PESTLINE

PESTLINE

Material Safety Data Sheets for Pesticides and Related Chemicals

VOLUME I

Occupational Health Services Inc.

VNR VAN NOSTRAND REINHOLD
New York

DISCLAIMER

Although great care has been taken by OHS in compiling and checking the information and data contained in Pestline™ to insure that it is current and accurate, OHS disclaims any and all liability for any errors, omissions, or inaccuracies in such information and data, whether attributable to inadvertence or otherwise, and for any consequences arising therefrom. The data provided hereunder neither purports to be nor constitutes legal or medical advice. It is further understood that OHS MAKES NO REPRESENTATIONS OR WARRANTIES OF ANY KIND INCLUDING BUT NOT LIMITED TO THE WARRANTIES OF FITNESS FOR A PARTICULAR PURPOSE OR MERCHANTABILITY, NOR ARE ANY SUCH REPRESENTATIONS OR WARRANTIES TO BE IMPLIED WITH RESPECT TO THE DATA FURNISHED, AND OHS ASSUMES NO RESPONSIBILITY WITH RESPECT TO CUSTOMERS, ITS EMPLOYEES, OR CLIENTS. OHS SHALL NOT BE LIABLE FOR ANY INCIDENTAL, SPECIAL, CONSEQUENTIAL, OR EXEMPLARY DAMAGES (INCLUDING DAMAGES FOR LOSS OF BUSINESS PROFITS, AND THE LIKE) RESULTING IN WHOLE OR IN PART, FROM CUSTOMERS USE OF DATA, EVEN IF OHS HAS BEEN ADVISED OF THE POSSIBILITY OF SUCH DAMAGES.

WARNING

Library of Congress Catalog Card Number 90-48902
ISBN 0-442-00697-7

Manufactured in the United States of America

Published by Van Nostrand Reinhold
115 Fifth Avenue
New York, New York 10003

Chapman and Hall
2-6 Boundary Row
London, SEJ 8HN

Thomas Nelson Australia
102 Dodds Street
South Melbourne 3205
Victoria, Australia

Nelson Canada
1120 Birchmount Road
Scarborough, Ontario MIK 5G4, Canada

16 15 14 13 12 11 10 9 8 7 6 5 4 3 2 1

Library of Congress Cataloging-in-Publication Data
Pestline: material safety data sheets for pesticides and related chemicals/by Occupational Health Services, Inc.
p. cm.
Includes bibliographical references and indexes.
"Volume 1 contains chemicals with PST numbers ranging from PST00020 through PST18670. Volume 2 contains PST18690 through PST86204"—Vol. 2, p.
ISBN 0-442-00697-7 (v. 1).—ISBN 0-442-00698-5 (v. 2)
1. Pesticides—Safety measures. 2. Agricultural chemicals—Safety measures. 3. Pesticides—Toxicology. 4. Agricultural chemicals—Toxicology. I. Occupational Health Services. II.Title: Pestline.
SB952.5. P48 1990
632'.95'0289—dc20

CONTENTS

PREFACE

The potential health and environmental risks associated with exposure to agricultural chemicals became evident during the 1970s with the banning of DDT, a potent insecticide that devastated some wildlife while persisting for years in the environment. Recent events, such as the cancer scare related to the growth regulator Alar, have heightened public awareness of the risks associated with pesticides. Government and industry have come to recognize the need to better communicate risk information to workers and the public.

Today, the Material Safety Data Sheet (MSDS) has become the most widely accepted means of communicating risk information. In response to the growing demand for technical information on pesticides, OHS created *Pestline*, a two-volume collection of MSDSs for more than 1000 pesticides and related chemicals. The MSDS is the culmination of an evolutionary process that has its roots in the eighteenth century.

During the late eighteenth century, the English developed the concept of "Failure to Warn," which today remains in various forms a part of all legal systems that subsequently sprang from English Common Law. "Failure to Warn" is a concept of liability that requires the innocent to be adequately warned when they may be subjected to one or more than one condition that might cause them injury, death, or both. The principle has been finely honed in recent years to include subjects other than physical dangers, such as can be found in financial transactions, investments, the transferring of properties, and even marriage contracts. Of the many nations and societies that have descended from England, none has come near to the extremes to which the United States legal system has raised this principle of law, to the point that it impinges daily upon the lives and activities of every citizen.

THE DESCENDENT VARIATIONS OF "FAILURE TO WARN"

"Failure to Warn" litigation has come to be a civilian enforcement tool that punishes through "Punitive Damages" the alleged wrongdoings of the financially influential when governmental inactions fail to fulfill those needs. The principle variations of the doctrine of "Failure to Warn" include:

1. "Right-To-Know"
2. "Full Disclosure"
3. "Punitive Damages"

The "Right-To-Know" and "Full Disclosure" doctrines or principles, at first glance, might seem the same or just different ways of saying the same thing. Though related to one another, they are treated entirely differently in the courts. Thus, corporations and other entities are required to build different defenses in structuring themselves for survival in this litigious society. "Right-To-Know" has, very recently (within the past 10 years), come to mean that anyone who is subject to any potentially harmful event or agent under the control of another must have been adequately and fully apprised of the dangers in a manner that can be proven to have been available to the injured party prior to the fact of the injury itself. The single greatest example of this principle at work can be found in tobacco products, where clear health warnings are and have been printed on each package for decades. These labels have effectively preempted personal injury suits by plaintiffs who claim tobacco companies failed to warn them of the risks associated with smoking. In such cases, the courts have presumed that the plaintiffs proceeded to use the products with full knowledge before the fact and did so willingly.

"Full Disclosure" goes beyond simple "Right-To-Know." Under this principle, a person or corporation who provides a service to the public is under a much broader requirement to disclose in advance to the purchaser all aspects of using the product or service, and it must be provable that such disclosure was made readily available to the purchaser. Many thousands of examples of this "Full Disclosure" doctrine or principle can be found in the securities industry. It might fairly be said that they have become legion.

As mentioned previously, "Failure to Warn" can result in civil litigation seeking "Punitive Damages." Such damages go beyond the normal compensation awarded the plaintiff and are designed to punish the defendant for a serious wrong. "Failure to Warn" the innocent of a condition that results in death or injury is, under the United States legal system, usually considered a serious wrong and grounds for "Punitive Damages."

PESTLINE AND THE DISCLOSURE DOCTRINES

Pestline is, to some degree, a product that fulfills the disclosure requirements of the principles outlined above. Its primary function is, however, rooted in the laws of nearly all of the 50 states and all of the Canadian Provinces. Nearly all such political subdivisions have passed laws requiring the existence of "Right-to-Know" documents of disclosure and warning for persons exposed to hazardous substances or conditions. It should be noted that of all chemical compounds, pesticides and drugs are the two most traditionally dangerous found in human society.

In addition to state and provincial laws requiring "Right-to-Know" documentation, there are powerful federal agencies, with overlapping powers and unclear lines of authority, that also require these same "Disclosure" documents.

Some of these agencies include:

1. Occupational Safety and Health Administration (OSHA)
2. Environmental Protection Agency (EPA)
3. United States Department of Agriculture (USDA)
4. Food and Drug Administration (FDA)
5. United States Department of Transportation (DOT)

It should be remembered that the legislative authority for all of the regulations promulgated by each of these agencies and departments has previously been enacted into law by the Congress of the United States.

OSHA created the progenitor Material Safety Data Sheet (MSDS) in the 1970s, with the original Form Number 20. In November of 1983, OSHA published the Hazard Communication standard, requiring chemical manufacturers to access the hazards of their chemicals and disclose this information to employees and downstream users via MSDS. The standard, which became effective in 1985, has since been expanded to cover all employers whose employees may be potentially exposed to hazardous chemicals. By act of congress, OSHA's authority is limited to the workplace; it does not have authority in the areas in which the EPA, USDA, and to some degree the FDA administer their respective controls over pesticides. There remain today many unanswered questions of jurisdiction, such as whether OSHA, the EPA, or the USDA have authority over worker exposures of hired employees on large farms who may be engaged in the mixing and application of pesticides.

The EPA is responsible for the regulation of the chemical pesticides listed in *Pestline* from two separate lines of legislative authority: the Federal Insecticide, Fungicide and Rodenticide Act (FIFRA) and the Superfund Amendments and Reauthorization Act (SARA).

Under FIFRA, the EPA carries the burden of governing all aspects of pesticides, with the exception of manufacturing worker occupational health conditions. These responsibilities include administration, mixing, labeling, disposal, registration, and toxicity review of manufacturer-provided data and licensing. Under SARA Title III, the EPA has promulgated regulations that require the states and their constituent political subdivisions to maintain MSDSs on the local inventory of hazardous chemicals that reside within their local boundaries. These local organizations are called LEPCs, or Local Emergency Planning Committees.

The FDA and USDA are responsible for enforcing pesticide tolerance levels set by EPA. These tolerances specify an upper limit of allowable pesticide residues on crops. The USDA enforces tolerances for residues found in meat, poultry, and dairy products. All other pesticide tolerances are enforced by the FDA.

DOT has promulgated certain regulations for the movement of pesticides or their hazardous wastes that require the labeling and classification of pesticide hazards. Further, DOT requires stringent packaging regulations on all goods shipped via air, rail, truck, or water. DOT also requires that shipping papers containing certain specific information accompany the pesticides, of which data is usually supplied from the MSDS, as presented in *Pestline*. In addition to the traditional shipping papers, DOT now requires that certain emergency response information accompany a hazardous shipment. Presently, the MSDS is the only document that fulfills that requirement.

The MSDS itself has become the principal instrument of data transmission for virtually all state and federal agencies. and that information is provided in unabridged form in Pestline.

We wish to acknowledge, with great appreciation, the dedicated work by the OHS research staff in Nashville, TN, especially Alison Barrett, Eric Boehme, Gerry Crownover, Scott Eckert, Ron Kirsch, and Linda Moore. Without their contributions this book would not have been possible. Special thanks go to John Bransford, President of OHS, and Jeff Hale, CEO of OHS, for their support and insight in the development of this project.

GUIDELINES FOR USING THE PESTLINE MSDS

This first edition of *Pestline* contains Material Safety Data Sheets (MSDSs) on more than 1000 agrochemicals. Most of these chemicals are registered as active pesticide ingredients with the Environmental Protection Agency (EPA) under the Federal Insecticide, Fungicide and Rodenticide Act (FIFRA). Some of the substances contained in the *Pestline* database are no longer registered for agricultural use in the United States. However, several U.S. companies continue to manufacture these chemicals, exporting them to other nations for use as pesticides.

Occupational Health Services, Inc. (OHS) produces and constantly updates thousands of MSDSs yearly. *Pestline* is a subset of that larger MSDS database. The MSDSs contained in *Pestline* are identified by a unique numbering system called the PST number. Two extensive indexes aid in finding a chemical of interest. The first index is organized alphabetically by chemical name, trade name, and synonym. The second index is organized by Chemical Abstract Service (CAS) number. Each index provides the appropriate PST number. Volume 1 contains chemicals with PST numbers ranging from PST00020 through PST18670. Volume 2 contains PST18690 through PST86204.

All of the MSDSs created by OHS, including those contained in *Pestline*, utilize a format based on the MSDS provisions of the Occupational Safety and Health Administration (OSHA) Hazard Communication Standard (HCS) 29 CFR 1910.1200. The following guidelines describe each section within the *Pestline* MSDS.

The first section of each MSDS always provides the name, address, and telephone number of the issuer of the MSDS.

SUBSTANCE IDENTIFICATION

SUBSTANCE/CHEMICAL NAME - OHS policy follows that of the HCS, which requires that chemicals be designated according to the nomenclature system developed by the International Union of Pure and Applied Chemistry (IUPAC), the CAS rules of nomenclature, or a name that will clearly identify the chemical for the purpose of conducting an evaluation. The CAS assigns a unique multidigit number to each chemical. OHS includes that number in this section.

SYNONYMS/COMMON NAMES - Designation or identification such as code name, code number, trade name, brand name, or generic name used to identify a chemical other than by its chemical name. OHS includes as many synonyms as possible, including the base name for all hydrates, salts, and isomers. The empirical formula is included when applicable. Code numbers include:

RCRA waste number (EPA)
UN and NA number (DOT)
STCC number (Standard Transportation Commodity Code)
PST number (A unique five-digit number assigned by OHS)

CHEMICAL FAMILY - Identifies the main functional groups of the chemical, as well as secondary functional groups.

MOLECULAR FORMULA - Structurally represents the substance, where space allows.

MOLECULAR WEIGHT - Supplies the weight of the substance in Daltons (atomic mass units).

CERCLA RATINGS - Quick reference indicator as to the severity of the hazards of the substance. Ratings are listed for health, fire, reactivity, and persistency on a scale of O to 3, 3 being the most hazardous, with U being unknown.

NFPA RATINGS - National Fire Protection Association quick reference indicators as to the severity of the hazards of the substance. Ratings, on a scale of O to 4, are listed for health, fire, and reactivity based on NFPA definitions in 704, 49, or 325 M.

COMPONENTS/CONTAMINANTS

COMPONENTS - Indicates the constituents of the material/substance that may pose a significant hazard. Single substances are generally listed as 100%. Components in mixtures are listed, and their percentages and CAS numbers included, if available.

CONTAMINANTS - Present in the substance in very small amounts, usually in parts per million (ppm) or less. Stabilizers and inhibitors are also included in this section.

EXPOSURE LIMITS - Established limits of an air contaminant to control potential exposure. The HCS requires the OSHA permissible exposure limit (PEL), the American Conference of Governmental Industrial Hygienists (ACGIH) threshold limit value (TLV), and any other exposure limits used or recommended by the chemical manufacturer, importer, or employer preparing the MSDS. In addition to the HCS requirements, OHS also includes National Institute for Occupational Safety and Health (NIOSH)-recommended exposure limits (RELs). Manufacturer exposure limits, industry consensus standards, and American Industrial Hygiene Association (AIHA) Workplace Environmental Exposure Levels (WEELs) are included only if the substance is not regulated or if the recommended limits are lower than those of OSHA, ACGIH, and NIOSH.

The following are other regulatory concerns covered under this category:

- CERCLA Reportable Quantities (RQs) - Environmental Exposure Limits;
- SARA Threshold Planning Quantities (TPQs), (RQs) - Environmental Exposure Limits;
- SARA Section 313 - Annual reporting on environmental releases; and
- California Proposition 65 - Environmental Health Warning requirements.

PHYSICAL DATA

OHS includes the following sections when information is available. If information is not available, NO DATA AVAILABLE is inserted in the categories.

DESCRIPTION - physical state, color, etc.

BOILING POINT - The temperature in degrees Fahrenheit and/or Centigrade at which a liquid boils (is converted to a gas).

MELTING POINT (FREEZING POINT) - The temperature at which conversion of a solid to a liquid (or liquid to a solid) begins.

SPECIFIC GRAVITY - The ratio of the weight of a volume of a substance to the weight of an equal volume of water. If the substance has a specific gravity greater than 1.0, it will sink in water; if less than 1.0, it will float in water.

VISCOSITY - A measure of the internal resistance to flow exhibited by a fluid.

VAPOR PRESSURE - The pressure (often expressed in millimeters of mercury - mmHg) characteristic at any given temperature of a vapor in equilibrium with its liquid or solid form. A high vapor pressure indicates that a liquid will evaporate readily (volatility). Materials with high vapor pressures can be especially dangerous when used in an enclosed area with poor ventilation. Materials with low vapor pressures may pose an inhalation hazard when sprayed. Also listed is the temperature at which the substance may become volatile.

EVAPORATION RATE - A value denoting the rate at which the substance evaporates compared to a standard such as ether (which evaporates very quickly) or to butyl acetate (which evaporates very slowly). The chemical used as the standard (either ether, butyl acetate, carbon tetrachloride, etc.) is listed.

PH - A value taken to represent the acidity or alkalinity of a substance. The pH of strong acids is 1-3; the pH of strong bases is 12-13. Neutrality is equal to a pH of 7.

WATER SOLUBILITY - The ability or tendency of the substance to blend uniformly with water.

ODOR THRESHOLD - The concentration, usually in ppm, at which an odor is detected.

VAPOR DENSITY - The relative weight or density of a vapor or gas compared with an equal volume of dry air.

SOLVENT SOLUBILITY - The ability or tendency of the substance to blend uniformly with another.

OTHER - This category is designed to include any special or extraordinary physical characteristics or properties of the substance.

FIRE AND EXPLOSION DATA

This section contains the physical hazards of the chemical, including the potential for fire, explosion, and reactivity.

FIRE AND EXPLOSION HAZARD - Qualifies the CERCLA and NFPA fire ratings utilizing the physical properties of the substance. Explains any other extraneous circumstances that could cause problems or hazards.

FLASH POINT - The lowest temperature, reported in degrees Fahrenheit and Centigrade, at which a liquid gives off enough vapor to ignite in air in the presence of an ignition source.

UPPER EXPLOSIVE LIMIT - Maximum concentration at which the substance will form a flammable (explosive) mixture with air. Above this level there will be too much fuel to support combustion.

LOWER EXPLOSIVE LIMIT - Minimum concentration at which the substance will form a flammable (explosive) mixture with air. Below this level there will be too little fuel to support combustion.

AUTOIGNITION TEMPERATURE - The lowest temperature at which the substance will ignite without an ignition source.

FLAMMABILITY CLASS - Based on OSHA 29 CFR 1910. 106 - Classification of flammable liquids. I to IIIB.

FIREFIGHTING MEDIA - A list of agents used to extinguish a fire involving the substance.

FIREFIGHTING PROCEDURES - Instructions on how to use the agents listed in firefighting media; steps to take, steps not to take.

TRANSPORTATION DATA

Provides DOT information on assigning hazard classifications, labeling requirements, and references for packaging requirements. Aids in completing shipping papers and choosing placards.

TOXICITY

This section is intended for the health professional/toxicologist and provides the following information, when available:

IRRITATION DATA - Compiled from the Registry of Toxic Effects of Chemical Substances (RTECS) animal irritancy testing data and, if available, the level of severity of irritation. Other sources of information may also be included.

TOXICITY DATA - Compiled from RTECS, journals, abstracts, and manufacturer animal toxicity testing data and, if available, any human data. This information determines whether the chemical is labeled toxic or highly toxic in the health effects section of the MSDS.

CARCINOGEN STATUS - OHS policy follows the HCS requirements. Under the HCS, a chemical is considered a carcinogen if it has been evaluated by the International Agency for Research on Cancer (IARC) and found to be a carcinogen or potential carcinogen; or it is listed as a carcinogen or potential carcinogen in the Annual Report on Carcinogens published by the National Toxicology Program (NTP); or it is regulated by OSHA as a carcinogen. If the NTP has published a technical report indicating some degree of carcinogenicity, but has not included this information in its annual report, OHS will summarize this information.

LOCAL EFFECTS - A list of the local effects labels used in the health effects section and by which route these labels have been assigned.

ACUTE TOXICITY LEVEL - An assessment by occupational exposure route of the available toxicity data.

TARGET EFFECTS - A list of all target organ labels used in the health effects section. A statement may also be made about other organs affected, but not affected severely enough to warrant a label.

AT INCREASED RISK - Lists medical conditions that are generally recognized as being aggravated by exposure to the chemical.

ADDITIONAL DATA - This is an optional category intended for significant information of which either a route of exposure is not known or the route is nonoccupational.

HEALTH EFFECTS AND FIRST AID

INHALATION/SKIN/EYE/INGESTION - This section contains health effects and first aid information on the primary routes of exposure. OHS reports the information in the following order:

1. **Label** - A word designating the significant toxicologic or characteristic effects of the substance (e.g., corrosive/toxic).
2. **Immediately Dangerous to Life or Health (IDLH) level** - A concentration in air at which an immediate danger to the life or health of an individual can occur within 30 minutes. Reported in inhalation only for purposes of respirator selection.
3. **Acute Exposure** - Effects that occur during an 8-hour workday or from a single exposure.
4. **Chronic Exposure** - Effects that occur from repeated or more than one exposure.
5. **First Aid** - Provides information on emergency and first aid procedures.

ANTIDOTE - Designed to inform trained personnel of substances that, when administered to an individual, have an antagonistic effect on the substance or chemical reaction brought about by the substance to which that individual has been exposed.

REACTIVITY

Qualifies the assigned CERCLA/NFPA reactivity rating. Explains the hazards due to exposure to natural forces (e.g., water, air, light, heat, shock, friction).

INCOMPATIBILITY - A list of substances that, when in the presence of the chemical, react dangerously. Includes a summary of the dangerous reaction.

DECOMPOSITION - A list of hazardous products that will evolve when the substance is exposed to heat.

POLYMERIZATION - A chemical reaction usually carried out with a catalyst, heat, or light, and often under high pressure, in which a large number of relatively simple molecules combine to form a chain-like macromolecule. OHS is primarily concerned with hazardous polymerizations (e.g., violent, explosive, exothermic).

STORAGE AND DISPOSAL

This section lists the general precautions to take when storing or disposing of the substance. RCRA waste numbers are included to aid in meeting disposal regulations governed by the EPA.

CONDITIONS TO AVOID

This section lists the general precautions that should be taken when handling the substance.

SPILL AND LEAK PROCEDURES

WATER RELEASE - Steps to be taken when the substance has spilled into a water supply. If applicable, the California Proposition 65 warning requirement is noted in this section.

AIR RELEASE - Steps to be taken when the substance has been released into the air.

SOIL RELEASE - Steps to be taken when the substance has spilled onto the ground.

OCCUPATIONAL SPILL - Steps to be taken when the substance has spilled in the workplace. If applicable, EPA reporting information (CERCLA/SARA RQs) is included to help comply with CERCLA and SARA notification requirements.

PROTECTIVE EQUIPMENT

VENTILATION - Recommends engineering controls (e.g., local exhaust) based on the toxicological and physical hazards of the substance.

RESPIRATORY PROTECTION - Includes OSHA requirements, when regulated, and NIOSH and ACGIH recommendations. If none of these apply, OHS makes a recommendation based on the toxicological and physical characteristics of the substance.

CLOTHING - Includes OSHA requirements, if regulated. If not, OHS recommends appropriate protective clothing based on the physical characteristics and toxicological and local effects of the substance.

GLOVES - Includes OSHA requirements, if regulated. If not, OHS recommends appropriate protective gloves based on the physical characteristics and toxicological and local effects of the substance.

EYE PROTECTION - Includes OSHA requirements, if regulated. If not, OHS recommends eye protection based on the physical characteristics and local effects of the substance.

CREATION DATE/REVISION DATE

This final section provides the original creation date for the MSDS, as well as the date of the last revision.

KEY TO ABBREVIATIONS

AAOHN American Association of Occupational Health Nurses
AAP Asbestos Action Program
ACFM Asbestos-Containing Friable Materials
ACGIH American Conference of Governmental Industrial Hygienists
ACS American Chemical Society
ADI Acceptable Daily Intake
ADN European agreement concerning international carriage of dangerous goods by inland waterways
ADNR ***and*** ADN /Rhine Regulations for the carriage of dangerous goods on the Rhine river
ADR European agreement concerning the international carriage of dangerous goods by road
AEA Atomic Energy Act
AFGE American Federation of Government Employees
AFL-CIO American Federation of Labor and Congress of Industrial Organizations
AHA American Heart Association
AHERA Asbestos Hazard Emergency Response Act
AIHA American Industrial Hygiene Association
AIHC American Industrial Health Council
AIMS American Institute of Merchant Shipping
ALJ Administrative Law Judge
AMA American Medical Association
ANPRM Advanced Notice of Proposed Rule Making
ANSI American National Standards Institute
AOMA American Occupational Medical Association
APHIS Animal and Plant Health Inspection Service
API American Petroleum Institute
ARDS Adult Respiratory Distress Syndrome
ASTM American Society for Testing Materials
AT Advanced Technology
ATSDR Agency for Toxic Substances and Disease Registry
BAT Best Available Technology
BDAT Best Demonstrated Available Technology
BCT Best Conventional Technology
BNA Bureau of National Affairs, Inc.
BOD Biochemical Oxygen Demand
BOS Bureau Of Standards
BPT Best Practical Technology
BSCC Biotechnology Science Coordinating Committee
CAA Clean Air Act (EPA)
CAER Community Awareness Emergency Response
CAMEO Computer-Aided Management of Emergency Operations
CAS Chemical Abstracts Service
CASN Chemical Abstracts Service Number
CBI Confidential Business Information
CD-ROM Compact Disc - Read Only Memory
CDC Centers for Disease Control
CEFIC Conseil European des Federations d'Industries Chemiques (European council of chemical manufacturers federations)
CEPP Community Emergency Preparedness Program
CEQ Council on Environmental Quality
CERCLA Comprehensive, Environmental Response, Compensation and Liability Act (Superfund, EPA)
CFR Code of Federal Regulations
CGL Comprehensive General Liability
CHIB Chemical Hazard Identification Branch
CHIP Chemical Hazard Information Profile
CHRIS Chemical Hazard Response Information System
CI Color Index
CIM International convention concerning the carriage of goods by rail
CISN Chemical Information Screening Network
CMA Chemical Manufacturers Association
COE Corps Of Engineers
COETDG Committee Of Experts on the Transport of Dangerous Goods, United Nations
COTR Contracting Officer's Technical Representative
CPSA Consumer Product Safety Act
CPSC Consumer Product Safety Commission
CRT Cathode Ray Tube
CSB Chemical Screening Branch
CUFT Center for the Utilization of Federal Technology
CWA Clean Water Act (EPA)
DAWN Drug Alert Warning Network
DEA Drug Enforcement Administration
DGP Dangerous Goods Panel
DHHS Department of Health and Human Services
DLA Defense Logistics Agency
DOD Department Of Defense
DOE Department Of Energy
DOI Department Of the Interior
DOJ Department Of Justice
DOL Department Of Labor
DOT Department Of Transportation
DRR Division of Research Resources (DHHS)
ECA Economic Commission for Africa
ECAD Existing Chemical Assessment Division

KEY TO ABBREVIATIONS

ECE	Economic Commission for Europe
ECLAC	Economic Commission for Latin America and the Carribean
ECMT	European Conference of Ministers of Transport
ECOSOC	Economic and Social Council, United Nations
ECTF	Existing Chemicals Task Force
EEC	European Economic Community
EEGL	Emergency Exposure Guidance Levels
EEL	Emergency Exposure Levels
EDF	Environmental Defense Fund
EHC	Environmental Health Committee
EHN	Environmental Health News
EIL	Environmental Impairment Liability
EIS	Environmental Impact Statement
EMS	Emergency procedures for ships carrying dangerous goods
ENT	ENTomology number
EP	Extraction Procedures
EPA	Environmental Protection Agency
EPCRA	Emergency Planning and Community Right-to-know Act
EPI	Environmental Policy Institute
ERCS	Emergency Response Cleanup Services
ERTKA	Employee Right-To-Know Act (state level)
ESCAP	Economic and Social Commission for Asia and the Pacific
ESCWA	Economic and Social Commission for Western Asia
ETS	Emergency Temporary Standard
FAA	Federal Aviation Administration
FACOSH	Federal Advisory Council on Occupational Safety and Health
FCCSET	Federal Coordinating Council for Science, Engineering and Technology
FDA	Food and Drug Administration
FDCA	Federal Food, Drug and Cosmetic Act
FEMA	Federal Emergency Management Agency
FEV	Forced Expiratory Volume
FFDCA	Federal Food, Drug and Cosmetic Act
FHCP	Federal Hazard Communication Program
FHSA	Federal Hazardous Substances Act
FIATA	International federation of forwarding agents
FIFRA	Federal Insecticide, Fungicide and Rodenticide Act (EPA)
FMCSR	Federal Motor Carrier Safety Regulations
FOET	Foundation On Economic Trends
FOIA	Freedom Of Information Act
FR	Federal Register
FLSA	Fair Labor Standards Act
FTCA	Federal Tort Claims Act
FSN	Federal Stock Number
FWPCA	Federal Water Pollution Control Act
FVC	Forced Vital Capacity
FYI	For Your Information
GAO	General Accounting Office
GE-15	Group of experts, economic commission for Europe
GPO	Government Printing Office
GRAS	Generally Recognized As Safe (FDA)
GRASP	Government Relations And Science Policy
HATS	Human Adipose Tissue Survey (EPA)
HAZBATE	HAZard aBATEment file (OSHA)
HAZCAP	HAZard communication Compliance Assistance Program
HHS	Health and Human Services
HMAC	Hazardous Materials Advisory Council
HMIS	Hazardous Materials Information System
HMTA	Hazardous Materials Transportation Act
HMTC	Hazardous Materials Technical Center
HSDB	Hazardous Substances Data Bank (NLM)
HSIA	Halogenated Solvents Industry Alliance
HSWA	Hazardous and Solid Waste Amendments
HUD	Housing and Urban Development
IAEA	International Atomic Energy Agency
IAFF	International Association of Fire Fighters
IAO	Industrial Assistance Office
IARC	International Agency for Research on Cancer
IATA	International Air Transportation Association
IBM	International Business Machines corp.
ICAO	International Civil Aviation Organization
ICSC	International Chemical Safety Card
IDLH	Immediately Dangerous to Life or Health
IISRP	International Institute for Synthetic Rubber Producers
ILO	International Labour Organization
IMDG	International Maritime Dangerous Goods code (IMO)
IMGS	International Medical Guide for Ships
IMIS	Integrated Management Information System (OSHA)
IMO	International Maritime Organization
INS	Immigration and Naturalization Service
IPM	Integrated Pest Management
IPSC	International Programme for Safety in Chemicals
IRCA	Immigration Reform and Control Act
ITC	Interagency Testing Committee (TSCA)
IUPAC	International Union of Pure and Applied Chemistry
KB	KiloByte
KG	KiloGram
L	Liter
LC5O	Lethal Concentration-5O
LCLO	Lethal Concentration-LOw

LD50 Lethal Dose-50
LDLO Lethal Dose-LOw
LEA Local Education Agencies
LEL Lower Exposure Limit
LEPC Local Emergency Planning Committee
LEPD Local Emergency Planning District
LFG Liquified Flammable Gas
LUST Leaking Underground Storage Tank
MAC Maximum Allowable Concentration
MOTC Ministry Of Transport, Canada
MOTJ Ministry Of Transport, Japan
MS Mail Stock
MAK Maximum Allowable concentration (German)
MB MegaByte
MCL Maximum Contaminant Level
MCLG Maximum Contaminant Level Goals
MCSAP Motor Carrier Safety Assistance Program
MFAG Medical First Aid Guide
MG MilliGram
MPU MicroProcessing Unit
MPRSA Marine Protection, Research and Sanctuaries Act
MSDS Material Safety Data Sheet
MSHA Mine Safety and Health Administration
MSHACT Mine Safety and Health ACT
MTB Materials Transportation Bureau
NA North American
NAAQS National Ambient Air Quality Standards
NACE National Association of Corrosion Engineers and health
NAS National Academy of Sciences
NASA National Aeronautics and Space Administration
NCI National Cancer Institute
NCP National Contingency Plan (Superfund)
NEI National Eye Institute
NEPA National Environmental Policy Act
NFFE National Federation of Federal Employees
NFPA National Fire Protection Agency
NHLBI National Heart, Lung and Blood Institute
NIDA National Institute of Drug Abuse
NIDR National Institute of Dental Research
NIEHS National Institute of Environmental Health Sciences
NIH National Institute of Health
NINCDS National Institute of Neurological and Communicative Disorders and Stroke
NIOSH National Institute for Occupational Safety and Health
NLM National Library of Medicine
NLRB National Labor Relations Board
NLS Noxious Liquid Substances
NOAA National Oceanic and Atmospheric Administration
NOEL No Observed Effect Level
NOES National Occupational Exposure Survey (NIOSH)
NOS Not Otherwise Specified
NPDES National Pollutant Discharge Elimination System
NPIRS National Pesticide Information and Retrieval System
NPL National Priorities List (Superfund)
NPRM Notice of Proposed Rule Making
NRC Nuclear Regulatory Commission
NRDC National Resources Defense Council
NSC National Safety Council
NSF National Science Foundation
NSPS New Source Performance Standard
NSTA National Science Teachers Association
NTP National Toxicology Program
OCIS OSHA Computerized Information System
OCM Office of Compliance Monitoring
OECD Organization for Economic Cooperative Development, Paris
OECM Office of Enforcement and Compliance Monitoring
OGC Office of General Council
OHEA Office of Health and Environmental Assessment
OHMR Office of Hazardous Material Regulation
OHMTADS Oil and Hazardous Materials / Technical Assistance Data System (EPA)
OHS Occupational Health Services, Inc.
OMB Office of Management and Budget
OPP Office of Pesticide Programs
OPTS Office of Pesticides and Toxic Substances
ORM Other Regulated Material
OSC On-Scene Coordinator
OSHA Occupational Safety and Health Administration
OSHACT Occupational Safety and Health ACT
OSHSPA Occupational Safety and Health State Plan Association
OSTP Office of Science and Technology Policy
OSW Office of Solid Waste
OTS Office of Toxic Substances
OWPE Office of Waste Programs Enforcement
PCL Permissible Concentration Limits
PEF Peak Expiratory Flowrate
PEL Permissible Exposure Limit
PMN PreManufacture Notification
POTW Publicly Owned Treatment Work
PPM Parts Per Million
PSC Public Service Commission

KEY TO ABBREVIATIONS

PSD	Prevention of Significant Deterioration
PSES	Pretreatment Standards for Existing Sources
PSNS	Pretreatment Standards for New Sources
QSAR	Quantitative Structure-Activity Relationship
RAB	Risk Analysis Branch
RAM	Random Access Memory
RCRA	Resource Conservation and Recovery Act (EPA)
RI/FS	Remedial Investigation / Feasibility Study (Superfund)
RIN	Regulatory Information Number
RMCL	Recommended Maximum Contaminant Level
RPAR	Rebuttable Presumption Against Registration
RPDB	Regulatory Program Development Branch
RP	Reportable Quantity
RSPA	Research and Special Programs Administration
RTECS	Registry of Toxic Effects of Chemical Substances
SAB	Scientific Advisory Board
SAP	Scientific Advisory Panel
SARA	Superfund Amendments and Reauthorization Act
SDWA	Safe Drinking Water Act
SERC	State Emergency Response Commission
SIC	Standard Industrial Classification
SIP	State Implementation Plan
SNUR	Significant New Use Rule
SODA	State Occupational Directors Association
SOLAS	Safety Of Life At Sea convention
SPEGLS	Short-term Public Emergency Guidance LevelS
STCC	Standard Transportation Commodity Code
STEL	Short-Term Exposure Limit
STLC	Soluble Threshold Limit Concentration
TAO	TSCA Assistance Office
TCLO	Toxic Concentration-LOw
TDLO	Toxic Dose-LOw
TLM	Threshold Limit Median
TLV	Threshold Limit Value
TPQ	Threshold Planning Quantity
TRDB	Test Rules Development Branch
TRI	Toxic Release Inventory (SARA Title III)
TSCA	Toxic Substances Control Act (EPA)
TSDF	Treatment, Storage and Disposal Facility
TSP	Total Suspended Particles
TSS	Total Suspended Solids
TTLC	Total Threshold Limit Concentration
TWA	Time-Weighted Average
UAW	United Auto Workers
UEL	Upper Exposure Limit
UG/M3	MicroGram per Cubic Meter
UIC	Underground Injection Control
UICPC	Underground Injection Control Practices Panel
UN	United Nations
UNEP	United Nations Environment Program
URW	United Rubber Workers
USCG	United States Coast Guard
USDA	United States Department of Agriculture
USDI	United States Department of the Interior
USWA	United Steel Workers of America
VA	Veterans Administration
VDT	Video Display Terminal
VFW	Veterans of Foreign Wars
VOC	Volatile Organic Chemical
VSD	Virtually Safe Dose
WHD	Wage and Hour Division (DOL)
WEEL	Workplace Environmental Exposure Level
WIPP	Waste Isolation Pilot Plant (DOE)
WHMIS	Workplace Hazardous Materials Information System (Canada)
WHO	World Health Organization
WQA	Water Quality Act

PESTLINE

MATERIAL SAFETY DATA SHEET

OCCUPATIONAL HEALTH SERVICES, INC.
AGRICULTURE AND PESTICIDE DIVISION
450 SEVENTH AVENUE, SUITE 2407
NEW YORK, NEW YORK 10123
1-800-445-MSDS OR (212) 967-1100

EMERGENCY CONTACT:
JOHN S. BRANSFORD, JR. (615) 292-1180

SUBSTANCE IDENTIFICATION

CAS-NUMBER 3383-96-8

SUBSTANCE: **TEMEPHOS**

TRADE NAMES/SYNONYMS: PHOSPHOROTHIOIC ACID, O,O'-(THIODI-4,1-PHENYLENE) O,O,O', O'-TETRAMETHYL ESTER; PHOSPHOROTHIOIC ACID, O,O',-(THIODI-P-PHENYLENE) O,O,O', O'-TETRAMETHYL ESTER; PHOSPHOROTHIOIC ACID, O,O-DIMETHYL ESTER, O,O-DIESTER WITH 4, 4'-THIODIPHENOL; O,O'(THIODI-4,1-PHENYLENE)PHOSPHOROTHIOIC ACID O,O,O', O'-TETRAMETHYL ESTER; O,O'(THIODI-4,1-PHENYLENE)BIS(O,O'-DIMETHYLPHOSPHOROTHIOATE); O,O,O',O'-TETRAMETHYL O,O'-THIODI-P-PHENYLENE BIS(PHOSPHOROTHIOATE); O,O,O',O'-TETRAMETHYL O,O'-THIODI-P-PHENYLENE DIPHOSPHOROTHIOATE; O,O'-(THIODI-P-PHENYLENE) O,O,O',O'-TETRAMETHYL DI(PHOSPHOROTHIOATE); O,O'-(THIODI-4,1-PHENYLENE) BIS(O,O-DIMETHYL PHOSPHOROTHIOATE); ABATE; ABATHION; AC 52160; BIOTHION; DIFOS; TEMEFOS; ENT 27,165; PST00020

CHEMICAL FAMILY: ORGANOPHOSPHATE

MOLECULAR FORMULA: C16-H20-O6-P2-S3

MOLECULAR WEIGHT: 466.48

CERCLA RATINGS (SCALE 0-3): HEALTH=3 FIRE=U REACTIVITY=0 PERSISTENCE=2

NFPA RATINGS (SCALE 0-4): HEALTH=3 FIRE=U REACTIVITY=0

COMPONENTS AND CONTAMINANTS

COMPONENT: TEMEPHOS ***PERCENT:*** 100
CAS# 3383-96-8

OTHER CONTAMINANTS: NONE

EXPOSURE LIMITS: TEMEPHOS: 5 MG/M3 OSHA TWA (RESPIRABLE FRACTION); 10 MG/M3 OSHA TWA (TOTAL DUST) 10 MG/M3 ACGIH TWA

PHYSICAL DATA

DESCRIPTION: WHITE CRYSTALLINE SOLID; TECHNICAL MATERIAL IS A BROWN VISCOUS LIQUID

BOILING POINT: 248 F (120 C) ***MELTING POINT:*** 86 F (30 C)

SPECIFIC GRAVITY: 1.32 ***VAPOR PRESSURE:*** 0.0000000717 MMHG

SOLUBILITY IN WATER: 25 PPB

SOLVENT SOLUBILITY: SOLUBLE IN ACETONITRILE, CARBON TETRACHLORIDE, DIETHYL ETHER, 1,2-DICHLOROETHANE, TOLUENE, LOWER ALKYL KETONES, CHLOROFORM, AROMATIC HYDROCARBONS, CHLORINATED HYDROCARBONS; INSOLUBLE IN ALIPHATIC HYDROCARBONS

FIRE AND EXPLOSION DATA

FIRE AND EXPLOSION HAZARD: UNKNOWN FIRE AND EXPLOSION HAZARD.

FIREFIGHTING MEDIA: DRY CHEMICAL, CARBON DIOXIDE, HALON, WATER SPRAY OR STANDARD FOAM (1987 EMERGENCY RESPONSE GUIDEBOOK, DOT P 5800.4). FOR LARGER FIRES, USE WATER SPRAY, FOG OR STANDARD FOAM (1987 EMERGENCY RESPONSE GUIDEBOOK, DOT P 5800.4).

FIREFIGHTING: MOVE CONTAINERS FROM FIRE AREA IF POSSIBLE. FIGHT FIRE FROM MAXIMUM DISTANCE. STAY AWAY FROM STORAGE TANK ENDS. DIKE FIRE CONTROL WATER FOR LATER DISPOSAL. DO NOT SCATTER MATERIAL (1987 EMERGENCY RESPONSE GUIDEBOOK, DOT P 5800.4, GUIDE PAGE 55). EXTINGUISH USING AGENT SUITABLE FOR TYPE OF SURROUNDING FIRE. AVOID BREATHING VAPORS AND DUSTS. KEEP UPWIND.

TOXICITY

TEMEPHOS: IRRITATION DATA: 500 MG/24 HOURS EYE-RABBIT MILD IRRITATION. TOXICITY DATA: 970 MG/KG SKIN-RABBIT LD50; 1370 MG/KG SKIN-RAT LD50; 1000 MG/KG ORAL-RAT LD50; 223 MG/KG ORAL-MOUSE LD50; 313 MG/KG ORAL-RABBIT LD50; 4700 MG/KG ORAL-MAMMAL LD50; 2302 MG/KG SUBCUTANEOUS-RAT LD50; 912 MG/KG INTRAPERITONEAL-RAT LD50; 683 MG/KG INTRAPERITONEAL-MOUSE LD50; 8600 MG/KG UNREPORTED-RAT LD50; 4 GM/KG UNREPORTED-MAMMAL LD50; REPRODUCTIVE EFFECTS DATA (RTECS). CARCINOGEN STATUS: NONE. ACUTE TOXICITY LEVEL: TOXIC BY DERMAL ABSORPTION AND MODERATELY TOXIC BY INGESTION. TARGET EFFECTS: CHOLINESTERASE INHIBITOR. POISONING MAY AFFECT THE NERVOUS SYSTEM.* AT INCREASED RISK FROM EXPOSURE: PERSONS WITH RESPIRATORY AILMENTS, RECENT EXPOSURE TO CHOLINESTERASE INHIBITORS OR IMPAIRED CHOLINESTERASE PRODUCTION, OR LIVER MALFUNCTION.* ADDITIONAL DATA: MAY CROSS THE PLACENTA. HIGH ENVIRONMENTAL TEMPERATURES OR EXPOSURE OF THE CHEMICAL TO VISIBLE OR ULTRAVIOLET LIGHT MAY ENHANCE THE TOXICITY. INTERACTIONS WITH MEDICATIONS MAY OCCUR.*
* MAY BE BASED ON GENERAL INFORMATION ON ORGANOPHOSPHATES.

HEALTH EFFECTS AND FIRST AID

INHALATION: TEMEPHOS: SEE INFORMATION ON ORGANOPHOSPHATES. ORGANOPHOSPHATES: CHOLINESTERASE INHIBITOR. **ACUTE EXPOSURE**- WHEN INHALED, THE FIRST EFFECTS OF CHOLINESTERASE INHIBITORS ARE USUALLY RESPIRATORY AND MAY INCLUDE NASAL HYPEREMIA AND WATERY DISCHARGE, COUGH, CHEST DISCOMFORT, DYSPNEA, AND WHEEZING DUE TO INCREASED BRONCHIAL SECRETIONS AND BRONCHOCONSTRICTION. IF SUFFICIENT AMOUNTS ARE ABSORBED, OTHER SYSTEMIC EFFECTS MAY BEGIN WITHIN A FEW MINUTES OR BE DELAYED FOR UP TO 12 HOURS. SYMPTOMS MAY INCLUDE PALLOR, NAUSEA, VOMITING, DIARRHEA, ABDOMINAL CRAMPS, HEADACHE, DIZZINESS, OCULAR PAIN, BLURRED VISION, MIOSIS OR IN SOME CASES, ESPECIALLY INITIALLY, MYDRIASIS, LACRIMATION, SALIVATION, SWEATING, AND CONFUSION. OTHER REPORTED CENTRAL NERVOUS SYSTEM OR NEUROMUSCULAR EFFECTS MAY INCLUDE ATAXIA, SLURRED SPEECH, AREFLEXIA, WEAKNESS, FATIGUE, FASCICULATIONS, TWITCHING, TREMORS POSSIBLY OF THE TONGUE AND EYELIDS, AND EVENTUALLY PARALYSIS OF THE EXTREMITIES AND POSSIBLY OF THE RESPIRATORY MUSCLES. IN SEVERE CASES THERE MAY ALSO BE INVOLUNTARY DEFECATION AND URINATION, CYANOSIS, PSYCHOSIS, HYPERGLYCEMIA, ACUTE PANCREATITIS, CARDIAC IRREGULARITIES, PULMONARY EDEMA, UNCONSCIOUSNESS, CONVULSIONS, AND COMA. DEATH IS PRIMARILY DUE TO RESPIRATORY FAILURE, ALTHOUGH CARDIOVASCULAR EFFECTS INCLUDING CARDIAC ARREST MAY ALSO BE IMPLICATED. LONG TERM SEQUELAE ARE RARE BUT MAY INCLUDE NEUROPSYCHIATRIC DISORDERS AND MYOPATHY WITH MUSCLE TENDERNESS. SOME ORGANOPHOSPHATES MAY CAUSE A DELAYED NEUROPATHY BEGINNING 1-4 WEEKS AFTER AN ACUTE EXPOSURE WHICH MAY OR MAY NOT HAVE CAUSED ACUTE CHOLINERGIC EFFECTS. NUMBNESS, TINGLING, WEAKNESS AND CRAMPING BEGINNING SYMMETRICALLY IN THE LOWER LIMBS MAY PROGRESS TO ATAXIA AND PARALYSIS. IN SEVERE CASES, UPPER LIMB INVOLVEMENT IS POSSIBLE AND FLACCID PARALYSIS MAY PROGRESS TO SPASTIC PARALYSIS WITH EXAGGERATED REFLEXES. IMPROVEMENT MAY OCCUR OVER MONTHS TO YEARS, BUT SOME RESIDUAL IMPAIRMENT USUALLY REMAINS. **CHRONIC EXPOSURE**- REPEATED OR PROLONGED EXPOSURE MAY RESULT IN THE EFFECTS OF ACUTE EXPOSURE INCLUDING THE DELAYED NEUROPATHY. OTHER EFFECTS REPORTED IN WORKERS REPEATEDLY EXPOSED INCLUDE IMPAIRED MEMORY AND CONCENTRATION, ACUTE PSYCHOSIS, SEVERE DEPRESSIONS, IRRITABILTY, CONFUSION, APATHY, EMOTIONAL LABILITY, SOCIAL WITHDRAWAL, CONFUSION, HEADACHE, SPEECH DIFFICULTIES, DELAYED REACTION TIMES, SPATIAL DISORIENTATION, NIGHTMARES, SLEEPWALKING, AND DROWSINESS OR INSOMNIA. AN INFLUENZA-LIKE CONDITION WITH HEADACHE, NAUSEA, WEAKNESS, ANOREXIA AND MALAISE HAS ALSO BEEN REPORTED.

FIRST AID- REMOVE FROM EXPOSURE AREA TO FRESH AIR IMMEDIATELY. IF BREATHING HAS STOPPED, GIVE ARTIFICIAL RESPIRATION. MAINTAIN AIRWAY AND BLOOD PRESSURE AND ADMINISTER OXYGEN IF AVAILABLE. KEEP AFFECTED PERSON WARM AND AT REST. TREAT SYMPTOMATICALLY AND SUPPORTIVELY. ADMINISTRATION OF OXYGEN SHOULD BE PERFORMED BY QUALIFIED PERSONNEL. GET MEDICAL ATTENTION IMMEDIATELY.

SKIN CONTACT: TEMEPHOS: TOXIC. 500 MG APPLIED TO RABBIT SKIN WAS MODERATELY IRRITATING. NO ADVERSE EFFECTS IN RATS WERE OBSERVED IN A 21-DAY REPEATED DERMAL STUDY AT DOSES OF 12 AND 60 MG/KG. ADVERSE EFFECTS ON THE FETUS WERE OBSERVED IN CHRONIC DERMAL STUDY OF PREGNANT RABBITS. SEE INFORMATION ON ORGANOPHOSPHATES. ORGANOPHOSPHATES: CHOLINESTERASE INHIBITOR. **ACUTE EXPOSURE**- LOCALIZED SWEATING AND FASCICULATIONS MAY OCCUR AT THE SITE OF CONTACT. IF SUFFICIENT AMOUNTS ARE ABSORBED, OTHER EFFECTS OF CHOLINESTERASE INHIBITION AS DESCRIBED IN ACUTE INHALATION MAY OCCUR. SYMPTOMS MAY BE DELAYED 2-3 HOURS, BUT USUALLY NO MORE THAN 12 HOURS. THE RATE OF ABSORPTION IS INCREASED BY THE PRESENCE OF DERMATITIS OR HIGH AMBIENT TEMPERATURES. DELAYED NEUROPATHY IS ALSO POSSIBLE. **CHRONIC EXPOSURE**- REPEATED OR PROLONGED EXPOSURE MAY CAUSE EFFECTS AS DESCRIBED IN ACUTE EXPOSURE. SOME ORGANOPHOSPHATES MAY CAUSE SENSITIZATION.

FIRST AID- REMOVE CONTAMINATED CLOTHING IMMEDIATELY. WASH CONTAMINATED AREAS WITH SOAP AND WATER FOLLOWED BY ALCOHOL (ARENA, POISONING, 4TH ED.). EMERGENCY PERSONNEL SHOULD WEAR GLOVES AND AVOID CONTAMINATION. TREAT RESPIRATORY DIFFICULTY WITH ARTIFICIAL RESPIRATION. GET MEDICAL ATTENTION IMMEDIATELY.

EYE CONTACT: TEMEPHOS: SEE INFORMATION ON ORGANOPHOSPHATES.
ORGANOPHOSPHATES: CHOLINESTERASE INHIBITOR. **ACUTE EXPOSURE-** DIRECT CONTACT MAY CAUSE PAIN, HYPEREMIA, LACRIMATION, TWITCHING OF THE EYELIDS, MIOSIS, AND CILIARY MUSCLE SPASM WITH LOSS OF ACCOMODATION, BLURRED OR DIMMED VISION AND BROWACHE. SOMETIMES MYDRIASIS MAY OCCUR INSTEAD OF MIOSIS. WITH SUFFICIENT EXPOSURE, OTHER SYMPTOMS OF CHOLINESTERASE INHIBITION AS DESCRIBED IN ACUTE INHALATION MAY OCCUR. **CHRONIC EXPOSURE-** REPEATED OR PROLONGED EXPOSURE MAY CAUSE EFFECTS AS DESCRIBED IN ACUTE EXPOSURE. SOME COMPOUNDS HAVE CAUSED TOXIC EFFECTS ON THE CRYSTALLINE LENS, CONJUNCTIVAL THICKENING AND OBSTRUCTION OF THE NASOLACRIMAL CANALS WHEN USED AS MIOTIC EYEDROPS.

FIRST AID- IRRIGATE EYES WITH WATER OR SALINE SOLUTION. IF SYMPTOMS OF POISONING OCCUR, TREAT RESPIRATORY DIFFICULTY WITH ARTIFICIAL RESPIRATION AND OXYGEN. OBSERVE PATIENT FOR AT LEAST 24-36 HOURS (GOSSELIN, CLINICAL TOXICOLOGY OF COMMERCIAL PRODUCTS, 5TH ED.). GET MEDICAL ATTENTION IMMEDIATELY. OXYGEN SHOULD BE ADMINISTERED BY QUALIFIED MEDICAL PERSONNEL.

INGESTION: TEMEPHOS: NO CHOLINESTERASE INHIBITION OR CLINICAL SYMPTOMS WERE OBSERVED IN A STUDY WITH HUMAN VOLUNTEERS WHO WERE FED DOSES OF 2 TO 256 MG/DAY FOR 5 DAYS OR CONSTANT DOSES OF 64 MG/DAY FOR FOUR WEEKS. FOCAL OR DIFFUSE NECROSIS OF THE LIVER OCCURED IN SOME RABBITS GIVEN 100 MG/KG/DAY FOR 5 DAYS. A DOSE OF 125 MG/KG FED TO CHICKENS OVER A 30-DAY PEROID PRODUCED TRANSIENT LEG WEAKNESS. SEE INFORMATION ON ORGANOPHOSPHATES.
ORGANOPHOSPHATES: CHOLINESTERASE INHIBITOR. **ACUTE EXPOSURE-** WHEN INGESTED, THE FIRST EFFECTS MAY BE NAUSEA, VOMITING, ANOREXIA, ABDOMINAL CRAMPS AND DIARRHEA. GASTROINTESTINAL ABSORPTION MAY CAUSE SYMPTOMS OF CHOLINESTERASE INHIBITION AS DESCRIBED IN ACUTE INHALATION. SYMPTOMS MAY BEGIN WITHIN MINUTES OR BE DELAYED FOR HOURS. DELAYED EFFECTS INCLUDING NEUROPATHY MAY ALSO OCCUR. **CHRONIC EXPOSURE-** REPEATED INGESTION MAY CAUSE EFFECTS AS DESCRIBED IN ACUTE EXPOSURE.

FIRST AID- IF PERSON IS ALERT AND RESPIRATION IS NOT DEPRESSED, GIVE SYRUP OF IPECAC FOLLOWED BY WATER (IF VOMITING OCCURS, KEEP HEAD BELOW HIPS TO PREVENT ASPIRATION). IF CONSCIOUSNESS LEVEL DECLINES OR VOMITING HAS NOT OCCURRED IN 15 MINUTES EMPTY STOMACH BY GASTRIC LAVAGE WITH THE AID OF CUFFED ENDOTRACHEAL TUBE USING ISOTONIC SALINE OR 5% SODIUM BICARBONATE FOLLOW WITH ACTIVATED CHARCOAL. ESTABLISH AND MAINTAIN AIRWAY. TREAT RESPIRATORY DIFFICULTY WITH ARTIFICIAL RESPIRATION AND OXYGEN. DO NOT GIVE MORPHINE, AMINOPHYLLINE, PHENOTHIAZINES, RESERPINE, FUROSEMIDE, OR ETHACRYNIC ACID (MORGAN, RECOGNITION AND MANAGEMENT OF PESTICIDE POISONINGS, 3RD ED.). TREAT SYMPTOMATICALLY AND SUPPORTIVELY. ADMINISTRATION OF OXYGEN AND LAVAGE MUST BE PERFORMED BY QUALIFIED MEDICAL PERSONNEL. GET MEDICAL ATTENTION IMMEDIATELY.

ANTIDOTE: THE FOLLOWING ANTIDOTE(S) HAVE BEEN RECOMMENDED. HOWEVER, THE DECISION AS TO WHETHER THE SEVERITY OF POISONING REQUIRES ADMINISTRATION OF ANY ANTIDOTE AND ACTUAL DOSE REQUIRED SHOULD BE MADE BY QUALIFIED MEDICAL PERSONNEL.
FOR CHOLINESTERASE INHIBITORS: ESTABLISH CLEAR AIRWAY AND TISSUE OXYGENATION BY ASPIRATION OF SECRETIONS, AND IF NECESSARY, BY ASSISTED PULMONARY VENTILATION WITH OXYGEN. IMPROVE TISSUE OXYGENATION AS MUCH AS POSSIBLE BEFORE ADMINISTERING ATROPINE TO MINIMIZE THE RISK OF VENTRICULAR FIBRILLATION. ADMINISTER ATROPINE SULFATE INTRAVENOUSLY, OR INTRAMUSCULARLY IF IV INJECTION IS NOT POSSIBLE. IN MODERATELY SEVERE POISONING ADMINISTER ATROPINE SULFATE, 0.4-2.0 MG REPEATED EVERY 15 MINUTES UNTIL ATROPINIZATION IS ACHIEVED (TACHYCARDIA, FLUSHING, DRY MOUTH, MYDRIASIS). MAINTAIN ATROPINIZATION BY REPEATED DOSES FOR 2-12 HOURS, OR LONGER, DEPENDING ON THE SEVERITY OF POISONING. THE APPEARANCE OF RALES IN THE LUNG BASES, MIOSIS, SALIVATION, NAUSEA, BRADYCARDIA, ARE ALL INDICATIONS OF INADEQUATE ATROPINIZATION. SEVERELY POISONED INDIVIDUALS MAY EXHIBIT REMARKABLE TOLERANCE TO ATROPINE; TWO OR MORE TIMES THE DOSAGES SUGGESTED ABOVE MAY BE NEEDED. PERSONS NOT POISONED OR ONLY SLIGHTLY POISONED, HOWEVER, MAY DEVELOP SIGNS OF ATROPINE TOXICITY FROM SUCH LARGE DOSAGES: FEVER, MUSCLE FIBRILLATIONS, AND DELIRIUM ARE THE MAIN SIGNS OF ATROPINE TOXICITY. IF THESE SIGNS APPEAR WHILE THE PATIENT IS FULLY ATROPINIZED, ATROPINE ADMINISTRATION SHOULD BE DISCONTINUED, AT LEAST TEMPORARILY. OBSERVE TREATED PATIENTS CLOSELY AT LEAST 24 HOURS TO INSURE THAT SYMPTOMS (POSSIBLY PULMONARY EDEMA) DO NOT RECUR AS ATROPINIZATION WEARS OFF. IN VERY SEVERE POISONINGS, METABOLIC DISPOSITION OF TOXICANT MAY REQUIRE SEVERAL HOURS OR DAYS DURING WHICH ATROPINIZATION MUST BE MAINTAINED. MARKEDLY LOWER LEVELS OF URINARY METABOLITES INDICATE THAT ATROPINE DOSAGE CAN BE TAPERED OFF. AS DOSAGE IS REDUCED, CHECK THE LUNG BASES FREQUENTLY FOR RALES. IF RALES ARE HEARD OR OTHER SYMPTOMS RETURN, RE-ESTABLISH ATROPINIZATION PROMPTLY (MORGAN, RECOGNITION AND MANAGEMENT OF PESTICIDE POISONINGS, 3RD ED.). ADMINISTRATION OF ANTIDOTE MUST BE PERFORMED BY QUALIFIED MEDICAL PERSONNEL.
IN CASES OF SEVERE POISONING BY ORGANOPHOSPHATE PESTICIDES IN WHICH RESPIRATORY DEPRESSION, MUSCLE WEAKNESS AND TWITCHINGS ARE SEVERE, GIVE PRALIDOXIME (PROTOPAM-AYERST, 2-PAM), 1.0 GRAM INTRAVENOUSLY AT NO MORE THAN 0.5 GRAM PER MINUTE. DOSAGE OF PRALIDOXIME MAY BE REPEATED IN 1-2 HOURS, THEN AT 10-12 HOUR INTERVALS IF NEEDED. IN VERY SEVERE POISONINGS, DOSAGE RATES MAY BE DOUBLED. TREATMENT WITH PRALIDOXIME WILL BE MOST EFFECTIVE IF GIVEN WITHIN THIRTY-SIX HOURS AFTER POISONING (MORGAN, RECOGNITION AND MANAGEMENT OF PESTICIDE POISONINGS, 3RD ED.). ANTIDOTE SHOULD BE ADMINISTERED BY QUALIFIED MEDICAL PERSONNEL.

REACTIVITY

REACTIVITY: STABLE UNDER NORMAL TEMPERATURES AND PRESSURES.
INCOMPATIBILITIES: TEMEPHOS: NO DATA AVAILABLE.
DECOMPOSITION: THERMAL DECOMPOSITION MAY RELEASE TOXIC OXIDES OF PHOSPHORUS AND SULFUR.
POLYMERIZATION: HAZARDOUS POLYMERIZATION HAS NOT BEEN REPORTED TO OCCUR UNDER NORMAL TEMPERATURES AND PRESSURES.

STORAGE AND DISPOSAL

OBSERVE ALL FEDERAL, STATE AND LOCAL REGULATIONS WHEN STORING OR DISPOSING OF THIS SUBSTANCE. FOR ASSISTANCE, CONTACT THE DISTRICT DIRECTOR OF THE ENVIRONMENTAL PROTECTION AGENCY.

STORAGE

STORE IN ACCORDANCE WITH 40 CFR 165 RECOMMENDED PROCEDURES FOR THE DISPOSAL AND STORAGE OF PESTICIDES AND PESTICIDE CONTAINERS.

DISPOSAL

DISPOSAL MUST BE IN ACCORDANCE WITH 40 CFR 165 RECOMMENDED PROCEDURES FOR THE DISPOSAL AND STORAGE OF PESTICIDES AND PESTICIDE CONTAINERS.

CONDITIONS TO AVOID

NONE REPORTED.

SPILL AND LEAK PROCEDURES

OCCUPATIONAL SPILL: DO NOT TOUCH SPILLED MATERIAL. STOP LEAK IF YOU CAN DO IT WITHOUT RISK. USE WATER SPRAY TO REDUCE VAPORS. FOR SMALL SPILLS, TAKE UP WITH SAND OR OTHER ABSORBENT MATERIAL AND PLACE INTO CONTAINERS FOR LATER DISPOSAL. FOR SMALL DRY SPILLS, WITH A CLEAN SHOVEL PLACE MATERIAL INTO CLEAN, DRY CONTAINERS AND COVER. MOVE CONTAINERS FROM SPILL AREA. FOR LARGER SPILLS, DIKE FAR AHEAD OF SPILL FOR LATER DISPOSAL. KEEP UNNECESSARY PEOPLE AWAY. ISOLATE HAZARD AREA AND DENY ENTRY. VENTILATE CLOSED SPACES BEFORE ENTERING.

PROTECTIVE EQUIPMENT

VENTILATION: PROVIDE LOCAL EXHAUST OR PROCESS ENCLOSURE VENTILATION TO MEET PUBLISHED EXPOSURE LIMITS.
RESPIRATOR: THE FOLLOWING RESPIRATORS ARE RECOMMENDED BASED ON INFORMATION FOUND IN THE PHYSICAL DATA, TOXICITY AND HEALTH EFFECTS SECTIONS. THEY ARE RANKED IN ORDER FROM MINIMUM TO MAXIMUM RESPIRATORY PROTECTION. THE SPECIFIC RESPIRATOR SELECTED MUST BE BASED ON CONTAMINATION LEVELS FOUND IN THE WORK PLACE, MUST NOT EXCEED THE WORKING LIMITS OF THE RESPIRATOR AND BE JOINTLY APPROVED BY THE NATIONAL INSTITUTE FOR OCCUPATIONAL SAFETY AND HEALTH AND THE MINE SAFETY AND HEALTH ADMINISTRATION (NIOSH-MSHA).
TYPE 'C' SUPPLIED-AIR RESPIRATOR WITH A FULL FACEPIECE OPERATED IN PRESSURE-DEMAND OR OTHER POSITIVE PRESSURE MODE OR WITH A FULL FACEPIECE, HELMET OR HOOD OPERATED IN CONTINOUS-FLOW MODE.
SELF-CONTAINED BREATHING APPARATUS WITH A FULL FACEPIECE OPERATED IN PRESSURE-DEMAND OR OTHER POSITIVE PRESSURE MODE.
FOR FIREFIGHTING AND OTHER IMMEDIATELY DANGEROUS TO LIFE OR HEALTH CONDITIONS:
SELF-CONTAINED BREATHING APPARATUS WITH FULL FACEPIECE OPERATED IN PRESSURE-DEMAND OR OTHER POSITIVE PRESSURE MODE.
SUPPLIED-AIR RESPIRATOR WITH FULL FACEPIECE AND OPERATED IN PRESSURE-DEMAND OR OTHER POSITIVE PRESSURE MODE IN COMBINATION WITH AN AUXILIARY SELF-CONTAINED BREATHING APPARATUS OPERATED IN PRESSURE-DEMAND OR OTHER POSITIVE PRESSURE MODE.
CLOTHING: EMPLOYEE MUST WEAR APPROPRIATE PROTECTIVE (IMPERVIOUS) CLOTHING AND EQUIPMENT TO PREVENT ANY POSSIBILITY OF SKIN CONTACT WITH THIS SUBSTANCE.
GLOVES: EMPLOYEE MUST WEAR APPROPRIATE PROTECTIVE GLOVES TO PREVENT CONTACT WITH THIS SUBSTANCE.

EYE PROTECTION: EMPLOYEE MUST WEAR SPLASH-PROOF OR DUST-RESISTANT SAFETY GOGGLES AND A FACESHIELD TO PREVENT CONTACT WITH THIS SUBSTANCE.
EMERGENCY WASH FACILITIES: WHERE THERE IS ANY POSSIBILITY THAT AN EMPLOYEE'S EYES AND/OR SKIN MAY BE EXPOSED TO THIS SUBSTANCE, THE EMPLOYER SHOULD PROVIDE AN EYE WASH FOUNTAIN AND QUICK DRENCH SHOWER WITHIN THE IMMEDIATE WORK AREA FOR EMERGENCY USE.

AUTHORIZED BY- OCCUPATIONAL HEALTH SERVICES, INC.
CREATION DATE: 10/05/89 ***REVISION DATE:*** 05/11/90

MATERIAL SAFETY DATA SHEET

OCCUPATIONAL HEALTH SERVICES, INC.
AGRICULTURE AND PESTICIDE DIVISION
450 SEVENTH AVENUE, SUITE 2407
NEW YORK, NEW YORK 10123
1-800-445-MSDS OR (212) 967-1100

EMERGENCY CONTACT:
JOHN S. BRANSFORD, JR. (615) 292-1180

SUBSTANCE IDENTIFICATION

CAS-NUMBER 30560-19-1
SUBSTANCE: **ACEPHATE**
TRADE NAMES/SYNONYMS: N-ACETYL-PHOSPHORAMIDOTHIOIC ACID O,O-DIMETHYL ESTER; ACETYLPHOSPHORAMIDOTHIOIC ACID O,S-DIMETHYL ESTER; O,S-DIMETHYLACETYLPHOSPHOROAMIDOTHIOATE; ACETAMIDOPHOS; DMAP; ORTHENE; ORTRAN; RE 12420; ENT 27 822; PST00065
CHEMICAL FAMILY: ORGANOPHOSPHATE
ESTER
AMIDE
MOLECULAR FORMULA: C4-H10-N-O3-P-S
MOLECULAR WEIGHT: 183.18
CERCLA RATINGS (SCALE 0-3): HEALTH=2 FIRE=U REACTIVITY=0 PERSISTENCE=1
NFPA RATINGS (SCALE 0-4): HEALTH=2 FIRE=U REACTIVITY=0

COMPONENTS AND CONTAMINANTS

COMPONENT: ACEPHATE ***PERCENT:*** 100.0
CAS# 30560-19-1
OTHER CONTAMINANTS: NONE
EXPOSURE LIMITS: NO OCCUPATIONAL EXPOSURE LIMITS ESTABLISHED BY OSHA, ACGIH, OR NIOSH.

PHYSICAL DATA

DESCRIPTION: WHITE CRYSTALLINE SOLID, SLIGHTLY HYGROSCOPIC
MELTING POINT: 198-199 F (92-93 C) ***SPECIFIC GRAVITY:*** 1.35
SOLUBILITY IN WATER: 65%
SOLVENT SOLUBILITY: ACETONE, ALCOHOL, AROMATIC SOLVENTS, POLAR ORGANIC SOLVENTS

FIRE AND EXPLOSION DATA

FIRE AND EXPLOSION HAZARD: UNKNOWN FIRE AND EXPLOSION HAZARD.
FIREFIGHTING MEDIA: DRY CHEMICAL, CARBON DIOXIDE, WATER SPRAY OR FOAM FOR LARGER FIRES, USE WATER SPRAY, FOG OR ALCOHOL FOAM
FIREFIGHTING: MOVE CONTAINER FROM FIRE AREA IF POSSIBLE. DO NOT SCATTER SPILLED MATERIAL WITH HIGH PRESSURE WATER STREAMS. DIKE FIRE CONTROL WATER FOR LATER DISPOSAL (1987 EMERGENCY RESPONSE GUIDEBOOK, DOT P 5800.4, GUIDE PAGE 31).
USE AGENTS SUITABLE FOR TYPE OF SURROUNDING FIRE. AVOID BREATHING HAZARDOUS VAPORS, KEEP UPWIND.

TOXICITY

ACEPHATE: TOXICITY DATA: 2200 MG/M3/5 HOURS INHALATION-MOUSE LCLO; 2000 MG/KG SKIN-RABBIT LD50; 700 MG/KG ORAL-RAT LD50; 233 MG/KG ORAL-MOUSE LD50; 681 MG/KG ORAL-DOG LDLO; 321 MG/KG ORAL-MAMMAL LD50; MUTAGENIC DATA (RTECS). CARCINOGEN STATUS: NONE ACUTE TOXICITY LEVEL: MODERATELY TOXIC BY DERMAL ABSORPTION AND INGESTION. TARGET EFFECTS: CHOLINESTERASE INHIBITOR. POISONING MAY AFFECT THE NERVOUS SYSTEM.* AT INCREASED RISK FROM EXPOSURE: PERSONS WITH RESPIRATORY AILMENTS, RECENT EXPOSURE TO CHOLINESTERASE INHIBITORS OR IMPAIRED CHOLINESTERASE PRODUCTION, OR LIVER MALFUNCTION.* ADDITIONAL DATA: MAY CROSS THE PLACENTA. HIGH ENVIRONMENTAL TEMPERATURES OR EXPOSURE OF THE CHEMICAL TO VISIBLE OR ULTRAVIOLET LIGHT MAY ENHANCE THE TOXICITY. INTERACTIONS WITH MEDICATIONS MAY OCCUR.*
* MAY BE BASED ON GENERAL INFORMATION ON ORGANOPHOSPHATES.

HEALTH EFFECTS AND FIRST AID

INHALATION: ACEPHATE: SEE INFORMATION ON ORGANOPHOSPHATES.
ORGANOPHOSPHATES: CHOLINESTERASE INHIBITOR. **ACUTE EXPOSURE-** WHEN INHALED, THE FIRST EFFECTS OF CHOLINESTERASE INHIBITORS ARE USUALLY RESPIRATORY AND MAY INCLUDE NASAL HYPEREMIA AND WATERY DISCHARGE, COUGH, CHEST DISCOMFORT, DYSPNEA, AND WHEEZING DUE TO INCREASED BRONCHIAL SECRETIONS AND BRONCHOCONSTRICTION. IF SUFFICIENT AMOUNTS ARE ABSORBED, OTHER SYSTEMIC EFFECTS MAY BEGIN WITHIN A FEW MINUTES OR BE DELAYED FOR UP TO 12 HOURS. SYMPTOMS MAY INCLUDE PALLOR, NAUSEA, VOMITING, DIARRHEA, ABDOMINAL CRAMPS, HEADACHE, DIZZINESS, OCULAR PAIN, BLURRED VISION, MIOSIS OR IN SOME CASES, ESPECIALLY INITIALLY, MYDRIASIS, LACRIMATION, SALIVATION, SWEATING, AND CONFUSION. OTHER REPORTED CENTRAL NERVOUS SYSTEM OR NEUROMUSCULAR EFFECTS MAY INCLUDE ATAXIA, SLURRED SPEECH, AREFLEXIA, WEAKNESS, FATIGUE, FASCICULATIONS, TWITCHING, TREMORS POSSIBLY OF THE TONGUE AND EYELIDS, AND EVENTUALLY PARALYSIS OF THE EXTREMITIES AND POSSIBLY OF THE RESPIRATORY MUSCLES. IN SEVERE CASES THERE MAY ALSO BE INVOLUNTARY DEFECATION AND URINATION, CYANOSIS, PSYCHOSIS, HYPERGLYCEMIA, ACUTE PANCREATITIS, CARDIAC IRREGULARITIES, PULMONARY EDEMA, UNCONSCIOUSNESS, CONVULSIONS, AND COMA. DEATH IS PRIMARILY DUE TO RESPIRATORY FAILURE, ALTHOUGH CARDIOVASCULAR EFFECTS INCLUDING CARDIAC ARREST MAY ALSO BE IMPLICATED. LONG TERM SEQUELAE ARE RARE BUT MAY INCLUDE NEUROPSYCHIATRIC DISORDERS AND MYOPATHY WITH MUSCLE TENDERNESS. SOME ORGANOPHOSPHATES MAY CAUSE A DELAYED NEUROPATHY BEGINNING 1-4 WEEKS AFTER AN ACUTE EXPOSURE WHICH MAY OR MAY NOT HAVE CAUSED ACUTE CHOLINERGIC EFFECTS. NUMBNESS, TINGLING, WEAKNESS AND CRAMPING BEGINNING SYMMETRICALLY IN THE LOWER LIMBS MAY PROGRESS TO ATAXIA AND PARALYSIS. IN SEVERE CASES, UPPER LIMB INVOLVEMENT IS POSSIBLE AND FLACCID PARALYSIS MAY PROGRESS TO SPASTIC PARALYSIS WITH EXAGGERATED REFLEXES. IMPROVEMENT MAY OCCUR OVER MONTHS TO YEARS, BUT SOME RESIDUAL IMPAIRMENT USUALLY REMAINS.
CHRONIC EXPOSURE- REPEATED OR PROLONGED EXPOSURE MAY RESULT IN THE EFFECTS OF ACUTE EXPOSURE INCLUDING THE DELAYED NEUROPATHY. OTHER EFFECTS REPORTED IN WORKERS REPEATEDLY EXPOSED INCLUDE IMPAIRED MEMORY AND CONCENTRATION, ACUTE PSYCHOSIS, SEVERE DEPRESSIONS, IRRITABILTY, CONFUSION, APATHY, EMOTIONAL LABILITY, SOCIAL WITHDRAWAL, CONFUSION, HEADACHE, SPEECH DIFFICULTIES, DELAYED REACTION TIMES, SPATIAL DISORIENTATION, NIGHTMARES, SLEEPWALKING, AND DROWSINESS OR INSOMNIA. AN INFLUENZA-LIKE CONDITION WITH HEADACHE, NAUSEA, WEAKNESS, ANOREXIA AND MALAISE HAS ALSO BEEN REPORTED.
FIRST AID- REMOVE FROM EXPOSURE AREA TO FRESH AIR IMMEDIATELY. IF BREATHING HAS STOPPED, GIVE ARTIFICIAL RESPIRATION. MAINTAIN AIRWAY AND BLOOD PRESSURE AND ADMINISTER OXYGEN IF AVAILABLE. KEEP AFFECTED PERSON WARM AND AT REST. TREAT SYMPTOMATICALLY AND SUPPORTIVELY. ADMINISTRATION OF OXYGEN SHOULD BE PERFORMED BY QUALIFIED PERSONNEL. GET MEDICAL ATTENTION IMMEDIATELY.

SKIN CONTACT: ACEPHATE: THIS SUBSTANCE WAS NOT IRRITATING TO RABBIT SKIN AND DID NOT PRODUCE ANY SENSITIZATION IN GUINEA PIGS. SEE INFORMATION ON ORGANOPHOSPHATES.
ORGANOPHOSPHATES: CHOLINESTERASE INHIBITOR. **ACUTE EXPOSURE-** LOCALIZED SWEATING AND FASCICULATIONS MAY OCCUR AT THE SITE OF CONTACT. IF SUFFICIENT AMOUNTS ARE ABSORBED, OTHER EFFECTS OF CHOLINESTERASE INHIBITION AS DESCRIBED IN ACUTE INHALATION MAY OCCUR. SYMPTOMS MAY BE DELAYED 2-3 HOURS, BUT USUALLY NO MORE THAN 12 HOURS. THE RATE OF ABSORPTION IS INCREASED BY THE PRESENCE OF DERMATITIS OR HIGH AMBIENT TEMPERATURES. DELAYED NEUROPATHY IS ALSO POSSIBLE. **CHRONIC EXPOSURE-** REPEATED OR PROLONGED EXPOSURE MAY CAUSE EFFECTS AS DESCRIBED IN ACUTE EXPOSURE. SOME ORGANOPHOSPHATES MAY CAUSE SENSITIZATION.
FIRST AID- REMOVE CONTAMINATED CLOTHING IMMEDIATELY. WASH CONTAMINATED AREAS WITH SOAP AND WATER FOLLOWED BY ALCOHOL (ARENA, POISONING, 4TH ED.). EMERGENCY PERSONNEL SHOULD WEAR GLOVES AND AVOID CONTAMINATION. TREAT RESPIRATORY DIFFICULTY WITH ARTIFICIAL RESPIRATION. GET MEDICAL ATTENTION IMMEDIATELY.

EYE CONTACT: ACEPHATE: EYE EXPOSURE IN THE RABBIT RESULTED IN SLIGHT CONJUNCTIVAL IRRITATION THAT HEALED IN A WEEK. SEE INFORMATION ON ORGANOPHOSPHATES.
ORGANOPHOSPHATES: CHOLINESTERASE INHIBITOR. **ACUTE EXPOSURE-** DIRECT CONTACT MAY CAUSE PAIN, HYPEREMIA, LACRIMATION, TWITCHING OF THE EYELIDS, MIOSIS, AND CILIARY MUSCLE SPASM WITH LOSS OF ACCOMODATION, BLURRED OR DIMMED VISION AND BROWACHE. SOMETIMES MYDRIASIS MAY

OCCUR INSTEAD OF MIOSIS. WITH SUFFICIENT EXPOSURE, OTHER SYMPTOMS OF CHOLINESTERASE INHIBITION AS DESCRIBED IN ACUTE INHALATION MAY OCCUR. **CHRONIC EXPOSURE-** REPEATED OR PROLONGED EXPOSURE MAY CAUSE EFFECTS AS DESCRIBED IN ACUTE EXPOSURE. SOME COMPOUNDS HAVE CAUSED TOXIC EFFECTS ON THE CRYSTALLINE LENS, CONJUNCTIVAL THICKENING AND OBSTRUCTION OF THE NASOLACRIMAL CANALS WHEN USED AS MIOTIC EYEDROPS.

FIRST AID- IRRIGATE EYES WITH WATER OR SALINE SOLUTION. IF SYMPTOMS OF POISONING OCCUR, TREAT RESPIRATORY DIFFICULTY WITH ARTIFICIAL RESPIRATION AND OXYGEN. OBSERVE PATIENT FOR AT LEAST 24-36 HOURS (GOSSELIN, CLINICAL TOXICOLOGY OF COMMERCIAL PRODUCTS, 5TH ED.). GET MEDICAL ATTENTION IMMEDIATELY. OXYGEN SHOULD BE ADMINISTERED BY QUALIFIED MEDICAL PERSONNEL.

INGESTION: ACEPHATE: STUDIES ON REPRODUCTIVE ACTIVITY SHOWED EFFECTS AT DIETARY LEVELS OF 100 PPM AND ABOVE AS EVIDENCED BY REDUCED SURVIVAL OF OFFSPRING. SEE INFORMATION ON ORGANOPHOSPHATES.
ORGANOPHOSPHATES: CHOLINESTERASE INHIBITOR. **ACUTE EXPOSURE-** WHEN INGESTED, THE FIRST EFFECTS MAY BE NAUSEA, VOMITING, ANOREXIA, ABDOMINAL CRAMPS AND DIARRHEA. GASTROINTESTINAL ABSORPTION MAY CAUSE SYMPTOMS OF CHOLINESTERASE INHIBITION AS DESCRIBED IN ACUTE INHALATION. SYMPTOMS MAY BEGIN WITHIN MINUTES OR BE DELAYED FOR HOURS. DELAYED EFFECTS INCLUDING NEUROPATHY MAY ALSO OCCUR. **CHRONIC EXPOSURE-** REPEATED INGESTION MAY CAUSE EFFECTS AS DESCRIBED IN ACUTE EXPOSURE.

FIRST AID- IF PERSON IS ALERT AND RESPIRATION IS NOT DEPRESSED, GIVE SYRUP OF IPECAC FOLLOWED BY WATER (IF VOMITING OCCURS, KEEP HEAD BELOW HIPS TO PREVENT ASPIRATION). IF CONSCIOUSNESS LEVEL DECLINES OR VOMITING HAS NOT OCCURRED IN 15 MINUTES EMPTY STOMACH BY GASTRIC LAVAGE WITH THE AID OF CUFFED ENDOTRACHEAL TUBE USING ISOTONIC SALINE OR 5% SODIUM BICARBONATE FOLLOW WITH ACTIVATED CHARCOAL. ESTABLISH AND MAINTAIN AIRWAY. TREAT RESPIRATORY DIFFICULTY WITH ARTIFICIAL RESPIRATION AND OXYGEN. DO NOT GIVE MORPHINE, AMINOPHYLLINE, PHENOTHIAZINES, RESERPINE, FUROSEMIDE, OR ETHACRYNIC ACID (MORGAN, RECOGNITION AND MANAGEMENT OF PESTICIDE POISONINGS, 3RD ED.). TREAT SYMPTOMATICALLY AND SUPPORTIVELY. ADMINISTRATION OF OXYGEN AND LAVAGE MUST BE PERFORMED BY QUALIFIED MEDICAL PERSONNEL. GET MEDICAL ATTENTION IMMEDIATELY.

ANTIDOTE: THE FOLLOWING ANTIDOTE(S) HAVE BEEN RECOMMENDED. HOWEVER, THE DECISION AS TO WHETHER THE SEVERITY OF POISONING REQUIRES ADMINISTRATION OF ANY ANTIDOTE AND ACTUAL DOSE REQUIRED SHOULD BE MADE BY QUALIFIED MEDICAL PERSONNEL. FOR CHOLINESTERASE INHIBITORS: ESTABLISH CLEAR AIRWAY AND TISSUE OXYGENATION BY ASPIRATION OF SECRETIONS, AND IF NECESSARY, BY ASSISTED PULMONARY VENTILATION WITH OXYGEN. IMPROVE TISSUE OXYGENATION AS MUCH AS POSSIBLE BEFORE ADMINISTERING ATROPINE TO MINIMIZE THE RISK OF VENTRICULAR FIBRILLATION. ADMINISTER ATROPINE SULFATE INTRAVENOUSLY, OR INTRAMUSCULARLY IF IV INJECTION IS NOT POSSIBLE. IN MODERATELY SEVERE POISONING ADMINISTER ATROPINE SULFATE, 0.4-2.0 MG REPEATED EVERY 15 MINUTES UNTIL ATROPINIZATION IS ACHIEVED (TACHYCARDIA, FLUSHING, DRY MOUTH, MYDRIASIS). MAINTAIN ATROPINIZATION BY REPEATED DOSES FOR 2-12 HOURS, OR LONGER, DEPENDING ON THE SEVERITY OF POISONING. THE APPEARANCE OF RALES IN THE LUNG BASES, MIOSIS, SALIVATION, NAUSEA, BRADYCARDIA, ARE ALL INDICATIONS OF INADEQUATE ATROPINIZATION. SEVERELY POISONED INDIVIDUALS MAY EXHIBIT REMARKABLE TOLERANCE TO ATROPINE; TWO OR MORE TIMES THE DOSAGES SUGGESTED ABOVE MAY BE NEEDED. PERSONS NOT POISONED OR ONLY SLIGHTLY POISONED, HOWEVER, MAY DEVELOP SIGNS OF ATROPINE TOXICITY FROM SUCH LARGE DOSAGES: FEVER, MUSCLE FIBRILLATIONS, AND DELIRIUM ARE THE MAIN SIGNS OF ATROPINE TOXICITY. IF THESE SIGNS APPEAR WHILE THE PATIENT IS FULLY ATROPINIZED, ATROPINE ADMINISTRATION SHOULD BE DISCONTINUED, AT LEAST TEMPORARILY. OBSERVE TREATED PATIENTS CLOSELY AT LEAST 24 HOURS TO INSURE THAT SYMPTOMS (POSSIBLY PULMONARY EDEMA) DO NOT RECUR AS ATROPINIZATION WEARS OFF. IN VERY SEVERE POISONINGS, METABOLIC DISPOSITION OF TOXICANT MAY REQUIRE SEVERAL HOURS OR DAYS DURING WHICH ATROPINIZATION MUST BE MAINTAINED. MARKEDLY LOWER LEVELS OF URINARY METABOLITES INDICATE THAT ATROPINE DOSAGE CAN BE TAPERED OFF. AS DOSAGE IS REDUCED, CHECK THE LUNG BASES FREQUENTLY FOR RALES. IF RALES ARE HEARD OR OTHER SYMPTOMS RETURN, RE-ESTABLISH ATROPINIZATION PROMPTLY (MORGAN, RECOGNITION AND MANAGEMENT OF PESTICIDE POISONINGS, 3RD ED.). ADMINISTRATION OF ANTIDOTE MUST BE PERFORMED BY QUALIFIED MEDICAL PERSONNEL.
IN CASES OF SEVERE POISONING BY ORGANOPHOSPHATE PESTICIDES IN WHICH RESPIRATORY DEPRESSION, MUSCLE WEAKNESS AND TWITCHINGS ARE SEVERE, GIVE PRALIDOXIME (PROTOPAM-AYERST, 2-PAM), 1.0 GRAM INTRAVENOUSLY AT NO MORE THAN 0.5 GRAM PER MINUTE. DOSAGE OF PRALIDOXIME MAY BE REPEATED IN 1-2 HOURS, THEN AT 10-12 HOUR INTERVALS IF NEEDED. IN VERY SEVERE POISONINGS, DOSAGE RATES MAY BE DOUBLED. TREATMENT WITH PRALIDOXIME WILL BE MOST EFFECTIVE IF GIVEN WITHIN THIRTY-SIX HOURS AFTER POISONING (MORGAN, RECOGNITION AND MANAGEMENT OF PESTICIDE POISONINGS, 3RD ED.). ANTIDOTE SHOULD BE ADMINISTERED BY QUALIFIED MEDICAL PERSONNEL.

REACTIVITY

REACTIVITY: RELATIVELY STABLE, BUT SENSITIVE TO HEAT AND DECOMPOSES RAPIDLY AT MELTING POINT.

INCOMPATIBILITIES: ACEPHATE: NO DATA AVAILABLE.

DECOMPOSITION: THERMAL DECOMPOSITION PRODUCTS MAY INCLUDE TOXIC AND HAZARDOUS FUMES OF SULFUR, NITROGEN AND PHOSPHORUS.

POLYMERIZATION: HAZARDOUS POLYMERIZATION HAS NOT BEEN REPORTED TO OCCUR UNDER NORMAL TEMPERATURES AND PRESSURES.

STORAGE AND DISPOSAL

OBSERVE ALL FEDERAL, STATE AND LOCAL REGULATIONS WHEN STORING OR DISPOSING OF THIS SUBSTANCE. FOR ASSISTANCE, CONTACT THE DISTRICT DIRECTOR OF THE ENVIRONMENTAL PROTECTION AGENCY.

****STORAGE****

DISPOSAL MUST BE IN ACCORDANCE WITH STANDARDS APPLICABLE TO GENERATORS OF HAZARDOUS WASTE, 40 CFR 262. EPA HAZARDOUS WASTE NUMBER D003.

****DISPOSAL****

DISPOSAL MUST BE IN ACCORDANCE WITH 40 CFR 165 RECOMMENDED PROCEDURES FOR THE DISPOSAL AND STORAGE OF PESTICIDES AND PESTICIDE CONTAINERS.

CONDITIONS TO AVOID

NONE REPORTED.

SPILL AND LEAK PROCEDURES

OCCUPATIONAL SPILL: SWEEP UP AND PLACE IN SUITABLE CLEAN, DRY CONTAINERS FOR RECLAMATION OR LATER DISPOSAL. DO NOT FLUSH SPILLED MATERIAL INTO SEWER. KEEP UNNECESSARY PEOPLE AWAY.

PROTECTIVE EQUIPMENT

VENTILATION: PROVIDE LOCAL EXHAUST VENTILATION SYSTEM.

RESPIRATOR: THE FOLLOWING RESPIRATORS ARE RECOMMENDED BASED ON INFORMATION FOUND IN THE PHYSICAL DATA, TOXICITY AND HEALTH EFFECTS SECTIONS. THEY ARE RANKED IN ORDER FROM MINIMUM TO MAXIMUM RESPIRATORY PROTECTION. THE SPECIFIC RESPIRATOR SELECTED MUST BE BASED ON CONTAMINATION LEVELS FOUND IN THE WORK PLACE, MUST NOT EXCEED THE WORKING LIMITS OF THE RESPIRATOR AND BE JOINTLY APPROVED BY THE NATIONAL INSTITUTE FOR OCCUPATIONAL SAFETY AND HEALTH AND THE MINE SAFETY AND HEALTH ADMINISTRATION (NIOSH-MSHA).
CHEMICAL CARTRIDGE RESPIRATOR WITH AN ORGANIC VAPOR CARTRIDGE(S) IN COMBINATION WITH A DUST AND MIST FILTER.
GAS MASK WITH ORGANIC VAPOR CANISTER (CHIN-STYLE OR FRONT- OR BACK-MOUNTED CANISTER) WITH A DUST AND MIST FILTER.
GAS MASK WITH ORGANIC VAPOR CANISTER (CHIN-STYLE OR FRONT- OR BACK-MOUNTED CANISTER) WITH A PARTICULATE FILTER.
POWERED AIR-PURIFYING RESPIRATOR WITH A HIGH-EFFICIENCY FILTER. TYPE 'C' SUPPLIED-AIR RESPIRATOR WITH A FULL FACEPIECE OPERATED IN A PRESSURE-DEMAND OR OTHER POSITIVE PRESSURE MODE.
SELF-CONTAINED BREATHING APPARATUS WITH A FULL FACEPIECE OPERATED IN PRESSURE-DEMAND OR OTHER POSITIVE PRESSURE MODE.
FOR FIREFIGHTING AND OTHER IMMEDIATELY DANGEROUS TO LIFE OR HEALTH CONDITIONS:
SELF-CONTAINED BREATHING APPARATUS WITH FULL FACEPIECE OPERATED IN PRESSURE-DEMAND OR OTHER POSITIVE PRESSURE MODE.
SUPPLIED-AIR RESPIRATOR WITH FULL FACEPIECE AND OPERATED IN PRESSURE-DEMAND OR OTHER POSITIVE PRESSURE MODE IN COMBINATION WITH AN AUXILIARY SELF-CONTAINED BREATHING APPARATUS OPERATED IN PRESSURE-DEMAND OR OTHER POSITIVE PRESSURE MODE.

CLOTHING: EMPLOYEE MUST WEAR APPROPRIATE PROTECTIVE (IMPERVIOUS) CLOTHING AND EQUIPMENT TO PREVENT REPEATED OR PROLONGED SKIN CONTACT WITH THIS SUBSTANCE.

GLOVES: EMPLOYEE MUST WEAR APPROPRIATE PROTECTIVE GLOVES TO PREVENT CONTACT WITH THIS SUBSTANCE.

EYE PROTECTION: EMPLOYEE MUST WEAR SPLASH-PROOF OR DUST-RESISTANT SAFETY GOGGLES TO PREVENT EYE CONTACT WITH THIS SUBSTANCE.
EMERGENCY EYE WASH: WHERE THERE IS ANY POSSIBILITY THAT AN EMPLOYEE'S EYES MAY BE EXPOSED TO THIS SUBSTANCE, THE EMPLOYER SHOULD PROVIDE AN EYE WASH FOUNTAIN WITHIN THE IMMEDIATE WORK AREA FOR EMERGENCY USE.

AUTHORIZED BY- OCCUPATIONAL HEALTH SERVICES, INC.
CREATION DATE: 10/04/89 ***REVISION DATE:*** 05/31/90

MATERIAL SAFETY DATA SHEET

OCCUPATIONAL HEALTH SERVICES, INC.
AGRICULTURE AND PESTICIDE DIVISION
450 SEVENTH AVENUE, SUITE 2407
NEW YORK, NEW YORK 10123
1-800-445-MSDS OR (212) 967-1100

EMERGENCY CONTACT:
JOHN S. BRANSFORD, JR. (615) 292-1180

SUBSTANCE IDENTIFICATION

CAS-NUMBER 919-54-0

SUBSTANCE: **ACETHION**

TRADE NAMES/SYNONYMS: ACETIC ACID, ((DIETHOXYPHOSPHINOTHIOYL)THIO)-, ETHYL ESTER; ACETIC ACID, MERCAPTO-, ETHYL ESTER, S-ESTER WITH O,O-DIETHYL PHOSPHORODITHIOATE; ((DIETHOXYPHOSPHINOTHIOYL)THIO)ACETIC ACID ETHYL ESTER; MERCAPTOACETIC ACID ETHYL ESTER, S-ESTER WITH O,O-DIETHYL PHOSPHORODITHIOATE; O,O-DIETHYL S-CARBOETHOXYMETHYL DITHIOPHOSPHATE; O,O-DIETHYL S-CARBOETHOXYMETHYL PHOSPHORODITHIOATE; DIETHYL S-(ETHOXYCARBONYLMETHYL)PHOSPHOROTHIOLOTHIONATE; ACETHIONE; ETHOXYPHAS; ETHOXYPHOS; ENT 25650; PST00117

CHEMICAL FAMILY: ORGANOPHOSPHATE

MOLECULAR FORMULA: C8-H17-O4-P-S2

MOLECULAR WEIGHT: 272.34

CERCLA RATINGS (SCALE 0-3): HEALTH=2 FIRE=U REACTIVITY=0 PERSISTENCE=0

NFPA RATINGS (SCALE 0-4): HEALTH=2 FIRE=U REACTIVITY=0

COMPONENTS AND CONTAMINANTS

COMPONENT: ACETHION ***PERCENT:*** 100
CAS# 919-54-0

OTHER CONTAMINANTS: NONE

EXPOSURE LIMITS: NO OCCUPATIONAL EXPOSURE LIMITS ESTABLISHED BY OSHA, ACGIH, OR NIOSH.

PHYSICAL DATA

DESCRIPTION: YELLOWISH LIQUID. ***BOILING POINT:*** 198 F (92 C) @ 0.01 MMHG

SPECIFIC GRAVITY: 1.176 ***EVAPORATION RATE:*** NOT AVAILABLE

SOLUBILITY IN WATER: NOT AVAILABLE

FIRE AND EXPLOSION DATA

FIRE AND EXPLOSION HAZARD: UNKNOWN FIRE AND EXPLOSION HAZARD.

FIREFIGHTING MEDIA: DRY CHEMICAL, CARBON DIOXIDE, HALON, WATER SPRAY OR STANDARD FOAM (1987 EMERGENCY RESPONSE GUIDEBOOK, DOT P 5800.4). FOR LARGER FIRES, USE WATER SPRAY, FOG OR STANDARD FOAM (1987 EMERGENCY RESPONSE GUIDEBOOK, DOT P 5800.4).

FIREFIGHTING: MOVE CONTAINERS FROM FIRE AREA IF POSSIBLE. FIGHT FIRE FROM MAXIMUM DISTANCE. STAY AWAY FROM STORAGE TANK ENDS. DIKE FIRE CONTROL WATER FOR LATER DISPOSAL. DO NOT SCATTER MATERIAL (1987 EMERGENCY RESPONSE GUIDEBOOK, DOT P 5800.4, GUIDE PAGE 55). EXTINGUISH USING AGENT SUITABLE FOR TYPE OF SURROUNDING FIRE. AVOID BREATHING VAPORS AND DUSTS. KEEP UPWIND.

TOXICITY

ACETHION: TOXICITY DATA: 1200 MG/KG ORAL-MOUSE LD50; 1100 MG/KG ORAL-RAT LD50; 1280 MG/KG INTRAPERITONEAL-MOUSE LD50; 1050 MG/KG UNKNOWN-RAT LD50. CARCINOGEN STATUS: NONE. ACUTE TOXICITY LEVEL: MODERATELY TOXIC BY INGESTION. TARGET EFFECTS: CHOLINESTERASE INHIBITOR. POISONING MAY AFFECT THE NERVOUS SYSTEM.* AT INCREASED RISK FROM EXPOSURE: PERSONS WITH RESPIRATORY AILMENTS, RECENT EXPOSURE TO CHOLINESTERASE INHIBITORS OR IMPAIRED CHOLINESTERASE PRODUCTION, OR LIVER MALFUNCTION.* ADDITIONAL DATA: MAY CROSS THE PLACENTA. HIGH ENVIRONMENTAL TEMPERATURES OR EXPOSURE OF THE CHEMICAL TO VISIBLE OR ULTRAVIOLET LIGHT MAY ENHANCE THE TOXICITY. INTERACTIONS WITH MEDICATIONS MAY OCCUR.*

* MAY BE BASED ON GENERAL INFORMATION ON ORGANOPHOSPHATES.

HEALTH EFFECTS AND FIRST AID

INHALATION: ACETHION: SEE INFORMATION ON ORGANOPHOSPHATES. ORGANOPHOSPHATES: CHOLINESTERASE INHIBITOR. **ACUTE EXPOSURE-** WHEN INHALED, THE FIRST EFFECTS OF CHOLINESTERASE INHIBITORS ARE USUALLY RESPIRATORY AND MAY INCLUDE NASAL HYPEREMIA AND WATERY DISCHARGE, COUGH, CHEST DISCOMFORT, DYSPNEA, AND WHEEZING DUE TO INCREASED BRONCHIAL SECRETIONS AND BRONCHOCONSTRICTION. IF SUFFICIENT AMOUNTS ARE ABSORBED, OTHER SYSTEMIC EFFECTS MAY BEGIN WITHIN A FEW MINUTES OR BE DELAYED FOR UP TO 12 HOURS. SYMPTOMS MAY INCLUDE PALLOR, NAUSEA, VOMITING, DIARRHEA, ABDOMINAL CRAMPS, HEADACHE, DIZZINESS, OCULAR PAIN, BLURRED VISION, MIOSIS OR IN SOME CASES, ESPECIALLY INITIALLY, MYDRIASIS, LACRIMATION, SALIVATION, SWEATING, AND CONFUSION. OTHER REPORTED CENTRAL NERVOUS SYSTEM OR NEUROMUSCULAR EFFECTS MAY INCLUDE ATAXIA, SLURRED SPEECH, AREFLEXIA, WEAKNESS, FATIGUE, FASCICULATIONS, TWITCHING, TREMORS POSSIBLY OF THE TONGUE AND EYELIDS, AND EVENTUALLY PARALYSIS OF THE EXTREMITIES AND POSSIBLY OF THE RESPIRATORY MUSCLES. IN SEVERE CASES THERE MAY ALSO BE INVOLUNTARY DEFECATION AND URINATION, CYANOSIS, PSYCHOSIS, HYPERGLYCEMIA, ACUTE PANCREATITIS, CARDIAC IRREGULARITIES, PULMONARY EDEMA, UNCONSCIOUSNESS, CONVULSIONS, AND COMA. DEATH IS PRIMARILY DUE TO RESPIRATORY FAILURE, ALTHOUGH CARDIOVASCULAR EFFECTS INCLUDING CARDIAC ARREST MAY ALSO BE IMPLICATED. LONG TERM SEQUELAE ARE RARE BUT MAY INCLUDE NEUROPSYCHIATRIC DISORDERS AND MYOPATHY WITH MUSCLE TENDERNESS. SOME ORGANOPHOSPHATES MAY CAUSE A DELAYED NEUROPATHY BEGINNING 1-4 WEEKS AFTER AN ACUTE EXPOSURE WHICH MAY OR MAY NOT HAVE CAUSED ACUTE CHOLINERGIC EFFECTS. NUMBNESS, TINGLING, WEAKNESS AND CRAMPING BEGINNING SYMMETRICALLY IN THE LOWER LIMBS MAY PROGRESS TO ATAXIA AND PARALYSIS. IN SEVERE CASES, UPPER LIMB INVOLVEMENT IS POSSIBLE AND FLACCID PARALYSIS MAY PROGRESS TO SPASTIC PARALYSIS WITH EXAGGERATED REFLEXES. IMPROVEMENT MAY OCCUR OVER MONTHS TO YEARS, BUT SOME RESIDUAL IMPAIRMENT USUALLY REMAINS. **CHRONIC EXPOSURE-** REPEATED OR PROLONGED EXPOSURE MAY RESULT IN THE EFFECTS OF ACUTE EXPOSURE INCLUDING THE DELAYED NEUROPATHY. OTHER EFFECTS REPORTED IN WORKERS REPEATEDLY EXPOSED INCLUDE IMPAIRED MEMORY AND CONCENTRATION, ACUTE PSYCHOSIS, SEVERE DEPRESSIONS, IRRITABILTY, CONFUSION, APATHY, EMOTIONAL LABILITY, SOCIAL WITHDRAWAL, CONFUSION, HEADACHE, SPEECH DIFFICULTIES, DELAYED REACTION TIMES, SPATIAL DISORIENTATION, NIGHTMARES, SLEEPWALKING, AND DROWSINESS OR INSOMNIA. AN INFLUENZA-LIKE CONDITION WITH HEADACHE, NAUSEA, WEAKNESS, ANOREXIA AND MALAISE HAS ALSO BEEN REPORTED.

FIRST AID- REMOVE FROM EXPOSURE AREA TO FRESH AIR IMMEDIATELY. IF BREATHING HAS STOPPED, GIVE ARTIFICIAL RESPIRATION. MAINTAIN AIRWAY AND BLOOD PRESSURE AND ADMINISTER OXYGEN IF AVAILABLE. KEEP AFFECTED PERSON WARM AND AT REST. TREAT SYMPTOMATICALLY AND SUPPORTIVELY. ADMINISTRATION OF OXYGEN SHOULD BE PERFORMED BY QUALIFIED PERSONNEL. GET MEDICAL ATTENTION IMMEDIATELY.

SKIN CONTACT: ACETHION: SEE INFORMATION ON ORGANOPHOSPHATES. ORGANOPHOSPHATES: CHOLINESTERASE INHIBITOR. **ACUTE EXPOSURE-** LOCALIZED SWEATING AND FASCICULATIONS MAY OCCUR AT THE SITE OF CONTACT. IF SUFFICIENT AMOUNTS ARE ABSORBED, OTHER EFFECTS OF CHOLINESTERASE INHIBITION AS DESCRIBED IN ACUTE INHALATION MAY OCCUR. SYMPTOMS MAY BE DELAYED 2-3 HOURS, BUT USUALLY NO MORE THAN 12 HOURS. THE RATE OF ABSORPTION IS INCREASED BY THE PRESENCE OF DERMATITIS OR HIGH AMBIENT TEMPERATURES. DELAYED NEUROPATHY IS ALSO POSSIBLE. **CHRONIC EXPOSURE-** REPEATED OR PROLONGED EXPOSURE MAY CAUSE EFFECTS AS DESCRIBED IN ACUTE EXPOSURE. SOME ORGANOPHOSPHATES MAY CAUSE SENSITIZATION.

FIRST AID- REMOVE CONTAMINATED CLOTHING IMMEDIATELY. WASH CONTAMINATED AREAS WITH SOAP AND WATER FOLLOWED BY ALCOHOL (ARENA, POISONING, 4TH ED.). EMERGENCY PERSONNEL SHOULD WEAR GLOVES AND AVOID CONTAMINATION. TREAT RESPIRATORY DIFFICULTY WITH ARTIFICIAL RESPIRATION. GET MEDICAL ATTENTION IMMEDIATELY.

EYE CONTACT: ACETHION: SEE INFORMATION ON ORGANOPHOSPHATES. ORGANOPHOSPHATES: CHOLINESTERASE INHIBITOR. **ACUTE EXPOSURE-** DIRECT CONTACT MAY CAUSE PAIN, HYPEREMIA, LACRIMATION, TWITCHING OF THE EYELIDS, MIOSIS, AND CILIARY MUSCLE SPASM WITH LOSS OF ACCOMODATION, BLURRED OR DIMMED VISION AND BROWACHE. SOMETIMES MYDRIASIS MAY OCCUR INSTEAD OF MIOSIS. WITH SUFFICIENT EXPOSURE, OTHER SYMPTOMS OF CHOLINESTERASE INHIBITION AS DESCRIBED IN ACUTE INHALATION MAY OCCUR. **CHRONIC EXPOSURE-** REPEATED OR PROLONGED EXPOSURE MAY CAUSE EFFECTS AS DESCRIBED IN ACUTE EXPOSURE. SOME COMPOUNDS HAVE CAUSED TOXIC EFFECTS ON THE CRYSTALLINE LENS, CONJUNCTIVAL THICKENING AND OBSTRUCTION OF THE NASOLACRIMAL CANALS WHEN USED AS MIOTIC EYEDROPS.

FIRST AID- IRRIGATE EYES WITH WATER OR SALINE SOLUTION. IF SYMPTOMS OF POISONING OCCUR, TREAT RESPIRATORY DIFFICULTY WITH ARTIFICIAL

RESPIRATION AND OXYGEN. OBSERVE PATIENT FOR AT LEAST 24-36 HOURS (GOSSELIN, CLINICAL TOXICOLOGY OF COMMERCIAL PRODUCTS, 5TH ED.). GET MEDICAL ATTENTION IMMEDIATELY. OXYGEN SHOULD BE ADMINISTERED BY QUALIFIED MEDICAL PERSONNEL.

INGESTION: ACETHION: SEE INFORMATION ON ORGANOPHOSPHATES. ORGANOPHOSPHATES: CHOLINESTERASE INHIBITOR. **ACUTE EXPOSURE**- WHEN INGESTED, THE FIRST EFFECTS MAY BE NAUSEA, VOMITING, ANOREXIA, ABDOMINAL CRAMPS AND DIARRHEA. GASTROINTESTINAL ABSORPTION MAY CAUSE SYMPTOMS OF CHOLINESTERASE INHIBITION AS DESCRIBED IN ACUTE INHALATION. SYMPTOMS MAY BEGIN WITHIN MINUTES OR BE DELAYED FOR HOURS. DELAYED EFFECTS INCLUDING NEUROPATHY MAY ALSO OCCUR. **CHRONIC EXPOSURE**- REPEATED INGESTION MAY CAUSE EFFECTS AS DESCRIBED IN ACUTE EXPOSURE.

FIRST AID- IF PERSON IS ALERT AND RESPIRATION IS NOT DEPRESSED, GIVE SYRUP OF IPECAC FOLLOWED BY WATER (IF VOMITING OCCURS, KEEP HEAD BELOW HIPS TO PREVENT ASPIRATION). IF CONSCIOUSNESS LEVEL DECLINES OR VOMITING HAS NOT OCCURRED IN 15 MINUTES EMPTY STOMACH BY GASTRIC LAVAGE WITH THE AID OF CUFFED ENDOTRACHEAL TUBE USING ISOTONIC SALINE OR 5% SODIUM BICARBONATE FOLLOW WITH ACTIVATED CHARCOAL. ESTABLISH AND MAINTAIN AIRWAY. TREAT RESPIRATORY DIFFICULTY WITH ARTIFICIAL RESPIRATION AND OXYGEN. DO NOT GIVE MORPHINE, AMINOPHYLLINE, PHENOTHIAZINES, RESERPINE, FUROSEMIDE, OR ETHACRYNIC ACID (MORGAN, RECOGNITION AND MANAGEMENT OF PESTICIDE POISONINGS, 3RD ED.). TREAT SYMPTOMATICALLY AND SUPPORTIVELY. ADMINISTRATION OF OXYGEN AND LAVAGE MUST BE PERFORMED BY QUALIFIED MEDICAL PERSONNEL. GET MEDICAL ATTENTION IMMEDIATELY.

ANTIDOTE: THE FOLLOWING ANTIDOTE(S) HAVE BEEN RECOMMENDED. HOWEVER, THE DECISION AS TO WHETHER THE SEVERITY OF POISONING REQUIRES ADMINISTRATION OF ANY ANTIDOTE AND ACTUAL DOSE REQUIRED SHOULD BE MADE BY QUALIFIED MEDICAL PERSONNEL.

FOR CHOLINESTERASE INHIBITORS: ESTABLISH CLEAR AIRWAY AND TISSUE OXYGENATION BY ASPIRATION OF SECRETIONS, AND IF NECESSARY, BY ASSISTED PULMONARY VENTILATION WITH OXYGEN. IMPROVE TISSUE OXYGENATION AS MUCH AS POSSIBLE BEFORE ADMINISTERING ATROPINE TO MINIMIZE THE RISK OF VENTRICULAR FIBRILLATION. ADMINISTER ATROPINE SULFATE INTRAVENOUSLY, OR INTRAMUSCULARLY IF IV INJECTION IS NOT POSSIBLE. IN MODERATELY SEVERE POISONING ADMINISTER ATROPINE SULFATE, 0.4-2.0 MG REPEATED EVERY 15 MINUTES UNTIL ATROPINIZATION IS ACHIEVED (TACHYCARDIA, FLUSHING, DRY MOUTH, MYDRIASIS). MAINTAIN ATROPINIZATION BY REPEATED DOSES FOR 2-12 HOURS, OR LONGER, DEPENDING ON THE SEVERITY OF POISONING. THE APPEARANCE OF RALES IN THE LUNG BASES, MIOSIS, SALIVATION, NAUSEA, BRADYCARDIA, ARE ALL INDICATIONS OF INADEQUATE ATROPINIZATION. SEVERELY POISONED INDIVIDUALS MAY EXHIBIT REMARKABLE TOLERANCE TO ATROPINE; TWO OR MORE TIMES THE DOSAGES SUGGESTED ABOVE MAY BE NEEDED. PERSONS NOT POISONED OR ONLY SLIGHTLY POISONED, HOWEVER, MAY DEVELOP SIGNS OF ATROPINE TOXICITY FROM SUCH LARGE DOSAGES: FEVER, MUSCLE FIBRILLATIONS, AND DELIRIUM ARE THE MAIN SIGNS OF ATROPINE TOXICITY. IF THESE SIGNS APPEAR WHILE THE PATIENT IS FULLY ATROPINIZED, ATROPINE ADMINISTRATION SHOULD BE DISCONTINUED, AT LEAST TEMPORARILY. OBSERVE TREATED PATIENTS CLOSELY AT LEAST 24 HOURS TO INSURE THAT SYMPTOMS (POSSIBLY PULMONARY EDEMA) DO NOT RECUR AS ATROPINIZATION WEARS OFF. IN VERY SEVERE POISONINGS, METABOLIC DISPOSITION OF TOXICANT MAY REQUIRE SEVERAL HOURS OR DAYS DURING WHICH ATROPINIZATION MUST BE MAINTAINED. MARKEDLY LOWER LEVELS OF URINARY METABOLITES INDICATE THAT ATROPINE DOSAGE CAN BE TAPERED OFF.

AS DOSAGE IS REDUCED, CHECK THE LUNG BASES FREQUENTLY FOR RALES. IF RALES ARE HEARD OR OTHER SYMPTOMS RETURN, RE-ESTABLISH ATROPINIZATION PROMPTLY (MORGAN, RECOGNITION AND MANAGEMENT OF PESTICIDE POISONINGS, 3RD ED.). ADMINISTRATION OF ANTIDOTE MUST BE PERFORMED BY QUALIFIED MEDICAL PERSONNEL.

IN CASES OF SEVERE POISONING BY ORGANOPHOSPHATE PESTICIDES IN WHICH RESPIRATORY DEPRESSION, MUSCLE WEAKNESS AND TWITCHINGS ARE SEVERE, GIVE PRALIDOXIME (PROTOPAM-AYERST, 2-PAM), 1.0 GRAM INTRAVENOUSLY AT NO MORE THAN 0.5 GRAM PER MINUTE. DOSAGE OF PRALIDOXIME MAY BE REPEATED IN 1-2 HOURS, THEN AT 10-12 HOUR INTERVALS IF NEEDED. IN VERY SEVERE POISONINGS, DOSAGE RATES MAY BE DOUBLED. TREATMENT WITH PRALIDOXIME WILL BE MOST EFFECTIVE IF GIVEN WITHIN THIRTY-SIX HOURS AFTER POISONING (MORGAN, RECOGNITION AND MANAGEMENT OF PESTICIDE POISONINGS, 3RD ED.). ANTIDOTE SHOULD BE ADMINISTERED BY QUALIFIED MEDICAL PERSONNEL.

REACTIVITY

REACTIVITY: STABLE UNDER NORMAL TEMPERATURES AND PRESSURES.

INCOMPATIBILITIES: ACETHION: NO DATA AVAILABLE.

DECOMPOSITION: THERMAL DECOMPOSITION MAY RELEASE TOXIC OXIDES OF PHOSPHORUS AND SULFUR.

POLYMERIZATION: HAZARDOUS POLYMERIZATION HAS NOT BEEN REPORTED TO OCCUR UNDER NORMAL TEMPERATURES AND PRESSURES.

STORAGE AND DISPOSAL

OBSERVE ALL FEDERAL, STATE AND LOCAL REGULATIONS WHEN STORING OR DISPOSING OF THIS SUBSTANCE. FOR ASSISTANCE, CONTACT THE DISTRICT DIRECTOR OF THE ENVIRONMENTAL PROTECTION AGENCY.

STORAGE

STORE IN ACCORDANCE WITH 40 CFR 165 RECOMMENDED PROCEDURES FOR THE DISPOSAL AND STORAGE OF PESTICIDES AND PESTICIDE CONTAINERS.

DISPOSAL

DISPOSAL MUST BE IN ACCORDANCE WITH 40 CFR 165 RECOMMENDED PROCEDURES FOR THE DISPOSAL AND STORAGE OF PESTICIDES AND PESTICIDE CONTAINERS.

CONDITIONS TO AVOID

NONE REPORTED.

SPILL AND LEAK PROCEDURES

OCCUPATIONAL SPILL: DO NOT TOUCH SPILLED MATERIAL. STOP LEAK IF YOU CAN DO IT WITHOUT RISK. USE WATER SPRAY TO REDUCE VAPORS. FOR SMALL SPILLS, TAKE UP WITH SAND OR OTHER ABSORBENT MATERIAL AND PLACE INTO CONTAINERS FOR LATER DISPOSAL. FOR SMALL DRY SPILLS, WITH A CLEAN SHOVEL PLACE MATERIAL INTO CLEAN, DRY CONTAINERS AND COVER. MOVE CONTAINERS FROM SPILL AREA. FOR LARGER SPILLS, DIKE FAR AHEAD OF SPILL FOR LATER DISPOSAL. KEEP UNNECESSARY PEOPLE AWAY. ISOLATE HAZARD AREA AND DENY ENTRY. VENTILATE CLOSED SPACES BEFORE ENTERING.

PROTECTIVE EQUIPMENT

VENTILATION: PROVIDE LOCAL EXHAUST VENTILATION SYSTEM.

RESPIRATOR: THE FOLLOWING RESPIRATORS ARE RECOMMENDED BASED ON INFORMATION FOUND IN THE PHYSICAL DATA, TOXICITY AND HEALTH EFFECTS SECTIONS. THEY ARE RANKED IN ORDER FROM MINIMUM TO MAXIMUM RESPIRATORY PROTECTION. THE SPECIFIC RESPIRATOR SELECTED MUST BE BASED ON CONTAMINATION LEVELS FOUND IN THE WORK PLACE, MUST NOT EXCEED THE WORKING LIMITS OF THE RESPIRATOR AND BE JOINTLY APPROVED BY THE NATIONAL INSTITUTE FOR OCCUPATIONAL SAFETY AND HEALTH AND THE MINE SAFETY AND HEALTH ADMINISTRATION (NIOSH-MSHA).

CHEMICAL CARTRIDGE RESPIRATOR WITH PESTICIDE CARTRIDGE.

GAS MASK WITH A PESTICIDE CANISTER (CHIN-STYLE OR FRONT- OR BACK-MOUNTED CANISTER).

TYPE 'C' SUPPLIED-AIR RESPIRATOR OPERATED IN THE PRESSURE-DEMAND OR OTHER POSITIVE PRESSURE OR CONTINUOUS-FLOW MODE.

SELF-CONTAINED BREATHING APPARATUS.

FOR FIREFIGHTING AND OTHER IMMEDIATELY DANGEROUS TO LIFE OR HEALTH CONDITIONS:

SELF-CONTAINED BREATHING APPARATUS WITH FULL FACEPIECE OPERATED IN PRESSURE-DEMAND OR OTHER POSITIVE PRESSURE MODE.

SUPPLIED-AIR RESPIRATOR WITH FULL FACEPIECE AND OPERATED IN PRESSURE-DEMAND OR OTHER POSITIVE PRESSURE MODE IN COMBINATION WITH AN AUXILIARY SELF-CONTAINED BREATHING APPARATUS OPERATED IN PRESSURE-DEMAND OR OTHER POSITIVE PRESSURE MODE.

CLOTHING: EMPLOYEE MUST WEAR APPROPRIATE PROTECTIVE (IMPERVIOUS) CLOTHING AND EQUIPMENT TO PREVENT REPEATED OR PROLONGED SKIN CONTACT WITH THIS SUBSTANCE.

GLOVES: EMPLOYEE MUST WEAR APPROPRIATE PROTECTIVE GLOVES TO PREVENT CONTACT WITH THIS SUBSTANCE.

EYE PROTECTION: EMPLOYEE MUST WEAR SPLASH-PROOF OR DUST-RESISTANT SAFETY GOGGLES TO PREVENT EYE CONTACT WITH THIS SUBSTANCE. EMERGENCY EYE WASH: WHERE THERE IS ANY POSSIBILITY THAT AN EMPLOYEE'S EYES MAY BE EXPOSED TO THIS SUBSTANCE, THE EMPLOYER SHOULD PROVIDE AN EYE WASH FOUNTAIN WITHIN THE IMMEDIATE WORK AREA FOR EMERGENCY USE.

AUTHORIZED BY- OCCUPATIONAL HEALTH SERVICES, INC.

CREATION DATE: 10/04/89 ***REVISION DATE:*** 08/06/90

MATERIAL SAFETY DATA SHEET

OCCUPATIONAL HEALTH SERVICES, INC.
AGRICULTURE AND PESTICIDE DIVISION

EMERGENCY CONTACT:
JOHN S. BRANSFORD, JR. (615) 292-1180

450 SEVENTH AVENUE, SUITE 2407
NEW YORK, NEW YORK 10123
1-800-445-MSDS OR (212) 967-1100

SUBSTANCE IDENTIFICATION

CAS-NUMBER 64-19-7

SUBSTANCE: <u>ACETIC ACID, GLACIAL</u>

TRADE NAMES/SYNONYMS: ACETIC ACID; GLACIAL ACETIC ACID; ETHANOIC ACID; VINEGAR ACID; ETHYLIC ACID; PYROLIGNEUS ACID; METHANECARBOXYLIC ACID; STCC 4931303; UN 2789; A-37; A-38; A-38C; A-38-P; A-38-SI; A-38-S; A-507; A-465; C2H4O2; PST00120

CHEMICAL FAMILY: CARBOXYLIC ACID, ALIPHATIC

MOLECULAR FORMULA: C-H3-C-O2-H

MOLECULAR WEIGHT: 60.05

CERCLA RATINGS (SCALE 0-3): HEALTH=2 FIRE=2 REACTIVITY=1 PERSISTENCE=0

NFPA RATINGS (SCALE 0-4): HEALTH=2 FIRE=2 REACTIVITY=1

COMPONENTS AND CONTAMINANTS

COMPONENT: ACETIC ACID, GLACIAL ***PERCENT:*** 100
CAS# 64-19-7

OTHER CONTAMINANTS: NONE

EXPOSURE LIMITS: ACETIC ACID, GLACIAL: 10 PPM (25 MG/M3) OSHA TWA 10 PPM (25 MG/M3) ACGIH TWA; 15 PPM (37 MG/M3) ACGIH STEL
5000 POUNDS CERCLA SECTION 103 REPORTABLE QUANTITY

PHYSICAL DATA

DESCRIPTION: CLEAR, COLORLESS LIQUID WITH A STRONG, PUNGENT, CHARACTERISTIC ODOR OF VINEGAR AND WHEN WELL DILUTED WITH WATER, AN ACID TASTE.

BOILING POINT: 244 F (118 C) ***MELTING POINT:*** 62 F (17 C)

SPECIFIC GRAVITY: 1.0492 ***VISCOSITY:*** 1.22 CPS @ 20 C

VAPOR PRESSURE: 11.8 MMHG @ 20 C ***EVAPORATION RATE:*** (BUTYL ACETATE=1) 0.97

PH: 2.4 (1.0 M SOL.) ***SOLUBILITY IN WATER:*** VERY SOLUBLE

ODOR THRESHOLD: 1.0 PPM ***VAPOR DENSITY:*** 2.07

SOLVENT SOLUBILITY: SOLUBLE IN ETHANOL, GLYCEROL, ETHER, ACETONE, BENZENE, CARBON TETRACHLORIDE; INSOLUBLE IN CARBON DISULFIDE, CHLOROFORM, DIMETHYL SULFOXIDE

FIRE AND EXPLOSION DATA

FIRE AND EXPLOSION HAZARD: MODERATE FIRE HAZARD WHEN EXPOSED TO HEAT OR FLAME.
VAPOR-AIR MIXTURES ARE EXPLOSIVE ABOVE FLASH POINT.
VAPORS ARE HEAVIER THAN AIR AND MAY TRAVEL A CONSIDERABLE DISTANCE TO A SOURCE OF IGNITION AND FLASH BACK.

FLASH POINT: 103 F (39 C) (CC) ***UPPER EXPLOSIVE LIMIT:*** 19.9% @ 200 F

LOWER EXPLOSIVE LIMIT: 4.0% ***AUTOIGNITION TEMP.:*** 867 F (464 C)

FLAMMABILITY CLASS(OSHA): II

FIREFIGHTING MEDIA: DRY CHEMICAL, CARBON DIOXIDE, HALON, WATER SPRAY OR STANDARD FOAM (1987 EMERGENCY RESPONSE GUIDEBOOK, DOT P 5800.4).
FOR LARGER FIRES, USE WATER SPRAY, FOG OR STANDARD FOAM (1987 EMERGENCY RESPONSE GUIDEBOOK, DOT P 5800.4).
ALCOHOL FOAM (NFPA 325M, FIRE HAZARD PROPERTIES OF FLAMMABLE LIQUIDS, GASES, AND VOLATILE SOLIDS, 1984).

FIREFIGHTING: MOVE CONTAINER FROM FIRE AREA IF POSSIBLE. DO NOT GET WATER INSIDE CONTAINER. COOL FIRE-EXPOSED CONTAINERS WITH WATER FROM SIDE UNTIL WELL AFTER FIRE IS OUT. STAY AWAY FROM STORAGE TANK ENDS. WITHDRAW IMMEDIATELY IN CASE OF RISING SOUND FROM VENTING SAFETY DEVICE OR ANY DISCOLORATION OF STORAGE TANK DUE TO FIRE (1987 EMERGENCY RESPONSE GUIDEBOOK, DOT P 5800.4, GUIDE PAGE 29).
USE FLOODING AMOUNTS OF WATER AS A FOG; SOLID STREAMS MAY BE INEFFECTIVE. COOL CONTAINERS WITH FLOODING AMOUNTS OF WATER FROM AS FAR A DISTANCE AS POSSIBLE. USE WATER SPRAY TO ABSORB CORROSIVE VAPORS. AVOID BREATHING CORROSIVE VAPORS; KEEP UPWIND.
FIRE FIGHTING PHASES: USE WATER SPRAY, DRY CHEMICAL, ALCOHOL FOAM, OR CARBON DIOXIDE. USE WATER TO KEEP FIRE-EXPOSED CONTAINERS COOL. IF A LEAK OR SPILL HAS NOT IGNITED, USE WATER SPRAY TO DISPERSE THE VAPORS AND TO PROTECT THE MEN ATTEMPTING TO STOP A LEAK. WATER SPRAY MAY BE USED TO FLUSH SPILLS AWAY FROM EXPOSURES AND TO DILUTE SPILLS TO NONFLAMMABLE MIXTURES (NFPA 49, HAZARDOUS CHEMICALS DATA, 1975).

TRANSPORTATION DATA

DEPARTMENT OF TRANSPORTATION HAZARD CLASSIFICATION 49 CFR 172.101: CORROSIVE MATERIAL DEPARTMENT OF TRANSPORTATION LABELING REQUIREMENTS 49 CFR 172.101 AND SUBPART E: CORROSIVE
DEPARTMENT OF TRANSPORTATION PACKAGING REQUIREMENTS: 49 CFR 173.245 EXCEPTIONS: 49 CFR 173.244

TOXICITY

ACETIC ACID, GLACIAL: IRRITATION DATA: 50 MG/24 HOURS SKIN-HUMAN MILD: 525 MG OPEN SKIN-RABBIT SEVERE; 50 MG/24 HOURS SKIN-RABBIT MILD; 20 MG/24 HOURS SKIN-RABBIT MODERATE; 50 UG OPEN EYE-RABBIT SEVERE; 5 MG/30 SECONDS RINSED EYE-RABBIT MILD. TOXICITY DATA: 816 PPM/3 MINUTES INHALATION-HUMAN TCLO; 16,000 PPM/4 HOURS INHALATION-RAT LCLO; 5620 PPM/1 HOUR INHALATION-MOUSE LC50; 1060 MG/KG SKIN-RABBIT LD50; 1470 UG/KG ORAL-HUMAN TDLO; 3310 MG/KG ORAL-RAT LD50; 1200 MG/KG ORAL-RABBIT LDLO; 1200 MG/KG SUBCUTANEOUS-RABBIT LDLO; 525 MG/KG INTRAVENOUS-MOUSE LD50; 1200 MG/KG RECTAL-RABBIT LDLO; 308 MG/KG UNREPORTED-MAN LDLO; MUTAGENIC DATA (RTECS); REPRODUCTIVE EFFECTS DATA (RTECS). CARCINOGEN STATUS: NONE. LOCAL EFFECTS: CORROSIVE- EYE, SKIN, MUCOUS MEMBRANES. ACUTE TOXICITY LEVEL: MODERATELY TOXIC BY INHALATION, DERMAL ABSORPTION, INGESTION. TARGET EFFECTS: POISONING MAY AFFECT THE LIVER, KIDNEYS, AND CARDIOVASCULAR SYSTEM. AT INCREASED RISK: PERSONS WITH A HISTORY OF RESPIRATORY, SKIN OR EYE DISEASE.

HEALTH EFFECTS AND FIRST AID

INHALATION: ACETIC ACID, GLACIAL: CORROSIVE. 1000 PPM IMMEDIATELY DANGEROUS TO LIFE OR HEALTH. **<u>ACUTE EXPOSURE</u>**- MAY CAUSE SEVERE IRRITATION OF THE RESPIRATORY TRACT. 50 PPM OR MORE IS INTOLERABLE TO MOST PERSONS AND RESULTS IN PHARYNGEAL EDEMA AND CHRONIC BRONCHITIS. OTHER SYMPTOMS MAY INCLUDE COUGHING, DYSPNEA, SHORTNESS OF BREATH, LARYNGITIS, PULMONARY EDEMA, BRONCHOPNEUMONIA AND HYPOTENSION. **<u>CHRONIC EXPOSURE</u>**- WORKERS REPEATEDLY EXPOSED TO CONCENTRATIONS UP TO 200 PPM HAVE BEEN FOUND TO SUFFER FROM PALPEBRAL EDEMA WITH HYPERTROPHY OF THE LYMPH NODES, CHRONIC PHARYNGITIS, CHRONIC BRONCHITIS AND IN SOME CASES, ASTHMATIC BRONCHITIS AND TRACES OF EROSION OF THE TEETH. COMPLAINTS OF DIGESTIVE DISORDERS WITH PYROSIS AND CONSTIPATION HAVE ALSO BEEN REPORTED.

FIRST AID- REMOVE FROM EXPOSURE AREA TO FRESH AIR IMMEDIATELY. IF BREATHING HAS STOPPED, GIVE ARTIFICIAL RESPIRATION. MAINTAIN AIRWAY AND BLOOD PRESSURE AND ADMINISTER OXYGEN IF AVAILABLE. KEEP AFFECTED PERSON WARM AND AT REST. TREAT SYMPTOMATICALLY AND SUPPORTIVELY. ADMINISTRATION OF OXYGEN SHOULD BE PERFORMED BY QUALIFIED PERSONNEL. GET MEDICAL ATTENTION IMMEDIATELY.

SKIN CONTACT: ACETIC ACID, GLACIAL: CORROSIVE. **<u>ACUTE EXPOSURE</u>**- DIRECT CONTACT MAY CAUSE SEVERE IRRITATION WITH PAIN, ERYTHEMA, BLISTERS, BURNS AND SUPERFICIAL DESTRUCTION OF THE SKIN WITH SLOW HEALING. THE SKIN MAY BECOME BLACKENED, HYPERKERATOTIC AND FISSURED. **<u>CHRONIC EXPOSURE</u>**- REPEATED AND PROLONGED CONTACT MAY CAUSE DARKENING OF THE SKIN, IRRITATION AND DERMATITIS.

FIRST AID- REMOVE CONTAMINATED CLOTHING AND SHOES IMMEDIATELY. WASH AFFECTED AREA WITH SOAP OR MILD DETERGENT AND LARGE AMOUNTS OF WATER UNTIL NO EVIDENCE OF CHEMICAL REMAINS (AT LEAST 15-20 MINUTES). IN CASE OF CHEMICAL BURNS, COVER AREA WITH STERILE, DRY DRESSING. BANDAGE SECURELY, BUT NOT TOO TIGHTLY. GET MEDICAL ATTENTION IMMEDIATELY.

EYE CONTACT: ACETIC ACID, GLACIAL: CORROSIVE. **<u>ACUTE EXPOSURE</u>**- DIRECT CONTACT CAUSES SEVERE IRRITATION, LACRIMATION, CORNEAL EROSION, OPACIFICATION, IRITIS AND POSSIBLY LOSS OF SIGHT IN HUMANS. REGENERATION OF THE EPITHELIUM MAY TAKE MANY MONTHS, BUT CORNEAL ANESTHESIA AND OPACITY WILL USUALLY BE PERMANENT. IN LESS SEVERE CASES, CONJUNCTIVITIS, PHOTOPHOBIA AND HYPEREMIA OF THE CONJUNCTIVA OCCURRED. THE VAPOR AND DILUTE SOLUTIONS MAY CAUSE CONJUNCTIVAL HYPEREMIA AND SOMETIMES INJURY TO THE CORNEAL EPITHELIUM. **<u>CHRONIC EXPOSURE</u>**- DEPENDING ON THE CONCENTRATION AND DURATION OF EXPOSURE, EFFECTS SIMILAR TO ACUTE EXPOSURE MAY OCCUR.

FIRST AID- WASH EYES IMMEDIATELY WITH LARGE AMOUNTS OF WATER, OCCASIONALLY LIFTING UPPER AND LOWER LIDS, UNTIL NO EVIDENCE OF CHEMICAL REMAINS (AT LEAST 15-20 MINUTES). CONTINUE IRRIGATING WITH NORMAL SALINE UNTIL THE PH HAS RETURNED TO NORMAL (30-60 MINUTES). COVER WITH STERILE BANDAGES. GET MEDICAL ATTENTION IMMEDIATELY.

INGESTION: ACETIC ACID, GLACIAL: CORROSIVE. **<u>ACUTE EXPOSURE</u>**- IN CASES OF ACCIDENTAL INGESTION, SEVERE ULCERONECROTIC LESIONS OF THE UPPER DIGESTIVE TRACT, STRICTURE OF THE ESOPHAGUS, AND PERFORATION OF THE ESOPHAGUS AND PYLORUS HAVE BEEN OBSERVED WITH HEMATEMESIS, DIARRHEA, SHOCK, HEMOGLOBINURIA FOLLOWED BY ANURIA AND UREMIA. OTHER SYMPTOMS MAY INCLUDE VOMITING, ABDOMINAL SPASMS, THIRST,

DIFFICULTY IN SWALLOWING, HYPOTHERMIA, RAPID AND WEAK PULSE, SLOW AND SHALLOW BREATHING, LARYNGITIS, BRONCHITIS, PULMONARY EDEMA, PNEUMONIA, HEMOLYSIS, ALBUMINURIA, HEMATURIA, TWITCHING, CONVULSIONS, CARDIOVASCULAR COLLAPSE, SHOCK AND DEATH. EFFECTS ON THE NEWBORN HAVE BEEN REPORTED IN RATS FROM 700 MG/KG, ADMINISTERED 18 DAYS AFTER GESTATION. **CHRONIC EXPOSURE**- NO DATA AVAILABLE.

FIRST AID- DO NOT USE GASTRIC LAVAGE OR EMESIS. DILUTE THE ACID IMMEDIATELY BY DRINKING LARGE QUANTITIES OF WATER OR MILK. IF VOMITING PERSISTS, ADMINISTER FLUIDS REPEATEDLY. INGESTED ACID MUST BE DILUTED APPROXIMATELY 100 FOLD TO RENDER IT HARMLESS TO TISSUES. MAINTAIN AIRWAY AND TREAT SHOCK (DREISBACH, HANDBOOK OF POISONING, 12TH ED.). GET MEDICAL ATTENTION IMMEDIATELY. IF VOMITING OCCURS, KEEP HEAD BELOW HIPS TO HELP PREVENT ASPIRATION.

ANTIDOTE: NO SPECIFIC ANTIDOTE. TREAT SYMPTOMATICALLY AND SUPPORTIVELY.

REACTIVITY

REACTIVITY: REACTS EXOTHERMICALLY WITH WATER.

INCOMPATIBILITIES: ACETIC ACID, GLACIAL: ACETALDEHYDE: VIOLENT, EXOTHERMIC POLYMERIZATION REACTION. ACETIC ANHYDRIDE + WATER: VIOLENT, EXOTHERMIC REACTION. 2-AMINOETHANOL: TEMPERATURE AND PRESSURE INCREASE IN CLOSED CONTAINER. AMMONIUM NITRATE: IGNITES ON WARMING, ESPECIALLY IF CONCENTRATED. 5-AZIDOTETRAZOLE: POSSIBLE EXPLOSIVE REACTION. BASES: EXOTHERMIC REACTION. BROMINE PENTAFLUORIDE: FIRE AND EXPLOSION HAZARD. CARBONATES: INCOMPATIBLE. CHLORINE TRIFLUORIDE: VIOLENT, POSSIBLY EXPLOSIVE REACTION. CHLOROSULFONIC ACID: TEMPERATURE AND PRESSURE INCREASE IN CLOSED CONTAINER. CHROMIC ACID: EXPLOSIVE REACTION IF NOT KEPT COLD. CHROMIUM TRIOXIDE: POSSIBLE FIRE AND EXPLOSION HAZARD. DIALLYL METHYL CARBINOL AND OZONE: EXPLOSIVE REACTION. ETHYLENE DIAMINE: TEMPERATURE AND PRESSURE INCREASE IN CLOSED CONTAINER. ETHYLENEIMINE: TEMPERATURE AND PRESSURE INCREASE IN CLOSED CONTAINER. HYDROGEN PEROXIDE: EXOTHERMIC REACTION ON HEATING WITH THE PRODUCTION OF PERACETIC ACID WHICH WILL EXPLODE AT 110 C. HYDROXIDES: INCOMPATIBLE. LEAD: CORRODES. METALS: ATTACKS MOST METALS, INCLUDING ZINC. NITRIC ACID: EXPLOSIVE REACTION IF NOT KEPT COLD. NITRIC ACID AND ACETONE: EXPLOSIVE REACTION (DELAYED) IN CLOSED CONTAINER. OLEUM: TEMPERATURE AND PRESSURE INCREASE IN CLOSED CONTAINER. OXIDIZERS: FIRE AND EXPLOSION HAZARD. PERCHLORIC ACID: EXPLOSIVE REACTION. PERMANGANATES: EXPLOSIVE REACTION IF NOT KEPT COLD. PHOSPHATES: INCOMPATIBLE. PHOSPHORUS ISOCYANATE: VIOLENT REACTION. PHOSPHORUS TRICHLORIDE: EXPLOSIVE REACTION. POTASSIUM HYDROXIDE: VIOLENT REACTION. POTASSIUM PERMANGANATE: POSSIBLE EXPLOSION IF INADEQUATELY COOLED. POTASSIUM TERT-BUTOXIDE: IGNITION REACTION. SODIUM HYDROXIDE: TEMPERATURE AND PRESSURE INCREASE IN CLOSED CONTAINER. SODIUM PEROXIDE: EXPLOSIVE REACTION IF NOT KEPT COLD. XYLENE: MAY FORM DETONABLE MIXTURES DURING TERPHTHALIC ACID PRODUCTION, THE PRESENCE OF WATER MAY DECREASE THE HAZARD.

DECOMPOSITION: THERMAL DECOMPOSITION PRODUCTS MAY INCLUDE TOXIC OXIDES OF CARBON.

POLYMERIZATION: HAZARDOUS POLYMERIZATION HAS NOT BEEN REPORTED TO OCCUR UNDER NORMAL TEMPERATURES AND PRESSURES.

STORAGE AND DISPOSAL

OBSERVE ALL FEDERAL, STATE AND LOCAL REGULATIONS WHEN STORING OR DISPOSING OF THIS SUBSTANCE. FOR ASSISTANCE, CONTACT THE DISTRICT DIRECTOR OF THE ENVIRONMENTAL PROTECTION AGENCY.

STORAGE

PROTECT AGAINST PHYSICAL DAMAGE. DETACHED STORAGE IS PREFERRED. SEPARATE FROM OXIDIZING MATERIALS AND AVOID STORAGE NEAR COMBUSTIBLE MATERIALS. KEEP ABOVE ITS FREEZING POINT (62 F) TO AVOID RUPTURE OF CARBOYS AND GLASS CONTAINERS (NFPA 49, HAZARDOUS CHEMICALS DATA, 1975).

BONDING AND GROUNDING: SUBSTANCES WITH LOW ELECTROCONDUCTIVITY, WHICH MAY BE IGNITED BY ELECTROSTATIC SPARKS, SHOULD BE STORED IN CONTAINERS WHICH MEET THE BONDING AND GROUNDING GUIDELINES SPECIFIED IN NFPA 77-1983, RECOMMENDED PRACTICE ON STATIC ELECTRICITY.

STORE AWAY FROM INCOMPATIBLE SUBSTANCES.

DISPOSAL

DISPOSAL MUST BE IN ACCORDANCE WITH STANDARDS APPLICABLE TO GENERATORS OF HAZARDOUS WASTE, 40 CFR 262. EPA HAZARDOUS WASTE NUMBER D002. 100 POUND CERCLA SECTION 103 REPORTABLE QUANTITY.

CONDITIONS TO AVOID

AVOID CONTACT WITH HEAT, SPARKS, FLAMES OR OTHER IGNITION SOURCES. VAPORS MAY BE EXPLOSIVE. MATERIAL IS CORROSIVE; AVOID CONTACT WITH SKIN OR EYES. DO NOT ALLOW CONTAMINATION OF WATER SOURCES.

USUAL SHIPPING CONTAINERS: GLASS AND POLYETHYLENE CARBOYS AND POLYETHYLENE-LINED DRUMS, TANK BARGES (NFPA 49, HAZARDOUS CHEMICALS DATA, 1975).

SPILL AND LEAK PROCEDURES

SOIL SPILL: DIG A HOLDING AREA SUCH AS A PIT, POND OR LAGOON TO CONTAIN SPILL AND DIKE SURFACE FLOW USING BARRIER OF SOIL, SANDBAGS, FOAMED POLYURETHANE OR FOAMED CONCRETE. ABSORB LIQUID MASS WITH FLY ASH OR CEMENT POWDER.

NEUTRALIZE WITH CAUSTIC SODA (NAOH) OR SODA ASH (NA2CO3)

AIR SPILL: KNOCK DOWN VAPORS WITH WATER SPRAY. KEEP UPWIND.

WATER USED TO KNOCK DOWN VAPORS MAY BECOME CORROSIVE OR TOXIC AND SHOULD BE CONTAINED PROPERLY FOR LATER DISPOSAL.

WATER SPILL: NEUTRALIZE WITH CAUSTIC SODA.

OCCUPATIONAL SPILL: SHUT OFF IGNITION SOURCES. DO NOT TOUCH SPILLED MATERIAL. STOP LEAK IF YOU CAN DO IT WITHOUT RISK. USE WATER SPRAY TO REDUCE VAPORS. DO NOT GET WATER INSIDE CONTAINER. FOR SMALL SPILLS, TAKE UP WITH SAND OR OTHER ABSORBENT MATERIAL AND PLACE INTO CONTAINERS FOR LATER DISPOSAL. FOR LARGER SPILLS, DIKE FAR AHEAD OF SPILL FOR LATER DISPOSAL. NO SMOKING, FLAMES OR FLARES IN HAZARD AREA. KEEP UNNECESSARY PEOPLE AWAY; ISOLATE HAZARD AREA AND DENY ENTRY.

REPORTABLE QUANTITY (RQ): 5000 POUNDS THE SUPERFUND AMENDMENTS AND REAUTHORIZATION ACT (SARA) SECTION 304 REQUIRES THAT A RELEASE EQUAL TO OR GREATER THAN THE REPORTABLE QUANTITY FOR THIS SUBSTANCE BE IMMEDIATELY REPORTED TO THE LOCAL EMERGENCY PLANNING COMMITTEE AND THE STATE EMERGENCY RESPONSE COMMISSION (40 CFR 355.40). IF THE RELEASE OF THIS SUBSTANCE IS REPORTABLE UNDER CERCLA SECTION 103, THE NATIONAL RESPONSE CENTER MUST BE NOTIFIED IMMEDIATELY AT (800) 424-8802 OR (202) 426-2675 IN THE METROPOLITAN WASHINGTON, D.C. AREA (40 CFR 302.6).

PROTECTIVE EQUIPMENT

VENTILATION: PROVIDE LOCAL EXHAUST VENTILATION SYSTEM TO MEET PUBLISHED EXPOSURE LIMITS.

RESPIRATOR: THE FOLLOWING RESPIRATORS AND MAXIMUM USE CONCENTRATIONS ARE RECOMMENDATIONS BY THE U.S. DEPARTMENT OF HEALTH AND HUMAN SERVICES, NIOSH POCKET GUIDE TO CHEMICAL HAZARDS; NIOSH CRITERIA DOCUMENTS OR BY THE U.S. DEPARTMENT OF LABOR, 29 CFR 1910 SUBPART Z. THE SPECIFIC RESPIRATOR SELECTED MUST BE BASED ON CONTAMINATION LEVELS FOUND IN THE WORK PLACE, MUST NOT EXCEED THE WORKING LIMITS OF THE RESPIRATOR AND BE JOINTLY APPROVED BY THE NATIONAL INSTITUTE FOR OCCUPATIONAL SAFETY AND HEALTH AND THE MINE SAFETY AND HEALTH ADMINISTRATION (NIOSH-MSHA).

ACETIC ACID, GLACIAL: 250 PPM- SUPPLIED-AIR RESPIRATOR OPERATED IN CONTINUOUS FLOW MODE. POWERED AIR-PURIFYING RESPIRATOR WITH ORGANIC VAPOR CARTRIDGE(S).

500 PPM- CHEMICAL CARTRIDGE RESPIRATOR WITH FULL FACEPIECE AND ORGANIC VAPOR CARTRIDGE(S). SELF-CONTAINED BREATHING APPARATUS WITH FULL FACEPIECE. SUPPLIED-AIR RESPIRATOR WITH FULL FACEPIECE. AIR-PURIFYING FULL FACEPIECE RESPIRATOR (GAS MASK) WITH CHIN-STYLE OR FRONT- OR BACK-MOUNTED ORGANIC VAPOR CANISTER. POWERED AIR-PURIFYING RESPIRATOR WITH TIGHT-FITTING FACEPIECE AND ORGANIC VAPOR CARTRIDGE(S).

1000 PPM- SUPPLIED-AIR RESPIRATOR WITH FULL FACEPIECE AND OPERATED IN PRESSURE-DEMAND OR OTHER POSITIVE PRESSURE MODE.

ESCAPE- AIR-PURIFYING FULL FACEPIECE RESPIRATOR (GAS MASK) WITH CHIN-STYLE OR FRONT- OR BACK-MOUNTED ORGANIC VAPOR CANISTER. ESCAPE-TYPE SELF-CONTAINED BREATHING APPARATUS.

FOR FIREFIGHTING AND OTHER IMMEDIATELY DANGEROUS TO LIFE OR HEALTH CONDITIONS:

SELF-CONTAINED BREATHING APPARATUS WITH FULL FACEPIECE OPERATED IN PRESSURE-DEMAND OR OTHER POSITIVE PRESSURE MODE. SUPPLIED-AIR RESPIRATOR WITH FULL FACEPIECE AND OPERATED IN PRESSURE-DEMAND OR OTHER POSITIVE PRESSURE MODE IN COMBINATION WITH AN AUXILIARY SELF-CONTAINED BREATHING APPARATUS OPERATED IN PRESSURE-DEMAND OR OTHER POSITIVE PRESSURE MODE.

CLOTHING: EMPLOYEE MUST WEAR APPROPRIATE PROTECTIVE (IMPERVIOUS) CLOTHING AND EQUIPMENT TO PREVENT ANY POSSIBILITY OF SKIN CONTACT WITH THIS SUBSTANCE.

GLOVES: EMPLOYEE MUST WEAR APPROPRIATE PROTECTIVE GLOVES TO PREVENT CONTACT WITH THIS SUBSTANCE.

EYE PROTECTION: EMPLOYEE MUST WEAR SPLASH-PROOF OR DUST-RESISTANT SAFETY GOGGLES AND A FACESHIELD TO PREVENT CONTACT WITH THIS SUBSTANCE.

EMERGENCY WASH FACILITIES: WHERE THERE IS ANY POSSIBILITY THAT AN EMPLOYEE'S EYES AND/OR SKIN MAY BE EXPOSED TO THIS SUBSTANCE, THE EMPLOYER SHOULD PROVIDE AN EYE WASH FOUNTAIN AND QUICK DRENCH SHOWER WITHIN THE IMMEDIATE WORK AREA FOR EMERGENCY USE.

AUTHORIZED BY- OCCUPATIONAL HEALTH SERVICES, INC.
CREATION DATE: 11/15/89 ***REVISION DATE:*** 06/12/90

MATERIAL SAFETY DATA SHEET

OCCUPATIONAL HEALTH SERVICES, INC.
AGRICULTURE AND PESTICIDE DIVISION
450 SEVENTH AVENUE, SUITE 2407
NEW YORK, NEW YORK 10123
1-800-445-MSDS OR (212) 967-1100

EMERGENCY CONTACT:
JOHN S. BRANSFORD, JR. (615) 292-1180

SUBSTANCE IDENTIFICATION

CAS-NUMBER 67-64-1
SUBSTANCE: **ACETONE**
TRADE NAMES/SYNONYMS: 2-PROPANONE; DIMETHYLFORMALDEHYDE; DIMETHYL KETONE; BETA-KETOPROPANE; METHYL KETONE; PROPANONENE; PYROACETIC ETHER; KTI ACETONE (HUGHES); RCRA U002; STCC 4908105; UN 1090; C3H60; PST00140
CHEMICAL FAMILY: KETONE, ALIPHATIC
MOLECULAR FORMULA: C-H3-C-(O)-C-H3
MOLECULAR WEIGHT: 58.08
CERCLA RATINGS (SCALE 0-3): HEALTH=1 FIRE=3 REACTIVITY=0 PERSISTENCE=0
NFPA RATINGS (SCALE 0-4): HEALTH=1 FIRE=3 REACTIVITY=0

COMPONENTS AND CONTAMINANTS

COMPONENT: ACETONE ***PERCENT:*** 100.0
CAS# 67-64-1
OTHER CONTAMINANTS: NONE
EXPOSURE LIMITS: ACETONE: 750 PPM (1780 MG/M3) OSHA TWA; 1000 PPM (2375 MG/M3) OSHA STEL 750 PPM (1780 MG/M3) ACGIH TWA; 1000 PPM (2375 MG/M3) ACGIH STEL 250 PPM (590 MG/M3) NIOSH RECOMMENDED 10 HOUR TWA 5000 POUNDS CERCLA SECTION 103 REPORTABLE QUANTITY SUBJECT TO SARA SECTION 313 ANNUAL TOXIC CHEMICAL RELEASE REPORTING

PHYSICAL DATA

DESCRIPTION: CLEAR, COLORLESS, VOLATILE LIQUID WITH A CHARACTERISTIC, SWEETISH MINT-LIKE ODOR AND SWEETISH TASTE. ***BOILING POINT:*** 133 F (56 C)
MELTING POINT: -139 F (-95 C) ***SPECIFIC GRAVITY:*** 0.7899 ***VOLATILITY:*** 100%
VAPOR PRESSURE: 180 MMHG @ 20 C ***EVAPORATION RATE:*** (BUTYL ACETATE=1) 6
SOLUBILITY IN WATER: VERY SOLUBLE ***ODOR THRESHOLD:*** 20 PPM
VAPOR DENSITY: 2.0
SOLVENT SOLUBILITY: SOLUBLE IN ALCOHOL, ETHER, BENZENE, CHLOROFORM, DIMETHYLFORMAMIDE AND MOST OILS.

FIRE AND EXPLOSION DATA

FIRE AND EXPLOSION HAZARD: DANGEROUS FIRE HAZARD WHEN EXPOSED TO HEAT OR FLAME.
VAPORS ARE HEAVIER THAN AIR AND MAY TRAVEL A CONSIDERABLE DISTANCE TO A SOURCE OF IGNITION AND FLASH BACK.
VAPOR-AIR MIXTURES ARE EXPLOSIVE.
FLASH POINT: -4 F (-20 C) (CC) ***UPPER EXPLOSIVE LIMIT:*** 13%
LOWER EXPLOSIVE LIMIT: 2.5% ***AUTOIGNITION TEMP.:*** 869 F (465 C)
FLAMMABILITY CLASS(OSHA): IB
FIREFIGHTING MEDIA: DRY CHEMICAL, CARBON DIOXIDE, HALON, WATER SPRAY OR ALCOHOL FOAM (1987 EMERGENCY RESPONSE GUIDEBOOK, DOT P 5800.4).
FOR LARGER FIRES, USE WATER SPRAY, FOG OR ALCOHOL FOAM (1987 EMERGENCY RESPONSE GUIDEBOOK, DOT P 5800.4).
ALCOHOL FOAM (NFPA 325M, FIRE HAZARD PROPERTIES OF FLAMMABLE LIQUIDS, GASES, AND VOLATILE SOLIDS, 1984).
FIREFIGHTING: MOVE CONTAINER FROM FIRE AREA IF POSSIBLE. COOL FIRE-EXPOSED CONTAINERS WITH WATER FROM SIDE UNTIL WELL AFTER FIRE IS OUT. STAY AWAY FROM STORAGE TANK ENDS. FOR MASSIVE FIRE IN STORAGE AREA, USE UNMANNED HOSE HOLDER OR MONITOR NOZZLES, ELSE WITHDRAW FROM AREA AND LET FIRE BURN. WITHDRAW IMMEDIATELY IN CASE OF RISING SOUND FROM VENTING SAFETY DEVICE OR ANY DISCOLORATION OF STORAGE TANK DUE TO FIRE (1987 EMERGENCY RESPONSE GUIDEBOOK, DOT P 5800.4, GUIDE PAGE 26). EXTINGUISH ONLY IF FLOW CAN BE STOPPED. USE FLOODING AMOUNTS OF WATER AS A FOG; SOLID STREAMS MAY BE INEFFECTIVE. COOL CONTAINERS WITH FLOODING AMOUNTS OF WATER FROM AS FAR A DISTANCE AS POSSIBLE. AVOID BREATHING VAPORS; KEEP UPWIND. IF FIRE IS UNCONTROLLABLE OR CONTAINERS ARE EXPOSED TO DIRECT FLAME, EVACUATE TO A RADIUS OF 1500 FEET.
CONSIDER EVACUATION OF DOWNWIND AREA IF MATERIAL IS LEAKING.
WATER MAY BE INEFFECTIVE (NFPA 325M, FIRE HAZARD PROPERTIES OF FLAMMABLE LIQUIDS, GASES, AND VOLATILE SOLIDS, 1984)

TRANSPORTATION DATA

DEPARTMENT OF TRANSPORTATION HAZARD CLASSIFICATION 49 CFR 172.101: FLAMMABLE LIQUID
DEPARTMENT OF TRANSPORTATION LABELING REQUIREMENTS 49 CFR 172.101 AND SUBPART E: FLAMMABLE LIQUID
DEPARTMENT OF TRANSPORTATION PACKAGING REQUIREMENTS: 49 CFR 173.119 EXCEPTIONS: 49 CFR 173.118

TOXICITY

ACETONE: IRRITATION DATA: 395 MG OPEN SKIN-RABBIT MILD; 500 MG/24 HOURS SKIN-RABBIT MILD; 500 PPM EYE-HUMAN; 3950 UG EYE-RABBIT SEVERE; 20 MG/24 HOURS EYE-RABBIT MODERATE. TOXICITY DATA: 500 PPM INHALATION-HUMAN TCLO; 440 UG/M3/6 MONTHS INHALATION-MAN TCLO; 10 MG/M3/6 HOURS INHALATION-MAN TCLO; 12000 PPM/4 HOURS INHALATION-MAN TCLO; 50100 MG/M3/8 HOURS INHALATION-RAT LC50; 110 GM/M3/1 HOUR INHALATION-MOUSE LCLO; 20 GM/KG SKIN-RABBIT LD50; 2857 MG/KG ORAL-MAN TDLO; 8 GM/KG ORAL-DOG LDLO; 5800 MG/KG ORAL-RAT LD50; 3000 MG/KG ORAL-MOUSE LD50; 5340 MG/KG ORAL-RABBIT LD50; 5 GM/KG SUBCUTANEOUS-DOG LDLO; 5000 MG/KG SUBCUTANEOUS-GUINEA PIG LDLO; 5500 MG/KG INTRAVENOUS-RAT LD50; 4 GM/KG INTRAVENOUS-MOUSE LDLO; 1576 MG/KG INTRAVENOUS-RABBIT LDLO; 500 MG/KG INTRAPERITONEAL-RAT LDLO; 1297 MG/KG INTRAPERITONEAL-MOUSE LD50; 8 GM/KG INTRAPERITONEAL-DOG LDLO; 1159 MG/KG UNREPORTED-MAN LDLO; MUTAGENIC DATA (RTECS); REPRODUCTIVE EFFECTS DATA (RTECS). CARCINOGEN STATUS: NONE. LOCAL EFFECTS: IRRITANT- INHALATION, SKIN, EYE. ACUTE TOXICITY LEVEL: MODERATELY TOXIC BY INHALATION; SLIGHTLY TOXIC BY DERMAL ABSORPTION AND INGESTION. TARGET EFFECTS: CENTRAL NERVOUS SYSTEM DEPRESSANT. AT INCREASED RISK FROM EXPOSURE- PERSONS WITH CHRONIC RESPIRATORY OR SKIN DISEASES. ADDITIONAL DATA: ALCOHOL MAY ENHANCE THE TOXIC EFFECTS.

HEALTH EFFECTS AND FIRST AID

INHALATION: ACETONE: IRRITANT/NARCOTIC. 20,000 PPM IMMEDIATELY DANGEROUS TO LIFE OR HEALTH. **ACUTE EXPOSURE-** VAPOR CONCENTRATIONS AROUND 1000 PPM MAY CAUSE SLIGHT TRANSIENT IRRITATION OF THE UPPER RESPIRATORY TRACT. EXPOSURE TO 12,000 PPM HAS CAUSED THROAT IRRITATION AND CENTRAL NERVOUS SYSTEM DEPRESSION WITH WEAKNESS OF THE LEGS, HEADACHE, DIZZINESS, DROWSINESS, NAUSEA AND A GENERAL FEELING OF MALAISE. OTHER POSSIBLE EFFECTS FROM EXPOSURE TO HIGH CONCENTRATIONS INCLUDE DRYNESS OF THE MOUTH AND THROAT, INCOORDINATION OF MOTION AND SPEECH, RESTLESSNESS, ANOREXIA, ABDOMINAL PAIN, VOMITING, SOMETIMES FOLLOWED BY HEMATEMESIS, HYPOTHERMIA, DYSPNEA, SLOW, IRREGULAR RESPIRATION, SLOW, WEAK PULSE, PROGRESSIVE COLLAPSE WITH STUPOR, AND IN SEVERE CASES, COMA. LIVER DAMAGE MAY BE INDICATED BY HIGH UROBILIN LEVELS AND JAUNDICE. KIDNEY DAMAGE MAY BE INDICATED BY ALBUMIN AND RED AND WHITE BLOOD CELLS IN THE URINE. BLOOD GLUCOSE LEVELS MAY BE AFFECTED AND FATAL KETOSIS IS POSSIBLE. **CHRONIC EXPOSURE-** WORKERS EXPOSED TO 500 PPM/6 HOURS/6 DAYS EXPERIENCED MUCOUS MEMBRANE IRRITATION, AN UNPLEASANT SMELL, HEAVY EYES, OVERNIGHT HEADACHE, AND GENERAL WEAKNESS ACCOMPANIED BY HEMATOLOGIC CHANGES. RECOVERY OCCURRED IN SEVERAL DAYS. WORKERS EXPOSED TO 1000 PPM FOR 3 HOURS/DAY FOR 7-15 YEARS REPORTED CHRONIC INFLAMMATION OF THE RESPIRATORY TRACT, STOMACH AND DUODENUM, DIZZINESS, LOSS OF STRENGTH, AND ASTHENIA. DROWSINESS, VERTIGO, SENSATION OF HEAT, AND COUGHING HAVE ALSO BEEN REPORTED FROM CHRONIC EXPOSURE TO LOW CONCENTRATIONS. REPRODUCTIVE EFFECTS HAVE BEEN REPORTED IN ANIMALS.
FIRST AID- REMOVE FROM EXPOSURE AREA TO FRESH AIR IMMEDIATELY. IF BREATHING HAS STOPPED, PERFORM ARTIFICIAL RESPIRATION. KEEP PERSON WARM AND AT REST. TREAT SYMPTOMATICALLY AND SUPPORTIVELY. GET MEDICAL ATTENTION IMMEDIATELY.

SKIN CONTACT: ACETONE: IRRITANT. **ACUTE EXPOSURE-** CONTACT WITH THE LIQUID CAUSED MILD IRRITATION IN RABBITS. CELLULAR DAMAGE TO THE OUTER LAYERS OF THE EPITHELIUM WITH MILD EDEMA AND HYPEREMIA HAS BEEN DEMONSTRATED IN HUMANS, BUT WAS READILY REVERSIBLE. SMALL AMOUNTS MAY BE ABSORBED THROUGH INTACT SKIN. **CHRONIC EXPOSURE-** REPEATED OR PROLONGED EXPOSURE MAY CAUSE DERMATITIS WITH DRYING, CRACKING, AND ERYTHEMA DUE TO THE DEFATTING ACTION ACCOMPANIED BY PERSISTENT PARESTHESIA OF THE FINGERS. THE AMOUNT ABSORBED THROUGH THE SKIN INCREASES DIRECTLY WITH THE FREQUENCY AND EXTENT OF THE EXPOSURE. 2

OR 3 GUINEA PIGS EXPOSED BY SKIN CONTACT FOR 3 WEEKS DEVELOPED CATARACTS BY THE END OF THREE MONTHS.

FIRST AID- REMOVE CONTAMINATED CLOTHING AND SHOES IMMEDIATELY. WASH AFFECTED AREA WITH SOAP OR MILD DETERGENT AND LARGE AMOUNTS OF WATER UNTIL NO EVIDENCE OF CHEMICAL REMAINS (APPROXIMATELY 15-20 MINUTES). GET MEDICAL ATTENTION IMMEDIATELY.

EYE CONTACT: ACETONE: IRRITANT. **ACUTE EXPOSURE-** IN HUMANS, VAPORS PRODUCE ONLY SLIGHT IRRITATION WHEN THE CONCENTRATION IS AT OR BELOW 1000 PPM. HOWEVER, HIGH VAPOR CONCENTRATIONS HAVE CAUSED CORNEAL EPITHELIAL AND CONJUNCTIVAL INJURY IN ANIMALS. LIQUID SPLASHED IN HUMAN EYES CAUSES AN IMMEDIATE STINGING SENSATION AND, IF WASHED PROMPTLY, DAMAGE ONLY TO THE CORNEAL EPITHELIUM CHARACTERIZED BY MICROSCOPIC GRAY DOTS AND A FOREIGN BODY SENSATION, WHICH HEALS COMPLETELY IN 1-2 DAYS. **CHRONIC EXPOSURE-** PROLONGED OR REPEATED EXPOSURE TO THE VAPORS MAY CAUSE IRRITATION OR CONJUNCTIVITIS.

FIRST AID- WASH EYES IMMEDIATELY WITH LARGE AMOUNTS OF WATER OR NORMAL SALINE, OCCASIONALLY LIFTING UPPER AND LOWER LIDS, UNTIL NO EVIDENCE OF CHEMICAL REMAINS (APPROXIMATELY 15-20 MINUTES). GET MEDICAL ATTENTION IMMEDIATELY.

INGESTION: ACETONE: NARCOTIC. **ACUTE EXPOSURE-** MAY CAUSE A FRUITY ODOR OF THE BREATH AND MUCOUS MEMBRANE AND GASTROENTERIC IRRITATION. IN ACUTE CASES, A LATENT PERIOD MAY BE FOLLOWED BY RESTLESSNESS, DIARRHEA, NAUSEA AND VOMITING PROCEEDING TO HEMATEMESIS AND PROGRESSIVE COLLAPSE WITH STUPOR. HEPATORENAL LESIONS HAVE BEEN REPORTED. THE BLOOD GLUCOSE LEVEL MAY BE AFFECTED AND KETOSIS MAY BE FATAL. 10-20 MILLILITERS HAVE BEEN TOLERATED WITHOUT ILL EFFECTS. LARGE AMOUNTS HAVE PRODUCED LETHARGY, PHARYNGEAL AND SOFT PALATE EROSIONS AND ERYTHEMA. 200 MILLILITERS HAVE CAUSED STUPOR WITHIN A HALF HOUR, FLUSHED CHEEKS, SHALLOW RESPIRATION, AND COMA WHICH LASTED FOR 12 HOURS. RENAL GLUCOSURIA PERSISTED FOR 5 MONTHS. **CHRONIC EXPOSURE-** NO DATA AVAILABLE.

FIRST AID- IF THE PERSON IS CONSCIOUS AND NOT CONVULSING, INDUCE EMESIS BY GIVING SYRUP OF IPECAC FOLLOWED BY WATER. (IF VOMITING OCCURS KEEP THE HEAD BELOW THE HIPS TO PREVENT ASPIRATION). REPEAT IN 20 MINUTES IF NOT EFFECTIVE INITIALLY. GIVE ACTIVATED CHARCOAL. IN PATIENTS WITH DEPRESSED RESPIRATION OR IF EMESIS IS NOT PRODUCED, PERFORM GASTRIC LAVAGE CAUTIOUSLY (DREISBACH, HANDBOOK OF POISONING, 12TH ED.). TREAT SYMPTOMATICALLY AND SUPPORTIVELY. GASTRIC LAVAGE SHOULD BE PERFORMED BY QUALIFIED MEDICAL PERSONNEL. GET MEDICAL ATTENTION IMMEDIATELY.

ANTIDOTE: NO SPECIFIC ANTIDOTE. TREAT SYMPTOMATICALLY AND SUPPORTIVELY.

REACTIVITY

REACTIVITY: STABLE UNDER NORMAL TEMPERATURES AND PRESSURES.

INCOMPATIBILITIES: ACETONE: ACIDS: INCOMPATIBLE. AMINES (ALIPHATIC): INCOMPATIBLE. BROMINE: VIOLENT REACTION WITH EXCESS AMOUNTS OF BROMINE. BROMINE TRIFLUORIDE: EXPLOSION ON CONTACT. BROMOFORM: VIOLENT REACTION IN PRESENCE OF BASES (E.G. POTASSIUM HYDROXIDE). CHLOROFORM: VIOLENT REACTION IN PRESENCE OF A BASE. CHROMIUM TRIOXIDE: IGNITION ON CONTACT AT AMBIENT TEMPERATURE. CHROMYL CHLORIDE: INCANDESCENT REACTION. DIOXYGEN DIFLUORIDE + SOLID CARBON DIOXIDE: EXPLOSION AT -78 C. HEXACHLOROMELAMINE: POSSIBLE EXPLOSION. HYDROGEN PEROXIDE: EXPLOSION. NITRIC ACID: IGNITION. NITRIC + ACETIC ACID MIXTURE: POSSIBLE EXPLOSION. NITRIC + SULFURIC ACID MIXTURE: VIOLENT OXIDATION. NITROSYL CHLORIDE: EXPLOSIVE REACTION. NITROSYL PERCHLORATE: IGNITION AND EXPLOSION. NITRYL PERCHLORATE: IGNITION AND EXPLOSION. OXIDIZERS (STRONG): FIRE AND EXPLOSION HAZARD. PERMONOSULFURIC ACID: EXPLOSION. PLASTICS: INCOMPATIBLE. PLATINUM + NITROSYL CHLORIDE: POSSIBLE EXPLOSION. POTASSIUM-TERT-BUTOXIDE: IGNITION. RAYON: INCOMPATIBLE. SODIUM HYPOBROMITE: EXPLOSION. SODIUM HYPOIODITE: POSSIBLE EXPLOSION. SULFUR DICHLORIDE: VIOLENT REACTION. SULFURIC ACID AND POTASSIUM BICHROMATE: IGNITION. THIODIGLYCOL + HYDROGEN PEROXIDE: POSSIBLE EXPLOSION. THIOTRIAZYL PERCHLORATE: POSSIBLE EXPLOSION. 1,1,1-TRICHLOROETHANE: EXOTHERMIC CONDENSATION BY A BASIC CATALYST. TRICHLOROMELAMINE: POSSIBLE EXPLOSION. SEE ALSO KETONES.
KETONES: ACETALDEHYDE: VIOLENT CONDENSATION REACTION. NITRIC ACID + HYDROGEN PEROXIDE: FORMATION OF EXPLOSIVE PRODUCT. PERCHLORIC ACID: VIOLENT DECOMPOSITION.

DECOMPOSITION: THERMAL DECOMPOSITION PRODUCTS MAY INCLUDE TOXIC OXIDES OF CARBON.

POLYMERIZATION: HAZARDOUS POLYMERIZATION HAS NOT BEEN REPORTED TO OCCUR UNDER NORMAL TEMPERATURES AND PRESSURES.

STORAGE AND DISPOSAL

OBSERVE ALL FEDERAL, STATE AND LOCAL REGULATIONS WHEN STORING OR DISPOSING OF THIS SUBSTANCE. FOR ASSISTANCE, CONTACT THE DISTRICT DIRECTOR OF THE ENVIRONMENTAL PROTECTION AGENCY.

****STORAGE****

STORE IN ACCORDANCE WITH 29 CFR 1910.106.
BONDING AND GROUNDING: SUBSTANCES WITH LOW ELECTROCONDUCTIVITY, WHICH MAY BE IGNITED BY ELECTROSTATIC SPARKS, SHOULD BE STORED IN CONTAINERS WHICH MEET THE BONDING AND GROUNDING GUIDELINES SPECIFIED IN NFPA 77-1983, RECOMMENDED PRACTICE ON STATIC ELECTRICITY.
STORE AWAY FROM INCOMPATIBLE SUBSTANCES.

****DISPOSAL****

DISPOSAL MUST BE IN ACCORDANCE WITH STANDARDS APPLICABLE TO GENERATORS OF HAZARDOUS WASTE, 40CFR 262. EPA HAZARDOUS WASTE NUMBER U002.

CONDITIONS TO AVOID

AVOID CONTACT WITH HEAT, SPARKS, FLAMES, OR OTHER SOURCES OF IGNITION. VAPORS MAY BE EXPLOSIVE AND POISONOUS; DO NOT ALLOW UNNECESSARY PERSONNEL IN AREA. DO NOT OVERHEAT CONTAINERS; CONTAINERS MAY VIOLENTLY RUPTURE AND TRAVEL A CONSIDERABLE DISTANCE IN HEAT OF FIRE.

SPILL AND LEAK PROCEDURES

OCCUPATIONAL SPILL: SHUT OFF IGNITION SOURCES. STOP LEAK IF YOU CAN DO IT WITHOUT RISK. USE WATER SPRAY TO REDUCE VAPORS. FOR SMALL SPILLS, TAKE UP WITH SAND OR OTHER ABSORBENT MATERIAL AND PLACE INTO CONTAINERS FOR LATER DISPOSAL. FOR LARGER SPILLS, DIKE FAR AHEAD OF SPILL FOR LATER DISPOSAL. NO SMOKING, FLAMES OR FLARES IN HAZARD AREA. KEEP UNNECESSARY PEOPLE AWAY; ISOLATE HAZARD AREA AND DENY ENTRY.

PROTECTIVE EQUIPMENT

VENTILATION: PROVIDE GENERAL DILUTION VENTILATION TO MEET PUBLISHED EXPOSURE LIMITS.

RESPIRATOR: THE FOLLOWING RESPIRATORS AND MAXIMUM USE CONCENTRATIONS ARE RECOMMENDATIONS BY THE U.S. DEPARTMENT OF HEALTH AND HUMAN SERVICES, NIOSH POCKET GUIDE TO CHEMICAL HAZARDS; NIOSH CRITERIA DOCUMENTS OR BY THE U.S. DEPARTMENT OF LABOR, 29 CFR 1910 SUBPART Z.
THE SPECIFIC RESPIRATOR SELECTED MUST BE BASED ON CONTAMINATION LEVELS FOUND IN THE WORK PLACE, MUST NOT EXCEED THE WORKING LIMITS OF THE RESPIRATOR AND BE JOINTLY APPROVED BY THE NATIONAL INSTITUTE FOR OCCUPATIONAL SAFETY AND HEALTH AND THE MINE SAFETY AND HEALTH ADMINISTRATION (NIOSH-MSHA).
ACETONE:
1000 PPM- ANY CHEMICAL CARTRIDGE RESPIRATOR WITH ORGANIC VAPOR CARTRIDGE(S). ANY POWERED AIR-PURIFYING RESPIRATOR WITH ORGANIC VAPOR CARTRIDGE(S). ANY SUPPLIED-AIR RESPIRATOR. ANY SELF-CONTAINED BREATHING APPARATUS.
6250 PPM- ANY SUPPLIED-AIR RESPIRATOR OPERATED IN A CONTINUOUS FLOW MODE.
12,500 PPM- ANY AIR-PURIFYING FULL FACEPIECE RESPIRATOR (GAS MASK) WITH A CHIN-STYLE OR FRONT- OR BACK-MOUNTED ORGANIC VAPOR CANISTER. ANY SUPPLIED-AIR RESPIRATOR WITH A FULL FACEPIECE. ANY SELF-CONTAINED BREATHING APPARATUS WITH A FULL FACEPIECE.
20,000 PPM- ANY SUPPLIED-AIR RESPIRATOR WITH A FULL FACEPIECE AND OPERATED IN A PRESSURE-DEMAND OR OTHER POSITIVE PRESSURE MODE.
ESCAPE- ANY AIR-PURIFYING FULL FACEPIECE RESPIRATOR (GAS MASK) WITH A CHIN-STYLE OR FRONT- OR BACK-MOUNTED ORGANIC VAPOR CANISTER. ANY APPROPRIATE ESCAPE-TYPE SELF-CONTAINED BREATHING APPARATUS.
FOR FIREFIGHTING AND OTHER IMMEDIATELY DANGEROUS TO LIFE OR HEALTH CONDITIONS:
SELF-CONTAINED BREATHING APPARATUS WITH FULL FACEPIECE OPERATED IN PRESSURE-DEMAND OR OTHER POSITIVE PRESSURE MODE.
SUPPLIED-AIR RESPIRATOR WITH FULL FACEPIECE AND OPERATED IN PRESSURE-DEMAND OR OTHER POSITIVE PRESSURE MODE IN COMBINATION WITH AN AUXILIARY SELF-CONTAINED BREATHING APPARATUS OPERATED IN PRESSURE-DEMAND OR OTHER POSITIVE PRESSURE MODE.

CLOTHING: EMPLOYEE MUST WEAR APPROPRIATE PROTECTIVE (IMPERVIOUS) CLOTHING AND EQUIPMENT TO PREVENT REPEATED OR PROLONGED SKIN CONTACT WITH THIS SUBSTANCE.

GLOVES: EMPLOYEE MUST WEAR APPROPRIATE PROTECTIVE GLOVES TO PREVENT CONTACT WITH THIS SUBSTANCE.

EYE PROTECTION: EMPLOYEE MUST WEAR SPLASH-PROOF OR DUST-RESISTANT SAFETY GOGGLES TO PREVENT EYE CONTACT WITH THIS SUBSTANCE.
EMERGENCY EYE WASH: WHERE THERE IS ANY POSSIBILITY THAT AN EMPLOYEE'S EYES MAY BE EXPOSED TO THIS SUBSTANCE, THE EMPLOYER SHOULD PROVIDE AN EYE WASH FOUNTAIN WITHIN THE IMMEDIATE WORK AREA FOR EMERGENCY USE.

AUTHORIZED BY- OCCUPATIONAL HEALTH SERVICES, INC.
CREATION DATE: 11/15/89 ***REVISION DATE:*** 05/14/90

MATERIAL SAFETY DATA SHEET

OCCUPATIONAL HEALTH SERVICES, INC.
AGRICULTURE AND PESTICIDE DIVISION
450 SEVENTH AVENUE, SUITE 2407
NEW YORK, NEW YORK 10123
1-800-445-MSDS OR (212) 967-1100

EMERGENCY CONTACT:
JOHN S. BRANSFORD, JR. (615) 292-1180

SUBSTANCE IDENTIFICATION

SUBSTANCE: ACIFLUORFEN AMINO METABOLITE
TRADE NAMES/SYNONYMS: PST00316
CHEMICAL FAMILY: ETHER, AROMATIC
HALOGEN
CARBOXYLIC ACID
CERCLA RATINGS (SCALE 0-3): HEALTH=U FIRE=1 REACTIVITY=0
PERSISTENCE=2
NFPA RATINGS (SCALE 0-4): HEALTH=U FIRE=1 REACTIVITY=0

COMPONENTS AND CONTAMINANTS

COMPONENT: ACIFLUORFEN AMINO METABOLITE ***PERCENT:*** 100.0
OTHER CONTAMINANTS: NONE
EXPOSURE LIMITS: NO OCCUPATIONAL EXPOSURE LIMITS ESTABLISHED BY OSHA, ACGIH, OR NIOSH.

PHYSICAL DATA

DESCRIPTION: BEIGE POWDER. ***MELTING POINT:*** NOT AVAILABLE
SPECIFIC GRAVITY: NOT AVAILABLE ***SOLUBILITY IN WATER:*** NOT AVAILABLE

FIRE AND EXPLOSION DATA

FIRE AND EXPLOSION HAZARD: SLIGHT FIRE HAZARD WHEN EXPOSED TO HEAT OR FLAME.
FIREFIGHTING MEDIA: DRY CHEMICAL, CARBON DIOXIDE, HALON, WATER SPRAY OR STANDARD FOAM (1987 EMERGENCY RESPONSE GUIDEBOOK, DOT P 5800.4).
FOR LARGER FIRES, USE WATER SPRAY, FOG OR STANDARD FOAM (1987 EMERGENCY RESPONSE GUIDEBOOK, DOT P 5800.4).
FIREFIGHTING: MOVE CONTAINER FROM FIRE AREA IF POSSIBLE. DO NOT SCATTER SPILLED MATERIAL WITH HIGH PRESSURE WATER STREAMS. DIKE FIRE CONTROL WATER FOR LATER DISPOSAL (1987 EMERGENCY RESPONSE GUIDEBOOK, DOT P 5800.4, GUIDE PAGE 31).
USE AGENTS SUITABLE FOR TYPE OF SURROUNDING FIRE. AVOID BREATHING HAZARDOUS VAPORS, KEEP UPWIND.

TOXICITY

ACIFLUORFEN AMINO METABOLITE: CARCINOGEN STATUS: NONE. ACUTE TOXICITY LEVEL: NO DATA AVAILABLE. TARGET EFFECTS: NO DATA AVAILABLE. ADDITIONAL DATA: REPEATED ABSORPTION OF CHLORINATED DIPHENYL ETHERS HAS RESULTED IN LIVER DAMAGE IN ANIMALS.

HEALTH EFFECTS AND FIRST AID

INHALATION: ACIFLUORFEN AMINO METABOLITE: **ACUTE EXPOSURE-** NO DATA AVAILABLE. **CHRONIC EXPOSURE-** NO DATA AVAILABLE.
FIRST AID- REMOVE FROM EXPOSURE AREA TO FRESH AIR IMMEDIATELY. IF BREATHING HAS STOPPED, PERFORM ARTIFICIAL RESPIRATION. KEEP PERSON WARM AND AT REST. TREAT SYMPTOMATICALLY AND SUPPORTIVELY. GET MEDICAL ATTENTION IMMEDIATELY.

SKIN CONTACT: ACIFLUORFEN AMINO METABOLITE: **ACUTE EXPOSURE-** NO DATA AVAILABLE. **CHRONIC EXPOSURE-** NO DATA AVAILABLE.
FIRST AID- REMOVE CONTAMINATED CLOTHING AND SHOES IMMEDIATELY. WASH AFFECTED AREA WITH SOAP OR MILD DETERGENT AND LARGE AMOUNTS OF WATER UNTIL NO EVIDENCE OF CHEMICAL REMAINS (APPROXIMATELY 15-20 MINUTES). GET MEDICAL ATTENTION IMMEDIATELY.

EYE CONTACT: ACIFLUORFEN AMINO METABOLITE: **ACUTE EXPOSURE-** NO DATA AVAILABLE. **CHRONIC EXPOSURE-** NO DATA AVAILABLE.
FIRST AID- WASH EYES IMMEDIATELY WITH LARGE AMOUNTS OF WATER OR NORMAL SALINE, OCCASIONALLY LIFTING UPPER AND LOWER LIDS, UNTIL NO EVIDENCE OF CHEMICAL REMAINS (APPROXIMATELY 15-20 MINUTES). GET MEDICAL ATTENTION IMMEDIATELY.

INGESTION: ACIFLUORFEN AMINO METABOLITE: **ACUTE EXPOSURE-** NO DATA AVAILABLE. **CHRONIC EXPOSURE-** NO DATA AVAILABLE.
FIRST AID- TREAT SYMPTOMATICALLY AND SUPPORTIVELY. GET MEDICAL ATTENTION IMMEDIATELY. IF VOMITING OCCURS, KEEP HEAD LOWER THAN HIPS TO PREVENT ASPIRATION.
ANTIDOTE: NO SPECIFIC ANTIDOTE. TREAT SYMPTOMATICALLY AND SUPPORTIVELY.

REACTIVITY

REACTIVITY: STABLE UNDER NORMAL TEMPERATURES AND PRESSURES.
INCOMPATIBILITIES: ACIFLUORFEN AMINO METABOLITE: OXIDIZERS (STRONG): FIRE AND EXPLOSION HAZARD.
DECOMPOSITION: THERMAL DECOMPOSITION MAY RELEASE TOXIC AND/OR HAZARDOUS GASES.
POLYMERIZATION: HAZARDOUS POLYMERIZATION HAS NOT BEEN REPORTED TO OCCUR UNDER NORMAL TEMPERATURES AND PRESSURES.

STORAGE AND DISPOSAL

OBSERVE ALL FEDERAL, STATE AND LOCAL REGULATIONS WHEN STORING OR DISPOSING OF THIS SUBSTANCE. FOR ASSISTANCE, CONTACT THE DISTRICT DIRECTOR OF THE ENVIRONMENTAL PROTECTION AGENCY.

****STORAGE****

STORE AWAY FROM INCOMPATIBLE SUBSTANCES.

CONDITIONS TO AVOID

MAY BURN BUT DOES NOT IGNITE READILY. AVOID CONTACT WITH STRONG OXIDIZERS, EXCESSIVE HEAT, SPARKS, OR OPEN FLAME.

SPILL AND LEAK PROCEDURES

OCCUPATIONAL SPILL: STOP LEAK IF YOU CAN DO IT WITHOUT RISK. FOR SMALL SPILLS, TAKE UP WITH SAND OR OTHER ABSORBENT MATERIAL AND PLACE INTO CLEAN, DRY CONTAINERS FOR LATER DISPOSAL. KEEP UNNECESSARY PEOPLE AWAY. ISOLATE HAZARD AREA AND DENY ENTRY.

PROTECTIVE EQUIPMENT

VENTILATION: PROVIDE LOCAL EXHAUST OR GENERAL DILUTION VENTILATION SYSTEM.
RESPIRATOR: THE FOLLOWING RESPIRATORS ARE RECOMMENDED BASED ON INFORMATION FOUND IN THE PHYSICAL DATA, TOXICITY AND HEALTH EFFECTS SECTIONS. THEY ARE RANKED IN ORDER FROM MINIMUM TO MAXIMUM RESPIRATORY PROTECTION. THE SPECIFIC RESPIRATOR SELECTED MUST BE BASED ON CONTAMINATION LEVELS FOUND IN THE WORK PLACE, MUST NOT EXCEED THE WORKING LIMITS OF THE RESPIRATOR AND BE JOINTLY APPROVED BY THE NATIONAL INSTITUTE FOR OCCUPATIONAL SAFETY AND HEALTH AND THE MINE SAFETY AND HEALTH ADMINISTRATION (NIOSH-MSHA).
CHEMICAL CARTRIDGE RESPIRATOR WITH AN ORGANIC VAPOR CARTRIDGE(S) WITH A FULL FACEPIECE AND ORGANIC VAPOR CARTRIDGE(S) IN COMBINATION WITH A DUST AND MIST FILTER.
POWERED AIR-PURIFYING RESPIRATOR WITH A TIGHT-FITTING FACEPIECE AND ORGANIC VAPOR CARTRIDGE(S) IN COMBINATION WITH A HIGH-EFFICIENCY PARTICULATE FILTER.
TYPE 'C' SUPPLIED-AIR RESPIRATOR WITH A FULL FACEPIECE OPERATED IN A PRESSURE-DEMAND OR OTHER POSITIVE PRESSURE MODE.
SELF-CONTAINED BREATHING APPARATUS WITH A FULL FACEPIECE OPERATED IN PRESSURE-DEMAND OR OTHER POSITIVE PRESSURE MODE.
FOR FIREFIGHTING AND OTHER IMMEDIATELY DANGEROUS TO LIFE OR HEALTH CONDITIONS:
SELF-CONTAINED BREATHING APPARATUS WITH FULL FACEPIECE OPERATED IN PRESSURE-DEMAND OR OTHER POSITIVE PRESSURE MODE.
SUPPLIED-AIR RESPIRATOR WITH FULL FACEPIECE AND OPERATED IN PRESSURE-DEMAND OR OTHER POSITIVE PRESSURE MODE IN COMBINATION WITH AN AUXILIARY SELF-CONTAINED BREATHING APPARATUS OPERATED IN PRESSURE-DEMAND OR OTHER POSITIVE PRESSURE MODE.
CLOTHING: EMPLOYEE MUST WEAR APPROPRIATE PROTECTIVE (IMPERVIOUS) CLOTHING AND EQUIPMENT TO PREVENT REPEATED OR PROLONGED SKIN CONTACT WITH THIS SUBSTANCE.
GLOVES: EMPLOYEE MUST WEAR APPROPRIATE PROTECTIVE GLOVES TO PREVENT CONTACT WITH THIS SUBSTANCE.
EYE PROTECTION: EMPLOYEE MUST WEAR SPLASH-PROOF OR DUST-RESISTANT SAFETY GOGGLES TO PREVENT EYE CONTACT WITH THIS SUBSTANCE.
EMERGENCY EYE WASH: WHERE THERE IS ANY POSSIBILITY THAT AN EMPLOYEE'S EYES MAY BE EXPOSED TO THIS SUBSTANCE, THE EMPLOYER SHOULD PROVIDE AN EYE WASH FOUNTAIN WITHIN THE IMMEDIATE WORK AREA FOR EMERGENCY USE.

AUTHORIZED BY- OCCUPATIONAL HEALTH SERVICES, INC.
CREATION DATE: 10/04/89 ***REVISION DATE:*** 05/07/90

MATERIAL SAFETY DATA SHEET

OCCUPATIONAL HEALTH SERVICES, INC.
AGRICULTURE AND PESTICIDE DIVISION
450 SEVENTH AVENUE, SUITE 2407
NEW YORK, NEW YORK 10123
1-800-445-MSDS OR (212) 967-1100

EMERGENCY CONTACT:
JOHN S. BRANSFORD, JR. (615) 292-1180

SUBSTANCE IDENTIFICATION

CAS-NUMBER 107-02-8
SUBSTANCE: **ACROLEIN, INHIBITED**
TRADE NAMES/SYNONYMS: ACRALDEHYDE; ACRYLALDEHYDE; ACRYLIC ALDEHYDE; ALLYL ALDEHYDE; 2-PROPENAL; PROP-2-EN-1-AL; 2-PROPEN-1-AL; ETHYLENE ALDEHYDE; AQUALIN; MAGNACIDE; PROPENAL; ACROLEIN; RCRA P003; STCC 4906410; UN 1092; C3H4O; PST00330
CHEMICAL FAMILY: ALDEHYDE, ALIPHATIC
MOLECULAR FORMULA: C-H2-C-H-C-H-O
MOLECULAR WEIGHT: 56.06
CERCLA RATINGS (SCALE 0-3): HEALTH=3 FIRE=3 REACTIVITY=2 PERSISTENCE=0
NFPA RATINGS (SCALE 0-4): HEALTH=3 FIRE=3 REACTIVITY=2

COMPONENTS AND CONTAMINANTS

COMPONENT: ACROLEIN ***PERCENT:*** >99.0
CAS# 107-02-8
OTHER CONTAMINANTS: MAY CONTAIN POLYMERIZATION INHIBITORS SUCH AS HYDROQUINONE.
EXPOSURE LIMITS: ACROLEIN, INHIBITED: 0.1 PPM (0.25 MG/M3) OSHA TWA; 0.3 PPM (0.8 MG/M3) OSHA STEL 0.1 PPM (0.25 MG/M3) ACGIH TWA; 0.3 PPM (0.8 MG/M3) ACGIH STEL
500 POUNDS SARA SECTION 302 THRESHOLD PLANNING QUANTITY 1 POUND SARA SECTION 304 REPORTABLE QUANTITY 1 POUND CERCLA SECTION 103 REPORTABLE QUANTITY SUBJECT TO SARA SECTION 313 ANNUAL TOXIC CHEMICAL RELEASE REPORTING

PHYSICAL DATA

DESCRIPTION: COLORLESS TO YELLOW, VOLATILE LIQUID WITH A PUNGENT ODOR.
BOILING POINT: 126-128 F (52-54 C) ***MELTING POINT:*** -124 F (-87 C)
SPECIFIC GRAVITY: 0.8410 ***VISCOSITY:*** 0.35 CPS @ 20 C ***VOLATILITY:*** 100%
VAPOR PRESSURE: 210 MMHG @ 20 C ***SOLUBILITY IN WATER:*** 20.6% @ 20 C
ODOR THRESHOLD: 1.5 PPM ***VAPOR DENSITY:*** 1.94
SOLVENT SOLUBILITY: SOLUBLE IN ALCOHOL, ETHER, ACETONE.

FIRE AND EXPLOSION DATA

FIRE AND EXPLOSION HAZARD: DANGEROUS FIRE HAZARD WHEN EXPOSED TO HEAT OR FLAME. VAPOR-AIR MIXTURES ARE EXPLOSIVE. VAPORS ARE HEAVIER THAN AIR AND MAY TRAVEL A CONSIDERABLE DISTANCE TO A SOURCE OF IGNITION AND FLASH BACK.
FLASH POINT: -15 F (-26 C) (CC) ***UPPER EXPLOSIVE LIMIT:*** 31.0%
LOWER EXPLOSIVE LIMIT: 2.8% ***AUTOIGNITION TEMP.:*** 428 F (220 C)
FLAMMABILITY CLASS(OSHA): IB
FIREFIGHTING MEDIA: DRY CHEMICAL, CARBON DIOXIDE, HALON, WATER SPRAY OR STANDARD FOAM (1987 EMERGENCY RESPONSE GUIDEBOOK, DOT P 5800.4).
FOR LARGER FIRES, USE WATER SPRAY, FOG OR STANDARD FOAM (1987 EMERGENCY RESPONSE GUIDEBOOK, DOT P 5800.4).
ALCOHOL FOAM (NFPA 325M, FIRE HAZARD PROPERTIES OF FLAMMABLE LIQUIDS, GASES, AND VOLATILE SOLIDS, 1984).
FIREFIGHTING: STAY AWAY FROM STORAGE TANK ENDS. DO NOT GET WATER INSIDE CONTAINER. COOL FIRE-EXPOSED CONTAINERS WITH WATER FROM SIDE UNTIL WELL AFTER FIRE IS OUT. FOR MASSIVE FIRE IN STORAGE AREA, USE UNMANNED HOSE HOLDER OR MONITOR NOZZLES, ELSE WITHDRAW FROM AREA AND LET FIRE BURN. WITHDRAW IMMEDIATELY IN CASE OF RISING SOUND FROM VENTING SAFETY DEVICE OR ANY DISCOLORATION OF STORAGE TANK DUE TO FIRE (1987 EMERGENCY RESPONSE GUIDEBOOK, DOT P 5800.4, GUIDE PAGE 30).
EXTINGUISH ONLY IF FLOW CAN BE STOPPED. USE FLOODING AMOUNTS OF WATER AS A FOG; SOLID STREAMS MAY BE INEFFECTIVE. COOL CONTAINERS WITH FLOODING AMOUNTS OF WATER FROM AS FAR A DISTANCE AS POSSIBLE. AVOID BREATHING POISONOUS VAPORS; KEEP UPWIND. IF FIRE IS UNCONTROLLABLE OR CONTAINERS EXPOSED TO DIRECT FLAME, EVACUATE FOR A RADIUS OF 5000 FEET. CONSIDER EVACUATION OF DOWNWIND AREA IF MATERIAL IS LEAKING. WATER MAY BE INEFFECTIVE (NFPA 325M, FIRE HAZARD PROPERTIES OF FLAMMABLE LIQUIDS, GASES, AND VOLATILE SOLIDS, 1984)

TRANSPORTATION DATA

DEPARTMENT OF TRANSPORTATION HAZARD CLASSIFICATION 49 CFR 172.101: FLAMMABLE LIQUID
DEPARTMENT OF TRANSPORTATION LABELING REQUIREMENTS 49 CFR 172.101 AND SUBPART E: FLAMMABLE LIQUID AND POISON
DEPARTMENT OF TRANSPORTATION PACKAGING REQUIREMENTS: 49 CFR 173.122 EXCEPTIONS: NONE

TOXICITY

ACROLEIN, INHIBITED: IRRITATION DATA: 500 PPB/12 MINUTES EYE-HUMAN; 1 MG EYE-RABBIT SEVERE; 50 UG/24 HOURS EYE-RABBIT SEVERE; 5 MG OPEN SKIN-RABBIT SEVERE; 2 MG/24 HOURS SKIN-RABBIT SEVERE. TOXICITY DATA: 1 PPM INHALATION-MAN TCLO; 153 PPM/10 MINUTES INHALATION-HUMAN LCLO; 5500 PPB INHALATION-HUMAN LCLO; 300 PPB/2 HOURS INHALATION-CHILD TCLO; 300 MG/M3/30 MINUTES INHALATION-RAT LC50; 66 PPM/6 HOURS INHALATION-MOUSE LC50; 24 MG/M3/6 HOURS INHALATION-RABBIT LCLO; 24 MG/M3/6 HOURS INHALATION-GUINEA PIG LCLO; 1570 MG/M3/2 HOURS INHALATION-CAT LCLO; 562 MG/KG SKIN-RABBIT LD50; 46 MG/KG ORAL-RAT LD50; 40 MG/KG ORAL-MOUSE LD50; 7 MG/KG ORAL-RABBIT LD50; 10 MG/KG ORAL-MAMMAL LDLO; 50 MG/KG SUBCUTANEOUS-RAT LD50; 30 MG/KG SUBCUTANEOUS-MOUSE LD50; 150 MG/KG SUBCUTANEOUS-RABBIT LDLO; 150 UG/KG SUBCUTANEOUS-GUINEA PIG LDLO; 15 MG/KG INTRAVENOUS-CAT LDLO; 4 MG/KG INTRAPERITONEAL-RAT LD50; 9008 UG/KG INTRAPERITONEAL-MOUSE LD50; 250 MG/KG INTRADERMAL-MAMMAL LDLO; 45 MG/KG UNREPORTED-MAMMAL LD50; MUTAGENIC DATA (RTECS); REPRODUCTIVE EFFECTS DATA (RTECS). CARCINOGEN STATUS: HUMAN INADEQUATE EVIDENCE, ANIMAL INADEQUATE EVIDENCE (IARC GROUP-3). LOCAL EFFECTS: CORROSIVE- INHALATION, SKIN, EYE, INGESTION; LACRIMATOR. ACUTE TOXICITY LEVEL: HIGHLY TOXIC BY INHALATION, INGESTION; TOXIC BY DERMAL ABSORPTION. TARGET EFFECTS: POISONING MAY AFFECT THE CENTRAL NERVOUS SYSTEM AND THE LIVER. AT INCREASED RISK FROM EXPOSURE: PERSONS WITH CHRONIC RESPIRATORY DISEASE.

HEALTH EFFECTS AND FIRST AID

INHALATION: ACROLEIN, INHIBITED: CORROSIVE/HIGHLY TOXIC. 5 PPM IMMEDIATELY DANGEROUS TO LIFE OR HEALTH. **ACUTE EXPOSURE-** HUMAN EXPOSURE TO 0.25 PPM MAY BE IRRITATING TO THE RESPIRATORY TRACT; 1 PPM FOR 5 MINUTES IS INTOLERABLE AND MAY CAUSE MARKED IRRITATION OF THE NOSE AND THROAT; AT HIGHER THAN 3 PPM, INJURY TO THE UPPER RESPIRATORY TRACT AND LUNGS AND PERSISTENT RESPIRATORY INSUFFICIENCY MAY BE EVIDENT. A 10 MINUTE EXPOSURE TO 150 PPM HAS BEEN LETHAL. ACROLEIN INCREASES AIRWAY RESISTANCE AND TIDAL VOLUME, AND DECREASES RESPIRATORY FREQUENCY. SYMPTOMS RELATED TO VAPOR EXPOSURE MAY INCLUDE SORE THROAT, COUGHING, HEADACHE, DIZZINESS, DROWSINESS, LIGHTHEADEDNESS, SYNCOPE, UPSET STOMACH, NAUSEA AND VOMITING, DIARRHEA, NASAL DISCHARGE, TRACHEOBRONCHITIS, SHORTNESS OF BREATH, TIGHTNESS AND CONGESTION IN THE CHEST, AND RARELY, PULMONARY EDEMA, WHICH MAY BE SLOW IN DEVELOPING. IF THE INDIVIDUAL RECOVERS FROM ACUTE EXPOSURE, THERE MAY BE PERMANENT RADIOLOGICAL AND FUNCTIONAL LUNG DAMAGE. LIVER INJURY MAY ALSO BE POSSIBLE. DEATH MAY OCCUR FROM PULMONARY EDEMA OR RESPIRATORY PARALYSIS. SENSITIZATION, MANIFESTED BY ASTHMATIC REACTIONS, HAS BEEN REPORTED IN SOME INDIVIDUALS. CATS EXPOSED TO 10 PPM FOR 3.5 HOURS EXHIBITED SYMPTOMS OF SALIVATION, RESPIRATORY IRRITATION, LACRIMATION AND MILD NARCOSIS. INHALATION HAS LED TO PNEUMONIA AND NEPHRITIS WITH DEATH FROM CARDIAC FAILURE IN EXPERIMENTAL ANIMALS. PATHOLOGIC FINDINGS HAVE INCLUDED HYPEREMIA, HEMORRHAGE OF THE LUNGS AND DEGENERATION OF THE BRONCHIAL EPITHELIUM. **CHRONIC EXPOSURE-** REPEATED AND PROLONGED EXPOSURE TO LOW, IRRITATING CONCENTRATIONS OF VAPOR MAY RESULT IN PROGRESSIVE LUNG INJURY AND CHRONIC RESPIRATORY DISEASE. RARELY, PULMONARY SENSITIZATION MAY OCCUR. PROLONGED EXPOSURE OF ANIMALS HAS LED TO IRRITATION OF THE NASAL MUCOSA. IN RATS EXPOSED TO 4 PPM/6 HOURS A DAY FOR 62 DAYS, BRONCHIOLAR NECROSIS AND FOCAL PULMONARY EDEMA WERE REPORTED. IN OTHER ANIMAL STUDIES WITH REPEATED LOW CONCENTRATION EXPOSURES, NO OVERT SYMPTOMS OF TOXICITY WERE NOTED. PATHOLOGIC FINDINGS INCLUDED NECROTIZING BRONCHITIS, EMPHYSEMA AND NON-SPECIFIC INFLAMMATION OF THE LIVER, KIDNEYS, LUNGS AND HEART. METAPLASTIC AND HYPERPLASTIC CHANGES OF THE TRACHEA AND NASAL CAVITY IN MAMMALS HAS RESULTED FROM REPEATED EXPOSURES.
FIRST AID- REMOVE FROM EXPOSURE AREA TO FRESH AIR IMMEDIATELY. IF BREATHING HAS STOPPED, GIVE ARTIFICIAL RESPIRATION. MAINTAIN AIRWAY AND

BLOOD PRESSURE AND ADMINISTER OXYGEN IF AVAILABLE. KEEP AFFECTED PERSON WARM AND AT REST. TREAT SYMPTOMATICALLY AND SUPPORTIVELY. ADMINISTRATION OF OXYGEN SHOULD BE PERFORMED BY QUALIFIED PERSONNEL. GET MEDICAL ATTENTION IMMEDIATELY.

SKIN CONTACT: ACROLEIN, INHIBITED: CORROSIVE/TOXIC. **ACUTE EXPOSURE**- CONTACT MAY CAUSE SEVERE IRRITATION WITH ERYTHEMA, EDEMA, VESICULATION, AND BURNS. NECROSIS HAS BEEN REPORTED FROM A 0.1% SOLUTION. SENSITIZATION REACTIONS AR POSSIBLE IN PREVIOUSLY EXPOSED INDIVIDUALS. MAY BE ABSORBED THROUGH THE SKIN AND CAUSE SYSTEMIC TOXICITY. THE LETHAL DOSE IN RABBITS IS 562 MG/KG. **CHRONIC EXPOSURE**- REPEATED OR PROLONGED CONTACT MAY CAUSE DERMATITIS OR POSSIBLY BURNS. SENSITIZATION DERMATITIS WITH HIVES AND RASH HAS BEEN REPORTED.
FIRST AID- REMOVE CONTAMINATED CLOTHING AND SHOES IMMEDIATELY. WASH AFFECTED AREA WITH SOAP OR MILD DETERGENT AND LARGE AMOUNTS OF WATER UNTIL NO EVIDENCE OF CHEMICAL REMAINS (AT LEAST 15-20 MINUTES). IN CASE OF CHEMICAL BURNS, COVER AREA WITH STERILE, DRY DRESSING. BANDAGE SECURELY, BUT NOT TOO TIGHTLY. GET MEDICAL ATTENTION IMMEDIATELY.

EYE CONTACT: ACROLEIN, INHIBITED: CORROSIVE/LACRIMATOR. **ACUTE EXPOSURE**- LACRIMATION MAY BE INDUCED AT 1 PPM IN LESS THAN 5 MINUTES. OTHER SYMPTOMS OF EXPOSURE TO ACROLEIN VAPORS MAY INCLUDE SEVERE IRRITATION WITH REDNESS, PAIN, INVOLUNTARY BLINKING, BURNING SENSATION, SWELLING OF EYELIDS, AND BLURRED VISION. DIRECT CONTACT WITH THE LIQUID MAY RESULT IN PALPEBRAL EDEMA, BLEPHAROCONJUNCTIVITIS, FIBRINOUS OR PURULENT DISCHARGE, BURNS, AND CORNEAL DAMAGE. **CHRONIC EXPOSURE**- EFFECTS DEPEND ON CONCENTRATION AND DURATION OF EXPOSURE. REPEATED OR PROLONGED CONTACT WITH CORROSIVE SUBSTANCES MAY RESULT IN CONJUNCTIVITIS OR EFFECTS AS IN ACUTE EXPOSURE.
FIRST AID- WASH EYES IMMEDIATELY WITH LARGE AMOUNTS OF WATER, OCCASIONALLY LIFTING UPPER AND LOWER LIDS, UNTIL NO EVIDENCE OF CHEMICAL REMAINS (AT LEAST 15-20 MINUTES). CONTINUE IRRIGATING WITH NORMAL SALINE UNTIL THE PH HAS RETURNED TO NORMAL (30-60 MINUTES). COVER WITH STERILE BANDAGES. GET MEDICAL ATTENTION IMMEDIATELY.

INGESTION: ACROLEIN, INHIBITED: CORROSIVE/HIGHLY TOXIC. **ACUTE EXPOSURE**- MAY CAUSE EFFECTS AS DETAILED IN ACUTE INHALATION. IN ADDITION, MAY CAUSE GASTROINTESTINAL DISTRESS WITH BURNS OF THE MOUTH, THROAT, ESOPHAGUS AND STOMACH, PAIN IN THE MOUTH, THROAT, CHEST, AND ABDOMEN, NAUSEA, BLOODY VOMITING, DIARRHEA, WEAKNESS, DIZZINESS, PULMONARY CONGESTION AND EDEMA, COLLAPSE, UNCONSCIOUSNESS, COMA, AND DEATH. **CHRONIC EXPOSURE**- REPEATED ADMINISTRATION IN DRINKING WATER TO RATS RESULTED IN MORE NUMEROUS ADENOMAS OF THE ADRENAL CORTEX IN FEMALES THAN IN UNTREATED CONTROLS.
FIRST AID- IF THE PERSON IS CONSCIOUS AND NOT CONVULSING, INDUCE EMESIS BY GIVING SYRUP OF IPECAC FOLLOWED BY WATER. (IF VOMITING OCCURS KEEP THE HEAD BELOW THE HIPS TO PREVENT ASPIRATION). REPEAT IN 20 MINUTES IF NOT EFFECTIVE INITIALLY. GIVE ACTIVATED CHARCOAL. IN PATIENTS WITH DEPRESSED RESPIRATION OR IF EMESIS IS NOT PRODUCED, PERFORM GASTRIC LAVAGE CAUTIOUSLY (DREISBACH, HANDBOOK OF POISONING, 12TH ED.). TREAT SYMPTOMATICALLY AND SUPPORTIVELY. GASTRIC LAVAGE SHOULD BE PERFORMED BY QUALIFIED MEDICAL PERSONNEL. GET MEDICAL ATTENTION IMMEDIATELY.
ANTIDOTE: NO SPECIFIC ANTIDOTE. TREAT SYMPTOMATICALLY AND SUPPORTIVELY.

REACTIVITY

REACTIVITY: FORMS UNSTABLE PEROXIDES ON CONTACT WITH AIR, HEAT OR SUNLIGHT. MAY UNDERGO EXOTHERMIC POLYMERIZATION ON EXPOSURE TO AIR, HEAT OR LIGHT.
INCOMPATIBILITIES: ACROLEIN, INHIBITED: ACIDS (STRONG): VIOLENT POLYMERIZATION. ALKALI: HAZARDOUS POLYMERIZATION. AMINES: EXOTHERMIC POLYMERIZATION. 2-AMINOETHANOL: TEMPERATURE AND PRESSURE INCREASE IN A CLOSED CONTAINER. AMMONIA: VIOLENT POLYMERIZATION. AMMONIUM HYDROXIDE: TEMPERATURE AND PRESSURE INCREASE IN A CLOSED CONTAINER. CARBON DIOXIDE: EXOTHERMIC POLYMERIZATION. CHLOROSULFONIC ACID: TEMPERATURE AND PRESSURE INCREASE IN A CLOSED CONTAINER. DIMETHYLAMINE: VIOLENT POLYMERIZATION. ETHYLENE DIAMINE: TEMPERATURE AND PRESSURE INCREASE IN A CLOSED CONTAINER. ETHYLENEIMINE: TEMPERATURE AND PRESSURE INCREASE IN A CLOSED CONTAINER. HYDROXIDES: VIOLENT POLYMERIZATION. METAL SALTS: INCOMPATIBLE. NITRIC ACID: TEMPERATURE AND PRESSURE INCREASE IN A CLOSED CONTAINER. OLEUM: TEMPERATURE AND PRESSURE INCREASE IN A CLOSED CONTAINER. OXIDIZERS (STRONG): FIRE AND EXPLOSION HAZARD. POTASSIUM HYDROXIDE: VIOLENT POLYMERIZATION. SODIUM HYDROXIDE: VIOLENT POLYMERIZATION. SULFUR DIOXIDE: EXOTHERMIC POLYMERIZATION. SULFURIC ACID: VIOLENT POLYMERIZATION. THIOUREA: EXOTHERMIC POLYMERIZATION.
DECOMPOSITION: THERMAL DECOMPOSITION PRODUCTS MAY INCLUDE TOXIC OXIDES OF CARBON.
POLYMERIZATION: READILY UNDERGOES POLYMERIZATION AT AMBIENT AND ELEVATED TEMPERATURES IF UNINHIBITED. IF POLYMERIZATION OCCURS IN A CLOSED CONTAINER, INCREASE IN TEMPERATURE AND PRESSURE MAY BE SUFFICIENT TO RUPTURE CONTAINER.

STORAGE AND DISPOSAL

OBSERVE ALL FEDERAL, STATE AND LOCAL REGULATIONS WHEN STORING OR DISPOSING OF THIS SUBSTANCE. FOR ASSISTANCE, CONTACT THE DISTRICT DIRECTOR OF THE ENVIRONMENTAL PROTECTION AGENCY.

****STORAGE****

STORE IN ACCORDANCE WITH 29 CFR 1910.106.
BONDING AND GROUNDING: SUBSTANCES WITH LOW ELECTROCONDUCTIVITY, WHICH MAY BE IGNITED BY ELECTROSTATIC SPARKS, SHOULD BE STORED IN CONTAINERS WHICH MEET THE BONDING AND GROUNDING GUIDELINES SPECIFIED IN NFPA 77-1983, RECOMMENDED PRACTICE ON STATIC ELECTRICITY.
PROTECT AGAINST PHYSICAL DAMAGE. OUTSIDE OR DETACHED STORAGE IS PREFERABLE. INSIDE STORAGE SHOULD BE IN A STANDARD FLAMMABLE LIQUIDS STORAGE ROOM OR CABINET; NO ALKALINE MATERIALS, SUCH AS CAUSTICS, AMMONIA OR AMINES OR OXIDIZING MATERIALS PERMITTED IN STORAGE ROOM OR CABINET. DO NOT STORE UNINHIBITED ACROLEIN UNDER ANY CIRCUMSTANCES (NFPA 49, HAZARDOUS CHEMICALS DATA, 1975).
THRESHOLD PLANNING QUANTITY (TPQ): THE SUPERFUND AMENDMENTS AND REAUTHORIZATION ACT (SARA) SECTION 302 REQUIRES THAT EACH FACILITY WHERE ANY EXTREMELY HAZARDOUS SUBSTANCE IS PRESENT IN A QUANTITY EQUAL TO OR GREATER THAN THE TPQ ESTABLISHED FOR THAT SUBSTANCE NOTIFY THE STATE EMERGENCY RESPONSE COMMISSION FOR THE STATE IN WHICH IT IS LOCATED. SECTION 303 OF SARA REQUIRES THESE FACILITIES TO PARTICIPATE IN LOCAL EMERGENCY RESPONSE PLANNING (40 CFR 355.30).
MAY FORM EXPLOSIVE PEROXIDES ON PROLONGED CONTACT WITH AIR. STORE IN A TIGHTLY CLOSED CONTAINER. PROTECT FROM EXPOSURE TO HEAT AND LIGHT. CHECK PEROXIDE CONTENT OFTEN; NEVER DISTILL TO DRYNESS.

****DISPOSAL****

DISPOSAL MUST BE IN ACCORDANCE WITH STANDARDS APPLICABLE TO GENERATORS OF HAZARDOUS WASTE, 40CFR 262. EPA HAZARDOUS WASTE NUMBER P003.

CONDITIONS TO AVOID

MATERIAL IS EXTREMELY FLAMMABLE; AVOID CONTACT WITH HEAT, SPARKS OR OPEN FLAME. DO NOT OVERHEAT CONTAINERS; CONTAINERS MAY EXPLODE IN HEAT OF FIRE. MATERIAL IS POISONOUS; AVOID CONTACT WITH SKIN AND INHALATION OF VAPORS. AVOID CONTAMINATION OF WATER SOURCES.

SPILL AND LEAK PROCEDURES

SOIL SPILL: DIG A HOLDING AREA SUCH AS PIT, POND OR LAGOON TO CONTAIN SPILL AND DIKE SURFACE FLOW WITH BARRIER OF SOIL, SANDBAGS, FOAMED POLYURETHANE OR FOAMED CONCRETE.
USE SODIUM BISULFATE (NA-H-SO4) TO NEUTRALIZE SPILL.
DIMINISH VAPOR AND FIRE HAZARD BY APPLICATION OF APPROPRIATE FOAM.
AIR SPILL: APPLY WATER SPRAY TO KNOCK DOWN VAPORS.
COMBUSTION PRODUCTS INCLUDE CORROSIVE OR TOXIC VAPORS.
WATER SPILL: LIMIT SPILL MOTION AND DISPERSION WITH NATURAL BARRIERS OR OIL SPILL CONTROL BOOMS. ADD SODIUM BISULFITE. IF DISSOLVED, AT A CONCENTRATION OF 10 PPM OR GREATER, APPLY ACTIVATED CARBON AT TEN TIMES THE AMOUNT THAT HAS BEEN SPILLED.
USE MECHANICAL DREDGES OR LIFTS TO EXTRACT IMMOBILIZED MASSES OF POLLUTION AND PRECIPITATES.
OCCUPATIONAL SPILL: SHUT OFF IGNITION SOURCES. DO NOT TOUCH SPILLED MATERIAL. STOP LEAK IF YOU CAN DO IT WITHOUT RISK. USE WATER SPRAY TO REDUCE VAPORS. FOR SMALL SPILLS, FLUSH AREA WITH FLOODING AMOUNTS OF WATER. DIKE FAR AHEAD OF SPILL FOR LATER DISPOSAL. NO SMOKING, FLAMES OR FLARES IN HAZARD AREA! KEEP UNNECESSARY PEOPLE AWAY; ISOLATE HAZARD AREA AND DENY ENTRY.
REPORTABLE QUANTITY (RQ): 1 POUND THE SUPERFUND AMENDMENTS AND REAUTHORIZATION ACT (SARA) SECTION 304 REQUIRES THAT A RELEASE EQUAL TO OR GREATER THAN THE REPORTABLE QUANTITY FOR THIS SUBSTANCE BE IMMEDIATELY REPORTED TO THE LOCAL EMERGENCY PLANNING COMMITTEE AND THE STATE EMERGENCY RESPONSE COMMISSION (40 CFR 355.40). IF THE RELEASE OF THIS SUBSTANCE IS REPORTABLE UNDER CERCLA SECTION 103, THE NATIONAL RESPONSE CENTER MUST BE NOTIFIED IMMEDIATELY AT (800) 424-8802 OR (202) 426-2675 IN THE METROPOLITAN WASHINGTON, D.C. AREA (40 CFR 302.6).

PROTECTIVE EQUIPMENT

VENTILATION: PROVIDE LOCAL EXHAUST OR PROCESS ENCLOSURE VENTILATION TO MEET THE PUBLISHED EXPOSURE LIMITS. VENTILATION EQUIPMENT MUST BE EXPLOSION-PROOF.

RESPIRATOR: THE FOLLOWING RESPIRATORS AND MAXIMUM USE CONCENTRATIONS ARE RECOMMENDATIONS BY THE U.S. DEPARTMENT OF HEALTH AND HUMAN SERVICES, NIOSH POCKET GUIDE TO CHEMICAL HAZARDS; NIOSH CRITERIA DOCUMENTS OR BY THE U.S. DEPARTMENT OF LABOR, 29 CFR 1910 SUBPART Z. THE SPECIFIC RESPIRATOR SELECTED MUST BE BASED ON CONTAMINATION LEVELS FOUND IN THE WORK PLACE, MUST NOT EXCEED THE WORKING LIMITS OF THE RESPIRATOR AND BE JOINTLY APPROVED BY THE NATIONAL INSTITUTE FOR OCCUPATIONAL SAFETY AND HEALTH AND THE MINE SAFETY AND HEALTH ADMINISTRATION (NIOSH-MSHA).

ACROLEIN, INHIBITED:

2.5 PPM- ANY SUPPLIED-AIR RESPIRATOR OPERATED IN A CONTINUOUS FLOW MODE. ANY POWERED AIR-PURIFYING RESPIRATOR WITH ORGANIC VAPOR CARTRIDGE(S).

5 PPM- ANY CHEMICAL CARTRIDGE RESPIRATOR WITH A FULL FACEPIECE AND ORGANIC VAPOR CARTRIDGE(S). ANY AIR-PURIFYING FULL FACEPIECE RESPIRATOR (GAS MASK) WITH A CHIN-STYLE OR FRONT- OR BACK-MOUNTED ORGANIC VAPOR CANISTER. ANY SELF-CONTAINED BREATHING APPARATUS WITH A FULL FACEPIECE. ANY SUPPLIED-AIR RESPIRATOR WITH A FULL FACEPIECE.

ESCAPE- ANY AIR-PURIFYING FULL FACEPIECE RESPIRATOR (GAS MASK) WITH A CHIN-STYLE OR FRONT- OR BACK-MOUNTED ORGANIC VAPOR CANISTER. ANY APPROPRIATE ESCAPE-TYPE SELF-CONTAINED BREATHING APPARATUS.

FOR FIREFIGHTING AND OTHER IMMEDIATELY DANGEROUS TO LIFE OR HEALTH CONDITIONS:

SELF-CONTAINED BREATHING APPARATUS WITH FULL FACEPIECE OPERATED IN PRESSURE-DEMAND OR OTHER POSITIVE PRESSURE MODE.

SUPPLIED-AIR RESPIRATOR WITH FULL FACEPIECE AND OPERATED IN PRESSURE-DEMAND OR OTHER POSITIVE PRESSURE MODE IN COMBINATION WITH AN AUXILIARY SELF-CONTAINED BREATHING APPARATUS OPERATED IN PRESSURE-DEMAND OR OTHER POSITIVE PRESSURE MODE.

CLOTHING: EMPLOYEE MUST WEAR APPROPRIATE PROTECTIVE (IMPERVIOUS) CLOTHING AND EQUIPMENT TO PREVENT ANY POSSIBILITY OF SKIN CONTACT WITH THIS SUBSTANCE.

GLOVES: EMPLOYEE MUST WEAR APPROPRIATE PROTECTIVE GLOVES TO PREVENT CONTACT WITH THIS SUBSTANCE.

EYE PROTECTION: EMPLOYEE MUST WEAR SPLASH-PROOF OR DUST-RESISTANT SAFETY GOGGLES AND A FACESHIELD TO PREVENT CONTACT WITH THIS SUBSTANCE.

EMERGENCY WASH FACILITIES: WHERE THERE IS ANY POSSIBILITY THAT AN EMPLOYEE'S EYES AND/OR SKIN MAY BE EXPOSED TO THIS SUBSTANCE, THE EMPLOYER SHOULD PROVIDE AN EYE WASH FOUNTAIN AND QUICK DRENCH SHOWER WITHIN THE IMMEDIATE WORK AREA FOR EMERGENCY USE.

AUTHORIZED BY- OCCUPATIONAL HEALTH SERVICES, INC.

CREATION DATE: 10/04/89 ***REVISION DATE:*** 06/26/90

MATERIAL SAFETY DATA SHEET

OCCUPATIONAL HEALTH SERVICES, INC.
AGRICULTURE AND PESTICIDE DIVISION
450 SEVENTH AVENUE, SUITE 2407
NEW YORK, NEW YORK 10123
1-800-445-MSDS OR (212) 967-1100

EMERGENCY CONTACT:
JOHN S. BRANSFORD, JR. (615) 292-1180

SUBSTANCE IDENTIFICATION

CAS-NUMBER 577-11-7

SUBSTANCE: **DIOCTYL SODIUM SULFOSUCCINATE**

TRADE NAMES/SYNONYMS: BUTANEDIOIC ACID, SULFO-, 1,4-BIS(2-ETHYLHEXYL) ESTER, SODIUM SALT; SULFOBUTANEDIOIC ACID 1,4-BIS(2-ETHYLHEXYL) ESTER, SODIUM SALT; SUCCINIC ACID, SULFO-, 1,4-BIS(2-ETHYLHEXYL) ESTER, SODIUM SALT; SULFOSUCCINIC ACID 1,4-BIS(2-ETHYLHEXYL) ESTER, SODIUM SALT; DIOCTYL SULFOSUCCINATE SODIUM; DIOCTYL SULFOSUCCINATE SODIUM SALT; DOCUSATE SODIUM; SODIUM DIOCTYL SULFOSUCCINATE; TRITON GR 5; TRITON GR 7; AEROSOL OT; ALPHASOL OT; DIOCTYLAL; DIOCTYL-MEDO FORTE; DIOTILAN; DIOVAC; DISONATE; DOXINATE; DOXOL; C20H38NAO7S; PST00406

CHEMICAL FAMILY: SURFACTANT

MOLECULAR FORMULA: C8-H17-O2-C-H2-C-H-(S-O3-NA)-C-O2-C8-H17

MOLECULAR WEIGHT: 444.56

CERCLA RATINGS (SCALE 0-3): HEALTH=3 FIRE=1 REACTIVITY=0 PERSISTENCE=0

NFPA RATINGS (SCALE 0-4): HEALTH=U FIRE=1 REACTIVITY=0

COMPONENTS AND CONTAMINANTS

COMPONENT: DIOCTYL SODIUM SULFOSUCCINATE ***PERCENT:*** 100.0

CAS# 577-11-7

OTHER CONTAMINANTS: NONE

EXPOSURE LIMITS: NO OCCUPATIONAL EXPOSURE LIMITS ESTABLISHED BY OSHA, ACGIH, OR NIOSH.

PHYSICAL DATA

DESCRIPTION: WHITE, WAX-LIKE, HYGROSCOPIC SOLID WITH A CHARACTERISTIC ODOR OF OCTYL ALCOHOL. ***MELTING POINT:*** 311 F (155 C) ***SPECIFIC GRAVITY:*** 1.1

VAPOR PRESSURE: NEGLIGIBLE ***EVAPORATION RATE:*** (BUTYL ACETATE=1) NEGLIGIBLE

SOLUBILITY IN WATER: 1.5% @ 25 C

SOLVENT SOLUBILITY: SOLUBLE IN ALCOHOL, GLYCEROL, CARBON TETRACHLORIDE, ACETONE, XYLENE, PETROLEUM ETHER, NAPHTHA, DIBUTYL PHTHALATE, VEGETABLE OILS, LIQUID PETROLATUM, HEXANE.

FIRE AND EXPLOSION DATA

FIRE AND EXPLOSION HAZARD: SLIGHT FIRE HAZARD WHEN EXPOSED TO HEAT OR FLAME.

DUST-AIR MIXTURES MAY IGNITE OR EXPLODE.

FIREFIGHTING MEDIA: DRY CHEMICAL, CARBON DIOXIDE, HALON, WATER SPRAY OR STANDARD FOAM (1987 EMERGENCY RESPONSE GUIDEBOOK, DOT P 5800.4).

FOR LARGER FIRES, USE WATER SPRAY, FOG OR STANDARD FOAM (1987 EMERGENCY RESPONSE GUIDEBOOK, DOT P 5800.4).

FIREFIGHTING: MOVE CONTAINER FROM FIRE AREA IF POSSIBLE. DO NOT SCATTER SPILLED MATERIAL WITH HIGH PRESSURE WATER STREAMS. DIKE FIRE CONTROL WATER FOR LATER DISPOSAL (1987 EMERGENCY RESPONSE GUIDEBOOK, DOT P 5800.4, GUIDE PAGE 31).

USE AGENTS SUITABLE FOR TYPE OF SURROUNDING FIRE. AVOID BREATHING HAZARDOUS VAPORS, KEEP UPWIND.

TOXICITY

DIOCTYL SODIUM SULFOSUCCINATE (AEROSOL (R) OT): IRRITATION DATA: 10 MG/24 HOURS SKIN-RABBIT MODERATE; 250 UG EYE-RABBIT MILD; 1% EYE-RABBIT SEVERE. TOXICITY DATA: >10,000 MG/KG SKIN-RABBIT LD50 (CYANAMID MSDS); 1900 MG/KG ORAL-RAT LD50; 2643 MG/KG ORAL-MOUSE LD50; 590 MG/KG INTRAPERITONEAL-RAT LD50; 60 MG/KG INTRAVENOUS-MOUSE LD50. CARCINOGEN STATUS: NONE. LOCAL EFFECTS: CORROSIVE- EYE; IRRITANT-INHALATION, SKIN. ACUTE TOXICITY LEVEL: MODERATELY TOXIC BY INGESTION; SLIGHTLY TOXIC BY DERMAL ABSORPTION. TARGET EFFECTS: NO DATA AVAILABLE.

HEALTH EFFECTS AND FIRST AID

INHALATION: DIOCTYL SODIUM SULFOSUCCINATE (AEROSOL (R) OT): IRRITANT.

ACUTE EXPOSURE- DUST MAY CAUSE IRRITATION TO THE RESPIRATORY TRACT.

CHRONIC EXPOSURE- NO DATA AVAILABLE.

FIRST AID- REMOVE FROM EXPOSURE AREA TO FRESH AIR IMMEDIATELY. IF BREATHING HAS STOPPED, PERFORM ARTIFICIAL RESPIRATION. KEEP PERSON WARM AND AT REST. TREAT SYMPTOMATICALLY AND SUPPORTIVELY. GET MEDICAL ATTENTION IMMEDIATELY.

SKIN CONTACT: DIOCTYL SODIUM SULFOSUCCINATE (AEROSOL (R) OT): IRRITANT. **ACUTE EXPOSURE-** MAY CAUSE IRRITATION DUE TO THE DEFATTING ACTION ON THE SKIN. **CHRONIC EXPOSURE-** REPEATED OR PROLONGED CONTACT WITH IRRITANTS MAY RESULT IN DERMATITIS.

FIRST AID- REMOVE CONTAMINATED CLOTHING AND SHOES IMMEDIATELY. WASH AFFECTED AREA WITH SOAP OR MILD DETERGENT AND LARGE AMOUNTS OF WATER UNTIL NO EVIDENCE OF CHEMICAL REMAINS (AT LEAST 15-20 MINUTES). IN CASE OF CHEMICAL BURNS, COVER AREA WITH STERILE, DRY DRESSING. BANDAGE SECURELY, BUT NOT TOO TIGHTLY. GET MEDICAL ATTENTION IMMEDIATELY.

EYE CONTACT: DIOCTYL SODIUM SULFOSUCCINATE (AEROSOL (R) OT): CORROSIVE. **ACUTE EXPOSURE-** MAY CAUSE SEVERE IRRITATION. A 10% SOLUTION APPLIED TO RABBIT EYES RESULTED IN SEVERE DAMAGE. SOLUTIONS OF 2% RESULTED IN REVERSIBLE DAMAGE. **CHRONIC EXPOSURE-** DEPENDING ON CONCENTRATION AND DURATION OF EXPOSURE, REPEATED OR PROLONGED CONTACT MAY RESULT IN SYMPTOMS SIMILAR TO THOSE SEEN IN ACUTE EXPOSURE.

FIRST AID- WASH EYES IMMEDIATELY WITH LARGE AMOUNTS OF WATER, OCCASIONALLY LIFTING UPPER AND LOWER LIDS, UNTIL NO EVIDENCE OF CHEMICAL REMAINS (AT LEAST 15-20 MINUTES). CONTINUE IRRIGATING WITH NORMAL SALINE UNTIL THE PH HAS RETURNED TO NORMAL (30-60 MINUTES). COVER WITH STERILE BANDAGES. GET MEDICAL ATTENTION IMMEDIATELY.

INGESTION: DIOCTYL SODIUM SULFOSUCCINATE (AEROSOL (R) OT): ACUTE EXPOSURE- MAY CAUSE GASTROENTERITIS, DIARRHEA, VOMITING, CRAMPING PAINS, NAUSEA, BLOATING AND ANOREXIA. CHRONIC EXPOSURE- IN CHRONIC FEEDING TESTS, FATALLY POISONED RATS SHOWED NO GROSS LESIONS OUTSIDE THE GASTROINTESTINAL TRACT.

FIRST AID- TREAT SYMPTOMATICALLY AND SUPPORTIVELY. GET MEDICAL ATTENTION IMMEDIATELY. IF VOMITING OCCURS, KEEP HEAD LOWER THAN HIPS TO PREVENT ASPIRATION.

ANTIDOTE: NO SPECIFIC ANTIDOTE. TREAT SYMPTOMATICALLY AND SUPPORTIVELY.

REACTIVITY

REACTIVITY: STABLE UNDER NORMAL TEMPERATURES AND PRESSURES.

INCOMPATIBILITIES: DIOCTYL SODIUM SULFOSUCCINATE (AEROSOL (R) OT): OXIDIZERS (STRONG): FIRE AND EXPLOSION HAZARD. STEEL: MAY CORRODE IN THE PRESENCE OF MOISTURE.

DECOMPOSITION: THERMAL DECOMPOSITION PRODUCTS MAY INCLUDE TOXIC OXIDES OF CARBON, NITROGEN, AND SULFUR.

POLYMERIZATION: HAZARDOUS POLYMERIZATION HAS NOT BEEN REPORTED TO OCCUR UNDER NORMAL TEMPERATURES AND PRESSURES.

STORAGE AND DISPOSAL

OBSERVE ALL FEDERAL, STATE AND LOCAL REGULATIONS WHEN STORING OR DISPOSING OF THIS SUBSTANCE. FOR ASSISTANCE, CONTACT THE DISTRICT DIRECTOR OF THE ENVIRONMENTAL PROTECTION AGENCY.

STORAGE

STORE AWAY FROM INCOMPATIBLE SUBSTANCES.
STORE IN A TIGHTLY CLOSED CONTAINER.

CONDITIONS TO AVOID

MAY BURN BUT DOES NOT IGNITE READILY. AVOID CONTACT WITH STRONG OXIDIZERS, EXCESSIVE HEAT, SPARKS, OR OPEN FLAME.

SPILL AND LEAK PROCEDURES

OCCUPATIONAL SPILL: SWEEP UP AND PLACE IN SUITABLE CLEAN, DRY CONTAINERS FOR RECLAMATION OR LATER DISPOSAL. DO NOT FLUSH SPILLED MATERIAL INTO SEWER. KEEP UNNECESSARY PEOPLE AWAY.

PROTECTIVE EQUIPMENT

VENTILATION: PROVIDE LOCAL EXHAUST OR PROCESS ENCLOSURE VENTILATION SYSTEM.

RESPIRATOR: THE FOLLOWING RESPIRATORS ARE RECOMMENDED BASED ON INFORMATION FOUND IN THE PHYSICAL DATA, TOXICITY AND HEALTH EFFECTS SECTIONS. THEY ARE RANKED IN ORDER FROM MINIMUM TO MAXIMUM RESPIRATORY PROTECTION. THE SPECIFIC RESPIRATOR SELECTED MUST BE BASED ON CONTAMINATION LEVELS FOUND IN THE WORK PLACE, MUST NOT EXCEED THE WORKING LIMITS OF THE RESPIRATOR AND BE JOINTLY APPROVED BY THE NATIONAL INSTITUTE FOR OCCUPATIONAL SAFETY AND HEALTH AND THE MINE SAFETY AND HEALTH ADMINISTRATION (NIOSH-MSHA).

DUST AND MIST RESPIRATOR WITH A FULL FACEPIECE.

AIR-PURIFYING FULL FACEPIECE RESPIRATOR WITH A HIGH-EFFICIENCY PARTICULATE FILTER.

POWERED AIR-PURIFYING RESPIRATOR WITH A TIGHT-FITTING FACEPIECE AND HIGH-EFFICIENCY PARTICULATE FILTER.

TYPE 'C' SUPPLIED-AIR RESPIRATOR WITH A FULL FACEPIECE OPERATED IN PRESSURE-DEMAND OR OTHER POSITIVE PRESSURE MODE OR WITH A FULL FACEPIECE, HELMET OR HOOD OPERATED IN CONTINUOUS-FLOW MODE.

SELF-CONTAINED BREATHING APPARATUS WITH A FULL FACEPIECE OPERATED IN PRESSURE-DEMAND OR OTHER POSITIVE PRESSURE MODE.

FOR FIREFIGHTING AND OTHER IMMEDIATELY DANGEROUS TO LIFE OR HEALTH CONDITIONS:

SELF-CONTAINED BREATHING APPARATUS WITH FULL FACEPIECE OPERATED IN PRESSURE-DEMAND OR OTHER POSITIVE PRESSURE MODE.

SUPPLIED-AIR RESPIRATOR WITH FULL FACEPIECE AND OPERATED IN PRESSURE-DEMAND OR OTHER POSITIVE PRESSURE MODE IN COMBINATION WITH AN AUXILIARY SELF-CONTAINED BREATHING APPARATUS OPERATED IN PRESSURE-DEMAND OR OTHER POSITIVE PRESSURE MODE.

CLOTHING: EMPLOYEE MUST WEAR APPROPRIATE PROTECTIVE (IMPERVIOUS) CLOTHING AND EQUIPMENT TO PREVENT REPEATED OR PROLONGED SKIN CONTACT WITH THIS SUBSTANCE.

GLOVES: EMPLOYEE MUST WEAR APPROPRIATE PROTECTIVE GLOVES TO PREVENT CONTACT WITH THIS SUBSTANCE.

EYE PROTECTION: EMPLOYEE MUST WEAR SPLASH-PROOF OR DUST-RESISTANT SAFETY GOGGLES AND A FACESHIELD TO PREVENT CONTACT WITH THIS SUBSTANCE.

EMERGENCY WASH FACILITIES: WHERE THERE IS ANY POSSIBILITY THAT AN EMPLOYEE'S EYES AND/OR SKIN MAY BE EXPOSED TO THIS SUBSTANCE, THE EMPLOYER SHOULD PROVIDE AN EYE WASH FOUNTAIN AND QUICK DRENCH SHOWER WITHIN THE IMMEDIATE WORK AREA FOR EMERGENCY USE.

AUTHORIZED BY- OCCUPATIONAL HEALTH SERVICES, INC.
CREATION DATE: 11/16/89 ***REVISION DATE:*** 05/31/90

MATERIAL SAFETY DATA SHEET

OCCUPATIONAL HEALTH SERVICES, INC.
AGRICULTURE AND PESTICIDE DIVISION
450 SEVENTH AVENUE, SUITE 2407
NEW YORK, NEW YORK 10123
1-800-445-MSDS OR (212) 967-1100

EMERGENCY CONTACT:
JOHN S. BRANSFORD, JR. (615) 292-1180

SUBSTANCE IDENTIFICATION

CAS-NUMBER 327-98-0

SUBSTANCE: TRICHLORONATE

TRADE NAMES/SYNONYMS: O-ETHYL O-(2,4,5-TRICHLOROPHENYL) ETHYLPHOSPHONOTHIOATE; O-ETHYL O-2,4,5-TRICHLOROPHENYL ETHYLPHOSPHONOTHIOATE; ETHYL 2,4,5-TRICHLOROPHENYL ETHYLPHOSPHONOTHIONATE; PHOSPHONOTHIOIC ACID, ETHYL-, O-ETHYL O-(2,4,5-TRICHLOROPHENYL)ESTER; ETHYLPHOSPHONOTHIOIC ACID O-ETHYL O-(2,4,5-TRICHLOROPHENYL)ESTER; AGRISIL; AGRITOX; BAY 37289; BAYER 37289; FITOSOL; PHYTOSOL; TRICHLORONAT; ENT 25712; C10H12CL3O2PS; PST00478

CHEMICAL FAMILY: PHOSPHOROTHIOATE
HALOGEN COMPOUND, AROMATIC

MOLECULAR FORMULA: C10-H12-CL3-O2-P-S

MOLECULAR WEIGHT: 333.60

CERCLA RATINGS (SCALE 0-3): HEALTH=3 FIRE=0 REACTIVITY=0 PERSISTENCE=3

NFPA RATINGS (SCALE 0-4): HEALTH=4 FIRE=0 REACTIVITY=0

COMPONENTS AND CONTAMINANTS

COMPONENT: TRICHLORONATE ***PERCENT:*** 100.0
CAS# 327-98-0

EXPOSURE LIMITS: NO OCCUPATIONAL EXPOSURE LIMITS ESTABLISHED BY OSHA, ACGIH, OR NIOSH.

TRICHLORONATE: 500 POUNDS SARA SECTION 302 THRESHOLD PLANNING QUANTITY
1 POUND SARA SECTION 304 REPORTABLE QUANTITY

PHYSICAL DATA

DESCRIPTION: AMBER LIQUID ***BOILING POINT:*** 226 F (108 C) @ 0.01 MMHG

SPECIFIC GRAVITY: 1.365 ***EVAPORATION RATE:*** NOT AVAILABLE

SOLUBILITY IN WATER: 50 PPM

SOLVENT SOLUBILITY: SOLUBLE IN DICHLOROMETHANE, PROPAN-2-OL, ALCOHOL, AND MOST ORGANIC SOLVENTS

FIRE AND EXPLOSION DATA

FIRE AND EXPLOSION HAZARD: NEGLIGIBLE FIRE HAZARD WHEN EXPOSED TO HEAT OR FLAME.

FIREFIGHTING MEDIA: DRY CHEMICAL, CARBON DIOXIDE, HALON, WATER SPRAY OR STANDARD FOAM (1987 EMERGENCY RESPONSE GUIDEBOOK, DOT P 5800.4).
FOR LARGER FIRES, USE WATER SPRAY, FOG OR STANDARD FOAM (1987 EMERGENCY RESPONSE GUIDEBOOK, DOT P 5800.4).

FIREFIGHTING: MOVE CONTAINERS FROM FIRE AREA IF POSSIBLE. FIGHT FIRE FROM MAXIMUM DISTANCE. STAY AWAY FROM STORAGE TANK ENDS. DIKE FIRE CONTROL WATER FOR LATER DISPOSAL. DO NOT SCATTER MATERIAL (1987 EMERGENCY RESPONSE GUIDEBOOK, DOT P 5800.4, GUIDE PAGE 55).

TRANSPORTATION DATA

DEPARTMENT OF TRANSPORTATION HAZARD CLASSIFICATION 49 CFR 172.101: POISON B

DEPARTMENT OF TRANSPORTATION LABELING REQUIREMENTS 49 CFR 172.101 AND SUBPART E: POISON

DEPARTMENT OF TRANSPORTATION PACKAGING REQUIREMENTS: 49 CFR 173.346 EXCEPTIONS: 49 CFR 173.345

TOXICITY

TRICHLORONATE: TOXICITY DATA: 700 MG/M3/4 HOURS INHALATION-RAT LCLO; 64 MG/KG SKIN-RAT LD50; 15 MG/KG ORAL-RAT LD50; 40 MG/KG ORAL-MOUSE LD50;

25 MG/KG ORAL-RABBIT LD50; 10 MG/KG ORAL-CAT LD50; 40 MG/KG ORAL-GUINEA PIG LD50; 35 MG/KG UNREPORTED-MAMMAL LD50. CARCINOGEN STATUS: NONE. ACUTE TOXICITY LEVEL: HIGHLY TOXIC BY DERMAL ABSORPTION AND INGESTION. TARGET EFFECTS: CHOLINESTERASE INHIBITOR. POISONING MAY AFFECT THE NERVOUS SYSTEM.* AT INCREASED RISK FROM EXPOSURE: PERSONS WITH RESPIRATORY AILMENTS, RECENT EXPOSURE TO CHOLINESTERASE INHIBITORS OR IMPAIRED CHOLINESTERASE PRODUCTION, OR LIVER MALFUNCTION.* ADDITIONAL DATA: MAY CROSS THE PLACENTA. HIGH ENVIRONMENTAL TEMPERATURES OR EXPOSURE OF THE CHEMICAL TO VISIBLE OR ULTRAVIOLET LIGHT MAY ENHANCE THE TOXICITY. INTERACTIONS WITH MEDICATIONS MAY OCCUR.*

* MAY BE BASED ON GENERAL INFORMATION ON ORGANOPHOSPHATES.

HEALTH EFFECTS AND FIRST AID

INHALATION: TRICHLORONATE: SEE INFORMATION ON ORGANOPHOSPHATES. ORGANOPHOSPHATES: CHOLINESTERASE INHIBITOR. **ACUTE EXPOSURE-** WHEN INHALED, THE FIRST EFFECTS OF CHOLINESTERASE INHIBITORS ARE USUALLY RESPIRATORY AND MAY INCLUDE NASAL HYPEREMIA AND WATERY DISCHARGE, COUGH, CHEST DISCOMFORT, DYSPNEA, AND WHEEZING DUE TO INCREASED BRONCHIAL SECRETIONS AND BRONCHOCONSTRICTION. IF SUFFICIENT AMOUNTS ARE ABSORBED, OTHER SYSTEMIC EFFECTS MAY BEGIN WITHIN A FEW MINUTES OR BE DELAYED FOR UP TO 12 HOURS. SYMPTOMS MAY INCLUDE PALLOR, NAUSEA, VOMITING, DIARRHEA, ABDOMINAL CRAMPS, HEADACHE, DIZZINESS, OCULAR PAIN, BLURRED VISION, MIOSIS OR IN SOME CASES, ESPECIALLY INITIALLY, MYDRIASIS, LACRIMATION, SALIVATION, SWEATING, AND CONFUSION. OTHER REPORTED CENTRAL NERVOUS SYSTEM OR NEUROMUSCULAR EFFECTS MAY INCLUDE ATAXIA, SLURRED SPEECH, AREFLEXIA, WEAKNESS, FATIGUE, FASCICULATIONS, TWITCHING, TREMORS POSSIBLY OF THE TONGUE AND EYELIDS, AND EVENTUALLY PARALYSIS OF THE EXTREMITIES AND POSSIBLY OF THE RESPIRATORY MUSCLES. IN SEVERE CASES THERE MAY ALSO BE INVOLUNTARY DEFECATION AND URINATION, CYANOSIS, PSYCHOSIS, HYPERGLYCEMIA, ACUTE PANCREATITIS, CARDIAC IRREGULARITIES, PULMONARY EDEMA, UNCONSCIOUSNESS, CONVULSIONS, AND COMA. DEATH IS PRIMARILY DUE TO RESPIRATORY FAILURE, ALTHOUGH CARDIOVASCULAR EFFECTS INCLUDING CARDIAC ARREST MAY ALSO BE IMPLICATED. LONG TERM SEQUELAE ARE RARE BUT MAY INCLUDE NEUROPSYCHIATRIC DISORDERS AND MYOPATHY WITH MUSCLE TENDERNESS. SOME ORGANOPHOSPHATES MAY CAUSE A DELAYED NEUROPATHY BEGINNING 1-4 WEEKS AFTER AN ACUTE EXPOSURE WHICH MAY OR MAY NOT HAVE CAUSED ACUTE CHOLINERGIC EFFECTS. NUMBNESS, TINGLING, WEAKNESS AND CRAMPING BEGINNING SYMMETRICALLY IN THE LOWER LIMBS MAY PROGRESS TO ATAXIA AND PARALYSIS. IN SEVERE CASES, UPPER LIMB INVOLVEMENT IS POSSIBLE AND FLACCID PARALYSIS MAY PROGRESS TO SPASTIC PARALYSIS WITH EXAGGERATED REFLEXES. IMPROVEMENT MAY OCCUR OVER MONTHS TO YEARS, BUT SOME RESIDUAL IMPAIRMENT USUALLY REMAINS. **CHRONIC EXPOSURE-** REPEATED OR PROLONGED EXPOSURE MAY RESULT IN THE EFFECTS OF ACUTE EXPOSURE INCLUDING THE DELAYED NEUROPATHY. OTHER EFFECTS REPORTED IN WORKERS REPEATEDLY EXPOSED INCLUDE IMPAIRED MEMORY AND CONCENTRATION, ACUTE PSYCHOSIS, SEVERE DEPRESSIONS, IRRITABILTY, CONFUSION, APATHY, EMOTIONAL LABILITY, SOCIAL WITHDRAWAL, CONFUSION, HEADACHE, SPEECH DIFFICULTIES, DELAYED REACTION TIMES, SPATIAL DISORIENTATION, NIGHTMARES, SLEEPWALKING, AND DROWSINESS OR INSOMNIA. AN INFLUENZA-LIKE CONDITION WITH HEADACHE, NAUSEA, WEAKNESS, ANOREXIA AND MALAISE HAS ALSO BEEN REPORTED.

FIRST AID- REMOVE FROM EXPOSURE AREA TO FRESH AIR IMMEDIATELY. IF BREATHING HAS STOPPED, GIVE ARTIFICIAL RESPIRATION. MAINTAIN AIRWAY AND BLOOD PRESSURE AND ADMINISTER OXYGEN IF AVAILABLE. KEEP AFFECTED PERSON WARM AND AT REST. TREAT SYMPTOMATICALLY AND SUPPORTIVELY. ADMINISTRATION OF OXYGEN SHOULD BE PERFORMED BY QUALIFIED PERSONNEL. GET MEDICAL ATTENTION IMMEDIATELY.

SKIN CONTACT: TRICHLORONATE: HIGHLY TOXIC. SEE INFORMATION ON ORGANOPHOSPHATES. ORGANOPHOSPHATES: CHOLINESTERASE INHIBITOR. **ACUTE EXPOSURE-** LOCALIZED SWEATING AND FASCICULATIONS MAY OCCUR AT THE SITE OF CONTACT. IF SUFFICIENT AMOUNTS ARE ABSORBED, OTHER EFFECTS OF CHOLINESTERASE INHIBITION AS DESCRIBED IN ACUTE INHALATION MAY OCCUR. SYMPTOMS MAY BE DELAYED 2-3 HOURS, BUT USUALLY NO MORE THAN 12 HOURS. THE RATE OF ABSORPTION IS INCREASED BY THE PRESENCE OF DERMATITIS OR HIGH AMBIENT TEMPERATURES. DELAYED NEUROPATHY IS ALSO POSSIBLE. **CHRONIC EXPOSURE-** REPEATED OR PROLONGED EXPOSURE MAY CAUSE EFFECTS AS DESCRIBED IN ACUTE EXPOSURE. SOME ORGANOPHOSPHATES MAY CAUSE SENSITIZATION.

FIRST AID- REMOVE CONTAMINATED CLOTHING IMMEDIATELY. WASH CONTAMINATED AREAS WITH SOAP AND WATER FOLLOWED BY ALCOHOL (ARENA, POISONING, 4TH ED.). EMERGENCY PERSONNEL SHOULD WEAR GLOVES AND AVOID CONTAMINATION. TREAT RESPIRATORY DIFFICULTY WITH ARTIFICIAL RESPIRATION. GET MEDICAL ATTENTION IMMEDIATELY.

EYE CONTACT: TRICHLORONATE: SEE INFORMATION ON ORGANOPHOSPHATES. ORGANOPHOSPHATES: CHOLINESTERASE INHIBITOR. **ACUTE EXPOSURE-** DIRECT CONTACT MAY CAUSE PAIN, HYPEREMIA, LACRIMATION, TWITCHING OF THE EYELIDS, MIOSIS, AND CILIARY MUSCLE SPASM WITH LOSS OF ACCOMODATION, BLURRED OR DIMMED VISION AND BROWACHE. SOMETIMES MYDRIASIS MAY OCCUR INSTEAD OF MIOSIS. WITH SUFFICIENT EXPOSURE, OTHER SYMPTOMS OF CHOLINESTERASE INHIBITION AS DESCRIBED IN ACUTE INHALATION MAY OCCUR. **CHRONIC EXPOSURE-** REPEATED OR PROLONGED EXPOSURE MAY CAUSE EFFECTS AS DESCRIBED IN ACUTE EXPOSURE. SOME COMPOUNDS HAVE CAUSED TOXIC EFFECTS ON THE CRYSTALLINE LENS, CONJUNCTIVAL THICKENING AND OBSTRUCTION OF THE NASOLACRIMAL CANALS WHEN USED AS MIOTIC EYEDROPS.

FIRST AID- IRRIGATE EYES WITH WATER OR SALINE SOLUTION. IF SYMPTOMS OF POISONING OCCUR, TREAT RESPIRATORY DIFFICULTY WITH ARTIFICIAL RESPIRATION AND OXYGEN. OBSERVE PATIENT FOR AT LEAST 24-36 HOURS (GOSSELIN, CLINICAL TOXICOLOGY OF COMMERCIAL PRODUCTS, 5TH ED.). GET MEDICAL ATTENTION IMMEDIATELY. OXYGEN SHOULD BE ADMINISTERED BY QUALIFIED MEDICAL PERSONNEL.

INGESTION: TRICHLORONATE: HIGHLY TOXIC. SEE INFORMATION ON ORGANOPHOSPHATES.
ORGANOPHOSPHATES: CHOLINESTERASE INHIBITOR. **ACUTE EXPOSURE-** WHEN INGESTED, THE FIRST EFFECTS MAY BE NAUSEA, VOMITING, ANOREXIA, ABDOMINAL CRAMPS AND DIARRHEA. GASTROINTESTINAL ABSORPTION MAY CAUSE SYMPTOMS OF CHOLINESTERASE INHIBITION AS DESCRIBED IN ACUTE INHALATION. SYMPTOMS MAY BEGIN WITHIN MINUTES OR BE DELAYED FOR HOURS. DELAYED EFFECTS INCLUDING NEUROPATHY MAY ALSO OCCUR. **CHRONIC EXPOSURE-** REPEATED INGESTION MAY CAUSE EFFECTS AS DESCRIBED IN ACUTE EXPOSURE.

FIRST AID- IF PERSON IS ALERT AND RESPIRATION IS NOT DEPRESSED, GIVE SYRUP OF IPECAC FOLLOWED BY WATER (IF VOMITING OCCURS, KEEP HEAD BELOW HIPS TO PREVENT ASPIRATION). IF CONSCIOUSNESS LEVEL DECLINES OR VOMITING HAS NOT OCCURRED IN 15 MINUTES EMPTY STOMACH BY GASTRIC LAVAGE WITH THE AID OF CUFFED ENDOTRACHEAL TUBE USING ISOTONIC SALINE OR 5% SODIUM BICARBONATE FOLLOW WITH ACTIVATED CHARCOAL. ESTABLISH AND MAINTAIN AIRWAY. TREAT RESPIRATORY DIFFICULTY WITH ARTIFICIAL RESPIRATION AND OXYGEN. DO NOT GIVE MORPHINE, AMINOPHYLLINE, PHENOTHIAZINES, RESERPINE, FUROSEMIDE, OR ETHACRYNIC ACID (MORGAN, RECOGNITION AND MANAGEMENT OF PESTICIDE POISONINGS, 3RD ED.). TREAT SYMPTOMATICALLY AND SUPPORTIVELY. ADMINISTRATION OF OXYGEN AND LAVAGE MUST BE PERFORMED BY QUALIFIED MEDICAL PERSONNEL. GET MEDICAL ATTENTION IMMEDIATELY.

ANTIDOTE: THE FOLLOWING ANTIDOTE(S) HAVE BEEN RECOMMENDED. HOWEVER, THE DECISION AS TO WHETHER THE SEVERITY OF POISONING REQUIRES ADMINISTRATION OF ANY ANTIDOTE AND ACTUAL DOSE REQUIRED SHOULD BE MADE BY QUALIFIED MEDICAL PERSONNEL.
FOR CHOLINESTERASE INHIBITORS: ESTABLISH CLEAR AIRWAY AND TISSUE OXYGENATION BY ASPIRATION OF SECRETIONS, AND IF NECESSARY, BY ASSISTED PULMONARY VENTILATION WITH OXYGEN. IMPROVE TISSUE OXYGENATION AS MUCH AS POSSIBLE BEFORE ADMINISTERING ATROPINE TO MINIMIZE THE RISK OF VENTRICULAR FIBRILLATION. ADMINISTER ATROPINE SULFATE INTRAVENOUSLY, OR INTRAMUSCULARLY IF IV INJECTION IS NOT POSSIBLE. IN MODERATELY SEVERE POISONING ADMINISTER ATROPINE SULFATE, 0.4-2.0 MG REPEATED EVERY 15 MINUTES UNTIL ATROPINIZATION IS ACHIEVED (TACHYCARDIA, FLUSHING, DRY MOUTH, MYDRIASIS). MAINTAIN ATROPINIZATION BY REPEATED DOSES FOR 2-12 HOURS, OR LONGER, DEPENDING ON THE SEVERITY OF POISONING. THE APPEARANCE OF RALES IN THE LUNG BASES, MIOSIS, SALIVATION, NAUSEA, BRADYCARDIA, ARE ALL INDICATIONS OF INADEQUATE ATROPINIZATION. SEVERELY POISONED INDIVIDUALS MAY EXHIBIT REMARKABLE TOLERANCE TO ATROPINE; TWO OR MORE TIMES THE DOSAGES SUGGESTED ABOVE MAY BE NEEDED. PERSONS NOT POISONED OR ONLY SLIGHTLY POISONED, HOWEVER, MAY DEVELOP SIGNS OF ATROPINE TOXICITY FROM SUCH LARGE DOSAGES: FEVER, MUSCLE FIBRILLATIONS, AND DELIRIUM ARE THE MAIN SIGNS OF ATROPINE TOXICITY. IF THESE SIGNS APPEAR WHILE THE PATIENT IS FULLY ATROPINIZED, ATROPINE ADMINISTRATION SHOULD BE DISCONTINUED, AT LEAST TEMPORARILY. OBSERVE TREATED PATIENTS CLOSELY AT LEAST 24 HOURS TO INSURE THAT SYMPTOMS (POSSIBLY PULMONARY EDEMA) DO NOT RECUR AS ATROPINIZATION WEARS OFF. IN VERY SEVERE POISONINGS, METABOLIC DISPOSITION OF TOXICANT MAY REQUIRE SEVERAL HOURS OR DAYS DURING WHICH ATROPINIZATION MUST BE MAINTAINED. MARKEDLY LOWER LEVELS OF URINARY METABOLITES INDICATE THAT ATROPINE DOSAGE CAN BE TAPERED OFF. AS DOSAGE IS REDUCED, CHECK THE LUNG BASES FREQUENTLY FOR RALES. IF RALES ARE HEARD OR OTHER SYMPTOMS RETURN, RE-ESTABLISH ATROPINIZATION PROMPTLY (MORGAN, RECOGNITION AND MANAGEMENT OF PESTICIDE POISONINGS, 3RD ED.). ADMINISTRATION OF ANTIDOTE MUST BE PERFORMED BY QUALIFIED MEDICAL PERSONNEL.

IN CASES OF SEVERE POISONING BY ORGANOPHOSPHATE PESTICIDES IN WHICH RESPIRATORY DEPRESSION, MUSCLE WEAKNESS AND TWITCHINGS ARE SEVERE, GIVE PRALIDOXIME (PROTOPAM-AYERST, 2-PAM), 1.0 GRAM INTRAVENOUSLY AT NO MORE THAN 0.5 GRAM PER MINUTE. DOSAGE OF PRALIDOXIME MAY BE REPEATED IN 1-2 HOURS, THEN AT 10-12 HOUR INTERVALS IF NEEDED. IN VERY SEVERE POISONINGS, DOSAGE RATES MAY BE DOUBLED. TREATMENT WITH PRALIDOXIME WILL BE MOST EFFECTIVE IF GIVEN WITHIN THIRTY-SIX HOURS AFTER POISONING (MORGAN, RECOGNITION AND MANAGEMENT OF PESTICIDE POISONINGS, 3RD ED.). ANTIDOTE SHOULD BE ADMINISTERED BY QUALIFIED MEDICAL PERSONNEL.

REACTIVITY

REACTIVITY: STABLE UNDER NORMAL TEMPERATURES AND PRESSURES.

INCOMPATIBILITIES: TRICHLORONATE: ALKALI: MAY CAUSE HYDROLYSIS.

DECOMPOSITION: THERMAL DECOMPOSITION MAY RELEASE TOXIC AND/OR HAZARDOUS GASES.

POLYMERIZATION: HAZARDOUS POLYMERIZATION HAS NOT BEEN REPORTED TO OCCUR UNDER NORMAL TEMPERATURES AND PRESSURES.

STORAGE AND DISPOSAL

OBSERVE ALL FEDERAL, STATE AND LOCAL REGULATIONS WHEN STORING OR DISPOSING OF THIS SUBSTANCE. FOR ASSISTANCE, CONTACT THE DISTRICT DIRECTOR OF THE ENVIRONMENTAL PROTECTION AGENCY.

STORAGE

STORE IN ACCORDANCE WITH 40 CFR 165 RECOMMENDED PROCEDURES FOR THE DISPOSAL AND STORAGE OF PESTICIDES AND PESTICIDE CONTAINERS.

STORE AWAY FROM INCOMPATIBLE SUBSTANCES.

THRESHOLD PLANNING QUANTITY (TPQ): THE SUPERFUND AMENDMENTS AND REAUTHORIZATION ACT (SARA) SECTION 302 REQUIRES THAT EACH FACILITY WHERE ANY EXTREMELY HAZARDOUS SUBSTANCE IS PRESENT IN A QUANTITY EQUAL TO OR GREATER THAN THE TPQ ESTABLISHED FOR THAT SUBSTANCE NOTIFY THE STATE EMERGENCY RESPONSE COMMISSION FOR THE STATE IN WHICH IT IS LOCATED. SECTION 303 OF SARA REQUIRES THESE FACILITIES TO PARTICIPATE IN LOCAL EMERGENCY RESPONSE PLANNING (40 CFR 355.30).

DISPOSAL

DISPOSAL MUST BE IN ACCORDANCE WITH 40 CFR 165 RECOMMENDED PROCEDURES FOR THE DISPOSAL AND STORAGE OF PESTICIDES AND PESTICIDE CONTAINERS.

CONDITIONS TO AVOID

MAY BURN BUT DOES NOT IGNITE READILY. CONTAINERS MAY EXPLODE IN HEAT OF FIRE.

SPILL AND LEAK PROCEDURES

OCCUPATIONAL SPILL: DO NOT TOUCH SPILLED MATERIAL. STOP LEAK IF YOU CAN DO IT WITHOUT RISK. USE WATER SPRAY TO REDUCE VAPORS. FOR SMALL SPILLS, TAKE UP WITH SAND OR OTHER ABSORBENT MATERIAL AND PLACE INTO CONTAINERS FOR LATER DISPOSAL. FOR SMALL DRY SPILLS, WITH A CLEAN SHOVEL PLACE MATERIAL INTO CLEAN, DRY CONTAINERS AND COVER. MOVE CONTAINERS FROM SPILL AREA. FOR LARGER SPILLS, DIKE FAR AHEAD OF SPILL FOR LATER DISPOSAL. KEEP UNNECESSARY PEOPLE AWAY. ISOLATE HAZARD AREA AND DENY ENTRY. VENTILATE CLOSED SPACES BEFORE ENTERING.

REPORTABLE QUANTITY (RQ): 1 POUND THE SUPERFUND AMENDMENTS AND REAUTHORIZATION ACT (SARA) SECTION 304 REQUIRES THAT A RELEASE EQUAL TO OR GREATER THAN THE REPORTABLE QUANTITY FOR THIS SUBSTANCE BE IMMEDIATELY REPORTED TO THE LOCAL EMERGENCY PLANNING COMMITTEE AND THE STATE EMERGENCY RESPONSE COMMISSION (40 CFR 355.40). IF THE RELEASE OF THIS SUBSTANCE IS REPORTABLE UNDER CERCLA SECTION 103, THE NATIONAL RESPONSE CENTER MUST BE NOTIFIED IMMEDIATELY AT (800) 424-8802 OR (202) 426-2675 IN THE METROPOLITAN WASHINGTON, D.C. AREA (40 CFR 302.6).

PROTECTIVE EQUIPMENT

VENTILATION: PROCESS ENCLOSURE RECOMMENDED.

RESPIRATOR: THE FOLLOWING RESPIRATORS ARE RECOMMENDED BASED ON INFORMATION FOUND IN THE PHYSICAL DATA, TOXICITY AND HEALTH EFFECTS SECTIONS. THEY ARE RANKED IN ORDER FROM MINIMUM TO MAXIMUM RESPIRATORY PROTECTION. THE SPECIFIC RESPIRATOR SELECTED MUST BE BASED ON CONTAMINATION LEVELS FOUND IN THE WORK PLACE, MUST NOT EXCEED THE WORKING LIMITS OF THE RESPIRATOR AND BE JOINTLY APPROVED BY THE NATIONAL INSTITUTE FOR OCCUPATIONAL SAFETY AND HEALTH AND THE MINE SAFETY AND HEALTH ADMINISTRATION (NIOSH-MSHA).

TYPE 'C' SUPPLIED-AIR RESPIRATOR WITH A FULL FACEPIECE OPERATED IN PRESSURE-DEMAND OR OTHER POSITIVE PRESSURE MODE OR WITH A FULL FACEPIECE, HELMET OR HOOD OPERATED IN CONTINOUS-FLOW MODE.

SELF-CONTAINED BREATHING APPARATUS WITH A FULL FACEPIECE OPERATED IN PRESSURE-DEMAND OR OTHER POSITIVE PRESSURE MODE.

FOR FIREFIGHTING AND OTHER IMMEDIATELY DANGEROUS TO LIFE OR HEALTH CONDITIONS:

SELF-CONTAINED BREATHING APPARATUS WITH FULL FACEPIECE OPERATED IN PRESSURE-DEMAND OR OTHER POSITIVE PRESSURE MODE.

SUPPLIED-AIR RESPIRATOR WITH FULL FACEPIECE AND OPERATED IN PRESSURE-DEMAND OR OTHER POSITIVE PRESSURE MODE IN COMBINATION WITH AN AUXILIARY SELF-CONTAINED BREATHING APPARATUS OPERATED IN PRESSURE-DEMAND OR OTHER POSITIVE PRESSURE MODE.

CLOTHING: EMPLOYEE MUST WEAR APPROPRIATE PROTECTIVE (IMPERVIOUS) CLOTHING AND EQUIPMENT TO PREVENT ANY POSSIBILITY OF SKIN CONTACT WITH THIS SUBSTANCE.

GLOVES: EMPLOYEE MUST WEAR APPROPRIATE PROTECTIVE GLOVES TO PREVENT CONTACT WITH THIS SUBSTANCE.

EYE PROTECTION: EMPLOYEE MUST WEAR SPLASH-PROOF OR DUST-RESISTANT SAFETY GOGGLES WITH OR WITHOUT A FACESHIELD TO PREVENT CONTACT WITH THIS SUBSTANCE.

EMERGENCY EYE WASH: WHERE THERE IS ANY POSSIBILITY THAT AN EMPLOYEE'S EYES MAY BE EXPOSED TO THIS SUBSTANCE, THE EMPLOYER SHOULD PROVIDE AN EYE WASH FOUNTAIN WITHIN THE IMMEDIATE WORK AREA FOR EMERGENCY USE.

AUTHORIZED BY- OCCUPATIONAL HEALTH SERVICES, INC.

CREATION DATE: 05/18/90 ***REVISION DATE:*** 05/18/90

MATERIAL SAFETY DATA SHEET

OCCUPATIONAL HEALTH SERVICES, INC.
AGRICULTURE AND PESTICIDE DIVISION
450 SEVENTH AVENUE, SUITE 2407
NEW YORK, NEW YORK 10123
1-800-445-MSDS OR (212) 967-1100

EMERGENCY CONTACT:
JOHN S. BRANSFORD, JR. (615) 292-1180

SUBSTANCE IDENTIFICATION

CAS-NUMBER 1757-18-2

SUBSTANCE: **AKTON**

TRADE NAMES/SYNONYMS: PHOSPHOROTHIOIC ACID, O-(2-CHLORO-1-(2,5-DICHLOROPHENYL)ETHYL O,O DIETHYL ESTER; PHOSPHOROTHIOIC ACID, O-(2-CHLORO-1-(2,5-DICHLOROPHENYL)VINYL) O,O-DIETHYL ESTER; O,O-DIETHYL O-(2-CHLORO-1-(2,5-DICHLOROPHENYL)VINYL)PHOSPHOROTHIOATE; 2-CHLORO-1-(2',5'-DICHLOROPHENYL)VINYL DIETHYL PHOSPHOROTHIONATE; OMS 1344; SD 9098; ENT 27,102; C12H14CL3O3PS; PST00493

CHEMICAL FAMILY: ORGANOPHOSPHATE

MOLECULAR FORMULA: C12-H14-CL3-O3-P-S

MOLECULAR WEIGHT: 375.64

CERCLA RATINGS (SCALE 0-3): HEALTH=3 FIRE=0 REACTIVITY=0 PERSISTENCE=3

NFPA RATINGS (SCALE 0-4): HEALTH=4 FIRE=0 REACTIVITY=0

COMPONENTS AND CONTAMINANTS

COMPONENT: AKTON ***PERCENT:*** 100

CAS# 1757-18-2

EXPOSURE LIMITS: NO OCCUPATIONAL EXPOSURE LIMITS ESTABLISHED BY OSHA, ACGIH, OR NIOSH.

PHYSICAL DATA

DESCRIPTION: BROWN LIQUID ***BOILING POINT:*** 293 F (145 C) @ 0.005 MMHG

SPECIFIC GRAVITY: NOT AVAILABLE ***EVAPORATION RATE:*** NOT AVAILABLE

SOLUBILITY IN WATER: 1.39 PPM

SOLVENT SOLUBILITY: SOLUBLE IN MOST ORGANIC SOLVENTS

FIRE AND EXPLOSION DATA

FIRE AND EXPLOSION HAZARD: NEGLIGIBLE FIRE HAZARD WHEN EXPOSED TO HEAT OR FLAME.

FIREFIGHTING MEDIA: DRY CHEMICAL, CARBON DIOXIDE, HALON, WATER SPRAY OR STANDARD FOAM (1987 EMERGENCY RESPONSE GUIDEBOOK, DOT P 5800.4). FOR LARGER FIRES, USE WATER SPRAY, FOG OR STANDARD FOAM (1987 EMERGENCY RESPONSE GUIDEBOOK, DOT P 5800.4).

FIREFIGHTING: MOVE CONTAINERS FROM FIRE AREA IF POSSIBLE. FIGHT FIRE FROM MAXIMUM DISTANCE. STAY AWAY FROM STORAGE TANK ENDS. DIKE FIRE CONTROL WATER FOR LATER DISPOSAL. DO NOT SCATTER MATERIAL (1987 EMERGENCY RESPONSE GUIDEBOOK, DOT P 5800.4, GUIDE PAGE 55).

TRANSPORTATION DATA

DEPARTMENT OF TRANSPORTATION HAZARD CLASSIFICATION 49 CFR 172.101: POISON B
DEPARTMENT OF TRANSPORTATION LABELING REQUIREMENTS 49 CFR 172.101 AND SUBPART E: POISON
DEPARTMENT OF TRANSPORTATION PACKAGING REQUIREMENTS: 49 CFR 173.346
EXCEPTIONS: 49 CFR 173.345

TOXICITY

AKTON: TOXICITY DATA: 177 MG/KG SKIN-RABBIT LD50; 42 MG/KG ORAL-RAT LD50; 89 MG/KG ORAL-MOUSE LD50. CARCINOGEN STATUS: NONE. ACUTE TOXICITY LEVEL: HIGHLY TOXIC BY DERMAL ABSORPTION AND INGESTION. TARGET EFFECTS: CHOLINESTERASE INHIBITOR. POISONING MAY AFFECT THE NERVOUS SYSTEM.* AT INCREASED RISK FROM EXPOSURE: PERSONS WITH RESPIRATORY AILMENTS, RECENT EXPOSURE TO CHOLINESTERASE INHIBITORS OR IMPAIRED CHOLINESTERASE PRODUCTION, OR LIVER MALFUNCTION.* ADDITIONAL DATA: MAY CROSS THE PLACENTA. HIGH ENVIRONMENTAL TEMPERATURES OR EXPOSURE OF THE CHEMICAL TO VISIBLE OR ULTRAVIOLET LIGHT MAY ENHANCE THE TOXICITY. INTERACTIONS WITH MEDICATIONS MAY OCCUR.*
* MAY BE BASED ON GENERAL INFORMATION ON ORGANOPHOSPHATES.

HEALTH EFFECTS AND FIRST AID

INHALATION: AKTON: SEE INFORMATION ON ORGANOPHOSPHATES.
ORGANOPHOSPHATES: CHOLINESTERASE INHIBITOR. **ACUTE EXPOSURE-** WHEN INHALED, THE FIRST EFFECTS OF CHOLINESTERASE INHIBITORS ARE USUALLY RESPIRATORY AND MAY INCLUDE NASAL HYPEREMIA AND WATERY DISCHARGE, COUGH, CHEST DISCOMFORT, DYSPNEA, AND WHEEZING DUE TO INCREASED BRONCHIAL SECRETIONS AND BRONCHOCONSTRICTION. IF SUFFICIENT AMOUNTS ARE ABSORBED, OTHER SYSTEMIC EFFECTS MAY BEGIN WITHIN A FEW MINUTES OR BE DELAYED FOR UP TO 12 HOURS. SYMPTOMS MAY INCLUDE PALLOR, NAUSEA, VOMITING, DIARRHEA, ABDOMINAL CRAMPS, HEADACHE, DIZZINESS, OCULAR PAIN, BLURRED VISION, MIOSIS OR IN SOME CASES, ESPECIALLY INITIALLY, MYDRIASIS, LACRIMATION, SALIVATION, SWEATING, AND CONFUSION. OTHER REPORTED CENTRAL NERVOUS SYSTEM OR NEUROMUSCULAR EFFECTS MAY INCLUDE ATAXIA, SLURRED SPEECH, AREFLEXIA, WEAKNESS, FATIGUE, FASCICULATIONS, TWITCHING, TREMORS POSSIBLY OF THE TONGUE AND EYELIDS, AND EVENTUALLY PARALYSIS OF THE EXTREMITIES AND POSSIBLY OF THE RESPIRATORY MUSCLES. IN SEVERE CASES THERE MAY ALSO BE INVOLUNTARY DEFECATION AND URINATION, CYANOSIS, PSYCHOSIS, HYPERGLYCEMIA, ACUTE PANCREATITIS, CARDIAC IRREGULARITIES, PULMONARY EDEMA, UNCONSCIOUSNESS, CONVULSIONS, AND COMA. DEATH IS PRIMARILY DUE TO RESPIRATORY FAILURE, ALTHOUGH CARDIOVASCULAR EFFECTS INCLUDING CARDIAC ARREST MAY ALSO BE IMPLICATED. LONG TERM SEQUELAE ARE RARE BUT MAY INCLUDE NEUROPSYCHIATRIC DISORDERS AND MYOPATHY WITH MUSCLE TENDERNESS. SOME ORGANOPHOSPHATES MAY CAUSE A DELAYED NEUROPATHY BEGINNING 1-4 WEEKS AFTER AN ACUTE EXPOSURE WHICH MAY OR MAY NOT HAVE CAUSED ACUTE CHOLINERGIC EFFECTS. NUMBNESS, TINGLING, WEAKNESS AND CRAMPING BEGINNING SYMMETRICALLY IN THE LOWER LIMBS MAY PROGRESS TO ATAXIA AND PARALYSIS. IN SEVERE CASES, UPPER LIMB INVOLVEMENT IS POSSIBLE AND FLACCID PARALYSIS MAY PROGRESS TO SPASTIC PARALYSIS WITH EXAGGERATED REFLEXES. IMPROVEMENT MAY OCCUR OVER MONTHS TO YEARS, BUT SOME RESIDUAL IMPAIRMENT USUALLY REMAINS.
CHRONIC EXPOSURE- REPEATED OR PROLONGED EXPOSURE MAY RESULT IN THE EFFECTS OF ACUTE EXPOSURE INCLUDING THE DELAYED NEUROPATHY. OTHER EFFECTS REPORTED IN WORKERS REPEATEDLY EXPOSED INCLUDE IMPAIRED MEMORY AND CONCENTRATION, ACUTE PSYCHOSIS, SEVERE DEPRESSIONS, IRRITABILTY, CONFUSION, APATHY, EMOTIONAL LABILITY, SOCIAL WITHDRAWAL, CONFUSION, HEADACHE, SPEECH DIFFICULTIES, DELAYED REACTION TIMES, SPATIAL DISORIENTATION, NIGHTMARES, SLEEPWALKING, AND DROWSINESS OR INSOMNIA. AN INFLUENZA-LIKE CONDITION WITH HEADACHE, NAUSEA, WEAKNESS, ANOREXIA AND MALAISE HAS ALSO BEEN REPORTED.

FIRST AID- REMOVE FROM EXPOSURE AREA TO FRESH AIR IMMEDIATELY. IF BREATHING HAS STOPPED, GIVE ARTIFICIAL RESPIRATION. MAINTAIN AIRWAY AND BLOOD PRESSURE AND ADMINISTER OXYGEN IF AVAILABLE. KEEP AFFECTED PERSON WARM AND AT REST. TREAT SYMPTOMATICALLY AND SUPPORTIVELY. ADMINISTRATION OF OXYGEN SHOULD BE PERFORMED BY QUALIFIED PERSONNEL. GET MEDICAL ATTENTION IMMEDIATELY.

SKIN CONTACT: AKTON: HIGHLY TOXIC. SEE INFORMATION ON ORGANOPHOSPHATES.
ORGANOPHOSPHATES: CHOLINESTERASE INHIBITOR. **ACUTE EXPOSURE-** LOCALIZED SWEATING AND FASCICULATIONS MAY OCCUR AT THE SITE OF CONTACT. IF SUFFICIENT AMOUNTS ARE ABSORBED, OTHER EFFECTS OF CHOLINESTERASE INHIBITION AS DESCRIBED IN ACUTE INHALATION MAY OCCUR. SYMPTOMS MAY BE DELAYED 2-3 HOURS, BUT USUALLY NO MORE THAN 12 HOURS. THE RATE OF ABSORPTION IS INCREASED BY THE PRESENCE OF DERMATITIS OR HIGH AMBIENT TEMPERATURES. DELAYED NEUROPATHY IS ALSO POSSIBLE. **CHRONIC EXPOSURE-** REPEATED OR PROLONGED EXPOSURE MAY CAUSE EFFECTS AS DESCRIBED IN ACUTE EXPOSURE. SOME ORGANOPHOSPHATES MAY CAUSE SENSITIZATION.

FIRST AID- REMOVE CONTAMINATED CLOTHING IMMEDIATELY. WASH CONTAMINATED AREAS WITH SOAP AND WATER FOLLOWED BY ALCOHOL (ARENA, POISONING, 4TH ED.). EMERGENCY PERSONNEL SHOULD WEAR GLOVES AND AVOID CONTAMINATION. TREAT RESPIRATORY DIFFICULTY WITH ARTIFICIAL RESPIRATION. GET MEDICAL ATTENTION IMMEDIATELY.

EYE CONTACT: AKTON: SEE INFORMATION ON ORGANOPHOSPHATES.
ORGANOPHOSPHATES: CHOLINESTERASE INHIBITOR. **ACUTE EXPOSURE-** DIRECT CONTACT MAY CAUSE PAIN, HYPEREMIA, LACRIMATION, TWITCHING OF THE EYELIDS, MIOSIS, AND CILIARY MUSCLE SPASM WITH LOSS OF ACCOMODATION, BLURRED OR DIMMED VISION AND BROWACHE. SOMETIMES MYDRIASIS MAY OCCUR INSTEAD OF MIOSIS. WITH SUFFICIENT EXPOSURE, OTHER SYMPTOMS OF CHOLINESTERASE INHIBITION AS DESCRIBED IN ACUTE INHALATION MAY OCCUR.
CHRONIC EXPOSURE- REPEATED OR PROLONGED EXPOSURE MAY CAUSE EFFECTS AS DESCRIBED IN ACUTE EXPOSURE. SOME COMPOUNDS HAVE CAUSED TOXIC EFFECTS ON THE CRYSTALLINE LENS, CONJUNCTIVAL THICKENING AND OBSTRUCTION OF THE NASOLACRIMAL CANALS WHEN USED AS MIOTIC EYEDROPS.

FIRST AID- IRRIGATE EYES WITH WATER OR SALINE SOLUTION. IF SYMPTOMS OF POISONING OCCUR, TREAT RESPIRATORY DIFFICULTY WITH ARTIFICIAL RESPIRATION AND OXYGEN. OBSERVE PATIENT FOR AT LEAST 24-36 HOURS (GOSSELIN, CLINICAL TOXICOLOGY OF COMMERCIAL PRODUCTS, 5TH ED.). GET MEDICAL ATTENTION IMMEDIATELY. OXYGEN SHOULD BE ADMINISTERED BY QUALIFIED MEDICAL PERSONNEL.

INGESTION: AKTON: HIGHLY TOXIC. SEE INFORMATION ON ORGANOPHOSPHATES.
ORGANOPHOSPHATES: CHOLINESTERASE INHIBITOR. **ACUTE EXPOSURE-** WHEN INGESTED, THE FIRST EFFECTS MAY BE NAUSEA, VOMITING, ANOREXIA, ABDOMINAL CRAMPS AND DIARRHEA. GASTROINTESTINAL ABSORPTION MAY CAUSE SYMPTOMS OF CHOLINESTERASE INHIBITION AS DESCRIBED IN ACUTE INHALATION. SYMPTOMS MAY BEGIN WITHIN MINUTES OR BE DELAYED FOR HOURS. DELAYED EFFECTS INCLUDING NEUROPATHY MAY ALSO OCCUR. **CHRONIC EXPOSURE-** REPEATED INGESTION MAY CAUSE EFFECTS AS DESCRIBED IN ACUTE EXPOSURE.

FIRST AID- IF PERSON IS ALERT AND RESPIRATION IS NOT DEPRESSED, GIVE SYRUP OF IPECAC FOLLOWED BY WATER (IF VOMITING OCCURS, KEEP HEAD BELOW HIPS TO PREVENT ASPIRATION). IF CONSCIOUSNESS LEVEL DECLINES OR VOMITING HAS NOT OCCURRED IN 15 MINUTES EMPTY STOMACH BY GASTRIC LAVAGE WITH THE AID OF CUFFED ENDOTRACHEAL TUBE USING ISOTONIC SALINE OR 5% SODIUM BICARBONATE FOLLOW WITH ACTIVATED CHARCOAL. ESTABLISH AND MAINTAIN AIRWAY. TREAT RESPIRATORY DIFFICULTY WITH ARTIFICIAL RESPIRATION AND OXYGEN. DO NOT GIVE MORPHINE, AMINOPHYLLINE, PHENOTHIAZINES, RESERPINE, FUROSEMIDE, OR ETHACRYNIC ACID (MORGAN, RECOGNITION AND MANAGEMENT OF PESTICIDE POISONINGS, 3RD ED.). TREAT SYMPTOMATICALLY AND SUPPORTIVELY. ADMINISTRATION OF OXYGEN AND LAVAGE MUST BE PERFORMED BY QUALIFIED MEDICAL PERSONNEL. GET MEDICAL ATTENTION IMMEDIATELY.

ANTIDOTE: THE FOLLOWING ANTIDOTE(S) HAVE BEEN RECOMMENDED. HOWEVER, THE DECISION AS TO WHETHER THE SEVERITY OF POISONING REQUIRES ADMINISTRATION OF ANY ANTIDOTE AND ACTUAL DOSE REQUIRED SHOULD BE MADE BY QUALIFIED MEDICAL PERSONNEL.
FOR CHOLINESTERASE INHIBITORS: ESTABLISH CLEAR AIRWAY AND TISSUE OXYGENATION BY ASPIRATION OF SECRETIONS, AND IF NECESSARY, BY ASSISTED PULMONARY VENTILATION WITH OXYGEN. IMPROVE TISSUE OXYGENATION AS MUCH AS POSSIBLE BEFORE ADMINISTERING ATROPINE TO MINIMIZE THE RISK OF VENTRICULAR FIBRILLATION. ADMINISTER ATROPINE SULFATE INTRAVENOUSLY, OR INTRAMUSCULARLY IF IV INJECTION IS NOT POSSIBLE. IN MODERATELY SEVERE POISONING ADMINISTER ATROPINE SULFATE, 0.4-2.0 MG REPEATED EVERY 15 MINUTES UNTIL ATROPINIZATION IS ACHIEVED (TACHYCARDIA, FLUSHING, DRY MOUTH, MYDRIASIS). MAINTAIN ATROPINIZATION BY REPEATED DOSES FOR 2-12 HOURS, OR LONGER, DEPENDING ON THE SEVERITY OF POISONING. THE APPEARANCE OF RALES IN THE LUNG BASES, MIOSIS, SALIVATION, NAUSEA, BRADYCARDIA, ARE ALL INDICATIONS OF INADEQUATE ATROPINIZATION. SEVERELY POISONED INDIVIDUALS MAY EXHIBIT REMARKABLE TOLERANCE TO ATROPINE; TWO OR MORE TIMES THE DOSAGES SUGGESTED ABOVE MAY BE NEEDED. PERSONS NOT POISONED OR ONLY SLIGHTLY POISONED, HOWEVER, MAY DEVELOP SIGNS OF ATROPINE TOXICITY FROM SUCH LARGE DOSAGES: FEVER, MUSCLE FIBRILLATIONS, AND DELIRIUM ARE THE MAIN SIGNS OF ATROPINE TOXICITY. IF THESE SIGNS APPEAR WHILE THE PATIENT IS FULLY ATROPINIZED, ATROPINE ADMINISTRATION SHOULD BE DISCONTINUED, AT LEAST TEMPORARILY. OBSERVE TREATED PATIENTS CLOSELY AT LEAST 24 HOURS TO INSURE THAT SYMPTOMS (POSSIBLY PULMONARY EDEMA) DO NOT RECUR AS ATROPINIZATION WEARS OFF. IN VERY SEVERE POISONINGS, METABOLIC DISPOSITION OF

TOXICANT MAY REQUIRE SEVERAL HOURS OR DAYS DURING WHICH ATROPINIZATION MUST BE MAINTAINED. MARKEDLY LOWER LEVELS OF URINARY METABOLITES INDICATE THAT ATROPINE DOSAGE CAN BE TAPERED OFF. AS DOSAGE IS REDUCED, CHECK THE LUNG BASES FREQUENTLY FOR RALES. IF RALES ARE HEARD OR OTHER SYMPTOMS RETURN, RE-ESTABLISH ATROPINIZATION PROMPTLY (MORGAN, RECOGNITION AND MANAGEMENT OF PESTICIDE POISONINGS, 3RD ED.). ADMINISTRATION OF ANTIDOTE MUST BE PERFORMED BY QUALIFIED MEDICAL PERSONNEL.

IN CASES OF SEVERE POISONING BY ORGANOPHOSPHATE PESTICIDES IN WHICH RESPIRATORY DEPRESSION, MUSCLE WEAKNESS AND TWITCHINGS ARE SEVERE, GIVE PRALIDOXIME (PROTOPAM-AYERST, 2-PAM), 1.0 GRAM INTRAVENOUSLY AT NO MORE THAN 0.5 GRAM PER MINUTE. DOSAGE OF PRALIDOXIME MAY BE REPEATED IN 1-2 HOURS, THEN AT 10-12 HOUR INTERVALS IF NEEDED. IN VERY SEVERE POISONINGS, DOSAGE RATES MAY BE DOUBLED. TREATMENT WITH PRALIDOXIME WILL BE MOST EFFECTIVE IF GIVEN WITHIN THIRTY-SIX HOURS AFTER POISONING (MORGAN, RECOGNITION AND MANAGEMENT OF PESTICIDE POISONINGS, 3RD ED.). ANTIDOTE SHOULD BE ADMINISTERED BY QUALIFIED MEDICAL PERSONNEL.

REACTIVITY

REACTIVITY: STABLE UNDER NORMAL TEMPERATURES AND PRESSURES.

INCOMPATIBILITIES: AKTON: NO DATA AVAILABLE.

DECOMPOSITION: THERMAL DECOMPOSITION MAY RELEASE TOXIC AND/OR HAZARDOUS GASES.

POLYMERIZATION: HAZARDOUS POLYMERIZATION HAS NOT BEEN REPORTED TO OCCUR UNDER NORMAL TEMPERATURES AND PRESSURES.

STORAGE AND DISPOSAL

OBSERVE ALL FEDERAL, STATE AND LOCAL REGULATIONS WHEN STORING OR DISPOSING OF THIS SUBSTANCE. FOR ASSISTANCE, CONTACT THE DISTRICT DIRECTOR OF THE ENVIRONMENTAL PROTECTION AGENCY.

STORAGE

STORE IN ACCORDANCE WITH 40 CFR 165 RECOMMENDED PROCEDURES FOR THE DISPOSAL AND STORAGE OF PESTICIDES AND PESTICIDE CONTAINERS.

DISPOSAL

DISPOSAL MUST BE IN ACCORDANCE WITH 40 CFR 165 RECOMMENDED PROCEDURES FOR THE DISPOSAL AND STORAGE OF PESTICIDES AND PESTICIDE CONTAINERS.

CONDITIONS TO AVOID

MAY BURN BUT DOES NOT IGNITE READILY. CONTAINERS MAY EXPLODE IN HEAT OF FIRE.

SPILL AND LEAK PROCEDURES

OCCUPATIONAL SPILL: DO NOT TOUCH SPILLED MATERIAL. STOP LEAK IF YOU CAN DO IT WITHOUT RISK. USE WATER SPRAY TO REDUCE VAPORS. FOR SMALL SPILLS, TAKE UP WITH SAND OR OTHER ABSORBENT MATERIAL AND PLACE INTO CONTAINERS FOR LATER DISPOSAL. FOR SMALL DRY SPILLS, WITH A CLEAN SHOVEL PLACE MATERIAL INTO CLEAN, DRY CONTAINERS AND COVER. MOVE CONTAINERS FROM SPILL AREA. FOR LARGER SPILLS, DIKE FAR AHEAD OF SPILL FOR LATER DISPOSAL. KEEP UNNECESSARY PEOPLE AWAY. ISOLATE HAZARD AREA AND DENY ENTRY. VENTILATE CLOSED SPACES BEFORE ENTERING.

PROTECTIVE EQUIPMENT

VENTILATION: PROCESS ENCLOSURE RECOMMENDED.

RESPIRATOR: THE FOLLOWING RESPIRATORS ARE RECOMMENDED BASED ON INFORMATION FOUND IN THE PHYSICAL DATA, TOXICITY AND HEALTH EFFECTS SECTIONS. THEY ARE RANKED IN ORDER FROM MINIMUM TO MAXIMUM RESPIRATORY PROTECTION. THE SPECIFIC RESPIRATOR SELECTED MUST BE BASED ON CONTAMINATION LEVELS FOUND IN THE WORK PLACE, MUST NOT EXCEED THE WORKING LIMITS OF THE RESPIRATOR AND BE JOINTLY APPROVED BY THE NATIONAL INSTITUTE FOR OCCUPATIONAL SAFETY AND HEALTH AND THE MINE SAFETY AND HEALTH ADMINISTRATION (NIOSH-MSHA).

TYPE 'C' SUPPLIED-AIR RESPIRATOR WITH A FULL FACEPIECE OPERATED IN PRESSURE-DEMAND OR OTHER POSITIVE PRESSURE MODE OR WITH A FULL FACEPIECE, HELMET OR HOOD OPERATED IN CONTINOUS-FLOW MODE.

SELF-CONTAINED BREATHING APPARATUS WITH A FULL FACEPIECE OPERATED IN PRESSURE-DEMAND OR OTHER POSITIVE PRESSURE MODE.

FOR FIREFIGHTING AND OTHER IMMEDIATELY DANGEROUS TO LIFE OR HEALTH CONDITIONS:

SELF-CONTAINED BREATHING APPARATUS WITH FULL FACEPIECE OPERATED IN PRESSURE-DEMAND OR OTHER POSITIVE PRESSURE MODE.

SUPPLIED-AIR RESPIRATOR WITH FULL FACEPIECE AND OPERATED IN PRESSURE-DEMAND OR OTHER POSITIVE PRESSURE MODE IN COMBINATION WITH AN AUXILIARY SELF-CONTAINED BREATHING APPARATUS OPERATED IN PRESSURE-DEMAND OR OTHER POSITIVE PRESSURE MODE.

CLOTHING: EMPLOYEE MUST WEAR APPROPRIATE PROTECTIVE (IMPERVIOUS) CLOTHING AND EQUIPMENT TO PREVENT ANY POSSIBILITY OF SKIN CONTACT WITH THIS SUBSTANCE.

GLOVES: EMPLOYEE MUST WEAR APPROPRIATE PROTECTIVE GLOVES TO PREVENT CONTACT WITH THIS SUBSTANCE.

EYE PROTECTION: EMPLOYEE MUST WEAR SPLASH-PROOF OR DUST-RESISTANT SAFETY GOGGLES WITH OR WITHOUT A FACESHIELD TO PREVENT CONTACT WITH THIS SUBSTANCE.

EMERGENCY EYE WASH: WHERE THERE IS ANY POSSIBILITY THAT AN EMPLOYEE'S EYES MAY BE EXPOSED TO THIS SUBSTANCE, THE EMPLOYER SHOULD PROVIDE AN EYE WASH FOUNTAIN WITHIN THE IMMEDIATE WORK AREA FOR EMERGENCY USE.

AUTHORIZED BY- OCCUPATIONAL HEALTH SERVICES, INC.

CREATION DATE: 10/04/89 ***REVISION DATE:*** 05/01/90

MATERIAL SAFETY DATA SHEET

OCCUPATIONAL HEALTH SERVICES, INC.
AGRICULTURE AND PESTICIDE DIVISION
450 SEVENTH AVENUE, SUITE 2407
NEW YORK, NEW YORK 10123
1-800-445-MSDS OR (212) 967-1100

EMERGENCY CONTACT:
JOHN S. BRANSFORD, JR. (615) 292-1180

SUBSTANCE IDENTIFICATION

CAS-NUMBER 116-06-3

SUBSTANCE: **ALDICARB**

TRADE NAMES/SYNONYMS: 2-METHYL-2-(METHYLTHIO)PROPIONALDEHYDE O-(METHYLCARBAMOYL)OXIME; 2-METHYL-2(METHYLTHIO)PROPANAL O-((METHYLAMINO)CARBONYL)OXIME; PROPANAL, 2-METHYL-2-(METHYLTHIO)-, O-((METHYLAMINO)CARBONYL)OXIME; PROPIONALDEHYDE, 2-METHYL-2-(METHYLTHIO)-, O-(METHYLCARBAMOYL)OXIME; OMS 771; TEMIK; UC 21149; RCRA P070; EPA SHAUGHNESSY CODE: 098301; NCI-C08640; ENT 27,093; C7H14N2O2S; PST00500

CHEMICAL FAMILY: CARBAMATE
OXIME

MOLECULAR FORMULA: C-H3-S-C-(C-H3)2-C-H-N-O-C-(O)-N-H-C-H3

MOLECULAR WEIGHT: 190.25

CERCLA RATINGS (SCALE 0-3): HEALTH=3 FIRE=1 REACTIVITY=0 PERSISTENCE=1

NFPA RATINGS (SCALE 0-4): HEALTH=4 FIRE=1 REACTIVITY=0

COMPONENTS AND CONTAMINANTS

COMPONENT: ALDICARB ***PERCENT:*** 100.00
CAS# 116-06-3

EXPOSURE LIMITS: NO OCCUPATIONAL EXPOSURE LIMITS ESTABLISHED BY OSHA, ACGIH, OR NIOSH.

ALDICARB: 100/10,000 POUNDS SARA SECTION 302 THRESHOLD PLANNING QUANTITY 1 POUND SARA SECTION 304 REPORTABLE QUANTITY 1 POUND CERCLA SECTION 103 REPORTABLE QUANTITY

PHYSICAL DATA

DESCRIPTION: ODORLESS, WHITE CRYSTALS WITH A SLIGHT SULFUR ODOR.

MELTING POINT: 212 F (100 C) ***SPECIFIC GRAVITY:*** 1.1950 @ 25 C

VAPOR PRESSURE: 0.05 MMHG @ 20 C ***SOLUBILITY IN WATER:*** 0.6% @ 25 C

SOLVENT SOLUBILITY: SOLUBLE IN ACETONE, BENZENE, ETHANOL, TOLUENE, CHLOROBENZENE, CHLOROFORM, ETHYLETHER, ISOPROPANE, METHYLENE CHLORIDE; SLIGHTLY SOLUBLE IN XYLENE; INSOLUBLE IN PARAFFINIC HYDROCARBONS.

FIRE AND EXPLOSION DATA

FIRE AND EXPLOSION HAZARD: SLIGHT FIRE HAZARD WHEN EXPOSED TO HEAT OR FLAME.

DUST-AIR MIXTURES MAY IGNITE OR EXPLODE.

FIREFIGHTING MEDIA: DRY CHEMICAL, CARBON DIOXIDE, HALON, WATER SPRAY OR STANDARD FOAM (1987 EMERGENCY RESPONSE GUIDEBOOK, DOT P 5800.4).

FOR LARGER FIRES, USE WATER SPRAY, FOG OR STANDARD FOAM (1987 EMERGENCY RESPONSE GUIDEBOOK, DOT P 5800.4).

FIREFIGHTING: MOVE CONTAINERS FROM FIRE AREA IF POSSIBLE (1987 EMERGENCY RESPONSE GUIDEBOOK, DOT P 5800.4, GUIDE PAGE 53).

EXTINGUISH ONLY IF FLOW CAN BE STOPPED. EXTINGUISH USING AGENT INDICATED. USE FLOODING AMOUNTS OF WATER AS A FOG. COOL CONTAINERS WITH

FLOODING AMOUNTS OF WATER FROM AS FAR A DISTANCE AS POSSIBLE. AVOID BREATHING POISONOUS VAPORS, KEEP UPWIND. CONSIDER EVACUATION OF DOWNWIND AREA IF MATERIAL IS LEAKING.

TRANSPORTATION DATA

DEPARTMENT OF TRANSPORTATION HAZARD CLASSIFICATION 49 CFR 172.101: POISON B

DEPARTMENT OF TRANSPORTATION LABELING REQUIREMENTS 49 CFR 172.101 AND SUBPART E: POISON

DEPARTMENT OF TRANSPORTATION PACKAGING REQUIREMENTS: 49 CFR 173.365 EXCEPTIONS: 49 CFR 173.364

TOXICITY

ALDICARB: TOXICITY DATA: 7.6 MG/M3/8 HOURS INHALATION-RAT LD67 (UNION CARBIDE TECHNICAL INFORMATION, 1975); 200 MG/M3 INHALATION-RAT LD100 (UNION CARBIDE TECHNICAL INFORMATION, 1975); 200 MG/M3 INHALATION-MOUSE LD100 (UNION CARBIDE TECHNICAL INFORMATION, 1975); 200 MG/M3 INHALATION-GUINEA PIG LC100 (UNION CARBIDE TECHNICAL INFORMATION, 1975); 200 MG/M3/5 HOURS INHALATION-RAT LC50; 5.0 MG/KG SKIN-RABBIT (85JFAN); 1400 MG/KG SKIN-RABBIT LD50; 2500 UG/KG SKIN-RAT LD50; 2400 MG/KG SKIN-GUINEA PIG LD50; 100 MG EYE-RABBIT LDLO (ALDICARB, EPA FACT SHEET, 1984); 650 UG/KG ORAL-RAT LD50; 300 UG/KG ORAL-MOUSE LD50; 666 UG/KG SUBCUTANEOUS-RAT LD50; 250 UG/KG SUBCUTANEOUS-MOUSE LD50; MUTAGENIC DATA (RTECS). CARCINOGEN STATUS: NONE. ACUTE TOXICITY LEVEL: HIGHLY TOXIC BY INHALATION, DERMAL ABSORPTION, AND INGESTION. TARGET EFFECTS: CHOLINESTERASE INHIBITOR. AT INCREASED RISK FROM EXPOSURE: PERSONS WITH ASTHMA, DIABETES, CARDIOVASCULAR DISEASE, MECHANICAL OBSTRUCTION OF THE GASTROINTESTINAL OR UROGENITAL TRACT, AND THOSE IN VAGOTONIC STATES.*

* MAY BE BASED ON GENERAL INFORMATION ON CARBAMATES.

AQUATIC TOXICITY: BLUEGILL SUNFISH LC50: 0.05-0.1 PPM/96 HOURS @ 24 C RAINBOW TROUT LC50: 0.5 PPM/96 HOURS @ 14 C GOLDFISH LC50: 8.3 PPM/48 HOURS @ 24 C BLUEGILL SUNFISH LC50: 1.45 PPM/96 HOURS @ 23 C RAINBOW TROUT LC50: 8.8 PPM/96 HOURS @ 13 C

HEALTH EFFECTS AND FIRST AID

INHALATION: ALDICARB: HIGHLY TOXIC. SEE INFORMATION ON CARBAMATES.

CARBAMATES: CHOLINESTERASE INHIBITOR. **ACUTE EXPOSURE-** WHEN INHALED, THE FIRST EFFECTS OF CHOLINESTERASE INHIBITION ARE USUALLY RESPIRATORY AND MAY INCLUDE NASAL HYPEREMIA AND WATERY DISCHARGE, CHEST DISCOMFORT, DYSPNEA, AND WHEEZING DUE TO INCREASED BRONCHIAL SECRETIONS AND BRONCHOCONSTRICTION. OTHER SYSTEMIC EFFECTS MAY BEGIN WITHIN A FEW MINUTES OR SEVERAL HOURS OF EXPOSURE. SYMPTOMS MAY INCLUDE NAUSEA, VOMITING, DIARRHEA, ABDOMINAL CRAMPS, HEADACHE, VERTIGO, OCULAR PAIN, CILIARY MUSCLE SPASM, BLURRING OR DIMNESS OF VISION, MIOSIS, OR IN SOME CASES MYDRIASIS, LACRIMATION, SALIVATION, SWEATING, AND CONFUSION. OTHER REPORTED CENTRAL NERVOUS SYSTEM OR NEUROMUSCULAR EFFECTS INCLUDE ATAXIA, SLURRED SPEECH, AREFLEXIA, WEAKNESS, FATIGUE, TWITCHING, FASCICULATION, TREMOR, AND EVENTUALLY PARALYSIS OF THE EXTREMITIES AND POSSIBLY OF THE RESPIRATORY MUSCLES. IN SEVERE CASES, THERE MAY ALSO BE INVOLUNTARY DEFECATION AND URINATION, BRADYCARDIA, HYPOTENSION, PULMONARY EDEMA, CONVULSIONS, COMA, AND DEATH FROM RESPIRATORY FAILURE OR CARDIAC ARREST. CARBAMATES GENERALLY DO NOT ACCUMULATE IN MAMMALIAN TISSUE AND THE CHOLINESTERASE INHIBITION REVERSES RATHER RAPIDLY. IN NON-FATAL CASES, THE ILLNESS GENERALLY LASTS LESS THAN 24 HOURS. **CHRONIC EXPOSURE-** PROLONGED OR REPEATED EXPOSURE MAY CAUSE EFFECTS AS DESCRIBED IN ACUTE EXPOSURE.

FIRST AID- REMOVE FROM EXPOSURE AREA TO FRESH AIR IMMEDIATELY. IF BREATHING HAS STOPPED, GIVE ARTIFICIAL RESPIRATION. MAINTAIN AIRWAY AND BLOOD PRESSURE AND ADMINISTER OXYGEN IF AVAILABLE. KEEP AFFECTED PERSON WARM AND AT REST. TREAT SYMPTOMATICALLY AND SUPPORTIVELY. ADMINISTRATION OF OXYGEN SHOULD BE PERFORMED BY QUALIFIED PERSONNEL. GET MEDICAL ATTENTION IMMEDIATELY.

SKIN CONTACT: ALDICARB: HIGHLY TOXIC. SEE INFORMATION ON CARBAMATES.

CARBAMATES: CHOLINESTERASE INHIBITOR. **ACUTE EXPOSURE-** SOME COMPOUNDS MAY CAUSE IRRITATION. LOCALIZED SWEATING AND FASCICULATIONS MAY OCCUR AT THE SITE OF CONTACT. IF SUFFICIENT AMOUNTS ARE ABSORBED THROUGH THE SKIN, OTHER EFFECTS OF CHOLINESTERASE INHIBITION MAY OCCUR AS DESCRIBED IN ACUTE INHALATION; SYMPTOMS MAY BE DELAYED FOR 2-3 HOURS, USUALLY NO MORE THAN 8 HOURS. **CHRONIC EXPOSURE-** REPEATED OR PROLONGED EXPOSURE MAY CAUSE EFFECTS AS DESCRIBED IN ACUTE EXPOSURE.

FIRST AID- REMOVE CONTAMINATED CLOTHING IMMEDIATELY. WASH CONTAMINATED AREAS WITH SOAP AND WATER FOLLOWED BY ALCOHOL (ARENA, POISONING, 4TH ED.). EMERGENCY PERSONNEL SHOULD WEAR GLOVES AND AVOID CONTAMINATION. TREAT RESPIRATORY DIFFICULTY WITH ARTIFICIAL RESPIRATION. GET MEDICAL ATTENTION IMMEDIATELY.

EYE CONTACT: ALDICARB: SEE INFORMATION ON CARBAMATES.

CARBAMATES: CHOLINESTERASE INHIBITOR. **ACUTE EXPOSURE-** DIRECT CONTACT MAY CAUSE PAIN, HYPEREMIA, LACRIMATION, TWITCHING OF THE EYELIDS, MIOSIS, AND CILIARY MUSCLE SPASM WITH LOSS OF ACCOMODATION, BLURRED OR DIMMED VISION AND BROWACHE. SOMETIMES MYDRIASIS MAY OCCUR INSTEAD OF MIOSIS. WITH SUFFICIENT EXPOSURE, OTHER SYMPTOMS OF CHOLINESTERASE INHIBITION MAY OCCUR AS DESCRIBED IN ACUTE INHALATION. **CHRONIC EXPOSURE-** PROLONGED EXPOSURE MAY CAUSE EFFECTS AS DESCRIBED IN ACUTE EXPOSURE. SOME COMPOUNDS HAVE CAUSED TOXIC EFFECTS ON THE CRYSTALLINE LENS, CONJUNCTIVAL THICKENING AND OBSTRUCTION OF NASOLACRIMAL CANALS WHEN USED AS MIOTIC EYE DROPS.

FIRST AID- IRRIGATE EYES WITH WATER OR SALINE SOLUTION. IF SYMPTOMS OF POISONING OCCUR, TREAT RESPIRATORY DIFFICULTY WITH ARTIFICIAL RESPIRATION AND OXYGEN. OBSERVE PATIENT FOR AT LEAST 24-36 HOURS (GOSSELIN, CLINICAL TOXICOLOGY OF COMMERCIAL PRODUCTS, 5TH ED.). GET MEDICAL ATTENTION IMMEDIATELY. OXYGEN SHOULD BE ADMINISTERED BY QUALIFIED MEDICAL PERSONNEL.

INGESTION: ALDICARB: HIGHLY TOXIC. IMMUNOTOXIC EFFECTS WERE OBSERVED IN ONE STUDY OF MICE RECEIVING A DIETARY LEVEL OF 1 PPB. SEE INFORMATION ON CARBAMATES.

CARBAMATES: CHOLINESTERASE INHIBITOR. **ACUTE EXPOSURE-** WHEN INGESTED, THE FIRST EFFECTS MAY BE NAUSEA, VOMITING, ANOREXIA, ABDOMINAL CRAMPS, AND DIARRHEA. WITH ABSORPTION FROM THE GASTROINTESTINAL TRACT, THE OTHER EFFECTS OF CHOLINESTERASE INHIBITION AS DESCRIBED IN ACUTE INHALATION MAY OCCUR; SYMPTOMS MAY BEGIN WITHIN MINUTES OR BE DELAYED SEVERAL HOURS. **CHRONIC EXPOSURE-** REPEATED INGESTION MAY CAUSE EFFECTS AS DESCRIBED IN ACUTE EXPOSURE.

FIRST AID- IF PERSON IS ALERT AND RESPIRATION IS NOT DEPRESSED, GIVE SYRUP OF IPECAC FOLLOWED BY WATER (IF VOMITING OCCURS, KEEP HEAD BELOW HIPS TO PREVENT ASPIRATION). IF CONSCIOUSNESS LEVEL DECLINES OR VOMITING HAS NOT OCCURRED IN 15 MINUTES EMPTY STOMACH BY GASTRIC LAVAGE WITH THE AID OF CUFFED ENDOTRACHEAL TUBE USING ISOTONIC SALINE OR 5% SODIUM BICARBONATE FOLLOW WITH ACTIVATED CHARCOAL. ESTABLISH AND MAINTAIN AIRWAY. TREAT RESPIRATORY DIFFICULTY WITH ARTIFICIAL RESPIRATION AND OXYGEN. DO NOT GIVE MORPHINE, AMINOPHYLLINE, PHENOTHIAZINES, RESERPINE, FUROSEMIDE, OR ETHACRYNIC ACID (MORGAN, RECOGNITION AND MANAGEMENT OF PESTICIDE POISONINGS, 3RD ED.). TREAT SYMPTOMATICALLY AND SUPPORTIVELY. ADMINISTRATION OF OXYGEN AND LAVAGE MUST BE PERFORMED BY QUALIFIED MEDICAL PERSONNEL. GET MEDICAL ATTENTION IMMEDIATELY.

ANTIDOTE: THE FOLLOWING ANTIDOTE HAS BEEN RECOMMENDED. HOWEVER, THE DECISION AS TO WHETHER THE SEVERITY OF POISONING REQUIRES ADMINISTRATION OF ANY ANTIDOTE AND ACTUAL DOSE REQUIRED SHOULD BE MADE BY QUALIFIED MEDICAL PERSONNEL.

FOR CHOLINESTERASE INHIBITORS: ESTABLISH CLEAR AIRWAY AND TISSUE OXYGENATION BY ASPIRATION OF SECRETIONS, AND IF NECESSARY, BY ASSISTED PULMONARY VENTILATION WITH OXYGEN. IMPROVE TISSUE OXYGENATION AS MUCH AS POSSIBLE BEFORE ADMINISTERING ATROPINE TO MINIMIZE THE RISK OF VENTRICULAR FIBRILLATION. ADMINISTER ATROPINE SULFATE INTRAVENOUSLY, OR INTRAMUSCULARLY IF IV INJECTION IS NOT POSSIBLE. IN MODERATELY SEVERE POISONING ADMINISTER ATROPINE SULFATE, 0.4-2.0 MG REPEATED EVERY 15 MINUTES UNTIL ATROPINIZATION IS ACHIEVED (TACHYCARDIA, FLUSHING, DRY MOUTH, MYDRIASIS). MAINTAIN ATROPINIZATION BY REPEATED DOSES FOR 2-12 HOURS, OR LONGER, DEPENDING ON THE SEVERITY OF POISONING. THE APPEARANCE OF RALES IN THE LUNG BASES, MIOSIS, SALIVATION, NAUSEA, BRADYCARDIA, ARE ALL INDICATIONS OF INADEQUATE ATROPINIZATION. SEVERELY POISONED INDIVIDUALS MAY EXHIBIT REMARKABLE TOLERANCE TO ATROPINE; TWO OR MORE TIMES THE DOSAGES SUGGESTED ABOVE MAY BE NEEDED. PERSONS NOT POISONED OR ONLY SLIGHTLY POISONED, HOWEVER, MAY DEVELOP SIGNS OF ATROPINE TOXICITY FROM SUCH LARGE DOSAGES: FEVER, MUSCLE FIBRILLATIONS, AND DELIRIUM ARE THE MAIN SIGNS OF ATROPINE TOXICITY. IF THESE SIGNS APPEAR WHILE THE PATIENT IS FULLY ATROPINIZED, ATROPINE ADMINISTRATION SHOULD BE DISCONTINUED, AT LEAST TEMPORARILY. OBSERVE TREATED PATIENTS CLOSELY AT LEAST 24 HOURS TO INSURE THAT SYMPTOMS (POSSIBLY PULMONARY EDEMA) DO NOT RECUR AS ATROPINIZATION WEARS OFF. IN VERY SEVERE POISONINGS, METABOLIC DISPOSITION OF TOXICANT MAY REQUIRE SEVERAL HOURS OR DAYS DURING WHICH ATROPINIZATION MUST BE MAINTAINED. MARKEDLY LOWER LEVELS OF URINARY METABOLITES INDICATE THAT ATROPINE DOSAGE CAN BE TAPERED OFF. AS DOSAGE IS REDUCED, CHECK THE LUNG BASES FREQUENTLY FOR RALES. IF RALES ARE HEARD OR OTHER SYMPTOMS RETURN, RE-ESTABLISH ATROPINIZATION PROMPTLY (MORGAN, RECOGNITION AND MANAGEMENT OF PESTICIDE

POISONINGS, 3RD ED.). ADMINISTRATION OF ANTIDOTE MUST BE PERFORMED BY QUALIFIED MEDICAL PERSONNEL.

REACTIVITY

REACTIVITY: STABLE UNDER NORMAL TEMPERATURES AND PRESSURES IN A CLOSED CONTAINER. PROLONGED EXPOSURE TO HEAT MAY RESULT IN DEGRADATION OF THE MATERIAL.

INCOMPATIBILITIES: ALDICARB: OXIDIZERS (STRONG): FIRE AND EXPLOSION HAZARD.

DECOMPOSITION: THERMAL DECOMPOSITION PRODUCTS MAY INCLUDE TOXIC OXIDES OF NITROGEN, SULFUR AND CARBON.

POLYMERIZATION: HAZARDOUS POLYMERIZATION HAS NOT BEEN REPORTED TO OCCUR UNDER NORMAL TEMPERATURES AND PRESSURES.

STORAGE AND DISPOSAL

OBSERVE ALL FEDERAL, STATE AND LOCAL REGULATIONS WHEN STORING OR DISPOSING OF THIS SUBSTANCE. FOR ASSISTANCE, CONTACT THE DISTRICT DIRECTOR OF THE ENVIRONMENTAL PROTECTION AGENCY.

STORAGE

STORE IN ACCORDANCE WITH 40 CFR 165 RECOMMENDED PROCEDURES FOR THE DISPOSAL AND STORAGE OF PESTICIDES AND PESTICIDE CONTAINERS.

STORE AWAY FROM INCOMPATIBLE SUBSTANCES.

STORE INDOORS IN ISOLATED, WELL-VENTILATED, CLEAN, DRY, COOL AREA. DO NOT STORE NEAR FOOD, FEED, OR OTHER ITEMS INTENDED FOR HUMAN OR ANIMAL CONSUMPTION.

THRESHOLD PLANNING QUANTITY (TPQ): THE SUPERFUND AMENDMENTS AND REAUTHORIZATION ACT (SARA) SECTION 302 REQUIRES THAT EACH FACILITY WHERE ANY EXTREMELY HAZARDOUS SUBSTANCE IS PRESENT IN A QUANTITY EQUAL TO OR GREATER THAN THE TPQ ESTABLISHED FOR THAT SUBSTANCE NOTIFY THE STATE EMERGENCY RESPONSE COMMISSION FOR THE STATE IN WHICH IT IS LOCATED. SECTION 303 OF SARA REQUIRES THESE FACILITIES TO PARTICIPATE IN LOCAL EMERGENCY RESPONSE PLANNING (40 CFR 355.30).

DISPOSAL

DISPOSAL MUST BE IN ACCORDANCE WITH STANDARDS APPLICABLE TO GENERATORS OF HAZARDOUS WASTE, 40CFR 262. EPA HAZARDOUS WASTE NUMBER P070.

DISPOSAL MUST BE IN ACCORDANCE WITH 40 CFR 165 RECOMMENDED PROCEDURES FOR THE DISPOSAL AND STORAGE OF PESTICIDES AND PESTICIDE CONTAINERS.

CONDITIONS TO AVOID

DO NOT MIX WITH WATER: THE RESULTANT SOLUTION MAY BE SERIOUSLY HAZARDOUS.

SPILL AND LEAK PROCEDURES

SOIL SPILL: PRECAUTIONS SHOULD BE TAKEN TO PREVENT THE LEACHING OF THIS MATERIAL INTO GROUNDWATER. FOR FURTHER INFORMATION, CONSULT THE MANUFACTURER.

OCCUPATIONAL SPILL: DO NOT FLUSH WITH WATER. DO NOT ALLOW MATERIAL TO CONTAMINATE ANY WATERWAYS. DO NOT GET DUST OR GRANULES ON SKIN OR IN EYES. DO NOT BREATHE DUST. WEAR PROTECTIVE CLOTHING AND EQUIPMENT WHEN HANDLING MATERIAL. SWEEP OR SHOVEL UP SPILLED MATERIAL AND PLACE INTO CLEAN DRY CONTAINER. DECONTAMINATE SPILL AREA USING PRESCRIBED DECONTAMINATING SOLUTION, CAUSTIC SODA SOLUTION, OR LIME. DECONTAMINATE ALL TOOLS AND EQUIPMENT, RINSE AND DRY. LAUNDER ALL CLOTHING.

REPORTABLE QUANTITY (RQ): 1 POUND THE SUPERFUND AMENDMENTS AND REAUTHORIZATION ACT (SARA) SECTION 304 REQUIRES THAT A RELEASE EQUAL TO OR GREATER THAN THE REPORTABLE QUANTITY FOR THIS SUBSTANCE BE IMMEDIATELY REPORTED TO THE LOCAL EMERGENCY PLANNING COMMITTEE AND THE STATE EMERGENCY RESPONSE COMMISSION (40 CFR 355.40). IF THE RELEASE OF THIS SUBSTANCE IS REPORTABLE UNDER CERCLA SECTION 103, THE NATIONAL RESPONSE CENTER MUST BE NOTIFIED IMMEDIATELY AT (800) 424-8802 OR (202) 426-2675 IN THE METROPOLITAN WASHINGTON, D.C. AREA (40 CFR 302.6).

PROTECTIVE EQUIPMENT

VENTILATION: PROCESS ENCLOSURE RECOMMENDED.

RESPIRATOR: THE FOLLOWING RESPIRATORS ARE RECOMMENDED BASED ON INFORMATION FOUND IN THE PHYSICAL DATA, TOXICITY AND HEALTH EFFECTS SECTIONS. THEY ARE RANKED IN ORDER FROM MINIMUM TO MAXIMUM RESPIRATORY PROTECTION. THE SPECIFIC RESPIRATOR SELECTED MUST BE BASED ON CONTAMINATION LEVELS FOUND IN THE WORK PLACE, MUST NOT EXCEED THE WORKING LIMITS OF THE RESPIRATOR AND BE JOINTLY APPROVED BY THE NATIONAL INSTITUTE FOR OCCUPATIONAL SAFETY AND HEALTH AND THE MINE SAFETY AND HEALTH ADMINISTRATION (NIOSH-MSHA).

TYPE 'C' SUPPLIED-AIR RESPIRATOR WITH A FULL FACEPIECE OPERATED IN PRESSURE-DEMAND OR OTHER POSITIVE PRESSURE MODE OR WITH A FULL FACEPIECE, HELMET OR HOOD OPERATED IN CONTINOUS-FLOW MODE.

SELF-CONTAINED BREATHING APPARATUS WITH A FULL FACEPIECE OPERATED IN PRESSURE-DEMAND OR OTHER POSITIVE PRESSURE MODE.

FOR FIREFIGHTING AND OTHER IMMEDIATELY DANGEROUS TO LIFE OR HEALTH CONDITIONS:

SELF-CONTAINED BREATHING APPARATUS WITH FULL FACEPIECE OPERATED IN PRESSURE-DEMAND OR OTHER POSITIVE PRESSURE MODE.

SUPPLIED-AIR RESPIRATOR WITH FULL FACEPIECE AND OPERATED IN PRESSURE-DEMAND OR OTHER POSITIVE PRESSURE MODE IN COMBINATION WITH AN AUXILIARY SELF-CONTAINED BREATHING APPARATUS OPERATED IN PRESSURE-DEMAND OR OTHER POSITIVE PRESSURE MODE.

CLOTHING: EMPLOYEE MUST WEAR APPROPRIATE PROTECTIVE (IMPERVIOUS) CLOTHING AND EQUIPMENT TO PREVENT ANY POSSIBILITY OF SKIN CONTACT WITH THIS SUBSTANCE.

GLOVES: EMPLOYEE MUST WEAR APPROPRIATE PROTECTIVE GLOVES TO PREVENT CONTACT WITH THIS SUBSTANCE.

EYE PROTECTION: EMPLOYEE MUST WEAR SPLASH-PROOF OR DUST-RESISTANT SAFETY GOGGLES AND A FACESHIELD TO PREVENT CONTACT WITH THIS SUBSTANCE. EMERGENCY WASH FACILITIES: WHERE THERE IS ANY POSSIBILITY THAT AN EMPLOYEE'S EYES AND/OR SKIN MAY BE EXPOSED TO THIS SUBSTANCE, THE EMPLOYER SHOULD PROVIDE AN EYE WASH FOUNTAIN AND QUICK DRENCH SHOWER WITHIN THE IMMEDIATE WORK AREA FOR EMERGENCY USE.

AUTHORIZED BY- OCCUPATIONAL HEALTH SERVICES, INC.

CREATION DATE: 10/04/89 ***REVISION DATE:*** 06/12/90

MATERIAL SAFETY DATA SHEET

OCCUPATIONAL HEALTH SERVICES, INC.
AGRICULTURE AND PESTICIDE DIVISION
450 SEVENTH AVENUE, SUITE 2407
NEW YORK, NEW YORK 10123
1-800-445-MSDS OR (212) 967-1100

EMERGENCY CONTACT:
JOHN S. BRANSFORD, JR. (615) 292-1180

SUBSTANCE IDENTIFICATION

CAS-NUMBER 1646-87-3

SUBSTANCE: <u>ALDICARB SULFOXIDE</u>

TRADE NAMES/SYNONYMS: PROPANOL, 2-METHYL-2-(METHYLSULFINYL)-, O-((METHYLAMINO)CARBONYL)OXIME; 2-METHYL-2-(METHYLSULFINYL)PROPANOL, O-((METHYLAMINO)CARBONYL)OXIME; PROPIONALDEHYDE, 2-METHYL-2-(METHYLSULFINYL)-, O-(METHYLCARBAMOYL) OXIME; 2-METHYL-2-(METHYLSULFINYL)PROPIONALDEHYDE-O-(METHYLCARBAMOYL)OXIME; TEMIK SULFOXIDE; C7H14N2O3S; PST00503

CHEMICAL FAMILY: CARBAMATE SULFOXIDE

MOLECULAR FORMULA: C7-H14-N2-O3-S

MOLECULAR WEIGHT: 206.29

CERCLA RATINGS (SCALE 0-3): HEALTH=3 FIRE=1 REACTIVITY=0 PERSISTENCE=3

NFPA RATINGS (SCALE 0-4): HEALTH=3 FIRE=1 REACTIVITY=0

COMPONENTS AND CONTAMINANTS

COMPONENT: ALDICARB SULFOXIDE ***PERCENT:*** 100.0
CAS# 1646-87-3

OTHER CONTAMINANTS: NONE

EXPOSURE LIMITS: NO OCCUPATIONAL EXPOSURE LIMITS ESTABLISHED BY OSHA, ACGIH, OR NIOSH.

PHYSICAL DATA

DESCRIPTION: WHITE CRYSTALS OR FLAKES. ***MELTING POINT:*** DECOMPOSES

SPECIFIC GRAVITY: NOT AVAILABLE ***SOLUBILITY IN WATER:*** INSOLUBLE

FIRE AND EXPLOSION DATA

FIRE AND EXPLOSION HAZARD: SLIGHT FIRE HAZARD WHEN EXPOSED TO HEAT OR FLAME.

FIREFIGHTING MEDIA: DRY CHEMICAL, CARBON DIOXIDE, HALON, WATER SPRAY OR STANDARD FOAM (1987 EMERGENCY RESPONSE GUIDEBOOK, DOT P 5800.4).
FOR LARGER FIRES, USE WATER SPRAY, FOG OR STANDARD FOAM (1987 EMERGENCY RESPONSE GUIDEBOOK, DOT P 5800.4).

FIREFIGHTING: MOVE CONTAINERS FROM FIRE AREA IF POSSIBLE (1987 EMERGENCY RESPONSE GUIDEBOOK, DOT P 5800.4, GUIDE PAGE 53).
EXTINGUISH USING AGENT SUITABLE FOR TYPE OF SURROUNDING FIRE. AVOID BREATHING VAPORS AND DUSTS. KEEP UPWIND.

TRANSPORTATION DATA

DEPARTMENT OF TRANSPORTATION HAZARD CLASSIFICATION 49 CFR 172.101: POISON B
DEPARTMENT OF TRANSPORTATION LABELING REQUIREMENTS 49 CFR 172.101 AND SUBPART E: POISON
DEPARTMENT OF TRANSPORTATION PACKAGING REQUIREMENTS: 49 CFR 173.365
EXCEPTIONS: 49 CFR 173.364

TOXICITY

ALDICARB SULFOXIDE: TOXICITY DATA: 54 UG/KG ORAL-WOMAN TDLO; 2100 UG/KG ORAL-RAT LD50. CARCINOGEN STATUS: NONE. ACUTE TOXICITY LEVEL: HIGHLY TOXIC BY INGESTION. TARGET EFFECTS: CHOLINESTERASE INHIBITOR. AT INCREASED RISK FROM EXPOSURE: PERSONS WITH ASTHMA, DIABETES, CARDIOVASCULAR DISEASE, MECHANICAL OBSTRUCTION OF THE GASTROINTESTINAL OR UROGENITAL TRACT, AND THOSE IN VAGOTONIC STATES.*

* MAY BE BASED ON GENERAL INFORMATION ON CARBAMATES.

HEALTH EFFECTS AND FIRST AID

INHALATION: ALDICARB SULFOXIDE: SEE INFORMATION ON CARBAMATES.
CARBAMATES: CHOLINESTERASE INHIBITOR. **ACUTE EXPOSURE-** WHEN INHALED, THE FIRST EFFECTS OF CHOLINESTERASE INHIBITION ARE USUALLY RESPIRATORY AND MAY INCLUDE NASAL HYPEREMIA AND WATERY DISCHARGE, CHEST DISCOMFORT, DYSPNEA, AND WHEEZING DUE TO INCREASED BRONCHIAL SECRETIONS AND BRONCHOCONSTRICTION. OTHER SYSTEMIC EFFECTS MAY BEGIN WITHIN A FEW MINUTES OR SEVERAL HOURS OF EXPOSURE. SYMPTOMS MAY INCLUDE NAUSEA, VOMITING, DIARRHEA, ABDOMINAL CRAMPS, HEADACHE, VERTIGO, OCULAR PAIN, CILIARY MUSCLE SPASM, BLURRING OR DIMNESS OF VISION, MIOSIS, OR IN SOME CASES MYDRIASIS, LACRIMATION, SALIVATION, SWEATING, AND CONFUSION. OTHER REPORTED CENTRAL NERVOUS SYSTEM OR NEUROMUSCULAR EFFECTS INCLUDE ATAXIA, SLURRED SPEECH, AREFLEXIA, WEAKNESS, FATIGUE, TWITCHING, FASCICULATION, TREMOR, AND EVENTUALLY PARALYSIS OF THE EXTREMITIES AND POSSIBLY OF THE RESPIRATORY MUSCLES. IN SEVERE CASES, THERE MAY ALSO BE INVOLUNTARY DEFECATION AND URINATION, BRADYCARDIA, HYPOTENSION, PULMONARY EDEMA, CONVULSIONS, COMA, AND DEATH FROM RESPIRATORY FAILURE OR CARDIAC ARREST. CARBAMATES GENERALLY DO NOT ACCUMULATE IN MAMMALIAN TISSUE AND THE CHOLINESTERASE INHIBITION REVERSES RATHER RAPIDLY. IN NON-FATAL CASES, THE ILLNESS GENERALLY LASTS LESS THAN 24 HOURS. **CHRONIC EXPOSURE-** PROLONGED OR REPEATED EXPOSURE MAY CAUSE EFFECTS AS DESCRIBED IN ACUTE EXPOSURE.

FIRST AID- REMOVE FROM EXPOSURE AREA TO FRESH AIR IMMEDIATELY. IF BREATHING HAS STOPPED, GIVE ARTIFICIAL RESPIRATION. MAINTAIN AIRWAY AND BLOOD PRESSURE AND ADMINISTER OXYGEN IF AVAILABLE. KEEP AFFECTED PERSON WARM AND AT REST. TREAT SYMPTOMATICALLY AND SUPPORTIVELY. ADMINISTRATION OF OXYGEN SHOULD BE PERFORMED BY QUALIFIED PERSONNEL. GET MEDICAL ATTENTION IMMEDIATELY.

SKIN CONTACT: ALDICARB SULFOXIDE: SEE INFORMATION ON CARBAMATES.
CARBAMATES: CHOLINESTERASE INHIBITOR. **ACUTE EXPOSURE-** SOME COMPOUNDS MAY CAUSE IRRITATION. LOCALIZED SWEATING AND FASCICULATIONS MAY OCCUR AT THE SITE OF CONTACT. IF SUFFICIENT AMOUNTS ARE ABSORBED THROUGH THE SKIN, OTHER EFFECTS OF CHOLINESTERASE INHIBITION MAY OCCUR AS DESCRIBED IN ACUTE INHALATION; SYMPTOMS MAY BE DELAYED FOR 2-3 HOURS, USUALLY NO MORE THAN 8 HOURS. **CHRONIC EXPOSURE-** REPEATED OR PROLONGED EXPOSURE MAY CAUSE EFFECTS AS DESCRIBED IN ACUTE EXPOSURE.

FIRST AID- REMOVE CONTAMINATED CLOTHING IMMEDIATELY. WASH CONTAMINATED AREAS WITH SOAP AND WATER FOLLOWED BY ALCOHOL (ARENA, POISONING, 4TH ED.). EMERGENCY PERSONNEL SHOULD WEAR GLOVES AND AVOID CONTAMINATION. TREAT RESPIRATORY DIFFICULTY WITH ARTIFICIAL RESPIRATION. GET MEDICAL ATTENTION IMMEDIATELY.

EYE CONTACT: ALDICARB SULFOXIDE: SEE INFORMATION ON CARBAMATES.
CARBAMATES: CHOLINESTERASE INHIBITOR. **ACUTE EXPOSURE-** DIRECT CONTACT MAY CAUSE PAIN, HYPEREMIA, LACRIMATION, TWITCHING OF THE EYELIDS, MIOSIS, AND CILIARY MUSCLE SPASM WITH LOSS OF ACCOMODATION, BLURRED OR DIMMED VISION AND BROWACHE. SOMETIMES MYDRIASIS MAY OCCUR INSTEAD OF MIOSIS. WITH SUFFICIENT EXPOSURE, OTHER SYMPTOMS OF CHOLINESTERASE INHIBITION MAY OCCUR AS DESCRIBED IN ACUTE INHALATION. **CHRONIC EXPOSURE-** PROLONGED EXPOSURE MAY CAUSE EFFECTS AS DESCRIBED IN ACUTE EXPOSURE. SOME COMPOUNDS HAVE CAUSED TOXIC EFFECTS ON THE CRYSTALLINE LENS, CONJUNCTIVAL THICKENING AND OBSTRUCTION OF NASOLACRIMAL CANALS WHEN USED AS MIOTIC EYE DROPS.

FIRST AID- IRRIGATE EYES WITH WATER OR SALINE SOLUTION. IF SYMPTOMS OF POISONING OCCUR, TREAT RESPIRATORY DIFFICULTY WITH ARTIFICIAL RESPIRATION AND OXYGEN. OBSERVE PATIENT FOR AT LEAST 24-36 HOURS (GOSSELIN, CLINICAL TOXICOLOGY OF COMMERCIAL PRODUCTS, 5TH ED.). GET MEDICAL ATTENTION IMMEDIATELY. OXYGEN SHOULD BE ADMINISTERED BY QUALIFIED MEDICAL PERSONNEL.

INGESTION: ALDICARB SULFOXIDE: HIGHLY TOXIC. SEE INFORMATION ON CARBAMATES.
CARBAMATES: CHOLINESTERASE INHIBITOR. **ACUTE EXPOSURE-** WHEN INGESTED, THE FIRST EFFECTS MAY BE NAUSEA, VOMITING, ANOREXIA, ABDOMINAL CRAMPS, AND DIARRHEA. WITH ABSORPTION FROM THE GASTROINTESTINAL TRACT, THE OTHER EFFECTS OF CHOLINESTERASE INHIBITION AS DESCRIBED IN ACUTE INHALATION MAY OCCUR; SYMPTOMS MAY BEGIN WITHIN MINUTES OR BE DELAYED SEVERAL HOURS. **CHRONIC EXPOSURE-** REPEATED INGESTION MAY CAUSE EFFECTS AS DESCRIBED IN ACUTE EXPOSURE.

FIRST AID- IF PERSON IS ALERT AND RESPIRATION IS NOT DEPRESSED, GIVE SYRUP OF IPECAC FOLLOWED BY WATER (IF VOMITING OCCURS, KEEP HEAD BELOW HIPS TO PREVENT ASPIRATION). IF CONSCIOUSNESS LEVEL DECLINES OR VOMITING HAS NOT OCCURRED IN 15 MINUTES EMPTY STOMACH BY GASTRIC LAVAGE WITH THE AID OF CUFFED ENDOTRACHEAL TUBE USING ISOTONIC SALINE OR 5% SODIUM BICARBONATE FOLLOW WITH ACTIVATED CHARCOAL. ESTABLISH AND MAINTAIN AIRWAY. TREAT RESPIRATORY DIFFICULTY WITH ARTIFICIAL RESPIRATION AND OXYGEN. DO NOT GIVE MORPHINE, AMINOPHYLLINE, PHENOTHIAZINES, RESERPINE, FUROSEMIDE, OR ETHACRYNIC ACID (MORGAN, RECOGNITION AND MANAGEMENT OF PESTICIDE POISONINGS, 3RD ED.). TREAT SYMPTOMATICALLY AND SUPPORTIVELY. ADMINISTRATION OF OXYGEN AND LAVAGE MUST BE PERFORMED BY QUALIFIED MEDICAL PERSONNEL. GET MEDICAL ATTENTION IMMEDIATELY.

ANTIDOTE: NO SPECIFIC ANTIDOTE. TREAT SYMPTOMATICALLY AND SUPPORTIVELY. FOR CHOLINESTERASE INHIBITORS: ESTABLISH CLEAR AIRWAY AND TISSUE OXYGENATION BY ASPIRATION OF SECRETIONS, AND IF NECESSARY, BY ASSISTED PULMONARY VENTILATION WITH OXYGEN. IMPROVE TISSUE OXYGENATION AS MUCH AS POSSIBLE BEFORE ADMINISTERING ATROPINE TO MINIMIZE THE RISK OF VENTRICULAR FIBRILLATION. ADMINISTER ATROPINE SULFATE INTRAVENOUSLY, OR INTRAMUSCULARLY IF IV INJECTION IS NOT POSSIBLE. IN MODERATELY SEVERE POISONING ADMINISTER ATROPINE SULFATE, 0.4-2.0 MG REPEATED EVERY 15 MINUTES UNTIL ATROPINIZATION IS ACHIEVED (TACHYCARDIA, FLUSHING, DRY MOUTH, MYDRIASIS). MAINTAIN ATROPINIZATION BY REPEATED DOSES FOR 2-12 HOURS, OR LONGER, DEPENDING ON THE SEVERITY OF POISONING. THE APPEARANCE OF RALES IN THE LUNG BASES, MIOSIS, SALIVATION, NAUSEA, BRADYCARDIA, ARE ALL INDICATIONS OF INADEQUATE ATROPINIZATION. SEVERELY POISONED INDIVIDUALS MAY EXHIBIT REMARKABLE TOLERANCE TO ATROPINE; TWO OR MORE TIMES THE DOSAGES SUGGESTED ABOVE MAY BE NEEDED. PERSONS NOT POISONED OR ONLY SLIGHTLY POISONED, HOWEVER, MAY DEVELOP SIGNS OF ATROPINE TOXICITY FROM SUCH LARGE DOSAGES: FEVER, MUSCLE FIBRILLATIONS, AND DELIRIUM ARE THE MAIN SIGNS OF ATROPINE TOXICITY. IF THESE SIGNS APPEAR WHILE THE PATIENT IS FULLY ATROPINIZED, ATROPINE ADMINISTRATION SHOULD BE DISCONTINUED, AT LEAST TEMPORARILY. OBSERVE TREATED PATIENTS CLOSELY AT LEAST 24 HOURS TO INSURE THAT SYMPTOMS (POSSIBLY PULMONARY EDEMA) DO NOT RECUR AS ATROPINIZATION WEARS OFF. IN VERY SEVERE POISONINGS, METABOLIC DISPOSITION OF TOXICANT MAY REQUIRE SEVERAL HOURS OR DAYS DURING WHICH ATROPINIZATION MUST BE MAINTAINED. MARKEDLY LOWER LEVELS OF URINARY METABOLITES INDICATE THAT ATROPINE DOSAGE CAN BE TAPERED OFF. AS DOSAGE IS REDUCED, CHECK THE LUNG BASES FREQUENTLY FOR RALES. IF RALES ARE HEARD OR OTHER SYMPTOMS RETURN, RE-ESTABLISH ATROPINIZATION PROMPTLY (MORGAN, RECOGNITION AND MANAGEMENT OF PESTICIDE POISONINGS, 3RD ED.). ADMINISTRATION OF ANTIDOTE MUST BE PERFORMED BY QUALIFIED MEDICAL PERSONNEL.

REACTIVITY

REACTIVITY: STABLE UNDER NORMAL TEMPERATURES AND PRESSURES.

INCOMPATIBILITIES: ALDICARB SULFOXIDE: OXIDIZERS (STRONG): FIRE AND EXPLOSION HAZARD.

DECOMPOSITION: THERMAL DECOMPOSITION PRODUCTS MAY INCLUDE HIGHLY TOXIC FUMES OF HYDROGEN CYANIDE, HYDROGEN SULFIDE AND TOXIC OXIDES OF NITROGEN, SULFUR, AND CARBON.

POLYMERIZATION: HAZARDOUS POLYMERIZATION HAS NOT BEEN REPORTED TO OCCUR UNDER NORMAL TEMPERATURES AND PRESSURES.

STORAGE AND DISPOSAL

OBSERVE ALL FEDERAL, STATE AND LOCAL REGULATIONS WHEN STORING OR DISPOSING OF THIS SUBSTANCE. FOR ASSISTANCE, CONTACT THE DISTRICT DIRECTOR OF THE ENVIRONMENTAL PROTECTION AGENCY.

STORAGE

STORE IN ACCORDANCE WITH 40 CFR 165 RECOMMENDED PROCEDURES FOR THE DISPOSAL AND STORAGE OF PESTICIDES AND PESTICIDE CONTAINERS.

STORE AWAY FROM INCOMPATIBLE SUBSTANCES.

DISPOSAL

DISPOSAL MUST BE IN ACCORDANCE WITH 40 CFR 165 RECOMMENDED PROCEDURES FOR THE DISPOSAL AND STORAGE OF PESTICIDES AND PESTICIDE CONTAINERS.

CONDITIONS TO AVOID

MAY BURN BUT DOES NOT IGNITE READILY.

SPILL AND LEAK PROCEDURES

OCCUPATIONAL SPILL: DO NOT TOUCH SPILLED MATERIAL. STOP LEAK IF YOU CAN DO IT WITHOUT RISK. FOR SMALL SPILLS, TAKE UP WITH SAND OR OTHER ABSORBENT MATERIAL AND PLACE INTO CONTAINERS FOR LATER DISPOSAL. FOR SMALL DRY SPILLS, WITH A CLEAN SHOVEL PLACE MATERIAL INTO CLEAN, DRY CONTAINER AND COVER. MOVE CONTAINERS FROM SPILL AREA. FOR LARGER SPILLS, DIKE FAR AHEAD OF SPILL FOR LATER DISPOSAL. KEEP UNNECESSARY PEOPLE AWAY. ISOLATE HAZARD AREA AND DENY ENTRY.

PROTECTIVE EQUIPMENT

VENTILATION: PROVIDE LOCAL EXHAUST OR PROCESS ENCLOSURE VENTILATION SYSTEM.

RESPIRATOR: THE FOLLOWING RESPIRATORS ARE RECOMMENDED BASED ON INFORMATION FOUND IN THE PHYSICAL DATA, TOXICITY AND HEALTH EFFECTS SECTIONS. THEY ARE RANKED IN ORDER FROM MINIMUM TO MAXIMUM RESPIRATORY PROTECTION. THE SPECIFIC RESPIRATOR SELECTED MUST BE BASED ON CONTAMINATION LEVELS FOUND IN THE WORK PLACE, MUST NOT EXCEED THE WORKING LIMITS OF THE RESPIRATOR AND BE JOINTLY APPROVED BY THE NATIONAL INSTITUTE FOR OCCUPATIONAL SAFETY AND HEALTH AND THE MINE SAFETY AND HEALTH ADMINISTRATION (NIOSH-MSHA).

CHEMICAL CARTRIDGE RESPIRATOR WITH AN ORGANIC VAPOR CARTRIDGE(S) WITH A FULL FACEPIECE AND ORGANIC VAPOR CARTRIDGE(S) IN COMBINATION WITH A DUST AND MIST FILTER.

POWERED AIR-PURIFYING RESPIRATOR WITH A TIGHT-FITTING FACEPIECE AND ORGANIC VAPOR CARTRIDGE(S) IN COMBINATION WITH A HIGH-EFFICIENCY PARTICULATE FILTER.

TYPE 'C' SUPPLIED-AIR RESPIRATOR WITH A FULL FACEPIECE OPERATED IN A PRESSURE-DEMAND OR OTHER POSITIVE PRESSURE MODE.

SELF-CONTAINED BREATHING APPARATUS WITH A FULL FACEPIECE OPERATED IN PRESSURE-DEMAND OR OTHER POSITIVE PRESSURE MODE.

FOR FIREFIGHTING AND OTHER IMMEDIATELY DANGEROUS TO LIFE OR HEALTH CONDITIONS:

SELF-CONTAINED BREATHING APPARATUS WITH FULL FACEPIECE OPERATED IN PRESSURE-DEMAND OR OTHER POSITIVE PRESSURE MODE.

SUPPLIED-AIR RESPIRATOR WITH FULL FACEPIECE AND OPERATED IN PRESSURE-DEMAND OR OTHER POSITIVE PRESSURE MODE IN COMBINATION WITH AN AUXILIARY SELF-CONTAINED BREATHING APPARATUS OPERATED IN PRESSURE-DEMAND OR OTHER POSITIVE PRESSURE MODE.

CLOTHING: EMPLOYEE MUST WEAR APPROPRIATE PROTECTIVE (IMPERVIOUS) CLOTHING AND EQUIPMENT TO PREVENT ANY POSSIBILITY OF SKIN CONTACT WITH THIS SUBSTANCE.

GLOVES: EMPLOYEE MUST WEAR APPROPRIATE PROTECTIVE GLOVES TO PREVENT CONTACT WITH THIS SUBSTANCE.

EYE PROTECTION: EMPLOYEE MUST WEAR SPLASH-PROOF OR DUST-RESISTANT SAFETY GOGGLES AND A FACESHIELD TO PREVENT CONTACT WITH THIS SUBSTANCE.

EMERGENCY WASH FACILITIES: WHERE THERE IS ANY POSSIBILITY THAT AN EMPLOYEE'S EYES AND/OR SKIN MAY BE EXPOSED TO THIS SUBSTANCE, THE EMPLOYER SHOULD PROVIDE AN EYE WASH FOUNTAIN AND QUICK DRENCH SHOWER WITHIN THE IMMEDIATE WORK AREA FOR EMERGENCY USE.

AUTHORIZED BY- OCCUPATIONAL HEALTH SERVICES, INC.

CREATION DATE: 10/04/89 ***REVISION DATE:*** 06/12/90

MATERIAL SAFETY DATA SHEET

OCCUPATIONAL HEALTH SERVICES, INC.
AGRICULTURE AND PESTICIDE DIVISION
450 SEVENTH AVENUE, SUITE 2407
NEW YORK, NEW YORK 10123
1-800-445-MSDS OR (212) 967-1100

EMERGENCY CONTACT:
JOHN S. BRANSFORD, JR. (615) 292-1180

SUBSTANCE IDENTIFICATION

CAS-NUMBER 15972-60-8

SUBSTANCE: **ALACHLOR**

TRADE NAMES/SYNONYMS: ACETAMIDE, 2-CHLORO-N-(2,6-DIETHYLPHENYL)-N-(METHOXYMETHYL)-; ACETANILIDE, 2-CHLORO-2',6'-DIETHYL-N-(METHOXYMETHYL)-; 2-CHLORO-N-(2,6-DIETHYLPHENYL)-N-(METHOXYMETHYL)ACETAMIDE; 2-CHLORO-2',6'-DIETHYL-N-(METHOXYMETHYL)ACETANILIDE; 2-CHLORO-2',6'-DIETHYL-N-METHOXYMETHYLACETANILIDE; ALPHA-CHLORO-2',6'-DIETHYL-N-METHOXYMETHYLACETANILIDE; ALANEX; CP 50144; LASSO; LAZO; METACHLOR; METHACHLOR; C14H20CLNO2; PST00506

CHEMICAL FAMILY: HALOGENATED ACETAMIDE

MOLECULAR FORMULA: C14-H20-CL-N-O2

MOLECULAR WEIGHT: 269.77

CERCLA RATINGS (SCALE 0-3): HEALTH=2 FIRE=1 REACTIVITY=0 PERSISTENCE=2

NFPA RATINGS (SCALE 0-4): HEALTH=U FIRE=1 REACTIVITY=0

COMPONENTS AND CONTAMINANTS

COMPONENT: ALACHLOR ***PERCENT:*** 100.0
CAS# 15972-60-8

OTHER CONTAMINANTS: NONE

EXPOSURE LIMITS: NO OCCUPATIONAL EXPOSURE LIMITS ESTABLISHED BY OSHA, ACGIH, OR NIOSH.

ALACHLOR: SUBJECT TO CALIFORNIA PROPOSITION 65 CANCER AND/OR REPRODUCTIVE TOXICITY WARNING AND RELEASE REQUIREMENTS- (JANUARY 1, 1989)

PHYSICAL DATA

DESCRIPTION: ODORLESS, CREAM-COLORED CRYSTALLINE SOLID.

BOILING POINT: 212 F (100 C) @ 0.02 MMHG ***MELTING POINT:*** 104-106 F (40-41 C)

SPECIFIC GRAVITY: 1.133 @ 25 C ***VAPOR PRESSURE:*** NEGLIGIBLE

SOLUBILITY IN WATER: 0.0242% @ 25 C

SOLVENT SOLUBILITY: SOLUBLE IN ETHER, ACETONE, BENZENE, ETHYL ACETATE, CHLOROFORM, AND ETHANOL; SPARINGLY SOLUBLE IN HEPTANE.

DECOMPOSES @ 221 F (105 C)

FIRE AND EXPLOSION DATA

FIRE AND EXPLOSION HAZARD: SLIGHT FIRE HAZARD WHEN EXPOSED TO HEAT OR FLAME.

FLASH POINT: >250 F (>121 C) (CC)

FIREFIGHTING MEDIA: DRY CHEMICAL, CARBON DIOXIDE, HALON, WATER SPRAY OR STANDARD FOAM (1987 EMERGENCY RESPONSE GUIDEBOOK, DOT P 5800.4).

FOR LARGER FIRES, USE WATER SPRAY, FOG OR STANDARD FOAM (1987 EMERGENCY RESPONSE GUIDEBOOK, DOT P 5800.4).

FIREFIGHTING: MOVE CONTAINER FROM FIRE AREA IF POSSIBLE. DO NOT SCATTER SPILLED MATERIAL WITH HIGH PRESSURE WATER STREAMS. DIKE FIRE CONTROL WATER FOR LATER DISPOSAL (1987 EMERGENCY RESPONSE GUIDEBOOK, DOT P 5800.4, GUIDE PAGE 31).

USE AGENTS SUITABLE FOR TYPE OF SURROUNDING FIRE. AVOID BREATHING HAZARDOUS VAPORS, KEEP UPWIND.

TOXICITY

ALACHLOR: TOXICITY DATA: 3500 MG/KG SKIN-RABBIT LD50; 930 MG/KG ORAL-RAT LD50; 462 MG/KG ORAL-MOUSE LD50; 3000 MG/KG ORAL-MAMMAL LD50; 1200 MG/KG UNREPORTED-MAMMAL LD50; MUTAGENIC DATA (RTECS); TUMORIGENIC DATA (RTECS). CARCINOGEN STATUS: NONE. ACUTE TOXICITY LEVEL: MODERATELY TOXIC BY INGESTION; SLIGHTLY TOXIC BY DERMAL ABSORPTION. TARGET EFFECTS: SENSITIZER- SKIN.

HEALTH EFFECTS AND FIRST AID

INHALATION: ALACHLOR: **ACUTE EXPOSURE-** SLIGHT TO NEGLIGIBLE EFFECTS WERE OBSERVED IN RATS EXPOSED TO 5100 MG/M3/4 HOURS. A CONCENTRATION OF 32600 MG/M3 WAS LETHAL TO RATS. **CHRONIC EXPOSURE-** NO DATA AVAILABLE.

FIRST AID- REMOVE FROM EXPOSURE AREA TO FRESH AIR IMMEDIATELY. IF BREATHING HAS STOPPED, PERFORM ARTIFICIAL RESPIRATION. KEEP PERSON WARM AND AT REST. TREAT SYMPTOMATICALLY AND SUPPORTIVELY. GET MEDICAL ATTENTION IMMEDIATELY.

SKIN CONTACT: ALACHLOR: SENSITIZER. **ACUTE EXPOSURE-** THIS MATERIAL WAS SLIGHTLY IRRITATING TO RABBIT SKIN. ALLERGIC SKIN REACTIONS MAY OCCUR IN PERSONS PREVIOUSLY EXPOSED. **CHRONIC EXPOSURE-** PROLONGED OR REPEATED EXPOSURE TO THIS MATERIAL MAY PRODUCE ALLERGIC SKIN REACTIONS IN SUSCEPTIBLE INDIVIDUALS. REPEATED APPLICATION OF ALACHLOR TO GUINEA PIG SKIN RESULTED IN ERYTHEMA, REDNESS, EDEMA, SWELLING, AND NECROSIS. REPEATED DERMAL APPLICATION OF 4.0 GM/KG PRODUCED SLIGHT TO MODERATE IRRITATION AND INCREASED PITUITARY WEIGHTS IN RABBITS.

FIRST AID- REMOVE CONTAMINATED CLOTHING AND SHOES IMMEDIATELY. WASH AFFECTED AREA WITH SOAP OR MILD DETERGENT AND LARGE AMOUNTS OF WATER UNTIL NO EVIDENCE OF CHEMICAL REMAINS (APPROXIMATELY 15-20 MINUTES). GET MEDICAL ATTENTION IMMEDIATELY.

EYE CONTACT: ALACHLOR: **ACUTE EXPOSURE-** EYE IRRITATION PRODUCED FROM CONTACT WITH TECHNICAL ALACHLOR HAS BEEN REPORTED. HOWEVER, TESTED IN RABBIT EYES, THIS MATERIAL WAS PRACTICALLY NONIRRITATING. **CHRONIC EXPOSURE-** NO DATA AVAILABLE.
FIRST AID- WASH EYES IMMEDIATELY WITH LARGE AMOUNTS OF WATER OR NORMAL SALINE, OCCASIONALLY LIFTING UPPER AND LOWER LIDS, UNTIL NO EVIDENCE OF CHEMICAL REMAINS (APPROXIMATELY 15-20 MINUTES). GET MEDICAL ATTENTION IMMEDIATELY.

INGESTION: ALACHLOR: **ACUTE EXPOSURE-** A LETHAL DOSE IN RATS WAS 930 MG/KG; SYMPTOMS WERE NOT REPORTED. **CHRONIC EXPOSURE-** EFFECTS OF GASTROINTESTINAL DISTURBANCES, HEMOLYTIC ANEMIA, DECREASED BODY WEIGHTS, INCREASED LIVER WEIGHTS AND INCREASED BROMOSULFOPHTHALEIN RETENTION WERE OBSERVED IN A 1-YEAR STUDY OF DOGS FED 10 MG/KG/DAY. HEPATOTOXICITY WAS CITED IN ANOTHER STUDY OF DOGS. MATERNAL AND FETAL TOXICITY WERE NOTED IN A STUDY OF PREGNANT RATS FED 400 MG/KG/DAY. IN A 3-GENERATION STUDY OF RATS, SOME KIDNEY EFFECTS WERE REPORTED AT A DOSE OF 30 MG/KG/DAY. EFFECTS OF OCULAR LESSIONS, HEPATOTOXICITY, TUMORS OF THE NASAL TURBINATE, STOMACH, LIVER, AND THYROID WERE PRODUCED IN RATS. LUNG BRONCHIOLAR-ALVEOLAR TUMORS IN FEMALES WERE OBSERVED IN MICE FED 260 MG/KG/DAY FOR 79 WEEKS.
FIRST AID- REMOVE BY GASTRIC LAVAGE AND CATHARSIS. MAINTAIN BLOOD PRESSURE AND AIRWAY. GIVE OXYGEN IF RESPIRATION IS DEPRESSED. DO NOT PERFORM GASTRIC LAVAGE IF VICTIM IS UNCONSCIOUS. GET MEDICAL ATTENTION IMMEDIATELY (DREISBACH, HANDBOOK OF POISONING, 12TH ED.).
ADMINISTRATION OF LAVAGE OR OXYGEN SHOULD BE PERFORMED BY QUALIFIED MEDICAL PERSONNEL.
ANTIDOTE: NO SPECIFIC ANTIDOTE. TREAT SYMPTOMATICALLY AND SUPPORTIVELY.

REACTIVITY

REACTIVITY: STABLE UNDER NORMAL TEMPERATURES AND PRESSURES.
INCOMPATIBILITIES: ALACHLOR: ACIDS (STRONG): HYDROLYZES. BASES (STRONG): HYDROLYZES. BLACK IRON: MAY CORRODE. STEEL: MAY CORRODE.
DECOMPOSITION: THERMAL DECOMPOSITION PRODUCTS MAY INCLUDE TOXIC OXIDES OF NITROGEN AND CARBON AND TOXIC AND CORROSIVE FUMES OF CHLORIDES.
POLYMERIZATION: HAZARDOUS POLYMERIZATION HAS NOT BEEN REPORTED TO OCCUR UNDER NORMAL TEMPERATURES AND PRESSURES.

STORAGE AND DISPOSAL

OBSERVE ALL FEDERAL, STATE AND LOCAL REGULATIONS WHEN STORING OR DISPOSING OF THIS SUBSTANCE. FOR ASSISTANCE, CONTACT THE DISTRICT DIRECTOR OF THE ENVIRONMENTAL PROTECTION AGENCY.

STORAGE

STORE IN ACCORDANCE WITH 40 CFR 165 RECOMMENDED PROCEDURES FOR THE DISPOSAL AND STORAGE OF PESTICIDES AND PESTICIDE CONTAINERS.
STORE AWAY FROM INCOMPATIBLE SUBSTANCES.
KEEP CONTAINER TIGHTLY CLOSED. PROTECT FROM EXPOSURE TO AIR OR LIGHT.

DISPOSAL

DISPOSAL MUST BE IN ACCORDANCE WITH 40 CFR 165 RECOMMENDED PROCEDURES FOR THE DISPOSAL AND STORAGE OF PESTICIDES AND PESTICIDE CONTAINERS.

CONDITIONS TO AVOID

MAY BURN BUT DOES NOT IGNITE READILY. AVOID CONTACT WITH STRONG OXIDIZERS, EXCESSIVE HEAT, SPARKS, OR OPEN FLAME.

SPILL AND LEAK PROCEDURES

WATER SPILL: THE CALIFORNIA SAFE DRINKING WATER AND TOXIC ENFORCEMENT ACT OF 1986 (PROPOSITION 65) PROHIBITS CONTAMINATING ANY KNOWN SOURCE OF DRINKING WATER WITH SUBSTANCES KNOWN TO CAUSE CANCER AND/OR REPRODUCTIVE TOXICITY.
OCCUPATIONAL SPILL: SWEEP UP AND PLACE IN SUITABLE CLEAN, DRY CONTAINERS FOR RECLAMATION OR LATER DISPOSAL. DO NOT FLUSH SPILLED MATERIAL INTO SEWER. KEEP UNNECESSARY PEOPLE AWAY.

PROTECTIVE EQUIPMENT

VENTILATION: PROVIDE LOCAL EXHAUST OR GENERAL DILUTION VENTILATION SYSTEM.
RESPIRATOR: THE FOLLOWING RESPIRATORS ARE RECOMMENDED BASED ON INFORMATION FOUND IN THE PHYSICAL DATA, TOXICITY AND HEALTH EFFECTS SECTIONS. THEY ARE RANKED IN ORDER FROM MINIMUM TO MAXIMUM RESPIRATORY PROTECTION. THE SPECIFIC RESPIRATOR SELECTED MUST BE BASED ON CONTAMINATION LEVELS FOUND IN THE WORK PLACE, MUST NOT EXCEED THE WORKING LIMITS OF THE RESPIRATOR AND BE JOINTLY APPROVED BY THE NATIONAL INSTITUTE FOR OCCUPATIONAL SAFETY AND HEALTH AND THE MINE SAFETY AND HEALTH ADMINISTRATION (NIOSH-MSHA).
CHEMICAL CARTRIDGE RESPIRATOR WITH AN ORGANIC VAPOR CARTRIDGE(S) WITH A FULL FACEPIECE AND ORGANIC VAPOR CARTRIDGE(S) IN COMBINATION WITH A DUST AND MIST FILTER.
POWERED AIR-PURIFYING RESPIRATOR WITH A TIGHT-FITTING FACEPIECE AND ORGANIC VAPOR CARTRIDGE(S) IN COMBINATION WITH A HIGH-EFFICIENCY PARTICULATE FILTER.
TYPE 'C' SUPPLIED-AIR RESPIRATOR WITH A FULL FACEPIECE OPERATED IN A PRESSURE-DEMAND OR OTHER POSITIVE PRESSURE MODE.
SELF-CONTAINED BREATHING APPARATUS WITH A FULL FACEPIECE OPERATED IN PRESSURE-DEMAND OR OTHER POSITIVE PRESSURE MODE.
FOR FIREFIGHTING AND OTHER IMMEDIATELY DANGEROUS TO LIFE OR HEALTH CONDITIONS:
SELF-CONTAINED BREATHING APPARATUS WITH FULL FACEPIECE OPERATED IN PRESSURE-DEMAND OR OTHER POSITIVE PRESSURE MODE.
SUPPLIED-AIR RESPIRATOR WITH FULL FACEPIECE AND OPERATED IN PRESSURE-DEMAND OR OTHER POSITIVE PRESSURE MODE IN COMBINATION WITH AN AUXILIARY SELF-CONTAINED BREATHING APPARATUS OPERATED IN PRESSURE-DEMAND OR OTHER POSITIVE PRESSURE MODE.
CLOTHING: EMPLOYEE MUST WEAR APPROPRIATE PROTECTIVE (IMPERVIOUS) CLOTHING AND EQUIPMENT TO PREVENT REPEATED OR PROLONGED SKIN CONTACT WITH THIS SUBSTANCE.
GLOVES: EMPLOYEE MUST WEAR APPROPRIATE PROTECTIVE GLOVES TO PREVENT CONTACT WITH THIS SUBSTANCE.
EYE PROTECTION: EMPLOYEE MUST WEAR SPLASH-PROOF OR DUST-RESISTANT SAFETY GOGGLES TO PREVENT EYE CONTACT WITH THIS SUBSTANCE.
EMERGENCY EYE WASH: WHERE THERE IS ANY POSSIBILITY THAT AN EMPLOYEE'S EYES MAY BE EXPOSED TO THIS SUBSTANCE, THE EMPLOYER SHOULD PROVIDE AN EYE WASH FOUNTAIN WITHIN THE IMMEDIATE WORK AREA FOR EMERGENCY USE.

AUTHORIZED BY- OCCUPATIONAL HEALTH SERVICES, INC.
CREATION DATE: 10/04/89 ***REVISION DATE:*** 05/31/90

MATERIAL SAFETY DATA SHEET

OCCUPATIONAL HEALTH SERVICES, INC.
AGRICULTURE AND PESTICIDE DIVISION
450 SEVENTH AVENUE, SUITE 2407
NEW YORK, NEW YORK 10123
1-800-445-MSDS OR (212) 967-1100

EMERGENCY CONTACT:
JOHN S. BRANSFORD, JR. (615) 292-1180

SUBSTANCE IDENTIFICATION

CAS-NUMBER 309-00-2
SUBSTANCE: **ALDRIN**
TRADE NAMES/SYNONYMS: 1,4:5,8-DIMETHANONAPHTHALENE, 1,2,3,4,10,10-HEXACHLORO-1,4,4A,5,8, 8A-HEXAHYDRO-, (1 ALPHA, 4 ALPHA, 4A BETA, 5 ALPHA, 8 ALPHA, 8A BETA)-; 1,4:5,8-DIMETHANONAPHTHALENE, 1,2,3,4,10,10-HEXACHLORO-1,4,4A,5,8 8A-HEXAHYDRO-, ENDO, EXO-; 1,2,3,4,10,10-HEXACHLORO-1,4,4A,5,8,8A-HEXAHYDRO-1,4,:5,8 -DIMETHANONAPHTHALENE; (1R,4S,4AS,5S,8R,8AR,)1,2,3,4,10,10-HEXACHLORO-1,4,4A,5,8,8A-HEXAHYDRO -1,4:5,8-DIMETHANONAPHTHALENE; 1,2,3,4,10,10-HEXACHLORO-1,4,4A,5,8,8A-HEXAHYDRO-EXO-1,4-ENDO-5,8 DIMETHANONAPHTHALENE; (1 ALPHA, 4 ALPHA, 4A BETA, 5 ALPHA, 8 ALPHA, 8A BETA)-1,2,3,4,10,10 HEXACHLORO-1,4,4A,5,8,8A-HEXAHYDRO-1,4:5,8-DIMETHANONAPHTHALENE; ENDO,EXO-1,2,3,4,10,10-HEXACHLORO-1,4,4A,5,8,8A-HEXAHYDRO-1,4:5,8 -DIMETHANONAPHTHALENE; HHDN; OCTALENE; ENT 15949; RCRA P004; STCC 4921403; C12H8CL6; PST00520
CHEMICAL FAMILY: HALOGEN COMPOUND, ALICYCLIC
MOLECULAR FORMULA: C12-H8-CL6
MOLECULAR WEIGHT: 364.93
CERCLA RATINGS (SCALE 0-3): HEALTH=3 FIRE=1 REACTIVITY=0 PERSISTENCE=3
NFPA RATINGS (SCALE 0-4): HEALTH=2 FIRE=0 REACTIVITY=0

COMPONENTS AND CONTAMINANTS

COMPONENT: ALDRIN ***PERCENT:*** 100
CAS# 309-00-2
OTHER CONTAMINANTS: NONE

EXPOSURE LIMITS: ALDRIN: 0.25 MG/M3 OSHA TWA (SKIN) 0.25 MG/M3 ACGIH TWA (SKIN) LOWEST DETECTABLE LIMIT NIOSH RECOMMENDED EXPOSURE CRITERIA 0.15 MG/M3 TWA BY NIOSH-VALIDATED METHOD
500/10,000 POUNDS SARA SECTION 302 THRESHOLD PLANNING QUANTITY 1 POUND SARA SECTION 304 REPORTABLE QUANTITY 1 POUND CERCLA SECTION 103 REPORTABLE QUANTITY SUBJECT TO SARA SECTION 313 ANNUAL TOXIC CHEMICAL RELEASE REPORTING SUBJECT TO CALIFORNIA PROPOSITION 65 CANCER AND/OR REPRODUCTIVE TOXICITY WARNING AND RELEASE REQUIREMENTS- (JULY 1, 1988)

PHYSICAL DATA

DESCRIPTION: ODORLESS, COLORLESS CRYSTALLINE SOLID
BOILING POINT: 293 F (145 C) @ 2 MMHG ***MELTING POINT:*** 220 F (104 C)
SPECIFIC GRAVITY: 1.70 ***VAPOR PRESSURE:*** NEGLIGIBLE
SOLUBILITY IN WATER: 0.027 PPB @ 20 C ***ODOR THRESHOLD:*** 0.017 MG/KG (IN H2O)
SOLVENT SOLUBILITY: SOLUBLE IN ACETONE, BENZENE, XYLENE, KETONES, ESTERS, PARAFFINS, AROMATICS, HALOGENATED SOLVENTS; SPARINGLY SOLUBLE IN ALCOHOLS

FIRE AND EXPLOSION DATA

FIRE AND EXPLOSION HAZARD: NEGLIGIBLE FIRE HAZARD WHEN EXPOSED TO HEAT OR FLAME.
FIREFIGHTING MEDIA: DRY CHEMICAL, CARBON DIOXIDE, HALON, WATER SPRAY OR STANDARD FOAM (1987 EMERGENCY RESPONSE GUIDEBOOK, DOT P 5800.4).
FOR LARGER FIRES, USE WATER SPRAY, FOG OR STANDARD FOAM (1987 EMERGENCY RESPONSE GUIDEBOOK, DOT P 5800.4).
FIREFIGHTING: MOVE CONTAINERS FROM FIRE AREA IF POSSIBLE. FIGHT FIRE FROM MAXIMUM DISTANCE. STAY AWAY FROM STORAGE TANK ENDS. DIKE FIRE CONTROL WATER FOR LATER DISPOSAL. DO NOT SCATTER MATERIAL (1987 EMERGENCY RESPONSE GUIDEBOOK, DOT P 5800.4, GUIDE PAGE 55).
EXTINGUISH ONLY IF FLOW CAN BE STOPPED; USE WATER IN FLOODING AMOUNTS AS A FOG, SOLID STREAMS MAY NOT BE EFFECTIVE. COOL CONTAINERS WITH FLOODING QUANTITIES OF WATER, APPLY FROM AS FAR A DISTANCE AS POSSIBLE. AVOID BREATHING TOXIC VAPORS, KEEP UPWIND.
FIRE FIGHTING PHASES: USE WATER SPRAY, DRY CHEMICAL, FOAM, OR CARBON DIOXIDE. USE WATER TO KEEP FIRE-EXPOSED CONTAINERS COOL. IF A LEAK OR SPILL HAS NOT IGNITED, USE WATER SPRAY TO DISPERSE THE VAPORS AND TO PROVIDE PROTECTION FOR THE MEN ATTEMPTING TO STOP A LEAK. WATER SPRAY MAY USED TO FLUSH SPILLS AWAY FROM EXPOSURES (NFPA 49, HAZARDOUS CHEMICALS DATA, 1975).

TRANSPORTATION DATA

DEPARTMENT OF TRANSPORTATION HAZARD CLASSIFICATION 49 CFR 172.101: POISON B
DEPARTMENT OF TRANSPORTATION LABELING REQUIREMENTS 49 CFR 172.101 AND SUBPART E: POISON
DEPARTMENT OF TRANSPORTATION PACKAGING REQUIREMENTS: 49 CFR 173.376 EXCEPTIONS: 49 CFR 173.364

TOXICITY

ALDRIN: TOXICITY DATA: 5800 UG/M3/4 HOURS INHALATION-RAT LCLO; 15 MG/KG SKIN-RABBIT LD50; 98 MG/KG SKIN-RAT LD50; 75 MG/KG SKIN-CAT LDLO; 14 MG/KG ORAL-HUMAN TDLO; 1250 UG/KG ORAL-CHILD LDLO; 39 MG/KG ORAL-RAT LD50; 44 MG/KG ORAL-MOUSE LD50; 50 MG/KG ORAL-RABBIT LD50; 33 MG/KG ORAL-GUINEA PIG LD50; 65 MG/KG ORAL-DOG LD50; 15 MG/KG ORAL-CAT LDLO; 100 MG/KG ORAL-HAMSTER LD50; 39 MG/KG ORAL-MAMMAL LD50; 1999 MG/KG INTRAPERITONEAL-DOG LD50; 100 MG/KG SUBCUTANEOUS-RABBIT LDLO; 62 MG/KG SUBCUTANEOUS-RAT LD50; 21 MG/KG INTRAVENOUS-MOUSE LD50; 150 MG/KG INTRAPERITONEAL-RAT LD50; 50 MG/KG INTRAPERITONEAL-MOUSE LD50; MUTAGENIC DATA (RTECS); REPRODUCTIVE EFFECTS DATA (RTECS); TUMORIGENIC DATA (RTECS). CARCINOGEN STATUS: HUMAN INADEQUATE EVIDENCE, ANIMAL LIMITED EVIDENCE (IARC GROUP-3). TESTED BY THE ORAL ROUTE, ALDRIN WAS CARCINOGENIC IN MICE, PRODUCING MALIGNANT LIVER NEOPLASMS, AND THYROID TUMORS WERE FOUND IN RATS. ACUTE TOXICITY LEVEL: HIGHLY TOXIC BY DERMAL ABSORPTION AND INGESTION. TARGET EFFECTS: CONVULSANT. POISONING MAY AFFECT THE LIVER, KIDNEYS, AND THYROID. ADDITION DATA: ALDRIN MAY BE STORED IN THE ADIPOSE TISSUES FOR WEEKS TO SEVERAL MONTHS BEFORE IT IS EXCRETED FROM THE BODY. INTENSE ACTIVITY AND STARVATION MAY MOBILIZE THE PESTICIDE RESULTING IN THE REAPPEARANCE OF TOXIC SYMPTOMS. IT MAY BE EXCRETED IN THE MILK OF LACTATING WOMEN AND IS TRANSFERRED TRANSPLACENTALLY TO THE FETUS. STIMULANTS SUCH AS EPINEPHRINE MAY INDUCE VENTRICULAR FIBRILLATION.

HEALTH EFFECTS AND FIRST AID

INHALATION: ALDRIN: CONVULSANT. **ACUTE EXPOSURE-** ONE HUMAN DEATH HAS BEEN REPORTED FROM INHALATION EXPOSURE. ALDRIN IS A CHLORINATED CYCLODIENE PESTICIDE. THESE PESTICIDES ARE ABSORBED FROM THE LUNGS AND MAY PRODUCE CENTRAL NERVOUS SYSTEM EFFECTS, INCLUDING CONVULSIONS, AS DESCRIBED IN ACUTE INGESTION. IN CASES OF GROSS OVEREXPOSURE, CONVULSIONS MAY OCCUR WITHOUT ANY PRIOR SYMPTOMS. ABNORMAL EEG PATTERNS MAY BE OBSERVED; THESE CHANGES IN EEG PATTERNS MAY PERSIST FOR WEEKS OR MONTHS WHILE NO OTHER OBSERVABLE SIGNS OF POISONING MAY EXIST. **CHRONIC EXPOSURE-** PROLONGED OR REPEATED EXPOSURE HAS CAUSED HEADACHE, DIZZINESS, NAUSEA AND VOMITING IN WORKERS. REPEATED EXPOSURE OF PREGNANT WOMEN MAY INCREASE THE RISK OF PREMATURE LABOR. PROLONGED EXPOSURE TO CHLORINATED CYCLODIENE PESTICIDES MAY RESULT IN THE ACCUMULATION IN THE BLOOD RESULTING IN A PROGRESSION OF SYMPTOMS OR IN A SUDDEN ONSET OF SYMPTOMS AS DESCRIBED IN ACUTE INGESTION.
FIRST AID- REMOVE FROM EXPOSURE AREA TO FRESH AIR IMMEDIATELY. IF BREATHING HAS STOPPED, GIVE ARTIFICIAL RESPIRATION. MAINTAIN AIRWAY AND BLOOD PRESSURE AND ADMINISTER OXYGEN IF AVAILABLE. KEEP AFFECTED PERSON WARM AND AT REST. TREAT SYMPTOMATICALLY AND SUPPORTIVELY. ADMINISTRATION OF OXYGEN SHOULD BE PERFORMED BY QUALIFIED PERSONNEL. GET MEDICAL ATTENTION IMMEDIATELY.

SKIN CONTACT: ALDRIN: CONVULSANT/HIGHLY TOXIC. **ACUTE EXPOSURE-** DERMATITIS ASSOCIATED WITH EXPOSURE TO ALDRIN IS RARE, HOWEVER, ONE CASE OF ACUTE ERYTHEMATOBULLOUS DERMATITIS HAS BEEN REPORTED. A LETHAL DOSE IN RABBITS FROM DERMAL ABSORPTION WAS 15 MG/KG. CHLORINATED CYCLODIENE PESTICIDES ARE ABSORBED FROM THE SKIN AND MAY PRODUCE CENTRAL NERVOUS SYSTEM EFFECTS, INCLUDING CONVULSIONS, AS DESCRIBED IN ACUTE INGESTION. IN CASES OF GROSS OVEREXPOSURE, CONVULSIONS MAY OCCUR WITHOUT ANY PRIOR SYMPTOMS. ABNORMAL EEG PATTERNS MAY BE OBSERVED; THESE CHANGES IN EEG PATTERNS MAY PERSIST FOR WEEKS OR MONTHS WHILE NO OTHER OBSERVABLE SIGNS OF POISONING MAY EXIST. **CHRONIC EXPOSURE-** PROLONGED OR REPEATED EXPOSURE TO CHLORINATED CYCLODIENE PESTICIDES MAY RESULT IN THE ACCUMULATION IN THE BLOOD RESULTING IN A PROGRESSION OF SYMPTOMS OR IN A SUDDEN ONSET OF SYMPTOMS AS DESCRIBED IN ACUTE INGESTION.
FIRST AID- REMOVE CONTAMINATED CLOTHING AND SHOES IMMEDIATELY. WASH AFFECTED AREA WITH SOAP OR MILD DETERGENT AND LARGE AMOUNTS OF WATER UNTIL NO EVIDENCE OF CHEMICAL REMAINS (APPROXIMATELY 15-20 MINUTES). GET MEDICAL ATTENTION IMMEDIATELY.

EYE CONTACT: ALDRIN: **ACUTE EXPOSURE-** NO DATA AVAILABLE. **CHRONIC EXPOSURE-** NO DATA AVAILABLE.
FIRST AID- WASH EYES IMMEDIATELY WITH LARGE AMOUNTS OF WATER OR NORMAL SALINE, OCCASIONALLY LIFTING UPPER AND LOWER LIDS, UNTIL NO EVIDENCE OF CHEMICAL REMAINS (APPROXIMATELY 15-20 MINUTES). GET MEDICAL ATTENTION IMMEDIATELY.

INGESTION: ALDRIN: CONVULSANT/LIMITED ANIMAL CARCINOGEN/HIGHLY TOXIC. **ACUTE EXPOSURE-** HYPEREXCITABILITY, ATAXIA, COLLAPSE AND COMA WERE DESCRIBED IN A FATAL POISONING. OTHER REPORTED EFFECTS INCLUDE HEMATURIA AND/OR ALBUMINURIA, AZOTEMIA AND CONVULSIONS. SYMPTOMS OF CHLORINATED CYCLODIENE PESTICIDES MAY INCLUDE HEADACHE, NAUSEA, VOMITING, MALAISE, DIZZINESS, MUSCLE TWITCHING, MYOCLONIC JERKING, CONVULSIVE SEIZURES, AND CARDIAC DYSRHYTHMIAS. IN CASES OF GROSS OVEREXPOSURE, CONVULSIONS MAY OCCUR WITHOUT ANY PRIOR SYMPTOMS. DEATH MAY OCCUR FROM ANOXIA, OR CARDIAC ARREST WITH RESPIRATORY FAILURE. SIGNS OF TOXIC NEPHROPATHY AND TOXIC HEPATITIS MAY DEVELOP. ABNORMAL EEG PATTERNS MAY BE OBSERVED; THESE CHANGES MAY PERSIST FOR WEEKS OR MONTHS WHILE NO OTHER OBSERVABLE SIGNS OF POISONING MAY EXIST. A HIGH INCIDENCE OF FETAL DEATH, CONGENITAL ANOMALIES, AND GROWTH RETARDATION WERE OBSERVED IN PREGNANT HAMSTERS FED 50 MG/KG. CONGENITAL ANOMALIES WERE ALSO PRODUCED AFTER PREGNANT MICE WERE FED 25 MG/KG. **CHRONIC EXPOSURE-** REPEATED INGESTION MAY CAUSE SYMPTOMS AS DESCRIBED IN ACUTE INGESTION. IN ONE CASE OF REPEATED INGESTION OF ALDRIN-TREATED SEED GRAIN, ADVERSE EFFECTS OF INDUCED MYOCLONIC CONVULSIONS, EEG CHANGES, MEMORY LOSS, LACK OF CONCENTRATION, VISUAL LIGHT FLASHES, AND TINNITUS WERE REPORTED. IN A THREE-GENERATION STUDY OF RATS, A REDUCED NUMBER OF PREGNANCIES AND SEVERELY INCREASED PUP MORTALITY WERE OBSERVED AT A DIETARY LEVEL OF 12.5 PPM AND 25 PPM (APPROXIMATELY 0.65 AND 1.3 MG/KG/DAY). INCREASED LIVER WEIGHTS AND DEGENERATIVE HEPATIC CELL CHANGES WERE ALSO OBSERVED IN RATS AT 25 PPM. PARENCHYMATOUS DEGENERATION OF THE LIVER AND KIDNEYS WAS REPORTED FROM A ONE-YEAR STUDY OF DOGS FED 0.02 AND 0.06 MG/KG/DAY. IN OTHER STUDIES, MALIGNANT LIVER NEOPLASMS WERE OBSERVED IN MICE AND THYROID TUMORS WERE FOUND IN RATS.

FIRST AID- IF THE PERSON IS CONSCIOUS AND NOT CONVULSING, REMOVE BY GIVING SYRUP OF IPECAC (IF VOMITING OCCURS, KEEP THE HEAD BELOW THE HIPS TO PREVENT ASPIRATION). GIVE ACTIVATED CHARCOAL FOLLOWED BY GASTRIC LAVAGE. FOLLOW WITH A SALINE CATHARTIC. DO NOT GIVE FATS OR OILS. INTESTINAL LAVAGE WITH 20% MANNITOL (200 ML) BY STOMACH TUBE IS ALSO USEFUL. GIVE ARTIFICIAL RESPIRATION WITH OXYGEN IF RESPIRATION IS DEPRESSED (DREISBACH, HANDBOOK OF POISONING, 12TH ED.). TREAT SYMPTOMATICALLY AND SUPPORTIVELY. LAVAGE AND ADMINISTRATION OF OXYGEN SHOULD BE PERFORMED BY QUALIFIED MEDICAL PERSONNEL. GET MEDICAL ATTENTION IMMEDIATELY.

ANTIDOTE: NO SPECIFIC ANTIDOTE. TREAT SYMPTOMATICALLY AND SUPPORTIVELY.

REACTIVITY

REACTIVITY: STABLE UNDER NORMAL TEMPERATURES AND PRESSURES.

INCOMPATIBILITIES: ALDRIN: ACID CATALYSTS: MAY REACT. ACID OXIDIZING AGENTS: MAY REACT. ACTIVE METALS: MAY REACT. CONCENTRATED MINERAL ACIDS: MAY REACT. OXIDIZING AGENT: MAY REACT. PHENOL: MAY REACT.

DECOMPOSITION: THERMAL DECOMPOSITION PRODUCTS MAY INCLUDE TOXIC AND/OR CORROSIVE VAPORS OF HYDROGEN CHLORIDE, CHLORINE, AND CARBON MONOXIDE.

POLYMERIZATION: HAZARDOUS POLYMERIZATION HAS NOT BEEN REPORTED TO OCCUR UNDER NORMAL TEMPERATURES AND PRESSURES.

STORAGE AND DISPOSAL

OBSERVE ALL FEDERAL, STATE AND LOCAL REGULATIONS WHEN STORING OR DISPOSING OF THIS SUBSTANCE. FOR ASSISTANCE, CONTACT THE DISTRICT DIRECTOR OF THE ENVIRONMENTAL PROTECTION AGENCY.

****STORAGE****

STORE IN ACCORDANCE WITH 40 CFR 165 RECOMMENDED PROCEDURES FOR THE DISPOSAL AND STORAGE OF PESTICIDES AND PESTICIDE CONTAINERS.

STORE AWAY FROM INCOMPATIBLE SUBSTANCES.

PROTECT AGAINST PHYSICAL DAMAGE. STORE IN COOL, DRY, WELL VENTILATED LOCATION, AWAY FROM ANY AREA WHERE THE FIRE HAZARD MAY BE ACUTE. OUTSIDE OR DETACHED STORAGE IS PREFERRED. SEPARATE LIQUID FORMULATION FROM OTHER STORAGE. (NFPA 49, HAZARDOUS CHEMICALS DATA, 1975).

THRESHOLD PLANNING QUANTITY (TPQ): THE SUPERFUND AMENDMENTS AND REAUTHORIZATION ACT (SARA) SECTION 302 REQUIRES THAT EACH FACILITY WHERE ANY EXTREMELY HAZARDOUS SUBSTANCE IS PRESENT IN A QUANTITY EQUAL TO OR GREATER THAN THE TPQ ESTABLISHED FOR THAT SUBSTANCE NOTIFY THE STATE EMERGENCY RESPONSE COMMISSION FOR THE STATE IN WHICH IT IS LOCATED. SECTION 303 OF SARA REQUIRES THESE FACILITIES TO PARTICIPATE IN LOCAL EMERGENCY RESPONSE PLANNING (40 CFR 355.30).

****DISPOSAL****

DISPOSAL MUST BE IN ACCORDANCE WITH STANDARDS APPLICABLE TO GENERATORS OF HAZARDOUS WASTE, 40CFR 262. EPA HAZARDOUS WASTE NUMBER P004.

CONDITIONS TO AVOID

MAY BURN BUT DOES NOT IGNITE READILY. CONTAINERS MAY EXPLODE IN HEAT OF FIRE.

SPILL AND LEAK PROCEDURES

SOIL SPILL: DIG HOLDING AREA SUCH AS LAGOON, POND OR PIT FOR CONTAINMENT. USE PROTECTIVE COVER SUCH AS A PLASTIC SHEET TO PREVENT MATERIAL FROM DISSOLVING IN FIRE EXTINGUISHING WATER OR RAIN.

WATER SPILL: TRAP SPILLED MATERIAL AT BOTTOM IN DEEP WATER POCKETS, EXCAVATED HOLDING AREAS OR WITHIN SAND BAG BARRIERS.

USE ACTIVATED CARBON TO ABSORB SPILLED SUBSTANCE THAT IS DISSOLVED.

USE SUCTION HOSES TO REMOVE TRAPPED SPILL MATERIAL.

USE MECHANICAL DREDGES OR LIFTS TO EXTRACT IMMOBILIZED MASSES OF POLLUTION AND PRECIPITATES.

OCCUPATIONAL SPILL: DO NOT TOUCH SPILLED MATERIAL. STOP LEAK IF YOU CAN DO IT WITHOUT RISK. USE WATER SPRAY TO REDUCE VAPORS. FOR SMALL SPILLS, TAKE UP WITH SAND OR OTHER ABSORBENT MATERIAL AND PLACE INTO CONTAINERS FOR LATER DISPOSAL. FOR SMALL DRY SPILLS, WITH A CLEAN SHOVEL PLACE MATERIAL INTO CLEAN, DRY CONTAINERS AND COVER. MOVE CONTAINERS FROM SPILL AREA. FOR LARGER SPILLS, DIKE FAR AHEAD OF SPILL FOR LATER DISPOSAL. KEEP UNNECESSARY PEOPLE AWAY. ISOLATE HAZARD AREA AND DENY ENTRY. VENTILATE CLOSED SPACES BEFORE ENTERING.

REPORTABLE QUANTITY (RQ): 1 POUND THE SUPERFUND AMENDMENTS AND REAUTHORIZATION ACT (SARA) SECTION 304 REQUIRES THAT A RELEASE EQUAL TO OR GREATER THAN THE REPORTABLE QUANTITY FOR THIS SUBSTANCE BE IMMEDIATELY REPORTED TO THE LOCAL EMERGENCY PLANNING COMMITTEE AND THE STATE EMERGENCY RESPONSE COMMISSION (40 CFR 355.40). IF THE RELEASE OF THIS SUBSTANCE IS REPORTABLE UNDER CERCLA SECTION 103, THE NATIONAL RESPONSE CENTER MUST BE NOTIFIED IMMEDIATELY AT (800) 424-8802 OR (202) 426-2675 IN THE METROPOLITAN WASHINGTON, D.C. AREA (40 CFR 302.6).

PROTECTIVE EQUIPMENT

VENTILATION: PROCESS ENCLOSURE RECOMMENDED TO MEET PUBLISHED EXPOSURE LIMITS.

RESPIRATOR: THE FOLLOWING RESPIRATORS AND MAXIMUM USE CONCENTRATIONS ARE RECOMMENDATIONS BY THE U.S. DEPARTMENT OF HEALTH AND HUMAN SERVICES, NIOSH POCKET GUIDE TO CHEMICAL HAZARDS; NIOSH CRITERIA DOCUMENTS OR BY THE U.S. DEPARTMENT OF LABOR, 29 CFR 1910 SUBPART Z. THE SPECIFIC RESPIRATOR SELECTED MUST BE BASED ON CONTAMINATION LEVELS FOUND IN THE WORK PLACE, MUST NOT EXCEED THE WORKING LIMITS OF THE RESPIRATOR AND BE JOINTLY APPROVED BY THE NATIONAL INSTITUTE FOR OCCUPATIONAL SAFETY AND HEALTH AND THE MINE SAFETY AND HEALTH ADMINISTRATION (NIOSH-MSHA).

AT ANY DETECTABLE CONCENTRATION:

SELF-CONTAINED BREATHING APPARATUS WITH FULL FACEPIECE OPERATED IN PRESSURE-DEMAND OR OTHER POSITIVE PRESSURE MODE. SUPPLIED-AIR RESPIRATOR WITH FULL FACEPIECE OPERATED IN PRESSURE-DEMAND OR OTHER POSITIVE PRESSURE MODE IN COMBINATION WITH AN AUXILIARY SELF-CONTAINED BREATHING APPARATUS OPERATED IN PRESSURE-DEMAND OR OTHER POSITIVE PRESSURE MODE.

ESCAPE- AIR-PURIFYING FULL FACEPIECE RESPIRATOR (GAS MASK) WITH A CHIN-STYLE OR FRONT- OR BACK-MOUNTED ORGANIC VAPOR CANISTER HAVING A HIGH-EFFICIENCY PARTICULATE FILTER. ESCAPE-TYPE SELF-CONTAINED BREATHING APPARATUS.

FOR FIREFIGHTING AND OTHER IMMEDIATELY DANGEROUS TO LIFE OR HEALTH CONDITIONS:

SELF-CONTAINED BREATHING APPARATUS WITH FULL FACEPIECE OPERATED IN PRESSURE-DEMAND OR OTHER POSITIVE PRESSURE MODE.

SUPPLIED-AIR RESPIRATOR WITH FULL FACEPIECE AND OPERATED IN PRESSURE-DEMAND OR OTHER POSITIVE PRESSURE MODE IN COMBINATION WITH AN AUXILIARY SELF-CONTAINED BREATHING APPARATUS OPERATED IN PRESSURE-DEMAND OR OTHER POSITIVE PRESSURE MODE.

CLOTHING: EMPLOYEE MUST WEAR APPROPRIATE PROTECTIVE (IMPERVIOUS) CLOTHING AND EQUIPMENT TO PREVENT ANY POSSIBILITY OF SKIN CONTACT WITH THIS SUBSTANCE.

GLOVES: EMPLOYEE MUST WEAR APPROPRIATE PROTECTIVE GLOVES TO PREVENT CONTACT WITH THIS SUBSTANCE.

EYE PROTECTION: EMPLOYEE MUST WEAR SPLASH-PROOF OR DUST-RESISTANT SAFETY GOGGLES AND A FACESHIELD TO PREVENT CONTACT WITH THIS SUBSTANCE.

EMERGENCY WASH FACILITIES: WHERE THERE IS ANY POSSIBILITY THAT AN EMPLOYEE'S EYES AND/OR SKIN MAY BE EXPOSED TO THIS SUBSTANCE, THE EMPLOYER SHOULD PROVIDE AN EYE WASH FOUNTAIN AND QUICK DRENCH SHOWER WITHIN THE IMMEDIATE WORK AREA FOR EMERGENCY USE.

AUTHORIZED BY- OCCUPATIONAL HEALTH SERVICES, INC.

CREATION DATE: 10/04/89 ***REVISION DATE:*** 06/26/90

MATERIAL SAFETY DATA SHEET

OCCUPATIONAL HEALTH SERVICES, INC.
AGRICULTURE AND PESTICIDE DIVISION
450 SEVENTH AVENUE, SUITE 2407
NEW YORK, NEW YORK 10123
1-800-445-MSDS OR (212) 967-1100

EMERGENCY CONTACT:
JOHN S. BRANSFORD, JR. (615) 292-1180

SUBSTANCE IDENTIFICATION

CAS-NUMBER 8001-54-5

SUBSTANCE: ALKYLDIMETHYLBENZYLAMMONIUM CHLORIDE

TRADE NAMES/SYNONYMS: BENZALKON; BENZALKONIUM CHLORIDE; BIONOL; BTC 824; DIMANIN; GERM-I-TOL; INTEXAN LB-50; NEO-GERMITOL; OSVAN; QUATRAMINE; ZEPHIRAN CHLORIDE; PST00537

CHEMICAL FAMILY: QUATERNARY AMMONIUM COMPOUND

CERCLA RATINGS (SCALE 0-3): HEALTH=3 FIRE=1 REACTIVITY=0 PERSISTENCE=2

NFPA RATINGS (SCALE 0-4): HEALTH=U FIRE=1 REACTIVITY=0

COMPONENTS AND CONTAMINANTS

COMPONENT: ALKYLDIMETHYLBENZYLAMMONIUM CHLORIDE ***PERCENT:*** 100.0
CAS# 8001-54-5

OTHER CONTAMINANTS: NONE

EXPOSURE LIMITS: NO OCCUPATIONAL EXPOSURE LIMITS ESTABLISHED BY OSHA, ACGIH, OR NIOSH.

PHYSICAL DATA

DESCRIPTION: WHITE OR YELLOWISH-WHITE, AMORPHOUS POWDER OR GELATINOUS SOLID WITH AN AROMATIC ODOR AND BITTER TASTE.

MELTING POINT: NOT AVAILABLE ***SPECIFIC GRAVITY:*** NOT AVAILABLE

PH: ALKALINE IN SOLUTION ***SOLUBILITY IN WATER:*** SOLUBLE

SOLVENT SOLUBILITY: SOLUBLE IN ALCOHOL, ACETONE; SLIGHTLY SOLUBLE IN BENZENE; ALMOST INSOLUBLE IN ETHER, ALIPHATIC HYDROCARBONS.

FIRE AND EXPLOSION DATA

FIRE AND EXPLOSION HAZARD: SLIGHT FIRE HAZARD WHEN EXPOSED TO HEAT OR FLAME.

FIREFIGHTING MEDIA: DRY CHEMICAL, CARBON DIOXIDE, HALON, WATER SPRAY OR STANDARD FOAM (1987 EMERGENCY RESPONSE GUIDEBOOK, DOT P 5800.4).
FOR LARGER FIRES, USE WATER SPRAY, FOG OR STANDARD FOAM (1987 EMERGENCY RESPONSE GUIDEBOOK, DOT P 5800.4).

FIREFIGHTING: MOVE CONTAINER FROM FIRE AREA IF POSSIBLE. DO NOT SCATTER SPILLED MATERIAL WITH HIGH PRESSURE WATER STREAMS. DIKE FIRE CONTROL WATER FOR LATER DISPOSAL (1987 EMERGENCY RESPONSE GUIDEBOOK, DOT P 5800.4, GUIDE PAGE 31).
USE AGENTS SUITABLE FOR TYPE OF SURROUNDING FIRE. AVOID BREATHING HAZARDOUS VAPORS, KEEP UPWIND.

TOXICITY

ALKYLDIMETHYLBENZYLAMMONIUM CHLORIDE: IRRITATION DATA: 150 UG/3 DAYS INTERMITTENT SKIN-HUMAN MILD; 50 UG EYE-HUMAN SEVERE; 2 MG/24 HOURS EYE-MONKEY SEVERE; 50 MG/24 HOURS SKIN-RABBIT MODERATE; 100 UG EYE-RABBIT; 1 MG/24 HOURS EYE-RABBIT SEVERE; 10 MG EYE-RABBIT MILD. TOXICITY DATA: 1560 MG/KG SKIN-RAT LD50; 266 MG/KG ORAL-WOMAN TDLO; 240 MG/KG ORAL-RAT LD50; 175 MG/KG ORAL-MOUSE LD50; 200 MG/KG ORAL-GUINEA PIG LD50; 400 MG/KG SUBCUTANEOUS-RAT LD50; 64 MG/KG SUBCUTANEOUS-MOUSE LD50; 13900 UG/KG INTRAVENOUS-RAT LD50; 10 MG/KG INTRAVENOUS-MOUSE LD50; 14500 UG/KG INTRAPERITONEAL-RAT LD50; 10 MG/KG INTRAPERITONEAL-MOUSE LDLO; 10 MG/KG INTRAPERITONEAL-GUINEA PIG LDLO; 7 MG/KG INTRAPERITONEAL-DOG LDLO; 12 MG/KG PARENTERAL-WOMAN LDLO; MUTAGENIC DATA (RTECS); REPRODUCTIVE EFFECTS DATA (RTECS). CARCINOGEN STATUS: NONE. LOCAL EFFECTS: CORROSIVE- INHALATION, SKIN, EYES, INGESTION. ACUTE TOXICITY: TOXIC BY INGESTION; MODERATELY TOXIC BY DERMAL ABSORPTION. TARGET EFFECTS: SENSITIZER- SKIN, EYE.

HEALTH EFFECTS AND FIRST AID

INHALATION: ALKYLDIMETHYLBENZYLAMMONIUM CHLORIDE: CORROSIVE. **ACUTE EXPOSURE-** CONCENTRATIONS AS LOW AS 0.1-0.5% MAY CAUSE IRRITATION OF THE MUCOUS MEMBRANES. STRONG AQUEOUS SOLUTIONS, 10-20%, HAVE PRODUCED SUPERFICIAL NECROSIS OF THE MUCOUS MEMBRANES. **CHRONIC EXPOSURE-** REPEATED OR PROLONGED EXPOSURE MAY CAUSE EFFECTS AS THOSE LISTED IN ACUTE EXPOSURE. ASTHMA DUE TO OCCUPATIONAL EXPOSURE HAS BEEN REPORTED.

FIRST AID- REMOVE FROM EXPOSURE AREA TO FRESH AIR IMMEDIATELY. IF BREATHING HAS STOPPED, GIVE ARTIFICIAL RESPIRATION. MAINTAIN AIRWAY AND BLOOD PRESSURE AND ADMINISTER OXYGEN IF AVAILABLE. KEEP AFFECTED PERSON WARM AND AT REST. TREAT SYMPTOMATICALLY AND SUPPORTIVELY. ADMINISTRATION OF OXYGEN SHOULD BE PERFORMED BY QUALIFIED PERSONNEL. GET MEDICAL ATTENTION IMMEDIATELY.

SKIN CONTACT: ALKYLDIMETHYLBENZYLAMMONIUM CHLORIDE: CORROSIVE/SENSITIZER. **ACUTE EXPOSURE-** CONCENTRATIONS EXCEEDING 1% CAN IRRITATE THE SKIN. CONCENTRATED AQUEOUS SOLUTIONS OF 10% ARE PRIMARY SKIN IRRITANTS. DAMAGE TO THE EPIDERMIS MAY OCCUR. SEVERE SKIN DAMAGE HAS BEEN REPORTED IN LABORATORY ANIMALS. **CHRONIC EXPOSURE-** ALLERGIC CONTACT DERMATITIS HAS OCCURRED IN INDIVIDUALS REPEATEDLY EXPOSED TO THIS MATERIAL.

FIRST AID- REMOVE CONTAMINATED CLOTHING AND SHOES IMMEDIATELY. WASH AFFECTED AREA WITH SOAP OR MILD DETERGENT AND LARGE AMOUNTS OF WATER UNTIL NO EVIDENCE OF CHEMICAL REMAINS (AT LEAST 15-20 MINUTES). IN CASE OF CHEMICAL BURNS, COVER AREA WITH STERILE, DRY DRESSING. BANDAGE SECURELY, BUT NOT TOO TIGHTLY. GET MEDICAL ATTENTION IMMEDIATELY.

EYE CONTACT: ALKYLDIMETHYLBENZYLAMMONIUM CHLORIDE: CORROSIVE/SENSITIZER. **ACUTE EXPOSURE-** A DROP OF 0.1% CONCENTRATION IN HUMAN EYES CAUSED MILD DISCOMFORT WHICH PERSISTED FOR 2 OR 3 HOURS AS A SLIGHT, SCRATCHY, FOREIGN-BODY TYPE SENSATION. HIGHER CONCENTRATIONS IN HUMAN EYES, SUCH AS 10%, CAN CAUSE VERY SERIOUS DAMAGE TO THE WHOLE CORNEA. IRRIGATION OF THE SURFACE OF RABBIT EYES WITH A 0.1% SOLUTION FOR 15 MINUTES PRODUCED SEVERE INJURY OF THE ENDOTHELIUM AND MUCH SWELLING. THE CORNEAS OF RABBIT EYES BECAME BLUE AND SWOLLEN, THEN COMPLETELY OPAQUE AND VASCULARIZED WITH THE FORMATION OF SCAR TISSUE AT THE 10% CONCENTRATION. **CHRONIC EXPOSURE-** ALLERGIC CONJUNCTIVITIS HAS DEVELOPED IN SOME INDIVIDUALS AFTER USING OPHTHALMIC SOLUTIONS CONTAINING THIS MATERIAL. A 0.1% CONCENTRATION APPLIED TO RABBIT EYES AS DROPS 2 OR 3 TIMES A DAY FOR 1 TO 3 MONTHS HAS CAUSED THICKENING AND ROUGHENING OF THE CORNEAL EPITHELIUM, WITH SUPERFICIAL VASCULARIZATION, BUT NO DEEPER DAMAGE.

FIRST AID- WASH EYES IMMEDIATELY WITH LARGE AMOUNTS OF WATER, OCCASIONALLY LIFTING UPPER AND LOWER LIDS, UNTIL NO EVIDENCE OF CHEMICAL REMAINS (AT LEAST 15-20 MINUTES). CONTINUE IRRIGATING WITH NORMAL SALINE UNTIL THE PH HAS RETURNED TO NORMAL (30-60 MINUTES). COVER WITH STERILE BANDAGES. GET MEDICAL ATTENTION IMMEDIATELY.

INGESTION: ALKYLDIMETHYLBENZYLAMMONIUM CHLORIDE: CORROSIVE/TOXIC. **ACUTE EXPOSURE-** CONCENTRATED SOLUTIONS MAY CAUSE AN IMMEDIATE BURNING PAIN IN THE MOUTH, THROAT, AND ABDOMEN WITH PROFUSE SALIVATION. EXPOSED AREAS OF MUCOUS MEMBRANES MAY ULCERATE. VOMITING MAY OCCUR, POSSIBLY WITH BLOOD. SIGNS OF CIRCULATORY SHOCK INCLUDING HYPOTENSION, LABORED BREATHING, AND CYANOSIS MAY OCCUR. RAPIDLY DEVELOPING APPREHENSION, RESTLESSNESS, CONFUSION, AND WEAKNESS MAY RESULT. WEAK CONVULSIVE MOVEMENTS MAY PRECEDE CENTRAL NERVOUS SYSTEM DEPRESSION. EROSION, ULCERATION AND PETECHIAL HEMORRHAGES MAY OCCUR THROUGHOUT THE SMALL INTESTINES. GLOTTIC, BRAIN, AND PULMONARY EDEMA HAVE BEEN REPORTED. DEATH MAY OCCUR WITHIN 1-2 HOURS AFTER INGESTION DUE TO ASPHYXIATION BECAUSE OF PARALYSIS OF THE MUSCLES OF RESPIRATION OR TO CARDIOVASCULAR COLLAPSE. EVEN IN PROMPT DEATH, CLOUDY SWELLING, PATCHY NECROSIS AND FATTY INFILTRATION OCCUR IN SUCH VISCERAL ORGANS AS HEART, LIVER, AND KIDNEYS. RENAL FAILURE MAY DEVELOP IN INDIVIDUALS THAT SURVIVED A PERIOD OF SEVERE HYPOTENSION. **CHRONIC EXPOSURE-** RATS REPEATEDLY FED THIS MATERIAL FOR SEVERAL WEEKS DIED OF INANITION ASSOCIATED WITH CHRONIC DIARRHEA; THE ONLY LESION FOUND WAS FOCAL HEMORRHAGIC NECROSIS OF THE GASTRIC MUCOSA. REPEATED ADMINISTRATION OF A 0.5% CONCENTRATION IN THE DIET WAS LETHAL TO RATS. REPEATED DOSAGES OF 25 MG/KG IN WATER WAS LETHAL TO ALL THREE DOGS TESTED; EFFECTS OF CONDITIONED SALIVATION, VOMITING, ENTERITIS, PULMONARY HEMORRHAGE, AND INFLAMMATION AND SLOUGHING OF THE MUCOSA WERE REPORTED.

FIRST AID- GIVE MILK OR ACTIVATED CHARCOAL AND REMOVE BY CATHARSIS WITH FLEET'S PHOSPHO-SODA, 15-60 ML DILUTED 1:4 WITH WATER. LAVAGE AND EMESIS ARE CONTRAINDICATED IN THE PRESENCE OF ESOPHAGEAL INJURY. GASTRIC LAVAGE SHOULD BE PERFORMED BY QUALIFIED MEDICAL PERSONNEL. GET MEDICAL ATTENTION IMMEDIATELY (DREISBACH, HANDBOOK OF POISONING, 12TH ED.). MAINTAIN AIRWAY, BLOOD PRESSURE AND RESPIRATION.

ANTIDOTE: NO SPECIFIC ANTIDOTE. TREAT SYMPTOMATICALLY AND SUPPORTIVELY.

REACTIVITY

REACTIVITY: STABLE UNDER NORMAL TEMPERATURES AND PRESSURES.

INCOMPATIBILITIES: ALKYLDIMETHYLBENZYLAMMONIUM CHLORIDE: OXIDIZERS (STRONG): FIRE AND EXPLOSION HAZARD.

DECOMPOSITION: THERMAL DECOMPOSITION PRODUCTS MAY INCLUDE TOXIC FUMES OF AMMONIA, CHLORIDES AND THE OXIDES OF NITROGEN.

POLYMERIZATION: HAZARDOUS POLYMERIZATION HAS NOT BEEN REPORTED TO OCCUR UNDER NORMAL TEMPERATURES AND PRESSURES.

STORAGE AND DISPOSAL

OBSERVE ALL FEDERAL, STATE AND LOCAL REGULATIONS WHEN STORING OR DISPOSING OF THIS SUBSTANCE. FOR ASSISTANCE, CONTACT THE DISTRICT DIRECTOR OF THE ENVIRONMENTAL PROTECTION AGENCY.

STORAGE

STORE IN ACCORDANCE WITH 40 CFR 165 RECOMMENDED PROCEDURES FOR THE DISPOSAL AND STORAGE OF PESTICIDES AND PESTICIDE CONTAINERS.
STORE AWAY FROM INCOMPATIBLE SUBSTANCES.
STORE IN A COOL, DRY PLACE; KEEP CONTAINER TIGHTLY CLOSED WHEN NOT IN USE.

DISPOSAL

DISPOSAL MUST BE IN ACCORDANCE WITH 40 CFR 165 RECOMMENDED PROCEDURES FOR THE DISPOSAL AND STORAGE OF PESTICIDES AND PESTICIDE CONTAINERS.

CONDITIONS TO AVOID

MAY BURN BUT DOES NOT IGNITE READILY. AVOID CONTACT WITH STRONG OXIDIZERS, EXCESSIVE HEAT, SPARKS, OR OPEN FLAME.

SPILL AND LEAK PROCEDURES

OCCUPATIONAL SPILL: SWEEP UP AND PLACE IN SUITABLE CLEAN, DRY CONTAINERS FOR RECLAMATION OR LATER DISPOSAL. DO NOT FLUSH SPILLED MATERIAL INTO SEWER. KEEP UNNECESSARY PEOPLE AWAY.

PROTECTIVE EQUIPMENT

VENTILATION: PROVIDE LOCAL EXHAUST OR GENERAL DILUTION VENTILATION SYSTEM.

RESPIRATOR: THE FOLLOWING RESPIRATORS ARE RECOMMENDED BASED ON INFORMATION FOUND IN THE PHYSICAL DATA, TOXICITY AND HEALTH EFFECTS SECTIONS. THEY ARE RANKED IN ORDER FROM MINIMUM TO MAXIMUM RESPIRATORY PROTECTION. THE SPECIFIC RESPIRATOR SELECTED MUST BE BASED ON CONTAMINATION LEVELS FOUND IN THE WORK PLACE, MUST NOT EXCEED THE WORKING LIMITS OF THE RESPIRATOR AND BE JOINTLY APPROVED BY THE NATIONAL INSTITUTE FOR OCCUPATIONAL SAFETY AND HEALTH AND THE MINE SAFETY AND HEALTH ADMINISTRATION (NIOSH-MSHA).

CHEMICAL CARTRIDGE RESPIRATOR WITH AN ORGANIC VAPOR CARTRIDGE(S) WITH A FULL FACEPIECE.

GAS MASK WITH ORGANIC VAPOR CANISTER (CHIN-STYLE OR FRONT- OR BACK-MOUNTED CANISTER) WITH A FULL FACEPIECE.

TYPE 'C' SUPPLIED-AIR RESPIRATOR WITH A FULL FACEPIECE OPERATED IN PRESSURE-DEMAND OR OTHER POSITIVE PRESSURE MODE OR WITH A FULL FACEPIECE, HELMET OR HOOD OPERATED IN CONTINUOUS-FLOW MODE.

SELF-CONTAINED BREATHING APPARATUS WITH A FULL FACEPIECE OPERATED IN PRESSURE-DEMAND OR OTHER POSITIVE PRESSURE MODE.

FOR FIREFIGHTING AND OTHER IMMEDIATELY DANGEROUS TO LIFE OR HEALTH CONDITIONS:

SELF-CONTAINED BREATHING APPARATUS WITH FULL FACEPIECE OPERATED IN PRESSURE-DEMAND OR OTHER POSITIVE PRESSURE MODE.

SUPPLIED-AIR RESPIRATOR WITH FULL FACEPIECE AND OPERATED IN PRESSURE-DEMAND OR OTHER POSITIVE PRESSURE MODE IN COMBINATION WITH AN AUXILIARY SELF-CONTAINED BREATHING APPARATUS OPERATED IN PRESSURE-DEMAND OR OTHER POSITIVE PRESSURE MODE.

CLOTHING: EMPLOYEE MUST WEAR APPROPRIATE PROTECTIVE (IMPERVIOUS) CLOTHING AND EQUIPMENT TO PREVENT ANY POSSIBILITY OF SKIN CONTACT WITH THIS SUBSTANCE.

GLOVES: EMPLOYEE MUST WEAR APPROPRIATE PROTECTIVE GLOVES TO PREVENT CONTACT WITH THIS SUBSTANCE.

EYE PROTECTION: EMPLOYEE MUST WEAR SPLASH-PROOF OR DUST-RESISTANT SAFETY GOGGLES AND A FACESHIELD TO PREVENT CONTACT WITH THIS SUBSTANCE.

EMERGENCY WASH FACILITIES: WHERE THERE IS ANY POSSIBILITY THAT AN EMPLOYEE'S EYES AND/OR SKIN MAY BE EXPOSED TO THIS SUBSTANCE, THE EMPLOYER SHOULD PROVIDE AN EYE WASH FOUNTAIN AND QUICK DRENCH SHOWER WITHIN THE IMMEDIATE WORK AREA FOR EMERGENCY USE.

AUTHORIZED BY- OCCUPATIONAL HEALTH SERVICES, INC.

CREATION DATE: 10/04/89 ***REVISION DATE:*** 05/31/90

MATERIAL SAFETY DATA SHEET

OCCUPATIONAL HEALTH SERVICES, INC.
AGRICULTURE AND PESTICIDE DIVISION
450 SEVENTH AVENUE, SUITE 2407
NEW YORK, NEW YORK 10123
1-800-445-MSDS OR (212) 967-1100

EMERGENCY CONTACT:
JOHN S. BRANSFORD, JR. (615) 292-1180

SUBSTANCE IDENTIFICATION

CAS-NUMBER 8001-54-5

SUBSTANCE: **ALKYL DIMETHYL ETHYLBENZYL AMMONIUM CHLORIDE**

TRADE NAMES/SYNONYMS: ALKYL(ETHYLPHENYL)METHYL)DIMETHYL QUARTENARY AMMONIUM CHLORIDES; BENIROL; BENZALKONIUM CHLORIDE; BTC 471; CEQUARTYL; DRAPOLEX; GERMINOL; GERMITOL; OCTYL/OCTADECYL DIMETHYL ETHYLBENZYL AMMONIUM CHLORIDES; ROCCAL; RODALON; ZEPHIRAN CHLORIDE; ZEPHIROL; PST00539

CHEMICAL FAMILY: QUATERNARY SALT

MOLECULAR FORMULA: C9-H13-CL-N-(C8-H17-37)

MOLECULAR WEIGHT: 183-423

CERCLA RATINGS (SCALE 0-3): HEALTH=3 FIRE=0 REACTIVITY=0 PERSISTENCE=0

NFPA RATINGS (SCALE 0-4): HEALTH=3 FIRE=0 REACTIVITY=0

COMPONENTS AND CONTAMINANTS

COMPONENT: ALKYL DIMETHYL ETHYLBENZYL AMMONIUM CHLORIDE ***PERCENT:*** 100

CAS# 8001-54-5

EXPOSURE LIMITS: NO OCCUPATIONAL EXPOSURE LIMITS ESTABLISHED BY OSHA, ACGIH, OR NIOSH.

PHYSICAL DATA

DESCRIPTION: WHITE OR YELLOWISH-WHITE AMORPHOUS POWDER OR GELATINOUS PIECES WITH AN AROMATIC ODOR AND A VERY BITTER TASTE. ***PH:*** ALKALINE

SOLUBILITY IN WATER: VERY SOLUBLE

SOLVENT SOLUBILITY: ALCOHOL, ACETONE, BENZENE, DIMETHYL SULFOXIDE

FIRE AND EXPLOSION DATA

FIRE AND EXPLOSION HAZARD: NEGLIGIBLE FIRE HAZARD WHEN EXPOSED TO HEAT OR FLAME.

FIREFIGHTING MEDIA: DRY CHEMICAL, CARBON DIOXIDE, HALON, WATER SPRAY OR STANDARD FOAM (1987 EMERGENCY RESPONSE GUIDEBOOK, DOT P 5800.4). FOR LARGER FIRES, USE WATER SPRAY, FOG OR STANDARD FOAM (1987 EMERGENCY RESPONSE GUIDEBOOK, DOT P 5800.4).

FIREFIGHTING: MOVE CONTAINER FROM FIRE AREA IF POSSIBLE. DO NOT SCATTER SPILLED MATERIAL WITH HIGH PRESSURE WATER STREAMS. DIKE FIRE CONTROL WATER FOR LATER DISPOSAL (1987 EMERGENCY RESPONSE GUIDEBOOK, DOT P 5800.4, GUIDE PAGE 31).

TOXICITY

ALKYL DIMETHYL ETHYLBENZYL AMMONIUM CHLORIDE: 2 MG EYE-RAT IRRITATION; 2 MG EYE-MOUSE SEVERE IRRITATION; 2 MG EYE-DOG IRRITATION; 2 MG EYE-RABBIT SEVERE IRRITATION; 8 UG EYE-RABBIT SEVERE IRRITATION; 10 MG EYE-RABBIT MILD IRRITATION; 2 MG EYE-GUINEA PIG IRRITATION; 2 MG EYE-HAMSTER SEVERE IRRITATION; 300 MG/KG ORAL-RAT LD50; 1420 MG/KG SKIN-RABBIT LD50; 150 MG/KG ORAL-MOUSE LD50; CARCINOGEN STATUS; NONE. ALKYL DIMETHYL ETHYLBENZYL AMMONIUM CHLORIDE IS A SEVERE EYE, MUCOUS MEMBRANE AND SKIN IRRITANT AND IS TOXIC.

HEALTH EFFECTS AND FIRST AID

INHALATION: ALKYL DIMETHYL ETHYLBENZYL AMMONIUM CHLORIDE: CORROSIVE.

ACUTE EXPOSURE- ALKYL DIMETHYL ETHYLBENZYL AMMONIUM CHLORIDE IS A BENZALKONIUM CHLORIDE. CONCENTRATIONS AS LOW AS 0.1-0.5% BENZALKONIUM CHLORIDE MAY BE IRRITATING TO MUCOUS MEMBRANES. STRONG AQUEOUS SOLUTIONS (10-20%) HAVE PRODUCED SUPERFICIAL NECROSIS OF THE MUCOUS MEMBRANES. **CHRONIC EXPOSURE-** PROLONGED OR REPEATED EXPOSURE MAY CAUSE EFFECTS AS THOSE LISTED IN ACUTE EXPOSURE. ASTHMA DUE TO OCCUPATIONAL EXPOSURE HAS BEEN REPORTED.

FIRST AID- REMOVE FROM EXPOSURE AREA TO FRESH AIR IMMEDIATELY. IF BREATHING HAS STOPPED, GIVE ARTIFICIAL RESPIRATION. MAINTAIN AIRWAY AND BLOOD PRESSURE AND ADMINISTER OXYGEN IF AVAILABLE. KEEP AFFECTED PERSON WARM AND AT REST. TREAT SYMPTOMATICALLY AND SUPPORTIVELY. ADMINISTRATION OF OXYGEN SHOULD BE PERFORMED BY QUALIFIED PERSONNEL. GET MEDICAL ATTENTION IMMEDIATELY.

SKIN CONTACT: ALKYL DIMETHYL ETHYLBENZYL AMMONIUM CHLORIDE: CORROSIVE.

ACUTE EXPOSURE- ALKYL DIMETHYL ETHYLBENZYL AMMONIUM CHLORIDE IS A BENZALKONIUM CHLORIDE WHICH MAY CAUSE SEVERE IRRITATION WITH REDNESS AND BURNS. CONCENTRATIONS OF AQUEOUS SOLUTIONS OF 10% OR LESS MAY BE IRRITATING. STRONGER SOLUTIONS HAVE PRODUCED SUPERFICIAL NECROSIS IN ANIMALS. A MODERATE DOSE OF ALKYL DIMETHYL ETHYLBENZYL AMMONIUM CHLORIDE WAS ABSORBED THROUGH RABBIT SKIN TO PRODUCE SOMNOLENCE, HEMORRHAGING AND DEATH. **CHRONIC EXPOSURE-** DEPENDING ON CONCENTRATION AND DURATION OF EXPOSURE, SYMPTOMS MAY BE AS THOSE OF ACUTE EXPOSURE. **FIRST AID-** REMOVE CONTAMINATED CLOTHING AND SHOES IMMEDIATELY. WASH AFFECTED AREA WITH SOAP OR MILD DETERGENT AND LARGE AMOUNTS OF WATER UNTIL NO EVIDENCE OF CHEMICAL REMAINS (AT LEAST 15-20 MINUTES). IN CASE OF CHEMICAL BURNS, COVER AREA WITH STERILE, DRY DRESSING. BANDAGE SECURELY, BUT NOT TOO TIGHTLY. GET MEDICAL ATTENTION IMMEDIATELY.

EYE CONTACT: ALKYL DIMETHYL ETHYLBENZYL AMMONIUM CHLORIDE: CORROSIVE. **ACUTE EXPOSURE**- ALKYL DIMETHYL ETHYLBENZYL AMMONIUM CHLORIDE IS A BENZALKONIUM CHLORIDE. BENZALKONIUM CHLORIDE HAS BEEN USED IN EYEDROPS OF CARBACHOL AND EPINEPHRINE TO INCREASE THE PENETRATION OF THESE DRUGS INTO THE EYE. FOR THIS APPLICATION BENZALKONIUM CHLORIDE HAS BEEN USED AT DILUTIONS OF 0.03% AND 0.025% AND A SINGLE DROP APPLIED TO HUMAN EYES CAUSED NO SENSATION OR INDICATION OF IRRITATION OR INJURY. A DROP OF A 0.1% CONCENTRATION TO HUMAN EYES CAUSED MILD DISCOMFORT WHICH PERSISTED FOR 2 TO 3 HOURS AS A SLIGHT, SCRATCHY, FOREIGN-BODY TYPE SENSATION. IRRIGATION OF THE SURFACE OF RABBIT EYES WITH A 0.1% SOLUTION FOR 15 MINUTES PRODUCED SEVERE INJURY OF THE ENDOTHELIUM AND MUCH SWELLING. HIGHER CONCENTRATIONS, SUCH AS 10%, HAVE CAUSED MORE EXTENSIVE AND SEVERE DAMAGE THE CORNEAS OF RABBIT EYES HAVE BECOME BLUE AND SWOLLEN, THEN COMPLETELY OPAQUE AND VASCULARIZED WITH THE FORMATION OF SCAR TISSUE OCCURRING AT THE 10% CONCENTRATION. **CHRONIC EXPOSURE**- APPLICATION 3 TO 4 TIMES DAILY FOR 2-8 WEEKS OF 0.03% AND 0.025% BENZALKONIUM CHLORIDE TO HUMAN EYES HAS BEEN NOTED TO CAUSE A "SANDY" SENSATION. A 0.1% CONCENTRATION APPLIED TO RABBIT EYES AS A DROP 2 TO 3 TIMES A DAY FOR 1 TO 3 MONTHS HAS CAUSED THICKENING AND ROUGHING OF THE CORNEAL EPITHELIUM, WITH SUPERFICIAL VASCULARIZATION, BUT NO DEEPER DAMAGE.

FIRST AID- WASH EYES IMMEDIATELY WITH LARGE AMOUNTS OF WATER, OCCASIONALLY LIFTING UPPER AND LOWER LIDS, UNTIL NO EVIDENCE OF CHEMICAL REMAINS (AT LEAST 15-20 MINUTES). CONTINUE IRRIGATING WITH NORMAL SALINE UNTIL THE PH HAS RETURNED TO NORMAL (30-60 MINUTES). COVER WITH STERILE BANDAGES. GET MEDICAL ATTENTION IMMEDIATELY.

INGESTION: ALKYL DIMETHYL ETHYLBENZYL AMMONIUM CHLORIDE: CORROSIVE/TOXIC. **ACUTE EXPOSURE**- A RELATIVELY LOW DOSE CAUSED SOMNOLENCE, HEMORRHAGING AND DEATH IN RATS. THIS SUBSTANCE IS A BENZALKONIUM CHLORIDE. INGESTION OF A CONCENTRATED SOLUTION OF BENZALKONIUM CHLORIDE MAY CAUSE IMMEDIATE BURNING PAIN IN THE MOUTH, THROAT, AND ABDOMEN, WITH PROFUSE SALIVATION. EXPOSED AREAS OF MUCOUS MEMBRANES MAY ULCERATE. STRONG AQUEOUS SOLUTIONS OF 10-20% COMMONLY PRODUCE SUPERFICIAL NECROSIS OF THE MUCOUS MEMBRANES. VOMITING MAY OCCUR, POSSIBLY WITH BLOOD. SIGNS OF CIRCULATORY SHOCK INCLUDING HYPOTENSION, LABORED BREATHING, AND CYANOSIS MAY OCCUR. RAPIDLY DEVELOPING APPREHENSION, RESTLESSNESS, CONFUSION, AND WEAKNESS MAY RESULT. WEAK CONVULSIVE MOVEMENTS MAY PRECEDE CENTRAL NERVOUS SYSTEM DEPRESSION. EROSION, ULCERATION AND PETECHIAL HEMORRHAGES MAY OCCUR THROUGHOUT THE SMALL INTESTINES. GLOTTIC, BRAIN, AND PULMONARY EDEMA HAVE BEEN REPORTED. THE MEAN LETHAL DOSE IS ESTIMATED TO BE BETWEEN 100 AND 700 MG/KG. DEATH MAY OCCUR WITHIN 1-2 HOURS AFTER INGESTION DUE TO ASPHYXIATION BECAUSE OF PARALYSIS OF THE MUSCLES OF RESPIRATION OR TO CARDIOVASCULAR COLLAPSE. EVEN IN PROMPT DEATH, CLOUDY SWELLING, PATCHY NECROSIS AND FATTY INFILTRATION OCCUR IN SUCH VISCERAL ORGANS AS HEART, LIVER, AND KIDNEYS. **CHRONIC EXPOSURE**- NO DATA AVAILABLE.

FIRST AID- GIVE MILK OR ACTIVATED CHARCOAL AND REMOVE BY CATHARSIS WITH FLEET'S PHOSPHO-SODA, 15-60 ML DILUTED 1:4 WITH WATER. LAVAGE AND EMESIS ARE CONTRAINDICATED IN THE PRESENCE OF ESOPHAGEAL INJURY. GASTRIC LAVAGE SHOULD BE PERFORMED BY QUALIFIED MEDICAL PERSONNEL. GET MEDICAL ATTENTION IMMEDIATELY (DREISBACH, HANDBOOK OF POISONING, 12TH ED.). MAINTAIN AIRWAY, BLOOD PRESSURE AND RESPIRATION.

REACTIVITY

REACTIVITY: STABLE UNDER NORMAL TEMPERATURES AND PRESSURES.

INCOMPATIBILITIES: ALKYL DIMETHYL ETHYLBENZYL AMMONIUM CHLORIDE: ALUMINUM: INCOMPATIBLE. BRASS: INCOMPATIBLE. COPPER: INCOMPATIBLE. BLACK IRON: INCOMPATIBLE. PLAIN STEEL: INCOMPATIBLE.

DECOMPOSITION: THERMAL DECOMPOSITION MAY RELEASE TOXIC AND/OR HAZARDOUS GASES.

POLYMERIZATION: HAZARDOUS POLYMERIZATION HAS NOT BEEN REPORTED TO OCCUR UNDER NORMAL TEMPERATURES AND PRESSURES.

CONDITIONS TO AVOID

MAY BURN BUT DOES NOT IGNITE READILY. AVOID CONTACT WITH STRONG OXIDIZERS, EXCESSIVE HEAT, SPARKS, OR OPEN FLAME.

SPILL AND LEAK PROCEDURES

OCCUPATIONAL SPILL: STOP LEAK IF YOU CAN DO IT WITHOUT RISK. FOR SMALL SPILLS, TAKE UP WITH SAND OR OTHER ABSORBENT MATERIAL AND PLACE INTO CLEAN, DRY CONTAINERS FOR LATER DISPOSAL. KEEP UNNECESSARY PEOPLE AWAY. ISOLATE HAZARD AREA AND DENY ENTRY.

PROTECTIVE EQUIPMENT

VENTILATION: PROVIDE LOCAL EXHAUST OR PROCESS ENCLOSURE VENTILATION TO MEET PUBLISHED EXPOSURE LIMITS.

RESPIRATOR: THE FOLLOWING RESPIRATORS ARE RECOMMENDED BASED ON INFORMATION FOUND IN THE PHYSICAL DATA, TOXICITY AND HEALTH EFFECTS SECTIONS. THEY ARE RANKED IN ORDER FROM MINIMUM TO MAXIMUM RESPIRATORY PROTECTION. THE SPECIFIC RESPIRATOR SELECTED MUST BE BASED ON CONTAMINATION LEVELS FOUND IN THE WORK PLACE, MUST NOT EXCEED THE WORKING LIMITS OF THE RESPIRATOR AND BE JOINTLY APPROVED BY THE NATIONAL INSTITUTE FOR OCCUPATIONAL SAFETY AND HEALTH AND THE MINE SAFETY AND HEALTH ADMINISTRATION (NIOSH-MSHA).

DUST AND MIST RESPIRATOR WITH A FULL FACEPIECE.

AIR-PURIFYING FULL FACEPIECE RESPIRATOR WITH A HIGH-EFFICIENCY PARTICULATE FILTER.

POWERED AIR-PURIFYING RESPIRATOR WITH A TIGHT-FITTING FACEPIECE AND HIGH-EFFICIENCY PARTICULATE FILTER.

TYPE 'C' SUPPLIED-AIR RESPIRATOR WITH A FULL FACEPIECE OPERATED IN PRESSURE-DEMAND OR OTHER POSITIVE PRESSURE MODE OR WITH A FULL FACEPIECE, HELMET OR HOOD OPERATED IN CONTINUOUS-FLOW MODE.

SELF-CONTAINED BREATHING APPARATUS WITH A FULL FACEPIECE OPERATED IN PRESSURE-DEMAND OR OTHER POSITIVE PRESSURE MODE.

FOR FIREFIGHTING AND OTHER IMMEDIATELY DANGEROUS TO LIFE OR HEALTH CONDITIONS:

SELF-CONTAINED BREATHING APPARATUS WITH FULL FACEPIECE OPERATED IN PRESSURE-DEMAND OR OTHER POSITIVE PRESSURE MODE.

SUPPLIED-AIR RESPIRATOR WITH FULL FACEPIECE AND OPERATED IN PRESSURE-DEMAND OR OTHER POSITIVE PRESSURE MODE IN COMBINATION WITH AN AUXILIARY SELF-CONTAINED BREATHING APPARATUS OPERATED IN PRESSURE-DEMAND OR OTHER POSITIVE PRESSURE MODE.

CLOTHING: EMPLOYEE MUST WEAR APPROPRIATE PROTECTIVE (IMPERVIOUS) CLOTHING AND EQUIPMENT TO PREVENT ANY POSSIBILITY OF SKIN CONTACT WITH THIS SUBSTANCE.

GLOVES: EMPLOYEE MUST WEAR APPROPRIATE PROTECTIVE GLOVES TO PREVENT CONTACT WITH THIS SUBSTANCE.

EYE PROTECTION: EMPLOYEE MUST WEAR SPLASH-PROOF OR DUST-RESISTANT SAFETY GOGGLES AND A FACESHIELD TO PREVENT CONTACT WITH THIS SUBSTANCE.

EMERGENCY WASH FACILITIES: WHERE THERE IS ANY POSSIBILITY THAT AN EMPLOYEE'S EYES AND/OR SKIN MAY BE EXPOSED TO THIS SUBSTANCE, THE EMPLOYER SHOULD PROVIDE AN EYE WASH FOUNTAIN AND QUICK DRENCH SHOWER WITHIN THE IMMEDIATE WORK AREA FOR EMERGENCY USE.

AUTHORIZED BY- OCCUPATIONAL HEALTH SERVICES, INC.

CREATION DATE: 10/04/89 ***REVISION DATE:*** 05/25/90

MATERIAL SAFETY DATA SHEET

OCCUPATIONAL HEALTH SERVICES, INC.	EMERGENCY CONTACT:
AGRICULTURE AND PESTICIDE DIVISION	JOHN S. BRANSFORD, JR. (615) 292-1180
450 SEVENTH AVENUE, SUITE 2407	
NEW YORK, NEW YORK 10123	
1-800-445-MSDS OR (212) 967-1100	

SUBSTANCE IDENTIFICATION

CAS-NUMBER 584-79-2

SUBSTANCE: **ALLETHRIN**

TRADE NAMES/SYNONYMS: 2,2-DIMETHYL-3-(2-METHYL-1-PROPENYL) CYCLOPROPANECARBOXYLIC ACID, 2-METHYL-4-OXO-3-(2-PROPENYL)-2-CYCLOPENTEN-1-YL ESTER; 2,2-DIMETHYL-3-(2-METHYLPROPENYL)-CYCLOPROPANECARBOXYLIC ACID, ESTER WITH 2-ALLYL-4-HYDROXY-3-METHYL-2-CYCLOPENTEN-1-ONE; 2-ALLYL-4-HYDROXY-3-METHYL-2-CYCLOPENTEN-1-ONE ESTER OF CHRYSANTHEMUMMONOCARBOXYLIC ACID; 2-METHYL-4-OXO-3-(2-CYCLOPENTEN-1-YL 2,2-DIMETHYL-3-(2-METHYL-1 -PROPENYL) CYCLOPROPANE CARBOXYLATE; (RS)-3-ALLYL-2-METHYL-4-OXOCYCLOPENT-2-ENYL(RS)-CIS/TRANS CHRYSANTHEMATE; ALLETHRONYL D,1-CIS,TRANS CHRYSANTHEMATE; D-ALLETHRIN; TRANS-ALLETHRIN; ALLYL CINERIN I; CINERIN I ALLYL HOMOLOG; BIOALLETHRIN; PYNAMIN; NIA 249; ENT 17,510; PST00550

CHEMICAL FAMILY: PYRETHROID (SYNTHETIC)

MOLECULAR FORMULA: C19-H26-O3

MOLECULAR WEIGHT: 302.45

CERCLA RATINGS (SCALE 0-3): HEALTH=3 FIRE=U REACTIVITY=0 PERSISTENCE=0

NFPA RATINGS (SCALE 0-4): HEALTH=3 FIRE=U REACTIVITY=0

COMPONENTS AND CONTAMINANTS

COMPONENT: ALLETHRIN ***PERCENT:*** 100
CAS# 584-79-2
OTHER CONTAMINANTS: NONE
EXPOSURE LIMITS: NO OCCUPATIONAL EXPOSURE LIMITS ESTABLISHED BY OSHA, ACGIH, OR NIOSH.

PHYSICAL DATA

DESCRIPTION: CLEAR, AMBER-COLORED VISCOUS LIQUID ***BOILING POINT:*** 320 F (160 C)
SPECIFIC GRAVITY: 1.005-1.015 ***EVAPORATION RATE:*** NOT AVAILABLE
SOLUBILITY IN WATER: INSOLUBLE
SOLVENT SOLUBILITY: ALCOHOL, KEROSENE, CARBON TETRACHLORIDE, NITROMETHANE, PETROLEUM ETHER, ETHYLENE DICHLORIDE, MOST ORGANIC SOLVENTS; MISCIBLE IN PETROLEUM OILS

FIRE AND EXPLOSION DATA

FIRE AND EXPLOSION HAZARD: UNKNOWN FIRE AND EXPLOSION HAZARD.
FIREFIGHTING MEDIA: DRY CHEMICAL, CARBON DIOXIDE, HALON, WATER SPRAY OR STANDARD FOAM (1987 EMERGENCY RESPONSE GUIDEBOOK, DOT P 5800.4). FOR LARGER FIRES, USE WATER SPRAY, FOG OR STANDARD FOAM (1987 EMERGENCY RESPONSE GUIDEBOOK, DOT P 5800.4).
FIREFIGHTING: MOVE CONTAINERS FROM FIRE AREA IF POSSIBLE. FIGHT FIRE FROM MAXIMUM DISTANCE. STAY AWAY FROM STORAGE TANK ENDS. DIKE FIRE CONTROL WATER FOR LATER DISPOSAL. DO NOT SCATTER MATERIAL (1987 EMERGENCY RESPONSE GUIDEBOOK, DOT P 5800.4, GUIDE PAGE 55). EXTINGUISH ONLY IF FLOW CAN BE STOPPED; USE FLOODING AMOUNTS OF WATER AS FOG, SOLID STREAMS MAY BE INEFFECTIVE. COOL CONTAINERS WITH FLOODING AMOUNTS OF WATER, APPLY FROM AS FAR A DISTANCE AS POSSIBLE. USE ALCOHOL FOAM, CARBON DIOXIDE OR DRY CHEMICAL. AVOID BREATHING TOXIC VAPORS, KEEP UPWIND.

TRANSPORTATION DATA

DEPARTMENT OF TRANSPORTATION HAZARD CLASSIFICATION 49 CFR 172.101: ORM-A
DEPARTMENT OF TRANSPORTATION LABELING REQUIREMENTS 49 CFR 172.101 AND SUBPART E: NONE
DEPARTMENT OF TRANSPORTATION PACKAGING REQUIREMENTS: 49 CFR 173.510 EXCEPTIONS: 49 CFR 173.505

TOXICITY

ALLETHRIN: TOXICITY DATA: 13,800 MG/M3/4 HOURS INHALATION-RAT LCLO; 11,332 MG/KG SKIN-RABBIT LD50; 860 MG/KG ORAL-RAT LD50; 370 MG/KG ORAL-MOUSE LD50; 4290 MG/KG ORAL-RABBIT LD50; 4 MG/KG INTRAVENOUS-RAT LDLO; 38 MG/KG INTRAPERITONEAL-MOUSE LD50; 11200 MG/KG INTRAPERITONEAL-RABBIT LD50; 4 MG/KG INTRACEREBRAL-MOUSE LDLO; 680 MG/KG UNREPORTED-RAT LD50; MUTAGENIC DATA (RTECS). CARCINOGEN STATUS: NONE. ACUTE TOXICITY LEVEL: MODERATELY TOXIC BY DERMAL ABSORPTION AND INGESTION. TARGET EFFECTS: CENTRAL NERVOUS SYSTEM STIMULANT. AT INCREASED RISK FROM EXPOSURE: PERSONS SENSITIVE TO RAGWEED POLLEN.

HEALTH EFFECTS AND FIRST AID

INHALATION: ALLETHRIN: **ACUTE EXPOSURE-** A HEAVY EXPOSURE TO ALLETHRIN MIST PRODUCED HYPERSENSITIVITY, MOTOR ATAXIA AND URINARY INCONTINENCE IN RATS AND MICE. CONCENTRATIONS GREATER THAN 2000 MG/KG FOR 2 HOURS CAUSED DEATH IN HALF OF THE ANIMALS TESTED. SYSTEMIC POISONING MAY OCCUR AS DETAILED IN ACUTE INGESTION. ALLERGIC ATTACKS IN SENSITIVE INDIVIDUALS MANIFESTED BY ASTHMA, VASOMOTOR RHINITIS AND ANAPHYLACTOID REACTIONS HAVE BEEN REPORTED DUE TO PYRETHRINS. HOWEVER, SYNTHETIC PYRETHROIDS ARE LESS LIKELY TO PRODUCE ALLERGIC REACTIONS. **CHRONIC EXPOSURE-** IN ONE STUDY OF ALLETHRIN, CHRONIC EXPOSURE OF RATS AND MICE TO MIST PREPARATIONS OF 123 MG/M3/3 HOURS 5 DAYS A WEEK FOR 4 WEEKS PRODUCED SOME UNSPECIFIED SYSTEMIC EFFECTS WITHOUT ANY ADVERSE EFFECTS ON THE MAJOR ORGANS AND TISSUES.
FIRST AID- REMOVE FROM EXPOSURE AREA TO FRESH AIR IMMEDIATELY. IF BREATHING HAS STOPPED, PERFORM ARTIFICIAL RESPIRATION. KEEP PERSON WARM AND AT REST. TREAT SYMPTOMATICALLY AND SUPPORTIVELY. GET MEDICAL ATTENTION IMMEDIATELY.

SKIN CONTACT: ALLETHRIN: **ACUTE EXPOSURE-** PARESTHESIA OF THE FACE HAS BEEN REPORTED WITH NUMBNESS, ITCHING, BURING, TINGLING AND WARMTH WITHOUT ANY DERMATITIS FOLLOWING DIRECT CONTACT OF SYNTHETIC PYRETHRINS WITH THE SKIN. THE EFFECT GENERALLY TAKES PLACE AFTER 1 HOUR AND MAY LAST FOR 24 HOURS. CONTACT WITH PYRETHRINS MAY CAUSE ALLERGIC ATTACKS IN SENSITIVE INDIVIDUALS MANIFESTED BY SEVERE DERMATITIS. HOWEVER, SYNTHETIC PYRETHROIDS ARE LESS LIKELY TO CAUSE ALLERGIC REACTIONS. **CHRONIC EXPOSURE-** NO DATA AVAILABLE.
FIRST AID- REMOVE CONTAMINATED CLOTHING AND SHOES IMMEDIATELY. WASH AFFECTED AREA WITH SOAP OR MILD DETERGENT AND LARGE AMOUNTS OF WATER UNTIL NO EVIDENCE OF CHEMICAL REMAINS (APPROXIMATELY 15-20 MINUTES). GET MEDICAL ATTENTION IMMEDIATELY.

EYE CONTACT: ALLETHRIN: **ACUTE EXPOSURE-** MASSIVE INSTILLATION OF ALLETHRIN INTO RABBIT EYES PRODUCED A SLIGHT, TRANSIENT CONGESTION OF CONJUNCTIVA OR LACRIMATION. **CHRONIC EXPOSURE-** NO DATA AVAILABLE.
FIRST AID- WASH EYES IMMEDIATELY WITH LARGE AMOUNTS OF WATER OR NORMAL SALINE, OCCASIONALLY LIFTING UPPER AND LOWER LIDS, UNTIL NO EVIDENCE OF CHEMICAL REMAINS (APPROXIMATELY 15-20 MINUTES). GET MEDICAL ATTENTION IMMEDIATELY.

INGESTION: ALLETHRIN: TOXIC. **ACUTE EXPOSURE-** INGESTION OF PYRETHRINS MAY CAUSE CENTRAL NERVOUS SYSTEM STIMULATION IN ANIMALS WITH NAUSEA, VOMITING, GASTROENTERITIS WITH DIARRHEA, HYPEREXCITABILITY, INCOORDINATION, TREMORS, CONVULSIVE TWITCHING, CONVULSIONS, BLOODY TEARS, URINARY INCONTINENCE, HYPERSENSITIVITY, MUSCULAR PARALYSIS, PROSTRATION AND COMA. LARGE DOSES ADMINISTERED TO GERBILS PRODUCED HYPERGLYCEMIA, REDUCED GLUCOSE TOLERENCE AND A REDUCTION IN TOTAL SERUM PROTEINS. DEATH IS DUE TO RESPIRATORY FAILURE. **CHRONIC EXPOSURE-** A DOSAGE OF 50 MG/KG BODY WEIGHT OF ALLETHRIN PER DAY FOR 2 YEARS PRODUCED NO DETECTABLE EFFECT IN THE DOG. SUBACUTE AND CHRONIC FEEDINGS OF LARGE AMOUNTS OF PYRETHROIDS TO RATS PRODUCED INCREASED LIVER AND KIDNEY WEIGHTS, LIVER SIZE, A HEPATIC LESIONS AND BILE DUCT HYPERPLASIA.
FIRST AID- REMOVE BY GASTRIC LAVAGE AND CATHARSIS. MAINTAIN BLOOD PRESSURE AND AIRWAY. GIVE OXYGEN IF RESPIRATION IS DEPRESSED. DO NOT PERFORM GASTRIC LAVAGE IF VICTIM IS UNCONSCIOUS. GET MEDICAL ATTENTION IMMEDIATELY (DREISBACH, HANDBOOK OF POISONING, 12TH ED.). ADMINISTRATION OF LAVAGE OR OXYGEN SHOULD BE PERFORMED BY QUALIFIED MEDICAL PERSONNEL.
ANTIDOTE: NO SPECIFIC ANTIDOTE. TREAT SYMPTOMATICALLY AND SUPPORTIVELY.

REACTIVITY

REACTIVITY: MAY DECOMPOSE UPON EXPOSURE TO HEAT OR LIGHT.
INCOMPATIBILITIES: ALLETHRIN: ALKALIES: INCOMPATIBLE.
DECOMPOSITION: THERMAL DECOMPOSITION MAY RELEASE TOXIC AND/OR HAZARDOUS GASES.
POLYMERIZATION: HAZARDOUS POLYMERIZATION HAS NOT BEEN REPORTED TO OCCUR UNDER NORMAL TEMPERATURES AND PRESSURES.

STORAGE AND DISPOSAL

OBSERVE ALL FEDERAL, STATE AND LOCAL REGULATIONS WHEN STORING OR DISPOSING OF THIS SUBSTANCE. FOR ASSISTANCE, CONTACT THE DISTRICT DIRECTOR OF THE ENVIRONMENTAL PROTECTION AGENCY.

STORAGE

STORE IN ACCORDANCE WITH 40 CFR 165 RECOMMENDED PROCEDURES FOR THE DISPOSAL AND STORAGE OF PESTICIDES AND PESTICIDE CONTAINERS. STORE AWAY FROM INCOMPATIBLE SUBSTANCES.

DISPOSAL

DISPOSAL MUST BE IN ACCORDANCE WITH 40 CFR 165 RECOMMENDED PROCEDURES FOR THE DISPOSAL AND STORAGE OF PESTICIDES AND PESTICIDE CONTAINERS.

CONDITIONS TO AVOID

NONE REPORTED.

SPILL AND LEAK PROCEDURES

OCCUPATIONAL SPILL: DO NOT TOUCH SPILLED MATERIAL. STOP LEAK IF YOU CAN DO IT WITHOUT RISK. USE WATER SPRAY TO REDUCE VAPORS. FOR SMALL SPILLS, TAKE UP WITH SAND OR OTHER ABSORBENT MATERIAL AND PLACE INTO CONTAINERS FOR LATER DISPOSAL. FOR SMALL DRY SPILLS, WITH A CLEAN SHOVEL PLACE MATERIAL INTO CLEAN, DRY CONTAINERS AND COVER. MOVE CONTAINERS FROM SPILL AREA. FOR LARGER SPILLS, DIKE FAR AHEAD OF SPILL FOR LATER DISPOSAL. KEEP UNNECESSARY PEOPLE AWAY. ISOLATE HAZARD AREA AND DENY ENTRY. VENTILATE CLOSED SPACES BEFORE ENTERING.

PROTECTIVE EQUIPMENT

VENTILATION: PROVIDE LOCAL EXHAUST OR PROCESS ENCLOSURE VENTILATION SYSTEM.

RESPIRATOR: THE FOLLOWING RESPIRATORS ARE RECOMMENDED BASED ON INFORMATION FOUND IN THE PHYSICAL DATA, TOXICITY AND HEALTH EFFECTS SECTIONS. THEY ARE RANKED IN ORDER FROM MINIMUM TO MAXIMUM RESPIRATORY PROTECTION. THE SPECIFIC RESPIRATOR SELECTED MUST BE BASED ON CONTAMINATION LEVELS FOUND IN THE WORK PLACE, MUST NOT EXCEED THE WORKING LIMITS OF THE RESPIRATOR AND BE JOINTLY APPROVED BY THE NATIONAL INSTITUTE FOR OCCUPATIONAL SAFETY AND HEALTH AND THE MINE SAFETY AND HEALTH ADMINISTRATION (NIOSH-MSHA).

CHEMICAL CARTRIDGE RESPIRATOR WITH PESTICIDE CARTRIDGE.

GAS MASK WITH A PESTICIDE CANISTER (CHIN-STYLE OR FRONT- OR BACK-MOUNTED CANISTER).

TYPE 'C' SUPPLIED-AIR RESPIRATOR OPERATED IN THE PRESSURE-DEMAND OR OTHER POSITIVE PRESSURE OR CONTINUOUS-FLOW MODE.

SELF-CONTAINED BREATHING APPARATUS.

FOR FIREFIGHTING AND OTHER IMMEDIATELY DANGEROUS TO LIFE OR HEALTH CONDITIONS:

SELF-CONTAINED BREATHING APPARATUS WITH FULL FACEPIECE OPERATED IN PRESSURE-DEMAND OR OTHER POSITIVE PRESSURE MODE.

SUPPLIED-AIR RESPIRATOR WITH FULL FACEPIECE AND OPERATED IN PRESSURE-DEMAND OR OTHER POSITIVE PRESSURE MODE IN COMBINATION WITH AN AUXILIARY SELF-CONTAINED BREATHING APPARATUS OPERATED IN PRESSURE-DEMAND OR OTHER POSITIVE PRESSURE MODE.

CLOTHING: EMPLOYEE MUST WEAR APPROPRIATE PROTECTIVE (IMPERVIOUS) CLOTHING AND EQUIPMENT TO PREVENT REPEATED OR PROLONGED SKIN CONTACT WITH THIS SUBSTANCE.

GLOVES: EMPLOYEE MUST WEAR APPROPRIATE PROTECTIVE GLOVES TO PREVENT CONTACT WITH THIS SUBSTANCE.

EYE PROTECTION: EMPLOYEE MUST WEAR SPLASH-PROOF OR DUST-RESISTANT SAFETY GOGGLES TO PREVENT EYE CONTACT WITH THIS SUBSTANCE.

EMERGENCY EYE WASH: WHERE THERE IS ANY POSSIBILITY THAT AN EMPLOYEE'S EYES MAY BE EXPOSED TO THIS SUBSTANCE, THE EMPLOYER SHOULD PROVIDE AN EYE WASH FOUNTAIN WITHIN THE IMMEDIATE WORK AREA FOR EMERGENCY USE.

AUTHORIZED BY- OCCUPATIONAL HEALTH SERVICES, INC.

CREATION DATE: 10/04/89 ***REVISION DATE:*** 05/18/90

MATERIAL SAFETY DATA SHEET

OCCUPATIONAL HEALTH SERVICES, INC.
AGRICULTURE AND PESTICIDE DIVISION
450 SEVENTH AVENUE, SUITE 2407
NEW YORK, NEW YORK 10123
1-800-445-MSDS OR (212) 967-1100

EMERGENCY CONTACT:
JOHN S. BRANSFORD, JR. (615) 292-1180

SUBSTANCE IDENTIFICATION

CAS-NUMBER 34624-48-1

SUBSTANCE: CIS-ALLETHRIN

TRADE NAMES/SYNONYMS: 2,2-DIMETHYL-3-(2-METHYL-1-PROPENYL)-CYCLOPROPANECARBOXYLIC ACID, 2-METHYL-4-OXO-3-(2-PROPENYL)-2-CYCLOPENTEN-1-YL ESTER; (+)-(Z)-2,2-DIMETHYL-3-(2-METHYLPROPENYL)-CYCLOPROPANECARBOXYLIC ACID, ESTER WITH 2-ALLYL-4-HYDROXY-3-METHYL-2-CYCLOPENTEN-1-ONE; (+)-CIS-ALLETHRIN; PST00551

CHEMICAL FAMILY: PYRETHROID (SYNTHETIC)

MOLECULAR FORMULA: C19-H26-O3

MOLECULAR WEIGHT: 302.45

CERCLA RATINGS (SCALE 0-3): HEALTH=3 FIRE=U REACTIVITY=0 PERSISTENCE=0

NFPA RATINGS (SCALE 0-4): HEALTH=3 FIRE=U REACTIVITY=0

COMPONENTS AND CONTAMINANTS

COMPONENT: CIS-ALLETHRIN ***PERCENT:*** 100
CAS# 34624-48-1

OTHER CONTAMINANTS: NONE

EXPOSURE LIMITS: NO OCCUPATIONAL EXPOSURE LIMITS ESTABLISHED BY OSHA, ACGIH, OR NIOSH.

PHYSICAL DATA

DESCRIPTION: VISCOUS LIQUID ***BOILING POINT:*** NOT AVAILABLE

SPECIFIC GRAVITY: NOT AVAILABLE ***EVAPORATION RATE:*** NOT AVAILABLE

SOLUBILITY IN WATER: INSOLUBLE

SOLVENT SOLUBILITY: ACETONE, BENZENE, ETHANOL, HEXANE, REFINED KEROSENE, ISOPARAFFINIC SOLVENTS, ORGANIC SOLVENTS

FIRE AND EXPLOSION DATA

FIRE AND EXPLOSION HAZARD: UNKNOWN FIRE AND EXPLOSION HAZARD.

FIREFIGHTING MEDIA: DRY CHEMICAL, CARBON DIOXIDE, HALON, WATER SPRAY OR STANDARD FOAM (1987 EMERGENCY RESPONSE GUIDEBOOK, DOT P 5800.4). FOR LARGER FIRES, USE WATER SPRAY, FOG OR STANDARD FOAM (1987 EMERGENCY RESPONSE GUIDEBOOK, DOT P 5800.4).

FIREFIGHTING: MOVE CONTAINERS FROM FIRE AREA IF POSSIBLE. FIGHT FIRE FROM MAXIMUM DISTANCE. STAY AWAY FROM STORAGE TANK ENDS. DIKE FIRE CONTROL WATER FOR LATER DISPOSAL. DO NOT SCATTER MATERIAL (1987 EMERGENCY RESPONSE GUIDEBOOK, DOT P 5800.4, GUIDE PAGE 55). EXTINGUISH ONLY IF FLOW CAN BE STOPPED; USE FLOODING AMOUNTS OF WATER AS FOG, SOLID STREAMS MAY BE INEFFECTIVE. COOL CONTAINERS WITH FLOODING AMOUNTS OF WATER, APPLY FROM AS FAR A DISTANCE AS POSSIBLE. USE ALCOHOL FOAM, CARBON DIOXIDE OR DRY CHEMICAL. AVOID BREATHING TOXIC VAPORS, KEEP UPWIND.

TRANSPORTATION DATA

DEPARTMENT OF TRANSPORTATION HAZARD CLASSIFICATION 49 CFR 172.101: ORM-A

DEPARTMENT OF TRANSPORTATION LABELING REQUIREMENTS 49 CFR 172.101 AND SUBPART E: NONE

DEPARTMENT OF TRANSPORTATION PACKAGING REQUIREMENTS: 49 CFR 173.510 EXCEPTIONS: 49 CFR 173.505

TOXICITY

CIS-ALLETHRIN: 260 MG/M3/2 HOURS INHALATION-MOUSE LCLO; 260 MG/M3/2 HOURS INHALATION-RAT LCLO; 210 MG/KG ORAL-MOUSE LD50; CARCINOGEN STATUS: NONE. CIS-ALLETHRIN IS TOXIC AND A CENTRAL NERVOUS SYSTEM STIMULANT IN ANIMALS.

HEALTH EFFECTS AND FIRST AID

INHALATION: CIS-ALLETHRIN: **ACUTE EXPOSURE-** CIS-ALLETHRIN IS A SYNTHETIC PYRETHRIN. SYNTHETIC PYRETHRINS, LIKE THE NATURAL PYRETHRINS, PRODUCE CENTRAL NERVOUS SYSTEM STIMULATION IN ANIMALS WITH SYMPTOMS OF NAUSEA, VOMITING, GASTROENTERITIS WITH DIARRHEA, HYPERSENSITIVITY, INCOORDINATION, TREMORS, MUSCULAR PARALYSIS, CONVULSION, COMA, AND DEATH DUE TO RESPIRATORY FAILURE. UNLIKE NATURAL PYRETHRINS, SYNTHETIC PYRETHRINS NORMALLY DO NOT PRODUCE ALLERGIC REACTIONS IN HUMANS. **CHRONIC EXPOSURE-** NO DATA AVAILABLE.

FIRST AID- REMOVE FROM EXPOSURE AREA TO FRESH AIR IMMEDIATELY. IF BREATHING HAS STOPPED, PERFORM ARTIFICIAL RESPIRATION. KEEP PERSON WARM AND AT REST. TREAT SYMPTOMATICALLY AND SUPPORTIVELY. GET MEDICAL ATTENTION IMMEDIATELY.

SKIN CONTACT: CIS-ALLETHRIN: ACUTE EXPSOURE- CIS-ALLETHRIN IS A SYNTHETIC PYRETHRIN. SYNTHETIC PYRETHRINS ARE NOT IRRITANTS TO RABBIT SKIN AND THE TOXICITY FROM DERMAL ABSORPTION IS USUALLY MODERATE TO LOW. UNLIKE NATURAL PYRETHRINS, SYNTHETIC PYRETHRINS NORMALLY DO NOT PRODUCE ALLERGIC REACTIONS IN HUMANS. HOWEVER, THERE HAVE BEEN SOME REPORTS OF CUTANEOUS PARESTHESIAS AMONG OCCUPATIONALLY EXPOSED INDIVIDUALS. THESE INDIVIDUALS COMPLAINED OF TINGLING, BURNING AND STINGING SENSATIONS ON THE EXPOSED SURFACE OF THE SKIN BEGINNING FROM 30 MINUTES TO 3 HOURS AFTER EXPOSURE. THE DURATION OF SYMPTOMS VARIED FROM 30 MINUTES TO 8 HOURS. **CHRONIC EXPOSURE-** NO DATA AVAILABLE.

FIRST AID- REMOVE CONTAMINATED CLOTHING AND SHOES IMMEDIATELY. WASH AFFECTED AREA WITH SOAP OR MILD DETERGENT AND LARGE AMOUNTS OF WATER UNTIL NO EVIDENCE OF CHEMICAL REMAINS (APPROXIMATELY 15-20 MINUTES). GET MEDICAL ATTENTION IMMEDIATELY.

EYE CONTACT: CIS-ALLETHRIN: **ACUTE EXPOSURE-** MASSIVE INSTILLATION OF ALLETHRIN INTO RABBIT EYES PRODUCED A SLIGHT, TRANSIENT CONGESTION OF CONJUNCTIVA OR LACRIMATION BUT THE EFFECT WAS NOT SEVERE ENOUGH TO BE CONSIDERED AN IRRITANT. **CHRONIC EXPOSURE-** NO DATA AVAILABLE.

FIRST AID- WASH EYES IMMEDIATELY WITH LARGE AMOUNTS OF WATER OR NORMAL SALINE, OCCASIONALLY LIFTING UPPER AND LOWER LIDS, UNTIL NO EVIDENCE OF CHEMICAL REMAINS (APPROXIMATELY 15-20 MINUTES). GET MEDICAL ATTENTION IMMEDIATELY.

INGESTION: CIS-ALLETHRIN: TOXIC. **ACUTE EXPOSURE-** A LOW DOSE OF CIS-ALLETHRIN WAS LETHAL IN MICE. CIS-ALLETHRIN IS A SYNTHETIC PYRETHRIN. SYNTHETIC PYRETHRINS, LIKE THE NATURAL PYRETHRINS, PRODUCE CENTRAL NERVOUS SYSTEM STIMULATION IN ANIMALS WITH SYMPTOMS OF NAUSEA,

VOMITING, GASTROENTERITIS WITH DIARRHEA, HYPERSENSITIVITY, INCOORDINATION, TREMORS, MUSCULAR PARALYSIS, CONVULSION, COMA, AND DEATH DUE TO RESPIRATORY FAILURE. **CHRONIC EXPOSURE-** INCREASED LIVER AND KIDNEY WEIGHTS WERE NOTED IN ANIMALS CHRONICALLY FED SYNTHETIC PYRETHRINS.

FIRST AID- TREAT SYMPTOMATICALLY AND SUPPORTIVELY. GET MEDICAL ATTENTION IMMEDIATELY. IF VOMITING OCCURS, KEEP HEAD LOWER THAN HIPS TO PREVENT ASPIRATION.

ANTIDOTE: NO SPECIFIC ANTIDOTE. TREAT SYMPTOMATICALLY AND SUPPORTIVELY.

REACTIVITY

REACTIVITY: MAY DECOMPOSE UPON EXPOSURE TO HEAT OR LIGHT.

INCOMPATIBILITIES: CIS-ALLETHRIN: ALKALIES: INCOMPATIBLE.

DECOMPOSITION: THERMAL DECOMPOSITION MAY RELEASE TOXIC AND/OR HAZARDOUS GASES.

POLYMERIZATION: HAZARDOUS POLYMERIZATION HAS NOT BEEN REPORTED TO OCCUR UNDER NORMAL TEMPERATURES AND PRESSURES.

STORAGE AND DISPOSAL

OBSERVE ALL FEDERAL, STATE AND LOCAL REGULATIONS WHEN STORING OR DISPOSING OF THIS SUBSTANCE. FOR ASSISTANCE, CONTACT THE DISTRICT DIRECTOR OF THE ENVIRONMENTAL PROTECTION AGENCY.

STORAGE

STORE IN ACCORDANCE WITH 40 CFR 165 RECOMMENDED PROCEDURES FOR THE DISPOSAL AND STORAGE OF PESTICIDES AND PESTICIDE CONTAINERS.

STORE AWAY FROM INCOMPATIBLE SUBSTANCES.

DISPOSAL

DISPOSAL MUST BE IN ACCORDANCE WITH 40 CFR 165 RECOMMENDED PROCEDURES FOR THE DISPOSAL AND STORAGE OF PESTICIDES AND PESTICIDE CONTAINERS.

CONDITIONS TO AVOID

MAY BURN BUT DOES NOT IGNITE READILY. CONTAINERS MAY EXPLODE IN HEAT OF FIRE.

SPILL AND LEAK PROCEDURES

OCCUPATIONAL SPILL: DO NOT TOUCH SPILLED MATERIAL. STOP LEAK IF YOU CAN DO IT WITHOUT RISK. USE WATER SPRAY TO REDUCE VAPORS. FOR SMALL SPILLS, TAKE UP WITH SAND OR OTHER ABSORBENT MATERIAL AND PLACE INTO CONTAINERS FOR LATER DISPOSAL. FOR SMALL DRY SPILLS, WITH A CLEAN SHOVEL PLACE MATERIAL INTO CLEAN, DRY CONTAINERS AND COVER. MOVE CONTAINERS FROM SPILL AREA. FOR LARGER SPILLS, DIKE FAR AHEAD OF SPILL FOR LATER DISPOSAL. KEEP UNNECESSARY PEOPLE AWAY. ISOLATE HAZARD AREA AND DENY ENTRY. VENTILATE CLOSED SPACES BEFORE ENTERING.

PROTECTIVE EQUIPMENT

VENTILATION: PROVIDE LOCAL EXHAUST OR PROCESS ENCLOSURE VENTILATION SYSTEM.

RESPIRATOR: THE FOLLOWING RESPIRATORS ARE RECOMMENDED BASED ON INFORMATION FOUND IN THE PHYSICAL DATA, TOXICITY AND HEALTH EFFECTS SECTIONS. THEY ARE RANKED IN ORDER FROM MINIMUM TO MAXIMUM RESPIRATORY PROTECTION. THE SPECIFIC RESPIRATOR SELECTED MUST BE BASED ON CONTAMINATION LEVELS FOUND IN THE WORK PLACE, MUST NOT EXCEED THE WORKING LIMITS OF THE RESPIRATOR AND BE JOINTLY APPROVED BY THE NATIONAL INSTITUTE FOR OCCUPATIONAL SAFETY AND HEALTH AND THE MINE SAFETY AND HEALTH ADMINISTRATION (NIOSH-MSHA).

CHEMICAL CARTRIDGE RESPIRATOR WITH PESTICIDE CARTRIDGE.

GAS MASK WITH A PESTICIDE CANISTER (CHIN-STYLE OR FRONT- OR BACK-MOUNTED CANISTER).

TYPE 'C' SUPPLIED-AIR RESPIRATOR OPERATED IN THE PRESSURE-DEMAND OR OTHER POSITIVE PRESSURE OR CONTINUOUS-FLOW MODE.

SELF-CONTAINED BREATHING APPARATUS.

FOR FIREFIGHTING AND OTHER IMMEDIATELY DANGEROUS TO LIFE OR HEALTH CONDITIONS:

SELF-CONTAINED BREATHING APPARATUS WITH FULL FACEPIECE OPERATED IN PRESSURE-DEMAND OR OTHER POSITIVE PRESSURE MODE.

SUPPLIED-AIR RESPIRATOR WITH FULL FACEPIECE AND OPERATED IN PRESSURE-DEMAND OR OTHER POSITIVE PRESSURE MODE IN COMBINATION WITH AN AUXILIARY SELF-CONTAINED BREATHING APPARATUS OPERATED IN PRESSURE-DEMAND OR OTHER POSITIVE PRESSURE MODE.

CLOTHING: EMPLOYEE MUST WEAR APPROPRIATE PROTECTIVE (IMPERVIOUS) CLOTHING AND EQUIPMENT TO PREVENT REPEATED OR PROLONGED SKIN CONTACT WITH THIS SUBSTANCE.

GLOVES: EMPLOYEE MUST WEAR APPROPRIATE PROTECTIVE GLOVES TO PREVENT CONTACT WITH THIS SUBSTANCE.

EYE PROTECTION: EMPLOYEE MUST WEAR SPLASH-PROOF OR DUST-RESISTANT SAFETY GOGGLES TO PREVENT EYE CONTACT WITH THIS SUBSTANCE.

EMERGENCY EYE WASH: WHERE THERE IS ANY POSSIBILITY THAT AN EMPLOYEE'S EYES MAY BE EXPOSED TO THIS SUBSTANCE, THE EMPLOYER SHOULD PROVIDE AN EYE WASH FOUNTAIN WITHIN THE IMMEDIATE WORK AREA FOR EMERGENCY USE.

AUTHORIZED BY- OCCUPATIONAL HEALTH SERVICES, INC.

CREATION DATE: 10/04/89 ***REVISION DATE:*** 03/28/90

MATERIAL SAFETY DATA SHEET

OCCUPATIONAL HEALTH SERVICES, INC.
AGRICULTURE AND PESTICIDE DIVISION
450 SEVENTH AVENUE, SUITE 2407
NEW YORK, NEW YORK 10123
1-800-445-MSDS OR (212) 967-1100

EMERGENCY CONTACT:
JOHN S. BRANSFORD, JR. (615) 292-1180

SUBSTANCE IDENTIFICATION

***SUBSTANCE:* D-TRANS-ALLETHRIN**

TRADE NAMES/SYNONYMS: DL-2-ALLYL-4-HYDROXY-3-METHYL-2-CYCLOPENTEN-1-ONE ESTER OF D-TRANS- 2,2-DIMETHYL-3-(2-METHYLPROPENYL)CYCLOPROPANECARBOXYLIC ACID; DL-2-ALLYL-4-HYDROXY-3-METHYL-2-CYCLOPENTEN-1-ONE ESTER OF D-TRANS CHRYSANTHEMUM MONOCARBOXYLIC ACID; (+)-TRANS-CHRYSANTHEMUMIC ACID ESTER OF (+-)-ALLETHROLONE; ALLYL HOMOLOG OF CINERIN I; BIOALLETHRIN; ENT 16275; PST00553

CHEMICAL FAMILY: PYRETHROID (SYNTHETIC)

MOLECULAR FORMULA: C19-H26-O3

MOLECULAR WEIGHT: 302.45

CERCLA RATINGS (SCALE 0-3): HEALTH=3 FIRE=2 REACTIVITY=0 PERSISTENCE=1

NFPA RATINGS (SCALE 0-4): HEALTH=U FIRE=2 REACTIVITY=0

COMPONENTS AND CONTAMINANTS

COMPONENT: D-TRANS-ALLETHRIN ***PERCENT:*** 100

EXPOSURE LIMITS: NO OCCUPATIONAL EXPOSURE LIMITS ESTABLISHED BY OSHA, ACGIH, OR NIOSH.

PHYSICAL DATA

DESCRIPTION: AMBER COLORED VISCOUS LIQUID WITH A SLIGHT AROMATIC ODOR.

BOILING POINT: 320 F (160 C) ***SPECIFIC GRAVITY:*** 0.997 @ 20 C

VAPOR PRESSURE: NOT AVAILABLE ***SOLUBILITY IN WATER:*** INSOLUBLE

SOLVENT SOLUBILITY: SOLUBLE IN ACETONE, BENZENE, ETHANOL, HEXANE, TOLUENE, METHYLENE CHLORIDE, METHANOL, REFINED KEROSENE.

FIRE AND EXPLOSION DATA

FIRE AND EXPLOSION HAZARD: MODERATE FIRE HAZARD WHEN EXPOSED TO HEAT OR FLAME.

FLASH POINT: >150 F (>66 C) (OC)

FIREFIGHTING MEDIA: DRY CHEMICAL, CARBON DIOXIDE, HALON, WATER SPRAY OR STANDARD FOAM (1987 EMERGENCY RESPONSE GUIDEBOOK, DOT P 5800.4). FOR LARGER FIRES, USE WATER SPRAY, FOG OR STANDARD FOAM (1987 EMERGENCY RESPONSE GUIDEBOOK, DOT P 5800.4).

FIREFIGHTING: MOVE CONTAINERS FROM FIRE AREA IF POSSIBLE. COOL CONTAINERS EXPOSED TO FLAMES WITH WATER FROM SIDE UNTIL WELL AFTER FIRE IS OUT. FIGHT FIRE FROM MAXIMUM DISTANCE. STAY AWAY FROM STORAGE TANK ENDS. DIKE FIRE CONTROL WATER FOR LATER DISPOSAL. DO NOT SCATTER MATERIAL. (1987 EMERGENCY RESPONSE GUIDEBOOK, DOT P 5800.4, GUIDE PAGE 57). EXTINGUISH ONLY IF FLOW CAN BE STOPPED. USE FLOODING AMOUNTS OF WATER AS A FOG; SOLID STREAMS MAY BE INEFFECTIVE. COOL CONTAINERS WITH FLOODING AMOUNTS OF WATER FROM AS FAR A DISTANCE AS POSSIBLE. AVOID BREATHING POISONOUS VAPORS, KEEP UPWIND.

TRANSPORTATION DATA

DEPARTMENT OF TRANSPORTATION HAZARD CLASSIFICATION 49 CFR 172.101: ORM-A

DEPARTMENT OF TRANSPORTATION LABELING REQUIREMENTS 49 CFR 172.101 AND SUBPART E: NONE

DEPARTMENT OF TRANSPORTATION PACKAGING REQUIREMENTS: 49 CFR 173.510 EXCEPTIONS: 49 CFR 173.505

TOXICITY

D-TRANS-ALLETHRIN: TOXICITY DATA: 425 MG/KG ORAL-RAT LD50; 330 MG/KG ORAL-MOUSE LD50; 4 MG/KG INTRAVENOUS-MOUSE LDLO. CARCINOGEN STATUS: NONE. ACUTE TOXICITY LEVEL: TOXIC BY INGESTION. TARGET EFFECTS: POISONING MAY AFFECT THE CENTRAL NERVOUS SYSTEM.*

* MAY BE BASED ON GENERAL INFORMATION ON PYRETHROIDS.

HEALTH EFFECTS AND FIRST AID

INHALATION: D-TRANS-ALLETHRIN: SEE INFORMATION ON PYRETHROIDS. PYRETHROIDS: **ACUTE EXPOSURE-** HEAVY EXPOSURE TO A MIST OF SOME PYRETHROIDS HAS PRODUCED HYPERSENSITIVIITY, ATAXIA, AND URINARY INCONTINENCE. CONVULSIONS MAY ALSO BE POSSIBLE. **CHRONIC EXPOSURE-** ANIMALS EXPOSED TO AEROSOLS OF SOME PYRETHROIDS FOR 3-4 HOURS/DAY FOR UP TO 4 WEEKS DID NOT EXHIBIT ANY SIGNIFICANT COMPOUND RELATED FINDINGS.

FIRST AID- REMOVE FROM EXPOSURE AREA TO FRESH AIR IMMEDIATELY. IF BREATHING HAS STOPPED, PERFORM ARTIFICIAL RESPIRATION. KEEP PERSON WARM AND AT REST. TREAT SYMPTOMATICALLY AND SUPPORTIVELY. GET MEDICAL ATTENTION IMMEDIATELY.

SKIN CONTACT: D-TRANS-ALLETHRIN: SEE INFORMATION ON PYRETHROIDS. PYRETHROIDS: **ACUTE EXPOSURE-** BASED ON ANIMAL AND HUMAN STUDIES AND HUMAN EXPERIENCES WITH SOME PYRETHROIDS, PRIMARY IRRITATION IS UNLIKELY. CUTANEOUS PARESTHESIAS MAY OCCUR INCLUDING NUMBNESS, ITCHING, BURNING, TINGLING AND WARMTH WITHOUT SIGNS OF IRRITATION. THESE EFFECTS MAY BE DELAYED FOR 30 MINUTES OR MORE AND LAST LESS THAN 24 HOURS. **CHRONIC EXPOSURE-** TESTS WITH SOME PYRETHROIDS ON HUMANS AND ANIMALS INDICATE SENSITIZATION IS UNLIKELY.

FIRST AID- REMOVE CONTAMINATED CLOTHING AND SHOES IMMEDIATELY. WASH AFFECTED AREA WITH SOAP OR MILD DETERGENT AND LARGE AMOUNTS OF WATER UNTIL NO EVIDENCE OF CHEMICAL REMAINS (APPROXIMATELY 15-20 MINUTES). GET MEDICAL ATTENTION IMMEDIATELY.

EYE CONTACT: D-TRANS-ALLETHRIN: SEE INFORMATION ON PYRETHROIDS. PYRETHROIDS: **ACUTE EXPOSURE-** MASSIVE INSTILLATION OF SOME PYRETHROIDS INTO RABBIT EYES PRODUCED ONLY A SLIGHT, TRANSIENT CONGESTION OF THE CONJUNCTIVA OR LACRIMATION. **CHRONIC EXPOSURE-** NO DATA AVAILABLE.

FIRST AID- WASH EYES IMMEDIATELY WITH LARGE AMOUNTS OF WATER OR NORMAL SALINE, OCCASIONALLY LIFTING UPPER AND LOWER LIDS, UNTIL NO EVIDENCE OF CHEMICAL REMAINS (APPROXIMATELY 15-20 MINUTES). GET MEDICAL ATTENTION IMMEDIATELY.

INGESTION: D-TRANS-ALLETHRIN: TOXIC. SEE INFORMATION ON PYRETHROIDS. PYRETHROIDS: **ACUTE EXPOSURE-** SOME PYRETHROIDS HAVE PRODUCED HYPERSENSITIVITY, NERVOUS IRRITABILITY, TREMORS, ATAXIA, AND URINARY INCONTINENCE IN ANIMALS. CONVULSIONS MAY ALSO BE POSSIBLE. **CHRONIC EXPOSURE-** INCREASED KIDNEY AND LIVER WEIGHTS AND HEPATIC HISTOPATHOLOGICAL CHANGES WERE NOTED IN ANIMALS CHRONICALLY FED SOME PYRETHROIDS.

FIRST AID- REMOVE BY GASTRIC LAVAGE AND CATHARSIS. MAINTAIN BLOOD PRESSURE AND AIRWAY. GIVE OXYGEN IF RESPIRATION IS DEPRESSED. DO NOT PERFORM GASTRIC LAVAGE IF VICTIM IS UNCONSCIOUS. GET MEDICAL ATTENTION IMMEDIATELY (DREISBACH, HANDBOOK OF POISONING, 12TH ED.). ADMINISTRATION OF LAVAGE OR OXYGEN SHOULD BE PERFORMED BY QUALIFIED MEDICAL PERSONNEL.

ANTIDOTE: NO SPECIFIC ANTIDOTE. TREAT SYMPTOMATICALLY AND SUPPORTIVELY.

REACTIVITY

REACTIVITY: STABLE UNDER NORMAL TEMPERATURES AND PRESSURES.

INCOMPATIBILITIES: D-TRANS-ALLETHRIN: ACIDS: INCOMPATIBLE. ALKALIES: INCOMPATIBLE. OXIDIZERS (STRONG): FIRE AND EXPLOSION HAZARD.

DECOMPOSITION: THERMAL DECOMPOSITION MAY RELEASE TOXIC AND/OR HAZARDOUS GASES.

POLYMERIZATION: POLYMERIZES ON STANDING.

STORAGE AND DISPOSAL

OBSERVE ALL FEDERAL, STATE AND LOCAL REGULATIONS WHEN STORING OR DISPOSING OF THIS SUBSTANCE. FOR ASSISTANCE, CONTACT THE DISTRICT DIRECTOR OF THE ENVIRONMENTAL PROTECTION AGENCY.

STORAGE

STORE IN ACCORDANCE WITH 40 CFR 165 RECOMMENDED PROCEDURES FOR THE DISPOSAL AND STORAGE OF PESTICIDES AND PESTICIDE CONTAINERS.
STORE AWAY FROM INCOMPATIBLE SUBSTANCES.

DISPOSAL

DISPOSAL MUST BE IN ACCORDANCE WITH 40 CFR 165 RECOMMENDED PROCEDURES FOR THE DISPOSAL AND STORAGE OF PESTICIDES AND PESTICIDE CONTAINERS.

CONDITIONS TO AVOID

MAY BE IGNITED BY HEAT, SPARKS OR FLAMES. CONTAINER MAY EXPLODE IN HEAT OF FIRE. VAPOR EXPLOSION AND POISON HAZARD INDOORS, OUTDOORS OR IN SEWERS.

SPILL AND LEAK PROCEDURES

SOIL SPILL: DIG HOLDING AREA SUCH AS LAGOON, POND OR PIT FOR CONTAINMENT. DIKE FLOW OF SPILLED MATERIAL USING SOIL OR SANDBAGS OR FOAMED BARRIERS SUCH AS POLYURETHANE OR CONCRETE.
USE CEMENT POWDER OR FLY ASH TO ABSORB LIQUID MASS.

WATER SPILL: USE ACTIVATED CARBON TO ABSORB SPILLED SUBSTANCE THAT IS DISSOLVED. USE MECHANICAL DREDGES OR LIFTS TO EXTRACT IMMOBILIZED MASSES OF POLLUTION AND PRECIPITATES.

OCCUPATIONAL SPILL: SHUT OFF IGNITION SOURCES. DO NOT TOUCH SPILLED MATERIAL. STOP LEAK IF YOU CAN DO IT WITHOUT RISK. USE WATER SPRAY TO REDUCE VAPORS. FOR SMALL SPILLS, TAKE UP WITH SAND OR OTHER ABSORBENT MATERIAL AND PLACE INTO CONTAINERS FOR LATER DISPOSAL. FOR SMALL DRY SPILLS, WITH CLEAN SHOVEL PLACE MATERIAL INTO CLEAN, DRY CONTAINERS AND COVER. MOVE CONTAINERS FROM SPILL AREA. FOR LARGER SPILLS, DIKE FAR AHEAD OF SPILL FOR LATER DISPOSAL. NO SMOKING, FLAMES OR FLARES IN HAZARD AREA! KEEP UNNECESSARY PEOPLE AWAY. ISOLATE HAZARD AREA AND DENY ENTRY. VENTILATE CLOSED SPACES BEFORE ENTERING.

PROTECTIVE EQUIPMENT

VENTILATION: PROVIDE LOCAL EXHAUST VENTILATION SYSTEM.

RESPIRATOR: THE FOLLOWING RESPIRATORS ARE RECOMMENDED BASED ON INFORMATION FOUND IN THE PHYSICAL DATA, TOXICITY AND HEALTH EFFECTS SECTIONS. THEY ARE RANKED IN ORDER FROM MINIMUM TO MAXIMUM RESPIRATORY PROTECTION. THE SPECIFIC RESPIRATOR SELECTED MUST BE BASED ON CONTAMINATION LEVELS FOUND IN THE WORK PLACE, MUST NOT EXCEED THE WORKING LIMITS OF THE RESPIRATOR AND BE JOINTLY APPROVED BY THE NATIONAL INSTITUTE FOR OCCUPATIONAL SAFETY AND HEALTH AND THE MINE SAFETY AND HEALTH ADMINISTRATION (NIOSH-MSHA).
CHEMICAL CARTRIDGE RESPIRATOR WITH PESTICIDE CARTRIDGE.
GAS MASK WITH A PESTICIDE CANISTER (CHIN-STYLE OR FRONT- OR BACK-MOUNTED CANISTER).
TYPE 'C' SUPPLIED-AIR RESPIRATOR OPERATED IN THE PRESSURE-DEMAND OR OTHER POSITIVE PRESSURE OR CONTINUOUS-FLOW MODE.
SELF-CONTAINED BREATHING APPARATUS.
FOR FIREFIGHTING AND OTHER IMMEDIATELY DANGEROUS TO LIFE OR HEALTH CONDITIONS:
SELF-CONTAINED BREATHING APPARATUS WITH FULL FACEPIECE OPERATED IN PRESSURE-DEMAND OR OTHER POSITIVE PRESSURE MODE.
SUPPLIED-AIR RESPIRATOR WITH FULL FACEPIECE AND OPERATED IN PRESSURE-DEMAND OR OTHER POSITIVE PRESSURE MODE IN COMBINATION WITH AN AUXILIARY SELF-CONTAINED BREATHING APPARATUS OPERATED IN PRESSURE-DEMAND OR OTHER POSITIVE PRESSURE MODE.

CLOTHING: EMPLOYEE MUST WEAR APPROPRIATE PROTECTIVE (IMPERVIOUS) CLOTHING AND EQUIPMENT TO PREVENT REPEATED OR PROLONGED SKIN CONTACT WITH THIS SUBSTANCE.

GLOVES: EMPLOYEE MUST WEAR APPROPRIATE PROTECTIVE GLOVES TO PREVENT CONTACT WITH THIS SUBSTANCE.

EYE PROTECTION: EMPLOYEE MUST WEAR SPLASH-PROOF OR DUST-RESISTANT SAFETY GOGGLES TO PREVENT EYE CONTACT WITH THIS SUBSTANCE.
EMERGENCY EYE WASH: WHERE THERE IS ANY POSSIBILITY THAT AN EMPLOYEE'S EYES MAY BE EXPOSED TO THIS SUBSTANCE, THE EMPLOYER SHOULD PROVIDE AN EYE WASH FOUNTAIN WITHIN THE IMMEDIATE WORK AREA FOR EMERGENCY USE.

AUTHORIZED BY- OCCUPATIONAL HEALTH SERVICES, INC.
CREATION DATE: 10/04/89 ***REVISION DATE:*** 03/28/90

MATERIAL SAFETY DATA SHEET

OCCUPATIONAL HEALTH SERVICES, INC.
AGRICULTURE AND PESTICIDE DIVISION
450 SEVENTH AVENUE, SUITE 2407
NEW YORK, NEW YORK 10123
1-800-445-MSDS OR (212) 967-1100

EMERGENCY CONTACT:
JOHN S. BRANSFORD, JR. (615) 292-1180

SUBSTANCE IDENTIFICATION

***SUBSTANCE:* ALLETHRIN (RACEMIC MIXTURE)**

TRADE NAMES/SYNONYMS: CYCLOPROPANECARBOXYLIC ACID, 2,2-DIMETHYL-3-(2-METHYLPROPENYL)-, ESTER WITH 2-ALLYL-4-HYDROXY-3-METHYL-2-CYCLOPENTEN-1-ONE, CIS-MISED WITH TRANS-2,2-DIMETHYL-3-(2-METHYL PROPENYL)CYCLOPROPANECARBOXYLIC ACID ESTER WITH 2-ALLYL-4-HYDROXY-3-METHYL-2-CYCLOPENTEN-1-ONE; PST00554

CHEMICAL FAMILY: PYRETHROID (SYNTHETIC)

MOLECULAR FORMULA: C19-H26-O3.4C19-H26-O3

MOLECULAR WEIGHT: 1512.25

CERCLA RATINGS (SCALE 0-3): HEALTH=2 FIRE=U REACTIVITY=0 PERSISTENCE=0

NFPA RATINGS (SCALE 0-4): HEALTH=2 FIRE=U REACTIVITY=0

COMPONENTS AND CONTAMINANTS

COMPONENT: ALLETHRIN (RACEMIC MIXTURE) ***PERCENT:*** 100

OTHER CONTAMINANTS: NONE

EXPOSURE LIMITS: NO OCCUPATIONAL EXPOSURE LIMITS ESTABLISHED BY OSHA, ACGIH, OR NIOSH.

PHYSICAL DATA

DESCRIPTION: CLEAR, AMBER-COLORED VISCOUS LIQUID ***BOILING POINT:*** 320 F (160 C)

SPECIFIC GRAVITY: NOT AVAILABLE ***EVAPORATION RATE:*** NOT AVAILABLE

SOLUBILITY IN WATER: INSOLUBLE

SOLVENT SOLUBILITY: ALCOHOL, KEROSENE, CARBON TETRACHLORIDE, NITROMETHANE, PETROLEUM ETHER, ETHYLENE DICHLORIDE, MOST ORGANIC SOLVENTS; MISCIBLE IN PETROLEUM OILS

FIRE AND EXPLOSION DATA

FIRE AND EXPLOSION HAZARD: UNKNOWN FIRE AND EXPLOSION HAZARD.

FIREFIGHTING MEDIA: DRY CHEMICAL, CARBON DIOXIDE, HALON, WATER SPRAY OR STANDARD FOAM (1987 EMERGENCY RESPONSE GUIDEBOOK, DOT P 5800.4). FOR LARGER FIRES, USE WATER SPRAY, FOG OR STANDARD FOAM (1987 EMERGENCY RESPONSE GUIDEBOOK, DOT P 5800.4).

FIREFIGHTING: MOVE CONTAINERS FROM FIRE AREA IF POSSIBLE. FIGHT FIRE FROM MAXIMUM DISTANCE. STAY AWAY FROM STORAGE TANK ENDS. DIKE FIRE CONTROL WATER FOR LATER DISPOSAL. DO NOT SCATTER MATERIAL (1987 EMERGENCY RESPONSE GUIDEBOOK, DOT P 5800.4, GUIDE PAGE 55). EXTINGUISH ONLY IF FLOW CAN BE STOPPED; USE FLOODING AMOUNTS OF WATER AS FOG, SOLID STREAMS MAY BE INEFFECTIVE. COOL CONTAINERS WITH FLOODING AMOUNTS OF WATER, APPLY FROM AS FAR A DISTANCE AS POSSIBLE. USE ALCOHOL FOAM, CARBON DIOXIDE OR DRY CHEMICAL. AVOID BREATHING TOXIC VAPORS, KEEP UPWIND.

TRANSPORTATION DATA

DEPARTMENT OF TRANSPORTATION HAZARD CLASSIFICATION 49 CFR 172.101: ORM-A

DEPARTMENT OF TRANSPORTATION LABELING REQUIREMENTS 49 CFR 172.101 AND SUBPART E: NONE

DEPARTMENT OF TRANSPORTATION PACKAGING REQUIREMENTS: 49 CFR 173.510 EXCEPTIONS: 49 CFR 173.505

TOXICITY

ALLETHRIN (RACEMIC MIXTURE): 720 MG/KG ORAL-RAT LD50; 500 MG/KG ORAL-MOUSE LD50; 260 MG/M3 INHALATION-RAT TCLO; 260 MG/M3 INHALATION-MOUSE TCLO; CARCINOGEN STATUS: NONE. ALLETHRIN (RACEMIC MIXTURE) IS A CENTRAL NERVOUS SYSTEM STIMULANT IN ANIMALS.

HEALTH EFFECTS AND FIRST AID

INHALATION: ALLETHRIN (RACEMIC MIXTURE): **ACUTE EXPOSURE-** SYNTHETIC PYRETHRINS LIKE THE NATURAL PYRETHRINS PRODUCE CENTRAL NERVOUS SYSTEM STIMULATION IN ANIMALS WITH SYMPTOMS OF NAUSEA, VOMITING, GASTROENTERITIS WITH DIARRHEA, HYPERSENSITIVITY, INCOORDINATION, TREMORS, MUSCULAR PARALYSIS, CONVULSION, COMA, AND DEATH DUE TO RESPIRATORY FAILURE. AT CONCENTRATION OF 2000 MG/KG, THIS MATERIAL PRODUCED SYMPTOMS OF HYPERSENSITIVITY, MOTOR ATAXIA, AND URINARY INCONTINENCE BUT NO FATALITIES IN MICE AND RATS. SYSTEMIC EFFECTS WERE FIRST NOTICED AT THE CONCENTRATION OF 260 MG/M3. **CHRONIC EXPOSURE-** IN ONE STUDY, CHRONIC EXPOSURE TO MIST PREPARATIONS OF ALLETHRIN OF 123 MG/M3/3 HOURS, 5 DAYS A WEEK FOR 4 WEEKS PRODUCED SOME SYSTEMIC EFFECTS WITHOUT ANY ADVERSE EFFECTS ON THE MAJOR ORGANS AND TISSUES.

FIRST AID- REMOVE FROM EXPOSURE AREA TO FRESH AIR IMMEDIATELY. IF BREATHING HAS STOPPED, PERFORM ARTIFICIAL RESPIRATION. KEEP PERSON WARM AND AT REST. TREAT SYMPTOMATICALLY AND SUPPORTIVELY. GET MEDICAL ATTENTION IMMEDIATELY.

SKIN CONTACT: ALLETHRIN (RACEMIC MIXTURE): **ACUTE EXPOSURE-** ALLETHRIN IS NOT ABSORBED THROUGH THE SKIN. SYNTHETIC PYRETHRINS ARE NOT IRRITANTS TO RABBIT SKIN AND THE TOXICITY FROM DERMAL ABSORPTION IS USUALLY MODERATE TO LOW. UNLIKE NATURAL PYRETHRINS, SYNTHETIC PYRETHRINS NORMALLY DO NOT PRODUCE ALLERGIC REACTIONS IN HUMANS. HOWEVER, THERE HAVE BEEN SOME REPORTS OF CUTANEOUS PARESTHESIAS AMONG OCCUPATIONALLY EXPOSED INDIVIDUALS. THESE INDIVIDUALS COMPLAINED OF TINGLING, BURNING AND STINGING SENSATIONS ON THE EXPOSED SURFACE OF THE SKIN ANYWHERE FROM 30 MINUTES UP TO 3 HOURS AFTER EXPOSURE. THE DURATION OF SYMPTOMS VARIED FROM 30 MINUTES TO 8 HOURS. **CHRONIC EXPOSURE-** NO DATA AVAILABLE.

FIRST AID- REMOVE CONTAMINATED CLOTHING AND SHOES IMMEDIATELY. WASH AFFECTED AREA WITH SOAP OR MILD DETERGENT AND LARGE AMOUNTS OF WATER UNTIL NO EVIDENCE OF CHEMICAL REMAINS (APPROXIMATELY 15-20 MINUTES). GET MEDICAL ATTENTION IMMEDIATELY.

EYE CONTACT: ALLETHRIN (RACEMIC MIXTURE): **ACUTE EXPOSURE-** MASSIVE INSTILLATION OF ALLETHRIN INTO RABBIT EYES PRODUCED A SLIGHT, TRANSIENT CONGESTION OF CONJUNCTIVA OR LACRIMATION BUT THE EFFECT WAS NOT SEVERE ENOUGH TO BE CONSIDERED AN IRRITANT. **CHRONIC EXPOSURE-** NO DATA AVAILABLE.

FIRST AID- WASH EYES IMMEDIATELY WITH LARGE AMOUNTS OF WATER OR NORMAL SALINE, OCCASIONALLY LIFTING UPPER AND LOWER LIDS, UNTIL NO EVIDENCE OF CHEMICAL REMAINS (APPROXIMATELY 15-20 MINUTES). GET MEDICAL ATTENTION IMMEDIATELY.

INGESTION: ALLETHRIN (RACEMIC MIXTURE): **ACUTE EXPOSURE-** SYNTHETIC PYRETHRINS LIKE THE NATURAL PYRETHRINS, PRODUCE CENTRAL NERVOUS SYSTEM STIMULATION IN ANIMALS WITH SYMPTOMS OF NAUSEA, VOMITING, GASTROENTERITIS WITH DIARRHEA, HYPERSENSITIVITY, INCOORDINATION, TREMORS, MUSCULAR PARALYSIS, CONVULSION, COMA, AND DEATH DUE TO RESPIRATORY FAILURE. THE AVERAGE LETHAL DOSE IN RATS WAS 720 MG/KG. **CHRONIC EXPOSURE-** 1000 TO 2500 PPM FED TO RATS FOR 6-MONTHS DID NOT PRODUCED ANY ADVERSE EFFECTS.

FIRST AID- TREAT SYMPTOMATICALLY AND SUPPORTIVELY. GET MEDICAL ATTENTION IMMEDIATELY. IF VOMITING OCCURS, KEEP HEAD LOWER THAN HIPS TO PREVENT ASPIRATION.

ANTIDOTE: NO SPECIFIC ANTIDOTE. TREAT SYMPTOMATICALLY AND SUPPORTIVELY.

REACTIVITY

REACTIVITY: MAY DECOMPOSE UPON EXPOSURE TO HEAT OR LIGHT.

INCOMPATIBILITIES: ALLETHRIN (RACEMIC MIXTURE): ALKALIES: INCOMPATIBLE.

DECOMPOSITION: THERMAL DECOMPOSITION MAY RELEASE TOXIC AND/OR HAZARDOUS GASES.

POLYMERIZATION: HAZARDOUS POLYMERIZATION HAS NOT BEEN REPORTED TO OCCUR UNDER NORMAL TEMPERATURES AND PRESSURES.

CONDITIONS TO AVOID

MAY BURN BUT DOES NOT IGNITE READILY. CONTAINERS MAY EXPLODE IN HEAT OF FIRE.

SPILL AND LEAK PROCEDURES

OCCUPATIONAL SPILL: DO NOT TOUCH SPILLED MATERIAL. STOP LEAK IF YOU CAN DO IT WITHOUT RISK. USE WATER SPRAY TO REDUCE VAPORS. FOR SMALL SPILLS, TAKE UP WITH SAND OR OTHER ABSORBENT MATERIAL AND PLACE INTO CONTAINERS FOR LATER DISPOSAL. FOR SMALL DRY SPILLS, WITH A CLEAN SHOVEL PLACE MATERIAL INTO CLEAN, DRY CONTAINERS AND COVER. MOVE CONTAINERS FROM SPILL AREA. FOR LARGER SPILLS, DIKE FAR AHEAD OF SPILL FOR LATER DISPOSAL. KEEP UNNECESSARY PEOPLE AWAY. ISOLATE HAZARD AREA AND DENY ENTRY. VENTILATE CLOSED SPACES BEFORE ENTERING.

PROTECTIVE EQUIPMENT

VENTILATION: PROVIDE LOCAL EXHAUST VENTILATION SYSTEM.

RESPIRATOR: THE FOLLOWING RESPIRATORS ARE RECOMMENDED BASED ON INFORMATION FOUND IN THE PHYSICAL DATA, TOXICITY AND HEALTH EFFECTS SECTIONS. THEY ARE RANKED IN ORDER FROM MINIMUM TO MAXIMUM RESPIRATORY PROTECTION. THE SPECIFIC RESPIRATOR SELECTED MUST BE BASED ON CONTAMINATION LEVELS FOUND IN THE WORK PLACE, MUST NOT EXCEED THE WORKING LIMITS OF THE RESPIRATOR AND BE JOINTLY APPROVED BY THE NATIONAL INSTITUTE FOR OCCUPATIONAL SAFETY AND HEALTH AND THE MINE SAFETY AND HEALTH ADMINISTRATION (NIOSH-MSHA).

CHEMICAL CARTRIDGE RESPIRATOR WITH PESTICIDE CARTRIDGE.

GAS MASK WITH A PESTICIDE CANISTER (CHIN-STYLE OR FRONT- OR BACK-MOUNTED CANISTER).
TYPE 'C' SUPPLIED-AIR RESPIRATOR OPERATED IN THE PRESSURE-DEMAND OR OTHER POSITIVE PRESSURE OR CONTINUOUS-FLOW MODE.
SELF-CONTAINED BREATHING APPARATUS.
FOR FIREFIGHTING AND OTHER IMMEDIATELY DANGEROUS TO LIFE OR HEALTH CONDITIONS:
SELF-CONTAINED BREATHING APPARATUS WITH FULL FACEPIECE OPERATED IN PRESSURE-DEMAND OR OTHER POSITIVE PRESSURE MODE.
SUPPLIED-AIR RESPIRATOR WITH FULL FACEPIECE AND OPERATED IN PRESSURE-DEMAND OR OTHER POSITIVE PRESSURE MODE IN COMBINATION WITH AN AUXILIARY SELF-CONTAINED BREATHING APPARATUS OPERATED IN PRESSURE-DEMAND OR OTHER POSITIVE PRESSURE MODE.
CLOTHING: EMPLOYEE MUST WEAR APPROPRIATE PROTECTIVE (IMPERVIOUS) CLOTHING AND EQUIPMENT TO PREVENT REPEATED OR PROLONGED SKIN CONTACT WITH THIS SUBSTANCE.
GLOVES: EMPLOYEE MUST WEAR APPROPRIATE PROTECTIVE GLOVES TO PREVENT CONTACT WITH THIS SUBSTANCE.
EYE PROTECTION: EMPLOYEE MUST WEAR SPLASH-PROOF OR DUST-RESISTANT SAFETY GOGGLES TO PREVENT EYE CONTACT WITH THIS SUBSTANCE.
EMERGENCY EYE WASH: WHERE THERE IS ANY POSSIBILITY THAT AN EMPLOYEE'S EYES MAY BE EXPOSED TO THIS SUBSTANCE, THE EMPLOYER SHOULD PROVIDE AN EYE WASH FOUNTAIN WITHIN THE IMMEDIATE WORK AREA FOR EMERGENCY USE.

AUTHORIZED BY- OCCUPATIONAL HEALTH SERVICES, INC.
CREATION DATE: 10/04/89 ***REVISION DATE:*** 03/28/90

MATERIAL SAFETY DATA SHEET

OCCUPATIONAL HEALTH SERVICES, INC.
AGRICULTURE AND PESTICIDE DIVISION
450 SEVENTH AVENUE, SUITE 2407
NEW YORK, NEW YORK 10123
1-800-445-MSDS OR (212) 967-1100

EMERGENCY CONTACT:
JOHN S. BRANSFORD, JR. (615) 292-1180

SUBSTANCE IDENTIFICATION

CAS-NUMBER 57-06-7
SUBSTANCE: ALLYL ISOTHIOCYANATE
TRADE NAMES/SYNONYMS: AITC; ALLYL MUSTARD OIL; MUSTARD OIL; ISOTHIOCYANIC ACID, ALLYL ESTER; 2-PROPENYL ISOTHIOCYANATE; REDSKIN; ALLYL ISOSULFOCYANATE; ALLYLSENEVOL; OIL OF MUSTARD, ARTIFICIAL; OLEUM SINAPIS VOLATILE; SYNTHETIC MUSTARD OIL; VOLATILE OIL OF MUSTARD; UN 1545; PST00680
CHEMICAL FAMILY: THIOCYANATE
MOLECULAR FORMULA: C4-H5-N-S
MOLECULAR WEIGHT: 99.16
CERCLA RATINGS (SCALE 0-3): HEALTH=3 FIRE=2 REACTIVITY=0 PERSISTENCE=0
NFPA RATINGS (SCALE 0-4): HEALTH=3 FIRE=2 REACTIVITY=0

COMPONENTS AND CONTAMINANTS

COMPONENT: ALLYL ISOTHIOCYANATE ***PERCENT:*** 100
CAS# 57-06-7
OTHER CONTAMINANTS: NONE
EXPOSURE LIMITS: NO OCCUPATIONAL EXPOSURE LIMITS ESTABLISHED BY OSHA, ACGIH, OR NIOSH.

PHYSICAL DATA

DESCRIPTION: COLORLESS TO PALE YELLOW, OILY LIQUID WITH A PUNGENT, IRRITATING ODOR; SHARP, BITING TASTE ***BOILING POINT:*** 304 F (151 C)
MELTING POINT: -112 F (-80 C) ***SPECIFIC GRAVITY:*** 1.0
VAPOR PRESSURE: 5 MMHG @ 25.3 C ***SOLUBILITY IN WATER:*** SLIGHTLY SOLUBLE
VAPOR DENSITY: 3.4
SOLVENT SOLUBILITY: ALCOHOL, ETHER, CARBON DISULFIDE, ORGANIC SOLVENTS

FIRE AND EXPLOSION DATA

FIRE AND EXPLOSION HAZARD: MODERATE FIRE HAZARD WHEN EXPOSED TO HEAT OR FLAME.
VAPOR-AIR MIXTURES ARE EXPLOSIVE ABOVE FLASH POINT.
VAPORS ARE HEAVIER THAN AIR AND MAY TRAVEL A CONSIDERABLE DISTANCE TO A SOURCE OF IGNITION AND FLASH BACK.
FLASH POINT: 115 F (46 C) (CC) ***FLAMMABILITY CLASS(OSHA):*** II
FIREFIGHTING MEDIA: DRY CHEMICAL, CARBON DIOXIDE, HALON, WATER SPRAY OR STANDARD FOAM (1987 EMERGENCY RESPONSE GUIDEBOOK, DOT P 5800.4).
FOR LARGER FIRES, USE WATER SPRAY, FOG OR STANDARD FOAM (1987 EMERGENCY RESPONSE GUIDEBOOK, DOT P 5800.4).
FIREFIGHTING: MOVE CONTAINERS FROM FIRE AREA IF POSSIBLE. COOL CONTAINERS EXPOSED TO FLAMES WITH WATER FROM SIDE UNTIL WELL AFTER FIRE IS OUT. FIGHT FIRE FROM MAXIMUM DISTANCE. STAY AWAY FROM STORAGE TANK ENDS. DIKE FIRE CONTROL WATER FOR LATER DISPOSAL. DO NOT SCATTER MATERIAL. (1987 EMERGENCY RESPONSE GUIDEBOOK, DOT P 5800.4, GUIDE PAGE 57).
EXTINGUISH ONLY IF FLOW CAN BE STOPPED. USE FLOODING AMOUNTS OF WATER AS A FOG; SOLID STREAMS MAY BE INEFFECTIVE. COOL CONTAINERS WITH FLOODING AMOUNTS OF WATER FROM AS FAR A DISTANCE AS POSSIBLE. AVOID BREATHING POISONOUS VAPORS, KEEP UPWIND.

TOXICITY

ALLYL ISOTHIOCYANATE: IRRITATION DATA: 2 MG EYE-RABBIT. TOXICITY DATA: 88 MG/KG SKIN-RABBIT LD50; 112 MG/KG ORAL-RAT LD50; 308 MG/KG ORAL-MOUSE LD50; 92 MG/KG SUBCUTANEOUS-RAT LD50; 80 MG/KG SUBCUTANEOUS-MOUSE LD50; 12 MG/KG INTRAVENOUS-RABBIT LDLO; 80 MG/KG INTRAPERITONEAL-RAT LDLO; 4 MG/KG INTRAPERITONEAL-MOUSE LDLO; MUTAGENIC DATA (RTECS); REPRODUCTIVE EFFECTS DATA (RTECS); TUMORIGENIC DATA (RTECS). CARCINOGEN STATUS: ANIMAL LIMITED EVIDENCE (IARC GROUP-3); THERE IS LIMITED EVIDENCE FOR THE CARCINOGENICITY OF ALLYL ISOTHIOCYANATE IN EXPERIMENTAL ANIMALS. IN THE ABSENCE OF EPIDEMIOLOGICAL DATA, NO EVALUATION COULD BE MADE OF THE CARCINOGENICITY OF ALLYL ISOTHIOCYANATE TO HUMANS. LOCAL EFFECTS: CORROSIVE- INHALATION, SKIN, AND EYES. ACUTE TOXICITY LEVEL: HIGHLY TOXIC BY DERMAL ABSORPTION AND TOXIC BY INGESTION. TARGET EFFECTS: SENSITIZER- PULMONARY.

HEALTH EFFECTS AND FIRST AID

INHALATION: ALLYL ISOTHIOCYANATE: SENSITIZER. **ACUTE EXPOSURE-** MAY CAUSE WATERING EYES, SNEEZING, AND ASTHMA IN PREVIOUSLY EXPOSED PERSONS. **CHRONIC EXPOSURE-** PROLONGED OR REPEATED EXPOSURE TO VAPORS MAY RESULT IN PULMONARY SENSITIZATION.
FIRST AID- REMOVE FROM EXPOSURE AREA TO FRESH AIR IMMEDIATELY. IF BREATHING HAS STOPPED, PERFORM ARTIFICIAL RESPIRATION. KEEP PERSON WARM AND AT REST. TREAT SYMPTOMATICALLY AND SUPPORTIVELY. GET MEDICAL ATTENTION IMMEDIATELY.

SKIN CONTACT: ALLYL ISOTHIOCYANATE: CORROSIVE/TOXIC. **ACUTE EXPOSURE-** UNDILUTED LIQUID MAY CAUSE ECZEMATOUS OR VESICULAR SKIN REACTIONS, AND VIOLENT IRRITATION. AQUEOUS SUPENSIONS OR OIL SOLUTIONS MAY CAUSE BLISTERING. ANIMAL STUDIES INDICATE THAT LETHAL AMOUNTS MAY BE ABSORBED THROUGH INTACT SKIN. **CHRONIC EXPOSURE-** PROLONGED OR REPEATED EXPOSURE MAY CAUSE DERMATITIS, BLISTERING, AND ULCERATION.
FIRST AID- REMOVE CONTAMINATED CLOTHING AND SHOES IMMEDIATELY. WASH AFFECTED AREA WITH SOAP OR MILD DETERGENT AND LARGE AMOUNTS OF WATER UNTIL NO EVIDENCE OF CHEMICAL REMAINS (AT LEAST 15-20 MINUTES). IN CASE OF CHEMICAL BURNS, COVER AREA WITH STERILE, DRY DRESSING. BANDAGE SECURELY, BUT NOT TOO TIGHTLY. GET MEDICAL ATTENTION IMMEDIATELY.

EYE CONTACT: ALLYL ISOTHIOCYANATE: CORROSIVE. **ACUTE EXPOSURE-** VAPORS MAY CAUSE LACRIMATION AND KERATITIS, WHICH MAY INTERFERE WITH VISION. LIQUID MAY CAUSE VIOLENT IRRITATION. A SINGLE DROP HAS CAUSED BLINDNESS. **CHRONIC EXPOSURE-** PROLONGED OR REPEATED EXPOSURE TO VAPORS MAY CAUSE LACRIMATION AND KERATITIS.
FIRST AID- WASH EYES IMMEDIATELY WITH LARGE AMOUNTS OF WATER OR NORMAL SALINE, OCCASIONALLY LIFTING UPPER AND LOWER LIDS, UNTIL NO EVIDENCE OF CHEMICAL REMAINS (APPROXIMATELY 15-20 MINUTES). GET MEDICAL ATTENTION IMMEDIATELY.

INGESTION: ALLYL ISOTHIOCYANATE: CORROSIVE/TOXIC/LIMITED ANIMAL CARCINOGEN. **ACUTE EXPOSURE-** MAY CAUSE CORROSION OF THE GASTROINTESTINAL TRACT AND DEATH. A SINGLE DOSE IN CORN OIL, BY GAVAGE ADMINISTRATION, CAUSED GROWTH RETARDATION, AND DOSE-RELATED, NON-SPECIFIC SIGNS OF TOXICITY IN MICE. A SINGLE DOSE CAUSED PORPHYRIN-LIKE DEPOSIT AROUND EYES AND NOSE, SCRAWNY APPEARANCE, AND ROUGH FUR IN RATS. DEATH OCCURRED WITHIN 4 HOURS TO 15 DAYS FOLLOWING INGESTION IN RATS. **CHRONIC EXPOSURE-** NO HUMAN DATA AVAILABLE. REPEATED ADMINISTRATION HAS RESULTED IN A DOSE-DEPENDENT THICKENING OF THE STOMACH MUCOSA AND THE URINARY-BLADDER WALL IN MICE, AND IN ADHESION OF THE STOMACH WALL TO THE PERITONEUM IN RATS. LETHALITY

BEGAN WITH 200 MG/KG IN RATS AND 50 MG/KG IN MICE. REPEATED GAVAGE ADMINISTRATION OF ALLYL ISOTHIOCYANATE IN CORN OIL RESULTED IN AN INCREASED INCIDENCE OF EPITHELIAL HYPERPLASIA AND TRANSITIONAL-CELL PAPILLOMAS OF THE URINARY BLADDER IN MALE RATS, AND SOME SUBCUTANEOUS FIBROSARCOMAS IN FEMALE RATS GIVEN HIGH DOSES.

FIRST AID- REMOVE BY GASTRIC LAVAGE OR EMESIS. MAINTAIN BLOOD PRESSURE AND AIRWAY. GIVE OXYGEN IF RESPIRATION IS DEPRESSED. DO NOT PERFORM GASTRIC LAVAGE OR EMESIS IF VICTIM IS UNCONSCIOUS. GET MEDICAL ATTENTION IMMEDIATELY (DREISBACH, HANDBOOK OF POISONING, 11TH ED.). ADMINISTRATION OF GASTRIC LAVAGE OR OXYGEN SHOULD BE PERFORMED BY QUALIFIED MEDICAL PERSONNEL.

ANTIDOTE: NO SPECIFIC ANTIDOTE. TREAT SYMPTOMATICALLY AND SUPPORTIVELY.

REACTIVITY

REACTIVITY: STABLE UNDER NORMAL TEMPERATURES AND PRESSURES.

INCOMPATIBILITIES: ALLYL ISOTHIOCYANATE: ACID, ACID FUMES: DECOMPOSITION WITH THE EVOLUTION OF HIGHLY TOXIC HYDROGEN CYANIDE. POWERFUL OXIDIZERS: IGNITION REACTION.

DECOMPOSITION: THERMAL DECOMPOSITION PRODUCTS MAY INCLUDE HIGHLY TOXIC HYDROGEN CYANIDE.

POLYMERIZATION: ALLYL ISOTHIOCYANATE: EXTENSIVE DECOMPOSITION WHEN HEATED TO 250 C IN GLASS AMPULE MAY HAVE BEEN THE RESULT OF POLYMERIZATION.

CONDITIONS TO AVOID

MAY BE IGNITED BY HEAT, SPARKS OR FLAMES. CONTAINER MAY EXPLODE IN HEAT OF FIRE. VAPOR EXPLOSION AND POISON HAZARD INDOORS, OUTDOORS OR IN SEWERS.

SPILL AND LEAK PROCEDURES

OCCUPATIONAL SPILL: SHUT OFF IGNITION SOURCES. DO NOT TOUCH SPILLED MATERIAL. STOP LEAK IF YOU CAN DO IT WITHOUT RISK. USE WATER SPRAY TO REDUCE VAPORS. FOR SMALL SPILLS, TAKE UP WITH SAND OR OTHER ABSORBENT MATERIAL AND PLACE INTO CONTAINERS FOR LATER DISPOSAL. FOR SMALL DRY SPILLS, WITH CLEAN SHOVEL PLACE MATERIAL INTO CLEAN, DRY CONTAINERS AND COVER. MOVE CONTAINERS FROM SPILL AREA. FOR LARGER SPILLS, DIKE FAR AHEAD OF SPILL FOR LATER DISPOSAL. NO SMOKING, FLAMES OR FLARES IN HAZARD AREA! KEEP UNNECESSARY PEOPLE AWAY. ISOLATE HAZARD AREA AND DENY ENTRY. VENTILATE CLOSED SPACES BEFORE ENTERING.

PROTECTIVE EQUIPMENT

VENTILATION: PROVIDE LOCAL EXHAUST OR PROCESS ENCLOSURE VENTILATION SYSTEM.

RESPIRATOR: THE FOLLOWING RESPIRATORS ARE RECOMMENDED BASED ON INFORMATION FOUND IN THE PHYSICAL DATA, TOXICITY AND HEALTH EFFECTS SECTIONS. THEY ARE RANKED IN ORDER FROM MINIMUM TO MAXIMUM RESPIRATORY PROTECTION. THE SPECIFIC RESPIRATOR SELECTED MUST BE BASED ON CONTAMINATION LEVELS FOUND IN THE WORK PLACE, MUST NOT EXCEED THE WORKING LIMITS OF THE RESPIRATOR AND BE JOINTLY APPROVED BY THE NATIONAL INSTITUTE FOR OCCUPATIONAL SAFETY AND HEALTH AND THE MINE SAFETY AND HEALTH ADMINISTRATION (NIOSH-MSHA).

TYPE 'C' SUPPLIED-AIR RESPIRATOR WITH A FULL FACEPIECE OPERATED IN PRESSURE-DEMAND OR OTHER POSITIVE PRESSURE MODE OR WITH A FULL FACEPIECE, HELMET OR HOOD OPERATED IN CONTINOUS-FLOW MODE.

SELF-CONTAINED BREATHING APPARATUS WITH A FULL FACEPIECE OPERATED IN PRESSURE-DEMAND OR OTHER POSITIVE PRESSURE MODE.

FOR FIREFIGHTING AND OTHER IMMEDIATELY DANGEROUS TO LIFE OR HEALTH CONDITIONS:

SELF-CONTAINED BREATHING APPARATUS WITH FULL FACEPIECE OPERATED IN PRESSURE-DEMAND OR OTHER POSITIVE PRESSURE MODE.

SUPPLIED-AIR RESPIRATOR WITH FULL FACEPIECE AND OPERATED IN PRESSURE-DEMAND OR OTHER POSITIVE PRESSURE MODE IN COMBINATION WITH AN AUXILIARY SELF-CONTAINED BREATHING APPARATUS OPERATED IN PRESSURE-DEMAND OR OTHER POSITIVE PRESSURE MODE.

CLOTHING: EMPLOYEE MUST WEAR APPROPRIATE PROTECTIVE (IMPERVIOUS) CLOTHING AND EQUIPMENT TO PREVENT ANY POSSIBILITY OF SKIN CONTACT WITH THIS SUBSTANCE.

GLOVES: EMPLOYEE MUST WEAR APPROPRIATE PROTECTIVE GLOVES TO PREVENT CONTACT WITH THIS SUBSTANCE.

EYE PROTECTION: EMPLOYEE MUST WEAR SPLASH-PROOF OR DUST-RESISTANT SAFETY GOGGLES AND A FACESHIELD TO PREVENT CONTACT WITH THIS SUBSTANCE.

EMERGENCY WASH FACILITIES: WHERE THERE IS ANY POSSIBILITY THAT AN EMPLOYEE'S EYES AND/OR SKIN MAY BE EXPOSED TO THIS SUBSTANCE, THE EMPLOYER SHOULD PROVIDE AN EYE WASH FOUNTAIN AND QUICK DRENCH SHOWER WITHIN THE IMMEDIATE WORK AREA FOR EMERGENCY USE.

AUTHORIZED BY- OCCUPATIONAL HEALTH SERVICES, INC.
CREATION DATE: 02/08/90 ***REVISION DATE:*** 06/26/90

MATERIAL SAFETY DATA SHEET

OCCUPATIONAL HEALTH SERVICES, INC.
AGRICULTURE AND PESTICIDE DIVISION
450 SEVENTH AVENUE, SUITE 2407
NEW YORK, NEW YORK 10123
1-800-445-MSDS OR (212) 967-1100

EMERGENCY CONTACT:
JOHN S. BRANSFORD, JR. (615) 292-1180

SUBSTANCE IDENTIFICATION

CAS-NUMBER 319-84-6

***SUBSTANCE:* <u>ALPHA-HEXACHLOROCYCLOHEXANE</u>**

TRADE NAMES/SYNONYMS: CYCLOHEXANE, 1,2,3,4,5,6-HEXACHLORO-, (1ALPHA,2ALPHA,3BETA,4ALPHA, 5BETA,6BETA)-; CYCLOHEXANE, 1,2,3,4,5,6-HEXACHLORO-, ALPHA-; (1ALPHA,2ALPHA,3BETA,4ALPHA,5BETA,6BETA)-1,2,3,4,5,6- HEXACHLOROCYCLOHEXANE; ALPHA-1,2,3,4,5,6,-HEXACHLOROCYCLOHEXANE; ALPHA-BENZENE HEXACHLORIDE; ALPHA-BENZOHEXACHLORIDE; ALPHA-BHC; ALPHA-HEXACHLORAN; ALPHA-HEXACHLORANE; ALPHA-HEXACHLORCYCLOHEXANE; 1,2,3,4,5,6-HEXACHLOROCYCLOHEXANE; HEXACHLOROCYCLOHEXANE; BHC; HCH; ENT 9,232; BENZENE HEXACHLORIDE; ALPHA-LINDANE; C6H6CL6; PST00770

CHEMICAL FAMILY: HALOGEN COMPOUND, ALICYCLIC

MOLECULAR FORMULA: C6-H6-CL6

MOLECULAR WEIGHT: 290.83

CERCLA RATINGS (SCALE 0-3): HEALTH=3 FIRE=0 REACTIVITY=0 PERSISTENCE=3

NFPA RATINGS (SCALE 0-4): HEALTH=U FIRE=0 REACTIVITY=0

COMPONENTS AND CONTAMINANTS

COMPONENT: ALPHA-HEXACHLOROCYCLOHEXANE ***PERCENT:*** 100.0
CAS# 319-84-6

OTHER CONTAMINANTS: NONE

EXPOSURE LIMITS: NO OCCUPATIONAL EXPOSURE LIMITS ESTABLISHED BY OSHA, ACGIH, OR NIOSH.

ALPHA-HEXACHLOROCYCLOHEXANE: 10 POUNDS CERCLA SECTION 103 REPORTABLE QUANTITY SUBJECT TO CALIFORNIA PROPOSITION 65 CANCER AND/OR REPRODUCTIVE TOXICITY WARNING AND RELEASE REQUIREMENTS-(OCTOBER 1, 1989)

PHYSICAL DATA

DESCRIPTION: COLORLESS, MONOCLINIC PRISMS. ***BOILING POINT:*** 550 F (288 C)

MELTING POINT: 318-320 F (159-160 C) ***SPECIFIC GRAVITY:*** 1.87

VAPOR PRESSURE: 0.02 MMHG @ 20 C ***SOLUBILITY IN WATER:*** 10 PPM

SOLVENT SOLUBILITY: SOLUBLE IN ACETONE; MODERATELY SOLUBLE IN BENZENE, CHLOROFORM, ETHER, ETHANOL, METHANOL, XYLENE, FATS AND OILS.

FIRE AND EXPLOSION DATA

FIRE AND EXPLOSION HAZARD: NEGLIGIBLE FIRE HAZARD WHEN EXPOSED TO HEAT OR FLAME.

FIREFIGHTING MEDIA: DRY CHEMICAL, CARBON DIOXIDE, HALON, WATER SPRAY OR STANDARD FOAM (1987 EMERGENCY RESPONSE GUIDEBOOK, DOT P 5800.4). FOR LARGER FIRES, USE WATER SPRAY, FOG OR STANDARD FOAM (1987 EMERGENCY RESPONSE GUIDEBOOK, DOT P 5800.4).

FIREFIGHTING: MOVE CONTAINERS FROM FIRE AREA IF POSSIBLE. FIGHT FIRE FROM MAXIMUM DISTANCE. STAY AWAY FROM STORAGE TANK ENDS. DIKE FIRE CONTROL WATER FOR LATER DISPOSAL. DO NOT SCATTER MATERIAL (1987 EMERGENCY RESPONSE GUIDEBOOK, DOT P 5800.4, GUIDE PAGE 55).

USE AGENTS SUITABLE FOR TYPE OF FIRE. COOL CONTAINERS WITH FLOODING AMOUNTS OF WATER. AVOID BREATHING VAPORS OR DUSTS, KEEP UPWIND.

TOXICITY

ALPHA-HEXACHLOROCYCLOHEXANE: TOXICITY DATA: 14 GM/KG ORAL-HUMAN LDLO; 177 MG/KG ORAL-RAT LD50; 78 MG/KG ORAL-MOUSE LD50; MUTAGENIC DATA (RTECS); TUMORIGENIC DATA (RTECS). CARCINOGEN STATUS: ANTICIPATED HUMAN CARCINOGEN (NTP); HUMAN INADEQUATE EVIDENCE, ANIMAL SUFFICIENT EVIDENCE (IARC GROUP-2B). A-HEXACHLOROCYCLOHEXANE PRODUCED LIVER TUMORS IN MICE BY ORAL ADMINISTRATION. ACUTE TOXICITY LEVEL: TOXIC BY INGESTION. TARGET EFFECTS: POISONING MAY AFFECT THE CENTRAL NERVOUS

SYSTEM AND THE LIVER. ADDITIONAL DATA: STIMULANTS SUCH AS EPINEPHRINE MAY INDUCE VENTRICULAR FIBRILLATION.

HEALTH EFFECTS AND FIRST AID

INHALATION: ALPHA-HEXACHLOROCYCLOHEXANE: **ACUTE EXPOSURE-** MAY CAUSE IRRITATION. **CHRONIC EXPOSURE-** NO DATA AVAILABLE.

FIRST AID- REMOVE FROM EXPOSURE AREA TO FRESH AIR IMMEDIATELY. IF BREATHING HAS STOPPED, PERFORM ARTIFICIAL RESPIRATION. KEEP PERSON WARM AND AT REST. TREAT SYMPTOMATICALLY AND SUPPORTIVELY. GET MEDICAL ATTENTION IMMEDIATELY.

SKIN CONTACT: ALPHA-HEXACHLOROCYCLOHEXANE: **ACUTE EXPOSURE-** MAY CAUSE IRRITATION. **CHRONIC EXPOSURE-** NO DATA AVAILABLE.

FIRST AID- REMOVE CONTAMINATED CLOTHING AND SHOES IMMEDIATELY. WASH AFFECTED AREA WITH SOAP OR MILD DETERGENT AND LARGE AMOUNTS OF WATER UNTIL NO EVIDENCE OF CHEMICAL REMAINS (APPROXIMATELY 15-20 MINUTES). GET MEDICAL ATTENTION IMMEDIATELY.

EYE CONTACT: ALPHA-HEXACHLOROCYCLOHEXANE: **ACUTE EXPOSURE-** MAY CAUSE IRRITATION. **CHRONIC EXPOSURE-** NO DATA AVAILABLE.

FIRST AID- WASH EYES IMMEDIATELY WITH LARGE AMOUNTS OF WATER OR NORMAL SALINE, OCCASIONALLY LIFTING UPPER AND LOWER LIDS, UNTIL NO EVIDENCE OF CHEMICAL REMAINS (APPROXIMATELY 15-20 MINUTES). GET MEDICAL ATTENTION IMMEDIATELY.

INGESTION: ALPHA-HEXACHLOROCYCLOHEXANE: CARCINOGEN/TOXIC. **ACUTE EXPOSURE-** A LETHAL DOSE IN RATS WAS 177 MG/KG; SYMPTOMS WERE NOT REPORTED. **CHRONIC EXPOSURE-** REDUCED WEIGHT GAIN, INCREASED MORTALITY, FATTY DEGENERATION AND FOCAL NECROSIS OF THE LIVER, AND CHRONIC NEPHRITIS WERE OBSERVED IN A STUDY OF RATS. CHANGES HAVE BEEN REPORTED IN THE PANCREAS, TESTES, LUNGS AND NASAL MUCOUS MEMBRANES OF ANIMALS FOLLOWING SUFFICIENTLY HIGH REPEATED ABSORPTION OF HEXACHLOROCYCLOHEXANE OR ONE OF ITS ISOMERS. BENIGN AND MALIGNANT LIVER TUMORS WERE INDUCED IN MICE FED ALPHA-HEXACHLOROCYCLOHEXANE.

FIRST AID- IF THE PERSON IS CONSCIOUS AND NOT CONVULSING, REMOVE BY GIVING SYRUP OF IPECAC (IF VOMITING OCCURS, KEEP THE HEAD BELOW THE HIPS TO PREVENT ASPIRATION). GIVE ACTIVATED CHARCOAL FOLLOWED BY GASTRIC LAVAGE. FOLLOW WITH A SALINE CATHARTIC. DO NOT GIVE FATS OR OILS. INTESTINAL LAVAGE WITH 20% MANNITOL (200 ML) BY STOMACH TUBE IS ALSO USEFUL. GIVE ARTIFICIAL RESPIRATION WITH OXYGEN IF RESPIRATION IS DEPRESSED (DREISBACH, HANDBOOK OF POISONING, 12TH ED.). TREAT SYMPTOMATICALLY AND SUPPORTIVELY. LAVAGE AND ADMINISTRATION OF OXYGEN SHOULD BE PERFORMED BY QUALIFIED MEDICAL PERSONNEL. GET MEDICAL ATTENTION IMMEDIATELY.

ANTIDOTE: NO SPECIFIC ANTIDOTE. TREAT SYMPTOMATICALLY AND SUPPORTIVELY.

REACTIVITY

REACTIVITY: STABLE UNDER NORMAL TEMPERATURES AND PRESSURES.

INCOMPATIBILITIES: 1,2,3,4,5,6-HEXACHLOROCYCLOHEXANE: ALKALIES- MAY DECOMPOSE. ALUMINUM: MAY DECOMPOSE. N,N-DIMETHYLACETAMIDE: EXOTHERMIC, POSSIBLE VIOLENT REACTION. DIMETHYLFORMAMIDE: POSSIBLE DANGEROUS REACTION. IRON: MAY DECOMPOSE. ZINC: MAY DECOMPOSE.

DECOMPOSITION: THERMAL DECOMPOSITION PRODUCTS MAY INCLUDE HIGHLY TOXIC FUMES OF PHOSGENE, TOXIC AND CORROSIVE FUMES OF CHLORIDES, AND OXIDES OF CARBON.

POLYMERIZATION: HAZARDOUS POLYMERIZATION HAS NOT BEEN REPORTED TO OCCUR UNDER NORMAL TEMPERATURES AND PRESSURES.

STORAGE AND DISPOSAL

OBSERVE ALL FEDERAL, STATE AND LOCAL REGULATIONS WHEN STORING OR DISPOSING OF THIS SUBSTANCE. FOR ASSISTANCE, CONTACT THE DISTRICT DIRECTOR OF THE ENVIRONMENTAL PROTECTION AGENCY.

****STORAGE****

STORE IN ACCORDANCE WITH 40 CFR 165 RECOMMENDED PROCEDURES FOR THE DISPOSAL AND STORAGE OF PESTICIDES AND PESTICIDE CONTAINERS.
STORE AWAY FROM INCOMPATIBLE SUBSTANCES.

****DISPOSAL****

DISPOSAL MUST BE IN ACCORDANCE WITH 40 CFR 165 RECOMMENDED PROCEDURES FOR THE DISPOSAL AND STORAGE OF PESTICIDES AND PESTICIDE CONTAINERS.

CONDITIONS TO AVOID

MAY BURN BUT DOES NOT IGNITE READILY. CONTAINERS MAY EXPLODE IN HEAT OF FIRE.

SPILL AND LEAK PROCEDURES

WATER SPILL: THE CALIFORNIA SAFE DRINKING WATER AND TOXIC ENFORCEMENT ACT OF 1986 (PROPOSITION 65) PROHIBITS CONTAMINATING ANY KNOWN SOURCE OF DRINKING WATER WITH SUBSTANCES KNOWN TO CAUSE CANCER AND/OR REPRODUCTIVE TOXICITY.

OCCUPATIONAL SPILL: DO NOT TOUCH SPILLED MATERIAL. STOP LEAK IF YOU CAN DO IT WITHOUT RISK. USE WATER SPRAY TO REDUCE VAPORS. FOR SMALL SPILLS, TAKE UP WITH SAND OR OTHER ABSORBENT MATERIAL AND PLACE INTO CONTAINERS FOR LATER DISPOSAL. FOR SMALL DRY SPILLS, WITH A CLEAN SHOVEL PLACE MATERIAL INTO CLEAN, DRY CONTAINERS AND COVER. MOVE CONTAINERS FROM SPILL AREA. FOR LARGER SPILLS, DIKE FAR AHEAD OF SPILL FOR LATER DISPOSAL. KEEP UNNECESSARY PEOPLE AWAY. ISOLATE HAZARD AREA AND DENY ENTRY. VENTILATE CLOSED SPACES BEFORE ENTERING. REPORTABLE QUANTITY (RQ): 10 POUNDS THE SUPERFUND AMENDMENTS AND REAUTHORIZATION ACT (SARA) SECTION 304 REQUIRES THAT A RELEASE EQUAL TO OR GREATER THAN THE REPORTABLE QUANTITY FOR THIS SUBSTANCE BE IMMEDIATELY REPORTED TO THE LOCAL EMERGENCY PLANNING COMMITTEE AND THE STATE EMERGENCY RESPONSE COMMISSION (40 CFR 355.40). IF THE RELEASE OF THIS SUBSTANCE IS REPORTABLE UNDER CERCLA SECTION 103, THE NATIONAL RESPONSE CENTER MUST BE NOTIFIED IMMEDIATELY AT (800) 424-8802 OR (202) 426-2675 IN THE METROPOLITAN WASHINGTON, D.C. AREA (40 CFR 302.6).

PROTECTIVE EQUIPMENT

VENTILATION: PROVIDE LOCAL EXHAUST OR PROCESS ENCLOSURE VENTILATION SYSTEM.

RESPIRATOR: THE FOLLOWING RESPIRATORS ARE RECOMMENDED BASED ON INFORMATION FOUND IN THE PHYSICAL DATA, TOXICITY AND HEALTH EFFECTS SECTIONS. THEY ARE RANKED IN ORDER FROM MINIMUM TO MAXIMUM RESPIRATORY PROTECTION. THE SPECIFIC RESPIRATOR SELECTED MUST BE BASED ON CONTAMINATION LEVELS FOUND IN THE WORK PLACE, MUST NOT EXCEED THE WORKING LIMITS OF THE RESPIRATOR AND BE JOINTLY APPROVED BY THE NATIONAL INSTITUTE FOR OCCUPATIONAL SAFETY AND HEALTH AND THE MINE SAFETY AND HEALTH ADMINISTRATION (NIOSH-MSHA).
TYPE 'C' SUPPLIED-AIR RESPIRATOR WITH A FULL FACEPIECE OPERATED IN PRESSURE-DEMAND OR OTHER POSITIVE PRESSURE MODE OR WITH A FULL FACEPIECE, HELMET OR HOOD OPERATED IN CONTINOUS-FLOW MODE.
SELF-CONTAINED BREATHING APPARATUS WITH A FULL FACEPIECE OPERATED IN PRESSURE-DEMAND OR OTHER POSITIVE PRESSURE MODE.
FOR FIREFIGHTING AND OTHER IMMEDIATELY DANGEROUS TO LIFE OR HEALTH CONDITIONS:
SELF-CONTAINED BREATHING APPARATUS WITH FULL FACEPIECE OPERATED IN PRESSURE-DEMAND OR OTHER POSITIVE PRESSURE MODE.
SUPPLIED-AIR RESPIRATOR WITH FULL FACEPIECE AND OPERATED IN PRESSURE-DEMAND OR OTHER POSITIVE PRESSURE MODE IN COMBINATION WITH AN AUXILIARY SELF-CONTAINED BREATHING APPARATUS OPERATED IN PRESSURE-DEMAND OR OTHER POSITIVE PRESSURE MODE.

CLOTHING: EMPLOYEE MUST WEAR APPROPRIATE PROTECTIVE (IMPERVIOUS) CLOTHING AND EQUIPMENT TO PREVENT REPEATED OR PROLONGED SKIN CONTACT WITH THIS SUBSTANCE.

GLOVES: EMPLOYEE MUST WEAR APPROPRIATE PROTECTIVE GLOVES TO PREVENT CONTACT WITH THIS SUBSTANCE.

EYE PROTECTION: EMPLOYEE MUST WEAR SPLASH-PROOF OR DUST-RESISTANT SAFETY GOGGLES WITH OR WITHOUT A FACESHIELD TO PREVENT CONTACT WITH THIS SUBSTANCE.
EMERGENCY EYE WASH: WHERE THERE IS ANY POSSIBILITY THAT AN EMPLOYEE'S EYES MAY BE EXPOSED TO THIS SUBSTANCE, THE EMPLOYER SHOULD PROVIDE AN EYE WASH FOUNTAIN WITHIN THE IMMEDIATE WORK AREA FOR EMERGENCY USE.

AUTHORIZED BY- OCCUPATIONAL HEALTH SERVICES, INC.
CREATION DATE: 10/04/89 ***REVISION DATE:*** 07/12/90

MATERIAL SAFETY DATA SHEET

OCCUPATIONAL HEALTH SERVICES, INC.
AGRICULTURE AND PESTICIDE DIVISION
450 SEVENTH AVENUE, SUITE 2407
NEW YORK, NEW YORK 10123
1-800-445-MSDS OR (212) 967-1100

EMERGENCY CONTACT:
JOHN S. BRANSFORD, JR. (615) 292-1180

SUBSTANCE IDENTIFICATION

CAS-NUMBER 15879-93-3

SUBSTANCE: **ALPHA-CHLORALOSE**

TRADE NAMES/SYNONYMS: ANHYDROGLUCOCHLORAL; APHOSAL; DULCIDOR; GLUCOCHLORAL; MUREX; SOMIO; ALPHA-D-GLUCHOCHLORALOSE; ALPHA-D-GLUCOFURANOSE-1,2-O-(2,2,2-TRICHLOROETHYLIDENE)-; CHLORALOSANE; C-287; PST00775

CHEMICAL FAMILY: HALOGEN COMPOUND, ALIPHATIC

MOLECULAR FORMULA: C8-H11-CL3-O6

MOLECULAR WEIGHT: 309.54

CERCLA RATINGS (SCALE 0-3): HEALTH=3 FIRE=0 REACTIVITY=0 PERSISTENCE=1

NFPA RATINGS (SCALE 0-4): HEALTH=3 FIRE=0 REACTIVITY=0

COMPONENTS AND CONTAMINANTS

COMPONENT: ALPHA-CHLORALOSE ***PERCENT:*** 100
CAS# 15879-93-3

OTHER CONTAMINANTS: NONE

EXPOSURE LIMITS: NO OCCUPATIONAL EXPOSURE LIMITS ESTABLISHED BY OSHA, ACGIH, OR NIOSH.

PHYSICAL DATA

DESCRIPTION: NEEDLES OR WHITE POWDER WITH A BITTER TASTE

MELTING POINT: 368.6 F (187 C) ***SOLUBILITY IN WATER:*** 6.7% @ 25C

SOLVENT SOLUBILITY: SOLUBLE IN ETHER, GLACIAL ACETIC ACID; SLIGHTLY SOLUBLE IN CHLOROFORM

FIRE AND EXPLOSION DATA

FIRE AND EXPLOSION HAZARD: NEGLIGIBLE FIRE HAZARD WHEN EXPOSED TO HEAT OR FLAME.

FIREFIGHTING MEDIA: DRY CHEMICAL, CARBON DIOXIDE, HALON, WATER SPRAY OR STANDARD FOAM (1987 EMERGENCY RESPONSE GUIDEBOOK, DOT P 5800.4). FOR LARGER FIRES, USE WATER SPRAY, FOG OR STANDARD FOAM (1987 EMERGENCY RESPONSE GUIDEBOOK, DOT P 5800.4).

FIREFIGHTING: NO ACUTE HAZARD. MOVE CONTAINER FROM FIRE AREA IF POSSIBLE. AVOID BREATHING VAPORS OR DUSTS; KEEP UPWIND.

TOXICITY

ALPHA-CHLORALOSE: TOXICITY DATA: 400 MG/KG ORAL-RAT LD50; 250 MG/KG ORAL-DOG LD50; 250 MG/KG ORAL-CAT LD50; 32 MG/KG ORAL-MOUSE LD50; 200 MG/KG SUBCUTANEOUS-RAT LDLO; 120 MG/KG INTRAVENOUS-DOG LDLO; 175 MG/KG INTRAPERITONEAL-MOUSE LD50; 400 MG/KG INTRAPERITONEAL-DOG LDLO; 150 MG/KG INTRAPERITONEAL-CAT LDLO; TUMORIGENIC DATA (RTECS).
CARCINOGEN STATUS: NONE. ACUTE TOXICITY LEVEL: TOXIC BY INGESTION.
TARGET EFFECTS: CENTRAL NERVOUS SYSTEM DEPRESSANT.

HEALTH EFFECTS AND FIRST AID

INHALATION: ALPHA-CHLOROLOSE: NARCOTIC. **ACUTE EXPOSURE-** MAY CAUSE CENTRAL NERVOUS SYSTEM DEPRESSION, DEPRESSED BREATHING, HYPNOSIS, HYPOTENSION, SLEEPINESS, AND MENTAL CONFUSION. **CHRONIC EXPOSURE-** NO DATA AVAILABLE.

FIRST AID- REMOVE FROM EXPOSURE AREA TO FRESH AIR IMMEDIATELY. IF BREATHING HAS STOPPED, PERFORM ARTIFICIAL RESPIRATION. KEEP PERSON WARM AND AT REST. TREAT SYMPTOMATICALLY AND SUPPORTIVELY. GET MEDICAL ATTENTION IMMEDIATELY.

SKIN CONTACT: ALPHA-CHLOROLOSE: IRRITANT. **ACUTE EXPOSURE-** MAY CAUSE IRRITATION AND PAIN. **CHRONIC EXPOSURE-** REPEATED OR PROLONGED CONTACT MAY CAUSE DERMATITIS.

FIRST AID- REMOVE CONTAMINATED CLOTHING AND SHOES IMMEDIATELY. WASH AFFECTED AREA WITH SOAP OR MILD DETERGENT AND LARGE AMOUNTS OF WATER UNTIL NO EVIDENCE OF CHEMICAL REMAINS (APPROXIMATELY 15-20 MINUTES). GET MEDICAL ATTENTION IMMEDIATELY.

EYE CONTACT: ALPHA-CHLOROLOSE: IRRITANT. **ACUTE EXPOSURE-** DIRECT CONTACT MAY CAUSE REDNESS AND IRRITATION. **CHRONIC EXPOSURE-** PROLONGED OR REPEATED EXPOSURE MAY CAUSE CONJUNCTIVITIS.

FIRST AID- WASH EYES IMMEDIATELY WITH LARGE AMOUNTS OF WATER OR NORMAL SALINE, OCCASIONALLY LIFTING UPPER AND LOWER LIDS, UNTIL NO EVIDENCE OF CHEMICAL REMAINS (APPROXIMATELY 15-20 MINUTES). GET MEDICAL ATTENTION IMMEDIATELY.

INGESTION: ALPHA-CHLOROLOSE: NARCOTIC. **ACUTE EXPOSURE-** MAY CAUSE RESPIRATORY DEPRESSION, HYPOTENSION, TACHYCARDIA, CARDIAC ARREST, OR COMA. LARGE DOSES MAY BE CORROSIVE TO THE DIGESTIVE TRACT. **CHRONIC EXPOSURE-** NO DATA AVAILABLE.

FIRST AID- IF PERSON IS CONSCIOUS, GIVE LARGE QUANTITIES OF WATER AND INDUCE VOMITING. DO NOT MAKE AN UNCONSCIOUS PERSON VOMIT OR DRINK ANYTHING. MAINTAIN BLOOD PRESSURE, AIRWAY, AND GIVE OXYGEN IF RESPIRATION IS DEPRESSED. GET MEDICAL ATTENTION.

ANTIDOTE: NO SPECIFIC ANTIDOTE. TREAT SYMPTOMATICALLY AND SUPPORTIVELY.

REACTIVITY

REACTIVITY: STABLE UNDER NORMAL TEMPERATURES AND PRESSURES.

INCOMPATIBILITIES: ALPHA-CHLOROLOSE: NO DATA AVAILABLE.

DECOMPOSITION: THERMAL DECOMPOSITION PRODUCTS MAY INCLUDE TOXIC AND/OR CORROSIVE VAPORS OF HYDROGEN CHLORIDE, CHLORINE, AND CARBON MONOXIDE.

POLYMERIZATION: HAZARDOUS POLYMERIZATION HAS NOT BEEN REPORTED TO OCCUR UNDER NORMAL TEMPERATURES AND PRESSURES.

CONDITIONS TO AVOID

MAY BURN BUT DOES NOT IGNITE READILY. AVOID CONTACT WITH STRONG OXIDIZERS, EXCESSIVE HEAT, SPARKS, OR OPEN FLAME.

SPILL AND LEAK PROCEDURES

OCCUPATIONAL SPILL: SWEEP UP AND PLACE IN SUITABLE CLEAN, DRY CONTAINERS FOR RECLAMATION OR LATER DISPOSAL. DO NOT FLUSH SPILLED MATERIAL INTO SEWER. KEEP UNNECESSARY PEOPLE AWAY.

PROTECTIVE EQUIPMENT

VENTILATION: PROVIDE LOCAL EXHAUST OR PROCESS ENCLOSURE VENTILATION SYSTEM.

RESPIRATOR: THE FOLLOWING RESPIRATORS ARE RECOMMENDED BASED ON INFORMATION FOUND IN THE PHYSICAL DATA, TOXICITY AND HEALTH EFFECTS SECTIONS. THEY ARE RANKED IN ORDER FROM MINIMUM TO MAXIMUM RESPIRATORY PROTECTION. THE SPECIFIC RESPIRATOR SELECTED MUST BE BASED ON CONTAMINATION LEVELS FOUND IN THE WORK PLACE, MUST NOT EXCEED THE WORKING LIMITS OF THE RESPIRATOR AND BE JOINTLY APPROVED BY THE NATIONAL INSTITUTE FOR OCCUPATIONAL SAFETY AND HEALTH AND THE MINE SAFETY AND HEALTH ADMINISTRATION (NIOSH-MSHA).
TYPE 'C' SUPPLIED-AIR RESPIRATOR WITH A FULL FACEPIECE OPERATED IN PRESSURE-DEMAND OR OTHER POSITIVE PRESSURE MODE OR WITH A FULL FACEPIECE, HELMET OR HOOD OPERATED IN CONTINOUS-FLOW MODE.
SELF-CONTAINED BREATHING APPARATUS WITH A FULL FACEPIECE OPERATED IN PRESSURE-DEMAND OR OTHER POSITIVE PRESSURE MODE.
FOR FIREFIGHTING AND OTHER IMMEDIATELY DANGEROUS TO LIFE OR HEALTH CONDITIONS:
SELF-CONTAINED BREATHING APPARATUS WITH FULL FACEPIECE OPERATED IN PRESSURE-DEMAND OR OTHER POSITIVE PRESSURE MODE.
SUPPLIED-AIR RESPIRATOR WITH FULL FACEPIECE AND OPERATED IN PRESSURE-DEMAND OR OTHER POSITIVE PRESSURE MODE IN COMBINATION WITH AN AUXILIARY SELF-CONTAINED BREATHING APPARATUS OPERATED IN PRESSURE-DEMAND OR OTHER POSITIVE PRESSURE MODE.

CLOTHING: EMPLOYEE MUST WEAR APPROPRIATE PROTECTIVE (IMPERVIOUS) CLOTHING AND EQUIPMENT TO PREVENT REPEATED OR PROLONGED SKIN CONTACT WITH THIS SUBSTANCE.

GLOVES: EMPLOYEE MUST WEAR APPROPRIATE PROTECTIVE GLOVES TO PREVENT CONTACT WITH THIS SUBSTANCE.

EYE PROTECTION: EMPLOYEE MUST WEAR SPLASH-PROOF OR DUST-RESISTANT SAFETY GOGGLES TO PREVENT EYE CONTACT WITH THIS SUBSTANCE.
EMERGENCY EYE WASH: WHERE THERE IS ANY POSSIBILITY THAT AN EMPLOYEE'S EYES MAY BE EXPOSED TO THIS SUBSTANCE, THE EMPLOYER SHOULD PROVIDE AN EYE WASH FOUNTAIN WITHIN THE IMMEDIATE WORK AREA FOR EMERGENCY USE.

AUTHORIZED BY- OCCUPATIONAL HEALTH SERVICES, INC.
CREATION DATE: 10/04/89 ***REVISION DATE:*** 05/31/90

MATERIAL SAFETY DATA SHEET

OCCUPATIONAL HEALTH SERVICES, INC.
AGRICULTURE AND PESTICIDE DIVISION
450 SEVENTH AVENUE, SUITE 2407
NEW YORK, NEW YORK 10123
1-800-445-MSDS OR (212) 967-1100

EMERGENCY CONTACT:
JOHN S. BRANSFORD, JR. (615) 292-1180

SUBSTANCE IDENTIFICATION

CAS-NUMBER 5103-71-9

SUBSTANCE: **ALPHA-CHLORDANE**

TRADE NAMES/SYNONYMS: 4,7-METHANO-1H-INDENE, 1,2,4,5,6,7,8,8-OCTACHLORO-2,3,3A,4,7,7A- HEXAHYDRO-, (1ALPHA,2ALPHA,3A ALPHA,4BETA,7BETA,7A ALPHA)-; (1ALPHA,2ALPHA,3A ALPHA,4BETA,7BETA,7A ALPHA)-1,2,4,5,6,7,8,8-OCTACHLORO-2,3,3A,4,7,7A-HEXAHYDRO-4,7-METHANO-1H-INDENE; 4,7-METHANOINDAN, 1ALPHA,2ALPHA,4BETA,5,6,7BETA,8,8-OCTACHLORO-3A ALPHA,4,7,7A ALPHA-TETRAHYDRO-; 1ALPHA,2ALPHA,4BETA,5,6,7BETA,8,8-OCTACHLORO-3A ALPHA,4,7,7A ALPHA- TETRAHYDRO-4,7-METHANOINDAN; CIS-CHLORDAN; ALPHA-CHLORDAN; CIS-CHLORDANE; CHLORDANE; C10H6CL8; PST00776

CHEMICAL FAMILY: HALOGEN COMPOUND, AROMATIC

MOLECULAR FORMULA: C10-H6-CL8

MOLECULAR WEIGHT: 409.80

CERCLA RATINGS (SCALE 0-3): HEALTH=3 FIRE=0 REACTIVITY=0 PERSISTENCE=3

NFPA RATINGS (SCALE 0-4): HEALTH=U FIRE=0 REACTIVITY=0

COMPONENTS AND CONTAMINANTS

COMPONENT: ALPHA-CHLORDANE ***PERCENT:*** 100.0 CAS# 5103-71-9

OTHER CONTAMINANTS: NONE

EXPOSURE LIMITS: ALPHA-CHLORDANE: 0.5 MG/M3 OSHA TWA (SKIN) 0.5 MG/M3 ACGIH TWA (SKIN); 2 MG/M3 ACGIH STEL (NOTICE OF INTENDED CHANGES 1988-89)

PHYSICAL DATA

DESCRIPTION: SOLID. ***BOILING POINT:*** 347 F (175 C) (DEC.) (APPROX.)

MELTING POINT: 223-225 F (106-107 C) ***SPECIFIC GRAVITY:*** 1.59-1.63 (APPROX.)

VAPOR PRESSURE: 0.00001 MMHG @ 20 C ***SOLUBILITY IN WATER:*** INSOLUBLE

SOLVENT SOLUBILITY: SOLUBLE IN ALIPHATIC AND AROMATIC HYDROCARBON SOLVENTS INCLUDING DEODORIZED KEROSENE.

FIRE AND EXPLOSION DATA

FIRE AND EXPLOSION HAZARD: NEGLIGIBLE FIRE HAZARD WHEN EXPOSED TO HEAT OR FLAME.

FIREFIGHTING MEDIA: DRY CHEMICAL, CARBON DIOXIDE, HALON, WATER SPRAY OR STANDARD FOAM (1987 EMERGENCY RESPONSE GUIDEBOOK, DOT P 5800.4). FOR LARGER FIRES, USE WATER SPRAY, FOG OR STANDARD FOAM (1987 EMERGENCY RESPONSE GUIDEBOOK, DOT P 5800.4).

FIREFIGHTING: MOVE CONTAINERS FROM FIRE AREA IF POSSIBLE (1987 EMERGENCY RESPONSE GUIDEBOOK, DOT P 5800.4, GUIDE PAGE 53).
EXTINGUISH USING AGENT SUITABLE FOR TYPE OF SURROUNDING FIRE. AVOID BREATHING VAPORS AND DUSTS. KEEP UPWIND.

TOXICITY

ALPHA-CHLORDANE: TOXICITY DATA: 500 MG/KG ORAL-RAT LD50; 125 MG/KG ORAL-MOUSE LD50; 290 MG/KG INTRAPERITONEAL-MOUSE LDLO; REPRODUCTIVE EFFECTS DATA (RTECS). CARCINOGEN STATUS: NONE. ACUTE TOXICITY LEVEL: TOXIC BY INGESTION. TARGET EFFECTS: POISONING MAY AFFECT THE LIVER, KIDNEYS, AND BLOOD.*

* MAY BE BASED ON GENERAL INFORMATION ON CHLORDANE.

CHLORDANE: TOXICITY DATA: 100 MG/M3/4 HOURS INHALATION-CAT LC50; 428 MG/KG SKIN-HUMAN LDLO; 780 MG/KG SKIN-RABBIT LD50; 690 MG/KG SKIN-RAT LD50; 29 MG/KG ORAL-HUMAN LDLO; 3071 UG/KG ORAL-MAN TDLO; 120 UG/KG ORAL-WOMAN LDLO; 200 MG/KG ORAL-RAT LD50; 145 MG/KG ORAL-MOUSE LD50; 100 MG/KG ORAL-RABBIT LD50; 1720 MG/KG ORAL-HAMSTER LD50; 180 MG/KG ORAL-MAMMAL LD50; 50 MG/KG ORAL-DOMESTIC ANIMAL LD50; 100 MG/KG INTRAVENOUS-MOUSE LD50; 10 MG/KG INTRAVENOUS-RABBIT LDLO; 343 MG/KG INTRAPERITONEAL-RAT LD50; 240 MG/KG INTRAPERITONEAL-MOUSE LDLO; 118 MG/KG UNREPORTED-MAN LDLO; MUTAGENIC DATA (RTECS); REPRODUCTIVE EFFECTS DATA (RTECS); TUMORIGENIC DATA (RTECS). CARCINOGEN STATUS: HUMAN INADEQUATE EVIDENCE; ANIMAL LIMITED EVIDENCE (IARC GROUP-3). HEPATOCELLULAR CARCINOMAS WERE PRODUCED IN MICE BY ORAL ADMINISTRATION. ACUTE TOXICITY LEVEL: HIGHLY TOXIC BY INHALATION; TOXIC BY DERMAL ABSORPTION AND INGESTION. TARGET EFFECTS: CONVULSANT. POISONING MAY ALSO AFFECT THE LIVER, KIDNEYS, AND BLOOD. AT INCREASED RISK FROM EXPOSURE: PERSONS WITH CONVULSIVE DISORDERS. ADDITIONAL DATA: CHLORDANE MAY BE STORED IN ADIPOSE TISSUE; INTENSE ACTIVITY AND STARVATION MAY MOBILIZE THE PESTICIDE RESULTING IN THE REAPPEARANCE OF TOXIC SYMPTOMS. IT CROSSES THE PLACENTA AND MAY BE EXCRETED IN HUMAN MILK. STUDIES OF 2 GROUPS OF WORKERS, ONE INVOLVED IN THE MANUFACTURE OF CHLORDANE, HEPTACHLOR, AND ENDRIN AND THE OTHER OF CHLORDANE AND HEPTACHLOR, REVEALED A STATISTICALLY SIGNIFICANT INCREASE IN DEATHS FROM CEREBROVASCULAR DISEASE IN THE FORMER BUT NOT THE LATTER; THE FORMER STUDY HAD METHODOLOGICAL DEFICIENCIES.

HEALTH EFFECTS AND FIRST AID

INHALATION: CHLORDANE: CONVULSANT/HIGHLY TOXIC. 500 MG/M3 IMMEDIATELY DANGEROUS TO LIFE OR HEALTH. **ACUTE EXPOSURE-** SYMPTOMS OF BLURRED VISION, COUGH, CONFUSION, ATAXIA, HEADACHE, WEAKNESS, DIZZINESS, AND DELIRIUM WERE REPORTED FROM INHALATION EXPOSURE TO CHLORDANE. SYMPTOMS OF CENTRAL NERVOUS SYSTEM STIMULATION MAY ALSO OCCUR AS DETAILED IN ACUTE INGESTION. **CHRONIC EXPOSURE-** HUMAN EXPOSURE TO VAPORS OF 7 PERCENT CHLORDANE FOR 15 MINUTES AT 3-DAY INTERVALS FOR PERIODS OF 15 WEEKS AND REPEATED A YEAR LATER, DID NOT RESULT IN SYMPTOMS OF TOXICITY. IN ADDITION TO THE SYMPTOMS OF ACUTE EXPOSURE, CHRONIC EXPOSURE OF HUMANS TO TECHNICAL CHLORDANE CONTAINING HEPTACHLOR AND OTHER CHEMICALS HAS CAUSED LIGHTHEADEDNESS, NAUSEA, COUGH, CHEST COMPLAINTS, TREMORS, ARTHRALGIAS, FATIGUE, THROMBOCYTOPENIC PURPURA, AND MARKED BRUISING. PANCYTOPENIA, APLASTIC, HEMOLYTIC, AND MEGALOBLASTIC ANEMIAS, LEUKEMIA, AND DEATH HAVE ALSO BEEN REPORTED. EXPOSURE OF MONKEYS TO 100-1,000 UG/M3 FOR 90 DAYS INDUCED A STATISTICALLY SIGNIFICANT INCIDENCE OF LEUKOPENIA AND THROMBOCYTOPENIA, WITH EFFECTS OCCURRING AT THE LOWEST DOSE TESTED.

FIRST AID- REMOVE FROM EXPOSURE AREA TO FRESH AIR IMMEDIATELY. IF BREATHING HAS STOPPED, GIVE ARTIFICIAL RESPIRATION. MAINTAIN AIRWAY AND BLOOD PRESSURE AND ADMINISTER OXYGEN IF AVAILABLE. KEEP AFFECTED PERSON WARM AND AT REST. TREAT SYMPTOMATICALLY AND SUPPORTIVELY. ADMINISTRATION OF OXYGEN SHOULD BE PERFORMED BY QUALIFIED PERSONNEL. GET MEDICAL ATTENTION IMMEDIATELY.

SKIN CONTACT: CHLORDANE: CONVULSANT/TOXIC. **ACUTE EXPOSURE-** MAY BE IRRITATING. SKIN ABSORPTION HAS CAUSED BLURRED VISION, CONFUSION, ATAXIA, HEADACHE, DIZZINESS, WEAKNESS, AND DELIRIUM. IN SEVERE POISONING, CONVULSIONS MAY DEVELOP AND COMA AND DEATH ARE POSSIBLE. IN ONE CASE OF OCCUPATIONAL EXPOSURE, A WOMAN BECAME CONFUSED AND DEVELOPED CONVULSIONS 40 MINUTES AFTER SPILLING A SOLUTION CONTAINING 25% CHLORDANE AND 25% DDT ON HER CLOTHING. SHE DIED SHORTLY THEREAFTER FROM RESPIRATORY FAILURE. **CHRONIC EXPOSURE-** REPEATED CONTACT CAUSED EPISODES OF PARESTHESIA, TWITCHING OF THE RIGHT HAND AND ARM, GRAND MAL SEIZURES, AND UNCONSCIOUSNESS. OTHER EFFECTS MAY OCCUR AS DETAILED IN CHRONIC INHALATION. REPEATED APPLICATION OF 50 MG/KG TO THE SKIN OF RATS FOR 3 OR 4 DAYS CAUSED 100% FATALITIES.

FIRST AID- REMOVE CONTAMINATED CLOTHING AND SHOES IMMEDIATELY. WASH AFFECTED AREA WITH SOAP OR MILD DETERGENT AND LARGE AMOUNTS OF WATER UNTIL NO EVIDENCE OF CHEMICAL REMAINS (APPROXIMATELY 15-20 MINUTES). GET MEDICAL ATTENTION IMMEDIATELY.

EYE CONTACT: CHLORDANE: **ACUTE EXPOSURE-** MAY BE IRRITATING. **CHRONIC EXPOSURE-** NO DATA AVAILABLE.

FIRST AID- WASH EYES IMMEDIATELY WITH LARGE AMOUNTS OF WATER OR NORMAL SALINE, OCCASIONALLY LIFTING UPPER AND LOWER LIDS, UNTIL NO EVIDENCE OF CHEMICAL REMAINS (APPROXIMATELY 15-20 MINUTES). GET MEDICAL ATTENTION IMMEDIATELY.

INGESTION: CHLORDANE: CONVULSANT/LIMITED ANIMAL CARCINOGEN/TOXIC. **ACUTE EXPOSURE-** MAY CAUSE ABDOMINAL PAIN, NAUSEA, VOMITING, AND DIARRHEA. CHLORDANE MAY STIMULATE THE CENTRAL NERVOUS SYSTEM WITH CONVULSIONS SOMETIMES APPEARING AS THE FIRST SYMPTOM OF POISONING. SYMPTOMS OF HEADACHE, BLURRED VISION, HYPEREXCITABILITY, MUSCLE TWITCHING, TREMOR, INCOORDINATION, AND ATAXIA MAY ALSO OCCUR. IN SEVERE CASES OF POISONING, COMA AND DEATH ARE POSSIBLE. EEG PATTERNS SUGGEST THAT DEATH IS DUE TO RESPIRATORY ARREST BETWEEN OR DURING CONVULSIVE EPISODES. CHLORDANE MAY BE EXCRETED SLOWLY FROM THE BODY; THE SERUM HALF-LIFE IN ONE CHILD WAS 88 DAYS. **CHRONIC EXPOSURE-** IN A TWO-YEAR FEEDING STUDY IN RATS, A DIETARY CONCENTRATION OF 150 PPM PRODUCED A NOTED RETARDATION OF GROWTH, LIVER AND KIDNEY DAMAGE, MYOCARDIAL DAMAGE, AND MILD INJURY TO THE LUNGS; MARKED DAMAGE TO THE LUNGS AND INCREASED MORTALITY WERE OBSERVED AT DIETARY CONCENTRATIONS OF 300 PPM. SIMILAR EFFECTS WERE REPORTED IN RABBITS ADMINISTERED 5 MG/KG/DAY. CHLORDANE PRODUCED LIVER NEOPLASMS IN MICE FOLLOWING ORAL ADMINISTRATION; RESULTS FOR RATS WERE INCONCLUSIVE. ORAL ADMINISTRATION OF CHLORDANE ENHANCED THE INCIDENCE OF LIVER TUMORS INDUCED IN MICE BY ORAL ADMINISTRATION OF N-NITROSODIETHYLAMINE. REPRODUCTIVE EFFECTS REPORTED IN ANIMALS INCLUDE DECREASED VIABILTIY OF OFFSPRING IN MICE FED 100 MG/KG/DAY FOR 4 MONTHS; DECREASED FERTILITY IN RATS AND MICE; AND EXCITABILITY AND TREMORS IN OFFSPRING WHEN KEPT WITH TREATED MOTHERS, BUT NOT WITH UNTREATED FEMALES.

FIRST AID- IF THE PERSON IS CONSCIOUS AND NOT CONVULSING, REMOVE BY GIVING SYRUP OF IPECAC (IF VOMITING OCCURS, KEEP THE HEAD BELOW THE HIPS TO PREVENT ASPIRATION). GIVE ACTIVATED CHARCOAL FOLLOWED BY GASTRIC LAVAGE. FOLLOW WITH A SALINE CATHARTIC. DO NOT GIVE FATS OR OILS.

INTESTINAL LAVAGE WITH 20% MANNITOL (200 ML) BY STOMACH TUBE IS ALSO USEFUL. GIVE ARTIFICIAL RESPIRATION WITH OXYGEN IF RESPIRATION IS DEPRESSED (DREISBACH, HANDBOOK OF POISONING, 12TH ED.). TREAT SYMPTOMATICALLY AND SUPPORTIVELY. LAVAGE AND ADMINISTRATION OF OXYGEN SHOULD BE PERFORMED BY QUALIFIED MEDICAL PERSONNEL. GET MEDICAL ATTENTION IMMEDIATELY.

ANTIDOTE: NO SPECIFIC ANTIDOTE. TREAT SYMPTOMATICALLY AND SUPPORTIVELY.

REACTIVITY

REACTIVITY: STABLE UNDER NORMAL TEMPERATURES AND PRESSURES.

INCOMPATIBILITIES: ALPHA-CHLORDANE: ALKALIES (WEAK): DECOMPOSES. OXIDIZERS (STRONG): FIRE AND EXPLOSION HAZARD. PLASTICS, RUBBER, AND COATINGS: MAY BE ATTACKED.

DECOMPOSITION: THERMAL DECOMPOSITION PRODUCTS MAY INCLUDE TOXIC AND CORROSIVE FUMES OF CHLORIDES AND PHOSGENE, AND TOXIC OXIDES OF CARBON.

POLYMERIZATION: HAZARDOUS POLYMERIZATION HAS NOT BEEN REPORTED TO OCCUR UNDER NORMAL TEMPERATURES AND PRESSURES.

STORAGE AND DISPOSAL

OBSERVE ALL FEDERAL, STATE AND LOCAL REGULATIONS WHEN STORING OR DISPOSING OF THIS SUBSTANCE. FOR ASSISTANCE, CONTACT THE DISTRICT DIRECTOR OF THE ENVIRONMENTAL PROTECTION AGENCY.

STORAGE

STORE AWAY FROM INCOMPATIBLE SUBSTANCES.

STORE IN ACCORDANCE WITH 40 CFR 165 RECOMMENDED PROCEDURES FOR THE DISPOSAL AND STORAGE OF PESTICIDES AND PESTICIDE CONTAINERS.

DISPOSAL

DISPOSAL MUST BE IN ACCORDANCE WITH 40 CFR 165 RECOMMENDED PROCEDURES FOR THE DISPOSAL AND STORAGE OF PESTICIDES AND PESTICIDE CONTAINERS.

CONDITIONS TO AVOID

MAY BURN BUT DOES NOT IGNITE READILY.

SPILL AND LEAK PROCEDURES

SOIL SPILL: DIG A HOLDING AREA SUCH AS A PIT, POND OR LAGOON TO CONTAIN SPILL AND DIKE SURFACE FLOW USING BARRIER OF SOIL, SANDBAGS, FOAMED POLYURETHANE OR FOAMED CONCRETE. ABSORB LIQUID MASS WITH FLY ASH OR CEMENT POWDER.

IMMOBILIZE SPILL WITH UNIVERSAL GELLING AGENT.

AIR SPILL: KNOCK DOWN VAPORS WITH WATER SPRAY. KEEP UPWIND. COMBUSTION PRODUCTS INCLUDE CORROSIVE OR TOXIC VAPORS.

WATER SPILL: TRAP SPILLED MATERIAL AT BOTTOM IN DEEP WATER POCKETS, EXCAVATED HOLDING AREAS OR WITHIN SAND BAG BARRIERS.

USE ACTIVATED CARBON TO ABSORB SPILLED SUBSTANCE THAT IS DISSOLVED.

USE MECHANICAL DREDGES OR LIFTS TO EXTRACT IMMOBILIZED MASSES OF POLLUTION AND PRECIPITATES.

OCCUPATIONAL SPILL: DO NOT TOUCH SPILLED MATERIAL. STOP LEAK IF YOU CAN DO IT WITHOUT RISK. FOR SMALL SPILLS, TAKE UP WITH SAND OR OTHER ABSORBENT MATERIAL AND PLACE INTO CONTAINERS FOR LATER DISPOSAL. FOR SMALL DRY SPILLS, WITH A CLEAN SHOVEL PLACE MATERIAL INTO CLEAN, DRY CONTAINER AND COVER. MOVE CONTAINERS FROM SPILL AREA. FOR LARGER SPILLS, DIKE FAR AHEAD OF SPILL FOR LATER DISPOSAL. KEEP UNNECESSARY PEOPLE AWAY. ISOLATE HAZARD AREA AND DENY ENTRY.

PROTECTIVE EQUIPMENT

VENTILATION: PROVIDE LOCAL EXHAUST VENTILATION AND/OR GENERAL DILUTION VENTILATION TO MEET PUBLISHED EXPOSURE LIMITS.

RESPIRATOR: THE FOLLOWING RESPIRATORS AND MAXIMUM USE CONCENTRATIONS ARE RECOMMENDATIONS BY THE U.S. DEPARTMENT OF HEALTH AND HUMAN SERVICES, NIOSH POCKET GUIDE TO CHEMICAL HAZARDS; NIOSH CRITERIA DOCUMENTS OR BY THE U.S. DEPARTMENT OF LABOR, 29 CFR 1910 SUBPART Z. THE SPECIFIC RESPIRATOR SELECTED MUST BE BASED ON CONTAMINATION LEVELS FOUND IN THE WORK PLACE, MUST NOT EXCEED THE WORKING LIMITS OF THE RESPIRATOR AND BE JOINTLY APPROVED BY THE NATIONAL INSTITUTE FOR OCCUPATIONAL SAFETY AND HEALTH AND THE MINE SAFETY AND HEALTH ADMINISTRATION (NIOSH-MSHA).

CHLORDANE:

5 MG/M3- ANY CHEMICAL CARTRIDGE RESPIRATOR WITH ORGANIC VAPOR CARTRIDGE(S) IN COMBINATION WITH A DUST, MIST, AND FUME FILTER. ANY SUPPLIED-AIR RESPIRATOR. ANY SELF-CONTAINED BREATHING APPARATUS.

12.5 MG/M3- ANY SUPPLIED-AIR RESPIRATOR OPERATED IN A CONTINUOUS FLOW MODE. ANY POWERED AIR-PURIFYING RESPIRATOR WITH ORGANIC VAPOR CARTRIDGE(S) IN COMBINATION WITH A DUST, MIST, AND FUME FILTER.

25 MG/M3- ANY CHEMICAL CARTRIDGE RESPIRATOR WITH A FULL FACEPIECE AND ORGANIC VAPOR CARTRIDGE(S) IN COMBINATION WITH A HIGH-EFFICIENCY PARTICULATE FILTER. ANY SUPPLIED-AIR RESPIRATOR WITH A FULL FACEPIECE. ANY SELF-CONTAINED BREATHING APPARATUS WITH A FULL FACEPIECE. ANY POWDERED AIR-PURIFYING RESPIRATOR WITH A TIGHT-FITTING FACEPIECE AND ORGANIC VAPOR CARTRIDGE(S) IN COMBINATION WITH A HIGH-EFFICIENCY PARTICULATE FILTER. ANY AIR-PURIFYING FULL FACEPIECE RESPIRATOR (GAS MASK) WITH A CHIN-STYLE OR FRONT- OR BACK-MOUNTED ORGANIC VAPOR CANISTER HAVING A HIGH-EFFICIENCY PARTICULATE FILTER.

500 MG/M3- ANY SUPPLIED-AIR RESPIRATOR WITH A HALF-MASK AND OPERATED IN A PRESSURE-DEMAND OR OTHER POSITIVE PRESSURE MODE.

ESCAPE- ANY AIR-PURIFYING FULL FACEPIECE RESPIRATOR (GAS MASK) WITH A CHIN-STYLE OR FRONT- OR BACK-MOUNTED ORGANIC VAPOR CANISTER HAVING A HIGH-EFFICIENCY PARTICULATE FILTER. ANY APPROPRIATE ESCAPE-TYPE SELF-CONTAINED BREATHING APPARATUS. FOR FIREFIGHTING AND OTHER IMMEDIATELY DANGEROUS TO LIFE OR HEALTH CONDITIONS:

SELF-CONTAINED BREATHING APPARATUS WITH FULL FACEPIECE OPERATED IN PRESSURE-DEMAND OR OTHER POSITIVE PRESSURE MODE.

SUPPLIED-AIR RESPIRATOR WITH FULL FACEPIECE AND OPERATED IN PRESSURE-DEMAND OR OTHER POSITIVE PRESSURE MODE IN COMBINATION WITH AN AUXILIARY SELF-CONTAINED BREATHING APPARATUS OPERATED IN PRESSURE-DEMAND OR OTHER POSITIVE PRESSURE MODE.

CLOTHING: EMPLOYEE MUST WEAR APPROPRIATE PROTECTIVE (IMPERVIOUS) CLOTHING AND EQUIPMENT TO PREVENT ANY POSSIBILITY OF SKIN CONTACT WITH THIS SUBSTANCE.

GLOVES: EMPLOYEE MUST WEAR APPROPRIATE PROTECTIVE GLOVES TO PREVENT CONTACT WITH THIS SUBSTANCE.

EYE PROTECTION: EMPLOYEE MUST WEAR SPLASH-PROOF OR DUST-RESISTANT SAFETY GOGGLES AND A FACESHIELD TO PREVENT CONTACT WITH THIS SUBSTANCE.

EMERGENCY WASH FACILITIES: WHERE THERE IS ANY POSSIBILITY THAT AN EMPLOYEE'S EYES AND/OR SKIN MAY BE EXPOSED TO THIS SUBSTANCE, THE EMPLOYER SHOULD PROVIDE AN EYE WASH FOUNTAIN AND QUICK DRENCH SHOWER WITHIN THE IMMEDIATE WORK AREA FOR EMERGENCY USE.

AUTHORIZED BY- OCCUPATIONAL HEALTH SERVICES, INC.

CREATION DATE: 10/04/89 ***REVISION DATE:*** 06/27/90

MATERIAL SAFETY DATA SHEET

OCCUPATIONAL HEALTH SERVICES, INC.
AGRICULTURE AND PESTICIDE DIVISION
450 SEVENTH AVENUE, SUITE 2407
NEW YORK, NEW YORK 10123
1-800-445-MSDS OR (212) 967-1100

EMERGENCY CONTACT:
JOHN S. BRANSFORD, JR. (615) 292-1180

SUBSTANCE IDENTIFICATION

CAS-NUMBER 959-98-8

SUBSTANCE: **ALPHA-ENDOSULFAN**

TRADE NAMES/SYNONYMS: 6,9-METHANO-2,4,3-BENZODIOXATHIEPIN, 6,7,8,9,10,10-HEXACHLORO-1, 5,5A,6,9,9A-HEXAHYDRO-, 3-OXIDE, (3 ALPHA, 5A BETA, 6 ALPHA, 9 ALPHA, 9A BETA)-; 5-NORBORNENE-2,3-DIMETHANOL,1,4,5,6,7,7-HEXACHLORO-,CYCLIC SULFITE, ENDO; (3 ALPHA, 5A BETA, 6 ALPHA, 9 ALPHA, 9A BETA) 6,7,8,9,10,10-HEXACHLORO -1,5,5A,6,9,9A-HEXAHYDRO-6,9,-METHANO-2,4,3-BENZODIOXATHIEPIN 3-OXIDE; ENDO-1,4,5,6,7,7-HEXACHLORO-5-NORBORNENE-2,3-DIMETHANOL CYCLIC SULFITE; ENDOSULFAN A; ALPHA-BENZOEPIN; ENDOSULFAN 1; ENDOSULFAN I; ALPHA-THIODAN; BETA-THIONEX; C9H6CL6O3S; PST00800

CHEMICAL FAMILY: HALOGEN COMPOUND, ALICYCLIC

MOLECULAR FORMULA: C9-H6-CL6-O3-S

MOLECULAR WEIGHT: 406.95

CERCLA RATINGS (SCALE 0-3): HEALTH=3 FIRE=0 REACTIVITY=0 PERSISTENCE=3

NFPA RATINGS (SCALE 0-4): HEALTH=3 FIRE=0 REACTIVITY=0

COMPONENTS AND CONTAMINANTS

COMPONENT: ALPHA-ENDOSULFAN ***PERCENT:*** 100

CAS# 959-98-8

OTHER CONTAMINANTS: NONE

EXPOSURE LIMITS: ALPHA-ENDOSULFAN: NO OCCUPATIONAL EXPSOURE LIMITS ESTABLISHED BY OSHA, ACGIH, OR NIOSH.

1 POUND CERCLA SECTION 103 REPORTABLE QUANTITY

PHYSICAL DATA

DESCRIPTION: CRYSTALLINE SOLID ***MELTING POINT:*** 223-230 F (106-110 C)
SPECIFIC GRAVITY: NOT AVAILABLE ***SOLUBILITY IN WATER:*** 530 UG/L
SOLVENT SOLUBILITY: ORGANIC SOLVENTS

FIRE AND EXPLOSION DATA

FIRE AND EXPLOSION HAZARD: NEGLIGIBLE FIRE HAZARD WHEN EXPOSED TO HEAT OR FLAME.

FIREFIGHTING MEDIA: DRY CHEMICAL, CARBON DIOXIDE, HALON, WATER SPRAY OR STANDARD FOAM (1987 EMERGENCY RESPONSE GUIDEBOOK, DOT P 5800.4). FOR LARGER FIRES, USE WATER SPRAY, FOG OR STANDARD FOAM (1987 EMERGENCY RESPONSE GUIDEBOOK, DOT P 5800.4).

FIREFIGHTING: MOVE CONTAINERS FROM FIRE AREA IF POSSIBLE. FIGHT FIRE FROM MAXIMUM DISTANCE. STAY AWAY FROM STORAGE TANK ENDS. DIKE FIRE CONTROL WATER FOR LATER DISPOSAL. DO NOT SCATTER MATERIAL (1987 EMERGENCY RESPONSE GUIDEBOOK, DOT P 5800.4, GUIDE PAGE 55).
USE AGENTS SUITABLE FOR TYPE OF FIRE. COOL CONTAINERS WITH FLOODING AMOUNTS OF WATER. AVOID BREATHING VAPORS OR DUSTS, KEEP UPWIND.

TOXICITY

ALPHA-ENDOSULFAN: TOXICITY DATA: 76 MG/KG ORAL-RAT LD50. CARCINOGEN STATUS: NONE. ACUTE TOXICITY: TOXIC BY INGESTION. TARGET EFFECTS: CONVULSANT.

HEALTH EFFECTS AND FIRST AID

INHALATION: ALPHA-ENDOSULFAN: CONVULSANT. **ACUTE EXPOSURE-** A LETHAL CONCENTRATION OF ENDOSULFAN IN RATS WAS 80 MG/M3/4 HOURS. ENDOSULFAN MAY BE ABSORBED FROM THE LUNGS AND PRODUCE CENTRAL NERVOUS SYSTEM STIMULATION WITH SYMPTOMS OF HEADACHE, RESTLESSNESS, IRRITABILITY, CONFUSION, MALAISE, DIZZINESS, WEAKNESS, NAUSEA, VOMITING, AND FLUSHING AND DRY MOUTH. FAINTING, EPILEPTIC CONVULSIONS AND ALTERED EEG PATTERNS MAY OCCUR. SOME OF THESE SYMPTOMS MAY BE DELAYED FOR SEVERAL HOURS AFTER EXPOSURE. ABSORPTION IS NORMALLY SLOW BUT IS INCREASED WHEN IN SOLUTION WITH ALCOHOLS, OILS AND EMULSIFIERS. IT DOES NOT ACCUMULATE SIGNIFICANTLY IN HUMAN TISSUE. **CHRONIC EXPOSURE-** PROLONGED OR REPEATED EXPOSURE MAY CAUSE EFFECTS AS DESCRIBED IN ACUTE EXPOSURE. ONE INDIVIDUAL EXPERIENCED FAINTING AND CONVULSIONS WHILE ASSIGNED TO CLEANING VATS CONTAINING RESIDUES OF ENDOSULFAN. TWO YEARS AFTER EXPOSURE, THIS PERSON HAD COGNITIVE AND EMOTIONAL DETERIORATION, SEVERE IMPAIRMENT OF MEMORY, GROSS IMPAIRMENT OF VISUAL MOTOR COORDINATION, AND INABILITY TO PERFORM ANY BUT THE SIMPLEST TASKS.

FIRST AID- REMOVE FROM EXPOSURE AREA TO FRESH AIR IMMEDIATELY. IF BREATHING HAS STOPPED, PERFORM ARTIFICIAL RESPIRATION. KEEP PERSON WARM AND AT REST. TREAT SYMPTOMATICALLY AND SUPPORTIVELY. GET MEDICAL ATTENTION IMMEDIATELY.

SKIN CONTACT: ALPHA-ENDOSULFAN: CONVULSANT. **ACUTE EXPOSURE-** A LETHAL DOSE OF ENDOSULFAN IN RABBITS BY DERMAL ABSORPTION WAS 90 MG/KG. ENDOSULFAN MAY BE ABSORBED FROM THE SKIN AND PRODUCE CENTRAL NERVOUS SYSTEM STIMULATION WITH SYMPTOMS OF HEADACHE, RESTLESSNESS, IRRITABILITY, CONFUSION, MALAISE, DIZZINESS, WEAKNESS, NAUSEA, VOMITING, AND FLUSHING AND DRY MOUTH. FAINTING, EPILEPTIC CONVULSIONS AND ALTERED EEG PATTERNS MAY OCCUR. SOME OF THESE SYMPTOMS MAY BE DELAYED FOR SEVERAL HOURS AFTER EXPOSURE. ABSORPTION IS NORMALLY SLOW BUT IS INCREASED WHEN IN SOLUTION WITH ALCOHOLS, OILS, AND EMULSIFIERS. IT DOES NOT ACCUMULATE SIGNIFICANTLY IN HUMAN TISSUE. **CHRONIC EXPOSURE-** PROLONGED OR REPEATED EXPOSURE MAY CAUSE EFFECTS AS DESCRIBED IN ACUTE EXPOSURE.

FIRST AID- REMOVE CONTAMINATED CLOTHING AND SHOES IMMEDIATELY. WASH AFFECTED AREA WITH SOAP OR MILD DETERGENT AND LARGE AMOUNTS OF WATER UNTIL NO EVIDENCE OF CHEMICAL REMAINS (APPROXIMATELY 15-20 MINUTES). GET MEDICAL ATTENTION IMMEDIATELY.

EYE CONTACT: ALPHA-ENDOSULFAN: **ACUTE EXPOSURE-** 83 MG OF ENDOSULFAN APPLIED TO THE EYES OF RABBITS PRODUCED SLIGHT CONJUNCTIVITIS WHICH CLEARED WITHIN 72 HOURS OF APPLICATION. **CHRONIC EXPOSURE-** NO DATA AVAILABLE.

FIRST AID- WASH EYES IMMEDIATELY WITH LARGE AMOUNTS OF WATER OR NORMAL SALINE, OCCASIONALLY LIFTING UPPER AND LOWER LIDS, UNTIL NO EVIDENCE OF CHEMICAL REMAINS (APPROXIMATELY 15-20 MINUTES). GET MEDICAL ATTENTION IMMEDIATELY.

INGESTION: ALPHA-ENDOSULFAN: CONVULSANT/TOXIC. **ACUTE EXPOSURE-** A LETHAL DOSE IN RATS WAS 76 MG/KG. INGESTION OF ENDOSULFAN MAY CAUSE GAGGING, VOMITING, DIARRHEA, AGITATION, TONIC-CLONIC CONVULSIONS, FOAMING AT THE MOUTH, DYSPNEA, APNEA, CYANOSIS, AND LOSS OF CONSCIOUSNESS. ONLY A SMALL DOSE OF ENDOSULFAN MAY BE FATAL. ONE 70-YEAR-OLD WOMAN DIED THREE HOURS AFTER TAKING ONLY "DROPS" OF AN ENDOSULFAN FORMULATION. PERSONS WHO TOOK LARGER DOSES DIED QUICKER, SOME IN LESS THAN AN HOUR. **CHRONIC EXPOSURE-** REPEATED DOSES OF ENDOSULFAN AT 6 MG/KG/DAY AND GREATER ON DAYS 6 TO 14 OF GESTATION INCREASED THE MORTALITY OF FEMALE RATS AND INCREASED THE RATES OF RESORPTION AND SKELETAL ABNORMALITY IN THEIR FETUSES. EFFECTS ON THE MALE REPRODUCTIVE SYSTEM WERE OBSERVED IN A STUDY OF ENDOSULFAN IN RATS. HISTOPATHOLOGICAL EXAMINATIONS OF THE LIVER AND KIDNEYS OF RATS FED A DAILY DIET UP TO 10 MG/KG OF ENDOSULFAN FOR 15 DAYS REVEALED DILATION OF SINUSOID AROUND CENTRAL VEINS, AREAS OF FOCAL NECROSIS AND DEGENERATION OF HEPATOCYTES AND MONONUCLEAR MONOLUCOCYTES, PROLIFERATION IN THE BILE DUCT, AND DEGENERATIVE ALTERATIONS IN THE EPITHELIAL LINING OF KIDNEY TUBULES. OTHER EFFECTS INCLUDED KUPFFER CELL HYPERPLASIA, INFLAMMATORY AREAS IN THE SUBPLEURAL OF THE LUNGS AND DILATION OF THE ALVEOLI, AND SEVERE DEGENERATION OF THE SEMINIFEROUS EPITHELIUM. AS EVALUATED BY RTECS, ORAL ADMINISTRATION OF ENDOSULFAN TO RATS RESULTED IN A STATISTICALLY SIGNIFICANT INCREASE IN THE INCIDENCE OF NEOPLASTIC TUMORS OF THE RESPIRATORY SYSTEM.

FIRST AID- IF THE PERSON IS CONSCIOUS AND NOT CONVULSING, REMOVE BY GIVING SYRUP OF IPECAC (IF VOMITING OCCURS, KEEP THE HEAD BELOW THE HIPS TO PREVENT ASPIRATION). GIVE ACTIVATED CHARCOAL FOLLOWED BY GASTRIC LAVAGE. FOLLOW WITH A SALINE CATHARTIC. DO NOT GIVE FATS OR OILS. INTESTINAL LAVAGE WITH 20% MANNITOL (200 ML) BY STOMACH TUBE IS ALSO USEFUL. GIVE ARTIFICIAL RESPIRATION WITH OXYGEN IF RESPIRATION IS DEPRESSED (DREISBACH, HANDBOOK OF POISONING, 12TH ED.). TREAT SYMPTOMATICALLY AND SUPPORTIVELY. LAVAGE AND ADMINISTRATION OF OXYGEN SHOULD BE PERFORMED BY QUALIFIED MEDICAL PERSONNEL. GET MEDICAL ATTENTION IMMEDIATELY.

ANTIDOTE: NO SPECIFIC ANTIDOTE. TREAT SYMPTOMATICALLY AND SUPPORTIVELY.

REACTIVITY

REACTIVITY: STABLE UNDER NORMAL TEMPERATURES AND PRESSURES IN AN ENCLOSED CONTAINER. CONTACT WITH MOISTURE MAY CAUSE DECOMPOSITION PRODUCING SULFUR DIOXIDE AND ENDOSULFAN ALCOHOL.

INCOMPATIBILITIES: ALPHA-ENDOSULFAN: ACIDS: MAY CAUSE DECOMPOSITION PRODUCING SULFUR DIOXIDE AND ENDOSULFAN ALCOHOL. BASES: MAY CAUSE DECOMPOSITION PRODUCING SULFUR DIOXIDE AND ENDOSULFAN ALCOHOL. IRON: MAY BE CORRODED.

DECOMPOSITION: THERMAL DECOMPOSITION MAY RELEASE TOXIC AND/OR HAZARDOUS GASES.

POLYMERIZATION: NO DATA AVAILABLE.

STORAGE AND DISPOSAL

OBSERVE ALL FEDERAL, STATE AND LOCAL REGULATIONS WHEN STORING OR DISPOSING OF THIS SUBSTANCE. FOR ASSISTANCE, CONTACT THE DISTRICT DIRECTOR OF THE ENVIRONMENTAL PROTECTION AGENCY.

****STORAGE****

STORE IN ACCORDANCE WITH 40 CFR 165 RECOMMENDED PROCEDURES FOR THE DISPOSAL AND STORAGE OF PESTICIDES AND PESTICIDE CONTAINERS.
STORE AWAY FROM INCOMPATIBLE SUBSTANCES.

****DISPOSAL****

DISPOSAL MUST BE IN ACCORDANCE WITH 40 CFR 165 RECOMMENDED PROCEDURES FOR THE DISPOSAL AND STORAGE OF PESTICIDES AND PESTICIDE CONTAINERS.

CONDITIONS TO AVOID

MAY BURN BUT DOES NOT IGNITE READILY. CONTAINERS MAY EXPLODE IN HEAT OF FIRE.

SPILL AND LEAK PROCEDURES

OCCUPATIONAL SPILL: DO NOT TOUCH SPILLED MATERIAL. STOP LEAK IF YOU CAN DO IT WITHOUT RISK. USE WATER SPRAY TO REDUCE VAPORS. FOR SMALL SPILLS, TAKE UP WITH SAND OR OTHER ABSORBENT MATERIAL AND PLACE INTO CONTAINERS FOR LATER DISPOSAL. FOR SMALL DRY SPILLS, WITH A CLEAN SHOVEL PLACE MATERIAL INTO CLEAN, DRY CONTAINERS AND COVER. MOVE CONTAINERS FROM SPILL AREA. FOR LARGER SPILLS, DIKE FAR AHEAD OF SPILL FOR LATER DISPOSAL. KEEP UNNECESSARY PEOPLE AWAY. ISOLATE HAZARD AREA AND DENY ENTRY. VENTILATE CLOSED SPACES BEFORE ENTERING. REPORTABLE QUANTITY (RQ): 1 POUND THE SUPERFUND AMENDMENTS AND REAUTHORIZATION ACT (SARA) SECTION 304 REQUIRES THAT A RELEASE EQUAL TO OR GREATER THAN THE REPORTABLE QUANTITY FOR THIS SUBSTANCE BE IMMEDIATELY REPORTED TO THE LOCAL EMERGENCY PLANNING COMMITTEE AND THE STATE EMERGENCY RESPONSE COMMISSION (40 CFR 355.40). IF THE RELEASE

OF THIS SUBSTANCE IS REPORTABLE UNDER CERCLA SECTION 103, THE NATIONAL RESPONSE CENTER MUST BE NOTIFIED IMMEDIATELY AT (800) 424-8802 OR (202) 426-2675 IN THE METROPOLITAN WASHINGTON, D.C. AREA (40 CFR 302.6).

PROTECTIVE EQUIPMENT

VENTILATION: PROVIDE LOCAL EXHAUST OR PROCESS ENCLOSURE VENTILATION SYSTEM.

RESPIRATOR: THE FOLLOWING RESPIRATORS ARE RECOMMENDED BASED ON INFORMATION FOUND IN THE PHYSICAL DATA, TOXICITY AND HEALTH EFFECTS SECTIONS. THEY ARE RANKED IN ORDER FROM MINIMUM TO MAXIMUM RESPIRATORY PROTECTION. THE SPECIFIC RESPIRATOR SELECTED MUST BE BASED ON CONTAMINATION LEVELS FOUND IN THE WORK PLACE, MUST NOT EXCEED THE WORKING LIMITS OF THE RESPIRATOR AND BE JOINTLY APPROVED BY THE NATIONAL INSTITUTE FOR OCCUPATIONAL SAFETY AND HEALTH AND THE MINE SAFETY AND HEALTH ADMINISTRATION (NIOSH-MSHA).

TYPE 'C' SUPPLIED-AIR RESPIRATOR WITH A FULL FACEPIECE OPERATED IN PRESSURE-DEMAND OR OTHER POSITIVE PRESSURE MODE OR WITH A FULL FACEPIECE, HELMET OR HOOD OPERATED IN CONTINOUS-FLOW MODE.

SELF-CONTAINED BREATHING APPARATUS WITH A FULL FACEPIECE OPERATED IN PRESSURE-DEMAND OR OTHER POSITIVE PRESSURE MODE.

FOR FIREFIGHTING AND OTHER IMMEDIATELY DANGEROUS TO LIFE OR HEALTH CONDITIONS:

SELF-CONTAINED BREATHING APPARATUS WITH FULL FACEPIECE OPERATED IN PRESSURE-DEMAND OR OTHER POSITIVE PRESSURE MODE.

SUPPLIED-AIR RESPIRATOR WITH FULL FACEPIECE AND OPERATED IN PRESSURE-DEMAND OR OTHER POSITIVE PRESSURE MODE IN COMBINATION WITH AN AUXILIARY SELF-CONTAINED BREATHING APPARATUS OPERATED IN PRESSURE-DEMAND OR OTHER POSITIVE PRESSURE MODE.

CLOTHING: EMPLOYEE MUST WEAR APPROPRIATE PROTECTIVE (IMPERVIOUS) CLOTHING AND EQUIPMENT TO PREVENT ANY POSSIBILITY OF SKIN CONTACT WITH THIS SUBSTANCE.

GLOVES: EMPLOYEE MUST WEAR APPROPRIATE PROTECTIVE GLOVES TO PREVENT CONTACT WITH THIS SUBSTANCE.

EYE PROTECTION: EMPLOYEE MUST WEAR SPLASH-PROOF OR DUST-RESISTANT SAFETY GOGGLES AND A FACESHIELD TO PREVENT CONTACT WITH THIS SUBSTANCE.

EMERGENCY WASH FACILITIES: WHERE THERE IS ANY POSSIBILITY THAT AN EMPLOYEE'S EYES AND/OR SKIN MAY BE EXPOSED TO THIS SUBSTANCE, THE EMPLOYER SHOULD PROVIDE AN EYE WASH FOUNTAIN AND QUICK DRENCH SHOWER WITHIN THE IMMEDIATE WORK AREA FOR EMERGENCY USE.

AUTHORIZED BY- OCCUPATIONAL HEALTH SERVICES, INC.

CREATION DATE: 10/04/89 ***REVISION DATE:*** 01/31/90

MATERIAL SAFETY DATA SHEET

OCCUPATIONAL HEALTH SERVICES, INC.
AGRICULTURE AND PESTICIDE DIVISION
450 SEVENTH AVENUE, SUITE 2407
NEW YORK, NEW YORK 10123
1-800-445-MSDS OR (212) 967-1100

EMERGENCY CONTACT:
JOHN S. BRANSFORD, JR. (615) 292-1180

SUBSTANCE IDENTIFICATION

CAS-NUMBER 7446-70-0

SUBSTANCE: <u>ALUMINUM CHLORIDE, ANHYDROUS</u>

TRADE NAMES/SYNONYMS: ALUMINUM TRICHLORIDE; TRICHLOROALUMINUM; ALUMINUM CHLORIDE; ALUMINUM CHLORIDE (1:3); UN 1726; A-574; A-575; ALUMINUM CHLORIDE (ALCL3); ALUMINUM TRICHLORIDE (ALCL3); ALCL3; PST00900

CHEMICAL FAMILY: INORGANIC SALT

MOLECULAR FORMULA: AL-CL3

MOLECULAR WEIGHT: 133.34

CERCLA RATINGS (SCALE 0-3): HEALTH=3 FIRE=0 REACTIVITY=2 PERSISTENCE=1

NFPA RATINGS (SCALE 0-4): HEALTH=3 FIRE=0 REACTIVITY=2

COMPONENTS AND CONTAMINANTS

COMPONENT: ALUMINUM CHLORIDE, ANHYDROUS ***PERCENT:*** 100.0
CAS# 7446-70-0

OTHER CONTAMINANTS: NONE

EXPOSURE LIMITS: ALUMINUM, SOLUBLE SALTS, (AS AL): 2 MG/M3 OSHA TWA 2 MG/M3 ACGIH TWA

PHYSICAL DATA

DESCRIPTION: WHITE, GRAY OR YELLOW DELIQUESCENT POWDER WITH A PUNGENT ODOR AND SWEET ASTRINGENT TASTE. ***BOILING POINT:*** 504 F (262 C) (DECOMPOSES)

MELTING POINT: 374 F (190 C) @ 1900 MMHG ***SPECIFIC GRAVITY:*** 2.44 @ 25 C

VAPOR PRESSURE: 1 MMHG @ 100 C ***PH:*** ACIDIC IN SOLUTION

SOLUBILITY IN WATER: REACTS

SOLVENT SOLUBILITY: SOLUBLE IN ABSOLUTE ALCOHOL, CARBON TETRACHLORIDE BENZOPHENONE, NITROBENZENE, ETHER, BENZENE; SLIGHTLY SOLUBLE CHLOROFORM.

FIRE AND EXPLOSION DATA

FIRE AND EXPLOSION HAZARD: NEGLIGIBLE FIRE HAZARD WHEN EXPOSED TO HEAT OR FLAME.

FIREFIGHTING MEDIA: DRY CHEMICAL, CARBON DIOXIDE OR HALON (1987 EMERGENCY RESPONSE GUIDEBOOK, DOT P 5800.4).

FOR LARGER FIRES, FLOOD AREA WITH WATER FROM A DISTANCE (1987 EMERGENCY RESPONSE GUIDEBOOK, DOT P 5800.4).

FIREFIGHTING: DO NOT GET SOLID STREAM OF WATER ON SPILLED MATERIAL. MOVE CONTAINERS FROM FIRE AREA IF POSSIBLE. COOL CONTAINERS EXPOSED TO FLAMES WITH WATER FROM SIDE UNTIL WELL AFTER FIRE IS OUT. KEEP AWAY FROM STORAGE TANK ENDS (1987 EMERGENCY RESPONSE GUIDEBOOK, DOT P 5800.4 GUIDE PAGE 39).

DO NOT USE WATER ON MATERIAL ITSELF. IF LARGE QUANTITIES OF COMBUSTIBLES ARE INVOLVED, USE WATER IN FLOODING QUANTITIES AS SPRAY OF FOG. KEEP MATERIAL OUT OF WATER SOURCES AND SEWERS. NEUTRALIZE SPILLED MATERIAL WITH CRUSHED LIMESTONE, SODA ASH, OR LIME. AVOID BREATHING VAPORS.

TRANSPORTATION DATA

DEPARTMENT OF TRANSPORTATION HAZARD CLASSIFICATION 49 CFR 172.101: CORROSIVE MATERIAL

DEPARTMENT OF TRANSPORTATION LABELING REQUIREMENTS 49 CFR 172.101 AND SUBPART E: CORROSIVE

DEPARTMENT OF TRANSPORTATION PACKAGING REQUIREMENTS: 49 CFR 173.245B EXCEPTIONS: 49 CFR 173.244

TOXICITY

ALUMINUM CHLORIDE: IRRITATION DATA: ANHYDROUS: NO DATA AVAILABLE. HEXAHYDRATE: 7500 UG/3 DAYS INTERMITTENT SKIN-HUMAN MILD. TOXICITY DATA: ANHYDROUS: 770 MG/KG ORAL-MOUSE LD50; 3730 MG/M3 ORAL-RAT LD50; MUTAGENIC DATA (RTECS); REPRODUCTIVE EFFECTS DATA (RTECS). HEXAHYDRATE: MUTAGENIC DATA (RTECS); REPRODUCTIVE EFFECTS DATA (RTECS). CARCINOGEN STATUS: NONE. LOCAL EFFECTS: CORROSIVE- EYE, SKIN, MUCOUS MEMBRANES. ACUTE TOXCITY LEVEL: MODERATELY TOXIC BY INGESTION. TARGET EFFECTS: POISONING MAY AFFECT THE LIVER AND KIDNEYS. AT INCREASED RISK FROM EXPOSURE: PERSONS WITH PRE-EXISTING SKIN DISORDERS, EYE PROBLEMS, OR IMPAIRED RESPIRATORY FUNCTION.

HEALTH EFFECTS AND FIRST AID

INHALATION: ALUMINUM CHLORIDE: CORROSIVE. **<u>ACUTE EXPOSURE-</u>** THE HEXAHYDRATE FORM IS IRRITATING TO MUCOUS MEMBRANES. THE ANHYDROUS FORMS CORROSIVE HYDROCHLORIC ACID ON CONTACT WITH MOISTURE. INHALATION OF CORROSIVE SUBSTANCES MAY CAUSE SYMPTOMS OF RESPIRATORY TRACT IRRITATION POSSIBLY INCLUDING COUGHING, CHOKING, PAIN IN THE NOSE, MOUTH AND THROAT AND BURNS OF THE MUCOUS MEMBRANES. IF SUFFICIENT QUANTITIES ARE INHALED, PULMONARY EDEMA MAY DEVELOP, OFTEN WITH A LATENT PERIOD OF E-72 HOURS. THE SYMPTOMS MAY INCLUDE TIGHTNESS IN THE CHEST, DYSPNEA, FROTHY SPUTUM, CYANOSIS, AND DIZZINESS. PHYSICAL FINDINGS MAY INCLUDE WEAK, RAPID PULSE, HYPOTENSION, HEMOCONCENTRATION AND MOIST RALES. **<u>CHRONIC EXPOSURE-</u>** DEPENDING ON THE CONCENTRATION AND DURATION OF EXPOSURE, REPEATED OR PROLONGED EXPOSURE TO CORROSIVE SUBSTANCES MAY CAUSE INFLAMMATORY AND ULCERATIVE CHANGES IN THE MOUTH, DENTAL DECAY AND POSSIBLY BRONCHIAL AND GASTROINTESTINAL DISTURBANCES.

FIRST AID- REMOVE FROM EXPOSURE AREA TO FRESH AIR IMMEDIATELY. IF BREATHING HAS STOPPED, GIVE ARTIFICIAL RESPIRATION. MAINTAIN AIRWAY AND BLOOD PRESSURE AND ADMINISTER OXYGEN IF AVAILABLE. KEEP AFFECTED PERSON WARM AND AT REST. TREAT SYMPTOMATICALLY AND SUPPORTIVELY. ADMINISTRATION OF OXYGEN SHOULD BE PERFORMED BY QUALIFIED PERSONNEL. GET MEDICAL ATTENTION IMMEDIATELY.

SKIN CONTACT: ALUMINUM CHLORIDE: CORROSIVE. **<u>ACUTE EXPOSURE-</u>** DIRECT CONTACT WITH THE HEXAHYDRATE FORM MAY CAUSE IRRITATION AND THE ANHYDROUS, ESPECIALLY ON MOIST SKIN, MAY CAUSE SEVERE IRRITATION, PAIN,

AND POSSIBLY BURNS. ALUMINUM SALTS ARE SUSPECTED OF BEING SENSITIZERS, HOWEVER ALLERGIC SENSITIVITY IS EXCEEDINGLY RARE. **CHRONIC EXPOSURE-** DEPENDING ON THE CONCENTRATION AND DURATION OF EXPOSURE, REPEATED OR PROLONGED CONTACT MAY RESULT IN IRRITATION, DERMATITIS, SCARRING AND SWEAT GLAND NECROSIS.

FIRST AID- REMOVE CONTAMINATED CLOTHING AND SHOES IMMEDIATELY. WASH AFFECTED AREA WITH SOAP OR MILD DETERGENT AND LARGE AMOUNTS OF WATER UNTIL NO EVIDENCE OF CHEMICAL REMAINS (AT LEAST 15-20 MINUTES). IN CASE OF CHEMICAL BURNS, COVER AREA WITH STERILE, DRY DRESSING. BANDAGE SECURELY, BUT NOT TOO TIGHTLY. GET MEDICAL ATTENTION IMMEDIATELY.

EYE CONTACT: ALUMINUM CHLORIDE: CORROSIVE. **ACUTE EXPOSURE-** WHEN THE HEXAHYDRATE WAS TESTED BY APPLYING 100 MG OF CRYSTALS TO THE CORNEA OF RABBITS, IMMEDIATE BLEPHAROSPASM OCCURRED. WHEN THE CRYSTALS WERE ALLOWED TO REMAIN UNTIL WASHED AWAY BY TEARS, THEY CAUSED TRANSIENT EPITHELIAL DAMAGE, AND A PERSISTENT FAINT NEBULA IN THE CORNEAL STROMA. THE ANHYDROUS FORM MAY CAUSE REDNESS, PAIN, BLURRED VISION, AND CORNEAL BURNS WHICH GENERALLY HEAL WITHIN 2 DAYS. **CHRONIC EXPOSURE-** EFFECTS DEPEND ON CONCENTRATION AND DURATION OF EXPOSURE. REPEATED OR PROLONGED CONTACT WITH CORROSIVE SUBSTANCES MAY RESULT IN CONJUNCTIVITIS OR EFFECTS AS IN ACUTE EXPOSURE.

FIRST AID- WASH EYES IMMEDIATELY WITH LARGE AMOUNTS OF WATER, OCCASIONALLY LIFTING UPPER AND LOWER LIDS, UNTIL NO EVIDENCE OF CHEMICAL REMAINS (AT LEAST 15-20 MINUTES). CONTINUE IRRIGATING WITH NORMAL SALINE UNTIL THE PH HAS RETURNED TO NORMAL (30-60 MINUTES). COVER WITH STERILE BANDAGES. GET MEDICAL ATTENTION IMMEDIATELY.

INGESTION: ALUMINUM CHLORIDE: CORROSIVE. **ACUTE EXPOSURE-** CORROSIVE METAL SALTS MAY CAUSE A BURNING PAIN IN THE MOUTH AND THROAT AND SEVERE BURNS OF THE MUCOUS MEMBRANES. THERE MAY BE DISCOLORATION OF THE TISSUES. SWALLOWING AND SPEECH MAY BE DIFFICULT AT FIRST AND THEN ALMOST IMPOSSIBLE. VOMITING, WATERY OR BLOODY DIARRHEA, TENESMUS, HEMOLYSIS, HEMATURIA, KIDNEY DAMAGE, ANURIA, LIVER DAMAGE WITH JAUNDICE, HYPOTENSION, COLLAPSE, AND CONVULSIONS MAY ALSO OCCUR. IN ANIMALS, LETHARGY, ANOREXIA AND DEATH OCCURRED AFTER ORAL DOSING. **CHRONIC EXPOSURE-** DEPENDING ON THE CONCENTRATION, REPEATED INGESTION OF CORROSIVE SUBSTANCES MAY RESULT IN EFFECTS AS WITH ACUTE INGESTION. LONG-TERM FEEDING OF RATS WITH ALUMINUM CHLORIDE AT 100 TO 200 MG/KG RETARDED GROWTH AND DISTURBED PHOSPHATE AND CARBOHYDRATE METABOLISM. REPRODUCTIVE EFFECTS HAVE BEEN REPORTED IN ANIMALS.

FIRST AID- DILUTE THE POISON IMMEDIATELY WITH LARGE AMOUNTS OF WATER OR MILK AND REMOVE BY GASTRIC LAVAGE UNLESS THE VICTIM IS ALREADY VOMITING. (DREISBACH, HANDBOOK OF POISONING, 12TH ED.) GET MEDICAL ATTENTION IMMEDIATELY. ADMINISTRATION OF GASTRIC LAVAGE SHOULD BE PERFORMED BY QUALIFIED MEDICAL PERSONNEL.

ANTIDOTE: NO SPECIFIC ANTIDOTE. TREAT SYMPTOMATICALLY AND SUPPORTIVELY.

REACTIVITY

REACTIVITY: STABLE AT NORMAL TEMPERATURE AND PRESSURES, BUT MAY DECOMPOSE ON PROLONGED STORAGE CREATING AN EXPLOSION HAZARD WHEN OPENED. REACTS VIOLENTLY WITH WATER, RELEASING TOXIC AND CORROSIVE HYDROGEN CHLORIDE WITH SUFFICIENT HEAT AND PRESSURE GENERATED TO RUPTURE CONTAINERS.

INCOMPATIBILITIES: ALUMINUM CHLORIDE ALKALI: MAY REACT EXPLOSIVELY. ALKENES: VIOLENT POLYMERIZATION POSSIBLE. ALLYL CHLORIDE: VIOLENT POLYMERIZATION POSSIBLE. BENZOYL CHLORIDE + NAPHTHALENE: VIOLENT REACTION POSSIBLE. ETHYLENE: VIOLENT POLYMERIZATION POSSIBLE. ETHYLENE OXIDE: VIOLENT POLYMERIZATION POSSIBLE. ISOBUTENE: VIOLENT POLYMERIZATION POSSIBLE. METALS: MAY CORRODE IN THE PRESENCE OF MOISTURE. NITROBENZENE: FORMS THERMALLY UNSTABLE MIXTURES. NITROBENZENE + PHENOL: VIOLENT EXPLOSION. NITROMETHANE + ORGANIC MATTER: POSSIBLE EXPLOSION. ORGANIC NITRO COMPOUNDS: VIGOROUS REACTION. OXYGEN DIFLUORIDE: EXPLODES. PERCHLORYL BENZENE: POSSIBLE EXPLOSION. PERCHLORYL FLUORIDE + BENZENE: FORMS EXPLOSIVE PRODUCTS. PHENYL AZIDE: VIOLENT EXPLOSION. POTASSIUM: FORMS IMPACT SENSITIVE MIXTURE. SODIUM: FORMS IMPACT SENSITIVE MIXTURE. SODIUM OXIDE: INCOMPATIBLE. SODIUM PEROXIDE + ALUMINUM: MAY REACT ON PROLONGED STORAGE. SODIUM TETRABORATE + BIS(2-METHOXYETHYL)ETHER: VIOLENT EXPLOSION.

DECOMPOSITION: THERMAL DECOMPOSITION PRODUCTS INCLUDES TOXIC AND CORROSIVE HYDROGEN CHLORIDE.

POLYMERIZATION: HAZARDOUS POLYMERIZATION HAS NOT BEEN REPORTED TO OCCUR UNDER NORMAL TEMPERATURES AND PRESSURES.

STORAGE AND DISPOSAL

OBSERVE ALL FEDERAL, STATE AND LOCAL REGULATIONS WHEN STORING OR DISPOSING OF THIS SUBSTANCE. FOR ASSISTANCE, CONTACT THE DISTRICT DIRECTOR OF THE ENVIRONMENTAL PROTECTION AGENCY.

STORAGE

STORE AWAY FROM INCOMPATIBLE SUBSTANCES.
STORE IN A COOL, DRY AREA PROTECTED FROM RAIN AND DIRECT SUNSHINE.
STORAGE IN SPRINKLERED BUILDINGS IS NOT RECOMMENDED (NFPA 49, HAZARDOUS CHEMICALS DATA, 1975).

CONDITIONS TO AVOID

MAY IGNITE OTHER COMBUSTIBLE MATERIALS (WOOD, PAPER, OIL, ETC.). VIOLENT REACTION WITH WATER. FLAMMABLE, POISONOUS GASES MAY ACCUMULATE IN CONFINED SPACES. RUNOFF TO SEWER MAY CREATE FIRE OR EXPLOSION HAZARD.

SPILL AND LEAK PROCEDURES

OCCUPATIONAL SPILL: KEEP COMBUSTIBLES (WOOD, PAPER, OIL, ETC.) AWAY FROM SPILLED MATERIAL. DO NOT TOUCH SPILLED MATERIAL. DO NOT GET WATER INSIDE CONTAINER. STOP LEAK IF YOU CAN DO IT WITHOUT RISK. USE WATER SPRAY TO REDUCE VAPORS. DO NOT PUT WATER ON LEAK OR SPILL AREA. CLEAN UP ONLY UNDER THE SUPERVISION OF AN EXPERT. DIKE SPILL FOR LATER DISPOSAL. DO NOT APPLY WATER UNLESS DIRECTED TO DO SO. KEEP UNNECESSARY PEOPLE AWAY. ISOLATE HAZARD AREA AND DENY ENTRY. VENTILATE CLOSED SPACES BEFORE ENTERING.

PROTECTIVE EQUIPMENT

VENTILATION: PROVIDE LOCAL EXHAUST OR PROCESS ENCLOSURE VENTILATION TO MEET PUBLISHED EXPOSURE LIMITS.

RESPIRATOR: THE FOLLOWING RESPIRATORS ARE RECOMMENDED BASED ON INFORMATION FOUND IN THE PHYSICAL DATA, TOXICITY AND HEALTH EFFECTS SECTIONS. THEY ARE RANKED IN ORDER FROM MINIMUM TO MAXIMUM RESPIRATORY PROTECTION. THE SPECIFIC RESPIRATOR SELECTED MUST BE BASED ON CONTAMINATION LEVELS FOUND IN THE WORK PLACE, MUST NOT EXCEED THE WORKING LIMITS OF THE RESPIRATOR AND BE JOINTLY APPROVED BY THE NATIONAL INSTITUTE FOR OCCUPATIONAL SAFETY AND HEALTH AND THE MINE SAFETY AND HEALTH ADMINISTRATION (NIOSH-MSHA).

DUST AND MIST RESPIRATOR WITH A FULL FACEPIECE.

AIR-PURIFYING FULL FACEPIECE RESPIRATOR WITH A HIGH-EFFICIENCY PARTICULATE FILTER.

POWERED AIR-PURIFYING RESPIRATOR WITH A TIGHT-FITTING FACEPIECE AND HIGH-EFFICIENCY PARTICULATE FILTER.

TYPE 'C' SUPPLIED-AIR RESPIRATOR WITH A FULL FACEPIECE OPERATED IN PRESSURE-DEMAND OR OTHER POSITIVE PRESSURE MODE OR WITH A FULL FACEPIECE, HELMET OR HOOD OPERATED IN CONTINUOUS-FLOW MODE.

SELF-CONTAINED BREATHING APPARATUS WITH A FULL FACEPIECE OPERATED IN PRESSURE-DEMAND OR OTHER POSITIVE PRESSURE MODE.

FOR FIREFIGHTING AND OTHER IMMEDIATELY DANGEROUS TO LIFE OR HEALTH CONDITIONS:

SELF-CONTAINED BREATHING APPARATUS WITH FULL FACEPIECE OPERATED IN PRESSURE-DEMAND OR OTHER POSITIVE PRESSURE MODE.

SUPPLIED-AIR RESPIRATOR WITH FULL FACEPIECE AND OPERATED IN PRESSURE-DEMAND OR OTHER POSITIVE PRESSURE MODE IN COMBINATION WITH AN AUXILIARY SELF-CONTAINED BREATHING APPARATUS OPERATED IN PRESSURE-DEMAND OR OTHER POSITIVE PRESSURE MODE.

CLOTHING: EMPLOYEE MUST WEAR APPROPRIATE PROTECTIVE (IMPERVIOUS) CLOTHING AND EQUIPMENT TO PREVENT ANY POSSIBILITY OF SKIN CONTACT WITH THIS SUBSTANCE.

GLOVES: EMPLOYEE MUST WEAR APPROPRIATE PROTECTIVE GLOVES TO PREVENT CONTACT WITH THIS SUBSTANCE.

EYE PROTECTION: EMPLOYEE MUST WEAR SPLASH-PROOF OR DUST-RESISTANT SAFETY GOGGLES AND A FACESHIELD TO PREVENT CONTACT WITH THIS SUBSTANCE.

EMERGENCY WASH FACILITIES: WHERE THERE IS ANY POSSIBILITY THAT AN EMPLOYEE'S EYES AND/OR SKIN MAY BE EXPOSED TO THIS SUBSTANCE, THE EMPLOYER SHOULD PROVIDE AN EYE WASH FOUNTAIN AND QUICK DRENCH SHOWER WITHIN THE IMMEDIATE WORK AREA FOR EMERGENCY USE.

AUTHORIZED BY- OCCUPATIONAL HEALTH SERVICES, INC.

CREATION DATE: 11/15/89 ***REVISION DATE:*** 03/28/90

MATERIAL SAFETY DATA SHEET

OCCUPATIONAL HEALTH SERVICES, INC.
AGRICULTURE AND PESTICIDE DIVISION
450 SEVENTH AVENUE, SUITE 2407
NEW YORK, NEW YORK 10123
1-800-445-MSDS OR (212) 967-1100

EMERGENCY CONTACT:
JOHN S. BRANSFORD, JR. (615) 292-1180

SUBSTANCE IDENTIFICATION

CAS-NUMBER 20859-73-8

SUBSTANCE: **ALUMINUM PHOSPHIDE**

TRADE NAMES/SYNONYMS: AL-PHOS; ALUMINUM MONOPHOSPHIDE; CELPHOS; DELICIA; DETIA-EX-B; QUICKPHOS; PHOSTOXIN (FORMULATION); AIP; DELICIA GASTOXIN; DELIA; DETIA GAS EX-B; STCC 4916305; UN 1397; RCRA P006; PST00970

CHEMICAL FAMILY: INORGANIC SALT

MOLECULAR FORMULA: AL-P

MOLECULAR WEIGHT: 57.95

CERCLA RATINGS (SCALE 0-3): HEALTH = 3 FIRE = 3 REACTIVITY = 1 PERSISTENCE = 3

NFPA RATINGS (SCALE 0-4): HEALTH = 3 FIRE = 3 REACTIVITY = 1

COMPONENTS AND CONTAMINANTS

COMPONENT: ALUMINUM PHOSPHIDE ***PERCENT:*** 100
CAS# 20859-73-8

OTHER CONTAMINANTS: NONE

EXPOSURE LIMITS: NO OCCUPATIONAL EXPOSURE LIMITS ESTABLISHED BY OSHA, ACGIH, OR NIOSH.
ALUMINUM PHOSPHIDE: 500 POUNDS SARA SECTION 302 THRESHOLD PLANNING QUANTITY 100 POUNDS SARA SECTION 304 REPORTABLE QUANTITY 100 POUNDS CERCLA SECTION 103 REPORTABLE QUANTITY

PHYSICAL DATA

DESCRIPTION: DARK GREY OR DARK YELLOW CRYSTALS ***BOILING POINT:*** >1832 F (>1000 C)

MELTING POINT: >1832 F (>1000 C) ***SPECIFIC GRAVITY:*** 2.9

SOLUBILITY IN WATER: INSOLUBLE ***VAPOR DENSITY:*** 2.9

FIRE AND EXPLOSION DATA

FIRE AND EXPLOSION HAZARD: DANGEROUS WHEN WET. CONTACT WITH WITH WATER OR DAMP AIR EVOLVES PHOSPHINE, A SPONTANEOUSLY FLAMMABLE GAS. VAPORS ARE HEAVIER THAN AIR AND MAY TRAVEL A CONSIDERABLE DISTANCE TO A SOURCE OF IGNITION AND FLASH BACK.

FIREFIGHTING MEDIA: DRY CHEMICAL, SODA ASH, LIME OR SAND (1987 EMERGENCY RESPONSE GUIDEBOOK, DOT P 5800.4).
SPECIAL POWDER, DRY SAND, NO HYDROUS EXTINGUISHING AGENTS.

FIREFIGHTING: MOVE CONTAINER FROM FIRE AREA IF POSSIBLE. DO NOT USE WATER OR FOAM! (1987 EMERGENCY RESPONSE GUIDEBOOK, DOT P 5800.4, GUIDE PAGE 41).
EXTINGUISH USING AGENT FOR TYPE OF FIRE. AVOID BREATHING FUMES FROM BURNING MATERIAL.

TRANSPORTATION DATA

DEPARTMENT OF TRANSPORTATION HAZARD CLASSIFICATION 49 CFR 172.101: FLAMMABLE SOLID
DEPARTMENT OF TRANSPORTATION LABELING REQUIREMENTS 49 CFR 172.101 AND SUBPART E: FLAMMABLE SOLID AND DANGEROUS WHEN WET
DEPARTMENT OF TRANSPORTATION PACKAGING REQUIREMENTS: 49 CFR 173.154 EXCEPTIONS: NONE

TOXICITY

ALUMINUM PHOSPHIDE: TOXICITY DATA: 2800 MG/M3 INHALATION-MAN LCLO. CARCINOGEN STATUS: NONE. LOCAL EFFECTS: IRRITANT- INHALATION, SKIN, AND EYES. ACUTE TOXICITY LEVEL: INSUFFICIENT DATA. TARGET EFFECTS: POISONING MAY AFFECT THE LIVER, KIDNEYS, CENTRAL NERVOUS SYSTEM, AND METABOLISM.

HEALTH EFFECTS AND FIRST AID

INHALATION: ALUMINUM PHOSPHIDE: IRRITANT/TOXIC. **ACUTE EXPOSURE-** MAY CAUSE SHORTNESS OF BREATH, HEADACHE, NAUSEA, AND DIZZINESS. AFTER A FEW HOURS, VOMITING, DIARRHEA, ABDOMINAL SPASMS AND MUSCULAR SPASMS MAY OCCUR. **CHRONIC EXPOSURE-** MAY AFFECT THE NERVOUS SYSTEM AND METABOLISM. LIVER AND KIDNEY DAMAGE MAY ALSO OCCUR.

FIRST AID- REMOVE FROM EXPOSURE AREA TO FRESH AIR IMMEDIATELY. IF BREATHING HAS STOPPED, PERFORM ARTIFICIAL RESPIRATION. KEEP PERSON WARM AND AT REST. TREAT SYMPTOMATICALLY AND SUPPORTIVELY. GET MEDICAL ATTENTION IMMEDIATELY.

SKIN CONTACT: ALUMINUM PHOSPHIDE: IRRITANT. **ACUTE EXPOSURE-** DIRECT CONTACT MAY RESULT IN IRRITATION. **CHRONIC EXPOSURE-** REPEATED OR PROLONGED EXPOSURE MAY RESULT IN DERMATITIS.

FIRST AID- REMOVE CONTAMINATED CLOTHING AND SHOES IMMEDIATELY. WASH AFFECTED AREA WITH SOAP OR MILD DETERGENT AND LARGE AMOUNTS OF WATER UNTIL NO EVIDENCE OF CHEMICAL REMAINS (APPROXIMATELY 15-20 MINUTES). GET MEDICAL ATTENTION IMMEDIATELY.

EYE CONTACT: ALUMINUM PHOSPHIDE: IRRITANT. **ACUTE EXPOSURE-** SOLID PARTICLES MAY CAUSE REDNESS, PAIN AND IRRITATION. **CHRONIC EXPOSURE-** MAY CAUSE CONJUNCTIVITIS.

FIRST AID- WASH EYES IMMEDIATELY WITH LARGE AMOUNTS OF WATER OR NORMAL SALINE, OCCASIONALLY LIFTING UPPER AND LOWER LIDS, UNTIL NO EVIDENCE OF CHEMICAL REMAINS (APPROXIMATELY 15-20 MINUTES). GET MEDICAL ATTENTION IMMEDIATELY.

INGESTION: ALUMINUM PHOSPHIDE: **ACUTE EXPOSURE-** MAY CAUSE HEADACHE, DIZZINESS, SHORTNESS OF BREATH, NAUSEA, VOMITING, DIARRHEA, ABDOMINAL AND MUSCULAR SPASMS. **CHRONIC EXPOSURE-** MAY AFFECT THE NERVOUS SYSTEM AND METABOLISM. LIVER AND KIDNEY DAMAGE MAY ALSO OCCUR.

FIRST AID- IF PERSON IS CONSCIOUS, GIVE LARGE QUANTITIES OF WATER. IF THERE IS NO EVIDENCE OF CORROSION, INDUCE VOMITING. TREAT SYMPTOMATICALLY AND SUPPORTIVELY. DO NOT MAKE AN UNCONSCIOUS PERSON VOMIT OR DRINK ANYTHING. GET MEDICAL ATTENTION. (DREISBACH, HANDBOOK OF POISONING 11TH, ED.)

ANTIDOTE: NO SPECIFIC ANTIDOTE. TREAT SYMPTOMATICALLY AND SUPPORTIVELY.

REACTIVITY

REACTIVITY: REACTS ON CONTACT WITH WATER OR MOIST AIR TO EVOLVE SPONTANEOUSLY FLAMMABLE PHOSPHINE GAS.

INCOMPATIBILITIES: ALUMINUM PHOSPHIDE: ACIDS: VIOLENT REACTION. OXIDIZERS: VIOLENT REACTION.

DECOMPOSITION: THERMAL DECOMPOSITION MAY RELEASE TOXIC AND HAZARDOUS PHOSPHINE AND TOXIC OXIDES OF PHOSPHORUS.

POLYMERIZATION: HAZARDOUS POLYMERIZATION HAS NOT BEEN REPORTED TO OCCUR UNDER NORMAL TEMPERATURES AND PRESSURES.

STORAGE AND DISPOSAL

OBSERVE ALL FEDERAL, STATE AND LOCAL REGULATIONS WHEN STORING OR DISPOSING OF THIS SUBSTANCE. FOR ASSISTANCE, CONTACT THE DISTRICT DIRECTOR OF THE ENVIRONMENTAL PROTECTION AGENCY.

****STORAGE****

THRESHOLD PLANNING QUANTITY (TPQ): THE SUPERFUND AMENDMENTS AND REAUTHORIZATION ACT (SARA) SECTION 302 REQUIRES THAT EACH FACILITY WHERE ANY EXTREMELY HAZARDOUS SUBSTANCE IS PRESENT IN A QUANTITY EQUAL TO OR GREATER THAN THE TPQ ESTABLISHED FOR THAT SUBSTANCE NOTIFY THE STATE EMERGENCY RESPONSE COMMISSION FOR THE STATE IN WHICH IT IS LOCATED. SECTION 303 OF SARA REQUIRES THESE FACILITIES TO PARTICIPATE IN LOCAL EMERGENCY RESPONSE PLANNING (40 CFR 355.30).

CONDITIONS TO AVOID

MAY BURN BUT DOES NOT IGNITE READILY.

SPILL AND LEAK PROCEDURES

OCCUPATIONAL SPILL: DO NOT TOUCH SPILLED MATERIAL. STOP LEAK IF YOU CAN DO IT WITHOUT RISK. FOR SMALL SPILLS, TAKE UP WITH SAND OR OTHER ABSORBENT MATERIAL AND PLACE INTO CONTAINERS FOR LATER DISPOSAL. FOR SMALL DRY SPILLS, WITH A CLEAN SHOVEL PLACE MATERIAL INTO CLEAN, DRY CONTAINER AND COVER. MOVE CONTAINERS FROM SPILL AREA. FOR LARGER SPILLS, DIKE FAR AHEAD OF SPILL FOR LATER DISPOSAL. KEEP UNNECESSARY PEOPLE AWAY. ISOLATE HAZARD AREA AND DENY ENTRY.
REPORTABLE QUANTITY (RQ): 100 POUNDS THE SUPERFUND AMENDMENTS AND REAUTHORIZATION ACT (SARA) SECTION 304 REQUIRES THAT A RELEASE EQUAL TO OR GREATER THAN THE REPORTABLE QUANTITY FOR THIS SUBSTANCE BE IMMEDIATELY REPORTED TO THE LOCAL EMERGENCY PLANNING COMMITTEE AND THE STATE EMERGENCY RESPONSE COMMISSION (40 CFR 355.40). IF THE RELEASE OF THIS SUBSTANCE IS REPORTABLE UNDER CERCLA SECTION 103, THE NATIONAL RESPONSE CENTER MUST BE NOTIFIED IMMEDIATELY AT (800) 424-8802 OR (202) 426-2675 IN THE METROPOLITAN WASHINGTON, D.C. AREA (40 CFR 302.6).

PROTECTIVE EQUIPMENT

VENTILATION: PROVIDE LOCAL EXHAUST OR PROCESS ENCLOSURE VENTILATION. VENTILATION EQUIPMENT MUST BE EXPLOSION-PROOF.

RESPIRATOR: THE FOLLOWING RESPIRATORS ARE RECOMMENDED BASED ON INFORMATION FOUND IN THE PHYSICAL DATA, TOXICITY AND HEALTH EFFECTS SECTIONS. THEY ARE RANKED IN ORDER FROM MINIMUM TO MAXIMUM RESPIRATORY PROTECTION. THE SPECIFIC RESPIRATOR SELECTED MUST BE BASED ON CONTAMINATION LEVELS FOUND IN THE WORK PLACE, MUST NOT EXCEED THE WORKING LIMITS OF THE RESPIRATOR AND BE JOINTLY APPROVED BY THE NATIONAL INSTITUTE FOR OCCUPATIONAL SAFETY AND HEALTH AND THE MINE SAFETY AND HEALTH ADMINISTRATION (NIOSH-MSHA).

TYPE 'C' SUPPLIED-AIR RESPIRATOR WITH A FULL FACEPIECE OPERATED IN PRESSURE-DEMAND OR OTHER POSITIVE PRESSURE MODE OR WITH A FULL FACEPIECE, HELMET OR HOOD OPERATED IN CONTINOUS-FLOW MODE.

SELF-CONTAINED BREATHING APPARATUS WITH A FULL FACEPIECE OPERATED IN PRESSURE-DEMAND OR OTHER POSITIVE PRESSURE MODE.

FOR FIREFIGHTING AND OTHER IMMEDIATELY DANGEROUS TO LIFE OR HEALTH CONDITIONS:

SELF-CONTAINED BREATHING APPARATUS WITH FULL FACEPIECE OPERATED IN PRESSURE-DEMAND OR OTHER POSITIVE PRESSURE MODE.

SUPPLIED-AIR RESPIRATOR WITH FULL FACEPIECE AND OPERATED IN PRESSURE-DEMAND OR OTHER POSITIVE PRESSURE MODE IN COMBINATION WITH AN AUXILIARY SELF-CONTAINED BREATHING APPARATUS OPERATED IN PRESSURE-DEMAND OR OTHER POSITIVE PRESSURE MODE.

CLOTHING: EMPLOYEE MUST WEAR APPROPRIATE PROTECTIVE (IMPERVIOUS) CLOTHING AND EQUIPMENT TO PREVENT REPEATED OR PROLONGED SKIN CONTACT WITH THIS SUBSTANCE.

GLOVES: EMPLOYEE MUST WEAR APPROPRIATE PROTECTIVE GLOVES TO PREVENT CONTACT WITH THIS SUBSTANCE.

EYE PROTECTION: EMPLOYEE MUST WEAR SPLASH-PROOF OR DUST-RESISTANT SAFETY GOGGLES TO PREVENT EYE CONTACT WITH THIS SUBSTANCE.

EMERGENCY EYE WASH: WHERE THERE IS ANY POSSIBILITY THAT AN EMPLOYEE'S EYES MAY BE EXPOSED TO THIS SUBSTANCE, THE EMPLOYER SHOULD PROVIDE AN EYE WASH FOUNTAIN WITHIN THE IMMEDIATE WORK AREA FOR EMERGENCY USE.

AUTHORIZED BY- OCCUPATIONAL HEALTH SERVICES, INC.

CREATION DATE: 10/04/89 ***REVISION DATE:*** 05/11/90

MATERIAL SAFETY DATA SHEET

OCCUPATIONAL HEALTH SERVICES, INC.
AGRICULTURE AND PESTICIDE DIVISION
450 SEVENTH AVENUE, SUITE 2407
NEW YORK, NEW YORK 10123
1-800-445-MSDS OR (212) 967-1100

EMERGENCY CONTACT:
JOHN S. BRANSFORD, JR. (615) 292-1180

SUBSTANCE IDENTIFICATION

CAS-NUMBER 10043-01-3

SUBSTANCE: **ALUMINUM SULFATE**

TRADE NAMES/SYNONYMS: ALUM; ALUMINUM ALUM; ALUMINUM TRISULFATE; CAKE ALUM; DIALUMINUM SULPHATE; PATENT ALUM; ALUMINUM SULPHATE; DIALUMINUM SULFATE; SULFATODIALUMINUM DISULFATE; DIALUMINUM TRISULFATE; SULFURIC ACID, ALUMINUM SALT; ALUMINUM SESQUISULFATE; STCC 4963303; NA 9078; A-611; A-613; AL2O12S3; PST00980

CHEMICAL FAMILY: INORGANIC SALT

MOLECULAR FORMULA: AL2-S3-O12

ILAR WEIGHT: 342.15

RATINGS (SCALE 0-3): HEALTH=3 FIRE=0 REACTIVITY=0

SISTENCE=3

RATINGS (SCALE 0-4): HEALTH=3 FIRE=0 REACTIVITY=0

COMPONENTS AND CONTAMINANTS

COMPONENT: ALUMINUM SULFATE ***PERCENT:*** 100

CAS# 10043-01-3

OTHER CONTAMINANTS: NONE

EXPOSURE LIMITS: ALUMINUM SULFATE: 2 MG(AL)/M3 ACGIH TWA
5000 POUNDS CERCLA SECTION 103 REPORTABLE QUANTITY

PHYSICAL DATA

DESCRIPTION: ODORLESS, WHITE TO GRAY, LUSTROUS CRYSTALS, GRANULES, OR POWDER WITH A SWEET TASTE BECOMING MILDLY ASTRINGENT.

MELTING POINT: 1418 F (770 C) DECOMPOSES ***SPECIFIC GRAVITY:*** 2.7

PH: >2.9 @ 5% SOLUTION ***SOLUBILITY IN WATER:*** 31% @ 0 C

SOLVENT SOLUBILITY: SOLUBLE IN DILUTE ACIDS; SLIGHTLY SOLUBLE IN ALCOHOL

FIRE AND EXPLOSION DATA

FIRE AND EXPLOSION HAZARD: NEGLIGIBLE FIRE HAZARD WHEN EXPOSED TO HEAT OR FLAME.

FIREFIGHTING MEDIA: DRY CHEMICAL, CARBON DIOXIDE, HALON, WATER SPRAY OR STANDARD FOAM (1987 EMERGENCY RESPONSE GUIDEBOOK, DOT P 5800.4). FOR LARGER FIRES, USE WATER SPRAY, FOG OR STANDARD FOAM (1987 EMERGENCY RESPONSE GUIDEBOOK, DOT P 5800.4).

FIREFIGHTING: MOVE CONTAINER FROM FIRE AREA IF POSSIBLE. DO NOT SCATTER SPILLED MATERIAL WITH HIGH PRESSURE WATER STREAMS. DIKE FIRE CONTROL WATER FOR LATER DISPOSAL (1987 EMERGENCY RESPONSE GUIDEBOOK, DOT P 5800.4, GUIDE PAGE 31).

USE AGENTS SUITABLE FOR TYPE OF FIRE. AVOID BREATHING VAPORS OR DUSTS, KEEP UPWIND.

TRANSPORTATION DATA

DEPARTMENT OF TRANSPORTATION HAZARD CLASSIFICATION 49 CFR 172.101: ORM-E

DEPARTMENT OF TRANSPORTATION LABELING REQUIREMENTS 49 CFR 172.101 AND SUBPART E: NONE

DEPARTMENT OF TRANSPORTATION PACKAGING REQUIREMENTS: 49 CFR 173.510 EXCEPTIONS: NONE

TOXICITY

ALUMINUM SULFATE: TOXICITY DATA: ANHYDROUS: 6207 MG/KG ORAL-MOUSE LD50; 1735 MG/KG INTRAPERITONEAL-MOUSE LD50; REPRODUCTIVE EFFECTS DATA (RTECS). OCTADECAHYDRATE: NO DATA AVAILABLE. CARCINOGEN STATUS: NONE. LOCAL EFFECTS: IRRITANT: INHALATION, SKIN, AND EYES. ACUTE TOXICITY LEVEL: SLIGHTLY TOXIC BY INGESTION. TARGET EFFECTS: NO DATA AVAILABLE.

HEALTH EFFECTS AND FIRST AID

INHALATION: ALUMINUM SULFATE: IRRITANT. **ACUTE EXPOSURE**- INHALATION MAY CAUSE IRRITATION OF MUCOUS MEMBRANES WITH SORE THROAT AND COUGH DUE TO SULFURIC ACID WHICH IS FORMED BY THE HYDROLYSIS OF THE SALT UPON CONTACT WITH MOISTURE. **CHRONIC EXPOSURE**- REPEATED OR PROLONGED EXPOSURE MAY CAUSE BRONCHIAL IRRITATION, LEADING TO NOCTURNAL WHEEZING, AND BREATHLESSNESS. PROLONGED INHALATION OF DUSTS CONTAINING HIGH CONCENTRATIONS OF ALUMINUM HAVE PRODUCED EMPHYSEMA, NON-NODULAR PULMONARY FIBROSIS AND FATALITIES.

FIRST AID- REMOVE FROM EXPOSURE AREA TO FRESH AIR IMMEDIATELY. IF BREATHING HAS STOPPED, PERFORM ARTIFICIAL RESPIRATION. KEEP PERSON WARM AND AT REST. TREAT SYMPTOMATICALLY AND SUPPORTIVELY. GET MEDICAL ATTENTION IMMEDIATELY.

SKIN CONTACT: ALUMINUM SULFATE: IRRITANT. **ACUTE EXPOSURE**- ALUMINUM SULFATE HYDROLYZES READILY WITH MOISTURE TO FORM SOME SULFURIC ACID WHICH MAY PRODUCE IRRITATION, DERMATOSES AND ECZEMA. EXCESSIVE FORMATION OF SULFURIC ACID MAY PRODUCE POSSIBLE BURNS. ALUMINUM SULFATE MAY RARELY CAUSE SKIN SENSITIZATION. **CHRONIC EXPOSURE**- REPEATED OR PROLONGED CONTACT WITH SOME SOLUBLE SALTS OF ALUMINUM RESULTS IN ACID IRRITATION FROM HYDROLYSIS. A CONGESTIVE, ANESTHETIC CONDITION OF THE FINGERS (ACROANESTHESIA) MAY OCCUR FROM PROLONGED CONTACT WITH ALUM. REPEATED EXPOSURE MAY RESULT IN SENSITIZATION.

FIRST AID- REMOVE CONTAMINATED CLOTHING AND SHOES IMMEDIATELY. WASH AFFECTED AREA WITH SOAP OR MILD DETERGENT AND LARGE AMOUNTS OF WATER UNTIL NO EVIDENCE OF CHEMICAL REMAINS (AT LEAST 15-20 MINUTES). IN CASE OF CHEMICAL BURNS, COVER AREA WITH STERILE, DRY DRESSING. BANDAGE SECURELY, BUT NOT TOO TIGHTLY. GET MEDICAL ATTENTION IMMEDIATELY.

EYE CONTACT: ALUMINUM SULFATE: IRRITANT. **ACUTE EXPOSURE**- MAY CAUSE IRRITATION, REDNESS, AND CORNEAL BURNS DUE TO THE REACTION OF THE COMPOUND WITH MOISTURE TO FORM SULFURIC ACID. **CHRONIC EXPOSURE**- REPEATED OR PROLONGED CONTACT WITH IRRITANTS MAY CAUSE CONJUNCTIVITIS OR EFFECTS SIMILAR TO THOSE FOR ACUTE EXPOSURE.

FIRST AID- WASH EYES IMMEDIATELY WITH LARGE AMOUNTS OF WATER, OCCASIONALLY LIFTING UPPER AND LOWER LIDS, UNTIL NO EVIDENCE OF CHEMICAL REMAINS (AT LEAST 15-20 MINUTES). CONTINUE IRRIGATING WITH NORMAL SALINE UNTIL THE PH HAS RETURNED TO NORMAL (30-60 MINUTES). COVER WITH STERILE BANDAGES. GET MEDICAL ATTENTION IMMEDIATELY.

INGESTION: ALUMINUM SULFATE: **ACUTE EXPOSURE-** INGESTION OF A LARGE DOSE WAS LETHAL IN MICE. ALUMINUM SALTS, PARTICULARLY CONCENTRATED SOLUTIONS (20%), MAY PRODUCE GINGIVAL NECROSIS AND FATAL HEMORRHAGIC GASTROENTERITIS, INCOORDINATION, CLONIC CONTRACTIONS, EVIDENCE OF NEPHRITIS AND DEATH. **CHRONIC EXPOSURE-** NO DATA AVAILABLE.

FIRST AID- TREAT SYMPTOMATICALLY AND SUPPORTIVELY. GET MEDICAL ATTENTION IMMEDIATELY. IF VOMITING OCCURS, KEEP HEAD LOWER THAN HIPS TO PREVENT ASPIRATION.

ANTIDOTE: NO SPECIFIC ANTIDOTE. TREAT SYMPTOMATICALLY AND SUPPORTIVELY.

REACTIVITY

REACTIVITY: STABLE UNDER NORMAL TEMPERATURES AND PRESSURES.

INCOMPATIBILITIES: ALUMINUM SULFATE: BASES: VIOLENT REACTION. METALS: MAY BE CORROSIVE IN THE PRESENCE OF MOISTURE.

DECOMPOSITION: THERMAL DECOMPOSITION MAY RELEASE TOXIC OXIDES OF SULFUR.

POLYMERIZATION: HAZARDOUS POLYMERIZATION HAS NOT BEEN REPORTED TO OCCUR UNDER NORMAL TEMPERATURES AND PRESSURES.

STORAGE AND DISPOSAL

OBSERVE ALL FEDERAL, STATE AND LOCAL REGULATIONS WHEN STORING OR DISPOSING OF THIS SUBSTANCE. FOR ASSISTANCE, CONTACT THE DISTRICT DIRECTOR OF THE ENVIRONMENTAL PROTECTION AGENCY.

****STORAGE****

STORE IN DRY, WELL-CLOSED CONTAINERS.
STORE AWAY FROM INCOMPATIBLE SUBSTANCES.

CONDITIONS TO AVOID

MAY BURN BUT DOES NOT IGNITE READILY. AVOID CONTACT WITH STRONG OXIDIZERS, EXCESSIVE HEAT, SPARKS, OR OPEN FLAME.

SPILL AND LEAK PROCEDURES

SOIL SPILL: DIG HOLDING AREA SUCH AS LAGOON, POND OR PIT FOR CONTAINMENT. USE PROTECTIVE COVER SUCH AS A PLASTIC SHEET TO PREVENT MATERIAL FROM DISSOLVING IN FIRE EXTINGUISHING WATER OR RAIN.

WATER SPILL: NEUTRALIZE WITH AGRICULTURAL LIME, SLAKED LIME, CRUSHED LIMESTONE, OR SODIUM BICARBONATE.
USE MECHANICAL DREDGES OR LIFTS TO EXTRACT IMMOBILIZED MASSES OF POLLUTION AND PRECIPITATES.

OCCUPATIONAL SPILL: SWEEP UP AND PLACE IN SUITABLE CLEAN, DRY CONTAINERS FOR RECLAMATION OR LATER DISPOSAL. DO NOT FLUSH SPILLED MATERIAL INTO SEWER. KEEP UNNECESSARY PEOPLE AWAY.
REPORTABLE QUANTITY (RQ): 5000 POUNDS THE SUPERFUND AMENDMENTS AND REAUTHORIZATION ACT (SARA) SECTION 304 REQUIRES THAT A RELEASE EQUAL TO OR GREATER THAN THE REPORTABLE QUANTITY FOR THIS SUBSTANCE BE IMMEDIATELY REPORTED TO THE LOCAL EMERGENCY PLANNING COMMITTEE AND THE STATE EMERGENCY RESPONSE COMMISSION (40 CFR 355.40). IF THE RELEASE OF THIS SUBSTANCE IS REPORTABLE UNDER CERCLA SECTION 103, THE NATIONAL RESPONSE CENTER MUST BE NOTIFIED IMMEDIATELY AT (800) 424-8802 OR (202) 426-2675 IN THE METROPOLITAN WASHINGTON, D.C. AREA (40 CFR 302.6).

PROTECTIVE EQUIPMENT

VENTILATION: PROVIDE LOCAL EXHAUST VENTILATION AND/OR GENERAL DILUTION VENTILATION TO MEET PUBLISHED EXPOSURE LIMITS.

RESPIRATOR: THE FOLLOWING RESPIRATORS ARE RECOMMENDED BASED ON INFORMATION FOUND IN THE PHYSICAL DATA, TOXICITY AND HEALTH EFFECTS SECTIONS. THEY ARE RANKED IN ORDER FROM MINIMUM TO MAXIMUM RESPIRATORY PROTECTION. THE SPECIFIC RESPIRATOR SELECTED MUST BE BASED ON CONTAMINATION LEVELS FOUND IN THE WORK PLACE, MUST NOT EXCEED THE WORKING LIMITS OF THE RESPIRATOR AND BE JOINTLY APPROVED BY THE NATIONAL INSTITUTE FOR OCCUPATIONAL SAFETY AND HEALTH AND THE MINE SAFETY AND HEALTH ADMINISTRATION (NIOSH-MSHA).
DUST AND MIST RESPIRATOR WITH A FULL FACEPIECE.
AIR-PURIFYING FULL FACEPIECE RESPIRATOR WITH A HIGH-EFFICIENCY PARTICULATE FILTER.
POWERED AIR-PURIFYING RESPIRATOR WITH A TIGHT-FITTING FACEPIECE AND HIGH-EFFICIENCY PARTICULATE FILTER.
TYPE 'C' SUPPLIED-AIR RESPIRATOR WITH A FULL FACEPIECE OPERATED IN PRESSURE-DEMAND OR OTHER POSITIVE PRESSURE MODE OR WITH A FULL FACEPIECE, HELMET OR HOOD OPERATED IN CONTINUOUS-FLOW MODE.
SELF-CONTAINED BREATHING APPARATUS WITH A FULL FACEPIECE OPERATED IN PRESSURE-DEMAND OR OTHER POSITIVE PRESSURE MODE.
FOR FIREFIGHTING AND OTHER IMMEDIATELY DANGEROUS TO LIFE OR HEALTH CONDITIONS:
SELF-CONTAINED BREATHING APPARATUS WITH FULL FACEPIECE OPERATED IN PRESSURE-DEMAND OR OTHER POSITIVE PRESSURE MODE.
SUPPLIED-AIR RESPIRATOR WITH FULL FACEPIECE AND OPERATED IN PRESSURE-DEMAND OR OTHER POSITIVE PRESSURE MODE IN COMBINATION WITH AN AUXILIARY SELF-CONTAINED BREATHING APPARATUS OPERATED IN PRESSURE-DEMAND OR OTHER POSITIVE PRESSURE MODE.

CLOTHING: EMPLOYEE MUST WEAR APPROPRIATE PROTECTIVE (IMPERVIOUS) CLOTHING AND EQUIPMENT TO PREVENT REPEATED OR PROLONGED SKIN CONTACT WITH THIS SUBSTANCE.

GLOVES: EMPLOYEE MUST WEAR APPROPRIATE PROTECTIVE GLOVES TO PREVENT CONTACT WITH THIS SUBSTANCE.

EYE PROTECTION: EMPLOYEE MUST WEAR SPLASH-PROOF OR DUST-RESISTANT SAFETY GOGGLES AND A FACESHIELD TO PREVENT CONTACT WITH THIS SUBSTANCE.
EMERGENCY WASH FACILITIES: WHERE THERE IS ANY POSSIBILITY THAT AN EMPLOYEE'S EYES AND/OR SKIN MAY BE EXPOSED TO THIS SUBSTANCE, THE EMPLOYER SHOULD PROVIDE AN EYE WASH FOUNTAIN AND QUICK DRENCH SHOWER WITHIN THE IMMEDIATE WORK AREA FOR EMERGENCY USE.

AUTHORIZED BY- OCCUPATIONAL HEALTH SERVICES, INC.
CREATION DATE: 11/15/89 ***REVISION DATE:*** 05/31/90

MATERIAL SAFETY DATA SHEET

OCCUPATIONAL HEALTH SERVICES, INC.
AGRICULTURE AND PESTICIDE DIVISION
450 SEVENTH AVENUE, SUITE 2407
NEW YORK, NEW YORK 10123
1-800-445-MSDS OR (212) 967-1100

EMERGENCY CONTACT:
JOHN S. BRANSFORD, JR. (615) 292-1180

SUBSTANCE IDENTIFICATION

CAS-NUMBER 7429-90-5

SUBSTANCE: **ALUMINUM, METALLIC, POWDER**

TRADE NAMES/SYNONYMS: ALUMINUM FLAKE; PYRO POWDER; ALUMINUM ELEMENT; ALUMINUM POWDER; ALUMINUM; 1XXX SERIES ALLOYS (CLADDINGS) (REYNOLDS METAL COMPANY); ATOMIZED ALUMINUM POWDER (ALCAN POWDERS & PIGMENTS); STCC 4916708; UN 1396; AL; PST01000

CHEMICAL FAMILY: METAL

MOLECULAR FORMULA: AL

MOLECULAR WEIGHT: 26.98

CERCLA RATINGS (SCALE 0-3): HEALTH=U FIRE=3 REACTIVITY=1 PERSISTENCE=3

NFPA RATINGS (SCALE 0-4): HEALTH=0 FIRE=1 REACTIVITY=1

COMPONENTS AND CONTAMINANTS

COMPONENT: ALUMINUM ***PERCENT:*** 100.0
CAS# 7429-90-5

OTHER CONTAMINANTS: NONE

EXPOSURE LIMITS: ALUMINUM, METALLIC, POWDER: 5 MG/M3 ACGIH TWA (PYRO POWDERS)
SUBJECT TO SARA SECTION 313 ANNUAL TOXIC CHEMICAL RELEASE REPORTING

PHYSICAL DATA

DESCRIPTION: ODORLESS, SILVER-WHITE POWDER. ***BOILING POINT:*** 4473 F (2467 C)

MELTING POINT: 1220 F (660 C) ***SPECIFIC GRAVITY:*** 2.702

VAPOR PRESSURE: 1 MMHG @ 1284 C ***SOLUBILITY IN WATER:*** REACTS

SOLVENT SOLUBILITY: INSOLUBLE IN ALCOHOL, CONCENTRATED NITRIC ACID, ACETIC ACID (HOT).

FIRE AND EXPLOSION DATA

FIRE AND EXPLOSION HAZARD: DANGEROUS FIRE HAZARD WHEN EXPOSED TO HEAT OR FLAME.
MAY IGNITE SPONTANEOUSLY ON EXPOSURE TO AIR.
DUST-AIR MIXTURES MAY IGNITE OR EXPLODE.

FLASH POINT: 1193 F (645 C) (CC) ***LOWER EXPLOSIVE LIMIT:*** 40 MG/L

AUTOIGNITION TEMP.: 1400 F (760 C)

FIREFIGHTING MEDIA: DRY CHEMICAL, SODA ASH, LIME OR SAND (1987 EMERGENCY RESPONSE GUIDEBOOK, DOT P 5800.4).
FOR LARGER FIRES, FLOOD AREA WITH WATER FROM A DISTANCE (1987 EMERGENCY RESPONSE GUIDEBOOK, DOT P 5800.4).

FIREFIGHTING: DO NOT GET WATER INSIDE CONTAINERS. MOVE CONTAINERS FROM FIRE AREA IF POSSIBLE. COOL CONTAINERS EXPOSED TO FLAMES WITH WATER FROM SIDE UNTIL WELL AFTER FIRE IS OUT. STAY AWAY FROM STORAGE TANK

ENDS. FOR MASSIVE FIRE IN STORAGE AREA, USE UNMANNED HOSE HOLDER OR MONITOR NOZZLES; ELSE WITHDRAW FROM AREA AND LET FIRE BURN (1987 EMERGENCY RESPONSE GUIDEBOOK, DOT P 5800.4, GUIDE PAGE 37).
DO NOT USE WATER! USE SUITABLE DRY POWDER. AVOID BREATHING DUSTS.

TRANSPORTATION DATA

DEPARTMENT OF TRANSPORTATION HAZARD CLASSIFICATION 49 CFR 172.101: FLAMMABLE SOLID
DEPARTMENT OF TRANSPORTATION LABELING REQUIREMENTS 49 CFR 172.101 AND SUBPART E: FLAMMABLE SOLID
DEPARTMENT OF TRANSPORTATION PACKAGING REQUIREMENTS: 49 CFR 173.232 EXCEPTIONS: 49 CFR 173.232

TOXICITY

ALUMINUM, METALLIC, POWDER: CARCINOGEN STATUS: NONE. LOCAL EFFECTS: IRRITANT- INHALATION, EYE. ACUTE TOXICITY LEVEL: NO DATA AVAILABLE.
TARGET EFFECTS: PROLONGED EXPOSURE MAY AFFECT THE LUNGS.

HEALTH EFFECTS AND FIRST AID

INHALATION: ALUMINUM POWDER: IRRITANT. **ACUTE EXPOSURE**- DUST MAY CAUSE RESPIRATORY IRRITATION WITH COUGHING AND SORE THROAT, MENTAL DETERIORATION, AND ENCEPHALOPATHY. DUST MAY COLLECT IN THE LUNGS. MASSIVE EXPOSURE LASTING 6 HOURS REPORTEDLY RESULTED IN THE DEATH OF ONE WORKER FROM DELAYED PULMONARY FIBROSIS. **CHRONIC EXPOSURE**- REPEATED OR PROLONGED CONTACT MAY CAUSE MUCOUS MEMBRANE IRRITATION AND "ALUMINOSIS" (AN ALUMINUM PNEUMOCONIOSIS). THE EVIDENCE IS NOT DEFINITIVE AND REPORTED EFFECTS FROM EXPOSURE MAY VARY FROM NO ILLNESS, SLIGHT X-RAY CHANGES, TO RAPIDLY PROGRESSIVE AND IRREVERSIBLE LUNG DISEASE. WORKERS CHRONICALLY EXPOSED TO FINE ALUMINUM POWDERS HAVE EXPERIENCED COUGHING WITH VARIABLE SPUTUM PRODUCTION, DYSPNEA OR TACHYPNEA, SPONTANEOUS PNEUMOTHORAX, CHEST PAIN ON RESPIRATION, EPIGASTRIC ABDOMINAL PAIN, LETHARGY, ANOREXIA, WEIGHT LOSS, BRONCHIAL ASTHMA, CARDIAC FAILURE, ENCEPHALOPATHY, AND DEATH DUE TO NODULAR INTERSTITIAL PULMONARY FIBROSIS AND EMPHYSEMA. DIAGNOSTIC TESTS REVEAL RELATIVE LYMPHOCYTOSIS, DECREASED VITAL CAPACITY, OPACITIES, AND BRONCHIAL MARKINGS IN THE LUNGS. EXCESSIVE LEVELS OF ALUMINUM HAVE BEEN FOUND IN THE BRAINS OF VICTIMS OF ALZHEIMER'S DISEASE.
FIRST AID- REMOVE FROM EXPOSURE AREA TO FRESH AIR IMMEDIATELY. IF BREATHING HAS STOPPED, PERFORM ARTIFICIAL RESPIRATION. KEEP PERSON WARM AND AT REST. TREAT SYMPTOMATICALLY AND SUPPORTIVELY. GET MEDICAL ATTENTION IMMEDIATELY.

SKIN CONTACT: ALUMINUM, METALLIC, POWDER: **ACUTE EXPOSURE**- DUST IS GENERALLY NON-IRRITATING. **CHRONIC EXPOSURE**- REPEATED OR PROLONGED CONTACT OF DUST WITH SKIN MOISTURE MAY CAUSE FORMATION OF IRRITATING SALTS WITH THE POSSIBILITY OF DERMATITIS AND SECONDARY INFECTION.
FIRST AID- REMOVE CONTAMINATED CLOTHING AND SHOES IMMEDIATELY. WASH AFFECTED AREA WITH SOAP OR MILD DETERGENT AND LARGE AMOUNTS OF WATER UNTIL NO EVIDENCE OF CHEMICAL REMAINS (APPROXIMATELY 15-20 MINUTES). GET MEDICAL ATTENTION IMMEDIATELY.

EYE CONTACT: ALUMINUM, METALLIC, POWDER: IRRITANT. **ACUTE EXPOSURE**- MAY CAUSE IRRITATION. DEPOSITION OF PARTICLES IN THE EYE MAY CAUSE CORNEAL NECROSIS. A LOW-GRADE UVEAL INFLAMMATION WITH POSTERIOR SYNECHIAS, PARTIAL ATROPHY OF THE IRIS, AND SMALL OPACITIES IN THE LENSES AND PIGMENTATION OF THE FUNDUS WAS REPORTED IN RABBITS. **CHRONIC EXPOSURE**- REPEATED OR PROLONGED CONTACT MAY CAUSE CONJUNCTIVITIS OR EFFECTS AS IN ACUTE EXPOSURE.
FIRST AID- WASH EYES IMMEDIATELY WITH LARGE AMOUNTS OF WATER OR NORMAL SALINE, OCCASIONALLY LIFTING UPPER AND LOWER LIDS, UNTIL NO EVIDENCE OF CHEMICAL REMAINS (APPROXIMATELY 15-20 MINUTES). GET MEDICAL ATTENTION IMMEDIATELY.

INGESTION: ALUMINUM, METALLIC, POWDER: **ACUTE EXPOSURE**- ALUMINUM IS POORLY ABSORBED AND MAY DECREASE ABSORPTION OF OTHER SUBSTANCES. LARGE DOSES MAY CAUSE GASTRIC IRRITATION. **CHRONIC EXPOSURE**- EXCESSIVE LEVELS OF ALUMINUM HAVE BEEN FOUND IN THE BRAINS OF VICTIMS OF ALZHEIMER'S DISEASE.
FIRST AID- TREAT SYMPTOMATICALLY AND SUPPORTIVELY. GET MEDICAL ATTENTION IMMEDIATELY. IF VOMITING OCCURS, KEEP HEAD LOWER THAN HIPS TO PREVENT ASPIRATION.

ANTIDOTE: NO SPECIFIC ANTIDOTE. TREAT SYMPTOMATICALLY AND SUPPORTIVELY.

REACTIVITY

REACTIVITY: REACTS EXOTHERMICALLY ON CONTACT WITH WATER, RELEASING FLAMMABLE HYDROGEN GAS.

INCOMPATIBILITIES: ALUMINUM: ACIDS: REACTS TO FORM FLAMMABLE HYDROGEN GAS. ALCOHOLS: VIGOROUS REACTION, WITH INCREASE IN TEMPERATURE AND PRESSURE. AMMONIUM NITRATE: EXPLOSIVE MIXTURE. AMMONIUM PEROXODISULFATE: POSSIBLE EXPLOSION. ANTIMONY: VIOLENT REACTION WHEN HEATED. ANTIMONY TRICHLORIDE (VAPOR): IGNITION. ARSENIC: VIOLENT REACTION WHEN HEATED. BARIUM PEROXIDE: IGNITION ON CONTACT. BASES: REACTS TO FORM FLAMMABLE HYDROGEN GAS. BISMUTH (POWDERED): PYROPHORIC MIXTURE. BISMUTH TRIOXIDE: EXPLODES ON HEATING. BROMINE: VIGOROUS REACTION. BROMINE PENTAFLUORIDE: VIOLENT REACTION AND POSSIBLE IGNITION. CARBON DIOXIDE: IGNITES WHEN HEATED. CARBON DIOXIDE + ALUMINUM HALIDES: INCANDESCENT REACTION. CARBON DISULFIDE (VAPOR): IGNITION. CARBON TETRACHLORIDE + METHANOL: POSSIBLE HAZARDOUS REACTION. CHLORINE: IGNITION. CHLORINE TRIFLUORIDE + CHARCOAL: POSSIBLE VIOLENT REACTION. CHLOROFLUOROHYDROCARBONS: FORMS SHOCK-SENSITIVE MIXTURE. CHLOROFORMAMIDINIUM NITRATE: EXPLOSIVE IGNITION. CHROMIC ANHYDRIDE: VIOLENT REACTION OR IGNITION. DIBORANE: FORMS SPONTANEOUSLY FLAMMABLE HYDRIDES. DISULFUR DIBROMIDE: VIOLENT REACTION. FLUORINE: ATTACKS. FORMIC ACID: INCANDESCENT REACTION. HALOCARBONS: EXPLODES ON CONTACT. HYDROCHLORIC ACID: VIOLENT REACTION. HYDROFLUORIC ACID: VIOLENT REACTION. HYDROGEN CHLORIDE: VIGOROUS EXOTHERMIC REACTION. INTERHALOGENS: POSSIBLE IGNITION OR EXPLOSIVE REACTION. IODINE + WATER: VIOLENT REACTION. IRON: EXOTHERMIC REACTION WITH EVOLUTION OF FLAMMABLE HYDROGEN GAS. MERCURY(II) SALTS: VIGOROUS REACTION. METAL BROMATES: FORMS SHOCK-SENSITIVE MIXTURE. METAL CHLORATES: FORMS SHOCK-SENSITIVE MIXTURE. METAL IODATES: FORMS SHOCK-SENSITIVE MIXTURE. METAL NITRATES: FORMS EXPLOSIVE MIXTURE. METAL OXIDES: VIOLENT OR EXPLOSIVE REACTION IF HEATED. METAL SULFATES: VIOLENT EXPLOSIVE REACTION. METHANOL: FORMS A DETONABLE MIXTURE. NIOBIUM OXIDE + SULFUR: DANGEROUS FIRE HAZARD. NITROGEN OXIDES: IGNITION. NITRYL FLUORIDE: INCANDESCES WHEN HEATED. NON-METALS: VIOLENT REACTION. NON-METAL HALIDES: IGNITION. OXIDIZERS: FIRE AND EXPLOSION HAZARD. OXYGEN: SPONTANEOUS IGNITION AND POSSIBLE EXPLOSION. PALLADIUM: EXOTHERMIC REACTION AT 600 C. PERFORMIC ACID: VIOLENT REACTION. PEROXIDES: POSSIBLE IGNITION OR EXPLOSION. PHOSGENE: SPONTANEOUS IGNITION. PICRIC ACID + WATER: POSSIBLE IGNITION. PLATINUM: RAPID EXOTHERMIC REACTION. SILICON + LEAD OXIDE: EXPLODES ON HEATING. SILICON STEEL: VIOLENT REACTION. SILVER CHLORIDE: POSSIBLE EXPLOSIVE REACTION. SODIUM CARBIDE: VIOLENT REACTION. SODIUM CARBONATE: POSSIBLE EXPLOSION ON HEATING. SODIUM DIURANATE: EXOTHERMIC REACTION. SODIUM HYDROXIDE: REACTS TO FORM EXPLOSIVE HYDROGEN GAS. SULFUR DIOXIDE: SPONTANEOUS IGNITION. ZINC: POSSIBLE FIRE HAZARD.

DECOMPOSITION: THERMAL DECOMPOSITION MAY RELEASE ACRID SMOKE AND IRRITATING FUMES.

POLYMERIZATION: HAZARDOUS POLYMERIZATION HAS NOT BEEN REPORTED TO OCCUR UNDER NORMAL TEMPERATURES AND PRESSURES.

STORAGE AND DISPOSAL

OBSERVE ALL FEDERAL, STATE AND LOCAL REGULATIONS WHEN STORING OR DISPOSING OF THIS SUBSTANCE. FOR ASSISTANCE, CONTACT THE DISTRICT DIRECTOR OF THE ENVIRONMENTAL PROTECTION AGENCY.

****STORAGE****

PROTECT CONTAINERS AGAINST PHYSICAL DAMAGE. KEEP DRY AND ISOLATE FROM ACIDS, CAUSTICS AND CHLORINATED HYDROCARBONS. SEPARATE FROM OXIDIZING MATERIALS. AVOID STORAGE NEAR COMBUSTIBLE MATERIALS (NFPA 49, HAZARDOUS CHEMICALS DATA, 1975)
STORE UNDER BENZENE, KEROSENE, OR OTHER LIQUID NOT CONTAINING OXYGEN. CONTACT WITH AIR MAY RESULT IN SPONTANEOUS IGNITION. DO NOT STORE UNDER HALOCARBON SOLVENTS.
STORE AWAY FROM INCOMPATIBLE SUBSTANCES.

****DISPOSAL****

DISPOSAL MUST BE IN ACCORDANCE WITH STANDARDS APPLICABLE TO GENERATORS OF HAZARDOUS WASTE, 40 CFR 262. EPA HAZARDOUS WASTE NUMBER D001. 100 POUND CERCLA SECTION 103 REPORTABLE QUANTITY.

CONDITIONS TO AVOID

MAY IGNITE ITSELF IF EXPOSED TO AIR AND MAY RE-IGNITE AFTER FIRE IS EXTINGUISHED. MAY BURN RAPIDLY WITH FLARE-BURNING EFFECT. RUNOFF TO SEWER MAY CREATE FIRE OR EXPLOSION HAZARD.

SPILL AND LEAK PROCEDURES

OCCUPATIONAL SPILL: DO NOT TOUCH SPILLED MATERIAL. STOP LEAK IF YOU CAN DO IT WITHOUT RISK. DO NOT GET WATER INSIDE CONTAINER. FOR SMALL SPILLS, FLUSH AREA WITH FLOODING AMOUNTS OF WATER. FOR LARGER SPILLS, DIKE SPILL FOR LATER DISPOSAL. KEEP UNNECESSARY PEOPLE AWAY. ISOLATE HAZARD AREA AND DENY ENTRY.

PROTECTIVE EQUIPMENT

VENTILATION: PROVIDE LOCAL EXHAUST OR PROCESS ENCLOSURE VENTILATION TO MEET PUBLISHED EXPOSURE LIMITS.

RESPIRATOR: THE FOLLOWING RESPIRATORS ARE RECOMMENDED BASED ON INFORMATION FOUND IN THE PHYSICAL DATA, TOXICITY AND HEALTH EFFECTS SECTIONS. THEY ARE RANKED IN ORDER FROM MINIMUM TO MAXIMUM RESPIRATORY PROTECTION. THE SPECIFIC RESPIRATOR SELECTED MUST BE BASED ON CONTAMINATION LEVELS FOUND IN THE WORK PLACE, MUST NOT EXCEED THE WORKING LIMITS OF THE RESPIRATOR AND BE JOINTLY APPROVED BY THE NATIONAL INSTITUTE FOR OCCUPATIONAL SAFETY AND HEALTH AND THE MINE SAFETY AND HEALTH ADMINISTRATION (NIOSH-MSHA).
DUST, MIST, AND FUME RESPIRATOR.
POWERED AIR-PURIFYING RESPIRATOR WITH A DUST, MIST, AND FUME FILTER.
TYPE 'C' SUPPLIED-AIR RESPIRATOR WITH A FULL FACEPIECE OPERATED IN PRESSURE-DEMAND OR OTHER POSITIVE PRESSURE MODE OR WITH A FULL FACEPIECE, HELMET OR HOOD OPERATED IN CONTINUOUS-FLOW MODE.
SELF-CONTAINED BREATHING APPARATUS WITH A FULL FACE PIECE OPERATED IN PRESSURE-DEMAND OR OTHER POSITIVE PRESSURE MODE.
FOR FIREFIGHTING AND OTHER IMMEDIATELY DANGEROUS TO LIFE OR HEALTH CONDITIONS:
SELF-CONTAINED BREATHING APPARATUS WITH FULL FACEPIECE OPERATED IN PRESSURE-DEMAND OR OTHER POSITIVE PRESSURE MODE.
SUPPLIED-AIR RESPIRATOR WITH FULL FACEPIECE AND OPERATED IN PRESSURE-DEMAND OR OTHER POSITIVE PRESSURE MODE IN COMBINATION WITH AN AUXILIARY SELF-CONTAINED BREATHING APPARATUS OPERATED IN PRESSURE-DEMAND OR OTHER POSITIVE PRESSURE MODE.

CLOTHING: EMPLOYEE MUST WEAR APPROPRIATE PROTECTIVE (IMPERVIOUS) CLOTHING AND EQUIPMENT TO PREVENT REPEATED OR PROLONGED SKIN CONTACT WITH THIS SUBSTANCE.

GLOVES: EMPLOYEE MUST WEAR APPROPRIATE PROTECTIVE GLOVES TO PREVENT CONTACT WITH THIS SUBSTANCE.

EYE PROTECTION: EMPLOYEE MUST WEAR SPLASH-PROOF OR DUST-RESISTANT SAFETY GOGGLES TO PREVENT EYE CONTACT WITH THIS SUBSTANCE.
EMERGENCY EYE WASH: WHERE THERE IS ANY POSSIBILITY THAT AN EMPLOYEE'S EYES MAY BE EXPOSED TO THIS SUBSTANCE, THE EMPLOYER SHOULD PROVIDE AN EYE WASH FOUNTAIN WITHIN THE IMMEDIATE WORK AREA FOR EMERGENCY USE.

AUTHORIZED BY- OCCUPATIONAL HEALTH SERVICES, INC.
CREATION DATE: 11/15/89 ***REVISION DATE:*** 03/28/90

MATERIAL SAFETY DATA SHEET

OCCUPATIONAL HEALTH SERVICES, INC.
AGRICULTURE AND PESTICIDE DIVISION
450 SEVENTH AVENUE, SUITE 2407
NEW YORK, NEW YORK 10123
1-800-445-MSDS OR (212) 967-1100

EMERGENCY CONTACT:
JOHN S. BRANSFORD, JR. (615) 292-1180

SUBSTANCE IDENTIFICATION

CAS-NUMBER 834-12-8

SUBSTANCE: AMETRYN

TRADE NAMES/SYNONYMS: 1,3,5-TRIAZINE-2,4-DIAMINE, N-ETHYL-N'-(1-METHYLETHYL)-6-(METHYLTHIO)-; S-TRIAZINE, 2-(ETHYLAMINO)-4-(ISOPROPYLAMINO)-6-(METHYLTHIO)-; N-ETHYL-N'-(1-METHYLETHYL)-6-(METHYLTHIO)-1,3,5-TRIAZINE-2,4-DIAMINE; 2-(ETHYLAMINO)-4-(ISOPROPYLAMINO)-6-(METHYLTHIO)-S-TRIAZINE; 2-ETHYLAMINO-4-ISOPROPYLAMINO-6-METHYLMERCAPTO-S-TRIAZINE; 2-METHYLTHIO-4-ETHYLAMINO-6-ISOPROPYLAMINO-S-TRIAZINE; 2-ETHYLAMINO-4-ISOPROPYLAMINO-6-METHYLTHIO-1,3,5-TRIAZINE 2-METHYLTHIO-4-ETHYLAMINO-6-ISOPROPYLAMINO-S-TRIAZINE; AMETRYNE; AMETREX; EVIK; G 34162; GESAPAX; C9H17N5S; PST01006

CHEMICAL FAMILY: S-TRIAZINE

MOLECULAR FORMULA: C9-H17-N5-S

MOLECULAR WEIGHT: 227.35

CERCLA RATINGS (SCALE 0-3): HEALTH=2 FIRE=1 REACTIVITY=0 PERSISTENCE=2

NFPA RATINGS (SCALE 0-4): HEALTH=2 FIRE=1 REACTIVITY=0

COMPONENTS AND CONTAMINANTS

COMPONENT: AMETRYN ***PERCENT:*** 100
CAS# 834-12-8

OTHER CONTAMINANTS: NONE

EXPOSURE LIMITS: NO OCCUPATIONAL EXPOSURE LIMITS ESTABLISHED BY OSHA, ACGIH, OR NIOSH.

PHYSICAL DATA

DESCRIPTION: COLORLESS CRYSTALLINE SOLID. ***MELTING POINT:*** 183-185 F (84-85 C)

SPECIFIC GRAVITY: 1.19 ***VAPOR PRESSURE:*** NEGLIGIBLE

SOLUBILITY IN WATER: 0.0185%

SOLVENT SOLUBILITY: SOLUBLE IN ALCOHOL, HEXANE, ACETONE, DICHLOROMETHANE, 1-OCTANOL, TOLUENE, ORGANIC SOLVENTS, ACIDS AND ALKALI.(

FIRE AND EXPLOSION DATA

FIRE AND EXPLOSION HAZARD: SLIGHT FIRE HAZARD WHEN EXPOSED TO HEAT OR FLAME.

FIREFIGHTING MEDIA: DRY CHEMICAL, CARBON DIOXIDE, HALON, WATER SPRAY OR STANDARD FOAM (1987 EMERGENCY RESPONSE GUIDEBOOK, DOT P 5800.4).
FOR LARGER FIRES, USE WATER SPRAY, FOG OR STANDARD FOAM (1987 EMERGENCY RESPONSE GUIDEBOOK, DOT P 5800.4).

FIREFIGHTING: MOVE CONTAINERS FROM FIRE AREA IF POSSIBLE (1987 EMERGENCY RESPONSE GUIDEBOOK, DOT P 5800.4, GUIDE PAGE 53).
EXTINGUISH USING AGENTS SUITABLE FOR SURROUNDING FIRE. USE FLOODING QUANTITIES OF WATER AS A FOG. KEEP MATERIAL OUT OF SEWERS AND WATER SOURCES. DO NOT TOUCH SPILLED MATERIAL. AVOID BREATHING HAZARDOUS FUMES; KEEP UPWIND.

TOXICITY

AMETRYN: IRRITATION DATA: 76 MG EYE-RABBIT MILD. TOXICITY DATA: 8160 MG/KG SKIN-RABBIT LD50; 508 MG/KG ORAL-RAT LD50; 965 MG/KG ORAL-MOUSE LD50. CARCINOGEN STATUS: NONE. ACUTE TOXICITY LEVEL: MODERATELY TOXIC BY INGESTION; SLIGHTLY TOXIC BY DERMAL ABSORPTION. TARGET EFFECTS: NO DATA AVAILABLE.

HEALTH EFFECTS AND FIRST AID

INHALATION: AMETRYN: ACUTE EXPOSURE- A LETHAL CONCENTRATION IN RATS IS GREATER THAN 2200 MG/M3/4 HOURS. SOME TRIAZINES ARE MILDLY IRRITATING TO THE UPPER RESPIRATORY TRACT. CHRONIC EXPOSURE- NO DATA AVAILABLE.

FIRST AID- REMOVE FROM EXPOSURE AREA TO FRESH AIR IMMEDIATELY. IF BREATHING HAS STOPPED, PERFORM ARTIFICIAL RESPIRATION. KEEP PERSON WARM AND AT REST. TREAT SYMPTOMATICALLY AND SUPPORTIVELY. GET MEDICAL ATTENTION IMMEDIATELY.

SKIN CONTACT: AMETRYN: ACUTE EXPOSURE- THIS MATERIAL WAS MILDLY IRRITATING TO RABBIT SKIN. A LETHAL DOSE BY DERMAL ABSORPTION IN RABBITS WAS 8160 MG/KG. CHRONIC EXPOSURE- NO DATA AVAILABLE.

FIRST AID- REMOVE CONTAMINATED CLOTHING AND SHOES IMMEDIATELY. WASH AFFECTED AREA WITH SOAP OR MILD DETERGENT AND LARGE AMOUNTS OF WATER UNTIL NO EVIDENCE OF CHEMICAL REMAINS (APPROXIMATELY 15-20 MINUTES). GET MEDICAL ATTENTION IMMEDIATELY.

EYE CONTACT: AMETRYN: ACUTE EXPOSURE- 76 MG WAS MILDLY IRRITATING TO RABBIT EYES. CHRONIC EXPOSURE- NO DATA AVAILABLE.

FIRST AID- WASH EYES IMMEDIATELY WITH LARGE AMOUNTS OF WATER OR NORMAL SALINE, OCCASIONALLY LIFTING UPPER AND LOWER LIDS, UNTIL NO EVIDENCE OF CHEMICAL REMAINS (APPROXIMATELY 15-20 MINUTES). GET MEDICAL ATTENTION IMMEDIATELY.

INGESTION: AMETRYN: ACUTE EXPOSURE- A LETHAL DOSE IN RATS WAS 508 MG/KG. CHRONIC EXPOSURE- DOSES OF 100 MG/KG PER DAY FOR 90 DAYS PRODUCED SLIGHT LIVER CHANGES IN RATS. LIVER CHANGES WERE ALSO REPORTED IN CHICKENS.

FIRST AID- REMOVE BY GASTRIC LAVAGE AND CATHARSIS. MAINTAIN BLOOD PRESSURE AND AIRWAY. GIVE OXYGEN IF RESPIRATION IS DEPRESSED. DO NOT PERFORM GASTRIC LAVAGE IF VICTIM IS UNCONSCIOUS. GET MEDICAL ATTENTION IMMEDIATELY (DREISBACH, HANDBOOK OF POISONING, 12TH ED.).
ADMINISTRATION OF LAVAGE OR OXYGEN SHOULD BE PERFORMED BY QUALIFIED MEDICAL PERSONNEL.

ANTIDOTE: NO SPECIFIC ANTIDOTE. TREAT SYMPTOMATICALLY AND SUPPORTIVELY.

REACTIVITY

REACTIVITY: STABLE UNDER NORMAL TEMPERATURES AND PRESSURES.

INCOMPATIBILITIES: AMETRYN: NO DATA AVAILABLE.

DECOMPOSITION: THERMAL DECOMPOSITION PRODUCTS MAY INCLUDE TOXIC OXIDES OF CARBON, NITROGEN, AND SULFUR.

POLYMERIZATION: HAZARDOUS POLYMERIZATION HAS NOT BEEN REPORTED TO OCCUR UNDER NORMAL TEMPERATURES AND PRESSURES.

STORAGE AND DISPOSAL

OBSERVE ALL FEDERAL, STATE AND LOCAL REGULATIONS WHEN STORING OR DISPOSING OF THIS SUBSTANCE. FOR ASSISTANCE, CONTACT THE DISTRICT DIRECTOR OF THE ENVIRONMENTAL PROTECTION AGENCY.

STORAGE

STORE IN ACCORDANCE WITH 40 CFR 165 RECOMMENDED PROCEDURES FOR THE DISPOSAL AND STORAGE OF PESTICIDES AND PESTICIDE CONTAINERS.

DISPOSAL

DISPOSAL MUST BE IN ACCORDANCE WITH 40 CFR 165 RECOMMENDED PROCEDURES FOR THE DISPOSAL AND STORAGE OF PESTICIDES AND PESTICIDE CONTAINERS.

CONDITIONS TO AVOID

MAY BURN BUT DOES NOT IGNITE READILY.

SPILL AND LEAK PROCEDURES

OCCUPATIONAL SPILL: DO NOT TOUCH SPILLED MATERIAL. STOP LEAK IF YOU CAN DO IT WITHOUT RISK. FOR SMALL SPILLS, TAKE UP WITH SAND OR OTHER ABSORBENT MATERIAL AND PLACE INTO CONTAINERS FOR LATER DISPOSAL. FOR SMALL DRY SPILLS, WITH A CLEAN SHOVEL PLACE MATERIAL INTO CLEAN, DRY CONTAINER AND COVER. MOVE CONTAINERS FROM SPILL AREA. FOR LARGER SPILLS, DIKE FAR AHEAD OF SPILL FOR LATER DISPOSAL. KEEP UNNECESSARY PEOPLE AWAY. ISOLATE HAZARD AREA AND DENY ENTRY.

PROTECTIVE EQUIPMENT

VENTILATION: PROVIDE LOCAL EXHAUST OR GENERAL DILUTION VENTILATION SYSTEM.

RESPIRATOR: THE FOLLOWING RESPIRATORS ARE RECOMMENDED BASED ON INFORMATION FOUND IN THE PHYSICAL DATA, TOXICITY AND HEALTH EFFECTS SECTIONS. THEY ARE RANKED IN ORDER FROM MINIMUM TO MAXIMUM RESPIRATORY PROTECTION. THE SPECIFIC RESPIRATOR SELECTED MUST BE BASED ON CONTAMINATION LEVELS FOUND IN THE WORK PLACE, MUST NOT EXCEED THE WORKING LIMITS OF THE RESPIRATOR AND BE JOINTLY APPROVED BY THE NATIONAL INSTITUTE FOR OCCUPATIONAL SAFETY AND HEALTH AND THE MINE SAFETY AND HEALTH ADMINISTRATION (NIOSH-MSHA).
CHEMICAL CARTRIDGE RESPIRATOR WITH AN ORGANIC VAPOR CARTRIDGE(S) IN COMBINATION WITH A DUST AND MIST FILTER.
GAS MASK WITH ORGANIC VAPOR CANISTER (CHIN-STYLE OR FRONT- OR BACK-MOUNTED CANISTER) WITH A DUST AND MIST FILTER.
GAS MASK WITH ORGANIC VAPOR CANISTER (CHIN-STYLE OR FRONT- OR BACK-MOUNTED CANISTER) WITH A PARTICULATE FILTER.
POWERED AIR-PURIFYING RESPIRATOR WITH A HIGH-EFFICIENCY FILTER.
TYPE 'C' SUPPLIED-AIR RESPIRATOR WITH A FULL FACEPIECE OPERATED IN A PRESSURE-DEMAND OR OTHER POSITIVE PRESSURE MODE.
SELF-CONTAINED BREATHING APPARATUS WITH A FULL FACEPIECE OPERATED IN PRESSURE-DEMAND OR OTHER POSITIVE PRESSURE MODE.
FOR FIREFIGHTING AND OTHER IMMEDIATELY DANGEROUS TO LIFE OR HEALTH CONDITIONS:
SELF-CONTAINED BREATHING APPARATUS WITH FULL FACEPIECE OPERATED IN PRESSURE-DEMAND OR OTHER POSITIVE PRESSURE MODE.
SUPPLIED-AIR RESPIRATOR WITH FULL FACEPIECE AND OPERATED IN PRESSURE-DEMAND OR OTHER POSITIVE PRESSURE MODE IN COMBINATION WITH AN AUXILIARY SELF-CONTAINED BREATHING APPARATUS OPERATED IN PRESSURE-DEMAND OR OTHER POSITIVE PRESSURE MODE.

CLOTHING: EMPLOYEE MUST WEAR APPROPRIATE PROTECTIVE (IMPERVIOUS) CLOTHING AND EQUIPMENT TO PREVENT REPEATED OR PROLONGED SKIN CONTACT WITH THIS SUBSTANCE.

GLOVES: EMPLOYEE MUST WEAR APPROPRIATE PROTECTIVE GLOVES TO PREVENT CONTACT WITH THIS SUBSTANCE.

EYE PROTECTION: EMPLOYEE MUST WEAR SPLASH-PROOF OR DUST-RESISTANT SAFETY GOGGLES TO PREVENT EYE CONTACT WITH THIS SUBSTANCE.
EMERGENCY EYE WASH: WHERE THERE IS ANY POSSIBILITY THAT AN EMPLOYEE'S EYES MAY BE EXPOSED TO THIS SUBSTANCE, THE EMPLOYER SHOULD PROVIDE AN EYE WASH FOUNTAIN WITHIN THE IMMEDIATE WORK AREA FOR EMERGENCY USE.

AUTHORIZED BY- OCCUPATIONAL HEALTH SERVICES, INC.
CREATION DATE: 10/04/89 ***REVISION DATE:*** 05/18/90

MATERIAL SAFETY DATA SHEET

OCCUPATIONAL HEALTH SERVICES, INC.
AGRICULTURE AND PESTICIDE DIVISION
450 SEVENTH AVENUE, SUITE 2407
NEW YORK, NEW YORK 10123
1-800-445-MSDS OR (212) 967-1100

EMERGENCY CONTACT:
JOHN S. BRANSFORD, JR. (615) 292-1180

SUBSTANCE IDENTIFICATION

CAS-NUMBER 919-76-6

SUBSTANCE: **AMIDITHION**

TRADE NAMES/SYNONYMS: PHOSPHORODITHIOIC ACID, S-(2-((2-METHOXYETHYL)AMINO)-2-OXOETHYL) O,O-DIMETHYL ESTER; PHOSPHORODITHIOIC ACID, O,O-DIMETHYL ESTER, S-ESTER WITH 2-MERCAPTO-N-(2-METHOXYETHYL)ACETAMIDE; S-2-METHOXYETHYLCARBAMOYLMETHYL O,O-DIMETHYL PHOSPHORODITHIOATE; 2-DIMETHOXYPHOSPHINOTHIOYLTHIO-N-(2-METHOXYETHYL)ACETAMIDE; S-(2-((2-METHOXYETHYL)AMINO-2-OXOETHYL) O,O-DIMETHYL PHOSPHORODITHIOATE; O,O-DIMETHYL PHOPHORODITHIOATE S-ESTER WITH 2-MERCAPTO-N-(2 -METHOXYETHYL ACETAMIDE; DIMETHYL S-(N-METHOXYETHYLCARBAMOYLMETHYL)PHOSPHOROTHIOLOTHIONATE; O,O-DIMETHYL-S-(N-METHOXYETHYL)-CARBAMOYLMETHYL PHOSPHORODITHIOATE; THIOCRON; ENT 27,160; PST01007

CHEMICAL FAMILY: ORGANOPHOSPHATE

MOLECULAR FORMULA: C7-H16-N-O4-P-S2

MOLECULAR WEIGHT: 273.33

CERCLA RATINGS (SCALE 0-3): HEALTH=3 FIRE=U REACTIVITY=0 PERSISTENCE=0

NFPA RATINGS (SCALE 0-4): HEALTH=3 FIRE=U REACTIVITY=0

COMPONENTS AND CONTAMINANTS

COMPONENT: AMIDITHION ***PERCENT:*** 100
CAS# 919-76-6

EXPOSURE LIMITS: NO OCCUPATIONAL EXPOSURE LIMITS ESTABLISHED BY OSHA, ACGIH, OR NIOSH.

PHYSICAL DATA

DESCRIPTION: CRYSTALLINE SOLID ***MELTING POINT:*** 115 F (46 C)
SPECIFIC GRAVITY: NOT AVAILABLE ***VAPOR PRESSURE:*** 0.000008 MMHG
SOLUBILITY IN WATER: 2%
SOLVENT SOLUBILITY: SOLUBLE IN POLAR ORGANIC SOLVENTS

FIRE AND EXPLOSION DATA

FIRE AND EXPLOSION HAZARD: UNKNOWN FIRE AND EXPLOSION HAZARD.

FIREFIGHTING MEDIA: DRY CHEMICAL, CARBON DIOXIDE, HALON, WATER SPRAY OR STANDARD FOAM (1987 EMERGENCY RESPONSE GUIDEBOOK, DOT P 5800.4).
FOR LARGER FIRES, USE WATER SPRAY, FOG OR STANDARD FOAM (1987 EMERGENCY RESPONSE GUIDEBOOK, DOT P 5800.4).

FIREFIGHTING: MOVE CONTAINERS FROM FIRE AREA IF POSSIBLE. FIGHT FIRE FROM MAXIMUM DISTANCE. STAY AWAY FROM STORAGE TANK ENDS. DIKE FIRE CONTROL WATER FOR LATER DISPOSAL. DO NOT SCATTER MATERIAL (1987 EMERGENCY RESPONSE GUIDEBOOK, DOT P 5800.4, GUIDE PAGE 55).
EXTINGUISH USING AGENT SUITABLE FOR TYPE OF SURROUNDING FIRE. AVOID BREATHING VAPORS AND DUSTS. KEEP UPWIND.

TOXICITY

AMIDITHION: TOXICITY DATA: 1600 MG/KG SKIN-RAT LD50; 420 MG/KG ORAL-RAT LD50. CARCINOGEN STATUS: NONE. ACUTE TOXICITY LEVEL: TOXIC BY INGESTION; MODERATELY TOXIC BY DERMAL ABSORPTION. TARGET EFFECTS: CHOLINESTERASE INHIBITOR. POISONING MAY AFFECT THE NERVOUS SYSTEM.* AT INCREASED RISK FROM EXPOSURE: PERSONS WITH RESPIRATORY AILMENTS, RECENT EXPOSURE TO CHOLINESTERASE INHIBITORS OR IMPAIRED CHOLINESTERASE PRODUCTION, OR LIVER MALFUNCTION.* ADDITIONAL DATA: MAY CROSS THE PLACENTA. HIGH ENVIRONMENTAL TEMPERATURES OR EXPOSURE OF THE CHEMICAL TO VISIBLE OR ULTRAVIOLET LIGHT MAY ENHANCE THE TOXICITY. INTERACTIONS WITH MEDICATIONS MAY OCCUR.*
* MAY BE BASED ON GENERAL INFORMATION ON ORGANOPHOSPHATES.

HEALTH EFFECTS AND FIRST AID

INHALATION: AMIDITHION: SEE INFORMATION ON ORGANOPHOSPHATES.
ORGANOPHOSPHATES: CHOLINESTERASE INHIBITOR. **ACUTE EXPOSURE**- WHEN INHALED, THE FIRST EFFECTS OF CHOLINESTERASE INHIBITORS ARE USUALLY RESPIRATORY AND MAY INCLUDE NASAL HYPEREMIA AND WATERY DISCHARGE, COUGH, CHEST DISCOMFORT, DYSPNEA, AND WHEEZING DUE TO INCREASED BRONCHIAL SECRETIONS AND BRONCHOCONSTRICTION. IF SUFFICIENT AMOUNTS

ARE ABSORBED, OTHER SYSTEMIC EFFECTS MAY BEGIN WITHIN A FEW MINUTES OR BE DELAYED FOR UP TO 12 HOURS. SYMPTOMS MAY INCLUDE PALLOR, NAUSEA, VOMITING, DIARRHEA, ABDOMINAL CRAMPS, HEADACHE, DIZZINESS, OCULAR PAIN, BLURRED VISION, MIOSIS OR IN SOME CASES, ESPECIALLY INITIALLY, MYDRIASIS, LACRIMATION, SALIVATION, SWEATING, AND CONFUSION. OTHER REPORTED CENTRAL NERVOUS SYSTEM OR NEUROMUSCULAR EFFECTS MAY INCLUDE ATAXIA, SLURRED SPEECH, AREFLEXIA, WEAKNESS, FATIGUE, FASCICULATIONS, TWITCHING, TREMORS POSSIBLY OF THE TONGUE AND EYELIDS, AND EVENTUALLY PARALYSIS OF THE EXTREMITIES AND POSSIBLY OF THE RESPIRATORY MUSCLES. IN SEVERE CASES THERE MAY ALSO BE INVOLUNTARY DEFECATION AND URINATION, CYANOSIS, PSYCHOSIS, HYPERGLYCEMIA, ACUTE PANCREATITIS, CARDIAC IRREGULARITIES, PULMONARY EDEMA, UNCONSCIOUSNESS, CONVULSIONS, AND COMA. DEATH IS PRIMARILY DUE TO RESPIRATORY FAILURE, ALTHOUGH CARDIOVASCULAR EFFECTS INCLUDING CARDIAC ARREST MAY ALSO BE IMPLICATED. LONG TERM SEQUELAE ARE RARE BUT MAY INCLUDE NEUROPSYCHIATRIC DISORDERS AND MYOPATHY WITH MUSCLE TENDERNESS. SOME ORGANOPHOSPHATES MAY CAUSE A DELAYED NEUROPATHY BEGINNING 1-4 WEEKS AFTER AN ACUTE EXPOSURE WHICH MAY OR MAY NOT HAVE CAUSED ACUTE CHOLINERGIC EFFECTS. NUMBNESS, TINGLING, WEAKNESS AND CRAMPING BEGINNING SYMMETRICALLY IN THE LOWER LIMBS MAY PROGRESS TO ATAXIA AND PARALYSIS. IN SEVERE CASES, UPPER LIMB INVOLVEMENT IS POSSIBLE AND FLACCID PARALYSIS MAY PROGRESS TO SPASTIC PARALYSIS WITH EXAGGERATED REFLEXES. IMPROVEMENT MAY OCCUR OVER MONTHS TO YEARS, BUT SOME RESIDUAL IMPAIRMENT USUALLY REMAINS. **CHRONIC EXPOSURE-** REPEATED OR PROLONGED EXPOSURE MAY RESULT IN THE EFFECTS OF ACUTE EXPOSURE INCLUDING THE DELAYED NEUROPATHY. OTHER EFFECTS REPORTED IN WORKERS REPEATEDLY EXPOSED INCLUDE IMPAIRED MEMORY AND CONCENTRATION, ACUTE PSYCHOSIS, SEVERE DEPRESSIONS, IRRITABILTY, CONFUSION, APATHY, EMOTIONAL LABILITY, SOCIAL WITHDRAWAL, CONFUSION, HEADACHE, SPEECH DIFFICULTIES, DELAYED REACTION TIMES, SPATIAL DISORIENTATION, NIGHTMARES, SLEEPWALKING, AND DROWSINESS OR INSOMNIA. AN INFLUENZA-LIKE CONDITION WITH HEADACHE, NAUSEA, WEAKNESS, ANOREXIA AND MALAISE HAS ALSO BEEN REPORTED.

FIRST AID- REMOVE FROM EXPOSURE AREA TO FRESH AIR IMMEDIATELY. IF BREATHING HAS STOPPED, GIVE ARTIFICIAL RESPIRATION. MAINTAIN AIRWAY AND BLOOD PRESSURE AND ADMINISTER OXYGEN IF AVAILABLE. KEEP AFFECTED PERSON WARM AND AT REST. TREAT SYMPTOMATICALLY AND SUPPORTIVELY. ADMINISTRATION OF OXYGEN SHOULD BE PERFORMED BY QUALIFIED PERSONNEL. GET MEDICAL ATTENTION IMMEDIATELY.

SKIN CONTACT: AMIDITHION: SEE INFORMATION ON ORGANOPHOSPHATES. ORGANOPHOSPHATES: CHOLINESTERASE INHIBITOR. **ACUTE EXPOSURE-** LOCALIZED SWEATING AND FASCICULATIONS MAY OCCUR AT THE SITE OF CONTACT. IF SUFFICIENT AMOUNTS ARE ABSORBED, OTHER EFFECTS OF CHOLINESTERASE INHIBITION AS DESCRIBED IN ACUTE INHALATION MAY OCCUR. SYMPTOMS MAY BE DELAYED 2-3 HOURS, BUT USUALLY NO MORE THAN 12 HOURS. THE RATE OF ABSORPTION IS INCREASED BY THE PRESENCE OF DERMATITIS OR HIGH AMBIENT TEMPERATURES. DELAYED NEUROPATHY IS ALSO POSSIBLE. **CHRONIC EXPOSURE-** REPEATED OR PROLONGED EXPOSURE MAY CAUSE EFFECTS AS DESCRIBED IN ACUTE EXPOSURE. SOME ORGANOPHOSPHATES MAY CAUSE SENSITIZATION.

FIRST AID- REMOVE CONTAMINATED CLOTHING IMMEDIATELY. WASH CONTAMINATED AREAS WITH SOAP AND WATER FOLLOWED BY ALCOHOL (ARENA, POISONING, 4TH ED.). EMERGENCY PERSONNEL SHOULD WEAR GLOVES AND AVOID CONTAMINATION. TREAT RESPIRATORY DIFFICULTY WITH ARTIFICIAL RESPIRATION. GET MEDICAL ATTENTION IMMEDIATELY.

EYE CONTACT: AMIDITHION: SEE INFORMATION ON ORGANOPHOSPHATES. ORGANOPHOSPHATES: CHOLINESTERASE INHIBITOR. **ACUTE EXPOSURE-** DIRECT CONTACT MAY CAUSE PAIN, HYPEREMIA, LACRIMATION, TWITCHING OF THE EYELIDS, MIOSIS, AND CILIARY MUSCLE SPASM WITH LOSS OF ACCOMODATION, BLURRED OR DIMMED VISION AND BROWACHE. SOMETIMES MYDRIASIS MAY OCCUR INSTEAD OF MIOSIS. WITH SUFFICIENT EXPOSURE, OTHER SYMPTOMS OF CHOLINESTERASE INHIBITION AS DESCRIBED IN ACUTE INHALATION MAY OCCUR. **CHRONIC EXPOSURE-** REPEATED OR PROLONGED EXPOSURE MAY CAUSE EFFECTS AS DESCRIBED IN ACUTE EXPOSURE. SOME COMPOUNDS HAVE CAUSED TOXIC EFFECTS ON THE CRYSTALLINE LENS, CONJUNCTIVAL THICKENING AND OBSTRUCTION OF THE NASOLACRIMAL CANALS WHEN USED AS MIOTIC EYEDROPS.

FIRST AID- IRRIGATE EYES WITH WATER OR SALINE SOLUTION. IF SYMPTOMS OF POISONING OCCUR, TREAT RESPIRATORY DIFFICULTY WITH ARTIFICIAL RESPIRATION AND OXYGEN. OBSERVE PATIENT FOR AT LEAST 24-36 HOURS (GOSSELIN, CLINICAL TOXICOLOGY OF COMMERCIAL PRODUCTS, 5TH ED.). GET MEDICAL ATTENTION IMMEDIATELY. OXYGEN SHOULD BE ADMINISTERED BY QUALIFIED MEDICAL PERSONNEL.

INGESTION: AMIDITHION: TOXIC. SEE INFORMATION ON ORGANOPHOSPHATES. ORGANOPHOSPHATES: CHOLINESTERASE INHIBITOR. **ACUTE EXPOSURE-** WHEN INGESTED, THE FIRST EFFECTS MAY BE NAUSEA, VOMITING, ANOREXIA, ABDOMINAL CRAMPS AND DIARRHEA. GASTROINTESTINAL ABSORPTION MAY CAUSE SYMPTOMS OF CHOLINESTERASE INHIBITION AS DESCRIBED IN ACUTE INHALATION. SYMPTOMS MAY BEGIN WITHIN MINUTES OR BE DELAYED FOR HOURS. DELAYED EFFECTS INCLUDING NEUROPATHY MAY ALSO OCCUR. **CHRONIC EXPOSURE-** REPEATED INGESTION MAY CAUSE EFFECTS AS DESCRIBED IN ACUTE EXPOSURE.

FIRST AID- IF PERSON IS ALERT AND RESPIRATION IS NOT DEPRESSED, GIVE SYRUP OF IPECAC FOLLOWED BY WATER (IF VOMITING OCCURS, KEEP HEAD BELOW HIPS TO PREVENT ASPIRATION). IF CONSCIOUSNESS LEVEL DECLINES OR VOMITING HAS NOT OCCURRED IN 15 MINUTES EMPTY STOMACH BY GASTRIC LAVAGE WITH THE AID OF CUFFED ENDOTRACHEAL TUBE USING ISOTONIC SALINE OR 5% SODIUM BICARBONATE FOLLOW WITH ACTIVATED CHARCOAL. ESTABLISH AND MAINTAIN AIRWAY. TREAT RESPIRATORY DIFFICULTY WITH ARTIFICIAL RESPIRATION AND OXYGEN. DO NOT GIVE MORPHINE, AMINOPHYLLINE, PHENOTHIAZINES, RESERPINE, FUROSEMIDE, OR ETHACRYNIC ACID (MORGAN, RECOGNITION AND MANAGEMENT OF PESTICIDE POISONINGS, 3RD ED.). TREAT SYMPTOMATICALLY AND SUPPORTIVELY. ADMINISTRATION OF OXYGEN AND LAVAGE MUST BE PERFORMED BY QUALIFIED MEDICAL PERSONNEL. GET MEDICAL ATTENTION IMMEDIATELY.

ANTIDOTE: THE FOLLOWING ANTIDOTE(S) HAVE BEEN RECOMMENDED. HOWEVER, THE DECISION AS TO WHETHER THE SEVERITY OF POISONING REQUIRES ADMINISTRATION OF ANY ANTIDOTE AND ACTUAL DOSE REQUIRED SHOULD BE MADE BY QUALIFIED MEDICAL PERSONNEL.

FOR CHOLINESTERASE INHIBITORS: ESTABLISH CLEAR AIRWAY AND TISSUE OXYGENATION BY ASPIRATION OF SECRETIONS, AND IF NECESSARY, BY ASSISTED PULMONARY VENTILATION WITH OXYGEN. IMPROVE TISSUE OXYGENATION AS MUCH AS POSSIBLE BEFORE ADMINISTERING ATROPINE TO MINIMIZE THE RISK OF VENTRICULAR FIBRILLATION. ADMINISTER ATROPINE SULFATE INTRAVENOUSLY, OR INTRAMUSCULARLY IF IV INJECTION IS NOT POSSIBLE. IN MODERATELY SEVERE POISONING ADMINISTER ATROPINE SULFATE, 0.4-2.0 MG REPEATED EVERY 15 MINUTES UNTIL ATROPINIZATION IS ACHIEVED (TACHYCARDIA, FLUSHING, DRY MOUTH, MYDRIASIS). MAINTAIN ATROPINIZATION BY REPEATED DOSES FOR 2-12 HOURS, OR LONGER, DEPENDING ON THE SEVERITY OF POISONING. THE APPEARANCE OF RALES IN THE LUNG BASES, MIOSIS, SALIVATION, NAUSEA, BRADYCARDIA, ARE ALL INDICATIONS OF INADEQUATE ATROPINIZATION. SEVERELY POISONED INDIVIDUALS MAY EXHIBIT REMARKABLE TOLERANCE TO ATROPINE; TWO OR MORE TIMES THE DOSAGES SUGGESTED ABOVE MAY BE NEEDED. PERSONS NOT POISONED OR ONLY SLIGHTLY POISONED, HOWEVER, MAY DEVELOP SIGNS OF ATROPINE TOXICITY FROM SUCH LARGE DOSAGES: FEVER, MUSCLE FIBRILLATIONS, AND DELIRIUM ARE THE MAIN SIGNS OF ATROPINE TOXICITY. IF THESE SIGNS APPEAR WHILE THE PATIENT IS FULLY ATROPINIZED, ATROPINE ADMINISTRATION SHOULD BE DISCONTINUED, AT LEAST TEMPORARILY. OBSERVE TREATED PATIENTS CLOSELY AT LEAST 24 HOURS TO INSURE THAT SYMPTOMS (POSSIBLY PULMONARY EDEMA) DO NOT RECUR AS ATROPINIZATION WEARS OFF. IN VERY SEVERE POISONINGS, METABOLIC DISPOSITION OF TOXICANT MAY REQUIRE SEVERAL HOURS OR DAYS DURING WHICH ATROPINIZATION MUST BE MAINTAINED. MARKEDLY LOWER LEVELS OF URINARY METABOLITES INDICATE THAT ATROPINE DOSAGE CAN BE TAPERED OFF. AS DOSAGE IS REDUCED, CHECK THE LUNG BASES FREQUENTLY FOR RALES. IF RALES ARE HEARD OR OTHER SYMPTOMS RETURN, RE-ESTABLISH ATROPINIZATION PROMPTLY (MORGAN, RECOGNITION AND MANAGEMENT OF PESTICIDE POISONINGS, 3RD ED.). ADMINISTRATION OF ANTIDOTE MUST BE PERFORMED BY QUALIFIED MEDICAL PERSONNEL.

IN CASES OF SEVERE POISONING BY ORGANOPHOSPHATE PESTICIDES IN WHICH RESPIRATORY DEPRESSION, MUSCLE WEAKNESS AND TWITCHINGS ARE SEVERE, GIVE PRALIDOXIME (PROTOPAM-AYERST, 2-PAM), 1.0 GRAM INTRAVENOUSLY AT NO MORE THAN 0.5 GRAM PER MINUTE. DOSAGE OF PRALIDOXIME MAY BE REPEATED IN 1-2 HOURS, THEN AT 10-12 HOUR INTERVALS IF NEEDED. IN VERY SEVERE POISONINGS, DOSAGE RATES MAY BE DOUBLED. TREATMENT WITH PRALIDOXIME WILL BE MOST EFFECTIVE IF GIVEN WITHIN THIRTY-SIX HOURS AFTER POISONING (MORGAN, RECOGNITION AND MANAGEMENT OF PESTICIDE POISONINGS, 3RD ED.). ANTIDOTE SHOULD BE ADMINISTERED BY QUALIFIED MEDICAL PERSONNEL.

REACTIVITY

REACTIVITY: STABLE UNDER NORMAL TEMPERATURES AND PRESSURES.

INCOMPATIBILITIES: AMIDITHION: ALKALI: HYDROLYZE.

DECOMPOSITION: THERMAL DECOMPOSITION PRODUCTS MAY INCLUDE TOXIC AND HAZARDOUS FUMES OF SULFUR, NITROGEN AND PHOSPHORUS.

POLYMERIZATION: HAZARDOUS POLYMERIZATION HAS NOT BEEN REPORTED TO OCCUR UNDER NORMAL TEMPERATURES AND PRESSURES.

STORAGE AND DISPOSAL

OBSERVE ALL FEDERAL, STATE AND LOCAL REGULATIONS WHEN STORING OR DISPOSING OF THIS SUBSTANCE. FOR ASSISTANCE, CONTACT THE DISTRICT DIRECTOR OF THE ENVIRONMENTAL PROTECTION AGENCY.

STORAGE

STORE IN ACCORDANCE WITH 40 CFR 165 RECOMMENDED PROCEDURES FOR THE DISPOSAL AND STORAGE OF PESTICIDES AND PESTICIDE CONTAINERS.
STORE AWAY FROM INCOMPATIBLE SUBSTANCES.

DISPOSAL

DISPOSAL MUST BE IN ACCORDANCE WITH 40 CFR 165 RECOMMENDED PROCEDURES FOR THE DISPOSAL AND STORAGE OF PESTICIDES AND PESTICIDE CONTAINERS.

CONDITIONS TO AVOID

NONE REPORTED.

SPILL AND LEAK PROCEDURES

OCCUPATIONAL SPILL: DO NOT TOUCH SPILLED MATERIAL. STOP LEAK IF YOU CAN DO IT WITHOUT RISK. USE WATER SPRAY TO REDUCE VAPORS. FOR SMALL SPILLS, TAKE UP WITH SAND OR OTHER ABSORBENT MATERIAL AND PLACE INTO CONTAINERS FOR LATER DISPOSAL. FOR SMALL DRY SPILLS, WITH A CLEAN SHOVEL PLACE MATERIAL INTO CLEAN, DRY CONTAINERS AND COVER. MOVE CONTAINERS FROM SPILL AREA. FOR LARGER SPILLS, DIKE FAR AHEAD OF SPILL FOR LATER DISPOSAL. KEEP UNNECESSARY PEOPLE AWAY. ISOLATE HAZARD AREA AND DENY ENTRY. VENTILATE CLOSED SPACES BEFORE ENTERING.

PROTECTIVE EQUIPMENT

VENTILATION: PROVIDE LOCAL EXHAUST OR GENERAL DILUTION VENTILATION SYSTEM.

RESPIRATOR: THE FOLLOWING RESPIRATORS ARE RECOMMENDED BASED ON INFORMATION FOUND IN THE PHYSICAL DATA, TOXICITY AND HEALTH EFFECTS SECTIONS. THEY ARE RANKED IN ORDER FROM MINIMUM TO MAXIMUM RESPIRATORY PROTECTION. THE SPECIFIC RESPIRATOR SELECTED MUST BE BASED ON CONTAMINATION LEVELS FOUND IN THE WORK PLACE, MUST NOT EXCEED THE WORKING LIMITS OF THE RESPIRATOR AND BE JOINTLY APPROVED BY THE NATIONAL INSTITUTE FOR OCCUPATIONAL SAFETY AND HEALTH AND THE MINE SAFETY AND HEALTH ADMINISTRATION (NIOSH-MSHA).
CHEMICAL CARTRIDGE RESPIRATOR WITH AN ORGANIC VAPOR CARTRIDGE(S) IN COMBINATION WITH A DUST AND MIST FILTER.
GAS MASK WITH ORGANIC VAPOR CANISTER (CHIN-STYLE OR FRONT- OR BACK-MOUNTED CANISTER) WITH A DUST AND MIST FILTER.
GAS MASK WITH ORGANIC VAPOR CANISTER (CHIN-STYLE OR FRONT- OR BACK-MOUNTED CANISTER) WITH A PARTICULATE FILTER.
POWERED AIR-PURIFYING RESPIRATOR WITH A HIGH-EFFICIENCY FILTER.
TYPE 'C' SUPPLIED-AIR RESPIRATOR WITH A FULL FACEPIECE OPERATED IN A PRESSURE-DEMAND OR OTHER POSITIVE PRESSURE MODE.
SELF-CONTAINED BREATHING APPARATUS WITH A FULL FACEPIECE OPERATED IN PRESSURE-DEMAND OR OTHER POSITIVE PRESSURE MODE.
FOR FIREFIGHTING AND OTHER IMMEDIATELY DANGEROUS TO LIFE OR HEALTH CONDITIONS:
SELF-CONTAINED BREATHING APPARATUS WITH FULL FACEPIECE OPERATED IN PRESSURE-DEMAND OR OTHER POSITIVE PRESSURE MODE.
SUPPLIED-AIR RESPIRATOR WITH FULL FACEPIECE AND OPERATED IN PRESSURE-DEMAND OR OTHER POSITIVE PRESSURE MODE IN COMBINATION WITH AN AUXILIARY SELF-CONTAINED BREATHING APPARATUS OPERATED IN PRESSURE-DEMAND OR OTHER POSITIVE PRESSURE MODE.

CLOTHING: EMPLOYEE MUST WEAR APPROPRIATE PROTECTIVE (IMPERVIOUS) CLOTHING AND EQUIPMENT TO PREVENT REPEATED OR PROLONGED SKIN CONTACT WITH THIS SUBSTANCE.

GLOVES: EMPLOYEE MUST WEAR APPROPRIATE PROTECTIVE GLOVES TO PREVENT CONTACT WITH THIS SUBSTANCE.

EYE PROTECTION: EMPLOYEE MUST WEAR SPLASH-PROOF OR DUST-RESISTANT SAFETY GOGGLES TO PREVENT EYE CONTACT WITH THIS SUBSTANCE.
EMERGENCY EYE WASH: WHERE THERE IS ANY POSSIBILITY THAT AN EMPLOYEE'S EYES MAY BE EXPOSED TO THIS SUBSTANCE, THE EMPLOYER SHOULD PROVIDE AN EYE WASH FOUNTAIN WITHIN THE IMMEDIATE WORK AREA FOR EMERGENCY USE.

AUTHORIZED BY- OCCUPATIONAL HEALTH SERVICES, INC.
CREATION DATE: 10/04/89 ***REVISION DATE:*** 06/07/90

MATERIAL SAFETY DATA SHEET

OCCUPATIONAL HEALTH SERVICES, INC.
AGRICULTURE AND PESTICIDE DIVISION
450 SEVENTH AVENUE, SUITE 2407
NEW YORK, NEW YORK 10123
1-800-445-MSDS OR (212) 967-1100

EMERGENCY CONTACT:
JOHN S. BRANSFORD, JR. (615) 292-1180

SUBSTANCE IDENTIFICATION

CAS-NUMBER 67485-29-4

SUBSTANCE: HYDRAMETHYLNON

TRADE NAMES/SYNONYMS: 2(1H)-PYRIMIDINONE, TETRAHYDRO-5,5-DIMETHYL-, (3-(4-(TRIFLUOROMETHYL) PHENYL-1-(2-(4-(TRIFLUOROMETHYL)PHENYL)ETHENYL)-2-PROPENYLIDENE) HYDRAZONE;
TETRAHYDRO-5,5-DIMETHYL-2(1H)-PYRIMIDINONE(3-(4-(TRIFLUOROMETHYL) PHENYL)-1-(2-(4-(TRIFLUOROMETHYL)PHENYL)ETHENYL)-2-PROPENYLIDENE) HYDRAZONE;
1,5-BIS(ALPHA,ALPHA,ALPHA-TRIFLUORO-P-TOLYL)1,4-PENTADIENE-3-ONE (1,4,5,6-TETRAHYDRO-5,5-DIMETHYL-2-PYRIMIDINYL)HYDRAZONE; 5,5-DIMETHYLPERHYDROPYRIMIDIN-2-ONE 4-TRIFLUOROMETHYL-ALPHA- (4-(4-TRILFLUOROMETHYLSTYRYL)CINNAMYLIDENEHYDRAZONE; AC 217300; AMDRO; C25H24F6N4; PST01009

CHEMICAL FAMILY: PYRIMIDINE HYDRAZONE

MOLECULAR FORMULA: C25-H24-F6-N4

MOLECULAR WEIGHT: 494.50

CERCLA RATINGS (SCALE 0-3): HEALTH=U FIRE=1 REACTIVITY=0 PERSISTENCE=2

NFPA RATINGS (SCALE 0-4): HEALTH=U FIRE=1 REACTIVITY=0

COMPONENTS AND CONTAMINANTS

COMPONENT: HYDRAMETHYLNON ***PERCENT:*** 100.0
CAS# 67485-29-4

OTHER CONTAMINANTS: NONE

EXPOSURE LIMITS: NO OCCUPATIONAL EXPOSURE LIMITS ESTABLISHED BY OSHA, ACGIH, OR NIOSH.

PHYSICAL DATA

DESCRIPTION: YELLOW TO ORANGE CRYSTALS. ***MELTING POINT:*** 365-374 F (185-190 C)

SPECIFIC GRAVITY: NOT AVAILABLE ***VAPOR PRESSURE:*** NEGLIGIBLE

SOLUBILITY IN WATER: 5-7 PPB @ 25 C

SOLVENT SOLUBILITY: SOLUBLE IN ACETONE, CHLOROBENZENE, HOT ETHYL ACETATE, METHYLENE CHLORIDE, XYLENE, DICHLOROETHANE; SLIGHTLY SOLUBLE IN ETHANOL, METHANOL, ISOPROPANOL.

FIRE AND EXPLOSION DATA

FIRE AND EXPLOSION HAZARD: SLIGHT FIRE HAZARD WHEN EXPOSED TO HEAT OR FLAME.

FIREFIGHTING MEDIA: DRY CHEMICAL, CARBON DIOXIDE, HALON, WATER SPRAY OR STANDARD FOAM (1987 EMERGENCY RESPONSE GUIDEBOOK, DOT P 5800.4).
FOR LARGER FIRES, USE WATER SPRAY, FOG OR STANDARD FOAM (1987 EMERGENCY RESPONSE GUIDEBOOK, DOT P 5800.4).

FIREFIGHTING: MOVE CONTAINERS FROM FIRE AREA IF POSSIBLE (1987 EMERGENCY RESPONSE GUIDEBOOK, DOT P 5800.4, GUIDE PAGE 53).
EXTINGUISH ONLY IF FLOW CAN BE STOPPED. EXTINGUISH USING AGENT INDICATED. USE FLOODING AMOUNTS OF WATER AS A FOG. COOL CONTAINERS WITH FLOODING AMOUNTS OF WATER FROM AS FAR A DISTANCE AS POSSIBLE. AVOID BREATHING POISONOUS VAPORS, KEEP UPWIND. CONSIDER EVACUATION OF DOWNWIND AREA IF MATERIAL IS LEAKING.

TOXICITY

HYDRAMETHYLNON: TOXICITY DATA: >5000 MG/KG SKIN-RABBIT LD50 (PEMNDP); 1131 MG/KG ORAL-RAT LD50. CARCINOGEN STATUS: NONE. ACUTE TOXICITY LEVEL: MODERATELY TOXIC BY INGESTION; SLIGHTLY TOXIC BY DERMAL ABSORPTION. TARGET EFFECTS: NO DATA AVAILABLE.

HEALTH EFFECTS AND FIRST AID

INHALATION: HYDRAMETHYLNON: **ACUTE EXPOSURE-** NO DATA AVAILABLE. **CHRONIC EXPOSURE-** NO DATA AVAILABLE.

FIRST AID- REMOVE FROM EXPOSURE AREA TO FRESH AIR IMMEDIATELY. IF BREATHING HAS STOPPED, PERFORM ARTIFICIAL RESPIRATION. KEEP PERSON

WARM AND AT REST. TREAT SYMPTOMATICALLY AND SUPPORTIVELY. GET MEDICAL ATTENTION IMMEDIATELY.

SKIN CONTACT: HYDRAMETHYLNON: **ACUTE EXPOSURE-** THIS MATERIAL WAS NOT IRRITATING TO RABBIT OR GUINEA PIG SKIN. **CHRONIC EXPOSURE-** NO DATA AVAILABLE.
FIRST AID- REMOVE CONTAMINATED CLOTHING AND SHOES IMMEDIATELY. WASH AFFECTED AREA WITH SOAP OR MILD DETERGENT AND LARGE AMOUNTS OF WATER UNTIL NO EVIDENCE OF CHEMICAL REMAINS (APPROXIMATELY 15-20 MINUTES). GET MEDICAL ATTENTION IMMEDIATELY.

EYE CONTACT: HYDRAMETHYLNON: **ACUTE EXPOSURE-** THIS MATERIAL WAS REVERSIBLY IRRITATING TO THE EYES OF RABBITS. **CHRONIC EXPOSURE-** NO DATA AVAILABLE.
FIRST AID- WASH EYES IMMEDIATELY WITH LARGE AMOUNTS OF WATER OR NORMAL SALINE, OCCASIONALLY LIFTING UPPER AND LOWER LIDS, UNTIL NO EVIDENCE OF CHEMICAL REMAINS (APPROXIMATELY 15-20 MINUTES). GET MEDICAL ATTENTION IMMEDIATELY.

INGESTION: HYDRAMETHYLNON: **ACUTE EXPOSURE-** A LETHAL DOSE IN RATS WAS 1131 MG/KG. SYMPTOMS WERE NOT REPORTED. **CHRONIC EXPOSURE-** THE NO EFFECT LEVEL HAS BEEN REPORTED AS 50 MG/KG FOR RATS AND 3 MG/KG FOR DOGS.
FIRST AID- REMOVE BY GASTRIC LAVAGE AND CATHARSIS. MAINTAIN BLOOD PRESSURE AND AIRWAY. GIVE OXYGEN IF RESPIRATION IS DEPRESSED. DO NOT PERFORM GASTRIC LAVAGE IF VICTIM IS UNCONSCIOUS. GET MEDICAL ATTENTION IMMEDIATELY (DREISBACH, HANDBOOK OF POISONING, 12TH ED.).
ADMINISTRATION OF LAVAGE OR OXYGEN SHOULD BE PERFORMED BY QUALIFIED MEDICAL PERSONNEL.
ANTIDOTE: NO SPECIFIC ANTIDOTE. TREAT SYMPTOMATICALLY AND SUPPORTIVELY.

REACTIVITY

REACTIVITY: STABLE UNDER NORMAL TEMPERATURES AND PRESSURES.
INCOMPATIBILITIES: HYDRAMETHYLNON: OXIDIZERS (STRONG): FIRE AND EXPLOSION HAZARD.
DECOMPOSITION: THERMAL DECOMPOSITION PRODUCTS MAY INCLUDE HIGHLY TOXIC FUMES OF FLUORIDES AND OXIDES OF NITROGEN AND CARBON.
POLYMERIZATION: HAZARDOUS POLYMERIZATION HAS NOT BEEN REPORTED TO OCCUR UNDER NORMAL TEMPERATURES AND PRESSURES.

STORAGE AND DISPOSAL

OBSERVE ALL FEDERAL, STATE AND LOCAL REGULATIONS WHEN STORING OR DISPOSING OF THIS SUBSTANCE. FOR ASSISTANCE, CONTACT THE DISTRICT DIRECTOR OF THE ENVIRONMENTAL PROTECTION AGENCY.

****STORAGE****

STORE IN ACCORDANCE WITH 40 CFR 165 RECOMMENDED PROCEDURES FOR THE DISPOSAL AND STORAGE OF PESTICIDES AND PESTICIDE CONTAINERS.
STORE AWAY FROM INCOMPATIBLE SUBSTANCES.
STORE IN A COOL, DRY PLACE PROTECTED AGAINST LIGHT.

****DISPOSAL****

DISPOSAL MUST BE IN ACCORDANCE WITH 40 CFR 165 RECOMMENDED PROCEDURES FOR THE DISPOSAL AND STORAGE OF PESTICIDES AND PESTICIDE CONTAINERS.

CONDITIONS TO AVOID

MAY BURN BUT DOES NOT IGNITE READILY.

SPILL AND LEAK PROCEDURES

OCCUPATIONAL SPILL: DO NOT TOUCH SPILLED MATERIAL. STOP LEAK IF YOU CAN DO IT WITHOUT RISK. FOR SMALL SPILLS, TAKE UP WITH SAND OR OTHER ABSORBENT MATERIAL AND PLACE INTO CONTAINERS FOR LATER DISPOSAL. FOR SMALL DRY SPILLS, WITH A CLEAN SHOVEL PLACE MATERIAL INTO CLEAN, DRY CONTAINER AND COVER. MOVE CONTAINERS FROM SPILL AREA. FOR LARGER SPILLS, DIKE FAR AHEAD OF SPILL FOR LATER DISPOSAL. KEEP UNNECESSARY PEOPLE AWAY. ISOLATE HAZARD AREA AND DENY ENTRY.

PROTECTIVE EQUIPMENT

VENTILATION: PROVIDE LOCAL EXHAUST OR GENERAL DILUTION VENTILATION SYSTEM.
RESPIRATOR: THE FOLLOWING RESPIRATORS ARE RECOMMENDED BASED ON INFORMATION FOUND IN THE PHYSICAL DATA, TOXICITY AND HEALTH EFFECTS SECTIONS. THEY ARE RANKED IN ORDER FROM MINIMUM TO MAXIMUM RESPIRATORY PROTECTION. THE SPECIFIC RESPIRATOR SELECTED MUST BE BASED ON CONTAMINATION LEVELS FOUND IN THE WORK PLACE, MUST NOT EXCEED THE WORKING LIMITS OF THE RESPIRATOR AND BE JOINTLY APPROVED BY THE NATIONAL INSTITUTE FOR OCCUPATIONAL SAFETY AND HEALTH AND THE MINE SAFETY AND HEALTH ADMINISTRATION (NIOSH-MSHA).
CHEMICAL CARTRIDGE RESPIRATOR WITH AN ORGANIC VAPOR CARTRIDGE(S) IN COMBINATION WITH A DUST AND MIST FILTER.
GAS MASK WITH ORGANIC VAPOR CANISTER (CHIN-STYLE OR FRONT- OR BACK-MOUNTED CANISTER) WITH A DUST AND MIST FILTER.
GAS MASK WITH ORGANIC VAPOR CANISTER (CHIN-STYLE OR FRONT- OR BACK-MOUNTED CANISTER) WITH A PARTICULATE FILTER.
POWERED AIR-PURIFYING RESPIRATOR WITH A HIGH-EFFICIENCY FILTER.
TYPE 'C' SUPPLIED-AIR RESPIRATOR WITH A FULL FACEPIECE OPERATED IN A PRESSURE-DEMAND OR OTHER POSITIVE PRESSURE MODE.
SELF-CONTAINED BREATHING APPARATUS WITH A FULL FACEPIECE OPERATED IN PRESSURE-DEMAND OR OTHER POSITIVE PRESSURE MODE.
FOR FIREFIGHTING AND OTHER IMMEDIATELY DANGEROUS TO LIFE OR HEALTH CONDITIONS:
SELF-CONTAINED BREATHING APPARATUS WITH FULL FACEPIECE OPERATED IN PRESSURE-DEMAND OR OTHER POSITIVE PRESSURE MODE.
SUPPLIED-AIR RESPIRATOR WITH FULL FACEPIECE AND OPERATED IN PRESSURE-DEMAND OR OTHER POSITIVE PRESSURE MODE IN COMBINATION WITH AN AUXILIARY SELF-CONTAINED BREATHING APPARATUS OPERATED IN PRESSURE-DEMAND OR OTHER POSITIVE PRESSURE MODE.
CLOTHING: EMPLOYEE MUST WEAR APPROPRIATE PROTECTIVE (IMPERVIOUS) CLOTHING AND EQUIPMENT TO PREVENT REPEATED OR PROLONGED SKIN CONTACT WITH THIS SUBSTANCE.
GLOVES: EMPLOYEE MUST WEAR APPROPRIATE PROTECTIVE GLOVES TO PREVENT CONTACT WITH THIS SUBSTANCE.
EYE PROTECTION: EMPLOYEE MUST WEAR SPLASH-PROOF OR DUST-RESISTANT SAFETY GOGGLES TO PREVENT EYE CONTACT WITH THIS SUBSTANCE.
EMERGENCY EYE WASH: WHERE THERE IS ANY POSSIBILITY THAT AN EMPLOYEE'S EYES MAY BE EXPOSED TO THIS SUBSTANCE, THE EMPLOYER SHOULD PROVIDE AN EYE WASH FOUNTAIN WITHIN THE IMMEDIATE WORK AREA FOR EMERGENCY USE.

AUTHORIZED BY- OCCUPATIONAL HEALTH SERVICES, INC.
CREATION DATE: 10/04/89 ***REVISION DATE:*** 05/14/90

MATERIAL SAFETY DATA SHEET

OCCUPATIONAL HEALTH SERVICES, INC.
AGRICULTURE AND PESTICIDE DIVISION
450 SEVENTH AVENUE, SUITE 2407
NEW YORK, NEW YORK 10123
1-800-445-MSDS OR (212) 967-1100

EMERGENCY CONTACT:
JOHN S. BRANSFORD, JR. (615) 292-1180

SUBSTANCE IDENTIFICATION

SUBSTANCE: **2-AMINO-4-CHLORO-6-ETHYLAMINE-S-TRIAZINE**
TRADE NAMES/SYNONYMS: SIMAZINE METABOLITE; C5H8CLN5; PST01011
CHEMICAL FAMILY: TRIAZINE
AMINE
MOLECULAR FORMULA: (CL)-C3-N3-(N-H2)-(N-H-C2-H5)
MOLECULAR WEIGHT: 173.61
CERCLA RATINGS (SCALE 0-3): HEALTH=U FIRE=1 REACTIVITY=0 PERSISTENCE=2
NFPA RATINGS (SCALE 0-4): HEALTH=U FIRE=1 REACTIVITY=0

COMPONENTS AND CONTAMINANTS

COMPONENT: 2-AMINO-4-CHLORO-6-ETHYLAMINE-S-TRIAZINE ***PERCENT:*** 100.0
OTHER CONTAMINANTS: NONE
EXPOSURE LIMITS: NO OCCUPATIONAL EXPOSURE LIMITS ESTABLISHED BY OSHA, ACGIH, OR NIOSH.

PHYSICAL DATA

DESCRIPTION: WHITE POWDER. ***MELTING POINT:*** 352-356 F (178-180 C)
SPECIFIC GRAVITY: NOT AVAILABLE ***SOLUBILITY IN WATER:*** NOT AVAILABLE

FIRE AND EXPLOSION DATA

FIRE AND EXPLOSION HAZARD: SLIGHT FIRE HAZARD WHEN EXPOSED TO HEAT OR FLAME.
FIREFIGHTING MEDIA: DRY CHEMICAL, CARBON DIOXIDE, HALON, WATER SPRAY OR STANDARD FOAM (1987 EMERGENCY RESPONSE GUIDEBOOK, DOT P 5800.4).
FOR LARGER FIRES, USE WATER SPRAY, FOG OR STANDARD FOAM (1987 EMERGENCY RESPONSE GUIDEBOOK, DOT P 5800.4). ***FIREFIGHTING:*** MOVE CONTAINERS FROM FIRE AREA IF POSSIBLE (1987 EMERGENCY RESPONSE

GUIDEBOOK, DOT P 5800.4, GUIDE PAGE 53).
EXTINGUISH USING AGENT SUITABLE FOR TYPE OF SURROUNDING FIRE. AVOID BREATHING VAPORS AND DUSTS. KEEP UPWIND.

TOXICITY

2-AMINO-4-CHLORO-6-ETHYLAMINE-S-TRIAZINE: TOXICITY DATA: 798 MG/KG ORAL-RAT LD50 (EPA). CARCINOGEN STATUS: NONE. ACUTE TOXICITY LEVEL: MODERATELY TOXIC BY INGESTION. TARGET EFFECTS: NO DATA AVAILABLE.

HEALTH EFFECTS AND FIRST AID

INHALATION: 2-AMINO-4-CHLORO-6-ETHYLAMINE-S-TRIAZINE: **ACUTE EXPOSURE-** NO DATA AVAILABLE. **CHRONIC EXPOSURE-** NO DATA AVAILABLE.
FIRST AID- REMOVE FROM EXPOSURE AREA TO FRESH AIR IMMEDIATELY. IF BREATHING HAS STOPPED, PERFORM ARTIFICIAL RESPIRATION. KEEP PERSON WARM AND AT REST. TREAT SYMPTOMATICALLY AND SUPPORTIVELY. GET MEDICAL ATTENTION IMMEDIATELY.

SKIN CONTACT: 2-AMINO-4-CHLORO-6-ETHYLAMINE-S-TRIAZINE: **ACUTE EXPOSURE-** NO DATA AVAILABLE. **CHRONIC EXPOSURE-** NO DATA AVAILABLE.
FIRST AID- REMOVE CONTAMINATED CLOTHING AND SHOES IMMEDIATELY. WASH AFFECTED AREA WITH SOAP OR MILD DETERGENT AND LARGE AMOUNTS OF WATER UNTIL NO EVIDENCE OF CHEMICAL REMAINS (APPROXIMATELY 15-20 MINUTES). GET MEDICAL ATTENTION IMMEDIATELY.

EYE CONTACT: 2-AMINO-4-CHLORO-6-ETHYLAMINE-S-TRIAZINE: **ACUTE EXPOSURE-** NO DATA AVAILABLE. **CHRONIC EXPOSURE-** NO DATA AVAILABLE.
FIRST AID- WASH EYES IMMEDIATELY WITH LARGE AMOUNTS OF WATER OR NORMAL SALINE, OCCASIONALLY LIFTING UPPER AND LOWER LIDS, UNTIL NO EVIDENCE OF CHEMICAL REMAINS (APPROXIMATELY 15-20 MINUTES). GET MEDICAL ATTENTION IMMEDIATELY.

INGESTION: 2-AMINO-4-CHLORO-6-ETHYLAMINE-S-TRIAZINE: **ACUTE EXPOSURE-** THE LETHAL DOSE REPORTED IN RATS WAS 798 MG/KG. THE SYMPTOMS WERE NOT REPORTED. **CHRONIC EXPOSURE-** NO DATA AVAILABLE.
FIRST AID- TREAT SYMPTOMATICALLY AND SUPPORTIVELY. GET MEDICAL ATTENTION IMMEDIATELY. IF VOMITING OCCURS, KEEP HEAD LOWER THAN HIPS TO PREVENT ASPIRATION.
ANTIDOTE: NO SPECIFIC ANTIDOTE. TREAT SYMPTOMATICALLY AND SUPPORTIVELY.

REACTIVITY

REACTIVITY: STABLE UNDER NORMAL TEMPERATURES AND PRESSURES.
INCOMPATIBILITIES: 2-AMINO-4-CHLORO-6-ETHYLAMINE-S-TRIAZINE: OXIDIZERS (STRONG): FIRE AND EXPLOSION HAZARD.
DECOMPOSITION: THERMAL DECOMPOSITION PRODUCTS MAY INCLUDE TOXIC OXIDES OF NITROGEN AND CARBON AND TOXIC AND CORROSIVE FUMES OF CHLORIDES.
POLYMERIZATION: HAZARDOUS POLYMERIZATION HAS NOT BEEN REPORTED TO OCCUR UNDER NORMAL TEMPERATURES AND PRESSURES.

STORAGE AND DISPOSAL

OBSERVE ALL FEDERAL, STATE AND LOCAL REGULATIONS WHEN STORING OR DISPOSING OF THIS SUBSTANCE. FOR ASSISTANCE, CONTACT THE DISTRICT DIRECTOR OF THE ENVIRONMENTAL PROTECTION AGENCY.

****STORAGE****

STORE AWAY FROM INCOMPATIBLE SUBSTANCES.

CONDITIONS TO AVOID

MAY BURN BUT DOES NOT IGNITE READILY.

SPILL AND LEAK PROCEDURES

OCCUPATIONAL SPILL: DO NOT TOUCH SPILLED MATERIAL. STOP LEAK IF YOU CAN DO IT WITHOUT RISK. FOR SMALL SPILLS, TAKE UP WITH SAND OR OTHER ABSORBENT MATERIAL AND PLACE INTO CONTAINERS FOR LATER DISPOSAL. FOR SMALL DRY SPILLS, WITH A CLEAN SHOVEL PLACE MATERIAL INTO CLEAN, DRY CONTAINER AND COVER. MOVE CONTAINERS FROM SPILL AREA. FOR LARGER SPILLS, DIKE FAR AHEAD OF SPILL FOR LATER DISPOSAL. KEEP UNNECESSARY PEOPLE AWAY. ISOLATE HAZARD AREA AND DENY ENTRY.

PROTECTIVE EQUIPMENT

VENTILATION: PROVIDE LOCAL EXHAUST OR GENERAL DILUTION VENTILATION SYSTEM.
RESPIRATOR: THE FOLLOWING RESPIRATORS ARE RECOMMENDED BASED ON INFORMATION FOUND IN THE PHYSICAL DATA, TOXICITY AND HEALTH EFFECTS SECTIONS. THEY ARE RANKED IN ORDER FROM MINIMUM TO MAXIMUM RESPIRATORY PROTECTION. THE SPECIFIC RESPIRATOR SELECTED MUST BE BASED ON CONTAMINATION LEVELS FOUND IN THE WORK PLACE, MUST NOT EXCEED THE WORKING LIMITS OF THE RESPIRATOR AND BE JOINTLY APPROVED BY THE NATIONAL INSTITUTE FOR OCCUPATIONAL SAFETY AND HEALTH AND THE MINE SAFETY AND HEALTH ADMINISTRATION (NIOSH-MSHA).
DUST AND MIST RESPIRATOR WITH A FULL FACEPIECE.
AIR-PURIFYING FULL FACEPIECE RESPIRATOR WITH A HIGH-EFFICIENCY PARTICULATE FILTER.
POWERED AIR-PURIFYING RESPIRATOR WITH A TIGHT-FITTING FACEPIECE AND HIGH-EFFICIENCY PARTICULATE FILTER.
TYPE 'C' SUPPLIED-AIR RESPIRATOR WITH A FULL FACEPIECE OPERATED IN PRESSURE-DEMAND OR OTHER POSITIVE PRESSURE MODE OR WITH A FULL FACEPIECE, HELMET OR HOOD OPERATED IN CONTINUOUS-FLOW MODE.
SELF-CONTAINED BREATHING APPARATUS WITH A FULL FACEPIECE OPERATED IN PRESSURE-DEMAND OR OTHER POSITIVE PRESSURE MODE.
FOR FIREFIGHTING AND OTHER IMMEDIATELY DANGEROUS TO LIFE OR HEALTH CONDITIONS:
SELF-CONTAINED BREATHING APPARATUS WITH FULL FACEPIECE OPERATED IN PRESSURE-DEMAND OR OTHER POSITIVE PRESSURE MODE.
SUPPLIED-AIR RESPIRATOR WITH FULL FACEPIECE AND OPERATED IN PRESSURE-DEMAND OR OTHER POSITIVE PRESSURE MODE IN COMBINATION WITH AN AUXILIARY SELF-CONTAINED BREATHING APPARATUS OPERATED IN PRESSURE-DEMAND OR OTHER POSITIVE PRESSURE MODE.
CLOTHING: EMPLOYEE MUST WEAR APPROPRIATE PROTECTIVE (IMPERVIOUS) CLOTHING AND EQUIPMENT TO PREVENT REPEATED OR PROLONGED SKIN CONTACT WITH THIS SUBSTANCE.
GLOVES: EMPLOYEE MUST WEAR APPROPRIATE PROTECTIVE GLOVES TO PREVENT CONTACT WITH THIS SUBSTANCE.
EYE PROTECTION: EMPLOYEE MUST WEAR SPLASH-PROOF OR DUST-RESISTANT SAFETY GOGGLES TO PREVENT EYE CONTACT WITH THIS SUBSTANCE.
EMERGENCY EYE WASH: WHERE THERE IS ANY POSSIBILITY THAT AN EMPLOYEE'S EYES MAY BE EXPOSED TO THIS SUBSTANCE, THE EMPLOYER SHOULD PROVIDE AN EYE WASH FOUNTAIN WITHIN THE IMMEDIATE WORK AREA FOR EMERGENCY USE.

AUTHORIZED BY- OCCUPATIONAL HEALTH SERVICES, INC.
CREATION DATE: 10/23/89 ***REVISION DATE:*** 05/25/90

MATERIAL SAFETY DATA SHEET

OCCUPATIONAL HEALTH SERVICES, INC.
AGRICULTURE AND PESTICIDE DIVISION
450 SEVENTH AVENUE, SUITE 2407
NEW YORK, NEW YORK 10123
1-800-445-MSDS OR (212) 967-1100

EMERGENCY CONTACT:
JOHN S. BRANSFORD, JR. (615) 292-1180

SUBSTANCE IDENTIFICATION

CAS-NUMBER 61-82-5
SUBSTANCE: **AMITROLE**
TRADE NAMES/SYNONYMS: 1H-1,2,4-TRIAZOL-3-AMINE; S-TRIAZOLE, 3-AMINO; 3-AMINO-S-TRIAZOLE; 3-AMINO-1H-1,2,4-TRIAZOLE; 1H-1,2,4-TRIAZOL-3-YLAMINE; AMINOTRIAZOLE; 3-AMINO-1,2,4-TRIAZOLE; 3-AMINOTRIAZOLE; AMITROL; 3,A-T; ATA; AZAPLANT; AZOLANE; CYTROL; CYTROLE; WEEDAZOL; ENT 25445; RCRA U011; C2H4N4; PST01040
CHEMICAL FAMILY: TRIAZOLE
AMINE
MOLECULAR FORMULA: (N-H2)-C2-N3-H2
MOLECULAR WEIGHT: 84.08
CERCLA RATINGS (SCALE 0-3): HEALTH=3 FIRE=1 REACTIVITY=0 PERSISTENCE=1
NFPA RATINGS (SCALE 0-4): HEALTH=U FIRE=1 REACTIVITY=0

COMPONENTS AND CONTAMINANTS

COMPONENT: AMITROLE ***PERCENT:*** 100
CAS# 61-82-5
OTHER CONTAMINANTS: NONE
EXPOSURE LIMITS: AMITROLE: 0.2 MG/M3 OSHA TWA 0.2 MG/M3 ACGIH TWA
10 POUNDS CERCLA SECTION 103 REPORTABLE QUANTITY. SUBJECT TO CALIFORNIA PROPOSITON 65 CANCER AND/OR REPRODUCTIVE TOXICITY WARNING AND RELEASE REQUIREMENTS- (JULY 1, 1987)

PHYSICAL DATA

DESCRIPTION: ODORLESS, COLORLESS TO WHITE CRYSTALLINE SOLID WITH A BITTER TASTE.
MELTING POINT: 318 F (159 C) ***SPECIFIC GRAVITY:*** 1.138 @ 20 C
VAPOR PRESSURE: NEGLIGIBLE ***PH:*** NEUTRAL ***SOLUBILITY IN WATER:*** 28% @ 25 C
SOLVENT SOLUBILITY: SOLUBLE IN CHLOROFORM, ALCOHOL, DICHLOROMETHANE, ACETONITRILE; SLIGHTLY SOLUBLE IN ETHYL ACETATE; INSOLUBLE IN ACETONE, ETHER, CARBON TETRACHLORIDE, NONPOLAR SOLVENTS, AND OILS.

FIRE AND EXPLOSION DATA

FIRE AND EXPLOSION HAZARD: SLIGHT FIRE HAZARD WHEN EXPOSED TO HEAT OR FLAME. DUST-AIR MIXTURES MAY IGNITE OR EXPLODE.
FIREFIGHTING MEDIA: DRY CHEMICAL, CARBON DIOXIDE, HALON, WATER SPRAY OR STANDARD FOAM (1987 EMERGENCY RESPONSE GUIDEBOOK, DOT P 5800.4). FOR LARGER FIRES, USE WATER SPRAY, FOG OR STANDARD FOAM (1987 EMERGENCY RESPONSE GUIDEBOOK, DOT P 5800.4).
FIREFIGHTING: MOVE CONTAINER FROM FIRE AREA IF POSSIBLE. DO NOT SCATTER SPILLED MATERIAL WITH HIGH PRESSURE WATER STREAMS. DIKE FIRE CONTROL WATER FOR LATER DISPOSAL (1987 EMERGENCY RESPONSE GUIDEBOOK, DOT P 5800.4, GUIDE PAGE 31).
USE AGENTS SUITABLE FOR TYPE OF SURROUNDING FIRE. AVOID BREATHING HAZARDOUS VAPORS, KEEP UPWIND.

TOXICITY

AMITROLE: TOXICITY DATA: >10,000 MG/KG SKIN-RAT LD50 (85JFAN); 1100 MG/KG ORAL-RAT LD50; 14700 MG/KG ORAL-MOUSE LD50; 200 MG/KG INTRAPERITONEAL-MOUSE LD50; MUTAGENIC DATA (RTECS); REPRODUCTIVE EFFECTS DATA (RTECS); TUMORIGENIC DATA (RTECS); CARCINOGEN STATUS: ANTICIPATED HUMAN CARCINOGEN (NTP); HUMAN INADEQUATE EVIDENCE, ANIMAL SUFFICIENT EVIDENCE (IARC GROUP-2B). BY ORAL ADMINISTRATION, AMITROLE PRODUCED THYROID AND BENIGN AND MALIGNANT LIVER TUMORS IN MICE AND BENIGN AND MALIGNANT THYROID AND BENIGN PITUITARY TUMORS IN RATS. ACUTE TOXICITY LEVEL: MODERATELY TOXIC BY INGESTION; SLIGHTLY TOXIC BY DERMAL ABSORPTION. TARGET EFFECTS: POISONING MAY AFFECT THE LIVER AND ENDOCRINE SYSTEM. ADDITIONAL DATA: MAY CROSS THE PLACENTA.

HEALTH EFFECTS AND FIRST AID

INHALATION: AMITROLE: **ACUTE EXPOSURE-** SYMPTOMS OF UPPER RESPIRATORY IRRITATION OR SYSTEMIC POISONING WERE NOT OBSERVED IN RATS EXPOSED TO AN AEROSOL OF 439 MG/M3 FOR 4 HOURS. **CHRONIC EXPOSURE-** SKIN RASH, VOMITING, DIARRHEA, AND NOSEBLEED HAVE BEEN REPORTED IN ASSOCIATION WITH AMITROLE APPLICATION. THERE WAS A STATISTICALLY SIGNIFICANT EXCESS OF ALL CANCERS AMONG RAILROAD WORKERS WHO WERE EXPOSED TO BOTH AMITROLE AND CHLOROPHENOXY HERBICIES, BUT NOT AMONG WORKERS EXPOSED MAINLY TO AMITROLE.
FIRST AID- REMOVE FROM EXPOSURE AREA TO FRESH AIR IMMEDIATELY. IF BREATHING HAS STOPPED, PERFORM ARTIFICIAL RESPIRATION. KEEP PERSON WARM AND AT REST. TREAT SYMPTOMATICALLY AND SUPPORTIVELY. GET MEDICAL ATTENTION IMMEDIATELY.

SKIN CONTACT: AMITROLE: **ACUTE EXPOSURE-** THIS MATERIAL WAS SLIGHTLY IRRITATING TO RABBIT SKIN. NO SYSTEMIC TOXICITY WAS OBSERVED IN RATS OR RABBITS RECEIVING A DERMAL APPLICATION OF 10,000 MG/KG. **CHRONIC EXPOSURE-** THERE WAS A STATISTICALLY SIGNIFICANT EXCESS OF ALL CANCERS AMONG RAILROAD WORKERS WHO WERE EXPOSED TO BOTH AMITROLE AND CHLOROPHENOXY HERBICIDES, BUT NOT AMONG WORKERS EXPOSED MAINLY TO AMITROLE.
FIRST AID- REMOVE CONTAMINATED CLOTHING AND SHOES IMMEDIATELY. WASH AFFECTED AREA WITH SOAP OR MILD DETERGENT AND LARGE AMOUNTS OF WATER UNTIL NO EVIDENCE OF CHEMICAL REMAINS (APPROXIMATELY 15-20 MINUTES). GET MEDICAL ATTENTION IMMEDIATELY.

EYE CONTACT: AMITROLE: **ACUTE EXPOSURE-** THIS MATERIAL WAS SLIGHTLY IRRITATING TO RABBIT EYES. **CHRONIC EXPOSURE-** NO DATA AVAILABLE.
FIRST AID- WASH EYES IMMEDIATELY WITH LARGE AMOUNTS OF WATER OR NORMAL SALINE, OCCASIONALLY LIFTING UPPER AND LOWER LIDS, UNTIL NO EVIDENCE OF CHEMICAL REMAINS (APPROXIMATELY 15-20 MINUTES). GET MEDICAL ATTENTION IMMEDIATELY.

INGESTION: AMITROLE: CARCINOGEN. **ACUTE EXPOSURE-** NO TOXIC EFFECTS WERE NOTED IN A WOMAN WHO INGESTED 20 MG/KG. A SINGLE DOSE OF 100 MG/KG PRODUCED A DECREASE IN THE IODINE UPTAKE BY THE THYROID IN HEALTHY PERSONS AND PERSONS WITH HYPERTHYROIDISM. IN ANIMAL STUDIES, POISONING WAS CHARACTERIZED BY INCREASED INTESTINAL PERISTALSIS, PULMONARY EDEMA, AND HEMORRHAGES IN VARIOUS ORGANS. REPRODUCTIVE EFFECTS HAVE BEEN REPORTED IN ANIMALS. **CHRONIC EXPOSURE-** REVERSIBLE THYROID EFFECTS OF GOITER, MORPHOLOGICAL CHANGES, AND ALTERED THYROID FUNCTION WERE OBSERVED IN LABORATORY ANIMALS. OTHER EFFECTS REPORTED IN ANIMALS INCLUDED PITUITARY CHANGES IN THE DOG, THYROID AND LIVER TUMORS IN MICE, AND HEPATIC EFFECTS AND THYROID AND PITUITARY TUMORS IN RATS. MALE MICE NURSED BY DAMS FED DIETS CONTAINING 500 MG/KG AMITROLE FROM DELIVERY UNTIL WEANING AND THEN MAINTAINED FOR 90 WEEKS ON A STANDARD DIET SHOWED A STATISTICALLY SIGNIFICANT INCREASED INCIDENCE OF LIVER CARCINOMAS. REPRODUCTIVE EFFECTS HAVE BEEN REPORTED IN ANIMALS.
FIRST AID- IF THE PERSON IS CONSCIOUS AND NOT CONVULSING, REMOVE BY GASTRIC LAVAGE AND FOLLOW WITH A CATHARTIC (DREISBACH, HANDBOOK OF POISONING, 12TH ED.). TREAT SYMPTOMATICALLY AND SUPPORTIVELY. GASTRIC LAVAGE SHOULD BE PERFORMED BY QUALIFIED MEDICAL PERSONNEL. GET MEDICAL ATTENTION IMMEDIATELY.
ANTIDOTE: NO SPECIFIC ANTIDOTE. TREAT SYMPTOMATICALLY AND SUPPORTIVELY.

REACTIVITY

REACTIVITY: STABLE UNDER NORMAL TEMPERATURES AND PRESSURES.
INCOMPATIBILITIES: AMITROLE: ALUMINUM: MAY CORRODE. COPPER: MAY CORRODE. IRON: MAY CORRODE.
DECOMPOSITION: THERMAL DECOMPOSITION PRODUCTS MAY INCLUDE TOXIC OXIDES OF CARBON AND NITROGEN.
POLYMERIZATION: HAZARDOUS POLYMERIZATION HAS NOT BEEN REPORTED TO OCCUR UNDER NORMAL TEMPERATURES AND PRESSURES.

STORAGE AND DISPOSAL

OBSERVE ALL FEDERAL, STATE AND LOCAL REGULATIONS WHEN STORING OR DISPOSING OF THIS SUBSTANCE. FOR ASSISTANCE, CONTACT THE DISTRICT DIRECTOR OF THE ENVIRONMENTAL PROTECTION AGENCY.

STORAGE

STORE IN ACCORDANCE WITH 40 CFR 165 RECOMMENDED PROCEDURES FOR THE DISPOSAL AND STORAGE OF PESTICIDES AND PESTICIDE CONTAINERS.
STORE AWAY FROM INCOMPATIBLE SUBSTANCES.

DISPOSAL

DISPOSAL MUST BE IN ACCORDANCE WITH STANDARDS APPLICABLE TO GENERATORS OF HAZARDOUS WASTE, 40CFR 262. EPA HAZARDOUS WASTE NUMBER U011.
DISPOSAL MUST BE IN ACCORDANCE WITH 40 CFR 165 RECOMMENDED PROCEDURES FOR THE DISPOSAL AND STORAGE OF PESTICIDES AND PESTICIDE CONTAINERS.

CONDITIONS TO AVOID

MAY BURN BUT DOES NOT IGNITE READILY. AVOID CONTACT WITH STRONG OXIDIZERS, EXCESSIVE HEAT, SPARKS, OR OPEN FLAME.

SPILL AND LEAK PROCEDURES

WATER SPILL: THE CALIFORNIA SAFE DRINKING WATER AND TOXIC ENFORCEMENT ACT OF 1986 (PROPOSITION 65) PROHIBITS CONTAMINATING ANY KNOWN SOURCE OF DRINKING WATER WITH SUBSTANCES KNOWN TO CAUSE CANCER AND/OR REPRODUCTIVE TOXICITY.
OCCUPATIONAL SPILL: SWEEP UP AND PLACE IN SUITABLE CLEAN, DRY CONTAINERS FOR RECLAMATION OR LATER DISPOSAL. DO NOT FLUSH SPILLED MATERIAL INTO SEWER. KEEP UNNECESSARY PEOPLE AWAY.
REPORTABLE QUANTITY (RQ): 10 POUNDS THE SUPERFUND AMENDMENTS AND REAUTHORIZATION ACT (SARA) SECTION 304 REQUIRES THAT A RELEASE EQUAL TO OR GREATER THAN THE REPORTABLE QUANTITY FOR THIS SUBSTANCE BE IMMEDIATELY REPORTED TO THE LOCAL EMERGENCY PLANNING COMMITTEE AND THE STATE EMERGENCY RESPONSE COMMISSION (40 CFR 355.40). IF THE RELEASE OF THIS SUBSTANCE IS REPORTABLE UNDER CERCLA SECTION 103, THE NATIONAL RESPONSE CENTER MUST BE NOTIFIED IMMEDIATELY AT (800) 424-8802 OR (202) 426-2675 IN THE METROPOLITAN WASHINGTON, D.C. AREA (40 CFR 302.6).

PROTECTIVE EQUIPMENT

VENTILATION: PROVIDE LOCAL EXHAUST OR PROCESS ENCLOSURE VENTILATION TO MEET PUBLISHED EXPOSURE LIMITS.
RESPIRATOR: THE FOLLOWING RESPIRATORS ARE RECOMMENDED BASED ON INFORMATION FOUND IN THE PHYSICAL DATA, TOXICITY AND HEALTH EFFECTS SECTIONS. THEY ARE RANKED IN ORDER FROM MINIMUM TO MAXIMUM RESPIRATORY PROTECTION. THE SPECIFIC RESPIRATOR SELECTED MUST BE BASED ON CONTAMINATION LEVELS FOUND IN THE WORK PLACE, MUST NOT EXCEED THE WORKING LIMITS OF THE RESPIRATOR AND BE JOINTLY APPROVED BY THE NATIONAL INSTITUTE FOR OCCUPATIONAL SAFETY AND HEALTH AND THE MINE SAFETY AND HEALTH ADMINISTRATION (NIOSH-MSHA).
TYPE 'C' SUPPLIED-AIR RESPIRATOR WITH A FULL FACEPIECE OPERATED IN PRESSURE-DEMAND OR OTHER POSITIVE PRESSURE MODE OR WITH A FULL

FACEPIECE, HELMET OR HOOD OPERATED IN CONTINOUS-FLOW MODE.
SELF-CONTAINED BREATHING APPARATUS WITH A FULL FACEPIECE OPERATED IN PRESSURE-DEMAND OR OTHER POSITIVE PRESSURE MODE.
FOR FIREFIGHTING AND OTHER IMMEDIATELY DANGEROUS TO LIFE OR HEALTH CONDITIONS:
SELF-CONTAINED BREATHING APPARATUS WITH FULL FACEPIECE OPERATED IN PRESSURE-DEMAND OR OTHER POSITIVE PRESSURE MODE.
SUPPLIED-AIR RESPIRATOR WITH FULL FACEPIECE AND OPERATED IN PRESSURE-DEMAND OR OTHER POSITIVE PRESSURE MODE IN COMBINATION WITH AN AUXILIARY SELF-CONTAINED BREATHING APPARATUS OPERATED IN PRESSURE-DEMAND OR OTHER POSITIVE PRESSURE MODE.

CLOTHING: EMPLOYEE MUST WEAR APPROPRIATE PROTECTIVE (IMPERVIOUS) CLOTHING AND EQUIPMENT TO PREVENT REPEATED OR PROLONGED SKIN CONTACT WITH THIS SUBSTANCE.

GLOVES: EMPLOYEE MUST WEAR APPROPRIATE PROTECTIVE GLOVES TO PREVENT CONTACT WITH THIS SUBSTANCE.

EYE PROTECTION: EMPLOYEE MUST WEAR SPLASH-PROOF OR DUST-RESISTANT SAFETY GOGGLES TO PREVENT EYE CONTACT WITH THIS SUBSTANCE.
EMERGENCY EYE WASH: WHERE THERE IS ANY POSSIBILITY THAT AN EMPLOYEE'S EYES MAY BE EXPOSED TO THIS SUBSTANCE, THE EMPLOYER SHOULD PROVIDE AN EYE WASH FOUNTAIN WITHIN THE IMMEDIATE WORK AREA FOR EMERGENCY USE.

AUTHORIZED BY- OCCUPATIONAL HEALTH SERVICES, INC.
CREATION DATE: 10/04/89 ***REVISION DATE:*** 07/12/90

MATERIAL SAFETY DATA SHEET

OCCUPATIONAL HEALTH SERVICES, INC.
AGRICULTURE AND PESTICIDE DIVISION
450 SEVENTH AVENUE, SUITE 2407
NEW YORK, NEW YORK 10123
1-800-445-MSDS OR (212) 967-1100

EMERGENCY CONTACT:
JOHN S. BRANSFORD, JR. (615) 292-1180

SUBSTANCE IDENTIFICATION

CAS-NUMBER 9080-17-5

SUBSTANCE: **AMMONIUM POLYSULFIDE SOLUTION**

TRADE NAMES/SYNONYMS: UN 2818; AMMONIUM SULFIDE SOLUTION, RED; PST01380

CERCLA RATINGS (SCALE 0-3): HEALTH=U FIRE=0 REACTIVITY=0 PERSISTENCE=1

NFPA RATINGS (SCALE 0-4): HEALTH=U FIRE=0 REACTIVITY=0

COMPONENTS AND CONTAMINANTS

COMPONENT: AMMONIUM POLYSULFIDE ***PERCENT:*** >1.0
CAS# 9080-17-5

COMPONENT: WATER ***PERCENT:*** REMAINDER

EXPOSURE LIMITS: NO OCCUPATIONAL EXPOSURE LIMITS ESTABLISHED BY OSHA, ACGIH, OR NIOSH.

PHYSICAL DATA

DESCRIPTION: CLEAR, YELLOW TO RED LIQUID WITH A FOUL (ROTTEN EGGS) ODOR OF AMMONIA AND HYDROGEN SULFIDE. ***BOILING POINT:*** NOT AVAILABLE
SPECIFIC GRAVITY: 1.10 ***PH:*** ALKALINE ***SOLUBILITY IN WATER:*** SOLUBLE

FIRE AND EXPLOSION DATA

FIRE AND EXPLOSION HAZARD: NEGLIGIBLE FIRE HAZARD WHEN EXPOSED TO HEAT OR FLAME.

FIREFIGHTING MEDIA: DRY CHEMICAL, CARBON DIOXIDE, HALON, WATER SPRAY OR STANDARD FOAM (1987 EMERGENCY RESPONSE GUIDEBOOK, DOT P 5800.4).
FOR LARGER FIRES, USE WATER SPRAY, FOG OR STANDARD FOAM (1987 EMERGENCY RESPONSE GUIDEBOOK, DOT P 5800.4).

FIREFIGHTING: MOVE CONTAINERS FROM FIRE AREA IF POSSIBLE. COOL CONTAINERS EXPOSED TO FLAMES WITH WATER FROM SIDE UNTIL WELL AFTER FIRE IS OUT. STAY AWAY FROM STORAGE TANK ENDS (1987 EMERGENCY RESPONSE GUIDEBOOK, DOT P 5800.4, GUIDE PAGE 60). EXTINGUISH USING AGENTS INDICATED; DO NOT USE WATER DIRECTLY ON MATERIAL. IF LARGE AMOUNTS OF COMBUSTIBLE MATERIALS ARE INVOLVED, USE WATER SPRAY OR FOG IN FLOODING AMOUNTS. USE WATER SPRAY TO ABSORB CORROSIVE VAPORS. COOL CONTAINERS WITH FLOODING AMOUNTS OF WATER FROM AS FAR A DISTANCE AS POSSIBLE. AVOID BREATHING CORROSIVE VAPORS; KEEP UPWIND.

TRANSPORTATION DATA

DEPARTMENT OF TRANSPORTATION HAZARD CLASSIFICATION 49 CFR 172.101: ORM-A
DEPARTMENT OF TRANSPORTATION LABELING REQUIREMENTS 49 CFR 172.101 AND SUBPART E: NONE
DEPARTMENT OF TRANSPORTATION PACKAGING REQUIREMENTS: 49 CFR 173.605 EXCEPTIONS: 49 CFR 173.505

TOXICITY

AMMONIUM POLYSULFIDE SOLUTION: CARCINOGEN STATUS: NONE. ACUTE TOXICITY LEVEL: NO DATA AVAILABLE. TARGET EFFECTS: NO DATA AVAILABLE.

HEALTH EFFECTS AND FIRST AID

INHALATION: AMMONIUM PHOSPHATE SOLUTION: **ACUTE EXPOSURE-** NO DATA AVAILABLE. HOWEVER DUE TO THE PRESENCE OF SULFIDES IRRITATION TO THE MUCOUS MEMBRANES MAY BE EXPECTED. DURING THE DECOMPOSITION OF THIS CHEMICAL HYDROGEN SULFIDE MAY BE RELEASED CAUSING IRRITATION TO MUCOUS MEMBRANES WITH HEADACHE, ANOSMIA, NAUSEA, RAWNESS IN THE THROAT, COUGH, DIZZINESS, DROWSINESS, AND PULMONARY EDEMA. **CHRONIC EXPOSURE-** NO DATA AVAILABLE. PROLONGED INHALATION OF HYDROGEN SULFIDE CAUSES PERSISTENT LOW BLOOD PRESSURE, NAUSEA, LOSS OF APPETITE, WEIGHT LOSS, IMPAIRED GAIT AND BALANCE AND CHRONIC COUGH.

FIRST AID- REMOVE FROM EXPOSURE AREA TO FRESH AIR IMMEDIATELY. IF BREATHING HAS STOPPED, GIVE ARTIFICIAL RESPIRATION. MAINTAIN AIRWAY AND BLOOD PRESSURE AND ADMINISTER OXYGEN IF AVAILABLE. KEEP AFFECTED PERSON WARM AND AT REST. TREAT SYMPTOMATICALLY AND SUPPORTIVELY. ADMINISTRATION OF OXYGEN SHOULD BE PERFORMED BY QUALIFIED PERSONNEL. GET MEDICAL ATTENTION IMMEDIATELY.

SKIN CONTACT: AMMONIUM POLYSULFIDE SOLUTION: **ACUTE EXPOSURE-** NO DATA AVAILABLE. HOWEVER, DUE TO IT'S ALKALINITY AND THE PRESENCE OF SULFIDES IT MAY CAUSE IRRITATION AND/OR SEVERE BURNS DEPENDING ON THE DURATION OF CONTACT. **CHRONIC EXPOSURE-** NO DATA AVAILABLE. MAY CAUSE DERMATITIS AFTER REPEATED OR PROLONGED EXPOSURE.

FIRST AID- REMOVE CONTAMINATED CLOTHING AND SHOES IMMEDIATELY. WASH AFFECTED AREA WITH SOAP OR MILD DETERGENT AND LARGE AMOUNTS OF WATER UNTIL NO EVIDENCE OF CHEMICAL REMAINS (AT LEAST 15-20 MINUTES). IN CASE OF CHEMICAL BURNS, COVER AREA WITH STERILE, DRY DRESSING. BANDAGE SECURELY, BUT NOT TOO TIGHTLY. GET MEDICAL ATTENTION IMMEDIATELY.

EYE CONTACT: AMMONIUM POLYSULFIDE SOLUTION: **ACUTE EXPOSURE-** NO DATA AVAILABLE. MAY BE IRRITATING AND CAUSE BURNS DUE TO IT'S ALKALINITY. **CHRONIC EXPOSURE-** NO DATA AVAILABLE. MAY CAUSE CONJUNCTIVITIS AFTER REPEATED OR PROLONGED EXPOSURE.

FIRST AID- WASH EYES IMMEDIATELY WITH LARGE AMOUNTS OF WATER, OCCASIONALLY LIFTING UPPER AND LOWER LIDS, UNTIL NO EVIDENCE OF CHEMICAL REMAINS (AT LEAST 15-20 MINUTES). CONTINUE IRRIGATING WITH NORMAL SALINE UNTIL THE PH HAS RETURNED TO NORMAL (30-60 MINUTES). COVER WITH STERILE BANDAGES. GET MEDICAL ATTENTION IMMEDIATELY.

INGESTION: AMMONIUM POLYSULFIDE SOLUTION: **ACUTE EXPOSURE-** NO DATA AVAILABLE. INGESTION OF SOME SOLUBLE SULFIDES CAUSES VOMITING, HEADACHE, CYANOSIS, RESPIRATORY DEPRESSION, FALL OF BLOOD PRESSURE, LOSS OF CONSCIOUSNESS, TREMORS, CONVULSIONS AND DEATH. **CHRONIC EXPOSURE-** NO DATA AVAILABLE.

FIRST AID- TREAT SYMPTOMATICALLY AND SUPPORTIVELY. GET MEDICAL ATTENTION IMMEDIATELY.

REACTIVITY

REACTIVITY: STABLE UNDER NORMAL TEMPERATURES AND PRESSURES.

INCOMPATIBILITIES: AMMONIUM POLYSULFIDE SOLUTION: ACIDS: MAY EVOLVE TOXIC AND FLAMMABLE HYDROGEN SULFIDE.

DECOMPOSITION: THERMAL DECOMPOSITION MAY RELEASE TOXIC FUMES OF AMMONIA, HYDROGEN SULFIDE, AND OXIDES OF SULFUR AND NITROGEN.

POLYMERIZATION: HAZARDOUS POLYMERIZATION HAS NOT BEEN REPORTED TO OCCUR UNDER NORMAL TEMPERATURES AND PRESSURES.

STORAGE AND DISPOSAL

OBSERVE ALL FEDERAL, STATE AND LOCAL REGULATIONS WHEN STORING OR DISPOSING OF THIS SUBSTANCE. FOR ASSISTANCE, CONTACT THE DISTRICT DIRECTOR OF THE ENVIRONMENTAL PROTECTION AGENCY.

****STORAGE****

STORE AWAY FROM INCOMPATIBLE SUBSTANCES.

CONDITIONS TO AVOID

MAY BURN BUT DOES NOT IGNITE READILY. FLAMMABLE, POISONOUS GASES MAY ACCUMULATE IN TANKS AND HOPPER CARS. MAY IGNITE COMBUSTIBLES (WOOD, PAPER, OIL, ETC.).

SPILL AND LEAK PROCEDURES

OCCUPATIONAL SPILL: DO NOT TOUCH SPILLED MATERIAL. STOP LEAK IF YOU CAN DO IT WITHOUT RISK. FOR SMALL SPILLS, TAKE UP WITH SAND OR OTHER ABSORBENT MATERIAL AND PLACE INTO CONTAINERS FOR LATER DISPOSAL. FOR SMALL DRY SPILLS, WITH CLEAN SHOVEL PLACE MATERIAL INTO CLEAN, DRY CONTAINER AND COVER. MOVE CONTAINERS FROM SPILL AREA. FOR LARGER SPILLS, DIKE FAR AHEAD OF SPILL FOR LATER DISPOSAL. KEEP UNNECESSARY PEOPLE AWAY. ISOLATE HAZARD AREA AND DENY ENTRY.

PROTECTIVE EQUIPMENT

VENTILATION: PROVIDE LOCAL EXHAUST OR GENERAL DILUTION VENTILATION SYSTEM.

RESPIRATOR: THE FOLLOWING RESPIRATORS ARE RECOMMENDED BASED ON INFORMATION FOUND IN THE PHYSICAL DATA, TOXICITY AND HEALTH EFFECTS SECTIONS. THEY ARE RANKED IN ORDER FROM MINIMUM TO MAXIMUM RESPIRATORY PROTECTION. THE SPECIFIC RESPIRATOR SELECTED MUST BE BASED ON CONTAMINATION LEVELS FOUND IN THE WORK PLACE, MUST NOT EXCEED THE WORKING LIMITS OF THE RESPIRATOR AND BE JOINTLY APPROVED BY THE NATIONAL INSTITUTE FOR OCCUPATIONAL SAFETY AND HEALTH AND THE MINE SAFETY AND HEALTH ADMINISTRATION (NIOSH-MSHA).

CHEMICAL CARTRIDGE RESPIRATOR WITH FULL FACEPIECE.

TYPE 'C' SUPPLIED-AIR RESPIRATOR WITH A FULL FACEPIECE OPERATED IN PRESSURE-DEMAND OR OTHER POSITIVE PRESSURE MODE OR WITH A FULL FACEPIECE, HELMET OR HOOD OPERATED IN CONTINUOUS-FLOW MODE.

SELF-CONTAINED BREATHING APPARATUS WITH A FULL FACEPIECE OPERATED IN PRESSURE-DEMAND OR OTHER POSITIVE PRESSURE MODE.

FOR FIREFIGHTING AND OTHER IMMEDIATELY DANGEROUS TO LIFE OR HEALTH CONDITIONS:

SELF-CONTAINED BREATHING APPARATUS WITH FULL FACEPIECE OPERATED IN PRESSURE-DEMAND OR OTHER POSITIVE PRESSURE MODE.

SUPPLIED-AIR RESPIRATOR WITH FULL FACEPIECE AND OPERATED IN PRESSURE-DEMAND OR OTHER POSITIVE PRESSURE MODE IN COMBINATION WITH AN AUXILIARY SELF-CONTAINED BREATHING APPARATUS OPERATED IN PRESSURE-DEMAND OR OTHER POSITIVE PRESSURE MODE.

CLOTHING: EMPLOYEE MUST WEAR APPROPRIATE PROTECTIVE (IMPERVIOUS) CLOTHING AND EQUIPMENT TO PREVENT REPEATED OR PROLONGED SKIN CONTACT WITH THIS SUBSTANCE.

GLOVES: EMPLOYEE MUST WEAR APPROPRIATE PROTECTIVE GLOVES TO PREVENT CONTACT WITH THIS SUBSTANCE.

EYE PROTECTION: EMPLOYEE MUST WEAR SPLASH-PROOF OR DUST-RESISTANT SAFETY GOGGLES AND A FACESHIELD TO PREVENT CONTACT WITH THIS SUBSTANCE.

EMERGENCY WASH FACILITIES: WHERE THERE IS ANY POSSIBILITY THAT AN EMPLOYEE'S EYES AND/OR SKIN MAY BE EXPOSED TO THIS SUBSTANCE, THE EMPLOYER SHOULD PROVIDE AN EYE WASH FOUNTAIN AND QUICK DRENCH SHOWER WITHIN THE IMMEDIATE WORK AREA FOR EMERGENCY USE.

AUTHORIZED BY- OCCUPATIONAL HEALTH SERVICES, INC.
CREATION DATE: 10/04/89 ***REVISION DATE:*** 05/18/90

MATERIAL SAFETY DATA SHEET

OCCUPATIONAL HEALTH SERVICES, INC.
AGRICULTURE AND PESTICIDE DIVISION
450 SEVENTH AVENUE, SUITE 2407
NEW YORK, NEW YORK 10123
1-800-445-MSDS OR (212) 967-1100

EMERGENCY CONTACT:
JOHN S. BRANSFORD, JR. (615) 292-1180

SUBSTANCE IDENTIFICATION

CAS-NUMBER 7773-06-0

SUBSTANCE: **AMMONIUM SULFAMATE**

TRADE NAMES/SYNONYMS: SULFAMIC ACID, MONOAMMONIUM SALT; AMMONIUM AMIDOSULFATE; AMMONIUM AMIDOSULFONATE; AMMONIUM AMIDOSULPHATE; AMMONIUM AMINOSULFONATE; AMMONIUM SULPHAMATE; MONOAMMONIUM SULFAMATE; AMS; AMCIDE; AMMATE; FELIDERM K; FYRAN 206K; IKURIN; SULFAMATE; STCC 4966732; NA 9089; H6N2O3S; PST01400

CHEMICAL FAMILY: INORGANIC SALT

MOLECULAR FORMULA: H6-N2-03-S

MOLECULAR WEIGHT: 114.13

CERCLA RATINGS (SCALE 0-3): HEALTH=2 FIRE=0 REACTIVITY=0 PERSISTENCE=0

NFPA RATINGS (SCALE 0-4): HEALTH=U FIRE=0 REACTIVITY=0

COMPONENTS AND CONTAMINANTS

COMPONENT: AMMONIUM SULFAMATE ***PERCENT:*** 100
CAS# 7773-06-0

OTHER CONTAMINANTS: NONE

EXPOSURE LIMITS: AMMONIUM SULFAMATE: 5 MG/M3 OSHA TWA (RESPIRABLE FRACTION); 10 MG/M3 OSHA TWA (TOTAL DUST) 10 MG/M3 ACGIH TWA 5000 POUNDS CERCLA SECTION 103 REPORTABLE QUANTITY

PHYSICAL DATA

DESCRIPTION: HYGROSCOPIC, WHITE CRYSTALLINE SOLID.

BOILING POINT: 320 F (160 C) DECOMPOSES ***MELTING POINT:*** 268 F (131 C)

SPECIFIC GRAVITY: >1 ***VAPOR PRESSURE:*** <1 MMHG @ 20 C ***PH:*** 4.9 @ 0.2 M

SOLUBILITY IN WATER: 68.4% @ 25 C

SOLVENT SOLUBILITY: SOLUBLE IN LIQUID AMMONIA; MODERATELY SOLUBLE IN GLYCEROL, GLYCOL, FORMAMIDE; SLIGHTLY SOLUBLE IN ETHANOL.

FIRE AND EXPLOSION DATA

FIRE AND EXPLOSION HAZARD: NEGLIGIBLE FIRE HAZARD WHEN EXPOSED TO HEAT OR FLAME.

FIREFIGHTING MEDIA: DRY CHEMICAL, CARBON DIOXIDE, HALON, WATER SPRAY OR STANDARD FOAM (1987 EMERGENCY RESPONSE GUIDEBOOK, DOT P 5800.4). FOR LARGER FIRES, USE WATER SPRAY, FOG OR STANDARD FOAM (1987 EMERGENCY RESPONSE GUIDEBOOK, DOT P 5800.4).

FIREFIGHTING: MOVE CONTAINER FROM FIRE AREA IF POSSIBLE. DO NOT SCATTER SPILLED MATERIAL WITH HIGH PRESSURE WATER STREAMS. DIKE FIRE CONTROL WATER FOR LATER DISPOSAL (1987 EMERGENCY RESPONSE GUIDEBOOK, DOT P 5800.4, GUIDE PAGE 31).

EXTINGUISH USING AGENTS SUITABLE FOR TYPE OF FIRE. AVOID BREATHING HAZARDOUS DUSTS OR VAPORS, KEEP UPWIND.

TRANSPORTATION DATA

DEPARTMENT OF TRANSPORTATION HAZARD CLASSIFICATION 49 CFR 172.101: ORM-E

DEPARTMENT OF TRANSPORTATION LABELING REQUIREMENTS 49 CFR 172.101 AND SUBPART E: NONE

DEPARTMENT OF TRANSPORTATION PACKAGING REQUIREMENTS: 49 CFR 173.510 EXCEPTIONS: NONE

TOXICITY

AMMONIUM SULFAMATE: TOXICITY DATA: 2 GM/KG ORAL-RAT LD50; 3100 MG/KG ORAL-MOUSE LD50; 800 MG/KG INTRAPERITONEAL-RAT LDLO. CARCINOGEN STATUS: NONE. ACUTE TOXICITY LEVEL: MODERATELY TOXIC BY INGESTION. TARGET EFFECTS: NO DATA AVAILABLE.

HEALTH EFFECTS AND FIRST AID

INHALATION: AMMONIUM SULFAMATE: 5000 MG/M3 IMMEDIATELY DANGEROUS TO LIFE OR HEALTH. **ACUTE EXPOSURE-** AN AEROSOL OF AMMONIUM SULFAMATE IN CONCENTRATIONS OF 0.25-0.5 G/L CAUSED DESQUAMATED CATARRH OF THE UPPER RESPIRATORY TRACT IN ANIMALS. **CHRONIC EXPOSURE-** NO DATA AVAILABLE.

FIRST AID- REMOVE FROM EXPOSURE AREA TO FRESH AIR IMMEDIATELY. IF BREATHING HAS STOPPED, PERFORM ARTIFICIAL RESPIRATION. KEEP PERSON WARM AND AT REST. TREAT SYMPTOMATICALLY AND SUPPORTIVELY. GET MEDICAL ATTENTION IMMEDIATELY.

SKIN CONTACT: AMMONIUM SULFAMATE: **ACUTE EXPOSURE-** THIS MATERIAL DID NOT PRODUCE ANY CONTACT IRRITATION OR EVIDENCE OF SENSITIZATION ON 194 HUMAN SUBJECTS. **CHRONIC EXPOSURE-** REPEATED APPLICATION OF A 4% SOLUTION TO THE SKIN OF 5 HUMAN VOLUNTEERS WAS NOT IRRITATING. REPEATED APPLICATION OF 20 OR 50% SOLUTIONS TO THE SHAVED SKIN OF RATS PRODUCED NO IRRITATION OR SIGNS OF TOXICITY.

FIRST AID- REMOVE CONTAMINATED CLOTHING AND SHOES IMMEDIATELY. WASH AFFECTED AREA WITH SOAP OR MILD DETERGENT AND LARGE AMOUNTS OF WATER UNTIL NO EVIDENCE OF CHEMICAL REMAINS (APPROXIMATELY 15-20 MINUTES). GET MEDICAL ATTENTION IMMEDIATELY.

EYE CONTACT: AMMONIUM SULFAMATE: **ACUTE EXPOSURE-** DUST MAY CAUSE IRRITATION. 0.5 ML OF A 4% SOLUTION PLACED IN THE CONJUNCTIVAL SAC OF A RABBIT'S EYE CAUSED NO IRRITATION. 0.1 ML OF A CONCENTRATED

FORMULATION CONTAINING 43% AMMONIUM SULFAMATE CAUSED A SLIGHT TO MODERATE CONJUNCTIVAL IRRITATION IN RABBIT EYES THAT CLEARED BY 72 HOURS IN ALL BUT ONE EYE. BY 7 DAYS, ALL EYES WERE NORMAL. **CHRONIC EXPOSURE-** NO DATA AVAILABLE.

FIRST AID- WASH EYES IMMEDIATELY WITH LARGE AMOUNTS OF WATER OR NORMAL SALINE, OCCASIONALLY LIFTING UPPER AND LOWER LIDS, UNTIL NO EVIDENCE OF CHEMICAL REMAINS (APPROXIMATELY 15-20 MINUTES). GET MEDICAL ATTENTION IMMEDIATELY.

INGESTION: AMMONIUM SULFAMATE: **ACUTE EXPOSURE-** MAY CAUSE GASTROINTESTINAL DISTURBANCES SUCH AS NAUSEA OR DIARRHEA. AN ACUTE DOSE OF A SOLUBLE CONCENTRATE CONTAINING 43% AMMONIUM SULFAMATE PRODUCED DEPRESSION, SALIVATION, BLOODY TEARS, AND COLLAPSE IN RATS. **CHRONIC EXPOSURE-** ADMINISTRATION OF A 2% CONCENTRATION IN THE DIET OF RATS FOR 105 DAYS PRODUCED AN INHIBITION IN GROWTH RATES OF RATS; NO EFFECTS WERE OBSERVED IN RATS AT THE 1% LEVEL.

FIRST AID- REMOVE BY GASTRIC LAVAGE AND CATHARSIS. MAINTAIN BLOOD PRESSURE AND AIRWAY. GIVE OXYGEN IF RESPIRATION IS DEPRESSED. DO NOT PERFORM GASTRIC LAVAGE IF VICTIM IS UNCONSCIOUS. GET MEDICAL ATTENTION IMMEDIATELY (DREISBACH, HANDBOOK OF POISONING, 12TH ED.).
ADMINISTRATION OF LAVAGE OR OXYGEN SHOULD BE PERFORMED BY QUALIFIED MEDICAL PERSONNEL.

ANTIDOTE: NO SPECIFIC ANTIDOTE. TREAT SYMPTOMATICALLY AND SUPPORTIVELY.

REACTIVITY

REACTIVITY: STABLE UNDER NORMAL TEMPERATURES AND PRESSURES.

INCOMPATIBILITIES: AMMONIUM SULFAMATE: ACIDS: MAY UNDERGO SPONTANEOUS HYDROLYSIS LIBERATING MUCH HEAT. CARBON STEEL: MAY CORRODE. COPPER: MAY CORRODE. BRASS: MAY CORRODE. BRONZE: MAY CORRODE. IRON: MAY CORRODE. METALS: MAY CORRODE. OXIDIZERS: INCOMPATIBLE. HOT WATER: INCOMPATIBLE.

DECOMPOSITION: THERMAL DECOMPOSITION MAY RELEASE TOXIC FUMES OF AMMONIA, HYDROGEN SULFIDE, AND OXIDES OF SULFUR AND NITROGEN.

POLYMERIZATION: HAZARDOUS POLYMERIZATION HAS NOT BEEN REPORTED TO OCCUR UNDER NORMAL TEMPERATURES AND PRESSURES.

STORAGE AND DISPOSAL

OBSERVE ALL FEDERAL, STATE AND LOCAL REGULATIONS WHEN STORING OR DISPOSING OF THIS SUBSTANCE. FOR ASSISTANCE, CONTACT THE DISTRICT DIRECTOR OF THE ENVIRONMENTAL PROTECTION AGENCY.

STORAGE

STORE AWAY FROM INCOMPATIBLE SUBSTANCES.

CONDITIONS TO AVOID

MAY BURN BUT DOES NOT IGNITE READILY. AVOID CONTACT WITH STRONG OXIDIZERS, EXCESSIVE HEAT, SPARKS, OR OPEN FLAME.

SPILL AND LEAK PROCEDURES

SOIL SPILL: DIG HOLDING AREA SUCH AS LAGOON, POND OR PIT FOR CONTAINMENT. USE PROTECTIVE COVER SUCH AS A PLASTIC SHEET TO PREVENT MATERIAL FROM DISSOLVING IN FIRE EXTINGUISHING WATER OR RAIN.

WATER SPILL: ADD CALCIUM HYPOCHLORITE TO SPILL.
ADJUST PH TO NEUTRAL (PH=7).
USE MECHANICAL DREDGES OR LIFTS TO EXTRACT IMMOBILIZED MASSES OF POLLUTION AND PRECIPITATES.

OCCUPATIONAL SPILL: STOP LEAK IF YOU CAN DO IT WITHOUT RISK. FOR SMALL SPILLS, TAKE UP WITH SAND OR OTHER ABSORBENT MATERIAL AND PLACE INTO CLEAN, DRY CONTAINERS FOR LATER DISPOSAL. KEEP UNNECESSARY PEOPLE AWAY. ISOLATE HAZARD AREA AND DENY ENTRY.
REPORTABLE QUANTITY (RQ): 5000 POUNDS THE SUPERFUND AMENDMENTS AND REAUTHORIZATION ACT (SARA) SECTION 304 REQUIRES THAT A RELEASE EQUAL TO OR GREATER THAN THE REPORTABLE QUANTITY FOR THIS SUBSTANCE BE IMMEDIATELY REPORTED TO THE LOCAL EMERGENCY PLANNING COMMITTEE AND THE STATE EMERGENCY RESPONSE COMMISSION (40 CFR 355.40). IF THE RELEASE OF THIS SUBSTANCE IS REPORTABLE UNDER CERCLA SECTION 103, THE NATIONAL RESPONSE CENTER MUST BE NOTIFIED IMMEDIATELY AT (800) 424-8802 OR (202) 426-2675 IN THE METROPOLITAN WASHINGTON, D.C. AREA (40 CFR 302.6).

PROTECTIVE EQUIPMENT

VENTILATION: PROVIDE LOCAL EXHAUST VENTILATION AND/OR GENERAL DILUTION VENTILATION TO MEET PUBLISHED EXPOSURE LIMITS.

RESPIRATOR: THE FOLLOWING RESPIRATORS AND MAXIMUM USE CONCENTRATIONS ARE RECOMMENDATIONS BY THE U.S. DEPARTMENT OF HEALTH AND HUMAN SERVICES, NIOSH POCKET GUIDE TO CHEMICAL HAZARDS; NIOSH CRITERIA DOCUMENTS OR BY THE U.S. DEPARTMENT OF LABOR, 29 CFR 1910 SUBPART Z. THE SPECIFIC RESPIRATOR SELECTED MUST BE BASED ON CONTAMINATION LEVELS FOUND IN THE WORK PLACE, MUST NOT EXCEED THE WORKING LIMITS OF THE RESPIRATOR AND BE JOINTLY APPROVED BY THE NATIONAL INSTITUTE FOR OCCUPATIONAL SAFETY AND HEALTH AND THE MINE SAFETY AND HEALTH ADMINISTRATION (NIOSH-MSHA).
AMMONIUM SULFAMATE:
50 MG/M3- ANY DUST AND MIST RESPIRATOR.
100 MG/M3- ANY DUST AND MIST RESPIRATOR EXCEPT SINGLE-USE AND QUARTER-MASK RESPIRATOR. ANY SUPPLIED-AIR RESPIRATOR.
250 MG/M3- ANY POWERED AIR-PURIFYING RESPIRATOR WITH DUST AND MIST FILTER. ANY SUPPLIED-AIR RESPIRATOR OPERATED IN CONTINUOUS FLOW MODE.
500 MG/M3- ANY AIR-PURIFYING FULL FACEPIECE RESPIRATOR WITH HIGH-EFFICIENCY PARTICULATE FILTER. ANY POWERED AIR-PURIFYING RESPIRATOR WITH TIGHT-FITTING FACEPIECE AND HIGH-EFFICIENCY PARTICULATE FILTER. ANY SUPPLIED-AIR RESPIRATOR WITH TIGHT-FITTING FACEPIECE OPERATED IN CONTINUOUS FLOW MODE. ANY SELF-CONTAINED BREATHING APPARATUS WITH FULL FACEPIECE. ANY SUPPLIED-AIR RESPIRATOR WITH FULL FACEPIECE.
5000 MG/M3- ANY SUPPLIED-AIR RESPIRATOR WITH HALF-MASK OPERATED IN PRESSURE-DEMAND OR OTHER POSITIVE PRESSURE MODE.
ESCAPE- ANY AIR-PURIFYING FULL FACEPIECE RESPIRATOR WITH HIGH-EFFICIENCY PARTICULATE. ANY APPROPRIATE ESCAPE-TYPE SELF-CONTAINED BREATHING APPARATUS.
FOR FIREFIGHTING AND OTHER IMMEDIATELY DANGEROUS TO LIFE OR HEALTH CONDITIONS:
SELF-CONTAINED BREATHING APPARATUS WITH FULL FACEPIECE OPERATED IN PRESSURE-DEMAND OR OTHER POSITIVE PRESSURE MODE.
SUPPLIED-AIR RESPIRATOR WITH FULL FACEPIECE AND OPERATED IN PRESSURE-DEMAND OR OTHER POSITIVE PRESSURE MODE IN COMBINATION WITH AN AUXILIARY SELF-CONTAINED BREATHING APPARATUS OPERATED IN PRESSURE-DEMAND OR OTHER POSITIVE PRESSURE MODE.

CLOTHING: PROTECTIVE CLOTHING NOT REQUIRED. AVOID REPEATED OR PROLONGED CONTACT WITH THIS SUBSTANCE.

GLOVES: PROTECTIVE GLOVES ARE NOT REQUIRED BUT RECOMMENDED.

EYE PROTECTION: EYE PROTECTION NOT REQUIRED, BUT ADVISABLE.

AUTHORIZED BY- OCCUPATIONAL HEALTH SERVICES, INC.
CREATION DATE: 10/04/89 ***REVISION DATE:*** 03/28/90

MATERIAL SAFETY DATA SHEET

OCCUPATIONAL HEALTH SERVICES, INC.
AGRICULTURE AND PESTICIDE DIVISION
450 SEVENTH AVENUE, SUITE 2407
NEW YORK, NEW YORK 10123
1-800-445-MSDS OR (212) 967-1100

EMERGENCY CONTACT:
JOHN S. BRANSFORD, JR. (615) 292-1180

SUBSTANCE IDENTIFICATION

CAS-NUMBER 7783-18-8

SUBSTANCE: **AMMONIUM THIOSULFATE**

TRADE NAMES/SYNONYMS: AMMONIUM HYPOSULFITE; THIOSULFURIC ACID, DIAMMONIUM SALT; DIAMMONIUM THIOSULFATE; THIO-SUL; STCC 4966750; NA 9093; PST01460

CHEMICAL FAMILY: INORGANIC SALT

MOLECULAR FORMULA: H8-N2-S2-O3

MOLECULAR WEIGHT: 148.20

CERCLA RATINGS (SCALE 0-3): HEALTH=2 FIRE=0 REACTIVITY=0 PERSISTENCE=0

NFPA RATINGS (SCALE 0-4): HEALTH=2 FIRE=0 REACTIVITY=0

COMPONENTS AND CONTAMINANTS

COMPONENT: AMMONIUM THIOSULFATE ***PERCENT:*** 100
CAS# 7783-18-8

OTHER CONTAMINANTS: NONE

EXPOSURE LIMITS: NO OCCUPATIONAL EXPOSURE LIMITS ESTABLISHED BY OSHA, ACGIH, OR NIOSH.

PHYSICAL DATA

DESCRIPTION: COLORLESS TO WHITE HYGROSCOPIC, MONOCLINIC CRYSTALS WITH AN AMMONIA ODOR. ***MELTING POINT:*** 302 F (150 C) DECOMPOSES

SPECIFIC GRAVITY: 1.679 ***PH:*** 6.5-7.0 (60% SOLN)

SOLUBILITY IN WATER: 103% @ 100 C

SOLVENT SOLUBILITY: SLIGHTLY SOLUBLE IN ACETONE; INSOLUBLE IN ETHER, ALCOHOL

FIRE AND EXPLOSION DATA

FIRE AND EXPLOSION HAZARD: NEGLIGIBLE FIRE HAZARD WHEN EXPOSED TO HEAT OR FLAME.

FIREFIGHTING MEDIA: DRY CHEMICAL, CARBON DIOXIDE, HALON, WATER SPRAY OR STANDARD FOAM (1987 EMERGENCY RESPONSE GUIDEBOOK, DOT P 5800.4).
FOR LARGER FIRES, USE WATER SPRAY, FOG OR STANDARD FOAM (1987 EMERGENCY RESPONSE GUIDEBOOK, DOT P 5800.4).

FIREFIGHTING: MOVE CONTAINER FROM FIRE AREA IF POSSIBLE. DO NOT SCATTER SPILLED MATERIAL WITH HIGH PRESSURE WATER STREAMS. DIKE FIRE CONTROL WATER FOR LATER DISPOSAL (1987 EMERGENCY RESPONSE GUIDEBOOK, DOT P 5800.4, GUIDE PAGE 31).
EXTINGUISH USING AGENT INDICATED. AVOID BREATHING HAZARDOUS VAPORS OR DUSTS; KEEP UPWIND.

TRANSPORTATION DATA

DEPARTMENT OF TRANSPORTATION HAZARD CLASSIFICATION 49 CFR 172.101: ORM-E
DEPARTMENT OF TRANSPORTATION LABELING REQUIREMENTS 49 CFR 172.101 AND SUBPART E: NONE
DEPARTMENT OF TRANSPORTATION PACKAGING REQUIREMENTS: 49 CFR 173.510 EXCEPTIONS: NONE

TOXICITY

AMMONIUM THIOSULFATE: TOXICITY DATA: 2890 MG/KG ORAL-RAT LD50; 1098 MG/KG ORAL-GUINEA PIG LD50. CARCINOGEN STATUS: NONE. ACUTE TOXICITY LEVEL: MODERATELY TOXIC BY INGESTION. TARGET EFFECTS: NO DATA AVAILABLE.

HEALTH EFFECTS AND FIRST AID

INHALATION: AMMONIUM THIOSULFATE: **ACUTE EXPOSURE-** INHALATION MAY CAUSE RESPIRATORY TRACT IRRITATION. **CHRONIC EXPOSURE-** NO DATA AVAILABLE.

FIRST AID- REMOVE FROM EXPOSURE AREA TO FRESH AIR IMMEDIATELY. IF BREATHING HAS STOPPED, PERFORM ARTIFICIAL RESPIRATION. KEEP PERSON WARM AND AT REST. TREAT SYMPTOMATICALLY AND SUPPORTIVELY. GET MEDICAL ATTENTION IMMEDIATELY.

SKIN CONTACT: AMMONIUM THIOSULFATE: **ACUTE EXPOSURE-** CONTACT WITH THE SKIN MAY BE IRRITATING. **CHRONIC EXPOSURE-** NO DATA AVAILABLE.

FIRST AID- REMOVE CONTAMINATED CLOTHING AND SHOES IMMEDIATELY. WASH AFFECTED AREA WITH SOAP OR MILD DETERGENT AND LARGE AMOUNTS OF WATER UNTIL NO EVIDENCE OF CHEMICAL REMAINS (APPROXIMATELY 15-20 MINUTES). GET MEDICAL ATTENTION IMMEDIATELY.

EYE CONTACT: AMMONIUM THIOSULFATE: **ACUTE EXPOSURE-** CONTACT WITH THE EYES MAY BE IRRITATING. **CHRONIC EXPOSURE-** NO DATA AVAILABLE.

FIRST AID- WASH EYES IMMEDIATELY WITH LARGE AMOUNTS OF WATER OR NORMAL SALINE, OCCASIONALLY LIFTING UPPER AND LOWER LIDS, UNTIL NO EVIDENCE OF CHEMICAL REMAINS (APPROXIMATELY 15-20 MINUTES). GET MEDICAL ATTENTION IMMEDIATELY.

INGESTION: AMMONIUM THIOSULFATE: **ACUTE EXPOSURE-** THE REPORTED LETHAL DOSE IN RATS IS 2890 MG/KG. THIOSULFATE SALTS MAY CAUSE OSMOTIC DISTURBANCES. THEY ARE POORLY ABSORBED FROM THE ALIMENTARY TRACT AND SO ACT AS AN OSMOTIC CATHARTIC. **CHRONIC EXPOSURE-** NO DATA AVAILABLE.

FIRST AID- TREAT SYMPTOMATICALLY AND SUPPORTIVELY. GET MEDICAL ATTENTION IMMEDIATELY. IF VOMITING OCCURS, KEEP HEAD LOWER THAN HIPS TO PREVENT ASPIRATION.

ANTIDOTE: NO SPECIFIC ANTIDOTE. TREAT SYMPTOMATICALLY AND SUPPORTIVELY.

REACTIVITY

REACTIVITY: STABLE UNDER NORMAL TEMPERATURES AND PRESSURES.

INCOMPATIBILITIES: AMMONIUM THIOSULFATE: SODIUM CHLORATE: FORMS EXPLOSIVE COMPOUNDS.

DECOMPOSITION: THERMAL DECOMPOSITION MAY RELEASE TOXIC FUMES OF AMMONIA, HYDROGEN SULFIDE, AND OXIDES OF SULFUR AND NITROGEN.

POLYMERIZATION: HAZARDOUS POLYMERIZATION HAS NOT BEEN REPORTED TO OCCUR UNDER NORMAL TEMPERATURES AND PRESSURES.

STORAGE AND DISPOSAL

OBSERVE ALL FEDERAL, STATE AND LOCAL REGULATIONS WHEN STORING OR DISPOSING OF THIS SUBSTANCE. FOR ASSISTANCE, CONTACT THE DISTRICT DIRECTOR OF THE ENVIRONMENTAL PROTECTION AGENCY.

****STORAGE****

STORE AWAY FROM INCOMPATIBLE SUBSTANCES.

CONDITIONS TO AVOID

MAY BURN BUT DOES NOT IGNITE READILY. AVOID CONTACT WITH STRONG OXIDIZERS, EXCESSIVE HEAT, SPARKS, OR OPEN FLAME.

SPILL AND LEAK PROCEDURES

SOIL SPILL: DIG HOLDING AREA SUCH AS LAGOON, POND OR PIT FOR CONTAINMENT.
USE PROTECTIVE COVER SUCH AS A PLASTIC SHEET TO PREVENT MATERIAL FROM DISSOLVING IN FIRE EXTINGUISHING WATER OR RAIN.

WATER SPILL: NEUTRALIZE WITH DILUTE ACID OR REMOVABLE STRONG ACID.
USE ACTIVATED CARBON TO ABSORB SPILLED SUBSTANCE THAT IS DISSOLVED.
USE MECHANICAL DREDGES OR LIFTS TO EXTRACT IMMOBILIZED MASSES OF POLLUTION AND PRECIPITATES.

OCCUPATIONAL SPILL: SWEEP UP AND PLACE IN SUITABLE CLEAN, DRY CONTAINERS FOR RECLAMATION OR LATER DISPOSAL. DO NOT FLUSH SPILLED MATERIAL INTO SEWER. KEEP UNNECESSARY PEOPLE AWAY.
USE EXTINGUISHING AGENT SUITABLE FOR TYPE OF SURROUNDING MATERIAL.
REPORTABLE QUANTITY (RQ): 5000 POUNDS THE SUPERFUND AMENDMENTS AND REAUTHORIZATION ACT (SARA) SECTION 304 REQUIRES THAT A RELEASE EQUAL TO OR GREATER THAN THE REPORTABLE QUANTITY FOR THIS SUBSTANCE BE IMMEDIATELY REPORTED TO THE LOCAL EMERGENCY PLANNING COMMITTEE AND THE STATE EMERGENCY RESPONSE COMMISSION (40 CFR 355.40). IF THE RELEASE OF THIS SUBSTANCE IS REPORTABLE UNDER CERCLA SECTION 103, THE NATIONAL RESPONSE CENTER MUST BE NOTIFIED IMMEDIATELY AT (800) 424-8802 OR (202) 426-2675 IN THE METROPOLITAN WASHINGTON, D.C. AREA (40 CFR 302.6).

PROTECTIVE EQUIPMENT

VENTILATION: PROVIDE LOCAL EXHAUST OR GENERAL DILUTION VENTILATION SYSTEM.

RESPIRATOR: THE FOLLOWING RESPIRATORS ARE RECOMMENDED BASED ON INFORMATION FOUND IN THE PHYSICAL DATA, TOXICITY AND HEALTH EFFECTS SECTIONS. THEY ARE RANKED IN ORDER FROM MINIMUM TO MAXIMUM RESPIRATORY PROTECTION. THE SPECIFIC RESPIRATOR SELECTED MUST BE BASED ON CONTAMINATION LEVELS FOUND IN THE WORK PLACE, MUST NOT EXCEED THE WORKING LIMITS OF THE RESPIRATOR AND BE JOINTLY APPROVED BY THE NATIONAL INSTITUTE FOR OCCUPATIONAL SAFETY AND HEALTH AND THE MINE SAFETY AND HEALTH ADMINISTRATION (NIOSH-MSHA).
DUST AND MIST RESPIRATOR WITH A FULL FACEPIECE.
AIR-PURIFYING FULL FACEPIECE RESPIRATOR WITH A HIGH-EFFICIENCY PARTICULATE FILTER.
POWERED AIR-PURIFYING RESPIRATOR WITH A TIGHT-FITTING FACEPIECE AND HIGH-EFFICIENCY PARTICULATE FILTER.
TYPE 'C' SUPPLIED-AIR RESPIRATOR WITH A FULL FACEPIECE OPERATED IN PRESSURE-DEMAND OR OTHER POSITIVE PRESSURE MODE OR WITH A FULL FACEPIECE, HELMET OR HOOD OPERATED IN CONTINUOUS-FLOW MODE.
SELF-CONTAINED BREATHING APPARATUS WITH A FULL FACEPIECE OPERATED IN PRESSURE-DEMAND OR OTHER POSITIVE PRESSURE MODE.
FOR FIREFIGHTING AND OTHER IMMEDIATELY DANGEROUS TO LIFE OR HEALTH CONDITIONS:
SELF-CONTAINED BREATHING APPARATUS WITH FULL FACEPIECE OPERATED IN PRESSURE-DEMAND OR OTHER POSITIVE PRESSURE MODE.
SUPPLIED-AIR RESPIRATOR WITH FULL FACEPIECE AND OPERATED IN PRESSURE-DEMAND OR OTHER POSITIVE PRESSURE MODE IN COMBINATION WITH AN AUXILIARY SELF-CONTAINED BREATHING APPARATUS OPERATED IN PRESSURE-DEMAND OR OTHER POSITIVE PRESSURE MODE.

CLOTHING: EMPLOYEE MUST WEAR APPROPRIATE PROTECTIVE (IMPERVIOUS) CLOTHING AND EQUIPMENT TO PREVENT REPEATED OR PROLONGED SKIN CONTACT WITH THIS SUBSTANCE.

GLOVES: EMPLOYEE MUST WEAR APPROPRIATE PROTECTIVE GLOVES TO PREVENT CONTACT WITH THIS SUBSTANCE.

EYE PROTECTION: EMPLOYEE MUST WEAR SPLASH-PROOF OR DUST-RESISTANT SAFETY GOGGLES TO PREVENT EYE CONTACT WITH THIS SUBSTANCE.
EMERGENCY EYE WASH: WHERE THERE IS ANY POSSIBILITY THAT AN EMPLOYEE'S EYES MAY BE EXPOSED TO THIS SUBSTANCE, THE EMPLOYER SHOULD PROVIDE AN EYE WASH FOUNTAIN WITHIN THE IMMEDIATE WORK AREA FOR EMERGENCY USE.

AUTHORIZED BY- OCCUPATIONAL HEALTH SERVICES, INC.
CREATION DATE: 11/17/89 ***REVISION DATE:*** 05/31/90

MATERIAL SAFETY DATA SHEET

OCCUPATIONAL HEALTH SERVICES, INC.
AGRICULTURE AND PESTICIDE DIVISION
450 SEVENTH AVENUE, SUITE 2407
NEW YORK, NEW YORK 10123
1-800-445-MSDS OR (212) 967-1100

EMERGENCY CONTACT:
JOHN S. BRANSFORD, JR. (615) 292-1180

SUBSTANCE IDENTIFICATION

CAS-NUMBER 101-05-3

SUBSTANCE: **ANILAZINE**

TRADE NAMES/SYNONYMS: 1,3,5-TRIAZIN-2-AMINE, 4,6-DICHLORO-N-(2-CHLOROPHENYL)-; S-TRIAZINE, 2,4-DICHLORO-6-(O-CHLOROANILINO)-; 4,6-DICHLORO-N-(2-CHLOROPHENYL)-1,3,5-TRIAZIN-2-AMINE; 2,4-DICHLORO-6-(O-CHLOROANILINO)-S-TRIAZINE; 2-CHLORO-N-(4,6-DICHLORO-1,3,5-TRIAZIN-2-YL)ANILINE; 2,4-DICHLORO-6-(2-CHLOROANILINO)-1,3,5-TRIAZINE; (O-CHLOROANILINO)DICHLOROTRIAZINE; ANILAZIN; ANIYALINE; B-622; BORTRYSAN; DYRENE; KEMATE; TRIAZIN; ZINOCHLOR; NCI-C08684; ENT 26,058; C9H5CL3N4; PST01526

CHEMICAL FAMILY: S-TRIAZINE

MOLECULAR FORMULA: CL2-N3-C3-N-H-C6-H4-CL

MOLECULAR WEIGHT: 275.51

CERCLA RATINGS (SCALE 0-3): HEALTH=2 FIRE=1 REACTIVITY=0 PERSISTENCE=2

NFPA RATINGS (SCALE 0-4): HEALTH=2 FIRE=1 REACTIVITY=0

COMPONENTS AND CONTAMINANTS

COMPONENT: ANILAZINE ***PERCENT:*** 100
CAS# 101-05-3

OTHER CONTAMINANTS: NONE

EXPOSURE LIMITS: NO OCCUPATIONAL EXPOSURE LIMITS ESTABLISHED BY OSHA, ACGIH, OR NIOSH.

PHYSICAL DATA

DESCRIPTION: WHITE TO TAN CRYSTALLINE SOLID.

MELTING POINT: 318-320 F (159-160 C) ***SPECIFIC GRAVITY:*** NOT AVAILABLE

SOLUBILITY IN WATER: INSOLUBLE

SOLVENT SOLUBILITY: SOLUBLE IN ACETONE, HYDROCARBONS AND CHLORINATED HYDROCARBONS, MOST ORGANIC SOLVENTS; SLIGHTLY SOLUBLE IN TOLUENE, XYLENE, CHLOROBENZENE.

FIRE AND EXPLOSION DATA

FIRE AND EXPLOSION HAZARD: SLIGHT FIRE HAZARD WHEN EXPOSED TO HEAT OR FLAME.

FIREFIGHTING MEDIA: DRY CHEMICAL, CARBON DIOXIDE, HALON, WATER SPRAY OR STANDARD FOAM (1987 EMERGENCY RESPONSE GUIDEBOOK, DOT P 5800.4).
FOR LARGER FIRES, USE WATER SPRAY, FOG OR STANDARD FOAM (1987 EMERGENCY RESPONSE GUIDEBOOK, DOT P 5800.4).

FIREFIGHTING: MOVE CONTAINERS FROM FIRE AREA IF POSSIBLE (1987 EMERGENCY RESPONSE GUIDEBOOK, DOT P 5800.4, GUIDE PAGE 53).
EXTINGUISH USING AGENTS SUITABLE FOR SURROUNDING FIRE. USE FLOODING QUANTITIES OF WATER AS A FOG. KEEP MATERIAL OUT OF SEWERS AND WATER SOURCES. DO NOT TOUCH SPILLED MATERIAL. AVOID BREATHING HAZARDOUS FUMES; KEEP UPWIND.

TOXICITY

ANILAZINE: IRRITATION DATA: 0.1% SKIN-MAN MODERATE; 500 MG SKIN-RABBIT SEVERE. TOXICITY DATA: 2700 MG/KG ORAL-RAT LD50; 6020 MG/KG ORAL-MOUSE LD50; 400 MG/KG ORAL-RABBIT LD50; 25 MG/KG INTRAPERITONEAL-RAT LD50; 50 MG/KG INTRAPERITONEAL-MOUSE LD50; MUTAGENIC DATA (RTECS). CARCINOGEN STATUS: NONE. LOCAL EFFECTS: IRRITANT- SKIN. ACUTE TOXICITY DATA: MODERATELY TOXIC BY INGESTION TARGET EFFECTS: NO DATA AVAILABLE.

HEALTH EFFECTS AND FIRST AID

INHALATION: ANILAZINE: **ACUTE EXPOSURE-** SOME TRIAZINES ARE MILDLY IRRITATING TO THE UPPER RESPIRATORY TRACT. **CHRONIC EXPOSURE-** NO DATA AVAILABLE.

FIRST AID- REMOVE FROM EXPOSURE AREA TO FRESH AIR IMMEDIATELY. IF BREATHING HAS STOPPED, PERFORM ARTIFICIAL RESPIRATION. KEEP PERSON WARM AND AT REST. TREAT SYMPTOMATICALLY AND SUPPORTIVELY. GET MEDICAL ATTENTION IMMEDIATELY.

SKIN CONTACT: ANILAZINE: IRRITANT. **ACUTE EXPOSURE-** 0.1% APPLIED TO HUMAN SKIN WAS MODERATELY IRRITATING. 9.4 GM/KG OF ANILAZINE APPLIED TO THE RABBIT SKIN IN THE FORM OF A PASTE (IN PEANUT OIL OR DIMETHYL PHTHALATE) PRODUCED LOCAL ERYTHEMA, EDEMA, ULCERATION, FISSURING, AND INCRUSTATION; SYSTEMIC EFFECTS OF TOXIC DEGENERATIVE CHANGES IN THE LIVER AND KIDNEYS ALSO OCCURRED. **CHRONIC EXPOSURE-** PROLONGED SKIN CONTACT MAY CAUSE IRRITATION.

FIRST AID- REMOVE CONTAMINATED CLOTHING AND SHOES IMMEDIATELY. WASH AFFECTED AREA WITH SOAP OR MILD DETERGENT AND LARGE AMOUNTS OF WATER UNTIL NO EVIDENCE OF CHEMICAL REMAINS (APPROXIMATELY 15-20 MINUTES). GET MEDICAL ATTENTION IMMEDIATELY.

EYE CONTACT: ANILAZINE: **ACUTE EXPOSURE-** SOME TRIAZINES ARE MILDLY IRRITATING TO THE EYES. **CHRONIC EXPOSURE-** NO DATA AVAILABLE.

FIRST AID- WASH EYES IMMEDIATELY WITH LARGE AMOUNTS OF WATER OR NORMAL SALINE, OCCASIONALLY LIFTING UPPER AND LOWER LIDS, UNTIL NO EVIDENCE OF CHEMICAL REMAINS (APPROXIMATELY 15-20 MINUTES). GET MEDICAL ATTENTION IMMEDIATELY.

INGESTION: ANILAZINE: **ACUTE EXPOSURE-** A LETHAL DOSE IN RATS WAS 2700 MG/KG; SYMPTOMS WERE NOT REPORTED. **CHRONIC EXPOSURE-** TOXIC DEGENERATION OF LIVER AND KIDNEYS WAS OBSERVED IN A 77-DAY STUDY OF RATS FED 30 AND 70 MG/KG/DAY. WEIGHT LOSS, ENLARGEMENT OF THE LIVER, KIDNEY, AND SPLEEN, AND DEATH WERE REPORTED FROM A STUDY OF DOGS FED 1.0 GM/KG/DAY OVER A PERIOD OF 681 DAYS.

FIRST AID- REMOVE BY GASTRIC LAVAGE AND CATHARSIS. MAINTAIN BLOOD PRESSURE AND AIRWAY. GIVE OXYGEN IF RESPIRATION IS DEPRESSED. DO NOT PERFORM GASTRIC LAVAGE IF VICTIM IS UNCONSCIOUS. GET MEDICAL ATTENTION IMMEDIATELY (DREISBACH, HANDBOOK OF POISONING, 12TH ED.).
ADMINISTRATION OF LAVAGE OR OXYGEN SHOULD BE PERFORMED BY QUALIFIED MEDICAL PERSONNEL.

ANTIDOTE: NO SPECIFIC ANTIDOTE. TREAT SYMPTOMATICALLY AND SUPPORTIVELY.

REACTIVITY

REACTIVITY: STABLE UNDER NORMAL TEMPERATURES AND PRESSURES.

INCOMPATIBILITIES: ANILAZINE: ALKALINE COMPOUNDS: HYDROLYSIS MAY OCCUR WHEN HEATED. OILS: INCOMPATIBLE.

DECOMPOSITION: THERMAL DECOMPOSITION PRODUCTS MAY INCLUDE TOXIC OXIDES OF NITROGEN AND CARBON AND TOXIC AND CORROSIVE FUMES OF CHLORIDES.

POLYMERIZATION: HAZARDOUS POLYMERIZATION HAS NOT BEEN REPORTED TO OCCUR UNDER NORMAL TEMPERATURES AND PRESSURES.

STORAGE AND DISPOSAL

OBSERVE ALL FEDERAL, STATE AND LOCAL REGULATIONS WHEN STORING OR DISPOSING OF THIS SUBSTANCE. FOR ASSISTANCE, CONTACT THE DISTRICT DIRECTOR OF THE ENVIRONMENTAL PROTECTION AGENCY.

STORAGE

STORE IN ACCORDANCE WITH 40 CFR 165 RECOMMENDED PROCEDURES FOR THE DISPOSAL AND STORAGE OF PESTICIDES AND PESTICIDE CONTAINERS.
STORE AWAY FROM INCOMPATIBLE SUBSTANCES.

DISPOSAL

DISPOSAL MUST BE IN ACCORDANCE WITH 40 CFR 165 RECOMMENDED PROCEDURES FOR THE DISPOSAL AND STORAGE OF PESTICIDES AND PESTICIDE CONTAINERS.

CONDITIONS TO AVOID

MAY BURN BUT DOES NOT IGNITE READILY.

SPILL AND LEAK PROCEDURES

OCCUPATIONAL SPILL: DO NOT TOUCH SPILLED MATERIAL. STOP LEAK IF YOU CAN DO IT WITHOUT RISK. FOR SMALL SPILLS, TAKE UP WITH SAND OR OTHER ABSORBENT MATERIAL AND PLACE INTO CONTAINERS FOR LATER DISPOSAL. FOR SMALL DRY SPILLS, WITH A CLEAN SHOVEL PLACE MATERIAL INTO CLEAN, DRY CONTAINER AND COVER. MOVE CONTAINERS FROM SPILL AREA. FOR LARGER SPILLS, DIKE FAR AHEAD OF SPILL FOR LATER DISPOSAL. KEEP UNNECESSARY PEOPLE AWAY. ISOLATE HAZARD AREA AND DENY ENTRY.

PROTECTIVE EQUIPMENT

VENTILATION: PROVIDE LOCAL EXHAUST OR GENERAL DILUTION VENTILATION SYSTEM.

RESPIRATOR: THE FOLLOWING RESPIRATORS ARE RECOMMENDED BASED ON INFORMATION FOUND IN THE PHYSICAL DATA, TOXICITY AND HEALTH EFFECTS SECTIONS. THEY ARE RANKED IN ORDER FROM MINIMUM TO MAXIMUM RESPIRATORY PROTECTION. THE SPECIFIC RESPIRATOR SELECTED MUST BE BASED ON CONTAMINATION LEVELS FOUND IN THE WORK PLACE, MUST NOT EXCEED THE WORKING LIMITS OF THE RESPIRATOR AND BE JOINTLY APPROVED BY THE NATIONAL INSTITUTE FOR OCCUPATIONAL SAFETY AND HEALTH AND THE MINE SAFETY AND HEALTH ADMINISTRATION (NIOSH-MSHA).

CHEMICAL CARTRIDGE RESPIRATOR WITH AN ORGANIC VAPOR CARTRIDGE(S) WITH A FULL FACEPIECE AND ORGANIC VAPOR CARTRIDGE(S) IN COMBINATION WITH A DUST AND MIST FILTER.
POWERED AIR-PURIFYING RESPIRATOR WITH A TIGHT-FITTING FACEPIECE AND ORGANIC VAPOR CARTRIDGE(S) IN COMBINATION WITH A HIGH-EFFICIENCY PARTICULATE FILTER.
TYPE 'C' SUPPLIED-AIR RESPIRATOR WITH A FULL FACEPIECE OPERATED IN A PRESSURE-DEMAND OR OTHER POSITIVE PRESSURE MODE. SELF-CONTAINED BREATHING APPARATUS WITH A FULL FACEPIECE OPERATED IN PRESSURE-DEMAND OR OTHER POSITIVE PRESSURE MODE.
FOR FIREFIGHTING AND OTHER IMMEDIATELY DANGEROUS TO LIFE OR HEALTH CONDITIONS:
SELF-CONTAINED BREATHING APPARATUS WITH FULL FACEPIECE OPERATED IN PRESSURE-DEMAND OR OTHER POSITIVE PRESSURE MODE.
SUPPLIED-AIR RESPIRATOR WITH FULL FACEPIECE AND OPERATED IN PRESSURE-DEMAND OR OTHER POSITIVE PRESSURE MODE IN COMBINATION WITH AN AUXILIARY SELF-CONTAINED BREATHING APPARATUS OPERATED IN PRESSURE-DEMAND OR OTHER POSITIVE PRESSURE MODE.

CLOTHING: EMPLOYEE MUST WEAR APPROPRIATE PROTECTIVE (IMPERVIOUS) CLOTHING AND EQUIPMENT TO PREVENT REPEATED OR PROLONGED SKIN CONTACT WITH THIS SUBSTANCE.

GLOVES: EMPLOYEE MUST WEAR APPROPRIATE PROTECTIVE GLOVES TO PREVENT CONTACT WITH THIS SUBSTANCE.

EYE PROTECTION: EMPLOYEE MUST WEAR SPLASH-PROOF OR DUST-RESISTANT SAFETY GOGGLES TO PREVENT EYE CONTACT WITH THIS SUBSTANCE.
EMERGENCY EYE WASH: WHERE THERE IS ANY POSSIBILITY THAT AN EMPLOYEE'S EYES MAY BE EXPOSED TO THIS SUBSTANCE, THE EMPLOYER SHOULD PROVIDE AN EYE WASH FOUNTAIN WITHIN THE IMMEDIATE WORK AREA FOR EMERGENCY USE.

AUTHORIZED BY- OCCUPATIONAL HEALTH SERVICES, INC.
CREATION DATE: 10/04/89 ***REVISION DATE:*** 05/07/90

MATERIAL SAFETY DATA SHEET

OCCUPATIONAL HEALTH SERVICES, INC.
AGRICULTURE AND PESTICIDE DIVISION
450 SEVENTH AVENUE, SUITE 2407
NEW YORK, NEW YORK 10123
1-800-445-MSDS OR (212) 967-1100

EMERGENCY CONTACT:
JOHN S. BRANSFORD, JR. (615) 292-1180

SUBSTANCE IDENTIFICATION

CAS-NUMBER 84-65-1
SUBSTANCE: **ANTHRAQUINONE**
TRADE NAMES/SYNONYMS: 9,10-ANTHRACENEDIONE; ANTHRADIONE; CORBIT; HEOLITE; 9,10-ANTHRAQUINONE; 9,10-DIOXOANTHRACENE; 9,10-DIHYDRO-9,10-DIKETOANTHRACENE; PST01600
CHEMICAL FAMILY: KETONE, AROMATIC
MOLECULAR FORMULA: C14-H8-O2
MOLECULAR WEIGHT: 208.22
CERCLA RATINGS (SCALE 0-3): HEALTH=1 FIRE=1 REACTIVITY=0 PERSISTENCE=3
NFPA RATINGS (SCALE 0-4): HEALTH=0 FIRE=1 REACTIVITY=0

COMPONENTS AND CONTAMINANTS

COMPONENT: ANTHRAQUINONE ***PERCENT:*** 100
CAS# 84-65-1
OTHER CONTAMINANTS: NONE
EXPOSURE LIMITS: NO OCCUPATIONAL EXPOSURE LIMITS ESTABLISHED BY OSHA, ACGIH, OR NIOSH.

PHYSICAL DATA

DESCRIPTION: COLORLESS TO LIGHT YELLOW CRYSTALS.
BOILING POINT: 714-718 F (379-381 C) ***MELTING POINT:*** 542-545 F (283-285 C)
SPECIFIC GRAVITY: 1.42-1.44 ***VAPOR PRESSURE:*** 1 MMHG @ 190 C
SOLUBILITY IN WATER: INSOLUBLE ***VAPOR DENSITY:*** 7.6
SOLVENT SOLUBILITY: ALCOHOL, ETHER, ACETONE, BENZENE, TOLUENE, CHL

FIRE AND EXPLOSION DATA

FIRE AND EXPLOSION HAZARD: SLIGHT FIRE HAZARD WHEN EXPOSED TO HEAT OR FLAME.
FLASH POINT: 365 F (185 C) (CC)
FIREFIGHTING MEDIA: DRY CHEMICAL, CARBON DIOXIDE, HALON, WATER SPRAY OR STANDARD FOAM (1987 EMERGENCY RESPONSE GUIDEBOOK, DOT P 5800.4). FOR LARGER FIRES, USE WATER SPRAY, FOG OR STANDARD FOAM (1987 EMERGENCY RESPONSE GUIDEBOOK, DOT P 5800.4).
FIREFIGHTING: NO ACUTE HAZARD. MOVE CONTAINER FROM FIRE AREA IF POSSIBLE. AVOID BREATHING VAPORS OR DUSTS; KEEP UPWIND.

TOXICITY

ANTHRAQUINONE: TOXICITY DATA: >5 GM/KG ORAL-MOUSE LD50 (85HSAI); 15 GM/KG ORAL-RAT LDLO; 3500 MG/KG INTRAPERITONEAL-RAT LD50; 3500 MG/KG UNREPORTED-MOUSE LD50; MUTAGENIC DATA (RTECS). CARCINOGEN STATUS: NONE. LOCAL EFFECTS: IRRITANT- INHALATION, SKIN, AND EYES. ACUTE TOXICITY LEVEL: SLIGHTLY TOXIC BY INGESTION. TARGET EFFECTS: SENSITIZER- SKIN.

HEALTH EFFECTS AND FIRST AID

INHALATION: ANTHRAQUINONE: IRRITANT. **ACUTE EXPOSURE-** INHALATION OF THE DUST MAY CAUSE IRRITATION OF THE RESPIRATORY TRACT. **CHRONIC EXPOSURE-** REPEATED OR PROLONGED EXPOSURE MAY CAUSE MUCOUS MEMBRANE IRRITATION.
FIRST AID- REMOVE FROM EXPOSURE AREA TO FRESH AIR IMMEDIATELY. IF BREATHING HAS STOPPED, PERFORM ARTIFICIAL RESPIRATION. KEEP PERSON WARM AND AT REST. TREAT SYMPTOMATICALLY AND SUPPORTIVELY. GET MEDICAL ATTENTION IMMEDIATELY.

SKIN CONTACT: ANTHRAQUINONE: IRRITANT/SENSITIZER. **ACUTE EXPOSURE-** CONTACT WITH THE SKIN MAY CAUSE IRRITATION. SENSITIZATION DERMATITIS MAY OCCUR IN PERSONS PREVIOSLY EXPOSED. **CHRONIC EXPOSURE-** REPEATED OR PROLONGED EXPOSURE MAY CAUSE SENSITIZATION DERMATITIS.
FIRST AID- REMOVE CONTAMINATED CLOTHING AND SHOES IMMEDIATELY. WASH AFFECTED AREA WITH SOAP OR MILD DETERGENT AND LARGE AMOUNTS OF WATER UNTIL NO EVIDENCE OF CHEMICAL REMAINS (APPROXIMATELY 15-20 MINUTES). GET MEDICAL ATTENTION IMMEDIATELY.

EYE CONTACT: ANTHRAQUINONE: IRRITANT. **ACUTE EXPOSURE-** CONTACT WITH THE EYES MAY CAUSE IRRITATION. THE CRYSTALS HAVE CAUSED IRRITATION AND INFLAMMATION IN EXPERIMENTAL ANIMAL EYES. THE SUBSTANCE IS PRACTICALLY INSOLUBLE IN WATER AND IT IS POSSIBLE THAT THE IRRITATION IS DUE TO A MECHANICAL ACTION OF THE POWDER. **CHRONIC EXPOSURE-** REPEATED OR PROLONGED EXPOSURE MAY CAUSE CONJUNCTIVITIS.
FIRST AID- WASH EYES IMMEDIATELY WITH LARGE AMOUNTS OF WATER OR NORMAL SALINE, OCCASIONALLY LIFTING UPPER AND LOWER LIDS, UNTIL NO EVIDENCE OF CHEMICAL REMAINS (APPROXIMATELY 15-20 MINUTES). GET MEDICAL ATTENTION IMMEDIATELY.

INGESTION: ANTHRAQUINONE: **ACUTE EXPOSURE-** ANTHRAQUINONES MAY CAUSE A LAXATIVE EFFECT AND PRODUCE A GREENISH OR BLUISH COLORED URINE. ONCE ABSORBED, THE SUBSTANCE MAY BE ELIMINATED IN THE MILK OF NURSING MOTHER. MICE FED 5 GM/KG SHOWED NO SYMPTOMS OR DEATH. **CHRONIC EXPOSURE-** NO DATA AVAILABLE.
FIRST AID- IF THE PERSON IS CONSCIOUS AND NOT CONVULSING, INDUCE EMESIS BY GIVING SYRUP OF IPECAC FOLLOWED BY WATER. (IF VOMITING OCCURS KEEP THE HEAD BELOW THE HIPS TO PREVENT ASPIRATION). REPEAT IN 20 MINUTES IF NOT EFFECTIVE INITIALLY. GIVE ACTIVATED CHARCOAL. IN PATIENTS WITH DEPRESSED RESPIRATION OR IF EMESIS IS NOT PRODUCED, PERFORM GASTRIC LAVAGE CAUTIOUSLY (DREISBACH, HANDBOOK OF POISONING, 12TH ED.). TREAT SYMPTOMATICALLY AND SUPPORTIVELY. GASTRIC LAVAGE SHOULD BE PERFORMED BY QUALIFIED MEDICAL PERSONNEL. GET MEDICAL ATTENTION IMMEDIATELY.
ANTIDOTE: NO SPECIFIC ANTIDOTE. TREAT SYMPTOMATICALLY AND SUPPORTIVELY.

REACTIVITY

REACTIVITY: STABLE UNDER NORMAL TEMPERATURES AND PRESSURES.
INCOMPATIBILITIES: ANTHRAQUINONE: NO DATA AVAILABLE.
DECOMPOSITION: THERMAL DECOMPOSITION MAY RELEASE TOXIC AND/OR HAZARDOUS GASES.
POLYMERIZATION: HAZARDOUS POLYMERIZATION HAS NOT BEEN REPORTED TO OCCUR UNDER NORMAL TEMPERATURES AND PRESSURES.

CONDITIONS TO AVOID

MAY BURN BUT DOES NOT IGNITE READILY. CONTAINER MAY EXPLODE IN HEAT OF FIRE.

SPILL AND LEAK PROCEDURES

OCCUPATIONAL SPILL: NO SPECIAL PRECAUTIONS INDICATED.

PROTECTIVE EQUIPMENT

VENTILATION: PROVIDE GENERAL DILUTION VENTILATION.

RESPIRATOR: THE FOLLOWING RESPIRATORS ARE RECOMMENDED BASED ON INFORMATION FOUND IN THE PHYSICAL DATA, TOXICITY AND HEALTH EFFECTS SECTIONS. THEY ARE RANKED IN ORDER FROM MINIMUM TO MAXIMUM RESPIRATORY PROTECTION. THE SPECIFIC RESPIRATOR SELECTED MUST BE BASED ON CONTAMINATION LEVELS FOUND IN THE WORK PLACE, MUST NOT EXCEED THE WORKING LIMITS OF THE RESPIRATOR AND BE JOINTLY APPROVED BY THE NATIONAL INSTITUTE FOR OCCUPATIONAL SAFETY AND HEALTH AND THE MINE SAFETY AND HEALTH ADMINISTRATION (NIOSH-MSHA).

CHEMICAL CARTRIDGE RESPIRATOR WITH FULL FACEPIECE AND ORGANIC VAPOR CARTRIDGE(S) IN COMBINATION WITH A DUST AND MIST FILTER.

CHEMICAL CARTRIDGE RESPIRATOR WITH FULL FACEPIECE AND ORGANIC VAPOR CARTRIDGE(S) IN COMBINATION WITH A HIGH-EFFICIENCY PARTICULATE FILTER.

GAS MASK WITH ORGANIC VAPOR CANISTER (CHIN-STYLE OR FRONT- OR BACK-MOUNTED CANISTER) WITH A FULL FACEPIECE AND A HIGH-EFFICIENCY PARTICULATE FILTER.

POWERED AIR-PURIFYING RESPIRATOR WITH TIGHT-FITTING FACEPIECE AND ORGANIC VAPOR CARTRIDGE(S) IN COMBINATION WITH A HIGH-EFFICIENCY PARTICULATE FILTER.

TYPE 'C' SUPPLIED-AIR RESPIRATOR WITH A FULL FACEPIECE OPERATED IN PRESSURE-DEMAND OR OTHER POSITIVE PRESSURE MODE OR WITH A FULL FACEPIECE, HELMET OR HOOD OPERATED IN CONTINUOUS-FLOW MODE.

SELF-CONTAINED BREATHING APPARATUS WITH A FULL FACEPIECE OPERATED IN PRESSURE-DEMAND OR OTHER POSITIVE PRESSURE MODE.

FOR FIREFIGHTING AND OTHER IMMEDIATELY DANGEROUS TO LIFE OR HEALTH CONDITIONS:

SELF-CONTAINED BREATHING APPARATUS WITH FULL FACEPIECE OPERATED IN PRESSURE-DEMAND OR OTHER POSITIVE PRESSURE MODE.

SUPPLIED-AIR RESPIRATOR WITH FULL FACEPIECE AND OPERATED IN PRESSURE-DEMAND OR OTHER POSITIVE PRESSURE MODE IN COMBINATION WITH AN AUXILIARY SELF-CONTAINED BREATHING APPARATUS OPERATED IN PRESSURE-DEMAND OR OTHER POSITIVE PRESSURE MODE.

CLOTHING: EMPLOYEE MUST WEAR APPROPRIATE PROTECTIVE (IMPERVIOUS) CLOTHING AND EQUIPMENT TO PREVENT REPEATED OR PROLONGED SKIN CONTACT WITH THIS SUBSTANCE.

GLOVES: EMPLOYEE MUST WEAR APPROPRIATE PROTECTIVE GLOVES TO PREVENT CONTACT WITH THIS SUBSTANCE.

EYE PROTECTION: EMPLOYEE MUST WEAR SPLASH-PROOF OR DUST-RESISTANT SAFETY GOGGLES TO PREVENT EYE CONTACT WITH THIS SUBSTANCE.

EMERGENCY EYE WASH: WHERE THERE IS ANY POSSIBILITY THAT AN EMPLOYEE'S EYES MAY BE EXPOSED TO THIS SUBSTANCE, THE EMPLOYER SHOULD PROVIDE AN EYE WASH FOUNTAIN WITHIN THE IMMEDIATE WORK AREA FOR EMERGENCY USE.

AUTHORIZED BY- OCCUPATIONAL HEALTH SERVICES, INC.

CREATION DATE: 10/04/89 ***REVISION DATE:*** 05/18/90

MATERIAL SAFETY DATA SHEET

OCCUPATIONAL HEALTH SERVICES, INC.
AGRICULTURE AND PESTICIDE DIVISION
450 SEVENTH AVENUE, SUITE 2407
NEW YORK, NEW YORK 10123
1-800-445-MSDS OR (212) 967-1100

EMERGENCY CONTACT:
JOHN S. BRANSFORD, JR. (615) 292-1180

SUBSTANCE IDENTIFICATION

CAS-NUMBER 28300-74-5

SUBSTANCE: **ANTIMONY POTASSIUM TARTRATE**

TRADE NAMES/SYNONYMS: POTASSIUM ANTIMONY TARTRATE; TARTAR EMETIC; TARTRATED ANTIMONY; TARTOX; TARTARIC ACID, ANTIMONY POTASSIUM SALT; ANTIMONY POTASSIUM TARTRATE SOLID; TARTARIZED ANTIMONY; POTASSIUM ANTIMONYL TARTRATE; POTASSIUM ANTIMONYL D-TARTRATE; C4H4KO7SB; A-865; PST01690

CHEMICAL FAMILY: ORGANOMETALLIC

MOLECULAR FORMULA: C4-H4-K-O7-SB

MOLECULAR WEIGHT: 324.93

CERCLA RATINGS (SCALE 0-3): HEALTH=3 FIRE=0 REACTIVITY=0 PERSISTENCE=3

NFPA RATINGS (SCALE 0-4): HEALTH=3 FIRE=0 REACTIVITY=0

COMPONENTS AND CONTAMINANTS

COMPONENT: ANTIMONY POTASSIUM TARTRATE ***PERCENT:*** 100
CAS# 28300-74-5

OTHER CONTAMINANTS: NONE

EXPOSURE LIMITS: ANTIMONY POTASSIUM TARTRATE: 0.5 MG(SB)/M3 OSHA TWA 0.5 MG(SB)/M3 ACGIH TWA 0.5 MG(SB)/M3 NIOSH RECOMMENDED TWA 100 POUNDS CERCLA SECTION 103 REPORTABLE QUANTITY SUBJECT TO SARA SECTION 313 ANNUAL TOXIC CHEMICAL RELEASE REPORTING

PHYSICAL DATA

DESCRIPTION: WHITE POWDER OR COLORLESS CRYSTALS WITH A SWEET, METALLIC TASTE.

MELTING POINT: LOSES H2O @ 212 F ***SPECIFIC GRAVITY:*** 2.6 @ 20 C

PH: 5-6 (AQUEOUS SOLN) ***SOLUBILITY IN WATER:*** 8.3%

FIRE AND EXPLOSION DATA

FIRE AND EXPLOSION HAZARD: NEGLIGIBLE FIRE HAZARD WHEN EXPOSED TO HEAT OR FLAME.

FIREFIGHTING MEDIA: DRY CHEMICAL, CARBON DIOXIDE, HALON, WATER SPRAY OR STANDARD FOAM (1987 EMERGENCY RESPONSE GUIDEBOOK, DOT P 5800.4).

FOR LARGER FIRES, USE WATER SPRAY, FOG OR STANDARD FOAM (1987 EMERGENCY RESPONSE GUIDEBOOK, DOT P 5800.4).

FIREFIGHTING: MOVE CONTAINERS FROM FIRE AREA IF POSSIBLE (1987 EMERGENCY RESPONSE GUIDEBOOK, DOT P 5800.4, GUIDE PAGE 53).

EXTINGUISH USING AGENT INDICATED; KEEP UPWIND, AVOID BREATHING VAPORS OR DUST.

TRANSPORTATION DATA

DEPARTMENT OF TRANSPORTATION HAZARD CLASSIFICATION 49 CFR 172.101: ORM-A

DEPARTMENT OF TRANSPORTATION LABELING REQUIREMENTS 49 CFR 172.101 AND SUBPART E: NONE

DEPARTMENT OF TRANSPORTATION PACKAGING REQUIREMENTS: 49 CFR 173.510 EXCEPTIONS: 49 CFR 173.505

TOXICITY

ANTIMONY POTASSIUM TARTRATE: TOXICITY DATA: 2 MG/KG ORAL-HUMAN LDLO; 115 MG/KG ORAL-RAT LD50; 600 MG/KG ORAL-MOUSE LDLO; 115 MG/KG ORAL-RABBIT LD50; 55 MG/KG SUBCUTANEOUS-MOUSE LD50; 1392 UG/KG INTRAVENOUS-HUMAN TDLO; 12 MG/KG/1 WEEK INTERMITTENT INTRAVENOUS-HUMAN LDLO; 249 MG/KG/9 DAYS INTERMITTENT INTRAVENOUS-MAN LD50; 45 MG/KG INTRAVENOUS-MOUSE LD50; 12 MG/KG INTRAVENOUS-RABBIT LD50; 11 MG/KG INTRAPERITONEAL-RAT LD50; 33 MG/KG INTRAPERITONEAL-MOUSE LD50; 15 MG/KG INTRAPERITONEAL-GUINEA PIG LD50; 33 MG/KG INTRAMUSCULAR-RAT LDLO; 55 MG/KG INTRAMUSCULAR-GUINEA PIG LDLO; MUTAGENIC DATA (RTECS). CARCINOGEN STATUS: NONE. LOCAL EFFECTS: IRRITANT- INHALATION, SKIN, AND EYES. ACUTE TOXICITY DATA: TOXIC BY INGESTION. TARGET EFFECTS: NO DATA AVAILABLE. AT INCREASED RISK FROM EXPOSURE: PERSONS WITH HEPATIC DISEASE. ADDITIONAL DATA: INTERACTIONS WITH MEDICATIONS HAVE BEEN REPORTED.

HEALTH EFFECTS AND FIRST AID

INHALATION: ANTIMONY POTASSIUM TARTRATE: IRRITANT. 80 MG(SB)/M3 IMMEDIATELY DANGEROUS TO LIFE OR HEALTH. **ACUTE EXPOSURE-** INHALATION MAY CAUSE MUCOUS MEMBRANE IRRITATION WITH SORE THROAT, COUGHING AND DYSPNEA. **CHRONIC EXPOSURE-** NO DATA AVAILABLE.

FIRST AID- REMOVE FROM EXPOSURE AREA TO FRESH AIR IMMEDIATELY. IF BREATHING HAS STOPPED, PERFORM ARTIFICIAL RESPIRATION. KEEP PERSON WARM AND AT REST. TREAT SYMPTOMATICALLY AND SUPPORTIVELY. GET MEDICAL ATTENTION IMMEDIATELY.

SKIN CONTACT: ANTIMONY POTASSIUM TARTRATE: IRRITANT. **ACUTE EXPOSURE-** CONTACT WITH ANTIMONY COMPOUNDS MAY CAUSE IRRITATION WITH REDNESS, PAIN AND POSSIBLE ULCERATION. **CHRONIC EXPOSURE-** REPEATED OR PROLONGED CONTACT WITH ANTIMONY COMPOUNDS MAY CAUSE DERMATITIS AND PAPULES, PUSTULES OR LESIONS ON EXPOSED MOIST AREAS OF THE BODY, RARELY INCLUDING THE FACIAL REGION.

FIRST AID- REMOVE CONTAMINATED CLOTHING AND SHOES IMMEDIATELY. WASH AFFECTED AREA WITH SOAP OR MILD DETERGENT AND LARGE AMOUNTS OF WATER UNTIL NO EVIDENCE OF CHEMICAL REMAINS (AT LEAST 15-20 MINUTES). IN CASE OF CHEMICAL BURNS, COVER AREA WITH STERILE, DRY DRESSING. BANDAGE SECURELY, BUT NOT TOO TIGHTLY. GET MEDICAL ATTENTION IMMEDIATELY.

EYE CONTACT: ANTIMONY POTASSIUM TARTRATE: IRRITANT. **ACUTE EXPOSURE-** CONTACT MAY CAUSE IRRITATION WITH REDNESS AND PAIN. KERATITIS AND ULCERATION HAVE BEEN REPORTED FROM EXPOSURE TO ANTIMONY COMPOUNDS. **CHRONIC EXPOSURE-** REPEATED OR PROLONGED CONTACT WITH IRRITANTS MAY CAUSE CONJUNCTIVITIS.

FIRST AID- WASH EYES IMMEDIATELY WITH LARGE AMOUNTS OF WATER, OCCASIONALLY LIFTING UPPER AND LOWER LIDS, UNTIL NO EVIDENCE OF CHEMICAL REMAINS (AT LEAST 15-20 MINUTES). CONTINUE IRRIGATING WITH NORMAL SALINE UNTIL THE PH HAS RETURNED TO NORMAL (30-60 MINUTES). COVER WITH STERILE BANDAGES. GET MEDICAL ATTENTION IMMEDIATELY.

INGESTION: ANTIMONY POTASSIUM TARTRATE: TOXIC. **ACUTE EXPOSURE-** INGESTION OF ANTIMONY COMPOUNDS MAY CAUSE VIOLENT IRRITATION OF THE NOSE, MOUTH, STOMACH AND INTESTINES, NAUSEA, VOMITING, SEVERE DIARRHEA WITH MUCOUS AND BLOOD AND ABDOMINAL CRAMPS. SLOW AND SHALLOW RESPIRATION, PULMONARY CONGESTION, MUSCULAR PAIN, SHOCK, COLLAPSE AND COMA MAY OCCUR. DEATH MAY OCCUR DUE TO CIRCULATORY AND RESPIRATORY FAILURE A FEW HOURS FOLLOWING INGESTION. HUMAN PATHOLOGIC FINDINGS MAY INCLUDE ULCERATIONS OF THE ESOPHAGUS AND STOMACH. IN SUBACUTE CASES, FATTY DEGENERATION OF THE LIVER, KIDNEY, AND HEART MAY BE PRESENT. **CHRONIC EXPOSURE-** REPEATED OR PROLONGED INGESTION OF ANTIMONY COMPOUNDS MAY CAUSE NAUSEA, ANOREXIA, HEADACHE, SLEEPLESSNESS, DIZZINESS AND LOWERED BODY TEMPERATURE. LIVER AND KIDNEY DEGENERATIVE CHANGES INCLUDING HEMORRHAGIC NEPHRITIS AND HEPATITIS WITH JAUNDICE ARE LATE MANIFESTATIONS. CHRONIC INCORPORATION OF ANTIMONY POTASSIUM TARTRATE AT 5 PPM INTO DRINKING WATER INCREASED THE MORTALITY RATE AND DECREASED SERUM GLUCOSE LEVELS IN RATS.

FIRST AID- REMOVE INGESTED ANTIMONY COMPOUNDS BY GASTRIC LAVAGE OR EMESIS. DO NOT PERFORM GASTRIC LAVAGE OR EMESIS IF VICTIM IS UNCONSCIOUS. GET MEDICAL ATTENTION IMMEDIATELY. (DREISBACH, HANDBOOK OF POISONING, 11TH ED.) TREATMENT SHOULD BE PERFORMED BY QUALIFIED MEDICAL PERSONNEL ONLY.

ANTIDOTE: THE FOLLOWING ANTIDOTE HAS BEEN RECOMMENDED. HOWEVER, THE DECISION AS TO WHETHER THE SEVERITY OF POISONING REQUIRES ADMINISTRATION OF ANY ANTIDOTE AND ACTUAL DOSE REQUIRED SHOULD BE MADE BY QUALIFIED MEDICAL PERSONNEL.

ANTIMONY POISONING: ADMINISTER DIMERCAPROL, 3 MG/KG (OR 0.3 ML/10 KG) EVERY 4 HOURS FOR THE FIRST 2 DAYS AND THEN 2 MG/KG EVERY 12 HOURS FOR A TOTAL OF 10 DAYS. DIMERCAPROL IS AVAILABLE AS A 10% SOLUTION IN OIL FOR INTRAMUSCULAR ADMINISTRATION (DREISBACH, HANDBOOK OF POISONING, 11TH ED.). ANTIDOTE SHOULD BE ADMINISTERED BY QUALIFIED MEDICAL PERSONNEL.

REACTIVITY

REACTIVITY: STABLE UNDER NORMAL TEMPERATURES AND PRESSURES.

INCOMPATIBILITIES: ANTIMONY POTASSIUM TARTRATE: ACACIA: INCOMPATIBLE. ACIDS: INCOMPATIBLE; MAY RELEASE HAZARDOUS AND TOXIC STIBINE. ALKALIES AND THEIR CARBONATES: INCOMPATIBLE. ANTIPYRINE: INCOMPATIBLE. ASTRINGENT INFUSIONS: INCOMPATIBLE. HALOGENATED ACIDS: INCOMPATIBLE. LEAD SALTS: INCOMPATIBLE. MERCURY BICHLORIDE: INCOMPATIBLE. OXIDIZERS: INCOMPATIBLE. TANNIC ACID: INCOMPATIBLE. TRIVALENT ANTIMONY AND PERCHLORIC ACID: EXPLOSIVE MIXTURE WHEN HOT.

DECOMPOSITION: THERMAL DECOMPOSITION PRODUCTS MAY INCLUDE TOXIC OXIDES OF ANTIMONY AND CARBON.

POLYMERIZATION: HAZARDOUS POLYMERIZATION HAS NOT BEEN REPORTED TO OCCUR UNDER NORMAL TEMPERATURES AND PRESSURES.

STORAGE AND DISPOSAL

OBSERVE ALL FEDERAL, STATE AND LOCAL REGULATIONS WHEN STORING OR DISPOSING OF THIS SUBSTANCE. FOR ASSISTANCE, CONTACT THE DISTRICT DIRECTOR OF THE ENVIRONMENTAL PROTECTION AGENCY.

STORAGE

STORE AWAY FROM INCOMPATIBLE SUBSTANCES.

CONDITIONS TO AVOID

AVOID CONTACT WITH ACIDS AND STRONG OXIDIZERS.

SPILL AND LEAK PROCEDURES

SOIL SPILL: DIG A HOLDING AREA SUCH AS PIT, POND OR LAGOON TO CONTAIN SPILLED MATERIAL. USE PROTECTIVE COVER SUCH AS A PLASTIC SHEET TO PREVENT DISSOLVING IN FIREFIGHTING WATER OR RAIN.

AIR SPILL: VAPORS OR DUST ARE IRRITATING OR TOXIC.

WATER SPILL: NEUTRALIZE WITH CAUSTIC SODA.

IF MATERIAL IS DISSOLVED, USE SODIUM SULFIDE SOLUTION TO PRECIPITATE HEAVY METALS.

USE MECHANICAL DREDGES OR LIFTS TO EXTRACT IMMOBILIZED MASSES OF POLLUTION AND PRECIPITATES.

ALLOW SPILLED MATERIAL TO AERATE.

OCCUPATIONAL SPILL: KEEP SPARKS, FLAME, AND OTHER SOURCES OF IGNITION AWAY. KEEP MATERIAL OUT OF WATER SOURCES AND SEWERS.

REPORTABLE QUANTITY (RQ): 100 POUNDS THE SUPERFUND AMENDMENTS AND REAUTHORIZATION ACT (SARA) SECTION 304 REQUIRES THAT A RELEASE EQUAL TO OR GREATER THAN THE REPORTABLE QUANTITY FOR THIS SUBSTANCE BE IMMEDIATELY REPORTED TO THE LOCAL EMERGENCY PLANNING COMMITTEE AND THE STATE EMERGENCY RESPONSE COMMISSION (40 CFR 355.40). IF THE RELEASE OF THIS SUBSTANCE IS REPORTABLE UNDER CERCLA SECTION 103, THE NATIONAL RESPONSE CENTER MUST BE NOTIFIED IMMEDIATELY AT (800) 424-8802 OR (202) 426-2675 IN THE METROPOLITAN WASHINGTON, D.C. AREA (40 CFR 302.6).

PROTECTIVE EQUIPMENT

VENTILATION: PROVIDE LOCAL EXHAUST OR PROCESS ENCLOSURE VENTILATION TO MEET PUBLISHED EXPOSURE LIMITS.

RESPIRATOR: THE FOLLOWING RESPIRATORS AND MAXIMUM USE CONCENTRATIONS ARE RECOMMENDATIONS BY THE U.S. DEPARTMENT OF HEALTH AND HUMAN SERVICES, NIOSH POCKET GUIDE TO CHEMICAL HAZARDS; NIOSH CRITERIA DOCUMENTS OR BY THE U.S. DEPARTMENT OF LABOR, 29 CFR 1910 SUBPART Z. THE SPECIFIC RESPIRATOR SELECTED MUST BE BASED ON CONTAMINATION LEVELS FOUND IN THE WORK PLACE, MUST NOT EXCEED THE WORKING LIMITS OF THE RESPIRATOR AND BE JOINTLY APPROVED BY THE NATIONAL INSTITUTE FOR OCCUPATIONAL SAFETY AND HEALTH AND THE MINE SAFETY AND HEALTH ADMINISTRATION (NIOSH-MSHA). ANTIMONY AND COMPOUNDS (AS SB):

FOR DUST OR MIST: 5 MG/M3- ANY DUST AND MIST RESPIRATOR, EXCEPT SINGLE USE AND QUARTER-MASK RESPIRATORS.

12.5 MG/M3- ANY POWERED AIR-PURIFYING RESPIRATOR WITH A DUST AND MIST FILTER.

FOR DUST, MIST OR FUME: 5 MG/M3- ANY SUPPLIED-AIR RESPIRATOR. ANY SELF-CONTAINED BREATHING APPARATUS.

12.5 MG/M3- ANY SUPPLIED-AIR RESPIRATOR OPERATED IN A CONTINUOUS FLOW MODE.

25 MG/M3- ANY AIR-PURIFYING FULL FACEPIECE RESPIRATOR WITH A HIGH-EFFICIENCY PARTICULATE FILTER. ANY POWERED AIR-PURIFYING RESPIRATOR WITH A TIGHT-FITTING FACEPIECE AND A HIGH-EFFICIENCY PARTICULATE FILTER. ANY SUPPLIED-AIR RESPIRATOR WITH A TIGHT-FITTING FACEPIECE OPERATED IN A CONTINUOUS FLOW MODE. ANY SELF-CONTAINED BREATHING APPARATUS WITH A FULL FACEPIECE. ANY SUPPLIED-AIR RESPIRATOR WITH A FULL FACEPIECE.

80 MG/M3- ANY SUPPLIED-AIR RESPIRATOR WITH A HALF-MASK AND OPERATED IN A PRESSURE-DEMAND OR OTHER POSITIVE PRESSURE MODE.

ESCAPE- ANY APPROPRIATE ESCAPE-TYPE SELF-CONTAINED BREATHING APPARATUS. ANY AIR-PURIFYING FULL FACEPIECE RESPIRATOR WITH A HIGH-EFFICIENCY PARTICULATE FILTER.

FOR FIREFIGHTING AND OTHER IMMEDIATELY DANGEROUS TO LIFE OR HEALTH CONDITIONS:

SELF-CONTAINED BREATHING APPARATUS WITH FULL FACEPIECE OPERATED IN PRESSURE-DEMAND OR OTHER POSITIVE PRESSURE MODE.

SUPPLIED-AIR RESPIRATOR WITH FULL FACEPIECE AND OPERATED IN PRESSURE-DEMAND OR OTHER POSITIVE PRESSURE MODE IN COMBINATION WITH AN AUXILIARY SELF-CONTAINED BREATHING APPARATUS OPERATED IN PRESSURE-DEMAND OR OTHER POSITIVE PRESSURE MODE.

CLOTHING: EMPLOYEE MUST WEAR APPROPRIATE PROTECTIVE (IMPERVIOUS) CLOTHING AND EQUIPMENT TO PREVENT REPEATED OR PROLONGED SKIN CONTACT WITH THIS SUBSTANCE.

GLOVES: EMPLOYEE MUST WEAR APPROPRIATE PROTECTIVE GLOVES TO PREVENT CONTACT WITH THIS SUBSTANCE.

EYE PROTECTION: EMPLOYEE MUST WEAR SPLASH-PROOF OR DUST-RESISTANT SAFETY GOGGLES TO PREVENT EYE CONTACT WITH THIS SUBSTANCE.

EMERGENCY EYE WASH: WHERE THERE IS ANY POSSIBILITY THAT AN EMPLOYEE'S EYES MAY BE EXPOSED TO THIS SUBSTANCE, THE EMPLOYER SHOULD PROVIDE AN EYE WASH FOUNTAIN WITHIN THE IMMEDIATE WORK AREA FOR EMERGENCY USE.

AUTHORIZED BY- OCCUPATIONAL HEALTH SERVICES, INC.

CREATION DATE: 02/08/90 ***REVISION DATE:*** 05/11/90

MATERIAL SAFETY DATA SHEET

OCCUPATIONAL HEALTH SERVICES, INC. EMERGENCY CONTACT:

AGRICULTURE AND PESTICIDE DIVISION JOHN S. BRANSFORD, JR. (615) 292-1180
450 SEVENTH AVENUE, SUITE 2407
NEW YORK, NEW YORK 10123
1-800-445-MSDS OR (212) 967-1100

SUBSTANCE IDENTIFICATION

CAS-NUMBER 86-88-4

SUBSTANCE: ANTU

TRADE NAMES/SYNONYMS: THIOUREA, 1-NAPHTHALENYL-; UREA, 1-(1-NAPHTHYL)-2-THIO-; 1-NAPHTHALENYLTHIOUREA; 1-(1-NAPHTHYL)-2-THIOUREA; ALPHA-NAPHTHYLTHIOCARBAMIDE; N-1-NAPHTHYLTHIOUREA; ALPHA-NAPHTHYLTHIOUREA; 1-NAPTHYLTHIOUREA; 1-(1-NAPHTHYL)THIOUREA; ALRATO; ANTURAT; BANTU; CHEMICAL 109; DIRAX; KRYSID; RATTRACK; SMEESANA; RCRA P072; UN 1651; C11H10N2S; PST01830

CHEMICAL FAMILY: NAPHTHALENE
THIOUREA

MOLECULAR FORMULA: H2-N-C-S-N-H-(1-C10-H7)

MOLECULAR WEIGHT: 202.27

CERCLA RATINGS (SCALE 0-3): HEALTH=3 FIRE=1 REACTIVITY=0 PERSISTENCE=1

NFPA RATINGS (SCALE 0-4): HEALTH=3 FIRE=1 REACTIVITY=0

COMPONENTS AND CONTAMINANTS

COMPONENT: ANTU ***PERCENT:*** 100.0
CAS# 86-88-4

OTHER CONTAMINANTS: TECHNICAL GRADES MAY CONTAIN 2-NAPHTHYLAMINE

EXPOSURE LIMITS: ANTU: 0.3 MG/M3 OSHA TWA 0.3 MG/M3 ACGIH TWA (SKIN) 500/10,000 POUNDS SARA SECTION 302 THRESHOLD PLANNING QUANTITY 100 POUNDS SARA SECTION 304 REPORTABLE QUANTITY 100 POUNDS CERCLA SECTION 103 REPORTABLE QUANTITY

BETA-NAPHTHYLAMINE: ACGIH A1-CONFIRMED HUMAN CARCINOGEN. NO EXPOSURE OR CONTACT BY ANY ROUTE- RESPIRATORY, SKIN, OR ORAL, AS DETECTED BY THE MOST SENSITIVE METHODS- SHALL BE PERMITTED.

10 POUNDS CERCLA SECTION 103 REPORTABLE QUANTITY SUBJECT TO SARA SECTION 313 ANNUAL TOXIC CHEMICAL RELEASE REPORTING SUBJECT TO CALIFORNIA PROPOSITION 65 CANCER AND/OR REPRODUCTIVE TOXICITY WARNING AND RELEASE REQUIREMENTS- (FEBRUARY 27, 1987)

PHYSICAL DATA

DESCRIPTION: ODORLESS, COLORLESS, CRYSTALLINE SOLID WITH A SLIGHTLY BITTER TASTE.

MELTING POINT: 388 F (198 C) ***SPECIFIC GRAVITY:*** >1.0

VAPOR PRESSURE: NEGLIGIBLE ***SOLUBILITY IN WATER:*** 0.06% @ 25 C

VAPOR DENSITY: 6.99

SOLVENT SOLUBILITY: SOLUBLE IN HOT ALCOHOL; MODERATELY SOLUBLE IN ACETONE, TRIETHYLENEGLYCOL; SLIGHTLY SOLUBLE IN MOST ORGANIC SOLVENTS.

FIRE AND EXPLOSION DATA

FIRE AND EXPLOSION HAZARD: SLIGHT FIRE HAZARD WHEN EXPOSED TO HEAT OR FLAME.

FIREFIGHTING MEDIA: DRY CHEMICAL, CARBON DIOXIDE, HALON, WATER SPRAY OR STANDARD FOAM (1987 EMERGENCY RESPONSE GUIDEBOOK, DOT P 5800.4).
FOR LARGER FIRES, USE WATER SPRAY, FOG OR STANDARD FOAM (1987 EMERGENCY RESPONSE GUIDEBOOK, DOT P 5800.4).

FIREFIGHTING: MOVE CONTAINERS FROM FIRE AREA IF POSSIBLE (1987 EMERGENCY RESPONSE GUIDEBOOK, DOT P 5800.4, GUIDE PAGE 53).
EXTINGUISH USING AGENT SUITABLE FOR TYPE OF SURROUNDING FIRE. AVOID BREATHING VAPORS AND DUSTS. KEEP UPWIND.

TRANSPORTATION DATA

DEPARTMENT OF TRANSPORTATION HAZARD CLASSIFICATION 49 CFR 172.101: POISON B

DEPARTMENT OF TRANSPORTATION LABELING REQUIREMENTS 49 CFR 172.101 AND SUBPART E: POISON

DEPARTMENT OF TRANSPORTATION PACKAGING REQUIREMENTS: 49 CFR 173.365 EXCEPTIONS: 49 CFR 173.364

TOXICITY

ANTU: TOXICITY DATA: 6 MG/KG ORAL-RAT LD50; 5 MG/KG ORAL-MOUSE LD50; 4250 MG/KG ORAL-MONKEY LD50; 380 UG/KG ORAL-DOG LD50; 500 MG/KG ORAL-CAT LD50; 50 MG/KG ORAL-PIG LDLO; 2470 UG/KG INTRAPERITONEAL-RAT LD50; 10 MG/KG INTRAPERITONEAL-MOUSE LD50; 175 MG/KG INTRAPERITONEAL-MONKEY LD50; 16 MG/KG INTRAPERITONEAL-DOG LD50; 350 MG/KG INTRAPERITONEAL-GUINEA PIG LD50; 588 MG/KG UNREPORTED-MAN LDLO; MUTAGENIC DATA (RTECS); TUMORIGENIC DATA (RTECS). CARCINOGEN STATUS: HUMAN INADEQUATE EVIDENCE, ANIMAL INADEQUATE EVIDENCE (IARC GROUP 3). CASE REPORTS AND EPIDEMIOLOGICAL STUDIES HAVE SHOWN THAT OCCUPATIONAL EXPOSURE TO 2-NAPHTHYLAMINE, EITHER ALONE OR AS AN IMPURITY IN OTHER COMPOUNDS, IS CAUSALLY ASSOCIATED WITH THE OCCURRENCE OF BLADDER CANCER. ACUTE TOXICITY LEVEL: HIGHLY TOXIC BY INGESTION. TARGET EFFECTS: POISONING MAY AFFECT THE RESPIRATORY SYSTEM AND LIVER. AT INCREASED RISK FROM EXPOSURE: PERSONS WITH IMPAIRED PULMONARY FUNCTION OR LIVER DISEASE.

BETA-NAPHTHYLAMINE: TOXICITY DATA: 727 MG/KG ORAL-RAT LD50; 200 MG/KG INTRAPERITONEAL-MOUSE LD50; 500 MG/KG UNREPORTED-DOG LDLO; MUTAGENIC DATA (RTECS); TUMORIGENIC DATA (RTECS). CARCINOGEN STATUS: OSHA CARCINOGEN; KNOWN HUMAN CARCINOGEN (NTP); ANIMAL SUFFICIENT EVIDENCE, HUMAN SUFFICIENT EVIDENCE (IARC GROUP 1). ORAL ADMINISTRATION OF BETA-NAPHTHYLAMINE RESULTED IN THE PRODUCTION OF BLADDER CANCERS IN DOGS, MONKEYS, AND HAMSTERS AND LIVER CANCERS IN MICE. EPIDEMIOLOGICAL STUDIES HAVE SHOWN THAT OCCUPATIONAL EXPOSURE TO BETA-NAPHTHYLAMINE IS STRONGLY ASSOCIATED WITH THE OCCURRENCE OF BLADDER CANCER. ACUTE TOXICITY LEVEL: MODERATELY TOXIC BY INGESTION. TARGET EFFECTS: POISONING MAY AFFECT THE BLOOD, BLADDER, LIVER AND KIDNEYS.

HEALTH EFFECTS AND FIRST AID

INHALATION: ANTU: 100 MG/M3 IMMEDIATELY DANGEROUS TO LIFE OR HEALTH.
ACUTE EXPOSURE- DUST CAUSES PULMONARY EDEMA AND PLEURAL EFFUSION IN ANIMALS. **CHRONIC EXPOSURE-** NO DATA AVAILABLE.

FIRST AID- REMOVE FROM EXPOSURE AREA TO FRESH AIR IMMEDIATELY. IF BREATHING HAS STOPPED, PERFORM ARTIFICIAL RESPIRATION. KEEP PERSON WARM AND AT REST. TREAT SYMPTOMATICALLY AND SUPPORTIVELY. GET MEDICAL ATTENTION IMMEDIATELY.

SKIN CONTACT: ANTU: **ACUTE EXPOSURE-** REPORTED NOT TO BE IRRITATING TO HUMAN SKIN. **CHRONIC EXPOSURE-** CONTACT ECZEMA WAS REPORTED FROM ONE CASE OF OCCUPATIONAL EXPOSURE TO ANTU. ONE STUDY INDICATED THAT ABSORPTION OF THIOUREA PRODUCTS THROUGH THE SKIN MAY RESULT IN DESTRUCTIVE CHANGES IN THE THYROID GLANDS.

FIRST AID- REMOVE CONTAMINATED CLOTHING AND SHOES IMMEDIATELY. WASH AFFECTED AREA WITH SOAP OR MILD DETERGENT AND LARGE AMOUNTS OF WATER UNTIL NO EVIDENCE OF CHEMICAL REMAINS (APPROXIMATELY 15-20 MINUTES). GET MEDICAL ATTENTION IMMEDIATELY.

EYE CONTACT: ANTU: **ACUTE EXPOSURE-** NO DATA AVAILABLE. **CHRONIC EXPOSURE-** NO DATA AVAILABLE.

FIRST AID- WASH EYES IMMEDIATELY WITH LARGE AMOUNTS OF WATER OR NORMAL SALINE, OCCASIONALLY LIFTING UPPER AND LOWER LIDS, UNTIL NO EVIDENCE OF CHEMICAL REMAINS (APPROXIMATELY 15-20 MINUTES). GET MEDICAL ATTENTION IMMEDIATELY.

INGESTION: ANTU: HIGHLY TOXIC. **ACUTE EXPOSURE-** MAY CAUSE VOMITING, DYSPNEA, CYANOSIS, AND PULMONARY RALES. IN ANIMALS, EFFECTS FROM POISONING INCLUDED LABORED RESPIRATION, MUSCULAR WEAKNESS, ALTERED CARBOHYDRATE METABOLISM, OLIGURIA AND ANURIA FROM GLOMERULAR INJURY, MILD LIVER DAMAGE, AND DEATH DUE TO PULMONARY EDEMA AND PLEURAL EFFUSION. **CHRONIC EXPOSURE-** REPEATED SUBLETHAL DOSES IN ANIMALS PRODUCED IMPAIRED WEIGHT GAIN, DEFORMITIES OF THE LEGS AND FEET, INHIBITION OF HAIR GROWTH AND DEFECTIVE HAIR PIGMENTATION, THYROID HYPERPLASIA, HYPERCHOLESTEROLEMIA, FATTY DEGENERATION OF THE LIVER, BILE DUCT PROLIFERATION, AND ALTERED ENZYMES ACTIVITIES.

FIRST AID- ADMINISTER SYRUP OF IPECAC, THEN 1-2 GLASSES OF WATER, TO INDUCE VOMITING. FOLLOW WITH ACTIVATED CHARCOAL, THEN 0.25 GM/KG SODIUM OR MAGNESIUM SULFATE IN 1-6 OUNCES WATER. GET MEDICAL ATTENTION. FIRST AID SHOULD BE ADMINISTERED BY QUALIFIED MEDICAL PERSONNEL. (MORGAN, RECOGNITION AND MANAGEMENT OF PESTICIDE POISONINGS, 3RD EDITION)

ANTIDOTE: NO SPECIFIC ANTIDOTE. TREAT SYMPTOMATICALLY AND SUPPORTIVELY.

REACTIVITY

REACTIVITY: STABLE UNDER NORMAL TEMPERATURES AND PRESSURES.

INCOMPATIBILITIES: ANTU: OXIDIZERS (STRONG): FIRE AND EXPLOSION HAZARD.

DECOMPOSITION: THERMAL DECOMPOSITION MAY RELEASE TOXIC OXIDES OF NITROGEN, SULFUR AND CARBON.

POLYMERIZATION: HAZARDOUS POLYMERIZATION HAS NOT BEEN REPORTED TO OCCUR UNDER NORMAL TEMPERATURES AND PRESSURES.

STORAGE AND DISPOSAL

OBSERVE ALL FEDERAL, STATE AND LOCAL REGULATIONS WHEN STORING OR DISPOSING OF THIS SUBSTANCE. FOR ASSISTANCE, CONTACT THE DISTRICT DIRECTOR OF THE ENVIRONMENTAL PROTECTION AGENCY.

STORAGE

STORE IN ACCORDANCE WITH 40 CFR 165 RECOMMENDED PROCEDURES FOR THE DISPOSAL AND STORAGE OF PESTICIDES AND PESTICIDE CONTAINERS.

THRESHOLD PLANNING QUANTITY (TPQ): THE SUPERFUND AMENDMENTS AND REAUTHORIZATION ACT (SARA) SECTION 302 REQUIRES THAT EACH FACILITY WHERE ANY EXTREMELY HAZARDOUS SUBSTANCE IS PRESENT IN A QUANTITY EQUAL TO OR GREATER THAN THE TPQ ESTABLISHED FOR THAT SUBSTANCE NOTIFY THE STATE EMERGENCY RESPONSE COMMISSION FOR THE STATE IN WHICH IT IS LOCATED. SECTION 303 OF SARA REQUIRES THESE FACILITIES TO PARTICIPATE IN LOCAL EMERGENCY RESPONSE PLANNING (40 CFR 355.30).

STORE AWAY FROM INCOMPATIBLE SUBSTANCES.

DISPOSAL

DISPOSAL MUST BE IN ACCORDANCE WITH STANDARDS APPLICABLE TO GENERATORS OF HAZARDOUS WASTE, 40CFR 262. EPA HAZARDOUS WASTE NUMBER P072.

CONDITIONS TO AVOID

MAY BURN BUT DOES NOT IGNITE READILY.

SPILL AND LEAK PROCEDURES

OCCUPATIONAL SPILL: DO NOT TOUCH SPILLED MATERIAL. STOP LEAK IF YOU CAN DO IT WITHOUT RISK. FOR SMALL SPILLS, TAKE UP WITH SAND OR OTHER ABSORBENT MATERIAL AND PLACE INTO CONTAINERS FOR LATER DISPOSAL. FOR SMALL DRY SPILLS, WITH A CLEAN SHOVEL PLACE MATERIAL INTO CLEAN, DRY CONTAINER AND COVER. MOVE CONTAINERS FROM SPILL AREA. FOR LARGER SPILLS, DIKE FAR AHEAD OF SPILL FOR LATER DISPOSAL. KEEP UNNECESSARY PEOPLE AWAY. ISOLATE HAZARD AREA AND DENY ENTRY.

REPORTABLE QUANTITY (RQ): 100 POUNDS THE SUPERFUND AMENDMENTS AND REAUTHORIZATION ACT (SARA) SECTION 304 REQUIRES THAT A RELEASE EQUAL TO OR GREATER THAN THE REPORTABLE QUANTITY FOR THIS SUBSTANCE BE IMMEDIATELY REPORTED TO THE LOCAL EMERGENCY PLANNING COMMITTEE AND THE STATE EMERGENCY RESPONSE COMMISSION (40 CFR 355.40). IF THE RELEASE OF THIS SUBSTANCE IS REPORTABLE UNDER CERCLA SECTION 103, THE NATIONAL RESPONSE CENTER MUST BE NOTIFIED IMMEDIATELY AT (800) 424-8802 OR (202) 426-2675 IN THE METROPOLITAN WASHINGTON, D.C. AREA (40 CFR 302.6).

PROTECTIVE EQUIPMENT

VENTILATION: PROVIDE LOCAL EXHAUST OR PROCESS ENCLOSURE VENTILATION TO MEET PUBLISHED EXPOSURE LIMITS.

RESPIRATOR: THE FOLLOWING RESPIRATORS AND MAXIMUM USE CONCENTRATIONS ARE RECOMMENDATIONS BY THE U.S. DEPARTMENT OF HEALTH AND HUMAN SERVICES, NIOSH POCKET GUIDE TO CHEMICAL HAZARDS; NIOSH CRITERIA DOCUMENTS OR BY THE U.S. DEPARTMENT OF LABOR, 29 CFR 1910 SUBPART Z. THE SPECIFIC RESPIRATOR SELECTED MUST BE BASED ON CONTAMINATION LEVELS FOUND IN THE WORK PLACE, MUST NOT EXCEED THE WORKING LIMITS OF THE RESPIRATOR AND BE JOINTLY APPROVED BY THE NATIONAL INSTITUTE FOR OCCUPATIONAL SAFETY AND HEALTH AND THE MINE SAFETY AND HEALTH ADMINISTRATION (NIOSH-MSHA).

ANTU: 3 MG/M3- ANY CHEMICAL CARTRIDGE RESPIRATOR WITH ORGANIC VAPOR CARTRIDGE(S) IN COMBINATION WITH A DUST, MIST, AND FUME FILTER. ANY SUPPLIED-AIR RESPIRATOR. ANY SELF-CONTAINED BREATHING APPARATUS.

7.5 MG/M3- ANY POWERED AIR-PURIFYING RESPIRATOR WITH ORGANIC VAPOR CARTRIDGE(S) IN COMBINATION WITH A DUST, MIST, AND FUME FILTER. ANY SUPPLIED-AIR RESPIRATOR OPERATED IN A CONTINUOUS FLOW MODE.

15 MG/M3- ANY CHEMICAL CARTRIDGE RESPIRATOR WITH A FULL FACEPIECE AND ORGANIC VAPOR CARTRIDGE(S) IN COMBINATION WITH A HIGH-EFFICIENCY PARTICULATE FILTER. ANY POWERED AIR-PURIFYING RESPIRATOR WITH A TIGHT-FITTING FACEPIECE AND ORGANIC VAPOR CARTRIDGE(S) IN COMBINATION WITH A HIGH-EFFICIENCY PARTICULATE FILTER. ANY SUPPLIED-AIR RESPIRATOR WITH A TIGHT-FITTING FACEPIECE OPERATED IN A CONTINUOS FLOW MODE. ANY SELF-CONTAINED BREATHING APPARATUS WITH A FULL FACEPIECE. ANY SUPPLIED-AIR RESPIRATOR WITH A FULL FACEPIECE. ANY AIR-PURIFYING FULL FACEPIECE RESPIRATOR (GAS MASK) WITH A CHIN-STYLE OR FRONT- OR BACK-MOUNTED ORGANIC VAPOR CANISTER HAVING A HIGH-EFFICIENCY PARTICULATE FILTER.

100 MG/M3- ANY SUPPLIED-AIR RESPIRATOR WITH A HALF-MASK AND OPERATED IN A PRESSURE-DEMAND OR OTHER POSITIVE PRESSURE MODE.

ESCAPE- ANY AIR-PURIFYING FULL FACEPIECE RESPIRATOR (GAS MASK) WITH A CHIN-STYLE OR FRONT- OR BACK-MOUNTED ORGANIC VAPOR CANISTER HAVING A HIGH-EFFICIENCY PARTICULATE FILTER. ANY APPROPRIATE ESCAPE-TYPE SELF-CONTAINED BREATHING APPARATUS.

FOR FIREFIGHTING AND OTHER IMMEDIATELY DANGEROUS TO LIFE OR HEALTH CONDITIONS:

SELF-CONTAINED BREATHING APPARATUS WITH FULL FACEPIECE OPERATED IN PRESSURE-DEMAND OR OTHER POSITIVE PRESSURE MODE.

SUPPLIED-AIR RESPIRATOR WITH FULL FACEPIECE AND OPERATED IN PRESSURE-DEMAND OR OTHER POSITIVE PRESSURE MODE IN COMBINATION WITH AN AUXILIARY SELF-CONTAINED BREATHING APPARATUS OPERATED IN PRESSURE-DEMAND OR OTHER POSITIVE PRESSURE MODE.

CLOTHING: EMPLOYEE MUST WEAR APPROPRIATE PROTECTIVE (IMPERVIOUS) CLOTHING AND EQUIPMENT TO PREVENT ANY POSSIBILITY OF SKIN CONTACT WITH THIS SUBSTANCE.

GLOVES: EMPLOYEE MUST WEAR APPROPRIATE PROTECTIVE GLOVES TO PREVENT CONTACT WITH THIS SUBSTANCE.

EYE PROTECTION: EMPLOYEE MUST WEAR SPLASH-PROOF OR DUST-RESISTANT SAFETY GOGGLES AND A FACESHIELD TO PREVENT CONTACT WITH THIS SUBSTANCE.

EMERGENCY WASH FACILITIES: WHERE THERE IS ANY POSSIBILITY THAT AN EMPLOYEE'S EYES AND/OR SKIN MAY BE EXPOSED TO THIS SUBSTANCE, THE EMPLOYER SHOULD PROVIDE AN EYE WASH FOUNTAIN AND QUICK DRENCH SHOWER WITHIN THE IMMEDIATE WORK AREA FOR EMERGENCY USE.

AUTHORIZED BY- OCCUPATIONAL HEALTH SERVICES, INC.

CREATION DATE: 10/04/89 ***REVISION DATE:*** 07/12/90

MATERIAL SAFETY DATA SHEET

OCCUPATIONAL HEALTH SERVICES, INC.
AGRICULTURE AND PESTICIDE DIVISION
450 SEVENTH AVENUE, SUITE 2407
NEW YORK, NEW YORK 10123
1-800-445-MSDS OR (212) 967-1100

EMERGENCY CONTACT:
JOHN S. BRANSFORD, JR. (615) 292-1180

SUBSTANCE IDENTIFICATION

CAS-NUMBER 140-57-8

SUBSTANCE: ARAMITE

TRADE NAMES/SYNONYMS: ARATRON; 2-(P-TERT-BUTYLPHENOXY)ISOPROPYL 2-CHLOROETHYL SULPHITE; NIAGARAMITE; ORTHO-MITE; CES; BETA-CHLOROETHYL-BETA-(P-TERT-BUTYLPHENOXY)-ALPHA-METHYLETHYL SULPHITE; ARAMIT; 88R; PST01850

CHEMICAL FAMILY: AROMATIC

MOLECULAR FORMULA: C15-H23-CL-O4-S

MOLECULAR WEIGHT: 334.89

CERCLA RATINGS (SCALE 0-3): HEALTH=3 FIRE=0 REACTIVITY=0 PERSISTENCE=2

NFPA RATINGS (SCALE 0-4): HEALTH=3 FIRE=0 REACTIVITY=0

COMPONENTS AND CONTAMINANTS

COMPONENT: ARAMITE ***PERCENT:*** 100
CAS# 140-57-8

OTHER CONTAMINANTS: NONE

EXPOSURE LIMITS: ARAMITE: NO OCCUPATIONAL EXPOSURE LIMITS ESTABLISHED BY OSHA, ACGIH, OR NIOSH.

SUBJECT TO CALIFORNIA PROPOSITION 65 CANCER AND/OR REPRODUCTIVE TOXICITY WARNING AND RELEASE REQUIREMENTS- (JULY 1, 1987)

PHYSICAL DATA

DESCRIPTION: CLEAR, LIGHT-COLORED OIL. ***BOILING POINT:*** 347 F (175 C) @ 0.1 MMHG

MELTING POINT: -35 F (-37 C) ***SPECIFIC GRAVITY:*** 1.148-1.152

VAPOR PRESSURE: <10 MMHG @ 25 C ***SOLUBILITY IN WATER:*** INSOLUBLE

SOLVENT SOLUBILITY: COMMON ORGANIC SOLVENTS

FIRE AND EXPLOSION DATA

FIRE AND EXPLOSION HAZARD: NEGLIGIBLE FIRE HAZARD WHEN EXPOSED TO HEAT OR FLAME.

FIREFIGHTING MEDIA: DRY CHEMICAL, CARBON DIOXIDE, HALON, WATER SPRAY OR STANDARD FOAM (1987 EMERGENCY RESPONSE GUIDEBOOK, DOT P 5800.4). FOR LARGER FIRES, USE WATER SPRAY, FOG OR STANDARD FOAM (1987 EMERGENCY RESPONSE GUIDEBOOK, DOT P 5800.4).

FIREFIGHTING: MOVE CONTAINER FROM FIRE AREA IF POSSIBLE. DO NOT SCATTER SPILLED MATERIAL WITH HIGH PRESSURE WATER STREAMS. DIKE FIRE CONTROL WATER FOR LATER DISPOSAL (1987 EMERGENCY RESPONSE GUIDEBOOK, DOT P 5800.4, GUIDE PAGE 31).

USE AGENTS SUITABLE FOR TYPE OF SURROUNDING FIRE. AVOID BREATHING HAZARDOUS VAPORS, KEEP UPWIND.

TOXICITY

ARAMITE: TOXICITY DATA: 429 MG/KG ORAL-HUMAN LDLO; 3900 MG/KG ORAL-RAT LD50; 3900 MG/KG ORAL-GUINEA PIG LD50; 200 MG/KG INTRAPERITONEAL-MOUSE LDLO; REPRODUCTIVE EFFECTS DATA (RTECS); TUMORIGENIC DATA (RTECS). CARCINOGEN STATUS: ANIMAL SUFFICIENT EVIDENCE (IARC GROUP-2B). PROLONGED ORAL ADMINISTRATION OF ARAMITE PRODUCED LIVER TUMORS IN THE RAT AND CARCINOMAS OF THE GALL BLADDER AND BILIARY DUCTS IN DOGS. LOCAL EFFECTS: IRRITANT- INHALATION, SKIN, AND EYES. ACUTE TOXICITY LEVEL: MODERATELY TOXIC BY INGESTION. TARGET EFFECTS: CENTRAL NERVOUS SYSTEM DEPRESSANT. POISONING MAY AFFECT THE LIVER AND KIDNEYS.

HEALTH EFFECTS AND FIRST AID

INHALATION: ARAMITE: IRRITANT. **ACUTE EXPOSURE-** MAY CAUSE IRRITATION TO THE MUCOUS MEMBRANES. **CHRONIC EXPOSURE-** NO DATA AVAILABLE.

FIRST AID- REMOVE FROM EXPOSURE AREA TO FRESH AIR IMMEDIATELY. IF BREATHING HAS STOPPED, PERFORM ARTIFICIAL RESPIRATION. KEEP PERSON WARM AND AT REST. TREAT SYMPTOMATICALLY AND SUPPORTIVELY. GET MEDICAL ATTENTION IMMEDIATELY.

SKIN CONTACT: ARAMITE: IRRITANT. **ACUTE EXPOSURE-** MAY CAUSE IRRITATION. **CHRONIC EXPOSURE-** REPEATED OR PROLONGED SKIN CONTACT WITH IRRITANTS MAY CAUSE DERMATITIS.

FIRST AID- REMOVE CONTAMINATED CLOTHING AND SHOES IMMEDIATELY. WASH AFFECTED AREA WITH SOAP OR MILD DETERGENT AND LARGE AMOUNTS OF WATER UNTIL NO EVIDENCE OF CHEMICAL REMAINS (APPROXIMATELY 15-20 MINUTES). GET MEDICAL ATTENTION IMMEDIATELY.

EYE CONTACT: ARAMITE: IRRITANT. **ACUTE EXPOSURE-** MAY CAUSE IRRITATION. **CHRONIC EXPOSURE-** REPEATED OR PROLONGED CONTACT WITH IRRITANTS MAY CAUSE CONJUNCTIVITIS.

FIRST AID- WASH EYES IMMEDIATELY WITH LARGE AMOUNTS OF WATER OR NORMAL SALINE, OCCASIONALLY LIFTING UPPER AND LOWER LIDS, UNTIL NO EVIDENCE OF CHEMICAL REMAINS (APPROXIMATELY 15-20 MINUTES). GET MEDICAL ATTENTION IMMEDIATELY.

INGESTION: ARAMITE: NARCOTIC/CARCINOGEN. **ACUTE EXPOSURE-** A LARGE ORAL DOSE MAY CAUSE CENTRAL NERVOUS SYSTEM DEPRESSION WITH HEADACHE, DIZZINESS, TREMORS, DROWSINESS, UNCONSCIOUSNESS, AND COMA. LIVER AND KIDNEY INJURY MAY OCCUR. AUTOPSY FINDINGS IN EXPERIMENTAL ANIMALS REVEALED A HEMORRHAGIC SYNDROME INVOLVING THE LUNGS. **CHRONIC EXPOSURE-** PROLONGED INGESTION HAS INDUCED HEPATIC ADENOMAS AND GALL BLADDER ADENOCARCINOMAS IN EXPERIMENTAL ANIMALS. EFFECTS ON THE NEWBORN HAVE BEEN REPORTED FROM ORAL ADMINISTRATION TO RATS FOR 12 WEEKS.

FIRST AID- INDUCE VOMITING AND FOLLOW WITH GASTRIC LAVAGE, SALINE CATHARTICS, AND FORCING OF FLUIDS. (TOXICOLOGY OF DRUGS AND CHEMICALS, DEICHMANN, 1969). DO NOT MAKE AN UNCONSCIOUS PERSON VOMIT. GET MEDICAL ATTENTION IMMEDIATELY.

ANTIDOTE: NO SPECIFIC ANTIDOTE. TREAT SYMPTOMATICALLY AND SUPPORTIVELY.

REACTIVITY

REACTIVITY: STABLE UNDER NORMAL TEMPERATURES AND PRESSURES.

INCOMPATIBILITIES: ARAMITE: NO DATA AVAILABLE.

DECOMPOSITION: THERMAL DECOMPOSITION MAY RELEASE TOXIC AND/OR HAZARDOUS GASES.
DECOMPOSITION OCCURS SLOWLY IN SUNLIGHT WITH FORMATION OF SULFUR DIOXIDE.

POLYMERIZATION: NO DATA AVAILABLE.

STORAGE AND DISPOSAL

OBSERVE ALL FEDERAL, STATE AND LOCAL REGULATIONS WHEN STORING OR DISPOSING OF THIS SUBSTANCE. FOR ASSISTANCE, CONTACT THE DISTRICT DIRECTOR OF THE ENVIRONMENTAL PROTECTION AGENCY.

CONDITIONS TO AVOID

MAY BURN BUT DOES NOT IGNITE READILY. AVOID CONTACT WITH STRONG OXIDIZERS, EXCESSIVE HEAT, SPARKS, OR OPEN FLAME.

SPILL AND LEAK PROCEDURES

WATER SPILL: THE CALIFORNIA SAFE DRINKING WATER AND TOXIC ENFORCEMENT ACT OF 1986 (PROPOSITION 65) PROHIBITS CONTAMINATING ANY KNOWN SOURCE OF DRINKING WATER WITH SUBSTANCES KNOWN TO CAUSE CANCER AND/OR REPRODUCTIVE TOXICITY.

OCCUPATIONAL SPILL: STOP LEAK IF YOU CAN DO IT WITHOUT RISK. FOR SMALL SPILLS, TAKE UP WITH SAND OR OTHER ABSORBENT MATERIAL AND PLACE INTO CLEAN, DRY CONTAINERS FOR LATER DISPOSAL. KEEP UNNECESSARY PEOPLE AWAY. ISOLATE HAZARD AREA AND DENY ENTRY.

PROTECTIVE EQUIPMENT

VENTILATION: PROVIDE LOCAL EXHAUST OR PROCESS ENCLOSURE VENTILATION SYSTEM.

RESPIRATOR: THE FOLLOWING RESPIRATORS ARE RECOMMENDED BASED ON INFORMATION FOUND IN THE PHYSICAL DATA, TOXICITY AND HEALTH EFFECTS SECTIONS. THEY ARE RANKED IN ORDER FROM MINIMUM TO MAXIMUM RESPIRATORY PROTECTION. THE SPECIFIC RESPIRATOR SELECTED MUST BE BASED ON CONTAMINATION LEVELS FOUND IN THE WORK PLACE, MUST NOT EXCEED THE WORKING LIMITS OF THE RESPIRATOR AND BE JOINTLY APPROVED BY THE NATIONAL INSTITUTE FOR OCCUPATIONAL SAFETY AND HEALTH AND THE MINE SAFETY AND HEALTH ADMINISTRATION (NIOSH-MSHA).
TYPE 'C' SUPPLIED-AIR RESPIRATOR WITH A FULL FACEPIECE OPERATED IN PRESSURE-DEMAND OR OTHER POSITIVE PRESSURE MODE OR WITH A FULL FACEPIECE, HELMET OR HOOD OPERATED IN CONTINOUS-FLOW MODE.
SELF-CONTAINED BREATHING APPARATUS WITH A FULL FACEPIECE OPERATED IN PRESSURE-DEMAND OR OTHER POSITIVE PRESSURE MODE.
FOR FIREFIGHTING AND OTHER IMMEDIATELY DANGEROUS TO LIFE OR HEALTH CONDITIONS:
SELF-CONTAINED BREATHING APPARATUS WITH FULL FACEPIECE OPERATED IN PRESSURE-DEMAND OR OTHER POSITIVE PRESSURE MODE.
SUPPLIED-AIR RESPIRATOR WITH FULL FACEPIECE AND OPERATED IN PRESSURE-DEMAND OR OTHER POSITIVE PRESSURE MODE IN COMBINATION WITH AN AUXILIARY SELF-CONTAINED BREATHING APPARATUS OPERATED IN PRESSURE-DEMAND OR OTHER POSITIVE PRESSURE MODE.

CLOTHING: EMPLOYEE MUST WEAR APPROPRIATE PROTECTIVE (IMPERVIOUS) CLOTHING AND EQUIPMENT TO PREVENT REPEATED OR PROLONGED SKIN CONTACT WITH THIS SUBSTANCE.

GLOVES: EMPLOYEE MUST WEAR APPROPRIATE PROTECTIVE GLOVES TO PREVENT CONTACT WITH THIS SUBSTANCE.

EYE PROTECTION: EMPLOYEE MUST WEAR SPLASH-PROOF OR DUST-RESISTANT SAFETY GOGGLES TO PREVENT EYE CONTACT WITH THIS SUBSTANCE.
EMERGENCY EYE WASH: WHERE THERE IS ANY POSSIBILITY THAT AN EMPLOYEE'S EYES MAY BE EXPOSED TO THIS SUBSTANCE, THE EMPLOYER SHOULD PROVIDE AN EYE WASH FOUNTAIN WITHIN THE IMMEDIATE WORK AREA FOR EMERGENCY USE.

AUTHORIZED BY- OCCUPATIONAL HEALTH SERVICES, INC.
CREATION DATE: 10/04/89 ***REVISION DATE:*** 07/12/90

MATERIAL SAFETY DATA SHEET

OCCUPATIONAL HEALTH SERVICES, INC.
AGRICULTURE AND PESTICIDE DIVISION
450 SEVENTH AVENUE, SUITE 2407
NEW YORK, NEW YORK 10123
1-800-445-MSDS OR (212) 967-1100

EMERGENCY CONTACT:
JOHN S. BRANSFORD, JR. (615) 292-1180

SUBSTANCE IDENTIFICATION

CAS-NUMBER 7778-39-4

SUBSTANCE: **ARSENIC ACID**

TRADE NAMES/SYNONYMS: ARSENATE; DESICCANT L-10; HI-YIELD DESICCANT H-10; ORTHOARSENIC ACID; ZOTOX; STCC 4923106; UN 1553; RCRA P010; PST01990

CHEMICAL FAMILY: INORGANIC ACID

MOLECULAR FORMULA: AS-H3-O4

MOLECULAR WEIGHT: 141.95

CERCLA RATINGS (SCALE 0-3): HEALTH=3 FIRE=0 REACTIVITY=0 PERSISTENCE=3

NFPA RATINGS (SCALE 0-4): HEALTH=3 FIRE=0 REACTIVITY=0

COMPONENTS AND CONTAMINANTS

COMPONENT: ARSENIC ACID ***PERCENT:*** 100
CAS# 7778-39-4

OTHER CONTAMINANTS: NONE

EXPOSURE LIMITS: ARSENIC ACID: 10 UG(AS)/M3 OSHA TWA 200 UG(AS)M3 ACGIH TWA 2 UG(AS)/M3 NIOSH RECOMMENDED 15 MINUTE CEILING
1 POUND CERCLA SECTION 103 REPORTABLE QUANTITY SUBJECT TO SARA SECTION 313 ANNUAL TOXIC CHEMICAL RELEASE REPORTING SUBJECT TO

CALIFORNIA PROPOSITION 65 CANCER AND/OR REPRODUCTIVE TOXICITY WARNING AND RELEASE REQUIREMENTS- (FEBRUARY 27, 1987)

PHYSICAL DATA

DESCRIPTION: ODORLESS, COLORLESS OR WHITE CRYSTALS. ***MELTING POINT:*** 205 F (96 C)

SPECIFIC GRAVITY: 2.2 ***SOLUBILITY IN WATER:*** SOLUBLE

SOLVENT SOLUBILITY: SOLUBLE IN ALCOHOL, GLYCEROL

FIRE AND EXPLOSION DATA

FIRE AND EXPLOSION HAZARD: SLIGHT FIRE HAZARD WHEN EXPOSED TO HEAT OR FLAME.

FLASH POINT: NONFLAMMABLE

FIREFIGHTING MEDIA: DRY CHEMICAL, CARBON DIOXIDE, HALON, WATER SPRAY OR STANDARD FOAM (1987 EMERGENCY RESPONSE GUIDEBOOK, DOT P 5800.4). FOR LARGER FIRES, USE WATER SPRAY, FOG OR STANDARD FOAM (1987 EMERGENCY RESPONSE GUIDEBOOK, DOT P 5800.4).

FIREFIGHTING: MOVE CONTAINERS FROM FIRE AREA IF POSSIBLE. FIGHT FIRE FROM MAXIMUM DISTANCE. STAY AWAY FROM STORAGE TANK ENDS. DIKE FIRE CONTROL WATER FOR LATER DISPOSAL. DO NOT SCATTER MATERIAL (1987 EMERGENCY RESPONSE GUIDEBOOK, DOT P 5800.4, GUIDE PAGE 55).
USE AGENT SUITABLE FOR TYPE OF FIRE; DO NOT USE WATER ON MATERIAL. FOR LARGE FIRES USE FLOODING QUANTITIES OF WATER AS SPRAY AND FOG. AVOID BREATHING CORROSIVE VAPORS, KEEP UPWIND.

TRANSPORTATION DATA

DEPARTMENT OF TRANSPORTATION HAZARD CLASSIFICATION 49 CFR 172.101: POISON B

DEPARTMENT OF TRANSPORTATION LABELING REQUIREMENTS 49 CFR 172.101 AND SUBPART E: POISON

DEPARTMENT OF TRANSPORTATION PACKAGING REQUIREMENTS: 49 CFR 173.366 EXCEPTIONS: 49 CFR 173.364

TOXICITY

ARSENIC ACID: TOXICITY DATA: ANHYDROUS: 48 MG/KG ORAL-RAT LD50; 10 MG/KG ORAL-DOG LDLO; 5 MG/KG ORAL-RABBIT LDLO; 100 MG/KG ORAL-PIGEON LDLO; 125 MG/KG ORAL-CHICKEN LDLO; MUTAGENIC DATA (RTECS); REPRODUCTIVE EFFECTS DATA (RTECS). HEMIHYDRATE: 6 MG/KG INTRAVENOUS-RABBIT LD50. CARCINOGEN STATUS: OSHA CARCINOGEN; KNOWN HUMAN CARCINOGEN (NTP); HUMAN SUFFICIENT EVIDENCE, ANIMAL LIMITED EVIDENCE (IARC GROUP-1). AN INCREASED INCIDENCE OF SKIN AND LUNG CANCER HAS BEEN ASSOCIATED WITH INORGANIC ARSENIC COMPOUNDS THROUGH MEDICAL TREATMENT, CONTAMINATED DRINKING WATER OR OCCUPATIONAL EXPOSURE. CANCERS AT OTHER SITES HAVE ALSO BEEN REPORTED, BUT A CLEAR ASSOCIATION HAS NOT BEEN CONFIRMED. LOCAL EFFECTS: IRRITANT- SKIN. ACUTE TOXICITY LEVELS: HIGHLY TOXIC BY INGESTION. TARGET EFFECTS: SENSITIZER- SKIN; NEUROTOXIN. POISONING MAY AFFECT THE LIVER, KIDNEYS, BONE MARROW, CENTRAL NERVOUS AND GASTROINTESTINAL SYSTEMS.

HEALTH EFFECTS AND FIRST AID

INHALATION: ARSENIC ACID: IRRITANT/NEUROTOXIN/CARCINOGEN. **ACUTE EXPOSURE**- INHALATION OF ARSENIC MAY CAUSE IRRITATION. DELAYED EFFECTS ARE PULMONARY EDEMA, RESTLESSNESS, DYSPNEA, CYANOSIS, DYSPHAGIA, COUGHING, FROTHY SPUTUM, RALES, AND HEMATURIA. **CHRONIC EXPOSURE**- REPEATED OR PROLONGED EXPOSURE MAY RESULT IN PERIPHERAL NEUROPATHY, OPTIC NEURITIS, ANESTHESIAS, AND PARESTHESIAS, AS INDICATED BY ATAXIA, TREMORS, INCOORDINATION, AND CONFUSION. TRACHIOBRONCHITIS AND SIGNS OF PULMONARY INSUFFICIENCY DUE TO EMPHYSEMA, BRONZING OF THE SKIN, ALOPECIA, LOCAL EDEMA, AND DERMATITIS MAY OCCUR. SOME ARSENIC COMPOUNDS MAY CAUSE RHINO-PHARYNGO-LARYNGITIS AND NASAL SEPTUM PERFORATION, NAUSEA, VOMITING, ABDOMINAL CRAMPS, DIARRHEA, SALIVATION, WEIGHT LOSS, HEMOLYTIC OR APLASTIC ANEMIA, LEUKOPENIA, NEPHRITIS, CIRRHOSIS, CARDIAC FAILURE. ARSENIC AND INORGANIC ARSENIC COMPOUNDS ARE CONSIDERED TO BE LUNG CARCINOGENS.

FIRST AID- REMOVE FROM EXPOSURE AREA TO FRESH AIR IMMEDIATELY. IF BREATHING HAS STOPPED, GIVE ARTIFICIAL RESPIRATION. MAINTAIN AIRWAY AND BLOOD PRESSURE AND ADMINISTER OXYGEN IF AVAILABLE. KEEP AFFECTED PERSON WARM AND AT REST. TREAT SYMPTOMATICALLY AND SUPPORTIVELY. ADMINISTRATION OF OXYGEN SHOULD BE PERFORMED BY QUALIFIED PERSONNEL. GET MEDICAL ATTENTION IMMEDIATELY.

SKIN CONTACT: ARSENIC ACID: IRRITANT/SENSITIZER/CARCINOGEN. **ACUTE EXPOSURE**- ARSENIC AND COMPOUNDS IRRITATE THE SKIN. SENSITIZATION DERMATITIS MAY OCCUR IN PREVIOUSLY EXPOSED PERSONS, CHARACTERIZED BY ECZEMA WITH SCALING AND HYPERPIGMENTATION OF THE SKIN AND HYPERKERATOSIS OF THE PALMS OF THE HANDS AND THE SOLES OF THE FEET. INORGANIC ARSENIC COMPOUNDS ARE SLIGHTLY ABSORBED THROUGH THE SKIN WHEN ADMINISTERED IN A LIPID VEHICLE. POISONING HAS CAUSED ALOPECIA, BRONZING OF THE SKIN, AND BRITTLE NAILS. **CHRONIC EXPOSURE**- REPEATED EXPOSURE MAY RESULT IN SENSITIZATION DERMATITIS. INORGANIC ARSENIC AND COMPOUNDS ARE SKIN CARCINOGENS.

FIRST AID- REMOVE CONTAMINATED CLOTHING AND SHOES IMMEDIATELY. WASH AFFECTED AREA WITH SOAP OR MILD DETERGENT AND LARGE AMOUNTS OF WATER UNTIL NO EVIDENCE OF CHEMICAL REMAINS (APPROXIMATELY 15-20 MINUTES). GET MEDICAL ATTENTION IMMEDIATELY.

EYE CONTACT: ARSENIC ACID: IRRITANT. **ACUTE EXPOSURE**- MAY CAUSE IRRITATION AND CONJUNCTIVITIS. POISONING HAS CAUSED EDEMA OF THE EYELIDS, CORNEAL NECROSIS, AND VISUAL DISTURBANCES. **CHRONIC EXPOSURE**- REPEATED OR PROLONGED EYE CONTACT WITH ARSENIC DUST MAY CAUSE CONJUNCTIVITIS. POISONING FROM INHALATION OR INGESTION HAS CAUSED OPTIC NEURITIS.

FIRST AID- WASH EYES IMMEDIATELY WITH LARGE AMOUNTS OF WATER OR NORMAL SALINE, OCCASIONALLY LIFTING UPPER AND LOWER LIDS, UNTIL NO EVIDENCE OF CHEMICAL REMAINS (APPROXIMATELY 15-20 MINUTES). GET MEDICAL ATTENTION IMMEDIATELY.

INGESTION: ARSENIC ACID: NEUROTOXIN/CARCINOGEN. **ACUTE EXPOSURE**- NON-FATAL DOSES MAY CAUSE RESTLESSNESS, NAUSEA, VOMITING, HEADACHE, DIZZINESS, CHILLS, CRAMPS, IRRITABILITY, AND PARALYSIS. JAUNDICE, OLIGURIA, AND ANURIA MAY OCCUR WITHIN 1-3 DAYS. FATAL DOSES MAY CAUSE GASTROINTESTINAL DISTURBANCES, BURNING PAIN IN THE THROAT, VOMITING, WATERY OR BLOODY DIARRHEA WITH MUCOUS, HYPOTENSION, WEAKNESS, CONVULSIONS, COMA AND DEATH FROM CIRCULATORY FAILURE. THERE IS EVIDENCE THAT ARSENIC COMPOUNDS MAY CROSS THE PLACENTAL BARRIER. RATS SHOWED FERTILITY EFFECTS WITH PRE-IMPLANTATION AND POST-IMPLANTATION MORTALITIES FOLLOWING ORAL ADMINISTRATION. **CHRONIC EXPOSURE**- CHRONIC POISONING MAY AFFECT THE CENTRAL NERVOUS SYSTEM, SKIN, GASTROINTESTINAL TRACT, CARDIOVASCULAR SYSTEM, KIDNEYS AND LIVER. ARSENIC MAY CAUSE CANCER OF THE LUNGS, LIVER, LARYNX, LYMPHATIC SYSTEM, OR VISCERA. IN ONE EPIDEMIOLOGICAL STUDY, SKIN CANCER WAS POSITIVELY CORRELATED WITH HIGH ARSENIC LEVELS IN DRINKING WATER.

FIRST AID- REMOVE BY GASTRIC LAVAGE OR EMESIS. FOLLOW WITH A SALINE CATHARTIC. MAINTAIN BLOOD PRESSURE, AIRWAY, AND GIVE OXYGEN IF RESPIRATION IS DEPRESSED. DO NOT PERFORM GASTRIC LAVAGE OR EMESIS IF VICTIM IS UNCONSCIOUS. GET MEDICAL ATTENTION IMMEDIATELY. (DREISBACH, HANDBOOK OF POISONING, 12TH ED.) ADMINISTRATION OF GASTRIC LAVAGE OR OXYGEN SHOULD BE PERFORMED BY QUALIFIED MEDICAL PERSONNEL.

ANTIDOTE: THE FOLLOWING ANTIDOTE HAS BEEN RECOMMENDED. HOWEVER, THE DECISION AS TO WHETHER THE SEVERITY OF POISONING REQUIRES ADMINISTRATION OF ANY ANTIDOTE AND ACTUAL DOSE REQUIRED SHOULD BE MADE BY QUALIFIED MEDICAL PERSONNEL.
ARSENIC POISONING: GIVE DIMERCAPROL, 3 MG/KG (OR 0.3 ML/KG) EVERY 4 HOURS FOR 2 DAYS AND THEN 2 MG/KG EVERY 2 HOURS FOR A TOTAL OF 10 DAYS. DIMERCAPROL IS AVAILABLE AS A 10% SOLUTION IN OIL FOR INTRAMUSCULAR ADMINISTRATION. NEXT, GIVE PENICILLAMINE, UP TO 100 MG/KG/DAY (MAXIMUM 1 G/DAY) DIVIDED INTO 4 DOSES FOR NO LONGER THAN 1 WEEK. IF A LONGER ADMINISTRATION PERIOD IS WARRANTED, DOSAGE SHOULD NOT EXCEED 40 MG/KG/DAY. GIVE THE DRUG ORALLY HALF AN HOUR BEFORE MEALS. DISCONTINUE ANTIDOTE WHEN URINE ARSENIC LEVEL FALLS BELOW 50 UG/24 HR. (DREISBACH, HANDBOOK OF POISONING, 12TH ED.). ANITDOTE SHOULD BE ADMINISTERED BY QUALIFIED MEDICAL PERSONNEL.

REACTIVITY

REACTIVITY: STABLE UNDER NORMAL TEMPERATURES AND PRESSURES.

INCOMPATIBILITIES: NONE KNOWN.

DECOMPOSITION: MAY RELEASE TOXIC AND HAZARDOUS ARSENIC FUMES UNDER THERMAL DECOMPOSITION.

POLYMERIZATION: HAZARDOUS POLYMERIZATION HAS NOT BEEN REPORTED TO OCCUR UNDER NORMAL TEMPERATURES AND PRESSURES.

STORAGE AND DISPOSAL

OBSERVE ALL FEDERAL, STATE AND LOCAL REGULATIONS WHEN STORING OR DISPOSING OF THIS SUBSTANCE. FOR ASSISTANCE, CONTACT THE DISTRICT DIRECTOR OF THE ENVIRONMENTAL PROTECTION AGENCY.

****DISPOSAL****

DISPOSAL MUST BE IN ACCORDANCE WITH STANDARDS APPLICABLE TO GENERATORS OF HAZARDOUS WASTE, 40CFR 262. EPA HAZARDOUS WASTE NUMBER P010.

CONDITIONS TO AVOID

MAY BURN BUT DOES NOT IGNITE READILY. CONTAINERS MAY EXPLODE IN HEAT OF FIRE.

SPILL AND LEAK PROCEDURES

WATER SPILL: THE CALIFORNIA SAFE DRINKING WATER AND TOXIC ENFORCEMENT ACT OF 1986 (PROPOSITION 65) PROHIBITS CONTAMINATING ANY KNOWN SOURCE OF DRINKING WATER WITH SUBSTANCES KNOWN TO CAUSE CANCER AND/OR REPRODUCTIVE TOXICITY.

OCCUPATIONAL SPILL: DO NOT TOUCH SPILLED MATERIAL. STOP LEAK IF YOU CAN DO IT WITHOUT RISK. USE WATER SPRAY TO REDUCE VAPORS. FOR SMALL SPILLS, TAKE UP WITH SAND OR OTHER ABSORBENT MATERIAL AND PLACE INTO CONTAINERS FOR LATER DISPOSAL. FOR SMALL DRY SPILLS, WITH A CLEAN SHOVEL PLACE MATERIAL INTO CLEAN, DRY CONTAINERS AND COVER. MOVE CONTAINERS FROM SPILL AREA. FOR LARGER SPILLS, DIKE FAR AHEAD OF SPILL FOR LATER DISPOSAL. KEEP UNNECESSARY PEOPLE AWAY. ISOLATE HAZARD AREA AND DENY ENTRY. VENTILATE CLOSED SPACES BEFORE ENTERING.
REPORTABLE QUANTITY (RQ): 1 POUND THE SUPERFUND AMENDMENTS AND REAUTHORIZATION ACT (SARA) SECTION 304 REQUIRES THAT A RELEASE EQUAL TO OR GREATER THAN THE REPORTABLE QUANTITY FOR THIS SUBSTANCE BE IMMEDIATELY REPORTED TO THE LOCAL EMERGENCY PLANNING COMMITTEE AND THE STATE EMERGENCY RESPONSE COMMISSION (40 CFR 355.40). IF THE RELEASE OF THIS SUBSTANCE IS REPORTABLE UNDER CERCLA SECTION 103, THE NATIONAL RESPONSE CENTER MUST BE NOTIFIED IMMEDIATELY AT (800) 424-8802 OR (202) 426-2675 IN THE METROPOLITAN WASHINGTON, D.C. AREA (40 CFR 302.6).

PROTECTIVE EQUIPMENT

VENTILATION: PROVIDE LOCAL EXHAUST OR PROCESS ENCLOSURE VENTILATION TO MEET PUBLISHED EXPOSURE LIMITS.

RESPIRATOR: THE FOLLOWING RESPIRATORS ARE THE MINIMUM LEGAL REQUIREMENTS AS SET FORTH BY THE OCCUPATIONAL SAFETY AND HEALTH ADMINISTRATION FOUND IN 29 CFR 1910, SUBPART Z.
RESPIRATORY PROTECTION FOR INORGANIC ARSENIC PARTICULATE EXCEPT THOSE WITH SIGNIFICANT VAPOR PRESSURE
CONCENTRATION OF INORGANIC ARSENIC (AS) REQUIRED RESPIRATOR OR CONDITION OF USE
UNKNOWN OR GREATER OR LESS THAN 20,000 ANY FULL FACEPIECE, SELF UG/M3 (20 MG/M3) OR FIREFIGHTING CONTAINED BREATHING APPARATUS, OPERATED IN POSITIVE PRESSURE MODE.
NOT GREATER THAN 20,000 UG/M3 SUPPLIED-AIR RESPIRATOR WITH FULL (20 MG/M3) FACEPIECE, HOOD OR HELMET OR SUIT AND OPERATED IN POSITIVE PRESSURE MODE.
NOT GREATER THAN 10,000 UG/M3 POWERED-AIR PURIFYING RESPIRATORS (10 MG/M3) IN ALL INLET FACE COVERINGS WITH HIGH EFFICIENCY FILTERS; OR HALF-MASK SUPPLIED-AIR RESPIRATOR OPERATED IN POSITIVE PRESSURE MODE.
NOT GREATER THAN 500 UG/M3 FULL FACEPIECE AIR-PURIFYING RESPIRATOR EQUIPPED WITH HIGH EFFICIENCY FILTERS; OR ANY FULL FACEPIECE SUPPLIED-AIR RESPIRATOR; OR ANY FULL FACEPIECE SELF-CONTAINED BREATHING APPARATUS. NOT GREATER THAN 100 UG/M3 HALF-MASK AIR-PURIFYING RESPIRATOR EQUIPPED WITH HIGH EFFICIENCY FILTERS; OR ANY HALF-MASK SUPPLIED-AIR RESPIRATOR.
(HIGH EFFICIENCY FILTER- 99.97% EFFICIENCY AGAINST 0.3 MICROMETER MONODISPERSE DIETHYL-HEXYL PHTHALATE (DOP) PARTICLES)
RESPIRATORY PROTECTION FOR INORGANIC ARSENICALS (SUCH AS ARSENIC TRICHLORIDE OR ARSENIC PHOSPHIDE) WITH SIGNIFICANT VAPOR PRESSURE.
CONCENTRATION OF INORGANIC ARSENIC (AS) REQUIRED RESPIRATOR OR CONDITION OF USE
UNKNOWN OR GREATER OR LESS THAN 20,000 ANY FULL FACEPIECE SELF-CONTAINED UG/M3 (20 MG/M3) BREATHING APPARATUS OPERATED IN POSITIVE PRESSURE MODE.
NOT GREATER THAN 20,000 UG/M3 SUPPLIED-AIR RESPIRATOR WITH A (20 MG/M3) FULL FACEPIECE, HOOD OR HELMET OR SUIT OPERATED IN POSITIVE PRESSURE MODE.
NOT GREATER THAN 10,000 UG/M3 HALF-MASK SUPPLIED AIR RESPIRATOR (10 MG/M3) OPERATED IN POSITIVE PRESSURE MODE.
NOT GREATER THAN 500 UG/M3 FRONT- OR BACK-MOUNTED GAS MASK EQUIPPED WITH HIGH-EFFICIENCY FILTERS AND ACID GAS CANISTER; OR ANY FULL FACEPIECE SUPPLIED AIR RESPIRATOR; OR ANY FULL FACEPIECE SELF-CONTAINED BREATHING APPARATUS.
NOT GREATER THAN 100 UG/M3 HALF-MASK AIR-PURIFYING RESPIRATOR EQUIPPED WITH HIGH EFFICIENCY FILTER AND ACID GAS CARTRIDGE; OR ANY HALF-MASK SUPPLIED-AIR RESPIRATOR.
(HIGH EFFICIENCY FILTER- 99.97% EFFICIENCY AGAINST 0.3 MICROMETER MONODISPERSE DIETHYL-HEXYL PHTHALATE (DOP) PARTICLES) (HALF-MASK RESPIRATORS SHALL NOT BE USED FOR PROTECTION AGAINST ARSENIC TRICHLORIDE, AS IT IS RAPIDLY ABSORBED THROUGH THE SKIN).
THE FOLLOWING RESPIRATORS AND MAXIMUM USE CONCENTRATIONS ARE RECOMMENDATIONS BY THE U.S. DEPARTMENT OF HEALTH AND HUMAN SERVICES, NIOSH POCKET GUIDE TO CHEMICAL HAZARDS; NIOSH CRITERIA DOCUMENTS OR BY THE U.S. DEPARTMENT OF LABOR, 29 CFR 1910 SUBPART Z.
THE SPECIFIC RESPIRATOR SELECTED MUST BE BASED ON CONTAMINATION LEVELS FOUND IN THE WORK PLACE, MUST NOT EXCEED THE WORKING LIMITS OF THE RESPIRATOR AND BE JOINTLY APPROVED BY THE NATIONAL INSTITUTE FOR OCCUPATIONAL SAFETY AND HEALTH AND THE MINE SAFETY AND HEALTH ADMINISTRATION (NIOSH-MSHA).
AT ANY DETECTABLE CONCENTRATION:
SELF-CONTAINED BREATHING APPARATUS WITH FULL FACEPIECE OPERATED IN PRESSURE-DEMAND OR OTHER POSITIVE PRESSURE MODE. SUPPLIED-AIR RESPIRATOR WITH FULL FACEPIECE OPERATED IN PRESSURE-DEMAND OR OTHER POSITIVE PRESSURE MODE IN COMBINATION WITH AN AUXILIARY SELF-CONTAINED BREATHING APPARATUS OPERATED IN PRESSURE-DEMAND OR OTHER POSITIVE PRESSURE MODE.
ESCAPE- AIR-PURIFYING FULL FACEPIECE RESPIRATOR (GAS MASK) WITH A CHIN-STYLE OR FRONT- OR BACK-MOUNTED ORGANIC VAPOR CANISTER HAVING A HIGH-EFFICIENCY PARTICULATE FILTER. ESCAPE-TYPE SELF-CONTAINED BREATHING APPARATUS.
FOR FIREFIGHTING AND OTHER IMMEDIATELY DANGEROUS TO LIFE OR HEALTH CONDITIONS:
SELF-CONTAINED BREATHING APPARATUS WITH FULL FACEPIECE OPERATED IN PRESSURE-DEMAND OR OTHER POSITIVE PRESSURE MODE.
SUPPLIED-AIR RESPIRATOR WITH FULL FACEPIECE AND OPERATED IN PRESSURE-DEMAND OR OTHER POSITIVE PRESSURE MODE IN COMBINATION WITH AN AUXILIARY SELF-CONTAINED BREATHING APPARATUS OPERATED IN PRESSURE-DEMAND OR OTHER POSITIVE PRESSURE MODE.

CLOTHING: EMPLOYEE MUST WEAR APPROPRIATE PROTECTIVE (IMPERVIOUS) CLOTHING AND EQUIPMENT TO PREVENT REPEATED OR PROLONGED SKIN CONTACT WITH THIS SUBSTANCE.
ARSENIC (INORGANIC): PROTECTIVE CLOTHING SHOULD MEET THE REQUIREMENTS FOR PROTECTIVE WORK CLOTHING AND EQUIPMENT IN 29 CFR 1910.1018(J).

GLOVES: EMPLOYEE MUST WEAR APPROPRIATE PROTECTIVE GLOVES TO PREVENT CONTACT WITH THIS SUBSTANCE.
ARSENIC (INORGANIC): PROTECTIVE GLOVES SHOULD MEET THE REQUIREMENTS FOR PROTECTIVE WORK CLOTHING AND EQUIPMENT IN 29 CFR 1910.1018(J).

EYE PROTECTION: EMPLOYEE MUST WEAR SPLASH-PROOF OR DUST-RESISTANT SAFETY GOGGLES TO PREVENT EYE CONTACT WITH THIS SUBSTANCE.
EMERGENCY EYE WASH: WHERE THERE IS ANY POSSIBILITY THAT AN EMPLOYEE'S EYES MAY BE EXPOSED TO THIS SUBSTANCE, THE EMPLOYER SHOULD PROVIDE AN EYE WASH FOUNTAIN WITHIN THE IMMEDIATE WORK AREA FOR EMERGENCY USE.
ARSENIC (INORGANIC): PROTECTIVE EYE EQUIPMENT SHOULD MEET THE REQUIREMENTS FOR PROTECTIVE WORK CLOTHING AND EQUIPMENT IN 29 CFR 1910.1018(J).

AUTHORIZED BY- OCCUPATIONAL HEALTH SERVICES, INC.
CREATION DATE: 10/04/89 ***REVISION DATE:*** 07/12/90

MATERIAL SAFETY DATA SHEET

OCCUPATIONAL HEALTH SERVICES, INC.
AGRICULTURE AND PESTICIDE DIVISION
450 SEVENTH AVENUE, SUITE 2407
NEW YORK, NEW YORK 10123
1-800-445-MSDS OR (212) 967-1100

EMERGENCY CONTACT:
JOHN S. BRANSFORD, JR. (615) 292-1180

SUBSTANCE IDENTIFICATION

CAS-NUMBER 1303-28-2

SUBSTANCE: **ARSENIC PENTOXIDE, SOLID**

TRADE NAMES/SYNONYMS: ARSENIC ACID; ARSENIC ACID ANHYDRIDE; ARSENIC ANHYDRIDE; ARSENIC OXIDE (AS2O5); ARSENIC(V) OXIDE; DIARSENIC PENTOXIDE; ARSENIC OXIDE; RCRA P011; STCC 4923112; UN 1559; AS2O5; PST02020

CHEMICAL FAMILY: METAL

MOLECULAR FORMULA: AS2-O5

MOLECULAR WEIGHT: 229.84

CERCLA RATINGS (SCALE 0-3): HEALTH=3 FIRE=0 REACTIVITY=0 PERSISTENCE=3

NFPA RATINGS (SCALE 0-4): HEALTH=3 FIRE=0 REACTIVITY=0

COMPONENTS AND CONTAMINANTS

COMPONENT: ARSENIC PENTOXIDE ***PERCENT:*** 100
CAS# 1303-28-2

OTHER CONTAMINANTS: NONE

EXPOSURE LIMITS: ARSENIC, INORGANIC AND SOLUBLE COMPOUNDS: 10 UG(AS)/M3 OSHA TWA 200 UG(AS)/M3 ACGIH TWA 2 UG(AS)/M3 NIOSH RECOMMENDED 15 MINUTE CEILING
SUBJECT TO SARA SECTION 313 ANNUAL TOXIC CHEMICAL RELEASE REPORTING
SUBJECT TO CALIFORNIA PROPOSITION 65 CANCER AND/OR REPRODUCTIVE TOXICITY WARNING AND RELEASE REQUIREMENTS- (FEBRUARY 27, 1987)
ARSENIC PENTOXIDE, SOLID: 100/10,000 POUNDS SARA SECTION 302 THRESHOLD PLANNING QUANTITY 5000 POUNDS SARA SECTION 304 REPORTABLE QUANTITY 1 POUND CERCLA SECTION 103 REPORTABLE QUANTITY

PHYSICAL DATA

DESCRIPTION: ODORLESS, WHITE, AMORPHOUS, DELIQUESCENT POWDER
BOILING POINT: SUBLIMES ***MELTING POINT:*** 599 F (315 C)
SPECIFIC GRAVITY: 4.1 ***VAPOR PRESSURE:*** NOT AVAILABLE
SOLUBILITY IN WATER: SOLUBLE
SOLVENT SOLUBILITY: ALCOHOLS, ACIDS, ALKALIES

FIRE AND EXPLOSION DATA

FIRE AND EXPLOSION HAZARD: NEGLIGIBLE FIRE HAZARD WHEN EXPOSED TO HEAT OR FLAME.

FLASH POINT: NONCOMBUSTIBLE

FIREFIGHTING MEDIA: DRY CHEMICAL, CARBON DIOXIDE, HALON, WATER SPRAY OR STANDARD FOAM (1987 EMERGENCY RESPONSE GUIDEBOOK, DOT P 5800.4).
FOR LARGER FIRES, USE WATER SPRAY, FOG OR STANDARD FOAM (1987 EMERGENCY RESPONSE GUIDEBOOK, DOT P 5800.4).

FIREFIGHTING: MOVE CONTAINERS FROM FIRE AREA IF POSSIBLE (1987 EMERGENCY RESPONSE GUIDEBOOK, DOT P 5800.4, GUIDE PAGE 53).
USE AGENTS FOR TYPE OF FIRE, USE WATER IN FLOODING AMOUNTS AS FOG. AVOID BREATHING CORROSIVE AND POISONOUS DUSTS AND FUMES, KEEP UPWIND.

TRANSPORTATION DATA

DEPARTMENT OF TRANSPORTATION HAZARD CLASSIFICATION 49 CFR 172.101: POISON B
DEPARTMENT OF TRANSPORTATION LABELING REQUIREMENTS 49 CFR 172.101 AND SUBPART E: POISON
DEPARTMENT OF TRANSPORTATION PACKAGING REQUIREMENTS: 49 CFR 173.365 EXCEPTIONS: 49 CFR 173.364

TOXICITY

ARSENIC PENTOXIDE: TOXICITY DATA: 8 MG/KG ORAL-RAT LD50; 55 MG/KG ORAL-MOUSE LD50; 12,400 UG/KG SUBCUTANEOUS-RABBIT LDLO; 6 MG/KG INTRAVENOUS-RABBIT LDLO; 18 GM/KG PARENTERAL-FROG LDLO; MUTAGENIC DATA (RTECS); REPRODUCTIVE EFFECTS DATA (RTECS). CARCINOGEN STATUS: OSHA CARCINOGEN; KNOWN HUMAN CARCINOGEN (NTP); HUMAN SUFFICIENT EVIDENCE, ANIMAL LIMITED EVIDENCE (IARC GROUP-1). AN INCREASED INCIDENCE OF SKIN AND LUNG CANCER HAS BEEN ASSOCIATED WITH INORGANIC ARSENIC COMPOUNDS THROUGH MEDICAL TREATMENT, CONTAMINATED DRINKING WATER OR OCCUPATIONAL EXPOSURE. CANCERS AT OTHER SITES HAVE ALSO BEEN REPORTED, BUT A CLEAR ASSOCIATION HAS NOT BEEN CONFIRMED. LOCAL EFFECTS: IRRITANT- INHALATION, SKIN, AND EYES. ACUTE TOXICITY LEVEL: HIGHLY TOXIC BY INGESTION. TARGET EFFECTS: SENSITIZER- SKIN; NEUROTOXIN.

HEALTH EFFECTS AND FIRST AID

INHALATION: ARSENIC PENTOXIDE: IRRITANT/NEUROTOXIN/CARCINOGEN. **ACUTE EXPOSURE-** INHALATION OF ARSENIC MAY CAUSE IRRITATION. DELAYED EFFECTS ARE PULMONARY EDEMA, RESTLESSNESS, DYSPNEA, CYANOSIS, DYSPHAGIA, COUGHING, FROTHY SPUTUM, RALES, AND HEMATURIA. **CHRONIC EXPOSURE-** REPEATED OR PROLONGED EXPOSURE MAY RESULT IN PERIPHERAL NEUROPATHY, OPTIC NEURITIS, ANESTHESIAS, AND PARESTHESIAS, AS INDICATED BY ATAXIA, TREMORS, INCOORDINATION, AND CONFUSION. TRACHIOBRONCHITIS AND SIGNS OF PULMONARY INSUFFICIENCY DUE TO EMPHYSEMA, BRONZING OF THE SKIN, ALOPECIA, LOCAL EDEMA, AND DERMATITIS MAY OCCUR. SOME ARSENIC COMPOUNDS MAY CAUSE RHINO-PHARYNGO-LARYNGITIS AND NASAL SEPTUM PERFORATION, NAUSEA, VOMITING, ABDOMINAL CRAMPS, DIARRHEA, SALIVATION, WEIGHT LOSS, HEMOLYTIC OR APLASTIC ANEMIA, LEUKOPENIA, NEPHRITIS, CIRRHOSIS, CARDIAC FAILURE. ARSENIC AND INORGANIC ARSENIC COMPOUNDS ARE CONSIDERED TO BE SKIN AND LUNG CARCINOGENS.

FIRST AID- REMOVE FROM EXPOSURE AREA TO FRESH AIR IMMEDIATELY. IF BREATHING HAS STOPPED, GIVE ARTIFICIAL RESPIRATION. MAINTAIN AIRWAY AND BLOOD PRESSURE AND ADMINISTER OXYGEN IF AVAILABLE. KEEP AFFECTED PERSON WARM AND AT REST. TREAT SYMPTOMATICALLY AND SUPPORTIVELY. ADMINISTRATION OF OXYGEN SHOULD BE PERFORMED BY QUALIFIED PERSONNEL. GET MEDICAL ATTENTION IMMEDIATELY.

SKIN CONTACT: ARSENIC PENTOXIDE: IRRITANT/SENSITIZER. **ACUTE EXPOSURE-** ARSENIC AND COMPOUNDS IRRITATE THE SKIN. SENSITIZATION DERMATITIS MAY OCCUR IN PREVIOUSLY EXPOSED PERSONS, CHARACTERIZED BY ECZEMA WITH SCALING AND HYPERPIGMENTATION OF THE SKIN AND HYPERKERATOSIS OF THE PALMS OF THE HANDS AND THE SOLES OF THE FEET. INORGANIC ARSENIC COMPOUNDS ARE SLIGHTLY ABSORBED THROUGH THE SKIN WHEN ADMINISTERED IN A LIPID VEHICLE. POISONING HAS CAUSED ALOPECIA, BRONZING OF THE SKIN, AND BRITTLE NAILS. **CHRONIC EXPOSURE-** REPEATED EXPOSURE MAY RESULT IN SENSITIZATION DERMATITIS. INORGANIC ARSENIC AND COMPOUNDS ARE SKIN CARCINOGENS; IT IS UNCLEAR WHETHER SKIN CONTACT CONTRIBUTES TO THE CARCINOGENICITY NORMALLY ATTRIBUTED TO INHALATION AND INGESTION.

FIRST AID- REMOVE CONTAMINATED CLOTHING AND SHOES IMMEDIATELY. WASH AFFECTED AREA WITH SOAP OR MILD DETERGENT AND LARGE AMOUNTS OF WATER UNTIL NO EVIDENCE OF CHEMICAL REMAINS (APPROXIMATELY 15-20 MINUTES). GET MEDICAL ATTENTION IMMEDIATELY.

EYE CONTACT: ARSENIC PENTOXIDE: IRRITANT. **ACUTE EXPOSURE-** MAY CAUSE IRRITATION AND CONJUNCTIVITIS. POISONING HAS CAUSED EDEMA OF THE EYELIDS, CORNEAL NECROSIS, AND VISUAL DISTURBANCES. **CHRONIC EXPOSURE-** REPEATED OR PROLONGED EYE CONTACT WITH ARSENIC DUST MAY CAUSE CONJUNCTIVITIS. POISONING FROM INHALATION OR INGESTION HAS CAUSED OPTIC NEURITIS.

FIRST AID- WASH EYES IMMEDIATELY WITH LARGE AMOUNTS OF WATER OR NORMAL SALINE, OCCASIONALLY LIFTING UPPER AND LOWER LIDS, UNTIL NO EVIDENCE OF CHEMICAL REMAINS (APPROXIMATELY 15-20 MINUTES). GET MEDICAL ATTENTION IMMEDIATELY.

INGESTION: ARSENIC PENTOXIDE: NEUROTOXIN/CARCINOGEN/HIGHLY TOXIC. **ACUTE EXPOSURE-** HALF OF THE RATS FED 8 MG/KG DIED; HALF OF THE MICE FED 55 MG/KG DIED. NON-FATAL DOSES MAY CAUSE RESTLESSNESS, NAUSEA, VOMITING, HEADACHE, DIZZINESS, CHILLS, CRAMPS, IRRITABILITY, AND PARALYSIS. JAUNDICE, OLIGURIA, AND ANURIA MAY OCCUR WITHIN 1-3 DAYS. FATAL DOSES MAY CAUSE GASTROINTESTINAL DISTURBANCES, BURNING PAIN IN THE THROAT, VOMITING, WATERY OR BLOODY DIARRHEA WITH MUCOUS, HYPOTENSION, WEAKNESS, CONVULSIONS, COMA AND DEATH FROM CIRCULATORY FAILURE. THERE IS EVIDENCE THAT ARSENIC COMPOUNDS MAY CROSS THE PLACENTAL BARRIER. RATS SHOWED FERTILITY EFFECTS WITH PRE-IMPLANTATION AND POST-IMPLANTATION MORTALITIES FOLLOWING INJECTION OF ARSENIC PENTOXIDE. **CHRONIC EXPOSURE-** CHRONIC POISONING MAY AFFECT THE CENTRAL NERVOUS SYSTEM, SKIN, GASTROINTESTINAL TRACT, CARDIOVASCULAR SYSTEM, KIDNEYS AND LIVER. ARSENIC MAY CAUSE CANCER OF THE LUNGS, LIVER, LARYNX, LYMPHATIC SYSTEM, OR VISCERA. IN ONE EPIDEMIOLOGICAL STUDY, SKIN CANCER WAS POSITIVELY CORRELATED WITH HIGH ARSENIC LEVELS IN DRINKING WATER.

FIRST AID- REMOVE BY GASTRIC LAVAGE OR EMESIS. FOLLOW WITH A SALINE CATHARTIC. MAINTAIN BLOOD PRESSURE, AIRWAY, AND GIVE OXYGEN IF RESPIRATION IS DEPRESSED. DO NOT PERFORM GASTRIC LAVAGE OR EMESIS IF VICTIM IS UNCONSCIOUS. GET MEDICAL ATTENTION IMMEDIATELY. (DREISBACH, HANDBOOK OF POISONING, 12TH ED.) ADMINISTRATION OF GASTRIC LAVAGE OR OXYGEN SHOULD BE PERFORMED BY QUALIFIED MEDICAL PERSONNEL.

ANTIDOTE: THE FOLLOWING ANTIDOTE HAS BEEN RECOMMENDED. HOWEVER, THE DECISION AS TO WHETHER THE SEVERITY OF POISONING REQUIRES ADMINISTRATION OF ANY ANTIDOTE AND ACTUAL DOSE REQUIRED SHOULD BE MADE BY QUALIFIED MEDICAL PERSONNEL.
ARSENIC POISONING: GIVE DIMERCAPROL, 3 MG/KG (OR 0.3 ML/KG) EVERY 4 HOURS FOR 2 DAYS AND THEN 2 MG/KG EVERY 2 HOURS FOR A TOTAL OF 10 DAYS. DIMERCAPROL IS AVAILABLE AS A 10% SOLUTION IN OIL FOR INTRAMUSCULAR ADMINISTRATION. NEXT, GIVE PENICILLAMINE, UP TO 100 MG/KG/DAY (MAXIMUM 1 G/DAY) DIVIDED INTO 4 DOSES FOR NO LONGER THAN 1 WEEK. IF A LONGER ADMINISTRATION PERIOD IS WARRANTED, DOSAGE SHOULD NOT EXCEED 40 MG/KG/DAY. GIVE THE DRUG ORALLY HALF AN HOUR BEFORE MEALS. DISCONTINUE ANTIDOTE WHEN URINE ARSENIC LEVEL FALLS BELOW 50 UG/24 HR. (DREISBACH, HANDBOOK OF POISONING, 12TH ED.). ANITDOTE SHOULD BE ADMINISTERED BY QUALIFIED MEDICAL PERSONNEL.

REACTIVITY

REACTIVITY: STABLE UNDER NORMAL TEMPERATURES AND PRESSURES.

INCOMPATIBILITIES: ARSENIC PENTOXIDE: BROMINE PENTAFLUORIDE: VIOLENT REACTION. DIRUBIDIUM ACETYLIDE: VIOLENT REACTION. CHLORINE TRIFLUORIDE: VIOLENT REACTION. MERCURY: VIOLENT REACTION. FLUORINE: VIOLENT

REACTION. OXIDIZING MATERIALS: VIOLENT REACTION. ACTIVE METALS: VIOLENT REACTION. ACIDS: MAY RELEASE HIGHLY TOXIC ARSENIC ANHYDRIDE.

DECOMPOSITION: THERMAL DECOMPOSITION MAY RELEASE TOXIC OXIDES OF ARSENIC AND SODIUM AND HIGHLY TOXIC ARSINE GAS.

POLYMERIZATION: HAZARDOUS POLYMERIZATION HAS NOT BEEN REPORTED TO OCCUR UNDER NORMAL TEMPERATURES AND PRESSURES.

STORAGE AND DISPOSAL

OBSERVE ALL FEDERAL, STATE AND LOCAL REGULATIONS WHEN STORING OR DISPOSING OF THIS SUBSTANCE. FOR ASSISTANCE, CONTACT THE DISTRICT DIRECTOR OF THE ENVIRONMENTAL PROTECTION AGENCY.

STORAGE

THRESHOLD PLANNING QUANTITY (TPQ): THE SUPERFUND AMENDMENTS AND REAUTHORIZATION ACT (SARA) SECTION 302 REQUIRES THAT EACH FACILITY WHERE ANY EXTREMELY HAZARDOUS SUBSTANCE IS PRESENT IN A QUANTITY EQUAL TO OR GREATER THAN THE TPQ ESTABLISHED FOR THAT SUBSTANCE NOTIFY THE STATE EMERGENCY RESPONSE COMMISSION FOR THE STATE IN WHICH IT IS LOCATED. SECTION 303 OF SARA REQUIRES THESE FACILITIES TO PARTICIPATE IN LOCAL EMERGENCY RESPONSE PLANNING (40 CFR 355.30).

STORE AWAY FROM INCOMPATIBLE SUBSTANCES.

DISPOSAL

DISPOSAL MUST BE IN ACCORDANCE WITH STANDARDS APPLICABLE TO GENERATORS OF HAZARDOUS WASTE, 40CFR 262. EPA HAZARDOUS WASTE NUMBER P011.

ARSENIC - REGULATORY LEVEL: 5.0 MG/L MATERIALS WHICH CONTAIN THE ABOVE SUBSTANCE AT OR ABOVE THE REGULATORY LEVEL MEET THE EPA CHARACTERISTIC OF TOXICITY, AND MUST BE DISPOSED OF IN ACCORDANCE WITH 40 CFR PART 262. EPA HAZARDOUS WASTE NUMBER D004.

CONDITIONS TO AVOID

MAY BURN BUT DOES NOT IGNITE READILY.

SPILL AND LEAK PROCEDURES

SOIL SPILL: DO NOT HANDLE PACKAGES WITHOUT FULL PROTECTIVE EQUIPMENT. DIG A PIT, POND, LAGOON OR HOLDING AREA TO CONTAIN LIQUID OR SOLID MATERIAL. COVER SOLIDS WITH A PLASTIC SHEET TO PREVENT DISSOLVING IN RAIN OR FIREFIGHTING WATER.

WATER SPILL: NEUTRALIZE WITH AGRICULTURAL LIME, SLAKED LIME, CRUSHED LIMESTONE OR SODIUM BICARBONATE.

ADD FERRIC CHLORIDE TO SPILL.

USE MECHANICAL DREDGES OR LIFTS TO EXTRACT IMMOBILIZED MASSES OF POLLUTION AND PRECIPITATES.

THE CALIFORNIA SAFE DRINKING WATER AND TOXIC ENFORCEMENT ACT OF 1986 (PROPOSITION 65) PROHIBITS CONTAMINATING ANY KNOWN SOURCE OF DRINKING WATER WITH SUBSTANCES KNOWN TO CAUSE CANCER AND/OR REPRODUCTIVE TOXICITY.

OCCUPATIONAL SPILL: DO NOT TOUCH SPILLED MATERIAL. STOP LEAK IF YOU CAN DO IT WITHOUT RISK. FOR SMALL SPILLS, TAKE UP WITH SAND OR OTHER ABSORBENT MATERIAL AND PLACE INTO CONTAINERS FOR LATER DISPOSAL. FOR SMALL DRY SPILLS, WITH A CLEAN SHOVEL PLACE MATERIAL INTO CLEAN, DRY CONTAINER AND COVER. MOVE CONTAINERS FROM SPILL AREA. FOR LARGER SPILLS, DIKE FAR AHEAD OF SPILL FOR LATER DISPOSAL. KEEP UNNECESSARY PEOPLE AWAY. ISOLATE HAZARD AREA AND DENY ENTRY.

REPORTABLE QUANTITY (RQ): THE SUPERFUND AMENDMENTS AND REAUTHORIZATION ACT (SARA) SECTION 304 REQUIRES THAT A RELEASE EQUAL TO OR GREATER THAN THE REPORTABLE QUANTITY ESTABLISHED FOR THAT SUBSTANCE BE IMMEDIATELY REPORTED TO THE LOCAL EMERGENCY PLANNING COMMITTEE AND THE STATE EMERGENCY RESPONSE COMMISSION (40 CFR 355.40). IF THE RELEASE OF THIS SUBSTANCE IS REPORTABLE UNDER CERCLA SECTION 103, THE NATIONAL RESPONSE CENTER MUST BE NOTIFIED IMMEDIATELY AT (800) 424-8802 OR (202) 426-2675 IN THE METROPOLITAN WASHINGTON, D.C. AREA (40 CFR 302.6).

PROTECTIVE EQUIPMENT

VENTILATION: PROVIDE LOCAL EXHAUST OR PROCESS ENCLOSURE VENTILATION TO MEET PUBLISHED EXPOSURE LIMITS.

ARSENIC (INORGANIC): VENTILATION SHOULD MEET THE REQUIREMENTS IN 29 CFR 1910.1018(G).

RESPIRATOR: THE FOLLOWING RESPIRATORS ARE THE MINIMUM LEGAL REQUIREMENTS AS SET FORTH BY THE OCCUPATIONAL SAFETY AND HEALTH ADMINISTRATION FOUND IN 29 CFR 1910, SUBPART Z.

RESPIRATORY PROTECTION FOR INORGANIC ARSENIC PARTICULATE EXCEPT THOSE WITH SIGNIFICANT VAPOR PRESSURE

CONCENTRATION OF INORGANIC ARSENIC (AS) REQUIRED RESPIRATOR OR CONDITION OF USE

UNKNOWN OR GREATER OR LESS THAN 20,000 ANY FULL FACEPIECE, SELF UG/M3 (20 MG/M3) OR FIREFIGHTING CONTAINED BREATHING APPARATUS, OPERATED IN POSITIVE PRESSURE MODE.

NOT GREATER THAN 20,000 UG/M3 SUPPLIED-AIR RESPIRATOR WITH FULL (20 MG/M3) FACEPIECE, HOOD OR HELMET OR SUIT AND OPERATED IN POSITIVE PRESSURE MODE.

NOT GREATER THAN 10,000 UG/M3 POWERED-AIR PURIFYING RESPIRATORS (10 MG/M3) IN ALL INLET FACE COVERINGS WITH HIGH EFFICIENCY FILTERS; OR HALF-MASK SUPPLIED-AIR RESPIRATOR OPERATED IN POSITIVE PRESSURE MODE.

NOT GREATER THAN 500 UG/M3 FULL FACEPIECE AIR-PURIFYING RESPIRATOR EQUIPPED WITH HIGH EFFICIENCY FILTERS; OR ANY FULL FACEPIECE SUPPLIED-AIR RESPIRATOR; OR ANY FULL FACEPIECE SELF-CONTAINED BREATHING APPARATUS. NOT GREATER THAN 100 UG/M3 HALF-MASK AIR-PURIFYING RESPIRATOR EQUIPPED WITH HIGH EFFICIENCY FILTERS; OR ANY HALF-MASK SUPPLIED-AIR RESPIRATOR.

(HIGH EFFICIENCY FILTER- 99.97% EFFICIENCY AGAINST 0.3 MICROMETER MONODISPERSE DIETHYL-HEXYL PHTHALATE (DOP) PARTICLES)

RESPIRATORY PROTECTION FOR INORGANIC ARSENICALS (SUCH AS ARSENIC TRICHLORIDE OR ARSENIC PHOSPHIDE) WITH SIGNIFICANT VAPOR PRESSURE.

CONCENTRATION OF INORGANIC ARSENIC (AS) REQUIRED RESPIRATOR OR CONDITION OF USE

UNKNOWN OR GREATER OR LESS THAN 20,000 ANY FULL FACEPIECE SELF-CONTAINED UG/M3 (20 MG/M3) BREATHING APPARATUS OPERATED IN POSITIVE PRESSURE MODE.

NOT GREATER THAN 20,000 UG/M3 SUPPLIED-AIR RESPIRATOR WITH A (20 MG/M3) FULL FACEPIECE, HOOD OR HELMET OR SUIT OPERATED IN POSITIVE PRESSURE MODE.

NOT GREATER THAN 10,000 UG/M3 HALF-MASK SUPPLIED AIR RESPIRATOR (10 MG/M3) OPERATED IN POSITIVE PRESSURE MODE.

NOT GREATER THAN 500 UG/M3 FRONT- OR BACK-MOUNTED GAS MASK EQUIPPED WITH HIGH-EFFICIENCY FILTERS AND ACID GAS CANISTER; OR ANY FULL FACEPIECE SUPPLIED AIR RESPIRATOR; OR ANY FULL FACEPIECE SELF-CONTAINED BREATHING APPARATUS.

NOT GREATER THAN 100 UG/M3 HALF-MASK AIR-PURIFYING RESPIRATOR EQUIPPED WITH HIGH EFFICIENCY FILTER AND ACID GAS CARTRIDGE; OR ANY HALF-MASK SUPPLIED-AIR RESPIRATOR.

(HIGH EFFICIENCY FILTER- 99.97% EFFICIENCY AGA'NST 0.3 MICROMETER MONODISPERSE DIETHYL-HEXYL PHTHALATE (DOP) PARTICLES) (HALF-MASK RESPIRATORS SHALL NOT BE USED FOR PROTECTION AGAINST ARSENIC TRICHLORIDE, AS IT IS RAPIDLY ABSORBED THROUGH THE SKIN).

THE FOLLOWING RESPIRATORS AND MAXIMUM USE CONCENTRATIONS ARE RECOMMENDATIONS BY THE U.S. DEPARTMENT OF HEALTH AND HUMAN SERVICES, NIOSH POCKET GUIDE TO CHEMICAL HAZARDS; NIOSH CRITERIA DOCUMENTS OR BY THE U.S. DEPARTMENT OF LABOR, 29 CFR 1910 SUBPART Z.

THE SPECIFIC RESPIRATOR SELECTED MUST BE BASED ON CONTAMINATION LEVELS FOUND IN THE WORK PLACE, MUST NOT EXCEED THE WORKING LIMITS OF THE RESPIRATOR AND BE JOINTLY APPROVED BY THE NATIONAL INSTITUTE FOR OCCUPATIONAL SAFETY AND HEALTH AND THE MINE SAFETY AND HEALTH ADMINISTRATION (NIOSH-MSHA).

AT ANY DETECTABLE CONCENTRATION:

SELF-CONTAINED BREATHING APPARATUS WITH FULL FACEPIECE OPERATED IN PRESSURE-DEMAND OR OTHER POSITIVE PRESSURE MODE. SUPPLIED-AIR RESPIRATOR WITH FULL FACEPIECE OPERATED IN PRESSURE-DEMAND OR OTHER POSITIVE PRESSURE MODE IN COMBINATION WITH AN AUXILIARY SELF-CONTAINED BREATHING APPARATUS OPERATED IN PRESSURE-DEMAND OR OTHER POSITIVE PRESSURE MODE.

ESCAPE- AIR-PURIFYING FULL FACEPIECE RESPIRATOR (GAS MASK) WITH A CHIN-STYLE OR FRONT- OR BACK-MOUNTED ORGANIC VAPOR CANISTER HAVING A HIGH-EFFICIENCY PARTICULATE FILTER. ESCAPE-TYPE SELF-CONTAINED BREATHING APPARATUS.

FOR FIREFIGHTING AND OTHER IMMEDIATELY DANGEROUS TO LIFE OR HEALTH CONDITIONS:

SELF-CONTAINED BREATHING APPARATUS WITH FULL FACEPIECE OPERATED IN PRESSURE-DEMAND OR OTHER POSITIVE PRESSURE MODE.

SUPPLIED-AIR RESPIRATOR WITH FULL FACEPIECE AND OPERATED IN PRESSURE-DEMAND OR OTHER POSITIVE PRESSURE MODE IN COMBINATION WITH AN AUXILIARY SELF-CONTAINED BREATHING APPARATUS OPERATED IN PRESSURE-DEMAND OR OTHER POSITIVE PRESSURE MODE.

CLOTHING: EMPLOYEE MUST WEAR APPROPRIATE PROTECTIVE (IMPERVIOUS) CLOTHING AND EQUIPMENT TO PREVENT REPEATED OR PROLONGED SKIN CONTACT WITH THIS SUBSTANCE.

ARSENIC (INORGANIC): PROTECTIVE CLOTHING SHOULD MEET THE REQUIREMENTS FOR PROTECTIVE WORK CLOTHING AND EQUIPMENT IN 29 CFR 1910.1018(J).

GLOVES: EMPLOYEE MUST WEAR APPROPRIATE PROTECTIVE GLOVES TO PREVENT CONTACT WITH THIS SUBSTANCE.

ARSENIC (INORGANIC): PROTECTIVE GLOVES SHOULD MEET THE REQUIREMENTS FOR PROTECTIVE WORK CLOTHING AND EQUIPMENT IN 29 CFR 1910.1018(J).

EYE PROTECTION: EMPLOYEE MUST WEAR SPLASH-PROOF OR DUST-RESISTANT SAFETY GOGGLES TO PREVENT EYE CONTACT WITH THIS SUBSTANCE.
EMERGENCY EYE WASH: WHERE THERE IS ANY POSSIBILITY THAT AN EMPLOYEE'S EYES MAY BE EXPOSED TO THIS SUBSTANCE, THE EMPLOYER SHOULD PROVIDE AN EYE WASH FOUNTAIN WITHIN THE IMMEDIATE WORK AREA FOR EMERGENCY USE.
ARSENIC (INORGANIC): PROTECTIVE EYE EQUIPMENT SHOULD MEET THE REQUIREMENTS FOR PROTECTIVE WORK CLOTHING AND EQUIPMENT IN 29 CFR 1910.1018(J).

AUTHORIZED BY- OCCUPATIONAL HEALTH SERVICES, INC.
CREATION DATE: 10/04/89 ***REVISION DATE:*** 07/13/90

MATERIAL SAFETY DATA SHEET

OCCUPATIONAL HEALTH SERVICES, INC.
AGRICULTURE AND PESTICIDE DIVISION
450 SEVENTH AVENUE, SUITE 2407
NEW YORK, NEW YORK 10123
1-800-445-MSDS OR (212) 967-1100

EMERGENCY CONTACT:
JOHN S. BRANSFORD, JR. (615) 292-1180

SUBSTANCE IDENTIFICATION

CAS-NUMBER 1327-53-3
SUBSTANCE: ARSENIC TRIOXIDE, SOLID
TRADE NAMES/SYNONYMS: ARSENIC OXIDE (AS2O3); ARSENIC SESQUIOXIDE (AS2O3); ARSENIC TRIOXIDE; ARSENICUM ALBUM; ARSENIOUC OXIDE; ARSENIC OXIDE; ARSENOUS ACID; ARSENOUS ACID ANHYDRIDE; ARSENIC SESQUIOXIDE; WHITE ARSENIC; ARSENOUS TRIOXIDE; CRUDE ARSENIC; ARSENOUS OXIDE; ARSENIC(III) OXIDE; ARSENOUS OXIDE ANHYDRIDE; RCRA P012; STCC 493115; UN 1561; A-59; AS2O3; PST02070
CHEMICAL FAMILY: METAL OXIDE
MOLECULAR FORMULA: AS2-O3
MOLECULAR WEIGHT: 197.84
CERCLA RATINGS (SCALE 0-3): HEALTH=3 FIRE=0 REACTIVITY=0 PERSISTENCE=3
NFPA RATINGS (SCALE 0-4): HEALTH=3 FIRE=0 REACTIVITY=0

COMPONENTS AND CONTAMINANTS

COMPONENT: ARSENIC TRIOXIDE ***PERCENT:*** 100.0
CAS# 1327-53-3
OTHER CONTAMINANTS: NONE
EXPOSURE LIMITS: ARSENIC, INORGANIC AND SOLUBLE COMPOUNDS: 10 UG(AS)/M3 OSHA TWA 200 UG(AS)/M3 ACGIH TWA 2 UG(AS)/M3 NIOSH RECOMMENDED 15 MINUTE CEILING
SUBJECT TO SARA SECTION 313 ANNUAL TOXIC CHEMICAL RELEASE REPORTING
SUBJECT TO CALIFORNIA PROPOSITION 65 CANCER AND/OR REPRODUCTIVE TOXICITY WARNING AND RELEASE REQUIREMENTS- (FEBRUARY 27, 1987)
ARSENIC TRIOXIDE, SOLID: ACGIH A2-SUSPECTED HUMAN CARCINOGEN (PRODUCTION).
100/10,000 POUNDS SARA SECTION 302 THRESHOLD PLANNING QUANTITY 5000 POUNDS SARA SECTION 304 REPORTABLE QUANTITY 1 POUND CERCLA SECTION 103 REPORTABLE QUANTITY

PHYSICAL DATA

DESCRIPTION: ODORLESS, TASTELESS, WHITE OR COLORLESS AMORPHOUS LUMPS OR CRYSTALLINE POWDER. ***BOILING POINT:*** 869 F (465 C)
MELTING POINT: 594 F (312 C) ***SPECIFIC GRAVITY:*** 3.738
VAPOR PRESSURE: 1 MMHG @ 212.5 C ***SOLUBILITY IN WATER:*** 3.7% @ 20 C
SOLVENT SOLUBILITY: SOLUBLE IN ACIDS, ALKALIES, DILUTE HYDROCHLORIC ACID, GLYCEROL, CARBONATE SOLUTIONS; INSOLUBLE IN CHLOROFORM, ETHER, ALCOHOL.

FIRE AND EXPLOSION DATA

FIRE AND EXPLOSION HAZARD: NEGLIGIBLE FIRE HAZARD WHEN EXPOSED TO HEAT OR FLAME.
FIREFIGHTING MEDIA: DRY CHEMICAL, CARBON DIOXIDE, HALON, WATER SPRAY OR STANDARD FOAM (1987 EMERGENCY RESPONSE GUIDEBOOK, DOT P 5800.4).
FOR LARGER FIRES, USE WATER SPRAY, FOG OR STANDARD FOAM (1987 EMERGENCY RESPONSE GUIDEBOOK, DOT P 5800.4).
FIREFIGHTING: MOVE CONTAINERS FROM FIRE AREA IF POSSIBLE (1987 EMERGENCY RESPONSE GUIDEBOOK, DOT P 5800.4, GUIDE PAGE 53).
USE AGENTS SUITABLE FOR TYPE OF FIRE, USE FLOODING AMOUNTS OF WATER AS A FOG. AVOID BREATHING POISONOUS VAPORS, KEEP UPWIND.

TRANSPORTATION DATA

DEPARTMENT OF TRANSPORTATION HAZARD CLASSIFICATION 49 CFR 172.101: POISON B
DEPARTMENT OF TRANSPORTATION LABELING REQUIREMENTS 49 CFR 172.101 AND SUBPART E: POISON
DEPARTMENT OF TRANSPORTATION PACKAGING REQUIREMENTS: 49 CFR 173.366 AND 49 CFR 173.368 EXCEPTIONS: 49 CFR 173.364

TOXICITY

ARSENIC TRIOXIDE, SOLID; TOXICITY DATA: 29 MG/KG ORAL-MAN LDLO; 1429 UG/KG ORAL-HUMAN LDLO; 14,600 UG/KG ORAL-RAT LD50; 31,500 UG/KG ORAL-MOUSE LD50; 20,190 UG/KG ORAL-RABBIT LD50; 10 MG/KG ORAL-DOG LDLO; 30 MG/KG ORAL-CATTLE LDLO; 8 MG/KG SUBCUTANEOUS-RAT LDLO; 9800 MG/KG SUBCUTANEOUS-MOUSE LD50; 6 MG/KG SUBCUTANEOUS-GUINEA PIG LDLO; 7 MG/KG SUBCUTANEOUS-RABBIT LDLO; 10,700 UG/KG INTRAVENOUS-MOUSE LD50; 10,560 UG/KG INTRAVENOUS-RABBIT LDLO; 871 MG/KG INTRAPERITONEAL-RAT LD50; 2 MG/KG INTRADERMAL-DOG LDLO; 4 GM/KG PARENTERAL-FROG LDLO; 2941 UG/KG UNREPORTED-MAN LDLO; MUTAGENIC DATA (RTECS); REPRODUCTIVE EFFECTS DATA (RTECS); TUMORIGENIC DATA (RTECS). CARCINOGEN STATUS: OSHA CARCINOGEN; KNOWN HUMAN CARCINOGEN (NTP); HUMAN SUFFICIENT EVIDENCE, ANIMAL LIMITED EVIDENCE (IARC GROUP-1). AN INCREASED INCIDENCE OF SKIN AND LUNG CANCER HAS BEEN ASSOICATED WITH INORGANIC ARSENIC COMPOUNDS THROUGH MEDICAL TREATMENT, CONTAMINATED DRINKING WATER OR OCCUPATIONAL EXPOSURE. CANCERS AT OTHER SITE HAVE ALSO BEEN REPORTED, BUT A CLEAR ASSOCIATION HAS NOT BEEN CONFIRMED. LOCAL EFFECTS: IRRITANT- INHALATION, SKIN AND EYE. ACUTE TOXICITY LEVEL: HIGHLY TOXIC BY INGESTION. TARGET EFFECTS: NEUROTOXIN; SENSITIZER- DERMAL. POISONING MAY ALSO AFFECT THE SKIN, GASTROINTESTINAL TRACT, LIVER, KIDNEYS, HEMATOPOIETIC AND CARDIOVASCULAR SYSTEMS. AT INCREASED RISK FROM EXPOSURE: PERSONS WITH PRE-EXISTING DIABETES, CARDIOVASCULAR DISEASES, ALLERGIC OR OTHER SKIN DISEASES, NEUROLOGIC, HEPATIC OR RENAL LESIONS.

HEALTH EFFECTS AND FIRST AID

INHALATION: ARSENIC TRIOXIDE, SOLID: IRRITANT/NEUROTOXIN/CARCINOGEN.
ACUTE EXPOSURE- INORGANIC ARSENIC CONPOUNDS MAY CAUSE IRRITATION OF THE RESPIRATORY TRACT WITH COUGH, FOAMY SPUTUM, PAIN IN THE CHEST, DYSPNEA, AND POSSIBLY PULMONARY EDEMA. THERE MAY BE CYANOSIS OF THE FACE, GIDDINESS, RESTLESSNESS, LASSITUDE, HEADACHE, EXTREME GENERAL WEAKNESS, AN INITIAL RISE, THEN FALL IN TEMPERATURE, HYPOTENSION, PAIN IN THE LIMBS, AND LEUKOCYTOSIS. DELAYED GASTROINTESTINAL SYMPTOMS MAY INCLUDE NAUSEA, VOMITING, COLIC AND DIARRHEA. ACUTE, SEVERE SYSTEMIC INTOXICATION BY INHALATION IS UNLIKELY, BUT IF SUFFICIENT AMOUNTS ARE ABSORBED, OTHER EFFECTS AS DESCRIBED IN ACUTE INGESTION ARE POSSIBLE. ONE CASE OF A SINGLE PROLONGED EXPOSURE TO AN ARSENICAL WEED SPRAY RESULTED IN MEGALOBLASTIC ANEMIA. CHRONIC EXPOSURE- REPEATED EXPOSURE TO INORGANIC ARSENIC COMPOUNDS MAY CAUSE WEAKNESS, PERSISTENT HEADACHE, ANOREXIA, WEIGHT LOSS, FATIGUE, PALLOR, MALAISE, LOW GRADE FEVER, SALIVATION, AND GASTROINTESTINAL DISTURBANCES WITH NAUSEA, OCCASIONAL VOMITING, A SENSE OF HEAVINESS IN THE STOMACH, COLIC AND DIARRHEA ALTERNATING WITH CONSTIPATION. EFFECTS ON MUCOUS MEMBRANES MAY RESULT IN CONJUNCTIVITIS WITH A SENSATION OF IRRITATION AND LACRIMATION, A CATARRHAL STATE OF THE NOSE, LARYNX, AND RESPIRATORY PASSAGES, CORYZA, HOARSENESS, MILD TRACHEOBRONCHITIS, AND STOMATITIS. PERFORATION OF THE NASAL SEPTUM MAY OCCUR. MANY FORMS OF SKIN LESIONS ARE POSSIBLE INCLUDING PIGMENTATION (MELANOSIS), ERYTHEMA, ECZEMA, KERATOSIS OF PALMS AND SOLES, LOCALIZED SUBCUTANEOUS EDEMA, ESPECIALLY OF THE EYELIDS, SCALING AND DESQUAMATION, BRITTLE NAILS, AND WHITE BANDS ON THE NAILS (MEES LINES), ALOPECIA AND VITILIGO. PERIPHERAL NEURITIS MAY DEVELOP, INITIALLY OF THE HANDS AND FEET, WHICH IS USUALLY SENSORY WITH PARESTHESIA, HYPESTHESIA, PAIN, BURNING, AND TENDERNESS. IN VERY SEVERE CASES, MOTOR PARALYSIS AND MUSCLE ATROPHY MAY OCCUR WITH FOOT AND WRIST DROP. EFFECTS ON THE LIVER, KIDNEY, MYOCARDIUM, AND BONE MARROW MAY OCCUR BUT ARE MORE COMMON WITH CHRONIC INGESTION. INORGANIC ARSENIC COMPOUNDS HAVE BEEN SHOWN TO BE LUNG AND SKIN CARCINOGENS IN HUMANS. THE LATENCY TIME BETWEEN ONSET OF EXPOSURE AND THE APPEARANCE OF CANCER IS USUALLY BETWEEN 15 AND 30 YEARS.
FIRST AID- REMOVE FROM EXPOSURE AREATO FRESH AIR IMMEDIATELY. IF BREATHING HAS STOPPED, PERFORMARTIFICIAL RESPIRATION. KEEP PERSON WARM AND AT REST.

TREAT SYMPTOMATICALLY AND SUPPORTIVELY. GET MEDICAL ATTENTION IMMEDIATELY.

SKIN CONTACT: ARSENIC TRIOXIDE, SOLID: IRRITANT/SENSITIZER. **ACUTE EXPOSURE-** ARSENIC AND INORGANIC ARSENIC COMPOUNDS IRRITATE THE SKIN WITH ERYTHEMA, ITCHING AND BURNING. SENSITIZATION DERMATITIS MAY OCCUR IN PREVIOUSLY EXPOSED PERSONS. INORGANIC ARSENIC COMPOUNDS ARE SLIGHTLY ABSORBED THROUGH THE SKIN WHEN ADMINISTERED IN A LIPID VEHICLE. POISONING HAS CAUSED ALOPECIA, BRONZING OF THE SKIN, AND BRITTLE NAILS. IF SUFFICIENT ABSORPTION OCCURS SEVERE GASTRITIS OR GASTROENTERITIS MAY OCCUR. **CHRONIC EXPOSURE-** OCCUPATIONAL EXPOSURE TO AIRBORNE ARSENIC MAY CAUSE BURNING AND ITCHING WITH TWO TYPES OF DERMATITIS DUE TO LOCAL IRRITATION OR SENSITIZATION. AN ECZEMATOUS TYPE WITH ERYTHEMA, SWELLING AND PAPULES OR VESICLES AND A FOLLICULAR TYPE WITH ERYTHEMA AND FOLLICULAR SWELLING OR PUSTULES. THE DERMATITIS IS USUALLY LOCALIZED ON THE MOST HEAVILY EXPOSED AREAS SUCH AS THE FACE, BACK OF THE NECK, FOREARMS, WRISTS AND HANDS. CHRONIC DERMAL LESIONS MAY FOLLOW THIS TYPE OF INITIAL REACTION, BUT USUALLY ONLY AFTER MANY YEARS OF EXPOSURE. HYPERKERATOSIS, WARTS AND MELANOSIS OF THE SKIN ARE CONSPICUOUS SIGNS. THESE CHRONIC SKIN LESIONS, PARTICULARLY THE HYPERKERATOSIS, MAY DEVELOP INTO PRECANCEROUS AND CANCEROUS LESIONS.

FIRST AID- REMOVE CONTAMINATED CLOTHING AND SHOES IMMEDIATELY. WASH AFFECTED AREA WITH SOAP OR MILD DETERGENT AND LARGE AMOUNTS OF WATER UNTIL NO EVIDENCE OF CHEMICAL REMAINS (APPROXIMATELY 15-20 MINUTES). GET MEDICAL ATTENTION IMMEDIATELY.

EYE CONTACT: ARSENIC TRIOXIDE, SOLID: IRRITANT. **ACUTE EXPOSURE-** ARSENICAL DUST MAY CAUSE IRRITATION CHARACTERIZED BY ITCHING, BURNING, WATERING OF THE EYES, PHOTOPHOBIA AND SOMETIMES HYPEREMIA AND CHEMOSIS. **CHRONIC EXPOSURE-** REPEATED OR PROLONGED CONTACT MAY CAUSE DISCOMFORT, EDEMA OF THE LIDS, AND CORNEAL INJURY AND OPACITY.

FIRST AID- WASH EYES IMMEDIATELY WITH LARGE AMOUNTS OF WATER OR NORMAL SALINE, OCCASIONALLY LIFTING UPPER AND LOWER LIDS, UNTIL NO EVIDENCE OF CHEMICAL REMAINS (APPROXIMATELY 15-20 MINUTES). GET MEDICAL ATTENTION IMMEDIATELY.

INGESTION: ARSENIC TRIOXIDE, SOLID: NEUROTOXIN/CARCINOGEN/HIGHLY TOXIC. **ACUTE EXPOSURE-** THE APPROXIMATE LETHAL DOSE IS 120 MG. A CASE OF INGESTION DURING THE 30TH WEEK OF PREGNANCY RESULTED IN MATERNAL TOXICITY; PREMATURE DELIVERY AND NEONATAL DEATH FOLLOWED. LARGE DOSES OF INORGANIC ARSENIC COMPOUNDS MAY CAUSE SYSTEMIC POISONING WITH SYMPTOMS USUALLY APPEARING ONE-HALF TO FOUR HOURS AFTER INGESTION. SYMPTOMS MAY INCLUDE BURNING AND PAIN IN THE CHEST, ESOPHAGUS, STOMACH AND BOWEL, CONSTRICTION IN THE THROAT, DYSPHAGIA, WEAKNESS, A SWEETISH METALLIC TASTE, VIOLENT GASTROENTERITIS WITH VOMITING, COPIUS WATERY OR BLOODY DIARRHEA CONTAINING SHREDS OF MUCOUS, AND DEHYDRATION WITH INTENSE THIRST AND MUSCULAR CRAMPS. THERE MAY BE A GARLIC ODOR TO THE BREATH, VOMIT, AND FECES. VERTIGO, FRONTAL HEADACHE, FEVER, SWEATING, RESTLESSNESS, CONFUSION, DELIRIUM AND EVEN MANIA MAY OCCUR. WITH LESS THAN LETHAL DOSES, SOME SYMPTOMS MAY DEVELOP WITHOUT PROMINENT GASTROINTESTINAL SIGNS. LATER SYMPTOMS MAY INCLUDE COLD, CLAMMY SKIN, CYANOSIS, RAPID, FEEBLE PULSE, HYPOTENSION, SHOCK, CARDIAC DISTURBANCES, INCLUDING VENTRICULAR FIBRILLATION, AND GENERAL PARALYSIS. DEATH WITHIN 1-48 HOURS IS USUALLY DUE TO CIRCULATORY FAILURE; COMA AND CONVULSIONS MAY OCCUR TERMINALLY. DEATH DELAYED 3-14 DAYS IS USUALLY DUE TO DEHYDRATION, ELECTROLYTE IMBALANCE AND GRADUAL HYPOTENSION. LIVER AND KIDNEY DEGENERATIVE CHANGES MAY BE PRESENT. IF THE ACUTE PHASE IS SURVIVED, DELAYED SEQUELAE MAY INCLUDE: A VARIETY OF SKIN LESIONS, ALOPECIA, MEES LINES, EDEMA OF THE FACE AND EYELIDS, AND CONJUNCTIVITIS; NEUROPATHY WITH SENSORY AND MOTOR INVOLVEMENT; ENCEPHALOPATHY; LIVER DAMAGE WITH MULTIPLE PROFILE ABNORMALITIES, JAUNDICE, AND HEPATOMEGALY; RENAL FAILURE WITH HEMATURIA, ALBUMINURIA, GLUCOSURIA, AND OLIGURIA OR ANURIA; AND ANEMIA AND AND LEUKOPENIA, ESPECIALLY NEUTROPENIA. WEAKNESS AND DIARRHEA MAY PERSIST FOR WEEKS. **CHRONIC EXPOSURE-** REPRODUCTIVE EFFECTS HAVE BEEN REPORTED IN ANIMALS. REPEATED INGESTION OF SMALL AMOUNTS OF INORGANIC ARSENIC COMPOUNDS MAY CAUSE EFFECTS AS DESCRIBED IN CHRONIC INHALATION. OTHER REPORTED SYMPTOMS MAY INCLUDE METALLIC TASTE, THIRST, GARLIC ODOR TO THE BREATH AND SWEAT, ANXIETY, HOT FLUSHES, ATAXIA, MENTAL CONFUSION, EDEMA OF THE ANKLES AND LOWER EYELIDS, NOSE BLEEDS AND BLEEDING GUMS. LIVER EFFECTS MAY INCLUDE JAUNDICE, HEPATOMEGALY, CIRRHOSIS, ASCITES, NON-CIRRHOTIC PORTAL HYPERTENSION, AND FATTY INFILTRATION AND CENTRAL NECROSIS. THE KIDNEYS MAY BE SEVERELY DAMAGED AND THERE MAY BE OLIGURIA, PROTEINURIA, HEMATURIA, AND CASTS. HEMATOLOGIC EFFECTS MAY INCLUDE ANEMIA, LEUKOPENIA, ESPECIALLY NEUTROPENIA, THROMBOCYTOPENIA WITHOUT SEVERE BLEEDING, DISTURBED ERYTHROPOIESIS, AND DISTURBED OR DEPRESSED MYELOPOIESIS. APLASTIC ANEMIA WITH SUBSEQUENT FATAL MYELOGENOUS LEUKEMIA HAS BEEN REPORTED. REPORTED CARDIOVASCULAR EFFECTS INCLUDE SEVERE CARDIAC PERIPHERAL EDEMA AND LEFT-SIDED HEART FAILURE AND GANGRENE OF THE EXTREMITIES DUE TO PERIPHERAL VASCULAR CHANGES. AN INCREASED INCIDENCE OF CHROMOSOMAL ABERRATIONS HAS BEEN OBSERVED IN PERSONS TREATED WITH ARSENICAL COMPOUNDS. CANCER IN HUMANS IS ASSOCIATED WITH CHRONIC INGESTION OF ARSENIC.

FIRST AID- REMOVE BY GASTRIC LAVAGE OR EMESIS. FOLLOW WITH A SALINE CATHARTIC. MAINTAIN BLOOD PRESSURE, AIRWAY, AND GIVE OXYGEN IF RESPIRATION IS DEPRESSED. DO NOT PERFORM GASTRIC LAVAGE OR EMESIS IF VICTIM IS UNCONSCIOUS. GET MEDICAL ATTENTION IMMEDIATELY. (DREISBACH, HANDBOOK OF POISONING, 12TH ED.) ADMINISTRATION OF GASTRIC LAVAGE OR OXYGEN SHOULD BE PERFORMED BY QUALIFIED MEDICAL PERSONNEL.

ANTIDOTE: THE FOLLOWING ANTIDOTE HAS BEEN RECOMMENDED. HOWEVER, THE DECISION AS TO WHETHER THE SEVERITY OF POISONING REQUIRES ADMINISTRATION OF ANY ANTIDOTE AND ACTUAL DOSE REQUIRED SHOULD BE MADE BY QUALIFIED MEDICAL PERSONNEL.

ARSENIC POISONING: GIVE DIMERCAPROL, 3 MG/KG (OR 0.3 ML/KG) EVERY 4 HOURS FOR 2 DAYS AND THEN 2 MG/KG EVERY 2 HOURS FOR A TOTAL OF 10 DAYS. DIMERCAPROL IS AVAILABLE AS A 10% SOLUTION IN OIL FOR INTRAMUSCULAR ADMINISTRATION. NEXT, GIVE PENICILLAMINE, UP TO 100 MG/KG/DAY (MAXIMUM 1 G/DAY) DIVIDED INTO 4 DOSES FOR NO LONGER THAN 1 WEEK. IF A LONGER ADMINISTRATION PERIOD IS WARRANTED, DOSAGE SHOULD NOT EXCEED 40 MG/KG/DAY. GIVE THE DRUG ORALLY HALF AN HOUR BEFORE MEALS. DISCONTINUE ANTIDOTE WHEN URINE ARSENIC LEVEL FALLS BELOW 50 UG/24 HR. (DREISBACH, HANDBOOK OF POISONING, 12TH ED.). ANITDOTE SHOULD BE ADMINISTERED BY QUALIFIED MEDICAL PERSONNEL.

REACTIVITY

REACTIVITY: STABLE UNDER NORMAL TEMPERATURES AND PRESSURES.

INCOMPATIBILITIES: ARSENIC TRIOXIDE, SOLID: ACIDS: VIGOROUS REACTION. ALUMINUM: CORROSIVE IN THE PRESENCE OF MOISTURE. CHLORINE TRIFLUORIDE: VIOLENT REACTION WITH POSSIBLE IGNITION. COPPER: CORROSIVE IN THE PRESENCE OF MOISTURE. FLUORINE: VIOLENT REACTION. HYDROGEN FLUORIDE: REACTS WITH INCANDESCENCE. IRON SOLUTIONS: CORRODES. MERCURY: VIGOROUS RECTION. METALS: CORROSIVE IN THE PRESENCE OF MOISTURE. OXYGEN DIFLUORIDE: VIGOROUS REACTION. RUBIDIUM CARBIDE: IGNITES. SODIUM CHLORATE: FORMS SPONTANEOUSLY FLAMMABLE MIXTURE. SODIUM NITRATE + IRON(II) SULFATE: SPONTANEOUS IGNITION. ZINC: EXPLODES WHEN HEATED.

DECOMPOSITION: THERMAL DECOMPOSITION MAY RELEASE TOXIC AND/OR HAZARDOUS GASES.

POLYMERIZATION: HAZARDOUS POLYMERIZATION HAS NOT BEEN REPORTED TO OCCUR UNDER NORMAL TEMPERATURES AND PRESSURES.

STORAGE AND DISPOSAL

OBSERVE ALL FEDERAL, STATE AND LOCAL REGULATIONS WHEN STORING OR DISPOSING OF THIS SUBSTANCE. FOR ASSISTANCE, CONTACT THE DISTRICT DIRECTOR OF THE ENVIRONMENTAL PROTECTION AGENCY.

****STORAGE****

STORE IN ACCORDANCE WITH 40 CFR 165 RECOMMENDED PROCEDURES FOR THE DISPOSAL AND STORAGE OF PESTICIDES AND PESTICIDE CONTAINERS.

STORE AWAY FROM INCOMPATIBLE SUBSTANCES.

KEEP IN A TIGHTLY CLOSED CONTAINER. STORE IN A COOL, DRY, VENTILATED AREA.

THRESHOLD PLANNING QUANTITY (TPQ): THE SUPERFUND AMENDMENTS AND REAUTHORIZATION ACT (SARA) SECTION 302 REQUIRES THAT EACH FACILITY WHERE ANY EXTREMELY HAZARDOUS SUBSTANCE IS PRESENT IN A QUANTITY EQUAL TO OR GREATER THAN THE TPQ ESTABLISHED FOR THAT SUBSTANCE NOTIFY THE STATE EMERGENCY RESPONSE COMMISSION FOR THE STATE IN WHICH IT IS LOCATED. SECTION 303 OF SARA REQUIRES THESE FACILITIES TO PARTICIPATE IN LOCAL EMERGENCY RESPONSE PLANNING (40 CFR 355.30).

****DISPOSAL****

DISPOSAL MUST BE IN ACCORDANCE WITH STANDARDS APPLICABLE TO GENERATORS OF HAZARDOUS WASTE, 40CFR 262. EPA HAZARDOUS WASTE NUMBER P012.

DISPOSAL MUST BE IN ACCORDANCE WITH 40 CFR 165 RECOMMENDED PROCEDURES FOR THE DISPOSAL AND STORAGE OF PESTICIDES AND PESTICIDE CONTAINERS.

ARSENIC - REGULATORY LEVEL: 5.0 MG/L MATERIALS WHICH CONTAIN THE ABOVE SUBSTANCE AT OR ABOVE THE REGULATORY LEVEL MEET THE EPA CHARACTERISTIC OF TOXICITY, AND MUST BE DISPOSED OF IN ACCORDANCE WITH 40 CFR PART 262. EPA HAZARDOUS WASTE NUMBER D004.

CONDITIONS TO AVOID

MAY BURN BUT DOES NOT IGNITE READILY.

SPILL AND LEAK PROCEDURES

SOIL SPILL: DIG A HOLDING AREA SUCH AS PIT, POND OR LAGOON TO CONTAIN SPILLED MATERIAL. USE PROTECTIVE COVER SUCH AS A PLASTIC SHEET TO PREVENT DISSOLVING IN FIREFIGHTING WATER OR RAIN.

WATER SPILL: ADD CALCIUM HYPOCHLORITE TO SPILL.

NEUTRALIZE WITH AGRICULTURAL LIME, SLAKED LIME, CRUSHED LIMESTONE, OR SODIUM BICARBONATE.

ADD FERRIC CHLORIDE TO SPILL.

USE MECHANICAL DREDGES OR LIFTS TO EXTRACT IMMOBILIZED MASSES OF POLLUTION AND PRECIPITATES.

THE CALIFORNIA SAFE DRINKING WATER AND TOXIC ENFORCEMENT ACT OF 1986 (PROPOSITION 65) PROHIBITS CONTAMINATING ANY KNOWN SOURCE OF DRINKING WATER WITH SUBSTANCES KNOWN TO CAUSE CANCER AND/OR REPRODUCTIVE TOXICITY.

OCCUPATIONAL SPILL: DO NOT TOUCH SPILLED MATERIAL. STOP LEAK IF YOU CAN DO IT WITHOUT RISK. FOR SMALL SPILLS, TAKE UP WITH SAND OR OTHER ABSORBENT MATERIAL AND PLACE INTO CONTAINERS FOR LATER DISPOSAL. FOR SMALL DRY SPILLS, WITH A CLEAN SHOVEL PLACE MATERIAL INTO CLEAN, DRY CONTAINER AND COVER. MOVE CONTAINERS FROM SPILL AREA. FOR LARGER SPILLS, DIKE FAR AHEAD OF SPILL FOR LATER DISPOSAL. KEEP UNNECESSARY PEOPLE AWAY. ISOLATE HAZARD AREA AND DENY ENTRY.

REPORTABLE QUANTITY (RQ): THE SUPERFUND AMENDMENTS AND REAUTHORIZATION ACT (SARA) SECTION 304 REQUIRES THAT A RELEASE EQUAL TO OR GREATER THAN THE REPORTABLE QUANTITY ESTABLISHED FOR THAT SUBSTANCE BE IMMEDIATELY REPORTED TO THE LOCAL EMERGENCY PLANNING COMMITTEE AND THE STATE EMERGENCY RESPONSE COMMISSION (40 CFR 355.40). IF THE RELEASE OF THIS SUBSTANCE IS REPORTABLE UNDER CERCLA SECTION 103, THE NATIONAL RESPONSE CENTER MUST BE NOTIFIED IMMEDIATELY AT (800) 424-8802 OR (202) 426-2675 IN THE METROPOLITAN WASHINGTON, D.C. AREA (40 CFR 302.6).

PROTECTIVE EQUIPMENT

VENTILATION: PROCESS ENCLOSURE RECOMMENDED TO MEET PUBLISHED EXPOSURE LIMITS.

ARSENIC (INORGANIC): VENTILATION SHOULD MEET THE REQUIREMENTS IN 29 CFR 1910.1018(G).

RESPIRATOR: THE FOLLOWING RESPIRATORS ARE THE MINIMUM LEGAL REQUIREMENTS AS SET FORTH BY THE OCCUPATIONAL SAFETY AND HEALTH ADMINISTRATION FOUND IN 29 CFR 1910, SUBPART Z.

RESPIRATORY PROTECTION FOR INORGANIC ARSENIC PARTICULATE EXCEPT THOSE WITH SIGNIFICANT VAPOR PRESSURE

CONCENTRATION OF INORGANIC ARSENIC (AS) REQUIRED RESPIRATOR OR CONDITION OF USE

UNKNOWN OR GREATER OR LESS THAN 20,000 UG/M3 (20 MG/M3) OR FIREFIGHTING ANY FULL FACEPIECE, SELF CONTAINED BREATHING APPARATUS, OPERATED IN POSITIVE PRESSURE MODE.

NOT GREATER THAN 20,000 UG/M3 FULL (20 MG/M3) SUPPLIED-AIR RESPIRATOR WITH FACEPIECE, HOOD OR HELMET OR SUIT AND OPERATED IN POSITIVE PRESSURE MODE.

NOT GREATER THAN 10,000 UG/M3 RESPIRATORS (10 MG/M3) POWERED-AIR PURIFYING IN ALL INLET FACE COVERINGS WITH HIGH EFFICIENCY FILTERS; OR HALF-MASK SUPPLIED-AIR RESPIRATOR OPERATED IN POSITIVE PRESSURE MODE.

NOT GREATER THAN 500 UG/M3 FULL FACEPIECE AIR-PURIFYING RESPIRATOR EQUIPPED WITH HIGH EFFICIENCY FILTERS; OR ANY FULL FACEPIECE SUPPLIED-AIR RESPIRATOR; OR ANY FULL FACEPIECE SELF-CONTAINED BREATHING APPARATUS. NOT GREATER THAN 100 UG/M3 HALF-MASK AIR-PURIFYING RESPIRATOR EQUIPPED WITH HIGH EFFICIENCY FILTERS; OR ANY HALF-MASK SUPPLIED-AIR RESPIRATOR.

(HIGH EFFICIENCY FILTER- 99.97% EFFICIENCY AGAINST 0.3 MICROMETER MONODISPERSE DIETHYL-HEXYL PHTHALATE (DOP) PARTICLES)

RESPIRATORY PROTECTION FOR INORGANIC ARSENICALS (SUCH AS ARSENIC TRICHLORIDE OR ARSENIC PHOSPHIDE) WITH SIGNIFICANT VAPOR PRESSURE.

CONCENTRATION OF INORGANIC ARSENIC (AS) REQUIRED RESPIRATOR OR CONDITION OF USE

UNKNOWN OR GREATER OR LESS THAN 20,000 CONTAINED UG/M3 (20 MG/M3) ANY FULL FACEPIECE SELF-BREATHING APPARATUS OPERATED IN POSITIVE PRESSURE MODE.

NOT GREATER THAN 20,000 UG/M3 (20 MG/M3) SUPPLIED-AIR RESPIRATOR WITH A FULL FACEPIECE, HOOD OR HELMET OR SUIT OPERATED IN POSITIVE PRESSURE MODE.

NOT GREATER THAN 10,000 UG/M3 RESPIRATOR (10 MG/M3) HALF-MASK SUPPLIED AIR OPERATED IN POSITIVE PRESSURE MODE.

NOT GREATER THAN 500 UG/M3 FRONT- OR BACK-MOUNTED GAS MASK EQUIPPED WITH HIGH-EFFICIENCY FILTERS AND ACID GAS CANISTER; OR ANY FULL FACEPIECE SUPPLIED AIR RESPIRATOR; OR ANY FULL FACEPIECE SELF-CONTAINED BREATHING APPARATUS.

NOT GREATER THAN 100 UG/M3 HALF-MASK AIR-PURIFYING RESPIRATOR EQUIPPED WITH HIGH EFFICIENCY FILTER AND ACID GAS CARTRIDGE; OR ANY HALF-MASK SUPPLIED-AIR RESPIRATOR.

(HIGH EFFICIENCY FILTER- 99.97% EFFICIENCY AGAINST 0.3 MICROMETER MONODISPERSE DIETHYL-HEXYL PHTHALATE (DOP) PARTICLES) (HALF-MASK RESPIRATORS SHALL NOT BE USED FOR PROTECTION AGAINST ARSENIC TRICHLORIDE, AS IT IS RAPIDLY ABSORBED THROUGH THE SKIN).

THE FOLLOWING RESPIRATORS AND MAXIMUM USE CONCENTRATIONS ARE RECOMMENDATIONS BY THE U.S. DEPARTMENT OF HEALTH AND HUMAN SERVICES, NIOSH POCKET GUIDE TO CHEMICAL HAZARDS OR NIOSH CRITERIA DOCUMENTS. THE SPECIFIC RESPIRATOR SELECTED MUST BE BASED ON CONTAMINATION LEVELS FOUND IN THE WORK PLACE AND BE JOINTLY APPROVED BY THE NATIONAL INSTITUTE OF OCCUPATIONAL SAFETY AND HEALTH AND THE MINE SAFETY AND HEALTH ADMINISTRATION.

AT ANY DETECTABLE CONCENTRATION:

SELF-CONTAINED BREATHING APPARATUS WITH FULL FACEPIECE OPERATED IN PRESSURE-DEMAND OR OTHER POSITIVE PRESSURE MODE. SUPPLIED-AIR RESPIRATOR WITH FULL FACEPIECE OPERATED IN PRESSURE-DEMAND OR OTHER POSITIVE PRESSURE MODE IN COMBINATION WITH AN AUXILIARY SELF-CONTAINED BREATHING APPARATUS OPERATED IN PRESSURE-DEMAND OR OTHER POSITIVE PRESSURE MODE.

ESCAPE- AIR-PURIFYING FULL FACEPIECE RESPIRATOR (GAS MASK) WITH A CHIN-STYLE OR FRONT- OR BACK-MOUNTED ACID GAS CANISTER HAVING A HIGH-EFFICIENCY PARTICULATE FILTER. ESCAPE-TYPE SELF-CONTAINED BREATHING APPARATUS.

FOR FIREFIGHTING AND OTHER IMMEDIATELY DANGEROUS TO LIFE OR HEALTH CONDITIONS:

SELF-CONTAINED BREATHING APPARATUS WITH FULL FACEPIECE OPERATED IN PRESSURE-DEMAND OR OTHER POSITIVE PRESSURE MODE.

SUPPLIED-AIR RESPIRATOR WITH FULL FACEPIECE AND OPERATED IN PRESSURE-DEMAND OR OTHER POSITIVE PRESSURE MODE IN COMBINATION WITH AN AUXILIARY SELF-CONTAINED BREATHING APPARATUS OPERATED IN PRESSURE-DEMAND OR OTHER POSITIVE PRESSURE MODE.

CLOTHING: EMPLOYEE MUST WEAR APPROPRIATE PROTECTIVE (IMPERVIOUS) CLOTHING AND EQUIPMENT TO PREVENT REPEATED OR PROLONGED SKIN CONTACT WITH THIS SUBSTANCE.

ARSENIC (INORGANIC): PROTECTIVE CLOTHING SHOULD MEET THE REQUIREMENTS FOR PROTECTIVE WORK CLOTHING AND EQUIPMENT IN 29 CFR 1910.1018(J).

GLOVES: EMPLOYEE MUST WEAR APPROPRIATE PROTECTIVE GLOVES TO PREVENT CONTACT WITH THIS SUBSTANCE.

ARSENIC (INORGANIC): PROTECTIVE GLOVES SHOULD MEET THE REQUIREMENTS FOR PROTECTIVE WORK CLOTHING AND EQUIPMENT IN 29 CFR 1910.1018(J).

EYE PROTECTION: EMPLOYEE MUST WEAR SPLASH-PROOF OR DUST-RESISTANT SAFETY GOGGLES TO PREVENT EYE CONTACT WITH THIS SUBSTANCE.

EMERGENCY EYE WASH: WHERE THERE IS ANY POSSIBILITY THAT AN EMPLOYEE'S EYES MAY BE EXPOSED TO THIS SUBSTANCE, THE EMPLOYER SHOULD PROVIDE AN EYE WASH FOUNTAIN WITHIN THE IMMEDIATE WORK AREA FOR EMERGENCY USE.

ARSENIC (INORGANIC): PROTECTIVE EYE EQUIPMENT SHOULD MEET THE REQUIREMENTS FOR PROTECTIVE WORK CLOTHING AND EQUIPMENT IN 29 CFR 1910.1018(J).

AUTHORIZED BY- OCCUPATIONAL HEALTH SERVICES, INC.
CREATION DATE: 10/04/89 ***REVISION DATE:*** 07/13/90

MATERIAL SAFETY DATA SHEET

OCCUPATIONAL HEALTH SERVICES, INC.
AGRICULTURE AND PESTICIDE DIVISION
450 SEVENTH AVENUE, SUITE 2407
NEW YORK, NEW YORK 10123
1-800-445-MSDS OR (212) 967-1100

EMERGENCY CONTACT:
JOHN S. BRANSFORD, JR. (615) 292-1180

SUBSTANCE IDENTIFICATION

CAS-NUMBER 7784-42-1
SUBSTANCE: ARSINE

TRADE NAMES/SYNONYMS: HYDROGEN ARSENIDE; ARSENIC TRIHYDRIDE; ARSENIC HYDRIDE; ARSENIURETTED HYDROGEN; ARSENOUS HYDRIDE; STCC 4920135; UN 2188; PST02100
CHEMICAL FAMILY: INORGANIC GAS
MOLECULAR FORMULA: AS-H3
MOLECULAR WEIGHT: 77.95
CERCLA RATINGS (SCALE 0-3): HEALTH=3 FIRE=3 REACTIVITY=0 PERSISTENCE=3
NFPA RATINGS (SCALE 0-4): HEALTH=4 FIRE=3 REACTIVITY=0

COMPONENTS AND CONTAMINANTS

COMPONENT: ARSINE ***PERCENT:*** 100
CAS# 7784-42-1
OTHER CONTAMINANTS: NONE
EXPOSURE LIMITS: ARSINE: 0.05 PPM (0.2 MG/M3) OSHA TWA 0.05 PPM (0.2 MG/M3) ACGIH TWA LOWEST FEASIBLE LIMITS NIOSH RECOMMENDED EXPOSURE CRITERIA; 2 UG/M3 NIOSH RECOMMENDED 15 MINUTE CEILING
100 POUNDS SARA SECTION 302 THRESHOLD PLANNING QUANTITY 1 POUND SARA SECTION 304 REPORTABLE QUANTITY SUBJECT TO SARA SECTION 313 ANNUAL TOXIC CHEMICAL RELEASE REPORTING SUBJECT TO CALIFORNIA PROPOSITION 65 CANCER AND/OR REPRODUCTIVE TOXICITY WARNING AND RELEASE REQUIREMENTS- (FEBRUARY 27, 1987)

PHYSICAL DATA

DESCRIPTION: COLORLESS GAS WITH A GARLIC-LIKE ODOR ***BOILING POINT:*** -81 F (-63 C)
MELTING POINT: -179 F (-117 C) ***SPECIFIC GRAVITY:*** 1.689 @ -55 C
VAPOR PRESSURE: 11,362 MMHG @ 21.1 C ***SOLUBILITY IN WATER:*** 20 ML/100 CC @ 20 C
ODOR THRESHOLD: 0.5 PPM ***VAPOR DENSITY:*** 2.7
SOLVENT SOLUBILITY: BENZENE, CHLOROFORM

FIRE AND EXPLOSION DATA

FIRE AND EXPLOSION HAZARD: DANGEROUS FIRE HAZARD WHEN EXPOSED TO HEAT OR FLAME.
MODERATE EXPLOSION HAZARD WHEN EXPOSED TO HEAT OR FLAME.
GAS IS HEAVIER THAN AIR AND MAY TRAVEL A CONSIDERABLE DISTANCE TO A SOURCE OF IGNITION AND FLASH BACK.
GAS-AIR MIXTURES ARE EXPLOSIVE.
UPPER EXPLOSIVE LIMIT: 100% ***LOWER EXPLOSIVE LIMIT:*** 4.5%
FIREFIGHTING MEDIA: LET BURN UNLESS LEAK CAN BE STOPPED IMMEDIATELY (1987 EMERGENCY RESPONSE GUIDEBOOK, DOT P 5800.4).
FOR LARGER FIRES, USE WATER SPRAY, FOG OR STANDARD FOAM (1987 EMERGENCY RESPONSE GUIDEBOOK, DOT P 5800.4).
FIREFIGHTING: MOVE CONTAINER FROM FIRE AREA IF POSSIBLE. STAY AWAY FROM STORAGE TANK ENDS. COOL FIRE-EXPOSED CONTAINERS FROM SIDE UNTIL WELL AFTER FIRE IS OUT. FOR MASSIVE FIRE IN STORAGE AREA, USE UNMANNED HOSE HOLDER OR MONITOR NOZZLES, ELSE WITHDRAW FROM AREA AND LET FIRE BURN. WITHDRAW IMMEDIATELY IN CASE OF RISING SOUND FROM VENTING SAFETY DEVICE OR ANY DISCOLORATION OF STORAGE TANK DUE TO FIRE (1987 EMERGENCY RESPONSE GUIDEBOOK, DOT P 5800.4, GUIDE PAGE 18).
EXTINGUISH ONLY IF FLOW CAN BE STOPPED; USE WATER IN FLOODING AMOUNTS AS FOG, SOLID STREAMS MAY NOT BE EFFECTIVE. COOL CONTAINERS WITH FLOODING AMOUNTS OF WATER, APPLY FROM AS FAR A DISTANCE AS POSSIBLE. AVOID BREATHING POISONOUS VAPORS, KEEP UPWIND. CONSIDER EVACUATION OF DOWNWIND AREA IF MATERIAL IS LEAKING.

TRANSPORTATION DATA

DEPARTMENT OF TRANSPORTATION HAZARD CLASSIFICATION 49 CFR 172.101: POISON A
DEPARTMENT OF TRANSPORTATION LABELING REQUIREMENTS 49 CFR 172.101 AND SUBPART E: POISON GAS AND FLAMMABLE GAS
DEPARTMENT OF TRANSPORTATION PACKAGING REQUIREMENTS: 49 CFR 173.328 EXCEPTIONS: NONE

TOXICITY

ARSINE: TOXICITY DATA: 25 PPM/30 MINUTES INHALATION-HUMAN LCLO; 300 PPM/5 MINUTES INHALATION-HUMAN LCLO; 3 PPM INHALATION-HUMAN TCLO; 325 UG/M3 INHALATION-MAN TCLO; 390 MG/M3/10 MINUTES INHALATION-RAT LC50; 250 MG/M3/10 MINUTES INHALATION-MOUSE LC50; 650 MG/M3/10 MINUTES INHALATION-RABBIT LC50; 1 GM/M3/10 MINUTES INHALATION-MAMMAL LC50; 350 MG/M3/10 MINUTES INHALATION-DOG LC50; 600 MG/M3/1 HOUR INHALATION-MONKEY LCLO; 150 MG/M3/20 MINUTES INHALATION-CAT LCLO; 2 MG/KG INTRAPERITONEAL-CAT LD50; 3 MG/KG INTRAPERITONEAL-MOUSE LD50; 2500 UG/KG INTRAPERITONEAL-RABBIT LD50. CARCINOGEN STATUS: OSHA CARCINOGEN; KNOWN HUMAN CARCINOGEN (NTP); HUMAN SUFFICIENT EVIDENCE, ANIMAL LIMITED EVIDENCE (IARC GROUP-1). AN INCREASED INCIDENCE OF SKIN AND LUNG CANCER HAS BEEN ASSOCIATED WITH INORGANIC ARSINIC COMPOUNDS THROUGH MEDICAL TREATMENT, CONTAMINATED DRINKING WATER OR OCCUPATIONAL EXPOSURE. CANCERS AT OTHER SITES HAVE ALSO BEEN REPORTED, BUT A CLEAR ASSOCIATION HAS NOT BEEN CONFIRMED. ACUTE TOXICITY LEVEL: HIGHLY TOXIC BY INHALATION. TARGET EFFECTS: HEMOLYTIC AGENT. POISONING MAY ALSO AFFECT THE BLOOD AND NERVOUS SYSTEM AND DAMAGE THE LIVER, KIDNEYS, HEART AND SPLEEN.

HEALTH EFFECTS AND FIRST AID

INHALATION: ARSINE: HEMOLYTIC AGENT/HIGHLY TOXIC. 6 PPM IMMEDIATELY DANGEROUS TO LIFE OR HEALTH. **ACUTE EXPOSURE-** SYMPTOMS MAY APPEAR IN 2-24 HOURS, BEGINNING WITH HEADACHE, MALAISE, WEAKNESS, DIZZINESS, DYSPHAGIA, CHEST PAIN, DYSPNEA, NAUSEA, VOMITING, ABDOMINAL PAIN AND GARLIC ODOR OF THE BREATH. SHOCK, COMA AND CARDIOVASCULAR COLLAPSE MAY OCCUR. MASSIVE HEMOLYSIS, HEMOGLOBINURIA, HEMATURIA AND ANEMIA MAY OCCUR. IN 24-48 HOURS, HEPATITIS, JAUNDICE AND HEPATOMEGALY MAY APPEAR. PULMONARY EDEMA WITH CYANOSIS IS POSSIBLE. OLIGURIA INDICATES NEPHRITIS. ANURIA OR CARDIAC FAILURE MAY BE FATAL. IN SOME CASES, BRONZING OF THE SKIN AND SCLERA MAY OCCUR. SYMPTOMS OF SEVERE ARSENIC POISONING, SUCH AS ENCEPHALOPATHY, RESTLESSNESS, MEMORY LOSS, AGITATION AND DISORIENTATION, HAVE OCCURRED SEVERAL DAYS AFTER EXPOSURE, FOLLOWED BY PERIPHERAL NEUROPATHY WITH NUMBNESS OF THE HANDS AND FEET, SEVERE MUSCLE WEAKNESS AND PHOTOPHOBIA. DEATH HAS OCCURRED FROM EXPOSURE TO 25 PPM IN AS SHORT A TIME AS 30 MINUTES. **CHRONIC EXPOSURE-** HEMOLYTIC ANEMIA MAY LEAD TO DAMAGE OF THE NERVOUS SYSTEM, HEART, LIVER, KIDNEYS, AND SPLEEN. SWELLING OF THE EYELIDS AND FACE HAS OCCURRED, BUT NOT IN ALL CASES.
FIRST AID- REMOVE FROM EXPOSURE AREA TO FRESH AIR IMMEDIATELY. IF BREATHING HAS STOPPED, GIVE ARTIFICIAL RESPIRATION. MAINTAIN AIRWAY AND BLOOD PRESSURE AND ADMINISTER OXYGEN IF AVAILABLE. KEEP AFFECTED PERSON WARM AND AT REST. TREAT SYMPTOMATICALLY AND SUPPORTIVELY. ADMINISTRATION OF OXYGEN SHOULD BE PERFORMED BY QUALIFIED PERSONNEL. GET MEDICAL ATTENTION IMMEDIATELY.

SKIN CONTACT: ARSINE: **ACUTE EXPOSURE-** NO IRRITATION HAS BEEN OBSERVED IN FATAL CASES. FROSTBITE MAY OCCUR FROM CONTACT WITH LIQUEFIED GAS. **CHRONIC EXPOSURE-** NO DATA AVAILABLE.
FIRST AID- IT IS UNLIKELY THAT EMERGENCY TREATMENT WILL BE REQUIRED. IF ADVERSE EFFECTS OCCUR, GET MEDICAL ATTENTION. IN CASE OF FROSTBITE, WARM AFFECTED SKIN IN WARM WATER AT A TEMPERATURE OF 107 F. IF WARM WATER IS NOT AVAILABLE OR IMPRACTICAL TO USE, GENTLY WRAP AFFECTED PART IN BLANKETS. ENCOURAGE VICTIM TO EXERCISE AFFECTED PART WHILE IT IS BEING WARMED. ALLOW CIRCULATION TO RETURN NATURALLY (MATHESON GAS, 6TH ED.). GET MEDICAL ATTENTION IMMEDIATELY.

EYE CONTACT: ARSINE: **ACUTE EXPOSURE-** NO IRRITATION HAS BEEN OBSERVED IN FATAL CASES. FROSTBITE MAY OCCUR FROM CONTACT WITH THE LIQUEFIED GAS. **CHRONIC EXPOSURE-** NO DATA AVAILABLE.
FIRST AID- WASH EYES IMMEDIATELY WITH LARGE AMOUNTS OF WATER, OCCASIONALLY LIFTING UPPER AND LOWER LIDS, UNTIL NO EVIDENCE OF CHEMICAL REMAINS (AT LEAST 15-20 MINUTES). CONTINUE IRRIGATING WITH NORMAL SALINE UNTIL THE PH HAS RETURNED TO NORMAL (30-60 MINUTES). COVER WITH STERILE BANDAGES. GET MEDICAL ATTENTION IMMEDIATELY.

INGESTION: ARSINE: **ACUTE EXPOSURE-** INGESTION OF A GAS IS UNLIKELY. **CHRONIC EXPOSURE-** NO DATA AVAILABLE.
FIRST AID- TREAT SYMPTOMATICALLY AND SUPPORTIVELY. GET MEDICAL ATTENTION IMMEDIATELY. IF VOMITING OCCURS, KEEP HEAD LOWER THAN HIPS TO PREVENT ASPIRATION.
ANTIDOTE: NO SPECIFIC ANTIDOTE. TREAT SYMPTOMATICALLY AND SUPPORTIVELY.

REACTIVITY

REACTIVITY: STABLE UNDER NORMAL TEMPERATURES AND PRESSURES.
INCOMPATIBILITIES: ARSINE: CHLORINE: POSSIBLE IGNITION. NITRIC ACID: POSSIBLE EXPLOSION. POTASSIUM AND LIQUID AMMONIA: VIGOROUS REACTION @ -78 C. OXIDIZERS: POSSIBLE EXPLOSION. FLUORINE: POSSIBLE IGNITION. NITROGEN TRICHLORIDE: POSSIBLE EXPLOSION.
DECOMPOSITION: MAY FORM TOXIC HAZARDOUS GAS WHEN HEATED TO 230 C, DEPOSITING ARSENIC WHICH VOLATILIZES AT 400 C. ON EXPOSURE TO LIGHT, MOIST ARSINE DECOMPOSES QUICKLY DEPOSITING SHINY BLACK ARSENIC.
POLYMERIZATION: HAZARDOUS POLYMERIZATION HAS NOT BEEN REPORTED TO OCCUR UNDER NORMAL TEMPERATURES AND PRESSURES.

STORAGE AND DISPOSAL

OBSERVE ALL FEDERAL, STATE AND LOCAL REGULATIONS WHEN STORING OR DISPOSING OF THIS SUBSTANCE. FOR ASSISTANCE, CONTACT THE DISTRICT DIRECTOR OF THE ENVIRONMENTAL PROTECTION AGENCY.

STORAGE

STORE AWAY FROM INCOMPATIBLE SUBSTANCES.

THRESHOLD PLANNING QUANTITY (TPQ): THE SUPERFUND AMENDMENTS AND REAUTHORIZATION ACT (SARA) SECTION 302 REQUIRES THAT EACH FACILITY WHERE ANY EXTREMELY HAZARDOUS SUBSTANCE IS PRESENT IN A QUANTITY EQUAL TO OR GREATER THAN THE TPQ ESTABLISHED FOR THAT SUBSTANCE NOTIFY THE STATE EMERGENCY RESPONSE COMMISSION FOR THE STATE IN WHICH IT IS LOCATED. SECTION 303 OF SARA REQUIRES THESE FACILITIES TO PARTICIPATE IN LOCAL EMERGENCY RESPONSE PLANNING (40 CFR 355.30).

CONDITIONS TO AVOID

AVOID CONTACT WITH HEAT, SPARKS, FLAMES, OR OTHER IGNITION SOURCES. VAPORS MAY BE EXPLOSIVE. MATERIAL IS EXTREMELY POISONOUS; AVOID INHALATION OF VAPORS OR CONTACT WITH SKIN. DO NOT ALLOW MATERIAL TO CONTAMINATE WATER SOURCES.

SPILL AND LEAK PROCEDURES

WATER SPILL: THE CALIFORNIA SAFE DRINKING WATER AND TOXIC ENFORCEMENT ACT OF 1986 (PROPOSITION 65) PROHIBITS CONTAMINATING ANY KNOWN SOURCE OF DRINKING WATER WITH SUBSTANCES KNOWN TO CAUSE CANCER AND/OR REPRODUCTIVE TOXICITY.

OCCUPATIONAL SPILL: SHUT OFF IGNITION SOUCES. STOP LEAK IF YOU CAN DO IT WITHOUT RISK. USE WATER SPRAY TO REDUCE VAPORS. ISOLATE AREA UNTIL GAS HAS DISPERSED. NO SMOKING, FLAMES OR FLARES IN HAZARD AREA! KEEP UNNECESSARY PEOPLE AWAY; ISOLATE HAZARD AREA AND DENY ENTRY. VENTILATE CLOSED SPACES BEFORE ENTERING THEM. EVACUATE AREA ENDANGERED BY GAS.

REPORTABLE QUANTITY (RQ): 1 POUND THE SUPERFUND AMENDMENTS AND REAUTHORIZATION ACT (SARA) SECTION 304 REQUIRES THAT A RELEASE EQUAL TO OR GREATER THAN THE REPORTABLE QUANTITY FOR THIS SUBSTANCE BE IMMEDIATELY REPORTED TO THE LOCAL EMERGENCY PLANNING COMMITTEE AND THE STATE EMERGENCY RESPONSE COMMISSION (40 CFR 355.40). IF THE RELEASE OF THIS SUBSTANCE IS REPORTABLE UNDER CERCLA SECTION 103, THE NATIONAL RESPONSE CENTER MUST BE NOTIFIED IMMEDIATELY AT (800) 424-8802 OR (202) 426-2675 IN THE METROPOLITAN WASHINGTON, D.C. AREA (40 CFR 302.6).

PROTECTIVE EQUIPMENT

VENTILATION: PROVIDE LOCAL EXHAUST OR PROCESS ENCLOSURE VENTILATION TO MEET THE PUBLISHED EXPOSURE LIMITS. VENTILATION EQUIPMENT MUST BE EXPLOSION-PROOF.

RESPIRATOR: THE FOLLOWING RESPIRATORS AND MAXIMUM USE CONCENTRATIONS ARE RECOMMENDATIONS BY THE U.S. DEPARTMENT OF HEALTH AND HUMAN SERVICES, NIOSH POCKET GUIDE TO CHEMICAL HAZARDS; NIOSH CRITERIA DOCUMENTS OR BY THE U.S. DEPARTMENT OF LABOR, 29 CFR 1910 SUBPART Z. THE SPECIFIC RESPIRATOR SELECTED MUST BE BASED ON CONTAMINATION LEVELS FOUND IN THE WORK PLACE, MUST NOT EXCEED THE WORKING LIMITS OF THE RESPIRATOR AND BE JOINTLY APPROVED BY THE NATIONAL INSTITUTE FOR OCCUPATIONAL SAFETY AND HEALTH AND THE MINE SAFETY AND HEALTH ADMINISTRATION (NIOSH-MSHA).

ARSINE (AT ANY DETECTABLE CONCENTRATION): ANY SELF-CONTAINED BREATHING APPARATUS WITH FULL FACEPIECE AND OPERATED IN PRESSURE-DEMAND OR OTHER POSITIVE PRESSURE MODE. ANY SUPPLIED-AIR WITH FULL FACEPIECE AND OPERATED IN PRESSURE-DEMAND OR OTHER POSITIVE PRESSURE MODE IN COMBINATION WITH AN AUXILIARY SELF-CONTAINED BREATHING APPARATUS OPERATED IN PRESSURE-DEMAND OR OTHER POSITIVE PRESSURE MODE.

ESCAPE- ANY AIR-PURIFYING FULL FACEPIECE RESPIRATOR (GAS-MASK) WITH CHIN-STYLE OR FRONT- OR BACK-MOUNTED CANISTER PROVIDING PROTECTION AGAINST ARSINE. ANY ESCAPE-TYPE SELF-CONTAINED BREATHING APPARATUS.

FOR FIREFIGHTING AND OTHER IMMEDIATELY DANGEROUS TO LIFE OR HEALTH CONDITIONS:

SELF-CONTAINED BREATHING APPARATUS WITH FULL FACEPIECE OPERATED IN PRESSURE-DEMAND OR OTHER POSITIVE PRESSURE MODE.

SUPPLIED-AIR RESPIRATOR WITH FULL FACEPIECE AND OPERATED IN PRESSURE-DEMAND OR OTHER POSITIVE PRESSURE MODE IN COMBINATION WITH AN AUXILIARY SELF-CONTAINED BREATHING APPARATUS OPERATED IN PRESSURE-DEMAND OR OTHER POSITIVE PRESSURE MODE.

CLOTHING: FOR THE GAS FORM, PROTECTIVE CLOTHING NOT REQUIRED. IF CONTACT WITH THE LIQUID FORM IS POSSIBLE, EMPLOYEE MUST WEAR APPROPRIATE PROTECTIVE CLOTHING AND EQUIPMENT TO PREVENT SKIN FROM FREEZING.

GLOVES: WEAR FULL PROTECTIVE, COLD INSULATING GLOVES.

EYE PROTECTION: FOR THE GAS FORM EYE PROTECTION IS NOT REQUIRED BUT RECOMMENDED. WHERE THERE IS ANY POSSIBILITY OF CONTACT WITH THE LIQUID FORM, EMPLOYEE MUST WEAR SPLASH-PROOF SAFETY GOGGLES AND A FACESHIELD TO PREVENT CONTACT WITH THIS SUBSTANCE. CONTACT LENSES SHOULD NOT BE WORN.

EMERGENCY WASH FACILITIES: WHERE THERE IS ANY POSSIBILITY THAT AN EMPLOYEE'S EYES AND/OR SKIN MAY BE EXPOSED TO THE LIQUID FORM OF THIS SUBSTANCE, THE EMPLOYER SHOULD PROVIDE AN EYE WASH FOUNTAIN AND QUICK DRENCH SHOWER WITHIN THE IMMEDIATE WORK AREA FOR EMERGENCY USE.

AUTHORIZED BY- OCCUPATIONAL HEALTH SERVICES, INC.
CREATION DATE: 10/04/89 ***REVISION DATE:*** 07/12/90

MATERIAL SAFETY DATA SHEET

OCCUPATIONAL HEALTH SERVICES, INC.
AGRICULTURE AND PESTICIDE DIVISION
450 SEVENTH AVENUE, SUITE 2407
NEW YORK, NEW YORK 10123
1-800-445-MSDS OR (212) 967-1100

EMERGENCY CONTACT:
JOHN S. BRANSFORD, JR. (615) 292-1180

SUBSTANCE IDENTIFICATION

CAS-NUMBER 8052-42-4

SUBSTANCE: ASPHALT

TRADE NAMES/SYNONYMS: ASPHALTUM; BITUMEN; JUDEAN PITCH; MINERAL PITCH; PETROLEUM PITCH; ROAD ASPHALT; ROAD TAR; TRINIDAD PITCH; PETROLEUM ASPHALT; NA 1999; PST02140

MOLECULAR FORMULA: VARIES

MOLECULAR WEIGHT: VARIABLE

CERCLA RATINGS (SCALE 0-3): HEALTH=3 FIRE=1 REACTIVITY=0 PERSISTENCE=3

NFPA RATINGS (SCALE 0-4): HEALTH=0 FIRE=1 REACTIVITY=0

COMPONENTS AND CONTAMINANTS

COMPONENT: ASPHALT ***PERCENT:*** >99
CAS# 8052-42-4

OTHER CONTAMINANTS: MAY CONTAIN SULFUR AND TRACES OF NICKEL, IRON OR VANADIUM

EXPOSURE LIMITS: ASPHALT (PETROLEUM) FUMES: 5 MG/M3 ACGIH TWA 5 MG/M3 NIOSH RECOMMENDED 15 MINUTE CEILING

SUBJECT TO CALIFORNIA PROPOSITION 65 CANCER AND/OR REPRODUCTIVE TOXICITY WARNING AND RELEASE REQUIREMENTS- (FEBRUARY 27, 1987)

HYDROGEN SULFIDE: 10 PPM (14 MG/M3) OSHA TWA; 15 PPM (21 MG/M3) OSHA STEL 10 PPM (14 MG/M3) ACGIH TWA; 15 PPM (21 MG/M3) ACGIH STEL 10 PPM NIOSH RECOMMENDED 10 MINUTE CEILING

500 POUNDS SARA SECTION 302 THRESHOLD PLANNING QUANTITY 100 POUNDS SARA SECTION 304 REPORTABLE QUANTITY 100 POUNDS CERCLA SECTION 103 REPORTABLE QUANTITY

PHYSICAL DATA

DESCRIPTION: BLACK OR BROWN MASS OR VISCOUS LIQUID

BOILING POINT: >700 F (>300 C) ***SPECIFIC GRAVITY:*** 1.1

SOLUBILITY IN WATER: INSOLUBLE

SOLVENT SOLUBILITY: OIL, TURPENTINE, PETROLEUM, CARBON DISULFIDE, CHLOROFORM, ETHER, ACETONE; INSOLUBLE IN ALCOHOL

FIRE AND EXPLOSION DATA

FIRE AND EXPLOSION HAZARD: SLIGHT FIRE HAZARD WHEN EXPOSED TO HEAT OR FLAME.

FLASH POINT: 400 F (204 C) (CC) ***AUTOIGNITION TEMP.:*** 905 F (485 C)

FLAMMABILITY CLASS(OSHA): IIIB

FIREFIGHTING MEDIA: DRY CHEMICAL, CARBON DIOXIDE, HALON, WATER SPRAY OR STANDARD FOAM (1987 EMERGENCY RESPONSE GUIDEBOOK, DOT P 5800.4). FOR LARGER FIRES, USE WATER SPRAY, FOG OR STANDARD FOAM (1987 EMERGENCY RESPONSE GUIDEBOOK, DOT P 5800.4).

FIREFIGHTING: MOVE CONTAINER FROM FIRE AREA IF POSSIBLE. COOL FIRE-EXPOSED CONTAINERS WITH WATER FROM SIDE UNTIL WELL AFTER FIRE IS OUT. STAY AWAY FROM STORAGE TANK ENDS. FOR MASSIVE FIRE IN STORAGE AREA, USE UNMANNED HOSE HOLDER OR MONITOR NOZZLES, ELSE WITHDRAW FROM AREA AND LET FIRE BURN. WITHDRAW IMMEDIATELY IN CASE OF RISING SOUND FROM VENTING SAFETY DEVICE OR ANY DISCOLORATION OF STORAGE TANK DUE TO

FIRE (1987 EMERGENCY RESPONSE GUIDEBOOK, DOT P 5800.4, GUIDE PAGE 27). EXTINGUISH ONLY IF FLOW CAN BE STOPPED; USE WATER IN FLOODING AMOUNTS AS FOG SOLID STREAMS MAY NOT BE EFFECTIVE. COOL CONTAINERS WITH FLOODING AMOUNTS OF WATER, APPLY FROM AS FAR A DISTANCE AS POSSIBLE. AVOID BREATHING TOXIC VAPORS, KEEP UPWIND.
WATER OR FOAM MAY CAUSE FROTHING (NFPA 325M, FIRE HAZARD PROPERTIES OF FLAMMABLE LIQUIDS, GASES, AND VOLATILE SOLIDS, 1984)

TRANSPORTATION DATA

DEPARTMENT OF TRANSPORTATION HAZARD CLASSIFICATION 49 CFR 172.101: ORM-C
DEPARTMENT OF TRANSPORTATION LABELING REQUIREMENTS 49 CFR 172.101 AND SUBPART E: NONE
DEPARTMENT OF TRANSPORTATION PACKAGING REQUIREMENTS: NONE
EXCEPTIONS: NONE

TOXICITY

ASPHALT: TOXICITY DATA: MUTAGENIC DATA (IARC); TUMORIGENIC DATA (RTECS). CARCINOGEN STATUS: HUMAN INADEQUATE EVIDENCE (IARC GROUP-3 FOR BITUMENS); ANIMAL SUFFICIENT EVIDENCE (IARC GROUP-2B FOR EXTRACTS OF STEAM-REFINED AND AIR-REFINED BITUMENS); ANIMAL LIMITED EVIDENCE (FOR STEAM-REFINED AND CRACKING-RESIDUE BITUMENS); ANIMAL INADEQUATE EVIDENCE (FOR AIR-REFINED BITUMENS). THERE IS INADEQUATE EVIDENCE THAT BITUMENS ALONE ARE CARCINOGENIC TO HUMANS. THERE IS SUFFICIENT EVIDENCE OF CARCINOGENICITY OF EXTRACTS OF STEAM-REFINED BITUMENS, AIR-REFINED BITUMENS, AND POOLED MIXTURES OF STEAM- AND AIR-REFINED BITUMENS IN EXPERIMENTAL ANIMALS. THERE IS LIMITED EVIDENCE FOR THE CARCINOGENICITY OF UNDILUTED STEAM-REFINED BITUMENS AND FOR CRACKING-RESIDUE BITUMENS IN EXPERIMENTAL ANIMALS. THERE IS INADEQUATE EVIDENCE FOR THE CARCINOGENICITY OF UNDILUTED AIR-REFINED BITUMENS IN EXPERIMENTAL ANIMALS. LOCAL EFFECTS: IRRITANT- INHALATION, SKIN, AND EYES. ACUTE TOXICITY LEVEL: NO DATA AVAILABLE. TARGET EFFECTS: POISONING MAY AFFECT THE RESPIRATORY SYSTEM.

HEALTH EFFECTS AND FIRST AID

INHALATION: ASPHALT: IRRITANT. **ACUTE EXPOSURE-** INHALATION OF FUMES FROM HOT ASPHALT MAY CAUSE IRRITATION OF THE MUCOUS MEMBRANES. WHEN HEATED, HYDROGEN SULFIDE, AND EXTREMELY TOXIC AND FLAMMABLE GAS MAY BE RELEASED AND ACCUMULATE IN ENCLOSED SPACES. HYDROGEN SULFIDE IS EXTREMELY IRRITATING AND AT 500-1000 PPM MAY CAUSE COMA, CONVULSIONS AND DEATH WITHIN 30 MINUTES. AT VERY HIGH CONCENTRATIONS, RESPIRATORY PARALYSIS AND DEATH FROM ASPHYXIA ARE IMMEDIATE. **CHRONIC EXPOSURE-** MICE WHICH INHALED AN AEROSOL OF PETROLEUM ASPHALT AND SMOKE FROM HEATED PETROLEUM ASPHALT SUFFERED CONGESTION, ACUTE BRONCHITIS, PNEUMONITIS, BRONCHIAL DILATION, ABSCESS FORMATION, EPITHELIAL ATROPHY AND NECROSIS. GUINEA PIGS AND RATS INHALING FUMES FROM HEATED ASPHALT SHOWED EFFECTS SUCH AS CHRONIC FIBROSING PNEUMONITIS WITH PERIBRONCHIAL ADENOMATOSIS; ONLY THE RATS DEVELOPED SQUAMOUS CELL METAPLASIA.
FIRST AID- REMOVE FROM EXPOSURE AREA TO FRESH AIR IMMEDIATELY. IF BREATHING HAS STOPPED, GIVE ARTIFICIAL RESPIRATION. MAINTAIN AIRWAY AND BLOOD PRESSURE AND ADMINISTER OXYGEN IF AVAILABLE. KEEP AFFECTED PERSON WARM AND AT REST. TREAT SYMPTOMATICALLY AND SUPPORTIVELY. ADMINISTRATION OF OXYGEN SHOULD BE PERFORMED BY QUALIFIED PERSONNEL. GET MEDICAL ATTENTION IMMEDIATELY.

SKIN CONTACT: ASPHALT: IRRITANT/CARCINOGEN. **ACUTE EXPOSURE-** CONTACT WITH FUMES FROM HOT ASPHALT MAY CAUSE IRRITATION. DIRECT CONTACT WITH HOT ASPHALT MAY CAUSE THERMAL BURNS. **CHRONIC EXPOSURE-** REPEATED OR PROLONGED CONTACT WITH FUMES FROM HOT ASPHALT MAY CAUSE DERMATITIS AND ACNE-LIKE LESIONS AS WELL AS MILD KERATOSES. THE GREENISH-YELLOW FUMES GIVEN OFF WHEN ASPHALT IS BOILED CAN CAUSE PHOTO-SENSITIZATION AND MELANOSIS. IN SOME STUDIES, REPEATED SKIN APPLICATION OF VARIOUS TYES OF BITUMENS RSULTED IN TUMORS IN MICE.
FIRST AID- IF CONTACT IS NOT WITH MOLTEN MATERIAL, REMOVE CONTAMINATED CLOTHING AND SHOES IMMEDIATELY. WASH AFFECTED AREA WITH SOAP OR MILD DETERGENT AND LARGE AMOUNTS OF WATER UNTIL NO EVIDENCE OF CHEMICAL REMAINS (APPROXIMATELY 15-20 MINUTES). GET MEDICAL ATTENTION IMMEDIATELY. BURNS FROM CONTACT WITH MOLTEN MATERIAL SHOULD BE TREATED LIKE THERMAL BURNS. COOL AFFECTED AREA AS QUICKLY AS POSSIBLE BY DRENCHING OR IMMERSING IN WATER UNTIL MATERIAL SOLIDIFIES. DO NOT ATTEMPT TO REMOVE SOLIDIFIED MATERIAL. COVER AREA WITH STERILE, DRY DRESSING. GET MEDICAL ATTENTION IMMEDIATELY.

EYE CONTACT: ASPHALT: IRRITANT. **ACUTE EXPOSURE-** FUMES FROM HOT ASPHALT MAY CAUSE IRRITATION. DIRECT CONTACT WITH HOT ASPHALT MAY CAUSE THERMAL BURNS. **CHRONIC EXPOSURE-** REPEATED OR PROLONGED EXPOSURE TO ASPHALT FUMES MAY CAUSE CONJUNCTIVITIS.
FIRST AID- WASH EYES IMMEDIATELY WITH LARGE AMOUNTS OF WATER, OCCASIONALLY LIFTING UPPER AND LOWER LIDS, UNTIL NO EVIDENCE OF CHEMICAL REMAINS (AT LEAST 15-20 MINUTES). CONTINUE IRRIGATING WITH NORMAL SALINE UNTIL THE PH HAS RETURNED TO NORMAL (30-60 MINUTES). COVER WITH STERILE BANDAGES. GET MEDICAL ATTENTION IMMEDIATELY.

INGESTION: ASPHALT: **ACUTE EXPOSURE-** MAY CAUSE NAUSEA AND IRRITATION OF THE GASTROINTESTINAL TRACT. **CHRONIC EXPOSURE-** ASPHALT WORKERS WHO WERE IN THE HABIT OF CHEWING ASPHALT AND SOMETIMES SWALLOWING IT HAVE BEEN REPORTED TO HAVE PYLORIC OBSTRUCTION BECAUSE THE INDIGESTIBLE MASS ACCUMULATES IN THE STOMACH FORMING A STONY CONCRETION.
FIRST AID- TREAT SYMPTOMATICALLY AND SUPPORTIVELY. GET MEDICAL ATTENTION IMMEDIATELY. IF VOMITING OCCURS, KEEP HEAD LOWER THAN HIPS TO PREVENT ASPIRATION.
ANTIDOTE: NO SPECIFIC ANTIDOTE. TREAT SYMPTOMATICALLY AND SUPPORTIVELY.

REACTIVITY

REACTIVITY: STABLE UNDER NORMAL TEMPERATURES AND PRESSURES.
INCOMPATIBILITIES: ASPHALT: FLUORINE: BURNS WITH SPATTERING AND SMALL FLAMES. NAPHTHA: READILY IGNITES. VOLATILE SOLVENTS: READILY IGNITES.
DECOMPOSITION: THERMAL DECOMPOSITION MAY RELEASE TOXIC AND/OR HAZARDOUS GASES.
POLYMERIZATION: HAZARDOUS POLYMERIZATION HAS NOT BEEN REPORTED TO OCCUR UNDER NORMAL TEMPERATURES AND PRESSURES.

CONDITIONS TO AVOID

AVOID CONTACT WITH HEAT, SPARKS, FLAMES, OR OTHER SOURCES OF IGNITION. VAPORS MAY BE EXPLOSIVE. AVOID OVERHEATING OF CONTAINERS; CONTAINERS MAY VIOLENTLY RUPTURE IN HEAT OF FIRE. AVOID CONTAMINATION OF WATER SOURCES.

SPILL AND LEAK PROCEDURES

WATER SPILL: THE CALIFORNIA SAFE DRINKING WATER AND TOXIC ENFORCEMENT ACT OF 1986 (PROPOSITION 65) PROHIBITS CONTAMINATING ANY KNOWN SOURCE OF DRINKING WATER WITH SUBSTANCES KNOWN TO CAUSE CANCER AND/OR REPRODUCTIVE TOXICITY.
OCCUPATIONAL SPILL: SHUT OFF IGNITION SOURCES. STOP LEAK IF YOU CAN DO IT WITHOUT RISK. USE WATER SPRAY TO REDUCE VAPORS. FOR SMALL SPILLS, TAKE UP WITH SAND OR OTHER ABSORBENT MATERIAL AND PLACE INTO CONTAINERS FOR LATER DISPOSAL. FOR LARGER SPILLS, DIKE FAR AHEAD OF SPILL FOR LATER DISPOSAL. NO SMOKING, FLAMES OR FLARES IN HAZARD AREA. KEEP UNNECESSARY PEOPLE AWAY; ISOLATE HAZARD AREA AND RESTRICT ENTRY.

PROTECTIVE EQUIPMENT

VENTILATION: PROVIDE LOCAL EXHAUST VENTILATION SYSTEM TO MEET PUBLISHED EXPOSURE LIMITS.
RESPIRATOR: THE FOLLOWING RESPIRATORS ARE RECOMMENDED BASED ON INFORMATION FOUND IN THE PHYSICAL DATA, TOXICITY AND HEALTH EFFECTS SECTIONS. THEY ARE RANKED IN ORDER FROM MINIMUM TO MAXIMUM RESPIRATORY PROTECTION. THE SPECIFIC RESPIRATOR SELECTED MUST BE BASED ON CONTAMINATION LEVELS FOUND IN THE WORK PLACE, MUST NOT EXCEED THE WORKING LIMITS OF THE RESPIRATOR AND BE JOINTLY APPROVED BY THE NATIONAL INSTITUTE FOR OCCUPATIONAL SAFETY AND HEALTH AND THE MINE SAFETY AND HEALTH ADMINISTRATION (NIOSH-MSHA).
TYPE 'C' SUPPLIED-AIR RESPIRATOR WITH A FULL FACEPIECE OPERATED IN PRESSURE-DEMAND OR OTHER POSITIVE PRESSURE MODE OR WITH A FULL FACEPIECE, HELMET OR HOOD OPERATED IN CONTINOUS-FLOW MODE.
SELF-CONTAINED BREATHING APPARATUS WITH A FULL FACEPIECE OPERATED IN PRESSURE-DEMAND OR OTHER POSITIVE PRESSURE MODE.
FOR FIREFIGHTING AND OTHER IMMEDIATELY DANGEROUS TO LIFE OR HEALTH CONDITIONS:
SELF-CONTAINED BREATHING APPARATUS WITH FULL FACEPIECE OPERATED IN PRESSURE-DEMAND OR OTHER POSITIVE PRESSURE MODE.
SUPPLIED-AIR RESPIRATOR WITH FULL FACEPIECE AND OPERATED IN PRESSURE-DEMAND OR OTHER POSITIVE PRESSURE MODE IN COMBINATION WITH AN AUXILIARY SELF-CONTAINED BREATHING APPARATUS OPERATED IN PRESSURE-DEMAND OR OTHER POSITIVE PRESSURE MODE.

CLOTHING: EMPLOYEE MUST WEAR APPROPRIATE PROTECTIVE (IMPERVIOUS) CLOTHING AND EQUIPMENT TO PREVENT REPEATED OR PROLONGED SKIN CONTACT WITH THIS SUBSTANCE.
GLOVES: EMPLOYEE MUST WEAR APPROPRIATE PROTECTIVE GLOVES TO PREVENT CONTACT WITH THIS SUBSTANCE.
EYE PROTECTION: EMPLOYEE MUST WEAR SPLASH-PROOF OR DUST-RESISTANT SAFETY GOGGLES WITH OR WITHOUT A FACESHIELD TO PREVENT CONTACT WITH THIS SUBSTANCE.
EMERGENCY EYE WASH: WHERE THERE IS ANY POSSIBILITY THAT AN EMPLOYEE'S EYES MAY BE EXPOSED TO THIS SUBSTANCE, THE EMPLOYER SHOULD PROVIDE AN EYE WASH FOUNTAIN WITHIN THE IMMEDIATE WORK AREA FOR EMERGENCY USE.

AUTHORIZED BY- OCCUPATIONAL HEALTH SERVICES, INC.
CREATION DATE: 10/04/89 ***REVISION DATE:*** 07/12/90

MATERIAL SAFETY DATA SHEET

OCCUPATIONAL HEALTH SERVICES, INC.
AGRICULTURE AND PESTICIDE DIVISION
450 SEVENTH AVENUE, SUITE 2407
NEW YORK, NEW YORK 10123
1-800-445-MSDS OR (212) 967-1100

EMERGENCY CONTACT:
JOHN S. BRANSFORD, JR. (615) 292-1180

SUBSTANCE IDENTIFICATION

CAS-NUMBER 1610-17-9
SUBSTANCE: **ATRATON**
TRADE NAMES/SYNONYMS: 1,3,5-TRIAZINE-2,4-DIAMINE, N-ETHYL-6-METHOXY-N'-(1-METHYLETHYL)-; S-TRIAZINE, 2-(ETHYLAMINO)-4-(ISOPROPYLAMINO)-6-METHOXY-; N-ETHYL-6-METHOXY-N'-(1-METHYLETHYL)-1,3,5-TRIAZINE-2,4-DIAMINE; 2-(ETHYLAMINO)-4-(ISOPROPYLAMINO)-6-METHOXY-S-TRIAZINE; 2-ETHYLAMINO-4-ISOPROPYLAMINO-6-METHOXY-1,3,5-TRIZAINE; ATRATONE; G 32293; GESATAMIN; C9H17N5O; PST02148
CHEMICAL FAMILY: S-TRIAZINE
MOLECULAR FORMULA: C9-H17-N5-O
MOLECULAR WEIGHT: 211.27
CERCLA RATINGS (SCALE 0-3): HEALTH=2 FIRE=1 REACTIVITY=0 PERSISTENCE=2
NFPA RATINGS (SCALE 0-4): HEALTH=2 FIRE=1 REACTIVITY=0

COMPONENTS AND CONTAMINANTS

COMPONENT: ATRATON ***PERCENT:*** 100.0
CAS# 1610-17-9
OTHER CONTAMINANTS: NONE
EXPOSURE LIMITS: NO OCCUPATIONAL EXPOSURE LIMITS ESTABLISHED BY OSHA, ACGIH, OR NIOSH.

PHYSICAL DATA

DESCRIPTION: COLORLESS TO WHITE SOLID. ***MELTING POINT:*** 201-205 F (94-96 C)
SPECIFIC GRAVITY: NOT AVAILABLE ***VAPOR PRESSURE:*** NEGLIGIBLE
SOLUBILITY IN WATER: 0.18 % @ 20 C
SOLVENT SOLUBILITY: SOLUBLE IN ETHANOL, ACETONE, AND MOST OTHER ORGANIC SOLVENTS.

FIRE AND EXPLOSION DATA

FIRE AND EXPLOSION HAZARD: SLIGHT FIRE HAZARD WHEN EXPOSED TO HEAT OR FLAME.
FIREFIGHTING MEDIA: DRY CHEMICAL, CARBON DIOXIDE, HALON, WATER SPRAY OR STANDARD FOAM (1987 EMERGENCY RESPONSE GUIDEBOOK, DOT P 5800.4).
FOR LARGER FIRES, USE WATER SPRAY, FOG OR STANDARD FOAM (1987 EMERGENCY RESPONSE GUIDEBOOK, DOT P 5800.4).
FIREFIGHTING: MOVE CONTAINERS FROM FIRE AREA IF POSSIBLE (1987 EMERGENCY RESPONSE GUIDEBOOK, DOT P 5800.4, GUIDE PAGE 53).
EXTINGUISH USING AGENTS SUITABLE FOR SURROUNDING FIRE. USE FLOODING QUANTITIES OF WATER AS A FOG. KEEP MATERIAL OUT OF SEWERS AND WATER SOURCES. DO NOT TOUCH SPILLED MATERIAL. AVOID BREATHING HAZARDOUS FUMES; KEEP UPWIND.

TOXICITY

ATRATON: TOXICITY DATA: 1465 MG/KG ORAL-RAT LD50; 905 MG/KG ORAL-MOUSE LD50. CARCINOGEN STATUS: NONE. ACUTE TOXICITY LEVEL: MODERATELY TOXIC BY INGESTION. TARGET EFFECTS: NO DATA AVAILABLE.

HEALTH EFFECTS AND FIRST AID

INHALATION: ATRATON: **ACUTE EXPOSURE-** SOME TRIAZINES ARE MILDLY IRRITATING TO THE UPPER RESPIRATORY TRACT. **CHRONIC EXPOSURE-** NO DATA AVAILABLE.
FIRST AID- REMOVE FROM EXPOSURE AREA TO FRESH AIR IMMEDIATELY. IF BREATHING HAS STOPPED, PERFORM ARTIFICIAL RESPIRATION. KEEP PERSON WARM AND AT REST. TREAT SYMPTOMATICALLY AND SUPPORTIVELY. GET MEDICAL ATTENTION IMMEDIATELY.

SKIN CONTACT: ATRATON: **ACUTE EXPOSURE-** SOME TRIAZINES ARE MILDLY IRRITATING TO THE SKIN. **CHRONIC EXPOSURE-** NO DATA AVAILABLE.
FIRST AID- REMOVE CONTAMINATED CLOTHING AND SHOES IMMEDIATELY. WASH AFFECTED AREA WITH SOAP OR MILD DETERGENT AND LARGE AMOUNTS OF WATER UNTIL NO EVIDENCE OF CHEMICAL REMAINS (APPROXIMATELY 15-20 MINUTES). GET MEDICAL ATTENTION IMMEDIATELY.

EYE CONTACT: ATRATON: **ACUTE EXPOSURE-** SOME TRIAZINES ARE MILDLY IRRITATING TO THE EYES. **CHRONIC EXPOSURE-** NO DATA AVAILABLE.
FIRST AID- WASH EYES IMMEDIATELY WITH LARGE AMOUNTS OF WATER OR NORMAL SALINE, OCCASIONALLY LIFTING UPPER AND LOWER LIDS, UNTIL NO EVIDENCE OF CHEMICAL REMAINS (APPROXIMATELY 15-20 MINUTES). GET MEDICAL ATTENTION IMMEDIATELY.

INGESTION: ATRATON: **ACUTE EXPOSURE-** A LETHAL DOSE IN RATS WAS 1465 MG/KG; NO SYMPTOMS WERE REPORTED. **CHRONIC EXPOSURE-** THE RESULTS FROM A 90-DAY STUDY OF A SERIES OF RATS FED VARIOUS FORMULATIONS OF ATRATON WAS THAT ALL BEHAVIORS WAS COMPARABLE WITH THE CONTROLS.
FIRST AID- TREAT SYMPTOMATICALLY AND SUPPORTIVELY. GET MEDICAL ATTENTION IMMEDIATELY. IF VOMITING OCCURS, KEEP HEAD LOWER THAN HIPS TO PREVENT ASPIRATION.
ANTIDOTE: NO SPECIFIC ANTIDOTE. TREAT SYMPTOMATICALLY AND SUPPORTIVELY.

REACTIVITY

REACTIVITY: STABLE UNDER NORMAL TEMPERATURES AND PRESSURES.
INCOMPATIBILITIES: ATRATON: NO DATA AVAILABLE.
DECOMPOSITION: THERMAL DECOMPOSITION PRODUCTS MAY INCLUDE TOXIC OXIDES OF CARBON AND NITROGEN.
POLYMERIZATION: HAZARDOUS POLYMERIZATION HAS NOT BEEN REPORTED TO OCCUR UNDER NORMAL TEMPERATURES AND PRESSURES.

STORAGE AND DISPOSAL

OBSERVE ALL FEDERAL, STATE AND LOCAL REGULATIONS WHEN STORING OR DISPOSING OF THIS SUBSTANCE. FOR ASSISTANCE, CONTACT THE DISTRICT DIRECTOR OF THE ENVIRONMENTAL PROTECTION AGENCY.

STORAGE

STORE IN ACCORDANCE WITH 40 CFR 165 RECOMMENDED PROCEDURES FOR THE DISPOSAL AND STORAGE OF PESTICIDES AND PESTICIDE CONTAINERS.

DISPOSAL

DISPOSAL MUST BE IN ACCORDANCE WITH 40 CFR 165 RECOMMENDED PROCEDURES FOR THE DISPOSAL AND STORAGE OF PESTICIDES AND PESTICIDE CONTAINERS.

CONDITIONS TO AVOID

MAY BURN BUT DOES NOT IGNITE READILY.

SPILL AND LEAK PROCEDURES

OCCUPATIONAL SPILL: DO NOT TOUCH SPILLED MATERIAL. STOP LEAK IF YOU CAN DO IT WITHOUT RISK. FOR SMALL SPILLS, TAKE UP WITH SAND OR OTHER ABSORBENT MATERIAL AND PLACE INTO CONTAINERS FOR LATER DISPOSAL. FOR SMALL DRY SPILLS, WITH A CLEAN SHOVEL PLACE MATERIAL INTO CLEAN, DRY CONTAINER AND COVER. MOVE CONTAINERS FROM SPILL AREA. FOR LARGER SPILLS, DIKE FAR AHEAD OF SPILL FOR LATER DISPOSAL. KEEP UNNECESSARY PEOPLE AWAY. ISOLATE HAZARD AREA AND DENY ENTRY.

PROTECTIVE EQUIPMENT

VENTILATION: PROVIDE LOCAL EXHAUST OR GENERAL DILUTION VENTILATION SYSTEM.
RESPIRATOR: THE FOLLOWING RESPIRATORS ARE RECOMMENDED BASED ON INFORMATION FOUND IN THE PHYSICAL DATA, TOXICITY AND HEALTH EFFECTS SECTIONS. THEY ARE RANKED IN ORDER FROM MINIMUM TO MAXIMUM RESPIRATORY PROTECTION. THE SPECIFIC RESPIRATOR SELECTED MUST BE BASED ON CONTAMINATION LEVELS FOUND IN THE WORK PLACE, MUST NOT EXCEED THE WORKING LIMITS OF THE RESPIRATOR AND BE JOINTLY APPROVED BY THE NATIONAL INSTITUTE FOR OCCUPATIONAL SAFETY AND HEALTH AND THE MINE SAFETY AND HEALTH ADMINISTRATION (NIOSH-MSHA).

CHEMICAL CARTRIDGE RESPIRATOR WITH AN ORGANIC VAPOR CARTRIDGE(S) WITH A FULL FACEPIECE AND ORGANIC VAPOR CARTRIDGE(S) IN COMBINATION WITH A DUST AND MIST FILTER.
POWERED AIR-PURIFYING RESPIRATOR WITH A TIGHT-FITTING FACEPIECE AND ORGANIC VAPOR CARTRIDGE(S) IN COMBINATION WITH A HIGH-EFFICIENCY PARTICULATE FILTER.
TYPE 'C' SUPPLIED-AIR RESPIRATOR WITH A FULL FACEPIECE OPERATED IN A PRESSURE-DEMAND OR OTHER POSITIVE PRESSURE MODE.
SELF-CONTAINED BREATHING APPARATUS WITH A FULL FACEPIECE OPERATED IN PRESSURE-DEMAND OR OTHER POSITIVE PRESSURE MODE.
FOR FIREFIGHTING AND OTHER IMMEDIATELY DANGEROUS TO LIFE OR HEALTH CONDITIONS:
SELF-CONTAINED BREATHING APPARATUS WITH FULL FACEPIECE OPERATED IN PRESSURE-DEMAND OR OTHER POSITIVE PRESSURE MODE.
SUPPLIED-AIR RESPIRATOR WITH FULL FACEPIECE AND OPERATED IN PRESSURE-DEMAND OR OTHER POSITIVE PRESSURE MODE IN COMBINATION WITH AN AUXILIARY SELF-CONTAINED BREATHING APPARATUS OPERATED IN PRESSURE-DEMAND OR OTHER POSITIVE PRESSURE MODE.

CLOTHING: EMPLOYEE MUST WEAR APPROPRIATE PROTECTIVE (IMPERVIOUS) CLOTHING AND EQUIPMENT TO PREVENT REPEATED OR PROLONGED SKIN CONTACT WITH THIS SUBSTANCE.

GLOVES: EMPLOYEE MUST WEAR APPROPRIATE PROTECTIVE GLOVES TO PREVENT CONTACT WITH THIS SUBSTANCE.

EYE PROTECTION: EMPLOYEE MUST WEAR SPLASH-PROOF OR DUST-RESISTANT SAFETY GOGGLES TO PREVENT EYE CONTACT WITH THIS SUBSTANCE.
EMERGENCY EYE WASH: WHERE THERE IS ANY POSSIBILITY THAT AN EMPLOYEE'S EYES MAY BE EXPOSED TO THIS SUBSTANCE, THE EMPLOYER SHOULD PROVIDE AN EYE WASH FOUNTAIN WITHIN THE IMMEDIATE WORK AREA FOR EMERGENCY USE.

AUTHORIZED BY- OCCUPATIONAL HEALTH SERVICES, INC.
CREATION DATE: 10/04/89 ***REVISION DATE:*** 05/09/90

MATERIAL SAFETY DATA SHEET

OCCUPATIONAL HEALTH SERVICES, INC.
AGRICULTURE AND PESTICIDE DIVISION
450 SEVENTH AVENUE, SUITE 2407
NEW YORK, NEW YORK 10123
1-800-445-MSDS OR (212) 967-1100

EMERGENCY CONTACT:
JOHN S. BRANSFORD, JR. (615) 292-1180

SUBSTANCE IDENTIFICATION

CAS-NUMBER 1912-24-9

SUBSTANCE: **ATRAZINE**

TRADE NAMES/SYNONYMS: 1,3,5-TRIAZINE-2,4-DIAMINE, 6-CHLORO-N-ETHYL-N'-(1-METHYLETHYL)-; S-TRIAZINE, 2-CHLORO-4-(ETHYLAMINO)-6-(ISOPROPYLAMINO)-; 6-CHLORO-N-ETHYL-N'-(1-METHYLETHYL)-1,3,5-TRIAZINE-2,4-DIAMINE; 2-CHLORO-4-ETHYLAMINO-6-ISOPROPYLAMINE-S-TRIAZINE; 2-CHLORO-4-(ETHYLAMINO)-6-(ISOPROPYLAMINO)-S-TRIAZINE; AATREX; AKTICON; AKTIKON; ARGEZIN; ATRATAF; ATRAZIN; G 30027; GESAPRIM; HERBATOXOL; HUNGAZIN; PRIMATOL A; RADAZIN; ZEAZIN; C8H14CLN5; PST02150

CHEMICAL FAMILY: S-TRIAZINE

MOLECULAR FORMULA: C8-H14-CL-N5

MOLECULAR WEIGHT: 215.68

CERCLA RATINGS (SCALE 0-3): HEALTH=2 FIRE=1 REACTIVITY=0 PERSISTENCE=3

NFPA RATINGS (SCALE 0-4): HEALTH=2 FIRE=1 REACTIVITY=0

COMPONENTS AND CONTAMINANTS

COMPONENT: ATRAZINE ***PERCENT:*** 100
CAS# 1912-24-9

OTHER CONTAMINANTS: NONE

EXPOSURE LIMITS: ATRAZINE: 5 MG/M3 OSHA TWA 5 MG/M3 ACGIH TWA

PHYSICAL DATA

DESCRIPTION: WHITE CRYSTALLINE SOLID. ***MELTING POINT:*** 340-345 F (171-174 C)

SPECIFIC GRAVITY: 1.187 ***VAPOR PRESSURE:*** NEGLIGIBLE

SOLUBILITY IN WATER: 0.007% @ 25 C

SOLVENT SOLUBILITY: SOLUBLE IN OCTAN-1-OL, CHLOROFORM, METHANOL, ETHER, N-PENTANE, ETHYL ACETATE, DIMETHYL SULFOXIDE.

FIRE AND EXPLOSION DATA

FIRE AND EXPLOSION HAZARD: SLIGHT FIRE HAZARD WHEN EXPOSED TO HEAT OR FLAME.

FIREFIGHTING MEDIA: DRY CHEMICAL, CARBON DIOXIDE, HALON, WATER SPRAY OR STANDARD FOAM (1987 EMERGENCY RESPONSE GUIDEBOOK, DOT P 5800.4).
FOR LARGER FIRES, USE WATER SPRAY, FOG OR STANDARD FOAM (1987 EMERGENCY RESPONSE GUIDEBOOK, DOT P 5800.4).

FIREFIGHTING: MOVE CONTAINERS FROM FIRE AREA IF POSSIBLE (1987 EMERGENCY RESPONSE GUIDEBOOK, DOT P 5800.4, GUIDE PAGE 53).
EXTINGUISH USING AGENTS SUITABLE FOR SURROUNDING FIRE. USE FLOODING QUANTITIES OF WATER AS A FOG. KEEP MATERIAL OUT OF SEWERS AND WATER SOURCES. DO NOT TOUCH SPILLED MATERIAL. AVOID BREATHING HAZARDOUS FUMES; KEEP UPWIND.

TOXICITY

ATRAZINE: IRRITATION DATA: 38 MG OPEN SKIN-RABBIT MILD; 6320 UG EYE-RABBIT SEVERE; 500 MG SKIN-MAMMAL MILD; 100 MG EYE-MAMMAL SEVERE. TOXICITY DATA: 5200 MG/M3/4 HOURS INHALATION-RAT LC50; 7500 MG/KG SKIN-RABBIT LD50; 672 MG/KG ORAL-RAT LD50; 850 MG/KG ORAL-MOUSE LD50; 750 MG/KG ORAL-RABBIT LD50; 1000 MG/KG ORAL-HAMSTER LD50; 235 MG/KG INTRAPERITONEAL-RAT LD50; 626 MG/KG INTRAPERITONEAL-MOUSE LD50; 1400 MG/KG UNREPORTED-MAMMAL LD50; MUTAGENIC DATA (RTECS); REPRODUCTIVE EFFECTS DATA (RTECS); TUMORIGENIC DATA (RTECS). CARCINOGEN STATUS: NONE. LOCAL EFFECTS: IRRITANT- EYE. ACUTE TOXICITY LEVEL: TOXIC BY INHALATION; MODERATELY TOXIC BY INGESTION; SLIGHTLY TOXIC BY DERMAL ABSORPTION. TARGET EFFECTS: NO DATA AVAILABLE.

HEALTH EFFECTS AND FIRST AID

INHALATION: ATRAZINE: TOXIC. **ACUTE EXPOSURE-** EXPOSURE TO LARGE CONCENTRATIONS OF DUST, AEROSOLS OR AQUEOUS EMULSIONS MAY CAUSE IRRITATION OF THE MUCOUS MEMBRANES. A LETHAL CONCENTRATION IN RATS WAS 5200 MG/M3/4 HOURS. **CHRONIC EXPOSURE-** NO DATA AVAILABLE.

FIRST AID- REMOVE FROM EXPOSURE AREA TO FRESH AIR IMMEDIATELY. IF BREATHING HAS STOPPED, PERFORM ARTIFICIAL RESPIRATION. KEEP PERSON WARM AND AT REST. TREAT SYMPTOMATICALLY AND SUPPORTIVELY. GET MEDICAL ATTENTION IMMEDIATELY.

SKIN CONTACT: ATRAZINE: **ACUTE EXPOSURE-** 38 MG APPLIED TO OPEN RABBIT SKIN WAS MILDLY IRRITATING. A CASE OF ALLERGIC REACTION FROM EXPOSURE TO ATRAZINE WAS REPORTED TO HAVE OCCURRED. ANIMAL STUDIES INDICATE SKIN ABSORPTION MAY OCCUR. **CHRONIC EXPOSURE-** PROLONGED OR REPEATED EXPOSURE MAY CAUSE DERMATITIS.

FIRST AID- REMOVE CONTAMINATED CLOTHING AND SHOES IMMEDIATELY. WASH AFFECTED AREA WITH SOAP OR MILD DETERGENT AND LARGE AMOUNTS OF WATER UNTIL NO EVIDENCE OF CHEMICAL REMAINS (APPROXIMATELY 15-20 MINUTES). GET MEDICAL ATTENTION IMMEDIATELY.

EYE CONTACT: ATRAZINE: IRRITANT. **ACUTE EXPOSURE-** 6320 UG APPLIED TO RABBIT EYES WAS SEVERELY IRRITATING. **CHRONIC EXPOSURE-** PROLONGED OR REPEATED EXPOSURE TO IRRITANTS MAY CAUSE CONJUNCTIVITIS.

FIRST AID- WASH EYES IMMEDIATELY WITH LARGE AMOUNTS OF WATER OR NORMAL SALINE, OCCASIONALLY LIFTING UPPER AND LOWER LIDS, UNTIL NO EVIDENCE OF CHEMICAL REMAINS (APPROXIMATELY 15-20 MINUTES). GET MEDICAL ATTENTION IMMEDIATELY.

INGESTION: ATRAZINE: **ACUTE EXPOSURE-** AFTER CONSUMING A LARGE ORAL DOSE OF ATRAZINE, RATS EXHIBITED MUSCULAR WEAKNESS, HYPOACTIVITY, PTOSIS, DYSPNEA, PROSTRATION, ATAXIA, CONVULSIONS, AND DEATH. **CHRONIC EXPOSURE-** FORTY PERCENT OF RATS THAT RECEIVED ATRAZINE ORALLY FOR 6 MONTHS AT A RATE OF 20 MG/KG/DAY DIED WITH SIGNS OF RESPIRATORY DISTRESS AND PARALYSIS OF THE LIMBS. MORPHOLOGICAL AND BIOCHEMICAL CHANGES IN THE BRAIN, HEART, LIVER, LUNGS, KIDNEY, OVARIES, AND ENDOCRINE ORGANS WERE OBSERVED. MATERNAL TOXICITY WAS OBSERVED IN PREGNANT RATS FED DOSES GREATER THAN 70 MG/KG/DAY AND IN PREGNANT RABBITS FED DOSES GREATER THAN 5 MG/KG/DAY. MINOR FETAL EFFECTS WERE NOTED IN RATS AT THIS LEVEL, AND IN RABBITS FETAL EFFECTS OCCURRED AT DOSES THAT PRODUCED SEVERE MATERNAL TOXICITY, 75 MG/KG/DAY. AN INCREASED INCIDENCE OF FIBROADENOMAS, CARCINOMAS OF THE MAMMARY GLANDS AND ALL MAMMARY TUMORS IN FEMALES WAS REPORTED FROM A 2-YEAR RAT STUDY.

FIRST AID- REMOVE BY GASTRIC LAVAGE AND CATHARSIS. MAINTAIN BLOOD PRESSURE AND AIRWAY. GIVE OXYGEN IF RESPIRATION IS DEPRESSED. DO NOT PERFORM GASTRIC LAVAGE IF VICTIM IS UNCONSCIOUS. GET MEDICAL ATTENTION IMMEDIATELY (DREISBACH, HANDBOOK OF POISONING, 12TH ED.).

ADMINISTRATION OF LAVAGE OR OXYGEN SHOULD BE PERFORMED BY QUALIFIED MEDICAL PERSONNEL.

ANTIDOTE: NO SPECIFIC ANTIDOTE. TREAT SYMPTOMATICALLY AND SUPPORTIVELY.

REACTIVITY

REACTIVITY: STABLE UNDER NORMAL TEMPERATURES AND PRESSURES.

INCOMPATIBILITIES: ATRAZINE: ALKALI: MAY BE HYDROLYZED AT HIGHER TEMPERATURES. MINERAL ACIDS: MAY BE HYDROLYZED AT HIGHER TEMPERATURES.

DECOMPOSITION: THERMAL DECOMPOSITION PRODUCTS MAY INCLUDE TOXIC AND CORROSIVE FUMES OF CHLORIDES AND TOXIC OXIDES OF NITROGEN.

POLYMERIZATION: HAZARDOUS POLYMERIZATION HAS NOT BEEN REPORTED TO OCCUR UNDER NORMAL TEMPERATURES AND PRESSURES.

STORAGE AND DISPOSAL

OBSERVE ALL FEDERAL, STATE AND LOCAL REGULATIONS WHEN STORING OR DISPOSING OF THIS SUBSTANCE. FOR ASSISTANCE, CONTACT THE DISTRICT DIRECTOR OF THE ENVIRONMENTAL PROTECTION AGENCY.

STORAGE

STORE IN ACCORDANCE WITH 40 CFR 165 RECOMMENDED PROCEDURES FOR THE DISPOSAL AND STORAGE OF PESTICIDES AND PESTICIDE CONTAINERS.
STORE AWAY FROM INCOMPATIBLE SUBSTANCES.

DISPOSAL

DISPOSAL MUST BE IN ACCORDANCE WITH 40 CFR 165 RECOMMENDED PROCEDURES FOR THE DISPOSAL AND STORAGE OF PESTICIDES AND PESTICIDE CONTAINERS.

CONDITIONS TO AVOID

MAY BURN BUT DOES NOT IGNITE READILY.

SPILL AND LEAK PROCEDURES

OCCUPATIONAL SPILL: DO NOT TOUCH SPILLED MATERIAL. STOP LEAK IF YOU CAN DO IT WITHOUT RISK. FOR SMALL SPILLS, TAKE UP WITH SAND OR OTHER ABSORBENT MATERIAL AND PLACE INTO CONTAINERS FOR LATER DISPOSAL. FOR SMALL DRY SPILLS, WITH A CLEAN SHOVEL PLACE MATERIAL INTO CLEAN, DRY CONTAINER AND COVER. MOVE CONTAINERS FROM SPILL AREA. FOR LARGER SPILLS, DIKE FAR AHEAD OF SPILL FOR LATER DISPOSAL. KEEP UNNECESSARY PEOPLE AWAY. ISOLATE HAZARD AREA AND DENY ENTRY.

PROTECTIVE EQUIPMENT

VENTILATION: PROVIDE LOCAL EXHAUST VENTILATION AND/OR GENERAL DILUTION VENTILATION TO MEET PUBLISHED EXPOSURE LIMITS.

RESPIRATOR: THE FOLLOWING RESPIRATORS ARE RECOMMENDED BASED ON INFORMATION FOUND IN THE PHYSICAL DATA, TOXICITY AND HEALTH EFFECTS SECTIONS. THEY ARE RANKED IN ORDER FROM MINIMUM TO MAXIMUM RESPIRATORY PROTECTION. THE SPECIFIC RESPIRATOR SELECTED MUST BE BASED ON CONTAMINATION LEVELS FOUND IN THE WORK PLACE, MUST NOT EXCEED THE WORKING LIMITS OF THE RESPIRATOR AND BE JOINTLY APPROVED BY THE NATIONAL INSTITUTE FOR OCCUPATIONAL SAFETY AND HEALTH AND THE MINE SAFETY AND HEALTH ADMINISTRATION (NIOSH-MSHA).
CHEMICAL CARTRIDGE RESPIRATOR WITH AN ORGANIC VAPOR CARTRIDGE(S) IN COMBINATION WITH A DUST AND MIST FILTER.
GAS MASK WITH ORGANIC VAPOR CANISTER (CHIN-STYLE OR FRONT- OR BACK-MOUNTED CANISTER) WITH A DUST AND MIST FILTER.
GAS MASK WITH ORGANIC VAPOR CANISTER (CHIN-STYLE OR FRONT- OR BACK-MOUNTED CANISTER) WITH A PARTICULATE FILTER.
POWERED AIR-PURIFYING RESPIRATOR WITH A HIGH-EFFICIENCY FILTER.
TYPE 'C' SUPPLIED-AIR RESPIRATOR WITH A FULL FACEPIECE OPERATED IN A PRESSURE-DEMAND OR OTHER POSITIVE PRESSURE MODE.
SELF-CONTAINED BREATHING APPARATUS WITH A FULL FACEPIECE OPERATED IN PRESSURE-DEMAND OR OTHER POSITIVE PRESSURE MODE.
FOR FIREFIGHTING AND OTHER IMMEDIATELY DANGEROUS TO LIFE OR HEALTH CONDITIONS:
SELF-CONTAINED BREATHING APPARATUS WITH FULL FACEPIECE OPERATED IN PRESSURE-DEMAND OR OTHER POSITIVE PRESSURE MODE.
SUPPLIED-AIR RESPIRATOR WITH FULL FACEPIECE AND OPERATED IN PRESSURE-DEMAND OR OTHER POSITIVE PRESSURE MODE IN COMBINATION WITH AN AUXILIARY SELF-CONTAINED BREATHING APPARATUS OPERATED IN PRESSURE-DEMAND OR OTHER POSITIVE PRESSURE MODE.

CLOTHING: EMPLOYEE MUST WEAR APPROPRIATE PROTECTIVE (IMPERVIOUS) CLOTHING AND EQUIPMENT TO PREVENT REPEATED OR PROLONGED SKIN CONTACT WITH THIS SUBSTANCE.

GLOVES: EMPLOYEE MUST WEAR APPROPRIATE PROTECTIVE GLOVES TO PREVENT CONTACT WITH THIS SUBSTANCE.

EYE PROTECTION: EMPLOYEE MUST WEAR SPLASH-PROOF OR DUST-RESISTANT SAFETY GOGGLES TO PREVENT EYE CONTACT WITH THIS SUBSTANCE.

EMERGENCY EYE WASH: WHERE THERE IS ANY POSSIBILITY THAT AN EMPLOYEE'S EYES MAY BE EXPOSED TO THIS SUBSTANCE, THE EMPLOYER SHOULD PROVIDE AN EYE WASH FOUNTAIN WITHIN THE IMMEDIATE WORK AREA FOR EMERGENCY USE.

AUTHORIZED BY- OCCUPATIONAL HEALTH SERVICES, INC.
CREATION DATE: 10/04/89 ***REVISION DATE:*** 05/09/90

MATERIAL SAFETY DATA SHEET

OCCUPATIONAL HEALTH SERVICES, INC.	EMERGENCY CONTACT:
AGRICULTURE AND PESTICIDE DIVISION	JOHN S. BRANSFORD, JR. (615) 292-1180
450 SEVENTH AVENUE, SUITE 2407	
NEW YORK, NEW YORK 10123	
1-800-445-MSDS OR (212) 967-1100	

SUBSTANCE IDENTIFICATION

CAS-NUMBER 65195-56-4

SUBSTANCE: <u>**AVERMECTIN B1B**</u>

TRADE NAMES/SYNONYMS: AVERMECTIN A1A, 5-O-DEMETHYL-25-DE(1-METHYLPROPYL)-25-(1-METHYLETHYL)-; 5-O-DEMETHYL-25-DE(1-METHYLPROPYL)-25-(1-METHYLETHYL)AVERMECTIN A1A; ANTIBIOTIC C 076B1B; C47H70O14; PST02156

CHEMICAL FAMILY: ANTIBIOTIC

MOLECULAR FORMULA: C47-H70-O14

MOLECULAR WEIGHT: 859.07

CERCLA RATINGS (SCALE 0-3): HEALTH=U FIRE=1 REACTIVITY=0 PERSISTENCE=0

NFPA RATINGS (SCALE 0-4): HEALTH=U FIRE=1 REACTIVITY=0

COMPONENTS AND CONTAMINANTS

COMPONENT: AVERMECTIN B1B ***PERCENT:*** 100.0
CAS# 65195-56-4

OTHER CONTAMINANTS: NONE

EXPOSURE LIMITS: NO OCCUPATIONAL EXPOSURE LIMITS ESTABLISHED BY OSHA, ACGIH, OR NIOSH.

PHYSICAL DATA

DESCRIPTION: SOLID. ***MELTING POINT:*** NOT AVAILABLE

SPECIFIC GRAVITY: NOT AVAILABLE ***SOLUBILITY IN WATER:*** NOT AVAILABLE

FIRE AND EXPLOSION DATA

FIRE AND EXPLOSION HAZARD: SLIGHT FIRE HAZARD WHEN EXPOSED TO HEAT OR FLAME.

FIREFIGHTING MEDIA: DRY CHEMICAL, CARBON DIOXIDE, HALON, WATER SPRAY OR STANDARD FOAM (1987 EMERGENCY RESPONSE GUIDEBOOK, DOT P 5800.4).
FOR LARGER FIRES, USE WATER SPRAY, FOG OR STANDARD FOAM (1987 EMERGENCY RESPONSE GUIDEBOOK, DOT P 5800.4).

FIREFIGHTING: MOVE CONTAINER FROM FIRE AREA IF POSSIBLE. DO NOT SCATTER SPILLED MATERIAL WITH HIGH PRESSURE WATER STREAMS. DIKE FIRE CONTROL WATER FOR LATER DISPOSAL (1987 EMERGENCY RESPONSE GUIDEBOOK, DOT P 5800.4, GUIDE PAGE 31).
USE AGENTS SUITABLE FOR TYPE OF SURROUNDING FIRE. AVOID BREATHING HAZARDOUS VAPORS, KEEP UPWIND.

TOXICITY

AVERMECTIN B1B: CARCINOGEN STATUS: NONE. ACUTE TOXICITY LEVEL: NO DATA AVAILABLE. TARGET EFFECTS: NO DATA AVAILABLE.

HEALTH EFFECTS AND FIRST AID

INHALATION: AVERMECTIN B1B: <u>**ACUTE EXPOSURE-**</u> NO DATA AVAILABLE. <u>**CHRONIC EXPOSURE-**</u> NO DATA AVAILABLE.

FIRST AID- REMOVE FROM EXPOSURE AREA TO FRESH AIR IMMEDIATELY. IF BREATHING HAS STOPPED, PERFORM ARTIFICIAL RESPIRATION. KEEP PERSON WARM AND AT REST. TREAT SYMPTOMATICALLY AND SUPPORTIVELY. GET MEDICAL ATTENTION IMMEDIATELY.

SKIN CONTACT: AVERMECTIN B1B: <u>**ACUTE EXPOSURE-**</u> NO DATA AVAILABLE. <u>**CHRONIC EXPOSURE-**</u> NO DATA AVAILABLE.

FIRST AID- REMOVE CONTAMINATED CLOTHING AND SHOES IMMEDIATELY. WASH AFFECTED AREA WITH SOAP OR MILD DETERGENT AND LARGE AMOUNTS OF

WATER UNTIL NO EVIDENCE OF CHEMICAL REMAINS (APPROXIMATELY 15-20 MINUTES). GET MEDICAL ATTENTION IMMEDIATELY.

EYE CONTACT: AVERMECTIN B1B: **ACUTE EXPOSURE-** NO DATA AVAILABLE. **CHRONIC EXPOSURE-** NO DATA AVAILABLE.
FIRST AID- WASH EYES IMMEDIATELY WITH LARGE AMOUNTS OF WATER OR NORMAL SALINE, OCCASIONALLY LIFTING UPPER AND LOWER LIDS, UNTIL NO EVIDENCE OF CHEMICAL REMAINS (APPROXIMATELY 15-20 MINUTES). GET MEDICAL ATTENTION IMMEDIATELY.

INGESTION: AVERMECTIN B1B: **ACUTE EXPOSURE-** NO DATA AVAILABLE. **CHRONIC EXPOSURE-** NO DATA AVAILABLE.
FIRST AID- TREAT SYMPTOMATICALLY AND SUPPORTIVELY. GET MEDICAL ATTENTION IMMEDIATELY. IF VOMITING OCCURS, KEEP HEAD LOWER THAN HIPS TO PREVENT ASPIRATION.
ANTIDOTE: NO SPECIFIC ANTIDOTE. TREAT SYMPTOMATICALLY AND SUPPORTIVELY.

REACTIVITY

REACTIVITY: STABLE UNDER NORMAL TEMPERATURES AND PRESSURES.
INCOMPATIBILITIES: AVERMECTIN B1B: OXIDIZERS (STRONG): FIRE AND EXPLOSION HAZARD.
DECOMPOSITION: THERMAL DECOMPOSITION PRODUCTS MAY INCLUDE TOXIC OXIDES OF CARBON.
POLYMERIZATION: HAZARDOUS POLYMERIZATION HAS NOT BEEN REPORTED TO OCCUR UNDER NORMAL TEMPERATURES AND PRESSURES.

STORAGE AND DISPOSAL

OBSERVE ALL FEDERAL, STATE AND LOCAL REGULATIONS WHEN STORING OR DISPOSING OF THIS SUBSTANCE. FOR ASSISTANCE, CONTACT THE DISTRICT DIRECTOR OF THE ENVIRONMENTAL PROTECTION AGENCY.

****STORAGE****

STORE AWAY FROM INCOMPATIBLE SUBSTANCES.

CONDITIONS TO AVOID

MAY BURN BUT DOES NOT IGNITE READILY. AVOID CONTACT WITH STRONG OXIDIZERS, EXCESSIVE HEAT, SPARKS, OR OPEN FLAME.

SPILL AND LEAK PROCEDURES

OCCUPATIONAL SPILL: SWEEP UP AND PLACE IN SUITABLE CLEAN, DRY CONTAINERS FOR RECLAMATION OR LATER DISPOSAL. DO NOT FLUSH SPILLED MATERIAL INTO SEWER. KEEP UNNECESSARY PEOPLE AWAY.

PROTECTIVE EQUIPMENT

VENTILATION: PROVIDE LOCAL EXHAUST OR GENERAL DILUTION VENTILATION SYSTEM.
RESPIRATOR: THE FOLLOWING RESPIRATORS ARE RECOMMENDED BASED ON INFORMATION FOUND IN THE PHYSICAL DATA, TOXICITY AND HEALTH EFFECTS SECTIONS. THEY ARE RANKED IN ORDER FROM MINIMUM TO MAXIMUM RESPIRATORY PROTECTION. THE SPECIFIC RESPIRATOR SELECTED MUST BE BASED ON CONTAMINATION LEVELS FOUND IN THE WORK PLACE, MUST NOT EXCEED THE WORKING LIMITS OF THE RESPIRATOR AND BE JOINTLY APPROVED BY THE NATIONAL INSTITUTE FOR OCCUPATIONAL SAFETY AND HEALTH AND THE MINE SAFETY AND HEALTH ADMINISTRATION (NIOSH-MSHA).
DUST AND MIST RESPIRATOR.
AIR-PURIFYING RESPIRATOR WITH A HIGH-EFFICIENCY PARTICULATE FILTER.
POWERED AIR-PURIFYING RESPIRATOR WITH A DUST AND MIST FILTER.
POWERED AIR-PURIFYING RESPIRATOR WITH A HIGH-EFFICIENCY PARTICULATE FILTER.
TYPE 'C' SUPPLIED-AIR RESPIRATOR OPERATED IN THE PRESSURE-DEMAND OR OTHER POSITIVE PRESSURE OR CONTINUOUS-FLOW MODE.
SELF-CONTAINED BREATHING APPARATUS.
FOR FIREFIGHTING AND OTHER IMMEDIATELY DANGEROUS TO LIFE OR HEALTH CONDITIONS:
SELF-CONTAINED BREATHING APPARATUS WITH FULL FACEPIECE OPERATED IN PRESSURE-DEMAND OR OTHER POSITIVE PRESSURE MODE.
SUPPLIED-AIR RESPIRATOR WITH FULL FACEPIECE AND OPERATED IN PRESSURE-DEMAND OR OTHER POSITIVE PRESSURE MODE IN COMBINATION WITH AN AUXILIARY SELF-CONTAINED BREATHING APPARATUS OPERATED IN PRESSURE-DEMAND OR OTHER POSITIVE PRESSURE MODE.
CLOTHING: EMPLOYEE MUST WEAR APPROPRIATE PROTECTIVE (IMPERVIOUS) CLOTHING AND EQUIPMENT TO PREVENT REPEATED OR PROLONGED SKIN CONTACT WITH THIS SUBSTANCE.
GLOVES: EMPLOYEE MUST WEAR APPROPRIATE PROTECTIVE GLOVES TO PREVENT CONTACT WITH THIS SUBSTANCE.
EYE PROTECTION: EMPLOYEE MUST WEAR SPLASH-PROOF OR DUST-RESISTANT SAFETY GOGGLES TO PREVENT EYE CONTACT WITH THIS SUBSTANCE.
EMERGENCY EYE WASH: WHERE THERE IS ANY POSSIBILITY THAT AN EMPLOYEE'S EYES MAY BE EXPOSED TO THIS SUBSTANCE, THE EMPLOYER SHOULD PROVIDE AN EYE WASH FOUNTAIN WITHIN THE IMMEDIATE WORK AREA FOR EMERGENCY USE.

AUTHORIZED BY- OCCUPATIONAL HEALTH SERVICES, INC.
CREATION DATE: 11/17/89 ***REVISION DATE:*** 05/31/90

MATERIAL SAFETY DATA SHEET

OCCUPATIONAL HEALTH SERVICES, INC.
AGRICULTURE AND PESTICIDE DIVISION
450 SEVENTH AVENUE, SUITE 2407
NEW YORK, NEW YORK 10123
1-800-445-MSDS OR (212) 967-1100

EMERGENCY CONTACT:
JOHN S. BRANSFORD, JR. (615) 292-1180

SUBSTANCE IDENTIFICATION

CAS-NUMBER 504-24-5
SUBSTANCE: AVITROL
TRADE NAMES/SYNONYMS: 4-AMINOPYRIDINE; 4-AP; VMI PHILIPS 1861; 4-PYRIDINAMINE; AMINO-4-PYRIDINE; GAMMA-AMINO PYRIDINE; P-AMINOPYRIDINE; VMI 10-3; AMINOPYRIDINE; RCRA P008; PST02180
CHEMICAL FAMILY: PYRIDINE
MOLECULAR FORMULA: C5-H6-N2 MOL WT: 94.13
CERCLA RATINGS (SCALE 0-3): HEALTH=3 FIRE=0 REACTIVITY=0 PERSISTENCE=2
NFPA RATINGS (SCALE 0-4): HEALTH=3 FIRE=0 REACTIVITY=0

COMPONENTS AND CONTAMINANTS

COMPONENT: AVITROL ***PERCENT:*** 100
CAS# 504-24-5
OTHER CONTAMINANTS: NONE
EXPOSURE LIMITS: NO OCCUPATIONAL EXPOSURE LIMITS ESTABLISHED BY OSHA, ACGIH, OR NIOSH.
AVITROL: 500/10,000 POUNDS SARA SECTION 302 THRESHOLD PLANNING QUANTITY 1000 POUNDS SARA SECTION 304 REPORTABLE QUANTITY 1000 POUNDS CERCLA SECTION 103 REPORTABLE QUANTITY

PHYSICAL DATA

DESCRIPTION: CRYSTALS. ***BOILING POINT:*** 523 F (273 C)
MELTING POINT: 316 F (158 C) ***SOLUBILITY IN WATER:*** SOLUBLE
SOLVENT SOLUBILITY: BENZENE, ETHER, ALCOHOL

FIRE AND EXPLOSION DATA

FIRE AND EXPLOSION HAZARD: NEGLIGIBLE FIRE HAZARD WHEN EXPOSED TO HEAT OR FLAME.
FIREFIGHTING MEDIA: DRY CHEMICAL, CARBON DIOXIDE, HALON, WATER SPRAY OR STANDARD FOAM (1987 EMERGENCY RESPONSE GUIDEBOOK, DOT P 5800.4).
FOR LARGER FIRES, WITHDRAW FROM AREA AND LET FIRE BURN (1987 EMERGENCY RESPONSE GUIDEBOOK, DOT P 5800.4).
FIREFIGHTING: MOVE CONTAINERS FROM FIRE AREA IF POSSIBLE (1987 EMERGENCY RESPONSE GUIDEBOOK, DOT P 5800.4, GUIDE PAGE 53).
EXTINGUISH USING AGENT SUITABLE FOR TYPE OF SURROUNDING FIRE. AVOID BREATHING VAPORS AND DUSTS. KEEP UPWIND.

TRANSPORTATION DATA

DEPARTMENT OF TRANSPORTATION HAZARD CLASSIFICATION 49 CFR 172.101: POISON B
DEPARTMENT OF TRANSPORTATION LABELING REQUIREMENTS 49 CFR 172.101 AND SUBPART E: POISON
DEPARTMENT OF TRANSPORTATION PACKAGING REQUIREMENTS: 49 CFR 173.365 EXCEPTIONS: 49 CFR 173.364

TOXICITY

AVITROL: TOXICITY DATA: 590 UG/KG ORAL-MAN LDLO; 21 MG/KG ORAL-RAT LD50; 3700 MG/KG ORAL-DOG LD50; 42 MG/KG ORAL-MOUSE LDLO; 19 MG/KG SUBCUTANEOUS-RAT LD50; 5 MG/KG SUBCUTANEOUS-MOUSE LDLO; 7 MG/KG INTRAVENOUS-MOUSE LD50; 5500 UG/KG INTRAVENOUS-RABBIT LD50; 6500 UG/KG INTRAPERITONEAL-RAT LD50; 10 MG/KG INTRAPERITONEAL-MOUSE LD50; 4 MG/KG INTRACEREBRAL-MOUSE LD50. CARCINOGEN STATUS: NONE. ACUTE TOXICITY LEVEL: HIGHLY TOXIC BY INGESTION. TARGET EFFECTS: CONVULSANT.

POISONING MAY AFFECT THE BLOOD. AT INCREASED RISK FROM EXPOSURE: PERSONS WITH A HISTORY OF CONVULSIONS.

HEALTH EFFECTS AND FIRST AID

INHALATION: AVITROL: **ACUTE EXPOSURE-** AMINO DERIVATIVES OF PYRIDINE ARE REPORTED NOT TO PRODUCE SIGNIFICANT METHEMOGLOBINEMIA IN RATS. HOWEVER, 2-AMINOPYRIDINE (A CLOSELY RELATED SUBSTANCE AND CONVULSANT) IS REPORTED TO CAUSE METHEMOGLOBINEMIA. EXPOSURE TO 2-AMINOPYRIDINE HAS ALSO CAUSED SEVERE HEADACHE, WEAKNESS, NAUSEA, FLUSHING OF THE EXTREMITIES, ELEVATED BLOOD PRESSURE, CONVULSIONS, AND A STUPOROUS STATE. **CHRONIC EXPOSURE-** NO DATA AVAILABLE.

FIRST AID- REMOVE FROM EXPOSURE AREA TO FRESH AIR IMMEDIATELY. IF BREATHING HAS STOPPED, GIVE ARTIFICIAL RESPIRATION. MAINTAIN AIRWAY AND BLOOD PRESSURE AND ADMINISTER OXYGEN IF AVAILABLE. KEEP AFFECTED PERSON WARM AND AT REST. TREAT SYMPTOMATICALLY AND SUPPORTIVELY. ADMINISTRATION OF OXYGEN SHOULD BE PERFORMED BY QUALIFIED PERSONNEL. GET MEDICAL ATTENTION IMMEDIATELY.

SKIN CONTACT: AVITROL: **ACUTE EXPOSURE-** MAY BE ABSORBED THROUGH THE SKIN. THERE ARE NO SPECIFIC REPORTS OF PERCUTANEOUS ABSORPTION, HOWEVER A WORKER WEARING CLOTHING CONTAMINATED WITH 2-AMINOPYRIDINE (A CLOSELY RELATED SUBSTANCE AND CONVULSANT) DEVELOPED DIZZINESS, HEADACHE, RESPIRATORY DISTRESS AND CONVULSIONS THAT PROGRESSED TO RESPIRATORY FAILURE AND DEATH. IT IS ASSUMED THAT SKIN ABSORPTION WAS AN IMPORTANT CONTRIBUTING FACTOR. AMINO DERIVATIVES OF PYRIDINE GENERALLY DO NOT PRODUCE SIGNIFICANT METHEMOGLOBINEMIA IN RATS. HOWEVER, 2-AMINOPYRIDINE HAS BEEN REPORTED TO BE A METHEMOGLOBIN FORMER. **CHRONIC EXPOSURE-** NO DATA AVAILABLE.

FIRST AID- REMOVE CONTAMINATED CLOTHING AND SHOES IMMEDIATELY. WASH AFFECTED AREA WITH SOAP OR MILD DETERGENT AND LARGE AMOUNTS OF WATER UNTIL NO EVIDENCE OF CHEMICAL REMAINS (APPROXIMATELY 15-20 MINUTES). GET MEDICAL ATTENTION IMMEDIATELY.

EYE CONTACT: AVITROL: **ACUTE EXPOSURE-** NO DATA AVAILABLE. HOWEVER, A 0.02 M AQUEOUS SOLUTION OF 2-AMINOPYRIDINE (A CLOSELY RELATED SUBSTANCE) TESTED IN RABBIT EYES FOR 10 MINUTES CAUSED ONLY TRANSIENT CORNEAL HAZE WITH A SLIGHT DELAY IN RETURN TO NORMAL. **CHRONIC EXPOSURE-** NO DATA AVAILABLE.

FIRST AID- WASH EYES IMMEDIATELY WITH LARGE AMOUNTS OF WATER OR NORMAL SALINE, OCCASIONALLY LIFTING UPPER AND LOWER LIDS, UNTIL NO EVIDENCE OF CHEMICAL REMAINS (APPROXIMATELY 15-20 MINUTES). GET MEDICAL ATTENTION IMMEDIATELY.

INGESTION: AVITROL: CONVULSANT/HIGHLY TOXIC. **ACUTE EXPOSURE-** AN ORAL DOSE OF 590 UG/KG RESULTED IN HALLUCINATIONS, DYSPNEA, NAUSEA AND DEATH IN MAN. A DOSE OF 20 MG/KG ADMINISTERED TO RATS WAS LETHAL TO 50% OF THE ANIMALS TESTED. AVITROL PRODUCES SYMPTOMS OF HYPEREXCITABILITY, SALIVATION, AND TREMORS PROGRESSING TO CLONIC AND TONIC CONVULSION AND DEATH AS A RESULT OF CARDIAC OR RESPIRATORY ARREST IN ANIMALS. IT MAY HAVE AN EXCITATORY EFFECT ON THE CENTRAL NERVOUS SYSTEM. AMINO DERIVATIVES OF PYRIDINE ARE REPORTED NOT TO PRODUCE SIGNIFICANT METHEMOGLOBINEMIA IN RATS. HOWEVER, STUDIES INDICATE 2-AMINOPYRIDINE TO BE A METHEMOGLOBIN FORMER IN HUMANS WITH SYMPTOMS DELAYED AS MUCH AS FOUR HOURS. THE FIRST SYMPTOMS TO DEVELOP ARE CYANOSIS WITH BLUENESS OF THE SKIN AND EARLOBES, AND HEADACHES THAT INCREASE IN SEVERITY WITH TIME. AS THE CONCENTRATION OF METHEMOGLOBIN INCREASES IN THE BLOOD, SYMPTOMS OF SHALLOW RESPIRATION AND DIZZINESS MAY APPEAR FOLLOWED BY CONFUSION, BLOOD PRESSURE FALL, LETHARGY AND STUPOR. AS THE CONCENTRATION OF METHEMOGLOBIN APPROACHES 70% OR HIGHER, CONVULSIONS OR COMA MAY OCCUR WITH THE POSSIBILITY OF DEATH. JAUNDICE PAIN ON URINATION, AND ANEMIA MAY APPEAR LATER IF DEATH DOES NOT OCCUR. **CHRONIC EXPOSURE-** NO DATA AVAILABLE.

FIRST AID- REMOVE BY GASTRIC LAVAGE OR EMESIS, USING ACTIVATED CHARCOAL. MAINTAIN AIRWAY AND BLOOD PRESSURE. GIVE OXYGEN IF RESPIRATION IS DEPRESSED (DREISBACH HANDBOOK OF POISONING, 11TH EDITION). GASTRIC LAVAGE OR EMESIS SHOULD NOT BE PERFORMED ON AN UNCONSCIOUS PERSON. LAVAGE SHOULD BE PERFORMED BY QUALIFIED MEDICAL PERSONNEL. GET MEDICAL ATTENTION IMMEDIATELY.

ANTIDOTE: NO SPECIFIC ANTIDOTE. TREAT SYMPTOMATICALLY AND SUPPORTIVELY.

REACTIVITY

REACTIVITY: STABLE UNDER NORMAL TEMPERATURES AND PRESSURES.

INCOMPATIBILITIES: NO DATA AVAILABLE.

DECOMPOSITION: THERMAL DECOMPOSITION PRODUCTS MAY INCLUDE TOXIC OXIDES OF CARBON AND NITROGEN.

POLYMERIZATION: HAZARDOUS POLYMERIZATION HAS NOT BEEN REPORTED TO OCCUR UNDER NORMAL TEMPERATURES AND PRESSURES.

STORAGE AND DISPOSAL

OBSERVE ALL FEDERAL, STATE AND LOCAL REGULATIONS WHEN STORING OR DISPOSING OF THIS SUBSTANCE. FOR ASSISTANCE, CONTACT THE DISTRICT DIRECTOR OF THE ENVIRONMENTAL PROTECTION AGENCY.

****STORAGE****

THRESHOLD PLANNING QUANTITY (TPQ): THE SUPERFUND AMENDMENTS AND REAUTHORIZATION ACT (SARA) SECTION 302 REQUIRES THAT EACH FACILITY WHERE ANY EXTREMELY HAZARDOUS SUBSTANCE IS PRESENT IN A QUANTITY EQUAL TO OR GREATER THAN THE TPQ ESTABLISHED FOR THAT SUBSTANCE NOTIFY THE STATE EMERGENCY RESPONSE COMMISSION FOR THE STATE IN WHICH IT IS LOCATED. SECTION 303 OF SARA REQUIRES THESE FACILITIES TO PARTICIPATE IN LOCAL EMERGENCY RESPONSE PLANNING (40 CFR 355.30).

CONDITIONS TO AVOID

MAY BURN BUT DOES NOT IGNITE READILY.

SPILL AND LEAK PROCEDURES

OCCUPATIONAL SPILL: DO NOT TOUCH SPILLED MATERIAL. STOP LEAK IF YOU CAN DO IT WITHOUT RISK. FOR SMALL SPILLS, TAKE UP WITH SAND OR OTHER ABSORBENT MATERIAL AND PLACE INTO CONTAINERS FOR LATER DISPOSAL. FOR SMALL DRY SPILLS, WITH A CLEAN SHOVEL PLACE MATERIAL INTO CLEAN, DRY CONTAINER AND COVER. MOVE CONTAINERS FROM SPILL AREA. FOR LARGER SPILLS, DIKE FAR AHEAD OF SPILL FOR LATER DISPOSAL. KEEP UNNECESSARY PEOPLE AWAY. ISOLATE HAZARD AREA AND DENY ENTRY.

REPORTABLE QUANTITY (RQ): 1000 POUNDS THE SUPERFUND AMENDMENTS AND REAUTHORIZATION ACT (SARA) SECTION 304 REQUIRES THAT A RELEASE EQUAL TO OR GREATER THAN THE REPORTABLE QUANTITY FOR THIS SUBSTANCE BE IMMEDIATELY REPORTED TO THE LOCAL EMERGENCY PLANNING COMMITTEE AND THE STATE EMERGENCY RESPONSE COMMISSION (40 CFR 355.40). IF THE RELEASE OF THIS SUBSTANCE IS REPORTABLE UNDER CERCLA SECTION 103, THE NATIONAL RESPONSE CENTER MUST BE NOTIFIED IMMEDIATELY AT (800) 424-8802 OR (202) 426-2675 IN THE METROPOLITAN WASHINGTON, D.C. AREA (40 CFR 302.6).

PROTECTIVE EQUIPMENT

VENTILATION: PROCESS ENCLOSURE RECOMMENDED TO MEET PUBLISHED EXPOSURE LIMITS.

RESPIRATOR: THE FOLLOWING RESPIRATORS ARE RECOMMENDED BASED ON INFORMATION FOUND IN THE PHYSICAL DATA, TOXICITY AND HEALTH EFFECTS SECTIONS. THEY ARE RANKED IN ORDER FROM MINIMUM TO MAXIMUM RESPIRATORY PROTECTION. THE SPECIFIC RESPIRATOR SELECTED MUST BE BASED ON CONTAMINATION LEVELS FOUND IN THE WORK PLACE, MUST NOT EXCEED THE WORKING LIMITS OF THE RESPIRATOR AND BE JOINTLY APPROVED BY THE NATIONAL INSTITUTE FOR OCCUPATIONAL SAFETY AND HEALTH AND THE MINE SAFETY AND HEALTH ADMINISTRATION (NIOSH-MSHA).

CHEMICAL CARTRIDGE RESPIRATOR WITH AN ORGANIC VAPOR CARTRIDGE(S) WITH A FULL FACEPIECE AND ORGANIC VAPOR CARTRIDGE(S) IN COMBINATION WITH A DUST AND MIST FILTER.

POWERED AIR-PURIFYING RESPIRATOR WITH A TIGHT-FITTING FACEPIECE AND ORGANIC VAPOR CARTRIDGE(S) IN COMBINATION WITH A HIGH-EFFICIENCY PARTICULATE FILTER.

TYPE 'C' SUPPLIED-AIR RESPIRATOR WITH A FULL FACEPIECE OPERATED IN A PRESSURE-DEMAND OR OTHER POSITIVE PRESSURE MODE.

SELF-CONTAINED BREATHING APPARATUS WITH A FULL FACEPIECE OPERATED IN PRESSURE-DEMAND OR OTHER POSITIVE PRESSURE MODE.

FOR FIREFIGHTING AND OTHER IMMEDIATELY DANGEROUS TO LIFE OR HEALTH CONDITIONS:

SELF-CONTAINED BREATHING APPARATUS WITH FULL FACEPIECE OPERATED IN PRESSURE-DEMAND OR OTHER POSITIVE PRESSURE MODE.

SUPPLIED-AIR RESPIRATOR WITH FULL FACEPIECE AND OPERATED IN PRESSURE-DEMAND OR OTHER POSITIVE PRESSURE MODE IN COMBINATION WITH AN AUXILIARY SELF-CONTAINED BREATHING APPARATUS OPERATED IN PRESSURE-DEMAND OR OTHER POSITIVE PRESSURE MODE.

CLOTHING: EMPLOYEE MUST WEAR APPROPRIATE PROTECTIVE (IMPERVIOUS) CLOTHING AND EQUIPMENT TO PREVENT ANY POSSIBILITY OF SKIN CONTACT WITH THIS SUBSTANCE.

GLOVES: EMPLOYEE MUST WEAR APPROPRIATE PROTECTIVE GLOVES TO PREVENT CONTACT WITH THIS SUBSTANCE.

EYE PROTECTION: EMPLOYEE MUST WEAR SPLASH-PROOF OR DUST-RESISTANT SAFETY GOGGLES AND A FACESHIELD TO PREVENT CONTACT WITH THIS SUBSTANCE.

EMERGENCY WASH FACILITIES: WHERE THERE IS ANY POSSIBILITY THAT AN EMPLOYEE'S EYES AND/OR SKIN MAY BE EXPOSED TO THIS SUBSTANCE, THE

EMPLOYER SHOULD PROVIDE AN EYE WASH FOUNTAIN AND QUICK DRENCH SHOWER WITHIN THE IMMEDIATE WORK AREA FOR EMERGENCY USE.

AUTHORIZED BY- OCCUPATIONAL HEALTH SERVICES, INC.
CREATION DATE: 10/04/89 ***REVISION DATE:*** 05/14/90

MATERIAL SAFETY DATA SHEET

OCCUPATIONAL HEALTH SERVICES, INC.
AGRICULTURE AND PESTICIDE DIVISION
450 SEVENTH AVENUE, SUITE 2407
NEW YORK, NEW YORK 10123
1-800-445-MSDS OR (212) 967-1100

EMERGENCY CONTACT:
JOHN S. BRANSFORD, JR. (615) 292-1180

SUBSTANCE IDENTIFICATION

CAS-NUMBER 2642-71-9

SUBSTANCE: **AZINPHOS-ETHYL**

TRADE NAMES/SYNONYMS: PHOSPHORODITHIOIC ACID, O,O-DIETHYL S-(4-OXO-1,2,3-BENZOTRIAZIN -3(4H)-YL)METHYL) ESTER; PHOSPHORODITHIOIC ACID, O,O-DIETHYL ESTER, S-ESTER WITH 3-(MERCAPTOMETHYL)-1,2,3-BENZOTRIAZIN-4(3H)-ONE; S-3,4-DIHYDRO-4-OXO-1,2,3-BENZOTRIAZIN-3-YLMETHYL O,O-DIETHYL PHOSPHORODITHIOATE; O,O-DIETHYL S-((4-OXO-1,2,3-BENZOTRIAZIN-3(4H-YL)METHYL) PHOSPHORODITHIOATE; O,O-DIETHYL PHOSPHORODITHIOATE S-ESTER WITH 3-(MERCAPTOMETHYL) -1,2,3-BENZOTRIAZIN-4(3H)-ONE; 3-DIETHOXYPHOSPHINOTHIOYLTHIOMETHYL-1,2,3-BENZOTRIAZIN-4(3H)-ONE; BAYER 16259; ETHYL AZINPHOS; ETHYL GUSATHION; ETHYL GUTHION; GUSATHION ETHYL; GUTHION ETHYL; R 1513; ENT 22,014; C12H16N3O3PS2; PST02205

CHEMICAL FAMILY: ORGANOPHOSPHATE

MOLECULAR FORMULA: C12-H16-N3-O3-P-S2

MOLECULAR WEIGHT: 345.40

CERCLA RATINGS (SCALE 0-3): HEALTH=3 FIRE=U REACTIVITY=0 PERSISTENCE=1

NFPA RATINGS (SCALE 0-4): HEALTH=4 FIRE=U REACTIVITY=0

COMPONENTS AND CONTAMINANTS

COMPONENT: AZINPHOS-ETHYL ***PERCENT:*** 100.0
CAS# 2642-71-9

OTHER CONTAMINANTS: NONE

EXPOSURE LIMITS: AZINPHOS-ETHYL: 100/10,000 POUNDS SARA SECTION 302 THRESHOLD PLANNING QUANTITY 1 POUND SATA SECTION 304 REPORTABLE QUANTITY 100/10,000 POUNDS SARA SECTION 302 THRESHOLD PLANNING QUANTITY 1 POUND SARA SECTION 304 REPORTABLE QUANTITY

PHYSICAL DATA

DESCRIPTION: COLORLESS CRYSTALS ***BOILING POINT:*** 232 F (111 C) @ 0.001 MMHG

MELTING POINT: 127 F (53 C) ***SPECIFIC GRAVITY:*** 1.284

VAPOR PRESSURE: 0.00000022 MMHG ***SOLUBILITY IN WATER:*** 4-5 PPM

SOLVENT SOLUBILITY: SOLUBLE IN DICHLOROMETHANE, TOLUENE, AND MOST ORGANIC SOLVENTS.

FIRE AND EXPLOSION DATA

FIRE AND EXPLOSION HAZARD: UNKNOWN FIRE AND EXPLOSION HAZARD.

FIREFIGHTING MEDIA: DRY CHEMICAL, CARBON DIOXIDE, HALON, WATER SPRAY OR STANDARD FOAM (1987 EMERGENCY RESPONSE GUIDEBOOK, DOT P 5800.4). FOR LARGER FIRES, USE WATER SPRAY, FOG OR STANDARD FOAM (1987 EMERGENCY RESPONSE GUIDEBOOK, DOT P 5800.4).

FIREFIGHTING: MOVE CONTAINERS FROM FIRE AREA IF POSSIBLE. FIGHT FIRE FROM MAXIMUM DISTANCE. STAY AWAY FROM STORAGE TANK ENDS. DIKE FIRE CONTROL WATER FOR LATER DISPOSAL. DO NOT SCATTER MATERIAL (1987 EMERGENCY RESPONSE GUIDEBOOK, DOT P 5800.4, GUIDE PAGE 55). EXTINGUISH ONLY IF FLOW CAN BE STOPPED; USE FLOODING AMOUNTS OF WATER AS FOG, SOLID STREAMS MAY BE INEFFECTIVE. COOL CONTAINERS WITH FLOODING AMOUNTS OF WATER FROM AS FAR A DISTANCE AS POSSIBLE. USE WATER SPRAY TO ABSORB TOXIC VAPORS. AVOID BREATHING TOXIC VAPORS; KEEP UPWIND. CONSIDER EVACUATION OF DOWNWIND AREA IF MATERIAL IS LEAKING.

TRANSPORTATION DATA

DEPARTMENT OF TRANSPORTATION HAZARD CLASSIFICATION 49 CFR 172.101: POISON B

DEPARTMENT OF TRANSPORTATION LABELING REQUIREMENTS 49 CFR 172.101 AND SUBPART E: POISON

DEPARTMENT OF TRANSPORTATION PACKAGING REQUIREMENTS: 49 CFR 173.365 EXCEPTIONS: 49 CFR 173.364

TOXICITY

AZINPHOS-ETHYL: TOXICITY DATA: 390 MG/M3 INHALATION-RAT LC50; 250 MG/KG SKIN-RAT LD50; 7 MG/KG ORAL-RAT LD50; 7500 UG/KG INTRAPERITONEAL-RAT LD50. CARCINOGEN STATUS: NONE. ACUTE TOXICITY LEVEL: HIGHLY TOXIC BY INHALATION AND INGESTION AND TOXIC BY DERMAL ABSORPTION. TARGET EFFECTS: CHOLINESTERASE INHIBITOR. POISONING MAY AFFECT THE NERVOUS SYSTEM.* AT INCREASED RISK FROM EXPOSURE: PERSONS WITH RESPIRATORY AILMENTS, RECENT EXPOSURE TO CHOLINESTERASE INHIBITORS OR IMPAIRED CHOLINESTERASE PRODUCTION, OR LIVER MALFUNCTION.* ADDITIONAL DATA: MAY CROSS THE PLACENTA. HIGH ENVIRONMENTAL TEMPERATURES OR EXPOSURE OF THE CHEMICAL TO VISIBLE OR ULTRAVIOLET LIGHT MAY ENHANCE THE TOXICITY. INTERACTIONS WITH MEDICATIONS MAY OCCUR.*
* MAY BE BASED ON GENERAL INFORMATION ON ORGANOPHOSPHATES.

HEALTH EFFECTS AND FIRST AID

INHALATION: AZINPHOS-ETHYL: HIGHLY TOXIC. SEE INFORMATION ON ORGANOPHOSPHATES.

ORGANOPHOSPHATES: CHOLINESTERASE INHIBITOR. **ACUTE EXPOSURE**- WHEN INHALED, THE FIRST EFFECTS OF CHOLINESTERASE INHIBITORS ARE USUALLY RESPIRATORY AND MAY INCLUDE NASAL HYPEREMIA AND WATERY DISCHARGE, COUGH, CHEST DISCOMFORT, DYSPNEA, AND WHEEZING DUE TO INCREASED BRONCHIAL SECRETIONS AND BRONCHOCONSTRICTION. IF SUFFICIENT AMOUNTS ARE ABSORBED, OTHER SYSTEMIC EFFECTS MAY BEGIN WITHIN A FEW MINUTES OR BE DELAYED FOR UP TO 12 HOURS. SYMPTOMS MAY INCLUDE PALLOR, NAUSEA, VOMITING, DIARRHEA, ABDOMINAL CRAMPS, HEADACHE, DIZZINESS, OCULAR PAIN, BLURRED VISION, MIOSIS OR IN SOME CASES, ESPECIALLY INITIALLY, MYDRIASIS, LACRIMATION, SALIVATION, SWEATING, AND CONFUSION. OTHER REPORTED CENTRAL NERVOUS SYSTEM OR NEUROMUSCULAR EFFECTS MAY INCLUDE ATAXIA, SLURRED SPEECH, AREFLEXIA, WEAKNESS, FATIGUE, FASCICULATIONS, TWITCHING, TREMORS POSSIBLY OF THE TONGUE AND EYELIDS, AND EVENTUALLY PARALYSIS OF THE EXTREMITIES AND POSSIBLY OF THE RESPIRATORY MUSCLES. IN SEVERE CASES THERE MAY ALSO BE INVOLUNTARY DEFECATION AND URINATION, CYANOSIS, PSYCHOSIS, HYPERGLYCEMIA, ACUTE PANCREATITIS, CARDIAC IRREGULARITIES, PULMONARY EDEMA, UNCONSCIOUSNESS, CONVULSIONS, AND COMA. DEATH IS PRIMARILY DUE TO RESPIRATORY FAILURE, ALTHOUGH CARDIOVASCULAR EFFECTS INCLUDING CARDIAC ARREST MAY ALSO BE IMPLICATED. LONG TERM SEQUELAE ARE RARE BUT MAY INCLUDE NEUROPSYCHIATRIC DISORDERS AND MYOPATHY WITH MUSCLE TENDERNESS. SOME ORGANOPHOSPHATES MAY CAUSE A DELAYED NEUROPATHY BEGINNING 1-4 WEEKS AFTER AN ACUTE EXPOSURE WHICH MAY OR MAY NOT HAVE CAUSED ACUTE CHOLINERGIC EFFECTS. NUMBNESS, TINGLING, WEAKNESS AND CRAMPING BEGINNING SYMMETRICALLY IN THE LOWER LIMBS MAY PROGRESS TO ATAXIA AND PARALYSIS. IN SEVERE CASES, UPPER LIMB INVOLVEMENT IS POSSIBLE AND FLACCID PARALYSIS MAY PROGRESS TO SPASTIC PARALYSIS WITH EXAGGERATED REFLEXES. IMPROVEMENT MAY OCCUR OVER MONTHS TO YEARS, BUT SOME RESIDUAL IMPAIRMENT USUALLY REMAINS.
CHRONIC EXPOSURE- REPEATED OR PROLONGED EXPOSURE MAY RESULT IN THE EFFECTS OF ACUTE EXPOSURE INCLUDING THE DELAYED NEUROPATHY. OTHER EFFECTS REPORTED IN WORKERS REPEATEDLY EXPOSED INCLUDE IMPAIRED MEMORY AND CONCENTRATION, ACUTE PSYCHOSIS, SEVERE DEPRESSIONS, IRRITABILTY, CONFUSION, APATHY, EMOTIONAL LABILITY, SOCIAL WITHDRAWAL, CONFUSION, HEADACHE, SPEECH DIFFICULTIES, DELAYED REACTION TIMES, SPATIAL DISORIENTATION, NIGHTMARES, SLEEPWALKING, AND DROWSINESS OR INSOMNIA. AN INFLUENZA-LIKE CONDITION WITH HEADACHE, NAUSEA, WEAKNESS, ANOREXIA AND MALAISE HAS ALSO BEEN REPORTED.

FIRST AID- REMOVE FROM EXPOSURE AREA TO FRESH AIR IMMEDIATELY. IF BREATHING HAS STOPPED, GIVE ARTIFICIAL RESPIRATION. MAINTAIN AIRWAY AND BLOOD PRESSURE AND ADMINISTER OXYGEN IF AVAILABLE. KEEP AFFECTED PERSON WARM AND AT REST. TREAT SYMPTOMATICALLY AND SUPPORTIVELY. ADMINISTRATION OF OXYGEN SHOULD BE PERFORMED BY QUALIFIED PERSONNEL. GET MEDICAL ATTENTION IMMEDIATELY.

SKIN CONTACT: AZINPHOS-ETHYL: TOXIC. SEE INFORMATION ON ORGANOPHOSPHATES.

ORGANOPHOSPHATES: CHOLINESTERASE INHIBITOR. **ACUTE EXPOSURE**- LOCALIZED SWEATING AND FASCICULATIONS MAY OCCUR AT THE SITE OF CONTACT. IF SUFFICIENT AMOUNTS ARE ABSORBED, OTHER EFFECTS OF CHOLINESTERASE INHIBITION AS DESCRIBED IN ACUTE INHALATION MAY OCCUR. SYMPTOMS MAY BE DELAYED 2-3 HOURS, BUT USUALLY NO MORE THAN 12 HOURS. THE RATE OF ABSORPTION IS INCREASED BY THE PRESENCE OF DERMATITIS OR HIGH AMBIENT TEMPERATURES. DELAYED NEUROPATHY IS ALSO

POSSIBLE. **CHRONIC EXPOSURE-** REPEATED OR PROLONGED EXPOSURE MAY CAUSE EFFECTS AS DESCRIBED IN ACUTE EXPOSURE. SOME ORGANOPHOSPHATES MAY CAUSE SENSITIZATION.

FIRST AID- REMOVE CONTAMINATED CLOTHING IMMEDIATELY. WASH CONTAMINATED AREAS WITH SOAP AND WATER FOLLOWED BY ALCOHOL (ARENA, POISONING, 4TH ED.). EMERGENCY PERSONNEL SHOULD WEAR GLOVES AND AVOID CONTAMINATION. TREAT RESPIRATORY DIFFICULTY WITH ARTIFICIAL RESPIRATION. GET MEDICAL ATTENTION IMMEDIATELY.

EYE CONTACT: AZINPHOS-ETHYL: SEE INFORMATION ON ORGANOPHOSPHATES. ORGANOPHOSPHATES: CHOLINESTERASE INHIBITOR. **ACUTE EXPOSURE-** DIRECT CONTACT MAY CAUSE PAIN, HYPEREMIA, LACRIMATION, TWITCHING OF THE EYELIDS, MIOSIS, AND CILIARY MUSCLE SPASM WITH LOSS OF ACCOMODATION, BLURRED OR DIMMED VISION AND BROWACHE. SOMETIMES MYDRIASIS MAY OCCUR INSTEAD OF MIOSIS. WITH SUFFICIENT EXPOSURE, OTHER SYMPTOMS OF CHOLINESTERASE INHIBITION AS DESCRIBED IN ACUTE INHALATION MAY OCCUR. **CHRONIC EXPOSURE-** REPEATED OR PROLONGED EXPOSURE MAY CAUSE EFFECTS AS DESCRIBED IN ACUTE EXPOSURE. SOME COMPOUNDS HAVE CAUSED TOXIC EFFECTS ON THE CRYSTALLINE LENS, CONJUNCTIVAL THICKENING AND OBSTRUCTION OF THE NASOLACRIMAL CANALS WHEN USED AS MIOTIC EYEDROPS.

FIRST AID- IRRIGATE EYES WITH WATER OR SALINE SOLUTION. IF SYMPTOMS OF POISONING OCCUR, TREAT RESPIRATORY DIFFICULTY WITH ARTIFICIAL RESPIRATION AND OXYGEN. OBSERVE PATIENT FOR AT LEAST 24-36 HOURS (GOSSELIN, CLINICAL TOXICOLOGY OF COMMERCIAL PRODUCTS, 5TH ED.). GET MEDICAL ATTENTION IMMEDIATELY. OXYGEN SHOULD BE ADMINISTERED BY QUALIFIED MEDICAL PERSONNEL.

INGESTION: AZINPHOS-ETHYL: HIGHLY TOXIC. SEE INFORMATION ON ORGANOPHOSPHATES.
ORGANOPHOSPHATES: CHOLINESTERASE INHIBITOR. **ACUTE EXPOSURE-** WHEN INGESTED, THE FIRST EFFECTS MAY BE NAUSEA, VOMITING, ANOREXIA, ABDOMINAL CRAMPS AND DIARRHEA. GASTROINTESTINAL ABSORPTION MAY CAUSE SYMPTOMS OF CHOLINESTERASE INHIBITION AS DESCRIBED IN ACUTE INHALATION. SYMPTOMS MAY BEGIN WITHIN MINUTES OR BE DELAYED FOR HOURS. DELAYED EFFECTS INCLUDING NEUROPATHY MAY ALSO OCCUR. **CHRONIC EXPOSURE-** REPEATED INGESTION MAY CAUSE EFFECTS AS DESCRIBED IN ACUTE EXPOSURE.

FIRST AID- IF PERSON IS ALERT AND RESPIRATION IS NOT DEPRESSED, GIVE SYRUP OF IPECAC FOLLOWED BY WATER (IF VOMITING OCCURS, KEEP HEAD BELOW HIPS TO PREVENT ASPIRATION). IF CONSCIOUSNESS LEVEL DECLINES OR VOMITING HAS NOT OCCURRED IN 15 MINUTES EMPTY STOMACH BY GASTRIC LAVAGE WITH THE AID OF CUFFED ENDOTRACHEAL TUBE USING ISOTONIC SALINE OR 5% SODIUM BICARBONATE FOLLOW WITH ACTIVATED CHARCOAL. ESTABLISH AND MAINTAIN AIRWAY. TREAT RESPIRATORY DIFFICULTY WITH ARTIFICIAL RESPIRATION AND OXYGEN. DO NOT GIVE MORPHINE, AMINOPHYLLINE, PHENOTHIAZINES, RESERPINE, FUROSEMIDE, OR ETHACRYNIC ACID (MORGAN, RECOGNITION AND MANAGEMENT OF PESTICIDE POISONINGS, 3RD ED.). TREAT SYMPTOMATICALLY AND SUPPORTIVELY. ADMINISTRATION OF OXYGEN AND LAVAGE MUST BE PERFORMED BY QUALIFIED MEDICAL PERSONNEL. GET MEDICAL ATTENTION IMMEDIATELY.

ANTIDOTE: THE FOLLOWING ANTIDOTE(S) HAVE BEEN RECOMMENDED. HOWEVER, THE DECISION AS TO WHETHER THE SEVERITY OF POISONING REQUIRES ADMINISTRATION OF ANY ANTIDOTE AND ACTUAL DOSE REQUIRED SHOULD BE MADE BY QUALIFIED MEDICAL PERSONNEL.
FOR CHOLINESTERASE INHIBITORS: ESTABLISH CLEAR AIRWAY AND TISSUE OXYGENATION BY ASPIRATION OF SECRETIONS, AND IF NECESSARY, BY ASSISTED PULMONARY VENTILATION WITH OXYGEN. IMPROVE TISSUE OXYGENATION AS MUCH AS POSSIBLE BEFORE ADMINISTERING ATROPINE TO MINIMIZE THE RISK OF VENTRICULAR FIBRILLATION. ADMINISTER ATROPINE SULFATE INTRAVENOUSLY, OR INTRAMUSCULARLY IF IV INJECTION IS NOT POSSIBLE. IN MODERATELY SEVERE POISONING ADMINISTER ATROPINE SULFATE, 0.4-2.0 MG REPEATED EVERY 15 MINUTES UNTIL ATROPINIZATION IS ACHIEVED (TACHYCARDIA, FLUSHING, DRY MOUTH, MYDRIASIS). MAINTAIN ATROPINIZATION BY REPEATED DOSES FOR 2-12 HOURS, OR LONGER, DEPENDING ON THE SEVERITY OF POISONING. THE APPEARANCE OF RALES IN THE LUNG BASES, MIOSIS, SALIVATION, NAUSEA, BRADYCARDIA, ARE ALL INDICATIONS OF INADEQUATE ATROPINIZATION.
SEVERELY POISONED INDIVIDUALS MAY EXHIBIT REMARKABLE TOLERANCE TO ATROPINE; TWO OR MORE TIMES THE DOSAGES SUGGESTED ABOVE MAY BE NEEDED. PERSONS NOT POISONED OR ONLY SLIGHTLY POISONED, HOWEVER, MAY DEVELOP SIGNS OF ATROPINE TOXICITY FROM SUCH LARGE DOSAGES: FEVER, MUSCLE FIBRILLATIONS, AND DELIRIUM ARE THE MAIN SIGNS OF ATROPINE TOXICITY. IF THESE SIGNS APPEAR WHILE THE PATIENT IS FULLY ATROPINIZED, ATROPINE ADMINISTRATION SHOULD BE DISCONTINUED, AT LEAST TEMPORARILY. OBSERVE TREATED PATIENTS CLOSELY AT LEAST 24 HOURS TO INSURE THAT SYMPTOMS (POSSIBLY PULMONARY EDEMA) DO NOT RECUR AS ATROPINIZATION WEARS OFF. IN VERY SEVERE POISONINGS, METABOLIC DISPOSITION OF TOXICANT MAY REQUIRE SEVERAL HOURS OR DAYS DURING WHICH ATROPINIZATION MUST BE MAINTAINED. MARKEDLY LOWER LEVELS OF URINARY METABOLITES INDICATE THAT ATROPINE DOSAGE CAN BE TAPERED OFF. AS DOSAGE IS REDUCED, CHECK THE LUNG BASES FREQUENTLY FOR RALES. IF RALES ARE HEARD OR OTHER SYMPTOMS RETURN, RE-ESTABLISH ATROPINIZATION PROMPTLY (MORGAN, RECOGNITION AND MANAGEMENT OF PESTICIDE POISONINGS, 3RD ED.). ADMINISTRATION OF ANTIDOTE MUST BE PERFORMED BY QUALIFIED MEDICAL PERSONNEL.
IN CASES OF SEVERE POISONING BY ORGANOPHOSPHATE PESTICIDES IN WHICH RESPIRATORY DEPRESSION, MUSCLE WEAKNESS AND TWITCHINGS ARE SEVERE, GIVE PRALIDOXIME (PROTOPAM-AYERST, 2-PAM), 1.0 GRAM INTRAVENOUSLY AT NO MORE THAN 0.5 GRAM PER MINUTE. DOSAGE OF PRALIDOXIME MAY BE REPEATED IN 1-2 HOURS, THEN AT 10-12 HOUR INTERVALS IF NEEDED. IN VERY SEVERE POISONINGS, DOSAGE RATES MAY BE DOUBLED. TREATMENT WITH PRALIDOXIME WILL BE MOST EFFECTIVE IF GIVEN WITHIN THIRTY-SIX HOURS AFTER POISONING (MORGAN, RECOGNITION AND MANAGEMENT OF PESTICIDE POISONINGS, 3RD ED.). ANTIDOTE SHOULD BE ADMINISTERED BY QUALIFIED MEDICAL PERSONNEL.

REACTIVITY

REACTIVITY: STABLE UNDER NORMAL TEMPERATURES AND PRESSURES.

INCOMPATIBILITIES: AZINPHOS-ETHYL: ALKALI: MAY CAUSE HYDROLYSIS. OXIDIZERS (STRONG): FIRE AND EXPLOSION HAZARD.

DECOMPOSITION: THERMAL DECOMPOSITION MAY RELEASE TOXIC OXIDES OF NITROGEN, PHOSPHORUS, SULFUR AND CARBON.

POLYMERIZATION: HAZARDOUS POLYMERIZATION HAS NOT BEEN REPORTED TO OCCUR UNDER NORMAL TEMPERATURES AND PRESSURES.

STORAGE AND DISPOSAL

OBSERVE ALL FEDERAL, STATE AND LOCAL REGULATIONS WHEN STORING OR DISPOSING OF THIS SUBSTANCE. FOR ASSISTANCE, CONTACT THE DISTRICT DIRECTOR OF THE ENVIRONMENTAL PROTECTION AGENCY.

STORAGE

STORE IN ACCORDANCE WITH 40 CFR 165 RECOMMENDED PROCEDURES FOR THE DISPOSAL AND STORAGE OF PESTICIDES AND PESTICIDE CONTAINERS.
STORE AWAY FROM INCOMPATIBLE SUBSTANCES.
STORE IN COOL DRY PLACE. KEEP AWAY FROM HEAT AND OPEN FLAME.
THRESHOLD PLANNING QUANTITY (TPQ): THE SUPERFUND AMENDMENTS AND REAUTHORIZATION ACT (SARA) SECTION 302 REQUIRES THAT EACH FACILITY WHERE ANY EXTREMELY HAZARDOUS SUBSTANCE IS PRESENT IN A QUANTITY EQUAL TO OR GREATER THAN THE TPQ ESTABLISHED FOR THAT SUBSTANCE NOTIFY THE STATE EMERGENCY RESPONSE COMMISSION FOR THE STATE IN WHICH IT IS LOCATED. SECTION 303 OF SARA REQUIRES THESE FACILITIES TO PARTICIPATE IN LOCAL EMERGENCY RESPONSE PLANNING (40 CFR 355.30).

DISPOSAL

DISPOSAL MUST BE IN ACCORDANCE WITH 40 CFR 165 RECOMMENDED PROCEDURES FOR THE DISPOSAL AND STORAGE OF PESTICIDES AND PESTICIDE CONTAINERS.

CONDITIONS TO AVOID

MAY BURN BUT DOES NOT IGNITE READILY. CONTAINERS MAY EXPLODE IN HEAT OF FIRE.

SPILL AND LEAK PROCEDURES

OCCUPATIONAL SPILL: DO NOT TOUCH SPILLED MATERIAL. STOP LEAK IF YOU CAN DO IT WITHOUT RISK. USE WATER SPRAY TO REDUCE VAPORS. FOR SMALL SPILLS, TAKE UP WITH SAND OR OTHER ABSORBENT MATERIAL AND PLACE INTO CONTAINERS FOR LATER DISPOSAL. FOR SMALL DRY SPILLS, WITH A CLEAN SHOVEL PLACE MATERIAL INTO CLEAN, DRY CONTAINERS AND COVER. MOVE CONTAINERS FROM SPILL AREA. FOR LARGER SPILLS, DIKE FAR AHEAD OF SPILL FOR LATER DISPOSAL. KEEP UNNECESSARY PEOPLE AWAY. ISOLATE HAZARD AREA AND DENY ENTRY. VENTILATE CLOSED SPACES BEFORE ENTERING.
REPORTABLE QUANTITY (RQ): 1 POUND THE SUPERFUND AMENDMENTS AND REAUTHORIZATION ACT (SARA) SECTION 304 REQUIRES THAT A RELEASE EQUAL TO OR GREATER THAN THE REPORTABLE QUANTITY FOR THIS SUBSTANCE BE IMMEDIATELY REPORTED TO THE LOCAL EMERGENCY PLANNING COMMITTEE AND THE STATE EMERGENCY RESPONSE COMMISSION (40 CFR 355.40). IF THE RELEASE OF THIS SUBSTANCE IS REPORTABLE UNDER CERCLA SECTION 103, THE NATIONAL RESPONSE CENTER MUST BE NOTIFIED IMMEDIATELY AT (800) 424-8802 OR (202) 426-2675 IN THE METROPOLITAN WASHINGTON, D.C. AREA (40 CFR 302.6).

PROTECTIVE EQUIPMENT

VENTILATION: PROCESS ENCLOSURE RECOMMENDED.

RESPIRATOR: THE FOLLOWING RESPIRATORS ARE RECOMMENDED BASED ON INFORMATION FOUND IN THE PHYSICAL DATA, TOXICITY AND HEALTH EFFECTS SECTIONS. THEY ARE RANKED IN ORDER FROM MINIMUM TO MAXIMUM

RESPIRATORY PROTECTION. THE SPECIFIC RESPIRATOR SELECTED MUST BE BASED ON CONTAMINATION LEVELS FOUND IN THE WORK PLACE, MUST NOT EXCEED THE WORKING LIMITS OF THE RESPIRATOR AND BE JOINTLY APPROVED BY THE NATIONAL INSTITUTE FOR OCCUPATIONAL SAFETY AND HEALTH AND THE MINE SAFETY AND HEALTH ADMINISTRATION (NIOSH-MSHA).
TYPE 'C' SUPPLIED-AIR RESPIRATOR WITH A FULL FACEPIECE OPERATED IN PRESSURE-DEMAND OR OTHER POSITIVE PRESSURE MODE OR WITH A FULL FACEPIECE, HELMET OR HOOD OPERATED IN CONTINOUS-FLOW MODE.
SELF-CONTAINED BREATHING APPARATUS WITH A FULL FACEPIECE OPERATED IN PRESSURE-DEMAND OR OTHER POSITIVE PRESSURE MODE.
FOR FIREFIGHTING AND OTHER IMMEDIATELY DANGEROUS TO LIFE OR HEALTH CONDITIONS:
SELF-CONTAINED BREATHING APPARATUS WITH FULL FACEPIECE OPERATED IN PRESSURE-DEMAND OR OTHER POSITIVE PRESSURE MODE.
SUPPLIED-AIR RESPIRATOR WITH FULL FACEPIECE AND OPERATED IN PRESSURE-DEMAND OR OTHER POSITIVE PRESSURE MODE IN COMBINATION WITH AN AUXILIARY SELF-CONTAINED BREATHING APPARATUS OPERATED IN PRESSURE-DEMAND OR OTHER POSITIVE PRESSURE MODE.

CLOTHING: EMPLOYEE MUST WEAR APPROPRIATE PROTECTIVE (IMPERVIOUS) CLOTHING AND EQUIPMENT TO PREVENT ANY POSSIBILITY OF SKIN CONTACT WITH THIS SUBSTANCE.

GLOVES: EMPLOYEE MUST WEAR APPROPRIATE PROTECTIVE GLOVES TO PREVENT CONTACT WITH THIS SUBSTANCE.

EYE PROTECTION: EMPLOYEE MUST WEAR SPLASH-PROOF OR DUST-RESISTANT SAFETY GOGGLES WITH OR WITHOUT A FACESHIELD TO PREVENT CONTACT WITH THIS SUBSTANCE.
EMERGENCY EYE WASH: WHERE THERE IS ANY POSSIBILITY THAT AN EMPLOYEE'S EYES MAY BE EXPOSED TO THIS SUBSTANCE, THE EMPLOYER SHOULD PROVIDE AN EYE WASH FOUNTAIN WITHIN THE IMMEDIATE WORK AREA FOR EMERGENCY USE.

AUTHORIZED BY- OCCUPATIONAL HEALTH SERVICES, INC.
CREATION DATE: 10/04/89 ***REVISION DATE:*** 04/26/90

MATERIAL SAFETY DATA SHEET

OCCUPATIONAL HEALTH SERVICES, INC.
AGRICULTURE AND PESTICIDE DIVISION
450 SEVENTH AVENUE, SUITE 2407
NEW YORK, NEW YORK 10123
1-800-445-MSDS OR (212) 967-1100

EMERGENCY CONTACT:
JOHN S. BRANSFORD, JR. (615) 292-1180

SUBSTANCE IDENTIFICATION

CAS-NUMBER 86-50-0

SUBSTANCE: **AZINPHOS-METHYL**

TRADE NAMES/SYNONYMS: PHOSPHORODITHIOIC ACID, O,O-DIMETHYL S-(4-OXO-1,2,3-BENZOTRIAZIN- 3(4H)-YL)METHYL) ESTER; PHOSPHORODITHIOIC ACID, O,O-DIMETHYL ESTER, S-ESTER WITH 3-(MERCAPTOMETHYL)-1,2,3-BENZOTRIAZIN-4(3H)-ONE; S-3,4-DIHYDRO-4-OXO-1,2,3-BENZOTRIAZIN-3-YLMETHYL O,O-DIMETHYL PHOSPHORODITHIOATE; S-3,4-DIHYDRO-4-OXOBENZO(D)(1,2,3)TRIAZIN-3-YLMETHYL O,O,-DIMETHYL PHOSPHORODITHIOATE; 3-DIMETHOXYPHOSPHINITHIOYLTHIOMETHYL-1,2,3-BENZOTRIAZIN-4(3H)-ONE; O,O-DIMETHYL S-((4-OXO-1,2,3-BENZOTRIAZIN-3(4H)-YL)METHYL) PHOSPHORODITHIOATE; O,O-DIMETHYL PHOSPHORODITHIOATE S-ESTER WITH 3-(MERCAPTOMETHYL)-1,2, 3-BENZOTRIAZIN-4(3H)-ONE; BAY 171476; GUTHION; GUSATHION M; OMS 186; ENT 23,233; STCC 4921528; C10H12N3O3PS2; PST02210

CHEMICAL FAMILY: ORGANOPHOSPHATE
HETEROCYCLIC NITROGEN

MOLECULAR FORMULA: C10-H12-N3-O3-P-S2

MOLECULAR WEIGHT: 317.34

CERCLA RATINGS (SCALE 0-3): HEALTH=3 FIRE=0 REACTIVITY=0 PERSISTENCE=1

NFPA RATINGS (SCALE 0-4): HEALTH=4 FIRE=0 REACTIVITY=0

COMPONENTS AND CONTAMINANTS

COMPONENT: AZINPHOS-METHYL ***PERCENT:*** 100
CAS# 86-50-0

EXPOSURE LIMITS: AZINPHOS-METHYL: 0.2 MG/M3 OSHA TWA (SKIN) 0.2 MG/M3 ACGIH TWA (SKIN) 0.6 MG/M3 ACGIH STEL (SKIN)
10/10,000 POUNDS SARA SECTION 304 THRESHOLD PLANNING QUANTITY 1 POUND SARA SECTION 304 REPORTABLE QUANTITY 1 POUND CERCLA SECTION 103 REPORTABLE QUANTITY

PHYSICAL DATA

DESCRIPTION: WHITE CRYSTALLINE SOLID; THE TECHNICAL MATERIAL FORMS A BROWN WAXY SOLID. ***BOILING POINT:*** DECOMPOSES ***MELTING POINT:*** 163 F (73 C)

SPECIFIC GRAVITY: 1.44 @ 20 C ***VAPOR PRESSURE:*** 0.0004 AT 20 C

SOLUBILITY IN WATER: 29 PPM @ 25 C

SOLVENT SOLUBILITY: SOLUBLE IN METHANOL, ETHANOL, PROPYLENE GLYCOL, XYLENE, TOLUENE, DICHLOROMETHANE, AND MOST ORGANIC SOLVENTS EXCEPT ALIPHATICS.

FIRE AND EXPLOSION DATA

FIRE AND EXPLOSION HAZARD: NEGLIGIBLE FIRE HAZARD WHEN EXPOSED TO HEAT OR FLAME.

FIREFIGHTING MEDIA: DRY CHEMICAL, CARBON DIOXIDE, HALON, WATER SPRAY OR STANDARD FOAM (1987 EMERGENCY RESPONSE GUIDEBOOK, DOT P 5800.4).
FOR LARGER FIRES, USE WATER SPRAY, FOG OR STANDARD FOAM (1987 EMERGENCY RESPONSE GUIDEBOOK, DOT P 5800.4).

FIREFIGHTING: MOVE CONTAINERS FROM FIRE AREA IF POSSIBLE. FIGHT FIRE FROM MAXIMUM DISTANCE. STAY AWAY FROM STORAGE TANK ENDS. DIKE FIRE CONTROL WATER FOR LATER DISPOSAL. DO NOT SCATTER MATERIAL (1987 EMERGENCY RESPONSE GUIDEBOOK, DOT P 5800.4, GUIDE PAGE 55).
EXTINGUISH ONLY IF FLOW CAN BE STOPPED; USE FLOODING AMOUNTS OF WATER AS FOG, SOLID STREAMS MAY BE INEFFECTIVE. COOL CONTAINERS WITH FLOODING AMOUNTS OF WATER FROM AS FAR A DISTANCE AS POSSIBLE. USE WATER SPRAY TO ABSORB TOXIC VAPORS. AVOID BREATHING TOXIC VAPORS; KEEP UPWIND. CONSIDER EVACUATION OF DOWNWIND AREA IF MATERIAL IS LEAKING.

TRANSPORTATION DATA

DEPARTMENT OF TRANSPORTATION HAZARD CLASSIFICATION 49 CFR 172.101: POISON B
DEPARTMENT OF TRANSPORTATION LABELING REQUIREMENTS 49 CFR 172.101 AND SUBPART E: POISON
DEPARTMENT OF TRANSPORTATION PACKAGING REQUIREMENTS: 49 CFR 173.365 EXCEPTIONS: 49 CFR 173.364

TOXICITY

AZINPHOS-METHYL: TOXICITY DATA: 69 MG/M3/1 HOUR INHALATION-RAT LC50; 88 MG/KG SKIN-RAT LD50; 65 MG/KG SKIN-MOUSE LD50; 7 MG/KG ORAL-RAT LD50; 15 MG/KG ORAL-MOUSE LD50; 80 MG/KG ORAL-GUINEA PIG LD50; 7500 UG/KG INTRAVENOUS-RAT LD50; 4900 UG/KG INTRAPERITONEAL-RAT LD50; 4 MG/KG INTRAPERITONEAL-MOUSE LD50; 40 MG/KG INTRAPERITONEAL-GUINEA PIG LD50; 15 MG/KG UNREPORTED-RAT LD50; MUTAGENIC DATA (RTECS); REPRODUCTIVE EFFECTS DATA (RTECS); TUMORIGENIC DATA (RTECS).
CARCINOGEN STATUS: NONE. ACUTE TOXICITY: HIGHLY TOXIC BY INHALATION, DERMAL ABSORPTION AND INGESTION. TARGET EFFECTS: CHOLINESTERASE INHIBITOR. POISONING MAY AFFECT THE NERVOUS SYSTEM.* AT INCREASED RISK FROM EXPOSURE: PERSONS WITH A HISTORY OF REDUCED PULMONARY FUNCTION, CONVULSIVE DISORDERS, OR RECENT EXPOSURE TO ANTICHOLINESTERASE AGENTS. ADDITIONAL DATA: MAY CROSS THE PLACENTA. HIGH ENVIRONMENTAL TEMPERATURES OR EXPOSURE OF THE CHEMICAL TO VISIBLE OR ULTRAVIOLET LIGHT MAY ENHANCE THE TOXICITY. INTERACTIONS WITH MEDICATIONS MAY OCCUR.*
* MAY BE BASED ON GENERAL INFORMATION ON ORGANOPHOSPHATES.

HEALTH EFFECTS AND FIRST AID

INHALATION: AZINPHOS-METHYL: 5 MG/M3 IMMEDIATELY DANGEROUS TO LIFE OR HEALTH. HIGHLY TOXIC. SEE INFORMATION ON ORGANOPHOSPHATES.
ORGANOPHOSPHATES: CHOLINESTERASE INHIBITOR. **ACUTE EXPOSURE-** WHEN INHALED, THE FIRST EFFECTS OF CHOLINESTERASE INHIBITORS ARE USUALLY RESPIRATORY AND MAY INCLUDE NASAL HYPEREMIA AND WATERY DISCHARGE, COUGH, CHEST DISCOMFORT, DYSPNEA, AND WHEEZING DUE TO INCREASED BRONCHIAL SECRETIONS AND BRONCHOCONSTRICTION. IF SUFFICIENT AMOUNTS ARE ABSORBED, OTHER SYSTEMIC EFFECTS MAY BEGIN WITHIN A FEW MINUTES OR BE DELAYED FOR UP TO 12 HOURS. SYMPTOMS MAY INCLUDE PALLOR, NAUSEA, VOMITING, DIARRHEA, ABDOMINAL CRAMPS, HEADACHE, DIZZINESS, OCULAR PAIN, BLURRED VISION, MIOSIS OR IN SOME CASES, ESPECIALLY INITIALLY, MYDRIASIS, LACRIMATION, SALIVATION, SWEATING, AND CONFUSION. OTHER REPORTED CENTRAL NERVOUS SYSTEM OR NEUROMUSCULAR EFFECTS MAY INCLUDE ATAXIA, SLURRED SPEECH, AREFLEXIA, WEAKNESS, FATIGUE, FASCICULATIONS, TWITCHING, TREMORS POSSIBLY OF THE TONGUE AND EYELIDS, AND EVENTUALLY PARALYSIS OF THE EXTREMITIES AND POSSIBLY OF THE RESPIRATORY MUSCLES. IN SEVERE CASES THERE MAY ALSO BE INVOLUNTARY DEFECATION AND URINATION, CYANOSIS, PSYCHOSIS, HYPERGLYCEMIA, ACUTE

PANCREATITIS, CARDIAC IRREGULARITIES, PULMONARY EDEMA, UNCONSCIOUSNESS, CONVULSIONS, AND COMA. DEATH IS PRIMARILY DUE TO RESPIRATORY FAILURE, ALTHOUGH CARDIOVASCULAR EFFECTS INCLUDING CARDIAC ARREST MAY ALSO BE IMPLICATED. LONG TERM SEQUELAE ARE RARE BUT MAY INCLUDE NEUROPSYCHIATRIC DISORDERS AND MYOPATHY WITH MUSCLE TENDERNESS. SOME ORGANOPHOSPHATES MAY CAUSE A DELAYED NEUROPATHY BEGINNING 1-4 WEEKS AFTER AN ACUTE EXPOSURE WHICH MAY OR MAY NOT HAVE CAUSED ACUTE CHOLINERGIC EFFECTS. NUMBNESS, TINGLING, WEAKNESS AND CRAMPING BEGINNING SYMMETRICALLY IN THE LOWER LIMBS MAY PROGRESS TO ATAXIA AND PARALYSIS. IN SEVERE CASES, UPPER LIMB INVOLVEMENT IS POSSIBLE AND FLACCID PARALYSIS MAY PROGRESS TO SPASTIC PARALYSIS WITH EXAGGERATED REFLEXES. IMPROVEMENT MAY OCCUR OVER MONTHS TO YEARS, BUT SOME RESIDUAL IMPAIRMENT USUALLY REMAINS. **CHRONIC EXPOSURE-** REPEATED OR PROLONGED EXPOSURE MAY RESULT IN THE EFFECTS OF ACUTE EXPOSURE INCLUDING THE DELAYED NEUROPATHY. OTHER EFFECTS REPORTED IN WORKERS REPEATEDLY EXPOSED INCLUDE IMPAIRED MEMORY AND CONCENTRATION, ACUTE PSYCHOSIS, SEVERE DEPRESSIONS, IRRITABILTY, CONFUSION, APATHY, EMOTIONAL LABILITY, SOCIAL WITHDRAWAL, CONFUSION, HEADACHE, SPEECH DIFFICULTIES, DELAYED REACTION TIMES, SPATIAL DISORIENTATION, NIGHTMARES, SLEEPWALKING, AND DROWSINESS OR INSOMNIA. AN INFLUENZA-LIKE CONDITION WITH HEADACHE, NAUSEA, WEAKNESS, ANOREXIA AND MALAISE HAS ALSO BEEN REPORTED.

FIRST AID- REMOVE FROM EXPOSURE AREA TO FRESH AIR IMMEDIATELY. IF BREATHING HAS STOPPED, GIVE ARTIFICIAL RESPIRATION. MAINTAIN AIRWAY AND BLOOD PRESSURE AND ADMINISTER OXYGEN IF AVAILABLE. KEEP AFFECTED PERSON WARM AND AT REST. TREAT SYMPTOMATICALLY AND SUPPORTIVELY. ADMINISTRATION OF OXYGEN SHOULD BE PERFORMED BY QUALIFIED PERSONNEL. GET MEDICAL ATTENTION IMMEDIATELY.

SKIN CONTACT: AZINPHOS-METHYL: HIGHLY TOXIC. SEE INFORMATION ON ORGANOPHOSPHATES.

ORGANOPHOSPHATES: CHOLINESTERASE INHIBITOR. **ACUTE EXPOSURE-** LOCALIZED SWEATING AND FASCICULATIONS MAY OCCUR AT THE SITE OF CONTACT. IF SUFFICIENT AMOUNTS ARE ABSORBED, OTHER EFFECTS OF CHOLINESTERASE INHIBITION AS DESCRIBED IN ACUTE INHALATION MAY OCCUR. SYMPTOMS MAY BE DELAYED 2-3 HOURS, BUT USUALLY NO MORE THAN 12 HOURS. THE RATE OF ABSORPTION IS INCREASED BY THE PRESENCE OF DERMATITIS OR HIGH AMBIENT TEMPERATURES. DELAYED NEUROPATHY IS ALSO POSSIBLE. **CHRONIC EXPOSURE-** REPEATED OR PROLONGED EXPOSURE MAY CAUSE EFFECTS AS DESCRIBED IN ACUTE EXPOSURE. SOME ORGANOPHOSPHATES MAY CAUSE SENSITIZATION.

FIRST AID- REMOVE CONTAMINATED CLOTHING IMMEDIATELY. WASH CONTAMINATED AREAS WITH SOAP AND WATER FOLLOWED BY ALCOHOL (ARENA, POISONING, 4TH ED.). EMERGENCY PERSONNEL SHOULD WEAR GLOVES AND AVOID CONTAMINATION. TREAT RESPIRATORY DIFFICULTY WITH ARTIFICIAL RESPIRATION. GET MEDICAL ATTENTION IMMEDIATELY.

EYE CONTACT: AZINPHOS-METHYL: SEE INFORMATION ON ORGANOPHOSPATES.

ORGANOPHOSPHATES: CHOLINESTERASE INHIBITOR. **ACUTE EXPOSURE-** DIRECT CONTACT MAY CAUSE PAIN, HYPEREMIA, LACRIMATION, TWITCHING OF THE EYELIDS, MIOSIS, AND CILIARY MUSCLE SPASM WITH LOSS OF ACCOMODATION, BLURRED OR DIMMED VISION AND BROWACHE. SOMETIMES MYDRIASIS MAY OCCUR INSTEAD OF MIOSIS. WITH SUFFICIENT EXPOSURE, OTHER SYMPTOMS OF CHOLINESTERASE INHIBITION AS DESCRIBED IN ACUTE INHALATION MAY OCCUR. **CHRONIC EXPOSURE-** REPEATED OR PROLONGED EXPOSURE MAY CAUSE EFFECTS AS DESCRIBED IN ACUTE EXPOSURE. SOME COMPOUNDS HAVE CAUSED TOXIC EFFECTS ON THE CRYSTALLINE LENS, CONJUNCTIVAL THICKENING AND OBSTRUCTION OF THE NASOLACRIMAL CANALS WHEN USED AS MIOTIC EYEDROPS.

FIRST AID- IRRIGATE EYES WITH WATER OR SALINE SOLUTION. IF SYMPTOMS OF POISONING OCCUR, TREAT RESPIRATORY DIFFICULTY WITH ARTIFICIAL RESPIRATION AND OXYGEN. OBSERVE PATIENT FOR AT LEAST 24-36 HOURS (GOSSELIN, CLINICAL TOXICOLOGY OF COMMERCIAL PRODUCTS, 5TH ED.). GET MEDICAL ATTENTION IMMEDIATELY. OXYGEN SHOULD BE ADMINISTERED BY QUALIFIED MEDICAL PERSONNEL.

INGESTION: AZINPHOS-METHYL: HIGHLY TOXIC. NO ADVERSE EFFECTS OR A SIGNIFICANT CHANGE IN CHOLINESTERASE LEVELS WERE OBSERVED IN SEVERAL VOLUNTEERS WHO INGESTED 20 MG/MAN/DAY FOR 30 DAYS. REPRODUCTIVE EFFECTS HAVE BEEN REPORTED IN ANIMALS. SEE INFORMATION ON ORGANOPHOSPHATES.

ORGANOPHOSPHATES: CHOLINESTERASE INHIBITOR. **ACUTE EXPOSURE-** WHEN INGESTED, THE FIRST EFFECTS MAY BE NAUSEA, VOMITING, ANOREXIA, ABDOMINAL CRAMPS AND DIARRHEA. GASTROINTESTINAL ABSORPTION MAY CAUSE SYMPTOMS OF CHOLINESTERASE INHIBITION AS DESCRIBED IN ACUTE INHALATION. SYMPTOMS MAY BEGIN WITHIN MINUTES OR BE DELAYED FOR HOURS. DELAYED EFFECTS INCLUDING NEUROPATHY MAY ALSO OCCUR. **CHRONIC EXPOSURE-** REPEATED INGESTION MAY CAUSE EFFECTS AS DESCRIBED IN ACUTE EXPOSURE.

FIRST AID- IF PERSON IS ALERT AND RESPIRATION IS NOT DEPRESSED, GIVE SYRUP OF IPECAC FOLLOWED BY WATER (IF VOMITING OCCURS, KEEP HEAD BELOW HIPS TO PREVENT ASPIRATION). IF CONSCIOUSNESS LEVEL DECLINES OR VOMITING HAS NOT OCCURRED IN 15 MINUTES EMPTY STOMACH BY GASTRIC LAVAGE WITH THE AID OF CUFFED ENDOTRACHEAL TUBE USING ISOTONIC SALINE OR 5% SODIUM BICARBONATE FOLLOW WITH ACTIVATED CHARCOAL. ESTABLISH AND MAINTAIN AIRWAY. TREAT RESPIRATORY DIFFICULTY WITH ARTIFICIAL RESPIRATION AND OXYGEN. DO NOT GIVE MORPHINE, AMINOPHYLLINE, PHENOTHIAZINES, RESERPINE, FUROSEMIDE, OR ETHACRYNIC ACID (MORGAN, RECOGNITION AND MANAGEMENT OF PESTICIDE POISONINGS, 3RD ED.). TREAT SYMPTOMATICALLY AND SUPPORTIVELY. ADMINISTRATION OF OXYGEN AND LAVAGE MUST BE PERFORMED BY QUALIFIED MEDICAL PERSONNEL. GET MEDICAL ATTENTION IMMEDIATELY.

ANTIDOTE: THE FOLLOWING ANTIDOTE(S) HAVE BEEN RECOMMENDED. HOWEVER, THE DECISION AS TO WHETHER THE SEVERITY OF POISONING REQUIRES ADMINISTRATION OF ANY ANTIDOTE AND ACTUAL DOSE REQUIRED SHOULD BE MADE BY QUALIFIED MEDICAL PERSONNEL.

FOR CHOLINESTERASE INHIBITORS: ESTABLISH CLEAR AIRWAY AND TISSUE OXYGENATION BY ASPIRATION OF SECRETIONS, AND IF NECESSARY, BY ASSISTED PULMONARY VENTILATION WITH OXYGEN. IMPROVE TISSUE OXYGENATION AS MUCH AS POSSIBLE BEFORE ADMINISTERING ATROPINE TO MINIMIZE THE RISK OF VENTRICULAR FIBRILLATION. ADMINISTER ATROPINE SULFATE INTRAVENOUSLY, OR INTRAMUSCULARLY IF IV INJECTION IS NOT POSSIBLE. IN MODERATELY SEVERE POISONING ADMINISTER ATROPINE SULFATE, 0.4-2.0 MG REPEATED EVERY 15 MINUTES UNTIL ATROPINIZATION IS ACHIEVED (TACHYCARDIA, FLUSHING, DRY MOUTH, MYDRIASIS). MAINTAIN ATROPINIZATION BY REPEATED DOSES FOR 2-12 HOURS, OR LONGER, DEPENDING ON THE SEVERITY OF POISONING. THE APPEARANCE OF RALES IN THE LUNG BASES, MIOSIS, SALIVATION, NAUSEA, BRADYCARDIA, ARE ALL INDICATIONS OF INADEQUATE ATROPINIZATION. SEVERELY POISONED INDIVIDUALS MAY EXHIBIT REMARKABLE TOLERANCE TO ATROPINE; TWO OR MORE TIMES THE DOSAGES SUGGESTED ABOVE MAY BE NEEDED. PERSONS NOT POISONED OR ONLY SLIGHTLY POISONED, HOWEVER, MAY DEVELOP SIGNS OF ATROPINE TOXICITY FROM SUCH LARGE DOSAGES: FEVER, MUSCLE FIBRILLATIONS, AND DELIRIUM ARE THE MAIN SIGNS OF ATROPINE TOXICITY. IF THESE SIGNS APPEAR WHILE THE PATIENT IS FULLY ATROPINIZED, ATROPINE ADMINISTRATION SHOULD BE DISCONTINUED, AT LEAST TEMPORARILY. OBSERVE TREATED PATIENTS CLOSELY AT LEAST 24 HOURS TO INSURE THAT SYMPTOMS (POSSIBLY PULMONARY EDEMA) DO NOT RECUR AS ATROPINIZATION WEARS OFF. IN VERY SEVERE POISONINGS, METABOLIC DISPOSITION OF TOXICANT MAY REQUIRE SEVERAL HOURS OR DAYS DURING WHICH ATROPINIZATION MUST BE MAINTAINED. MARKEDLY LOWER LEVELS OF URINARY METABOLITES INDICATE THAT ATROPINE DOSAGE CAN BE TAPERED OFF. AS DOSAGE IS REDUCED, CHECK THE LUNG BASES FREQUENTLY FOR RALES. IF RALES ARE HEARD OR OTHER SYMPTOMS RETURN, RE-ESTABLISH ATROPINIZATION PROMPTLY (MORGAN, RECOGNITION AND MANAGEMENT OF PESTICIDE POISONINGS, 3RD ED.). ADMINISTRATION OF ANTIDOTE MUST BE PERFORMED BY QUALIFIED MEDICAL PERSONNEL.

IN CASES OF SEVERE POISONING BY ORGANOPHOSPHATE PESTICIDES IN WHICH RESPIRATORY DEPRESSION, MUSCLE WEAKNESS AND TWITCHINGS ARE SEVERE, GIVE PRALIDOXIME (PROTOPAM-AYERST, 2-PAM), 1.0 GRAM INTRAVENOUSLY AT NO MORE THAN 0.5 GRAM PER MINUTE. DOSAGE OF PRALIDOXIME MAY BE REPEATED IN 1-2 HOURS, THEN AT 10-12 HOUR INTERVALS IF NEEDED. IN VERY SEVERE POISONINGS, DOSAGE RATES MAY BE DOUBLED. TREATMENT WITH PRALIDOXIME WILL BE MOST EFFECTIVE IF GIVEN WITHIN THIRTY-SIX HOURS AFTER POISONING (MORGAN, RECOGNITION AND MANAGEMENT OF PESTICIDE POISONINGS, 3RD ED.). ANTIDOTE SHOULD BE ADMINISTERED BY QUALIFIED MEDICAL PERSONNEL.

REACTIVITY

REACTIVITY: STABLE UNDER NORMAL TEMPERATURES AND PRESSURES. HOWEVER, HIGH TEMPERATURES MAY CAUSE GAS EVOLUTION AND THE DEVELOPMENT OF PRESSURE IN ENCLOSED CONTAINERS. UNSTABLE ABOVE 200 C.

INCOMPATIBILITIES: AZINPHOS-METHYL: ACID: MAY HYDROLYZE. ALKALI (COLD): MAY HYDROLYZE. STRONG OXIDIZERS: MAY CAUSE FIRE AND EXPLOSION HAZARD.

DECOMPOSITION: THERMAL DECOMPOSITION MAY RELEASE TOXIC OXIDES OF NITROGEN, PHOSPHORUS, SULFUR AND CARBON.

POLYMERIZATION: HAZARDOUS POLYMERIZATION HAS NOT BEEN REPORTED TO OCCUR UNDER NORMAL TEMPERATURES AND PRESSURES.

STORAGE AND DISPOSAL

OBSERVE ALL FEDERAL, STATE AND LOCAL REGULATIONS WHEN STORING OR DISPOSING OF THIS SUBSTANCE. FOR ASSISTANCE, CONTACT THE DISTRICT DIRECTOR OF THE ENVIRONMENTAL PROTECTION AGENCY.

STORAGE

STORE IN ACCORDANCE WITH 40 CFR 165 RECOMMENDED PROCEDURES FOR THE DISPOSAL AND STORAGE OF PESTICIDES AND PESTICIDE CONTAINERS.
STORE AWAY FROM INCOMPATIBLE SUBSTANCES.
THRESHOLD PLANNING QUANTITY (TPQ): THE SUPERFUND AMENDMENTS AND REAUTHORIZATION ACT (SARA) SECTION 302 REQUIRES THAT EACH FACILITY WHERE ANY EXTREMELY HAZARDOUS SUBSTANCE IS PRESENT IN A QUANTITY EQUAL TO OR GREATER THAN THE TPQ ESTABLISHED FOR THAT SUBSTANCE NOTIFY THE STATE EMERGENCY RESPONSE COMMISSION FOR THE STATE IN WHICH IT IS LOCATED. SECTION 303 OF SARA REQUIRES THESE FACILITIES TO PARTICIPATE IN LOCAL EMERGENCY RESPONSE PLANNING (40 CFR 355.30).

DISPOSAL

DISPOSAL MUST BE IN ACCORDANCE WITH 40 CFR 165 RECOMMENDED PROCEDURES FOR THE DISPOSAL AND STORAGE OF PESTICIDES AND PESTICIDE CONTAINERS.

CONDITIONS TO AVOID

MAY BURN BUT DOES NOT IGNITE READILY. CONTAINERS MAY EXPLODE IN HEAT OF FIRE.

SPILL AND LEAK PROCEDURES

SOIL SPILL: DIG A HOLDING AREA SUCH AS A PIT, POND OR LAGOON TO CONTAIN SPILL AND DIKE SURFACE FLOW USING BARRIER OF SOIL, SANDBAGS, FOAMED POLYURETHANE OR FOAMED CONCRETE. ABSORB LIQUID MASS WITH FLY ASH OR CEMENT POWDER.

AIR SPILL: KNOCK DOWN VAPORS WITH WATER SPRAY. KEEP UPWIND.

WATER SPILL: IF DISSOLVED, AT A CONCENTRATION OF 10 PPM OR GREATER, APPLY ACTIVATED CARBON AT TEN TIMES THE AMOUNT THAT HAS BEEN SPILLED.
USE MECHANICAL DREDGES OR LIFTS TO EXTRACT IMMOBILIZED MASSES OF POLLUTION AND PRECIPITATES.

OCCUPATIONAL SPILL: DO NOT TOUCH SPILLED MATERIAL. STOP LEAK IF YOU CAN DO IT WITHOUT RISK. USE WATER SPRAY TO REDUCE VAPORS. FOR SMALL SPILLS, TAKE UP WITH SAND OR OTHER ABSORBENT MATERIAL AND PLACE INTO CONTAINERS FOR LATER DISPOSAL. FOR SMALL DRY SPILLS, WITH A CLEAN SHOVEL PLACE MATERIAL INTO CLEAN, DRY CONTAINERS AND COVER. MOVE CONTAINERS FROM SPILL AREA. FOR LARGER SPILLS, DIKE FAR AHEAD OF SPILL FOR LATER DISPOSAL. KEEP UNNECESSARY PEOPLE AWAY. ISOLATE HAZARD AREA AND DENY ENTRY. VENTILATE CLOSED SPACES BEFORE ENTERING.
REPORTABLE QUANTITY (RQ): 1 POUND THE SUPERFUND AMENDMENTS AND REAUTHORIZATION ACT (SARA) SECTION 304 REQUIRES THAT A RELEASE EQUAL TO OR GREATER THAN THE REPORTABLE QUANTITY FOR THIS SUBSTANCE BE IMMEDIATELY REPORTED TO THE LOCAL EMERGENCY PLANNING COMMITTEE AND THE STATE EMERGENCY RESPONSE COMMISSION (40 CFR 355.40). IF THE RELEASE OF THIS SUBSTANCE IS REPORTABLE UNDER CERCLA SECTION 103, THE NATIONAL RESPONSE CENTER MUST BE NOTIFIED IMMEDIATELY AT (800) 424-8802 OR (202) 426-2675 IN THE METROPOLITAN WASHINGTON, D.C. AREA (40 CFR 302.6).

PROTECTIVE EQUIPMENT

VENTILATION: PROCESS ENCLOSURE RECOMMENDED TO MEET PUBLISHED EXPOSURE LIMITS.

RESPIRATOR: THE FOLLOWING RESPIRATORS AND MAXIMUM USE CONCENTRATIONS ARE RECOMMENDATIONS BY THE U.S. DEPARTMENT OF HEALTH AND HUMAN SERVICES, NIOSH POCKET GUIDE TO CHEMICAL HAZARDS; NIOSH CRITERIA DOCUMENTS OR BY THE U.S. DEPARTMENT OF LABOR, 29 CFR 1910 SUBPART Z. THE SPECIFIC RESPIRATOR SELECTED MUST BE BASED ON CONTAMINATION LEVELS FOUND IN THE WORK PLACE, MUST NOT EXCEED THE WORKING LIMITS OF THE RESPIRATOR AND BE JOINTLY APPROVED BY THE NATIONAL INSTITUTE FOR OCCUPATIONAL SAFETY AND HEALTH AND THE MINE SAFETY AND HEALTH ADMINISTRATION (NIOSH-MSHA).
2 MG/M3- ANY SUPPLIED-AIR RESPIRATOR. ANY SELF-CONTAINED BREATHING APPARATUS. ANY CHEMICAL CARTRIDGE RESPIRATOR WITH ORGANIC VAPOR CARTRIDGE(S) IN COMBINATION WITH A DUST, MIST, AND FUME FILTER.
5 MG/M3- ANY POWERED AIR-PURIFYING RESPIRATOR WITH ORGANIC VAPOR CARTRIDGE(S) IN COMBINATION WITH A DUST, MIST, AND FUME FILTER. ANY SUPPLIED-AIR RESPIRATOR OPERATED IN A CONTINUOUS FLOW MODE. ANY CHEMICAL CARTRIDGE RESPIRATOR WITH A FULL FACEPIECE AND ORGANIC VAPOR CARTRIDGES(S) IN COMBINATION WITH A HIGH-EFFICIENCY PARTICULATE FILTER. ANY POWERED AIR-PURIFYING RESPIRATOR WITH A TIGHT-FITTING FACEPIECE AND ORGANIC VAPOR CARTRIDGE(S) IN COMBINATION WITH A HIGH-EFFICIENCY PARTICULATE FILTER. ANY SUPPLIED-AIR RESPIRATOR WITH A TIGHT-FITTING FACEPIECE OPERATED IN A CONTINUOUS FLOW MODE. ANY SELF-CONTAINED BREATHING APPARATUS WITH A FACEPIECE. ANY SUPPLIED-AIR RESPIRATOR WITH A FULL FACEPIECE. ANY AIR-PURIFYING FULL FACEPIECE RESPIRATOR (GAS MASK) WITH A CHIN-STYLE OR FRONT- OR BACK-MOUNTED ORGANIC VAPOR CANISTER IN COMBINATION WITH A HIGH-EFFICIENCY PARTICULATE FILTER.
ESCAPE- ANY AIR-PURIFYING FULL FACEPIECE RESPIRATOR (GAS MASK) WITH A CHIN-STYLE OF FRONT- OR BACK-MOUNTED ORGANIC VAPOR CANISTER HAVING A HIGH-EFFICIENCY PARTICULATE FILTER. ANY APPROPRIATE ESCAPE-TYPE SELF-CONTAINED BREATHING APPARATUS.
FOR FIREFIGHTING AND OTHER IMMEDIATELY DANGEROUS TO LIFE OR HEALTH CONDITIONS:
SELF-CONTAINED BREATHING APPARATUS WITH FULL FACEPIECE OPERATED IN PRESSURE-DEMAND OR OTHER POSITIVE PRESSURE MODE.
SUPPLIED-AIR RESPIRATOR WITH FULL FACEPIECE AND OPERATED IN PRESSURE-DEMAND OR OTHER POSITIVE PRESSURE MODE IN COMBINATION WITH AN AUXILIARY SELF-CONTAINED BREATHING APPARATUS OPERATED IN PRESSURE-DEMAND OR OTHER POSITIVE PRESSURE MODE.

CLOTHING: EMPLOYEE MUST WEAR APPROPRIATE PROTECTIVE (IMPERVIOUS) CLOTHING AND EQUIPMENT TO PREVENT ANY POSSIBILITY OF SKIN CONTACT WITH THIS SUBSTANCE.

GLOVES: EMPLOYEE MUST WEAR APPROPRIATE PROTECTIVE GLOVES TO PREVENT CONTACT WITH THIS SUBSTANCE.

EYE PROTECTION: EMPLOYEE MUST WEAR SPLASH-PROOF OR DUST-RESISTANT SAFETY GOGGLES AND A FACESHIELD TO PREVENT CONTACT WITH THIS SUBSTANCE.
EMERGENCY WASH FACILITIES: WHERE THERE IS ANY POSSIBILITY THAT AN EMPLOYEE'S EYES AND/OR SKIN MAY BE EXPOSED TO THIS SUBSTANCE, THE EMPLOYER SHOULD PROVIDE AN EYE WASH FOUNTAIN AND QUICK DRENCH SHOWER WITHIN THE IMMEDIATE WORK AREA FOR EMERGENCY USE.

AUTHORIZED BY- OCCUPATIONAL HEALTH SERVICES, INC.
CREATION DATE: 10/04/89 ***REVISION DATE:*** 05/01/90

MATERIAL SAFETY DATA SHEET

OCCUPATIONAL HEALTH SERVICES, INC.
AGRICULTURE AND PESTICIDE DIVISION
450 SEVENTH AVENUE, SUITE 2407
NEW YORK, NEW YORK 10123
1-800-445-MSDS OR (212) 967-1100

EMERGENCY CONTACT:
JOHN S. BRANSFORD, JR. (615) 292-1180

SUBSTANCE IDENTIFICATION

CAS-NUMBER 4658-28-0

SUBSTANCE: **AZIPROTRYN**

TRADE NAMES/SYNONYMS: 1,3,5-TRIAZIN-2-AMINE, 4-AZIDO-N-(1-METHYLETHYL)-6-(METHYLTHIO)-; S-TRIAZINE, 2-AZIDO-4-(ISOPROPYLAMINO)-6-(METHYLTHIO)-; 4-AZIDO-N-(1-METHYLETHYL)-6-(METHYLTHIO)-1,3,5-TRIAZIN-2-AMINE; 2-AZIDO-4-(ISOPROPYLAMINO)-6-(METHYLTHIO)-S-TRIAZINE,; 4-AZIDO-N-ISOPROPYL-6-METHYLTHIO-1,3,5-TRIAZIN-2-YLAMINE; 2-AZIDO-4-ISOPROPYLAMINO-6-METHYLTHIO-1,3,5-TRIAZINE; 2-AZIDO-4-ISOPROPYLAMINO-6-METHYLTHIO-S-TRIAZINE; AZIPROTRYNE; BRASORAN; C 7019; CIBA C 7019; MESORANIL; MEZURON; C7H11N7S; PST02216

CHEMICAL FAMILY: S-TRIAZINE

MOLECULAR FORMULA: C7-H11-N7-S

MOLECULAR WEIGHT: 225.31

CERCLA RATINGS (SCALE 0-3): HEALTH=2 FIRE=1 REACTIVITY=0 PERSISTENCE=2

NFPA RATINGS (SCALE 0-4): HEALTH=2 FIRE=1 REACTIVITY=0

COMPONENTS AND CONTAMINANTS

COMPONENT: AZIPROTRYN ***PERCENT:*** 100.0
CAS# 4658-28-0

OTHER CONTAMINANTS: NONE

EXPOSURE LIMITS: NO OCCUPATIONAL EXPOSURE LIMITS ESTABLISHED BY OSHA, ACGIH, OR NIOSH.

PHYSICAL DATA

DESCRIPTION: COLORLESS CRYSTALLINE POWDER ***MELTING POINT:*** 203-205 F (95-96 C)

SPECIFIC GRAVITY: 1.40 ***VAPOR PRESSURE:*** 0.000002 MMHG @ 20 C

SOLUBILITY IN WATER: 55 PPM @ 20 C

SOLVENT SOLUBILITY: SLIGHTLY SOUBLE IN DICHLOROMETHANE, ETHYL ACETATE, BENZENE, ACETONE, PROPAN-2-OL.

FIRE AND EXPLOSION DATA

FIRE AND EXPLOSION HAZARD: SLIGHT FIRE HAZARD WHEN EXPOSED TO HEAT OR FLAME.

FIREFIGHTING MEDIA: DRY CHEMICAL, CARBON DIOXIDE, HALON, WATER SPRAY OR STANDARD FOAM (1987 EMERGENCY RESPONSE GUIDEBOOK, DOT P 5800.4). FOR LARGER FIRES, USE WATER SPRAY, FOG OR STANDARD FOAM (1987 EMERGENCY RESPONSE GUIDEBOOK, DOT P 5800.4).

FIREFIGHTING: MOVE CONTAINERS FROM FIRE AREA IF POSSIBLE (1987 EMERGENCY RESPONSE GUIDEBOOK, DOT P 5800.4, GUIDE PAGE 53). EXTINGUISH USING AGENTS SUITABLE FOR SURROUNDING FIRE. USE FLOODING QUANTITIES OF WATER AS A FOG. KEEP MATERIAL OUT OF SEWERS AND WATER SOURCES. DO NOT TOUCH SPILLED MATERIAL. AVOID BREATHING HAZARDOUS FUMES; KEEP UPWIND.

TOXICITY

AZIPROTRYN: TOXICITY DATA: 3600 MG/KG ORAL-RAT LD50; 1800 MG/KG ORAL-RABBIT LD50; 2970 MG/KG ORAL-MOUSE LD50; 265 MG/KG INTRAPERITONEAL-MOUSE LD50. CARCINOGEN STATUS: NONE. ACUTE TOXICITY LEVEL: MODERATELY TOXIC BY INGESTION. TARGET EFFECTS: NO DATA AVAILABLE.

HEALTH EFFECTS AND FIRST AID

INHALATION: AZIPROTRYN: **ACUTE EXPOSURE-** A LETHAL CONCENTRATION IN RATS IS GREATER THAN 208 MG/M3/6 HOURS. SOME TRIAZINES ARE MILDLY IRRITATING TO THE UPPER RESPIRATORY TRACT. **CHRONIC EXPOSURE-** NO DATA AVAILABLE.

FIRST AID- REMOVE FROM EXPOSURE AREA TO FRESH AIR IMMEDIATELY. IF BREATHING HAS STOPPED, PERFORM ARTIFICIAL RESPIRATION. KEEP PERSON WARM AND AT REST. TREAT SYMPTOMATICALLY AND SUPPORTIVELY. GET MEDICAL ATTENTION IMMEDIATELY.

SKIN CONTACT: AZIPROTRYN: **ACUTE EXPOSURE-** THIS MATERIAL WAS NOT IRRITATING TO RABBIT SKIN. A LETHAL DOSE BY DERMAL ABSORPTION IN RATS WAS GREATER THAN 3000 MG/KG. **CHRONIC EXPOSURE-** NO DATA AVAILABLE.

FIRST AID- REMOVE CONTAMINATED CLOTHING AND SHOES IMMEDIATELY. WASH AFFECTED AREA WITH SOAP OR MILD DETERGENT AND LARGE AMOUNTS OF WATER UNTIL NO EVIDENCE OF CHEMICAL REMAINS (APPROXIMATELY 15-20 MINUTES). GET MEDICAL ATTENTION IMMEDIATELY.

EYE CONTACT: AZIPROTRYN: **ACUTE EXPOSURE-** THIS MATERIAL WAS SLIGHTLY IRRITATING TO RABBIT EYES. **CHRONIC EXPOSURE-** NO DATA AVAILABLE.

FIRST AID- WASH EYES IMMEDIATELY WITH LARGE AMOUNTS OF WATER OR NORMAL SALINE, OCCASIONALLY LIFTING UPPER AND LOWER LIDS, UNTIL NO EVIDENCE OF CHEMICAL REMAINS (APPROXIMATELY 15-20 MINUTES). GET MEDICAL ATTENTION IMMEDIATELY.

INGESTION: AZIPROTRYN: **ACUTE EXPOSURE-** A LETHAL DOSE IN RATS WAS 3600 MG/KG; SYMPTOMS WERE NOT REPORTED. **CHRONIC EXPOSURE-** NO ADVERSE EFFECTS WERE OBSERVED IN STUDIES OF RATS OR DOGS FED 50 MG/KG/DAY FOR 90 DAYS.

FIRST AID- TREAT SYMPTOMATICALLY AND SUPPORTIVELY. GET MEDICAL ATTENTION IMMEDIATELY. IF VOMITING OCCURS, KEEP HEAD LOWER THAN HIPS TO PREVENT ASPIRATION.

ANTIDOTE: NO SPECIFIC ANTIDOTE. TREAT SYMPTOMATICALLY AND SUPPORTIVELY.

REACTIVITY

REACTIVITY: STABLE UNDER NORMAL TEMPERATURES AND PRESSURES.

INCOMPATIBILITIES: AZIPROTRYN: ALKALIES: MAY HYDROLYZE.

DECOMPOSITION: THERMAL DECOMPOSITION PRODUCTS MAY INCLUDE TOXIC OXIDES OF CARBON, NITROGEN, AND SULFUR.

POLYMERIZATION: HAZARDOUS POLYMERIZATION HAS NOT BEEN REPORTED TO OCCUR UNDER NORMAL TEMPERATURES AND PRESSURES.

STORAGE AND DISPOSAL

OBSERVE ALL FEDERAL, STATE AND LOCAL REGULATIONS WHEN STORING OR DISPOSING OF THIS SUBSTANCE. FOR ASSISTANCE, CONTACT THE DISTRICT DIRECTOR OF THE ENVIRONMENTAL PROTECTION AGENCY.

****STORAGE****

STORE IN ACCORDANCE WITH 40 CFR 165 RECOMMENDED PROCEDURES FOR THE DISPOSAL AND STORAGE OF PESTICIDES AND PESTICIDE CONTAINERS. STORE AWAY FROM INCOMPATIBLE SUBSTANCES.

****DISPOSAL****

DISPOSAL MUST BE IN ACCORDANCE WITH 40 CFR 165 RECOMMENDED PROCEDURES FOR THE DISPOSAL AND STORAGE OF PESTICIDES AND PESTICIDE CONTAINERS.

CONDITIONS TO AVOID

MAY BURN BUT DOES NOT IGNITE READILY.

SPILL AND LEAK PROCEDURES

OCCUPATIONAL SPILL: DO NOT TOUCH SPILLED MATERIAL. STOP LEAK IF YOU CAN DO IT WITHOUT RISK. FOR SMALL SPILLS, TAKE UP WITH SAND OR OTHER ABSORBENT MATERIAL AND PLACE INTO CONTAINERS FOR LATER DISPOSAL. FOR SMALL DRY SPILLS, WITH A CLEAN SHOVEL PLACE MATERIAL INTO CLEAN, DRY CONTAINER AND COVER. MOVE CONTAINERS FROM SPILL AREA. FOR LARGER SPILLS, DIKE FAR AHEAD OF SPILL FOR LATER DISPOSAL. KEEP UNNECESSARY PEOPLE AWAY. ISOLATE HAZARD AREA AND DENY ENTRY.

PROTECTIVE EQUIPMENT

VENTILATION: PROVIDE LOCAL EXHAUST OR GENERAL DILUTION VENTILATION SYSTEM.

RESPIRATOR: THE FOLLOWING RESPIRATORS ARE RECOMMENDED BASED ON INFORMATION FOUND IN THE PHYSICAL DATA, TOXICITY AND HEALTH EFFECTS SECTIONS. THEY ARE RANKED IN ORDER FROM MINIMUM TO MAXIMUM RESPIRATORY PROTECTION. THE SPECIFIC RESPIRATOR SELECTED MUST BE BASED ON CONTAMINATION LEVELS FOUND IN THE WORK PLACE, MUST NOT EXCEED THE WORKING LIMITS OF THE RESPIRATOR AND BE JOINTLY APPROVED BY THE NATIONAL INSTITUTE FOR OCCUPATIONAL SAFETY AND HEALTH AND THE MINE SAFETY AND HEALTH ADMINISTRATION (NIOSH-MSHA).

CHEMICAL CARTRIDGE RESPIRATOR WITH AN ORGANIC VAPOR CARTRIDGE(S) IN COMBINATION WITH A DUST AND MIST FILTER.

GAS MASK WITH ORGANIC VAPOR CANISTER (CHIN-STYLE OR FRONT- OR BACK-MOUNTED CANISTER) WITH A DUST AND MIST FILTER.

GAS MASK WITH ORGANIC VAPOR CANISTER (CHIN-STYLE OR FRONT- OR BACK-MOUNTED CANISTER) WITH A PARTICULATE FILTER.

POWERED AIR-PURIFYING RESPIRATOR WITH A HIGH-EFFICIENCY FILTER.

TYPE 'C' SUPPLIED-AIR RESPIRATOR WITH A FULL FACEPIECE OPERATED IN A PRESSURE-DEMAND OR OTHER POSITIVE PRESSURE MODE.

SELF-CONTAINED BREATHING APPARATUS WITH A FULL FACEPIECE OPERATED IN PRESSURE-DEMAND OR OTHER POSITIVE PRESSURE MODE.

FOR FIREFIGHTING AND OTHER IMMEDIATELY DANGEROUS TO LIFE OR HEALTH CONDITIONS:

SELF-CONTAINED BREATHING APPARATUS WITH FULL FACEPIECE OPERATED IN PRESSURE-DEMAND OR OTHER POSITIVE PRESSURE MODE. SUPPLIED-AIR RESPIRATOR WITH FULL FACEPIECE AND OPERATED IN PRESSURE-DEMAND OR OTHER POSITIVE PRESSURE MODE IN COMBINATION WITH AN AUXILIARY SELF-CONTAINED BREATHING APPARATUS OPERATED IN PRESSURE-DEMAND OR OTHER POSITIVE PRESSURE MODE.

CLOTHING: EMPLOYEE MUST WEAR APPROPRIATE PROTECTIVE (IMPERVIOUS) CLOTHING AND EQUIPMENT TO PREVENT REPEATED OR PROLONGED SKIN CONTACT WITH THIS SUBSTANCE.

GLOVES: EMPLOYEE MUST WEAR APPROPRIATE PROTECTIVE GLOVES TO PREVENT CONTACT WITH THIS SUBSTANCE.

EYE PROTECTION: EMPLOYEE MUST WEAR SPLASH-PROOF OR DUST-RESISTANT SAFETY GOGGLES TO PREVENT EYE CONTACT WITH THIS SUBSTANCE. EMERGENCY EYE WASH: WHERE THERE IS ANY POSSIBILITY THAT AN EMPLOYEE'S EYES MAY BE EXPOSED TO THIS SUBSTANCE, THE EMPLOYER SHOULD PROVIDE AN EYE WASH FOUNTAIN WITHIN THE IMMEDIATE WORK AREA FOR EMERGENCY USE.

AUTHORIZED BY- OCCUPATIONAL HEALTH SERVICES, INC.
CREATION DATE: 10/04/89 ***REVISION DATE:*** 05/11/90

MATERIAL SAFETY DATA SHEET

OCCUPATIONAL HEALTH SERVICES, INC.
AGRICULTURE AND PESTICIDE DIVISION
450 SEVENTH AVENUE, SUITE 2407
NEW YORK, NEW YORK 10123
1-800-445-MSDS OR (212) 967-1100

EMERGENCY CONTACT:
JOHN S. BRANSFORD, JR. (615) 292-1180

SUBSTANCE IDENTIFICATION

CAS-NUMBER 671-04-5

SUBSTANCE: **CARBANOLATE**

TRADE NAMES/SYNONYMS: PHENOL, 2-CHLORO-4,5-DIMETHYL-, METHYLCARBAMATE; CARBAMIC ACID, METHYL-, 6-CHLORO-3,4-XYLYL ESTER; 6-CHLORO-3,4-XYLYL ESTER METHYLCARBAMIC ACID; 2-CHLORO-4,5-DIMETHYLPHENYL METHYLCARBAMATE; 6-CHLORO-3,4-XYLYL METHYLCARBAMATE; BANOL; U-12927; SOK; C10H12CLNO2; PST02250

CHEMICAL FAMILY: CARBAMATE
HALOGEN COMPOUND, AROMATIC
MOLECULAR FORMULA: C10-H12-CL-N-O2
MOLECULAR WEIGHT: 213.68
CERCLA RATINGS (SCALE 0-3): HEALTH=3 FIRE=0 REACTIVITY=0
PERSISTENCE=3
NFPA RATINGS (SCALE 0-4): HEALTH=3 FIRE=0 REACTIVITY=0

COMPONENTS AND CONTAMINANTS

COMPONENT: CARBANOLATE ***PERCENT:*** 100.0
CAS# 671-04-5
OTHER CONTAMINANTS: NONE
EXPOSURE LIMITS: NO OCCUPATIONAL EXPOSURE LIMITS ESTABLISHED BY OSHA, ACGIH, OR NIOSH.

PHYSICAL DATA

DESCRIPTION: WHITE CRYSTALLINE SOLID. ***MELTING POINT:*** 266-271 F (130-133 C)
SPECIFIC GRAVITY: NOT AVAILABLE ***SOLUBILITY IN WATER:*** SLIGHTLY SOLUBLE
SOLVENT SOLUBILITY: SOLUBLE IN ACETONE, BENZENE, TOLUENE, XYLENE, METHYLENE CHLORIDE, CHLOROFORM, KEROSENE, HEAVY AROMATIC NAPHTHA

FIRE AND EXPLOSION DATA

FIRE AND EXPLOSION HAZARD: NEGLIGIBLE FIRE HAZARD WHEN EXPOSED TO HEAT OR FLAME.
FIREFIGHTING MEDIA: DRY CHEMICAL, CARBON DIOXIDE, HALON, WATER SPRAY OR STANDARD FOAM (1987 EMERGENCY RESPONSE GUIDEBOOK, DOT P 5800.4). FOR LARGER FIRES, USE WATER SPRAY, FOG OR STANDARD FOAM (1987 EMERGENCY RESPONSE GUIDEBOOK, DOT P 5800.4).
FIREFIGHTING: MOVE CONTAINERS FROM FIRE AREA IF POSSIBLE. FIGHT FIRE FROM MAXIMUM DISTANCE. STAY AWAY FROM STORAGE TANK ENDS. DIKE FIRE CONTROL WATER FOR LATER DISPOSAL. DO NOT SCATTER MATERIAL (1987 EMERGENCY RESPONSE GUIDEBOOK, DOT P 5800.4, GUIDE PAGE 55). EXTINGUISH ONLY IF FLOW CAN BE STOPPED. EXTINGUISH USING AGENT INDICATED. USE FLOODING AMOUNTS OF WATER AS A FOG. COOL CONTAINERS WITH FLOODING AMOUNTS OF WATER FROM AS FAR A DISTANCE AS POSSIBLE. AVOID BREATHING POISONOUS VAPORS, KEEP UPWIND. CONSIDER EVACUATION OF DOWNWIND AREA IF MATERIAL IS LEAKING.

TRANSPORTATION DATA

DEPARTMENT OF TRANSPORTATION HAZARD CLASSIFICATION 49 CFR 172.101: POISON B
DEPARTMENT OF TRANSPORTATION LABELING REQUIREMENTS 49 CFR 172.101 AND SUBPART E: POISON
DEPARTMENT OF TRANSPORTATION PACKAGING REQUIREMENTS: 49 CFR 173.365 EXCEPTIONS: 49 CFR 173.364

TOXICITY

CARBANOLATE: TOXICITY DATA: 30 MG/KG ORAL-RAT LD50; 300 MG/KG ORAL-MOUSE LD50; 3 MG/KG INTRAVENOUS-RAT LD50; 11,200 UG/KG INTRAPERITONEAL-RAT LD50; 4600 UG/KG INTRAPERITONEAL-MOUSE LD50; 24 MG/KG INTRAMUSCULAR-RAT LD50; 293 MG/KG UNREPORTED-RAT LD50. CARCINOGEN STATUS: NONE. ACUTE TOXICITY LEVEL: HIGHLY TOXIC BY INGESTION. TARGET EFFECTS: CHOLINESTERASE INHIBITOR. AT INCREASED RISK FROM EXPOSURE: PERSONS WITH ASTHMA, DIABETES, CARDIOVASCULAR DISEASE, MECHANICAL OBSTRUCTION OF THE GASTROINTESTINAL OR UROGENITAL TRACT, AND THOSE IN VAGOTONIC STATES.*
* MAY BE BASED ON GENERAL INFORMATION ON CARBAMATES.

HEALTH EFFECTS AND FIRST AID

INHALATION: CARBANOLATE: SEE INFORMATION ON CARBAMATES.
CARBAMATES: CHOLINESTERASE INHIBITOR. **ACUTE EXPOSURE-** WHEN INHALED, THE FIRST EFFECTS OF CHOLINESTERASE INHIBITION ARE USUALLY RESPIRATORY AND MAY INCLUDE NASAL HYPEREMIA AND WATERY DISCHARGE, CHEST DISCOMFORT, DYSPNEA, AND WHEEZING DUE TO INCREASED BRONCHIAL SECRETIONS AND BRONCHOCONSTRICTION. OTHER SYSTEMIC EFFECTS MAY BEGIN WITHIN A FEW MINUTES OR SEVERAL HOURS OF EXPOSURE. SYMPTOMS MAY INCLUDE NAUSEA, VOMITING, DIARRHEA, ABDOMINAL CRAMPS, HEADACHE, VERTIGO, OCULAR PAIN, CILIARY MUSCLE SPASM, BLURRING OR DIMNESS OF VISION, MIOSIS, OR IN SOME CASES MYDRIASIS, LACRIMATION, SALIVATION, SWEATING, AND CONFUSION. OTHER REPORTED CENTRAL NERVOUS SYSTEM OR NEUROMUSCULAR EFFECTS INCLUDE ATAXIA, SLURRED SPEECH, AREFLEXIA, WEAKNESS, FATIGUE, TWITCHING, FASCICULATION, TREMOR, AND EVENTUALLY PARALYSIS OF THE EXTREMITIES AND POSSIBLY OF THE RESPIRATORY MUSCLES. IN SEVERE CASES, THERE MAY ALSO BE INVOLUNTARY DEFECATION AND URINATION, BRADYCARDIA, HYPOTENSION, PULMONARY EDEMA, CONVULSIONS, COMA, AND DEATH FROM RESPIRATORY FAILURE OR CARDIAC ARREST. CARBAMATES GENERALLY DO NOT ACCUMULATE IN MAMMALIAN TISSUE AND THE CHOLINESTERASE INHIBITION REVERSES RATHER RAPIDLY. IN NON-FATAL CASES, THE ILLNESS GENERALLY LASTS LESS THAN 24 HOURS. **CHRONIC EXPOSURE-** PROLONGED OR REPEATED EXPOSURE MAY CAUSE EFFECTS AS DESCRIBED IN ACUTE EXPOSURE.
FIRST AID- REMOVE FROM EXPOSURE AREA TO FRESH AIR IMMEDIATELY. IF BREATHING HAS STOPPED, GIVE ARTIFICIAL RESPIRATION. MAINTAIN AIRWAY AND BLOOD PRESSURE AND ADMINISTER OXYGEN IF AVAILABLE. KEEP AFFECTED PERSON WARM AND AT REST. TREAT SYMPTOMATICALLY AND SUPPORTIVELY. ADMINISTRATION OF OXYGEN SHOULD BE PERFORMED BY QUALIFIED PERSONNEL. GET MEDICAL ATTENTION IMMEDIATELY.

SKIN CONTACT: CARBANOLATE: SEE INFORMATION ON CARBAMATES.
CARBAMATES: CHOLINESTERASE INHIBITOR. **ACUTE EXPOSURE-** SOME COMPOUNDS MAY CAUSE IRRITATION. LOCALIZED SWEATING AND FASCICULATIONS MAY OCCUR AT THE SITE OF CONTACT. IF SUFFICIENT AMOUNTS ARE ABSORBED THROUGH THE SKIN, OTHER EFFECTS OF CHOLINESTERASE INHIBITION MAY OCCUR AS DESCRIBED IN ACUTE INHALATION; SYMPTOMS MAY BE DELAYED FOR 2-3 HOURS, USUALLY NO MORE THAN 8 HOURS. **CHRONIC EXPOSURE-** REPEATED OR PROLONGED EXPOSURE MAY CAUSE EFFECTS AS DESCRIBED IN ACUTE EXPOSURE.
FIRST AID- REMOVE CONTAMINATED CLOTHING IMMEDIATELY. WASH CONTAMINATED AREAS WITH SOAP AND WATER FOLLOWED BY ALCOHOL (ARENA, POISONING, 4TH ED.). EMERGENCY PERSONNEL SHOULD WEAR GLOVES AND AVOID CONTAMINATION. TREAT RESPIRATORY DIFFICULTY WITH ARTIFICIAL RESPIRATION. GET MEDICAL ATTENTION IMMEDIATELY.

EYE CONTACT: CARBANOLATE: SEE INFORMATION ON CARBAMATES. CARBAMATES: CHOLINESTERASE INHIBITOR. **ACUTE EXPOSURE-** DIRECT CONTACT MAY CAUSE PAIN, HYPEREMIA, LACRIMATION, TWITCHING OF THE EYELIDS, MIOSIS, AND CILIARY MUSCLE SPASM WITH LOSS OF ACCOMODATION, BLURRED OR DIMMED VISION AND BROWACHE. SOMETIMES MYDRIASIS MAY OCCUR INSTEAD OF MIOSIS. WITH SUFFICIENT EXPOSURE, OTHER SYMPTOMS OF CHOLINESTERASE INHIBITION MAY OCCUR AS DESCRIBED IN ACUTE INHALATION. **CHRONIC EXPOSURE-** PROLONGED EXPOSURE MAY CAUSE EFFECTS AS DESCRIBED IN ACUTE EXPOSURE. SOME COMPOUNDS HAVE CAUSED TOXIC EFFECTS ON THE CRYSTALLINE LENS, CONJUNCTIVAL THICKENING AND OBSTRUCTION OF NASOLACRIMAL CANALS WHEN USED AS MIOTIC EYE DROPS.
FIRST AID- IRRIGATE EYES WITH WATER OR SALINE SOLUTION. IF SYMPTOMS OF POISONING OCCUR, TREAT RESPIRATORY DIFFICULTY WITH ARTIFICIAL RESPIRATION AND OXYGEN. OBSERVE PATIENT FOR AT LEAST 24-36 HOURS (GOSSELIN, CLINICAL TOXICOLOGY OF COMMERCIAL PRODUCTS, 5TH ED.). GET MEDICAL ATTENTION IMMEDIATELY. OXYGEN SHOULD BE ADMINISTERED BY QUALIFIED MEDICAL PERSONNEL.

INGESTION: CARBANOLATE: HIGHLY TOXIC. SEE INFORMATION ON CARBAMATES.
CARBAMATES: CHOLINESTERASE INHIBITOR. **ACUTE EXPOSURE-** WHEN INGESTED, THE FIRST EFFECTS MAY BE NAUSEA, VOMITING, ANOREXIA, ABDOMINAL CRAMPS, AND DIARRHEA. WITH ABSORPTION FROM THE GASTROINTESTINAL TRACT, THE OTHER EFFECTS OF CHOLINESTERASE INHIBITION AS DESCRIBED IN ACUTE INHALATION MAY OCCUR; SYMPTOMS MAY BEGIN WITHIN MINUTES OR BE DELAYED SEVERAL HOURS. **CHRONIC EXPOSURE-** REPEATED INGESTION MAY CAUSE EFFECTS AS DESCRIBED IN ACUTE EXPOSURE.
FIRST AID- IF PERSON IS ALERT AND RESPIRATION IS NOT DEPRESSED, GIVE SYRUP OF IPECAC FOLLOWED BY WATER (IF VOMITING OCCURS, KEEP HEAD BELOW HIPS TO PREVENT ASPIRATION). IF CONSCIOUSNESS LEVEL DECLINES OR VOMITING HAS NOT OCCURRED IN 15 MINUTES EMPTY STOMACH BY GASTRIC LAVAGE WITH THE AID OF CUFFED ENDOTRACHEAL TUBE USING ISOTONIC SALINE OR 5% SODIUM BICARBONATE FOLLOW WITH ACTIVATED CHARCOAL. ESTABLISH AND MAINTAIN AIRWAY. TREAT RESPIRATORY DIFFICULTY WITH ARTIFICIAL RESPIRATION AND OXYGEN. DO NOT GIVE MORPHINE, AMINOPHYLLINE, PHENOTHIAZINES, RESERPINE, FUROSEMIDE, OR ETHACRYNIC ACID (MORGAN, RECOGNITION AND MANAGEMENT OF PESTICIDE POISONINGS, 3RD ED.). TREAT SYMPTOMATICALLY AND SUPPORTIVELY. ADMINISTRATION OF OXYGEN AND LAVAGE MUST BE PERFORMED BY QUALIFIED MEDICAL PERSONNEL. GET MEDICAL ATTENTION IMMEDIATELY.
ANTIDOTE: THE FOLLOWING ANTIDOTE HAS BEEN RECOMMENDED. HOWEVER, THE DECISION AS TO WHETHER THE SEVERITY OF POISONING REQUIRES ADMINISTRATION OF ANY ANTIDOTE AND ACTUAL DOSE REQUIRED SHOULD BE MADE BY QUALIFIED MEDICAL PERSONNEL.
FOR CHOLINESTERASE INHIBITORS: ESTABLISH CLEAR AIRWAY AND TISSUE OXYGENATION BY ASPIRATION OF SECRETIONS, AND IF NECESSARY, BY ASSISTED PULMONARY VENTILATION WITH OXYGEN. IMPROVE TISSUE OXYGENATION AS MUCH AS POSSIBLE BEFORE ADMINISTERING ATROPINE TO MINIMIZE THE RISK OF VENTRICULAR FIBRILLATION. ADMINISTER ATROPINE SULFATE INTRAVENOUSLY, OR INTRAMUSCULARLY IF IV INJECTION IS NOT POSSIBLE. IN MODERATELY SEVERE POISONING ADMINISTER ATROPINE SULFATE, 0.4-2.0 MG REPEATED EVERY

15 MINUTES UNTIL ATROPINIZATION IS ACHIEVED (TACHYCARDIA, FLUSHING, DRY MOUTH, MYDRIASIS). MAINTAIN ATROPINIZATION BY REPEATED DOSES FOR 2-12 HOURS, OR LONGER, DEPENDING ON THE SEVERITY OF POISONING. THE APPEARANCE OF RALES IN THE LUNG BASES, MIOSIS, SALIVATION, NAUSEA, BRADYCARDIA, ARE ALL INDICATIONS OF INADEQUATE ATROPINIZATION. SEVERELY POISONED INDIVIDUALS MAY EXHIBIT REMARKABLE TOLERANCE TO ATROPINE; TWO OR MORE TIMES THE DOSAGES SUGGESTED ABOVE MAY BE NEEDED. PERSONS NOT POISONED OR ONLY SLIGHTLY POISONED, HOWEVER, MAY DEVELOP SIGNS OF ATROPINE TOXICITY FROM SUCH LARGE DOSAGES: FEVER, MUSCLE FIBRILLATIONS, AND DELIRIUM ARE THE MAIN SIGNS OF ATROPINE TOXICITY. IF THESE SIGNS APPEAR WHILE THE PATIENT IS FULLY ATROPINIZED, ATROPINE ADMINISTRATION SHOULD BE DISCONTINUED, AT LEAST TEMPORARILY. OBSERVE TREATED PATIENTS CLOSELY AT LEAST 24 HOURS TO INSURE THAT SYMPTOMS (POSSIBLY PULMONARY EDEMA) DO NOT RECUR AS ATROPINIZATION WEARS OFF. IN VERY SEVERE POISONINGS, METABOLIC DISPOSITION OF TOXICANT MAY REQUIRE SEVERAL HOURS OR DAYS DURING WHICH ATROPINIZATION MUST BE MAINTAINED. MARKEDLY LOWER LEVELS OF URINARY METABOLITES INDICATE THAT ATROPINE DOSAGE CAN BE TAPERED OFF. AS DOSAGE IS REDUCED, CHECK THE LUNG BASES FREQUENTLY FOR RALES. IF RALES ARE HEARD OR OTHER SYMPTOMS RETURN, RE-ESTABLISH ATROPINIZATION PROMPTLY (MORGAN, RECOGNITION AND MANAGEMENT OF PESTICIDE POISONINGS, 3RD ED.). ADMINISTRATION OF ANTIDOTE MUST BE PERFORMED BY QUALIFIED MEDICAL PERSONNEL.

REACTIVITY

REACTIVITY: NO DATA AVAILABLE.

INCOMPATIBILITIES: CARBANOLATE: ALKALINE CONDITIONS (>PH 8.5): MAY CAUSE DECOMPOSITION. OXIDIZERS (STRONG): FIRE AND EXPLOSION HAZARD.

DECOMPOSITION: THERMAL DECOMPOSITION MAY EMIT TOXIC FUMES OF CHLORIDE AND OXIDES OF NITROGEN AND CARBON.

POLYMERIZATION: HAZARDOUS POLYMERIZATION HAS NOT BEEN REPORTED TO OCCUR UNDER NORMAL TEMPERATURES AND PRESSURES.

STORAGE AND DISPOSAL

OBSERVE ALL FEDERAL, STATE AND LOCAL REGULATIONS WHEN STORING OR DISPOSING OF THIS SUBSTANCE. FOR ASSISTANCE, CONTACT THE DISTRICT DIRECTOR OF THE ENVIRONMENTAL PROTECTION AGENCY.

STORAGE

STORE IN ACCORDANCE WITH 40 CFR 165 RECOMMENDED PROCEDURES FOR THE DISPOSAL AND STORAGE OF PESTICIDES AND PESTICIDE CONTAINERS.
STORE AWAY FROM INCOMPATIBLE SUBSTANCES.

DISPOSAL

DISPOSAL MUST BE IN ACCORDANCE WITH 40 CFR 165 RECOMMENDED PROCEDURES FOR THE DISPOSAL AND STORAGE OF PESTICIDES AND PESTICIDE CONTAINERS.

CONDITIONS TO AVOID

NONE REPORTED.

SPILL AND LEAK PROCEDURES

OCCUPATIONAL SPILL: DO NOT TOUCH SPILLED MATERIAL. STOP LEAK IF YOU CAN DO IT WITHOUT RISK. USE WATER SPRAY TO REDUCE VAPORS. FOR SMALL SPILLS, TAKE UP WITH SAND OR OTHER ABSORBENT MATERIAL AND PLACE INTO CONTAINERS FOR LATER DISPOSAL. FOR SMALL DRY SPILLS, WITH A CLEAN SHOVEL PLACE MATERIAL INTO CLEAN, DRY CONTAINERS AND COVER. MOVE CONTAINERS FROM SPILL AREA. FOR LARGER SPILLS, DIKE FAR AHEAD OF SPILL FOR LATER DISPOSAL. KEEP UNNECESSARY PEOPLE AWAY. ISOLATE HAZARD AREA AND DENY ENTRY. VENTILATE CLOSED SPACES BEFORE ENTERING.

PROTECTIVE EQUIPMENT

VENTILATION: PROCESS ENCLOSURE RECOMMENDED.

RESPIRATOR: THE FOLLOWING RESPIRATORS ARE RECOMMENDED BASED ON INFORMATION FOUND IN THE PHYSICAL DATA, TOXICITY AND HEALTH EFFECTS SECTIONS. THEY ARE RANKED IN ORDER FROM MINIMUM TO MAXIMUM RESPIRATORY PROTECTION. THE SPECIFIC RESPIRATOR SELECTED MUST BE BASED ON CONTAMINATION LEVELS FOUND IN THE WORK PLACE, MUST NOT EXCEED THE WORKING LIMITS OF THE RESPIRATOR AND BE JOINTLY APPROVED BY THE NATIONAL INSTITUTE FOR OCCUPATIONAL SAFETY AND HEALTH AND THE MINE SAFETY AND HEALTH ADMINISTRATION (NIOSH-MSHA).
TYPE 'C' SUPPLIED-AIR RESPIRATOR WITH A FULL FACEPIECE OPERATED IN PRESSURE-DEMAND OR OTHER POSITIVE PRESSURE MODE OR WITH A FULL FACEPIECE, HELMET OR HOOD OPERATED IN CONTINOUS-FLOW MODE.
SELF-CONTAINED BREATHING APPARATUS WITH A FULL FACEPIECE OPERATED IN PRESSURE-DEMAND OR OTHER POSITIVE PRESSURE MODE.
FOR FIREFIGHTING AND OTHER IMMEDIATELY DANGEROUS TO LIFE OR HEALTH CONDITIONS:
SELF-CONTAINED BREATHING APPARATUS WITH FULL FACEPIECE OPERATED IN PRESSURE-DEMAND OR OTHER POSITIVE PRESSURE MODE.
SUPPLIED-AIR RESPIRATOR WITH FULL FACEPIECE AND OPERATED IN PRESSURE-DEMAND OR OTHER POSITIVE PRESSURE MODE IN COMBINATION WITH AN AUXILIARY SELF-CONTAINED BREATHING APPARATUS OPERATED IN PRESSURE-DEMAND OR OTHER POSITIVE PRESSURE MODE.

CLOTHING: EMPLOYEE MUST WEAR APPROPRIATE PROTECTIVE (IMPERVIOUS) CLOTHING AND EQUIPMENT TO PREVENT ANY POSSIBILITY OF SKIN CONTACT WITH THIS SUBSTANCE.

GLOVES: EMPLOYEE MUST WEAR APPROPRIATE PROTECTIVE GLOVES TO PREVENT CONTACT WITH THIS SUBSTANCE.

EYE PROTECTION: EMPLOYEE MUST WEAR SPLASH-PROOF OR DUST-RESISTANT SAFETY GOGGLES AND A FACESHIELD TO PREVENT CONTACT WITH THIS SUBSTANCE.
EMERGENCY WASH FACILITIES: WHERE THERE IS ANY POSSIBILITY THAT AN EMPLOYEE'S EYES AND/OR SKIN MAY BE EXPOSED TO THIS SUBSTANCE, THE EMPLOYER SHOULD PROVIDE AN EYE WASH FOUNTAIN AND QUICK DRENCH SHOWER WITHIN THE IMMEDIATE WORK AREA FOR EMERGENCY USE.

AUTHORIZED BY- OCCUPATIONAL HEALTH SERVICES, INC.
CREATION DATE: 10/04/89 ***REVISION DATE:*** 06/12/90

MATERIAL SAFETY DATA SHEET

OCCUPATIONAL HEALTH SERVICES, INC.
AGRICULTURE AND PESTICIDE DIVISION
450 SEVENTH AVENUE, SUITE 2407
NEW YORK, NEW YORK 10123
1-800-445-MSDS OR (212) 967-1100

EMERGENCY CONTACT:
JOHN S. BRANSFORD, JR. (615) 292-1180

SUBSTANCE IDENTIFICATION

CAS-NUMBER 1918-00-9

SUBSTANCE: DICAMBA

TRADE NAMES/SYNONYMS: 3,6-DICHLORO-2-METHOXYBENZOIC ACID; 3,6-DICHLORO-O-ANISIC ACID; 2-METHOXY-3,6-DICHLOROBENZOIC ACID; BENZOIC ACID, 3,6-DICHLORO-2-METHOXY-; BANVEL; BANEX; BANFEL; DIANAT; MDBA; MEDIBEN; VELSICOL COMPOUND R; VELSICOL 58-CS-11; STCC 4963337; C8H6CL2O3; PST02260

CHEMICAL FAMILY: CARBOXYLIC ACID, AROMATIC HALOGEN

MOLECULAR FORMULA: CL2-C-H3-O-C6-H2-C-O2-H

MOLECULAR WEIGHT: 221.04

CERCLA RATINGS (SCALE 0-3): HEALTH=2 FIRE=1 REACTIVITY=0 PERSISTENCE=1

NFPA RATINGS (SCALE 0-4): HEALTH=U FIRE=1 REACTIVITY=0

COMPONENTS AND CONTAMINANTS

COMPONENT: DICAMBA ***PERCENT:*** 100.0
CAS# 1918-00-9

OTHER CONTAMINANTS: MAY CONTAIN 50 PPB 2,7 DICHLORODIBENZO-P-DIOXIN

EXPOSURE LIMITS: NO OCCUPATIONAL EXPOSURE LIMITS ESTABLISHED BY OSHA, ACGIH, OR NIOSH.
DICAMBA: 1000 POUNDS CERCLA SECTION 103 REPORTABLE QUANTITY

PHYSICAL DATA

DESCRIPTION: COLORLESS TO LIGHT TAN CRYSTALLINE SOLID.

MELTING POINT: 237-241 F (114-116 C) ***SPECIFIC GRAVITY:*** 1.57 @ 25 C

VAPOR PRESSURE: 0.00375 MMHG @ 100 C ***SOLUBILITY IN WATER:*** 0.65% @ 25 C

ODOR THRESHOLD: 250.8 PPM ***VAPOR DENSITY:*** 7.64

SOLVENT SOLUBILITY: SOLUBLE IN ETHANOL, CYCLOHEXANONE, ACETONE, KETONES, DICHLOROMETHANE, DIOXANE, TOLUENE; MODERATELY SOLUBLE IN XYLENE. DECOMPOSES @ APPROXIMATELY 392 F (200 C).

FIRE AND EXPLOSION DATA

FIRE AND EXPLOSION HAZARD: SLIGHT FIRE HAZARD WHEN EXPOSED TO HEAT OR FLAME.
DUST-AIR MIXTURES MAY IGNITE OR EXPLODE.

FLASH POINT: 390 F (199 C) (OC)

FIREFIGHTING MEDIA: DRY CHEMICAL, CARBON DIOXIDE, HALON, WATER SPRAY OR STANDARD FOAM (1987 EMERGENCY RESPONSE GUIDEBOOK, DOT P 5800.4).

FOR LARGER FIRES, USE WATER SPRAY, FOG OR STANDARD FOAM (1987 EMERGENCY RESPONSE GUIDEBOOK, DOT P 5800.4).

FIREFIGHTING: MOVE CONTAINER FROM FIRE AREA IF POSSIBLE. DO NOT SCATTER SPILLED MATERIAL WITH HIGH PRESSURE WATER STREAMS. DIKE FIRE CONTROL WATER FOR LATER DISPOSAL (1987 EMERGENCY RESPONSE GUIDEBOOK, DOT P 5800.4, GUIDE PAGE 31).

USE AGENTS SUITABLE FOR TYPE OF SURROUNDING FIRE. AVOID BREATHING HAZARDOUS VAPORS, KEEP UPWIND.

TOXICITY

DICAMBA: TOXICITY DATA: >200 MG/L INHALATION-RAT LC50 (EPA HEALTH ADVISORY, 1988); >2000 MG/KG SKIN-RABBIT LD50 (EPA HEALTH ADVISORY, 1988); 1039 MG/KG ORAL-RAT LD50; 1190 MG/KG ORAL-MOUSE LD50; 2000 MG/KG ORAL-RABBIT LD50; 3000 MG/KG ORAL-GUINEA PIG LD50; 1000 MG/KG UNREPORTED-MAMMAL LD50; 700 MG/KG UNREPORTED-MOUSE LD50; MUTAGENIC DATA (RTECS). CARCINOGEN STATUS: NONE. LOCAL EFFECTS: CORROSIVE- EYE. ACUTE TOXICITY LEVEL: MODERATELY TOXIC BY INGESTION; SLIGHTLY TOXIC BY INHALATION AND DERMAL ABSORPTION. TARGET EFFECTS: SENSITIZER- SKIN.

HEALTH EFFECTS AND FIRST AID

INHALATION: DICAMBA: **ACUTE EXPOSURE-** MAY CAUSE IRRITATION OF THE MUCOUS MEMBRANES. **CHRONIC EXPOSURE-** EFFECTS OF MUSCLE CRAMPS, DYSPNEA, NAUSEA, VOMITING, SKIN RASHES, LOSS OF VOICE OR SWELLING OF CERVICAL GLAND WERE OBSERVED AMONG EXPOSED WORKERS.

FIRST AID- REMOVE FROM EXPOSURE AREA TO FRESH AIR IMMEDIATELY. IF BREATHING HAS STOPPED, PERFORM ARTIFICIAL RESPIRATION. KEEP PERSON WARM AND AT REST. TREAT SYMPTOMATICALLY AND SUPPORTIVELY. GET MEDICAL ATTENTION IMMEDIATELY.

SKIN CONTACT: DICAMBA: SENSITIZER. **ACUTE EXPOSURE-** THIS MATERIAL WAS SLIGHTLY TO MODERATELY IRRITATING TO RABBIT SKIN. IT PRODUCED MODERATE SENSITIZATION IN GUINEA PIGS. **CHRONIC EXPOSURE-** 500 MG/KG/DAY APPLIED TO RABBIT SKIN FOR 3 WEEKS WAS MODERATELY IRRITATING. PROLONGED OR REPEATED EXPOSURE MAY CAUSE SENSITIZATION. EFFECTS OF MUSCLE CRAMPS, DYSPNEA, NAUSEA, VOMITING, SKIN RASHES, LOSS OF VOICE OR SWELLING OF CERVICAL GLANDS WERE OBSERVED AMONG EXPOSED WORKERS.

FIRST AID- REMOVE CONTAMINATED CLOTHING AND SHOES IMMEDIATELY. WASH AFFECTED AREA WITH SOAP OR MILD DETERGENT AND LARGE AMOUNTS OF WATER UNTIL NO EVIDENCE OF CHEMICAL REMAINS (APPROXIMATELY 15-20 MINUTES). GET MEDICAL ATTENTION IMMEDIATELY.

EYE CONTACT: DICAMBA: CORROSIVE. **ACUTE EXPOSURE-** THIS MATERIAL WAS EXTREMELY IRRITATING AND CORROSIVE TO RABBIT EYES; EFFECTS HAVE INCLUDED IRREVERSIBLE EYE DAMAGE AND PANNUS. **CHRONIC EXPOSURE-** EFFECTS DEPEND ON CONCENTRATION AND DURATION OF EXPOSURE. REPEATED OR PROLONGED CONTACT WITH CORROSIVE SUBSTANCES MAY RESULT IN CONJUNCTIVITIS OR EFFECTS AS IN ACUTE EXPOSURE.

FIRST AID- WASH EYES IMMEDIATELY WITH LARGE AMOUNTS OF WATER OR NORMAL SALINE, OCCASIONALLY LIFTING UPPER AND LOWER LIDS, UNTIL NO EVIDENCE OF CHEMICAL REMAINS (APPROXIMATELY 15-20 MINUTES). GET MEDICAL ATTENTION IMMEDIATELY.

INGESTION: DICAMBA: **ACUTE EXPOSURE-** IN ANIMALS, ACUTE DOSES PRODUCED MYOTONIC MUSCULAR SPASMS, EXHAUSTION, URINARY INCONTINENCE, DYSPNEA, CYANOSIS, AND SOME DEATHS. MINOR LUNG HEMORRHAGES WERE FOUND IN SOME ANIMALS. MOST SURVIVORS RECOVERED IN 2 TO 3 DAYS AND SHOWED NO MACROSCOPIC PATHOLOGY. **CHRONIC EXPOSURE-** SLIGHTLY DECREASED BODY WEIGHT GAIN AND FOOD CONSUMPTION AND EVIDENCE OF REDUCED GLYCOGEN STORAGE WERE NOTED IN RATS AT 500 MG/KG/DAY FOR 90 DAYS. MATERNAL TOXICITY, SLIGHTLY REDUCED FETAL BODY WEIGHTS, AND INCREASED POST-IMPLANTATION LOSS WERE OBSERVED IN A STUDY OF PREGNANT RABBITS.

FIRST AID- IF THE PERSON IS CONSCIOUS AND NOT CONVULSING, REMOVE BY GIVING SYRUP OF IPECAC (IF VOMITING OCCURS, KEEP THE HEAD BELOW THE HIPS TO PREVENT ASPIRATION). GIVE ACTIVATED CHARCOAL FOLLOWED BY GASTRIC LAVAGE. FOLLOW WITH A SALINE CATHARTIC. DO NOT GIVE FATS OR OILS. INTESTINAL LAVAGE WITH 20% MANNITOL (200 ML) BY STOMACH TUBE IS ALSO USEFUL. GIVE ARTIFICIAL RESPIRATION WITH OXYGEN IF RESPIRATION IS DEPRESSED (DREISBACH, HANDBOOK OF POISONING, 12TH ED.). TREAT SYMPTOMATICALLY AND SUPPORTIVELY. LAVAGE AND ADMINISTRATION OF OXYGEN SHOULD BE PERFORMED BY QUALIFIED MEDICAL PERSONNEL. GET MEDICAL ATTENTION IMMEDIATELY.

ANTIDOTE: NO SPECIFIC ANTIDOTE. TREAT SYMPTOMATICALLY AND SUPPORTIVELY.

REACTIVITY

REACTIVITY: STABLE UNDER NORMAL TEMPERATURES AND PRESSURES.

INCOMPATIBILITIES: DICAMBA: OXIDIZERS (STRONG): FIRE AND EXPLOSION HAZARD.

DECOMPOSITION: THERMAL DECOMPOSITION PRODUCTS MAY INCLUDE TOXIC AND CORROSIVE FUMES OF CHLORIDES AND TOXIC OXIDES OF CARBON.

POLYMERIZATION: HAZARDOUS POLYMERIZATION HAS NOT BEEN REPORTED TO OCCUR UNDER NORMAL TEMPERATURES AND PRESSURES.

STORAGE AND DISPOSAL

OBSERVE ALL FEDERAL, STATE AND LOCAL REGULATIONS WHEN STORING OR DISPOSING OF THIS SUBSTANCE. FOR ASSISTANCE, CONTACT THE DISTRICT DIRECTOR OF THE ENVIRONMENTAL PROTECTION AGENCY.

****STORAGE****

STORE IN ACCORDANCE WITH 40 CFR 165 RECOMMENDED PROCEDURES FOR THE DISPOSAL AND STORAGE OF PESTICIDES AND PESTICIDE CONTAINERS.

STORE AWAY FROM INCOMPATIBLE SUBSTANCES.

****DISPOSAL****

DISPOSAL MUST BE IN ACCORDANCE WITH 40 CFR 165 RECOMMENDED PROCEDURES FOR THE DISPOSAL AND STORAGE OF PESTICIDES AND PESTICIDE CONTAINERS.

CONDITIONS TO AVOID

MAY BURN BUT DOES NOT IGNITE READILY. AVOID CONTACT WITH STRONG OXIDIZERS, EXCESSIVE HEAT, SPARKS, OR OPEN FLAME.

SPILL AND LEAK PROCEDURES

SOIL SPILL: DIG A HOLDING AREA SUCH AS PIT, POND OR LAGOON TO CONTAIN SPILLED MATERIAL. USE PROTECTIVE COVER SUCH AS A PLASTIC SHEET TO PREVENT DISSOLVING IN FIREFIGHTING WATER OR RAIN.

WATER SPILL: USE ACTIVATED CARBON TO ABSORB SPILLED SUBSTANCE THAT IS DISSOLVED. USE MECHANICAL DREDGES OR LIFTS TO EXTRACT IMMOBILIZED MASSES OF POLLUTION AND PRECIPITATES.

OCCUPATIONAL SPILL: SWEEP UP AND PLACE IN SUITABLE CLEAN, DRY CONTAINERS FOR RECLAMATION OR LATER DISPOSAL. DO NOT FLUSH SPILLED MATERIAL INTO SEWER. KEEP UNNECESSARY PEOPLE AWAY.

REPORTABLE QUANTITY (RQ): 1000 POUNDS THE SUPERFUND AMENDMENTS AND REAUTHORIZATION ACT (SARA) SECTION 304 REQUIRES THAT A RELEASE EQUAL TO OR GREATER THAN THE REPORTABLE QUANTITY FOR THIS SUBSTANCE BE IMMEDIATELY REPORTED TO THE LOCAL EMERGENCY PLANNING COMMITTEE AND THE STATE EMERGENCY RESPONSE COMMISSION (40 CFR 355.40). IF THE RELEASE OF THIS SUBSTANCE IS REPORTABLE UNDER CERCLA SECTION 103, THE NATIONAL RESPONSE CENTER MUST BE NOTIFIED IMMEDIATELY AT (800) 424-8802 OR (202) 426-2675 IN THE METROPOLITAN WASHINGTON, D.C. AREA (40 CFR 302.6).

PROTECTIVE EQUIPMENT

VENTILATION: PROVIDE LOCAL EXHAUST OR GENERAL DILUTION VENTILATION SYSTEM.

RESPIRATOR: THE FOLLOWING RESPIRATORS ARE RECOMMENDED BASED ON INFORMATION FOUND IN THE PHYSICAL DATA, TOXICITY AND HEALTH EFFECTS SECTIONS. THEY ARE RANKED IN ORDER FROM MINIMUM TO MAXIMUM RESPIRATORY PROTECTION. THE SPECIFIC RESPIRATOR SELECTED MUST BE BASED ON CONTAMINATION LEVELS FOUND IN THE WORK PLACE, MUST NOT EXCEED THE WORKING LIMITS OF THE RESPIRATOR AND BE JOINTLY APPROVED BY THE NATIONAL INSTITUTE FOR OCCUPATIONAL SAFETY AND HEALTH AND THE MINE SAFETY AND HEALTH ADMINISTRATION (NIOSH-MSHA).

CHEMICAL CARTRIDGE RESPIRATOR WITH AN ORGANIC VAPOR CARTRIDGE(S) WITH A FULL FACEPIECE AND ORGANIC VAPOR CARTRIDGE(S) IN COMBINATION WITH A DUST AND MIST FILTER.

POWERED AIR-PURIFYING RESPIRATOR WITH A TIGHT-FITTING FACEPIECE AND ORGANIC VAPOR CARTRIDGE(S) IN COMBINATION WITH A HIGH-EFFICIENCY PARTICULATE FILTER.

TYPE 'C' SUPPLIED-AIR RESPIRATOR WITH A FULL FACEPIECE OPERATED IN A PRESSURE-DEMAND OR OTHER POSITIVE PRESSURE MODE.

SELF-CONTAINED BREATHING APPARATUS WITH A FULL FACEPIECE OPERATED IN PRESSURE-DEMAND OR OTHER POSITIVE PRESSURE MODE.

FOR FIREFIGHTING AND OTHER IMMEDIATELY DANGEROUS TO LIFE OR HEALTH CONDITIONS:

SELF-CONTAINED BREATHING APPARATUS WITH FULL FACEPIECE OPERATED IN PRESSURE-DEMAND OR OTHER POSITIVE PRESSURE MODE.

SUPPLIED-AIR RESPIRATOR WITH FULL FACEPIECE AND OPERATED IN PRESSURE-DEMAND OR OTHER POSITIVE PRESSURE MODE IN COMBINATION WITH AN AUXILIARY SELF-CONTAINED BREATHING APPARATUS OPERATED IN PRESSURE-DEMAND OR OTHER POSITIVE PRESSURE MODE.

CLOTHING: EMPLOYEE MUST WEAR APPROPRIATE PROTECTIVE (IMPERVIOUS) CLOTHING AND EQUIPMENT TO PREVENT REPEATED OR PROLONGED SKIN CONTACT WITH THIS SUBSTANCE.

GLOVES: EMPLOYEE MUST WEARAPPROPRIATE PROTECTIVE GLOVES TO PREVENT CONTACT WITH THIS SUBSTANCE.

EYE PROTECTION: EMPLOYEE MUST WEAR SPLASH-PROOF OR DUST-RESISTANT SAFETY GOGGLES TO PREVENT EYE CONTACT WITH THIS SUBSTANCE.
EMERGENCY EYE WASH: WHERE THERE IS ANY POSSIBILITY THAT AN EMPLOYEE'S EYES MAY BE EXPOSED TO THIS SUBSTANCE, THE EMPLOYER SHOULD PROVIDE AN EYE WASH FOUNTAIN WITHIN THE IMMEDIATE WORK AREA FOR EMERGENCY USE.

AUTHORIZED BY- OCCUPATIONAL HEALTH SERVICES, INC.
CREATION DATE: 10/04/89 ***REVISION DATE:*** 05/31/90

MATERIAL SAFETY DATA SHEET

OCCUPATIONAL HEALTH SERVICES, INC.
AGRICULTURE AND PESTICIDE DIVISION
450 SEVENTH AVENUE, SUITE 2407
NEW YORK, NEW YORK 10123
1-800-445-MSDS OR (212) 967-1100

EMERGENCY CONTACT:
JOHN S. BRANSFORD, JR. (615) 292-1180

SUBSTANCE IDENTIFICATION

CAS-NUMBER 114-26-1
SUBSTANCE: **O-ISOPROPOXYPHENYL METHYLCARBAMATE**
TRADE NAMES/SYNONYMS: 2-(1-METHYLETHOXY)PHENOL METHYLCARBAMATE; METHYLCARBAMIC ACID, O-ISOPROPOXYPHENYL ESTER; PHENOL, 2-(1-METHYLETHOXY)-, METHYLCARBAMATE; CARBAMIC ACID, METHYL-, O-ISOPROPOXYPHENYL ESTER; O-ISOPROPOXYPHENYL N-METHYLCARBAMATE; 2-ISOPROPOXYPHENYL METHYLCARBAMATE; 2-ISOPROPOXYPHENYL N-METHYLCARBAMATE; N-METHYL-2-ISOPROPOXYPHENYLCARBAMATE; 2-(1-METHYLETHOXY)PHENYL METHYLCARBAMATE; PROPOXUR; ARPROCARB; BAYER 39007; BAYGON; BLATTANEX; PROPOGON; SENDRAN; UNDEN; OMS 33; ENT 25,671; C11H15NO3; PST02540
CHEMICAL FAMILY: CARBAMATE
ETHER, AROMATIC
MOLECULAR FORMULA: C11-H15-N-O3
MOLECULAR WEIGHT: 209.27
CERCLA RATINGS (SCALE 0-3): HEALTH=3 FIRE=U REACTIVITY=0 PERSISTENCE=3
NFPA RATINGS (SCALE 0-4): HEALTH=4 FIRE=U REACTIVITY=0

COMPONENTS AND CONTAMINANTS

COMPONENT: O-ISOPROPOXYPHENYL METHYLCARBAMATE ***PERCENT:*** 100.0
CAS# 114-26-1
OTHER CONTAMINANTS: NONE
EXPOSURE LIMITS: O-ISOPROPOXYPHENYL METHYLCARBAMATE: 0.5 MG/M3 OSHA TWA 0.5 MG/M3 ACGIH TWA
SUBJECT TO SARA SECTION 313 ANNUAL TOXIC CHEMICAL RELEASE REPORTING

PHYSICAL DATA

DESCRIPTION: WHITE CRYSTALLINE POWDER WITH A FAINT ODOR
MELTING POINT: 198 F (92 C) ***SPECIFIC GRAVITY:*** NOT AVAILABLE
VAPOR PRESSURE: 0.000065 MMHG @ 20 C ***SOLUBILITY IN WATER:*** 0.2%
SOLVENT SOLUBILITY: MOST ORGANIC POLAR SOLVENTS, ACETONE, AND METHANOL

FIRE AND EXPLOSION DATA

FIRE AND EXPLOSION HAZARD: UNKNOWN FIRE AND EXPLOSION HAZARD.
FIREFIGHTING MEDIA: DRY CHEMICAL, CARBON DIOXIDE, WATER SPRAY OR FOAM FOR LARGER FIRES, USE WATER SPRAY, FOG OR ALCOHOL FOAM
FIREFIGHTING: MOVE CONTAINER FROM FIRE AREA IF POSSIBLE. DO NOT SCATTER SPILLED MATERIAL WITH MORE WATER THAN NEEDED FOR FIRE CONTROL. DIKE FIRE CONTROL WATER FOR LATER DISPOSAL
USE AGENTS SUITABLE FOR TYPE OF SURROUNDING FIRE. AVOID BREATHING HAZARDOUS VAPORS, KEEP UPWIND.

TRANSPORTATION DATA

DEPARTMENT OF TRANSPORTATION HAZARD CLASSIFICATION 49 CFR 172.101: POISON B
DEPARTMENT OF TRANSPORTATION LABELING REQUIREMENTS 49 CFR 172.101 AND SUBPART E: POISON

TOXICITY

O-ISOPROPOXYPHENYL METHYLCARBAMATE: TOXICITY DATA: 1440 MG/M3/1 HOUR INHALATION-RAT LC50; 800 MG/KG SKIN-RAT LD50; 24 MG/KG ORAL-WOMAN LDLO; 70 MG/KG ORAL-RAT LD50; 23500 UG/KG ORAL-MOUSE LD50; 40 MG/KG ORAL-GUINEA PIG LD50; 11400 UG/KG SUBCUTANEOUS-MOUSE LD50; 56 MG/KG SUBCUTANEOUS-RAT LD50; 11 MG/KG INTRAVENOUS-RAT LD50; 30 MG/KG INTRAPERITONEAL-RAT LD50; 12 MG/KG INTRAPERITONEAL-MOUSE LD50; 500 MG/KG INTRAPERITONEAL-HAMSTER LD50; 53 MG/KG INTRAMUSCULAR-RAT LD50; 100 MG/KG UNREPORTED-RAT LD50; 100 MG/KG UNREPORTED-MAMMAL LD50; MUTAGENIC DATA (RTECS); REPRODUCTIVE EFFECTS DATA (RTECS). CARCINOGEN STATUS: NONE. ACUTE TOXICITY LEVEL: HIGHLY TOXIC BY INHALATION; TOXIC BY DERMAL ABSORPTION AND INGESTION. TARGET EFFECTS: CHOLINESTERASE INHIBITOR. AT INCREASED RISK FROM EXPOSURE: PERSONS WITH ASTHMA, DIABETES, CARDIOVASCULAR DISEASE, MECHANICAL OBSTRUCTION OF THE GASTROINTESTINAL OR UROGENITAL TRACT, AND THOSE IN VAGOTONIC STATES.*
* MAY BE BASED ON GENERAL INFORMATION ON CARBAMATES.

HEALTH EFFECTS AND FIRST AID

INHALATION: O-ISOPROPOXYPHENYL METHYLCARBAMATE: HIGHLY TOXIC. SEE INFORMATION ON CARBAMATES.
CARBAMATES: CHOLINESTERASE INHIBITOR. **ACUTE EXPOSURE-** WHEN INHALED, THE FIRST EFFECTS OF CHOLINESTERASE INHIBITION ARE USUALLY RESPIRATORY AND MAY INCLUDE NASAL HYPEREMIA AND WATERY DISCHARGE, CHEST DISCOMFORT, DYSPNEA, AND WHEEZING DUE TO INCREASED BRONCHIAL SECRETIONS AND BRONCHOCONSTRICTION. OTHER SYSTEMIC EFFECTS MAY BEGIN WITHIN A FEW MINUTES OR SEVERAL HOURS OF EXPOSURE. SYMPTOMS MAY INCLUDE NAUSEA, VOMITING, DIARRHEA, ABDOMINAL CRAMPS, HEADACHE, VERTIGO, OCULAR PAIN, CILIARY MUSCLE SPASM, BLURRING OR DIMNESS OF VISION, MIOSIS, OR IN SOME CASES MYDRIASIS, LACRIMATION, SALIVATION, SWEATING, AND CONFUSION. OTHER REPORTED CENTRAL NERVOUS SYSTEM OR NEUROMUSCULAR EFFECTS INCLUDE ATAXIA, SLURRED SPEECH, AREFLEXIA, WEAKNESS, FATIGUE, TWITCHING, FASCICULATION, TREMOR, AND EVENTUALLY PARALYSIS OF THE EXTREMITIES AND POSSIBLY OF THE RESPIRATORY MUSCLES. IN SEVERE CASES, THERE MAY ALSO BE INVOLUNTARY DEFECATION AND URINATION, BRADYCARDIA, HYPOTENSION, PULMONARY EDEMA, CONVULSIONS, COMA, AND DEATH FROM RESPIRATORY FAILURE OR CARDIAC ARREST. CARBAMATES GENERALLY DO NOT ACCUMULATE IN MAMMALIAN TISSUE AND THE CHOLINESTERASE INHIBITION REVERSES RATHER RAPIDLY. IN NON-FATAL CASES, THE ILLNESS GENERALLY LASTS LESS THAN 24 HOURS. **CHRONIC EXPOSURE-** PROLONGED OR REPEATED EXPOSURE MAY CAUSE EFFECTS AS DESCRIBED IN ACUTE EXPOSURE.
FIRST AID- REMOVE FROM EXPOSURE AREA TO FRESH AIR IMMEDIATELY. IF BREATHING HAS STOPPED, GIVE ARTIFICIAL RESPIRATION. MAINTAIN AIRWAY AND BLOOD PRESSURE AND ADMINISTER OXYGEN IF AVAILABLE. KEEP AFFECTED PERSON WARM AND AT REST. TREAT SYMPTOMATICALLY AND SUPPORTIVELY. ADMINISTRATION OF OXYGEN SHOULD BE PERFORMED BY QUALIFIED PERSONNEL. GET MEDICAL ATTENTION IMMEDIATELY.

SKIN CONTACT: O-ISOPROPOXYPHENYL METHYLCARBAMATE: TOXIC. SEE INFORMATION ON CARBAMATES.
CARBAMATES: CHOLINESTERASE INHIBITOR. **ACUTE EXPOSURE-** SOME COMPOUNDS MAY CAUSE IRRITATION. LOCALIZED SWEATING AND FASCICULATIONS MAY OCCUR AT THE SITE OF CONTACT. IF SUFFICIENT AMOUNTS ARE ABSORBED THROUGH THE SKIN, OTHER EFFECTS OF CHOLINESTERASE INHIBITION MAY OCCUR AS DESCRIBED IN ACUTE INHALATION; SYMPTOMS MAY BE DELAYED FOR 2-3 HOURS, USUALLY NO MORE THAN 8 HOURS. **CHRONIC EXPOSURE-** REPEATED OR PROLONGED EXPOSURE MAY CAUSE EFFECTS AS DESCRIBED IN ACUTE EXPOSURE.
FIRST AID- REMOVE CONTAMINATED CLOTHING IMMEDIATELY. WASH CONTAMINATED AREAS WITH SOAP AND WATER FOLLOWED BY ALCOHOL (ARENA, POISONING, 4TH ED.). EMERGENCY PERSONNEL SHOULD WEAR GLOVES AND AVOID CONTAMINATION. TREAT RESPIRATORY DIFFICULTY WITH ARTIFICIAL RESPIRATION. GET MEDICAL ATTENTION IMMEDIATELY.

EYE CONTACT: O-ISOPROPOXYPHENYL METHYLCARBAMATE: SEE INFORMATION ON CARBAMATES.
CARBAMATES: CHOLINESTERASE INHIBITOR. **ACUTE EXPOSURE-** DIRECT CONTACT MAY CAUSE PAIN, HYPEREMIA, LACRIMATION, TWITCHING OF THE EYELIDS, MIOSIS, AND CILIARY MUSCLE SPASM WITH LOSS OF ACCOMODATION, BLURRED OR DIMMED VISION AND BROWACHE. SOMETIMES MYDRIASIS MAY OCCUR INSTEAD OF MIOSIS. WITH SUFFICIENT EXPOSURE, OTHER SYMPTOMS OF CHOLINESTERASE INHIBITION MAY OCCUR AS DESCRIBED IN ACUTE INHALATION. **CHRONIC EXPOSURE-** PROLONGED EXPOSURE MAY CAUSE EFFECTS AS DESCRIBED IN ACUTE EXPOSURE. SOME COMPOUNDS HAVE CAUSED TOXIC EFFECTS ON THE CRYSTALLINE LENS, CONJUNCTIVAL THICKENING AND OBSTRUCTION OF NASOLACRIMAL CANALS WHEN USED AS MIOTIC EYE DROPS.
FIRST AID- IRRIGATE EYES WITH WATER OR SALINE SOLUTION. IF SYMPTOMS OF POISONING OCCUR, TREAT RESPIRATORY DIFFICULTY WITH ARTIFICIAL

RESPIRATION AND OXYGEN. OBSERVE PATIENT FOR AT LEAST 24-36 HOURS (GOSSELIN, CLINICAL TOXICOLOGY OF COMMERCIAL PRODUCTS, 5TH ED.). GET MEDICAL ATTENTION IMMEDIATELY. OXYGEN SHOULD BE ADMINISTERED BY QUALIFIED MEDICAL PERSONNEL.

INGESTION: O-ISOPROPOXYPHENYL METHYLCARBAMATE: TOXIC. CHRONIC INGESTION OF A DIETARY LEVEL OF 1,000 PPM FROM DAY 6 OF GESTATION TO DAY 15 OF LACTATION PRODUCED SLIGHTLY REDUCED WEIGHT GAIN OF THE DAMS AND TH BIRTH WEIGHT OF THE YOUNG. THE YOUNG ALSO SHOWED A SIGNIFICANT DELAY IN DEVELOPING, THE STARTLE REFLEX AND SHOWED SOME DIFFERENCES IN THE EEG. SOME HISTOLOGICAL CHANGES IN THE LIVER AND DEPRESSED CHOLINESTERASE ACTIVITY OF THE BRAIN AND BLOOD WERE OBSERVED IN A STUDY OF RATS FED A DIETARY LEVEL OF 1,000 AND 2,000 PPM. SEE INFORMATION ON CARBAMATES.

CARBAMATES: CHOLINESTERASE INHIBITOR. **ACUTE EXPOSURE-** WHEN INGESTED, THE FIRST EFFECTS MAY BE NAUSEA, VOMITING, ANOREXIA, ABDOMINAL CRAMPS, AND DIARRHEA. WITH ABSORPTION FROM THE GASTROINTESTINAL TRACT, THE OTHER EFFECTS OF CHOLINESTERASE INHIBITION AS DESCRIBED IN ACUTE INHALATION MAY OCCUR; SYMPTOMS MAY BEGIN WITHIN MINUTES OR BE DELAYED SEVERAL HOURS. **CHRONIC EXPOSURE-** REPEATED INGESTION MAY CAUSE EFFECTS AS DESCRIBED IN ACUTE EXPOSURE.

FIRST AID- IF PERSON IS ALERT AND RESPIRATION IS NOT DEPRESSED, GIVE SYRUP OF IPECAC FOLLOWED BY WATER (IF VOMITING OCCURS, KEEP HEAD BELOW HIPS TO PREVENT ASPIRATION). IF CONSCIOUSNESS LEVEL DECLINES OR VOMITING HAS NOT OCCURRED IN 15 MINUTES EMPTY STOMACH BY GASTRIC LAVAGE WITH THE AID OF CUFFED ENDOTRACHEAL TUBE USING ISOTONIC SALINE OR 5% SODIUM BICARBONATE FOLLOW WITH ACTIVATED CHARCOAL. ESTABLISH AND MAINTAIN AIRWAY. TREAT RESPIRATORY DIFFICULTY WITH ARTIFICIAL RESPIRATION AND OXYGEN. DO NOT GIVE MORPHINE, AMINOPHYLLINE, PHENOTHIAZINES, RESERPINE, FUROSEMIDE, OR ETHACRYNIC ACID (MORGAN, RECOGNITION AND MANAGEMENT OF PESTICIDE POISONINGS, 3RD ED.). TREAT SYMPTOMATICALLY AND SUPPORTIVELY. ADMINISTRATION OF OXYGEN AND LAVAGE MUST BE PERFORMED BY QUALIFIED MEDICAL PERSONNEL. GET MEDICAL ATTENTION IMMEDIATELY.

ANTIDOTE: THE FOLLOWING ANTIDOTE HAS BEEN RECOMMENDED. HOWEVER, THE DECISION AS TO WHETHER THE SEVERITY OF POISONING REQUIRES ADMINISTRATION OF ANY ANTIDOTE AND ACTUAL DOSE REQUIRED SHOULD BE MADE BY QUALIFIED MEDICAL PERSONNEL.

FOR CHOLINESTERASE INHIBITORS: ESTABLISH CLEAR AIRWAY AND TISSUE OXYGENATION BY ASPIRATION OF SECRETIONS, AND IF NECESSARY, BY ASSISTED PULMONARY VENTILATION WITH OXYGEN. IMPROVE TISSUE OXYGENATION AS MUCH AS POSSIBLE BEFORE ADMINISTERING ATROPINE TO MINIMIZE THE RISK OF VENTRICULAR FIBRILLATION. ADMINISTER ATROPINE SULFATE INTRAVENOUSLY, OR INTRAMUSCULARLY IF IV INJECTION IS NOT POSSIBLE. IN MODERATELY SEVERE POISONING ADMINISTER ATROPINE SULFATE, 0.4-2.0 MG REPEATED EVERY 15 MINUTES UNTIL ATROPINIZATION IS ACHIEVED (TACHYCARDIA, FLUSHING, DRY MOUTH, MYDRIASIS). MAINTAIN ATROPINIZATION BY REPEATED DOSES FOR 2-12 HOURS, OR LONGER, DEPENDING ON THE SEVERITY OF POISONING. THE APPEARANCE OF RALES IN THE LUNG BASES, MIOSIS, SALIVATION, NAUSEA, BRADYCARDIA, ARE ALL INDICATIONS OF INADEQUATE ATROPINIZATION. SEVERELY POISONED INDIVIDUALS MAY EXHIBIT REMARKABLE TOLERANCE TO ATROPINE; TWO OR MORE TIMES THE DOSAGES SUGGESTED ABOVE MAY BE NEEDED. PERSONS NOT POISONED OR ONLY SLIGHTLY POISONED, HOWEVER, MAY DEVELOP SIGNS OF ATROPINE TOXICITY FROM SUCH LARGE DOSAGES: FEVER, MUSCLE FIBRILLATIONS, AND DELIRIUM ARE THE MAIN SIGNS OF ATROPINE TOXICITY. IF THESE SIGNS APPEAR WHILE THE PATIENT IS FULLY ATROPINIZED, ATROPINE ADMINISTRATION SHOULD BE DISCONTINUED, AT LEAST TEMPORARILY. OBSERVE TREATED PATIENTS CLOSELY AT LEAST 24 HOURS TO INSURE THAT SYMPTOMS (POSSIBLY PULMONARY EDEMA) DO NOT RECUR AS ATROPINIZATION WEARS OFF. IN VERY SEVERE POISONINGS, METABOLIC DISPOSITION OF TOXICANT MAY REQUIRE SEVERAL HOURS OR DAYS DURING WHICH ATROPINIZATION MUST BE MAINTAINED. MARKEDLY LOWER LEVELS OF URINARY METABOLITES INDICATE THAT ATROPINE DOSAGE CAN BE TAPERED OFF. AS DOSAGE IS REDUCED, CHECK THE LUNG BASES FREQUENTLY FOR RALES. IF RALES ARE HEARD OR OTHER SYMPTOMS RETURN, RE-ESTABLISH ATROPINIZATION PROMPTLY (MORGAN, RECOGNITION AND MANAGEMENT OF PESTICIDE POISONINGS, 3RD ED.). ADMINISTRATION OF ANTIDOTE MUST BE PERFORMED BY QUALIFIED MEDICAL PERSONNEL.

REACTIVITY

REACTIVITY: STABLE UNDER NORMAL TEMPERATURES AND PRESSURES.

INCOMPATIBILITIES: O-ISOPROPOXYPHENYL METHYLCARBAMATE: ALKALINE CONDITIONS: IS UNSTABLE.

DECOMPOSITION: THERMAL DECOMPOSITION PRODUCTS MAY INCLUDE TOXIC OXIDES OF NITROGEN AND METHYL ISOCYANATE.

POLYMERIZATION: HAZARDOUS POLYMERIZATION HAS NOT BEEN REPORTED TO OCCUR UNDER NORMAL TEMPERATURES AND PRESSURES.

STORAGE AND DISPOSAL

OBSERVE ALL FEDERAL, STATE AND LOCAL REGULATIONS WHEN STORING OR DISPOSING OF THIS SUBSTANCE. FOR ASSISTANCE, CONTACT THE DISTRICT DIRECTOR OF THE ENVIRONMENTAL PROTECTION AGENCY.

****STORAGE****

STORE IN ACCORDANCE WITH 40 CFR 165 RECOMMENDED PROCEDURES FOR THE DISPOSAL AND STORAGE OF PESTICIDES AND PESTICIDE CONTAINERS.
STORE AWAY FROM INCOMPATIBLE SUBSTANCES.

****DISPOSAL****

DISPOSAL MUST BE IN ACCORDANCE WITH 40 CFR 165 RECOMMENDED PROCEDURES FOR THE DISPOSAL AND STORAGE OF PESTICIDES AND PESTICIDE CONTAINERS.

CONDITIONS TO AVOID

NONE REPORTED.

SPILL AND LEAK PROCEDURES

OCCUPATIONAL SPILL: SWEEP UP AND PLACE IN SUITABLE CLEAN, DRY CONTAINERS FOR RECLAMATION OR LATER DISPOSAL. DO NOT FLUSH SPILLED MATERIAL INTO SEWER. KEEP UNNECESSARY PEOPLE AWAY.

PROTECTIVE EQUIPMENT

VENTILATION: PROCESS ENCLOSURE RECOMMENDED TO MEET PUBLISHED EXPOSURE LIMITS.

RESPIRATOR: THE FOLLOWING RESPIRATORS ARE RECOMMENDED BASED ON INFORMATION FOUND IN THE PHYSICAL DATA, TOXICITY AND HEALTH EFFECTS SECTIONS. THEY ARE RANKED IN ORDER FROM MINIMUM TO MAXIMUM RESPIRATORY PROTECTION. THE SPECIFIC RESPIRATOR SELECTED MUST BE BASED ON CONTAMINATION LEVELS FOUND IN THE WORK PLACE, MUST NOT EXCEED THE WORKING LIMITS OF THE RESPIRATOR AND BE JOINTLY APPROVED BY THE NATIONAL INSTITUTE FOR OCCUPATIONAL SAFETY AND HEALTH AND THE MINE SAFETY AND HEALTH ADMINISTRATION (NIOSH-MSHA).

TYPE 'C' SUPPLIED-AIR RESPIRATOR WITH A FULL FACEPIECE OPERATED IN PRESSURE-DEMAND OR OTHER POSITIVE PRESSURE MODE OR WITH A FULL FACEPIECE, HELMET OR HOOD OPERATED IN CONTINOUS-FLOW MODE.

SELF-CONTAINED BREATHING APPARATUS WITH A FULL FACEPIECE OPERATED IN PRESSURE-DEMAND OR OTHER POSITIVE PRESSURE MODE.

FOR FIREFIGHTING AND OTHER IMMEDIATELY DANGEROUS TO LIFE OR HEALTH CONDITIONS:

SELF-CONTAINED BREATHING APPARATUS WITH FULL FACEPIECE OPERATED IN PRESSURE-DEMAND OR OTHER POSITIVE PRESSURE MODE.

SUPPLIED-AIR RESPIRATOR WITH FULL FACEPIECE AND OPERATED IN PRESSURE-DEMAND OR OTHER POSITIVE PRESSURE MODE IN COMBINATION WITH AN AUXILIARY SELF-CONTAINED BREATHING APPARATUS OPERATED IN PRESSURE-DEMAND OR OTHER POSITIVE PRESSURE MODE.

CLOTHING: EMPLOYEE MUST WEAR APPROPRIATE PROTECTIVE (IMPERVIOUS) CLOTHING AND EQUIPMENT TO PREVENT ANY POSSIBILITY OF SKIN CONTACT WITH THIS SUBSTANCE.

GLOVES: EMPLOYEE MUST WEAR APPROPRIATE PROTECTIVE GLOVES TO PREVENT CONTACT WITH THIS SUBSTANCE.

EYE PROTECTION: EMPLOYEE MUST WEAR SPLASH-PROOF OR DUST-RESISTANT SAFETY GOGGLES AND A FACESHIELD TO PREVENT CONTACT WITH THIS SUBSTANCE.

EMERGENCY WASH FACILITIES: WHERE THERE IS ANY POSSIBILITY THAT AN EMPLOYEE'S EYES AND/OR SKIN MAY BE EXPOSED TO THIS SUBSTANCE, THE EMPLOYER SHOULD PROVIDE AN EYE WASH FOUNTAIN AND QUICK DRENCH SHOWER WITHIN THE IMMEDIATE WORK AREA FOR EMERGENCY USE.

AUTHORIZED BY- OCCUPATIONAL HEALTH SERVICES, INC.

CREATION DATE: 10/04/89 ***REVISION DATE:*** 06/12/90

MATERIAL SAFETY DATA SHEET

OCCUPATIONAL HEALTH SERVICES, INC.
AGRICULTURE AND PESTICIDE DIVISION
450 SEVENTH AVENUE, SUITE 2407
NEW YORK, NEW YORK 10123
1-800-445-MSDS OR (212) 967-1100

EMERGENCY CONTACT:
JOHN S. BRANSFORD, JR. (615) 292-1180

SUBSTANCE IDENTIFICATION

CAS-NUMBER 55-38-9

SUBSTANCE: FENTHION

TRADE NAMES/SYNONYMS: PHOSPHOROTHIOIC ACID, O,O-DIMETHYL O-(3-METHYL-4-(METHYLTHIO)PHENYL) ESTER; PHOSPHOROTHIOIC ACID, O,O-DIMETHYL O-(4-(METHYLTHIO)-M-TOLYL) ESTER; PHOSPHOROTHIOIC ACID, DIMETHYL (4-(METHYLTHIO)-M-TOLYL) ESTER; O,O-DIMETHYL O-4-METHYLTHIO-M-TOLYL PHOSPHOROTHIOATE; O,O-DIMETHYL O-(3-METHYL-4-(METHYLTHIO)PHENYL) PHOSPHOROTHIOATE; O,O-DIMETHYL O-(4-(METHYLTHIO)-M-TOLYL) PHOSPHOROTHIOATE; PHOSPHOROTHIOIC ACID ((H3PO3S)), O,O-DIMETHYL O-4-(METHYLTHIO)-M-TOLYL ESTER; BAYER 29493; ENT 25540; S 1752; BAYCID (FORMULATION); BAYTEX (FORMULATION); ENTEX (FORMULATION); LEBAYCID (FORMULATION); MERCAPTOPHOS (FORMULATION); QUELETOX (FORMULATION); SPOTTON (FORMULATION); C10H15O3PS2; PST02550

CHEMICAL FAMILY: ORGANOPHOSPHATE

MOLECULAR FORMULA: (C-H3-O)2-P-(S)-O-C6-H3-(C-H3)-S-C-H3

MOLECULAR WEIGHT: 278.34

CERCLA RATINGS (SCALE 0-3): HEALTH=3 FIRE=2 REACTIVITY=0 PERSISTENCE=1

NFPA RATINGS (SCALE 0-4): HEALTH=3 FIRE=2 REACTIVITY=0

COMPONENTS AND CONTAMINANTS

COMPONENT: FENTHION ***PERCENT:*** 100.0
CAS# 55-38-9

OTHER CONTAMINANTS: NONE

EXPOSURE LIMITS: FENTHION: 0.2 MG/M3 OSHA TWA (SKIN) 0.2 MG/M3 ACGIH TWA (SKIN)

PHYSICAL DATA

DESCRIPTION: COLORLESS LIQUID WITH A SLIGHT ODOR OF GARLIC.

BOILING POINT: 189 F (87 C) @ 0.01 MMHG ***SPECIFIC GRAVITY:*** 1.245

VAPOR PRESSURE: NEGLIGIBLE ***SOLUBILITY IN WATER:*** 55 PPM @ 20 C

SOLVENT SOLUBILITY: SOLUBLE IN ALCOHOL, ETHER, ACETONE, DICHLOROMETHANE AND ISOPROPANOL; INSOLUBLE IN ALIPHATIC HYDROCARBONS.

FIRE AND EXPLOSION DATA

FIRE AND EXPLOSION HAZARD: MODERATE FIRE HAZARD WHEN EXPOSED TO HEAT OR FLAME.

FLASH POINT: > 180 F (>82 C)

FIREFIGHTING MEDIA: DRY CHEMICA:., CARBON DIOXIDE, HALON, WATER SPRAY OR STANDARD FOAM (1987 EMERGENCY RESPONSE GUIDEBOOK, DOT P 5800.4). FOR LARGER FIRES, USE WATER SPRAY, FOG OR STANDARD FOAM (1987 EMERGENCY RESPONSE GUIDEBOOK, DOT P 5800.4).

FIREFIGHTING: MOVE CONTAINERS FROM FIRE AREA IF POSSIBLE. COOL CONTAINERS EXPOSED TO FLAMES WITH WATER FROM SIDE UNTIL WELL AFTER FIRE IS OUT. FIGHT FIRE FROM MAXIMUM DISTANCE. STAY AWAY FROM STORAGE TANK ENDS. DIKE FIRE CONTROL WATER FOR LATER DISPOSAL. DO NOT SCATTER MATERIAL. (1987 EMERGENCY RESPONSE GUIDEBOOK, DOT P 5800.4, GUIDE PAGE 57). EXTINGUISH ONLY IF FLOW CAN BE STOPPED. USE FLOODING AMOUNTS OF WATER AS A FOG; SOLID STREAMS MAY BE INEFFECTIVE. COOL CONTAINERS WITH FLOODING AMOUNTS OF WATER FROM AS FAR A DISTANCE AS POSSIBLE. AVOID BREATHING POISONOUS VAPORS, KEEP UPWIND.

TOXICITY

FENTHION: TOXICITY DATA: 2.4-3.0 MG/L/1 HOUR INHALATION-RAT LC50 (85JFAN); 1 GM/M3/2 HOURS INHALATION-RAT LCLO; 1 GM/M3/2 HOURS INHALATION-MOUSE LDLO; 1 GM/M3/2 HOURS INHALATION-RABBIT LCLO; 1 GM/M3/2 HOURS INHALATION-GUINEA PIG LCLO; 330 MG/KG SKIN-RAT LD50; 500 MG/KG SKIN-MOUSE LD50; 98 MG/KG SKIN-DOMESTIC ANIMAL LD50; 180 MG/KG ORAL-RAT LD50; 88,100 UG/KG ORAL-MOUSE LD50; 150 MG/KG ORAL-RABBIT LD50; 257 MG/KG ORAL-MAN TDLO; 105 MG/KG ORAL-MAMMAL LD50; 260 MG/KG ORAL-GUINEA PIG LD50; 144 MG/KG SUBCUTANEOUS-MOUSE LD50; 320 MG/KG INTRAVENOUS-MOUSE LD50; 260 MG/KG INTRAPERITONEAL-RAT LD50; 125 MG/KG INTRAPERITONEAL-MOUSE LD50; 310 MG/KG INTRAPERITONEAL-GUINEA PIG LD50; 50 MG/KG INTRACEREBRAL-MOUSE LD50; 46,200 UG/KG INTRAMUSCULAR-MAMMAL LD50; 46 MG/KG INTRAMUSCULAR-DOMESTIC ANIMAL LD50; 50 MG/KG UNREPORTED-HUMAN LDLO; MUTAGENIC DATA (RTECS); REPRODUCTIVE EFFECTS DATA (RTECS); TUMORIGENIC DATA (RTECS). CARCINOGEN STATUS: NONE. ACUTE TOXICITY LEVEL: TOXIC BY DERMAL ABSORPTION; TOXIC BY INHALATION AND INGESTION. TARGET EFFECTS: CHOLINESTERASE INHIBITOR. POISONING MAY AFFECT THE NERVOUS SYSTEM.* AT INCREASED RISK FROM EXPOSURE: PERSONS WITH RESPIRATORY AILMENTS, RECENT EXPOSURE TO CHOLINESTERASE INHIBITORS OR IMPAIRED CHOLINESTERASE PRODUCTION, OR LIVER MALFUNCTION.* ADDITIONAL DATA: MAY CROSS THE PLACENTA. HIGH ENVIRONMENTAL TEMPERATURES OR EXPOSURE OF THE CHEMICAL TO VISIBLE OR ULTRAVIOLET LIGHT MAY ENHANCE THE TOXICITY. INTERACTIONS WITH MEDICATIONS MAY OCCUR.* * MAY BE BASED ON GENERAL INFORMATION ON ORGANOPHOSPHATES.

HEALTH EFFECTS AND FIRST AID

INHALATION: FENTHION: TOXIC. SEE INFORMATION ON ORGANOPHOSPHATES. ORGANOPHOSPHATES: CHOLINESTERASE INHIBITOR. **ACUTE EXPOSURE-** WHEN INHALED, THE FIRST EFFECTS OF CHOLINESTERASE INHIBITORS ARE USUALLY RESPIRATORY AND MAY INCLUDE NASAL HYPEREMIA AND WATERY DISCHARGE, COUGH, CHEST DISCOMFORT, DYSPNEA, AND WHEEZING DUE TO INCREASED BRONCHIAL SECRETIONS AND BRONCHOCONSTRICTION. IF SUFFICIENT AMOUNTS ARE ABSORBED, OTHER SYSTEMIC EFFECTS MAY BEGIN WITHIN A FEW MINUTES OR BE DELAYED FOR UP TO 12 HOURS. SYMPTOMS MAY INCLUDE PALLOR, NAUSEA, VOMITING, DIARRHEA, ABDOMINAL CRAMPS, HEADACHE, DIZZINESS, OCULAR PAIN, BLURRED VISION, MIOSIS OR IN SOME CASES, ESPECIALLY INITIALLY, MYDRIASIS, LACRIMATION, SALIVATION, SWEATING, AND CONFUSION. OTHER REPORTED CENTRAL NERVOUS SYSTEM OR NEUROMUSCULAR EFFECTS MAY INCLUDE ATAXIA, SLURRED SPEECH, AREFLEXIA, WEAKNESS, FATIGUE, FASCICULATIONS, TWITCHING, TREMORS POSSIBLY OF THE TONGUE AND EYELIDS, AND EVENTUALLY PARALYSIS OF THE EXTREMITIES AND POSSIBLY OF THE RESPIRATORY MUSCLES. IN SEVERE CASES THERE MAY ALSO BE INVOLUNTARY DEFECATION AND URINATION, CYANOSIS, PSYCHOSIS, HYPERGLYCEMIA, ACUTE PANCREATITIS, CARDIAC IRREGULARITIES, PULMONARY EDEMA, UNCONSCIOUSNESS, CONVULSIONS, AND COMA. DEATH IS PRIMARILY DUE TO RESPIRATORY FAILURE, ALTHOUGH CARDIOVASCULAR EFFECTS INCLUDING CARDIAC ARREST MAY ALSO BE IMPLICATED. LONG TERM SEQUELAE ARE RARE BUT MAY INCLUDE NEUROPSYCHIATRIC DISORDERS AND MYOPATHY WITH MUSCLE TENDERNESS. SOME ORGANOPHOSPHATES MAY CAUSE A DELAYED NEUROPATHY BEGINNING 1-4 WEEKS AFTER AN ACUTE EXPOSURE WHICH MAY OR MAY NOT HAVE CAUSED ACUTE CHOLINERGIC EFFECTS. NUMBNESS, TINGLING, WEAKNESS AND CRAMPING BEGINNING SYMMETRICALLY IN THE LOWER LIMBS MAY PROGRESS TO ATAXIA AND PARALYSIS. IN SEVERE CASES, UPPER LIMB INVOLVEMENT IS POSSIBLE AND FLACCID PARALYSIS MAY PROGRESS TO SPASTIC PARALYSIS WITH EXAGGERATED REFLEXES. IMPROVEMENT MAY OCCUR OVER MONTHS TO YEARS, BUT SOME RESIDUAL IMPAIRMENT USUALLY REMAINS. **CHRONIC EXPOSURE-** REPEATED OR PROLONGED EXPOSURE MAY RESULT IN THE EFFECTS OF ACUTE EXPOSURE INCLUDING THE DELAYED NEUROPATHY.
OTHER EFFECTS REPORTED IN WORKERS REPEATEDLY EXPOSED INCLUDE IMPAIRED MEMORY AND CONCENTRATION, ACUTE PSYCHOSIS, SEVERE DEPRESSIONS, IRRITABILTY, CONFUSION, APATHY, EMOTIONAL LABILITY, SOCIAL WITHDRAWAL, CONFUSION, HEADACHE, SPEECH DIFFICULTIES, DELAYED REACTION TIMES, SPATIAL DISORIENTATION, NIGHTMARES, SLEEPWALKING, AND DROWSINESS OR INSOMNIA. AN INFLUENZA-LIKE CONDITION WITH HEADACHE, NAUSEA, WEAKNESS, ANOREXIA AND MALAISE HAS ALSO BEEN REPORTED.

FIRST AID- REMOVE FROM EXPOSURE AREA TO FRESH AIR IMMEDIATELY. IF BREATHING HAS STOPPED, GIVE ARTIFICIAL RESPIRATION. MAINTAIN AIRWAY AND BLOOD PRESSURE AND ADMINISTER OXYGEN IF AVAILABLE. KEEP AFFECTED PERSON WARM AND AT REST. TREAT SYMPTOMATICALLY AND SUPPORTIVELY. ADMINISTRATION OF OXYGEN SHOULD BE PERFORMED BY QUALIFIED PERSONNEL. GET MEDICAL ATTENTION IMMEDIATELY.

SKIN CONTACT: FENTHION: TOXIC. SEE INFORMATION ON ORGANOPHOSPHATES. ORGANOPHOSPHATES: CHOLINESTERASE INHIBITOR. **ACUTE EXPOSURE-** LOCALIZED SWEATING AND FASCICULATIONS MAY OCCUR AT THE SITE OF CONTACT. IF SUFFICIENT AMOUNTS ARE ABSORBED, OTHER EFFECTS OF CHOLINESTERASE INHIBITION AS DESCRIBED IN ACUTE INHALATION MAY OCCUR. SYMPTOMS MAY BE DELAYED 2-3 HOURS, BUT USUALLY NO MORE THAN 12 HOURS. THE RATE OF ABSORPTION IS INCREASED BY THE PRESENCE OF DERMATITIS OR HIGH AMBIENT TEMPERATURES. DELAYED NEUROPATHY IS ALSO POSSIBLE. **CHRONIC EXPOSURE-** REPEATED OR PROLONGED EXPOSURE MAY CAUSE EFFECTS AS DESCRIBED IN ACUTE EXPOSURE. SOME ORGANOPHOSPHATES MAY CAUSE SENSITIZATION.

FIRST AID- REMOVE CONTAMINATED CLOTHING IMMEDIATELY. WASH CONTAMINATED AREAS WITH SOAP AND WATER FOLLOWED BY ALCOHOL (ARENA, POISONING, 4TH ED.). EMERGENCY PERSONNEL SHOULD WEAR GLOVES AND AVOID CONTAMINATION. TREAT RESPIRATORY DIFFICULTY WITH ARTIFICIAL RESPIRATION. GET MEDICAL ATTENTION IMMEDIATELY.

EYE CONTACT: FENTHION: SEE INFORMATION ON ORGANOPHOSPHATES. ORGANOPHOSPHATES: CHOLINESTERASE INHIBITOR. **ACUTE EXPOSURE-** DIRECT CONTACT MAY CAUSE PAIN, HYPEREMIA, LACRIMATION, TWITCHING OF THE EYELIDS, MIOSIS, AND CILIARY MUSCLE SPASM WITH LOSS OF ACCOMODATION, BLURRED OR DIMMED VISION AND BROWACHE. SOMETIMES MYDRIASIS MAY OCCUR INSTEAD OF MIOSIS. WITH SUFFICIENT EXPOSURE, OTHER SYMPTOMS OF CHOLINESTERASE INHIBITION AS DESCRIBED IN ACUTE INHALATION MAY OCCUR. **CHRONIC EXPOSURE-** REPEATED OR PROLONGED EXPOSURE MAY CAUSE EFFECTS AS DESCRIBED IN ACUTE EXPOSURE. SOME COMPOUNDS HAVE CAUSED TOXIC

EFFECTS ON THE CRYSTALLINE LENS, CONJUNCTIVAL THICKENING AND OBSTRUCTION OF THE NASOLACRIMAL CANALS WHEN USED AS MIOTIC EYEDROPS.

FIRST AID- IRRIGATE EYES WITH WATER OR SALINE SOLUTION. IF SYMPTOMS OF POISONING OCCUR, TREAT RESPIRATORY DIFFICULTY WITH ARTIFICIAL RESPIRATION AND OXYGEN. OBSERVE PATIENT FOR AT LEAST 24-36 HOURS (GOSSELIN, CLINICAL TOXICOLOGY OF COMMERCIAL PRODUCTS, 5TH ED.). GET MEDICAL ATTENTION IMMEDIATELY. OXYGEN SHOULD BE ADMINISTERED BY QUALIFIED MEDICAL PERSONNEL.

INGESTION: FENTHION: TOXIC. SEE INFORMATION ON ORGANOPHOSPHATES. REPRODUCTIVE EFFECTS HAVE BEEN REPORTED IN ANIMALS.
ORGANOPHOSPHATES: CHOLINESTERASE INHIBITOR. **ACUTE EXPOSURE**- WHEN INGESTED, THE FIRST EFFECTS MAY BE NAUSEA, VOMITING, ANOREXIA, ABDOMINAL CRAMPS AND DIARRHEA. GASTROINTESTINAL ABSORPTION MAY CAUSE SYMPTOMS OF CHOLINESTERASE INHIBITION AS DESCRIBED IN ACUTE INHALATION. SYMPTOMS MAY BEGIN WITHIN MINUTES OR BE DELAYED FOR HOURS. DELAYED EFFECTS INCLUDING NEUROPATHY MAY ALSO OCCUR. **CHRONIC EXPOSURE**- REPEATED INGESTION MAY CAUSE EFFECTS AS DESCRIBED IN ACUTE EXPOSURE.

FIRST AID- IF PERSON IS ALERT AND RESPIRATION IS NOT DEPRESSED, GIVE SYRUP OF IPECAC FOLLOWED BY WATER (IF VOMITING OCCURS, KEEP HEAD BELOW HIPS TO PREVENT ASPIRATION). IF CONSCIOUSNESS LEVEL DECLINES OR VOMITING HAS NOT OCCURRED IN 15 MINUTES EMPTY STOMACH BY GASTRIC LAVAGE WITH THE AID OF CUFFED ENDOTRACHEAL TUBE USING ISOTONIC SALINE OR 5% SODIUM BICARBONATE FOLLOW WITH ACTIVATED CHARCOAL. ESTABLISH AND MAINTAIN AIRWAY. TREAT RESPIRATORY DIFFICULTY WITH ARTIFICIAL RESPIRATION AND OXYGEN. DO NOT GIVE MORPHINE, AMINOPHYLLINE, PHENOTHIAZINES, RESERPINE, FUROSEMIDE, OR ETHACRYNIC ACID (MORGAN, RECOGNITION AND MANAGEMENT OF PESTICIDE POISONINGS, 3RD ED.). TREAT SYMPTOMATICALLY AND SUPPORTIVELY. ADMINISTRATION OF OXYGEN AND LAVAGE MUST BE PERFORMED BY QUALIFIED MEDICAL PERSONNEL. GET MEDICAL ATTENTION IMMEDIATELY.

ANTIDOTE: THE FOLLOWING ANTIDOTE(S) HAVE BEEN RECOMMENDED. HOWEVER, THE DECISION AS TO WHETHER THE SEVERITY OF POISONING REQUIRES ADMINISTRATION OF ANY ANTIDOTE AND ACTUAL DOSE REQUIRED SHOULD BE MADE BY QUALIFIED MEDICAL PERSONNEL.
FOR CHOLINESTERASE INHIBITORS: ESTABLISH CLEAR AIRWAY AND TISSUE OXYGENATION BY ASPIRATION OF SECRETIONS, AND IF NECESSARY, BY ASSISTED PULMONARY VENTILATION WITH OXYGEN. IMPROVE TISSUE OXYGENATION AS MUCH AS POSSIBLE BEFORE ADMINISTERING ATROPINE TO MINIMIZE THE RISK OF VENTRICULAR FIBRILLATION. ADMINISTER ATROPINE SULFATE INTRAVENOUSLY, OR INTRAMUSCULARLY IF IV INJECTION IS NOT POSSIBLE. IN MODERATELY SEVERE POISONING ADMINISTER ATROPINE SULFATE, 0.4-2.0 MG REPEATED EVERY 15 MINUTES UNTIL ATROPINIZATION IS ACHIEVED (TACHYCARDIA, FLUSHING, DRY MOUTH, MYDRIASIS). MAINTAIN ATROPINIZATION BY REPEATED DOSES FOR 2-12 HOURS, OR LONGER, DEPENDING ON THE SEVERITY OF POISONING. THE APPEARANCE OF RALES IN THE LUNG BASES, MIOSIS, SALIVATION, NAUSEA, BRADYCARDIA, ARE ALL INDICATIONS OF INADEQUATE ATROPINIZATION. SEVERELY POISONED INDIVIDUALS MAY EXHIBIT REMARKABLE TOLERANCE TO ATROPINE; TWO OR MORE TIMES THE DOSAGES SUGGESTED ABOVE MAY BE NEEDED. PERSONS NOT POISONED OR ONLY SLIGHTLY POISONED, HOWEVER, MAY DEVELOP SIGNS OF ATROPINE TOXICITY FROM SUCH LARGE DOSAGES: FEVER, MUSCLE FIBRILLATIONS, AND DELIRIUM ARE THE MAIN SIGNS OF ATROPINE TOXICITY. IF THESE SIGNS APPEAR WHILE THE PATIENT IS FULLY ATROPINIZED, ATROPINE ADMINISTRATION SHOULD BE DISCONTINUED, AT LEAST TEMPORARILY. OBSERVE TREATED PATIENTS CLOSELY AT LEAST 24 HOURS TO INSURE THAT SYMPTOMS (POSSIBLY PULMONARY EDEMA) DO NOT RECUR AS ATROPINIZATION WEARS OFF. IN VERY SEVERE POISONINGS, METABOLIC DISPOSITION OF TOXICANT MAY REQUIRE SEVERAL HOURS OR DAYS DURING WHICH ATROPINIZATION MUST BE MAINTAINED. MARKEDLY LOWER LEVELS OF URINARY METABOLITES INDICATE THAT ATROPINE DOSAGE CAN BE TAPERED OFF. AS DOSAGE IS REDUCED, CHECK THE LUNG BASES FREQUENTLY FOR RALES. IF RALES ARE HEARD OR OTHER SYMPTOMS RETURN, RE-ESTABLISH ATROPINIZATION PROMPTLY (MORGAN, RECOGNITION AND MANAGEMENT OF PESTICIDE POISONINGS, 3RD ED.). ADMINISTRATION OF ANTIDOTE MUST BE PERFORMED BY QUALIFIED MEDICAL PERSONNEL.
IN CASES OF SEVERE POISONING BY ORGANOPHOSPHATE PESTICIDES IN WHICH RESPIRATORY DEPRESSION, MUSCLE WEAKNESS AND TWITCHINGS ARE SEVERE, GIVE PRALIDOXIME (PROTOPAM-AYERST, 2-PAM), 1.0 GRAM INTRAVENOUSLY AT NO MORE THAN 0.5 GRAM PER MINUTE. DOSAGE OF PRALIDOXIME MAY BE REPEATED IN 1-2 HOURS, THEN AT 10-12 HOUR INTERVALS IF NEEDED. IN VERY SEVERE POISONINGS, DOSAGE RATES MAY BE DOUBLED. TREATMENT WITH PRALIDOXIME WILL BE MOST EFFECTIVE IF GIVEN WITHIN THIRTY-SIX HOURS AFTER POISONING (MORGAN, RECOGNITION AND MANAGEMENT OF PESTICIDE POISONINGS, 3RD ED.). ANTIDOTE SHOULD BE ADMINISTERED BY QUALIFIED MEDICAL PERSONNEL.

REACTIVITY

REACTIVITY: STABLE UNDER NORMAL TEMPERATURES AND PRESSURES.

INCOMPATIBILITIES: FENTHION: OXIDIZERS (STRONG): FIRE AND EXPLOSION HAZARD.

DECOMPOSITION: THERMAL DECOMPOSITION PRODUCTS MAY INCLUDE TOXIC OXIDES OF CARBON, SULFUR, AND PHOSPHORUS.

POLYMERIZATION: HAZARDOUS POLYMERIZATION HAS NOT BEEN REPORTED TO OCCUR UNDER NORMAL TEMPERATURES AND PRESSURES.

STORAGE AND DISPOSAL

OBSERVE ALL FEDERAL, STATE AND LOCAL REGULATIONS WHEN STORING OR DISPOSING OF THIS SUBSTANCE. FOR ASSISTANCE, CONTACT THE DISTRICT DIRECTOR OF THE ENVIRONMENTAL PROTECTION AGENCY.

****STORAGE****

STORE IN ACCORDANCE WITH 40 CFR 165 RECOMMENDED PROCEDURES FOR THE DISPOSAL AND STORAGE OF PESTICIDES AND PESTICIDE CONTAINERS.
STORE AWAY FROM INCOMPATIBLE SUBSTANCES.

****DISPOSAL****

DISPOSAL MUST BE IN ACCORDANCE WITH 40 CFR 165 RECOMMENDED PROCEDURES FOR THE DISPOSAL AND STORAGE OF PESTICIDES AND PESTICIDE CONTAINERS.

CONDITIONS TO AVOID

MAY BE IGNITED BY HEAT, SPARKS OR FLAMES. CONTAINER MAY EXPLODE IN HEAT OF FIRE. VAPOR EXPLOSION AND POISON HAZARD INDOORS, OUTDOORS OR IN SEWERS.

SPILL AND LEAK PROCEDURES

OCCUPATIONAL SPILL: SHUT OFF IGNITION SOURCES. DO NOT TOUCH SPILLED MATERIAL. STOP LEAK IF YOU CAN DO IT WITHOUT RISK. USE WATER SPRAY TO REDUCE VAPORS. FOR SMALL SPILLS, TAKE UP WITH SAND OR OTHER ABSORBENT MATERIAL AND PLACE INTO CONTAINERS FOR LATER DISPOSAL. FOR SMALL DRY SPILLS, WITH CLEAN SHOVEL PLACE MATERIAL INTO CLEAN, DRY CONTAINERS AND COVER. MOVE CONTAINERS FROM SPILL AREA. FOR LARGER SPILLS, DIKE FAR AHEAD OF SPILL FOR LATER DISPOSAL. NO SMOKING, FLAMES OR FLARES IN HAZARD AREA! KEEP UNNECESSARY PEOPLE AWAY. ISOLATE HAZARD AREA AND DENY ENTRY. VENTILATE CLOSED SPACES BEFORE ENTERING.

PROTECTIVE EQUIPMENT

VENTILATION: PROVIDE LOCAL EXHAUST OR PROCESS ENCLOSURE VENTILATION TO MEET PUBLISHED EXPOSURE LIMITS.

RESPIRATOR: THE FOLLOWING RESPIRATORS ARE RECOMMENDED BASED ON INFORMATION FOUND IN THE PHYSICAL DATA, TOXICITY AND HEALTH EFFECTS SECTIONS. THEY ARE RANKED IN ORDER FROM MINIMUM TO MAXIMUM RESPIRATORY PROTECTION. THE SPECIFIC RESPIRATOR SELECTED MUST BE BASED ON CONTAMINATION LEVELS FOUND IN THE WORK PLACE, MUST NOT EXCEED THE WORKING LIMITS OF THE RESPIRATOR AND BE JOINTLY APPROVED BY THE NATIONAL INSTITUTE FOR OCCUPATIONAL SAFETY AND HEALTH AND THE MINE SAFETY AND HEALTH ADMINISTRATION (NIOSH-MSHA).
TYPE 'C' SUPPLIED-AIR RESPIRATOR WITH A FULL FACEPIECE OPERATED IN PRESSURE-DEMAND OR OTHER POSITIVE PRESSURE MODE OR WITH A FULL FACEPIECE, HELMET OR HOOD OPERATED IN CONTINOUS-FLOW MODE.
SELF-CONTAINED BREATHING APPARATUS WITH A FULL FACEPIECE OPERATED IN PRESSURE-DEMAND OR OTHER POSITIVE PRESSURE MODE.
FOR FIREFIGHTING AND OTHER IMMEDIATELY DANGEROUS TO LIFE OR HEALTH CONDITIONS:
SELF-CONTAINED BREATHING APPARATUS WITH FULL FACEPIECE OPERATED IN PRESSURE-DEMAND OR OTHER POSITIVE PRESSURE MODE.
SUPPLIED-AIR RESPIRATOR WITH FULL FACEPIECE AND OPERATED IN PRESSURE-DEMAND OR OTHER POSITIVE PRESSURE MODE IN COMBINATION WITH AN AUXILIARY SELF-CONTAINED BREATHING APPARATUS OPERATED IN PRESSURE-DEMAND OR OTHER POSITIVE PRESSURE MODE.

CLOTHING: EMPLOYEE MUST WEAR APPROPRIATE PROTECTIVE (IMPERVIOUS) CLOTHING AND EQUIPMENT TO PREVENT ANY POSSIBILITY OF SKIN CONTACT WITH THIS SUBSTANCE.

GLOVES: EMPLOYEE MUST WEAR APPROPRIATE PROTECTIVE GLOVES TO PREVENT CONTACT WITH THIS SUBSTANCE.

EYE PROTECTION: EMPLOYEE MUST WEAR SPLASH-PROOF OR DUST-RESISTANT SAFETY GOGGLES AND A FACESHIELD TO PREVENT CONTACT WITH THIS SUBSTANCE.
EMERGENCY WASH FACILITIES: WHERE THERE IS ANY POSSIBILITY THAT AN EMPLOYEE'S EYES AND/OR SKIN MAY BE EXPOSED TO THIS SUBSTANCE, THE EMPLOYER SHOULD PROVIDE AN EYE WASH FOUNTAIN AND QUICK DRENCH SHOWER WITHIN THE IMMEDIATE WORK AREA FOR EMERGENCY USE.

AUTHORIZED BY- OCCUPATIONAL HEALTH SERVICES, INC.
CREATION DATE: 10/04/89 ***REVISION DATE:*** 05/09/90

MATERIAL SAFETY DATA SHEET

OCCUPATIONAL HEALTH SERVICES, INC.
AGRICULTURE AND PESTICIDE DIVISION
450 SEVENTH AVENUE, SUITE 2407
NEW YORK, NEW YORK 10123
1-800-445-MSDS OR (212) 967-1100

EMERGENCY CONTACT:
JOHN S. BRANSFORD, JR. (615) 292-1180

SUBSTANCE IDENTIFICATION

CAS-NUMBER 6552-12-1
SUBSTANCE: FENTHION OXYGEN ANALOG
TRADE NAMES/SYNONYMS: PHOSPHORIC ACID, DIMETHYL 3-METHYL-4-(METHYLTHIO)PHENYL ESTER; PHOSPHORIC ACID, DIMETHYL 4-(METHYLTHIO)-M-TOLYL ESTER; O,O-DIMETHYL-O-(4-(METHYLTHIO)-M-TOLYL)PHOSPHATE; FENTHION OXON; MERCAPTOPHOS OXON; BAYTEX OXON; ENTEX OXON; TIGUVON OXON; HEBURID OXON; FENOXON; DIMETHYL 3-METHYL-4-(METHYLTHIO)PHENYL PHOSPHATE; DIMETHYL 4-(METHYLTHIO)-M-TOLYL PHOSPHATE; C10H15O4PS; PST02551
CHEMICAL FAMILY: ORGANOPHOSPHATE
MOLECULAR FORMULA: C-H3-S-C6-H3-(C-H3)-O-P-(O)-(O-C-H3)2
MOLECULAR WEIGHT: 262.28
CERCLA RATINGS (SCALE 0-3): HEALTH=3 FIRE=2 REACTIVITY=0 PERSISTENCE=1
NFPA RATINGS (SCALE 0-4): HEALTH=U FIRE=2 REACTIVITY=0

COMPONENTS AND CONTAMINANTS

COMPONENT: FENTHION OXYGEN ANALOG ***PERCENT:*** 100.0
CAS# 6552-12-1
OTHER CONTAMINANTS: NONE
EXPOSURE LIMITS: NO OCCUPATIONAL EXPOSURE LIMITS ESTABLISHED BY OSHA, ACGIH, OR NIOSH.

PHYSICAL DATA

DESCRIPTION: CLEAR LIQUID. ***BOILING POINT:*** NOT AVAILABLE
SPECIFIC GRAVITY: NOT AVAILABLE ***SOLUBILITY IN WATER:*** NOT AVAILABLE

FIRE AND EXPLOSION DATA

FIRE AND EXPLOSION HAZARD: MODERATE FIRE HAZARD WHEN EXPOSED TO HEAT OR FLAME.
FLASH POINT: >180 F (>82 C) (APPROXIMATE)
FIREFIGHTING MEDIA: DRY CHEMICAL, CARBON DIOXIDE, HALON, WATER SPRAY OR STANDARD FOAM (1987 EMERGENCY RESPONSE GUIDEBOOK, DOT P 5800.4). FOR LARGER FIRES, USE WATER SPRAY, FOG OR STANDARD FOAM (1987 EMERGENCY RESPONSE GUIDEBOOK, DOT P 5800.4).
FIREFIGHTING: MOVE CONTAINERS FROM FIRE AREA IF POSSIBLE. FIGHT FIRE FROM MAXIMUM DISTANCE. STAY AWAY FROM STORAGE TANK ENDS. DIKE FIRE CONTROL WATER FOR LATER DISPOSAL. DO NOT SCATTER MATERIAL (1987 EMERGENCY RESPONSE GUIDEBOOK, DOT P 5800.4, GUIDE PAGE 55). EXTINGUISH ONLY IF FLOW CAN BE STOPPED. USE FLOODING AMOUNTS OF WATER AS A FOG; SOLID STREAMS MAY BE INEFFECTIVE. COOL CONTAINERS WITH FLOODING AMOUNTS OF WATER FROM AS FAR A DISTANCE AS POSSIBLE. AVOID BREATHING POISONOUS VAPORS, KEEP UPWIND.

TOXICITY

FENTHION OXYGEN ANALOG: TOXICITY DATA: 125 MG/KG ORAL-RAT LDLO; 130 MG/KG ORAL-MOUSE LD50; 26 MG/KG INTRAPERITONEAL-RAT LD50. CARCINOGEN STATUS: NONE. ACUTE TOXICITY LEVEL: TOXIC BY INGESTION. TARGET EFFECTS: CHOLINESTERASE INHIBITOR. POISONING MAY AFFECT THE NERVOUS SYSTEM.* AT INCREASED RISK FROM EXPOSURE: PERSONS WITH RESPIRATORY AILMENTS, RECENT EXPOSURE TO CHOLINESTERASE INHIBITORS OR IMPAIRED CHOLINESTERASE PRODUCTION, OR LIVER MALFUNCTION.* ADDITIONAL DATA: MAY CROSS THE PLACENTA. HIGH ENVIRONMENTAL TEMPERATURES OR EXPOSURE OF THE CHEMICAL TO VISIBLE OR ULTRAVIOLET LIGHT MAY ENHANCE THE TOXICITY. INTERACTIONS WITH MEDICATIONS MAY OCCUR.*
* MAY BE BASED ON GENERAL INFORMATION ON ORGANOPHOSPHATES.

HEALTH EFFECTS AND FIRST AID

INHALATION: FENTHION OXYGEN ANALOG: SEE INFORMATION ON ORGANOPHOSPHATES.
ORGANOPHOSPHATES: CHOLINESTERASE INHIBITOR. **ACUTE EXPOSURE-** WHEN INHALED, THE FIRST EFFECTS OF CHOLINESTERASE INHIBITORS ARE USUALLY RESPIRATORY AND MAY INCLUDE NASAL HYPEREMIA AND WATERY DISCHARGE, COUGH, CHEST DISCOMFORT, DYSPNEA, AND WHEEZING DUE TO INCREASED BRONCHIAL SECRETIONS AND BRONCHOCONSTRICTION. IF SUFFICIENT AMOUNTS ARE ABSORBED, OTHER SYSTEMIC EFFECTS MAY BEGIN WITHIN A FEW MINUTES OR BE DELAYED FOR UP TO 12 HOURS. SYMPTOMS MAY INCLUDE PALLOR, NAUSEA, VOMITING, DIARRHEA, ABDOMINAL CRAMPS, HEADACHE, DIZZINESS, OCULAR PAIN, BLURRED VISION, MIOSIS OR IN SOME CASES, ESPECIALLY INITIALLY, MYDRIASIS, LACRIMATION, SALIVATION, SWEATING, AND CONFUSION. OTHER REPORTED CENTRAL NERVOUS SYSTEM OR NEUROMUSCULAR EFFECTS MAY INCLUDE ATAXIA, SLURRED SPEECH, AREFLEXIA, WEAKNESS, FATIGUE, FASCICULATIONS, TWITCHING, TREMORS POSSIBLY OF THE TONGUE AND EYELIDS, AND EVENTUALLY PARALYSIS OF THE EXTREMITIES AND POSSIBLY OF THE RESPIRATORY MUSCLES. IN SEVERE CASES THERE MAY ALSO BE INVOLUNTARY DEFECATION AND URINATION, CYANOSIS, PSYCHOSIS, HYPERGLYCEMIA, ACUTE PANCREATITIS, CARDIAC IRREGULARITIES, PULMONARY EDEMA, UNCONSCIOUSNESS, CONVULSIONS, AND COMA. DEATH IS PRIMARILY DUE TO RESPIRATORY FAILURE, ALTHOUGH CARDIOVASCULAR EFFECTS INCLUDING CARDIAC ARREST MAY ALSO BE IMPLICATED. LONG TERM SEQUELAE ARE RARE BUT MAY INCLUDE NEUROPSYCHIATRIC DISORDERS AND MYOPATHY WITH MUSCLE TENDERNESS. SOME ORGANOPHOSPHATES MAY CAUSE A DELAYED NEUROPATHY BEGINNING 1-4 WEEKS AFTER AN ACUTE EXPOSURE WHICH MAY OR MAY NOT HAVE CAUSED ACUTE CHOLINERGIC EFFECTS. NUMBNESS, TINGLING, WEAKNESS AND CRAMPING BEGINNING SYMMETRICALLY IN THE LOWER LIMBS MAY PROGRESS TO ATAXIA AND PARALYSIS. IN SEVERE CASES, UPPER LIMB INVOLVEMENT IS POSSIBLE AND FLACCID PARALYSIS MAY PROGRESS TO SPASTIC PARALYSIS WITH EXAGGERATED REFLEXES. IMPROVEMENT MAY OCCUR OVER MONTHS TO YEARS, BUT SOME RESIDUAL IMPAIRMENT USUALLY REMAINS. **CHRONIC EXPOSURE-** REPEATED OR PROLONGED EXPOSURE MAY RESULT IN THE EFFECTS OF ACUTE EXPOSURE INCLUDING THE DELAYED NEUROPATHY. OTHER EFFECTS REPORTED IN WORKERS REPEATEDLY EXPOSED INCLUDE IMPAIRED MEMORY AND CONCENTRATION, ACUTE PSYCHOSIS, SEVERE DEPRESSIONS, IRRITABILTY, CONFUSION, APATHY, EMOTIONAL LABILITY, SOCIAL WITHDRAWAL, CONFUSION, HEADACHE, SPEECH DIFFICULTIES, DELAYED REACTION TIMES, SPATIAL DISORIENTATION, NIGHTMARES, SLEEPWALKING, AND DROWSINESS OR INSOMNIA. AN INFLUENZA-LIKE CONDITION WITH HEADACHE, NAUSEA, WEAKNESS, ANOREXIA AND MALAISE HAS ALSO BEEN REPORTED.
FIRST AID- REMOVE FROM EXPOSURE AREA TO FRESH AIR IMMEDIATELY. IF BREATHING HAS STOPPED, GIVE ARTIFICIAL RESPIRATION. MAINTAIN AIRWAY AND BLOOD PRESSURE AND ADMINISTER OXYGEN IF AVAILABLE. KEEP AFFECTED PERSON WARM AND AT REST. TREAT SYMPTOMATICALLY AND SUPPORTIVELY. ADMINISTRATION OF OXYGEN SHOULD BE PERFORMED BY QUALIFIED PERSONNEL. GET MEDICAL ATTENTION IMMEDIATELY.

SKIN CONTACT: FENTHION OXYGEN ANALOG: SEE INFORMATION ON ORGANOPHOSPHATES.
ORGANOPHOSPHATES: CHOLINESTERASE INHIBITOR. **ACUTE EXPOSURE-** LOCALIZED SWEATING AND FASCICULATIONS MAY OCCUR AT THE SITE OF CONTACT. IF SUFFICIENT AMOUNTS ARE ABSORBED, OTHER EFFECTS OF CHOLINESTERASE INHIBITION AS DESCRIBED IN ACUTE INHALATION MAY OCCUR. SYMPTOMS MAY BE DELAYED 2-3 HOURS, BUT USUALLY NO MORE THAN 12 HOURS. THE RATE OF ABSORPTION IS INCREASED BY THE PRESENCE OF DERMATITIS OR HIGH AMBIENT TEMPERATURES. DELAYED NEUROPATHY IS ALSO POSSIBLE. **CHRONIC EXPOSURE-** REPEATED OR PROLONGED EXPOSURE MAY CAUSE EFFECTS AS DESCRIBED IN ACUTE EXPOSURE. SOME ORGANOPHOSPHATES MAY CAUSE SENSITIZATION.
FIRST AID- REMOVE CONTAMINATED CLOTHING IMMEDIATELY. WASH CONTAMINATED AREAS WITH SOAP AND WATER FOLLOWED BY ALCOHOL (ARENA, POISONING, 4TH ED.). EMERGENCY PERSONNEL SHOULD WEAR GLOVES AND AVOID CONTAMINATION. TREAT RESPIRATORY DIFFICULTY WITH ARTIFICIAL RESPIRATION. GET MEDICAL ATTENTION IMMEDIATELY.

EYE CONTACT: FENTHION OXYGEN ANALOG: SEE INFORMATION ON ORGANOPHOSPHATES. ORGANOPHOSPHATES: CHOLINESTERASE INHIBITOR. **ACUTE EXPOSURE-** DIRECT CONTACT MAY CAUSE PAIN, HYPEREMIA, LACRIMATION, TWITCHING OF THE EYELIDS, MIOSIS, AND CILIARY MUSCLE SPASM WITH LOSS OF ACCOMODATION, BLURRED OR DIMMED VISION AND BROWACHE. SOMETIMES MYDRIASIS MAY OCCUR INSTEAD OF MIOSIS. WITH SUFFICIENT EXPOSURE, OTHER SYMPTOMS OF CHOLINESTERASE INHIBITION AS DESCRIBED IN ACUTE INHALATION MAY OCCUR. **CHRONIC EXPOSURE-** REPEATED OR PROLONGED EXPOSURE MAY CAUSE EFFECTS AS DESCRIBED IN ACUTE EXPOSURE. SOME COMPOUNDS HAVE CAUSED TOXIC EFFECTS ON THE CRYSTALLINE LENS, CONJUNCTIVAL THICKENING AND OBSTRUCTION OF THE NASOLACRIMAL CANALS WHEN USED AS MIOTIC EYEDROPS.

FIRST AID- IRRIGATE EYES WITH WATER OR SALINE SOLUTION. IF SYMPTOMS OF POISONING OCCUR, TREAT RESPIRATORY DIFFICULTY WITH ARTIFICIAL RESPIRATION AND OXYGEN. OBSERVE PATIENT FOR AT LEAST 24-36 HOURS (GOSSELIN, CLINICAL TOXICOLOGY OF COMMERCIAL PRODUCTS, 5TH ED.). GET MEDICAL ATTENTION IMMEDIATELY. OXYGEN SHOULD BE ADMINISTERED BY QUALIFIED MEDICAL PERSONNEL.

INGESTION: FENTHION OXYGEN ANALOG: TOXIC. SEE INFORMATION ON ORGANOPHOSPHATES.
ORGANOPHOSPHATES: CHOLINESTERASE INHIBITOR. **ACUTE EXPOSURE**- WHEN INGESTED, THE FIRST EFFECTS MAY BE NAUSEA, VOMITING, ANOREXIA, ABDOMINAL CRAMPS AND DIARRHEA. GASTROINTESTINAL ABSORPTION MAY CAUSE SYMPTOMS OF CHOLINESTERASE INHIBITION AS DESCRIBED IN ACUTE INHALATION. SYMPTOMS MAY BEGIN WITHIN MINUTES OR BE DELAYED FOR HOURS. DELAYED EFFECTS INCLUDING NEUROPATHY MAY ALSO OCCUR. **CHRONIC EXPOSURE**- REPEATED INGESTION MAY CAUSE EFFECTS AS DESCRIBED IN ACUTE EXPOSURE.

FIRST AID- IF PERSON IS ALERT AND RESPIRATION IS NOT DEPRESSED, GIVE SYRUP OF IPECAC FOLLOWED BY WATER (IF VOMITING OCCURS, KEEP HEAD BELOW HIPS TO PREVENT ASPIRATION). IF CONSCIOUSNESS LEVEL DECLINES OR VOMITING HAS NOT OCCURRED IN 15 MINUTES EMPTY STOMACH BY GASTRIC LAVAGE WITH THE AID OF CUFFED ENDOTRACHEAL TUBE USING ISOTONIC SALINE OR 5% SODIUM BICARBONATE FOLLOW WITH ACTIVATED CHARCOAL. ESTABLISH AND MAINTAIN AIRWAY. TREAT RESPIRATORY DIFFICULTY WITH ARTIFICIAL RESPIRATION AND OXYGEN. DO NOT GIVE MORPHINE, AMINOPHYLLINE, PHENOTHIAZINES, RESERPINE, FUROSEMIDE, OR ETHACRYNIC ACID (MORGAN, RECOGNITION AND MANAGEMENT OF PESTICIDE POISONINGS, 3RD ED.). TREAT SYMPTOMATICALLY AND SUPPORTIVELY. ADMINISTRATION OF OXYGEN AND LAVAGE MUST BE PERFORMED BY QUALIFIED MEDICAL PERSONNEL. GET MEDICAL ATTENTION IMMEDIATELY.

ANTIDOTE: THE FOLLOWING ANTIDOTE(S) HAVE BEEN RECOMMENDED. HOWEVER, THE DECISION AS TO WHETHER THE SEVERITY OF POISONING REQUIRES ADMINISTRATION OF ANY ANTIDOTE AND ACTUAL DOSE REQUIRED SHOULD BE MADE BY QUALIFIED MEDICAL PERSONNEL.
FOR CHOLINESTERASE INHIBITORS: ESTABLISH CLEAR AIRWAY AND TISSUE OXYGENATION BY ASPIRATION OF SECRETIONS, AND IF NECESSARY, BY ASSISTED PULMONARY VENTILATION WITH OXYGEN. IMPROVE TISSUE OXYGENATION AS MUCH AS POSSIBLE BEFORE ADMINISTERING ATROPINE TO MINIMIZE THE RISK OF VENTRICULAR FIBRILLATION. ADMINISTER ATROPINE SULFATE INTRAVENOUSLY, OR INTRAMUSCULARLY IF IV INJECTION IS NOT POSSIBLE. IN MODERATELY SEVERE POISONING ADMINISTER ATROPINE SULFATE, 0.4-2.0 MG REPEATED EVERY 15 MINUTES UNTIL ATROPINIZATION IS ACHIEVED (TACHYCARDIA, FLUSHING, DRY MOUTH, MYDRIASIS). MAINTAIN ATROPINIZATION BY REPEATED DOSES FOR 2-12 HOURS, OR LONGER, DEPENDING ON THE SEVERITY OF POISONING. THE APPEARANCE OF RALES IN THE LUNG BASES, MIOSIS, SALIVATION, NAUSEA, BRADYCARDIA, ARE ALL INDICATIONS OF INADEQUATE ATROPINIZATION. SEVERELY POISONED INDIVIDUALS MAY EXHIBIT REMARKABLE TOLERANCE TO ATROPINE; TWO OR MORE TIMES THE DOSAGES SUGGESTED ABOVE MAY BE NEEDED. PERSONS NOT POISONED OR ONLY SLIGHTLY POISONED, HOWEVER, MAY DEVELOP SIGNS OF ATROPINE TOXICITY FROM SUCH LARGE DOSAGES: FEVER, MUSCLE FIBRILLATIONS, AND DELIRIUM ARE THE MAIN SIGNS OF ATROPINE TOXICITY. IF THESE SIGNS APPEAR WHILE THE PATIENT IS FULLY ATROPINIZED, ATROPINE ADMINISTRATION SHOULD BE DISCONTINUED, AT LEAST TEMPORARILY. OBSERVE TREATED PATIENTS CLOSELY AT LEAST 24 HOURS TO INSURE THAT SYMPTOMS (POSSIBLY PULMONARY EDEMA) DO NOT RECUR AS ATROPINIZATION WEARS OFF. IN VERY SEVERE POISONINGS, METABOLIC DISPOSITION OF TOXICANT MAY REQUIRE SEVERAL HOURS OR DAYS DURING WHICH ATROPINIZATION MUST BE MAINTAINED. MARKEDLY LOWER LEVELS OF URINARY METABOLITES INDICATE THAT ATROPINE DOSAGE CAN BE TAPERED OFF. AS DOSAGE IS REDUCED, CHECK THE LUNG BASES FREQUENTLY FOR RALES. IF RALES ARE HEARD OR OTHER SYMPTOMS RETURN, RE-ESTABLISH ATROPINIZATION PROMPTLY (MORGAN, RECOGNITION AND MANAGEMENT OF PESTICIDE POISONINGS, 3RD ED.). ADMINISTRATION OF ANTIDOTE MUST BE PERFORMED BY QUALIFIED MEDICAL PERSONNEL.
IN CASES OF SEVERE POISONING BY ORGANOPHOSPHATE PESTICIDES IN WHICH RESPIRATORY DEPRESSION, MUSCLE WEAKNESS AND TWITCHINGS ARE SEVERE, GIVE PRALIDOXIME (PROTOPAM-AYERST, 2-PAM), 1.0 GRAM INTRAVENOUSLY AT NO MORE THAN 0.5 GRAM PER MINUTE. DOSAGE OF PRALIDOXIME MAY BE REPEATED IN 1-2 HOURS, THEN AT 10-12 HOUR INTERVALS IF NEEDED. IN VERY SEVERE POISONINGS, DOSAGE RATES MAY BE DOUBLED. TREATMENT WITH PRALIDOXIME WILL BE MOST EFFECTIVE IF GIVEN WITHIN THIRTY-SIX HOURS AFTER POISONING (MORGAN, RECOGNITION AND MANAGEMENT OF PESTICIDE POISONINGS, 3RD ED.). ANTIDOTE SHOULD BE ADMINISTERED BY QUALIFIED MEDICAL PERSONNEL.

REACTIVITY

REACTIVITY: STABLE UNDER NORMAL TEMPERATURES AND PRESSURES.

INCOMPATIBILITIES: FENTHION OXYGEN ANALOG: OXIDIZERS (STRONG): FIRE AND EXPLOSION HAZARD.

DECOMPOSITION: THERMAL DECOMPOSITION PRODUCTS MAY INCLUDE TOXIC OXIDES OF CARBON, SULFUR, AND PHOSPHORUS.

POLYMERIZATION: HAZARDOUS POLYMERIZATION HAS NOT BEEN REPORTED TO OCCUR UNDER NORMAL TEMPERATURES AND PRESSURES.

STORAGE AND DISPOSAL

OBSERVE ALL FEDERAL, STATE AND LOCAL REGULATIONS WHEN STORING OR DISPOSING OF THIS SUBSTANCE. FOR ASSISTANCE, CONTACT THE DISTRICT DIRECTOR OF THE ENVIRONMENTAL PROTECTION AGENCY.

****STORAGE****

STORE AWAY FROM INCOMPATIBLE SUBSTANCES.
STORE IN ACCORDANCE WITH 40 CFR 165 RECOMMENDED PROCEDURES FOR THE DISPOSAL AND STORAGE OF PESTICIDES AND PESTICIDE CONTAINERS.

****DISPOSAL****

DISPOSAL MUST BE IN ACCORDANCE WITH 40 CFR 165 RECOMMENDED PROCEDURES FOR THE DISPOSAL AND STORAGE OF PESTICIDES AND PESTICIDE CONTAINERS.

CONDITIONS TO AVOID

MAY BE IGNITED BY HEAT, SPARKS OR FLAMES. CONTAINER MAY EXPLODE IN HEAT OF FIRE. VAPOR EXPLOSION AND POISON HAZARD INDOORS, OUTDOORS OR IN SEWERS.

SPILL AND LEAK PROCEDURES

OCCUPATIONAL SPILL: SHUT OFF IGNITION SOURCES. DO NOT TOUCH SPILLED MATERIAL. STOP LEAK IF YOU CAN DO IT WITHOUT RISK. USE WATER SPRAY TO REDUCE VAPORS. FOR SMALL SPILLS, TAKE UP WITH SAND OR OTHER ABSORBENT MATERIAL AND PLACE INTO CONTAINERS FOR LATER DISPOSAL. FOR SMALL DRY SPILLS, WITH CLEAN SHOVEL PLACE MATERIAL INTO CLEAN, DRY CONTAINERS AND COVER. MOVE CONTAINERS FROM SPILL AREA. FOR LARGER SPILLS, DIKE FAR AHEAD OF SPILL FOR LATER DISPOSAL. NO SMOKING, FLAMES OR FLARES IN HAZARD AREA! KEEP UNNECESSARY PEOPLE AWAY. ISOLATE HAZARD AREA AND DENY ENTRY. VENTILATE CLOSED SPACES BEFORE ENTERING.

PROTECTIVE EQUIPMENT

VENTILATION: PROVIDE LOCAL EXHAUST OR PROCESS ENCLOSURE VENTILATION SYSTEM.

RESPIRATOR: THE FOLLOWING RESPIRATORS ARE RECOMMENDED BASED ON INFORMATION FOUND IN THE PHYSICAL DATA, TOXICITY AND HEALTH EFFECTS SECTIONS. THEY ARE RANKED IN ORDER FROM MINIMUM TO MAXIMUM RESPIRATORY PROTECTION. THE SPECIFIC RESPIRATOR SELECTED MUST BE BASED ON CONTAMINATION LEVELS FOUND IN THE WORK PLACE, MUST NOT EXCEED THE WORKING LIMITS OF THE RESPIRATOR AND BE JOINTLY APPROVED BY THE NATIONAL INSTITUTE FOR OCCUPATIONAL SAFETY AND HEALTH AND THE MINE SAFETY AND HEALTH ADMINISTRATION (NIOSH-MSHA).
TYPE 'C' SUPPLIED-AIR RESPIRATOR WITH A FULL FACEPIECE OPERATED IN PRESSURE-DEMAND OR OTHER POSITIVE PRESSURE MODE OR WITH A FULL FACEPIECE, HELMET OR HOOD OPERATED IN CONTINOUS-FLOW MODE.
SELF-CONTAINED BREATHING APPARATUS WITH A FULL FACEPIECE OPERATED IN PRESSURE-DEMAND OR OTHER POSITIVE PRESSURE MODE.
FOR FIREFIGHTING AND OTHER IMMEDIATELY DANGEROUS TO LIFE OR HEALTH CONDITIONS:
SELF-CONTAINED BREATHING APPARATUS WITH FULL FACEPIECE OPERATED IN PRESSURE-DEMAND OR OTHER POSITIVE PRESSURE MODE.
SUPPLIED-AIR RESPIRATOR WITH FULL FACEPIECE AND OPERATED IN PRESSURE-DEMAND OR OTHER POSITIVE PRESSURE MODE IN COMBINATION WITH AN AUXILIARY SELF-CONTAINED BREATHING APPARATUS OPERATED IN PRESSURE-DEMAND OR OTHER POSITIVE PRESSURE MODE.

CLOTHING: EMPLOYEE MUST WEAR APPROPRIATE PROTECTIVE (IMPERVIOUS) CLOTHING AND EQUIPMENT TO PREVENT ANY POSSIBILITY OF SKIN CONTACT WITH THIS SUBSTANCE.

GLOVES: EMPLOYEE MUST WEAR APPROPRIATE PROTECTIVE GLOVES TO PREVENT CONTACT WITH THIS SUBSTANCE.

EYE PROTECTION: EMPLOYEE MUST WEAR SPLASH-PROOF OR DUST-RESISTANT SAFETY GOGGLES AND A FACESHIELD TO PREVENT CONTACT WITH THIS SUBSTANCE.
EMERGENCY WASH FACILITIES: WHERE THERE IS ANY POSSIBILITY THAT AN EMPLOYEE'S EYES AND/OR SKIN MAY BE EXPOSED TO THIS SUBSTANCE, THE EMPLOYER SHOULD PROVIDE AN EYE WASH FOUNTAIN AND QUICK DRENCH SHOWER WITHIN THE IMMEDIATE WORK AREA FOR EMERGENCY USE.

AUTHORIZED BY- OCCUPATIONAL HEALTH SERVICES, INC.
CREATION DATE: 10/04/89 ***REVISION DATE:*** 04/27/90

MATERIAL SAFETY DATA SHEET

OCCUPATIONAL HEALTH SERVICES, INC.
AGRICULTURE AND PESTICIDE DIVISION
450 SEVENTH AVENUE, SUITE 2407
NEW YORK, NEW YORK 10123
1-800-445-MSDS OR (212) 967-1100

EMERGENCY CONTACT:
JOHN S. BRANSFORD, JR. (615) 292-1180

SUBSTANCE IDENTIFICATION

CAS-NUMBER 14086-35-2

SUBSTANCE: FENTHION OXON SULFONE

TRADE NAMES/SYNONYMS: PHOSPHORIC ACID, DIMETHYL 3-METHYL-4-(METHYLSULFINYL)PHENYL ESTER; PHOSPHORIC ACID, DIMETHYL 4-(METHYLSULFONYL)-M-TOLYL ESTER; FENOXON SULFONE; FENTHION O-ANALOG SULFONE; O,O-DIMETHYL-O-(4-(METHYLSULFONYL)-M-TOLYL)PHOSPHATE; MERCAPTOPHOS OXON SULFONE; TIGUVON OXON SULFONE; HEBACID OXON SULFONE; BAYTEX OXON SULFONE; ENTEX OXON SULFONE; DIMETHYL 3-METHYL-4-(METHYLSULFINYL)PHENYL PHOSPHOROTHIOATE; DIMETHYL 4-(METHYLSULFONYL)-M-TOLYL PHOSPHOROTHIOATE; C10H15O6PS; PST02552

CHEMICAL FAMILY: ORGANOPHOSPHATE SULFONE

MOLECULAR FORMULA: C-H3-S-O2-C6-H3-(C-H3)-O-P-(O)-(O-C-H3)2

MOLECULAR WEIGHT: 294.27

CERCLA RATINGS (SCALE 0-3): HEALTH=3 FIRE=1 REACTIVITY=0 PERSISTENCE=1

NFPA RATINGS (SCALE 0-4): HEALTH=3 FIRE=1 REACTIVITY=0

COMPONENTS AND CONTAMINANTS

COMPONENT: FENTHION OXON SULFONE ***PERCENT:*** 100.0
CAS# 14086-35-2

OTHER CONTAMINANTS: NONE

EXPOSURE LIMITS: NO OCCUPATIONAL EXPOSURE LIMITS ESTABLISHED BY OSHA, ACGIH, OR NIOSH.

PHYSICAL DATA

DESCRIPTION: WHITE POWDER. ***MELTING POINT:*** NOT AVAILABLE

SPECIFIC GRAVITY: NOT AVAILABLE ***SOLUBILITY IN WATER:*** NOT AVAILABLE

FIRE AND EXPLOSION DATA

FIRE AND EXPLOSION HAZARD: SLIGHT FIRE HAZARD WHEN EXPOSED TO HEAT OR FLAME.

FIREFIGHTING MEDIA: DRY CHEMICAL, CARBON DIOXIDE, HALON, WATER SPRAY OR STANDARD FOAM (1987 EMERGENCY RESPONSE GUIDEBOOK, DOT P 5800.4).
FOR LARGER FIRES, USE WATER SPRAY, FOG OR STANDARD FOAM (1987 EMERGENCY RESPONSE GUIDEBOOK, DOT P 5800.4).

FIREFIGHTING: MOVE CONTAINERS FROM FIRE AREA IF POSSIBLE (1987 EMERGENCY RESPONSE GUIDEBOOK, DOT P 5800.4, GUIDE PAGE 53).
EXTINGUISH USING AGENT SUITABLE FOR TYPE OF SURROUNDING FIRE. AVOID BREATHING VAPORS AND DUSTS. KEEP UPWIND.

TRANSPORTATION DATA

DEPARTMENT OF TRANSPORTATION HAZARD CLASSIFICATION 49 CFR 172.101: POISON B
DEPARTMENT OF TRANSPORTATION LABELING REQUIREMENTS 49 CFR 172.101 AND SUBPART E: POISON
DEPARTMENT OF TRANSPORTATION PACKAGING REQUIREMENTS: 49 CFR 173.365 EXCEPTIONS: 49 CFR 173.364

TOXICITY

FENTHION OXON SULFONE: TOXICITY DATA: 30 MG/KG ORAL-RAT LD50; 9 MG/KG INTRAPERITONEAL-RAT LD50. CARCINOGEN STATUS: NONE. ACUTE TOXICITY LEVEL: HIGHLY TOXIC BY INGESTION. TARGET EFFECTS: CHOLINESTERASE INHIBITOR. POISONING MAY AFFECT THE NERVOUS SYSTEM.* AT INCREASED RISK FROM EXPOSURE: PERSONS WITH RESPIRATORY AILMENTS, RECENT EXPOSURE TO CHOLINESTERASE INHIBITORS OR IMPAIRED CHOLINESTERASE PRODUCTION, OR LIVER MALFUNCTION.* ADDITIONAL DATA: MAY CROSS THE PLACENTA. HIGH ENVIRONMENTAL TEMPERATURES OR EXPOSURE OF THE CHEMICAL TO VISIBLE OR ULTRAVIOLET LIGHT MAY ENHANCE THE TOXICITY. INTERACTIONS WITH MEDICATIONS MAY OCCUR.*
* MAY BE BASED ON GENERAL INFORMATION ON ORGANOPHOSPHATES.

HEALTH EFFECTS AND FIRST AID

INHALATION: FENTHION OXON SULFONE: SEE INFORMATION ON ORGANOPHOSPHATES.
ORGANOPHOSPHATES: CHOLINESTERASE INHIBITOR. **ACUTE EXPOSURE**- WHEN INHALED, THE FIRST EFFECTS OF CHOLINESTERASE INHIBITORS ARE USUALLY RESPIRATORY AND MAY INCLUDE NASAL HYPEREMIA AND WATERY DISCHARGE, COUGH, CHEST DISCOMFORT, DYSPNEA, AND WHEEZING DUE TO INCREASED BRONCHIAL SECRETIONS AND BRONCHOCONSTRICTION. IF SUFFICIENT AMOUNTS ARE ABSORBED, OTHER SYSTEMIC EFFECTS MAY BEGIN WITHIN A FEW MINUTES OR BE DELAYED FOR UP TO 12 HOURS. SYMPTOMS MAY INCLUDE PALLOR, NAUSEA, VOMITING, DIARRHEA, ABDOMINAL CRAMPS, HEADACHE, DIZZINESS, OCULAR PAIN, BLURRED VISION, MIOSIS OR IN SOME CASES, ESPECIALLY INITIALLY, MYDRIASIS, LACRIMATION, SALIVATION, SWEATING, AND CONFUSION. OTHER REPORTED CENTRAL NERVOUS SYSTEM OR NEUROMUSCULAR EFFECTS MAY INCLUDE ATAXIA, SLURRED SPEECH, AREFLEXIA, WEAKNESS, FATIGUE, FASCICULATIONS, TWITCHING, TREMORS POSSIBLY OF THE TONGUE AND EYELIDS, AND EVENTUALLY PARALYSIS OF THE EXTREMITIES AND POSSIBLY OF THE RESPIRATORY MUSCLES. IN SEVERE CASES THERE MAY ALSO BE INVOLUNTARY DEFECATION AND URINATION, CYANOSIS, PSYCHOSIS, HYPERGLYCEMIA, ACUTE PANCREATITIS, CARDIAC IRREGULARITIES, PULMONARY EDEMA, UNCONSCIOUSNESS, CONVULSIONS, AND COMA. DEATH IS PRIMARILY DUE TO RESPIRATORY FAILURE, ALTHOUGH CARDIOVASCULAR EFFECTS INCLUDING CARDIAC ARREST MAY ALSO BE IMPLICATED. LONG TERM SEQUELAE ARE RARE BUT MAY INCLUDE NEUROPSYCHIATRIC DISORDERS AND MYOPATHY WITH MUSCLE TENDERNESS. SOME ORGANOPHOSPHATES MAY CAUSE A DELAYED NEUROPATHY BEGINNING 1-4 WEEKS AFTER AN ACUTE EXPOSURE WHICH MAY OR MAY NOT HAVE CAUSED ACUTE CHOLINERGIC EFFECTS. NUMBNESS, TINGLING, WEAKNESS AND CRAMPING BEGINNING SYMMETRICALLY IN THE LOWER LIMBS MAY PROGRESS TO ATAXIA AND PARALYSIS. IN SEVERE CASES, UPPER LIMB INVOLVEMENT IS POSSIBLE AND FLACCID PARALYSIS MAY PROGRESS TO SPASTIC PARALYSIS WITH EXAGGERATED REFLEXES. IMPROVEMENT MAY OCCUR OVER MONTHS TO YEARS, BUT SOME RESIDUAL IMPAIRMENT USUALLY REMAINS.
CHRONIC EXPOSURE- REPEATED OR PROLONGED EXPOSURE MAY RESULT IN THE EFFECTS OF ACUTE EXPOSURE INCLUDING THE DELAYED NEUROPATHY. OTHER EFFECTS REPORTED IN WORKERS REPEATEDLY EXPOSED INCLUDE IMPAIRED MEMORY AND CONCENTRATION, ACUTE PSYCHOSIS, SEVERE DEPRESSIONS, IRRITABILTY, CONFUSION, APATHY, EMOTIONAL LABILITY, SOCIAL WITHDRAWAL, CONFUSION, HEADACHE, SPEECH DIFFICULTIES, DELAYED REACTION TIMES, SPATIAL DISORIENTATION, NIGHTMARES, SLEEPWALKING, AND DROWSINESS OR INSOMNIA. AN INFLUENZA-LIKE CONDITION WITH HEADACHE, NAUSEA, WEAKNESS, ANOREXIA AND MALAISE HAS ALSO BEEN REPORTED.

FIRST AID- REMOVE FROM EXPOSURE AREA TO FRESH AIR IMMEDIATELY. IF BREATHING HAS STOPPED, GIVE ARTIFICIAL RESPIRATION. MAINTAIN AIRWAY AND BLOOD PRESSURE AND ADMINISTER OXYGEN IF AVAILABLE. KEEP AFFECTED PERSON WARM AND AT REST. TREAT SYMPTOMATICALLY AND SUPPORTIVELY. ADMINISTRATION OF OXYGEN SHOULD BE PERFORMED BY QUALIFIED PERSONNEL. GET MEDICAL ATTENTION IMMEDIATELY.

SKIN CONTACT: FENTHION OXON SULFONE: SEE INFORMATION ON ORGANOPHOSPHATES.
ORGANOPHOSPHATES: CHOLINESTERASE INHIBITOR. **ACUTE EXPOSURE**- LOCALIZED SWEATING AND FASCICULATIONS MAY OCCUR AT THE SITE OF CONTACT. IF SUFFICIENT AMOUNTS ARE ABSORBED, OTHER EFFECTS OF CHOLINESTERASE INHIBITION AS DESCRIBED IN ACUTE INHALATION MAY OCCUR. SYMPTOMS MAY BE DELAYED 2-3 HOURS, BUT USUALLY NO MORE THAN 12 HOURS. THE RATE OF ABSORPTION IS INCREASED BY THE PRESENCE OF DERMATITIS OR HIGH AMBIENT TEMPERATURES. DELAYED NEUROPATHY IS ALSO POSSIBLE. **CHRONIC EXPOSURE**- REPEATED OR PROLONGED EXPOSURE MAY CAUSE EFFECTS AS DESCRIBED IN ACUTE EXPOSURE. SOME ORGANOPHOSPHATES MAY CAUSE SENSITIZATION.

FIRST AID- REMOVE CONTAMINATED CLOTHING IMMEDIATELY. WASH CONTAMINATED AREAS WITH SOAP AND WATER FOLLOWED BY ALCOHOL (ARENA, POISONING, 4TH ED.). EMERGENCY PERSONNEL SHOULD WEAR GLOVES AND AVOID CONTAMINATION. TREAT RESPIRATORY DIFFICULTY WITH ARTIFICIAL RESPIRATION. GET MEDICAL ATTENTION IMMEDIATELY.

EYE CONTACT: FENTHION OXON SULFONE: SEE INFORMATION ON ORGANOPHOSPHATES.
ORGANOPHOSPHATES: CHOLINESTERASE INHIBITOR. **ACUTE EXPOSURE**- DIRECT CONTACT MAY CAUSE PAIN, HYPEREMIA, LACRIMATION, TWITCHING OF THE EYELIDS, MIOSIS, AND CILIARY MUSCLE SPASM WITH LOSS OF ACCOMODATION, BLURRED OR DIMMED VISION AND BROWACHE. SOMETIMES MYDRIASIS MAY OCCUR INSTEAD OF MIOSIS. WITH SUFFICIENT EXPOSURE, OTHER SYMPTOMS OF CHOLINESTERASE INHIBITION AS DESCRIBED IN ACUTE INHALATION MAY OCCUR. **CHRONIC EXPOSURE**- REPEATED OR PROLONGED EXPOSURE MAY CAUSE EFFECTS AS DESCRIBED IN ACUTE EXPOSURE. SOME COMPOUNDS HAVE CAUSED TOXIC

EFFECTS ON THE CRYSTALLINE LENS, CONJUNCTIVAL THICKENING AND OBSTRUCTION OF THE NASOLACRIMAL CANALS WHEN USED AS MIOTIC EYEDROPS.

FIRST AID- IRRIGATE EYES WITH WATER OR SALINE SOLUTION. IF SYMPTOMS OF POISONING OCCUR, TREAT RESPIRATORY DIFFICULTY WITH ARTIFICIAL RESPIRATION AND OXYGEN. OBSERVE PATIENT FOR AT LEAST 24-36 HOURS (GOSSELIN, CLINICAL TOXICOLOGY OF COMMERCIAL PRODUCTS, 5TH ED.). GET MEDICAL ATTENTION IMMEDIATELY. OXYGEN SHOULD BE ADMINISTERED BY QUALIFIED MEDICAL PERSONNEL.

INGESTION: FENTHION OXON SULFONE: HIGHLY TOXIC. SEE INFORMATION ON ORGANOPHOSPHATES.

ORGANOPHOSPHATES: CHOLINESTERASE INHIBITOR. **ACUTE EXPOSURE**- WHEN INGESTED, THE FIRST EFFECTS MAY BE NAUSEA, VOMITING, ANOREXIA, ABDOMINAL CRAMPS AND DIARRHEA. GASTROINTESTINAL ABSORPTION MAY CAUSE SYMPTOMS OF CHOLINESTERASE INHIBITION AS DESCRIBED IN ACUTE INHALATION. SYMPTOMS MAY BEGIN WITHIN MINUTES OR BE DELAYED FOR HOURS. DELAYED EFFECTS INCLUDING NEUROPATHY MAY ALSO OCCUR. **CHRONIC EXPOSURE**- REPEATED INGESTION MAY CAUSE EFFECTS AS DESCRIBED IN ACUTE EXPOSURE.

FIRST AID- IF PERSON IS ALERT AND RESPIRATION IS NOT DEPRESSED, GIVE SYRUP OF IPECAC FOLLOWED BY WATER (IF VOMITING OCCURS, KEEP HEAD BELOW HIPS TO PREVENT ASPIRATION). IF CONSCIOUSNESS LEVEL DECLINES OR VOMITING HAS NOT OCCURRED IN 15 MINUTES EMPTY STOMACH BY GASTRIC LAVAGE WITH THE AID OF CUFFED ENDOTRACHEAL TUBE USING ISOTONIC SALINE OR 5% SODIUM BICARBONATE FOLLOW WITH ACTIVATED CHARCOAL. ESTABLISH AND MAINTAIN AIRWAY. TREAT RESPIRATORY DIFFICULTY WITH ARTIFICIAL RESPIRATION AND. OXYGEN. DO NOT GIVE MORPHINE, AMINOPHYLLINE, PHENOTHIAZINES, RESERPINE, FUROSEMIDE, OR ETHACRYNIC ACID (MORGAN, RECOGNITION AND MANAGEMENT OF PESTICIDE POISONINGS, 3RD ED.). TREAT SYMPTOMATICALLY AND SUPPORTIVELY. ADMINISTRATION OF OXYGEN AND LAVAGE MUST BE PERFORMED BY QUALIFIED MEDICAL PERSONNEL. GET MEDICAL ATTENTION IMMEDIATELY.

ANTIDOTE: THE FOLLOWING ANTIDOTE(S) HAVE BEEN RECOMMENDED. HOWEVER, THE DECISION AS TO WHETHER THE SEVERITY OF POISONING REQUIRES ADMINISTRATION OF ANY ANTIDOTE AND ACTUAL DOSE REQUIRED SHOULD BE MADE BY QUALIFIED MEDICAL PERSONNEL.

FOR CHOLINESTERASE INHIBITORS: ESTABLISH CLEAR AIRWAY AND TISSUE OXYGENATION BY ASPIRATION OF SECRETIONS, AND IF NECESSARY, BY ASSISTED PULMONARY VENTILATION WITH OXYGEN. IMPROVE TISSUE OXYGENATION AS MUCH AS POSSIBLE BEFORE ADMINISTERING ATROPINE TO MINIMIZE THE RISK OF VENTRICULAR FIBRILLATION. ADMINISTER ATROPINE SULFATE INTRAVENOUSLY, OR INTRAMUSCULARLY IF IV INJECTION IS NOT POSSIBLE. IN MODERATELY SEVERE POISONING ADMINISTER ATROPINE SULFATE, 0.4-2.0 MG REPEATED EVERY 15 MINUTES UNTIL ATROPINIZATION IS ACHIEVED (TACHYCARDIA, FLUSHING, DRY MOUTH, MYDRIASIS). MAINTAIN ATROPINIZATION BY REPEATED DOSES FOR 2-12 HOURS, OR LONGER, DEPENDING ON THE SEVERITY OF POISONING. THE APPEARANCE OF RALES IN THE LUNG BASES, MIOSIS, SALIVATION, NAUSEA, BRADYCARDIA, ARE ALL INDICATIONS OF INADEQUATE ATROPINIZATION. SEVERELY POISONED INDIVIDUALS MAY EXHIBIT REMARKABLE TOLERANCE TO ATROPINE; TWO OR MORE TIMES THE DOSAGES SUGGESTED ABOVE MAY BE NEEDED. PERSONS NOT POISONED OR ONLY SLIGHTLY POISONED, HOWEVER, MAY DEVELOP SIGNS OF ATROPINE TOXICITY FROM SUCH LARGE DOSAGES: FEVER, MUSCLE FIBRILLATIONS, AND DELIRIUM ARE THE MAIN SIGNS OF ATROPINE TOXICITY. IF THESE SIGNS APPEAR WHILE THE PATIENT IS FULLY ATROPINIZED, ATROPINE ADMINISTRATION SHOULD BE DISCONTINUED, AT LEAST TEMPORARILY. OBSERVE TREATED PATIENTS CLOSELY AT LEAST 24 HOURS TO INSURE THAT SYMPTOMS (POSSIBLY PULMONARY EDEMA) DO NOT RECUR AS ATROPINIZATION WEARS OFF. IN VERY SEVERE POISONINGS, METABOLIC DISPOSITION OF TOXICANT MAY REQUIRE SEVERAL HOURS OR DAYS DURING WHICH ATROPINIZATION MUST BE MAINTAINED. MARKEDLY LOWER LEVELS OF URINARY METABOLITES INDICATE THAT ATROPINE DOSAGE CAN BE TAPERED OFF. AS DOSAGE IS REDUCED, CHECK THE LUNG BASES FREQUENTLY FOR RALES. IF RALES ARE HEARD OR OTHER SYMPTOMS RETURN, RE-ESTABLISH ATROPINIZATION PROMPTLY (MORGAN, RECOGNITION AND MANAGEMENT OF PESTICIDE POISONINGS, 3RD ED.). ADMINISTRATION OF ANTIDOTE MUST BE PERFORMED BY QUALIFIED MEDICAL PERSONNEL.

IN CASES OF SEVERE POISONING BY ORGANOPHOSPHATE PESTICIDES IN WHICH RESPIRATORY DEPRESSION, MUSCLE WEAKNESS AND TWITCHINGS ARE SEVERE, GIVE PRALIDOXIME (PROTOPAM-AYERST, 2-PAM), 1.0 GRAM INTRAVENOUSLY AT NO MORE THAN 0.5 GRAM PER MINUTE. DOSAGE OF PRALIDOXIME MAY BE REPEATED IN 1-2 HOURS, THEN AT 10-12 HOUR INTERVALS IF NEEDED. IN VERY SEVERE POISONINGS, DOSAGE RATES MAY BE DOUBLED. TREATMENT WITH PRALIDOXIME WILL BE MOST EFFECTIVE IF GIVEN WITHIN THIRTY-SIX HOURS AFTER POISONING (MORGAN, RECOGNITION AND MANAGEMENT OF PESTICIDE POISONINGS, 3RD ED.). ANTIDOTE SHOULD BE ADMINISTERED BY QUALIFIED MEDICAL PERSONNEL.

REACTIVITY

REACTIVITY: STABLE UNDER NORMAL TEMPERATURES AND PRESSURES.

INCOMPATIBILITIES: FENTHION OXON SULFONE: OXIDIZERS (STRONG): FIRE AND EXPLOSION HAZARD.

DECOMPOSITION: THERMAL DECOMPOSITION PRODUCTS MAY INCLUDE TOXIC OXIDES OF CARBON, SULFUR, AND PHOSPHORUS.

POLYMERIZATION: HAZARDOUS POLYMERIZATION HAS NOT BEEN REPORTED TO OCCUR UNDER NORMAL TEMPERATURES AND PRESSURES.

STORAGE AND DISPOSAL

OBSERVE ALL FEDERAL, STATE AND LOCAL REGULATIONS WHEN STORING OR DISPOSING OF THIS SUBSTANCE. FOR ASSISTANCE, CONTACT THE DISTRICT DIRECTOR OF THE ENVIRONMENTAL PROTECTION AGENCY.

STORAGE

STORE AWAY FROM INCOMPATIBLE SUBSTANCES.

STORE IN ACCORDANCE WITH 40 CFR 165 RECOMMENDED PROCEDURES FOR THE DISPOSAL AND STORAGE OF PESTICIDES AND PESTICIDE CONTAINERS.

DISPOSAL

DISPOSAL MUST BE IN ACCORDANCE WITH 40 CFR 165 RECOMMENDED PROCEDURES FOR THE DISPOSAL AND STORAGE OF PESTICIDES AND PESTICIDE CONTAINERS.

CONDITIONS TO AVOID

MAY BURN BUT DOES NOT IGNITE READILY.

SPILL AND LEAK PROCEDURES

OCCUPATIONAL SPILL: DO NOT TOUCH SPILLED MATERIAL. STOP LEAK IF YOU CAN DO IT WITHOUT RISK. FOR SMALL SPILLS, TAKE UP WITH SAND OR OTHER ABSORBENT MATERIAL AND PLACE INTO CONTAINERS FOR LATER DISPOSAL. FOR SMALL DRY SPILLS, WITH A CLEAN SHOVEL PLACE MATERIAL INTO CLEAN, DRY CONTAINER AND COVER. MOVE CONTAINERS FROM SPILL AREA. FOR LARGER SPILLS, DIKE FAR AHEAD OF SPILL FOR LATER DISPOSAL. KEEP UNNECESSARY PEOPLE AWAY. ISOLATE HAZARD AREA AND DENY ENTRY.

PROTECTIVE EQUIPMENT

VENTILATION: PROVIDE LOCAL EXHAUST OR PROCESS ENCLOSURE VENTILATION SYSTEM.

RESPIRATOR: THE FOLLOWING RESPIRATORS ARE RECOMMENDED BASED ON INFORMATION FOUND IN THE PHYSICAL DATA, TOXICITY AND HEALTH EFFECTS SECTIONS. THEY ARE RANKED IN ORDER FROM MINIMUM TO MAXIMUM RESPIRATORY PROTECTION. THE SPECIFIC RESPIRATOR SELECTED MUST BE BASED ON CONTAMINATION LEVELS FOUND IN THE WORK PLACE, MUST NOT EXCEED THE WORKING LIMITS OF THE RESPIRATOR AND BE JOINTLY APPROVED BY THE NATIONAL INSTITUTE FOR OCCUPATIONAL SAFETY AND HEALTH AND THE MINE SAFETY AND HEALTH ADMINISTRATION (NIOSH-MSHA).

TYPE 'C' SUPPLIED-AIR RESPIRATOR WITH A FULL FACEPIECE OPERATED IN PRESSURE-DEMAND OR OTHER POSITIVE PRESSURE MODE OR WITH A FULL FACEPIECE, HELMET OR HOOD OPERATED IN CONTINOUS-FLOW MODE.

SELF-CONTAINED BREATHING APPARATUS WITH A FULL FACEPIECE OPERATED IN PRESSURE-DEMAND OR OTHER POSITIVE PRESSURE MODE.

FOR FIREFIGHTING AND OTHER IMMEDIATELY DANGEROUS TO LIFE OR HEALTH CONDITIONS:

SELF-CONTAINED BREATHING APPARATUS WITH FULL FACEPIECE OPERATED IN PRESSURE-DEMAND OR OTHER POSITIVE PRESSURE MODE.

SUPPLIED-AIR RESPIRATOR WITH FULL FACEPIECE AND OPERATED IN PRESSURE-DEMAND OR OTHER POSITIVE PRESSURE MODE IN COMBINATION WITH AN AUXILIARY SELF-CONTAINED BREATHING APPARATUS OPERATED IN PRESSURE-DEMAND OR OTHER POSITIVE PRESSURE MODE.

CLOTHING: EMPLOYEE MUST WEAR APPROPRIATE PROTECTIVE (IMPERVIOUS) CLOTHING AND EQUIPMENT TO PREVENT ANY POSSIBILITY OF SKIN CONTACT WITH THIS SUBSTANCE.

GLOVES: EMPLOYEE MUST WEAR APPROPRIATE PROTECTIVE GLOVES TO PREVENT CONTACT WITH THIS SUBSTANCE.

EYE PROTECTION: EMPLOYEE MUST WEAR SPLASH-PROOF OR DUST-RESISTANT SAFETY GOGGLES AND A FACESHIELD TO PREVENT CONTACT WITH THIS SUBSTANCE.

EMERGENCY WASH FACILITIES: WHERE THERE IS ANY POSSIBILITY THAT AN EMPLOYEE'S EYES AND/OR SKIN MAY BE EXPOSED TO THIS SUBSTANCE, THE EMPLOYER SHOULD PROVIDE AN EYE WASH FOUNTAIN AND QUICK DRENCH SHOWER WITHIN THE IMMEDIATE WORK AREA FOR EMERGENCY USE.

AUTHORIZED BY- OCCUPATIONAL HEALTH SERVICES, INC.

CREATION DATE: 10/04/89 ***REVISION DATE:*** 04/27/90

MATERIAL SAFETY DATA SHEET

OCCUPATIONAL HEALTH SERVICES, INC.
AGRICULTURE AND PESTICIDE DIVISION
450 SEVENTH AVENUE, SUITE 2407
NEW YORK, NEW YORK 10123
1-800-445-MSDS OR (212) 967-1100

EMERGENCY CONTACT:
JOHN S. BRANSFORD, JR. (615) 292-1180

SUBSTANCE IDENTIFICATION

CAS-NUMBER 6552-13-2

SUBSTANCE: **FENTHION OXON SULFOXIDE**

TRADE NAMES/SYNONYMS: PHOSPHORIC ACID, DIMETHYL 3-METHYL-4-(METHYLSULFINYL)PHENYL ESTER; PHOSPHORIC ACID, DIMETHYL 4-(METHYLSULFINYL)-M-TOLYL ESTER; O,O-DIMETHYL-O-(4(METHYLSULFINYL)-M-TOLYL)PHOSPHATE; MERCAPTOPHOS OXON SULFOXIDE; BAYTEX OXON SULFOXIDE; ENTEX OXON SULFOXIDE; TIGUVON OXON SULFOXIDE; FENOXON SULFOXIDE; DIMETHYL 3-METHYL-4-(METHYLSULFINYL)PHENYL PHOSPHATE; DIMETHYL 4-(METHYLSULFINYL)-M-TOLYL PHOSPHATE; C10H15O5PS; PST02553

CHEMICAL FAMILY: ORGANOPHOSPHATE

MOLECULAR FORMULA: C-H3-S-O-C6-H3-(C-H3)-O-P-(O)-(O-C-H3)2

MOLECULAR WEIGHT: 278.28

CERCLA RATINGS (SCALE 0-3): HEALTH=U FIRE=1 REACTIVITY=0 PERSISTENCE=1

NFPA RATINGS (SCALE 0-4): HEALTH=U FIRE=1 REACTIVITY=0

COMPONENTS AND CONTAMINANTS

COMPONENT: FENTHION OXON SULFOXIDE ***PERCENT:*** 100.0
CAS# 6552-13-2

OTHER CONTAMINANTS: NONE

EXPOSURE LIMITS: NO OCCUPATIONAL EXPOSURE LIMITS ESTABLISHED BY OSHA, ACGIH, OR NIOSH.

PHYSICAL DATA

DESCRIPTION: WHITE POWDER. ***MELTING POINT:*** NOT AVAILABLE

SPECIFIC GRAVITY: NOT AVAILABLE ***SOLUBILITY IN WATER:*** NOT AVAILABLE

FIRE AND EXPLOSION DATA

FIRE AND EXPLOSION HAZARD: SLIGHT FIRE HAZARD WHEN EXPOSED TO HEAT OR FLAME.

FIREFIGHTING MEDIA: DRY CHEMICAL, CARBON DIOXIDE, HALON, WATER SPRAY OR STANDARD FOAM (1987 EMERGENCY RESPONSE GUIDEBOOK, DOT P 5800.4).
FOR LARGER FIRES, USE WATER SPRAY, FOG OR STANDARD FOAM (1987 EMERGENCY RESPONSE GUIDEBOOK, DOT P 5800.4).

FIREFIGHTING: MOVE CONTAINERS FROM FIRE AREA IF POSSIBLE (1987 EMERGENCY RESPONSE GUIDEBOOK, DOT P 5800.4, GUIDE PAGE 53).
EXTINGUISH USING AGENT SUITABLE FOR TYPE OF SURROUNDING FIRE. AVOID BREATHING VAPORS AND DUSTS. KEEP UPWIND.

TRANSPORTATION DATA

DEPARTMENT OF TRANSPORTATION HAZARD CLASSIFICATION 49 CFR 172.101: POISON B
DEPARTMENT OF TRANSPORTATION LABELING REQUIREMENTS 49 CFR 172.101 AND SUBPART E: POISON
DEPARTMENT OF TRANSPORTATION PACKAGING REQUIREMENTS: 49 {CFR 173.377 EXCEPTIONS: 49 CFR 173.377

TOXICITY

FENTHION OXON SULFOXIDE: TOXICITY DATA: 50 MG/KG ORAL-RAT LD50 (FDA); 22 MG/KG INTRAPERITONEAL-RAT LD50. CARCINOGEN STATUS: NONE. ACUTE TOXICITY LEVEL: HIGHLY TOXIC BY INGESTION. TARGET EFFECTS: CHOLINESTERASE INHIBITOR. POISONING MAY AFFECT THE NERVOUS SYSTEM.* AT INCREASED RISK FROM EXPOSURE: PERSONS WITH RESPIRATORY AILMENTS, RECENT EXPOSURE TO CHOLINESTERASE INHIBITORS OR IMPAIRED CHOLINESTERASE PRODUCTION, OR LIVER MALFUNCTION.* ADDITIONAL DATA: MAY CROSS THE PLACENTA. HIGH ENVIRONMENTAL TEMPERATURES OR EXPOSURE OF THE CHEMICAL TO VISIBLE OR ULTRAVIOLET LIGHT MAY ENHANCE THE TOXICITY. INTERACTIONS WITH MEDICATIONS MAY OCCUR.*
* MAY BE BASED ON GENERAL INFORMATION ON ORGANOPHOSPHATES.

HEALTH EFFECTS AND FIRST AID

INHALATION: FENTHION OXON SULFOXIDE: SEE INFORMATION ON ORGANOPHOSPHATES.
ORGANOPHOSPHATES: CHOLINESTERASE INHIBITOR. **ACUTE EXPOSURE-** WHEN INHALED, THE FIRST EFFECTS OF CHOLINESTERASE INHIBITORS ARE USUALLY RESPIRATORY AND MAY INCLUDE NASAL HYPEREMIA AND WATERY DISCHARGE, COUGH, CHEST DISCOMFORT, DYSPNEA, AND WHEEZING DUE TO INCREASED BRONCHIAL SECRETIONS AND BRONCHOCONSTRICTION. IF SUFFICIENT AMOUNTS ARE ABSORBED, OTHER SYSTEMIC EFFECTS MAY BEGIN WITHIN A FEW MINUTES OR BE DELAYED FOR UP TO 12 HOURS. SYMPTOMS MAY INCLUDE PALLOR, NAUSEA, VOMITING, DIARRHEA, ABDOMINAL CRAMPS, HEADACHE, DIZZINESS, OCULAR PAIN, BLURRED VISION, MIOSIS OR IN SOME CASES, ESPECIALLY INITIALLY, MYDRIASIS, LACRIMATION, SALIVATION, SWEATING, AND CONFUSION. OTHER REPORTED CENTRAL NERVOUS SYSTEM OR NEUROMUSCULAR EFFECTS MAY INCLUDE ATAXIA, SLURRED SPEECH, AREFLEXIA, WEAKNESS, FATIGUE, FASCICULATIONS, TWITCHING, TREMORS POSSIBLY OF THE TONGUE AND EYELIDS, AND EVENTUALLY PARALYSIS OF THE EXTREMITIES AND POSSIBLY OF THE RESPIRATORY MUSCLES. IN SEVERE CASES THERE MAY ALSO BE INVOLUNTARY DEFECATION AND URINATION, CYANOSIS, PSYCHOSIS, HYPERGLYCEMIA, ACUTE PANCREATITIS, CARDIAC IRREGULARITIES, PULMONARY EDEMA, UNCONSCIOUSNESS, CONVULSIONS, AND COMA. DEATH IS PRIMARILY DUE TO RESPIRATORY FAILURE, ALTHOUGH CARDIOVASCULAR EFFECTS INCLUDING CARDIAC ARREST MAY ALSO BE IMPLICATED. LONG TERM SEQUELAE ARE RARE BUT MAY INCLUDE NEUROPSYCHIATRIC DISORDERS AND MYOPATHY WITH MUSCLE TENDERNESS. SOME ORGANOPHOSPHATES MAY CAUSE A DELAYED NEUROPATHY BEGINNING 1-4 WEEKS AFTER AN ACUTE EXPOSURE WHICH MAY OR MAY NOT HAVE CAUSED ACUTE CHOLINERGIC EFFECTS. NUMBNESS, TINGLING, WEAKNESS AND CRAMPING BEGINNING SYMMETRICALLY IN THE LOWER LIMBS MAY PROGRESS TO ATAXIA AND PARALYSIS. IN SEVERE CASES, UPPER LIMB INVOLVEMENT IS POSSIBLE AND FLACCID PARALYSIS MAY PROGRESS TO SPASTIC PARALYSIS WITH EXAGGERATED REFLEXES. IMPROVEMENT MAY OCCUR OVER MONTHS TO YEARS, BUT SOME RESIDUAL IMPAIRMENT USUALLY REMAINS.
CHRONIC EXPOSURE- REPEATED OR PROLONGED EXPOSURE MAY RESULT IN THE EFFECTS OF ACUTE EXPOSURE INCLUDING THE DELAYED NEUROPATHY. OTHER EFFECTS REPORTED IN WORKERS REPEATEDLY EXPOSED INCLUDE IMPAIRED MEMORY AND CONCENTRATION, ACUTE PSYCHOSIS, SEVERE DEPRESSIONS, IRRITABILTY, CONFUSION, APATHY, EMOTIONAL LABILITY, SOCIAL WITHDRAWAL, CONFUSION, HEADACHE, SPEECH DIFFICULTIES, DELAYED REACTION TIMES, SPATIAL DISORIENTATION, NIGHTMARES, SLEEPWALKING, AND DROWSINESS OR INSOMNIA. AN INFLUENZA-LIKE CONDITION WITH HEADACHE, NAUSEA, WEAKNESS, ANOREXIA AND MALAISE HAS ALSO BEEN REPORTED.

FIRST AID- REMOVE FROM EXPOSURE AREA TO FRESH AIR IMMEDIATELY. IF BREATHING HAS STOPPED, GIVE ARTIFICIAL RESPIRATION. MAINTAIN AIRWAY AND BLOOD PRESSURE AND ADMINISTER OXYGEN IF AVAILABLE. KEEP AFFECTED PERSON WARM AND AT REST. TREAT SYMPTOMATICALLY AND SUPPORTIVELY. ADMINISTRATION OF OXYGEN SHOULD BE PERFORMED BY QUALIFIED PERSONNEL. GET MEDICAL ATTENTION IMMEDIATELY.

SKIN CONTACT: FENTHION OXON SULFOXIDE: SEE INFORMATION ON ORGANOPHOSPHATES.
ORGANOPHOSPHATES: CHOLINESTERASE INHIBITOR. **ACUTE EXPOSURE-** LOCALIZED SWEATING AND FASCICULATIONS MAY OCCUR AT THE SITE OF CONTACT. IF SUFFICIENT AMOUNTS ARE ABSORBED, OTHER EFFECTS OF CHOLINESTERASE INHIBITION AS DESCRIBED IN ACUTE INHALATION MAY OCCUR. SYMPTOMS MAY BE DELAYED 2-3 HOURS, BUT USUALLY NO MORE THAN 12 HOURS. THE RATE OF ABSORPTION IS INCREASED BY THE PRESENCE OF DERMATITIS OR HIGH AMBIENT TEMPERATURES. DELAYED NEUROPATHY IS ALSO POSSIBLE. **CHRONIC EXPOSURE-** REPEATED OR PROLONGED EXPOSURE MAY CAUSE EFFECTS AS DESCRIBED IN ACUTE EXPOSURE. SOME ORGANOPHOSPHATES MAY CAUSE SENSITIZATION.

FIRST AID- REMOVE CONTAMINATED CLOTHING IMMEDIATELY. WASH CONTAMINATED AREAS WITH SOAP AND WATER FOLLOWED BY ALCOHOL (ARENA, POISONING, 4TH ED.). EMERGENCY PERSONNEL SHOULD WEAR GLOVES AND AVOID CONTAMINATION. TREAT RESPIRATORY DIFFICULTY WITH ARTIFICIAL RESPIRATION. GET MEDICAL ATTENTION IMMEDIATELY.

EYE CONTACT: FENTHION OXON SULFOXIDE: SEE INFORMATION ON ORGANOPHOSPHATES.
ORGANOPHOSPHATES: CHOLINESTERASE INHIBITOR. **ACUTE EXPOSURE-** DIRECT CONTACT MAY CAUSE PAIN, HYPEREMIA, LACRIMATION, TWITCHING OF THE EYELIDS, MIOSIS, AND CILIARY MUSCLE SPASM WITH LOSS OF ACCOMODATION, BLURRED OR DIMMED VISION AND BROWACHE. SOMETIMES MYDRIASIS MAY OCCUR INSTEAD OF MIOSIS. WITH SUFFICIENT EXPOSURE, OTHER SYMPTOMS OF CHOLINESTERASE INHIBITION AS DESCRIBED IN ACUTE INHALATION MAY OCCUR. **CHRONIC EXPOSURE-** REPEATED OR PROLONGED EXPOSURE MAY CAUSE EFFECTS AS DESCRIBED IN ACUTE EXPOSURE. SOME COMPOUNDS HAVE CAUSED TOXIC EFFECTS ON THE CRYSTALLINE LENS, CONJUNCTIVAL THICKENING AND OBSTRUCTION OF THE NASOLACRIMAL CANALS WHEN USED AS MIOTIC EYEDROPS.

FIRST AID- IRRIGATE EYES WITH WATER OR SALINE SOLUTION. IF SYMPTOMS OF POISONING OCCUR, TREAT RESPIRATORY DIFFICULTY WITH ARTIFICIAL RESPIRATION AND OXYGEN. OBSERVE PATIENT FOR AT LEAST 24-36 HOURS (GOSSELIN, CLINICAL TOXICOLOGY OF COMMERCIAL PRODUCTS, 5TH ED.). GET MEDICAL ATTENTION IMMEDIATELY. OXYGEN SHOULD BE ADMINISTERED BY QUALIFIED MEDICAL PERSONNEL.

INGESTION: FENTHION OXON SULFOXIDE: HIGHLY TOXIC. SEE INFORMATION ON ORGANOPHOSPHATES.

ORGANOPHOSPHATES: CHOLINESTERASE INHIBITOR. **ACUTE EXPOSURE**- WHEN INGESTED, THE FIRST EFFECTS MAY BE NAUSEA, VOMITING, ANOREXIA, ABDOMINAL CRAMPS AND DIARRHEA. GASTROINTESTINAL ABSORPTION MAY CAUSE SYMPTOMS OF CHOLINESTERASE INHIBITION AS DESCRIBED IN ACUTE INHALATION. SYMPTOMS MAY BEGIN WITHIN MINUTES OR BE DELAYED FOR HOURS. DELAYED EFFECTS INCLUDING NEUROPATHY MAY ALSO OCCUR. **CHRONIC EXPOSURE**- REPEATED INGESTION MAY CAUSE EFFECTS AS DESCRIBED IN ACUTE EXPOSURE.

FIRST AID- IF PERSON IS ALERT AND RESPIRATION IS NOT DEPRESSED, GIVE SYRUP OF IPECAC FOLLOWED BY WATER (IF VOMITING OCCURS, KEEP HEAD BELOW HIPS TO PREVENT ASPIRATION). IF CONSCIOUSNESS LEVEL DECLINES OR VOMITING HAS NOT OCCURRED IN 15 MINUTES EMPTY STOMACH BY GASTRIC LAVAGE WITH THE AID OF CUFFED ENDOTRACHEAL TUBE USING ISOTONIC SALINE OR 5% SODIUM BICARBONATE FOLLOW WITH ACTIVATED CHARCOAL. ESTABLISH AND MAINTAIN AIRWAY. TREAT RESPIRATORY DIFFICULTY WITH ARTIFICIAL RESPIRATION AND OXYGEN. DO NOT GIVE MORPHINE, AMINOPHYLLINE, PHENOTHIAZINES, RESERPINE, FUROSEMIDE, OR ETHACRYNIC ACID (MORGAN, RECOGNITION AND MANAGEMENT OF PESTICIDE POISONINGS, 3RD ED.). TREAT SYMPTOMATICALLY AND SUPPORTIVELY. ADMINISTRATION OF OXYGEN AND LAVAGE MUST BE PERFORMED BY QUALIFIED MEDICAL PERSONNEL. GET MEDICAL ATTENTION IMMEDIATELY.

ANTIDOTE: THE FOLLOWING ANTIDOTE(S) HAVE BEEN RECOMMENDED. HOWEVER, THE DECISION AS TO WHETHER THE SEVERITY OF POISONING REQUIRES ADMINISTRATION OF ANY ANTIDOTE AND ACTUAL DOSE REQUIRED SHOULD BE MADE BY QUALIFIED MEDICAL PERSONNEL.

FOR CHOLINESTERASE INHIBITORS: ESTABLISH CLEAR AIRWAY AND TISSUE OXYGENATION BY ASPIRATION OF SECRETIONS, AND IF NECESSARY, BY ASSISTED PULMONARY VENTILATION WITH OXYGEN. IMPROVE TISSUE OXYGENATION AS MUCH AS POSSIBLE BEFORE ADMINISTERING ATROPINE TO MINIMIZE THE RISK OF VENTRICULAR FIBRILLATION. ADMINISTER ATROPINE SULFATE INTRAVENOUSLY, OR INTRAMUSCULARLY IF IV INJECTION IS NOT POSSIBLE. IN MODERATELY SEVERE POISONING ADMINISTER ATROPINE SULFATE, 0.4-2.0 MG REPEATED EVERY 15 MINUTES UNTIL ATROPINIZATION IS ACHIEVED (TACHYCARDIA, FLUSHING, DRY MOUTH, MYDRIASIS). MAINTAIN ATROPINIZATION BY REPEATED DOSES FOR 2-12 HOURS, OR LONGER, DEPENDING ON THE SEVERITY OF POISONING. THE APPEARANCE OF RALES IN THE LUNG BASES, MIOSIS, SALIVATION, NAUSEA, BRADYCARDIA, ARE ALL INDICATIONS OF INADEQUATE ATROPINIZATION. SEVERELY POISONED INDIVIDUALS MAY EXHIBIT REMARKABLE TOLERANCE TO ATROPINE; TWO OR MORE TIMES THE DOSAGES SUGGESTED ABOVE MAY BE NEEDED. PERSONS NOT POISONED OR ONLY SLIGHTLY POISONED, HOWEVER, MAY DEVELOP SIGNS OF ATROPINE TOXICITY FROM SUCH LARGE DOSAGES: FEVER, MUSCLE FIBRILLATIONS, AND DELIRIUM ARE THE MAIN SIGNS OF ATROPINE TOXICITY. IF THESE SIGNS APPEAR WHILE THE PATIENT IS FULLY ATROPINIZED, ATROPINE ADMINISTRATION SHOULD BE DISCONTINUED, AT LEAST TEMPORARILY. OBSERVE TREATED PATIENTS CLOSELY AT LEAST 24 HOURS TO INSURE THAT SYMPTOMS (POSSIBLY PULMONARY EDEMA) DO NOT RECUR AS ATROPINIZATION WEARS OFF. IN VERY SEVERE POISONINGS, METABOLIC DISPOSITION OF TOXICANT MAY REQUIRE SEVERAL HOURS OR DAYS DURING WHICH ATROPINIZATION MUST BE MAINTAINED. MARKEDLY LOWER LEVELS OF URINARY METABOLITES INDICATE THAT ATROPINE DOSAGE CAN BE TAPERED OFF. AS DOSAGE IS REDUCED, CHECK THE LUNG BASES FREQUENTLY FOR RALES. IF RALES ARE HEARD OR OTHER SYMPTOMS RETURN, RE-ESTABLISH ATROPINIZATION PROMPTLY (MORGAN, RECOGNITION AND MANAGEMENT OF PESTICIDE POISONINGS, 3RD ED.). ADMINISTRATION OF ANTIDOTE MUST BE PERFORMED BY QUALIFIED MEDICAL PERSONNEL.

IN CASES OF SEVERE POISONING BY ORGANOPHOSPHATE PESTICIDES IN WHICH RESPIRATORY DEPRESSION, MUSCLE WEAKNESS AND TWITCHINGS ARE SEVERE, GIVE PRALIDOXIME (PROTOPAM-AYERST, 2-PAM), 1.0 GRAM INTRAVENOUSLY AT NO MORE THAN 0.5 GRAM PER MINUTE. DOSAGE OF PRALIDOXIME MAY BE REPEATED IN 1-2 HOURS, THEN AT 10-12 HOUR INTERVALS IF NEEDED. IN VERY SEVERE POISONINGS, DOSAGE RATES MAY BE DOUBLED. TREATMENT WITH PRALIDOXIME WILL BE MOST EFFECTIVE IF GIVEN WITHIN THIRTY-SIX HOURS AFTER POISONING (MORGAN, RECOGNITION AND MANAGEMENT OF PESTICIDE POISONINGS, 3RD ED.). ANTIDOTE SHOULD BE ADMINISTERED BY QUALIFIED MEDICAL PERSONNEL.

REACTIVITY

REACTIVITY: STABLE UNDER NORMAL TEMPERATURES AND PRESSURES.

INCOMPATIBILITIES: FENTHION OXON SULFOXIDE: OXIDIZER (STRONG): FIRE AND EXPLOSION HAZARD.

DECOMPOSITION: THERMAL DECOMPOSITION PRODUCTS MAY INCLUDE TOXIC OXIDES OF CARBON, SULFUR, AND PHOSPHORUS.

POLYMERIZATION: HAZARDOUS POLYMERIZATION HAS NOT BEEN REPORTED TO OCCUR UNDER NORMAL TEMPERATURES AND PRESSURES.

STORAGE AND DISPOSAL

OBSERVE ALL FEDERAL, STATE AND LOCAL REGULATIONS WHEN STORING OR DISPOSING OF THIS SUBSTANCE. FOR ASSISTANCE, CONTACT THE DISTRICT DIRECTOR OF THE ENVIRONMENTAL PROTECTION AGENCY.

****STORAGE****

STORE AWAY FROM INCOMPATIBLE SUBSTANCES.

STORE IN ACCORDANCE WITH 40 CFR 165 RECOMMENDED PROCEDURES FOR THE DISPOSAL AND STORAGE OF PESTICIDES AND PESTICIDE CONTAINERS.

****DISPOSAL****

DISPOSAL MUST BE IN ACCORDANCE WITH 40 CFR 165 RECOMMENDED PROCEDURES FOR THE DISPOSAL AND STORAGE OF PESTICIDES AND PESTICIDE CONTAINERS.

CONDITIONS TO AVOID

MAY BURN BUT DOES NOT IGNITE READILY.

SPILL AND LEAK PROCEDURES

OCCUPATIONAL SPILL: DO NOT TOUCH SPILLED MATERIAL. STOP LEAK IF YOU CAN DO IT WITHOUT RISK. FOR SMALL SPILLS, TAKE UP WITH SAND OR OTHER ABSORBENT MATERIAL AND PLACE INTO CONTAINERS FOR LATER DISPOSAL. FOR SMALL DRY SPILLS, WITH A CLEAN SHOVEL PLACE MATERIAL INTO CLEAN, DRY CONTAINER AND COVER. MOVE CONTAINERS FROM SPILL AREA. FOR LARGER SPILLS, DIKE FAR AHEAD OF SPILL FOR LATER DISPOSAL. KEEP UNNECESSARY PEOPLE AWAY. ISOLATE HAZARD AREA AND DENY ENTRY.

PROTECTIVE EQUIPMENT

VENTILATION: PROVIDE LOCAL EXHAUST OR PROCESS ENCLOSURE VENTILATION SYSTEM.

RESPIRATOR: THE FOLLOWING RESPIRATORS ARE RECOMMENDED BASED ON INFORMATION FOUND IN THE PHYSICAL DATA, TOXICITY AND HEALTH EFFECTS SECTIONS. THEY ARE RANKED IN ORDER FROM MINIMUM TO MAXIMUM RESPIRATORY PROTECTION. THE SPECIFIC RESPIRATOR SELECTED MUST BE BASED ON CONTAMINATION LEVELS FOUND IN THE WORK PLACE, MUST NOT EXCEED THE WORKING LIMITS OF THE RESPIRATOR AND BE JOINTLY APPROVED BY THE NATIONAL INSTITUTE FOR OCCUPATIONAL SAFETY AND HEALTH AND THE MINE SAFETY AND HEALTH ADMINISTRATION (NIOSH-MSHA).

TYPE 'C' SUPPLIED-AIR RESPIRATOR WITH A FULL FACEPIECE OPERATED IN PRESSURE-DEMAND OR OTHER POSITIVE PRESSURE MODE OR WITH A FULL FACEPIECE, HELMET OR HOOD OPERATED IN CONTINOUS-FLOW MODE.

SELF-CONTAINED BREATHING APPARATUS WITH A FULL FACEPIECE OPERATED IN PRESSURE-DEMAND OR OTHER POSITIVE PRESSURE MODE.

FOR FIREFIGHTING AND OTHER IMMEDIATELY DANGEROUS TO LIFE OR HEALTH CONDITIONS:

SELF-CONTAINED BREATHING APPARATUS WITH FULL FACEPIECE OPERATED IN PRESSURE-DEMAND OR OTHER POSITIVE PRESSURE MODE.

SUPPLIED-AIR RESPIRATOR WITH FULL FACEPIECE AND OPERATED IN PRESSURE-DEMAND OR OTHER POSITIVE PRESSURE MODE IN COMBINATION WITH AN AUXILIARY SELF-CONTAINED BREATHING APPARATUS OPERATED IN PRESSURE-DEMAND OR OTHER POSITIVE PRESSURE MODE.

CLOTHING: EMPLOYEE MUST WEAR APPROPRIATE PROTECTIVE (IMPERVIOUS) CLOTHING AND EQUIPMENT TO PREVENT ANY POSSIBILITY OF SKIN CONTACT WITH THIS SUBSTANCE.

GLOVES: EMPLOYEE MUST WEAR APPROPRIATE PROTECTIVE GLOVES TO PREVENT CONTACT WITH THIS SUBSTANCE.

EYE PROTECTION: EMPLOYEE MUST WEAR SPLASH-PROOF OR DUST-RESISTANT SAFETY GOGGLES AND A FACESHIELD TO PREVENT CONTACT WITH THIS SUBSTANCE.

EMERGENCY WASH FACILITIES: WHERE THERE IS ANY POSSIBILITY THAT AN EMPLOYEE'S EYES AND/OR SKIN MAY BE EXPOSED TO THIS SUBSTANCE, THE EMPLOYER SHOULD PROVIDE AN EYE WASH FOUNTAIN AND QUICK DRENCH SHOWER WITHIN THE IMMEDIATE WORK AREA FOR EMERGENCY USE.

AUTHORIZED BY- OCCUPATIONAL HEALTH SERVICES, INC.

CREATION DATE: 10/04/89 ***REVISION DATE:*** 05/03/90

MATERIAL SAFETY DATA SHEET

OCCUPATIONAL HEALTH SERVICES, INC.
AGRICULTURE AND PESTICIDE DIVISION
450 SEVENTH AVENUE, SUITE 2407
NEW YORK, NEW YORK 10123
1-800-445-MSDS OR (212) 967-1100

EMERGENCY CONTACT:
JOHN S. BRANSFORD, JR. (615) 292-1180

SUBSTANCE IDENTIFICATION

CAS-NUMBER 3761-42-0

SUBSTANCE: **FENTHION SULFONE**

TRADE NAMES/SYNONYMS: PHOSPHOROTHIOIC ACID, O,O-DIMETHYL O-(3-METHYL-4-(METHYLSULFONYL) PHENYL) ESTER; PHOSPHOROTHIOIC ACID, O,O-DIMETHYL O-(4-(METHYLSULFONYL)-M-TOLYL ESTER; BAYTEX SULFONE; O,O-DIMETHYL O-(3-METHYL-4-(METHYLSULFONYL) PHOSPHOROTHIOATE; O,O-DIMETHYL O-(4-METHYLSULFONYL)-M-TOLYL PHOSPHOROTHIOATE; C10H15O5PS2; PST02554

CHEMICAL FAMILY: ORGANOPHOSPHATE SULFONE

MOLECULAR FORMULA: C-H3-S-(O)2-C6-H3-(C-H3)-O-P-S-(O-C-H3)2

MOLECULAR WEIGHT: 310.34

CERCLA RATINGS (SCALE 0-3): HEALTH=3 FIRE=1 REACTIVITY=0 PERSISTENCE=1

NFPA RATINGS (SCALE 0-4): HEALTH=U FIRE=1 REACTIVITY=0

COMPONENTS AND CONTAMINANTS

COMPONENT: FENTHION SULFONE ***PERCENT:*** 100.0
CAS# 3761-42-0

OTHER CONTAMINANTS: NONE

EXPOSURE LIMITS: NO OCCUPATIONAL EXPOSURE LIMITS ESTABLISHED BY OSHA, ACGIH, OR NIOSH.

PHYSICAL DATA

DESCRIPTION: BEIGE POWDER. ***MELTING POINT:*** NOT AVAILABLE
SPECIFIC GRAVITY: NOT AVAILABLE ***SOLUBILITY IN WATER:*** NOT AVAILABLE

FIRE AND EXPLOSION DATA

FIRE AND EXPLOSION HAZARD: SLIGHT FIRE HAZARD WHEN EXPOSED TO HEAT OR FLAME.

FIREFIGHTING MEDIA: DRY CHEMICAL, CARBON DIOXIDE, HALON, WATER SPRAY OR STANDARD FOAM (1987 EMERGENCY RESPONSE GUIDEBOOK, DOT P 5800.4).
FOR LARGER FIRES, USE WATER SPRAY, FOG OR STANDARD FOAM (1987 EMERGENCY RESPONSE GUIDEBOOK, DOT P 5800.4).

FIREFIGHTING: MOVE CONTAINERS FROM FIRE AREA IF POSSIBLE (1987 EMERGENCY RESPONSE GUIDEBOOK, DOT P 5800.4, GUIDE PAGE 53).
EXTINGUISH USING AGENT SUITABLE FOR TYPE OF SURROUNDING FIRE. AVOID BREATHING VAPORS AND DUSTS. KEEP UPWIND.

TOXICITY

FENTHION SULFONE: TOXICITY DATA: 125 MG/KG ORAL-RAT LD50; 210 MG/KG ORAL-MOUSE LD50; 250 M/KG INTRAPERITONEAL-RAT LD50; 25 MG/KG INTRACEREBRAL-MOUSE LD50. CARCINOGEN STATUS: NONE. ACUTE TOXICITY LEVEL: TOXIC BY INGESTION. TARGET EFFECTS: CHOLINESTERASE INHIBITOR. POISONING MAY AFFECT THE NERVOUS SYSTEM. * AT INCREASED RISK FROM EXPOSURE: PERSONS WITH RESPIRATORY AILMENTS, RECENT EXPOSURE TO CHOLINESTERASE INHIBITORS OR IMPAIRED CHOLINESTERASE PRODUCTION, OR LIVER MALFUNCTION.* ADDITIONAL DATA: MAY CROSS THE PLACENTA. HIGH ENVIRONMENTAL TEMPERATURES OR EXPOSURE OF THE CHEMICAL TO VISIBLE OR ULTRAVIOLET LIGHT MAY ENHANCE THE TOXICITY. INTERACTIONS WITH MEDICATIONS MAY OCCUR.*
* MAY BE BASED ON GENERAL INFORMATION ON ORGANOPHOSPHATES.

HEALTH EFFECTS AND FIRST AID

INHALATION: FENTHION SULFONE: SEE INFORMATION ON ORGANOPHOSPHATES.
ORGANOPHOSPHATES: CHOLINESTERASE INHIBITOR. **ACUTE EXPOSURE-** WHEN INHALED, THE FIRST EFFECTS OF CHOLINESTERASE INHIBITORS ARE USUALLY RESPIRATORY AND MAY INCLUDE NASAL HYPEREMIA AND WATERY DISCHARGE, COUGH, CHEST DISCOMFORT, DYSPNEA, AND WHEEZING DUE TO INCREASED BRONCHIAL SECRETIONS AND BRONCHOCONSTRICTION. IF SUFFICIENT AMOUNTS ARE ABSORBED, OTHER SYSTEMIC EFFECTS MAY BEGIN WITHIN A FEW MINUTES OR BE DELAYED FOR UP TO 12 HOURS. SYMPTOMS MAY INCLUDE PALLOR, NAUSEA, VOMITING, DIARRHEA, ABDOMINAL CRAMPS, HEADACHE, DIZZINESS, OCULAR PAIN, BLURRED VISION, MIOSIS OR IN SOME CASES, ESPECIALLY INITIALLY, MYDRIASIS, LACRIMATION, SALIVATION, SWEATING, AND CONFUSION. OTHER REPORTED CENTRAL NERVOUS SYSTEM OR NEUROMUSCULAR EFFECTS MAY INCLUDE ATAXIA, SLURRED SPEECH, AREFLEXIA, WEAKNESS, FATIGUE, FASCICULATIONS, TWITCHING, TREMORS POSSIBLY OF THE TONGUE AND EYELIDS, AND EVENTUALLY PARALYSIS OF THE EXTREMITIES AND POSSIBLY OF THE RESPIRATORY MUSCLES. IN SEVERE CASES THERE MAY ALSO BE INVOLUNTARY DEFECATION AND URINATION, CYANOSIS, PSYCHOSIS, HYPERGLYCEMIA, ACUTE PANCREATITIS, CARDIAC IRREGULARITIES, PULMONARY EDEMA, UNCONSCIOUSNESS, CONVULSIONS, AND COMA. DEATH IS PRIMARILY DUE TO RESPIRATORY FAILURE, ALTHOUGH CARDIOVASCULAR EFFECTS INCLUDING CARDIAC ARREST MAY ALSO BE IMPLICATED. LONG TERM SEQUELAE ARE RARE BUT MAY INCLUDE NEUROPSYCHIATRIC DISORDERS AND MYOPATHY WITH MUSCLE TENDERNESS. SOME ORGANOPHOSPHATES MAY CAUSE A DELAYED NEUROPATHY BEGINNING 1-4 WEEKS AFTER AN ACUTE EXPOSURE WHICH MAY OR MAY NOT HAVE CAUSED ACUTE CHOLINERGIC EFFECTS. NUMBNESS, TINGLING, WEAKNESS AND CRAMPING BEGINNING SYMMETRICALLY IN THE LOWER LIMBS MAY PROGRESS TO ATAXIA AND PARALYSIS. IN SEVERE CASES, UPPER LIMB INVOLVEMENT IS POSSIBLE AND FLACCID PARALYSIS MAY PROGRESS TO SPASTIC PARALYSIS WITH EXAGGERATED REFLEXES. IMPROVEMENT MAY OCCUR OVER MONTHS TO YEARS, BUT SOME RESIDUAL IMPAIRMENT USUALLY REMAINS.
CHRONIC EXPOSURE- REPEATED OR PROLONGED EXPOSURE MAY RESULT IN THE EFFECTS OF ACUTE EXPOSURE INCLUDING THE DELAYED NEUROPATHY. OTHER EFFECTS REPORTED IN WORKERS REPEATEDLY EXPOSED INCLUDE IMPAIRED MEMORY AND CONCENTRATION, ACUTE PSYCHOSIS, SEVERE DEPRESSIONS, IRRITABILTY, CONFUSION, APATHY, EMOTIONAL LABILITY, SOCIAL WITHDRAWAL, CONFUSION, HEADACHE, SPEECH DIFFICULTIES, DELAYED REACTION TIMES, SPATIAL DISORIENTATION, NIGHTMARES, SLEEPWALKING, AND DROWSINESS OR INSOMNIA. AN INFLUENZA-LIKE CONDITION WITH HEADACHE, NAUSEA, WEAKNESS, ANOREXIA AND MALAISE HAS ALSO BEEN REPORTED.

FIRST AID- REMOVE FROM EXPOSURE AREA TO FRESH AIR IMMEDIATELY. IF BREATHING HAS STOPPED, GIVE ARTIFICIAL RESPIRATION. MAINTAIN AIRWAY AND BLOOD PRESSURE AND ADMINISTER OXYGEN IF AVAILABLE. KEEP AFFECTED PERSON WARM AND AT REST. TREAT SYMPTOMATICALLY AND SUPPORTIVELY. ADMINISTRATION OF OXYGEN SHOULD BE PERFORMED BY QUALIFIED PERSONNEL. GET MEDICAL ATTENTION IMMEDIATELY.

SKIN CONTACT: FENTHION SULFONE: SEE INFORMATION ON ORGANOPHOSPHATES.
ORGANOPHOSPHATES: CHOLINESTERASE INHIBITOR. **ACUTE EXPOSURE-** LOCALIZED SWEATING AND FASCICULATIONS MAY OCCUR AT THE SITE OF CONTACT. IF SUFFICIENT AMOUNTS ARE ABSORBED, OTHER EFFECTS OF CHOLINESTERASE INHIBITION AS DESCRIBED IN ACUTE INHALATION MAY OCCUR. SYMPTOMS MAY BE DELAYED 2-3 HOURS, BUT USUALLY NO MORE THAN 12 HOURS. THE RATE OF ABSORPTION IS INCREASED BY THE PRESENCE OF DERMATITIS OR HIGH AMBIENT TEMPERATURES. DELAYED NEUROPATHY IS ALSO POSSIBLE. **CHRONIC EXPOSURE-** REPEATED OR PROLONGED EXPOSURE MAY CAUSE EFFECTS AS DESCRIBED IN ACUTE EXPOSURE. SOME ORGANOPHOSPHATES MAY CAUSE SENSITIZATION.

FIRST AID- REMOVE CONTAMINATED CLOTHING IMMEDIATELY. WASH CONTAMINATED AREAS WITH SOAP AND WATER FOLLOWED BY ALCOHOL (ARENA, POISONING, 4TH ED.). EMERGENCY PERSONNEL SHOULD WEAR GLOVES AND AVOID CONTAMINATION. TREAT RESPIRATORY DIFFICULTY WITH ARTIFICIAL RESPIRATION. GET MEDICAL ATTENTION IMMEDIATELY.

EYE CONTACT: FENTHION SULFONE: SEE INFORMATION ON ORGANOPHOSPHATES.
ORGANOPHOSPHATES: CHOLINESTERASE INHIBITOR. **ACUTE EXPOSURE-** DIRECT CONTACT MAY CAUSE PAIN, HYPEREMIA, LACRIMATION, TWITCHING OF THE EYELIDS, MIOSIS, AND CILIARY MUSCLE SPASM WITH LOSS OF ACCOMODATION, BLURRED OR DIMMED VISION AND BROWACHE. SOMETIMES MYDRIASIS MAY OCCUR INSTEAD OF MIOSIS. WITH SUFFICIENT EXPOSURE, OTHER SYMPTOMS OF CHOLINESTERASE INHIBITION AS DESCRIBED IN ACUTE INHALATION MAY OCCUR.
CHRONIC EXPOSURE- REPEATED OR PROLONGED EXPOSURE MAY CAUSE EFFECTS AS DESCRIBED IN ACUTE EXPOSURE. SOME COMPOUNDS HAVE CAUSED TOXIC EFFECTS ON THE CRYSTALLINE LENS, CONJUNCTIVAL THICKENING AND OBSTRUCTION OF THE NASOLACRIMAL CANALS WHEN USED AS MIOTIC EYEDROPS.

FIRST AID- IRRIGATE EYES WITH WATER OR SALINE SOLUTION. IF SYMPTOMS OF POISONING OCCUR, TREAT RESPIRATORY DIFFICULTY WITH ARTIFICIAL RESPIRATION AND OXYGEN. OBSERVE PATIENT FOR AT LEAST 24-36 HOURS (GOSSELIN, CLINICAL TOXICOLOGY OF COMMERCIAL PRODUCTS, 5TH ED.). GET MEDICAL ATTENTION IMMEDIATELY. OXYGEN SHOULD BE ADMINISTERED BY QUALIFIED MEDICAL PERSONNEL.

INGESTION: FENTHION SULFONE: TOXIC. SEE INFORMATION ON ORGANOPHOSPHATES.
ORGANOPHOSPHATES: CHOLINESTERASE INHIBITOR. **ACUTE EXPOSURE-** WHEN INGESTED, THE FIRST EFFECTS MAY BE NAUSEA, VOMITING, ANOREXIA, ABDOMINAL CRAMPS AND DIARRHEA. GASTROINTESTINAL ABSORPTION MAY CAUSE SYMPTOMS OF CHOLINESTERASE INHIBITION AS DESCRIBED IN ACUTE INHALATION. SYMPTOMS MAY BEGIN WITHIN MINUTES OR BE DELAYED FOR

HOURS. DELAYED EFFECTS INCLUDING NEUROPATHY MAY ALSO OCCUR. **CHRONIC EXPOSURE-** REPEATED INGESTION MAY CAUSE EFFECTS AS DESCRIBED IN ACUTE EXPOSURE.

FIRST AID- IF PERSON IS ALERT AND RESPIRATION IS NOT DEPRESSED, GIVE SYRUP OF IPECAC FOLLOWED BY WATER (IF VOMITING OCCURS, KEEP HEAD BELOW HIPS TO PREVENT ASPIRATION). IF CONSCIOUSNESS LEVEL DECLINES OR VOMITING HAS NOT OCCURRED IN 15 MINUTES EMPTY STOMACH BY GASTRIC LAVAGE WITH THE AID OF CUFFED ENDOTRACHEAL TUBE USING ISOTONIC SALINE OR 5% SODIUM BICARBONATE FOLLOW WITH ACTIVATED CHARCOAL. ESTABLISH AND MAINTAIN AIRWAY. TREAT RESPIRATORY DIFFICULTY WITH ARTIFICIAL RESPIRATION AND OXYGEN. DO NOT GIVE MORPHINE, AMINOPHYLLINE, PHENOTHIAZINES, RESERPINE, FUROSEMIDE, OR ETHACRYNIC ACID (MORGAN, RECOGNITION AND MANAGEMENT OF PESTICIDE POISONINGS, 3RD ED.). TREAT SYMPTOMATICALLY AND SUPPORTIVELY. ADMINISTRATION OF OXYGEN AND LAVAGE MUST BE PERFORMED BY QUALIFIED MEDICAL PERSONNEL. GET MEDICAL ATTENTION IMMEDIATELY.

ANTIDOTE: THE FOLLOWING ANTIDOTE(S) HAVE BEEN RECOMMENDED. HOWEVER, THE DECISION AS TO WHETHER THE SEVERITY OF POISONING REQUIRES ADMINISTRATION OF ANY ANTIDOTE AND ACTUAL DOSE REQUIRED SHOULD BE MADE BY QUALIFIED MEDICAL PERSONNEL.

FOR CHOLINESTERASE INHIBITORS: ESTABLISH CLEAR AIRWAY AND TISSUE OXYGENATION BY ASPIRATION OF SECRETIONS, AND IF NECESSARY, BY ASSISTED PULMONARY VENTILATION WITH OXYGEN. IMPROVE TISSUE OXYGENATION AS MUCH AS POSSIBLE BEFORE ADMINISTERING ATROPINE TO MINIMIZE THE RISK OF VENTRICULAR FIBRILLATION. ADMINISTER ATROPINE SULFATE INTRAVENOUSLY, OR INTRAMUSCULARLY IF IV INJECTION IS NOT POSSIBLE. IN MODERATELY SEVERE POISONING ADMINISTER ATROPINE SULFATE, 0.4-2.0 MG REPEATED EVERY 15 MINUTES UNTIL ATROPINIZATION IS ACHIEVED (TACHYCARDIA, FLUSHING, DRY MOUTH, MYDRIASIS). MAINTAIN ATROPINIZATION BY REPEATED DOSES FOR 2-12 HOURS, OR LONGER, DEPENDING ON THE SEVERITY OF POISONING. THE APPEARANCE OF RALES IN THE LUNG BASES, MIOSIS, SALIVATION, NAUSEA, BRADYCARDIA, ARE ALL INDICATIONS OF INADEQUATE ATROPINIZATION. SEVERELY POISONED INDIVIDUALS MAY EXHIBIT REMARKABLE TOLERANCE TO ATROPINE; TWO OR MORE TIMES THE DOSAGES SUGGESTED ABOVE MAY BE NEEDED. PERSONS NOT POISONED OR ONLY SLIGHTLY POISONED, HOWEVER, MAY DEVELOP SIGNS OF ATROPINE TOXICITY FROM SUCH LARGE DOSAGES: FEVER, MUSCLE FIBRILLATIONS, AND DELIRIUM ARE THE MAIN SIGNS OF ATROPINE TOXICITY. IF THESE SIGNS APPEAR WHILE THE PATIENT IS FULLY ATROPINIZED, ATROPINE ADMINISTRATION SHOULD BE DISCONTINUED, AT LEAST TEMPORARILY. OBSERVE TREATED PATIENTS CLOSELY AT LEAST 24 HOURS TO INSURE THAT SYMPTOMS (POSSIBLY PULMONARY EDEMA) DO NOT RECUR AS ATROPINIZATION WEARS OFF. IN VERY SEVERE POISONINGS, METABOLIC DISPOSITION OF TOXICANT MAY REQUIRE SEVERAL HOURS OR DAYS DURING WHICH ATROPINIZATION MUST BE MAINTAINED. MARKEDLY LOWER LEVELS OF URINARY METABOLITES INDICATE THAT ATROPINE DOSAGE CAN BE TAPERED OFF. AS DOSAGE IS REDUCED, CHECK THE LUNG BASES FREQUENTLY FOR RALES. IF RALES ARE HEARD OR OTHER SYMPTOMS RETURN, RE-ESTABLISH ATROPINIZATION PROMPTLY (MORGAN, RECOGNITION AND MANAGEMENT OF PESTICIDE POISONINGS, 3RD ED.). ADMINISTRATION OF ANTIDOTE MUST BE PERFORMED BY QUALIFIED MEDICAL PERSONNEL.

IN CASES OF SEVERE POISONING BY ORGANOPHOSPHATE PESTICIDES IN WHICH RESPIRATORY DEPRESSION, MUSCLE WEAKNESS AND TWITCHINGS ARE SEVERE, GIVE PRALIDOXIME (PROTOPAM-AYERST, 2-PAM), 1.0 GRAM INTRAVENOUSLY AT NO MORE THAN 0.5 GRAM PER MINUTE. DOSAGE OF PRALIDOXIME MAY BE REPEATED IN 1-2 HOURS, THEN AT 10-12 HOUR INTERVALS IF NEEDED. IN VERY SEVERE POISONINGS, DOSAGE RATES MAY BE DOUBLED. TREATMENT WITH PRALIDOXIME WILL BE MOST EFFECTIVE IF GIVEN WITHIN THIRTY-SIX HOURS AFTER POISONING (MORGAN, RECOGNITION AND MANAGEMENT OF PESTICIDE POISONINGS, 3RD ED.). ANTIDOTE SHOULD BE ADMINISTERED BY QUALIFIED MEDICAL PERSONNEL.

REACTIVITY

REACTIVITY: STABLE UNDER NORMAL TEMPERATURES AND PRESSURES.

INCOMPATIBILITIES: FENTHION SULFONE: OXIDIZERS (STRONG): FIRE AND EXPLOSION HAZARD.

DECOMPOSITION: THERMAL DECOMPOSITION PRODUCTS MAY INCLUDE TOXIC OXIDES OF CARBON, SULFUR, AND PHOSPHORUS.

POLYMERIZATION: HAZARDOUS POLYMERIZATION HAS NOT BEEN REPORTED TO OCCUR UNDER NORMAL TEMPERATURES AND PRESSURES.

STORAGE AND DISPOSAL

OBSERVE ALL FEDERAL, STATE AND LOCAL REGULATIONS WHEN STORING OR DISPOSING OF THIS SUBSTANCE. FOR ASSISTANCE, CONTACT THE DISTRICT DIRECTOR OF THE ENVIRONMENTAL PROTECTION AGENCY.

****STORAGE****

STORE AWAY FROM INCOMPATIBLE SUBSTANCES.

STORE IN ACCORDANCE WITH 40 CFR 165 RECOMMENDED PROCEDURES FOR THE DISPOSAL AND STORAGE OF PESTICIDES AND PESTICIDE CONTAINERS.

****DISPOSAL****

DISPOSAL MUST BE IN ACCORDANCE WITH 40 CFR 165 RECOMMENDED PROCEDURES FOR THE DISPOSAL AND STORAGE OF PESTICIDES AND PESTICIDE CONTAINERS.

CONDITIONS TO AVOID

MAY BURN BUT DOES NOT IGNITE READILY.

SPILL AND LEAK PROCEDURES

OCCUPATIONAL SPILL: DO NOT TOUCH SPILLED MATERIAL. STOP LEAK IF YOU CAN DO IT WITHOUT RISK. FOR SMALL SPILLS, TAKE UP WITH SAND OR OTHER ABSORBENT MATERIAL AND PLACE INTO CONTAINERS FOR LATER DISPOSAL. FOR SMALL DRY SPILLS, WITH A CLEAN SHOVEL PLACE MATERIAL INTO CLEAN, DRY CONTAINER AND COVER. MOVE CONTAINERS FROM SPILL AREA. FOR LARGER SPILLS, DIKE FAR AHEAD OF SPILL FOR LATER DISPOSAL. KEEP UNNECESSARY PEOPLE AWAY. ISOLATE HAZARD AREA AND DENY ENTRY.

PROTECTIVE EQUIPMENT

VENTILATION: PROVIDE LOCAL EXHAUST OR PROCESS ENCLOSURE VENTILATION SYSTEM.

RESPIRATOR: THE FOLLOWING RESPIRATORS ARE RECOMMENDED BASED ON INFORMATION FOUND IN THE PHYSICAL DATA, TOXICITY AND HEALTH EFFECTS SECTIONS. THEY ARE RANKED IN ORDER FROM MINIMUM TO MAXIMUM RESPIRATORY PROTECTION. THE SPECIFIC RESPIRATOR SELECTED MUST BE BASED ON CONTAMINATION LEVELS FOUND IN THE WORK PLACE, MUST NOT EXCEED THE WORKING LIMITS OF THE RESPIRATOR AND BE JOINTLY APPROVED BY THE NATIONAL INSTITUTE FOR OCCUPATIONAL SAFETY AND HEALTH AND THE MINE SAFETY AND HEALTH ADMINISTRATION (NIOSH-MSHA).

TYPE 'C' SUPPLIED-AIR RESPIRATOR WITH A FULL FACEPIECE OPERATED IN PRESSURE-DEMAND OR OTHER POSITIVE PRESSURE MODE OR WITH A FULL FACEPIECE, HELMET OR HOOD OPERATED IN CONTINOUS-FLOW MODE.

SELF-CONTAINED BREATHING APPARATUS WITH A FULL FACEPIECE OPERATED IN PRESSURE-DEMAND OR OTHER POSITIVE PRESSURE MODE.

FOR FIREFIGHTING AND OTHER IMMEDIATELY DANGEROUS TO LIFE OR HEALTH CONDITIONS:

SELF-CONTAINED BREATHING APPARATUS WITH FULL FACEPIECE OPERATED IN PRESSURE-DEMAND OR OTHER POSITIVE PRESSURE MODE.

SUPPLIED-AIR RESPIRATOR WITH FULL FACEPIECE AND OPERATED IN PRESSURE-DEMAND OR OTHER POSITIVE PRESSURE MODE IN COMBINATION WITH AN AUXILIARY SELF-CONTAINED BREATHING APPARATUS OPERATED IN PRESSURE-DEMAND OR OTHER POSITIVE PRESSURE MODE.

CLOTHING: EMPLOYEE MUST WEAR APPROPRIATE PROTECTIVE (IMPERVIOUS) CLOTHING AND EQUIPMENT TO PREVENT ANY POSSIBILITY OF SKIN CONTACT WITH THIS SUBSTANCE.

GLOVES: EMPLOYEE MUST WEAR APPROPRIATE PROTECTIVE GLOVES TO PREVENT CONTACT WITH THIS SUBSTANCE.

EYE PROTECTION: EMPLOYEE MUST WEAR SPLASH-PROOF OR DUST-RESISTANT SAFETY GOGGLES AND A FACESHIELD TO PREVENT CONTACT WITH THIS SUBSTANCE.

EMERGENCY WASH FACILITIES: WHERE THERE IS ANY POSSIBILITY THAT AN EMPLOYEE'S EYES AND/OR SKIN MAY BE EXPOSED TO THIS SUBSTANCE, THE EMPLOYER SHOULD PROVIDE AN EYE WASH FOUNTAIN AND QUICK DRENCH SHOWER WITHIN THE IMMEDIATE WORK AREA FOR EMERGENCY USE.

AUTHORIZED BY- OCCUPATIONAL HEALTH SERVICES, INC.

CREATION DATE: 10/04/89 ***REVISION DATE:*** 04/27/90

MATERIAL SAFETY DATA SHEET

OCCUPATIONAL HEALTH SERVICES, INC.
AGRICULTURE AND PESTICIDE DIVISION
450 SEVENTH AVENUE, SUITE 2407
NEW YORK, NEW YORK 10123
1-800-445-MSDS OR (212) 967-1100

EMERGENCY CONTACT:
JOHN S. BRANSFORD, JR. (615) 292-1180

SUBSTANCE IDENTIFICATION

CAS-NUMBER 3761-41-9

SUBSTANCE: **FENTHION SULFOXIDE**

TRADE NAMES/SYNONYMS: PHOSPHOROTHIOIC ACID, O,O-DIMETHYL O-(3-METHYL-4-(METHYLSULFINYL) PHENYL) ESTER; PHOSPHOROTHIOIC ACID, O,O-DIMETHYL O-(4-

(METHYLSULFINYL)-M-TOLYL) ESTER; O,O-DIMETHYL O-(3-METHYL-4-(METHYLSULFINYL)PHENYL) PHOSPHOROTHIOATE; O,O-DIMETHYL O-(4-(METHYLSULFINYL)M-TOLYL) PHOSPHOROTHIOATE; MESULFENFOS; FENSULFOXIDE; C10H15O4PS2; PST02555

CHEMICAL FAMILY: ORGANOPHOSPHATE SULFOXIDE

MOLECULAR FORMULA: C-H3-S-(O)-C6-H3-(C-H3)-O-P-S-(O-C-H3)2

MOLECULAR WEIGHT: 294.34

CERCLA RATINGS (SCALE 0-3): HEALTH=3 FIRE=1 REACTIVITY=0 PERSISTENCE=1

NFPA RATINGS (SCALE 0-4): HEALTH=U FIRE=1 REACTIVITY=0

COMPONENTS AND CONTAMINANTS

COMPONENT: FENTHION SULFOXIDE ***PERCENT:*** 100.0
CAS# 3761-41-9

OTHER CONTAMINANTS: NONE

EXPOSURE LIMITS: NO OCCUPATIONAL EXPOSURE LIMITS ESTABLISHED BY OSHA, ACGIH, OR NIOSH.

PHYSICAL DATA

DESCRIPTION: WHITE POWDER. ***MELTING POINT:*** NOT AVAILABLE
SPECIFIC GRAVITY: NOT AVAILABLE ***SOLUBILITY IN WATER:*** NOT AVAILABLE

FIRE AND EXPLOSION DATA

FIRE AND EXPLOSION HAZARD: SLIGHT FIRE HAZARD WHEN EXPOSED TO HEAT OR FLAME.

FIREFIGHTING MEDIA: DRY CHEMICAL, CARBON DIOXIDE, HALON, WATER SPRAY OR STANDARD FOAM (1987 EMERGENCY RESPONSE GUIDEBOOK, DOT P 5800.4). FOR LARGER FIRES, USE WATER SPRAY, FOG OR STANDARD FOAM (1987 EMERGENCY RESPONSE GUIDEBOOK, DOT P 5800.4).

FIREFIGHTING: MOVE CONTAINERS FROM FIRE AREA IF POSSIBLE (1987 EMERGENCY RESPONSE GUIDEBOOK, DOT P 5800.4, GUIDE PAGE 53).
EXTINGUISH USING AGENT SUITABLE FOR TYPE OF SURROUNDING FIRE. AVOID BREATHING VAPORS AND DUSTS. KEEP UPWIND.

TOXICITY

FENTHION SULFOXIDE: TOXICITY DATA: 125 MG/KG ORAL-RAT LD50; 220 MG/KG ORAL-MOUSE LD50; 250 MG/KG INTRAPERITONEAL-RAT LD50; 5 MG/KG INTRACEREBRAL-MOUSE LD50. CARCINOGEN STATUS: NONE. ACUTE TOXICITY LEVEL: TOXIC BY INGESTION. TARGET EFFECTS: CHOLINESTERASE INHIBITOR. POISONING MAY AFFECT THE NERVOUS SYSTEM.* AT INCREASED RISK FROM EXPOSURE: PERSONS WITH RESPIRATORY AILMENTS, RECENT EXPOSURE TO CHOLINESTERASE INHIBITORS OR IMPAIRED CHOLINESTERASE PRODUCTION, OR LIVER MALFUNCTION.* ADDITIONAL DATA: MAY CROSS THE PLACENTA. HIGH ENVIRONMENTAL TEMPERATURES OR EXPOSURE OF THE CHEMICAL TO VISIBLE OR ULTRAVIOLET LIGHT MAY ENHANCE THE TOXICITY. INTERACTIONS WITH MEDICATIONS MAY OCCUR.*
* MAY BE BASED ON GENERAL INFORMATION ON ORGANOPHOSPHATES.

HEALTH EFFECTS AND FIRST AID

INHALATION: FENTHION SULFOXIDE: SEE INFORMATION ON ORGANOPHOSPHATES. ORGANOPHOSPHATES: CHOLINESTERASE INHIBITOR. **ACUTE EXPOSURE-** WHEN INHALED, THE FIRST EFFECTS OF CHOLINESTERASE INHIBITORS ARE USUALLY RESPIRATORY AND MAY INCLUDE NASAL HYPEREMIA AND WATERY DISCHARGE, COUGH, CHEST DISCOMFORT, DYSPNEA, AND WHEEZING DUE TO INCREASED BRONCHIAL SECRETIONS AND BRONCHOCONSTRICTION. IF SUFFICIENT AMOUNTS ARE ABSORBED, OTHER SYSTEMIC EFFECTS MAY BEGIN WITHIN A FEW MINUTES OR BE DELAYED FOR UP TO 12 HOURS. SYMPTOMS MAY INCLUDE PALLOR, NAUSEA, VOMITING, DIARRHEA, ABDOMINAL CRAMPS, HEADACHE, DIZZINESS, OCULAR PAIN, BLURRED VISION, MIOSIS OR IN SOME CASES, ESPECIALLY INITIALLY, MYDRIASIS, LACRIMATION, SALIVATION, SWEATING, AND CONFUSION. OTHER REPORTED CENTRAL NERVOUS SYSTEM OR NEUROMUSCULAR EFFECTS MAY INCLUDE ATAXIA, SLURRED SPEECH, AREFLEXIA, WEAKNESS, FATIGUE, FASCICULATIONS, TWITCHING, TREMORS POSSIBLY OF THE TONGUE AND EYELIDS, AND EVENTUALLY PARALYSIS OF THE EXTREMITIES AND POSSIBLY OF THE RESPIRATORY MUSCLES. IN SEVERE CASES THERE MAY ALSO BE INVOLUNTARY DEFECATION AND URINATION, CYANOSIS, PSYCHOSIS, HYPERGLYCEMIA, ACUTE PANCREATITIS, CARDIAC IRREGULARITIES, PULMONARY EDEMA, UNCONSCIOUSNESS, CONVULSIONS, AND COMA. DEATH IS PRIMARILY DUE TO RESPIRATORY FAILURE, ALTHOUGH CARDIOVASCULAR EFFECTS INCLUDING CARDIAC ARREST MAY ALSO BE IMPLICATED. LONG TERM SEQUELAE ARE RARE BUT MAY INCLUDE NEUROPSYCHIATRIC DISORDERS AND MYOPATHY WITH MUSCLE TENDERNESS. SOME ORGANOPHOSPHATES MAY CAUSE A DELAYED NEUROPATHY BEGINNING 1-4 WEEKS AFTER AN ACUTE EXPOSURE WHICH MAY OR MAY NOT HAVE CAUSED ACUTE CHOLINERGIC EFFECTS. NUMBNESS, TINGLING, WEAKNESS AND CRAMPING BEGINNING SYMMETRICALLY IN THE LOWER LIMBS MAY PROGRESS TO ATAXIA AND PARALYSIS. IN SEVERE CASES, UPPER LIMB INVOLVEMENT IS POSSIBLE AND FLACCID PARALYSIS MAY PROGRESS TO SPASTIC PARALYSIS WITH EXAGGERATED REFLEXES. IMPROVEMENT MAY OCCUR OVER MONTHS TO YEARS, BUT SOME RESIDUAL IMPAIRMENT USUALLY REMAINS. **CHRONIC EXPOSURE-** REPEATED OR PROLONGED EXPOSURE MAY RESULT IN THE EFFECTS OF ACUTE EXPOSURE INCLUDING THE DELAYED NEUROPATHY. OTHER EFFECTS REPORTED IN WORKERS REPEATEDLY EXPOSED INCLUDE IMPAIRED MEMORY AND CONCENTRATION, ACUTE PSYCHOSIS, SEVERE DEPRESSIONS, IRRITABILTY, CONFUSION, APATHY, EMOTIONAL LABILITY, SOCIAL WITHDRAWAL, CONFUSION, HEADACHE, SPEECH DIFFICULTIES, DELAYED REACTION TIMES, SPATIAL DISORIENTATION, NIGHTMARES, SLEEPWALKING, AND DROWSINESS OR INSOMNIA. AN INFLUENZA-LIKE CONDITION WITH HEADACHE, NAUSEA, WEAKNESS, ANOREXIA AND MALAISE HAS ALSO BEEN REPORTED.

FIRST AID- REMOVE FROM EXPOSURE AREA TO FRESH AIR IMMEDIATELY. IF BREATHING HAS STOPPED, GIVE ARTIFICIAL RESPIRATION. MAINTAIN AIRWAY AND BLOOD PRESSURE AND ADMINISTER OXYGEN IF AVAILABLE. KEEP AFFECTED PERSON WARM AND AT REST. TREAT SYMPTOMATICALLY AND SUPPORTIVELY. ADMINISTRATION OF OXYGEN SHOULD BE PERFORMED BY QUALIFIED PERSONNEL. GET MEDICAL ATTENTION IMMEDIATELY.

SKIN CONTACT: FENTHION SULFOXIDE: SEE INFORMATION ON ORGANOPHOSPHATES. ORGANOPHOSPHATES: CHOLINESTERASE INHIBITOR. **ACUTE EXPOSURE-** LOCALIZED SWEATING AND FASCICULATIONS MAY OCCUR AT THE SITE OF CONTACT. IF SUFFICIENT AMOUNTS ARE ABSORBED, OTHER EFFECTS OF CHOLINESTERASE INHIBITION AS DESCRIBED IN ACUTE INHALATION MAY OCCUR. SYMPTOMS MAY BE DELAYED 2-3 HOURS, BUT USUALLY NO MORE THAN 12 HOURS. THE RATE OF ABSORPTION IS INCREASED BY THE PRESENCE OF DERMATITIS OR HIGH AMBIENT TEMPERATURES. DELAYED NEUROPATHY IS ALSO POSSIBLE. **CHRONIC EXPOSURE-** REPEATED OR PROLONGED EXPOSURE MAY CAUSE EFFECTS AS DESCRIBED IN ACUTE EXPOSURE. SOME ORGANOPHOSPHATES MAY CAUSE SENSITIZATION.

FIRST AID- REMOVE CONTAMINATED CLOTHING IMMEDIATELY. WASH CONTAMINATED AREAS WITH SOAP AND WATER FOLLOWED BY ALCOHOL (ARENA, POISONING, 4TH ED.). EMERGENCY PERSONNEL SHOULD WEAR GLOVES AND AVOID CONTAMINATION. TREAT RESPIRATORY DIFFICULTY WITH ARTIFICIAL RESPIRATION. GET MEDICAL ATTENTION IMMEDIATELY.

EYE CONTACT: FENTHION SULFOXIDE: SEE INFORMATION ON ORGANOPHOSPHATES. ORGANOPHOSPHATES: CHOLINESTERASE INHIBITOR. **ACUTE EXPOSURE-** DIRECT CONTACT MAY CAUSE PAIN, HYPEREMIA, LACRIMATION, TWITCHING OF THE EYELIDS, MIOSIS, AND CILIARY MUSCLE SPASM WITH LOSS OF ACCOMODATION, BLURRED OR DIMMED VISION AND BROWACHE. SOMETIMES MYDRIASIS MAY OCCUR INSTEAD OF MIOSIS. WITH SUFFICIENT EXPOSURE, OTHER SYMPTOMS OF CHOLINESTERASE INHIBITION AS DESCRIBED IN ACUTE INHALATION MAY OCCUR. **CHRONIC EXPOSURE-** REPEATED OR PROLONGED EXPOSURE MAY CAUSE EFFECTS AS DESCRIBED IN ACUTE EXPOSURE. SOME COMPOUNDS HAVE CAUSED TOXIC EFFECTS ON THE CRYSTALLINE LENS, CONJUNCTIVAL THICKENING AND OBSTRUCTION OF THE NASOLACRIMAL CANALS WHEN USED AS MIOTIC EYEDROPS.

FIRST AID- IRRIGATE EYES WITH WATER OR SALINE SOLUTION. IF SYMPTOMS OF POISONING OCCUR, TREAT RESPIRATORY DIFFICULTY WITH ARTIFICIAL RESPIRATION AND OXYGEN. OBSERVE PATIENT FOR AT LEAST 24-36 HOURS (GOSSELIN, CLINICAL TOXICOLOGY OF COMMERCIAL PRODUCTS, 5TH ED.). GET MEDICAL ATTENTION IMMEDIATELY. OXYGEN SHOULD BE ADMINISTERED BY QUALIFIED MEDICAL PERSONNEL.

INGESTION: FENTHION SULFOXIDE: TOXIC. SEE INFORMATION ON ORGANOPHOSPHATES.
ORGANOPHOSPHATES: CHOLINESTERASE INHIBITOR. **ACUTE EXPOSURE-** WHEN INGESTED, THE FIRST EFFECTS MAY BE NAUSEA, VOMITING, ANOREXIA, ABDOMINAL CRAMPS AND DIARRHEA. GASTROINTESTINAL ABSORPTION MAY CAUSE SYMPTOMS OF CHOLINESTERASE INHIBITION AS DESCRIBED IN ACUTE INHALATION. SYMPTOMS MAY BEGIN WITHIN MINUTES OR BE DELAYED FOR HOURS. DELAYED EFFECTS INCLUDING NEUROPATHY MAY ALSO OCCUR. **CHRONIC EXPOSURE-** REPEATED INGESTION MAY CAUSE EFFECTS AS DESCRIBED IN ACUTE EXPOSURE.

FIRST AID- IF PERSON IS ALERT AND RESPIRATION IS NOT DEPRESSED, GIVE SYRUP OF IPECAC FOLLOWED BY WATER (IF VOMITING OCCURS, KEEP HEAD BELOW HIPS TO PREVENT ASPIRATION). IF CONSCIOUSNESS LEVEL DECLINES OR VOMITING HAS NOT OCCURRED IN 15 MINUTES EMPTY STOMACH BY GASTRIC LAVAGE WITH THE AID OF CUFFED ENDOTRACHEAL TUBE USING ISOTONIC SALINE OR 5% SODIUM BICARBONATE FOLLOW WITH ACTIVATED CHARCOAL. ESTABLISH AND MAINTAIN AIRWAY. TREAT RESPIRATORY DIFFICULTY WITH ARTIFICIAL RESPIRATION AND OXYGEN. DO NOT GIVE MORPHINE, AMINOPHYLLINE, PHENOTHIAZINES, RESERPINE, FUROSEMIDE, OR ETHACRYNIC ACID (MORGAN, RECOGNITION AND MANAGEMENT OF PESTICIDE POISONINGS, 3RD ED.). TREAT SYMPTOMATICALLY AND

SUPPORTIVELY. ADMINISTRATION OF OXYGEN AND LAVAGE MUST BE PERFORMED BY QUALIFIED MEDICAL PERSONNEL. GET MEDICAL ATTENTION IMMEDIATELY.

ANTIDOTE: THE FOLLOWING ANTIDOTE(S) HAVE BEEN RECOMMENDED. HOWEVER, THE DECISION AS TO WHETHER THE SEVERITY OF POISONING REQUIRES ADMINISTRATION OF ANY ANTIDOTE AND ACTUAL DOSE REQUIRED SHOULD BE MADE BY QUALIFIED MEDICAL PERSONNEL.

FOR CHOLINESTERASE INHIBITORS: ESTABLISH CLEAR AIRWAY AND TISSUE OXYGENATION BY ASPIRATION OF SECRETIONS, AND IF NECESSARY, BY ASSISTED PULMONARY VENTILATION WITH OXYGEN. IMPROVE TISSUE OXYGENATION AS MUCH AS POSSIBLE BEFORE ADMINISTERING ATROPINE TO MINIMIZE THE RISK OF VENTRICULAR FIBRILLATION. ADMINISTER ATROPINE SULFATE INTRAVENOUSLY, OR INTRAMUSCULARLY IF IV INJECTION IS NOT POSSIBLE. IN MODERATELY SEVERE POISONING ADMINISTER ATROPINE SULFATE, 0.4-2.0 MG REPEATED EVERY 15 MINUTES UNTIL ATROPINIZATION IS ACHIEVED (TACHYCARDIA, FLUSHING, DRY MOUTH, MYDRIASIS). MAINTAIN ATROPINIZATION BY REPEATED DOSES FOR 2-12 HOURS, OR LONGER, DEPENDING ON THE SEVERITY OF POISONING. THE APPEARANCE OF RALES IN THE LUNG BASES, MIOSIS, SALIVATION, NAUSEA, BRADYCARDIA, ARE ALL INDICATIONS OF INADEQUATE ATROPINIZATION. SEVERELY POISONED INDIVIDUALS MAY EXHIBIT REMARKABLE TOLERANCE TO ATROPINE; TWO OR MORE TIMES THE DOSAGES SUGGESTED ABOVE MAY BE NEEDED. PERSONS NOT POISONED OR ONLY SLIGHTLY POISONED, HOWEVER, MAY DEVELOP SIGNS OF ATROPINE TOXICITY FROM SUCH LARGE DOSAGES: FEVER, MUSCLE FIBRILLATIONS, AND DELIRIUM ARE THE MAIN SIGNS OF ATROPINE TOXICITY. IF THESE SIGNS APPEAR WHILE THE PATIENT IS FULLY ATROPINIZED, ATROPINE ADMINISTRATION SHOULD BE DISCONTINUED, AT LEAST TEMPORARILY. OBSERVE TREATED PATIENTS CLOSELY AT LEAST 24 HOURS TO INSURE THAT SYMPTOMS (POSSIBLY PULMONARY EDEMA) DO NOT RECUR AS ATROPINIZATION WEARS OFF. IN VERY SEVERE POISONINGS, METABOLIC DISPOSITION OF TOXICANT MAY REQUIRE SEVERAL HOURS OR DAYS DURING WHICH ATROPINIZATION MUST BE MAINTAINED. MARKEDLY LOWER LEVELS OF URINARY METABOLITES INDICATE THAT ATROPINE DOSAGE CAN BE TAPERED OFF. AS DOSAGE IS REDUCED, CHECK THE LUNG BASES FREQUENTLY FOR RALES. IF RALES ARE HEARD OR OTHER SYMPTOMS RETURN, RE-ESTABLISH ATROPINIZATION PROMPTLY (MORGAN, RECOGNITION AND MANAGEMENT OF PESTICIDE POISONINGS, 3RD ED.). ADMINISTRATION OF ANTIDOTE MUST BE PERFORMED BY QUALIFIED MEDICAL PERSONNEL.

IN CASES OF SEVERE POISONING BY ORGANOPHOSPHATE PESTICIDES IN WHICH RESPIRATORY DEPRESSION, MUSCLE WEAKNESS AND TWITCHINGS ARE SEVERE, GIVE PRALIDOXIME (PROTOPAM-AYERST, 2-PAM), 1.0 GRAM INTRAVENOUSLY AT NO MORE THAN 0.5 GRAM PER MINUTE. DOSAGE OF PRALIDOXIME MAY BE REPEATED IN 1-2 HOURS, THEN AT 10-12 HOUR INTERVALS IF NEEDED. IN VERY SEVERE POISONINGS, DOSAGE RATES MAY BE DOUBLED. TREATMENT WITH PRALIDOXIME WILL BE MOST EFFECTIVE IF GIVEN WITHIN THIRTY-SIX HOURS AFTER POISONING (MORGAN, RECOGNITION AND MANAGEMENT OF PESTICIDE POISONINGS, 3RD ED.). ANTIDOTE SHOULD BE ADMINISTERED BY QUALIFIED MEDICAL PERSONNEL.

REACTIVITY

REACTIVITY: STABLE UNDER NORMAL TEMPERATURES AND PRESSURES.

INCOMPATIBILITIES: FENTHION SULFOXIDE: OXIDIZERS (STRONG): FIRE AND EXPLOSION HAZARD.

DECOMPOSITION: THERMAL DECOMPOSITION PRODUCTS MAY INCLUDE TOXIC OXIDES OF CARBON, NITROGEN, AND SULFUR.

POLYMERIZATION: HAZARDOUS POLYMERIZATION HAS NOT BEEN REPORTED TO OCCUR UNDER NORMAL TEMPERATURES AND PRESSURES.

STORAGE AND DISPOSAL

OBSERVE ALL FEDERAL, STATE AND LOCAL REGULATIONS WHEN STORING OR DISPOSING OF THIS SUBSTANCE. FOR ASSISTANCE, CONTACT THE DISTRICT DIRECTOR OF THE ENVIRONMENTAL PROTECTION AGENCY.

****STORAGE****

STORE AWAY FROM INCOMPATIBLE SUBSTANCES.

STORE IN ACCORDANCE WITH 40 CFR 165 RECOMMENDED PROCEDURES FOR THE DISPOSAL AND STORAGE OF PESTICIDES AND PESTICIDE CONTAINERS.

****DISPOSAL****

DISPOSAL MUST BE IN ACCORDANCE WITH 40 CFR 165 RECOMMENDED PROCEDURES FOR THE DISPOSAL AND STORAGE OF PESTICIDES AND PESTICIDE CONTAINERS.

CONDITIONS TO AVOID

MAY BURN BUT DOES NOT IGNITE READILY.

SPILL AND LEAK PROCEDURES

OCCUPATIONAL SPILL: DO NOT TOUCH SPILLED MATERIAL. STOP LEAK IF YOU CAN DO IT WITHOUT RISK. FOR SMALL SPILLS, TAKE UP WITH SAND OR OTHER ABSORBENT MATERIAL AND PLACE INTO CONTAINERS FOR LATER DISPOSAL. FOR SMALL DRY SPILLS, WITH A CLEAN SHOVEL PLACE MATERIAL INTO CLEAN, DRY CONTAINER AND COVER. MOVE CONTAINERS FROM SPILL AREA. FOR LARGER SPILLS, DIKE FAR AHEAD OF SPILL FOR LATER DISPOSAL. KEEP UNNECESSARY PEOPLE AWAY. ISOLATE HAZARD AREA AND DENY ENTRY.

PROTECTIVE EQUIPMENT

VENTILATION: PROVIDE LOCAL EXHAUST OR PROCESS ENCLOSURE VENTILATION SYSTEM.

RESPIRATOR: THE FOLLOWING RESPIRATORS ARE RECOMMENDED BASED ON INFORMATION FOUND IN THE PHYSICAL DATA, TOXICITY AND HEALTH EFFECTS SECTIONS. THEY ARE RANKED IN ORDER FROM MINIMUM TO MAXIMUM RESPIRATORY PROTECTION. THE SPECIFIC RESPIRATOR SELECTED MUST BE BASED ON CONTAMINATION LEVELS FOUND IN THE WORK PLACE, MUST NOT EXCEED THE WORKING LIMITS OF THE RESPIRATOR AND BE JOINTLY APPROVED BY THE NATIONAL INSTITUTE FOR OCCUPATIONAL SAFETY AND HEALTH AND THE MINE SAFETY AND HEALTH ADMINISTRATION (NIOSH-MSHA).

TYPE 'C' SUPPLIED-AIR RESPIRATOR WITH A FULL FACEPIECE OPERATED IN PRESSURE-DEMAND OR OTHER POSITIVE PRESSURE MODE OR WITH A FULL FACEPIECE, HELMET OR HOOD OPERATED IN CONTINOUS-FLOW MODE.

SELF-CONTAINED BREATHING APPARATUS WITH A FULL FACEPIECE OPERATED IN PRESSURE-DEMAND OR OTHER POSITIVE PRESSURE MODE.

FOR FIREFIGHTING AND OTHER IMMEDIATELY DANGEROUS TO LIFE OR HEALTH CONDITIONS:

SELF-CONTAINED BREATHING APPARATUS WITH FULL FACEPIECE OPERATED IN PRESSURE-DEMAND OR OTHER POSITIVE PRESSURE MODE.

SUPPLIED-AIR RESPIRATOR WITH FULL FACEPIECE AND OPERATED IN PRESSURE-DEMAND OR OTHER POSITIVE PRESSURE MODE IN COMBINATION WITH AN AUXILIARY SELF-CONTAINED BREATHING APPARATUS OPERATED IN PRESSURE-DEMAND OR OTHER POSITIVE PRESSURE MODE.

CLOTHING: EMPLOYEE MUST WEAR APPROPRIATE PROTECTIVE (IMPERVIOUS) CLOTHING AND EQUIPMENT TO PREVENT ANY POSSIBILITY OF SKIN CONTACT WITH THIS SUBSTANCE.

GLOVES: EMPLOYEE MUST WEAR APPROPRIATE PROTECTIVE GLOVES TO PREVENT CONTACT WITH THIS SUBSTANCE.

EYE PROTECTION: EMPLOYEE MUST WEAR SPLASH-PROOF OR DUST-RESISTANT SAFETY GOGGLES AND A FACESHIELD TO PREVENT CONTACT WITH THIS SUBSTANCE.

EMERGENCY WASH FACILITIES: WHERE THERE IS ANY POSSIBILITY THAT AN EMPLOYEE'S EYES AND/OR SKIN MAY BE EXPOSED TO THIS SUBSTANCE, THE EMPLOYER SHOULD PROVIDE AN EYE WASH FOUNTAIN AND QUICK DRENCH SHOWER WITHIN THE IMMEDIATE WORK AREA FOR EMERGENCY USE.

AUTHORIZED BY- OCCUPATIONAL HEALTH SERVICES, INC.

CREATION DATE: 10/04/89 ***REVISION DATE:*** 04/27/90

MATERIAL SAFETY DATA SHEET

OCCUPATIONAL HEALTH SERVICES, INC.
AGRICULTURE AND PESTICIDE DIVISION
450 SEVENTH AVENUE, SUITE 2407
NEW YORK, NEW YORK 10123
1-800-445-MSDS OR (212) 967-1100

EMERGENCY CONTACT:
JOHN S. BRANSFORD, JR. (615) 292-1180

SUBSTANCE IDENTIFICATION

CAS-NUMBER 22781-23-3

SUBSTANCE: **BENDIOCARB**

TRADE NAMES/SYNONYMS: 1,3-BENZODIOXOL-4-OL, 2,2-DIMETHYL-, METHYLCARBAMATE; CARBAMIC ACID, METHYL-, 2,3-(ISOPROPYLIDENEDIOXY)PHENYL ESTER; 2,2-DIMETHYL-1,3-BENZODIOXOL-4-OL METHYLCARBAMATE; METHYLCARBAMIC ACID 2,3-(ISOPROPYLIDENEDIOXY)PHENYL ESTER; 2,2-DIMETHYL-1,3-BENZODIOXOL-4-YL METHYLCARBAMATE; 2,3-ISOPROPYLIDENEDIOXYPHENYL METHYLCARBAMATE; BENCARBATE; DYCARB; FICAM; GARVOX; NC 6897; NIOMIL; TATTOO; C11H13NO4; PST02560

CHEMICAL FAMILY: CARBAMATE ESTER, CARBOXYLIC, AROMATIC

MOLECULAR FORMULA: C11-H13-N-O4

MOLECULAR WEIGHT: 223.25
CERCLA RATINGS (SCALE 0-3): HEALTH=3 FIRE=U REACTIVITY=0 PERSISTENCE=2
NFPA RATINGS (SCALE 0-4): HEALTH=3 FIRE=U REACTIVITY=0

COMPONENTS AND CONTAMINANTS

COMPONENT: BENDIOCARB ***PERCENT:*** 100.0
CAS# 22781-23-3
OTHER CONTAMINANTS: NONE
EXPOSURE LIMITS: NO OCCUPATIONAL EXPOSURE LIMITS ESTABLISHED BY OSHA, ACGIH, OR NIOSH.

PHYSICAL DATA

DESCRIPTION: WHITE CRYSTALLINE SOLID ***MELTING POINT:*** 264 F (129 C)
SPECIFIC GRAVITY: NOT AVAILABLE ***VAPOR PRESSURE:*** .000005 MMHG @ 25 C
SOLUBILITY IN WATER: 40 PPM
SOLVENT SOLUBILITY: SOLUBLE IN DICHLOROMETHANE, ACETONE, CHLOROFORM, DIOXANE; SLIGHTLY SOLUBLE IN O-XYLENE, BENZENE, AND ETHANOL

FIRE AND EXPLOSION DATA

FIRE AND EXPLOSION HAZARD: UNKNOWN FIRE AND EXPLOSION HAZARD.
FIREFIGHTING MEDIA: DRY CHEMICAL, CARBON DIOXIDE, HALON, WATER SPRAY OR STANDARD FOAM (1987 EMERGENCY RESPONSE GUIDEBOOK, DOT P 5800.4).
FOR LARGER FIRES, USE WATER SPRAY, FOG OR STANDARD FOAM (1987 EMERGENCY RESPONSE GUIDEBOOK, DOT P 5800.4).
FIREFIGHTING: MOVE CONTAINER FROM FIRE AREA IF POSSIBLE. DO NOT SCATTER SPILLED MATERIAL WITH HIGH PRESSURE WATER STREAMS. DIKE FIRE CONTROL WATER FOR LATER DISPOSAL (1987 EMERGENCY RESPONSE GUIDEBOOK, DOT P 5800.4, GUIDE PAGE 31).
USE AGENTS SUITABLE FOR TYPE OF SURROUNDING FIRE. AVOID BREATHING HAZARDOUS VAPORS, KEEP UPWIND.

TRANSPORTATION DATA

DEPARTMENT OF TRANSPORTATION HAZARD CLASSIFICATION 49 CFR 172.101: POISON B
DEPARTMENT OF TRANSPORTATION LABELING REQUIREMENTS 49 CFR 172.101 AND SUBPART E: POISON
DEPARTMENT OF TRANSPORTATION PACKAGING REQUIREMENTS: 49 CFR 173.365 EXCEPTIONS: 49 CFR 173.364

TOXICITY

BENDIOCARB: TOXICITY DATA: 566 MG/KG SKIN-RAT LD50; 40 MG/KG ORAL-RAT LD50; 45 MG/KG ORAL-MOUSE LD50; 35 MG/KG ORAL-RABBIT LD50; 35 MG/KG ORAL-GUINEA PIG LD50; 35 MG/KG ORAL-MAMMAL LD50. CARCINOGEN STATUS: NONE. ACUTE TOXICITY: HIGHLY TOXIC BY INGESTION; TOXIC BY DERMAL ABSORPTION. TARGET EFFECTS: CHOLINESTERASE INHIBITOR. AT INCREASED RISK FROM EXPOSURE: PERSONS WITH ASTHMA, DIABETES, CARDIOVASCULAR DISEASE, MECHANICAL OBSTRUCTION OF THE GASTROINTESTINAL OR UROGENITAL TRACT, AND THOSE IN VAGOTONIC STATES.*
* MAY BE BASED ON GENERAL INFORMATION ON CARBAMATES.

HEALTH EFFECTS AND FIRST AID

INHALATION: BENDIOCARB: SEE INFORMATION ON CARBAMATES. CARBAMATES: CHOLINESTERASE INHIBITOR. **ACUTE EXPOSURE**- WHEN INHALED, THE FIRST EFFECTS OF CHOLINESTERASE INHIBITION ARE USUALLY RESPIRATORY AND MAY INCLUDE NASAL HYPEREMIA AND WATERY DISCHARGE, CHEST DISCOMFORT, DYSPNEA, AND WHEEZING DUE TO INCREASED BRONCHIAL SECRETIONS AND BRONCHOCONSTRICTION. OTHER SYSTEMIC EFFECTS MAY BEGIN WITHIN A FEW MINUTES OR SEVERAL HOURS OF EXPOSURE. SYMPTOMS MAY INCLUDE NAUSEA, VOMITING, DIARRHEA, ABDOMINAL CRAMPS, HEADACHE, VERTIGO, OCULAR PAIN, CILIARY MUSCLE SPASM, BLURRING OR DIMNESS OF VISION, MIOSIS, OR IN SOME CASES MYDRIASIS, LACRIMATION, SALIVATION, SWEATING, AND CONFUSION. OTHER REPORTED CENTRAL NERVOUS SYSTEM OR NEUROMUSCULAR EFFECTS INCLUDE ATAXIA, SLURRED SPEECH, AREFLEXIA, WEAKNESS, FATIGUE, TWITCHING, FASCICULATION, TREMOR, AND EVENTUALLY PARALYSIS OF THE EXTREMITIES AND POSSIBLY OF THE RESPIRATORY MUSCLES. IN SEVERE CASES, THERE MAY ALSO BE INVOLUNTARY DEFECATION AND URINATION, BRADYCARDIA, HYPOTENSION, PULMONARY EDEMA, CONVULSIONS, COMA, AND DEATH FROM RESPIRATORY FAILURE OR CARDIAC ARREST. CARBAMATES GENERALLY DO NOT ACCUMULATE IN MAMMALIAN TISSUE AND THE CHOLINESTERASE INHIBITION REVERSES RATHER RAPIDLY. IN NON-FATAL CASES, THE ILLNESS GENERALLY LASTS LESS THAN 24 HOURS. **CHRONIC EXPOSURE**- PROLONGED OR REPEATED EXPOSURE MAY CAUSE EFFECTS AS DESCRIBED IN ACUTE EXPOSURE.
FIRST AID- REMOVE FROM EXPOSURE AREA TO FRESH AIR IMMEDIATELY. IF BREATHING HAS STOPPED, GIVE ARTIFICIAL RESPIRATION. MAINTAIN AIRWAY AND BLOOD PRESSURE AND ADMINISTER OXYGEN IF AVAILABLE. KEEP AFFECTED PERSON WARM AND AT REST. TREAT SYMPTOMATICALLY AND SUPPORTIVELY. ADMINISTRATION OF OXYGEN SHOULD BE PERFORMED BY QUALIFIED PERSONNEL. GET MEDICAL ATTENTION IMMEDIATELY.

SKIN CONTACT: BENDIOCARB: TOXIC. SEE INFORMATION ON CARBAMATES. CARBAMATES: CHOLINESTERASE INHIBITOR. **ACUTE EXPOSURE**- SOME COMPOUNDS MAY CAUSE IRRITATION. LOCALIZED SWEATING AND FASCICULATIONS MAY OCCUR AT THE SITE OF CONTACT. IF SUFFICIENT AMOUNTS ARE ABSORBED THROUGH THE SKIN, OTHER EFFECTS OF CHOLINESTERASE INHIBITION MAY OCCUR AS DESCRIBED IN ACUTE INHALATION; SYMPTOMS MAY BE DELAYED FOR 2-3 HOURS, USUALLY NO MORE THAN 8 HOURS. **CHRONIC EXPOSURE**- REPEATED OR PROLONGED EXPOSURE MAY CAUSE EFFECTS AS DESCRIBED IN ACUTE EXPOSURE.
FIRST AID- REMOVE CONTAMINATED CLOTHING IMMEDIATELY. WASH CONTAMINATED AREAS WITH SOAP AND WATER FOLLOWED BY ALCOHOL (ARENA, POISONING, 4TH ED.). EMERGENCY PERSONNEL SHOULD WEAR GLOVES AND AVOID CONTAMINATION. TREAT RESPIRATORY DIFFICULTY WITH ARTIFICIAL RESPIRATION. GET MEDICAL ATTENTION IMMEDIATELY.

EYE CONTACT: BENDIOCARB: SEE INFORMATION ON CARBAMATES. CARBAMATES: CHOLINESTERASE INHIBITOR. **ACUTE EXPOSURE**- DIRECT CONTACT MAY CAUSE PAIN, HYPEREMIA, LACRIMATION, TWITCHING OF THE EYELIDS, MIOSIS, AND CILIARY MUSCLE SPASM WITH LOSS OF ACCOMODATION, BLURRED OR DIMMED VISION AND BROWACHE. SOMETIMES MYDRIASIS MAY OCCUR INSTEAD OF MIOSIS. WITH SUFFICIENT EXPOSURE, OTHER SYMPTOMS OF CHOLINESTERASE INHIBITION MAY OCCUR AS DESCRIBED IN ACUTE INHALATION. **CHRONIC EXPOSURE**- PROLONGED EXPOSURE MAY CAUSE EFFECTS AS DESCRIBED IN ACUTE EXPOSURE. SOME COMPOUNDS HAVE CAUSED TOXIC EFFECTS ON THE CRYSTALLINE LENS, CONJUNCTIVAL THICKENING AND OBSTRUCTION OF NASOLACRIMAL CANALS WHEN USED AS MIOTIC EYE DROPS.
FIRST AID- IRRIGATE EYES WITH WATER OR SALINE SOLUTION. IF SYMPTOMS OF POISONING OCCUR, TREAT RESPIRATORY DIFFICULTY WITH ARTIFICIAL RESPIRATION AND OXYGEN. OBSERVE PATIENT FOR AT LEAST 24-36 HOURS (GOSSELIN, CLINICAL TOXICOLOGY OF COMMERCIAL PRODUCTS, 5TH ED.). GET MEDICAL ATTENTION IMMEDIATELY. OXYGEN SHOULD BE ADMINISTERED BY QUALIFIED MEDICAL PERSONNEL.

INGESTION: BENDIOCARB: HIGHLY TOXIC. SEE INFORMATION ON CARBAMATES. CARBAMATES: CHOLINESTERASE INHIBITOR. **ACUTE EXPOSURE**- WHEN INGESTED, THE FIRST EFFECTS MAY BE NAUSEA, VOMITING, ANOREXIA, ABDOMINAL CRAMPS, AND DIARRHEA. WITH ABSORPTION FROM THE GASTROINTESTINAL TRACT, THE OTHER EFFECTS OF CHOLINESTERASE INHIBITION AS DESCRIBED IN ACUTE INHALATION MAY OCCUR; SYMPTOMS MAY BEGIN WITHIN MINUTES OR BE DELAYED SEVERAL HOURS. **CHRONIC EXPOSURE**- REPEATED INGESTION MAY CAUSE EFFECTS AS DESCRIBED IN ACUTE EXPOSURE.
FIRST AID- IF PERSON IS ALERT AND RESPIRATION IS NOT DEPRESSED, GIVE SYRUP OF IPECAC FOLLOWED BY WATER (IF VOMITING OCCURS, KEEP HEAD BELOW HIPS TO PREVENT ASPIRATION). IF CONSCIOUSNESS LEVEL DECLINES OR VOMITING HAS NOT OCCURRED IN 15 MINUTES EMPTY STOMACH BY GASTRIC LAVAGE WITH THE AID OF CUFFED ENDOTRACHEAL TUBE USING ISOTONIC SALINE OR 5% SODIUM BICARBONATE FOLLOW WITH ACTIVATED CHARCOAL. ESTABLISH AND MAINTAIN AIRWAY. TREAT RESPIRATORY DIFFICULTY WITH ARTIFICIAL RESPIRATION AND OXYGEN. DO NOT GIVE MORPHINE, AMINOPHYLLINE, PHENOTHIAZINES, RESERPINE, FUROSEMIDE, OR ETHACRYNIC ACID (MORGAN, RECOGNITION AND MANAGEMENT OF PESTICIDE POISONINGS, 3RD ED.). TREAT SYMPTOMATICALLY AND SUPPORTIVELY. ADMINISTRATION OF OXYGEN AND LAVAGE MUST BE PERFORMED BY QUALIFIED MEDICAL PERSONNEL. GET MEDICAL ATTENTION IMMEDIATELY.
ANTIDOTE: THE FOLLOWING ANTIDOTE HAS BEEN RECOMMENDED. HOWEVER, THE DECISION AS TO WHETHER THE SEVERITY OF POISONING REQUIRES ADMINISTRATION OF ANY ANTIDOTE AND ACTUAL DOSE REQUIRED SHOULD BE MADE BY QUALIFIED MEDICAL PERSONNEL.
FOR CHOLINESTERASE INHIBITORS: ESTABLISH CLEAR AIRWAY AND TISSUE OXYGENATION BY ASPIRATION OF SECRETIONS, AND IF NECESSARY, BY ASSISTED PULMONARY VENTILATION WITH OXYGEN. IMPROVE TISSUE OXYGENATION AS MUCH AS POSSIBLE BEFORE ADMINISTERING ATROPINE TO MINIMIZE THE RISK OF VENTRICULAR FIBRILLATION. ADMINISTER ATROPINE SULFATE INTRAVENOUSLY, OR INTRAMUSCULARLY IF IV INJECTION IS NOT POSSIBLE. IN MODERATELY SEVERE POISONING ADMINISTER ATROPINE SULFATE, 0.4-2.0 MG REPEATED EVERY 15 MINUTES UNTIL ATROPINIZATION IS ACHIEVED (TACHYCARDIA, FLUSHING, DRY MOUTH, MYDRIASIS). MAINTAIN ATROPINIZATION BY REPEATED DOSES FOR 2-12 HOURS, OR LONGER, DEPENDING ON THE SEVERITY OF POISONING. THE APPEARANCE OF RALES IN THE LUNG BASES, MIOSIS, SALIVATION, NAUSEA, BRADYCARDIA, ARE ALL INDICATIONS OF INADEQUATE ATROPINIZATION. SEVERELY POISONED INDIVIDUALS MAY EXHIBIT REMARKABLE TOLERANCE TO ATROPINE; TWO OR MORE TIMES THE DOSAGES SUGGESTED ABOVE MAY BE NEEDED. PERSONS NOT POISONED OR ONLY SLIGHTLY POISONED, HOWEVER, MAY

DEVELOP SIGNS OF ATROPINE TOXICITY FROM SUCH LARGE DOSAGES: FEVER, MUSCLE FIBRILLATIONS, AND DELIRIUM ARE THE MAIN SIGNS OF ATROPINE TOXICITY. IF THESE SIGNS APPEAR WHILE THE PATIENT IS FULLY ATROPINIZED, ATROPINE ADMINISTRATION SHOULD BE DISCONTINUED, AT LEAST TEMPORARILY. OBSERVE TREATED PATIENTS CLOSELY AT LEAST 24 HOURS TO INSURE THAT SYMPTOMS (POSSIBLY PULMONARY EDEMA) DO NOT RECUR AS ATROPINIZATION WEARS OFF. IN VERY SEVERE POISONINGS, METABOLIC DISPOSITION OF TOXICANT MAY REQUIRE SEVERAL HOURS OR DAYS DURING WHICH ATROPINIZATION MUST BE MAINTAINED. MARKEDLY LOWER LEVELS OF URINARY METABOLITES INDICATE THAT ATROPINE DOSAGE CAN BE TAPERED OFF. AS DOSAGE IS REDUCED, CHECK THE LUNG BASES FREQUENTLY FOR RALES. IF RALES ARE HEARD OR OTHER SYMPTOMS RETURN, RE-ESTABLISH ATROPINIZATION PROMPTLY (MORGAN, RECOGNITION AND MANAGEMENT OF PESTICIDE POISONINGS, 3RD ED.). ADMINISTRATION OF ANTIDOTE MUST BE PERFORMED BY QUALIFIED MEDICAL PERSONNEL.

REACTIVITY

REACTIVITY: STABLE UNDER NORMAL TEMPERATURES AND PRESSURES.

INCOMPATIBILITIES: BENDIOCARB: NO DATA AVAILABLE.

DECOMPOSITION: THERMAL DECOMPOSITION PRODUCTS MAY INCLUDE TOXIC OXIDES OF NITROGEN.

POLYMERIZATION: HAZARDOUS POLYMERIZATION HAS NOT BEEN REPORTED TO OCCUR UNDER NORMAL TEMPERATURES AND PRESSURES.

STORAGE AND DISPOSAL

OBSERVE ALL FEDERAL, STATE AND LOCAL REGULATIONS WHEN STORING OR DISPOSING OF THIS SUBSTANCE. FOR ASSISTANCE, CONTACT THE DISTRICT DIRECTOR OF THE ENVIRONMENTAL PROTECTION AGENCY.

STORAGE

STORE IN ACCORDANCE WITH 40 CFR 165 RECOMMENDED PROCEDURES FOR THE DISPOSAL AND STORAGE OF PESTICIDES AND PESTICIDE CONTAINERS.

DISPOSAL

DISPOSAL MUST BE IN ACCORDANCE WITH 40 CFR 165 RECOMMENDED PROCEDURES FOR THE DISPOSAL AND STORAGE OF PESTICIDES AND PESTICIDE CONTAINERS.

CONDITIONS TO AVOID

NONE REPORTED.

SPILL AND LEAK PROCEDURES

OCCUPATIONAL SPILL: SWEEP UP AND PLACE IN SUITABLE CLEAN, DRY CONTAINERS FOR RECLAMATION OR LATER DISPOSAL. DO NOT FLUSH SPILLED MATERIAL INTO SEWER. KEEP UNNECESSARY PEOPLE AWAY.

PROTECTIVE EQUIPMENT

VENTILATION: PROVIDE LOCAL EXHAUST OR PROCESS ENCLOSURE VENTILATION SYSTEM.

RESPIRATOR: THE FOLLOWING RESPIRATORS ARE RECOMMENDED BASED ON INFORMATION FOUND IN THE PHYSICAL DATA, TOXICITY AND HEALTH EFFECTS SECTIONS. THEY ARE RANKED IN ORDER FROM MINIMUM TO MAXIMUM RESPIRATORY PROTECTION. THE SPECIFIC RESPIRATOR SELECTED MUST BE BASED ON CONTAMINATION LEVELS FOUND IN THE WORK PLACE, MUST NOT EXCEED THE WORKING LIMITS OF THE RESPIRATOR AND BE JOINTLY APPROVED BY THE NATIONAL INSTITUTE FOR OCCUPATIONAL SAFETY AND HEALTH AND THE MINE SAFETY AND HEALTH ADMINISTRATION (NIOSH-MSHA).

TYPE 'C' SUPPLIED-AIR RESPIRATOR WITH A FULL FACEPIECE OPERATED IN PRESSURE-DEMAND OR OTHER POSITIVE PRESSURE MODE OR WITH A FULL FACEPIECE, HELMET OR HOOD OPERATED IN CONTINOUS-FLOW MODE.

SELF-CONTAINED BREATHING APPARATUS WITH A FULL FACEPIECE OPERATED IN PRESSURE-DEMAND OR OTHER POSITIVE PRESSURE MODE.

FOR FIREFIGHTING AND OTHER IMMEDIATELY DANGEROUS TO LIFE OR HEALTH CONDITIONS:

SELF-CONTAINED BREATHING APPARATUS WITH FULL FACEPIECE OPERATED IN PRESSURE-DEMAND OR OTHER POSITIVE PRESSURE MODE.

SUPPLIED-AIR RESPIRATOR WITH FULL FACEPIECE AND OPERATED IN PRESSURE-DEMAND OR OTHER POSITIVE PRESSURE MODE IN COMBINATION WITH AN AUXILIARY SELF-CONTAINED BREATHING APPARATUS OPERATED IN PRESSURE-DEMAND OR OTHER POSITIVE PRESSURE MODE.

CLOTHING: EMPLOYEE MUST WEAR APPROPRIATE PROTECTIVE (IMPERVIOUS) CLOTHING AND EQUIPMENT TO PREVENT ANY POSSIBILITY OF SKIN CONTACT WITH THIS SUBSTANCE.

GLOVES: EMPLOYEE MUST WEAR APPROPRIATE PROTECTIVE GLOVES TO PREVENT CONTACT WITH THIS SUBSTANCE.

EYE PROTECTION: EMPLOYEE MUST WEAR SPLASH-PROOF OR DUST-RESISTANT SAFETY GOGGLES WITH OR WITHOUT A FACESHIELD TO PREVENT CONTACT WITH THIS SUBSTANCE. EMERGENCY EYE WASH: WHERE THERE IS ANY POSSIBILITY THAT AN EMPLOYEE'S EYES MAY BE EXPOSED TO THIS SUBSTANCE, THE EMPLOYER SHOULD PROVIDE AN EYE WASH FOUNTAIN WITHIN THE IMMEDIATE WORK AREA FOR EMERGENCY USE.

AUTHORIZED BY- OCCUPATIONAL HEALTH SERVICES, INC.

CREATION DATE: 10/04/89 ***REVISION DATE:*** 06/12/90

MATERIAL SAFETY DATA SHEET

OCCUPATIONAL HEALTH SERVICES, INC.
AGRICULTURE AND PESTICIDE DIVISION
450 SEVENTH AVENUE, SUITE 2407
NEW YORK, NEW YORK 10123
1-800-445-MSDS OR (212) 967-1100

EMERGENCY CONTACT:
JOHN S. BRANSFORD, JR. (615) 292-1180

SUBSTANCE IDENTIFICATION

CAS-NUMBER 1861-40-1

SUBSTANCE: **BENFLURALIN**

TRADE NAMES/SYNONYMS: BENZENAMINE, N-BUTYL-N-ETHYL-2,6-DINITRO-4-(TRIFLUOROMETHYL)-; P-TOLUIDINE, N-BUTYL-N-ETHYL-ALPHA,ALPHA,ALPHA-TRIFLUORO-2,6-DINITRO-; N-BUTYL-N-ETHYL-2,6-DINITRO-4-(TRIFLUOROMETHYL)BENZENAMINE; N-BUTYL-N-ETHYL-ALPHA,ALPHA,ALPHA-TRIFLUORO-2,6-DINITRO-P-TOLUIDINE; N-BUTYL-N-ETHYL-2,6-DINITRO-4-TRIFLUOROMETHYLANILINE; BALAN; BENEFEX; BENEFIN; BALFIN; BETHRODINE; BINNELL; BONALAN; EL 110; FLUBALEX; BANAFINE; BENALAN; QUILAN; C13H16F3N3O4; PST02570

CHEMICAL FAMILY: AROMATIC
AMINE
HALOGEN

MOLECULAR FORMULA: C13-H16-F3-N3-O4

MOLECULAR WEIGHT: 335.32

CERCLA RATINGS (SCALE 0-3): HEALTH=U FIRE=0 REACTIVITY=0 PERSISTENCE=2

NFPA RATINGS (SCALE 0-4): HEALTH=U FIRE=0 REACTIVITY=0

COMPONENTS AND CONTAMINANTS

COMPONENT: BENFLURALIN ***PERCENT:*** 100.0
CAS# 1861-40-1

EXPOSURE LIMITS: NO OCCUPATIONAL EXPOSURE LIMITS ESTABLISHED BY OSHA, ACGIH, OR NIOSH.

PHYSICAL DATA

DESCRIPTION: YELLOW-ORANGE CRYSTALINE SOLID

MELTING POINT: 149-151.7 F (65-66 C) ***SPECIFIC GRAVITY:*** NOT AVAILABLE

VAPOR PRESSURE: 0.0004 @ 30 C ***SOLUBILITY IN WATER:*** 0.01% @ 25 C

SOLVENT SOLUBILITY: SOLUBLE IN ACETONE, XYLENE, AND MOST ORGANIC SOLVENTS; SLIGHTLY SOLUBLE IN ETHANOL.

FIRE AND EXPLOSION DATA

FIRE AND EXPLOSION HAZARD: NEGLIGIBLE FIRE HAZARD WHEN EXPOSED TO HEAT OR FLAME.

FIREFIGHTING MEDIA: DRY CHEMICAL, CARBON DIOXIDE, HALON, WATER SPRAY OR STANDARD FOAM (1987 EMERGENCY RESPONSE GUIDEBOOK, DOT P 5800.4). FOR LARGER FIRES, USE WATER SPRAY, FOG OR STANDARD FOAM (1987 EMERGENCY RESPONSE GUIDEBOOK, DOT P 5800.4).

FIREFIGHTING: NO ACUTE HAZARD. MOVE CONTAINER FROM FIRE AREA IF POSSIBLE. AVOID BREATHING VAPORS OR DUSTS; KEEP UPWIND.

TOXICITY

BENFLURALIN: TOXICITY DATA: 10 GM/KG ORAL-RAT LD50; 5 GM/KG ORAL-MOUSE LD50. CARCINOGEN STATUS: NONE. ACUTE TOXICITY: SLIGHTLY TOXIC BY INGESTION. TARGET EFFECTS: NO DATA AVAILABLE.

HEALTH EFFECTS AND FIRST AID

INHALATION: BENFLURALIN: **ACUTE EXPOSURE**- NO DATA AVAILABLE. **CHRONIC EXPOSURE**- NO DATA AVAILABLE.

FIRST AID- REMOVE FROM EXPOSURE AREA TO FRESH AIR IMMEDIATELY. IF BREATHING HAS STOPPED, PERFORM ARTIFICIAL RESPIRATION. KEEP PERSON WARM AND AT REST. TREAT SYMPTOMATICALLY AND SUPPORTIVELY. GET MEDICAL ATTENTION IMMEDIATELY.

SKIN CONTACT: BENFLURALIN: **ACUTE EXPOSURE-** 200 MG/KG APPLIED TO THE SKIN OF RABBITS WAS NOT IRRITATING. BENFLURALIN MAY CAUSE SKIN SENSITIZATION REACTIONS IN SOME INDIVIDUALS. **CHRONIC EXPOSURE-** NO DATA AVAILABLE.
FIRST AID- REMOVE CONTAMINATED CLOTHING AND SHOES IMMEDIATELY. WASH AFFECTED AREA WITH SOAP OR MILD DETERGENT AND LARGE AMOUNTS OF WATER UNTIL NO EVIDENCE OF CHEMICAL REMAINS (APPROXIMATELY 15-20 MINUTES). GET MEDICAL ATTENTION IMMEDIATELY.

EYE CONTACT: BENFLURALIN: **ACUTE EXPOSURE-** THIS MATERIAL WAS NOT IRRITATING TO RABBIT EYES. CERTAIN FORMULATIONS CONTAINING BENFLURALIN HAVE CAUSED SEVERE EYE IRRITATION IN LABORATORY ANIMALS. **CHRONIC EXPOSURE-** NO DATA AVAILABLE. **FIRST AID-** WASH EYES IMMEDIATELY WITH LARGE AMOUNTS OF WATER OR NORMAL SALINE, OCCASIONALLY LIFTING UPPER AND LOWER LIDS, UNTIL NO EVIDENCE OF CHEMICAL REMAINS (APPROXIMATELY 15-20 MINUTES). GET MEDICAL ATTENTION IMMEDIATELY.

INGESTION: BENFLURALIN: **ACUTE EXPOSURE-** A LETHAL DOSE IN RATS WAS 10 GM/KG; SYMPTOMS WERE NOT REPORTED. **CHRONIC EXPOSURE-** RATS AND DOGS SHOWED NO ILL EFFECT WHEN FED A DIETARY LEVEL OF 1,000 PPM FOR 2 YEARS.
FIRST AID- REMOVE BY GASTRIC LAVAGE AND CATHARSIS. MAINTAIN BLOOD PRESSURE AND AIRWAY. GIVE OXYGEN IF RESPIRATION IS DEPRESSED. DO NOT PERFORM GASTRIC LAVAGE IF VICTIM IS UNCONSCIOUS. GET MEDICAL ATTENTION IMMEDIATELY (DREISBACH, HANDBOOK OF POISONING, 12TH ED.).
ADMINISTRATION OF LAVAGE OR OXYGEN SHOULD BE PERFORMED BY QUALIFIED MEDICAL PERSONNEL.
ANTIDOTE: NO SPECIFIC ANTIDOTE. TREAT SYMPTOMATICALLY AND SUPPORTIVELY.

REACTIVITY

REACTIVITY: STABLE UNDER NORMAL TEMPERATURES AND PRESSURES.
INCOMPATIBILITIES: BENFLURALIN: OXIDIZERS (STRONG): FIRE AND EXPLOSION HAZARD.
DECOMPOSITION: THERMAL DECOMPOSITION MAY RELEASE TOXIC AND/OR HAZARDOUS GASES.
POLYMERIZATION: HAZARDOUS POLYMERIZATION HAS NOT BEEN REPORTED TO OCCUR UNDER NORMAL TEMPERATURES AND PRESSURES.

STORAGE AND DISPOSAL

OBSERVE ALL FEDERAL, STATE AND LOCAL REGULATIONS WHEN STORING OR DISPOSING OF THIS SUBSTANCE. FOR ASSISTANCE, CONTACT THE DISTRICT DIRECTOR OF THE ENVIRONMENTAL PROTECTION AGENCY.

****STORAGE****

STORE IN ACCORDANCE WITH 40 CFR 165 RECOMMENDED PROCEDURES FOR THE DISPOSAL AND STORAGE OF PESTICIDES AND PESTICIDE CONTAINERS.

****DISPOSAL****

DISPOSAL MUST BE IN ACCORDANCE WITH 40 CFR 165 RECOMMENDED PROCEDURES FOR THE DISPOSAL AND STORAGE OF PESTICIDES AND PESTICIDE CONTAINERS.

CONDITIONS TO AVOID

MAY BURN BUT DOES NOT IGNITE READILY. AVOID CONTACT WITH STRONG OXIDIZERS, EXCESSIVE HEAT, SPARKS, OR OPEN FLAME.

SPILL AND LEAK PROCEDURES

OCCUPATIONAL SPILL: SWEEP UP AND PLACE IN SUITABLE CLEAN, DRY CONTAINERS FOR RECLAMATION OR LATER DISPOSAL. DO NOT FLUSH SPILLED MATERIAL INTO SEWER. KEEP UNNECESSARY PEOPLE AWAY.

PROTECTIVE EQUIPMENT

VENTILATION: PROVIDE GENERAL DILUTION VENTILATION.
RESPIRATOR: THE FOLLOWING RESPIRATORS ARE RECOMMENDED BASED ON INFORMATION FOUND IN THE PHYSICAL DATA, TOXICITY AND HEALTH EFFECTS SECTIONS. THEY ARE RANKED IN ORDER FROM MINIMUM TO MAXIMUM RESPIRATORY PROTECTION. THE SPECIFIC RESPIRATOR SELECTED MUST BE BASED ON CONTAMINATION LEVELS FOUND IN THE WORK PLACE, MUST NOT EXCEED THE WORKING LIMITS OF THE RESPIRATOR AND BE JOINTLY APPROVED BY THE NATIONAL INSTITUTE FOR OCCUPATIONAL SAFETY AND HEALTH AND THE MINE SAFETY AND HEALTH ADMINISTRATION (NIOSH-MSHA).
CHEMICAL CARTRIDGE RESPIRATOR WITH AN ORGANIC VAPOR CARTRIDGE(S) IN COMBINATION WITH A DUST AND MIST FILTER.
GAS MASK WITH ORGANIC VAPOR CANISTER (CHIN-STYLE OR FRONT- OR BACK-MOUNTED CANISTER) WITH A DUST AND MIST FILTER.
GAS MASK WITH ORGANIC VAPOR CANISTER (CHIN-STYLE OR FRONT- OR BACK-MOUNTED CANISTER) WITH A PARTICULATE FILTER.
POWERED AIR-PURIFYING RESPIRATOR WITH A HIGH-EFFICIENCY FILTER.
TYPE 'C' SUPPLIED-AIR RESPIRATOR WITH A FULL FACEPIECE OPERATED IN A PRESSURE-DEMAND OR OTHER POSITIVE PRESSURE MODE.
SELF-CONTAINED BREATHING APPARATUS WITH A FULL FACEPIECE OPERATED IN PRESSURE-DEMAND OR OTHER POSITIVE PRESSURE MODE.
FOR FIREFIGHTING AND OTHER IMMEDIATELY DANGEROUS TO LIFE OR HEALTH CONDITIONS:
SELF-CONTAINED BREATHING APPARATUS WITH FULL FACEPIECE OPERATED IN PRESSURE-DEMAND OR OTHER POSITIVE PRESSURE MODE.
SUPPLIED-AIR RESPIRATOR WITH FULL FACEPIECE AND OPERATED IN PRESSURE-DEMAND OR OTHER POSITIVE PRESSURE MODE IN COMBINATION WITH AN AUXILIARY SELF-CONTAINED BREATHING APPARATUS OPERATED IN PRESSURE-DEMAND OR OTHER POSITIVE PRESSURE MODE.
CLOTHING: EMPLOYEE MUST WEAR APPROPRIATE PROTECTIVE (IMPERVIOUS) CLOTHING AND EQUIPMENT TO PREVENT REPEATED OR PROLONGED SKIN CONTACT WITH THIS SUBSTANCE.
GLOVES: EMPLOYEE MUST WEAR APPROPRIATE PROTECTIVE GLOVES TO PREVENT CONTACT WITH THIS SUBSTANCE.
EYE PROTECTION: EMPLOYEE MUST WEAR SPLASH-PROOF OR DUST-RESISTANT SAFETY GOGGLES TO PREVENT EYE CONTACT WITH THIS SUBSTANCE.
EMERGENCY EYE WASH: WHERE THERE IS ANY POSSIBILITY THAT AN EMPLOYEE'S EYES MAY BE EXPOSED TO THIS SUBSTANCE, THE EMPLOYER SHOULD PROVIDE AN EYE WASH FOUNTAIN WITHIN THE IMMEDIATE WORK AREA FOR EMERGENCY USE.

AUTHORIZED BY- OCCUPATIONAL HEALTH SERVICES, INC.
CREATION DATE: 10/04/89 ***REVISION DATE:*** 05/31/90

MATERIAL SAFETY DATA SHEET

OCCUPATIONAL HEALTH SERVICES, INC.
AGRICULTURE AND PESTICIDE DIVISION
450 SEVENTH AVENUE, SUITE 2407
NEW YORK, NEW YORK 10123
1-800-445-MSDS OR (212) 967-1100

EMERGENCY CONTACT:
JOHN S. BRANSFORD, JR. (615) 292-1180

SUBSTANCE IDENTIFICATION

CAS-NUMBER 17804-35-2
SUBSTANCE: **BENOMYL**
TRADE NAMES/SYNONYMS: CARBAMIC ACID, (1-((BUTYLAMINO)CARBONYL)-1H-BENZIMIDAZOL-2-YL)- METHYL ESTER; (1-((BUTYLAMINO)CARBONYL)-1H-BENZIMIDAZOL-2-YL)CARBAMIC ACID METHYL ESTER; 2-BENZIMIDAZOLECARBAMIC ACID, 1-(BUTYLCARBAMOYL)-, METHYL ESTER; 1-(BUTYLCARBAMOYL)-2-BENZIMIDAZOLECARBAMIC ACID METHYL ESTER; METHYL 1-(BUTYLCARBAMOYL)-2-BENZIMIDAZOLECARBAMATE; METHYL 1-(BUTYLCARBAMOYL)BENZIMIDAZOL-2-YLCARBAMATE; METHYL (1-((BUTYLAMINO)CARBONYL)-1H-BENZIMIDAZOL-2-YL)CARBAMATE; AGROCIT; BENLATE; DU PONT 1991; FUNDAZOL; FUNGICIDE D-1991; TERSAN 1991; UZGEN; C14H18N4O3; PST02580
CHEMICAL FAMILY: BENZIMIDAZOLE
MOLECULAR FORMULA: C14-H18-N4-O3
MOLECULAR WEIGHT: 290.32
CERCLA RATINGS (SCALE 0-3): HEALTH=1 FIRE=0 REACTIVITY=0 PERSISTENCE=2
NFPA RATINGS (SCALE 0-4): HEALTH=1 FIRE=0 REACTIVITY=0

COMPONENTS AND CONTAMINANTS

COMPONENT: BENOMYL ***PERCENT:*** 100.0
CAS# 17804-35-2
EXPOSURE LIMITS: BENOMYL: 5 MG/M3 OSHA TWA (RESPIRABLE FRACTION); 10 MG/M3 OSHA TWA (TOTAL DUST) 10 MG/M3 ACGIH TWA (TOTAL DUST)

PHYSICAL DATA

DESCRIPTION: COLORLESS, CRYSTALINE SOLID WITH A FAINT ACRID ODOR
MELTING POINT: DECOMPOSES WITHOUT MELTING ***SPECIFIC GRAVITY:*** NOT AVAILABLE
VAPOR PRESSURE: NEGLIGIBLE ***SOLUBILITY IN WATER:*** 3.8 PPM
SOLVENT SOLUBILITY: SOLUBLE IN CHLOROFORM, XYLENE, ACETONE, HEPTANE, DIMETHYLFORMAMIDE; INSOLUBLE IN OIL

FIRE AND EXPLOSION DATA

FIRE AND EXPLOSION HAZARD: NEGLIGIBLE FIRE HAZARD WHEN EXPOSED TO HEAT OR FLAME.

FIREFIGHTING MEDIA: DRY CHEMICAL, CARBON DIOXIDE, HALON, WATER SPRAY OR STANDARD FOAM (1987 EMERGENCY RESPONSE GUIDEBOOK, DOT P 5800.4). FOR LARGER FIRES, USE WATER SPRAY, FOG OR STANDARD FOAM (1987 EMERGENCY RESPONSE GUIDEBOOK, DOT P 5800.4).

FIREFIGHTING: NO ACUTE HAZARD. MOVE CONTAINER FROM FIRE AREA IF POSSIBLE. AVOID BREATHING VAPORS OR DUSTS; KEEP UPWIND.

TOXICITY

BENOMYL: IRRITATION DATA: 0.1% SKIN-MAN MILD. TOXICITY DATA: 10 GM/KG ORAL-RAT LD50; 5600 MG/KG ORAL-MOUSE LD50; 9920 MG/KG UNREPORTED-RAT LD50; 10 GM/KG UNREPORTED-MAMMAL LD50; MUTAGENIC DATA (RTECS); REPRODUCTIVE EFFECTS DATA (RTECS). CARCINOGEN STATUS: NONE. ACUTE TOXICITY LEVEL: SLIGHTLY TOXIC BY INGESTION. TARGET EFFECTS: SENSITIZER-SKIN. AT INCREASED RISK FROM EXPOSURE: PERSONS EXPOSED TO HIGH LEVELS OF BENOMYL MIGHT BE AT AN INCREASED MUTAGENIC RISK IN THE FORM OF HERITABLE SPINDLE EFFECTS.

HEALTH EFFECTS AND FIRST AID

INHALATION: BENOMYL: **ACUTE EXPOSURE-** A LETHAL CONCENTRATION IN RATS IS GREATER THAN 2000 MG/M3/4 HOURS. A REDUCTION OF SPERMATOGENIC ACTIVITY WAS OBSERVED IN DOGS AND RATS EXPOSED TO THIS MATERIAL. **CHRONIC EXPOSURE-** A CHRONIC INHALATION STUDY INVOLVING RATS EXPOSED TO A CONCENTRATION OF 0.1 MG/LITER OF BENOMYL DUST FOR THREE WEEKS, PRODUCED NO CLINICAL OR HISTOPATHOLOGIC EVIDENCE OF ACCUMULATIVE EFFECTS IN THE RAT.

FIRST AID- REMOVE FROM EXPOSURE AREA TO FRESH AIR IMMEDIATELY. IF BREATHING HAS STOPPED, PERFORM ARTIFICIAL RESPIRATION. KEEP PERSON WARM AND AT REST. TREAT SYMPTOMATICALLY AND SUPPORTIVELY. GET MEDICAL ATTENTION IMMEDIATELY.

SKIN CONTACT: BENOMYL: SENSITIZER. **ACUTE EXPOSURE-** THIS MATERIAL WAS MILDLY IRRITATING TO HUMAN SKIN. SENSITIZATION DERMATITIS MAY OCCUR IN PERSONS PREVIOUSLY EXPOSED. **CHRONIC EXPOSURE-** PROLONGED OR REPEATED EXPOSURE MAY CAUSE SENSITIZATION DERMATITIS.

FIRST AID- REMOVE CONTAMINATED CLOTHING AND SHOES IMMEDIATELY. WASH AFFECTED AREA WITH SOAP OR MILD DETERGENT AND LARGE AMOUNTS OF WATER UNTIL NO EVIDENCE OF CHEMICAL REMAINS (APPROXIMATELY 15-20 MINUTES). GET MEDICAL ATTENTION IMMEDIATELY.

EYE CONTACT: BENOMYL: **ACUTE EXPOSURE-** 10 MG OF A 50% POWDER OR 0.1 ML OF 10% SOLUTION IN MINERAL OIL PRODUCED TEMPORARY MILD CONJUNCTIVAL IRRITATION WHEN APPLIED TO RABBIT EYES. **CHRONIC EXPOSURE-** NO DATA AVAILABLE.

FIRST AID- WASH EYES IMMEDIATELY WITH LARGE AMOUNTS OF WATER OR NORMAL SALINE, OCCASIONALLY LIFTING UPPER AND LOWER LIDS, UNTIL NO EVIDENCE OF CHEMICAL REMAINS (APPROXIMATELY 15-20 MINUTES). GET MEDICAL ATTENTION IMMEDIATELY.

INGESTION: BENOMYL: **ACUTE EXPOSURE-** A LETHAL DOSE IN RATS WAS 10 GM/KG. THIS MATERIAL IS RAPIDLY METABOLIZED; IN ONE STUDY 85% OF A DOSE OF 900 MG/KG FED TO RATS WAS METABOLIZED WITHIN ONE HOUR TO CARBENDAZIM. **CHRONIC EXPOSURE-** IN A TWO-YEAR FEEDING STUDY AT 2500 PPM (0.25%), THERE WAS IMPAIRED LIVER FUNCTION AND HISTOLOGICAL EVIDENCE OF CIRRHOSIS IN DOGS; AT THE SAME CONCENTRATION, NO TOXIC EFFECTS WERE PRODUCED IN RATS. RESIDUE DATA ON RAT AND DOG TISSUES AFTER 2-YEAR STUDY INDICATE THAT BENOMYL AND ITS METABOLITIES DO NOT ACCUMULATE IN ANIMAL TISSUES. EFFECTS ON THE FETUS, FERTILITY, NEWBORN AND MALE REPRODUCTIVE SYSTEM AS WELL AS FETAL DEVELOPMENTAL ABNORMALITIES WERE OBSERVED IN STUDIES OF MICE AND RATS. AN EPA REPORT BY THE OFFICE OF PESTICIDES AND TOXIC SUBSTANCES INDICATED THAT BENOMYL WAS AN HEPATOCARCINOGEN IN MICE.

FIRST AID- TREAT SYMPTOMATICALLY AND SUPPORTIVELY. GET MEDICAL ATTENTION IMMEDIATELY. IF VOMITING OCCURS, KEEP HEAD LOWER THAN HIPS TO PREVENT ASPIRATION.

ANTIDOTE: NO SPECIFIC ANTIDOTE. TREAT SYMPTOMATICALLY AND SUPPORTIVELY.

REACTIVITY

REACTIVITY: STABLE UNDER NORMAL TEMPERATURES AND PRESSURES.

INCOMPATIBILITIES: BENOMYL: ALKALINE CONDITIONS: MAY CAUSE HYDROLYSIS. NEUTRAL SOLUTIONS: MAY CAUSE HYDROLYSIS.

DECOMPOSITION: THERMAL DECOMPOSITION MAY RELEASE TOXIC OXIDES OF CARBON AND NITROGEN.

POLYMERIZATION: HAZARDOUS POLYMERIZATION HAS NOT BEEN REPORTED TO OCCUR UNDER NORMAL TEMPERATURES AND PRESSURES.

STORAGE AND DISPOSAL

OBSERVE ALL FEDERAL, STATE AND LOCAL REGULATIONS WHEN STORING OR DISPOSING OF THIS SUBSTANCE. FOR ASSISTANCE, CONTACT THE DISTRICT DIRECTOR OF THE ENVIRONMENTAL PROTECTION AGENCY.

****STORAGE****

STORE IN ACCORDANCE WITH 40 CFR 165 RECOMMENDED PROCEDURES FOR THE DISPOSAL AND STORAGE OF PESTICIDES AND PESTICIDE CONTAINERS.
STORE AWAY FROM INCOMPATIBLE SUBSTANCES.
STORE IN A TIGHTLY CLOSED CONTAINER AVOIDING CONTACT WITH MOISTURE.

****DISPOSAL****

DISPOSAL MUST BE IN ACCORDANCE WITH 40 CFR 165 RECOMMENDED PROCEDURES FOR THE DISPOSAL AND STORAGE OF PESTICIDES AND PESTICIDE CONTAINERS.

CONDITIONS TO AVOID

MAY BURN BUT DOES NOT IGNITE READILY. AVOID CONTACT WITH STRONG OXIDIZERS, EXCESSIVE HEAT, SPARKS, OR OPEN FLAME.

SPILL AND LEAK PROCEDURES

OCCUPATIONAL SPILL: SWEEP UP AND PLACE IN SUITABLE CLEAN, DRY CONTAINERS FOR RECLAMATION OR LATER DISPOSAL. DO NOT FLUSH SPILLED MATERIAL INTO SEWER. KEEP UNNECESSARY PEOPLE AWAY.

PROTECTIVE EQUIPMENT

VENTILATION: PROVIDE GENERAL DILUTION VENTILATION TO MEET PUBLISHED EXPOSURE LIMITS.

RESPIRATOR: THE FOLLOWING RESPIRATORS ARE RECOMMENDED BASED ON INFORMATION FOUND IN THE PHYSICAL DATA, TOXICITY AND HEALTH EFFECTS SECTIONS. THEY ARE RANKED IN ORDER FROM MINIMUM TO MAXIMUM RESPIRATORY PROTECTION. THE SPECIFIC RESPIRATOR SELECTED MUST BE BASED ON CONTAMINATION LEVELS FOUND IN THE WORK PLACE, MUST NOT EXCEED THE WORKING LIMITS OF THE RESPIRATOR AND BE JOINTLY APPROVED BY THE NATIONAL INSTITUTE FOR OCCUPATIONAL SAFETY AND HEALTH AND THE MINE SAFETY AND HEALTH ADMINISTRATION (NIOSH-MSHA).
CHEMICAL CARTRIDGE RESPIRATOR WITH AN ORGANIC VAPOR CARTRIDGE(S) IN COMBINATION WITH A DUST AND MIST FILTER.
GAS MASK WITH ORGANIC VAPOR CANISTER (CHIN-STYLE OR FRONT- OR BACK-MOUNTED CANISTER) WITH A DUST AND MIST FILTER.
GAS MASK WITH ORGANIC VAPOR CANISTER (CHIN-STYLE OR FRONT- OR BACK-MOUNTED CANISTER) WITH A PARTICULATE FILTER.
POWERED AIR-PURIFYING RESPIRATOR WITH A HIGH-EFFICIENCY FILTER.
TYPE 'C' SUPPLIED-AIR RESPIRATOR WITH A FULL FACEPIECE OPERATED IN A PRESSURE-DEMAND OR OTHER POSITIVE PRESSURE MODE.
SELF-CONTAINED BREATHING APPARATUS WITH A FULL FACEPIECE OPERATED IN PRESSURE-DEMAND OR OTHER POSITIVE PRESSURE MODE.
FOR FIREFIGHTING AND OTHER IMMEDIATELY DANGEROUS TO LIFE OR HEALTH CONDITIONS:
SELF-CONTAINED BREATHING APPARATUS WITH FULL FACEPIECE OPERATED IN PRESSURE-DEMAND OR OTHER POSITIVE PRESSURE MODE.
SUPPLIED-AIR RESPIRATOR WITH FULL FACEPIECE AND OPERATED IN PRESSURE-DEMAND OR OTHER POSITIVE PRESSURE MODE IN COMBINATION WITH AN AUXILIARY SELF-CONTAINED BREATHING APPARATUS OPERATED IN PRESSURE-DEMAND OR OTHER POSITIVE PRESSURE MODE.

CLOTHING: EMPLOYEE MUST WEAR APPROPRIATE PROTECTIVE (IMPERVIOUS) CLOTHING AND EQUIPMENT TO PREVENT REPEATED OR PROLONGED SKIN CONTACT WITH THIS SUBSTANCE.

GLOVES: EMPLOYEE MUST WEAR APPROPRIATE PROTECTIVE GLOVES TO PREVENT CONTACT WITH THIS SUBSTANCE.

EYE PROTECTION: EMPLOYEE MUST WEAR SPLASH-PROOF OR DUST-RESISTANT SAFETY GOGGLES TO PREVENT EYE CONTACT WITH THIS SUBSTANCE.
EMERGENCY EYE WASH: WHERE THERE IS ANY POSSIBILITY THAT AN EMPLOYEE'S EYES MAY BE EXPOSED TO THIS SUBSTANCE, THE EMPLOYER SHOULD PROVIDE AN EYE WASH FOUNTAIN WITHIN THE IMMEDIATE WORK AREA FOR EMERGENCY USE.

AUTHORIZED BY- OCCUPATIONAL HEALTH SERVICES, INC.
CREATION DATE: 10/04/89 ***REVISION DATE:*** 05/31/90

MATERIAL SAFETY DATA SHEET

OCCUPATIONAL HEALTH SERVICES, INC. AGRICULTURE AND PESTICIDE DIVISION

EMERGENCY CONTACT: JOHN S. BRANSFORD, JR. (615) 292-1180

450 SEVENTH AVENUE, SUITE 2407
NEW YORK, NEW YORK 10123
1-800-445-MSDS OR (212) 967-1100

SUBSTANCE IDENTIFICATION

SUBSTANCE: **BENTAZON A.I.B.A. METABOLITE**

TRADE NAMES/SYNONYMS: BENTAZON AMINO ISOPROPYL BENZOIC ACID METABOLITE; 2-AMINO-N-ISOPROPYL BENZAMIDE; BASAGRAN AIBA METABOLITE; C10H14ON2; PST02581

CHEMICAL FAMILY: AMINE, AROMATIC; AMIDE

MOLECULAR FORMULA: C6-H4-(N-H2)-C-(O)-N-H-C-H-(C-H3)2

MOLECULAR WEIGHT: 178.23

CERCLA RATINGS (SCALE 0-3): HEALTH=U FIRE=1 REACTIVITY=0 PERSISTENCE=2

NFPA RATINGS (SCALE 0-4): HEALTH=U FIRE=1 REACTIVITY=0

COMPONENTS AND CONTAMINANTS

COMPONENT: BENTAZON A.I.B.A. METABOLITE ***PERCENT:*** 100.0

OTHER CONTAMINANTS: NONE

EXPOSURE LIMITS: NO OCCUPATIONAL EXPOSURE LIMITS ESTABLISHED BY OSHA, ACGIH, OR NIOSH.

PHYSICAL DATA

DESCRIPTION: WHITE POWDER. ***MELTING POINT:*** 297 F (147 C)

SPECIFIC GRAVITY: NOT AVAILABLE ***SOLUBILITY IN WATER:*** NOT AVAILABLE

FIRE AND EXPLOSION DATA

FIRE AND EXPLOSION HAZARD: SLIGHT FIRE HAZARD WHEN EXPOSED TO HEAT OR FLAME.

FIREFIGHTING MEDIA: DRY CHEMICAL, CARBON DIOXIDE, HALON, WATER SPRAY OR STANDARD FOAM (1987 EMERGENCY RESPONSE GUIDEBOOK, DOT P 5800.4).
FOR LARGER FIRES, USE WATER SPRAY, FOG OR STANDARD FOAM (1987 EMERGENCY RESPONSE GUIDEBOOK, DOT P 5800.4).

FIREFIGHTING: MOVE CONTAINER FROM FIRE AREA IF POSSIBLE. DO NOT SCATTER SPILLED MATERIAL WITH HIGH PRESSURE WATER STREAMS. DIKE FIRE CONTROL WATER FOR LATER DISPOSAL (1987 EMERGENCY RESPONSE GUIDEBOOK, DOT P 5800.4, GUIDE PAGE 31).
USE AGENTS SUITABLE FOR TYPE OF SURROUNDING FIRE. AVOID BREATHING HAZARDOUS VAPORS, KEEP UPWIND.

TOXICITY

BENTAZON A.I.B.A. METABOLITE: CARCINOGEN STATUS: NONE. ACUTE TOXICITY LEVEL: NO DATA AVAILABLE. TARGET EFFECTS: NO DATA AVAILABLE.

HEALTH EFFECTS AND FIRST AID

INHALATION: BENTAZON A.I.B.A. METABOLITE: **ACUTE EXPOSURE-** NO SPECIFIC DATA AVAILABLE. MANY AROMATIC AMINES CAUSE METHEMOGLOBINEMIA; SOME ARE CARCINOGENIC. **CHRONIC EXPOSURE-** NO SPECIFIC DATA AVAILABLE. SOME AROMATIC AMINES ARE PULMONARY SENSITIZERS.

FIRST AID- REMOVE FROM EXPOSURE AREA TO FRESH AIR IMMEDIATELY. IF BREATHING HAS STOPPED, PERFORM ARTIFICIAL RESPIRATION. KEEP PERSON WARM AND AT REST. TREAT SYMPTOMATICALLY AND SUPPORTIVELY. GET MEDICAL ATTENTION IMMEDIATELY.

SKIN CONTACT: BENTAZON A.I.B.A. METABOLITE: **ACUTE EXPOSURE-** NO SPECIFIC DATA AVAILABLE. MANY AROMATIC AMINES AND AMIDES ARE ABSORBED THROUGH INTACT SKIN. **CHRONIC EXPOSURE-** NO SPECIFIC DATA AVAILABLE. REPEATED OR PROLONGED EXPOSURE TO AROMATIC AMINES MAY RESULT IN ALLERGIC DERMATITIS.

FIRST AID- REMOVE CONTAMINATED CLOTHING AND SHOES IMMEDIATELY. WASH AFFECTED AREA WITH SOAP OR MILD DETERGENT AND LARGE AMOUNTS OF WATER UNTIL NO EVIDENCE OF CHEMICAL REMAINS (APPROXIMATELY 15-20 MINUTES). GET MEDICAL ATTENTION IMMEDIATELY.

EYE CONTACT: BENTAZON A.I.B.A. METABOLITE: **ACUTE EXPOSURE-** NO DATA AVAILABLE. **CHRONIC EXPOSURE-** NO DATA AVAILABLE.

FIRST AID- WASH EYES IMMEDIATELY WITH LARGE AMOUNTS OF WATER OR NORMAL SALINE, OCCASIONALLY LIFTING UPPER AND LOWER LIDS, UNTIL NO EVIDENCE OF CHEMICAL REMAINS (APPROXIMATELY 15-20 MINUTES). GET MEDICAL ATTENTION IMMEDIATELY.

INGESTION: BENTAZON A.I.B.A. METABOLITE: **ACUTE EXPOSURE-** NO DATA AVAILABLE. **CHRONIC EXPOSURE-** NO DATA AVAILABLE.

FIRST AID- TREAT SYMPTOMATICALLY AND SUPPORTIVELY. GET MEDICAL ATTENTION IMMEDIATELY. IF VOMITING OCCURS, KEEP HEAD LOWER THAN HIPS TO PREVENT ASPIRATION.

ANTIDOTE: NO SPECIFIC ANTIDOTE. TREAT SYMPTOMATICALLY AND SUPPORTIVELY.

REACTIVITY

REACTIVITY: STABLE UNDER NORMAL TEMPERATURES AND PRESSURES.

INCOMPATIBILITIES: BENTAZON A.I.B.A. METABOLITE: OXIDIZERS (STRONG): FIRE AND EXPLOSION HAZARD.

DECOMPOSITION: THERMAL DECOMPOSITION MAY RELEASE TOXIC OXIDES OF NITROGEN AND SULFUR.

POLYMERIZATION: HAZARDOUS POLYMERIZATION HAS NOT BEEN REPORTED TO OCCUR UNDER NORMAL TEMPERATURES AND PRESSURES.

STORAGE AND DISPOSAL

OBSERVE ALL FEDERAL, STATE AND LOCAL REGULATIONS WHEN STORING OR DISPOSING OF THIS SUBSTANCE. FOR ASSISTANCE, CONTACT THE DISTRICT DIRECTOR OF THE ENVIRONMENTAL PROTECTION AGENCY.

****STORAGE****

STORE IN ACCORDANCE WITH 40 CFR 165 RECOMMENDED PROCEDURES FOR THE DISPOSAL AND STORAGE OF PESTICIDES AND PESTICIDE CONTAINERS.
STORE AWAY FROM INCOMPATIBLE SUBSTANCES.

****DISPOSAL****

DISPOSAL MUST BE IN ACCORDANCE WITH 40 CFR 165 RECOMMENDED PROCEDURES FOR THE DISPOSAL AND STORAGE OF PESTICIDES AND PESTICIDE CONTAINERS.

CONDITIONS TO AVOID

MAY BURN BUT DOES NOT IGNITE READILY. AVOID CONTACT WITH STRONG OXIDIZERS, EXCESSIVE HEAT, SPARKS, OR OPEN FLAME.

SPILL AND LEAK PROCEDURES

OCCUPATIONAL SPILL: SWEEP UP AND PLACE IN SUITABLE CLEAN, DRY CONTAINERS FOR RECLAMATION OR LATER DISPOSAL. DO NOT FLUSH SPILLED MATERIAL INTO SEWER. KEEP UNNECESSARY PEOPLE AWAY.

PROTECTIVE EQUIPMENT

VENTILATION: PROVIDE LOCAL EXHAUST OR PROCESS ENCLOSURE VENTILATION SYSTEM.

RESPIRATOR: THE FOLLOWING RESPIRATORS ARE RECOMMENDED BASED ON INFORMATION FOUND IN THE PHYSICAL DATA, TOXICITY AND HEALTH EFFECTS SECTIONS. THEY ARE RANKED IN ORDER FROM MINIMUM TO MAXIMUM RESPIRATORY PROTECTION. THE SPECIFIC RESPIRATOR SELECTED MUST BE BASED ON CONTAMINATION LEVELS FOUND IN THE WORK PLACE, MUST NOT EXCEED THE WORKING LIMITS OF THE RESPIRATOR AND BE JOINTLY APPROVED BY THE NATIONAL INSTITUTE FOR OCCUPATIONAL SAFETY AND HEALTH AND THE MINE SAFETY AND HEALTH ADMINISTRATION (NIOSH-MSHA).
CHEMICAL CARTRIDGE RESPIRATOR WITH AN ORGANIC VAPOR CARTRIDGE(S) WITH A FULL FACEPIECE AND ORGANIC VAPOR CARTRIDGE(S) IN COMBINATION WITH A DUST AND MIST FILTER.
POWERED AIR-PURIFYING RESPIRATOR WITH A TIGHT-FITTING FACEPIECE AND ORGANIC VAPOR CARTRIDGE(S) IN COMBINATION WITH A HIGH-EFFICIENCY PARTICULATE FILTER.
TYPE 'C' SUPPLIED-AIR RESPIRATOR WITH A FULL FACEPIECE OPERATED IN A PRESSURE-DEMAND OR OTHER POSITIVE PRESSURE MODE.
SELF-CONTAINED BREATHING APPARATUS WITH A FULL FACEPIECE OPERATED IN PRESSURE-DEMAND OR OTHER POSITIVE PRESSURE MODE.
FOR FIREFIGHTING AND OTHER IMMEDIATELY DANGEROUS TO LIFE OR HEALTH CONDITIONS:
SELF-CONTAINED BREATHING APPARATUS WITH FULL FACEPIECE OPERATED IN PRESSURE-DEMAND OR OTHER POSITIVE PRESSURE MODE.
SUPPLIED-AIR RESPIRATOR WITH FULL FACEPIECE AND OPERATED IN PRESSURE-DEMAND OR OTHER POSITIVE PRESSURE MODE IN COMBINATION WITH AN AUXILIARY SELF-CONTAINED BREATHING APPARATUS OPERATED IN PRESSURE-DEMAND OR OTHER POSITIVE PRESSURE MODE.

CLOTHING: EMPLOYEE MUST WEAR APPROPRIATE PROTECTIVE (IMPERVIOUS) CLOTHING AND EQUIPMENT TO PREVENT REPEATED OR PROLONGED SKIN CONTACT WITH THIS SUBSTANCE.

GLOVES: EMPLOYEE MUST WEAR APPROPRIATE PROTECTIVE GLOVES TO PREVENT CONTACT WITH THIS SUBSTANCE.

EYE PROTECTION: EMPLOYEE MUST WEAR SPLASH-PROOF OR DUST-RESISTANT SAFETY GOGGLES TO PREVENT EYE CONTACT WITH THIS SUBSTANCE.
EMERGENCY EYE WASH: WHERE THERE IS ANY POSSIBILITY THAT AN EMPLOYEE'S EYES MAY BE EXPOSED TO THIS SUBSTANCE, THE EMPLOYER SHOULD PROVIDE AN EYE WASH FOUNTAIN WITHIN THE IMMEDIATE WORK AREA FOR EMERGENCY USE.

AUTHORIZED BY- OCCUPATIONAL HEALTH SERVICES, INC.
CREATION DATE: 10/04/89 ***REVISION DATE:*** 05/31/90

MATERIAL SAFETY DATA SHEET

OCCUPATIONAL HEALTH SERVICES, INC.
AGRICULTURE AND PESTICIDE DIVISION
450 SEVENTH AVENUE, SUITE 2407
NEW YORK, NEW YORK 10123
1-800-445-MSDS OR (212) 967-1100

EMERGENCY CONTACT:
JOHN S. BRANSFORD, JR. (615) 292-1180

SUBSTANCE IDENTIFICATION

SUBSTANCE: **BENSULIDE OXYGEN ANALOG**

TRADE NAMES/SYNONYMS: BENSULIDE OXON; PREFAROXON; BETASAN OXON; S-(O,O-DIISOPROPYL PHOSPHOROTHIOATE) ESTER OF N-(2-MERCAPTOETHYL) BENZENE SULFONAMIDE; C14H24NO5PS2; PST02582

CHEMICAL FAMILY: PHOSPHOROTHIOATE SULFONAMIDE

MOLECULAR FORMULA: C14-H24-N-O5-P-S2

MOLECULAR WEIGHT: 381.45

CERCLA RATINGS (SCALE 0-3): HEALTH=U FIRE=1 REACTIVITY=0 PERSISTENCE=0

NFPA RATINGS (SCALE 0-4): HEALTH=U FIRE=1 REACTIVITY=0

COMPONENTS AND CONTAMINANTS

COMPONENT: BENSULIDE OXYGEN ANALOG ***PERCENT:*** 100.0

OTHER CONTAMINANTS: NONE

EXPOSURE LIMITS: NO OCCUPATIONAL EXPOSURE LIMITS ESTABLISHED BY OSHA, ACGIH, OR NIOSH.

PHYSICAL DATA

DESCRIPTION: WHITE POWDER. ***MELTING POINT:*** NOT AVAILABLE

SPECIFIC GRAVITY: NOT AVAILABLE ***SOLUBILITY IN WATER:*** NOT AVAILABLE

FIRE AND EXPLOSION DATA

FIRE AND EXPLOSION HAZARD: SLIGHT FIRE HAZARD WHEN EXPOSED TO HEAT OR FLAME.

FIREFIGHTING MEDIA: DRY CHEMICAL, CARBON DIOXIDE, HALON, WATER SPRAY OR STANDARD FOAM (1987 EMERGENCY RESPONSE GUIDEBOOK, DOT P 5800.4). FOR LARGER FIRES, USE WATER SPRAY, FOG OR STANDARD FOAM (1987 EMERGENCY RESPONSE GUIDEBOOK, DOT P 5800.4).

FIREFIGHTING: MOVE CONTAINERS FROM FIRE AREA IF POSSIBLE (1987 EMERGENCY RESPONSE GUIDEBOOK, DOT P 5800.4, GUIDE PAGE 53).
EXTINGUISH USING AGENT SUITABLE FOR TYPE OF SURROUNDING FIRE. AVOID BREATHING VAPORS AND DUSTS. KEEP UPWIND.

TOXICITY

BENSULIDE OXYGEN ANALOG: CARCINOGEN STATUS: NONE. ACUTE TOXICITY LEVEL: NO DATA AVAILABLE. TARGET EFFECTS: CHOLINESTERASE INHIBITOR. POISONING MAY AFFECT THE NERVOUS SYSTEM.* AT INCREASED RISK FROM EXPOSURE: PERSONS WITH RESPIRATORY AILMENTS, RECENT EXPOSURE TO CHOLINESTERASE INHIBITORS OR IMPAIRED CHOLINESTERASE PRODUCTION, OR LIVER MALFUNCTION.* ADDITIONAL DATA: MAY CROSS THE PLACENTA. HIGH ENVIRONMENTAL TEMPERATURES OR EXPOSURE OF THE CHEMICAL TO VISIBLE OR ULTRAVIOLET LIGHT MAY ENHANCE THE TOXICITY. INTERACTIONS WITH MEDICATIONS MAY OCCUR.*

* MAY BE BASED ON GENERAL INFORMATION ON ORGANOPHOSPHATES.

HEALTH EFFECTS AND FIRST AID

INHALATION: BENSULIDE OXYGEN ANALOG: SEE INFORMATION ON ORGANOPHOSPHATES.
ORGANOPHOSPHATES: CHOLINESTERASE INHIBITOR. **ACUTE EXPOSURE-** WHEN INHALED, THE FIRST EFFECTS OF CHOLINESTERASE INHIBITORS ARE USUALLY RESPIRATORY AND MAY INCLUDE NASAL HYPEREMIA AND WATERY DISCHARGE, COUGH, CHEST DISCOMFORT, DYSPNEA, AND WHEEZING DUE TO INCREASED BRONCHIAL SECRETIONS AND BRONCHOCONSTRICTION. IF SUFFICIENT AMOUNTS ARE ABSORBED, OTHER SYSTEMIC EFFECTS MAY BEGIN WITHIN A FEW MINUTES OR BE DELAYED FOR UP TO 12 HOURS. SYMPTOMS MAY INCLUDE PALLOR, NAUSEA, VOMITING, DIARRHEA, ABDOMINAL CRAMPS, HEADACHE, DIZZINESS, OCULAR PAIN, BLURRED VISION, MIOSIS OR IN SOME CASES, ESPECIALLY INITIALLY, MYDRIASIS, LACRIMATION, SALIVATION, SWEATING, AND CONFUSION. OTHER REPORTED CENTRAL NERVOUS SYSTEM OR NEUROMUSCULAR EFFECTS MAY INCLUDE ATAXIA, SLURRED SPEECH, AREFLEXIA, WEAKNESS, FATIGUE, FASCICULATIONS, TWITCHING, TREMORS POSSIBLY OF THE TONGUE AND EYELIDS, AND EVENTUALLY PARALYSIS OF THE EXTREMITIES AND POSSIBLY OF THE RESPIRATORY MUSCLES. IN SEVERE CASES THERE MAY ALSO BE INVOLUNTARY DEFECATION AND URINATION, CYANOSIS, PSYCHOSIS, HYPERGLYCEMIA, ACUTE PANCREATITIS, CARDIAC IRREGULARITIES, PULMONARY EDEMA, UNCONSCIOUSNESS, CONVULSIONS, AND COMA. DEATH IS PRIMARILY DUE TO RESPIRATORY FAILURE, ALTHOUGH CARDIOVASCULAR EFFECTS INCLUDING CARDIAC ARREST MAY ALSO BE IMPLICATED. LONG TERM SEQUELAE ARE RARE BUT MAY INCLUDE NEUROPSYCHIATRIC DISORDERS AND MYOPATHY WITH MUSCLE TENDERNESS. SOME ORGANOPHOSPHATES MAY CAUSE A DELAYED NEUROPATHY BEGINNING 1-4 WEEKS AFTER AN ACUTE EXPOSURE WHICH MAY OR MAY NOT HAVE CAUSED ACUTE CHOLINERGIC EFFECTS. NUMBNESS, TINGLING, WEAKNESS AND CRAMPING BEGINNING SYMMETRICALLY IN THE LOWER LIMBS MAY PROGRESS TO ATAXIA AND PARALYSIS. IN SEVERE CASES, UPPER LIMB INVOLVEMENT IS POSSIBLE AND FLACCID PARALYSIS MAY PROGRESS TO SPASTIC PARALYSIS WITH EXAGGERATED REFLEXES. IMPROVEMENT MAY OCCUR OVER MONTHS TO YEARS, BUT SOME RESIDUAL IMPAIRMENT USUALLY REMAINS.
CHRONIC EXPOSURE- REPEATED OR PROLONGED EXPOSURE MAY RESULT IN THE EFFECTS OF ACUTE EXPOSURE INCLUDING THE DELAYED NEUROPATHY. OTHER EFFECTS REPORTED IN WORKERS REPEATEDLY EXPOSED INCLUDE IMPAIRED MEMORY AND CONCENTRATION, ACUTE PSYCHOSIS, SEVERE DEPRESSIONS, IRRITABILTY, CONFUSION, APATHY, EMOTIONAL LABILITY, SOCIAL WITHDRAWAL, CONFUSION, HEADACHE, SPEECH DIFFICULTIES, DELAYED REACTION TIMES, SPATIAL DISORIENTATION, NIGHTMARES, SLEEPWALKING, AND DROWSINESS OR INSOMNIA. AN INFLUENZA-LIKE CONDITION WITH HEADACHE, NAUSEA, WEAKNESS, ANOREXIA AND MALAISE HAS ALSO BEEN REPORTED.

FIRST AID- REMOVE FROM EXPOSURE AREA TO FRESH AIR IMMEDIATELY. IF BREATHING HAS STOPPED, GIVE ARTIFICIAL RESPIRATION. MAINTAIN AIRWAY AND BLOOD PRESSURE AND ADMINISTER OXYGEN IF AVAILABLE. KEEP AFFECTED PERSON WARM AND AT REST. TREAT SYMPTOMATICALLY AND SUPPORTIVELY. ADMINISTRATION OF OXYGEN SHOULD BE PERFORMED BY QUALIFIED PERSONNEL. GET MEDICAL ATTENTION IMMEDIATELY.

SKIN CONTACT: BENSULIDE OXYGEN ANALOG: SEE INFORMATION ON ORGANOPHOSPHATES.
ORGANOPHOSPHATES: CHOLINESTERASE INHIBITOR. **ACUTE EXPOSURE-** LOCALIZED SWEATING AND FASCICULATIONS MAY OCCUR AT THE SITE OF CONTACT. IF SUFFICIENT AMOUNTS ARE ABSORBED, OTHER EFFECTS OF CHOLINESTERASE INHIBITION AS DESCRIBED IN ACUTE INHALATION MAY OCCUR. SYMPTOMS MAY BE DELAYED 2-3 HOURS, BUT USUALLY NO MORE THAN 12 HOURS. THE RATE OF ABSORPTION IS INCREASED BY THE PRESENCE OF DERMATITIS OR HIGH AMBIENT TEMPERATURES. DELAYED NEUROPATHY IS ALSO POSSIBLE. **CHRONIC EXPOSURE-** REPEATED OR PROLONGED EXPOSURE MAY CAUSE EFFECTS AS DESCRIBED IN ACUTE EXPOSURE. SOME ORGANOPHOSPHATES MAY CAUSE SENSITIZATION.

FIRST AID- REMOVE CONTAMINATED CLOTHING IMMEDIATELY. WASH CONTAMINATED AREAS WITH SOAP AND WATER FOLLOWED BY ALCOHOL (ARENA, POISONING, 4TH ED.). EMERGENCY PERSONNEL SHOULD WEAR GLOVES AND AVOID CONTAMINATION. TREAT RESPIRATORY DIFFICULTY WITH ARTIFICIAL RESPIRATION. GET MEDICAL ATTENTION IMMEDIATELY.

EYE CONTACT: BENSULIDE OXYGEN ANALOG: APPLICATION OF BENSULIDE TO RABBIT EYES CAUSED MILD IRRITATION. SEE INFORMATION ON ORGANOPHOSPHATES.
ORGANOPHOSPHATES: CHOLINESTERASE INHIBITOR. **ACUTE EXPOSURE-** DIRECT CONTACT MAY CAUSE PAIN, HYPEREMIA, LACRIMATION, TWITCHING OF THE EYELIDS, MIOSIS, AND CILIARY MUSCLE SPASM WITH LOSS OF ACCOMODATION, BLURRED OR DIMMED VISION AND BROWACHE. SOMETIMES MYDRIASIS MAY OCCUR INSTEAD OF MIOSIS. WITH SUFFICIENT EXPOSURE, OTHER SYMPTOMS OF CHOLINESTERASE INHIBITION AS DESCRIBED IN ACUTE INHALATION MAY OCCUR.
CHRONIC EXPOSURE- REPEATED OR PROLONGED EXPOSURE MAY CAUSE EFFECTS AS DESCRIBED IN ACUTE EXPOSURE. SOME COMPOUNDS HAVE CAUSED TOXIC EFFECTS ON THE CRYSTALLINE LENS, CONJUNCTIVAL THICKENING AND OBSTRUCTION OF THE NASOLACRIMAL CANALS WHEN USED AS MIOTIC EYEDROPS.

FIRST AID- IRRIGATE EYES WITH WATER OR SALINE SOLUTION. IF SYMPTOMS OF POISONING OCCUR, TREAT RESPIRATORY DIFFICULTY WITH ARTIFICIAL RESPIRATION AND OXYGEN. OBSERVE PATIENT FOR AT LEAST 24-36 HOURS (GOSSELIN, CLINICAL TOXICOLOGY OF COMMERCIAL PRODUCTS, 5TH ED.). GET MEDICAL ATTENTION IMMEDIATELY. OXYGEN SHOULD BE ADMINISTERED BY QUALIFIED MEDICAL PERSONNEL.

INGESTION: BENSULIDE OXYGEN ANALOG: IN CHRONIC STUDIES, ANIMALS FED BENSULIDE EXPERIENCED LIVER AND KIDNEY CHANGES. SEE INFORMATION ON ORGANOPHOSPHATES.
ORGANOPHOSPHATES: CHOLINESTERASE INHIBITOR. **ACUTE EXPOSURE-** WHEN INGESTED, THE FIRST EFFECTS MAY BE NAUSEA, VOMITING, ANOREXIA,

ABDOMINAL CRAMPS AND DIARRHEA. GASTROINTESTINAL ABSORPTION MAY CAUSE SYMPTOMS OF CHOLINESTERASE INHIBITION AS DESCRIBED IN ACUTE INHALATION. SYMPTOMS MAY BEGIN WITHIN MINUTES OR BE DELAYED FOR HOURS. DELAYED EFFECTS INCLUDING NEUROPATHY MAY ALSO OCCUR. **CHRONIC EXPOSURE-** REPEATED INGESTION MAY CAUSE EFFECTS AS DESCRIBED IN ACUTE EXPOSURE.

FIRST AID- IF PERSON IS ALERT AND RESPIRATION IS NOT DEPRESSED, GIVE SYRUP OF IPECAC FOLLOWED BY WATER (IF VOMITING OCCURS, KEEP HEAD BELOW HIPS TO PREVENT ASPIRATION). IF CONSCIOUSNESS LEVEL DECLINES OR VOMITING HAS NOT OCCURRED IN 15 MINUTES EMPTY STOMACH BY GASTRIC LAVAGE WITH THE AID OF CUFFED ENDOTRACHEAL TUBE USING ISOTONIC SALINE OR 5% SODIUM BICARBONATE FOLLOW WITH ACTIVATED CHARCOAL. ESTABLISH AND MAINTAIN AIRWAY. TREAT RESPIRATORY DIFFICULTY WITH ARTIFICIAL RESPIRATION AND OXYGEN. DO NOT GIVE MORPHINE, AMINOPHYLLINE, PHENOTHIAZINES, RESERPINE, FUROSEMIDE, OR ETHACRYNIC ACID (MORGAN, RECOGNITION AND MANAGEMENT OF PESTICIDE POISONINGS, 3RD ED.). TREAT SYMPTOMATICALLY AND SUPPORTIVELY. ADMINISTRATION OF OXYGEN AND LAVAGE MUST BE PERFORMED BY QUALIFIED MEDICAL PERSONNEL. GET MEDICAL ATTENTION IMMEDIATELY.

ANTIDOTE: THE FOLLOWING ANTIDOTE(S) HAVE BEEN RECOMMENDED. HOWEVER, THE DECISION AS TO WHETHER THE SEVERITY OF POISONING REQUIRES ADMINISTRATION OF ANY ANTIDOTE AND ACTUAL DOSE REQUIRED SHOULD BE MADE BY QUALIFIED MEDICAL PERSONNEL.

FOR CHOLINESTERASE INHIBITORS: ESTABLISH CLEAR AIRWAY AND TISSUE OXYGENATION BY ASPIRATION OF SECRETIONS, AND IF NECESSARY, BY ASSISTED PULMONARY VENTILATION WITH OXYGEN. IMPROVE TISSUE OXYGENATION AS MUCH AS POSSIBLE BEFORE ADMINISTERING ATROPINE TO MINIMIZE THE RISK OF VENTRICULAR FIBRILLATION. ADMINISTER ATROPINE SULFATE INTRAVENOUSLY, OR INTRAMUSCULARLY IF IV INJECTION IS NOT POSSIBLE. IN MODERATELY SEVERE POISONING ADMINISTER ATROPINE SULFATE, 0.4-2.0 MG REPEATED EVERY 15 MINUTES UNTIL ATROPINIZATION IS ACHIEVED (TACHYCARDIA, FLUSHING, DRY MOUTH, MYDRIASIS). MAINTAIN ATROPINIZATION BY REPEATED DOSES FOR 2-12 HOURS, OR LONGER, DEPENDING ON THE SEVERITY OF POISONING. THE APPEARANCE OF RALES IN THE LUNG BASES, MIOSIS, SALIVATION, NAUSEA, BRADYCARDIA, ARE ALL INDICATIONS OF INADEQUATE ATROPINIZATION. SEVERELY POISONED INDIVIDUALS MAY EXHIBIT REMARKABLE TOLERANCE TO ATROPINE; TWO OR MORE TIMES THE DOSAGES SUGGESTED ABOVE MAY BE NEEDED. PERSONS NOT POISONED OR ONLY SLIGHTLY POISONED, HOWEVER, MAY DEVELOP SIGNS OF ATROPINE TOXICITY FROM SUCH LARGE DOSAGES: FEVER, MUSCLE FIBRILLATIONS, AND DELIRIUM ARE THE MAIN SIGNS OF ATROPINE TOXICITY. IF THESE SIGNS APPEAR WHILE THE PATIENT IS FULLY ATROPINIZED, ATROPINE ADMINISTRATION SHOULD BE DISCONTINUED, AT LEAST TEMPORARILY. OBSERVE TREATED PATIENTS CLOSELY AT LEAST 24 HOURS TO INSURE THAT SYMPTOMS (POSSIBLY PULMONARY EDEMA) DO NOT RECUR AS ATROPINIZATION WEARS OFF. IN VERY SEVERE POISONINGS, METABOLIC DISPOSITION OF TOXICANT MAY REQUIRE SEVERAL HOURS OR DAYS DURING WHICH ATROPINIZATION MUST BE MAINTAINED. MARKEDLY LOWER LEVELS OF URINARY METABOLITES INDICATE THAT ATROPINE DOSAGE CAN BE TAPERED OFF. AS DOSAGE IS REDUCED, CHECK THE LUNG BASES FREQUENTLY FOR RALES. IF RALES ARE HEARD OR OTHER SYMPTOMS RETURN, RE-ESTABLISH ATROPINIZATION PROMPTLY (MORGAN, RECOGNITION AND MANAGEMENT OF PESTICIDE POISONINGS, 3RD ED.). ADMINISTRATION OF ANTIDOTE MUST BE PERFORMED BY QUALIFIED MEDICAL PERSONNEL.

IN CASES OF SEVERE POISONING BY ORGANOPHOSPHATE PESTICIDES IN WHICH RESPIRATORY DEPRESSION, MUSCLE WEAKNESS AND TWITCHINGS ARE SEVERE, GIVE PRALIDOXIME (PROTOPAM-AYERST, 2-PAM), 1.0 GRAM INTRAVENOUSLY AT NO MORE THAN 0.5 GRAM PER MINUTE. DOSAGE OF PRALIDOXIME MAY BE REPEATED IN 1-2 HOURS, THEN AT 10-12 HOUR INTERVALS IF NEEDED. IN VERY SEVERE POISONINGS, DOSAGE RATES MAY BE DOUBLED. TREATMENT WITH PRALIDOXIME WILL BE MOST EFFECTIVE IF GIVEN WITHIN THIRTY-SIX HOURS AFTER POISONING (MORGAN, RECOGNITION AND MANAGEMENT OF PESTICIDE POISONINGS, 3RD ED.). ANTIDOTE SHOULD BE ADMINISTERED BY QUALIFIED MEDICAL PERSONNEL.

REACTIVITY

REACTIVITY: STABLE UNDER NORMAL TEMPERATURES AND PRESSURES.

INCOMPATIBILITIES: BENSULIDE OXYGEN ANALOG: OXIDIZERS (STRONG): FIRE AND EXPLOSION HAZARD.

DECOMPOSITION: THERMAL DECOMPOSITION MAY RELEASE TOXIC OXIDES OF NITROGEN, PHOSPHORUS, SULFUR AND CARBON.

POLYMERIZATION: HAZARDOUS POLYMERIZATION HAS NOT BEEN REPORTED TO OCCUR UNDER NORMAL TEMPERATURES AND PRESSURES.

STORAGE AND DISPOSAL

OBSERVE ALL FEDERAL, STATE AND LOCAL REGULATIONS WHEN STORING OR DISPOSING OF THIS SUBSTANCE. FOR ASSISTANCE, CONTACT THE DISTRICT DIRECTOR OF THE ENVIRONMENTAL PROTECTION AGENCY.

****STORAGE****

STORE IN ACCORDANCE WITH 40 CFR 165 RECOMMENDED PROCEDURES FOR THE DISPOSAL AND STORAGE OF PESTICIDES AND PESTICIDE CONTAINERS.
STORE AWAY FROM INCOMPATIBLE SUBSTANCES.

****DISPOSAL****

DISPOSAL MUST BE IN ACCORDANCE WITH 40 CFR 165 RECOMMENDED PROCEDURES FOR THE DISPOSAL AND STORAGE OF PESTICIDES AND PESTICIDE CONTAINERS.

CONDITIONS TO AVOID

MAY BURN BUT DOES NOT IGNITE READILY.

SPILL AND LEAK PROCEDURES

OCCUPATIONAL SPILL: DO NOT TOUCH SPILLED MATERIAL. STOP LEAK IF YOU CAN DO IT WITHOUT RISK. FOR SMALL SPILLS, TAKE UP WITH SAND OR OTHER ABSORBENT MATERIAL AND PLACE INTO CONTAINERS FOR LATER DISPOSAL. FOR SMALL DRY SPILLS, WITH A CLEAN SHOVEL PLACE MATERIAL INTO CLEAN, DRY CONTAINER AND COVER. MOVE CONTAINERS FROM SPILL AREA. FOR LARGER SPILLS, DIKE FAR AHEAD OF SPILL FOR LATER DISPOSAL. KEEP UNNECESSARY PEOPLE AWAY. ISOLATE HAZARD AREA AND DENY ENTRY.

PROTECTIVE EQUIPMENT

VENTILATION: PROVIDE LOCAL EXHAUST OR GENERAL DILUTION VENTILATION SYSTEM.

RESPIRATOR: THE FOLLOWING RESPIRATORS ARE RECOMMENDED BASED ON INFORMATION FOUND IN THE PHYSICAL DATA, TOXICITY AND HEALTH EFFECTS SECTIONS. THEY ARE RANKED IN ORDER FROM MINIMUM TO MAXIMUM RESPIRATORY PROTECTION. THE SPECIFIC RESPIRATOR SELECTED MUST BE BASED ON CONTAMINATION LEVELS FOUND IN THE WORK PLACE, MUST NOT EXCEED THE WORKING LIMITS OF THE RESPIRATOR AND BE JOINTLY APPROVED BY THE NATIONAL INSTITUTE FOR OCCUPATIONAL SAFETY AND HEALTH AND THE MINE SAFETY AND HEALTH ADMINISTRATION (NIOSH-MSHA).

TYPE 'C' SUPPLIED-AIR RESPIRATOR WITH A FULL FACEPIECE OPERATED IN PRESSURE-DEMAND OR OTHER POSITIVE PRESSURE MODE OR WITH A FULL FACEPIECE, HELMET OR HOOD OPERATED IN CONTINOUS-FLOW MODE.

SELF-CONTAINED BREATHING APPARATUS WITH A FULL FACEPIECE OPERATED IN PRESSURE-DEMAND OR OTHER POSITIVE PRESSURE MODE.

FOR FIREFIGHTING AND OTHER IMMEDIATELY DANGEROUS TO LIFE OR HEALTH CONDITIONS:

SELF-CONTAINED BREATHING APPARATUS WITH FULL FACEPIECE OPERATED IN PRESSURE-DEMAND OR OTHER POSITIVE PRESSURE MODE.

SUPPLIED-AIR RESPIRATOR WITH FULL FACEPIECE AND OPERATED IN PRESSURE-DEMAND OR OTHER POSITIVE PRESSURE MODE IN COMBINATION WITH AN AUXILIARY SELF-CONTAINED BREATHING APPARATUS OPERATED IN PRESSURE-DEMAND OR OTHER POSITIVE PRESSURE MODE.

CLOTHING: EMPLOYEE MUST WEAR APPROPRIATE PROTECTIVE (IMPERVIOUS) CLOTHING AND EQUIPMENT TO PREVENT ANY POSSIBILITY OF SKIN CONTACT WITH THIS SUBSTANCE.

GLOVES: EMPLOYEE MUST WEAR APPROPRIATE PROTECTIVE GLOVES TO PREVENT CONTACT WITH THIS SUBSTANCE.

EYE PROTECTION: EMPLOYEE MUST WEAR SPLASH-PROOF OR DUST-RESISTANT SAFETY GOGGLES TO PREVENT EYE CONTACT WITH THIS SUBSTANCE.

EMERGENCY EYE WASH: WHERE THERE IS ANY POSSIBILITY THAT AN EMPLOYEE'S EYES MAY BE EXPOSED TO THIS SUBSTANCE, THE EMPLOYER SHOULD PROVIDE AN EYE WASH FOUNTAIN WITHIN THE IMMEDIATE WORK AREA FOR EMERGENCY USE.

AUTHORIZED BY- OCCUPATIONAL HEALTH SERVICES, INC.
CREATION DATE: 10/04/89 ***REVISION DATE:*** 04/23/90

MATERIAL SAFETY DATA SHEET

OCCUPATIONAL HEALTH SERVICES, INC.
AGRICULTURE AND PESTICIDE DIVISION
450 SEVENTH AVENUE, SUITE 2407
NEW YORK, NEW YORK 10123
1-800-445-MSDS OR (212) 967-1100

EMERGENCY CONTACT:
JOHN S. BRANSFORD, JR. (615) 292-1180

SUBSTANCE IDENTIFICATION

CAS-NUMBER 741-58-2

SUBSTANCE: **BENSULIDE**

TRADE NAMES/SYNONYMS: PHOSPHORODITHIOIC ACID, O,O-BIS(1-METHYLETHYL) S-(2-((PHENYLSULFONYL) AMINO)ETHYL) ESTER; PHOSPHORODITHIOIC ACID , O,O-DIISOPROPYL ESTER, S-ESTER WITH N- (2-MERCAPTOETHYL)BENZENESULFONAMIDE; S-(O,O-DIISOPROPYL PHOSPHORODITHIOATE)ESTER OF N-(2-MERCAPTOETHYL) BENZENESULFONAMIDE; O,O-BIS(1-METHYLETHYL)-S-(2-((PHENYLSULFONYL)AMINO)ETHYL) PHOSPHORODITHIOATE; N-(2-(O,O-DIISOPROPYLDITHIOPHOSPHORYL)ETHYL)BENZENESULFONAMIDE; BETASAN; DISAN; PREFAR; C14H24NO4PS3; PST02583

CHEMICAL FAMILY: PHOSPHOROTHIOATE ESTER, NON-CARBOXYLIC SULFONAMIDE

MOLECULAR FORMULA: C14-H24-N-O4-P-S3

MOLECULAR WEIGHT: 397.54

CERCLA RATINGS (SCALE 0-3): HEALTH=3 FIRE=1 REACTIVITY=0 PERSISTENCE=3

NFPA RATINGS (SCALE 0-4): HEALTH=U FIRE=1 REACTIVITY=0

COMPONENTS AND CONTAMINANTS

COMPONENT: BENSULIDE ***PERCENT:*** 100.0

CAS# 741-58-2

OTHER CONTAMINANTS: NONE

EXPOSURE LIMITS: NO OCCUPATIONAL EXPOSURE LIMITS ESTABLISHED BY OSHA, ACGIH, OR NIOSH.

PHYSICAL DATA

DESCRIPTION: COLORLESS SOLID. ***BOILING POINT:*** >392 F (>200 C) (DECOMPOSES)

MELTING POINT: 94 F (34 C) ***SPECIFIC GRAVITY:*** 1.23 @ 20 C

VAPOR PRESSURE: NEGLIGIBLE ***SOLUBILITY IN WATER:*** 25 PPM @ 25 C

SOLVENT SOLUBILITY: SOLUBLE IN ACETONE, ETHANOL, METHYL ISOBUTYL KETONE AND XYLENE; VERY SLIGHTLY SOLUBLE IN KEROSENE.

FIRE AND EXPLOSION DATA

FIRE AND EXPLOSION HAZARD: SLIGHT FIRE HAZARD WHEN EXPOSED TO HEAT OR FLAME.

FIREFIGHTING MEDIA: DRY CHEMICAL, CARBON DIOXIDE, HALON, WATER SPRAY OR STANDARD FOAM (1987 EMERGENCY RESPONSE GUIDEBOOK, DOT P 5800.4).
FOR LARGER FIRES, USE WATER SPRAY, FOG OR STANDARD FOAM (1987 EMERGENCY RESPONSE GUIDEBOOK, DOT P 5800.4).

FIREFIGHTING: MOVE CONTAINERS FROM FIRE AREA IF POSSIBLE (1987 EMERGENCY RESPONSE GUIDEBOOK, DOT P 5800.4, GUIDE PAGE 53).
EXTINGUISH USING AGENT SUITABLE FOR TYPE OF SURROUNDING FIRE. AVOID BREATHING VAPORS AND DUSTS. KEEP UPWIND.

TOXICITY

BENSULIDE: TOXICITY DATA: 2000 MG/KG SKIN-RABBIT LD50; 3950 MG/KG SKIN-RAT LD50; 271 MG/KG ORAL-RAT LD50; 770 MG/KG UNREPORTED-RAT LD50. CARCINOGEN STATUS: NONE. ACUTE TOXICITY LEVEL: TOXIC BY INGESTION; MODERATELY TOXIC BY DERMAL ABSORPTION. TARGET EFFECTS: CHOLINESTERASE INHIBITOR. POISONING MAY AFFECT THE NERVOUS SYSTEM.* AT INCREASED RISK FROM EXPOSURE: PERSONS WITH RESPIRATORY AILMENTS, RECENT EXPOSURE TO CHOLINESTERASE INHIBITORS OR IMPAIRED CHOLINESTERASE PRODUCTION, OR LIVER MALFUNCTION.* ADDITIONAL DATA: MAY CROSS THE PLACENTA. HIGH ENVIRONMENTAL TEMPERATURES OR EXPOSURE OF THE CHEMICAL TO VISIBLE OR ULTRAVIOLET LIGHT MAY ENHANCE THE TOXICITY. INTERACTIONS WITH MEDICATIONS MAY OCCUR.*
* MAY BE BASED ON GENERAL INFORMATION ON ORGANOPHOSPHATES.

HEALTH EFFECTS AND FIRST AID

INHALATION: BENSULIDE: SEE INFORMATION ON ORGANOPHOSPHATES.
ORGANOPHOSPHATES: CHOLINESTERASE INHIBITOR. **ACUTE EXPOSURE-** WHEN INHALED, THE FIRST EFFECTS OF CHOLINESTERASE INHIBITORS ARE USUALLY RESPIRATORY AND MAY INCLUDE NASAL HYPEREMIA AND WATERY DISCHARGE, COUGH, CHEST DISCOMFORT, DYSPNEA, AND WHEEZING DUE TO INCREASED BRONCHIAL SECRETIONS AND BRONCHOCONSTRICTION. IF SUFFICIENT AMOUNTS ARE ABSORBED, OTHER SYSTEMIC EFFECTS MAY BEGIN WITHIN A FEW MINUTES OR BE DELAYED FOR UP TO 12 HOURS. SYMPTOMS MAY INCLUDE PALLOR, NAUSEA, VOMITING, DIARRHEA, ABDOMINAL CRAMPS, HEADACHE, DIZZINESS, OCULAR PAIN, BLURRED VISION, MIOSIS OR IN SOME CASES, ESPECIALLY INITIALLY, MYDRIASIS, LACRIMATION, SALIVATION, SWEATING, AND CONFUSION. OTHER REPORTED CENTRAL NERVOUS SYSTEM OR NEUROMUSCULAR EFFECTS MAY INCLUDE ATAXIA, SLURRED SPEECH, AREFLEXIA, WEAKNESS, FATIGUE, FASCICULATIONS, TWITCHING, TREMORS POSSIBLY OF THE TONGUE AND EYELIDS, AND EVENTUALLY PARALYSIS OF THE EXTREMITIES AND POSSIBLY OF THE RESPIRATORY MUSCLES. IN SEVERE CASES THERE MAY ALSO BE INVOLUNTARY DEFECATION AND URINATION, CYANOSIS, PSYCHOSIS, HYPERGLYCEMIA, ACUTE PANCREATITIS, CARDIAC IRREGULARITIES, PULMONARY EDEMA, UNCONSCIOUSNESS, CONVULSIONS, AND COMA. DEATH IS PRIMARILY DUE TO RESPIRATORY FAILURE, ALTHOUGH CARDIOVASCULAR EFFECTS INCLUDING CARDIAC ARREST MAY ALSO BE IMPLICATED. LONG TERM SEQUELAE ARE RARE BUT MAY INCLUDE NEUROPSYCHIATRIC DISORDERS AND MYOPATHY WITH MUSCLE TENDERNESS. SOME ORGANOPHOSPHATES MAY CAUSE A DELAYED NEUROPATHY BEGINNING 1-4 WEEKS AFTER AN ACUTE EXPOSURE WHICH MAY OR MAY NOT HAVE CAUSED ACUTE CHOLINERGIC EFFECTS. NUMBNESS, TINGLING, WEAKNESS AND CRAMPING BEGINNING SYMMETRICALLY IN THE LOWER LIMBS MAY PROGRESS TO ATAXIA AND PARALYSIS. IN SEVERE CASES, UPPER LIMB INVOLVEMENT IS POSSIBLE AND FLACCID PARALYSIS MAY PROGRESS TO SPASTIC PARALYSIS WITH EXAGGERATED REFLEXES. IMPROVEMENT MAY OCCUR OVER MONTHS TO YEARS, BUT SOME RESIDUAL IMPAIRMENT USUALLY REMAINS.
CHRONIC EXPOSURE- REPEATED OR PROLONGED EXPOSURE MAY RESULT IN THE EFFECTS OF ACUTE EXPOSURE INCLUDING THE DELAYED NEUROPATHY. OTHER EFFECTS REPORTED IN WORKERS REPEATEDLY EXPOSED INCLUDE IMPAIRED MEMORY AND CONCENTRATION, ACUTE PSYCHOSIS, SEVERE DEPRESSIONS, IRRITABILTY, CONFUSION, APATHY, EMOTIONAL LABILITY, SOCIAL WITHDRAWAL, CONFUSION, HEADACHE, SPEECH DIFFICULTIES, DELAYED REACTION TIMES, SPATIAL DISORIENTATION, NIGHTMARES, SLEEPWALKING, AND DROWSINESS OR INSOMNIA. AN INFLUENZA-LIKE CONDITION WITH HEADACHE, NAUSEA, WEAKNESS, ANOREXIA AND MALAISE HAS ALSO BEEN REPORTED.

FIRST AID- REMOVE FROM EXPOSURE AREA TO FRESH AIR IMMEDIATELY. IF BREATHING HAS STOPPED, GIVE ARTIFICIAL RESPIRATION. MAINTAIN AIRWAY AND BLOOD PRESSURE AND ADMINISTER OXYGEN IF AVAILABLE. KEEP AFFECTED PERSON WARM AND AT REST. TREAT SYMPTOMATICALLY AND SUPPORTIVELY. ADMINISTRATION OF OXYGEN SHOULD BE PERFORMED BY QUALIFIED PERSONNEL. GET MEDICAL ATTENTION IMMEDIATELY.

SKIN CONTACT: BENSULIDE: SEE INFORMATION ON ORGANOPHOSPHATES.
ORGANOPHOSPHATES: CHOLINESTERASE INHIBITOR. **ACUTE EXPOSURE-** LOCALIZED SWEATING AND FASCICULATIONS MAY OCCUR AT THE SITE OF CONTACT. IF SUFFICIENT AMOUNTS ARE ABSORBED, OTHER EFFECTS OF CHOLINESTERASE INHIBITION AS DESCRIBED IN ACUTE INHALATION MAY OCCUR. SYMPTOMS MAY BE DELAYED 2-3 HOURS, BUT USUALLY NO MORE THAN 12 HOURS. THE RATE OF ABSORPTION IS INCREASED BY THE PRESENCE OF DERMATITIS OR HIGH AMBIENT TEMPERATURES. DELAYED NEUROPATHY IS ALSO POSSIBLE. **CHRONIC EXPOSURE-** REPEATED OR PROLONGED EXPOSURE MAY CAUSE EFFECTS AS DESCRIBED IN ACUTE EXPOSURE. SOME ORGANOPHOSPHATES MAY CAUSE SENSITIZATION.

FIRST AID- REMOVE CONTAMINATED CLOTHING IMMEDIATELY. WASH CONTAMINATED AREAS WITH SOAP AND WATER FOLLOWED BY ALCOHOL (ARENA, POISONING, 4TH ED.). EMERGENCY PERSONNEL SHOULD WEAR GLOVES AND AVOID CONTAMINATION. TREAT RESPIRATORY DIFFICULTY WITH ARTIFICIAL RESPIRATION. GET MEDICAL ATTENTION IMMEDIATELY.

EYE CONTACT: BENSULIDE: APPLICATION TO RABBIT EYES CAUSED MILD IRRITATION. SEE INFORMATION ON ORGANOPHOSPHATES.
ORGANOPHOSPHATES: CHOLINESTERASE INHIBITOR. **ACUTE EXPOSURE-** DIRECT CONTACT MAY CAUSE PAIN, HYPEREMIA, LACRIMATION, TWITCHING OF THE EYELIDS, MIOSIS, AND CILIARY MUSCLE SPASM WITH LOSS OF ACCOMODATION, BLURRED OR DIMMED VISION AND BROWACHE. SOMETIMES MYDRIASIS MAY OCCUR INSTEAD OF MIOSIS. WITH SUFFICIENT EXPOSURE, OTHER SYMPTOMS OF CHOLINESTERASE INHIBITION AS DESCRIBED IN ACUTE INHALATION MAY OCCUR. **CHRONIC EXPOSURE-** REPEATED OR PROLONGED EXPOSURE MAY CAUSE EFFECTS AS DESCRIBED IN ACUTE EXPOSURE. SOME COMPOUNDS HAVE CAUSED TOXIC EFFECTS ON THE CRYSTALLINE LENS, CONJUNCTIVAL THICKENING AND OBSTRUCTION OF THE NASOLACRIMAL CANALS WHEN USED AS MIOTIC EYEDROPS.

FIRST AID- IRRIGATE EYES WITH WATER OR SALINE SOLUTION. IF SYMPTOMS OF POISONING OCCUR, TREAT RESPIRATORY DIFFICULTY WITH ARTIFICIAL RESPIRATION AND OXYGEN. OBSERVE PATIENT FOR AT LEAST 24-36 HOURS (GOSSELIN, CLINICAL TOXICOLOGY OF COMMERCIAL PRODUCTS, 5TH ED.). GET MEDICAL ATTENTION IMMEDIATELY. OXYGEN SHOULD BE ADMINISTERED BY QUALIFIED MEDICAL PERSONNEL.

INGESTION: BENSULIDE: TOXIC. IN CHRONIC FEEDING STUDIES IN ANIMALS, RENAL CHANGES AND DEGENERATIVE LIVER CHANGES OCCURRED. SEE INFORMATION ON ORGANOPHOSPHATES.
ORGANOPHOSPHATES: CHOLINESTERASE INHIBITOR. **ACUTE EXPOSURE-** WHEN INGESTED, THE FIRST EFFECTS MAY BE NAUSEA, VOMITING, ANOREXIA, ABDOMINAL CRAMPS AND DIARRHEA. GASTROINTESTINAL ABSORPTION MAY CAUSE SYMPTOMS OF CHOLINESTERASE INHIBITION AS DESCRIBED IN ACUTE INHALATION. SYMPTOMS MAY BEGIN WITHIN MINUTES OR BE DELAYED FOR

HOURS. DELAYED EFFECTS INCLUDING NEUROPATHY MAY ALSO OCCUR. **CHRONIC EXPOSURE-** REPEATED INGESTION MAY CAUSE EFFECTS AS DESCRIBED IN ACUTE EXPOSURE.

FIRST AID- IF PERSON IS ALERT AND RESPIRATION IS NOT DEPRESSED, GIVE SYRUP OF IPECAC FOLLOWED BY WATER (IF VOMITING OCCURS, KEEP HEAD BELOW HIPS TO PREVENT ASPIRATION). IF CONSCIOUSNESS LEVEL DECLINES OR VOMITING HAS NOT OCCURRED IN 15 MINUTES EMPTY STOMACH BY GASTRIC LAVAGE WITH THE AID OF CUFFED ENDOTRACHEAL TUBE USING ISOTONIC SALINE OR 5% SODIUM BICARBONATE FOLLOW WITH ACTIVATED CHARCOAL. ESTABLISH AND MAINTAIN AIRWAY. TREAT RESPIRATORY DIFFICULTY WITH ARTIFICIAL RESPIRATION AND OXYGEN. DO NOT GIVE MORPHINE, AMINOPHYLLINE, PHENOTHIAZINES, RESERPINE, FUROSEMIDE, OR ETHACRYNIC ACID (MORGAN, RECOGNITION AND MANAGEMENT OF PESTICIDE POISONINGS, 3RD ED.). TREAT SYMPTOMATICALLY AND SUPPORTIVELY. ADMINISTRATION OF OXYGEN AND LAVAGE MUST BE PERFORMED BY QUALIFIED MEDICAL PERSONNEL. GET MEDICAL ATTENTION IMMEDIATELY.

ANTIDOTE: THE FOLLOWING ANTIDOTE(S) HAVE BEEN RECOMMENDED. HOWEVER, THE DECISION AS TO WHETHER THE SEVERITY OF POISONING REQUIRES ADMINISTRATION OF ANY ANTIDOTE AND ACTUAL DOSE REQUIRED SHOULD BE MADE BY QUALIFIED MEDICAL PERSONNEL.

FOR CHOLINESTERASE INHIBITORS: ESTABLISH CLEAR AIRWAY AND TISSUE OXYGENATION BY ASPIRATION OF SECRETIONS, AND IF NECESSARY, BY ASSISTED PULMONARY VENTILATION WITH OXYGEN. IMPROVE TISSUE OXYGENATION AS MUCH AS POSSIBLE BEFORE ADMINISTERING ATROPINE TO MINIMIZE THE RISK OF VENTRICULAR FIBRILLATION. ADMINISTER ATROPINE SULFATE INTRAVENOUSLY, OR INTRAMUSCULARLY IF IV INJECTION IS NOT POSSIBLE. IN MODERATELY SEVERE POISONING ADMINISTER ATROPINE SULFATE, 0.4-2.0 MG REPEATED EVERY 15 MINUTES UNTIL ATROPINIZATION IS ACHIEVED (TACHYCARDIA, FLUSHING, DRY MOUTH, MYDRIASIS). MAINTAIN ATROPINIZATION BY REPEATED DOSES FOR 2-12 HOURS, OR LONGER, DEPENDING ON THE SEVERITY OF POISONING. THE APPEARANCE OF RALES IN THE LUNG BASES, MIOSIS, SALIVATION, NAUSEA, BRADYCARDIA, ARE ALL INDICATIONS OF INADEQUATE ATROPINIZATION. SEVERELY POISONED INDIVIDUALS MAY EXHIBIT REMARKABLE TOLERANCE TO ATROPINE; TWO OR MORE TIMES THE DOSAGES SUGGESTED ABOVE MAY BE NEEDED. PERSONS NOT POISONED OR ONLY SLIGHTLY POISONED, HOWEVER, MAY DEVELOP SIGNS OF ATROPINE TOXICITY FROM SUCH LARGE DOSAGES: FEVER, MUSCLE FIBRILLATIONS, AND DELIRIUM ARE THE MAIN SIGNS OF ATROPINE TOXICITY. IF THESE SIGNS APPEAR WHILE THE PATIENT IS FULLY ATROPINIZED, ATROPINE ADMINISTRATION SHOULD BE DISCONTINUED, AT LEAST TEMPORARILY. OBSERVE TREATED PATIENTS CLOSELY AT LEAST 24 HOURS TO INSURE THAT SYMPTOMS (POSSIBLY PULMONARY EDEMA) DO NOT RECUR AS ATROPINIZATION WEARS OFF. IN VERY SEVERE POISONINGS, METABOLIC DISPOSITION OF TOXICANT MAY REQUIRE SEVERAL HOURS OR DAYS DURING WHICH ATROPINIZATION MUST BE MAINTAINED. MARKEDLY LOWER LEVELS OF URINARY METABOLITES INDICATE THAT ATROPINE DOSAGE CAN BE TAPERED OFF. AS DOSAGE IS REDUCED, CHECK THE LUNG BASES FREQUENTLY FOR RALES. IF RALES ARE HEARD OR OTHER SYMPTOMS RETURN, RE-ESTABLISH ATROPINIZATION PROMPTLY (MORGAN, RECOGNITION AND MANAGEMENT OF PESTICIDE POISONINGS, 3RD ED.). ADMINISTRATION OF ANTIDOTE MUST BE PERFORMED BY QUALIFIED MEDICAL PERSONNEL.

IN CASES OF SEVERE POISONING BY ORGANOPHOSPHATE PESTICIDES IN WHICH RESPIRATORY DEPRESSION, MUSCLE WEAKNESS AND TWITCHINGS ARE SEVERE, GIVE PRALIDOXIME (PROTOPAM-AYERST, 2-PAM), 1.0 GRAM INTRAVENOUSLY AT NO MORE THAN 0.5 GRAM PER MINUTE. DOSAGE OF PRALIDOXIME MAY BE REPEATED IN 1-2 HOURS, THEN AT 10-12 HOUR INTERVALS IF NEEDED. IN VERY SEVERE POISONINGS, DOSAGE RATES MAY BE DOUBLED. TREATMENT WITH PRALIDOXIME WILL BE MOST EFFECTIVE IF GIVEN WITHIN THIRTY-SIX HOURS AFTER POISONING (MORGAN, RECOGNITION AND MANAGEMENT OF PESTICIDE POISONINGS, 3RD ED.). ANTIDOTE SHOULD BE ADMINISTERED BY QUALIFIED MEDICAL PERSONNEL.

REACTIVITY

REACTIVITY: STABLE UNDER NORMAL TEMPERATURES AND PRESSURES.

INCOMPATIBILITIES: BENSULIDE: OXIDIZERS (STRONG): FIRE AND EXPLOSION HAZARD.

DECOMPOSITION: THERMAL DECOMPOSITION MAY RELEASE TOXIC OXIDES OF NITROGEN, PHOSPHORUS, SULFUR AND CARBON.

POLYMERIZATION: HAZARDOUS POLYMERIZATION HAS NOT BEEN REPORTED TO OCCUR UNDER NORMAL TEMPERATURES AND PRESSURES.

STORAGE AND DISPOSAL

OBSERVE ALL FEDERAL, STATE AND LOCAL REGULATIONS WHEN STORING OR DISPOSING OF THIS SUBSTANCE. FOR ASSISTANCE, CONTACT THE DISTRICT DIRECTOR OF THE ENVIRONMENTAL PROTECTION AGENCY.

STORAGE

STORE IN ACCORDANCE WITH 40 CFR 165 RECOMMENDED PROCEDURES FOR THE DISPOSAL AND STORAGE OF PESTICIDES AND PESTICIDE CONTAINERS.
STORE AWAY FROM INCOMPATIBLE SUBSTANCES.

DISPOSAL

DISPOSAL MUST BE IN ACCORDANCE WITH 40 CFR 165 RECOMMENDED PROCEDURES FOR THE DISPOSAL AND STORAGE OF PESTICIDES AND PESTICIDE CONTAINERS.

CONDITIONS TO AVOID

MAY BURN BUT DOES NOT IGNITE READILY.

SPILL AND LEAK PROCEDURES

OCCUPATIONAL SPILL: DO NOT TOUCH SPILLED MATERIAL. STOP LEAK IF YOU CAN DO IT WITHOUT RISK. FOR SMALL SPILLS, TAKE UP WITH SAND OR OTHER ABSORBENT MATERIAL AND PLACE INTO CONTAINERS FOR LATER DISPOSAL. FOR SMALL DRY SPILLS, WITH A CLEAN SHOVEL PLACE MATERIAL INTO CLEAN, DRY CONTAINER AND COVER. MOVE CONTAINERS FROM SPILL AREA. FOR LARGER SPILLS, DIKE FAR AHEAD OF SPILL FOR LATER DISPOSAL. KEEP UNNECESSARY PEOPLE AWAY. ISOLATE HAZARD AREA AND DENY ENTRY.

PROTECTIVE EQUIPMENT

VENTILATION: PROVIDE LOCAL EXHAUST OR GENERAL DILUTION VENTILATION SYSTEM.

RESPIRATOR: THE FOLLOWING RESPIRATORS ARE RECOMMENDED BASED ON INFORMATION FOUND IN THE PHYSICAL DATA, TOXICITY AND HEALTH EFFECTS SECTIONS. THEY ARE RANKED IN ORDER FROM MINIMUM TO MAXIMUM RESPIRATORY PROTECTION. THE SPECIFIC RESPIRATOR SELECTED MUST BE BASED ON CONTAMINATION LEVELS FOUND IN THE WORK PLACE, MUST NOT EXCEED THE WORKING LIMITS OF THE RESPIRATOR AND BE JOINTLY APPROVED BY THE NATIONAL INSTITUTE FOR OCCUPATIONAL SAFETY AND HEALTH AND THE MINE SAFETY AND HEALTH ADMINISTRATION (NIOSH-MSHA).

TYPE 'C' SUPPLIED-AIR RESPIRATOR WITH A FULL FACEPIECE OPERATED IN PRESSURE-DEMAND OR OTHER POSITIVE PRESSURE MODE OR WITH A FULL FACEPIECE, HELMET OR HOOD OPERATED IN CONTINOUS-FLOW MODE.

SELF-CONTAINED BREATHING APPARATUS WITH A FULL FACEPIECE OPERATED IN PRESSURE-DEMAND OR OTHER POSITIVE PRESSURE MODE.

FOR FIREFIGHTING AND OTHER IMMEDIATELY DANGEROUS TO LIFE OR HEALTH CONDITIONS:

SELF-CONTAINED BREATHING APPARATUS WITH FULL FACEPIECE OPERATED IN PRESSURE-DEMAND OR OTHER POSITIVE PRESSURE MODE.

SUPPLIED-AIR RESPIRATOR WITH FULL FACEPIECE AND OPERATED IN PRESSURE-DEMAND OR OTHER POSITIVE PRESSURE MODE IN COMBINATION WITH AN AUXILIARY SELF-CONTAINED BREATHING APPARATUS OPERATED IN PRESSURE-DEMAND OR OTHER POSITIVE PRESSURE MODE.

CLOTHING: EMPLOYEE MUST WEAR APPROPRIATE PROTECTIVE (IMPERVIOUS) CLOTHING AND EQUIPMENT TO PREVENT ANY POSSIBILITY OF SKIN CONTACT WITH THIS SUBSTANCE.

GLOVES: EMPLOYEE MUST WEAR APPROPRIATE PROTECTIVE GLOVES TO PREVENT CONTACT WITH THIS SUBSTANCE.

EYE PROTECTION: EMPLOYEE MUST WEAR SPLASH-PROOF OR DUST-RESISTANT SAFETY GOGGLES TO PREVENT EYE CONTACT WITH THIS SUBSTANCE.

EMERGENCY EYE WASH: WHERE THERE IS ANY POSSIBILITY THAT AN EMPLOYEE'S EYES MAY BE EXPOSED TO THIS SUBSTANCE, THE EMPLOYER SHOULD PROVIDE AN EYE WASH FOUNTAIN WITHIN THE IMMEDIATE WORK AREA FOR EMERGENCY USE.

AUTHORIZED BY- OCCUPATIONAL HEALTH SERVICES, INC.
CREATION DATE: 10/04/89 ***REVISION DATE:*** 04/25/90

MATERIAL SAFETY DATA SHEET

OCCUPATIONAL HEALTH SERVICES, INC.
AGRICULTURE AND PESTICIDE DIVISION
450 SEVENTH AVENUE, SUITE 2407
NEW YORK, NEW YORK 10123
1-800-445-MSDS OR (212) 967-1100

EMERGENCY CONTACT:
JOHN S. BRANSFORD, JR. (615) 292-1180

SUBSTANCE IDENTIFICATION

CAS-NUMBER 25057-89-0

SUBSTANCE: **BENTAZON**

TRADE NAMES/SYNONYMS: 3-(1-METHYLETHYL)-1H-2,1,3-BENZOTHIADIAZIN-4(3H)-ONE 2,2-DIOXIDE; 3-ISOPROPYL-1H-2,1,3-BENZOTHIADIAZIN-4(3H)-ONE 2,2-DIOXIDE; 3-ISOPROPYL-1H-BENZO-2,1,3-THIADIAZIN-4-ONE 2,2-DIOXIDE; 1H-2,1,3-BENZOTHIADIAZIN-4(3H)-ONE, 3-(1-METHYLETHYL)-, 2,2-DIOXIDE; 1H-2,1,3-

BENZOTHIADIAZIN-4(3H)-ONE, 3-IOSPROPYL-, 2,2-DIOXIDE; BASAGRAN; BENDIOXIDE; BENTAZONE; C10H12N2O3S; PST02584

CHEMICAL FAMILY: BENZOTHIAZINE

MOLECULAR FORMULA: C10-H12-N2-O3-S

MOLECULAR WEIGHT: 240.28

CERCLA RATINGS (SCALE 0-3): HEALTH=2 FIRE=1 REACTIVITY=0 PERSISTENCE=2

NFPA RATINGS (SCALE 0-4): HEALTH=2 FIRE=1 REACTIVITY=0

COMPONENTS AND CONTAMINANTS

COMPONENT: BENTAZON ***PERCENT:*** 100.0
CAS# 25057-89-0

OTHER CONTAMINANTS: NONE

EXPOSURE LIMITS: NO OCCUPATIONAL EXPOSURE LIMITS ESTABLISHED BY OSHA, ACGIH, OR NIOSH.

PHYSICAL DATA

DESCRIPTION: COLORLESS OR WHITE CRYSTALLINE POWDER.

MELTING POINT: 279-282 F (137-139 C) ***SPECIFIC GRAVITY:*** NOT AVAILABLE

VAPOR PRESSURE: NEGLIGIBLE ***SOLUBILITY IN WATER:*** 0.05% @ 20 C

SOLVENT SOLUBILITY: SOLUBLE IN ACETONE, BENZENE, CHLOROFORM, ETHANOL. DECOMPOSES ABOVE 392 F (200 C)

FIRE AND EXPLOSION DATA

FIRE AND EXPLOSION HAZARD: SLIGHT FIRE HAZARD WHEN EXPOSED TO HEAT OR FLAME.

FIREFIGHTING MEDIA: DRY CHEMICAL, CARBON DIOXIDE, HALON, WATER SPRAY OR STANDARD FOAM (1987 EMERGENCY RESPONSE GUIDEBOOK, DOT P 5800.4).
FOR LARGER FIRES, USE WATER SPRAY, FOG OR STANDARD FOAM (1987 EMERGENCY RESPONSE GUIDEBOOK, DOT P 5800.4).

FIREFIGHTING: MOVE CONTAINER FROM FIRE AREA IF POSSIBLE. DO NOT SCATTER SPILLED MATERIAL WITH HIGH PRESSURE WATER STREAMS. DIKE FIRE CONTROL WATER FOR LATER DISPOSAL (1987 EMERGENCY RESPONSE GUIDEBOOK, DOT P 5800.4, GUIDE PAGE 31).
USE AGENTS SUITABLE FOR TYPE OF SURROUNDING FIRE. AVOID BREATHING HAZARDOUS VAPORS, KEEP UPWIND.

TOXICITY

BENTAZON: TOXICITY DATA: 2500 MG/KG SKIN-RAT LD50; 1100 MG/KG ORAL-RAT LD50; 750 MG/KG ORAL-RABBIT LD50; 500 MG/KG ORAL-CAT LD50; 450 MG/KG ORAL-DOG LD50; REPRODUCTIVE EFFECTS DATA (RTECS). CARCINOGEN STATUS: NONE. LOCAL EFFECTS: IRRITANT- INHALATION, SKIN, AND EYES. ACUTE TOXICITY LEVEL: MODERATELY TOXIC BY INGESTION AND SLIGHTLY TOXIC BY DERMAL ABSORPTION. TARGET EFFECTS: NO DATA AVAILABLE.

HEALTH EFFECTS AND FIRST AID

INHALATION: BENTAZON: IRRITANT. **ACUTE EXPOSURE-** MAY CAUSE IRRITATION OF THE MUCOUS MEMBRANES. **CHRONIC EXPOSURE-** PROLONGED OR REPEATED EXPOSURE MAY CAUSE IRRITATION OF OF THE MUCOUS MEMBRANES.

FIRST AID- REMOVE FROM EXPOSURE AREA TO FRESH AIR IMMEDIATELY. IF BREATHING HAS STOPPED, PERFORM ARTIFICIAL RESPIRATION. KEEP PERSON WARM AND AT REST. TREAT SYMPTOMATICALLY AND SUPPORTIVELY. GET MEDICAL ATTENTION IMMEDIATELY.

SKIN CONTACT: BENTAZON: IRRITANT. **ACUTE EXPOSURE-** MAY CAUSE IRRITATION. **CHRONIC EXPOSURE-** PROLONGED OR REPEATED EXPOSURE MAY CAUSE DERMATITIS.

FIRST AID- REMOVE CONTAMINATED CLOTHING AND SHOES IMMEDIATELY. WASH AFFECTED AREA WITH SOAP OR MILD DETERGENT AND LARGE AMOUNTS OF WATER UNTIL NO EVIDENCE OF CHEMICAL REMAINS (APPROXIMATELY 15-20 MINUTES). GET MEDICAL ATTENTION IMMEDIATELY.

EYE CONTACT: BENTAZON: IRRITANT. **ACUTE EXPOSURE-** MAY CAUSE IRRITATION. **CHRONIC EXPOSURE-** PROLONGED OR REPEATED EXPOSURE MAY CAUSE CONJUNCTIVITIS.

FIRST AID- WASH EYES IMMEDIATELY WITH LARGE AMOUNTS OF WATER OR NORMAL SALINE, OCCASIONALLY LIFTING UPPER AND LOWER LIDS, UNTIL NO EVIDENCE OF CHEMICAL REMAINS (APPROXIMATELY 15-20 MINUTES). GET MEDICAL ATTENTION IMMEDIATELY.

INGESTION: BENTAZON: **ACUTE EXPOSURE-** MAY CAUSE VOMITING, DIARRHEA, DYSPNEA, TREMORS, AND WEAKNESS. **CHRONIC EXPOSURE-** NO DATA AVAILABLE.

FIRST AID- REMOVE BY GASTRIC LAVAGE AND CATHARSIS. MAINTAIN BLOOD PRESSURE AND AIRWAY. GIVE OXYGEN IF RESPIRATION IS DEPRESSED. DO NOT PERFORM GASTRIC LAVAGE IF VICTIM IS UNCONSCIOUS. GET MEDICAL ATTENTION IMMEDIATELY (DREISBACH, HANDBOOK OF POISONING, 12TH ED.).
ADMINISTRATION OF LAVAGE OR OXYGEN SHOULD BE PERFORMED BY QUALIFIED MEDICAL PERSONNEL.

ANTIDOTE: NO SPECIFIC ANTIDOTE. TREAT SYMPTOMATICALLY AND SUPPORTIVELY.

REACTIVITY

REACTIVITY: STABLE UNDER NORMAL TEMPERATURES AND PRESSURES.

INCOMPATIBILITIES: BENTAZON: OXIDIZERS (STRONG): FIRE AND EXPLOSION HAZARD. SEE ALSO KETONES.
KETONES: ACETALDEHYDE: VIOLENT CONDENSATION REACTION. NITRIC ACID + HYDROGEN PEROXIDE: FORMATION OF EXPLOSIVE PRODUCT. PERCHLORIC ACID: VIOLENT DECOMPOSITION.

DECOMPOSITION: THERMAL DECOMPOSITION MAY RELEASE TOXIC OXIDES OF NITROGEN AND SULFUR.

POLYMERIZATION: HAZARDOUS POLYMERIZATION HAS NOT BEEN REPORTED TO OCCUR UNDER NORMAL TEMPERATURES AND PRESSURES.

STORAGE AND DISPOSAL

OBSERVE ALL FEDERAL, STATE AND LOCAL REGULATIONS WHEN STORING OR DISPOSING OF THIS SUBSTANCE. FOR ASSISTANCE, CONTACT THE DISTRICT DIRECTOR OF THE ENVIRONMENTAL PROTECTION AGENCY.

****STORAGE****

STORE IN ACCORDANCE WITH 40 CFR 165 RECOMMENDED PROCEDURES FOR THE DISPOSAL AND STORAGE OF PESTICIDES AND PESTICIDE CONTAINERS.
STORE AWAY FROM INCOMPATIBLE SUBSTANCES.

****DISPOSAL****

DISPOSAL MUST BE IN ACCORDANCE WITH 40 CFR 165 RECOMMENDED PROCEDURES FOR THE DISPOSAL AND STORAGE OF PESTICIDES AND PESTICIDE CONTAINERS.

CONDITIONS TO AVOID

MAY BURN BUT DOES NOT IGNITE READILY. AVOID CONTACT WITH STRONG OXIDIZERS, EXCESSIVE HEAT, SPARKS, OR OPEN FLAME.

SPILL AND LEAK PROCEDURES

OCCUPATIONAL SPILL: SWEEP UP AND PLACE IN SUITABLE CLEAN, DRY CONTAINERS FOR RECLAMATION OR LATER DISPOSAL. DO NOT FLUSH SPILLED MATERIAL INTO SEWER. KEEP UNNECESSARY PEOPLE AWAY.

PROTECTIVE EQUIPMENT

VENTILATION: PROVIDE LOCAL EXHAUST VENTILATION SYSTEM.

RESPIRATOR: THE FOLLOWING RESPIRATORS ARE RECOMMENDED BASED ON INFORMATION FOUND IN THE PHYSICAL DATA, TOXICITY AND HEALTH EFFECTS SECTIONS. THEY ARE RANKED IN ORDER FROM MINIMUM TO MAXIMUM RESPIRATORY PROTECTION. THE SPECIFIC RESPIRATOR SELECTED MUST BE BASED ON CONTAMINATION LEVELS FOUND IN THE WORK PLACE, MUST NOT EXCEED THE WORKING LIMITS OF THE RESPIRATOR AND BE JOINTLY APPROVED BY THE NATIONAL INSTITUTE FOR OCCUPATIONAL SAFETY AND HEALTH AND THE MINE SAFETY AND HEALTH ADMINISTRATION (NIOSH-MSHA).
CHEMICAL CARTRIDGE RESPIRATOR WITH AN ORGANIC VAPOR CARTRIDGE(S) WITH A FULL FACEPIECE AND ORGANIC VAPOR CARTRIDGE(S) IN COMBINATION WITH A DUST AND MIST FILTER.
POWERED AIR-PURIFYING RESPIRATOR WITH A TIGHT-FITTING FACEPIECE AND ORGANIC VAPOR CARTRIDGE(S) IN COMBINATION WITH A HIGH-EFFICIENCY PARTICULATE FILTER.
TYPE 'C' SUPPLIED-AIR RESPIRATOR WITH A FULL FACEPIECE OPERATED IN A PRESSURE-DEMAND OR OTHER POSITIVE PRESSURE MODE.
SELF-CONTAINED BREATHING APPARATUS WITH A FULL FACEPIECE OPERATED IN PRESSURE-DEMAND OR OTHER POSITIVE PRESSURE MODE. FOR FIREFIGHTING AND OTHER IMMEDIATELY DANGEROUS TO LIFE OR HEALTH CONDITIONS:
SELF-CONTAINED BREATHING APPARATUS WITH FULL FACEPIECE OPERATED IN PRESSURE-DEMAND OR OTHER POSITIVE PRESSURE MODE.
SUPPLIED-AIR RESPIRATOR WITH FULL FACEPIECE AND OPERATED IN PRESSURE-DEMAND OR OTHER POSITIVE PRESSURE MODE IN COMBINATION WITH AN AUXILIARY SELF-CONTAINED BREATHING APPARATUS OPERATED IN PRESSURE-DEMAND OR OTHER POSITIVE PRESSURE MODE.

CLOTHING: EMPLOYEE MUST WEAR APPROPRIATE PROTECTIVE (IMPERVIOUS) CLOTHING AND EQUIPMENT TO PREVENT REPEATED OR PROLONGED SKIN CONTACT WITH THIS SUBSTANCE.

GLOVES: EMPLOYEE MUST WEAR APPROPRIATE PROTECTIVE GLOVES TO PREVENT CONTACT WITH THIS SUBSTANCE.

EYE PROTECTION: EMPLOYEE MUST WEAR SPLASH-PROOF OR DUST-RESISTANT SAFETY GOGGLES TO PREVENT EYE CONTACT WITH THIS SUBSTANCE.
EMERGENCY EYE WASH: WHERE THERE IS ANY POSSIBILITY THAT AN EMPLOYEE'S EYES MAY BE EXPOSED TO THIS SUBSTANCE, THE EMPLOYER SHOULD PROVIDE AN EYE WASH FOUNTAIN WITHIN THE IMMEDIATE WORK AREA FOR EMERGENCY USE.

AUTHORIZED BY- OCCUPATIONAL HEALTH SERVICES, INC.
CREATION DATE: 10/04/89 ***REVISION DATE:*** 05/31/90

MATERIAL SAFETY DATA SHEET

OCCUPATIONAL HEALTH SERVICES, INC.
AGRICULTURE AND PESTICIDE DIVISION
450 SEVENTH AVENUE, SUITE 2407
NEW YORK, NEW YORK 10123
1-800-445-MSDS OR (212) 967-1100

EMERGENCY CONTACT:
JOHN S. BRANSFORD, JR. (615) 292-1180

SUBSTANCE IDENTIFICATION

CAS-NUMBER 100-52-7
SUBSTANCE: **BENZALDEHYDE**
TRADE NAMES/SYNONYMS: ARTIFICIAL ALMOND OIL; BENZENECARBONAL; PHENYLMETHANAL; BENZOIC ALDEHYDE; BENZENE METHYLAL; BENZALDEHYDE FFC; OIL OF BITTER ALMOND; ARTIFICAL ESSENTIAL ALMOND OIL; BENZENECARBOXALDEHYDE; NA 1989; C7H6O; PST02590
CHEMICAL FAMILY: ALDEHYDE, AROMATIC
MOLECULAR FORMULA: C6-H5-C-H-O
MOLECULAR WEIGHT: 106.12
CERCLA RATINGS (SCALE 0-3): HEALTH=3 FIRE=2 REACTIVITY=0 PERSISTENCE=1
NFPA RATINGS (SCALE 0-4): HEALTH=2 FIRE=2 REACTIVITY=0

COMPONENTS AND CONTAMINANTS

COMPONENT: BENZALDEHYDE ***PERCENT:*** 100.0
CAS# 100-52-7
OTHER CONTAMINANTS: NONE
EXPOSURE LIMITS: NO OCCUPATIONAL EXPOSURE LIMITS ESTABLISHED BY OSHA, ACGIH, OR NIOSH.

PHYSICAL DATA

DESCRIPTION: COLORLESS TO PALE YELLOW LIQUID WITH A BITTER ALMOND ODOR AND
BURNING AROMATIC TASTE. ***BOILING POINT:*** 352 F (178 C)
MELTING POINT: -15 F (-26 C) ***SPECIFIC GRAVITY:*** 1.0415 @ 10 C
VAPOR PRESSURE: 1 MMHG @ 26.2 C ***SOLUBILITY IN WATER:*** 0.29%
ODOR THRESHOLD: 0.3-1.3 MG/M3 ***VAPOR DENSITY:*** 3.65
SOLVENT SOLUBILITY: SOLUBLE IN ALCOHOL, ETHER, ACETONE, BENZENE, LIGROIN, FIXED AND VOLATILE OILS, CONCENTRATED SULFURIC ACID, LIQUID CARBON DIOXIDE, LIQUID AMMONIA, METHYLAMINE, DIETHYLAMINE, CHLOROFORM, PETROLEUM ETHER.

FIRE AND EXPLOSION DATA

FIRE AND EXPLOSION HAZARD: MODERATE FIRE HAZARD WHEN EXPOSED TO HEAT OR FLAME.
VAPORS ARE HEAVIER THAN AIR AND MAY TRAVEL A CONSIDERABLE DISTANCE TO A SOURCE OF IGNITION AND FLASH BACK.
VAPOR-AIR MIXTURES ARE EXPLOSIVE ABOVE FLASH POINT.
FLASH POINT: 145 F (63 C) (CC) ***LOWER EXPLOSIVE LIMIT:*** 1.4%
AUTOIGNITION TEMP.: 377 F (192 F) ***FLAMMABILITY CLASS(OSHA):*** IIIA
FIREFIGHTING MEDIA: DRY CHEMICAL, CARBON DIOXIDE, HALON, WATER SPRAY OR ALCOHOL FOAM (1987 EMERGENCY RESPONSE GUIDEBOOK, DOT P 5800.4).
FOR LARGER FIRES, USE WATER SPRAY, FOG OR ALCOHOL FOAM (1987 EMERGENCY RESPONSE GUIDEBOOK, DOT P 5800.4).
FIREFIGHTING: MOVE CONTAINER FROM FIRE AREA IF POSSIBLE. COOL FIRE-EXPOSED CONTAINERS WITH WATER FROM SIDE UNTIL WELL AFTER FIRE IS OUT. STAY AWAY FROM STORAGE TANK ENDS. FOR MASSIVE FIRE IN STORAGE AREA, USE UNMANNED HOSE HOLDER OR MONITOR NOZZLES, ELSE WITHDRAW FROM AREA AND LET FIRE BURN. WITHDRAW IMMEDIATELY IN CASE OF RISING SOUND FROM VENTING SAFETY DEVICE OR ANY DISCOLORATION OF STORAGE TANK DUE TO FIRE (1987 EMERGENCY RESPONSE GUIDEBOOK, DOT P 5800.4, GUIDE PAGE 26). EXTINGUISH ONLY IF FLOW CAN BE STOPPED. USE WATER IN FLOODING QUANTITIES AS A FOG; SOLID STREAMS MAY NOT BE EFFECTIVE. COOL CONTAINERS WITH FLOODING QUANTITIES OF WATER, APPLIED FROM AS FAR A DISTANCE AS POSSIBLE. AVOID BREATHING TOXIC VAPORS; KEEP UPWIND.
WATER MAY BE USED TO BLANKET FIRE (NFPA 325M FIRE HAZARD PROPERTIES OF FLAMMABLE LIQUIDS, GASES, AND VOLATILE SOLIDS, 1984)

TRANSPORTATION DATA

DEPARTMENT OF TRANSPORTATION HAZARD CLASSIFICATION 49 CFR 172.101: COMBUSTIBLE LIQUID
DEPARTMENT OF TRANSPORTATION LABELING REQUIREMENTS 49 CFR 172.101 AND SUBPART E: NONE
DEPARTMENT OF TRANSPORTATION PACKAGING REQUIREMENTS: NONE
EXCEPTIONS: 49 CFR 173.118A

TOXICITY

BENZALDEHYDE: IRRITATION DATA: 500 MG/24 HOURS SKIN-RABBIT MODERATE. TOXICITY DATA: >1250 MG/KG SKIN-RABBIT LD50 (NTP TR 378); 1300 MG/KG ORAL-RAT LD50; 2020 MG/KG ORAL MOUSE (85GMAT); 1000 MG/KG ORAL-GUINEA PIG LD50; 5000 MG/KG SUBCUTANEOUS-RAT LDLO; 5000 MG/KG SUBCUTANEOUS-RABBIT LD50; 1020 MG/KG INTRAPERITONEAL-MOUSE LD50 (NTP TR 378); MUTAGENIC DATA (RTECS). CARCINOGEN STATUS: NONE. THERE WAS SOME EVIDENCE OF CARCINOGENIC ACTIVITY FOR MICE AS EVIDENCED BY INCREASED INCIDENCES OF SQUAMOUS CELL PAPILLOMAS AND HYPERPLASIA OF THE FORESTOMACH. THERE WAS NO EVIDENCE OF CARCINOGENIC ACTIVITY FOR RATS (NTP TR 378). LOCAL EFFECTS: IRRITANT- INHALATION, SKIN, EYE. ACUTE TOXICITY LEVEL: MODERATELY TOXIC BY DERMAL ABSORPTION, INGESTION. TARGET EFFECTS: CENTRAL NERVOUS SYSTEM DEPRESSANT; SENSITIZER-DERMAL. ADDITIONAL DATA: ALCOHOL MAY ENHANCE THE TOXIC EFFECTS. CROSS SENSITIZATION WITH BENZOIC ACID, VANILLA, AND BALSAM OF PERU IS POSSIBLE.

HEALTH EFFECTS AND FIRST AID

INHALATION: BENZALDEHYDE: IRRITANT/NARCOTIC. **ACUTE EXPOSURE-** MAY CAUSE IRRITATION OF THE RESPIRATORY TRACT WITH DYSPNEA, SORE THROAT, AND COUGHING. HIGH CONCENTRATIONS MAY CAUSE CENTRAL NERVOUS SYSTEM DEPRESSION WITH NAUSEA, VOMITING, HEADACHE, LIGHTHEADEDNESS, DULLNESS, AND NARCOSIS; EXTREME EXPOSURES MAY CAUSE LUNG INJURY, CONVULSIONS, AND RESPIRATORY FAILURE. **CHRONIC EXPOSURE-** REPEATED INHALATION OF 26 MG/M3 HAS CAUSED HEMATOLOGICAL CHANGES IN ANIMALS.
FIRST AID- REMOVE FROM EXPOSURE AREA TO FRESH AIR IMMEDIATELY. IF BREATHING HAS STOPPED, PERFORM ARTIFICIAL RESPIRATION. KEEP PERSON WARM AND AT REST. TREAT SYMPTOMATICALLY AND SUPPORTIVELY. GET MEDICAL ATTENTION IMMEDIATELY.

SKIN CONTACT: BENZALDEHYDE: IRRITANT/SENSITIZER. **ACUTE EXPOSURE-** CONTACT WITH THE LIQUID MAY CAUSE IRRITATION WITH REDNESS, PAIN, AND WEAK LOCAL ANESTHESIA. SENSITIZATION REACTIONS MAY OCCUR IN PREVIOUSLY EXPOSED PERSONS. SOME ABSORPTION THROUGH THE SKIN MAY OCCUR. **CHRONIC EXPOSURE-** REPEATED OR PROLONGED CONTACT MAY CAUSE DEFATTING OF THE SKIN. SENSITIZATION WITH DERMATITIS OR URTICARIA MAY ALSO OCCUR.
FIRST AID- REMOVE CONTAMINATED CLOTHING AND SHOES IMMEDIATELY. WASH AFFECTED AREA WITH SOAP OR MILD DETERGENT AND LARGE AMOUNTS OF WATER UNTIL NO EVIDENCE OF CHEMICAL REMAINS (APPROXIMATELY 15-20 MINUTES). GET MEDICAL ATTENTION IMMEDIATELY.

EYE CONTACT: BENZALDEHYDE: IRRITANT. **ACUTE EXPOSURE-** VAPORS MAY CAUSE SLIGHT IRRITATION. DIRECT CONTACT OR HIGH VAPOR CONCENTRATIONS MAY CAUSE IRRITATION WITH LACRIMATION, REDNESS, AND PAIN. IN SEVERE CASES, EYE INJURY MAY OCCUR. **CHRONIC EXPOSURE-** REPEATED OR PROLONGED EXPOSURE TO IRRITANTS MAY CAUSE CONJUNCTIVITIS.
FIRST AID- WASH EYES IMMEDIATELY WITH LARGE AMOUNTS OF WATER OR NORMAL SALINE, OCCASIONALLY LIFTING UPPER AND LOWER LIDS, UNTIL NO EVIDENCE OF CHEMICAL REMAINS (APPROXIMATELY 15-20 MINUTES). GET MEDICAL ATTENTION IMMEDIATELY.

INGESTION: BENZALDEHYDE: NARCOTIC. **ACUTE EXPOSURE-** MAY CAUSE SORE THROAT, CENTRAL NERVOUS SYSTEM DEPRESSION, NAUSEA, VOMITING, ABDOMINAL PAIN, HEADACHE, DIZZINESS, DULLNESS, CONVULSIONS, AND RESPIRATORY FAILURE. THE ESTIMATED LETHAL DOSE IN HUMANS IS 2 OUNCES. **CHRONIC EXPOSURE-** RATS FED 800 MG/KG/DAY FOR 12-16 DAYS EXHIBITED TREMORS, HYPEREXCITABILITY OR INACTIVITY, AND SOME DEATHS. IN 13 WEEK STUDIES, THERE WERE COMPOUND-RELATED LESIONS OF THE BRAIN, HYPERPLASIA AND/OR HYPERKERATOSIS OF THE FORESTOMACH, AND LIVER AND KIDNEY DAMAGE IN RATS, AND KIDNEY LESIONS IN MICE. IN 2 YEAR STUDIES, THERE WAS SOME EVIDENCE FOR CARCINOGENIC ACTIVITY IN MICE BASED ON INCREASED INCIDENCES OF SQUAMOUS CELL PAPILLOMAS AND HYPERPLASIA OF THE FORESTOMACH.
FIRST AID- IF THE PERSON IS CONSCIOUS AND NOT CONVULSING, INDUCE EMESIS BY GIVING SYRUP OF IPECAC FOLLOWED BY WATER. (IF VOMITING OCCURS KEEP THE HEAD BELOW THE HIPS TO PREVENT ASPIRATION). REPEAT IN 20 MINUTES IF NOT EFFECTIVE INITIALLY. GIVE ACTIVATED CHARCOAL. IN PATIENTS WITH DEPRESSED RESPIRATION OR IF EMESIS IS NOT PRODUCED, PERFORM GASTRIC LAVAGE

CAUTIOUSLY (DREISBACH, HANDBOOK OF POISONING, 12TH ED.). TREAT SYMPTOMATICALLY AND SUPPORTIVELY. GASTRIC LAVAGE SHOULD BE PERFORMED BY QUALIFIED MEDICAL PERSONNEL. GET MEDICAL ATTENTION IMMEDIATELY.

ANTIDOTE: NO SPECIFIC ANTIDOTE. TREAT SYMPTOMATICALLY AND SUPPORTIVELY.

REACTIVITY

REACTIVITY: STABLE UNDER NORMAL TEMPERATURES AND PRESSURES.

INCOMPATIBILITIES: BENZALDEHYDE: ALKALINE CYANIDE SOLUTIONS: MAY INITIATE EXOTHERMIC CONDENSATION REACTION. BASES (STRONG): MAY INITIATE EXOTHERMIC CONDENSATION REACTION. OXIDIZERS (STRONG): FIRE AND EXPLOSION HAZARD. PERFORMIC ACID: VIOLENT REACTION. REDUCING AGENTS (STRONG): MAY INITIATE EXOTHERMIC CONDENSATION REACTION.

DECOMPOSITION: THERMAL DECOMPOSITION PRODUCTS MAY INCLUDE TOXIC OXIDES OF CARBON.

POLYMERIZATION: MAY UNDERGO EXOTHERMIC CONDENSATION REACTION ON CONTACT WITH STRONG BASES, REDUCING AGENTS AND ALKALINE CYANIDE SOLUTIONS.

STORAGE AND DISPOSAL

OBSERVE ALL FEDERAL, STATE AND LOCAL REGULATIONS WHEN STORING OR DISPOSING OF THIS SUBSTANCE. FOR ASSISTANCE, CONTACT THE DISTRICT DIRECTOR OF THE ENVIRONMENTAL PROTECTION AGENCY.

STORAGE

STORE IN ACCORDANCE WITH 29 CFR 1910.106.

BONDING AND GROUNDING: SUBSTANCES WITH LOW ELECTROCONDUCTIVITY, WHICH MAY BE IGNITED BY ELECTROSTATIC SPARKS, SHOULD BE STORED IN CONTAINERS WHICH MEET THE BONDING AND GROUNDING GUIDELINES SPECIFIED IN NFPA 77-1983, RECOMMENDED PRACTICE ON STATIC ELECTRICITY.

STORE AWAY FROM INCOMPATIBLE SUBSTANCES.

KEEP CONTAINER TIGHTLY CLOSED. PROTECT FROM EXPOSURE TO AIR OR LIGHT.

CONDITIONS TO AVOID

AVOID CONTACT WITH HEAT, SPARKS, FLAMES, OR OTHER SOURCES OF IGNITION. VAPORS MAY BE EXPLOSIVE AND POISONOUS; DO NOT ALLOW UNNECESSARY PERSONNEL IN AREA. DO NOT OVERHEAT CONTAINERS; CONTAINERS MAY VIOLENTLY RUPTURE AND TRAVEL A CONSIDERABLE DISTANCE IN HEAT OF FIRE.

SPILL AND LEAK PROCEDURES

OCCUPATIONAL SPILL: SHUT OFF IGNITION SOURCES. STOP LEAK IF YOU CAN DO IT WITHOUT RISK. USE WATER SPRAY TO REDUCE VAPORS. FOR SMALL SPILLS, TAKE UP WITH SAND OR OTHER ABSORBENT MATERIAL AND PLACE INTO CONTAINERS FOR LATER DISPOSAL. FOR LARGER SPILLS, DIKE FAR AHEAD OF SPILL FOR LATER DISPOSAL. NO SMOKING, FLAMES OR FLARES IN HAZARD AREA. KEEP UNNECESSARY PEOPLE AWAY; ISOLATE HAZARD AREA AND DENY ENTRY.

PROTECTIVE EQUIPMENT

VENTILATION: PROVIDE LOCAL EXHAUST VENTILATION SYSTEM.

RESPIRATOR: THE FOLLOWING RESPIRATORS ARE RECOMMENDED BASED ON INFORMATION FOUND IN THE PHYSICAL DATA, TOXICITY AND HEALTH EFFECTS SECTIONS. THEY ARE RANKED IN ORDER FROM MINIMUM TO MAXIMUM RESPIRATORY PROTECTION. THE SPECIFIC RESPIRATOR SELECTED MUST BE BASED ON CONTAMINATION LEVELS FOUND IN THE WORK PLACE, MUST NOT EXCEED THE WORKING LIMITS OF THE RESPIRATOR AND BE JOINTLY APPROVED BY THE NATIONAL INSTITUTE FOR OCCUPATIONAL SAFETY AND HEALTH AND THE MINE SAFETY AND HEALTH ADMINISTRATION (NIOSH-MSHA).

TYPE 'C' SUPPLIED-AIR RESPIRATOR WITH A FULL FACEPIECE OPERATED IN PRESSURE-DEMAND OR OTHER POSITIVE PRESSURE MODE OR WITH A FULL FACEPIECE, HELMET OR HOOD OPERATED IN CONTINOUS-FLOW MODE.

SELF-CONTAINED BREATHING APPARATUS WITH A FULL FACEPIECE OPERATED IN PRESSURE-DEMAND OR OTHER POSITIVE PRESSURE MODE.

FOR FIREFIGHTING AND OTHER IMMEDIATELY DANGEROUS TO LIFE OR HEALTH CONDITIONS:

SELF-CONTAINED BREATHING APPARATUS WITH FULL FACEPIECE OPERATED IN PRESSURE-DEMAND OR OTHER POSITIVE PRESSURE MODE. SUPPLIED-AIR RESPIRATOR WITH FULL FACEPIECE AND OPERATED IN PRESSURE-DEMAND OR OTHER POSITIVE PRESSURE MODE IN COMBINATION WITH AN AUXILIARY SELF-CONTAINED BREATHING APPARATUS OPERATED IN PRESSURE-DEMAND OR OTHER POSITIVE PRESSURE MODE.

CLOTHING: EMPLOYEE MUST WEAR APPROPRIATE PROTECTIVE (IMPERVIOUS) CLOTHING AND EQUIPMENT TO PREVENT REPEATED OR PROLONGED SKIN CONTACT WITH THIS SUBSTANCE.

GLOVES: EMPLOYEE MUST WEAR APPROPRIATE PROTECTIVE GLOVES TO PREVENT CONTACT WITH THIS SUBSTANCE.

EYE PROTECTION: EMPLOYEE MUST WEAR SPLASH-PROOF OR DUST-RESISTANT SAFETY GOGGLES TO PREVENT CONTACT WITH THIS SUBSTANCE.

EMERGENCY WASH FACILITIES: WHERE THERE IS ANY POSSIBILITY THAT AN EMPLOYEE'S EYES AND/OR SKIN MAY BE EXPOSED TO THIS SUBSTANCE, THE EMPLOYER SHOULD PROVIDE AN EYE WASH FOUNTAIN AND QUICK DRENCH SHOWER WITHIN THE IMMEDIATE WORK AREA FOR EMERGENCY USE.

AUTHORIZED BY- OCCUPATIONAL HEALTH SERVICES, INC.

CREATION DATE: 10/04/89 ***REVISION DATE:*** 03/28/90

MATERIAL SAFETY DATA SHEET

OCCUPATIONAL HEALTH SERVICES, INC.
AGRICULTURE AND PESTICIDE DIVISION
450 SEVENTH AVENUE, SUITE 2407
NEW YORK, NEW YORK 10123
1-800-445-MSDS OR (212) 967-1100

EMERGENCY CONTACT:
JOHN S. BRANSFORD, JR. (615) 292-1180

SUBSTANCE IDENTIFICATION

CAS-NUMBER 65-85-0

SUBSTANCE: BENZOIC ACID

TRADE NAMES/SYNONYMS: BENZENECARBOXYLIC ACID; CARBOXYBENZENE; DRACYLIC ACID; PHENYL CARBOXYLIC ACID; PHENYLFORMIC ACID; RETARDER BA; TENN-PLAS; RETARDEX; SOLVO POWDER; SALVO LIQUID; PHENYLCARBOXYLIC ACID; BENZOATE; BENZENEMETHANOIC ACID; BENZENEFORMIC ACID; STCC 4966340; C7H6O2; PST02720

CHEMICAL FAMILY: CARBOXYLIC ACID, AROMATIC

MOLECULAR FORMULA: C6-H5-C-O2-H

MOLECULAR WEIGHT: 122.12

CERCLA RATINGS (SCALE 0-3): HEALTH=2 FIRE=1 REACTIVITY=0 PERSISTENCE=2

NFPA RATINGS (SCALE 0-4): HEALTH=2 FIRE=1 REACTIVITY=U

COMPONENTS AND CONTAMINANTS

COMPONENT: BENZOIC ACID ***PERCENT:*** 100
CAS# 65-85-0

EXPOSURE LIMITS: BENZOIC ACID: NO OCCUPATIONAL EXPOSURE LIMITS ESTABLISHED BY OSHA, ACGIH, OR NIOSH.
5000 POUNDS CERCLA SECTION 103 REPORTABLE QUANTITY

PHYSICAL DATA

DESCRIPTION: WHITE POWDER OR CRYSTALS WITH AN ODOR OF BENZOIN OR BENZALDEHYDE.

BOILING POINT: 480 F (249 C) ***MELTING POINT:*** 252 F (122 C)

SPECIFIC GRAVITY: 1.2659 @ 15 C ***VAPOR PRESSURE:*** 1 MMHG @ 205 F

PH: 2.8 @ SATD SOLUTION ***SOLUBILITY IN WATER:*** 2.9% @ 20 C

VAPOR DENSITY: 4.2

SOLVENT SOLUBILITY: SOLUBLE IN ALCOHOL, ETHER, BENZENE, CHLOROFORM, ACETONE, CARBON DISULFIDE, OIL OF TURPENTINE, CARBON TETRACHLORIDE, FIXED AND VOLATILE OILS; SLIGHTLY SOLUBLE IN PETROLEUM ETHER, HEXANE

FIRE AND EXPLOSION DATA

FIRE AND EXPLOSION HAZARD: SLIGHT FIRE HAZARD WHEN EXPOSED TO HEAT OR FLAME. DUST/AIR MIXTURES MAY BE EXPLOSIVE ABOVE THE FLASH POINT. VAPOR FROM MOLTEN BENZOIC ACID MAY FORM EXPLOSIVE MIXTURE WITH AIR.

FLASH POINT: 250 F (121 C) ***UPPER EXPLOSIVE LIMIT:*** 35 G/FT3 (OPTIMUM)

LOWER EXPLOSIVE LIMIT: 3 G/FT3 ***AUTOIGNITION TEMP.:*** 1060 F (571 C)

FIREFIGHTING MEDIA: DRY CHEMICAL, CARBON DIOXIDE, HALON, WATER SPRAY OR STANDARD FOAM (1987 EMERGENCY RESPONSE GUIDEBOOK, DOT P 5800.4).
FOR LARGER FIRES, USE WATER SPRAY, FOG OR STANDARD FOAM (1987 EMERGENCY RESPONSE GUIDEBOOK, DOT P 5800.4).

FIREFIGHTING: MOVE CONTAINER FROM FIRE AREA IF POSSIBLE. DO NOT SCATTER SPILLED MATERIAL WITH HIGH PRESSURE WATER STREAMS. DIKE FIRE CONTROL WATER FOR LATER DISPOSAL (1987 EMERGENCY RESPONSE GUIDEBOOK, DOT P 5800.4, GUIDE PAGE 31).
USE WATER IN FLOODING QUANTITIES AS A FOG; SOLID STREAMS OF WATER MAY BE INEFFECTIVE. COOL AFFECTED CONTAINERS WITH FLOODING QUANTITIES OF WATER APPLYING WATER FROM AS FAR A DISTANCE AS POSSIBLE. AVOID BREATHING VAPORS OR DUSTS.

TOXICITY

BENZOIC ACID: IRRITATION DATA: 22 MG/3 DAYS INTERMITTENT SKIN-HUMAN MODERATE; 500 MG/24 HOURS SKIN-RABBIT MILD; 100 MG EYE-RABBIT SEVERE.

TOXICITY DATA: 6 MG/KG SKIN-HUMAN TDLO; 500 MG/KG ORAL-MAN LDLO; 1700 MG/KG ORAL-RAT LD50; 1940 MG/KG ORAL-MOUSE LD50; 2 GM/KG ORAL-GUINEA PIG LDLO; 2000 MG/KG ORAL-DOG LD50; 2000 MG/KG ORAL-CAT LD50; 2000 MG/KG ORAL-RABBIT LDLO; 2000 MG/KG SUBCUTANEOUS-RABBIT LDLO; 1400 MG/KG INTRAPERITONEAL-GUINEA PIG LDLO; 1460 MG/KG INTRAPERITONEAL-MOUSE LD50; MUTAGENIC DATA (RTECS). CARCINOGEN STATUS: NONE. LOCAL EFFECTS: IRRITANT- INHALATION, SKIN, AND EYES. ACUTE TOXICITY LEVEL: MODERATELY TOXIC BY INGESTION. TARGET EFFECTS: POISONING MAY AFFECT THE RESPIRATORY AND CENTRAL NERVOUS SYSTEM.

HEALTH EFFECTS AND FIRST AID

INHALATION: BENZOIC ACID: **ACUTE EXPOSURE-** DUST MAY CAUSE MILD RESPIRATORY IRRITATION WITH SORE THROAT AND COUGHING. **CHRONIC EXPOSURE-** NO DATA AVAILABLE.

FIRST AID- REMOVE FROM EXPOSURE AREA TO FRESH AIR IMMEDIATELY. IF BREATHING HAS STOPPED, PERFORM ARTIFICIAL RESPIRATION. KEEP PERSON WARM AND AT REST. TREAT SYMPTOMATICALLY AND SUPPORTIVELY. GET MEDICAL ATTENTION IMMEDIATELY.

SKIN CONTACT: BENZOIC ACID: **ACUTE EXPOSURE-** DUST AND LIQUID MAY CAUSE MILD IRRITATION AND REDNESS. CONCENTRATIONS UP TO 0.2%, MAY ELICIT AN IMMEDIATE SKIN REACTION VARYING FROM ERYTHEMA TO A NON-IMMUNOLOGIC CONTACT URTICARIA IN SOME PERSONS. **CHRONIC EXPOSURE-** REPEATED APPLICATION TO HUMAN SKIN PRODUCED MODERATE IRRITATION.

FIRST AID- REMOVE CONTAMINATED CLOTHING AND SHOES IMMEDIATELY. WASH AFFECTED AREA WITH SOAP OR MILD DETERGENT AND LARGE AMOUNTS OF WATER UNTIL NO EVIDENCE OF CHEMICAL REMAINS (APPROXIMATELY 15-20 MINUTES). GET MEDICAL ATTENTION IMMEDIATELY.

EYE CONTACT: BENZOIC ACID: IRRITANT. **ACUTE EXPOSURE-** DUST MAY CAUSE STRONG IRRITATION AND REDNESS. **CHRONIC EXPOSURE-** REPEATED OR PROLONGED CONTACT WITH IRRITANTS MAY CAUSE CONJUNCTIVITIS.

FIRST AID- WASH EYES IMMEDIATELY WITH LARGE AMOUNTS OF WATER OR NORMAL SALINE, OCCASIONALLY LIFTING UPPER AND LOWER LIDS, UNTIL NO EVIDENCE OF CHEMICAL REMAINS (APPROXIMATELY 15-20 MINUTES). GET MEDICAL ATTENTION IMMEDIATELY.

INGESTION: BENZOIC ACID: **ACUTE EXPOSURE-** LARGE DOSES MAY CAUSE SORE THROAT, GASTRIC PAIN, NAUSEA, VOMITING, AND POSSIBLE ALLERGIC REACTIONS. A 67 KG MAN INGESTED 50 GM WITHOUT ILL EFFECTS. **CHRONIC EXPOSURE-** A DAILY INTAKE OF 4-6 GRAMS PRODUCED NO TOXIC EFFECTS OUTSIDE OF GASTRIC IRRITATION. LARGER DOSES MAY HAVE SYSTEMIC EFFECTS SIMILAR TO SALICYLATES AND MAY INCLUDE DISTURBANCES IN ACID BASE BALANCE, TREMOR AND CONVULSIONS.

FIRST AID- TREAT SYMPTOMATICALLY AND SUPPORTIVELY. GET MEDICAL ATTENTION IMMEDIATELY. IF VOMITING OCCURS, KEEP HEAD LOWER THAN HIPS TO PREVENT ASPIRATION.

ANTIDOTE: NO SPECIFIC ANTIDOTE. TREAT SYMPTOMATICALLY AND SUPPORTIVELY.

REACTIVITY

REACTIVITY: STABLE UNDER NORMAL TEMPERATURES AND PRESSURES.

INCOMPATIBILITIES: BENZOIC ACID: OXIDIZERS (STRONG): VIGOROUS EXOTHERMIC REACTION.

DECOMPOSITION: THERMAL DECOMPOSITION PRODUCTS MAY INCLUDE TOXIC OXIDES OF CARBON.

POLYMERIZATION: HAZARDOUS POLYMERIZATION HAS NOT BEEN REPORTED TO OCCUR UNDER NORMAL TEMPERATURES AND PRESSURES.

STORAGE AND DISPOSAL

OBSERVE ALL FEDERAL, STATE AND LOCAL REGULATIONS WHEN STORING OR DISPOSING OF THIS SUBSTANCE. FOR ASSISTANCE, CONTACT THE DISTRICT DIRECTOR OF THE ENVIRONMENTAL PROTECTION AGENCY.

STORAGE

STORE AWAY FROM INCOMPATIBLE SUBSTANCES.

CONDITIONS TO AVOID

MAY BURN BUT DOES NOT IGNITE READILY. AVOID CONTACT WITH STRONG OXIDIZERS, EXCESSIVE HEAT, SPARKS, OR OPEN FLAME.

SPILL AND LEAK PROCEDURES

SOIL SPILL: DIG HOLDING AREA SUCH AS LAGOON, POND OR PIT FOR CONTAINMENT.

USE PROTECTIVE COVER SUCH AS A PLASTIC SHEET TO PREVENT MATERIAL FROM DISSOLVING IN FIRE EXTINGUISHING WATER OR RAIN.

WATER SPILL: USE ACTIVATED CARBON TO ABSORB SPILLED SUBSTANCE THAT IS DISSOLVED.

USE MECHANICAL DREDGES OR LIFTS TO EXTRACT IMMOBILIZED MASSES OF POLLUTION AND PRECIPITATES.

USE SUCTION HOSES TO REMOVE TRAPPED SPILL MATERIAL.

OCCUPATIONAL SPILL: SWEEP UP AND PLACE IN SUITABLE CLEAN, DRY CONTAINERS FOR RECLAMATION OR LATER DISPOSAL. DO NOT FLUSH SPILLED MATERIAL INTO SEWER. KEEP UNNECESSARY PEOPLE AWAY.

REPORTABLE QUANTITY (RQ): 5000 POUNDS THE SUPERFUND AMENDMENTS AND REAUTHORIZATION ACT (SARA) SECTION 304 REQUIRES THAT A RELEASE EQUAL TO OR GREATER THAN THE REPORTABLE QUANTITY FOR THIS SUBSTANCE BE IMMEDIATELY REPORTED TO THE LOCAL EMERGENCY PLANNING COMMITTEE AND THE STATE EMERGENCY RESPONSE COMMISSION (40 CFR 355.40). IF THE RELEASE OF THIS SUBSTANCE IS REPORTABLE UNDER CERCLA SECTION 103, THE NATIONAL RESPONSE CENTER MUST BE NOTIFIED IMMEDIATELY AT (800) 424-8802 OR (202) 426-2675 IN THE METROPOLITAN WASHINGTON, D.C. AREA (40 CFR 302.6).

PROTECTIVE EQUIPMENT

VENTILATION: PROVIDE LOCAL EXHAUST OR GENERAL DILUTION VENTILATION SYSTEM.

RESPIRATOR: THE FOLLOWING RESPIRATORS ARE RECOMMENDED BASED ON INFORMATION FOUND IN THE PHYSICAL DATA, TOXICITY AND HEALTH EFFECTS SECTIONS. THEY ARE RANKED IN ORDER FROM MINIMUM TO MAXIMUM RESPIRATORY PROTECTION. THE SPECIFIC RESPIRATOR SELECTED MUST BE BASED ON CONTAMINATION LEVELS FOUND IN THE WORK PLACE, MUST NOT EXCEED THE WORKING LIMITS OF THE RESPIRATOR AND BE JOINTLY APPROVED BY THE NATIONAL INSTITUTE FOR OCCUPATIONAL SAFETY AND HEALTH AND THE MINE SAFETY AND HEALTH ADMINISTRATION (NIOSH-MSHA).

CHEMICAL CARTRIDGE RESPIRATOR WITH FULL FACEPIECE AND ORGANIC VAPOR CARTRIDGE(S) IN COMBINATION WITH A DUST AND MIST FILTER.

CHEMICAL CARTRIDGE RESPIRATOR WITH FULL FACEPIECE AND ORGANIC VAPOR CARTRIDGE(S) IN COMBINATION WITH A HIGH-EFFICIENCY PARTICULATE FILTER.

GAS MASK WITH ORGANIC VAPOR CANISTER (CHIN-STYLE OR FRONT- OR BACK-MOUNTED CANISTER) WITH A FULL FACEPIECE AND A HIGH-EFFICIENCY PARTICULATE FILTER.

POWERED AIR-PURIFYING RESPIRATOR WITH TIGHT-FITTING FACEPIECE AND ORGANIC VAPOR CARTRIDGE(S) IN COMBINATION WITH A HIGH-EFFICIENCY PARTICULATE FILTER.

TYPE 'C' SUPPLIED-AIR RESPIRATOR WITH A FULL FACEPIECE OPERATED IN PRESSURE-DEMAND OR OTHER POSITIVE PRESSURE MODE OR WITH A FULL FACEPIECE, HELMET OR HOOD OPERATED IN CONTINUOUS-FLOW MODE.

SELF-CONTAINED BREATHING APPARATUS WITH A FULL FACEPIECE OPERATED IN PRESSURE-DEMAND OR OTHER POSITIVE PRESSURE MODE.

FOR FIREFIGHTING AND OTHER IMMEDIATELY DANGEROUS TO LIFE OR HEALTH CONDITIONS:

SELF-CONTAINED BREATHING APPARATUS WITH FULL FACEPIECE OPERATED IN PRESSURE-DEMAND OR OTHER POSITIVE PRESSURE MODE.

SUPPLIED-AIR RESPIRATOR WITH FULL FACEPIECE AND OPERATED IN PRESSURE-DEMAND OR OTHER POSITIVE PRESSURE MODE IN COMBINATION WITH AN AUXILIARY SELF-CONTAINED BREATHING APPARATUS OPERATED IN PRESSURE-DEMAND OR OTHER POSITIVE PRESSURE MODE.

CLOTHING: EMPLOYEE MUST WEAR APPROPRIATE PROTECTIVE (IMPERVIOUS) CLOTHING AND EQUIPMENT TO PREVENT REPEATED OR PROLONGED SKIN CONTACT WITH THIS SUBSTANCE.

GLOVES: EMPLOYEE MUST WEAR APPROPRIATE PROTECTIVE GLOVES TO PREVENT CONTACT WITH THIS SUBSTANCE.

EYE PROTECTION: EMPLOYEE MUST WEAR SPLASH-PROOF OR DUST-RESISTANT SAFETY GOGGLES TO PREVENT EYE CONTACT WITH THIS SUBSTANCE.

EMERGENCY EYE WASH: WHERE THERE IS ANY POSSIBILITY THAT AN EMPLOYEE'S EYES MAY BE EXPOSED TO THIS SUBSTANCE, THE EMPLOYER SHOULD PROVIDE AN EYE WASH FOUNTAIN WITHIN THE IMMEDIATE WORK AREA FOR EMERGENCY USE.

AUTHORIZED BY- OCCUPATIONAL HEALTH SERVICES, INC.

CREATION DATE: 11/15/89 ***REVISION DATE:*** 05/31/90

MATERIAL SAFETY DATA SHEET

OCCUPATIONAL HEALTH SERVICES, INC.
AGRICULTURE AND PESTICIDE DIVISION
450 SEVENTH AVENUE, SUITE 2407
NEW YORK, NEW YORK 10123
1-800-445-MSDS OR (212) 967-1100

EMERGENCY CONTACT:
JOHN S. BRANSFORD, JR. (615) 292-1180

SUBSTANCE IDENTIFICATION

CAS-NUMBER 100-51-6

SUBSTANCE: **BENZYL ALCOHOL**

TRADE NAMES/SYNONYMS: BENZENEMETHANOL; BENZENECARBINOL; (HYDROXYMETHYL)BENZENE; ALPHA-HYDROXYTOLUENE; PHENYLCARBINOL; PHENYLMETHANOL; PHENYLMETHYL ALCOHOL; ALPHA-TOLUENOL; C7H8O; PST02800

CHEMICAL FAMILY: ALCOHOL
AROMATIC

MOLECULAR FORMULA: C6-H5-C-H2-O-H

MOLECULAR WEIGHT: 108.15

CERCLA RATINGS (SCALE 0-3): HEALTH=3 FIRE=1 REACTIVITY=0 PERSISTENCE=1

NFPA RATINGS (SCALE 0-4): HEALTH=2 FIRE=1 REACTIVITY=0

COMPONENTS AND CONTAMINANTS

COMPONENT: BENZYL ALCOHOL ***PERCENT:*** 100.0
CAS# 100-51-6

OTHER CONTAMINANTS: NONE

EXPOSURE LIMITS: NO OCCUPATIONAL EXPOSURE LIMITS ESTABLISHED BY OSHA, ACGIH, OR NIOSH.

PHYSICAL DATA

DESCRIPTION: COLORLESS LIQUID WITH A FAINT AROMATIC ODOR AND A SHARP, BURNING TASTE.

BOILING POINT: 401 F (205 C) ***MELTING POINT:*** 5 F (-15 C)

SPECIFIC GRAVITY: 1.0419 @ 24 C ***VAPOR PRESSURE:*** 0.04 MMHG @ 20 C

SOLUBILITY IN WATER: 3.5% @ 20 C ***VAPOR DENSITY:*** 3.72

SOLVENT SOLUBILITY: SOLUBLE IN ALCOHOL, ETHER, CHLOROFORM, ACETONE, BENZENE, AROMATIC HYDROCARBONS.

FIRE AND EXPLOSION DATA

FIRE AND EXPLOSION HAZARD: SLIGHT FIRE HAZARD WHEN EXPOSED TO HEAT OR FLAME.

FLASH POINT: 213 F (101 C) (CC) ***AUTOIGNITION TEMP.:*** 817 F (436 C)

FLAMMABILITY CLASS(OSHA): IIIB

FIREFIGHTING MEDIA: DRY CHEMICAL, CARBON DIOXIDE, HALON, WATER SPRAY OR STANDARD FOAM (1987 EMERGENCY RESPONSE GUIDEBOOK, DOT P 5800.4).
FOR LARGER FIRES, USE WATER SPRAY, FOG OR STANDARD FOAM (1987 EMERGENCY RESPONSE GUIDEBOOK, DOT P 5800.4).
ALCOHOL FOAM (NFPA 325M, FIRE HAZARD PROPERTIES OF FLAMMABLE LIQUIDS, GASES, AND VOLATILE SOLIDS, 1984).

FIREFIGHTING: MOVE CONTAINER FROM FIRE AREA IF POSSIBLE. DO NOT SCATTER SPILLED MATERIAL WITH HIGH PRESSURE WATER STREAMS. DIKE FIRE CONTROL WATER FOR LATER DISPOSAL (1987 EMERGENCY RESPONSE GUIDEBOOK, DOT P 5800.4, GUIDE PAGE 31).
USE AGENTS SUITABLE FOR TYPE OF SURROUNDING FIRE. AVOID BREATHING HAZARDOUS VAPORS, KEEP UPWIND.
WATER OR FOAM MAY CAUSE FROTHING (NFPA 325M, FIRE HAZARD PROPERTIES OF FLAMMABLE LIQUIDS, GASES, AND VOLATILE SOLIDS, 1984)

TOXICITY

BENZYL ALCOHOL: IRRITATION DATA: 16 MG/48 HOURS SKIN-MAN MILD; 10 MG/24 HOURS OPEN SKIN-RABBIT MILD; 100 MG/24 HOURS SKIN-RABBIT MODERATE; 100% SKIN-PIG MODERATE; 750 UG OPEN EYE-RABBIT SEVERE. TOXICITY DATA: 2000 PPM/4 HOURS INHALATION-RAT LCLO; 1000 PPM/8 HOURS INHALATION-RAT LC50 (THIDD6); 2000 MG/KG SKIN-RABBIT LD50; 10 GM/KG SKIN-CAT LDLO; 1230 MG/KG ORAL-RAT LD50; 1580 MG/KG ORAL-MOUSE LD50; 1040 MG/KG ORAL-RABBIT LD50; 1700 MG/KG SUBCUTANEOUS-RAT LDLO; 53 MG/KG INTRAVENOUS-RAT LD50; 324 MG/KG INTRAVENOUS-MOUSE LD50; 50 MG/KG INTRAVENOUS-DOG LDLO; 625 MG/KG INTRAVENOUS-CAT LDLO; 400 MG/KG INTRAPERITONEAL-RAT LD50; 650 MG/KG INTRAPERITONEAL-MOUSE LD50; 400 MG/KG INTRAPERITONEAL-GUINEA PIG LDLO; 9 MG/KG PARENTERAL-DOG LDLO; 441 MG/KG INTRAARTERIAL-RAT LD50; MUTAGENIC DATA (RTECS); REPRODUCTIVE EFFECTS DATA (RTECS). CARCINOGEN STATUS: NONE. LOCAL EFFECTS: IRRITANT- INHALATION, SKIN, EYES. ACUTE TOXICITY LEVEL: TOXIC BY INHALATION; MODERATELY TOXIC BY DERMAL ABSORPTION, INGESTION. TARGET EFFECTS: CENTRAL NERVOUS SYSTEM DEPRESSANT. ADDITIONAL DATA: ALCOHOL MAY ENHANCE THE TOXIC EFFECTS.

HEALTH EFFECTS AND FIRST AID

INHALATION: BENZYL ALCOHOL: IRRITANT/NARCOTIC/TOXIC. **ACUTE EXPOSURE-** MAY CAUSE IRRITATION OF THE RESPIRATORY TRACT AND A BURNING SENSATION. HIGH VAPOR CONCENTRATIONS MAY CAUSE HEADACHE, SORE THROAT, COUGHING, WHEEZING, LARYNGITIS, DYSPNEA, VERTIGO, WEAKNESS, HYPOTENSION, DULLNESS, FATIGUE, NAUSEA, VOMITING, DIARRHEA, AND ABDOMINAL PAIN. IN SEVERE CASES, RESPIRATORY STIMULATION FOLLOWED BY RESPIRATORY AND MUSCULAR PARALYSIS, CONVULSIONS, NARCOSIS, AND DEATH MAY OCCUR. **CHRONIC EXPOSURE-** PROLONGED EXPOSURE MAY CAUSE LUNG DAMAGE, GASTROINTESTINAL DISTURBANCES, AND NARCOTIC EFFECTS.

FIRST AID- REMOVE FROM EXPOSURE AREA TO FRESH AIR IMMEDIATELY. IF BREATHING HAS STOPPED, PERFORM ARTIFICIAL RESPIRATION. KEEP PERSON WARM AND AT REST. TREAT SYMPTOMATICALLY AND SUPPORTIVELY. GET MEDICAL ATTENTION IMMEDIATELY.

SKIN CONTACT: BENZYL ALCOHOL: IRRITANT/NARCOTIC. **ACUTE EXPOSURE-** CONTACT MAY CAUSE REDNESS, PAIN, TISSUE INJURY, AND TEMPORARY ANESTHESIA. IF ABSORBED THROUGH THE SKIN, EFFECTS AS DESCRIBED IN ACUTE INHALATION MAY OCCUR. ALTHOUGH RARE, SENSITIZATION IN PREVIOUSLY EXPOSED INDIVIDUALS HAS BEEN REPORTED. CROSS REACTIONS WITH BALSAM OF PERU MAY ALSO OCCUR. **CHRONIC EXPOSURE-** REPEATED OR PROLONGED EXPOSURE MAY CAUSE IRRITATION AND SENSITIZATION DERMATITIS.

FIRST AID- REMOVE CONTAMINATED CLOTHING AND SHOES IMMEDIATELY. WASH AFFECTED AREA WITH SOAP OR MILD DETERGENT AND LARGE AMOUNTS OF WATER UNTIL NO EVIDENCE OF CHEMICAL REMAINS (APPROXIMATELY 15-20 MINUTES). GET MEDICAL ATTENTION IMMEDIATELY.

EYE CONTACT: BENZYL ALCOHOL: IRRITANT. **ACUTE EXPOSURE-** CONTACT MAY CAUSE SEVERE IRRITATION OF THE CONJUNCTIVAL MEMBRANES, CLOUDINESS OF THE CORNEA, REDNESS, PAIN, TEARING, AND BLURRED VISION: FULL STRENGTH BENZYL ALCOHOL, TESTED BY THE APPLICATION OF A DROP INTO RABBIT EYES, RATED 8 ON A SCALE OF 1-10. **CHRONIC EXPOSURE-** REPEATED OR PROLONGED EXPOSURE TO IRRITANTS MAY CAUSE CONJUNCTIVITIS.

FIRST AID- WASH EYES IMMEDIATELY WITH LARGE AMOUNTS OF WATER OR NORMAL SALINE, OCCASIONALLY LIFTING UPPER AND LOWER LIDS, UNTIL NO EVIDENCE OF CHEMICAL REMAINS (APPROXIMATELY 15-20 MINUTES). GET MEDICAL ATTENTION IMMEDIATELY.

INGESTION: BENZYL ALCOHOL: **ACUTE EXPOSURE-** INGESTION OF LARGE VOLUMES MAY CAUSE EFFECTS AS DESCRIBED IN ACUTE INHALATION. IF ASPIRATED INTO THE LUNGS, CHEMICAL PNEUMONITIS MAY OCCUR. SINGLE DOSES CAUSED DEPRESSION AND COMA WITHIN 10-15 MINUTES, EXCITABILITY, AND DEATH IN RATS. **CHRONIC EXPOSURE-** IN 16 DAY STUDIES, RODENTS FED 1000 MG/KG/DAY EXHIBITED LETHARGY, BLOOD AROUND THE MOUTH AND NOSE, SUBCUTANEOUS HEMORRHAGES, BLOOD IN THE URINARY AND GASTROINTESTINAL TRACTS, AND SOME DEATHS; AT 2000 MG/KG/DAY ALL DIED BEFORE THE END OF THE STUDY. IN 13 WEEK STUDIES, 800 MG/KG/DAY CAUSED STAGGERING, RESPIRATORY DIFFICULTIES, LETHARGY, HEMORRHAGES, AND HISTOLOGICAL LESIONS OF THE BRAIN, THYMUS, SKELETAL MUSCLES, AND KIDNEYS IN RATS, AND SOME DEATHS IN MICE. REPRODUCTIVE EFFECTS HAVE BEEN REPORTED IN ANIMALS.

FIRST AID- IF THE PERSON IS CONSCIOUS AND NOT CONVULSING, REMOVE BY INDUCING EMESIS FOLLOWED BY ACTIVATED CHARCOAL (DREISBACH, HANDBOOK OF POISONING, 12TH ED.). KEEP THE HEAD BELOW THE HIPS TO PREVENT ASPIRATION. TREAT SYMPTOMATICALLY AND SUPPORTIVELY. GET MEDICAL ATTENTION IMMEDIATELY.

ANTIDOTE: NO SPECIFIC ANTIDOTE. TREAT SYMPTOMATICALLY AND SUPPORTIVELY.

REACTIVITY

REACTIVITY: STABLE UNDER NORMAL TEMPERATURES AND PRESSURES.

INCOMPATIBILITIES: BENZYL ALCOHOL: ACIDS: INCOMPATIBLE. ACIDS + IRON: MAY POLYMERIZE EXOTHERMICALLY AT ELEVATED TEMPERATURES. ALUMINUM: MAY BE ATTACKED ON HEATING. HYDROGEN BROMIDE + IRON: POLYMERIZES EXOTHERMICALLY ABOVE 100 C. NITRIC ACID: FIRE AND EXPLOSION HAZARD. OXIDIZERS (STRONG): FIRE AND EXPLOSION HAZARD. PERMANGANATES: FIRE AND EXPLOSION HAZARD. PLASTICS: MAY BE ATTACKED. SULFURIC ACID: DECOMPOSES EXPLOSIVELY AT 180 C.

DECOMPOSITION: THERMAL DECOMPOSITION PRODUCTS MAY INCLUDE TOXIC OXIDES OF CARBON.

POLYMERIZATION: HAZARDOUS POLYMERIZATION HAS NOT BEEN REPORTED TO OCCUR UNDER NORMAL TEMPERATURES AND PRESSURES.

STORAGE AND DISPOSAL

OBSERVE ALL FEDERAL, STATE AND LOCAL REGULATIONS WHEN STORING OR DISPOSING OF THIS SUBSTANCE. FOR ASSISTANCE, CONTACT THE DISTRICT DIRECTOR OF THE ENVIRONMENTAL PROTECTION AGENCY.

****STORAGE****

STORE IN ACCORDANCE WITH 29 CFR 1910.106.
KEEP IN A TIGHTLY CLOSED CONTAINER. STORE IN A COOL, DRY, VENTILATED AREA.
STORE AWAY FROM INCOMPATIBLE SUBSTANCES.

CONDITIONS TO AVOID

MAY BURN BUT DOES NOT IGNITE READILY. AVOID CONTACT WITH STRONG OXIDIZERS, EXCESSIVE HEAT, SPARKS, OR OPEN FLAME.

SPILL AND LEAK PROCEDURES

OCCUPATIONAL SPILL: STOP LEAK IF YOU CAN DO IT WITHOUT RISK. FOR SMALL SPILLS, TAKE UP WITH SAND OR OTHER ABSORBENT MATERIAL AND PLACE INTO CLEAN, DRY CONTAINERS FOR LATER DISPOSAL. KEEP UNNECESSARY PEOPLE AWAY. ISOLATE HAZARD AREA AND DENY ENTRY.

PROTECTIVE EQUIPMENT

VENTILATION: PROVIDE LOCAL EXHAUST VENTILATION SYSTEM.

RESPIRATOR: THE FOLLOWING RESPIRATORS ARE RECOMMENDED BASED ON INFORMATION FOUND IN THE PHYSICAL DATA, TOXICITY AND HEALTH EFFECTS SECTIONS. THEY ARE RANKED IN ORDER FROM MINIMUM TO MAXIMUM RESPIRATORY PROTECTION. THE SPECIFIC RESPIRATOR SELECTED MUST BE BASED ON CONTAMINATION LEVELS FOUND IN THE WORK PLACE, MUST NOT EXCEED THE WORKING LIMITS OF THE RESPIRATOR AND BE JOINTLY APPROVED BY THE NATIONAL INSTITUTE FOR OCCUPATIONAL SAFETY AND HEALTH AND THE MINE SAFETY AND HEALTH ADMINISTRATION (NIOSH-MSHA).

TYPE 'C' SUPPLIED-AIR RESPIRATOR WITH A FULL FACEPIECE OPERATED IN PRESSURE-DEMAND OR OTHER POSITIVE PRESSURE MODE OR WITH A FULL FACEPIECE, HELMET OR HOOD OPERATED IN CONTINOUS-FLOW MODE.

SELF-CONTAINED BREATHING APPARATUS WITH A FULL FACEPIECE OPERATED IN PRESSURE-DEMAND OR OTHER POSITIVE PRESSURE MODE.

FOR FIREFIGHTING AND OTHER IMMEDIATELY DANGEROUS TO LIFE OR HEALTH CONDITIONS:

SELF-CONTAINED BREATHING APPARATUS WITH FULL FACEPIECE OPERATED IN PRESSURE-DEMAND OR OTHER POSITIVE PRESSURE MODE.

SUPPLIED-AIR RESPIRATOR WITH FULL FACEPIECE AND OPERATED IN PRESSURE-DEMAND OR OTHER POSITIVE PRESSURE MODE IN COMBINATION WITH AN AUXILIARY SELF-CONTAINED BREATHING APPARATUS OPERATED IN PRESSURE-DEMAND OR OTHER POSITIVE PRESSURE MODE.

CLOTHING: EMPLOYEE MUST WEAR APPROPRIATE PROTECTIVE (IMPERVIOUS) CLOTHING AND EQUIPMENT TO PREVENT REPEATED OR PROLONGED SKIN CONTACT WITH THIS SUBSTANCE.

GLOVES: EMPLOYEE MUST WEAR APPROPRIATE PROTECTIVE GLOVES TO PREVENT CONTACT WITH THIS SUBSTANCE.

EYE PROTECTION: EMPLOYEE MUST WEAR SPLASH-PROOF OR DUST-RESISTANT SAFETY GOGGLES AND A FACESHIELD TO PREVENT CONTACT WITH THIS SUBSTANCE.

EMERGENCY WASH FACILITIES: WHERE THERE IS ANY POSSIBILITY THAT AN EMPLOYEE'S EYES AND/OR SKIN MAY BE EXPOSED TO THIS SUBSTANCE, THE EMPLOYER SHOULD PROVIDE AN EYE WASH FOUNTAIN AND QUICK DRENCH SHOWER WITHIN THE IMMEDIATE WORK AREA FOR EMERGENCY USE.

AUTHORIZED BY- OCCUPATIONAL HEALTH SERVICES, INC.

CREATION DATE: 11/15/89 ***REVISION DATE:*** 03/02/90

MATERIAL SAFETY DATA SHEET

OCCUPATIONAL HEALTH SERVICES, INC.
AGRICULTURE AND PESTICIDE DIVISION
450 SEVENTH AVENUE, SUITE 2407
NEW YORK, NEW YORK 10123
1-800-445-MSDS OR (212) 967-1100

EMERGENCY CONTACT:
JOHN S. BRANSFORD, JR. (615) 292-1180

SUBSTANCE IDENTIFICATION

CAS-NUMBER 120-51-4

SUBSTANCE: BENZYL BENZOATE

TRADE NAMES/SYNONYMS: BENZOIC ACID, BENZYL ESTER; ASCABIN; ASCABIOL; BENZOIC ACID, PHENYLMETHYL ESTER; BENYLATE; BENZYLETS; COLEBENZ; NOVOSCABIN; BENZYL BENZENECARBOXYLATE; BENZYL PHENYLFORMATE; PERUSCABIN; VENZONATE; VANZOATE; SCABAGEN; SCABANCA; SCABIDE; SCABIOZON; SCOBENOL; PST02805

CHEMICAL FAMILY: ESTER, CARBOXYLIC, AROMATIC

MOLECULAR FORMULA: C14-H12-O2

MOLECULAR WEIGHT: 212.26

CERCLA RATINGS (SCALE 0-3): HEALTH=3 FIRE=1 REACTIVITY=0 PERSISTENCE=1

NFPA RATINGS (SCALE 0-4): HEALTH=1 FIRE=1 REACTIVITY=0

COMPONENTS AND CONTAMINANTS

COMPONENT: BENZYL BENZOATE ***PERCENT:*** 100
CAS# 120-51-4

OTHER CONTAMINANTS: NONE

EXPOSURE LIMITS: NO OCCUPATIONAL EXPOSURE LIMITS ESTABLISHED BY OSHA, ACGIH, OR NIOSH.

PHYSICAL DATA

DESCRIPTION: COLORLESS LEAFLETS OR OILY LIQUID WITH A FAINT PLEASANT, AROMATIC ODOR AND A SHARP BURNING TASTE.

BOILING POINT: 614 F (323 C)

MELTING POINT: 70 F (21 C) ***SPECIFIC GRAVITY:*** 1.114

VAPOR PRESSURE: 1.3 MMHG @ 44 C ***SOLUBILITY IN WATER:*** INSOLUBLE

VAPOR DENSITY: 7.31

SOLVENT SOLUBILITY: SOLUBLE IN ALCOHOL, CHLOROFORM, ETHER, OILS; INSOLUBLE IN GLYCEROL

FIRE AND EXPLOSION DATA

FIRE AND EXPLOSION HAZARD: SLIGHT FIRE HAZARD WHEN EXPOSED TO HEAT OR FLAME.

FLASH POINT: 298 F (148 C) (CC) ***AUTOIGNITION TEMP.:*** 896 F (480 C)

FLAMMABILITY CLASS(OSHA): IIIB

FIREFIGHTING MEDIA: DRY CHEMICAL, CARBON DIOXIDE, HALON, WATER SPRAY OR STANDARD FOAM (1987 EMERGENCY RESPONSE GUIDEBOOK, DOT P 5800.4). FOR LARGER FIRES, USE WATER SPRAY, FOG OR STANDARD FOAM (1987 EMERGENCY RESPONSE GUIDEBOOK, DOT P 5800.4).

FIREFIGHTING: MOVE CONTAINER FROM FIRE AREA IF POSSIBLE. DO NOT SCATTER SPILLED MATERIAL WITH HIGH PRESSURE WATER STREAMS. DIKE FIRE CONTROL WATER FOR LATER DISPOSAL (1987 EMERGENCY RESPONSE GUIDEBOOK, DOT P 5800.4, GUIDE PAGE 31).

USE AGENTS SUITABLE FOR TYPE OF SURROUNDING FIRE. AVOID BREATHING HAZARDOUS VAPORS, KEEP UPWIND.

TOXICITY

BENZYL BENZOATE: TOXICITY DATA: 4000 MG/KG SKIN-RABBIT LD50; 4000 MG/KG SKIN-RAT LD50; 1700 MG/KG ORAL-RAT LD50; 1400 MG/KG ORAL-MOUSELD50; 1680 MG/KG ORAL-RABBIT LD50; 1000 MG/KG ORAL-GUINEA PIG LD50; 2240 MG/KG ORAL-CAT LD50; CARCINOGEN STATUS: NONE. LOCAL EFFECTS: IRRITANT-INHALATION, SKIN, AND EYES. ACUTE TOXICITY LEVEL: MODERATELY TOXIC BY INGESTION AND SLIGHTLY TOXIC BY DERMAL ABSORPTION. TARGET EFFECTS: TRAMUSCULAR, INTRAPERITONEAL OR INTRAVENOUS INJECTION.

HEALTH EFFECTS AND FIRST AID

INHALATION: BENZYL BENZOATE: IRRITANT. **ACUTE EXPOSURE-** VAPORS AT A HIGH TEMPERATURE MAY CAUSE MUCOUS MEMBRANE IRRITATION, SORE THROAT, COUGHING AND SHORTNESS OF BREATH. **CHRONIC EXPOSURE-** NO DATA AVAILABLE.

FIRST AID- REMOVE FROM EXPOSURE AREA TO FRESH AIR IMMEDIATELY. IF BREATHING HAS STOPPED, PERFORM ARTIFICIAL RESPIRATION. KEEP PERSON WARM AND AT REST. TREAT SYMPTOMATICALLY AND SUPPORTIVELY. GET MEDICAL ATTENTION IMMEDIATELY.

SKIN CONTACT: BENZYL BENZOATE: IRRITANT. **ACUTE EXPOSURE-** CONTACT MAY CAUSE IRRITATION WITH REDNESS AND PAIN. BENZYL BENZOATE HAS BEEN APPLIED TO THE SKIN MEDICALLY IN THE TREATMENT OF SCABIES. SYSTEMIC POISONING MAY OCCUR DUE TO DERMAL ABSORPTION OF LARGE AMOUNTS. **CHRONIC EXPOSURE-** INTENSIVE CONTACT WITH THE SKIN MAY CAUSE DERMATITIS AFTER REPEATED OR PROLONGED EXPOSURE.

FIRST AID- REMOVE CONTAMINATED CLOTHING AND SHOES IMMEDIATELY. WASH AFFECTED AREA WITH SOAP OR MILD DETERGENT AND LARGE AMOUNTS OF WATER UNTIL NO EVIDENCE OF CHEMICAL REMAINS (APPROXIMATELY 15-20 MINUTES). GET MEDICAL ATTENTION IMMEDIATELY.

EYE CONTACT: BENZYL BENZOATE: IRRITANT. **ACUTE EXPOSURE-** DIRECT CONTACT WITH THE LIQUID OR VAPORS MAY CAUSE IRRITATION, REDNESS AND PAIN, BUT NO DAMAGE HAS BEEN REPORTED. **CHRONIC EXPOSURE-** REPEATED OR PROLONGED CONTACT MAY CAUSE CONJUNCTIVITIS.

FIRST AID- WASH EYES IMMEDIATELY WITH LARGE AMOUNTS OF WATER OR NORMAL SALINE, OCCASIONALLY LIFTING UPPER AND LOWER LIDS, UNTIL NO EVIDENCE OF CHEMICAL REMAINS (APPROXIMATELY 15-20 MINUTES). GET MEDICAL ATTENTION IMMEDIATELY.

INGESTION: BENZYL BENZOATE: TOXIC. **ACUTE EXPOSURE-** MAY CAUSE ABDOMINAL PAIN AND NAUSEA. IN LABORATORY ANIMALS, 1 GM/KG HAS CAUSED PROGRESSIVE INCOORDINATION, CENTRAL NERVOUS EXCITATION AND

CONVULSIONS LEADING POSSIBLY TO DEATH. BENZYL BENZOATE GIVEN IN MODERATELY LARGE DOSES TO LABORATORY ANIMALS HAS PRODUCED A CATHARTIC AND EMETIC EFFECT. **CHRONIC EXPOSURE**- NO DATA AVAILABLE.

FIRST AID- REMOVE BY GASTRIC LAVAGE OR EMESIS. MAINTAIN BLOOD PRESSURE AND AIRWAY. GIVE OXYGEN IF RESPIRATION IS DEPRESSED. DO NOT PERFORM GASTRIC LAVAGE OR EMESIS IF VICTIM IS UNCONSCIOUS. GET MEDICAL ATTENTION IMMEDIATELY (DREISBACH, HANDBOOK OF POISONING, 11TH ED.). ADMINISTRATION OF GASTRIC LAVAGE OR OXYGEN SHOULD BE PERFORMED BY QUALIFIED MEDICAL PERSONNEL.

ANTIDOTE: NO SPECIFIC ANTIDOTE. TREAT SYMPTOMATICALLY AND SUPPORTIVELY.

REACTIVITY

REACTIVITY: STABLE UNDER NORMAL TEMPERATURES AND PRESSURES.

INCOMPATIBILITIES: BENZYL BENZOATE: STRONG OXIDIZERS: VIOLENT REACTION.

DECOMPOSITION: THERMAL DECOMPOSITION MAY RELEASE ACRID SMOKE AND IRRITATING FUMES.

POLYMERIZATION: HAZARDOUS POLYMERIZATION HAS NOT BEEN REPORTED TO OCCUR UNDER NORMAL TEMPERATURES AND PRESSURES.

CONDITIONS TO AVOID

MAY BURN BUT DOES NOT IGNITE READILY. AVOID CONTACT WITH STRONG OXIDIZERS, EXCESSIVE HEAT, SPARKS, OR OPEN FLAME.

SPILL AND LEAK PROCEDURES

OCCUPATIONAL SPILL: STOP LEAK IF YOU CAN DO IT WITHOUT RISK. FOR SMALL SPILLS, TAKE UP WITH SAND OR OTHER ABSORBENT MATERIAL AND PLACE INTO CLEAN, DRY CONTAINERS FOR LATER DISPOSAL. KEEP UNNECESSARY PEOPLE AWAY. ISOLATE HAZARD AREA AND DENY ENTRY.

PROTECTIVE EQUIPMENT

VENTILATION: PROVIDE LOCAL EXHAUST OR PROCESS ENCLOSURE VENTILATION SYSTEM.

RESPIRATOR: THE FOLLOWING RESPIRATORS ARE RECOMMENDED BASED ON INFORMATION FOUND IN THE PHYSICAL DATA, TOXICITY AND HEALTH EFFECTS SECTIONS. THEY ARE RANKED IN ORDER FROM MINIMUM TO MAXIMUM RESPIRATORY PROTECTION. THE SPECIFIC RESPIRATOR SELECTED MUST BE BASED ON CONTAMINATION LEVELS FOUND IN THE WORK PLACE, MUST NOT EXCEED THE WORKING LIMITS OF THE RESPIRATOR AND BE JOINTLY APPROVED BY THE NATIONAL INSTITUTE FOR OCCUPATIONAL SAFETY AND HEALTH AND THE MINE SAFETY AND HEALTH ADMINISTRATION (NIOSH-MSHA).

TYPE 'C' SUPPLIED-AIR RESPIRATOR WITH A FULL FACEPIECE OPERATED IN PRESSURE-DEMAND OR OTHER POSITIVE PRESSURE MODE OR WITH A FULL FACEPIECE, HELMET OR HOOD OPERATED IN CONTINOUS-FLOW MODE.

SELF-CONTAINED BREATHING APPARATUS WITH A FULL FACEPIECE OPERATED IN PRESSURE-DEMAND OR OTHER POSITIVE PRESSURE MODE.

FOR FIREFIGHTING AND OTHER IMMEDIATELY DANGEROUS TO LIFE OR HEALTH CONDITIONS:

SELF-CONTAINED BREATHING APPARATUS WITH FULL FACEPIECE OPERATED IN PRESSURE-DEMAND OR OTHER POSITIVE PRESSURE MODE.

SUPPLIED-AIR RESPIRATOR WITH FULL FACEPIECE AND OPERATED IN PRESSURE-DEMAND OR OTHER POSITIVE PRESSURE MODE IN COMBINATION WITH AN AUXILIARY SELF-CONTAINED BREATHING APPARATUS OPERATED IN PRESSURE-DEMAND OR OTHER POSITIVE PRESSURE MODE.

CLOTHING: EMPLOYEE MUST WEAR APPROPRIATE PROTECTIVE (IMPERVIOUS) CLOTHING AND EQUIPMENT TO PREVENT REPEATED OR PROLONGED SKIN CONTACT WITH THIS SUBSTANCE.

GLOVES: EMPLOYEE MUST WEAR APPROPRIATE PROTECTIVE GLOVES TO PREVENT CONTACT WITH THIS SUBSTANCE.

EYE PROTECTION: EMPLOYEE MUST WEAR SPLASH-PROOF OR DUST-RESISTANT SAFETY GOGGLES TO PREVENT EYE CONTACT WITH THIS SUBSTANCE.

EMERGENCY EYE WASH: WHERE THERE IS ANY POSSIBILITY THAT AN EMPLOYEE'S EYES MAY BE EXPOSED TO THIS SUBSTANCE, THE EMPLOYER SHOULD PROVIDE AN EYE WASH FOUNTAIN WITHIN THE IMMEDIATE WORK AREA FOR EMERGENCY USE.

AUTHORIZED BY- OCCUPATIONAL HEALTH SERVICES, INC.

CREATION DATE: 11/15/89 ***REVISION DATE:*** 05/04/90

MATERIAL SAFETY DATA SHEET

OCCUPATIONAL HEALTH SERVICES, INC. EMERGENCY CONTACT:
AGRICULTURE AND PESTICIDE DIVISION JOHN S. BRANSFORD, JR. (615) 292-1180
450 SEVENTH AVENUE, SUITE 2407
NEW YORK, NEW YORK 10123
1-800-445-MSDS OR (212) 967-1100

SUBSTANCE IDENTIFICATION

CAS-NUMBER 1014-70-6

SUBSTANCE: **SIMETRYN**

TRADE NAMES/SYNONYMS: 1,3,5-TRIAZINE-2,4-DIAMINE, N,N'-DIETHYL-6-(METHYLTHIO)-; S-TRIAZINE, 2,4-BIS(ETHYLAMINO)-6-(METHYLTHIO)-; N,N'-DIETHYL-6-(METHYLTHIO)-1,3,5-TRIAZINE-2,4-DIAMINE; 2,4-BIS(ETHYLAMINO)-6-(METHYLTHIO)-S-TRIAZINE; 2,4-BIS(ETHYLAMINO)-6-(METHYLTHIO)-1,3,5-TRIAZINE; 2-METHYLTHIO-4,6-BIS(MONOETHYLAMINO)-S-TRIAZINE; 2,4-BIS(ETHYLAMINO)-6-METHYLTHIO-2,3,5-TRIAZINE; 2,4-DI(ETHYLAMINO)-6-METHYLTHIO-1,3,5-TRIAZINE; G 32911; GY-BON; SIMETRYNE; C8H15N5S; PST02838

CHEMICAL FAMILY: S-TRIAZINE

MOLECULAR FORMULA: C8-H15-N5-S

MOLECULAR WEIGHT: 213.32

CERCLA RATINGS (SCALE 0-3): HEALTH=2 FIRE=1 REACTIVITY=0 PERSISTENCE=2

NFPA RATINGS (SCALE 0-4): HEALTH=2 FIRE=1 REACTIVITY=0

COMPONENTS AND CONTAMINANTS

COMPONENT: SIMETRYN ***PERCENT:*** 100.0
CAS# 1014-70-6

OTHER CONTAMINANTS: NONE

EXPOSURE LIMITS: NO OCCUPATIONAL EXPOSURE LIMITS ESTABLISHED BY OSHA, ACGIH, OR NIOSH.

PHYSICAL DATA

DESCRIPTION: CRYSTALS ***MELTING POINT:*** 180-181 F (82-83 C)

SPECIFIC GRAVITY: NOT AVAILABLE ***SOLUBILITY IN WATER:*** 450 PPM @ 25 C

FIRE AND EXPLOSION DATA

FIRE AND EXPLOSION HAZARD: SLIGHT FIRE HAZARD WHEN EXPOSED TO HEAT OR FLAME.

FIREFIGHTING MEDIA: DRY CHEMICAL, CARBON DIOXIDE, HALON, WATER SPRAY OR STANDARD FOAM (1987 EMERGENCY RESPONSE GUIDEBOOK, DOT P 5800.4). FOR LARGER FIRES, USE WATER SPRAY, FOG OR STANDARD FOAM (1987 EMERGENCY RESPONSE GUIDEBOOK, DOT P 5800.4).

FIREFIGHTING: MOVE CONTAINERS FROM FIRE AREA IF POSSIBLE (1987 EMERGENCY RESPONSE GUIDEBOOK, DOT P 5800.4, GUIDE PAGE 53).
EXTINGUISH USING AGENTS SUITABLE FOR SURROUNDING FIRE. USE FLOODING QUANTITIES OF WATER AS A FOG. KEEP MATERIAL OUT OF SEWERS AND WATER SOURCES. DO NOT TOUCH SPILLED MATERIAL. AVOID BREATHING HAZARDOUS FUMES; KEEP UPWIND.

TOXICITY

SIMETRYN: TOXICITY DATA: 750 MG/KG ORAL-RAT LD50. CARCINOGEN STATUS: NONE. ACUTE TOXICITY LEVEL: MODERATELY TOXIC BY INGESTION. TARGET EFFECTS: NO DATA AVAILABLE.

HEALTH EFFECTS AND FIRST AID

INHALATION: SIMETRYN: **ACUTE EXPOSURE**- SOME TRIAZINES ARE MILDLY IRRITATING TO THE UPPER RESPIRATORY TRACT. **CHRONIC EXPOSURE**- NO DATA AVAILABLE.

FIRST AID- REMOVE FROM EXPOSURE AREA TO FRESH AIR IMMEDIATELY. IF BREATHING HAS STOPPED, PERFORM ARTIFICIAL RESPIRATION. KEEP PERSON WARM AND AT REST. TREAT SYMPTOMATICALLY AND SUPPORTIVELY. GET MEDICAL ATTENTION IMMEDIATELY.

SKIN CONTACT: SIMETRYN: **ACUTE EXPOSURE**- SOME TRIAZINES ARE MILDLY IRRITATING TO THE SKIN. **CHRONIC EXPOSURE**- NO DATA AVAILABLE.

FIRST AID- REMOVE CONTAMINATED CLOTHING AND SHOES IMMEDIATELY. WASH AFFECTED AREA WITH SOAP OR MILD DETERGENT AND LARGE AMOUNTS OF WATER UNTIL NO EVIDENCE OF CHEMICAL REMAINS (APPROXIMATELY 15-20 MINUTES). GET MEDICAL ATTENTION IMMEDIATELY.

EYE CONTACT: SIMETRYN: **ACUTE EXPOSURE**- SOME TRIAZINES ARE MILDLY IRRITATING TO THE EYES. **CHRONIC EXPOSURE**- NO DATA AVAILABLE.

FIRST AID- WASH EYES IMMEDIATELY WITH LARGE AMOUNTS OF WATER OR NORMAL SALINE, OCCASIONALLY LIFTING UPPER AND LOWER LIDS, UNTIL NO EVIDENCE OF CHEMICAL REMAINS (APPROXIMATELY 15-20 MINUTES). GET MEDICAL ATTENTION IMMEDIATELY.

INGESTION: SIMETRYN: **ACUTE EXPOSURE-** A LETHAL DOSE IN RATS WAS 750 MG/KG; SYMPTOMS WERE NOT REPORTED. **CHRONIC EXPOSURE-** NO DATA AVAILABLE.

FIRST AID- REMOVE BY GASTRIC LAVAGE AND CATHARSIS. MAINTAIN BLOOD PRESSURE AND AIRWAY. GIVE OXYGEN IF RESPIRATION IS DEPRESSED. DO NOT PERFORM GASTRIC LAVAGE IF VICTIM IS UNCONSCIOUS. GET MEDICAL ATTENTION IMMEDIATELY (DREISBACH, HANDBOOK OF POISONING, 12TH ED.).
ADMINISTRATION OF LAVAGE OR OXYGEN SHOULD BE PERFORMED BY QUALIFIED MEDICAL PERSONNEL.

ANTIDOTE: NO SPECIFIC ANTIDOTE. TREAT SYMPTOMATICALLY AND SUPPORTIVELY.

REACTIVITY

REACTIVITY: STABLE UNDER NORMAL TEMPERATURES AND PRESSURES.

INCOMPATIBILITIES: SIMETRYN: NO DATA AVAILABLE.

DECOMPOSITION: THERMAL DECOMPOSITION PRODUCTS MAY INCLUDE TOXIC OXIDES OF CARBON, NITROGEN, AND SULFUR.

POLYMERIZATION: HAZARDOUS POLYMERIZATION HAS NOT BEEN REPORTED TO OCCUR UNDER NORMAL TEMPERATURES AND PRESSURES.

STORAGE AND DISPOSAL

OBSERVE ALL FEDERAL, STATE AND LOCAL REGULATIONS WHEN STORING OR DISPOSING OF THIS SUBSTANCE. FOR ASSISTANCE, CONTACT THE DISTRICT DIRECTOR OF THE ENVIRONMENTAL PROTECTION AGENCY.

****STORAGE****

STORE IN ACCORDANCE WITH 40 CFR 165 RECOMMENDED PROCEDURES FOR THE DISPOSAL AND STORAGE OF PESTICIDES AND PESTICIDE CONTAINERS.

****DISPOSAL****

DISPOSAL MUST BE IN ACCORDANCE WITH 40 CFR 165 RECOMMENDED PROCEDURES FOR THE DISPOSAL AND STORAGE OF PESTICIDES AND PESTICIDE CONTAINERS.

CONDITIONS TO AVOID

MAY BURN BUT DOES NOT IGNITE READILY.

SPILL AND LEAK PROCEDURES

OCCUPATIONAL SPILL: DO NOT TOUCH SPILLED MATERIAL. STOP LEAK IF YOU CAN DO IT WITHOUT RISK. FOR SMALL SPILLS, TAKE UP WITH SAND OR OTHER ABSORBENT MATERIAL AND PLACE INTO CONTAINERS FOR LATER DISPOSAL. FOR SMALL DRY SPILLS, WITH A CLEAN SHOVEL PLACE MATERIAL INTO CLEAN, DRY CONTAINER AND COVER. MOVE CONTAINERS FROM SPILL AREA. FOR LARGER SPILLS, DIKE FAR AHEAD OF SPILL FOR LATER DISPOSAL. KEEP UNNECESSARY PEOPLE AWAY. ISOLATE HAZARD AREA AND DENY ENTRY.

PROTECTIVE EQUIPMENT

VENTILATION: PROVIDE LOCAL EXHAUST OR GENERAL DILUTION VENTILATION SYSTEM.

RESPIRATOR: THE FOLLOWING RESPIRATORS ARE RECOMMENDED BASED ON INFORMATION FOUND IN THE PHYSICAL DATA, TOXICITY AND HEALTH EFFECTS SECTIONS. THEY ARE RANKED IN ORDER FROM MINIMUM TO MAXIMUM RESPIRATORY PROTECTION. THE SPECIFIC RESPIRATOR SELECTED MUST BE BASED ON CONTAMINATION LEVELS FOUND IN THE WORK PLACE, MUST NOT EXCEED THE WORKING LIMITS OF THE RESPIRATOR AND BE JOINTLY APPROVED BY THE NATIONAL INSTITUTE FOR OCCUPATIONAL SAFETY AND HEALTH AND THE MINE SAFETY AND HEALTH ADMINISTRATION (NIOSH-MSHA).
CHEMICAL CARTRIDGE RESPIRATOR WITH AN ORGANIC VAPOR CARTRIDGE(S) WITH A FULL FACEPIECE AND ORGANIC VAPOR CARTRIDGE(S) IN COMBINATION WITH A DUST AND MIST FILTER.
POWERED AIR-PURIFYING RESPIRATOR WITH A TIGHT-FITTING FACEPIECE AND ORGANIC VAPOR CARTRIDGE(S) IN COMBINATION WITH A HIGH-EFFICIENCY PARTICULATE FILTER.
TYPE 'C' SUPPLIED-AIR RESPIRATOR WITH A FULL FACEPIECE OPERATED IN A PRESSURE-DEMAND OR OTHER POSITIVE PRESSURE MODE.
SELF-CONTAINED BREATHING APPARATUS WITH A FULL FACEPIECE OPERATED IN PRESSURE-DEMAND OR OTHER POSITIVE PRESSURE MODE.
FOR FIREFIGHTING AND OTHER IMMEDIATELY DANGEROUS TO LIFE OR HEALTH CONDITIONS:
SELF-CONTAINED BREATHING APPARATUS WITH FULL FACEPIECE OPERATED IN PRESSURE-DEMAND OR OTHER POSITIVE PRESSURE MODE.
SUPPLIED-AIR RESPIRATOR WITH FULL FACEPIECE AND OPERATED IN PRESSURE-DEMAND OR OTHER POSITIVE PRESSURE MODE IN COMBINATION WITH AN AUXILIARY SELF-CONTAINED BREATHING APPARATUS OPERATED IN PRESSURE-DEMAND OR OTHER POSITIVE PRESSURE MODE.

CLOTHING: EMPLOYEE MUST WEAR APPROPRIATE PROTECTIVE (IMPERVIOUS) CLOTHING AND EQUIPMENT TO PREVENT REPEATED OR PROLONGED SKIN CONTACT WITH THIS SUBSTANCE.

GLOVES: EMPLOYEE MUST WEAR APPROPRIATE PROTECTIVE GLOVES TO PREVENT CONTACT WITH THIS SUBSTANCE.

EYE PROTECTION: EMPLOYEE MUST WEAR SPLASH-PROOF OR DUST-RESISTANT SAFETY GOGGLES TO PREVENT EYE CONTACT WITH THIS SUBSTANCE.
EMERGENCY EYE WASH: WHERE THERE IS ANY POSSIBILITY THAT AN EMPLOYEE'S EYES MAY BE EXPOSED TO THIS SUBSTANCE, THE EMPLOYER SHOULD PROVIDE AN EYE WASH FOUNTAIN WITHIN THE IMMEDIATE WORK AREA FOR EMERGENCY USE.

AUTHORIZED BY- OCCUPATIONAL HEALTH SERVICES, INC.
CREATION DATE: 10/05/89 ***REVISION DATE:*** 05/07/90

MATERIAL SAFETY DATA SHEET

OCCUPATIONAL HEALTH SERVICES, INC.
AGRICULTURE AND PESTICIDE DIVISION
450 SEVENTH AVENUE, SUITE 2407
NEW YORK, NEW YORK 10123
1-800-445-MSDS OR (212) 967-1100

EMERGENCY CONTACT:
JOHN S. BRANSFORD, JR. (615) 292-1180

SUBSTANCE IDENTIFICATION

CAS-NUMBER 319-85-7

SUBSTANCE: **BETA-HEXACHLOROCYCLOHEXANE**

TRADE NAMES/SYNONYMS: CYCLOHEXANE, 1,2,3,4,5,6-HEXACHLORO-, (1ALPHA,2BETA,3ALPHA,4BETA, 5ALPHA,6BETA)-; (1ALPHA,2BETA,3ALPHA,4BETA,5ALPHA,6BETA)-1,2,3,4,5,6-HEXACHLOROCYCLOHEXANE; CYCLOHEXANE, 1,2,3,4,5,6-HEXACHLORO-, BETA-; BETA-1,2,3,4,5,6-HEXACHLOROCYCLOHEXANE; BETA-BENZENE HEXACHLORIDE; 1,2,3,4,5,6,-HEXACHLOROCYCLOHEXANE; HEXACHLOROCYCLOHEXANE; HCH; BHC; ENT 9,233; BETA-BHC; BETA-HCH; BETA-HEXACHLOROBENZENE; HEXACHLOROBENZENE; C6H6CL6; PST03010

CHEMICAL FAMILY: HALOGEN COMPOUND, ALICYCLIC

MOLECULAR FORMULA: C6-H6-CL6

MOLECULAR WEIGHT: 290.83

CERCLA RATINGS (SCALE 0-3): HEALTH=3 FIRE=0 REACTIVITY=0 PERSISTENCE=3

NFPA RATINGS (SCALE 0-4): HEALTH=U FIRE=0 REACTIVITY=0

COMPONENTS AND CONTAMINANTS

COMPONENT: BETA-HEXACHLOROCYCLOHEXANE ***PERCENT:*** 100.0
CAS# 319-85-7

OTHER CONTAMINANTS: NONE.

EXPOSURE LIMITS: NO OCCUPATIONAL EXPOSURE LIMITS ESTABLISHED BY OSHA, ACGIH, OR NIOSH.
BETA-HEXACHLOROCYCLOHEXANE: 1 POUND CERCLA SECTION 103 REPORTABLE QUANTITY SUBJECT TO CALIFORNIA PROPOSITION 65 CANCER AND/OR REPRODUCTIVE TOXICITY WARNING AND RELEASE REQUIREMENTS- (OCTOBER 1, 1989)

PHYSICAL DATA

DESCRIPTION: CUBIC CRYSTALS. ***BOILING POINT:*** 140 F (60 C) @ 0.58 MMHG

MELTING POINT: 597-599 F (314-315 C) (SUBLIMES)

SPECIFIC GRAVITY: 1.89 @ 19C

VAPOR PRESSURE: 0.005 MMHG @ 20 C ***SOLUBILITY IN WATER:*** 5 PPM

SOLVENT SOLUBILITY: SOLUBLE IN ACETONE; MODERATELY SOLUBLE IN BENZENE, CHLOROFORM, ETHER, METHANOL, XYLENE, FATS, OILS, AND KEROSENE.

FIRE AND EXPLOSION DATA

FIRE AND EXPLOSION HAZARD: NEGLIGIBLE FIRE HAZARD WHEN EXPOSED TO HEAT OR FLAME.

FIREFIGHTING MEDIA: DRY CHEMICAL, CARBON DIOXIDE, HALON, WATER SPRAY OR STANDARD FOAM (1987 EMERGENCY RESPONSE GUIDEBOOK, DOT P 5800.4).
FOR LARGER FIRES, USE WATER SPRAY, FOG OR STANDARD FOAM (1987 EMERGENCY RESPONSE GUIDEBOOK, DOT P 5800.4).

FIREFIGHTING: MOVE CONTAINERS FROM FIRE AREA IF POSSIBLE. FIGHT FIRE FROM MAXIMUM DISTANCE. STAY AWAY FROM STORAGE TANK ENDS. DIKE FIRE CONTROL WATER FOR LATER DISPOSAL. DO NOT SCATTER MATERIAL (1987 EMERGENCY RESPONSE GUIDEBOOK, DOT P 5800.4, GUIDE PAGE 55).
USE AGENTS SUITABLE FOR TYPE OF FIRE. COOL CONTAINERS WITH FLOODING AMOUNTS OF WATER. AVOID BREATHING VAPORS OR DUSTS, KEEP UPWIND.

TOXICITY

BETA-HEXACHLOROCYCLOHEXANE: TOXICITY DATA: 6000 MG/KG ORAL-RAT LD50; 1500 MG/KG ORAL-MOUSE LDLO; 2000 MG/KG ORAL-RAT LD50 (IARC, 1979); TUMORIGENIC DATA (RTECS). CARCINOGEN STATUS: ANTICIPATED HUMAN CARCINOGEN (NTP); HUMAN INADEQUATE EVIDENCE, ANIMAL LIMITED EVIDENCE (IARC GROUP-2B). B-HEXACHLOROCYCLOHEXANE PRODUCED LIVER TUMORS IN MICE BY ORAL ADMINISTRATION. ACUTE TOXICITY LEVEL: MODERATELY TOXIC BY INGESTION. TARGET EFFECTS: POISONING MAY AFFECT THE LIVER. CENTRAL NERVOUS SYSTEM DEPRESSION WAS OBSERVED IN ANIMAL STUDIES. ADDITIONAL DATA: STIMULANTS SUCH AS EPINEPHRINE MAY INDUCE VENTRICULAR FIBRILLATION.

HEALTH EFFECTS AND FIRST AID

INHALATION: BETA-HEXACHLOROCYCLOHEXANE: **ACUTE EXPOSURE-** MAY CAUSE IRRITATION. **CHRONIC EXPOSURE-** NO DATA AVAILABLE.

FIRST AID- REMOVE FROM EXPOSURE AREA TO FRESH AIR IMMEDIATELY. IF BREATHING HAS STOPPED, PERFORM ARTIFICIAL RESPIRATION. KEEP PERSON WARM AND AT REST. TREAT SYMPTOMATICALLY AND SUPPORTIVELY. GET MEDICAL ATTENTION IMMEDIATELY.

SKIN CONTACT: BETA-HEXACHLOROCYCLOHEXANE: **ACUTE EXPOSURE-** MAY CAUSE IRRITATION. **CHRONIC EXPOSURE-** NO DATA AVAILABLE.

FIRST AID- REMOVE CONTAMINATED CLOTHING AND SHOES IMMEDIATELY. WASH AFFECTED AREA WITH SOAP OR MILD DETERGENT AND LARGE AMOUNTS OF WATER UNTIL NO EVIDENCE OF CHEMICAL REMAINS (APPROXIMATELY 15-20 MINUTES). GET MEDICAL ATTENTION IMMEDIATELY.

EYE CONTACT: BETA-HEXACHLOROCYCLOHEXANE: **ACUTE EXPOSURE-** MAY CAUSE IRRITATION. **CHRONIC EXPOSURE-** NO DATA AVAILABLE.

FIRST AID- WASH EYES IMMEDIATELY WITH LARGE AMOUNTS OF WATER OR NORMAL SALINE, OCCASIONALLY LIFTING UPPER AND LOWER LIDS, UNTIL NO EVIDENCE OF CHEMICAL REMAINS (APPROXIMATELY 15-20 MINUTES). GET MEDICAL ATTENTION IMMEDIATELY.

INGESTION: BETA-HEXACHLOROCYCLOHEXANE: CARCINOGEN. **ACUTE EXPOSURE-** A LETHAL DOSE IN RATS WAS 2000 MG/KG; SYMPTOMS WERE NOT REPORTED. **CHRONIC EXPOSURE-** INCREASED MORTALITY, FATTY DEGENERATION AND FOCAL NECROSIS OF THE LIVER WERE OBSERVED IN A STUDY OF RATS. CHANGES HAVE BEEN REPORTED IN THE KIDNEYS, PANCREAS, TESTES, LUNGS AND NASAL MUCOUS MEMBRANES OF ANIMALS FOLLOWING SUFFICIENTLY HIGH REPEATED ABSORPTION OF HEXACHLOROCYCLOHEXANE OR ONE OF ITS ISOMERS. BENIGN AND MALIGNANT LIVER TUMORS WERE INDUCED IN MICE FED BETA-HEXACHLOROCYCLOHEXANE.

FIRST AID- IF THE PERSON IS CONSCIOUS AND NOT CONVULSING, REMOVE BY GIVING SYRUP OF IPECAC (IF VOMITING OCCURS, KEEP THE HEAD BELOW THE HIPS TO PREVENT ASPIRATION). GIVE ACTIVATED CHARCOAL FOLLOWED BY GASTRIC LAVAGE. FOLLOW WITH A SALINE CATHARTIC. DO NOT GIVE FATS OR OILS. INTESTINAL LAVAGE WITH 20% MANNITOL (200 ML) BY STOMACH TUBE IS ALSO USEFUL. GIVE ARTIFICIAL RESPIRATION WITH OXYGEN IF RESPIRATION IS DEPRESSED (DREISBACH, HANDBOOK OF POISONING, 12TH ED.). TREAT SYMPTOMATICALLY AND SUPPORTIVELY. LAVAGE AND ADMINISTRATION OF OXYGEN SHOULD BE PERFORMED BY QUALIFIED MEDICAL PERSONNEL. GET MEDICAL ATTENTION IMMEDIATELY.

ANTIDOTE: NO SPECIFIC ANTIDOTE. TREAT SYMPTOMATICALLY AND SUPPORTIVELY.

REACTIVITY

REACTIVITY: STABLE UNDER NORMAL TEMPERATURES AND PRESSURES.

INCOMPATIBILITIES: 1,2,3,4,5,6-HEXACHLOROCYCLOHEXANE: ALKALIES- MAY DECOMPOSE. ALUMINUM: MAY DECOMPOSE. N,N-DIMETHYLACETAMIDE: EXOTHERMIC, POSSIBLE VIOLENT REACTION. DIMETHYLFORMAMIDE: POSSIBLE DANGEROUS REACTION. IRON: MAY DECOMPOSE. ZINC: MAY DECOMPOSE.

DECOMPOSITION: THERMAL DECOMPOSITION PRODUCTS MAY INCLUDE HIGHLY TOXIC FUMES OF PHOSGENE, TOXIC AND CORROSIVE FUMES OF CHLORIDES, AND OXIDES OF CARBON.

POLYMERIZATION: HAZARDOUS POLYMERIZATION HAS NOT BEEN REPORTED TO OCCUR UNDER NORMAL TEMPERATURES AND PRESSURES.

STORAGE AND DISPOSAL

OBSERVE ALL FEDERAL, STATE AND LOCAL REGULATIONS WHEN STORING OR DISPOSING OF THIS SUBSTANCE. FOR ASSISTANCE, CONTACT THE DISTRICT DIRECTOR OF THE ENVIRONMENTAL PROTECTION AGENCY.

****STORAGE****

STORE IN ACCORDANCE WITH 40 CFR 165 RECOMMENDED PROCEDURES FOR THE DISPOSAL AND STORAGE OF PESTICIDES AND PESTICIDE CONTAINERS.
STORE AWAY FROM INCOMPATIBLE SUBSTANCES.

****DISPOSAL****

DISPOSAL MUST BE IN ACCORDANCE WITH 40 CFR 165 RECOMMENDED PROCEDURES FOR THE DISPOSAL AND STORAGE OF PESTICIDES AND PESTICIDE CONTAINERS.

CONDITIONS TO AVOID

MAY BURN BUT DOES NOT IGNITE READILY. CONTAINERS MAY EXPLODE IN HEAT OF FIRE.

SPILL AND LEAK PROCEDURES

WATER SPILL: THE CALIFORNIA SAFE DRINKING WATER AND TOXIC ENFORCEMENT ACT OF 1986 (PROPOSITION 65) PROHIBITS CONTAMINATING ANY KNOWN SOURCE OF DRINKING WATER WITH SUBSTANCES KNOWN TO CAUSE CANCER AND/OR REPRODUCTIVE TOXICITY.

OCCUPATIONAL SPILL: DO NOT TOUCH SPILLED MATERIAL. STOP LEAK IF YOU CAN DO IT WITHOUT RISK. USE WATER SPRAY TO REDUCE VAPORS. FOR SMALL SPILLS, TAKE UP WITH SAND OR OTHER ABSORBENT MATERIAL AND PLACE INTO CONTAINERS FOR LATER DISPOSAL. FOR SMALL DRY SPILLS, WITH A CLEAN SHOVEL PLACE MATERIAL INTO CLEAN, DRY CONTAINERS AND COVER. MOVE CONTAINERS FROM SPILL AREA. FOR LARGER SPILLS, DIKE FAR AHEAD OF SPILL FOR LATER DISPOSAL. KEEP UNNECESSARY PEOPLE AWAY. ISOLATE HAZARD AREA AND DENY ENTRY. VENTILATE CLOSED SPACES BEFORE ENTERING. REPORTABLE QUANTITY (RQ): 1 POUND THE SUPERFUND AMENDMENTS AND REAUTHORIZATION ACT (SARA) SECTION 304 REQUIRES THAT A RELEASE EQUAL TO OR GREATER THAN THE REPORTABLE QUANTITY FOR THIS SUBSTANCE BE IMMEDIATELY REPORTED TO THE LOCAL EMERGENCY PLANNING COMMITTEE AND THE STATE EMERGENCY RESPONSE COMMISSION (40 CFR 355.40). IF THE RELEASE OF THIS SUBSTANCE IS REPORTABLE UNDER CERCLA SECTION 103, THE NATIONAL RESPONSE CENTER MUST BE NOTIFIED IMMEDIATELY AT (800) 424-8802 OR (202) 426-2675 IN THE METROPOLITAN WASHINGTON, D.C. AREA (40 CFR 302.6).

PROTECTIVE EQUIPMENT

VENTILATION: PROVIDE LOCAL EXHAUST OR PROCESS ENCLOSURE VENTILATION SYSTEM.

RESPIRATOR: THE FOLLOWING RESPIRATORS ARE RECOMMENDED BASED ON INFORMATION FOUND IN THE PHYSICAL DATA, TOXICITY AND HEALTH EFFECTS SECTIONS. THEY ARE RANKED IN ORDER FROM MINIMUM TO MAXIMUM RESPIRATORY PROTECTION. THE SPECIFIC RESPIRATOR SELECTED MUST BE BASED ON CONTAMINATION LEVELS FOUND IN THE WORK PLACE, MUST NOT EXCEED THE WORKING LIMITS OF THE RESPIRATOR AND BE JOINTLY APPROVED BY THE NATIONAL INSTITUTE FOR OCCUPATIONAL SAFETY AND HEALTH AND THE MINE SAFETY AND HEALTH ADMINISTRATION (NIOSH-MSHA).
TYPE 'C' SUPPLIED-AIR RESPIRATOR WITH A FULL FACEPIECE OPERATED IN PRESSURE-DEMAND OR OTHER POSITIVE PRESSURE MODE OR WITH A FULL FACEPIECE, HELMET OR HOOD OPERATED IN CONTINOUS-FLOW MODE.
SELF-CONTAINED BREATHING APPARATUS WITH A FULL FACEPIECE OPERATED IN PRESSURE-DEMAND OR OTHER POSITIVE PRESSURE MODE.
FOR FIREFIGHTING AND OTHER IMMEDIATELY DANGEROUS TO LIFE OR HEALTH CONDITIONS:
SELF-CONTAINED BREATHING APPARATUS WITH FULL FACEPIECE OPERATED IN PRESSURE-DEMAND OR OTHER POSITIVE PRESSURE MODE.
SUPPLIED-AIR RESPIRATOR WITH FULL FACEPIECE AND OPERATED IN PRESSURE-DEMAND OR OTHER POSITIVE PRESSURE MODE IN COMBINATION WITH AN AUXILIARY SELF-CONTAINED BREATHING APPARATUS OPERATED IN PRESSURE-DEMAND OR OTHER POSITIVE PRESSURE MODE.

CLOTHING: EMPLOYEE MUST WEAR APPROPRIATE PROTECTIVE (IMPERVIOUS) CLOTHING AND EQUIPMENT TO PREVENT ANY POSSIBILITY OF SKIN CONTACT WITH THIS SUBSTANCE.

GLOVES: EMPLOYEE MUST WEAR APPROPRIATE PROTECTIVE GLOVES TO PREVENT CONTACT WITH THIS SUBSTANCE.

EYE PROTECTION: EMPLOYEE MUST WEAR SPLASH-PROOF OR DUST-RESISTANT SAFETY GOGGLES WITH OR WITHOUT A FACESHIELD TO PREVENT CONTACT WITH THIS SUBSTANCE.
EMERGENCY EYE WASH: WHERE THERE IS ANY POSSIBILITY THAT AN EMPLOYEE'S EYES MAY BE EXPOSED TO THIS SUBSTANCE, THE EMPLOYER SHOULD PROVIDE AN EYE WASH FOUNTAIN WITHIN THE IMMEDIATE WORK AREA FOR EMERGENCY USE.

AUTHORIZED BY- OCCUPATIONAL HEALTH SERVICES, INC.
CREATION DATE: 10/04/89 ***REVISION DATE:*** 07/12/90

MATERIAL SAFETY DATA SHEET

OCCUPATIONAL HEALTH SERVICES, INC.
AGRICULTURE AND PESTICIDE DIVISION
450 SEVENTH AVENUE, SUITE 2407
NEW YORK, NEW YORK 10123
1-800-445-MSDS OR (212) 967-1100

EMERGENCY CONTACT:
JOHN S. BRANSFORD, JR. (615) 292-1180

SUBSTANCE IDENTIFICATION

CAS-NUMBER 33213-65-9

SUBSTANCE: **BETA-ENDOSULFAN**

TRADE NAMES/SYNONYMS: 6,9-METHANO-2,4,3-BENZODIOXATHIEPIN, 6,7,8,9,10,10-HEXACHLORO-1, 5,5A,6,9,9A-HEXAHYDRO-, 3-OXIDE, (3 ALPHA, 5A ALPHA, 6 BETA, 9 BETA, 9A ALPHA)-; 5-NORBORNENE-2,3-DIMETHANOL,1,4,5,6,7,7-HEXACHLORO-,CYCLIC SULFITE, EXO-; (3 ALPHA, 5A ALPHA, 6 BETA, 9 BETA, 9A ALPHA) 6,7,8,9,10,10-HEXACHLORO -1,5,5A,6,9,9A-HEXAHYDRO-6,9,-METHANO-2,4,3-BENZODIOXATHIEPIN 3-OXIDE; EXO-1,4,5,6,7,7-HEXACHLORO-5-NORBORNENE-2,3-DIMETHANOL CYCLIC SULFITE; ENDOSULFAN B; BETA-BENZOEPIN; ENDOSULFAN 2; ENDOSULFAN II; GENERAL WEED KILLER; BETA-THIODAN; ALPHA-THIONEX; C9H6CL6O3S; PST03040

CHEMICAL FAMILY: HALOGEN COMPOUND, AROMATIC

MOLECULAR FORMULA: C9-H6-CL6-O3-S

MOLECULAR WEIGHT: 406.95

CERCLA RATINGS (SCALE 0-3): HEALTH=3 FIRE=0 REACTIVITY=0 PERSISTENCE=3

NFPA RATINGS (SCALE 0-4): HEALTH=3 FIRE=0 REACTIVITY=0

COMPONENTS AND CONTAMINANTS

COMPONENT: BETA-ENDOSULFAN ***PERCENT:*** 100
CAS# 33213-65-9

OTHER CONTAMINANTS: NONE

EXPOSURE LIMITS: BETA-ENDOSULFAN: NO OCCUPATIONAL EXPOSURE LIMITS ESTABLISHED BY OSHA, ACGIH, OR NIOSH.
1 POUND CERCLA SECTION 103 REPORTABLE QUANTITY

PHYSICAL DATA

DESCRIPTION: CRYSTALLINE SOLID ***MELTING POINT:*** 406-410 F (208-210 C)

SPECIFIC GRAVITY: NOT AVAILABLE ***SOLUBILITY IN WATER:*** 280 UG/L

SOLVENT SOLUBILITY: SOLUBLE IN ORGANIC SOLVENTS

FIRE AND EXPLOSION DATA

FIRE AND EXPLOSION HAZARD: NEGLIGIBLE FIRE HAZARD WHEN EXPOSED TO HEAT OR FLAME.

FIREFIGHTING MEDIA: DRY CHEMICAL, CARBON DIOXIDE, HALON, WATER SPRAY OR STANDARD FOAM (1987 EMERGENCY RESPONSE GUIDEBOOK, DOT P 5800.4).
FOR LARGER FIRES, USE WATER SPRAY, FOG OR STANDARD FOAM (1987 EMERGENCY RESPONSE GUIDEBOOK, DOT P 5800.4).

FIREFIGHTING: MOVE CONTAINERS FROM FIRE AREA IF POSSIBLE. FIGHT FIRE FROM MAXIMUM DISTANCE. STAY AWAY FROM STORAGE TANK ENDS. DIKE FIRE CONTROL WATER FOR LATER DISPOSAL. DO NOT SCATTER MATERIAL (1987 EMERGENCY RESPONSE GUIDEBOOK, DOT P 5800.4, GUIDE PAGE 55).
USE AGENTS SUITABLE FOR TYPE OF FIRE. COOL CONTAINERS WITH FLOODING AMOUNTS OF WATER. AVOID BREATHING VAPORS OR DUSTS, KEEP UPWIND.

TOXICITY

BETA-ENDOSULFAN: TOXICITY DATA: 240 MG/KG ORAL-RAT LD50. CARCINOGEN STATUS: NONE. ACUTE TOXICITY: TOXIC BY INGESTION. TARGET EFFECTS: CONVULSANT.

HEALTH EFFECTS AND FIRST AID

INHALATION: BETA-ENDOSULFAN: CONVULSANT. **ACUTE EXPOSURE-** A LETHAL CONCENTRATION OF ENDOSULFAN IN RATS WAS 80 MG/M3/4 HOURS. ENDOSULFAN MAY BE ABSORBED FROM THE LUNGS AND PRODUCE CENTRAL NERVOUS SYSTEM STIMULATION WITH SYMPTOMS OF HEADACHE, RESTLESSNESS, IRRITABILITY, CONFUSION, MALAISE, DIZZINESS, WEAKNESS, NAUSEA, VOMITING, AND FLUSHING AND DRY MOUTH. FAINTING, EPILEPTIC CONVULSIONS AND ALTERED EEG PATTERNS MAY OCCUR. SOME OF THESE SYMPTOMS MAY BE DELAYED FOR SEVERAL HOURS AFTER EXPOSURE. ABSORPTION IS NORMALLY SLOW BUT IS INCREASED WHEN IN SOLUTION WITH ALCOHOLS, OILS AND EMULSIFIERS. IT DOES NOT ACCUMULATE SIGNIFICANTLY IN HUMAN TISSUE. **CHRONIC EXPOSURE-** PROLONGED OR REPEATED EXPOSURE MAY CAUSE EFFECTS AS DESCRIBED IN ACUTE EXPOSURE. ONE INDIVIDUAL EXPERIENCED FAINTING AND CONVULSIONS WHILE ASSIGNED TO CLEANING VATS CONTAINING RESIDUES OF ENDOSULFAN. TWO YEARS AFTER EXPOSURE, THIS PERSON HAD COGNITIVE AND EMOTIONAL DETERIORATION, SEVERE IMPAIRMENT OF MEMORY, GROSS IMPAIRMENT OF VISUAL MOTOR COORDINATION, AND INABILITY TO PERFORM ANY BUT THE SIMPLEST TASKS.

FIRST AID- REMOVE FROM EXPOSURE AREA TO FRESH AIR IMMEDIATELY. IF BREATHING HAS STOPPED, PERFORM ARTIFICIAL RESPIRATION. KEEP PERSON WARM AND AT REST. TREAT SYMPTOMATICALLY AND SUPPORTIVELY. GET MEDICAL ATTENTION IMMEDIATELY.

SKIN CONTACT: BETA-ENDOSULFAN: CONVULSANT. **ACUTE EXPOSURE-** A LETHAL DOSE OF ENDOSULFAN IN RABBITS BY DERMAL ABSORPTION WAS 90 MG/KG. ENDOSULFAN MAY BE ABSORBED FROM THE SKIN AND PRODUCE CENTRAL NERVOUS SYSTEM STIMULATION WITH SYMPTOMS OF HEADACHE, RESTLESSNESS, IRRITABILITY, CONFUSION, MALAISE, DIZZINESS, WEAKNESS, NAUSEA, VOMITING, AND FLUSHING AND DRY MOUTH. FAINTING, EPILEPTIC CONVULSIONS AND ALTERED EEG PATTERNS MAY OCCUR. SOME OF THESE SYMPTOMS MAY BE DELAYED FOR SEVERAL HOURS AFTER EXPOSURE. ABSORPTION IS NORMALLY SLOW BUT IS INCREASED WHEN IN SOLUTION WITH ALCOHOLS, OILS, AND EMULSIFIERS. IT DOES NOT ACCUMULATE SIGNIFICANTLY IN HUMAN TISSUE. **CHRONIC EXPOSURE-** PROLONGED OR REPEATED EXPOSURE MAY CAUSE EFFECTS AS DESCRIBED IN ACUTE EXPOSURE.

FIRST AID- REMOVE CONTAMINATED CLOTHING AND SHOES IMMEDIATELY. WASH AFFECTED AREA WITH SOAP OR MILD DETERGENT AND LARGE AMOUNTS OF WATER UNTIL NO EVIDENCE OF CHEMICAL REMAINS (APPROXIMATELY 15-20 MINUTES). GET MEDICAL ATTENTION IMMEDIATELY.

EYE CONTACT: ALPHA-ENDOSULFAN: **ACUTE EXPOSURE-** 83 MG OF ENDOSULFAN APPLIED TO THE EYES OF RABBITS PRODUCED SLIGHT CONJUNCTIVITIS WHICH CLEARED WITHIN 72 HOURS OF APPLICATION. **CHRONIC EXPOSURE-** NO DATA AVAILABLE.

FIRST AID- WASH EYES IMMEDIATELY WITH LARGE AMOUNTS OF WATER OR NORMAL SALINE, OCCASIONALLY LIFTING UPPER AND LOWER LIDS, UNTIL NO EVIDENCE OF CHEMICAL REMAINS (APPROXIMATELY 15-20 MINUTES). GET MEDICAL ATTENTION IMMEDIATELY.

INGESTION: BETA-ENDOSULFAN: CONVULSANT/TOXIC. **ACUTE EXPOSURE-** A LETHAL DOSE IN RATS WAS 240 MG/KG. INGESTION OF ENDOSULFAN MAY CAUSE GAGGING, VOMITING, DIARRHEA, AGITATION, TONIC-CLONIC CONVULSIONS, FOAMING AT THE MOUTH, DYSPNEA, APNEA, CYANOSIS, AND LOSS OF CONSCIOUSNESS. ONLY A SMALL DOSE OF ENDOSULFAN MAY BE FATAL. ONE 70-YEAR-OLD WOMAN DIED THREE HOURS AFTER TAKING ONLY "DROPS" OF AN ENDOSULFAN FORMULATION. PERSONS WHO TOOK LARGER DOSES DIED QUICKER, SOME IN LESS THAN AN HOUR. **CHRONIC EXPOSURE-** REPEATED DOSES OF ENDOSULFAN AT 5 MG/KG/DAY AND GREATER ON DAYS 6 TO 14 OF GESTATION INCREASED THE MORTALITY OF FEMALE RATS AND INCREASED THE RATES OF RESORPTION AND SKELETAL ABNORMALITY IN THEIR FETUSES. EFFECTS ON THE MALE REPRODUCTIVE SYSTEM WERE OBSERVED IN A STUDY OF ENDOSULFAN IN RATS. HISTOPATHOLOGICAL EXAMINATIONS OF THE LIVER AND KIDNEYS OF RATS FED A DAILY DIET UP TO 10 MG/KG OF ENDOSULFAN FOR 15 DAYS REVEALED DILATION OF SINUSOID AROUND CENTRAL VEINS, AREAS OF FOCAL NECROSIS AND DEGENERATION OF HEPATOCYTES AND MONONUCLEAR MONOLUCOCYTES, PROLIFERATION IN THE BILE DUCT, AND DEGENERATIVE ALTERATIONS IN THE EPITHELIAL LINING OF KIDNEY TUBULES. OTHER EFFECTS INCLUDED KUPFFER CELL HYPERPLASIA, INFLAMMATORY AREAS IN THE SUBPLEURAL OF THE LUNGS AND DILATION OF THE ALVEOLI, AND SEVERE DEGENERATION OF THE SEMINIFEROUS EPITHELIUM. AS EVALUATED BY RTECS, ORAL ADMINISTRATION OF ENDOSULFAN TO RATS RESULTED IN A STATISTICALLY SIGNIFICANT INCREASE IN THE INCIDENCE OF NEOPLASTIC TUMORS OF THE RESPIRATORY SYSTEM.

FIRST AID- IF THE PERSON IS CONSCIOUS AND NOT CONVULSING, REMOVE BY GIVING SYRUP OF IPECAC (IF VOMITING OCCURS, KEEP THE HEAD BELOW THE HIPS TO PREVENT ASPIRATION). GIVE ACTIVATED CHARCOAL FOLLOWED BY GASTRIC LAVAGE. FOLLOW WITH A SALINE CATHARTIC. DO NOT GIVE FATS OR OILS. INTESTINAL LAVAGE WITH 20% MANNITOL (200 ML) BY STOMACH TUBE IS ALSO USEFUL. GIVE ARTIFICIAL RESPIRATION WITH OXYGEN IF RESPIRATION IS DEPRESSED (DREISBACH, HANDBOOK OF POISONING, 12TH ED.). TREAT SYMPTOMATICALLY AND SUPPORTIVELY. LAVAGE AND ADMINISTRATION OF OXYGEN SHOULD BE PERFORMED BY QUALIFIED MEDICAL PERSONNEL. GET MEDICAL ATTENTION IMMEDIATELY.

ANTIDOTE: NO SPECIFIC ANTIDOTE. TREAT SYMPTOMATICALLY AND SUPPORTIVELY.

REACTIVITY

REACTIVITY: STABLE UNDER NORMAL TEMPERATURES AND PRESSURES IN AN ENCLOSED CONTAINER. CONTACT WITH MOISTURE MAY CAUSE DECOMPOSITION PRODUCING SULFUR DIOXIDE AND ENDOSULFAN ALCOHOL.

INCOMPATIBILITIES: BETA-ENDOSULFAN: ACIDS: MAY CAUSE DECOMPOSITION PRODUCING SULFUR DIOXIDE AND ENDOSULFAN ALCOHOL. BASES: MAY CAUSE DECOMPOSITION PRODUCING SULFUR DIOXIDE AND ENDOSULFAN ALCOHOL. IRON: MAY BE CORRODED.

DECOMPOSITION: THERMAL DECOMPOSITION MAY RELEASE TOXIC AND/OR HAZARDOUS GASES.
POLYMERIZATION: NO DATA AVAILABLE.

STORAGE AND DISPOSAL

OBSERVE ALL FEDERAL, STATE AND LOCAL REGULATIONS WHEN STORING OR DISPOSING OF THIS SUBSTANCE. FOR ASSISTANCE, CONTACT THE DISTRICT DIRECTOR OF THE ENVIRONMENTAL PROTECTION AGENCY.

****STORAGE****

STORE IN ACCORDANCE WITH 40 CFR 165 RECOMMENDED PROCEDURES FOR THE DISPOSAL AND STORAGE OF PESTICIDES AND PESTICIDE CONTAINERS.
STORE AWAY FROM INCOMPATIBLE SUBSTANCES.

****DISPOSAL****

DISPOSAL MUST BE IN ACCORDANCE WITH 40 CFR 165 RECOMMENDED PROCEDURES FOR THE DISPOSAL AND STORAGE OF PESTICIDES AND PESTICIDE CONTAINERS.

CONDITIONS TO AVOID

MAY BURN BUT DOES NOT IGNITE READILY. CONTAINERS MAY EXPLODE IN HEAT OF FIRE.

SPILL AND LEAK PROCEDURES

OCCUPATIONAL SPILL: DO NOT TOUCH SPILLED MATERIAL. STOP LEAK IF YOU CAN DO IT WITHOUT RISK. USE WATER SPRAY TO REDUCE VAPORS. FOR SMALL SPILLS, TAKE UP WITH SAND OR OTHER ABSORBENT MATERIAL AND PLACE INTO CONTAINERS FOR LATER DISPOSAL. FOR SMALL DRY SPILLS, WITH A CLEAN SHOVEL PLACE MATERIAL INTO CLEAN, DRY CONTAINERS AND COVER. MOVE CONTAINERS FROM SPILL AREA. FOR LARGER SPILLS, DIKE FAR AHEAD OF SPILL FOR LATER DISPOSAL. KEEP UNNECESSARY PEOPLE AWAY. ISOLATE HAZARD AREA AND DENY ENTRY. VENTILATE CLOSED SPACES BEFORE ENTERING. REPORTABLE QUANTITY (RQ): 1 POUND THE SUPERFUND AMENDMENTS AND REAUTHORIZATION ACT (SARA) SECTION 304 REQUIRES THAT A RELEASE EQUAL TO OR GREATER THAN THE REPORTABLE QUANTITY FOR THIS SUBSTANCE BE IMMEDIATELY REPORTED TO THE LOCAL EMERGENCY PLANNING COMMITTEE AND THE STATE EMERGENCY RESPONSE COMMISSION (40 CFR 355.40). IF THE RELEASE OF THIS SUBSTANCE IS REPORTABLE UNDER CERCLA SECTION 103, THE NATIONAL RESPONSE CENTER MUST BE NOTIFIED IMMEDIATELY AT (800) 424-8802 OR (202) 426-2675 IN THE METROPOLITAN WASHINGTON, D.C. AREA (40 CFR 302.6).

PROTECTIVE EQUIPMENT

VENTILATION: PROVIDE LOCAL EXHAUST OR PROCESS ENCLOSURE VENTILATION SYSTEM.

RESPIRATOR: THE FOLLOWING RESPIRATORS ARE RECOMMENDED BASED ON INFORMATION FOUND IN THE PHYSICAL DATA, TOXICITY AND HEALTH EFFECTS SECTIONS. THEY ARE RANKED IN ORDER FROM MINIMUM TO MAXIMUM RESPIRATORY PROTECTION. THE SPECIFIC RESPIRATOR SELECTED MUST BE BASED ON CONTAMINATION LEVELS FOUND IN THE WORK PLACE, MUST NOT EXCEED THE WORKING LIMITS OF THE RESPIRATOR AND BE JOINTLY APPROVED BY THE NATIONAL INSTITUTE FOR OCCUPATIONAL SAFETY AND HEALTH AND THE MINE SAFETY AND HEALTH ADMINISTRATION (NIOSH-MSHA).
TYPE 'C' SUPPLIED-AIR RESPIRATOR WITH A FULL FACEPIECE OPERATED IN PRESSURE-DEMAND OR OTHER POSITIVE PRESSURE MODE OR WITH A FULL FACEPIECE, HELMET OR HOOD OPERATED IN CONTINOUS-FLOW MODE.
SELF-CONTAINED BREATHING APPARATUS WITH A FULL FACEPIECE OPERATED IN PRESSURE-DEMAND OR OTHER POSITIVE PRESSURE MODE.
FOR FIREFIGHTING AND OTHER IMMEDIATELY DANGEROUS TO LIFE OR HEALTH CONDITIONS:
SELF-CONTAINED BREATHING APPARATUS WITH FULL FACEPIECE OPERATED IN PRESSURE-DEMAND OR OTHER POSITIVE PRESSURE MODE.
SUPPLIED-AIR RESPIRATOR WITH FULL FACEPIECE AND OPERATED IN PRESSURE-DEMAND OR OTHER POSITIVE PRESSURE MODE IN COMBINATION WITH AN AUXILIARY SELF-CONTAINED BREATHING APPARATUS OPERATED IN PRESSURE-DEMAND OR OTHER POSITIVE PRESSURE MODE.

CLOTHING: EMPLOYEE MUST WEAR APPROPRIATE PROTECTIVE (IMPERVIOUS) CLOTHING AND EQUIPMENT TO PREVENT ANY POSSIBILITY OF SKIN CONTACT WITH THIS SUBSTANCE.

GLOVES: EMPLOYEE MUST WEAR APPROPRIATE PROTECTIVE GLOVES TO PREVENT CONTACT WITH THIS SUBSTANCE.

EYE PROTECTION: EMPLOYEE MUST WEAR SPLASH-PROOF OR DUST-RESISTANT SAFETY GOGGLES AND A FACESHIELD TO PREVENT CONTACT WITH THIS SUBSTANCE.
EMERGENCY WASH FACILITIES: WHERE THERE IS ANY POSSIBILITY THAT AN EMPLOYEE'S EYES AND/OR SKIN MAY BE EXPOSED TO THIS SUBSTANCE, THE EMPLOYER SHOULD PROVIDE AN EYE WASH FOUNTAIN AND QUICK DRENCH SHOWER WITHIN THE IMMEDIATE WORK AREA FOR EMERGENCY USE.

AUTHORIZED BY- OCCUPATIONAL HEALTH SERVICES, INC.
CREATION DATE: 10/04/89 ***REVISION DATE:*** 01/31/90

MATERIAL SAFETY DATA SHEET

OCCUPATIONAL HEALTH SERVICES, INC.
AGRICULTURE AND PESTICIDE DIVISION
450 SEVENTH AVENUE, SUITE 2407
NEW YORK, NEW YORK 10123
1-800-445-MSDS OR (212) 967-1100

EMERGENCY CONTACT:
JOHN S. BRANSFORD, JR. (615) 292-1180

SUBSTANCE IDENTIFICATION

CAS-NUMBER 135-19-3
SUBSTANCE: **2-NAPHTHOL**
TRADE NAMES/SYNONYMS: BETA-NAPTHOL; BETA-NAPHTHYLALCOHOL; BETA-NAPHTHYL HYD-ROXIDE; BETA-MONOXYNAPHTHALENE; ISONAPHTHOL; 2-HYDROXYNAPHTHLALENE; BETA-HYD-ROXYNAPHTHALENE; AZOGEN DEVELOPER; C.I. 37500; DEVELOPER AMS; DEVELOPER BN; DEVELOPER SODIUM; 171-T; PST03050
CHEMICAL FAMILY: HYDROXYL, AROMATIC
MOLECULAR FORMULA: C10-H8-O
MOLECULAR WEIGHT: 144.18
CERCLA RATINGS (SCALE 0-3): HEALTH=2 FIRE=1 REACTIVITY=0 PERSISTENCE=1
NFPA RATINGS (SCALE 0-4): HEALTH=2 FIRE=1 REACTIVITY=0

COMPONENTS AND CONTAMINANTS

COMPONENT: 2-NAPHTHOL ***PERCENT:*** 100
CAS# 135-19-3
OTHER CONTAMINANTS: NONE
EXPOSURE LIMITS: NO OCCUPATIONAL EXPOSURE LIMITS ESTABLISHED BY OSHA, ACGIH, OR NIOSH.

PHYSICAL DATA

DESCRIPTION: WHITE-YELLOWISH WHITE CRYSTALS, SLIGHT PHENOLIC ODOR
BOILING POINT: 545 F (285 C) SUBLIMES ***MELTING POINT:*** 252 F (122 C)
SPECIFIC GRAVITY: 1.2 ***VAPOR PRESSURE:*** 3.6 MMHG @ 130 C
SOLUBILITY IN WATER: SLIGHTLY SOLUBLE ***VAPOR DENSITY:*** 4.97
SOLVENT SOLUBILITY: CHLOROFORM, ETHANOL, ALCOHOL, GLYCERINE, ALKALI HYDROXIDES

FIRE AND EXPLOSION DATA

FIRE AND EXPLOSION HAZARD: SLIGHT FIRE HAZARD WHEN EXPOSED TO HEAT OR FLAME.
FLASH POINT: 307 F (153 C) (CC)
FIREFIGHTING MEDIA: DRY CHEMICAL, CARBON DIOXIDE, HALON, WATER SPRAY OR ALCOHOL FOAM (1987 EMERGENCY RESPONSE GUIDEBOOK, DOT P 5800.4).
FOR LARGER FIRES, USE WATER SPRAY, FOG OR ALCOHOL FOAM (1987 EMERGENCY RESPONSE GUIDEBOOK, DOT P 5800.4).
FIREFIGHTING: MOVE CONTAINER FROM FIRE AREA IF POSSIBLE. COOL FIRE-EXPOSED CONTAINERS WITH WATER FROM SIDE UNTIL WELL AFTER FIRE IS OUT. STAY AWAY FROM STORAGE TANK ENDS. FOR MASSIVE FIRE IN STORAGE AREA, USE UNMANNED HOSE HOLDER OR MONITOR NOZZLES, ELSE WITHDRAW FROM AREA AND LET FIRE BURN. WITHDRAW IMMEDIATELY IN CASE OF RISING SOUND FROM VENTING SAFETY DEVICE OR ANY DISCOLORATION OF STORAGE TANK DUE TO FIRE (1987 EMERGENCY RESPONSE GUIDEBOOK, DOT P 5800.4, GUIDE PAGE 26). EXTINGUISH ONLY IF FLOW CAN BE STOPPED; USE FLOODING AMOUNTS OF WATER AS A FOG, SOLID STREAMS MAY BE INEFFECTIVE. COOL CONTAINERS WITH FLOODING AMOUNTS OF WATER, APPLY FROM AS FAR A DISTANCE AS POSSIBLE. AVOID BREATHING VAPORS, KEEP UPWIND.

TOXICITY

2-NAPHTHOL: IRRITATION DATA: 500 MG/24 HOURS SKIN-RABBIT MILD; 100 MG EYE-RABBIT MODERATE. TOXICITY DATA: 1960 MG/KG ORAL-RAT LD50; 100 MG/KG ORAL-MOUSE LDLO; 3800 MG/KG ORAL-RABBIT LDLO; 1335 MG/KG ORAL-GUINEA PIG LD50; 100 MG/KG ORAL-CAT LDLO; 2940 MG/KG SUBCUTANEOUS-RAT LDLO; 100 MG/KG SUBCUTANEOUS-MOUSE LDLO; 3 GM/KG SUBCUTANEOUS-RABBIT LDLO; 2670 MG/KG SUBCUTANEOUS-GUINEA PIG LDLO; 97500 MG/KG INTRAPERITONEAL-MOUSE LD50; 3800 MG/KG UNREPORTED-RABBIT LDLO; MUTAGENIC DATA (RTECS). CARCINOGEN STATUS: NONE. LOCAL EFFECTS: CORROSIVE- INHALATION, SKIN, AND EYES. ACUTE TOXICITY LEVEL: MODERATELY TOXIC BY INGESTION. TARGET EFFECTS: SENSITIZER- SKIN.

HEALTH EFFECTS AND FIRST AID

INHALATION: 2-NAPHTHOL: CORROSIVE. **ACUTE EXPOSURE-** MAY CAUSE PROFUSE SWEATING, INTENSE THIRST, NAUSEA, VOMITING, DIARRHEA, HYPERACTIVITY, STUPOR, HYPOTENSION, HYPERPNEA, ABDOMINAL PAIN, HEMOLYSIS, CONVULSIONS, COMA AND PULMONARY EDEMA FOLLOWED BY PNEUMONIA. IF DEATH FROM RESPIRATORY FAILURE IS NOT IMMEDIATE, JAUNDICE AND OLIGURIA MAY OCCUR. **CHRONIC EXPOSURE-** REPEATED EXPOSURE MAY CAUSE SYMPTOMS DESCRIBED FOR ACUTE POISONING.

FIRST AID- REMOVE FROM EXPOSURE AREA TO FRESH AIR IMMEDIATELY. IF BREATHING HAS STOPPED, GIVE ARTIFICIAL RESPIRATION. MAINTAIN AIRWAY AND BLOOD PRESSURE AND ADMINISTER OXYGEN IF AVAILABLE. KEEP AFFECTED PERSON WARM AND AT REST. TREAT SYMPTOMATICALLY AND SUPPORTIVELY. ADMINISTRATION OF OXYGEN SHOULD BE PERFORMED BY QUALIFIED PERSONNEL. GET MEDICAL ATTENTION IMMEDIATELY.

SKIN CONTACT: 2-NAPHTHOL: CORROSIVE/SENSITIZER. **ACUTE EXPOSURE-** LOCAL EFFECTS MAY INCLUDE BLANCHING, ERYTHEMA, AND TISSUE DESTRUCTION. MAY BE ABSORBED THROUGH SKIN TO CAUSE PROFUSE SWEATING, INTENSE THIRST, NAUSEA, VOMITING, HYPERACTIVITY, STUPOR, HYPOTENSION, ABDOMINAL PAIN, HEMOLYSIS, CONVULSIONS, COMA, AND PULMONARY EDEMA FOLLOWED BY PNEUMONIA. IF DEATH FROM RESPIRATORY FAILURE IS NOT IMMEDIATE, JAUNDICE AND OLIGURIA OR ANURIA MAY OCCUR. MAY CAUSE SENSITIZATION DERMATITIS IN PREVIOUSLY EXPOSED PERSONS. **CHRONIC EXPOSURE-** PROLONGED OR REPEATED CONTACT MAY RESULT IN SENSITIZATION. PROLONGED CONTACT MAY CAUSE BLADDER TUMORS, HEMOLYTIC ANEMIA, AND LENS OPACITIES.

FIRST AID- REMOVE CONTAMINATED CLOTHING AND SHOES IMMEDIATELY. WASH AFFECTED AREA WITH SOAP OR MILD DETERGENT AND LARGE AMOUNTS OF WATER UNTIL NO EVIDENCE OF CHEMICAL REMAINS (AT LEAST 15-20 MINUTES). IN CASE OF CHEMICAL BURNS, COVER AREA WITH STERILE, DRY DRESSING. BANDAGE SECURELY, BUT NOT TOO TIGHTLY. GET MEDICAL ATTENTION IMMEDIATELY.

EYE CONTACT: 2-NAPHTHOL: CORROSIVE. **ACUTE EXPOSURE-** IRRITATION, REDNESS AND PAIN MAY OCCUR FROM EXPOSURE. **CHRONIC EXPOSURE-** MAY BE ABSORBED WITH PROLONGED CONTACT CAUSING LENS OPACITIES AND CORNEAL DAMAGE.

FIRST AID- WASH EYES IMMEDIATELY WITH LARGE AMOUNTS OF WATER, OCCASIONALLY LIFTING UPPER AND LOWER LIDS, UNTIL NO EVIDENCE OF CHEMICAL REMAINS (AT LEAST 15-20 MINUTES). CONTINUE IRRIGATING WITH NORMAL SALINE UNTIL THE PH HAS RETURNED TO NORMAL (30-60 MINUTES). COVER WITH STERILE BANDAGES. GET MEDICAL ATTENTION IMMEDIATELY.

INGESTION: 2-NAPHTHOL: CORROSIVE. **ACUTE EXPOSURE-** MAY CAUSE PROFUSE SWEATING, INTENSE THIRST, NAUSEA, VOMITING, ABDOMINAL PAIN, DIARRHEA, HYPERACTIVITY, STUPOR, HYPOTENSION, HYPERPNEA, HEMOLYSIS, CONVULSIONS, AND COMA. ASPIRATION MAY CAUSE PULMONARY EDEMA FOLLOWED BY PNEUMONIA. IF DEATH IS NOT IMMEDIATE, JAUNDICE AND OLIGURIA OR ANURIA MAY OCCUR. **CHRONIC EXPOSURE-** PROLONGED EXPOSURE FROM INGESTION MAY CAUSE MANY OF THE SYMPTOMS OF ACUTE EXPOSURE.

FIRST AID- IN THE ABSENCE OF CORROSIVE INJURY, REMOVE POISON BY IPECAC EMESIS. ACTIVATED CHARCOAL IS ALSO USEFUL. FOLLOW WITH 240 ML OF MILK. GASTRIC LAVAGE AND EMESIS ARE CONTRAINDICATED IN THE PRESENCE OF ESOPHAGEAL INJURY (DREISBACH, HANDBOOK OF POISONING, 12TH EDITION). GET MEDICAL ATTENTION IMMEDIATELY.

ANTIDOTE: NO SPECIFIC ANTIDOTE. TREAT SYMPTOMATICALLY AND SUPPORTIVELY.

REACTIVITY

REACTIVITY: STABLE UNDER NORMAL TEMPERATURES AND PRESSURES.

INCOMPATIBILITIES: 2-NAPHTHOL: ACIDS: REACTS VIOLENTLY. STRONG ACIDS: REACTS VIOLENTLY.

DECOMPOSITION: THERMAL DECOMPOSITION MAY RELEASE TOXIC AND/OR HAZARDOUS GASES.

POLYMERIZATION: HAZARDOUS POLYMERIZATION HAS NOT BEEN REPORTED TO OCCUR UNDER NORMAL TEMPERATURES AND PRESSURES.

CONDITIONS TO AVOID

DARKENS UPON EXPOSURE TO LIGHT.

SPILL AND LEAK PROCEDURES

SWEEP UP AND PLACE IN SUITABLE CLEAN, DRY CONTAINERS FOR RECLAMATION OR LATER DISPOSAL. DO NOT FLUSH MATERIAL INTO SEWER. KEEP UNNECESSARY PEOPLE AWAY.

PROTECTIVE EQUIPMENT

VENTILATION: PROVIDE LOCAL EXHAUST OR GENERAL DILUTION VENTILATION SYSTEM.

RESPIRATOR: THE FOLLOWING RESPIRATORS ARE RECOMMENDED BASED ON INFORMATION FOUND IN THE PHYSICAL DATA, TOXICITY AND HEALTH EFFECTS SECTIONS. THEY ARE RANKED IN ORDER FROM MINIMUM TO MAXIMUM RESPIRATORY PROTECTION. THE SPECIFIC RESPIRATOR SELECTED MUST BE BASED ON CONTAMINATION LEVELS FOUND IN THE WORK PLACE, MUST NOT EXCEED THE WORKING LIMITS OF THE RESPIRATOR AND BE JOINTLY APPROVED BY THE NATIONAL INSTITUTE FOR OCCUPATIONAL SAFETY AND HEALTH AND THE MINE SAFETY AND HEALTH ADMINISTRATION (NIOSH-MSHA).

CHEMICAL CARTRIDGE RESPIRATOR WITH FULL FACEPIECE AND ORGANIC VAPOR CARTRIDGE(S) IN COMBINATION WITH A DUST AND MIST FILTER.

CHEMICAL CARTRIDGE RESPIRATOR WITH FULL FACEPIECE AND ORGANIC VAPOR CARTRIDGE(S) IN COMBINATION WITH A HIGH-EFFICIENCY PARTICULATE FILTER.

GAS MASK WITH ORGANIC VAPOR CANISTER (CHIN-STYLE OR FRONT- OR BACK-MOUNTED CANISTER) WITH A FULL FACEPIECE AND A HIGH-EFFICIENCY PARTICULATE FILTER.

POWERED AIR-PURIFYING RESPIRATOR WITH TIGHT-FITTING FACEPIECE AND ORGANIC VAPOR CARTRIDGE(S) IN COMBINATION WITH A HIGH-EFFICIENCY PARTICULATE FILTER.

TYPE 'C' SUPPLIED-AIR RESPIRATOR WITH A FULL FACEPIECE OPERATED IN PRESSURE-DEMAND OR OTHER POSITIVE PRESSURE MODE OR WITH A FULL FACEPIECE, HELMET OR HOOD OPERATED IN CONTINUOUS-FLOW MODE.

SELF-CONTAINED BREATHING APPARATUS WITH A FULL FACEPIECE OPERATED IN PRESSURE-DEMAND OR OTHER POSITIVE PRESSURE MODE.

FOR FIREFIGHTING AND OTHER IMMEDIATELY DANGEROUS TO LIFE OR HEALTH CONDITIONS:

SELF-CONTAINED BREATHING APPARATUS WITH FULL FACEPIECE OPERATED IN PRESSURE-DEMAND OR OTHER POSITIVE PRESSURE MODE.

SUPPLIED-AIR RESPIRATOR WITH FULL FACEPIECE AND OPERATED IN PRESSURE-DEMAND OR OTHER POSITIVE PRESSURE MODE IN COMBINATION WITH AN AUXILIARY SELF-CONTAINED BREATHING APPARATUS OPERATED IN PRESSURE-DEMAND OR OTHER POSITIVE PRESSURE MODE.

CLOTHING: EMPLOYEE MUST WEAR APPROPRIATE PROTECTIVE (IMPERVIOUS) CLOTHING AND EQUIPMENT TO PREVENT ANY POSSIBILITY OF SKIN CONTACT WITH THIS SUBSTANCE.

GLOVES: EMPLOYEE MUST WEAR APPROPRIATE PROTECTIVE GLOVES TO PREVENT CONTACT WITH THIS SUBSTANCE.

EYE PROTECTION: EMPLOYEE MUST WEAR SPLASH-PROOF OR DUST-RESISTANT SAFETY GOGGLES TO PREVENT EYE CONTACT WITH THIS SUBSTANCE.

EMERGENCY EYE WASH: WHERE THERE IS ANY POSSIBILITY THAT AN EMPLOYEE'S EYES MAY BE EXPOSED TO THIS SUBSTANCE, THE EMPLOYER SHOULD PROVIDE AN EYE WASH FOUNTAIN WITHIN THE IMMEDIATE WORK AREA FOR EMERGENCY USE.

AUTHORIZED BY- OCCUPATIONAL HEALTH SERVICES, INC.

CREATION DATE: 10/05/89 ***REVISION DATE:*** 05/09/90

MATERIAL SAFETY DATA SHEET

OCCUPATIONAL HEALTH SERVICES, INC.
AGRICULTURE AND PESTICIDE DIVISION
450 SEVENTH AVENUE, SUITE 2407
NEW YORK, NEW YORK 10123
1-800-445-MSDS OR (212) 967-1100

EMERGENCY CONTACT:
JOHN S. BRANSFORD, JR. (615) 292-1180

SUBSTANCE IDENTIFICATION

CAS-NUMBER 138-87-4

SUBSTANCE: **BETA-TERPINEOL**

TRADE NAMES/SYNONYMS: CYCLOHEXANOL,1-METHYL-4-(1-METHYLETHENYL)-; 1-METHYL-4-(1-METHYLETHENYL)CYCLOHEXANOL; P-MENTH-8-EN-1-OL; PARA-MENTH-8-EN-1-OL; PST03075

CHEMICAL FAMILY: TERPENE

MOLECULAR FORMULA: C10-H18-O

MOLECULAR WEIGHT: 154.25

CERCLA RATINGS (SCALE 0-3): HEALTH=U FIRE=U REACTIVITY=U PERSISTENCE=1

NFPA RATINGS (SCALE 0-4): HEALTH=U FIRE=U REACTIVITY=U

COMPONENTS AND CONTAMINANTS

COMPONENT: BETA-TERPINEOL ***PERCENT:*** 100
CAS# 138-87-4

OTHER CONTAMINANTS: NONE

EXPOSURE LIMITS: NO OCCUPATIONAL EXPOSURE LIMITS ESTABLISHED BY OSHA, ACGIH, OR NIOSH.

PHYSICAL DATA

DESCRIPTION: SOLID. ***BOILING POINT:*** 408-410 F (209-210 C)
MELTING POINT: 90-91 F (32-33 C) ***SPECIFIC GRAVITY:*** 0.919
SOLUBILITY IN WATER: NOT AVAILABLE

FIRE AND EXPLOSION DATA

FIRE AND EXPLOSION HAZARD: UNKNOWN FIRE AND EXPLOSION HAZARD.
FIREFIGHTING MEDIA: DRY CHEMICAL, CARBON DIOXIDE, WATER SPRAY OR FOAM FOR LARGER FIRES, USE WATER SPRAY, FOG OR ALCOHOL FOAM
FIREFIGHTING: MOVE CONTAINER FROM FIRE AREA IF POSSIBLE. DO NOT SCATTER SPILLED MATERIAL WITH MORE WATER THAN NEEDED FOR FIRE CONTROL. DIKE FIRE CONTROL WATER FOR LATER DISPOSAL
USE AGENTS SUITABLE FOR TYPE OF SURROUNDING FIRE. AVOID BREATHING HAZARDOUS VAPORS, KEEP UPWIND.

TOXICITY

BETA-TERPINEOL: TOXICITY DATA: MUTAGENIC DATA (RTECS). CARCINOGEN STATUS: NONE. ACUTE TOXICITY LEVEL: NO DATA AVAILABLE. TARGET EFFECTS: POISONING MAY AFFECT THE CENTRAL NERVOUS SYSTEM.

HEALTH EFFECTS AND FIRST AID

INHALATION: TERPINEOL: **ACUTE EXPOSURE-** NO SPECIFIC DATA AVAILABLE. EXPOSURE TO SOME TERPINEOLS MAY CAUSE IRRITATION TO MUCOUS MEMBRANES. SYSTEMIC EFFECTS MAY INCLUDE WEAKNESS AND CENTRAL NERVOUS SYSTEM DEPRESSION, WITH HYPOTHERMIA AND RESPIRATORY FAILURE. **CHRONIC EXPOSURE-** NO DATA AVAILABLE.
FIRST AID- REMOVE FROM EXPOSURE AREA TO FRESH AIR IMMEDIATELY. IF BREATHING HAS STOPPED, PERFORM ARTIFICIAL RESPIRATION. KEEP PERSON WARM AND AT REST. TREAT SYMPTOMATICALLY AND SUPPORTIVELY. GET MEDICAL ATTENTION IMMEDIATELY.

SKIN CONTACT: TERPINEOL: **ACUTE EXPOSURE-** NO SPECIFIC DATA AVAILABLE. CONTACT WITH SOME TERPINEOLS MAY CAUSE IRRITATION, WITH ERYTHEMA AND ITCHING. **CHRONIC EXPOSURE-** NO DATA AVAILABLE.
FIRST AID- REMOVE CONTAMINATED CLOTHING AND SHOES IMMEDIATELY. WASH AFFECTED AREA WITH SOAP OR MILD DETERGENT AND LARGE AMOUNTS OF WATER UNTIL NO EVIDENCE OF CHEMICAL REMAINS (APPROXIMATELY 15-20 MINUTES). GET MEDICAL ATTENTION IMMEDIATELY.

EYE CONTACT: TERPINEOL: **ACUTE EXPOSURE-** NO SPECIFIC DATA AVAILABLE. EXPOSURE TO SOME TERPINEOLS MAY CAUSE IRRITATION TO THE EYES. **CHRONIC EXPOSURE-** NO DATA AVAILABLE.
FIRST AID- WASH EYES IMMEDIATELY WITH LARGE AMOUNTS OF WATER OR NORMAL SALINE, OCCASIONALLY LIFTING UPPER AND LOWER LIDS, UNTIL NO EVIDENCE OF CHEMICAL REMAINS (APPROXIMATELY 15-20 MINUTES). GET MEDICAL ATTENTION IMMEDIATELY.

INGESTION: TERPINEOL: **ACUTE EXPOSURE-** NO SPECIFIC DATA AVAILABLE. INGESTION OF SOME TERPINEOLS MAY CAUSE HEMORRHAGIC GASTRITIS. ASPIRATION AND PULMONARY INFILTRATION MAY OCCUR. CHRONIC EXPOSSURE- NO DATA AVAILABLE.
FIRST AID- TREAT SYMPTOMATICALLY AND SUPPORTIVELY. GET MEDICAL ATTENTION IMMEDIATELY. IF VOMITING OCCURS, KEEP HEAD LOWER THAN HIPS TO PREVENT ASPIRATION.
ANTIDOTE: NO SPECIFIC ANTIDOTE. TREAT SYMPTOMATICALLY AND SUPPORTIVELY.

REACTIVITY

REACTIVITY: NO DATA AVAILABLE.
INCOMPATIBILITIES: TERPENES: NITRIC ACID + DIBORANE: IGNITION. OXIDIZERS (STRONG): FIRE AND EXPLOSION HAZARD.
DECOMPOSITION: THERMAL DECOMPOSITION MAY RELEASE TOXIC AND/OR HAZARDOUS GASES.
POLYMERIZATION: NO DATA AVAILABLE.

STORAGE AND DISPOSAL

OBSERVE ALL FEDERAL, STATE AND LOCAL REGULATIONS WHEN STORING OR DISPOSING OF THIS SUBSTANCE. FOR ASSISTANCE, CONTACT THE DISTRICT DIRECTOR OF THE ENVIRONMENTAL PROTECTION AGENCY.

CONDITIONS TO AVOID

NONE REPORTED.

SPILL AND LEAK PROCEDURES

OCCUPATIONAL SPILL: NO SPECIAL PRECAUTIONS INDICATED.

PROTECTIVE EQUIPMENT

VENTILATION: PROVIDE LOCAL EXHAUST OR PROCESS ENCLOSURE VENTILATION. VENTILATION EQUIPMENT MUST BE EXPLOSION-PROOF.
RESPIRATOR: THE FOLLOWING RESPIRATORS ARE RECOMMENDED BASED ON INFORMATION FOUND IN THE PHYSICAL DATA, TOXICITY AND HEALTH EFFECTS SECTIONS. THEY ARE RANKED IN ORDER FROM MINIMUM TO MAXIMUM RESPIRATORY PROTECTION. THE SPECIFIC RESPIRATOR SELECTED MUST BE BASED ON CONTAMINATION LEVELS FOUND IN THE WORK PLACE, MUST NOT EXCEED THE WORKING LIMITS OF THE RESPIRATOR AND BE JOINTLY APPROVED BY THE NATIONAL INSTITUTE FOR OCCUPATIONAL SAFETY AND HEALTH AND THE MINE SAFETY AND HEALTH ADMINISTRATION (NIOSH-MSHA).
CHEMICAL CARTRIDGE RESPIRATOR WITH AN ORGANIC VAPOR CARTRIDGE(S) WITH A FULL FACEPIECE.
GAS MASK WITH ORGANIC VAPOR CANISTER (CHIN-STYLE OR FRONT- OR BACK-MOUNTED CANISTER) WITH A FULL FACEPIECE.
TYPE 'C' SUPPLIED-AIR RESPIRATOR WITH A FULL FACEPIECE OPERATED IN PRESSURE-DEMAND OR OTHER POSITIVE PRESSURE MODE OR WITH A FULL FACEPIECE, HELMET OR HOOD OPERATED IN CONTINUOUS-FLOW MODE.
SELF-CONTAINED BREATHING APPARATUS WITH A FULL FACEPIECE OPERATED IN PRESSURE-DEMAND OR OTHER POSITIVE PRESSURE MODE.
FOR FIREFIGHTING AND OTHER IMMEDIATELY DANGEROUS TO LIFE OR HEALTH CONDITIONS:
SELF-CONTAINED BREATHING APPARATUS WITH FULL FACEPIECE OPERATED IN PRESSURE-DEMAND OR OTHER POSITIVE PRESSURE MODE.
SUPPLIED-AIR RESPIRATOR WITH FULL FACEPIECE AND OPERATED IN PRESSURE-DEMAND OR OTHER POSITIVE PRESSURE MODE IN COMBINATION WITH AN AUXILIARY SELF-CONTAINED BREATHING APPARATUS OPERATED IN PRESSURE-DEMAND OR OTHER POSITIVE PRESSURE MODE.
CLOTHING: EMPLOYEE MUST WEAR APPROPRIATE PROTECTIVE (IMPERVIOUS) CLOTHING AND EQUIPMENT TO PREVENT REPEATED OR PROLONGED SKIN CONTACT WITH THIS SUBSTANCE.
GLOVES: EMPLOYEE MUST WEAR APPROPRIATE PROTECTIVE GLOVES TO PREVENT CONTACT WITH THIS SUBSTANCE.
EYE PROTECTION: EMPLOYEE MUST WEAR SPLASH-PROOF OR DUST-RESISTANT SAFETY GOGGLES TO PREVENT EYE CONTACT WITH THIS SUBSTANCE.
EMERGENCY EYE WASH: WHERE THERE IS ANY POSSIBILITY THAT AN EMPLOYEE'S EYES MAY BE EXPOSED TO THIS SUBSTANCE, THE EMPLOYER SHOULD PROVIDE AN EYE WASH FOUNTAIN WITHIN THE IMMEDIATE WORK AREA FOR EMERGENCY USE.

AUTHORIZED BY- OCCUPATIONAL HEALTH SERVICES, INC.
CREATION DATE: 10/04/89 ***REVISION DATE:*** 05/08/90

MATERIAL SAFETY DATA SHEET

OCCUPATIONAL HEALTH SERVICES, INC.
AGRICULTURE AND PESTICIDE DIVISION
450 SEVENTH AVENUE, SUITE 2407
NEW YORK, NEW YORK 10123
1-800-445-MSDS OR (212) 967-1100

EMERGENCY CONTACT:
JOHN S. BRANSFORD, JR. (615) 292-1180

SUBSTANCE IDENTIFICATION

CAS-NUMBER 608-73-1
SUBSTANCE: **1,2,3,4,5,6-HEXACHLOROCYCLOHEXANE**
TRADE NAMES/SYNONYMS: BENZENE HEXACHLORIDE; BHC; HCH; HEXACHLOROCYCLOHEXANE; ENT 8,601; CYCLOHEXANE, 1,2,3,4,5,6-HEXACHLORO-; HEXACHLOROBENZENE; C6H6CL6; PST03080
CHEMICAL FAMILY: HALOGEN COMPOUND, ALICYCLIC
MOLECULAR FORMULA: C6-H6-CL6
MOLECULAR WEIGHT: 290.83
CERCLA RATINGS (SCALE 0-3): HEALTH=3 FIRE=0 REACTIVITY=0 PERSISTENCE=3
NFPA RATINGS (SCALE 0-4): HEALTH=3 FIRE=0 REACTIVITY=0

COMPONENTS AND CONTAMINANTS

COMPONENT: 1,2,3,4,5,6-HEXACHLOROCYCLOHEXANE ***PERCENT:*** 100.0
CAS# 608-73-1

OTHER CONTAMINANTS: NONE

EXPOSURE LIMITS: NO OCCUPATIONAL EXPOSURE LIMITS ESTABLISHED BY OSHA, ACGIH, OR NIOSH.
1,2,3,4,5,6-HEXACHLOROCYCLOHEXANE: SUBJECT TO CALIFORNIA PROPOSITION 65 CANCER AND/OR REPRODUCTIVE TOXICITY WARNING AND RELEASE REQUIREMENTS (OCTOBER 1, 1987).

PHYSICAL DATA

DESCRIPTION: WHITE TO YELLOWISH POWDER OR FLAKES WITH A MUSTY ODOR.

MELTING POINT: NOT AVAILABLE ***SPECIFIC GRAVITY:*** 1.87

VAPOR PRESSURE: 0.03 MMHG @ 20 C ***SOLUBILITY IN WATER:*** 10-32 PPM

SOLVENT SOLUBILITY: SOLUBLE IN CHLOROFORM, ALCOHOL, ACETONE, ETHER, BENZENE, AND CHLORINATED HYDROCARBON SOLVENTS; MODERATELY SOLUBLE IN FATS AND OILS; SLIGHTLY SOLUBLE IN KEROSENE.

FIRE AND EXPLOSION DATA

FIRE AND EXPLOSION HAZARD: NEGLIGIBLE FIRE HAZARD WHEN EXPOSED TO HEAT OR FLAME.

FIREFIGHTING MEDIA: DRY CHEMICAL, CARBON DIOXIDE, HALON, WATER SPRAY OR STANDARD FOAM (1987 EMERGENCY RESPONSE GUIDEBOOK, DOT P 5800.4).
FOR LARGER FIRES, USE WATER SPRAY, FOG OR STANDARD FOAM (1987 EMERGENCY RESPONSE GUIDEBOOK, DOT P 5800.4).

FIREFIGHTING: MOVE CONTAINERS FROM FIRE AREA IF POSSIBLE. FIGHT FIRE FROM MAXIMUM DISTANCE. STAY AWAY FROM STORAGE TANK ENDS. DIKE FIRE CONTROL WATER FOR LATER DISPOSAL. DO NOT SCATTER MATERIAL (1987 EMERGENCY RESPONSE GUIDEBOOK, DOT P 5800.4, GUIDE PAGE 55).
USE AGENTS SUITABLE FOR TYPE OF FIRE. COOL CONTAINERS WITH FLOODING AMOUNTS OF WATER. AVOID BREATHING VAPORS OR DUSTS, KEEP UPWIND.

TOXICITY

1,2,3,4,5,6-HEXACHLOROCYCLOHEXANE: TOXICITY DATA: 400 UG/KG/3 DAYS INHALATION-MAN TCLO; 900 MG/KG SKIN-RAT LD50; 100 MG/KG ORAL-RAT LD50; 59 MG/KG ORAL-MOUSE LD50; 1400 MG/KG ORAL-GUINEA PIG LDLO; 75 MG/KG SUBCUTANEOUS-RABBIT LD50; MUTAGENIC DATA (RTECS); REPRODUCTIVE EFFECTS DATA (RTECS); TUMORIGENIC DATA (RTECS). CARCINOGEN STATUS: ANTICIPATED HUMAN CARCINOGEN (NTP); HUMAN INADEQUATE EVIDENCE, ANIMAL SUFFICIENT EVIDENCE (IARC GROUP-2B). TECHNICAL HEXACHLOROCYCLOHEXANE PRODUCED LIVER TUMORS AND LYMPHORETICULAR NEOPLASMS IN MICE BY ORAL ADMINISTRATION. HEXACHLOROCYCLOHEXANE INCREASED THE INCIDENCE OF LIVER NEOPLASMS IN RATS PREVIOUSLY EXPOSED TO N-NITROSODIETHYLAMINE. LOCAL EFFECTS: IRRITANT- EYE, SKIN, MUCOUS MEMBRANES. ACUTE TOXICITY: TOXIC BY DERMAL ABSORPTION AND INGESTION. TARGET EFFECTS: CONVULSANT. POISONING MAY AFFECT THE BLOOD AND LIVER. AT INCREASED RISK FROM EXPOSURE: PERSONS WITH LIVER AND BLOOD DISEASES. ADDITIONAL DATA: THIS MATERIAL MAY BE EXCRETED IN THE MILK OF LACTATING WOMEN. STIMULANTS SUCH AS EPINEPHRINE MAY INDUCE VENTRICULAR FIBRILLATION.

HEALTH EFFECTS AND FIRST AID

INHALATION: 1,2,3,4,5,6-HEXACHLOROCYCLOHEXANE: IRRITANT/CONVULSANT.
ACUTE EXPOSURE- THE VAPORS MAY CAUSE IRRITATION OF THE NOSE, THROAT, AND MUCOUS MEMBRANES. THIS MATERIAL MAY BE ABSORBED FROM THE LUNGS AND PRODUCE CENTRAL NERVOUS SYSTEM EFFECTS WITH SYMPTOMS OF MOTOR HYPEREXCITABILITY THAT MAY INCLUDE MUSCLE TWITCHING, MYOCLONIC JERKING, AND CONVULSIVE SEIZURES. THE CONVULSIONS MAY OCCUR WITH PERIODS OF UNCONSCIOUSNESS. OTHER SYMPTOMS MAY INCLUDE HEADACHE, NAUSEA, VOMITING, MALAISE, AND DIZZINESS. IN CASES OF GROSS OVEREXPOSURE, CONVULSIONS MAY OCCUR WITHOUT ANY PRIOR SYMPTOMS. ABNORMAL EEG PATTERNS MAY BE OBSERVED; THESE CHANGES IN EEG PATTERNS MAY PERSIST FOR WEEKS OR MONTHS WHILE NO OTHER OBSERVABLE SIGNS OF POISONING MAY EXIST. **CHRONIC EXPOSURE-** PROLONGED OR REPEATED EXPOSURE MAY CAUSE SYMPTOMS AS DESCRIBED IN ACUTE EXPOSURE. EXPOSURE TO 400 UG/KG/3 DAYS PRODUCED SYSTEMIC POISONING IN MAN. SYMPTOMS OF DEPRESSION, HEADACHE, VOMITING, ASTHENIA, EPILEPTIFORM ATTACKS, SLEEPLESSNESS, PROFUSE PERSPIRATION, VARIOUS ABNORMAL REFLEXES AND NEUROLOGICAL SIGNS WERE REPORTED IN ONE CASE OF OCCUPATIONAL EXPOSURE TO THE GAMMA ISOMER OF 1,2,3,4,5, 6-HEXACHLOROCYCLOHEXANE. SEVERAL INCIDENCES OF DIMINUTION OF VISION AND BLINDNESS HAVE ALSO BEEN REPORTED IN SOME CASES OF SYSTEMIC POISONING. REPORTS SUGGEST THAT 1,2,3,4,5,6-HEXACHLOROCYCLOHEXANE IS CAPABLE OF CAUSING BLOOD DYSCRASIAS, PRIMARILY APLASTIC ANEMIA; HOWEVER, THESE REPORTS HAVE NOT BEEN CONFIRMED.

FIRST AID- REMOVE FROM EXPOSURE AREA TO FRESH AIR IMMEDIATELY. IF BREATHING HAS STOPPED, PERFORM ARTIFICIAL RESPIRATION. KEEP PERSON WARM AND AT REST. TREAT SYMPTOMATICALLY AND SUPPORTIVELY. GET MEDICAL ATTENTION IMMEDIATELY.

SKIN CONTACT: 1,2,3,4,5,6-HEXACHLOROCYCLOHEXANE: IRRITANT/CONVULSANT/TOXIC. **ACUTE EXPOSURE-** MAY CAUSE IRRITATION. A LETHAL DOSE IN RATS BY DERMAL ABSORPTION WAS 900 MG/KG. THIS SUBSTANCE MAY BE ABSORBED THROUGH THE SKIN AND PRODUCE CENTRAL NERVOUS SYSTEM EFFECTS WITH SYMPTOMS OF MOTOR HYPEREXCITABILITY THAT MAY INCLUDE MUSCLE TWITCHING, MYOCLONIC JERKING, AND CONVULSIVE SEIZURES. THE CONVULSIONS MAY OCCUR WITH PERIODS OF UNCONSCIOUSNESS. OTHER SYMPTOMS MAY INCLUDE HEADACHE, NAUSEA, VOMITING, MALAISE, AND DIZZINESS. IN CASES OF GROSS OVEREXPOSURE, CONVULSIONS MAY OCCUR WITHOUT ANY PRIOR SYMPTOMS. ABNORMAL EEG PATTERNS MAY BE OBSERVED, THESE CHANGES IN EEG PATTERNS MAY PERSIST FOR WEEKS OR MONTHS WHILE NO OTHER OBSERVABLE SIGNS OF POISONING MAY EXIST. **CHRONIC EXPOSURE-** PROLONGED OR REPEATED EXPOSURE MAY CAUSE DERMATITIS AND URTICARIA. OTHER SYSTEMIC EFFECTS MAY OCCUR AS DETAILED IN ACUTE EXPOSURE AND CHRONIC INHALATION.

FIRST AID- REMOVE CONTAMINATED CLOTHING AND SHOES IMMEDIATELY. WASH AFFECTED AREA WITH SOAP OR MILD DETERGENT AND LARGE AMOUNTS OF WATER UNTIL NO EVIDENCE OF CHEMICAL REMAINS (APPROXIMATELY 15-20 MINUTES). GET MEDICAL ATTENTION IMMEDIATELY.

EYE CONTACT: 1,2,3,4,5,6-HEXACHLOROCYCLOHEXANE: IRRITANT. **ACUTE EXPOSURE-** MAY CAUSE IRRITATION. **CHRONIC EXPOSURE-** PROLONGED OR REPEATED EXPOSURE MAY CAUSE CONJUNCTIVITIS.

FIRST AID- WASH EYES IMMEDIATELY WITH LARGE AMOUNTS OF WATER OR NORMAL SALINE, OCCASIONALLY LIFTING UPPER AND LOWER LIDS, UNTIL NO EVIDENCE OF CHEMICAL REMAINS (APPROXIMATELY 15-20 MINUTES). GET MEDICAL ATTENTION IMMEDIATELY.

INGESTION: 1,2,3,4,5,6-HEXACHLOROCYCLOHEXANE: CONVULSANT/CARCINOGEN/TOXIC. **ACUTE EXPOSURE-** A LETHAL DOSE IN RATS WAS 100 MG/KG. SYMPTOMS OF MALAISE, FAINTNESS, DIZZINESS, NAUSEA, VOMITING, MUSCLE SPASMS, ATAXIA, RESTLESSNESS, TREMOR, CYANOSIS, AND FACIAL PALLOR WERE REPORTED IN CASES OF ACCIDENTAL POISONING. CLONIC AND TONIC CONVULSIONS ALONG WITH UNCONSCIOUSNESS WERE ALSO CHARACTERISTIC SYMPTOMS OF POISONING. POSTICAL COMA OF VARIABLE DURATION LEADING TO RESPIRATORY FAILURE OCCURRED IN FATAL CASES. IN SOME CASES, RETROGRADE AMNESIA WAS REPORTED. **CHRONIC EXPOSURE-** REPRODUCTIVE EFFECTS HAVE BEEN REPORTED IN ANIMALS. LIVER TUMORS AND LYMPHORETICULAR NEOPLASMS WERE OBSERVED IN MICE CHRONICALLY FED 1,2,3,4,5,6-HEXACHLOROCYCLOHEXANE.

FIRST AID- IF THE PERSON IS CONSCIOUS AND NOT CONVULSING, REMOVE BY GIVING SYRUP OF IPECAC (IF VOMITING OCCURS, KEEP THE HEAD BELOW THE HIPS TO PREVENT ASPIRATION). GIVE ACTIVATED CHARCOAL FOLLOWED BY GASTRIC LAVAGE. FOLLOW WITH A SALINE CATHARTIC. DO NOT GIVE FATS OR OILS. INTESTINAL LAVAGE WITH 20% MANNITOL (200 ML) BY STOMACH TUBE IS ALSO USEFUL. GIVE ARTIFICIAL RESPIRATION WITH OXYGEN IF RESPIRATION IS DEPRESSED (DREISBACH, HANDBOOK OF POISONING, 12TH ED.). TREAT SYMPTOMATICALLY AND SUPPORTIVELY. LAVAGE AND ADMINISTRATION OF OXYGEN SHOULD BE PERFORMED BY QUALIFIED MEDICAL PERSONNEL. GET MEDICAL ATTENTION IMMEDIATELY.

REACTIVITY

REACTIVITY: STABLE UNDER NORMAL TEMPERATURES AND PRESSURES.

INCOMPATIBILITIES: 1,2,3,4,5,6-HEXACHLOROCYCLOHEXANE: ALKALIES- MAY DECOMPOSE. ALUMINUM: MAY DECOMPOSE. N,N-DIMETHYLACETAMIDE: EXOTHERMIC, POSSIBLE VIOLENT REACTION. DIMETHYLFORMAMIDE: POSSIBLE DANGEROUS REACTION. IRON: MAY DECOMPOSE. ZINC: MAY DECOMPOSE.

DECOMPOSITION: THERMAL DECOMPOSITION PRODUCTS MAY INCLUDE HIGHLY TOXIC FUMES OF PHOSGENE, TOXIC AND CORROSIVE FUMES OF CHLORIDES, AND OXIDES OF CARBON.

POLYMERIZATION: HAZARDOUS POLYMERIZATION HAS NOT BEEN REPORTED TO OCCUR UNDER NORMAL TEMPERATURES AND PRESSURES.

STORAGE AND DISPOSAL

OBSERVE ALL FEDERAL, STATE AND LOCAL REGULATIONS WHEN STORING OR DISPOSING OF THIS SUBSTANCE. FOR ASSISTANCE, CONTACT THE DISTRICT DIRECTOR OF THE ENVIRONMENTAL PROTECTION AGENCY.

****STORAGE****

STORE IN ACCORDANCE WITH 40 CFR 165 RECOMMENDED PROCEDURES FOR THE DISPOSAL AND STORAGE OF PESTICIDES AND PESTICIDE CONTAINERS.
STORE AWAY FROM INCOMPATIBLE SUBSTANCES.

****DISPOSAL****

DISPOSAL MUST BE IN ACCORDANCE WITH 40 CFR 165 RECOMMENDED PROCEDURES FOR THE DISPOSAL AND STORAGE OF PESTICIDES AND PESTICIDE CONTAINERS.

CONDITIONS TO AVOID

MAY BURN BUT DOES NOT IGNITE READILY. CONTAINERS MAY EXPLODE IN HEAT OF FIRE.

SPILL AND LEAK PROCEDURES

WATER SPILL: THE CALIFORNIA SAFE DRINKING WATER AND TOXIC ENFORCEMENT ACT OF 1986 (PROPOSITION 65) PROHIBITS CONTAMINATING ANY KNOWN SOURCE OF DRINKING WATER WITH SUBSTANCES KNOWN TO CAUSE CANCER AND/OR REPRODUCTIVE TOXICITY.

OCCUPATIONAL SPILL: DO NOT TOUCH SPILLED MATERIAL. STOP LEAK IF YOU CAN DO IT WITHOUT RISK. USE WATER SPRAY TO REDUCE VAPORS. FOR SMALL SPILLS, TAKE UP WITH SAND OR OTHER ABSORBENT MATERIAL AND PLACE INTO CONTAINERS FOR LATER DISPOSAL. FOR SMALL DRY SPILLS, WITH A CLEAN SHOVEL PLACE MATERIAL INTO CLEAN, DRY CONTAINERS AND COVER. MOVE CONTAINERS FROM SPILL AREA. FOR LARGER SPILLS, DIKE FAR AHEAD OF SPILL FOR LATER DISPOSAL. KEEP UNNECESSARY PEOPLE AWAY. ISOLATE HAZARD AREA AND DENY ENTRY. VENTILATE CLOSED SPACES BEFORE ENTERING.

PROTECTIVE EQUIPMENT

VENTILATION: PROVIDE LOCAL EXHAUST OR PROCESS ENCLOSURE VENTILATION SYSTEM.

RESPIRATOR: THE FOLLOWING RESPIRATORS ARE RECOMMENDED BASED ON INFORMATION FOUND IN THE PHYSICAL DATA, TOXICITY AND HEALTH EFFECTS SECTIONS. THEY ARE RANKED IN ORDER FROM MINIMUM TO MAXIMUM RESPIRATORY PROTECTION. THE SPECIFIC RESPIRATOR SELECTED MUST BE BASED ON CONTAMINATION LEVELS FOUND IN THE WORK PLACE, MUST NOT EXCEED THE WORKING LIMITS OF THE RESPIRATOR AND BE JOINTLY APPROVED BY THE NATIONAL INSTITUTE FOR OCCUPATIONAL SAFETY AND HEALTH AND THE MINE SAFETY AND HEALTH ADMINISTRATION (NIOSH-MSHA).

TYPE 'C' SUPPLIED-AIR RESPIRATOR WITH A FULL FACEPIECE OPERATED IN PRESSURE-DEMAND OR OTHER POSITIVE PRESSURE MODE OR WITH A FULL FACEPIECE, HELMET OR HOOD OPERATED IN CONTINOUS-FLOW MODE.

SELF-CONTAINED BREATHING APPARATUS WITH A FULL FACEPIECE OPERATED IN PRESSURE-DEMAND OR OTHER POSITIVE PRESSURE MODE.

FOR FIREFIGHTING AND OTHER IMMEDIATELY DANGEROUS TO LIFE OR HEALTH CONDITIONS:

SELF-CONTAINED BREATHING APPARATUS WITH FULL FACEPIECE OPERATED IN PRESSURE-DEMAND OR OTHER POSITIVE PRESSURE MODE.

SUPPLIED-AIR RESPIRATOR WITH FULL FACEPIECE AND OPERATED IN PRESSURE-DEMAND OR OTHER POSITIVE PRESSURE MODE IN COMBINATION WITH AN AUXILIARY SELF-CONTAINED BREATHING APPARATUS OPERATED IN PRESSURE-DEMAND OR OTHER POSITIVE PRESSURE MODE.

CLOTHING: EMPLOYEE MUST WEAR APPROPRIATE PROTECTIVE (IMPERVIOUS) CLOTHING AND EQUIPMENT TO PREVENT ANY POSSIBILITY OF SKIN CONTACT WITH THIS SUBSTANCE.

GLOVES: EMPLOYEE MUST WEAR APPROPRIATE PROTECTIVE GLOVES TO PREVENT CONTACT WITH THIS SUBSTANCE.

EYE PROTECTION: EMPLOYEE MUST WEAR SPLASH-PROOF OR DUST-RESISTANT SAFETY GOGGLES WITH OR WITHOUT A FACESHIELD TO PREVENT CONTACT WITH THIS SUBSTANCE.

EMERGENCY EYE WASH: WHERE THERE IS ANY POSSIBILITY THAT AN EMPLOYEE'S EYES MAY BE EXPOSED TO THIS SUBSTANCE, THE EMPLOYER SHOULD PROVIDE AN EYE WASH FOUNTAIN WITHIN THE IMMEDIATE WORK AREA FOR EMERGENCY USE.

AUTHORIZED BY- OCCUPATIONAL HEALTH SERVICES, INC.
CREATION DATE: 10/05/89 ***REVISION DATE:*** 07/12/90

MATERIAL SAFETY DATA SHEET

OCCUPATIONAL HEALTH SERVICES, INC.
AGRICULTURE AND PESTICIDE DIVISION
450 SEVENTH AVENUE, SUITE 2407
NEW YORK, NEW YORK 10123
1-800-445-MSDS OR (212) 967-1100

EMERGENCY CONTACT:
JOHN S. BRANSFORD, JR. (615) 292-1180

SUBSTANCE IDENTIFICATION

CAS-NUMBER 141-66-2

SUBSTANCE: DICROTOPHOS

TRADE NAMES/SYNONYMS: PHOSPHORIC ACID, 3-(DIMETHYLAMINO)-1-METHYL-3-OXO-1-PROPENYL DIMETHYL ESTER, (E)-; PHOSPHORIC ACID, DIMETHYL ESTER, ESTER WITH 3-HYDROXY-N,N -DIMETHYLCROTONAMIDE, (E)-; (E)-2-DIMETHYLCARBAMOYL-1-METHYLVINYL DIMETHYL PHOSPHATE; 3-DIMETHOXYPHOSPHINOYLOXY-N,N-DIMETHYLISOCROTONAMIDE; 3-DIMETHOXYPHOSPHINYLOXY-N,N-DIMETHYLISOCROTONAMIDE; (E)-3-(DIMETHYLAMINO)-1-METHYL-3-OXO-1-PROPENYL DIMETHYL PHOSPHATE; DIMETHYL PHOSPHATE ESTER WITH (E)-3-HYDROXY-N,N-DIMETHYLCROTONAMIDE; 2-DIMETHYL CIS-2-DIMETHYL-CARBAMOYL-1-METHYLVINYL PHOSPHATE; 3-(DIMETHOXYPHOSPHINYLOXY)-N,N-DIMETHYL-CIS-CROTONAMIDE; BIDRIN; CARBICRON; EKTAFOS; C 709; DIAPADRIN; SD 3562; ENT 24,482; PST03090

CHEMICAL FAMILY: ORGANOPHOSPHATE

MOLECULAR FORMULA: C8-H16-N-O5-P

MOLECULAR WEIGHT: 237.21

CERCLA RATINGS (SCALE 0-3): HEALTH=3 FIRE=1 REACTIVITY=0 PERSISTENCE=0

NFPA RATINGS (SCALE 0-4): HEALTH=4 FIRE=1 REACTIVITY=0

COMPONENTS AND CONTAMINANTS

COMPONENT: DICROTOPHOS ***PERCENT:*** 100
CAS# 141-66-2

EXPOSURE LIMITS: DICROTOPHOS: 0.25 MG/M3 OSHA TWA (SKIN) 0.25 MG/M3 ACGIH TWA (SKIN)
100 POUNDS SARA SECTION 302 THRESHOLD PLANNING QUANTITY 1 POUND SARA SECTION 304 REPORTABLE QUANTITY

PHYSICAL DATA

DESCRIPTION: YELLOWISH LIQUID; COMMERCIAL GRADE IS BROWN WITH A MILD ESTER ODOR

BOILING POINT: 266 F (130 C) @ 0.1 MMHG ***SPECIFIC GRAVITY:*** 1.216

SOLUBILITY IN WATER: MISCIBLE

SOLVENT SOLUBILITY: SOLUBLE IN ACETONE, ALCOHOL, ISOBUTANOL, HEXYLENE GLYCOL, XYLENE, DIACETONE; SLIGHTLY SOLUBLE IN KEROSENE AND DIESEL FUEL

FIRE AND EXPLOSION DATA

FIRE AND EXPLOSION HAZARD: SLIGHT FIRE HAZARD WHEN EXPOSED TO HEAT OR FLAME.

FLASH POINT: >200 F (93 C) ***FLAMMABILITY CLASS(OSHA):*** IIIB

FIREFIGHTING MEDIA: DRY CHEMICAL, CARBON DIOXIDE, HALON, WATER SPRAY OR STANDARD FOAM (1987 EMERGENCY RESPONSE GUIDEBOOK, DOT P 5800.4). FOR LARGER FIRES, USE WATER SPRAY, FOG OR STANDARD FOAM (1987 EMERGENCY RESPONSE GUIDEBOOK, DOT P 5800.4).

FIREFIGHTING: MOVE CONTAINERS FROM FIRE AREA IF POSSIBLE. FIGHT FIRE FROM MAXIMUM DISTANCE. STAY AWAY FROM STORAGE TANK ENDS. DIKE FIRE CONTROL WATER FOR LATER DISPOSAL. DO NOT SCATTER MATERIAL (1987 EMERGENCY RESPONSE GUIDEBOOK, DOT P 5800.4, GUIDE PAGE 55). EXTINGUISH ONLY IF FLOW CAN BE STOPPED; USE FLOODING AMOUNTS OF WATER AS FOG, SOLID STREAMS MAY BE INEFFECTIVE. COOL CONTAINERS WITH FLOODING AMOUNTS OF WATER FROM AS FAR A DISTANCE AS POSSIBLE. USE WATER SPRAY TO ABSORB TOXIC VAPORS. AVOID BREATHING TOXIC VAPORS; KEEP UPWIND. CONSIDER EVACUATION OF DOWNWIND AREA IF MATERIAL IS LEAKING.

TRANSPORTATION DATA

DEPARTMENT OF TRANSPORTATION HAZARD CLASSIFICATION 49 CFR 172.101: POISON B

DEPARTMENT OF TRANSPORTATION LABELING REQUIREMENTS 49 CFR 172.101 AND SUBPART E: POISON

DEPARTMENT OF TRANSPORTATION PACKAGING REQUIREMENTS: 49 CFR 173.346 EXCEPTIONS: 49 CFR 173.345

TOXICITY

DICROTOPHOS: TOXICITY DATA: 90 MG/M3/4 HOURS INHALATION-RAT LC50; 168 MG/KG SKIN-RABBIT LD50; 42 MG/KG SKIN-RAT LD50; 13 MG/KG ORAL-RAT LD50; 11 MG/KG ORAL-MOUSE LD50; 8137 UG/KG SUBCUTANEOUS-RAT LD50; 11,500 UG/KG SUBCUTANEOUS-MOUSE LD50; 9900 UG/KG INTRAVENOUS-MOUSE LD50; 9500 UG/KG INTRAPERITONEAL-MOUSE LD50; 22 MG/KG UNREPORTED-RAT LD50; MUTAGENIC DATA (RTECS). CARCINOGEN STATUS: NONE. ACUTE TOXICITY LEVEL: HIGHLY TOXIC BY INHALATION, DERMAL ABSORPTION, AND INGESTION. TARGET EFFECTS: CHOLINESTERASE INHIBITOR. AT INCREASED RISK FROM EXPOSURE: PERSONS WITH RESPIRATORY AILMENTS, RECENT EXPOSURE TO CHOLINESTERASE INHIBITORS OR IMPAIRED CHOLINESTERASE PRODUCTION, OR LIVER MALFUNCTION.* ADDITIONAL DATA: MAY CROSS THE PLACENTA. HIGH ENVIRONMENTAL TEMPERATURES OR EXPOSURE OF THE CHEMICAL TO VISIBLE OR ULTRAVIOLET LIGHT MAY ENHANCE THE TOXICITY. INTERACTIONS WITH MEDICATIONS MAY OCCUR.*

* MAY BE BASED ON GENERAL INFORMATION ON ORGANOPHOSPHATES.

HEALTH EFFECTS AND FIRST AID

INHALATION: DICROTOPHOS: HIGHLY TOXIC. SEE INFORMATION ON ORGANOPHOSPHATES.

ORGANOPHOSPHATES: CHOLINESTERASE INHIBITOR. **ACUTE EXPOSURE-** WHEN INHALED, THE FIRST EFFECTS OF CHOLINESTERASE INHIBITORS ARE USUALLY RESPIRATORY AND MAY INCLUDE NASAL HYPEREMIA AND WATERY DISCHARGE, COUGH, CHEST DISCOMFORT, DYSPNEA, AND WHEEZING DUE TO INCREASED BRONCHIAL SECRETIONS AND BRONCHOCONSTRICTION. IF SUFFICIENT AMOUNTS ARE ABSORBED, OTHER SYSTEMIC EFFECTS MAY BEGIN WITHIN A FEW MINUTES OR BE DELAYED FOR UP TO 12 HOURS. SYMPTOMS MAY INCLUDE PALLOR, NAUSEA, VOMITING, DIARRHEA, ABDOMINAL CRAMPS, HEADACHE, DIZZINESS, OCULAR PAIN, BLURRED VISION, MIOSIS OR IN SOME CASES, ESPECIALLY INITIALLY, MYDRIASIS, LACRIMATION, SALIVATION, SWEATING, AND CONFUSION. OTHER REPORTED CENTRAL NERVOUS SYSTEM OR NEUROMUSCULAR EFFECTS MAY INCLUDE ATAXIA, SLURRED SPEECH, AREFLEXIA, WEAKNESS, FATIGUE, FASCICULATIONS, TWITCHING, TREMORS POSSIBLY OF THE TONGUE AND EYELIDS, AND EVENTUALLY PARALYSIS OF THE EXTREMITIES AND POSSIBLY OF THE RESPIRATORY MUSCLES. IN SEVERE CASES THERE MAY ALSO BE INVOLUNTARY DEFECATION AND URINATION, CYANOSIS, PSYCHOSIS, HYPERGLYCEMIA, ACUTE PANCREATITIS, CARDIAC IRREGULARITIES, PULMONARY EDEMA, UNCONSCIOUSNESS, CONVULSIONS, AND COMA. DEATH IS PRIMARILY DUE TO RESPIRATORY FAILURE, ALTHOUGH CARDIOVASCULAR EFFECTS INCLUDING CARDIAC ARREST MAY ALSO BE IMPLICATED. LONG TERM SEQUELAE ARE RARE BUT MAY INCLUDE NEUROPSYCHIATRIC DISORDERS AND MYOPATHY WITH MUSCLE TENDERNESS. **CHRONIC EXPOSURE-** REPEATED OR PROLONGED EXPOSURE MAY RESULT IN THE EFFECTS OF ACUTE EXPOSURE. OTHER EFFECTS REPORTED IN WORKERS REPEATEDLY EXPOSED INCLUDE IMPAIRED MEMORY AND CONCENTRATION, ACUTE PSYCHOSIS, SEVERE DEPRESSIONS, IRRITABILTY, CONFUSION, APATHY, EMOTIONAL LABILITY, SOCIAL WITHDRAWAL, CONFUSION, HEADACHE, SPEECH DIFFICULTIES, DELAYED REACTION TIMES, SPATIAL DISORIENTATION, NIGHTMARES, SLEEPWALKING, AND DROWSINESS OR INSOMNIA. AN INFLUENZA-LIKE CONDITION WITH HEADACHE, NAUSEA, WEAKNESS, ANOREXIA AND MALAISE HAS ALSO BEEN REPORTED.

FIRST AID- REMOVE FROM EXPOSURE AREA TO FRESH AIR IMMEDIATELY. IF BREATHING HAS STOPPED, GIVE ARTIFICIAL RESPIRATION. MAINTAIN AIRWAY AND BLOOD PRESSURE AND ADMINISTER OXYGEN IF AVAILABLE. KEEP AFFECTED PERSON WARM AND AT REST. TREAT SYMPTOMATICALLY AND SUPPORTIVELY. ADMINISTRATION OF OXYGEN SHOULD BE PERFORMED BY QUALIFIED PERSONNEL. GET MEDICAL ATTENTION IMMEDIATELY.

SKIN CONTACT: DICROTOPHOS: HIGHLY TOXIC. SEE INFORMATION ON ORGANOPHOSPHATES.

ORGANOPHOSPHATES: CHOLINESTERASE INHIBITOR. **ACUTE EXPOSURE-** LOCALIZED SWEATING AND FASCICULATIONS MAY OCCUR AT THE SITE OF CONTACT. IF SUFFICIENT AMOUNTS ARE ABSORBED, OTHER EFFECTS OF CHOLINESTERASE INHIBITION AS DESCRIBED IN ACUTE INHALATION MAY OCCUR. SYMPTOMS MAY BE DELAYED 2-3 HOURS, BUT USUALLY NO MORE THAN 12 HOURS. THE RATE OF ABSORPTION IS INCREASED BY THE PRESENCE OF DERMATITIS OR HIGH AMBIENT TEMPERATURES. **CHRONIC EXPOSURE-** REPEATED OR PROLONGED EXPOSURE MAY CAUSE EFFECTS AS DESCRIBED IN ACUTE EXPOSURE. SOME ORGANOPHOSPHATES MAY CAUSE SENSITIZATION.

FIRST AID- REMOVE CONTAMINATED CLOTHING IMMEDIATELY. WASH CONTAMINATED AREAS WITH SOAP AND WATER FOLLOWED BY ALCOHOL (ARENA, POISONING, 4TH ED.). EMERGENCY PERSONNEL SHOULD WEAR GLOVES AND AVOID CONTAMINATION. TREAT RESPIRATORY DIFFICULTY WITH ARTIFICIAL RESPIRATION. GET MEDICAL ATTENTION IMMEDIATELY.

EYE CONTACT: DICROTOPHOS: SEE INFORMATION ON ORGANOPHOSPHATES.

ORGANOPHOSPHATES: CHOLINESTERASE INHIBITOR. **ACUTE EXPOSURE-** DIRECT CONTACT MAY CAUSE PAIN, HYPEREMIA, LACRIMATION, TWITCHING OF THE EYELIDS, MIOSIS, AND CILIARY MUSCLE SPASM WITH LOSS OF ACCOMODATION, BLURRED OR DIMMED VISION AND BROWACHE. SOMETIMES MYDRIASIS MAY OCCUR INSTEAD OF MIOSIS. WITH SUFFICIENT EXPOSURE, OTHER SYMPTOMS OF CHOLINESTERASE INHIBITION AS DESCRIBED IN ACUTE INHALATION MAY OCCUR. **CHRONIC EXPOSURE-** REPEATED OR PROLONGED EXPOSURE MAY CAUSE EFFECTS AS DESCRIBED IN ACUTE EXPOSURE. SOME COMPOUNDS HAVE CAUSED TOXIC EFFECTS ON THE CRYSTALLINE LENS, CONJUNCTIVAL THICKENING AND OBSTRUCTION OF THE NASOLACRIMAL CANALS WHEN USED AS MIOTIC EYEDROPS.

FIRST AID- IRRIGATE EYES WITH WATER OR SALINE SOLUTION. IF SYMPTOMS OF POISONING OCCUR, TREAT RESPIRATORY DIFFICULTY WITH ARTIFICIAL RESPIRATION AND OXYGEN. OBSERVE PATIENT FOR AT LEAST 24-36 HOURS (GOSSELIN, CLINICAL TOXICOLOGY OF COMMERCIAL PRODUCTS, 5TH ED.). GET MEDICAL ATTENTION IMMEDIATELY. OXYGEN SHOULD BE ADMINISTERED BY QUALIFIED MEDICAL PERSONNEL.

INGESTION: DICROTOPHOS: HIGHLY TOXIC. DICROTOPHOS DID NOT CAUSE DEMYELINIZATION BY THE STANDARD CHICKEN TEST. SEE INFORMATION ON ORGANOPHOSPHATES.

ORGANOPHOSPHATES: CHOLINESTERASE INHIBITOR. **ACUTE EXPOSURE-** WHEN INGESTED, THE FIRST EFFECTS MAY BE NAUSEA, VOMITING, ANOREXIA, ABDOMINAL CRAMPS AND DIARRHEA. GASTROINTESTINAL ABSORPTION MAY CAUSE THE SYMPTOMS OF CHOLINESTERASE INHIBITION AS DESCRIBED IN ACUTE INHALATION. SYMPTOMS MAY BEGIN WITHIN MINUTES OR BE DELAYED. **CHRONIC EXPOSURE-** REPEATED INGESTION MAY CAUSE EFFECTS AS DESCRIBED IN ACUTE EXPOSURE.

FIRST AID- IF PERSON IS ALERT AND RESPIRATION IS NOT DEPRESSED, GIVE SYRUP OF IPECAC FOLLOWED BY WATER (IF VOMITING OCCURS, KEEP HEAD BELOW HIPS TO PREVENT ASPIRATION). IF CONSCIOUSNESS LEVEL DECLINES OR VOMITING HAS NOT OCCURRED IN 15 MINUTES EMPTY STOMACH BY GASTRIC LAVAGE WITH THE AID OF CUFFED ENDOTRACHEAL TUBE USING ISOTONIC SALINE OR 5% SODIUM BICARBONATE FOLLOW WITH ACTIVATED CHARCOAL. ESTABLISH AND MAINTAIN AIRWAY. TREAT RESPIRATORY DIFFICULTY WITH ARTIFICIAL RESPIRATION AND OXYGEN. DO NOT GIVE MORPHINE, AMINOPHYLLINE, PHENOTHIAZINES, RESERPINE, FUROSEMIDE, OR ETHACRYNIC ACID (MORGAN, RECOGNITION AND MANAGEMENT OF PESTICIDE POISONINGS, 3RD ED.). TREAT SYMPTOMATICALLY AND SUPPORTIVELY. ADMINISTRATION OF OXYGEN AND LAVAGE MUST BE PERFORMED BY QUALIFIED MEDICAL PERSONNEL. GET MEDICAL ATTENTION IMMEDIATELY.

ANTIDOTE: THE FOLLOWING ANTIDOTE(S) HAVE BEEN RECOMMENDED. HOWEVER, THE DECISION AS TO WHETHER THE SEVERITY OF POISONING REQUIRES ADMINISTRATION OF ANY ANTIDOTE AND ACTUAL DOSE REQUIRED SHOULD BE MADE BY QUALIFIED MEDICAL PERSONNEL.

FOR CHOLINESTERASE INHIBITORS: ESTABLISH CLEAR AIRWAY AND TISSUE OXYGENATION BY ASPIRATION OF SECRETIONS, AND IF NECESSARY, BY ASSISTED PULMONARY VENTILATION WITH OXYGEN. IMPROVE TISSUE OXYGENATION AS MUCH AS POSSIBLE BEFORE ADMINISTERING ATROPINE TO MINIMIZE THE RISK OF VENTRICULAR FIBRILLATION. ADMINISTER ATROPINE SULFATE INTRAVENOUSLY, OR INTRAMUSCULARLY IF IV INJECTION IS NOT POSSIBLE. IN MODERATELY SEVERE POISONING ADMINISTER ATROPINE SULFATE, 0.4-2.0 MG REPEATED EVERY 15 MINUTES UNTIL ATROPINIZATION IS ACHIEVED (TACHYCARDIA, FLUSHING, DRY MOUTH, MYDRIASIS). MAINTAIN ATROPINIZATION BY REPEATED DOSES FOR 2-12 HOURS, OR LONGER, DEPENDING ON THE SEVERITY OF POISONING. THE APPEARANCE OF RALES IN THE LUNG BASES, MIOSIS, SALIVATION, NAUSEA, BRADYCARDIA, ARE ALL INDICATIONS OF INADEQUATE ATROPINIZATION. SEVERELY POISONED INDIVIDUALS MAY EXHIBIT REMARKABLE TOLERANCE TO ATROPINE; TWO OR MORE TIMES THE DOSAGES SUGGESTED ABOVE MAY BE NEEDED. PERSONS NOT POISONED OR ONLY SLIGHTLY POISONED, HOWEVER, MAY DEVELOP SIGNS OF ATROPINE TOXICITY FROM SUCH LARGE DOSAGES: FEVER, MUSCLE FIBRILLATIONS, AND DELIRIUM ARE THE MAIN SIGNS OF ATROPINE TOXICITY. IF THESE SIGNS APPEAR WHILE THE PATIENT IS FULLY ATROPINIZED, ATROPINE ADMINISTRATION SHOULD BE DISCONTINUED, AT LEAST TEMPORARILY. OBSERVE TREATED PATIENTS CLOSELY AT LEAST 24 HOURS TO INSURE THAT SYMPTOMS (POSSIBLY PULMONARY EDEMA) DO NOT RECUR AS ATROPINIZATION WEARS OFF. IN VERY SEVERE POISONINGS, METABOLIC DISPOSITION OF TOXICANT MAY REQUIRE SEVERAL HOURS OR DAYS DURING WHICH ATROPINIZATION MUST BE MAINTAINED. MARKEDLY LOWER LEVELS OF URINARY METABOLITES INDICATE THAT ATROPINE DOSAGE CAN BE TAPERED OFF. AS DOSAGE IS REDUCED, CHECK THE LUNG BASES FREQUENTLY FOR RALES. IF RALES ARE HEARD OR OTHER SYMPTOMS RETURN, RE-ESTABLISH ATROPINIZATION PROMPTLY (MORGAN, RECOGNITION AND MANAGEMENT OF PESTICIDE POISONINGS, 3RD ED.). ADMINISTRATION OF ANTIDOTE MUST BE PERFORMED BY QUALIFIED MEDICAL PERSONNEL.

IN CASES OF SEVERE POISONING BY ORGANOPHOSPHATE PESTICIDES IN WHICH RESPIRATORY DEPRESSION, MUSCLE WEAKNESS AND TWITCHINGS ARE SEVERE, GIVE PRALIDOXIME (PROTOPAM-AYERST, 2-PAM), 1.0 GRAM INTRAVENOUSLY AT NO MORE THAN 0.5 GRAM PER MINUTE. DOSAGE OF PRALIDOXIME MAY BE REPEATED IN 1-2 HOURS, THEN AT 10-12 HOUR INTERVALS IF NEEDED. IN VERY SEVERE POISONINGS, DOSAGE RATES MAY BE DOUBLED. TREATMENT WITH PRALIDOXIME WILL BE MOST EFFECTIVE IF GIVEN WITHIN THIRTY-SIX HOURS AFTER POISONING (MORGAN, RECOGNITION AND MANAGEMENT OF PESTICIDE POISONINGS, 3RD ED.). ANTIDOTE SHOULD BE ADMINISTERED BY QUALIFIED MEDICAL PERSONNEL.

REACTIVITY

REACTIVITY: STABLE WHEN STORED IN GLASS OR POLYTHENE CONTAINERS $<$ 104 F (40 C), BUT IS DECOMPOSED AFTER PROLONGED STORAGE AT 131 F (55 C).

INCOMPATIBILITIES: DICROTOPHOS: CAST IRON: CORROSIVE. MILD STEEL: CORROSIVE. BRASS: CORROSIVE. STAINLESS STEEL: SOME GRADES MAY CORRODE.

DECOMPOSITION: THERMAL DECOMPOSITION MAY RELEASE TOXIC AND/OR HAZARDOUS GASES.

POLYMERIZATION: HAZARDOUS POLYMERIZATION HAS NOT BEEN REPORTED TO OCCUR UNDER NORMAL TEMPERATURES AND PRESSURES.

STORAGE AND DISPOSAL

OBSERVE ALL FEDERAL, STATE AND LOCAL REGULATIONS WHEN STORING OR DISPOSING OF THIS SUBSTANCE. FOR ASSISTANCE, CONTACT THE DISTRICT DIRECTOR OF THE ENVIRONMENTAL PROTECTION AGENCY.

STORAGE

STORE IN ACCORDANCE WITH 40 CFR 165 RECOMMENDED PROCEDURES FOR THE DISPOSAL AND STORAGE OF PESTICIDES AND PESTICIDE CONTAINERS.
STORE AWAY FROM INCOMPATIBLE SUBSTANCES.
THRESHOLD PLANNING QUANTITY (TPQ): THE SUPERFUND AMENDMENTS AND REAUTHORIZATION ACT (SARA) SECTION 302 REQUIRES THAT EACH FACILITY WHERE ANY EXTREMELY HAZARDOUS SUBSTANCE IS PRESENT IN A QUANTITY EQUAL TO OR GREATER THAN THE TPQ ESTABLISHED FOR THAT SUBSTANCE NOTIFY THE STATE EMERGENCY RESPONSE COMMISSION FOR THE STATE IN WHICH IT IS LOCATED. SECTION 303 OF SARA REQUIRES THESE FACILITIES TO PARTICIPATE IN LOCAL EMERGENCY RESPONSE PLANNING (40 CFR 355.30).

DISPOSAL

DISPOSAL MUST BE IN ACCORDANCE WITH 40 CFR 165 RECOMMENDED PROCEDURES FOR THE DISPOSAL AND STORAGE OF PESTICIDES AND PESTICIDE CONTAINERS.

CONDITIONS TO AVOID

KEEP AWAY FROM HEAT AND OPEN FLAME.

SPILL AND LEAK PROCEDURES

OCCUPATIONAL SPILL: DO NOT TOUCH SPILLED MATERIAL. STOP LEAK IF YOU CAN DO IT WITHOUT RISK. USE WATER SPRAY TO REDUCE VAPORS. FOR SMALL SPILLS, TAKE UP WITH SAND OR OTHER ABSORBENT MATERIAL AND PLACE INTO CONTAINERS FOR LATER DISPOSAL. FOR SMALL DRY SPILLS, WITH A CLEAN SHOVEL PLACE MATERIAL INTO CLEAN, DRY CONTAINERS AND COVER. MOVE CONTAINERS FROM SPILL AREA. FOR LARGER SPILLS, DIKE FAR AHEAD OF SPILL FOR LATER DISPOSAL. KEEP UNNECESSARY PEOPLE AWAY. ISOLATE HAZARD AREA AND DENY ENTRY. VENTILATE CLOSED SPACES BEFORE ENTERING.
REPORTABLE QUANTITY (RQ): 1 POUND THE SUPERFUND AMENDMENTS AND REAUTHORIZATION ACT (SARA) SECTION 304 REQUIRES THAT A RELEASE EQUAL TO OR GREATER THAN THE REPORTABLE QUANTITY FOR THIS SUBSTANCE BE IMMEDIATELY REPORTED TO THE LOCAL EMERGENCY PLANNING COMMITTEE AND THE STATE EMERGENCY RESPONSE COMMISSION (40 CFR 355.40). IF THE RELEASE OF THIS SUBSTANCE IS REPORTABLE UNDER CERCLA SECTION 103, THE NATIONAL RESPONSE CENTER MUST BE NOTIFIED IMMEDIATELY AT (800) 424-8802 OR (202) 426-2675 IN THE METROPOLITAN WASHINGTON, D.C. AREA (40 CFR 302.6).

PROTECTIVE EQUIPMENT

VENTILATION: PROCESS ENCLOSURE RECOMMENDED.

RESPIRATOR: THE FOLLOWING RESPIRATORS ARE RECOMMENDED BASED ON INFORMATION FOUND IN THE PHYSICAL DATA, TOXICITY AND HEALTH EFFECTS SECTIONS. THEY ARE RANKED IN ORDER FROM MINIMUM TO MAXIMUM RESPIRATORY PROTECTION. THE SPECIFIC RESPIRATOR SELECTED MUST BE BASED ON CONTAMINATION LEVELS FOUND IN THE WORK PLACE, MUST NOT EXCEED THE WORKING LIMITS OF THE RESPIRATOR AND BE JOINTLY APPROVED BY THE NATIONAL INSTITUTE FOR OCCUPATIONAL SAFETY AND HEALTH AND THE MINE SAFETY AND HEALTH ADMINISTRATION (NIOSH-MSHA).
TYPE 'C' SUPPLIED-AIR RESPIRATOR WITH A FULL FACEPIECE OPERATED IN PRESSURE-DEMAND OR OTHER POSITIVE PRESSURE MODE OR WITH A FULL FACEPIECE, HELMET OR HOOD OPERATED IN CONTINOUS-FLOW MODE.
SELF-CONTAINED BREATHING APPARATUS WITH A FULL FACEPIECE OPERATED IN PRESSURE-DEMAND OR OTHER POSITIVE PRESSURE MODE.
FOR FIREFIGHTING AND OTHER IMMEDIATELY DANGEROUS TO LIFE OR HEALTH CONDITIONS:
SELF-CONTAINED BREATHING APPARATUS WITH FULL FACEPIECE OPERATED IN PRESSURE-DEMAND OR OTHER POSITIVE PRESSURE MODE.
SUPPLIED-AIR RESPIRATOR WITH FULL FACEPIECE AND OPERATED IN PRESSURE-DEMAND OR OTHER POSITIVE PRESSURE MODE IN COMBINATION WITH AN AUXILIARY SELF-CONTAINED BREATHING APPARATUS OPERATED IN PRESSURE-DEMAND OR OTHER POSITIVE PRESSURE MODE.

CLOTHING: EMPLOYEE MUST WEAR APPROPRIATE PROTECTIVE (IMPERVIOUS) CLOTHING AND EQUIPMENT TO PREVENT ANY POSSIBILITY OF SKIN CONTACT WITH THIS SUBSTANCE.

GLOVES: EMPLOYEE MUST WEAR APPROPRIATE PROTECTIVE GLOVES TO PREVENT CONTACT WITH THIS SUBSTANCE.

EYE PROTECTION: EMPLOYEE MUST WEAR SPLASH-PROOF OR DUST-RESISTANT SAFETY GOGGLES AND A FACESHIELD TO PREVENT CONTACT WITH THIS SUBSTANCE.
EMERGENCY WASH FACILITIES: WHERE THERE IS ANY POSSIBILITY THAT AN EMPLOYEE'S EYES AND/OR SKIN MAY BE EXPOSED TO THIS SUBSTANCE, THE EMPLOYER SHOULD PROVIDE AN EYE WASH FOUNTAIN AND QUICK DRENCH SHOWER WITHIN THE IMMEDIATE WORK AREA FOR EMERGENCY USE.

AUTHORIZED BY- OCCUPATIONAL HEALTH SERVICES, INC.
CREATION DATE: 10/04/89 ***REVISION DATE:*** 06/20/90

MATERIAL SAFETY DATA SHEET

OCCUPATIONAL HEALTH SERVICES, INC.
AGRICULTURE AND PESTICIDE DIVISION
450 SEVENTH AVENUE, SUITE 2407
NEW YORK, NEW YORK 10123
1-800-445-MSDS OR (212) 967-1100

EMERGENCY CONTACT:
JOHN S. BRANSFORD, JR. (615) 292-1180

SUBSTANCE IDENTIFICATION

CAS-NUMBER 42795-00-6

SUBSTANCE: SULPROFOS OXYGEN ANALOG SULFONE

TRADE NAMES/SYNONYMS: O-ETHYL O-(4-(METHYLSULFONYL)PHENYL)S-PROPYL-PHOSPHOROTHIOATE; BAY NTN 9306 OXYGEN ANALOG SULFONE; BOLSTAR OXYGEN ANALOG SULFONE; BOLDSTAR O.A. SULFONE; PHOSPHOROTHIOIC ACID, O-ETHYL O-(4-(METHYLSULFONYL)PHENYL) S-PROPYL ESTER; BOLDSTAR OXON SULFONE (FORMULATION); SULPROFOS OXON SULFONE; C12H19O5PS2; PST03231

CHEMICAL FAMILY: PHOSPHOROTHIOATE SULFONYL

MOLECULAR FORMULA: C12-H19-O5-P-S2

MOLECULAR WEIGHT: 338.37

CERCLA RATINGS (SCALE 0-3): HEALTH=U FIRE=U REACTIVITY=0 PERSISTENCE=0

NFPA RATINGS (SCALE 0-4): HEALTH=U FIRE=U REACTIVITY=0

COMPONENTS AND CONTAMINANTS

COMPONENT: SULPROFOS OXYGEN ANALOG SULFONE ***PERCENT:*** 100.0
CAS# 42795-00-6

OTHER CONTAMINANTS: NONE

EXPOSURE LIMITS: NO OCCUPATIONAL EXPOSURE LIMITS ESTABLISHED BY OSHA, ACGIH, OR NIOSH.

PHYSICAL DATA

DESCRIPTION: CLEAR LIQUID. ***BOILING POINT:*** NOT AVAILABLE
SPECIFIC GRAVITY: NOT AVAILABLE ***VAPOR PRESSURE:*** NOT AVAILABLE
SOLUBILITY IN WATER: NOT AVAILABLE

FIRE AND EXPLOSION DATA

FIRE AND EXPLOSION HAZARD: UNKNOWN FIRE AND EXPLOSION HAZARD.

FIREFIGHTING MEDIA: DRY CHEMICAL, CARBON DIOXIDE, HALON, WATER SPRAY OR STANDARD FOAM (1987 EMERGENCY RESPONSE GUIDEBOOK, DOT P 5800.4).
FOR LARGER FIRES, USE WATER SPRAY, FOG OR STANDARD FOAM (1987 EMERGENCY RESPONSE GUIDEBOOK, DOT P 5800.4).

FIREFIGHTING: MOVE CONTAINER FROM FIRE AREA IF POSSIBLE. DIKE FIRE CONTROL WATER FOR LATER DISPOSAL; DO NOT SCATTER THE MATERIAL. COOL FIRE-EXPOSED CONTAINERS WITH WATER FROM SIDE UNTIL WELL AFTER FIRE IS OUT. STAY AWAY FROM STORAGE TANK ENDS. WITHDRAW IMMEDIATELY IN CASE OF RISING SOUND FROM VENTING SAFETY DEVICE OR ANY DISCOLORATION OF STORAGE TANK DUE TO FIRE (1987 EMERGENCY RESPONSE GUIDEBOOK, DOT P 5800.4, GUIDE PAGE 28).
EXTINGUISH ONLY IF FLOW CAN BE STOPPED. USE FLOODING AMOUNTS OF WATER AS A FOG; SOLID STREAMS MAY BE INEFFECTIVE. COOL CONTAINERS WITH FLOODING AMOUNTS OF WATER FROM AS FAR A DISTANCE AS POSSIBLE. AVOID BREATHING POISONOUS VAPORS, KEEP UPWIND.

TOXICITY

SULPROFOS OXYGEN ANALOG SULFONE: TOXICITY DATA: 74 MG/KG ORAL-RAT LD50 (EPA). CARCINOGEN STATUS: NONE. ACUTE TOXICITY LEVEL: TOXIC BY INGESTION. TARGET EFFECTS: CHOLINESTERASE INHIBITOR. POISONING MAY AFFECT THE NERVOUS SYSTEM.* AT INCREASED RISK FROM EXPOSURE: PERSONS WITH RESPIRATORY AILMENTS, RECENT EXPOSURE TO CHOLINESTERASE INHIBITORS OR IMPAIRED CHOLINESTERASE PRODUCTION, OR LIVER MALFUNCTION.* ADDITIONAL DATA: MAY CROSS THE PLACENTA. HIGH

ENVIRONMENTAL TEMPERATURES OR EXPOSURE OF THE CHEMICAL TO VISIBLE OR ULTRAVIOLET LIGHT MAY ENHANCE THE TOXICITY. INTERACTIONS WITH MEDICATIONS MAY OCCUR.*

* MAY BE BASED ON GENERAL INFORMATION ON ORGANOPHOSPHATES.

HEALTH EFFECTS AND FIRST AID

INHALATION: SULPROFOS OXYGEN ANALOG SULFONE: SEE INFORMATION ON ORGANOPHOSPHATES.

ORGANOPHOSPHATES: CHOLINESTERASE INHIBITOR. **ACUTE EXPOSURE-** WHEN INHALED, THE FIRST EFFECTS OF CHOLINESTERASE INHIBITORS ARE USUALLY RESPIRATORY AND MAY INCLUDE NASAL HYPEREMIA AND WATERY DISCHARGE, COUGH, CHEST DISCOMFORT, DYSPNEA, AND WHEEZING DUE TO INCREASED BRONCHIAL SECRETIONS AND BRONCHOCONSTRICTION. IF SUFFICIENT AMOUNTS ARE ABSORBED, OTHER SYSTEMIC EFFECTS MAY BEGIN WITHIN A FEW MINUTES OR BE DELAYED FOR UP TO 12 HOURS. SYMPTOMS MAY INCLUDE PALLOR, NAUSEA, VOMITING, DIARRHEA, ABDOMINAL CRAMPS, HEADACHE, DIZZINESS, OCULAR PAIN, BLURRED VISION, MIOSIS OR IN SOME CASES, ESPECIALLY INITIALLY, MYDRIASIS, LACRIMATION, SALIVATION, SWEATING, AND CONFUSION. OTHER REPORTED CENTRAL NERVOUS SYSTEM OR NEUROMUSCULAR EFFECTS MAY INCLUDE ATAXIA, SLURRED SPEECH, AREFLEXIA, WEAKNESS, FATIGUE, FASCICULATIONS, TWITCHING, TREMORS POSSIBLY OF THE TONGUE AND EYELIDS, AND EVENTUALLY PARALYSIS OF THE EXTREMITIES AND POSSIBLY OF THE RESPIRATORY MUSCLES. IN SEVERE CASES THERE MAY ALSO BE INVOLUNTARY DEFECATION AND URINATION, CYANOSIS, PSYCHOSIS, HYPERGLYCEMIA, ACUTE PANCREATITIS, CARDIAC IRREGULARITIES, PULMONARY EDEMA, UNCONSCIOUSNESS, CONVULSIONS, AND COMA. DEATH IS PRIMARILY DUE TO RESPIRATORY FAILURE, ALTHOUGH CARDIOVASCULAR EFFECTS INCLUDING CARDIAC ARREST MAY ALSO BE IMPLICATED. LONG TERM SEQUELAE ARE RARE BUT MAY INCLUDE NEUROPSYCHIATRIC DISORDERS AND MYOPATHY WITH MUSCLE TENDERNESS. SOME ORGANOPHOSPHATES MAY CAUSE A DELAYED NEUROPATHY BEGINNING 1-4 WEEKS AFTER AN ACUTE EXPOSURE WHICH MAY OR MAY NOT HAVE CAUSED ACUTE CHOLINERGIC EFFECTS. NUMBNESS, TINGLING, WEAKNESS AND CRAMPING BEGINNING SYMMETRICALLY IN THE LOWER LIMBS MAY PROGRESS TO ATAXIA AND PARALYSIS. IN SEVERE CASES, UPPER LIMB INVOLVEMENT IS POSSIBLE AND FLACCID PARALYSIS MAY PROGRESS TO SPASTIC PARALYSIS WITH EXAGGERATED REFLEXES. IMPROVEMENT MAY OCCUR OVER MONTHS TO YEARS, BUT SOME RESIDUAL IMPAIRMENT USUALLY REMAINS. **CHRONIC EXPOSURE-** REPEATED OR PROLONGED EXPOSURE MAY RESULT IN THE EFFECTS OF ACUTE EXPOSURE INCLUDING THE DELAYED NEUROPATHY. OTHER EFFECTS REPORTED IN WORKERS REPEATEDLY EXPOSED INCLUDE IMPAIRED MEMORY AND CONCENTRATION, ACUTE PSYCHOSIS, SEVERE DEPRESSIONS, IRRITABILTY, CONFUSION, APATHY, EMOTIONAL LABILITY, SOCIAL WITHDRAWAL, CONFUSION, HEADACHE, SPEECH DIFFICULTIES, DELAYED REACTION TIMES, SPATIAL DISORIENTATION, NIGHTMARES, SLEEPWALKING, AND DROWSINESS OR INSOMNIA. AN INFLUENZA-LIKE CONDITION WITH HEADACHE, NAUSEA, WEAKNESS, ANOREXIA AND MALAISE HAS ALSO BEEN REPORTED.

FIRST AID- REMOVE FROM EXPOSURE AREA TO FRESH AIR IMMEDIATELY. IF BREATHING HAS STOPPED, GIVE ARTIFICIAL RESPIRATION. MAINTAIN AIRWAY AND BLOOD PRESSURE AND ADMINISTER OXYGEN IF AVAILABLE. KEEP AFFECTED PERSON WARM AND AT REST. TREAT SYMPTOMATICALLY AND SUPPORTIVELY. ADMINISTRATION OF OXYGEN SHOULD BE PERFORMED BY QUALIFIED PERSONNEL. GET MEDICAL ATTENTION IMMEDIATELY.

SKIN CONTACT: SULPROFOS OXYGEN ANALOG SULFONE: SEE INFORMATION ON ORGANOPHOSPHATES.

ORGANOPHOSPHATES: CHOLINESTERASE INHIBITOR. **ACUTE EXPOSURE-** LOCALIZED SWEATING AND FASCICULATIONS MAY OCCUR AT THE SITE OF CONTACT. IF SUFFICIENT AMOUNTS ARE ABSORBED, OTHER EFFECTS OF CHOLINESTERASE INHIBITION AS DESCRIBED IN ACUTE INHALATION MAY OCCUR. SYMPTOMS MAY BE DELAYED 2-3 HOURS, BUT USUALLY NO MORE THAN 12 HOURS. THE RATE OF ABSORPTION IS INCREASED BY THE PRESENCE OF DERMATITIS OR HIGH AMBIENT TEMPERATURES. DELAYED NEUROPATHY IS ALSO POSSIBLE. **CHRONIC EXPOSURE-** REPEATED OR PROLONGED EXPOSURE MAY CAUSE EFFECTS AS DESCRIBED IN ACUTE EXPOSURE. SOME ORGANOPHOSPHATES MAY CAUSE SENSITIZATION.

FIRST AID- REMOVE CONTAMINATED CLOTHING IMMEDIATELY. WASH CONTAMINATED AREAS WITH SOAP AND WATER FOLLOWED BY ALCOHOL (ARENA, POISONING, 4TH ED.). EMERGENCY PERSONNEL SHOULD WEAR GLOVES AND AVOID CONTAMINATION. TREAT RESPIRATORY DIFFICULTY WITH ARTIFICIAL RESPIRATION. GET MEDICAL ATTENTION IMMEDIATELY.

EYE CONTACT: SULPROFOS OXYGEN ANALOG SULFONE: SEE INFORMATION ON ORGANOPHOSPHATES.

ORGANOPHOSPHATES: CHOLINESTERASE INHIBITOR. **ACUTE EXPOSURE-** DIRECT CONTACT MAY CAUSE PAIN, HYPEREMIA, LACRIMATION, TWITCHING OF THE EYELIDS, MIOSIS, AND CILIARY MUSCLE SPASM WITH LOSS OF ACCOMODATION, BLURRED OR DIMMED VISION AND BROWACHE. SOMETIMES MYDRIASIS MAY OCCUR INSTEAD OF MIOSIS. WITH SUFFICIENT EXPOSURE, OTHER SYMPTOMS OF CHOLINESTERASE INHIBITION AS DESCRIBED IN ACUTE INHALATION MAY OCCUR. **CHRONIC EXPOSURE-** REPEATED OR PROLONGED EXPOSURE MAY CAUSE EFFECTS AS DESCRIBED IN ACUTE EXPOSURE. SOME COMPOUNDS HAVE CAUSED TOXIC EFFECTS ON THE CRYSTALLINE LENS, CONJUNCTIVAL THICKENING AND OBSTRUCTION OF THE NASOLACRIMAL CANALS WHEN USED AS MIOTIC EYEDROPS.

FIRST AID- IRRIGATE EYES WITH WATER OR SALINE SOLUTION. IF SYMPTOMS OF POISONING OCCUR, TREAT RESPIRATORY DIFFICULTY WITH ARTIFICIAL RESPIRATION AND OXYGEN. OBSERVE PATIENT FOR AT LEAST 24-36 HOURS (GOSSELIN, CLINICAL TOXICOLOGY OF COMMERCIAL PRODUCTS, 5TH ED.). GET MEDICAL ATTENTION IMMEDIATELY. OXYGEN SHOULD BE ADMINISTERED BY QUALIFIED MEDICAL PERSONNEL.

INGESTION: SULPROFOS OXYGEN ANALOG SULFONE: TOXIC. SEE INFORMATION ON ORGANOPHOSPHATES. THE REPORTED LETHAL DOSE IN RATS WAS 74 MG/KG.

ORGANOPHOSPHATES: CHOLINESTERASE INHIBITOR. **ACUTE EXPOSURE-** WHEN INGESTED, THE FIRST EFFECTS MAY BE NAUSEA, VOMITING, ANOREXIA, ABDOMINAL CRAMPS AND DIARRHEA. GASTROINTESTINAL ABSORPTION MAY CAUSE SYMPTOMS OF CHOLINESTERASE INHIBITION AS DESCRIBED IN ACUTE INHALATION. SYMPTOMS MAY BEGIN WITHIN MINUTES OR BE DELAYED FOR HOURS. DELAYED EFFECTS INCLUDING NEUROPATHY MAY ALSO OCCUR. **CHRONIC EXPOSURE-** REPEATED INGESTION MAY CAUSE EFFECTS AS DESCRIBED IN ACUTE EXPOSURE.

FIRST AID- IF PERSON IS ALERT AND RESPIRATION IS NOT DEPRESSED, GIVE SYRUP OF IPECAC FOLLOWED BY WATER (IF VOMITING OCCURS, KEEP HEAD BELOW HIPS TO PREVENT ASPIRATION). IF CONSCIOUSNESS LEVEL DECLINES OR VOMITING HAS NOT OCCURRED IN 15 MINUTES EMPTY STOMACH BY GASTRIC LAVAGE WITH THE AID OF CUFFED ENDOTRACHEAL TUBE USING ISOTONIC SALINE OR 5% SODIUM BICARBONATE FOLLOW WITH ACTIVATED CHARCOAL. ESTABLISH AND MAINTAIN AIRWAY. TREAT RESPIRATORY DIFFICULTY WITH ARTIFICIAL RESPIRATION AND OXYGEN. DO NOT GIVE MORPHINE, AMINOPHYLLINE, PHENOTHIAZINES, RESERPINE, FUROSEMIDE, OR ETHACRYNIC ACID (MORGAN, RECOGNITION AND MANAGEMENT OF PESTICIDE POISONINGS, 3RD ED.). TREAT SYMPTOMATICALLY AND SUPPORTIVELY. ADMINISTRATION OF OXYGEN AND LAVAGE MUST BE PERFORMED BY QUALIFIED MEDICAL PERSONNEL. GET MEDICAL ATTENTION IMMEDIATELY.

ANTIDOTE: THE FOLLOWING ANTIDOTE HAS BEEN RECOMMENDED. HOWEVER, THE DECISION AS TO WHETHER THE SEVERITY OF POISONING REQUIRES ADMINISTRATION OF ANY ANTIDOTE AND ACTUAL DOSE REQUIRED SHOULD BE MADE BY QUALIFIED MEDICAL PERSONNEL. FOR CHOLINESTERASE INHIBITORS: ESTABLISH CLEAR AIRWAY AND TISSUE OXYGENATION BY ASPIRATION OF SECRETIONS, AND IF NECESSARY, BY ASSISTED PULMONARY VENTILATION WITH OXYGEN. IMPROVE TISSUE OXYGENATION AS MUCH AS POSSIBLE BEFORE ADMINISTERING ATROPINE TO MINIMIZE THE RISK OF VENTRICULAR FIBRILLATION. ADMINISTER ATROPINE SULFATE INTRAVENOUSLY, OR INTRAMUSCULARLY IF IV INJECTION IS NOT POSSIBLE. IN MODERATELY SEVERE POISONING ADMINISTER ATROPINE SULFATE, 0.4-2.0 MG REPEATED EVERY 15 MINUTES UNTIL ATROPINIZATION IS ACHIEVED (TACHYCARDIA, FLUSHING, DRY MOUTH, MYDRIASIS). MAINTAIN ATROPINIZATION BY REPEATED DOSES FOR 2-12 HOURS, OR LONGER, DEPENDING ON THE SEVERITY OF POISONING. THE APPEARANCE OF RALES IN THE LUNG BASES, MIOSIS, SALIVATION, NAUSEA, BRADYCARDIA, ARE ALL INDICATIONS OF INADEQUATE ATROPINIZATION. SEVERELY POISONED INDIVIDUALS MAY EXHIBIT REMARKABLE TOLERANCE TO ATROPINE; TWO OR MORE TIMES THE DOSAGES SUGGESTED ABOVE MAY BE NEEDED. PERSONS NOT POISONED OR ONLY SLIGHTLY POISONED, HOWEVER, MAY DEVELOP SIGNS OF ATROPINE TOXICITY FROM SUCH LARGE DOSAGES: FEVER, MUSCLE FIBRILLATIONS, AND DELIRIUM ARE THE MAIN SIGNS OF ATROPINE TOXICITY. IF THESE SIGNS APPEAR WHILE THE PATIENT IS FULLY ATROPINIZED, ATROPINE ADMINISTRATION SHOULD BE DISCONTINUED, AT LEAST TEMPORARILY. OBSERVE TREATED PATIENTS CLOSELY AT LEAST 24 HOURS TO INSURE THAT SYMPTOMS (POSSIBLY PULMONARY EDEMA) DO NOT RECUR AS ATROPINIZATION WEARS OFF. IN VERY SEVERE POISONINGS, METABOLIC DISPOSITION OF TOXICANT MAY REQUIRE SEVERAL HOURS OR DAYS DURING WHICH ATROPINIZATION MUST BE MAINTAINED. MARKEDLY LOWER LEVELS OF URINARY METABOLITES INDICATE THAT ATROPINE DOSAGE CAN BE TAPERED OFF. AS DOSAGE IS REDUCED, CHECK THE LUNG BASES FREQUENTLY FOR RALES. IF RALES ARE HEARD OR OTHER SYMPTOMS RETURN, RE-ESTABLISH ATROPINIZATION PROMPTLY (MORGAN, RECOGNITION AND MANAGEMENT OF PESTICIDE POISONINGS, 3RD ED.). ADMINISTRATION OF ANTIDOTE MUST BE PERFORMED BY QUALIFIED MEDICAL PERSONNEL.

IN CASES OF SEVERE POISONING BY ORGANOPHOSPHATE PESTICIDES IN WHICH RESPIRATORY DEPRESSION, MUSCLE WEAKNESS AND TWITCHINGS ARE SEVERE, GIVE PRALIDOXIME (PROTOPAM-AYERST, 2-PAM), 1.0 GRAM INTRAVENOUSLY AT NO MORE THAN 0.5 GRAM PER MINUTE. DOSAGE OF PRALIDOXIME MAY BE REPEATED IN 1-2 HOURS, THEN AT 10-12 HOUR INTERVALS IF NEEDED. IN VERY

SEVERE POISONINGS, DOSAGE RATES MAY BE DOUBLED. TREATMENT WITH PRALIDOXIME WILL BE MOST EFFECTIVE IF GIVEN WITHIN THIRTY-SIX HOURS AFTER POISONING (MORGAN, RECOGNITION AND MANAGEMENT OF PESTICIDE POISONINGS, 3RD ED.). ANTIDOTE SHOULD BE ADMINISTERED BY QUALIFIED MEDICAL PERSONNEL.

REACTIVITY

REACTIVITY: STABLE UNDER NORMAL TEMPERATURES AND PRESSURES.

INCOMPATIBILITIES: SULPROFOS OXYGEN ANALOG SULFONE: OXIDIZERS (STRONG): FIRE AND EXPLOSION HAZARD.

DECOMPOSITION: THERMAL DECOMPOSITION PRODUCTS MAY INCLUDE TOXIC OXIDES OF CARBON, SULFUR, AND PHOSPHORUS.

POLYMERIZATION: HAZARDOUS POLYMERIZATION HAS NOT BEEN REPORTED TO OCCUR UNDER NORMAL TEMPERATURES AND PRESSURES.

STORAGE AND DISPOSAL

OBSERVE ALL FEDERAL, STATE AND LOCAL REGULATIONS WHEN STORING OR DISPOSING OF THIS SUBSTANCE. FOR ASSISTANCE, CONTACT THE DISTRICT DIRECTOR OF THE ENVIRONMENTAL PROTECTION AGENCY.

STORAGE

STORE AWAY FROM INCOMPATIBLE SUBSTANCES.

STORE IN TIGHTLY CLOSED CONTAINERS; PREVENT EXPOSURE TO MOISTURE.

CONDITIONS TO AVOID

AVOID CONTACT WITH HEAT, SPARKS, FLAMES OR OTHER IGNITION SOURCES. VAPORS MAY BE EXPLOSIVE. MATERIAL IS POISONOUS; AVOID INHALATION OF VAPORS OR CONTACT WITH SKIN. DO NOT ALLOW MATERIAL TO CONTAMINATE WATER SOURCES.

SPILL AND LEAK PROCEDURES

OCCUPATIONAL SPILL: SHUT OFF IGNITION SOURCES. DO NOT TOUCH SPILLED MATERIAL. STOP LEAK IF YOU CAN DO IT WITHOUT RISK. USE WATER SPRAY TO REDUCE VAPORS. FOR SMALL SPILLS, TAKE UP WITH SAND OR OTHER ABSORBENT MATERIAL AND PLACE INTO CONTAINERS FOR LATER DISPOSAL. FOR LARGER SPILLS, DIKE FAR AHEAD OF SPILL FOR LATER DISPOSAL. NO SMOKING, FLAMES OR FLARES IN HAZARD AREA! KEEP UNNECESSARY PEOPLE AWAY; ISOLATE HAZARD AREA AND DENY ENTRY.

PROTECTIVE EQUIPMENT

VENTILATION: PROVIDE LOCAL EXHAUST OR PROCESS ENCLOSURE VENTILATION SYSTEM.

RESPIRATOR: THE FOLLOWING RESPIRATORS ARE RECOMMENDED BASED ON INFORMATION FOUND IN THE PHYSICAL DATA, TOXICITY AND HEALTH EFFECTS SECTIONS. THEY ARE RANKED IN ORDER FROM MINIMUM TO MAXIMUM RESPIRATORY PROTECTION. THE SPECIFIC RESPIRATOR SELECTED MUST BE BASED ON CONTAMINATION LEVELS FOUND IN THE WORK PLACE, MUST NOT EXCEED THE WORKING LIMITS OF THE RESPIRATOR AND BE JOINTLY APPROVED BY THE NATIONAL INSTITUTE FOR OCCUPATIONAL SAFETY AND HEALTH AND THE MINE SAFETY AND HEALTH ADMINISTRATION (NIOSH-MSHA).

CHEMICAL CARTRIDGE RESPIRATOR WITH FULL FACEPIECE AND PESTICIDE CARTRIDGE.

TYPE 'C' SUPPLIED-AIR RESPIRATOR WITH A FULL FACEPIECE OPERATED IN PRESSURE-DEMAND OR OTHER POSITIVE PRESSURE MODE OR WITH A FULL FACEPIECE, HELMET OR HOOD OPERATED IN CONTINUOUS-FLOW MODE.

SELF-CONTAINED BREATHING APPARATUS OPERATED IN PRESSURE-DEMAND OR OTHER POSITIVE PRESSURE MODE.

FOR FIREFIGHTING AND OTHER IMMEDIATELY DANGEROUS TO LIFE OR HEALTH CONDITIONS:

SELF-CONTAINED BREATHING APPARATUS WITH FULL FACEPIECE OPERATED IN PRESSURE-DEMAND OR OTHER POSITIVE PRESSURE MODE.

SUPPLIED-AIR RESPIRATOR WITH FULL FACEPIECE AND OPERATED IN PRESSURE-DEMAND OR OTHER POSITIVE PRESSURE MODE IN COMBINATION WITH AN AUXILIARY SELF-CONTAINED BREATHING APPARATUS OPERATED IN PRESSURE-DEMAND OR OTHER POSITIVE PRESSURE MODE.

CLOTHING: EMPLOYEE MUST WEAR APPROPRIATE PROTECTIVE (IMPERVIOUS) CLOTHING AND EQUIPMENT TO PREVENT ANY POSSIBILITY OF SKIN CONTACT WITH THIS SUBSTANCE.

GLOVES: EMPLOYEE MUST WEAR APPROPRIATE PROTECTIVE GLOVES TO PREVENT CONTACT WITH THIS SUBSTANCE.

EYE PROTECTION: EMPLOYEE MUST WEAR SPLASH-PROOF OR DUST-RESISTANT SAFETY GOGGLES AND A FACESHIELD TO PREVENT CONTACT WITH THIS SUBSTANCE.

EMERGENCY WASH FACILITIES: WHERE THERE IS ANY POSSIBILITY THAT AN EMPLOYEE'S EYES AND/OR SKIN MAY BE EXPOSED TO THIS SUBSTANCE, THE EMPLOYER SHOULD PROVIDE AN EYE WASH FOUNTAIN AND QUICK DRENCH SHOWER WITHIN THE IMMEDIATE WORK AREA FOR EMERGENCY USE.

AUTHORIZED BY- OCCUPATIONAL HEALTH SERVICES, INC.

CREATION DATE: 02/08/90 ***REVISION DATE:*** 05/02/90

MATERIAL SAFETY DATA SHEET

OCCUPATIONAL HEALTH SERVICES, INC.
AGRICULTURE AND PESTICIDE DIVISION
450 SEVENTH AVENUE, SUITE 2407
NEW YORK, NEW YORK 10123
1-800-445-MSDS OR (212) 967-1100

EMERGENCY CONTACT:
JOHN S. BRANSFORD, JR. (615) 292-1180

SUBSTANCE IDENTIFICATION

CAS-NUMBER 122-10-1

SUBSTANCE: **BOMYL**

TRADE NAMES/SYNONYMS: 2-PENTENEDIOIC ACID, 3-((DIMETHOXYPHOSPHINYL)OXY)-, DIMETHYL ESTER; GLUTACONIC ACID, 3-HYDROXY-, DIMETHYL ESTER, DIMETHYL PHOSPHATE; 3-HYDROXY-2-PENTENEDIOIC ACID DIMETHYL ESTER DIMETHYL PHOSPHATE; 3-HYDROXYGLUTACONIC ACID DIMETHYL ESTER DIMETHYL PHOSPHATE; DIMETHYL 1,3 BIS(CARBOMETHOXY)-1-PROPEN-2-YL PHOSPHATE; DIMETHYL 1,3 DI(CARBOMETHOXY)-1-PROPEN-2-YL PHOSPHATE; DIMETHYL 3-HYDROXYGLUTACONATE DIMETHYL PHOSPHATE; 3-((DIMETHOXYPHOSPHINYL)OXY-2-PENTENEDIOIC ACID DIMETHYL ESTER; GC 3707; SWAT; ENT 24,833; C9H15O8P; PST03240

CHEMICAL FAMILY: ORGANOPHOSPHATE

MOLECULAR FORMULA: C9-H15-O8-P

MOLECULAR WEIGHT: 282.21

CERCLA RATINGS (SCALE 0-3): HEALTH=3 FIRE=0 REACTIVITY=0 PERSISTENCE=0

NFPA RATINGS (SCALE 0-4): HEALTH=4 FIRE=0 REACTIVITY=0

COMPONENTS AND CONTAMINANTS

COMPONENT: BOMYL ***PERCENT:*** 100

CAS# 122-10-1

EXPOSURE LIMITS: NO OCCUPATIONAL EXPOSURE LIMITS ESTABLISHED BY OSHA, ACGIH, OR NIOSH.

PHYSICAL DATA

DESCRIPTION: LIQUID ***BOILING POINT:*** 311-327 F (155-164 C) @ 2 MMHG

SPECIFIC GRAVITY: 1.2 ***SOLUBILITY IN WATER:*** INSOLUBLE

SOLVENT SOLUBILITY: SOLUBLE IN ACETONE, ALCOHOL, PROPYLENE GLYCOL, XYLENE, METHANOL, ETHANOL, AND MOST ORGANIC SOLVENTS EXCEPT ALIPHATIC HYDROCARBONS; INSOLUBLE IN PETROLEUM ETHER AND KEROSENE

FIRE AND EXPLOSION DATA

FIRE AND EXPLOSION HAZARD: NEGLIGIBLE FIRE HAZARD WHEN EXPOSED TO HEAT OR FLAME.

FIREFIGHTING MEDIA: DRY CHEMICAL, CARBON DIOXIDE, HALON, WATER SPRAY OR STANDARD FOAM (1987 EMERGENCY RESPONSE GUIDEBOOK, DOT P 5800.4). FOR LARGER FIRES, USE WATER SPRAY, FOG OR STANDARD FOAM (1987 EMERGENCY RESPONSE GUIDEBOOK, DOT P 5800.4).

FIREFIGHTING: MOVE CONTAINERS FROM FIRE AREA IF POSSIBLE. FIGHT FIRE FROM MAXIMUM DISTANCE. STAY AWAY FROM STORAGE TANK ENDS. DIKE FIRE CONTROL WATER FOR LATER DISPOSAL. DO NOT SCATTER MATERIAL (1987 EMERGENCY RESPONSE GUIDEBOOK, DOT P 5800.4, GUIDE PAGE 55). EXTINGUISH USING AGENT SUITABLE FOR TYPE OF SURROUNDING FIRE. AVOID BREATHING VAPORS AND DUSTS. KEEP UPWIND.

TRANSPORTATION DATA

DEPARTMENT OF TRANSPORTATION HAZARD CLASSIFICATION 49 CFR 172.101: POISON B

DEPARTMENT OF TRANSPORTATION LABELING REQUIREMENTS 49 CFR 172.101 AND SUBPART E: POISON

DEPARTMENT OF TRANSPORTATION PACKAGING REQUIREMENTS: 49 CFR 173.346 EXCEPTIONS: 49 CFR 173.345

TOXICITY

BOMYL: TOXICITY DATA: 20 MG/KG SKIN-RABBIT LD50; 31 MG/KG ORAL-RAT LD50. CARCINOGEN STATUS: NONE. ACUTE TOXICITY LEVEL: HIGHLY TOXIC BY DERMAL ABSORPTION AND INGESTION. TARGET EFFECTS: CHOLINESTERASE INHIBITOR. POISONING MAY AFFECT THE NERVOUS SYSTEM.* AT INCREASED RISK

FROM EXPOSURE: PERSONS WITH RESPIRATORY AILMENTS, RECENT EXPOSURE TO CHOLINESTERASE INHIBITORS OR IMPAIRED CHOLINESTERASE PRODUCTION, OR LIVER MALFUNCTION.* ADDITIONAL DATA: MAY CROSS THE PLACENTA. HIGH ENVIRONMENTAL TEMPERATURES OR EXPOSURE OF THE CHEMICAL TO VISIBLE OR ULTRAVIOLET LIGHT MAY ENHANCE THE TOXICITY. INTERACTIONS WITH MEDICATIONS MAY OCCUR.*

* MAY BE BASED ON GENERAL INFORMATION ON ORGANOPHOSPHATES.

HEALTH EFFECTS AND FIRST AID

INHALATION: BOMYL: SEE INFORMATION ON ORGANOPHOSPHATES.
ORGANOPHOSPHATES: CHOLINESTERASE INHIBITOR. **ACUTE EXPOSURE-** WHEN INHALED, THE FIRST EFFECTS OF CHOLINESTERASE INHIBITORS ARE USUALLY RESPIRATORY AND MAY INCLUDE NASAL HYPEREMIA AND WATERY DISCHARGE, COUGH, CHEST DISCOMFORT, DYSPNEA, AND WHEEZING DUE TO INCREASED BRONCHIAL SECRETIONS AND BRONCHOCONSTRICTION. IF SUFFICIENT AMOUNTS ARE ABSORBED, OTHER SYSTEMIC EFFECTS MAY BEGIN WITHIN A FEW MINUTES OR BE DELAYED FOR UP TO 12 HOURS. SYMPTOMS MAY INCLUDE PALLOR, NAUSEA, VOMITING, DIARRHEA, ABDOMINAL CRAMPS, HEADACHE, DIZZINESS, OCULAR PAIN, BLURRED VISION, MIOSIS OR IN SOME CASES, ESPECIALLY INITIALLY, MYDRIASIS, LACRIMATION, SALIVATION, SWEATING, AND CONFUSION. OTHER REPORTED CENTRAL NERVOUS SYSTEM OR NEUROMUSCULAR EFFECTS MAY INCLUDE ATAXIA, SLURRED SPEECH, AREFLEXIA, WEAKNESS, FATIGUE, FASCICULATIONS, TWITCHING, TREMORS POSSIBLY OF THE TONGUE AND EYELIDS, AND EVENTUALLY PARALYSIS OF THE EXTREMITIES AND POSSIBLY OF THE RESPIRATORY MUSCLES. IN SEVERE CASES THERE MAY ALSO BE INVOLUNTARY DEFECATION AND URINATION, CYANOSIS, PSYCHOSIS, HYPERGLYCEMIA, ACUTE PANCREATITIS, CARDIAC IRREGULARITIES, PULMONARY EDEMA, UNCONSCIOUSNESS, CONVULSIONS, AND COMA. DEATH IS PRIMARILY DUE TO RESPIRATORY FAILURE, ALTHOUGH CARDIOVASCULAR EFFECTS INCLUDING CARDIAC ARREST MAY ALSO BE IMPLICATED. LONG TERM SEQUELAE ARE RARE BUT MAY INCLUDE NEUROPSYCHIATRIC DISORDERS AND MYOPATHY WITH MUSCLE TENDERNESS. SOME ORGANOPHOSPHATES MAY CAUSE A DELAYED NEUROPATHY BEGINNING 1-4 WEEKS AFTER AN ACUTE EXPOSURE WHICH MAY OR MAY NOT HAVE CAUSED ACUTE CHOLINERGIC EFFECTS. NUMBNESS, TINGLING, WEAKNESS AND CRAMPING BEGINNING SYMMETRICALLY IN THE LOWER LIMBS MAY PROGRESS TO ATAXIA AND PARALYSIS. IN SEVERE CASES, UPPER LIMB INVOLVEMENT IS POSSIBLE AND FLACCID PARALYSIS MAY PROGRESS TO SPASTIC PARALYSIS WITH EXAGGERATED REFLEXES. IMPROVEMENT MAY OCCUR OVER MONTHS TO YEARS, BUT SOME RESIDUAL IMPAIRMENT USUALLY REMAINS. **CHRONIC EXPOSURE-** REPEATED OR PROLONGED EXPOSURE MAY RESULT IN THE EFFECTS OF ACUTE EXPOSURE INCLUDING THE DELAYED NEUROPATHY. OTHER EFFECTS REPORTED IN WORKERS REPEATEDLY EXPOSED INCLUDE IMPAIRED MEMORY AND CONCENTRATION, ACUTE PSYCHOSIS, SEVERE DEPRESSIONS, IRRITABILTY, CONFUSION, APATHY, EMOTIONAL LABILITY, SOCIAL WITHDRAWAL, CONFUSION, HEADACHE, SPEECH DIFFICULTIES, DELAYED REACTION TIMES, SPATIAL DISORIENTATION, NIGHTMARES, SLEEPWALKING, AND DROWSINESS OR INSOMNIA. AN INFLUENZA-LIKE CONDITION WITH HEADACHE, NAUSEA, WEAKNESS, ANOREXIA AND MALAISE HAS ALSO BEEN REPORTED.

FIRST AID- REMOVE FROM EXPOSURE AREA TO FRESH AIR IMMEDIATELY. IF BREATHING HAS STOPPED, GIVE ARTIFICIAL RESPIRATION. MAINTAIN AIRWAY AND BLOOD PRESSURE AND ADMINISTER OXYGEN IF AVAILABLE. KEEP AFFECTED PERSON WARM AND AT REST. TREAT SYMPTOMATICALLY AND SUPPORTIVELY. ADMINISTRATION OF OXYGEN SHOULD BE PERFORMED BY QUALIFIED PERSONNEL. GET MEDICAL ATTENTION IMMEDIATELY.

SKIN CONTACT: BOMYL: HIGHLY TOXIC. SEE INFORMATION ON ORGANOPHOSPHATES.
ORGANOPHOSPHATES: CHOLINESTERASE INHIBITOR. **ACUTE EXPOSURE-** LOCALIZED SWEATING AND FASCICULATIONS MAY OCCUR AT THE SITE OF CONTACT. IF SUFFICIENT AMOUNTS ARE ABSORBED, OTHER EFFECTS OF CHOLINESTERASE INHIBITION AS DESCRIBED IN ACUTE INHALATION MAY OCCUR. SYMPTOMS MAY BE DELAYED 2-3 HOURS, BUT USUALLY NO MORE THAN 12 HOURS. THE RATE OF ABSORPTION IS INCREASED BY THE PRESENCE OF DERMATITIS OR HIGH AMBIENT TEMPERATURES. DELAYED NEUROPATHY IS ALSO POSSIBLE. **CHRONIC EXPOSURE-** REPEATED OR PROLONGED EXPOSURE MAY CAUSE EFFECTS AS DESCRIBED IN ACUTE EXPOSURE. SOME ORGANOPHOSPHATES MAY CAUSE SENSITIZATION.

FIRST AID- REMOVE CONTAMINATED CLOTHING IMMEDIATELY. WASH CONTAMINATED AREAS WITH SOAP AND WATER FOLLOWED BY ALCOHOL (ARENA, POISONING, 4TH ED.). EMERGENCY PERSONNEL SHOULD WEAR GLOVES AND AVOID CONTAMINATION. TREAT RESPIRATORY DIFFICULTY WITH ARTIFICIAL RESPIRATION. GET MEDICAL ATTENTION IMMEDIATELY.

EYE CONTACT: BOMYL: SEE INFORMATION ON ORGANOPHOSPHATES.
ORGANOPHOSPHATES: CHOLINESTERASE INHIBITOR. **ACUTE EXPOSURE-** DIRECT CONTACT MAY CAUSE PAIN, HYPEREMIA, LACRIMATION, TWITCHING OF THE EYELIDS, MIOSIS, AND CILIARY MUSCLE SPASM WITH LOSS OF ACCOMODATION, BLURRED OR DIMMED VISION AND BROWACHE. SOMETIMES MYDRIASIS MAY OCCUR INSTEAD OF MIOSIS. WITH SUFFICIENT EXPOSURE, OTHER SYMPTOMS OF CHOLINESTERASE INHIBITION AS DESCRIBED IN ACUTE INHALATION MAY OCCUR. **CHRONIC EXPOSURE-** REPEATED OR PROLONGED EXPOSURE MAY CAUSE EFFECTS AS DESCRIBED IN ACUTE EXPOSURE. SOME COMPOUNDS HAVE CAUSED TOXIC EFFECTS ON THE CRYSTALLINE LENS, CONJUNCTIVAL THICKENING AND OBSTRUCTION OF THE NASOLACRIMAL CANALS WHEN USED AS MIOTIC EYEDROPS.

FIRST AID- IRRIGATE EYES WITH WATER OR SALINE SOLUTION. IF SYMPTOMS OF POISONING OCCUR, TREAT RESPIRATORY DIFFICULTY WITH ARTIFICIAL RESPIRATION AND OXYGEN. OBSERVE PATIENT FOR AT LEAST 24-36 HOURS (GOSSELIN, CLINICAL TOXICOLOGY OF COMMERCIAL PRODUCTS, 5TH ED.). GET MEDICAL ATTENTION IMMEDIATELY. OXYGEN SHOULD BE ADMINISTERED BY QUALIFIED MEDICAL PERSONNEL.

INGESTION: BOMYL: HIGHLY TOXIC. SEE INFORMATION ON ORGANOPHOSPHATES.
ORGANOPHOSPHATES: CHOLINESTERASE INHIBITOR. **ACUTE EXPOSURE-** WHEN INGESTED, THE FIRST EFFECTS MAY BE NAUSEA, VOMITING, ANOREXIA, ABDOMINAL CRAMPS AND DIARRHEA. GASTROINTESTINAL ABSORPTION MAY CAUSE SYMPTOMS OF CHOLINESTERASE INHIBITION AS DESCRIBED IN ACUTE INHALATION. SYMPTOMS MAY BEGIN WITHIN MINUTES OR BE DELAYED FOR HOURS. DELAYED EFFECTS INCLUDING NEUROPATHY MAY ALSO OCCUR. **CHRONIC EXPOSURE-** REPEATED INGESTION MAY CAUSE EFFECTS AS DESCRIBED IN ACUTE EXPOSURE.

FIRST AID- IF PERSON IS ALERT AND RESPIRATION IS NOT DEPRESSED, GIVE SYRUP OF IPECAC FOLLOWED BY WATER (IF VOMITING OCCURS, KEEP HEAD BELOW HIPS TO PREVENT ASPIRATION). IF CONSCIOUSNESS LEVEL DECLINES OR VOMITING HAS NOT OCCURRED IN 15 MINUTES EMPTY STOMACH BY GASTRIC LAVAGE WITH THE AID OF CUFFED ENDOTRACHEAL TUBE USING ISOTONIC SALINE OR 5% SODIUM BICARBONATE FOLLOW WITH ACTIVATED CHARCOAL. ESTABLISH AND MAINTAIN AIRWAY. TREAT RESPIRATORY DIFFICULTY WITH ARTIFICIAL RESPIRATION AND OXYGEN. DO NOT GIVE MORPHINE, AMINOPHYLLINE, PHENOTHIAZINES, RESERPINE, FUROSEMIDE, OR ETHACRYNIC ACID (MORGAN, RECOGNITION AND MANAGEMENT OF PESTICIDE POISONINGS, 3RD ED.). TREAT SYMPTOMATICALLY AND SUPPORTIVELY. ADMINISTRATION OF OXYGEN AND LAVAGE MUST BE PERFORMED BY QUALIFIED MEDICAL PERSONNEL. GET MEDICAL ATTENTION IMMEDIATELY.

ANTIDOTE: THE FOLLOWING ANTIDOTE(S) HAVE BEEN RECOMMENDED. HOWEVER, THE DECISION AS TO WHETHER THE SEVERITY OF POISONING REQUIRES ADMINISTRATION OF ANY ANTIDOTE AND ACTUAL DOSE REQUIRED SHOULD BE MADE BY QUALIFIED MEDICAL PERSONNEL.
FOR CHOLINESTERASE INHIBITORS: ESTABLISH CLEAR AIRWAY AND TISSUE OXYGENATION BY ASPIRATION OF SECRETIONS, AND IF NECESSARY, BY ASSISTED PULMONARY VENTILATION WITH OXYGEN. IMPROVE TISSUE OXYGENATION AS MUCH AS POSSIBLE BEFORE ADMINISTERING ATROPINE TO MINIMIZE THE RISK OF VENTRICULAR FIBRILLATION. ADMINISTER ATROPINE SULFATE INTRAVENOUSLY, OR INTRAMUSCULARLY IF IV INJECTION IS NOT POSSIBLE. IN MODERATELY SEVERE POISONING ADMINISTER ATROPINE SULFATE, 0.4-2.0 MG REPEATED EVERY 15 MINUTES UNTIL ATROPINIZATION IS ACHIEVED (TACHYCARDIA, FLUSHING, DRY MOUTH, MYDRIASIS). MAINTAIN ATROPINIZATION BY REPEATED DOSES FOR 2-12 HOURS, OR LONGER, DEPENDING ON THE SEVERITY OF POISONING. THE APPEARANCE OF RALES IN THE LUNG BASES, MIOSIS, SALIVATION, NAUSEA, BRADYCARDIA, ARE ALL INDICATIONS OF INADEQUATE ATROPINIZATION. SEVERELY POISONED INDIVIDUALS MAY EXHIBIT REMARKABLE TOLERANCE TO ATROPINE; TWO OR MORE TIMES THE DOSAGES SUGGESTED ABOVE MAY BE NEEDED. PERSONS NOT POISONED OR ONLY SLIGHTLY POISONED, HOWEVER, MAY DEVELOP SIGNS OF ATROPINE TOXICITY FROM SUCH LARGE DOSAGES: FEVER, MUSCLE FIBRILLATIONS, AND DELIRIUM ARE THE MAIN SIGNS OF ATROPINE TOXICITY. IF THESE SIGNS APPEAR WHILE THE PATIENT IS FULLY ATROPINIZED, ATROPINE ADMINISTRATION SHOULD BE DISCONTINUED, AT LEAST TEMPORARILY. OBSERVE TREATED PATIENTS CLOSELY AT LEAST 24 HOURS TO INSURE THAT SYMPTOMS (POSSIBLY PULMONARY EDEMA) DO NOT RECUR AS ATROPINIZATION WEARS OFF. IN VERY SEVERE POISONINGS, METABOLIC DISPOSITION OF TOXICANT MAY REQUIRE SEVERAL HOURS OR DAYS DURING WHICH ATROPINIZATION MUST BE MAINTAINED. MARKEDLY LOWER LEVELS OF URINARY METABOLITES INDICATE THAT ATROPINE DOSAGE CAN BE TAPERED OFF. AS DOSAGE IS REDUCED, CHECK THE LUNG BASES FREQUENTLY FOR RALES. IF RALES ARE HEARD OR OTHER SYMPTOMS RETURN, RE-ESTABLISH ATROPINIZATION PROMPTLY (MORGAN, RECOGNITION AND MANAGEMENT OF PESTICIDE POISONINGS, 3RD ED.). ADMINISTRATION OF ANTIDOTE MUST BE PERFORMED BY QUALIFIED MEDICAL PERSONNEL.
IN CASES OF SEVERE POISONING BY ORGANOPHOSPHATE PESTICIDES IN WHICH RESPIRATORY DEPRESSION, MUSCLE WEAKNESS AND TWITCHINGS ARE SEVERE, GIVE PRALIDOXIME (PROTOPAM-AYERST, 2-PAM), 1.0 GRAM INTRAVENOUSLY AT NO MORE THAN 0.5 GRAM PER MINUTE. DOSAGE OF PRALIDOXIME MAY BE REPEATED IN 1-2 HOURS, THEN AT 10-12 HOUR INTERVALS IF NEEDED. IN VERY

SEVERE POISONINGS, DOSAGE RATES MAY BE DOUBLED. TREATMENT WITH PRALIDOXIME WILL BE MOST EFFECTIVE IF GIVEN WITHIN THIRTY-SIX HOURS AFTER POISONING (MORGAN, RECOGNITION AND MANAGEMENT OF PESTICIDE POISONINGS, 3RD ED.). ANTIDOTE SHOULD BE ADMINISTERED BY QUALIFIED MEDICAL PERSONNEL.

REACTIVITY

REACTIVITY: STABLE UNDER NORMAL TEMPERATURES AND PRESSURES.

INCOMPATIBILITIES: BOMYL: IRON: MAY CORRODE. STEEL: MAY CORRODE. BRASS: MAY CORRODE.

DECOMPOSITION: THERMAL DECOMPOSITION MAY RELEASE TOXIC AND/OR HAZARDOUS GASES.

POLYMERIZATION: HAZARDOUS POLYMERIZATION HAS NOT BEEN REPORTED TO OCCUR UNDER NORMAL TEMPERATURES AND PRESSURES.

STORAGE AND DISPOSAL

OBSERVE ALL FEDERAL, STATE AND LOCAL REGULATIONS WHEN STORING OR DISPOSING OF THIS SUBSTANCE. FOR ASSISTANCE, CONTACT THE DISTRICT DIRECTOR OF THE ENVIRONMENTAL PROTECTION AGENCY.

****STORAGE****

STORE IN ACCORDANCE WITH 40 CFR 165 RECOMMENDED PROCEDURES FOR THE DISPOSAL AND STORAGE OF PESTICIDES AND PESTICIDE CONTAINERS.
STORE AWAY FROM INCOMPATIBLE SUBSTANCES.

****DISPOSAL****

DISPOSAL MUST BE IN ACCORDANCE WITH 40 CFR 165 RECOMMENDED PROCEDURES FOR THE DISPOSAL AND STORAGE OF PESTICIDES AND PESTICIDE CONTAINERS.

CONDITIONS TO AVOID

MAY BURN BUT DOES NOT IGNITE READILY. CONTAINERS MAY EXPLODE IN HEAT OF FIRE.

SPILL AND LEAK PROCEDURES

OCCUPATIONAL SPILL: DO NOT TOUCH SPILLED MATERIAL. STOP LEAK IF YOU CAN DO IT WITHOUT RISK. USE WATER SPRAY TO REDUCE VAPORS. FOR SMALL SPILLS, TAKE UP WITH SAND OR OTHER ABSORBENT MATERIAL AND PLACE INTO CONTAINERS FOR LATER DISPOSAL. FOR SMALL DRY SPILLS, WITH A CLEAN SHOVEL PLACE MATERIAL INTO CLEAN, DRY CONTAINERS AND COVER. MOVE CONTAINERS FROM SPILL AREA. FOR LARGER SPILLS, DIKE FAR AHEAD OF SPILL FOR LATER DISPOSAL. KEEP UNNECESSARY PEOPLE AWAY. ISOLATE HAZARD AREA AND DENY ENTRY. VENTILATE CLOSED SPACES BEFORE ENTERING.

PROTECTIVE EQUIPMENT

VENTILATION: PROCESS ENCLOSURE RECOMMENDED.

RESPIRATOR: THE FOLLOWING RESPIRATORS ARE RECOMMENDED BASED ON INFORMATION FOUND IN THE PHYSICAL DATA, TOXICITY AND HEALTH EFFECTS SECTIONS. THEY ARE RANKED IN ORDER FROM MINIMUM TO MAXIMUM RESPIRATORY PROTECTION. THE SPECIFIC RESPIRATOR SELECTED MUST BE BASED ON CONTAMINATION LEVELS FOUND IN THE WORK PLACE, MUST NOT EXCEED THE WORKING LIMITS OF THE RESPIRATOR AND BE JOINTLY APPROVED BY THE NATIONAL INSTITUTE FOR OCCUPATIONAL SAFETY AND HEALTH AND THE MINE SAFETY AND HEALTH ADMINISTRATION (NIOSH-MSHA).
TYPE 'C' SUPPLIED-AIR RESPIRATOR WITH A FULL FACEPIECE OPERATED IN PRESSURE-DEMAND OR OTHER POSITIVE PRESSURE MODE OR WITH A FULL FACEPIECE, HELMET OR HOOD OPERATED IN CONTINOUS-FLOW MODE.
SELF-CONTAINED BREATHING APPARATUS WITH A FULL FACEPIECE OPERATED IN PRESSURE-DEMAND OR OTHER POSITIVE PRESSURE MODE.
FOR FIREFIGHTING AND OTHER IMMEDIATELY DANGEROUS TO LIFE OR HEALTH CONDITIONS:
SELF-CONTAINED BREATHING APPARATUS WITH FULL FACEPIECE OPERATED IN PRESSURE-DEMAND OR OTHER POSITIVE PRESSURE MODE.
SUPPLIED-AIR RESPIRATOR WITH FULL FACEPIECE AND OPERATED IN PRESSURE-DEMAND OR OTHER POSITIVE PRESSURE MODE IN COMBINATION WITH AN AUXILIARY SELF-CONTAINED BREATHING APPARATUS OPERATED IN PRESSURE-DEMAND OR OTHER POSITIVE PRESSURE MODE.

CLOTHING: EMPLOYEE MUST WEAR APPROPRIATE PROTECTIVE (IMPERVIOUS) CLOTHING AND EQUIPMENT TO PREVENT ANY POSSIBILITY OF SKIN CONTACT WITH THIS SUBSTANCE.

GLOVES: EMPLOYEE MUST WEAR APPROPRIATE PROTECTIVE GLOVES TO PREVENT CONTACT WITH THIS SUBSTANCE.

EYE PROTECTION: EMPLOYEE MUST WEAR SPLASH-PROOF OR DUST-RESISTANT SAFETY GOGGLES WITH OR WITHOUT A FACESHIELD TO PREVENT CONTACT WITH THIS SUBSTANCE.
EMERGENCY EYE WASH: WHERE THERE IS ANY POSSIBILITY THAT AN EMPLOYEE'S EYES MAY BE EXPOSED TO THIS SUBSTANCE, THE EMPLOYER SHOULD PROVIDE AN EYE WASH FOUNTAIN WITHIN THE IMMEDIATE WORK AREA FOR EMERGENCY USE.

AUTHORIZED BY- OCCUPATIONAL HEALTH SERVICES, INC.
CREATION DATE: 10/04/89 ***REVISION DATE:*** 04/27/90

MATERIAL SAFETY DATA SHEET

OCCUPATIONAL HEALTH SERVICES, INC.
AGRICULTURE AND PESTICIDE DIVISION
450 SEVENTH AVENUE, SUITE 2407
NEW YORK, NEW YORK 10123
1-800-445-MSDS OR (212) 967-1100

EMERGENCY CONTACT:
JOHN S. BRANSFORD, JR. (615) 292-1180

SUBSTANCE IDENTIFICATION

CAS-NUMBER 8001-85-2

SUBSTANCE: BONE OIL

TRADE NAMES/SYNONYMS: ANIMAL OIL; DIPPEL'S OIL; OIL OF HARTSHORN; TEPPEL'S OIL; PST03250

CHEMICAL FAMILY: AMINE, ALKYL-ARYL
HYDROCARBON, ALIPHATIC

CERCLA RATINGS (SCALE 0-3): HEALTH=2 FIRE=U REACTIVITY=0 PERSISTENCE=0

NFPA RATINGS (SCALE 0-4): HEALTH=2 FIRE=U REACTIVITY=0

COMPONENTS AND CONTAMINANTS

COMPONENT: BONE OIL ***PERCENT:*** 100
CAS# 8001-85-2

OTHER CONTAMINANTS: NONE

EXPOSURE LIMITS: NO OCCUPATIONAL EXPOSURE LIMITS ESTABLISHED BY OSHA, ACGIH, OR NIOSH.

PHYSICAL DATA

DESCRIPTION: DARK BROWN OR BLACK LIQUID WITH AN OFFENSIVE, FETID ODOR

BOILING POINT: 176 F (80 C) ***SPECIFIC GRAVITY:*** 0.900-0.980

SOLUBILITY IN WATER: INSOLUBLE

FIRE AND EXPLOSION DATA

FIRE AND EXPLOSION HAZARD: UNKNOWN FIRE AND EXPLOSION HAZARD.

FIREFIGHTING MEDIA: DRY CHEMICAL, CARBON DIOXIDE, HALON, WATER SPRAY OR STANDARD FOAM (1987 EMERGENCY RESPONSE GUIDEBOOK, DOT P 5800.4).
FOR LARGER FIRES, USE WATER SPRAY, FOG OR STANDARD FOAM (1987 EMERGENCY RESPONSE GUIDEBOOK, DOT P 5800.4).

FIREFIGHTING: MOVE CONTAINER FROM FIRE AREA IF POSSIBLE. COOL FIRE-EXPOSED CONTAINERS WITH WATER FROM SIDE UNTIL WELL AFTER FIRE IS OUT. STAY AWAY FROM STORAGE TANK ENDS. FOR MASSIVE FIRE IN STORAGE AREA, USE UNMANNED HOSE HOLDER OR MONITOR NOZZLES, ELSE WITHDRAW FROM AREA AND LET FIRE BURN. WITHDRAW IMMEDIATELY IN CASE OF RISING SOUND FROM VENTING SAFETY DEVICE OR ANY DISCOLORATION OF STORAGE TANK DUE TO FIRE (1987 EMERGENCY RESPONSE GUIDEBOOK, DOT P 5800.4, GUIDE PAGE 27).
EXTINGUISH ONLY IF FLOW CAN BE STOPPED; USE FLOODING AMOUNTS OF WATER AS A FOG, SOLID STREAMS MAY BE INEFFECTIVE. COOL CONTAINERS WITH FLOODING AMOUNTS OF WATER, APPLY FROM AS FAR A DISTANCE AS POSSIBLE. AVOID BREATHING VAPORS, KEEP UPWIND.

TOXICITY

BONE OIL: TOXICITY DATA: 800 MG/KG ORAL-RAT LDLO. CARCINOGEN STATUS: NONE. ACUTE TOXICITY LEVEL: INSUFFICIENT DATA. TARGET EFFECTS: METHEMOGLOBIN FORMER.

HEALTH EFFECTS AND FIRST AID

INHALATION: BONE OIL: ACUTE EXPOSURE- NO DATA AVAILABLE. CHRONIC EXPOSURE- NO DATA AVAILABLE.

FIRST AID- REMOVE FROM EXPOSURE AREA TO FRESH AIR IMMEDIATELY. IF BREATHING HAS STOPPED, PERFORM ARTIFICIAL RESPIRATION. KEEP PERSON WARM AND AT REST. TREAT SYMPTOMATICALLY AND SUPPORTIVELY. GET MEDICAL ATTENTION IMMEDIATELY.

SKIN CONTACT: BONE OIL: ACUTE EXPOSURE- NO DATA AVAILABLE. CHRONIC EXPOSURE- NO DATA AVAILABLE.

FIRST AID- REMOVE CONTAMINATED CLOTHING AND SHOES IMMEDIATELY. WASH AFFECTED AREA WITH SOAP OR MILD DETERGENT AND LARGE AMOUNTS OF

WATER UNTIL NO EVIDENCE OF CHEMICAL REMAINS (APPROXIMATELY 15-20 MINUTES). GET MEDICAL ATTENTION IMMEDIATELY.

EYE CONTACT: BONE OIL: **ACUTE EXPOSURE**-NO DATA AVAILABLE. **CHRONIC EXPOSURE**- NO DATA AVAILABLE.
FIRST AID- WASH EYES IMMEDIATELY WITH LARGE AMOUNTS OF WATER OR NORMAL SALINE, OCCASIONALLY LIFTING UPPER AND LOWER LIDS, UNTIL NO EVIDENCE OF CHEMICAL REMAINS (APPROXIMATELY 15-20 MINUTES). GET MEDICAL ATTENTION IMMEDIATELY.

INGESTION: BONE OIL: METHEMOGLOBIN FORMER. **ACUTE EXPOSURE**- MAY CAUSE FORMATION OF METHEMOGLOBIN WITH SYMPTOMS INCLUDING CYANOSIS, HEADACHE, DIZZINESS, DYSPNEA, STUPOR, RESPIRATION DEPRESSION, AND POSSIBLY DEATH. RATS GIVEN ORAL DOSES OF 31 GM/KG TERMINATED IN 4 MINUTES DUE TO RESPIRATORY ARREST. DOSES OF 10 GM/KG TO RATS PRODUCED AN INITIAL WEAKNESS OF THE HIND LEGS WITHIN 5 MINUTES, DEPRESSION WITH 15 MINUTES AND DEATH IN LESS THAN 2 HOURS. DOSES AS SMALL AS 350 MG/KG RESULTED IN DEPRESSION. **CHRONIC EXPOSURE**- NO DATA AVAILABLE.
FIRST AID- REMOVE BY GASTRIC LAVAGE OR EMESIS. MAINTAIN BLOOD PRESSURE AND AIRWAY. GIVE OXYGEN IF RESPIRATION IS DEPRESSED. DO NOT PERFORM GASTRIC LAVAGE OR EMESIS IF VICTIM IS UNCONSCIOUS. GET MEDICAL ATTENTION IMMEDIATELY (DREISBACH, HANDBOOK OF POISONING, 11TH ED.). ADMINISTRATION OF GASTRIC LAVAGE OR OXYGEN SHOULD BE PERFORMED BY QUALIFIED MEDICAL PERSONNEL.
ANTIDOTE: THE FOLLOWING ANTIDOTE HAS BEEN RECOMMENDED. HOWEVER, THE DECISION AS TO WHETHER THE SEVERITY OF POISONING REQUIRES ADMINISTRATION OF ANY ANTIDOTE AND ACTUAL DOSE REQUIRED SHOULD BE MADE BY QUALIFIED MEDICAL PERSONNEL.
METHEMOGLOBINEMIA: (WHEN METHEMOGLOBIN CONCENTRATION IS OVER 25-40% OR IN PRESENCE OF SYMPTOMS.) GIVE METHYLENE BLUE, 1% SOLUTION, 0.1 ML/KG INTRAVENOUSLY OVER A 10-MINUTE PERIOD. CYANOSIS MAY DISAPPEAR WITHIN MINUTES OR PERSIST LONGER DEPENDING ON DEGREE OF METHEMOGLOBINEMIA. INTRAVENOUS ADMINISTRATION OF THERAPEUTIC DOSES OF METHYLENE BLUE MAY CAUSE A RISE IN BLOOD PRESSURE, NAUSEA, AND DIZZINESS. LARGER DOSES (>500 MG) CAUSE VOMITING, DIARRHEA, CHEST PAIN, MENTAL CONFUSION, CYANOSIS, AND SWEATING. HEMOLYTIC ANEMIA HAS ALSO OCCURRED SEVERAL DAYS AFTER ADMINISTRATION. THESE EFFECTS ARE TEMPORARY, AND FATALITIES HAVE NOT BEEN REPORTED. IF METHYLENE BLUE IS NOT AVAILABLE, GIVE ASCORBIC ACID, 1 GRAM SLOWLY INTRAVENOUSLY. WITHOUT TREATMENT, METHEMOGLOBINEMIA LEVELS OF 20-30% REVERT TO NORMAL WITHIN 3 DAYS (DREISBACH, HANDBOOK OF POISONING, 12TH ED.). ANTIDOTE SHOULD BE ADMINISTERED BY QUALIFIED MEDICAL PERSONNEL.

REACTIVITY

REACTIVITY: STABLE UNDER NORMAL TEMPERATURES AND PRESSURES.
INCOMPATIBILITIES: BONE OIL: NO DATA AVAILABLE.
DECOMPOSITION: THERMAL DECOMPOSITION PRODUCTS MAY INCLUDE TOXIC OXIDES OF CARBON AND NITROGEN.
POLYMERIZATION: HAZARDOUS POLYMERIZATION HAS NOT BEEN REPORTED TO OCCUR UNDER NORMAL TEMPERATURES AND PRESSURES.

CONDITIONS TO AVOID

NONE REPORTED.

SPILL AND LEAK PROCEDURES

OCCUPATIONAL SPILL: NO SPECIAL PRECAUTIONS INDICATED.

PROTECTIVE EQUIPMENT

VENTILATION: PROVIDE LOCAL EXHAUST VENTILATION SYSTEM.
RESPIRATOR: THE FOLLOWING RESPIRATORS ARE RECOMMENDED BASED ON INFORMATION FOUND IN THE PHYSICAL DATA, TOXICITY AND HEALTH EFFECTS SECTIONS. THEY ARE RANKED IN ORDER FROM MINIMUM TO MAXIMUM RESPIRATORY PROTECTION. THE SPECIFIC RESPIRATOR SELECTED MUST BE BASED ON CONTAMINATION LEVELS FOUND IN THE WORK PLACE, MUST NOT EXCEED THE WORKING LIMITS OF THE RESPIRATOR AND BE JOINTLY APPROVED BY THE NATIONAL INSTITUTE FOR OCCUPATIONAL SAFETY AND HEALTH AND THE MINE SAFETY AND HEALTH ADMINISTRATION (NIOSH-MSHA).
CHEMICAL CARTRIDGE RESPIRATOR WITH AN ORGANIC VAPOR CARTRIDGE(S) WITH A FULL FACEPIECE.
GAS MASK WITH ORGANIC VAPOR CANISTER (CHIN-STYLE OR FRONT- OR BACK-MOUNTED CANISTER) WITH A FULL FACEPIECE.
TYPE 'C' SUPPLIED-AIR RESPIRATOR WITH A FULL FACEPIECE OPERATED IN PRESSURE-DEMAND OR OTHER POSITIVE PRESSURE MODE OR WITH A FULL FACEPIECE, HELMET OR HOOD OPERATED IN CONTINUOUS-FLOW MODE.
SELF-CONTAINED BREATHING APPARATUS WITH A FULL FACEPIECE OPERATED IN PRESSURE-DEMAND OR OTHER POSITIVE PRESSURE MODE.
FOR FIREFIGHTING AND OTHER IMMEDIATELY DANGEROUS TO LIFE OR HEALTH CONDITIONS:
SELF-CONTAINED BREATHING APPARATUS WITH FULL FACEPIECE OPERATED IN PRESSURE-DEMAND OR OTHER POSITIVE PRESSURE MODE.
SUPPLIED-AIR RESPIRATOR WITH FULL FACEPIECE AND OPERATED IN PRESSURE-DEMAND OR OTHER POSITIVE PRESSURE MODE IN COMBINATION WITH AN AUXILIARY SELF-CONTAINED BREATHING APPARATUS OPERATED IN PRESSURE-DEMAND OR OTHER POSITIVE PRESSURE MODE.
CLOTHING: EMPLOYEE MUST WEAR APPROPRIATE PROTECTIVE (IMPERVIOUS) CLOTHING AND EQUIPMENT TO PREVENT REPEATED OR PROLONGED SKIN CONTACT WITH THIS SUBSTANCE.
GLOVES: EMPLOYEE MUST WEAR APPROPRIATE PROTECTIVE GLOVES TO PREVENT CONTACT WITH THIS SUBSTANCE.
EYE PROTECTION: EMPLOYEE MUST WEAR SPLASH-PROOF OR DUST-RESISTANT SAFETY GOGGLES TO PREVENT EYE CONTACT WITH THIS SUBSTANCE.
EMERGENCY EYE WASH: WHERE THERE IS ANY POSSIBILITY THAT AN EMPLOYEE'S EYES MAY BE EXPOSED TO THIS SUBSTANCE, THE EMPLOYER SHOULD PROVIDE AN EYE WASH FOUNTAIN WITHIN THE IMMEDIATE WORK AREA FOR EMERGENCY USE.

AUTHORIZED BY- OCCUPATIONAL HEALTH SERVICES, INC.
CREATION DATE: 10/04/89 ***REVISION DATE:*** 05/18/90

MATERIAL SAFETY DATA SHEET

OCCUPATIONAL HEALTH SERVICES, INC.
AGRICULTURE AND PESTICIDE DIVISION
450 SEVENTH AVENUE, SUITE 2407
NEW YORK, NEW YORK 10123
1-800-445-MSDS OR (212) 967-1100

EMERGENCY CONTACT:
JOHN S. BRANSFORD, JR. (615) 292-1180

SUBSTANCE IDENTIFICATION

CAS-NUMBER 10043-35-3
SUBSTANCE: **BORIC ACID**
TRADE NAMES/SYNONYMS: BORIC ACID (H3BO3); BORACIC ACID; BORIC TRIHYDROXIDE; ORTHOBORIC ACID; ORTHOBORIC ACID (B(OH)3); ORTHOBORIC ACID (H3BO3); TRIHYDROXYBORANE; BH3O3; PST03260
CHEMICAL FAMILY: INORGANIC ACID
MOLECULAR FORMULA: H3-B-O3
MOLECULAR WEIGHT: 61.84
CERCLA RATINGS (SCALE 0-3): HEALTH=3 FIRE=0 REACTIVITY=0 PERSISTENCE=0
NFPA RATINGS (SCALE 0-4): HEALTH=3 FIRE=0 REACTIVITY=0

COMPONENTS AND CONTAMINANTS

COMPONENT: BORIC ACID ***PERCENT:*** 100.0
CAS# 10043-35-3
OTHER CONTAMINANTS: NONE
EXPOSURE LIMITS: NO OCCUPATIONAL EXPOSURE LIMITS ESTABLISHED BY OSHA, ACGIH, OR NIOSH.

PHYSICAL DATA

DESCRIPTION: ODORLESS, COLORLESS, TRANSPARENT CRYSTALS OR WHITE GRANULES OR POWDER; SLIGHTLY UNCTUOUS TO THE TOUCH.
MELTING POINT: 338-356 F (170-180 C) (DECOMPOSES)
SPECIFIC GRAVITY: 1.435 @ 15 C ***VAPOR PRESSURE:*** 2.6 MMHG @ 20 C
PH: 5.1 @ 0.6% SOLUTION ***SOLUBILITY IN WATER:*** 6.35% @ 30 C
SOLVENT SOLUBILITY: SOLUBLE IN BOILING ALCOHOL AND GLYCEROL; MODERATELY SOLUBLE IN LIQUID AMMONIA; SLIGHTLY SOLUBLE IN ACETONE; VERY SLIGHTLY SOLUBLE IN ETHER.

FIRE AND EXPLOSION DATA

FIRE AND EXPLOSION HAZARD: NEGLIGIBLE FIRE HAZARD WHEN EXPOSED TO HEAT OR FLAME.
FIREFIGHTING MEDIA: EXTINGUISH USING AGENT SUITABLE FOR TYPE OF SURROUNDING FIRE.
FIREFIGHTING: NO ACUTE HAZARD. MOVE CONTAINER FROM FIRE AREA IF POSSIBLE. AVOID BREATHING VAPORS OR DUSTS; KEEP UPWIND.

TOXICITY

BORIC ACID: IRRITATION DATA: 15 MG/3 DAYS INTERMITTENT SKIN-HUMAN MILD. TOXICITY DATA: 28 MG/M3/4 HOURS INHALATION-RAT LCLO; 4 GM/KG/4 DAYS SKIN-CHILD LDLO; 1500 MG/KG SKIN-CHILD LDLO; 1200 MG/KG SKIN-INFANT LDLO; 2430 MG/KG SKIN-MAN LDLO; 500 MG/KG ORAL-CHILD TDLO; 800 MG/KG/4 WEEKS INTERMITTENT ORAL-INFANT TDLO; 934 MG/KG ORAL-INFANT LDLO; 200 MG/KG ORAL-WOMAN LDLO; 2660 MG/KG ORAL-RAT LD50; 3450 MG/KG ORAL-MOUSE LD50; 4 GM/KG ORAL-RABBIT LDLO; 1 GM/KG ORAL-GUINEA PIG LDLO; 1780 MG/KG ORAL-DOG LDLO; 1100 MG/KG SUBCUTANEOUS-INFANT LDLO; 1400 MG/KG SUBCUTANEOUS-RAT LD50; 1740 MG/KG SUBCUTANEOUS-MOUSE LD50; 1200 MG/KG SUBCUTANEOUS-GUINEA PIG LD50; 1000 MG/KG SUBCUTANEOUS-DOG LDLO; 150 MG/KG SUBCUTANEOUS-RABBIT LDLO; 1330 MG/KG INTRAVENOUS-RAT LD50; 1240 MG/KG INTRAVENOUS-MOUSE LD50; 800 MG/KG INTRAVENOUS-RABBIT LDLO; 800 MG/KG INTRAPERITONEAL-MOUSE LDLO; 1 GM/KG PARENTERAL-DOG LDLO; 670 MG/KG PARENTERAL-RABBIT LDLO; 170 MG/KG UNREPORTED-MAN TDLO; 147 MG/KG UNREPORTED-MAN TDLO; MUTAGENIC DATA (RTECS); REPRODUCTIVE EFFECTS DATA (RTECS). CARCINOGEN STATUS: NONE. LOCAL EFFECTS: IRRITANT- INHALATION, SKIN. ACUTE TOXICITY LEVEL: MODERATELY TOXIC BY INGESTION. TARGET EFFECTS: NEPHROTOXIN; CENTRAL NERVOUS SYSTEM DEPRESSANT. POISONING MAY AFFECT THE GASTROINTESTINAL SYSTEM AND CIRCULATORY SYSTEM. ADDITIONAL DATA: MAY CROSS THE PLACENTA.

HEALTH EFFECTS AND FIRST AID

INHALATION: BORIC ACID: IRRITANT/NARCOTIC/NEPHROTOXIN. **ACUTE EXPOSURE-** MAY CAUSE IRRITATION TO THE MUCOUS MEMBRANES, SORE THROAT, AND COUGHING. ABSORPTION THROUGH THE MUCOUS MEMBRANES MAY CAUSE SYSTEMIC POISONING AS DESCRIBED IN ACUTE INGESTION. **CHRONIC EXPOSURE-** WORKERS EXPOSED TO DUST LEVELS >31 MG/M3 SHOWED ATROPHIC AND SUBATROPHIC CHANGES OF RESPIRATORY MUCOUS MEMBRANES. PROLONGED INHALATION MAY CAUSE POISONING AS DESCRIBED IN CHRONIC INGESTION. REPRODUCTIVE EFFECTS HAVE BEEN REPORTED IN ANIMALS.

FIRST AID- REMOVE FROM EXPOSURE AREA TO FRESH AIR IMMEDIATELY. IF BREATHING HAS STOPPED, PERFORM ARTIFICIAL RESPIRATION. KEEP PERSON WARM AND AT REST. TREAT SYMPTOMATICALLY AND SUPPORTIVELY. GET MEDICAL ATTENTION IMMEDIATELY.

SKIN CONTACT: BORIC ACID: IRRITANT/NARCOTIC/NEPHROTOXIN. **ACUTE EXPOSURE-** MAY CAUSE IRRITATION. DEATHS HAVE OCCURRED BY SKIN ABSORPTION, PARTICULARLY IN INFANTS AND ESPECIALLY IF SKIN IS DAMAGED, ABRADED OR BURNED. SYSTEMIC POISONING MAY CAUSE EFFECTS AS IN ACUTE INGESTION. **CHRONIC EXPOSURE-** REPEATED OR PROLONGED CONTACT MAY CAUSE DERMATITIS. STUDIES IN OLD LITERATURE INDICATE PROLONGED SKIN ABSORPTION MAY CAUSE HALLUCINATIONS OF VISION, DECREASE OF VISUAL ACUITY, AND DIPLOPIA. OTHER SYSTEMIC EFFECTS MAY OCCUR AS DESCRIBED IN CHRONIC INGESTION.

FIRST AID- REMOVE CONTAMINATED CLOTHING AND SHOES IMMEDIATELY. WASH AFFECTED AREA WITH SOAP OR MILD DETERGENT AND LARGE AMOUNTS OF WATER UNTIL NO EVIDENCE OF CHEMICAL REMAINS (APPROXIMATELY 15-20 MINUTES). GET MEDICAL ATTENTION IMMEDIATELY.

EYE CONTACT: BORIC ACID: **ACUTE EXPOSURE-** REPORTED TO BE NON-IRRITATING TO THE EYES. **CHRONIC EXPOSURE-** NO DATA AVAILABLE.

FIRST AID- WASH EYES IMMEDIATELY WITH LARGE AMOUNTS OF WATER OR NORMAL SALINE, OCCASIONALLY LIFTING UPPER AND LOWER LIDS, UNTIL NO EVIDENCE OF CHEMICAL REMAINS (APPROXIMATELY 15-20 MINUTES). GET MEDICAL ATTENTION IMMEDIATELY.

INGESTION: BORIC ACID: NARCOTIC/NEPHROTOXIN. **ACUTE EXPOSURE-** INGESTION MAY CAUSE NAUSEA, EPIGASTRIC PAIN, HEMORRHAGIC GASTRITIS, BLOODY VOMIT AND DIARRHEA, WEAKNESS, LETHARGY, HEADACHE, RESTLESSNESS, TREMORS AND TWITCHING OF FACIAL MUSCLES AND EXTREMITIES, INTERMITTENT CONVULSIONS, AND EVENTUAL CENTRAL NERVOUS SYSTEM DEPRESSION WITH CONFUSION, DROWSINESS, AND PROSTRATION. SHOCK MAY OCCUR WITH COLD, CLAMMY SKIN, CYANOSIS, HYPOTENSION, TACHYCARDIA, WEAK PULSE, DELIRIUM AND COMA. DEATH FROM CIRCULATORY FAILURE, CENTRAL NERVOUS SYSTEM DEPRESSION OR RENAL FAILURE MAY OCCUR IMMEDIATELY OR IN 4-7 DAYS. ERYTHRODERMA MAY OCCUR, FOLLOWED BY DESQUAMATION, EXCORIATION, BLISTERING, BULLAE, AND LESIONS, TYPICALLY LOCATED ON THE PALMS, SOLES, BUTTOCKS, AND SCROTUM. THE PHARYNX AND TYMPANIC MEMBRANES MAY ALSO BE AFFECTED. KIDNEY DAMAGE MAY BE INDICATED BY OLIGURIA, ALBUMINURIA AND ANURIA. LIVER DAMAGE WITH JAUNDICE AND HEPATOMEGALY IS RARE. OTHER SYMPTOMS OF POISONING ARE ACIDOSIS, INTRAVASCULAR COAGULATION, ANEMIA, VISUAL DISTURBANCES, AND FEVER. **CHRONIC EXPOSURE-** REPEATED INGESTION MAY CAUSE GASTROINTESTINAL IRRITATION AND DISTURBANCES, LOSS OF APPETITE, DISTURBED DIGESTION, NAUSEA, POSSIBLY VOMITING, ERYTHEMATOUS RASH WHICH MAY BECOME HARD AND PURPURIC, DRYNESS OF SKIN AND MUCOUS MEMBRANES, REDDENING OF THE TONGUE, CRACKING OF THE LIPS, LOSS OF HAIR, CONJUNCTIVITIS, PALPEBRAL EDEMA AND KIDNEY INJURY. ANIMAL STUDIES INDICATE PROLONGED INGESTION MAY CAUSE A VARIETY OF REPRODUCTIVE EFFECTS. IN FEMALE RATS THE OVARIES AND FALLOPIAN TUBES WERE AFFECTED, AND IN MALES THE TESTES, EPIDIDYMIS, AND SPERM DUCT WERE AFFECTED.

FIRST AID- MAINTAIN RESPIRATION. REMOVE BY IPECAC EMESIS FOLLOWED BY ACTIVATED CHARCOAL. GASTRIC LAVAGE MAY BE USEFUL. TREAT ANURIA. (DREISBACH HANDBOOK OF POISONING, 11TH ED.) GET MEDICAL ATTENTION IMMEDIATELY. TREATMENT SHOULD BE PERFORMED BY QUALIFIED MEDICAL PERSONNEL.

ANTIDOTE: NO SPECIFIC ANTIDOTE. TREAT SYMPTOMATICALLY AND SUPPORTIVELY.

REACTIVITY

REACTIVITY: STABLE UNDER NORMAL TEMPERATURES AND PRESSURES.

INCOMPATIBILITIES: BORIC ACID: ACETIC ANHYDRIDE: EXPLOSIVE REACTION ON HEATING. IRON: MAY BE CORROSIVE IN PRESENCE OF MOISTURE. POTASSIUM: POSSIBLE VIOLENT OR EXPLOSIVE REACTION.

DECOMPOSITION: THE SUBSTANCE GRADUALLY LOSES WATER @ 100-160 C FORMING METABORIC ACID, THEN PYROBORIC ACID, AND FINALLY BORIC ANHYDRIDE.

POLYMERIZATION: HAZARDOUS POLYMERIZATION HAS NOT BEEN REPORTED TO OCCUR UNDER NORMAL TEMPERATURES AND PRESSURES.

STORAGE AND DISPOSAL

OBSERVE ALL FEDERAL, STATE AND LOCAL REGULATIONS WHEN STORING OR DISPOSING OF THIS SUBSTANCE. FOR ASSISTANCE, CONTACT THE DISTRICT DIRECTOR OF THE ENVIRONMENTAL PROTECTION AGENCY.

STORAGE

STORE AWAY FROM INCOMPATIBLE SUBSTANCES.

CONDITIONS TO AVOID

NO REPORTS FOUND.

SPILL AND LEAK PROCEDURES

OCCUPATIONAL SPILL: SWEEP UP AND PLACE IN SUITABLE CLEAN, DRY CONTAINERS FOR RECLAMATION OR LATER DISPOSAL. DO NOT FLUSH SPILLED MATERIAL INTO SEWER. KEEP UNNECESSARY PEOPLE AWAY.

PROTECTIVE EQUIPMENT

VENTILATION: PROVIDE LOCAL EXHAUST OR GENERAL DILUTION VENTILATION SYSTEM.

RESPIRATOR: THE FOLLOWING RESPIRATORS ARE RECOMMENDED BASED ON INFORMATION FOUND IN THE PHYSICAL DATA, TOXICITY AND HEALTH EFFECTS SECTIONS. THEY ARE RANKED IN ORDER FROM MINIMUM TO MAXIMUM RESPIRATORY PROTECTION. THE SPECIFIC RESPIRATOR SELECTED MUST BE BASED ON CONTAMINATION LEVELS FOUND IN THE WORK PLACE, MUST NOT EXCEED THE WORKING LIMITS OF THE RESPIRATOR AND BE JOINTLY APPROVED BY THE NATIONAL INSTITUTE FOR OCCUPATIONAL SAFETY AND HEALTH AND THE MINE SAFETY AND HEALTH ADMINISTRATION (NIOSH-MSHA).

TYPE 'C' SUPPLIED-AIR RESPIRATOR WITH A FULL FACEPIECE OPERATED IN PRESSURE-DEMAND OR OTHER POSITIVE PRESSURE MODE OR WITH A FULL FACEPIECE, HELMET OR HOOD OPERATED IN CONTINOUS-FLOW MODE.

SELF-CONTAINED BREATHING APPARATUS WITH A FULL FACEPIECE OPERATED IN PRESSURE-DEMAND OR OTHER POSITIVE PRESSURE MODE.

FOR FIREFIGHTING AND OTHER IMMEDIATELY DANGEROUS TO LIFE OR HEALTH CONDITIONS:

SELF-CONTAINED BREATHING APPARATUS WITH FULL FACEPIECE OPERATED IN PRESSURE-DEMAND OR OTHER POSITIVE PRESSURE MODE.

SUPPLIED-AIR RESPIRATOR WITH FULL FACEPIECE AND OPERATED IN PRESSURE-DEMAND OR OTHER POSITIVE PRESSURE MODE IN COMBINATION WITH AN AUXILIARY SELF-CONTAINED BREATHING APPARATUS OPERATED IN PRESSURE-DEMAND OR OTHER POSITIVE PRESSURE MODE.

CLOTHING: EMPLOYEE MUST WEAR APPROPRIATE PROTECTIVE (IMPERVIOUS) CLOTHING AND EQUIPMENT TO PREVENT REPEATED OR PROLONGED SKIN CONTACT WITH THIS SUBSTANCE.

GLOVES: EMPLOYEE MUST WEAR APPROPRIATE PROTECTIVE GLOVES TO PREVENT CONTACT WITH THIS SUBSTANCE.

EYE PROTECTION: EMPLOYEE MUST WEAR SPLASH-PROOF OR DUST-RESISTANT SAFETY GOGGLES TO PREVENT EYE CONTACT WITH THIS SUBSTANCE.

EMERGENCY EYE WASH: WHERE THERE IS ANY POSSIBILITY THAT AN EMPLOYEE'S EYES MAY BE EXPOSED TO THIS SUBSTANCE, THE EMPLOYER SHOULD PROVIDE AN EYE WASH FOUNTAIN WITHIN THE IMMEDIATE WORK AREA FOR EMERGENCY USE.

AUTHORIZED BY- OCCUPATIONAL HEALTH SERVICES, INC.
CREATION DATE: 10/04/89 ***REVISION DATE:*** 05/31/90

MATERIAL SAFETY DATA SHEET

OCCUPATIONAL HEALTH SERVICES, INC.
AGRICULTURE AND PESTICIDE DIVISION
450 SEVENTH AVENUE, SUITE 2407
NEW YORK, NEW YORK 10123
1-800-445-MSDS OR (212) 967-1100

EMERGENCY CONTACT:
JOHN S. BRANSFORD, JR. (615) 292-1180

SUBSTANCE IDENTIFICATION

CAS-NUMBER 1303-86-2
SUBSTANCE: **BORON OXIDE**
TRADE NAMES/SYNONYMS: ANHYDROUS BORIC ACID; BORIC ANHYDRIDE; BORIC OXIDE; BORON SESQUIOXIDE; BORON TRIOXIDE; FUSED BORIC ACID; DIBORON TRIOXIDE; BORON OXIDE (B2O3); BORIC OXIDE (B2O3); A-76; B2O3; PST03290
CHEMICAL FAMILY: NON-METALLIC OXIDE
MOLECULAR FORMULA: O-B-O-B-O
MOLECULAR WEIGHT: 69.62
CERCLA RATINGS (SCALE 0-3): HEALTH=2 FIRE=0 REACTIVITY=0 PERSISTENCE=3
NFPA RATINGS (SCALE 0-4): HEALTH=2 FIRE=0 REACTIVITY=0

COMPONENTS AND CONTAMINANTS

COMPONENT: BORON OXIDE ***PERCENT:*** 100
CAS# 1303-86-2
OTHER CONTAMINANTS: NONE
EXPOSURE LIMITS: BORON OXIDE: 10 MG/M3 OSHA TWA (TOTAL DUST) 10 MG/M3 ACGIH TWA

PHYSICAL DATA

DESCRIPTION: ODORLESS, HYGROSCOPIC WHITE POWDER OR CRYSTALLINE SOLID WITH A SLIGHTLY BITTER TASTE. ***BOILING POINT:*** 3380 F (1860 C)
MELTING POINT: 838-846 F (448-452 C) ***SOLUBILITY IN WATER:*** 2.77% @ 20 C
SOLVENT SOLUBILITY: SOLUBLE IN ETHYL ALCOHOL, GLYCEROL; SLIGHTLY SOLUBLE IN ACIDS.
SPECIFIC GRAVITY: 2.46 (CRYSTALLINE); 1.84 (AMORPHOUS)

FIRE AND EXPLOSION DATA

FIRE AND EXPLOSION HAZARD: NEGLIGIBLE FIRE HAZARD WHEN EXPOSED TO HEAT OR FLAME.
FIREFIGHTING MEDIA: EXTINGUISH USING AGENT SUITABLE FOR TYPE OF SURROUNDING FIRE.
FIREFIGHTING: NO ACUTE HAZARD. MOVE CONTAINER FROM FIRE AREA IF POSSIBLE. AVOID BREATHING VAPORS OR DUSTS; KEEP UPWIND.

TOXICITY

BORON OXIDE (BORIC ANHYDRIDE): IRRITATION DATA: 1 GM SKIN-RABBIT; 50 MG EYE-RABBIT. TOXICITY DATA: 3163 MG/KG ORAL-MOUSE LD50; 1868 MG/KG INTRAPERITONEAL-MOUSE LD50. CARCINOGEN STATUS: NONE. LOCAL EFFECTS: IRRITANT- INHALATION, SKIN, AND EYES. ACUTE TOXICITY LEVEL: MODERATELY TOXIC BY INGESTION. TARGET EFFECTS: POISONING MAY AFFECT THE LIVER, KIDNEYS, AND CIRCULATORY SYSTEM.

HEALTH EFFECTS AND FIRST AID

INHALATION: BORON OXIDE (BORIC ANHYDRIDE): IRRITANT. **ACUTE EXPOSURE-** INHALATION OF DUST PARTICLES OR HIGH LEVELS OF AEROSOL MAY CAUSE IRRITATION TO THE NOSE, THROAT, AND RESPIRATORY TRACT. EXPOSURE TO FUMES MAY CAUSE AN INCREASE IN BODY TEMPERATURE, SHORTNESS OF BREATH, DIZZINESS, DOUBLE VISION, AND GENERALIZED SEVERE MYALGIA, WITH SYMPTOMS CLEARING UPON REMOVAL FROM EXPOSURE. **CHRONIC EXPOSURE-** REPEATED OR PROLONGED ABSORPTION MAY CAUSE WEIGHT LOSS, DYSPROTEINAEMIA, CARBOHYDRATE METABOLISM DISORDERS, MODERATE LIVER AND KIDNEY CHANGES, AND VASCULAR DISORDERS. REPEATED EXPOSURE OF RATS TO 470 MG/M3 FOR 10 WEEKS CAUSED MILD NASAL IRRITATION AND TO 77 MG/M3 FOR 23 WEEKS RESULTED IN ELEVATED CREATININE AND BORON CONTENT OF THE URINE, IN ADDITION TO INCREASED URINARY VOLUME.
FIRST AID- REMOVE FROM EXPOSURE AREA TO FRESH AIR IMMEDIATELY. IF BREATHING HAS STOPPED, PERFORM ARTIFICIAL RESPIRATION. KEEP PERSON WARM AND AT REST. TREAT SYMPTOMATICALLY AND SUPPORTIVELY. GET MEDICAL ATTENTION IMMEDIATELY.

SKIN CONTACT: BORON OXIDE (BORIC ANHYDRIDE): IRRITANT. **ACUTE EXPOSURE-** DIRECT CONTACT MAY CAUSE IRRITATION DUE TO BORON OXIDE BEING CONVERTED TO BORIC ACID. TOPICAL APPLICATION OF BORON OXIDE DUST TO THE CLIPPED BACKS OF RABBITS RESULTED IN ERYTHEMA THAT PERSISTED FOR 2-3 DAYS. **CHRONIC EXPOSURE-** REPEATED OR PROLONGED ABSORPTION MAY CAUSE WEIGHT LOSS, CARBOHYDRATE METABOLISM DISORDERS, MODERATE CHANGES OF THE LIVER AND KIDNEYS, VASCULAR DISORDERS, AND PROTEINEMIA.
FIRST AID- REMOVE CONTAMINATED CLOTHING AND SHOES IMMEDIATELY. WASH AFFECTED AREA WITH SOAP OR MILD DETERGENT AND LARGE AMOUNTS OF WATER UNTIL NO EVIDENCE OF CHEMICAL REMAINS (APPROXIMATELY 15-20 MINUTES). GET MEDICAL ATTENTION IMMEDIATELY.

EYE CONTACT: BORON OXIDE (BORIC ANHYDRIDE): IRRITANT. **ACUTE EXPOSURE-** DIRECT CONTACT WITH DUST PARTICLES CAUSED ALMOST IMMEDIATE IRRITATION AND CONJUNCTIVITIS IN RABBITS, DUE TO BORON OXIDE BEING CONVERTED TO BORIC ACID. **CHRONIC EXPOSURE-** REPEATED OR PROLONGED EXPOSURE MAY CAUSE CONJUNCTIVITIS.
FIRST AID- WASH EYES IMMEDIATELY WITH LARGE AMOUNTS OF WATER OR NORMAL SALINE, OCCASIONALLY LIFTING UPPER AND LOWER LIDS, UNTIL NO EVIDENCE OF CHEMICAL REMAINS (APPROXIMATELY 15-20 MINUTES). GET MEDICAL ATTENTION IMMEDIATELY.

INGESTION: BORON OXIDE (BORIC ANHYDRIDE): **ACUTE EXPOSURE-** INGESTION OF LARGE AMOUNTS MAY RESULT IN GASTROINTESTINAL DISTURBANCES. **CHRONIC EXPOSURE-** REPEATED OR PROLONGED ABSORPTION MAY CAUSE WEIGHT LOSS, CARBOHYDRATE METABOLISM DISORDERS, MODERATE CHANGES OF THE LIVER AND KIDNEYS, VASCULAR DISORDERS, AND PROTEINEMIA.
FIRST AID- IF THE PERSON IS CONSCIOUS AND NOT CONVULSING, INDUCE EMESIS BY GIVING SYRUP OF IPECAC FOLLOWED BY WATER. (IF VOMITING OCCURS KEEP THE HEAD BELOW THE HIPS TO PREVENT ASPIRATION). REPEAT IN 20 MINUTES IF NOT EFFECTIVE INITIALLY. GIVE ACTIVATED CHARCOAL. IN PATIENTS WITH DEPRESSED RESPIRATION OR IF EMESIS IS NOT PRODUCED, PERFORM GASTRIC LAVAGE CAUTIOUSLY (DREISBACH, HANDBOOK OF POISONING, 12TH ED.). TREAT SYMPTOMATICALLY AND SUPPORTIVELY. GASTRIC LAVAGE SHOULD BE PERFORMED BY QUALIFIED MEDICAL PERSONNEL. GET MEDICAL ATTENTION IMMEDIATELY.
ANTIDOTE: NO SPECIFIC ANTIDOTE. TREAT SYMPTOMATICALLY AND SUPPORTIVELY.

REACTIVITY

REACTIVITY: STABLE UNDER NORMAL TEMPERATURES AND PRESSURES.
INCOMPATIBILITIES: BORON OXIDE (BORIC ANHYDRIDE): BROMINE PENTAFLUORIDE: VIOLENT REACTION AND POSSIBLE IGNITION.
DECOMPOSITION: THERMAL DECOMPOSITION MAY RELEASE TOXIC AND/OR HAZARDOUS GASES.
POLYMERIZATION: HAZARDOUS POLYMERIZATION HAS NOT BEEN REPORTED TO OCCUR UNDER NORMAL TEMPERATURES AND PRESSURES.

STORAGE AND DISPOSAL

OBSERVE ALL FEDERAL, STATE AND LOCAL REGULATIONS WHEN STORING OR DISPOSING OF THIS SUBSTANCE. FOR ASSISTANCE, CONTACT THE DISTRICT DIRECTOR OF THE ENVIRONMENTAL PROTECTION AGENCY.

****STORAGE****

STORE AWAY FROM INCOMPATIBLE SUBSTANCES.

CONDITIONS TO AVOID

PREVENT DISPERSION OF DUST IN AIR.

SPILL AND LEAK PROCEDURES

OCCUPATIONAL SPILL: FOR LARGE SPILLS, SWEEP UP WITH A MINIMUM OF DUSTING AND PLACE INTO SUITABLE CLEAN, DRY CONTAINERS FOR RECLAMATION OR LATER DISPOSAL.
RESIDUE SHOULD BE CLEANED UP USING A HIGH-EFFICIENCY PARTICULATE FILTER VACUUM.

PROTECTIVE EQUIPMENT

VENTILATION: PROVIDE LOCAL EXHAUST VENTILATION AND/OR GENERAL DILUTION VENTILATION TO MEET PUBLISHED EXPOSURE LIMITS.
RESPIRATOR: THE FOLLOWING RESPIRATORS AND MAXIMUM USE CONCENTRATIONS ARE RECOMMENDATIONS BY THE U.S. DEPARTMENT OF HEALTH AND HUMAN SERVICES, NIOSH POCKET GUIDE TO CHEMICAL HAZARDS; NIOSH CRITERIA DOCUMENTS OR BY THE U.S. DEPARTMENT OF LABOR, 29 CFR 1910 SUBPART Z. THE SPECIFIC RESPIRATOR SELECTED MUST BE BASED ON CONTAMINATION LEVELS FOUND IN THE WORK PLACE, MUST NOT EXCEED THE WORKING LIMITS OF

THE RESPIRATOR AND BE JOINTLY APPROVED BY THE NATIONAL INSTITUTE FOR OCCUPATIONAL SAFETY AND HEALTH AND THE MINE SAFETY AND HEALTH ADMINISTRATION (NIOSH-MSHA).
BORON OXIDE:
50 MG/M3- ANY DUST AND MIST RESPIRATOR.
100 MG/M3- ANY DUST AND MIST RESPIRATOR EXCEPT SINGLE-USE AND QUARTER-MASK RESPIRATORS. ANY SUPPLIED-AIR RESPIRATOR. ANY SELF-CONTAINED BREATHING APPARATUS.
250 MG/M3- ANY POWERED AIR-PURIFYING RESPIRATOR WITH DUST AND MIST FILTER. ANY SUPPLIED-AIR RESPIRATOR OPERATED IN CONTINUOUS FLOW MODE.
500 MG/M3- ANY SELF-CONTAINED BREATHING APPARATUS WITH FULL FACEPIECE. ANY SUPPLIED-AIR RESPIRATOR WITH FULL FACEPIECE. ANY AIR-PURIFYING FULL FACEPIECE RESPIRATOR WITH HIGH-EFFICIENCY PARTICULATE FILTER. ANY POWERED AIR-PURIFYING RESPIRATOR WITH TIGHT-FITTING FACEPIECE AND HIGH-EFFICIENCY PARTICULATE FILTER.
7500 MG/M3- ANY SUPPLIED-AIR RESPIRATOR WITH FULL FACEPIECE OPERATED IN PRESSURE DEMAND OR OTHER POSITIVE PRESSURE MODE.
ESCAPE- ANY AIR-PURIFYING FULL FACEPIECE RESPIRATOR WITH HIGH-EFFICIENCY PARTICULATE FILTER. ANY APPROPRIATE ESCAPE-TYPE SELF-CONTAINED BREATHING APPARATUS.
FOR FIREFIGHTING AND OTHER IMMEDIATELY DANGEROUS TO LIFE OR HEALTH CONDITIONS:
SELF-CONTAINED BREATHING APPARATUS WITH FULL FACEPIECE OPERATED IN PRESSURE-DEMAND OR OTHER POSITIVE PRESSURE MODE.
SUPPLIED-AIR RESPIRATOR WITH FULL FACEPIECE AND OPERATED IN PRESSURE-DEMAND OR OTHER POSITIVE PRESSURE MODE IN COMBINATION WITH AN AUXILIARY SELF-CONTAINED BREATHING APPARATUS OPERATED IN PRESSURE-DEMAND OR OTHER POSITIVE PRESSURE MODE.

CLOTHING: EMPLOYEE MUST WEAR APPROPRIATE PROTECTIVE (IMPERVIOUS) CLOTHING AND EQUIPMENT TO PREVENT REPEATED OR PROLONGED SKIN CONTACT WITH THIS SUBSTANCE.

GLOVES: EMPLOYEE MUST WEAR APPROPRIATE PROTECTIVE GLOVES TO PREVENT CONTACT WITH THIS SUBSTANCE.

EYE PROTECTION: EMPLOYEE MUST WEAR SPLASH-PROOF OR DUST-RESISTANT SAFETY GOGGLES TO PREVENT EYE CONTACT WITH THIS SUBSTANCE.
EMERGENCY EYE WASH: WHERE THERE IS ANY POSSIBILITY THAT AN EMPLOYEE'S EYES MAY BE EXPOSED TO THIS SUBSTANCE, THE EMPLOYER SHOULD PROVIDE AN EYE WASH FOUNTAIN WITHIN THE IMMEDIATE WORK AREA FOR EMERGENCY USE.

AUTHORIZED BY- OCCUPATIONAL HEALTH SERVICES, INC.
CREATION DATE: 10/04/89 ***REVISION DATE:*** 05/09/90

MATERIAL SAFETY DATA SHEET

OCCUPATIONAL HEALTH SERVICES, INC.
AGRICULTURE AND PESTICIDE DIVISION
450 SEVENTH AVENUE, SUITE 2407
NEW YORK, NEW YORK 10123
1-800-445-MSDS OR (212) 967-1100

EMERGENCY CONTACT:
JOHN S. BRANSFORD, JR. (615) 292-1180

SUBSTANCE IDENTIFICATION

CAS-NUMBER 3766-81-2

SUBSTANCE: **FENOBUCARB**

TRADE NAMES/SYNONYMS: PHENOL, 2-(1-METHYLPROPYL)-, METHYLCARBAMATE; 2-(1-METHYLPROPYL)PHENOL METHYLCARBAMATE; CARBAMIC ACID, METHYL-, O-SEC-BUTYLPHENYL ESTER; METHYLCARBAMIC ACID O-SEC-BUTYLPHENYL ESTER; BASSA; O-SEC-BUTYLPHENYL METHYLCARBAMATE; 2-SEC-BUTYLPHENYL METHYLCARBAMATE; BPMC; BAYER 41 367C; C12H17NO2; PST03324

CHEMICAL FAMILY: CARBAMATE

MOLECULAR FORMULA: C12-H17-N-O2

MOLECULAR WEIGHT: 207.30

CERCLA RATINGS (SCALE 0-3): HEALTH=3 FIRE=1 REACTIVITY=0 PERSISTENCE=1

NFPA RATINGS (SCALE 0-4): HEALTH=3 FIRE=1 REACTIVITY=0

COMPONENTS AND CONTAMINANTS

COMPONENT: FENOBUCARB ***PERCENT:*** 100.0
CAS# 3766-81-2

OTHER CONTAMINANTS: NONE

EXPOSURE LIMITS: NO OCCUPATIONAL EXPOSURE LIMITS ESTABLISHED BY OSHA, ACGIH, OR NIOSH.

PHYSICAL DATA

DESCRIPTION: PALE YELLOW TO PALE REDDISH CRYSTALS. ***BOILING POINT:*** NOT AVAILABLE

MELTING POINT: 88-90 F (31-32 C) ***SPECIFIC GRAVITY:*** 1.035 @ 30 C

VAPOR PRESSURE: 0.00036 MMHG @ 20 C ***SOLUBILITY IN WATER:*** 0.061% @ 30 C

SOLVENT SOLUBILITY: SOLUBLE IN ACETONE, BENZENE, TOLUENE, XYLENE AND CHLOROFORM.

FIRE AND EXPLOSION DATA

FIRE AND EXPLOSION HAZARD: SLIGHT FIRE HAZARD WHEN EXPOSED TO HEAT OR FLAME.
DUST-AIR MIXTURES MAY IGNITE OR EXPLODE.

FLASH POINT: 270 F (132 C)

FIREFIGHTING MEDIA: DRY CHEMICAL, CARBON DIOXIDE, HALON, WATER SPRAY OR STANDARD FOAM (1987 EMERGENCY RESPONSE GUIDEBOOK, DOT P 5800.4).
FOR LARGER FIRES, USE WATER SPRAY, FOG OR STANDARD FOAM (1987 EMERGENCY RESPONSE GUIDEBOOK, DOT P 5800.4).

FIREFIGHTING: MOVE CONTAINERS FROM FIRE AREA IF POSSIBLE (1987 EMERGENCY RESPONSE GUIDEBOOK, DOT P 5800.4, GUIDE PAGE 53).
EXTINGUISH USING AGENT SUITABLE FOR TYPE OF SURROUNDING FIRE. AVOID BREATHING VAPORS AND DUSTS. KEEP UPWIND.

TOXICITY

FENOBUCARB: TOXICITIY DATA: 3.3 MG/L/4 HOURS INHALATION-RAT LC50 (RHONE-POULENC MSDS); >2000 MG/KG SKIN-RABBIT LD50 (RHONE-POULENC MSDS); 340 MG/KG SKIN-MOUSE LD50; 350 MG/KG ORAL-RAT LD50; 173 MG/KG ORAL-MOUSE LD50; 42 MG/KG INTRAVENOUS-MOUSE LD50; 140 MG/KG INTRAPERITONEAL-MOUSE LD50. CARCINOGEN STATUS: NONE. ACUTE TOXICITY LEVEL: TOXIC BY INHALATION, DERMAL ABSORPTION, INGESTION. TARGET EFFECTS: CHOLINESTERASE INHIBITOR. AT INCREASED RISK FROM EXPOSURE: PERSONS WITH ASTHMA, DIABETES, CARDIOVASCULAR DISEASE, MECHANICAL OBSTRUCTION OF THE GASTROINTESTINAL OR UROGENITAL TRACT, AND THOSE IN VAGOTONIC STATES.*
* MAY BE BASED ON GENERAL INFORMATION ON CARBAMATES.

HEALTH EFFECTS AND FIRST AID

INHALATION: FENOBUCARB: TOXIC. DUST MAY CAUSE IRRITATION, COUGHING, AND EXPECTORATION. SEE INFORMATION ON CARBAMATES.
CARBAMATES: CHOLINESTERASE INHIBITOR. **ACUTE EXPOSURE**- WHEN INHALED, THE FIRST EFFECTS OF CHOLINESTERASE INHIBITION ARE USUALLY RESPIRATORY AND MAY INCLUDE NASAL HYPEREMIA AND WATERY DISCHARGE, CHEST DISCOMFORT, DYSPNEA, AND WHEEZING DUE TO INCREASED BRONCHIAL SECRETIONS AND BRONCHOCONSTRICTION. OTHER SYSTEMIC EFFECTS MAY BEGIN WITHIN A FEW MINUTES OR SEVERAL HOURS OF EXPOSURE. SYMPTOMS MAY INCLUDE NAUSEA, VOMITING, DIARRHEA, ABDOMINAL CRAMPS, HEADACHE, VERTIGO, OCULAR PAIN, CILIARY MUSCLE SPASM, BLURRING OR DIMNESS OF VISION, MIOSIS, OR IN SOME CASES MYDRIASIS, LACRIMATION, SALIVATION, SWEATING, AND CONFUSION. OTHER REPORTED CENTRAL NERVOUS SYSTEM OR NEUROMUSCULAR EFFECTS INCLUDE ATAXIA, SLURRED SPEECH, AREFLEXIA, WEAKNESS, FATIGUE, TWITCHING, FASCICULATION, TREMOR, AND EVENTUALLY PARALYSIS OF THE EXTREMITIES AND POSSIBLY OF THE RESPIRATORY MUSCLES. IN SEVERE CASES, THERE MAY ALSO BE INVOLUNTARY DEFECATION AND URINATION, BRADYCARDIA, HYPOTENSION, PULMONARY EDEMA, CONVULSIONS, COMA, AND DEATH FROM RESPIRATORY FAILURE OR CARDIAC ARREST. CARBAMATES GENERALLY DO NOT ACCUMULATE IN MAMMALIAN TISSUE AND THE CHOLINESTERASE INHIBITION REVERSES RATHER RAPIDLY. IN NON-FATAL CASES, THE ILLNESS GENERALLY LASTS LESS THAN 24 HOURS. **CHRONIC EXPOSURE**- PROLONGED OR REPEATED EXPOSURE MAY CAUSE EFFECTS AS DESCRIBED IN ACUTE EXPOSURE.

FIRST AID- REMOVE FROM EXPOSURE AREA TO FRESH AIR IMMEDIATELY. IF BREATHING HAS STOPPED, GIVE ARTIFICIAL RESPIRATION. MAINTAIN AIRWAY AND BLOOD PRESSURE AND ADMINISTER OXYGEN IF AVAILABLE. KEEP AFFECTED PERSON WARM AND AT REST. TREAT SYMPTOMATICALLY AND SUPPORTIVELY. ADMINISTRATION OF OXYGEN SHOULD BE PERFORMED BY QUALIFIED PERSONNEL. GET MEDICAL ATTENTION IMMEDIATELY.

SKIN CONTACT: FENOBUCARB: TOXIC. CONTACT MAY CAUSE MINIMAL IRRITATION. SEE INFORMATION ON CARBAMATES.
CARBAMATES: CHOLINESTERASE INHIBITOR. **ACUTE EXPOSURE**- SOME COMPOUNDS MAY CAUSE IRRITATION. LOCALIZED SWEATING AND FASCICULATIONS MAY OCCUR AT THE SITE OF CONTACT. IF SUFFICIENT AMOUNTS ARE ABSORBED THROUGH THE SKIN, OTHER EFFECTS OF CHOLINESTERASE INHIBITION MAY OCCUR AS DESCRIBED IN ACUTE INHALATION; SYMPTOMS MAY BE DELAYED FOR 2-3 HOURS, USUALLY NO MORE THAN 8

HOURS. **CHRONIC EXPOSURE-** REPEATED OR PROLONGED EXPOSURE MAY CAUSE EFFECTS AS DESCRIBED IN ACUTE EXPOSURE.

FIRST AID- REMOVE CONTAMINATED CLOTHING IMMEDIATELY. WASH CONTAMINATED AREAS WITH SOAP AND WATER FOLLOWED BY ALCOHOL (ARENA, POISONING, 4TH ED.). EMERGENCY PERSONNEL SHOULD WEAR GLOVES AND AVOID CONTAMINATION. TREAT RESPIRATORY DIFFICULTY WITH ARTIFICIAL RESPIRATION. GET MEDICAL ATTENTION IMMEDIATELY.

EYE CONTACT: FENOBUCARB: CONTACT MAY CAUSE MINIMAL IRRITATION. SEE INFORMATION ON CARBAMATES.
CARBAMATES: CHOLINESTERASE INHIBITOR. **ACUTE EXPOSURE-** DIRECT CONTACT MAY CAUSE PAIN, HYPEREMIA, LACRIMATION, TWITCHING OF THE EYELIDS, MIOSIS, AND CILIARY MUSCLE SPASM WITH LOSS OF ACCOMODATION, BLURRED OR DIMMED VISION AND BROWACHE. SOMETIMES MYDRIASIS MAY OCCUR INSTEAD OF MIOSIS. WITH SUFFICIENT EXPOSURE, OTHER SYMPTOMS OF CHOLINESTERASE INHIBITION MAY OCCUR AS DESCRIBED IN ACUTE INHALATION. **CHRONIC EXPOSURE-** PROLONGED EXPOSURE MAY CAUSE EFFECTS AS DESCRIBED IN ACUTE EXPOSURE. SOME COMPOUNDS HAVE CAUSED TOXIC EFFECTS ON THE CRYSTALLINE LENS, CONJUNCTIVAL THICKENING AND OBSTRUCTION OF NASOLACRIMAL CANALS WHEN USED AS MIOTIC EYE DROPS.

FIRST AID- IRRIGATE EYES WITH WATER OR SALINE SOLUTION. IF SYMPTOMS OF POISONING OCCUR, TREAT RESPIRATORY DIFFICULTY WITH ARTIFICIAL RESPIRATION AND OXYGEN. OBSERVE PATIENT FOR AT LEAST 24-36 HOURS (GOSSELIN, CLINICAL TOXICOLOGY OF COMMERCIAL PRODUCTS, 5TH ED.). GET MEDICAL ATTENTION IMMEDIATELY. OXYGEN SHOULD BE ADMINISTERED BY QUALIFIED MEDICAL PERSONNEL.

INGESTION: FENOBUCARB: TOXIC. IN DOMESTIC ANIMALS, DEATH FOLLOWED ECG CHANGES. PATHOLOGIC FINDINGS INCLUDED PETECHIAL HEMORRHAGES OF THE KIDNEYS, HEART, THYMUS, URINARY BLADDER, AND RESPIRATORY MUSCLES, ENLARGEMENT OF LYMPH NODES, AND ESOPHAGEAL ULCERATION. SEE INFORMATION ON CARBAMATES.
CARBAMATES: CHOLINESTERASE INHIBITOR. **ACUTE EXPOSURE-** WHEN INGESTED, THE FIRST EFFECTS MAY BE NAUSEA, VOMITING, ANOREXIA, ABDOMINAL CRAMPS, AND DIARRHEA. WITH ABSORPTION FROM THE GASTROINTESTINAL TRACT, THE OTHER EFFECTS OF CHOLINESTERASE INHIBITION AS DESCRIBED IN ACUTE INHALATION MAY OCCUR; SYMPTOMS MAY BEGIN WITHIN MINUTES OR BE DELAYED SEVERAL HOURS. **CHRONIC EXPOSURE-** REPEATED INGESTION MAY CAUSE EFFECTS AS DESCRIBED IN ACUTE EXPOSURE.

FIRST AID- IF PERSON IS ALERT AND RESPIRATION IS NOT DEPRESSED, GIVE SYRUP OF IPECAC FOLLOWED BY WATER (IF VOMITING OCCURS, KEEP HEAD BELOW HIPS TO PREVENT ASPIRATION). IF CONSCIOUSNESS LEVEL DECLINES OR VOMITING HAS NOT OCCURRED IN 15 MINUTES EMPTY STOMACH BY GASTRIC LAVAGE WITH THE AID OF CUFFED ENDOTRACHEAL TUBE USING ISOTONIC SALINE OR 5% SODIUM BICARBONATE FOLLOW WITH ACTIVATED CHARCOAL. ESTABLISH AND MAINTAIN AIRWAY. TREAT RESPIRATORY DIFFICULTY WITH ARTIFICIAL RESPIRATION AND OXYGEN. DO NOT GIVE MORPHINE, AMINOPHYLLINE, PHENOTHIAZINES, RESERPINE, FUROSEMIDE, OR ETHACRYNIC ACID (MORGAN, RECOGNITION AND MANAGEMENT OF PESTICIDE POISONINGS, 3RD ED.). TREAT SYMPTOMATICALLY AND SUPPORTIVELY. ADMINISTRATION OF OXYGEN AND LAVAGE MUST BE PERFORMED BY QUALIFIED MEDICAL PERSONNEL. GET MEDICAL ATTENTION IMMEDIATELY.

ANTIDOTE: THE FOLLOWING ANTIDOTE(S) HAVE BEEN RECOMMENDED. HOWEVER, THE DECISION AS TO WHETHER THE SEVERITY OF POISONING REQUIRES ADMINISTRATION OF ANY ANTIDOTE AND ACTUAL DOSE REQUIRED SHOULD BE MADE BY QUALIFIED MEDICAL PERSONNEL.
FOR CHOLINESTERASE INHIBITORS: ESTABLISH CLEAR AIRWAY AND TISSUE OXYGENATION BY ASPIRATION OF SECRETIONS, AND IF NECESSARY, BY ASSISTED PULMONARY VENTILATION WITH OXYGEN. IMPROVE TISSUE OXYGENATION AS MUCH AS POSSIBLE BEFORE ADMINISTERING ATROPINE TO MINIMIZE THE RISK OF VENTRICULAR FIBRILLATION. ADMINISTER ATROPINE SULFATE INTRAVENOUSLY, OR INTRAMUSCULARLY IF IV INJECTION IS NOT POSSIBLE. IN MODERATELY SEVERE POISONING ADMINISTER ATROPINE SULFATE, 0.4-2.0 MG REPEATED EVERY 15 MINUTES UNTIL ATROPINIZATION IS ACHIEVED (TACHYCARDIA, FLUSHING, DRY MOUTH, MYDRIASIS). MAINTAIN ATROPINIZATION BY REPEATED DOSES FOR 2-12 HOURS, OR LONGER, DEPENDING ON THE SEVERITY OF POISONING. THE APPEARANCE OF RALES IN THE LUNG BASES, MIOSIS, SALIVATION, NAUSEA, BRADYCARDIA, ARE ALL INDICATIONS OF INADEQUATE ATROPINIZATION. SEVERELY POISONED INDIVIDUALS MAY EXHIBIT REMARKABLE TOLERANCE TO ATROPINE; TWO OR MORE TIMES THE DOSAGES SUGGESTED ABOVE MAY BE NEEDED. PERSONS NOT POISONED OR ONLY SLIGHTLY POISONED, HOWEVER, MAY DEVELOP SIGNS OF ATROPINE TOXICITY FROM SUCH LARGE DOSAGES: FEVER, MUSCLE FIBRILLATIONS, AND DELIRIUM ARE THE MAIN SIGNS OF ATROPINE TOXICITY. IF THESE SIGNS APPEAR WHILE THE PATIENT IS FULLY ATROPINIZED, ATROPINE ADMINISTRATION SHOULD BE DISCONTINUED, AT LEAST TEMPORARILY. OBSERVE TREATED PATIENTS CLOSELY AT LEAST 24 HOURS TO INSURE THAT SYMPTOMS (POSSIBLY PULMONARY EDEMA) DO NOT RECUR AS ATROPINIZATION WEARS OFF. IN VERY SEVERE POISONINGS, METABOLIC DISPOSITION OF TOXICANT MAY REQUIRE SEVERAL HOURS OR DAYS DURING WHICH ATROPINIZATION MUST BE MAINTAINED. MARKEDLY LOWER LEVELS OF URINARY METABOLITES INDICATE THAT ATROPINE DOSAGE CAN BE TAPERED OFF. AS DOSAGE IS REDUCED, CHECK THE LUNG BASES FREQUENTLY FOR RALES. IF RALES ARE HEARD OR OTHER SYMPTOMS RETURN, RE-ESTABLISH ATROPINIZATION PROMPTLY (MORGAN, RECOGNITION AND MANAGEMENT OF PESTICIDE POISONINGS, 3RD ED.). ADMINISTRATION OF ANTIDOTE MUST BE PERFORMED BY QUALIFIED MEDICAL PERSONNEL.
PRALIDOXIME (PROTOPAM-AYERST, 2-PAM) IS OF DOUBTFUL VALUE IN POISONINGS BY CARBAMATE INHIBITORS OF CHOLINESTERASE. ATROPINE ALONE IS ALMOST ALWAYS AN ADEQUATE ANTIDOTE. PRALIDOXIME IS PROBABLY CONTRAINDICATED IN POISONING BY CARBARYL SPECIFICALLY, AND OTHER MONOMETHYLATED CARBAMATES. IF A VICTIM OF DIMETHYLCARBAMATE INSECTICIDE POISONING FAILS TO RESPOND PROMPTLY AND ADEQUATELY TO ATROPINE, OR IF POISONING INVOLVES A COMBINATION OF CARBAMATE AND ORGANOPHOSPHATE, A DILUTE SOLUTION OF PRALIDOXIME (TOTAL DOSE IN 250 ML 5% GLUCOSE SOLUTION) MAY BE GIVEN CAUTIOUSLY INTRAVENOUSLY. ADULT DOSAGE IS 1 GRAM (MORGAN, RECOGNITION AND MANAGEMENT OF PESTICIDE POISONINGS, THIRD EDITION; HAYES, PESTICIDES STUDIED IN MAN, 1982).

REACTIVITY

REACTIVITY: STABLE UNDER NORMAL TEMPERATURES AND PRESSURES.

INCOMPATIBILITIES: FENOBUCARB: ACIDS (STRONG): EXOTHERMIC REACTION. ALKALIES (STRONG): EXOTHERMIC REACTION. OXIDIZERS (STRONG): FIRE AND EXPLOSION HAZARD.

DECOMPOSITION: THERMAL DECOMPOSITION PRODUCTS MAY INCLUDE TOXIC OXIDES OF CARBON AND NITROGEN.

POLYMERIZATION: HAZARDOUS POLYMERIZATION HAS NOT BEEN REPORTED TO OCCUR UNDER NORMAL TEMPERATURES AND PRESSURES.

STORAGE AND DISPOSAL

OBSERVE ALL FEDERAL, STATE AND LOCAL REGULATIONS WHEN STORING OR DISPOSING OF THIS SUBSTANCE. FOR ASSISTANCE, CONTACT THE DISTRICT DIRECTOR OF THE ENVIRONMENTAL PROTECTION AGENCY.

****STORAGE****

STORE IN ACCORDANCE WITH 40 CFR 165 RECOMMENDED PROCEDURES FOR THE DISPOSAL AND STORAGE OF PESTICIDES AND PESTICIDE CONTAINERS.
DO NOT STORE AT TEMPERATURES ABOVE 194 F (90 C) FOR PROLONGED PERIODS OF TIME.

****DISPOSAL****

DISPOSAL MUST BE IN ACCORDANCE WITH 40 CFR 165 RECOMMENDED PROCEDURES FOR THE DISPOSAL AND STORAGE OF PESTICIDES AND PESTICIDE CONTAINERS.

CONDITIONS TO AVOID

MAY BURN BUT DOES NOT IGNITE READILY.
PREVENT DISPERSION OF DUST IN AIR.

SPILL AND LEAK PROCEDURES

OCCUPATIONAL SPILL: DO NOT TOUCH SPILLED MATERIAL. STOP LEAK IF YOU CAN DO IT WITHOUT RISK. FOR SMALL SPILLS, TAKE UP WITH SAND OR OTHER ABSORBENT MATERIAL AND PLACE INTO CONTAINERS FOR LATER DISPOSAL. FOR SMALL DRY SPILLS, WITH A CLEAN SHOVEL PLACE MATERIAL INTO CLEAN, DRY CONTAINER AND COVER. MOVE CONTAINERS FROM SPILL AREA. FOR LARGER SPILLS, DIKE FAR AHEAD OF SPILL FOR LATER DISPOSAL. KEEP UNNECESSARY PEOPLE AWAY. ISOLATE HAZARD AREA AND DENY ENTRY.

PROTECTIVE EQUIPMENT

VENTILATION: PROVIDE LOCAL EXHAUST OR PROCESS ENCLOSURE VENTILATION SYSTEM.

RESPIRATOR: THE FOLLOWING RESPIRATORS ARE RECOMMENDED BASED ON INFORMATION FOUND IN THE PHYSICAL DATA, TOXICITY AND HEALTH EFFECTS SECTIONS. THEY ARE RANKED IN ORDER FROM MINIMUM TO MAXIMUM RESPIRATORY PROTECTION. THE SPECIFIC RESPIRATOR SELECTED MUST BE BASED ON CONTAMINATION LEVELS FOUND IN THE WORK PLACE, MUST NOT EXCEED THE WORKING LIMITS OF THE RESPIRATOR AND BE JOINTLY APPROVED BY THE NATIONAL INSTITUTE FOR OCCUPATIONAL SAFETY AND HEALTH AND THE MINE SAFETY AND HEALTH ADMINISTRATION (NIOSH-MSHA).
TYPE 'C' SUPPLIED-AIR RESPIRATOR WITH A FULL FACEPIECE OPERATED IN PRESSURE-DEMAND OR OTHER POSITIVE PRESSURE MODE OR WITH A FULL FACEPIECE, HELMET OR HOOD OPERATED IN CONTINOUS-FLOW MODE.
SELF-CONTAINED BREATHING APPARATUS WITH A FULL FACEPIECE OPERATED IN PRESSURE-DEMAND OR OTHER POSITIVE PRESSURE MODE.
FOR FIREFIGHTING AND OTHER IMMEDIATELY DANGEROUS TO LIFE OR HEALTH CONDITIONS:

SELF-CONTAINED BREATHING APPARATUS WITH FULL FACEPIECE OPERATED IN PRESSURE-DEMAND OR OTHER POSITIVE PRESSURE MODE.
SUPPLIED-AIR RESPIRATOR WITH FULL FACEPIECE AND OPERATED IN PRESSURE-DEMAND OR OTHER POSITIVE PRESSURE MODE IN COMBINATION WITH AN AUXILIARY SELF-CONTAINED BREATHING APPARATUS OPERATED IN PRESSURE-DEMAND OR OTHER POSITIVE PRESSURE MODE.
CLOTHING: EMPLOYEE MUST WEAR APPROPRIATE PROTECTIVE (IMPERVIOUS) CLOTHING AND EQUIPMENT TO PREVENT ANY POSSIBILITY OF SKIN CONTACT WITH THIS SUBSTANCE.
GLOVES: EMPLOYEE MUST WEAR APPROPRIATE PROTECTIVE GLOVES TO PREVENT CONTACT WITH THIS SUBSTANCE.
EYE PROTECTION: EMPLOYEE MUST WEAR SPLASH-PROOF OR DUST-RESISTANT SAFETY GOGGLES WITH OR WITHOUT A FACESHIELD TO PREVENT CONTACT WITH THIS SUBSTANCE.
EMERGENCY EYE WASH: WHERE THERE IS ANY POSSIBILITY THAT AN EMPLOYEE'S EYES MAY BE EXPOSED TO THIS SUBSTANCE, THE EMPLOYER SHOULD PROVIDE AN EYE WASH FOUNTAIN WITHIN THE IMMEDIATE WORK AREA FOR EMERGENCY USE.

AUTHORIZED BY- OCCUPATIONAL HEALTH SERVICES, INC.
CREATION DATE: 10/04/89 ***REVISION DATE:*** 06/12/90

MATERIAL SAFETY DATA SHEET

OCCUPATIONAL HEALTH SERVICES, INC.
AGRICULTURE AND PESTICIDE DIVISION
450 SEVENTH AVENUE, SUITE 2407
NEW YORK, NEW YORK 10123
1-800-445-MSDS OR (212) 967-1100

EMERGENCY CONTACT:
JOHN S. BRANSFORD, JR. (615) 292-1180

SUBSTANCE IDENTIFICATION

CAS-NUMBER 56073-10-0
SUBSTANCE: BRODIFACOUM
TRADE NAMES/SYNONYMS: 2H-1-BENZOPYRAN-2-ONE, 3-(3-(4'-BROMO(1,1'-BIPHENYL)-4-YL)- 1,2,3,4-TETRAHYDRO-1-NAPHTHALENYL)-4-HYDROXY-; 3-(3-(4'-BROMO(1,1'-BIPHENYL)-4-YL)-1,2,3,4-TETRAHYDRO-1-NAPHTHALENYL)-4-HYDROXY-2H-1-BENZOPYRAN-2-ONE; 3-(3-(4'-BROMOBIPHENYL-4-YL)-1,2,3,4-TETRAHYDRO-1-NAPHTHYL-4- HYDROXYCOUMARIN; HAVOC; KLERAT; PP-581; RATAK +; TALON; VOLAK; VOLID; WBA 8119; C31H23BRO3; PST03327
CHEMICAL FAMILY: COUMARIN
MOLECULAR FORMULA: C31-H23-BR-O3
MOLECULAR WEIGHT: 523.44
CERCLA RATINGS (SCALE 0-3): HEALTH=3 FIRE=1 REACTIVITY=0 PERSISTENCE=2
NFPA RATINGS (SCALE 0-4): HEALTH=4 FIRE=1 REACTIVITY=0

COMPONENTS AND CONTAMINANTS

COMPONENT: BRODIFACOUM ***PERCENT:*** 100.0
CAS# 56073-10-0
EXPOSURE LIMITS: NO OCCUPATIONAL EXPOSURE LIMITS ESTABLISHED BY OSHA, ACGIH, OR NIOSH.

PHYSICAL DATA

DESCRIPTION: OFF-WHITE TO FAWN POWDER.
MELTING POINT: 442-450 F (228-232C)
SPECIFIC GRAVITY: NOT AVAILABLE ***VAPOR PRESSURE:*** NEGLIGIBLE
SOLUBILITY IN WATER: 10 PPM
SOLVENT SOLUBILITY: SOLUBLE IN ACETONE, CHLOROFORM; MODERATELY SOLUBLE IN BENZENE, ETHANOL; INSOLUBLE IN PETROLEUM ETHER.

FIRE AND EXPLOSION DATA

FIRE AND EXPLOSION HAZARD: SLIGHT FIRE HAZARD WHEN EXPOSED TO HEAT OR FLAME.
FIREFIGHTING MEDIA: DRY CHEMICAL, CARBON DIOXIDE, HALON, WATER SPRAY OR STANDARD FOAM (1987 EMERGENCY RESPONSE GUIDEBOOK, DOT P 5800.4). FOR LARGER FIRES, USE WATER SPRAY, FOG OR STANDARD FOAM (1987 EMERGENCY RESPONSE GUIDEBOOK, DOT P 5800.4).
FIREFIGHTING: MOVE CONTAINERS FROM FIRE AREA IF POSSIBLE. FIGHT FIRE FROM MAXIMUM DISTANCE. STAY AWAY FROM STORAGE TANK ENDS. DIKE FIRE CONTROL WATER FOR LATER DISPOSAL. DO NOT SCATTER MATERIAL (1987 EMERGENCY RESPONSE GUIDEBOOK, DOT P 5800.4, GUIDE PAGE 55). EXTINGUISH USING AGENT SUITABLE FOR TYPE OF SURROUNDING FIRE. AVOID BREATHING VAPORS AND DUSTS. KEEP UPWIND.

TRANSPORTATION DATA

DEPARTMENT OF TRANSPORTATION HAZARD CLASSIFICATION 49 CFR 172.101: POISON B
DEPARTMENT OF TRANSPORTATION LABELING REQUIREMENTS 49 CFR 172.101 AND SUBPART E: POISON
DEPARTMENT OF TRANSPORTATION PACKAGING REQUIREMENTS: 49 CFR 173.365 EXCEPTIONS: 49 CFR 173.364

TOXICITY

BRODIFACOUM: TOXICITY DATA: 50 MG/KG SKIN-RAT LD50; 120 UG/KG ORAL-MAN TDLO; 160 UG/KG ORAL-RAT LD50; 290 UG/KG ORAL-MOUSE LD50; 200 UG/KG ORAL-RABBIT LD50; 2800 UG/KG ORAL-GUINEA PIG LD50; 250 UG/KG ORAL-DOG LD50; 25 MG/KG ORAL-CAT LD50; 1 MG/KG ORAL-GERBIL LD50; 1320 UG/KG ORAL-MAMMAL LD50; 3 MG/KG ORAL-DOMESTIC ANIMAL LDLO. CARCINOGEN STATUS: NONE. ACUTE TOXICITY LEVEL: HIGHLY TOXIC BY DERMAL ABSORPTION AND INGESTION. TARGET EFFECTS: HEMORRHAGIC AGENT. AT INCREASED RISK FROM EXPOSURE: PERSONS WITH BLOOD DYSCRASIAS WITH BLEEDING TENDENCIES, LIVER OR KIDNEY DISEASE, ULCERS OF THE GASTROINTESTINAL TRACT, OR HYPERTENSION.* ADDITIONAL DATA: INTERACTIONS WITH MEDICATIONS HAVE BEEN REPORTED.*
*MAY BE BASED ON GENERAL INFORMATION ON COUMARIN DERIVATIVES.

HEALTH EFFECTS AND FIRST AID

INHALATION: BRODIFACOUM: SEE INFORMATION ON COUMARIN DERIVATIVES.
COUMARIN DERIVATIVES: HEMORRHAGIC AGENT. **ACUTE EXPOSURE-** ABSORPTION BY THE LUNGS MAY RESULT IN HEMORRHAGIC EFFECTS AS DESCRIBED IN CHRONIC EXPOSURE. SEVERE CASES MAY BE FATAL. **CHRONIC EXPOSURE-** REPEATED ABSORPTION MAY CAUSE THE INHIBITION OF PROTHROMBIN SYNTHESIS AND DAMAGE TO CAPILLARY PERMEABILITY RESULTING IN WIDESPREAD INTERNAL HEMORRHAGE WITH ASSOCIATED EFFECTS OF NOSEBLEED, HEMATOMA, HEMATURIA, WIDESPREAD BRUISING, AND ANEMIA.
FIRST AID- REMOVE FROM EXPOSURE AREA TO FRESH AIR IMMEDIATELY. IF BREATHING HAS STOPPED, PERFORM ARTIFICIAL RESPIRATION. KEEP PERSON WARM AND AT REST. TREAT SYMPTOMATICALLY AND SUPPORTIVELY. GET MEDICAL ATTENTION IMMEDIATELY.

SKIN CONTACT: BRODIFACOUM: HIGHLY TOXIC. SEE INFORMATION ON COUMARIN DERIVATIVES.
COUMARIN DERIVATIVES: HEMORRHAGIC AGENT. **ACUTE EXPOSURE-** ABSORPTION THROUGH THE SKIN MAY RESULT IN HEMORRHAGIC EFFECTS AS DESCRIBED IN CHRONIC EXPOSURE. SEVERE CASES MAY BE FATAL. **CHRONIC EXPOSURE-** REPEATED ABSORPTION MAY CAUSE THE INHIBITION OF PROTHROMBIN SYNTHESIS AND DAMAGE TO CAPILLARY PERMEABILITY RESULTING IN WIDESPREAD INTERNAL HEMORRHAGE WITH ASSOCIATED EFFECTS OF NOSEBLEED, HEMATOMA, HEMATURIA, WIDESPREAD BRUISING, AND ANEMIA.
FIRST AID- REMOVE CONTAMINATED CLOTHING AND SHOES IMMEDIATELY. WASH AFFECTED AREA WITH SOAP OR MILD DETERGENT AND LARGE AMOUNTS OF WATER UNTIL NO EVIDENCE OF CHEMICAL REMAINS (APPROXIMATELY 15-20 MINUTES). GET MEDICAL ATTENTION IMMEDIATELY.

EYE CONTACT: BRODIFACOUM: **ACUTE EXPOSURE-** NO DATA AVAILABLE. **CHRONIC EXPOSURE-** NO DATA AVAILABLE.
FIRST AID- WASH EYES IMMEDIATELY WITH LARGE AMOUNTS OF WATER OR NORMAL SALINE, OCCASIONALLY LIFTING UPPER AND LOWER LIDS, UNTIL NO EVIDENCE OF CHEMICAL REMAINS (APPROXIMATELY 15-20 MINUTES). GET MEDICAL ATTENTION IMMEDIATELY.

INGESTION: BRODIFACOUM: HIGHLY TOXIC. SEE INFORMATION ON COUMARIN DERIVATIVES.
COUMARIN DERIVATIVES: HEMORRHAGIC AGENT. **ACUTE EXPOSURE-** MAY BE READILY ABSORBED FROM THE GASTROINTESTINAL TRACT AND CAUSE THE INHIBITION OF PROTHROMBIN SYNTHESIS AND DAMAGE TO CAPILLARY PERMEABILITY RESULTING IN WIDESPREAD INTERNAL HEMORRHAGE ACCOMPANIED BY THE HEMORRHAGIC SYMPTOMS AS DESCRIBED IN CHRONIC EXPOSURE. SEVERE CASES MAY BE FATAL. **CHRONIC EXPOSURE-** REPEATED INGESTION MAY CAUSE NOSEBLEED, BLEEDING GUMS AND PHARYNX, PETECHIAL RASH, WIDESPREAD BRUISING, HEMATOMA, HEMOPTYSIS, HEMATEMESIS, HEMATURIA, BLOODY STOOLS, BLEEDING INTO THE ORGANS, GASTROINTESTINAL TRACT, JOINTS, ABDOMINAL OR RETROPERITONEAL AREA WITH ABDOMINAL, BACK, JOINT AND LIMB PAIN AND CEREBROVASCULAR ACCIDENT. ANEMIA ACCOMPANIED BY WEAKNESS, PALLOR, AND SHOCK MAY OCCUR. SEVERE HEMORRHAGING MAY CAUSE DEATH. THERAPEUTIC USE OF SOME COUMARIN

DERIVATIVES HAS INFREQUENTLY PRODUCED GASTROINTESTINAL DISTURBANCES, ELEVATED TRANSAMINASE, URTICARIA, DERMATITIS, LEUKOPENIA, ALOPECIA, FEVER, HYPERSENSITIVITY REACTIONS, AND RARELY SKIN NECROSIS.

FIRST AID- IF ONLY A FEW GRAINS OF ANTICOAGULANT BAIT HAVE BEEN INGESTED BY AN ADULT OR CHILD HAVING NO ANTECEDENT LIVER OR BLOOD CLOTTING DISEASE, TREATMENT IS PROBABLY UNNECESSARY. IF LARGE AMOUNTS OF ANTICOAGULANT WERE INGESTED IN THE PRECEDING 2-3 HOURS, INDUCE VOMITING WITH SYRUP OF IPECAC, FOLLOWED BY 1-2 GLASSES OF WATER. FOLLOWING EMESIS, GIVE ACTIVATED CHARCOAL IN 4-6 OUNCES OF WATER TO LIMIT ABSORPTION OF ANTICOAGULANT REMAINING IN THE GUT. OBSERVE PATIENT 4-5 DAYS AFTER INGESTION. (MORGAN, RECOGNITION AND MANAGEMENT OF PESTICIDE POISONINGS, THIRD EDITION). GET MEDICAL ATTENTION.

ANTIDOTE: THE FOLLOWING ANTIDOTE HAS BEEN RECOMMENDED. HOWEVER, THE DECISION AS TO WHETHER THE SEVERITY OF POISONING REQUIRES ADMINISTRATION OF ANY ANTIDOTE AND ACTUAL DOSE REQUIRED SHOULD BE MADE BY QUALIFIED MEDICAL PERSONNEL.

OVERDOSE OF ANTICOAGULANTS: VITAMIN K IS A SPECIFIC ANTIDOTE. VITAMIN K1 EMULSION IS THE PREFERRED FORM. THE INITIAL SUBCUTANEOUS OR INTRAMUSCULAR DOSE IN ADULTS IS 5 TO 10 MG (UP TO 25 MG), REPEATED ONCE IF NECESSARY. ONLY IN VICTIMS WHO ARE BLEEDING SEVERLY OR OTHERWISE IN SERIOUS DISTRESS SHOULD THE DRUG BE GIVEN INTRAVENOUSLY AND THEN AT A RATE NO FASTER THAN 1 MG/MINUTE. IF NECESSARY, ON SUBSEQUENT DAYS, VITAMIN K1 SHOULD BE CONTINUED AT A REDUCED LEVEL UNTIL THE PROTHROMBIN TIME RETURNS TO NORMAL. VITAMIN K1 IS PREFERABLE TO K1 OXIDE (DOSE 0.5-2.5) AND CERTAINLY PREFERABLE TO MENADIONE OR MENADIONE SODIUM BISULFITE (GOSSELIN, CLINICAL TOXICOLOGY OF COMMERCIAL PRODUCTS, 5TH ED.). ANTIDOTE SHOULD BE ADMINISTERED BY QUALIFIED MEDICAL PERSONNEL.

REACTIVITY

REACTIVITY: STABLE UNDER NORMAL TEMPERATURES AND PRESSURES.

INCOMPATIBILITIES: BRODIFACOUM: OXIDIZERS (STRONG): FIRE AND EXPLOSION HAZARD.

DECOMPOSITION: THERMAL DECOMPOSITION PRODUCTS MAY INCLUDE TOXIC AND CORROSIVE FUMES OF BROMIDES AND TOXIC OXIDES OF CARBON.

POLYMERIZATION: HAZARDOUS POLYMERIZATION HAS NOT BEEN REPORTED TO OCCUR UNDER NORMAL TEMPERATURES AND PRESSURES.

STORAGE AND DISPOSAL

OBSERVE ALL FEDERAL, STATE AND LOCAL REGULATIONS WHEN STORING OR DISPOSING OF THIS SUBSTANCE. FOR ASSISTANCE, CONTACT THE DISTRICT DIRECTOR OF THE ENVIRONMENTAL PROTECTION AGENCY.

STORAGE

STORE IN ACCORDANCE WITH 40 CFR 165 RECOMMENDED PROCEDURES FOR THE DISPOSAL AND STORAGE OF PESTICIDES AND PESTICIDE CONTAINERS.

STORE AWAY FROM INCOMPATIBLE SUBSTANCES.

DISPOSAL

DISPOSAL MUST BE IN ACCORDANCE WITH 40 CFR 165 RECOMMENDED PROCEDURES FOR THE DISPOSAL AND STORAGE OF PESTICIDES AND PESTICIDE CONTAINERS.

CONDITIONS TO AVOID

MAY BURN BUT DOES NOT IGNITE READILY. CONTAINERS MAY EXPLODE IN HEAT OF FIRE.

SPILL AND LEAK PROCEDURES

OCCUPATIONAL SPILL: DO NOT TOUCH SPILLED MATERIAL. STOP LEAK IF YOU CAN DO IT WITHOUT RISK. USE WATER SPRAY TO REDUCE VAPORS. FOR SMALL SPILLS, TAKE UP WITH SAND OR OTHER ABSORBENT MATERIAL AND PLACE INTO CONTAINERS FOR LATER DISPOSAL. FOR SMALL DRY SPILLS, WITH A CLEAN SHOVEL PLACE MATERIAL INTO CLEAN, DRY CONTAINERS AND COVER. MOVE CONTAINERS FROM SPILL AREA. FOR LARGER SPILLS, DIKE FAR AHEAD OF SPILL FOR LATER DISPOSAL. KEEP UNNECESSARY PEOPLE AWAY. ISOLATE HAZARD AREA AND DENY ENTRY. VENTILATE CLOSED SPACES BEFORE ENTERING.

PROTECTIVE EQUIPMENT

VENTILATION: PROVIDE LOCAL EXHAUST OR PROCESS ENCLOSURE VENTILATION SYSTEM.

RESPIRATOR: THE FOLLOWING RESPIRATORS AND MAXIMUM USE CONCENTRATIONS ARE RECOMMENDATIONS BY THE U.S. DEPARTMENT OF HEALTH AND HUMAN SERVICES, NIOSH POCKET GUIDE TO CHEMICAL HAZARDS; NIOSH CRITERIA DOCUMENTS OR BY THE U.S. DEPARTMENT OF LABOR, 29 CFR 1910 SUBPART Z. THE SPECIFIC RESPIRATOR SELECTED MUST BE BASED ON CONTAMINATION LEVELS FOUND IN THE WORK PLACE, MUST NOT EXCEED THE WORKING LIMITS OF THE RESPIRATOR AND BE JOINTLY APPROVED BY THE NATIONAL INSTITUTE FOR OCCUPATIONAL SAFETY AND HEALTH AND THE MINE SAFETY AND HEALTH ADMINISTRATION (NIOSH-MSHA).

TYPE 'C' SUPPLIED-AIR RESPIRATOR WITH A FULL FACEPIECE OPERATED IN PRESSURE-DEMAND OR OTHER POSITIVE PRESSURE MODE OR WITH A FULL FACEPIECE, HELMET OR HOOD OPERATED IN CONTINOUS-FLOW MODE.

SELF-CONTAINED BREATHING APPARATUS WITH A FULL FACEPIECE OPERATED IN PRESSURE-DEMAND OR OTHER POSITIVE PRESSURE MODE.

FOR FIREFIGHTING AND OTHER IMMEDIATELY DANGEROUS TO LIFE OR HEALTH CONDITIONS: SELF-CONTAINED BREATHING APPARATUS WITH FULL FACEPIECE OPERATED IN PRESSURE-DEMAND OR OTHER POSITIVE PRESSURE MODE.

SUPPLIED-AIR RESPIRATOR WITH FULL FACEPIECE AND OPERATED IN PRESSURE-DEMAND OR OTHER POSITIVE PRESSURE MODE IN COMBINATION WITH AN AUXILIARY SELF-CONTAINED BREATHING APPARATUS OPERATED IN PRESSURE-DEMAND OR OTHER POSITIVE PRESSURE MODE.

CLOTHING: EMPLOYEE MUST WEAR APPROPRIATE PROTECTIVE (IMPERVIOUS) CLOTHING AND EQUIPMENT TO PREVENT ANY POSSIBILITY OF SKIN CONTACT WITH THIS SUBSTANCE.

GLOVES: EMPLOYEE MUST WEAR APPROPRIATE PROTECTIVE GLOVES TO PREVENT CONTACT WITH THIS SUBSTANCE.

EYE PROTECTION: EMPLOYEE MUST WEAR SPLASH-PROOF OR DUST-RESISTANT SAFETY GOGGLES WITH OR WITHOUT A FACESHIELD TO PREVENT CONTACT WITH THIS SUBSTANCE.

EMERGENCY EYE WASH: WHERE THERE IS ANY POSSIBILITY THAT AN EMPLOYEE'S EYES MAY BE EXPOSED TO THIS SUBSTANCE, THE EMPLOYER SHOULD PROVIDE AN EYE WASH FOUNTAIN WITHIN THE IMMEDIATE WORK AREA FOR EMERGENCY USE.

AUTHORIZED BY- OCCUPATIONAL HEALTH SERVICES, INC.

CREATION DATE: 10/04/89 ***REVISION DATE:*** 05/14/90

MATERIAL SAFETY DATA SHEET

OCCUPATIONAL HEALTH SERVICES, INC.
AGRICULTURE AND PESTICIDE DIVISION
450 SEVENTH AVENUE, SUITE 2407
NEW YORK, NEW YORK 10123
1-800-445-MSDS OR (212) 967-1100

EMERGENCY CONTACT:
JOHN S. BRANSFORD, JR. (615) 292-1180

SUBSTANCE IDENTIFICATION

CAS-NUMBER 314-40-9

SUBSTANCE: BROMACIL

TRADE NAMES/SYNONYMS: 2,4(1H,3H)-PYRIMIDINEDIONE, 5-BROMO-6-METHYL-3-(1-METHYLPROPYL)-; 5-BROMO-6-METHYL-3-(1-METHYLPROPYL)-2,4(1H,3H)-PYRIMIDINEDIONE; URACIL, 5-BROMO-3-SEC-BUTYL-6-METHYL-; 5-BROMO-3-SEC-BUTYL-6-METHYLURACIL; BROMAZIL; HERBICIDE 976; HYVAREX; HYVAR X; KROVAR II; UROX B; HYVAR X-WS; C9H13BRN2O2; PST03330

CHEMICAL FAMILY: HETEROCYCLIC NITROGEN
HALOGEN COMPOUND, AROMATIC

MOLECULAR FORMULA: C9-H13-BR-N2-O2

MOLECULAR WEIGHT: 261.11

CERCLA RATINGS (SCALE 0-3): HEALTH=2 FIRE=1 REACTIVITY=0 PERSISTENCE=3

NFPA RATINGS (SCALE 0-4): HEALTH=2 FIRE=1 REACTIVITY=0

COMPONENTS AND CONTAMINANTS

COMPONENT: BROMACIL ***PERCENT:*** 100
CAS# 314-40-9

OTHER CONTAMINANTS: NONE

EXPOSURE LIMITS: BROMACIL: 1 PPM (10 MG/M3) OSHA TWA 1 PPM (10 MG/M3) ACGIH TWA

PHYSICAL DATA

DESCRIPTION: ODORLESS, WHITE CRYSTALLINE SOLID.

MELTING POINT: 316-320 F (158-160 C) ***SPECIFIC GRAVITY:*** 1.55

VAPOR PRESSURE: 0.0008 MMHG @ 100 C ***SOLUBILITY IN WATER:*** 0.0815% @ 25 C

SOLVENT SOLUBILITY: MODERATELY SOLUBLE IN STRONG AQUEOUS BASES, ACETONE, ACETONITRILE AND ETHANOL; SPARINGLY SOLUBLE IN HYDROCARBONS

FIRE AND EXPLOSION DATA

FIRE AND EXPLOSION HAZARD: SLIGHT FIRE HAZARD WHEN EXPOSED TO HEAT OR FLAME.

FIREFIGHTING MEDIA: DRY CHEMICAL, CARBON DIOXIDE, HALON, WATER SPRAY OR STANDARD FOAM (1987 EMERGENCY RESPONSE GUIDEBOOK, DOT P 5800.4).
FOR LARGER FIRES, USE WATER SPRAY, FOG OR STANDARD FOAM (1987 EMERGENCY RESPONSE GUIDEBOOK, DOT P 5800.4).

FIREFIGHTING: MOVE CONTAINER FROM FIRE AREA IF POSSIBLE. DO NOT SCATTER SPILLED MATERIAL WITH HIGH PRESSURE WATER STREAMS. DIKE FIRE CONTROL WATER FOR LATER DISPOSAL (1987 EMERGENCY RESPONSE GUIDEBOOK, DOT P 5800.4, GUIDE PAGE 31).
USE AGENTS SUITABLE FOR TYPE OF SURROUNDING FIRE. AVOID BREATHING HAZARDOUS VAPORS, KEEP UPWIND.

TOXICITY

BROMACIL: TOXICITY DATA: 641 MG/KG ORAL-RAT LD50; 3040 MG/KG ORAL-MOUSE LD50; MUTAGENIC DATA (RTECS); REPRODUCTIVE EFFECTS DATA (RTECS). CARCINOGEN STATUS: NONE. ACUTE TOXICITY LEVEL: MODERATELY TOXIC BY INGESTION. TARGET EFFECTS: NO DATA AVAILABLE.

HEALTH EFFECTS AND FIRST AID

INHALATION: BROMACIL **ACUTE EXPOSURE-** NO DEATHS WERE REPORTED IN A STUDY OF RATS EXPOSED TO A CONCENTRATION OF 4800 MG/M3/4 HOURS. **CHRONIC EXPOSURE-** FETOTOXICITY AND FETAL DEVELOPMENTAL ABNORMALITIES WERE OBSERVED IN A STUDY OF PREGNANT RATS REPEATEDLY EXPOSED TO BROMACIL.

FIRST AID- REMOVE FROM EXPOSURE AREA TO FRESH AIR IMMEDIATELY. IF BREATHING HAS STOPPED, PERFORM ARTIFICIAL RESPIRATION. KEEP PERSON WARM AND AT REST. TREAT SYMPTOMATICALLY AND SUPPORTIVELY. GET MEDICAL ATTENTION IMMEDIATELY.

SKIN CONTACT: BROMACIL **ACUTE EXPOSURE-** THIS MATERIAL WAS MILDLY IRRITATING TO GUINEA PIG SKIN. NO SIGNS OF SYSTEMIC TOXICITY WERE OBSERVED IN RABBITS AFTER DERMAL APPLICATION OF 5000 MG/KG. **CHRONIC EXPOSURE-** NO DATA AVAILABLE.

FIRST AID- REMOVE CONTAMINATED CLOTHING AND SHOES IMMEDIATELY. WASH AFFECTED AREA WITH SOAP OR MILD DETERGENT AND LARGE AMOUNTS OF WATER UNTIL NO EVIDENCE OF CHEMICAL REMAINS (APPROXIMATELY 15-20 MINUTES). GET MEDICAL ATTENTION IMMEDIATELY.

EYE CONTACT: BROMACIL **ACUTE EXPOSURE-** THIS MATERIAL PRODUCED SLIGHT TRANSIENT CONJUNCTIVAL IRRITATION WITHOUT CORNEAL INJURY IN RABBIT EYES. **CHRONIC EXPOSURE-** NO DATA AVAILABLE.

FIRST AID- WASH EYES IMMEDIATELY WITH LARGE AMOUNTS OF WATER OR NORMAL SALINE, OCCASIONALLY LIFTING UPPER AND LOWER LIDS, UNTIL NO EVIDENCE OF CHEMICAL REMAINS (APPROXIMATELY 15-20 MINUTES). GET MEDICAL ATTENTION IMMEDIATELY.

INGESTION: BROMACIL **ACUTE EXPOSURE-** AS LITTLE AS 100 MG/KG CAUSED VOMITING, SALIVATION, MUSCULAR WEAKNESS, EXCITABILITY, DIARRHEA, AND MYDRIASIS IN DOGS. RATS EXPERIENCED INITIAL WEIGHT LOSS, PALLOR, PROSTRATION AND RAPID RESPIRATION WHEN FED SINGLE DOSES. **CHRONIC EXPOSURE-** ABNORMAL THYROID PATHOLOGY AND SLIGHTLY LOWER FEMALE BODY WEIGHT WAS OBSERVED IN A STUDY OF RATS FED A DIETARY LEVEL OF 1250 PPM. 1500 MG/KG/DAY WAS LETHAL TO RATS AFTER 5 DAYS; AN AUTOPSY REVEALED FOCAL LIVER CELL HYPERTROPHY AND HYPERPLASIA.

FIRST AID- REMOVE BY GASTRIC LAVAGE AND CATHARSIS. MAINTAIN BLOOD PRESSURE AND AIRWAY. GIVE OXYGEN IF RESPIRATION IS DEPRESSED. DO NOT PERFORM GASTRIC LAVAGE IF VICTIM IS UNCONSCIOUS. GET MEDICAL ATTENTION IMMEDIATELY (DREISBACH, HANDBOOK OF POISONING, 12TH ED.).
ADMINISTRATION OF LAVAGE OR OXYGEN SHOULD BE PERFORMED BY QUALIFIED MEDICAL PERSONNEL.

ANTIDOTE: NO SPECIFIC ANTIDOTE. TREAT SYMPTOMATICALLY AND SUPPORTIVELY.

REACTIVITY

REACTIVITY: STABLE UNDER NORMAL TEMPERATURES AND PRESSURES.

INCOMPATIBILITIES: BROMACIL: ACIDS (STRONG): SLOWLY DECOMPOSES. OXIDIZERS (STRONG): FIRE AND EXPLOSION HAZARD.

DECOMPOSITION: THERMAL DECOMPOSITION PRODUCTS MAY INCLUDE TOXIC AND CORROSIVE FUMES OF BROMIDES, AND TOXIC OXIDES OF CARBON AND NITROGEN.

POLYMERIZATION: HAZARDOUS POLYMERIZATION HAS NOT BEEN REPORTED TO OCCUR UNDER NORMAL TEMPERATURES AND PRESSURES.

STORAGE AND DISPOSAL

OBSERVE ALL FEDERAL, STATE AND LOCAL REGULATIONS WHEN STORING OR DISPOSING OF THIS SUBSTANCE. FOR ASSISTANCE, CONTACT THE DISTRICT DIRECTOR OF THE ENVIRONMENTAL PROTECTION AGENCY.

****STORAGE****

STORE IN ACCORDANCE WITH 40 CFR 165 RECOMMENDED PROCEDURES FOR THE DISPOSAL AND STORAGE OF PESTICIDES AND PESTICIDE CONTAINERS.
STORE AWAY FROM INCOMPATIBLE SUBSTANCES.
KEEP COOL AND DRY.

****DISPOSAL****

DISPOSAL MUST BE IN ACCORDANCE WITH 40 CFR 165 RECOMMENDED PROCEDURES FOR THE DISPOSAL AND STORAGE OF PESTICIDES AND PESTICIDE CONTAINERS.

CONDITIONS TO AVOID

MAY BURN BUT DOES NOT IGNITE READILY. AVOID CONTACT WITH STRONG OXIDIZERS, EXCESSIVE HEAT, SPARKS, OR OPEN FLAME.

SPILL AND LEAK PROCEDURES

OCCUPATIONAL SPILL: STOP LEAK IF YOU CAN DO IT WITHOUT RISK. FOR SMALL SPILLS, TAKE UP WITH SAND OR OTHER ABSORBENT MATERIAL AND PLACE INTO CLEAN, DRY CONTAINERS FOR LATER DISPOSAL. KEEP UNNECESSARY PEOPLE AWAY. ISOLATE HAZARD AREA AND DENY ENTRY.

PROTECTIVE EQUIPMENT

VENTILATION: PROVIDE LOCAL EXHAUST VENTILATION AND/OR GENERAL DILUTION VENTILATION TO MEET PUBLISHED EXPOSURE LIMITS.

RESPIRATOR: THE FOLLOWING RESPIRATORS ARE RECOMMENDED BASED ON INFORMATION FOUND IN THE PHYSICAL DATA, TOXICITY AND HEALTH EFFECTS SECTIONS. THEY ARE RANKED IN ORDER FROM MINIMUM TO MAXIMUM RESPIRATORY PROTECTION. THE SPECIFIC RESPIRATOR SELECTED MUST BE BASED ON CONTAMINATION LEVELS FOUND IN THE WORK PLACE, MUST NOT EXCEED THE WORKING LIMITS OF THE RESPIRATOR AND BE JOINTLY APPROVED BY THE NATIONAL INSTITUTE FOR OCCUPATIONAL SAFETY AND HEALTH AND THE MINE SAFETY AND HEALTH ADMINISTRATION (NIOSH-MSHA).
CHEMICAL CARTRIDGE RESPIRATOR WITH AN ORGANIC VAPOR CARTRIDGE(S) IN COMBINATION WITH A DUST AND MIST FILTER.
GAS MASK WITH ORGANIC VAPOR CANISTER (CHIN-STYLE OR FRONT- OR BACK-MOUNTED CANISTER) WITH A DUST AND MIST FILTER.
GAS MASK WITH ORGANIC VAPOR CANISTER (CHIN-STYLE OR FRONT- OR BACK-MOUNTED CANISTER) WITH A PARTICULATE FILTER.
POWERED AIR-PURIFYING RESPIRATOR WITH A HIGH-EFFICIENCY FILTER.
TYPE 'C' SUPPLIED-AIR RESPIRATOR WITH A FULL FACEPIECE OPERATED IN A PRESSURE-DEMAND OR OTHER POSITIVE PRESSURE MODE.
SELF-CONTAINED BREATHING APPARATUS WITH A FULL FACEPIECE OPERATED IN PRESSURE-DEMAND OR OTHER POSITIVE PRESSURE MODE.
FOR FIREFIGHTING AND OTHER IMMEDIATELY DANGEROUS TO LIFE OR HEALTH CONDITIONS:
SELF-CONTAINED BREATHING APPARATUS WITH FULL FACEPIECE OPERATED IN PRESSURE-DEMAND OR OTHER POSITIVE PRESSURE MODE.
SUPPLIED-AIR RESPIRATOR WITH FULL FACEPIECE AND OPERATED IN PRESSURE-DEMAND OR OTHER POSITIVE PRESSURE MODE IN COMBINATION WITH AN AUXILIARY SELF-CONTAINED BREATHING APPARATUS OPERATED IN PRESSURE-DEMAND OR OTHER POSITIVE PRESSURE MODE.

CLOTHING: EMPLOYEE MUST WEAR APPROPRIATE PROTECTIVE (IMPERVIOUS) CLOTHING AND EQUIPMENT TO PREVENT REPEATED OR PROLONGED SKIN CONTACT WITH THIS SUBSTANCE.

GLOVES: EMPLOYEE MUST WEAR APPROPRIATE PROTECTIVE GLOVES TO PREVENT CONTACT WITH THIS SUBSTANCE.

EYE PROTECTION: EMPLOYEE MUST WEAR SPLASH-PROOF OR DUST-RESISTANT SAFETY GOGGLES TO PREVENT EYE CONTACT WITH THIS SUBSTANCE.
EMERGENCY EYE WASH: WHERE THERE IS ANY POSSIBILITY THAT AN EMPLOYEE'S EYES MAY BE EXPOSED TO THIS SUBSTANCE, THE EMPLOYER SHOULD PROVIDE AN EYE WASH FOUNTAIN WITHIN THE IMMEDIATE WORK AREA FOR EMERGENCY USE.

AUTHORIZED BY- OCCUPATIONAL HEALTH SERVICES, INC.
CREATION DATE: 10/04/89 ***REVISION DATE:*** 05/07/90

MATERIAL SAFETY DATA SHEET

OCCUPATIONAL HEALTH SERVICES, INC.
AGRICULTURE AND PESTICIDE DIVISION
450 SEVENTH AVENUE, SUITE 2407
NEW YORK, NEW YORK 10123
1-800-445-MSDS OR (212) 967-1100

EMERGENCY CONTACT:
JOHN S. BRANSFORD, JR. (615) 292-1180

SUBSTANCE IDENTIFICATION

CAS-NUMBER 28772-56-7

SUBSTANCE: **BROMADIOLONE**

TRADE NAMES/SYNONYMS: 2H-1-BENZOPYRAN-2-ONE, 3-(3-(4'-BROMO(1,1'-BIPHENYL)-4-YL)-3-HYDROXY- 1-PHENYLPROPYL)-4-HYDROXY-; COUMARIN, 3-(ALPHA-(P-(P-BROMOPHENYL)-BETA-HYDROXYPHENETHYL)BENZYL)-4-HYDROXY-; 3-(3-(4'-BROMO(1,1'-BIPHENYL)-4-YL)-3-HYDROXY-1-PHENYLPROPYL)-4- HYDROXY-2H-1-BENZOPYRAN-2-ONE; 3-(ALPHA-(P-(P-BROMOPHENYL)-BETA-HYDROXYPHENETHYL)BENZYL)-4-HYDROXY- COUMARIN; 3-(3-(4'-BROMOBIPHENYL-4-YL)-3-HYDROXY-1-PHENYLPROPYL)-4-HYDROXY- COUMARIN; MAKI; SUPERCAID; C30H23BRO4; PST03334

CHEMICAL FAMILY: COUMARIN

MOLECULAR FORMULA: C30-H23-BR-O4

MOLECULAR WEIGHT: 527.42

CERCLA RATINGS (SCALE 0-3): HEALTH=3 FIRE=1 REACTIVITY=0 PERSISTENCE=2

NFPA RATINGS (SCALE 0-4): HEALTH=4 FIRE=1 REACTIVITY=0

COMPONENTS AND CONTAMINANTS

COMPONENT: BROMADIOLONE ***PERCENT:*** 100.0
CAS# 28772-56-7

OTHER CONTAMINANTS: NONE

EXPOSURE LIMITS: BROMADIOLONE: NO OCCUPATIONAL EXPOSURE LIMITS ESTABLISHED BY OSHA, ACGIH, OR NIOSH.

100/10,000 POUNDS SARA SECTION 302 THRESHOLD PLANNING QUANTITY 1 POUND SARA SECTION 304 REPORTABLE QUANTITY

PHYSICAL DATA

DESCRIPTION: YELLOWISH POWDER. ***MELTING POINT:*** 392-410 F (200-210 C)

SPECIFIC GRAVITY: NOT AVAILABLE ***SOLUBILITY IN WATER:*** 19 PPM @ 20 C

SOLVENT SOLUBILITY: SOLUBLE IN ACETONE, DIMETHYLFORMAMIDE; SLIGHTLY SOLUBLE IN CHLOROFORM, ETHYL ACETATE, ETHANOL, CARBON TETRAACHLORIDE; INSOLUBLE IN ETHER, HEXANE.

FIRE AND EXPLOSION DATA

FIRE AND EXPLOSION HAZARD: SLIGHT FIRE HAZARD WHEN EXPOSED TO HEAT OR FLAME.

FIREFIGHTING MEDIA: DRY CHEMICAL, CARBON DIOXIDE, HALON, WATER SPRAY OR STANDARD FOAM (1987 EMERGENCY RESPONSE GUIDEBOOK, DOT P 5800.4).
FOR LARGER FIRES, USE WATER SPRAY, FOG OR STANDARD FOAM (1987 EMERGENCY RESPONSE GUIDEBOOK, DOT P 5800.4).

FIREFIGHTING: MOVE CONTAINERS FROM FIRE AREA IF POSSIBLE. FIGHT FIRE FROM MAXIMUM DISTANCE. STAY AWAY FROM STORAGE TANK ENDS. DIKE FIRE CONTROL WATER FOR LATER DISPOSAL. DO NOT SCATTER MATERIAL (1987 EMERGENCY RESPONSE GUIDEBOOK, DOT P 5800.4, GUIDE PAGE 55).
EXTINGUISH USING AGENT SUITABLE FOR TYPE OF SURROUNDING FIRE. AVOID BREATHING VAPORS AND DUSTS. KEEP UPWIND.

TRANSPORTATION DATA

DEPARTMENT OF TRANSPORTATION HAZARD CLASSIFICATION 49 CFR 172.101: POISON B

DEPARTMENT OF TRANSPORTATION LABELING REQUIREMENTS 49 CFR 172.101 AND SUBPART E: POISON

DEPARTMENT OF TRANSPORTATION PACKAGING REQUIREMENTS: 49 CFR 173.365 EXCEPTIONS: 49 CFR 173.364

TOXICITY

BROMADIOLONE: TOXICITY DATA: 2100 UG/KG SKIN-RABBIT LD50; 490 UG/KG ORAL-RAT LD50; 1750 UG/KG ORAL-MOUSE LD50; 1 MG/KG ORAL-RABBIT LD50. CARCINOGEN STATUS: NONE. ACUTE TOXICITY LEVEL: HIGHLY TOXIC BY DERMAL ABSORPTION AND INGESTION. TARGET EFFECTS: HEMORRHAGIC AGENT. AT INCREASED RISK FROM EXPOSURE: PERSONS WITH BLOOD DYSCRASIAS, BLEEDING TENDENCIES, LIVER OR KIDNEY DISEASE, ULCERS OF THE GASTROINTESTINAL TRACT, OR HYPERTENSION.* ADDITIONAL DATA: INTERACTIONS WITH MEDICATIONS HAVE BEEN REPORTED.*

* MAY BE BASED ON GENERAL INFORMATION ON COUMARIN DERIVATIVES.

HEALTH EFFECTS AND FIRST AID

INHALATION: BROMADIOLONE: SEE INFORMATION ON COUMARIN DERIVATIVES.
COUMARIN DERIVATIVES: HEMORRHAGIC AGENT. **ACUTE EXPOSURE-** ABSORPTION BY THE LUNGS MAY RESULT IN HEMORRHAGIC EFFECTS AS DESCRIBED IN CHRONIC EXPOSURE. SEVERE CASES MAY BE FATAL. **CHRONIC EXPOSURE-** REPEATED ABSORPTION MAY CAUSE THE INHIBITION OF PROTHROMBIN SYNTHESIS AND DAMAGE TO CAPILLARY PERMEABILITY RESULTING IN WIDESPREAD INTERNAL HEMORRHAGE WITH ASSOCIATED EFFECTS OF NOSEBLEED, HEMATOMA, HEMATURIA, WIDESPREAD BRUISING, AND ANEMIA.

FIRST AID- REMOVE FROM EXPOSURE AREA TO FRESH AIR IMMEDIATELY. IF BREATHING HAS STOPPED, PERFORM ARTIFICIAL RESPIRATION. KEEP PERSON WARM AND AT REST. TREAT SYMPTOMATICALLY AND SUPPORTIVELY. GET MEDICAL ATTENTION IMMEDIATELY.

SKIN CONTACT: BROMADIOLONE: HIGHLY TOXIC. SEE INFORMATION ON COUMARIN DERIVATIVES.
COUMARIN DERIVATIVES: HEMORRHAGIC AGENT. **ACUTE EXPOSURE-** ABSORPTION THROUGH THE SKIN MAY RESULT IN HEMORRHAGIC EFFECTS AS DESCRIBED IN CHRONIC EXPOSURE. SEVERE CASES MAY BE FATAL. **CHRONIC EXPOSURE-** REPEATED ABSORPTION MAY CAUSE THE INHIBITION OF PROTHROMBIN SYNTHESIS AND DAMAGE TO CAPILLARY PERMEABILITY RESULTING IN WIDESPREAD INTERNAL HEMORRHAGE WITH ASSOCIATED EFFECTS OF NOSEBLEED, HEMATOMA, HEMATURIA, WIDESPREAD BRUISING, AND ANEMIA.

FIRST AID- REMOVE CONTAMINATED CLOTHING AND SHOES IMMEDIATELY. WASH AFFECTED AREA WITH SOAP OR MILD DETERGENT AND LARGE AMOUNTS OF WATER UNTIL NO EVIDENCE OF CHEMICAL REMAINS (APPROXIMATELY 15-20 MINUTES). GET MEDICAL ATTENTION IMMEDIATELY.

EYE CONTACT: BROMADIOLONE: **ACUTE EXPOSURE-** NO DATA AVAILABLE. **CHRONIC EXPOSURE-** NO DATA AVAILABLE.

FIRST AID- WASH EYES IMMEDIATELY WITH LARGE AMOUNTS OF WATER OR NORMAL SALINE, OCCASIONALLY LIFTING UPPER AND LOWER LIDS, UNTIL NO EVIDENCE OF CHEMICAL REMAINS (APPROXIMATELY 15-20 MINUTES). GET MEDICAL ATTENTION IMMEDIATELY.

INGESTION: BROMADIOLONE: HIGHLY TOXIC. SEE INFORMATION ON COUMARIN DERIVATIVES.
COUMARIN DERIVATIVES: HEMORRHAGIC AGENT. **ACUTE EXPOSURE-** MAY BE READILY ABSORBED FROM THE GASTROINTESTINAL TRACT AND CAUSE THE INHIBITION OF PROTHROMBIN SYNTHESIS AND DAMAGE TO CAPILLARY PERMEABILITY RESULTING IN WIDESPREAD INTERNAL HEMORRHAGE ACCOMPANIED BY THE HEMORRHAGIC SYMPTOMS AS DESCRIBED IN CHRONIC EXPOSURE. SEVERE CASES MAY BE FATAL. **CHRONIC EXPOSURE-** REPEATED INGESTION MAY CAUSE NOSEBLEED, BLEEDING GUMS AND PHARYNX, PETECHIAL RASH, WIDESPREAD BRUISING, HEMATOMA, HEMOPTYSIS, HEMATEMESIS, HEMATURIA, BLOODY STOOLS, BLEEDING INTO THE ORGANS, GASTROINTESTINAL TRACT, JOINTS, ABDOMINAL OR RETROPERITONEAL AREA WITH ABDOMINAL, BACK, JOINT AND LIMB PAIN AND CEREBROVASCULAR ACCIDENT. ANEMIA ACCOMPANIED BY WEAKNESS, PALLOR, AND SHOCK MAY OCCUR. SEVERE HEMORRHAGING MAY CAUSE DEATH. THERAPEUTIC USE OF SOME COUMARIN DERIVATIVES HAS INFREQUENTLY PRODUCED GASTROINTESTINAL DISTURBANCES, ELEVATED TRANSAMINASE, URTICARIA, DERMATITIS, LEUKOPENIA, ALOPECIA, FEVER, HYPERSENSITIVITY REACTIONS, AND RARELY SKIN NECROSIS.

FIRST AID- IF ONLY A FEW GRAINS OF ANTICOAGULANT BAIT HAVE BEEN INGESTED BY AN ADULT OR CHILD HAVING NO ANTECEDENT LIVER OR BLOOD CLOTTING DISEASE, TREATMENT IS PROBABLY UNNECESSARY. IF LARGE AMOUNTS OF ANTICOAGULANT WERE INGESTED IN THE PRECEDING 2-3 HOURS, INDUCE VOMITING WITH SYRUP OF IPECAC, FOLLOWED BY 1-2 GLASSES OF WATER. FOLLOWING EMESIS, GIVE ACTIVATED CHARCOAL IN 4-6 OUNCES OF WATER TO LIMIT ABSORPTION OF ANTICOAGULANT REMAINING IN THE GUT. OBSERVE PATIENT 4-5 DAYS AFTER INGESTION. (MORGAN, RECOGNITION AND MANAGEMENT OF PESTICIDE POISONINGS, THIRD EDITION). GET MEDICAL ATTENTION.

ANTIDOTE: THE FOLLOWING ANTIDOTE HAS BEEN RECOMMENDED. HOWEVER, THE DECISION AS TO WHETHER THE SEVERITY OF POISONING REQUIRES ADMINISTRATION OF ANY ANTIDOTE AND ACTUAL DOSE REQUIRED SHOULD BE MADE BY QUALIFIED MEDICAL PERSONNEL.
OVERDOSE OF ANTICOAGULANTS: VITAMIN K IS A SPECIFIC ANTIDOTE. VITAMIN K1 EMULSION IS THE PREFERRED FORM. THE INITIAL SUBCUTANEOUS OR INTRAMUSCULAR DOSE IN ADULTS IS 5 TO 10 MG (UP TO 25 MG), REPEATED ONCE IF NECESSARY. ONLY IN VICTIMS WHO ARE BLEEDING SEVERLY OR OTHERWISE IN SERIOUS DISTRESS SHOULD THE DRUG BE GIVEN INTRAVENOUSLY AND THEN AT A RATE NO FASTER THAN 1 MG/MINUTE. IF NECESSARY, ON SUBSEQUENT DAYS, VITAMIN K1 SHOULD BE CONTINUED AT A REDUCED LEVEL UNTIL THE PROTHROMBIN TIME RETURNS TO NORMAL. VITAMIN K1 IS PREFERABLE TO K1 OXIDE (DOSE 0.5-2.5) AND CERTAINLY PREFERABLE TO MENADIONE OR MENADIONE SODIUM BISULFITE (GOSSELIN, CLINICAL TOXICOLOGY OF COMMERCIAL PRODUCTS, 5TH ED.). ANTIDOTE SHOULD BE ADMINISTERED BY QUALIFIED MEDICAL PERSONNEL.

REACTIVITY

REACTIVITY: STABLE UNDER NORMAL TEMPERATURES AND PRESSURES.

INCOMPATIBILITIES: BROMADIOLONE: ALKALIES: INCOMPATIBLE. OXIDIZERS (STRONG): FIRE AND EXPLOSION HAZARD.

DECOMPOSITION: THERMAL DECOMPOSITION PRODUCTS MAY INCLUDE TOXIC AND CORROSIVE FUMES OF BROMIDES AND TOXIC OXIDES OF CARBON.
POLYMERIZATION: HAZARDOUS POLYMERIZATION HAS NOT BEEN REPORTED TO OCCUR UNDER NORMAL TEMPERATURES AND PRESSURES.

STORAGE AND DISPOSAL

OBSERVE ALL FEDERAL, STATE AND LOCAL REGULATIONS WHEN STORING OR DISPOSING OF THIS SUBSTANCE. FOR ASSISTANCE, CONTACT THE DISTRICT DIRECTOR OF THE ENVIRONMENTAL PROTECTION AGENCY.

****STORAGE****

STORE IN ACCORDANCE WITH 40 CFR 165 RECOMMENDED PROCEDURES FOR THE DISPOSAL AND STORAGE OF PESTICIDES AND PESTICIDE CONTAINERS.
STORE AWAY FROM INCOMPATIBLE SUBSTANCES.
THRESHOLD PLANNING QUANTITY (TPQ): THE SUPERFUND AMENDMENTS AND REAUTHORIZATION ACT (SARA) SECTION 302 REQUIRES THAT EACH FACILITY WHERE ANY EXTREMELY HAZARDOUS SUBSTANCE IS PRESENT IN A QUANTITY EQUAL TO OR GREATER THAN THE TPQ ESTABLISHED FOR THAT SUBSTANCE NOTIFY THE STATE EMERGENCY RESPONSE COMMISSION FOR THE STATE IN WHICH IT IS LOCATED. SECTION 303 OF SARA REQUIRES THESE FACILITIES TO PARTICIPATE IN LOCAL EMERGENCY RESPONSE PLANNING (40 CFR 355.30).

****DISPOSAL****

DISPOSAL MUST BE IN ACCORDANCE WITH 40 CFR 165 RECOMMENDED PROCEDURES FOR THE DISPOSAL AND STORAGE OF PESTICIDES AND PESTICIDE CONTAINERS.

CONDITIONS TO AVOID

MAY BURN BUT DOES NOT IGNITE READILY. CONTAINERS MAY EXPLODE IN HEAT OF FIRE.

SPILL AND LEAK PROCEDURES

OCCUPATIONAL SPILL: DO NOT TOUCH SPILLED MATERIAL. STOP LEAK IF YOU CAN DO IT WITHOUT RISK. USE WATER SPRAY TO REDUCE VAPORS. FOR SMALL SPILLS, TAKE UP WITH SAND OR OTHER ABSORBENT MATERIAL AND PLACE INTO CONTAINERS FOR LATER DISPOSAL. FOR SMALL DRY SPILLS, WITH A CLEAN SHOVEL PLACE MATERIAL INTO CLEAN, DRY CONTAINERS AND COVER. MOVE CONTAINERS FROM SPILL AREA. FOR LARGER SPILLS, DIKE FAR AHEAD OF SPILL FOR LATER DISPOSAL. KEEP UNNECESSARY PEOPLE AWAY. ISOLATE HAZARD AREA AND DENY ENTRY. VENTILATE CLOSED SPACES BEFORE ENTERING.
REPORTABLE QUANTITY (RQ): 1 POUND THE SUPERFUND AMENDMENTS AND REAUTHORIZATION ACT (SARA) SECTION 304 REQUIRES THAT A RELEASE EQUAL TO OR GREATER THAN THE REPORTABLE QUANTITY FOR THIS SUBSTANCE BE IMMEDIATELY REPORTED TO THE LOCAL EMERGENCY PLANNING COMMITTEE AND THE STATE EMERGENCY RESPONSE COMMISSION (40 CFR 355.40). IF THE RELEASE OF THIS SUBSTANCE IS REPORTABLE UNDER CERCLA SECTION 103, THE NATIONAL RESPONSE CENTER MUST BE NOTIFIED IMMEDIATELY AT (800) 424-8802 OR (202) 426-2675 IN THE METROPOLITAN WASHINGTON, D.C. AREA (40 CFR 302.6).

PROTECTIVE EQUIPMENT

VENTILATION: PROCESS ENCLOSURE RECOMMENDED.
RESPIRATOR: THE FOLLOWING RESPIRATORS ARE RECOMMENDED BASED ON INFORMATION FOUND IN THE PHYSICAL DATA, TOXICITY AND HEALTH EFFECTS SECTIONS. THEY ARE RANKED IN ORDER FROM MINIMUM TO MAXIMUM RESPIRATORY PROTECTION. THE SPECIFIC RESPIRATOR SELECTED MUST BE BASED ON CONTAMINATION LEVELS FOUND IN THE WORK PLACE, MUST NOT EXCEED THE WORKING LIMITS OF THE RESPIRATOR AND BE JOINTLY APPROVED BY THE NATIONAL INSTITUTE FOR OCCUPATIONAL SAFETY AND HEALTH AND THE MINE SAFETY AND HEALTH ADMINISTRATION (NIOSH-MSHA).
TYPE 'C' SUPPLIED-AIR RESPIRATOR WITH A FULL FACEPIECE OPERATED IN PRESSURE-DEMAND OR OTHER POSITIVE PRESSURE MODE OR WITH A FULL FACEPIECE, HELMET OR HOOD OPERATED IN CONTINOUS-FLOW MODE.
SELF-CONTAINED BREATHING APPARATUS WITH A FULL FACEPIECE OPERATED IN PRESSURE-DEMAND OR OTHER POSITIVE PRESSURE MODE.
FOR FIREFIGHTING AND OTHER IMMEDIATELY DANGEROUS TO LIFE OR HEALTH CONDITIONS:
SELF-CONTAINED BREATHING APPARATUS WITH FULL FACEPIECE OPERATED IN PRESSURE-DEMAND OR OTHER POSITIVE PRESSURE MODE.
SUPPLIED-AIR RESPIRATOR WITH FULL FACEPIECE AND OPERATED IN PRESSURE-DEMAND OR OTHER POSITIVE PRESSURE MODE IN COMBINATION WITH AN AUXILIARY SELF-CONTAINED BREATHING APPARATUS OPERATED IN PRESSURE-DEMAND OR OTHER POSITIVE PRESSURE MODE.
CLOTHING: EMPLOYEE MUST WEAR APPROPRIATE PROTECTIVE (IMPERVIOUS) CLOTHING AND EQUIPMENT TO PREVENT ANY POSSIBILITY OF SKIN CONTACT WITH THIS SUBSTANCE.
GLOVES: EMPLOYEE MUST WEAR APPROPRIATE PROTECTIVE GLOVES TO PREVENT CONTACT WITH THIS SUBSTANCE.
EYE PROTECTION: EMPLOYEE MUST WEAR SPLASH-PROOF OR DUST-RESISTANT SAFETY GOGGLES WITH OR WITHOUT A FACESHIELD TO PREVENT CONTACT WITH THIS SUBSTANCE.
EMERGENCY EYE WASH: WHERE THERE IS ANY POSSIBILITY THAT AN EMPLOYEE'S EYES MAY BE EXPOSED TO THIS SUBSTANCE, THE EMPLOYER SHOULD PROVIDE AN EYE WASH FOUNTAIN WITHIN THE IMMEDIATE WORK AREA FOR EMERGENCY USE.

AUTHORIZED BY- OCCUPATIONAL HEALTH SERVICES, INC.
CREATION DATE: 10/04/89 ***REVISION DATE:*** 03/28/90

MATERIAL SAFETY DATA SHEET

OCCUPATIONAL HEALTH SERVICES, INC.
AGRICULTURE AND PESTICIDE DIVISION
450 SEVENTH AVENUE, SUITE 2407
NEW YORK, NEW YORK 10123
1-800-445-MSDS OR (212) 967-1100

EMERGENCY CONTACT:
JOHN S. BRANSFORD, JR. (615) 292-1180

SUBSTANCE IDENTIFICATION

CAS-NUMBER 7726-95-6
SUBSTANCE: BROMINE
TRADE NAMES/SYNONYMS: UN 1744; B-385; PST03340
CHEMICAL FAMILY: HALOGEN
MOLECULAR FORMULA: BR2
MOLECULAR WEIGHT: 160
CERCLA RATINGS (SCALE 0-3): HEALTH=3 FIRE=0 REACTIVITY=0 PERSISTENCE=0
NFPA RATINGS (SCALE 0-4): HEALTH=4 FIRE=0 REACTIVITY=0

COMPONENTS AND CONTAMINANTS

COMPONENT: BROMINE ***PERCENT:*** 100
CAS# 7726-95-6
OTHER CONTAMINANTS: NONE
EXPOSURE LIMITS: BROMINE: 0.1 PPM (0.7 MG/M3) OSHA TWA; 0.3 PPM (2 MG/M3) OSHA STEL 0.1 PPM (0.7 MG/M3) ACGIH TWA; 0.3 PPM (2 MG/M3) ACGIH STEL 500 POUNDS SARA SECTION 302 THRESHOLD PLANNING QUANTITY 1 POUND SARA SECTION 304 REPORTABLE QUANTITY

PHYSICAL DATA

DESCRIPTION: HEAVY RED-BROWN LIQUID WITH A PUNGENT ODOR.
BOILING POINT: 138 F (59 C) ***MELTING POINT:*** 19 F (-7 C)
SPECIFIC GRAVITY: 3.11 ***VAPOR PRESSURE:*** 175 MMHG @ 20 C
SOLUBILITY IN WATER: 3.5% ***ODOR THRESHOLD:*** 0.05 PPM ***VAPOR DENSITY:*** 5.5
SOLVENT SOLUBILITY: ALCOHOL, ETHER, CHLOROFORM, CCL4, CARBON DISULFIDE

FIRE AND EXPLOSION DATA

FIRE AND EXPLOSION HAZARD: NEGLIGIBLE FIRE HAZARD WHEN EXPOSED TO HEAT OR FLAME.
FIREFIGHTING MEDIA: DRY CHEMICAL, CARBON DIOXIDE, HALON, WATER SPRAY OR ALCOHOL FOAM (1987 EMERGENCY RESPONSE GUIDEBOOK, DOT P 5800.4).
FOR LARGER FIRES, USE WATER SPRAY, FOG OR STANDARD FOAM (1987 EMERGENCY RESPONSE GUIDEBOOK, DOT P 5800.4).
FIREFIGHTING: MOVE CONTAINERS FROM FIRE AREA IF POSSIBLE. COOL CONTAINERS EXPOSED TO FLAMES WITH WATER FROM SIDE UNTIL WELL AFTER FIRE IS OUT. STAY AWAY FROM STORAGE TANK ENDS (1987 EMERGENCY RESPONSE GUIDEBOOK, DOT P 5800.4, GUIDE PAGE 59).
USE AGENTS SUITABLE FOR TYPE OF FIRE; USE WATER IN FLOODING AMOUNTS AS FOG. COOL CONTAINERS WITH FLOODING AMOUNTS OF WATER, APPLY FROM AS FAR A DISTANCE AS POSSIBLE. AVOID BREATHING POISONOUS AND CORROSIVE VAPORS, KEEP UPWIND. EVACUATE TO A RADIUS OF 2500 FEET FOR LEAKS.
FIRE FIGHTING PHASES: USE LARGE AMOUNTS OF WATER TO COOL CONTAINERS AND WASH AWAY SPILLS. HYPO SOLUTION (SODIUM THIO SULFATE) OR LIME WATER SHOULD BE POURED OVER SMALL LIQUID SPILLS. ANHYDROUS AMMONIA VAPOR RELEASED FROM A SAFE DISTANCE CAN BE USED TO NEUTRALIZE LARGE QUANTITIES OF BROMINE VAPOR. AVOID AQUEOUS AMMONIA AS IT MIGHT REACT VIOLENTLY WITH LIQUID BROMINE (NFPA 49, HAZARDOUS CHEMICALS DATA, 1975).

TRANSPORTATION DATA

DEPARTMENT OF TRANSPORTATION HAZARD CLASSIFICATION 49 CFR 172.101: CORROSIVE MATERIAL

DEPARTMENT OF TRANSPORTATION LABELING REQUIREMENTS 49 CFR 172.101 AND SUBPART E: CORROSIVE
DEPARTMENT OF TRANSPORTATION PACKAGING REQUIREMENTS: 49 CFR 173.252 EXCEPTIONS: NONE

TOXICITY

BROMINE: TOXICITY DATA: 1000 PPM INHALATION-HUMAN LCLO; 750 PPM/9 MINUTES INHALATION-MOUSE LC50; 140 PPM/7 HOURS INHALATION-CAT LCLO; 140 PPM/7 HOURS INHALATION-GUINEA PIG LCLO; 180 PPM/6.5 HOURS INHALATION-RABBIT LCLO; 14 MG/KG ORAL-HUMAN LDLO. CARCINOGEN STATUS: NONE. LOCAL EFFECTS: CORROSIVE- INHALATION, SKIN, AND EYES. ACUTE TOXICITY LEVEL: TOXIC BY INHALATION. TARGET EFFECTS: NO DATA AVAILABLE.

HEALTH EFFECTS AND FIRST AID

INHALATION: BROMINE: CORROSIVE/TOXIC. 10 PPM IMMEDIATELY DANGEROUS TO LIFE OR HEALTH. **ACUTE EXPOSURE-** 3.5 PPM HAS A DETECTABLE ODOR; 10 PPM IS SEVERELY IRRITATING AND MAY BE INTOLERABLE; 40-60 PPM IS DANGEROUS FOR BRIEF EXPOSURES; 1000 PPM IS RAPIDLY FATAL. INHALATION OF SMALL AMOUNTS MAY CAUSE COPIOUS MUCOUS SECRETION, COUGHING, NOSEBLEED, FEELING OF OPPRESSION, EPISTAXIS, VERTIGO, DIZZINESS AND HEADACHE. DELAYED SYMPTOMS MAY INCLUDE NAUSEA, DIARRHEA, STOMACH PAINS, HOARSENESS, RESPIRATORY DIFFICULTY WITH ASTHMA, CREPITATIONS IN THE LUNGS AND A GENERALIZED VESICULAR OR MORBILLIFORM RASH. INHALATION OF HIGH CONCENTRATIONS MAY CAUSE INFLAMMATORY LESIONS OF THE MUCOUS MEMBRANES OF THE UPPER RESPIRATORY TRACT AND FATAL CHEMICAL BURNS OF THE LUNGS. THE TONGUE AND PALATE MAY APPEAR INFLAMED AND EDEMATOUS AND GLOTTAL SPASMS AND ASTHMATIC BRONCHITITS MAY OCCUR. EXPIRED AIR MAY HAVE A CHARACTERISTIC ODOR. PULMONARY EDEMA AND PNEUMONITIS MAY BE DELAYED FOR SEVERAL HOURS. THE PATHOLOGY OF ANIMALS EXPOSED TO 300 PPM FOR 3 HOURS SHOWED PULMONARY EDEMA, PSEUDOMEMBRANOUS DEPOSIT ON THE TRACHEA AND BRONCHI, AND HEMORRHAGES OF THE GASTRIC MUCOSA. FUNCTIONAL DISTURBANCES OF THE CENTRAL NERVOUS SYSTEM WERE OBSERVED IN ANIMALS THAT DIED SEVERAL DAYS AFTER EXPOSURE. **CHRONIC EXPOSURE-** PROLONGED OR REPEATED EXPOSURE TO CONCENTRATIONS LESS THAN 0.1 MG/M3 MAY CAUSE HEADACHE, CHEST PAINS, ANOREXIA, INDIGESTION, IRRITABILITY AND JOINT PAINS. PERSONS EXPOSED TO 3-6 TIMES THE EXPOSURE LIMIT FOR 1 YEAR COMPLAIN OF HEADACHE, PAIN IN THE REGION OF THE HEART, INCREASING IRRITABILITY, LOSS OF APPETITE, JOINT PAINS AND DYSPEPSIA. AFTER 5-6 YEARS OF EXPOSURE TO THIS LEVEL THERE MAY BE LOSS OF CORNEAL REFLEXES, PHARYNGITIS, VEGETATIVE DISORDERS AND THYROID HYPERPLASIA ACCOMPANIED BY THYROID DYSFUNCTION. CARDIOVASCULAR DISORDERS MAY OCCUR IN THE FORM OF MYOCARDIAL DEGENERATION AND HYPOTENSION. FUNCTIONAL AND SECRETORY DISORDERS OF THE DIGESTIVE TRACT MAY ALSO OCCUR. HEMATOLOGIC EFFECTS MAY INCLUDE LEUKOPOIESIS AND LEUKOCYTOSIS. BROMINE MAY BE DEPOSITED IN TISSUE AND MAY ACCUMULATE TO CAUSE CENTRAL NERVOUS SYSTEM DISORDERS.

FIRST AID- REMOVE FROM EXPOSURE AREA TO FRESH AIR IMMEDIATELY. IF BREATHING HAS STOPPED, PERFORM ARTIFICIAL RESPIRATION. KEEP PERSON WARM AND AT REST. TREAT SYMPTOMATICALLY AND SUPPORTIVELY. GET MEDICAL ATTENTION IMMEDIATELY.

SKIN CONTACT: BROMINE: CORROSIVE. **ACUTE EXPOSURE-** DIRECT CONTACT WITH THE LIQUID MAY CAUSE A MILD, COOLING SENSATION FOLLOWED BY A BURNING SENSATION. IF NOT REMOVED PROMPTLY, DEEP SURFACE BURNS MAY RESULT WITH BROWN DISCOLORATION AND DEEP-SEATED, SLOW HEALING ULCERS. SECOND AND THIRD DEGREE BURNS ARE POSSIBLE. **CHRONIC EXPOSURE-** PROLONGED OR REPEATED CONTACT MAY CAUSE DERMATITIS AND SLOW HEALING ULCERS.

FIRST AID- REMOVE CONTAMINATED CLOTHING AND SHOES IMMEDIATELY. WASH AFFECTED AREA WITH SOAP OR MILD DETERGENT AND LARGE AMOUNTS OF WATER UNTIL NO EVIDENCE OF CHEMICAL REMAINS (AT LEAST 15-20 MINUTES). IN CASE OF CHEMICAL BURNS, COVER AREA WITH STERILE, DRY DRESSING. BANDAGE SECURELY, BUT NOT TOO TIGHTLY. GET MEDICAL ATTENTION IMMEDIATELY.

EYE CONTACT: BROMINE: CORROSIVE. **ACUTE EXPOSURE-** VAPORS MAY BE VERY IRRITATING TO THE EYES. DIRECT CONTACT WITH THE LIQUID MAY CAUSE BURNS. ANIMALS EXPOSED TO 180 PPM FOR 7 HOURS CAUSED SEVERE EYE IRRITATION WITH CLOUDING OF THE CORNEA. **CHRONIC EXPOSURE-** PROLONGED OR REPEATED EXPOSURE AT CONCENTRATIONS BELOW 3.5 PPM CAUSED LACRIMATION.

FIRST AID- WASH EYES IMMEDIATELY WITH LARGE AMOUNTS OF WATER, OCCASIONALLY LIFTING UPPER AND LOWER LIDS, UNTIL NO EVIDENCE OF CHEMICAL REMAINS (AT LEAST 15-20 MINUTES). CONTINUE IRRIGATING WITH NORMAL SALINE UNTIL THE PH HAS RETURNED TO NORMAL (30-60 MINUTES). COVER WITH STERILE BANDAGES. GET MEDICAL ATTENTION IMMEDIATELY.

INGESTION: BROMINE: CORROSIVE. **ACUTE EXPOSURE-** INGESTION OF BROMINE MAY CAUSE SEVERE GASTROENTERITIS AND DEATH. **CHRONIC EXPOSURE-** NOT REPORTED TO OCCUR IN HUMANS.

FIRST AID- DO NOT USE GASTRIC LAVAGE OR EMESIS. DILUTE CHEMICAL IMMEDIATELY BY DRINKING LARGE AMOUNTS OF WATER OR MILK. IF VOMITING PERSISTS, ADMINISTER FLUIDS REPEATEDLY. DO NOT GIVE AN UNCONSCIOUS PERSON ANYTHING TO DRINK. GET MEDICAL ATTENTION.

ANTIDOTE: NO SPECIFIC ANTIDOTE. TREAT SYMPTOMATICALLY AND SUPPORTIVELY.

REACTIVITY

REACTIVITY: STABLE UNDER NORMAL TEMPERATURES AND PRESSURES.

INCOMPATIBILITIES: BROMINE: ACETALDEHYDE: POSSIBLE VIOLENT REACTION. ACETYLENE: VIOLENT REACTION. ACRYLONITRILE: VIOLENT POLYMERIZATION. ALUMINUM (POWDERED): VIOLENT REACTION. AMMONIA, ANHYDROUS: VIOLENT REACTION. ANTIMONY: IGNITION REACTION. BROMINE TRIFLUORIDE: INCANDESCENT REACTION. CALCIUM NITRIDE: INCANDESCENT REACTION. CESIUM MONOXIDE: INCANDESCENT REACTION. CESIUM CARBIDE ACETYLENE: IGNITION REACTION. COPPER HYDRIDE: IGNITION REACTION. DIETHYL ETHER: IGNITION OR EXPLOSIVE REACTION. N,N-DIMETHYLFORMAMIDE: HIGHLY EXOTHERMIC REACTION. ETHYLPHOSPHINE: PROBABLE EXPLOSIVE REACTION. FLUORINE: IGNITION AT ROOM TEMPERATURE. HYDROGEN: EXPLOSIVE REACTION. MAGNESIUM PHOSPHIDE: IGNITION REACTION ON HEATING. METALS: SODIUM: EXPLOSIVE REACTION. POTASSIUM: IGNITION REACTION. ALUMINUM: VIOLENT REACTION. MERCURY: VIOLENT REACTION. TITANIUM: VIOLENT REACTION. LITHIUM: EXPLOSIVE REACTION BY STRONG IMPACT. METAL ACETYLIDE: COPPER ACETYLIDE: IGNITION REACTION. RUBIDIUM ACETYLIDE: IGNITION REACTION. METAL AZIDE: POSSIBLE EXPLOSIVE REACTION. METAL CARBONATES: ALKALI EARTH METAL CARBONATES: IGNITION REACTION. IRON CARBONATES: IGNITION REACTION. URANIUM CARBONATES: IGNITION REACTION. ZIRCONIUM CARBONATES: IGNITION REACTION. METHANOL: INTENSE EXOTHERMIC REACTION. NICKEL CARBONYL: EXPLOSVIE REACTION. NITROGEN TRIIODIDE AND AMMONIA: EXPLOSIVE REACTION. OXYGEN DIFLUORIDE: EXPLOSIVE REACTION ON HEATING. OZONE: FORMATION OF EXPLOSIVE MIXTURE. PHOSPHORUS: INCANDESCENT REACTION. RUBIDIUM CARBIDE ACETYLENE: IGNITION REACTION. SILANE: VIOLENT REACTION. SODIUM CARBIDE: PROBABLE EXPLOSIVE REACTION. SODIUM CARBIDE ACETYLENE: IGNITION REACTION.

DECOMPOSITION: THERMAL DECOMPOSITION MAY RELEASE TOXIC AND CORROSIVE BROMIDES.

POLYMERIZATION: BROMINE UNDERGOES VIOLENT POLYMERIZATION IN REACTION WITH ACRYLONITRILE.

STORAGE AND DISPOSAL

STORAGE: PROTECT AGAINST PHYSICAL DAMAGE. STORE IN COOL, DRY AREA, OUT OF DIRECT SUNLIGHT. SEPARATE FROM COMBUSTIBLE, ORGANIC OR OTHER READILY OXIDIZABLE MATERIALS. KEEP ABOVE 20 F TO PREVENT FREEZING BUT AVOID HEATING ABOVE ATMOSPHERIC TEMPERATURES AS VAPOR PRESSURE INCREASE COULD RUPTURE CONTAINER (NFPA 49, HAZARDOUS CHEMICALS DATA, 1975).

THRESHOLD PLANNING QUANTITY (TPQ): THE SUPERFUND AMENDMENTS AND REAUTHORIZATION ACT (SARA) SECTION 302 REQUIRES THAT EACH FACILITY WHERE ANY EXTREMELY HAZARDOUS SUBSTANCE IS PRESENT IN A QUANTITY EQUAL TO OR GREATER THAN THE TPQ ESTABLISHED FOR THAT SUBSTANCE NOTIFY THE STATE EMERGENCY RESPONSE COMMISSION FOR THE STATE IN WHICH IT IS LOCATED. SECTION 303 OF SARA REQUIRES THESE FACILITIES TO PARTICIPATE IN LOCAL EMERGENCY RESPONSE PLANNING (40 CFR 355.30).

CONDITIONS TO AVOID

MAY BURN BUT DOES NOT IGNITE READILY. MAY IGNITE COMBUSTIBLES (WOOD, PAPER, OIL, ETC.).

USUAL SHIPPING CONTAINERS: QUART GLASS BOTTLES, LEAD-LINED STEEL, NICKEL OR MONEL DRUMS TO 10-GALLON SIZE, AND NICKEL-CLAD OR LEAD-LINED TANK CARS (NFPA 49, HAZARDOUS CHEMICALS DATA, 1975).

SPILL AND LEAK PROCEDURES

OCCUPATIONAL SPILL: DO NOT TOUCH SPILLED MATERIAL. STOP LEAK IF YOU CAN DO IT WITHOUT RISK. USE WATER SPRAY TO REDUCE VAPORS. FOR SMALL SPILLS, TAKE UP WITH SAND OR OTHER ABSORBENT MATERIAL AND PLACE INTO CONTAINERS FOR LATER DISPOSAL. FOR LARGER SPILLS, DIKE SPILL FOR LATER DISPOSAL. KEEP UNNECESSARY PEOPLE AWAY. ISOLATE HAZARD AREA AND DENY ENTRY.

REPORTABLE QUANTITY (RQ): 1 POUND THE SUPERFUND AMENDMENTS AND REAUTHORIZATION ACT (SARA) SECTION 304 REQUIRES THAT A RELEASE EQUAL TO OR GREATER THAN THE REPORTABLE QUANTITY FOR THIS SUBSTANCE BE IMMEDIATELY REPORTED TO THE LOCAL EMERGENCY PLANNING COMMITTEE AND THE STATE EMERGENCY RESPONSE COMMISSION (40 CFR 355.40). IF THE RELEASE

OF THIS SUBSTANCE IS REPORTABLE UNDER CERCLA SECTION 103, THE NATIONAL RESPONSE CENTER MUST BE NOTIFIED IMMEDIATELY AT (800) 424-8802 OR (202) 426-2675 IN THE METROPOLITAN WASHINGTON, D.C. AREA (40 CFR 302.6).

PROTECTIVE EQUIPMENT

VENTILATION: PROVIDE LOCAL EXHAUST OR PROCESS ENCLOSURE VENTILATION TO MEET PUBLISHED EXPOSURE LIMITS.

RESPIRATOR: THE FOLLOWING RESPIRATORS AND MAXIMUM USE CONCENTRATIONS ARE RECOMMENDATIONS BY THE U.S. DEPARTMENT OF HEALTH AND HUMAN SERVICES, NIOSH POCKET GUIDE TO CHEMICAL HAZARDS; NIOSH CRITERIA DOCUMENTS OR BY THE U.S. DEPARTMENT OF LABOR, 29 CFR 1910 SUBPART Z. THE SPECIFIC RESPIRATOR SELECTED MUST BE BASED ON CONTAMINATION LEVELS FOUND IN THE WORK PLACE, MUST NOT EXCEED THE WORKING LIMITS OF THE RESPIRATOR AND BE JOINTLY APPROVED BY THE NATIONAL INSTITUTE FOR OCCUPATIONAL SAFETY AND HEALTH AND THE MINE SAFETY AND HEALTH ADMINISTRATION (NIOSH-MSHA).

RESPIRATOR SELECTION FOR BROMINE:

CONCENTRATION SUGGESTED RESPIRATORS

2.5 PPM -ANY SUPPLIED-AIR RESPIRATOR OPERATED IN A CONTINUOUS FLOW MODE. -ANY POWERED AIR-PURIFYING RESPIRATOR WTIH CARTRIDGE(S) PROVIDING PROTECTION AGAINST BROMINE.

5 PPM -ANY CHEMICAL CARTRIDGE RESPIRATOR WITH A FULL FACEPIECE AND CARTRIDGE(S) PROVIDING PROTECTION AGAINST BROMINE. -ANY AIR-PURIFYING FULL FACEPIECE RESPIRATOR (GAS MASK) WITH A CHIN-STYLE OR FRONT- OR BACK-MOUNTED CANISTER PROVIDING PROTECTION AGAINST BROMINE. -ANY SELF-CONTAINED BREATHING APPARATUS WITH A FULL FACEPIECE. -ANY POWERED AIR-PURIFYING RESPIRATOR WITH A TIGHT-FITTING FACEPIECE AND CARTRIDGE(S) PROVIDING PROTECTION AGAINST BROMINE. -ANY SUPPLIED AIR RESPIRATOR WITH A FULL FACEPIECE. 10 PPM -ANY SUPPLIED AIR RESPIRATOR WITH A FULL FACEPIECE AND OPERATED IN A PRESSURE-DEMAND OR OTHER POSITIVE PRESSURE MODE.

EMERGENCY OR PLANNED -ANY SELF CONTAINED BREATHING APPARATUS WITH A ENTRY INTO UNKNOWN OR FULL FACEPIECE. IDLH CONDITIONS -ANY SUPPLIED AIR RESPIRATOR WITH A FULL FACEPIECE AND OPERATED IN PRESSURE-DEMAND OR OTHER POSITIVE PRESSURE MODE IN COMBINATION WTIH AN AUXILIARY SELF-CONTAINED BREATHING APPARATUS OPERATED IN PRESSURE-DEMAND OR OTHER POSITIVE PRESSURE MODE.

FOR FIREFIGHTING AND OTHER IMMEDIATELY DANGEROUS TO LIFE OR HEALTH CONDITIONS:

SELF-CONTAINED BREATHING APPARATUS WITH FULL FACEPIECE OPERATED IN PRESSURE-DEMAND OR OTHER POSITIVE PRESSURE MODE.

SUPPLIED-AIR RESPIRATOR WITH FULL FACEPIECE AND OPERATED IN PRESSURE-DEMAND OR OTHER POSITIVE PRESSURE MODE IN COMBINATION WITH AN AUXILIARY SELF-CONTAINED BREATHING APPARATUS OPERATED IN PRESSURE-DEMAND OR OTHER POSITIVE PRESSURE MODE.

CLOTHING: EMPLOYEE MUST WEAR APPROPRIATE PROTECTIVE (IMPERVIOUS) CLOTHING AND EQUIPMENT TO PREVENT ANY POSSIBILITY OF SKIN CONTACT WITH THIS SUBSTANCE.

GLOVES: EMPLOYEE MUST WEAR APPROPRIATE PROTECTIVE GLOVES TO PREVENT CONTACT WITH THIS SUBSTANCE.

EYE PROTECTION: EMPLOYEE MUST WEAR SPLASH-PROOF OR DUST-RESISTANT SAFETY GOGGLES AND A FACESHIELD TO PREVENT CONTACT WITH THIS SUBSTANCE.

EMERGENCY WASH FACILITIES: WHERE THERE IS ANY POSSIBILITY THAT AN EMPLOYEE'S EYES AND/OR SKIN MAY BE EXPOSED TO THIS SUBSTANCE, THE EMPLOYER SHOULD PROVIDE AN EYE WASH FOUNTAIN AND QUICK DRENCH SHOWER WITHIN THE IMMEDIATE WORK AREA FOR EMERGENCY USE.

AUTHORIZED BY- OCCUPATIONAL HEALTH SERVICES, INC.

CREATION DATE: 11/15/89 ***REVISION DATE:*** 05/16/90

MATERIAL SAFETY DATA SHEET

OCCUPATIONAL HEALTH SERVICES, INC.
AGRICULTURE AND PESTICIDE DIVISION
450 SEVENTH AVENUE, SUITE 2407
NEW YORK, NEW YORK 10123
1-800-445-MSDS OR (212) 967-1100

EMERGENCY CONTACT:
JOHN S. BRANSFORD, JR. (615) 292-1180

SUBSTANCE IDENTIFICATION

SUBSTANCE: BRONCO HERBICIDE

TRADE NAMES/SYNONYMS: EPA REG. NO. 524-341; PST03451

CHEMICAL FAMILY: MIXTURE, PESTICIDE FORMULATION

CERCLA RATINGS (SCALE 0-3): HEALTH=U FIRE=2 REACTIVITY=0 PERSISTENCE=2

NFPA RATINGS (SCALE 0-4): HEALTH=U FIRE=2 REACTIVITY=0

COMPONENTS AND CONTAMINANTS

COMPONENT: ALACHLOR ***PERCENT:*** 27.6
CAS# 15972-60-8

COMPONENT: GLYPHOSATE ISOPROPYLAMINE SALT ***PERCENT:*** 14.8
CAS# 38641-94-0

COMPONENT: INERT INGREDIENTS ***PERCENT:*** 57.6
INCLUDING:
CHLOROBENZENE CAS# 108-90-7
EMULSIFIERS

EXPOSURE LIMITS: ALACHLOR: SUBJECT TO CALIFORNIA PROPOSITION 65 CANCER AND/OR REPRODUCTIVE TOXICITY WARNING AND RELEASE REQUIREMENTS-(JANUARY 1, 1989)

CHLOROBENZENE: 75 PPM (350 MG/M3) OSHA TWA 75 PPM (350 MG/M3) ACGIH TWA (NOTICE OF INTENDED CHANGES 1989-1990)

100 POUNDS CERCLA SECTION 103 REPORTABLE QUANTITY SUBJECT TO SARA SECTION 313 ANNUAL TOXIC CHEMICAL RELEASE REPORTING

PHYSICAL DATA

DESCRIPTION: MILKY SOLUTION WITH ODOR SIMILAR TO SHOE POLISH.

BOILING POINT: NOT AVAILABLE ***SPECIFIC GRAVITY:*** 1.133

VAPOR PRESSURE: 25 MMHG @ 25 C ***SOLUBILITY IN WATER:*** SOLUBLE

FIRE AND EXPLOSION DATA

FIRE AND EXPLOSION HAZARD: MODERATE FIRE HAZARD WHEN EXPOSED TO HEAT OR FLAME.

FLASH POINT: 105 F (41 C) ***FLAMMABILITY CLASS(OSHA):*** II

FIREFIGHTING MEDIA: DRY CHEMICAL, CARBON DIOXIDE, HALON, WATER SPRAY OR STANDARD FOAM (1987 EMERGENCY RESPONSE GUIDEBOOK, DOT P 5800.4). FOR LARGER FIRES, USE WATER SPRAY, FOG OR STANDARD FOAM (1987 EMERGENCY RESPONSE GUIDEBOOK, DOT P 5800.4).

FIREFIGHTING: MOVE CONTAINERS FROM FIRE AREA IF POSSIBLE. COOL CONTAINERS EXPOSED TO FLAMES WITH WATER FROM SIDE UNTIL WELL AFTER FIRE IS OUT. FIGHT FIRE FROM MAXIMUM DISTANCE. STAY AWAY FROM STORAGE TANK ENDS. DIKE FIRE CONTROL WATER FOR LATER DISPOSAL. DO NOT SCATTER MATERIAL. (1987 EMERGENCY RESPONSE GUIDEBOOK, DOT P 5800.4, GUIDE PAGE 57). EXTINGUISH ONLY IF FLOW CAN BE STOPPED. USE FLOODING AMOUNTS OF WATER AS A FOG; SOLID STREAMS MAY BE INEFFECTIVE. COOL CONTAINERS WITH FLOODING AMOUNTS OF WATER FROM AS FAR A DISTANCE AS POSSIBLE. AVOID BREATHING POISONOUS VAPORS, KEEP UPWIND.

TRANSPORTATION DATA

DEPARTMENT OF TRANSPORTATION HAZARD CLASSIFICATION 49 CFR 172.101: COMBUSTIBLE LIQUID

DEPARTMENT OF TRANSPORTATION LABELING REQUIREMENTS 49 CFR 172.101 AND SUBPART E: NONE

DEPARTMENT OF TRANSPORTATION PACKAGING REQUIREMENTS: NONE EXCEPTIONS: 49 CFR 173.118A

TOXICITY

BRONCO HERBICIDE: TOXICITY LEVEL: 3152 MG/KG ORAL-RAT LD50; >5,000 MG/KG SKIN-RABBIT LD50. CARCINOGEN STATUS: NONE. LOCAL EFFECTS: CORROSIVE- EYE. ACUTE TOXICITY LEVEL: MODERATELY TOXIC BY INGESTION. TARGET EFFECTS: SENSITIZER- DERMAL; CENTRAL NERVOUS SYSTEM DEPRESSANT.

ALACHLOR: TOXICITY DATA: 3500 MG/KG SKIN-RABBIT LD50; 930 MG/KG ORAL-RAT LD50; 462 MG/KG ORAL-MOUSE LD50; 3000 MG/KG ORAL-MAMMAL LD50; 1200 MG/KG UNREPORTED-MAMMAL LD50; MUTAGENIC DATA (RTECS); TUMORIGENIC DATA (RTECS). CARCINOGEN STATUS: NONE. ACUTE TOXICITY LEVEL: MODERATELY TOXIC BY INGESTION; SLIGHTLY TOXIC BY DERMAL ABSORPTION. TARGET EFFECTS: SENSITIZER- SKIN. GLYPHOSATE ISOPROPYLAMINE SALT: TOXICITY DATA: 5480 MG/KG ORAL-RAT LD50; 3750 MG/KG SKIN-RABBIT LD50 (PEMNDP); MUTAGENIC DATA (RTECS). CARCINOGEN STATUS: NONE. ACUTE TOXICITY LEVEL: SLIGHTLY TOXIC BY DERMAL ABSORPTION AND INGESTION. TARGET EFFECTS: NO DATA AVAILABLE.

CHLOROBENZENE: TOXICITY DATA: 15 GM/M3 INHALATION-MOUSE LCLO; 2290 MG/KG ORAL-RAT LD50; 2250 MG/KG ORAL-RABBIT LD50; 2300 MG/KG ORAL-MOUSE LD50; 2250 MG/KG ORAL-GUINEA PIG LD50; 7000 MG/KG SUBCUTANEOUS-RAT LDLO; 7400 MG/KG INTRAPERITONEAL-RAT LDLO; 515 MG/KG INTRAPERITONEAL-MOUSE LD50; 4100 MG/KG INTRAPERITONEAL-GUINEA PIG LDLO; 2300 MG/KG UNREPORTED-MAMMAL LD50; MUTAGENIC DATA (RTECS);

REPRODUCTIVE EFFECTS DATA (RTECS). CARCINOGEN STATUS: NONE. LOCAL EFFECTS: IRRITANT- INHALATION, SKIN, EYE. ACUTE TOXICITY LEVEL: MODERATELY TOXIC BY INGESTION. TARGET EFFECTS: CENTRAL NERVOUS SYSTEM DEPRESSANT. POISONING MAY AFFECT THE LIVER AND KIDNEYS. AT INCREASED RISK FROM EXPOSURE: PERSONS WITH PREEXISTING SKIN, LIVER, KIDNEY, OR CHRONIC RESPIRATORY DISEASES. ADDITIONAL DATA: GASTROENTERIC ABSORPTION IS ENHANCED BY THE PRESENCE OF FATS OR OILS. ALCOHOL MAY ENHANCE THE TOXIC EFFECTS.

HEALTH EFFECTS AND FIRST AID

INHALATION: BRONCO HERBICIDE: NARCOTIC. **ACUTE EXPOSURE**- MAY CAUSE IRRITATION OF THE MUCOUS MEMBRANES. EXCESSIVE EXPOSURE TO THIS MATERIAL MAY CAUSE CENTRAL NERVOUS SYSTEM DEPRESSION WITH RESULTING EFFECTS OF HEADACHE, DIZZINESS, DROWSINESS, INCOORDINATION AND UNCONSCIOUSNESS AND METHEMOGLOBINEMIA WITH CYANOSIS DUE TO THE SOLVENT, CHLOROBENZENE, CONTAINED IN THIS PRODUCT. **CHRONIC EXPOSURE**- PROLONGED OR REPEATED EXPOSURE MAY CAUSE EFFECTS AS LISTED IN ACUTE EXPOSURE. REPEATED EXPOSURE TO CHLOROBENZENE PRODUCED NEUROMUSCULAR EFFECTS IN WORKERS AND EFFECTS ON THE LUNG, LIVER, AND KIDNEYS IN ANIMALS.

FIRST AID- REMOVE FROM EXPOSURE AREA TO FRESH AIR IMMEDIATELY. IF BREATHING HAS STOPPED, PERFORM ARTIFICIAL RESPIRATION. KEEP PERSON WARM AND AT REST. TREAT SYMPTOMATICALLY AND SUPPORTIVELY. GET MEDICAL ATTENTION IMMEDIATELY.

SKIN CONTACT: BRONCO HERBICIDE: SENSITIZER. **ACUTE EXPOSURE**- APPLICATION TO RABBIT SKIN PRODUCED SLIGHT IRRITATION AND SLIGHT TO MODERATE EDEMA THAT HAD HEALED WITHIN 6 TO 14 DAYS. SENSITIZATION REACTIONS MAY OCCUR IN PERSONS PREVIOUSLY EXPOSED. ACNEFORM ERUPTIONS MAY OCCUR DUE TO CHLOROBENZENE. **CHRONIC EXPOSURE**- PROLONGED OR REPEATED EXPOSURE MAY CAUSE ALLERGIC SKIN REACTIONS IN SUSCEPTIBLE INDIVIDUALS.

FIRST AID- REMOVE CONTAMINATED CLOTHING AND SHOES IMMEDIATELY. WASH AFFECTED AREA WITH SOAP OR MILD DETERGENT AND LARGE AMOUNTS OF WATER UNTIL NO EVIDENCE OF CHEMICAL REMAINS (APPROXIMATELY 15-20 MINUTES). GET MEDICAL ATTENTION IMMEDIATELY.

EYE CONTACT: BRONCO HERBICIDE: CORROSIVE. **ACUTE EXPOSURE**- APPLICATION TO RABBIT EYES PRODUCED SEVERE IRRITATION AND CORNEAL EFFECTS IN 5 OF 6 ANIMALS TESTED THAT REQUIRED 10 TO 19 DAYS TO HEAL AFTER EXPOSURE. A SLIGHT DEGREE OF CORNEAL OPACITY OBSERVED IN THE EYE OF ONE RABBIT REQUIRED MORE THAN 34 DAYS TO HEAL. **CHRONIC EXPOSURE**- NO DATA AVAILABLE.

FIRST AID- WASH EYES IMMEDIATELY WITH LARGE AMOUNTS OF WATER, OCCASIONALLY LIFTING UPPER AND LOWER LIDS, UNTIL NO EVIDENCE OF CHEMICAL REMAINS (AT LEAST 15-20 MINUTES). CONTINUE IRRIGATING WITH NORMAL SALINE UNTIL THE PH HAS RETURNED TO NORMAL (30-60 MINUTES). COVER WITH STERILE BANDAGES. GET MEDICAL ATTENTION IMMEDIATELY.

INGESTION: BRONCO HERBICIDE: NARCOTIC. **ACUTE EXPOSURE**- INGESTION MAY PRODUCE CENTRAL NERVOUS SYSTEM DEPRESSION WITH RESULTING EFFECTS OF HEADACHE, DIZZINESS, DROWSINESS, INCOORDINATION AND UNCONSCIOUSNESS AND METHEMOGLOBINEMIA WITH CYANOSIS DUE TO THE SOLVENT CHLOROBENZENE CONTAINED IN THIS MATERIAL. **CHRONIC EXPOSURE**- IN CHRONIC ADMINISTRATION STUDIES OF ALACHLOR, MATERNAL AND FETAL TOXICITY WAS OBSERVED IN RATS, HEPATOTOXICITY WAS REPORTED IN DOGS AND RATS; LIVER EFFECTS WERE NOTED IN RATS; AND TUMORS WERE PRODUCED IN RATS AND MICE. CHRONIC ADMINISTRATION OF CHLOROBENZENE PRODUCED EFFECTS ON THE LIVER, EOSINOPHILIA, AND INHIBITION OF ERYTHROPOIESIS AND THROMBOCYTOSIS IN RATS.

FIRST AID- TREAT SYMPTOMATICALLY AND SUPPORTIVELY. GET MEDICAL ATTENTION IMMEDIATELY. IF VOMITING OCCURS, KEEP HEAD LOWER THAN HIPS TO PREVENT ASPIRATION.

REACTIVITY

REACTIVITY: STABLE UNDER NORMAL TEMPERATURES AND PRESSURES.

INCOMPATIBILITIES: BRONCO HERBICIDE: OXIDIZERS (STRONG): FIRE AND EXPLOSION HAZARD. STEEL (GALVANIZED OR UNLINED): MAY REACT PRODUCING A HIGHLY COMBUSTIBLE GAS.

DECOMPOSITION: THERMAL DECOMPOSITION PRODUCTS MAY INCLUDE TOXIC AND CORROSIVE FUMES OF CHLORIDES AND TOXIC OXIDES OF CARBON.

POLYMERIZATION: HAZARDOUS POLYMERIZATION HAS NOT BEEN REPORTED TO OCCUR UNDER NORMAL TEMPERATURES AND PRESSURES.

STORAGE AND DISPOSAL

OBSERVE ALL FEDERAL, STATE AND LOCAL REGULATIONS WHEN STORING OR DISPOSING OF THIS SUBSTANCE. FOR ASSISTANCE, CONTACT THE DISTRICT DIRECTOR OF THE ENVIRONMENTAL PROTECTION AGENCY.

****STORAGE****

STORE IN ACCORDANCE WITH 29 CFR 1910.106.

BONDING AND GROUNDING: SUBSTANCES WITH LOW ELECTROCONDUCTIVITY, WHICH MAY BE IGNITED BY ELECTROSTATIC SPARKS, SHOULD BE STORED IN CONTAINERS WHICH MEET THE BONDING AND GROUNDING GUIDELINES SPECIFIED IN NFPA 77-1983, RECOMMENDED PRACTICE ON STATIC ELECTRICITY.

STORE IN ACCORDANCE WITH 40 CFR 165 RECOMMENDED PROCEDURES FOR THE DISPOSAL AND STORAGE OF PESTICIDES AND PESTICIDE CONTAINERS.

DO NOT STORE THIS MATERIAL IN GALVANIZED OR UNLINED STEEL DUE TO THE POSSIBLE REACTION OF THIS PRODUCT RESULTING IN THE FORMATION OF HIGHLY COMBUSTIBLE GAS MIXTURE THAT CAN BE IGNITED BY OPEN FLAME, SPARK, WELDER'S TORCH, LIGHTED CIGARETTE OR OTHER IGNITION SOURCE.

STORE AWAY FROM INCOMPATIBLE SUBSTANCES.

****DISPOSAL****

DISPOSAL MUST BE IN ACCORDANCE WITH STANDARDS APPLICABLE TO GENERATORS OF HAZARDOUS WASTE, 40 CFR 262. EPA HAZARDOUS WASTE NUMBER D001. 100 POUND CERCLA SECTION 103 REPORTABLE QUANTITY.

DISPOSAL MUST BE IN ACCORDANCE WITH 40 CFR 165 RECOMMENDED PROCEDURES FOR THE DISPOSAL AND STORAGE OF PESTICIDES AND PESTICIDE CONTAINERS.

CHLOROBENZENE - REGULATORY LEVEL: 100.0 MG/L MATERIALS WHICH CONTAIN THE ABOVE SUBSTANCE AT OR ABOVE THE REGULATORY LEVEL MEET THE EPA CHARACTERISTIC OF TOXICITY, AND MUST BE DISPOSED OF IN ACCORDANCE WITH 40 CFR PART 262. EPA HAZARDOUS WASTE NUMBER D021.

CONDITIONS TO AVOID

MAY BE IGNITED BY HEAT, SPARKS OR FLAMES. CONTAINER MAY EXPLODE IN HEAT OF FIRE. VAPOR EXPLOSION AND POISON HAZARD INDOORS, OUTDOORS OR IN SEWERS.

SPILL AND LEAK PROCEDURES

OCCUPATIONAL SPILL: SHUT OFF IGNITION SOURCES. DO NOT TOUCH SPILLED MATERIAL. STOP LEAK IF YOU CAN DO IT WITHOUT RISK. USE WATER SPRAY TO REDUCE VAPORS. FOR SMALL SPILLS, TAKE UP WITH SAND OR OTHER ABSORBENT MATERIAL AND PLACE INTO CONTAINERS FOR LATER DISPOSAL. FOR SMALL DRY SPILLS, WITH CLEAN SHOVEL PLACE MATERIAL INTO CLEAN, DRY CONTAINERS AND COVER. MOVE CONTAINERS FROM SPILL AREA. FOR LARGER SPILLS, DIKE FAR AHEAD OF SPILL FOR LATER DISPOSAL. NO SMOKING, FLAMES OR FLARES IN HAZARD AREA! KEEP UNNECESSARY PEOPLE AWAY. ISOLATE HAZARD AREA AND DENY ENTRY. VENTILATE CLOSED SPACES BEFORE ENTERING.

PROTECTIVE EQUIPMENT

VENTILATION: PROVIDE LOCAL EXHAUST OR GENERAL DILUTION VENTILATION SYSTEM.

RESPIRATOR: THE FOLLOWING RESPIRATORS ARE RECOMMENDED BASED ON INFORMATION FOUND IN THE PHYSICAL DATA, TOXICITY AND HEALTH EFFECTS SECTIONS. THEY ARE RANKED IN ORDER FROM MINIMUM TO MAXIMUM RESPIRATORY PROTECTION. THE SPECIFIC RESPIRATOR SELECTED MUST BE BASED ON CONTAMINATION LEVELS FOUND IN THE WORK PLACE, MUST NOT EXCEED THE WORKING LIMITS OF THE RESPIRATOR AND BE JOINTLY APPROVED BY THE NATIONAL INSTITUTE FOR OCCUPATIONAL SAFETY AND HEALTH AND THE MINE SAFETY AND HEALTH ADMINISTRATION (NIOSH-MSHA).

CHEMICAL CARTRIDGE RESPIRATOR WITH FULL FACEPIECE AND PESTICIDE CARTRIDGE.

TYPE 'C' SUPPLIED-AIR RESPIRATOR WITH A FULL FACEPIECE OPERATED IN PRESSURE-DEMAND OR OTHER POSITIVE PRESSURE MODE OR WITH A FULL FACEPIECE, HELMET OR HOOD OPERATED IN CONTINUOUS-FLOW MODE.

SELF-CONTAINED BREATHING APPARATUS OPERATED IN PRESSURE-DEMAND OR OTHER POSITIVE PRESSURE MODE.

FOR FIREFIGHTING AND OTHER IMMEDIATELY DANGEROUS TO LIFE OR HEALTH CONDITIONS:

SELF-CONTAINED BREATHING APPARATUS WITH FULL FACEPIECE OPERATED IN PRESSURE-DEMAND OR OTHER POSITIVE PRESSURE MODE.

SUPPLIED-AIR RESPIRATOR WITH FULL FACEPIECE AND OPERATED IN PRESSURE-DEMAND OR OTHER POSITIVE PRESSURE MODE IN COMBINATION WITH AN AUXILIARY SELF-CONTAINED BREATHING APPARATUS OPERATED IN PRESSURE-DEMAND OR OTHER POSITIVE PRESSURE MODE.

CLOTHING: EMPLOYEE MUST WEAR APPROPRIATE PROTECTIVE (IMPERVIOUS) CLOTHING AND EQUIPMENT TO PREVENT REPEATED OR PROLONGED SKIN CONTACT WITH THIS SUBSTANCE.

GLOVES: EMPLOYEE MUST WEAR APPROPRIATE PROTECTIVE GLOVES TO PREVENT CONTACT WITH THIS SUBSTANCE.

EYE PROTECTION: EMPLOYEE MUST WEAR SPLASH-PROOF OR DUST-RESISTANT SAFETY GOGGLES AND A FACESHIELD TO PREVENT CONTACT WITH THIS SUBSTANCE.

EMERGENCY WASH FACILITIES: WHERE THERE IS ANY POSSIBILITY THAT AN EMPLOYEE'S EYES AND/OR SKIN MAY BE EXPOSED TO THIS SUBSTANCE, THE EMPLOYER SHOULD PROVIDE AN EYE WASH FOUNTAIN AND QUICK DRENCH SHOWER WITHIN THE IMMEDIATE WORK AREA FOR EMERGENCY USE.

AUTHORIZED BY- OCCUPATIONAL HEALTH SERVICES, INC.
CREATION DATE: 10/04/89 ***REVISION DATE:*** 07/13/90

MATERIAL SAFETY DATA SHEET

OCCUPATIONAL HEALTH SERVICES, INC.
AGRICULTURE AND PESTICIDE DIVISION
450 SEVENTH AVENUE, SUITE 2407
NEW YORK, NEW YORK 10123
1-800-445-MSDS OR (212) 967-1100

EMERGENCY CONTACT:
JOHN S. BRANSFORD, JR. (615) 292-1180

SUBSTANCE IDENTIFICATION

CAS-NUMBER 4824-78-6
SUBSTANCE: **BROMOPHOS-ETHYL**
TRADE NAMES/SYNONYMS: PHOSPHOROTHIOIC ACID, O-(4-BROMO-2,5-DICHLOROPHENYL) O,O-DIETHYL ESTER; O-4-BROMO-2,5-DICHLOROPHENYL O,O-DIETHYL PHOSPHOROTHIOATE; O-(4-BROMO-2,5-DICHLOROPHENYL) O,O-DIETHYL PHOSPHOROTHIOATE; 4-BROMO-2,5-DICHLOROPHENYL DIMETHYL PHOSPHOROTHIONATE; ETHYL BROMOPHOS; FILARIOL; NEXAGAN; OMS 659; ENT 27 258; PST03458
CHEMICAL FAMILY: ORGANOPHOSPHATE
MOLECULAR FORMULA: C10-H12-BR-CL2-O3-P-S
MOLECULAR WEIGHT: 394.06
CERCLA RATINGS (SCALE 0-3): HEALTH=3 FIRE=0 REACTIVITY=U PERSISTENCE=3
NFPA RATINGS (SCALE 0-4): HEALTH=3 FIRE=0 REACTIVITY=U

COMPONENTS AND CONTAMINANTS

COMPONENT: BROMOPHOS-ETHYL ***PERCENT:*** 100
CAS# 4824-78-6
EXPOSURE LIMITS: NO OCCUPATIONAL EXPOSURE LIMITS ESTABLISHED BY OSHA, ACGIH, OR NIOSH.

PHYSICAL DATA

DESCRIPTION: COLORLESS TO PALE YELLOW OIL
BOILING POINT: 252-272 F (122-133 C) @ 0.001 MMHG ***SPECIFIC GRAVITY:*** 1.52-1.55
VAPOR PRESSURE: 0.000046 MMHG @ 30 C ***SOLUBILITY IN WATER:*** 2 MG/L
SOLVENT SOLUBILITY: SOLUBLE IN MOST ORGANIC SOLVENTS

FIRE AND EXPLOSION DATA

FIRE AND EXPLOSION HAZARD: NEGLIGIBLE FIRE HAZARD WHEN EXPOSED TO HEAT OR FLAME.
FIREFIGHTING MEDIA: DRY CHEMICAL, CARBON DIOXIDE, HALON, WATER SPRAY OR STANDARD FOAM (1987 EMERGENCY RESPONSE GUIDEBOOK, DOT P 5800.4). FOR LARGER FIRES, USE WATER SPRAY, FOG OR STANDARD FOAM (1987 EMERGENCY RESPONSE GUIDEBOOK, DOT P 5800.4).
FIREFIGHTING: MOVE CONTAINERS FROM FIRE AREA IF POSSIBLE. FIGHT FIRE FROM MAXIMUM DISTANCE. STAY AWAY FROM STORAGE TANK ENDS. DIKE FIRE CONTROL WATER FOR LATER DISPOSAL. DO NOT SCATTER MATERIAL (1987 EMERGENCY RESPONSE GUIDEBOOK, DOT P 5800.4, GUIDE PAGE 55). EXTINGUISH USING AGENT SUITABLE FOR TYPE OF SURROUNDING FIRE. AVOID BREATHING VAPORS AND DUSTS. KEEP UPWIND.

TOXICITY

BROMOPHOS-ETHYL: TOXICITY DATA: 16600 PPB/2 HOURS INHALATION-RAT LCLO; 2600 MG/M3/1.7 HOURS INHALATION-RAT LC50 (PEMNDP); 500 MG/KG SKIN-RABBIT LD50; 1000 MG/KG SKIN-RAT LD50; 52 MG/KG ORAL-RAT LD50; 48 MG/KG ORAL-RAT LD50 (PEMNDP); 210 MG/KG ORAL-MOUSE LD50;28 MG/KG ORAL-RABBIT LD50; 100 MG/KG ORAL-GUINEA PIG LDLO; 125 MG/KG ORAL DOMESTIC ANIMAL LDLO; 360 MG/KG ORAL-DOG LD50; 60 MG/KG INTRAPERITONEAL-RAT LD50; 25 MG/KG INTRAPERITONEAL-MOUSE LD50; 238 MG/KG UNREPORTED-RAT LD50. CARCINOGEN STATUS: NONE. ACUTE TOXICITY LEVEL: HIGHLY TOXIC BY INGESTION; TOXIC BY INHALATION AND DERMAL ABSORPTION. TARGET EFFECTS: CHOLINESTERASE INHIBITOR. POISONING MAY AFFECT THE NERVOUS SYSTEM.* AT INCREASED RISK FROM EXPOSURE: PERSONS WITH RESPIRATORY AILMENTS, RECENT EXPOSURE TO CHOLINESTERASE INHIBITORS OR IMPAIRED CHOLINESTERASE PRODUCTION, OR LIVER MALFUNCTION.* ADDITIONAL DATA: MAY CROSS THE PLACENTA. HIGH ENVIRONMENTAL TEMPERATURES OR EXPOSURE OF THE CHEMICAL TO VISIBLE OR ULTRAVIOLET LIGHT MAY ENHANCE THE TOXICITY. INTERACTIONS WITH MEDICATIONS MAY OCCUR.*
* MAY BE BASED ON GENERAL INFORMATION ON ORGANOPHOSPHATES.

HEALTH EFFECTS AND FIRST AID

INHALATION: BROMOPHOS-ETHYL: TOXIC. SEE INFORMATION ON ORGANOPHOSPHATES.
ORGANOPHOSPHATES: CHOLINESTERASE INHIBITOR. **ACUTE EXPOSURE-** WHEN INHALED, THE FIRST EFFECTS OF CHOLINESTERASE INHIBITORS ARE USUALLY RESPIRATORY AND MAY INCLUDE NASAL HYPEREMIA AND WATERY DISCHARGE, COUGH, CHEST DISCOMFORT, DYSPNEA, AND WHEEZING DUE TO INCREASED BRONCHIAL SECRETIONS AND BRONCHOCONSTRICTION. IF SUFFICIENT AMOUNTS ARE ABSORBED, OTHER SYSTEMIC EFFECTS MAY BEGIN WITHIN A FEW MINUTES OR BE DELAYED FOR UP TO 12 HOURS. SYMPTOMS MAY INCLUDE PALLOR, NAUSEA, VOMITING, DIARRHEA, ABDOMINAL CRAMPS, HEADACHE, DIZZINESS, OCULAR PAIN, BLURRED VISION, MIOSIS OR IN SOME CASES, ESPECIALLY INITIALLY, MYDRIASIS, LACRIMATION, SALIVATION, SWEATING, AND CONFUSION. OTHER REPORTED CENTRAL NERVOUS SYSTEM OR NEUROMUSCULAR EFFECTS MAY INCLUDE ATAXIA, SLURRED SPEECH, AREFLEXIA, WEAKNESS, FATIGUE, FASCICULATIONS, TWITCHING, TREMORS POSSIBLY OF THE TONGUE AND EYELIDS, AND EVENTUALLY PARALYSIS OF THE EXTREMITIES AND POSSIBLY OF THE RESPIRATORY MUSCLES. IN SEVERE CASES THERE MAY ALSO BE INVOLUNTARY DEFECATION AND URINATION, CYANOSIS, PSYCHOSIS, HYPERGLYCEMIA, ACUTE PANCREATITIS, CARDIAC IRREGULARITIES, PULMONARY EDEMA, UNCONSCIOUSNESS, CONVULSIONS, AND COMA. DEATH IS PRIMARILY DUE TO RESPIRATORY FAILURE, ALTHOUGH CARDIOVASCULAR EFFECTS INCLUDING CARDIAC ARREST MAY ALSO BE IMPLICATED. LONG TERM SEQUELAE ARE RARE BUT MAY INCLUDE NEUROPSYCHIATRIC DISORDERS AND MYOPATHY WITH MUSCLE TENDERNESS. SOME ORGANOPHOSPHATES MAY CAUSE A DELAYED NEUROPATHY BEGINNING 1-4 WEEKS AFTER AN ACUTE EXPOSURE WHICH MAY OR MAY NOT HAVE CAUSED ACUTE CHOLINERGIC EFFECTS. NUMBNESS, TINGLING, WEAKNESS AND CRAMPING BEGINNING SYMMETRICALLY IN THE LOWER LIMBS MAY PROGRESS TO ATAXIA AND PARALYSIS. IN SEVERE CASES, UPPER LIMB INVOLVEMENT IS POSSIBLE AND FLACCID PARALYSIS MAY PROGRESS TO SPASTIC PARALYSIS WITH EXAGGERATED REFLEXES. IMPROVEMENT MAY OCCUR OVER MONTHS TO YEARS, BUT SOME RESIDUAL IMPAIRMENT USUALLY REMAINS.
CHRONIC EXPOSURE- REPEATED OR PROLONGED EXPOSURE MAY RESULT IN THE EFFECTS OF ACUTE EXPOSURE INCLUDING THE DELAYED NEUROPATHY. OTHER EFFECTS REPORTED IN WORKERS REPEATEDLY EXPOSED INCLUDE IMPAIRED MEMORY AND CONCENTRATION, ACUTE PSYCHOSIS, SEVERE DEPRESSIONS, IRRITABILTY, CONFUSION, APATHY, EMOTIONAL LABILITY, SOCIAL WITHDRAWAL, CONFUSION, HEADACHE, SPEECH DIFFICULTIES, DELAYED REACTION TIMES, SPATIAL DISORIENTATION, NIGHTMARES, SLEEPWALKING, AND DROWSINESS OR INSOMNIA. AN INFLUENZA-LIKE CONDITION WITH HEADACHE, NAUSEA, WEAKNESS, ANOREXIA AND MALAISE HAS ALSO BEEN REPORTED.
FIRST AID- REMOVE FROM EXPOSURE AREA TO FRESH AIR IMMEDIATELY. IF BREATHING HAS STOPPED, GIVE ARTIFICIAL RESPIRATION. MAINTAIN AIRWAY AND BLOOD PRESSURE AND ADMINISTER OXYGEN IF AVAILABLE. KEEP AFFECTED PERSON WARM AND AT REST. TREAT SYMPTOMATICALLY AND SUPPORTIVELY. ADMINISTRATION OF OXYGEN SHOULD BE PERFORMED BY QUALIFIED PERSONNEL. GET MEDICAL ATTENTION IMMEDIATELY.

SKIN CONTACT: BROMOPHOS-ETHYL: TOXIC. SEE INFORMATION ON ORGANOPHOSPHATES.
ORGANOPHOSPHATES: CHOLINESTERASE INHIBITOR. **ACUTE EXPOSURE-** LOCALIZED SWEATING AND FASCICULATIONS MAY OCCUR AT THE SITE OF CONTACT. IF SUFFICIENT AMOUNTS ARE ABSORBED, OTHER EFFECTS OF CHOLINESTERASE INHIBITION AS DESCRIBED IN ACUTE INHALATION MAY OCCUR. SYMPTOMS MAY BE DELAYED 2-3 HOURS, BUT USUALLY NO MORE THAN 12 HOURS. THE RATE OF ABSORPTION IS INCREASED BY THE PRESENCE OF DERMATITIS OR HIGH AMBIENT TEMPERATURES. DELAYED NEUROPATHY IS ALSO POSSIBLE. **CHRONIC EXPOSURE-** REPEATED OR PROLONGED EXPOSURE MAY CAUSE EFFECTS AS DESCRIBED IN ACUTE EXPOSURE. SOME ORGANOPHOSPHATES MAY CAUSE SENSITIZATION.
FIRST AID- REMOVE CONTAMINATED CLOTHING IMMEDIATELY. WASH CONTAMINATED AREAS WITH SOAP AND WATER FOLLOWED BY ALCOHOL (ARENA, POISONING, 4TH ED.). EMERGENCY PERSONNEL SHOULD WEAR GLOVES AND AVOID CONTAMINATION. TREAT RESPIRATORY DIFFICULTY WITH ARTIFICIAL RESPIRATION. GET MEDICAL ATTENTION IMMEDIATELY.

EYE CONTACT: BROMOPHOS-ETHYL: SEE INFORMATION ON ORGANOPHOSPHATES.
ORGANOPHOSPHATES: CHOLINESTERASE INHIBITOR. **ACUTE EXPOSURE-** DIRECT CONTACT MAY CAUSE PAIN, HYPEREMIA, LACRIMATION, TWITCHING OF THE

EYELIDS, MIOSIS, AND CILIARY MUSCLE SPASM WITH LOSS OF ACCOMODATION, BLURRED OR DIMMED VISION AND BROWACHE. SOMETIMES MYDRIASIS MAY OCCUR INSTEAD OF MIOSIS. WITH SUFFICIENT EXPOSURE, OTHER SYMPTOMS OF CHOLINESTERASE INHIBITION AS DESCRIBED IN ACUTE INHALATION MAY OCCUR. **CHRONIC EXPOSURE**- REPEATED OR PROLONGED EXPOSURE MAY CAUSE EFFECTS AS DESCRIBED IN ACUTE EXPOSURE. SOME COMPOUNDS HAVE CAUSED TOXIC EFFECTS ON THE CRYSTALLINE LENS, CONJUNCTIVAL THICKENING AND OBSTRUCTION OF THE NASOLACRIMAL CANALS WHEN USED AS MIOTIC EYEDROPS.

FIRST AID- IRRIGATE EYES WITH WATER OR SALINE SOLUTION. IF SYMPTOMS OF POISONING OCCUR, TREAT RESPIRATORY DIFFICULTY WITH ARTIFICIAL RESPIRATION AND OXYGEN. OBSERVE PATIENT FOR AT LEAST 24-36 HOURS (GOSSELIN, CLINICAL TOXICOLOGY OF COMMERCIAL PRODUCTS, 5TH ED.). GET MEDICAL ATTENTION IMMEDIATELY. OXYGEN SHOULD BE ADMINISTERED BY QUALIFIED MEDICAL PERSONNEL.

INGESTION: BROMOPHOS-ETHYL: HIGHLY TOXIC. SEE INFORMATION ON ORGANOPHOSPHATES.

ORGANOPHOSPHATES: CHOLINESTERASE INHIBITOR. **ACUTE EXPOSURE**- WHEN INGESTED, THE FIRST EFFECTS MAY BE NAUSEA, VOMITING, ANOREXIA, ABDOMINAL CRAMPS AND DIARRHEA. GASTROINTESTINAL ABSORPTION MAY CAUSE SYMPTOMS OF CHOLINESTERASE INHIBITION AS DESCRIBED IN ACUTE INHALATION. SYMPTOMS MAY BEGIN WITHIN MINUTES OR BE DELAYED FOR HOURS. DELAYED EFFECTS INCLUDING NEUROPATHY MAY ALSO OCCUR. **CHRONIC EXPOSURE**- REPEATED INGESTION MAY CAUSE EFFECTS AS DESCRIBED IN ACUTE EXPOSURE.

FIRST AID- IF PERSON IS ALERT AND RESPIRATION IS NOT DEPRESSED, GIVE SYRUP OF IPECAC FOLLOWED BY WATER (IF VOMITING OCCURS, KEEP HEAD BELOW HIPS TO PREVENT ASPIRATION). IF CONSCIOUSNESS LEVEL DECLINES OR VOMITING HAS NOT OCCURRED IN 15 MINUTES EMPTY STOMACH BY GASTRIC LAVAGE WITH THE AID OF CUFFED ENDOTRACHEAL TUBE USING ISOTONIC SALINE OR 5% SODIUM BICARBONATE FOLLOW WITH ACTIVATED CHARCOAL. ESTABLISH AND MAINTAIN AIRWAY. TREAT RESPIRATORY DIFFICULTY WITH ARTIFICIAL RESPIRATION AND OXYGEN. DO NOT GIVE MORPHINE, AMINOPHYLLINE, PHENOTHIAZINES, RESERPINE, FUROSEMIDE, OR ETHACRYNIC ACID (MORGAN, RECOGNITION AND MANAGEMENT OF PESTICIDE POISONINGS, 3RD ED.). TREAT SYMPTOMATICALLY AND SUPPORTIVELY. ADMINISTRATION OF OXYGEN AND LAVAGE MUST BE PERFORMED BY QUALIFIED MEDICAL PERSONNEL. GET MEDICAL ATTENTION IMMEDIATELY.

ANTIDOTE: THE FOLLOWING ANTIDOTE(S) HAVE BEEN RECOMMENDED. HOWEVER, THE DECISION AS TO WHETHER THE SEVERITY OF POISONING REQUIRES ADMINISTRATION OF ANY ANTIDOTE AND ACTUAL DOSE REQUIRED SHOULD BE MADE BY QUALIFIED MEDICAL PERSONNEL.

FOR CHOLINESTERASE INHIBITORS: ESTABLISH CLEAR AIRWAY AND TISSUE OXYGENATION BY ASPIRATION OF SECRETIONS, AND IF NECESSARY, BY ASSISTED PULMONARY VENTILATION WITH OXYGEN. IMPROVE TISSUE OXYGENATION AS MUCH AS POSSIBLE BEFORE ADMINISTERING ATROPINE TO MINIMIZE THE RISK OF VENTRICULAR FIBRILLATION. ADMINISTER ATROPINE SULFATE INTRAVENOUSLY, OR INTRAMUSCULARLY IF IV INJECTION IS NOT POSSIBLE. IN MODERATELY SEVERE POISONING ADMINISTER ATROPINE SULFATE, 0.4-2.0 MG REPEATED EVERY 15 MINUTES UNTIL ATROPINIZATION IS ACHIEVED (TACHYCARDIA, FLUSHING, DRY MOUTH, MYDRIASIS). MAINTAIN ATROPINIZATION BY REPEATED DOSES FOR 2-12 HOURS, OR LONGER, DEPENDING ON THE SEVERITY OF POISONING. THE APPEARANCE OF RALES IN THE LUNG BASES, MIOSIS, SALIVATION, NAUSEA, BRADYCARDIA, ARE ALL INDICATIONS OF INADEQUATE ATROPINIZATION. SEVERELY POISONED INDIVIDUALS MAY EXHIBIT REMARKABLE TOLERANCE TO ATROPINE; TWO OR MORE TIMES THE DOSAGES SUGGESTED ABOVE MAY BE NEEDED. PERSONS NOT POISONED OR ONLY SLIGHTLY POISONED, HOWEVER, MAY DEVELOP SIGNS OF ATROPINE TOXICITY FROM SUCH LARGE DOSAGES: FEVER, MUSCLE FIBRILLATIONS, AND DELIRIUM ARE THE MAIN SIGNS OF ATROPINE TOXICITY. IF THESE SIGNS APPEAR WHILE THE PATIENT IS FULLY ATROPINIZED, ATROPINE ADMINISTRATION SHOULD BE DISCONTINUED, AT LEAST TEMPORARILY. OBSERVE TREATED PATIENTS CLOSELY AT LEAST 24 HOURS TO INSURE THAT SYMPTOMS (POSSIBLY PULMONARY EDEMA) DO NOT RECUR AS ATROPINIZATION WEARS OFF. IN VERY SEVERE POISONINGS, METABOLIC DISPOSITION OF TOXICANT MAY REQUIRE SEVERAL HOURS OR DAYS DURING WHICH ATROPINIZATION MUST BE MAINTAINED. MARKEDLY LOWER LEVELS OF URINARY METABOLITES INDICATE THAT ATROPINE DOSAGE CAN BE TAPERED OFF. AS DOSAGE IS REDUCED, CHECK THE LUNG BASES FREQUENTLY FOR RALES. IF RALES ARE HEARD OR OTHER SYMPTOMS RETURN, RE-ESTABLISH ATROPINIZATION PROMPTLY (MORGAN, RECOGNITION AND MANAGEMENT OF PESTICIDE POISONINGS, 3RD ED.). ADMINISTRATION OF ANTIDOTE MUST BE PERFORMED BY QUALIFIED MEDICAL PERSONNEL.

IN CASES OF SEVERE POISONING BY ORGANOPHOSPHATE PESTICIDES IN WHICH RESPIRATORY DEPRESSION, MUSCLE WEAKNESS AND TWITCHINGS ARE SEVERE, GIVE PRALIDOXIME (PROTOPAM-AYERST, 2-PAM), 1.0 GRAM INTRAVENOUSLY AT NO MORE THAN 0.5 GRAM PER MINUTE. DOSAGE OF PRALIDOXIME MAY BE REPEATED IN 1-2 HOURS, THEN AT 10-12 HOUR INTERVALS IF NEEDED. IN VERY SEVERE POISONINGS, DOSAGE RATES MAY BE DOUBLED. TREATMENT WITH PRALIDOXIME WILL BE MOST EFFECTIVE IF GIVEN WITHIN THIRTY-SIX HOURS AFTER POISONING (MORGAN, RECOGNITION AND MANAGEMENT OF PESTICIDE POISONINGS, 3RD ED.). ANTIDOTE SHOULD BE ADMINISTERED BY QUALIFIED MEDICAL PERSONNEL.

REACTIVITY

REACTIVITY: NO SPECIFIC DATA AVAILABLE. HOWEVER, A NUMBER OF PHOSPHATE AND THIOPHOSPHATE ESTERS ARE OF LIMITED THERMAL STABILITY AND UNDERGO HIGHLY EXOTHERMIC SELF-ACCELERATING DECOMPOSITION REACTIONS.

INCOMPATIBILITIES: BROMOPHOS-ETHYL: ALKALINE CONDITIONS (PH >9): MAY CAUSE HYDROLYSIS. ORGANOMETAL FUNGICIDES: INCOMPATIBLE. SULFUR: INCOMPATIBLE.

DECOMPOSITION: THERMAL DECOMPOSITION MAY RELEASE TOXIC OXIDES OF SULFUR, PHOSPHOROUS AND HAZARDOUS FUMES OF HYDROGEN BROMIDE AND HYDROGEN CHLORIDE.

POLYMERIZATION: HAZARDOUS POLYMERIZATION HAS NOT BEEN REPORTED TO OCCUR UNDER NORMAL TEMPERATURES AND PRESSURES.

STORAGE AND DISPOSAL

OBSERVE ALL FEDERAL, STATE AND LOCAL REGULATIONS WHEN STORING OR DISPOSING OF THIS SUBSTANCE. FOR ASSISTANCE, CONTACT THE DISTRICT DIRECTOR OF THE ENVIRONMENTAL PROTECTION AGENCY.

****STORAGE****

STORE IN ACCORDANCE WITH 40 CFR 165 RECOMMENDED PROCEDURES FOR THE DISPOSAL AND STORAGE OF PESTICIDES AND PESTICIDE CONTAINERS.
STORE AWAY FROM INCOMPATIBLE SUBSTANCES.

****DISPOSAL****

DISPOSAL MUST BE IN ACCORDANCE WITH 40 CFR 165 RECOMMENDED PROCEDURES FOR THE DISPOSAL AND STORAGE OF PESTICIDES AND PESTICIDE CONTAINERS.

CONDITIONS TO AVOID

NONE REPORTED.

SPILL AND LEAK PROCEDURES

OCCUPATIONAL SPILL: DO NOT TOUCH SPILLED MATERIAL. STOP LEAK IF YOU CAN DO IT WITHOUT RISK. USE WATER SPRAY TO REDUCE VAPORS. FOR SMALL SPILLS, TAKE UP WITH SAND OR OTHER ABSORBENT MATERIAL AND PLACE INTO CONTAINERS FOR LATER DISPOSAL. FOR SMALL DRY SPILLS, WITH A CLEAN SHOVEL PLACE MATERIAL INTO CLEAN, DRY CONTAINERS AND COVER. MOVE CONTAINERS FROM SPILL AREA. FOR LARGER SPILLS, DIKE FAR AHEAD OF SPILL FOR LATER DISPOSAL. KEEP UNNECESSARY PEOPLE AWAY. ISOLATE HAZARD AREA AND DENY ENTRY. VENTILATE CLOSED SPACES BEFORE ENTERING.

PROTECTIVE EQUIPMENT

VENTILATION: PROVIDE LOCAL EXHAUST OR PROCESS ENCLOSURE VENTILATION SYSTEM.

RESPIRATOR: THE FOLLOWING RESPIRATORS ARE RECOMMENDED BASED ON INFORMATION FOUND IN THE PHYSICAL DATA, TOXICITY AND HEALTH EFFECTS SECTIONS. THEY ARE RANKED IN ORDER FROM MINIMUM TO MAXIMUM RESPIRATORY PROTECTION. THE SPECIFIC RESPIRATOR SELECTED MUST BE BASED ON CONTAMINATION LEVELS FOUND IN THE WORK PLACE, MUST NOT EXCEED THE WORKING LIMITS OF THE RESPIRATOR AND BE JOINTLY APPROVED BY THE NATIONAL INSTITUTE FOR OCCUPATIONAL SAFETY AND HEALTH AND THE MINE SAFETY AND HEALTH ADMINISTRATION (NIOSH-MSHA).

TYPE 'C' SUPPLIED-AIR RESPIRATOR WITH A FULL FACEPIECE OPERATED IN PRESSURE-DEMAND OR OTHER POSITIVE PRESSURE MODE OR WITH A FULL FACEPIECE, HELMET OR HOOD OPERATED IN CONTINOUS-FLOW MODE.

SELF-CONTAINED BREATHING APPARATUS WITH A FULL FACEPIECE OPERATED IN PRESSURE-DEMAND OR OTHER POSITIVE PRESSURE MODE.

FOR FIREFIGHTING AND OTHER IMMEDIATELY DANGEROUS TO LIFE OR HEALTH CONDITIONS:

SELF-CONTAINED BREATHING APPARATUS WITH FULL FACEPIECE OPERATED IN PRESSURE-DEMAND OR OTHER POSITIVE PRESSURE MODE.

SUPPLIED-AIR RESPIRATOR WITH FULL FACEPIECE AND OPERATED IN PRESSURE-DEMAND OR OTHER POSITIVE PRESSURE MODE IN COMBINATION WITH AN AUXILIARY SELF-CONTAINED BREATHING APPARATUS OPERATED IN PRESSURE-DEMAND OR OTHER POSITIVE PRESSURE MODE.

CLOTHING: EMPLOYEE MUST WEAR APPROPRIATE PROTECTIVE (IMPERVIOUS) CLOTHING AND EQUIPMENT TO PREVENT ANY POSSIBILITY OF SKIN CONTACT WITH THIS SUBSTANCE.

GLOVES: EMPLOYEE MUST WEAR APPROPRIATE PROTECTIVE GLOVES TO PREVENT CONTACT WITH THIS SUBSTANCE.

EYE PROTECTION: EMPLOYEE MUST WEAR SPLASH-PROOF OR DUST-RESISTANT SAFETY GOGGLES AND A FACESHIELD TO PREVENT CONTACT WITH THIS SUBSTANCE.
EMERGENCY WASH FACILITIES: WHERE THERE IS ANY POSSIBILITY THAT AN EMPLOYEE'S EYES AND/OR SKIN MAY BE EXPOSED TO THIS SUBSTANCE, THE EMPLOYER SHOULD PROVIDE AN EYE WASH FOUNTAIN AND QUICK DRENCH SHOWER WITHIN THE IMMEDIATE WORK AREA FOR EMERGENCY USE.

AUTHORIZED BY- OCCUPATIONAL HEALTH SERVICES, INC.
CREATION DATE: 10/04/89 ***REVISION DATE:*** 05/09/90

MATERIAL SAFETY DATA SHEET

OCCUPATIONAL HEALTH SERVICES, INC.
AGRICULTURE AND PESTICIDE DIVISION
450 SEVENTH AVENUE, SUITE 2407
NEW YORK, NEW YORK 10123
1-800-445-MSDS OR (212) 967-1100

EMERGENCY CONTACT:
JOHN S. BRANSFORD, JR. (615) 292-1180

SUBSTANCE IDENTIFICATION

CAS-NUMBER 8065-36-9
SUBSTANCE: BUFENCARB
TRADE NAMES/SYNONYMS: PHENOL, 3-(1-ETHYLPROPYL)-, METHYLCARBAMATE, MIXTURE WITH 3- (1-METHYLBUTYL)PHENYL METHYLCARBAMATE; 3-(1-ETHYLPROPYL)PHENOL METHYLCARBAMATE MIXTURE WITH 3-(1-METHYLBUTYL) PHENYL METHYLCARBAMATE; METHYLCARBAMIC ACID M-(1-ETHYLPROPYL)PHENYL ESTER MIXTURE WITH M-(1-METHYLBUTYL)PHENYL ESTER; BUX; METALCAMAT; METALKAMATE; ORTHO 5353; OMS 227; ENT 27127; C13H19NO2; PST03480
CHEMICAL FAMILY: CARBAMATE
MOLECULAR FORMULA: C13-H19-N-O2
MOLECULAR WEIGHT: 221.30
CERCLA RATINGS (SCALE 0-3): HEALTH=3 FIRE=1 REACTIVITY=0 PERSISTENCE=1
NFPA RATINGS (SCALE 0-4): HEALTH=3 FIRE=1 REACTIVITY=0

COMPONENTS AND CONTAMINANTS

COMPONENT: BUFENCARB ***PERCENT:*** 100.0
CAS# 8065-36-9
OTHER CONTAMINANTS: NONE
EXPOSURE LIMITS: NO OCCUPATIONAL EXPOSURE LIMITS ESTABLISHED BY OSHA, ACGIH, OR NIOSH.

PHYSICAL DATA

DESCRIPTION: YELLOW TO AMBER SOLID. ***BOILING POINT:*** 257 F (125 C) @ 0.04 MMHG
MELTING POINT: 79-102 F (26-39 C) ***SPECIFIC GRAVITY:*** 1.024 @ 26 C
VAPOR PRESSURE: 0.00003 MMHG @ 30 C
SOLUBILITY IN WATER: <0.005% @ 25C
SOLVENT SOLUBILITY: SOLUBLE IN METHANOL AND XYLENE; LESS SOLUBLE IN HEXANE AND OTHER ALIPHATIC HYDROCARBONS.

FIRE AND EXPLOSION DATA

FIRE AND EXPLOSION HAZARD: SLIGHT FIRE HAZARD WHEN EXPOSED TO HEAT OR FLAME.
FIREFIGHTING MEDIA: DRY CHEMICAL, CARBON DIOXIDE, HALON, WATER SPRAY OR STANDARD FOAM (1987 EMERGENCY RESPONSE GUIDEBOOK, DOT P 5800.4). FOR LARGER FIRES, USE WATER SPRAY, FOG OR STANDARD FOAM (1987 EMERGENCY RESPONSE GUIDEBOOK, DOT P 5800.4).
FIREFIGHTING: MOVE CONTAINERS FROM FIRE AREA IF POSSIBLE. FIGHT FIRE FROM MAXIMUM DISTANCE. STAY AWAY FROM STORAGE TANK ENDS. DIKE FIRE CONTROL WATER FOR LATER DISPOSAL. DO NOT SCATTER MATERIAL (1987 EMERGENCY RESPONSE GUIDEBOOK, DOT P 5800.4, GUIDE PAGE 55). EXTINGUISH USING AGENTS SUITABLE FOR TYPE OF SURROUNDING FIRE. USE FLOODING AMOUNTS OF WATER AS FOG. AVOID BREATHING TOXIC DUST AND FUMES FROM BURNING MATERIAL; KEEP UPWIND.

TOXICITY

BUFENCARB: TOXICITY DATA: 400 MG/KG SKIN-RABBIT LD50; 163 MG/KG SKIN-RAT LD50; 1400 MG/KG SKIN-DOG LD50; 61 MG/KG ORAL-RAT LD50; CARCINOGEN STATUS: NONE. ACUTE TOXICITY: TOXIC BY DERMAL ABSORPTION AND INGESTION. TARGET EFFECTS: CHOLINESTERASE INHIBITOR. AT INCREASED RISK FROM EXPOSURE: PERSONS WITH ASTHMA, DIABETES, CARDIOVASCULAR DISEASE, MECHANICAL OBSTRUCTION OF THE GASTROINTESTINAL OR UROGENITAL TRACT, AND THOSE IN VAGOTONIC STATES.*
* MAY BE BASED ON GENERAL INFORMATION ON CARBAMATES.

HEALTH EFFECTS AND FIRST AID

INHALATION: BUFENCARB: SEE INFORMATION ON CARBAMATES.
CARBAMATES: CHOLINESTERASE INHIBITOR. **ACUTE EXPOSURE-** WHEN INHALED, THE FIRST EFFECTS OF CHOLINESTERASE INHIBITION ARE USUALLY RESPIRATORY AND MAY INCLUDE NASAL HYPEREMIA AND WATERY DISCHARGE, CHEST DISCOMFORT, DYSPNEA, AND WHEEZING DUE TO INCREASED BRONCHIAL SECRETIONS AND BRONCHOCONSTRICTION. OTHER SYSTEMIC EFFECTS MAY BEGIN WITHIN A FEW MINUTES OR SEVERAL HOURS OF EXPOSURE. SYMPTOMS MAY INCLUDE NAUSEA, VOMITING, DIARRHEA, ABDOMINAL CRAMPS, HEADACHE, VERTIGO, OCULAR PAIN, CILIARY MUSCLE SPASM, BLURRING OR DIMNESS OF VISION, MIOSIS, OR IN SOME CASES MYDRIASIS, LACRIMATION, SALIVATION, SWEATING, AND CONFUSION. OTHER REPORTED CENTRAL NERVOUS SYSTEM OR NEUROMUSCULAR EFFECTS INCLUDE ATAXIA, SLURRED SPEECH, AREFLEXIA, WEAKNESS, FATIGUE, TWITCHING, FASCICULATION, TREMOR, AND EVENTUALLY PARALYSIS OF THE EXTREMITIES AND POSSIBLY OF THE RESPIRATORY MUSCLES. IN SEVERE CASES, THERE MAY ALSO BE INVOLUNTARY DEFECATION AND URINATION, BRADYCARDIA, HYPOTENSION, PULMONARY EDEMA, CONVULSIONS, COMA, AND DEATH FROM RESPIRATORY FAILURE OR CARDIAC ARREST. CARBAMATES GENERALLY DO NOT ACCUMULATE IN MAMMALIAN TISSUE AND THE CHOLINESTERASE INHIBITION REVERSES RATHER RAPIDLY. IN NON-FATAL CASES, THE ILLNESS GENERALLY LASTS LESS THAN 24 HOURS. **CHRONIC EXPOSURE-** PROLONGED OR REPEATED EXPOSURE MAY CAUSE EFFECTS AS DESCRIBED IN ACUTE EXPOSURE.
FIRST AID- REMOVE FROM EXPOSURE AREA TO FRESH AIR IMMEDIATELY. IF BREATHING HAS STOPPED, GIVE ARTIFICIAL RESPIRATION. MAINTAIN AIRWAY AND BLOOD PRESSURE AND ADMINISTER OXYGEN IF AVAILABLE. KEEP AFFECTED PERSON WARM AND AT REST. TREAT SYMPTOMATICALLY AND SUPPORTIVELY. ADMINISTRATION OF OXYGEN SHOULD BE PERFORMED BY QUALIFIED PERSONNEL. GET MEDICAL ATTENTION IMMEDIATELY.

SKIN CONTACT: BUFENCARB: TOXIC. SEE INFORMATION ON CARBAMATES.
CARBAMATES: CHOLINESTERASE INHIBITOR. **ACUTE EXPOSURE-** SOME COMPOUNDS MAY CAUSE IRRITATION. LOCALIZED SWEATING AND FASCICULATIONS MAY OCCUR AT THE SITE OF CONTACT. IF SUFFICIENT AMOUNTS ARE ABSORBED THROUGH THE SKIN, OTHER EFFECTS OF CHOLINESTERASE INHIBITION MAY OCCUR AS DESCRIBED IN ACUTE INHALATION; SYMPTOMS MAY BE DELAYED FOR 2-3 HOURS, USUALLY NO MORE THAN 8 HOURS. **CHRONIC EXPOSURE-** REPEATED OR PROLONGED EXPOSURE MAY CAUSE EFFECTS AS DESCRIBED IN ACUTE EXPOSURE.
FIRST AID- REMOVE CONTAMINATED CLOTHING IMMEDIATELY. WASH CONTAMINATED AREAS WITH SOAP AND WATER FOLLOWED BY ALCOHOL (ARENA, POISONING, 4TH ED.). EMERGENCY PERSONNEL SHOULD WEAR GLOVES AND AVOID CONTAMINATION. TREAT RESPIRATORY DIFFICULTY WITH ARTIFICIAL RESPIRATION. GET MEDICAL ATTENTION IMMEDIATELY.

EYE CONTACT: BUFENCARB: SEE INFORMATION ON CARBAMATES.
CARBAMATES: CHOLINESTERASE INHIBITOR. **ACUTE EXPOSURE-** DIRECT CONTACT MAY CAUSE PAIN, HYPEREMIA, LACRIMATION, TWITCHING OF THE EYELIDS, MIOSIS, AND CILIARY MUSCLE SPASM WITH LOSS OF ACCOMODATION, BLURRED OR DIMMED VISION AND BROWACHE. SOMETIMES MYDRIASIS MAY OCCUR INSTEAD OF MIOSIS. WITH SUFFICIENT EXPOSURE, OTHER SYMPTOMS OF CHOLINESTERASE INHIBITION MAY OCCUR AS DESCRIBED IN ACUTE INHALATION. **CHRONIC EXPOSURE-** PROLONGED EXPOSURE MAY CAUSE EFFECTS AS DESCRIBED IN ACUTE EXPOSURE. SOME COMPOUNDS HAVE CAUSED TOXIC EFFECTS ON THE CRYSTALLINE LENS, CONJUNCTIVAL THICKENING AND OBSTRUCTION OF NASOLACRIMAL CANALS WHEN USED AS MIOTIC EYE DROPS.
FIRST AID- IRRIGATE EYES WITH WATER OR SALINE SOLUTION. IF SYMPTOMS OF POISONING OCCUR, TREAT RESPIRATORY DIFFICULTY WITH ARTIFICIAL RESPIRATION AND OXYGEN. OBSERVE PATIENT FOR AT LEAST 24-36 HOURS (GOSSELIN, CLINICAL TOXICOLOGY OF COMMERCIAL PRODUCTS, 5TH ED.). GET MEDICAL ATTENTION IMMEDIATELY. OXYGEN SHOULD BE ADMINISTERED BY QUALIFIED MEDICAL PERSONNEL.

INGESTION: BUFENCARB: TOXIC. SEE INFORMATION ON CARBAMATES.
CARBAMATES: CHOLINESTERASE INHIBITOR. **ACUTE EXPOSURE-** WHEN INGESTED, THE FIRST EFFECTS MAY BE NAUSEA, VOMITING, ANOREXIA, ABDOMINAL CRAMPS, AND DIARRHEA. WITH ABSORPTION FROM THE GASTROINTESTINAL TRACT, THE OTHER EFFECTS OF CHOLINESTERASE INHIBITION AS DESCRIBED IN ACUTE INHALATION MAY OCCUR; SYMPTOMS MAY BEGIN WITHIN MINUTES OR BE

DELAYED SEVERAL HOURS. **CHRONIC EXPOSURE-** REPEATED INGESTION MAY CAUSE EFFECTS AS DESCRIBED IN ACUTE EXPOSURE.

FIRST AID- IF PERSON IS ALERT AND RESPIRATION IS NOT DEPRESSED, GIVE SYRUP OF IPECAC FOLLOWED BY WATER (IF VOMITING OCCURS, KEEP HEAD BELOW HIPS TO PREVENT ASPIRATION). IF CONSCIOUSNESS LEVEL DECLINES OR VOMITING HAS NOT OCCURRED IN 15 MINUTES EMPTY STOMACH BY GASTRIC LAVAGE WITH THE AID OF CUFFED ENDOTRACHEAL TUBE USING ISOTONIC SALINE OR 5% SODIUM BICARBONATE FOLLOW WITH ACTIVATED CHARCOAL. ESTABLISH AND MAINTAIN AIRWAY. TREAT RESPIRATORY DIFFICULTY WITH ARTIFICIAL RESPIRATION AND OXYGEN. DO NOT GIVE MORPHINE, AMINOPHYLLINE, PHENOTHIAZINES, RESERPINE, FUROSEMIDE, OR ETHACRYNIC ACID (MORGAN, RECOGNITION AND MANAGEMENT OF PESTICIDE POISONINGS, 3RD ED.). TREAT SYMPTOMATICALLY AND SUPPORTIVELY. ADMINISTRATION OF OXYGEN AND LAVAGE MUST BE PERFORMED BY QUALIFIED MEDICAL PERSONNEL. GET MEDICAL ATTENTION IMMEDIATELY.

ANTIDOTE: THE FOLLOWING ANTIDOTE HAS BEEN RECOMMENDED. HOWEVER, THE DECISION AS TO WHETHER THE SEVERITY OF POISONING REQUIRES ADMINISTRATION OF ANY ANTIDOTE AND ACTUAL DOSE REQUIRED SHOULD BE MADE BY QUALIFIED MEDICAL PERSONNEL.

FOR CHOLINESTERASE INHIBITORS: ESTABLISH CLEAR AIRWAY AND TISSUE OXYGENATION BY ASPIRATION OF SECRETIONS, AND IF NECESSARY, BY ASSISTED PULMONARY VENTILATION WITH OXYGEN. IMPROVE TISSUE OXYGENATION AS MUCH AS POSSIBLE BEFORE ADMINISTERING ATROPINE TO MINIMIZE THE RISK OF VENTRICULAR FIBRILLATION. ADMINISTER ATROPINE SULFATE INTRAVENOUSLY, OR INTRAMUSCULARLY IF IV INJECTION IS NOT POSSIBLE. IN MODERATELY SEVERE POISONING ADMINISTER ATROPINE SULFATE, 0.4-2.0 MG REPEATED EVERY 15 MINUTES UNTIL ATROPINIZATION IS ACHIEVED (TACHYCARDIA, FLUSHING, DRY MOUTH, MYDRIASIS). MAINTAIN ATROPINIZATION BY REPEATED DOSES FOR 2-12 HOURS, OR LONGER, DEPENDING ON THE SEVERITY OF POISONING. THE APPEARANCE OF RALES IN THE LUNG BASES, MIOSIS, SALIVATION, NAUSEA, BRADYCARDIA, ARE ALL INDICATIONS OF INADEQUATE ATROPINIZATION. SEVERELY POISONED INDIVIDUALS MAY EXHIBIT REMARKABLE TOLERANCE TO ATROPINE; TWO OR MORE TIMES THE DOSAGES SUGGESTED ABOVE MAY BE NEEDED. PERSONS NOT POISONED OR ONLY SLIGHTLY POISONED, HOWEVER, MAY DEVELOP SIGNS OF ATROPINE TOXICITY FROM SUCH LARGE DOSAGES: FEVER, MUSCLE FIBRILLATIONS, AND DELIRIUM ARE THE MAIN SIGNS OF ATROPINE TOXICITY. IF THESE SIGNS APPEAR WHILE THE PATIENT IS FULLY ATROPINIZED, ATROPINE ADMINISTRATION SHOULD BE DISCONTINUED, AT LEAST TEMPORARILY. OBSERVE TREATED PATIENTS CLOSELY AT LEAST 24 HOURS TO INSURE THAT SYMPTOMS (POSSIBLY PULMONARY EDEMA) DO NOT RECUR AS ATROPINIZATION WEARS OFF. IN VERY SEVERE POISONINGS, METABOLIC DISPOSITION OF TOXICANT MAY REQUIRE SEVERAL HOURS OR DAYS DURING WHICH ATROPINIZATION MUST BE MAINTAINED. MARKEDLY LOWER LEVELS OF URINARY METABOLITES INDICATE THAT ATROPINE DOSAGE CAN BE TAPERED OFF. AS DOSAGE IS REDUCED, CHECK THE LUNG BASES FREQUENTLY FOR RALES. IF RALES ARE HEARD OR OTHER SYMPTOMS RETURN, RE-ESTABLISH ATROPINIZATION PROMPTLY (MORGAN, RECOGNITION AND MANAGEMENT OF PESTICIDE POISONINGS, 3RD ED.). ADMINISTRATION OF ANTIDOTE MUST BE PERFORMED BY QUALIFIED MEDICAL PERSONNEL.

REACTIVITY

REACTIVITY: STABLE UNDER NORMAL TEMPERATURES AND PRESSURES.

INCOMPATIBILITIES: BUFENCARB: ALKALIS: HYDROLYZES. OXIDIZERS (STRONG): FIRE AND EXPLOSION HAZARD.

DECOMPOSITION: THERMAL DECOMPOSITION PRODUCTS MAY INCLUDE TOXIC OXIDES OF CARBON AND NITROGEN.

POLYMERIZATION: HAZARDOUS POLYMERIZATION HAS NOT BEEN REPORTED TO OCCUR UNDER NORMAL TEMPERATURES AND PRESSURES.

STORAGE AND DISPOSAL

OBSERVE ALL FEDERAL, STATE AND LOCAL REGULATIONS WHEN STORING OR DISPOSING OF THIS SUBSTANCE. FOR ASSISTANCE, CONTACT THE DISTRICT DIRECTOR OF THE ENVIRONMENTAL PROTECTION AGENCY.

STORAGE

STORE IN ACCORDANCE WITH 40 CFR 165 RECOMMENDED PROCEDURES FOR THE DISPOSAL AND STORAGE OF PESTICIDES AND PESTICIDE CONTAINERS.
STORE AWAY FROM INCOMPATIBLE SUBSTANCES.

DISPOSAL

DISPOSAL MUST BE IN ACCORDANCE WITH 40 CFR 165 RECOMMENDED PROCEDURES FOR THE DISPOSAL AND STORAGE OF PESTICIDES AND PESTICIDE CONTAINERS.

CONDITIONS TO AVOID

MAY BURN BUT DOES NOT IGNITE READILY. CONTAINERS MAY EXPLODE IN HEAT OF FIRE.

SPILL AND LEAK PROCEDURES

OCCUPATIONAL SPILL: DO NOT TOUCH SPILLED MATERIAL. STOP LEAK IF YOU CAN DO IT WITHOUT RISK. USE WATER SPRAY TO REDUCE VAPORS. FOR SMALL SPILLS, TAKE UP WITH SAND OR OTHER ABSORBENT MATERIAL AND PLACE INTO CONTAINERS FOR LATER DISPOSAL. FOR SMALL DRY SPILLS, WITH A CLEAN SHOVEL PLACE MATERIAL INTO CLEAN, DRY CONTAINERS AND COVER. MOVE CONTAINERS FROM SPILL AREA. FOR LARGER SPILLS, DIKE FAR AHEAD OF SPILL FOR LATER DISPOSAL. KEEP UNNECESSARY PEOPLE AWAY. ISOLATE HAZARD AREA AND DENY ENTRY. VENTILATE CLOSED SPACES BEFORE ENTERING.

PROTECTIVE EQUIPMENT

VENTILATION: PROVIDE LOCAL EXHAUST OR PROCESS ENCLOSURE VENTILATION SYSTEM.

RESPIRATOR: THE FOLLOWING RESPIRATORS ARE RECOMMENDED BASED ON INFORMATION FOUND IN THE PHYSICAL DATA, TOXICITY AND HEALTH EFFECTS SECTIONS. THEY ARE RANKED IN ORDER FROM MINIMUM TO MAXIMUM RESPIRATORY PROTECTION. THE SPECIFIC RESPIRATOR SELECTED MUST BE BASED ON CONTAMINATION LEVELS FOUND IN THE WORK PLACE, MUST NOT EXCEED THE WORKING LIMITS OF THE RESPIRATOR AND BE JOINTLY APPROVED BY THE NATIONAL INSTITUTE FOR OCCUPATIONAL SAFETY AND HEALTH AND THE MINE SAFETY AND HEALTH ADMINISTRATION (NIOSH-MSHA).

TYPE 'C' SUPPLIED-AIR RESPIRATOR WITH A FULL FACEPIECE OPERATED IN PRESSURE-DEMAND OR OTHER POSITIVE PRESSURE MODE OR WITH A FULL FACEPIECE, HELMET OR HOOD OPERATED IN CONTINOUS-FLOW MODE.

SELF-CONTAINED BREATHING APPARATUS WITH A FULL FACEPIECE OPERATED IN PRESSURE-DEMAND OR OTHER POSITIVE PRESSURE MODE.

FOR FIREFIGHTING AND OTHER IMMEDIATELY DANGEROUS TO LIFE OR HEALTH CONDITIONS:

SELF-CONTAINED BREATHING APPARATUS WITH FULL FACEPIECE OPERATED IN PRESSURE-DEMAND OR OTHER POSITIVE PRESSURE MODE.

SUPPLIED-AIR RESPIRATOR WITH FULL FACEPIECE AND OPERATED IN PRESSURE-DEMAND OR OTHER POSITIVE PRESSURE MODE IN COMBINATION WITH AN AUXILIARY SELF-CONTAINED BREATHING APPARATUS OPERATED IN PRESSURE-DEMAND OR OTHER POSITIVE PRESSURE MODE.

CLOTHING: EMPLOYEE MUST WEAR APPROPRIATE PROTECTIVE (IMPERVIOUS) CLOTHING AND EQUIPMENT TO PREVENT ANY POSSIBILITY OF SKIN CONTACT WITH THIS SUBSTANCE.

GLOVES: EMPLOYEE MUST WEAR APPROPRIATE PROTECTIVE GLOVES TO PREVENT CONTACT WITH THIS SUBSTANCE.

EYE PROTECTION: EMPLOYEE MUST WEAR SPLASH-PROOF OR DUST-RESISTANT SAFETY GOGGLES WITH OR WITHOUT A FACESHIELD TO PREVENT CONTACT WITH THIS SUBSTANCE.

EMERGENCY EYE WASH: WHERE THERE IS ANY POSSIBILITY THAT AN EMPLOYEE'S EYES MAY BE EXPOSED TO THIS SUBSTANCE, THE EMPLOYER SHOULD PROVIDE AN EYE WASH FOUNTAIN WITHIN THE IMMEDIATE WORK AREA FOR EMERGENCY USE.

AUTHORIZED BY- OCCUPATIONAL HEALTH SERVICES, INC.
CREATION DATE: 10/04/89 ***REVISION DATE:*** 06/12/90

MATERIAL SAFETY DATA SHEET

OCCUPATIONAL HEALTH SERVICES, INC.
AGRICULTURE AND PESTICIDE DIVISION
450 SEVENTH AVENUE, SUITE 2407
NEW YORK, NEW YORK 10123
1-800-445-MSDS OR (212) 967-1100

EMERGENCY CONTACT:
JOHN S. BRANSFORD, JR. (615) 292-1180

SUBSTANCE IDENTIFICATION

CAS-NUMBER 55-98-1

SUBSTANCE: **BUSULFAN**

TRADE NAMES/SYNONYMS: 1,4-BIS(METHANESULFONOXY)BUTANE; MISULBAN; MYLERAN; 1,4-BUTANEDIOL DIMETHANESULFONATE; C.B. 2041; MITOSANI; SALFABUTIN; TETRAMETHYLENE BIS(METHANESULFONATE); METHANESULFONIC ACID, TETRAMETHYLENE ESTER; 1,4-DIMETHANESULFONYLOXYBUTANE; GT 41; GT 2041; MABLIN; 1,4-BUTANEDIOL DIMETHANESULPHONATE; PST03482

MOLECULAR FORMULA: C6-H14-O6-S2

MOLECULAR WEIGHT: 246.32

CERCLA RATINGS (SCALE 0-3): HEALTH=3 FIRE=0 REACTIVITY=1 PERSISTENCE=1

NFPA RATINGS (SCALE 0-4): HEALTH=3 FIRE=0 REACTIVITY=1

COMPONENTS AND CONTAMINANTS

COMPONENT: BUSULFAN ***PERCENT:*** 100.0
CAS# 55-98-1

EXPOSURE LIMITS: NO OCCUPATIONAL EXPOSURE LIMITS ESTABLISHED BY OSHA, ACGIH, OR NIOSH.
BUSULFAN: SUBJECT TO CALIFORNIA PROPOSITION 65 CANCER AND/OR REPRODUCTIVE TOXICITY WARNING AND RELEASE REQUIREMENTS- (FEBRUARY 27, 1987)

PHYSICAL DATA

DESCRIPTION: WHITE CRYSTALLINE POWDER ***MELTING POINT:*** 237 C (114 C)
SOLUBILITY IN WATER: ALMOST INSOLUBLE
SOLVENT SOLUBILITY: ACETONE, ALCOHOL

FIRE AND EXPLOSION DATA

FIRE AND EXPLOSION HAZARD: NEGLIGIBLE FIRE HAZARD WHEN EXPOSED TO HEAT OR FLAME.

FIREFIGHTING MEDIA: DRY CHEMICAL, CARBON DIOXIDE, HALON, WATER SPRAY OR STANDARD FOAM (1987 EMERGENCY RESPONSE GUIDEBOOK, DOT P 5800.4).
FOR LARGER FIRES, USE WATER SPRAY, FOG OR STANDARD FOAM (1987 EMERGENCY RESPONSE GUIDEBOOK, DOT P 5800.4).

FIREFIGHTING: MOVE CONTAINERS FROM FIRE AREA IF POSSIBLE. FIGHT FIRE FROM MAXIMUM DISTANCE. STAY AWAY FROM STORAGE TANK ENDS. DIKE FIRE CONTROL WATER FOR LATER DISPOSAL. DO NOT SCATTER MATERIAL (1987 EMERGENCY RESPONSE GUIDEBOOK, DOT P 5800.4, GUIDE PAGE 55).
EXTINGUISH ONLY IF FLOW CAN BE STOPPED. EXTINGUISH USING AGENT INDICATED. USE FLOODING AMOUNTS OF WATER AS A FOG. COOL CONTAINERS WITH FLOODING AMOUNTS OF WATER FROM AS FAR A DISTANCE AS POSSIBLE. AVOID BREATHING POISONOUS VAPORS, KEEP UPWIND. CONSIDER EVACUATION OF DOWNWIND AREA IF MATERIAL IS LEAKING.

TRANSPORTATION DATA

DEPARTMENT OF TRANSPORTATION HAZARD CLASSIFICATION 49 CFR 172.101: POISON B
DEPARTMENT OF TRANSPORTATION LABELING REQUIREMENTS 49 CFR 172.101 AND SUBPART E: POISON
DEPARTMENT OF TRANSPORTATION PACKAGING REQUIREMENTS: 49 CFR 173.365 EXCEPTIONS: 49 CFR 173.364

TOXICITY

BUSULFAN: TOXICITY DATA: 8 MG/KG/2 DAYS-INTERMITTENT ORAL-MAN TDLO; 798 MG/KG 8 YEARS ORAL-WOMAN TDLO; 110 MG/KG ORAL-MOUSE LD50; 22 MG/KG SUBCUTANEOUS-RAT LD50; 63 MG/KG SUBCUTANEOUS-MOUSE LD50; 1800 UG/KG INTRAVENOUS-RAT LD50; 8 MG/KG INTRAVENOUS-MONKEY LDLO; 8 MG/KG INTRAVENOUS-DOG LDLO; 18 MG/KG INTRAPERITONEAL-RAT LD50; 86 MG/KG INTRAPERITONEAL-MOUSE LD50; 46 MG/KG UNREPORTED-MOUSE LD50; 20 MG/KG UNREPORTED-RAT LD50; MUTAGENIC DATA (RTECS); REPRODUCTIVE EFFECTS DATA (RTECS); TUMORIGENIC DATA (RTECS). CARCINOGEN STATUS: KNOWN HUMAN CARCINOGEN (NTP); HUMAN SUFFICIENT EVIDENCE, ANIMAL LIMITED EVIDENCE (IARC GROUP-1). LEUKEMIA PATIENTS TREATED WITH BUSULFAN DEVELOPED MANY DIFFERENT CYTOLOGICAL ABNORMALITIES, AND SOME DEVELOPED CARCINOMAS. INTRAPERITONEAL ADMINISTRATION INDUCED T-CELL LYMPHOMAS IN MALE MICE. INTRAVENOUS ADMINISTRATION INDUCED AN INCREASED INCIDENCE OF THYMIC LYMPHOMAS AND OVARIAN TUMORS IN FEMALE MICE. ACUTE TOXICITY LEVEL: TOXIC BY INGESTION. TARGET EFFECTS: NO DATA AVAILABLE.

HEALTH EFFECTS AND FIRST AID

INHALATION: BUSULFAN: **ACUTE EXPOSURE-** NO DATA AVAILABLE. **CHRONIC EXPOSURE-** NO DATA AVAILABLE.

FIRST AID- REMOVE FROM EXPOSURE AREA TO FRESH AIR IMMEDIATELY. IF BREATHING HAS STOPPED, PERFORM ARTIFICIAL RESPIRATION. KEEP PERSON WARM AND AT REST. TREAT SYMPTOMATICALLY AND SUPPORTIVELY. GET MEDICAL ATTENTION IMMEDIATELY.

SKIN CONTACT: BUSULFAN: **ACUTE EXPOSURE-** NO DATA AVAILABLE. **CHRONIC EXPOSURE-** NO DATA AVAILABLE.

FIRST AID- REMOVE CONTAMINATED CLOTHING AND SHOES IMMEDIATELY. WASH AFFECTED AREA WITH SOAP OR MILD DETERGENT AND LARGE AMOUNTS OF WATER UNTIL NO EVIDENCE OF CHEMICAL REMAINS (APPROXIMATELY 15-20 MINUTES). GET MEDICAL ATTENTION IMMEDIATELY.

EYE CONTACT: BUSULFAN: **ACUTE EXPOSURE-** NO DATA AVAILABLE. DUST MAY CAUSE IRRITATION. **CHRONIC EXPOSURE-** NO DATA AVAILABLE.

FIRST AID- WASH EYES IMMEDIATELY WITH LARGE AMOUNTS OF WATER OR NORMAL SALINE, OCCASIONALLY LIFTING UPPER AND LOWER LIDS, UNTIL NO EVIDENCE OF CHEMICAL REMAINS (APPROXIMATELY 15-20 MINUTES). GET MEDICAL ATTENTION IMMEDIATELY.

INGESTION: BUSULFAN: HIGHLY TOXIC. **ACUTE EXPOSURE-** OVERDOSE OF ANTICANCER AGENTS MAY CAUSE LEUKOPENIA, GRANULOCYTOPENIA, THROMBOCYTOPENIA, HYPOPLASIA OF ALL ELEMENTS OF BONE MARROW, NAUSEA, VOMITING, DIARRHEA AND ANOREXIA. **CHRONIC EXPOSURE-** THE MOST FREQUENT SERIOUS SIDE EFFECT OF BUSULFAN THERAPY IS THE INDUCTION OF BONE MARROW FAILURE RESULTING IN SEVERE PANCYTOPENIA (WHICH MAY BE DUE TO FAILURE TO STOP ADMINISTRATION OF THE DRUG SOON ENOUGH). RECOVERY FROM BUSULFAN-INDUCED PANCYTOPENIA MAY TAKE FROM 1 MONTH TO 2 YEARS. DEVELOPMENT OF BRONCHOPULMONARY DYSPLASIA WITH PULMONARY FIBROSIS IS A RARE COMPLICATION. SYMPTOMS OF "BUSULFAN-LUNG", INSIDIOUS ONSET OF COUGH, DYSPNEA AND LOW-GRADE FEVER, MAY DEVELOP FROM 8 MONTHS TO 10 YEARS AFTER INITIATION OF THERAPY. DIMINISHED PULMONARY FUNCTION MAY OCCUR. CELLULAR DYSPLASIA MAY OCCUR IN MANY OTHER ORGANS, ALSO. CYTOLOGIC ABNORMALITIES MAY BE CHARACTERIZED BY GIANT HYPERCHROMATIC NUCLEI IN LYMPH NODES, PANCREAS, THYROID, ADRENAL GLANDS, LIVER AND BONE MARROW. EPITHELIAL DYSPLASIA AND CHROMOSOMAL ABERRATIONS HAVE BEEN OBSERVED IN CELLS FROM PATIENTS RECEIVING BUSULFAN. SECOND MALIGNANCIES HAVE BEEN REPORTED IN PATIENTS ON BUSULFAN THERAPY, WITH A MEAN LATENT PERIOD OF 62 MONTHS (BASED ON A MEAN TOTAL DOSE OF 643 MG). BUSULFAN MAY CAUSE FETAL DAMAGE WHEN ADMINISTERED TO PREGNANT WOMEN. NON-TERATOGENIC EFFECTS MAY INCLUDE LOW BIRTH WEIGHT INFANTS, AND ANEMIA AND NEUTROPENIA AT BIRTH. IN PREGNANT RATS, BUSULFAN PRODUCES STERILITY IN MALE AND FEMALE OFFSPRING. THIS CONDITION HAS NOT BEEN REPORTED IN HUMANS. OVARIAN SUPPRESSION AND AMENORRHEA WITH MENOPAUSE-LIKE SYMPTOMS MAY OCCUR IN PREMENOPAUSAL PATIENTS. BUSULFAN INTERFERES WITH SPERMATOGENESIS IN EXPERIMENTAL ANIMALS, AND THERE ARE CLINICAL REPORTS OF IMPOTENCE, STERILITY, AZOOSPERMIA AND TESTICULAR ATROPHY IN MALE PATIENTS. DERMATOLOGIC EFFECTS INCLUDE HYPERPIGMENTATION, CHEILOSIS AND ANHIDROSIS. BUSULFAN EXERTS OCULAR TOXICITY. IT MAY INTERFERE WITH THE PRODUCTION OF LENS NUCLEIC ACID DURING MITOSIS OF THE LENS EPITHELIUM. CATARACTS WERE EXPERIMENTALLY INDUCED IN RATS BY FEEDING 7.5-20.0 MG/KG. AN IRREVERSIBLE CATARACT IS COMPLETELY DEVELOPED IN 5-7 WEEKS. OTHER REPORTED ADVERSE REACTIONS MAY INCLUDE UTICARIA, ALOPECIA, PORPHYRIA CUTANEA TARDA, GLOTTITIS, ORAL MUCOUS MEMBRANE DRYING, GYNECOMASTIA, CHOLESTATIC JAUNDICE AND MYASTHENIA GRAVIS.

FIRST AID- TREAT SYMPTOMATICALLY AND SUPPORTIVELY. GET MEDICAL ATTENTION IMMEDIATELY. IF VOMITING OCCURS, KEEP HEAD LOWER THAN HIPS TO PREVENT ASPIRATION.

REACTIVITY

REACTIVITY: STABLE IN DRY FORM. SLOW HYDROLYSIS IN WATER.
INCOMPATIBILITIES: BUSULFAN: STRONG OXIDIZERS: FIRE AND EXPLOSION HAZARD.
DECOMPOSITION: THERMAL DECOMPOSITION PRODUCTS MAY INCLUDE TOXIC OXIDES OF SULFUR AND CARBON.
POLYMERIZATION: HAZARDOUS POLYMERIZATION HAS NOT BEEN REPORTED TO OCCUR UNDER NORMAL TEMPERATURES AND PRESSURES.

STORAGE AND DISPOSAL

OBSERVE ALL FEDERAL, STATE AND LOCAL REGULATIONS WHEN STORING OR DISPOSING OF THIS SUBSTANCE. FOR ASSISTANCE, CONTACT THE DISTRICT DIRECTOR OF THE ENVIRONMENTAL PROTECTION AGENCY.

CONDITIONS TO AVOID

AVOID CONTACT WITH HEAT, SPARKS OR OPEN FLAMES. STORE AWAY FROM OTHER COMBUSTIBLE MATERIALS (WOOD, PAPER, OIL, ETC.).KEEP CONTAINERS COOL IN FIRE CONDITIONS. AVOID CONTAMINATION OF WATER SOURCES AND SEWERS WITH RUNOFF WATER.

SPILL AND LEAK PROCEDURES

WATER SPILL: THE CALIFORNIA SAFE DRINKING WATER AND TOXIC ENFORCEMENT ACT OF 1986 (PROPOSITION 65) PROHIBITS CONTAMINATING ANY KNOWN SOURCE OF DRINKING WATER WITH SUBSTANCES KNOWN TO CAUSE CANCER AND/OR REPRODUCTIVE TOXICITY.

OCCUPATIONAL SPILL: SHUT OFF IGNITION SOURCES. DO NOT TOUCH SPILLED MATERIAL. FOR SMALL SPILLS, TAKE UP WITH SAND OR OTHER ABSORBENT MATERIAL AND PLACE INTO CONTAINERS FOR LATER DISPOSAL. FOR LARGER SPILLS, DIKE FAR AHEAD OF SPILL FOR LATER DISPOSAL. NO SMOKING, FLAMES OR FLARES IN HAZARD AREA! KEEP UNNECESSARY PEOPLE AWAY; ISOLATE HAZARD AREA AND DENY ENTRY.

PROTECTIVE EQUIPMENT

VENTILATION: PROVIDE LOCAL EXHAUST OR GENERAL DILUTION VENTILATION SYSTEM.

RESPIRATOR: THE FOLLOWING RESPIRATORS ARE RECOMMENDED BASED ON INFORMATION FOUND IN THE PHYSICAL DATA, TOXICITY AND HEALTH EFFECTS SECTIONS. THEY ARE RANKED IN ORDER FROM MINIMUM TO MAXIMUM RESPIRATORY PROTECTION. THE SPECIFIC RESPIRATOR SELECTED MUST BE BASED ON CONTAMINATION LEVELS FOUND IN THE WORK PLACE, MUST NOT EXCEED THE WORKING LIMITS OF THE RESPIRATOR AND BE JOINTLY APPROVED BY THE NATIONAL INSTITUTE FOR OCCUPATIONAL SAFETY AND HEALTH AND THE MINE SAFETY AND HEALTH ADMINISTRATION (NIOSH-MSHA).

TYPE 'C' SUPPLIED-AIR RESPIRATOR WITH A FULL FACEPIECE OPERATED IN PRESSURE-DEMAND OR OTHER POSITIVE PRESSURE MODE OR WITH A FULL FACEPIECE, HELMET OR HOOD OPERATED IN CONTINOUS-FLOW MODE.

SELF-CONTAINED BREATHING APPARATUS WITH A FULL FACEPIECE OPERATED IN PRESSURE-DEMAND OR OTHER POSITIVE PRESSURE MODE.

FOR FIREFIGHTING AND OTHER IMMEDIATELY DANGEROUS TO LIFE OR HEALTH CONDITIONS:

SELF-CONTAINED BREATHING APPARATUS WITH FULL FACEPIECE OPERATED IN PRESSURE-DEMAND OR OTHER POSITIVE PRESSURE MODE.

SUPPLIED-AIR RESPIRATOR WITH FULL FACEPIECE AND OPERATED IN PRESSURE-DEMAND OR OTHER POSITIVE PRESSURE MODE IN COMBINATION WITH AN AUXILIARY SELF-CONTAINED BREATHING APPARATUS OPERATED IN PRESSURE-DEMAND OR OTHER POSITIVE PRESSURE MODE.

CLOTHING: PROTECTIVE CLOTHING NOT REQUIRED. AVOID REPEATED OR PROLONGED CONTACT WITH THIS SUBSTANCE.

GLOVES: PROTECTIVE GLOVES ARE NOT REQUIRED BUT RECOMMENDED.

EYE PROTECTION: EYE PROTECTION NOT REQUIRED, BUT ADVISABLE.

AUTHORIZED BY- OCCUPATIONAL HEALTH SERVICES, INC.

CREATION DATE: 10/04/89 ***REVISION DATE:*** 06/27/90

MATERIAL SAFETY DATA SHEET

OCCUPATIONAL HEALTH SERVICES, INC.
AGRICULTURE AND PESTICIDE DIVISION
450 SEVENTH AVENUE, SUITE 2407
NEW YORK, NEW YORK 10123
1-800-445-MSDS OR (212) 967-1100

EMERGENCY CONTACT:
JOHN S. BRANSFORD, JR. (615) 292-1180

SUBSTANCE IDENTIFICATION

CAS-NUMBER 23184-66-9

SUBSTANCE: **BUTACHLOR**

TRADE NAMES/SYNONYMS: 2-CHLORO-2',6'-DIETHYL-N-(BUTOXYMETHYL)ACETANILIDE; N-(BUTOXYMETHYL)-2-CHLORO-N-(2,6-DIETHYLPHENYL)ACETAMIDE; 2-CHLORO-DIETHYL-N-(BUTOXYMETHYL)ACETANILIDE; N-BUTOXYMETHYL-2-CHLORO-2',6'-DIETHYLACETANILIDE; ACETAMIDE, N-(BUTOXYMETHYL)-2-CHLORO-N-(2,6-DIETHYLPHENYL); ACETANILIDE, N-(BUTOXYMETHYL)-2-CHLORO-2',6'-DIETHYL-; N-BUTOXYMETHYL-ALPHA-CHLORO-2',6'-DIETHYLACETANILIDE; BUTACLOR; BUTANEX; CP 53619; HILTACHLOR; LAMBAST; MACHETE; C17H26CLNO2; PST03497

CHEMICAL FAMILY: AMIDE

MOLECULAR FORMULA: C17-H26-CL-N-O2

MOLECULAR WEIGHT: 311.89

CERCLA RATINGS (SCALE 0-3): HEALTH=2 FIRE=U REACTIVITY=0 PERSISTENCE=2

NFPA RATINGS (SCALE 0-4): HEALTH=2 FIRE=U REACTIVITY=0

COMPONENTS AND CONTAMINANTS

COMPONENT: BUTACHLOR ***PERCENT:*** 100
CAS# 23184-66-9

OTHER CONTAMINANTS: NONE

EXPOSURE LIMITS: NO OCCUPATIONAL EXPOSURE LIMITS ESTABLISHED BY OSHA, ACGIH, OR NIOSH.

PHYSICAL DATA

DESCRIPTION: AMBER TO LIGHT YELLOW COLORED LIQUID.

BOILING POINT: 312 F (156 C) @ 0.5 MMHG ***MELTING POINT:*** <23 F (<-5 C)

SPECIFIC GRAVITY: 1.070 ***VAPOR PRESSURE:*** NEGLIGIBLE

SOLUBILITY IN WATER: 23 PPM @ 24 C

SOLVENT SOLUBILITY: SOLUBLE IN ACETONE, BENZENE, ETHANOL, METHANOL, HEXANE, ETHYL ACETATE, AND MOST ORGANIC SOLVENTS
DECOMPOSES @ 329 F (165 C)

FIRE AND EXPLOSION DATA

FIRE AND EXPLOSION HAZARD: UNKNOWN FIRE AND EXPLOSION HAZARD.

FIREFIGHTING MEDIA: DRY CHEMICAL, CARBON DIOXIDE, HALON, WATER SPRAY OR STANDARD FOAM (1987 EMERGENCY RESPONSE GUIDEBOOK, DOT P 5800.4).
FOR LARGER FIRES, USE WATER SPRAY, FOG OR STANDARD FOAM (1987 EMERGENCY RESPONSE GUIDEBOOK, DOT P 5800.4).

FIREFIGHTING: MOVE CONTAINER FROM FIRE AREA IF POSSIBLE. DO NOT SCATTER SPILLED MATERIAL WITH HIGH PRESSURE WATER STREAMS. DIKE FIRE CONTROL WATER FOR LATER DISPOSAL (1987 EMERGENCY RESPONSE GUIDEBOOK, DOT P 5800.4, GUIDE PAGE 31).
EXTINGUISH ONLY IF FLOW CAN BE STOPPED; USE FLOODING AMOUNTS OF WATER AS A FOG, SOLID STREAMS MAY BE INEFFECTIVE. COOL CONTAINERS WITH FLOODING AMOUNTS OF WATER, APPLY FROM AS FAR A DISTANCE AS POSSIBLE. AVOID BREATHING VAPORS, KEEP UPWIND.

TOXICITY

BUTACHLOR: TOXICITY DATA: 4080 MG/KG SKIN-RABBIT LD50; 1740 MG/KG ORAL-RAT LD50; MUTAGENIC DATA (RTECS). CARCINOGEN STATUS: NONE. LOCAL EFFECTS: IRRITANT- INHALATION, SKIN, AND EYES. ACUTE TOXICITY LEVEL: MODERATELY TOXIC BY INGESTION AND SLIGHTLY TOXIC BY DERMAL ABSORPTION. TARGET EFFECTS: SENSITIZER- SKIN.

HEALTH EFFECTS AND FIRST AID

INHALATION: BUTACHLOR: IRRITANT. **ACUTE EXPOSURE-** MAY CAUSE UPPER RESPIRATORY TRACT AND MUCOUS MEMBRANE IRRITATION. **CHRONIC EXPOSURE-** NO DATA AVAILABLE.

FIRST AID- REMOVE FROM EXPOSURE AREA TO FRESH AIR IMMEDIATELY. IF BREATHING HAS STOPPED, PERFORM ARTIFICIAL RESPIRATION. KEEP PERSON WARM AND AT REST. TREAT SYMPTOMATICALLY AND SUPPORTIVELY. GET MEDICAL ATTENTION IMMEDIATELY.

SKIN CONTACT: BUTACHLOR: IRRITANT/SENSITIZER. **ACUTE EXPOSURE-** MAY CAUSE IRRITATION. ALLERGIC SKIN REACTIONS MAY OCCUR IN PREVIOUSLY EXPOSED INDIVIDUALS. A LETHAL DOSE IN RABBITS BY DERMAL ABSORPTION WAS 4080 MG/KG; SYMPTOMS WERE NOT REPORTED. **CHRONIC EXPOSURE-** REPEATED OR PROLONGED CONTACT MAY CAUSE ALLERGIC SKIN REACTIONS.

FIRST AID- REMOVE CONTAMINATED CLOTHING AND SHOES IMMEDIATELY. WASH AFFECTED AREA WITH SOAP OR MILD DETERGENT AND LARGE AMOUNTS OF WATER UNTIL NO EVIDENCE OF CHEMICAL REMAINS (APPROXIMATELY 15-20 MINUTES). GET MEDICAL ATTENTION IMMEDIATELY.

EYE CONTACT: BUTACHLOR: IRRITANT. **ACUTE EXPOSURE-** MAY CAUSE IRRITATION. **CHRONIC EXPOSURE-** REPEATED OR PROLONGED EXPOSURE TO IRRITANTS MAY RESULT IN CONJUNCTIVITIS.

FIRST AID- WASH EYES IMMEDIATELY WITH LARGE AMOUNTS OF WATER OR NORMAL SALINE, OCCASIONALLY LIFTING UPPER AND LOWER LIDS, UNTIL NO EVIDENCE OF CHEMICAL REMAINS (APPROXIMATELY 15-20 MINUTES). GET MEDICAL ATTENTION IMMEDIATELY.

INGESTION: BUTACHLOR: **ACUTE EXPOSURE-** A LETHAL DOSE IN RATS WAS 1740 MG/KG; SYMPTOMS WERE NOT REPORTED. POISONING BY PROPACHLOR, A SIMILAR COMPOUND, CAUSES MUSCLE WEAKNESS, SALIVATION, TREMORS, COLLAPSE, COMA, AND DEATH IN ANIMALS. **CHRONIC EXPOSURE-** INCREASED LIVER WEIGHT WAS OBSERVED IN FEMALE RATS FED BUTACHLOR AT A RATE OF 100 MG/KG/DAY.

FIRST AID- REMOVE BY GASTRIC LAVAGE AND CATHARSIS. MAINTAIN BLOOD PRESSURE AND AIRWAY. GIVE OXYGEN IF RESPIRATION IS DEPRESSED. DO NOT PERFORM GASTRIC LAVAGE IF VICTIM IS UNCONSCIOUS. GET MEDICAL ATTENTION IMMEDIATELY (DREISBACH, HANDBOOK OF POISONING, 12TH ED.).
ADMINISTRATION OF LAVAGE OR OXYGEN SHOULD BE PERFORMED BY QUALIFIED MEDICAL PERSONNEL.

ANTIDOTE: NO SPECIFIC ANTIDOTE. TREAT SYMPTOMATICALLY AND SUPPORTIVELY.

REACTIVITY

REACTIVITY: STABLE UNDER NORMAL TEMPERATURES AND PRESSURES.

INCOMPATIBILITIES: BUTACHLOR: ACIDS (STRONG): HYDROLYZE. ALKALIS (STRONG): HYDROLYZE. IRON: MAY CORRODE. STEEL: MAY CORRODE.

DECOMPOSITION: THERMAL DECOMPOSITION MAY RELEASE CORROSIVE FUMES OF HYDROGEN CHLORIDE AND TOXIC OXIDES OF NITROGEN AND CARBON.
POLYMERIZATION: HAZARDOUS POLYMERIZATION HAS NOT BEEN REPORTED TO OCCUR UNDER NORMAL TEMPERATURES AND PRESSURES.

STORAGE AND DISPOSAL

OBSERVE ALL FEDERAL, STATE AND LOCAL REGULATIONS WHEN STORING OR DISPOSING OF THIS SUBSTANCE. FOR ASSISTANCE, CONTACT THE DISTRICT DIRECTOR OF THE ENVIRONMENTAL PROTECTION AGENCY.

****STORAGE****

STORE IN ACCORDANCE WITH 40 CFR 165 RECOMMENDED PROCEDURES FOR THE DISPOSAL AND STORAGE OF PESTICIDES AND PESTICIDE CONTAINERS.
STORE AWAY FROM INCOMPATIBLE SUBSTANCES.

****DISPOSAL****

DISPOSAL MUST BE IN ACCORDANCE WITH 40 CFR 165 RECOMMENDED PROCEDURES FOR THE DISPOSAL AND STORAGE OF PESTICIDES AND PESTICIDE CONTAINERS.

CONDITIONS TO AVOID

MAY BURN BUT DOES NOT IGNITE READILY. AVOID CONTACT WITH STRONG OXIDIZERS, EXCESSIVE HEAT, SPARKS, OR OPEN FLAME.

SPILL AND LEAK PROCEDURES

OCCUPATIONAL SPILL: STOP LEAK IF YOU CAN DO IT WITHOUT RISK. FOR SMALL SPILLS, TAKE UP WITH SAND OR OTHER ABSORBENT MATERIAL AND PLACE INTO CLEAN, DRY CONTAINERS FOR LATER DISPOSAL. KEEP UNNECESSARY PEOPLE AWAY. ISOLATE HAZARD AREA AND DENY ENTRY.

PROTECTIVE EQUIPMENT

VENTILATION: PROVIDE LOCAL EXHAUST VENTILATION SYSTEM.
RESPIRATOR: THE FOLLOWING RESPIRATORS ARE RECOMMENDED BASED ON INFORMATION FOUND IN THE PHYSICAL DATA, TOXICITY AND HEALTH EFFECTS SECTIONS. THEY ARE RANKED IN ORDER FROM MINIMUM TO MAXIMUM RESPIRATORY PROTECTION. THE SPECIFIC RESPIRATOR SELECTED MUST BE BASED ON CONTAMINATION LEVELS FOUND IN THE WORK PLACE, MUST NOT EXCEED THE WORKING LIMITS OF THE RESPIRATOR AND BE JOINTLY APPROVED BY THE NATIONAL INSTITUTE FOR OCCUPATIONAL SAFETY AND HEALTH AND THE MINE SAFETY AND HEALTH ADMINISTRATION (NIOSH-MSHA).
CHEMICAL CARTRIDGE RESPIRATOR WITH FULL FACEPIECE AND PESTICIDE CARTRIDGE.
TYPE 'C' SUPPLIED-AIR RESPIRATOR WITH A FULL FACEPIECE OPERATED IN PRESSURE-DEMAND OR OTHER POSITIVE PRESSURE MODE OR WITH A FULL FACEPIECE, HELMET OR HOOD OPERATED IN CONTINUOUS-FLOW MODE.
SELF-CONTAINED BREATHING APPARATUS OPERATED IN PRESSURE-DEMAND OR OTHER POSITIVE PRESSURE MODE.
FOR FIREFIGHTING AND OTHER IMMEDIATELY DANGEROUS TO LIFE OR HEALTH CONDITIONS:
SELF-CONTAINED BREATHING APPARATUS WITH FULL FACEPIECE OPERATED IN PRESSURE-DEMAND OR OTHER POSITIVE PRESSURE MODE.
SUPPLIED-AIR RESPIRATOR WITH FULL FACEPIECE AND OPERATED IN PRESSURE-DEMAND OR OTHER POSITIVE PRESSURE MODE IN COMBINATION WITH AN AUXILIARY SELF-CONTAINED BREATHING APPARATUS OPERATED IN PRESSURE-DEMAND OR OTHER POSITIVE PRESSURE MODE.
CLOTHING: EMPLOYEE MUST WEAR APPROPRIATE PROTECTIVE (IMPERVIOUS) CLOTHING AND EQUIPMENT TO PREVENT REPEATED OR PROLONGED SKIN CONTACT WITH THIS SUBSTANCE.
GLOVES: EMPLOYEE MUST WEAR APPROPRIATE PROTECTIVE GLOVES TO PREVENT CONTACT WITH THIS SUBSTANCE.
EYE PROTECTION: EMPLOYEE MUST WEAR SPLASH-PROOF OR DUST-RESISTANT SAFETY GOGGLES TO PREVENT EYE CONTACT WITH THIS SUBSTANCE.
EMERGENCY EYE WASH: WHERE THERE IS ANY POSSIBILITY THAT AN EMPLOYEE'S EYES MAY BE EXPOSED TO THIS SUBSTANCE, THE EMPLOYER SHOULD PROVIDE AN EYE WASH FOUNTAIN WITHIN THE IMMEDIATE WORK AREA FOR EMERGENCY USE.

AUTHORIZED BY- OCCUPATIONAL HEALTH SERVICES, INC.
CREATION DATE: 10/04/89 ***REVISION DATE:*** 05/10/90

MATERIAL SAFETY DATA SHEET

OCCUPATIONAL HEALTH SERVICES, INC. EMERGENCY CONTACT:
AGRICULTURE AND PESTICIDE DIVISION JOHN S. BRANSFORD, JR. (615) 292-1180
450 SEVENTH AVENUE, SUITE 2407
NEW YORK, NEW YORK 10123
1-800-445-MSDS OR (212) 967-1100

SUBSTANCE IDENTIFICATION

CAS-NUMBER 3766-60-7
SUBSTANCE: BUTURON
TRADE NAMES/SYNONYMS: UREA, N'-(4-CHLOROPHENYL)-N-METHYL-N-(1-METHYL-2-PROPYNYL)-; UREA, 3-(P-CHLOROPHENYL)-1-METHYL-1-(1-METHYL-2-PROPYNYL)-; 3-(4-CHLOROPHENYL)-1-METHYL-1-(1-METHYLPROP-2-YNYL)UREA; N'-(4-CHLOROPHENYL)-N-METHYL-N-(1-METHYL-2-PROPYNYL)UREA; 3-(P-CHLOROPHENYL)-1-METHYL-1-(1-METHYL-2-PROPYNYL)UREA; ARISAN; BUTYRON; EPTAPUR; H 95; C12H13CLN2O; PST03523
CHEMICAL FAMILY: SUBSTITUTED UREA
HALOGEN COMPOUND, AROMATIC
MOLECULAR FORMULA: C12-H13-CL-N2-O
MOLECULAR WEIGHT: 236.72
CERCLA RATINGS (SCALE 0-3): HEALTH=3 FIRE=1 REACTIVITY=0 PERSISTENCE=3
NFPA RATINGS (SCALE 0-4): HEALTH=3 FIRE=1 REACTIVITY=0

COMPONENTS AND CONTAMINANTS

COMPONENT: BUTURON ***PERCENT:*** 100
CAS# 3766-60-7
OTHER CONTAMINANTS: NONE
EXPOSURE LIMITS: NO OCCUPATIONAL EXPOSURE LIMITS ESTABLISHED BY OSHA, ACGIH, OR NIOSH.

PHYSICAL DATA

DESCRIPTION: COLORLESS OR WHITE SOLID.
MELTING POINT: 293-295 F (145-146C)
SPECIFIC GRAVITY: NOT AVAILABLE ***VAPOR PRESSURE:*** NEGLIGIBLE
SOLUBILITY IN WATER: 0.003%
SOLVENT SOLUBILITY: SOLUBLE IN ACETONE, METHANOL AND BENZENE.

FIRE AND EXPLOSION DATA

FIRE AND EXPLOSION HAZARD: SLIGHT FIRE HAZARD WHEN EXPOSED TO HEAT OR FLAME.
FIREFIGHTING MEDIA: DRY CHEMICAL, CARBON DIOXIDE, HALON, WATER SPRAY OR STANDARD FOAM (1987 EMERGENCY RESPONSE GUIDEBOOK, DOT P 5800.4). FOR LARGER FIRES, USE WATER SPRAY, FOG OR STANDARD FOAM (1987 EMERGENCY RESPONSE GUIDEBOOK, DOT P 5800.4).
FIREFIGHTING: MOVE CONTAINERS FROM FIRE AREA IF POSSIBLE. FIGHT FIRE FROM MAXIMUM DISTANCE. STAY AWAY FROM STORAGE TANK ENDS. DIKE FIRE CONTROL WATER FOR LATER DISPOSAL. DO NOT SCATTER MATERIAL (1987 EMERGENCY RESPONSE GUIDEBOOK, DOT P 5800.4, GUIDE PAGE 55). EXTINGUISH USING AGENT SUITABLE FOR TYPE OF SURROUNDING FIRE. USE WATER IN FLOODING QUANTITIES AS FOG. KEEP SPARKS, FLAMES AND OTHER SOURCES OF IGNITION AWAY. KEEP MATERIAL OUT OF WATER SOURCES AND SEWERS. DO NOT TOUCH MATERIAL AND AVOID BREATHING DUSTS AND FUMES FROM BURNING MATERIAL. KEEP UPWIND.

TOXICITY

BUTURON: TOXICITY DATA: 1791 MG/KG ORAL-RAT LD50; 1791 MG/KG ORAL-MOUSE LD50 (ARTODN 38,261,77); 500 MG/KG INTRAPERITONEAL-MOUSE LD50; REPRODUCTIVE EFFECTS DATA (RTECS). CARCINOGEN STATUS: NONE. ACUTE TOXICITY LEVEL: MODERATELY TOXIC BY INGESTION. TARGET EFFECTS: NO DATA AVAILABLE.

HEALTH EFFECTS AND FIRST AID

INHALATION: BUTURON: **ACUTE EXPOSURE-** MANY UREA DERIVATIVE HERBICIDES ARE MODERATELY IRRITATING TO THE MUCOUS MEMBRANES. **CHRONIC EXPOSURE-** NO DATA AVAILABLE.
FIRST AID- REMOVE FROM EXPOSURE AREA TO FRESH AIR IMMEDIATELY. IF BREATHING HAS STOPPED, PERFORM ARTIFICIAL RESPIRATION. KEEP PERSON WARM AND AT REST. TREAT SYMPTOMATICALLY AND SUPPORTIVELY. GET MEDICAL ATTENTION IMMEDIATELY.

SKIN CONTACT: BUTURON: **ACUTE EXPOSURE-** THIS MATERIAL APPLIED TO THE BACKS OF RABBITS PRODUCED A SLIGHT ERYTHEMA. **CHRONIC EXPOSURE-** NO DATA AVAILABLE.
FIRST AID- REMOVE CONTAMINATED CLOTHING AND SHOES IMMEDIATELY. WASH AFFECTED AREA WITH SOAP OR MILD DETERGENT AND LARGE AMOUNTS OF WATER UNTIL NO EVIDENCE OF CHEMICAL REMAINS (APPROXIMATELY 15-20 MINUTES). GET MEDICAL ATTENTION IMMEDIATELY.

EYE CONTACT: BUTURON: **ACUTE EXPOSURE-** MANY UREA DERIVATIVE HERBICIDES ARE MODERATELY IRRITATING TO THE EYES. **CHRONIC EXPOSURE-** NO DATA AVAILABLE.

FIRST AID- WASH EYES IMMEDIATELY WITH LARGE AMOUNTS OF WATER OR NORMAL SALINE, OCCASIONALLY LIFTING UPPER AND LOWER LIDS, UNTIL NO EVIDENCE OF CHEMICAL REMAINS (APPROXIMATELY 15-20 MINUTES). GET MEDICAL ATTENTION IMMEDIATELY.

INGESTION: BUTURON: **ACUTE EXPOSURE-** A LETHAL DOSE IN RATS WAS 3.0 GM/KG. **CHRONIC EXPOSURE-** RATS TOLERATED 500 PPM IN FOOD FOR 120 DAYS WITHOUT ILL EFFECTS. AN INCREASE OF POSTIMPLANTATIVE LOSSES AND CLEAR RETARDATION OF FETAL DEVELOPMENT WHICH INCLUDED AN INCREASE IN THE NUMBER OF CLEFT PALATES AND EXENCEPHALY WERE OBSERVED IN A STUDY OF PREGNANT MICE FED BUTURON.

FIRST AID- REMOVE BY GASTRIC LAVAGE AND CATHARSIS. MAINTAIN BLOOD PRESSURE AND AIRWAY. GIVE OXYGEN IF RESPIRATION IS DEPRESSED. DO NOT PERFORM GASTRIC LAVAGE IF VICTIM IS UNCONSCIOUS. GET MEDICAL ATTENTION IMMEDIATELY (DREISBACH, HANDBOOK OF POISONING, 12TH ED.).
ADMINISTRATION OF LAVAGE OR OXYGEN SHOULD BE PERFORMED BY QUALIFIED MEDICAL PERSONNEL.

ANTIDOTE: NO SPECIFIC ANTIDOTE. TREAT SYMPTOMATICALLY AND SUPPORTIVELY.

REACTIVITY

REACTIVITY: STABLE UNDER NORMAL TEMPERATURES AND PRESSURES.

INCOMPATIBILITIES: BUTURON: OXIDIZERS (STRONG): FIRE AND EXPLOSION HAZARD.

DECOMPOSITION: THERMAL DECOMPOSITION PRODUCTS MAY INCLUDE TOXIC OXIDES OF NITROGEN AND CARBON AND TOXIC AND CORROSIVE FUMES OF CHLORIDES.

POLYMERIZATION: HAZARDOUS POLYMERIZATION HAS NOT BEEN REPORTED TO OCCUR UNDER NORMAL TEMPERATURES AND PRESSURES.

STORAGE AND DISPOSAL

OBSERVE ALL FEDERAL, STATE AND LOCAL REGULATIONS WHEN STORING OR DISPOSING OF THIS SUBSTANCE. FOR ASSISTANCE, CONTACT THE DISTRICT DIRECTOR OF THE ENVIRONMENTAL PROTECTION AGENCY.

STORAGE

STORE IN ACCORDANCE WITH 40 CFR 165 RECOMMENDED PROCEDURES FOR THE DISPOSAL AND STORAGE OF PESTICIDES AND PESTICIDE CONTAINERS.
STORE AWAY FROM INCOMPATIBLE SUBSTANCES.

DISPOSAL

DISPOSAL MUST BE IN ACCORDANCE WITH 40 CFR 165 RECOMMENDED PROCEDURES FOR THE DISPOSAL AND STORAGE OF PESTICIDES AND PESTICIDE CONTAINERS.

CONDITIONS TO AVOID

MAY BURN BUT DOES NOT IGNITE READILY. CONTAINERS MAY EXPLODE IN HEAT OF FIRE.

SPILL AND LEAK PROCEDURES

OCCUPATIONAL SPILL: DO NOT TOUCH SPILLED MATERIAL. STOP LEAK IF YOU CAN DO IT WITHOUT RISK. USE WATER SPRAY TO REDUCE VAPORS. FOR SMALL SPILLS, TAKE UP WITH SAND OR OTHER ABSORBENT MATERIAL AND PLACE INTO CONTAINERS FOR LATER DISPOSAL. FOR SMALL DRY SPILLS, WITH A CLEAN SHOVEL PLACE MATERIAL INTO CLEAN, DRY CONTAINERS AND COVER. MOVE CONTAINERS FROM SPILL AREA. FOR LARGER SPILLS, DIKE FAR AHEAD OF SPILL FOR LATER DISPOSAL. KEEP UNNECESSARY PEOPLE AWAY. ISOLATE HAZARD AREA AND DENY ENTRY. VENTILATE CLOSED SPACES BEFORE ENTERING.

PROTECTIVE EQUIPMENT

VENTILATION: PROVIDE LOCAL EXHAUST VENTILATION SYSTEM.

RESPIRATOR: THE FOLLOWING RESPIRATORS ARE RECOMMENDED BASED ON INFORMATION FOUND IN THE PHYSICAL DATA, TOXICITY AND HEALTH EFFECTS SECTIONS. THEY ARE RANKED IN ORDER FROM MINIMUM TO MAXIMUM RESPIRATORY PROTECTION. THE SPECIFIC RESPIRATOR SELECTED MUST BE BASED ON CONTAMINATION LEVELS FOUND IN THE WORK PLACE, MUST NOT EXCEED THE WORKING LIMITS OF THE RESPIRATOR AND BE JOINTLY APPROVED BY THE NATIONAL INSTITUTE FOR OCCUPATIONAL SAFETY AND HEALTH AND THE MINE SAFETY AND HEALTH ADMINISTRATION (NIOSH-MSHA).
CHEMICAL CARTRIDGE RESPIRATOR WITH AN ORGANIC VAPOR CARTRIDGE(S) WITH A FULL FACEPIECE AND ORGANIC VAPOR CARTRIDGE(S) IN COMBINATION WITH A DUST AND MIST FILTER.
POWERED AIR-PURIFYING RESPIRATOR WITH A TIGHT-FITTING FACEPIECE AND ORGANIC VAPOR CARTRIDGE(S) IN COMBINATION WITH A HIGH-EFFICIENCY PARTICULATE FILTER.
TYPE 'C' SUPPLIED-AIR RESPIRATOR WITH A FULL FACEPIECE OPERATED IN A PRESSURE-DEMAND OR OTHER POSITIVE PRESSURE MODE.
SELF-CONTAINED BREATHING APPARATUS WITH A FULL FACEPIECE OPERATED IN PRESSURE-DEMAND OR OTHER POSITIVE PRESSURE MODE.
FOR FIREFIGHTING AND OTHER IMMEDIATELY DANGEROUS TO LIFE OR HEALTH CONDITIONS:
SELF-CONTAINED BREATHING APPARATUS WITH FULL FACEPIECE OPERATED IN PRESSURE-DEMAND OR OTHER POSITIVE PRESSURE MODE.
SUPPLIED-AIR RESPIRATOR WITH FULL FACEPIECE AND OPERATED IN PRESSURE-DEMAND OR OTHER POSITIVE PRESSURE MODE IN COMBINATION WITH AN AUXILIARY SELF-CONTAINED BREATHING APPARATUS OPERATED IN PRESSURE-DEMAND OR OTHER POSITIVE PRESSURE MODE.

CLOTHING: EMPLOYEE MUST WEAR APPROPRIATE PROTECTIVE (IMPERVIOUS) CLOTHING AND EQUIPMENT TO PREVENT REPEATED OR PROLONGED SKIN CONTACT WITH THIS SUBSTANCE.

GLOVES: EMPLOYEE MUST WEAR APPROPRIATE PROTECTIVE GLOVES TO PREVENT CONTACT WITH THIS SUBSTANCE.

EYE PROTECTION: EMPLOYEE MUST WEAR SPLASH-PROOF OR DUST-RESISTANT SAFETY GOGGLES TO PREVENT EYE CONTACT WITH THIS SUBSTANCE.
EMERGENCY EYE WASH: WHERE THERE IS ANY POSSIBILITY THAT AN EMPLOYEE'S EYES MAY BE EXPOSED TO THIS SUBSTANCE, THE EMPLOYER SHOULD PROVIDE AN EYE WASH FOUNTAIN WITHIN THE IMMEDIATE WORK AREA FOR EMERGENCY USE.

AUTHORIZED BY- OCCUPATIONAL HEALTH SERVICES, INC.
CREATION DATE: 10/04/89 ***REVISION DATE:*** 05/11/90

MATERIAL SAFETY DATA SHEET

OCCUPATIONAL HEALTH SERVICES, INC.
AGRICULTURE AND PESTICIDE DIVISION
450 SEVENTH AVENUE, SUITE 2407
NEW YORK, NEW YORK 10123
1-800-445-MSDS OR (212) 967-1100

EMERGENCY CONTACT:
JOHN S. BRANSFORD, JR. (615) 292-1180

SUBSTANCE IDENTIFICATION

CAS-NUMBER 33629-47-9

SUBSTANCE: **BUTRALIN**

TRADE NAMES/SYNONYMS: BENZENAMINE, 4-(1,1-DIMETHYLETHYL)-N-(1-METHYLPROPYL)-2,6-DINITRO-; ANILINE, N-SEC-BUTYL-4-TERT-BUTYL-2,6-DINITRO-; 4-(1,1-DIMETHYLETHYL)-N-(1-METHYLPROPYL)-2,6-DINITROBENZENAMINE; N-SEC-BUTYL-4-TERT-BUTYL-2,6-DINITROANILINE; A-820; AMCHEM 70-25; AMEX; BUTALIN; DIBUTALIN; TAMEX; C14H21N3O4; PST03525

CHEMICAL FAMILY: AMINE, AROMATIC

MOLECULAR FORMULA: C14-H21-N3-O4

MOLECULAR WEIGHT: 295.34

CERCLA RATINGS (SCALE 0-3): HEALTH=U FIRE=2 REACTIVITY=0 PERSISTENCE=2

NFPA RATINGS (SCALE 0-4): HEALTH=U FIRE=2 REACTIVITY=0

COMPONENTS AND CONTAMINANTS

COMPONENT: BUTRALIN ***PERCENT:*** 100
CAS# 33629-47-9

OTHER CONTAMINANTS: NONE

EXPOSURE LIMITS: NO OCCUPATIONAL EXPOSURE LIMITS ESTABLISHED BY OSHA, ACGIH, OR NIOSH.

PHYSICAL DATA

DESCRIPTION: YELLOW-ORANGE CRYSTALS WITH A SLIGHT AROMATIC ODOR

BOILING POINT: 273-277 F (134-136 C) 0.5 MMHG

MELTING POINT: 140-141 F (60-61 C) ***VAPOR PRESSURE:*** 0.000013 MMHG @ 25 C

SOLUBILITY IN WATER: 0.1%

SOLVENT SOLUBILITY: SOLUBLE IN ACETONE, BENZENE, BUTANONE, XYLENE, CARBON TETRACHLORIDE, ETHANOL, METHANOL
DECOMPOSES @ 509 F (265 C)

FIRE AND EXPLOSION DATA

FIRE AND EXPLOSION HAZARD: MODERATE FIRE HAZARD WHEN EXPOSED TO HEAT OR FLAME.

FLASH POINT: 97 F (36 C) ***FLAMMABILITY CLASS(OSHA):*** IC

FIREFIGHTING MEDIA: DRY CHEMICAL, CARBON DIOXIDE, HALON, WATER SPRAY OR STANDARD FOAM (1987 EMERGENCY RESPONSE GUIDEBOOK, DOT P 5800.4).

FOR LARGER FIRES, USE WATER SPRAY, FOG OR STANDARD FOAM (1987 EMERGENCY RESPONSE GUIDEBOOK, DOT P 5800.4).

FIREFIGHTING: MOVE CONTAINER FROM FIRE AREA IF POSSIBLE. COOL FIRE-EXPOSED CONTAINERS WITH WATER FROM SIDE UNTIL WELL AFTER FIRE IS OUT. STAY AWAY FROM STORAGE TANK ENDS. FOR MASSIVE FIRE IN STORAGE AREA, USE UNMANNED HOSE HOLDER OR MONITOR NOZZLES, ELSE WITHDRAW FROM AREA AND LET FIRE BURN. WITHDRAW IMMEDIATELY IN CASE OF RISING SOUND FROM VENTING SAFETY DEVICE OR ANY DISCOLORATION OF STORAGE TANK DUE TO FIRE (1987 EMERGENCY RESPONSE GUIDEBOOK, DOT P 5800.4, GUIDE PAGE 27). EXTINGUISH ONLY IF FLOW CAN BE STOPPED; USE FLOODING AMOUNTS OF WATER AS A FOG, SOLID STREAMS MAY BE INEFFECTIVE. COOL CONTAINERS WITH FLOODING AMOUNTS OF WATER, APPLY FROM AS FAR A DISTANCE AS POSSIBLE. AVOID BREATHING VAPORS, KEEP UPWIND.

TRANSPORTATION DATA

DEPARTMENT OF TRANSPORTATION HAZARD CLASSIFICATION 49 CFR 172.101: FLAMMABLE SOLID

DEPARTMENT OF TRANSPORTATION LABELING REQUIREMENTS 49 CFR 172.101 AND SUBPART E: FLAMMABLE SOLID

DEPARTMENT OF TRANSPORTATION PACKAGING REQUIREMENTS: 49 CFR 173.154 EXCEPTIONS: 49 CFR 173.153

TOXICITY

BUTRALIN: TOXICITY DATA: 10200 MG/KG SKIN-RABBIT LD50; 2500 MG/KG ORAL-RAT LD50. CARCINOGEN STATUS: NONE. ACUTE TOXICITY LEVEL: MODERATELY TOXIC BY INGESTION; SLIGHTLY TOXIC BY DERMAL ABSORPTION. TARGET EFFECTS: NO DATA AVAILABLE.

HEALTH EFFECTS AND FIRST AID

INHALATION: BUTRALIN: **ACUTE EXPOSURE**- SOME SUBSTITUTED DINITROANILINE HERBICIDES ARE IRRITATING TO THE MUCOUS MEMBRANES. **CHRONIC EXPOSURE**- NO DATA AVAILABLE.

FIRST AID- REMOVE FROM EXPOSURE AREA TO FRESH AIR IMMEDIATELY. IF BREATHING HAS STOPPED, PERFORM ARTIFICIAL RESPIRATION. KEEP PERSON WARM AND AT REST. TREAT SYMPTOMATICALLY AND SUPPORTIVELY. GET MEDICAL ATTENTION IMMEDIATELY.

SKIN CONTACT: BUTRALIN: **ACUTE EXPOSURE**- MAY CAUSE IRRITATION. **CHRONIC EXPOSURE**- NO DATA AVAILABLE.

FIRST AID- REMOVE CONTAMINATED CLOTHING AND SHOES IMMEDIATELY. WASH AFFECTED AREA WITH SOAP OR MILD DETERGENT AND LARGE AMOUNTS OF WATER UNTIL NO EVIDENCE OF CHEMICAL REMAINS (APPROXIMATELY 15-20 MINUTES). GET MEDICAL ATTENTION IMMEDIATELY.

EYE CONTACT: BUTRALIN: **ACUTE EXPOSURE**- MAY CAUSE IRRITATION. **CHRONIC EXPOSURE**- NO DATA AVAILABLE.

FIRST AID- WASH EYES IMMEDIATELY WITH LARGE AMOUNTS OF WATER OR NORMAL SALINE, OCCASIONALLY LIFTING UPPER AND LOWER LIDS, UNTIL NO EVIDENCE OF CHEMICAL REMAINS (APPROXIMATELY 15-20 MINUTES). GET MEDICAL ATTENTION IMMEDIATELY.

INGESTION: BUTRALIN: **ACUTE EXPOSURE**- A LETHAL DOSE IN RATS IS 2500 MG/KG; THE SYMPTOMS WERE NOT REPORTED. **CHRONIC EXPOSURE**- NO DATA AVAILABLE.

FIRST AID- TREAT SYMPTOMATICALLY AND SUPPORTIVELY. GET MEDICAL ATTENTION IMMEDIATELY. IF VOMITING OCCURS, KEEP HEAD LOWER THAN HIPS TO PREVENT ASPIRATION.

ANTIDOTE: NO SPECIFIC ANTIDOTE. TREAT SYMPTOMATICALLY AND SUPPORTIVELY.

REACTIVITY

REACTIVITY: STABLE UNDER NORMAL TEMPERATURES AND PRESSURES.

INCOMPATIBILITIES: BUTRALIN: OXIDIZERS (STRONG): FIRE AND EXPLOSION HAZARD. PLASTICS AND RUBBERS: SOME FORMS MAY BE DISTORTED OR PERMEATED.

DECOMPOSITION: THERMAL DECOMPOSITION MAY RELEASE ACRID SMOKE AND IRRITATING FUMES.

POLYMERIZATION: HAZARDOUS POLYMERIZATION HAS NOT BEEN REPORTED TO OCCUR UNDER NORMAL TEMPERATURES AND PRESSURES.

STORAGE AND DISPOSAL

OBSERVE ALL FEDERAL, STATE AND LOCAL REGULATIONS WHEN STORING OR DISPOSING OF THIS SUBSTANCE. FOR ASSISTANCE, CONTACT THE DISTRICT DIRECTOR OF THE ENVIRONMENTAL PROTECTION AGENCY.

STORAGE

STORE IN ACCORDANCE WITH 40 CFR 165 RECOMMENDED PROCEDURES FOR THE DISPOSAL AND STORAGE OF PESTICIDES AND PESTICIDE CONTAINERS.

DISPOSAL

DISPOSAL MUST BE IN ACCORDANCE WITH 40 CFR 165 RECOMMENDED PROCEDURES FOR THE DISPOSAL AND STORAGE OF PESTICIDES AND PESTICIDE CONTAINERS.

CONDITIONS TO AVOID

AVOID CONTACT WITH HEAT, SPARKS, FLAMES, OR OTHER SOURCES OF IGNITION. VAPORS MAY BE EXPLOSIVE. AVOID OVERHEATING OF CONTAINERS; CONTAINERS MAY VIOLENTLY RUPTURE IN HEAT OF FIRE. AVOID CONTAMINATION OF WATER SOURCES.

SPILL AND LEAK PROCEDURES

OCCUPATIONAL SPILL: SHUT OFF IGNITION SOURCES. STOP LEAK IF YOU CAN DO IT WITHOUT RISK. USE WATER SPRAY TO REDUCE VAPORS. FOR SMALL SPILLS, TAKE UP WITH SAND OR OTHER ABSORBENT MATERIAL AND PLACE INTO CONTAINERS FOR LATER DISPOSAL. FOR LARGER SPILLS, DIKE FAR AHEAD OF SPILL FOR LATER DISPOSAL. NO SMOKING, FLAMES OR FLARES IN HAZARD AREA. KEEP UNNECESSARY PEOPLE AWAY; ISOLATE HAZARD AREA AND RESTRICT ENTRY.

PROTECTIVE EQUIPMENT

VENTILATION: PROVIDE GENERAL DILUTION VENTILATION.

RESPIRATOR: THE FOLLOWING RESPIRATORS ARE RECOMMENDED BASED ON INFORMATION FOUND IN THE PHYSICAL DATA, TOXICITY AND HEALTH EFFECTS SECTIONS. THEY ARE RANKED IN ORDER FROM MINIMUM TO MAXIMUM RESPIRATORY PROTECTION. THE SPECIFIC RESPIRATOR SELECTED MUST BE BASED ON CONTAMINATION LEVELS FOUND IN THE WORK PLACE, MUST NOT EXCEED THE WORKING LIMITS OF THE RESPIRATOR AND BE JOINTLY APPROVED BY THE NATIONAL INSTITUTE FOR OCCUPATIONAL SAFETY AND HEALTH AND THE MINE SAFETY AND HEALTH ADMINISTRATION (NIOSH-MSHA).

CHEMICAL CARTRIDGE RESPIRATOR WITH AN ORGANIC VAPOR CARTRIDGE(S) WITH A FULL FACEPIECE AND ORGANIC VAPOR CARTRIDGE(S) IN COMBINATION WITH A DUST AND MIST FILTER.

POWERED AIR-PURIFYING RESPIRATOR WITH A TIGHT-FITTING FACEPIECE AND ORGANIC VAPOR CARTRIDGE(S) IN COMBINATION WITH A HIGH-EFFICIENCY PARTICULATE FILTER.

TYPE 'C' SUPPLIED-AIR RESPIRATOR WITH A FULL FACEPIECE OPERATED IN A PRESSURE-DEMAND OR OTHER POSITIVE PRESSURE MODE.

SELF-CONTAINED BREATHING APPARATUS WITH A FULL FACEPIECE OPERATED IN PRESSURE-DEMAND OR OTHER POSITIVE PRESSURE MODE.

FOR FIREFIGHTING AND OTHER IMMEDIATELY DANGEROUS TO LIFE OR HEALTH CONDITIONS:

SELF-CONTAINED BREATHING APPARATUS WITH FULL FACEPIECE OPERATED IN PRESSURE-DEMAND OR OTHER POSITIVE PRESSURE MODE.

SUPPLIED-AIR RESPIRATOR WITH FULL FACEPIECE AND OPERATED IN PRESSURE-DEMAND OR OTHER POSITIVE PRESSURE MODE IN COMBINATION WITH AN AUXILIARY SELF-CONTAINED BREATHING APPARATUS OPERATED IN PRESSURE-DEMAND OR OTHER POSITIVE PRESSURE MODE.

CLOTHING: EMPLOYEE MUST WEAR APPROPRIATE PROTECTIVE (IMPERVIOUS) CLOTHING AND EQUIPMENT TO PREVENT REPEATED OR PROLONGED SKIN CONTACT WITH THIS SUBSTANCE.

GLOVES: EMPLOYEE MUST WEAR APPROPRIATE PROTECTIVE GLOVES TO PREVENT CONTACT WITH THIS SUBSTANCE.

EYE PROTECTION: EMPLOYEE MUST WEAR SPLASH-PROOF OR DUST-RESISTANT SAFETY GOGGLES TO PREVENT EYE CONTACT WITH THIS SUBSTANCE.

EMERGENCY EYE WASH: WHERE THERE IS ANY POSSIBILITY THAT AN EMPLOYEE'S EYES MAY BE EXPOSED TO THIS SUBSTANCE, THE EMPLOYER SHOULD PROVIDE AN EYE WASH FOUNTAIN WITHIN THE IMMEDIATE WORK AREA FOR EMERGENCY USE.

AUTHORIZED BY- OCCUPATIONAL HEALTH SERVICES, INC.

CREATION DATE: 10/04/89 ***REVISION DATE:*** 05/07/90

MATERIAL SAFETY DATA SHEET

OCCUPATIONAL HEALTH SERVICES, INC.
AGRICULTURE AND PESTICIDE DIVISION
450 SEVENTH AVENUE, SUITE 2407
NEW YORK, NEW YORK 10123
1-800-445-MSDS OR (212) 967-1100

EMERGENCY CONTACT:
JOHN S. BRANSFORD, JR. (615) 292-1180

SUBSTANCE IDENTIFICATION

CAS-NUMBER 111-76-2

***SUBSTANCE:* BUTYL CELLOSOLVE**

TRADE NAMES/SYNONYMS: ETHANOL, 2-BUTOXY-; BUTYL OXITOL; ETHYLENE GLYCOL MONOBUTYL ETHER; 2-BUTOXYETHANOL; BETA-BUTOXYETHANOL; BUTYL GLYCOL; ETHYLENE GLYCOL BUTYL ETHER; ETHYLENE GLYCOL N-BUTYL ETHER; DOWANOL EB; GLYCOL BUTYL ETHER; GLYCOL MONOBUTYL ETHER; MONOBUTYL GLYCOL ETHER; GAFCOL EB; BUTYL MONOETHER GLYCOL; ETHYLENE GLYCOL MONO-N-BUTYL ETHER; EKTASOLVE EB; SOLVENT, THINNER AND SCREEN WASH (NAZ-DAR CO.); SCREEN INK REDUCER (COLONIAL PRINTING INK CO.); UN 2369; C6H14O2; PST03540

CHEMICAL FAMILY: ETHER, ALIPHATIC

MOLECULAR FORMULA: C4-H9-O-C-H2-C-H2-O-H

MOLECULAR WEIGHT: 118.18

CERCLA RATINGS (SCALE 0-3): HEALTH=3 FIRE=2 REACTIVITY=0 PERSISTENCE=0

NFPA RATINGS (SCALE 0-4): HEALTH=2 FIRE=2 REACTIVITY=0

COMPONENTS AND CONTAMINANTS

COMPONENT: BUTYL CELLOSOLVE ***PERCENT:*** 100
CAS# 111-76-2

OTHER CONTAMINANTS: NONE

EXPOSURE LIMITS: BUTYL CELLOSOLVE (ETHYLENE GLYCOL MONOBUTYL ETHER): 25 PPM (120 MG/M3) OSHA TWA (SKIN) 25 PPM (120 MG/M3) ACGIH TWA (SKIN) SUBJECT TO SARA SECTION 313 ANNUAL TOXIC CHEMICAL RELEASE REPORTING

PHYSICAL DATA

DESCRIPTION: COLORLESS LIQUID WITH A MILD, ETHEREAL ODOR.

BOILING POINT: 340 F (171 C) ***MELTING POINT:*** -94 F (-70 C)

SPECIFIC GRAVITY: 0.9015 ***VISCOSITY:*** 3.5 CST @ 25 C

VAPOR PRESSURE: 0.76 MMHG @ 20 C ***EVAPORATION RATE:*** (BUTYL ACETATE=1) 0.06

SOLUBILITY IN WATER: SOLUBLE ***VAPOR DENSITY:*** 4.1

SOLVENT SOLUBILITY: SOLUBLE IN ALCOHOL, ETHER, MOST ORGANIC SOLVENTS, MINERAL OIL

FIRE AND EXPLOSION DATA

FIRE AND EXPLOSION HAZARD: MODERATE FIRE HAZARD WHEN EXPOSED TO HEAT OR FLAME.
VAPORS ARE HEAVIER THAN AIR AND MAY TRAVEL A CONSIDERABLE DISTANCE TO A SOURCE OF IGNITION AND FLASH BACK.
VAPOR-AIR MIXTURES ARE EXPLOSIVE ABOVE FLASH POINT.

FLASH POINT: 143 F (62 C) (CC) ***UPPER EXPLOSIVE LIMIT:*** 12.7 % @ 275 F

LOWER EXPLOSIVE LIMIT: 1.1% @ 200 F ***AUTOIGNITION TEMP.:*** 460 F (238 C)

FLAMMABILITY CLASS(OSHA): IIIA

FIREFIGHTING MEDIA: DRY CHEMICAL, CARBON DIOXIDE, HALON, WATER SPRAY OR ALCOHOL FOAM (1987 EMERGENCY RESPONSE GUIDEBOOK, DOT P 5800.4).
FOR LARGER FIRES, USE WATER SPRAY, FOG OR ALCOHOL FOAM (1987 EMERGENCY RESPONSE GUIDEBOOK, DOT P 5800.4).
ALCOHOL FOAM (NFPA 325M, FIRE HAZARD PROPERTIES OF FLAMMABLE LIQUIDS, GASES, AND VOLATILE SOLIDS, 1984).

FIREFIGHTING: MOVE CONTAINER FROM FIRE AREA IF POSSIBLE. COOL FIRE-EXPOSED CONTAINERS WITH WATER FROM SIDE UNTIL WELL AFTER FIRE IS OUT. STAY AWAY FROM STORAGE TANK ENDS. FOR MASSIVE FIRE IN STORAGE AREA, USE UNMANNED HOSE HOLDER OR MONITOR NOZZLES, ELSE WITHDRAW FROM AREA AND LET FIRE BURN. WITHDRAW IMMEDIATELY IN CASE OF RISING SOUND FROM VENTING SAFETY DEVICE OR ANY DISCOLORATION OF STORAGE TANK DUE TO FIRE (1987 EMERGENCY RESPONSE GUIDEBOOK, DOT P 5800.4, GUIDE PAGE 26). EXTINGUISH ONLY IF FLOW CAN BE STOPPED; USE FLOODING AMOUNTS OF WATER AS A FOG, SOLID STREAMS MAY BE INEFFECTIVE. COOL CONTAINERS WITH FLOODING AMOUNTS OF WATER, APPLY FROM AS FAR A DISTANCE AS POSSIBLE. AVOID BREATHING VAPORS, KEEP UPWIND.

TRANSPORTATION DATA

DEPARTMENT OF TRANSPORTATION HAZARD CLASSIFICATION 49 CFR 172.101: COMBUSTIBLE LIQUID
DEPARTMENT OF TRANSPORTATION LABELING REQUIREMENTS 49 CFR 172.101 AND SUBPART E: NONE
DEPARTMENT OF TRANSPORTATION PACKAGING REQUIREMENTS: NONE
EXCEPTIONS: 49 CFR 173.118A

TOXICITY

BUTYL CELLOSOLVE (ETHYLENE GLYCOL MONOBUTYL ETHER): IRRITATION DATA: 500 MG OPEN SKIN-RABBIT MILD; 18 MG EYE-RABBIT; 100 MG/24 HOURS EYE-RABBIT MODERATE. TOXICITY DATA: 195 PPM/8 HOURS INHALATION-HUMAN TCLO; 100 PPM INHALATION-HUMAN TCLO; 700 PPM/7 HOURS INHALATION-MOUSE LC50; 2900 MG/M3 INHALATION-RAT LC50; 220 MG/KG SKIN-RABBIT LD50; 230 MG/KG SKIN-GUINEA PIG LD50; 600 MG/KG ORAL-WOMAN TDLO; 470 MG/KG ORAL-RAT LD50; 1230 MG/KG ORAL-MOUSE LD50; 300 MG/KG ORAL-RABBIT LD50; 1200 MG/KG ORAL-GUINEA PIG LD50; 500 MG/KG SUBCUTANEOUS-MOUSE LDLO; 340 MG/KG INTRAVENOUS-RAT LD50; 1130 MG/KG INTRAVENOUS-MOUSE LD50; 280 MG/KG INTRAVENOUS-RABBIT LD50; 220 MG/KG INTRAPERITONEAL-RAT LD50; 536 MG/KG INTRAPERITONEAL-MOUSE LD50; 220 MG/KG INTRAPERITONEAL-RABBIT LD50; 1500 MG/KG UNREPORTED-MAMMAL LD50; REPRODUCTIVE EFFECTS DATA (RTECS). CARCINOGEN STATUS: NONE. LOCAL EFFECTS: IRRITANT-INHALATION, SKIN, EYE. ACUTE TOXICITY LEVEL: TOXIC BY INHALATION, DERMAL ABSORPTION, INGESTION. TARGET EFFECTS: CENTRAL NERVOUS SYSTEM DEPRESSANT; NEPHROTOXIN; HEMOLYTIC AGENT. POISONING MAY ALSO AFFECT THE LIVER.

HEALTH EFFECTS AND FIRST AID

INHALATION: BUTYL CELLOSOLVE (ETHYLENE GLYCOL MONOBUTYL ETHER): IRRITANT/NARCOTIC/HEMOLYTIC AGENT/NEPHROTOXIN/TOXIC. 700 PPM IMMEDIATELY DANGEROUS TO LIFE OR HEALTH. **ACUTE EXPOSURE-** INHALATION OF VAPORS MAY CAUSE IRRITATION OF THE UPPER RESPIRATORY TRACT AND DYSPNEA. SOME CELLOSOLVES MAY CAUSE VOMITING, NAUSEA, DIARRHEA, ANEMIA, POSSIBLE ABDOMINAL AND LUMBAR PAIN, AND SYMPTOMS OF CENTRAL NERVOUS SYSTEM DEPRESSION INCLUDING HEADACHE, DIZZINESS, DROWSINESS, WEAKNESS, TREMORS, AND NARCOSIS. SEVERE EXPOSURES MAY RESULT IN ANOREXIA, WEIGHT LOSS, APATHY, VISCERAL CONGESTION, HEMORRHAGING OF THE LUNGS, AND LIVER AND KIDNEY DAMAGE. KIDNEY EFFECTS MAY INCLUDE TRANSIENT POLYURIA, ALBUMINURIA, HEMATURIA, HEMOGLOBINURIA, OLIGURIA PROGRESSING TO ANURIA, AND ACUTE RENAL FAILURE. EFFECTS ON THE BLOOD MAY INCLUDE ERYTHROPENIA, RETICULOCYTOSIS, LEUKOCYTOSIS, GRANULOCYTOSIS, AND INCREASED ERYTHROCYTE FRAGILITY WHICH MAY RESULT IN HEMOLYSIS. PULMONARY EDEMA AND BONE MARROW DEPRESSION HAVE ALSO BEEN REPORTED. INHALATION OF 700 PPM/7 HOURS RESULTED IN DEATH IN MICE DUE TO LUNG AND KIDNEY INJURY. **CHRONIC EXPOSURE-** REPEATED OR PROLONGED EXPOSURE TO VAPOR CONCENTRATIONS WOULD BE EXPECTED TO CAUSE IRRITATION OF THE RESPIRATORY TRACT, NARCOSIS, AND LIVER AND KIDNEY DAMAGE IN HUMANS. IN ANIMALS, REPEATED EXPOSURES TO 100-400 PPM MAY CAUSE VISCERAL EFFECTS AND MILD HEMOLYTIC ANEMIA; OVEREXPOSURE TO VAPORS MAY RESULT IN FATIGUE AND LETHARGY, HEADACHE, NAUSEA, ANOREXIA, AND TREMOR; AND OVEREXPOSURE TO HIGH CONCENTRATIONS MAY RESULT IN LIVER AND KIDNEY INJURY, HEMOGLOBINURIA, GREATLY INCREASED ERYTHROCYTE FRAGILITY, PULMONARY HEMORRHAGE, AND DEATH FROM RENAL FAILURE. EFFECTS ON THE FEMALE REPRODUCTIVE SYSTEM, FERTILITY, AND SPECIFIC DEVELOPMENTAL ABNORMALITIES HAVE BEEN REPORTED FROM EXPOSURE OF PREGNANT RATS AND RABBITS TO BUTYL CELLOSOLVE.

FIRST AID- REMOVE FROM EXPOSURE AREA TO FRESH AIR IMMEDIATELY. IF BREATHING HAS STOPPED, PERFORM ARTIFICIAL RESPIRATION. KEEP PERSON WARM AND AT REST. TREAT SYMPTOMATICALLY AND SUPPORTIVELY. GET MEDICAL ATTENTION IMMEDIATELY.

SKIN CONTACT: BUTYL CELLOSOLVE (ETHYLENE GLYCOL MONOBUTYL ETHER): IRRITANT/NARCOTIC/HEMOLYTIC AGENT/NEPHROTOXIN/TOXIC. **ACUTE EXPOSURE-** DIRECT CONTACT WITH THE LIQUID MAY CAUSE IRRITATION WITH REDNESS. BUTYL CELLOSOLVE MAY BE RAPIDLY ABSORBED THROUGH INTACT SKIN TO CAUSE NAUSEA, VOMITING, DIARRHEA, ANEMIA, ABDOMINAL AND LUMBAR PAIN, AND SYMPTOMS OF CENTRAL NERVOUS SYSTEM DEPRESSION INCLUDING HEADACHE, DROWSINESS, DIZZINESS, WEAKNESS, TREMORS, AND NARCOSIS. SEVERE EXPOSURES MAY RESULT IN ANOREXIA, WEIGHT LOSS, APATHY, VISCERAL CONGESTION, HEMORRHAGING OF THE LUNGS, AND LIVER AND KIDNEY DAMAGE. KIDNEY EFFECTS MAY INCLUDE TRANSIENT POLYURIA, ALBUMINURIA, HEMATURIA, HEMOGLOBINURIA, OLIGURIA PROGRESSING TO ANURIA, AND ACUTE RENAL FAILURE. EFFECTS ON THE BLOOD MAY INCLUDE ERYTHROPENIA, RETICULOCYTOSIS, LEUKOCYTOSIS, GRANULOCYTOSIS, AND INCREASED ERYTHROCYTE FRAGILITY WHICH MAY RESULT IN HEMOLYSIS. PULMONARY EDEMA AND BONE MARROW DEPRESSION HAVE ALSO BEEN REPORTED. **CHRONIC EXPOSURE-** REPEATED OR PROLONGED CONTACT MAY CAUSE DEFATTING OF THE SKIN, DERMATITIS, AND SYMPTOMS AS IN ACUTE EXPOSURE.

FIRST AID- REMOVE CONTAMINATED CLOTHING AND SHOES IMMEDIATELY. WASH AFFECTED AREA WITH SOAP OR MILD DETERGENT AND LARGE AMOUNTS OF WATER UNTIL NO EVIDENCE OF CHEMICAL REMAINS (APPROXIMATELY 15-20 MINUTES). GET MEDICAL ATTENTION IMMEDIATELY.

EYE CONTACT: BUTYL CELLOSOLVE (ETHYLENE GLYCOL MONOBUTYL ETHER): IRRITANT. **ACUTE EXPOSURE-** EXPOSURE TO VAPOR CONCENTRATIONS OF >100 PPM MAY CAUSE IRRITATION WITH MILD PAIN, REDNESS, AND LACRIMATION. DIRECT CONTACT WITH THE LIQUID CAUSED IRRITATION WITH REDDENING AND SWELLING OF THE CONJUNCTIVA, PAIN, AND SLIGHT TRANSITORY CORNEAL CLOUDING IN RABBITS. THE DEGREE OF INJURY WAS GRADED 4 ON A SCALE OF 1-

10 AFTER 24 HOURS. **CHRONIC EXPOSURE-** REPEATED OR PROLONGED EXPOSURE MAY CAUSE CONJUNCTIVITIS.

FIRST AID- WASH EYES IMMEDIATELY WITH LARGE AMOUNTS OF WATER OR NORMAL SALINE, OCCASIONALLY LIFTING UPPER AND LOWER LIDS, UNTIL NO EVIDENCE OF CHEMICAL REMAINS (APPROXIMATELY 15-20 MINUTES). GET MEDICAL ATTENTION IMMEDIATELY.

INGESTION: BUTYL CELLOSOLVE (ETHYLENE GLYCOL MONOBUTYL ETHER): NARCOTIC/HEMOLYTIC AGENT/NEPHROTOXIC/TOXIC. **ACUTE EXPOSURE-** MAY CAUSE SOUR TASTE, TONGUE NUMBNESS, NAUSEA, VOMITING, DIARRHEA, ABDOMINAL AND LUMBAR PAIN, AND EFFECTS ON THE CENTRAL NERVOUS SYSTEM INCLUDING HEADACHE, DROWSINESS, DIZZINESS, WEAKNESS, TREMORS, AND NARCOSIS. SEVERE EXPOSURES MAY RESULT IN ANOREXIA, WEIGHT LOSS, APATHY, VISCERAL CONGESTION, HEMORRHAGING OF THE LUNGS, AND LIVER AND KIDNEY DAMAGE. KIDNEY EFFECTS MAY INCLUDE TRANSIENT POLYURIA, ALBUMINURIA, HEMATURIA, HEMOGLOBINURIA, OLIGURIA PROGRESSING TO ANURIA, AND ACUTE RENAL EFFECTS ON THE BLOOD MAY INCLUDE ERYTHROPENIA, RETICULOCYTOSIS, LEUKOCYTOSIS, GRANULOCYTOSIS, AND INCREASED ERYTHROCYTE FRAGILITY WHICH MAY RESULT IN HEMOLYSIS. PULMONARY EDEMA AND BONE MARROW DEPRESSION HAVE ALSO BEEN REPORTED. ANIMALS GIVEN FATAL DOSES DIED FROM NARCOSIS WHEN DEATH WAS PROMPT; DELAYED DEATHS RESULTED FROM CONGESTED LUNGS AND SEVERE KIDNEY DAMAGE. **CHRONIC EXPOSURE-** REPEATED OR PROLONGED INGESTION MAY CAUSE GROWTH DEPRESSION, INCREASED LIVER AND KIDNEY DAMAGE, AND EFFECTS AS IN ACUTE EXPOSURE. DELAYED DEATHS IN ANIMALS ARE GENERALLY A RESULT OF LUNG CONGESTION AND/OR RENAL FAILURE. EFFECTS ON FERTILITY HAVE BEEN REPORTED FROM EXPOSURE OF PREGNANT MICE TO BUTYL CELLOSOLVE.

FIRST AID- REMOVE BY GASTRIC LAVAGE OR EMESIS. MAINTAIN BLOOD PRESSURE AND AIRWAY. GIVE OXYGEN IF RESPIRATION IS DEPRESSED. DO NOT PERFORM GASTRIC LAVAGE OR EMESIS IF VICTIM IS UNCONSCIOUS. GET MEDICAL ATTENTION IMMEDIATELY (DREISBACH, HANDBOOK OF POISONING, 11TH ED.). ADMINISTRATION OF GASTRIC LAVAGE OR OXYGEN SHOULD BE PERFORMED BY QUALIFIED MEDICAL PERSONNEL.

ANTIDOTE: NO SPECIFIC ANTIDOTE. TREAT SYMPTOMATICALLY AND SUPPORTIVELY.

REACTIVITY

REACTIVITY: STABLE UNDER NORMAL TEMPERATURES AND PRESSURES.

INCOMPATIBILITIES: BUTYL CELLOSOLVE (ETHYLENE GLYCOL MONOBUTYL ETHER): CAUSTICS (STRONG): DECOMPOSITION. OXIDIZERS (STRONG): FIRE AND EXPLOSION HAZARD.

DECOMPOSITION: THERMAL DECOMPOSITION PRODUCTS MAY INCLUDE TOXIC OXIDES OF CARBON.

POLYMERIZATION: HAZARDOUS POLYMERIZATION HAS NOT BEEN REPORTED TO OCCUR UNDER NORMAL TEMPERATURES AND PRESSURES.

STORAGE AND DISPOSAL

OBSERVE ALL FEDERAL, STATE AND LOCAL REGULATIONS WHEN STORING OR DISPOSING OF THIS SUBSTANCE. FOR ASSISTANCE, CONTACT THE DISTRICT DIRECTOR OF THE ENVIRONMENTAL PROTECTION AGENCY.

****STORAGE****

STORE IN ACCORDANCE WITH 29 CFR 1910.106.

BONDING AND GROUNDING: SUBSTANCES WITH LOW ELECTROCONDUCTIVITY, WHICH MAY BE IGNITED BY ELECTROSTATIC SPARKS, SHOULD BE STORED IN CONTAINERS WHICH MEET THE BONDING AND GROUNDING GUIDELINES SPECIFIED IN NFPA 77-1983, RECOMMENDED PRACTICE ON STATIC ELECTRICITY.

STORE AWAY FROM INCOMPATIBLE SUBSTANCES.

CONDITIONS TO AVOID

AVOID CONTACT WITH HEAT, SPARKS, FLAMES, OR OTHER SOURCES OF IGNITION. VAPORS MAY BE EXPLOSIVE AND POISONOUS; DO NOT ALLOW UNNECESSARY PERSONNEL IN AREA. DO NOT OVERHEAT CONTAINERS; CONTAINERS MAY VIOLENTLY RUPTURE AND TRAVEL A CONSIDERABLE DISTANCE IN HEAT OF FIRE.

SPILL AND LEAK PROCEDURES

OCCUPATIONAL SPILL: SHUT OFF IGNITION SOURCES. STOP LEAK IF YOU CAN DO IT WITHOUT RISK. USE WATER SPRAY TO REDUCE VAPORS. FOR SMALL SPILLS, TAKE UP WITH SAND OR OTHER ABSORBENT MATERIAL AND PLACE INTO CONTAINERS FOR LATER DISPOSAL. FOR LARGER SPILLS, DIKE FAR AHEAD OF SPILL FOR LATER DISPOSAL. NO SMOKING, FLAMES OR FLARES IN HAZARD AREA. KEEP UNNECESSARY PEOPLE AWAY; ISOLATE HAZARD AREA AND DENY ENTRY.

PROTECTIVE EQUIPMENT

VENTILATION: PROVIDE LOCAL EXHAUST OR PROCESS ENCLOSURE VENTILATION TO MEET PUBLISHED EXPOSURE LIMITS.

RESPIRATOR: THE FOLLOWING RESPIRATORS AND MAXIMUM USE CONCENTRATIONS ARE RECOMMENDATIONS BY THE U.S. DEPARTMENT OF HEALTH AND HUMAN SERVICES, NIOSH POCKET GUIDE TO CHEMICAL HAZARDS; NIOSH CRITERIA DOCUMENTS OR BY THE U.S. DEPARTMENT OF LABOR, 29 CFR 1910 SUBPART Z. THE SPECIFIC RESPIRATOR SELECTED MUST BE BASED ON CONTAMINATION LEVELS FOUND IN THE WORK PLACE, MUST NOT EXCEED THE WORKING LIMITS OF THE RESPIRATOR AND BE JOINTLY APPROVED BY THE NATIONAL INSTITUTE FOR OCCUPATIONAL SAFETY AND HEALTH AND THE MINE SAFETY AND HEALTH ADMINISTRATION (NIOSH-MSHA).

BUTYL CELLOSOLVE:

250 PPM- ANY SUPPLIED-AIR RESPIRATOR. ANY SELF-CONTAINED BREATHING APPARATUS.

625 PPM- ANY POWERED AIR-PURIFYING RESPIRATOR WITH ORGANIC VAPOR CARTRIDGE(S). ANY SUPPLIED-AIR RESPIRATOR OPERATED IN A CONTINUOUS FLOW MODE.

700 PPM- ANY AIR-PURIFYING FULL FACEPIECE RESPIRATOR (GAS MASK) WITH A CHIN-STYLE OR FRONT- OR BACK-MOUNTED ORGANIC VAPOR CANISTER. ANY CHEMICAL CARTRIDGE RESPIRATOR WITH A FULL FACEPIECE AND ORGANIC VAPOR CARTRIDGE(S). ANY SUPPLIED-AIR RESPIRATOR WITH A FULL FACEPIECE. ANY SELF-CONTAINED BREATHING APPARATUS WITH A FULL FACEPIECE.

ESCAPE- ANY AIR-PURIFYING FULL FACEPIECE RESPIRATOR (GAS MASK) WITH A CHIN-STYLE OR FRONT- OR BACK-MOUNTED ORGANIC VAPOR CANISTER. ANY APPROPRIATE ESCAPE-TYPE SELF-CONTAINED BREATHING APPARATUS.

FOR FIREFIGHTING AND OTHER IMMEDIATELY DANGEROUS TO LIFE OR HEALTH CONDITIONS:

SELF-CONTAINED BREATHING APPARATUS WITH FULL FACEPIECE OPERATED IN PRESSURE-DEMAND OR OTHER POSITIVE PRESSURE MODE.

SUPPLIED-AIR RESPIRATOR WITH FULL FACEPIECE AND OPERATED IN PRESSURE-DEMAND OR OTHER POSITIVE PRESSURE MODE IN COMBINATION WITH AN AUXILIARY SELF-CONTAINED BREATHING APPARATUS OPERATED IN PRESSURE-DEMAND OR OTHER POSITIVE PRESSURE MODE. ***CLOTHING:*** EMPLOYEE MUST WEAR APPROPRIATE PROTECTIVE (IMPERVIOUS) CLOTHING AND EQUIPMENT TO PREVENT ANY POSSIBILITY OF SKIN CONTACT WITH THIS SUBSTANCE.

GLOVES: EMPLOYEE MUST WEAR APPROPRIATE PROTECTIVE GLOVES TO PREVENT CONTACT WITH THIS SUBSTANCE.

EYE PROTECTION: EMPLOYEE MUST WEAR SPLASH-PROOF OR DUST-RESISTANT SAFETY GOGGLES AND A FACESHIELD TO PREVENT CONTACT WITH THIS SUBSTANCE.

EMERGENCY WASH FACILITIES: WHERE THERE IS ANY POSSIBILITY THAT AN EMPLOYEE'S EYES AND/OR SKIN MAY BE EXPOSED TO THIS SUBSTANCE, THE EMPLOYER SHOULD PROVIDE AN EYE WASH FOUNTAIN AND QUICK DRENCH SHOWER WITHIN THE IMMEDIATE WORK AREA FOR EMERGENCY USE.

AUTHORIZED BY- OCCUPATIONAL HEALTH SERVICES, INC.

CREATION DATE: 10/04/89 ***REVISION DATE:*** 05/07/90

MATERIAL SAFETY DATA SHEET

OCCUPATIONAL HEALTH SERVICES, INC.
AGRICULTURE AND PESTICIDE DIVISION
450 SEVENTH AVENUE, SUITE 2407
NEW YORK, NEW YORK 10123
1-800-445-MSDS OR (212) 967-1100

EMERGENCY CONTACT:
JOHN S. BRANSFORD, JR. (615) 292-1180

SUBSTANCE IDENTIFICATION

CAS-NUMBER 1689-84-5

SUBSTANCE: **BROMOXYNIL**

TRADE NAMES/SYNONYMS: BENZONITRILE, 3,5-DIBROMO-4-HYDROXY-; 3,5-DIBROMO-4-HYDROXYBENZONITRILE; 3-5-DIBROMO-4-HYDROXYPHENYL CYANIDE; 2,6-DIBROMO-4-CYANOPHENOL; BROMINAL; BROMINIL; BROXYNIL; BUCTRIL; PARDNER; ENT 20,852; C7H3BR2NO; PST03542

CHEMICAL FAMILY: ESTER
HALOGEN COMPOUND, AROMATIC
NITRILE, AROMATIC

MOLECULAR FORMULA: C-N-C6-H2-BR2-O-H

MOLECULAR WEIGHT: 276.92

CERCLA RATINGS (SCALE 0-3): HEALTH=3 FIRE=1 REACTIVITY=0 PERSISTENCE=3

NFPA RATINGS (SCALE 0-4): HEALTH=U FIRE=1 REACTIVITY=0

COMPONENTS AND CONTAMINANTS

COMPONENT: BROMOXYNIL ***PERCENT:*** 100
CAS# 1689-84-5

EXPOSURE LIMITS: NO OCCUPATIONAL EXPOSURE LIMITS ESTABLISHED BY OSHA, ACGIH, OR NIOSH.

PHYSICAL DATA

DESCRIPTION: COLORLESS SOLID ***MELTING POINT:*** 381-383 F (194-195 C)
SPECIFIC GRAVITY: NOT AVAILABLE ***SOLUBILITY IN WATER:*** 130 PPM
SOLVENT SOLUBILITY: SOLUBLE IN ACETONE, TETRAHYDROFURAN; SLIGHTLY SOLUBLE IN METHANOL AND PETROLEUM OILS
SUBLIMATION PT: 275 F (135 C) @ 0.15 MMHG

FIRE AND EXPLOSION DATA

FIRE AND EXPLOSION HAZARD: SLIGHT FIRE HAZARD WHEN EXPOSED TO HEAT OR FLAME.

FIREFIGHTING MEDIA: DRY CHEMICAL, CARBON DIOXIDE, HALON, WATER SPRAY OR STANDARD FOAM (1987 EMERGENCY RESPONSE GUIDEBOOK, DOT P 5800.4).
FOR LARGER FIRES, USE WATER SPRAY, FOG OR STANDARD FOAM (1987 EMERGENCY RESPONSE GUIDEBOOK, DOT P 5800.4).

FIREFIGHTING: MOVE CONTAINERS FROM FIRE AREA IF POSSIBLE (1987 EMERGENCY RESPONSE GUIDEBOOK, DOT P 5800.4, GUIDE PAGE 53).
EXTINGUISH FIRE USING AGENTS SUITABLE FOR TYPE OF SURROUNDING FIRE. USE WATER IN FLOODING AMOUNTS AS A FOG. AVOID BREATHING DUSTS AND FUMES FROM BURNING MATERIAL; KEEP UPWIND.

TOXICITY

BROMOXYNIL: TOXICITY DATA: 3660 MG/KG SKIN-RABBIT LD50; 190 MG/KG ORAL-RAT LD50; 110 MG/KG ORAL-MOUSE LD50; 260 MG/KG ORAL-RABBIT LD50; 63 MG/KG ORAL-GUINEA PIG LD50; 100 MG/KG ORAL-DOG LD50; 56 MG/KG INTRAVENOUS-MOUSE LD50; 190 MG/KG UNREPORTED-MAMMAL LD50.
CARCINOGEN STATUS: NONE. ACUTE TOXICITY LEVEL: TOXIC BY INGESTION; SLIGHTLY TOXIC BY DERMAL ABSORPTION. TARGET EFFECTS: NO DATA AVAILABLE.

HEALTH EFFECTS AND FIRST AID

INHALATION: BROMOXYNIL: **ACUTE EXPOSURE**- NO DATA AVAILABLE. **CHRONIC EXPOSURE**- NO DATA AVAILABLE.

FIRST AID- REMOVE FROM EXPOSURE AREA TO FRESH AIR IMMEDIATELY. IF BREATHING HAS STOPPED, PERFORM ARTIFICIAL RESPIRATION. KEEP PERSON WARM AND AT REST. TREAT SYMPTOMATICALLY AND SUPPORTIVELY. GET MEDICAL ATTENTION IMMEDIATELY.

SKIN CONTACT: BROMOXYNIL: **ACUTE EXPOSURE**- A LETHAL DOSE IN RABBITS BY DERMAL ABSORPTION WAS 3660 MG/KG. **CHRONIC EXPOSURE**- NO DATA AVAILABLE.

FIRST AID- REMOVE CONTAMINATED CLOTHING AND SHOES IMMEDIATELY. WASH AFFECTED AREA WITH SOAP OR MILD DETERGENT AND LARGE AMOUNTS OF WATER UNTIL NO EVIDENCE OF CHEMICAL REMAINS (APPROXIMATELY 15-20 MINUTES). GET MEDICAL ATTENTION IMMEDIATELY.

EYE CONTACT: BROMOXYNIL: **ACUTE EXPOSURE**- BROMOXYNIL, APPLIED TO THE EYES OF RABBITS, PRODUCED TRANSIENT IRRITATION. **CHRONIC EXPOSURE**- NO DATA AVAILABLE.

FIRST AID- WASH EYES IMMEDIATELY WITH LARGE AMOUNTS OF WATER OR NORMAL SALINE, OCCASIONALLY LIFTING UPPER AND LOWER LIDS, UNTIL NO EVIDENCE OF CHEMICAL REMAINS (APPROXIMATELY 15-20 MINUTES). GET MEDICAL ATTENTION IMMEDIATELY.

INGESTION: BROMOXYNIL: TOXIC. **ACUTE EXPOSURE**- A LETHAL DOSE IN RATS WAS 190 MG/KG; NO SYMPTOMS WERE REPORTED. **CHRONIC EXPOSURE**- REDUCED BODY WEIGHT WAS OBSERVED IN SUBCHRONIC FEEDING STUDIES IN RATS AND DOGS. INCREASED FETAL WEIGHT, INCREASED UTERINE DEATHS, AND INCREASED NUMBER OF FETUSES WITH AN EXTRA 14TH RIB WERE NOTED IN A STUDY OF PREGNANT RATS FED 35 MG/KG/DAY. REPEATED DOSES OF 60 MG/KG/DAY IN PREGNANT RABBITS RESULTED IN HYDROCEPHALUS, MICROPHTHALMIA, ANOPHTHALMIA, AND SEVERE DEFECTS IN OSSIFICATION OF THE SKULL. A COMBINED INCIDENCE OF ADENOMAS AND CARCINOMAS IN THE LIVER WAS NOTED IN A STUDY OF MALE MICE.

FIRST AID- REMOVE BY GASTRIC LAVAGE AND CATHARSIS. MAINTAIN BLOOD PRESSURE AND AIRWAY. GIVE OXYGEN IF RESPIRATION IS DEPRESSED. DO NOT PERFORM GASTRIC LAVAGE IF VICTIM IS UNCONSCIOUS. GET MEDICAL ATTENTION IMMEDIATELY (DREISBACH, HANDBOOK OF POISONING, 12TH ED.).
ADMINISTRATION OF LAVAGE OR OXYGEN SHOULD BE PERFORMED BY QUALIFIED MEDICAL PERSONNEL.

ANTIDOTE: NO SPECIFIC ANTIDOTE. TREAT SYMPTOMATICALLY AND SUPPORTIVELY.

REACTIVITY

REACTIVITY: STABLE UNDER NORMAL TEMPERATURES AND PRESSURES.
INCOMPATIBILITIES: BROMOXYNIL: NO DATA AVAILABLE.
DECOMPOSITION: THERMAL DECOMPOSITION MAY RELEASE CORROSIVE BROMINE AND TOXIC OXIDES OF NITROGEN.
POLYMERIZATION: HAZARDOUS POLYMERIZATION HAS NOT BEEN REPORTED TO OCCUR UNDER NORMAL TEMPERATURES AND PRESSURES.

STORAGE AND DISPOSAL

OBSERVE ALL FEDERAL, STATE AND LOCAL REGULATIONS WHEN STORING OR DISPOSING OF THIS SUBSTANCE. FOR ASSISTANCE, CONTACT THE DISTRICT DIRECTOR OF THE ENVIRONMENTAL PROTECTION AGENCY.

****STORAGE****

STORE IN ACCORDANCE WITH 40 CFR 165 RECOMMENDED PROCEDURES FOR THE DISPOSAL AND STORAGE OF PESTICIDES AND PESTICIDE CONTAINERS.

****DISPOSAL****

DISPOSAL MUST BE IN ACCORDANCE WITH 40 CFR 165 RECOMMENDED PROCEDURES FOR THE DISPOSAL AND STORAGE OF PESTICIDES AND PESTICIDE CONTAINERS.

CONDITIONS TO AVOID

MAY BURN BUT DOES NOT IGNITE READILY.

SPILL AND LEAK PROCEDURES

OCCUPATIONAL SPILL: DO NOT TOUCH SPILLED MATERIAL. STOP LEAK IF YOU CAN DO IT WITHOUT RISK. FOR SMALL SPILLS, TAKE UP WITH SAND OR OTHER ABSORBENT MATERIAL AND PLACE INTO CONTAINERS FOR LATER DISPOSAL. FOR SMALL DRY SPILLS, WITH A CLEAN SHOVEL PLACE MATERIAL INTO CLEAN, DRY CONTAINER AND COVER. MOVE CONTAINERS FROM SPILL AREA. FOR LARGER SPILLS, DIKE FAR AHEAD OF SPILL FOR LATER DISPOSAL. KEEP UNNECESSARY PEOPLE AWAY. ISOLATE HAZARD AREA AND DENY ENTRY.

PROTECTIVE EQUIPMENT

VENTILATION: PROVIDE LOCAL EXHAUST OR GENERAL DILUTION VENTILATION SYSTEM.

RESPIRATOR: THE FOLLOWING RESPIRATORS ARE RECOMMENDED BASED ON INFORMATION FOUND IN THE PHYSICAL DATA, TOXICITY AND HEALTH EFFECTS SECTIONS. THEY ARE RANKED IN ORDER FROM MINIMUM TO MAXIMUM RESPIRATORY PROTECTION. THE SPECIFIC RESPIRATOR SELECTED MUST BE BASED ON CONTAMINATION LEVELS FOUND IN THE WORK PLACE, MUST NOT EXCEED THE WORKING LIMITS OF THE RESPIRATOR AND BE JOINTLY APPROVED BY THE NATIONAL INSTITUTE FOR OCCUPATIONAL SAFETY AND HEALTH AND THE MINE SAFETY AND HEALTH ADMINISTRATION (NIOSH-MSHA).
CHEMICAL CARTRIDGE RESPIRATOR WITH AN ORGANIC VAPOR CARTRIDGE(S) IN COMBINATION WITH A DUST AND MIST FILTER.
GAS MASK WITH ORGANIC VAPOR CANISTER (CHIN-STYLE OR FRONT- OR BACK-MOUNTED CANISTER) WITH A DUST AND MIST FILTER.
GAS MASK WITH ORGANIC VAPOR CANISTER (CHIN-STYLE OR FRONT- OR BACK-MOUNTED CANISTER) WITH A PARTICULATE FILTER.
POWERED AIR-PURIFYING RESPIRATOR WITH A HIGH-EFFICIENCY FILTER.
TYPE 'C' SUPPLIED-AIR RESPIRATOR WITH A FULL FACEPIECE OPERATED IN A PRESSURE-DEMAND OR OTHER POSITIVE PRESSURE MODE.
SELF-CONTAINED BREATHING APPARATUS WITH A FULL FACEPIECE OPERATED IN PRESSURE-DEMAND OR OTHER POSITIVE PRESSURE MODE.
FOR FIREFIGHTING AND OTHER IMMEDIATELY DANGEROUS TO LIFE OR HEALTH CONDITIONS: SELF-CONTAINED BREATHING APPARATUS WITH FULL FACEPIECE OPERATED IN PRESSURE-DEMAND OR OTHER POSITIVE PRESSURE MODE.
SUPPLIED-AIR RESPIRATOR WITH FULL FACEPIECE AND OPERATED IN PRESSURE-DEMAND OR OTHER POSITIVE PRESSURE MODE IN COMBINATION WITH AN AUXILIARY SELF-CONTAINED BREATHING APPARATUS OPERATED IN PRESSURE-DEMAND OR OTHER POSITIVE PRESSURE MODE.

CLOTHING: EMPLOYEE MUST WEAR APPROPRIATE PROTECTIVE (IMPERVIOUS) CLOTHING AND EQUIPMENT TO PREVENT REPEATED OR PROLONGED SKIN CONTACT WITH THIS SUBSTANCE.

GLOVES: EMPLOYEE MUST WEAR APPROPRIATE PROTECTIVE GLOVES TO PREVENT CONTACT WITH THIS SUBSTANCE.

EYE PROTECTION: EMPLOYEE MUST WEAR SPLASH-PROOF OR DUST-RESISTANT SAFETY GOGGLES TO PREVENT EYE CONTACT WITH THIS SUBSTANCE.
EMERGENCY EYE WASH: WHERE THERE IS ANY POSSIBILITY THAT AN EMPLOYEE'S EYES MAY BE EXPOSED TO THIS SUBSTANCE, THE EMPLOYER SHOULD PROVIDE AN EYE WASH FOUNTAIN WITHIN THE IMMEDIATE WORK AREA FOR EMERGENCY USE.

AUTHORIZED BY- OCCUPATIONAL HEALTH SERVICES, INC.
CREATION DATE: 10/04/89 ***REVISION DATE:*** 05/08/90

MATERIAL SAFETY DATA SHEET

OCCUPATIONAL HEALTH SERVICES, INC.
AGRICULTURE AND PESTICIDE DIVISION
450 SEVENTH AVENUE, SUITE 2407
NEW YORK, NEW YORK 10123
1-800-445-MSDS OR (212) 967-1100

EMERGENCY CONTACT:
JOHN S. BRANSFORD, JR. (615) 292-1180

SUBSTANCE IDENTIFICATION

CAS-NUMBER 1689-99-2

SUBSTANCE: **BROMOXYNIL OCTANOATE**

TRADE NAMES/SYNONYMS: OCTANOIC ACID, 2,6-DIBROMO-4-CYANOPHENYL ESTER; OCTANOIC ACID, ESTER WITH 3,5-DIBROMO-4-HYDROXYBENZONITRILE; BROMOXYNIL OCTANOIC ACID ESTER; BROMOXYNIL N-OCTANOYL ESTER; 2,6-DIBROMO-4-CYANOPHENYL OCTANOATE; 3,5-DIBROMO-4-OCTANOYLOXY-BENZONITRILE; BROMOXYNILOCTANOATE; NPH 1320; C15H17BR2NO2; PST03543

CHEMICAL FAMILY: ESTER
HALOGEN COMPOUND, AROMATIC
NITRILE, AROMATIC

MOLECULAR FORMULA: C-N-C6-H2-BR2-O-C-O-(C-H2)6-C-H3

MOLECULAR WEIGHT: 403

CERCLA RATINGS (SCALE 0-3): HEALTH=3 FIRE=1 REACTIVITY=0 PERSISTENCE=3

NFPA RATINGS (SCALE 0-4): HEALTH=3 FIRE=1 REACTIVITY=0

COMPONENTS AND CONTAMINANTS

COMPONENT: BROMOXYNIL OCTANOATE ***PERCENT:*** 100
CAS# 1689-99-2

EXPOSURE LIMITS: NO OCCUPATIONAL EXPOSURE LIMITS ESTABLISHED BY OSHA, ACGIH, OR NIOSH.

PHYSICAL DATA

DESCRIPTION: CREAM COLORED, WAXY SOLID.

MELTING POINT: 113-115 F (45-46C)

SPECIFIC GRAVITY: NOT AVAILABLE ***SOLUBILITY IN WATER:*** INSOLUBLE

SOLVENT SOLUBILITY: SOLUBLE IN ACETONE, ETHANOL, BENZENE, CHLOROFORM, METHYLENE CHLORIDE, XYLENE, CYCLOHEXANONE, CARBON TETRACHLORIDE, NAPHTHA, METHANOL, N-PROPANOL
SUBLIMATION PT: 190 F (90 C) @ 0.1 MMHG

FIRE AND EXPLOSION DATA

FIRE AND EXPLOSION HAZARD: SLIGHT FIRE HAZARD WHEN EXPOSED TO HEAT OR FLAME.

FIREFIGHTING MEDIA: DRY CHEMICAL, CARBON DIOXIDE, HALON, WATER SPRAY OR STANDARD FOAM (1987 EMERGENCY RESPONSE GUIDEBOOK, DOT P 5800.4).
FOR LARGER FIRES, USE WATER SPRAY, FOG OR STANDARD FOAM (1987 EMERGENCY RESPONSE GUIDEBOOK, DOT P 5800.4).

FIREFIGHTING: MOVE CONTAINERS FROM FIRE AREA IF POSSIBLE (1987 EMERGENCY RESPONSE GUIDEBOOK, DOT P 5800.4, GUIDE PAGE 53).
EXTINGUISH FIRE USING AGENTS SUITABLE FOR TYPE OF SURROUNDING FIRE. USE WATER IN FLOODING AMOUNTS AS A FOG. AVOID BREATHING DUSTS AND FUMES FROM BURNING MATERIAL; KEEP UPWIND.

TOXICITY

BROMOXYNIL OCTANOATE: TOXICITY DATA: 1675 MG/KG SKIN-RABBIT LD50; 250 MG/KG ORAL-RAT LD50; 245 MG/KG ORAL-MOUSE LD50; 2 GM/KG ORAL-RABBIT LD50; 420 MG/KG UNREPORTED-MAMMAL LD50. CARCINOGEN STATUS: NONE. ACUTE TOXICITY LEVEL: TOXIC BY INGESTION; MODERATELY TOXIC BY DERMAL ABSORPTION. TARGET EFFECTS: NO DATA AVAILABLE.

HEALTH EFFECTS AND FIRST AID

INHALATION: BROMOXYNIL OCTANOATE: **ACUTE EXPOSURE-** NO DATA AVAILABLE. **CHRONIC EXPOSURE-** NO DATA AVAILABLE.

FIRST AID- REMOVE FROM EXPOSURE AREA TO FRESH AIR IMMEDIATELY. IF BREATHING HAS STOPPED, PERFORM ARTIFICIAL RESPIRATION. KEEP PERSON WARM AND AT REST. TREAT SYMPTOMATICALLY AND SUPPORTIVELY. GET MEDICAL ATTENTION IMMEDIATELY.

SKIN CONTACT: BROMOXYNIL OCTANOATE: **ACUTE EXPOSURE-** A LETHAL DOSE IN RABBITS BY DERMAL ABSORPTION WAS 1675 MG/KG. **CHRONIC EXPOSURE-** NO DATA AVAILABLE.

FIRST AID- REMOVE CONTAMINATED CLOTHING AND SHOES IMMEDIATELY. WASH AFFECTED AREA WITH SOAP OR MILD DETERGENT AND LARGE AMOUNTS OF WATER UNTIL NO EVIDENCE OF CHEMICAL REMAINS (APPROXIMATELY 15-20 MINUTES). GET MEDICAL ATTENTION IMMEDIATELY.

EYE CONTACT: BROMOXYNIL OCTANOATE: **ACUTE EXPOSURE-** BROMOXYNIL, APPLIED TO THE EYES OF RABBITS, PRODUCED TRANSIENT IRRITATION. **CHRONIC EXPOSURE-** NO DATA AVAILABLE.

FIRST AID- WASH EYES IMMEDIATELY WITH LARGE AMOUNTS OF WATER OR NORMAL SALINE, OCCASIONALLY LIFTING UPPER AND LOWER LIDS, UNTIL NO EVIDENCE OF CHEMICAL REMAINS (APPROXIMATELY 15-20 MINUTES). GET MEDICAL ATTENTION IMMEDIATELY.

INGESTION: BROMOXYNIL OCTANOATE: TOXIC. **ACUTE EXPOSURE-** A LETHAL DOSE IN RATS WAS 250 MG/KG; NO SYMPTOMS WERE REPORTED. **CHRONIC EXPOSURE-** IN A 90-DAY FEEDING STUDY OF RATS, NO ADVERSE EFFECTS WERE OBSERVED AT DAILY DOSES OF 15.6 MG/KG.

FIRST AID- REMOVE BY GASTRIC LAVAGE AND CATHARSIS. MAINTAIN BLOOD PRESSURE AND AIRWAY. GIVE OXYGEN IF RESPIRATION IS DEPRESSED. DO NOT PERFORM GASTRIC LAVAGE IF VICTIM IS UNCONSCIOUS. GET MEDICAL ATTENTION IMMEDIATELY (DREISBACH, HANDBOOK OF POISONING, 12TH ED.).
ADMINISTRATION OF LAVAGE OR OXYGEN SHOULD BE PERFORMED BY QUALIFIED MEDICAL PERSONNEL.

ANTIDOTE: NO SPECIFIC ANTIDOTE. TREAT SYMPTOMATICALLY AND SUPPORTIVELY.

REACTIVITY

REACTIVITY: STABLE UNDER NORMAL TEMPERATURES AND PRESSURES.

INCOMPATIBILITIES: BROMOXYNIL OCTANOATE: ALKALINE CONDITIONS (PH>9): MAY CAUSE HYDROLYSIS TO BROMOXYNIL. COMBUSTIBLE MATERIALS: INCOMPATIBLE.

DECOMPOSITION: THERMAL DECOMPOSITION MAY RELEASE CORROSIVE BROMINE AND TOXIC OXIDES OF NITROGEN.

POLYMERIZATION: HAZARDOUS POLYMERIZATION HAS NOT BEEN REPORTED TO OCCUR UNDER NORMAL TEMPERATURES AND PRESSURES.

STORAGE AND DISPOSAL

OBSERVE ALL FEDERAL, STATE AND LOCAL REGULATIONS WHEN STORING OR DISPOSING OF THIS SUBSTANCE. FOR ASSISTANCE, CONTACT THE DISTRICT DIRECTOR OF THE ENVIRONMENTAL PROTECTION AGENCY.

STORAGE

STORE IN ACCORDANCE WITH 40 CFR 165 RECOMMENDED PROCEDURES FOR THE DISPOSAL AND STORAGE OF PESTICIDES AND PESTICIDE CONTAINERS.
STORE AWAY FROM INCOMPATIBLE SUBSTANCES.

DISPOSAL

DISPOSAL MUST BE IN ACCORDANCE WITH 40 CFR 165 RECOMMENDED PROCEDURES FOR THE DISPOSAL AND STORAGE OF PESTICIDES AND PESTICIDE CONTAINERS.

CONDITIONS TO AVOID

MAY BURN BUT DOES NOT IGNITE READILY.

SPILL AND LEAK PROCEDURES

OCCUPATIONAL SPILL: DO NOT TOUCH SPILLED MATERIAL. STOP LEAK IF YOU CAN DO IT WITHOUT RISK. FOR SMALL SPILLS, TAKE UP WITH SAND OR OTHER ABSORBENT MATERIAL AND PLACE INTO CONTAINERS FOR LATER DISPOSAL. FOR SMALL DRY SPILLS, WITH A CLEAN SHOVEL PLACE MATERIAL INTO CLEAN, DRY CONTAINER AND COVER. MOVE CONTAINERS FROM SPILL AREA. FOR LARGER SPILLS, DIKE FAR AHEAD OF SPILL FOR LATER DISPOSAL. KEEP UNNECESSARY PEOPLE AWAY. ISOLATE HAZARD AREA AND DENY ENTRY.

PROTECTIVE EQUIPMENT

VENTILATION: PROVIDE LOCAL EXHAUST OR GENERAL DILUTION VENTILATION SYSTEM.

RESPIRATOR: THE FOLLOWING RESPIRATORS ARE RECOMMENDED BASED ON INFORMATION FOUND IN THE PHYSICAL DATA, TOXICITY AND HEALTH EFFECTS SECTIONS. THEY ARE RANKED IN ORDER FROM MINIMUM TO MAXIMUM RESPIRATORY PROTECTION. THE SPECIFIC RESPIRATOR SELECTED MUST BE BASED ON CONTAMINATION LEVELS FOUND IN THE WORK PLACE, MUST NOT EXCEED THE WORKING LIMITS OF THE RESPIRATOR AND BE JOINTLY APPROVED BY THE NATIONAL INSTITUTE FOR OCCUPATIONAL SAFETY AND HEALTH AND THE MINE SAFETY AND HEALTH ADMINISTRATION (NIOSH-MSHA).
CHEMICAL CARTRIDGE RESPIRATOR WITH AN ORGANIC VAPOR CARTRIDGE(S) IN COMBINATION WITH A DUST AND MIST FILTER.
GAS MASK WITH ORGANIC VAPOR CANISTER (CHIN-STYLE OR FRONT- OR BACK-MOUNTED CANISTER) WITH A DUST AND MIST FILTER.
GAS MASK WITH ORGANIC VAPOR CANISTER (CHIN-STYLE OR FRONT- OR BACK-MOUNTED CANISTER) WITH A PARTICULATE FILTER.
POWERED AIR-PURIFYING RESPIRATOR WITH A HIGH-EFFICIENCY FILTER.

TYPE 'C' SUPPLIED-AIR RESPIRATOR WITH A FULL FACEPIECE OPERATED IN A PRESSURE-DEMAND OR OTHER POSITIVE PRESSURE MODE.
SELF-CONTAINED BREATHING APPARATUS WITH A FULL FACEPIECE OPERATED IN PRESSURE-DEMAND OR OTHER POSITIVE PRESSURE MODE. FOR FIREFIGHTING AND OTHER IMMEDIATELY DANGEROUS TO LIFE OR HEALTH CONDITIONS:
SELF-CONTAINED BREATHING APPARATUS WITH FULL FACEPIECE OPERATED IN PRESSURE-DEMAND OR OTHER POSITIVE PRESSURE MODE.
SUPPLIED-AIR RESPIRATOR WITH FULL FACEPIECE AND OPERATED IN PRESSURE-DEMAND OR OTHER POSITIVE PRESSURE MODE IN COMBINATION WITH AN AUXILIARY SELF-CONTAINED BREATHING APPARATUS OPERATED IN PRESSURE-DEMAND OR OTHER POSITIVE PRESSURE MODE.

CLOTHING: EMPLOYEE MUST WEAR APPROPRIATE PROTECTIVE (IMPERVIOUS) CLOTHING AND EQUIPMENT TO PREVENT REPEATED OR PROLONGED SKIN CONTACT WITH THIS SUBSTANCE.

GLOVES: EMPLOYEE MUST WEAR APPROPRIATE PROTECTIVE GLOVES TO PREVENT CONTACT WITH THIS SUBSTANCE.

EYE PROTECTION: EMPLOYEE MUST WEAR SPLASH-PROOF OR DUST-RESISTANT SAFETY GOGGLES TO PREVENT EYE CONTACT WITH THIS SUBSTANCE.
EMERGENCY EYE WASH: WHERE THERE IS ANY POSSIBILITY THAT AN EMPLOYEE'S EYES MAY BE EXPOSED TO THIS SUBSTANCE, THE EMPLOYER SHOULD PROVIDE AN EYE WASH FOUNTAIN WITHIN THE IMMEDIATE WORK AREA FOR EMERGENCY USE.

AUTHORIZED BY- OCCUPATIONAL HEALTH SERVICES, INC.
CREATION DATE: 10/04/89 ***REVISION DATE:*** 05/08/90

MATERIAL SAFETY DATA SHEET

OCCUPATIONAL HEALTH SERVICES, INC.
AGRICULTURE AND PESTICIDE DIVISION
450 SEVENTH AVENUE, SUITE 2407
NEW YORK, NEW YORK 10123
1-800-445-MSDS OR (212) 967-1100

EMERGENCY CONTACT:
JOHN S. BRANSFORD, JR. (615) 292-1180

SUBSTANCE IDENTIFICATION

CAS-NUMBER 75-60-5

SUBSTANCE: **CACODYLIC ACID**

TRADE NAMES/SYNONYMS: HYDROXYDIMETHYLARSINE OXIDE; DIMETHYLARSINIC ACID; DIMETHYLHYDROXYARSINE OXIDE; ANSAR 138; ARSAN; SILVISAR 510; SYLVICOR; PHYTAR; SALVO; RAD-E-CATE; RCRA U136; UN 1572; ARSINIC ACID, DIMETHYL-; C2H7ASO2; PST03710

CHEMICAL FAMILY: ORGANIC ARSENIC

MOLECULAR FORMULA: C2-H7-AS-O2

MOLECULAR WEIGHT: 138.01

CERCLA RATINGS (SCALE 0-3): HEALTH=3 FIRE=0 REACTIVITY=0 PERSISTENCE=3

NFPA RATINGS (SCALE 0-4): HEALTH=3 FIRE=0 REACTIVITY=0

COMPONENTS AND CONTAMINANTS

COMPONENT: CACODYLIC ACID ***PERCENT:*** 100%
CAS# 75-60-5

OTHER CONTAMINANTS: NONE

EXPOSURE LIMITS: CACODYLIC ACID: 0.5 MG(AS)/M3 OSHA TWA 0.2 MG(AS)/M3 ACGIH TWA
1 POUND CERCLA SECTION 103 REPORTABLE QUANTITY SUBJECT TO SARA SECTION 313 ANNUAL TOXIC CHEMICAL RELEASE REPORTING SUBJECT TO CALIFORNIA PROPOSITION 65 CANCER AND/OR REPRODUCTIVE TOXICITY WARNING AND RELEASE REQUIREMENTS- (FEBRUARY 27, 1987)

PHYSICAL DATA

DESCRIPTION: COLORLESS PRISMS OR WHITE POWDER, HYGROSCOPIC WITH AN OFFENSIVE ODOR ***BOILING POINT:*** >392 F (>200 C)

MELTING POINT: 378 F (192 C) ***SPECIFIC GRAVITY:*** >1.1 ***PH:*** ACIDIC

SOLUBILITY IN WATER: 83% @ 22 C

SOLVENT SOLUBILITY: ETHANOL, ACETIC ACID;

FIRE AND EXPLOSION DATA

FIRE AND EXPLOSION HAZARD: NEGLIGIBLE FIRE HAZARD WHEN EXPOSED TO HEAT OR FLAME.

FIREFIGHTING MEDIA: DRY CHEMICAL, CARBON DIOXIDE, HALON, WATER SPRAY OR STANDARD FOAM (1987 EMERGENCY RESPONSE GUIDEBOOK, DOT P 5800.4).
FOR LARGER FIRES, USE WATER SPRAY, FOG OR STANDARD FOAM (1987 EMERGENCY RESPONSE GUIDEBOOK, DOT P 5800.4).

FIREFIGHTING: MOVE CONTAINER FROM FIRE AREA IF POSSIBLE. DO NOT SCATTER SPILLED MATERIAL WITH HIGH PRESSURE WATER STREAMS. DIKE FIRE CONTROL WATER FOR LATER DISPOSAL (1987 EMERGENCY RESPONSE GUIDEBOOK, DOT P 5800.4, GUIDE PAGE 31).
USE AGENTS SUITABLE FOR TYPE OF SURROUNDING FIRE. AVOID BREATHING HAZARDOUS VAPORS, KEEP UPWIND.

TOXICITY

CACODYLIC ACID: IRRITATION DATA: 2600 MG/M3/2 HOURS SKIN-MOUSE; 2600 MG/M3/2 HOURS EYE-MOUSE; 2600 MG/M3/2 HOURS SKIN-RAT; 2600 MG/M3/2 HOURS EYE-RAT. TOXICITY DATA: 3900 MG/M3 INHALATION-RAT LC50 (IARC); 644 MG/KG ORAL-RAT LD50; 500 MG/KG INTRAPERITONEAL-MOUSE LD50; 185 MG/KG UNREPORTED-MOUSE LD50; MUTAGENIC DATA (RTECS); REPRODUCTIVE EFFECTS DATA (RTECS); TUMORIGENIC DATA (RTECS). CARCINOGEN STATUS: NONE. NO ADEQUATE DATA ON ORGANIC ARSENICALS WERE AVAILABLE FOR EVALUATION. LOCAL EFFECTS: IRRITANT- INHALATION, SKIN, AND EYE. ACUTE TOXICITY LEVEL: TOXIC BY INHALATION; MODERATELY TOXIC BY INGESTION. TARGET EFFECTS: POISONING MAY AFFECT THE HEART, KIDNEYS, DIGESTIVE TRACT, AND SKIN.

HEALTH EFFECTS AND FIRST AID

INHALATION: CACODYLIC ACID: IRRITANT/TOXIC. **ACUTE EXPOSURE-** FORESTRY WORKERS EXPOSED TO DIMETHYLARSENIC ACID HERBICIDES HAD ELEVATED URINARY LEVELS OF ARSENIC, BUT NO CLINICAL SIGNS OF TOXICITY WERE REPORTED. IN RATS, CACODYLIC ACID IS ABSORBED MORE READILY BY INHALATION THAN INGESTION, AND MODERATE DOSES ARE LETHAL. IN PERSONS EXPOSED TO SUFFICIENT ARSENICAL DUST, THE ONSET OF ILLNESS IS USUALLY CHARACTERIZED BY DYSPNEA WITH OPPRESSION AND PAIN IN THE CHEST, FOLLOWED BY NAUSEA AND DIARRHEA. SEVERE ARSENIC POISONING CAUSES VOMITING, PROFUSE AND WATERY DIARRHEA FOLLOWED BY DEHYDRATION, ELECTROLYTE IMBALANCE, GRADUAL FALL IN BLOOD PRESSURE AND POSSIBLE DEATH WITHIN 3 TO 14 DAYS. OTHER PERSISTANT SEQUELLAE OF ARSENIC POISONING INCLUDE: GARLIC ODOR TO THE BREATH, URINE AND SWEAT, CIRRHOSIS OF THE LIVER, HYPOPLASTIC BONE MARROW, RENAL INSUFFICIENCY AND LOSS OF SENSORY AND MOTOR FUNCTIONS. **CHRONIC EXPOSURE-** EXCESSIVE INHALATION OF ARSENICAL DUSTS MAY CAUSE COUGHING, RHINITIS, PULMONARY IRRITATION, BRONCHITIS OR PNEUMONIA.

FIRST AID- REMOVE FROM EXPOSURE AREA TO FRESH AIR IMMEDIATELY. IF BREATHING HAS STOPPED, PERFORM ARTIFICIAL RESPIRATION. KEEP PERSON WARM AND AT REST. TREAT SYMPTOMATICALLY AND SUPPORTIVELY. GET MEDICAL ATTENTION IMMEDIATELY.

SKIN CONTACT: CACODYLIC ACID: IRRITANT. **ACUTE EXPOSURE-** DIRECT CONTACT MAY CAUSE IRRITATION, WHICH MAY BE GREATER IN THE PRESENCE OF IMPURITIES. EXCESSIVE EXPOSURE MAY RESULT IN ABSORPTION OF TOXIC AMOUNTS AND MAY PRODUCE DERMATITIS OR SKIN ERUPTIONS. **CHRONIC EXPOSURE-** REPEATED OR PROLONGED EXPOSURE TO ARSENICALS MAY PRODUCE ERYTHEMATOUS, PUSTULAR OR ULCERATIVE DERMATITIS, PERHAPS DUE TO LOCAL ACTION ON CAPILLARIES.

FIRST AID- REMOVE CONTAMINATED CLOTHING AND SHOES IMMEDIATELY. WASH AFFECTED AREA WITH SOAP OR MILD DETERGENT AND LARGE AMOUNTS OF WATER UNTIL NO EVIDENCE OF CHEMICAL REMAINS (APPROXIMATELY 15-20 MINUTES). GET MEDICAL ATTENTION IMMEDIATELY.

EYE CONTACT: CACODYLIC ACID: IRRITANT. **ACUTE EXPOSURE-** DUST MAY CAUSE IRRITATION. **CHRONIC EXPOSURE-** MAY CAUSE CONJUNCTIVITIS. PROLONGED EXPOSURE TO ARSENICALS HAS CAUSED ERUPTIONS OF EYELIDS, CONJUNCTIVA AND EVEN THE CORNEA.

FIRST AID- WASH EYES IMMEDIATELY WITH LARGE AMOUNTS OF WATER OR NORMAL SALINE, OCCASIONALLY LIFTING UPPER AND LOWER LIDS, UNTIL NO EVIDENCE OF CHEMICAL REMAINS (APPROXIMATELY 15-20 MINUTES). GET MEDICAL ATTENTION IMMEDIATELY.

INGESTION: CACODYLIC ACID: **ACUTE EXPOSURE-** METHYLATED PENTAVALENT ARSENICALS ARE CONSIDERABLY LESS TOXIC THAN TRIVALENT INORGANIC ARSENICALS. IN FACT, METHYLATION IS THE PRINCIPLE MECHANISM OF DETOXIFICATION AND ELIMINATION OF INORGANIC ARSENICAL IN MAMMALS. HOWEVER, ARSENIC MAY BE RELEASED SLOWLY, PERHAPS DUE TO GASTRIC PH OR INTESTINAL BACTERIAL ACTION, TO PRODUCE DELAYED ARSENIC POISONING. ARSENIC POISONING CAUSES DILATION AND INCREASED PERMEABILITY OF CAPILLARIES, ESPECIALLY IN THE INTESTINAL TRACT REGARDLESS OF THE ROUTE OF EXPOSURE. LOCAL ACTION ON CAPILLARIES CAN CAUSE CONGESTION AND STASIS, THROMBOSIS, ISCHEMIA AND NECROSIS. SEVERE ARSENIC POISONING MAY CAUSE VOMITING, PROFUSE AND WATERY DIARRHEA FOLLOWED BY DEHYDRATION, ELECTROLYTE IMBALANCE, GRADUALLY FALLING BLOOD PRESSURE

AND POSSIBLE DEATH WITHIN 3 TO 14 DAYS. IF THE ACUTE PHASE IS SURVIVED, SKIN ERUPTIONS MAY OCCUR AND PROGRESS TO EXFOLIATIVE DERMATITIS. DERMATITIS MAY BE PROMINENT ON THE PALMS AND SOLES. WHITE TRANSVERSE BANDS IN THE NAILS FREQUENTLY APPEAR IN ABOUT 6 WEEKS AND ACCOMPANY POLYNEUROPATHY, WHICH OFTEN APPEARS IN 1 TO 3 WEEKS AFTER EXPOSURE. POLYNEUROPATHY INVOLVES PARATHESIS, PAIN, BURNING AND TENDERNESS OF AFFECTED LIMBS. PERIPHERAL CIRCULATORY DIFFICULTY CHARACTERIZED BY BLANCHING OR FLUSHING SKIN MAY OCCUR, ESPECIALLY IN THE FINGERS. OTHER PERSISTENT SEQUELLAE OF ARSENIC POISONING INCLUDE: A GARLIC ODOR IMPARTED TO BREATH, URINE, AND SWEAT, CIRRHOSIS, HYPOPLASTIC BONE MARROW, RENAL INSUFFICIENCY AND LOSS OF SENSORY AND MOTOR FUNCTIONS. **CHRONIC EXPOSURE**- REPEATED EXPOSURE TO LOW LEVELS OF ARSENIC MAY PRODUCE INCREASED TOLERANCE FOR ARSENIC. ARSENIC COMPOUNDS ACCUMULATE IN THE SKIN, HAIR AND NAILS. SIGNS OF CHRONIC ARSENIC POISONING INCLUDE LOSS OF APPETITE, WEIGHT LOSS, WEAKNESS, NAUSEA, ALTERNATING DIARRHEA AND CONSTIPATION, COLIC, PERIPHERAL NEUROPATHY, DERMATITIS, DYSCHROMIA, HYPERKERATOSIS OF PLANTAR SURFACES, ALOPECIA, GIDDINESS AND HEADACHE. PROLONGED EXPOSURE MAY CAUSE GRADUAL MENTAL AND PHYSICAL DETERIORATION AND A STATE OF CACHEXIA. POLYNEUROPATHY, SIMILAR TO ACUTE EXPOSURE, MAY OCCUR, AS WELL AS DISTURBANCES OF SIGHT, TASTE, SMELL AND BLADDER FUNCTION. EXPOSURE TO ARSENIC HAS BEEN ASSOCIATED WITH INCREASED INCIDENCE OF SKIN AND OTHER CANCERS. ORAL DOSES TO RATS AND MICE DURING PREGNANCY HAVE PRODUCED EMBRYOTOXICITY AND DEVELOPMENTAL CHANGES IN THE EMBRYOS.

FIRST AID- REMOVE BY GASTRIC LAVAGE OR EMESIS. FOLLOW WITH A SALINE CATHARTIC. MAINTAIN BLOOD PRESSURE, AIRWAY, AND GIVE OXYGEN IF RESPIRATION IS DEPRESSED. DO NOT PERFORM GASTRIC LAVAGE OR EMESIS IF VICTIM IS UNCONSCIOUS. GET MEDICAL ATTENTION IMMEDIATELY. (DREISBACH, HANDBOOK OF POISONING, 12TH ED.) ADMINISTRATION OF GASTRIC LAVAGE OR OXYGEN SHOULD BE PERFORMED BY QUALIFIED MEDICAL PERSONNEL.

ANTIDOTE: THE FOLLOWING ANTIDOTE HAS BEEN RECOMMENDED. HOWEVER, THE DECISION AS TO WHETHER THE SEVERITY OF POISONING REQUIRES ADMINISTRATION OF ANY ANTIDOTE AND ACTUAL DOSE REQUIRED SHOULD BE MADE BY QUALIFIED MEDICAL PERSONNEL.

ARSENIC POISONING: GIVE DIMERCAPROL, 3 MG/KG (OR 0.3 ML/KG) EVERY 4 HOURS FOR 2 DAYS AND THEN 2 MG/KG EVERY 2 HOURS FOR A TOTAL OF 10 DAYS. DIMERCAPROL IS AVAILABLE AS A 10% SOLUTION IN OIL FOR INTRAMUSCULAR ADMINISTRATION. NEXT, GIVE PENICILLAMINE, UP TO 100 MG/KG/DAY (MAXIMUM 1 G/DAY) DIVIDED INTO 4 DOSES FOR NO LONGER THAN 1 WEEK. IF A LONGER ADMINISTRATION PERIOD IS WARRANTED, DOSAGE SHOULD NOT EXCEED 40 MG/KG/DAY. GIVE THE DRUG ORALLY HALF AN HOUR BEFORE MEALS. DISCONTINUE ANTIDOTE WHEN URINE ARSENIC LEVEL FALLS BELOW 50 UG/24 HR. (DREISBACH, HANDBOOK OF POISONING, 12TH ED.). ANITDOTE SHOULD BE ADMINISTERED BY QUALIFIED MEDICAL PERSONNEL.

REACTIVITY

REACTIVITY: STABLE UNDER NORMAL TEMPERATURES AND PRESSURES.

INCOMPATIBILITIES: CACODYLIC ACID: ACIDS: REACTS TO RELEASE EXTREMELY TOXIC DIMETHYL ARSINE. ACTIVE METALS (FE, AL, ZN): WHEN IN AQUEOUS SOLUTION REACTS TO RELEASE TOXIC ARSENIC FUMES. STRONG OXIDIZERS: REACTS. AIR: MAY CAUSE OXIDIZATION.

DECOMPOSITION: THERMAL DECOMPOSITION PRODUCTS MAY INCLUDE TOXIC OXIDES OF ARSENIC AND CARBON.

POLYMERIZATION: HAZARDOUS POLYMERIZATION HAS NOT BEEN REPORTED TO OCCUR UNDER NORMAL TEMPERATURES AND PRESSURES.

STORAGE AND DISPOSAL

OBSERVE ALL FEDERAL, STATE AND LOCAL REGULATIONS WHEN STORING OR DISPOSING OF THIS SUBSTANCE. FOR ASSISTANCE, CONTACT THE DISTRICT DIRECTOR OF THE ENVIRONMENTAL PROTECTION AGENCY.

CONDITIONS TO AVOID

MAY BURN BUT DOES NOT IGNITE READILY.

SPILL AND LEAK PROCEDURES

WATER SPILL: THE CALIFORNIA SAFE DRINKING WATER AND TOXIC ENFORCEMENT ACT OF 1986 (PROPOSITION 65) PROHIBITS CONTAMINATING ANY KNOWN SOURCE OF DRINKING WATER WITH SUBSTANCES KNOWN TO CAUSE CANCER AND/OR REPRODUCTIVE TOXICITY.

OCCUPATIONAL SPILL: DO NOT TOUCH SPILLED MATERIAL. STOP LEAK IF YOU CAN DO IT WITHOUT RISK. FOR SMALL SPILLS, TAKE UP WITH SAND OR OTHER ABSORBENT MATERIAL AND PLACE INTO CONTAINERS FOR LATER DISPOSAL. FOR SMALL DRY SPILLS, WITH A CLEAN SHOVEL PLACE MATERIAL INTO CLEAN, DRY CONTAINER AND COVER. MOVE CONTAINERS FROM SPILL AREA. FOR LARGER SPILLS, DIKE FAR AHEAD OF SPILL FOR LATER DISPOSAL. KEEP UNNECESSARY PEOPLE AWAY. ISOLATE HAZARD AREA AND DENY ENTRY.

REPORTABLE QUANTITY (RQ): 1 POUND THE SUPERFUND AMENDMENTS AND REAUTHORIZATION ACT (SARA) SECTION 304 REQUIRES THAT A RELEASE EQUAL TO OR GREATER THAN THE REPORTABLE QUANTITY FOR THIS SUBSTANCE BE IMMEDIATELY REPORTED TO THE LOCAL EMERGENCY PLANNING COMMITTEE AND THE STATE EMERGENCY RESPONSE COMMISSION (40 CFR 355.40). IF THE RELEASE OF THIS SUBSTANCE IS REPORTABLE UNDER CERCLA SECTION 103, THE NATIONAL RESPONSE CENTER MUST BE NOTIFIED IMMEDIATELY AT (800) 424-8802 OR (202) 426-2675 IN THE METROPOLITAN WASHINGTON, D.C. AREA (40 CFR 302.6).

PROTECTIVE EQUIPMENT

VENTILATION: PROVIDE LOCAL EXHAUST OR PROCESS ENCLOSURE VENTILATION TO MEET PUBLISHED EXPOSURE LIMITS.

RESPIRATOR: THE FOLLOWING RESPIRATORS ARE RECOMMENDED BASED ON INFORMATION FOUND IN THE PHYSICAL DATA, TOXICITY AND HEALTH EFFECTS SECTIONS. THEY ARE RANKED IN ORDER FROM MINIMUM TO MAXIMUM RESPIRATORY PROTECTION. THE SPECIFIC RESPIRATOR SELECTED MUST BE BASED ON CONTAMINATION LEVELS FOUND IN THE WORK PLACE, MUST NOT EXCEED THE WORKING LIMITS OF THE RESPIRATOR AND BE JOINTLY APPROVED BY THE NATIONAL INSTITUTE FOR OCCUPATIONAL SAFETY AND HEALTH AND THE MINE SAFETY AND HEALTH ADMINISTRATION (NIOSH-MSHA).

AT ANY DETECTABLE CONCENTRATION:

SELF-CONTAINED BREATHING APPARATUS WITH FULL FACEPIECE OPERATED IN PRESSURE-DEMAND OR OTHER POSITIVE PRESSURE MODE. SUPPLIED-AIR RESPIRATOR WITH FULL FACEPIECE OPERATED IN PRESSURE-DEMAND OR OTHER POSITIVE PRESSURE MODE IN COMBINATION WITH AN AUXILIARY SELF-CONTAINED BREATHING APPARATUS OPERATED IN PRESSURE-DEMAND OR OTHER POSITIVE PRESSURE MODE.

ESCAPE- AIR-PURIFYING FULL FACEPIECE RESPIRATOR (GAS MASK) WITH A CHIN-STYLE OR FRONT- OR BACK-MOUNTED ACID GAS CANISTER HAVING A HIGH-EFFICIENCY PARTICULATE FILTER. ESCAPE-TYPE SELF-CONTAINED BREATHING APPARATUS.

FOR FIREFIGHTING AND OTHER IMMEDIATELY DANGEROUS TO LIFE OR HEALTH CONDITIONS:

SELF-CONTAINED BREATHING APPARATUS WITH FULL FACEPIECE OPERATED IN PRESSURE-DEMAND OR OTHER POSITIVE PRESSURE MODE.

SUPPLIED-AIR RESPIRATOR WITH FULL FACEPIECE AND OPERATED IN PRESSURE-DEMAND OR OTHER POSITIVE PRESSURE MODE IN COMBINATION WITH AN AUXILIARY SELF-CONTAINED BREATHING APPARATUS OPERATED IN PRESSURE-DEMAND OR OTHER POSITIVE PRESSURE MODE.

CLOTHING: EMPLOYEE MUST WEAR APPROPRIATE PROTECTIVE (IMPERVIOUS) CLOTHING AND EQUIPMENT TO PREVENT REPEATED OR PROLONGED SKIN CONTACT WITH THIS SUBSTANCE.

GLOVES: EMPLOYEE MUST WEAR APPROPRIATE PROTECTIVE GLOVES TO PREVENT CONTACT WITH THIS SUBSTANCE.

EYE PROTECTION: EMPLOYEE MUST WEAR SPLASH-PROOF OR DUST-RESISTANT SAFETY GOGGLES TO PREVENT EYE CONTACT WITH THIS SUBSTANCE.

EMERGENCY EYE WASH: WHERE THERE IS ANY POSSIBILITY THAT AN EMPLOYEE'S EYES MAY BE EXPOSED TO THIS SUBSTANCE, THE EMPLOYER SHOULD PROVIDE AN EYE WASH FOUNTAIN WITHIN THE IMMEDIATE WORK AREA FOR EMERGENCY USE.

AUTHORIZED BY- OCCUPATIONAL HEALTH SERVICES, INC.

CREATION DATE: 10/04/89 ***REVISION DATE:*** 05/18/90

MATERIAL SAFETY DATA SHEET

OCCUPATIONAL HEALTH SERVICES, INC.
AGRICULTURE AND PESTICIDE DIVISION
450 SEVENTH AVENUE, SUITE 2407
NEW YORK, NEW YORK 10123
1-800-445-MSDS OR (212) 967-1100

EMERGENCY CONTACT:
JOHN S. BRANSFORD, JR. (615) 292-1180

SUBSTANCE IDENTIFICATION

CAS-NUMBER 10108-64-2

SUBSTANCE: **CADMIUM CHLORIDE**

TRADE NAMES/SYNONYMS: CADMIUM DICHLORIDE; DICHLOROCADMIUM; STCC 4962505; CADMIUM CHLORIDE (CDCL2); CDCL2; PST03740

CHEMICAL FAMILY: INORGANIC SALT

MOLECULAR FORMULA: CD-CL2

MOLECULAR WEIGHT: 183.32

CERCLA RATINGS (SCALE 0-3): HEALTH=3 FIRE=0 REACTIVITY=0 PERSISTENCE=1
NFPA RATINGS (SCALE 0-4): HEALTH=3 FIRE=0 REACTIVITY=0

COMPONENTS AND CONTAMINANTS

COMPONENT: CADMIUM CHLORIDE ***PERCENT:*** 100.0
CAS# 10108-64-2
OTHER CONTAMINANTS: NONE
EXPOSURE LIMITS: CADMIUM: * OSHA EXPOSURE LIMIT REMOVED AS PER OSHA INSTRUCTION PUB 8-1.4 0.05 MG(CD)/M3 ACGIH TWA (DUST, SALTS) (NOTICE OF INTENDED CHANGES 1987-1988) LOWEST FEASIBLE LIMIT NIOSH RECOMMENDED EXPOSURE CRITERIA
SUBJECT TO SARA SECTION 313 ANNUAL TOXIC CHEMICAL RELEASE REPORTING
SUBJECT TO CALIFORNIA PROPOSITION 65 CANCER AND/OR REPRODUCTIVE TOXICITY WARNING AND RELEASE REQUIREMENTS- (OCTOBER 1, 1987)
CADMIUM CHLORIDE: 10 POUNDS CERCLA SECTION 103 REPORTABLE QUANTITY

PHYSICAL DATA

DESCRIPTION: ODORLESS, COLORLESS OR WHITE, HYGROSCOPIC, HEXAGONAL, CRYSTALLINE SOLID.
BOILING POINT: 1760 F (960 C) ***MELTING POINT:*** 1054 F (568 C)
SPECIFIC GRAVITY: 4.047 @ 25 C ***VAPOR PRESSURE:*** 10 MMHG @ 656 C
SOLUBILITY IN WATER: 140% @ 20 C
SOLVENT SOLUBILITY: SOLUBLE IN ACETONE; SLIGHTLY SOLUBLE IN ETHANOL, METHANOL; INSOLUBLE IN ETHER.

FIRE AND EXPLOSION DATA

FIRE AND EXPLOSION HAZARD: NEGLIGIBLE FIRE HAZARD WHEN EXPOSED TO HEAT OR FLAME.
FIREFIGHTING MEDIA: DRY CHEMICAL, CARBON DIOXIDE, HALON, WATER SPRAY OR STANDARD FOAM (1987 EMERGENCY RESPONSE GUIDEBOOK, DOT P 5800.4).
FOR LARGER FIRES, USE WATER SPRAY, FOG OR STANDARD FOAM (1987 EMERGENCY RESPONSE GUIDEBOOK, DOT P 5800.4).
FIREFIGHTING: MOVE CONTAINERS FROM FIRE AREA IF POSSIBLE (1987 EMERGENCY RESPONSE GUIDEBOOK, DOT P 5800.4, GUIDE PAGE 53).
EXTINGUISH USING AGENTS SUITABLE FOR TYPE OF FIRE. AVOID BREATHING POISONOUS VAPORS, KEEP UPWIND.

TOXICITY

CADMIUM CHLORIDE: TOXICITY DATA: ANHYDROUS: 3 GM/KG ORAL-WOMAN LDLO; 88 MG/KG ORAL-RAT LD50; 60 MG/KG ORAL-MOUSE LD50; 70 MG/KG ORAL-RABBIT LDLO; 63 MG/KG ORAL-GUINEA PIG LD50; 233 MG/KG SKIN-GUINEA PIG LDLO; 420 MG/M3/30 MINUTES INHALATION-DOG LC90; 2300 MG/M3 INHALATION-MOUSE LC50; 6 MG/KG SUBCUTANEOUS-RAT LDLO; 3200 UG/KG SUBCUTANEOUS-MOUSE LD50; 18 MG/KG SUBCUTANEOUS-RABBIT LDLO; 25 MG/KG SUBCUTANEOUS-CAT LDLO; 7500 UG/KG SUBCUTANEOUS-GERBIL LDLO; 5 MG/KG INTRAVENOUS-CAT LDLO; 5 MG/KG INTRAVENOUS-DOG LDLO; 3500 UG/KG INTRAVENOUS-MOUSE LD50; 2 MG/KG INTRAVENOUS-RABBIT LDLO; 1800 UG/KG INTRAPERITONEAL-RAT LD50; 9300 UG/KG INTRAPERITONEAL-MOUSE LD50; 233 MG/KG INTRAPERITONEAL-GUINEA PIG LDLO; 88 MG/KG UNREPORTED-MAMMAL LD50; MUTAGENIC DATA (RTECS); REPRODUCTIVE EFFECTS DATA (RTECS); TUMORIGENIC DATA (RTECS). MONOHYDRATE: REPRODUCTIVE EFFECTS DATA (RTECS); TUMORIGENIC DATA (RTECS). DIHYDRATE: REPRODUCTIVE EFFECTS DATA (RTECS); TUMORIGENIC DATA (RTECS). HYDRATE (2:5): 194 MG/KG ORAL-MOUSE LD50; 7 MG/KG INTRAPERITONEAL-MOUSE LD50; MUTAGENIC DATA (RTECS); REPRODUCTIVE EFFECTS DATA (RTECS). CARCINOGEN STATUS: ANTICIPATED HUMAN CARCINOGEN (NTP); HUMAN LIMITED EVIDENCE, ANIMAL SUFFICIENT EVIDENCE (IARC GROUP-2A). MALE RATS EXPOSED CONTINUOUSLY TO CADMIUM CHLORIDE AEROSOLS DEVELOPED A DOSE-RELATED INCREASE IN LUNG CANCERS. TESTICULAR ATROPHY FOLLOWED BY TESTICULAR TUMORS OCCURRED IN RATS AND MICE AND LOCAL SARCOMAS OCCURRED IN RATS FOLLOWING SUBCUTANEOUS ADMINISTRATION. STUDIES HAVE SUGGESTED THAT HUMAN EXPOSURE TO CADMIUM IN SOME FORM (PRIMARILY THE OXIDE) IS ASSOCIATED WITH INCREASED RISKS OF PROSTATIC AND RESPIRATORY CANCERS. LOCAL EFFECTS: IRRITANT- EYE, SKIN, MUCOUS MEMBRANES. ACUTE TOXICITY LEVEL: TOXIC BY INHALATION AND INGESTION. TARGET EFFECTS: POISONING MAY AFFECT THE KIDNEYS, BONE, BLOOD AND LIVER, AND THE RESPIRATORY, NERVOUS, CARDIOVASCULAR AND GASTROINTESTINAL SYSTEMS. AT INCREASED RISK FROM EXPOSURE: PERSONS WITH KIDNEY, LIVER, OR RESPIRATORY DISORDERS. ADDITIONAL INFORMATION: NEITHER EYE NOR RESPIRATORY IRRITATION IS ENOUGH TO PREVENT EXPOSURE WHICH MAY CAUSE SERIOUS SYSTEMIC POISONING.

HEALTH EFFECTS AND FIRST AID

INHALATION: CADMIUM CHLORIDE: CARCINOGEN/TOXIC. SEE INFORMATION ON CADMIUM COMPOUNDS. RATS EXPOSED TO CADMIUM CHLORIDE AEROSOLS BY INHALATION ALMOST CONTINUOUSLY FOR 18 MONTHS, AND OBSERVED FOR AN ADDITIONAL 13 MONTHS, DEVELOPED PRIMARY LUNG CARCINOMAS IN 71% OF THOSE EXPOSED TO 50 UG/M3, 52.6% EXPOSED TO 25 UG/M3, AND 15.4% EXPOSED TO 12.5 UG/M3. REPRODUCTIVE EFFECTS HAVE BEEN REPORTED IN ANIMALS.
CADMIUM COMPOUNDS: NEPHROTOXIN. **ACUTE EXPOSURE-** EXPOSURE TO SUFFICIENTLY HIGH CONCENTRATIONS OF CADMIUM DUSTS MAY RESULT IN UPPER RESPIRATORY TRACT IRRITATION WITH DELAYED SYMPTOMS OF COUGH, CHEST PAIN, DIZZINESS, ABDOMINAL PAIN, NAUSEA AND VOMITING. SEVERE EXPOSURES MAY RESULT IN LUNG, KIDNEY OR LIVER DAMAGE OR DEATH FROM MASSIVE PULMONARY EDEMA. **CHRONIC EXPOSURE-** CADMIUM IS HIGHLY CUMULATIVE AND RESPIRATORY EFFECTS FROM REPEATED OR PROLONGED EXPOSURE TO DUSTS OR FUMES MAY INCLUDE RHINITIS, BRONCHITIS, EMPHYSEMA, COUGH, DYSPNEA, ABNORMAL LUNG FUNCTION, OBSTRUCTIVE DISEASE, AND POSSIBLY FIBROSIS. ULCERATION OF THE NASAL SEPTUM AND YELLOW DISCOLORATION OF THE TEETH MAY OCCUR. CADMIUM INDUCED KIDNEY DAMAGE IS IRREVERSIBLE AND MAY PROGRESS AFTER EXPOSURE CEASES; SOME CASES OF PROGRESSION TO KIDNEY FAILURE HAVE BEEN DESCRIBED. PROTEINURIA IS USUALLY THE FIRST SIGN OF DAMAGE AND MAY BE ASSOCIATED WITH GLUCOSURIA, AMINOACIDURIA, DECREASED CONCENTRATING CAPACITY, INCREASED EXCRETION OF CALCIUM AND PHOSPHORUS, AND DECREASED CREATININE EXCRETION. CALCIURIA MAY FAVOR THE DEVELOPMENT OF KIDNEY STONES. OSTEOMALACIA, OSTEOPOROSIS, AND SPONTANEOUS AND PSUEDOFRACTURES MAY OCCUR AND MAY BE MANIFESTED AS BACK PAIN, PAIN IN THE EXTREMITIES, DIFFICULTY IN WALKING, AND PAIN ON BONE PRESSURE. OTHER EFFECTS MAY INCLUDE IRRITABILITY, WEIGHT LOSS, FATIGUE, MILD TO MODERATE ANEMIA, EOSINOPHILIA, DAMAGE TO THE OLFACTORY NERVE WITH ANOSMIA, AND LIVER DAMAGE. AN EPIDEMIOLOGICAL STUDY SUGGESTS A RELATIONSHIP BETWEEN CADMIUM LEVELS IN AIR AND CARDIOVASCULAR DISEASE, BUT A CAUSAL ASSOCIATION HAS NOT BEEN PROVED. OCCUPATIONAL EXPOSURE TO CADMIUM IS IMPLICATED IN A SIGNIFICANT INCREASE IN THE INCIDENCE OF PROSTATIC AND RESPIRATORY CANCERS. ONE STUDY ALSO REPORTS A SIGNIFICANT INCREASE IN RENAL CANCERS IN THOSE WITH INFERRED OCCUPATIONAL EXPOSURE TO CADMIUM.
FIRST AID- REMOVE FROM EXPOSURE AREA TO FRESH AIR IMMEDIATELY. IF BREATHING HAS STOPPED, PERFORM ARTIFICIAL RESPIRATION. KEEP PERSON WARM AND AT REST. TREAT SYMPTOMATICALLY AND SUPPORTIVELY. GET MEDICAL ATTENTION IMMEDIATELY.

SKIN CONTACT: CADMIUM CHLORIDE: IRRITANT. **ACUTE EXPOSURE-** A 2% AQUEOUS SOLUTION WAS TESTED FOR SENSITIVITY ON 1502 PATIENTS, 25 (1.7%) HAD A REACTION WHICH INVESTIGATORS ATTRIBUTED TO AN IRRITANT EFFECT. SKIN ABSORPTION MAY OCCUR AND CAUSE CADMIUM POISONING AS DETAILED IN ACUTE INGESTION. **CHRONIC EXPOSURE-** REPEATED OR PROLONGED EXPOSURE TO IRRITANTS MAY RESULT IN DERMATITIS.
FIRST AID- REMOVE CONTAMINATED CLOTHING AND SHOES IMMEDIATELY. WASH AFFECTED AREA WITH SOAP OR MILD DETERGENT AND LARGE AMOUNTS OF WATER UNTIL NO EVIDENCE OF CHEMICAL REMAINS (APPROXIMATELY 15-20 MINUTES). GET MEDICAL ATTENTION IMMEDIATELY.

EYE CONTACT: CADMIUM CHLORIDE: IRRITANT. **ACUTE EXPOSURE-** MAY CAUSE IRRITATION. AQUEOUS SOLUTIONS APPLIED TO RABBIT EYES FOR 10 MINUTES AFTER MECHANICAL REMOVAL OF THE CORNEAL EPITHELIUM CAUSED TOTAL OPACIFICATION AND SCARRING OF THE CORNEA. **CHRONIC EXPOSURE-** REPEATED OR PROLONGED CONTACT WITH IRRITANTS MAY RESULT IN CONJUNCTIVITIS.
FIRST AID- WASH EYES IMMEDIATELY WITH LARGE AMOUNTS OF WATER OR NORMAL SALINE, OCCASIONALLY LIFTING UPPER AND LOWER LIDS, UNTIL NO EVIDENCE OF CHEMICAL REMAINS (APPROXIMATELY 15-20 MINUTES). GET MEDICAL ATTENTION IMMEDIATELY.

INGESTION: CADMIUM CHLORIDE: TOXIC. SEE INFORMATION ON CADMIUM COMPOUNDS. A INGESTION OF 150 GRAMS OF CADMIUM CHLORIDE PRODUCED FACIAL EDEMA, VOMITING, HYPOTENSION, RESPIRATORY ARREST, METABOLIC ACIDOSIS, PULMONARY EDEMA, OLIGURIA AND FINALLY DEATH 30 HOURS AFTER INGESTION. WHEN CADMIUM CHLORIDE WAS ADMINISTERED IN THE DRINKING WATER TO RATS FOR PROLONGED PERIODS, A 50% REDUCTION IN HEMOGLOBIN WAS FOUND. REPRODUCTIVE EFFECTS HAVE BEEN REPORTED IN ANIMALS.
CADMIUM COMPOUNDS: NEPHROTOXIN. **ACUTE EXPOSURE-** THE PERSISTENT VOMITING INDUCED BY CADMIUM COMPOUNDS MAY LIMIT THE AMOUNT RETAINED, BUT IF SUFFICIENT AMOUNTS ARE ABSORBED, SYMPTOMS OF SYSTEMIC TOXICITY MAY BEGIN WITHIN 15 MINUTES TO 2 HOURS. SALIVATION, CHOKING, SEVERE NAUSEA, ABDOMINAL PAIN, DIARRHEA, TENESMUS, BLURRED VISION, DIZZINESS, HEADACHE, MUSCULAR CRAMPS, EXHAUSTION, COLLAPSE, SHOCK, UNCONSCIOUSNESS AND RARELY, CONVULSIONS MAY OCCUR. RECOVERY MAY BEGIN WITHIN 5-10 HOURS; SEQUELAE MAY INCLUDE DELAYED LIVER AND KIDNEY DAMAGE. SINGLE DOSES OF 10-20 MG OF SOLUBLE CADMIUM

SALTS HAVE INDUCED SEVERE TOXIC EFFECTS AND DOSES ABOVE 300 MG MAY BE FATAL. DEATH DUE TO SHOCK AND DEHYDRATION MAY OCCUR WITHIN 24 HOURS OR MAY BE DELAYED 7-14 DAYS AND BE DUE TO RENAL FAILURE OR CARDIOPULMONARY DEPRESSION. **CHRONIC EXPOSURE-** CADMIUM IS HIGHLY CUMULATIVE AND PROLONGED LOW LEVEL EXPOSURE MAY CAUSE IRREVERSIBLE RENAL TUBULAR DYSFUNCTION AND BONE EFFECTS AS DESCRIBED IN CHRONIC INHALATION. CHRONIC EXPOSURE TO CADMIUM IN WATER AS THE CHLORIDE CAUSED HYPERTENSION IN RATS. FUNCTIONAL CHANGES IN THE LIVER, PANCREAS AND ADRENAL GLANDS HAVE ALSO BEEN REPORTED IN ANIMALS.

FIRST AID- IF EXTENSIVE VOMITING HAS NOT OCCURRED, THE SUBSTANCE SHOULD BE REMOVED BY EMESIS OR GASTRIC LAVAGE PROVIDED THAT THE PATIENT IS CONSCIOUS AND CONVULSIONS ARE NOT PRESENT. KEEP HEAD BELOW HIPS DURING VOMITING TO PREVENT ASPIRATION. DO NOT ATTEMPT TO MAKE AN UNCONSCIOUS PERSON VOMIT. TREAT SYMPTOMATICALLY AND SUPPORTIVELY. GET MEDICAL ATTENTION IMMEDIATELY (DREISBACH, HANDBOOK OF POISONING, 12TH ED.). TREATMENT SHOULD BE PERFORMED BY QUALIFIED MEDICAL PERSONNEL.

ANTIDOTE: THE FOLLOWING ANTIDOTE HAS BEEN RECOMMENDED. HOWEVER, THE DECISION AS TO WHETHER THE SEVERITY OF POISONING REQUIRES ADMINISTRATION OF ANY ANTIDOTE AND ACTUAL DOSE REQUIRED SHOULD BE MADE BY QUALIFIED MEDICAL PERSONNEL.

CADMIUM POISONING: DO NOT GIVE DIMERCAPROL (BAL). IF SYMPTOMS PERSIST, THE ADMINISTRATION OF CALCIUM DISODIUM EDETATE IS RECOMMENDED. GIVE 15-25 MG/KG (0.08-0.125 ML OF 20% SOLUTION PER KILOGRAM OF BODY WEIGHT) IN 250-500 ML OF 5% DEXTROSE INTRAVENOUSLY OVER A 1 TO 2 HOUR PERIOD, TWICE DAILY. THE MAXIMUM DOSE SHOULD NOT EXCEED 50 MG/KG/DAY. THE DRUG SHOULD BE GIVEN IN 5-DAY COURSES WITH A REST PERIOD OF AT LEAST 2 DAYS BETWEEN COURSES. AFTER THE FIRST COURSE, SUBSEQUENT COURSES SHOULD NOT EXCEED 50 MG/KG/DAY. DAILY URINALYSES SHOULD BE DONE DURING THE TREATMENT PERIOD. THE DOSAGE SHOULD BE REDUCED IF ANY UNUSUAL URINARY FINDINGS APPEAR. FOR INTRAMUSCULAR ADMINISTRATION, GIVE 20% SOLUTION (200 MG/ML), 12.5 MG/KG BODY WEIGHT EVERY 4-6 HOURS. DILUTE EACH DOSE WITH AN EQUAL VOLUME OF 1% PROCAINE. DOSE LIMITATION IS THE SAME AS THAT GIVEN ABOVE (DREISBACH, HANDBOOK OF POISONING, 12TH ED.). ANTIDOTE SHOULD BE ADMINISTERED BY QUALIFIED MEDICAL PERSONNEL.

REACTIVITY

REACTIVITY: STABLE UNDER NORMAL TEMPERATURES AND PRESSURES.

INCOMPATIBILITIES: CADMIUM CHLORIDE: BROMINE TRIFLUORIDE: ATTACKS. POTASSIUM: FORMS IMPACT SENSITIVE MIXTURE.

DECOMPOSITION: THERMAL DECOMPOSITION PRODUCTS MAY INCLUDE TOXIC OXIDES OF CADMIUM AND TOXIC AND CORROSIVE FUMES OF CHLORIDES.

POLYMERIZATION: HAZARDOUS POLYMERIZATION HAS NOT BEEN REPORTED TO OCCUR UNDER NORMAL TEMPERATURES AND PRESSURES.

STORAGE AND DISPOSAL

OBSERVE ALL FEDERAL, STATE AND LOCAL REGULATIONS WHEN STORING OR DISPOSING OF THIS SUBSTANCE. FOR ASSISTANCE, CONTACT THE DISTRICT DIRECTOR OF THE ENVIRONMENTAL PROTECTION AGENCY.

STORAGE

STORE AWAY FROM INCOMPATIBLE SUBSTANCES.

KEEP IN A TIGHTLY CLOSED CONTAINER. STORE IN A COOL, DRY, VENTILATED AREA.

DISPOSAL

CADMIUM - REGULATORY LEVEL: 1.0 MG/L MATERIALS WHICH CONTAIN THE ABOVE SUBSTANCE AT OR ABOVE THE REGULATORY LEVEL MEET THE EPA CHARACTERISTIC OF TOXICITY, AND MUST BE DISPOSED OF IN ACCORDANCE WITH 40 CFR PART 262. EPA HAZARDOUS WASTE NUMBER D006.

CONDITIONS TO AVOID

MAY BURN BUT DOES NOT IGNITE READILY.

PREVENT DISPERSION OF DUST IN AIR.

SPILL AND LEAK PROCEDURES

SOIL SPILL: DIG A HOLDING AREA SUCH AS PIT, POND OR LAGOON TO CONTAIN SPILLED MATERIAL. USE PROTECTIVE COVER SUCH AS A PLASTIC SHEET TO PREVENT DISSOLVING IN FIREFIGHTING WATER OR RAIN.

WATER SPILL: ADD SUITABLE AGENT TO NEUTRALIZE SPILLED MATERIAL TO PH-7. ADD FERRIC CHLORIDE TO SPILL.

USE MECHANICAL DREDGES OR LIFTS TO EXTRACT IMMOBILIZED MASSES OF POLLUTION AND PRECIPITATES.

THE CALIFORNIA SAFE DRINKING WATER AND TOXIC ENFORCEMENT ACT OF 1986 (PROPOSITION 65) PROHIBITS CONTAMINATING ANY KNOWN SOURCE OF DRINKING WATER WITH SUBSTANCES KNOWN TO CAUSE CANCER AND/OR REPRODUCTIVE TOXICITY.

OCCUPATIONAL SPILL: DO NOT TOUCH SPILLED MATERIAL. STOP LEAK IF YOU CAN DO IT WITHOUT RISK. FOR SMALL SPILLS, TAKE UP WITH SAND OR OTHER ABSORBENT MATERIAL AND PLACE INTO CONTAINERS FOR LATER DISPOSAL. FOR SMALL DRY SPILLS, WITH A CLEAN SHOVEL PLACE MATERIAL INTO CLEAN, DRY CONTAINER AND COVER. MOVE CONTAINERS FROM SPILL AREA. FOR LARGER SPILLS, DIKE FAR AHEAD OF SPILL FOR LATER DISPOSAL. KEEP UNNECESSARY PEOPLE AWAY. ISOLATE HAZARD AREA AND DENY ENTRY.

REPORTABLE QUANTITY (RQ): 10 POUNDS THE SUPERFUND AMENDMENTS AND REAUTHORIZATION ACT (SARA) SECTION 304 REQUIRES THAT A RELEASE EQUAL TO OR GREATER THAN THE REPORTABLE QUANTITY FOR THIS SUBSTANCE BE IMMEDIATELY REPORTED TO THE LOCAL EMERGENCY PLANNING COMMITTEE AND THE STATE EMERGENCY RESPONSE COMMISSION (40 CFR 355.40). IF THE RELEASE OF THIS SUBSTANCE IS REPORTABLE UNDER CERCLA SECTION 103, THE NATIONAL RESPONSE CENTER MUST BE NOTIFIED IMMEDIATELY AT (800) 424-8802 OR (202) 426-2675 IN THE METROPOLITAN WASHINGTON, D.C. AREA (40 CFR 302.6).

PROTECTIVE EQUIPMENT

VENTILATION: PROVIDE LOCAL EXHAUST OR PROCESS ENCLOSURE VENTILATION TO MEET PUBLISHED EXPOSURE LIMITS.

RESPIRATOR: THE FOLLOWING RESPIRATORS AND MAXIMUM USE CONCENTRATIONS ARE RECOMMENDATIONS BY THE U.S. DEPARTMENT OF HEALTH AND HUMAN SERVICES, NIOSH POCKET GUIDE TO CHEMICAL HAZARDS; NIOSH CRITERIA DOCUMENTS OR BY THE U.S. DEPARTMENT OF LABOR, 29 CFR 1910 SUBPART Z. THE SPECIFIC RESPIRATOR SELECTED MUST BE BASED ON CONTAMINATION LEVELS FOUND IN THE WORK PLACE, MUST NOT EXCEED THE WORKING LIMITS OF THE RESPIRATOR AND BE JOINTLY APPROVED BY THE NATIONAL INSTITUTE FOR OCCUPATIONAL SAFETY AND HEALTH AND THE MINE SAFETY AND HEALTH ADMINISTRATION (NIOSH-MSHA).

CADMIUM DUST AND FUME (AS CD): AT ANY DETECTABLE CONCENTRATION: ANY SELF-CONTAINED BREATHING APPARATUS WITH FULL FACEPIECE OPERATED IN PRESSURE-DEMAND OR OTHER POSITIVE PRESSURE MODE. ANY SUPPLIED-AIR RESPIRATOR WITH FULL FACEPIECE OPERATED IN PRESSURE-DEMAND OR OTHER POSITIVE PRESSURE MODE IN COMBINATION WITH AN AUXILIARY SELF-CONTAINED BREATHING APPARATUS OPERATED IN PRESSURE-DEMAND OR OTHER POSITIVE PRESSURE MODE.

ESCAPE- ANY AIR-PURIFYING FULL FACEPIECE RESPIRATOR WITH HIGH-EFFICIENCY PARTICULATE FILTER. ANY APPROPRIATE ESCAPE-TYPE SELF-CONTAINED BREATHING APPARATUS.

FOR FIREFIGHTING AND OTHER IMMEDIATELY DANGEROUS TO LIFE OR HEALTH CONDITIONS:

SELF-CONTAINED BREATHING APPARATUS WITH FULL FACEPIECE OPERATED IN PRESSURE-DEMAND OR OTHER POSITIVE PRESSURE MODE.

SUPPLIED-AIR RESPIRATOR WITH FULL FACEPIECE AND OPERATED IN PRESSURE-DEMAND OR OTHER POSITIVE PRESSURE MODE IN COMBINATION WITH AN AUXILIARY SELF-CONTAINED BREATHING APPARATUS OPERATED IN PRESSURE-DEMAND OR OTHER POSITIVE PRESSURE MODE.

CLOTHING: EMPLOYEE MUST WEAR APPROPRIATE PROTECTIVE (IMPERVIOUS) CLOTHING AND EQUIPMENT TO PREVENT ANY POSSIBILITY OF SKIN CONTACT WITH THIS SUBSTANCE.

GLOVES: EMPLOYEE MUST WEAR APPROPRIATE PROTECTIVE GLOVES TO PREVENT CONTACT WITH THIS SUBSTANCE.

EYE PROTECTION: EMPLOYEE MUST WEAR SPLASH-PROOF OR DUST-RESISTANT SAFETY GOGGLES TO PREVENT CONTACT WITH THIS SUBSTANCE.

EMERGENCY WASH FACILITIES: WHERE THERE IS ANY POSSIBILITY THAT AN EMPLOYEE'S EYES AND/OR SKIN MAY BE EXPOSED TO THIS SUBSTANCE, THE EMPLOYER SHOULD PROVIDE AN EYE WASH FOUNTAIN AND QUICK DRENCH SHOWER WITHIN THE IMMEDIATE WORK AREA FOR EMERGENCY USE.

AUTHORIZED BY- OCCUPATIONAL HEALTH SERVICES, INC.

CREATION DATE: 10/04/89 ***REVISION DATE:*** 07/13/90

MATERIAL SAFETY DATA SHEET

OCCUPATIONAL HEALTH SERVICES, INC.
AGRICULTURE AND PESTICIDE DIVISION
450 SEVENTH AVENUE, SUITE 2407
NEW YORK, NEW YORK 10123
1-800-445-MSDS OR (212) 967-1100

EMERGENCY CONTACT:
JOHN S. BRANSFORD, JR. (615) 292-1180

SUBSTANCE IDENTIFICATION

CAS-NUMBER 7778-44-1

SUBSTANCE: **CALCIUM ARSENATE**

TRADE NAMES/SYNONYMS: TRICALCIUM ORTHO-ARSENATE; CALCIUM ORTHOARSENATE; PENCAL; ARSENIC ACID, CALCIUM SALT (2:3); CUCUMBER DUST; CHIP-CAL; FENCAL; KALO; KILMAG; CALCIUM ARSENAT; CALCIUM ARSENATE, SOLID; CHIP-CAL GRANALAR; FLAC; SECURITY; SPRACAL; STCC 4923217; UN 1573; PST03850

CHEMICAL FAMILY: INORGANIC SALT

MOLECULAR FORMULA: AS2-CA3-O8 ***MOLECULAR WEIGHT:*** 398.08

CERCLA RATINGS (SCALE 0-3): HEALTH=3 FIRE=0 REACTIVITY=0 PERSISTENCE=3

NFPA RATINGS (SCALE 0-4): HEALTH=3 FIRE=0 REACTIVITY=0

COMPONENTS AND CONTAMINANTS

COMPONENT: CALCIUM ARSENATE ***PERCENT:*** 100
CAS# 7778-44-1

OTHER CONTAMINANTS: NONE

EXPOSURE LIMITS: CALCIUM ARSENATE: 10 UG(AS)/M3 OSHA TWA 200 UG(AS)/M3 ACGIH TWA LOWEST FEASIBLE LIMIT NIOSH RECOMMENDED EXPOSURE CRITERIA; 2 UG(AS)/M3 NIOSH RECOMMENDED 15 MINUTE CEILING
500/10,000 POUNDS SARA SECTION 302 THRESHOLD PLANNING QUANTITY 1000 POUNDS SARA SECTION 304 REPORTABLE QUANTITY 1 POUND CERCLA SECTION 103 REPORTABLE QUANTITY SUBJECT TO SARA SECTION 313 ANNUAL TOXIC CHEMICAL RELEASE REPORTING SUBJECT TO CALIFORNIA PROPOSITION 65 CANCER AND/OR REPRODUCTIVE TOXICITY WARNING AND RELEASE REQUIREMENTS- (FEBRUARY 27, 1987)

PHYSICAL DATA

DESCRIPTION: COLORLESS, ODORLESS SOLID ***BOILING POINT:*** DECOMPOSES

MELTING POINT: 34 F (1 C)DECOMPOSES ***SPECIFIC GRAVITY:*** 3.6

VAPOR PRESSURE: NOT AVAILABLE ***SOLUBILITY IN WATER:*** 0.013% @ 25 C

SOLVENT SOLUBILITY: DILUTE ACIDS

FIRE AND EXPLOSION DATA

FIRE AND EXPLOSION HAZARD: NEGLIGIBLE FIRE HAZARD WHEN EXPOSED TO HEAT OR FLAME.

FLASH POINT: NONCOMBUSTIBLE

FIREFIGHTING MEDIA: DRY CHEMICAL, CARBON DIOXIDE, HALON, WATER SPRAY OR STANDARD FOAM (1987 EMERGENCY RESPONSE GUIDEBOOK, DOT P 5800.4).
FOR LARGER FIRES, USE WATER SPRAY, FOG OR STANDARD FOAM (1987 EMERGENCY RESPONSE GUIDEBOOK, DOT P 5800.4).

FIREFIGHTING: MOVE CONTAINERS FROM FIRE AREA IF POSSIBLE (1987 EMERGENCY RESPONSE GUIDEBOOK, DOT P 5800.4, GUIDE PAGE 53).
EXTINGUISH USING AGENTS SUITABLE FOR TYPE OF SURROUNDING FIRE. AVOID BREATHING POISONOUS VAPORS, KEEP UPWIND.

TRANSPORTATION DATA

DEPARTMENT OF TRANSPORTATION HAZARD CLASSIFICATION 49 CFR 172.101: POISON B

DEPARTMENT OF TRANSPORTATION LABELING REQUIREMENTS 49 CFR 172.101 AND SUBPART E: POISON

DEPARTMENT OF TRANSPORTATION PACKAGING REQUIREMENTS: 49 CFR 173.367 AND 49 CFR 173.368 EXCEPTIONS: 49 CFR 173.364

TOXICITY

CALCIUM ARSENATE: TOXICITY DATA: 2400 MG/KG SKIN-RAT LD50; 20 MG/KG ORAL-RAT LD50; 794 MG/KG ORAL-MOUSE LD50; 50 MG/KG ORAL-RABBIT LDLO; 38 MG/KG ORAL-DOG LD50; TUMORIGENIC DATA (RTECS). CARCINOGEN STATUS: OSHA CARCINOGEN; KNOWN HUMAN CARCINOGEN (NTP); HUMAN SUFFICIENT EVIDENCE, ANIMAL LIMITED EVIDENCE (IARC GROUP-1). AN INCREASED INCIDENCE OF SKIN AND LUNG CANCER HAS BEEN ASSOCIATED WITH INORGANIC ARSENIC COMPOUNDS THROUGH MEDICAL TREATMENT, CONTAMINATED DRINKING WATER OR OCCUPATIONAL EXPOSURE. CANCERS AT OTHER SIGHTS HAVE ALSO BEEN REPORTED, BUT A CLEAR ASSOCIATION HAS NOT BEEN CONFIRMED. LOCAL EFFECTS: IRRITANT- INHALATION, SKIN, EYE. ACUTE TOXICITY LEVEL: HIGHLY TOXIC BY INGESTION; SLIGHTLY TOXIC BY DERMAL ABSORPTION. TARGET EFFECTS: SENSITIZER- SKIN; NEUROTOXIN. POISONING MAY ALSO AFFECT THE LIVER, KIDNEYS, BONE MARROW, CENTRAL NERVOUS SYSTEM, AND THE GASTROINTESTINAL TRACT.

HEALTH EFFECTS AND FIRST AID

INHALATION: CALCIUM ARSENATE: IRRITANT/NEUROTOXIN/CARCINOGEN. 100 MG/M3 IMMEDIATELY DANGEROUS TO LIFE OR HEALTH. **ACUTE EXPOSURE-** INHALATION OF INORGANIC ARSENIC COMPOUNDS IS THE MOST COMMON CAUSE OF POISONING. THE ACUTE SYMPTOMS ARE COUGH, CHEST PAIN, DYSPNEA, GIDDINESS, HEADACHE, AND EXTREME GENERAL WEAKNESS. THE MUCOUS MEMBRANES MAY BECOME SEVERLY INFLAMED. **CHRONIC EXPOSURE-** REPEATED OR PROLONGED EXPOSURE MAY RESULT IN PERIPHERAL NEUROPATHY, OPTIC NEURITIS, ANESTHESIAS, AND PARESTHESIAS, AS INDICATED BY ATAXIA, TREMORS, INCOORDINATION AND CONFUSION. BRONZING OF THE SKIN WITH ALOPECIA, LOCAL EDEMA AND DERMATITIS MAY OCCUR. OTHER EFFECTS ARE CIRRHOSIS, NAUSEA, VOMITING, ABDOMINAL CRAMPS, AND SALIVATION, HEMOLYTIC OR APLASTIC ANEMIA WITH WEIGHT LOSS, NEPHRITIS AND CARDIAC FAILURE. ARSENIC AND INORGANIC ARSENIC COMPOUNDS, SUCH AS CALCIUM ARSENATE, ARE CONSIDERED TO BE LUNG AND SKIN CARCINOGENS.

FIRST AID- REMOVE FROM EXPOSURE AREA TO FRESH AIR IMMEDIATELY. IF BREATHING HAS STOPPED, GIVE ARTIFICIAL RESPIRATION. MAINTAIN AIRWAY AND BLOOD PRESSURE AND ADMINISTER OXYGEN IF AVAILABLE. KEEP AFFECTED PERSON WARM AND AT REST. TREAT SYMPTOMATICALLY AND SUPPORTIVELY. ADMINISTRATION OF OXYGEN SHOULD BE PERFORMED BY QUALIFIED PERSONNEL. GET MEDICAL ATTENTION IMMEDIATELY.

SKIN CONTACT: CALCIUM ARSENATE: IRRITANT/SENSITIZER. **ACUTE EXPOSURE-** 2400 MG/KG APPLIED TO THE SKIN OF RATS KILLED HALF OF THOSE SO TESTED. IRRITATION AND CONTACT DERMATITIS MAY BE PRODUCED, INCLUDING ECZEMA WITH SCALING AND HYPERPIGMENTATION OF THE SKIN AND HYPERKERATOSIS OF THE PALMS OF THE HANDS AND THE SOLES OF THE FEET. INORGANIC ARSENIC COMPOUNDS ARE SLIGHTLY ABSORBED THROUGH THE SKIN WHEN ADMINISTERED IN A LIPID VEHICLE. POISONING HAS CAUSED ALOPECIA, BRONZING OF THE SKIN, AND BRITTLE NAILS WITH STRIATIONS (MEE'S LINES). **CHRONIC EXPOSURE-** REPEATED EXPOSURE MAY RESULT IN SENSITIZATION DERMATITIS. SKIN CANCER MAY BE A RESULT OF ARSENIC POISONING; IT IS UNCLEAR WHETHER SKIN CONTACT MAY PRODUCE THE CARCINOGENICITY, IN ADDITION TO INHALATION AND INGESTION.

FIRST AID- REMOVE CONTAMINATED CLOTHING AND SHOES IMMEDIATELY. WASH AFFECTED AREA WITH SOAP OR MILD DETERGENT AND LARGE AMOUNTS OF WATER UNTIL NO EVIDENCE OF CHEMICAL REMAINS (APPROXIMATELY 15-20 MINUTES). GET MEDICAL ATTENTION IMMEDIATELY.

EYE CONTACT: CALCIUM ARSENATE: IRRITANT. **ACUTE EXPOSURE-** MAY CAUSE IRRITATION AND CONJUNCTIVITIS. POISONING HAS CAUSED EDEMA OF THE EYELIDS, CORNEAL NECROSIS, AND VISUAL DISTURBANCES. **CHRONIC EXPOSURE-** REPEATED OR PROLONGED EYE CONTACT WITH ARSENIC DUST MAY CAUSE CONJUNCTIVITIS. POISONING FROM INHALATION OR INGESTION HAS CAUSED OPTIC NEURITIS.

FIRST AID- WASH EYES IMMEDIATELY WITH LARGE AMOUNTS OF WATER OR NORMAL SALINE, OCCASIONALLY LIFTING UPPER AND LOWER LIDS, UNTIL NO EVIDENCE OF CHEMICAL REMAINS (APPROXIMATELY 15-20 MINUTES). GET MEDICAL ATTENTION IMMEDIATELY.

INGESTION: CALCIUM ARSENATE: NEUROTOXIN/CARCINOGEN/HIGHLY TOXIC. **ACUTE EXPOSURE-** NON-FATAL DOSES MAY CAUSE RESTLESSNESS, NAUSEA, VOMITING, HEADACHE, DIZZINESS, CHILLS, CRAMPS, IRRITABILITY, AND PARALYSIS. JAUNDICE OLIGURIA, AND ANURIA MAY OCCUR WITHIN 1-3 DAYS. FATAL DOSES MAY CAUSE GASTROINTESTINAL DISTURBANCES, A BURNING PAIN IN THE THROAT, VOMITING, WATERY OR BLOODY DIARRHEA WITH MUCOUS, HYPOTENSION, WEAKNESS, CONVULSIONS, AND COMA AND DEATH FROM RESPIRATORY AND CIRCULATORY FAILURE. **CHRONIC EXPOSURE-** CHRONIC POISONING MAY AFFECT THE CENTRAL NERVOUS SYSTEM, CAUSING POLYNEURITIS, OPTIC NEURITIS, ANESTHESIAS, AND PARENTHESIAS SUCH AS BURNING PAINS IN THE HANDS AND FEET. THE SKIN MAY BECOME BRONZED WITH LOCALIZED EDEMA AND DERMATITIS. THE GASTROINTESTINAL TRACT IS AFFECTED, WITH NAUSEA AND VOMITING, CRAMPS, SALIVATION, AND POSSIBLE CIRRHOSIS OF THE LIVER. THE GENERAL EFFECTS ARE ANEMIA AND WEIGHT LOSS. INORGANIC ARSENIC COMPOUNDS HAVE BEEN SHOWN TO CAUSE SKIN AND LUNG CANCER IN HUMANS.

FIRST AID- REMOVE BY GASTRIC LAVAGE OR EMESIS. FOLLOW WITH A SALINE CATHARTIC. MAINTAIN BLOOD PRESSURE, AIRWAY, AND GIVE OXYGEN IF RESPIRATION IS DEPRESSED. DO NOT PERFORM GASTRIC LAVAGE OR EMESIS IF VICTIM IS UNCONSCIOUS. GET MEDICAL ATTENTION IMMEDIATELY. (DREISBACH, HANDBOOK OF POISONING, 12TH ED.) ADMINISTRATION OF GASTRIC LAVAGE OR OXYGEN SHOULD BE PERFORMED BY QUALIFIED MEDICAL PERSONNEL.

ANTIDOTE: THE FOLLOWING ANTIDOTE HAS BEEN RECOMMENDED. HOWEVER, THE DECISION AS TO WHETHER THE SEVERITY OF POISONING REQUIRES ADMINISTRATION OF ANY ANTIDOTE AND ACTUAL DOSE REQUIRED SHOULD BE MADE BY QUALIFIED MEDICAL PERSONNEL.
ARSENIC POISONING: GIVE DIMERCAPROL, 3 MG/KG (OR 0.3 ML/KG) EVERY 4 HOURS FOR 2 DAYS AND THEN 2 MG/KG EVERY 2 HOURS FOR A TOTAL OF 10 DAYS. DIMERCAPROL IS AVAILABLE AS A 10% SOLUTION IN OIL FOR INTRAMUSCULAR ADMINISTRATION. NEXT, GIVE PENICILLAMINE, UP TO 100 MG/KG/DAY (MAXIMUM 1 G/DAY) DIVIDED INTO 4 DOSES FOR NO LONGER THAN 1

WEEK. IF A LONGER ADMINISTRATION PERIOD IS WARRANTED, DOSAGE SHOULD NOT EXCEED 40 MG/KG/DAY. GIVE THE DRUG ORALLY HALF AN HOUR BEFORE MEALS. DISCONTINUE ANTIDOTE WHEN URINE ARSENIC LEVEL FALLS BELOW 50 UG/24 HR. (DREISBACH, HANDBOOK OF POISONING, 12TH ED.). ANITDOTE SHOULD BE ADMINISTERED BY QUALIFIED MEDICAL PERSONNEL.

REACTIVITY

REACTIVITY: STABLE UNDER NORMAL TEMPERATURES AND PRESSURES.

INCOMPATIBILITIES: CALCIUM ARSENATE: OXIDIZING MATERIALS- MAY REACT.

DECOMPOSITION: TOXIC FUMES OF ARSENIC ARE EMITTED ON THERMAL OR ACIDIC DECOMPOSITION.

POLYMERIZATION: HAZARDOUS POLYMERIZATION HAS NOT BEEN REPORTED TO OCCUR UNDER NORMAL TEMPERATURES AND PRESSURES.

STORAGE AND DISPOSAL

OBSERVE ALL FEDERAL, STATE AND LOCAL REGULATIONS WHEN STORING OR DISPOSING OF THIS SUBSTANCE. FOR ASSISTANCE, CONTACT THE DISTRICT DIRECTOR OF THE ENVIRONMENTAL PROTECTION AGENCY.

****STORAGE****

THRESHOLD PLANNING QUANTITY (TPQ): THE SUPERFUND AMENDMENTS AND REAUTHORIZATION ACT (SARA) SECTION 302 REQUIRES THAT EACH FACILITY WHERE ANY EXTREMELY HAZARDOUS SUBSTANCE IS PRESENT IN A QUANTITY EQUAL TO OR GREATER THAN THE TPQ ESTABLISHED FOR THAT SUBSTANCE NOTIFY THE STATE EMERGENCY RESPONSE COMMISSION FOR THE STATE IN WHICH IT IS LOCATED. SECTION 303 OF SARA REQUIRES THESE FACILITIES TO PARTICIPATE IN LOCAL EMERGENCY RESPONSE PLANNING (40 CFR 355.30). STORE AWAY FROM INCOMPATIBLE SUBSTANCES.

CONDITIONS TO AVOID

MAY BURN BUT DOES NOT IGNITE READILY.

SPILL AND LEAK PROCEDURES

SOIL SPILL: DO NOT HANDLE PACKAGES WITHOUT FULL PROTECTIVE EQUIPMENT. DIG A PIT, POND, LAGOON OR HOLDING AREA TO CONTAIN LIQUID OR SOLID MATERIAL. COVER SOLIDS WITH A PLASTIC SHEET TO PREVENT DISSOLVING IN RAIN OR FIREFIGHTING WATER.

WATER SPILL: USE DREDGES OR LIFTS TO EXTRACT IMMOBILIZED MASSES OF POLLUTION AND PRECIPITATES. ADD SUITABLE AGENT TO NEUTRALIZE MATERIAL TO PH-7. ADD CALCIUM HYPOCHLORITE TO SPILL. ADD FERRIC CHLORIDE TO SPILL. NEUTRALIZE WITH AGRICULTURAL LIME, SLAKED LIME, CRUSHED LIMESTONE, OR SODIUM BICARBONATE.

THE CALIFORNIA SAFE DRINKING WATER AND TOXIC ENFORCEMENT ACT OF 1986 (PROPOSITION 65) PROHIBITS CONTAMINATING ANY KNOWN SOURCE OF DRINKING WATER WITH SUBSTANCES KNOWN TO CAUSE CANCER AND/OR REPRODUCTIVE TOXICITY.

OCCUPATIONAL SPILL: DO NOT TOUCH SPILLED MATERIAL. STOP LEAK IF YOU CAN DO IT WITHOUT RISK. FOR SMALL SPILLS, TAKE UP WITH SAND OR OTHER ABSORBENT MATERIAL AND PLACE INTO CONTAINERS FOR LATER DISPOSAL. FOR SMALL DRY SPILLS, WITH A CLEAN SHOVEL PLACE MATERIAL INTO CLEAN, DRY CONTAINER AND COVER. MOVE CONTAINERS FROM SPILL AREA. FOR LARGER SPILLS, DIKE FAR AHEAD OF SPILL FOR LATER DISPOSAL. KEEP UNNECESSARY PEOPLE AWAY. ISOLATE HAZARD AREA AND DENY ENTRY.

REPORTABLE QUANTITY (RQ): THE SUPERFUND AMENDMENTS AND REAUTHORIZATION ACT (SARA) SECTION 304 REQUIRES THAT A RELEASE EQUAL TO OR GREATER THAN THE REPORTABLE QUANTITY ESTABLISHED FOR THAT SUBSTANCE BE IMMEDIATELY REPORTED TO THE LOCAL EMERGENCY PLANNING COMMITTEE AND THE STATE EMERGENCY RESPONSE COMMISSION (40 CFR 355.40). IF THE RELEASE OF THIS SUBSTANCE IS REPORTABLE UNDER CERCLA SECTION 103, THE NATIONAL RESPONSE CENTER MUST BE NOTIFIED IMMEDIATELY AT (800) 424-8802 OR (202) 426-2675 IN THE METROPOLITAN WASHINGTON, D.C. AREA (40 CFR 302.6).

PROTECTIVE EQUIPMENT

VENTILATION: PROCESS ENCLOSURE RECOMMENDED.

ARSENIC (INORGANIC): VENTILATION SHOULD MEET THE REQUIREMENTS IN 29 CFR 1910.1018(G).

RESPIRATOR: THE FOLLOWING RESPIRATORS ARE THE MINIMUM LEGAL REQUIREMENTS AS SET FORTH BY THE OCCUPATIONAL SAFETY AND HEALTH ADMINISTRATION FOUND IN 29 CFR 1910, SUBPART Z.

RESPIRATORY PROTECTION FOR INORGANIC ARSENIC PARTICULATE EXCEPT THOSE WITH SIGNIFICANT VAPOR PRESSURE

CONCENTRATION OF INORGANIC ARSENIC (AS) REQUIRED RESPIRATOR OR CONDITION OF USE

UNKNOWN OR GREATER OR LESS THAN 20,000 UG/M3 (20 MG/M3) OR FIREFIGHTING ANY FULL FACEPIECE, SELF CONTAINED BREATHING APPARATUS, OPERATED IN POSITIVE PRESSURE MODE.

NOT GREATER THAN 20,000 UG/M3 FULL (20 MG/M3) SUPPLIED-AIR RESPIRATOR WITH FACEPIECE, HOOD OR HELMET OR SUIT AND OPERATED IN POSITIVE PRESSURE MODE.

NOT GREATER THAN 10,000 UG/M3 RESPIRATORS (10 MG/M3) POWERED-AIR PURIFYING IN ALL INLET FACE COVERINGS WITH HIGH EFFICIENCY FILTERS; OR HALF-MASK SUPPLIED-AIR RESPIRATOR OPERATED IN POSITIVE PRESSURE MODE.

NOT GREATER THAN 500 UG/M3 FULL FACEPIECE AIR-PURIFYING RESPIRATOR EQUIPPED WITH HIGH EFFICIENCY FILTERS; OR ANY FULL FACEPIECE SUPPLIED-AIR RESPIRATOR; OR ANY FULL FACEPIECE SELF-CONTAINED BREATHING APPARATUS. NOT GREATER THAN 100 UG/M3 HALF-MASK AIR-PURIFYING RESPIRATOR EQUIPPED WITH HIGH EFFICIENCY FILTERS; OR ANY HALF-MASK SUPPLIED-AIR RESPIRATOR.

(HIGH EFFICIENCY FILTER- 99.97% EFFICIENCY AGAINST 0.3 MICROMETER MONODISPERSE DIETHYL-HEXYL PHTHALATE (DOP) PARTICLES)

RESPIRATORY PROTECTION FOR INORGANIC ARSENICALS (SUCH AS ARSENIC TRICHLORIDE OR ARSENIC PHOSPHIDE) WITH SIGNIFICANT VAPOR PRESSURE.

CONCENTRATION OF INORGANIC ARSENIC (AS) REQUIRED RESPIRATOR OR CONDITION OF USE

UNKNOWN OR GREATER OR LESS THAN 20,000 CONTAINED UG/M3 (20 MG/M3) ANY FULL FACEPIECE SELF-BREATHING APPARATUS OPERATED IN POSITIVE PRESSURE MODE.

NOT GREATER THAN 20,000 UG/M3 (20 MG/M3) SUPPLIED-AIR RESPIRATOR WITH A FULL FACEPIECE, HOOD OR HELMET OR SUIT OPERATED IN POSITIVE PRESSURE MODE.

NOT GREATER THAN 10,000 UG/M3 RESPIRATOR (10 MG/M3) HALF-MASK SUPPLIED AIR OPERATED IN POSITIVE PRESSURE MODE.

NOT GREATER THAN 500 UG/M3 FRONT- OR BACK-MOUNTED GAS MASK EQUIPPED WITH HIGH-EFFICIENCY FILTERS AND ACID GAS CANISTER; OR ANY FULL FACEPIECE SUPPLIED AIR RESPIRATOR; OR ANY FULL FACEPIECE SELF-CONTAINED BREATHING APPARATUS.

NOT GREATER THAN 100 UG/M3 HALF-MASK AIR-PURIFYING RESPIRATOR EQUIPPED WITH HIGH EFFICIENCY FILTER AND ACID GAS CARTRIDGE; OR ANY HALF-MASK SUPPLIED-AIR RESPIRATOR.

(HIGH EFFICIENCY FILTER- 99.97% EFFICIENCY AGAINST 0.3 MICROMETER MONODISPERSE DIETHYL-HEXYL PHTHALATE (DOP) PARTICLES) (HALF-MASK RESPIRATORS SHALL NOT BE USED FOR PROTECTION AGAINST ARSENIC TRICHLORIDE, AS IT IS RAPIDLY ABSORBED THROUGH THE SKIN).

THE FOLLOWING RESPIRATORS AND MAXIMUM USE CONCENTRATIONS ARE RECOMMENDATIONS BY THE U.S. DEPARTMENT OF HEALTH AND HUMAN SERVICES, NIOSH POCKET GUIDE TO CHEMICAL HAZARDS; NIOSH CRITERIA DOCUMENTS OR BY THE U.S. DEPARTMENT OF LABOR, 29 CFR 1910 SUBPART Z. THE SPECIFIC RESPIRATOR SELECTED MUST BE BASED ON CONTAMINATION LEVELS FOUND IN THE WORK PLACE, MUST NOT EXCEED THE WORKING LIMITS OF THE RESPIRATOR AND BE JOINTLY APPROVED BY THE NATIONAL INSTITUTE FOR OCCUPATIONAL SAFETY AND HEALTH AND THE MINE SAFETY AND HEALTH ADMINISTRATION (NIOSH-MSHA).

AT ANY DETECTABLE CONCENTRATION:

SELF-CONTAINED BREATHING APPARATUS WITH FULL FACEPIECE OPERATED IN PRESSURE-DEMAND OR OTHER POSITIVE PRESSURE MODE. SUPPLIED-AIR RESPIRATOR WITH FULL FACEPIECE OPERATED IN PRESSURE-DEMAND OR OTHER POSITIVE PRESSURE MODE IN COMBINATION WITH AN AUXILIARY SELF-CONTAINED BREATHING APPARATUS OPERATED IN PRESSURE-DEMAND OR OTHER POSITIVE PRESSURE MODE.

ESCAPE- AIR-PURIFYING FULL FACEPIECE RESPIRATOR (GAS MASK) WITH A CHIN-STYLE OR FRONT- OR BACK-MOUNTED ORGANIC VAPOR CANISTER HAVING A HIGH-EFFICIENCY PARTICULATE FILTER. ESCAPE-TYPE SELF-CONTAINED BREATHING APPARATUS.

FOR FIREFIGHTING AND OTHER IMMEDIATELY DANGEROUS TO LIFE OR HEALTH CONDITIONS:

SELF-CONTAINED BREATHING APPARATUS WITH FULL FACEPIECE OPERATED IN PRESSURE-DEMAND OR OTHER POSITIVE PRESSURE MODE.

SUPPLIED-AIR RESPIRATOR WITH FULL FACEPIECE AND OPERATED IN PRESSURE-DEMAND OR OTHER POSITIVE PRESSURE MODE IN COMBINATION WITH AN AUXILIARY SELF-CONTAINED BREATHING APPARATUS OPERATED IN PRESSURE-DEMAND OR OTHER POSITIVE PRESSURE MODE.

CLOTHING: EMPLOYEE MUST WEAR APPROPRIATE PROTECTIVE (IMPERVIOUS) CLOTHING AND EQUIPMENT TO PREVENT REPEATED OR PROLONGED SKIN CONTACT WITH THIS SUBSTANCE.

ARSENIC (INORGANIC): PROTECTIVE CLOTHING SHOULD MEET THE REQUIREMENTS FOR PROTECTIVE WORK CLOTHING AND EQUIPMENT IN 29 CFR 1910.1018(J).

GLOVES: EMPLOYEE MUST WEAR APPROPRIATE PROTECTIVE GLOVES TO PREVENT CONTACT WITH THIS SUBSTANCE.

ARSENIC (INORGANIC): PROTECTIVE GLOVES SHOULD MEET THE REQUIREMENTS FOR PROTECTIVE WORK CLOTHING AND EQUIPMENT IN 29 CFR 1910.1018(J).

EYE PROTECTION: EMPLOYEE MUST WEAR SPLASH-PROOF OR DUST-RESISTANT SAFETY GOGGLES TO PREVENT EYE CONTACT WITH THIS SUBSTANCE.
EMERGENCY EYE WASH: WHERE THERE IS ANY POSSIBILITY THAT AN EMPLOYEE'S EYES MAY BE EXPOSED TO THIS SUBSTANCE, THE EMPLOYER SHOULD PROVIDE AN EYE WASH FOUNTAIN WITHIN THE IMMEDIATE WORK AREA FOR EMERGENCY USE.
ARSENIC (INORGANIC): PROTECTIVE EYE EQUIPMENT SHOULD MEET THE REQUIREMENTS FOR PROTECTIVE WORK CLOTHING AND EQUIPMENT IN 29 CFR 1910.1018(J).

AUTHORIZED BY- OCCUPATIONAL HEALTH SERVICES, INC.
CREATION DATE: 10/04/89 ***REVISION DATE:*** 07/12/90

MATERIAL SAFETY DATA SHEET

OCCUPATIONAL HEALTH SERVICES, INC.
AGRICULTURE AND PESTICIDE DIVISION
450 SEVENTH AVENUE, SUITE 2407
NEW YORK, NEW YORK 10123
1-800-445-MSDS OR (212) 967-1100

EMERGENCY CONTACT:
JOHN S. BRANSFORD, JR. (615) 292-1180

SUBSTANCE IDENTIFICATION

CAS-NUMBER 10137-74-3
SUBSTANCE: **CALCIUM CHLORATE**
TRADE NAMES/SYNONYMS: CHLORIC ACID, CALCIUM SALT; STCC 4918713; UN 1452; PST03890
CHEMICAL FAMILY: INORGANIC SALT
MOLECULAR FORMULA: CA-CL2-O6
MOLECULAR WEIGHT: 206.98
CERCLA RATINGS (SCALE 0-3): HEALTH=2 FIRE=0 REACTIVITY=2 PERSISTENCE=0
NFPA RATINGS (SCALE 0-4): HEALTH=2 FIRE=0 REACTIVITY=2

COMPONENTS AND CONTAMINANTS

COMPONENT: CALCIUM CHLORATE ***PERCENT:*** 100
CAS# 10137-74-3
OTHER CONTAMINANTS: NONE
EXPOSURE LIMITS: NO OCCUPATIONAL EXPOSURE LIMITS ESTABLISHED BY OSHA, ACGIH, OR NIOSH.

PHYSICAL DATA

DESCRIPTION: ODORLESS, MONOCLINIC, YELLOWISH-WHITE, DELIQUESCENT CRYSTALS
BOILING POINT: DECOMPOSES ***MELTING POINT:*** 644 F (340 C)
SPECIFIC GRAVITY: 2.7 @ 0 C ***SOLUBILITY IN WATER:*** SOLUBLE
SOLVENT SOLUBILITY: ALCOHOL, ACETONE

FIRE AND EXPLOSION DATA

FIRE AND EXPLOSION HAZARD: NEGLIGIBLE FIRE HAZARD WHEN EXPOSED TO HEAT OR FLAME.
OXIDIZER: OXIDIZERS DECOMPOSE, ESPECIALLY WHEN HEATED, TO YIELD OXYGEN OR OTHER GASES WHICH WILL INCREASE THE BURNING RATE OF COMBUSTIBLE MATTER. CONTACT WITH EASILY OXIDIZABLE, ORGANIC, OR OTHER COMBUSTIBLE MATERIALS MAY RESULT IN IGNITION, VIOLENT COMBUSTION OR EXPLOSION.
FIREFIGHTING MEDIA: DRY CHEMICAL, CARBON DIOXIDE, HALON OR WATER SPRAY (1987 EMERGENCY RESPONSE GUIDEBOOK, DOT P 5800.4).
FOR LARGER FIRES, USE WATER SPRAY OR FOG (1987 EMERGENCY RESPONSE GUIDEBOOK, DOT P 5800.4).
FIREFIGHTING: MOVE CONTAINERS FROM FIRE AREA IF POSSIBLE. COOL CONTAINERS EXPOSED TO FLAMES WITH WATER FROM SIDE UNTIL WELL AFTER FIRE IS OUT. STAY AWAY FROM STORAGE TANK ENDS. FOR MASSIVE FIRE IN STORAGE AREA, USE UNMANNED HOSE HOLDER OR MONITOR NOZZLES; ELSE WITHDRAW FROM AREA AND LET FIRE BURN (1987 EMERGENCY RESPONSE GUIDEBOOK, DOT P 5800.4, GUIDE PAGE 35)
USE FLOODING AMOUNTS OF WATER. COOL CONTAINERS WITH FLOODING AMOUNTS OF WATER, APPLY FROM AS FAR A DISTANCE AS POSSIBLE. EVACUATE TO A RADIUS OF 2500 FEET FOR UNCONTROLLABLE FIRES.
FIRE FIGHTING PHASES: DO NOT USE WATER, VASPORIZING LIQUIDS OR FOAM. CARBON DIOXIDE IS INEFFECTIVE. SMOTHER WITH SUITABLE DRY POWDER (NFPA 49, HAZARDOUS CHEMICALS DATA, 1975).

TRANSPORTATION DATA

DEPARTMENT OF TRANSPORTATION HAZARD CLASSIFICATION 49 CFR 172.101: OXIDIZER
DEPARTMENT OF TRANSPORTATION LABELING REQUIREMENTS 49 CFR 172.101 AND SUBPART E: OXIDIZER
DEPARTMENT OF TRANSPORTATION PACKAGING REQUIREMENTS: 49 CFR 173.163 EXCEPTIONS: 49 CFR 173.153

TOXICITY

CALCIUM CHLORATE: TOXICITY DATA: ANHYDROUS: 4500 MG/KG ORAL-RAT LDLO; 625 MG/KG INTRAPERITONEAL-RAT LDLO. DIHYDRATE: 4500 MG/KG ORAL-RAT LD50. CARCINOGEN STATUS: NONE. LOCAL EFFECTS: IRRITANT- INHALATION, SKIN, AND EYES. ACUTE TOXICITY LEVEL: MODERATELY TOXIC BY INGESTION. TARGET EFFECTS: NO DATA AVAILABLE.

HEALTH EFFECTS AND FIRST AID

INHALATION: CALCIUM CHLORATE: IRRITANT. **ACUTE EXPOSURE-** MAY CAUSE SORE THROAT, COUGHING, HEADACHE, DIZZINESS, AND FAINTNESS. **CHRONIC EXPOSURE-** NO DATA AVAILABLE.
FIRST AID- REMOVE FROM EXPOSURE AREA TO FRESH AIR IMMEDIATELY. IF BREATHING HAS STOPPED, PERFORM ARTIFICIAL RESPIRATION. KEEP PERSON WARM AND AT REST. TREAT SYMPTOMATICALLY AND SUPPORTIVELY. GET MEDICAL ATTENTION IMMEDIATELY.

SKIN CONTACT: CALCIUM CHLORATE: IRRITANT. **ACUTE EXPOSURE-** MAY CAUSE IRRITATION. **CHRONIC EXPOSURE-** REPEATED OR PROLONGED CONTACT MAY CAUSE DERMATITIS.
FIRST AID- REMOVE CONTAMINATED CLOTHING AND SHOES IMMEDIATELY. WASH AFFECTED AREA WITH SOAP OR MILD DETERGENT AND LARGE AMOUNTS OF WATER UNTIL NO EVIDENCE OF CHEMICAL REMAINS (APPROXIMATELY 15-20 MINUTES). GET MEDICAL ATTENTION IMMEDIATELY.

EYE CONTACT: CALCIUM CHLORATE: IRRITANT. **ACUTE EXPOSURE-** CONTACT MAY CAUSE REDNESS AND IRRITATION. **CHRONIC EXPOSURE-** PROLONGED OR REPEATED EXPOSURE MAY CAUSE CONJUNCTIVITIS.
FIRST AID- WASH EYES IMMEDIATELY WITH LARGE AMOUNTS OF WATER OR NORMAL SALINE, OCCASIONALLY LIFTING UPPER AND LOWER LIDS, UNTIL NO EVIDENCE OF CHEMICAL REMAINS (APPROXIMATELY 15-20 MINUTES). GET MEDICAL ATTENTION IMMEDIATELY.

INGESTION: CALCIUM CHLORATE: **ACUTE EXPOSURE-** INGESTION MAY CAUSE PALLOR, NAUSEA, VOMITING, DIARRHEA, SHORTNESS OF BREATH, AND ABDOMINAL PAIN. THE CHLORATE ION IS IRRITATING TO MUCOUS MEMBRANES IN CONCENTRATED SOLUTION, AND AFTER ABSORPTION, IT PRODUCES METHEMOGLOBINEMIA BY VIRTUE OF ITS OXIDIZING PROPERTIES. HOWEVER, THE CHLORATE IS NOT REDUCED IN THE PROCESS BUT ACTS AS A CATALYST, SO THAT A SMALL AMOUNT OF CHLORATE CAN PRODUCE A LARGE AMOUNT METHEMOGLOBIN. CHLORATES MAY ALSO CAUSE INCREASED PRODUCTION OF HEINZ BODIES AND HEMOLYSIS. CYANOSIS, CENTRAL NERVOUS SYSTEM DEPRESSION, CONFUSION, CONVULSIONS, AND ANURIA MAY OCCUR. THE FATAL DOSE OF CHLORATES IS ESTIMATED TO BE 15 GRAMS FOR ADULTS AND 2 GRAMS FOR CHILDREN. PATHOLOGIC FINDINGS IN DEATHS FROM CHLORATES ARE GASTROINTESTINAL CONGESTION AND CORROSION, KIDNEY INJURY, LIVER DAMAGE, AND CHOCOLATE COLOR OF THE BLOOD. **CHRONIC EXPOSURE-** REPEATED OR PROLONGED EXPOSURE TO CHLORATES IN DOSES LESS THAN NECESSARY TO PRODUCE SYMPTOMS OF ACUTE POISONING MAY CAUSE LOSS OF APPETITE AND WEIGHT LOSS.
FIRST AID- REMOVE CHEMICAL BY IPECAC EMESIS. GIVE ACTIVATED CHARCOAL. DO NOT MAKE AN UNCONSCIOUS PERSON VOMIT OR DRINK ANYTHING. USE AIRWAY-PROTECTED LAVAGE IF RESPIRATION IS DEPRESSED. (DREISBACH, HANDBOOK OF POISONING , 11TH ED.) LAVAGE MUST BE PERFORMED BY QUALIFIED MEDICAL PERSONNEL.
ANTIDOTE: THE FOLLOWING ANTIDOTE HAS BEEN RECOMMENDED. HOWEVER, THE DECISION AS TO WHETHER THE SEVERITY OF POISONING REQUIRES ADMINISTRATION OF ANY ANTIDOTE AND ACTUAL DOSE REQUIRED SHOULD BE MADE BY QUALIFIED MEDICAL PERSONNEL. CHLORATE POISONING: GIVE SODIUM THIOSULFATE, 2-5 GRAMS IN 200 ML OF 5% SODIUM BICARBONATE, ORALLY, TO DECOMPOSE CHLORATES. METHYLENE BLUE IS NOT USEFUL FOR REVERSING CHLORATE METHEMOGLOBINEMIA AND MAY BE HAZARDOUS. ASCORBIC ACID ACTS SLOWLY (DREISBACH, HANDBOOK OF POISONING, 11TH ED.). ANTIDOTE SHOULD BE ADMINISTERED BY QUALIFIED MEDICAL PERSONNEL.

REACTIVITY

REACTIVITY: MAY BE EXPLODED OR IGNITED BY FRICTION, SHOCK, OR HEAT, ESPECIALLY WHEN CONTAMINATED, OR IN CONTACT WITH, COMBUSTIBLE OR OXIDIZABLE MATERIALS.

INCOMPATIBILITIES: CALCIUM CHLORATE: AMMONIUM COMPOUNDS: MAY FORM EXPLOSIVE MIXTURES. FINELY DIVIDED ARSENIC: WITH FINELY DIVIDED CALCIUM CHLORATE CAN BE EXPLODED BY HEAT, PERCUSSION, AND SOMETIMES BY LIGHT FRICTION. CHARCOAL: MIXTURE MAY LIBERATE OXYGEN AND HEAT EXPLOSIVELY. CARBON: WITH FINELY DIVIDED CALCIUM CHLORATE CAN EXPLODE WITH HEAT, PERCUSSION, AND SOMETIMES BY LIGHT FRICTION. FINELY DIVIDED COPPER: WITH FINELY DIVIDED CALCIUM CHLORATE MAY EXPLODE WITH HEAT, PERCUSSION, AND SOMETIMES LIGHT FRICTION. MANGANESE DIOXIDE: MIXTURE MAY LIBERATE OXYGEN AND HEAT EXPLOSIVELY BY HEAT, SHOCK, FRICTION, AGE, OR STATIC ELECTRICITY. FINELY DIVIDED METAL SULFIDES: WITH FINELY DIVIDED CALCIUM CHLORATE CAN BE EXPLODED BY HEAT, PERCUSSION, AND SOMETIMES LIGHT FRICTION. ORGANIC ACIDS (DIBASIC): EXPLOSIVE CHLORINE DIOXIDE IS EVOLVED WHEN MIXTURE IS HEATED ABOVE ROOM TEMPERATURE. ORGANIC MATTER: MIXTURE MAY LIBERATE OXYGEN AND HEAT EXPLOSIVELY. RED PHOSPHORUS: MIXTURE BURSTS INTO FLAMES AFTER A FEW MOMENTS. SULFUR: MIXTURE MAY LIBERATE OXYGEN AND HEAT EXPLOSIVELY. WHITE PHOSPHORUS: MOIST CALCIUM CHLORIDE MAY EXPLODE UPON CONTACT.

DECOMPOSITION: THERMAL DECOMPOSITION MAY RELEASE TOXIC CALCIUM DIOXIDE AND CORROSIVE HYDROGEN CHLORIDE FUMES.

POLYMERIZATION: HAZARDOUS POLYMERIZATION HAS NOT BEEN REPORTED TO OCCUR UNDER NORMAL TEMPERATURES AND PRESSURES.

STORAGE AND DISPOSAL

STORAGE: PROTECT AGAINST PHYSICAL DAMAGE. SEPARATE FROM COMBUSTIBLE, ORGANIC, OR OTHER READILY OXIDIZABLE MATERIALS, ACIDS, AMMONIUM SALTS, SULFUR, AND FLAMMABLE VAPORS. AVOID STORAGE ON WOODEN FLOORS. IMMEDIATELY REMOVE AND DISPOSE OF ANY SPILLED CHLORATE (NFPA 49, HAZARDOUS CHEMICALS DATA, 1975).

CONDITIONS TO AVOID

AVOID CONTACT WITH COMBUSTIBLE MATERIALS (WOOD, PAPER, FUEL, OILS, ETC); IGNITION OR EXPLOSION MAY RESULT. AVOID CONTAMINATION OF WATER SOURCES.

USUAL SHIPPING CONTAINERS: GLASS BOTTLES, CANS, DRUMS (NFPA 49, HAZARDOUS CHEMICALS DATA, 1975).

SPILL AND LEAK PROCEDURES

OCCUPATIONAL SPILL: KEEP COMBUSTIBLES (WOOD, PAPER, OIL, ETC) AWAY FROM SPILLED MATERIAL. DO NOT TOUCH SPILLED MATERIAL. FOR SMALL DRY SPILLS, WITH CLEAN SHOVEL PLACE MATERIAL INTO CLEAN, DRY CONTAINER AND COVER; MOVE CONTAINERS FROM SPILL AREA. FOR SMALL LIQUID SPILLS, TAKE UP WITH SAND, EARTH OR OTHER ABSORBENT MATERIAL AND PLACE INTO CONTAINERS FOR LATER DISPOSAL. FOR LARGER SPILLS, DIKE FAR AHEAD OF SPILL FOR LATER DISPOSAL. KEEP UNNECESSARY PEOPLE AWAY. ISOLATE HAZARD AREA AND DENY ENTRY.

PROTECTIVE EQUIPMENT

VENTILATION: PROVIDE LOCAL EXHAUST OR GENERAL DILUTION VENTILATION SYSTEM.

RESPIRATOR: THE FOLLOWING RESPIRATORS ARE RECOMMENDED BASED ON INFORMATION FOUND IN THE PHYSICAL DATA, TOXICITY AND HEALTH EFFECTS SECTIONS. THEY ARE RANKED IN ORDER FROM MINIMUM TO MAXIMUM RESPIRATORY PROTECTION. THE SPECIFIC RESPIRATOR SELECTED MUST BE BASED ON CONTAMINATION LEVELS FOUND IN THE WORK PLACE, MUST NOT EXCEED THE WORKING LIMITS OF THE RESPIRATOR AND BE JOINTLY APPROVED BY THE NATIONAL INSTITUTE FOR OCCUPATIONAL SAFETY AND HEALTH AND THE MINE SAFETY AND HEALTH ADMINISTRATION (NIOSH-MSHA).

DUST AND MIST RESPIRATOR WITH A FULL FACEPIECE.

AIR-PURIFYING FULL FACEPIECE RESPIRATOR WITH A HIGH-EFFICIENCY PARTICULATE FILTER.

POWERED AIR-PURIFYING RESPIRATOR WITH A TIGHT-FITTING FACEPIECE AND HIGH-EFFICIENCY PARTICULATE FILTER.

TYPE 'C' SUPPLIED-AIR RESPIRATOR WITH A FULL FACEPIECE OPERATED IN PRESSURE-DEMAND OR OTHER POSITIVE PRESSURE MODE OR WITH A FULL FACEPIECE, HELMET OR HOOD OPERATED IN CONTINUOUS-FLOW MODE.

SELF-CONTAINED BREATHING APPARATUS WITH A FULL FACEPIECE OPERATED IN PRESSURE-DEMAND OR OTHER POSITIVE PRESSURE MODE.

FOR FIREFIGHTING AND OTHER IMMEDIATELY DANGEROUS TO LIFE OR HEALTH CONDITIONS:

SELF-CONTAINED BREATHING APPARATUS WITH FULL FACEPIECE OPERATED IN PRESSURE-DEMAND OR OTHER POSITIVE PRESSURE MODE.

SUPPLIED-AIR RESPIRATOR WITH FULL FACEPIECE AND OPERATED IN PRESSURE-DEMAND OR OTHER POSITIVE PRESSURE MODE IN COMBINATION WITH AN AUXILIARY SELF-CONTAINED BREATHING APPARATUS OPERATED IN PRESSURE-DEMAND OR OTHER POSITIVE PRESSURE MODE.

CLOTHING: EMPLOYEE MUST WEAR APPROPRIATE PROTECTIVE (IMPERVIOUS) CLOTHING AND EQUIPMENT TO PREVENT REPEATED OR PROLONGED SKIN CONTACT WITH THIS SUBSTANCE.

GLOVES: EMPLOYEE MUST WEAR APPROPRIATE PROTECTIVE GLOVES TO PREVENT CONTACT WITH THIS SUBSTANCE.

EYE PROTECTION: EMPLOYEE MUST WEAR SPLASH-PROOF OR DUST-RESISTANT SAFETY GOGGLES TO PREVENT EYE CONTACT WITH THIS SUBSTANCE. EMERGENCY EYE WASH: WHERE THERE IS ANY POSSIBILITY THAT AN EMPLOYEE'S EYES MAY BE EXPOSED TO THIS SUBSTANCE, THE EMPLOYER SHOULD PROVIDE AN EYE WASH FOUNTAIN WITHIN THE IMMEDIATE WORK AREA FOR EMERGENCY USE.

AUTHORIZED BY- OCCUPATIONAL HEALTH SERVICES, INC.
CREATION DATE: 11/16/89 ***REVISION DATE:*** 05/18/90

MATERIAL SAFETY DATA SHEET

OCCUPATIONAL HEALTH SERVICES, INC.
AGRICULTURE AND PESTICIDE DIVISION
450 SEVENTH AVENUE, SUITE 2407
NEW YORK, NEW YORK 10123
1-800-445-MSDS OR (212) 967-1100

EMERGENCY CONTACT:
JOHN S. BRANSFORD, JR. (615) 292-1180

SUBSTANCE IDENTIFICATION

CAS-NUMBER 10043-52-4

SUBSTANCE: CALCIUM CHLORIDE

TRADE NAMES/SYNONYMS: CALCIUM DICHLORIDE; CALCOSAN; URAMINE MC; CALCIUM CHLORIDE (CACL2); CACL2; PST03900

CHEMICAL FAMILY: INORGANIC SALT

MOLECULAR FORMULA: CA-CL2

MOLECULAR WEIGHT: 110.99

CERCLA RATINGS (SCALE 0-3): HEALTH=3 FIRE=0 REACTIVITY=1 PERSISTENCE=0

NFPA RATINGS (SCALE 0-4): HEALTH=U FIRE=0 REACTIVITY=1

COMPONENTS AND CONTAMINANTS

COMPONENT: CALCIUM CHLORIDE ***PERCENT:*** 100.0
CAS# 10043-52-4

OTHER CONTAMINANTS: NONE

EXPOSURE LIMITS: CALCIUM CHLORIDE: NO OCCUPATIONAL EXPOSURE LIMITS ESTABLISHED BY OSHA, ACGIH, OR NIOSH.
MALLINCKRODT INCORPORATED RECOMMENDS 5 MG/M3 TWA.

PHYSICAL DATA

DESCRIPTION: COLORLESS, DELIQUESCENT CRYSTALS. ***BOILING POINT:*** >2912 F (>1600 C)

MELTING POINT: 1440 F (782 C) ***SPECIFIC GRAVITY:*** 2.15 @ 25 C

SOLUBILITY IN WATER: 74.5% @ 20 C

SOLVENT SOLUBILITY: SOLUBLE IN ALCOHOL, ACETIC ACID, ACETONE.

FIRE AND EXPLOSION DATA

FIRE AND EXPLOSION HAZARD: NEGLIGIBLE FIRE HAZARD WHEN EXPOSED TO HEAT OR FLAME.

FIREFIGHTING MEDIA: EXTINGUISH USING AGENT SUITABLE FOR TYPE OF SURROUNDING FIRE.

FIREFIGHTING: NO ACUTE HAZARD. MOVE CONTAINER FROM FIRE AREA IF POSSIBLE. AVOID BREATHING VAPORS OR DUSTS; KEEP UPWIND.

TOXICITY

CALCIUM CHLORIDE: TOXICITY DATA: ANHYDROUS: 1000 MG/KG ORAL-RAT LD50; 1384 MG/KG ORAL-RABBIT LDLO; 1940 MG/KG ORAL-MOUSE LD50; 264 MG/KG INTRAPERITONEAL-RAT LD50; 161 MG/KG INTRAVENOUS-RAT LDLO; 25 MG/KG INTRAMUSCULAR-RAT LD50; 245 MG/KG INTRAPERITONEAL-MOUSE LD50; 110 MG/KG INTRAPERITONEAL-DOG LDLO; 274 MG/KG SUBCUTANEOUS-DOG LDLO; 274 MG/KG INTRAVENOUS-DOG LDLO; 249 MG/KG SUBCUTANEOUS-CAT LDLO; 249 MG/KG INTRAVENOUS-CAT LDLO; 42 MG/KG INTRAVENOUS-MOUSE LD50; 274 MG/KG INTRAVENOUS-RABBIT LDLO; 823 MG/KG SUBCUTANEOUS-MOUSE LD50; 2630 MG/KG SUBCUTANEOUS-RAT LD50; 472 MG/KG SUBCUTANEOUS-RABBIT LDLO; 150 MG/KG INTRAVENOUS-GUINEA PIG LDLO; 300 MG/KG INTRAARTERIAL-GUINEA PIG LDLO; 20 MG/KG/1 HOUR INTRAVENOUS-WOMEN TDLO; MUTAGENIC DATA (RTECS); TUMORIGENIC DATA (RTECS). DIHYDRATE: 20500 MG/KG

INTRAPERITONEAL-MOUSE LD50. CARCINOGEN STATUS: NONE. LOCAL EFFECTS: CORROSIVE-SKIN; IRRITANT-EYE, MUCOUS MEMBRANE. ACUTE TOXICITY LEVEL: MODERATELY TOXIC BY INGESTION. TARGET EFFECTS: NO DATA AVAILABLE.

HEALTH EFFECTS AND FIRST AID

INHALATION: CALCIUM CHLORIDE: IRRITANT. **ACUTE EXPOSURE-** INHALATION OF DUST MAY CAUSE IRRITATION WITH COUGHING AND SHORTNESS OF BREATH. **CHRONIC EXPOSURE-** WORKERS PACKING DRY CALCIUM CHLORIDE REPORTED A BURNING SENSATION AND PAIN IN THE NASAL CAVITIES, OCCASIONAL NOSE BLEED, AND TICKLING IN THE THROAT. PERFORATION OF THE NASAL SEPTUM HAS BEEN REPORTED.

FIRST AID- REMOVE FROM EXPOSURE AREA TO FRESH AIR IMMEDIATELY. IF BREATHING HAS STOPPED, PERFORM ARTIFICIAL RESPIRATION. KEEP PERSON WARM AND AT REST. TREAT SYMPTOMATICALLY AND SUPPORTIVELY. GET MEDICAL ATTENTION IMMEDIATELY.

SKIN CONTACT: CALCIUM CHLORIDE: CORROSIVE. **ACUTE EXPOSURE-** DIRECT CONTACT WITH DUST OR SOLUTIONS MAY CAUSE SEVERE IRRITATION, ERYTHEMA, BLISTERING, EXFOLIATION, ULCERATION, NECROSIS AND SCARRING. THE DEGREE OF CORROSION DEPENDS ON THE CONCENTRATION AND DURATION OF CONTACT. **CHRONIC EXPOSURE-** EFFECTS DEPEND ON CONCENTRATION AND DURATION OF EXPOSURE. REPEATED OR PROLONGED CONTACT WITH CORROSIVE SUBSTANCES MAY RESULT IN DERMATITIS OR EFFECTS SIMILAR TO THOSE IN ACUTE EXPOSURE.

FIRST AID- REMOVE CONTAMINATED CLOTHING AND SHOES IMMEDIATELY. WASH AFFECTED AREA WITH SOAP OR MILD DETERGENT AND LARGE AMOUNTS OF WATER UNTIL NO EVIDENCE OF CHEMICAL REMAINS (AT LEAST 15-20 MINUTES). IN CASE OF CHEMICAL BURNS, COVER AREA WITH STERILE, DRY DRESSING. BANDAGE SECURELY, BUT NOT TOO TIGHTLY. GET MEDICAL ATTENTION IMMEDIATELY.

EYE CONTACT: CALCIUM CHLORIDE: IRRITANT. **ACUTE EXPOSURE-** DIRECT CONTACT WITH THE DUST MAY CAUSE IRRITATION WITH REDNESS AND PAIN AND SUPERFICIAL INJURY. LACRIMATION AND EYE DISCHARGE MAY ALSO OCCUR. DIRECT CONTACT OF CALCIUM CHLORIDE IN SOLUTION IS ESSENTIALLY INNOCUOUS. APPLICATION OF 2-10% SOLUTION TO RABBIT EYES CAUSED NO PERMANENT INJURY. **CHRONIC EXPOSURE-** REPEATED OR PROLONGED EXPOSURE TO EYE IRRITANTS MAY RESULT IN CONJUNCTIVITIS.

FIRST AID- WASH EYES IMMEDIATELY WITH LARGE AMOUNTS OF WATER OR NORMAL SALINE, OCCASIONALLY LIFTING UPPER AND LOWER LIDS, UNTIL NO EVIDENCE OF CHEMICAL REMAINS (APPROXIMATELY 15-20 MINUTES). GET MEDICAL ATTENTION IMMEDIATELY.

INGESTION: CALCIUM CHLORIDE: **ACUTE EXPOSURE-** MAY CAUSE ABDOMINAL SPASMS AND NAUSEA. OVERDOSES MAY CAUSE GASTROINTESTINAL TRACT OR CARDIOVASCULAR IRREGULARITIES. THE FATAL DOSE IS ESTIMATED TO BE 30 GM. **CHRONIC EXPOSURE-** IT IS USED AS A FOOD ADDITIVE.

FIRST AID- TREAT SYMPTOMATICALLY AND SUPPORTIVELY. GET MEDICAL ATTENTION IMMEDIATELY. IF VOMITING OCCURS, KEEP HEAD LOWER THAN HIPS TO PREVENT ASPIRATION.

ANTIDOTE: NO SPECIFIC ANTIDOTE. TREAT SYMPTOMATICALLY AND SUPPORTIVELY.

REACTIVITY

REACTIVITY: REACTS EXOTHERMICALLY WITH WATER.

INCOMPATIBILITIES: CALCIUM CHLORIDE: BORIC OXIDE + CALCIUM OXIDE: POSSIBLE VIOLENT INCANDESCENT REACTION. BROMINE TRIFLUORIDE: POSSIBLE VIOLENT REACTION. FURAN-2-PEROXYCARBOXYLIC ACID: EXPLODES. METALS: CORROSIVE IN THE PRESENCE OF MOISTURE. METHYL VINYL ETHER: MAY INITIATE EXOTHERMIC POLYMERIZATION. ZINC: CORRODES, RELEASING FLAMMABLE HYDROGEN GAS.

DECOMPOSITION: THERMAL DECOMPOSITION PRODUCTS MAY INCLUDE TOXIC AND CORROSIVE FUMES OF CHLORINE.

POLYMERIZATION: HAZARDOUS POLYMERIZATION HAS NOT BEEN REPORTED TO OCCUR UNDER NORMAL TEMPERATURES AND PRESSURES.

STORAGE AND DISPOSAL

OBSERVE ALL FEDERAL, STATE AND LOCAL REGULATIONS WHEN STORING OR DISPOSING OF THIS SUBSTANCE. FOR ASSISTANCE, CONTACT THE DISTRICT DIRECTOR OF THE ENVIRONMENTAL PROTECTION AGENCY.

STORAGE

STORE AWAY FROM INCOMPATIBLE SUBSTANCES.
STORE IN A TIGHTLY CLOSED CONTAINER.

CONDITIONS TO AVOID

NO REPORTS FOUND.

SPILL AND LEAK PROCEDURES

OCCUPATIONAL SPILL: SWEEP UP AND PLACE IN SUITABLE CLEAN, DRY CONTAINERS FOR RECLAMATION OR LATER DISPOSAL. DO NOT FLUSH SPILLED MATERIAL INTO SEWER. KEEP UNNECESSARY PEOPLE AWAY.

PROTECTIVE EQUIPMENT

VENTILATION: PROVIDE LOCAL EXHAUST OR PROCESS ENCLOSURE VENTILATION SYSTEM.

RESPIRATOR: THE FOLLOWING RESPIRATORS ARE RECOMMENDED BASED ON INFORMATION FOUND IN THE PHYSICAL DATA, TOXICITY AND HEALTH EFFECTS SECTIONS. THEY ARE RANKED IN ORDER FROM MINIMUM TO MAXIMUM RESPIRATORY PROTECTION. THE SPECIFIC RESPIRATOR SELECTED MUST BE BASED ON CONTAMINATION LEVELS FOUND IN THE WORK PLACE, MUST NOT EXCEED THE WORKING LIMITS OF THE RESPIRATOR AND BE JOINTLY APPROVED BY THE NATIONAL INSTITUTE FOR OCCUPATIONAL SAFETY AND HEALTH AND THE MINE SAFETY AND HEALTH ADMINISTRATION (NIOSH-MSHA).
DUST AND MIST RESPIRATOR WITH A FULL FACEPIECE.
AIR-PURIFYING FULL FACEPIECE RESPIRATOR WITH A HIGH-EFFICIENCY PARTICULATE FILTER.
POWERED AIR-PURIFYING RESPIRATOR WITH A TIGHT-FITTING FACEPIECE AND HIGH-EFFICIENCY PARTICULATE FILTER.
TYPE 'C' SUPPLIED-AIR RESPIRATOR WITH A FULL FACEPIECE OPERATED IN PRESSURE-DEMAND OR OTHER POSITIVE PRESSURE MODE OR WITH A FULL FACEPIECE, HELMET OR HOOD OPERATED IN CONTINUOUS-FLOW MODE.
SELF-CONTAINED BREATHING APPARATUS WITH A FULL FACEPIECE OPERATED IN PRESSURE-DEMAND OR OTHER POSITIVE PRESSURE MODE. FOR FIREFIGHTING AND OTHER IMMEDIATELY DANGEROUS TO LIFE OR HEALTH CONDITIONS:
SELF-CONTAINED BREATHING APPARATUS WITH FULL FACEPIECE OPERATED IN PRESSURE-DEMAND OR OTHER POSITIVE PRESSURE MODE.
SUPPLIED-AIR RESPIRATOR WITH FULL FACEPIECE AND OPERATED IN PRESSURE-DEMAND OR OTHER POSITIVE PRESSURE MODE IN COMBINATION WITH AN AUXILIARY SELF-CONTAINED BREATHING APPARATUS OPERATED IN PRESSURE-DEMAND OR OTHER POSITIVE PRESSURE MODE.

CLOTHING: EMPLOYEE MUST WEAR APPROPRIATE PROTECTIVE (IMPERVIOUS) CLOTHING AND EQUIPMENT TO PREVENT ANY POSSIBILITY OF SKIN CONTACT WITH THIS SUBSTANCE.

GLOVES: EMPLOYEE MUST WEAR APPROPRIATE PROTECTIVE GLOVES TO PREVENT CONTACT WITH THIS SUBSTANCE.

EYE PROTECTION: EMPLOYEE MUST WEAR SPLASH-PROOF OR DUST-RESISTANT SAFETY GOGGLES AND A FACESHIELD TO PREVENT CONTACT WITH THIS SUBSTANCE.
EMERGENCY WASH FACILITIES: WHERE THERE IS ANY POSSIBILITY THAT AN EMPLOYEE'S EYES AND/OR SKIN MAY BE EXPOSED TO THIS SUBSTANCE, THE EMPLOYER SHOULD PROVIDE AN EYE WASH FOUNTAIN AND QUICK DRENCH SHOWER WITHIN THE IMMEDIATE WORK AREA FOR EMERGENCY USE.

AUTHORIZED BY- OCCUPATIONAL HEALTH SERVICES, INC.
CREATION DATE: 11/16/89 ***REVISION DATE:*** 05/31/90

MATERIAL SAFETY DATA SHEET

OCCUPATIONAL HEALTH SERVICES, INC.
AGRICULTURE AND PESTICIDE DIVISION
450 SEVENTH AVENUE, SUITE 2407
NEW YORK, NEW YORK 10123
1-800-445-MSDS OR (212) 967-1100

EMERGENCY CONTACT:
JOHN S. BRANSFORD, JR. (615) 292-1180

SUBSTANCE IDENTIFICATION

CAS-NUMBER 156-62-7

SUBSTANCE: **CALCIUM CYANAMIDE, NOT HYDRATED**

TRADE NAMES/SYNONYMS: CALCIUM CARBIMIDE; CYANAMID; CYANAMIDE, CALCIUM SALT; CALCIUM CYANAMID; NITROLIME; UN 1403; PST03930

CHEMICAL FAMILY: CYANAMIDE

MOLECULAR FORMULA: CA-C-N2 MOL WT: 80.11

CERCLA RATINGS (SCALE 0-3): HEALTH=3 FIRE=0 REACTIVITY=3 PERSISTENCE=0

NFPA RATINGS (SCALE 0-4): HEALTH=3 FIRE=0 REACTIVITY=3

COMPONENTS AND CONTAMINANTS

COMPONENT: CALCIUM CYANAMIDE ***PERCENT:*** >99
COMPONENT: CALCIUM CARBIDE ***PERCENT:*** >0.1

OTHER CONTAMINANTS: CARBON, CALCIUM HYDROXIDE, CALCIUM OXIDE, CALCIUM CARBONATE

EXPOSURE LIMITS: CALCIUM CYANAMIDE: 0.5 MG/M3 OSHA TWA 0.5 MG/M3 ACGIH TWA

SUBJECT TO SARA SECTION 313 ANNUAL TOXIC CHEMICAL RELEASE REPORTING

PHYSICAL DATA

DESCRIPTION: WHITE TO GRAYISH-BLACK CRYSTALLINE SOLID OR GRANULES

MELTING POINT: 2372 F (1300 C) ***SPECIFIC GRAVITY:*** 2.3

SOLUBILITY IN WATER: DECOMPOSES

SOLVENT SOLUBILITY: DECOMPOSES IN ALL KNOWN SOLVENTS

FIRE AND EXPLOSION DATA

FIRE AND EXPLOSION HAZARD: DANGEROUS WHEN WET! DECOMPOSES IN WATER, RELEASING HIGHLY FLAMMABLE AND EXPLOSIVE ACETYLENE.

FLASH POINT: NONFLAMMABLE

FIREFIGHTING MEDIA: DRY CHEMICAL, SODA ASH, LIME OR SAND (1987 EMERGENCY RESPONSE GUIDEBOOK, DOT P 5800.4).

FOR LARGER FIRE, WITHDRAW FROM AREA AND LET FIRE BURN.

FIREFIGHTING: MOVE CONTAINER FROM FIRE AREA IF POSSIBLE. DO NOT SCATTER SPILLED MATERIAL WITH HIGH PRESSURE WATER STREAMS. DIKE FIRE CONTROL WATER FOR LATER DISPOSAL (1987 EMERGENCY RESPONSE GUIDEBOOK, DOT P 5800.4, GUIDE PAGE 31).

USE AGENTS SUITABLE FOR TYPE OF SURROUNDING FIRE. AVOID BREATHING HAZARDOUS VAPORS, KEEP UPWIND.

TRANSPORTATION DATA

DEPARTMENT OF TRANSPORTATION HAZARD CLASSIFICATION 49 CFR 172.101: ORM-C

DEPARTMENT OF TRANSPORTATION LABELING REQUIREMENTS 49 CFR 172.101 AND SUBPART E: NONE

DEPARTMENT OF TRANSPORTATION PACKAGING REQUIREMENTS: 49 CFR 173.945 EXCEPTIONS: NONE

TOXICITY

CALCIUM CYANAMIDE: TOXICITY DATA: 590 MG/KG SKIN-RABBIT LD50; 571 MG/KG ORAL-HUMAN LDLO; 158 MG/KG ORAL-RAT LD50; 334 MG/KG ORAL-MOUSE LD50; 1400 MG/KG ORAL-RABBIT LD50; 125 MG/KG INTRAVENOUS-RAT LD50; 282 MG/KG INTRAVENOUS-MOUSE LD50; 100 MG/KG INTRAPERITONEAL-MOUSE LD50; 1000 MG/KG UNREPORTED-RAT LD50; MUTAGENIC DATA (RTECS); TUMORIGENIC DATA (RTECS). CARCINOGEN STATUS: NONE. LOCAL EFFECTS: IRRITANT-INHALATION, SKIN, AND EYES. ACUTE TOXICITY LEVEL: TOXIC BY DERMAL ABSORPTION AND INGESTION. TARGET EFFECTS: POISONING MAY AFFECT THE CARDIOVASCULAR SYSTEM. ADDITIONAL DATA: THIS CHEMICAL DOES NOT EXHIBIT CYANIDE TOXICITY. ALCOHOLIC BEVERAGES ENHANCE THE TOXICITY OF CALCIUM CYANAMIDE.

HEALTH EFFECTS AND FIRST AID

INHALATION: CALCIUM CYANAMIDE: IRRITANT. **ACUTE EXPOSURE-** HIGH LEVELS MAY PRODUCE NASAL AND THROAT IRRITATION, NASAL ULCERATION, RHINITIS AND GINGIVITIS. HEADACHE, FLUSHING OF THE SKIN, DYSPNEA, HYPOTENSION, RAPID PULSE, RESPIRATION AND SHOCK MAY OCCUR, ESPECIALLY IF ETHYL ALCOHOL IS CONSUMED FOLLOWING EXPOSURE. **CHRONIC EXPOSURE-** HAS NOT BEEN REPORTED IN HUMANS.

FIRST AID- REMOVE FROM EXPOSURE AREA TO FRESH AIR IMMEDIATELY. IF BREATHING HAS STOPPED, PERFORM ARTIFICIAL RESPIRATION. KEEP PERSON WARM AND AT REST. TREAT SYMPTOMATICALLY AND SUPPORTIVELY. GET MEDICAL ATTENTION IMMEDIATELY.

SKIN CONTACT: CALCIUM CYANAMIDE: IRRITANT. **ACUTE EXPOSURE-** CONTACT MAY CAUSE IRRITATION, WITH ERYTHEMA AND ECZEMA, PARTICULARLY ON THE MOIST AREAS OF THE SKIN. PROLONGED CONTACT MAY LEAD TO ULCERATION, WITH BLACK AREAS OF NECROSIS. **CHRONIC EXPOSURE-** REPEATED OR PROLONGED CONTACT MAY RESULT IN THE FORMATION OF DERMATITIS.

FIRST AID- REMOVE CONTAMINATED CLOTHING AND SHOES IMMEDIATELY. WASH AFFECTED AREA WITH SOAP OR MILD DETERGENT AND LARGE AMOUNTS OF WATER UNTIL NO EVIDENCE OF CHEMICAL REMAINS (APPROXIMATELY 15-20 MINUTES). GET MEDICAL ATTENTION IMMEDIATELY.

EYE CONTACT: CALCIUM CYANAMIDE: IRRITANT. **ACUTE EXPOSURE-** VAPOR OR DIRECT CONTACT MAY CAUSE IRRITATION. **CHRONIC EXPOSURE-** REPEATED OR PROLONGED EXPOSURE MAY CAUSE CONJUNCTIVITIS.

FIRST AID- WASH EYES IMMEDIATELY WITH LARGE AMOUNTS OF WATER OR NORMAL SALINE, OCCASIONALLY LIFTING UPPER AND LOWER LIDS, UNTIL NO EVIDENCE OF CHEMICAL REMAINS (APPROXIMATELY 15-20 MINUTES). GET MEDICAL ATTENTION IMMEDIATELY.

INGESTION: CALCIUM CYANAMIDE: NARCOTIC. **ACUTE EXPOSURE-** INGESTION MAY CAUSE THE SAME SYSTEMIC EFFECTS AS INHALATION: HEADACHE, DIZZINESS, HYPOTENSION, RAPID RESPIRATION, SHOCK, ESPECIALLY WITH ETHYL ALCOHOL CONSUMPTION AFTER EXPOSURE. **CHRONIC EXPOSURE-** HAS NOT BEEN REPORTED IN HUMANS.

FIRST AID- REMOVE BY GASTRIC LAVAGE OR EMESIS. MAINTAIN BLOOD PRESSURE AND AIRWAY. GIVE OXYGEN IF RESPIRATION IS DEPRESSED. DO NOT PERFORM GASTRIC LAVAGE OR EMESIS IF VICTIM IS UNCONSCIOUS. GET MEDICAL ATTENTION IMMEDIATELY (DREISBACH, HANDBOOK OF POISONING, 11TH ED.). ADMINISTRATION OF GASTRIC LAVAGE OR OXYGEN SHOULD BE PERFORMED BY QUALIFIED MEDICAL PERSONNEL.

ANTIDOTE: NO SPECIFIC ANTIDOTE. TREAT SYMPTOMATICALLY AND SUPPORTIVELY.

REACTIVITY

REACTIVITY: CALCIUM CYANAMIDE: DANGEROUS WHEN WET! RELEASES HIGHLY FLAMMABLE AND EXPLOSIVE ACETYLENE. REACTS VIGOROUSLY WITH ACIDS.

INCOMPATIBILITIES: CALCIUM CYANAMIDE: WATER: RELEASES HIGHLY FLAMMABLE AND EXPLOSIVE ACETYLENE. ACIDS: VIGOROUS REACTION.

DECOMPOSITION: THERMAL DECOMPOSITION MAY RELEASE HIGHLY TOXIC VAPORS OF HYDROGEN CYANIDE, AND TOXIC OXIDES OF NITROGEN AND CARBON.

POLYMERIZATION: HAZARDOUS POLYMERIZATION HAS NOT BEEN REPORTED TO OCCUR UNDER NORMAL TEMPERATURES AND PRESSURES.

CONDITIONS TO AVOID

MAY IGNITE ITSELF IF EXPOSED TO AIR OR IN PRESENCE OF MOISTURE. MAY RE-IGNITE AFTER FIRE IS EXTINGUISHED. VIOLENT REACTION WITH WATER PRODUCES FLAMMABLE GAS. RUNOFF TO SEWER MAY CREATE FIRE OR EXPLOSION HAZARD.

SPILL AND LEAK PROCEDURES

SOIL SPILL: DIG A PIT, POND, LAGOON OR HOLDING AREA TO CONTAIN LIQUID OR SOLID MATERIAL. COVER SOLIDS WITH A PLASTIC SHEET TO PREVENT DISSOLVING IN RAIN OR FIREFIGHTING WATER.

WATER SPILL: USE ACTIVATED CARBON TO ABSORB SPILLED SUBSTANCE THAT IS DISSOLVED.

USE SUCTION HOSES TO REMOVE TRAPPED SPILL MATERIAL.

USE MECHANICAL DREDGES OR LIFTS TO EXTRACT IMMOBILIZED MASSES OF POLLUTION AND PRECIPITATES.

OCCUPATIONAL SPILL: SHUT OFF IGNITION SOURCES. DO NOT TOUCH SPILLED MATERIAL. STOP LEAK IF YOU CAN DO IT WITHOUT RISK. DO NOT GET WATER ON SPILLED MATERIAL OR INSIDE THE CONTAINER. FOR SMALL DRY SPILLS, WITH CLEAN SHOVEL PLACE MATERIAL INTO CLEAN, DRY CONTAINER AND COVER; MOVE CONTAINERS FROM SPILL AREA. FOR SMALL LIQUID SPILLS, TAKE UP WITH SAND OR OTHER ABSORBENT MATERIAL AND PLACE INTO CONTAINERS FOR LATER DISPOSAL. FOR LARGER SPILLS, DIKE SPILL FOR LATER DISPOSAL. COVER POWDER SPILLS WITH PLASTIC SHEET OR TARP TO MINIMIZE SPREADING. KEEP UNNECESSARY PEOPLE AWAY. ISOLATE HAZARD AREA AND DENY ENTRY.

PROTECTIVE EQUIPMENT

VENTILATION: PROCESS ENCLOSURE RECOMMENDED TO MEET PUBLISHED EXPOSURE LIMITS.

RESPIRATOR: THE FOLLOWING RESPIRATORS ARE RECOMMENDED BASED ON INFORMATION FOUND IN THE PHYSICAL DATA, TOXICITY AND HEALTH EFFECTS SECTIONS. THEY ARE RANKED IN ORDER FROM MINIMUM TO MAXIMUM RESPIRATORY PROTECTION. THE SPECIFIC RESPIRATOR SELECTED MUST BE BASED ON CONTAMINATION LEVELS FOUND IN THE WORK PLACE, MUST NOT EXCEED THE WORKING LIMITS OF THE RESPIRATOR AND BE JOINTLY APPROVED BY THE NATIONAL INSTITUTE FOR OCCUPATIONAL SAFETY AND HEALTH AND THE MINE SAFETY AND HEALTH ADMINISTRATION (NIOSH-MSHA).

TYPE 'C' SUPPLIED-AIR RESPIRATOR WITH A FULL FACEPIECE OPERATED IN PRESSURE-DEMAND OR OTHER POSITIVE PRESSURE MODE OR WITH A FULL FACEPIECE, HELMET OR HOOD OPERATED IN CONTINOUS-FLOW MODE.

SELF-CONTAINED BREATHING APPARATUS WITH A FULL FACEPIECE OPERATED IN PRESSURE-DEMAND OR OTHER POSITIVE PRESSURE MODE.

FOR FIREFIGHTING AND OTHER IMMEDIATELY DANGEROUS TO LIFE OR HEALTH CONDITIONS:

SELF-CONTAINED BREATHING APPARATUS WITH FULL FACEPIECE OPERATED IN PRESSURE-DEMAND OR OTHER POSITIVE PRESSURE MODE.

SUPPLIED-AIR RESPIRATOR WITH FULL FACEPIECE AND OPERATED IN PRESSURE-DEMAND OR OTHER POSITIVE PRESSURE MODE IN COMBINATION WITH AN AUXILIARY SELF-CONTAINED BREATHING APPARATUS OPERATED IN PRESSURE-DEMAND OR OTHER POSITIVE PRESSURE MODE.

CLOTHING: EMPLOYEE MUST WEAR APPROPRIATE PROTECTIVE (IMPERVIOUS) CLOTHING AND EQUIPMENT TO PREVENT ANY POSSIBILITY OF SKIN CONTACT WITH THIS SUBSTANCE.

GLOVES: EMPLOYEE MUST WEAR APPROPRIATE PROTECTIVE GLOVES TO PREVENT CONTACT WITH THIS SUBSTANCE.

EYE PROTECTION: EMPLOYEE MUST WEAR SPLASH-PROOF OR DUST-RESISTANT SAFETY GOGGLES AND A FACESHIELD TO PREVENT CONTACT WITH THIS SUBSTANCE.
EMERGENCY WASH FACILITIES: WHERE THERE IS ANY POSSIBILITY THAT AN EMPLOYEE'S EYES AND/OR SKIN MAY BE EXPOSED TO THIS SUBSTANCE, THE EMPLOYER SHOULD PROVIDE AN EYE WASH FOUNTAIN AND QUICK DRENCH SHOWER WITHIN THE IMMEDIATE WORK AREA FOR EMERGENCY USE.

AUTHORIZED BY- OCCUPATIONAL HEALTH SERVICES, INC.
CREATION DATE: 11/15/89 ***REVISION DATE:*** 05/18/90

MATERIAL SAFETY DATA SHEET

OCCUPATIONAL HEALTH SERVICES, INC.
AGRICULTURE AND PESTICIDE DIVISION
450 SEVENTH AVENUE, SUITE 2407
NEW YORK, NEW YORK 10123
1-800-445-MSDS OR (212) 967-1100

EMERGENCY CONTACT:
JOHN S. BRANSFORD, JR. (615) 292-1180

SUBSTANCE IDENTIFICATION

CAS-NUMBER 1305-62-0
SUBSTANCE: CALCIUM HYDROXIDE
TRADE NAMES/SYNONYMS: HYDRATED LIME; CALCIUM HYDRATE; LIME WATER; SLAKED LIME; CAUSTIC LIME; BIOCALC; CALCIUM DIHYDROXIDE; CALCIT; CALCIUM HYDROXIDE (CA(OH)2); CAH2O2; PST03980
CHEMICAL FAMILY: INORGANIC BASE
MOLECULAR FORMULA: CA-(OH)2
MOLECULAR WEIGHT: 74.09
CERCLA RATINGS (SCALE 0-3): HEALTH=1 FIRE=0 REACTIVITY=0 PERSISTENCE=0
NFPA RATINGS (SCALE 0-4): HEALTH=U FIRE=0 REACTIVITY=0

COMPONENTS AND CONTAMINANTS

COMPONENT: CALCIUM HYDROXIDE ***PERCENT:*** 100.0
CAS# 1305-62-0
OTHER CONTAMINANTS: NONE
EXPOSURE LIMITS: CALCIUM HYDROXIDE: 5 MG/M3 OSHA TWA (RESPIRABLE FRACTION); 15 MG/M3 OSHA TWA (TOTAL DUST) 5 MG/M3 ACGIH TWA

PHYSICAL DATA

DESCRIPTION: ODORLESS, WHITE, CRYSTALLINE POWDER WITH A SLIGHTLY BITTER TASTE.
MELTING POINT: 1076 F (580 C) (DECOMPOSES) ***SPECIFIC GRAVITY:*** 2.24
PH: 12.4 @ SATD SOLUTION ***SOLUBILITY IN WATER:*** 0.185% @ 0 C
SOLVENT SOLUBILITY: SOLUBLE IN AMMONIUM SALT SOLUTIONS, GLYCEROL, SUGAR, SATURATED SUGAR SOLUTIONS; INSOLUBLE IN ALCOHOL.

FIRE AND EXPLOSION DATA

FIRE AND EXPLOSION HAZARD: NEGLIGIBLE FIRE HAZARD WHEN EXPOSED TO HEAT OR FLAME.
FIREFIGHTING MEDIA: EXTINGUISH USING AGENT SUITABLE FOR TYPE OF SURROUNDING FIRE.
FIREFIGHTING: NO ACUTE HAZARD. MOVE CONTAINER FROM FIRE AREA IF POSSIBLE. AVOID BREATHING VAPORS OR DUSTS; KEEP UPWIND.

TOXICITY

CALCIUM HYDROXIDE: IRRITATION DATA: 10 MG EYE-RABBIT SEVERE. TOXICITY DATA: 7340 MG/KG ORAL-RAT LD50; 7300 MG/KG ORAL-MOUSE LD50; MUTAGENIC DATA (RTECS). CARCINOGEN STATUS: NONE. LOCAL EFFECTS: CORROSIVE- INHALATION, SKIN, EYE, INGESTION. ACUTE TOXICITY LEVEL: SLIGHTLY TOXIC BY INGESTION. TARGET EFFECTS: NO DATA AVAILABLE. AT INCREASED RISK FROM EXPOSURE: PERSONS WITH PREEXISTING SKIN DISORDERS.

HEALTH EFFECTS AND FIRST AID

INHALATION: CALCIUM HYDROXIDE: CORROSIVE. SEE INFORMATION ON ALKALINE CORROSIVES.
ALKALINE CORROSIVES: **ACUTE EXPOSURE-** MAY CAUSE IRRITATION OF THE RESPIRATORY TRACT WITH COUGHING, CHOKING, PAIN AND POSSIBLY BURNS OF THE MUCOUS MEMBRANES. IN SOME CASES, PULMONARY EDEMA MAY DEVELOP, EITHER IMMEDIATELY IN SEVERE CASES OR MORE OFTEN WITH A LATENT PERIOD OF 5-72 HOURS. THE SYMPTOMS MAY INCLUDE TIGHTNESS IN THE CHEST, DYSPNEA, FROTHY SPUTUM, CYANOSIS, AND DIZZINESS. PHYSICAL FINDINGS MAY INCLUDE HYPOTENSION, WEAK AND RAPID PULSE AND MOIST RALES. SEVERE CASES MAY BE FATAL. **CHRONIC EXPOSURE-** DEPENDING ON THE CONCENTRATION AND DURATION OF EXPOSURE, REPEATED OR PROLONGED EXPOSURE MAY CAUSE INFLAMMATORY AND ULCERATIVE CHANGES IN THE MOUTH AND POSSIBLY BRONCHIAL AND GASTROINTESTINAL DISTURBANCES.
FIRST AID- REMOVE FROM EXPOSURE AREA TO FRESH AIR IMMEDIATELY. IF BREATHING HAS STOPPED, GIVE ARTIFICIAL RESPIRATION. MAINTAIN AIRWAY AND BLOOD PRESSURE AND ADMINISTER OXYGEN IF AVAILABLE. KEEP AFFECTED PERSON WARM AND AT REST. TREAT SYMPTOMATICALLY AND SUPPORTIVELY. ADMINISTRATION OF OXYGEN SHOULD BE PERFORMED BY QUALIFIED PERSONNEL. GET MEDICAL ATTENTION IMMEDIATELY.

SKIN CONTACT: CALCIUM HYDROXIDE: CORROSIVE. SEE INFORMATION ON ALKALINE CORROSIVES.
ALKALINE CORROSIVES: **ACUTE EXPOSURE-** DIRECT CONTACT MAY CAUSE SEVERE PAIN, BURNS AND POSSIBLY BROWNISH STAINS. THE CORRODED AREAS MAY BE SOFT, GELATINOUS AND NECROTIC AND THE TISSUE DESTRUCTION MAY BE DEEP. **CHRONIC EXPOSURE-** EFFECTS DEPEND ON THE CONCENTRATION AND DURATION OF EXPOSURE. REPEATED OR PROLONGED CONTACT MAY CAUSE DERMATITIS OR EFFECTS SIMILAR TO ACUTE EXPOSURE.
FIRST AID- REMOVE CONTAMINATED CLOTHING AND SHOES IMMEDIATELY. WASH AFFECTED AREA WITH SOAP OR MILD DETERGENT AND LARGE AMOUNTS OF WATER UNTIL NO EVIDENCE OF CHEMICAL REMAINS (AT LEAST 15-20 MINUTES). IN CASE OF CHEMICAL BURNS, COVER AREA WITH STERILE, DRY DRESSING. BANDAGE SECURELY, BUT NOT TOO TIGHTLY. GET MEDICAL ATTENTION IMMEDIATELY.

EYE CONTACT: CALCIUM HYDROXIDE: CORROSIVE. SEE INFORMATION ON ALKALINE CORROSIVES. CORNEAS SEVERELY BURNED TYPICALLY ARE ANESTHETIZED FOR MANY DAYS PRESUMABLY DUE TO DAMAGE TO THE CORNEAL NERVES. GLAUCOMA MAY BE A LATE COMPLICATION POSSIBLY CAUSED BY SCARRING AND BLOCKAGE OF AQUEOUS OUTFLOW CHANNELS.
ALKALINE CORROSIVES: **ACUTE EXPOSURE-** DIRECT CONTACT MAY CAUSE PAIN AND BURNS. THERE MAY BE EDEMA, DESTRUCTION OF EPITHELIUM, CORNEAL OPACIFICATION AND IRITIS. WHEN DAMAGE IS LESS THAN EXCESSIVE, THESE SYMPTOMS TEND TO AMELIORATE. IN SEVERE BURNS, THE FULL EXTENT OF THE INJURY MAY NOT BE IMMEDIATELY APPARENT. LATE COMPLICATIONS MAY INCLUDE PERSISTENT EDEMA, VASCULARIZATION AND SCARRING OF THE CORNEA, PERMANENT OPACITY, STAPHYLOMA, CATARACT, SYMBLEPHARON AND BLINDNESS. **CHRONIC EXPOSURE-** EFFECTS DEPEND ON CONCENTRATION AND DURATION OF EXPOSURE. REPEATED OR PROLONGED CONTACT MAY RESULT IN CONJUNCTIVITIS OR EFFECTS AS IN ACUTE EXPOSURE.
FIRST AID- IMMEDIATELY AND VIGOROUSLY IRRIGATE EYES WITH RUNNING WATER TO REMOVE SOLID AND SEMISOLID MATERIAL FROM THE CORNEA AND CONJUNCTIVAL SACS; IT MAY BE NECESSARY TO DOUBLE EVERT THE LIDS AND SWAB OR BRUSH AWAY THE MATERIAL. THIS PROCEDURE IS FACILITATED BY APPLICATION OF A LOCAL ANESTHETIC AND BY USE OF A SOLUTION OF NEAR-NEUTRAL 0.01 TO 0.05 M SODIUM EDETATE (EDTA) FOR IRRIGATION TO AID IN LOOSENING AND DISSOLVING THE SOLID. (GRANT, TOXICOLOGY OF THE EYE, 2ND ED.). GET MEDICAL ATTENTION IMMEDIATELY.

INGESTION: CALCIUM HYDROXIDE: CORROSIVE. SEE INFORMATION ON ALKALINE CORROSIVES. RATS GIVEN WATER CONTAINING 50 OR 350 MG OF CALCIUM HYDROXIDE PER LITER SHOWED RESTLESSNESS, AGGRESSIVENESS, AND HAD A REDUCED FOOD INTAKE AFTER 2 MONTHS. AFTER 3 MONTHS THERE WAS A LOSS IN BODY WEIGHT, DECREASED ERYTHROCYTE AND PHAGOCYTE COUNTS, AND DECREASED HEMOGLOBIN. PATHOLOGIC EXAMINATION REVEALED INFLAMMATION OF THE SMALL INTESTINE AND DYSTROPHIC CHANGES OF THE STOMACH, KIDNEYS, AND LIVER.
ALKALINE CORROSIVES: **ACUTE EXPOSURE-** MAY CAUSE IMMEDIATE PAIN, CIRCUMORAL BURNS AND CORROSION OF THE MUCOUS MEMBRANES WHICH AT FIRST TURN WHITE AND SOAPY AND THEN BECOME BROWN, EDEMATOUS AND ULCERATED. THERE MAY BE PROFUSE SALIVATION AND DIFFICULTY OR INABILITY TO SWALLOW OR SPEAK. EVEN WHEN THERE IS NO EVIDENCE OF ORAL BURNS, THE ESOPHAGUS AND STOMACH MAY BE INVOLVED WITH BURNING PAIN, VOMITING AND DIARRHEA. THE VOMITUS MAY BE THICK AND SLIMY WITH MUCOUS, AND LATER CONTAIN BLOOD AND SHREDS OF MUCOSA. EPIGLOTTAL EDEMA MAY RESULT IN RESPIRATORY DISTRESS AND POSSIBLY ASPHYXIA. SHOCK WITH MARKED HYPOTENSION, WEAK AND RAPID PULSE, SHALLOW RESPIRATION, AND CLAMMY SKIN MAY OCCUR. CIRCULATORY COLLAPSE MAY ENSUE, AND IF UNCORRECTED, LEAD TO RENAL FAILURE. IN SEVERE CASES, ESOPHAGEAL OR GASTRIC PERFORATION ARE POSSIBLE AND MAY BE ACCOMPANIED BY MEDIASTINITIS, SUBSTERNAL PAIN, PERITONITIS, ABDOMINAL RIGIDITY, AND FEVER. ESOPHAGEAL, AND POSSIBLY GASTRIC OR PYLORIC STRICTURE, MAY OCCUR WITHIN A FEW WEEKS, BUT MAY BE DELAYED FOR MONTHS OR EVEN

YEARS. DEATH MAY RESULT WITHIN A SHORT TIME FROM ASPHYXIA, CIRCULATORY COLLAPSE, OR ASPIRATION OF EVEN MINUTE AMOUNTS. IF DEATH IS DELAYED IT MAY BE DUE TO THE COMPLICATIONS OF PERFORATION, PNEUMONIA, OR THE EFFECTS OF STRICTURE FORMATION. **CHRONIC EXPOSURE-** DEPENDING ON THE CONCENTRATION, REPEATED INGESTION MAY RESULT IN INFLAMMATORY AND ULCERATIVE EFFECTS ON THE ORAL MUCOUS MEMBRANES AND OTHER EFFECTS AS WITH ACUTE INGESTION.

FIRST AID- DILUTE THE ALKALI BY GIVING WATER OR MILK IMMEDIATELY AND ALLOW VOMITING TO OCCUR. AVOID GASTRIC LAVAGE OR EMETICS. ESOPHAGOSCOPY IS THE ONLY WAY TO EXCLUDE THE POSSIBLITY OF CORROSION IN THE UPPER GASTROINTESTINAL TRACT; IF CORROSION IS SUSPECTED, ESOPHAGOSCOPY SHOULD USUALLY BE PERFORMED WITHIN 24 HOURS (DREISBACH, HANDBOOK OF POISONING, 12TH ED.). MAINTAIN AIRWAY AND TREAT SHOCK. IF VOMITING OCCURS, KEEP HEAD BELOW HIPS TO HELP PREVENT ASPIRATION. GET MEDICAL ATTENTION IMMEDIATELY.

ANTIDOTE: NO SPECIFIC ANTIDOTE. TREAT SYMPTOMATICALLY AND SUPPORTIVELY.

REACTIVITY

REACTIVITY: STABLE UNDER NORMAL TEMPERATURES AND PRESSURES.

INCOMPATIBILITIES: CALCIUM HYDROXIDE: ACIDS: EXOTHERMIC REACTION. CHLORINATED PHENOLS + POTASSIUM NITRATE: MAY FORM CHLORINATED BENZODIOXINS. MALEIC ANHYDRIDE: EXPLOSIVE DECOMPOSITION OF MALEIC ANHYDRIDE. NITROPARAFFINS: FORMS EXPLOSIVE SALT. PHOSPHORUS: MAY FORM FLAMMABLE PRODUCTS WHEN HEATED.

DECOMPOSITION: THERMAL DECOMPOSITION MAY PRODUCE CALCIUM OXIDE OR CALCIUM CARBONATE.

POLYMERIZATION: HAZARDOUS POLYMERIZATION HAS NOT BEEN REPORTED TO OCCUR UNDER NORMAL TEMPERATURES AND PRESSURES.

STORAGE AND DISPOSAL

OBSERVE ALL FEDERAL, STATE AND LOCAL REGULATIONS WHEN STORING OR DISPOSING OF THIS SUBSTANCE. FOR ASSISTANCE, CONTACT THE DISTRICT DIRECTOR OF THE ENVIRONMENTAL PROTECTION AGENCY.

****STORAGE****

STORE AWAY FROM INCOMPATIBLE SUBSTANCES.
STORE IN A TIGHTLY CLOSED CONTAINER.

CONDITIONS TO AVOID

NO REPORTS FOUND.

SPILL AND LEAK PROCEDURES

OCCUPATIONAL SPILL: SWEEP UP AND PLACE IN SUITABLE CLEAN, DRY CONTAINERS FOR RECLAMATION OR LATER DISPOSAL. DO NOT FLUSH SPILLED MATERIAL INTO SEWER. KEEP UNNECESSARY PEOPLE AWAY.

PROTECTIVE EQUIPMENT

VENTILATION: PROVIDE LOCAL EXHAUST OR PROCESS ENCLOSURE VENTILATION TO MEET PUBLISHED EXPOSURE LIMITS.

RESPIRATOR: THE FOLLOWING RESPIRATORS ARE RECOMMENDED BASED ON INFORMATION FOUND IN THE PHYSICAL DATA, TOXICITY AND HEALTH EFFECTS SECTIONS. THEY ARE RANKED IN ORDER FROM MINIMUM TO MAXIMUM RESPIRATORY PROTECTION. THE SPECIFIC RESPIRATOR SELECTED MUST BE BASED ON CONTAMINATION LEVELS FOUND IN THE WORK PLACE, MUST NOT EXCEED THE WORKING LIMITS OF THE RESPIRATOR AND BE JOINTLY APPROVED BY THE NATIONAL INSTITUTE FOR OCCUPATIONAL SAFETY AND HEALTH AND THE MINE SAFETY AND HEALTH ADMINISTRATION (NIOSH-MSHA).

DUST AND MIST RESPIRATOR WITH A FULL FACEPIECE.

AIR-PURIFYING FULL FACEPIECE RESPIRATOR WITH A HIGH-EFFICIENCY PARTICULATE FILTER.

POWERED AIR-PURIFYING RESPIRATOR WITH A TIGHT-FITTING FACEPIECE AND HIGH-EFFICIENCY PARTICULATE FILTER.

TYPE 'C' SUPPLIED-AIR RESPIRATOR WITH A FULL FACEPIECE OPERATED IN PRESSURE-DEMAND OR OTHER POSITIVE PRESSURE MODE OR WITH A FULL FACEPIECE, HELMET OR HOOD OPERATED IN CONTINUOUS-FLOW MODE.

SELF-CONTAINED BREATHING APPARATUS WITH A FULL FACEPIECE OPERATED IN PRESSURE-DEMAND OR OTHER POSITIVE PRESSURE MODE.

FOR FIREFIGHTING AND OTHER IMMEDIATELY DANGEROUS TO LIFE OR HEALTH CONDITIONS:

SELF-CONTAINED BREATHING APPARATUS WITH FULL FACEPIECE OPERATED IN PRESSURE-DEMAND OR OTHER POSITIVE PRESSURE MODE.

SUPPLIED-AIR RESPIRATOR WITH FULL FACEPIECE AND OPERATED IN PRESSURE-DEMAND OR OTHER POSITIVE PRESSURE MODE IN COMBINATION WITH AN AUXILIARY SELF-CONTAINED BREATHING APPARATUS OPERATED IN PRESSURE-DEMAND OR OTHER POSITIVE PRESSURE MODE.

CLOTHING: EMPLOYEE MUST WEAR APPROPRIATE PROTECTIVE (IMPERVIOUS) CLOTHING AND EQUIPMENT TO PREVENT ANY POSSIBILITY OF SKIN CONTACT WITH THIS SUBSTANCE.

GLOVES: EMPLOYEE MUST WEAR APPROPRIATE PROTECTIVE GLOVES TO PREVENT CONTACT WITH THIS SUBSTANCE.

EYE PROTECTION: EMPLOYEE MUST WEAR SPLASH-PROOF OR DUST-RESISTANT SAFETY GOGGLES AND A FACESHIELD TO PREVENT CONTACT WITH THIS SUBSTANCE.

EMERGENCY WASH FACILITIES: WHERE THERE IS ANY POSSIBILITY THAT AN EMPLOYEE'S EYES AND/OR SKIN MAY BE EXPOSED TO THIS SUBSTANCE, THE EMPLOYER SHOULD PROVIDE AN EYE WASH FOUNTAIN AND QUICK DRENCH SHOWER WITHIN THE IMMEDIATE WORK AREA FOR EMERGENCY USE.

AUTHORIZED BY- OCCUPATIONAL HEALTH SERVICES, INC.

CREATION DATE: 11/17/89 ***REVISION DATE:*** 05/31/90

MATERIAL SAFETY DATA SHEET

OCCUPATIONAL HEALTH SERVICES, INC.
AGRICULTURE AND PESTICIDE DIVISION
450 SEVENTH AVENUE, SUITE 2407
NEW YORK, NEW YORK 10123
1-800-445-MSDS OR (212) 967-1100

EMERGENCY CONTACT:
JOHN S. BRANSFORD, JR. (615) 292-1180

SUBSTANCE IDENTIFICATION

CAS-NUMBER 7778-54-3

SUBSTANCE: **CALCIUM HYPOCHLORITE**

TRADE NAMES/SYNONYMS: B-K POWDER; HYPOCHLOROUS ACID, CALCIUM SALT; CALCIUM OXYCHLORIDE; CAPORIT; LOSANTIN; CHLORINATED LIME; CHLORIDE OF LIME; LIME CHLORIDE; STCC 4918715; UN 1748; C-99; C-100; PST03990

CHEMICAL FAMILY: INORGANIC SALT

MOLECULAR FORMULA: CA-CL2-O2

MOLECULAR WEIGHT: 142.98

CERCLA RATINGS (SCALE 0-3): HEALTH=1 FIRE=0 REACTIVITY=2 PERSISTENCE=0

NFPA RATINGS (SCALE 0-4): HEALTH=1 FIRE=0 REACTIVITY=2

COMPONENTS AND CONTAMINANTS

COMPONENT: CALCIUM HYPOCHLORITE ***PERCENT:*** 90-94%
COMPONENT: CALCIUM HYPOCHLORATE ***PERCENT:*** <6%
COMPONENT: CALCIUM CHLORIDE ***PERCENT:*** <6%
COMPONENT: CALCIUM CARBONATE ***PERCENT:*** <6%
COMPONENT: CALCIUM HYDROXIDE ***PERCENT:*** <6%

OTHER CONTAMINANTS: NONE

EXPOSURE LIMITS: CALCIUM HYPOCHLORITE: NO OCCUPATIONAL EXPOSURE LIMITS ESTABLISHED BY OSHA, ACGIH, OR NIOSH.
10 POUNDS CERCLA SECTION 103 REPORTABLE QUANTITY

PHYSICAL DATA

DESCRIPTION: WHITE GRANULES WITH A STRONG CHLORINE ODOR.

MELTING POINT: 212 F (100 C) DECOMPOSES ***SPECIFIC GRAVITY:*** 2.35

SOLUBILITY IN WATER: DECOMPOSES

SOLVENT SOLUBILITY: INSOLUBLE IN ALCOHOLS, DILUTE ACIDS

FIRE AND EXPLOSION DATA

FIRE AND EXPLOSION HAZARD: NEGLIGIBLE FIRE HAZARD WHEN EXPOSED TO HEAT OR FLAME.

OXIDIZER: OXIDIZERS DECOMPOSE, ESPECIALLY WHEN HEATED, TO YIELD OXYGEN OR OTHER GASES WHICH WILL INCREASE THE BURNING RATE OF COMBUSTIBLE MATTER. CONTACT WITH EASILY OXIDIZABLE, ORGANIC, OR OTHER COMBUSTIBLE MATERIALS MAY RESULT IN IGNITION, VIOLENT COMBUSTION OR EXPLOSION.

FIREFIGHTING MEDIA: DRY CHEMICAL, CARBON DIOXIDE, HALON OR WATER SPRAY (1987 EMERGENCY RESPONSE GUIDEBOOK, DOT P 5800.4).

FOR LARGER FIRES, USE WATER SPRAY OR FOG (1987 EMERGENCY RESPONSE GUIDEBOOK, DOT P 5800.4).

FIREFIGHTING: MOVE CONTAINERS FROM FIRE AREA IF POSSIBLE. COOL CONTAINERS EXPOSED TO FLAMES WITH WATER FROM SIDE UNTIL WELL AFTER FIRE IS OUT. STAY AWAY FROM STORAGE TANK ENDS. FOR MASSIVE FIRE IN STORAGE AREA, USE UNMANNED HOSE HOLDER OR MONITOR NOZZLES; ELSE WITHDRAW FROM AREA AND LET FIRE BURN (1987 EMERGENCY RESPONSE GUIDEBOOK, DOT P 5800.4 GUIDE PAGE 45).

FLOOD WITH WATER. COOL CONTAINERS WITH FLOODING AMOUNTS OF WATER

FROM AS FAR A DISTANCE AS POSSIBLE. AVOID BREATHING VAPORS OR DUSTS. EVACUATE TO A RADIUS OF 2500 FEET FOR UNCONTROLLABLE FIRES.

TRANSPORTATION DATA

DEPARTMENT OF TRANSPORTATION HAZARD CLASSIFICATION 49 CFR 172.101: OXIDIZER
DEPARTMENT OF TRANSPORTATION LABELING REQUIREMENTS 49 CFR 172.101 AND SUBPART E: OXIDIZER
DEPARTMENT OF TRANSPORTATION PACKAGING REQUIREMENTS: 49 CFR 173.217 EXCEPTIONS: 49 CFR 173.153

TOXICITY

CALCIUM HYPOCHLORITE: TOXICITY DATA: 850 MG/KG ORAL-RAT LD50; MUTAGENIC DATA (RTECS). CARCINOGEN STATUS: NONE. LOCAL EFFECTS: CORROSIVE- INHALATION, SKIN, AND EYES. ACUTE TOXICITY LEVEL: MODERATELY TOXIC BY INGESTION. TARGET EFFECTS: NO DATA AVAILABLE.

HEALTH EFFECTS AND FIRST AID

INHALATION: CALCIUM HYPOCHLORITE. CORROSIVE. **ACUTE EXPOSURE-** MAY SEVERELY IRRITATE THE MUCOUS MEMBRANES OF THE RESPIRATORY TRACT AND CAUSE NASAL ULCERS, NASAL SEPTAL NECROSIS, AND LARYNGEAL EDEMA. COUGHING, SORE THROAT, GINGIVITIS, DAMAGE TO THE TEETH, SHORTNESS OF BREATH, LABORED BREATHING, LARYNGITIS, AND PULMONARY EDEMA MAY OCCUR. SYMPTOMS OF PULMONARY EDEMA MAY INCLUDE TIGHTNESS IN THE CHEST, DYSPNEA, FROTHY SPUTUM, CYANOSIS, AND DIZZINESS. PHYSICAL FINDINGS MAY INCLUDE WEAK, RAPID PULSE, HYPOTENSION, HEMOCONCENTRATION AND MOIST RALES. **CHRONIC EXPOSURE-** DEPENDING ON THE CONCENTRATION AND DURATION OF EXPOSURE, REPEATED OR PROLONGED EXPOSURE TO CORROSIVE SUBSTANCES MAY CAUSE INFLAMMATORY AND ULCERATIVE CHANGES IN THE MOUTH AND POSSIBLY BRONCHIAL AND GASTROINTESTINAL DISTURBANCES.

FIRST AID- REMOVE FROM EXPOSURE AREA TO FRESH AIR IMMEDIATELY. IF BREATHING HAS STOPPED, GIVE ARTIFICIAL RESPIRATION. MAINTAIN AIRWAY AND BLOOD PRESSURE AND ADMINISTER OXYGEN IF AVAILABLE. KEEP AFFECTED PERSON WARM AND AT REST. TREAT SYMPTOMATICALLY AND SUPPORTIVELY. ADMINISTRATION OF OXYGEN SHOULD BE PERFORMED BY QUALIFIED PERSONNEL. GET MEDICAL ATTENTION IMMEDIATELY.

SKIN CONTACT: CALCIUM HYPOCHLORITE: CORROSIVE. **ACUTE EXPOSURE-** DRYING, LOCALIZED DERMATITIS, REDNESS, PAIN, AND SEVERE IRRITATION MAY OCCUR. **CHRONIC EXPOSURE-** REPEATED OR PROLONGED EXPOSURE MAY CAUSE DERMATITIS.

FIRST AID- REMOVE CONTAMINATED CLOTHING AND SHOES IMMEDIATELY. WASH AFFECTED AREA WITH SOAP OR MILD DETERGENT AND LARGE AMOUNTS OF WATER UNTIL NO EVIDENCE OF CHEMICAL REMAINS (AT LEAST 15-20 MINUTES). IN CASE OF CHEMICAL BURNS, COVER AREA WITH STERILE, DRY DRESSING. BANDAGE SECURELY, BUT NOT TOO TIGHTLY. GET MEDICAL ATTENTION IMMEDIATELY.

EYE CONTACT: CALCIUM HYPOCHLORITE: CORROSIVE. **ACUTE EXPOSURE-** THE DEGREE OF INJURY DEPENDS ON THE CONCENTRATION AND DURATION OF CONTACT. SEVERE IRRITATION MAY OCCUR WITH REDNESS, PAIN, BLEPHARITIS, CONJUNCTIVITIS, BLURRED VISION, AND CORNEAL ULCERS. EXPERIMENTAL APPLICATION OF A 5% AQUEOUS SOLUTION TO THE EYES OF RABBITS FOLLOWED BY IRRIGATION WITH WATER CAUSED SUPERFICIAL LOSS OF EPITHILIUM FROM CORNEAS AND CONJUNCTIVAS. **CHRONIC EXPOSURE-** REPEATED OR PROLONGED EXPOSURE MAY LEAD TO CONJUNCTIVITIS OR EFFECTS AS IN ACUTE EXPOSURE. EFFECTS DEPEND ON CONCENTRATION AND DURATION OF EXPOSURE.

FIRST AID- WASH EYES IMMEDIATELY WITH LARGE AMOUNTS OF WATER, OCCASIONALLY LIFTING UPPER AND LOWER LIDS, UNTIL NO EVIDENCE OF CHEMICAL REMAINS (AT LEAST 15-20 MINUTES). CONTINUE IRRIGATING WITH NORMAL SALINE UNTIL THE PH HAS RETURNED TO NORMAL (30-60 MINUTES). COVER WITH STERILE BANDAGES. GET MEDICAL ATTENTION IMMEDIATELY.

INGESTION: CALCIUM HYPOCHLORITE: CORROSIVE. **ACUTE EXPOSURE-** EDEMA AND CORROSION OF THE MOUTH, PHARYNX, LARYNX, AND STOMACH MAY OCCUR ALONG WITH SORE THROAT, ABDOMINAL PAIN, VOMITING, AND SEVERE GASTRITIS. **CHRONIC EXPOSURE-** DEPENDING ON THE CONCENTRATION, REPEATED INGESTION OF ALKALINE SUBSTANCES MAY RESULT IN INFLAMMATORY AND ULCERATIVE EFFECTS ON THE ORAL MUCOUS MEMBRANES.

FIRST AID- REMOVE BY GASTRIC LAVAGE OR EMESIS. MAINTAIN BLOOD PRESSURE AND AIRWAY. GIVE OXYGEN IF RESPIRATION IS DEPRESSED. DO NOT PERFORM GASTRIC LAVAGE OR EMESIS IF VICTIM IS UNCONSCIOUS. GET MEDICAL ATTENTION IMMEDIATELY (DREISBACH, HANDBOOK OF POISONING, 11TH ED.). ADMINISTRATION OF GASTRIC LAVAGE OR OXYGEN SHOULD BE PERFORMED BY QUALIFIED MEDICAL PERSONNEL.

ANTIDOTE: NO SPECIFIC ANTIDOTE. TREAT SYMPTOMATICALLY AND SUPPORTIVELY.

REACTIVITY

REACTIVITY: MAY UNDERGO ACCELERATED DECOMPOSITION WITH EVOLUTION OF HEAT AND POSSIBLE RUPTURE OF CONTAINER. EXOTHERMIC REACTION WITH WATER YIELDING CHLORINE GAS.

INCOMPATIBILITIES: CALCIUM HYPOCHLORITE: ACETYLENE: FORMATION OF EXPLOSIVE CHLOROACETYLENES. ACIDS: REACTS WITH EVOLUTION OF CHLORINE GAS. ACIDS + CYANIDES: EXPLOSIVE REACTION. AMINES (PRIMARY): REACTION TO FORM NORMAL CHLORAMINES WHICH ARE EXPLOSIVE. AMMONIUM CHLORIDE: EXPLOSION HAZARD. ANTHRACENE: HEATS ON CONTACT. CARBON TETRACHLORIDE: EXPLOSIVE REACTION. CHARCOAL (FINELY DIVIDED): EXPLOSIVE WHEN HEATED. N,N-DICHLOROMETHYLAMINE: VIOLENT EXPLOSION ON WARMING. DIETHYLENE GLYCOL MONOMETHYL ETHER: IGNITION. ETHANEDIOL: EXPLOSIVE REACTION. ETHYL ALCOHOL: VIOLENT EXPLOSION AFTER SHORT TIME. GLYCEROL: SPONTANEOUS IGNITION OF GLYCEROL. GREASE: VIOLENT REACTION. HYDROCHLORIC ACID: REACTION RELEASES COPIOUS AMOUNTS OF CHLORINE GAS. IRON OXIDE: CONTAINERS MAY EXPLODE. ISOBUTANETHIOL: EXPLOSIVE REACTION. MANGANESE OXIDE: CONTAINERS MAY EXPLODE. MERCAPTANS: VIOLENT REACTION. METALS: CORROSIVE IN THE PRESENCE OF MOISTURE. METHANOL: VIOLENT EXPLOSION AFTER SHORT TIME. METHYL CARBITAL: FIRE HAZARD. NITROMETHANE: DELAYED BUT VIOLENT REACTION WITH POWDERED CALCIUM HYPOCHLORITE, ESPECIALLY WHEN CONFINED, AS IN A PLASTIC BAG. OIL: VIOLENT REACTION. ORGANIC MATTER: CALCIUM HYPOCHLORITE CONTAMINATED WITH 1% OF VARIOUS COMMON ORGANIC MATERIALS REACTED WHEN HEATED. THE REACTION VARIED FROM MILD FLAME AT 350 F WITH WOOD, TO VIOLENT EXPLOSION AT 275 F WITH OIL. ORGANIC SULFIDES: VIOLENT REACTION WITH THE POSSIBILITY OF A FLASH FIRE. PHENOL: EXOTHERMIC REACTION, PRODUCING TOXIC FUMES WHICH MAY IGNITE. 1-PROPANETHIOL: EXPLOSIVE REACTION. PROPYL MERCAPTANS: FIRE HAZARD. SULFUR: VIOLENT, EXOTHERMIC REACTION. TURPENTINE: EXPLOSIVE REACTION. UREA: FORMATION OF SPONTANEOUSLY EXPLOSIVE NITROGEN TRICHLORIDE.

DECOMPOSITION: THERMAL DECOMPOSITION RELEASES OXYGEN AND TOXIC CHLORINE GAS.

POLYMERIZATION: HAZARDOUS POLYMERIZATION HAS NOT BEEN REPORTED TO OCCUR UNDER NORMAL TEMPERATURES AND PRESSURES.

STORAGE AND DISPOSAL

OBSERVE ALL FEDERAL, STATE AND LOCAL REGULATIONS WHEN STORING OR DISPOSING OF THIS SUBSTANCE. FOR ASSISTANCE, CONTACT THE DISTRICT DIRECTOR OF THE ENVIRONMENTAL PROTECTION AGENCY.

****STORAGE****

PROTECT AGAINST PHYSICAL DAMAGE. SOTRE IN A COOL, DRY, WELL VENTILATED PLACE AWAY FROM COMBUSTIBLE MATERIALS. DRUMS MAY RUPTURE FROM EXPOSURE TO HEAT, PARTICULARLY IF CHLORINE CONTENT IS HIGH. AVOID STORAGE FOR PROLONGED PERIODS, PARTICULARLY AT SUMMER TEMPERATURES (NFPA 49, HAZARDOUS CHEMICALS DATA, 1975).
STORE AWAY FROM INCOMPATIBLE SUBSTANCES.

CONDITIONS TO AVOID

MAY IGNITE OTHER COMBUSTIBLE MATERIALS (WOOD, PAPER, OIL, ETC.). REACTION WITH FUELS MAY BE VIOLENT. FLAMMABLE POISONOUS GASES MAY ACCUMULATE IN TANKS AND HOPPER CARS. RUNOFF TO SEWER MAY CREATE FIRE OR EXPLOSION HAZARD.
USUAL SHIPPING CONTAINERS: AIRTIGHT CANS, WOODEN BARRELS, STEEL DRUMS, FIBER DRUMS (NFPA 49, HAZARDOUS CHEMICALS DATA, 1975).

SPILL AND LEAK PROCEDURES

SOIL SPILL: DIG HOLDING AREA SUCH AS LAGOON, POND OR PIT FOR CONTAINMENT. USE PROTECTIVE COVER SUCH AS A PLASTIC SHEET TO PREVENT MATERIAL FROM DISSOLVING IN FIRE EXTINGUISHING WATER OR RAIN.

WATER SPILL: ADD SODIUM BISULFITE.
ADD SODA ASH.
ADD SUITABLE AGENT TO NEUTRALIZE SPILLED MATERIAL TO PH-7.
USE MECHANICAL DREDGES OR LIFTS TO EXTRACT IMMOBILIZED MASSES OF POLLUTION AND PRECIPITATES.

OCCUPATIONAL SPILL: KEEP COMBUSTIBLES (WOOD, PAPER, OIL, ETC.) AWAY FROM SPILLED MATERIAL. DO NOT TOUCH SPILLED MATERIAL. STOP LEAK IF YOU CAN DO IT WITHOUT RISK. USE WATER SPRAY TO REDUCE VAPORS. DO NOT GET WATER INSIDE CONTAINER. FOR SMALL DRY SPILLS, WITH CLEAN SHOVEL PLACE MATERIAL INTO CLEAN, DRY CONTAINER AND COVER. MOVE CONTAINERS FROM SPILL AREA. FOR SMALL LIQUID SPILLS, FLUSH AREA WITH FLOODING AMOUNTS OF WATER. FOR LARGER SPILLS, DIKE FAR AHEAD OF SPILL FOR LATER DISPOSAL. KEEP UNNECESSARY PEOPLE AWAY. ISOLATE HAZARD AREA AND DENY ENTRY. REPORTABLE QUANTITY (RQ): 10 POUNDS THE SUPERFUND AMENDMENTS AND REAUTHORIZATION ACT (SARA) SECTION 304 REQUIRES THAT A RELEASE EQUAL

TO OR GREATER THAN THE REPORTABLE QUANTITY FOR THIS SUBSTANCE BE IMMEDIATELY REPORTED TO THE LOCAL EMERGENCY PLANNING COMMITTEE AND THE STATE EMERGENCY RESPONSE COMMISSION (40 CFR 355.40). IF THE RELEASE OF THIS SUBSTANCE IS REPORTABLE UNDER CERCLA SECTION 103, THE NATIONAL RESPONSE CENTER MUST BE NOTIFIED IMMEDIATELY AT (800) 424-8802 OR (202) 426-2675 IN THE METROPOLITAN WASHINGTON, D.C. AREA (40 CFR 302.6).

PROTECTIVE EQUIPMENT

VENTILATION: PROVIDE LOCAL EXHAUST OR GENERAL DILUTION VENTILATION SYSTEM.

RESPIRATOR: THE FOLLOWING RESPIRATORS ARE RECOMMENDED BASED ON INFORMATION FOUND IN THE PHYSICAL DATA, TOXICITY AND HEALTH EFFECTS SECTIONS. THEY ARE RANKED IN ORDER FROM MINIMUM TO MAXIMUM RESPIRATORY PROTECTION. THE SPECIFIC RESPIRATOR SELECTED MUST BE BASED ON CONTAMINATION LEVELS FOUND IN THE WORK PLACE, MUST NOT EXCEED THE WORKING LIMITS OF THE RESPIRATOR AND BE JOINTLY APPROVED BY THE NATIONAL INSTITUTE FOR OCCUPATIONAL SAFETY AND HEALTH AND THE MINE SAFETY AND HEALTH ADMINISTRATION (NIOSH-MSHA).

DUST AND MIST RESPIRATOR WITH A FULL FACEPIECE.

AIR-PURIFYING FULL FACEPIECE RESPIRATOR WITH A HIGH-EFFICIENCY PARTICULATE FILTER.

POWERED AIR-PURIFYING RESPIRATOR WITH A TIGHT-FITTING FACEPIECE AND HIGH-EFFICIENCY PARTICULATE FILTER.

TYPE 'C' SUPPLIED-AIR RESPIRATOR WITH A FULL FACEPIECE OPERATED IN PRESSURE-DEMAND OR OTHER POSITIVE PRESSURE MODE OR WITH A FULL FACEPIECE, HELMET OR HOOD OPERATED IN CONTINUOUS-FLOW MODE.

SELF-CONTAINED BREATHING APPARATUS WITH A FULL FACEPIECE OPERATED IN PRESSURE-DEMAND OR OTHER POSITIVE PRESSURE MODE.

FOR FIREFIGHTING AND OTHER IMMEDIATELY DANGEROUS TO LIFE OR HEALTH CONDITIONS:

SELF-CONTAINED BREATHING APPARATUS WITH FULL FACEPIECE OPERATED IN PRESSURE-DEMAND OR OTHER POSITIVE PRESSURE MODE.

SUPPLIED-AIR RESPIRATOR WITH FULL FACEPIECE AND OPERATED IN PRESSURE-DEMAND OR OTHER POSITIVE PRESSURE MODE IN COMBINATION WITH AN AUXILIARY SELF-CONTAINED BREATHING APPARATUS OPERATED IN PRESSURE-DEMAND OR OTHER POSITIVE PRESSURE MODE.

CLOTHING: EMPLOYEE MUST WEAR APPROPRIATE PROTECTIVE (IMPERVIOUS) CLOTHING AND EQUIPMENT TO PREVENT ANY POSSIBILITY OF SKIN CONTACT WITH THIS SUBSTANCE.

GLOVES: EMPLOYEE MUST WEAR APPROPRIATE PROTECTIVE GLOVES TO PREVENT CONTACT WITH THIS SUBSTANCE.

EYE PROTECTION: EMPLOYEE MUST WEAR SPLASH-PROOF OR DUST-RESISTANT SAFETY GOGGLES AND A FACESHIELD TO PREVENT CONTACT WITH THIS SUBSTANCE.

EMERGENCY WASH FACILITIES: WHERE THERE IS ANY POSSIBILITY THAT AN EMPLOYEE'S EYES AND/OR SKIN MAY BE EXPOSED TO THIS SUBSTANCE, THE EMPLOYER SHOULD PROVIDE AN EYE WASH FOUNTAIN AND QUICK DRENCH SHOWER WITHIN THE IMMEDIATE WORK AREA FOR EMERGENCY USE.

AUTHORIZED BY- OCCUPATIONAL HEALTH SERVICES, INC.
CREATION DATE: 10/04/89 ***REVISION DATE:*** 05/16/90

MATERIAL SAFETY DATA SHEET

OCCUPATIONAL HEALTH SERVICES, INC.
AGRICULTURE AND PESTICIDE DIVISION
450 SEVENTH AVENUE, SUITE 2407
NEW YORK, NEW YORK 10123
1-800-445-MSDS OR (212) 967-1100

EMERGENCY CONTACT:
JOHN S. BRANSFORD, JR. (615) 292-1180

SUBSTANCE IDENTIFICATION

CAS-NUMBER 1305-78-8

SUBSTANCE: CALCIUM OXIDE

TRADE NAMES/SYNONYMS: CALCIUM OXIDE (CAO); CALCIA; CALCIUM MONOXIDE; CALX; CALXYL; QUICKLIME; PEBBLE LIME; LIME; BURNT LIME; CAUSTIC LIME; UNSLAKED LIME; LIME, UNSLAKED; CALCIA (CAO); STCC 4944515; UN 1910; CAO; PST04030

CHEMICAL FAMILY: METAL OXIDE

MOLECULAR FORMULA: CA-O

MOLECULAR WEIGHT: 56.08

CERCLA RATINGS (SCALE 0-3): HEALTH = U FIRE = 0 REACTIVITY = 2 PERSISTENCE = 0

NFPA RATINGS (SCALE 0-4): HEALTH = 1 FIRE = 0 REACTIVITY = 1

COMPONENTS AND CONTAMINANTS

COMPONENT: CALCIUM OXIDE ***PERCENT:*** 100.0
CAS# 1305-78-8

OTHER CONTAMINANTS: NONE

EXPOSURE LIMITS: CALCIUM OXIDE: 5 MG/M3 OSHA TWA 2 MG/M3 ACGIH TWA

PHYSICAL DATA

DESCRIPTION: ODORLESS, WHITE OR GRAYISH-WHITE HYGROSCOPIC, GRANULAR POWDER, CRYSTALS, OR LUMPS WITH A BITTER TASTE. ***BOILING POINT:*** 5162 F (2850 C)

MELTING POINT: 4737 F (2614 C) ***SPECIFIC GRAVITY:*** 3.25-3.38

PH: 12.5 @ 0.12% SOLN ***SOLUBILITY IN WATER:*** REACTS

SOLVENT SOLUBILITY: SOLUBLE IN GLYCEROL, SUGAR SOLUTIONS; PRACTICALLY INSOLUBLE IN ALCOHOL.

FIRE AND EXPLOSION DATA

FIRE AND EXPLOSION HAZARD: NEGLIGIBLE FIRE HAZARD WHEN EXPOSED TO HEAT OR FLAME.

FIREFIGHTING MEDIA: DRY CHEMICAL, CARBON DIOXIDE, HALON, WATER SPRAY OR STANDARD FOAM (1987 EMERGENCY RESPONSE GUIDEBOOK, DOT P 5800.4). FOR LARGER FIRES, USE WATER SPRAY, FOG OR STANDARD FOAM (1987 EMERGENCY RESPONSE GUIDEBOOK, DOT P 5800.4).

FIREFIGHTING: MOVE CONTAINERS FROM FIRE AREA IF POSSIBLE. COOL CONTAINERS EXPOSED TO FLAMES WITH WATER FROM SIDE UNTIL WELL AFTER FIRE IS OUT. STAY AWAY FROM STORAGE TANK ENDS (1987 EMERGENCY RESPONSE GUIDEBOOK, DOT P 5800.4, GUIDE PAGE 60).

EXTINGUISH FIRE USING AGENT SUITABLE FOR TYPE OF SURROUNDING FIRE. COOL CONTAINERS WITH FLOODING QUANTITIES OF WATER, BUT DO NOT USE WATER ON MATERIAL ITSELF. AVOID CONTAMINATING WATER SOURCES AND SEWERS. AVOID BREATHING VAPORS OR DUST.

TRANSPORTATION DATA

DEPARTMENT OF TRANSPORTATION HAZARD CLASSIFICATION 49 CFR 172.101: ORM-B

DEPARTMENT OF TRANSPORTATION LABELING REQUIREMENTS 49 CFR 172.101 AND SUBPART E: NONE

DEPARTMENT OF TRANSPORTATION PACKAGING REQUIREMENTS: 49 CFR 173.850 EXCEPTIONS: 49 CFR 173.505

TOXICITY

CALCIUM OXIDE: CARCINOGEN STATUS: NONE. LOCAL EFFECTS: CORROSIVE-INHALATION, SKIN, EYE, INGESTION. ACUTE TOXICITY LEVEL: NO DATA AVAILABLE. TARGET EFFECTS: NO DATA AVAILABLE. AT INCREASED RISK FROM EXPOSURE: PERSONS WITH CHRONIC RESPIRATORY DISEASE OR SKIN DISEASE.

HEALTH EFFECTS AND FIRST AID

INHALATION: CALCIUM OXIDE: CORROSIVE. 250 MG/M3 IMMEDIATELY DANGEROUS TO LIFE OR HEALTH. **ACUTE EXPOSURE-** MAY CAUSE SEVERE IRRITATION OF THE MUCOUS MEMBRANES WITH SORE THROAT, COUGHING, AND DYSPNEA. BRONCHITIS AND PNEUMONITIS HAVE ALSO BEEN REPORTED. DELAYED PULMONARY EDEMA MAY OCCUR IN SEVERE CASES. **CHRONIC EXPOSURE-** DEPENDING ON THE CONCENTRATION AND DURATION OF EXPOSURE, REPEATED OR PROLONGED EXPOSURE MAY CAUSE INFLAMMATION AND ULCERATION OF THE NASAL AND BUCCAL MUCOSA, PERFORATION OF THE NASAL SEPTUM, AND POSSIBLY BRONCHIAL AND GASTROINTESTINAL DISTURBANCES.

FIRST AID- REMOVE FROM EXPOSURE AREA TO FRESH AIR IMMEDIATELY. IF BREATHING HAS STOPPED, GIVE ARTIFICIAL RESPIRATION. MAINTAIN AIRWAY AND BLOOD PRESSURE AND ADMINISTER OXYGEN IF AVAILABLE. KEEP AFFECTED PERSON WARM AND AT REST. TREAT SYMPTOMATICALLY AND SUPPORTIVELY. ADMINISTRATION OF OXYGEN SHOULD BE PERFORMED BY QUALIFIED PERSONNEL. GET MEDICAL ATTENTION IMMEDIATELY.

SKIN CONTACT: CALCIUM OXIDE: CORROSIVE. **ACUTE EXPOSURE-** CONTACT, ESPECIALLY WITH MOIST SKIN, MAY CAUSE SEVERE IRRITATION WITH PAIN, REDNESS, BURNS, AND ULCERATION. BURNS SEVERE ENOUGH TO BE FATAL HAVE RESULTED FROM MASSIVE EXPOSURE. **CHRONIC EXPOSURE-** EFFECTS DEPEND ON THE CONCENTRATION AND DURATION OF EXPOSURE. REPEATED OR PROLONGED CONTACT MAY CAUSE DERMATITIS, WITH DESQUAMATION AND VESICULAR RASH, FISSURING AND BRITTLENESS OF THE NAILS, OR EFFECTS SIMILAR TO ACUTE EXPOSURE.

FIRST AID- REMOVE CONTAMINATED CLOTHING AND SHOES IMMEDIATELY. WASH AFFECTED AREA WITH SOAP OR MILD DETERGENT AND LARGE AMOUNTS OF

WATER UNTIL NO EVIDENCE OF CHEMICAL REMAINS (AT LEAST 15-20 MINUTES). IN CASE OF CHEMICAL BURNS, COVER AREA WITH STERILE, DRY DRESSING. BANDAGE SECURELY, BUT NOT TOO TIGHTLY. GET MEDICAL ATTENTION IMMEDIATELY.

EYE CONTACT: CALCIUM OXIDE: CORROSIVE. **ACUTE EXPOSURE-** UPON CONTACT, DUST MAY REACT WITH MOISTURE AND PROTEIN IN THE EYE AND FORM CLUMPS OF MOIST COMPOUND, WHICH ARE OFTEN LODGED DEEP IN THE CONJUNCTIVA. THE DEGREE OF INJURY DEPENDS ON THE CONCENTRATION AND DURATION OF CONTACT. THERE MAY BE SEVERE IRRITATION, EDEMA, HYPEREMIA, PAIN, LACRIMATION, BLURRED VISION, SPASMODIC BLINKING, CORNEAL OPACITIES, ULCERATION AND PERFORATION, SOMETIMES WITH LOSS OF VISION. **CHRONIC EXPOSURE-** EFFECTS DEPEND ON THE CONCENTRATION AND DURATION OF EXPOSURE. REPEATED OR PROLONGED CONTACT MAY RESULT IN CONJUNCTIVITIS OR EFFECTS AS IN ACUTE EXPOSURE.

FIRST AID- WASH EYES IMMEDIATELY WITH LARGE AMOUNTS OF WATER, OCCASIONALLY LIFTING UPPER AND LOWER LIDS, UNTIL NO EVIDENCE OF CHEMICAL REMAINS (AT LEAST 15-20 MINUTES). CONTINUE IRRIGATING WITH NORMAL SALINE UNTIL THE PH HAS RETURNED TO NORMAL (30-60 MINUTES). COVER WITH STERILE BANDAGES. GET MEDICAL ATTENTION IMMEDIATELY.

INGESTION: CALCIUM OXIDE: CORROSIVE. SEE INFORMATION ON ALKALINE CORROSIVES.

ALKALINE CORROSIVES: **ACUTE EXPOSURE-** MAY CAUSE IMMEDIATE PAIN, CIRCUMORAL BURNS AND CORROSION OF THE MUCOUS MEMBRANES WHICH AT FIRST TURN WHITE AND SOAPY AND THEN BECOME BROWN, EDEMATOUS AND ULCERATED. THERE MAY BE PROFUSE SALIVATION AND DIFFICULTY OR INABILITY TO SWALLOW OR SPEAK. EVEN WHEN THERE IS NO EVIDENCE OF ORAL BURNS, THE ESOPHAGUS AND STOMACH MAY BE INVOLVED WITH BURNING PAIN, VOMITING AND DIARRHEA. THE VOMITUS MAY BE THICK AND SLIMY WITH MUCOUS, AND LATER CONTAIN BLOOD AND SHREDS OF MUCOSA. EPIGLOTTAL EDEMA MAY RESULT IN RESPIRATORY DISTRESS AND POSSIBLY ASPHYXIA. SHOCK WITH MARKED HYPOTENSION, WEAK AND RAPID PULSE, SHALLOW RESPIRATION, AND CLAMMY SKIN MAY OCCUR. CIRCULATORY COLLAPSE MAY ENSUE, AND IF UNCORRECTED, LEAD TO RENAL FAILURE. IN SEVERE CASES, ESOPHAGEAL OR GASTRIC PERFORATION ARE POSSIBLE AND MAY BE ACCOMPANIED BY MEDIASTINITIS, SUBSTERNAL PAIN, PERITONITIS, ABDOMINAL RIGIDITY, AND FEVER. ESOPHAGEAL, AND POSSIBLY GASTRIC OR PYLORIC STRICTURE, MAY OCCUR WITHIN A FEW WEEKS, BUT MAY BE DELAYED FOR MONTHS OR EVEN YEARS. DEATH MAY RESULT WITHIN A SHORT TIME FROM ASPHYXIA, CIRCULATORY COLLAPSE, OR ASPIRATION OF EVEN MINUTE AMOUNTS. IF DEATH IS DELAYED IT MAY BE DUE TO THE COMPLICATIONS OF PERFORATION, PNEUMONIA, OR THE EFFECTS OF STRICTURE FORMATION. **CHRONIC EXPOSURE-** DEPENDING ON THE CONCENTRATION, REPEATED INGESTION MAY RESULT IN INFLAMMATORY AND ULCERATIVE EFFECTS ON THE ORAL MUCOUS MEMBRANES AND OTHER EFFECTS AS WITH ACUTE INGESTION.

FIRST AID- DILUTE THE ALKALI BY GIVING WATER OR MILK IMMEDIATELY AND ALLOW VOMITING TO OCCUR. AVOID GASTRIC LAVAGE OR EMETICS. ESOPHAGOSCOPY IS THE ONLY WAY TO EXCLUDE THE POSSIBLITY OF CORROSION IN THE UPPER GASTROINTESTINAL TRACT; IF CORROSION IS SUSPECTED, ESOPHAGOSCOPY SHOULD USUALLY BE PERFORMED WITHIN 24 HOURS (DREISBACH, HANDBOOK OF POISONING, 12TH ED.). MAINTAIN AIRWAY AND TREAT SHOCK. IF VOMITING OCCURS, KEEP HEAD BELOW HIPS TO HELP PREVENT ASPIRATION. GET MEDICAL ATTENTION IMMEDIATELY.

ANTIDOTE: NO SPECIFIC ANTIDOTE. TREAT SYMPTOMATICALLY AND SUPPORTIVELY.

REACTIVITY

REACTIVITY: VIOLENT, EXOTHERMIC REACTION WITH WATER YIELDING CORROSIVE CALCIUM HYDROXIDE. REACTION TEMPERATURES MAY REACH AS HIGH AS 800-900 C, AND PROCEED WITH EXPLOSIVE VIOLENCE. THE BULK MATERIAL REACTS SLOWLY WITH WATER, HOWEVER, THE POWDERED MATERIAL REACTS AFTER A FEW MINUTES DELAY. ADDITION OF WATER TO A CLOSED CONTAINER MAY RUPTURE THE CONTAINER.

INCOMPATIBILITIES: CALCIUM OXIDE: ACIDS: EXOTHERMIC REACTION. BORIC ACID + CALCIUM CHLORIDE (FUSED): INCANDESCENT REACTION. BROMINE PENTAFLUORIDE: VIOLENT REACTION, IGNITION OFTEN OCCURRING. CHLORINE TRIFLUORIDE: VIOLENT REACTION, IGNITION OFTEN OCCURRING. ETHANOL: POSSIBLE IGNITION AND EXPLOSION IF EXPOSED TO MOISTURE OR HEAT. FLUORINE: INCANDESCENT EXOTHERMIC REACTION. HYDROGEN FLUORIDE: VIOLENT, INCANDESCENT REACTION. INTERHALOGEN COMPOUNDS: IGNITION. ORGANIC MATERIALS: FIRE AND EXPLOSION HAZARD. PHOSPHORUS PENTOXIDE: VIOLENT REACTION IF WARMED OR MOISTENED.

DECOMPOSITION: THERMAL DECOMPOSITION MAY RELEASE TOXIC AND/OR HAZARDOUS GASES.

POLYMERIZATION: HAZARDOUS POLYMERIZATION HAS NOT BEEN REPORTED TO OCCUR UNDER NORMAL TEMPERATURES AND PRESSURES.

STORAGE AND DISPOSAL

OBSERVE ALL FEDERAL, STATE AND LOCAL REGULATIONS WHEN STORING OR DISPOSING OF THIS SUBSTANCE. FOR ASSISTANCE, CONTACT THE DISTRICT DIRECTOR OF THE ENVIRONMENTAL PROTECTION AGENCY.

****STORAGE****

PROTECT AGAINST PHYSICAL DAMAGE AND STORE IN A DRY PLACE AWAY FROM WATER OR MOISTURE (NFPA 49, HAZARDOUS CHEMICALS DATA, 1975). STORE AWAY FROM INCOMPATIBLE SUBSTANCES.

****DISPOSAL****

DISPOSAL MUST BE IN ACCORDANCE WITH STANDARDS APPLICABLE TO GENERATORS OF HAZARDOUS WASTE, 40 CFR 262. EPA HAZARDOUS WASTE NUMBER D003. 100 POUND CERCLA SECTION 103 REPORTABLE QUANTITY.

CONDITIONS TO AVOID

MAY BURN BUT DOES NOT IGNITE READILY. FLAMMABLE, POISONOUS GASES MAY ACCUMULATE IN TANKS AND HOPPER CARS. MAY IGNITE COMBUSTIBLES (WOOD, PAPER, OIL, ETC.).

SPILL AND LEAK PROCEDURES

SOIL SPILL: USE PROTECTIVE COVER SUCH AS A PLASTIC SHEET TO PREVENT MATERIAL FROM DISSOLVING IN FIRE EXTINGUISHING WATER OR RAIN.

OCCUPATIONAL SPILL: DO NOT TOUCH SPILLED MATERIAL. STOP LEAK IF YOU CAN DO IT WITHOUT RISK. FOR SMALL SPILLS, TAKE UP WITH SAND OR OTHER ABSORBENT MATERIAL AND PLACE INTO CONTAINERS FOR LATER DISPOSAL. FOR SMALL DRY SPILLS, WITH CLEAN SHOVEL PLACE MATERIAL INTO CLEAN, DRY CONTAINER AND COVER. MOVE CONTAINERS FROM SPILL AREA. FOR LARGER SPILLS, DIKE FAR AHEAD OF SPILL FOR LATER DISPOSAL. KEEP UNNECESSARY PEOPLE AWAY. ISOLATE HAZARD AREA AND DENY ENTRY.

PROTECTIVE EQUIPMENT

VENTILATION: PROVIDE LOCAL EXHAUST VENTILATION AND/OR GENERAL DILUTION VENTILATION TO MEET PUBLISHED EXPOSURE LIMITS.

RESPIRATOR: THE FOLLOWING RESPIRATORS AND MAXIMUM USE CONCENTRATIONS ARE RECOMMENDATIONS BY THE U.S. DEPARTMENT OF HEALTH AND HUMAN SERVICES, NIOSH POCKET GUIDE TO CHEMICAL HAZARDS; NIOSH CRITERIA DOCUMENTS OR BY THE U.S. DEPARTMENT OF LABOR, 29 CFR 1910 SUBPART Z. THE SPECIFIC RESPIRATOR SELECTED MUST BE BASED ON CONTAMINATION LEVELS FOUND IN THE WORK PLACE, MUST NOT EXCEED THE WORKING LIMITS OF THE RESPIRATOR AND BE JOINTLY APPROVED BY THE NATIONAL INSTITUTE FOR OCCUPATIONAL SAFETY AND HEALTH AND THE MINE SAFETY AND HEALTH ADMINISTRATION (NIOSH-MSHA).

CALCIUM OXIDE:

10 MG/M3- ANY DUST AND MIST RESPIRATOR.

20 MG/M3- ANY DUST AND MIST RESPIRATOR EXCEPT SINGLE-USE AND QUARTER-MASK RESPIRATORS. ANY SUPPLIED-AIR RESPIRATOR. ANY SELF-CONTAINED BREATHING APPARATUS.

50 MG/M3- ANY POWERED AIR-PURIFYING RESPIRATOR WITH A HIGH-EFFICIENCY PARTICULATE FILTER. ANY SUPPLIED-AIR RESPIRATOR OPERATED IN A CONTINUOUS FLOW MODE.

100 MG/M3- ANY AIR-PURIFYING FULL FACEPIECE RESPIRATOR WITH A HIGH-EFFICIENCY PARTICULATE FILTER. ANY SELF-CONTAINED BREATHING APPARATUS WITH A FULL FACEPIECE. ANY SUPPLIED-AIR RESPIRATOR WITH A FULL FACEPIECE. ANY POWERED AIR-PURIFYING RESPIRATOR WITH A TIGHT-FITTING FACEPIECE AND A HIGH-EFFICIENCY PARTICULATE FILTER.

250 MG/M3- ANY SUPPLIED-AIR RESPIRATOR WITH A HALF-MASK AND OPERATED IN A PRESSURE-DEMAND OR OTHER POSITIVE PRESSURE MODE.

ESCAPE- ANY AIR-PURIFYING FULL FACEPIECE RESPIRATOR WITH A HIGH-EFFICIENCY PARTICULATE FILTER. ANY APPROPRIATE ESCAPE-TYPE SELF-CONTAINED BREATHING APPARATUS.

FOR FIREFIGHTING AND OTHER IMMEDIATELY DANGEROUS TO LIFE OR HEALTH CONDITIONS:

SELF-CONTAINED BREATHING APPARATUS WITH FULL FACEPIECE OPERATED IN PRESSURE-DEMAND OR OTHER POSITIVE PRESSURE MODE.

SUPPLIED-AIR RESPIRATOR WITH FULL FACEPIECE AND OPERATED IN PRESSURE-DEMAND OR OTHER POSITIVE PRESSURE MODE IN COMBINATION WITH AN AUXILIARY SELF-CONTAINED BREATHING APPARATUS OPERATED IN PRESSURE-DEMAND OR OTHER POSITIVE PRESSURE MODE.

CLOTHING: EMPLOYEE MUST WEAR APPROPRIATE PROTECTIVE (IMPERVIOUS) CLOTHING AND EQUIPMENT TO PREVENT ANY POSSIBILITY OF SKIN CONTACT WITH THIS SUBSTANCE.

GLOVES: EMPLOYEE MUST WEAR APPROPRIATE PROTECTIVE GLOVES TO PREVENT CONTACT WITH THIS SUBSTANCE.

EYE PROTECTION: EMPLOYEE MUST WEAR SPLASH-PROOF OR DUST-RESISTANT SAFETY GOGGLES AND A FACESHIELD TO PREVENT CONTACT WITH THIS SUBSTANCE. EMERGENCY WASH FACILITIES: WHERE THERE IS ANY POSSIBILITY

THAT AN EMPLOYEE'S EYES AND/OR SKIN MAY BE EXPOSED TO THIS SUBSTANCE, THE EMPLOYER SHOULD PROVIDE AN EYE WASH FOUNTAIN AND QUICK DRENCH SHOWER WITHIN THE IMMEDIATE WORK AREA FOR EMERGENCY USE.

AUTHORIZED BY- OCCUPATIONAL HEALTH SERVICES, INC.
CREATION DATE: 11/17/89 ***REVISION DATE:*** 03/28/90

MATERIAL SAFETY DATA SHEET

OCCUPATIONAL HEALTH SERVICES, INC.
AGRICULTURE AND PESTICIDE DIVISION
450 SEVENTH AVENUE, SUITE 2407
NEW YORK, NEW YORK 10123
1-800-445-MSDS OR (212) 967-1100

EMERGENCY CONTACT:
JOHN S. BRANSFORD, JR. (615) 292-1180

SUBSTANCE IDENTIFICATION

CAS-NUMBER 7778-18-9
SUBSTANCE: **CALCIUM SULFATE, ANHYDROUS**
TRADE NAMES/SYNONYMS: SULFURIC ACID, CALCIUM SALT (1:1); CALCIUM SULFATE; ANHYDROUS CALCIUM SULFATE; CALCIUM SULFATE(CASO4); CALCIUM SULFATE(1:1); CALCIUM SULPHATE; SULFURIC ACID CALCIUM SALT; CRYSALBA; DRIERITE; GIBS; NATURAL ANHYDRITE; KARSTENITE; MURIACITE; ANHYDROUS SULFATE OF LIME; ANHYDROUS GYPSUM; CAAO4S; PST04110
CHEMICAL FAMILY: INORGANIC SALT
MOLECULAR FORMULA: CA-S-O4
MOLECULAR WEIGHT: 136.14
CERCLA RATINGS (SCALE 0-3): HEALTH=U FIRE=0 REACTIVITY=0 PERSISTENCE=0
NFPA RATINGS (SCALE 0-4): HEALTH=U FIRE=0 REACTIVITY=0

COMPONENTS AND CONTAMINANTS

COMPONENT: CALCIUM SULFATE, ANHYDROUS ***PERCENT:*** 100
CAS# 7778-18-9
OTHER CONTAMINANTS: NONE
EXPOSURE LIMITS: NUISANCE PARTICULATES (NUISANCE DUST): 5 MG/M3 OSHA TWA (RESPIRABLE DUST); 15 MG/M3 OSHA TWA (TOTAL DUST) 10 MG/M3 ACGIH TWA (TOTAL DUST) (NO ASBESTOS AND < 1% CRYSTALLINE SILICA)

PHYSICAL DATA

DESCRIPTION: ODORLESS WHITE WITH A BLUE, GRAY OR REDDISH TINGE OR BRICK RED, RHOMBIC OR MONOCLINIC CRYSTALS OR POWDER. ***MELTING POINT:*** 2642 F (1450 C)
SPECIFIC GRAVITY: 2.964 ***SOLUBILITY IN WATER:*** 0.2%
SOLVENT SOLUBILITY: SOLUBLE IN ACIDS, AMMONIUM SALTS, GLYCEROL, SODIUM SULFATE.
HARDNESS (MOHS): 3-3.5

FIRE AND EXPLOSION DATA

FIRE AND EXPLOSION HAZARD: NEGLIGIBLE FIRE HAZARD WHEN EXPOSED TO HEAT OR FLAME.
FIREFIGHTING MEDIA: EXTINGUISH USING AGENT SUITABLE FOR TYPE OF SURROUNDING FIRE.
FIREFIGHTING: NO ACUTE HAZARD. MOVE CONTAINER FROM FIRE AREA IF POSSIBLE. AVOID BREATHING VAPORS OR DUSTS; KEEP UPWIND.

TOXICITY

CALCIUM SULFATE: ANHYDROUS: NO DATA AVAILABLE. HEMIHYDRATE: NO DATA AVAILABLE. MONOHYDRATE: NO DATA AVAILABLE. DIHYDRATE: 194 GM/M3/10 YEAR INTERMITTENT INHALATION-HUMAN TCLO; PENTAHYDRATE: NO DATA AVAILABLE. TUMORIGENIC DATA (RTECS). CARCINOGEN STATUS: NONE. ACUTE TOXICITY LEVEL: INSUFFICIENT DATA. TARGET EFFECTS: NUISANCE DUST.

HEALTH EFFECTS AND FIRST AID

INHALATION: CALCIUM SULFATE: NUISANCE DUST. **ACUTE EXPOSURE-** EXCESSIVE CONCENTRATIONS OF NUISANCE DUSTS MAY CAUSE UNPLEASANT DEPOSITS IN THE NASAL PASSAGES AND COUGH. **CHRONIC EXPOSURE-** NUISANCE DUSTS HAVE A LONG HISTORY OF LITTLE ADVERSE EFFECT ON LUNGS AND DO NOT PRODUCE SIGNIFICANT ORGANIC DISEASE, TOXIC EFFECT OR SCAR TISSURE FORMATION WHEN EXPOSURES ARE KEPT UNDER REASONABLE CONTROL. HOWEVER, ONE STUDY REPORTS NASAL EFFECTS, FIBROSING ALVEOLITIS AND OTHER LUNG CHANGES FROM A CONCENTRATION OF 194 GM/M3 FOR A TEN YEAR PERIOD OF INTERMITTENT EXPOSURES IN HUMANS. INHALATION OF GYPSUM, WHICH IS HYDRATED CALCIUM SULFATE, HAS BEEN REPORTED TO CAUSE IRRITATION OF THE RESPIRATORY TRACT, CHRONIC RHINITIS, LARYNGITIS, PHARYNGITIS, IMPAIRED SENSE OF SMELL AND TASTE, EPISTAXIS, AND REACTIONS OF THE TRACHEAL AND BRONCHIAL MEMBRANES IN EXPOSED WORKERS. EXPERIMENTAL ANIMALS EXPOSED DEVELOPED PNEUMONIA, INTERSTITIAL PNEUMOSCLEROSIS, AND BLOOD AND LYMPH CIRCULATION DISORDERS IN THE LUNGS. HOWEVER, THIS MAY BE DUE TO HIGH CONCENTRATIONS OF FURNACE GASES OR SMOKE.
FIRST AID- REMOVE FROM EXPOSURE AREA TO FRESH AIR IMMEDIATELY. IF BREATHING HAS STOPPED, PERFORM ARTIFICIAL RESPIRATION. KEEP PERSON WARM AND AT REST. TREAT SYMPTOMATICALLY AND SUPPORTIVELY. GET MEDICAL ATTENTION IMMEDIATELY.

SKIN CONTACT: CALCIUM SULFATE: **ACUTE EXPOSURE-** EXCESSIVE CONCENTRATIONS OF NUISANCE DUSTS IN THE WORKROOM AIR MAY CAUSE UNPLEASANT DEPOSITS ON THE SKIN. INJURY MAY OCCUR DUE TO THE RIGOROUS SKIN CLEANSING PROCEDURES NECESSARY FOR REMOVAL. **CHRONIC EXPOSURE-** PLASTER OF PARIS (HYDRATED CALCIUM SULFATE WITH 5% WATER) MAY CAUSE A DERMATOSIS TO DEVELOP.
FIRST AID- REMOVE CONTAMINATED CLOTHING AND SHOES IMMEDIATELY. WASH AFFECTED AREA WITH SOAP OR MILD DETERGENT AND LARGE AMOUNTS OF WATER UNTIL NO EVIDENCE OF CHEMICAL REMAINS (APPROXIMATELY 15-20 MINUTES). GET MEDICAL ATTENTION IMMEDIATELY.

EYE CONTACT: CALCIUM SULFATE: **ACUTE EXPOSURE-** CALCIUM SULFATE APPLIED EXPERIMENTALLY AS A WATERY PASTE TO RABBIT EYES HAS BEEN FOUND TO BE INNOCUOUS. HOWEVER, EXCESSIVE CONCENTRATIONS OF NUISANCE DUSTS MAY SERIOUSLY REDUCE VISIBILITY. **CHRONIC EXPOSURE-** REPEATED OR PROLONGED EXPOSURE TO HYDRATED CALCIUM SULFATE DUST HAS BEEN REPORTED TO CAUSE CONJUNCTIVITIS IN EXPOSED WORKERS.
FIRST AID- WASH EYES IMMEDIATELY WITH LARGE AMOUNTS OF WATER OR NORMAL SALINE, OCCASIONALLY LIFTING UPPER AND LOWER LIDS, UNTIL NO EVIDENCE OF CHEMICAL REMAINS (APPROXIMATELY 15-20 MINUTES). GET MEDICAL ATTENTION IMMEDIATELY.

INGESTION: CALCIUM SULFATE: **ACUTE EXPOSURE-** SINCE IT HARDENS QUICKLY AFTER ABSORBING MOISTURE, INGESTION OF PLASTER OF PARIS (ANHYDROUS CALCIUM SULFATE OR DIHYDRATE WITH 5% WATER) MAY CAUSE OBSTRUCTION PARTICULARLY IN THE PYLORUS. CALCIUM SALTS MAY CAUSE GASTRIC IRRITATION DUE IN PART TO OSMOTIC DISTURBANCES. THE ESTIMATED HUMAN LETHAL DOSE FOR HYDROUS CALCIUM SULFATE IS 0.5 TO 5.0 GM/KG. **CHRONIC EXPOSURE-** NO DATA AVAILABLE.
FIRST AID- GIVE GLYCERIN OR GELATIN SOLUTIONS OR LARGE AMOUNTS OF WATER TO DELAY SETTING PROCESS (DEICHMANN, TOXICOLOGY OR DRUGS AND CHEMICALS, 1969). TREAT SYMTOMATICALLY AND SUPPORTIVELY. GET MEDICAL ATTENTION IMMEDIATELY.
ANTIDOTE: NO SPECIFIC ANTIDOTE. TREAT SYMPTOMATICALLY AND SUPPORTIVELY.

REACTIVITY

REACTIVITY: STABLE UNDER NORMAL TEMPERATURES AND PRESSURES.
INCOMPATIBILITIES: CALCIUM SULFATE: ALUMINUM: VIOLENT OR EXPLOSIVE REDUCTION REACTION. DIAZOMETHANE (VAPOR): MAY EXPLODE ON CONTACT. PHOSPHORUS (RED): POSSIBLE FIRE HAZARD.
DECOMPOSITION: THERMAL DECOMPOSITION MAY RELEASE TOXIC OXIDES OF SULFUR.
POLYMERIZATION: HAZARDOUS POLYMERIZATION HAS NOT BEEN REPORTED TO OCCUR UNDER NORMAL TEMPERATURES AND PRESSURES.

STORAGE AND DISPOSAL

OBSERVE ALL FEDERAL, STATE AND LOCAL REGULATIONS WHEN STORING OR DISPOSING OF THIS SUBSTANCE. FOR ASSISTANCE, CONTACT THE DISTRICT DIRECTOR OF THE ENVIRONMENTAL PROTECTION AGENCY.

STORAGE

STORE AWAY FROM INCOMPATIBLE SUBSTANCES.

CONDITIONS TO AVOID

NONE REPORTED.

SPILL AND LEAK PROCEDURES

OCCUPATIONAL SPILL: NO SPECIAL PRECAUTIONS INDICATED.

PROTECTIVE EQUIPMENT

VENTILATION: PROVIDE LOCAL EXHAUST VENTILATION AND/OR GENERAL DILUTION VENTILATION TO MEET PUBLISHED EXPOSURE LIMITS.
RESPIRATOR: THE FOLLOWING RESPIRATORS ARE RECOMMENDED BASED ON INFORMATION FOUND IN THE PHYSICAL DATA, TOXICITY AND HEALTH EFFECTS SECTIONS. THEY ARE RANKED IN ORDER FROM MINIMUM TO MAXIMUM

RESPIRATORY PROTECTION. THE SPECIFIC RESPIRATOR SELECTED MUST BE BASED ON CONTAMINATION LEVELS FOUND IN THE WORK PLACE, MUST NOT EXCEED THE WORKING LIMITS OF THE RESPIRATOR AND BE JOINTLY APPROVED BY THE NATIONAL INSTITUTE FOR OCCUPATIONAL SAFETY AND HEALTH AND THE MINE SAFETY AND HEALTH ADMINISTRATION (NIOSH-MSHA).
DUST AND MIST RESPIRATOR.
AIR-PURIFYING RESPIRATOR WITH A HIGH-EFFICIENCY PARTICULATE FILTER.
POWERED AIR-PURIFYING RESPIRATOR WITH A DUST AND MIST FILTER.
POWERED AIR-PURIFYING RESPIRATOR WITH A HIGH-EFFICIENCY PARTICULATE FILTER.
TYPE 'C' SUPPLIED-AIR RESPIRATOR OPERATED IN THE PRESSURE-DEMAND OR OTHER POSITIVE PRESSURE OR CONTINUOUS-FLOW MODE.
SELF-CONTAINED BREATHING APPARATUS.
FOR FIREFIGHTING AND OTHER IMMEDIATELY DANGEROUS TO LIFE OR HEALTH CONDITIONS:
SELF-CONTAINED BREATHING APPARATUS WITH FULL FACEPIECE OPERATED IN PRESSURE-DEMAND OR OTHER POSITIVE PRESSURE MODE.
SUPPLIED-AIR RESPIRATOR WITH FULL FACEPIECE AND OPERATED IN PRESSURE-DEMAND OR OTHER POSITIVE PRESSURE MODE IN COMBINATION WITH AN AUXILIARY SELF-CONTAINED BREATHING APPARATUS OPERATED IN PRESSURE-DEMAND OR OTHER POSITIVE PRESSURE MODE.

CLOTHING: PROTECTIVE CLOTHING NOT REQUIRED. AVOID REPEATED OR PROLONGED CONTACT WITH THIS SUBSTANCE.

GLOVES: PROTECTIVE GLOVES ARE NOT REQUIRED BUT RECOMMENDED.

EYE PROTECTION: EYE PROTECTION NOT REQUIRED, BUT ADVISABLE.

AUTHORIZED BY- OCCUPATIONAL HEALTH SERVICES, INC.
CREATION DATE: 11/17/89 ***REVISION DATE:*** 05/18/90

MATERIAL SAFETY DATA SHEET

OCCUPATIONAL HEALTH SERVICES, INC.
AGRICULTURE AND PESTICIDE DIVISION
450 SEVENTH AVENUE, SUITE 2407
NEW YORK, NEW YORK 10123
1-800-445-MSDS OR (212) 967-1100

EMERGENCY CONTACT:
JOHN S. BRANSFORD, JR. (615) 292-1180

SUBSTANCE IDENTIFICATION

CAS-NUMBER 76-22-2

SUBSTANCE: CAMPHOR

TRADE NAMES/SYNONYMS: 1,7,7-TRIMETHYL-BICYCLO(2.2.1)HEPTAN-2-ONE; 2-BORNANONE; ROOT BARK SPIRIT; 1,7,7-TRIMETHYLNORCAMPHOR; 2-CAMPHONE; SYNTHETIC CAMPHOR; GUM CAMPHOR; ROOT BARK OIL; SPIRIT OF CAMPHOR; UN 2717; PST04130

CHEMICAL FAMILY: KETONE, ALICYCLIC

MOLECULAR FORMULA: C10-H16-O

MOLECULAR WEIGHT: 152.26

CERCLA RATINGS (SCALE 0-3): HEALTH=3 FIRE=2 REACTIVITY=0 PERSISTENCE=2

NFPA RATINGS (SCALE 0-4): HEALTH=0 FIRE=2 REACTIVITY=0

COMPONENTS AND CONTAMINANTS

COMPONENT: CAMPHOR ***PERCENT:*** 100
CAS# 76-22-2

OTHER CONTAMINANTS: NONE

EXPOSURE LIMITS: CAMPHOR: 2 MG/M3 OSHA TWA 12 MG/M3 ACGIH TWA; 18 MG/M3 ACGIH STEL

PHYSICAL DATA

DESCRIPTION: COLORLESS OR WHITE CUBIC CRYSTALS, GRANULES, OR CRYSTALLINE MASS WITH A FAMILIAR, FRAGRANT AND PENETRATING AROMATIC ODOR AND SLIGHTLY BITTER AND COOLING TASTE ***BOILING POINT:*** 399 F (204 C)

MELTING POINT: 345-354 F (174-179 C) ***SPECIFIC GRAVITY:*** 0.990

VAPOR PRESSURE: 0.18 MMHG @ 20 C ***SOLUBILITY IN WATER:*** 0.1% AT 25 C

ODOR THRESHOLD: 1.6 PPM ***VAPOR DENSITY:*** 5.24

SOLVENT SOLUBILITY: ALCOHOL, ETHER, CHLOROFORM, BENZENE, ACETONE, OIL OF TURPENTINE, GLACIAL ACETIC ACID, ANILINE, DINITROBENZENE, CARBON DISULFIDE ***VOLATILITY:*** SUBLIMES APPRECIABLY AT ROOM TEMPERATURE

FIRE AND EXPLOSION DATA

FIRE AND EXPLOSION HAZARD: MODERATE FIRE HAZARD WHEN EXPOSED TO HEAT OR FLAME.
VAPORS ARE HEAVIER THAN AIR AND MAY TRAVEL A CONSIDERABLE DISTANCE TO A SOURCE OF IGNITION AND FLASH BACK.
VAPOR-AIR MIXTURES ARE EXPLOSIVE ABOVE FLASH POINT.

FLASH POINT: 150 F (65.5 C) ***UPPER EXPLOSIVE LIMIT:*** 3.5%

LOWER EXPLOSIVE LIMIT: 0.6% ***AUTOIGNITION TEMP.:*** 871 F (466 C)

FIREFIGHTING MEDIA: DRY CHEMICAL, CARBON DIOXIDE, HALON, WATER SPRAY OR STANDARD FOAM (1987 EMERGENCY RESPONSE GUIDEBOOK, DOT P 5800.4).
FOR LARGER FIRES, USE WATER SPRAY, FOG OR STANDARD FOAM (1987 EMERGENCY RESPONSE GUIDEBOOK, DOT P 5800.4).

FIREFIGHTING: MOVE CONTAINER FROM FIRE AREA IF POSSIBLE. COOL FIRE-EXPOSED CONTAINERS WITH WATER FROM SIDE UNTIL WELL AFTER FIRE IS OUT. STAY AWAY FROM STORAGE TANK ENDS. FOR MASSIVE FIRE IN STORAGE AREA, USE UNMANNED HOSE HOLDER OR MONITOR NOZZLES, ELSE WITHDRAW FROM AREA AND LET FIRE BURN. WITHDRAW IMMEDIATELY IN CASE OF RISING SOUND FROM VENTING SAFETY DEVICE OR ANY DISCOLORATION OF STORAGE TANK DUE TO FIRE (1987 EMERGENCY RESPONSE GUIDEBOOK, DOT P 5800.4, GUIDE PAGE 27). EXTINGUISH ONLY IF FLOW CAN BE STOPPED; USE FLOODING AMOUNTS OF WATER AS A FOG, SOLID STREAMS MAY BE INEFFECTIVE. COOL CONTAINERS WITH FLOODING AMOUNTS OF WATER, APPLY FROM AS FAR A DISTANCE AS POSSIBLE. AVOID BREATHING VAPORS, KEEP UPWIND.

TRANSPORTATION DATA

DEPARTMENT OF TRANSPORTATION HAZARD CLASSIFICATION 49 CFR 172.101: FLAMMABLE SOLID
DEPARTMENT OF TRANSPORTATION LABELING REQUIREMENTS 49 CFR 172.101 AND SUBPART E: FLAMMABLE SOLID
DEPARTMENT OF TRANSPORTATION PACKAGING REQUIREMENTS: 49 CFR 173.154 EXCEPTIONS: 49 CFR 173.153

TOXICITY

CAMPHOR: TOXICITY DATA: 400 MG/M3/3 HOURS INHALATION-MOUSE LCLO; 70 MG/KG ORAL-INFANT LDLO; 1310 MG/KG ORAL-MOUSE LD50; 800 MG/KG ORAL-DOG LDLO; 2000 MG/KG ORAL-RABBIT LDLO; 70 MG/KG SUBCUTANEOUS-RAT LD50; 200 MG/KG SUBCUTANEOUS-MOUSE LDLO; 900 MG/KG INTRAPERITONEAL-RAT LDLO; 3000 MG/KG INTRAPERITONEAL-MOUSE LD50; 400 MG/KG INTRAPERITONEAL-CAT LDLO; 100 MG/KG UNREPORTED-CHILD LDLO; 29 MG/KG UNREPORTED-MAN LDLO. CARCINOGEN STATUS: NONE. LOCAL EFFECTS: IRRITANT- INHALATION, SKIN, AND EYES. ACUTE TOXICITY LEVEL: MODERATELY TOXIC BY INGESTION. TARGET EFFECTS: POISONING MAY AFFECT THE CENTRAL NERVOUS SYSTEM. AT INCREASED RISK FROM EXPOSURE: PERSONS WITH CONVULSIVE DISORDERS.

HEALTH EFFECTS AND FIRST AID

INHALATION: CAMPHOR: IRRITANT/NARCOTIC/CONVULSANT. 200 MG/M3 IMMEDIATELY DANGEROUS TO LIFE OR HEALTH. **ACUTE EXPOSURE-** LOW LEVELS MAY CAUSE MUCOUS MEMBRANE IRRITATION AND ANOSMIA. HIGHER CONCENTRATIONS MAY CAUSE BURNING IN THE MOUTH AND THROAT, THIRST, FEELING OF TENSION, IRRATIONAL BEHAVIOR, EXCITEMENT, RAPID PULSE, TWITCHING OF FACIAL MUSCLES, MUSCLE SPASMS, AND CONVULSIONS, FOLLOWED BY CENTRAL NERVOUS SYSTEM DEPRESSION WITH DIZZINESS, RIGIDITY, SLOW RESPIRATION, UNCONSCIOUSNESS, AND COMA. DEATH MAY OCCUR FROM RESPIRATORY FAILURE. **CHRONIC EXPOSURE-** REPEATED OVEREXPOSURE MAY RESULT IN ANOSMIA.

FIRST AID- REMOVE FROM EXPOSURE AREA TO FRESH AIR IMMEDIATELY. IF BREATHING HAS STOPPED, PERFORM ARTIFICIAL RESPIRATION. KEEP PERSON WARM AND AT REST. TREAT SYMPTOMATICALLY AND SUPPORTIVELY. GET MEDICAL ATTENTION IMMEDIATELY.

SKIN CONTACT: CAMPHOR: IRRITANT. **ACUTE EXPOSURE-** MAY CAUSE IRRITATION. **CHRONIC EXPOSURE-** REPEATED OR PROLONGED CONTACT MAY CAUSE DERMATITIS.

FIRST AID- REMOVE CONTAMINATED CLOTHING AND SHOES IMMEDIATELY. WASH AFFECTED AREA WITH SOAP OR MILD DETERGENT AND LARGE AMOUNTS OF WATER UNTIL NO EVIDENCE OF CHEMICAL REMAINS (APPROXIMATELY 15-20 MINUTES). GET MEDICAL ATTENTION IMMEDIATELY.

EYE CONTACT: CAMPHOR: IRRITANT. **ACUTE EXPOSURE-** MAY CAUSE IRRITATION. **CHRONIC EXPOSURE-** REPEATED OR PROLONGED CONTACT MAY CAUSE CONJUNCTIVITIS.

FIRST AID- WASH EYES IMMEDIATELY WITH LARGE AMOUNTS OF WATER OR NORMAL SALINE, OCCASIONALLY LIFTING UPPER AND LOWER LIDS, UNTIL NO EVIDENCE OF CHEMICAL REMAINS (APPROXIMATELY 15-20 MINUTES). GET MEDICAL ATTENTION IMMEDIATELY.

INGESTION: CAMPHOR: NARCOTIC/CONVULSANT. **ACUTE EXPOSURE-** MAY CAUSE BURNING IN THE MOUTH AND THROAT, NAUSEA, VOMITING, THIRST, FEELING OF TENSION, IRRATIONAL BEHAVIOR, EXCITEMENT, RAPID PULSE, TWITCHING OF FACIAL MUSCLES, MUSCLE SPASMS, AND CONVULSIONS, FOLLOWED BY CENTRAL NERVOUS SYSTEM DEPRESSION WITH DIZZINESS, RIGIDITY, SLOW RESPIRATION, UNCONSCIOUSNESS, AND COMA. DEATH IS POSSIBLE FROM RESPIRATORY FAILURE. IT IS MODERATELY TOXIC IN ANIMALS BUT APPEARS TO BE MUCH MORE TOXIC IN HUMANS WITH A FATAL DOSE OF AROUND 2 GRAMS. **CHRONIC EXPOSURE-** NO DATA AVAILABLE.

FIRST AID- ESTABLISH AIRWAY AND MAINTAIN RESPIRATION. AFTER CONVULSIONS ARE CONTROLLED, REMOVE SWALLOWED POISON BY AIRWAY-PROTECTED GASTRIC LAVAGE FOLLOWED BY 30-60 ML OF FLEET'S PHOSPHO-SODA DILUTED 1:4 IN WATER. GASTRIC LAVAGE SHOULD BE PERFORMED BY QUALIFIED MEDICAL PERSONNEL (DREISBACH, HANDBOOK OF POISONING, 12TH ED.). GET MEDICAL ATTENTION IMMEDIATELY.

ANTIDOTE: NO SPECIFIC ANTIDOTE. TREAT SYMPTOMATICALLY AND SUPPORTIVELY.

REACTIVITY

REACTIVITY: STABLE UNDER NORMAL TEMPERATURES AND PRESSURES.

INCOMPATIBILITIES: CAMPHOR: CHROMIC ANHYDRIDE: INCOMPATIBLE. OXIDIZERS (STRONG): FIRE AND EXPLOSION HAZARD. POTASSIUM PERMANGANATE: INCOMPATIBLE.

DECOMPOSITION: THERMAL DECOMPOSITION MAY RELEASE TOXIC AND/OR HAZARDOUS GASES.

POLYMERIZATION: HAZARDOUS POLYMERIZATION HAS NOT BEEN REPORTED TO OCCUR UNDER NORMAL TEMPERATURES AND PRESSURES.

CONDITIONS TO AVOID

AVOID CONTACT WITH HEAT, SPARKS, FLAMES, OR OTHER SOURCES OF IGNITION. VAPORS MAY BE EXPLOSIVE. AVOID OVERHEATING OF CONTAINERS; CONTAINERS MAY VIOLENTLY RUPTURE IN HEAT OF FIRE. AVOID CONTAMINATION OF WATER SOURCES.

SPILL AND LEAK PROCEDURES

OCCUPATIONAL SPILL: SHUT OFF IGNITION SOURCES. STOP LEAK IF YOU CAN DO IT WITHOUT RISK. USE WATER SPRAY TO REDUCE VAPORS. FOR SMALL SPILLS, TAKE UP WITH SAND OR OTHER ABSORBENT MATERIAL AND PLACE INTO CONTAINERS FOR LATER DISPOSAL. FOR LARGER SPILLS, DIKE FAR AHEAD OF SPILL FOR LATER DISPOSAL. NO SMOKING, FLAMES OR FLARES IN HAZARD AREA. KEEP UNNECESSARY PEOPLE AWAY; ISOLATE HAZARD AREA AND RESTRICT ENTRY.

PROTECTIVE EQUIPMENT

VENTILATION: PROVIDE LOCAL EXHAUST OR PROCESS ENCLOSURE VENTILATION TO MEET PUBLISHED EXPOSURE LIMITS.

RESPIRATOR: THE FOLLOWING RESPIRATORS AND MAXIMUM USE CONCENTRATIONS ARE RECOMMENDATIONS BY THE U.S. DEPARTMENT OF HEALTH AND HUMAN SERVICES, NIOSH POCKET GUIDE TO CHEMICAL HAZARDS; NIOSH CRITERIA DOCUMENTS OR BY THE U.S. DEPARTMENT OF LABOR, 29 CFR 1910 SUBPART Z. THE SPECIFIC RESPIRATOR SELECTED MUST BE BASED ON CONTAMINATION LEVELS FOUND IN THE WORK PLACE, MUST NOT EXCEED THE WORKING LIMITS OF THE RESPIRATOR AND BE JOINTLY APPROVED BY THE NATIONAL INSTITUTE FOR OCCUPATIONAL SAFETY AND HEALTH AND THE MINE SAFETY AND HEALTH ADMINISTRATION (NIOSH-MSHA).

CAMPHOR:

50 MG/M3- ANY SUPPLIED-AIR RESPIRATOR OPERATED IN A CONTINUOUS FLOW MODE. ANY POWERED AIR-PURIFYING RESPIRATOR WITH ORGANIC VAPOR CARTRIDGE(S) IN COMBINATION WITH A DUST AND MIST FILTER.

100 MG/M3- ANY CHEMICAL CARTRIDGE RESPIRATOR WITH A FULL FACEPIECE AND ORGANIC VAPOR CARTRIDGE(S) IN COMBINATION WITH A DUST AND MIST FILTER. ANY AIR-PURIFYING FULL FACEPIECE RESPIRATOR (GAS MASK) WITH A CHIN-STYLE OR FRONT OR BACK-MOUNTED ORGANIC VAPOR CANISTER HAVING A HIGH-EFFICIENCY PARTICULATE FILTER. ANY POWERED AIR-PURIFYING RESPIRATOR WITH A TIGHT-FITTING FACEPIECE AND ORGANIC VAPOR CARTRIDGE(S) IN COMBINATION WITH A HIGH-EFFICIENCY PARTICULATE FILTER. ANY SELF-CONTAINED BREATHING APPARATUS WITH A FULL FACEPIECE. ANY SUPPLIED-AIR RESPIRATOR WITH A FULL FACEPIECE.

200 MG/M3- ANY SUPPLIED-AIR RESPIRATOR WITH A FULL FACEPIECE AND OPERATED IN A PRESSURE-DEMAND OR OTHER POSITIVE PRESSURE MODE.

ESCAPE- ANY AIR-PURIFYING FULL FACEPIECE RESPIRATOR (GAS MASK) WITH A CHIN-STYLE OR FRONT OR BACK-MOUNTED ORGANIC CANISTER HAVING A HIGH-EFFICIENCY PARTICULATE FILTER. ANY APPROPRIATE ESCAPE-TYPE SELF-CONTAINED BREATHING APPARATUS.

FOR FIREFIGHTING AND OTHER IMMEDIATELY DANGEROUS TO LIFE OR HEALTH CONDITIONS:

SELF-CONTAINED BREATHING APPARATUS WITH FULL FACEPIECE OPERATED IN PRESSURE-DEMAND OR OTHER POSITIVE PRESSURE MODE.

SUPPLIED-AIR RESPIRATOR WITH FULL FACEPIECE AND OPERATED IN PRESSURE-DEMAND OR OTHER POSITIVE PRESSURE MODE IN COMBINATION WITH AN AUXILIARY SELF-CONTAINED BREATHING APPARATUS OPERATED IN PRESSURE-DEMAND OR OTHER POSITIVE PRESSURE MODE.

CLOTHING: EMPLOYEE MUST WEAR APPROPRIATE PROTECTIVE (IMPERVIOUS) CLOTHING AND EQUIPMENT TO PREVENT REPEATED OR PROLONGED SKIN CONTACT WITH THIS SUBSTANCE.

GLOVES: EMPLOYEE MUST WEAR APPROPRIATE PROTECTIVE GLOVES TO PREVENT CONTACT WITH THIS SUBSTANCE.

EYE PROTECTION: EMPLOYEE MUST WEAR SPLASH-PROOF OR DUST-RESISTANT SAFETY GOGGLES TO PREVENT EYE CONTACT WITH THIS SUBSTANCE.

EMERGENCY EYE WASH: WHERE THERE IS ANY POSSIBILITY THAT AN EMPLOYEE'S EYES MAY BE EXPOSED TO THIS SUBSTANCE, THE EMPLOYER SHOULD PROVIDE AN EYE WASH FOUNTAIN WITHIN THE IMMEDIATE WORK AREA FOR EMERGENCY USE.

AUTHORIZED BY- OCCUPATIONAL HEALTH SERVICES, INC.

CREATION DATE: 10/04/89 ***REVISION DATE:*** 05/17/90

MATERIAL SAFETY DATA SHEET

OCCUPATIONAL HEALTH SERVICES, INC.
AGRICULTURE AND PESTICIDE DIVISION
450 SEVENTH AVENUE, SUITE 2407
NEW YORK, NEW YORK 10123
1-800-445-MSDS OR (212) 967-1100

EMERGENCY CONTACT:
JOHN S. BRANSFORD, JR. (615) 292-1180

SUBSTANCE IDENTIFICATION

CAS-NUMBER 8008-51-3

SUBSTANCE: **CAMPHOR OIL**

TRADE NAMES/SYNONYMS: CAMPHOR OIL, RECTIFIED; CAMPHOR OIL WHITE; CAMPHOR OIL YELLOW; LIGHT CAMPHOR OIL; FORMOSE OIL OF CAMPHOR; WHITE CAMPHOR OIL; JAPANESE, OIL OF CAMPHOR; JAPANESE CAMPHOR OIL; OIL CAMPHOR SASSAFRASSY; PST04140

CHEMICAL FAMILY: HYDROAROMATIC TERPENE

CERCLA RATINGS (SCALE 0-3): HEALTH=2 FIRE=2 REACTIVITY=0 PERSISTENCE=0

NFPA RATINGS (SCALE 0-4): HEALTH=2 FIRE=2 REACTIVITY=0

COMPONENTS AND CONTAMINANTS

COMPONENT: CAMPHOR OIL ***PERCENT:*** 100
CAS# 8008-51-3

OTHER CONTAMINANTS: NONE

EXPOSURE LIMITS: NO OCCUPATIONAL EXPOSURE LIMITS ESTABLISHED BY OSHA, ACGIH, OR NIOSH.

PHYSICAL DATA

DESCRIPTION: COLORLESS OR YELLOWISH, OILY LIQUID WITH AN ODOR OF CAMPHOR

BOILING POINT: 175-200 F (347-392 C) ***SPECIFIC GRAVITY:*** 0.875-0.900

SOLUBILITY IN WATER: INSOLUBLE

SOLVENT SOLUBILITY: CHLOROFORM, ETHER, OILS, ALCOHOL

FIRE AND EXPLOSION DATA

FIRE AND EXPLOSION HAZARD: MODERATE FIRE HAZARD WHEN EXPOSED TO HEAT OR FLAME.

FLASH POINT: 117 F (47 C) (CC) ***FLAMMABILITY CLASS(OSHA):*** II

FIREFIGHTING MEDIA: DRY CHEMICAL, CARBON DIOXIDE, HALON, WATER SPRAY OR STANDARD FOAM (1987 EMERGENCY RESPONSE GUIDEBOOK, DOT P 5800.4). FOR LARGER FIRES, USE WATER SPRAY, FOG OR STANDARD FOAM (1987 EMERGENCY RESPONSE GUIDEBOOK, DOT P 5800.4).

FIREFIGHTING: MOVE CONTAINER FROM FIRE AREA IF POSSIBLE. COOL FIRE-EXPOSED CONTAINERS WITH WATER FROM SIDE UNTIL WELL AFTER FIRE IS OUT. STAY AWAY FROM STORAGE TANK ENDS. FOR MASSIVE FIRE IN STORAGE AREA, USE UNMANNED HOSE HOLDER OR MONITOR NOZZLES, ELSE WITHDRAW FROM AREA AND LET FIRE BURN. WITHDRAW IMMEDIATELY IN CASE OF RISING SOUND FROM VENTING SAFETY DEVICE OR ANY DISCOLORATION OF STORAGE TANK DUE TO FIRE (1987 EMERGENCY RESPONSE GUIDEBOOK, DOT P 5800.4, GUIDE PAGE 27). EXTINGUISH ONLY IF FLOW CAN BE STOPPED; USE WATER IN FLOODING QUANTITIES AS FOG, SOLID STREAMS MAY NOT BE EFFECTIVE. COOL CONTAINERS WITH FLOODING AMOUNTS OF WATER, APPLY FROM AS FAR A DISTANCE AS

QUANTITIES AS FOG, SOLID STREAMS MAY NOT BE EFFECTIVE. COOL CONTAINERS WITH FLOODING AMOUNTS OF WATER, APPLY FROM AS FAR A DISTANCE AS POSSIBLE. AVOID BREATHING TOXIC VAPORS, KEEP UPWIND.

TRANSPORTATION DATA

DEPARTMENT OF TRANSPORTATION HAZARD CLASSIFICATION 49 CFR 172.101: COMBUSTIBLE LIQUID
DEPARTMENT OF TRANSPORTATION LABELING REQUIREMENTS 49 CFR 172.101 AND SUBPART E: NONE
DEPARTMENT OF TRANSPORTATION PACKAGING REQUIREMENTS: NONE
EXCEPTIONS: 49 CFR 173.118A

TOXICITY

CAMPHOR OIL: IRRITATION DATA: 500 MG/24 HOURS SKIN-RABBIT MILD. TOXICITY DATA: 29 MG/KG ORAL-HUMAN TDLO; 50 MG/KG ORAL-CHILD LDLO; 3730 MG/KG ORAL-RAT LD50. CARCINOGEN STATUS: NONE. LOCAL EFFECTS: IRRITANT- SKIN. ACUTE TOXICITY LEVEL: MODERATELY TOXIC BY INGESTION. TARGET EFFECTS: CONVULSANT.

HEALTH EFFECTS AND FIRST AID

INHALATION: CAMPHOR OIL: **ACUTE EXPOSURE-** NO DATA AVAILABLE. **CHRONIC EXPOSURE-** NO DATA AVAILABLE.
FIRST AID- REMOVE FROM EXPOSURE AREA TO FRESH AIR IMMEDIATELY. IF BREATHING HAS STOPPED, PERFORM ARTIFICIAL RESPIRATION. KEEP PERSON WARM AND AT REST. TREAT SYMPTOMATICALLY AND SUPPORTIVELY. GET MEDICAL ATTENTION IMMEDIATELY.

SKIN CONTACT: CAMPHOR OIL: **ACUTE EXPOSURE-** HAS CAUSED MILD IRRITATION TO RABBIT SKIN. **CHRONIC EXPOSURE-** NO DATA AVAILABLE.
FIRST AID- REMOVE CONTAMINATED CLOTHING AND SHOES IMMEDIATELY. WASH AFFECTED AREA WITH SOAP OR MILD DETERGENT AND LARGE AMOUNTS OF WATER UNTIL NO EVIDENCE OF CHEMICAL REMAINS (APPROXIMATELY 15-20 MINUTES). GET MEDICAL ATTENTION IMMEDIATELY.

EYE CONTACT: CAMPHOR OIL: **ACUTE EXPOSURE-** NO DATA AVAILABLE. MAY BE IRRITATING. **CHRONIC EXPOSURE-** NO DATA AVAILABLE.
FIRST AID- WASH EYES IMMEDIATELY WITH LARGE AMOUNTS OF WATER OR NORMAL SALINE, OCCASIONALLY LIFTING UPPER AND LOWER LIDS, UNTIL NO EVIDENCE OF CHEMICAL REMAINS (APPROXIMATELY 15-20 MINUTES). GET MEDICAL ATTENTION IMMEDIATELY.

INGESTION: CAMPHOR OIL: CONVULSANT. **ACUTE EXPOSURE-** HAS CAUSED TREMOR, CONVULSIONS, RESPIRATORY DEPRESSION AND DEATH IN HUMANS. MAY CAUSE SYMPTOMS SIMILAR TO THOSE OF CAMPHOR POISONING INCLUDING BURNING IN THE MOUTH AND THROAT, NAUSEA, VOMITING,THIRST, FEELING OF TENSION, IRRATIONAL BEHAVIOR, EXCITEMENT, RAPID PULSE, TWITCHING OF FACIAL MUSCLES, MUSCLE SPASMS, AND CONVULSIONS, FOLLOWED BY CENTRAL NERVOUS SYSTEM DEPRESSION WITH DIZZINESS, RIGIDITY, SLOW RESPIRATION, UNCONSCIOUSNESS, AND COMA. DEATH IS POSSIBLE FROM RESPIRATORY FAILURE. CAMPHOR OIL IS MODERATELY TOXIC IN ANIMALS BUT APPEARS TO BE MUCH MORE TOXIC IN HUMANS BASED ON AVAILABLE DATA. **CHRONIC EXPOSURE-** NO DATA AVAILABLE.
FIRST AID- ESTABLISH AIRWAY AND MAINTAIN RESPIRATION. AFTER CONVULSIONS ARE CONTROLLED, REMOVE SWALLOWED POISON BY AIRWAY-PROTECTED GASTRIC LAVAGE FOLLOWED BY 30-60 ML OF FLEET'S PHOSPHO-SODA DILUTED 1:4 IN WATER. GASTRIC LAVAGE SHOULD BE PERFORMED BY QUALIFIED MEDICAL PERSONNEL (DREISBACH, HANDBOOK OF POISONING, 12TH ED.). GET MEDICAL ATTENTION IMMEDIATELY.
ANTIDOTE: NO SPECIFIC ANTIDOTE. TREAT SYMPTOMATICALLY AND SUPPORTIVELY.

REACTIVITY

REACTIVITY: STABLE UNDER NORMAL TEMPERATURES AND PRESSURES.
INCOMPATIBILITIES: CAMPHOR OIL: NO DATA AVAILABLE.
DECOMPOSITION: THERMAL DECOMPOSITION MAY RELEASE ACRID SMOKE AND IRRITATING FUMES.
POLYMERIZATION: HAZARDOUS POLYMERIZATION HAS NOT BEEN REPORTED TO OCCUR UNDER NORMAL TEMPERATURES AND PRESSURES.

CONDITIONS TO AVOID

AVOID CONTACT WITH HEAT, SPARKS, FLAMES, OR OTHER SOURCES OF IGNITION. VAPORS MAY BE EXPLOSIVE. AVOID OVERHEATING OF CONTAINERS; CONTAINERS MAY VIOLENTLY RUPTURE IN HEAT OF FIRE. AVOID CONTAMINATION OF WATER SOURCES.
KEEP TIGHTLY CLOSED AND PROTECTED FROM LIGHT.

SPILL AND LEAK PROCEDURES

OCCUPATIONAL SPILL: SHUT OFF IGNITION SOURCES. STOP LEAK IF YOU CAN DO IT WITHOUT RISK. USE WATER SPRAY TO REDUCE VAPORS. FOR SMALL SPILLS, TAKE UP WITH SAND OR OTHER ABSORBENT MATERIAL AND PLACE INTO CONTAINERS FOR LATER DISPOSAL. FOR LARGER SPILLS, DIKE FAR AHEAD OF SPILL FOR LATER DISPOSAL. NO SMOKING, FLAMES OR FLARES IN HAZARD AREA. KEEP UNNECESSARY PEOPLE AWAY; ISOLATE HAZARD AREA AND RESTRICT ENTRY.

PROTECTIVE EQUIPMENT

VENTILATION: PROVIDE LOCAL EXHAUST VENTILATION SYSTEM TO MEET PUBLISHED EXPOSURE LIMITS.
RESPIRATOR: THE FOLLOWING RESPIRATORS ARE RECOMMENDED BASED ON INFORMATION FOUND IN THE PHYSICAL DATA, TOXICITY AND HEALTH EFFECTS SECTIONS. THEY ARE RANKED IN ORDER FROM MINIMUM TO MAXIMUM RESPIRATORY PROTECTION. THE SPECIFIC RESPIRATOR SELECTED MUST BE BASED ON CONTAMINATION LEVELS FOUND IN THE WORK PLACE, MUST NOT EXCEED THE WORKING LIMITS OF THE RESPIRATOR AND BE JOINTLY APPROVED BY THE NATIONAL INSTITUTE FOR OCCUPATIONAL SAFETY AND HEALTH AND THE MINE SAFETY AND HEALTH ADMINISTRATION (NIOSH-MSHA).
CHEMICAL CARTRIDGE RESPIRATOR WITH AN ORGANIC VAPOR CARTRIDGE(S) WITH A FULL FACEPIECE.
GAS MASK WITH ORGANIC VAPOR CANISTER (CHIN-STYLE OR FRONT- OR BACK-MOUNTED CANISTER) WITH A FULL FACEPIECE.
TYPE 'C' SUPPLIED-AIR RESPIRATOR WITH A FULL FACEPIECE OPERATED IN PRESSURE-DEMAND OR OTHER POSITIVE PRESSURE MODE OR WITH A FULL FACEPIECE, HELMET OR HOOD OPERATED IN CONTINUOUS-FLOW MODE.
SELF-CONTAINED BREATHING APPARATUS WITH A FULL FACEPIECE OPERATED IN PRESSURE-DEMAND OR OTHER POSITIVE PRESSURE MODE.
FOR FIREFIGHTING AND OTHER IMMEDIATELY DANGEROUS TO LIFE OR HEALTH CONDITIONS:
SELF-CONTAINED BREATHING APPARATUS WITH FULL FACEPIECE OPERATED IN PRESSURE-DEMAND OR OTHER POSITIVE PRESSURE MODE.
SUPPLIED-AIR RESPIRATOR WITH FULL FACEPIECE AND OPERATED IN PRESSURE-DEMAND OR OTHER POSITIVE PRESSURE MODE IN COMBINATION WITH AN AUXILIARY SELF-CONTAINED BREATHING APPARATUS OPERATED IN PRESSURE-DEMAND OR OTHER POSITIVE PRESSURE MODE.
CLOTHING: EMPLOYEE MUST WEAR APPROPRIATE PROTECTIVE (IMPERVIOUS) CLOTHING AND EQUIPMENT TO PREVENT REPEATED OR PROLONGED SKIN CONTACT WITH THIS SUBSTANCE.
GLOVES: EMPLOYEE MUST WEAR APPROPRIATE PROTECTIVE GLOVES TO PREVENT CONTACT WITH THIS SUBSTANCE.
EYE PROTECTION: EMPLOYEE MUST WEAR SPLASH-PROOF OR DUST-RESISTANT SAFETY GOGGLES TO PREVENT EYE CONTACT WITH THIS SUBSTANCE.
EMERGENCY EYE WASH: WHERE THERE IS ANY POSSIBILITY THAT AN EMPLOYEE'S EYES MAY BE EXPOSED TO THIS SUBSTANCE, THE EMPLOYER SHOULD PROVIDE AN EYE WASH FOUNTAIN WITHIN THE IMMEDIATE WORK AREA FOR EMERGENCY USE.

AUTHORIZED BY- OCCUPATIONAL HEALTH SERVICES, INC.
CREATION DATE: 10/04/89 ***REVISION DATE:*** 05/17/90

MATERIAL SAFETY DATA SHEET

OCCUPATIONAL HEALTH SERVICES, INC.
AGRICULTURE AND PESTICIDE DIVISION
450 SEVENTH AVENUE, SUITE 2407
NEW YORK, NEW YORK 10123
1-800-445-MSDS OR (212) 967-1100

EMERGENCY CONTACT:
JOHN S. BRANSFORD, JR. (615) 292-1180

SUBSTANCE IDENTIFICATION

CAS-NUMBER 8007-47-4
***SUBSTANCE:* CANADA BALSAM**
TRADE NAMES/SYNONYMS: CANADA TURPENTINE; BALSAM OF FIR; B-10; PST04145
CHEMICAL FAMILY: LIQUID OLEORESIN.
MOLECULAR FORMULA: VARIES MOL WT: VARIES
CERCLA RATINGS (SCALE 0-3): HEALTH=U FIRE=0 REACTIVITY=0 PERSISTENCE=1
NFPA RATINGS (SCALE 0-4): HEALTH=U FIRE=0 REACTIVITY=0

COMPONENTS AND CONTAMINANTS

COMPONENT: CANADA BALSAM ***PERCENT:*** 100
CAS# 8007-47-4
OTHER CONTAMINANTS: NONE

EXPOSURE LIMITS: CANADA BALSAM: NONE ESTABLISHED.

PHYSICAL DATA

DESCRIPTION: YELLOWISH TO GREENISH, VISCID, TRANSPARENT, SLIGHTLY FLUORESCENT LIQUID WITH AN AGREEABLE PINE-LIKE ODOR AND BITTER TASTE.
SPECIFIC GRAVITY: 0.915 ***EVAPORATION RATE:*** (ETHER = 1) > 1
SOLUBILITY IN WATER: INSOLUBLE ***VAPOR DENSITY:*** > 1
SOLVENT SOLUBILITY: BENZENE, CHLOROFORM, XYLENE, ETHER, ALCOHOL

FIRE AND EXPLOSION DATA

FIRE AND EXPLOSION HAZARD: NEGLIGIBLE FIRE HAZARD WHEN EXPOSED TO HEAT OR FLAME.
FIREFIGHTING MEDIA: DRY CHEMICAL, CARBON DIOXIDE, HALON, WATER SPRAY OR STANDARD FOAM (1987 EMERGENCY RESPONSE GUIDEBOOK, DOT P 5800.4). FOR LARGER FIRES, USE WATER SPRAY, FOG OR STANDARD FOAM (1987 EMERGENCY RESPONSE GUIDEBOOK, DOT P 5800.4).
FIREFIGHTING: MOVE CONTAINER FROM FIRE AREA IF POSSIBLE. COOL FIRE-EXPOSED CONTAINERS WITH WATER FROM SIDE UNTIL WELL AFTER FIRE IS OUT. STAY AWAY FROM STORAGE TANK ENDS. FOR MASSIVE FIRE IN STORAGE AREA, USE UNMANNED HOSE HOLDER OR MONITOR NOZZLES, ELSE WITHDRAW FROM AREA AND LET FIRE BURN. WITHDRAW IMMEDIATELY IN CASE OF RISING SOUND FROM VENTING SAFETY DEVICE OR ANY DISCOLORATION OF STORAGE TANK DUE TO FIRE (1987 EMERGENCY RESPONSE GUIDEBOOK, DOT P 5800.4, GUIDE PAGE 27). EXTINGUISH ONLY IF FLOW CAN BE STOPPED; USE FLOODING AMOUNTS OF WATER AS A FOG, SOLID STREAMS MAY BE INEFFECTIVE. COOL CONTAINERS WITH FLOODING AMOUNTS OF WATER, APPLY FROM AS FAR A DISTANCE AS POSSIBLE. AVOID BREATHING VAPORS, KEEP UPWIND.

TOXICITY

CANADA BALSAM: CARCINOGEN STATUS: NONE. LOCAL EFFECTS: IRRITANT- SKIN AND EYES. ACUTE TOXICITY LEVEL: NO DATA AVAILABLE. TARGET EFFECTS: NO DATA AVAILABLE.

HEALTH EFFECTS AND FIRST AID

INHALATION: CANADA BALSAM: **ACUTE EXPOSURE**- NO DATA AVAILABLE. **CHRONIC EXPOSURE**- NO DATA AVAILABLE.
FIRST AID- REMOVE FROM EXPOSURE AREA TO FRESH AIR IMMEDIATELY. IF BREATHING HAS STOPPED, PERFORM ARTIFICIAL RESPIRATION. KEEP PERSON WARM AND AT REST. TREAT SYMPTOMATICALLY AND SUPPORTIVELY. GET MEDICAL ATTENTION IMMEDIATELY.

SKIN CONTACT: CANADA BALSAM: IRRITANT. **ACUTE EXPOSURE**- MAY CAUSE IRRITATION. **CHRONIC EXPOSURE**- PROLONGED OR REPEATED EXPOSURE MAY CAUSE DERMATITIS.
FIRST AID- REMOVE CONTAMINATED CLOTHING AND SHOES IMMEDIATELY. WASH AFFECTED AREA WITH SOAP OR MILD DETERGENT AND LARGE AMOUNTS OF WATER UNTIL NO EVIDENCE OF CHEMICAL REMAINS (APPROXIMATELY 15-20 MINUTES). GET MEDICAL ATTENTION IMMEDIATELY.

EYE CONTACT: CANADA BALSAM: IRRITANT. **ACUTE EXPOSURE**- MAY CAUSE IRRITATION. **CHRONIC EXPOSURE**- PROLONGED OR REPEATED EXPOSURE MAY CAUSE CONJUNCTIVITIS.
FIRST AID- WASH EYES IMMEDIATELY WITH LARGE AMOUNTS OF WATER OR NORMAL SALINE, OCCASIONALLY LIFTING UPPER AND LOWER LIDS, UNTIL NO EVIDENCE OF CHEMICAL REMAINS (APPROXIMATELY 15-20 MINUTES). GET MEDICAL ATTENTION IMMEDIATELY.

INGESTION: CANADA BALSAM: **ACUTE EXPOSURE**- NO DATA AVAILABLE. **CHRONIC EXPOSURE**- NO DATA AVAILABLE.
FIRST AID- TREAT SYMPTOMATICALLY AND SUPPORTIVELY. GET MEDICAL ATTENTION IMMEDIATELY. IF VOMITING OCCURS, KEEP HEAD LOWER THAN HIPS TO PREVENT ASPIRATION.
ANTIDOTE: NO SPECIFIC ANTIDOTE. TREAT SYMPTOMATICALLY AND SUPPORTIVELY.

REACTIVITY

REACTIVITY: STABLE UNDER NORMAL TEMPERATURES AND PRESSURES.
INCOMPATIBILITIES: CANADA BALSAM: OXIDIZERS: INCOMPATIBLE.
DECOMPOSITION: THERMAL DECOMPOSITION PRODUCTS MAY INCLUDE TOXIC OXIDES OF CARBON.
POLYMERIZATION: HAZARDOUS POLYMERIZATION HAS NOT BEEN REPORTED TO OCCUR UNDER NORMAL TEMPERATURES AND PRESSURES.

CONDITIONS TO AVOID

KEEP AWAY FROM HEAT AND OPEN FLAME.

SPILL AND LEAK PROCEDURES

OCCUPATIONAL SPILL: SOAK UP SPILL WITH VERMICULITE OR OTHER ABSORBENT MATERIAL AND PLACE INTO SUITABLE CONTAINERS FOR LATER DISPOSAL.

PROTECTIVE EQUIPMENT

VENTILATION: PROVIDE LOCAL EXHAUST OR PROCESS ENCLOSURE VENTILATION TO MEET PUBLISHED EXPOSURE LIMITS.
RESPIRATOR: THE FOLLOWING RESPIRATORS ARE RECOMMENDED BASED ON INFORMATION FOUND IN THE PHYSICAL DATA, TOXICITY AND HEALTH EFFECTS SECTIONS. THEY ARE RANKED IN ORDER FROM MINIMUM TO MAXIMUM RESPIRATORY PROTECTION. THE SPECIFIC RESPIRATOR SELECTED MUST BE BASED ON CONTAMINATION LEVELS FOUND IN THE WORK PLACE, MUST NOT EXCEED THE WORKING LIMITS OF THE RESPIRATOR AND BE JOINTLY APPROVED BY THE NATIONAL INSTITUTE FOR OCCUPATIONAL SAFETY AND HEALTH AND THE MINE SAFETY AND HEALTH ADMINISTRATION (NIOSH-MSHA).
CHEMICAL CARTRIDGE RESPIRATOR WITH AN ORGANIC VAPOR CARTRIDGE(S) WITH A FULL FACEPIECE.
GAS MASK WITH ORGANIC VAPOR CANISTER (CHIN-STYLE OR FRONT- OR BACK-MOUNTED CANISTER) WITH A FULL FACEPIECE.
TYPE 'C' SUPPLIED-AIR RESPIRATOR WITH A FULL FACEPIECE OPERATED IN PRESSURE-DEMAND OR OTHER POSITIVE PRESSURE MODE OR WITH A FULL FACEPIECE, HELMET OR HOOD OPERATED IN CONTINUOUS-FLOW MODE.
SELF-CONTAINED BREATHING APPARATUS WITH A FULL FACEPIECE OPERATED IN PRESSURE-DEMAND OR OTHER POSITIVE PRESSURE MODE.
FOR FIREFIGHTING AND OTHER IMMEDIATELY DANGEROUS TO LIFE OR HEALTH CONDITIONS:
SELF-CONTAINED BREATHING APPARATUS WITH FULL FACEPIECE OPERATED IN PRESSURE-DEMAND OR OTHER POSITIVE PRESSURE MODE.
SUPPLIED-AIR RESPIRATOR WITH FULL FACEPIECE AND OPERATED IN PRESSURE-DEMAND OR OTHER POSITIVE PRESSURE MODE IN COMBINATION WITH AN AUXILIARY SELF-CONTAINED BREATHING APPARATUS OPERATED IN PRESSURE-DEMAND OR OTHER POSITIVE PRESSURE MODE.
CLOTHING: PROTECTIVE CLOTHING NOT REQUIRED. AVOID REPEATED OR PROLONGED CONTACT WITH THIS SUBSTANCE.
GLOVES: PROTECTIVE GLOVES ARE NOT REQUIRED BUT RECOMMENDED.
EYE PROTECTION: EYE PROTECTION NOT REQUIRED, BUT ADVISABLE.

AUTHORIZED BY- OCCUPATIONAL HEALTH SERVICES, INC.
CREATION DATE: 10/04/89 ***REVISION DATE:*** 05/18/90

MATERIAL SAFETY DATA SHEET

OCCUPATIONAL HEALTH SERVICES, INC.
AGRICULTURE AND PESTICIDE DIVISION
450 SEVENTH AVENUE, SUITE 2407
NEW YORK, NEW YORK 10123
1-800-445-MSDS OR (212) 967-1100

EMERGENCY CONTACT:
JOHN S. BRANSFORD, JR. (615) 292-1180

SUBSTANCE IDENTIFICATION

CAS-NUMBER 2425-06-1
SUBSTANCE: **CAPTAFOL**
TRADE NAMES/SYNONYMS: 3A,4,7,7A-TETRAHYDRO-2-((1,1,2,2-TETRACHLOROETHYL)THIO)-1H-ISOINDOLE- 1,3(2H)-DIONE; N-((1,1,2,2-TETRACHLOROETHYL)THIO)-4-CYCLOHEXENE-1,2-DICARBOXIMIDE; ALFLOC 7020; ALFLOC 7046; ARBORSEAL; CS 5623; DIFOLATAN; DIFOLATAN BOW; DIFOLATAN 4F; FOLCID; FOLTAF; HAIPEN 50; NALCO 7046; ORTHO 5865; PROXEL EF; TERRAZOL; DIFOLATAN 4F1; PST04200
CHEMICAL FAMILY: HALOGEN
THIOL (MERCAPTAN)
HYDROCARBON, ALICYCLIC
MOLECULAR FORMULA: C10-H9-CL4-N-02-S
MOLECULAR WEIGHT: 349.09
CERCLA RATINGS (SCALE 0-3): HEALTH = 2 FIRE = U REACTIVITY = U PERSISTENCE = 3
NFPA RATINGS (SCALE 0-4): HEALTH = 2 FIRE = U REACTIVITY = U

COMPONENTS AND CONTAMINANTS

COMPONENT: CAPTAFOL ***PERCENT:*** 100
CAS# 2425-06-1
OTHER CONTAMINANTS: NONE

EXPOSURE LIMITS: CAPTAFOL: 0.1 MG/M3 OSHA TWA 0.1 MG/M3 ACGIH TWA (SKIN) SUBJECT TO CALIFORNIA PROPOSITION 65 CANCER AND/OR REPRODUCTIVE TOXICITY WARNING AND RELEASE REQUIREMENTS- (OCTOBER 1, 1988)

PHYSICAL DATA

DESCRIPTION: A COLORLESS OR WHITE CRYSTALLINE SOLID, WITH A CHARACTERISTIC PYNGENT ODOR
MELTING POINT: 322 F (161 C) ***SPECIFIC GRAVITY:*** NOT AVAILABLE
VAPOR PRESSURE: NEGLIGIBLE @ 25 C ***SOLUBILITY IN WATER:*** 0.014%
SOLVENT SOLUBILITY: ACETONE, BENZENE, CHLORINATED SOLVENTS; SLIGHTLY SOLUBLE IN ALCOHOLS

FIRE AND EXPLOSION DATA

FIRE AND EXPLOSION HAZARD: UNKNOWN FIRE AND EXPLOSION HAZARD.
FIREFIGHTING MEDIA: DRY CHEMICAL, CARBON DIOXIDE, WATER SPRAY OR FOAM FOR LARGER FIRES, USE WATER SPRAY, FOG OR ALCOHOL FOAM
FIREFIGHTING: MOVE CONTAINER FROM FIRE AREA IF POSSIBLE. DO NOT SCATTER SPILLED MATERIAL WITH MORE WATER THAN NEEDED FOR FIRE CONTROL. DIKE FIRE CONTROL WATER FOR LATER DISPOSAL
USE AGENTS SUITABLE FOR TYPE OF SURROUNDING FIRE. AVOID BREATHING HAZARDOUS VAPORS, KEEP UPWIND.

TOXICITY

CAPTAFOL: TOXICITY DATA: >15,400 MG/KG SKIN-RABBIT LD50 (38MKAJ); 2500 MG/KG ORAL-RAT LD50; 3 MG/KG INTRAPERITONEAL-MOUSE LDLO; MUTAGENIC DATA (RTECS); REPRODUCTIVE EFFECTS DATA (RTECS); TUMORIGENIC DATA (RTECS). CARCINOGEN STATUS: NONE. LOCAL EFFECTS: IRRITANT- INHALATION, SKIN, AND EYES. ACUTE TOXICITY LEVEL: MODERATELY TOXIC BY INGESTION AND SLIGHTLY TOXIC BY DERMAL ABSORPTION. TARGET EFFECTS: SENSITIZER- PULMONARY AND SKIN.

HEALTH EFFECTS AND FIRST AID

INHALATION: CAPTAFOL: IRRITANT/SENSITIZER. **ACUTE EXPOSURE-** MAY CAUSE IRRITATION OF MUCOUS MEMBRANES WITH WHEEZING, STOMATITIS, AND PAINFUL BRONCHITIS. SENSITIZATION REACTIONS MAY OCCUR IN PREVIOUSLY EXPOSED PERSONS. **CHRONIC EXPOSURE-** REPEATED OR PROLONGED EXPOSURE MAY CAUSE SENSITIZATION.
FIRST AID- REMOVE FROM EXPOSURE AREA TO FRESH AIR IMMEDIATELY. IF BREATHING HAS STOPPED, PERFORM ARTIFICIAL RESPIRATION. KEEP PERSON WARM AND AT REST. TREAT SYMPTOMATICALLY AND SUPPORTIVELY. GET MEDICAL ATTENTION IMMEDIATELY.

SKIN CONTACT: CAPTAFOL: IRRITANT/SENSITIZER. **ACUTE EXPOSURE-** MAY CAUSE IRRITATION, OFTEN PHOTOTOXIC, WITH ITCHING, ERYTHEMA, VESICULATION, AND LOCAL EDEMA, ESPECIALLY OF THE HANDS, FACE, AND EYELIDS. SYSTEMIC POISONING MAY OCCUR WITH HYPERTENSION, PROTEIN AND UROBILINOGEN IN THE URINE, DEPRESSION OF LIVER FUNCTION, ANEMIA, AND DEPRESSION OF CHOLINESTERASE ACTIVITY. SENSITIZATION REACTIONS MAY OCCUR IN PREVIOUSLY EXPOSED PERSONS. **CHRONIC EXPOSURE-** REPEATED OR PROLONGED EXPOSURE MAY CAUSE LOCAL AND SYSTEMIC EFFECTS AS DETAILED IN ACUTE EXPOSURE. SENSITIZATION HAS BEEN REPORTED IN 10-40% OF THOSE CHRONICALLY EXPOSED.
FIRST AID- REMOVE CONTAMINATED CLOTHING AND SHOES IMMEDIATELY. WASH AFFECTED AREA WITH SOAP OR MILD DETERGENT AND LARGE AMOUNTS OF WATER UNTIL NO EVIDENCE OF CHEMICAL REMAINS (APPROXIMATELY 15-20 MINUTES). GET MEDICAL ATTENTION IMMEDIATELY.

EYE CONTACT: CAPTAFOL: IRRITANT. **ACUTE EXPOSURE-** MAY CAUSE IRRITATION THAT IS LOCALIZED TO THE CONJUNCTIVA. **CHRONIC EXPOSURE-** REPEATED AND PROLONGED EXPOSURE MAY CAUSE CHEMICAL OR ALLERGIC CONJUNCTIVITIS.
FIRST AID- WASH EYES IMMEDIATELY WITH LARGE AMOUNTS OF WATER OR NORMAL SALINE, OCCASIONALLY LIFTING UPPER AND LOWER LIDS, UNTIL NO EVIDENCE OF CHEMICAL REMAINS (APPROXIMATELY 15-20 MINUTES). GET MEDICAL ATTENTION IMMEDIATELY.

INGESTION: CAPTAFOL: **ACUTE EXPOSURE-** EFFECTS ON THE EMBRYO OR FETUS AND FETAL DEVELOPMENTAL ABNORMALITIES HAVE BEEN REPORTED FROM THE INGESTION OF A SINGLE DOSE DURING GESTATION IN HAMSTERS. EFFECTS ON THE EMBRYO OR FETUS HAVE BEEN REPORTED FROM THE ADMINISTRATION OF A SINGLE DOSE ON THE FIFTH DAY PRIOR TO MATING IN MALE RATS. **CHRONIC EXPOSURE-** RAT FEEDING STUDIES REPORTED GROWTH DEPRESSION AND SOME LIVER AND KIDNEY CHANGES FOLLOWING EXPOSURE TO 1500 AND 5000 PPM AND AN INCREASE IN MORTALITY AT THE 5000 PPM LEVEL. PROLONGED INGESTION OF 100 OR 300 MG/KG/DAY IN DOGS CAUSED VOMITING, DIARRHEA, ANEMIA, WEIGHT LOSS, GROWTH DEFICIENCY, AND DEPRESSION. EFFECTS ON FERTILITY HAVE BEEN REPORTED FROM REPEATED INGESTION DURING PREGNANCY IN RABBITS. EFFECTS ON THE NEWBORN HAVE BEEN REPORTED FROM PROLONGED EXPOSURE IN RATS. AS EVALUATED BY RTECS, ADMINISTRATION TO MICE BY INGESTION RESULTED IN A STATISTICALLY SIGNIFICANT INCREASE IN THE INCIDENCE OF CARCINOGENIC GASTROINTESTINAL AND LIVER TUMORS.
FIRST AID- REMOVE BY GASTRIC LAVAGE AND CATHARSIS. MAINTAIN BLOOD PRESSURE AND AIRWAY. GIVE OXYGEN IF RESPIRATION IS DEPRESSED. DO NOT PERFORM GASTRIC LAVAGE IF VICTIM IS UNCONSCIOUS. GET MEDICAL ATTENTION IMMEDIATELY (DREISBACH, HANDBOOK OF POISONING, 12TH ED.). ADMINISTRATION OF LAVAGE OR OXYGEN SHOULD BE PERFORMED BY QUALIFIED MEDICAL PERSONNEL.
ANTIDOTE: NO SPECIFIC ANTIDOTE. TREAT SYMPTOMATICALLY AND SUPPORTIVELY.

REACTIVITY

REACTIVITY: NO DATA AVAILABLE.
INCOMPATIBILITIES: CAPTAFOL: ACID OR ACID FUMES: EVOLVES HIGHLY TOXIC CHLORIDE FUMES UPON THEIR CONTACT. STRONG ALKALINE CONDITIONS: UNSTABLE.
DECOMPOSITION: THERMAL DECOMPOSITION PRODUCTS MAY INCLUDE HIGHLY TOXIC FUMES OF CHLORIDE, SULFUR OXIDES, AND PHOSGENE.
POLYMERIZATION: HAZARDOUS POLYMERIZATION HAS NOT BEEN REPORTED TO OCCUR UNDER NORMAL TEMPERATURES AND PRESSURES.

STORAGE AND DISPOSAL

OBSERVE ALL FEDERAL, STATE AND LOCAL REGULATIONS WHEN STORING OR DISPOSING OF THIS SUBSTANCE. FOR ASSISTANCE, CONTACT THE DISTRICT DIRECTOR OF THE ENVIRONMENTAL PROTECTION AGENCY.

CONDITIONS TO AVOID

NONE REPORTED.

SPILL AND LEAK PROCEDURES

WATER SPILL: THE CALIFORNIA SAFE DRINKING WATER AND TOXIC ENFORCEMENT ACT OF 1986 (PROPOSITION 65) PROHIBITS CONTAMINATING ANY KNOWN SOURCE OF DRINKING WATER WITH SUBSTANCES KNOWN TO CAUSE CANCER AND/OR REPRODUCTIVE TOXICITY.
OCCUPATIONAL SPILL: SWEEP UP AND PLACE IN SUITABLE CLEAN, DRY CONTAINERS FOR RECLAMATION OR LATER DISPOSAL. DO NOT FLUSH SPILLED MATERIAL INTO SEWER. KEEP UNNECESSARY PEOPLE AWAY.

PROTECTIVE EQUIPMENT

VENTILATION: PROVIDE LOCAL EXHAUST OR GENERAL DILUTION VENTILATION TO MEET PUBLISHED EXPOSURE LIMITS. VENTILATION EQUIPMENT MUST BE EXPLOSION-PROOF.
RESPIRATOR: THE FOLLOWING RESPIRATORS ARE RECOMMENDED BASED ON INFORMATION FOUND IN THE PHYSICAL DATA, TOXICITY AND HEALTH EFFECTS SECTIONS. THEY ARE RANKED IN ORDER FROM MINIMUM TO MAXIMUM RESPIRATORY PROTECTION. THE SPECIFIC RESPIRATOR SELECTED MUST BE BASED ON CONTAMINATION LEVELS FOUND IN THE WORK PLACE, MUST NOT EXCEED THE WORKING LIMITS OF THE RESPIRATOR AND BE JOINTLY APPROVED BY THE NATIONAL INSTITUTE FOR OCCUPATIONAL SAFETY AND HEALTH AND THE MINE SAFETY AND HEALTH ADMINISTRATION (NIOSH-MSHA).
TYPE 'C' SUPPLIED-AIR RESPIRATOR WITH A FULL FACEPIECE OPERATED IN PRESSURE-DEMAND OR OTHER POSITIVE PRESSURE MODE OR WITH A FULL FACEPIECE, HELMET OR HOOD OPERATED IN CONTINOUS-FLOW MODE.
SELF-CONTAINED BREATHING APPARATUS WITH A FULL FACEPIECE OPERATED IN PRESSURE-DEMAND OR OTHER POSITIVE PRESSURE MODE.
FOR FIREFIGHTING AND OTHER IMMEDIATELY DANGEROUS TO LIFE OR HEALTH CONDITIONS:
SELF-CONTAINED BREATHING APPARATUS WITH FULL FACEPIECE OPERATED IN PRESSURE-DEMAND OR OTHER POSITIVE PRESSURE MODE.
SUPPLIED-AIR RESPIRATOR WITH FULL FACEPIECE AND OPERATED IN PRESSURE-DEMAND OR OTHER POSITIVE PRESSURE MODE IN COMBINATION WITH AN AUXILIARY SELF-CONTAINED BREATHING APPARATUS OPERATED IN PRESSURE-DEMAND OR OTHER POSITIVE PRESSURE MODE.
CLOTHING: EMPLOYEE MUST WEAR APPROPRIATE PROTECTIVE (IMPERVIOUS) CLOTHING AND EQUIPMENT TO PREVENT REPEATED OR PROLONGED SKIN CONTACT WITH THIS SUBSTANCE.
GLOVES: EMPLOYEE MUST WEAR APPROPRIATE PROTECTIVE GLOVES TO PREVENT CONTACT WITH THIS SUBSTANCE.
EYE PROTECTION: EMPLOYEE MUST WEAR SPLASH-PROOF OR DUST-RESISTANT SAFETY GOGGLES TO PREVENT EYE CONTACT WITH THIS SUBSTANCE.
EMERGENCY EYE WASH: WHERE THERE IS ANY POSSIBILITY THAT AN EMPLOYEE'S EYES MAY BE EXPOSED TO THIS SUBSTANCE, THE EMPLOYER SHOULD PROVIDE AN EYE WASH FOUNTAIN WITHIN THE IMMEDIATE WORK AREA FOR EMERGENCY USE.

AUTHORIZED BY- OCCUPATIONAL HEALTH SERVICES, INC.
CREATION DATE: 10/04/89 ***REVISION DATE:*** 05/31/90

MATERIAL SAFETY DATA SHEET

OCCUPATIONAL HEALTH SERVICES, INC.
AGRICULTURE AND PESTICIDE DIVISION
450 SEVENTH AVENUE, SUITE 2407
NEW YORK, NEW YORK 10123
1-800-445-MSDS OR (212) 967-1100

EMERGENCY CONTACT:
JOHN S. BRANSFORD, JR. (615) 292-1180

SUBSTANCE IDENTIFICATION

CAS-NUMBER 133-06-2
SUBSTANCE: CAPTAN
TRADE NAMES/SYNONYMS: N-TRICHLOROMETHYLTHIO-CIS-DELTA(SUP 4)-CYCLOHEXENE-1,2-DICARBOXIMIDE; N-(TRICHLOROMETHYLMERCAPTO)-DELTA(SUP 4)-TETRAHYDROPHTHALIMIDE; N-((TRICHLOROMETHYL)THIO)-4-CYCLOHEXENE-1,2-DICARBOXIMIDE; N-TRICHLOROMETHYLMERCAPTO-4-CYCLOHEXENE-1,2-DICARBOXIMIDE; N-TRICHLOROMETHYLTHIOCYCLOHEX-4-ENE-1,2-DICARBOXIMIDE; N-TRICHLOROMETHYLTHIO-3A,4,7,7-TETRAHYDROPHTHALIMIDE; N-((TRICHLOROMETHYL)THIO)TETRAHYDROPHTHALIMIDE; N-(TRICHLOROMETHYL)THIO-4-CYCLOHEXENE-1,2-DICARBOXIMIDE; 3A,4,7,7A-TETRAHYDRO-2-((TRICHLOROMETHYL)THIO)-1H-ISOINDOLE-1,3(2H)- DIONE; TRICHLOROMETHYL-CYCLOHEXENE DICARBOMIDE; AMERCIDE; CAPTAF; CAPTAF 85W; NCI-000077; CAPTANE; ORTHOCIDE; MERPAN; STCC 4961164; NA 9099; PST04210
CHEMICAL FAMILY: PHTHALIMIDE
MOLECULAR FORMULA: C9-H8-CL3-N-O2-S
MOLECULAR WEIGHT: 300.59
CERCLA RATINGS (SCALE 0-3): HEALTH=3 FIRE=0 REACTIVITY=0 PERSISTENCE=3
NFPA RATINGS (SCALE 0-4): HEALTH=3 FIRE=0 REACTIVITY=0

COMPONENTS AND CONTAMINANTS

COMPONENT: CAPTAN ***PERCENT:*** 100
CAS# 133-06-2
OTHER CONTAMINANTS: NONE
EXPOSURE LIMITS: CAPTAN: 5 MG/M3 OSHA TWA 5 MG/M3 ACGIH TWA
10 POUNDS CERCLA SECTION 103 REPORTABLE QUANTITY SUBJECT TO SARA SECTION 313 ANNUAL TOXIC CHEMICAL RELEASE REPORTING SUBJECT TO CALIFORNIA PROPOSITION 65 CANCER AND/OR REPRODUCTIVE TOXICITY WARNING AND RELEASE REQUIREMENTS- (JANUARY 1, 1990)

PHYSICAL DATA

DESCRIPTION: WHITE TO CREAM POWDER, OR ODORLESS CRYSTALS WITH A SLIGHT ODOR
BOILING POINT: NOT AVAILABLE ***MELTING POINT:*** 352 F (178 C)
SPECIFIC GRAVITY: 1.74 ***SOLUBILITY IN WATER:*** INSOLUBLE
SOLVENT SOLUBILITY: ACETONE, BENZENE, TOLUENE, ETHYLENE DICHLORIDE, CHLOROFORM, TETRACHLOROETHANE, CYCLOHEXANONE, DIOXANE, HEPTANE, ETHANOL, ETHER

FIRE AND EXPLOSION DATA

FIRE AND EXPLOSION HAZARD: NEGLIGIBLE FIRE HAZARD WHEN EXPOSED TO HEAT OR FLAME.
FIREFIGHTING MEDIA: DRY CHEMICAL, CARBON DIOXIDE, HALON, WATER SPRAY OR STANDARD FOAM (1987 EMERGENCY RESPONSE GUIDEBOOK, DOT P 5800.4).
FOR LARGER FIRES, USE WATER SPRAY, FOG OR STANDARD FOAM (1987 EMERGENCY RESPONSE GUIDEBOOK, DOT P 5800.4).
FIREFIGHTING: NO ACUTE HAZARD. MOVE CONTAINER FROM FIRE AREA IF POSSIBLE. AVOID BREATHING VAPORS OR DUSTS; KEEP UPWIND.

TRANSPORTATION DATA

DEPARTMENT OF TRANSPORTATION HAZARD CLASSIFICATION 49 CFR 172.101: ORM-E
DEPARTMENT OF TRANSPORTATION LABELING REQUIREMENTS 49 CFR 172.101 AND SUBPART E: NONE
DEPARTMENT OF TRANSPORTATION PACKAGING REQUIREMENTS: 49 CFR 173.510 EXCEPTIONS: NONE

TOXICITY

CAPTAN: TOXICITY DATA: 5000 MG/M3/2 HOURS INHALATION-MOUSE LC50; 1071 MG/KG ORAL-HUMAN LDLO; 9 GM/KG ORAL-RAT LD50; 30 MG/KG INTRAPERITONEAL-MOUSE LD50; 2650 MG/KG UNREPORTED-RAT LD50; 138 MG/KG UNREPORTED-MOUSE LD50; 740 MG/KG UNREPORTED-RABBIT LD50; MUTAGENIC DATA (RTECS); REPRODUCTIVE EFFECTS DATA (RTECS); TUMORIGENIC DATA (RTECS). CARCINOGEN STATUS: ANIMAL LIMITED EVIDENCE (IARC GROUP-3). CAPTAN PRODUCED DUODENAL TUMORS BY ORAL ADMINISTRATION IN ONE STRAIN OF MICE. LOCAL EFFECTS: IRRITANT-INHALATION, SKIN, AND EYES. ACUTE TOXICITY LEVEL: TOXIC BY INHALATION AND SLIGHTLY TOXIC BY INGESTION. TARGET EFFECTS: SENSITIZER- SKIN. POISONING MAY AFFECT THE CARDIOVASCULAR SYSTEM, LIVER, AND KIDNEYS.

HEALTH EFFECTS AND FIRST AID

INHALATION: CAPTAN: IRRITANT/TOXIC. **ACUTE EXPOSURE-** MAY CAUSE RESPIRATORY IRRITATION AND BRONCHITIS. **CHRONIC EXPOSURE-** NO DATA AVAILABLE.
FIRST AID- REMOVE FROM EXPOSURE AREA TO FRESH AIR IMMEDIATELY. IF BREATHING HAS STOPPED, PERFORM ARTIFICIAL RESPIRATION. KEEP PERSON WARM AND AT REST. TREAT SYMPTOMATICALLY AND SUPPORTIVELY. GET MEDICAL ATTENTION IMMEDIATELY.

SKIN CONTACT: CAPTAN: IRRITANT/SENSITIZER. **ACUTE EXPOSURE-** MAY CAUSE IRRITATION. SENSITIZATION WAS DEMONSTRATED AMONG VOLUNTEERS FOLLOWING SKIN APPLICATION. EFFECTS IN ANIMALS INCLUDE URTICARIA. **CHRONIC EXPOSURE-** REPEATED AND PROLONGED CONTACT MAY CAUSE SENSITIZATION DERMATITIS.
FIRST AID- REMOVE CONTAMINATED CLOTHING AND SHOES IMMEDIATELY. WASH AFFECTED AREA WITH SOAP OR MILD DETERGENT AND LARGE AMOUNTS OF WATER UNTIL NO EVIDENCE OF CHEMICAL REMAINS (APPROXIMATELY 15-20 MINUTES). GET MEDICAL ATTENTION IMMEDIATELY.

EYE CONTACT: CAPTAN: IRRITANT. **ACUTE EXPOSURE-** MAY CAUSE IRRITATION. **CHRONIC EXPOSURE-** REPEATED AND PROLONGED CONTACT MAY CAUSE CONJUNCTIVITIS.
FIRST AID- WASH EYES IMMEDIATELY WITH LARGE AMOUNTS OF WATER OR NORMAL SALINE, OCCASIONALLY LIFTING UPPER AND LOWER LIDS, UNTIL NO EVIDENCE OF CHEMICAL REMAINS (APPROXIMATELY 15-20 MINUTES). GET MEDICAL ATTENTION IMMEDIATELY.

INGESTION: CAPTAN: HEMORRHAGIC AGENT/LIMITED ANIMAL CARCINOGEN. **ACUTE EXPOSURE-** LARGE AMOUNTS MAY CAUSE VOMITING, DIARRHEA, GASTROINTESTINAL IRRITATION, DYSPNEA, LACRIMATION AND DEPRESSION. ANIMALS EXPOSED TO HIGH DOSES EXHIBITED HYPOTHERMIA, IRRITABILITY, LISTLESSNESS, ANOREXIA, HYPOREFLEXIA AND OLIGURIA WITH A MARKED GLYCOSURIA AND HEMATURIA ON THE FIRST DAY. FOLLOWING LARGE DOSES, DEATH IS DUE TO CARDIAC OR RESPIRATORY FAILURE. WITH SMALLER DOSES DEATH MAY BE DELAYED AND IS THEN APPARENTLY CAUSED BY INFILTRATIVE MENINGITIS SECONDARY TO CAPILLARY HEMORRHAGES. ANIMALS DYING EARLY SHOWED MARKED HEMORRHAGIC CAPILLARY-VENOUS CONGESTION IN THE STOMACH, HEART, LUNGS AND HIGHLY VASCULAR ORGANS, INCLUDING THE THYMUS. WHEN DEATH WAS DELAYED, AUTOPSY SHOWED LEUKOCYTIC INVASION OF THE MENINGES, FATTY DEGENERATION OF THE HEART AND RENAL TUBULES, STRESS RESPONSE IN ADRENALS, SPLEEN AND THYMUS, AND DEGENERATIVE CHANGES IN THE PANCREAS, SALIVARY GLANDS AND TESTES. **CHRONIC EXPOSURE-** POTENTIAL HUMAN EXPOSURE EXISTS BECAUSE IT IS A RESIDUE FOUND ON MANY FRUITS PERMITTED FOR HUMAN CONSUMPTION. ADVERSE EFFECTS HAVE NOT BEEN REPORTED. PREGNANT ANIMAL FEEDING STUDIES PRODUCED FETAL DEATH, STILLBIRTH, DEVELOPMENTAL ABNORMALITIES OF THE MUSCULOSKELETAL AND CARDIOVASCULAR SYSTEMS AND OTHER EFFECTS ON THE FETUSES AND NEWBORNS. MATERNAL PROBLEMS INCLUDED EFFECTS ON THE UTERUS, CERVIX AND VAGINA. MICE, CHRONICALLY FED, EXHIBITED TUMORS OF THE GASTROINTESTINAL TRACT.
FIRST AID- REMOVE BY GASTRIC LAVAGE AND CATHARSIS. MAINTAIN BLOOD PRESSURE AND AIRWAY. GIVE OXYGEN IF RESPIRATION IS DEPRESSED. DO NOT PERFORM GASTRIC LAVAGE IF VICTIM IS UNCONSCIOUS. GET MEDICAL ATTENTION IMMEDIATELY (DREISBACH, HANDBOOK OF POISONING, 12TH ED.). ADMINISTRATION OF LAVAGE OR OXYGEN SHOULD BE PERFORMED BY QUALIFIED MEDICAL PERSONNEL.
ANTIDOTE: NO SPECIFIC ANTIDOTE. TREAT SYMPTOMATICALLY AND SUPPORTIVELY.

REACTIVITY

REACTIVITY: STABLE UNDER NORMAL TEMPERATURES AND PRESSURES.
INCOMPATIBILITIES: CAPTAN: NO DATA AVAILABLE.
DECOMPOSITION: THERMAL DECOMPOSITION MAY RELEASE TOXIC AND/OR HAZARDOUS GASES.

POLYMERIZATION: HAZARDOUS POLYMERIZATION HAS NOT BEEN REPORTED TO OCCUR UNDER NORMAL TEMPERATURES AND PRESSURES.

CONDITIONS TO AVOID

NONE REPORTED.

SPILL AND LEAK PROCEDURES

WATER SPILL: THE CALIFORNIA SAFE DRINKING WATER AND TOXIC ENFORCEMENT ACT OF 1986 (PROPOSITION 65) PROHIBITS CONTAMINATING ANY KNOWN SOURCE OF DRINKING WATER WITH SUBSTANCES KNOWN TO CAUSE CANCER AND/OR REPRODUCTIVE TOXICITY.

OCCUPATIONAL SPILL: NO SPECIAL PRECAUTIONS INDICATED.

REPORTABLE QUANTITY (RQ): 10 POUNDS THE SUPERFUND AMENDMENTS AND REAUTHORIZATION ACT (SARA) SECTION 304 REQUIRES THAT A RELEASE EQUAL TO OR GREATER THAN THE REPORTABLE QUANTITY FOR THIS SUBSTANCE BE IMMEDIATELY REPORTED TO THE LOCAL EMERGENCY PLANNING COMMITTEE AND THE STATE EMERGENCY RESPONSE COMMISSION (40 CFR 355.40). IF THE RELEASE OF THIS SUBSTANCE IS REPORTABLE UNDER CERCLA SECTION 103, THE NATIONAL RESPONSE CENTER MUST BE NOTIFIED IMMEDIATELY AT (800) 424-8802 OR (202) 426-2675 IN THE METROPOLITAN WASHINGTON, D.C. AREA (40 CFR 302.6).

PROTECTIVE EQUIPMENT

VENTILATION: PROVIDE LOCAL EXHAUST OR PROCESS ENCLOSURE VENTILATION TO MEET PUBLISHED EXPOSURE LIMITS.

RESPIRATOR: THE FOLLOWING RESPIRATORS ARE RECOMMENDED BASED ON INFORMATION FOUND IN THE PHYSICAL DATA, TOXICITY AND HEALTH EFFECTS SECTIONS. THEY ARE RANKED IN ORDER FROM MINIMUM TO MAXIMUM RESPIRATORY PROTECTION. THE SPECIFIC RESPIRATOR SELECTED MUST BE BASED ON CONTAMINATION LEVELS FOUND IN THE WORK PLACE, MUST NOT EXCEED THE WORKING LIMITS OF THE RESPIRATOR AND BE JOINTLY APPROVED BY THE NATIONAL INSTITUTE FOR OCCUPATIONAL SAFETY AND HEALTH AND THE MINE SAFETY AND HEALTH ADMINISTRATION (NIOSH-MSHA).

TYPE 'C' SUPPLIED-AIR RESPIRATOR WITH A FULL FACEPIECE OPERATED IN PRESSURE-DEMAND OR OTHER POSITIVE PRESSURE MODE OR WITH A FULL FACEPIECE, HELMET OR HOOD OPERATED IN CONTINOUS-FLOW MODE.

SELF-CONTAINED BREATHING APPARATUS WITH A FULL FACEPIECE OPERATED IN PRESSURE-DEMAND OR OTHER POSITIVE PRESSURE MODE.

FOR FIREFIGHTING AND OTHER IMMEDIATELY DANGEROUS TO LIFE OR HEALTH CONDITIONS:

SELF-CONTAINED BREATHING APPARATUS WITH FULL FACEPIECE OPERATED IN PRESSURE-DEMAND OR OTHER POSITIVE PRESSURE MODE.

SUPPLIED-AIR RESPIRATOR WITH FULL FACEPIECE AND OPERATED IN PRESSURE-DEMAND OR OTHER POSITIVE PRESSURE MODE IN COMBINATION WITH AN AUXILIARY SELF-CONTAINED BREATHING APPARATUS OPERATED IN PRESSURE-DEMAND OR OTHER POSITIVE PRESSURE MODE.

CLOTHING: EMPLOYEE MUST WEAR APPROPRIATE PROTECTIVE (IMPERVIOUS) CLOTHING AND EQUIPMENT TO PREVENT REPEATED OR PROLONGED SKIN CONTACT WITH THIS SUBSTANCE.

GLOVES: EMPLOYEE MUST WEAR APPROPRIATE PROTECTIVE GLOVES TO PREVENT CONTACT WITH THIS SUBSTANCE.

EYE PROTECTION: EMPLOYEE MUST WEAR SPLASH-PROOF OR DUST-RESISTANT SAFETY GOGGLES TO PREVENT EYE CONTACT WITH THIS SUBSTANCE.

EMERGENCY EYE WASH: WHERE THERE IS ANY POSSIBILITY THAT AN EMPLOYEE'S EYES MAY BE EXPOSED TO THIS SUBSTANCE, THE EMPLOYER SHOULD PROVIDE AN EYE WASH FOUNTAIN WITHIN THE IMMEDIATE WORK AREA FOR EMERGENCY USE.

AUTHORIZED BY- OCCUPATIONAL HEALTH SERVICES, INC.

CREATION DATE: 10/04/89 ***REVISION DATE:*** 06/27/90

MATERIAL SAFETY DATA SHEET

OCCUPATIONAL HEALTH SERVICES, INC.
AGRICULTURE AND PESTICIDE DIVISION
450 SEVENTH AVENUE, SUITE 2407
NEW YORK, NEW YORK 10123
1-800-445-MSDS OR (212) 967-1100

EMERGENCY CONTACT:
JOHN S. BRANSFORD, JR. (615) 292-1180

SUBSTANCE IDENTIFICATION

CAS-NUMBER 63-25-2

SUBSTANCE: CARBARYL

TRADE NAMES/SYNONYMS: 1-NAPHTHALENOL, METHYLCARBAMATE; CARBAMIC ACID, METHYL-, 1-NAPHTHYL ESTER; METHYL CARBAMIC ACID 1-NAPHTHYL ESTER; 1-NAPHTHYL N-METHYLCARBAMATE; 1-NAPHTHYL METHYL CARBAMATE; 1-NAPHTHALENYL METHYLCARBAMATE; METHYLCARBAMIC ACID, 1-NAPHTHYL ESTER; N-METHYL-1-NAPHTHYLCARBAMATE; ALPHA-NAPHTHALENYL METHYLCARBAMATE; ALPHA-NAPHTHYL METHYLCARBAMATE; SEVIN; ENT 23,969; STCC 4941122; PST04220

CHEMICAL FAMILY: CARBAMATE

MOLECULAR FORMULA: C12-H11-N-O2

MOLECULAR WEIGHT: 201.24

CERCLA RATINGS (SCALE 0-3): HEALTH=3 FIRE=0 REACTIVITY=0 PERSISTENCE=3

NFPA RATINGS (SCALE 0-4): HEALTH=U FIRE=0 REACTIVITY=0

COMPONENTS AND CONTAMINANTS

COMPONENT: CARBARYL ***PERCENT:*** 100.00

CAS# 63-25-2

EXPOSURE LIMITS: CARBARYL: 5 MG/M3 OSHA TWA 5 MG/M3 ACGIH TWA 5 MG/M3 NIOSH RECOMMENDED 10 HOUR TWA

100 POUNDS CERCLA SECTION 103 REPORTABLE QUANTITY SUBJECT TO SARA SECTION 313 ANNUAL TOXIC CHEMICAL RELEASE REPORTING

PHYSICAL DATA

DESCRIPTION: ODORLESS, WHITE CRYSTALLINE SOLID ***BOILING POINT:*** DECOMPOSES

MELTING POINT: 288 F (142 C) ***SPECIFIC GRAVITY:*** 1.232

VAPOR PRESSURE: <0.005 MMHG @ 26 C ***SOLUBILITY IN WATER:*** 40 PPM

SOLVENT SOLUBILITY: SOLUBLE IN ACETONE, ISOPHORONE, CYCLOHEXANONE, DIMETHYLFORMAMIDE, DIMETHYL SULPHOXIDE, MIXED CRESOLS, PETROLEUM OILS, AND MOST POLAR SOLVENTS; SLIGHTLY SOLUBLE IN METHANOL.

FIRE AND EXPLOSION DATA

FIRE AND EXPLOSION HAZARD: NEGLIGIBLE FIRE HAZARD WHEN EXPOSED TO HEAT OR FLAME.

FLASH POINT: 380 F (193 C) (OC) ***UPPER EXPLOSIVE LIMIT:*** NOT AVAILABLE

LOWER EXPLOSIVE LIMIT: 0.02 OZ/FT3 ***AUTOIGNITION TEMP.:*** 1157 F (625 C)

FIREFIGHTING MEDIA: DRY CHEMICAL, CARBON DIOXIDE, HALON, WATER SPRAY OR STANDARD FOAM (1987 EMERGENCY RESPONSE GUIDEBOOK, DOT P 5800.4).

FOR LARGER FIRES, USE WATER SPRAY, FOG OR STANDARD FOAM (1987 EMERGENCY RESPONSE GUIDEBOOK, DOT P 5800.4).

FIREFIGHTING: MOVE CONTAINERS FROM FIRE AREA IF POSSIBLE. FIGHT FIRE FROM MAXIMUM DISTANCE. STAY AWAY FROM STORAGE TANK ENDS. DIKE FIRE CONTROL WATER FOR LATER DISPOSAL. DO NOT SCATTER MATERIAL (1987 EMERGENCY RESPONSE GUIDEBOOK, DOT P 5800.4, GUIDE PAGE 55).

EXTINGUISH ONLY IF FLOW CAN BE STOPPED. EXTINGUISH USING AGENT INDICATED. USE FLOODING AMOUNTS OF WATER AS A FOG. COOL CONTAINERS WITH FLOODING AMOUNTS OF WATER FROM AS FAR A DISTANCE AS POSSIBLE. AVOID BREATHING POISONOUS VAPORS, KEEP UPWIND. CONSIDER EVACUATION OF DOWNWIND AREA IF MATERIAL IS LEAKING.

TRANSPORTATION DATA

DEPARTMENT OF TRANSPORTATION HAZARD CLASSIFICATION 49 CFR 172.101: ORM-A

DEPARTMENT OF TRANSPORTATION LABELING REQUIREMENTS 49 CFR 172.101 AND SUBPART E: NONE

DEPARTMENT OF TRANSPORTATION PACKAGING REQUIREMENTS: 49 CFR 173.510 EXCEPTIONS: 49 CFR 173.505

TOXICITY

CARBARYL: IRRITATION DATA: 500 MG/24 HOURS EYE-RABBIT MILD; 12 MG/24 HOURS SKIN-RABBIT SEVERE. TOXICITY DATA: 2000 MG/KG SKIN-RABBIT LD50; 4000 MG/KG SKIN-RAT LD50; 500 MG/KG ORAL-MAN TDLO; 230 MG/KG ORAL-RAT LD50; 128 MG/KG ORAL-MOUSE LD50; 710 MG/KG ORAL-RABBIT LD50; 250 MG/KG ORAL-GUINEA PIG LD50; 250 MG/KG ORAL-HAMSTER LDLO; 150 MG/KG ORAL-CAT LD50; 491 MG/KG ORAL-GERBIL LD50; 1400 MG/KG SUBCUTANEOUS-RAT LD50; 640 MG/KG INTRAPERITONEAL-HAMSTER LD50; 6717 MG/KG SUBCUTANEOUS-MOUSE LD50; 41900 UG/KG INTRAVENOUS-RAT LD50; 64 MG/KG INTRAPERITONEAL-RAT LD50; 25 MG/KG INTRAPERITONEAL-MOUSE LD50; MUTAGENIC DATA (RTECS); REPRODUCTIVE EFFECTS DATA (RTECS); TUMORIGENIC DATA (RTECS). CARCINOGEN STATUS: ANIMAL INADEQUATE EVIDENCE (IARC GROUP-3). LOCAL EFFECTS: IRRITANT- INHALATION, SKIN AND EYE. ACUTE TOXICITY: TOXIC BY INGESTION; MODERATELY TOXIC BY DERMAL ABSORPTION. TARGET EFFECTS: CHOLINESTERASE INHIBITOR. AT INCREASED RISK FROM EXPOSURE: PERSONS WITH CARDIOVASCULAR, HEPATIC, AND RENAL DISEASES, GLAUCOMA, CENTRAL NERVOUS SYSTEMS ABNORMALITIES, AND USING ANTICHOLINERGIC DRUGS.

HEALTH EFFECTS AND FIRST AID

INHALATION: CARBARYL: IRRITANT. 600 MG/M3 IMMEDIATELY DANGEROUS TO LIFE OR HEALTH. MAY CAUSE IRRITATION OF THE MUCOUS MEMBRANES. IN ONE REPORT, WORKERS EXPOSED TO CONCENTRATIONS RANGING FROM 0.23 TO 31 MG/M3 FOR A 19 MONTH PERIOD EXCRETED UP TO 80 MG 1-NAPHTHOL/DAY; 1-NAPHTHOL IS A METABOLITE OF CARBARYL. THERE WAS ONLY A SLIGHT DEPRESSION OF BLOOD ACETYLCHOLINESTERASE. THERE WERE NO SIGNS OR SYMPTOMS OF ANTICHOLINESTERASE ACTIVITY. SEE INFORMATION ON CARBAMATES.

CARBAMATES: CHOLINESTERASE INHIBITOR. **ACUTE EXPOSURE-** WHEN INHALED, THE FIRST EFFECTS OF CHOLINESTERASE INHIBITION ARE USUALLY RESPIRATORY AND MAY INCLUDE NASAL HYPEREMIA AND WATERY DISCHARGE, CHEST DISCOMFORT, DYSPNEA, AND WHEEZING DUE TO INCREASED BRONCHIAL SECRETIONS AND BRONCHOCONSTRICTION. OTHER SYSTEMIC EFFECTS MAY BEGIN WITHIN A FEW MINUTES OR SEVERAL HOURS OF EXPOSURE. SYMPTOMS MAY INCLUDE NAUSEA, VOMITING, DIARRHEA, ABDOMINAL CRAMPS, HEADACHE, VERTIGO, OCULAR PAIN, CILIARY MUSCLE SPASM, BLURRING OR DIMNESS OF VISION, MIOSIS, OR IN SOME CASES MYDRIASIS, LACRIMATION, SALIVATION, SWEATING, AND CONFUSION. OTHER REPORTED CENTRAL NERVOUS SYSTEM OR NEUROMUSCULAR EFFECTS INCLUDE ATAXIA, SLURRED SPEECH, AREFLEXIA, WEAKNESS, FATIGUE, TWITCHING, FASCICULATION, TREMOR, AND EVENTUALLY PARALYSIS OF THE EXTREMITIES AND POSSIBLY OF THE RESPIRATORY MUSCLES. IN SEVERE CASES, THERE MAY ALSO BE INVOLUNTARY DEFECATION AND URINATION, BRADYCARDIA, HYPOTENSION, PULMONARY EDEMA, CONVULSIONS, COMA, AND DEATH FROM RESPIRATORY FAILURE OR CARDIAC ARREST. CARBAMATES GENERALLY DO NOT ACCUMULATE IN MAMMALIAN TISSUE AND THE CHOLINESTERASE INHIBITION REVERSES RATHER RAPIDLY. IN NON-FATAL CASES, THE ILLNESS GENERALLY LASTS LESS THAN 24 HOURS. **CHRONIC EXPOSURE-** PROLONGED OR REPEATED EXPOSURE MAY CAUSE EFFECTS AS DESCRIBED IN ACUTE EXPOSURE.

FIRST AID- REMOVE FROM EXPOSURE AREA TO FRESH AIR IMMEDIATELY. IF BREATHING HAS STOPPED, GIVE ARTIFICIAL RESPIRATION. MAINTAIN AIRWAY AND BLOOD PRESSURE AND ADMINISTER OXYGEN IF AVAILABLE. KEEP AFFECTED PERSON WARM AND AT REST. TREAT SYMPTOMATICALLY AND SUPPORTIVELY. ADMINISTRATION OF OXYGEN SHOULD BE PERFORMED BY QUALIFIED PERSONNEL. GET MEDICAL ATTENTION IMMEDIATELY.

SKIN CONTACT: CARBARYL: IRRITANT. 12 MG APPLIED TO RABBIT SKIN PRODUCED SEVERE IRRITATION. GUINEA PIGS WERE WEAKLY SENSITIZED IN A SKIN-SENSITIVITY TEST. PROLONGED OR REPEATED CONTACT MAY CAUSE DERMATITIS. SEE INFORMATION ON CARBAMATES.

CARBAMATES: CHOLINESTERASE INHIBITOR. **ACUTE EXPOSURE-** SOME COMPOUNDS MAY CAUSE IRRITATION. LOCALIZED SWEATING AND FASCICULATIONS MAY OCCUR AT THE SITE OF CONTACT. IF SUFFICIENT AMOUNTS ARE ABSORBED THROUGH THE SKIN, OTHER EFFECTS OF CHOLINESTERASE INHIBITION MAY OCCUR AS DESCRIBED IN ACUTE INHALATION; SYMPTOMS MAY BE DELAYED FOR 2-3 HOURS, USUALLY NO MORE THAN 8 HOURS. **CHRONIC EXPOSURE-** REPEATED OR PROLONGED EXPOSURE MAY CAUSE EFFECTS AS DESCRIBED IN ACUTE EXPOSURE.

FIRST AID- REMOVE CONTAMINATED CLOTHING IMMEDIATELY. WASH CONTAMINATED AREAS WITH SOAP AND WATER FOLLOWED BY ALCOHOL (ARENA, POISONING, 4TH ED.). EMERGENCY PERSONNEL SHOULD WEAR GLOVES AND AVOID CONTAMINATION. TREAT RESPIRATORY DIFFICULTY WITH ARTIFICIAL RESPIRATION. GET MEDICAL ATTENTION IMMEDIATELY.

EYE CONTACT: CARBARYL: IRRITANT. TRACES OF CORNEAL NECROSIS OCCURRED WHEN 50 MG OF DUST WAS APPLIED TO RABBIT'S EYES. SEE INFORMATION ON CARBAMATES.

CARBAMATES: CHOLINESTERASE INHIBITOR. **ACUTE EXPOSURE-** DIRECT CONTACT MAY CAUSE PAIN, HYPEREMIA, LACRIMATION, TWITCHING OF THE EYELIDS, MIOSIS, AND CILIARY MUSCLE SPASM WITH LOSS OF ACCOMODATION, BLURRED OR DIMMED VISION AND BROWACHE. SOMETIMES MYDRIASIS MAY OCCUR INSTEAD OF MIOSIS. WITH SUFFICIENT EXPOSURE, OTHER SYMPTOMS OF CHOLINESTERASE INHIBITION MAY OCCUR AS DESCRIBED IN ACUTE INHALATION. **CHRONIC EXPOSURE-** PROLONGED EXPOSURE MAY CAUSE EFFECTS AS DESCRIBED IN ACUTE EXPOSURE. SOME COMPOUNDS HAVE CAUSED TOXIC EFFECTS ON THE CRYSTALLINE LENS, CONJUNCTIVAL THICKENING AND OBSTRUCTION OF NASOLACRIMAL CANALS WHEN USED AS MIOTIC EYE DROPS.

FIRST AID- IRRIGATE EYES WITH WATER OR SALINE SOLUTION. IF SYMPTOMS OF POISONING OCCUR, TREAT RESPIRATORY DIFFICULTY WITH ARTIFICIAL RESPIRATION AND OXYGEN. OBSERVE PATIENT FOR AT LEAST 24-36 HOURS (GOSSELIN, CLINICAL TOXICOLOGY OF COMMERCIAL PRODUCTS, 5TH ED.). GET MEDICAL ATTENTION IMMEDIATELY. OXYGEN SHOULD BE ADMINISTERED BY QUALIFIED MEDICAL PERSONNEL.

INGESTION: CARBARYL: TOXIC. SIX MALE VOLUNTEERS WHO INGESTED AN ORAL DOSAGE OF 0.12 TO 0.13 MG/KG/DAY FOR 6 WEEKS DEVELOPED A SLIGHT, TRANSIENT DECREASE IN THE ABILITY OF THEIR KIDNEYS TO REABSORB AMINO ACIDS WITH NO OTHER APPARENT EFFECTS THAT COULD BE RELATED TO CARBARYL. REPEATED DIETARY ADMINISTRATION HAS PRODUCED SLIGHT KIDNEY DAMAGE IN DOGS AND DISTURBANCES IN CARBOHYDRATE AND PROTEIN METABOLISM IN RABBITS. EFFECTS ON THE PITUITARY GLAND WITH IMPAIRMENT OF THYROID AND GONADAL FUNCTION AND LIVER DAMAGE WERE OBSERVED IN STUDIES OF RATS. CARBARYL ADMINISTERED ORALLY DURING ORGANOGENESIS WAS TERATOGENIC IN GUINEA PIGS AT A DOSE OF 300 MG/KG AND IN DOGS AT A DOSE OF 25 MG/KG. DEGENERATIVE CHANGES IN THE TESTES AND PROLONGED ESTRUS CYCLE HAVE BEEN REPORTED IN RATS. SEE INFORMATION ON CARBAMATES.

CARBAMATES: CHOLINESTERASE INHIBITOR. **ACUTE EXPOSURE-** WHEN INGESTED, THE FIRST EFFECTS MAY BE NAUSEA, VOMITING, ANOREXIA, ABDOMINAL CRAMPS, AND DIARRHEA. WITH ABSORPTION FROM THE GASTROINTESTINAL TRACT, THE OTHER EFFECTS OF CHOLINESTERASE INHIBITION AS DESCRIBED IN ACUTE INHALATION MAY OCCUR; SYMPTOMS MAY BEGIN WITHIN MINUTES OR BE DELAYED SEVERAL HOURS. **CHRONIC EXPOSURE-** REPEATED INGESTION MAY CAUSE EFFECTS AS DESCRIBED IN ACUTE EXPOSURE.

FIRST AID- IF PERSON IS ALERT AND RESPIRATION IS NOT DEPRESSED, GIVE SYRUP OF IPECAC FOLLOWED BY WATER (IF VOMITING OCCURS, KEEP HEAD BELOW HIPS TO PREVENT ASPIRATION). IF CONSCIOUSNESS LEVEL DECLINES OR VOMITING HAS NOT OCCURRED IN 15 MINUTES EMPTY STOMACH BY GASTRIC LAVAGE WITH THE AID OF CUFFED ENDOTRACHEAL TUBE USING ISOTONIC SALINE OR 5% SODIUM BICARBONATE FOLLOW WITH ACTIVATED CHARCOAL. ESTABLISH AND MAINTAIN AIRWAY. TREAT RESPIRATORY DIFFICULTY WITH ARTIFICIAL RESPIRATION AND OXYGEN. DO NOT GIVE MORPHINE, AMINOPHYLLINE, PHENOTHIAZINES, RESERPINE, FUROSEMIDE, OR ETHACRYNIC ACID (MORGAN, RECOGNITION AND MANAGEMENT OF PESTICIDE POISONINGS, 3RD ED.). TREAT SYMPTOMATICALLY AND SUPPORTIVELY. ADMINISTRATION OF OXYGEN AND LAVAGE MUST BE PERFORMED BY QUALIFIED MEDICAL PERSONNEL. GET MEDICAL ATTENTION IMMEDIATELY.

ANTIDOTE: THE FOLLOWING ANTIDOTE HAS BEEN RECOMMENDED. HOWEVER, THE DECISION AS TO WHETHER THE SEVERITY OF POISONING REQUIRES ADMINISTRATION OF ANY ANTIDOTE AND ACTUAL DOSE REQUIRED SHOULD BE MADE BY QUALIFIED MEDICAL PERSONNEL.

FOR CHOLINESTERASE INHIBITORS: ESTABLISH CLEAR AIRWAY AND TISSUE OXYGENATION BY ASPIRATION OF SECRETIONS, AND IF NECESSARY, BY ASSISTED PULMONARY VENTILATION WITH OXYGEN. IMPROVE TISSUE OXYGENATION AS MUCH AS POSSIBLE BEFORE ADMINISTERING ATROPINE TO MINIMIZE THE RISK OF VENTRICULAR FIBRILLATION. ADMINISTER ATROPINE SULFATE INTRAVENOUSLY, OR INTRAMUSCULARLY IF IV INJECTION IS NOT POSSIBLE. IN MODERATELY SEVERE POISONING ADMINISTER ATROPINE SULFATE, 0.4-2.0 MG REPEATED EVERY 15 MINUTES UNTIL ATROPINIZATION IS ACHIEVED (TACHYCARDIA, FLUSHING, DRY MOUTH, MYDRIASIS). MAINTAIN ATROPINIZATION BY REPEATED DOSES FOR 2-12 HOURS, OR LONGER, DEPENDING ON THE SEVERITY OF POISONING. THE APPEARANCE OF RALES IN THE LUNG BASES, MIOSIS, SALIVATION, NAUSEA, BRADYCARDIA, ARE ALL INDICATIONS OF INADEQUATE ATROPINIZATION. SEVERELY POISONED INDIVIDUALS MAY EXHIBIT REMARKABLE TOLERANCE TO ATROPINE; TWO OR MORE TIMES THE DOSAGES SUGGESTED ABOVE MAY BE NEEDED. PERSONS NOT POISONED OR ONLY SLIGHTLY POISONED, HOWEVER, MAY DEVELOP SIGNS OF ATROPINE TOXICITY FROM SUCH LARGE DOSAGES: FEVER, MUSCLE FIBRILLATIONS, AND DELIRIUM ARE THE MAIN SIGNS OF ATROPINE TOXICITY. IF THESE SIGNS APPEAR WHILE THE PATIENT IS FULLY ATROPINIZED, ATROPINE ADMINISTRATION SHOULD BE DISCONTINUED, AT LEAST TEMPORARILY. OBSERVE TREATED PATIENTS CLOSELY AT LEAST 24 HOURS TO INSURE THAT SYMPTOMS (POSSIBLY PULMONARY EDEMA) DO NOT RECUR AS ATROPINIZATION WEARS OFF. IN VERY SEVERE POISONINGS, METABOLIC DISPOSITION OF TOXICANT MAY REQUIRE SEVERAL HOURS OR DAYS DURING WHICH ATROPINIZATION MUST BE MAINTAINED. MARKEDLY LOWER LEVELS OF URINARY METABOLITES INDICATE THAT ATROPINE DOSAGE CAN BE TAPERED OFF. AS DOSAGE IS REDUCED, CHECK THE LUNG BASES FREQUENTLY FOR RALES. IF RALES ARE HEARD OR OTHER SYMPTOMS RETURN, RE-ESTABLISH ATROPINIZATION PROMPTLY (MORGAN, RECOGNITION AND MANAGEMENT OF PESTICIDE POISONINGS, 3RD ED.). ADMINISTRATION OF ANTIDOTE MUST BE PERFORMED BY QUALIFIED MEDICAL PERSONNEL.

REACTIVITY

REACTIVITY: STABLE UNDER NORMAL TEMPERATURES AND PRESSURES.

INCOMPATIBILITIES: CARBARYL: ALKALIS: HYDROLYZED RAPIDLY WHEN MIXED. OXIDIZERS (STRONG): MAY REACT.

DECOMPOSITION: THERMAL DECOMPOSITION PRODUCTS MAY INCLUDE TOXIC OXIDES OF NITROGEN.

POLYMERIZATION: HAZARDOUS POLYMERIZATION HAS NOT BEEN REPORTED TO OCCUR UNDER NORMAL TEMPERATURES AND PRESSURES.

STORAGE AND DISPOSAL

OBSERVE ALL FEDERAL, STATE AND LOCAL REGULATIONS WHEN STORING OR DISPOSING OF THIS SUBSTANCE. FOR ASSISTANCE, CONTACT THE DISTRICT DIRECTOR OF THE ENVIRONMENTAL PROTECTION AGENCY.

STORAGE

STORE IN ACCORDANCE WITH 40 CFR 165 RECOMMENDED PROCEDURES FOR THE DISPOSAL AND STORAGE OF PESTICIDES AND PESTICIDE CONTAINERS.
STORE AWAY FROM INCOMPATIBLE SUBSTANCES.

DISPOSAL

DISPOSAL MUST BE IN ACCORDANCE WITH 40 CFR 165 RECOMMENDED PROCEDURES FOR THE DISPOSAL AND STORAGE OF PESTICIDES AND PESTICIDE CONTAINERS.

CONDITIONS TO AVOID

NONE REPORTED.

SPILL AND LEAK PROCEDURES

SOIL SPILL: DIG HOLDING AREA SUCH AS LAGOON, POND OR PIT FOR CONTAINMENT. USE PROTECTIVE COVER SUCH AS A PLASTIC SHEET TO PREVENT MATERIAL FROM DISSOLVING IN FIRE EXTINGUISHING WATER OR RAIN.

WATER SPILL: IF DISSOLVED, AT A CONCENTRATION OF 10 PPM OR GREATER, APPLY ACTIVATED CARBON AT TEN TIMES THE AMOUNT THAT HAS BEEN SPILLED.
USE SUCTION HOSES TO REMOVE TRAPPED SPILL MATERIAL. USE MECHANICAL DREDGES OR LIFTS TO EXTRACT IMMOBILIZED MASSES OF POLLUTION AND PRECIPITATES.

OCCUPATIONAL SPILL: DO NOT TOUCH SPILLED MATERIAL. STOP LEAK IF YOU CAN DO IT WITHOUT RISK. USE WATER SPRAY TO REDUCE VAPORS. FOR SMALL SPILLS, TAKE UP WITH SAND OR OTHER ABSORBENT MATERIAL AND PLACE INTO CONTAINERS FOR LATER DISPOSAL. FOR SMALL DRY SPILLS, WITH A CLEAN SHOVEL PLACE MATERIAL INTO CLEAN, DRY CONTAINERS AND COVER. MOVE CONTAINERS FROM SPILL AREA. FOR LARGER SPILLS, DIKE FAR AHEAD OF SPILL FOR LATER DISPOSAL. KEEP UNNECESSARY PEOPLE AWAY. ISOLATE HAZARD AREA AND DENY ENTRY. VENTILATE CLOSED SPACES BEFORE ENTERING.
REPORTABLE QUANTITY (RQ): 100 POUNDS THE SUPERFUND AMENDMENTS AND REAUTHORIZATION ACT (SARA) SECTION 304 REQUIRES THAT A RELEASE EQUAL TO OR GREATER THAN THE REPORTABLE QUANTITY FOR THIS SUBSTANCE BE IMMEDIATELY REPORTED TO THE LOCAL EMERGENCY PLANNING COMMITTEE AND THE STATE EMERGENCY RESPONSE COMMISSION (40 CFR 355.40). IF THE RELEASE OF THIS SUBSTANCE IS REPORTABLE UNDER CERCLA SECTION 103, THE NATIONAL RESPONSE CENTER MUST BE NOTIFIED IMMEDIATELY AT (800) 424-8802 OR (202) 426-2675 IN THE METROPOLITAN WASHINGTON, D.C. AREA (40 CFR 302.6).

PROTECTIVE EQUIPMENT

VENTILATION: PROVIDE LOCAL EXHAUST VENTILATION AND/OR GENERAL DILUTION VENTILATION TO MEET PUBLISHED EXPOSURE LIMITS.

RESPIRATOR: THE FOLLOWING RESPIRATORS AND MAXIMUM USE CONCENTRATIONS ARE RECOMMENDATIONS BY THE U.S. DEPARTMENT OF HEALTH AND HUMAN SERVICES, NIOSH POCKET GUIDE TO CHEMICAL HAZARDS; NIOSH CRITERIA DOCUMENTS OR BY THE U.S. DEPARTMENT OF LABOR, 29 CFR 1910 SUBPART Z.
THE SPECIFIC RESPIRATOR SELECTED MUST BE BASED ON CONTAMINATION LEVELS FOUND IN THE WORK PLACE, MUST NOT EXCEED THE WORKING LIMITS OF THE RESPIRATOR AND BE JOINTLY APPROVED BY THE NATIONAL INSTITUTE FOR OCCUPATIONAL SAFETY AND HEALTH AND THE MINE SAFETY AND HEALTH ADMINISTRATION (NIOSH-MSHA).
50 MG/M3- ANY SUPPLIED-AIR RESPIRATOR. ANY SELF-CONTAINED BREATHING APPARATUS.
125 MG/M3- ANY SUPPLIED-AIR RESPIRATOR OPERATED IN A CONTINUOUS FLOW MODE.
250 MG/M3- ANY SELF-CONTAINED BREATHING APPARATUS WITH A FULL FACEPIECE. ANY SUPPLIED-AIR RESPIRATOR WITH A FULL FACEPIECE.
625 MG/M3- ANY SUPPLIED-AIR RESPIRATOR WITH A HALF-MASK AND OPERATED IN A PRESSURE-DEMAND OR OTHER POSITIVE PRESSURE MODE.
ESCAPE- ANY AIR-PURIFYING FULL FACEPIECE RESPIRATOR (GAS MASK) WITH A CHIN-STYLE OR FRONT- OR BACK-MOUNTED ORGANIC VAPOR CANISTER HAVING A HIGH-EFFICIENCY PARTICULATE FILTER. ANY APPROPRIATE ESCAPE-TYPE SELF-CONTAINED BREATHING APPARATUS.
FOR FIREFIGHTING AND OTHER IMMEDIATELY DANGEROUS TO LIFE OR HEALTH CONDITIONS:
SELF-CONTAINED BREATHING APPARATUS WITH FULL FACEPIECE OPERATED IN PRESSURE-DEMAND OR OTHER POSITIVE PRESSURE MODE.
SUPPLIED-AIR RESPIRATOR WITH FULL FACEPIECE AND OPERATED IN PRESSURE-DEMAND OR OTHER POSITIVE PRESSURE MODE IN COMBINATION WITH AN AUXILIARY SELF-CONTAINED BREATHING APPARATUS OPERATED IN PRESSURE-DEMAND OR OTHER POSITIVE PRESSURE MODE.

CLOTHING: EMPLOYEE MUST WEAR APPROPRIATE PROTECTIVE (IMPERVIOUS) CLOTHING AND EQUIPMENT TO PREVENT REPEATED OR PROLONGED SKIN CONTACT WITH THIS SUBSTANCE.

GLOVES: EMPLOYEE MUST WEAR APPROPRIATE PROTECTIVE GLOVES TO PREVENT CONTACT WITH THIS SUBSTANCE.

EYE PROTECTION: EMPLOYEE MUST WEAR SPLASH-PROOF OR DUST-RESISTANT SAFETY GOGGLES TO PREVENT EYE CONTACT WITH THIS SUBSTANCE.
EMERGENCY EYE WASH: WHERE THERE IS ANY POSSIBILITY THAT AN EMPLOYEE'S EYES MAY BE EXPOSED TO THIS SUBSTANCE, THE EMPLOYER SHOULD PROVIDE AN EYE WASH FOUNTAIN WITHIN THE IMMEDIATE WORK AREA FOR EMERGENCY USE.

AUTHORIZED BY- OCCUPATIONAL HEALTH SERVICES, INC.
CREATION DATE: 10/04/89 ***REVISION DATE:*** 06/27/90

MATERIAL SAFETY DATA SHEET

OCCUPATIONAL HEALTH SERVICES, INC.
AGRICULTURE AND PESTICIDE DIVISION
450 SEVENTH AVENUE, SUITE 2407
NEW YORK, NEW YORK 10123
1-800-445-MSDS OR (212) 967-1100

EMERGENCY CONTACT:
JOHN S. BRANSFORD, JR. (615) 292-1180

SUBSTANCE IDENTIFICATION

CAS-NUMBER 1563-66-2

SUBSTANCE: CARBOFURAN

TRADE NAMES/SYNONYMS: 7-BENZOFURANOL, 2,3-DIHYDRO-2,2-DIMETHYL-, METHYLCARBAMATE; CARBAMIC ACID, METHYL-, 2,3-DIHYDRO-2,2-DIMETHYL-7-BENZOFURANYL ESTER; 2,3-DIHYDRO-2,2-DIMETHYL-7-BENZOFURANOL METHYLCARBAMATE; METHYLCARBAMIC ACID 2,3-DIHYDRO-2,2-DIMETHYL-7-BENZOFURANYL ESTER; 2,3-DIHYDRO-2,2-DIMETHYLBENZOFURAN-7-YL METHYLCARBAMATE; 2,3-DIHYDRO-2,2-DIMETHYL-7-BENZOFURANYL METHYLCARBAMATE; 2,3-DIHYDRO-2,2-DIMETHYL-7-BENZOFURANOL-N-METHYLCARBAMATE; BAY 70143; CHINUFUR; CURATERR; FURADAN; NIA 10242; NIAGARA 10242; ENT 27164; STCC 4921525; C12H15NO3; PST04240

CHEMICAL FAMILY: FURAN DERIVATIVE
CARBAMATE

MOLECULAR FORMULA: C12-H15-N-O3

MOLECULAR WEIGHT: 221.28

CERCLA RATINGS (SCALE 0-3): HEALTH=3 FIRE=0 REACTIVITY=0 PERSISTENCE=3

NFPA RATINGS (SCALE 0-4): HEALTH=4 FIRE=0 REACTIVITY=0

COMPONENTS AND CONTAMINANTS

COMPONENT: CARBOFURAN ***PERCENT:*** 100
CAS# 1563-66-2

OTHER CONTAMINANTS: NONE

EXPOSURE LIMITS: CARBOFURAN: 0.1 MG/M3 OSHA TWA 0.1 MG/M3 ACGIH TWA 10/10,000 POUNDS SARA SECTION 302 THRESHOLD PLANNING QUANTITY 10 POUNDS SARA SECTION 304 REPORTABLE QUANTITY 10 POUNDS CERCLA SECTION 103 REPORTABLE QUANTITY

PHYSICAL DATA

DESCRIPTION: ODORLESS, WHITE CRYSTALLINE SOLID

MELTING POINT: 302-307 F (150-153 C) ***SPECIFIC GRAVITY:*** 1.180 @ 20 C

VAPOR PRESSURE: 0.00002 MMHG @ 33 C ***EVAPORATION RATE:*** NOT AVAILABLE

SOLUBILITY IN WATER: 700 PPM @ 25 C

SOLVENT SOLUBILITY: ACETONE, BENZENE, DIMETHYLFORMAMIDE, DIMETHYLSULFOXIDE, ACETONITRILE, CYCLOHEXANE, 1-METHYLPYRROLID-2-ONE

FIRE AND EXPLOSION DATA

FIRE AND EXPLOSION HAZARD: NEGLIGIBLE FIRE HAZARD WHEN EXPOSED TO HEAT OR FLAME.

FIREFIGHTING MEDIA: DRY CHEMICAL, CARBON DIOXIDE, HALON, WATER SPRAY OR STANDARD FOAM (1987 EMERGENCY RESPONSE GUIDEBOOK, DOT P 5800.4).
FOR LARGER FIRES, USE WATER SPRAY, FOG OR STANDARD FOAM (1987 EMERGENCY RESPONSE GUIDEBOOK, DOT P 5800.4).

FIREFIGHTING: MOVE CONTAINERS FROM FIRE AREA IF POSSIBLE. FIGHT FIRE FROM MAXIMUM DISTANCE. STAY AWAY FROM STORAGE TANK ENDS. DIKE FIRE CONTROL WATER FOR LATER DISPOSAL. DO NOT SCATTER MATERIAL (1987 EMERGENCY RESPONSE GUIDEBOOK, DOT P 5800.4, GUIDE PAGE 55).
EXTINGUISH USING AGENTS SUITABLE FOR TYPE OF SURROUNDING FIRE. USE

FLOODING AMOUNTS OF WATER AS FOG. AVOID BREATHING TOXIC DUST AND FUMES FROM BURNING MATERIAL; KEEP UPWIND.

TRANSPORTATION DATA

DEPARTMENT OF TRANSPORTATION HAZARD CLASSIFICATION 49 CFR 172.101: POISON B
DEPARTMENT OF TRANSPORTATION LABELING REQUIREMENTS 49 CFR 172.101 AND SUBPART E: POISON
DEPARTMENT OF TRANSPORTATION PACKAGING REQUIREMENTS: 49 CFR 173.365 EXCEPTIONS: 49 CFR 173.364

TOXICITY

CARBOFURAN: TOXICITY DATA: 85 MG/M3 INHALATION-RAT LC50; 52 MG/M3 INHALATION-DOG LC50; 43 MG/KG/4 HOURS INHALATION-GUINEA PIG LC50; 885 MG/KG SKIN-RABBIT LD50; 120 MG/KG SKIN-RAT LD50; 837 MG/KG SKIN-MAMMAL LD50; 5 MG/KG ORAL-RAT LD50; 2 MG/KG ORAL-MOUSE LD50; 19 MG/KG ORAL-DOG LD50; 450 UG/KG INTRAVENOUS-MOUSE LD50; 19 MG/KG UNREPORTED-RAT LD50; 5 MG/KG UNREPORTED-MOUSE LD50; MUTAGENIC DATA (RTECS); REPRODUCTIVE EFFECTS DATA (RTECS). CARCINOGEN STATUS: NONE. ACUTE TOXICITY LEVEL: HIGHLY TOXIC BY INHALATION AND INGESTION; TOXIC BY DERMAL ABSORPTION. TARGET EFFECTS: CHOLINESTERASE INHIBITOR. AT INCREASED RISK FROM EXPOSURE: PERSONS WITH ASTHMA, DIABETES, CARDIOVASCULAR DISEASE, MECHANICAL OBSTRUCTION OF THE GASTROINTESTINAL OR UROGENITAL TRACT, AND THOSE IN VAGOTONIC STATES.*

* MAY BE BASED ON GENERAL INFORMATION ON CARBAMATES.

HEALTH EFFECTS AND FIRST AID

INHALATION: CARBOFURAN: HIGHLY TOXIC. SEE INFORMATION ON CARBAMATES. CARBAMATES: CHOLINESTERASE INHIBITOR. **ACUTE EXPOSURE**- WHEN INHALED, THE FIRST EFFECTS OF CHOLINESTERASE INHIBITION ARE USUALLY RESPIRATORY AND MAY INCLUDE NASAL HYPEREMIA AND WATERY DISCHARGE, CHEST DISCOMFORT, DYSPNEA, AND WHEEZING DUE TO INCREASED BRONCHIAL SECRETIONS AND BRONCHOCONSTRICTION. OTHER SYSTEMIC EFFECTS MAY BEGIN WITHIN A FEW MINUTES OR SEVERAL HOURS OF EXPOSURE. SYMPTOMS MAY INCLUDE NAUSEA, VOMITING, DIARRHEA, ABDOMINAL CRAMPS, HEADACHE, VERTIGO, OCULAR PAIN, CILIARY MUSCLE SPASM, BLURRING OR DIMNESS OF VISION, MIOSIS, OR IN SOME CASES MYDRIASIS, LACRIMATION, SALIVATION, SWEATING, AND CONFUSION. OTHER REPORTED CENTRAL NERVOUS SYSTEM OR NEUROMUSCULAR EFFECTS INCLUDE ATAXIA, SLURRED SPEECH, AREFLEXIA, WEAKNESS, FATIGUE, TWITCHING, FASCICULATION, TREMOR, AND EVENTUALLY PARALYSIS OF THE EXTREMITIES AND POSSIBLY OF THE RESPIRATORY MUSCLES. IN SEVERE CASES, THERE MAY ALSO BE INVOLUNTARY DEFECATION AND URINATION, BRADYCARDIA, HYPOTENSION, PULMONARY EDEMA, CONVULSIONS, COMA, AND DEATH FROM RESPIRATORY FAILURE OR CARDIAC ARREST. CARBAMATES GENERALLY DO NOT ACCUMULATE IN MAMMALIAN TISSUE AND THE CHOLINESTERASE INHIBITION REVERSES RATHER RAPIDLY. IN NON-FATAL CASES, THE ILLNESS GENERALLY LASTS LESS THAN 24 HOURS. **CHRONIC EXPOSURE**- PROLONGED OR REPEATED EXPOSURE MAY CAUSE EFFECTS AS DESCRIBED IN ACUTE EXPOSURE.

FIRST AID- REMOVE FROM EXPOSURE AREA TO FRESH AIR IMMEDIATELY. IF BREATHING HAS STOPPED, GIVE ARTIFICIAL RESPIRATION. MAINTAIN AIRWAY AND BLOOD PRESSURE AND ADMINISTER OXYGEN IF AVAILABLE. KEEP AFFECTED PERSON WARM AND AT REST. TREAT SYMPTOMATICALLY AND SUPPORTIVELY. ADMINISTRATION OF OXYGEN SHOULD BE PERFORMED BY QUALIFIED PERSONNEL. GET MEDICAL ATTENTION IMMEDIATELY.

SKIN CONTACT: CARBOFURAN: TOXIC. SEE INFORMATION ON CARBAMATES. CARBAMATES: CHOLINESTERASE INHIBITOR. **ACUTE EXPOSURE**- SOME COMPOUNDS MAY CAUSE IRRITATION. LOCALIZED SWEATING AND FASCICULATIONS MAY OCCUR AT THE SITE OF CONTACT. IF SUFFICIENT AMOUNTS ARE ABSORBED THROUGH THE SKIN, OTHER EFFECTS OF CHOLINESTERASE INHIBITION MAY OCCUR AS DESCRIBED IN ACUTE INHALATION; SYMPTOMS MAY BE DELAYED FOR 2-3 HOURS, USUALLY NO MORE THAN 8 HOURS. **CHRONIC EXPOSURE**- REPEATED OR PROLONGED EXPOSURE MAY CAUSE EFFECTS AS DESCRIBED IN ACUTE EXPOSURE.

FIRST AID- REMOVE CONTAMINATED CLOTHING IMMEDIATELY. WASH CONTAMINATED AREAS WITH SOAP AND WATER FOLLOWED BY ALCOHOL (ARENA, POISONING, 4TH ED.). EMERGENCY PERSONNEL SHOULD WEAR GLOVES AND AVOID CONTAMINATION. TREAT RESPIRATORY DIFFICULTY WITH ARTIFICIAL RESPIRATION. GET MEDICAL ATTENTION IMMEDIATELY.

EYE CONTACT: CARBOFURAN: FORMULATIONS OF 25% WETTABLE POWDER AND 75% WETTABLE POWDER WERE LETHAL WHEN APPLIED TO RABBIT EYES AT DOSES OF 21.5 MG/KG AND 18.0 MG/KG, RESPECTIVELY. SEE INFORMATION ON CARBAMATES. CARBAMATES: CHOLINESTERASE INHIBITOR. **ACUTE EXPOSURE**- DIRECT CONTACT MAY CAUSE PAIN, HYPEREMIA, LACRIMATION, TWITCHING OF THE EYELIDS, MIOSIS, AND CILIARY MUSCLE SPASM WITH LOSS OF ACCOMODATION, BLURRED OR DIMMED VISION AND BROWACHE. SOMETIMES MYDRIASIS MAY OCCUR INSTEAD OF MIOSIS. WITH SUFFICIENT EXPOSURE, OTHER SYMPTOMS OF CHOLINESTERASE INHIBITION MAY OCCUR AS DESCRIBED IN ACUTE INHALATION. **CHRONIC EXPOSURE**- PROLONGED EXPOSURE MAY CAUSE EFFECTS AS DESCRIBED IN ACUTE EXPOSURE. SOME COMPOUNDS HAVE CAUSED TOXIC EFFECTS ON THE CRYSTALLINE LENS, CONJUNCTIVAL THICKENING AND OBSTRUCTION OF NASOLACRIMAL CANALS WHEN USED AS MIOTIC EYE DROPS.

FIRST AID- IRRIGATE EYES WITH WATER OR SALINE SOLUTION. IF SYMPTOMS OF POISONING OCCUR, TREAT RESPIRATORY DIFFICULTY WITH ARTIFICIAL RESPIRATION AND OXYGEN. OBSERVE PATIENT FOR AT LEAST 24-36 HOURS (GOSSELIN, CLINICAL TOXICOLOGY OF COMMERCIAL PRODUCTS, 5TH ED.). GET MEDICAL ATTENTION IMMEDIATELY. OXYGEN SHOULD BE ADMINISTERED BY QUALIFIED MEDICAL PERSONNEL.

INGESTION: CARBOFURAN: HIGHLY TOXIC. ADVERSE EFFECTS ON THE NEWBORN AND FETAL DEVELOPMENTAL ABNORMALITIES WERE REPORTED FROM A CHRONIC INGESTION STUDY OF PREGNANT MICE. SEE INFORMATIN ON CARBAMATES. CARBAMATES: CHOLINESTERASE INHIBITOR. **ACUTE EXPOSURE**- WHEN INGESTED, THE FIRST EFFECTS MAY BE NAUSEA, VOMITING, ANOREXIA, ABDOMINAL CRAMPS, AND DIARRHEA. WITH ABSORPTION FROM THE GASTROINTESTINAL TRACT, THE OTHER EFFECTS OF CHOLINESTERASE INHIBITION AS DESCRIBED IN ACUTE INHALATION MAY OCCUR; SYMPTOMS MAY BEGIN WITHIN MINUTES OR BE DELAYED SEVERAL HOURS. **CHRONIC EXPOSURE**- REPEATED INGESTION MAY CAUSE EFFECTS AS DESCRIBED IN ACUTE EXPOSURE.

FIRST AID- IF PERSON IS ALERT AND RESPIRATION IS NOT DEPRESSED, GIVE SYRUP OF IPECAC FOLLOWED BY WATER (IF VOMITING OCCURS, KEEP HEAD BELOW HIPS TO PREVENT ASPIRATION). IF CONSCIOUSNESS LEVEL DECLINES OR VOMITING HAS NOT OCCURRED IN 15 MINUTES EMPTY STOMACH BY GASTRIC LAVAGE WITH THE AID OF CUFFED ENDOTRACHEAL TUBE USING ISOTONIC SALINE OR 5% SODIUM BICARBONATE FOLLOW WITH ACTIVATED CHARCOAL. ESTABLISH AND MAINTAIN AIRWAY. TREAT RESPIRATORY DIFFICULTY WITH ARTIFICIAL RESPIRATION AND OXYGEN. DO NOT GIVE MORPHINE, AMINOPHYLLINE, PHENOTHIAZINES, RESERPINE, FUROSEMIDE, OR ETHACRYNIC ACID (MORGAN, RECOGNITION AND MANAGEMENT OF PESTICIDE POISONINGS, 3RD ED.). TREAT SYMPTOMATICALLY AND SUPPORTIVELY. ADMINISTRATION OF OXYGEN AND LAVAGE MUST BE PERFORMED BY QUALIFIED MEDICAL PERSONNEL. GET MEDICAL ATTENTION IMMEDIATELY.

ANTIDOTE: THE FOLLOWING ANTIDOTE HAS BEEN RECOMMENDED. HOWEVER, THE DECISION AS TO WHETHER THE SEVERITY OF POISONING REQUIRES ADMINISTRATION OF ANY ANTIDOTE AND ACTUAL DOSE REQUIRED SHOULD BE MADE BY QUALIFIED MEDICAL PERSONNEL.

FOR CHOLINESTERASE INHIBITORS: ESTABLISH CLEAR AIRWAY AND TISSUE OXYGENATION BY ASPIRATION OF SECRETIONS, AND IF NECESSARY, BY ASSISTED PULMONARY VENTILATION WITH OXYGEN. IMPROVE TISSUE OXYGENATION AS MUCH AS POSSIBLE BEFORE ADMINISTERING ATROPINE TO MINIMIZE THE RISK OF VENTRICULAR FIBRILLATION. ADMINISTER ATROPINE SULFATE INTRAVENOUSLY, OR INTRAMUSCULARLY IF IV INJECTION IS NOT POSSIBLE. IN MODERATELY SEVERE POISONING ADMINISTER ATROPINE SULFATE, 0.4-2.0 MG REPEATED EVERY 15 MINUTES UNTIL ATROPINIZATION IS ACHIEVED (TACHYCARDIA, FLUSHING, DRY MOUTH, MYDRIASIS). MAINTAIN ATROPINIZATION BY REPEATED DOSES FOR 2-12 HOURS, OR LONGER, DEPENDING ON THE SEVERITY OF POISONING. THE APPEARANCE OF RALES IN THE LUNG BASES, MIOSIS, SALIVATION, NAUSEA, BRADYCARDIA, ARE ALL INDICATIONS OF INADEQUATE ATROPINIZATION. SEVERELY POISONED INDIVIDUALS MAY EXHIBIT REMARKABLE TOLERANCE TO ATROPINE; TWO OR MORE TIMES THE DOSAGES SUGGESTED ABOVE MAY BE NEEDED. PERSONS NOT POISONED OR ONLY SLIGHTLY POISONED, HOWEVER, MAY DEVELOP SIGNS OF ATROPINE TOXICITY FROM SUCH LARGE DOSAGES: FEVER, MUSCLE FIBRILLATIONS, AND DELIRIUM ARE THE MAIN SIGNS OF ATROPINE TOXICITY. IF THESE SIGNS APPEAR WHILE THE PATIENT IS FULLY ATROPINIZED, ATROPINE ADMINISTRATION SHOULD BE DISCONTINUED, AT LEAST TEMPORARILY. OBSERVE TREATED PATIENTS CLOSELY AT LEAST 24 HOURS TO INSURE THAT SYMPTOMS (POSSIBLY PULMONARY EDEMA) DO NOT RECUR AS ATROPINIZATION WEARS OFF. IN VERY SEVERE POISONINGS, METABOLIC DISPOSITION OF TOXICANT MAY REQUIRE SEVERAL HOURS OR DAYS DURING WHICH ATROPINIZATION MUST BE MAINTAINED. MARKEDLY LOWER LEVELS OF URINARY METABOLITES INDICATE THAT ATROPINE DOSAGE CAN BE TAPERED OFF. AS DOSAGE IS REDUCED, CHECK THE LUNG BASES FREQUENTLY FOR RALES. IF RALES ARE HEARD OR OTHER SYMPTOMS RETURN, RE-ESTABLISH ATROPINIZATION PROMPTLY (MORGAN, RECOGNITION AND MANAGEMENT OF PESTICIDE POISONINGS, 3RD ED.). ADMINISTRATION OF ANTIDOTE MUST BE PERFORMED BY QUALIFIED MEDICAL PERSONNEL.

REACTIVITY

REACTIVITY: STABLE UNDER NORMAL TEMPERATURES AND PRESSURES.

INCOMPATIBILITIES: CARBOFURAN: ALKALINE MEDIA: MAY CAUSE HYDROLYSIS. ACIDIC CONDITIONS (STRONG): MAY CAUSE HYDROLYSIS. OXIDIZERS (STRONG): FIRE AND EXPLOSION HAZARD.
DECOMPOSITION: THERMAL DECOMPOSITION PRODUCTS MAY INCLUDE TOXIC OXIDES OF NITROGEN.
POLYMERIZATION: HAZARDOUS POLYMERIZATION HAS NOT BEEN REPORTED TO OCCUR UNDER NORMAL TEMPERATURES AND PRESSURES.

STORAGE AND DISPOSAL

OBSERVE ALL FEDERAL, STATE AND LOCAL REGULATIONS WHEN STORING OR DISPOSING OF THIS SUBSTANCE. FOR ASSISTANCE, CONTACT THE DISTRICT DIRECTOR OF THE ENVIRONMENTAL PROTECTION AGENCY.

STORAGE

STORE IN ACCORDANCE WITH 40 CFR 165 RECOMMENDED PROCEDURES FOR THE DISPOSAL AND STORAGE OF PESTICIDES AND PESTICIDE CONTAINERS.
STORE AWAY FROM INCOMPATIBLE SUBSTANCES.
THRESHOLD PLANNING QUANTITY (TPQ): THE SUPERFUND AMENDMENTS AND REAUTHORIZATION ACT (SARA) SECTION 302 REQUIRES THAT EACH FACILITY WHERE ANY EXTREMELY HAZARDOUS SUBSTANCE IS PRESENT IN A QUANTITY EQUAL TO OR GREATER THAN THE TPQ ESTABLISHED FOR THAT SUBSTANCE NOTIFY THE STATE EMERGENCY RESPONSE COMMISSION FOR THE STATE IN WHICH IT IS LOCATED. SECTION 303 OF SARA REQUIRES THESE FACILITIES TO PARTICIPATE IN LOCAL EMERGENCY RESPONSE PLANNING (40 CFR 355.30).

DISPOSAL

DISPOSAL MUST BE IN ACCORDANCE WITH 40 CFR 165 RECOMMENDED PROCEDURES FOR THE DISPOSAL AND STORAGE OF PESTICIDES AND PESTICIDE CONTAINERS.

CONDITIONS TO AVOID

NONE REPORTED.

SPILL AND LEAK PROCEDURES

SOIL SPILL: DIG A HOLDING AREA SUCH AS PIT, POND OR LAGOON TO CONTAIN SPILLED MATERIAL. USE PROTECTIVE COVER SUCH AS A PLASTIC SHEET TO PREVENT DISSOLVING IN FIREFIGHTING WATER OR RAIN.
WATER SPILL: TRAP SPILLED MATERIAL AT BOTTOM IN DEEP WATER POCKETS, EXCAVATED HOLDING AREAS OR WITHIN SAND BAG BARRIERS.
IF DISSOLVED, AT A CONCENTRATION OF 10 PPM OR GREATER, APPLY ACTIVATED CARBON AT TEN TIMES THE AMOUNT THAT HAS BEEN SPILLED.
USE MECHANICAL DREDGES OR LIFTS TO EXTRACT IMMOBILIZED MASSES OF POLLUTION AND PRECIPITATES.
OCCUPATIONAL SPILL: DO NOT TOUCH SPILLED MATERIAL. STOP LEAK IF YOU CAN DO IT WITHOUT RISK. USE WATER SPRAY TO REDUCE VAPORS. FOR SMALL SPILLS, TAKE UP WITH SAND OR OTHER ABSORBENT MATERIAL AND PLACE INTO CONTAINERS FOR LATER DISPOSAL. FOR SMALL DRY SPILLS, WITH A CLEAN SHOVEL PLACE MATERIAL INTO CLEAN, DRY CONTAINERS AND COVER. MOVE CONTAINERS FROM SPILL AREA. FOR LARGER SPILLS, DIKE FAR AHEAD OF SPILL FOR LATER DISPOSAL. KEEP UNNECESSARY PEOPLE AWAY. ISOLATE HAZARD AREA AND DENY ENTRY. VENTILATE CLOSED SPACES BEFORE ENTERING.
REPORTABLE QUANTITY (RQ): 10 POUNDS THE SUPERFUND AMENDMENTS AND REAUTHORIZATION ACT (SARA) SECTION 304 REQUIRES THAT A RELEASE EQUAL TO OR GREATER THAN THE REPORTABLE QUANTITY FOR THIS SUBSTANCE BE IMMEDIATELY REPORTED TO THE LOCAL EMERGENCY PLANNING COMMITTEE AND THE STATE EMERGENCY RESPONSE COMMISSION (40 CFR 355.40). IF THE RELEASE OF THIS SUBSTANCE IS REPORTABLE UNDER CERCLA SECTION 103, THE NATIONAL RESPONSE CENTER MUST BE NOTIFIED IMMEDIATELY AT (800) 424-8802 OR (202) 426-2675 IN THE METROPOLITAN WASHINGTON, D.C. AREA (40 CFR 302.6).

PROTECTIVE EQUIPMENT

VENTILATION: PROCESS ENCLOSURE RECOMMENDED TO MEET PUBLISHED EXPOSURE LIMITS.
RESPIRATOR: THE FOLLOWING RESPIRATORS ARE RECOMMENDED BASED ON INFORMATION FOUND IN THE PHYSICAL DATA, TOXICITY AND HEALTH EFFECTS SECTIONS. THEY ARE RANKED IN ORDER FROM MINIMUM TO MAXIMUM RESPIRATORY PROTECTION. THE SPECIFIC RESPIRATOR SELECTED MUST BE BASED ON CONTAMINATION LEVELS FOUND IN THE WORK PLACE, MUST NOT EXCEED THE WORKING LIMITS OF THE RESPIRATOR AND BE JOINTLY APPROVED BY THE NATIONAL INSTITUTE FOR OCCUPATIONAL SAFETY AND HEALTH AND THE MINE SAFETY AND HEALTH ADMINISTRATION (NIOSH-MSHA).
TYPE 'C' SUPPLIED-AIR RESPIRATOR WITH A FULL FACEPIECE OPERATED IN PRESSURE-DEMAND OR OTHER POSITIVE PRESSURE MODE OR WITH A FULL FACEPIECE, HELMET OR HOOD OPERATED IN CONTINOUS-FLOW MODE.
SELF-CONTAINED BREATHING APPARATUS WITH A FULL FACEPIECE OPERATED IN PRESSURE-DEMAND OR OTHER POSITIVE PRESSURE MODE.
FOR FIREFIGHTING AND OTHER IMMEDIATELY DANGEROUS TO LIFE OR HEALTH CONDITIONS:
SELF-CONTAINED BREATHING APPARATUS WITH FULL FACEPIECE OPERATED IN PRESSURE-DEMAND OR OTHER POSITIVE PRESSURE MODE.
SUPPLIED-AIR RESPIRATOR WITH FULL FACEPIECE AND OPERATED IN PRESSURE-DEMAND OR OTHER POSITIVE PRESSURE MODE IN COMBINATION WITH AN AUXILIARY SELF-CONTAINED BREATHING APPARATUS OPERATED IN PRESSURE-DEMAND OR OTHER POSITIVE PRESSURE MODE.
CLOTHING: EMPLOYEE MUST WEAR APPROPRIATE PROTECTIVE (IMPERVIOUS) CLOTHING AND EQUIPMENT TO PREVENT ANY POSSIBILITY OF SKIN CONTACT WITH THIS SUBSTANCE.
GLOVES: EMPLOYEE MUST WEAR APPROPRIATE PROTECTIVE GLOVES TO PREVENT CONTACT WITH THIS SUBSTANCE.
EYE PROTECTION: EMPLOYEE MUST WEAR SPLASH-PROOF OR DUST-RESISTANT SAFETY GOGGLES AND A FACESHIELD TO PREVENT CONTACT WITH THIS SUBSTANCE. EMERGENCY WASH FACILITIES: WHERE THERE IS ANY POSSIBILITY THAT AN EMPLOYEE'S EYES AND/OR SKIN MAY BE EXPOSED TO THIS SUBSTANCE, THE EMPLOYER SHOULD PROVIDE AN EYE WASH FOUNTAIN AND QUICK DRENCH SHOWER WITHIN THE IMMEDIATE WORK AREA FOR EMERGENCY USE.

AUTHORIZED BY- OCCUPATIONAL HEALTH SERVICES, INC.
CREATION DATE: 10/04/89 ***REVISION DATE:*** 06/12/90

MATERIAL SAFETY DATA SHEET

OCCUPATIONAL HEALTH SERVICES, INC.
AGRICULTURE AND PESTICIDE DIVISION
450 SEVENTH AVENUE, SUITE 2407
NEW YORK, NEW YORK 10123
1-800-445-MSDS OR (212) 967-1100

EMERGENCY CONTACT:
JOHN S. BRANSFORD, JR. (615) 292-1180

SUBSTANCE IDENTIFICATION

CAS-NUMBER 7440-44-0
SUBSTANCE: CARBON, ACTIVATED
TRADE NAMES/SYNONYMS: ACTIVATED CARBON; ANTHRASORB; CARBON-12; CARBON ELEMENT; ELEMENTAL CARBON; FILTRASORB; GROSAFE; NACAR; NITTAN; NORIT; SHIRASAGI; SUCHAR; SUPERSORBON; DARCO KB; STCC 4917310; UN 1362; C; PST04246
CHEMICAL FAMILY: NON-METALLIC ELEMENT
MOLECULAR FORMULA: C
MOLECULAR WEIGHT: 12.011
CERCLA RATINGS (SCALE 0-3): HEALTH=3 FIRE=3 REACTIVITY=0 PERSISTENCE=1
NFPA RATINGS (SCALE 0-4): HEALTH=U FIRE=3 REACTIVITY=0

COMPONENTS AND CONTAMINANTS

COMPONENT: CARBON, ACTIVATED ***PERCENT:*** 100.0
CAS# 7440-44-0
OTHER CONTAMINANTS: NONE
EXPOSURE LIMITS: NO OCCUPATIONAL EXPOSURE LIMITS ESTABLISHED BY OSHA, ACGIH, OR NIOSH.

PHYSICAL DATA

DESCRIPTION: ODORLESS, BLACK AMORPHOUS SOLID.
MELTING POINT: 6606-6687 F (3652-3697 C) (SUBLIMES) ***SPECIFIC GRAVITY:*** 1.8-2.1
VAPOR PRESSURE: 1 MMHG @ 3586 C ***SOLUBILITY IN WATER:*** INSOLUBLE
SOLVENT SOLUBILITY: INSOLUBLE IN ACIDS AND ALKALI.

FIRE AND EXPLOSION DATA

FIRE AND EXPLOSION HAZARD: MAY IGNITE SPONTANEOUSLY ON EXPOSURE TO AIR. DANGEROUS FIRE HAZARD WHEN EXPOSED TO HEAT OR FLAME.
DUST-AIR MIXTURES MAY IGNITE OR EXPLODE.
FIREFIGHTING MEDIA: DRY CHEMICAL, SAND, WATER SPRAY OR FOAM (1987 EMERGENCY RESPONSE GUIDEBOOK, DOT P 5800.4).
FOR LARGER FIRES, USE WATER SPRAY, FOG OR STANDARD FOAM (1987 EMERGENCY RESPONSE GUIDEBOOK, DOT P 5800.4).
FIREFIGHTING: MOVE CONTAINER FROM FIRE AREA IF POSSIBLE. COOL CONTAINERS EXPOSED TO FLAME WITH WATER FROM SIDE UNTIL WELL AFTER FIRE IS OUT. STAY AWAY FROM STORAGE TANK ENDS. FOR MASSIVE FIRE IN CARGO AREA, USE UNMANNED HOSE HOLDER OR MONITOR NOZZLES; ELSE WITHDRAW AND LET FIRE BURN (1987 EMERGENCY RESPONSE GUIDEBOOK, DOT P 5800.4, GUIDE PAGE 32).

EXTINGUISH USING AGENTS INDICATED. MOVE MATERIAL FROM FIRE ONLY IF SAFE AND PRACTICAL. USE WATER ONLY IN FLOODING AMOUNTS.

TRANSPORTATION DATA

DEPARTMENT OF TRANSPORTATION HAZARD CLASSIFICATION 49 CFR 172.101: FLAMMABLE SOLID

DEPARTMENT OF TRANSPORTATION LABELING REQUIREMENTS 49 CFR 172.101 AND SUBPART E: FLAMMABLE SOLID

DEPARTMENT OF TRANSPORTATION PACKAGING REQUIREMENTS: 49 CFR 173.162 EXCEPTIONS: 49 CFR 173.162

TOXICITY

CARBON, ACTIVATED: TOXICITY DATA: 440 MG/KG INTRAVENOUS-MOUSE LD50; REPRODUCTIVE EFFECTS DATA (RTECS). CARCINOGEN STATUS: NONE. ACUTE TOXICITY LEVEL: INSUFFICIENT DATA. TARGET EFFECTS: NO DATA AVAILABLE.

HEALTH EFFECTS AND FIRST AID

INHALATION: CARBON, ACTIVATED: **ACUTE EXPOSURE-** INHALATION OF DUST MAY CAUSE SLIGHT MUCOUS MEMBRANE IRRITATION. **CHRONIC EXPOSURE-** REPEATED OR PROLONGED EXPOUSRE MAY CAUSE SLIGHT IRRITATION.

FIRST AID- REMOVE FROM EXPOSURE AREA TO FRESH AIR IMMEDIATELY. IF BREATHING HAS STOPPED, PERFORM ARTIFICIAL RESPIRATION. KEEP PERSON WARM AND AT REST. TREAT SYMPTOMATICALLY AND SUPPORTIVELY. GET MEDICAL ATTENTION IMMEDIATELY.

SKIN CONTACT: CARBON, ACTIVATED: **ACUTE EXPOSURE-** NO DATA AVAILABLE. **CHRONIC EXPOSURE-** NO DATA AVAILABLE.

FIRST AID- REMOVE CONTAMINATED CLOTHING AND SHOES IMMEDIATELY. WASH AFFECTED AREA WITH SOAP OR MILD DETERGENT AND LARGE AMOUNTS OF WATER UNTIL NO EVIDENCE OF CHEMICAL REMAINS (APPROXIMATELY 15-20 MINUTES). GET MEDICAL ATTENTION IMMEDIATELY.

EYE CONTACT: CARBON, ACTIVATED: **ACUTE EXPOSURE-** CONTACT WITH DUST MAY CAUSE MECHANICAL IRRITATION. **CHRONIC EXPOSURE-** REPEATED OR PROLONGED EXPOSURE MAY CAUSE MECHANICAL IRRITATION.

FIRST AID- WASH EYES IMMEDIATELY WITH LARGE AMOUNTS OF WATER OR NORMAL SALINE, OCCASIONALLY LIFTING UPPER AND LOWER LIDS, UNTIL NO EVIDENCE OF CHEMICAL REMAINS (APPROXIMATELY 15-20 MINUTES). GET MEDICAL ATTENTION IMMEDIATELY.

INGESTION: CARBON, ACTIVATED: **ACUTE EXPOSURE-** NO DATA AVAILABLE. **CHRONIC EXPOSURE-** NO DATA AVAILABLE.

FIRST AID- TREAT SYMPTOMATICALLY AND SUPPORTIVELY. GET MEDICAL ATTENTION IMMEDIATELY. IF VOMITING OCCURS, KEEP HEAD LOWER THAN HIPS TO PREVENT ASPIRATION.

ANTIDOTE: NO SPECIFIC ANTIDOTE. TREAT SYMPTOMATICALLY AND SUPPORTIVELY.

REACTIVITY

REACTIVITY: STABLE UNDER NORMAL TEMPERATURES AND PRESSURES IN A CLOSED CONTAINER. MAY UNDERGO SPONTANEOUS IGNITION ON EXPOSURE TO AIR; THIS MAY BE ACCELERATED BY THE PRESENCE OF MOISTURE.

INCOMPATIBILITIES: CARBON: ALKALI METALS: CONTACT MAY RESULT IN AN EXOTHERMIC REACTION WITH IGNITION OR AN EXPLOSION. AMMONIUM NITRATE: POSSIBLE EXPLOSION WHEN HEATED. AMMONIUM PERCHLORATE: POSSIBLE EXPLOSION ON HEATING. BROMATES: CONTACT IS LIKELY TO RESULT IN IGNITION OR AN EXPLOSION. CALCIUM HYPOCHLORITE: POSSIBLE EXPLOSION ON HEATING. CHLORATES: CONTACT IS LIKELY TO RESULT IN IGNITION OR AN EXPLOSION. CHLORINE MONOXIDE: EXPLODES. CHROMATES: INCOMPATIBLE. DICHLORINE OXIDE: EXPLOSION REACTION. HALOGENS: CONTACT OF CARBON WITH ANY HALOGEN IS LIABLE TO RESULT IN IGNITION OR AN EXPLOSION. INTERHALOGENS: CONTACT OF CARBON WITH ANY INTERHALOGEN IS LIABLE TO RESULT IN IGNITION OR AN EXPLOSION. IODATES: CONTACT IS LIKELY TO RESULT IN IGNITION OR AN EXPLOSION. IODINE PENTOXIDE: EXPLODES WHEN WARMED. METAL NITRATES: CONTACT IS LIKELY TO RESULT IN IGNITION OR AN EXPLOSION. NITRIC ACID: VIOLENT REACTION. NITROGEN OXIDE: IGNITION WITH INCANDESCENCE. NITROGEN TRIFLUORIDE: EXPLOSION AT REDUCED TEMPERATURES. OILS (UNSATURATED): FIRE AND EXPLOSION HAZARD. OXIDES: CONTACT WITH MANY OXIDES IS LIKELY TO RESULT IN IGNITION OR AN EXPLOSION. OXIDIZERS (STRONG): FIRE AND EXPLOSION HAZARD. OXOSALTS: CONTACT IS LIKELY TO RESULT IN IGNITION OR AN EXPLOSION. OXYGEN: MAY RESULT IN IGNITION OR AN EXPLOSION. OXYGEN DIFLUORIDE: POSSIBLE EXPLOSION. PEROXIDES: CONTACT IS LIKELY TO RESULT IN IGNITION OR AN EXPLOSION. PEROXYFORMIC ACID: VIOLENT OXIDATION. PEROXYFUROIC ACID: EXPLOSIVE DECOMPOSITION. POTASSIUM PERMANGANATE: IGNITION ON HEATING. SODIUM SULFIDE: MAY UNDERGO SPONTANEOUS HEATING. TRIOXYGEN DIFLUORIDE: IGNITION WITH POSSIBLE EXPLOSION.

DECOMPOSITION: THERMAL DECOMPOSITION PRODUCTS MAY INCLUDE TOXIC OXIDES OF CARBON.

POLYMERIZATION: HAZARDOUS POLYMERIZATION HAS NOT BEEN REPORTED TO OCCUR UNDER NORMAL TEMPERATURES AND PRESSURES.

STORAGE AND DISPOSAL

OBSERVE ALL FEDERAL, STATE AND LOCAL REGULATIONS WHEN STORING OR DISPOSING OF THIS SUBSTANCE. FOR ASSISTANCE, CONTACT THE DISTRICT DIRECTOR OF THE ENVIRONMENTAL PROTECTION AGENCY.

****STORAGE****

STORE AWAY FROM INCOMPATIBLE SUBSTANCES.

****DISPOSAL****

DISPOSAL MUST BE IN ACCORDANCE WITH STANDARDS APPLICABLE TO GENERATORS OF HAZARDOUS WASTE, 40 CFR 262. EPA HAZARDOUS WASTE NUMBER D001. 100 POUND CERCLA SECTION 103 REPORTABLE QUANTITY.

CONDITIONS TO AVOID

AVOID CONTACT WITH HEAT, SPARKS, FLAMES OR OTHER SOURCES OF IGNITION. MATERIAL IS EXTREMELY FLAMMABLE AND MAY BURN RAPIDLY WITH FLARE-BURNING EFFECT.

AVOID DISPERSION OF DUST IN AIR. FINELY DIVIDED PARTICLES, DUST, OR FUMES MAY BE FLAMMABLE OR EXPLOSIVE. KEEP AWAY FROM SPARKS OR IGNITION SOURCES.

SPILL AND LEAK PROCEDURES

OCCUPATIONAL SPILL: SHUT OFF IGNITION SOURCES. DO NOT TOUCH SPILLED MATERIAL. FOR SMALL SPILLS, WITH CLEAN SHOVEL, PLACE MATERIAL INTO CLEAN, DRY CONTAINER AND COVER; MOVE CONTAINERS FROM SPILL AREA. FOR LARGER SPILLS, WET DOWN WITH WATER AND DIKE FOR LATER DISPOSAL. NO SMOKING, FLAMES OR FLARES IN HAZARD AREA! KEEP UNNECESSARY PEOPLE AWAY. ISOLATE HAZARD AREA AND DENY ENTRY.

RESIDUE SHOULD BE CLEANED UP USING A HIGH-EFFICIENCY PARTICULATE FILTER VACUUM.

PROTECTIVE EQUIPMENT

VENTILATION: PROVIDE LOCAL EXHAUST OR PROCESS ENCLOSURE VENTILATION. VENTILATION EQUIPMENT MUST BE EXPLOSION-PROOF.

RESPIRATOR: THE FOLLOWING RESPIRATORS ARE RECOMMENDED BASED ON INFORMATION FOUND IN THE PHYSICAL DATA, TOXICITY AND HEALTH EFFECTS SECTIONS. THEY ARE RANKED IN ORDER FROM MINIMUM TO MAXIMUM RESPIRATORY PROTECTION. THE SPECIFIC RESPIRATOR SELECTED MUST BE BASED ON CONTAMINATION LEVELS FOUND IN THE WORK PLACE, MUST NOT EXCEED THE WORKING LIMITS OF THE RESPIRATOR AND BE JOINTLY APPROVED BY THE NATIONAL INSTITUTE FOR OCCUPATIONAL SAFETY AND HEALTH AND THE MINE SAFETY AND HEALTH ADMINISTRATION (NIOSH-MSHA).

DUST AND MIST RESPIRATOR.

AIR-PURIFYING RESPIRATOR WITH A HIGH-EFFICIENCY PARTICULATE FILTER.

POWERED AIR-PURIFYING RESPIRATOR WITH A DUST AND MIST FILTER.

POWERED AIR-PURIFYING RESPIRATOR WITH A HIGH-EFFICIENCY PARTICULATE FILTER.

TYPE 'C' SUPPLIED-AIR RESPIRATOR OPERATED IN THE PRESSURE-DEMAND OR OTHER POSITIVE PRESSURE OR CONTINUOUS-FLOW MODE.

SELF-CONTAINED BREATHING APPARATUS.

FOR FIREFIGHTING AND OTHER IMMEDIATELY DANGEROUS TO LIFE OR HEALTH CONDITIONS:

SELF-CONTAINED BREATHING APPARATUS WITH FULL FACEPIECE OPERATED IN PRESSURE-DEMAND OR OTHER POSITIVE PRESSURE MODE.

SUPPLIED-AIR RESPIRATOR WITH FULL FACEPIECE AND OPERATED IN PRESSURE-DEMAND OR OTHER POSITIVE PRESSURE MODE IN COMBINATION WITH AN AUXILIARY SELF-CONTAINED BREATHING APPARATUS OPERATED IN PRESSURE-DEMAND OR OTHER POSITIVE PRESSURE MODE.

CLOTHING: EMPLOYEE MUST WEAR APPROPRIATE PROTECTIVE (IMPERVIOUS) CLOTHING AND EQUIPMENT TO PREVENT REPEATED OR PROLONGED SKIN CONTACT WITH THIS SUBSTANCE.

GLOVES: EMPLOYEE MUST WEAR APPROPRIATE PROTECTIVE GLOVES TO PREVENT CONTACT WITH THIS SUBSTANCE.

EYE PROTECTION: EMPLOYEE MUST WEAR SPLASH-PROOF OR DUST-RESISTANT SAFETY GOGGLES TO PREVENT EYE CONTACT WITH THIS SUBSTANCE. EMERGENCY EYE WASH: WHERE THERE IS ANY POSSIBILITY THAT AN EMPLOYEE'S EYES MAY BE EXPOSED TO THIS SUBSTANCE, THE EMPLOYER SHOULD PROVIDE AN EYE WASH FOUNTAIN WITHIN THE IMMEDIATE WORK AREA FOR EMERGENCY USE.

AUTHORIZED BY- OCCUPATIONAL HEALTH SERVICES, INC.

CREATION DATE: 11/15/89 ***REVISION DATE:*** 03/28/90

MATERIAL SAFETY DATA SHEET

OCCUPATIONAL HEALTH SERVICES, INC.
AGRICULTURE AND PESTICIDE DIVISION
450 SEVENTH AVENUE, SUITE 2407
NEW YORK, NEW YORK 10123
1-800-445-MSDS OR (212) 967-1100

EMERGENCY CONTACT:
JOHN S. BRANSFORD, JR. (615) 292-1180

SUBSTANCE IDENTIFICATION

CAS-NUMBER 56-23-5

SUBSTANCE: CARBON TETRACHLORIDE

TRADE NAMES/SYNONYMS: METHANE, TETRACHLORO-; CARBON CHLORIDE (CCL4); PERCHLOROMETHANE; TETRACHLORMETHANE; BENZINOFORM; NECATORINA; R 10; R 10 (REFRIGERANT); RCRA U211; UN 1846; STCC 4940320; CCL4; PST04310

CHEMICAL FAMILY: HALOGEN COMPOUND, ALIPHATIC

MOLECULAR FORMULA: C-CL4

MOLECULAR WEIGHT: 153.82

CERCLA RATINGS (SCALE 0-3): HEALTH=3 FIRE=0 REACTIVITY=0 PERSISTENCE=3

NFPA RATINGS (SCALE 0-4): HEALTH=U FIRE=0 REACTIVITY=0

COMPONENTS AND CONTAMINANTS

COMPONENT: CARBON TETRACHLORIDE ***PERCENT:*** 100.0
CAS# 56-23-5

OTHER CONTAMINANTS: NONE

EXPOSURE LIMITS: CARBON TETRACHLORIDE: 2 PPM (12.6 MG/M3) OSHA TWA 5 PPM (30 MG/M3) ACGIH TWA (SKIN) ACGIH A2-SUSPECTED HUMAN CARCINOGEN. 2 PPM NIOSH RECOMMENDED 60 MINUTE CEILING (45 LITER SAMPLE)
10 POUNDS CERCLA SECTION 103 REPORTABLE QUANTITY SUBJECT TO SARA SECTION 313 ANNUAL TOXIC CHEMICAL RELEASE REPORTING SUBJECT TO CALIFORNIA PROPOSITION 65 CANCER AND/OR REPRODUCTIVE TOXICITY WARNING AND RELEASE REQUIREMENTS- (OCTOBER 1, 1987)

PHYSICAL DATA

DESCRIPTION: CLEAR, COLORLESS HEAVY LIQUID WITH CHARACTERISTIC ODOR.

BOILING POINT: 171 F (77 C) ***MELTING POINT:*** -9 F (-23 C)

SPECIFIC GRAVITY: 1.5940 ***VOLATILITY:*** 100%

VAPOR PRESSURE: 91.3 MMHG @ 20 C ***EVAPORATION RATE:*** (BUTYL ACETATE=1) 12.8

SOLUBILITY IN WATER: 0.08% @ 20 C ***ODOR THRESHOLD:*** 50 PPM

VAPOR DENSITY: 5.32

SOLVENT SOLUBILITY: SOLUBLE IN ALCOHOL, BENZENE, CHLOROFORM, ETHER, CARBON DISULFIDE, PETROLEUM ETHER, SOLVENT NAPTHA AND MOST FIXED, VOLATILE OILS AND ACETONE.

FIRE AND EXPLOSION DATA

FIRE AND EXPLOSION HAZARD: NEGLIGIBLE FIRE HAZARD WHEN EXPOSED TO HEAT OR FLAME.

FLASH POINT: NONE

FIREFIGHTING MEDIA: DRY CHEMICAL, CARBON DIOXIDE, HALON, WATER SPRAY OR STANDARD FOAM (1987 EMERGENCY RESPONSE GUIDEBOOK, DOT P 5800.4).
FOR LARGER FIRES, USE WATER SPRAY, FOG OR STANDARD FOAM (1987 EMERGENCY RESPONSE GUIDEBOOK, DOT P 5800.4).

FIREFIGHTING: MOVE CONTAINERS FROM FIRE AREA IF POSSIBLE. FIGHT FIRE FROM MAXIMUM DISTANCE. STAY AWAY FROM STORAGE TANK ENDS. DIKE FIRE CONTROL WATER FOR LATER DISPOSAL. DO NOT SCATTER MATERIAL (1987 EMERGENCY RESPONSE GUIDEBOOK, DOT P 5800.4, GUIDE PAGE 55).
USE SUITABLE AGENT FOR SURROUNDING FIRE. AVOID BREATHING VAPORS OR DUSTS, KEEP UPWIND.

TRANSPORTATION DATA

DEPARTMENT OF TRANSPORTATION HAZARD CLASSIFICATION 49 CFR 172.101: ORM-A
DEPARTMENT OF TRANSPORTATION LABELING REQUIREMENTS 49 CFR 172.101 AND SUBPART E: NONE
DEPARTMENT OF TRANSPORTATION PACKAGING REQUIREMENTS: 49 CFR 173.620 EXCEPTIONS: 49 CFR 173.505

TOXICITY

CARBON TETRACHLORIDE: IRRITATION DATA: 4 MG SKIN-RABBIT MILD; 500 MG/24 HOURS SKIN-RABBIT MILD; 2200 UG/30 SECONDS EYE-RABBIT MILD; 500 MG/24 HOURS EYE-RABBIT MILD. TOXICITY DATA: 20 PPM INHALATION-HUMAN TCLO; 1000 PPM INHALATION-HUMAN LCLO; 45 PPM/3 DAYS INHALATION-HUMAN TCLO; 317 PPM/30 MINUTES INHALATION-HUMAN TCLO; 5 PPH/5 MINUTES INHALATION-HUMAN LCLO; 8000 PPM/4 HOURS INHALATION-RAT LC50; 9526 PPM/8 HOURS INHALATION-MOUSE LC50; 20,000 PPM/2 HOURS INHALATION-GUINEA PIG LCLO; 38,110 PPM/2 HOURS INHALATION-CAT LCLO; 14,620 PPM/8 HOURS INHALATION-DOG LCLO; 34,500 MG/M3 INHALATION-MAMMAL LC50; 5070 MG/KG SKIN-RAT LD50; 1700 MG/KG ORAL-MAN TDLO; 1800 MG/KG ORAL-WOMAN TDLO; 2350 MG/KG ORAL-RAT LD50; 8263 MG/KG ORAL-MOUSE LD50; 5760 MG/KG MG/KG ORAL-RABBIT LD50; 5760 MG/KG ORAL-GUINEA PIG LD50; 1 GM/KG ORAL-DOG LDLO; 31 GM/KG SUBCUTANEOUS-MOUSE LD50; 3000 MG/KG SUBCUTANEOUS-RABBIT LDLO; 300 MG/KG SUBCUTANEOUS-CAT LDLO; 5840 MG/KG INTRAVENOUS-RABBIT LD50; 125 MG/KG INTRAVENOUS-DOG LDLO; 1500 MG/KG INTRAPERITONEAL-RAT LD50; 572 MG/KG INTRAPERITONEAL-MOUSE LD50; 478 MG/KG INTRAPERITONEAL-RABBIT LDLO; 1500 MG/KG INTRAPERITONEAL-DOG LD50; 93 MG/KG UNREPORTED-MAN LDLO; MUTAGENIC DATA (RTECS); REPRODUCTIVE EFFECTS DATA (RTECS); TUMORIGENIC DATA (RTECS).
CARCINOGEN STATUS: ANTICIPATED HUMAN CARCINOGEN (NTP); ANIMAL SUFFICIENT EVIDENCE, HUMAN INADEQUATE EVIDENCE (IARC GROUP-2B). CARBON TETRACHLORIDE WAS TESTED IN SEVERAL EXPERIMENTS IN MICE BY ORAL AND INTRARECTAL ADMINISTRATION AND IN RATS BY ORAL AND SUBCUTANEOUS ADMINISTRATION AND BY INHALATION EXPOSURE. IN VARIOUS STRAINS OF MICE, IT PRODUCED LIVER TUMORS, INCLUDING HEPATOCELLULAR CARCINOMAS. IN VARIOUS STRAINS OF RATS, IT PRODUCED BENIGN AND MALIGNANT LIVER TUMORS; AND IN ONE EXPERIMENT WITH SUBCUTANEOUS INJECTION, AN INCREASED INCIDENCE OF MAMMARY ADENOCARCINOMAS WAS OBSERVED.
ACUTE TOXICITY LEVEL: MODERATELY TOXIC BY INHALATION, INGESTION; SLIGHTLY TOXIC BY DERMAL ABSORPTION. TARGET EFFECTS: CENTRAL NERVOUS SYSTEM DEPRESSANT; NEPHROTOXIN; HEPATOTOXIN. POISONING MAY ALSO AFFECT THE CARDIOVASCULAR SYSTEM. AT INCREASED RISK FROM EXPOSURE: PERSONS WITH PRE-EXISTING LIVER AND/OR KIDNEY DAMAGE AND ALCOHOLICS. ADDITIONAL DATA: MAY CROSS THE PLACENTA AND BE EXCRETED IN BREAST MILK. ONE STUDY SHOWS AN INCREASED RISK OF LEUKEMIA FOR CHILDREN WHOSE FATHERS HAD OCCUPATIONAL EXPOSURE TO CHLORINATED SOLVENTS AFTER THE BIRTH OF THE CHILD. STIMULANTS SUCH AS EPINEPHRINE MAY INDUCE VENTRICULAR FIBRILLATION. ALCOHOLS, HALOALKANES, KETONES, BARBITURATES, PCB'S, PBB'S, AND DDT MAY ENHANCE THE TOXIC EFFECTS.

HEALTH EFFECTS AND FIRST AID

INHALATION: CARBON TETRACHLORIDE:
NARCOTIC/NEPHROTOXIN/HEPATOTOXIN/CARCINOGEN. **ACUTE EXPOSURE-** MAY CAUSE IRRITATION. EXPOSURE TO 25-117 PPM HAS CAUSED NAUSEA, HEADACHE, DIZZINESS, DEPRESSION, NARCOSIS, DYSPEPSIA, RESTRICTED VISION, AND LIVER DAMAGE. UNCONSCIOUSNESS, COMA AND DEATH MAY OCCUR AT 1000-2000 PPM/60-90 MINUTES. DEATH MAY BE DUE TO RESPIRATORY ARREST OR CIRCULATORY COLLAPSE, OR OCCASIONALLY, VENTRICULAR FIBRILLATION. OTHER EFFECTS MAY INCLUDE ABDOMINAL PAIN, DIARRHEA, VOMITING, HEMATEMESIS, MENTAL CONFUSION, HYPOTENSION, AND CONVULSIONS. IF DEATH IS NOT IMMEDIATE, AN ASYMPTOMATIC PERIOD OF SEVERAL DAYS MAY BE FOLLOWED BY KIDNEY NECROSIS WITH ALBUMINURIA, OLIGURIA OR ANURIA, EDEMA, PULMONARY EDEMA, AND UREMIA. HEPATIC NECROSIS WITH FATTY ACCUMULATION MAY OCCUR WITH SYMPTOMS OF NAUSEA, ANOREXIA, FLATULANCE, VOMITING, STOMACHACHE, JAUNDICE, AND AN ENLARGED AND TENDER LIVER. LIVER FAILURE MAY BE ACCOMPANIED BY ENCEPHALOPATHY. IN NON-FATAL CASES, KIDNEY AND LIVER FUNCTION MAY RETURN TO NORMAL. OTHER ORGANS THAT MAY BE AFFECTED INCLUDE PANCREAS, ADRENALS, TESTES, SPLEEN, PITUITARY, AND THYROID. HEPATIC NECROSIS, NEPHROSIS AND DEATH OCCURRED IN AN ALCOHOLIC EXPOSED TO 250 PPM/15 MINUTES; SLIGHT HEADACHE WAS REPORTED IN NON-ALCOHOLICS. **CHRONIC EXPOSURE-** REPEATED OR PROLONGED EXPOSURE MAY CAUSE EFFECTS AS IN ACUTE INHALATION. OTHER EFFECTS MAY INCLUDE ANEMIA, AND VARIOUS VISUAL DISTURBANCES SUCH AS BLIND SPOTS, SPOTS BEFORE EYES, VISUAL HAZE, AND RESTRICTIONS OF COLOR FIELDS WHICH MAY INDICATE OPTIC NEURITIS OR ATROPHY. CASE REPORTS HAVE DESCRIBED LIVER TUMORS ASSOCIATED WITH CIRRHOSIS IN EXPOSED PERSONS. A MORTALITY STUDY OF LAUNDRY AND DRY CLEANING WORKERS EXPOSED TO CARBON TETRACHLORIDE AND A VARIETY OF OTHER SOLVENTS SUGGESTS AN EXCESS OF RESPIRATORY CANCERS, LIVER TUMORS, CERVICAL CANCERS, AND LEUKEMIA. IN RATS, CHRONIC INHALATION PRODUCED BENIGN AND MALIGNANT LIVER TUMORS. REPRODUCTIVE EFFECTS REPORTED IN ANIMALS INCLUDE A DECREASE IN FERTILITY, EMBRYOTOXICITY, FETOTOXICITY, AND A MODERATE TO MARKED DEGENERATION OF TESTICULAR GERMINAL EPITHELIUM.

FIRST AID- REMOVE FROM EXPOSURE AREA TO FRESH AIR IMMEDIATELY. IF BREATHING HAS STOPPED, PERFORM ARTIFICIAL RESPIRATION. KEEP PERSON WARM AND AT REST. TREAT SYMPTOMATICALLY AND SUPPORTIVELY. GET MEDICAL ATTENTION IMMEDIATELY.

SKIN CONTACT: CARBON TETRACHLORIDE: NARCOTIC/NEPHROTOXIN/HEPATOTOXIN. **ACUTE EXPOSURE-** CONTACT WITH THE LIQUID MAY CAUSE DISTINCT PAIN WITH ERYTHEMA, HYPEREMIA, AND WHEAL FORMATION FOLLOWED BY VESICATION; SKIN ERUPTIONS ARE SOMETIMES SEEN. MAY BE ABSORBED THROUGH THE SKIN TO CAUSE EFFECTS AS DETAILED IN ACUTE INHALATION. **CHRONIC EXPOSURE-** REPEATED OR PROLONGED CONTACT MAY RESULT IN IRRITATION AND DERMATITIS DUE TO THE DEFATTING ACTION ON THE SKIN. TOXIC AMOUNTS MAY BE ABSORBED THROUGH THE SKIN TO CAUSE EFFECTS AS DETAILED IN CHRONIC INHALATION.

FIRST AID- REMOVE CONTAMINATED CLOTHING AND SHOES IMMEDIATELY. WASH AFFECTED AREA WITH SOAP OR MILD DETERGENT AND LARGE AMOUNTS OF WATER UNTIL NO EVIDENCE OF CHEMICAL REMAINS (APPROXIMATELY 15-20 MINUTES). GET MEDICAL ATTENTION IMMEDIATELY.

EYE CONTACT: CARBON TETRACHLORIDE: **ACUTE EXPOSURE-** CONTACT WITH LIQUID OR VAPOR MAY CAUSE SLIGHT, TRANSIENT IRRITATION AND MINOR CONJUNCTIVAL INJURY. **CHRONIC EXPOSURE-** NO DATA AVAILABLE.

FIRST AID- WASH EYES IMMEDIATELY WITH LARGE AMOUNTS OF WATER OR NORMAL SALINE, OCCASIONALLY LIFTING UPPER AND LOWER LIDS, UNTIL NO EVIDENCE OF CHEMICAL REMAINS (APPROXIMATELY 15-20 MINUTES). GET MEDICAL ATTENTION IMMEDIATELY.

INGESTION: CARBON TETRACHLORIDE: NARCOTIC/NEPHROTOXIN/HEPATOTOXIN/CARCINOGEN. **ACUTE EXPOSURE-** MAY CAUSE EFFECTS AS IN ACUTE INHALATION. ASPIRATION MAY PRODUCE PRIMARY PULMONARY EDEMA. DOSES OF 40-48 MG/KG PRODUCED LIVER INJURY IN ANIMALS. INGESTION OF 1.5 ML HAS CAUSED DEATH. **CHRONIC EXPOSURE-** REPEATED ADMINISTRATION TO ANIMALS HAS PRODUCED LIVER AND KIDNEY CHANGES. ADMINISTRATION TO ANIMALS PRODUCED LIVER TUMORS, INCLUDING HEPATOCELLULAR CARCINOMAS, IN VARIOUS STRAINS OF MICE; AND IN RATS CAUSED BENIGN AND MALIGNANT LIVER TUMORS. AS EVALUATED BY RTECS, ADMINISTRATION TO MICE RESULTED IN A STATISTICALLY SIGNIFICANT INCREASE IN THE INCIDENCE OF NEOPLASTIC TUMORS OF THE SKIN. ADMINISTRATION DURING GESTATION PRODUCED MARKED MATERNAL TOXICITY AND TOTAL RESORPTION OF FETUSES IN SOME ANIMALS, BUT NO TERATOGENICITY OR OTHER ADVERSE EFFECTS ON SURVIVORS.

FIRST AID- IF THE PERSON IS CONSCIOUS AND NOT CONVULSING, INDUCE EMESIS BY GIVING SYRUP OF IPECAC (KEEPING THE HEAD BELOW THE HIPS TO PREVENT ASPIRATION), FOLLOWED BY WATER. REPEAT IN 20 MINUTES IF NOT EFFECTIVE INITIALLY. IN PATIENTS WITH DEPRESSED RESPIRATION OR IF EMESIS IS NOT PRODUCED, PERFORM GASTRIC LAVAGE CAUTIOUSLY (DREISBACH, HANDBOOK OF POISONING, 12TH ED.). TREAT SYMPTOMATICALLY AND SUPPORTIVELY. GASTRIC LAVAGE SHOULD BE PERFORMED BY QUALIFIED MEDICAL PERSONNEL. GET MEDICAL ATTENTION IMMEDIATELY.

ANTIDOTE: NO SPECIFIC ANTIDOTE. TREAT SYMPTOMATICALLY AND SUPPORTIVELY.

REACTIVITY

REACTIVITY: STABLE UNDER NORMAL TEMPERATURES AND PRESSURES.

INCOMPATIBILITIES: CARBON TETRACHLORIDE: ALLYL ALCOHOL: FORMS EXPLOSIVE PRODUCTS. ALUMINUM OXIDE AND COBALT/MOLYBDENUM: EXOTHERMIC REACTION IN PRESENCE OF AIR ALUMINUM TRICHLORIDE: INCOMPATIBLE. BENZOYL PEROXIDE: INCOMPATIBLE. BENZOYL PEROXIDE AND ETHYLENE: VIOLENT EXPLOSION REACTION. BORANES: POTENTIALLY EXPLOSIVE REACTION ON CONTACT. BROMINE TRIFLUORIDE: EXOTHERMIC REACTION. CALCIUM DISILIDE: POSSIBLE EXPLOSION ON IMPACT. CALCIUM HYPOCHLORITE: EXPLOSIVE REACTION ON HEATING. CHLORINE TRIFLUORIDE: FORMS EXPLOSIVE MIXTURE. DIMETHYLACETAMIDE: EXOTHERMIC REACTION WITH INCREASE IN PRESSURE OR VIGOROUS REACTION IN PRESENCE OF IRON. DIMETHYLFORMAMIDE: VIOLENT REACTION IN PRESENCE OF IRON OR AT TEMPERATURES BELOW 100 C. DINITROGEN TETRAOXIDE: FORMATION OF SHOCK-SENSITIVE MIXTURE. ETHYLENE: MAY FORM EXPLOSIVE MIXTURE. . FLUORINE: VIOLENT REACTION OR POSSIBLE EXPLOSION. HEXACHLOROCYCLOHEXANE: VIGOROUS REACTION. METALS: POSSIBLE EXPLOSION ON HEATING OR IMPACT. OXYGEN (LIQUID): VIGOROUS EXPLOSION REACTION. PLASTICS, RUBBER AND COATINGS: MAY BE ATTACKED. POTASSIUM TERT-BUTOXIDE: IGNITION REACTION. SILANES (DI-, TRI-, TETRA-): EXOTHERMIC REACTION WITH POSSIBLE EXPLOSION. SILVER PERCHLORATE AND HYDROGEN CHLORIDE: PRODUCES EXPLOSIVE MIXTURE. TRIETHYLDIALUMINUM SESQUICHLORIDES: FORMATION OF HEAT-SENSITIVE PRODUCT. TETRAETHYLENEPENTAMINE: POSSIBLE EXPLOSION REACTION. WAX (BURNING): EXPLOSIVE REACTION.

DECOMPOSITION: THERMAL DECOMPOSITION PRODUCTS MAY INCLUDE TOXIC AND CORROSIVE FUMES OF CHLORIDES AND PHOSGENE, AND TOXIC OXIDES OF CARBON.

POLYMERIZATION: HAZARDOUS POLYMERIZATION HAS NOT BEEN REPORTED TO OCCUR UNDER NORMAL TEMPERATURES AND PRESSURES.

STORAGE AND DISPOSAL

OBSERVE ALL FEDERAL, STATE AND LOCAL REGULATIONS WHEN STORING OR DISPOSING OF THIS SUBSTANCE. FOR ASSISTANCE, CONTACT THE DISTRICT DIRECTOR OF THE ENVIRONMENTAL PROTECTION AGENCY.

****STORAGE****

STORE AWAY FROM INCOMPATIBLE SUBSTANCES.

PROTECT AGAINST PHYSICAL DAMAGE. STORE IN A COOL, DRY WELL VENTILATED LOCATION, AWAY FROM ANY AREA WHERE THE FIRE HAZARD MAY BE ACUTE (NFPA 49, HAZARDOUS CHEMICALS DATA, 1975).

****DISPOSAL****

DISPOSAL MUST BE IN ACCORDANCE WITH STANDARDS APPLICABLE TO GENERATORS OF HAZARDOUS WASTE, 40CFR 262. EPA HAZARDOUS WASTE NUMBER U211.

CARBON TETRACHLORIDE - REGULATORY LEVEL: 0.5 MG/L MATERIALS WHICH CONTAIN THE ABOVE SUBSTANCE AT OR ABOVE THE REGULATORY LEVEL MEET THE EPA CHARACTERISTIC OF TOXICITY, AND MUST BE DISPOSED OF IN ACCORDANCE WITH 40 CFR PART 262. EPA HAZARDOUS WASTE NUMBER D019.

CONDITIONS TO AVOID

MAY BURN BUT DOES NOT IGNITE READILY. CONTAINERS MAY EXPLODE IN HEAT OF FIRE.

SPILL AND LEAK PROCEDURES

SOIL SPILL: DIG A HOLDING AREA SUCH AS A PIT, POND OR LAGOON TO CONTAIN SPILL AND DIKE SURFACE FLOW USING BARRIER OF SOIL, SANDBAGS, FOAMED POLYURETHANE OR FOAMED CONCRETE. ABSORB LIQUID MASS WITH FLY ASH OR CEMENT POWDER.

IMMOBILIZE SPILL WITH UNIVERSAL GELLING AGENT.

AIR SPILL: KNOCK DOWN VAPORS WITH WATER SPRAY. KEEP UPWIND. COMBUSTION PRODUCTS INCLUDE CORROSIVE OR TOXIC VAPORS.

WATER SPILL: TRAP SPILLED MATERIAL AT BOTTOM IN DEEP WATER POCKETS, EXCAVATED HOLDING AREAS OR WITHIN SAND BAG BARRIERS.

USE SUCTION HOSES TO REMOVE TRAPPED SPILL MATERIAL.

USE ACTIVATED CARBON TO ABSORB SPILLED SUBSTANCE THAT IS DISSOLVED.

USE MECHANICAL DREDGES OR LIFTS TO EXTRACT IMMOBILIZED MASSES OF POLLUTION AND PRECIPITATES.

THE CALIFORNIA SAFE DRINKING WATER AND TOXIC ENFORCEMENT ACT OF 1986 (PROPOSITION 65) PROHIBITS CONTAMINATING ANY KNOWN SOURCE OF DRINKING WATER WITH SUBSTANCES KNOWN TO CAUSE CANCER AND/OR REPRODUCTIVE TOXICITY.

OCCUPATIONAL SPILL: DO NOT TOUCH SPILLED MATERIAL. STOP LEAK IF YOU CAN DO IT WITHOUT RISK. USE WATER SPRAY TO REDUCE VAPORS. FOR SMALL SPILLS, TAKE UP WITH SAND OR OTHER ABSORBENT MATERIAL AND PLACE INTO CONTAINERS FOR LATER DISPOSAL. FOR SMALL DRY SPILLS, WITH A CLEAN SHOVEL PLACE MATERIAL INTO CLEAN, DRY CONTAINERS AND COVER. MOVE CONTAINERS FROM SPILL AREA. FOR LARGER SPILLS, DIKE FAR AHEAD OF SPILL FOR LATER DISPOSAL. KEEP UNNECESSARY PEOPLE AWAY. ISOLATE HAZARD AREA AND DENY ENTRY. VENTILATE CLOSED SPACES BEFORE ENTERING.

REPORTABLE QUANTITY (RQ): 5000 POUNDS THE SUPERFUND AMENDMENTS AND REAUTHORIZATION ACT (SARA) SECTION 304 REQUIRES THAT A RELEASE EQUAL TO OR GREATER THAN THE REPORTABLE QUANTITY FOR THIS SUBSTANCE BE IMMEDIATELY REPORTED TO THE LOCAL EMERGENCY PLANNING COMMITTEE AND THE STATE EMERGENCY RESPONSE COMMISSION (40 CFR 355.40). IF THE RELEASE OF THIS SUBSTANCE IS REPORTABLE UNDER CERCLA SECTION 103, THE NATIONAL RESPONSE CENTER MUST BE NOTIFIED IMMEDIATELY AT (800) 424-8802 OR (202) 426-2675 IN THE METROPOLITAN WASHINGTON, D.C. AREA (40 CFR 302.6).

PROTECTIVE EQUIPMENT

VENTILATION: PROVIDE LOCAL EXHAUST VENTILATION AND/OR GENERAL DILUTION VENTILATION TO MEET PUBLISHED EXPOSURE LIMITS.

RESPIRATOR: THE FOLLOWING RESPIRATORS AND MAXIMUM USE CONCENTRATIONS ARE RECOMMENDATIONS BY THE U.S. DEPARTMENT OF HEALTH AND HUMAN SERVICES, NIOSH POCKET GUIDE TO CHEMICAL HAZARDS; NIOSH CRITERIA DOCUMENTS OR BY THE U.S. DEPARTMENT OF LABOR, 29 CFR 1910 SUBPART Z. THE SPECIFIC RESPIRATOR SELECTED MUST BE BASED ON C ONTAMINATION LEVELS FOUND IN THE WORK PLACE, MUST NOT EXCEED THE WORKING LIMITS OF THE RESPIRATOR AND BE JOINTLY APPROVED BY THE NATIONAL INSTITUTE FOR OCCUPATIONAL SAFETY AND HEALTH AND THE MINE SAFETY AND HEALTH ADMINISTRATION (NIOSH-MSHA).

CARBON TETRACHLORIDE:

AT ANY DETECTABLE CONCENTRATION: ANY SELF-CONTAINED BREATHING APPARATUS WITH FULL FACEPIECE AND OPERATED IN A PRESSURE-DEMAND OR OTHER POSITIVE PRESSURE MODE. ANY SUPPLIED-AIR RESPIRATOR WITH A FULL FACEPIECE AND OPERATED IN A PRESSURE-DEMAND OR OTHER POSITIVE PRESSURE MODE IN COMBINATION WITH AN AUXILIARY SELF-CONTAINED

BREATHING APPARATUS OPERATED IN PRESSURE-DEMAND OR OTHER POSITIVE PRESSURE MODE.
ESCAPE- ANY AIR-PURIFYING FULL FACEPIECE RESPIRATOR (GAS MASK) WITH A CHIN-STYLE OR FRONT- OR BACK-MOUNTED ORGANIC VAPOR CANISTER. ANY APPROPRIATE ESCAPE-TYPE SELF-CONTAINED BREATHING APPARATUS.
FOR FIREFIGHTING AND OTHER IMMEDIATELY DANGEROUS TO LIFE OR HEALTH CONDITIONS:
SELF-CONTAINED BREATHING APPARATUS WITH FULL FACEPIECE OPERATED IN PRESSURE-DEMAND OR OTHER POSITIVE PRESSURE MODE.
SUPPLIED-AIR RESPIRATOR WITH FULL FACEPIECE AND OPERATED IN PRESSURE-DEMAND OR OTHER POSITIVE PRESSURE MODE IN COMBINATION WITH AN AUXILIARY SELF-CONTAINED BREATHING APPARATUS OPERATED IN PRESSURE-DEMAND OR OTHER POSITIVE PRESSURE MODE.

CLOTHING: EMPLOYEE MUST WEAR APPROPRIATE PROTECTIVE (IMPERVIOUS) CLOTHING AND EQUIPMENT TO PREVENT REPEATED OR PROLONGED SKIN CONTACT WITH THIS SUBSTANCE.

GLOVES: EMPLOYEE MUST WEAR APPROPRIATE PROTECTIVE GLOVES TO PREVENT CONTACT WITH THIS SUBSTANCE.

EYE PROTECTION: EMPLOYEE MUST WEAR SPLASH-PROOF OR DUST-RESISTANT SAFETY GOGGLES TO PREVENT EYE CONTACT WITH THIS SUBSTANCE.
EMERGENCY EYE WASH: WHERE THERE IS ANY POSSIBILITY THAT AN EMPLOYEE'S EYES MAY BE EXPOSED TO THIS SUBSTANCE, THE EMPLOYER SHOULD PROVIDE AN EYE WASH FOUNTAIN WITHIN THE IMMEDIATE WORK AREA FOR EMERGENCY USE.

AUTHORIZED BY- OCCUPATIONAL HEALTH SERVICES, INC.
CREATION DATE: 10/04/89 ***REVISION DATE:*** 07/13/90

MATERIAL SAFETY DATA SHEET

OCCUPATIONAL HEALTH SERVICES, INC.
AGRICULTURE AND PESTICIDE DIVISION
450 SEVENTH AVENUE, SUITE 2407
NEW YORK, NEW YORK 10123
1-800-445-MSDS OR (212) 967-1100

EMERGENCY CONTACT:
JOHN S. BRANSFORD, JR. (615) 292-1180

SUBSTANCE IDENTIFICATION

CAS-NUMBER 786-19-6

SUBSTANCE: <u>CARBOPHENOTHION</u>

TRADE NAMES/SYNONYMS: PHOSPHORODITHIOIC ACID, S-(((4-CHLOROPHENYL)THIO)METHYL) O,O-DIETHYL ESTER; PHOSPHORODITHIOIC ACID, S-(((P-CHLOROPHENYL)THIO)METHYL) O,O-DIETHYL ESTER; O,O-DIETHYL-S-4-CHLOROPHENYL-THIOMETHYL PHOSPHOROTHIONATE; S-4-CHLOROPHENYLTHIOMETHYL O,O-DIETHYL PHOSPHORODITHIOATE; S-(((P-CHLOROPHENYL)THIO)METHYL) O,O-DIETHYL PHOSPHORODITHIOATE; S-(P-CHLOROPHENYLTHIOMETHYL)DIETHYL PHOSPHOROTHIOLOTHIONATE; O,O-DIETHYL-S-P-CHLOROPHENYLTHIOMETHYL PHOSPHORODITHIOATE; ACARITHION; CARBOFENOTHION; CARBOFENTHION; ETHYL CARBOPHENOTHION; GARRATHION; HEXATHION; STAUFFER R 1303; TRITHION; OMS 244; C11H16CLO2PS3; PST04340

CHEMICAL FAMILY: ORGANOPHOSPHATE

MOLECULAR FORMULA: (C-H3-C-H2-O)2-P-(S)-S-C-H2-S-C6-H4-CL

MOLECULAR WEIGHT: 342.85

CERCLA RATINGS (SCALE 0-3): HEALTH=3 FIRE=U REACTIVITY=0 PERSISTENCE=2

NFPA RATINGS (SCALE 0-4): HEALTH=3 FIRE=U REACTIVITY=0

COMPONENTS AND CONTAMINANTS

COMPONENT: CARBOPHENOTHION ***PERCENT:*** 100.0
CAS# 786-19-6

OTHER CONTAMINANTS: NONE

EXPOSURE LIMITS: NO OCCUPATIONAL EXPOSURE LIMITS ESTABLISHED BY OSHA, ACGIH, OR NIOSH.
CARBOPHENOTHION: 500 POUNDS SARA SECTION 302 THRESHOLD PLANNING QUANTITY 1 POUND SARA SECTION 304 REPORTABLE QUANTITY

PHYSICAL DATA

DESCRIPTION: COLORLESS TO LIGHT AMBER LIQUID WITH A MERCAPTAN-LIKE ODOR.

BOILING POINT: 180 F (82 C) @ 0.01 MMHG ***SPECIFIC GRAVITY:*** 1.271 @ 25 C

VAPOR PRESSURE: NEGLIGIBLE ***SOLUBILITY IN WATER:*** <2 PPM @ 20 C

SOLVENT SOLUBILITY: SOLUBLE IN ACETONE, ETHANOL, KEROSENE, XYLENE, METHYL ISOBUTYL KETONE, VEGETABLE OILS, OTHER ORGANIC SOLVENTS.

FIRE AND EXPLOSION DATA

FIRE AND EXPLOSION HAZARD: UNKNOWN FIRE AND EXPLOSION HAZARD.

FLASH POINT: NOT AVAILABLE

FIREFIGHTING MEDIA: DRY CHEMICAL, CARBON DIOXIDE, HALON, WATER SPRAY OR STANDARD FOAM (1987 EMERGENCY RESPONSE GUIDEBOOK, DOT P 5800.4).
FOR LARGER FIRES, USE WATER SPRAY, FOG OR STANDARD FOAM (1987 EMERGENCY RESPONSE GUIDEBOOK, DOT P 5800.4).

FIREFIGHTING: MOVE CONTAINER FROM FIRE AREA IF POSSIBLE. DIKE FIRE CONTROL WATER FOR LATER DISPOSAL; DO NOT SCATTER THE MATERIAL. COOL FIRE-EXPOSED CONTAINERS WITH WATER FROM SIDE UNTIL WELL AFTER FIRE IS OUT. STAY AWAY FROM STORAGE TANK ENDS. WITHDRAW IMMEDIATELY IN CASE OF RISING SOUND FROM VENTING SAFETY DEVICE OR ANY DISCOLORATION OF STORAGE TANK DUE TO FIRE (1987 EMERGENCY RESPONSE GUIDEBOOK, DOT P 5800.4, GUIDE PAGE 28).
EXTINGUISH ONLY IF FLOW CAN BE STOPPED. USE FLOODING AMOUNTS OF WATER AS A FOG; SOLID STREAMS MAY BE INEFFECTIVE. COOL CONTAINERS WITH FLOODING AMOUNTS OF WATER FROM AS FAR A DISTANCE AS POSSIBLE. AVOID BREATHING POISONOUS VAPORS, KEEP UPWIND.

TRANSPORTATION DATA

DEPARTMENT OF TRANSPORTATION HAZARD CLASSIFICATION 49 CFR 172.101: POISON B
DEPARTMENT OF TRANSPORTATION LABELING REQUIREMENTS 49 CFR 172.101 AND SUBPART E: POISON
DEPARTMENT OF TRANSPORTATION PACKAGING REQUIREMENTS: 49 CFR 173.359 EXCEPTIONS: 49 CFR 173.359

TOXICITY

CARBOPHENOTHION: TOXICITY DATA: 1270 MG/KG SKIN-RABBIT LD50; 27 MG/KG SKIN-RAT LD50; 6800 UG/KG ORAL-RAT LD50; 1250 MG/KG ORAL-RABBIT LD50; 218 MG/KG ORAL-MOUSE LD50; 6 MG/KG INTRAPERITONEAL-RAT LD50; 27 MG/KG INTRAPERITONEAL-MOUSE LD50; MUTAGENIC DATA (RTECS). CARCINOGEN STATUS: NONE. ACUTE TOXICITY LEVEL: HIGHLY TOXIC BY INGESTION; MODERATELY TOXIC BY DERMAL ABSORPTION. TARGET EFFECTS: CHOLINESTERASE INHIBITOR. POISONING MAY AFFECT THE NERVOUS SYSTEM.* AT INCREASED RISK FROM EXPOSURE: PERSONS WITH RESPIRATORY AILMENTS, RECENT EXPOSURE TO CHOLINESTERASE INHIBITORS OR IMPAIRED CHOLINESTERASE PRODUCTION, OR LIVER MALFUNCTION.* ADDITIONAL DATA: MAY CROSS THE PLACENTA. HIGH ENVIRONMENTAL TEMPERATURES OR EXPOSURE OF THE CHEMICAL TO VISIBLE OR ULTRAVIOLET LIGHT MAY ENHANCE THE TOXICITY. INTERACTIONS WITH MEDICATIONS MAY OCCUR.*
* MAY BE BASED ON GENERAL INFORMATION ON ORGANOPHOSPHATES.

HEALTH EFFECTS AND FIRST AID

INHALATION: CARBOPHENOTHION: SCHIZOPHRENIC AND DEPRESSIVE REACTIONS HAVE BEEN REPORTED AFTER EXPOSURE TO CARBOPHENOTHION AND OTHER ORGANOPHOSPHATES FOR 1.5-10 YEARS. SEE INFORMATION ON ORGANOPHOSPHATES.
ORGANOPHOSPHATES: CHOLINESTERASE INHIBITOR. **<u>ACUTE EXPOSURE</u>**- WHEN INHALED, THE FIRST EFFECTS OF CHOLINESTERASE INHIBITORS ARE USUALLY RESPIRATORY AND MAY INCLUDE NASAL HYPEREMIA AND WATERY DISCHARGE, COUGH, CHEST DISCOMFORT, DYSPNEA, AND WHEEZING DUE TO INCREASED BRONCHIAL SECRETIONS AND BRONCHOCONSTRICTION. IF SUFFICIENT AMOUNTS ARE ABSORBED, OTHER SYSTEMIC EFFECTS MAY BEGIN WITHIN A FEW MINUTES OR BE DELAYED FOR UP TO 12 HOURS. SYMPTOMS MAY INCLUDE PALLOR, NAUSEA, VOMITING, DIARRHEA, ABDOMINAL CRAMPS, HEADACHE, DIZZINESS, OCULAR PAIN, BLURRED VISION, MIOSIS OR IN SOME CASES, ESPECIALLY INITIALLY, MYDRIASIS, LACRIMATION, SALIVATION, SWEATING, AND CONFUSION. OTHER REPORTED CENTRAL NERVOUS SYSTEM OR NEUROMUSCULAR EFFECTS MAY INCLUDE ATAXIA, SLURRED SPEECH, AREFLEXIA, WEAKNESS, FATIGUE, FASCICULATIONS, TWITCHING, TREMORS POSSIBLY OF THE TONGUE AND EYELIDS, AND EVENTUALLY PARALYSIS OF THE EXTREMITIES AND POSSIBLY OF THE RESPIRATORY MUSCLES. IN SEVERE CASES THERE MAY ALSO BE INVOLUNTARY DEFECATION AND URINATION, CYANOSIS, PSYCHOSIS, HYPERGLYCEMIA, ACUTE PANCREATITIS, CARDIAC IRREGULARITIES, PULMONARY EDEMA, UNCONSCIOUSNESS, CONVULSIONS, AND COMA. DEATH IS PRIMARILY DUE TO RESPIRATORY FAILURE, ALTHOUGH CARDIOVASCULAR EFFECTS INCLUDING CARDIAC ARREST MAY ALSO BE IMPLICATED. LONG TERM SEQUELAE ARE RARE BUT MAY INCLUDE NEUROPSYCHIATRIC DISORDERS AND MYOPATHY WITH MUSCLE TENDERNESS. SOME ORGANOPHOSPHATES MAY CAUSE A DELAYED NEUROPATHY BEGINNING 1-4 WEEKS AFTER AN ACUTE EXPOSURE WHICH MAY OR MAY NOT HAVE CAUSED ACUTE CHOLINERGIC EFFECTS. NUMBNESS, TINGLING, WEAKNESS AND CRAMPING BEGINNING SYMMETRICALLY IN THE LOWER LIMBS MAY PROGRESS TO ATAXIA AND PARALYSIS. IN SEVERE CASES, UPPER LIMB INVOLVEMENT IS POSSIBLE AND FLACCID PARALYSIS MAY PROGRESS TO SPASTIC

PARALYSIS WITH EXAGGERATED REFLEXES. IMPROVEMENT MAY OCCUR OVER MONTHS TO YEARS, BUT SOME RESIDUAL IMPAIRMENT USUALLY REMAINS. **CHRONIC EXPOSURE-** REPEATED OR PROLONGED EXPOSURE MAY RESULT IN THE EFFECTS OF ACUTE EXPOSURE INCLUDING THE DELAYED NEUROPATHY. OTHER EFFECTS REPORTED IN WORKERS REPEATEDLY EXPOSED INCLUDE IMPAIRED MEMORY AND CONCENTRATION, ACUTE PSYCHOSIS, SEVERE DEPRESSIONS, IRRITABILTY, CONFUSION, APATHY, EMOTIONAL LABILITY, SOCIAL WITHDRAWAL, CONFUSION, HEADACHE, SPEECH DIFFICULTIES, DELAYED REACTION TIMES, SPATIAL DISORIENTATION, NIGHTMARES, SLEEPWALKING, AND DROWSINESS OR INSOMNIA. AN INFLUENZA-LIKE CONDITION WITH HEADACHE, NAUSEA, WEAKNESS, ANOREXIA AND MALAISE HAS ALSO BEEN REPORTED.

FIRST AID- REMOVE FROM EXPOSURE AREA TO FRESH AIR IMMEDIATELY. IF BREATHING HAS STOPPED, GIVE ARTIFICIAL RESPIRATION. MAINTAIN AIRWAY AND BLOOD PRESSURE AND ADMINISTER OXYGEN IF AVAILABLE. KEEP AFFECTED PERSON WARM AND AT REST. TREAT SYMPTOMATICALLY AND SUPPORTIVELY. ADMINISTRATION OF OXYGEN SHOULD BE PERFORMED BY QUALIFIED PERSONNEL. GET MEDICAL ATTENTION IMMEDIATELY.

SKIN CONTACT: CARBOPHENOTHION: SCHIZOPHRENIC AND DEPRESSIVE REACTIONS HAVE BEEN REPORTED AFTER EXPOSURE TO CARBOPHENOTHION AND OTHER ORGANOPHOSPHATES FOR 1.5-10 YEARS. SEE INFORMATION ON ORGANOPHOSPHATES.
ORGANOPHOSPHATES: CHOLINESTERASE INHIBITOR. **ACUTE EXPOSURE-** LOCALIZED SWEATING AND FASCICULATIONS MAY OCCUR AT THE SITE OF CONTACT. IF SUFFICIENT AMOUNTS ARE ABSORBED, OTHER EFFECTS OF CHOLINESTERASE INHIBITION AS DESCRIBED IN ACUTE INHALATION MAY OCCUR. SYMPTOMS MAY BE DELAYED 2-3 HOURS, BUT USUALLY NO MORE THAN 12 HOURS. THE RATE OF ABSORPTION IS INCREASED BY THE PRESENCE OF DERMATITIS OR HIGH AMBIENT TEMPERATURES. DELAYED NEUROPATHY IS ALSO POSSIBLE. **CHRONIC EXPOSURE-** REPEATED OR PROLONGED EXPOSURE MAY CAUSE EFFECTS AS DESCRIBED IN ACUTE EXPOSURE. SOME ORGANOPHOSPHATES MAY CAUSE SENSITIZATION.

FIRST AID- REMOVE CONTAMINATED CLOTHING IMMEDIATELY. WASH CONTAMINATED AREAS WITH SOAP AND WATER FOLLOWED BY ALCOHOL (ARENA, POISONING, 4TH ED.). EMERGENCY PERSONNEL SHOULD WEAR GLOVES AND AVOID CONTAMINATION. TREAT RESPIRATORY DIFFICULTY WITH ARTIFICIAL RESPIRATION. GET MEDICAL ATTENTION IMMEDIATELY.

EYE CONTACT: CARBOPHENOTHION: SEE INFORMATION ON ORGANOPHOSPHATES.
ORGANOPHOSPHATES: CHOLINESTERASE INHIBITOR. **ACUTE EXPOSURE-** DIRECT CONTACT MAY CAUSE PAIN, HYPEREMIA, LACRIMATION, TWITCHING OF THE EYELIDS, MIOSIS, AND CILIARY MUSCLE SPASM WITH LOSS OF ACCOMODATION, BLURRED OR DIMMED VISION AND BROWACHE. SOMETIMES MYDRIASIS MAY OCCUR INSTEAD OF MIOSIS. WITH SUFFICIENT EXPOSURE, OTHER SYMPTOMS OF CHOLINESTERASE INHIBITION AS DESCRIBED IN ACUTE INHALATION MAY OCCUR. **CHRONIC EXPOSURE-** REPEATED OR PROLONGED EXPOSURE MAY CAUSE EFFECTS AS DESCRIBED IN ACUTE EXPOSURE. SOME COMPOUNDS HAVE CAUSED TOXIC EFFECTS ON THE CRYSTALLINE LENS, CONJUNCTIVAL THICKENING AND OBSTRUCTION OF THE NASOLACRIMAL CANALS WHEN USED AS MIOTIC EYEDROPS.

FIRST AID- IRRIGATE EYES WITH WATER OR SALINE SOLUTION. IF SYMPTOMS OF POISONING OCCUR, TREAT RESPIRATORY DIFFICULTY WITH ARTIFICIAL RESPIRATION AND OXYGEN. OBSERVE PATIENT FOR AT LEAST 24-36 HOURS (GOSSELIN, CLINICAL TOXICOLOGY OF COMMERCIAL PRODUCTS, 5TH ED.). GET MEDICAL ATTENTION IMMEDIATELY. OXYGEN SHOULD BE ADMINISTERED BY QUALIFIED MEDICAL PERSONNEL.

INGESTION: CARBOPHENOTHION: HIGHLY TOXIC. IN A 3 GENERATION STUDY, RATS FED 20 PPM COMMERCIAL GRADE CARBOPHENOTHION EXPERIENCED INCREASED FETAL RESORPTIONS AND FETOTOXICITY. SEE INFORMATION ON ORGANOPHOSPHATES.
ORGANOPHOSPHATES: CHOLINESTERASE INHIBITOR. **ACUTE EXPOSURE-** WHEN INGESTED, THE FIRST EFFECTS MAY BE NAUSEA, VOMITING, ANOREXIA, ABDOMINAL CRAMPS AND DIARRHEA. GASTROINTESTINAL ABSORPTION MAY CAUSE SYMPTOMS OF CHOLINESTERASE INHIBITION AS DESCRIBED IN ACUTE INHALATION. SYMPTOMS MAY BEGIN WITHIN MINUTES OR BE DELAYED FOR HOURS. DELAYED EFFECTS INCLUDING NEUROPATHY MAY ALSO OCCUR. **CHRONIC EXPOSURE-** REPEATED INGESTION MAY CAUSE EFFECTS AS DESCRIBED IN ACUTE EXPOSURE.

FIRST AID- IF PERSON IS ALERT AND RESPIRATION IS NOT DEPRESSED, GIVE SYRUP OF IPECAC FOLLOWED BY WATER (IF VOMITING OCCURS, KEEP HEAD BELOW HIPS TO PREVENT ASPIRATION). IF CONSCIOUSNESS LEVEL DECLINES OR VOMITING HAS NOT OCCURRED IN 15 MINUTES EMPTY STOMACH BY GASTRIC LAVAGE WITH THE AID OF CUFFED ENDOTRACHEAL TUBE USING ISOTONIC SALINE OR 5% SODIUM BICARBONATE FOLLOW WITH ACTIVATED CHARCOAL. ESTABLISH AND MAINTAIN AIRWAY. TREAT RESPIRATORY DIFFICULTY WITH ARTIFICIAL RESPIRATION AND OXYGEN. DO NOT GIVE MORPHINE, AMINOPHYLLINE, PHENOTHIAZINES, RESERPINE, FUROSEMIDE, OR ETHACRYNIC ACID (MORGAN, RECOGNITION AND MANAGEMENT OF PESTICIDE POISONINGS, 3RD ED.). TREAT SYMPTOMATICALLY AND SUPPORTIVELY. ADMINISTRATION OF OXYGEN AND LAVAGE MUST BE PERFORMED BY QUALIFIED MEDICAL PERSONNEL. GET MEDICAL ATTENTION IMMEDIATELY.

ANTIDOTE: THE FOLLOWING ANTIDOTE(S) HAVE BEEN RECOMMENDED. HOWEVER, THE DECISION AS TO WHETHER THE SEVERITY OF POISONING REQUIRES ADMINISTRATION OF ANY ANTIDOTE AND ACTUAL DOSE REQUIRED SHOULD BE MADE BY QUALIFIED MEDICAL PERSONNEL.
FOR CHOLINESTERASE INHIBITORS: ESTABLISH CLEAR AIRWAY AND TISSUE OXYGENATION BY ASPIRATION OF SECRETIONS, AND IF NECESSARY, BY ASSISTED PULMONARY VENTILATION WITH OXYGEN. IMPROVE TISSUE OXYGENATION AS MUCH AS POSSIBLE BEFORE ADMINISTERING ATROPINE TO MINIMIZE THE RISK OF VENTRICULAR FIBRILLATION. ADMINISTER ATROPINE SULFATE INTRAVENOUSLY, OR INTRAMUSCULARLY IF IV INJECTION IS NOT POSSIBLE. IN MODERATELY SEVERE POISONING ADMINISTER ATROPINE SULFATE, 0.4-2.0 MG REPEATED EVERY 15 MINUTES UNTIL ATROPINIZATION IS ACHIEVED (TACHYCARDIA, FLUSHING, DRY MOUTH, MYDRIASIS). MAINTAIN ATROPINIZATION BY REPEATED DOSES FOR 2-12 HOURS, OR LONGER, DEPENDING ON THE SEVERITY OF POISONING. THE APPEARANCE OF RALES IN THE LUNG BASES, MIOSIS, SALIVATION, NAUSEA, BRADYCARDIA, ARE ALL INDICATIONS OF INADEQUATE ATROPINIZATION. SEVERELY POISONED INDIVIDUALS MAY EXHIBIT REMARKABLE TOLERANCE TO ATROPINE; TWO OR MORE TIMES THE DOSAGES SUGGESTED ABOVE MAY BE NEEDED. PERSONS NOT POISONED OR ONLY SLIGHTLY POISONED, HOWEVER, MAY DEVELOP SIGNS OF ATROPINE TOXICITY FROM SUCH LARGE DOSAGES: FEVER, MUSCLE FIBRILLATIONS, AND DELIRIUM ARE THE MAIN SIGNS OF ATROPINE TOXICITY. IF THESE SIGNS APPEAR WHILE THE PATIENT IS FULLY ATROPINIZED, ATROPINE ADMINISTRATION SHOULD BE DISCONTINUED, AT LEAST TEMPORARILY. OBSERVE TREATED PATIENTS CLOSELY AT LEAST 24 HOURS TO INSURE THAT SYMPTOMS (POSSIBLY PULMONARY EDEMA) DO NOT RECUR AS ATROPINIZATION WEARS OFF. IN VERY SEVERE POISONINGS, METABOLIC DISPOSITION OF TOXICANT MAY REQUIRE SEVERAL HOURS OR DAYS DURING WHICH ATROPINIZATION MUST BE MAINTAINED. MARKEDLY LOWER LEVELS OF URINARY METABOLITES INDICATE THAT ATROPINE DOSAGE CAN BE TAPERED OFF. AS DOSAGE IS REDUCED, CHECK THE LUNG BASES FREQUENTLY FOR RALES. IF RALES ARE HEARD OR OTHER SYMPTOMS RETURN, RE-ESTABLISH ATROPINIZATION PROMPTLY (MORGAN, RECOGNITION AND MANAGEMENT OF PESTICIDE POISONINGS, 3RD ED.). ADMINISTRATION OF ANTIDOTE MUST BE PERFORMED BY QUALIFIED MEDICAL PERSONNEL. IN CASES OF SEVERE POISONING BY ORGANOPHOSPHATE PESTICIDES IN WHICH RESPIRATORY DEPRESSION, MUSCLE WEAKNESS AND TWITCHINGS ARE SEVERE, GIVE PRALIDOXIME (PROTOPAM-AYERST, 2-PAM), 1.0 GRAM INTRAVENOUSLY AT NO MORE THAN 0.5 GRAM PER MINUTE. DOSAGE OF PRALIDOXIME MAY BE REPEATED IN 1-2 HOURS, THEN AT 10-12 HOUR INTERVALS IF NEEDED. IN VERY SEVERE POISONINGS, DOSAGE RATES MAY BE DOUBLED. TREATMENT WITH PRALIDOXIME WILL BE MOST EFFECTIVE IF GIVEN WITHIN THIRTY-SIX HOURS AFTER POISONING (MORGAN, RECOGNITION AND MANAGEMENT OF PESTICIDE POISONINGS, 3RD ED.). ANTIDOTE SHOULD BE ADMINISTERED BY QUALIFIED MEDICAL PERSONNEL.

REACTIVITY

REACTIVITY: STABLE UNDER NORMAL TEMPERATURES AND PRESSURES.

INCOMPATIBILITIES: CARBOPHENOTHION: OXIDIZERS (STRONG): FIRE AND EXPLOSION HAZARD.

DECOMPOSITION: THERMAL DECOMPOSITION MAY RELEASE TOXIC AND/OR HAZARDOUS GASES.

POLYMERIZATION: HAZARDOUS POLYMERIZATION HAS NOT BEEN REPORTED TO OCCUR UNDER NORMAL TEMPERATURES AND PRESSURES.

STORAGE AND DISPOSAL

OBSERVE ALL FEDERAL, STATE AND LOCAL REGULATIONS WHEN STORING OR DISPOSING OF THIS SUBSTANCE. FOR ASSISTANCE, CONTACT THE DISTRICT DIRECTOR OF THE ENVIRONMENTAL PROTECTION AGENCY.

****STORAGE****

STORE IN ACCORDANCE WITH 40 CFR 165 RECOMMENDED PROCEDURES FOR THE DISPOSAL AND STORAGE OF PESTICIDES AND PESTICIDE CONTAINERS.
STORE AWAY FROM INCOMPATIBLE SUBSTANCES.
THRESHOLD PLANNING QUANTITY (TPQ): THE SUPERFUND AMENDMENTS AND REAUTHORIZATION ACT (SARA) SECTION 302 REQUIRES THAT EACH FACILITY WHERE ANY EXTREMELY HAZARDOUS SUBSTANCE IS PRESENT IN A QUANTITY EQUAL TO OR GREATER THAN THE TPQ ESTABLISHED FOR THAT SUBSTANCE NOTIFY THE STATE EMERGENCY RESPONSE COMMISSION FOR THE STATE IN WHICH IT IS LOCATED. SECTION 303 OF SARA REQUIRES THESE FACILITIES TO PARTICIPATE IN LOCAL EMERGENCY RESPONSE PLANNING (40 CFR 355.30).

****DISPOSAL****

DISPOSAL MUST BE IN ACCORDANCE WITH 40 CFR 165 RECOMMENDED PROCEDURES FOR THE DISPOSAL AND STORAGE OF PESTICIDES AND PESTICIDE CONTAINERS.

CONDITIONS TO AVOID

AVOID CONTACT WITH HEAT, SPARKS, FLAMES OR OTHER IGNITION SOURCES. VAPORS MAY BE EXPLOSIVE. MATERIAL IS POISONOUS; AVOID INHALATION OF VAPORS OR CONTACT WITH SKIN. DO NOT ALLOW MATERIAL TO CONTAMINATE WATER SOURCES.

SPILL AND LEAK PROCEDURES

OCCUPATIONAL SPILL: SHUT OFF IGNITION SOURCES. DO NOT TOUCH SPILLED MATERIAL. STOP LEAK IF YOU CAN DO IT WITHOUT RISK. USE WATER SPRAY TO REDUCE VAPORS. FOR SMALL SPILLS, TAKE UP WITH SAND OR OTHER ABSORBENT MATERIAL AND PLACE INTO CONTAINERS FOR LATER DISPOSAL. FOR LARGER SPILLS, DIKE FAR AHEAD OF SPILL FOR LATER DISPOSAL. NO SMOKING, FLAMES OR FLARES IN HAZARD AREA! KEEP UNNECESSARY PEOPLE AWAY; ISOLATE HAZARD AREA AND DENY ENTRY.

REPORTABLE QUANTITY (RQ): 1 POUND THE SUPERFUND AMENDMENTS AND REAUTHORIZATION ACT (SARA) SECTION 304 REQUIRES THAT A RELEASE EQUAL TO OR GREATER THAN THE REPORTABLE QUANTITY FOR THIS SUBSTANCE BE IMMEDIATELY REPORTED TO THE LOCAL EMERGENCY PLANNING COMMITTEE AND THE STATE EMERGENCY RESPONSE COMMISSION (40 CFR 355.40). IF THE RELEASE OF THIS SUBSTANCE IS REPORTABLE UNDER CERCLA SECTION 103, THE NATIONAL RESPONSE CENTER MUST BE NOTIFIED IMMEDIATELY AT (800) 424-8802 OR (202) 426-2675 IN THE METROPOLITAN WASHINGTON, D.C. AREA (40 CFR 302.6).

PROTECTIVE EQUIPMENT

VENTILATION: PROVIDE LOCAL EXHAUST OR GENERAL DILUTION VENTILATION. VENTILATION EQUIPMENT MUST BE EXPLOSION-PROOF.

RESPIRATOR: THE FOLLOWING RESPIRATORS ARE RECOMMENDED BASED ON INFORMATION FOUND IN THE PHYSICAL DATA, TOXICITY AND HEALTH EFFECTS SECTIONS. THEY ARE RANKED IN ORDER FROM MINIMUM TO MAXIMUM RESPIRATORY PROTECTION. THE SPECIFIC RESPIRATOR SELECTED MUST BE BASED ON CONTAMINATION LEVELS FOUND IN THE WORK PLACE, MUST NOT EXCEED THE WORKING LIMITS OF THE RESPIRATOR AND BE JOINTLY APPROVED BY THE NATIONAL INSTITUTE FOR OCCUPATIONAL SAFETY AND HEALTH AND THE MINE SAFETY AND HEALTH ADMINISTRATION (NIOSH-MSHA).

CHEMICAL CARTRIDGE RESPIRATOR WITH FULL FACEPIECE AND PESTICIDE CARTRIDGE.

TYPE 'C' SUPPLIED-AIR RESPIRATOR WITH A FULL FACEPIECE OPERATED IN PRESSURE-DEMAND OR OTHER POSITIVE PRESSURE MODE OR WITH A FULL FACEPIECE, HELMET OR HOOD OPERATED IN CONTINUOUS-FLOW MODE.

SELF-CONTAINED BREATHING APPARATUS OPERATED IN PRESSURE-DEMAND OR OTHER POSITIVE PRESSURE MODE.

FOR FIREFIGHTING AND OTHER IMMEDIATELY DANGEROUS TO LIFE OR HEALTH CONDITIONS:

SELF-CONTAINED BREATHING APPARATUS WITH FULL FACEPIECE OPERATED IN PRESSURE-DEMAND OR OTHER POSITIVE PRESSURE MODE. SUPPLIED-AIR RESPIRATOR WITH FULL FACEPIECE AND OPERATED IN PRESSURE-DEMAND OR OTHER POSITIVE PRESSURE MODE IN COMBINATION WITH AN AUXILIARY SELF-CONTAINED BREATHING APPARATUS OPERATED IN PRESSURE-DEMAND OR OTHER POSITIVE PRESSURE MODE.

CLOTHING: EMPLOYEE MUST WEAR APPROPRIATE PROTECTIVE (IMPERVIOUS) CLOTHING AND EQUIPMENT TO PREVENT ANY POSSIBILITY OF SKIN CONTACT WITH THIS SUBSTANCE.

GLOVES: EMPLOYEE MUST WEAR APPROPRIATE PROTECTIVE GLOVES TO PREVENT CONTACT WITH THIS SUBSTANCE.

EYE PROTECTION: EMPLOYEE MUST WEAR SPLASH-PROOF OR DUST-RESISTANT SAFETY GOGGLES TO PREVENT EYE CONTACT WITH THIS SUBSTANCE.

EMERGENCY EYE WASH: WHERE THERE IS ANY POSSIBILITY THAT AN EMPLOYEE'S EYES MAY BE EXPOSED TO THIS SUBSTANCE, THE EMPLOYER SHOULD PROVIDE AN EYE WASH FOUNTAIN WITHIN THE IMMEDIATE WORK AREA FOR EMERGENCY USE.

AUTHORIZED BY- OCCUPATIONAL HEALTH SERVICES, INC.

CREATION DATE: 10/04/89 ***REVISION DATE:*** 05/01/90

MATERIAL SAFETY DATA SHEET

OCCUPATIONAL HEALTH SERVICES, INC.
AGRICULTURE AND PESTICIDE DIVISION
460 SEVENTH AVENUE, SUITE 2407
NEW YORK, NEW YORK 10123
1-800-445-MSDS OR (212) 967-1100

EMERGENCY CONTACT:
JOHN S. BRANSFORD, JR. (615) 292-1180

SUBSTANCE IDENTIFICATION

CAS-NUMBER 7173-84-4

SUBSTANCE: **CARBOPHENOTHION OXYGEN ANALOG**

TRADE NAMES/SYNONYMS: S-(P-CHLOROPHENYLMETHYL-THIO)-O,O-DIETHYL PHOSPHOROTHIOATE; PHOSPHOROTHIOIC ACID, S-(((4-CHLOROPHENYL)THIO)METHYL) O,O-DIETHYL ESTER; PHOSPHOROTHIOIC ACID, S-(((P-CHLOROPHENYL)THIO)METHYL) O,O-DIETHYL ESTER; S-(((4-CHLOROPHENYL)THIO)METHYL O,O-DIETHYLPHOSPHOROTHIOATE; S-(((P-CHLOROPHENYL)THIO)METHYL O,O-DIETHYLPHORPHOROTHIOATE; CARBOPHENOTHION OXON; CARBOPHENOXON; R 1472; C11H16CLO3PS2; PST04341

CHEMICAL FAMILY: ORGANOPHOSPHATE

MOLECULAR FORMULA: (C-H3-C-H2-O)2-P-(O)-S-C-H2-S-C6-H4-CL

MOLECULAR WEIGHT: 326.79

CERCLA RATINGS (SCALE 0-3): HEALTH=3 FIRE=U REACTIVITY=0 PERSISTENCE=2

NFPA RATINGS (SCALE 0-4): HEALTH=3 FIRE=U REACTIVITY=0

COMPONENTS AND CONTAMINANTS

COMPONENT: CARBOPHENOTHION OXYGEN ANALOG ***PERCENT:*** 100.0
CAS# 7173-84-4

OTHER CONTAMINANTS: NONE

EXPOSURE LIMITS: NO OCCUPATIONAL EXPOSURE LIMITS ESTABLISHED BY OSHA, ACGIH, OR NIOSH.

PHYSICAL DATA

DESCRIPTION: LIGHT YELLOW LIQUID. ***BOILING POINT:*** NOT AVAILABLE

SPECIFIC GRAVITY: NOT AVAILABLE ***SOLUBILITY IN WATER:*** NOT AVAILABLE

FIRE AND EXPLOSION DATA

FIRE AND EXPLOSION HAZARD: UNKNOWN FIRE AND EXPLOSION HAZARD.

FLASH POINT: NOT AVAILABLE

FIREFIGHTING MEDIA: DRY CHEMICAL, CARBON DIOXIDE, HALON, WATER SPRAY OR STANDARD FOAM (1987 EMERGENCY RESPONSE GUIDEBOOK, DOT P 5800.4).
FOR LARGER FIRES, USE WATER SPRAY, FOG OR STANDARD FOAM (1987 EMERGENCY RESPONSE GUIDEBOOK, DOT P 5800.4).

FIREFIGHTING: MOVE CONTAINER FROM FIRE AREA IF POSSIBLE. DIKE FIRE CONTROL WATER FOR LATER DISPOSAL; DO NOT SCATTER THE MATERIAL. COOL FIRE-EXPOSED CONTAINERS WITH WATER FROM SIDE UNTIL WELL AFTER FIRE IS OUT. STAY AWAY FROM STORAGE TANK ENDS. WITHDRAW IMMEDIATELY IN CASE OF RISING SOUND FROM VENTING SAFETY DEVICE OR ANY DISCOLORATION OF STORAGE TANK DUE TO FIRE (1987 EMERGENCY RESPONSE GUIDEBOOK, DOT P 5800.4, GUIDE PAGE 28).
EXTINGUISH ONLY IF FLOW CAN BE STOPPED. USE FLOODING AMOUNTS OF WATER AS A FOG; SOLID STREAMS MAY BE INEFFECTIVE. COOL CONTAINERS WITH FLOODING AMOUNTS OF WATER FROM AS FAR A DISTANCE AS POSSIBLE. AVOID BREATHING POISONOUS VAPORS, KEEP UPWIND.

TRANSPORTATION DATA

DEPARTMENT OF TRANSPORTATION HAZARD CLASSIFICATION 49 CFR 172.101: POISON B

DEPARTMENT OF TRANSPORTATION LABELING REQUIREMENTS 49 CFR 172.101 AND SUBPART E: POISON

DEPARTMENT OF TRANSPORTATION PACKAGING REQUIREMENTS: 49 CFR 173.346 EXCEPTIONS: 49 CFR 173.345

TOXICITY

CARBOPHENOTHION OXYGEN ANALOG: TOXICITY DATA: 220 MG/KG SKIN-MOUSE LD50; 165 MG/KG ORAL-MOUSE LD50; <30 MG/KG ORAL-RAT LD50 (STAUFFER). CARCINOGEN STATUS: NONE. ACUTE TOXICITY LEVEL: HIGHLY TOXIC BY INGESTION; TOXIC BY DERMAL ABSORPTION. TARGET EFFECTS: CHOLINESTERASE INHIBITOR. POISONING MAY AFFECT THE NERVOUS SYSTEM.* AT INCREASED RISK FROM EXPOSURE: PERSONS WITH RESPIRATORY AILMENTS, RECENT EXPOSURE TO CHOLINESTERASE INHIBITORS OR IMPAIRED CHOLINESTERASE PRODUCTION, OR LIVER MALFUNCTION.* ADDITIONAL DATA: MAY CROSS THE PLACENTA. HIGH ENVIRONMENTAL TEMPERATURES OR EXPOSURE OF THE CHEMICAL TO VISIBLE OR ULTRAVIOLET LIGHT MAY ENHANCE THE TOXICITY. INTERACTIONS WITH MEDICATIONS MAY OCCUR.*

* MAY BE BASED ON GENERAL INFORMATION ON ORGANOPHOSPHATES.

HEALTH EFFECTS AND FIRST AID

INHALATION: CARBOPHENOTHION OXYGEN ANALOG: SCHIZOPHRENIC AND DEPRESSIVE REACTIONS HAVE BEEN REPORTED AFTER EXPOSURE TO CARBOPHENOTHION FOR 1.5-10 YEARS. SEE INFORMATION ON ORGANOPHOSPHATES.
ORGANOPHOSPHATES: CHOLINESTERASE INHIBITOR. **ACUTE EXPOSURE-** WHEN INHALED, THE FIRST EFFECTS OF CHOLINESTERASE INHIBITORS ARE USUALLY RESPIRATORY AND MAY INCLUDE NASAL HYPEREMIA AND WATERY DISCHARGE, COUGH, CHEST DISCOMFORT, DYSPNEA, AND WHEEZING DUE TO INCREASED BRONCHIAL SECRETIONS AND BRONCHOCONSTRICTION. IF SUFFICIENT AMOUNTS ARE ABSORBED, OTHER SYSTEMIC EFFECTS MAY BEGIN WITHIN A FEW MINUTES OR BE DELAYED FOR UP TO 12 HOURS. SYMPTOMS MAY INCLUDE PALLOR, NAUSEA, VOMITING, DIARRHEA, ABDOMINAL CRAMPS, HEADACHE, DIZZINESS, OCULAR PAIN, BLURRED VISION, MIOSIS OR IN SOME CASES, ESPECIALLY INITIALLY, MYDRIASIS, LACRIMATION, SALIVATION, SWEATING, AND CONFUSION. OTHER REPORTED CENTRAL NERVOUS SYSTEM OR NEUROMUSCULAR EFFECTS MAY INCLUDE ATAXIA, SLURRED SPEECH, AREFLEXIA, WEAKNESS, FATIGUE, FASCICULATIONS, TWITCHING, TREMORS POSSIBLY OF THE TONGUE AND EYELIDS, AND EVENTUALLY PARALYSIS OF THE EXTREMITIES AND POSSIBLY OF THE RESPIRATORY MUSCLES. IN SEVERE CASES THERE MAY ALSO BE INVOLUNTARY DEFECATION AND URINATION, CYANOSIS, PSYCHOSIS, HYPERGLYCEMIA, ACUTE PANCREATITIS, CARDIAC IRREGULARITIES, PULMONARY EDEMA, UNCONSCIOUSNESS, CONVULSIONS, AND COMA. DEATH IS PRIMARILY DUE TO RESPIRATORY FAILURE, ALTHOUGH CARDIOVASCULAR EFFECTS INCLUDING CARDIAC ARREST MAY ALSO BE IMPLICATED. LONG TERM SEQUELAE ARE RARE BUT MAY INCLUDE NEUROPSYCHIATRIC DISORDERS AND MYOPATHY WITH MUSCLE TENDERNESS. SOME ORGANOPHOSPHATES MAY CAUSE A DELAYED NEUROPATHY BEGINNING 1-4 WEEKS AFTER AN ACUTE EXPOSURE WHICH MAY OR MAY NOT HAVE CAUSED ACUTE CHOLINERGIC EFFECTS. NUMBNESS, TINGLING, WEAKNESS AND CRAMPING BEGINNING SYMMETRICALLY IN THE LOWER LIMBS MAY PROGRESS TO ATAXIA AND PARALYSIS. IN SEVERE CASES, UPPER LIMB INVOLVEMENT IS POSSIBLE AND FLACCID PARALYSIS MAY PROGRESS TO SPASTIC PARALYSIS WITH EXAGGERATED REFLEXES. IMPROVEMENT MAY OCCUR OVER MONTHS TO YEARS, BUT SOME RESIDUAL IMPAIRMENT USUALLY REMAINS.
CHRONIC EXPOSURE- REPEATED OR PROLONGED EXPOSURE MAY RESULT IN THE EFFECTS OF ACUTE EXPOSURE INCLUDING THE DELAYED NEUROPATHY.
OTHER EFFECTS REPORTED IN WORKERS REPEATEDLY EXPOSED INCLUDE IMPAIRED MEMORY AND CONCENTRATION, ACUTE PSYCHOSIS, SEVERE DEPRESSIONS, IRRITABILTY, CONFUSION, APATHY, EMOTIONAL LABILITY, SOCIAL WITHDRAWAL, CONFUSION, HEADACHE, SPEECH DIFFICULTIES, DELAYED REACTION TIMES, SPATIAL DISORIENTATION, NIGHTMARES, SLEEPWALKING, AND DROWSINESS OR INSOMNIA. AN INFLUENZA-LIKE CONDITION WITH HEADACHE, NAUSEA, WEAKNESS, ANOREXIA AND MALAISE HAS ALSO BEEN REPORTED.

FIRST AID- REMOVE FROM EXPOSURE AREA TO FRESH AIR IMMEDIATELY. IF BREATHING HAS STOPPED, GIVE ARTIFICIAL RESPIRATION. MAINTAIN AIRWAY AND BLOOD PRESSURE AND ADMINISTER OXYGEN IF AVAILABLE. KEEP AFFECTED PERSON WARM AND AT REST. TREAT SYMPTOMATICALLY AND SUPPORTIVELY. ADMINISTRATION OF OXYGEN SHOULD BE PERFORMED BY QUALIFIED PERSONNEL. GET MEDICAL ATTENTION IMMEDIATELY.

SKIN CONTACT: CARBOPHENOTHION OXYGEN ANALOG: TOXIC. SCHIZOPHRENIC AND DEPRESSIVE REACTIONS HAVE BEEN REPORTED AFTER EXPOSURE TO CARBOPHENOTHION FOR 1.5-10 YEARS. SEE INFORMATION ON ORGANOPHOSPHATES.
ORGANOPHOSPHATES: CHOLINESTERASE INHIBITOR. **ACUTE EXPOSURE-** LOCALIZED SWEATING AND FASCICULATIONS MAY OCCUR AT THE SITE OF CONTACT. IF SUFFICIENT AMOUNTS ARE ABSORBED, OTHER EFFECTS OF CHOLINESTERASE INHIBITION AS DESCRIBED IN ACUTE INHALATION MAY OCCUR. SYMPTOMS MAY BE DELAYED 2-3 HOURS, BUT USUALLY NO MORE THAN 12 HOURS. THE RATE OF ABSORPTION IS INCREASED BY THE PRESENCE OF DERMATITIS OR HIGH AMBIENT TEMPERATURES. DELAYED NEUROPATHY IS ALSO POSSIBLE. **CHRONIC EXPOSURE-** REPEATED OR PROLONGED EXPOSURE MAY CAUSE EFFECTS AS DESCRIBED IN ACUTE EXPOSURE. SOME ORGANOPHOSPHATES MAY CAUSE SENSITIZATION.

FIRST AID- REMOVE CONTAMINATED CLOTHING IMMEDIATELY. WASH CONTAMINATED AREAS WITH SOAP AND WATER FOLLOWED BY ALCOHOL (ARENA, POISONING, 4TH ED.). EMERGENCY PERSONNEL SHOULD WEAR GLOVES AND AVOID CONTAMINATION. TREAT RESPIRATORY DIFFICULTY WITH ARTIFICIAL RESPIRATION. GET MEDICAL ATTENTION IMMEDIATELY.

EYE CONTACT: CARBOPHENOTHION OXYGEN ANALOG: SEE INFORMATION ON ORGANOPHOSPHATES.
ORGANOPHOSPHATES: CHOLINESTERASE INHIBITOR. **ACUTE EXPOSURE-** DIRECT CONTACT MAY CAUSE PAIN, HYPEREMIA, LACRIMATION, TWITCHING OF THE EYELIDS, MIOSIS, AND CILIARY MUSCLE SPASM WITH LOSS OF ACCOMODATION, BLURRED OR DIMMED VISION AND BROWACHE. SOMETIMES MYDRIASIS MAY OCCUR INSTEAD OF MIOSIS. WITH SUFFICIENT EXPOSURE, OTHER SYMPTOMS OF CHOLINESTERASE INHIBITION AS DESCRIBED IN ACUTE INHALATION MAY OCCUR. **CHRONIC EXPOSURE-** REPEATED OR PROLONGED EXPOSURE MAY CAUSE EFFECTS AS DESCRIBED IN ACUTE EXPOSURE. SOME COMPOUNDS HAVE CAUSED TOXIC EFFECTS ON THE CRYSTALLINE LENS, CONJUNCTIVAL THICKENING AND OBSTRUCTION OF THE NASOLACRIMAL CANALS WHEN USED AS MIOTIC EYEDROPS.

FIRST AID- IRRIGATE EYES WITH WATER OR SALINE SOLUTION. IF SYMPTOMS OF POISONING OCCUR, TREAT RESPIRATORY DIFFICULTY WITH ARTIFICIAL RESPIRATION AND OXYGEN. OBSERVE PATIENT FOR AT LEAST 24-36 HOURS (GOSSELIN, CLINICAL TOXICOLOGY OF COMMERCIAL PRODUCTS, 5TH ED.). GET MEDICAL ATTENTION IMMEDIATELY. OXYGEN SHOULD BE ADMINISTERED BY QUALIFIED MEDICAL PERSONNEL.

INGESTION: CARBOPHENOTHION OXYGEN ANALOG: HIGHLY TOXIC. IN A 3 GENERATION STUDY, RATS FED 20 PPM COMMERCIAL GRADE CARBOPHENOTHION EXPERIENCED INCREASED FETAL RESORPTIONS AND FETOTOXICITY. SEE INFORMATION ON ORGANOPHOSPHATES.
ORGANOPHOSPHATES: CHOLINESTERASE INHIBITOR. **ACUTE EXPOSURE-** WHEN INGESTED, THE FIRST EFFECTS MAY BE NAUSEA, VOMITING, ANOREXIA, ABDOMINAL CRAMPS AND DIARRHEA. GASTROINTESTINAL ABSORPTION MAY CAUSE SYMPTOMS OF CHOLINESTERASE INHIBITION AS DESCRIBED IN ACUTE INHALATION. SYMPTOMS MAY BEGIN WITHIN MINUTES OR BE DELAYED FOR HOURS. DELAYED EFFECTS INCLUDING NEUROPATHY MAY ALSO OCCUR. **CHRONIC EXPOSURE-** REPEATED INGESTION MAY CAUSE EFFECTS AS DESCRIBED IN ACUTE EXPOSURE.

FIRST AID- IF PERSON IS ALERT AND RESPIRATION IS NOT DEPRESSED, GIVE SYRUP OF IPECAC FOLLOWED BY WATER (IF VOMITING OCCURS, KEEP HEAD BELOW HIPS TO PREVENT ASPIRATION). IF CONSCIOUSNESS LEVEL DECLINES OR VOMITING HAS NOT OCCURRED IN 15 MINUTES EMPTY STOMACH BY GASTRIC LAVAGE WITH THE AID OF CUFFED ENDOTRACHEAL TUBE USING ISOTONIC SALINE OR 5% SODIUM BICARBONATE FOLLOW WITH ACTIVATED CHARCOAL. ESTABLISH AND MAINTAIN AIRWAY. TREAT RESPIRATORY DIFFICULTY WITH ARTIFICIAL RESPIRATION AND OXYGEN. DO NOT GIVE MORPHINE, AMINOPHYLLINE, PHENOTHIAZINES, RESERPINE, FUROSEMIDE, OR ETHACRYNIC ACID (MORGAN, RECOGNITION AND MANAGEMENT OF PESTICIDE POISONINGS, 3RD ED.). TREAT SYMPTOMATICALLY AND SUPPORTIVELY. ADMINISTRATION OF OXYGEN AND LAVAGE MUST BE PERFORMED BY QUALIFIED MEDICAL PERSONNEL. GET MEDICAL ATTENTION IMMEDIATELY.

ANTIDOTE: THE FOLLOWING ANTIDOTE(S) HAVE BEEN RECOMMENDED. HOWEVER, THE DECISION AS TO WHETHER THE SEVERITY OF POISONING REQUIRES ADMINISTRATION OF ANY ANTIDOTE AND ACTUAL DOSE REQUIRED SHOULD BE MADE BY QUALIFIED MEDICAL PERSONNEL.
FOR CHOLINESTERASE INHIBITORS: ESTABLISH CLEAR AIRWAY AND TISSUE OXYGENATION BY ASPIRATION OF SECRETIONS, AND IF NECESSARY, BY ASSISTED PULMONARY VENTILATION WITH OXYGEN. IMPROVE TISSUE OXYGENATION AS MUCH AS POSSIBLE BEFORE ADMINISTERING ATROPINE TO MINIMIZE THE RISK OF VENTRICULAR FIBRILLATION. ADMINISTER ATROPINE SULFATE INTRAVENOUSLY, OR INTRAMUSCULARLY IF IV INJECTION IS NOT POSSIBLE. IN MODERATELY SEVERE POISONING ADMINISTER ATROPINE SULFATE, 0.4-2.0 MG REPEATED EVERY 15 MINUTES UNTIL ATROPINIZATION IS ACHIEVED (TACHYCARDIA, FLUSHING, DRY MOUTH, MYDRIASIS). MAINTAIN ATROPINIZATION BY REPEATED DOSES FOR 2-12 HOURS, OR LONGER, DEPENDING ON THE SEVERITY OF POISONING. THE APPEARANCE OF RALES IN THE LUNG BASES, MIOSIS, SALIVATION, NAUSEA, BRADYCARDIA, ARE ALL INDICATIONS OF INADEQUATE ATROPINIZATION. SEVERELY POISONED INDIVIDUALS MAY EXHIBIT REMARKABLE TOLERANCE TO ATROPINE; TWO OR MORE TIMES THE DOSAGES SUGGESTED ABOVE MAY BE NEEDED. PERSONS NOT POISONED OR ONLY SLIGHTLY POISONED, HOWEVER, MAY DEVELOP SIGNS OF ATROPINE TOXICITY FROM SUCH LARGE DOSAGES: FEVER, MUSCLE FIBRILLATIONS, AND DELIRIUM ARE THE MAIN SIGNS OF ATROPINE TOXICITY. IF THESE SIGNS APPEAR WHILE THE PATIENT IS FULLY ATROPINIZED, ATROPINE ADMINISTRATION SHOULD BE DISCONTINUED, AT LEAST TEMPORARILY. OBSERVE TREATED PATIENTS CLOSELY AT LEAST 24 HOURS TO INSURE THAT SYMPTOMS (POSSIBLY PULMONARY EDEMA) DO NOT RECUR AS ATROPINIZATION WEARS OFF. IN VERY SEVERE POISONINGS, METABOLIC DISPOSITION OF TOXICANT MAY REQUIRE SEVERAL HOURS OR DAYS DURING WHICH ATROPINIZATION MUST BE MAINTAINED. MARKEDLY LOWER LEVELS OF URINARY METABOLITES INDICATE THAT ATROPINE DOSAGE CAN BE TAPERED OFF. AS DOSAGE IS REDUCED, CHECK THE LUNG BASES FREQUENTLY FOR RALES. IF RALES ARE HEARD OR OTHER SYMPTOMS RETURN, RE-ESTABLISH ATROPINIZATION PROMPTLY (MORGAN, RECOGNITION AND MANAGEMENT OF PESTICIDE POISONINGS, 3RD ED.). ADMINISTRATION OF ANTIDOTE MUST BE PERFORMED BY QUALIFIED MEDICAL PERSONNEL.
IN CASES OF SEVERE POISONING BY ORGANOPHOSPHATE PESTICIDES IN WHICH RESPIRATORY DEPRESSION, MUSCLE WEAKNESS AND TWITCHINGS ARE SEVERE, GIVE PRALIDOXIME (PROTOPAM-AYERST, 2-PAM), 1.0 GRAM INTRAVENOUSLY AT NO MORE THAN 0.5 GRAM PER MINUTE. DOSAGE OF PRALIDOXIME MAY BE

REPEATED IN 1-2 HOURS, THEN AT 10-12 HOUR INTERVALS IF NEEDED. IN VERY SEVERE POISONINGS, DOSAGE RATES MAY BE DOUBLED. TREATMENT WITH PRALIDOXIME WILL BE MOST EFFECTIVE IF GIVEN WITHIN THIRTY-SIX HOURS AFTER POISONING (MORGAN, RECOGNITION AND MANAGEMENT OF PESTICIDE POISONINGS, 3RD ED.). ANTIDOTE SHOULD BE ADMINISTERED BY QUALIFIED MEDICAL PERSONNEL.

REACTIVITY

REACTIVITY: STABLE UNDER NORMAL TEMPERATURES AND PRESSURES.
INCOMPATIBILITIES: CARBOPHENOTHION OXYGEN ANALOG: OXIDIZERS (STRONG): FIRE AND EXPLOSION HAZARD.
DECOMPOSITION: THERMAL DECOMPOSITION PRODUCTS MAY INCLUDE TOXIC OXIDES OF SULFUR AND CARBON.
POLYMERIZATION: HAZARDOUS POLYMERIZATION HAS NOT BEEN REPORTED TO OCCUR UNDER NORMAL TEMPERATURES AND PRESSURES.

STORAGE AND DISPOSAL

OBSERVE ALL FEDERAL, STATE AND LOCAL REGULATIONS WHEN STORING OR DISPOSING OF THIS SUBSTANCE. FOR ASSISTANCE, CONTACT THE DISTRICT DIRECTOR OF THE ENVIRONMENTAL PROTECTION AGENCY.

STORAGE

STORE IN ACCORDANCE WITH 40 CFR 165 RECOMMENDED PROCEDURES FOR THE DISPOSAL AND STORAGE OF PESTICIDES AND PESTICIDE CONTAINERS.
STORE IN A TIGHTLY CLOSED CONTAINER AT TEMPERATURES NOT EXCEEDING 39 F (4 C).
STORE AWAY FROM INCOMPATIBLE SUBSTANCES.

DISPOSAL

DISPOSAL MUST BE IN ACCORDANCE WITH 40 CFR 165 RECOMMENDED PROCEDURES FOR THE DISPOSAL AND STORAGE OF PESTICIDES AND PESTICIDE CONTAINERS.

CONDITIONS TO AVOID

AVOID CONTACT WITH HEAT, SPARKS, FLAMES OR OTHER IGNITION SOURCES. VAPORS MAY BE EXPLOSIVE. MATERIAL IS POISONOUS; AVOID INHALATION OF VAPORS OR CONTACT WITH SKIN. DO NOT ALLOW MATERIAL TO CONTAMINATE WATER SOURCES.

SPILL AND LEAK PROCEDURES

OCCUPATIONAL SPILL: SHUT OFF IGNITION SOURCES. DO NOT TOUCH SPILLED MATERIAL. STOP LEAK IF YOU CAN DO IT WITHOUT RISK. USE WATER SPRAY TO REDUCE VAPORS. FOR SMALL SPILLS, TAKE UP WITH SAND OR OTHER ABSORBENT MATERIAL AND PLACE INTO CONTAINERS FOR LATER DISPOSAL. FOR LARGER SPILLS, DIKE FAR AHEAD OF SPILL FOR LATER DISPOSAL. NO SMOKING, FLAMES OR FLARES IN HAZARD AREA! KEEP UNNECESSARY PEOPLE AWAY; ISOLATE HAZARD AREA AND DENY ENTRY.

PROTECTIVE EQUIPMENT

VENTILATION: PROVIDE LOCAL EXHAUST VENTILATION. VENTILATION EQUIPMENT MUST BE EXPLOSION PROOF.
RESPIRATOR: THE FOLLOWING RESPIRATORS ARE RECOMMENDED BASED ON INFORMATION FOUND IN THE PHYSICAL DATA, TOXICITY AND HEALTH EFFECTS SECTIONS. THEY ARE RANKED IN ORDER FROM MINIMUM TO MAXIMUM RESPIRATORY PROTECTION. THE SPECIFIC RESPIRATOR SELECTED MUST BE BASED ON CONTAMINATION LEVELS FOUND IN THE WORK PLACE, MUST NOT EXCEED THE WORKING LIMITS OF THE RESPIRATOR AND BE JOINTLY APPROVED BY THE NATIONAL INSTITUTE FOR OCCUPATIONAL SAFETY AND HEALTH AND THE MINE SAFETY AND HEALTH ADMINISTRATION (NIOSH-MSHA).
CHEMICAL CARTRIDGE RESPIRATOR WITH FULL FACEPIECE AND PESTICIDE CARTRIDGE.
TYPE 'C' SUPPLIED-AIR RESPIRATOR WITH A FULL FACEPIECE OPERATED IN PRESSURE-DEMAND OR OTHER POSITIVE PRESSURE MODE OR WITH A FULL FACEPIECE, HELMET OR HOOD OPERATED IN CONTINUOUS-FLOW MODE.
SELF-CONTAINED BREATHING APPARATUS OPERATED IN PRESSURE-DEMAND OR OTHER POSITIVE PRESSURE MODE.
FOR FIREFIGHTING AND OTHER IMMEDIATELY DANGEROUS TO LIFE OR HEALTH CONDITIONS:
SELF-CONTAINED BREATHING APPARATUS WITH FULL FACEPIECE OPERATED IN PRESSURE-DEMAND OR OTHER POSITIVE PRESSURE MODE.
SUPPLIED-AIR RESPIRATOR WITH FULL FACEPIECE AND OPERATED IN PRESSURE-DEMAND OR OTHER POSITIVE PRESSURE MODE IN COMBINATION WITH AN AUXILIARY SELF-CONTAINED BREATHING APPARATUS OPERATED IN PRESSURE-DEMAND OR OTHER POSITIVE PRESSURE MODE.
CLOTHING: EMPLOYEE MUST WEAR APPROPRIATE PROTECTIVE (IMPERVIOUS) CLOTHING AND EQUIPMENT TO PREVENT ANY POSSIBILITY OF SKIN CONTACT WITH THIS SUBSTANCE.
GLOVES: EMPLOYEE MUST WEAR APPROPRIATE PROTECTIVE GLOVES TO PREVENT CONTACT WITH THIS SUBSTANCE.
EYE PROTECTION: EMPLOYEE MUST WEAR SPLASH-PROOF OR DUST-RESISTANT SAFETY GOGGLES TO PREVENT EYE CONTACT WITH THIS SUBSTANCE.
EMERGENCY EYE WASH: WHERE THERE IS ANY POSSIBILITY THAT AN EMPLOYEE'S EYES MAY BE EXPOSED TO THIS SUBSTANCE, THE EMPLOYER SHOULD PROVIDE AN EYE WASH FOUNTAIN WITHIN THE IMMEDIATE WORK AREA FOR EMERGENCY USE.

AUTHORIZED BY- OCCUPATIONAL HEALTH SERVICES, INC.
CREATION DATE: 10/04/89 ***REVISION DATE:*** 04/27/90

MATERIAL SAFETY DATA SHEET

OCCUPATIONAL HEALTH SERVICES, INC.
AGRICULTURE AND PESTICIDE DIVISION
450 SEVENTH AVENUE, SUITE 2407
NEW YORK, NEW YORK 10123
1-800-445-MSDS OR (212) 967-1100

EMERGENCY CONTACT:
JOHN S. BRANSFORD, JR. (615) 292-1180

SUBSTANCE IDENTIFICATION

CAS-NUMBER 16662-87-6
SUBSTANCE: **CARBOPHENOTHION OXYGEN ANALOG SULFONE**
TRADE NAMES/SYNONYMS: S-((P-CHLOROPHENYLSULFONYL)METHYL)-O,O-DIETHYL PHOSPHOROTHIOATE; TRITHION O2 ANALOG SULFONE; PHOSPHOROTHIOIC ACID, S-(((4-CHLOROPHENYL)SULFONYL)METHYL) O,O- DIETHYL ESTER; PHOSPHOROTHIOIC ACID, S-(((P-CHLOROPHENYL)SULFONYL)METHYL) O,O- DIETHYL ESTER; CARBOPHENOXON SULFONE; C11H16CLO5PS2; PST04342
CHEMICAL FAMILY: ORGANOPHOSPHATE SULFONE
MOLECULAR FORMULA: CL-(C6-H4)-S-O2-C-H2-S-P-(O)-(O-C2-H5)2
MOLECULAR WEIGHT: 258.80
CERCLA RATINGS (SCALE 0-3): HEALTH=3 FIRE=1 REACTIVITY=0 PERSISTENCE=2
NFPA RATINGS (SCALE 0-4): HEALTH=3 FIRE=1 REACTIVITY=0

COMPONENTS AND CONTAMINANTS

COMPONENT: CARBOPHENOTHION OXYGEN ANALOG SULFONE ***PERCENT:*** 100.0
CAS# 16662-87-6
OTHER CONTAMINANTS: NONE
EXPOSURE LIMITS: NO OCCUPATIONAL EXPOSURE LIMITS ESTABLISHED BY OSHA, ACGIH, OR NIOSH.

PHYSICAL DATA

DESCRIPTION: WHITE POWDER. ***MELTING POINT:*** NOT AVAILABLE
SPECIFIC GRAVITY: NOT AVAILABLE ***SOLUBILITY IN WATER:*** NOT AVAILABLE

FIRE AND EXPLOSION DATA

FIRE AND EXPLOSION HAZARD: SLIGHT FIRE HAZARD WHEN EXPOSED TO HEAT OR FLAME.

FIREFIGHTING MEDIA: DRY CHEMICAL, CARBON DIOXIDE, HALON, WATER SPRAY OR STANDARD FOAM (1987 EMERGENCY RESPONSE GUIDEBOOK, DOT P 5800.4).
FOR LARGER FIRES, USE WATER SPRAY, FOG OR STANDARD FOAM (1987 EMERGENCY RESPONSE GUIDEBOOK, DOT P 5800.4).
FIREFIGHTING: MOVE CONTAINERS FROM FIRE AREA IF POSSIBLE (1987 EMERGENCY RESPONSE GUIDEBOOK, DOT P 5800.4, GUIDE PAGE 53).
EXTINGUISH USING AGENT SUITABLE FOR TYPE OF SURROUNDING FIRE. AVOID BREATHING VAPORS AND DUSTS. KEEP UPWIND.

TRANSPORTATION DATA

DEPARTMENT OF TRANSPORTATION HAZARD CLASSIFICATION 49 CFR 172.101: POISON B
DEPARTMENT OF TRANSPORTATION LABELING REQUIREMENTS 49 CFR 172.101 AND SUBPART E: POISON
DEPARTMENT OF TRANSPORTATION PACKAGING REQUIREMENTS: 49 CFR 173.365 EXCEPTIONS: 49 CFR 173.364

TOXICITY

CARBOPHENOTHION OXYGEN ANALOG SULFONE: TOXICITY DATA: <30 MG/KG ORAL-RAT LD50 (STAUFFER). CARCINOGEN STATUS: NONE. ACUTE TOXICITY LEVEL: HIGHLY TOXIC BY INGESTION. TARGET EFFECTS: CHOLINESTERASE

INHIBITOR. POISONING MAY AFFECT THE NERVOUS SYSTEM.* AT INCREASED RISK FROM EXPOSURE: PERSONS WITH RESPIRATORY AILMENTS, RECENT EXPOSURE TO CHOLINESTERASE INHIBITORS OR IMPAIRED CHOLINESTERASE PRODUCTION, OR LIVER MALFUNCTION.* ADDITIONAL DATA: MAY CROSS THE PLACENTA. HIGH ENVIRONMENTAL TEMPERATURES OR EXPOSURE OF THE CHEMICAL TO VISIBLE OR ULTRAVIOLET LIGHT MAY ENHANCE THE TOXICITY. INTERACTIONS WITH MEDICATIONS MAY OCCUR.*

* MAY BE BASED ON GENERAL INFORMATION ON ORGANOPHOSPHATES.

HEALTH EFFECTS AND FIRST AID

INHALATION: CARBOPHENOTHION OXYGEN ANALOG SULFONE: SCHIZOPHRENIC AND DEPRESSIVE REACTIONS HAVE BEEN REPORTED AFTER EXPOSURE TO CARBOPHENOTHION FOR 1.5-10 YEARS. SEE INFORMATION ON ORGANOPHOSPHATES.

ORGANOPHOSPHATES: CHOLINESTERASE INHIBITOR. **ACUTE EXPOSURE-** WHEN INHALED, THE FIRST EFFECTS OF CHOLINESTERASE INHIBITORS ARE USUALLY RESPIRATORY AND MAY INCLUDE NASAL HYPEREMIA AND WATERY DISCHARGE, COUGH, CHEST DISCOMFORT, DYSPNEA, AND WHEEZING DUE TO INCREASED BRONCHIAL SECRETIONS AND BRONCHOCONSTRICTION. IF SUFFICIENT AMOUNTS ARE ABSORBED, OTHER SYSTEMIC EFFECTS MAY BEGIN WITHIN A FEW MINUTES OR BE DELAYED FOR UP TO 12 HOURS. SYMPTOMS MAY INCLUDE PALLOR, NAUSEA, VOMITING, DIARRHEA, ABDOMINAL CRAMPS, HEADACHE, DIZZINESS, OCULAR PAIN, BLURRED VISION, MIOSIS OR IN SOME CASES, ESPECIALLY INITIALLY, MYDRIASIS, LACRIMATION, SALIVATION, SWEATING, AND CONFUSION. OTHER REPORTED CENTRAL NERVOUS SYSTEM OR NEUROMUSCULAR EFFECTS MAY INCLUDE ATAXIA, SLURRED SPEECH, AREFLEXIA, WEAKNESS, FATIGUE, FASCICULATIONS, TWITCHING, TREMORS POSSIBLY OF THE TONGUE AND EYELIDS, AND EVENTUALLY PARALYSIS OF THE EXTREMITIES AND POSSIBLY OF THE RESPIRATORY MUSCLES. IN SEVERE CASES THERE MAY ALSO BE INVOLUNTARY DEFECATION AND URINATION, CYANOSIS, PSYCHOSIS, HYPERGLYCEMIA, ACUTE PANCREATITIS, CARDIAC IRREGULARITIES, PULMONARY EDEMA, UNCONSCIOUSNESS, CONVULSIONS, AND COMA. DEATH IS PRIMARILY DUE TO RESPIRATORY FAILURE, ALTHOUGH CARDIOVASCULAR EFFECTS INCLUDING CARDIAC ARREST MAY ALSO BE IMPLICATED. LONG TERM SEQUELAE ARE RARE BUT MAY INCLUDE NEUROPSYCHIATRIC DISORDERS AND MYOPATHY WITH MUSCLE TENDERNESS. SOME ORGANOPHOSPHATES MAY CAUSE A DELAYED NEUROPATHY BEGINNING 1-4 WEEKS AFTER AN ACUTE EXPOSURE WHICH MAY OR MAY NOT HAVE CAUSED ACUTE CHOLINERGIC EFFECTS. NUMBNESS, TINGLING, WEAKNESS AND CRAMPING BEGINNING SYMMETRICALLY IN THE LOWER LIMBS MAY PROGRESS TO ATAXIA AND PARALYSIS. IN SEVERE CASES, UPPER LIMB INVOLVEMENT IS POSSIBLE AND FLACCID PARALYSIS MAY PROGRESS TO SPASTIC PARALYSIS WITH EXAGGERATED REFLEXES. IMPROVEMENT MAY OCCUR OVER MONTHS TO YEARS, BUT SOME RESIDUAL IMPAIRMENT USUALLY REMAINS.

CHRONIC EXPOSURE- REPEATED OR PROLONGED EXPOSURE MAY RESULT IN THE EFFECTS OF ACUTE EXPOSURE INCLUDING THE DELAYED NEUROPATHY. OTHER EFFECTS REPORTED IN WORKERS REPEATEDLY EXPOSED INCLUDE IMPAIRED MEMORY AND CONCENTRATION, ACUTE PSYCHOSIS, SEVERE DEPRESSIONS, IRRITABILTY, CONFUSION, APATHY, EMOTIONAL LABILITY, SOCIAL WITHDRAWAL, CONFUSION, HEADACHE, SPEECH DIFFICULTIES, DELAYED REACTION TIMES, SPATIAL DISORIENTATION, NIGHTMARES, SLEEPWALKING, AND DROWSINESS OR INSOMNIA. AN INFLUENZA-LIKE CONDITION WITH HEADACHE, NAUSEA, WEAKNESS, ANOREXIA AND MALAISE HAS ALSO BEEN REPORTED.

FIRST AID- REMOVE FROM EXPOSURE AREA TO FRESH AIR IMMEDIATELY. IF BREATHING HAS STOPPED, GIVE ARTIFICIAL RESPIRATION. MAINTAIN AIRWAY AND BLOOD PRESSURE AND ADMINISTER OXYGEN IF AVAILABLE. KEEP AFFECTED PERSON WARM AND AT REST. TREAT SYMPTOMATICALLY AND SUPPORTIVELY. ADMINISTRATION OF OXYGEN SHOULD BE PERFORMED BY QUALIFIED PERSONNEL. GET MEDICAL ATTENTION IMMEDIATELY.

SKIN CONTACT: CARBOPHENOTHION OXYGEN ANALOG SULFONE: SCHIZOPHRENIC AND DEPRESSIVE REACTIONS HAVE BEEN REPORTED AFTER EXPOSURE TO CARBOPHENOTHION FOR 1.5-10 YEARS. SEE INFORMATION ON ORGANOPHOSPHATES.

ORGANOPHOSPHATES: CHOLINESTERASE INHIBITOR. **ACUTE EXPOSURE-** LOCALIZED SWEATING AND FASCICULATIONS MAY OCCUR AT THE SITE OF CONTACT. IF SUFFICIENT AMOUNTS ARE ABSORBED, OTHER EFFECTS OF CHOLINESTERASE INHIBITION AS DESCRIBED IN ACUTE INHALATION MAY OCCUR. SYMPTOMS MAY BE DELAYED 2-3 HOURS, BUT USUALLY NO MORE THAN 12 HOURS. THE RATE OF ABSORPTION IS INCREASED BY THE PRESENCE OF DERMATITIS OR HIGH AMBIENT TEMPERATURES. DELAYED NEUROPATHY IS ALSO POSSIBLE. **CHRONIC EXPOSURE-** REPEATED OR PROLONGED EXPOSURE MAY CAUSE EFFECTS AS DESCRIBED IN ACUTE EXPOSURE. SOME ORGANOPHOSPHATES MAY CAUSE SENSITIZATION.

FIRST AID- REMOVE CONTAMINATED CLOTHING IMMEDIATELY. WASH CONTAMINATED AREAS WITH SOAP AND WATER FOLLOWED BY ALCOHOL (ARENA, POISONING, 4TH ED.). EMERGENCY PERSONNEL SHOULD WEAR GLOVES AND AVOID CONTAMINATION. TREAT RESPIRATORY DIFFICULTY WITH ARTIFICIAL RESPIRATION. GET MEDICAL ATTENTION IMMEDIATELY.

EYE CONTACT: CARBOPHENOTHION OXYGEN ANALOG SULFONE: SEE INFORMATION ON ORGANOPHOSPHATES.

ORGANOPHOSPHATES: CHOLINESTERASE INHIBITOR. **ACUTE EXPOSURE-** DIRECT CONTACT MAY CAUSE PAIN, HYPEREMIA, LACRIMATION, TWITCHING OF THE EYELIDS, MIOSIS, AND CILIARY MUSCLE SPASM WITH LOSS OF ACCOMODATION, BLURRED OR DIMMED VISION AND BROWACHE. SOMETIMES MYDRIASIS MAY OCCUR INSTEAD OF MIOSIS. WITH SUFFICIENT EXPOSURE, OTHER SYMPTOMS OF CHOLINESTERASE INHIBITION AS DESCRIBED IN ACUTE INHALATION MAY OCCUR. **CHRONIC EXPOSURE-** REPEATED OR PROLONGED EXPOSURE MAY CAUSE EFFECTS AS DESCRIBED IN ACUTE EXPOSURE. SOME COMPOUNDS HAVE CAUSED TOXIC EFFECTS ON THE CRYSTALLINE LENS, CONJUNCTIVAL THICKENING AND OBSTRUCTION OF THE NASOLACRIMAL CANALS WHEN USED AS MIOTIC EYEDROPS.

FIRST AID- IRRIGATE EYES WITH WATER OR SALINE SOLUTION. IF SYMPTOMS OF POISONING OCCUR, TREAT RESPIRATORY DIFFICULTY WITH ARTIFICIAL RESPIRATION AND OXYGEN. OBSERVE PATIENT FOR AT LEAST 24-36 HOURS (GOSSELIN, CLINICAL TOXICOLOGY OF COMMERCIAL PRODUCTS, 5TH ED.). GET MEDICAL ATTENTION IMMEDIATELY. OXYGEN SHOULD BE ADMINISTERED BY QUALIFIED MEDICAL PERSONNEL.

INGESTION: CARBOPHENOTHION OXYGEN ANALOG SULFONE: HIGHLY TOXIC. IN A 3 GENERATION STUDY, RATS FED 20 PPM COMMERCIAL GRADE CARBOPHENOTHION EXPERIENCED INCREASED FETAL RESORPTIONS AND FETOTOXICITY. SEE INFORMATION ON ORGANOPHOSPHATES.

ORGANOPHOSPHATES: CHOLINESTERASE INHIBITOR. **ACUTE EXPOSURE-** WHEN INGESTED, THE FIRST EFFECTS MAY BE NAUSEA, VOMITING, ANOREXIA, ABDOMINAL CRAMPS AND DIARRHEA. GASTROINTESTINAL ABSORPTION MAY CAUSE SYMPTOMS OF CHOLINESTERASE INHIBITION AS DESCRIBED IN ACUTE INHALATION. SYMPTOMS MAY BEGIN WITHIN MINUTES OR BE DELAYED FOR HOURS. DELAYED EFFECTS INCLUDING NEUROPATHY MAY ALSO OCCUR. **CHRONIC EXPOSURE-** REPEATED INGESTION MAY CAUSE EFFECTS AS DESCRIBED IN ACUTE EXPOSURE.

FIRST AID- IF PERSON IS ALERT AND RESPIRATION IS NOT DEPRESSED, GIVE SYRUP OF IPECAC FOLLOWED BY WATER (IF VOMITING OCCURS, KEEP HEAD BELOW HIPS TO PREVENT ASPIRATION). IF CONSCIOUSNESS LEVEL DECLINES OR VOMITING HAS NOT OCCURRED IN 15 MINUTES EMPTY STOMACH BY GASTRIC LAVAGE WITH THE AID OF CUFFED ENDOTRACHEAL TUBE USING ISOTONIC SALINE OR 5% SODIUM BICARBONATE FOLLOW WITH ACTIVATED CHARCOAL. ESTABLISH AND MAINTAIN AIRWAY. TREAT RESPIRATORY DIFFICULTY WITH ARTIFICIAL RESPIRATION AND OXYGEN. DO NOT GIVE MORPHINE, AMINOPHYLLINE, PHENOTHIAZINES, RESERPINE, FUROSEMIDE, OR ETHACRYNIC ACID (MORGAN, RECOGNITION AND MANAGEMENT OF PESTICIDE POISONINGS, 3RD ED.). TREAT SYMPTOMATICALLY AND SUPPORTIVELY. ADMINISTRATION OF OXYGEN AND LAVAGE MUST BE PERFORMED BY QUALIFIED MEDICAL PERSONNEL. GET MEDICAL ATTENTION IMMEDIATELY.

ANTIDOTE: THE FOLLOWING ANTIDOTE HAS BEEN RECOMMENDED. HOWEVER, THE DECISION AS TO WHETHER THE SEVERITY OF POISONING REQUIRES ADMINISTRATION OF ANY ANTIDOTE AND ACTUAL DOSE REQUIRED SHOULD BE MADE BY QUALIFIED MEDICAL PERSONNEL.

FOR CHOLINESTERASE INHIBITORS: ESTABLISH CLEAR AIRWAY AND TISSUE OXYGENATION BY ASPIRATION OF SECRETIONS, AND IF NECESSARY, BY ASSISTED PULMONARY VENTILATION WITH OXYGEN. IMPROVE TISSUE OXYGENATION AS MUCH AS POSSIBLE BEFORE ADMINISTERING ATROPINE TO MINIMIZE THE RISK OF VENTRICULAR FIBRILLATION. ADMINISTER ATROPINE SULFATE INTRAVENOUSLY, OR INTRAMUSCULARLY IF IV INJECTION IS NOT POSSIBLE. IN MODERATELY SEVERE POISONING ADMINISTER ATROPINE SULFATE, 0.4-2.0 MG REPEATED EVERY 15 MINUTES UNTIL ATROPINIZATION IS ACHIEVED (TACHYCARDIA, FLUSHING, DRY MOUTH, MYDRIASIS). MAINTAIN ATROPINIZATION BY REPEATED DOSES FOR 2-12 HOURS, OR LONGER, DEPENDING ON THE SEVERITY OF POISONING. THE APPEARANCE OF RALES IN THE LUNG BASES, MIOSIS, SALIVATION, NAUSEA, BRADYCARDIA, ARE ALL INDICATIONS OF INADEQUATE ATROPINIZATION. SEVERELY POISONED INDIVIDUALS MAY EXHIBIT REMARKABLE TOLERANCE TO ATROPINE; TWO OR MORE TIMES THE DOSAGES SUGGESTED ABOVE MAY BE NEEDED. PERSONS NOT POISONED OR ONLY SLIGHTLY POISONED, HOWEVER, MAY DEVELOP SIGNS OF ATROPINE TOXICITY FROM SUCH LARGE DOSAGES: FEVER, MUSCLE FIBRILLATIONS, AND DELIRIUM ARE THE MAIN SIGNS OF ATROPINE TOXICITY. IF THESE SIGNS APPEAR WHILE THE PATIENT IS FULLY ATROPINIZED, ATROPINE ADMINISTRATION SHOULD BE DISCONTINUED, AT LEAST TEMPORARILY. OBSERVE TREATED PATIENTS CLOSELY AT LEAST 24 HOURS TO INSURE THAT SYMPTOMS (POSSIBLY PULMONARY EDEMA) DO NOT RECUR AS ATROPINIZATION WEARS OFF. IN VERY SEVERE POISONINGS, METABOLIC DISPOSITION OF TOXICANT MAY REQUIRE SEVERAL HOURS OR DAYS DURING WHICH ATROPINIZATION MUST BE MAINTAINED. MARKEDLY LOWER LEVELS OF URINARY METABOLITES INDICATE THAT ATROPINE DOSAGE CAN BE TAPERED OFF. AS

DOSAGE IS REDUCED, CHECK THE LUNG BASES FREQUENTLY FOR RALES. IF RALES ARE HEARD OR OTHER SYMPTOMS RETURN, RE-ESTABLISH ATROPINIZATION PROMPTLY (MORGAN, RECOGNITION AND MANAGEMENT OF PESTICIDE POISONINGS, 3RD ED.). ADMINISTRATION OF ANTIDOTE MUST BE PERFORMED BY QUALIFIED MEDICAL PERSONNEL.
IN CASES OF SEVERE POISONING BY ORGANOPHOSPHATE PESTICIDES IN WHICH RESPIRATORY DEPRESSION, MUSCLE WEAKNESS AND TWITCHINGS ARE SEVERE, GIVE PRALIDOXIME (PROTOPAM-AYERST, 2-PAM), 1.0 GRAM INTRAVENOUSLY AT NO MORE THAN 0.5 GRAM PER MINUTE. DOSAGE OF PRALIDOXIME MAY BE REPEATED IN 1-2 HOURS, THEN AT 10-12 HOUR INTERVALS IF NEEDED. IN VERY SEVERE POISONINGS, DOSAGE RATES MAY BE DOUBLED. TREATMENT WITH PRALIDOXIME WILL BE MOST EFFECTIVE IF GIVEN WITHIN THIRTY-SIX HOURS AFTER POISONING (MORGAN, RECOGNITION AND MANAGEMENT OF PESTICIDE POISONINGS, 3RD ED.). ANTIDOTE SHOULD BE ADMINISTERED BY QUALIFIED MEDICAL PERSONNEL.

REACTIVITY

REACTIVITY: STABLE UNDER NORMAL TEMPERATURES AND PRESSURES.
INCOMPATIBILITIES: CARBOPHENOTHION OXYGEN ANALOG SULFONE: OXIDIZERS (STRONG): FIRE AND EXPLOSION HAZARD.
DECOMPOSITION: THERMAL DECOMPOSITION PRODUCTS MAY INCLUDE TOXIC OXIDES OF SULFUR AND CARBON.
POLYMERIZATION: HAZARDOUS POLYMERIZATION HAS NOT BEEN REPORTED TO OCCUR UNDER NORMAL TEMPERATURES AND PRESSURES.

STORAGE AND DISPOSAL

OBSERVE ALL FEDERAL, STATE AND LOCAL REGULATIONS WHEN STORING OR DISPOSING OF THIS SUBSTANCE. FOR ASSISTANCE, CONTACT THE DISTRICT DIRECTOR OF THE ENVIRONMENTAL PROTECTION AGENCY.

STORAGE

STORE IN ACCORDANCE WITH 40 CFR 165 RECOMMENDED PROCEDURES FOR THE DISPOSAL AND STORAGE OF PESTICIDES AND PESTICIDE CONTAINERS.
STORE AWAY FROM INCOMPATIBLE SUBSTANCES.

DISPOSAL

DISPOSAL MUST BE IN ACCORDANCE WITH 40 CFR 165 RECOMMENDED PROCEDURES FOR THE DISPOSAL AND STORAGE OF PESTICIDES AND PESTICIDE CONTAINERS.

CONDITIONS TO AVOID

MAY BURN BUT DOES NOT IGNITE READILY.

SPILL AND LEAK PROCEDURES

OCCUPATIONAL SPILL: DO NOT TOUCH SPILLED MATERIAL. STOP LEAK IF YOU CAN DO IT WITHOUT RISK. FOR SMALL SPILLS, TAKE UP WITH SAND OR OTHER ABSORBENT MATERIAL AND PLACE INTO CONTAINERS FOR LATER DISPOSAL. FOR SMALL DRY SPILLS, WITH A CLEAN SHOVEL PLACE MATERIAL INTO CLEAN, DRY CONTAINER AND COVER. MOVE CONTAINERS FROM SPILL AREA. FOR LARGER SPILLS, DIKE FAR AHEAD OF SPILL FOR LATER DISPOSAL. KEEP UNNECESSARY PEOPLE AWAY. ISOLATE HAZARD AREA AND DENY ENTRY.

PROTECTIVE EQUIPMENT

VENTILATION: PROVIDE LOCAL EXHAUST OR GENERAL DILUTION VENTILATION SYSTEM.
RESPIRATOR: THE FOLLOWING RESPIRATORS ARE RECOMMENDED BASED ON INFORMATION FOUND IN THE PHYSICAL DATA, TOXICITY AND HEALTH EFFECTS SECTIONS. THEY ARE RANKED IN ORDER FROM MINIMUM TO MAXIMUM RESPIRATORY PROTECTION. THE SPECIFIC RESPIRATOR SELECTED MUST BE BASED ON CONTAMINATION LEVELS FOUND IN THE WORK PLACE, MUST NOT EXCEED THE WORKING LIMITS OF THE RESPIRATOR AND BE JOINTLY APPROVED BY THE NATIONAL INSTITUTE FOR OCCUPATIONAL SAFETY AND HEALTH AND THE MINE SAFETY AND HEALTH ADMINISTRATION (NIOSH-MSHA).
CHEMICAL CARTRIDGE RESPIRATOR WITH AN ORGANIC VAPOR CARTRIDGE(S) WITH A FULL FACEPIECE AND ORGANIC VAPOR CARTRIDGE(S) IN COMBINATION WITH A DUST AND MIST FILTER.
POWERED AIR-PURIFYING RESPIRATOR WITH A TIGHT-FITTING FACEPIECE AND ORGANIC VAPOR CARTRIDGE(S) IN COMBINATION WITH A HIGH-EFFICIENCY PARTICULATE FILTER.
TYPE 'C' SUPPLIED-AIR RESPIRATOR WITH A FULL FACEPIECE OPERATED IN A PRESSURE-DEMAND OR OTHER POSITIVE PRESSURE MODE.
SELF-CONTAINED BREATHING APPARATUS WITH A FULL FACEPIECE OPERATED IN PRESSURE-DEMAND OR OTHER POSITIVE PRESSURE MODE.
FOR FIREFIGHTING AND OTHER IMMEDIATELY DANGEROUS TO LIFE OR HEALTH CONDITIONS:
SELF-CONTAINED BREATHING APPARATUS WITH FULL FACEPIECE OPERATED IN PRESSURE-DEMAND OR OTHER POSITIVE PRESSURE MODE.
SUPPLIED-AIR RESPIRATOR WITH FULL FACEPIECE AND OPERATED IN PRESSURE-DEMAND OR OTHER POSITIVE PRESSURE MODE IN COMBINATION WITH AN AUXILIARY SELF-CONTAINED BREATHING APPARATUS OPERATED IN PRESSURE-DEMAND OR OTHER POSITIVE PRESSURE MODE.
CLOTHING: EMPLOYEE MUST WEAR APPROPRIATE PROTECTIVE (IMPERVIOUS) CLOTHING AND EQUIPMENT TO PREVENT ANY POSSIBILITY OF SKIN CONTACT WITH THIS SUBSTANCE.
GLOVES: EMPLOYEE MUST WEAR APPROPRIATE PROTECTIVE GLOVES TO PREVENT CONTACT WITH THIS SUBSTANCE.
EYE PROTECTION: EMPLOYEE MUST WEAR SPLASH-PROOF OR DUST-RESISTANT SAFETY GOGGLES TO PREVENT EYE CONTACT WITH THIS SUBSTANCE.
EMERGENCY EYE WASH: WHERE THERE IS ANY POSSIBILITY THAT AN EMPLOYEE'S EYES MAY BE EXPOSED TO THIS SUBSTANCE, THE EMPLOYER SHOULD PROVIDE AN EYE WASH FOUNTAIN WITHIN THE IMMEDIATE WORK AREA FOR EMERGENCY USE.

AUTHORIZED BY- OCCUPATIONAL HEALTH SERVICES, INC.
CREATION DATE: 10/04/89 ***REVISION DATE:*** 05/07/90

MATERIAL SAFETY DATA SHEET

OCCUPATIONAL HEALTH SERVICES, INC.
AGRICULTURE AND PESTICIDE DIVISION
450 SEVENTH AVENUE, SUITE 2407
NEW YORK, NEW YORK 10123
1-800-445-MSDS OR (212) 967-1100

EMERGENCY CONTACT:
JOHN S. BRANSFORD, JR. (615) 292-1180

SUBSTANCE IDENTIFICATION

CAS-NUMBER 16662-86-5
SUBSTANCE: **CARBOPHENOTHION OXYGEN ANALOG SULFOXIDE**
TRADE NAMES/SYNONYMS: PHOSPHOROTHIOIC ACID, S-(((4-CHLOROPHENYL)SULFINYL)METHYL) O,O-DIETHYL ESTER; PHOSPHOROTHIOIC ACID, S-(((P-CHLOROPHENYL)SULFINYL)METHYL) O,O-DIETHYL ESTER; S-(((4-CHLOROPHENYL)SULFINYL)METHYL) O,O-DIETHYL PHOSPHOROTHIOATE; S-(((P-CHLOROPHENYL)SULFINYL)METHYL) O,O-DIETHYL PHOSPHOROTHIOATE; CARBOPHENOTHION OXON SULFOXIDE; CARBOPHENOXON SULFOXIDE; S-(P-CHLOROPHENYLSULFINYLMETHYL)-O,O-DIETHYL PHOSPHOROTHIOATE; TRITHION O.A. SULFOXIDE; C11H16CLO4PS2; PST04343
CHEMICAL FAMILY: ORGANOPHOSPHATE SULFOXIDE
MOLECULAR FORMULA: CL-(C6-H4)-S-(O)-C-H2-S-P-(O)-(O-C2-H5)2
MOLECULAR WEIGHT: 342.80
CERCLA RATINGS (SCALE 0-3): HEALTH=3 FIRE=U REACTIVITY=0 PERSISTENCE=2
NFPA RATINGS (SCALE 0-4): HEALTH=3 FIRE=U REACTIVITY=0

COMPONENTS AND CONTAMINANTS

COMPONENT: CARBOPHENOTHION OXYGEN ANALOG SULFOXIDE ***PERCENT:*** 100.0
CAS# 16662-86-5
OTHER CONTAMINANTS: NONE
EXPOSURE LIMITS: NO OCCUPATIONAL EXPOSURE LIMITS ESTABLISHED BY OSHA, ACGIH, OR NIOSH.

PHYSICAL DATA

DESCRIPTION: YELLOW LIQUID. ***BOILING POINT:*** NOT AVAILABLE
SPECIFIC GRAVITY: NOT AVAILABLE ***SOLUBILITY IN WATER:*** NOT AVAILABLE

FIRE AND EXPLOSION DATA

FIRE AND EXPLOSION HAZARD: UNKNOWN FIRE AND EXPLOSION HAZARD.
FLASH POINT: NOT AVAILABLE
FIREFIGHTING MEDIA: DRY CHEMICAL, CARBON DIOXIDE, HALON, WATER SPRAY OR STANDARD FOAM (1987 EMERGENCY RESPONSE GUIDEBOOK, DOT P 5800.4).
FOR LARGER FIRES, USE WATER SPRAY, FOG OR STANDARD FOAM (1987 EMERGENCY RESPONSE GUIDEBOOK, DOT P 5800.4).
FIREFIGHTING: MOVE CONTAINER FROM FIRE AREA IF POSSIBLE. DIKE FIRE CONTROL WATER FOR LATER DISPOSAL; DO NOT SCATTER THE MATERIAL. COOL FIRE-EXPOSED CONTAINERS WITH WATER FROM SIDE UNTIL WELL AFTER FIRE IS OUT. STAY AWAY FROM STORAGE TANK ENDS. WITHDRAW IMMEDIATELY IN CASE OF RISING SOUND FROM VENTING SAFETY DEVICE OR ANY DISCOLORATION OF STORAGE TANK DUE TO FIRE (1987 EMERGENCY RESPONSE GUIDEBOOK, DOT P 5800.4, GUIDE PAGE 28).

EXTINGUISH ONLY IF FLOW CAN BE STOPPED. USE FLOODING AMOUNTS OF WATER AS A FOG; SOLID STREAMS MAY BE INEFFECTIVE. COOL CONTAINERS WITH FLOODING AMOUNTS OF WATER FROM AS FAR A DISTANCE AS POSSIBLE. AVOID BREATHING POISONOUS VAPORS, KEEP UPWIND.

TRANSPORTATION DATA

DEPARTMENT OF TRANSPORTATION HAZARD CLASSIFICATION 49 CFR 172.101: POISON B

DEPARTMENT OF TRANSPORTATION LABELING REQUIREMENTS 49 CFR 172.101 AND SUBPART E: POISON

DEPARTMENT OF TRANSPORTATION PACKAGING REQUIREMENTS: 49 CFR 173.346 EXCEPTIONS: 49 CFR 173.345

TOXICITY

CARBOPHENOTHION OXYGEN ANALOG SULFOXIDE: TOXICITY DATA: 30 MG/KG ORAL-RAT LD50 (STAUFFER). CARCINOGEN STATUS: NONE. ACUTE TOXICITY LEVEL: HIGHLY TOXIC BY INGESTION. TARGET EFFECTS: CHOLINESTERASE INHIBITOR. POISONING MAY AFFECT THE NERVOUS SYSTEM.* AT INCREASED RISK FROM EXPOSURE: PERSONS WITH RESPIRATORY AILMENTS, RECENT EXPOSURE TO CHOLINESTERASE INHIBITORS OR IMPAIRED CHOLINESTERASE PRODUCTION, OR LIVER MALFUNCTION.* ADDITIONAL DATA: MAY CROSS THE PLACENTA. HIGH ENVIRONMENTAL TEMPERATURES OR EXPOSURE OF THE CHEMICAL TO VISIBLE OR ULTRAVIOLET LIGHT MAY ENHANCE THE TOXICITY. INTERACTIONS WITH MEDICATIONS MAY OCCUR.*

* MAY BE BASED ON GENERAL INFORMATION ON ORGANOPHOSPHATES.

HEALTH EFFECTS AND FIRST AID

INHALATION: CARBOPHENOTHION OXYGEN ANALOG SULFOXIDE: SCHIZOPHRENIC AND DEPRESSIVE REACTIONS HAVE BEEN REPORTED AFTER EXPOSURE TO CARBOPHENOTHION FOR 1.5-10 YEARS. SEE INFORMATION ON ORGANOPHOSPHATES.

ORGANOPHOSPHATES: CHOLINESTERASE INHIBITOR. **ACUTE EXPOSURE-** WHEN INHALED, THE FIRST EFFECTS OF CHOLINESTERASE INHIBITORS ARE USUALLY RESPIRATORY AND MAY INCLUDE NASAL HYPEREMIA AND WATERY DISCHARGE, COUGH, CHEST DISCOMFORT, DYSPNEA, AND WHEEZING DUE TO INCREASED BRONCHIAL SECRETIONS AND BRONCHOCONSTRICTION. IF SUFFICIENT AMOUNTS ARE ABSORBED, OTHER SYSTEMIC EFFECTS MAY BEGIN WITHIN A FEW MINUTES OR BE DELAYED FOR UP TO 12 HOURS. SYMPTOMS MAY INCLUDE PALLOR, NAUSEA, VOMITING, DIARRHEA, ABDOMINAL CRAMPS, HEADACHE, DIZZINESS, OCULAR PAIN, BLURRED VISION, MIOSIS OR IN SOME CASES, ESPECIALLY INITIALLY, MYDRIASIS, LACRIMATION, SALIVATION, SWEATING, AND CONFUSION. OTHER REPORTED CENTRAL NERVOUS SYSTEM OR NEUROMUSCULAR EFFECTS MAY INCLUDE ATAXIA, SLURRED SPEECH, AREFLEXIA, WEAKNESS, FATIGUE, FASCICULATIONS, TWITCHING, TREMORS POSSIBLY OF THE TONGUE AND EYELIDS, AND EVENTUALLY PARALYSIS OF THE EXTREMITIES AND POSSIBLY OF THE RESPIRATORY MUSCLES. IN SEVERE CASES THERE MAY ALSO BE INVOLUNTARY DEFECATION AND URINATION, CYANOSIS, PSYCHOSIS, HYPERGLYCEMIA, ACUTE PANCREATITIS, CARDIAC IRREGULARITIES, PULMONARY EDEMA, UNCONSCIOUSNESS, CONVULSIONS, AND COMA. DEATH IS PRIMARILY DUE TO RESPIRATORY FAILURE, ALTHOUGH CARDIOVASCULAR EFFECTS INCLUDING CARDIAC ARREST MAY ALSO BE IMPLICATED. LONG TERM SEQUELAE ARE RARE BUT MAY INCLUDE NEUROPSYCHIATRIC DISORDERS AND MYOPATHY WITH MUSCLE TENDERNESS. SOME ORGANOPHOSPHATES MAY CAUSE A DELAYED NEUROPATHY BEGINNING 1-4 WEEKS AFTER AN ACUTE EXPOSURE WHICH MAY OR MAY NOT HAVE CAUSED ACUTE CHOLINERGIC EFFECTS. NUMBNESS, TINGLING, WEAKNESS AND CRAMPING BEGINNING SYMMETRICALLY IN THE LOWER LIMBS MAY PROGRESS TO ATAXIA AND PARALYSIS. IN SEVERE CASES, UPPER LIMB INVOLVEMENT IS POSSIBLE AND FLACCID PARALYSIS MAY PROGRESS TO SPASTIC PARALYSIS WITH EXAGGERATED REFLEXES. IMPROVEMENT MAY OCCUR OVER MONTHS TO YEARS, BUT SOME RESIDUAL IMPAIRMENT USUALLY REMAINS. **CHRONIC EXPOSURE-** REPEATED OR PROLONGED EXPOSURE MAY RESULT IN THE EFFECTS OF ACUTE EXPOSURE INCLUDING THE DELAYED NEUROPATHY. OTHER EFFECTS REPORTED IN WORKERS REPEATEDLY EXPOSED INCLUDE IMPAIRED MEMORY AND CONCENTRATION, ACUTE PSYCHOSIS, SEVERE DEPRESSIONS, IRRITABILTY, CONFUSION, APATHY, EMOTIONAL LABILITY, SOCIAL WITHDRAWAL, CONFUSION, HEADACHE, SPEECH DIFFICULTIES, DELAYED REACTION TIMES, SPATIAL DISORIENTATION, NIGHTMARES, SLEEPWALKING, AND DROWSINESS OR INSOMNIA. AN INFLUENZA-LIKE CONDITION WITH HEADACHE, NAUSEA, WEAKNESS, ANOREXIA AND MALAISE HAS ALSO BEEN REPORTED.

FIRST AID- REMOVE FROM EXPOSURE AREA TO FRESH AIR IMMEDIATELY. IF BREATHING HAS STOPPED, GIVE ARTIFICIAL RESPIRATION. MAINTAIN AIRWAY AND BLOOD PRESSURE AND ADMINISTER OXYGEN IF AVAILABLE. KEEP AFFECTED PERSON WARM AND AT REST. TREAT SYMPTOMATICALLY AND SUPPORTIVELY. ADMINISTRATION OF OXYGEN SHOULD BE PERFORMED BY QUALIFIED PERSONNEL. GET MEDICAL ATTENTION IMMEDIATELY.

SKIN CONTACT: CARBOPHENOTHION OXYGEN ANALOG SULFOXIDE: SCHIZOPHRENIC AND DEPRESSIVE REACTIONS HAVE BEEN REPORTED AFTER EXPOSURE TO CARBOPHENOTHION FOR 1.5-10 YEARS. SEE INFORMATION ON ORGANOPHOSPHATES.

ORGANOPHOSPHATES: CHOLINESTERASE INHIBITOR. **ACUTE EXPOSURE-** LOCALIZED SWEATING AND FASCICULATIONS MAY OCCUR AT THE SITE OF CONTACT. IF SUFFICIENT AMOUNTS ARE ABSORBED, OTHER EFFECTS OF CHOLINESTERASE INHIBITION AS DESCRIBED IN ACUTE INHALATION MAY OCCUR. SYMPTOMS MAY BE DELAYED 2-3 HOURS, BUT USUALLY NO MORE THAN 12 HOURS. THE RATE OF ABSORPTION IS INCREASED BY THE PRESENCE OF DERMATITIS OR HIGH AMBIENT TEMPERATURES. DELAYED NEUROPATHY IS ALSO POSSIBLE. **CHRONIC EXPOSURE-** REPEATED OR PROLONGED EXPOSURE MAY CAUSE EFFECTS AS DESCRIBED IN ACUTE EXPOSURE. SOME ORGANOPHOSPHATES MAY CAUSE SENSITIZATION.

FIRST AID- REMOVE CONTAMINATED CLOTHING IMMEDIATELY. WASH CONTAMINATED AREAS WITH SOAP AND WATER FOLLOWED BY ALCOHOL (ARENA, POISONING, 4TH ED.). EMERGENCY PERSONNEL SHOULD WEAR GLOVES AND AVOID CONTAMINATION. TREAT RESPIRATORY DIFFICULTY WITH ARTIFICIAL RESPIRATION. GET MEDICAL ATTENTION IMMEDIATELY.

EYE CONTACT: CARBOPHENOTHION OXYGEN ANALOG SULFOXIDE: SEE INFORMATION ON ORGANOPHOSPHATES.

ORGANOPHOSPHATES: CHOLINESTERASE INHIBITOR. **ACUTE EXPOSURE-** DIRECT CONTACT MAY CAUSE PAIN, HYPEREMIA, LACRIMATION, TWITCHING OF THE EYELIDS, MIOSIS, AND CILIARY MUSCLE SPASM WITH LOSS OF ACCOMODATION, BLURRED OR DIMMED VISION AND BROWACHE. SOMETIMES MYDRIASIS MAY OCCUR INSTEAD OF MIOSIS. WITH SUFFICIENT EXPOSURE, OTHER SYMPTOMS OF CHOLINESTERASE INHIBITION AS DESCRIBED IN ACUTE INHALATION MAY OCCUR. **CHRONIC EXPOSURE-** REPEATED OR PROLONGED EXPOSURE MAY CAUSE EFFECTS AS DESCRIBED IN ACUTE EXPOSURE. SOME COMPOUNDS HAVE CAUSED TOXIC EFFECTS ON THE CRYSTALLINE LENS, CONJUNCTIVAL THICKENING AND OBSTRUCTION OF THE NASOLACRIMAL CANALS WHEN USED AS MIOTIC EYEDROPS.

FIRST AID- IRRIGATE EYES WITH WATER OR SALINE SOLUTION. IF SYMPTOMS OF POISONING OCCUR, TREAT RESPIRATORY DIFFICULTY WITH ARTIFICIAL RESPIRATION AND OXYGEN. OBSERVE PATIENT FOR AT LEAST 24-36 HOURS (GOSSELIN, CLINICAL TOXICOLOGY OF COMMERCIAL PRODUCTS, 5TH ED.). GET MEDICAL ATTENTION IMMEDIATELY. OXYGEN SHOULD BE ADMINISTERED BY QUALIFIED MEDICAL PERSONNEL.

INGESTION: CARBOPHENOTHION OXYGEN ANALOG SULFOXIDE: HIGHLY TOXIC. IN A 3 GENERATION STUDY, RATS FED 20 PPM COMMERCIAL GRADE CARBOPHENOTHION EXPERIENCED INCREASED FETAL RESORPTIONS AND FETOTOXICITY. SEE INFORMATION ON ORGANOPHOSPHATES.

ORGANOPHOSPHATES: CHOLINESTERASE INHIBITOR. **ACUTE EXPOSURE-** WHEN INGESTED, THE FIRST EFFECTS MAY BE NAUSEA, VOMITING, ANOREXIA, ABDOMINAL CRAMPS AND DIARRHEA. GASTROINTESTINAL ABSORPTION MAY CAUSE SYMPTOMS OF CHOLINESTERASE INHIBITION AS DESCRIBED IN ACUTE INHALATION. SYMPTOMS MAY BEGIN WITHIN MINUTES OR BE DELAYED FOR HOURS. DELAYED EFFECTS INCLUDING NEUROPATHY MAY ALSO OCCUR. **CHRONIC EXPOSURE-** REPEATED INGESTION MAY CAUSE EFFECTS AS DESCRIBED IN ACUTE EXPOSURE.

FIRST AID- IF PERSON IS ALERT AND RESPIRATION IS NOT DEPRESSED, GIVE SYRUP OF IPECAC FOLLOWED BY WATER (IF VOMITING OCCURS, KEEP HEAD BELOW HIPS TO PREVENT ASPIRATION). IF CONSCIOUSNESS LEVEL DECLINES OR VOMITING HAS NOT OCCURRED IN 15 MINUTES EMPTY STOMACH BY GASTRIC LAVAGE WITH THE AID OF CUFFED ENDOTRACHEAL TUBE USING ISOTONIC SALINE OR 5% SODIUM BICARBONATE FOLLOW WITH ACTIVATED CHARCOAL. ESTABLISH AND MAINTAIN AIRWAY. TREAT RESPIRATORY DIFFICULTY WITH ARTIFICIAL RESPIRATION AND OXYGEN. DO NOT GIVE MORPHINE, AMINOPHYLLINE, PHENOTHIAZINES, RESERPINE, FUROSEMIDE, OR ETHACRYNIC ACID (MORGAN, RECOGNITION AND MANAGEMENT OF PESTICIDE POISONINGS, 3RD ED.). TREAT SYMPTOMATICALLY AND SUPPORTIVELY. ADMINISTRATION OF OXYGEN AND LAVAGE MUST BE PERFORMED BY QUALIFIED MEDICAL PERSONNEL. GET MEDICAL ATTENTION IMMEDIATELY.

ANTIDOTE: THE FOLLOWING ANTIDOTE(S) HAVE BEEN RECOMMENDED. HOWEVER, THE DECISION AS TO WHETHER THE SEVERITY OF POISONING REQUIRES ADMINISTRATION OF ANY ANTIDOTE AND ACTUAL DOSE REQUIRED SHOULD BE MADE BY QUALIFIED MEDICAL PERSONNEL.

FOR CHOLINESTERASE INHIBITORS: ESTABLISH CLEAR AIRWAY AND TISSUE OXYGENATION BY ASPIRATION OF SECRETIONS, AND IF NECESSARY, BY ASSISTED PULMONARY VENTILATION WITH OXYGEN. IMPROVE TISSUE OXYGENATION AS MUCH AS POSSIBLE BEFORE ADMINISTERING ATROPINE TO MINIMIZE THE RISK OF VENTRICULAR FIBRILLATION. ADMINISTER ATROPINE SULFATE INTRAVENOUSLY, OR INTRAMUSCULARLY IF IV INJECTION IS NOT POSSIBLE. IN MODERATELY SEVERE POISONING ADMINISTER ATROPINE SULFATE, 0.4-2.0 MG REPEATED EVERY 15 MINUTES UNTIL ATROPINIZATION IS ACHIEVED (TACHYCARDIA, FLUSHING, DRY

MOUTH, MYDRIASIS). MAINTAIN ATROPINIZATION BY REPEATED DOSES FOR 2-12 HOURS, OR LONGER, DEPENDING ON THE SEVERITY OF POISONING. THE APPEARANCE OF RALES IN THE LUNG BASES, MIOSIS, SALIVATION, NAUSEA, BRADYCARDIA, ARE ALL INDICATIONS OF INADEQUATE ATROPINIZATION. SEVERELY POISONED INDIVIDUALS MAY EXHIBIT REMARKABLE TOLERANCE TO ATROPINE; TWO OR MORE TIMES THE DOSAGES SUGGESTED ABOVE MAY BE NEEDED. PERSONS NOT POISONED OR ONLY SLIGHTLY POISONED, HOWEVER, MAY DEVELOP SIGNS OF ATROPINE TOXICITY FROM SUCH LARGE DOSAGES: FEVER, MUSCLE FIBRILLATIONS, AND DELIRIUM ARE THE MAIN SIGNS OF ATROPINE TOXICITY. IF THESE SIGNS APPEAR WHILE THE PATIENT IS FULLY ATROPINIZED, ATROPINE ADMINISTRATION SHOULD BE DISCONTINUED, AT LEAST TEMPORARILY. OBSERVE TREATED PATIENTS CLOSELY AT LEAST 24 HOURS TO INSURE THAT SYMPTOMS (POSSIBLY PULMONARY EDEMA) DO NOT RECUR AS ATROPINIZATION WEARS OFF. IN VERY SEVERE POISONINGS, METABOLIC DISPOSITION OF TOXICANT MAY REQUIRE SEVERAL HOURS OR DAYS DURING WHICH ATROPINIZATION MUST BE MAINTAINED. MARKEDLY LOWER LEVELS OF URINARY METABOLITES INDICATE THAT ATROPINE DOSAGE CAN BE TAPERED OFF. AS DOSAGE IS REDUCED, CHECK THE LUNG BASES FREQUENTLY FOR RALES. IF RALES ARE HEARD OR OTHER SYMPTOMS RETURN, RE-ESTABLISH ATROPINIZATION PROMPTLY (MORGAN, RECOGNITION AND MANAGEMENT OF PESTICIDE POISONINGS, 3RD ED.). ADMINISTRATION OF ANTIDOTE MUST BE PERFORMED BY QUALIFIED MEDICAL PERSONNEL.

IN CASES OF SEVERE POISONING BY ORGANOPHOSPHATE PESTICIDES IN WHICH RESPIRATORY DEPRESSION, MUSCLE WEAKNESS AND TWITCHINGS ARE SEVERE, GIVE PRALIDOXIME (PROTOPAM-AYERST, 2-PAM), 1.0 GRAM INTRAVENOUSLY AT NO MORE THAN 0.5 GRAM PER MINUTE. DOSAGE OF PRALIDOXIME MAY BE REPEATED IN 1-2 HOURS, THEN AT 10-12 HOUR INTERVALS IF NEEDED. IN VERY SEVERE POISONINGS, DOSAGE RATES MAY BE DOUBLED. TREATMENT WITH PRALIDOXIME WILL BE MOST EFFECTIVE IF GIVEN WITHIN THIRTY-SIX HOURS AFTER POISONING (MORGAN, RECOGNITION AND MANAGEMENT OF PESTICIDE POISONINGS, 3RD ED.). ANTIDOTE SHOULD BE ADMINISTERED BY QUALIFIED MEDICAL PERSONNEL.

REACTIVITY

REACTIVITY: STABLE UNDER NORMAL TEMPERATURES AND PRESSURES.

INCOMPATIBILITIES: CARBOPHENOTHION OXYGEN ANALOG SULFOXIDE: OXIDIZERS (STRONG): FIRE AND EXPLOSION HAZARD.

DECOMPOSITION: THERMAL DECOMPOSITION PRODUCTS MAY INCLUDE TOXIC OXIDES OF SULFUR AND CARBON.

POLYMERIZATION: HAZARDOUS POLYMERIZATION HAS NOT BEEN REPORTED TO OCCUR UNDER NORMAL TEMPERATURES AND PRESSURES.

STORAGE AND DISPOSAL

OBSERVE ALL FEDERAL, STATE AND LOCAL REGULATIONS WHEN STORING OR DISPOSING OF THIS SUBSTANCE. FOR ASSISTANCE, CONTACT THE DISTRICT DIRECTOR OF THE ENVIRONMENTAL PROTECTION AGENCY.

****STORAGE****

STORE IN ACCORDANCE WITH 40 CFR 165 RECOMMENDED PROCEDURES FOR THE DISPOSAL AND STORAGE OF PESTICIDES AND PESTICIDE CONTAINERS.

STORE AWAY FROM INCOMPATIBLE SUBSTANCES.

****DISPOSAL****

DISPOSAL MUST BE IN ACCORDANCE WITH 40 CFR 165 RECOMMENDED PROCEDURES FOR THE DISPOSAL AND STORAGE OF PESTICIDES AND PESTICIDE CONTAINERS.

CONDITIONS TO AVOID

AVOID CONTACT WITH HEAT, SPARKS, FLAMES OR OTHER IGNITION SOURCES. VAPORS MAY BE EXPLOSIVE. MATERIAL IS POISONOUS; AVOID INHALATION OF VAPORS OR CONTACT WITH SKIN. DO NOT ALLOW MATERIAL TO CONTAMINATE WATER SOURCES.

SPILL AND LEAK PROCEDURES

OCCUPATIONAL SPILL: SHUT OFF IGNITION SOURCES. DO NOT TOUCH SPILLED MATERIAL. STOP LEAK IF YOU CAN DO IT WITHOUT RISK. USE WATER SPRAY TO REDUCE VAPORS. FOR SMALL SPILLS, TAKE UP WITH SAND OR OTHER ABSORBENT MATERIAL AND PLACE INTO CONTAINERS FOR LATER DISPOSAL. FOR LARGER SPILLS, DIKE FAR AHEAD OF SPILL FOR LATER DISPOSAL. NO SMOKING, FLAMES OR FLARES IN HAZARD AREA! KEEP UNNECESSARY PEOPLE AWAY; ISOLATE HAZARD AREA AND DENY ENTRY.

PROTECTIVE EQUIPMENT

VENTILATION: PROVIDE LOCAL EXHAUST VENTILATION. VENTILATION EQUIPMENT MUST BE EXPLOSION PROOF.

RESPIRATOR: THE FOLLOWING RESPIRATORS ARE RECOMMENDED BASED ON INFORMATION FOUND IN THE PHYSICAL DATA, TOXICITY AND HEALTH EFFECTS SECTIONS. THEY ARE RANKED IN ORDER FROM MINIMUM TO MAXIMUM RESPIRATORY PROTECTION. THE SPECIFIC RESPIRATOR SELECTED MUST BE BASED ON CONTAMINATION LEVELS FOUND IN THE WORK PLACE, MUST NOT EXCEED THE WORKING LIMITS OF THE RESPIRATOR AND BE JOINTLY APPROVED BY THE NATIONAL INSTITUTE FOR OCCUPATIONAL SAFETY AND HEALTH AND THE MINE SAFETY AND HEALTH ADMINISTRATION (NIOSH-MSHA).

CHEMICAL CARTRIDGE RESPIRATOR WITH FULL FACEPIECE AND PESTICIDE CARTRIDGE.

TYPE 'C' SUPPLIED-AIR RESPIRATOR WITH A FULL FACEPIECE OPERATED IN PRESSURE-DEMAND OR OTHER POSITIVE PRESSURE MODE OR WITH A FULL FACEPIECE, HELMET OR HOOD OPERATED IN CONTINUOUS-FLOW MODE.

SELF-CONTAINED BREATHING APPARATUS OPERATED IN PRESSURE-DEMAND OR OTHER POSITIVE PRESSURE MODE.

FOR FIREFIGHTING AND OTHER IMMEDIATELY DANGEROUS TO LIFE OR HEALTH CONDITIONS:

SELF-CONTAINED BREATHING APPARATUS WITH FULL FACEPIECE OPERATED IN PRESSURE-DEMAND OR OTHER POSITIVE PRESSURE MODE.

SUPPLIED-AIR RESPIRATOR WITH FULL FACEPIECE AND OPERATED IN PRESSURE-DEMAND OR OTHER POSITIVE PRESSURE MODE IN COMBINATION WITH AN AUXILIARY SELF-CONTAINED BREATHING APPARATUS OPERATED IN PRESSURE-DEMAND OR OTHER POSITIVE PRESSURE MODE.

CLOTHING: EMPLOYEE MUST WEAR APPROPRIATE PROTECTIVE (IMPERVIOUS) CLOTHING AND EQUIPMENT TO PREVENT ANY POSSIBILITY OF SKIN CONTACT WITH THIS SUBSTANCE.

GLOVES: EMPLOYEE MUST WEAR APPROPRIATE PROTECTIVE GLOVES TO PREVENT CONTACT WITH THIS SUBSTANCE.

EYE PROTECTION: EMPLOYEE MUST WEAR SPLASH-PROOF OR DUST-RESISTANT SAFETY GOGGLES TO PREVENT EYE CONTACT WITH THIS SUBSTANCE.

EMERGENCY EYE WASH: WHERE THERE IS ANY POSSIBILITY THAT AN EMPLOYEE'S EYES MAY BE EXPOSED TO THIS SUBSTANCE, THE EMPLOYER SHOULD PROVIDE AN EYE WASH FOUNTAIN WITHIN THE IMMEDIATE WORK AREA FOR EMERGENCY USE.

AUTHORIZED BY- OCCUPATIONAL HEALTH SERVICES, INC.

CREATION DATE: 10/04/89 ***REVISION DATE:*** 04/27/90

MATERIAL SAFETY DATA SHEET

OCCUPATIONAL HEALTH SERVICES, INC.
AGRICULTURE AND PESTICIDE DIVISION
450 SEVENTH AVENUE, SUITE 2407
NEW YORK, NEW YORK 10123
1-800-445-MSDS OR (212) 967-1100

EMERGENCY CONTACT:
JOHN S. BRANSFORD, JR. (615) 292-1180

SUBSTANCE IDENTIFICATION

CAS-NUMBER 16662-85-4

SUBSTANCE: <u>CARBOPHENOTHION SULFONE</u>

TRADE NAMES/SYNONYMS: S(P-CHLOROPHENYLSULFONYLMETHYL)-O,O-DIETHYLPHOSPHORODITHIOATE; TRITHION SULFONE; PHOSPHORODITHIOIC ACID, S-(((4-CHLOROPHENYL)SULFONYL)METHYL) O,O- DIETHYL ESTER; PHOSPHORODITHIOIC ACID, S-(((P-CHLOROPHENYL)SULFONYL)METHYL) O,O-DIETHYL ESTER; C11H16CLO4PS3; PST04344

CHEMICAL FAMILY: ORGANOPHOSPHATE SULFONE

MOLECULAR FORMULA: CL-(C6-H4)-S-O2-C-H2-S-P-(S)-(O-C2-H5)2

MOLECULAR WEIGHT: 374.87

CERCLA RATINGS (SCALE 0-3): HEALTH=3 FIRE=1 REACTIVITY=0 PERSISTENCE=2

NFPA RATINGS (SCALE 0-4): HEALTH=3 FIRE=1 REACTIVITY=0

COMPONENTS AND CONTAMINANTS

COMPONENT: CARBOPHENOTHION SULFONE ***PERCENT:*** 100.0
CAS# 16662-85-4

OTHER CONTAMINANTS: NONE

EXPOSURE LIMITS: NO OCCUPATIONAL EXPOSURE LIMITS ESTABLISHED BY OSHA, ACGIH, OR NIOSH.

PHYSICAL DATA

DESCRIPTION: WHITE POWDER. ***MELTING POINT:*** 208 F (98 C)

SPECIFIC GRAVITY: NOT AVAILABLE ***SOLUBILITY IN WATER:*** NOT AVAILABLE

FIRE AND EXPLOSION DATA

FIRE AND EXPLOSION HAZARD: SLIGHT FIRE HAZARD WHEN EXPOSED TO HEAT OR FLAME.

FIREFIGHTING MEDIA: DRY CHEMICAL, CARBON DIOXIDE, HALON, WATER SPRAY OR STANDARD FOAM (1987 EMERGENCY RESPONSE GUIDEBOOK, DOT P 5800.4). FOR LARGER FIRES, USE WATER SPRAY, FOG OR STANDARD FOAM (1987 EMERGENCY RESPONSE GUIDEBOOK, DOT P 5800.4).

FIREFIGHTING: MOVE CONTAINERS FROM FIRE AREA IF POSSIBLE (1987 EMERGENCY RESPONSE GUIDEBOOK, DOT P 5800.4, GUIDE PAGE 53).
EXTINGUISH ONLY IF FLOW CAN BE STOPPED. EXTINGUISH USING AGENT INDICATED. USE FLOODING AMOUNTS OF WATER AS A FOG. COOL CONTAINERS WITH FLOODING AMOUNTS OF WATER FROM AS FAR A DISTANCE AS POSSIBLE. AVOID BREATHING POISONOUS VAPORS, KEEP UPWIND. CONSIDER EVACUATION OF DOWNWIND AREA IF MATERIAL IS LEAKING.

TRANSPORTATION DATA

DEPARTMENT OF TRANSPORTATION HAZARD CLASSIFICATION 49 CFR 172.101: POISON B

DEPARTMENT OF TRANSPORTATION LABELING REQUIREMENTS 49 CFR 172.101 AND SUBPART E: POISON

DEPARTMENT OF TRANSPORTATION PACKAGING REQUIREMENTS: 49 CFR 173.365 EXCEPTIONS: 49 CFR 173.364

TOXICITY

CARBOPHENOTHION SULFONE: TOXICITY DATA: 30 MG/KG ORAL-RAT LD50 (STAUFFER). CARCINOGEN STATUS: NONE. ACUTE TOXICITY LEVEL: HIGHLY TOXIC BY INGESTION. TARGET EFFECTS: CHOLINESTERASE INHIBITOR. POISONING MAY AFFECT THE NERVOUS SYSTEM.* AT INCREASED RISK FROM EXPOSURE: PERSONS WITH RESPIRATORY AILMENTS, RECENT EXPOSURE TO CHOLINESTERASE INHIBITORS OR IMPAIRED CHOLINESTERASE PRODUCTION, OR LIVER MALFUNCTION.* ADDITIONAL DATA: MAY CROSS THE PLACENTA. HIGH ENVIRONMENTAL TEMPERATURES OR EXPOSURE OF THE CHEMICAL TO VISIBLE OR ULTRAVIOLET LIGHT MAY ENHANCE THE TOXICITY. INTERACTIONS WITH MEDICATIONS MAY OCCUR.*

* MAY BE BASED ON GENERAL INFORMATION ON ORGANOPHOSPHATES.

HEALTH EFFECTS AND FIRST AID

INHALATION: CARBOPHENOTHION SULFONE: SCHIZOPHRENIC AND DEPRESSIVE REACTIONS HAVE BEEN REPORTED AFTER EXPOSURE TO CARBOPHENOTHION FOR 1.5-10 YEARS. SEE INFORMATION ON ORGANOPHOSPHATES.
ORGANOPHOSPHATES: CHOLINESTERASE INHIBITOR. **ACUTE EXPOSURE-** WHEN INHALED, THE FIRST EFFECTS OF CHOLINESTERASE INHIBITORS ARE USUALLY RESPIRATORY AND MAY INCLUDE NASAL HYPEREMIA AND WATERY DISCHARGE, COUGH, CHEST DISCOMFORT, DYSPNEA, AND WHEEZING DUE TO INCREASED BRONCHIAL SECRETIONS AND BRONCHOCONSTRICTION. IF SUFFICIENT AMOUNTS ARE ABSORBED, OTHER SYSTEMIC EFFECTS MAY BEGIN WITHIN A FEW MINUTES OR BE DELAYED FOR UP TO 12 HOURS. SYMPTOMS MAY INCLUDE PALLOR, NAUSEA, VOMITING, DIARRHEA, ABDOMINAL CRAMPS, HEADACHE, DIZZINESS, OCULAR PAIN, BLURRED VISION, MIOSIS OR IN SOME CASES, ESPECIALLY INITIALLY, MYDRIASIS, LACRIMATION, SALIVATION, SWEATING, AND CONFUSION. OTHER REPORTED CENTRAL NERVOUS SYSTEM OR NEUROMUSCULAR EFFECTS MAY INCLUDE ATAXIA, SLURRED SPEECH, AREFLEXIA, WEAKNESS, FATIGUE, FASCICULATIONS, TWITCHING, TREMORS POSSIBLY OF THE TONGUE AND EYELIDS, AND EVENTUALLY PARALYSIS OF THE EXTREMITIES AND POSSIBLY OF THE RESPIRATORY MUSCLES. IN SEVERE CASES THERE MAY ALSO BE INVOLUNTARY DEFECATION AND URINATION, CYANOSIS, PSYCHOSIS, HYPERGLYCEMIA, ACUTE PANCREATITIS, CARDIAC IRREGULARITIES, PULMONARY EDEMA, UNCONSCIOUSNESS, CONVULSIONS, AND COMA. DEATH IS PRIMARILY DUE TO RESPIRATORY FAILURE, ALTHOUGH CARDIOVASCULAR EFFECTS INCLUDING CARDIAC ARREST MAY ALSO BE IMPLICATED. LONG TERM SEQUELAE ARE RARE BUT MAY INCLUDE NEUROPSYCHIATRIC DISORDERS AND MYOPATHY WITH MUSCLE TENDERNESS. SOME ORGANOPHOSPHATES MAY CAUSE A DELAYED NEUROPATHY BEGINNING 1-4 WEEKS AFTER AN ACUTE EXPOSURE WHICH MAY OR MAY NOT HAVE CAUSED ACUTE CHOLINERGIC EFFECTS. NUMBNESS, TINGLING, WEAKNESS AND CRAMPING BEGINNING SYMMETRICALLY IN THE LOWER LIMBS MAY PROGRESS TO ATAXIA AND PARALYSIS. IN SEVERE CASES, UPPER LIMB INVOLVEMENT IS POSSIBLE AND FLACCID PARALYSIS MAY PROGRESS TO SPASTIC PARALYSIS WITH EXAGGERATED REFLEXES. IMPROVEMENT MAY OCCUR OVER MONTHS TO YEARS, BUT SOME RESIDUAL IMPAIRMENT USUALLY REMAINS. **CHRONIC EXPOSURE-** REPEATED OR PROLONGED EXPOSURE MAY RESULT IN THE EFFECTS OF ACUTE EXPOSURE INCLUDING THE DELAYED NEUROPATHY. OTHER EFFECTS REPORTED IN WORKERS REPEATEDLY EXPOSED INCLUDE IMPAIRED MEMORY AND CONCENTRATION, ACUTE PSYCHOSIS, SEVERE DEPRESSIONS, IRRITABILTY, CONFUSION, APATHY, EMOTIONAL LABILITY, SOCIAL WITHDRAWAL, CONFUSION, HEADACHE, SPEECH DIFFICULTIES, DELAYED REACTION TIMES, SPATIAL DISORIENTATION, NIGHTMARES, SLEEPWALKING, AND DROWSINESS OR INSOMNIA. AN INFLUENZA-LIKE CONDITION WITH HEADACHE, NAUSEA, WEAKNESS, ANOREXIA AND MALAISE HAS ALSO BEEN REPORTED.

FIRST AID- REMOVE FROM EXPOSURE AREA TO FRESH AIR IMMEDIATELY. IF BREATHING HAS STOPPED, GIVE ARTIFICIAL RESPIRATION. MAINTAIN AIRWAY AND BLOOD PRESSURE AND ADMINISTER OXYGEN IF AVAILABLE. KEEP AFFECTED PERSON WARM AND AT REST. TREAT SYMPTOMATICALLY AND SUPPORTIVELY. ADMINISTRATION OF OXYGEN SHOULD BE PERFORMED BY QUALIFIED PERSONNEL. GET MEDICAL ATTENTION IMMEDIATELY.

SKIN CONTACT: CARBOPHENOTHION SULFONE: SCHIZOPHRENIC AND DEPRESSIVE REACTIONS HAVE BEEN REPORTED AFTER EXPOSURE TO CARBOPHENOTHION FOR 1.5-10 YEARS. SEE INFORMATION ON ORGANOPHOSPHATES.
ORGANOPHOSPHATES: CHOLINESTERASE INHIBITOR. **ACUTE EXPOSURE-** LOCALIZED SWEATING AND FASCICULATIONS MAY OCCUR AT THE SITE OF CONTACT. IF SUFFICIENT AMOUNTS ARE ABSORBED, OTHER EFFECTS OF CHOLINESTERASE INHIBITION AS DESCRIBED IN ACUTE INHALATION MAY OCCUR. SYMPTOMS MAY BE DELAYED 2-3 HOURS, BUT USUALLY NO MORE THAN 12 HOURS. THE RATE OF ABSORPTION IS INCREASED BY THE PRESENCE OF DERMATITIS OR HIGH AMBIENT TEMPERATURES. DELAYED NEUROPATHY IS ALSO POSSIBLE. **CHRONIC EXPOSURE-** REPEATED OR PROLONGED EXPOSURE MAY CAUSE EFFECTS AS DESCRIBED IN ACUTE EXPOSURE. SOME ORGANOPHOSPHATES MAY CAUSE SENSITIZATION.

FIRST AID- REMOVE CONTAMINATED CLOTHING IMMEDIATELY. WASH CONTAMINATED AREAS WITH SOAP AND WATER FOLLOWED BY ALCOHOL (ARENA, POISONING, 4TH ED.). EMERGENCY PERSONNEL SHOULD WEAR GLOVES AND AVOID CONTAMINATION. TREAT RESPIRATORY DIFFICULTY WITH ARTIFICIAL RESPIRATION. GET MEDICAL ATTENTION IMMEDIATELY.

EYE CONTACT: CARBOPHENOTHION SULFONE: SEE INFORMATION ON ORGANOPHOSPHATES.
ORGANOPHOSPHATES: CHOLINESTERASE INHIBITOR. **ACUTE EXPOSURE-** DIRECT CONTACT MAY CAUSE PAIN, HYPEREMIA, LACRIMATION, TWITCHING OF THE EYELIDS, MIOSIS, AND CILIARY MUSCLE SPASM WITH LOSS OF ACCOMODATION, BLURRED OR DIMMED VISION AND BROWACHE. SOMETIMES MYDRIASIS MAY OCCUR INSTEAD OF MIOSIS. WITH SUFFICIENT EXPOSURE, OTHER SYMPTOMS OF CHOLINESTERASE INHIBITION AS DESCRIBED IN ACUTE INHALATION MAY OCCUR. **CHRONIC EXPOSURE-** REPEATED OR PROLONGED EXPOSURE MAY CAUSE EFFECTS AS DESCRIBED IN ACUTE EXPOSURE. SOME COMPOUNDS HAVE CAUSED TOXIC EFFECTS ON THE CRYSTALLINE LENS, CONJUNCTIVAL THICKENING AND OBSTRUCTION OF THE NASOLACRIMAL CANALS WHEN USED AS MIOTIC EYEDROPS.

FIRST AID- IRRIGATE EYES WITH WATER OR SALINE SOLUTION. IF SYMPTOMS OF POISONING OCCUR, TREAT RESPIRATORY DIFFICULTY WITH ARTIFICIAL RESPIRATION AND OXYGEN. OBSERVE PATIENT FOR AT LEAST 24-36 HOURS (GOSSELIN, CLINICAL TOXICOLOGY OF COMMERCIAL PRODUCTS, 5TH ED.). GET MEDICAL ATTENTION IMMEDIATELY. OXYGEN SHOULD BE ADMINISTERED BY QUALIFIED MEDICAL PERSONNEL.

INGESTION: CARBOPHENOTHION SULFONE: HIGHLY TOXIC. IN A 3 GENERATION STUDY, RATS FED 20 PPM COMMERCIAL GRADE CARBOPHENOTHION EXPERIENCED INCREASED FETAL RESORPTIONS AND FETOTOXICITY. SEE INFORMATION ON ORGANOPHOSPHATES.
ORGANOPHOSPHATES: CHOLINESTERASE INHIBITOR. **ACUTE EXPOSURE-** WHEN INGESTED, THE FIRST EFFECTS MAY BE NAUSEA, VOMITING, ANOREXIA, ABDOMINAL CRAMPS AND DIARRHEA. GASTROINTESTINAL ABSORPTION MAY CAUSE SYMPTOMS OF CHOLINESTERASE INHIBITION AS DESCRIBED IN ACUTE INHALATION. SYMPTOMS MAY BEGIN WITHIN MINUTES OR BE DELAYED FOR HOURS. DELAYED EFFECTS INCLUDING NEUROPATHY MAY ALSO OCCUR. **CHRONIC EXPOSURE-** REPEATED INGESTION MAY CAUSE EFFECTS AS DESCRIBED IN ACUTE EXPOSURE.

FIRST AID- IF PERSON IS ALERT AND RESPIRATION IS NOT DEPRESSED, GIVE SYRUP OF IPECAC FOLLOWED BY WATER (IF VOMITING OCCURS, KEEP HEAD BELOW HIPS TO PREVENT ASPIRATION). IF CONSCIOUSNESS LEVEL DECLINES OR VOMITING HAS NOT OCCURRED IN 15 MINUTES EMPTY STOMACH BY GASTRIC LAVAGE WITH THE AID OF CUFFED ENDOTRACHEAL TUBE USING ISOTONIC SALINE OR 5% SODIUM BICARBONATE FOLLOW WITH ACTIVATED CHARCOAL. ESTABLISH AND MAINTAIN AIRWAY. TREAT RESPIRATORY DIFFICULTY WITH ARTIFICIAL RESPIRATION AND OXYGEN. DO NOT GIVE MORPHINE, AMINOPHYLLINE, PHENOTHIAZINES, RESERPINE, FUROSEMIDE, OR ETHACRYNIC ACID (MORGAN, RECOGNITION AND MANAGEMENT OF PESTICIDE POISONINGS, 3RD ED.). TREAT SYMPTOMATICALLY AND SUPPORTIVELY. ADMINISTRATION OF OXYGEN AND LAVAGE MUST BE PERFORMED BY QUALIFIED MEDICAL PERSONNEL. GET MEDICAL ATTENTION IMMEDIATELY.

ANTIDOTE: THE FOLLOWING ANTIDOTE(S) HAVE BEEN RECOMMENDED. HOWEVER, THE DECISION AS TO WHETHER THE SEVERITY OF POISONING REQUIRES ADMINISTRATION OF ANY ANTIDOTE AND ACTUAL DOSE REQUIRED SHOULD BE MADE BY QUALIFIED MEDICAL PERSONNEL.

FOR CHOLINESTERASE INHIBITORS: ESTABLISH CLEAR AIRWAY AND TISSUE OXYGENATION BY ASPIRATION OF SECRETIONS, AND IF NECESSARY, BY ASSISTED PULMONARY VENTILATION WITH OXYGEN. IMPROVE TISSUE OXYGENATION AS MUCH AS POSSIBLE BEFORE ADMINISTERING ATROPINE TO MINIMIZE THE RISK OF VENTRICULAR FIBRILLATION. ADMINISTER ATROPINE SULFATE INTRAVENOUSLY, OR INTRAMUSCULARLY IF IV INJECTION IS NOT POSSIBLE. IN MODERATELY SEVERE POISONING ADMINISTER ATROPINE SULFATE, 0.4-2.0 MG REPEATED EVERY 15 MINUTES UNTIL ATROPINIZATION IS ACHIEVED (TACHYCARDIA, FLUSHING, DRY MOUTH, MYDRIASIS). MAINTAIN ATROPINIZATION BY REPEATED DOSES FOR 2-12 HOURS, OR LONGER, DEPENDING ON THE SEVERITY OF POISONING. THE APPEARANCE OF RALES IN THE LUNG BASES, MIOSIS, SALIVATION, NAUSEA, BRADYCARDIA, ARE ALL INDICATIONS OF INADEQUATE ATROPINIZATION.
SEVERELY POISONED INDIVIDUALS MAY EXHIBIT REMARKABLE TOLERANCE TO ATROPINE; TWO OR MORE TIMES THE DOSAGES SUGGESTED ABOVE MAY BE NEEDED. PERSONS NOT POISONED OR ONLY SLIGHTLY POISONED, HOWEVER, MAY DEVELOP SIGNS OF ATROPINE TOXICITY FROM SUCH LARGE DOSAGES: FEVER, MUSCLE FIBRILLATIONS, AND DELIRIUM ARE THE MAIN SIGNS OF ATROPINE TOXICITY. IF THESE SIGNS APPEAR WHILE THE PATIENT IS FULLY ATROPINIZED, ATROPINE ADMINISTRATION SHOULD BE DISCONTINUED, AT LEAST TEMPORARILY. OBSERVE TREATED PATIENTS CLOSELY AT LEAST 24 HOURS TO INSURE THAT SYMPTOMS (POSSIBLY PULMONARY EDEMA) DO NOT RECUR AS ATROPINIZATION WEARS OFF. IN VERY SEVERE POISONINGS, METABOLIC DISPOSITION OF TOXICANT MAY REQUIRE SEVERAL HOURS OR DAYS DURING WHICH ATROPINIZATION MUST BE MAINTAINED. MARKEDLY LOWER LEVELS OF URINARY METABOLITES INDICATE THAT ATROPINE DOSAGE CAN BE TAPERED OFF. AS DOSAGE IS REDUCED, CHECK THE LUNG BASES FREQUENTLY FOR RALES. IF RALES ARE HEARD OR OTHER SYMPTOMS RETURN, RE-ESTABLISH ATROPINIZATION PROMPTLY (MORGAN, RECOGNITION AND MANAGEMENT OF PESTICIDE POISONINGS, 3RD ED.). ADMINISTRATION OF ANTIDOTE MUST BE PERFORMED BY QUALIFIED MEDICAL PERSONNEL.
IN CASES OF SEVERE POISONING BY ORGANOPHOSPHATE PESTICIDES IN WHICH RESPIRATORY DEPRESSION, MUSCLE WEAKNESS AND TWITCHINGS ARE SEVERE, GIVE PRALIDOXIME (PROTOPAM-AYERST, 2-PAM), 1.0 GRAM INTRAVENOUSLY AT NO MORE THAN 0.5 GRAM PER MINUTE. DOSAGE OF PRALIDOXIME MAY BE REPEATED IN 1-2 HOURS, THEN AT 10-12 HOUR INTERVALS IF NEEDED. IN VERY SEVERE POISONINGS, DOSAGE RATES MAY BE DOUBLED. TREATMENT WITH PRALIDOXIME WILL BE MOST EFFECTIVE IF GIVEN WITHIN THIRTY-SIX HOURS AFTER POISONING (MORGAN, RECOGNITION AND MANAGEMENT OF PESTICIDE POISONINGS, 3RD ED.). ANTIDOTE SHOULD BE ADMINISTERED BY QUALIFIED MEDICAL PERSONNEL.

REACTIVITY

REACTIVITY: STABLE UNDER NORMAL TEMPERATURES AND PRESSURES.
INCOMPATIBILITIES: CARBOPHENOTHION SULFONE: OXIDIZERS (STRONG): FIRE AND EXPLOSION HAZARD.
DECOMPOSITION: THERMAL DECOMPOSITION PRODUCTS MAY INCLUDE TOXIC OXIDES OF SULFUR AND CARBON.
POLYMERIZATION: HAZARDOUS POLYMERIZATION HAS NOT BEEN REPORTED TO OCCUR UNDER NORMAL TEMPERATURES AND PRESSURES.

STORAGE AND DISPOSAL

OBSERVE ALL FEDERAL, STATE AND LOCAL REGULATIONS WHEN STORING OR DISPOSING OF THIS SUBSTANCE. FOR ASSISTANCE, CONTACT THE DISTRICT DIRECTOR OF THE ENVIRONMENTAL PROTECTION AGENCY.

STORAGE

STORE IN ACCORDANCE WITH 40 CFR 165 RECOMMENDED PROCEDURES FOR THE DISPOSAL AND STORAGE OF PESTICIDES AND PESTICIDE CONTAINERS.
STORE AWAY FROM INCOMPATIBLE SUBSTANCES.

DISPOSAL

DISPOSAL MUST BE IN ACCORDANCE WITH 40 CFR 165 RECOMMENDED PROCEDURES FOR THE DISPOSAL AND STORAGE OF PESTICIDES AND PESTICIDE CONTAINERS.

CONDITIONS TO AVOID

MAY BURN BUT DOES NOT IGNITE READILY.

SPILL AND LEAK PROCEDURES

OCCUPATIONAL SPILL: DO NOT TOUCH SPILLED MATERIAL. STOP LEAK IF YOU CAN DO IT WITHOUT RISK. FOR SMALL SPILLS, TAKE UP WITH SAND OR OTHER ABSORBENT MATERIAL AND PLACE INTO CONTAINERS FOR LATER DISPOSAL. FOR SMALL DRY SPILLS, WITH A CLEAN SHOVEL PLACE MATERIAL INTO CLEAN, DRY CONTAINER AND COVER. MOVE CONTAINERS FROM SPILL AREA. FOR LARGER SPILLS, DIKE FAR AHEAD OF SPILL FOR LATER DISPOSAL. KEEP UNNECESSARY PEOPLE AWAY. ISOLATE HAZARD AREA AND DENY ENTRY.

PROTECTIVE EQUIPMENT

VENTILATION: PROVIDE LOCAL EXHAUST OR GENERAL DILUTION VENTILATION SYSTEM.
RESPIRATOR: THE FOLLOWING RESPIRATORS ARE RECOMMENDED BASED ON INFORMATION FOUND IN THE PHYSICAL DATA, TOXICITY AND HEALTH EFFECTS SECTIONS. THEY ARE RANKED IN ORDER FROM MINIMUM TO MAXIMUM RESPIRATORY PROTECTION. THE SPECIFIC RESPIRATOR SELECTED MUST BE BASED ON CONTAMINATION LEVELS FOUND IN THE WORK PLACE, MUST NOT EXCEED THE WORKING LIMITS OF THE RESPIRATOR AND BE JOINTLY APPROVED BY THE NATIONAL INSTITUTE FOR OCCUPATIONAL SAFETY AND HEALTH AND THE MINE SAFETY AND HEALTH ADMINISTRATION (NIOSH-MSHA).
CHEMICAL CARTRIDGE RESPIRATOR WITH AN ORGANIC VAPOR CARTRIDGE(S) WITH A FULL FACEPIECE AND ORGANIC VAPOR CARTRIDGE(S) IN COMBINATION WITH A DUST AND MIST FILTER.
POWERED AIR-PURIFYING RESPIRATOR WITH A TIGHT-FITTING FACEPIECE AND ORGANIC VAPOR CARTRIDGE(S) IN COMBINATION WITH A HIGH-EFFICIENCY PARTICULATE FILTER.
TYPE 'C' SUPPLIED-AIR RESPIRATOR WITH A FULL FACEPIECE OPERATED IN A PRESSURE-DEMAND OR OTHER POSITIVE PRESSURE MODE.
SELF-CONTAINED BREATHING APPARATUS WITH A FULL FACEPIECE OPERATED IN PRESSURE-DEMAND OR OTHER POSITIVE PRESSURE MODE.
FOR FIREFIGHTING AND OTHER IMMEDIATELY DANGEROUS TO LIFE OR HEALTH CONDITIONS:
SELF-CONTAINED BREATHING APPARATUS WITH FULL FACEPIECE OPERATED IN PRESSURE-DEMAND OR OTHER POSITIVE PRESSURE MODE.
SUPPLIED-AIR RESPIRATOR WITH FULL FACEPIECE AND OPERATED IN PRESSURE-DEMAND OR OTHER POSITIVE PRESSURE MODE IN COMBINATION WITH AN AUXILIARY SELF-CONTAINED BREATHING APPARATUS OPERATED IN PRESSURE-DEMAND OR OTHER POSITIVE PRESSURE MODE.
CLOTHING: EMPLOYEE MUST WEAR APPROPRIATE PROTECTIVE (IMPERVIOUS) CLOTHING AND EQUIPMENT TO PREVENT ANY POSSIBILITY OF SKIN CONTACT WITH THIS SUBSTANCE.
GLOVES: EMPLOYEE MUST WEAR APPROPRIATE PROTECTIVE GLOVES TO PREVENT CONTACT WITH THIS SUBSTANCE.
EYE PROTECTION: EMPLOYEE MUST WEAR SPLASH-PROOF OR DUST-RESISTANT SAFETY GOGGLES TO PREVENT EYE CONTACT WITH THIS SUBSTANCE.
EMERGENCY EYE WASH: WHERE THERE IS ANY POSSIBILITY THAT AN EMPLOYEE'S EYES MAY BE EXPOSED TO THIS SUBSTANCE, THE EMPLOYER SHOULD PROVIDE AN EYE WASH FOUNTAIN WITHIN THE IMMEDIATE WORK AREA FOR EMERGENCY USE.

AUTHORIZED BY- OCCUPATIONAL HEALTH SERVICES, INC.
CREATION DATE: 10/04/89 ***REVISION DATE:*** 05/07/90

MATERIAL SAFETY DATA SHEET

OCCUPATIONAL HEALTH SERVICES, INC.	EMERGENCY CONTACT:
AGRICULTURE AND PESTICIDE DIVISION	JOHN S. BRANSFORD, JR. (615) 292-1180
450 SEVENTH AVENUE, SUITE 2407	
NEW YORK, NEW YORK 10123	
1-800-445-MSDS OR (212) 967-1100	

SUBSTANCE IDENTIFICATION

CAS-NUMBER 17297-40-4
SUBSTANCE: **CARBOPHENOTHION SULFOXIDE**
TRADE NAMES/SYNONYMS: S-(P-CHLOROPHENYLSULFINYLMETHYL)-O,O-DIETHYLPHOSPHORODITHIOATE; TRITHION SULFOXIDE; PHOSPHORODITHIOIC ACID, S-(((4-CHLOROPHENYL)SULFINYL)METHYL) O,O- DIETHYL ESTER; PHOSPHORODITHIOIC ACID, S-(((P-CHLOROPHENYL)SULFINYL)METHYL) O,O-DIETHYL ESTER; CARBOFENOTHION SULFOXIDE; C11H16CLO3PS3; PST04345
CHEMICAL FAMILY: ORGANOPHOSPHATE SULFOXIDE
MOLECULAR FORMULA: CL-(C6-H4)-S-(O)-C-H2 S-P-(S)-(O-C2-H5)2
MOLECULAR WEIGHT: 358.87
CERCLA RATINGS (SCALE 0-3): HEALTH=3 FIRE=U REACTIVITY=0 PERSISTENCE=2
NFPA RATINGS (SCALE 0-4): HEALTH=3 FIRE=U REACTIVITY=0

COMPONENTS AND CONTAMINANTS

COMPONENT: CARBOPHENOTHION SULFOXIDE ***PERCENT:*** 100.0
CAS# 17297-40-4
OTHER CONTAMINANTS: NONE

EXPOSURE LIMITS: NO OCCUPATIONAL EXPOSURE LIMITS ESTABLISHED BY OSHA, ACGIH, OR NIOSH.

PHYSICAL DATA

DESCRIPTION: YELLOW LIQUID. ***BOILING POINT:*** NOT AVAILABLE
SPECIFIC GRAVITY: NOT AVAILABLE ***SOLUBILITY IN WATER:*** NOT AVAILABLE

FIRE AND EXPLOSION DATA

FIRE AND EXPLOSION HAZARD: UNKNOWN FIRE AND EXPLOSION HAZARD.
FLASH POINT: NOT AVAILABLE
FIREFIGHTING MEDIA: DRY CHEMICAL, CARBON DIOXIDE, HALON, WATER SPRAY OR STANDARD FOAM (1987 EMERGENCY RESPONSE GUIDEBOOK, DOT P 5800.4). FOR LARGER FIRES, USE WATER SPRAY, FOG OR STANDARD FOAM (1987 EMERGENCY RESPONSE GUIDEBOOK, DOT P 5800.4).
FIREFIGHTING: MOVE CONTAINER FROM FIRE AREA IF POSSIBLE. DIKE FIRE CONTROL WATER FOR LATER DISPOSAL; DO NOT SCATTER THE MATERIAL. COOL FIRE-EXPOSED CONTAINERS WITH WATER FROM SIDE UNTIL WELL AFTER FIRE IS OUT. STAY AWAY FROM STORAGE TANK ENDS. WITHDRAW IMMEDIATELY IN CASE OF RISING SOUND FROM VENTING SAFETY DEVICE OR ANY DISCOLORATION OF STORAGE TANK DUE TO FIRE (1987 EMERGENCY RESPONSE GUIDEBOOK, DOT P 5800.4, GUIDE PAGE 28).
EXTINGUISH ONLY IF FLOW CAN BE STOPPED. USE FLOODING AMOUNTS OF WATER AS A FOG; SOLID STREAMS MAY BE INEFFECTIVE. COOL CONTAINERS WITH FLOODING AMOUNTS OF WATER FROM AS FAR A DISTANCE AS POSSIBLE. AVOID BREATHING POISONOUS VAPORS, KEEP UPWIND.

TRANSPORTATION DATA

DEPARTMENT OF TRANSPORTATION HAZARD CLASSIFICATION 49 CFR 172.101: POISON B
DEPARTMENT OF TRANSPORTATION LABELING REQUIREMENTS 49 CFR 172.101 AND SUBPART E: POISON
DEPARTMENT OF TRANSPORTATION PACKAGING REQUIREMENTS: 49 CFR 173.346 EXCEPTIONS: 49 CFR 173.345

TOXICITY

CARBOPHENOTHION SULFOXIDE: TOXICITY DATA: 30 MG/KG ORAL-RAT LD50 (STAUFFER). CARCINOGEN STATUS: NONE. ACUTE TOXICITY LEVEL: HIGHLY TOXIC BY INGESTION. TARGET EFFECTS: CHOLINESTERASE INHIBITOR. POISONING MAY AFFECT THE NERVOUS SYSTEM.* AT INCREASED RISK FROM EXPOSURE: PERSONS WITH RESPIRATORY AILMENTS, RECENT EXPOSURE TO CHOLINESTERASE INHIBITORS OR IMPAIRED CHOLINESTERASE PRODUCTION, OR LIVER MALFUNCTION.* ADDITIONAL DATA: MAY CROSS THE PLACENTA. HIGH ENVIRONMENTAL TEMPERATURES OR EXPOSURE OF THE CHEMICAL TO VISIBLE OR ULTRAVIOLET LIGHT MAY ENHANCE THE TOXICITY. INTERACTIONS WITH MEDICATIONS MAY OCCUR.*
* MAY BE BASED ON GENERAL INFORMATION ON ORGANOPHOSPHATES.

HEALTH EFFECTS AND FIRST AID

INHALATION: CARBOPHENOTHION SULFOXIDE: SCHIZOPHRENIC AND DEPRESSIVE REACTIONS HAVE BEEN REPORTED AFTER EXPOSURE TO CARBOPHENOTHION FOR 1.5-10 YEARS. SEE INFORMATION ON ORGANOPHOSPHATES.
ORGANOPHOSPHATES: CHOLINESTERASE INHIBITOR. **ACUTE EXPOSURE-** WHEN INHALED, THE FIRST EFFECTS OF CHOLINESTERASE INHIBITORS ARE USUALLY RESPIRATORY AND MAY INCLUDE NASAL HYPEREMIA AND WATERY DISCHARGE, COUGH, CHEST DISCOMFORT, DYSPNEA, AND WHEEZING DUE TO INCREASED BRONCHIAL SECRETIONS AND BRONCHOCONSTRICTION. IF SUFFICIENT AMOUNTS ARE ABSORBED, OTHER SYSTEMIC EFFECTS MAY BEGIN WITHIN A FEW MINUTES OR BE DELAYED FOR UP TO 12 HOURS. SYMPTOMS MAY INCLUDE PALLOR, NAUSEA, VOMITING, DIARRHEA, ABDOMINAL CRAMPS, HEADACHE, DIZZINESS, OCULAR PAIN, BLURRED VISION, MIOSIS OR IN SOME CASES, ESPECIALLY INITIALLY, MYDRIASIS, LACRIMATION, SALIVATION, SWEATING, AND CONFUSION. OTHER REPORTED CENTRAL NERVOUS SYSTEM OR NEUROMUSCULAR EFFECTS MAY INCLUDE ATAXIA, SLURRED SPEECH, AREFLEXIA, WEAKNESS, FATIGUE, FASCICULATIONS, TWITCHING, TREMORS POSSIBLY OF THE TONGUE AND EYELIDS, AND EVENTUALLY PARALYSIS OF THE EXTREMITIES AND POSSIBLY OF THE RESPIRATORY MUSCLES. IN SEVERE CASES THERE MAY ALSO BE INVOLUNTARY DEFECATION AND URINATION, CYANOSIS, PSYCHOSIS, HYPERGLYCEMIA, ACUTE PANCREATITIS, CARDIAC IRREGULARITIES, PULMONARY EDEMA, UNCONSCIOUSNESS, CONVULSIONS, AND COMA. DEATH IS PRIMARILY DUE TO RESPIRATORY FAILURE, ALTHOUGH CARDIOVASCULAR EFFECTS INCLUDING CARDIAC ARREST MAY ALSO BE IMPLICATED. LONG TERM SEQUELAE ARE RARE BUT MAY INCLUDE NEUROPSYCHIATRIC DISORDERS AND MYOPATHY WITH MUSCLE TENDERNESS. SOME ORGANOPHOSPHATES MAY CAUSE A DELAYED NEUROPATHY BEGINNING 1-4 WEEKS AFTER AN ACUTE EXPOSURE WHICH MAY OR MAY NOT HAVE CAUSED ACUTE CHOLINERGIC EFFECTS. NUMBNESS, TINGLING, WEAKNESS AND CRAMPING BEGINNING SYMMETRICALLY IN THE LOWER LIMBS MAY PROGRESS TO ATAXIA AND PARALYSIS. IN SEVERE CASES, UPPER LIMB INVOLVEMENT IS POSSIBLE AND FLACCID PARALYSIS MAY PROGRESS TO SPASTIC PARALYSIS WITH EXAGGERATED REFLEXES. IMPROVEMENT MAY OCCUR OVER MONTHS TO YEARS, BUT SOME RESIDUAL IMPAIRMENT USUALLY REMAINS.
CHRONIC EXPOSURE- REPEATED OR PROLONGED EXPOSURE MAY RESULT IN THE EFFECTS OF ACUTE EXPOSURE INCLUDING THE DELAYED NEUROPATHY. OTHER EFFECTS REPORTED IN WORKERS REPEATEDLY EXPOSED INCLUDE IMPAIRED MEMORY AND CONCENTRATION, ACUTE PSYCHOSIS, SEVERE DEPRESSIONS, IRRITABILTY, CONFUSION, APATHY, EMOTIONAL LABILITY, SOCIAL WITHDRAWAL, CONFUSION, HEADACHE, SPEECH DIFFICULTIES, DELAYED REACTION TIMES, SPATIAL DISORIENTATION, NIGHTMARES, SLEEPWALKING, AND DROWSINESS OR INSOMNIA. AN INFLUENZA-LIKE CONDITION WITH HEADACHE, NAUSEA, WEAKNESS, ANOREXIA AND MALAISE HAS ALSO BEEN REPORTED.
FIRST AID- REMOVE FROM EXPOSURE AREA TO FRESH AIR IMMEDIATELY. IF BREATHING HAS STOPPED, GIVE ARTIFICIAL RESPIRATION. MAINTAIN AIRWAY AND BLOOD PRESSURE AND ADMINISTER OXYGEN IF AVAILABLE. KEEP AFFECTED PERSON WARM AND AT REST. TREAT SYMPTOMATICALLY AND SUPPORTIVELY. ADMINISTRATION OF OXYGEN SHOULD BE PERFORMED BY QUALIFIED PERSONNEL. GET MEDICAL ATTENTION IMMEDIATELY.

SKIN CONTACT: CARBOPHENOTHION SULFOXIDE: SCHIZOPHRENIC AND DEPRESSIVE REACTIONS HAVE BEEN REPORTED AFTER EXPOSURE TO CARBOPHENOTHION FOR 1.5-10 YEARS. SEE INFORMATION ON ORGANOPHOSPHATES.
ORGANOPHOSPHATES: CHOLINESTERASE INHIBITOR. **ACUTE EXPOSURE-** LOCALIZED SWEATING AND FASCICULATIONS MAY OCCUR AT THE SITE OF CONTACT. IF SUFFICIENT AMOUNTS ARE ABSORBED, OTHER EFFECTS OF CHOLINESTERASE INHIBITION AS DESCRIBED IN ACUTE INHALATION MAY OCCUR. SYMPTOMS MAY BE DELAYED 2-3 HOURS, BUT USUALLY NO MORE THAN 12 HOURS. THE RATE OF ABSORPTION IS INCREASED BY THE PRESENCE OF DERMATITIS OR HIGH AMBIENT TEMPERATURES. DELAYED NEUROPATHY IS ALSO POSSIBLE. **CHRONIC EXPOSURE-** REPEATED OR PROLONGED EXPOSURE MAY CAUSE EFFECTS AS DESCRIBED IN ACUTE EXPOSURE. SOME ORGANOPHOSPHATES MAY CAUSE SENSITIZATION.
FIRST AID- REMOVE CONTAMINATED CLOTHING IMMEDIATELY. WASH CONTAMINATED AREAS WITH SOAP AND WATER FOLLOWED BY ALCOHOL (ARENA, POISONING, 4TH ED.). EMERGENCY PERSONNEL SHOULD WEAR GLOVES AND AVOID CONTAMINATION. TREAT RESPIRATORY DIFFICULTY WITH ARTIFICIAL RESPIRATION. GET MEDICAL ATTENTION IMMEDIATELY.

EYE CONTACT: CARBOPHENOTHION SULFOXIDE: SEE INFORMATION ON ORGANOPHOSPHATES.
ORGANOPHOSPHATES: CHOLINESTERASE INHIBITOR. **ACUTE EXPOSURE-** DIRECT CONTACT MAY CAUSE PAIN, HYPEREMIA, LACRIMATION, TWITCHING OF THE EYELIDS, MIOSIS, AND CILIARY MUSCLE SPASM WITH LOSS OF ACCOMODATION, BLURRED OR DIMMED VISION AND BROWACHE. SOMETIMES MYDRIASIS MAY OCCUR INSTEAD OF MIOSIS. WITH SUFFICIENT EXPOSURE, OTHER SYMPTOMS OF CHOLINESTERASE INHIBITION AS DESCRIBED IN ACUTE INHALATION MAY OCCUR. **CHRONIC EXPOSURE-** REPEATED OR PROLONGED EXPOSURE MAY CAUSE EFFECTS AS DESCRIBED IN ACUTE EXPOSURE. SOME COMPOUNDS HAVE CAUSED TOXIC EFFECTS ON THE CRYSTALLINE LENS, CONJUNCTIVAL THICKENING AND OBSTRUCTION OF THE NASOLACRIMAL CANALS WHEN USED AS MIOTIC EYEDROPS.
FIRST AID- IRRIGATE EYES WITH WATER OR SALINE SOLUTION. IF SYMPTOMS OF POISONING OCCUR, TREAT RESPIRATORY DIFFICULTY WITH ARTIFICIAL RESPIRATION AND OXYGEN. OBSERVE PATIENT FOR AT LEAST 24-36 HOURS (GOSSELIN, CLINICAL TOXICOLOGY OF COMMERCIAL PRODUCTS, 5TH ED.). GET MEDICAL ATTENTION IMMEDIATELY. OXYGEN SHOULD BE ADMINISTERED BY QUALIFIED MEDICAL PERSONNEL.

INGESTION: CARBOPHENOTHION SULFOXIDE: HIGHLY TOXIC. IN A 3 GENERATION STUDY, RATS FED 20 PPM COMMERCIAL GRADE CARBOPHENOTHION EXPERIENCED INCREASED FETAL RESORPTIONS AND FETOTOXICITY. SEE INFORMATION ON ORGANOPHOSPHATES.
ORGANOPHOSPHATES: CHOLINESTERASE INHIBITOR. **ACUTE EXPOSURE-** WHEN INGESTED, THE FIRST EFFECTS MAY BE NAUSEA, VOMITING, ANOREXIA, ABDOMINAL CRAMPS AND DIARRHEA. GASTROINTESTINAL ABSORPTION MAY CAUSE SYMPTOMS OF CHOLINESTERASE INHIBITION AS DESCRIBED IN ACUTE INHALATION. SYMPTOMS MAY BEGIN WITHIN MINUTES OR BE DELAYED FOR HOURS. DELAYED EFFECTS INCLUDING NEUROPATHY MAY ALSO OCCUR. **CHRONIC EXPOSURE-** REPEATED INGESTION MAY CAUSE EFFECTS AS DESCRIBED IN ACUTE EXPOSURE.
FIRST AID- IF PERSON IS ALERT AND RESPIRATION IS NOT DEPRESSED, GIVE SYRUP OF IPECAC FOLLOWED BY WATER (IF VOMITING OCCURS, KEEP HEAD BELOW HIPS TO PREVENT ASPIRATION). IF CONSCIOUSNESS LEVEL DECLINES OR VOMITING HAS NOT OCCURRED IN 15 MINUTES EMPTY STOMACH BY GASTRIC LAVAGE WITH THE AID OF CUFFED ENDOTRACHEAL TUBE USING ISOTONIC SALINE OR 5% SODIUM

BICARBONATE FOLLOW WITH ACTIVATED CHARCOAL. ESTABLISH AND MAINTAIN AIRWAY. TREAT RESPIRATORY DIFFICULTY WITH ARTIFICIAL RESPIRATION AND OXYGEN. DO NOT GIVE MORPHINE, AMINOPHYLLINE, PHENOTHIAZINES, RESERPINE, FUROSEMIDE, OR ETHACRYNIC ACID (MORGAN, RECOGNITION AND MANAGEMENT OF PESTICIDE POISONINGS, 3RD ED.). TREAT SYMPTOMATICALLY AND SUPPORTIVELY. ADMINISTRATION OF OXYGEN AND LAVAGE MUST BE PERFORMED BY QUALIFIED MEDICAL PERSONNEL. GET MEDICAL ATTENTION IMMEDIATELY.

ANTIDOTE: THE FOLLOWING ANTIDOTE(S) HAVE BEEN RECOMMENDED. HOWEVER, THE DECISION AS TO WHETHER THE SEVERITY OF POISONING REQUIRES ADMINISTRATION OF ANY ANTIDOTE AND ACTUAL DOSE REQUIRED SHOULD BE MADE BY QUALIFIED MEDICAL PERSONNEL.

FOR CHOLINESTERASE INHIBITORS: ESTABLISH CLEAR AIRWAY AND TISSUE OXYGENATION BY ASPIRATION OF SECRETIONS, AND IF NECESSARY, BY ASSISTED PULMONARY VENTILATION WITH OXYGEN. IMPROVE TISSUE OXYGENATION AS MUCH AS POSSIBLE BEFORE ADMINISTERING ATROPINE TO MINIMIZE THE RISK OF VENTRICULAR FIBRILLATION. ADMINISTER ATROPINE SULFATE INTRAVENOUSLY, OR INTRAMUSCULARLY IF IV INJECTION IS NOT POSSIBLE. IN MODERATELY SEVERE POISONING ADMINISTER ATROPINE SULFATE, 0.4-2.0 MG REPEATED EVERY 15 MINUTES UNTIL ATROPINIZATION IS ACHIEVED (TACHYCARDIA, FLUSHING, DRY MOUTH, MYDRIASIS). MAINTAIN ATROPINIZATION BY REPEATED DOSES FOR 2-12 HOURS, OR LONGER, DEPENDING ON THE SEVERITY OF POISONING. THE APPEARANCE OF RALES IN THE LUNG BASES, MIOSIS, SALIVATION, NAUSEA, BRADYCARDIA, ARE ALL INDICATIONS OF INADEQUATE ATROPINIZATION. SEVERELY POISONED INDIVIDUALS MAY EXHIBIT REMARKABLE TOLERANCE TO ATROPINE; TWO OR MORE TIMES THE DOSAGES SUGGESTED ABOVE MAY BE NEEDED. PERSONS NOT POISONED OR ONLY SLIGHTLY POISONED, HOWEVER, MAY DEVELOP SIGNS OF ATROPINE TOXICITY FROM SUCH LARGE DOSAGES: FEVER, MUSCLE FIBRILLATIONS, AND DELIRIUM ARE THE MAIN SIGNS OF ATROPINE TOXICITY. IF THESE SIGNS APPEAR WHILE THE PATIENT IS FULLY ATROPINIZED, ATROPINE ADMINISTRATION SHOULD BE DISCONTINUED, AT LEAST TEMPORARILY. OBSERVE TREATED PATIENTS CLOSELY AT LEAST 24 HOURS TO INSURE THAT SYMPTOMS (POSSIBLY PULMONARY EDEMA) DO NOT RECUR AS ATROPINIZATION WEARS OFF. IN VERY SEVERE POISONINGS, METABOLIC DISPOSITION OF TOXICANT MAY REQUIRE SEVERAL HOURS OR DAYS DURING WHICH ATROPINIZATION MUST BE MAINTAINED. MARKEDLY LOWER LEVELS OF URINARY METABOLITES INDICATE THAT ATROPINE DOSAGE CAN BE TAPERED OFF. AS DOSAGE IS REDUCED, CHECK THE LUNG BASES FREQUENTLY FOR RALES. IF RALES ARE HEARD OR OTHER SYMPTOMS RETURN, RE-ESTABLISH ATROPINIZATION PROMPTLY (MORGAN, RECOGNITION AND MANAGEMENT OF PESTICIDE POISONINGS, 3RD ED.). ADMINISTRATION OF ANTIDOTE MUST BE PERFORMED BY QUALIFIED MEDICAL PERSONNEL.

IN CASES OF SEVERE POISONING BY ORGANOPHOSPHATE PESTICIDES IN WHICH RESPIRATORY DEPRESSION, MUSCLE WEAKNESS AND TWITCHINGS ARE SEVERE, GIVE PRALIDOXIME (PROTOPAM-AYERST, 2-PAM), 1.0 GRAM INTRAVENOUSLY AT NO MORE THAN 0.5 GRAM PER MINUTE. DOSAGE OF PRALIDOXIME MAY BE REPEATED IN 1-2 HOURS, THEN AT 10-12 HOUR INTERVALS IF NEEDED. IN VERY SEVERE POISONINGS, DOSAGE RATES MAY BE DOUBLED. TREATMENT WITH PRALIDOXIME WILL BE MOST EFFECTIVE IF GIVEN WITHIN THIRTY-SIX HOURS AFTER POISONING (MORGAN, RECOGNITION AND MANAGEMENT OF PESTICIDE POISONINGS, 3RD ED.). ANTIDOTE SHOULD BE ADMINISTERED BY QUALIFIED MEDICAL PERSONNEL.

REACTIVITY

REACTIVITY: STABLE UNDER NORMAL TEMPERATURES AND PRESSURES.

INCOMPATIBILITIES: CARBOPHENOTHION SULFOXIDE: OXIDIZERS (STRONG): FIRE AND EXPLOSION HAZARD.

DECOMPOSITION: THERMAL DECOMPOSITION PRODUCTS MAY INCLUDE TOXIC OXIDES OF SULFUR AND CARBON.

POLYMERIZATION: HAZARDOUS POLYMERIZATION HAS NOT BEEN REPORTED TO OCCUR UNDER NORMAL TEMPERATURES AND PRESSURES.

STORAGE AND DISPOSAL

OBSERVE ALL FEDERAL, STATE AND LOCAL REGULATIONS WHEN STORING OR DISPOSING OF THIS SUBSTANCE. FOR ASSISTANCE, CONTACT THE DISTRICT DIRECTOR OF THE ENVIRONMENTAL PROTECTION AGENCY.

STORAGE

STORE IN ACCORDANCE WITH 40 CFR 165 RECOMMENDED PROCEDURES FOR THE DISPOSAL AND STORAGE OF PESTICIDES AND PESTICIDE CONTAINERS.

STORE AWAY FROM INCOMPATIBLE SUBSTANCES.

DISPOSAL

DISPOSAL MUST BE IN ACCORDANCE WITH 40 CFR 165 RECOMMENDED PROCEDURES FOR THE DISPOSAL AND STORAGE OF PESTICIDES AND PESTICIDE CONTAINERS.

CONDITIONS TO AVOID

AVOID CONTACT WITH HEAT, SPARKS, FLAMES OR OTHER IGNITION SOURCES. VAPORS MAY BE EXPLOSIVE. MATERIAL IS POISONOUS; AVOID INHALATION OF VAPORS OR CONTACT WITH SKIN. DO NOT ALLOW MATERIAL TO CONTAMINATE WATER SOURCES.

SPILL AND LEAK PROCEDURES

OCCUPATIONAL SPILL: SHUT OFF IGNITION SOURCES. DO NOT TOUCH SPILLED MATERIAL. STOP LEAK IF YOU CAN DO IT WITHOUT RISK. USE WATER SPRAY TO REDUCE VAPORS. FOR SMALL SPILLS, TAKE UP WITH SAND OR OTHER ABSORBENT MATERIAL AND PLACE INTO CONTAINERS FOR LATER DISPOSAL. FOR LARGER SPILLS, DIKE FAR AHEAD OF SPILL FOR LATER DISPOSAL. NO SMOKING, FLAMES OR FLARES IN HAZARD AREA! KEEP UNNECESSARY PEOPLE AWAY; ISOLATE HAZARD AREA AND DENY ENTRY.

PROTECTIVE EQUIPMENT

VENTILATION: PROVIDE LOCAL EXHAUST VENTILATION. VENTILATION EQUIPMENT MUST BE EXPLOSION PROOF.

RESPIRATOR: THE FOLLOWING RESPIRATORS ARE RECOMMENDED BASED ON INFORMATION FOUND IN THE PHYSICAL DATA, TOXICITY AND HEALTH EFFECTS SECTIONS. THEY ARE RANKED IN ORDER FROM MINIMUM TO MAXIMUM RESPIRATORY PROTECTION. THE SPECIFIC RESPIRATOR SELECTED MUST BE BASED ON CONTAMINATION LEVELS FOUND IN THE WORK PLACE, MUST NOT EXCEED THE WORKING LIMITS OF THE RESPIRATOR AND BE JOINTLY APPROVED BY THE NATIONAL INSTITUTE FOR OCCUPATIONAL SAFETY AND HEALTH AND THE MINE SAFETY AND HEALTH ADMINISTRATION (NIOSH-MSHA).

CHEMICAL CARTRIDGE RESPIRATOR WITH FULL FACEPIECE AND PESTICIDE CARTRIDGE.

TYPE 'C' SUPPLIED-AIR RESPIRATOR WITH A FULL FACEPIECE OPERATED IN PRESSURE-DEMAND OR OTHER POSITIVE PRESSURE MODE OR WITH A FULL FACEPIECE, HELMET OR HOOD OPERATED IN CONTINUOUS-FLOW MODE.

SELF-CONTAINED BREATHING APPARATUS OPERATED IN PRESSURE-DEMAND OR OTHER POSITIVE PRESSURE MODE.

FOR FIREFIGHTING AND OTHER IMMEDIATELY DANGEROUS TO LIFE OR HEALTH CONDITIONS:

SELF-CONTAINED BREATHING APPARATUS WITH FULL FACEPIECE OPERATED IN PRESSURE-DEMAND OR OTHER POSITIVE PRESSURE MODE.

SUPPLIED-AIR RESPIRATOR WITH FULL FACEPIECE AND OPERATED IN PRESSURE-DEMAND OR OTHER POSITIVE PRESSURE MODE IN COMBINATION WITH AN AUXILIARY SELF-CONTAINED BREATHING APPARATUS OPERATED IN PRESSURE-DEMAND OR OTHER POSITIVE PRESSURE MODE.

CLOTHING: EMPLOYEE MUST WEAR APPROPRIATE PROTECTIVE (IMPERVIOUS) CLOTHING AND EQUIPMENT TO PREVENT ANY POSSIBILITY OF SKIN CONTACT WITH THIS SUBSTANCE.

GLOVES: EMPLOYEE MUST WEAR APPROPRIATE PROTECTIVE GLOVES TO PREVENT CONTACT WITH THIS SUBSTANCE.

EYE PROTECTION: EMPLOYEE MUST WEAR SPLASH-PROOF OR DUST-RESISTANT SAFETY GOGGLES TO PREVENT EYE CONTACT WITH THIS SUBSTANCE.

EMERGENCY EYE WASH: WHERE THERE IS ANY POSSIBILITY THAT AN EMPLOYEE'S EYES MAY BE EXPOSED TO THIS SUBSTANCE, THE EMPLOYER SHOULD PROVIDE AN EYE WASH FOUNTAIN WITHIN THE IMMEDIATE WORK AREA FOR EMERGENCY USE.

AUTHORIZED BY- OCCUPATIONAL HEALTH SERVICES, INC.

CREATION DATE: 10/04/89 ***REVISION DATE:*** 04/27/90

MATERIAL SAFETY DATA SHEET

OCCUPATIONAL HEALTH SERVICES, INC.
AGRICULTURE AND PESTICIDE DIVISION
450 SEVENTH AVENUE, SUITE 2407
NEW YORK, NEW YORK 10123
1-800-445-MSDS OR (212) 967-1100

EMERGENCY CONTACT:
JOHN S. BRANSFORD, JR. (615) 292-1180

SUBSTANCE IDENTIFICATION

CAS-NUMBER 5234-68-4

SUBSTANCE: CARBOXIN

TRADE NAMES/SYNONYMS: 1,4-OXATHIIN-3-CARBOXAMIDE, 5,6-DIHYDRO-2-METHYL-N-PHENYL-; 1,4-OXATHIIN-3-CARBOXANILIDE, 5,6-DIHYDRO-2-METHYL-; 5,6-DIHYDRO-2-METHYL-N-PHENYL-1,4-OXATHIIN-3-CARBOXAMIDE; 2,3-DIHYDRO-5-CARBOXANILIDO-6-METHYL-1,4-OXATHIIN; 5,6-DIHYDRO-2-METHYL-1,4-OXATHI-IN-3-CARBOXANILIDE; 5,6-DIHYDRO-2-METHYL-1,4-OXATHI-INE-3-CARBOXANILIDE; 2,3-DIHYDRO-6-METHYL-5-PHENYLCARBAMOYL-1,4-OXATHIIN; 5,6-DIHYDRO-2-

METHYL-1,4-OXATHIIN-3-CARBOXANILIDE; CARBOXINE; D 735; DCMO; DMOC; VITAVAX; C12H13NO2S; PST04348

CHEMICAL FAMILY: OXATHION

MOLECULAR FORMULA: C12-H13-N-O2-S

MOLECULAR WEIGHT: 235.32

CERCLA RATINGS (SCALE 0-3): HEALTH=2 FIRE=1 REACTIVITY=0 PERSISTENCE=1

NFPA RATINGS (SCALE 0-4): HEALTH=2 FIRE=1 REACTIVITY=0

COMPONENTS AND CONTAMINANTS

COMPONENT: CARBOXIN ***PERCENT:*** 97

COMPONENT: RELATED COMPOUNDS, INERT INGREDIENTS ***PERCENT:*** 3

EXPOSURE LIMITS: NO OCCUPATIONAL EXPOSURE LIMITS ESTABLISHED BY OSHA, ACGIH, OR NIOSH.

PHYSICAL DATA

DESCRIPTION: OFF-WHITE, CRYSTALLINE SOLID WITH A FAINT ODOR

MELTING POINT: 199 F (93 C) ***SPECIFIC GRAVITY:*** 1.22

VAPOR PRESSURE: <1.0 MMHG @ 20 C ***SOLUBILITY IN WATER:*** 170 PPM

SOLVENT SOLUBILITY: SOLUBLE IN ACETONE, METHANOL, BENZENE, ETHANOL, AND DIMETHYL SULPHOXIDE

FIRE AND EXPLOSION DATA

FIRE AND EXPLOSION HAZARD: SLIGHT FIRE HAZARD WHEN EXPOSED TO HEAT OR FLAME.

FLASH POINT: 397 F (203 C) (OC) ***LOWER EXPLOSIVE LIMIT:*** 0.052 OZ/FT3

AUTOIGNITION TEMP.: 784 F (418 C)

FIREFIGHTING MEDIA: DRY CHEMICAL, CARBON DIOXIDE, WATER SPRAY OR FOAM FOR LARGER FIRES, USE WATER SPRAY, FOG OR ALCOHOL FOAM

FIREFIGHTING: MOVE CONTAINER FROM FIRE AREA IF POSSIBLE. DO NOT SCATTER SPILLED MATERIAL WITH MORE WATER THAN NEEDED FOR FIRE CONTROL. DIKE FIRE CONTROL WATER FOR LATER DISPOSAL

USE AGENTS SUITABLE FOR TYPE OF SURROUNDING FIRE. AVOID BREATHING HAZARDOUS VAPORS, KEEP UPWIND.

TOXICITY

CARBOXIN: TOXICITY DATA: 8 GM/KG SKIN-RABBIT LD50; 1050 MG/KG SKIN-RAT LD50; 430 MG/KG ORAL-RAT LD50; 3200 MG/KG ORAL-MOUSE LD50; 3200 MG/KG UNREPORTED-MAMMAL LD50; MUTAGENIC DATA (RTECS). CARCINOGEN STATUS: NONE. ACUTE TOXICITY LEVEL: TOXIC BY INGESTION AND SLIGHTLY TOXIC BY DERMAL ABSORPTION. TARGET EFFECTS: NO DATA AVAILABLE.

HEALTH EFFECTS AND FIRST AID

INHALATION: CARBOXIN: **ACUTE EXPOSURE**- NO MORTALITY WAS OBSERVED IN RATS AFTER A ONE HOUR EXPOSURE TO A CONCENTRATION OF 20 ML/L. **CHRONIC EXPOSURE**- NO DATA AVAILABLE.

FIRST AID- REMOVE FROM EXPOSURE AREA TO FRESH AIR IMMEDIATELY. IF BREATHING HAS STOPPED, PERFORM ARTIFICIAL RESPIRATION. KEEP PERSON WARM AND AT REST. TREAT SYMPTOMATICALLY AND SUPPORTIVELY. GET MEDICAL ATTENTION IMMEDIATELY.

SKIN CONTACT: CARBOXIN: **ACUTE EXPOSURE**- 500 MG APPLIED TO RABBIT SKIN DID NOT PRODUCED IRRITATION. A DOSE OF 8 GM/KG OF A 50% AQUEOUS SLURRY WAS NOT LETHAL TO RABBITS BY DERMAL ABSORPTION. **CHRONIC EXPOSURE**- NO ADVERSE EFFECTS IN RABBITS WERE REPORTED FROM A 21-DAY DERMAL STUDY OF 3.0 GM/KG.

FIRST AID- REMOVE CONTAMINATED CLOTHING AND SHOES IMMEDIATELY. WASH AFFECTED AREA WITH SOAP OR MILD DETERGENT AND LARGE AMOUNTS OF WATER UNTIL NO EVIDENCE OF CHEMICAL REMAINS (APPROXIMATELY 15-20 MINUTES). GET MEDICAL ATTENTION IMMEDIATELY.

EYE CONTACT: CARBOXIN: **ACUTE EXPOSURE**- MAY CAUSE EYE IRRITATION. A 100 MG OF 75% WETTABLE POWDER/DUST FORMULATION APPLIED TO RABBIT EYES PRODUCED MARKED AND PERSISTENT CONJUNCTIVAL EFFECTS, IRIS IRRITATION, AND CORNEAL OPACITY THAT WAS STILL PRESENT AFTER 14 DAYS OF APPLICATION. **CHRONIC EXPOSURE**- NO DATA AVAILABLE.

FIRST AID- WASH EYES IMMEDIATELY WITH LARGE AMOUNTS OF WATER OR NORMAL SALINE, OCCASIONALLY LIFTING UPPER AND LOWER LIDS, UNTIL NO EVIDENCE OF CHEMICAL REMAINS (APPROXIMATELY 15-20 MINUTES). GET MEDICAL ATTENTION IMMEDIATELY.

INGESTION: CARBOXIN: TOXIC. **ACUTE EXPOSURE**- A LETHAL DOSE IN RATS WAS 430 MG/KG. CARBOXIN INHIBITS OXIDATIVE METABOLISM AND SUCCINIC DEHYDROGENASE IN MITOCHONDRIA OF LIVER AND BONE. **CHRONIC EXPOSURE**- DEGENERATIVE RENAL CHANGES WERE OBSERVED IN A 90-DAY FEEDING STUDY IN RATS AT THE 600 PPM LEVEL. POOR SURVIVAL AND WEIGHT GAIN DEPRESSION WERE REPORTED IN RATS FROM A 2 YEAR FEEDING STUDY AT THE 600 PPM LEVEL.

FIRST AID- REMOVE BY GASTRIC LAVAGE AND CATHARSIS. MAINTAIN BLOOD PRESSURE AND AIRWAY. GIVE OXYGEN IF RESPIRATION IS DEPRESSED. DO NOT PERFORM GASTRIC LAVAGE IF VICTIM IS UNCONSCIOUS. GET MEDICAL ATTENTION IMMEDIATELY (DREISBACH, HANDBOOK OF POISONING, 12TH ED.). ADMINISTRATION OF LAVAGE OR OXYGEN SHOULD BE PERFORMED BY QUALIFIED MEDICAL PERSONNEL.

ANTIDOTE: NO SPECIFIC ANTIDOTE. TREAT SYMPTOMATICALLY AND SUPPORTIVELY.

REACTIVITY

REACTIVITY: STABLE UNDER NORMAL CONDITIONS IN AN ENCLOSED CONTAINER. IT IS READILY INACTIVATED BY ULTRAVIOLET LIGHT AND SUNLIGHT.

INCOMPATIBILITIES: CARBOXIN: ACIDS (STRONG): INCOMPATIBLE. HIGHLY ALKALINE CONDITIONS: INCOMPATIBLE. OXIDIZERS: INCOMPATIBLE.

DECOMPOSITION: THERMAL DECOMPOSITION MAY RELEASE TOXIC OXIDES OF NITROGEN AND SULFUR.

POLYMERIZATION: HAZARDOUS POLYMERIZATION HAS NOT BEEN REPORTED TO OCCUR UNDER NORMAL TEMPERATURES AND PRESSURES.

STORAGE AND DISPOSAL

OBSERVE ALL FEDERAL, STATE AND LOCAL REGULATIONS WHEN STORING OR DISPOSING OF THIS SUBSTANCE. FOR ASSISTANCE, CONTACT THE DISTRICT DIRECTOR OF THE ENVIRONMENTAL PROTECTION AGENCY.

****STORAGE****

STORE IN ACCORDANCE WITH 40 CFR 165 RECOMMENDED PROCEDURES FOR THE DISPOSAL AND STORAGE OF PESTICIDES AND PESTICIDE CONTAINERS.

STORE AWAY FROM INCOMPATIBLE SUBSTANCES.

STORE IN A COOL, DRY PLACE.

****DISPOSAL****

DISPOSAL MUST BE IN ACCORDANCE WITH 40 CFR 165 RECOMMENDED PROCEDURES FOR THE DISPOSAL AND STORAGE OF PESTICIDES AND PESTICIDE CONTAINERS.

CONDITIONS TO AVOID

NONE REPORTED.

SPILL AND LEAK PROCEDURES

OCCUPATIONAL SPILL: REMOVE BY SWEEPING OR VACUUMING.

PROTECTIVE EQUIPMENT

VENTILATION: PROVIDE LOCAL EXHAUST OR GENERAL DILUTION VENTILATION SYSTEM.

RESPIRATOR: THE FOLLOWING RESPIRATORS ARE RECOMMENDED BASED ON INFORMATION FOUND IN THE PHYSICAL DATA, TOXICITY AND HEALTH EFFECTS SECTIONS. THEY ARE RANKED IN ORDER FROM MINIMUM TO MAXIMUM RESPIRATORY PROTECTION. THE SPECIFIC RESPIRATOR SELECTED MUST BE BASED ON CONTAMINATION LEVELS FOUND IN THE WORK PLACE, MUST NOT EXCEED THE WORKING LIMITS OF THE RESPIRATOR AND BE JOINTLY APPROVED BY THE NATIONAL INSTITUTE FOR OCCUPATIONAL SAFETY AND HEALTH AND THE MINE SAFETY AND HEALTH ADMINISTRATION (NIOSH-MSHA).

CHEMICAL CARTRIDGE RESPIRATOR WITH AN ORGANIC VAPOR CARTRIDGE(S) WITH A FULL FACEPIECE AND ORGANIC VAPOR CARTRIDGE(S) IN COMBINATION WITH A DUST AND MIST FILTER.

POWERED AIR-PURIFYING RESPIRATOR WITH A TIGHT-FITTING FACEPIECE AND ORGANIC VAPOR CARTRIDGE(S) IN COMBINATION WITH A HIGH-EFFICIENCY PARTICULATE FILTER.

TYPE 'C' SUPPLIED-AIR RESPIRATOR WITH A FULL FACEPIECE OPERATED IN A PRESSURE-DEMAND OR OTHER POSITIVE PRESSURE MODE.

SELF-CONTAINED BREATHING APPARATUS WITH A FULL FACEPIECE OPERATED IN PRESSURE-DEMAND OR OTHER POSITIVE PRESSURE MODE.

FOR FIREFIGHTING AND OTHER IMMEDIATELY DANGEROUS TO LIFE OR HEALTH CONDITIONS:

SELF-CONTAINED BREATHING APPARATUS WITH FULL FACEPIECE OPERATED IN PRESSURE-DEMAND OR OTHER POSITIVE PRESSURE MODE.

SUPPLIED-AIR RESPIRATOR WITH FULL FACEPIECE AND OPERATED IN PRESSURE-DEMAND OR OTHER POSITIVE PRESSURE MODE IN COMBINATION WITH AN AUXILIARY SELF-CONTAINED BREATHING APPARATUS OPERATED IN PRESSURE-DEMAND OR OTHER POSITIVE PRESSURE MODE.

CLOTHING: EMPLOYEE MUST WEAR APPROPRIATE PROTECTIVE (IMPERVIOUS) CLOTHING AND EQUIPMENT TO PREVENT REPEATED OR PROLONGED SKIN CONTACT WITH THIS SUBSTANCE.

GLOVES: EMPLOYEE MUST WEAR APPROPRIATE PROTECTIVE GLOVES TO PREVENT CONTACT WITH THIS SUBSTANCE.

EYE PROTECTION: EMPLOYEE MUST WEAR SPLASH-PROOF OR DUST-RESISTANT SAFETY GOGGLES TO PREVENT EYE CONTACT WITH THIS SUBSTANCE.

EMERGENCY EYE WASH: WHERE THERE IS ANY POSSIBILITY THAT AN EMPLOYEE'S EYES MAY BE EXPOSED TO THIS SUBSTANCE, THE EMPLOYER SHOULD PROVIDE AN EYE WASH FOUNTAIN WITHIN THE IMMEDIATE WORK AREA FOR EMERGENCY USE.

AUTHORIZED BY- OCCUPATIONAL HEALTH SERVICES, INC.
CREATION DATE: 10/04/89 ***REVISION DATE:*** 05/14/90

MATERIAL SAFETY DATA SHEET

OCCUPATIONAL HEALTH SERVICES, INC.
AGRICULTURE AND PESTICIDE DIVISION
450 SEVENTH AVENUE, SUITE 2407
NEW YORK, NEW YORK 10123
1-800-445-MSDS OR (212) 967-1100

EMERGENCY CONTACT:
JOHN S. BRANSFORD, JR. (615) 292-1180

SUBSTANCE IDENTIFICATION

CAS-NUMBER 9003-01-4

SUBSTANCE: POLYACRYLIC ACID

TRADE NAMES/SYNONYMS: ACRYLIC ACID, POLYMERS; ACRYLIC ACID RESIN; CARBOXY POLYMETHYLENE; CARBOPOL; CARBOXYVINYL POLYMER; CARBOMER; CARPOLENE; GOOD-RITE K-700; HALOFLEX 208; JURIMER AC 10H; POLY(ACRYLIC ACID); 2-PROPENOIC ACID HOMOPOLYMER; RACRYL; TEXCRYL; VERSICOL E 7; VISCALEX; VISCON 103; WS 24; XPA; ZINPOL; PST04349

CHEMICAL FAMILY: ACRYLIC ACID POLYMER

MOLECULAR FORMULA: (C3-H4-O2)X

MOLECULAR WEIGHT: VARIES

CERCLA RATINGS (SCALE 0-3): HEALTH=U FIRE=1 REACTIVITY=0 PERSISTENCE=0

NFPA RATINGS (SCALE 0-4): HEALTH=U FIRE=1 REACTIVITY=0

COMPONENTS AND CONTAMINANTS

COMPONENT: POLYACRYLIC ACID ***PERCENT:*** 100
CAS# 9003-01-4

EXPOSURE LIMITS: POLYACRYLIC ACID: NONE ESTABLISHED
BF GOODRICH COMPANY RECOMMENDS USING LIMITS FOR NUISANCE DUST: 5 MG/M3 OSHA TWA (RESPIRABLE DUST) 10 MG/M3 ACGIH TWA (TOTAL DUST)

PHYSICAL DATA

DESCRIPTION: WHITE FLUFFY POWDER, WITH A SLIGHT ACIDIC ODOR.

MELTING POINT: NOT AVAILABLE ***SPECIFIC GRAVITY:*** 1.41 ***VOLATILITY:*** 2.0% H2O

PH: 2.5-3.0 (1% AQUEOUS) ***SOLUBILITY IN WATER:*** SOLUBLE

SOLVENT SOLUBILITY: DIOXANE, DIMETHYLFORMAMIDE, ETHANOL, METHANOL, ISOPROPANOL; INSOLUBLE IN ETHER, BENZENE AND CYCLOHEXANE.

FIRE AND EXPLOSION DATA

FIRE AND EXPLOSION HAZARD: SLIGHT FIRE HAZARD WHEN EXPOSED TO HEAT OR FLAME.

LOWER EXPLOSIVE LIMIT: 0.325 OZ/FT3 ***AUTOIGNITION TEMP.:*** 968 F (520 C)

FLAMMABILITY CLASS(OSHA): IIIB

FIREFIGHTING MEDIA: DRY CHEMICAL, CARBON DIOXIDE, HALON, WATER SPRAY OR STANDARD FOAM (1987 EMERGENCY RESPONSE GUIDEBOOK, DOT P 5800.4).
FOR LARGER FIRES, USE WATER SPRAY, FOG OR STANDARD FOAM (1987 EMERGENCY RESPONSE GUIDEBOOK, DOT P 5800.4).

FIREFIGHTING: MOVE CONTAINER FROM FIRE AREA IF POSSIBLE. DO NOT SCATTER SPILLED MATERIAL WITH HIGH PRESSURE WATER STREAMS. DIKE FIRE CONTROL WATER FOR LATER DISPOSAL (1987 EMERGENCY RESPONSE GUIDEBOOK, DOT P 5800.4, GUIDE PAGE 31).
USE AGENTS SUITABLE FOR TYPE OF SURROUNDING FIRE. AVOID BREATHING HAZARDOUS VAPORS, KEEP UPWIND.

TOXICITY

POLYACRYLIC ACID: TOXICITY DATA: 2500 MG/KG ORAL-RAT LD50; 70 MG/KG INTRAVENOUS-MOUSE LD50. CARCINOGEN STATUS: NONE (IARC GROUP-3). ACUTE TOXICITY LEVEL: MODERATELY TOXIC BY INGESTION. TARGET EFFECTS: NO DATA AVAILABLE.

HEALTH EFFECTS AND FIRST AID

INHALATION: POLYACRYLIC ACID: **ACUTE EXPOSURE**- NO DATA AVAILABLE. MAY CAUSE IRRITATION OF THE MUCOUS MEMBRANES. **CHRONIC EXPOSURE**- NO DATA AVAILABLE.

FIRST AID- REMOVE FROM EXPOSURE AREA TO FRESH AIR IMMEDIATELY. IF BREATHING HAS STOPPED, PERFORM ARTIFICIAL RESPIRATION. KEEP PERSON WARM AND AT REST. TREAT SYMPTOMATICALLY AND SUPPORTIVELY. GET MEDICAL ATTENTION IMMEDIATELY.

SKIN CONTACT: POLYACRYLIC ACID: **ACUTE EXPOSURE**- NO DATA AVAILABLE. MAY CAUSE IRRITATION. **CHRONIC EXPOSURE**- NO DATA AVAILABLE.

FIRST AID- REMOVE CONTAMINATED CLOTHING AND SHOES IMMEDIATELY. WASH AFFECTED AREA WITH SOAP OR MILD DETERGENT AND LARGE AMOUNTS OF WATER UNTIL NO EVIDENCE OF CHEMICAL REMAINS (APPROXIMATELY 15-20 MINUTES). GET MEDICAL ATTENTION IMMEDIATELY.

EYE CONTACT: POLYACRYLIC ACID: **ACUTE EXPOSURE**- DIRECT CONTACT MAY CAUSE EYE IRRITATION. A GELATINOUS FILM MAY FORM AS A RESULT OF THE REACTION BETWEEN THIS CHEMICAL AND MOISTURE. IRRITATION EXPERIENCED, IF ANY, IS EXPECTED TO BE A PHYSICAL RATHER THAN A CHEMICAL EFFECT. **CHRONIC EXPOSURE**- MAY CAUSE CONJUNCTIVITIS AFTER REPEATED OR PROLONGED EXPOSURE.

FIRST AID- WASH EYES IMMEDIATELY WITH LARGE AMOUNTS OF WATER OR NORMAL SALINE, OCCASIONALLY LIFTING UPPER AND LOWER LIDS, UNTIL NO EVIDENCE OF CHEMICAL REMAINS (APPROXIMATELY 15-20 MINUTES). GET MEDICAL ATTENTION IMMEDIATELY.

INGESTION: POLYACRYLIC ACID: **ACUTE EXPOSURE**- IT IS POORLY ABSORBED BY THE GASTROINTESTINAL TRACT AND THEREFORE IS THOUGHT TO BE ESSENTIALLY NONTOXIC. **CHRONIC EXPOSURE**- NO DATA AVAILABLE.

FIRST AID- TREAT SYMPTOMATICALLY AND SUPPORTIVELY. GET MEDICAL ATTENTION IMMEDIATELY. IF VOMITING OCCURS, KEEP HEAD LOWER THAN HIPS TO PREVENT ASPIRATION.

ANTIDOTE: NO SPECIFIC ANTIDOTE. TREAT SYMPTOMATICALLY AND SUPPORTIVELY.

REACTIVITY

REACTIVITY: STABLE UNDER NORMAL TEMPERATURES AND PRESSURES.

INCOMPATIBILITIES: POLYACRYLIC ACID: AMMONIA: MAY REACT WITH INTENSE HEAT. BASIC AMINES: MAY REACT WITH INTENSE HEAT. POTASSIUM HYDROXIDE: MAY REACT WITH INTENSE HEAT. SODIUM HYDROXIDE: MAY REACT WITH INTENSE HEAT. STRONG BASIC MATERIALS: MAY REACT WITH INTENSE HEAT.

DECOMPOSITION: THERMAL DECOMPOSITION PRODUCTS MAY INCLUDE TOXIC OXIDES OF CARBON.

POLYMERIZATION: HAZARDOUS POLYMERIZATION HAS NOT BEEN REPORTED TO OCCUR UNDER NORMAL TEMPERATURES AND PRESSURES.

CONDITIONS TO AVOID

MAY BURN BUT DOES NOT IGNITE READILY. AVOID CONTACT WITH STRONG OXIDIZERS, EXCESSIVE HEAT, SPARKS, OR OPEN FLAME.

SPILL AND LEAK PROCEDURES

OCCUPATIONAL SPILL: SWEEP UP AND PLACE IN SUITABLE CLEAN, DRY CONTAINERS FOR RECLAMATION OR LATER DISPOSAL. DO NOT FLUSH SPILLED MATERIAL INTO SEWER. KEEP UNNECESSARY PEOPLE AWAY.

PROTECTIVE EQUIPMENT

VENTILATION: PROVIDE LOCAL EXHAUST OR GENERAL DILUTION VENTILATION SYSTEM.

RESPIRATOR: THE FOLLOWING RESPIRATORS ARE RECOMMENDED BASED ON INFORMATION FOUND IN THE PHYSICAL DATA, TOXICITY AND HEALTH EFFECTS SECTIONS. THEY ARE RANKED IN ORDER FROM MINIMUM TO MAXIMUM RESPIRATORY PROTECTION. THE SPECIFIC RESPIRATOR SELECTED MUST BE BASED ON CONTAMINATION LEVELS FOUND IN THE WORK PLACE, MUST NOT EXCEED THE WORKING LIMITS OF THE RESPIRATOR AND BE JOINTLY APPROVED BY THE NATIONAL INSTITUTE FOR OCCUPATIONAL SAFETY AND HEALTH AND THE MINE SAFETY AND HEALTH ADMINISTRATION (NIOSH-MSHA).
DUST AND MIST RESPIRATOR WITH A FULL FACEPIECE.
AIR-PURIFYING FULL FACEPIECE RESPIRATOR WITH A HIGH-EFFICIENCY PARTICULATE FILTER.
POWERED AIR-PURIFYING RESPIRATOR WITH A TIGHT-FITTING FACEPIECE AND HIGH-EFFICIENCY PARTICULATE FILTER.
TYPE 'C' SUPPLIED-AIR RESPIRATOR WITH A FULL FACEPIECE OPERATED IN PRESSURE-DEMAND OR OTHER POSITIVE PRESSURE MODE OR WITH A FULL FACEPIECE, HELMET OR HOOD OPERATED IN CONTINUOUS-FLOW MODE.
SELF-CONTAINED BREATHING APPARATUS WITH A FULL FACEPIECE OPERATED IN PRESSURE-DEMAND OR OTHER POSITIVE PRESSURE MODE.

FOR FIREFIGHTING AND OTHER IMMEDIATELY DANGEROUS TO LIFE OR HEALTH CONDITIONS:
SELF-CONTAINED BREATHING APPARATUS WITH FULL FACEPIECE OPERATED IN PRESSURE-DEMAND OR OTHER POSITIVE PRESSURE MODE.
SUPPLIED-AIR RESPIRATOR WITH FULL FACEPIECE AND OPERATED IN PRESSURE-DEMAND OR OTHER POSITIVE PRESSURE MODE IN COMBINATION WITH AN AUXILIARY SELF-CONTAINED BREATHING APPARATUS OPERATED IN PRESSURE-DEMAND OR OTHER POSITIVE PRESSURE MODE.

CLOTHING: EMPLOYEE MUST WEAR APPROPRIATE PROTECTIVE (IMPERVIOUS) CLOTHING AND EQUIPMENT TO PREVENT REPEATED OR PROLONGED SKIN CONTACT WITH THIS SUBSTANCE.

GLOVES: EMPLOYEE MUST WEAR APPROPRIATE PROTECTIVE GLOVES TO PREVENT CONTACT WITH THIS SUBSTANCE.

EYE PROTECTION: EMPLOYEE MUST WEAR SPLASH-PROOF OR DUST-RESISTANT SAFETY GOGGLES TO PREVENT EYE CONTACT WITH THIS SUBSTANCE.
EMERGENCY EYE WASH: WHERE THERE IS ANY POSSIBILITY THAT AN EMPLOYEE'S EYES MAY BE EXPOSED TO THIS SUBSTANCE, THE EMPLOYER SHOULD PROVIDE AN EYE WASH FOUNTAIN WITHIN THE IMMEDIATE WORK AREA FOR EMERGENCY USE.

AUTHORIZED BY- OCCUPATIONAL HEALTH SERVICES, INC.
CREATION DATE: 11/17/89 ***REVISION DATE:*** 07/12/90

MATERIAL SAFETY DATA SHEET

OCCUPATIONAL HEALTH SERVICES, INC.
AGRICULTURE AND PESTICIDE DIVISION
450 SEVENTH AVENUE, SUITE 2407
NEW YORK, NEW YORK 10123
1-800-445-MSDS OR (212) 967-1100

EMERGENCY CONTACT:
JOHN S. BRANSFORD, JR. (615) 292-1180

SUBSTANCE IDENTIFICATION

CAS-NUMBER 15263-52-2

SUBSTANCE: **CARTAP HYDROCHLORIDE**

TRADE NAMES/SYNONYMS: CARBAMOTHIOIC ACID, S,S'-(2-(SIMETHYLAMINO)-1,3-PROPANEDIYL) ESTER, MONOHYDROCHLORIDE; CARBAMIC ACID, THIO-, S,S'-(2-(DIMETHYLAMINO)TRIMETHYLENE) ESTER, MONOHYDROCHLORIDE; PADAN; VEGETOX; 1,3-BIS(CARBAMOYLTHIO)-2-(N,N-DIMETHYLAMINO)PROPANE HYDROCHLORIDE; S,S'-(2-DIMETHYLAMINOTRIMETHYLENE) BIS(THIOCARBAMATE) HYDROCHLORIDE; 1,3-DI(CARBAMOYLTHIO)-2-DIMETHYLAMINOPROPANE-HYDROCHLORIDE; S,S'-(2-(DIMETHYLAMINO)-1,3-PROPANEDIYL) DICARBANOTHIOATE HYDROCHLORIDE; CARTAP; C7H16CLN3O2S2; PST04359

CHEMICAL FAMILY: THIOCARBAMATE
AMINE SALT

MOLECULAR FORMULA: C7-H15-N3-O2-S2.CL-H

MOLECULAR WEIGHT: 273.83

CERCLA RATINGS (SCALE 0-3): HEALTH=3 FIRE=1 REACTIVITY=0 PERSISTENCE=1

NFPA RATINGS (SCALE 0-4): HEALTH=U FIRE=1 REACTIVITY=0

COMPONENTS AND CONTAMINANTS

COMPONENT: CARTAP HYDROCHLORIDE ***PERCENT:*** 100.0
CAS# 15263-52-2

OTHER CONTAMINANTS: NONE

EXPOSURE LIMITS: NO OCCUPATIONAL EXPOSURE LIMITS ESTABLISHED BY OSHA, ACGIH, OR NIOSH.

PHYSICAL DATA

DESCRIPTION: COLORLESS TO WHITE, HYGROSCOPIC, CRYSTALLINE SOLID.

MELTING POINT: 354-358 F (179-181 C) (DECOMPOSES)

SPECIFIC GRAVITY: NOT AVAILABLE ***SOLUBILITY IN WATER:*** 20%

SOLVENT SOLUBILITY: SLIGHTLY SOLUBLE IN METHANOL AND ETHANOL; INSOLUBLE IN ACETONE, ETHER, CHLOROFORM, BENZENE, ETHYL ACETATE, AND N-HEXANE.

FIRE AND EXPLOSION DATA

FIRE AND EXPLOSION HAZARD: SLIGHT FIRE HAZARD WHEN EXPOSED TO HEAT OR FLAME.

FIREFIGHTING MEDIA: DRY CHEMICAL, CARBON DIOXIDE, HALON, WATER SPRAY OR STANDARD FOAM (1987 EMERGENCY RESPONSE GUIDEBOOK, DOT P 5800.4).
FOR LARGER FIRES, USE WATER SPRAY, FOG OR STANDARD FOAM (1987 EMERGENCY RESPONSE GUIDEBOOK, DOT P 5800.4).

FIREFIGHTING: MOVE CONTAINERS FROM FIRE AREA IF POSSIBLE (1987 EMERGENCY RESPONSE GUIDEBOOK, DOT P 5800.4, GUIDE PAGE 53).
EXTINGUISH USING AGENT SUITABLE FOR TYPE OF SURROUNDING FIRE. AVOID BREATHING VAPORS AND DUSTS. KEEP UPWIND.

TOXICITY

CARTAP HYDROCHLORIDE: TOXICITY DATA: >1000 MG/KG SKIN-MOUSE LD50 (85JFAN); 250 MG/KG ORAL-RAT LD50; 165 MG/KG ORAL-MOUSE LD50; 59 MG/KG INTRAVENOUS-MOUSE LD50; REPRODUCTIVE EFFECTS (RTECS). CARCINOGEN STATUS: NONE. ACUTE TOXICITY LEVEL: TOXIC BY INGESTION. TARGET EFFECTS: POISONING MAY AFFECT THE NERVOUS AND ENDOCRINE SYSTEMS.* ADDITIONAL DATA: THE USE OF ALCOHOL GREATLY INCREASES THE TOXICITY OF THIOCARBAMATES.
* MAY BE BASED ON GENERAL INFORMATION ON THIOCARBAMIC ACID ESTERS.

HEALTH EFFECTS AND FIRST AID

INHALATION: CARTAP HYDROCHLORIDE: **ACUTE EXPOSURE-** NO DATA AVAILABLE.
CHRONIC EXPOSURE- PROLONGED OR REPEATED EXPOSURE TO SOME THIOCARBAMATES MAY CAUSE RHINITIS, PHARYNGITIS AND BRONCHITIS.

FIRST AID- REMOVE FROM EXPOSURE AREA TO FRESH AIR IMMEDIATELY. IF BREATHING HAS STOPPED, PERFORM ARTIFICIAL RESPIRATION. KEEP PERSON WARM AND AT REST. TREAT SYMPTOMATICALLY AND SUPPORTIVELY. GET MEDICAL ATTENTION IMMEDIATELY.

SKIN CONTACT: CARTAP HYDROCHLORIDE: **ACUTE EXPOSURE-** NO SKIN IRRITATION WAS OBSERVED IN RABBITS. THE REPORTED LD50 IN MICE WAS >1000 MG/KG; THE SYMPTOMS WERE NOT REPORTED. **CHRONIC EXPOSURE-** PROLONGED OR REPEATED EXPOSURE TO SOME THIOCARBAMATES MAY CAUSE INSIGNIFICANT DERMATITIS.

FIRST AID- REMOVE CONTAMINATED CLOTHING AND SHOES IMMEDIATELY. WASH AFFECTED AREA WITH SOAP OR MILD DETERGENT AND LARGE AMOUNTS OF WATER UNTIL NO EVIDENCE OF CHEMICAL REMAINS (APPROXIMATELY 15-20 MINUTES). GET MEDICAL ATTENTION IMMEDIATELY.

EYE CONTACT: CARTAP HYDROCHLORIDE: **ACUTE EXPOSURE-** NO EYE IRRITATION WAS OBSERVED IN RABBITS. **CHRONIC EXPOSURE-** PROLONGED OR REPEATED EXPOSURE TO SOME THIOCARBAMATES MAY CAUSE MILD CONJUNCTIVITIS.

FIRST AID- WASH EYES IMMEDIATELY WITH LARGE AMOUNTS OF WATER OR NORMAL SALINE, OCCASIONALLY LIFTING UPPER AND LOWER LIDS, UNTIL NO EVIDENCE OF CHEMICAL REMAINS (APPROXIMATELY 15-20 MINUTES). GET MEDICAL ATTENTION IMMEDIATELY.

INGESTION: CARTAP HYDROCHLORIDE: TOXIC. **ACUTE EXPOSURE-** THE REPORTED LETHAL DOSE IN RATS WAS 250 MG/KG; THE SYMPTOMS WERE NOT REPORTED. **CHRONIC EXPOSURE-** DOSES UP TO 100 MG/KG DURING ORGANOGENESIS CAUSED MINOR SKELETAL CHANGES WHICH WERE ASCRIBED TO MATERNAL TOXICITY.

FIRST AID- IF EXTENSIVE VOMITING HAS NOT OCCURRED, THE SUBSTANCE SHOULD BE REMOVED BY EMESIS OR GASTRIC LAVAGE PROVIDED THAT THE PATIENT IS CONSCIOUS AND CONVULSIONS ARE NOT PRESENT. KEEP HEAD BELOW HIPS DURING VOMITING TO PREVENT ASPIRATION. DO NOT ATTEMPT TO MAKE AN UNCONSCIOUS PERSON VOMIT. TREAT SYMPTOMATICALLY AND SUPPORTIVELY. GET MEDICAL ATTENTION IMMEDIATELY (DREISBACH, HANDBOOK OF POISONING, 12TH ED.). TREATMENT SHOULD BE PERFORMED BY QUALIFIED MEDICAL PERSONNEL.

ANTIDOTE: NO SPECIFIC ANTIDOTE. TREAT SYMPTOMATICALLY AND SUPPORTIVELY.

REACTIVITY

REACTIVITY: STABLE UNDER NORMAL TEMPERATURES AND PRESSURES.

INCOMPATIBILITIES: CARTAP HYDROCHLORIDE: METALS: MAY CORRODE. OXIDIZERS (STRONG): FIRE AND EXPLOSION HAZARD.

DECOMPOSITION: THERMAL DECOMPOSITION PRODUCTS MAY INCLUDE TOXIC OXIDES OF NITROGEN, SULFUR, AND CARBON, AND TOXIC AND CORROSIVE FUMES OF CHLORIDES.

POLYMERIZATION: HAZARDOUS POLYMERIZATION HAS NOT BEEN REPORTED TO OCCUR UNDER NORMAL TEMPERATURES AND PRESSURES.

STORAGE AND DISPOSAL

OBSERVE ALL FEDERAL, STATE AND LOCAL REGULATIONS WHEN STORING OR DISPOSING OF THIS SUBSTANCE. FOR ASSISTANCE, CONTACT THE DISTRICT DIRECTOR OF THE ENVIRONMENTAL PROTECTION AGENCY.

****STORAGE****

STORE IN ACCORDANCE WITH 40 CFR 165 RECOMMENDED PROCEDURES FOR THE DISPOSAL AND STORAGE OF PESTICIDES AND PESTICIDE CONTAINERS.
STORE AWAY FROM INCOMPATIBLE SUBSTANCES.

DISPOSAL

DISPOSAL MUST BE IN ACCORDANCE WITH 40 CFR 165 RECOMMENDED PROCEDURES FOR THE DISPOSAL AND STORAGE OF PESTICIDES AND PESTICIDE CONTAINERS.

CONDITIONS TO AVOID

MAY BURN BUT DOES NOT IGNITE READILY.

SPILL AND LEAK PROCEDURES

OCCUPATIONAL SPILL: DO NOT TOUCH SPILLED MATERIAL. STOP LEAK IF YOU CAN DO IT WITHOUT RISK. FOR SMALL SPILLS, TAKE UP WITH SAND OR OTHER ABSORBENT MATERIAL AND PLACE INTO CONTAINERS FOR LATER DISPOSAL. FOR SMALL DRY SPILLS, WITH A CLEAN SHOVEL PLACE MATERIAL INTO CLEAN, DRY CONTAINER AND COVER. MOVE CONTAINERS FROM SPILL AREA. FOR LARGER SPILLS, DIKE FAR AHEAD OF SPILL FOR LATER DISPOSAL. KEEP UNNECESSARY PEOPLE AWAY. ISOLATE HAZARD AREA AND DENY ENTRY.

PROTECTIVE EQUIPMENT

VENTILATION: PROVIDE LOCAL EXHAUST OR PROCESS ENCLOSURE VENTILATION SYSTEM.

RESPIRATOR: THE FOLLOWING RESPIRATORS ARE RECOMMENDED BASED ON INFORMATION FOUND IN THE PHYSICAL DATA, TOXICITY AND HEALTH EFFECTS SECTIONS. THEY ARE RANKED IN ORDER FROM MINIMUM TO MAXIMUM RESPIRATORY PROTECTION. THE SPECIFIC RESPIRATOR SELECTED MUST BE BASED ON CONTAMINATION LEVELS FOUND IN THE WORK PLACE, MUST NOT EXCEED THE WORKING LIMITS OF THE RESPIRATOR AND BE JOINTLY APPROVED BY THE NATIONAL INSTITUTE FOR OCCUPATIONAL SAFETY AND HEALTH AND THE MINE SAFETY AND HEALTH ADMINISTRATION (NIOSH-MSHA).

CHEMICAL CARTRIDGE RESPIRATOR WITH AN ORGANIC VAPOR CARTRIDGE(S) IN COMBINATION WITH A DUST AND MIST FILTER.

GAS MASK WITH ORGANIC VAPOR CANISTER (CHIN-STYLE OR FRONT- OR BACK-MOUNTED CANISTER) WITH A DUST AND MIST FILTER. GAS MASK WITH ORGANIC VAPOR CANISTER (CHIN-STYLE OR FRONT- OR BACK-MOUNTED CANISTER) WITH A PARTICULATE FILTER.

POWERED AIR-PURIFYING RESPIRATOR WITH A HIGH-EFFICIENCY FILTER.

TYPE 'C' SUPPLIED-AIR RESPIRATOR WITH A FULL FACEPIECE OPERATED IN A PRESSURE-DEMAND OR OTHER POSITIVE PRESSURE MODE.

SELF-CONTAINED BREATHING APPARATUS WITH A FULL FACEPIECE OPERATED IN PRESSURE-DEMAND OR OTHER POSITIVE PRESSURE MODE.

FOR FIREFIGHTING AND OTHER IMMEDIATELY DANGEROUS TO LIFE OR HEALTH CONDITIONS:

SELF-CONTAINED BREATHING APPARATUS WITH FULL FACEPIECE OPERATED IN PRESSURE-DEMAND OR OTHER POSITIVE PRESSURE MODE.

SUPPLIED-AIR RESPIRATOR WITH FULL FACEPIECE AND OPERATED IN PRESSURE-DEMAND OR OTHER POSITIVE PRESSURE MODE IN COMBINATION WITH AN AUXILIARY SELF-CONTAINED BREATHING APPARATUS OPERATED IN PRESSURE-DEMAND OR OTHER POSITIVE PRESSURE MODE.

CLOTHING: EMPLOYEE MUST WEAR APPROPRIATE PROTECTIVE (IMPERVIOUS) CLOTHING AND EQUIPMENT TO PREVENT ANY POSSIBILITY OF SKIN CONTACT WITH THIS SUBSTANCE.

GLOVES: EMPLOYEE MUST WEAR APPROPRIATE PROTECTIVE GLOVES TO PREVENT CONTACT WITH THIS SUBSTANCE.

EYE PROTECTION: EMPLOYEE MUST WEAR SPLASH-PROOF OR DUST-RESISTANT SAFETY GOGGLES AND A FACESHIELD TO PREVENT CONTACT WITH THIS SUBSTANCE.

EMERGENCY WASH FACILITIES: WHERE THERE IS ANY POSSIBILITY THAT AN EMPLOYEE'S EYES AND/OR SKIN MAY BE EXPOSED TO THIS SUBSTANCE, THE EMPLOYER SHOULD PROVIDE AN EYE WASH FOUNTAIN AND QUICK DRENCH SHOWER WITHIN THE IMMEDIATE WORK AREA FOR EMERGENCY USE.

AUTHORIZED BY- OCCUPATIONAL HEALTH SERVICES, INC.
CREATION DATE: 02/08/90 ***REVISION DATE:*** 05/07/90

MATERIAL SAFETY DATA SHEET

OCCUPATIONAL HEALTH SERVICES, INC.
AGRICULTURE AND PESTICIDE DIVISION
450 SEVENTH AVENUE, SUITE 2407
NEW YORK, NEW YORK 10123
1-800-445-MSDS OR (212) 967-1100

EMERGENCY CONTACT:
JOHN S. BRANSFORD, JR. (615) 292-1180

SUBSTANCE IDENTIFICATION

CAS-NUMBER 120-80-9

***SUBSTANCE:* <u>CATECHOL</u>**

TRADE NAMES/SYNONYMS: PYROCATECHOL; O-DIHYDROXYBENZENE; 1,2-BENZENEDIOL; C.I. 76500; O-HYDROXYPHENOL; O-BENZENEDIOL; C.I. OXIDATION BASE 26; OXYPHENIC ACID; O-DIOXYBENZENE; O-DIPHENOL; O-HYDROQUINONE; 2-HYDROXYPHENOL; CATECHIN; DURAFUR DEVELOPER C; 1,2-DIHYDROXYBENZENE; FOURAMINE PCH; FOURRINE 68; PYROCATECHUIC ACID; P-370; PST04360

CHEMICAL FAMILY: HYDROXYL, AROMATIC

MOLECULAR FORMULA: C6-H6-O2

MOLECULAR WEIGHT: 110.11

CERCLA RATINGS (SCALE 0-3): HEALTH=3 FIRE=1 REACTIVITY=0 PERSISTENCE=2

NFPA RATINGS (SCALE 0-4): HEALTH=3 FIRE=1 REACTIVITY=0

COMPONENTS AND CONTAMINANTS

COMPONENT: CATECHOL ***PERCENT:*** 100
CAS# 120-80-9

OTHER CONTAMINANTS: NONE

EXPOSURE LIMITS: CATECHOL: 5 PPM (20 MG/M3) OSHA TWA (SKIN) 5 PPM (20 MG/M3) ACGIH TWA
SUBJECT TO SARA SECTION 313 ANNUAL TOXIC CHEMICAL RELEASE REPORTING

PHYSICAL DATA

DESCRIPTION: COLORLESS, CRYSTALLINE SOLID WHICH DISCOLORS TO BROWN ON EXPOSURE TO AIR AND LIGHT, ESPECIALLY IN THE PRESENCE OF MOISTURE

BOILING POINT: 473 F (245 C) ***MELTING POINT:*** 219-223 F (104-106 C)

SPECIFIC GRAVITY: 1.371 ***VAPOR PRESSURE:*** 10 MMHG @ 118 C

SOLUBILITY IN WATER: SOLUBLE ***VAPOR DENSITY:*** 3.8

SOLVENT SOLUBILITY: ALCOHOL, ETHER, ACETONE, BENZENE, CHOLRINE, PYRIDINE, AQUEOUS ALKALIES

FIRE AND EXPLOSION DATA

FIRE AND EXPLOSION HAZARD: SLIGHT FIRE HAZARD WHEN EXPOSED TO HEAT OR FLAME.

FLASH POINT: 261 F (127 C)(CC)

FIREFIGHTING MEDIA: DRY CHEMICAL, CARBON DIOXIDE, HALON, WATER SPRAY OR ALCOHOL FOAM (1987 EMERGENCY RESPONSE GUIDEBOOK, DOT P 5800.4).
FOR LARGER FIRES, USE WATER SPRAY, FOG OR ALCOHOL FOAM (1987 EMERGENCY RESPONSE GUIDEBOOK, DOT P 5800.4).

FIREFIGHTING: MOVE CONTAINER FROM FIRE AREA IF POSSIBLE. DO NOT SCATTER SPILLED MATERIAL WITH HIGH PRESSURE WATER STREAMS. DIKE FIRE CONTROL WATER FOR LATER DISPOSAL (1987 EMERGENCY RESPONSE GUIDEBOOK, DOT P 5800.4, GUIDE PAGE 31).
USE AGENTS SUITABLE FOR TYPE OF SURROUNDING FIRE. AVOID BREATHING HAZARDOUS VAPORS, KEEP UPWIND.

TOXICITY

CATECHOL: TOXICITY DATA: 800 MG/KG SKIN-RABBIT LD50; 260 MG/KG ORAL-RAT LD50; 260 MG/KG ORAL-MOUSE LD50; 200 MG/KG ORAL-RABBIT LDLO; 240 MG/KG ORAL-MAMMAL LD50; 130 MG/KG ORAL-DOG LDLO; 100 MG/KG ORAL-CAT LDLO; 210 MG/KG ORAL-GUINEA PIG LD50; 247 MG/KG SUBCUTANEOUS-MOUSE LD50; 200 MG/KG SUBCUTANEOUS-GUINEA PIG LDLO; 225 MG/KG SUBCUTANEOUS-RABBIT LDLO; 110 MG/KG SUBCUTANEOUS-RAT LDLO; 40 MG/KG INTRAVENOUS-DOG LDLO; 175 MG/KG INTRAPERITONEAL-MOUSE LD50; 150 MG/KG INTRAPERITONEAL-GUINEA PIG LDLO; MUTAGENIC DATA (RTECS); REPRODUCTIVE EFFECTS DATA (RTECS). CARCINOGEN STATUS: ANIMAL INADEQUATE EVIDENCE (IARC GROUP-3). IN SKIN PAINTING STUDIES IN MICE, IT INCREASED THE CARCINOGENIC EFFECTS OF BENZO(A)PYRENE ON THE SKIN. LOCAL EFFECTS: CORROSIVE- INHALATION, SKIN, AND EYES. ACUTE TOXICITY LEVEL: TOXIC BY DERMAL ABSORPTION AND INGESTION. TARGET EFFECTS: SENSITIZER- DERMAL; CONVULSANT; METHEMOGLOBIN FORMER; CENTRAL NERVOUS SYSTEM DEPRESSANT. POISONING MAY AFFECT THE LIVER AND KIDNEYS.

HEALTH EFFECTS AND FIRST AID

INHALATION: CATECHOL: CORROSIVE/NARCOTIC/CONVULSANT/METHEMOGLOBIN FORMER. **<u>ACUTE EXPOSURE</u>**- MAY CAUSE SEVERE IRRITATION TO THE RESPIRATORY TRACT, SORE THROAT, COUGHING, LABORED BREATHING, ABDOMINAL SPASMS, PROFUSE SWEATING, INTENSE THIRST, NAUSEA, VOMITING, DIARRHEA, HYPERACTIVITY, STUPOR, CENTRAL NERVOUS SYSTEM DEPRESSION WITH WEAKNESS, DIZZINESS, DROWSINESS, METHEMOGLOBINEMIA WITH CYANOSIS AND FALL IN BLOOD PRESSURE, HYPERPNEA, ABDOMINAL PAIN, HEMOLYSIS, CONVULSIONS, COMA AND PULMONARY EDEMA FOLLOWED BY PNEUMONIA. IF DEATH FROM RESPIRATORY FAILURE IS NOT IMMEDIATE, JAUNDICE AND OLIGURIA OR ANURIA MAY OCCUR. **<u>CHRONIC EXPOSURE</u>**- REPEATED AND PROLONGED CONTACT MAY CAUSE SYMPTOMS DESCRIBED FOR ACUTE POISONING AND LIVER AND KIDNEY DAMAGE.

FIRST AID- REMOVE FROM EXPOSURE AREA TO FRESH AIR IMMEDIATELY. IF BREATHING HAS STOPPED, GIVE ARTIFICIAL RESPIRATION. MAINTAIN AIRWAY AND BLOOD PRESSURE AND ADMINISTER OXYGEN IF AVAILABLE. KEEP AFFECTED PERSON WARM AND AT REST. TREAT SYMPTOMATICALLY AND SUPPORTIVELY. ADMINISTRATION OF OXYGEN SHOULD BE PERFORMED BY QUALIFIED PERSONNEL. GET MEDICAL ATTENTION IMMEDIATELY.

SKIN CONTACT: CATECHOL: CORROSIVE/NARCOTIC/CONVULSANT/SENSITIZER/METHEMOGLOBIN FORMER/TOXIC. **ACUTE EXPOSURE-** MAY CAUSE SEVERE IRRITATION, SENSITIZATION DERMATITIS, PROFUSE SWEATING, INTENSE THIRST, NAUSEA, VOMITING, DIARRHEA, HYPERACTIVITY, STUPOR, CENTRAL NERVOUS SYSTEM DEPRESSION WITH WEAKNESS, DIZZINESS AND DROWSINESS, METHEMOGLOBINEMIA WITH CYANOSIS AND FALL IN BLOOD PRESSURE, HYPERPNEA, ABDOMINAL PAIN, HEMOLYSIS, CONVULSIONS, COMA AND PULMONARY EDEMA FOLLOWED BY PNEUMONIA. IF DEATH FROM RESPIRATORY FAILURE IS NOT IMMEDIATE, JAUNDICE AND OLIGURIA OR ANURIA MAY OCCUR. RABBITS,EXPOSED TO 800 MG/KG, EXHIBITED WEIGHT LOSS OR DECREASED WEIGHT GAIN. **CHRONIC EXPOSURE-** REPEATED AND PROLONGED CONTACT MAY CAUSE SENSITIZATION DERMATITIS AND SYMPTOMS SIMILAR TO THOSE DESCRIBED FOR ACUTE POISONING.

FIRST AID- REMOVE CONTAMINATED CLOTHING AND SHOES IMMEDIATELY. WASH AFFECTED AREA WITH SOAP OR MILD DETERGENT AND LARGE AMOUNTS OF WATER UNTIL NO EVIDENCE OF CHEMICAL REMAINS (AT LEAST 15-20 MINUTES). IN CASE OF CHEMICAL BURNS, COVER AREA WITH STERILE, DRY DRESSING. BANDAGE SECURELY, BUT NOT TOO TIGHTLY. GET MEDICAL ATTENTION IMMEDIATELY.

EYE CONTACT: CATECHOL: CORROSIVE. **ACUTE EXPOSURE-** MAY CAUSE SEVERE IRRITATION, PAIN, BLURRED VISION AND SLOW HEALING BURNS. **CHRONIC EXPOSURE-** REPEATED AND PROLONGED CONTACT MAY CAUSE CONJUNCTIVITIS.

FIRST AID- WASH EYES IMMEDIATELY WITH LARGE AMOUNTS OF WATER, OCCASIONALLY LIFTING UPPER AND LOWER LIDS, UNTIL NO EVIDENCE OF CHEMICAL REMAINS (AT LEAST 15-20 MINUTES). CONTINUE IRRIGATING WITH NORMAL SALINE UNTIL THE PH HAS RETURNED TO NORMAL (30-60 MINUTES). COVER WITH STERILE BANDAGES. GET MEDICAL ATTENTION IMMEDIATELY.

INGESTION: CATECHOL: CORROSIVE/NARCOTIC/CONVULSANT/METHEMOGLOBIN FORMER/TOXIC. **ACUTE EXPOSURE-** MAY CAUSE SEVERE IRRITATION, PROFUSE SWEATING, INTENSE THIRST, NAUSEA, VOMITING, DIARRHEA, HYPERACTIVITY, STUPOR, CENTRAL NERVOUS SYSTEM DEPRESSION WITH WEAKNESS, DIZZINESS AND DROWSINESS, METHEMOGLOBINEMIA WITH CYANOSIS AND FALL IN BLOOD PRESSURE, HYPERPNEA, ABDOMINAL PAIN, HEMOLYSIS, CONVULSIONS, COMA AND PULMONARY EDEMA FOLLOWED BY PNEUMONIA. IF DEATH FROM RESPIRATORY FAILURE IS NOT IMMEDIATE, JAUNDICE AND OLIGURIA OR ANURIA MAY OCCUR. MAMMALS, EXPOSED TO 240 MG/KG, EXHIBITED A CHANGE IN MOTOR ACTIVITY, MUSCLES CONTRACTIONS OR SPASTICITY AND DYSPNEA. **CHRONIC EXPOSURE-** REPEATED EXPOSURE MAY LEAD TO SYMPTOMS SIMILAR TO THOSE DESCRIBED FROM ACUTE POISONING.

FIRST AID- IF VICTIM IS CONSCIOUS, AND IF CORROSIVE INJURY IS ABSENT, REMOVE POISON BY GASTRIC LAVAGE OR EMESIS. ACTIVATED CHARCOAL IS USEFUL. FOLLOW WITH 240 ML OF MILK. GASTRIC LAVAGE AND EMESIS ARE NOT TO BE USED IN THE PRESENCE OF ESOPHAGEAL INJURY (DREISBACH, HANDBOOK OF POISONING, 12TH ED.). GASTRIC LAVAGE SHOULD BE PERFORMED BY QUALIFIED MEDICAL PERSONNEL. GET MEDICAL ATTENTION IMMEDIATELY.

ANTIDOTE: THE FOLLOWING ANTIDOTE HAS BEEN RECOMMENDED. HOWEVER, THE DECISION AS TO WHETHER THE SEVERITY OF POISONING REQUIRES ADMINISTRATION OF ANY ANTIDOTE AND ACTUAL DOSE REQUIRED SHOULD BE MADE BY QUALIFIED MEDICAL PERSONNEL.

METHEMOGLOBINEMIA: (WHEN METHEMOGLOBIN CONCENTRATION IS OVER 25-40% OR IN PRESENCE OF SYMPTOMS.) GIVE METHYLENE BLUE, 1% SOLUTION, 0.1 ML/KG INTRAVENOUSLY OVER A 10-MINUTE PERIOD. CYANOSIS MAY DISAPPEAR WITHIN MINUTES OR PERSIST LONGER DEPENDING ON DEGREE OF METHEMOGLOBINEMIA. INTRAVENOUS ADMINISTRATION OF THERAPEUTIC DOSES OF METHYLENE BLUE MAY CAUSE A RISE IN BLOOD PRESSURE, NAUSEA, AND DIZZINESS. LARGER DOSES (>500 MG) CAUSE VOMITING, DIARRHEA, CHEST PAIN, MENTAL CONFUSION, CYANOSIS, AND SWEATING. HEMOLYTIC ANEMIA HAS ALSO OCCURRED SEVERAL DAYS AFTER ADMINISTRATION. THESE EFFECTS ARE TEMPORARY, AND FATALITIES HAVE NOT BEEN REPORTED. IF METHYLENE BLUE IS NOT AVAILABLE, GIVE ASCORBIC ACID, 1 GRAM SLOWLY INTRAVENOUSLY. WITHOUT TREATMENT, METHEMOGLOBINEMIA LEVELS OF 20-30% REVERT TO NORMAL WITHIN 3 DAYS (DREISBACH, HANDBOOK OF POISONING, 12TH ED.). ANTIDOTE SHOULD BE ADMINISTERED BY QUALIFIED MEDICAL PERSONNEL.

REACTIVITY

REACTIVITY: STABLE UNDER NORMAL TEMPERATURES AND PRESSURES.

INCOMPATIBILITIES: CATECHOL: AMMONIACAL SILVER NITRATE: REDUCES. FEHLING'S SOLUTION: REDUCES. OXIDIZING MATERIALS: REACT. NITRIC ACID: EXPLODES.

DECOMPOSITION: THERMAL DECOMPOSITION PRODUCTS MAY INCLUDE TOXIC OXIDES OF CARBON.

POLYMERIZATION: HAZARDOUS POLYMERIZATION HAS NOT BEEN REPORTED TO OCCUR UNDER NORMAL TEMPERATURES AND PRESSURES.

CONDITIONS TO AVOID

MAY BURN BUT DOES NOT IGNITE READILY. AVOID CONTACT WITH STRONG OXIDIZERS, EXCESSIVE HEAT, SPARKS, OR OPEN FLAME.

SPILL AND LEAK PROCEDURES

OCCUPATIONAL SPILL: SWEEP UP AND PLACE IN SUITABLE CLEAN, DRY CONTAINERS FOR RECLAMATION OR LATER DISPOSAL. DO NOT FLUSH SPILLED MATERIAL INTO SEWER. KEEP UNNECESSARY PEOPLE AWAY.

PROTECTIVE EQUIPMENT

VENTILATION: PROVIDE LOCAL EXHAUST OR PROCESS ENCLOSURE VENTILATION TO MEET PUBLISHED EXPOSURE LIMITS.

RESPIRATOR: THE FOLLOWING RESPIRATORS ARE RECOMMENDED BASED ON INFORMATION FOUND IN THE PHYSICAL DATA, TOXICITY AND HEALTH EFFECTS SECTIONS. THEY ARE RANKED IN ORDER FROM MINIMUM TO MAXIMUM RESPIRATORY PROTECTION. THE SPECIFIC RESPIRATOR SELECTED MUST BE BASED ON CONTAMINATION LEVELS FOUND IN THE WORK PLACE, MUST NOT EXCEED THE WORKING LIMITS OF THE RESPIRATOR AND BE JOINTLY APPROVED BY THE NATIONAL INSTITUTE FOR OCCUPATIONAL SAFETY AND HEALTH AND THE MINE SAFETY AND HEALTH ADMINISTRATION (NIOSH-MSHA).

TYPE 'C' SUPPLIED-AIR RESPIRATOR WITH A FULL FACEPIECE OPERATED IN PRESSURE-DEMAND OR OTHER POSITIVE PRESSURE MODE OR WITH A FULL FACEPIECE, HELMET OR HOOD OPERATED IN CONTINOUS-FLOW MODE.

SELF-CONTAINED BREATHING APPARATUS WITH A FULL FACEPIECE OPERATED IN PRESSURE-DEMAND OR OTHER POSITIVE PRESSURE MODE.

FOR FIREFIGHTING AND OTHER IMMEDIATELY DANGEROUS TO LIFE OR HEALTH CONDITIONS:

SELF-CONTAINED BREATHING APPARATUS WITH FULL FACEPIECE OPERATED IN PRESSURE-DEMAND OR OTHER POSITIVE PRESSURE MODE.

SUPPLIED-AIR RESPIRATOR WITH FULL FACEPIECE AND OPERATED IN PRESSURE-DEMAND OR OTHER POSITIVE PRESSURE MODE IN COMBINATION WITH AN AUXILIARY SELF-CONTAINED BREATHING APPARATUS OPERATED IN PRESSURE-DEMAND OR OTHER POSITIVE PRESSURE MODE.

CLOTHING: EMPLOYEE MUST WEAR APPROPRIATE PROTECTIVE (IMPERVIOUS) CLOTHING AND EQUIPMENT TO PREVENT ANY POSSIBILITY OF SKIN CONTACT WITH THIS SUBSTANCE.

GLOVES: EMPLOYEE MUST WEAR APPROPRIATE PROTECTIVE GLOVES TO PREVENT CONTACT WITH THIS SUBSTANCE.

EYE PROTECTION: EMPLOYEE MUST WEAR SPLASH-PROOF OR DUST-RESISTANT SAFETY GOGGLES AND A FACESHIELD TO PREVENT CONTACT WITH THIS SUBSTANCE.

EMERGENCY WASH FACILITIES: WHERE THERE IS ANY POSSIBILITY THAT AN EMPLOYEE'S EYES AND/OR SKIN MAY BE EXPOSED TO THIS SUBSTANCE, THE EMPLOYER SHOULD PROVIDE AN EYE WASH FOUNTAIN AND QUICK DRENCH SHOWER WITHIN THE IMMEDIATE WORK AREA FOR EMERGENCY USE.

AUTHORIZED BY- OCCUPATIONAL HEALTH SERVICES, INC.

CREATION DATE: 10/04/89 ***REVISION DATE:*** 06/27/90

MATERIAL SAFETY DATA SHEET

OCCUPATIONAL HEALTH SERVICES, INC.
AGRICULTURE AND PESTICIDE DIVISION
450 SEVENTH AVENUE, SUITE 2407
NEW YORK, NEW YORK 10123
1-800-445-MSDS OR (212) 967-1100

EMERGENCY CONTACT:
JOHN S. BRANSFORD, JR. (615) 292-1180

SUBSTANCE IDENTIFICATION

CAS-NUMBER 8000-27-9

SUBSTANCE: CEDARWOOD OIL

TRADE NAMES/SYNONYMS: OIL CEDAR; RED CEDARWOOD OIL; CEDRUS ATLANTICA OIL; PST04365

CERCLA RATINGS (SCALE 0-3): HEALTH=U FIRE=1 REACTIVITY=0 PERSISTENCE=0

NFPA RATINGS (SCALE 0-4): HEALTH = U FIRE = 1 REACTIVITY = 0

COMPONENTS AND CONTAMINANTS

COMPONENT: CEDARWOOD OIL ***PERCENT:*** 100
CAS# 8000-27-9

OTHER CONTAMINANTS: NONE

EXPOSURE LIMITS: NO OCCUPATIONAL EXPOSURE LIMITS ESTABLISHED BY OSHA, ACGIH, OR NIOSH.

PHYSICAL DATA

DESCRIPTION: COLORLESS TO SLIGHTLY YELLOW VISCOUS LIQUID.

BOILING POINT: NOT AVAILABLE ***SPECIFIC GRAVITY:*** 0.947

EVAPORATION RATE: (ETHER = 1) > 1 ***SOLUBILITY IN WATER:*** INSOLUBLE

SOLVENT SOLUBILITY: ETHER, 90% ALCOHOL

FIRE AND EXPLOSION DATA

FIRE AND EXPLOSION HAZARD: SLIGHT FIRE HAZARD WHEN EXPOSED TO HEAT OR FLAME.

FLASH POINT: > 230 F (> 110 C)

FIREFIGHTING MEDIA: DRY CHEMICAL, CARBON DIOXIDE, HALON, WATER SPRAY OR STANDARD FOAM (1987 EMERGENCY RESPONSE GUIDEBOOK, DOT P 5800.4). FOR LARGER FIRES, USE WATER SPRAY, FOG OR STANDARD FOAM (1987 EMERGENCY RESPONSE GUIDEBOOK, DOT P 5800.4).

FIREFIGHTING: NO ACUTE HAZARD. MOVE CONTAINER FROM FIRE AREA IF POSSIBLE. AVOID BREATHING VAPORS OR DUSTS; KEEP UPWIND.

TOXICITY

CEDARWOOD OIL: IRRITATION DATA: 500 MG/24 HOURS SKIN-RABBIT MODERATE. CARCINOGEN STATUS: NONE. LOCAL EFFECTS: IRRITANT- SKIN. ACUTE TOXICITY LEVEL: NO DATA AVAILABLE. TARGET EFFECTS: NO DATA AVAILABLE.

HEALTH EFFECTS AND FIRST AID

INHALATION: CEDARWOOD OIL: **ACUTE EXPOSURE-** ASPIRATION INTO THE LUNGS MAY CAUSE CHEMICAL PNEUMONITIS. **CHRONIC EXPOSURE-** NO DATA AVAILABLE.

FIRST AID- REMOVE FROM EXPOSURE AREA TO FRESH AIR IMMEDIATELY. IF BREATHING HAS STOPPED, PERFORM ARTIFICIAL RESPIRATION. KEEP PERSON WARM AND AT REST. TREAT SYMPTOMATICALLY AND SUPPORTIVELY. GET MEDICAL ATTENTION IMMEDIATELY.

SKIN CONTACT: CEDARWOOD OIL: IRRITANT. **ACUTE EXPOSURE-** MAY CAUSE IRRITATION. 500 MG APPLIED TO RABBIT SKIN FOR 24 HOURS RESULTED IN MODERATE IRRITATION. **CHRONIC EXPOSURE-** REPEATED OR PROLONGED CONTACT MAY CAUSE DERMATITIS.

FIRST AID- REMOVE CONTAMINATED CLOTHING AND SHOES IMMEDIATELY. WASH AFFECTED AREA WITH SOAP OR MILD DETERGENT AND LARGE AMOUNTS OF WATER UNTIL NO EVIDENCE OF CHEMICAL REMAINS (APPROXIMATELY 15-20 MINUTES). GET MEDICAL ATTENTION IMMEDIATELY.

EYE CONTACT: CEDARWOOD OIL: **ACUTE EXPOSURE-** NO DATA AVAILABLE. **CHRONIC EXPOSURE-** NO DATA AVAILABLE.

FIRST AID- WASH EYES IMMEDIATELY WITH LARGE AMOUNTS OF WATER OR NORMAL SALINE, OCCASIONALLY LIFTING UPPER AND LOWER LIDS, UNTIL NO EVIDENCE OF CHEMICAL REMAINS (APPROXIMATELY 15-20 MINUTES). GET MEDICAL ATTENTION IMMEDIATELY.

INGESTION: CEDARWOOD OIL: **ACUTE EXPOSURE-** INGESTION OF VOLATILE OILS MAY RESULT IN CENTRAL NERVOUS SYSTEM EFFECTS DUE TO THEIR LIPID SOLUBILITY. ASPIRATION INTO THE LUNGS MAY RESULT IN CHEMICAL PNEUMONITIS. **CHRONIC EXPOSURE-** NO DATA AVAILABLE.

FIRST AID- TREAT SYMPTOMATICALLY AND SUPPORTIVELY. GET MEDICAL ATTENTION IMMEDIATELY. IF VOMITING OCCURS, KEEP HEAD LOWER THAN HIPS TO PREVENT ASPIRATION.

ANTIDOTE: NO SPECIFIC ANTIDOTE. TREAT SYMPTOMATICALLY AND SUPPORTIVELY.

REACTIVITY

REACTIVITY: STABLE UNDER NORMAL TEMPERATURES AND PRESSURES.

INCOMPATIBILITIES: CEDARWOOD OIL: NO DATA AVAILABLE.

DECOMPOSITION: THERMAL DECOMPOSITION PRODUCTS MAY INCLUDE TOXIC OXIDES OF CARBON.

POLYMERIZATION: HAZARDOUS POLYMERIZATION HAS NOT BEEN REPORTED TO OCCUR UNDER NORMAL TEMPERATURES AND PRESSURES.

CONDITIONS TO AVOID

NONE REPORTED.

SPILL AND LEAK PROCEDURES

OCCUPATIONAL SPILL: NO SPECIAL PRECAUTIONS INDICATED.

PROTECTIVE EQUIPMENT

VENTILATION: PROVIDE LOCAL EXHAUST OR GENERAL DILUTION VENTILATION SYSTEM.

RESPIRATOR: THE FOLLOWING RESPIRATORS ARE RECOMMENDED BASED ON INFORMATION FOUND IN THE PHYSICAL DATA, TOXICITY AND HEALTH EFFECTS SECTIONS. THEY ARE RANKED IN ORDER FROM MINIMUM TO MAXIMUM RESPIRATORY PROTECTION. THE SPECIFIC RESPIRATOR SELECTED MUST BE BASED ON CONTAMINATION LEVELS FOUND IN THE WORK PLACE, MUST NOT EXCEED THE WORKING LIMITS OF THE RESPIRATOR AND BE JOINTLY APPROVED BY THE NATIONAL INSTITUTE FOR OCCUPATIONAL SAFETY AND HEALTH AND THE MINE SAFETY AND HEALTH ADMINISTRATION (NIOSH-MSHA).

CHEMICAL CARTRIDGE RESPIRATOR WITH AN ORGANIC VAPOR CARTRIDGE(S) WITH A FULL FACEPIECE.

GAS MASK WITH ORGANIC VAPOR CANISTER (CHIN-STYLE OR FRONT- OR BACK-MOUNTED CANISTER) WITH A FULL FACEPIECE.

TYPE 'C' SUPPLIED-AIR RESPIRATOR WITH A FULL FACEPIECE OPERATED IN PRESSURE-DEMAND OR OTHER POSITIVE PRESSURE MODE OR WITH A FULL FACEPIECE, HELMET OR HOOD OPERATED IN CONTINUOUS-FLOW MODE.

SELF-CONTAINED BREATHING APPARATUS WITH A FULL FACEPIECE OPERATED IN PRESSURE-DEMAND OR OTHER POSITIVE PRESSURE MODE.

FOR FIREFIGHTING AND OTHER IMMEDIATELY DANGEROUS TO LIFE OR HEALTH CONDITIONS:

SELF-CONTAINED BREATHING APPARATUS WITH FULL FACEPIECE OPERATED IN PRESSURE-DEMAND OR OTHER POSITIVE PRESSURE MODE.

SUPPLIED-AIR RESPIRATOR WITH FULL FACEPIECE AND OPERATED IN PRESSURE-DEMAND OR OTHER POSITIVE PRESSURE MODE IN COMBINATION WITH AN AUXILIARY SELF-CONTAINED BREATHING APPARATUS OPERATED IN PRESSURE-DEMAND OR OTHER POSITIVE PRESSURE MODE.

CLOTHING: EMPLOYEE MUST WEAR APPROPRIATE PROTECTIVE (IMPERVIOUS) CLOTHING AND EQUIPMENT TO PREVENT REPEATED OR PROLONGED SKIN CONTACT WITH THIS SUBSTANCE.

GLOVES: EMPLOYEE MUST WEAR APPROPRIATE PROTECTIVE GLOVES TO PREVENT CONTACT WITH THIS SUBSTANCE.

EYE PROTECTION: EMPLOYEE MUST WEAR SPLASH-PROOF OR DUST-RESISTANT SAFETY GOGGLES TO PREVENT EYE CONTACT WITH THIS SUBSTANCE.

EMERGENCY EYE WASH: WHERE THERE IS ANY POSSIBILITY THAT AN EMPLOYEE'S EYES MAY BE EXPOSED TO THIS SUBSTANCE, THE EMPLOYER SHOULD PROVIDE AN EYE WASH FOUNTAIN WITHIN THE IMMEDIATE WORK AREA FOR EMERGENCY USE.

AUTHORIZED BY- OCCUPATIONAL HEALTH SERVICES, INC.

CREATION DATE: 10/04/89 ***REVISION DATE:*** 05/17/90

MATERIAL SAFETY DATA SHEET

OCCUPATIONAL HEALTH SERVICES, INC.
AGRICULTURE AND PESTICIDE DIVISION
450 SEVENTH AVENUE, SUITE 2407
NEW YORK, NEW YORK 10123
1-800-445-MSDS OR (212) 967-1100

EMERGENCY CONTACT:
JOHN S. BRANSFORD, JR. (615) 292-1180

SUBSTANCE IDENTIFICATION

CAS-NUMBER 36653-82-4

SUBSTANCE: **CETYL ALCOHOL**

TRADE NAMES/SYNONYMS: 1-HEXADECANOL; N-CETYL ALCOHOL; CETYLIC ALCOHOL; HEXADECANOL; N-HEXADECANOL; N-1-HEXADECANOL; 1-HEXADECYL ALCOHOL; HEXADECYL ALCOHOL; PALMITOYL ALCOHOL; ETHAL; ETHOL; CETOL; C16H34O; PST04525

CHEMICAL FAMILY: HYDROXYL, ALIPHATIC

MOLECULAR FORMULA: C-H3-(C-H2)14-C-H2-O-H

MOLECULAR WEIGHT: 242.45

CERCLA RATINGS (SCALE 0-3): HEALTH = 2 FIRE = 1 REACTIVITY = 0 PERSISTENCE = 0

NFPA RATINGS (SCALE 0-4): HEALTH = U FIRE = 1 REACTIVITY = 0

COMPONENTS AND CONTAMINANTS

COMPONENT: CETYL ALCOHOL ***PERCENT:*** 100.0
CAS# 36653-82-4

OTHER CONTAMINANTS: NONE

EXPOSURE LIMITS: NO OCCUPATIONAL EXPOSURE LIMITS ESTABLISHED BY OSHA, ACGIH, OR NIOSH.

PHYSICAL DATA

DESCRIPTION: WHITE, WAXY SOLID, FLAKES OR POWDERY GRANULES WITH A FAINT ODOR.

BOILING POINT: 651 F (344 C) ***MELTING POINT:*** 122 F (50 C)

SPECIFIC GRAVITY: 0.8176 @ 50 C ***VISCOSITY:*** 53 CPS @ 75 C

VAPOR PRESSURE: <0.1 MMHG @ 20 C ***SOLUBILITY IN WATER:*** INSOLUBLE

SOLVENT SOLUBILITY: SOLUBLE IN ALCOHOL, CHLOROFORM, ETHER, BENZENE AND ACETONE.

FIRE AND EXPLOSION DATA

FIRE AND EXPLOSION HAZARD: SLIGHT FIRE HAZARD WHEN EXPOSED TO HEAT OR FLAME. ***FLASH POINT:*** >230 F (>110 C)

FIREFIGHTING MEDIA: DRY CHEMICAL, CARBON DIOXIDE, HALON, WATER SPRAY OR ALCOHOL FOAM (1987 EMERGENCY RESPONSE GUIDEBOOK, DOT P 5800.4). FOR LARGER FIRES, USE WATER SPRAY, FOG OR ALCOHOL FOAM (1987 EMERGENCY RESPONSE GUIDEBOOK, DOT P 5800.4).

FIREFIGHTING: MOVE CONTAINER FROM FIRE AREA IF POSSIBLE. COOL FIRE-EXPOSED CONTAINERS WITH WATER FROM SIDE UNTIL WELL AFTER FIRE IS OUT. STAY AWAY FROM STORAGE TANK ENDS. FOR MASSIVE FIRE IN STORAGE AREA, USE UNMANNED HOSE HOLDER OR MONITOR NOZZLES, ELSE WITHDRAW FROM AREA AND LET FIRE BURN. WITHDRAW IMMEDIATELY IN CASE OF RISING SOUND FROM VENTING SAFETY DEVICE OR ANY DISCOLORATION OF STORAGE TANK DUE TO FIRE (1987 EMERGENCY RESPONSE GUIDEBOOK, DOT P 5800.4, GUIDE PAGE 26). EXTINGUISH ONLY IF FLOW CAN BE STOPPED; USE WATER IN FLOODING AMOUNTS AS FOG, SOLID STREAMS MAY NOT BE EFFECTIVE. COOL CONTAINERS WITH FLOODING AMOUNTS OF WATER, APPLY FROM AS FAR A DISTANCE AS POSSIBLE. AVOID BREATHING VAPORS, KEEP UPWIND.

TOXICITY

CETYL ALCOHOL: IRRITATION DATA: 75 MG/3 DAYS INTERMITTENT SKIN-HUMAN MILD; 50 MG/48 HOURS SKIN-MAN MILD; 100 MG/24 HOURS SKIN-RAT SEVERE; 2600 MG/KG/24 HOURS SKIN-RABBIT MILD; 100 MG/24 HOURS SKIN-RABBIT SEVERE; 100% SKIN-GUINEA PIG MILD; 100 MG/24 HOURS SKIN-GUINEA PIG MODERATE; 82 MG EYE-RABBIT MILD. TOXICITY DATA: 2220 MG/M3/6 HOURS INHALATION-RAT LCLO; 10 GM/KG SKIN-GUINEA PIG LDLO; 5 GM/KG ORAL-RAT LD50; 3200 MG/KG ORAL-MOUSE LD50; 1600 MG/KG INTRAPERITONEAL-RAT LD50; 1600 MG/KG INTRAPERITONEAL-MOUSE LD50. CARCINOGEN STATUS: NONE. LOCAL EFFECTS: IRRITANT- SKIN. ACUTE TOXICITY LEVEL: MODERATELY TOXIC BY INGESTION. TARGET EFFECTS: NO DATA AVAILABLE. ADDITIONAL DATA: CROSS SENSITIVITY WITH STEARYL ALCOHOL MAY OCCUR.

HEALTH EFFECTS AND FIRST AID

INHALATION: CETYL ALCOHOL: **ACUTE EXPOSURE-** INHALATION OF 258 MG/M3 FOR 6 HOURS CAUSED SLIGHT LOCAL IRRITATION IN RATS, MICE, AND GUINEA PIGS; 2220 MG/M3 FOR 6 HOURS CAUSED DEATH WITHIN 2 DAYS IN RATS. **CHRONIC EXPOSURE-** NO DATA AVAILABLE.

FIRST AID- REMOVE FROM EXPOSURE AREA TO FRESH AIR IMMEDIATELY. IF BREATHING HAS STOPPED, PERFORM ARTIFICIAL RESPIRATION. KEEP PERSON WARM AND AT REST. TREAT SYMPTOMATICALLY AND SUPPORTIVELY. GET MEDICAL ATTENTION IMMEDIATELY.

SKIN CONTACT: CETYL ALCOHOL: IRRITANT. **ACUTE EXPOSURE-** CONTACT MAY CAUSE IRRITATION. SENSITIZATION REACTIONS WITH URTICARIA MAY OCCUR, BUT ARE RARE. **CHRONIC EXPOSURE-** REPEATED OR PROLONGED CONTACT WITH IRRITANTS MAY CAUSE DERMATITIS. REPEATED CONTACT MAY ALSO CAUSE SENSITIZATION.

FIRST AID- REMOVE CONTAMINATED CLOTHING AND SHOES IMMEDIATELY. WASH AFFECTED AREA WITH SOAP OR MILD DETERGENT AND LARGE AMOUNTS OF WATER UNTIL NO EVIDENCE OF CHEMICAL REMAINS (APPROXIMATELY 15-20 MINUTES). GET MEDICAL ATTENTION IMMEDIATELY.

EYE CONTACT: CETYL ALCOHOL: **ACUTE EXPOSURE-** INSTILLATION OF 0.1 ML OF THE UNDILUTED MATERIAL CAUSED SLIGHT CONJUNCTIVAL IRRITATION IN RABBITS. **CHRONIC EXPOSURE-** NO DATA AVAILABLE.

FIRST AID- WASH EYES IMMEDIATELY WITH LARGE AMOUNTS OF WATER OR NORMAL SALINE, OCCASIONALLY LIFTING UPPER AND LOWER LIDS, UNTIL NO EVIDENCE OF CHEMICAL REMAINS (APPROXIMATELY 15-20 MINUTES). GET MEDICAL ATTENTION IMMEDIATELY.

INGESTION: CETYL ALCOHOL: **ACUTE EXPOSURE-** THE LD50 REPORTED IN RATS WAS 6400 MG/KG; SYMPTOMS WERE NOT REPORTED. **CHRONIC EXPOSURE-** NO DATA AVAILABLE.

FIRST AID- TREAT SYMPTOMATICALLY AND SUPPORTIVELY. GET MEDICAL ATTENTION IMMEDIATELY. IF VOMITING OCCURS, KEEP HEAD LOWER THAN HIPS TO PREVENT ASPIRATION.

ANTIDOTE: NO SPECIFIC ANTIDOTE. TREAT SYMPTOMATICALLY AND SUPPORTIVELY.

REACTIVITY

REACTIVITY: STABLE UNDER NORMAL TEMPERATURES AND PRESSURES.

INCOMPATIBILITIES: CETYL ALCOHOL: MINERAL ACIDS (STRONG): INCOMPATIBLE. OXIDIZERS (STRONG): FIRE AND EXPLOSION HAZARD. SEE ALSO ALCOHOLS. ALCOHOLS: ACETALDEHYDE: VIOLENT CONDENSATION REACTION. BARIUM PERCHLORATE: FORMATION OF HIGHLY EXPLOSIVE PERCHLORIC ESTER ON REFLUXING. CHLORINE: FORMATION OF HIGHLY EXPLOSIVE ALKYL HYPOCHLORITES. DIETHYL ALUMINUM BROMIDE: SPONTANEOUS IGNITION. ETHYLENE OXIDE: POSSIBLE EXPLOSION. HEXAMETHYLENE DIISOCYANATE: POSSIBLE EXPLOSION IN ABSENCE OF SOLVENT. HYDROGEN PEROXIDE + SULFURIC ACID: POSSIBLE EXPLOSION. HYPOCHLOROUS ACID: FORMATION OF HIGHLY EXPLOSIVE ALKYL HYPOCHLORITES. ISOCYANATES: POSSIBLE EXPLOSION IN ABSENCE OF SOLVENT. LITHIUM ALUMINUM HYDRIDE: VIGOROUS REACTION. NITROGEN TETROXIDE: POSSIBLE EXPLOSION. PERCHLORIC ACID (HOT): DANGEROUS INTERACTION. PERMONOSULFURIC ACID: POSSIBLE EXPLOSION ON CONTACT WITH PRIMARY OR SECONDARY ALCOHOLS. TRI-ISO-BUTYL ALUMINUM: VIOLENT REACTION.

DECOMPOSITION: THERMAL DECOMPOSITION PRODUCTS MAY INCLUDE TOXIC OXIDES OF CARBON.

POLYMERIZATION: HAZARDOUS POLYMERIZATION HAS NOT BEEN REPORTED TO OCCUR UNDER NORMAL TEMPERATURES AND PRESSURES.

STORAGE AND DISPOSAL

OBSERVE ALL FEDERAL, STATE AND LOCAL REGULATIONS WHEN STORING OR DISPOSING OF THIS SUBSTANCE. FOR ASSISTANCE, CONTACT THE DISTRICT DIRECTOR OF THE ENVIRONMENTAL PROTECTION AGENCY.

STORAGE

STORE AWAY FROM INCOMPATIBLE SUBSTANCES.

CONDITIONS TO AVOID

AVOID CONTACT WITH HEAT, SPARKS, FLAMES, OR OTHER SOURCES OF IGNITION. VAPORS MAY BE EXPLOSIVE AND POISONOUS; DO NOT ALLOW UNNECESSARY PERSONNEL IN AREA. DO NOT OVERHEAT CONTAINERS; CONTAINERS MAY VIOLENTLY RUPTURE AND TRAVEL A CONSIDERABLE DISTANCE IN HEAT OF FIRE.

SPILL AND LEAK PROCEDURES

OCCUPATIONAL SPILL: SHUT OFF IGNITION SOURCES. STOP LEAK IF YOU CAN DO IT WITHOUT RISK. USE WATER SPRAY TO REDUCE VAPORS. FOR SMALL SPILLS, TAKE UP WITH SAND OR OTHER ABSORBENT MATERIAL AND PLACE INTO CONTAINERS FOR LATER DISPOSAL. FOR LARGER SPILLS, DIKE FAR AHEAD OF SPILL FOR LATER DISPOSAL. NO SMOKING, FLAMES OR FLARES IN HAZARD AREA. KEEP UNNECESSARY PEOPLE AWAY; ISOLATE HAZARD AREA AND DENY ENTRY.

PROTECTIVE EQUIPMENT

VENTILATION: PROVIDE LOCAL EXHAUST OR GENERAL DILUTION VENTILATION SYSTEM.

RESPIRATOR: THE FOLLOWING RESPIRATORS ARE RECOMMENDED BASED ON INFORMATION FOUND IN THE PHYSICAL DATA, TOXICITY AND HEALTH EFFECTS SECTIONS. THEY ARE RANKED IN ORDER FROM MINIMUM TO MAXIMUM RESPIRATORY PROTECTION. THE SPECIFIC RESPIRATOR SELECTED MUST BE BASED ON CONTAMINATION LEVELS FOUND IN THE WORK PLACE, MUST NOT EXCEED THE WORKING LIMITS OF THE RESPIRATOR AND BE JOINTLY APPROVED BY THE NATIONAL INSTITUTE FOR OCCUPATIONAL SAFETY AND HEALTH AND THE MINE SAFETY AND HEALTH ADMINISTRATION (NIOSH-MSHA).

DUST AND MIST RESPIRATOR.

AIR-PURIFYING RESPIRATOR WITH A HIGH-EFFICIENCY PARTICULATE FILTER.

POWERED AIR-PURIFYING RESPIRATOR WITH A DUST AND MIST FILTER.

POWERED AIR-PURIFYING RESPIRATOR WITH A HIGH-EFFICIENCY PARTICULATE FILTER.

TYPE 'C' SUPPLIED-AIR RESPIRATOR OPERATED IN THE PRESSURE-DEMAND OR OTHER POSITIVE PRESSURE OR CONTINUOUS-FLOW MODE.

SELF-CONTAINED BREATHING APPARATUS.

FOR FIREFIGHTING AND OTHER IMMEDIATELY DANGEROUS TO LIFE OR HEALTH CONDITIONS:

SELF-CONTAINED BREATHING APPARATUS WITH FULL FACEPIECE OPERATED IN PRESSURE-DEMAND OR OTHER POSITIVE PRESSURE MODE.

SUPPLIED-AIR RESPIRATOR WITH FULL FACEPIECE AND OPERATED IN PRESSURE-DEMAND OR OTHER POSITIVE PRESSURE MODE IN COMBINATION WITH AN AUXILIARY SELF-CONTAINED BREATHING APPARATUS OPERATED IN PRESSURE-DEMAND OR OTHER POSITIVE PRESSURE MODE.

CLOTHING: EMPLOYEE MUST WEAR APPROPRIATE PROTECTIVE (IMPERVIOUS) CLOTHING AND EQUIPMENT TO PREVENT REPEATED OR PROLONGED SKIN CONTACT WITH THIS SUBSTANCE.
GLOVES: EMPLOYEE MUST WEAR APPROPRIATE PROTECTIVE GLOVES TO PREVENT CONTACT WITH THIS SUBSTANCE.
EYE PROTECTION: EMPLOYEE MUST WEAR SPLASH-PROOF OR DUST-RESISTANT SAFETY GOGGLES TO PREVENT EYE CONTACT WITH THIS SUBSTANCE.
EMERGENCY EYE WASH: WHERE THERE IS ANY POSSIBILITY THAT AN EMPLOYEE'S EYES MAY BE EXPOSED TO THIS SUBSTANCE, THE EMPLOYER SHOULD PROVIDE AN EYE WASH FOUNTAIN WITHIN THE IMMEDIATE WORK AREA FOR EMERGENCY USE.

AUTHORIZED BY- OCCUPATIONAL HEALTH SERVICES, INC.
CREATION DATE: 11/15/89 ***REVISION DATE:*** 05/24/90

MATERIAL SAFETY DATA SHEET

OCCUPATIONAL HEALTH SERVICES, INC.
AGRICULTURE AND PESTICIDE DIVISION
450 SEVENTH AVENUE, SUITE 2407
NEW YORK, NEW YORK 10123
1-800-445-MSDS OR (212) 967-1100

EMERGENCY CONTACT:
JOHN S. BRANSFORD, JR. (615) 292-1180

SUBSTANCE IDENTIFICATION

CAS-NUMBER 13360-45-7
SUBSTANCE: CHLORBROMURON
TRADE NAMES/SYNONYMS: UREA, N'-(4-BROMO-3-CHLOROPHENYL)-N-METHOXY-N-METHYL-; UREA, 3-(4-BROMO-3-CHLOROPHENYL)-1-METHOXY-1-METHYL-; N'-(4-BROMO-3-CHLOROPHENYL)-N-METHOXY-N-METHYLUREA; 3-(4-BROMO-3-CHLOROPHENYL)-1-METHOXY-1-METHYLUREA; BROMEX; C 6313; CHLOROBROMURON; MALORAN; C9H10BRCLN2O2; PST04552
CHEMICAL FAMILY: SUBSTITUTED UREA
HALOGEN COMPOUND, AROMATIC
MOLECULAR FORMULA: C9-H10-BR-CL-N2-O2
MOLECULAR WEIGHT: 293.57
CERCLA RATINGS (SCALE 0-3): HEALTH=2 FIRE=1 REACTIVITY=0 PERSISTENCE=3
NFPA RATINGS (SCALE 0-4): HEALTH=2 FIRE=1 REACTIVITY=0

COMPONENTS AND CONTAMINANTS

COMPONENT: CHLORBROMURON ***PERCENT:*** 100
CAS# 13360-45-7
OTHER CONTAMINANTS: NONE
EXPOSURE LIMITS: NO OCCUPATIONAL EXPOSURE LIMITS ESTABLISHED BY OSHA, ACGIH, OR NIOSH.

PHYSICAL DATA

DESCRIPTION: COLORLESS TO OFF-WHITE CRYSTALLINE SOLID.
MELTING POINT: 203-207 F (95-97 C) ***SPECIFIC GRAVITY:*** 1.69
VAPOR PRESSURE: NEGLIGIBLE ***SOLUBILITY IN WATER:*** 0.0035%
SOLVENT SOLUBILITY: SOLUBLE IN ACETONE, BENZENE, DICHLOROMETHANE, HEXANE, 2-PROPANOL, DIMETHYLFORMAMIDE; MODERATELY SOLUBLE IN XYLENE.

FIRE AND EXPLOSION DATA

FIRE AND EXPLOSION HAZARD: SLIGHT FIRE HAZARD WHEN EXPOSED TO HEAT OR FLAME.
FIREFIGHTING MEDIA: DRY CHEMICAL, CARBON DIOXIDE, HALON, WATER SPRAY OR STANDARD FOAM (1987 EMERGENCY RESPONSE GUIDEBOOK, DOT P 5800.4). FOR LARGER FIRES, USE WATER SPRAY, FOG OR STANDARD FOAM (1987 EMERGENCY RESPONSE GUIDEBOOK, DOT P 5800.4).
FIREFIGHTING: MOVE CONTAINERS FROM FIRE AREA IF POSSIBLE. FIGHT FIRE FROM MAXIMUM DISTANCE. STAY AWAY FROM STORAGE TANK ENDS. DIKE FIRE CONTROL WATER FOR LATER DISPOSAL. DO NOT SCATTER MATERIAL (1987 EMERGENCY RESPONSE GUIDEBOOK, DOT P 5800.4, GUIDE PAGE 55).
EXTINGUISH USING AGENT SUITABLE FOR TYPE OF SURROUNDING FIRE. USE WATER IN FLOODING QUANTITIES AS FOG. KEEP SPARKS, FLAMES AND OTHER SOURCES OF IGNITION AWAY. KEEP MATERIAL OUT OF WATER SOURCES AND SEWERS. DO NOT TOUCH MATERIAL AND AVOID BREATHING DUSTS AND FUMES FROM BURNING MATERIAL. KEEP UPWIND.

TOXICITY

CHLORBROMURON: IRRITATION DATA: 50 MG EYE-RABBIT MODERATE. TOXICITY DATA: 2150 MG/KG ORAL-RAT LD50. CARCINOGEN STATUS: NONE. LOCAL EFFECTS: IRRITANT- EYES. ACUTE TOXICITY LEVEL: MODERATELY TOXIC BY INGESTION. TARGET EFFECTS: NO DATA AVAILABLE.

HEALTH EFFECTS AND FIRST AID

INHALATION: CHLORBROMURON: **ACUTE EXPOSURE-** A LETHAL CONCENTRATION IN RATS WAS GREATER THAN 1050 MG/M3/6 HOURS. MANY SUBSTITUTED UREA HERBICIDES ARE MODERATELY IRRITATING TO THE MUCOUS MEMBRANES.
CHRONIC EXPOSURE- NO DATA AVAILABLE.
FIRST AID- REMOVE FROM EXPOSURE AREA TO FRESH AIR IMMEDIATELY. IF BREATHING HAS STOPPED, PERFORM ARTIFICIAL RESPIRATION. KEEP PERSON WARM AND AT REST. TREAT SYMPTOMATICALLY AND SUPPORTIVELY. GET MEDICAL ATTENTION IMMEDIATELY.

SKIN CONTACT: CHLORBROMURON **ACUTE EXPOSURE-** THIS MATERIAL WAS SLIGHTLY IRRITATING TO RABBIT SKIN. A LETHAL DOSE IN RATS BY DERMAL ABSORPTION WAS GREATER THAN 2000 MG/KG. **CHRONIC EXPOSURE-** NO DATA AVAILABLE.
FIRST AID- REMOVE CONTAMINATED CLOTHING AND SHOES IMMEDIATELY. WASH AFFECTED AREA WITH SOAP OR MILD DETERGENT AND LARGE AMOUNTS OF WATER UNTIL NO EVIDENCE OF CHEMICAL REMAINS (APPROXIMATELY 15-20 MINUTES). GET MEDICAL ATTENTION IMMEDIATELY.

EYE CONTACT: CHLORBROMURON: IRRITANT. **ACUTE EXPOSURE-** 50 MG APPLIED TO RABBIT EYES WAS MODERATELY IRRITATING. **CHRONIC EXPOSURE-** REPEATED OR PROLONGED CONTACT WITH IRRITANTS MAY CAUSE CONJUNCTIVITIS.
FIRST AID- WASH EYES IMMEDIATELY WITH LARGE AMOUNTS OF WATER OR NORMAL SALINE, OCCASIONALLY LIFTING UPPER AND LOWER LIDS, UNTIL NO EVIDENCE OF CHEMICAL REMAINS (APPROXIMATELY 15-20 MINUTES). GET MEDICAL ATTENTION IMMEDIATELY.

INGESTION: CHLORBROMURON: **ACUTE EXPOSURE-** A LETHAL DOSE IN RATS WAS 2150 MG/KG; SYMPTOMS WERE NOT REPORTED. **CHRONIC EXPOSURE-** A SIGNIFICANT DECREASE IN BODY WEIGHT AND AN INCREASE IN LIVER/BODY WEIGHT RATIO WERE NOTED IN A 28-DAY STUDY OF RATS AT A DIETARY LEVEL OF 1000 PPM.
FIRST AID- REMOVE BY GASTRIC LAVAGE AND CATHARSIS. MAINTAIN BLOOD PRESSURE AND AIRWAY. GIVE OXYGEN IF RESPIRATION IS DEPRESSED. DO NOT PERFORM GASTRIC LAVAGE IF VICTIM IS UNCONSCIOUS. GET MEDICAL ATTENTION IMMEDIATELY (DREISBACH, HANDBOOK OF POISONING, 12TH ED.). ADMINISTRATION OF LAVAGE OR OXYGEN SHOULD BE PERFORMED BY QUALIFIED MEDICAL PERSONNEL.
ANTIDOTE: NO SPECIFIC ANTIDOTE. TREAT SYMPTOMATICALLY AND SUPPORTIVELY.

REACTIVITY

REACTIVITY: STABLE UNDER NORMAL TEMPERATURES AND PRESSURES.
INCOMPATIBILITIES: CHLORBROMURON: ACIDS (STRONG): HYDROLYZES. ALKALIES (STRONG): HYDROLYZES.
DECOMPOSITION: THERMAL DECOMPOSITION PRODUCTS MAY INCLUDE TOXIC OXIDES OF NITROGEN AND CARBON, AND TOXIC AND CORROSIVE FUMES OF CHLORIDES AND BROMIDES.
POLYMERIZATION: HAZARDOUS POLYMERIZATION HAS NOT BEEN REPORTED TO OCCUR UNDER NORMAL TEMPERATURES AND PRESSURES.

STORAGE AND DISPOSAL

OBSERVE ALL FEDERAL, STATE AND LOCAL REGULATIONS WHEN STORING OR DISPOSING OF THIS SUBSTANCE. FOR ASSISTANCE, CONTACT THE DISTRICT DIRECTOR OF THE ENVIRONMENTAL PROTECTION AGENCY.

****STORAGE****

STORE IN ACCORDANCE WITH 40 CFR 165 RECOMMENDED PROCEDURES FOR THE DISPOSAL AND STORAGE OF PESTICIDES AND PESTICIDE CONTAINERS.
STORE AWAY FROM INCOMPATIBLE SUBSTANCES.

****DISPOSAL****

DISPOSAL MUST BE IN ACCORDANCE WITH 40 CFR 165 RECOMMENDED PROCEDURES FOR THE DISPOSAL AND STORAGE OF PESTICIDES AND PESTICIDE CONTAINERS.

CONDITIONS TO AVOID

MAY BURN BUT DOES NOT IGNITE READILY. CONTAINERS MAY EXPLODE IN HEAT OF FIRE.

SPILL AND LEAK PROCEDURES

OCCUPATIONAL SPILL: DO NOT TOUCH SPILLED MATERIAL. STOP LEAK IF YOU CAN DO IT WITHOUT RISK. USE WATER SPRAY TO REDUCE VAPORS. FOR SMALL SPILLS, TAKE UP WITH SAND OR OTHER ABSORBENT MATERIAL AND PLACE INTO

CONTAINERS FOR LATER DISPOSAL. FOR SMALL DRY SPILLS, WITH A CLEAN SHOVEL PLACE MATERIAL INTO CLEAN, DRY CONTAINERS AND COVER. MOVE CONTAINERS FROM SPILL AREA. FOR LARGER SPILLS, DIKE FAR AHEAD OF SPILL FOR LATER DISPOSAL. KEEP UNNECESSARY PEOPLE AWAY. ISOLATE HAZARD AREA AND DENY ENTRY. VENTILATE CLOSED SPACES BEFORE ENTERING.

PROTECTIVE EQUIPMENT

VENTILATION: PROVIDE LOCAL EXHAUST OR GENERAL DILUTION VENTILATION SYSTEM.

RESPIRATOR: THE FOLLOWING RESPIRATORS ARE RECOMMENDED BASED ON INFORMATION FOUND IN THE PHYSICAL DATA, TOXICITY AND HEALTH EFFECTS SECTIONS. THEY ARE RANKED IN ORDER FROM MINIMUM TO MAXIMUM RESPIRATORY PROTECTION. THE SPECIFIC RESPIRATOR SELECTED MUST BE BASED ON CONTAMINATION LEVELS FOUND IN THE WORK PLACE, MUST NOT EXCEED THE WORKING LIMITS OF THE RESPIRATOR AND BE JOINTLY APPROVED BY THE NATIONAL INSTITUTE FOR OCCUPATIONAL SAFETY AND HEALTH AND THE MINE SAFETY AND HEALTH ADMINISTRATION (NIOSH-MSHA).

CHEMICAL CARTRIDGE RESPIRATOR WITH AN ORGANIC VAPOR CARTRIDGE(S) WITH A FULL FACEPIECE AND ORGANIC VAPOR CARTRIDGE(S) IN COMBINATION WITH A DUST AND MIST FILTER.

POWERED AIR-PURIFYING RESPIRATOR WITH A TIGHT-FITTING FACEPIECE AND ORGANIC VAPOR CARTRIDGE(S) IN COMBINATION WITH A HIGH-EFFICIENCY PARTICULATE FILTER.

TYPE 'C' SUPPLIED-AIR RESPIRATOR WITH A FULL FACEPIECE OPERATED IN A PRESSURE-DEMAND OR OTHER POSITIVE PRESSURE MODE. SELF-CONTAINED BREATHING APPARATUS WITH A FULL FACEPIECE OPERATED IN PRESSURE-DEMAND OR OTHER POSITIVE PRESSURE MODE.

FOR FIREFIGHTING AND OTHER IMMEDIATELY DANGEROUS TO LIFE OR HEALTH CONDITIONS:

SELF-CONTAINED BREATHING APPARATUS WITH FULL FACEPIECE OPERATED IN PRESSURE-DEMAND OR OTHER POSITIVE PRESSURE MODE.

SUPPLIED-AIR RESPIRATOR WITH FULL FACEPIECE AND OPERATED IN PRESSURE-DEMAND OR OTHER POSITIVE PRESSURE MODE IN COMBINATION WITH AN AUXILIARY SELF-CONTAINED BREATHING APPARATUS OPERATED IN PRESSURE-DEMAND OR OTHER POSITIVE PRESSURE MODE.

CLOTHING: EMPLOYEE MUST WEAR APPROPRIATE PROTECTIVE (IMPERVIOUS) CLOTHING AND EQUIPMENT TO PREVENT REPEATED OR PROLONGED SKIN CONTACT WITH THIS SUBSTANCE.

GLOVES: EMPLOYEE MUST WEAR APPROPRIATE PROTECTIVE GLOVES TO PREVENT CONTACT WITH THIS SUBSTANCE.

EYE PROTECTION: EMPLOYEE MUST WEAR SPLASH-PROOF OR DUST-RESISTANT SAFETY GOGGLES TO PREVENT EYE CONTACT WITH THIS SUBSTANCE.

EMERGENCY EYE WASH: WHERE THERE IS ANY POSSIBILITY THAT AN EMPLOYEE'S EYES MAY BE EXPOSED TO THIS SUBSTANCE, THE EMPLOYER SHOULD PROVIDE AN EYE WASH FOUNTAIN WITHIN THE IMMEDIATE WORK AREA FOR EMERGENCY USE.

AUTHORIZED BY- OCCUPATIONAL HEALTH SERVICES, INC.

CREATION DATE: 10/04/89 ***REVISION DATE:*** 05/08/90

MATERIAL SAFETY DATA SHEET

OCCUPATIONAL HEALTH SERVICES, INC.
AGRICULTURE AND PESTICIDE DIVISION
450 SEVENTH AVENUE, SUITE 2407
NEW YORK, NEW YORK 10123
1-800-445-MSDS OR (212) 967-1100

EMERGENCY CONTACT:
JOHN S. BRANSFORD, JR. (615) 292-1180

SUBSTANCE IDENTIFICATION

CAS-NUMBER 57-74-9

SUBSTANCE: CHLORDANE

TRADE NAMES/SYNONYMS:

1,2,4,5,6,7,8,8-OCTACHLORO-2,3,3A,4,7,7A-HEXAHYDRO-4,7-METHANO-1H -INDENE; 1,2,4,5,6,7,8,8-OCTACHLORO-3A,4,7,7A-TETRAHYDRO-4,7-METHANOINDAN; 4,7-METHANO-1H-INDENE, 1,2,4,5,6,7,8,8-OCTACHLORO-2,3,3A,4,7, 7A-HEXAHYDRO-; 4,7-METHANOINDAN, 1,2,4,5,6,7,8,8-OCTACHLORO-3A,4,7,7A-TETRAHYDRO-; 1,2,4,5,6,7,8,8-OCTACHLORO-2,3,3A,4,7,7A-HEXAHYDRO-4,7-METHANOINDENE; 1,2,4,5,6,7,8,8-OCTACHLORO-4,7-METHANE-3A,4,7,7A-TETRAHYDROINDANE; 1,2,4,5,6,7,8,8-OCTACHLORO-3A,4,7,7A-TETRAHYDRO-4,7-METHANOINDANE; CHLORINDAN; CORTILAN-NEU; TAT; TOXICHLOR; NCI-COOO99; ENT 9,932; STCC 4909320; OMS 1437; RCRA U036; UN 2762; C10H6CL8; PST04560

CHEMICAL FAMILY: HALOGEN COMPOUND, AROMATIC

MOLECULAR FORMULA: C10-H6-CL8

MOLECULAR WEIGHT: 409.76

CERCLA RATINGS (SCALE 0-3): HEALTH=3 FIRE=0 REACTIVITY=0 PERSISTENCE=3

NFPA RATINGS (SCALE 0-4): HEALTH=4 FIRE=0 REACTIVITY=0

COMPONENTS AND CONTAMINANTS

COMPONENT: CHLORDANE ***PERCENT:*** 100.0
CAS# 57-74-9

OTHER CONTAMINANTS: NONE

EXPOSURE LIMITS: CHLORDANE: 0.5 MG/M3 OSHA TWA (SKIN) 0.5 MG/M3 ACGIH TWA (SKIN); 2 MG/M3 ACGIH STEL (NOTICE OF INTENDED CHANGES 1988-89) 1000 POUNDS SARA SECTION 302 THRESHOLD PLANNING QUANTITY 1 POUND SARA SECTION 304 REPORTABLE QUANTITY 1 POUND CERCLA SECTION 103 REPORTABLE QUANTITY SUBJECT TO SARA SECTION 313 ANNUAL TOXIC CHEMICAL RELEASE REPORTING SUBJECT TO CALIFORNIA PROPOSITION 65 CANCER AND/OR REPRODUCTIVE TOXICITY WARNING AND RELEASE REQUIREMENTS- (JULY 1, 1988)

PHYSICAL DATA

DESCRIPTION: COLORLESS OR AMBER-COLORED LIQUID WITH A CHORINE-LIKE ODOR.

BOILING POINT: 347 F (175 C) @ 2 MMHG (DECOMPOSES)

SPECIFIC GRAVITY: 1.59-1.63

VISCOSITY: 6900 CPS @ 25 C ***VAPOR PRESSURE:*** 0.00001 MMHG @ 25 C

EVAPORATION RATE: NOT AVAILABLE ***SOLUBILITY IN WATER:*** 0.1 PPM @ 25 C

VAPOR DENSITY: 14

SOLVENT SOLUBILITY: SOLUBLE IN ALIPHATIC AND AROMATIC HYDROCARBON SOLVENTS INCLUDING DEODORIZED KEROSENE AND TRICHLORETHYLENE.

FIRE AND EXPLOSION DATA

FIRE AND EXPLOSION HAZARD: NEGLIGIBLE FIRE HAZARD WHEN EXPOSED TO HEAT OR FLAME.

FIREFIGHTING MEDIA: DRY CHEMICAL, CARBON DIOXIDE, HALON, WATER SPRAY OR STANDARD FOAM (1987 EMERGENCY RESPONSE GUIDEBOOK, DOT P 5800.4). FOR LARGER FIRES, USE WATER SPRAY, FOG OR STANDARD FOAM (1987 EMERGENCY RESPONSE GUIDEBOOK, DOT P 5800.4).

FIREFIGHTING: MOVE CONTAINERS FROM FIRE AREA IF POSSIBLE. FIGHT FIRE FROM MAXIMUM DISTANCE. STAY AWAY FROM STORAGE TANK ENDS. DIKE FIRE CONTROL WATER FOR LATER DISPOSAL. DO NOT SCATTER MATERIAL (1987 EMERGENCY RESPONSE GUIDEBOOK, DOT P 5800.4, GUIDE PAGE 55). EXTINGUISH ONLY IF FLOW CAN BE STOPPED. EXTINGUISH USING AGENT INDICATED. USE FLOODING AMOUNTS OF WATER AS A FOG. COOL CONTAINERS WITH FLOODING AMOUNTS OF WATER FROM AS FAR A DISTANCE AS POSSIBLE. AVOID BREATHING POISONOUS VAPORS, KEEP UPWIND. CONSIDER EVACUATION OF DOWNWIND AREA IF MATERIAL IS LEAKING.

TOXICITY

CHLORDANE: TOXICITY DATA: 100 MG/M3/4 HOURS INHALATION-CAT LC50; 428 MG/KG SKIN-HUMAN LDLO; 780 MG/KG SKIN-RABBIT LD50; 690 MG/KG SKIN-RAT LD50; 29 MG/KG ORAL-HUMAN LDLO; 3071 UG/KG ORAL-MAN TDLO; 120 UG/KG ORAL-WOMAN LDLO; 200 MG/KG ORAL-RAT LD50; 145 MG/KG ORAL-MOUSE LD50; 100 MG/KG ORAL-RABBIT LD50; 1720 MG/KG ORAL-HAMSTER LD50; 180 MG/KG ORAL-MAMMAL LD50; 50 MG/KG ORAL-DOMESTIC ANIMAL LD50; 100 MG/KG INTRAVENOUS-MOUSE LD50; 10 MG/KG INTRAVENOUS-RABBIT LDLO; 343 MG/KG INTRAPERITONEAL-RAT LD50; 240 MG/KG INTRAPERITONEAL-MOUSE LDLO; 118 MG/KG UNREPORTED-MAN LDLO; MUTAGENIC DATA (RTECS); REPRODUCTIVE EFFECTS DATA (RTECS); TUMORIGENIC DATA (RTECS). CARCINOGEN STATUS: HUMAN INADEQUATE EVIDENCE; ANIMAL LIMITED EVIDENCE (IARC GROUP-3). HEPATOCELLULAR CARCINOMAS WERE PRODUCED IN MICE BY ORAL ADMINISTRATION. ACUTE TOXICITY LEVEL: HIGHLY TOXIC BY INHALATION; TOXIC BY DERMAL ABSORPTION AND INGESTION. TARGET EFFECTS: CONVULSANT. POISONING MAY ALSO AFFECT THE LIVER, KIDNEYS, AND BLOOD. AT INCREASED RISK FROM EXPOSURE: PERSONS WITH CONVULSIVE DISORDERS. ADDITIONAL DATA: CHLORDANE MAY BE STORED IN ADIPOSE TISSUE; INTENSE ACTIVITY AND STARVATION MAY MOBILIZE THE PESTICIDE RESULTING IN THE REAPPEARANCE OF TOXIC SYMPTOMS. IT CROSSES THE PLACENTA AND MAY BE EXCRETED IN HUMAN MILK. STUDIES OF 2 GROUPS OF WORKERS, ONE INVOLVED IN THE MANUFACTURE OF CHLORDANE, HEPTACHLOR, AND ENDRIN AND THE OTHER OF CHLORDANE AND HEPTACHLOR, REVEALED A STATISTICALLY SIGNIFICANT INCREASE IN DEATHS FROM CEREBROVASCULAR DISEASE IN THE FORMER BUT NOT THE LATTER; THE FORMER STUDY HAD METHODOLOGICAL DEFICIENCIES.

HEALTH EFFECTS AND FIRST AID

INHALATION: CHLORDANE: CONVULSANT/HIGHLY TOXIC. 500 MG/M3 IMMEDIATELY DANGEROUS TO LIFE OR HEALTH. **ACUTE EXPOSURE-** SYMPTOMS OF BLURRED VISION, COUGH, CONFUSION, ATAXIA, HEADACHE, WEAKNESS, DIZZINESS, AND DELIRIUM WERE REPORTED FROM INHALATION EXPOSURE TO CHLORDANE. SYMPTOMS OF CENTRAL NERVOUS SYSTEM STIMULATION MAY ALSO OCCUR AS DETAILED IN ACUTE INGESTION. **CHRONIC EXPOSURE-** HUMAN EXPOSURE TO VAPORS OF 7 PERCENT CHLORDANE FOR 15 MINUTES AT 3-DAY INTERVALS FOR PERIODS OF 15 WEEKS AND REPEATED A YEAR LATER, DID NOT RESULT IN SYMPTOMS OF TOXICITY. IN ADDITION TO THE SYMPTOMS OF ACUTE EXPOSURE, CHRONIC EXPOSURE OF HUMANS TO TECHNICAL CHLORDANE CONTAINING HEPTACHLOR AND OTHER CHEMICALS HAS CAUSED LIGHTHEADEDNESS, NAUSEA, COUGH, CHEST COMPLAINTS, TREMORS, ARTHRALGIAS, FATIGUE, THROMBOCYTOPENIC PURPURA, AND MARKED BRUISING. PANCYTOPENIA, APLASTIC, HEMOLYTIC, AND MEGALOBLASTIC ANEMIAS, LEUKEMIA, AND DEATH HAVE ALSO BEEN REPORTED. EXPOSURE OF MONKEYS TO 100-1,000 UG/M3 FOR 90 DAYS INDUCED A STATISTICALLY SIGNIFICANT INCIDENCE OF LEUKOPENIA AND THROMBOCYTOPENIA, WITH EFFECTS OCCURRING AT THE LOWEST DOSE TESTED.

FIRST AID- REMOVE FROM EXPOSURE AREA TO FRESH AIR IMMEDIATELY. IF BREATHING HAS STOPPED, GIVE ARTIFICIAL RESPIRATION. MAINTAIN AIRWAY AND BLOOD PRESSURE AND ADMINISTER OXYGEN IF AVAILABLE. KEEP AFFECTED PERSON WARM AND AT REST. TREAT SYMPTOMATICALLY AND SUPPORTIVELY. ADMINISTRATION OF OXYGEN SHOULD BE PERFORMED BY QUALIFIED PERSONNEL. GET MEDICAL ATTENTION IMMEDIATELY.

SKIN CONTACT: CHLORDANE: CONVULSANT/TOXIC. **ACUTE EXPOSURE-** MAY BE IRRITATING. SKIN ABSORPTION HAS CAUSED BLURRED VISION, CONFUSION, ATAXIA, HEADACHE, DIZZINESS, WEAKNESS, AND DELIRIUM. IN SEVERE POISONING, CONVULSIONS MAY DEVELOP AND COMA AND DEATH ARE POSSIBLE. IN ONE CASE OF OCCUPATIONAL EXPOSURE, A WOMAN BECAME CONFUSED AND DEVELOPED CONVULSIONS 40 MINUTES AFTER SPILLING A SOLUTION CONTAINING 25% CHLORDANE AND 26% DDT ON HER CLOTHING. SHE DIED SHORTLY THEREAFTER FROM RESPIRATORY FAILURE. **CHRONIC EXPOSURE-** REPEATED CONTACT CAUSED EPISODES OF PARESTHESIA, TWITCHING OF THE RIGHT HAND AND ARM, GRAND MAL SEIZURES, AND UNCONSCIOUSNESS. OTHER EFFECTS MAY OCCUR AS DETAILED IN CHRONIC INHALATION. REPEATED APPLICATION OF 50 MG/KG TO THE SKIN OF RATS FOR 3 OR 4 DAYS CAUSED 100% FATALITIES.

FIRST AID- REMOVE CONTAMINATED CLOTHING AND SHOES IMMEDIATELY. WASH AFFECTED AREA WITH SOAP OR MILD DETERGENT AND LARGE AMOUNTS OF WATER UNTIL NO EVIDENCE OF CHEMICAL REMAINS (APPROXIMATELY 15-20 MINUTES). GET MEDICAL ATTENTION IMMEDIATELY.

EYE CONTACT: CHLORDANE: **ACUTE EXPOSURE-** MAY BE IRRITATING. **CHRONIC EXPOSURE-** NO DATA AVAILABLE.

FIRST AID- WASH EYES IMMEDIATELY WITH LARGE AMOUNTS OF WATER OR NORMAL SALINE, OCCASIONALLY LIFTING UPPER AND LOWER LIDS, UNTIL NO EVIDENCE OF CHEMICAL REMAINS (APPROXIMATELY 15-20 MINUTES). GET MEDICAL ATTENTION IMMEDIATELY.

INGESTION: CHLORDANE: CONVULSANT/LIMITED ANIMAL CARCINOGEN/TOXIC. **ACUTE EXPOSURE-** MAY CAUSE ABDOMINAL PAIN, NAUSEA, VOMITING, AND DIARRHEA. CHLORDANE MAY STIMULATE THE CENTRAL NERVOUS SYSTEM WITH CONVULSIONS SOMETIMES APPEARING AS THE FIRST SYMPTOM OF POISONING. SYMPTOMS OF HEADACHE, BLURRED VISION, HYPEREXCITABILITY, MUSCLE TWITCHING, TREMOR, INCOORDINATION, AND ATAXIA MAY ALSO OCCUR. IN SEVERE CASES OF POISONING, COMA AND DEATH ARE POSSIBLE. EEG PATTERNS SUGGEST THAT DEATH IS DUE TO RESPIRATORY ARREST BETWEEN OR DURING CONVULSIVE EPISODES. CHLORDANE MAY BE EXCRETED SLOWLY FROM THE BODY; THE SERUM HALF-LIFE IN ONE CHILD WAS 88 DAYS. **CHRONIC EXPOSURE-** IN A TWO-YEAR FEEDING STUDY IN RATS, A DIETARY CONCENTRATION OF 150 PPM PRODUCED A NOTED RETARDATION OF GROWTH, LIVER AND KIDNEY DAMAGE, MYOCARDIAL DAMAGE, AND MILD INJURY TO THE LUNGS; MARKED DAMAGE TO THE LUNGS AND INCREASED MORTALITY WERE OBSERVED AT DIETARY CONCENTRATIONS OF 300 PPM. SIMILAR EFFECTS WERE REPORTED IN RABBITS ADMINISTERED 5 MG/KG/DAY. CHLORDANE PRODUCED LIVER NEOPLASMS IN MICE FOLLOWING ORAL ADMINISTRATION; RESULTS FOR RATS WERE INCONCLUSIVE. ORAL ADMINISTRATION OF CHLORDANE ENHANCED THE INCIDENCE OF LIVER TUMORS INDUCED IN MICE BY ORAL ADMINISTRATION OF N-NITROSODIETHYLAMINE. REPRODUCTIVE EFFECTS REPORTED IN ANIMALS INCLUDE DECREASED VIABILTIY OF OFFSPRING IN MICE FED 100 MG/KG/DAY FOR 4 MONTHS; DECREASED FERTILITY IN RATS AND MICE; AND EXCITABILITY AND TREMORS IN OFFSPRING WHEN KEPT WITH TREATED MOTHERS, BUT NOT WITH UNTREATED FEMALES.

FIRST AID- IF THE PERSON IS CONSCIOUS AND NOT CONVULSING, REMOVE BY GIVING SYRUP OF IPECAC (IF VOMITING OCCURS, KEEP THE HEAD BELOW THE HIPS TO PREVENT ASPIRATION). GIVE ACTIVATED CHARCOAL FOLLOWED BY GASTRIC LAVAGE. FOLLOW WITH A SALINE CATHARTIC. DO NOT GIVE FATS OR OILS. INTESTINAL LAVAGE WITH 20% MANNITOL (200 ML) BY STOMACH TUBE IS ALSO USEFUL. GIVE ARTIFICIAL RESPIRATION WITH OXYGEN IF RESPIRATION IS DEPRESSED (DREISBACH, HANDBOOK OF POISONING, 12TH ED.). TREAT SYMPTOMATICALLY AND SUPPORTIVELY. LAVAGE AND ADMINISTRATION OF OXYGEN SHOULD BE PERFORMED BY QUALIFIED MEDICAL PERSONNEL. GET MEDICAL ATTENTION IMMEDIATELY.

ANTIDOTE: NO SPECIFIC ANTIDOTE. TREAT SYMPTOMATICALLY AND SUPPORTIVELY.

REACTIVITY

REACTIVITY: STABLE UNDER NORMAL TEMPERATURES AND PRESSURES.

INCOMPATIBILITIES: CHLORDANE: ALKALIES (WEAK): DECOMPOSES. OXIDIZERS (STRONG): FIRE AND EXPLOSION HAZARD. PLASTICS, RUBBER, COATINGS: MAY BE ATTACKED.

DECOMPOSITION: THERMAL DECOMPOSITION PRODUCTS MAY INCLUDE TOXIC AND CORROSIVE FUMES OF CHLORIDES AND PHOSGENE, AND TOXIC OXIDES OF CARBON.

POLYMERIZATION: HAZARDOUS POLYMERIZATION HAS NOT BEEN REPORTED TO OCCUR UNDER NORMAL TEMPERATURES AND PRESSURES.

STORAGE AND DISPOSAL

OBSERVE ALL FEDERAL, STATE AND LOCAL REGULATIONS WHEN STORING OR DISPOSING OF THIS SUBSTANCE. FOR ASSISTANCE, CONTACT THE DISTRICT DIRECTOR OF THE ENVIRONMENTAL PROTECTION AGENCY.

****STORAGE****

STORE IN ACCORDANCE WITH 40 CFR 165 RECOMMENDED PROCEDURES FOR THE DISPOSAL AND STORAGE OF PESTICIDES AND PESTICIDE CONTAINERS.

STORE AWAY FROM INCOMPATIBLE SUBSTANCES.

THRESHOLD PLANNING QUANTITY (TPQ): THE SUPERFUND AMENDMENTS AND REAUTHORIZATION ACT (SARA) SECTION 302 REQUIRES THAT EACH FACILITY WHERE ANY EXTREMELY HAZARDOUS SUBSTANCE IS PRESENT IN A QUANTITY EQUAL TO OR GREATER THAN THE TPQ ESTABLISHED FOR THAT SUBSTANCE NOTIFY THE STATE EMERGENCY RESPONSE COMMISSION FOR THE STATE IN WHICH IT IS LOCATED. SECTION 303 OF SARA REQUIRES THESE FACILITIES TO PARTICIPATE IN LOCAL EMERGENCY RESPONSE PLANNING (40 CFR 355.30).

****DISPOSAL****

DISPOSAL MUST BE IN ACCORDANCE WITH 40 CFR 165 RECOMMENDED PROCEDURES FOR THE DISPOSAL AND STORAGE OF PESTICIDES AND PESTICIDE CONTAINERS.

DISPOSAL MUST BE IN ACCORDANCE WITH STANDARDS APPLICABLE TO GENERATORS OF HAZARDOUS WASTE, 40CFR 262. EPA HAZARDOUS WASTE NUMBER U036.

CHLORDANE - REGULATORY LEVEL: 0.03 MG/L MATERIALS WHICH CONTAIN THE ABOVE SUBSTANCE AT OR ABOVE THE REGULATORY LEVEL MEET THE EPA CHARACTERISTIC OF TOXICITY, AND MUST BE DISPOSED OF IN ACCORDANCE WITH 40 CFR PART 262. EPA HAZARDOUS WASTE NUMBER D020.

CONDITIONS TO AVOID

MAY BURN BUT DOES NOT IGNITE READILY. CONTAINERS MAY EXPLODE IN HEAT OF FIRE.

SPILL AND LEAK PROCEDURES

SOIL SPILL: DIG A HOLDING AREA SUCH AS A PIT, POND OR LAGOON TO CONTAIN SPILL AND DIKE SURFACE FLOW USING BARRIER OF SOIL, SANDBAGS, FOAMED POLYURETHANE OR FOAMED CONCRETE. ABSORB LIQUID MASS WITH FLY ASH OR CEMENT POWDER.

IMMOBILIZE SPILL WITH UNIVERSAL GELLING AGENT.

AIR SPILL: KNOCK DOWN VAPORS WITH WATER SPRAY. KEEP UPWIND. COMBUSTION PRODUCTS INCLUDE CORROSIVE OR TOXIC VAPORS.

WATER SPILL: TRAP SPILLED MATERIAL AT BOTTOM IN DEEP WATER POCKETS, EXCAVATED HOLDING AREAS OR WITHIN SAND BAG BARRIERS.

USE ACTIVATED CARBON TO ABSORB SPILLED SUBSTANCE THAT IS DISSOLVED.

USE MECHANICAL DREDGES OR LIFTS TO EXTRACT IMMOBILIZED MASSES OF POLLUTION AND PRECIPITATES.

THE CALIFORNIA SAFE DRINKING WATER AND TOXIC ENFORCEMENT ACT OF 1986 (PROPOSITION 65) PROHIBITS CONTAMINATING ANY KNOWN SOURCE OF DRINKING WATER WITH SUBSTANCES KNOWN TO CAUSE CANCER AND/OR REPRODUCTIVE TOXICITY.

OCCUPATIONAL SPILL: DO NOT TOUCH SPILLED MATERIAL. STOP LEAK IF YOU CAN DO IT WITHOUT RISK. USE WATER SPRAY TO REDUCE VAPORS. FOR SMALL SPILLS, TAKE UP WITH SAND OR OTHER ABSORBENT MATERIAL AND PLACE INTO CONTAINERS FOR LATER DISPOSAL. FOR SMALL DRY SPILLS, WITH A CLEAN SHOVEL PLACE MATERIAL INTO CLEAN, DRY CONTAINERS AND COVER. MOVE CONTAINERS FROM SPILL AREA. FOR LARGER SPILLS, DIKE FAR AHEAD OF SPILL FOR LATER DISPOSAL. KEEP UNNECESSARY PEOPLE AWAY. ISOLATE HAZARD AREA AND DENY ENTRY. VENTILATE CLOSED SPACES BEFORE ENTERING.

REPORTABLE QUANTITY (RQ): 1 POUND THE SUPERFUND AMENDMENTS AND REAUTHORIZATION ACT (SARA) SECTION 304 REQUIRES THAT A RELEASE EQUAL TO OR GREATER THAN THE REPORTABLE QUANTITY FOR THIS SUBSTANCE BE IMMEDIATELY REPORTED TO THE LOCAL EMERGENCY PLANNING COMMITTEE AND THE STATE EMERGENCY RESPONSE COMMISSION (40 CFR 355.40). IF THE RELEASE OF THIS SUBSTANCE IS REPORTABLE UNDER CERCLA SECTION 103, THE NATIONAL RESPONSE CENTER MUST BE NOTIFIED IMMEDIATELY AT (800) 424-8802 OR (202) 426-2675 IN THE METROPOLITAN WASHINGTON, D.C. AREA (40 CFR 302.6).

PROTECTIVE EQUIPMENT

VENTILATION: PROVIDE LOCAL EXHAUST VENTILATION AND/OR GENERAL DILUTION VENTILATION TO MEET PUBLISHED EXPOSURE LIMITS.

RESPIRATOR: THE FOLLOWING RESPIRATORS AND MAXIMUM USE CONCENTRATIONS ARE RECOMMENDATIONS BY THE U.S. DEPARTMENT OF HEALTH AND HUMAN SERVICES, NIOSH POCKET GUIDE TO CHEMICAL HAZARDS; NIOSH CRITERIA DOCUMENTS OR BY THE U.S. DEPARTMENT OF LABOR, 29 CFR 1910 SUBPART Z. THE SPECIFIC RESPIRATOR SELECTED MUST BE BASED ON CONTAMINATION LEVELS FOUND IN THE WORK PLACE, MUST NOT EXCEED THE WORKING LIMITS OF THE RESPIRATOR AND BE JOINTLY APPROVED BY THE NATIONAL INSTITUTE FOR OCCUPATIONAL SAFETY AND HEALTH AND THE MINE SAFETY AND HEALTH ADMINISTRATION (NIOSH-MSHA).

CHLORDANE:

5 MG/M3- ANY CHEMICAL CARTRIDGE RESPIRATOR WITH ORGANIC VAPOR CARTRIDGE(S) IN COMBINATION WITH A DUST, MIST, AND FUME FILTER. ANY SUPPLIED-AIR RESPIRATOR. ANY SELF-CONTAINED BREATHING APPARATUS.

12.5 MG/M3- ANY SUPPLIED-AIR RESPIRATOR OPERATED IN A CONTINUOUS FLOW MODE. ANY POWERED AIR-PURIFYING RESPIRATOR WITH ORGANIC VAPOR CARTRIDGE(S) IN COMBINATION WITH A DUST, MIST, AND FUME FILTER.

25 MG/M3- ANY CHEMICAL CARTRIDGE RESPIRATOR WITH A FULL FACEPIECE AND ORGANIC VAPOR CARTRIDGE(S) IN COMBINATION WITH A HIGH-EFFICIENCY PARTICULATE FILTER. ANY SUPPLIED-AIR RESPIRATOR WITH A FULL FACEPIECE. ANY SELF-CONTAINED BREATHING APPARATUS WITH A FULL FACEPIECE. ANY POWDERED AIR-PURIFYING RESPIRATOR WITH A TIGHT-FITTING FACEPIECE AND ORGANIC VAPOR CARTRIDGE(S) IN COMBINATION WITH A HIGH-EFFICIENCY PARTICULATE FILTER. ANY AIR-PURIFYING FULL FACEPIECE RESPIRATOR (GAS MASK) WITH A CHIN-STYLE OR FRONT- OR BACK-MOUNTED ORGANIC VAPOR CANISTER HAVING A HIGH-EFFICIENCY PARTICULATE FILTER.

500 MG/M3- ANY SUPPLIED-AIR RESPIRATOR WITH A HALF-MASK AND OPERATED IN A PRESSURE-DEMAND OR OTHER POSITIVE PRESSURE MODE.

ESCAPE- ANY AIR-PURIFYING FULL FACEPIECE RESPIRATOR (GAS MASK) WITH A CHIN-STYLE OR FRONT- OR BACK-MOUNTED ORGANIC VAPOR CANISTER HAVING A HIGH-EFFICIENCY PARTICULATE FILTER. ANY APPROPRIATE ESCAPE-TYPE SELF-CONTAINED BREATHING APPARATUS.

FOR FIREFIGHTING AND OTHER IMMEDIATELY DANGEROUS TO LIFE OR HEALTH CONDITIONS:

SELF-CONTAINED BREATHING APPARATUS WITH FULL FACEPIECE OPERATED IN PRESSURE-DEMAND OR OTHER POSITIVE PRESSURE MODE.

SUPPLIED-AIR RESPIRATOR WITH FULL FACEPIECE AND OPERATED IN PRESSURE-DEMAND OR OTHER POSITIVE PRESSURE MODE IN COMBINATION WITH AN AUXILIARY SELF-CONTAINED BREATHING APPARATUS OPERATED IN PRESSURE-DEMAND OR OTHER POSITIVE PRESSURE MODE.

CLOTHING: EMPLOYEE MUST WEAR APPROPRIATE PROTECTIVE (IMPERVIOUS) CLOTHING AND EQUIPMENT TO PREVENT ANY POSSIBILITY OF SKIN CONTACT WITH THIS SUBSTANCE.

GLOVES: EMPLOYEE MUST WEAR APPROPRIATE PROTECTIVE GLOVES TO PREVENT CONTACT WITH THIS SUBSTANCE.

EYE PROTECTION: EMPLOYEE MUST WEAR SPLASH-PROOF OR DUST-RESISTANT SAFETY GOGGLES AND A FACESHIELD TO PREVENT CONTACT WITH THIS SUBSTANCE.

EMERGENCY WASH FACILITIES: WHERE THERE IS ANY POSSIBILITY THAT AN EMPLOYEE'S EYES AND/OR SKIN MAY BE EXPOSED TO THIS SUBSTANCE, THE EMPLOYER SHOULD PROVIDE AN EYE WASH FOUNTAIN AND QUICK DRENCH SHOWER WITHIN THE IMMEDIATE WORK AREA FOR EMERGENCY USE.

AUTHORIZED BY- OCCUPATIONAL HEALTH SERVICES, INC.
CREATION DATE: 10/04/89 ***REVISION DATE:*** 07/13/90

MATERIAL SAFETY DATA SHEET

OCCUPATIONAL HEALTH SERVICES, INC.
AGRICULTURE AND PESTICIDE DIVISION
450 SEVENTH AVENUE, SUITE 2407
NEW YORK, NEW YORK 10123
1-800-445-MSDS OR (212) 967-1100

EMERGENCY CONTACT:
JOHN S. BRANSFORD, JR. (615) 292-1180

SUBSTANCE IDENTIFICATION

CAS-NUMBER 3734-48-3

SUBSTANCE: CHLORDENE

TRADE NAMES/SYNONYMS: 4,7-METHANO-1H-INDENE, 4,5,6,7,8,8-HEXACHLORO-3A,4,7,7A-TETRAHYDRO-; 4,5,6,7,8,8-HEXACHLORO-3A,4,7,7A-TETRAHYDRO-4,7-METHANO-1H-INDENE; 4,7-METHANOINDENE, 4,5,6,7,8,8-HEXACHLORO-3A,4,7,7A-TETRAHYDRO-; 4,5,6,7,8,8-HEXACHLORO-3A,4,7,7A-TETRAHYDRO-4,7-METHANOINDENE; C10H6CL6; PST04565

CHEMICAL FAMILY: HALOGEN COMPOUND, ALICYCLIC

MOLECULAR FORMULA: C10-H6-CL6

MOLECULAR WEIGHT: 338.86

CERCLA RATINGS (SCALE 0-3): HEALTH=3 FIRE=1 REACTIVITY=0 PERSISTENCE=3

NFPA RATINGS (SCALE 0-4): HEALTH=4 FIRE=1 REACTIVITY=0

COMPONENTS AND CONTAMINANTS

COMPONENT: CHLORDENE ***PERCENT:*** 100.0
CAS# 3734-48-3

OTHER CONTAMINANTS: NONE

EXPOSURE LIMITS: NO OCCUPATIONAL EXPOSURE LIMITS ESTABLISHED BY OSHA, ACGIH, OR NIOSH.

PHYSICAL DATA

DESCRIPTION: WHITE SOLID. ***MELTING POINT:*** DECOMPOSES

SPECIFIC GRAVITY: NOT AVAILABLE ***SOLUBILITY IN WATER:*** NOT AVAILABLE

FIRE AND EXPLOSION DATA

FIRE AND EXPLOSION HAZARD: SLIGHT FIRE HAZARD WHEN EXPOSED TO HEAT OR FLAME.

FIREFIGHTING MEDIA: DRY CHEMICAL, CARBON DIOXIDE, HALON, WATER SPRAY OR STANDARD FOAM (1987 EMERGENCY RESPONSE GUIDEBOOK, DOT P 5800.4). FOR LARGER FIRES, USE WATER SPRAY, FOG OR STANDARD FOAM (1987 EMERGENCY RESPONSE GUIDEBOOK, DOT P 5800.4).

FIREFIGHTING: MOVE CONTAINERS FROM FIRE AREA IF POSSIBLE (1987 EMERGENCY RESPONSE GUIDEBOOK, DOT P 5800.4, GUIDE PAGE 53).
EXTINGUISH USING AGENT SUITABLE FOR TYPE OF SURROUNDING FIRE. AVOID BREATHING VAPORS AND DUSTS. KEEP UPWIND.

TOXICITY

CHLORDENE: IRRITATION DATA: 500 MG/24 HOURS EYE-RABBIT MILD. TOXICITY DATA: 2 GM/M3 INHALATION-HUMAN LCLO; 2 GM/M3 INHALATION-RAT LC50; 69 MG/KG SKIN-HUMAN LDLO; 690 MG/KG SKIN-RAT LD50; 583 MG/KG ORAL-HUMAN LDLO; REPRODUCTIVE EFFECTS DATA (RTECS). CARCINOGEN STATUS: NONE. ACUTE TOXICITY LEVEL: HIGHLY TOXIC BY INHALATION; TOXIC BY DERMAL ABSORPTION. TARGET EFFECTS: POISONING MAY AFFECT THE LIVER, KIDNEYS, BLOOD, AND CARDIOVASCULAR SYSTEM.* AT INCREASED RISK FROM EXPOSURE: PERSONS WITH CONVULSIVE DISORDERS.* ADDITIONAL DATA: MAY BE STORED IN ADIPOSE TISSUE; MAY CROSS THE PLACENTA AND BE EXCRETED IN HUMAN MILK. STIMULANTS SUCH AS EPINEPHRINE MAY INDUCE VENTRICULAR FIBRILLATIONS.*
* MAY BE BASED ON GENERAL INFORMATION ON CHLORINATED CYCLODIENE DERIVATIVES.

HEALTH EFFECTS AND FIRST AID

INHALATION: CHLORDENE: HIGHLY TOXIC. **ACUTE EXPOSURE-** CHLORINATED CYCLODIENE DERIVATIVES MAY PRODUCE HEADACHE, NAUSEA, VOMITING, MALAISE, DIZZINESS, APPREHENSION, PARESTHESIA, HYPERIRRITABILITY, ATAXIA, MUSCLE TWITCHING, MYOCLONIC JERKING, AND CONVULSIVE SEIZURES. IN SEVERE CASES, CONVULSIONS MAY OCCUR WITHOUT ANY PRIOR SYMPTOMS. THE CONVULSIONS MAY BE CONTINUOUS WITH ELEVATED BODY TEMPERATURE, UNCONSCIOUSNESS, LABORED BREATHING WITH VIGOROUS, RAPID HEART BEAT, AND DEATH FROM RESPIRATORY DEPRESSION. **CHRONIC EXPOSURE-** CHRONIC INTOXICATION FROM CHLORINATED CYCLODIENE DERIVATIVES MAY BE CHARACTERIZED BY NERVOUS SYSTEM, LIVER, AND KIDNEY DAMAGE, CARDIOVASCULAR DISTURBANCES, AND BLOOD AND CAPILLARY DISTURBANCES. IN ADDITION TO THE SYMPTOMS DETAILED IN ACUTE EXPOSURE, ANOREXIA, BLURRED VISION, AND DROWSINESS MAY ALSO OCCUR.

FIRST AID- REMOVE FROM EXPOSURE AREA TO FRESH AIR IMMEDIATELY. IF BREATHING HAS STOPPED, PERFORM ARTIFICIAL RESPIRATION. KEEP PERSON WARM AND AT REST. TREAT SYMPTOMATICALLY AND SUPPORTIVELY. GET MEDICAL ATTENTION IMMEDIATELY.

SKIN CONTACT: CHLORDENE: TOXIC. **ACUTE EXPOSURE-** CHLORINATED CYCLODIENE DERIVATIVES MAY PRODUCE HEADACHE, NAUSEA, VOMITING, MALAISE, DIZZINESS, APPREHENSION, PARESTHESIA, HYPERIRRITABILITY, ATAXIA, MUSCLE TWITCHING, MYOCLONIC JERKING, AND CONVULSIVE SEIZURES. IN SEVERE CASES, CONVULSIONS MAY OCCUR WITHOUT ANY PRIOR SYMPTOMS. THE CONVULSIONS MAY BE CONTINUOUS WITH ELEVATED BODY TEMPERATURES, UNCONSCIOUSNESS, LABORED BREATHING WITH VIGOROUS, RAPID HEART BEAT, AND DEATH FROM RESPIRATORY DEPRESSION. **CHRONIC EXPOSURE-** CHRONIC INTOXICATION FROM CHLORINATED CYCLODIENE DERIVATIVES MAY BE CHARACTERIZED BY NERVOUS SYSTEM, LIVER, AND KIDNEY DAMAGE, CARDIOVASCULAR DISTURBANCES, AND BLOOD AND CAPILLARY DISTURBANCES. IN ADDITION TO THE SYMPTOMS DETAILED IN ACUTE EXPOSURE, SKIN IRRITATION, ANOREXIA, BLURRED VISION, AND DROWSINESS MAY ALSO OCCUR.

FIRST AID- REMOVE CONTAMINATED CLOTHING AND SHOES IMMEDIATELY. WASH AFFECTED AREA WITH SOAP OR MILD DETERGENT AND LARGE AMOUNTS OF WATER UNTIL NO EVIDENCE OF CHEMICAL REMAINS (APPROXIMATELY 15-20 MINUTES). GET MEDICAL ATTENTION IMMEDIATELY.

EYE CONTACT: CHLORDENE: **ACUTE EXPOSURE-** MAY PRODUCE MILD IRRITATION. **CHRONIC EXPOSURE-** NO DATA AVAILABLE.

FIRST AID- WASH EYES IMMEDIATELY WITH LARGE AMOUNTS OF WATER OR NORMAL SALINE, OCCASIONALLY LIFTING UPPER AND LOWER LIDS, UNTIL NO EVIDENCE OF CHEMICAL REMAINS (APPROXIMATELY 15-20 MINUTES). GET MEDICAL ATTENTION IMMEDIATELY.

INGESTION: CHLORDENE: **ACUTE EXPOSURE-** CHLORINATED CYCLODIENE DERIVATIVES MAY PRODUCE HEADACHE, NAUSEA, VOMITING, MALAISE, DIZZINESS, APPREHENSION, PARESTHESIA, HYPERIRRITABILITY, ATAXIA, MUSCLE TWITCHING, MYOCLONIC JERKING, AND CONVULSIVE SEIZURES. IN SEVERE CASES, CONVULSIONS MAY OCCUR WITHOUT ANY PRIOR SYMPTOMS. THE CONVULSIONS MAY BE CONTINUOUS WITH ELEVATED BODY TEMPERATURE, UNCONSCIOUSNESS, LABORED BREATHING WITH VIGOROUS, RAPID HEART BEAT, AND DEATH FROM RESPIRATORY DEPRESSION. **CHRONIC EXPOSURE-** REPEATED ADMINISTRATION OF CHLORDENE TO PIGEONS PRODUCED CYTOLOGIC CHANGES IN LIVER CELLS. REPRODUCTIVE EFFECTS HAVE BEEN REPORTED IN ANIMALS. CHRONIC INTOXICATION FROM CHLORINATED CYCLODIENE DERIVATIVES MAY BE CHARACTERIZED BY NERVOUS SYSTEM, LIVER, AND KIDNEY DAMAGE, AND CARDIOVASCULAR, BLOOD, AND CAPILLARY DISTURBANCES. IN ADDITION TO THE SYMPTOMS DETAILED IN ACUTE EXPOSURE, ANOREXIA, BLURRED VISION, AND DROWSINESS MAY ALSO OCCUR.

FIRST AID- IF THE PERSON IS CONSCIOUS AND NOT CONVULSING, REMOVE BY GIVING SYRUP OF IPECAC (IF VOMITING OCCURS, KEEP THE HEAD BELOW THE HIPS TO PREVENT ASPIRATION). GIVE ACTIVATED CHARCOAL FOLLOWED BY GASTRIC LAVAGE. FOLLOW WITH A SALINE CATHARTIC. DO NOT GIVE FATS OR OILS. INTESTINAL LAVAGE WITH 20% MANNITOL (200 ML) BY STOMACH TUBE IS ALSO USEFUL. GIVE ARTIFICIAL RESPIRATION WITH OXYGEN IF RESPIRATION IS DEPRESSED (DREISBACH, HANDBOOK OF POISONING, 12TH ED.). TREAT SYMPTOMATICALLY AND SUPPORTIVELY. LAVAGE AND ADMINISTRATION OF OXYGEN SHOULD BE PERFORMED BY QUALIFIED MEDICAL PERSONNEL. GET MEDICAL ATTENTION IMMEDIATELY.

ANTIDOTE: NO SPECIFIC ANTIDOTE. TREAT SYMPTOMATICALLY AND SUPPORTIVELY.

REACTIVITY

REACTIVITY: STABLE UNDER NORMAL TEMPERATURES AND PRESSURES.

INCOMPATIBILITIES: CHLORDENE: OXIDIZERS (STRONG): FIRE AND EXPLOSION HAZARD.

DECOMPOSITION: THERMAL DECOMPOSITION PRODUCTS MAY INCLUDE TOXIC AND CORROSIVE FUMES OF CHLORINE.

POLYMERIZATION: HAZARDOUS POLYMERIZATION HAS NOT BEEN REPORTED TO OCCUR UNDER NORMAL TEMPERATURES AND PRESSURES.

STORAGE AND DISPOSAL

OBSERVE ALL FEDERAL, STATE AND LOCAL REGULATIONS WHEN STORING OR DISPOSING OF THIS SUBSTANCE. FOR ASSISTANCE, CONTACT THE DISTRICT DIRECTOR OF THE ENVIRONMENTAL PROTECTION AGENCY.

****STORAGE****

STORE IN ACCORDANCE WITH 40 CFR 165 RECOMMENDED PROCEDURES FOR THE DISPOSAL AND STORAGE OF PESTICIDES AND PESTICIDE CONTAINERS.
STORE AWAY FROM INCOMPATIBLE SUBSTANCES.

****DISPOSAL****

DISPOSAL MUST BE IN ACCORDANCE WITH 40 CFR 165 RECOMMENDED PROCEDURES FOR THE DISPOSAL AND STORAGE OF PESTICIDES AND PESTICIDE CONTAINERS.

CONDITIONS TO AVOID

MAY BURN BUT DOES NOT IGNITE READILY.

SPILL AND LEAK PROCEDURES

OCCUPATIONAL SPILL: DO NOT TOUCH SPILLED MATERIAL. STOP LEAK IF YOU CAN DO IT WITHOUT RISK. FOR SMALL SPILLS, TAKE UP WITH SAND OR OTHER ABSORBENT MATERIAL AND PLACE INTO CONTAINERS FOR LATER DISPOSAL. FOR SMALL DRY SPILLS, WITH A CLEAN SHOVEL PLACE MATERIAL INTO CLEAN, DRY CONTAINER AND COVER. MOVE CONTAINERS FROM SPILL AREA. FOR LARGER SPILLS, DIKE FAR AHEAD OF SPILL FOR LATER DISPOSAL. KEEP UNNECESSARY PEOPLE AWAY. ISOLATE HAZARD AREA AND DENY ENTRY.

PROTECTIVE EQUIPMENT

VENTILATION: PROCESS ENCLOSURE RECOMMENDED.

RESPIRATOR: THE FOLLOWING RESPIRATORS ARE RECOMMENDED BASED ON INFORMATION FOUND IN THE PHYSICAL DATA, TOXICITY AND HEALTH EFFECTS SECTIONS. THEY ARE RANKED IN ORDER FROM MINIMUM TO MAXIMUM RESPIRATORY PROTECTION. THE SPECIFIC RESPIRATOR SELECTED MUST BE BASED ON CONTAMINATION LEVELS FOUND IN THE WORK PLACE, MUST NOT EXCEED THE WORKING LIMITS OF THE RESPIRATOR AND BE JOINTLY APPROVED BY THE NATIONAL INSTITUTE FOR OCCUPATIONAL SAFETY AND HEALTH AND THE MINE SAFETY AND HEALTH ADMINISTRATION (NIOSH-MSHA).

TYPE 'C' SUPPLIED-AIR RESPIRATOR WITH A FULL FACEPIECE OPERATED IN PRESSURE-DEMAND OR OTHER POSITIVE PRESSURE MODE OR WITH A FULL FACEPIECE, HELMET OR HOOD OPERATED IN CONTINOUS-FLOW MODE.

SELF-CONTAINED BREATHING APPARATUS WITH A FULL FACEPIECE OPERATED IN PRESSURE-DEMAND OR OTHER POSITIVE PRESSURE MODE.

FOR FIREFIGHTING AND OTHER IMMEDIATELY DANGEROUS TO LIFE OR HEALTH CONDITIONS:

SELF-CONTAINED BREATHING APPARATUS WITH FULL FACEPIECE OPERATED IN PRESSURE-DEMAND OR OTHER POSITIVE PRESSURE MODE.

SUPPLIED-AIR RESPIRATOR WITH FULL FACEPIECE AND OPERATED IN PRESSURE-DEMAND OR OTHER POSITIVE PRESSURE MODE IN COMBINATION WITH AN AUXILIARY SELF-CONTAINED BREATHING APPARATUS OPERATED IN PRESSURE-DEMAND OR OTHER POSITIVE PRESSURE MODE.

CLOTHING: EMPLOYEE MUST WEAR APPROPRIATE PROTECTIVE (IMPERVIOUS) CLOTHING AND EQUIPMENT TO PREVENT ANY POSSIBILITY OF SKIN CONTACT WITH THIS SUBSTANCE.

GLOVES: EMPLOYEE MUST WEAR APPROPRIATE PROTECTIVE GLOVES TO PREVENT CONTACT WITH THIS SUBSTANCE.

EYE PROTECTION: EMPLOYEE MUST WEAR SPLASH-PROOF OR DUST-RESISTANT SAFETY GOGGLES AND A FACESHIELD TO PREVENT CONTACT WITH THIS SUBSTANCE.

EMERGENCY WASH FACILITIES: WHERE THERE IS ANY POSSIBILITY THAT AN EMPLOYEE'S EYES AND/OR SKIN MAY BE EXPOSED TO THIS SUBSTANCE, THE EMPLOYER SHOULD PROVIDE AN EYE WASH FOUNTAIN AND QUICK DRENCH SHOWER WITHIN THE IMMEDIATE WORK AREA FOR EMERGENCY USE.

AUTHORIZED BY- OCCUPATIONAL HEALTH SERVICES, INC.
CREATION DATE: 02/08/90 ***REVISION DATE:*** 05/10/90

MATERIAL SAFETY DATA SHEET

OCCUPATIONAL HEALTH SERVICES, INC.
AGRICULTURE AND PESTICIDE DIVISION
450 SEVENTH AVENUE, SUITE 2407
NEW YORK, NEW YORK 10123
1-800-445-MSDS OR (212) 967-1100

EMERGENCY CONTACT:
JOHN S. BRANSFORD, JR. (615) 292-1180

SUBSTANCE IDENTIFICATION

CAS-NUMBER 56534-02-2

SUBSTANCE: **ALPHA-CHLORDENE**

TRADE NAMES/SYNONYMS: 1,4-ETHENOPENTALENE, 1,2,3,5,7,8-HEXACHLORO-1,3A,4,5,6,6A-HEXAHYDRO-, (1ALPHA,3A ALPHA,4BETA,5ALPHA,6A ALPHA)-; (1ALPHA,3A ALPHA,4BETA,5ALPHA,6A ALPHA)-1,2,3,5,7,8-HEXACHLORO-1,3A,4,5,6,6A-HEXAHYDRO-1,4-ETHENOPENTALENE; CHLORDENE; C10H6CL6; PST04566

CHEMICAL FAMILY: HALOGEN COMPOUND, ALICYCLIC

MOLECULAR FORMULA: C10-H6-CL6

MOLECULAR WEIGHT: 338.86

CERCLA RATINGS (SCALE 0-3): HEALTH=U FIRE=1 REACTIVITY=0 PERSISTENCE=3

NFPA RATINGS (SCALE 0-4): HEALTH=U FIRE=1 REACTIVITY=0

COMPONENTS AND CONTAMINANTS

COMPONENT: ALPHA-CHLORDENE ***PERCENT:*** 100.0
CAS# 56534-02-2
OTHER CONTAMINANTS: NONE
EXPOSURE LIMITS: NO OCCUPATIONAL EXPOSURE LIMITS ESTABLISHED BY OSHA, ACGIH, OR NIOSH.

PHYSICAL DATA

DESCRIPTION: WHITE SOLID. ***MELTING POINT:*** NOT AVAILABLE
SPECIFIC GRAVITY: NOT AVAILABLE ***SOLUBILITY IN WATER:*** NOT AVAILABLE

FIRE AND EXPLOSION DATA

FIRE AND EXPLOSION HAZARD: SLIGHT FIRE HAZARD WHEN EXPOSED TO HEAT OR FLAME.
FIREFIGHTING MEDIA: DRY CHEMICAL, CARBON DIOXIDE, HALON, WATER SPRAY OR STANDARD FOAM (1987 EMERGENCY RESPONSE GUIDEBOOK, DOT P 5800.4).
FOR LARGER FIRES, USE WATER SPRAY, FOG OR STANDARD FOAM (1987 EMERGENCY RESPONSE GUIDEBOOK, DOT P 5800.4).
FIREFIGHTING: MOVE CONTAINERS FROM FIRE AREA IF POSSIBLE (1987 EMERGENCY RESPONSE GUIDEBOOK, DOT P 5800.4, GUIDE PAGE 53).
EXTINGUISH USING AGENT SUITABLE FOR TYPE OF SURROUNDING FIRE. AVOID BREATHING VAPORS AND DUSTS. KEEP UPWIND.

TOXICITY

ALPHA-CHLORDENE: TOXICITY DATA: 10200 MG/KG ORAL-RAT LD50. CARCINOGEN STATUS: NONE. ACUTE TOXICITY LEVEL: SLIGHTLY TOXIC BY INGESTION. TARGET EFFECTS: POISONING MAY AFFECT THE LIVER, KIDNEYS, BLOOD, AND CARDIOVASCULAR SYSTEM.* AT INCREASED RISK FROM EXPOSURE: PERSONS WITH CONVULSIVE DISORDERS.* ADDITIONAL DATA: MAY BE STORED IN ADIPOSE TISSUE; MAY CROSS THE PLACENTA AND BE EXCRETED IN HUMAN MILK. STIMULANTS SUCH AS EPINEPHRINE MAY INDUCE VENTRICULAR FIBRILLATION.*
* MAY BE BASED ON GENERAL INFORMATION ON CHLORINATED CYCLODIENE DERIVATIVES.

HEALTH EFFECTS AND FIRST AID

INHALATION: ALPHA-CHLORDENE: **ACUTE EXPOSURE-** CHLORINATED CYCLODIENE DERIVATIVES MAY PRODUCE HEADACHE, NAUSEA, VOMITING, MALAISE, DIZZINESS, APPREHENSION, PARESTHESIA, HYPERIRRITABILITY, ATAXIA, MUSCLE TWITCHING, MYOCLONIC JERKING, AND CONVULSIVE SEIZURES. IN SEVERE CASES, CONVULSIONS MAY OCCUR WITHOUT ANY ANY PRIOR SYMPTOMS. THE CONVULSIONS MAY BE CONTINUOUS WITH ELEVATED BODY TEMPERATURE, UNCONSCIOUSNESS, LABORED BREATHING WITH VIGOROUS, RAPID HEART BEAT, AND DEATH FROM RESPIRATORY DEPRESSION. **CHRONIC EXPOSURE-** CHRONIC INTOXICATION FROM CHLORINATED CYCLODIENE DERIVATIVES MAY BE CHARACTERIZED BY NERVOUS SYSTEM, LIVER, AND KIDNEY DAMAGE, CARDIOVASCULAR DISTURBANCES, AND BLOOD AND CAPILLARY DISTURBANCES. IN ADDITION TO THE SYMPTOMS DETAILED IN ACUTE EXPOSURE, ANOREXIA, BLURRED VISION, AND DROWSINESS MAY ALSO OCCUR.
FIRST AID- REMOVE FROM EXPOSURE AREA TO FRESH AIR IMMEDIATELY. IF BREATHING HAS STOPPED, PERFORM ARTIFICIAL RESPIRATION. KEEP PERSON WARM AND AT REST. TREAT SYMPTOMATICALLY AND SUPPORTIVELY. GET MEDICAL ATTENTION IMMEDIATELY.

SKIN CONTACT: ALPHA-CHLORDENE: **ACUTE EXPOSURE-** CHLORINATED CYCLODIENE DERIVATIVES MAY PRODUCE HEADACHE, NAUSEA, VOMITING, MALAISE, DIZZINESS, APPREHENSION, PARESTHESIA, HYPERIRRITABILITY, ATAXIA, MUSCLE TWITCHING, MYOCLONIC JERKING, AND CONVULSIVE SEIZURES. IN SEVERE CASES, CONVULSIONS MAY OCCUR WITHOUT ANY PRIOR SYMPTOMS. THE CONVULSIONS MAY BE CONTINUOUS WITH ELEVATED BODY TEMPERATURES, UNCONSCIOUSNESS, LABORED BREATHING WITH VIGOROUS, RAPID HEART BEAT, AND DEATH FROM RESPIRATORY DEPRESSION. **CHRONIC EXPOSURE-** CHRONIC INTOXICATION FROM CHLORINATED CYCLODIENE DERIVATIVES MAY BE CHARACTERIZED BY NERVOUS SYSTEM, LIVER, AND KIDNEY DAMAGE, CARDIOVASCULAR DISTURBANCES, AND BLOOD AND CAPILLARY DISTURBANCES. IN ADDITION TO THE SYMPTOMS DETAILED IN ACUTE EXPOSURE, SKIN IRRITATION, ANOREXIA, BLURRED VISION, AND DROWSINESS MAY ALSO OCCUR.
FIRST AID- REMOVE CONTAMINATED CLOTHING AND SHOES IMMEDIATELY. WASH AFFECTED AREA WITH SOAP OR MILD DETERGENT AND LARGE AMOUNTS OF WATER UNTIL NO EVIDENCE OF CHEMICAL REMAINS (APPROXIMATELY 15-20 MINUTES). GET MEDICAL ATTENTION IMMEDIATELY.

EYE CONTACT: ALPHA-CHLORDENE: **ACUTE EXPOSURE-** NO DATA AVAILABLE. **CHRONIC EXPOSURE-** NO DATA AVAILABLE.
FIRST AID- WASH EYES IMMEDIATELY WITH LARGE AMOUNTS OF WATER OR NORMAL SALINE, OCCASIONALLY LIFTING UPPER AND LOWER LIDS, UNTIL NO EVIDENCE OF CHEMICAL REMAINS (APPROXIMATELY 15-20 MINUTES). GET MEDICAL ATTENTION IMMEDIATELY.

INGESTION: ALPHA-CHLORDENE: **ACUTE EXPOSURE-** CHLORINATED CYCLODIENE DERIVATIVES MAY PRODUCE HEADACHE, NAUSEA, VOMITING, MALAISE, DIZZINESS, APPREHENSION, PARESTHESIA, HYPERIRRITABILITY, ATAXIA, MUSCLE TWITCHING, MYOCLONIC JERKING, AND CONVULSIVE SEIZURES. IN SEVERE CASES, CONVULSIONS MAY OCCUR WITHOUT ANY PRIOR SYMPTOMS. THE CONVULSIONS MAY BE CONTINUOUS WITH ELEVATED BODY TEMPERATURE, UNCONSCIOUSNESS, LABORED BREATHING WITH VIGOROUS, RAPID HEART BEAT, AND DEATH FROM RESPIRATORY DEPRESSION. **CHRONIC EXPOSURE-** CHRONIC INTOXICATION FROM CHLORINATED CYCLODIENE DERIVATIVES MAY BE CHARACTERIZED BY NERVOUS SYSTEM, LIVER, AND KIDNEY DAMAGE, CARDIOVASCULAR DISTURBANCES, AND BLOOD AND CAPILLARY DISTURBANCES. IN ADDITION TO THE SYMPTOMS DETAILED IN ACUTE EXPOSURE, ANOREXIA, BLURRED VISION, AND DROWSINESS MAY ALSO OCCUR.
FIRST AID- IF THE PERSON IS CONSCIOUS AND NOT CONVULSING, REMOVE BY GIVING SYRUP OF IPECAC (IF VOMITING OCCURS, KEEP THE HEAD BELOW THE HIPS TO PREVENT ASPIRATION). GIVE ACTIVATED CHARCOAL FOLLOWED BY GASTRIC LAVAGE. FOLLOW WITH A SALINE CATHARTIC. DO NOT GIVE FATS OR OILS. INTESTINAL LAVAGE WITH 20% MANNITOL (200 ML) BY STOMACH TUBE IS ALSO USEFUL. GIVE ARTIFICIAL RESPIRATION WITH OXYGEN IF RESPIRATION IS DEPRESSED (DREISBACH, HANDBOOK OF POISONING, 12TH ED.). TREAT SYMPTOMATICALLY AND SUPPORTIVELY. LAVAGE AND ADMINISTRATION OF OXYGEN SHOULD BE PERFORMED BY QUALIFIED MEDICAL PERSONNEL. GET MEDICAL ATTENTION IMMEDIATELY.
ANTIDOTE: NO SPECIFIC ANTIDOTE. TREAT SYMPTOMATICALLY AND SUPPORTIVELY.

REACTIVITY

REACTIVITY: STABLE UNDER NORMAL TEMPERATURES AND PRESSURES.
INCOMPATIBILITIES: ALPHA-CHLORDENE: OXIDIZERS (STRONG): FIRE AND EXPLOSION HAZARD.
DECOMPOSITION: THERMAL DECOMPOSITION PRODUCTS MAY INCLUDE TOXIC AND CORROSIVE FUMES OF CHLORINE.
POLYMERIZATION: HAZARDOUS POLYMERIZATION HAS NOT BEEN REPORTED TO OCCUR UNDER NORMAL TEMPERATURES AND PRESSURES.

STORAGE AND DISPOSAL

OBSERVE ALL FEDERAL, STATE AND LOCAL REGULATIONS WHEN STORING OR DISPOSING OF THIS SUBSTANCE. FOR ASSISTANCE, CONTACT THE DISTRICT DIRECTOR OF THE ENVIRONMENTAL PROTECTION AGENCY.

STORAGE

STORE IN ACCORDANCE WITH 40 CFR 165 RECOMMENDED PROCEDURES FOR THE DISPOSAL AND STORAGE OF PESTICIDES AND PESTICIDE CONTAINERS.
STORE AWAY FROM INCOMPATIBLE SUBSTANCES.

DISPOSAL

DISPOSAL MUST BE IN ACCORDANCE WITH 40 CFR 165 RECOMMENDED PROCEDURES FOR THE DISPOSAL AND STORAGE OF PESTICIDES AND PESTICIDE CONTAINERS.

CONDITIONS TO AVOID

MAY BURN BUT DOES NOT IGNITE READILY.

SPILL AND LEAK PROCEDURES

OCCUPATIONAL SPILL: DO NOT TOUCH SPILLED MATERIAL. STOP LEAK IF YOU CAN DO IT WITHOUT RISK. FOR SMALL SPILLS, TAKE UP WITH SAND OR OTHER ABSORBENT MATERIAL AND PLACE INTO CONTAINERS FOR LATER DISPOSAL. FOR SMALL DRY SPILLS, WITH A CLEAN SHOVEL PLACE MATERIAL INTO CLEAN, DRY CONTAINER AND COVER. MOVE CONTAINERS FROM SPILL AREA. FOR LARGER SPILLS, DIKE FAR AHEAD OF SPILL FOR LATER DISPOSAL. KEEP UNNECESSARY PEOPLE AWAY. ISOLATE HAZARD AREA AND DENY ENTRY.

PROTECTIVE EQUIPMENT

VENTILATION: PROVIDE LOCAL EXHAUST OR GENERAL DILUTION VENTILATION SYSTEM.
RESPIRATOR: THE FOLLOWING RESPIRATORS ARE RECOMMENDED BASED ON INFORMATION FOUND IN THE PHYSICAL DATA, TOXICITY AND HEALTH EFFECTS SECTIONS. THEY ARE RANKED IN ORDER FROM MINIMUM TO MAXIMUM RESPIRATORY PROTECTION. THE SPECIFIC RESPIRATOR SELECTED MUST BE BASED ON CONTAMINATION LEVELS FOUND IN THE WORK PLACE, MUST NOT EXCEED THE WORKING LIMITS OF THE RESPIRATOR AND BE JOINTLY APPROVED BY THE NATIONAL INSTITUTE FOR OCCUPATIONAL SAFETY AND HEALTH AND THE MINE SAFETY AND HEALTH ADMINISTRATION (NIOSH-MSHA).
CHEMICAL CARTRIDGE RESPIRATOR WITH AN ORGANIC VAPOR CARTRIDGE(S) WITH A FULL FACEPIECE AND ORGANIC VAPOR CARTRIDGE(S) IN COMBINATION WITH A DUST AND MIST FILTER.
POWERED AIR-PURIFYING RESPIRATOR WITH A TIGHT-FITTING FACEPIECE AND

ORGANIC VAPOR CARTRIDGE(S) IN COMBINATION WITH A HIGH-EFFICIENCY PARTICULATE FILTER.
TYPE 'C' SUPPLIED-AIR RESPIRATOR WITH A FULL FACEPIECE OPERATED IN A PRESSURE-DEMAND OR OTHER POSITIVE PRESSURE MODE.
SELF-CONTAINED BREATHING APPARATUS WITH A FULL FACEPIECE OPERATED IN PRESSURE-DEMAND OR OTHER POSITIVE PRESSURE MODE.
FOR FIREFIGHTING AND OTHER IMMEDIATELY DANGEROUS TO LIFE OR HEALTH CONDITIONS:
SELF-CONTAINED BREATHING APPARATUS WITH FULL FACEPIECE OPERATED IN PRESSURE-DEMAND OR OTHER POSITIVE PRESSURE MODE.
SUPPLIED-AIR RESPIRATOR WITH FULL FACEPIECE AND OPERATED IN PRESSURE-DEMAND OR OTHER POSITIVE PRESSURE MODE IN COMBINATION WITH AN AUXILIARY SELF-CONTAINED BREATHING APPARATUS OPERATED IN PRESSURE-DEMAND OR OTHER POSITIVE PRESSURE MODE.

CLOTHING: EMPLOYEE MUST WEAR APPROPRIATE PROTECTIVE (IMPERVIOUS) CLOTHING AND EQUIPMENT TO PREVENT REPEATED OR PROLONGED SKIN CONTACT WITH THIS SUBSTANCE.

GLOVES: EMPLOYEE MUST WEAR APPROPRIATE PROTECTIVE GLOVES TO PREVENT CONTACT WITH THIS SUBSTANCE.

EYE PROTECTION: EMPLOYEE MUST WEAR SPLASH-PROOF OR DUST-RESISTANT SAFETY GOGGLES TO PREVENT EYE CONTACT WITH THIS SUBSTANCE.
EMERGENCY EYE WASH: WHERE THERE IS ANY POSSIBILITY THAT AN EMPLOYEE'S EYES MAY BE EXPOSED TO THIS SUBSTANCE, THE EMPLOYER SHOULD PROVIDE AN EYE WASH FOUNTAIN WITHIN THE IMMEDIATE WORK AREA FOR EMERGENCY USE.

AUTHORIZED BY- OCCUPATIONAL HEALTH SERVICES, INC.
CREATION DATE: 02/08/90 ***REVISION DATE:*** 05/07/90

MATERIAL SAFETY DATA SHEET

OCCUPATIONAL HEALTH SERVICES, INC.
AGRICULTURE AND PESTICIDE DIVISION
450 SEVENTH AVENUE, SUITE 2407
NEW YORK, NEW YORK 10123
1-800-445-MSDS OR (212) 967-1100

EMERGENCY CONTACT:
JOHN S. BRANSFORD, JR. (615) 292-1180

SUBSTANCE IDENTIFICATION

CAS-NUMBER 56641-38-4
SUBSTANCE: **GAMMA-CHLORDENE**
TRADE NAMES/SYNONYMS: 1,6-METHANO-1H-INDENE, 2,3,3A,4,5,8-HEXACHLORO-3A,6,7,7A-TETRAHYDRO-, (1ALPHA,3A BETA,6ALPHA,7A BETA,8R*)-; (1ALPHA,3A BETA,6ALPHA,7A BETA,8R*)-2,3,3A,4,5,8-HEXACHLORO-3A,6,7 7A-TETRAHYDRO-1,6-METHANO-1H-INDENE; CHLORDENE; C10H6CL6; PST04567
CHEMICAL FAMILY: HALOGEN COMPOUND, ALICYCLIC
MOLECULAR FORMULA: C10-H6-CL6
MOLECULAR WEIGHT: 338.86
CERCLA RATINGS (SCALE 0-3): HEALTH=U FIRE=1 REACTIVITY=0 PERSISTENCE=3
NFPA RATINGS (SCALE 0-4): HEALTH=U FIRE=1 REACTIVITY=0

COMPONENTS AND CONTAMINANTS

COMPONENT: GAMMA-CHLORDENE ***PERCENT:*** 100.0
CAS# 56641-38-4
OTHER CONTAMINANTS: NONE
EXPOSURE LIMITS: NO OCCUPATIONAL EXPOSURE LIMITS ESTABLISHED BY OSHA, ACGIH, OR NIOSH.

PHYSICAL DATA

DESCRIPTION: WHITE SOLID. ***MELTING POINT:*** NOT AVAILABLE
SPECIFIC GRAVITY: NOT AVAILABLE ***SOLUBILITY IN WATER:*** NOT AVAILABLE

FIRE AND EXPLOSION DATA

FIRE AND EXPLOSION HAZARD: SLIGHT FIRE HAZARD WHEN EXPOSED TO HEAT OR FLAME.

FIREFIGHTING MEDIA: DRY CHEMICAL, CARBON DIOXIDE, HALON, WATER SPRAY OR STANDARD FOAM (1987 EMERGENCY RESPONSE GUIDEBOOK, DOT P 5800.4).
FOR LARGER FIRES, USE WATER SPRAY, FOG OR STANDARD FOAM (1987 EMERGENCY RESPONSE GUIDEBOOK, DOT P 5800.4).

FIREFIGHTING: MOVE CONTAINERS FROM FIRE AREA IF POSSIBLE (1987 EMERGENCY RESPONSE GUIDEBOOK, DOT P 5800.4, GUIDE PAGE 53).
EXTINGUISH USING AGENT SUITABLE FOR TYPE OF SURROUNDING FIRE. AVOID BREATHING VAPORS AND DUSTS. KEEP UPWIND.

TOXICITY

GAMMA-CHLORDENE: TOXICITY DATA: 4600 MG/KG ORAL-RAT LD50. CARCINOGEN STATUS: NONE. ACUTE TOXICITY LEVEL: MODERATELY TOXIC BY INGESTION. TARGET EFFECTS: POISONING MAY AFFECT THE LIVER, KIDNEYS, BLOOD, AND CARDIOVASCULAR SYSTEM.* AT INCREASED RISK FROM EXPOSURE: PERSONS WITH CONVULSIVE DISORDERS.* ADDITIONAL DATA: MAY BE STORED IN ADIPOSE TISSUE; MAY CROSS THE PLACENTA AND BE EXCRETED IN HUMAN MILK. STIMULANTS SUCH AS EPINEPHRINE MAY INDUCE VENTRICULAR FIBRILLATIONS.*
* MAY BE BASED ON GENERAL INFORMATION ON CHLORINATED CYCLODIENE DERIVATIVES.

HEALTH EFFECTS AND FIRST AID

INHALATION: GAMMA-CHLORDENE: **ACUTE EXPOSURE-** CHLORINATED CYCLODIENE DERIVATIVES MAY PRODUCE HEADACHE, NAUSEA, VOMITING, MALAISE, DIZZINESS, APPREHENSION, PARESTHESIA, HYPERIRRITABILITY, ATAXIA, MUSCLE TWITCHING, MYOCLONIC JERKING, AND CONVULSIVE SEIZURES. IN SEVERE CASES, CONVULSIONS MAY OCCUR WITHOUT ANY ANY PRIOR SYMPTOMS. THE CONVULSIONS MAY BE CONTINUOUS WITH ELEVATED BODY TEMPERATURE, UNCONSCIOUSNESS, LABORED BREATHING WITH VIGOROUS, RAPID HEART BEAT, AND DEATH FROM RESPIRATORY DEPRESSION. **CHRONIC EXPOSURE-** CHRONIC INTOXICATION FROM CHLORINATED CYCLODIENE DERIVATIVES MAY BE CHARACTERIZED BY NERVOUS SYSTEM, LIVER, AND KIDNEY DAMAGE, CARDIOVASCULAR DISTURBANCES, AND BLOOD AND CAPILLARY DISTURBANCES. IN ADDITION TO THE SYMPTOMS DETAILED IN ACUTE EXPOSURE, ANOREXIA, BLURRED VISION, AND DROWSINESS MAY ALSO OCCUR.
FIRST AID- REMOVE FROM EXPOSURE AREA TO FRESH AIR IMMEDIATELY. IF BREATHING HAS STOPPED, PERFORM ARTIFICIAL RESPIRATION. KEEP PERSON WARM AND AT REST. TREAT SYMPTOMATICALLY AND SUPPORTIVELY. GET MEDICAL ATTENTION IMMEDIATELY.

SKIN CONTACT: GAMMA-CHLORDENE: **ACUTE EXPOSURE-** CHLORINATED CYCLODIENE DERIVATIVES MAY PRODUCE HEADACHE, NAUSEA, VOMITING, MALAISE, DIZZINESS, APPREHENSION, PARESTHESIA, HYPERIRRITABILITY, ATAXIA, MUSCLE TWITCHING, MYOCLONIC JERKING, AND CONVULSIVE SEIZURES. IN SEVERE CASES, CONVULSIONS MAY OCCUR WITHOUT ANY PRIOR SYMPTOMS. THE CONVULSIONS MAY BE CONTINUOUS WITH ELEVATED BODY TEMPERATURES, UNCONSCIOUSNESS, LABORED BREATHING WITH VIGOROUS, RAPID HEART BEAT, AND DEATH FROM RESPIRATORY DEPRESSION. **CHRONIC EXPOSURE-** CHRONIC INTOXICATION FROM CHLORINATED CYCLODIENE DERIVATIVES MAY BE CHARACTERIZED BY NERVOUS SYSTEM, LIVER, AND KIDNEY DAMAGE, CARDIOVASCULAR DISTURBANCES, AND BLOOD AND CAPILLARY DISTURBANCES. IN ADDITION TO THE SYMPTOMS DETAILED IN ACUTE EXPOSURE, SKIN IRRITATION, ANOREXIA, BLURRED VISION, AND DROWSINESS MAY ALSO OCCUR.
FIRST AID- REMOVE CONTAMINATED CLOTHING AND SHOES IMMEDIATELY. WASH AFFECTED AREA WITH SOAP OR MILD DETERGENT AND LARGE AMOUNTS OF WATER UNTIL NO EVIDENCE OF CHEMICAL REMAINS (APPROXIMATELY 15-20 MINUTES). GET MEDICAL ATTENTION IMMEDIATELY.

EYE CONTACT: GAMMA-CHLORDENE: **ACUTE EXPOSURE-** NO DATA AVAILABLE. **CHRONIC EXPOSURE-** NO DATA AVAILABLE.
FIRST AID- WASH EYES IMMEDIATELY WITH LARGE AMOUNTS OF WATER OR NORMAL SALINE, OCCASIONALLY LIFTING UPPER AND LOWER LIDS, UNTIL NO EVIDENCE OF CHEMICAL REMAINS (APPROXIMATELY 15-20 MINUTES). GET MEDICAL ATTENTION IMMEDIATELY.

INGESTION: GAMMA-CHLORDENE: **ACUTE EXPOSURE-** CHLORINATED CYCLODIENE DERIVATIVES MAY PRODUCE HEADACHE, NAUSEA, VOMITING, MALAISE, DIZZINESS, APPREHENSION, PARESTHESIA, HYPERIRRITABILITY, ATAXIA, MUSCLE TWITCHING, MYOCLONIC JERKING, AND CONVULSIVE SEIZURES. IN SEVERE CASES, CONVULSIONS MAY OCCUR WITHOUT ANY PRIOR SYMPTOMS. THE CONVULSIONS MAY BE CONTINUOUS WITH ELEVATED BODY TEMPERATURE, UNCONSCIOUSNESS, LABORED BREATHING WITH VIGOROUS, RAPID HEART BEAT, AND DEATH FROM RESPIRATORY DEPRESSION. **CHRONIC EXPOSURE-** CHRONIC INTOXICATION FROM CHLORINATED CYCLODIENE DERIVATIVES MAY BE CHARACTERIZED BY NERVOUS SYSTEM, LIVER, AND KIDNEY DAMAGE, CARDIOVASCULAR DISTURBANCES, AND BLOOD AND CAPILLARY DISTURBANCES. IN ADDITION TO THE SYMPTOMS DETAILED IN ACUTE EXPOSURE, ANOREXIA, BLURRED VISION, AND DROWSINESS MAY ALSO OCCUR.
FIRST AID- IF THE PERSON IS CONSCIOUS AND NOT CONVULSING, REMOVE BY GIVING SYRUP OF IPECAC (IF VOMITING OCCURS, KEEP THE HEAD BELOW THE HIPS TO PREVENT ASPIRATION). GIVE ACTIVATED CHARCOAL FOLLOWED BY GASTRIC LAVAGE. FOLLOW WITH A SALINE CATHARTIC. DO NOT GIVE FATS OR OILS. INTESTINAL LAVAGE WITH 20% MANNITOL (200 ML) BY STOMACH TUBE IS ALSO

USEFUL. GIVE ARTIFICIAL RESPIRATION WITH OXYGEN IF RESPIRATION IS DEPRESSED (DREISBACH, HANDBOOK OF POISONING, 12TH ED.). TREAT SYMPTOMATICALLY AND SUPPORTIVELY. LAVAGE AND ADMINISTRATION OF OXYGEN SHOULD BE PERFORMED BY QUALIFIED MEDICAL PERSONNEL. GET MEDICAL ATTENTION IMMEDIATELY.

ANTIDOTE: NO SPECIFIC ANTIDOTE. TREAT SYMPTOMATICALLY AND SUPPORTIVELY.

REACTIVITY

REACTIVITY: STABLE UNDER NORMAL TEMPERATURES AND PRESSURES.

INCOMPATIBILITIES: GAMMA-CHLORDENE: OXIDIZERS (STRONG): FIRE AND EXPLOSION HAZARD.

DECOMPOSITION: THERMAL DECOMPOSITION PRODUCTS MAY INCLUDE TOXIC AND CORROSIVE FUMES OF CHLORINE.

POLYMERIZATION: HAZARDOUS POLYMERIZATION HAS NOT BEEN REPORTED TO OCCUR UNDER NORMAL TEMPERATURES AND PRESSURES.

STORAGE AND DISPOSAL

OBSERVE ALL FEDERAL, STATE AND LOCAL REGULATIONS WHEN STORING OR DISPOSING OF THIS SUBSTANCE. FOR ASSISTANCE, CONTACT THE DISTRICT DIRECTOR OF THE ENVIRONMENTAL PROTECTION AGENCY.

STORAGE

STORE IN ACCORDANCE WITH 40 CFR 165 RECOMMENDED PROCEDURES FOR THE DISPOSAL AND STORAGE OF PESTICIDES AND PESTICIDE CONTAINERS.
STORE AWAY FROM INCOMPATIBLE SUBSTANCES.

DISPOSAL

DISPOSAL MUST BE IN ACCORDANCE WITH 40 CFR 165 RECOMMENDED PROCEDURES FOR THE DISPOSAL AND STORAGE OF PESTICIDES AND PESTICIDE CONTAINERS.

CONDITIONS TO AVOID

MAY BURN BUT DOES NOT IGNITE READILY.

SPILL AND LEAK PROCEDURES

OCCUPATIONAL SPILL: DO NOT TOUCH SPILLED MATERIAL. STOP LEAK IF YOU CAN DO IT WITHOUT RISK. FOR SMALL SPILLS, TAKE UP WITH SAND OR OTHER ABSORBENT MATERIAL AND PLACE INTO CONTAINERS FOR LATER DISPOSAL. FOR SMALL DRY SPILLS, WITH A CLEAN SHOVEL PLACE MATERIAL INTO CLEAN, DRY CONTAINER AND COVER. MOVE CONTAINERS FROM SPILL AREA. FOR LARGER SPILLS, DIKE FAR AHEAD OF SPILL FOR LATER DISPOSAL. KEEP UNNECESSARY PEOPLE AWAY. ISOLATE HAZARD AREA AND DENY ENTRY.

PROTECTIVE EQUIPMENT

VENTILATION: PROVIDE LOCAL EXHAUST OR GENERAL DILUTION VENTILATION SYSTEM.

RESPIRATOR: THE FOLLOWING RESPIRATORS ARE RECOMMENDED BASED ON INFORMATION FOUND IN THE PHYSICAL DATA, TOXICITY AND HEALTH EFFECTS SECTIONS. THEY ARE RANKED IN ORDER FROM MINIMUM TO MAXIMUM RESPIRATORY PROTECTION. THE SPECIFIC RESPIRATOR SELECTED MUST BE BASED ON CONTAMINATION LEVELS FOUND IN THE WORK PLACE, MUST NOT EXCEED THE WORKING LIMITS OF THE RESPIRATOR AND BE JOINTLY APPROVED BY THE NATIONAL INSTITUTE FOR OCCUPATIONAL SAFETY AND HEALTH AND THE MINE SAFETY AND HEALTH ADMINISTRATION (NIOSH-MSHA).
CHEMICAL CARTRIDGE RESPIRATOR WITH AN ORGANIC VAPOR CARTRIDGE(S) WITH A FULL FACEPIECE AND ORGANIC VAPOR CARTRIDGE(S) IN COMBINATION WITH A DUST AND MIST FILTER.
POWERED AIR-PURIFYING RESPIRATOR WITH A TIGHT-FITTING FACEPIECE AND ORGANIC VAPOR CARTRIDGE(S) IN COMBINATION WITH A HIGH-EFFICIENCY PARTICULATE FILTER.
TYPE 'C' SUPPLIED-AIR RESPIRATOR WITH A FULL FACEPIECE OPERATED IN A PRESSURE-DEMAND OR OTHER POSITIVE PRESSURE MODE.
SELF-CONTAINED BREATHING APPARATUS WITH A FULL FACEPIECE OPERATED IN PRESSURE-DEMAND OR OTHER POSITIVE PRESSURE MODE.
FOR FIREFIGHTING AND OTHER IMMEDIATELY DANGEROUS TO LIFE OR HEALTH CONDITIONS:
SELF-CONTAINED BREATHING APPARATUS WITH FULL FACEPIECE OPERATED IN PRESSURE-DEMAND OR OTHER POSITIVE PRESSURE MODE.
SUPPLIED-AIR RESPIRATOR WITH FULL FACEPIECE AND OPERATED IN PRESSURE-DEMAND OR OTHER POSITIVE PRESSURE MODE IN COMBINATION WITH AN AUXILIARY SELF-CONTAINED BREATHING APPARATUS OPERATED IN PRESSURE-DEMAND OR OTHER POSITIVE PRESSURE MODE.

CLOTHING: EMPLOYEE MUST WEAR APPROPRIATE PROTECTIVE (IMPERVIOUS) CLOTHING AND EQUIPMENT TO PREVENT REPEATED OR PROLONGED SKIN CONTACT WITH THIS SUBSTANCE.

GLOVES: EMPLOYEE MUST WEAR APPROPRIATE PROTECTIVE GLOVES TO PREVENT CONTACT WITH THIS SUBSTANCE.

EYE PROTECTION: EMPLOYEE MUST WEAR SPLASH-PROOF OR DUST-RESISTANT SAFETY GOGGLES TO PREVENT EYE CONTACT WITH THIS SUBSTANCE.
EMERGENCY EYE WASH: WHERE THERE IS ANY POSSIBILITY THAT AN EMPLOYEE'S EYES MAY BE EXPOSED TO THIS SUBSTANCE, THE EMPLOYER SHOULD PROVIDE AN EYE WASH FOUNTAIN WITHIN THE IMMEDIATE WORK AREA FOR EMERGENCY USE.

AUTHORIZED BY- OCCUPATIONAL HEALTH SERVICES, INC.
CREATION DATE: 02/08/90 ***REVISION DATE:*** 05/07/90

MATERIAL SAFETY DATA SHEET

OCCUPATIONAL HEALTH SERVICES, INC.
AGRICULTURE AND PESTICIDE DIVISION
450 SEVENTH AVENUE, SUITE 2407
NEW YORK, NEW YORK 10123
1-800-445-MSDS OR (212) 967-1100

EMERGENCY CONTACT:
JOHN S. BRANSFORD, JR. (615) 292-1180

SUBSTANCE IDENTIFICATION

CAS-NUMBER 6164-98-3

SUBSTANCE: CHLORDIMEFORM

TRADE NAMES/SYNONYMS: METHANIMIDAMIDE, N'-(4-CHLORO-2-METHYLPHENYL) N,N-DIMETHYL-; FORMAMIDINE, N'-(4-CHLORO-O-TOLYL) N,N-DIMETHYL-; N'-(4-CHLORO-2-METHYLPHENYL)-N,N-DIMETHYLMETHANIMIDAMIDE; N'-(4-CHLORO-O-TOLYL)-N,N-DIMETHYLFORMAMIDINE; CHLOROPHENAMIDIN; CHLOROPHENAMIDINE; CHLORPHENAMIDINE; CIBA 8514; FUNDAL; GALECRON; RS 141; SCHERING 36,268; OMS 1209; ENT 27335; C10H13CLN2; PST04570

CHEMICAL FAMILY: HALOGEN COMPOUND, AROMATIC AMIDINE

MOLECULAR FORMULA: CL-C-H3-C6-H3-N-C-H-N-(C-H3)2

MOLECULAR WEIGHT: 196.67

CERCLA RATINGS (SCALE 0-3): HEALTH=3 FIRE=1 REACTIVITY=0 PERSISTENCE=3

NFPA RATINGS (SCALE 0-4): HEALTH=3 FIRE=1 REACTIVITY=0

COMPONENTS AND CONTAMINANTS

COMPONENT: CHLORDIMEFORM ***PERCENT:*** 100
CAS# 6164-98-3

OTHER CONTAMINANTS: NONE

EXPOSURE LIMITS: NO OCCUPATIONAL EXPOSURE LIMITS ESTABLISHED BY OSHA, ACGIH, OR NIOSH.
CHLODIMEFORM: SUBJECT TO CALIFORNIA PROPOSITION 65 CANCER AND/OR REPRODUCTIVE TOXICITY WARNING AND RELEASE REQUIREMENTS- (JANUARY 1, 1989)

PHYSICAL DATA

DESCRIPTION: COLORLESS CRYSTALS ***BOILING POINT:*** 313-315 F (156-157 C) @ 14 MMHG

MELTING POINT: 95 F (35 C) ***SPECIFIC GRAVITY:*** 1.105

VAPOR PRESSURE: 0.00035 MMHG ***SOLUBILITY IN WATER:*** 250 PPM

SOLVENT SOLUBILITY: SOLUBLE IN ACETONE, BENZENE, CHLOROFORM, ETHYL ACETATE, HEXANE, METHANOL

FIRE AND EXPLOSION DATA

FIRE AND EXPLOSION HAZARD: SLIGHT FIRE HAZARD WHEN EXPOSED TO HEAT OR FLAME.

FIREFIGHTING MEDIA: DRY CHEMICAL, CARBON DIOXIDE, HALON, WATER SPRAY OR STANDARD FOAM (1987 EMERGENCY RESPONSE GUIDEBOOK, DOT P 5800.4).
FOR LARGER FIRES, USE WATER SPRAY, FOG OR STANDARD FOAM (1987 EMERGENCY RESPONSE GUIDEBOOK, DOT P 5800.4).

FIREFIGHTING: MOVE CONTAINERS FROM FIRE AREA IF POSSIBLE. FIGHT FIRE FROM MAXIMUM DISTANCE. STAY AWAY FROM STORAGE TANK ENDS. DIKE FIRE CONTROL WATER FOR LATER DISPOSAL. DO NOT SCATTER MATERIAL (1987 EMERGENCY RESPONSE GUIDEBOOK, DOT P 5800.4, GUIDE PAGE 55).
USE AGENTS SUITABLE FOR TYPE OF FIRE. COOL CONTAINERS WITH FLOODING AMOUNTS OF WATER. AVOID BREATHING VAPORS OR DUSTS, KEEP UPWIND.

TOXICITY

CHLORDIMEFORM: IRRITATION DATA: 100 MG EYE-RABBIT SEVERE. TOXICITY DATA: 640 MG/KG SKIN-RABBIT LD50; 263 MG/KG SKIN-RAT LD50; 225 MG/KG SKIN-MOUSE LD50; 160 MG/KG ORAL-RAT LD50; 160 MG/KG ORAL-MOUSE LD50; 625 MG/KG ORAL-RABBIT LD50; 90 MG/KG INTRAPERITONEAL-RAT LD50; 71

MG/KG INTRAPERITONEAL-MOUSE LD50; MUTAGENIC DATA (RTECS); REPRODUCTIVE EFFECTS DATA (RTECS); TUMORIGENIC DATA (RTECS). CARCINOGEN STATUS: ANIMAL INADEQUATE EVIDENCE (IARC GROUP-3). THE AVAILABLE DATA ARE INSUFFICIENT TO EVALUATE THE CARCINOGENICITY OF CHLORDIMEFORM TO HUMANS. HOWEVER, EXPERIMENTS IN MICE PROVIDE SUFFICIENT EVIDENCE THAT PARA-CHLORO-ORTHO-TOLUIDINE, A METABOLITE OF CHLORDIMEFORM, IS CARCINOGENIC TO EXPERIMENTAL ANIMALS. LOCAL EFFECTS: IRRITANT- EYES. ACUTE TOXICITY DATA: TOXIC BY DERMAL ABSORPTION AND INGESTION. TARGET EFFECTS: POISONING MAY AFFECT THE URINARY BLADDER, AND THE CARDIOVASCULAR AND NERVOUS SYSTEMS.

HEALTH EFFECTS AND FIRST AID

INHALATION: CHLORDIMEFORM: **ACUTE EXPOSURE-** MAY CAUSE NAUSEA, VOMITING AND LETHARGY. MASSIVE EXPOSURE TO CHLORDIMEFORM MAY CAUSE EFFECTS AS LISTED IN CHRONIC EXPOSURE. **CHRONIC EXPOSURE-** SYMPTOMS OF INCREASED URINARY FREQUENCY, GROSS HEMATURIA, URETHRAL DISCHARGE, ABDOMINAL AND BACK PAIN, AND A HOT SENSATION ALL OVER WERE REPORTED AMONG WORKERS EXPOSED TO CHLORDIMEFORM. OTHER EFFECTS OF BLADDER IRRITATION, SLEEPINESS, SKIN RASH, ANOREXIA, DIZZINESS, AND A SWEET TASTE IN THE MOUTH ALSO OCCURRED. UROLOGICAL EXAMINATION OF SOME WORKERS REVEALED HEMATURIA AND PYURIA, PROTEINURIA, LOW CREATININE CLEARANCE, DECREASED SERUM COMPLEMENT LEVEL, ELEVATED SERUM GLUTAMIC OXALOACETIC TRANSAMINASE, SMALL URINARY BLADDER CAPACITY AND URETERAL REFLUX; SEVERE HEMORRHAGIC CYSTITIS WAS DETERMINED BY CYSTOSCOPIC EXAMINATION. THESE EFFECTS WERE COMPLETELY REVERSED WITHIN A THREE TO EIGHT WEEK PERIOD.

FIRST AID- REMOVE FROM EXPOSURE AREA TO FRESH AIR IMMEDIATELY. IF BREATHING HAS STOPPED, PERFORM ARTIFICIAL RESPIRATION. KEEP PERSON WARM AND AT REST. TREAT SYMPTOMATICALLY AND SUPPORTIVELY. GET MEDICAL ATTENTION IMMEDIATELY.

SKIN CONTACT: CHLORDIMEFORM: TOXIC. **ACUTE EXPOSURE-** THIS MATERIAL DOES NOT IRRITATE THE SKIN OF ANIMALS. A LETHAL DOSE BY DERMAL ABSORPTION IN RABBITS WAS 640 MG/KG. AN APPLICATION OF A LETHAL DOSE IN RATS PRODUCED PALE LIVER AND HEMORRHAGIC STOMACH CONTENTS. **CHRONIC EXPOSURE-** SYMPTOMS OF INCREASED URINARY FREQUENCY, GROSS HEMATURIA, URETHRAL DISCHARGE, ABDOMINAL AND BACK PAIN, AND A HOT SENSATION ALL OVER WERE REPORTED AMONG WORKERS EXPOSED TO CHLORDIMEFORM. OTHER EFFECTS OF BLADDER IRRITATION, SLEEPINESS, SKIN RASH, ANOREXIA, DIZZINESS, AND A SWEET TASTE IN THE MOUTH ALSO OCCURRED. UROLOGICAL EXAMINATION OF SOME WORKERS REVEALED HEMATURIA AND PYURIA, PROTEINURIA, LOW CREATININE CLEARANCE, DECREASED SERUM COMPLEMENT LEVEL, ELEVATED SERUM GLUTAMIC OXALOACETIC TRANSAMINASE, SMALL URINARY BLADDER CAPACITY AND URETERAL REFLUX; SEVERE HEMORRHAGIC CYSTITIS WAS DETERMINED BY CYSTOSCOPIC EXAMINATION. THESE EFFECTS WERE COMPLETELY REVERSED WITHIN A THREE TO EIGHT WEEK PERIOD.

FIRST AID- REMOVE CONTAMINATED CLOTHING AND SHOES IMMEDIATELY. WASH AFFECTED AREA WITH SOAP OR MILD DETERGENT AND LARGE AMOUNTS OF WATER UNTIL NO EVIDENCE OF CHEMICAL REMAINS (APPROXIMATELY 15-20 MINUTES). GET MEDICAL ATTENTION IMMEDIATELY.

EYE CONTACT: CHLORDIMEFORM: IRRITANT. **ACUTE EXPOSURE-** A 100 MG APPLIED TO THE EYES OF RABBITS WAS SEVERELY IRRITATING. **CHRONIC EXPOSURE-** NO DATA AVAILABLE.

FIRST AID- WASH EYES IMMEDIATELY WITH LARGE AMOUNTS OF WATER OR NORMAL SALINE, OCCASIONALLY LIFTING UPPER AND LOWER LIDS, UNTIL NO EVIDENCE OF CHEMICAL REMAINS (APPROXIMATELY 15-20 MINUTES). GET MEDICAL ATTENTION IMMEDIATELY.

INGESTION: CHLORDIMEFORM: TOXIC. **ACUTE EXPOSURE-** A LETHAL DOSE IN RAT WAS 160 MG/KG. ORAL ADMINISTRATION IN DOGS PRODUCED CONGESTION OF LIVER, KIDNEYS, AND LUNGS AS WELL AS EDEMA AND HEMORRHAGE OF THE LUNGS. **CHRONIC EXPOSURE-** EFFECTS OF BILE DUCT HYPERPLASIA, LIVER CELL CHANGES, DECREASED BODY WEIGHT AND FOOD CONSUMPTION, AND METHEMOGLOBIN FORMATION WERE REPORTED FROM A TWO-YEAR STUDY WITH RATS. IN STUDIES OF DOGS FOR A PERIOD OF 90 DAYS TO 2 YEARS, EFFECTS OF BILE DUCT HYPERPLASIA, INCREASED SPLEEN TO BODY WEIGHT RATIOS, INCREASED SERUM ALKALINE PHOSPHATASE, INCREASED WHITE BLOOD CELL COUNT, AND PIGMENT DEPOSITION IN THE KIDNEYS WERE OBSERVED. EFFECTS OF REDUCED LACTATION AND WEIGHT OF WEANLINGS WERE NOTED IN A 3-GENERATION RAT REPRODUCTION STUDY. A SLOWER OVERALL DEVELOPMENT OF THE ABILITY TO SWIM WAS OBSERVED AMONG THE PROGENY OF FEMALE RATS FED CHLORDIMEFORM WHILE PREGNANT. AS EVALUATED BY RTECS, ORAL ADMINISTRATION TO RATS RESULTED IN A STATISTICALLY SIGNIFICANT INCREASE IN THE INCIDENCE OF CARCINOGENIC TUMORS OF THE VASCULAR AND RESPIRATORY SYSTEM. PARA-CHLORO-ORTHO-TOLUIDINE, A METABOLITE OF CHLORDIMEFORM, PRODUCED CARCINOGENIC EFFECTS IN MICE.

FIRST AID- REMOVE BY GASTRIC LAVAGE AND CATHARSIS. MAINTAIN BLOOD PRESSURE AND AIRWAY. GIVE OXYGEN IF RESPIRATION IS DEPRESSED. DO NOT PERFORM GASTRIC LAVAGE IF VICTIM IS UNCONSCIOUS. GET MEDICAL ATTENTION IMMEDIATELY (DREISBACH, HANDBOOK OF POISONING, 12TH ED.).
ADMINISTRATION OF LAVAGE OR OXYGEN SHOULD BE PERFORMED BY QUALIFIED MEDICAL PERSONNEL.

ANTIDOTE: NO SPECIFIC ANTIDOTE. TREAT SYMPTOMATICALLY AND SUPPORTIVELY.

REACTIVITY

REACTIVITY: STABLE UNDER NORMAL TEMPERATURES AND PRESSURES.

INCOMPATIBILITIES: CHLORDIMEFORM: ACIDIC MEDIA: MAY CAUSE HYDROLYSIS. ALKALINE MEDIA: MAY CAUSE HYDROLYSIS. NEUTRAL MEDIA: MAY CAUSE HYDROLYSIS.

DECOMPOSITION: THERMAL DECOMPOSITION PRODUCTS MAY INCLUDE TOXIC AND CORROSIVE FUMES OF CHLORIDES AND PHOSGENE, AND TOXIC OXIDES OF CARBON.

POLYMERIZATION: HAZARDOUS POLYMERIZATION HAS NOT BEEN REPORTED TO OCCUR UNDER NORMAL TEMPERATURES AND PRESSURES.

STORAGE AND DISPOSAL

OBSERVE ALL FEDERAL, STATE AND LOCAL REGULATIONS WHEN STORING OR DISPOSING OF THIS SUBSTANCE. FOR ASSISTANCE, CONTACT THE DISTRICT DIRECTOR OF THE ENVIRONMENTAL PROTECTION AGENCY.

****STORAGE****

STORE IN ACCORDANCE WITH 40 CFR 165 RECOMMENDED PROCEDURES FOR THE DISPOSAL AND STORAGE OF PESTICIDES AND PESTICIDE CONTAINERS.
STORE IN A COOL, DRY PLACE; KEEP CONTAINER TIGHTLY CLOSED WHEN NOT IN USE.
STORE AWAY FROM INCOMPATIBLE SUBSTANCES.

****DISPOSAL****

DISPOSAL MUST BE IN ACCORDANCE WITH 40 CFR 165 RECOMMENDED PROCEDURES FOR THE DISPOSAL AND STORAGE OF PESTICIDES AND PESTICIDE CONTAINERS.

CONDITIONS TO AVOID

MAY BURN BUT DOES NOT IGNITE READILY. CONTAINERS MAY EXPLODE IN HEAT OF FIRE.

SPILL AND LEAK PROCEDURES

WATER SPILL: THE CALIFORNIA SAFE DRINKING WATER AND TOXIC ENFORCEMENT ACT OF 1986 (PROPOSITION 65) PROHIBITS CONTAMINATING ANY KNOWN SOURCE OF DRINKING WATER WITH SUBSTANCES KNOWN TO CAUSE CANCER AND/OR REPRODUCTIVE TOXICITY.

OCCUPATIONAL SPILL: DO NOT TOUCH SPILLED MATERIAL. STOP LEAK IF YOU CAN DO IT WITHOUT RISK. USE WATER SPRAY TO REDUCE VAPORS. FOR SMALL SPILLS, TAKE UP WITH SAND OR OTHER ABSORBENT MATERIAL AND PLACE INTO CONTAINERS FOR LATER DISPOSAL. FOR SMALL DRY SPILLS, WITH A CLEAN SHOVEL PLACE MATERIAL INTO CLEAN, DRY CONTAINERS AND COVER. MOVE CONTAINERS FROM SPILL AREA. FOR LARGER SPILLS, DIKE FAR AHEAD OF SPILL FOR LATER DISPOSAL. KEEP UNNECESSARY PEOPLE AWAY. ISOLATE HAZARD AREA AND DENY ENTRY. VENTILATE CLOSED SPACES BEFORE ENTERING.

PROTECTIVE EQUIPMENT

VENTILATION: PROVIDE LOCAL EXHAUST OR PROCESS ENCLOSURE VENTILATION SYSTEM.

RESPIRATOR: THE FOLLOWING RESPIRATORS ARE RECOMMENDED BASED ON INFORMATION FOUND IN THE PHYSICAL DATA, TOXICITY AND HEALTH EFFECTS SECTIONS. THEY ARE RANKED IN ORDER FROM MINIMUM TO MAXIMUM RESPIRATORY PROTECTION. THE SPECIFIC RESPIRATOR SELECTED MUST BE BASED ON CONTAMINATION LEVELS FOUND IN THE WORK PLACE, MUST NOT EXCEED THE WORKING LIMITS OF THE RESPIRATOR AND BE JOINTLY APPROVED BY THE NATIONAL INSTITUTE FOR OCCUPATIONAL SAFETY AND HEALTH AND THE MINE SAFETY AND HEALTH ADMINISTRATION (NIOSH-MSHA).
TYPE 'C' SUPPLIED-AIR RESPIRATOR WITH A FULL FACEPIECE OPERATED IN PRESSURE-DEMAND OR OTHER POSITIVE PRESSURE MODE OR WITH A FULL FACEPIECE, HELMET OR HOOD OPERATED IN CONTINOUS-FLOW MODE.
SELF-CONTAINED BREATHING APPARATUS WITH A FULL FACEPIECE OPERATED IN PRESSURE-DEMAND OR OTHER POSITIVE PRESSURE MODE.
FOR FIREFIGHTING AND OTHER IMMEDIATELY DANGEROUS TO LIFE OR HEALTH CONDITIONS:
SELF-CONTAINED BREATHING APPARATUS WITH FULL FACEPIECE OPERATED IN PRESSURE-DEMAND OR OTHER POSITIVE PRESSURE MODE.
SUPPLIED-AIR RESPIRATOR WITH FULL FACEPIECE AND OPERATED IN PRESSURE-DEMAND OR OTHER POSITIVE PRESSURE MODE IN COMBINATION WITH AN

AUXILIARY SELF-CONTAINED BREATHING APPARATUS OPERATED IN PRESSURE-DEMAND OR OTHER POSITIVE PRESSURE MODE.

CLOTHING: EMPLOYEE MUST WEAR APPROPRIATE PROTECTIVE (IMPERVIOUS) CLOTHING AND EQUIPMENT TO PREVENT ANY POSSIBILITY OF SKIN CONTACT WITH THIS SUBSTANCE.

GLOVES: EMPLOYEE MUST WEAR APPROPRIATE PROTECTIVE GLOVES TO PREVENT CONTACT WITH THIS SUBSTANCE.

EYE PROTECTION: EMPLOYEE MUST WEAR SPLASH-PROOF OR DUST-RESISTANT SAFETY GOGGLES AND A FACESHIELD TO PREVENT CONTACT WITH THIS SUBSTANCE.

EMERGENCY WASH FACILITIES: WHERE THERE IS ANY POSSIBILITY THAT AN EMPLOYEE'S EYES AND/OR SKIN MAY BE EXPOSED TO THIS SUBSTANCE, THE EMPLOYER SHOULD PROVIDE AN EYE WASH FOUNTAIN AND QUICK DRENCH SHOWER WITHIN THE IMMEDIATE WORK AREA FOR EMERGENCY USE.

AUTHORIZED BY- OCCUPATIONAL HEALTH SERVICES, INC.

CREATION DATE: 10/04/89 ***REVISION DATE:*** 06/27/90

MATERIAL SAFETY DATA SHEET

OCCUPATIONAL HEALTH SERVICES, INC.
AGRICULTURE AND PESTICIDE DIVISION
450 SEVENTH AVENUE, SUITE 2407
NEW YORK, NEW YORK 10123
1-800-445-MSDS OR (212) 967-1100

EMERGENCY CONTACT:
JOHN S. BRANSFORD, JR. (615) 292-1180

SUBSTANCE IDENTIFICATION

CAS-NUMBER 470-90-6

SUBSTANCE: CHLORFENVINPHOS

TRADE NAMES/SYNONYMS: PHOSPHORIC ACID, 2-CHLORO-1-(2,4-DICHLOROPHENYL)ETHENYL DIETHYL ESTER; PHOSPHORIC ACID, 2-CHLORO-1-(2,4-DICHLOROPHENYL)VINYL DIETHYL ESTER; 2-CHLORO-1-(2,4-DICHLOROPHENYL)ETHENYL DIETHYL PHOSPHATE; 2-CHLORO-1-(2,4-DICHLOROPHENYL)VINYL DIETHYL PHOSPHATE; O,O-DIETHYL-O-(2-CHLORO-1-(2,4-DICHLOROPHENYL)VINYL) PHOSPHATE; 2,4-DICHLORO-ALPHA-(CHLOROMETHYLENE)BENZYL ALCOHOL DIETHYL PHOSPHATE; BIRLANE; COMPOUND 4072; CVP; DERMATON; OMS 1328; SAPECRON; SD 7859; SUPONA; APACHLOR; ENT 24969; O,O-DIETHYL-O-1-(',4'-DICHLORO-PHENYL)-2-CHLOROVINYLPHOSPHATE; STELADENE; VINYLPHATE; C12H14CL3O4P; PST04575

CHEMICAL FAMILY: ORGANOPHOSPHATE HALOGEN

MOLECULAR FORMULA: (C6-H3-CL2)-C-(C-H-CL)-P-O2-(C2-H5-O)2

MOLECULAR WEIGHT: 359.56

CERCLA RATINGS (SCALE 0-3): HEALTH=3 FIRE=U REACTIVITY=0 PERSISTENCE=3

NFPA RATINGS (SCALE 0-4): HEALTH=4 FIRE=U REACTIVITY=0

COMPONENTS AND CONTAMINANTS

COMPONENT: CHLORFENVINPHOS ***PERCENT:*** 100.0
CAS# 470-90-6

OTHER CONTAMINANTS: NONE

EXPOSURE LIMITS: NO OCCUPATIONAL EXPOSURE LIMITS ESTABLISHED BY OSHA, ACGIH, OR NIOSH.

CHLORFENVINPHOS: 500 POUNDS SARA SECTION 302 THRESHOLD PLANNING QUANTITY 1 POUND SARA SECTION 304 REPORTABLE QUANTITY

PHYSICAL DATA

DESCRIPTION: AMBER LIQUID WITH A MILD ODOR.

BOILING POINT: 333-338 F (167-170) C @ 0.5 MMHG

MELTING POINT: -3--9 F (-23--19 C) ***SPECIFIC GRAVITY:*** 1.36 @ 20 C

VAPOR PRESSURE: NEGLIGIBLE ***EVAPORATION RATE:*** NOT AVAILABLE

SOLUBILITY IN WATER: 0.0145% @ 23 C

SOLVENT SOLUBILITY: SOLUBLE IN ACETONE, DICHLOROMETHANE, ALCOHOL, HEXANE, KEROSENE, PROPYLENE GLYCOL, XYTLENE, POLYETHYLENE GLYCOL AND AROMATIC HYDROCARBONS.

FIRE AND EXPLOSION DATA

FIRE AND EXPLOSION HAZARD: UNKNOWN FIRE AND EXPLOSION HAZARD.

FLASH POINT: NOT AVAILABLE

FIREFIGHTING MEDIA: DRY CHEMICAL, CARBON DIOXIDE, HALON, WATER SPRAY OR STANDARD FOAM (1987 EMERGENCY RESPONSE GUIDEBOOK, DOT P 5800.4). FOR LARGER FIRES, USE WATER SPRAY, FOG OR STANDARD FOAM (1987 EMERGENCY RESPONSE GUIDEBOOK, DOT P 5800.4).

FIREFIGHTING: MOVE CONTAINERS FROM FIRE AREA IF POSSIBLE. COOL CONTAINERS EXPOSED TO FLAMES WITH WATER FROM SIDE UNTIL WELL AFTER FIRE IS OUT. FIGHT FIRE FROM MAXIMUM DISTANCE. STAY AWAY FROM STORAGE TANK ENDS. DIKE FIRE CONTROL WATER FOR LATER DISPOSAL. DO NOT SCATTER MATERIAL. (1987 EMERGENCY RESPONSE GUIDEBOOK, DOT P 5800.4, GUIDE PAGE 57). EXTINGUISH ONLY IF FLOW CAN BE STOPPED. USE FLOODING AMOUNTS OF WATER AS A FOG; SOLID STREAMS MAY BE INEFFECTIVE. COOL CONTAINERS WITH FLOODING AMOUNTS OF WATER FROM AS FAR A DISTANCE AS POSSIBLE. AVOID BREATHING POISONOUS VAPORS, KEEP UPWIND.

TRANSPORTATION DATA

DEPARTMENT OF TRANSPORTATION HAZARD CLASSIFICATION 49 CFR 172.101: POISON B

DEPARTMENT OF TRANSPORTATION LABELING REQUIREMENTS 49 CFR 172.101 AND SUBPART E: POISON

DEPARTMENT OF TRANSPORTATION PACKAGING REQUIREMENTS: 49 CFR 173.346 EXCEPTIONS: 49 CFR 173.345

TOXICITY

CHLORFENVINPHOS: TOXICITY DATA: 50 MG/M3/4 HOURS INHALATION-RAT LC50; 10 MG/KG SKIN-HUMAN TDLO; 400 MG/KG SKIN-RABBIT LD50; 26,400 UG/KG SKIN-RAT LD50; 336 MG/KG SKIN-MOUSE LD50; 10 MG/KG ORAL-RAT LD50; 65 MG/KG ORAL-MOUSE LD50; 300 MG/KG ORAL-RABBIT LD50; 1200 MG/KG ORAL-DOG LD50; 125 MG/KG ORAL-GUINEA PIG LD50; 71,250 UG/KG ORAL-DOMESTIC ANIMAL LD50; 20 MG/KG ORAL-CATTLE LD50; 7 MG/KG SUBCUTANEOUS-RAT LD50; 339 MG/KG SUBCUTANEOUS-MOUSE LD50; 6600 UG/KG INTRAVENOUS-RAT LD50; 87 MG/KG INTRAVENOUS-MOUSE LD50; 51 MG/KG INTRAVENOUS-DOG LD50; 8500 UG/KG INTRAPERITONEAL-RAT LD50; 87 MG/KG INTRAPERITONEAL-MOUSE LD50; MUTAGENIC DATA (RTECS). CARCINOGEN STATUS: NONE. ACUTE TOXICITY LEVEL: HIGHLY TOXIC BY INHALATION AND INGESTION; TOXIC BY DERMAL ABSORPTION. TARGET EFFECTS: CHOLINESTERASE INHIBITOR. AT INCREASED RISK FROM EXPOSURE: PERSONS WITH RESPIRATORY AILMENTS, RECENT EXPOSURE TO CHOLINESTERASE INHIBITORS OR IMPAIRED CHOLINESTERASE PRODUCTION, OR LIVER MALFUNCTION.* ADDITIONAL DATA: MAY CROSS THE PLACENTA. HIGH ENVIRONMENTAL TEMPERATURES OR EXPOSURE OF THE CHEMICAL TO VISIBLE OR ULTRAVIOLET LIGHT MAY ENHANCE THE TOXICITY. INTERACTIONS WITH MEDICATIONS MAY OCCUR.*

* MAY BE BASED ON GENERAL INFORMATION ON ORGANOPHOSPHATES.

HEALTH EFFECTS AND FIRST AID

INHALATION: CHLORFENVINPHOS: HIGHLY TOXIC. SEE INFORMATION ON ORGANOPHOSPHATES.

ORGANOPHOSPHATES: CHOLINESTERASE INHIBITOR. **ACUTE EXPOSURE-** WHEN INHALED, THE FIRST EFFECTS OF CHOLINESTERASE INHIBITORS ARE USUALLY RESPIRATORY AND MAY INCLUDE NASAL HYPEREMIA AND WATERY DISCHARGE, COUGH, CHEST DISCOMFORT, DYSPNEA, AND WHEEZING DUE TO INCREASED BRONCHIAL SECRETIONS AND BRONCHOCONSTRICTION. IF SUFFICIENT AMOUNTS ARE ABSORBED, OTHER SYSTEMIC EFFECTS MAY BEGIN WITHIN A FEW MINUTES OR BE DELAYED FOR UP TO 12 HOURS. SYMPTOMS MAY INCLUDE PALLOR, NAUSEA, VOMITING, DIARRHEA, ABDOMINAL CRAMPS, HEADACHE, DIZZINESS, OCULAR PAIN, BLURRED VISION, MIOSIS OR IN SOME CASES, ESPECIALLY INITIALLY, MYDRIASIS, LACRIMATION, SALIVATION, SWEATING, AND CONFUSION. OTHER REPORTED CENTRAL NERVOUS SYSTEM OR NEUROMUSCULAR EFFECTS MAY INCLUDE ATAXIA, SLURRED SPEECH, AREFLEXIA, WEAKNESS, FATIGUE, FASCICULATIONS, TWITCHING, TREMORS POSSIBLY OF THE TONGUE AND EYELIDS, AND EVENTUALLY PARALYSIS OF THE EXTREMITIES AND POSSIBLY OF THE RESPIRATORY MUSCLES. IN SEVERE CASES THERE MAY ALSO BE INVOLUNTARY DEFECATION AND URINATION, CYANOSIS, PSYCHOSIS, HYPERGLYCEMIA, ACUTE PANCREATITIS, CARDIAC IRREGULARITIES, PULMONARY EDEMA, UNCONSCIOUSNESS, CONVULSIONS, AND COMA. DEATH IS PRIMARILY DUE TO RESPIRATORY FAILURE, ALTHOUGH CARDIOVASCULAR EFFECTS INCLUDING CARDIAC ARREST MAY ALSO BE IMPLICATED. LONG TERM SEQUELAE ARE RARE BUT MAY INCLUDE NEUROPSYCHIATRIC DISORDERS AND MYOPATHY WITH MUSCLE TENDERNESS. **CHRONIC EXPOSURE-** REPEATED OR PROLONGED EXPOSURE MAY RESULT IN THE EFFECTS OF ACUTE EXPOSURE. OTHER EFFECTS REPORTED IN WORKERS REPEATEDLY EXPOSED INCLUDE IMPAIRED MEMORY AND CONCENTRATION, ACUTE PSYCHOSIS, SEVERE DEPRESSIONS, IRRITABILTY, CONFUSION, APATHY, EMOTIONAL LABILITY, SOCIAL WITHDRAWAL, CONFUSION, HEADACHE, SPEECH DIFFICULTIES, DELAYED REACTION TIMES, SPATIAL DISORIENTATION, NIGHTMARES, SLEEPWALKING, AND DROWSINESS OR INSOMNIA. AN INFLUENZA-LIKE CONDITION WITH HEADACHE, NAUSEA, WEAKNESS, ANOREXIA AND MALAISE HAS ALSO BEEN REPORTED.

FIRST AID- REMOVE FROM EXPOSURE AREATO FRESH AIR IMMEDIATELY. IF BREATHING HAS STOPPED, GIVE ARTIFICIAL RESPIRATION. MAINTAIN AIRWAY AND BLOOD PRESSURE AND

ADMINISTER OXYGEN IF AVAILABLE. KEEP AFFECTED PERSON WARM AND AT REST. TREAT SYMPTOMATICALLY AND SUPPORTIVELY. ADMINISTRATION OF OXYGEN SHOULD BE PERFORMED BY QUALIFIED PERSONNEL. GET MEDICAL ATTENTION IMMEDIATELY.

SKIN CONTACT: CHLORFENVINPHOS: TOXIC. A DOSE OF 10 MG/KG OF CHLORFENVINPHOS IN AN EMULSIFIABLE CONCENTRATE FORMULATION APPLIED TO THE FOREARM OF NINE VOLUNTEERS, FOR FOUR HOURS, PRODUCED CHOLINESTERASE INHIBITION. SEE INFORMATION ON ORGANOPHOSPHATES. ORGANOPHOSPHATES: CHOLINESTERASE INHIBITOR. **ACUTE EXPOSURE**- LOCALIZED SWEATING AND FASCICULATIONS MAY OCCUR AT THE SITE OF CONTACT. IF SUFFICIENT AMOUNTS ARE ABSORBED, OTHER EFFECTS OF CHOLINESTERASE INHIBITION AS DESCRIBED IN ACUTE INHALATION MAY OCCUR. SYMPTOMS MAY BE DELAYED 2-3 HOURS, BUT USUALLY NO MORE THAN 12 HOURS. THE RATE OF ABSORPTION IS INCREASED BY THE PRESENCE OF DERMATITIS OR HIGH AMBIENT TEMPERATURES. **CHRONIC EXPOSURE**- REPEATED OR PROLONGED EXPOSURE MAY CAUSE EFFECTS AS DESCRIBED IN ACUTE EXPOSURE. SOME ORGANOPHOSPHATES MAY CAUSE SENSITIZATION.

FIRST AID- REMOVE CONTAMINATED CLOTHING IMMEDIATELY. WASH CONTAMINATED AREAS WITH SOAP AND WATER FOLLOWED BY ALCOHOL (ARENA, POISONING, 4TH ED.). EMERGENCY PERSONNEL SHOULD WEAR GLOVES AND AVOID CONTAMINATION. TREAT RESPIRATORY DIFFICULTY WITH ARTIFICIAL RESPIRATION. GET MEDICAL ATTENTION IMMEDIATELY.

EYE CONTACT: CHLORFENVINPHOS: SEE INFORMATION ON ORGANOPHOSPHATES. ORGANOPHOSPHATES: CHOLINESTERASE INHIBITOR. **ACUTE EXPOSURE**- DIRECT CONTACT MAY CAUSE PAIN, HYPEREMIA, LACRIMATION, TWITCHING OF THE EYELIDS, MIOSIS, AND CILIARY MUSCLE SPASM WITH LOSS OF ACCOMODATION, BLURRED OR DIMMED VISION AND BROWACHE. SOMETIMES MYDRIASIS MAY OCCUR INSTEAD OF MIOSIS. WITH SUFFICIENT EXPOSURE, OTHER SYMPTOMS OF CHOLINESTERASE INHIBITION AS DESCRIBED IN ACUTE INHALATION MAY OCCUR. **CHRONIC EXPOSURE**- REPEATED OR PROLONGED EXPOSURE MAY CAUSE EFFECTS AS DESCRIBED IN ACUTE EXPOSURE. SOME COMPOUNDS HAVE CAUSED TOXIC EFFECTS ON THE CRYSTALLINE LENS, CONJUNCTIVAL THICKENING AND OBSTRUCTION OF THE NASOLACRIMAL CANALS WHEN USED AS MIOTIC EYEDROPS.

FIRST AID- IRRIGATE EYES WITH WATER OR SALINE SOLUTION. IF SYMPTOMS OF POISONING OCCUR, TREAT RESPIRATORY DIFFICULTY WITH ARTIFICIAL RESPIRATION AND OXYGEN. OBSERVE PATIENT FOR AT LEAST 24-36 HOURS (GOSSELIN, CLINICAL TOXICOLOGY OF COMMERCIAL PRODUCTS, 5TH ED.). GET MEDICAL ATTENTION IMMEDIATELY. OXYGEN SHOULD BE ADMINISTERED BY QUALIFIED MEDICAL PERSONNEL.

INGESTION: CHLORFENVINPHOS: HIGHLY TOXIC. A STUDY OF HENS FOR NEUROLOGICAL DAMAGE DUE TO REPEATED INGESTION OF CHLORFENVINPHOS WAS NEGATIVE. EFFECTS OF REDUCED FERTILITY AND REDUCED SURVIVAL OF OFFSPRING WERE OBSERVED IN A THREE-GENERATION STUDY WITH RATS. SEE INFORMATION ON ORGANOPHOSPHATES.
ORGANOPHOSPHATES: CHOLINESTERASE INHIBITOR. **ACUTE EXPOSURE**- WHEN INGESTED, THE FIRST EFFECTS MAY BE NAUSEA, VOMITING, ANOREXIA, ABDOMINAL CRAMPS AND DIARRHEA. GASTROINTESTINAL ABSORPTION MAY CAUSE THE SYMPTOMS OF CHOLINESTERASE INHIBITION AS DESCRIBED IN ACUTE INHALATION. SYMPTOMS MAY BEGIN WITHIN MINUTES OR BE DELAYED. **CHRONIC EXPOSURE**- REPEATED INGESTION MAY CAUSE EFFECTS AS DESCRIBED IN ACUTE EXPOSURE.

FIRST AID- IF PERSON IS ALERT AND RESPIRATION IS NOT DEPRESSED, GIVE SYRUP OF IPECAC FOLLOWED BY WATER (IF VOMITING OCCURS, KEEP HEAD BELOW HIPS TO PREVENT ASPIRATION). IF CONSCIOUSNESS LEVEL DECLINES OR VOMITING HAS NOT OCCURRED IN 15 MINUTES EMPTY STOMACH BY GASTRIC LAVAGE WITH THE AID OF CUFFED ENDOTRACHEAL TUBE USING ISOTONIC SALINE OR 5% SODIUM BICARBONATE FOLLOW WITH ACTIVATED CHARCOAL. ESTABLISH AND MAINTAIN AIRWAY. TREAT RESPIRATORY DIFFICULTY WITH ARTIFICIAL RESPIRATION AND OXYGEN. DO NOT GIVE MORPHINE, AMINOPHYLLINE, PHENOTHIAZINES, RESERPINE, FUROSEMIDE, OR ETHACRYNIC ACID (MORGAN, RECOGNITION AND MANAGEMENT OF PESTICIDE POISONINGS, 3RD ED.). TREAT SYMPTOMATICALLY AND SUPPORTIVELY. ADMINISTRATION OF OXYGEN AND LAVAGE MUST BE PERFORMED BY QUALIFIED MEDICAL PERSONNEL. GET MEDICAL ATTENTION IMMEDIATELY.

ANTIDOTE: THE FOLLOWING ANTIDOTE(S) HAVE BEEN RECOMMENDED. HOWEVER, THE DECISION AS TO WHETHER THE SEVERITY OF POISONING REQUIRES ADMINISTRATION OF ANY ANTIDOTE AND ACTUAL DOSE REQUIRED SHOULD BE MADE BY QUALIFIED MEDICAL PERSONNEL.
FOR CHOLINESTERASE INHIBITORS: ESTABLISH CLEAR AIRWAY AND TISSUE OXYGENATION BY ASPIRATION OF SECRETIONS, AND IF NECESSARY, BY ASSISTED PULMONARY VENTILATION WITH OXYGEN. IMPROVE TISSUE OXYGENATION AS MUCH AS POSSIBLE BEFORE ADMINISTERING ATROPINE TO MINIMIZE THE RISK OF VENTRICULAR FIBRILLATION. ADMINISTER ATROPINE SULFATE INTRAVENOUSLY, OR INTRAMUSCULARLY IF IV INJECTION IS NOT POSSIBLE. IN MODERATELY SEVERE POISONING ADMINISTER ATROPINE SULFATE, 0.4-2.0 MG REPEATED EVERY 15 MINUTES UNTIL ATROPINIZATION IS ACHIEVED (TACHYCARDIA, FLUSHING, DRY MOUTH, MYDRIASIS). MAINTAIN ATROPINIZATION BY REPEATED DOSES FOR 2-12 HOURS, OR LONGER, DEPENDING ON THE SEVERITY OF POISONING. THE APPEARANCE OF RALES IN THE LUNG BASES, MIOSIS, SALIVATION, NAUSEA, BRADYCARDIA, ARE ALL INDICATIONS OF INADEQUATE ATROPINIZATION. SEVERELY POISONED INDIVIDUALS MAY EXHIBIT REMARKABLE TOLERANCE TO ATROPINE; TWO OR MORE TIMES THE DOSAGES SUGGESTED ABOVE MAY BE NEEDED. PERSONS NOT POISONED OR ONLY SLIGHTLY POISONED, HOWEVER, MAY DEVELOP SIGNS OF ATROPINE TOXICITY FROM SUCH LARGE DOSAGES: FEVER, MUSCLE FIBRILLATIONS, AND DELIRIUM ARE THE MAIN SIGNS OF ATROPINE TOXICITY. IF THESE SIGNS APPEAR WHILE THE PATIENT IS FULLY ATROPINIZED, ATROPINE ADMINISTRATION SHOULD BE DISCONTINUED, AT LEAST TEMPORARILY. OBSERVE TREATED PATIENTS CLOSELY AT LEAST 24 HOURS TO INSURE THAT SYMPTOMS (POSSIBLY PULMONARY EDEMA) DO NOT RECUR AS ATROPINIZATION WEARS OFF. IN VERY SEVERE POISONINGS, METABOLIC DISPOSITION OF TOXICANT MAY REQUIRE SEVERAL HOURS OR DAYS DURING WHICH ATROPINIZATION MUST BE MAINTAINED. MARKEDLY LOWER LEVELS OF URINARY METABOLITES INDICATE THAT ATROPINE DOSAGE CAN BE TAPERED OFF. AS DOSAGE IS REDUCED, CHECK THE LUNG BASES FREQUENTLY FOR RALES. IF RALES ARE HEARD OR OTHER SYMPTOMS RETURN, RE-ESTABLISH ATROPINIZATION PROMPTLY (MORGAN, RECOGNITION AND MANAGEMENT OF PESTICIDE POISONINGS, 3RD ED.). ADMINISTRATION OF ANTIDOTE MUST BE PERFORMED BY QUALIFIED MEDICAL PERSONNEL.
IN CASES OF SEVERE POISONING BY ORGANOPHOSPHATE PESTICIDES IN WHICH RESPIRATORY DEPRESSION, MUSCLE WEAKNESS AND TWITCHINGS ARE SEVERE, GIVE PRALIDOXIME (PROTOPAM-AYERST, 2-PAM), 1.0 GRAM INTRAVENOUSLY AT NO MORE THAN 0.5 GRAM PER MINUTE. DOSAGE OF PRALIDOXIME MAY BE REPEATED IN 1-2 HOURS, THEN AT 10-12 HOUR INTERVALS IF NEEDED. IN VERY SEVERE POISONINGS, DOSAGE RATES MAY BE DOUBLED. TREATMENT WITH PRALIDOXIME WILL BE MOST EFFECTIVE IF GIVEN WITHIN THIRTY-SIX HOURS AFTER POISONING (MORGAN, RECOGNITION AND MANAGEMENT OF PESTICIDE POISONINGS, 3RD ED.). ANTIDOTE SHOULD BE ADMINISTERED BY QUALIFIED MEDICAL PERSONNEL.

REACTIVITY

REACTIVITY: STABLE UNDER NORMAL TEMPERATURES AND PRESSURES.

INCOMPATIBILITIES: CHLORFENVINPHOS: METALS: MAY BE CORROSIVE. OXIDIZERS (STRONG): FIRE AND EXPLOSION HAZARD.

DECOMPOSITION: THERMAL DECOMPOSITION RELEASES CORROSIVE FUMES OF HYDROGEN CHLORIDE AND TOXIC OXIDES OF PHOSPHORUS AND SULFUR.

POLYMERIZATION: HAZARDOUS POLYMERIZATION HAS NOT BEEN REPORTED TO OCCUR UNDER NORMAL TEMPERATURES AND PRESSURES.

STORAGE AND DISPOSAL

OBSERVE ALL FEDERAL, STATE AND LOCAL REGULATIONS WHEN STORING OR DISPOSING OF THIS SUBSTANCE. FOR ASSISTANCE, CONTACT THE DISTRICT DIRECTOR OF THE ENVIRONMENTAL PROTECTION AGENCY.

****STORAGE****

STORE IN ACCORDANCE WITH 40 CFR 165 RECOMMENDED PROCEDURES FOR THE DISPOSAL AND STORAGE OF PESTICIDES AND PESTICIDE CONTAINERS.
STORE AWAY FROM INCOMPATIBLE SUBSTANCES.
THRESHOLD PLANNING QUANTITY (TPQ): THE SUPERFUND AMENDMENTS AND REAUTHORIZATION ACT (SARA) SECTION 302 REQUIRES THAT EACH FACILITY WHERE ANY EXTREMELY HAZARDOUS SUBSTANCE IS PRESENT IN A QUANTITY EQUAL TO OR GREATER THAN THE TPQ ESTABLISHED FOR THAT SUBSTANCE NOTIFY THE STATE EMERGENCY RESPONSE COMMISSION FOR THE STATE IN WHICH IT IS LOCATED. SECTION 303 OF SARA REQUIRES THESE FACILITIES TO PARTICIPATE IN LOCAL EMERGENCY RESPONSE PLANNING (40 CFR 355.30).

****DISPOSAL****

DISPOSAL MUST BE IN ACCORDANCE WITH 40 CFR 165 RECOMMENDED PROCEDURES FOR THE DISPOSAL AND STORAGE OF PESTICIDES AND PESTICIDE CONTAINERS.

CONDITIONS TO AVOID

MAY BE IGNITED BY HEAT, SPARKS OR FLAMES. CONTAINER MAY EXPLODE IN HEAT OF FIRE. VAPOR EXPLOSION AND POISON HAZARD INDOORS, OUTDOORS OR IN SEWERS.

SPILL AND LEAK PROCEDURES

OCCUPATIONAL SPILL: SHUT OFF IGNITION SOURCES. DO NOT TOUCH SPILLED MATERIAL. STOP LEAK IF YOU CAN DO IT WITHOUT RISK. USE WATER SPRAY TO REDUCE VAPORS. FOR SMALL SPILLS, TAKE UP WITH SAND OR OTHER ABSORBENT

MATERIAL AND PLACE INTO CONTAINERS FOR LATER DISPOSAL. FOR SMALL DRY SPILLS, WITH CLEAN SHOVEL PLACE MATERIAL INTO CLEAN, DRY CONTAINERS AND COVER. MOVE CONTAINERS FROM SPILL AREA. FOR LARGER SPILLS, DIKE FAR AHEAD OF SPILL FOR LATER DISPOSAL. NO SMOKING, FLAMES OR FLARES IN HAZARD AREA! KEEP UNNECESSARY PEOPLE AWAY. ISOLATE HAZARD AREA AND DENY ENTRY. VENTILATE CLOSED SPACES BEFORE ENTERING.

REPORTABLE QUANTITY (RQ): 1 POUND THE SUPERFUND AMENDMENTS AND REAUTHORIZATION ACT (SARA) SECTION 304 REQUIRES THAT A RELEASE EQUAL TO OR GREATER THAN THE REPORTABLE QUANTITY FOR THIS SUBSTANCE BE IMMEDIATELY REPORTED TO THE LOCAL EMERGENCY PLANNING COMMITTEE AND THE STATE EMERGENCY RESPONSE COMMISSION (40 CFR 355.40). IF THE RELEASE OF THIS SUBSTANCE IS REPORTABLE UNDER CERCLA SECTION 103, THE NATIONAL RESPONSE CENTER MUST BE NOTIFIED IMMEDIATELY AT (800) 424-8802 OR (202) 426-2675 IN THE METROPOLITAN WASHINGTON, D.C. AREA (40 CFR 302.6).

PROTECTIVE EQUIPMENT

VENTILATION: PROCESS ENCLOSURE RECOMMENDED.

RESPIRATOR: THE FOLLOWING RESPIRATORS ARE RECOMMENDED BASED ON INFORMATION FOUND IN THE PHYSICAL DATA, TOXICITY AND HEALTH EFFECTS SECTIONS. THEY ARE RANKED IN ORDER FROM MINIMUM TO MAXIMUM RESPIRATORY PROTECTION. THE SPECIFIC RESPIRATOR SELECTED MUST BE BASED ON CONTAMINATION LEVELS FOUND IN THE WORK PLACE, MUST NOT EXCEED THE WORKING LIMITS OF THE RESPIRATOR AND BE JOINTLY APPROVED BY THE NATIONAL INSTITUTE FOR OCCUPATIONAL SAFETY AND HEALTH AND THE MINE SAFETY AND HEALTH ADMINISTRATION (NIOSH-MSHA).

TYPE 'C' SUPPLIED-AIR RESPIRATOR WITH A FULL FACEPIECE OPERATED IN PRESSURE-DEMAND OR OTHER POSITIVE PRESSURE MODE OR WITH A FULL FACEPIECE, HELMET OR HOOD OPERATED IN CONTINOUS-FLOW MODE.

SELF-CONTAINED BREATHING APPARATUS WITH A FULL FACEPIECE OPERATED IN PRESSURE-DEMAND OR OTHER POSITIVE PRESSURE MODE.

FOR FIREFIGHTING AND OTHER IMMEDIATELY DANGEROUS TO LIFE OR HEALTH CONDITIONS: SELF-CONTAINED BREATHING APPARATUS WITH FULL FACEPIECE OPERATED IN PRESSURE-DEMAND OR OTHER POSITIVE PRESSURE MODE.

SUPPLIED-AIR RESPIRATOR WITH FULL FACEPIECE AND OPERATED IN PRESSURE-DEMAND OR OTHER POSITIVE PRESSURE MODE IN COMBINATION WITH AN AUXILIARY SELF-CONTAINED BREATHING APPARATUS OPERATED IN PRESSURE-DEMAND OR OTHER POSITIVE PRESSURE MODE.

CLOTHING: EMPLOYEE MUST WEAR APPROPRIATE PROTECTIVE (IMPERVIOUS) CLOTHING AND EQUIPMENT TO PREVENT ANY POSSIBILITY OF SKIN CONTACT WITH THIS SUBSTANCE.

GLOVES: EMPLOYEE MUST WEAR APPROPRIATE PROTECTIVE GLOVES TO PREVENT CONTACT WITH THIS SUBSTANCE.

EYE PROTECTION: EMPLOYEE MUST WEAR SPLASH-PROOF OR DUST-RESISTANT SAFETY GOGGLES AND A FACESHIELD TO PREVENT CONTACT WITH THIS SUBSTANCE.

EMERGENCY WASH FACILITIES: WHERE THERE IS ANY POSSIBILITY THAT AN EMPLOYEE'S EYES AND/OR SKIN MAY BE EXPOSED TO THIS SUBSTANCE, THE EMPLOYER SHOULD PROVIDE AN EYE WASH FOUNTAIN AND QUICK DRENCH SHOWER WITHIN THE IMMEDIATE WORK AREA FOR EMERGENCY USE.

AUTHORIZED BY- OCCUPATIONAL HEALTH SERVICES, INC.

CREATION DATE: 10/04/89 ***REVISION DATE:*** 06/20/90

MATERIAL SAFETY DATA SHEET

OCCUPATIONAL HEALTH SERVICES, INC.
AGRICULTURE AND PESTICIDE DIVISION
450 SEVENTH AVENUE, SUITE 2407
NEW YORK, NEW YORK 10123
1-800-445-MSDS OR (212) 967-1100

EMERGENCY CONTACT:
JOHN S. BRANSFORD, JR. (615) 292-1180

SUBSTANCE IDENTIFICATION

CAS-NUMBER 7782-50-5

SUBSTANCE: CHLORINE

TRADE NAMES/SYNONYMS: CHLORINE MOLECULAR; CHLORINE MOL.; DIATOMIC CHLORINE; DICHLORINE; MOLECULAR CHLORINE; STCC 4904120; UN 1017; CL2; PST04600

CHEMICAL FAMILY: HALOGEN
INORGANIC GAS

MOLECULAR FORMULA: CL2

MOLECULAR WEIGHT: 70.906

CERCLA RATINGS (SCALE 0-3): HEALTH=3 FIRE=0 REACTIVITY=0 PERSISTENCE=0

NFPA RATINGS (SCALE 0-4): HEALTH=3 FIRE=0 REACTIVITY=0

COMPONENTS AND CONTAMINANTS

COMPONENT: CHLORINE ***PERCENT:*** 100.0
CAS# 7782-50-5

OTHER CONTAMINANTS: NONE

EXPOSURE LIMITS: CHLORINE: 0.5 PPM (1.5 MG/M3) OSHA TWA; 1 PPM (3 MG/M3) OSHA STEL 0.5 PPM (1.5 MG/M3) ACGIH TWA; 1 PPM (3 MG/M3) ACGIH STEL 0.5 PPM NIOSH RECOMMENDED 15 MINUTE CEILING

100 POUNDS SARA SECTION 302 THRESHOLD PLANNING QUANTITY 10 POUNDS SARA SECTION 304 REPORTABLE QUANTITY 10 POUNDS CERCLA SECTION 103 REPORTABLE QUANTITY SUBJECT TO SARA SECTION 313 ANNUAL TOXIC CHEMICAL RELEASE REPORTING.

PHYSICAL DATA

DESCRIPTION: PALE GREENISH-YELLOW GAS WITH A CHARACTERISTIC, SUFFOCATING ODOR.

BOILING POINT: -31 F (-35 C) ***MELTING POINT:*** -150 F (-101 C)

SPECIFIC GRAVITY: 3.214 G/L @ 0 C ***VISCOSITY:*** 0.01327 CPS @ 20 C

VAPOR PRESSURE: 5168 MMHG @ 21 C ***SOLUBILITY IN WATER:*** 1.46% @ 0 C

ODOR THRESHOLD: 0.01 PPM ***VAPOR DENSITY:*** 2.49

SOLVENT SOLUBILITY: SOLUBLE IN ALKALIES.

FIRE AND EXPLOSION DATA

FIRE AND EXPLOSION HAZARD: NEGLIGIBLE FIRE HAZARD WHEN EXPOSED TO HEAT OR FLAME.

OXIDIZER: OXIDIZERS DECOMPOSE, ESPECIALLY WHEN HEATED, TO YIELD OXYGEN OR OTHER GASES WHICH WILL INCREASE THE BURNING RATE OF COMBUSTIBLE MATTER. CONTACT WITH EASILY OXIDIZABLE, ORGANIC, OR OTHER COMBUSTIBLE MATERIALS MAY RESULT IN IGNITION, VIOLENT COMBUSTION OR EXPLOSION.

FIREFIGHTING MEDIA: DRY CHEMICAL, CARBON DIOXIDE OR HALON (1987 EMERGENCY RESPONSE GUIDEBOOK, DOT P 5800.4).

FOR LARGER FIRES, USE WATER SPRAY, FOG OR STANDARD FOAM (1987 EMERGENCY RESPONSE GUIDEBOOK, DOT P 5800.4).

FIREFIGHTING: MOVE CONTAINER FROM FIRE AREA IF POSSIBLE. STAY AWAY FROM STORAGE TANK ENDS. COOL FIRE-EXPOSED CONTAINERS WITH WATER FROM SIDE UNTIL WELL AFTER FIRE IS OUT. FOR MASSIVE FIRE IN STORAGE AREA, USE UNMANNED HOSE HOLDER OR MONITOR NOZZLES, ELSE WITHDRAW FROM AREA AND LET BURN (1987 EMERGENCY RESPONSE GUIDEBOOK, DOT P 5800.4, GUIDE PAGE 20).

EXTINGUISH USING AGENTS SUITABLE FOR TYPE OF FIRE. COOL CONTAINERS WITH FLOODING AMOUNTS OF WATER, APPLY FROM AS FAR A DISTANCE AS POSSIBLE. AVOID BREATHING POISONOUS VAPORS, KEEP UPWIND. EVACUTE TO A RADIUS OF 2500 FEET IF MATERIAL IS LEAKING.

TRANSPORTATION DATA

DEPARTMENT OF TRANSPORTATION HAZARD CLASSIFICATION 49 CFR 172.101: NONFLAMMABLE GAS

DEPARTMENT OF TRANSPORTATION LABELING REQUIREMENTS 49 CFR 172.101 AND SUBPART E: NONFLAMMABLE GAS AND POISON

DEPARTMENT OF TRANSPORTATION PACKAGING REQUIREMENTS: 49 CFR 173.304; 49 CFR 173.314 AND 49 CFR 173.315 EXCEPTIONS: NONE

TOXICITY

CHLORINE: TOXICITY DATA: 2530 MG/M3/30 MINUTES INHALATION-HUMAN LCLO; 500 PPM/5 MINUTES INHALATION-HUMAN LCLO; 293 PPM/1 HOUR INHALATION-RAT LC50; 137 PPM/1 HOUR INHALATION-MOUSE LC50; 660 PPM/4 HOURS INHALATION-RABBIT LCLO; 330 PPM/7 HOURS INHALATION-GUINEA PIG LCLO; 800 PPM/30 MINUTES INHALATION-DOG LCLO; 660 PPM/4 HOURS INHALATION-CAT LCLO, 500 PPM/5 MINUTES INHALATION-MAMMAL LCLO; MUTAGENIC DATA (RTECS); REPRODUCTIVE EFFECTS DATA (RTECS). CARCINOGEN STATUS: NONE. LOCAL EFFECTS: CORROSIVE- SKIN, EYE; IRRITANT- MUCOUS MEMBRANES. ACUTE TOXICITY LEVEL: TOXIC BY INHALATION. TARGET EFFECTS: POISONING MAY AFFECT THE LUNGS. AT INCREASED RISK FROM EXPOSURE: PERSONS WITH PRE-EXISTING HEART DISEASE OR TUBERCULOSIS.

HEALTH EFFECTS AND FIRST AID

INHALATION: CHLORINE: CORROSIVE/TOXIC. 30 PPM IMMEDIATELY DANGEROUS TO LIFE OR HEALTH. ACUTE EXPOSURE- MUCOUS MEMBRANE IRRITATION MAY OCCUR AT 0.2 TO 16 PPM AND COUGH AT 30 PPM. INHALATION OF 500 PPM FOR 5 MINUTES HAS BEEN LETHAL IN HUMANS AND 1000 PPM MAY BE FATAL AFTER A FEW DEEP BREATHS. OCCUPATIONAL EXPOSURES HAVE RESULTED IN BURNING OF THE NOSE AND MOUTH WITH RHINORRHEA, RESPIRATORY DISTRESS WITH COUGHING, CHOKING, WHEEZING, RALES, RETCHING, HEMOPTYSIS, SUBSTERNAL

PAIN, DYSPNEA, AND CYANOSIS. TRACHEOBRONCHITIS, PROGRESSING TO IMMEDIATE OR POSSIBLY DELAYED PULMONARY EDEMA AND OCCASIONAL PNEUMONITIS HAVE ALSO BEEN REPORTED. COUGH GENERALLY INCREASES IN FREQUENCY AND SEVERITY AFTER TWO TO THREE DAYS AND BECAME PRODUCTIVE OF THICK MUCOPURULENT SPUTUM, WHICH DISAPPEARS BY THE END OF 14 DAYS. LUNG DAMAGE IS USUALLY NOT PERMANENT; RESPIRATORY DISTRESS USUALLY SUBSIDES WITHIN 72 HOURS. AT HIGH CONCENTRATIONS, CHLORINE MAY ACT AS AN ASPHYXIANT BY CAUSING CRAMPS OF THE LARYNX MUSCLES AND SWELLING OF THE THE MUCOUS MEMBRANES. OTHER SYMPTOMS MAY INCLUDE SALIVATION, ANXIETY, SNEEZING, PALLOR OR REDNESS OF THE FACE, WEAKNESS, HOARSENESS, HEADACHE, DIZZINESS, AND GENERAL EXCITEMENT AND RESTLESSNESS. MASSIVE INHALATION MAY ALSO CAUSE DEATH BY CARDIAC ARREST. **CHRONIC EXPOSURE**- PERSONS REPEATEDLY EXPOSED TO LOW CONCENTRATIONS MAY DEVELOP CHLORACNE, OLFACTORY DEFICIENCY AND TOLERANCE BUILD-UP. PROLONGED AND REPEATED EXPOSURE TO 0.8-1.0 PPM MAY CAUSE PERMANENT, ALTHOUGH MODERATE REDUCTION IN PULMONARY FUNCTION. CHRONIC EXPOSURE AT 5 PPM MAY RESULT IN INFLAMMATION OF THE MUCOUS MEMBRANES OF THE NOSE, DISEASE OF THE BRONCHI, AND INCREASED SUSCEPTIBILITY TO RESPIRATORY INFECTION INCLUDING TUBERCULOSIS. DENTAL EROSION MAY OCCUR. ANIMALS SURVIVING SUBLETHAL EXPOSURES FOR 15 TO 193 DAYS AFTER GASSING SHOWED MARKED EMPHYSEMA.

FIRST AID- REMOVE FROM EXPOSURE AREA TO FRESH AIR IMMEDIATELY. IF BREATHING HAS STOPPED, GIVE ARTIFICIAL RESPIRATION. MAINTAIN AIRWAY AND BLOOD PRESSURE AND ADMINISTER OXYGEN IF AVAILABLE. KEEP AFFECTED PERSON WARM AND AT REST. TREAT SYMPTOMATICALLY AND SUPPORTIVELY. ADMINISTRATION OF OXYGEN SHOULD BE PERFORMED BY QUALIFIED PERSONNEL. GET MEDICAL ATTENTION IMMEDIATELY.

SKIN CONTACT: CHLORINE: CORROSIVE. **ACUTE EXPOSURE**- HIGH VAPOR CONCENTRATIONS MAY IRRITATE THE SKIN AND CAUSE BURNING AND PRICKING SENSATIONS, INFLAMMATION, AND VESICLE FORMATION. CONTACT WITH LIQUID MAY CAUSE BURNS, BLISTERING, TISSUE DESTRUCTION, AND FROSTBITE. **CHRONIC EXPOSURE**- EFFECTS DEPEND ON THE CONCENTRATION AND DURATION OF EXPOSURE. REPEATED OR PROLONGED CONTACT MAY RESULT IN DERMATITIS OR EFFECTS SIMILAR TO ACUTE EXPOSURE.

FIRST AID- REMOVE CONTAMINATED CLOTHING AND SHOES IMMEDIATELY. WASH AFFECTED AREA WITH SOAP OR MILD DETERGENT AND LARGE AMOUNTS OF WATER UNTIL NO EVIDENCE OF CHEMICAL REMAINS (AT LEAST 15-20 MINUTES). IN CASE OF CHEMICAL BURNS, COVER AREA WITH STERILE, DRY DRESSING. BANDAGE SECURELY, BUT NOT TOO TIGHTLY. GET MEDICAL ATTENTION IMMEDIATELY.

EYE CONTACT: CHLORINE: CORROSIVE. **ACUTE EXPOSURE**- EXPOSURE TO CONCENTRATIONS OF CHLORINE GAS AS LOW AS 3-6 PPM MAY CAUSE REDNESS, PAIN, BLURRED VISION, AND LACRIMATION. DIRECT CONTACT WITH LIQUID MAY CAUSE BURNS. CHLORINE DISSOLVED IN WATER, AND PLACED INTO THE ANTERIOR CHAMBERS OF RABBIT EYES CAUSED SEVERE INFLAMMATION, CORNEAL OPACITY, IRIS ATROPHY AND INJURY TO THE LENS. **CHRONIC EXPOSURE**- EFFECTS DEPEND ON THE CONCENTRATION AND DURATION OF EXPOSURE. REPEATED OR PROLONGED EXPOSURE MAY CAUSE CONJUNCTIVITIS OR EFFECTS AS IN ACUTE EXPOSURE.

FIRST AID- WASH EYES IMMEDIATELY WITH LARGE AMOUNTS OF WATER, OCCASIONALLY LIFTING UPPER AND LOWER LIDS, UNTIL NO EVIDENCE OF CHEMICAL REMAINS (AT LEAST 15-20 MINUTES). CONTINUE IRRIGATING WITH NORMAL SALINE UNTIL THE PH HAS RETURNED TO NORMAL (30-60 MINUTES). COVER WITH STERILE BANDAGES. GET MEDICAL ATTENTION IMMEDIATELY.

INGESTION: CHLORINE: **ACUTE EXPOSURE**- INGESTION OF A GAS IS VERY UNLIKELY. INGESTION OF THE LIQUID MAY CAUSE BURNS OF THE LIPS, MOUTH AND MUCOUS MEMBRANES OF THE GASTROINTESTINAL TRACT, POSSIBLE ULCERATION OR PERFORATION, ABDOMINAL PAIN, TACHYCARDIA, PROSTRATION AND CIRCULATORY COLLAPSE. **CHRONIC EXPOSURE**- NO DATA AVAILABLE.

FIRST AID- DO NOT USE GASTRIC LAVAGE OR EMESIS. DILUTE THE ACID IMMEDIATELY BY DRINKING LARGE QUANTITIES OF WATER OR MILK. IF VOMITING PERSISTS, ADMINISTER FLUIDS REPEATEDLY. INGESTED ACID MUST BE DILUTED APPROXIMATELY 100 FOLD TO RENDER IT HARMLESS TO TISSUES. MAINTAIN AIRWAY AND TREAT SHOCK (DREISBACH, HANDBOOK OF POISONING, 12TH ED.). GET MEDICAL ATTENTION IMMEDIATELY. IF VOMITING OCCURS, KEEP HEAD BELOW HIPS TO HELP PREVENT ASPIRATION.

ANTIDOTE: NO SPECIFIC ANTIDOTE. TREAT SYMPTOMATICALLY AND SUPPORTIVELY.

REACTIVITY

REACTIVITY: STABLE UNDER NORMAL TEMPERATURES AND PRESSURES.

INCOMPATIBILITIES: CHLORINE: ACETYLENE: EXPLOSIVE REACTION. ALCOHOLS: FORMATION OF EXPLOSIVE ALKYL HYPOCHLORITES. ALKYL ISOTHIOUREA SALTS: FORMATION OF EXPLOSIVE NITROGEN TRICHLORIDE. AMMONIA: EXPLODES WHEN HEATED. ANTIMONY: IGNITION REACTION. ARSENIC: SPONTANEOUS IGNITION. N-ARYLSULFINAMIDES: POSSIBLE VIOLENT REACTION. BENZENE: EXPLOSIVE REACTION CATALYZED BY LIGHT. BORON: IGNITES ON CONTACT. BROMINE PENTAFLUORIDE: EXPLOSIVE REACTION. CALCIUM CHLORITE: FORMS EXPLOSIVE CHLORINE DIOXIDE. CALCIUM NITRIDE: INCANDESCENT REACTION. CARBON (ACTIVATED): IGNITES ON CONTACT. CARBON DISULFIDE: EXPLOSIVE REACTION IN THE PRESENCE OF IRON CATALYST. CESIUM NITRIDE: ATTACKED BY CHLORINE. 3-CHLOROPROPYNE: POSSIBLE EXPLOSION. CHROMYL CHLORIDE + CARBON: POSSIBLE EXPLOSION. COMBUSTIBLE MATERIALS: CONTACT WITH THE LIQUID IS LIKELY TO RESULT IN AN EXPLOSION. CONTACT WITH THE GAS MAY RESULT IN IGNITION OR AN EXPLOSION. DIBORANE: EXPLODES ON CONTACT AT AMBIENT TEMPERATURES. DICHLOROMETHYLARSINE: POSSIBLE EXPLOSION. DIETHYL ETHER: EXPLODES. DIETHYLZINC: IGNITION. DIMETHYLFORMAMIDE: EXPLOSION HAZARD. DIMETHYL PHOSPHORAMIDATE: MAY FORM EXPLOSIVE NITROGEN TRICHLORIDE. DIOXYGEN DIFLUORIDE: IGNITION OR EXPLOSIVE REACTION. DISILYL OXIDE: EXPLOSIVE REACTION. 4,4'-DITHIODIMORPHOLINE: MAY FORM EXPLOSIVE COMPOUND. ETHYLENE: EXPLOSIVE REACTION IN THE PRESENCE OF LIGHT OR CATALYSTS. ETHYLENE IMINE: FORMATION OF EXPLOSIVE 1-CHLOROETHYLENE IMINE. ETHYLPHOSPHINE: EXPLOSION ON CONTACT. FLAMMABLE COMPOUNDS: CONTACT WITH THE LIQUID IS LIKELY TO RESULT IN AN EXPLOSION. CONTACT WITH THE GAS MAY RESULT IN IGNITION OR AN EXPLOSION. FLUORINE: IGNITION FOLLOWED BY EXPLOSION ON SPARKING. HEXACHLORODISILANE: IGNITION ABOVE 300 C WITH POSSIBLE EXPLOSION. HYDRAZINE: IGNITION REACTION. HYDROCARBONS: CONTACT WITH THE LIQUID IS LIKELY TO RESULT IN AN EXPLOSION. CONTACT WITH THE GAS MAY RESULT IN IGNITION OR AN EXPLOSION. ADDITION OF A LEWIS ACID TO CHLORINE-HYDROCARBON MIXTURES WILL RESULT IN THE RELEASE OF LARGE VOLUMES OF HYDROGEN CHLORIDE. HYDROGEN: EXPLOSIVE MIXTURES. HYDROGEN PEROXIDE + POTASSIUM HYDROXIDE: LUMINESCENT REACTION. HYDROXYLAMINE: SPONTANEOUS IGNITION. IODINE: VIOLENT REACTION. IRON CARBIDE: INCANDESCENT REACTION. LITHIUM SILICIDE: INCANDESCENT REACTION WHEN HEATED. METALS AND ALLOYS: IGNITION ON CONTACT; SOME METALS MAY BE CORRODED IN THE PRESENCE OF MOISTURE. METAL ACETYLIDES: IGNITION REACTION. METAL HYDRIDES: IGNITION. METAL OXIDES: VIGOROUS REACTION AND POSSIBLE IGNITION. METAL PHOSPHIDES: IGNITION. NITROGEN COMPOUNDS: MAY FORM EXPLOSIVE NITROGEN TRICHLORIDE. NITROGEN TRIIODIDE: EXPLOSIVE REACTION ON CONTACT. NON-METAL HYDRIDES: IGNITE ON CONTACT. OXYGEN: EXPLOSION ON HEATING. OXYGEN DIFLUORIDE: EXPLODES ON WARMING. PHENYLMAGNESIUM BROMIDE: POSSIBLE EXPLOSION. PHOSPHOROUS: EXPLOSIVE REACTION ON CONTACT WITH THE LIQUID; IGNITION ON CONTACT WITH THE GAS. PHOSPHOROUS COMPOUNDS: IGNITION. PHOSPHOROUS ISOCYANATE: VIGOROUS REACTION. POLYCHLOROBIPHENYL: EXOTHERMIC REACTION. (POLY)OXOMONOSILANE: IGNITION. POTASSIUM HALIDES: IGNITION. SILICON: IGNITES ON CONTACT WITH GASEOUS CHLORINE AT AMBIENT TEMPERATURES. SILOXANES: POSSIBLE EXPLOSION ON HEATING. SODIUM HYDROXIDE: VIOLENT REACTION. STANNOUS FLUORIDE: REACTION OCCURS WITH FLAMING. STIBINE: EXPLOSIVE REACTION IF HEATED. SULFAMIC ACID: MAY FORM EXPLOSIVE NITROGEN TRICHLORIDE. SULFIDES: IGNITION. TELLURIUM: INCANDESCENT REACTION. TETRAMETHYLDIARSINE: SPONTANEOUS IGNITION. TETRAMETHYLSILANE: POSSIBLE EXPLOSION IN PRESENCE OF A CATALYST. TETRASELENIUM TETRANITRIDE: EXPLOSION ON CONTACT. TRIALKYLBORANES: IGNITION REACTION. TRIMETHYL THIONOPHOSPHATE: POSSIBLE EXPLOSION. VANADIUM (POWDER): EXPLOSION ON CONTACT WITH THE LIQUID.

DECOMPOSITION: THERMAL DECOMPOSITION PRODUCTS MAY INCLUDE TOXIC AND CORROSIVE FUMES OF CHLORINE.

POLYMERIZATION: HAZARDOUS POLYMERIZATION HAS NOT BEEN REPORTED TO OCCUR UNDER NORMAL TEMPERATURES AND PRESSURES.

STORAGE AND DISPOSAL

OBSERVE ALL FEDERAL, STATE AND LOCAL REGULATIONS WHEN STORING OR DISPOSING OF THIS SUBSTANCE. FOR ASSISTANCE, CONTACT THE DISTRICT DIRECTOR OF THE ENVIRONMENTAL PROTECTION AGENCY.

STORAGE

PROTECT AGAINST PHYSICAL DAMAGE. SEPARATE FROM COMBUSTIBLE, ORGANIC OR EASILY OXIDIZABLE MATERIALS AND ESPECIALLY ISOLATE FROM ACETYLENE, AMMONIA, HYDROGEN, HYDROCARBONS, ETHER, TURPENTINE, AND FINELY DIVIDED METALS. STORE OUTDOORS OR IN A WELL-VENTILATED, DETACHED OR SEGREGATED AREAS OF NONCOMBUSTIBLE CONSTRUCTION (NFPA 49, HAZARDOUS CHEMICALS DATA, 1975).

STORE AWAY FROM INCOMPATIBLE SUBSTANCES.

CONSULT NFPA PUBLICATION 43C, STORAGE OF GASEOUS OXIDIZING MATERIALS, FOR STORAGE REQUIREMENTS.

THRESHOLD PLANNING QUANTITY (TPQ): THE SUPERFUND AMENDMENTS AND REAUTHORIZATION ACT (SARA) SECTION 302 REQUIRES THAT EACH FACILITY WHERE ANY EXTREMELY HAZARDOUS SUBSTANCE IS PRESENT IN A QUANTITY

EQUAL TO OR GREATER THAN THE TPQ ESTABLISHED FOR THAT SUBSTANCE NOTIFY THE STATE EMERGENCY RESPONSE COMMISSION FOR THE STATE IN WHICH IT IS LOCATED. SECTION 303 OF SARA REQUIRES THESE FACILITIES TO PARTICIPATE IN LOCAL EMERGENCY RESPONSE PLANNING (40 CFR 355.30).

DISPOSAL

DISPOSAL MUST BE IN ACCORDANCE WITH STANDARDS APPLICABLE TO GENERATORS OF HAZARDOUS WASTE, 40 CFR 262. EPA HAZARDOUS WASTE NUMBER D001. 100 POUND CERCLA SECTION 103 REPORTABLE QUANTITY.

CONDITIONS TO AVOID

AVOID CONTACT WITH COMBUSTIBLE MATERIALS (WOOD, PAPER, OIL, ETC); CONTACT MAY RESULT IN IGNITION OR EXPLOSION. MATERIAL MAY BE POISONOUS; AVOID INHALATION OF VAPORS OR CONTACT WITH SKIN. DO NOT ALLOW MATERIAL TO CONTAMINATE WATER SOURCES.

SPILL AND LEAK PROCEDURES

SOIL SPILL: DIG A PIT, POND, LAGOON OR HOLDING AREA TO CONTAIN LIQUID OR SOLID MATERIAL. DIKE SURFACE FLOW USING SOIL, SANDBAGS, FOAMED POLYURETHANE OR FOAMED CONCRETE. ABSORB BULK LIQUID WITH FLY ASH OR CEMENT POWDER. ADD CAUSTIC SODA.

AIR SPILL: APPLY WATER SPRAY TO KNOCK DOWN AND REDUCE VAPORS. KNOCK-DOWN WATER IS CORROSIVE AND TOXIC AND SHOULD BE DIKED FOR CONTAINMENT AND LATER DISPOSAL.

WATER SPILL: NEUTRALIZE WITH CAUSTIC SODA.

IF DISSOLVED, AT A CONCENTRATION OF 10 PPM OR GREATER, APPLY ACTIVATED CARBON AT TEN TIMES THE AMOUNT THAT HAS BEEN SPILLED.

USE MECHANICAL DREDGES OR LIFTS TO EXTRACT IMMOBILIZED MASSES OF POLLUTION AND PRECIPITATES.

OCCUPATIONAL SPILL: STOP LEAK IF YOU CAN DO IT WITHOUT RISK. KEEP COMBUSTIBLES AWAY FROM SPILLED MATERIAL. KEEP UNNECESSARY PEOPLE AWAY; ISOLATE AREA AND DENY ENTRY UNTIL GAS HAS DISPERSED. VENTILATE CLOSED SPACES BEFORE ENTERING.

REPORTABLE QUANTITY (RQ): 10 POUNDS THE SUPERFUND AMENDMENTS AND REAUTHORIZATION ACT (SARA) SECTION 304 REQUIRES THAT A RELEASE EQUAL TO OR GREATER THAN THE REPORTABLE QUANTITY FOR THIS SUBSTANCE BE IMMEDIATELY REPORTED TO THE LOCAL EMERGENCY PLANNING COMMITTEE AND THE STATE EMERGENCY RESPONSE COMMISSION (40 CFR 355.40). IF THE RELEASE OF THIS SUBSTANCE IS REPORTABLE UNDER CERCLA SECTION 103, THE NATIONAL RESPONSE CENTER MUST BE NOTIFIED IMMEDIATELY AT (800) 424-8802 OR (202) 426-2675 IN THE METROPOLITAN WASHINGTON, D.C. AREA (40 CFR 302.6).

PROTECTIVE EQUIPMENT

VENTILATION: PROVIDE LOCAL EXHAUST OR PROCESS ENCLOSURE VENTILATION TO MEET PUBLISHED EXPOSURE LIMITS.

RESPIRATOR: THE FOLLOWING RESPIRATORS AND MAXIMUM USE CONCENTRATIONS ARE RECOMMENDATIONS BY THE U.S. DEPARTMENT OF HEALTH AND HUMAN SERVICES, NIOSH POCKET GUIDE TO CHEMICAL HAZARDS; NIOSH CRITERIA DOCUMENTS OR BY THE U.S. DEPARTMENT OF LABOR, 29 CFR 1910 SUBPART Z. THE SPECIFIC RESPIRATOR SELECTED MUST BE BASED ON CONTAMINATION LEVELS FOUND IN THE WORK PLACE, MUST NOT EXCEED THE WORKING LIMITS OF THE RESPIRATOR AND BE JOINTLY APPROVED BY THE NATIONAL INSTITUTE FOR OCCUPATIONAL SAFETY AND HEALTH AND THE MINE SAFETY AND HEALTH ADMINISTRATION (NIOSH-MSHA).

CHLORINE:

5 PPM- CHEMICAL CARTRIDGE RESPIRATOR WITH CARTRIDGE(S) PROVIDING PROTECTION AGAINST CHLORINE. SUPPLIED-AIR RESPIRATOR. SELF-CONTAINED BREATHING APPARATUS.

10 PPM- POWERED AIR-PURIFYING RESPIRATOR WITH CARTRIDGE(S) PROVIDING PROTECTION AGAINST CHLORINE. CHEMICAL CARTRIDGE RESPIRATOR WITH FULL FACEPIECE AND CARTRIDGE(S) PROVIDING PROTECTION AGAINST CHLORINE.

12.5 PPM- SUPPLIED-AIR RESPIRATOR OPERATED IN A CONTINUOUS FLOW MODE. POWERED AIR-PURIFYING RESPIRATOR WITH CARTRIDGE(S) PROVIDING PROTECTION AGAINST CHLORINE.

25 PPM- SELF-CONTAINED BREATHING APPARATUS WITH FULL FACEPIECE. SUPPLIED-AIR RESPIRATOR WITH FULL FACEPIECE. AIR-PURIFYING FULL FACEPIECE RESPIRATOR (GAS MASK) WITH CHIN-STYLE OR FRONT- OR BACK-MOUNTED CANISTER PROVIDING PROTECTION AGAINST CHLORINE.

30 PPM- SUPPLIED-AIR RESPIRATOR WITH HALF-MASK AND OPERATED IN A PRESSURE-DEMAND OR OTHER POSITIVE PRESSURE MODE.

ESCAPE- AIR-PURIFYING FULL FACEPIECE RESPIRATOR (GAS MASK) WITH A CHIN-STYLE OR FRONT- OR BACK-MOUNTED CANISTER PROVIDING PROTECTION AGAINST CHLORINE. ESCAPE-TYPE SELF-CONTAINED BREATHING APPARATUS.

FOR FIREFIGHTING AND OTHER IMMEDIATELY DANGEROUS TO LIFE OR HEALTH CONDITIONS:

SELF-CONTAINED BREATHING APPARATUS WITH FULL FACEPIECE OPERATED IN PRESSURE-DEMAND OR OTHER POSITIVE PRESSURE MODE.

SUPPLIED-AIR RESPIRATOR WITH FULL FACEPIECE AND OPERATED IN PRESSURE-DEMAND OR OTHER POSITIVE PRESSURE MODE IN COMBINATION WITH AN AUXILIARY SELF-CONTAINED BREATHING APPARATUS OPERATED IN PRESSURE-DEMAND OR OTHER POSITIVE PRESSURE MODE.

CLOTHING: EMPLOYEE MUST WEAR APPROPRIATE PROTECTIVE (IMPERVIOUS) CLOTHING AND EQUIPMENT TO PREVENT ANY POSSIBILITY OF SKIN CONTACT WITH THIS SUBSTANCE.

GLOVES: EMPLOYEE MUST WEAR APPROPRIATE PROTECTIVE GLOVES TO PREVENT CONTACT WITH THIS SUBSTANCE.

EYE PROTECTION: EMPLOYEE MUST WEAR SPLASH-PROOF OR DUST-RESISTANT SAFETY GOGGLES AND A FACESHIELD TO PREVENT CONTACT WITH THIS SUBSTANCE. EMERGENCY WASH FACILITIES: WHERE THERE IS ANY POSSIBILITY THAT AN EMPLOYEE'S EYES AND/OR SKIN MAY BE EXPOSED TO THIS SUBSTANCE, THE EMPLOYER SHOULD PROVIDE AN EYE WASH FOUNTAIN AND QUICK DRENCH SHOWER WITHIN THE IMMEDIATE WORK AREA FOR EMERGENCY USE.

AUTHORIZED BY- OCCUPATIONAL HEALTH SERVICES, INC.

CREATION DATE: 11/15/89 ***REVISION DATE:*** 05/16/90

MATERIAL SAFETY DATA SHEET

OCCUPATIONAL HEALTH SERVICES, INC.
AGRICULTURE AND PESTICIDE DIVISION
450 SEVENTH AVENUE, SUITE 2407
NEW YORK, NEW YORK 10123
1-800-445-MSDS OR (212) 967-1100

EMERGENCY CONTACT:
JOHN S. BRANSFORD, JR. (615) 292-1180

SUBSTANCE IDENTIFICATION

CAS-NUMBER 10049-04-4

SUBSTANCE: CHLORINE DIOXIDE

TRADE NAMES/SYNONYMS: CHLORINE OXIDE; ANTHIUM DIOXCIDE; CHLORINE(IV) OXIDE; CHLOROPEROXYL; CHLORYL RADICAL; DOXCIDE 50; ALCIDE; CHLORINE PEROXIDE; EZ FLOW; PUROGENE; CHLORINE OXIDE (CLO2); STCC 4918110; CLO2; PST04610

CHEMICAL FAMILY: INORGANIC ACID

MOLECULAR FORMULA: CL-O2

MOLECULAR WEIGHT: 67.46

CERCLA RATINGS (SCALE 0-3): HEALTH=3 FIRE=3 REACTIVITY=3 PERSISTENCE=0

NFPA RATINGS (SCALE 0-4): HEALTH=3 FIRE=3 REACTIVITY=3

COMPONENTS AND CONTAMINANTS

COMPONENT: CHLORINE DIOXIDE ***PERCENT:*** 100

CAS# 10049-04-4

OTHER CONTAMINANTS: NONE

EXPOSURE LIMITS: CHLORINE DIOXIDE: 0.1 PPM (0.3 MG/M3) OSHA TWA; 0.3 PPM (0.9 MG/M3) OSHA STEL 0.1 PPM (0.3 MG/M3) ACGIH TWA; 0.3 PPM (0.9 MG/M3) ACGIH STEL

SUBJECT TO SARA SECTION 313 ANNUAL TOXIC CHEMICAL RELEASE REPORTING

PHYSICAL DATA

DESCRIPTION: YELLOW TO REDDISH-YELLOW GAS WITH AN UNPLEASANT ODOR SIMILAR TO CHLORINE AND REMINISCENT OF NITRIC ACID ***BOILING POINT:*** 50 F (10 C)

MELTING POINT: -76 F (-60 C) ***SPECIFIC GRAVITY:*** 1.6

VAPOR PRESSURE: >1 ATM @ 20 C ***PH:*** ACIDIC ***SOLUBILITY IN WATER:*** 0.8%

ODOR THRESHOLD: 0.1 PPM ***VAPOR DENSITY:*** 2.3

FIRE AND EXPLOSION DATA

FIRE AND EXPLOSION HAZARD: DANGEROUS FIRE HAZARD WHEN EXPOSED TO HEAT OR FLAME.

DANGEROUS EXPLOSION HAZARD WHEN EXPOSED TO HEAT OR FLAME.

UPPER EXPLOSIVE LIMIT: EXPLOSIVE ***LOWER EXPLOSIVE LIMIT:*** 10%

FIREFIGHTING MEDIA: WATER ONLY, NO DRY CHEMICAL, CARBON DIOXIDE OR HALON (1987 EMERGENCY RESPONSE GUIDEBOOK, DOT P 5800.4).

FOR LARGER FIRES, FLOOD AREA WITH WATER FROM A DISTANCE (1987 EMERGENCY RESPONSE GUIDEBOOK, DOT P 5800.4).

FIREFIGHTING: DO NOT MOVE CONTAINERS IF EXPOSURE TO HEAT HAS OCCURRED. COOL CONTAINERS EXPOSED TO FLAMES WITH WATER FROM SIDE UNTIL WELL AFTER FIRE IS OUT. STAY AWAY FROM STORAGE TANK ENDS. FOR MASSIVE FIRE IN CARGO AREA, USE UNMANNED HOSE HOLDER OR MONITOR NOZZLES; ELSE

WITHDRAW FROM AREA AND LET FIRE BURN (1987 EMERGENCY RESPONSE GUIDEBOOK, DOT P 5800.4, GUIDE PAGE 47).
EXTINGUISH USING AGENTS INDICATED. COOL FIRE EXPOSED CONTAINERS WITH FLOODING AMOUNTS OF WATER APPLIED FROM AS FAR A DISTANCE AS POSSIBLE.
AVOID BREATHING HAZARDOUS VAPORS. EVACUATE TO A RADIUS OF 1600 FEET IF FIRE BECOMES UNCONTROLLABLE.

TRANSPORTATION DATA

DEPARTMENT OF TRANSPORTATION HAZARD CLASSIFICATION 49 CFR 172.101: FORBIDDEN
DEPARTMENT OF TRANSPORTATION LABELING REQUIREMENTS 49 CFR 172.101 AND SUBPART E: NONE

TOXICITY

CHLORINE DIOXIDE: IRRITATION DATA: 100 MG EYE-RABBIT MILD. TOXICITY DATA: 292 MG/KG ORAL-RAT LD50; 500 PPM/15 MINUTES INHALATION-RAT LCLO; 140 MG/KG UNREPORTED-RAT LD50; MUTAGENIC DATA (RTECS); REPRODUCTIVE EFFECTS DATA (RTECS). CARCINOGEN STATUS: NONE. LOCAL EFFECTS: CORROSIVE- INHALATION, SKIN, EYES. ACUTE TOXICITY LEVEL: TOXIC BY INGESTION. TARGET EFFECTS: NO DATA AVAILABLE.

HEALTH EFFECTS AND FIRST AID

INHALATION: CHLORINE DIOXIDE: CORROSIVE/HIGHLY TOXIC. 10 PPM IMMEDIATELY DANGEROUS TO LIFE OR HEALTH. **ACUTE EXPOSURE-** INHALATION OF >5 PPM MAY CAUSE SYMPTOMS OF SEVERE RESPIRATORY TRACT IRRITATION POSSIBLY INCLUDING COUGHING, CHOKING, WHEEZING, PAIN IN THE NOSE, MOUTH, AND THROAT, RHINITIS, AND BURNS OF THE MUCOUS MEMBRANES. IF SUFFICIENT QUANTITIES ARE INHALED, PULMONARY EDEMA AND BRONCHITIS MAY DEVELOP, OFTEN WITH A LATENT PERIOD OF 5-72 HOURS. THE SYMPTOMS MAY INCLUDE TIGHTNESS IN THE CHEST, HEADACHE, DYSPNEA, FROTHY SPUTUM, VOMITING, CYANOSIS, AND DIZZINESS. PHYSICAL FINDINGS MAY INCLUDE WEAK, RAPID PULSE, HYPOTENSION, MOIST RALES, AND HEMOCONCENTRATION. RECOVERY MAY BE PROLONGED AND RELAPSES ARE POSSIBLE. IN SEVERE EXPOSURES, DEATH DUE TO ANOXIA MAY OCCUR WITHIN A FEW HOURS AFTER ONSET OF PULMONARY EDEMA SYMPTOMS OR FOLLOWING A RELAPSE. INHALATION OF 150 PPM/15 MINUTES WAS LETHAL TO RATS. **CHRONIC EXPOSURE-** REPEATED OR PROLONGED INHALATION OF CHLORINE DIOXIDE FOR SEVERAL YEARS BY A CHEMIST RESULTED IN CHRONIC BRONCHITIS AND EMPHYSEMA, WITH INCREASING DYSPNEA AND ASTHMATIC BRONCHITIS. REPEATED INHALATION OF VAPOR CONCENTRATIONS OF 19 PPM RESULTED IN DEATH TO A WORKER. REPEATED EXPOSURE TO 10 PPM/DAY/10-13 DAYS RESULTED IN NASAL AND OCULAR DISCHARGE, DYSPNEA, AND DEATH IN RATS.
FIRST AID- REMOVE FROM EXPOSURE AREA TO FRESH AIR IMMEDIATELY. IF BREATHING HAS STOPPED, GIVE ARTIFICIAL RESPIRATION. MAINTAIN AIRWAY AND BLOOD PRESSURE AND ADMINISTER OXYGEN IF AVAILABLE. KEEP AFFECTED PERSON WARM AND AT REST. TREAT SYMPTOMATICALLY AND SUPPORTIVELY. ADMINISTRATION OF OXYGEN SHOULD BE PERFORMED BY QUALIFIED PERSONNEL. GET MEDICAL ATTENTION IMMEDIATELY.

SKIN CONTACT: CHLORINE DIOXIDE: CORROSIVE. **ACUTE EXPOSURE-** DIRECT CONTACT MAY CAUSE SEVERE PAIN, BURNS, AND POSSIBLY BROWNISH OR YELLOWISH STAINS. BURNS MAY BE DEEP WITH SHARP EDGES AND HEAL SLOWLY WITH SCAR TISSUE FORMATION. **CHRONIC EXPOSURE-** EFFECTS DEPEND ON THE CONCENTRATION AND DURATION OF EXPOSURE. REPEATED OR PROLONGED CONTACT WITH ACIDIC SUBSTANCES MAY RESULT IN DERMATITIS OR EFFECTS SIMILAR TO ACUTE EXPOSURE.
FIRST AID- REMOVE CONTAMINATED CLOTHING AND SHOES IMMEDIATELY. WASH AFFECTED AREA WITH SOAP OR MILD DETERGENT AND LARGE AMOUNTS OF WATER UNTIL NO EVIDENCE OF CHEMICAL REMAINS (AT LEAST 15-20 MINUTES). IN CASE OF CHEMICAL BURNS, COVER AREA WITH STERILE, DRY DRESSING. BANDAGE SECURELY, BUT NOT TOO TIGHTLY. GET MEDICAL ATTENTION IMMEDIATELY.

EYE CONTACT: CHLORINE DIOXIDE: CORROSIVE. **ACUTE EXPOSURE-** DIRECT CONTACT MAY CAUSE PAIN, LACRIMATION, BLURRED VISION, PHOTOPHOBIA, AND BURNS, POSSIBLY SEVERE. THE DEGREE OF INJURY DEPENDS ON THE CONCENTRATION AND DURATION OF CONTACT. IN MILD BURNS, THE EPITHELIUM REGENERATES RAPIDLY AND THE EYE RECOVERS COMPLETELY. IN SEVERE CASES, THE EXTENT OF INJURY MAY NOT BE FULLY APPARENT FOR SEVERAL WEEKS. ULTIMATELY, THE WHOLE CORNEA MAY BECOME DEEPLY VASCULARIZED AND OPAQUE RESULTING IN BLINDNESS. IN THE WORST CASES, THE EYE MAY BE TOTALLY DESTROYED. **CHRONIC EXPOSURE-** EFFECTS DEPEND ON THE CONCENTRATION AND DURATION OF EXPOSURE. REPEATED OR PROLONGED EXPOSURE TO ACIDIC SUBSTANCES MAY CAUSE CONJUNCTIVITIS OR EFFECTS AS IN ACUTE EXPOSURE.
FIRST AID- WASH EYES IMMEDIATELY WITH LARGE AMOUNTS OF WATER, OCCASIONALLY LIFTING UPPER AND LOWER LIDS, UNTIL NO EVIDENCE OF CHEMICAL REMAINS (AT LEAST 15-20 MINUTES). CONTINUE IRRIGATING WITH NORMAL SALINE UNTIL THE PH HAS RETURNED TO NORMAL (30-60 MINUTES). COVER WITH STERILE BANDAGES. GET MEDICAL ATTENTION IMMEDIATELY.

INGESTION: CHLORINE DIOXIDE: TOXIC. **ACUTE EXPOSURE-** INGESTION OF 292 MG/KG WAS LETHAL TO RATS. **CHRONIC EXPOSURE-** EFFECTS ON THE NEWBORN AND ON FERTILITY HAVE BEEN REPORTED FROM PROLONGED INGESTION OF CHLORINE DIOXIDE BY PREGNANT MICE AND RATS.
FIRST AID- TREAT SYMPTOMATICALLY AND SUPPORTIVELY. GET MEDICAL ATTENTION IMMEDIATELY. IF VOMITING OCCURS, KEEP HEAD LOWER THAN HIPS TO PREVENT ASPIRATION.
ANTIDOTE: NO SPECIFIC ANTIDOTE. TREAT SYMPTOMATICALLY AND SUPPORTIVELY.

REACTIVITY

REACTIVITY: STRONG OXIDANT. REACTS VIOLENTLY WITH COMBUSTIBLE AND REDUCING MATERIALS. REACTS WITH WATER TO FORM PERCHLORIC ACID. THE SUBSTANCE AND SOLUTIONS OVER 10% CAN DECOMPOSE EXPLOSIVELY WHEN EXPOSED TO SUNLIGHT, HEAT, SHOCK OR FRICTION.
INCOMPATIBILITIES: CHLORINE DIOXIDE: CARBON MONOXIDE: EXPLOSION ON MIXING. DIFLUOROAMINE: INTERACTION IN THE GAS PHASE IS EXPLOSIVE. HYDROGEN: POSSIBLE EXPLOSION. MERCURY: CHLORINE DIOXIDE EXPLODES ON SHAKING WITH MERCURY. ORGANIC MATERIAL: ORGANIC MATERIAL IN CONTACT WITH CHLORINE DIOXIDE CAN BE EXPLODED BY SHOCK OR SPARKS. PHOSPHORUS: IGNITION OR EXPLOSION. PHOSPHORUS PENTACHLORIDE: PROBABLE EXPLOSION. POTASSIUM HYDROXIDE: THE LIQUID OR GASEOUS OXIDE WILL EXPLODE IN CONTACT WITH SOLID POTASSIUM HYDROXIDE OR ITS CONCENTRATED SOLUTION. SULFUR: PROBABLE IGNITION AND EXPLOSION. SUGAR: POSSIBLE IGNITION AND EXPLOSION. LIGHT: EXPLOSIVE DECOMPOSITION.
DECOMPOSITION: THERMAL DECOMPOSITION MAY RELEASE CORROSIVE FUMES OF HYDROGEN CHLORIDE OR TOXIC CHLORINE GAS.
POLYMERIZATION: HAZARDOUS POLYMERIZATION HAS NOT BEEN REPORTED TO OCCUR UNDER NORMAL TEMPERATURES AND PRESSURES.

CONDITIONS TO AVOID

MAY IGNITE WITH OTHER COMBUSTIBLE MATERIALS (WOOD, PAPER, OIL, ETC.). MIXTURE WITH FUELS MAY EXPLODE. FLAMMABLE, POISONOUS GASES MAY ACCUMULATE IN TANKS AND HOPPER CARS. CONTAINER MAY EXPLODE IN HEAT OF FIRE. MAY EXPLODE FROM FRICTION, HEAT OR CONTAMINATION. RUNOFF TO SEWER MAY CREATE FIRE OR EXPLOSION HAZARD.

SPILL AND LEAK PROCEDURES

OCCUPATIONAL SPILL: KEEP COMBUSTIBLES (WOOD, PAPER, OIL, ETC.) AWAY FROM SPILLED MATERIAL. DO NOT TOUCH SPILLED MATERIAL. STOP LEAK IF YOU CAN DO IT WITHOUT RISK. USE WATER SPRAY TO REDUCE VAPORS. FOR SMALL SPILLS, FLUSH AREA WITH FLOODING AMOUNTS OF WATER. FOR LARGER SPILLS, DIKE SPILL FOR LATER DISPOSAL. KEEP UNNECESSARY PEOPLE AWAY. ISOLATE HAZARD AREA AND DENY ENTRY.

PROTECTIVE EQUIPMENT

VENTILATION: PROVIDE LOCAL EXHAUST OR PROCESS ENCLOSURE VENTILATION TO MEET THE PUBLISHED EXPOSURE LIMITS. VENTILATION EQUIPMENT MUST BE EXPLOSION-PROOF.
RESPIRATOR: THE FOLLOWING RESPIRATORS AND MAXIMUM USE CONCENTRATIONS ARE RECOMMENDATIONS BY THE U.S. DEPARTMENT OF HEALTH AND HUMAN SERVICES, NIOSH POCKET GUIDE TO CHEMICAL HAZARDS; NIOSH CRITERIA DOCUMENTS OR BY THE U.S. DEPARTMENT OF LABOR, 29 CFR 1910 SUBPART Z. THE SPECIFIC RESPIRATOR SELECTED MUST BE BASED ON CONTAMINATION LEVELS FOUND IN THE WORK PLACE, MUST NOT EXCEED THE WORKING LIMITS OF THE RESPIRATOR AND BE JOINTLY APPROVED BY THE NATIONAL INSTITUTE FOR OCCUPATIONAL SAFETY AND HEALTH AND THE MINE SAFETY AND HEALTH ADMINISTRATION (NIOSH-MSHA).
CHLORINE DIOXIDE:
2.5 PPM- ANY SUPPLIED-AIR RESPIRATOR OPERATED IN A CONTINUOUS FLOW MODE. ANY POWERED AIR-PURIFYING RESPIRATOR WITH CARTRIDGE(S) PROVIDING PROTECTION AGAINST CHLORINE DIOXIDE.
5 PPM- ANY CHEMICAL CARTRIDGE RESPIRATOR WITH A FULL FACEPIECE AND CARTRIDGE(S) PROVIDING PROTECTION AGAINST CHLORINE DIOXIDE. ANY AIR-PURIFYING FULL FACEPIECE RESPIRATOR (GAS MASK) WITH A CHIN-STYLE OR FRONT- OR BACK-MOUNTED CANISTER PROVIDING PROTECTION AGAINST CHLORINE DIOXIDE. ANY SELF-CONTAINED BREATHING APPARATUS WITH A FULL FACEPIECE. ANY SUPPLIED-AIR RESPIRATOR WITH A FULL FACEPIECE.
10 PPM- ANY SUPPLIED-AIR RESPIRATOR WITH A FULL FACEPIECE AND OPERATED IN A PRESSURE-DEMAND OR OTHER POSITIVE PRESSURE MODE. ESCAPE- ANY AIR-PURIFYING FULL FACEPIECE RESPIRATOR (GAS MASK) WITH A CHIN-STYLE OR FRONT- OR BACK-MOUNTED CANISTER PROVIDING PROTECTION AGAINST

CHLORINE DIOXIDE. ANY APPROPRIATE ESCAPE-TYPE SELF-CONTAINED BREATHING APPARATUS.
**** NOTE: DO NOT USE OXIDIZABLE SORBENTS.****
FOR FIREFIGHTING AND OTHER IMMEDIATELY DANGEROUS TO LIFE OR HEALTH CONDITIONS:
SELF-CONTAINED BREATHING APPARATUS WITH FULL FACEPIECE OPERATED IN PRESSURE-DEMAND OR OTHER POSITIVE PRESSURE MODE.
SUPPLIED-AIR RESPIRATOR WITH FULL FACEPIECE AND OPERATED IN PRESSURE-DEMAND OR OTHER POSITIVE PRESSURE MODE IN COMBINATION WITH AN AUXILIARY SELF-CONTAINED BREATHING APPARATUS OPERATED IN PRESSURE-DEMAND OR OTHER POSITIVE PRESSURE MODE.

CLOTHING: EMPLOYEE MUST WEAR APPROPRIATE PROTECTIVE (IMPERVIOUS) CLOTHING AND EQUIPMENT TO PREVENT ANY POSSIBILITY OF SKIN CONTACT WITH THIS SUBSTANCE.

GLOVES: EMPLOYEE MUST WEAR APPROPRIATE PROTECTIVE GLOVES TO PREVENT CONTACT WITH THIS SUBSTANCE.

EYE PROTECTION: EMPLOYEE MUST WEAR SPLASH-PROOF OR DUST-RESISTANT SAFETY GOGGLES AND A FACESHIELD TO PREVENT CONTACT WITH THIS SUBSTANCE.
EMERGENCY WASH FACILITIES: WHERE THERE IS ANY POSSIBILITY THAT AN EMPLOYEE'S EYES AND/OR SKIN MAY BE EXPOSED TO THIS SUBSTANCE, THE EMPLOYER SHOULD PROVIDE AN EYE WASH FOUNTAIN AND QUICK DRENCH SHOWER WITHIN THE IMMEDIATE WORK AREA FOR EMERGENCY USE.

AUTHORIZED BY- OCCUPATIONAL HEALTH SERVICES, INC.
CREATION DATE: 11/15/89 ***REVISION DATE:*** 07/11/90

MATERIAL SAFETY DATA SHEET

OCCUPATIONAL HEALTH SERVICES, INC.
AGRICULTURE AND PESTICIDE DIVISION
450 SEVENTH AVENUE, SUITE 2407
NEW YORK, NEW YORK 10123
1-800-445-MSDS OR (212) 967-1100

EMERGENCY CONTACT:
JOHN S. BRANSFORD, JR. (615) 292-1180

SUBSTANCE IDENTIFICATION

CAS-NUMBER 24934-91-6
SUBSTANCE: CHLORMEPHOS
TRADE NAMES/SYNONYMS: S-(CHLOROMETHYL) O,O-DIETHYL ESTER PHOSPHORODITHIOIC ACID; S-CHLOROMETHYL O,O-DIETHYL PHOSPHORODITHIOATE; S-(CHLOROMETHYL) O,O-DIETHYL PHOSPHORODITHIOATE; PHOSPHORODITHIOIC ACID, S-(CHLOROMETHYL) O,O-DIETHYL ESTER; DOTAN; MC 2188; C5H12CLO2PS2; PST04655
CHEMICAL FAMILY: ORGANOPHOSPHATE
MOLECULAR FORMULA: C5-H12-CL-O2-P-S2
MOLECULAR WEIGHT: 234.71
CERCLA RATINGS (SCALE 0-3): HEALTH=3 FIRE=1 REACTIVITY=0 PERSISTENCE=0
NFPA RATINGS (SCALE 0-4): HEALTH=4 FIRE=1 REACTIVITY=0

COMPONENTS AND CONTAMINANTS

COMPONENT: CHLORMEPHOS ***PERCENT:*** 100
CAS# 24934-91-6
EXPOSURE LIMITS: NO OCCUPATIONAL EXPOSURE LIMITS ESTABLISHED BY OSHA, ACGIH, OR NIOSH.
CHLORMEPHOS: 500 POUNDS SARA SECTION 302 THRESHOLD PLANNING QUANTITY 1 POUND SARA SECTION 304 REPORTABLE QUANTITY

PHYSICAL DATA

DESCRIPTION: COLORLESS LIQUID ***BOILING POINT:*** 178-185 F (81-85 C) @ 0.1 MMHG
SPECIFIC GRAVITY: 1.260 ***VAPOR PRESSURE:*** 0.0057 MMHG @ 30 C
EVAPORATION RATE: NOT AVAILABLE ***SOLUBILITY IN WATER:*** 60 PPM
SOLVENT SOLUBILITY: SOLUBLE IN MOST ORGANIC SOLVENTS

FIRE AND EXPLOSION DATA

FIRE AND EXPLOSION HAZARD: NEGLIGIBLE FIRE HAZARD WHEN EXPOSED TO HEAT OR FLAME.
FIREFIGHTING MEDIA: DRY CHEMICAL, CARBON DIOXIDE, HALON, WATER SPRAY OR STANDARD FOAM (1987 EMERGENCY RESPONSE GUIDEBOOK, DOT P 5800.4).
FOR LARGER FIRES, USE WATER SPRAY, FOG OR STANDARD FOAM (1987 EMERGENCY RESPONSE GUIDEBOOK, DOT P 5800.4).
FIREFIGHTING: MOVE CONTAINERS FROM FIRE AREA IF POSSIBLE. FIGHT FIRE FROM MAXIMUM DISTANCE. STAY AWAY FROM STORAGE TANK ENDS. DIKE FIRE CONTROL WATER FOR LATER DISPOSAL. DO NOT SCATTER MATERIAL (1987 EMERGENCY RESPONSE GUIDEBOOK, DOT P 5800.4, GUIDE PAGE 55).
EXTINGUISH USING AGENT SUITABLE FOR TYPE OF SURROUNDING FIRE. AVOID BREATHING VAPORS AND DUSTS. KEEP UPWIND.

TRANSPORTATION DATA

DEPARTMENT OF TRANSPORTATION HAZARD CLASSIFICATION 49 CFR 172.101: POISON B
DEPARTMENT OF TRANSPORTATION LABELING REQUIREMENTS 49 CFR 172.101 AND SUBPART E: POISON
DEPARTMENT OF TRANSPORTATION PACKAGING REQUIREMENTS: 49 CFR 173.346 EXCEPTIONS: 49 CFR 173.345

TOXICITY

CHLORMEPHOS: TOXICITY DATA: 27 MG/KG SKIN-RAT LD50; 7 MG/KG ORAL-RAT LD50. CARCINOGEN STATUS: NONE. ACUTE TOXICITY LEVEL: HIGHLY TOXIC BY DERMAL ABSORPTION AND INGESTION. TARGET EFFECTS: CHOLINESTERASE INHIBITOR. POISONING MAY AFFECT THE NERVOUS SYSTEM.* AT INCREASED RISK FROM EXPOSURE: PERSONS WITH RESPIRATORY AILMENTS, RECENT EXPOSURE TO CHOLINESTERASE INHIBITORS OR IMPAIRED CHOLINESTERASE PRODUCTION OR LIVER MALFUNCTION.* ADDITIONAL DATA: MAY CROSS THE PLACENTA. HIGH ENVIRONMENTAL TEMPERATURES OR EXPOSURE OF THE CHEMICAL TO VISIBLE OR ULTRAVIOLET LIGHT MAY ENHANCE THE TOXICITY. INTERACTIONS WITH MEDICATIONS MAY OCCUR.*
* MAY BE BASED ON GENERAL INFORMATION ON ORGANOPHOSPHATES.

HEALTH EFFECTS AND FIRST AID

INHALATION: CHLORMEPHOS: SEE INFORMATION ON ORGANOPHOSPHATES.
ORGANOPHOSPHATES: CHOLINESTERASE INHIBITOR. **ACUTE EXPOSURE-** WHEN INHALED, THE FIRST EFFECTS OF CHOLINESTERASE INHIBITORS ARE USUALLY RESPIRATORY AND MAY INCLUDE NASAL HYPEREMIA AND WATERY DISCHARGE, COUGH, CHEST DISCOMFORT, DYSPNEA, AND WHEEZING DUE TO INCREASED BRONCHIAL SECRETIONS AND BRONCHOCONSTRICTION. IF SUFFICIENT AMOUNTS ARE ABSORBED, OTHER SYSTEMIC EFFECTS MAY BEGIN WITHIN A FEW MINUTES OR BE DELAYED FOR UP TO 12 HOURS. SYMPTOMS MAY INCLUDE PALLOR, NAUSEA, VOMITING, DIARRHEA, ABDOMINAL CRAMPS, HEADACHE, DIZZINESS, OCULAR PAIN, BLURRED VISION, MIOSIS OR IN SOME CASES, ESPECIALLY INITIALLY, MYDRIASIS, LACRIMATION, SALIVATION, SWEATING, AND CONFUSION. OTHER REPORTED CENTRAL NERVOUS SYSTEM OR NEUROMUSCULAR EFFECTS MAY INCLUDE ATAXIA, SLURRED SPEECH, AREFLEXIA, WEAKNESS, FATIGUE, FASCICULATIONS, TWITCHING, TREMORS POSSIBLY OF THE TONGUE AND EYELIDS, AND EVENTUALLY PARALYSIS OF THE EXTREMITIES AND POSSIBLY OF THE RESPIRATORY MUSCLES. IN SEVERE CASES THERE MAY ALSO BE INVOLUNTARY DEFECATION AND URINATION, CYANOSIS, PSYCHOSIS, HYPERGLYCEMIA, ACUTE PANCREATITIS, CARDIAC IRREGULARITIES, PULMONARY EDEMA, UNCONSCIOUSNESS, CONVULSIONS, AND COMA. DEATH IS PRIMARILY DUE TO RESPIRATORY FAILURE, ALTHOUGH CARDIOVASCULAR EFFECTS INCLUDING CARDIAC ARREST MAY ALSO BE IMPLICATED. LONG TERM SEQUELAE ARE RARE BUT MAY INCLUDE NEUROPSYCHIATRIC DISORDERS AND MYOPATHY WITH MUSCLE TENDERNESS. SOME ORGANOPHOSPHATES MAY CAUSE A DELAYED NEUROPATHY BEGINNING 1-4 WEEKS AFTER AN ACUTE EXPOSURE WHICH MAY OR MAY NOT HAVE CAUSED ACUTE CHOLINERGIC EFFECTS. NUMBNESS, TINGLING, WEAKNESS AND CRAMPING BEGINNING SYMMETRICALLY IN THE LOWER LIMBS MAY PROGRESS TO ATAXIA AND PARALYSIS. IN SEVERE CASES, UPPER LIMB INVOLVEMENT IS POSSIBLE AND FLACCID PARALYSIS MAY PROGRESS TO SPASTIC PARALYSIS WITH EXAGGERATED REFLEXES. IMPROVEMENT MAY OCCUR OVER MONTHS TO YEARS, BUT SOME RESIDUAL IMPAIRMENT USUALLY REMAINS.
CHRONIC EXPOSURE- REPEATED OR PROLONGED EXPOSURE MAY RESULT IN THE EFFECTS OF ACUTE EXPOSURE INCLUDING THE DELAYED NEUROPATHY. OTHER EFFECTS REPORTED IN WORKERS REPEATEDLY EXPOSED INCLUDE IMPAIRED MEMORY AND CONCENTRATION, ACUTE PSYCHOSIS, SEVERE DEPRESSIONS, IRRITABILTY, CONFUSION, APATHY, EMOTIONAL LABILITY, SOCIAL WITHDRAWAL, CONFUSION, HEADACHE, SPEECH DIFFICULTIES, DELAYED REACTION TIMES, SPATIAL DISORIENTATION, NIGHTMARES, SLEEPWALKING, AND DROWSINESS OR INSOMNIA. AN INFLUENZA-LIKE CONDITION WITH HEADACHE, NAUSEA, WEAKNESS, ANOREXIA AND MALAISE HAS ALSO BEEN REPORTED.

FIRST AID- REMOVE FROM EXPOSURE AREA TO FRESH AIR IMMEDIATELY. IF BREATHING HAS STOPPED, GIVE ARTIFICIAL RESPIRATION. MAINTAIN AIRWAY AND BLOOD PRESSURE AND ADMINISTER OXYGEN IF AVAILABLE. KEEP AFFECTED PERSON WARM AND AT REST. TREAT SYMPTOMATICALLY AND SUPPORTIVELY. ADMINISTRATION OF OXYGEN SHOULD BE PERFORMED BY QUALIFIED PERSONNEL. GET MEDICAL ATTENTION IMMEDIATELY.

SKIN CONTACT: CHLORMEPHOS: HIGHLY TOXIC. SEE INFORMATION ON ORGANOPHOSPHATES. ORGANOPHOSPHATES: CHOLINESTERASE INHIBITOR. **ACUTE EXPOSURE-** LOCALIZED SWEATING AND FASCICULATIONS MAY OCCUR AT THE SITE OF CONTACT. IF SUFFICIENT AMOUNTS ARE ABSORBED, OTHER EFFECTS OF CHOLINESTERASE INHIBITION AS DESCRIBED IN ACUTE INHALATION MAY OCCUR. SYMPTOMS MAY BE DELAYED 2-3 HOURS, BUT USUALLY NO MORE THAN 12 HOURS. THE RATE OF ABSORPTION IS INCREASED BY THE PRESENCE OF DERMATITIS OR HIGH AMBIENT TEMPERATURES. DELAYED NEUROPATHY IS ALSO POSSIBLE. **CHRONIC EXPOSURE-** REPEATED OR PROLONGED EXPOSURE MAY CAUSE EFFECTS AS DESCRIBED IN ACUTE EXPOSURE. SOME ORGANOPHOSPHATES MAY CAUSE SENSITIZATION.

FIRST AID- REMOVE CONTAMINATED CLOTHING IMMEDIATELY. WASH CONTAMINATED AREAS WITH SOAP AND WATER FOLLOWED BY ALCOHOL (ARENA, POISONING, 4TH ED.). EMERGENCY PERSONNEL SHOULD WEAR GLOVES AND AVOID CONTAMINATION. TREAT RESPIRATORY DIFFICULTY WITH ARTIFICIAL RESPIRATION. GET MEDICAL ATTENTION IMMEDIATELY.

EYE CONTACT: CHLORMEPHOS: SEE INFORMATION ON ORGANOPHOSPHATES. ORGANOPHOSPHATES: CHOLINESTERASE INHIBITOR. **ACUTE EXPOSURE-** DIRECT CONTACT MAY CAUSE PAIN, HYPEREMIA, LACRIMATION, TWITCHING OF THE EYELIDS, MIOSIS, AND CILIARY MUSCLE SPASM WITH LOSS OF ACCOMODATION, BLURRED OR DIMMED VISION AND BROWACHE. SOMETIMES MYDRIASIS MAY OCCUR INSTEAD OF MIOSIS. WITH SUFFICIENT EXPOSURE, OTHER SYMPTOMS OF CHOLINESTERASE INHIBITION AS DESCRIBED IN ACUTE INHALATION MAY OCCUR. **CHRONIC EXPOSURE-** REPEATED OR PROLONGED EXPOSURE MAY CAUSE EFFECTS AS DESCRIBED IN ACUTE EXPOSURE. SOME COMPOUNDS HAVE CAUSED TOXIC EFFECTS ON THE CRYSTALLINE LENS, CONJUNCTIVAL THICKENING AND OBSTRUCTION OF THE NASOLACRIMAL CANALS WHEN USED AS MIOTIC EYEDROPS.

FIRST AID- IRRIGATE EYES WITH WATER OR SALINE SOLUTION. IF SYMPTOMS OF POISONING OCCUR, TREAT RESPIRATORY DIFFICULTY WITH ARTIFICIAL RESPIRATION AND OXYGEN. OBSERVE PATIENT FOR AT LEAST 24-36 HOURS (GOSSELIN, CLINICAL TOXICOLOGY OF COMMERCIAL PRODUCTS, 5TH ED.). GET MEDICAL ATTENTION IMMEDIATELY. OXYGEN SHOULD BE ADMINISTERED BY QUALIFIED MEDICAL PERSONNEL.

INGESTION: CHLORMEPHOS: HIGHLY TOXIC. SEE INFORMATION ON ORGANOPHOSPHATES.
ORGANOPHOSPHATES: CHOLINESTERASE INHIBITOR. **ACUTE EXPOSURE-** WHEN INGESTED, THE FIRST EFFECTS MAY BE NAUSEA, VOMITING, ANOREXIA, ABDOMINAL CRAMPS AND DIARRHEA. GASTROINTESTINAL ABSORPTION MAY CAUSE SYMPTOMS OF CHOLINESTERASE INHIBITION AS DESCRIBED IN ACUTE INHALATION. SYMPTOMS MAY BEGIN WITHIN MINUTES OR BE DELAYED FOR HOURS. DELAYED EFFECTS INCLUDING NEUROPATHY MAY ALSO OCCUR. **CHRONIC EXPOSURE-** REPEATED INGESTION MAY CAUSE EFFECTS AS DESCRIBED IN ACUTE EXPOSURE.

FIRST AID- IF PERSON IS ALERT AND RESPIRATION IS NOT DEPRESSED, GIVE SYRUP OF IPECAC FOLLOWED BY WATER (IF VOMITING OCCURS, KEEP HEAD BELOW HIPS TO PREVENT ASPIRATION). IF CONSCIOUSNESS LEVEL DECLINES OR VOMITING HAS NOT OCCURRED IN 15 MINUTES EMPTY STOMACH BY GASTRIC LAVAGE WITH THE AID OF CUFFED ENDOTRACHEAL TUBE USING ISOTONIC SALINE OR 5% SODIUM BICARBONATE FOLLOW WITH ACTIVATED CHARCOAL. ESTABLISH AND MAINTAIN AIRWAY. TREAT RESPIRATORY DIFFICULTY WITH ARTIFICIAL RESPIRATION AND OXYGEN. DO NOT GIVE MORPHINE, AMINOPHYLLINE, PHENOTHIAZINES, RESERPINE, FUROSEMIDE, OR ETHACRYNIC ACID (MORGAN, RECOGNITION AND MANAGEMENT OF PESTICIDE POISONINGS, 3RD ED.). TREAT SYMPTOMATICALLY AND SUPPORTIVELY. ADMINISTRATION OF OXYGEN AND LAVAGE MUST BE PERFORMED BY QUALIFIED MEDICAL PERSONNEL. GET MEDICAL ATTENTION IMMEDIATELY.

ANTIDOTE: THE FOLLOWING ANTIDOTE(S) HAVE BEEN RECOMMENDED. HOWEVER, THE DECISION AS TO WHETHER THE SEVERITY OF POISONING REQUIRES ADMINISTRATION OF ANY ANTIDOTE AND ACTUAL DOSE REQUIRED SHOULD BE MADE BY QUALIFIED MEDICAL PERSONNEL.
FOR CHOLINESTERASE INHIBITORS: ESTABLISH CLEAR AIRWAY AND TISSUE OXYGENATION BY ASPIRATION OF SECRETIONS, AND IF NECESSARY, BY ASSISTED PULMONARY VENTILATION WITH OXYGEN. IMPROVE TISSUE OXYGENATION AS MUCH AS POSSIBLE BEFORE ADMINISTERING ATROPINE TO MINIMIZE THE RISK OF VENTRICULAR FIBRILLATION. ADMINISTER ATROPINE SULFATE INTRAVENOUSLY, OR INTRAMUSCULARLY IF IV INJECTION IS NOT POSSIBLE. IN MODERATELY SEVERE POISONING ADMINISTER ATROPINE SULFATE, 0.4-2.0 MG REPEATED EVERY 15 MINUTES UNTIL ATROPINIZATION IS ACHIEVED (TACHYCARDIA, FLUSHING, DRY MOUTH, MYDRIASIS). MAINTAIN ATROPINIZATION BY REPEATED DOSES FOR 2-12 HOURS, OR LONGER, DEPENDING ON THE SEVERITY OF POISONING. THE APPEARANCE OF RALES IN THE LUNG BASES, MIOSIS, SALIVATION, NAUSEA, BRADYCARDIA, ARE ALL INDICATIONS OF INADEQUATE ATROPINIZATION.
SEVERELY POISONED INDIVIDUALS MAY EXHIBIT REMARKABLE TOLERANCE TO ATROPINE; TWO OR MORE TIMES THE DOSAGES SUGGESTED ABOVE MAY BE NEEDED. PERSONS NOT POISONED OR ONLY SLIGHTLY POISONED, HOWEVER, MAY DEVELOP SIGNS OF ATROPINE TOXICITY FROM SUCH LARGE DOSAGES: FEVER, MUSCLE FIBRILLATIONS, AND DELIRIUM ARE THE MAIN SIGNS OF ATROPINE TOXICITY. IF THESE SIGNS APPEAR WHILE THE PATIENT IS FULLY ATROPINIZED, ATROPINE ADMINISTRATION SHOULD BE DISCONTINUED, AT LEAST TEMPORARILY. OBSERVE TREATED PATIENTS CLOSELY AT LEAST 24 HOURS TO INSURE THAT SYMPTOMS (POSSIBLY PULMONARY EDEMA) DO NOT RECUR AS ATROPINIZATION WEARS OFF. IN VERY SEVERE POISONINGS, METABOLIC DISPOSITION OF TOXICANT MAY REQUIRE SEVERAL HOURS OR DAYS DURING WHICH ATROPINIZATION MUST BE MAINTAINED. MARKEDLY LOWER LEVELS OF URINARY METABOLITES INDICATE THAT ATROPINE DOSAGE CAN BE TAPERED OFF. AS DOSAGE IS REDUCED, CHECK THE LUNG BASES FREQUENTLY FOR RALES. IF RALES ARE HEARD OR OTHER SYMPTOMS RETURN, RE-ESTABLISH ATROPINIZATION PROMPTLY (MORGAN, RECOGNITION AND MANAGEMENT OF PESTICIDE POISONINGS, 3RD ED.). ADMINISTRATION OF ANTIDOTE MUST BE PERFORMED BY QUALIFIED MEDICAL PERSONNEL.
IN CASES OF SEVERE POISONING BY ORGANOPHOSPHATE PESTICIDES IN WHICH RESPIRATORY DEPRESSION, MUSCLE WEAKNESS AND TWITCHINGS ARE SEVERE, GIVE PRALIDOXIME (PROTOPAM-AYERST, 2-PAM), 1.0 GRAM INTRAVENOUSLY AT NO MORE THAN 0.5 GRAM PER MINUTE. DOSAGE OF PRALIDOXIME MAY BE REPEATED IN 1-2 HOURS, THEN AT 10-12 HOUR INTERVALS IF NEEDED. IN VERY SEVERE POISONINGS, DOSAGE RATES MAY BE DOUBLED. TREATMENT WITH PRALIDOXIME WILL BE MOST EFFECTIVE IF GIVEN WITHIN THIRTY-SIX HOURS AFTER POISONING (MORGAN, RECOGNITION AND MANAGEMENT OF PESTICIDE POISONINGS, 3RD ED.). ANTIDOTE SHOULD BE ADMINISTERED BY QUALIFIED MEDICAL PERSONNEL.

REACTIVITY

REACTIVITY: STABLE UNDER NORMAL TEMPERATURES AND PRESSURES.

INCOMPATIBILITIES: CHLORMEPHOS: METALS: MAY BE CORROSIVE. OXIDIZERS (STRONG): FIRE AND EXPLOSION HAZARD.

DECOMPOSITION: THERMAL DECOMPOSITION MAY RELEASE TOXIC AND/OR HAZARDOUS GASES.

POLYMERIZATION: HAZARDOUS POLYMERIZATION HAS NOT BEEN REPORTED TO OCCUR UNDER NORMAL TEMPERATURES AND PRESSURES.

STORAGE AND DISPOSAL

OBSERVE ALL FEDERAL, STATE AND LOCAL REGULATIONS WHEN STORING OR DISPOSING OF THIS SUBSTANCE. FOR ASSISTANCE, CONTACT THE DISTRICT DIRECTOR OF THE ENVIRONMENTAL PROTECTION AGENCY.

STORAGE

STORE IN ACCORDANCE WITH 40 CFR 165 RECOMMENDED PROCEDURES FOR THE DISPOSAL AND STORAGE OF PESTICIDES AND PESTICIDE CONTAINERS.
STORE AWAY FROM INCOMPATIBLE SUBSTANCES.
THRESHOLD PLANNING QUANTITY (TPQ): THE SUPERFUND AMENDMENTS AND REAUTHORIZATION ACT (SARA) SECTION 302 REQUIRES THAT EACH FACILITY WHERE ANY EXTREMELY HAZARDOUS SUBSTANCE IS PRESENT IN A QUANTITY EQUAL TO OR GREATER THAN THE TPQ ESTABLISHED FOR THAT SUBSTANCE NOTIFY THE STATE EMERGENCY RESPONSE COMMISSION FOR THE STATE IN WHICH IT IS LOCATED. SECTION 303 OF SARA REQUIRES THESE FACILITIES TO PARTICIPATE IN LOCAL EMERGENCY RESPONSE PLANNING (40 CFR 355.30).

DISPOSAL

DISPOSAL MUST BE IN ACCORDANCE WITH 40 CFR 165 RECOMMENDED PROCEDURES FOR THE DISPOSAL AND STORAGE OF PESTICIDES AND PESTICIDE CONTAINERS.

CONDITIONS TO AVOID

MAY BURN BUT DOES NOT IGNITE READILY. CONTAINERS MAY EXPLODE IN HEAT OF FIRE.

SPILL AND LEAK PROCEDURES

OCCUPATIONAL SPILL: DO NOT TOUCH SPILLED MATERIAL. STOP LEAK IF YOU CAN DO IT WITHOUT RISK. USE WATER SPRAY TO REDUCE VAPORS. FOR SMALL SPILLS, TAKE UP WITH SAND OR OTHER ABSORBENT MATERIAL AND PLACE INTO CONTAINERS FOR LATER DISPOSAL. FOR SMALL DRY SPILLS, WITH A CLEAN SHOVEL PLACE MATERIAL INTO CLEAN, DRY CONTAINERS AND COVER. MOVE CONTAINERS FROM SPILL AREA. FOR LARGER SPILLS, DIKE FAR AHEAD OF SPILL FOR LATER DISPOSAL. KEEP UNNECESSARY PEOPLE AWAY. ISOLATE HAZARD AREA AND DENY ENTRY. VENTILATE CLOSED SPACES BEFORE ENTERING.
REPORTABLE QUANTITY (RQ): 1 POUND THE SUPERFUND AMENDMENTS AND REAUTHORIZATION ACT (SARA) SECTION 304 REQUIRES THAT A RELEASE EQUAL TO OR GREATER THAN THE REPORTABLE QUANTITY FOR THIS SUBSTANCE BE IMMEDIATELY REPORTED TO THE LOCAL EMERGENCY PLANNING COMMITTEE AND THE STATE EMERGENCY RESPONSE COMMISSION (40 CFR 355.40). IF THE RELEASE OF THIS SUBSTANCE IS REPORTABLE UNDER CERCLA SECTION 103, THE NATIONAL

RESPONSE CENTER MUST BE NOTIFIED IMMEDIATELY AT (800) 424-8802 OR (202) 426-2675 IN THE METROPOLITAN WASHINGTON, D.C. AREA (40 CFR 302.6).

PROTECTIVE EQUIPMENT

VENTILATION: PROCESS ENCLOSURE RECOMMENDED.

RESPIRATOR: THE FOLLOWING RESPIRATORS ARE RECOMMENDED BASED ON INFORMATION FOUND IN THE PHYSICAL DATA, TOXICITY AND HEALTH EFFECTS SECTIONS. THEY ARE RANKED IN ORDER FROM MINIMUM TO MAXIMUM RESPIRATORY PROTECTION. THE SPECIFIC RESPIRATOR SELECTED MUST BE BASED ON CONTAMINATION LEVELS FOUND IN THE WORK PLACE, MUST NOT EXCEED THE WORKING LIMITS OF THE RESPIRATOR AND BE JOINTLY APPROVED BY THE NATIONAL INSTITUTE FOR OCCUPATIONAL SAFETY AND HEALTH AND THE MINE SAFETY AND HEALTH ADMINISTRATION (NIOSH-MSHA).

TYPE 'C' SUPPLIED-AIR RESPIRATOR WITH A FULL FACEPIECE OPERATED IN PRESSURE-DEMAND OR OTHER POSITIVE PRESSURE MODE OR WITH A FULL FACEPIECE, HELMET OR HOOD OPERATED IN CONTINOUS-FLOW MODE.

SELF-CONTAINED BREATHING APPARATUS WITH A FULL FACEPIECE OPERATED IN PRESSURE-DEMAND OR OTHER POSITIVE PRESSURE MODE.

FOR FIREFIGHTING AND OTHER IMMEDIATELY DANGEROUS TO LIFE OR HEALTH CONDITIONS:

SELF-CONTAINED BREATHING APPARATUS WITH FULL FACEPIECE OPERATED IN PRESSURE-DEMAND OR OTHER POSITIVE PRESSURE MODE.

SUPPLIED-AIR RESPIRATOR WITH FULL FACEPIECE AND OPERATED IN PRESSURE-DEMAND OR OTHER POSITIVE PRESSURE MODE IN COMBINATION WITH AN AUXILIARY SELF-CONTAINED BREATHING APPARATUS OPERATED IN PRESSURE-DEMAND OR OTHER POSITIVE PRESSURE MODE.

CLOTHING: EMPLOYEE MUST WEAR APPROPRIATE PROTECTIVE (IMPERVIOUS) CLOTHING AND EQUIPMENT TO PREVENT ANY POSSIBILITY OF SKIN CONTACT WITH THIS SUBSTANCE.

GLOVES: EMPLOYEE MUST WEAR APPROPRIATE PROTECTIVE GLOVES TO PREVENT CONTACT WITH THIS SUBSTANCE.

EYE PROTECTION: EMPLOYEE MUST WEAR SPLASH-PROOF OR DUST-RESISTANT SAFETY GOGGLES AND A FACESHIELD TO PREVENT CONTACT WITH THIS SUBSTANCE.

EMERGENCY WASH FACILITIES: WHERE THERE IS ANY POSSIBILITY THAT AN EMPLOYEE'S EYES AND/OR SKIN MAY BE EXPOSED TO THIS SUBSTANCE, THE EMPLOYER SHOULD PROVIDE AN EYE WASH FOUNTAIN AND QUICK DRENCH SHOWER WITHIN THE IMMEDIATE WORK AREA FOR EMERGENCY USE.

AUTHORIZED BY- OCCUPATIONAL HEALTH SERVICES, INC.
CREATION DATE: 02/08/90 ***REVISION DATE:*** 05/02/90

MATERIAL SAFETY DATA SHEET

OCCUPATIONAL HEALTH SERVICES, INC.
AGRICULTURE AND PESTICIDE DIVISION
450 SEVENTH AVENUE, SUITE 2407
NEW YORK, NEW YORK 10123
1-800-445-MSDS OR (212) 967-1100

EMERGENCY CONTACT:
JOHN S. BRANSFORD, JR. (615) 292-1180

SUBSTANCE IDENTIFICATION

CAS-NUMBER 510-15-6

SUBSTANCE: <u>CHLOROBENZILATE</u>

TRADE NAMES/SYNONYMS: BENZENEACETIC ACID, 4-CHLORO-ALPHA-(4-CHLOROPHENYL)-ALPHA-HYDROXY-, ETHYL ESTER; BENZILIC ACID, 4,4'-DICHLORO-, ETHYL ESTER; 4-CHLORO-ALPHA-(4-CHLOROPHENYL)-ALPHA-HYDROXYBENZENEACETIC ACID ETHYL ESTER; 4,4'-DICHLOROBENZILIC ACID ETHYL ESTER; ETHYL 4,4'-DICHLOROBENZILATE; ETHYL 4-CHLORO-ALPHA-(4-CHLOROPHENYL)-ALPHA-HYDROXYBENZENEACETATE; ETHYL 2-HYDROXY-2,2-BIS(4-CHLOROPHENYL)ACETATE; ETHYL P,P'-DICHLOROBENZILATE; ACAR; ACARABEN; AKAR; BENZILAN; CHLORBENZYLATE; NCI-C60413; NCI-C00408; ENT 18596; RCRA U038; C16H14CL2O3; PST04740

CHEMICAL FAMILY: ESTER
HALOGEN COMPOUND, AROMATIC

MOLECULAR FORMULA: C16-H14-CL2-O3

MOLECULAR WEIGHT: 325.20

CERCLA RATINGS (SCALE 0-3): HEALTH=3 FIRE=2 REACTIVITY=0 PERSISTENCE=3

NFPA RATINGS (SCALE 0-4): HEALTH=3 FIRE=2 REACTIVITY=0

COMPONENTS AND CONTAMINANTS

COMPONENT: CHLOROBENZILATE ***PERCENT:*** 100
CAS# 510-15-6

OTHER CONTAMINANTS: NONE

EXPOSURE LIMITS: NO OCCUPATIONAL EXPOSURE LIMITS ESTABLISHED BY OSHA, ACGIH, OR NIOSH.
CHLOROBENZILATE: 10 POUNDS CERCLA SECTION 103 REPORTABLE QUANTITY
SUBJECT TO SARA SECTION 313 ANNUAL TOXIC CHEMICAL RELEASE REPORTING
SUBJECT TO CALIFORNIA PROPOSITION 65 CANCER AND/OR REPRODUCTIVE TOXICITY WARNING AND RELEASE REQUIREMENTS- (JANUARY 1, 1990)

PHYSICAL DATA

DESCRIPTION: YELLOW SOLID. ***BOILING POINT:*** 313-316 F (156-158 C) AT 0.07 MMHG

MELTING POINT: 95-99 F (35-37 C) ***SPECIFIC GRAVITY:*** 1.2816 (AT 90%)

VAPOR PRESSURE: 0.0000022 MMHG @ 20C ***SOLUBILITY IN WATER:*** 10 PPM

SOLVENT SOLUBILITY: SOLUBLE IN ACETONE, DICHLOROMETHANE, METHANOL, TOLUENE, HEXANE, OCTAN-1-OL, BENZENE, ALCOHOL, ETHANOL, DIMETHYLSULFOXIDE, PETROLEUM OILS, ORGANIC SOLVENTS.

FIRE AND EXPLOSION DATA

FIRE AND EXPLOSION HAZARD: MODERATE FIRE HAZARD WHEN EXPOSED TO HEAT OR FLAME.

FLASH POINT: 104 F (40 C) (CC) ***FLAMMABILITY CLASS(OSHA):*** II

FIREFIGHTING MEDIA: DRY CHEMICAL, CARBON DIOXIDE, HALON, WATER SPRAY OR STANDARD FOAM (1987 EMERGENCY RESPONSE GUIDEBOOK, DOT P 5800.4).
FOR LARGER FIRES, USE WATER SPRAY, FOG OR STANDARD FOAM (1987 EMERGENCY RESPONSE GUIDEBOOK, DOT P 5800.4).

FIREFIGHTING: MOVE CONTAINERS FROM FIRE AREA IF POSSIBLE. FIGHT FIRE FROM MAXIMUM DISTANCE. STAY AWAY FROM STORAGE TANK ENDS. DIKE FIRE CONTROL WATER FOR LATER DISPOSAL. DO NOT SCATTER MATERIAL (1987 EMERGENCY RESPONSE GUIDEBOOK, DOT P 5800.4, GUIDE PAGE 55).
USE AGENTS SUITABLE FOR TYPE OF FIRE. COOL CONTAINERS WITH FLOODING AMOUNTS OF WATER. AVOID BREATHING VAPORS OR DUSTS, KEEP UPWIND.

TRANSPORTATION DATA

DEPARTMENT OF TRANSPORTATION HAZARD CLASSIFICATION 49 CFR 172.101: COMBUSTIBLE LIQUID
DEPARTMENT OF TRANSPORTATION LABELING REQUIREMENTS 49 CFR 172.101 AND SUBPART E: NONE
DEPARTMENT OF TRANSPORTATION PACKAGING REQUIREMENTS: NONE
EXCEPTIONS: 49 CFR 173.118A

TOXICITY

CHLOROBENZILATE: IRRITATION DATA: 125 MG OPEN SKIN-RABBIT MILD; 25 MG EYE-RABBIT MODERATE. TOXICITY DATA: 700 MG/KG ORAL-RAT LD50; 729 MG/KG ORAL-MOUSE LD50; 700 MG/KG ORAL-HAMSTER LD50; MUTAGENIC DATA (RTECS); TUMORIGENIC DATA (RTECS). CARCINOGEN STATUS: ANIMAL LIMITED EVIDENCE (IARC GROUP-3). ORAL ADMINISTRATION OF CHLOROBENZILATE INDUCED HEPATOCELLULAR CARCINOMAS IN BOTH SEXES OF ONE STRAIN OF MICE AND IN MALES OF TWO OTHER STRAINS. LOCAL EFFECTS: IRRITANT- EYE. ACUTE TOXICITY DATA: MODERATELY TOXIC BY INGESTION. TARGET EFFECTS: POISONING MAY AFFECT THE NERVOUS SYSTEM, KIDNEYS AND LIVER. ADDITIONAL DATA: MAY BE STORED IN THE ADIPOSE TISSUES; INTENSE ACTIVITY AND STARVATION MAY MOBILIZE THE PESTICIDE RESULTING IN THE REAPPEARANCE OF TOXIC SYMPTOMS. MAY BE EXCRETED IN BREAST MILK. STIMULANTS SUCH AS EPINEPHRINE MAY INDUCE VENTRICULAR FIBRILLATION.

HEALTH EFFECTS AND FIRST AID

INHALATION: CHLOROBENZILATE: **<u>ACUTE EXPOSURE</u>**- COMPLAINTS OF MUSCLE PAINS, ATAXIA, MILD DELIRIUM AND FEVER WERE REPORTED FROM ONE CASE OF OCCUPATIONAL EXPOSURE TO CHLOROBENZILATE. THIS CHEMICAL IS AN ORGANOCHLORINE PESTICIDE. THESE PESTICIDES HAVE DIRECT ACTION ON THE CENTRAL NERVOUS SYSTEM PRODUCING SYMPTOMS OF APPREHENSION, EXCITABILITY, DIZZINESS, HEADACHE, DISORIENTATION, WEAKNESS, PARESTHESIAS, MUSCLE TWITCHING, TREMORS, AND CONVULSIONS. SYMPTOMS OF POISONING MAY OCCUR WITHIN SEVERAL HOURS AFTER OVEREXPOSURE.
<u>CHRONIC EXPOSURE</u>- PROLONGED OR REPEATED EXPOSURE TO ORGANOCHLORINE PESTICIDES MAY CAUSE EFFECTS AS DESCRIBED IN ACUTE EXPOSURE.

FIRST AID- REMOVE FROM EXPOSURE AREA TO FRESH AIR IMMEDIATELY. IF BREATHING HAS STOPPED, PERFORM ARTIFICIAL RESPIRATION. KEEP PERSON WARM AND AT REST. TREAT SYMPTOMATICALLY AND SUPPORTIVELY. GET MEDICAL ATTENTION IMMEDIATELY.

SKIN CONTACT: CHLOROBENZILATE: **<u>ACUTE EXPOSURE</u>**- THIS PRODUCT WAS MILDLY IRRITATING TO RABBIT SKIN. COMPLAINTS OF MUSCLE PAINS, ATAXIA, MILD DELIRIUM AND FEVER WAS REPORTED IN ONE CASE OF OCCUPATIONAL EXPOSURE

TO CHLOROBENZILATE. ORGANOCHLORINE PESTICIDES ARE ABSORBED THROUGH THE SKIN AND PRODUCE SYMPTOMS OF APPREHENSION, EXCITABILITY, DIZZINESS, HEADACHE, DISORIENTATION, WEAKNESS, PARESTHESIAS, MUSCLE TWITCHING, TREMORS, AND CONVULSIONS. SYMPTOMS OF POISONING MAY OCCUR WITHIN SEVERAL HOURS AFTER OVEREXPOSURE. **CHRONIC EXPOSURE-** PROLONGED OR REPEATED EXPOSURE TO ORGANOCHLORINE PESTICIDES MAY CAUSE EFFECTS AS DESCRIBED IN ACUTE EXPOSURE.

FIRST AID- REMOVE CONTAMINATED CLOTHING AND SHOES IMMEDIATELY. WASH AFFECTED AREA WITH SOAP OR MILD DETERGENT AND LARGE AMOUNTS OF WATER UNTIL NO EVIDENCE OF CHEMICAL REMAINS (APPROXIMATELY 15-20 MINUTES). GET MEDICAL ATTENTION IMMEDIATELY.

EYE CONTACT: CHLOROBENZILATE: IRRITANT. **ACUTE EXPOSURE-** MAY CAUSE IRRITATION. **CHRONIC EXPOSURE-** REPEATED OR PROLONGED EXPOSURE TO IRRITANTS MAY CAUSE CONJUNCTIVITIS.

FIRST AID- WASH EYES IMMEDIATELY WITH LARGE AMOUNTS OF WATER OR NORMAL SALINE, OCCASIONALLY LIFTING UPPER AND LOWER LIDS, UNTIL NO EVIDENCE OF CHEMICAL REMAINS (APPROXIMATELY 15-20 MINUTES). GET MEDICAL ATTENTION IMMEDIATELY.

INGESTION: CHLOROBENZILATE: LIMITED ANIMAL CARCINOGEN. **ACUTE EXPOSURE-** A LETHAL DOSE IN RATS WAS 700 MG/KG. ADVERSE EFFECTS OBSERVED IN ANIMALS INCLUDED DEPRESSED MOTOR ACTIVITY, LACRIMATION, A RAPID WHEEZING RESPIRATION, COMA, AND DEATH. CHLOROBENZILATE IS EXCRETED RAPIDLY BY HUMANS, USUALLY WITHIN 3-4 DAYS OF INGESTION. INGESTION OF ORGANOCHLORINE PESTICIDES MAY CAUSE GASTROINTESTINAL EFFECTS OF NAUSEA, VOMITING, DIARRHEA, AND STOMACH PAINS. OTHER SYMPTOMS OF APPREHENSION, EXCITABILITY, DIZZINESS, HEADACHE, DISORIENTATION, WEAKNESS, PARESTHESIAS, MUSCLE TWITCHING, TREMOR, AND CONVULSIONS MAY OCCUR. DEATH MAY BE DUE TO RESPIRATORY FAILURE OR VENTRICULAR FIBRILLATION. SYMPTOMS MAY APPEAR WITHIN SEVERAL HOURS OF OVEREXPOSURE. **CHRONIC EXPOSURE-** LIVER ENLARGEMENT WAS OBSERVED IN ONE STUDY OF FEMALE RATS FED 100 MG/KG IN THE DIET FOR FOUR WEEKS. TESTICULAR ATROPHY IN MALE RATS WAS REPORTED FROM A TWO-YEAR STUDY. STATISTICALLY SIGNIFICANT INCREASES IN THE NUMBER OF TOTAL TUMORS AND OF HEPATOCELLULAR CARCINOMAS WERE REPORTED FROM TWO STUDIES OF MICE.

FIRST AID- IF THE PERSON IS CONSCIOUS AND NOT CONVULSING, REMOVE BY GIVING SYRUP OF IPECAC (IF VOMITING OCCURS, KEEP THE HEAD BELOW THE HIPS TO PREVENT ASPIRATION). GIVE ACTIVATED CHARCOAL FOLLOWED BY GASTRIC LAVAGE. FOLLOW WITH A SALINE CATHARTIC. DO NOT GIVE FATS OR OILS. INTESTINAL LAVAGE WITH 20% MANNITOL (200 ML) BY STOMACH TUBE IS ALSO USEFUL. GIVE ARTIFICIAL RESPIRATION WITH OXYGEN IF RESPIRATION IS DEPRESSED (DREISBACH, HANDBOOK OF POISONING, 12TH ED.). TREAT SYMPTOMATICALLY AND SUPPORTIVELY. LAVAGE AND ADMINISTRATION OF OXYGEN SHOULD BE PERFORMED BY QUALIFIED MEDICAL PERSONNEL. GET MEDICAL ATTENTION IMMEDIATELY.

ANTIDOTE: NO SPECIFIC ANTIDOTE. TREAT SYMPTOMATICALLY AND SUPPORTIVELY.

REACTIVITY

REACTIVITY: STABLE UNDER NORMAL TEMPERATURES AND PRESSURES.

INCOMPATIBILITIES: CHLOROBENZILATE: ACIDS (STRONG): MAY CAUSE HYDROLYSIS. ALKALIES: MAY CAUSE HYDROLYSIS. LIME: MAY REACT

DECOMPOSITION: THERMAL DECOMPOSITION PRODUCTS MAY INCLUDE TOXIC AND CORROSIVE FUMES OF CHLORIDES AND TOXIC OXIDES OF CARBON.

POLYMERIZATION: HAZARDOUS POLYMERIZATION HAS NOT BEEN REPORTED TO OCCUR UNDER NORMAL TEMPERATURES AND PRESSURES.

STORAGE AND DISPOSAL

OBSERVE ALL FEDERAL, STATE AND LOCAL REGULATIONS WHEN STORING OR DISPOSING OF THIS SUBSTANCE. FOR ASSISTANCE, CONTACT THE DISTRICT DIRECTOR OF THE ENVIRONMENTAL PROTECTION AGENCY.

****STORAGE****

STORE IN ACCORDANCE WITH 29 CFR 1910.106.

STORE IN ACCORDANCE WITH 40 CFR 165 RECOMMENDED PROCEDURES FOR THE DISPOSAL AND STORAGE OF PESTICIDES AND PESTICIDE CONTAINERS.

BONDING AND GROUNDING: SUBSTANCES WITH LOW ELECTROCONDUCTIVITY, WHICH MAY BE IGNITED BY ELECTROSTATIC SPARKS, SHOULD BE STORED IN CONTAINERS WHICH MEET THE BONDING AND GROUNDING GUIDELINES SPECIFIED IN NFPA 77-1983, RECOMMENDED PRACTICE ON STATIC ELECTRICITY.

STORE AWAY FROM INCOMPATIBLE SUBSTANCES.

****DISPOSAL****

DISPOSAL MUST BE IN ACCORDANCE WITH STANDARDS APPLICABLE TO GENERATORS OF HAZARDOUS WASTE, 40 CFR 262. EPA HAZARDOUS WASTE NUMBER D001. 100 POUND CERCLA SECTION 103 REPORTABLE QUANTITY.

DISPOSAL MUST BE IN ACCORDANCE WITH STANDARDS APPLICABLE TO GENERATORS OF HAZARDOUS WASTE, 40CFR 262. EPA HAZARDOUS WASTE NUMBER U038.

CONDITIONS TO AVOID

MAY BURN BUT DOES NOT IGNITE READILY. CONTAINERS MAY EXPLODE IN HEAT OF FIRE.

SPILL AND LEAK PROCEDURES

WATER SPILL: THE CALIFORNIA SAFE DRINKING WATER AND TOXIC ENFORCEMENT ACT OF 1986 (PROPOSITION 65) PROHIBITS CONTAMINATING ANY KNOWN SOURCE OF DRINKING WATER WITH SUBSTANCES KNOWN TO CAUSE CANCER AND/OR REPRODUCTIVE TOXICITY.

OCCUPATIONAL SPILL: SWEEP UP AND PLACE IN SUITABLE CLEAN, DRY CONTAINERS FOR RECLAMATION OR LATER DISPOSAL. DO NOT FLUSH SPILLED MATERIAL INTO SEWER. KEEP UNNECESSARY PEOPLE AWAY.

REPORTABLE QUANTITY (RQ): 10 POUNDS THE SUPERFUND AMENDMENTS AND REAUTHORIZATION ACT (SARA) SECTION 304 REQUIRES THAT A RELEASE EQUAL TO OR GREATER THAN THE REPORTABLE QUANTITY FOR THIS SUBSTANCE BE IMMEDIATELY REPORTED TO THE LOCAL EMERGENCY PLANNING COMMITTEE AND THE STATE EMERGENCY RESPONSE COMMISSION (40 CFR 355.40). IF THE RELEASE OF THIS SUBSTANCE IS REPORTABLE UNDER CERCLA SECTION 103, THE NATIONAL RESPONSE CENTER MUST BE NOTIFIED IMMEDIATELY AT (800) 424-8802 OR (202) 426-2675 IN THE METROPOLITAN WASHINGTON, D.C. AREA (40 CFR 302.6).

PROTECTIVE EQUIPMENT

VENTILATION: PROVIDE LOCAL EXHAUST OR PROCESS ENCLOSURE VENTILATION SYSTEM.

RESPIRATOR: THE FOLLOWING RESPIRATORS ARE RECOMMENDED BASED ON INFORMATION FOUND IN THE PHYSICAL DATA, TOXICITY AND HEALTH EFFECTS SECTIONS. THEY ARE RANKED IN ORDER FROM MINIMUM TO MAXIMUM RESPIRATORY PROTECTION. THE SPECIFIC RESPIRATOR SELECTED MUST BE BASED ON CONTAMINATION LEVELS FOUND IN THE WORK PLACE, MUST NOT EXCEED THE WORKING LIMITS OF THE RESPIRATOR AND BE JOINTLY APPROVED BY THE NATIONAL INSTITUTE FOR OCCUPATIONAL SAFETY AND HEALTH AND THE MINE SAFETY AND HEALTH ADMINISTRATION (NIOSH-MSHA).

TYPE 'C' SUPPLIED-AIR RESPIRATOR WITH A FULL FACEPIECE OPERATED IN PRESSURE-DEMAND OR OTHER POSITIVE PRESSURE MODE OR WITH A FULL FACEPIECE, HELMET OR HOOD OPERATED IN CONTINOUS-FLOW MODE.

SELF-CONTAINED BREATHING APPARATUS WITH A FULL FACEPIECE OPERATED IN PRESSURE-DEMAND OR OTHER POSITIVE PRESSURE MODE.

FOR FIREFIGHTING AND OTHER IMMEDIATELY DANGEROUS TO LIFE OR HEALTH CONDITIONS:

SELF-CONTAINED BREATHING APPARATUS WITH FULL FACEPIECE OPERATED IN PRESSURE-DEMAND OR OTHER POSITIVE PRESSURE MODE.

SUPPLIED-AIR RESPIRATOR WITH FULL FACEPIECE AND OPERATED IN PRESSURE-DEMAND OR OTHER POSITIVE PRESSURE MODE IN COMBINATION WITH AN AUXILIARY SELF-CONTAINED BREATHING APPARATUS OPERATED IN PRESSURE-DEMAND OR OTHER POSITIVE PRESSURE MODE.

CLOTHING: EMPLOYEE MUST WEAR APPROPRIATE PROTECTIVE (IMPERVIOUS) CLOTHING AND EQUIPMENT TO PREVENT REPEATED OR PROLONGED SKIN CONTACT WITH THIS SUBSTANCE.

GLOVES: EMPLOYEE MUST WEAR APPROPRIATE PROTECTIVE GLOVES TO PREVENT CONTACT WITH THIS SUBSTANCE.

EYE PROTECTION: EMPLOYEE MUST WEAR SPLASH-PROOF OR DUST-RESISTANT SAFETY GOGGLES TO PREVENT EYE CONTACT WITH THIS SUBSTANCE.

EMERGENCY EYE WASH: WHERE THERE IS ANY POSSIBILITY THAT AN EMPLOYEE'S EYES MAY BE EXPOSED TO THIS SUBSTANCE, THE EMPLOYER SHOULD PROVIDE AN EYE WASH FOUNTAIN WITHIN THE IMMEDIATE WORK AREA FOR EMERGENCY USE.

AUTHORIZED BY- OCCUPATIONAL HEALTH SERVICES, INC.

CREATION DATE: 10/04/89 ***REVISION DATE:*** 07/13/90

MATERIAL SAFETY DATA SHEET

OCCUPATIONAL HEALTH SERVICES, INC.	EMERGENCY CONTACT:
AGRICULTURE AND PESTICIDE DIVISION	JOHN S. BRANSFORD, JR. (615) 292-1180
450 SEVENTH AVENUE, SUITE 2407	
NEW YORK, NEW YORK 10123	

450 SEVENTH AVENUE, SUITE 2407
NEW YORK, NEW YORK 10123
1-800-445-MSDS OR (212) 967-1100

SUBSTANCE IDENTIFICATION

CAS-NUMBER 4329-12-8

SUBSTANCE: **1-CHLORO-3-(2,2-DICHLORO-1-(4-CHLOROPHENYL)ETHYL)BENZENE**

TRADE NAMES/SYNONYMS: BENZENE, 1-CHLORO-3-(2,2-DICHLORO-1-(4-CHLOROPHENYL)ETHYL)-; ETHANE, 1,1-DICHLORO-2-(M-CHLOROPHENYL)-2-(P-CHLOROPHENYL)-; 1,1-DICHLORO-2-(M-CHLOROPHENYL)-2-(P-CHLOROPHENYL)ETHANE; M,P'-DDD; 2-(M-CHLOROPHENYL) 2-(P-CHLOROPHENYL-1,1-DICHLOROETHANE; M,P'-TDE; DDD-M,P'; TDE-M,P'; C14H10CL4; PST04752

CHEMICAL FAMILY: HALOGEN COMPOUND, AROMATIC

MOLECULAR FORMULA: (C6-H4-CL)2-C-H-C-H-CL2

MOLECULAR WEIGHT: 319.97

CERCLA RATINGS (SCALE 0-3): HEALTH=U FIRE=1 REACTIVITY=0 PERSISTENCE=2

NFPA RATINGS (SCALE 0-4): HEALTH=U FIRE=1 REACTIVITY=0

COMPONENTS AND CONTAMINANTS

COMPONENT: 1-CHLORO-3-(2,2-DICHLORO-1-(4-CHLOROPHENYL)-ETHYL)BENZENE ***PERCENT:*** 100.0
CAS# 4329-12-8

OTHER CONTAMINANTS: NONE

EXPOSURE LIMITS: NO OCCUPATIONAL EXPOSURE LIMITS ESTABLISHED BY OSHA, ACGIH, OR NIOSH.

PHYSICAL DATA

DESCRIPTION: WHITE POWDER. ***MELTING POINT:*** 126-127 F ((52-53 C)

SPECIFIC GRAVITY: NOT AVAILABLE ***SOLUBILITY IN WATER:*** NOT AVAILABLE

FIRE AND EXPLOSION DATA

FIRE AND EXPLOSION HAZARD: SLIGHT FIRE HAZARD WHEN EXPOSED TO HEAT OR FLAME.
DUST-AIR MIXTURES MAY IGNITE OR EXPLODE.

FIREFIGHTING MEDIA: DRY CHEMICAL, CARBON DIOXIDE, HALON, WATER SPRAY OR STANDARD FOAM (1987 EMERGENCY RESPONSE GUIDEBOOK, DOT P 5800.4).
FOR LARGER FIRES, USE WATER SPRAY, FOG OR STANDARD FOAM (1987 EMERGENCY RESPONSE GUIDEBOOK, DOT P 5800.4).

FIREFIGHTING: MOVE CONTAINER FROM FIRE AREA IF POSSIBLE. DO NOT SCATTER SPILLED MATERIAL WITH HIGH PRESSURE WATER STREAMS. DIKE FIRE CONTROL WATER FOR LATER DISPOSAL (1987 EMERGENCY RESPONSE GUIDEBOOK, DOT P 5800.4, GUIDE PAGE 31).
USE AGENTS SUITABLE FOR TYPE OF SURROUNDING FIRE. AVOID BREATHING HAZARDOUS VAPORS, KEEP UPWIND.

TOXICITY

1-CHLORO-3-(2,2-DICHLORO-1-(4-CHLOROPHENYL)ETHYL)BENZENE: TOXICITY DATA: 3400 MG/KG ORAL-RAT LD50 (EPA). CARCINOGEN STATUS: NONE. ACUTE TOXICITY DATA: MODERATELY TOXIC BY INGESTION. TARGET EFFECTS: CONVULSANT. POISONING MAY AFFECT THE LIVER AND KIDNEYS.* ADDITIONAL DATA: DDT ANALOGUE. MAY CROSS THE PLACENTA AND BE EXCRETED IN BREAST MILK. MAY IMPAIR FERTILITY. STIMULANTS SUCH AS EPINEPHRINE OR EPHEDRINE MAY INDUCE VENTRICULAR FIBRILLATION.*
* MAY BE BASED ON GENERAL INFORMATION ON ORGANOCHLORINE PESTICIDES.

HEALTH EFFECTS AND FIRST AID

INHALATION: 1-CHLORO-3-(2,2-DICHLORO-1-(4-CHLOROPHENYL)ETHYL)BENZENE:
ACUTE EXPOSURE- EFFECTS AS DESCRIBED FOR ORGANOCHLORINE PESTICIDES IN ACUTE INGESTION MAY OCCUR IF SUFFICIENT AMOUNTS ARE ABSORBED FROM THE LUNGS. **CHRONIC EXPOSURE-** A STUDY OF OCCUPATIONAL EXPOSURE TO DDT REPORTED A HIGHER FREQUENCY OF WHITE BLOOD CELLS WITH CHROMOSOMAL ABNORMALITIES AMONG WORKERS WITH HIGH DDT BLOOD LEVELS; ANOTHER STUDY REPORTED MENSTRUAL IRREGULARITIES AS THE MOST FREQUENT COMPLAINT AMONG MIGRANT FARM WORKERS. PROLONGED OR REPEATED EXPOSURE TO ORGANOCHLORINE PESTICIDES MAY CAUSE EFFECTS AS DESCRIBED IN ACUTE INGESTION.

FIRST AID- REMOVE FROM EXPOSURE AREA TO FRESH AIR IMMEDIATELY. IF BREATHING HAS STOPPED, PERFORM ARTIFICIAL RESPIRATION. KEEP PERSON WARM AND AT REST. TREAT SYMPTOMATICALLY AND SUPPORTIVELY. GET MEDICAL ATTENTION IMMEDIATELY.

SKIN CONTACT: 1-CHLORO-3-(2,2-DICHLORO-1-(4-CHLOROPHENYL)ETHYL)BENZENE:
ACUTE EXPOSURE- EFFECTS AS DESCRIBED FOR ORGANOCHLORINE PESTICIDES IN ACUTE INGESTION MAY OCCUR IF SUFFICIENT AMOUNTS ARE ABSORBED THROUGH THE THE SKIN. **CHRONIC EXPOSURE-** A STUDY OF OCCUPATIONAL EXPOSURE TO DDT REPORTED A HIGHER FREQUENCY OF WHITE BLOOD CELLS WITH CHROMOSOMAL ABNORMALITIES AMONG WORKERS WITH HIGH DDT BLOOD LEVELS; ANOTHER STUDY REPORTED MENSTRUAL IRREGULARITIES AS THE MOST FREQUENT COMPLAINT AMONG MIGRANT FARM WORKERS. PROLONGED OR REPEATED EXPOSURE TO ORGANOCHLORINE PESTICIDES MAY CAUSE EFFECTS AS DESCRIBED IN ACUTE INGESTION.

FIRST AID- REMOVE CONTAMINATED CLOTHING AND SHOES IMMEDIATELY. WASH AFFECTED AREA WITH SOAP OR MILD DETERGENT AND LARGE AMOUNTS OF WATER UNTIL NO EVIDENCE OF CHEMICAL REMAINS (APPROXIMATELY 15-20 MINUTES). GET MEDICAL ATTENTION IMMEDIATELY.

EYE CONTACT: 1-CHLORO-3-(2,2-DICHLORO-1-(4-CHLOROPHENYL)ETHYL)BENZENE:
ACUTE EXPOSURE- NO DATA AVAILABLE. **CHRONIC EXPOSURE-** NO DATA AVAILABLE.

FIRST AID- WASH EYES IMMEDIATELY WITH LARGE AMOUNTS OF WATER OR NORMAL SALINE, OCCASIONALLY LIFTING UPPER AND LOWER LIDS, UNTIL NO EVIDENCE OF CHEMICAL REMAINS (APPROXIMATELY 15-20 MINUTES). GET MEDICAL ATTENTION IMMEDIATELY.

INGESTION: 1-CHLORO-3-(2,2-DICHLORO-1-(4-CHLOROPHENYL)ETHYL)BENZENE: **ACUTE EXPOSURE-** INGESTION OF ORGANOCHLORINE PESTICIDES MAY CAUSE GASTROINTESTINAL EFFECTS OF NAUSEA, VOMITING, DIARRHEA, AND STOMACH PAINS. OTHER SYMPTOMS OF CONFUSION, APPREHENSION, IRRITABILITY, EXCITABILITY, DIZZINESS, HEADACHE, DISORIENTATION, WEAKNESS, PARESTHESIAS, MUSCLE TWITCHING, TREMOR, STUPOR, COMA, AND CONVULSIONS MAY OCCUR. SIGNS OF LIVER AND KIDNEY DAMAGE MAY DEVELOP. DEATH MAY BE DUE TO RESPIRATORY FAILURE OR VENTRICULAR FIBRILLATION. SYMPTOMS OF POISONING MAY OCCUR SEVERAL HOURS AFTER INGESTION. **CHRONIC EXPOSURE-** REPEATED EXPOSURE TO ORGANOCHLORINE PESTICIDES MAY CAUSE EFFECTS AS DESCRIBED IN ACUTE EXPOSURE.

FIRST AID- IF THE PERSON IS CONSCIOUS AND NOT CONVULSING, REMOVE BY GIVING SYRUP OF IPECAC (IF VOMITING OCCURS, KEEP THE HEAD BELOW THE HIPS TO PREVENT ASPIRATION). GIVE ACTIVATED CHARCOAL FOLLOWED BY GASTRIC LAVAGE. FOLLOW WITH A SALINE CATHARTIC. DO NOT GIVE FATS OR OILS. INTESTINAL LAVAGE WITH 20% MANNITOL (200 ML) BY STOMACH TUBE IS ALSO USEFUL. GIVE ARTIFICIAL RESPIRATION WITH OXYGEN IF RESPIRATION IS DEPRESSED (DREISBACH, HANDBOOK OF POISONING, 12TH ED.). TREAT SYMPTOMATICALLY AND SUPPORTIVELY. LAVAGE AND ADMINISTRATION OF OXYGEN SHOULD BE PERFORMED BY QUALIFIED MEDICAL PERSONNEL. GET MEDICAL ATTENTION IMMEDIATELY.

ANTIDOTE: NO SPECIFIC ANTIDOTE. TREAT SYMPTOMATICALLY AND SUPPORTIVELY.

REACTIVITY

REACTIVITY: STABLE UNDER NORMAL TEMPERATURES AND PRESSURES.

INCOMPATIBILITIES: 1-CHLORO-3-(2,2-DICHLORO-1-(4-CHLOROPHENYL)ETHYL)BENZENE: OXIDIZERS (STRONG): FIRE AND EXPLOSION HAZARD.

DECOMPOSITION: THERMAL DECOMPOSITION PRODUCTS MAY INCLUDE TOXIC AND CORROSIVE FUMES OF CHLORIDES AND TOXIC OXIDES OF CARBON.

POLYMERIZATION: HAZARDOUS POLYMERIZATION HAS NOT BEEN REPORTED TO OCCUR UNDER NORMAL TEMPERATURES AND PRESSURES.

STORAGE AND DISPOSAL

OBSERVE ALL FEDERAL, STATE AND LOCAL REGULATIONS WHEN STORING OR DISPOSING OF THIS SUBSTANCE. FOR ASSISTANCE, CONTACT THE DISTRICT DIRECTOR OF THE ENVIRONMENTAL PROTECTION AGENCY.

STORAGE

STORE IN ACCORDANCE WITH 40 CFR 165 RECOMMENDED PROCEDURES FOR THE DISPOSAL AND STORAGE OF PESTICIDES AND PESTICIDE CONTAINERS.
STORE AWAY FROM INCOMPATIBLE SUBSTANCES.

DISPOSAL

DISPOSAL MUST BE IN ACCORDANCE WITH 40 CFR 165 RECOMMENDED PROCEDURES FOR THE DISPOSAL AND STORAGE OF PESTICIDES AND PESTICIDE CONTAINERS.

CONDITIONS TO AVOID

MAY BURN BUT DOES NOT IGNITE READILY. AVOID CONTACT WITH STRONG OXIDIZERS, EXCESSIVE HEAT, SPARKS, OR OPEN FLAME.

SPILL AND LEAK PROCEDURES

OCCUPATIONAL SPILL: SWEEP UP AND PLACE IN SUITABLE CLEAN, DRY CONTAINERS FOR RECLAMATION OR LATER DISPOSAL. DO NOT FLUSH SPILLED MATERIAL INTO SEWER. KEEP UNNECESSARY PEOPLE AWAY.

SYSTEM.

RESPIRATOR: THE FOLLOWING RESPIRATORS ARE RECOMMENDED BASED ON INFORMATION FOUND IN THE PHYSICAL DATA, TOXICITY AND HEALTH EFFECTS SECTIONS. THEY ARE RANKED IN ORDER FROM MINIMUM TO MAXIMUM RESPIRATORY PROTECTION. THE SPECIFIC RESPIRATOR SELECTED MUST BE BASED ON CONTAMINATION LEVELS FOUND IN THE WORK PLACE, MUST NOT EXCEED THE WORKING LIMITS OF THE RESPIRATOR AND BE JOINTLY APPROVED BY THE NATIONAL INSTITUTE FOR OCCUPATIONAL SAFETY AND HEALTH AND THE MINE SAFETY AND HEALTH ADMINISTRATION (NIOSH-MSHA).

CHEMICAL CARTRIDGE RESPIRATOR WITH AN ORGANIC VAPOR CARTRIDGE(S) IN COMBINATION WITH A DUST AND MIST FILTER.

GAS MASK WITH ORGANIC VAPOR CANISTER (CHIN-STYLE OR FRONT- OR BACK-MOUNTED CANISTER) WITH A DUST AND MIST FILTER.

GAS MASK WITH ORGANIC VAPOR CANISTER (CHIN-STYLE OR FRONT- OR BACK-MOUNTED CANISTER) WITH A PARTICULATE FILTER.

POWERED AIR-PURIFYING RESPIRATOR WITH A HIGH-EFFICIENCY FILTER.

TYPE 'C' SUPPLIED-AIR RESPIRATOR WITH A FULL FACEPIECE OPERATED IN A PRESSURE-DEMAND OR OTHER POSITIVE PRESSURE MODE.

SELF-CONTAINED BREATHING APPARATUS WITH A FULL FACEPIECE OPERATED IN PRESSURE-DEMAND OR OTHER POSITIVE PRESSURE MODE.

FOR FIREFIGHTING AND OTHER IMMEDIATELY DANGEROUS TO LIFE OR HEALTH CONDITIONS:

SELF-CONTAINED BREATHING APPARATUS WITH FULL FACEPIECE OPERATED IN PRESSURE-DEMAND OR OTHER POSITIVE PRESSURE MODE.

SUPPLIED-AIR RESPIRATOR WITH FULL FACEPIECE AND OPERATED IN PRESSURE-DEMAND OR OTHER POSITIVE PRESSURE MODE IN COMBINATION WITH AN AUXILIARY SELF-CONTAINED BREATHING APPARATUS OPERATED IN PRESSURE-DEMAND OR OTHER POSITIVE PRESSURE MODE.

CLOTHING: EMPLOYEE MUST WEAR APPROPRIATE PROTECTIVE (IMPERVIOUS) CLOTHING AND EQUIPMENT TO PREVENT REPEATED OR PROLONGED SKIN CONTACT WITH THIS SUBSTANCE.

GLOVES: EMPLOYEE MUST WEAR APPROPRIATE PROTECTIVE GLOVES TO PREVENT CONTACT WITH THIS SUBSTANCE.

EYE PROTECTION: EMPLOYEE MUST WEAR SPLASH-PROOF OR DUST-RESISTANT SAFETY GOGGLES TO PREVENT EYE CONTACT WITH THIS SUBSTANCE.

EMERGENCY EYE WASH: WHERE THERE IS ANY POSSIBILITY THAT AN EMPLOYEE'S EYES MAY BE EXPOSED TO THIS SUBSTANCE, THE EMPLOYER SHOULD PROVIDE AN EYE WASH FOUNTAIN WITHIN THE IMMEDIATE WORK AREA FOR EMERGENCY USE.

AUTHORIZED BY- OCCUPATIONAL HEALTH SERVICES, INC.

CREATION DATE: 03/22/90 ***REVISION DATE:*** 05/31/90

MATERIAL SAFETY DATA SHEET

OCCUPATIONAL HEALTH SERVICES, INC.
AGRICULTURE AND PESTICIDE DIVISION
450 SEVENTH AVENUE, SUITE 2407
NEW YORK, NEW YORK 10123
1-800-445-MSDS OR (212) 967-1100

EMERGENCY CONTACT:
JOHN S. BRANSFORD, JR. (615) 292-1180

SUBSTANCE IDENTIFICATION

CAS-NUMBER 14835-94-0

SUBSTANCE: **1-CHLORO-2-(O-CHLOROPHENYL)-2-(P-CHLOROPHENYL)ETHYLENE**

TRADE NAMES/SYNONYMS: BENZENE, 1-CHLORO-2-(2-CHLORO-1-(4-CHLOROPHENYL)ETHENYL-; ETHYLENE, 2-CHLORO-1-(O-CHLOROPHENYL)-1-(P-CHLOROPHENYL)-; 2-CHLORO-1-(O-CHLOROPHENYLO-1-(P-CHLOROPHENYL)ETHYLENE; O,P'-DDD OLEFIN; O,P'-DDMU; O,P'-TDE OLEFIN; 1-CHLORO-2-(2-CHLORO-1-(4-CHLOROPHENYL)ETHENYL)BENZENE; C14H9CL3; PST04753

CHEMICAL FAMILY: HALOGEN COMPOUND, AROMATIC

MOLECULAR FORMULA: (C6-H4-CL)2-C-C-H-CL

MOLECULAR WEIGHT: 283.58

CERCLA RATINGS (SCALE 0-3): HEALTH=U FIRE=U REACTIVITY=0 PERSISTENCE=2

NFPA RATINGS (SCALE 0-4): HEALTH=U FIRE=U REACTIVITY=0

COMPONENTS AND CONTAMINANTS

COMPONENT: 1-CHLORO-2-(O-CHLOROPHENYL)-2-(P-CHLOROPHENYL) ETHYLENE ***PERCENT:*** 100.0

CAS# 14835-94-0

OTHER CONTAMINANTS: NONE

EXPOSURE LIMITS: NO OCCUPATIONAL EXPOSURE LIMITS ESTABLISHED BY OSHA, ACGIH, OR NIOSH.

PHYSICAL DATA

DESCRIPTION: CLEAR LIQUID. ***BOILING POINT:*** NOT AVAILABLE

SPECIFIC GRAVITY: NOT AVAILABLE ***EVAPORATION RATE:*** NOT AVAILABLE

SOLUBILITY IN WATER: NOT AVAILABLE

FIRE AND EXPLOSION DATA

FIRE AND EXPLOSION HAZARD: UNKNOWN FIRE AND EXPLOSION HAZARD.

FLASH POINT: NOT AVAILABLE

FIREFIGHTING MEDIA: DRY CHEMICAL, CARBON DIOXIDE, HALON, WATER SPRAY OR STANDARD FOAM (1987 EMERGENCY RESPONSE GUIDEBOOK, DOT P 5800.4). FOR LARGER FIRES, USE WATER SPRAY, FOG OR STANDARD FOAM (1987 EMERGENCY RESPONSE GUIDEBOOK, DOT P 5800.4).

FIREFIGHTING: MOVE CONTAINER FROM FIRE AREA IF POSSIBLE. COOL FIRE-EXPOSED CONTAINERS WITH WATER FROM SIDE UNTIL WELL AFTER FIRE IS OUT. STAY AWAY FROM STORAGE TANK ENDS. FOR MASSIVE FIRE IN STORAGE AREA, USE UNMANNED HOSE HOLDER OR MONITOR NOZZLES, ELSE WITHDRAW FROM AREA AND LET FIRE BURN. WITHDRAW IMMEDIATELY IN CASE OF RISING SOUND FROM VENTING SAFETY DEVICE OR ANY DISCOLORATION OF STORAGE TANK DUE TO FIRE (1987 EMERGENCY RESPONSE GUIDEBOOK, DOT P 5800.4, GUIDE PAGE 27). EXTINGUISH ONLY IF FLOW CAN BE STOPPED; USE FLOODING AMOUNTS OF WATER AS A FOG, SOLID STREAMS MAY BE INEFFECTIVE. COOL CONTAINERS WITH FLOODING AMOUNTS OF WATER, APPLY FROM AS FAR A DISTANCE AS POSSIBLE. AVOID BREATHING VAPORS, KEEP UPWIND.

TOXICITY

1-CHLORO-2-(O-CHLOROPHENYL)-2-(P-CHLOROPHENYL)ETHYLENE: CARCINOGEN STATUS: NONE. ACUTE TOXCITY DATA: NO DATA AVAILABLE. TARGET EFFECTS: CONVULSANT. POISONING MAY AFFECT THE LIVER AND KIDNEYS.* ADDITIONAL DATA: DDT METABOLITE. MAY CROSS THE PLACENTA AND BE EXCRETED IN BREAST MILK. MAY IMPAIR FERTILITY. STIMULANTS SUCH AS EPINEPHRINE OR EPHEDRINE MAY INDUCE VENTRICULAR FIBRILLATION.*

* MAY BE BASED ON GENERAL INFORMATION ON ORGANOCHLORINE PESTICIDES.

HEALTH EFFECTS AND FIRST AID

INHALATION: 1-CHLORO-2-(O-CHLOROPHENYL)-2-(P-CHLOROPHENYL)ETHYLENE:

ACUTE EXPOSURE- EFFECTS AS DESCRIBED FOR ORGANOCHLORINE PESTICIDES IN ACUTE INGESTION MAY OCCUR IF SUFFICIENT AMOUNTS ARE ABSORBED FROM THE LUNGS. **CHRONIC EXPOSURE-** A STUDY OF OCCUPATIONAL EXPOSURE TO DDT REPORTED A HIGHER FREQUENCY OF WHITE BLOOD CELLS WITH CHROMOSOMAL ABNORMALITIES AMONG WORKERS WITH HIGH DDT BLOOD LEVELS; ANOTHER STUDY REPORTED MENSTRUAL IRREGULARITIES AS THE MOST FREQUENT COMPLAINT AMONG MIGRANT FARM WORKERS. PROLONGED OR REPEATED EXPOSURE TO ORGANOCHLORINE PESTICIDES MAY CAUSE EFFECTS AS DESCRIBED IN ACUTE INGESTION.

FIRST AID- REMOVE FROM EXPOSURE AREA TO FRESH AIR IMMEDIATELY. IF BREATHING HAS STOPPED, PERFORM ARTIFICIAL RESPIRATION. KEEP PERSON WARM AND AT REST. TREAT SYMPTOMATICALLY AND SUPPORTIVELY. GET MEDICAL ATTENTION IMMEDIATELY.

SKIN CONTACT: 1-CHLORO-2-(O-CHLOROPHENYL)-2-(P-CHLOROPHENYL)ETHYLENE:

ACUTE EXPOSURE- EFFECTS AS DESCRIBED FOR ORGANOCHLORINE PESTICIDES IN ACUTE INGESTION MAY OCCUR IF SUFFICIENT AMOUNTS ARE ABSORBED THROUGH THE THE SKIN. **CHRONIC EXPOSURE-** A STUDY OF OCCUPATIONAL EXPOSURE TO DDT REPORTED A HIGHER FREQUENCY OF WHITE BLOOD CELLS WITH CHROMOSOMAL ABNORMALITIES AMONG WORKERS WITH HIGH DDT BLOOD LEVELS; ANOTHER STUDY REPORTED MENSTRUAL IRREGULARITIES AS THE MOST FREQUENT COMPLAINT AMONG MIGRANT FARM WORKERS. PROLONGED OR REPEATED EXPOSURE TO ORGANOCHLORINE PESTICIDES MAY CAUSE EFFECTS AS DESCRIBED IN ACUTE INGESTION.

FIRST AID- REMOVE CONTAMINATED CLOTHING AND SHOES IMMEDIATELY. WASH AFFECTED AREA WITH SOAP OR MILD DETERGENT AND LARGE AMOUNTS OF WATER UNTIL NO EVIDENCE OF CHEMICAL REMAINS (APPROXIMATELY 15-20 MINUTES). GET MEDICAL ATTENTION IMMEDIATELY.

EYE CONTACT: 1-CHLORO-2-(O-CHLOROPHENYL)-2-(P-CHLOROPHENYL)ETHYLENE:

ACUTE EXPOSURE- NO DATA AVAILABLE. **CHRONIC EXPOSURE-** NO DATA AVAILABLE.

FIRST AID- WASH EYES IMMEDIATELY WITH LARGE AMOUNTS OF WATER OR NORMAL SALINE, OCCASIONALLY LIFTING UPPER AND LOWER LIDS, UNTIL NO EVIDENCE OF CHEMICAL REMAINS (APPROXIMATELY 15-20 MINUTES). GET MEDICAL ATTENTION IMMEDIATELY.

INGESTION: 1-CHLORO-2-(O-CHLOROPHENYL)-2-(P-CHLOROPHENYL)ETHYLENE: **ACUTE EXPOSURE**- INGESTION OF ORGANOCHLORINE PESTICIDES MAY CAUSE GASTROINTESTINAL EFFECTS OF NAUSEA, VOMITING, DIARRHEA, AND STOMACH PAINS. OTHER SYMPTOMS OF CONFUSION, APPREHENSION, IRRITABILITY, EXCITABILITY, DIZZINESS, HEADACHE, DISORIENTATION, WEAKNESS, PARESTHESIAS, MUSCLE TWITCHING, TREMOR, STUPOR, COMA, AND CONVULSIONS MAY OCCUR. SIGNS OF LIVER AND KIDNEY DAMAGE MAY DEVELOP. DEATH MAY BE DUE TO RESPIRATORY FAILURE OR VENTRICULAR FIBRILLATION. SYMPTOMS OF POISONING MAY OCCUR SEVERAL HOURS AFTER INGESTION. **CHRONIC EXPOSURE**- REPEATED EXPOSURE TO ORGANOCHLORINE PESTICIDES MAY CAUSE EFFECTS AS DESCRIBED IN ACUTE EXPOSURE.

FIRST AID- IF THE PERSON IS CONSCIOUS AND NOT CONVULSING, REMOVE BY GIVING SYRUP OF IPECAC (IF VOMITING OCCURS, KEEP THE HEAD BELOW THE HIPS TO PREVENT ASPIRATION). GIVE ACTIVATED CHARCOAL FOLLOWED BY GASTRIC LAVAGE. FOLLOW WITH A SALINE CATHARTIC. DO NOT GIVE FATS OR OILS. INTESTINAL LAVAGE WITH 20% MANNITOL (200 ML) BY STOMACH TUBE IS ALSO USEFUL. GIVE ARTIFICIAL RESPIRATION WITH OXYGEN IF RESPIRATION IS DEPRESSED (DREISBACH, HANDBOOK OF POISONING, 12TH ED.). TREAT SYMPTOMATICALLY AND SUPPORTIVELY. LAVAGE AND ADMINISTRATION OF OXYGEN SHOULD BE PERFORMED BY QUALIFIED MEDICAL PERSONNEL. GET MEDICAL ATTENTION IMMEDIATELY.

REACTIVITY

REACTIVITY: STABLE UNDER NORMAL TEMPERATURES AND PRESSURES.

INCOMPATIBILITIES: 1-CHLORO-2-(O-CHLOROPHENYL)-2-(P-CHLOROPHENYL)ETHYLENE: OXIDIZERS (STRONG): FIRE AND EXPLOSION HAZARD.

DECOMPOSITION: THERMAL DECOMPOSITION PRODUCTS MAY INCLUDE TOXIC AND CORROSIVE FUMES OF CHLORIDES AND TOXIC OXIDES OF CARBON.

POLYMERIZATION: HAZARDOUS POLYMERIZATION HAS NOT BEEN REPORTED TO OCCUR UNDER NORMAL TEMPERATURES AND PRESSURES.

STORAGE AND DISPOSAL

OBSERVE ALL FEDERAL, STATE AND LOCAL REGULATIONS WHEN STORING OR DISPOSING OF THIS SUBSTANCE. FOR ASSISTANCE, CONTACT THE DISTRICT DIRECTOR OF THE ENVIRONMENTAL PROTECTION AGENCY.

STORAGE

STORE IN ACCORDANCE WITH 40 CFR 165 RECOMMENDED PROCEDURES FOR THE DISPOSAL AND STORAGE OF PESTICIDES AND PESTICIDE CONTAINERS.

STORE AWAY FROM INCOMPATIBLE SUBSTANCES.

DISPOSAL

DISPOSAL MUST BE IN ACCORDANCE WITH 40 CFR 165 RECOMMENDED PROCEDURES FOR THE DISPOSAL AND STORAGE OF PESTICIDES AND PESTICIDE CONTAINERS.

CONDITIONS TO AVOID

AVOID CONTACT WITH HEAT, SPARKS, FLAMES, OR OTHER SOURCES OF IGNITION. VAPORS MAY BE EXPLOSIVE. AVOID OVERHEATING OF CONTAINERS; CONTAINERS MAY VIOLENTLY RUPTURE IN HEAT OF FIRE. AVOID CONTAMINATION OF WATER SOURCES.

SPILL AND LEAK PROCEDURES

OCCUPATIONAL SPILL: SHUT OFF IGNITION SOURCES. STOP LEAK IF YOU CAN DO IT WITHOUT RISK. USE WATER SPRAY TO REDUCE VAPORS. FOR SMALL SPILLS, TAKE UP WITH SAND OR OTHER ABSORBENT MATERIAL AND PLACE INTO CONTAINERS FOR LATER DISPOSAL. FOR LARGER SPILLS, DIKE FAR AHEAD OF SPILL FOR LATER DISPOSAL. NO SMOKING, FLAMES OR FLARES IN HAZARD AREA. KEEP UNNECESSARY PEOPLE AWAY; ISOLATE HAZARD AREA AND RESTRICT ENTRY.

PROTECTIVE EQUIPMENT

VENTILATION: PROVIDE LOCAL EXHAUST OR GENERAL DILUTION VENTILATION SYSTEM.

RESPIRATOR: THE FOLLOWING RESPIRATORS ARE RECOMMENDED BASED ON INFORMATION FOUND IN THE PHYSICAL DATA, TOXICITY AND HEALTH EFFECTS SECTIONS. THEY ARE RANKED IN ORDER FROM MINIMUM TO MAXIMUM RESPIRATORY PROTECTION. THE SPECIFIC RESPIRATOR SELECTED MUST BE BASED ON CONTAMINATION LEVELS FOUND IN THE WORK PLACE, MUST NOT EXCEED THE WORKING LIMITS OF THE RESPIRATOR AND BE JOINTLY APPROVED BY THE NATIONAL INSTITUTE FOR OCCUPATIONAL SAFETY AND HEALTH AND THE MINE SAFETY AND HEALTH ADMINISTRATION (NIOSH-MSHA).

CHEMICAL CARTRIDGE RESPIRATOR WITH PESTICIDE CARTRIDGE.

GAS MASK WITH A PESTICIDE CANISTER (CHIN-STYLE OR FRONT- OR BACK-MOUNTED CANISTER).

TYPE 'C' SUPPLIED-AIR RESPIRATOR OPERATED IN THE PRESSURE-DEMAND OR OTHER POSITIVE PRESSURE OR CONTINUOUS-FLOW MODE.

SELF-CONTAINED BREATHING APPARATUS.

FOR FIREFIGHTING AND OTHER IMMEDIATELY DANGEROUS TO LIFE OR HEALTH CONDITIONS:

SELF-CONTAINED BREATHING APPARATUS WITH FULL FACEPIECE OPERATED IN PRESSURE-DEMAND OR OTHER POSITIVE PRESSURE MODE.

SUPPLIED-AIR RESPIRATOR WITH FULL FACEPIECE AND OPERATED IN PRESSURE-DEMAND OR OTHER POSITIVE PRESSURE MODE IN COMBINATION WITH AN AUXILIARY SELF-CONTAINED BREATHING APPARATUS OPERATED IN PRESSURE-DEMAND OR OTHER POSITIVE PRESSURE MODE.

CLOTHING: EMPLOYEE MUST WEAR APPROPRIATE PROTECTIVE (IMPERVIOUS) CLOTHING AND EQUIPMENT TO PREVENT REPEATED OR PROLONGED SKIN CONTACT WITH THIS SUBSTANCE.

GLOVES: EMPLOYEE MUST WEAR APPROPRIATE PROTECTIVE GLOVES TO PREVENT CONTACT WITH THIS SUBSTANCE.

EYE PROTECTION: EMPLOYEE MUST WEAR SPLASH-PROOF OR DUST-RESISTANT SAFETY GOGGLES TO PREVENT EYE CONTACT WITH THIS SUBSTANCE.

EMERGENCY EYE WASH: WHERE THERE IS ANY POSSIBILITY THAT AN EMPLOYEE'S EYES MAY BE EXPOSED TO THIS SUBSTANCE, THE EMPLOYER SHOULD PROVIDE AN EYE WASH FOUNTAIN WITHIN THE IMMEDIATE WORK AREA FOR EMERGENCY USE.

AUTHORIZED BY- OCCUPATIONAL HEALTH SERVICES, INC.

CREATION DATE: 03/22/90 ***REVISION DATE:*** 05/17/90

MATERIAL SAFETY DATA SHEET

OCCUPATIONAL HEALTH SERVICES, INC.
AGRICULTURE AND PESTICIDE DIVISION
450 SEVENTH AVENUE, SUITE 2407
NEW YORK, NEW YORK 10123
1-800-445-MSDS OR (212) 967-1100

EMERGENCY CONTACT:
JOHN S. BRANSFORD, JR. (615) 292-1180

SUBSTANCE IDENTIFICATION

CAS-NUMBER 3691-35-8

SUBSTANCE: **CHLOROPHACINONE**

TRADE NAMES/SYNONYMS: 1H-INDENE-1,3(2H)-DIONE, 2-((4-CHLOROPHENYL)PHENYLACETYL)-; 1,3-INDANDIONE, 2-((P-CHLOROPHENYL)PHENYLACETYL)-; 2-((4-CHLOROPHENYL)PHENYLACETYL)-1H-INDENE-1,3(2H)-DIONE; 2-((P-CHLOROPHENYL)PHENYLACETYL)-1,3-INDANDIONE; 2-(2-(4-CHLOROPHENYL)-2-PHENYLACETYL)INDAN-1,3-DIONE; 2-(2-(4-CHLOROPHENYL)-2-PHENYLACETYL)INDANE-1,3-DIONE; CAID; CHLORPHACINONE; CHLORPHENACONE; LIPHADIONE; LM 91; ROZOL; C23H15CLO3; PST04826

CHEMICAL FAMILY: INDANDIONE
HALOGEN COMPOUND, AROMATIC

MOLECULAR FORMULA: C23-H15-CL-O3

MOLECULAR WEIGHT: 374.83

CERCLA RATINGS (SCALE 0-3): HEALTH=3 FIRE=1 REACTIVITY=0 PERSISTENCE=2

NFPA RATINGS (SCALE 0-4): HEALTH=4 FIRE=1 REACTIVITY=0

COMPONENTS AND CONTAMINANTS

COMPONENT: CHLOROPHACINONE ***PERCENT:*** 100.0
CAS# 3691-35-8

OTHER CONTAMINANTS: NONE

EXPOSURE LIMITS: NO OCCUPATIONAL EXPOSURE LIMITS ESTABLISHED BY OSHA, ACGIH, OR NIOSH.

CHLOROPHACINONE: 100/10,000 POUNDS SARA SECTION 302 THRESHOLD PLANNING QUANTITY 1 POUND SARA SECTION 304 REPORTABLE QUANTITY

PHYSICAL DATA

DESCRIPTION: PALE YELLOW CRYSTALLINE SOLID. ***MELTING POINT:*** 284 F (140 C)

SPECIFIC GRAVITY: NOT AVAILABLE ***VAPOR PRESSURE:*** NEGLIGIBLE @ 20 C

SOLUBILITY IN WATER: SPARINGLY SOLUBLE

SOLVENT SOLUBILITY: SOLUBLE IN ACETONE, ETHANOL, ETHYL ACETATE AND OTHER ORGANIC SOLVENTS.

FIRE AND EXPLOSION DATA

FIRE AND EXPLOSION HAZARD: SLIGHT FIRE HAZARD WHEN EXPOSED TO HEAT OR FLAME.

FIREFIGHTING MEDIA: DRY CHEMICAL, CARBON DIOXIDE, HALON, WATER SPRAY OR STANDARD FOAM (1987 EMERGENCY RESPONSE GUIDEBOOK, DOT P 5800.4).

FOR LARGER FIRES, USE WATER SPRAY, FOG OR STANDARD FOAM (1987 EMERGENCY RESPONSE GUIDEBOOK, DOT P 5800.4).

FIREFIGHTING: MOVE CONTAINERS FROM FIRE AREA IF POSSIBLE (1987 EMERGENCY RESPONSE GUIDEBOOK, DOT P 5800.4, GUIDE PAGE 53).

EXTINGUISH USING AGENT SUITABLE FOR TYPE OF SURROUNDING FIRE. AVOID BREATHING VAPORS AND DUSTS. KEEP UPWIND.

TRANSPORTATION DATA

DEPARTMENT OF TRANSPORTATION HAZARD CLASSIFICATION 49 CFR 172.101: POISON B

DEPARTMENT OF TRANSPORTATION LABELING REQUIREMENTS 49 CFR 172.101 AND SUBPART E: POISON

DEPARTMENT OF TRANSPORTATION PACKAGING REQUIREMENTS: 49 CFR 173.365 EXCEPTIONS: 49 CFR 173.364

TOXICITY

CHLOROPHACINONE: TOXICITY DATA: 200 MG/KG SKIN-RABBIT LD50; 2100 UG/KG ORAL-RAT LD50; 1060 UG/KG ORAL-MOUSE LD50; 50 MG/KG ORAL-RABBIT LD50; 7500 UG/KG ORAL-MAMMAL LD50. CARCINOGEN STATUS: NONE. ACUTE TOXICITY LEVEL: HIGHLY TOXIC BY DERMAL ABSORPTION AND INGESTION. TARGET EFFECTS: HEMORRHAGIC AGENT. AT INCREASED RISK FROM EXPOSURE: PERSONS WITH BLOOD DYSCRASIAS, BLEEDING TENDENCIES, LIVER OR KIDNEY DISEASE, ULCERS OF THE GASTROINTESTINAL TRACT, OR HYPERTENSION.*

* MAY BE BASED ON GENERAL INFORMATION ON INDANDIONE DERIVATIVES.

HEALTH EFFECTS AND FIRST AID

INHALATION: CHLOROPHACINONE: SEE INFORMATION ON INDANDIONE DERIVATIVES.

INDANDIONE DERIVATIVES: HEMORRHAGIC AGENT. **ACUTE EXPOSURE-** ABSORPTION BY THE LUNGS MAY RESULT IN HEMORRHAGIC EFFECTS AS DESCRIBED IN CHRONIC EXPOSURE. SEVERE CASES MAY BE FATAL. **CHRONIC EXPOSURE-** REPEATED ABSORPTION MAY CAUSE THE INHIBITION OF PROTHROMBIN SYNTHESIS AND DAMAGE TO CAPILLARY PERMEABILITY RESULTING IN WIDESPREAD INTERNAL HEMORRHAGE WITH ASSOCIATED EFFECTS OF NOSEBLEED, HEMATOMA, HEMATURIA, WIDESPREAD BRUISING, AND ANEMIA.

FIRST AID- REMOVE FROM EXPOSURE AREA TO FRESH AIR IMMEDIATELY. IF BREATHING HAS STOPPED, PERFORM ARTIFICIAL RESPIRATION. KEEP PERSON WARM AND AT REST. TREAT SYMPTOMATICALLY AND SUPPORTIVELY. GET MEDICAL ATTENTION IMMEDIATELY.

SKIN CONTACT: CHLOROPHACINONE: HIGHLY TOXIC. SEE INFORMATION ON INDANDIONE DERIVATIVES. THE LETHAL DOSE IN RABBITS WAS 200 MG/KG.

INDANDIONE DERIVATIVES: HEMORRHAGIC AGENT. **ACUTE EXPOSURE-** ABSORPTION THROUGH THE SKIN MAY RESULT IN HEMORRHAGIC EFFECTS AS DESCRIBED IN CHRONIC EXPOSURE. SEVERE CASES MAY BE FATAL. **CHRONIC EXPOSURE-** REPEATED ABSORPTION MAY CAUSE THE INHIBITION OF PROTHROMBIN SYNTHESIS AND DAMAGE TO CAPILLARY PERMEABILITY RESULTING IN WIDESPREAD INTERNAL HEMORRHAGE WITH ASSOCIATED EFFECTS OF NOSEBLEED, HEMATOMA, HEMATURIA, WIDESPREAD BRUISING, AND ANEMIA.

FIRST AID- REMOVE CONTAMINATED CLOTHING AND SHOES IMMEDIATELY. WASH AFFECTED AREA WITH SOAP OR MILD DETERGENT AND LARGE AMOUNTS OF WATER UNTIL NO EVIDENCE OF CHEMICAL REMAINS (APPROXIMATELY 15-20 MINUTES). GET MEDICAL ATTENTION IMMEDIATELY.

EYE CONTACT: CHLOROPHACINONE: **ACUTE EXPOSURE-** NO DATA AVAILABLE. **CHRONIC EXPOSURE-** NO DATA AVAILABLE.

FIRST AID- WASH EYES IMMEDIATELY WITH LARGE AMOUNTS OF WATER OR NORMAL SALINE, OCCASIONALLY LIFTING UPPER AND LOWER LIDS, UNTIL NO EVIDENCE OF CHEMICAL REMAINS (APPROXIMATELY 15-20 MINUTES). GET MEDICAL ATTENTION IMMEDIATELY.

INGESTION: CHLOROPHACINONE: HIGHLY TOXIC. SEE INFORMATION ON INDANDIONE DERIVATIVES.

INDANDIONE DERIVATIVES: HEMORRHAGIC AGENT. **ACUTE EXPOSURE-** LETHAL DOSES IN ANIMALS HAVE PRODUCED LABORED BREATHING, PROGRESSIVE MUSCULAR WEAKNESS, HYPEREXCITABILITY, PULMONARY CONGESTION, VENOUS ENGORGEMENT, AND CARDIAC STANDSTILL. **CHRONIC EXPOSURE-** MAY BE READILY ABSORBED FROM THE GASTROINTESTINAL TRACT AND CAUSE THE INHIBITION OF PROTHROMBIN SYNTHESIS AND DAMAGE TO CAPILLARY PERMEABILITY. HEMORRHAGIC EFFECTS FROM SYSTEMIC ABSORPTION MAY INCLUDE NOSEBLEED, BLEEDING GUMS AND PHARYNX, PETECHIAL RASH, WIDESPREAD BRUISING, HEMATOMA, HEMOPTYSIS, HEMATEMESIS, HEMATURIA, BLOODY STOOLS, BLEEDING INTO THE ORGANS, GASTROINTESTINAL TRACT, JOINTS, ABDOMINAL OR RETROPERITONEAL AREA WITH ABDOMINAL, BACK, JOINT AND LIMB PAIN AND CEREBROVASCULAR ACCIDENT. ANEMIA ACCOMPANIED BY WEAKNESS, PALLOR, AND SHOCK MAY OCCUR. SEVERE HEMORRHAGING MAY CAUSE DEATH. THERAPEUTIC USE OF SOME INDANDIONE DERIVATIVES HAS PRODUCED SIDE EFFECTS OF AGRANULOCYTOSIS, THROMBOCYTOPENIA, PYREXIA, DIARRHEA, STEATORRHEA, HEPATITIS, RENAL TUBULAR NECROSIS, EXFOLIATIVE DERMATITIS AND PARALYSIS OF ACCOMMODATION.

FIRST AID- IF ONLY A FEW GRAINS OF ANTICOAGULANT BAIT HAVE BEEN INGESTED BY AN ADULT OR CHILD HAVING NO ANTECEDENT LIVER OR BLOOD CLOTTING DISEASE, TREATMENT IS PROBABLY UNNECESSARY. IF LARGE AMOUNTS OF ANTICOAGULANT WERE INGESTED IN THE PRECEDING 2-3 HOURS, INDUCE VOMITING WITH SYRUP OF IPECAC, FOLLOWED BY 1-2 GLASSES OF WATER. FOLLOWING EMESIS, GIVE ACTIVATED CHARCOAL IN 4-6 OUNCES OF WATER TO LIMIT ABSORPTION OF ANTICOAGULANT REMAINING IN THE GUT. OBSERVE PATIENT 4-5 DAYS AFTER INGESTION. (MORGAN, RECOGNITION AND MANAGEMENT OF PESTICIDE POISONINGS, THIRD EDITION). GET MEDICAL ATTENTION.

ANTIDOTE: THE FOLLOWING ANTIDOTE HAS BEEN RECOMMENDED. HOWEVER, THE DECISION AS TO WHETHER THE SEVERITY OF POISONING REQUIRES ADMINISTRATION OF ANY ANTIDOTE AND ACTUAL DOSE REQUIRED SHOULD BE MADE BY QUALIFIED MEDICAL PERSONNEL.

OVERDOSE OF ANTICOAGULANTS: VITAMIN K IS A SPECIFIC ANTIDOTE. VITAMIN K1 EMULSION IS THE PREFERRED FORM. THE INITIAL SUBCUTANEOUS OR INTRAMUSCULAR DOSE IN ADULTS IS 5 TO 10 MG (UP TO 25 MG), REPEATED ONCE IF NECESSARY. ONLY IN VICTIMS WHO ARE BLEEDING SEVERLY OR OTHERWISE IN SERIOUS DISTRESS SHOULD THE DRUG BE GIVEN INTRAVENOUSLY AND THEN AT A RATE NO FASTER THAN 1 MG/MINUTE. IF NECESSARY, ON SUBSEQUENT DAYS, VITAMIN K1 SHOULD BE CONTINUED AT A REDUCED LEVEL UNTIL THE PROTHROMBIN TIME RETURNS TO NORMAL. VITAMIN K1 IS PREFERABLE TO K1 OXIDE (DOSE 0.5-2.5) AND CERTAINLY PREFERABLE TO MENADIONE OR MENADIONE SODIUM BISULFITE (GOSSELIN, CLINICAL TOXICOLOGY OF COMMERCIAL PRODUCTS, 5TH ED.). ANTIDOTE SHOULD BE ADMINISTERED BY QUALIFIED MEDICAL PERSONNEL.

REACTIVITY

REACTIVITY: STABLE UNDER NORMAL TEMPERATURES AND PRESSURES.

INCOMPATIBILITIES: CHLOROPHACINONE: OXIDIZERS (STRONG): FIRE AND EXPLOSION HAZARD.

DECOMPOSITION: THERMAL DECOMPOSITION PRODUCTS MAY INCLUDE TOXIC AND CORROSIVE FUMES OF CHLORIDES AND TOXIC OXIDES OF CARBON.

POLYMERIZATION: HAZARDOUS POLYMERIZATION HAS NOT BEEN REPORTED TO OCCUR UNDER NORMAL TEMPERATURES AND PRESSURES.

STORAGE AND DISPOSAL

OBSERVE ALL FEDERAL, STATE AND LOCAL REGULATIONS WHEN STORING OR DISPOSING OF THIS SUBSTANCE. FOR ASSISTANCE, CONTACT THE DISTRICT DIRECTOR OF THE ENVIRONMENTAL PROTECTION AGENCY.

STORAGE

STORE IN ACCORDANCE WITH 40 CFR 165 RECOMMENDED PROCEDURES FOR THE DISPOSAL AND STORAGE OF PESTICIDES AND PESTICIDE CONTAINERS.

STORE AWAY FROM INCOMPATIBLE SUBSTANCES.

THRESHOLD PLANNING QUANTITY (TPQ): THE SUPERFUND AMENDMENTS AND REAUTHORIZATION ACT (SARA) SECTION 302 REQUIRES THAT EACH FACILITY WHERE ANY EXTREMELY HAZARDOUS SUBSTANCE IS PRESENT IN A QUANTITY EQUAL TO OR GREATER THAN THE TPQ ESTABLISHED FOR THAT SUBSTANCE NOTIFY THE STATE EMERGENCY RESPONSE COMMISSION FOR THE STATE IN WHICH IT IS LOCATED. SECTION 303 OF SARA REQUIRES THESE FACILITIES TO PARTICIPATE IN LOCAL EMERGENCY RESPONSE PLANNING (40 CFR 355.30).

DISPOSAL

DISPOSAL MUST BE IN ACCORDANCE WITH 40 CFR 165 RECOMMENDED PROCEDURES FOR THE DISPOSAL AND STORAGE OF PESTICIDES AND PESTICIDE CONTAINERS.

CONDITIONS TO AVOID

MAY BURN BUT DOES NOT IGNITE READILY.

SPILL AND LEAK PROCEDURES

OCCUPATIONAL SPILL: DO NOT TOUCH SPILLED MATERIAL. STOP LEAK IF YOU CAN DO IT WITHOUT RISK. FOR SMALL SPILLS, TAKE UP WITH SAND OR OTHER ABSORBENT MATERIAL AND PLACE INTO CONTAINERS FOR LATER DISPOSAL. FOR SMALL DRY SPILLS, WITH A CLEAN SHOVEL PLACE MATERIAL INTO CLEAN, DRY CONTAINER AND COVER. MOVE CONTAINERS FROM SPILL AREA. FOR LARGER SPILLS, DIKE FAR AHEAD OF SPILL FOR LATER DISPOSAL. KEEP UNNECESSARY PEOPLE AWAY. ISOLATE HAZARD AREA AND DENY ENTRY.

REPORTABLE QUANTITY (RQ): 1 POUND THE SUPERFUND AMENDMENTS AND REAUTHORIZATION ACT (SARA) SECTION 304 REQUIRES THAT A RELEASE EQUAL TO OR GREATER THAN THE REPORTABLE QUANTITY FOR THIS SUBSTANCE BE IMMEDIATELY REPORTED TO THE LOCAL EMERGENCY PLANNING COMMITTEE AND THE STATE EMERGENCY RESPONSE COMMISSION (40 CFR 355.40). IF THE RELEASE OF THIS SUBSTANCE IS REPORTABLE UNDER CERCLA SECTION 103, THE NATIONAL

RESPONSE CENTER MUST BE NOTIFIED IMMEDIATELY AT (800) 424-8802 OR (202) 426-2675 IN THE METROPOLITAN WASHINGTON, D.C. AREA (40 CFR 302.6).

PROTECTIVE EQUIPMENT

VENTILATION: PROVIDE LOCAL EXHAUST OR GENERAL DILUTION VENTILATION SYSTEM.

RESPIRATOR: THE FOLLOWING RESPIRATORS ARE RECOMMENDED BASED ON INFORMATION FOUND IN THE PHYSICAL DATA, TOXICITY AND HEALTH EFFECTS SECTIONS. THEY ARE RANKED IN ORDER FROM MINIMUM TO MAXIMUM RESPIRATORY PROTECTION. THE SPECIFIC RESPIRATOR SELECTED MUST BE BASED ON CONTAMINATION LEVELS FOUND IN THE WORK PLACE, MUST NOT EXCEED THE WORKING LIMITS OF THE RESPIRATOR AND BE JOINTLY APPROVED BY THE NATIONAL INSTITUTE FOR OCCUPATIONAL SAFETY AND HEALTH AND THE MINE SAFETY AND HEALTH ADMINISTRATION (NIOSH-MSHA).

TYPE 'C' SUPPLIED-AIR RESPIRATOR WITH A FULL FACEPIECE OPERATED IN PRESSURE-DEMAND OR OTHER POSITIVE PRESSURE MODE OR WITH A FULL FACEPIECE, HELMET OR HOOD OPERATED IN CONTINOUS-FLOW MODE.

SELF-CONTAINED BREATHING APPARATUS WITH A FULL FACEPIECE OPERATED IN PRESSURE-DEMAND OR OTHER POSITIVE PRESSURE MODE.

FOR FIREFIGHTING AND OTHER IMMEDIATELY DANGEROUS TO LIFE OR HEALTH CONDITIONS:

SELF-CONTAINED BREATHING APPARATUS WITH FULL FACEPIECE OPERATED IN PRESSURE-DEMAND OR OTHER POSITIVE PRESSURE MODE.

SUPPLIED-AIR RESPIRATOR WITH FULL FACEPIECE AND OPERATED IN PRESSURE-DEMAND OR OTHER POSITIVE PRESSURE MODE IN COMBINATION WITH AN AUXILIARY SELF-CONTAINED BREATHING APPARATUS OPERATED IN PRESSURE-DEMAND OR OTHER POSITIVE PRESSURE MODE.

CLOTHING: EMPLOYEE MUST WEAR APPROPRIATE PROTECTIVE (IMPERVIOUS) CLOTHING AND EQUIPMENT TO PREVENT ANY POSSIBILITY OF SKIN CONTACT WITH THIS SUBSTANCE.

GLOVES: EMPLOYEE MUST WEAR APPROPRIATE PROTECTIVE GLOVES TO PREVENT CONTACT WITH THIS SUBSTANCE.

EYE PROTECTION: EMPLOYEE MUST WEAR SPLASH-PROOF OR DUST-RESISTANT SAFETY GOGGLES WITH OR WITHOUT A FACESHIELD TO PREVENT CONTACT WITH THIS SUBSTANCE.

EMERGENCY EYE WASH: WHERE THERE IS ANY POSSIBILITY THAT AN EMPLOYEE'S EYES MAY BE EXPOSED TO THIS SUBSTANCE, THE EMPLOYER SHOULD PROVIDE AN EYE WASH FOUNTAIN WITHIN THE IMMEDIATE WORK AREA FOR EMERGENCY USE.

AUTHORIZED BY- OCCUPATIONAL HEALTH SERVICES, INC.

CREATION DATE: 10/04/89 ***REVISION DATE:*** 03/28/90

MATERIAL SAFETY DATA SHEET

OCCUPATIONAL HEALTH SERVICES, INC.
AGRICULTURE AND PESTICIDE DIVISION
450 SEVENTH AVENUE, SUITE 2407
NEW YORK, NEW YORK 10123
1-800-445-MSDS OR (212) 967-1100

EMERGENCY CONTACT:
JOHN S. BRANSFORD, JR. (615) 292-1180

SUBSTANCE IDENTIFICATION

CAS-NUMBER 76-06-2

SUBSTANCE: **CHLOROPICRIN**

TRADE NAMES/SYNONYMS: NITROCHLOROMETHANE; TRICHLORONITROMETHANE; PICRIDE; CHLOR-O-PIC; PICFUME; TRI-CLOR; CHLOROPICRIN, LIQUID; AQUINITE; DOLOCHLOR; G 25; LARVACIDE; MICROLYSIN; PROFUME A; S 1; NITROCHLOROFORM; PIC-CLOR; PS; STCC 4921414; UN 1580; PST04830

CHEMICAL FAMILY: NITRO HALOGEN COMPOUND, ALIPHATIC

MOLECULAR FORMULA: C-CL3-N-O2 MOL WT: 164.37

CERCLA RATINGS (SCALE 0-3): HEALTH=3 FIRE=0 REACTIVITY=3 PERSISTENCE=3

NFPA RATINGS (SCALE 0-4): HEALTH=4 FIRE=0 REACTIVITY=3

COMPONENTS AND CONTAMINANTS

COMPONENT: CHLOROPICRIN ***PERCENT:*** 100

CAS# 76-06-2

OTHER CONTAMINANTS: NONE

EXPOSURE LIMITS: CHLOROPICRIN: 0.1 PPM OSHA TWA 0.1 PPM (0.7 MG/M3) ACGIH TWA; 0.3 PPM (2 MG/M3) ACGIH STEL (NOTICE OF INTENDED CHANGES 1988-89)

PHYSICAL DATA

DESCRIPTION: OILY, COLORLESS LIQUID, EXTREMELY IRRITATING ODOR.

BOILING POINT: 233 F (112 C) ***MELTING POINT:*** -83 F (-64 C)

SPECIFIC GRAVITY: 1.7 ***VAPOR PRESSURE:*** 20 MM @ 20 C

SOLUBILITY IN WATER: 0.2% @ 20 C ***ODOR THRESHOLD:*** 1.1 PPM

VAPOR DENSITY: 5.7

SOLVENT SOLUBILITY: ALCOHOL, ETHER, ACETONE, BENZENE, ACETIC ACID

FIRE AND EXPLOSION DATA

FIRE AND EXPLOSION HAZARD: NEGLIGIBLE FIRE HAZARD WHEN EXPOSED TO HEAT OR FLAME.

FLASH POINT: NONFLAMMABLE ***FLAMMABILITY CLASS(OSHA):*** IIIB

FIREFIGHTING MEDIA: DRY CHEMICAL, CARBON DIOXIDE, HALON, WATER SPRAY OR STANDARD FOAM (1987 EMERGENCY RESPONSE GUIDEBOOK, DOT P 5800.4). FOR LARGER FIRES, USE WATER SPRAY, FOG OR STANDARD FOAM (1987 EMERGENCY RESPONSE GUIDEBOOK, DOT P 5800.4).

FIREFIGHTING: MOVE CONTAINERS FROM FIRE AREA IF POSSIBLE. COOL CONTAINERS EXPOSED TO FLAMES WITH WATER FROM SIDE UNTIL WELL AFTER FIRE IS OUT. STAY AWAY FROM STORAGE TANK ENDS. FOR MASSIVE FIRE IN STORAGE AREA, USE UNMANNED HOSE HOLDER OR MONITOR NOZZLES; ELSE WITHDRAW FROM AREA AND LET FIRE BURN (1987 EMERGENCY RESPONSE GUIDEBOOK, DOT P 5800.4, GUIDE PAGE 56).

EXTINGUISH USING AGENTS SUITABLE FOR TYPE OF SURROUNDING FIRE. USE FLOODING AMOUNTS OF WATER AS FOG. AVOID BREATHING POISONOUS VAPORS; KEEP UPWIND. CONSIDER EVACUATION OF DOWNWIND AREA IF MATERIAL IS LEAKING.

TRANSPORTATION DATA

DEPARTMENT OF TRANSPORTATION HAZARD CLASSIFICATION 49 CFR 172.101: POISON B

DEPARTMENT OF TRANSPORTATION LABELING REQUIREMENTS 49 CFR 172.101 AND SUBPART E: POISON

DEPARTMENT OF TRANSPORTATION PACKAGING REQUIREMENTS: 49 CFR 173.357 EXCEPTIONS: NONE

TOXICITY

CHLOROPICRIN: TOXICITY DATA: 2 MG/M3 INHALATION-HUMAN TCLO; 2000 MG/M3/10 MINUTES INHALATION-HUMAN LCLO; 66 MG/M3/4 HOURS INHALATION-MOUSE LC50; 800 MG/M3/20 MINUTES INHALATION-CAT LCLO; 800 MG/M3/20 MINUTES INHALATION-RABBIT LC50; 800 MG/M3/20 MINUTES INHALATION-GUINEA PIG LCLO; 250 MG/KG ORAL-RAT LD50; 4200 UG/KG INTRAVENOUS-GUINEA PIG LD50; 25 MG/KG INTRAPERITONEAL-MOUSE LD50; MUTAGENIC DATA (RTECS); TUMORIGENIC DATA (RTECS). CARCINOGEN STATUS: NONE. LOCAL EFFECTS: CORROSIVE- INHALATION, SKIN, AND EYES; LACRIMATOR. ACUTE TOXICITY LEVEL: HIGHLY TOXIC BY INHALATION; TOXIC BY INGESTION. TARGET EFFECTS: METHEMOGLOBIN FORMER. POISONING MAY AFFECT THE RESPIRATORY AND CARDIOVASCULAR SYSTEMS.

HEALTH EFFECTS AND FIRST AID

INHALATION: CHLOROPICRIN: CORROSIVE/METHEMOGLOBIN FORMER/HIGHLY TOXIC. 4 PPM IMMEDIATELY DANGEROUS TO LIFE OR HEALTH. **ACUTE EXPOSURE-** MAY CAUSE IRRITATION, SORE THROAT, COUGHING, LABORED BREATHING, DIZZINESS, NAUSEA, VOMITING, CYANOSIS, FAINTNESS, AND PULMONARY EDEMA. LOW METHEMOGLOBIN LEVELS MAY RESULT IN HEADACHE, WEAKNESS, AND DYSPNEA. HIGH METHEMOGLOBIN LEVELS MAY RESULT IN STUPOR, RESPIRATORY DEPRESSION, AND CHOCOLATE COLORED BLOOD FROM LACK OF OXYGENATION. **CHRONIC EXPOSURE-** PROLONGED AND REPEATED EXPOSURE MAY CAUSE HEART AND LUNG DAMAGE AND PULMONARY EDEMA WITH POSSIBLE COMA AND DEATH.

FIRST AID- REMOVE FROM EXPOSURE AREA TO FRESH AIR IMMEDIATELY. IF BREATHING HAS STOPPED, GIVE ARTIFICIAL RESPIRATION. MAINTAIN AIRWAY AND BLOOD PRESSURE AND ADMINISTER OXYGEN IF AVAILABLE. KEEP AFFECTED PERSON WARM AND AT REST. TREAT SYMPTOMATICALLY AND SUPPORTIVELY. ADMINISTRATION OF OXYGEN SHOULD BE PERFORMED BY QUALIFIED PERSONNEL. GET MEDICAL ATTENTION IMMEDIATELY.

SKIN CONTACT: CHLOROPICRIN: CORROSIVE/METHEMOGLOBIN FORMER. **ACUTE EXPOSURE-** MAY CAUSE IRRITATION, REDNESS, PAIN AND SKIN BURNS. IT IS ABSORBED THROUGH THE SKIN AND MAY RESULT IN METHEMOGLOBINEMIA. LOW METHEMOGLOBIN LEVELS MAY RESULT IN HEADACHE, WEAKNESS, AND DYSPNEA. HIGH METHEMOGLOBIN LEVELS MAY RESULT IN STUPOR, RESPIRATORY DEPRESSION, AND CHOCOLATE COLORED BLOOD FROM LACK OF OXYGENATION. **CHRONIC EXPOSURE-** PROLONGED AND REPEATED EXPOSURE MAY CAUSE DERMATITIS AND SKIN BURNS.

FIRST AID- REMOVE CONTAMINATED CLOTHING AND SHOES IMMEDIATELY. WASH AFFECTED AREA WITH SOAP OR MILD DETERGENT AND LARGE AMOUNTS OF

WATER UNTIL NO EVIDENCE OF CHEMICAL REMAINS (AT LEAST 15-20 MINUTES). IN CASE OF CHEMICAL BURNS, COVER AREA WITH STERILE, DRY DRESSING. BANDAGE SECURELY, BUT NOT TOO TIGHTLY. GET MEDICAL ATTENTION IMMEDIATELY.

EYE CONTACT: CHLOROPICRIN: CORROSIVE/LACRIMATOR. **ACUTE EXPOSURE**- MAY CAUSE IRRITATION, REDNESS, PAIN, LACRIMATION, BLURRED VISION AND CORNEAL DAMAGE. **CHRONIC EXPOSURE**- MAY CAUSE CORNEAL DAMAGE AND CONJUNCTIVITIS.

FIRST AID- WASH EYES IMMEDIATELY WITH LARGE AMOUNTS OF WATER, OCCASIONALLY LIFTING UPPER AND LOWER LIDS, UNTIL NO EVIDENCE OF CHEMICAL REMAINS (AT LEAST 15-20 MINUTES). CONTINUE IRRIGATING WITH NORMAL SALINE UNTIL THE PH HAS RETURNED TO NORMAL (30-60 MINUTES). COVER WITH STERILE BANDAGES. GET MEDICAL ATTENTION IMMEDIATELY.

INGESTION: CHLOROPICRIN: CORROSIVE/METHEMOGLOBIN FORMER/TOXIC. **ACUTE EXPOSURE**- MAY CAUSE IRRITATION, SORE THROAT, COUGHING, LABORED BREATHING, DIZZINESS, NAUSEA, VOMITING, CYANOSIS, AND FAINTNESS. INGESTION OF LIQUID CAN CAUSE SEVERE GASTROENTERITIS. LOW METHEMOGLOBIN LEVELS MAY RESULT IN HEADACHE, WEAKNESS, AND DYSPNEA. HIGH METHEMOGLOBIN LEVELS MAY RESULT IN STUPOR, RESPIRATORY DEPRESSION, AND CHOCOLATE COLORED BLOOD FROM LACK OF OXYGENATION. **CHRONIC EXPOSURE**- MAY CAUSE HEART AND LUNG DAMAGE.

FIRST AID- REMOVE BY GASTRIC LAVAGE OR EMESIS USING ACTIVATED CHARCOAL. (DREISBACH, HANDBOOK OF POISONING, 11TH EDITION) GASTRIC LAVAGE OR EMESIS SHOULD NOT BE PERFORMED ON AN UNCONSCIOUS PERSON. TREATMENT SHOULD BE ADMINISTERED BY QUALIFIED MEDICAL PERSONNEL. GET MEDICAL ATTENTION IMMEDIATELY.

ANTIDOTE: THE FOLLOWING ANTIDOTE HAS BEEN RECOMMENDED. HOWEVER, THE DECISION AS TO WHETHER THE SEVERITY OF POISONING REQUIRES ADMINISTRATION OF ANY ANTIDOTE AND ACTUAL DOSE REQUIRED SHOULD BE MADE BY QUALIFIED MEDICAL PERSONNEL.
METHEMOGLOBINEMIA: (WHEN METHEMOGLOBIN CONCENTRATION IS OVER 25-40% OR IN PRESENCE OF SYMPTOMS.) GIVE METHYLENE BLUE, 1% SOLUTION, 0.1 ML/KG INTRAVENOUSLY OVER A 10-MINUTE PERIOD. CYANOSIS MAY DISAPPEAR WITHIN MINUTES OR PERSIST LONGER DEPENDING ON DEGREE OF METHEMOGLOBINEMIA. INTRAVENOUS ADMINISTRATION OF THERAPEUTIC DOSES OF METHYLENE BLUE MAY CAUSE A RISE IN BLOOD PRESSURE, NAUSEA, AND DIZZINESS. LARGER DOSES (>500 MG) CAUSE VOMITING, DIARRHEA, CHEST PAIN, MENTAL CONFUSION, CYANOSIS, AND SWEATING. HEMOLYTIC ANEMIA HAS ALSO OCCURRED SEVERAL DAYS AFTER ADMINISTRATION. THESE EFFECTS ARE TEMPORARY, AND FATALITIES HAVE NOT BEEN REPORTED. IF METHYLENE BLUE IS NOT AVAILABLE, GIVE ASCORBIC ACID, 1 GRAM SLOWLY INTRAVENOUSLY. WITHOUT TREATMENT, METHEMOGLOBINEMIA LEVELS OF 20-30% REVERT TO NORMAL WITHIN 3 DAYS (DREISBACH, HANDBOOK OF POISONING, 12TH ED.). ANTIDOTE SHOULD BE ADMINISTERED BY QUALIFIED MEDICAL PERSONNEL.

REACTIVITY

REACTIVITY: CHLOROPICRIN: BULK CONTAINERS CAN BE SHOCK DETONATED.

INCOMPATIBILITIES: CHLOROPICRIN: ANILINE: VIOLENT REACTION. BROMO-2-PROPYNE: EXPLOSIVE, SHOCK- AND HEAT- SENSITIVE. SODIUM HYDROXIDE: REACTS VIOLENTLY SODIUM METHOXIDE: BELOW 50 C, NITRO COMPOUND WILL ACCUMULATE AND CAUSE A VIOLENT AND DANGEROUS EXOTHERMIC REACTION. STRONG OXIDIZERS: POSSIBLE VIOLENT REACTION.

DECOMPOSITION: CHLOROPICRIN: THERMAL DECOMPOSITION PRODUCES CORROSIVE FUMES OF HYDROGEN CHLORIDE AND TOXIC OXIDES OF NITROGEN AND CARBON.

POLYMERIZATION: HAZARDOUS POLYMERIZATION HAS NOT BEEN REPORTED TO OCCUR UNDER NORMAL TEMPERATURES AND PRESSURES.

STORAGE AND DISPOSAL

STORAGE: PROTECT AGAINST PHYSICAL DAMAGE. OUTSIDE OR DETACHED STORAGE IS PREFERRED. INSIDE STORAGE SHOULD BE IN A WELL-VENTILATED AREA (NFPA 49, HAZARDOUS CHEMICALS DATA, 1975).

CONDITIONS TO AVOID

MAY BURN BUT DOES NOT IGNITE READILY. MAY EXPLODE FROM FRICTION, HEAT OR CONTAMINATION.

SPILL AND LEAK PROCEDURES

OCCUPATIONAL SPILL: DO NOT TOUCH SPILLED MATERIAL. STOP LEAK IF YOU CAN DO IT WITHOUT RISK. USE WATER SPRAY TO REDUCE VAPORS. FOR SMALL SPILLS, TAKE UP WITH SAND OR OTHER ABSORBENT MATERIAL AND PLACE INTO CONTAINERS FOR LATER DISPOSAL. FOR SMALL DRY SPILLS, WITH CLEAN SHOVEL PLACE MATERIAL INTO CLEAN, DRY CONTAINERS AND COVER. MOVE CONTAINERS FROM SPILL AREA. FOR LARGER SPILLS, DIKE FAR AHEAD OF SPILL FOR LATER DISPOSAL. KEEP UNNECESSARY PEOPLE AWAY. ISOLATE HAZARD AREA AND DENY ENTRY. VENTILATE CLOSED SPACES BEFORE ENTERING.

PROTECTIVE EQUIPMENT

VENTILATION: PROVIDE LOCAL EXHAUST OR PROCESS ENCLOSURE VENTILATION TO MEET PUBLISHED EXPOSURE LIMITS.

RESPIRATOR: THE FOLLOWING RESPIRATORS AND MAXIMUM USE CONCENTRATIONS ARE RECOMMENDATIONS BY THE U.S. DEPARTMENT OF HEALTH AND HUMAN SERVICES, NIOSH POCKET GUIDE TO CHEMICAL HAZARDS; NIOSH CRITERIA DOCUMENTS OR BY THE U.S. DEPARTMENT OF LABOR, 29 CFR 1910 SUBPART Z. THE SPECIFIC RESPIRATOR SELECTED MUST BE BASED ON CONTAMINATION LEVELS FOUND IN THE WORK PLACE, MUST NOT EXCEED THE WORKING LIMITS OF THE RESPIRATOR AND BE JOINTLY APPROVED BY THE NATIONAL INSTITUTE FOR OCCUPATIONAL SAFETY AND HEALTH AND THE MINE SAFETY AND HEALTH ADMINISTRATION (NIOSH-MSHA).
FOR CHLOROPICRIN:
2.5 PPM- ANY SUPPLIED-AIR RESPIRATOR OPERATED IN A CONTINUOUS FLOW MODE. ANY POWERED AIR-PURIFYING RESPIRATOR WITH ORGANIC VAPOR CARTRIDGE(S).
4 PPM- ANY SELF-CONTAINED BREATHING APPARATUS WITH A FULL FACEPIECE. ANY SUPPLIED-AIR RESPIRATOR WITH A FULL FACEPIECE. ANY CHEMICAL CARTRIDGE RESPIRATOR WITH A FULL FACEPIECE AND ORGANIC VAPOR CARTRIDGE(S). ANY AIR-PURIFYING FULL FACEPIECE RESPIRATOR (GAS MASK) WITH A CHIN-STYLE OR FRONT OR BACK-MOUNTED ORGANIC VAPOR CANISTER.
ESCAPE- ANY AIR-PURIFYING FULL FACEPIECE RESPIRATOR (GAS MASK) WITH A CHIN-STYLE OR FRONT OR BACK-MOUNTED ORGANIC VAPOR CANISTER. ANY APPROPRIATE ESCAPE-TYPE SELF-CONTAINED BREATHING APPARATUS.
FOR FIREFIGHTING AND OTHER IMMEDIATELY DANGEROUS TO LIFE OR HEALTH CONDITIONS:
SELF-CONTAINED BREATHING APPARATUS WITH FULL FACEPIECE OPERATED IN PRESSURE-DEMAND OR OTHER POSITIVE PRESSURE MODE.
SUPPLIED-AIR RESPIRATOR WITH FULL FACEPIECE AND OPERATED IN PRESSURE-DEMAND OR OTHER POSITIVE PRESSURE MODE IN COMBINATION WITH AN AUXILIARY SELF-CONTAINED BREATHING APPARATUS OPERATED IN PRESSURE-DEMAND OR OTHER POSITIVE PRESSURE MODE.

CLOTHING: EMPLOYEE MUST WEAR APPROPRIATE PROTECTIVE (IMPERVIOUS) CLOTHING AND EQUIPMENT TO PREVENT ANY POSSIBILITY OF SKIN CONTACT WITH THIS SUBSTANCE.

GLOVES: EMPLOYEE MUST WEAR APPROPRIATE PROTECTIVE GLOVES TO PREVENT CONTACT WITH THIS SUBSTANCE.

EYE PROTECTION: EMPLOYEE MUST WEAR SPLASH-PROOF OR DUST-RESISTANT SAFETY GOGGLES AND A FACESHIELD TO PREVENT CONTACT WITH THIS SUBSTANCE.
EMERGENCY WASH FACILITIES: WHERE THERE IS ANY POSSIBILITY THAT AN EMPLOYEE'S EYES AND/OR SKIN MAY BE EXPOSED TO THIS SUBSTANCE, THE EMPLOYER SHOULD PROVIDE AN EYE WASH FOUNTAIN AND QUICK DRENCH SHOWER WITHIN THE IMMEDIATE WORK AREA FOR EMERGENCY USE.

AUTHORIZED BY- OCCUPATIONAL HEALTH SERVICES, INC.
CREATION DATE: 10/04/89 ***REVISION DATE:*** 05/18/90

MATERIAL SAFETY DATA SHEET

OCCUPATIONAL HEALTH SERVICES, INC.
AGRICULTURE AND PESTICIDE DIVISION
450 SEVENTH AVENUE, SUITE 2407
NEW YORK, NEW YORK 10123
1-800-445-MSDS OR (212) 967-1100

EMERGENCY CONTACT:
JOHN S. BRANSFORD, JR. (615) 292-1180

SUBSTANCE IDENTIFICATION

CAS-NUMBER 1897-45-6

SUBSTANCE: **CHLOROTHALONIL**

TRADE NAMES/SYNONYMS: 2,4,5,6-TETRACHLORO-1,3-BENZENEDICARBONITRILE; TETRACHLOROISOPHTHALONITRILE; 1,3-BENZENEDICARBONITRILE, 2,4,5,6-TETRACHLORO-; 1,3-DICYANOTETRACHLOROBENZENE; ISOPHTHALONITRILE, TETRACHLORO-; M-TETRACHLOROPHTHALONITRILE; TETRACHLORO-META-PHTHALODINITRILE; BRAVO; DAC 2787; DACONIL; FORTURF; NOPCOCIDE N 96; TERMIL; THALONIL; C8CL4N2; PST04890

CHEMICAL FAMILY: HALOGEN COMPOUND, AROMATIC NITRILE

MOLECULAR FORMULA: C8-CL4-N2

MOLECULAR WEIGHT: 265.89

MOLECULAR FORMULA: C8-CL4-N2
MOLECULAR WEIGHT: 265.89
CERCLA RATINGS (SCALE 0-3): HEALTH = 3 FIRE = 1 REACTIVITY = 0 PERSISTENCE = 3
NFPA RATINGS (SCALE 0-4): HEALTH = U FIRE = 1 REACTIVITY = 0

COMPONENTS AND CONTAMINANTS

COMPONENT: CHLOROTHALONIL ***PERCENT:*** 100.0
CAS# 1897-45-6
OTHER CONTAMINANTS: NONE
EXPOSURE LIMITS: NO OCCUPATIONAL EXPOSURE LIMITS ESTABLISHED BY OSHA, ACGIH, OR NIOSH.
CHLOROTHALONIL: SUBJECT TO SARA SECTION 313 ANNUAL TOXIC CHEMICAL RELEASE REPORTING SUBJECT TO CALIFORNIA PROPOSITION 65 CANCER AND/OR REPRODUCTIVE TOXICITY WARNING AND RELEASE REQUIREMENTS- (JANUARY 1, 1989)

PHYSICAL DATA

DESCRIPTION: ODORLESS, WHITE CRYSTALLINE SOLID.
BOILING POINT: 662 F (350C)
MELTING POINT: 482-484 F (250-251 C) ***SPECIFIC GRAVITY:*** 1.7 @ 25 C
VAPOR PRESSURE: <0.01 MMHG AT 40 C ***SOLUBILITY IN WATER:*** 0.6 PPM @ 25 C
SOLVENT SOLUBILITY: SOLUBLE IN BENZENE; MODERATELY SOLUBLE IN XYLENE, CYCLOHEXANONE, ACETONE, KEROSENE, DIMETHYLFORMAMIDE, DIMETHYL SULFOXIDE, BUTANONE AND METHYL ETHYL KETONE.
SUBLIMES READILY ABOVE 200 C

FIRE AND EXPLOSION DATA

FIRE AND EXPLOSION HAZARD: SLIGHT FIRE HAZARD WHEN EXPOSED TO HEAT OR FLAME.
FIREFIGHTING MEDIA: DRY CHEMICAL, CARBON DIOXIDE, HALON, WATER SPRAY OR STANDARD FOAM (1987 EMERGENCY RESPONSE GUIDEBOOK, DOT P 5800.4).
FOR LARGER FIRES, USE WATER SPRAY, FOG OR STANDARD FOAM (1987 EMERGENCY RESPONSE GUIDEBOOK, DOT P 5800.4).
FIREFIGHTING: MOVE CONTAINER FROM FIRE AREA IF POSSIBLE. DO NOT SCATTER SPILLED MATERIAL WITH HIGH PRESSURE WATER STREAMS. DIKE FIRE CONTROL WATER FOR LATER DISPOSAL (1987 EMERGENCY RESPONSE GUIDEBOOK, DOT P 5800.4, GUIDE PAGE 31).
USE AGENTS SUITABLE FOR TYPE OF SURROUNDING FIRE. AVOID BREATHING HAZARDOUS VAPORS, KEEP UPWIND.

TOXICITY

CHLOROTHALONIL: TOXICITY DATA: >4.7 MG/L INHALATION-RAT LC50 (85JFAN); >10,000 MG/KG SKIN-RABBIT LD50 (85JFAN); 10 GM/KG ORAL-RAT LD50; 3700 MG/KG ORAL-MOUSE LD50; 2500 UG/KG INTRAPERITONEAL-MOUSE LD50; MUTAGENIC DATA (RTECS); TUMORIGENIC DATA (RTECS). CARCINOGEN STATUS: ANIMAL LIMITED EVIDENCE (IARC GROUP-3). ADMINISTRATION IN THE DIET PRODUCED ADENOMAS AND ADENOCARCINOMAS OF THE KIDNEY IN RATS, BUT NO EVIDENCE OF CARCINOGENICITY IN MICE. NO DATA WAS AVAILABLE TO EVALUATE THE CARCINOGENICITY OF CHLOROTHALONIL TO HUMANS. LOCAL EFFECTS: IRRITANT- INHALATION, SKIN, EYE. ACUTE TOXICITY LEVEL: SLIGHTLY TOXIC BY DERMAL ABSORPTION AND INGESTION. TARGET EFFECTS: SENSITIZER-DERMAL. POISONING MAY ALSO AFFECT THE KIDNEYS.

HEALTH EFFECTS AND FIRST AID

INHALATION: CHLOROTHALONIL: IRRITANT. **ACUTE EXPOSURE-** MAY CAUSE MODERATE IRRITATION. THE LETHAL DOSE REPORTED IN RATS WAS >4.7 MG/L. **CHRONIC EXPOSURE-** NO DATA AVAILABLE.
FIRST AID- REMOVE FROM EXPOSURE AREA TO FRESH AIR IMMEDIATELY. IF BREATHING HAS STOPPED, PERFORM ARTIFICIAL RESPIRATION. KEEP PERSON WARM AND AT REST. TREAT SYMPTOMATICALLY AND SUPPORTIVELY. GET MEDICAL ATTENTION IMMEDIATELY.

SKIN CONTACT: CHLOROTHALONIL: IRRITANT/SENSITIZER. **ACUTE EXPOSURE-** MAY CAUSE MODERATE IRRITATION. SENSITIZATION DERMATITIS MAY OCCUR IN PREVIOUSLY EXPOSED INDIVIDUALS. **CHRONIC EXPOSURE-** REPEATED AND PROLONGED EXPOSURE MAY CAUSE DERMATITIS WITH PRURITUS, ERYTHEMA, AND EDEMA DUE TO IRRITATION OR SENSITIZATION. PHOTOSENSITIZATION MAY OCCUR.
FIRST AID- REMOVE CONTAMINATED CLOTHING AND SHOES IMMEDIATELY. WASH AFFECTED AREA WITH SOAP OR MILD DETERGENT AND LARGE AMOUNTS OF WATER UNTIL NO EVIDENCE OF CHEMICAL REMAINS (APPROXIMATELY 15-20 MINUTES). GET MEDICAL ATTENTION IMMEDIATELY.

EYE CONTACT: CHLOROTHALONIL: IRRITANT. **ACUTE EXPOSURE-** 3 MG APPLIED TO THE EYES OF RABBITS PRODUCED CONJUNCTIVITIS THAT LARGELY SUBSIDED WITHIN 7 DAYS OF APPLICATION. IN ANOTHER STUDY, 100 MG APPLIED TO THE EYES OF RABBITS CAUSED MARKED IRRITATION AND CORNEAL OPACITIES. **CHRONIC EXPOSURE-** REPEATED OR PROLONGED CONTACT WITH IRRITANTS MAY CAUSE CONJUNCTIVITIS.
FIRST AID- WASH EYES IMMEDIATELY WITH LARGE AMOUNTS OF WATER OR NORMAL SALINE, OCCASIONALLY LIFTING UPPER AND LOWER LIDS, UNTIL NO EVIDENCE OF CHEMICAL REMAINS (APPROXIMATELY 15-20 MINUTES). GET MEDICAL ATTENTION IMMEDIATELY.

INGESTION: CHLOROTHALONIL: LIMITED ANIMAL CARCINOGEN. **ACUTE EXPOSURE-** ANIMALS GIVEN ACUTELY TOXIC DOSES EXHIBITED SEDATION FOLLOWED BY INCREASED WEAKNESS AND DEATH. **CHRONIC EXPOSURE-** IN A CHRONIC FEEDING STUDY AT THE 1% LEVEL, RATS EVENTUALLY DEVELOPED ATAXIA, TACHYPNEA, EPISTAXIS, DERMATITIS, HEMATURIA, HYPERACTIVITY, VAGINAL BLEEDING, AND BRIGHT YELLOW URINE. NODULAR MASSES PROGRESSING TO ABSCESSES AND RENAL TUMORS DEVELOPED IN SOME ANIMALS. OTHER REPORTED EFFECTS INCLUDE KIDNEY CHANGES WITH HYPERTROPHY, DILATATION, CYTOPLASMIC VACUOLATION, AND HYPERPLASIA OF THE EPITHELIAL CELLS OF THE TUBULES, AND GROSSLY ENLARGED, GREENISH-BROWN, GRANULAR KIDNEYS. LIVER, THYROID, AND STOMACH IRREGULARITIES HAVE ALSO BEEN REPORTED. RESULTS OF A THREE GENERATION REPRODUCTIVE EFFECTS STUDY INCLUDED GROWTH SUPPRESSION IN THE PUPS AND KIDNEY AND GASTROINTESTINAL TRACT PATHOLOGY.
FIRST AID- REMOVE BY GASTRIC LAVAGE AND CATHARSIS. MAINTAIN BLOOD PRESSURE AND AIRWAY. GIVE OXYGEN IF RESPIRATION IS DEPRESSED. DO NOT PERFORM GASTRIC LAVAGE IF VICTIM IS UNCONSCIOUS. GET MEDICAL ATTENTION IMMEDIATELY (DREISBACH, HANDBOOK OF POISONING, 12TH ED.).
ADMINISTRATION OF LAVAGE OR OXYGEN SHOULD BE PERFORMED BY QUALIFIED MEDICAL PERSONNEL.
ANTIDOTE: NO SPECIFIC ANTIDOTE. TREAT SYMPTOMATICALLY AND SUPPORTIVELY.

REACTIVITY

REACTIVITY: STABLE UNDER NORMAL TEMPERATURES AND PRESSURES.
INCOMPATIBILITIES: CHLOROTHALONIL: OXIDIZERS (STRONG): FIRE AND EXPLOSION HAZARD. THIOL-CONTAINING COMPOUNDS: HIGHLY REACTIVE.
DECOMPOSITION: THERMAL DECOMPOSITION PRODUCTS MAY INCLUDE HIGHLY TOXIC FUMES OF HYDROGEN CYANIDE.
THERMAL DECOMPOSITION MAY YIELD CHLORIDE FUMES AND TOXIC OXIDES OF NITROGEN.
POLYMERIZATION: HAZARDOUS POLYMERIZATION HAS NOT BEEN REPORTED TO OCCUR UNDER NORMAL TEMPERATURES AND PRESSURES.

STORAGE AND DISPOSAL

OBSERVE ALL FEDERAL, STATE AND LOCAL REGULATIONS WHEN STORING OR DISPOSING OF THIS SUBSTANCE. FOR ASSISTANCE, CONTACT THE DISTRICT DIRECTOR OF THE ENVIRONMENTAL PROTECTION AGENCY.

****STORAGE****

STORE IN ACCORDANCE WITH 40 CFR 165 RECOMMENDED PROCEDURES FOR THE DISPOSAL AND STORAGE OF PESTICIDES AND PESTICIDE CONTAINERS.
STORE AWAY FROM INCOMPATIBLE SUBSTANCES.

****DISPOSAL****

DISPOSAL MUST BE IN ACCORDANCE WITH 40 CFR 165 RECOMMENDED PROCEDURES FOR THE DISPOSAL AND STORAGE OF PESTICIDES AND PESTICIDE CONTAINERS.

CONDITIONS TO AVOID

MAY BURN BUT DOES NOT IGNITE READILY. AVOID CONTACT WITH STRONG OXIDIZERS, EXCESSIVE HEAT, SPARKS, OR OPEN FLAME.

SPILL AND LEAK PROCEDURES

WATER SPILL: THE CALIFORNIA SAFE DRINKING WATER AND TOXIC ENFORCEMENT ACT OF 1986 (PROPOSITION 65) PROHIBITS CONTAMINATING ANY KNOWN SOURCE OF DRINKING WATER WITH SUBSTANCES KNOWN TO CAUSE CANCER AND/OR REPRODUCTIVE TOXICITY.
OCCUPATIONAL SPILL: STOP LEAK IF YOU CAN DO IT WITHOUT RISK. FOR SMALL SPILLS, TAKE UP WITH SAND OR OTHER ABSORBENT MATERIAL AND PLACE INTO CLEAN, DRY CONTAINERS FOR LATER DISPOSAL. KEEP UNNECESSARY PEOPLE AWAY. ISOLATE HAZARD AREA AND DENY ENTRY.

PROTECTIVE EQUIPMENT

VENTILATION: PROVIDE LOCAL EXHAUST OR PROCESS ENCLOSURE VENTILATION SYSTEM.
RESPIRATOR: THE FOLLOWING RESPIRATORS ARE RECOMMENDED BASED ON INFORMATION FOUND IN THE PHYSICAL DATA, TOXICITY AND HEALTH EFFECTS SECTIONS. THEY ARE RANKED IN ORDER FROM MINIMUM TO MAXIMUM RESPIRATORY PROTECTION. THE SPECIFIC RESPIRATOR SELECTED MUST BE BASED

NATIONAL INSTITUTE FOR OCCUPATIONAL SAFETY AND HEALTH AND THE MINE SAFETY AND HEALTH ADMINISTRATION (NIOSH-MSHA).
CHEMICAL CARTRIDGE RESPIRATOR WITH AN ORGANIC VAPOR CARTRIDGE(S) WITH A FULL FACEPIECE AND ORGANIC VAPOR CARTRIDGE(S) IN COMBINATION WITH A DUST AND MIST FILTER.
POWERED AIR-PURIFYING RESPIRATOR WITH A TIGHT-FITTING FACEPIECE AND ORGANIC VAPOR CARTRIDGE(S) IN COMBINATION WITH A HIGH-EFFICIENCY PARTICULATE FILTER.
TYPE 'C' SUPPLIED-AIR RESPIRATOR WITH A FULL FACEPIECE OPERATED IN A PRESSURE-DEMAND OR OTHER POSITIVE PRESSURE MODE.
SELF-CONTAINED BREATHING APPARATUS WITH A FULL FACEPIECE OPERATED IN PRESSURE-DEMAND OR OTHER POSITIVE PRESSURE MODE.
FOR FIREFIGHTING AND OTHER IMMEDIATELY DANGEROUS TO LIFE OR HEALTH CONDITIONS:
SELF-CONTAINED BREATHING APPARATUS WITH FULL FACEPIECE OPERATED IN PRESSURE-DEMAND OR OTHER POSITIVE PRESSURE MODE.
SUPPLIED-AIR RESPIRATOR WITH FULL FACEPIECE AND OPERATED IN PRESSURE-DEMAND OR OTHER POSITIVE PRESSURE MODE IN COMBINATION WITH AN AUXILIARY SELF-CONTAINED BREATHING APPARATUS OPERATED IN PRESSURE-DEMAND OR OTHER POSITIVE PRESSURE MODE.

CLOTHING: EMPLOYEE MUST WEAR APPROPRIATE PROTECTIVE (IMPERVIOUS) CLOTHING AND EQUIPMENT TO PREVENT REPEATED OR PROLONGED SKIN CONTACT WITH THIS SUBSTANCE.

GLOVES: EMPLOYEE MUST WEAR APPROPRIATE PROTECTIVE GLOVES TO PREVENT CONTACT WITH THIS SUBSTANCE.

EYE PROTECTION: EMPLOYEE MUST WEAR SPLASH-PROOF OR DUST-RESISTANT SAFETY GOGGLES TO PREVENT EYE CONTACT WITH THIS SUBSTANCE.
EMERGENCY EYE WASH: WHERE THERE IS ANY POSSIBILITY THAT AN EMPLOYEE'S EYES MAY BE EXPOSED TO THIS SUBSTANCE, THE EMPLOYER SHOULD PROVIDE AN EYE WASH FOUNTAIN WITHIN THE IMMEDIATE WORK AREA FOR EMERGENCY USE.

AUTHORIZED BY- OCCUPATIONAL HEALTH SERVICES, INC.
CREATION DATE: 10/04/89 ***REVISION DATE:*** 07/13/90

MATERIAL SAFETY DATA SHEET

OCCUPATIONAL HEALTH SERVICES, INC.
AGRICULTURE AND PESTICIDE DIVISION
450 SEVENTH AVENUE, SUITE 2407
NEW YORK, NEW YORK 10123
1-800-445-MSDS OR (212) 967-1100

EMERGENCY CONTACT:
JOHN S. BRANSFORD, JR. (615) 292-1180

SUBSTANCE IDENTIFICATION

CAS-NUMBER 1982-47-4

SUBSTANCE: CHLOROXURON

TRADE NAMES/SYNONYMS: UREA, N'-(4-(4-CHLOROPHENOXY)PHENYL)-N,N-DIMETHYL-; UREA, 3-(P-(P-CHLOROPHENOXY)PHENYL)-1,1-DIMETHYL-; N'-(4-(4-CHLOROPHENOXY)PHENYL)-N,N-DIMETHYLUREA; 3-(P-(P-CHLOROPHENOXY)PHENYL)-1,1-DIMETHYLUREA; 3-(4-(4-CHLOROPHENOXY)PHENYL)-1,1-DIMETHYLUREA; C 1983; CHLOROXIFENIDIM; NOREX; TENORAN; C15H15CLN2O2; PST04905

CHEMICAL FAMILY: SUBSTITUTED UREA
HALOGEN COMPOUND, AROMATIC

MOLECULAR FORMULA: C15-H15-CL-N2-O2

MOLECULAR WEIGHT: 290.77

CERCLA RATINGS (SCALE 0-3): HEALTH=2 FIRE=1 REACTIVITY=0 PERSISTENCE=3

NFPA RATINGS (SCALE 0-4): HEALTH=2 FIRE=1 REACTIVITY=0

COMPONENTS AND CONTAMINANTS

COMPONENT: CHLOROXURON ***PERCENT:*** 100
CAS# 1982-47-4

OTHER CONTAMINANTS: NONE

EXPOSURE LIMITS: CHLOROXURON: NO OCCUPATIONAL EXPOSURE LIMITS ESTABLISHED BY OSHA, ACGIH, OR NIOSH.
500/10,000 POUNDS SARA SECTION 302 THRESHOLD PLANNING QUANTITY 1 POUND SARA SECTION 304 REPORTABLE QUANTITY

PHYSICAL DATA

DESCRIPTION: WHITE CRYSTALLINE SOLID. ***MELTING POINT:*** 304-306 F (151-152 C)

SPECIFIC GRAVITY: 1.34 ***VAPOR PRESSURE:*** NEGLIGIBLE

SOLUBILITY IN WATER: 0.0004%

SOLVENT SOLUBILITY: SOLUBLE IN DICHLOROMETHANE, ACETONE, CHLOROFORM, DIMETHYL FORMAMIDE, METHANOL; SLIGHTLY SOLUBLE IN TOLUENE, ALCOHOL, ETHER.

FIRE AND EXPLOSION DATA

FIRE AND EXPLOSION HAZARD: SLIGHT FIRE HAZARD WHEN EXPOSED TO HEAT OR FLAME.

FIREFIGHTING MEDIA: DRY CHEMICAL, CARBON DIOXIDE, HALON, WATER SPRAY OR STANDARD FOAM (1987 EMERGENCY RESPONSE GUIDEBOOK, DOT P 5800.4).
FOR LARGER FIRES, USE WATER SPRAY, FOG OR STANDARD FOAM (1987 EMERGENCY RESPONSE GUIDEBOOK, DOT P 5800.4).

FIREFIGHTING: MOVE CONTAINERS FROM FIRE AREA IF POSSIBLE (1987 EMERGENCY RESPONSE GUIDEBOOK, DOT P 5800.4, GUIDE PAGE 53).
EXTINGUISH USING AGENTS SUITABLE FOR SURROUNDING FIRE. USE FLOODING QUANTITIES OF WATER AS A FOG. KEEP MATERIAL OUT OF SEWERS AND WATER SOURCES. DO NOT TOUCH SPILLED MATERIAL. AVOID BREATHING HAZARDOUS FUMES; KEEP UPWIND.

TOXICITY

CHLOROXURON: TOXICITY DATA: 3700 MG/KG ORAL-RAT LD50; 10 MG/KG ORAL-DOG LD50; 1000 MG/KG UNREPORTED-RAT LD50. CARCINOGEN STATUS: NONE. ACUTE TOXICITY LEVEL: MODERATELY TOXIC BY INGESTION. TARGET EFFECTS: NO DATA AVAILABLE.

HEALTH EFFECTS AND FIRST AID

INHALATION: CHLOROXURON: **ACUTE EXPOSURE**- A LETHAL CONCENTRATION IN RATS WAS GREATER THAN 1350 MG/M3/6 HOURS. MANY UREA DERIVATIVE HERBICIDES ARE MODERATELY IRRITATING TO THE MUCOUS MEMBRANES.
CHRONIC EXPOSURE- NO DATA AVAILABLE.

FIRST AID- REMOVE FROM EXPOSURE AREA TO FRESH AIR IMMEDIATELY. IF BREATHING HAS STOPPED, PERFORM ARTIFICIAL RESPIRATION. KEEP PERSON WARM AND AT REST. TREAT SYMPTOMATICALLY AND SUPPORTIVELY. GET MEDICAL ATTENTION IMMEDIATELY.

SKIN CONTACT: CHLOROXURON: **ACUTE EXPOSURE**- THIS MATERIAL WAS SLIGHTLY IRRITATING TO RABBIT SKIN. A LETHAL DOSE IN RABBITS BY DERMAL ABSORPTION WAS GREATER THAN 10,000 MG/KG. **CHRONIC EXPOSURE**- NO DATA AVAILABLE.

FIRST AID- REMOVE CONTAMINATED CLOTHING AND SHOES IMMEDIATELY. WASH AFFECTED AREA WITH SOAP OR MILD DETERGENT AND LARGE AMOUNTS OF WATER UNTIL NO EVIDENCE OF CHEMICAL REMAINS (APPROXIMATELY 15-20 MINUTES). GET MEDICAL ATTENTION IMMEDIATELY.

EYE CONTACT: CHLOROXURON: **ACUTE EXPOSURE**- THIS MATERIAL WAS SLIGHTLY IRRITATING TO RABBIT EYES. **CHRONIC EXPOSURE**- NO DATA AVAILABLE.

FIRST AID- WASH EYES IMMEDIATELY WITH LARGE AMOUNTS OF WATER OR NORMAL SALINE, OCCASIONALLY LIFTING UPPER AND LOWER LIDS, UNTIL NO EVIDENCE OF CHEMICAL REMAINS (APPROXIMATELY 15-20 MINUTES). GET MEDICAL ATTENTION IMMEDIATELY.

INGESTION: CHLOROXURON: **ACUTE EXPOSURE**- A LETHAL DOSE IN RATS WAS 3700 MG/KG. **CHRONIC EXPOSURE**- NO ADVERSE EFFECTS WERE OBSERVED IN SUBCHRONIC STUDIES OF RATS FED 30 MG/KG/DAY OR DOGS FED 16.7 MG/KG/DAY.

FIRST AID- TREAT SYMPTOMATICALLY AND SUPPORTIVELY. GET MEDICAL ATTENTION IMMEDIATELY. IF VOMITING OCCURS, KEEP HEAD LOWER THAN HIPS TO PREVENT ASPIRATION.

ANTIDOTE: NO SPECIFIC ANTIDOTE. TREAT SYMPTOMATICALLY AND SUPPORTIVELY.

REACTIVITY

REACTIVITY: STABLE UNDER NORMAL TEMPERATURES AND PRESSURES.

INCOMPATIBILITIES: CHLOROXURON: OXIDIZERS (STRONG): FIRE AND EXPLOSION HAZARD.

DECOMPOSITION: THERMAL DECOMPOSITION PRODUCTS MAY INCLUDE TOXIC OXIDES OF NITROGEN AND CARBON AND TOXIC AND CORROSIVE FUMES OF CHLORIDES.

POLYMERIZATION: HAZARDOUS POLYMERIZATION HAS NOT BEEN REPORTED TO OCCUR UNDER NORMAL TEMPERATURES AND PRESSURES.

STORAGE AND DISPOSAL

OBSERVE ALL FEDERAL, STATE AND LOCAL REGULATIONS WHEN STORING OR DISPOSING OF THIS SUBSTANCE. FOR ASSISTANCE, CONTACT THE DISTRICT DIRECTOR OF THE ENVIRONMENTAL PROTECTION AGENCY.

****STORAGE****

STORE IN ACCORDANCE WITH 40 CFR 165 RECOMMENDED PROCEDURES FOR THE

DISPOSAL AND STORAGE OF PESTICIDES AND PESTICIDE CONTAINERS.
THRESHOLD PLANNING QUANTITY (TPQ): THE SUPERFUND AMENDMENTS AND REAUTHORIZATION ACT (SARA) SECTION 302 REQUIRES THAT EACH FACILITY WHERE ANY EXTREMELY HAZARDOUS SUBSTANCE IS PRESENT IN A QUANTITY EQUAL TO OR GREATER THAN THE TPQ ESTABLISHED FOR THAT SUBSTANCE NOTIFY THE STATE EMERGENCY RESPONSE COMMISSION FOR THE STATE IN WHICH IT IS LOCATED. SECTION 303 OF SARA REQUIRES THESE FACILITIES TO PARTICIPATE IN LOCAL EMERGENCY RESPONSE PLANNING (40 CFR 355.30).
STORE AWAY FROM INCOMPATIBLE SUBSTANCES.

DISPOSAL

DISPOSAL MUST BE IN ACCORDANCE WITH 40 CFR 165 RECOMMENDED PROCEDURES FOR THE DISPOSAL AND STORAGE OF PESTICIDES AND PESTICIDE CONTAINERS.

CONDITIONS TO AVOID

MAY BURN BUT DOES NOT IGNITE READILY.

SPILL AND LEAK PROCEDURES

OCCUPATIONAL SPILL: DO NOT TOUCH SPILLED MATERIAL. STOP LEAK IF YOU CAN DO IT WITHOUT RISK. FOR SMALL SPILLS, TAKE UP WITH SAND OR OTHER ABSORBENT MATERIAL AND PLACE INTO CONTAINERS FOR LATER DISPOSAL. FOR SMALL DRY SPILLS, WITH A CLEAN SHOVEL PLACE MATERIAL INTO CLEAN, DRY CONTAINER AND COVER. MOVE CONTAINERS FROM SPILL AREA. FOR LARGER SPILLS, DIKE FAR AHEAD OF SPILL FOR LATER DISPOSAL. KEEP UNNECESSARY PEOPLE AWAY. ISOLATE HAZARD AREA AND DENY ENTRY.
REPORTABLE QUANTITY (RQ): 1 POUND THE SUPERFUND AMENDMENTS AND REAUTHORIZATION ACT (SARA) SECTION 304 REQUIRES THAT A RELEASE EQUAL TO OR GREATER THAN THE REPORTABLE QUANTITY FOR THIS SUBSTANCE BE IMMEDIATELY REPORTED TO THE LOCAL EMERGENCY PLANNING COMMITTEE AND THE STATE EMERGENCY RESPONSE COMMISSION (40 CFR 355.40). IF THE RELEASE OF THIS SUBSTANCE IS REPORTABLE UNDER CERCLA SECTION 103, THE NATIONAL RESPONSE CENTER MUST BE NOTIFIED IMMEDIATELY AT (800) 424-8802 OR (202) 426-2675 IN THE METROPOLITAN WASHINGTON, D.C. AREA (40 CFR 302.6).

PROTECTIVE EQUIPMENT

VENTILATION: PROVIDE LOCAL EXHAUST VENTILATION SYSTEM.
RESPIRATOR: THE FOLLOWING RESPIRATORS ARE RECOMMENDED BASED ON INFORMATION FOUND IN THE PHYSICAL DATA, TOXICITY AND HEALTH EFFECTS SECTIONS. THEY ARE RANKED IN ORDER FROM MINIMUM TO MAXIMUM RESPIRATORY PROTECTION. THE SPECIFIC RESPIRATOR SELECTED MUST BE BASED ON CONTAMINATION LEVELS FOUND IN THE WORK PLACE, MUST NOT EXCEED THE WORKING LIMITS OF THE RESPIRATOR AND BE JOINTLY APPROVED BY THE NATIONAL INSTITUTE FOR OCCUPATIONAL SAFETY AND HEALTH AND THE MINE SAFETY AND HEALTH ADMINISTRATION (NIOSH-MSHA).
CHEMICAL CARTRIDGE RESPIRATOR WITH AN ORGANIC VAPOR CARTRIDGE(S) WITH A FULL FACEPIECE AND ORGANIC VAPOR CARTRIDGE(S) IN COMBINATION WITH A DUST AND MIST FILTER.
POWERED AIR-PURIFYING RESPIRATOR WITH A TIGHT-FITTING FACEPIECE AND ORGANIC VAPOR CARTRIDGE(S) IN COMBINATION WITH A HIGH-EFFICIENCY PARTICULATE FILTER.
TYPE 'C' SUPPLIED-AIR RESPIRATOR WITH A FULL FACEPIECE OPERATED IN A PRESSURE-DEMAND OR OTHER POSITIVE PRESSURE MODE.
SELF-CONTAINED BREATHING APPARATUS WITH A FULL FACEPIECE OPERATED IN PRESSURE-DEMAND OR OTHER POSITIVE PRESSURE MODE.
FOR FIREFIGHTING AND OTHER IMMEDIATELY DANGEROUS TO LIFE OR HEALTH CONDITIONS:
SELF-CONTAINED BREATHING APPARATUS WITH FULL FACEPIECE OPERATED IN PRESSURE-DEMAND OR OTHER POSITIVE PRESSURE MODE.
SUPPLIED-AIR RESPIRATOR WITH FULL FACEPIECE AND OPERATED IN PRESSURE-DEMAND OR OTHER POSITIVE PRESSURE MODE IN COMBINATION WITH AN AUXILIARY SELF-CONTAINED BREATHING APPARATUS OPERATED IN PRESSURE-DEMAND OR OTHER POSITIVE PRESSURE MODE.
CLOTHING: EMPLOYEE MUST WEAR APPROPRIATE PROTECTIVE (IMPERVIOUS) CLOTHING AND EQUIPMENT TO PREVENT REPEATED OR PROLONGED SKIN CONTACT WITH THIS SUBSTANCE.
GLOVES: EMPLOYEE MUST WEAR APPROPRIATE PROTECTIVE GLOVES TO PREVENT CONTACT WITH THIS SUBSTANCE.
EYE PROTECTION: EMPLOYEE MUST WEAR SPLASH-PROOF OR DUST-RESISTANT SAFETY GOGGLES TO PREVENT EYE CONTACT WITH THIS SUBSTANCE.
EMERGENCY EYE WASH: WHERE THERE IS ANY POSSIBILITY THAT AN EMPLOYEE'S EYES MAY BE EXPOSED TO THIS SUBSTANCE, THE EMPLOYER SHOULD PROVIDE AN EYE WASH FOUNTAIN WITHIN THE IMMEDIATE WORK AREA FOR EMERGENCY USE.

AUTHORIZED BY- OCCUPATIONAL HEALTH SERVICES, INC.

CREATION DATE: 10/04/89 ***REVISION DATE:*** 05/14/90

MATERIAL SAFETY DATA SHEET

OCCUPATIONAL HEALTH SERVICES, INC.
AGRICULTURE AND PESTICIDE DIVISION
450 SEVENTH AVENUE, SUITE 2407
NEW YORK, NEW YORK 10123
1-800-445-MSDS OR (212) 967-1100

EMERGENCY CONTACT:
JOHN S. BRANSFORD, JR. (615) 292-1180

SUBSTANCE IDENTIFICATION

CAS-NUMBER 2921-88-2
SUBSTANCE: **CHLORPYRIFOS**
TRADE NAMES/SYNONYMS: PHOSPHOROTHIOIC ACID, O,O-DIETHYL O-(3,5,6-TRICHLORO-2-PYRIDINYL) ESTER; PHOSPHOROTHIOIC ACID, O,O-DIETHYL O-(3,5,6-TRICHLORO-2-PYRIDYL) ESTER; O,O-DIETHYL O-3,5,6-TRICHLORO-2-PYRIDYL PHOSPHOROTHIOATE; O,O-DIETHYL O-(3,5,6-TRICHLORO-2-PYRIDYL) PHOSPHOROTHIOATE; O,O-DIETHYL O-(3,5,6-TRICHLORO-2-PYRIDINYL) PHOSPHOROTHIOATE; DIETHYL 3,5,6-TRICHLORO-2-PYRIDYL PHOSPHOROTHIONATE; CHLOROPYRIPHOS; CHLOROPYRIFOS; CHLORPYRIPHOS; CORBAN; DOWCO 179; DURSBAN; KILLMASTER; LORSBAN; OMS 971; ENT 27311; STCC 4941124; C9H11CL3NO3PS; PST04910
CHEMICAL FAMILY: ORGANOPHOSPHATE
HALOGEN COMPOUND, AROMATIC
MOLECULAR FORMULA: C9-H11-CL3-N-O3-P-S
MOLECULAR WEIGHT: 350.57
CERCLA RATINGS (SCALE 0-3): HEALTH=3 FIRE=U REACTIVITY=1 PERSISTENCE=3
NFPA RATINGS (SCALE 0-4): HEALTH=3 FIRE=U REACTIVITY=1

COMPONENTS AND CONTAMINANTS

COMPONENT: CHLORPYRIFOS ***PERCENT:*** 100
CAS# 2921-88-2
EXPOSURE LIMITS: CHLORPYRIFOS: 0.2 MG/M3 OSHA TWA (SKIN) 0.2 MG/M3 ACGIH TWA (SKIN); 0.6 MG/M3 ACGIH STEL (NOTICE OF INTENDED CHANGES 1988-89)
1 POUND CERCLA SECTION 103 REPORTABLE QUANTITY

PHYSICAL DATA

DESCRIPTION: WHITE CRYSTALLINE SOLID WITH A MILD MERCAPTAN ODOR
MELTING POINT: 106-108 F (41-42 C) ***SPECIFIC GRAVITY:*** 1.398 @ 43 C
VAPOR PRESSURE: 0.0000187 MMHG @ 25C ***SOLUBILITY IN WATER:*** 2 PPM @ 25 C
SOLVENT SOLUBILITY: SOLUBLE IN ACETONE, BENZENE, CHLOROFORM, ETHANOL, ISOOCTANE, METHANOL, AND ORGANIC SOLVENTS

FIRE AND EXPLOSION DATA

FIRE AND EXPLOSION HAZARD: UNKNOWN FIRE AND EXPLOSION HAZARD.
FIREFIGHTING MEDIA: DRY CHEMICAL, CARBON DIOXIDE, HALON, WATER SPRAY OR STANDARD FOAM (1987 EMERGENCY RESPONSE GUIDEBOOK, DOT P 5800.4).
FOR LARGER FIRES, USE WATER SPRAY, FOG OR STANDARD FOAM (1987 EMERGENCY RESPONSE GUIDEBOOK, DOT P 5800.4).
FIREFIGHTING: MOVE CONTAINERS FROM FIRE AREA IF POSSIBLE. FIGHT FIRE FROM MAXIMUM DISTANCE. STAY AWAY FROM STORAGE TANK ENDS. DIKE FIRE CONTROL WATER FOR LATER DISPOSAL. DO NOT SCATTER MATERIAL (1987 EMERGENCY RESPONSE GUIDEBOOK, DOT P 5800.4, GUIDE PAGE 55).
EXTINGUISH ONLY IF FLOW CAN BE STOPPED; USE FLOODING AMOUNTS OF WATER AS FOG, SOLID STREAMS MAY BE INEFFECTIVE. COOL CONTAINERS WITH FLOODING AMOUNTS OF WATER FROM AS FAR A DISTANCE AS POSSIBLE. USE WATER SPRAY TO ABSORB TOXIC VAPORS. AVOID BREATHING TOXIC VAPORS; KEEP UPWIND. CONSIDER EVACUATION OF DOWNWIND AREA IF MATERIAL IS LEAKING.

TRANSPORTATION DATA

DEPARTMENT OF TRANSPORTATION HAZARD CLASSIFICATION 49 CFR 172.101: ORM-A
DEPARTMENT OF TRANSPORTATION LABELING REQUIREMENTS 49 CFR 172.101 AND SUBPART E: NONE
DEPARTMENT OF TRANSPORTATION PACKAGING REQUIREMENTS: 49 CFR 173.510 EXCEPTIONS: 49 CFR 173.505

TOXICITY

CHLORPYRIFOS: TOXICITY DATA: 78 MG/KG INHALATION-RAT LD50; 94 MG/KG

TOXICITY

CHLORPYRIFOS: TOXICITY DATA: 78 MG/KG INHALATION-RAT LD50; 94 MG/KG INHALATION-MOUSE LD50; 2000 MG/KG SKIN-RABBIT LD50; 202 MG/KG SKIN-RAT LD50; 300 MG/KG ORAL-MAN TDLO; 82 MG/KG ORAL-RAT LD50; 60 MG/KG ORAL-MOUSE LD50; 1000 MG/KG ORAL-RABBIT LD50; 504 MG/KG ORAL-GUINEA PIG LD50; 100 MG/KG SUBCUTANEOUS-GUINEA PIG LDLO; 192 MG/KG INTRAPERITONEAL-MOUSE LD50; 150 MG/KG UNREPORTED-RAT LD50; 163 MG/KG UNREPORTED-MAMMAL LD50; MUTAGENIC DATA (RTECS); REPRODUCTIVE EFFECTS DATA (RTECS). CARCINOGEN STATUS: NONE. LOCAL EFFECTS: IRRITANT-SKIN, EYE. ACUTE TOXICITY LEVEL: TOXIC BY INGESTION; MODERATELY TOXIC BY DERMAL ABSORPTION. TARGET EFFECTS: CHOLINESTERASE INHIBITOR. AT INCREASED RISK FROM EXPOSURE: PERSONS WITH RESPIRATORY AILMENTS, RECENT EXPOSURE TO CHOLINESTERASE INHIBITORS OR IMPAIRED CHOLINESTERASE PRODUCTION, OR LIVER MALFUNCTION.* ADDITIONAL DATA: MAY CROSS THE PLACENTA. HIGH ENVIRONMENTAL TEMPERATURES OR EXPOSURE OF THE CHEMICAL TO VISIBLE OR ULTRAVIOLET LIGHT MAY ENHANCE THE TOXICITY. INTERACTIONS WITH MEDICATIONS MAY OCCUR.*

* MAY BE BASED ON GENERAL INFORMATION ON ORGANOPHOSPHATES.

HEALTH EFFECTS AND FIRST AID

INHALATION: CHLORPYRIFOS: SEE INFORMATION ON ORGANOPHOSPHATES.

ORGANOPHOSPHATES: CHOLINESTERASE INHIBITOR. **ACUTE EXPOSURE-** WHEN INHALED, THE FIRST EFFECTS OF CHOLINESTERASE INHIBITORS ARE USUALLY RESPIRATORY AND MAY INCLUDE NASAL HYPEREMIA AND WATERY DISCHARGE, COUGH, CHEST DISCOMFORT, DYSPNEA, AND WHEEZING DUE TO INCREASED BRONCHIAL SECRETIONS AND BRONCHOCONSTRICTION. IF SUFFICIENT AMOUNTS ARE ABSORBED, OTHER SYSTEMIC EFFECTS MAY BEGIN WITHIN A FEW MINUTES OR BE DELAYED FOR UP TO 12 HOURS. SYMPTOMS MAY INCLUDE PALLOR, NAUSEA, VOMITING, DIARRHEA, ABDOMINAL CRAMPS, HEADACHE, DIZZINESS, OCULAR PAIN, BLURRED VISION, MIOSIS OR IN SOME CASES, ESPECIALLY INITIALLY, MYDRIASIS, LACRIMATION, SALIVATION, SWEATING, AND CONFUSION. OTHER REPORTED CENTRAL NERVOUS SYSTEM OR NEUROMUSCULAR EFFECTS MAY INCLUDE ATAXIA, SLURRED SPEECH, AREFLEXIA, WEAKNESS, FATIGUE, FASCICULATIONS, TWITCHING, TREMORS POSSIBLY OF THE TONGUE AND EYELIDS, AND EVENTUALLY PARALYSIS OF THE EXTREMITIES AND POSSIBLY OF THE RESPIRATORY MUSCLES. IN SEVERE CASES THERE MAY ALSO BE INVOLUNTARY DEFECATION AND URINATION, CYANOSIS, PSYCHOSIS, HYPERGLYCEMIA, ACUTE PANCREATITIS, CARDIAC IRREGULARITIES, PULMONARY EDEMA, UNCONSCIOUSNESS, CONVULSIONS, AND COMA. DEATH IS PRIMARILY DUE TO RESPIRATORY FAILURE, ALTHOUGH CARDIOVASCULAR EFFECTS INCLUDING CARDIAC ARREST MAY ALSO BE IMPLICATED. LONG TERM SEQUELAE ARE RARE BUT MAY INCLUDE NEUROPSYCHIATRIC DISORDERS AND MYOPATHY WITH MUSCLE TENDERNESS. **CHRONIC EXPOSURE-** REPEATED OR PROLONGED EXPOSURE MAY RESULT IN THE EFFECTS OF ACUTE EXPOSURE. OTHER EFFECTS REPORTED IN WORKERS REPEATEDLY EXPOSED INCLUDE IMPAIRED MEMORY AND CONCENTRATION, ACUTE PSYCHOSIS, SEVERE DEPRESSIONS, IRRITABILTY, CONFUSION, APATHY, EMOTIONAL LABILITY, SOCIAL WITHDRAWAL, CONFUSION, HEADACHE, SPEECH DIFFICULTIES, DELAYED REACTION TIMES, SPATIAL DISORIENTATION, NIGHTMARES, SLEEPWALKING, AND DROWSINESS OR INSOMNIA. AN INFLUENZA-LIKE CONDITION WITH HEADACHE, NAUSEA, WEAKNESS, ANOREXIA AND MALAISE HAS ALSO BEEN REPORTED.

FIRST AID- REMOVE FROM EXPOSURE AREA TO FRESH AIR IMMEDIATELY. IF BREATHING HAS STOPPED, GIVE ARTIFICIAL RESPIRATION. MAINTAIN AIRWAY AND BLOOD PRESSURE AND ADMINISTER OXYGEN IF AVAILABLE. KEEP AFFECTED PERSON WARM AND AT REST. TREAT SYMPTOMATICALLY AND SUPPORTIVELY. ADMINISTRATION OF OXYGEN SHOULD BE PERFORMED BY QUALIFIED PERSONNEL. GET MEDICAL ATTENTION IMMEDIATELY.

SKIN CONTACT: CHLORPYRIFOS: IRRITANT. MAY CAUSE IRRITATION. FOUR DOSES OF 25 MG/KG APPLIED TO THE SKIN OF HUMANS FOR 12 HOURS EACH PRODUCED DEPRESSED PLASMA CHOLINESTERASE LEVELS. SEE INFORMATION ON ORHANOPHOSPHATES.

ORGANOPHOSPHATES: CHOLINESTERASE INHIBITOR. **ACUTE EXPOSURE-** LOCALIZED SWEATING AND FASCICULATIONS MAY OCCUR AT THE SITE OF CONTACT. IF SUFFICIENT AMOUNTS ARE ABSORBED, OTHER EFFECTS OF CHOLINESTERASE INHIBITION AS DESCRIBED IN ACUTE INHALATION MAY OCCUR. SYMPTOMS MAY BE DELAYED 2-3 HOURS, BUT USUALLY NO MORE THAN 12 HOURS. THE RATE OF ABSORPTION IS INCREASED BY THE PRESENCE OF DERMATITIS OR HIGH AMBIENT TEMPERATURES. **CHRONIC EXPOSURE-** REPEATED OR PROLONGED EXPOSURE MAY CAUSE EFFECTS AS DESCRIBED IN ACUTE EXPOSURE. SOME ORGANOPHOSPHATES MAY CAUSE SENSITIZATION.

FIRST AID- REMOVE CONTAMINATED CLOTHING IMMEDIATELY. WASH CONTAMINATED AREAS WITH SOAP AND WATER FOLLOWED BY ALCOHOL (ARENA, POISONING, 4TH ED.). EMERGENCY PERSONNEL SHOULD WEAR GLOVES AND AVOID CONTAMINATION. TREAT RESPIRATORY DIFFICULTY WITH ARTIFICIAL RESPIRATION. GET MEDICAL ATTENTION IMMEDIATELY.

EYE CONTACT: CHLORPYRIFOS: IRRITANT. MAY CAUSE IRRITATION. SEE INFORMATION ON ORGANOPHOSPHATES.

ORGANOPHOSPHATES: CHOLINESTERASE INHIBITOR. **ACUTE EXPOSURE-** DIRECT CONTACT MAY CAUSE PAIN, HYPEREMIA, LACRIMATION, TWITCHING OF THE EYELIDS, MIOSIS, AND CILIARY MUSCLE SPASM WITH LOSS OF ACCOMODATION, BLURRED OR DIMMED VISION AND BROWACHE. SOMETIMES MYDRIASIS MAY OCCUR INSTEAD OF MIOSIS. WITH SUFFICIENT EXPOSURE, OTHER SYMPTOMS OF CHOLINESTERASE INHIBITION AS DESCRIBED IN ACUTE INHALATION MAY OCCUR. **CHRONIC EXPOSURE-** REPEATED OR PROLONGED EXPOSURE MAY CAUSE EFFECTS AS DESCRIBED IN ACUTE EXPOSURE. SOME COMPOUNDS HAVE CAUSED TOXIC EFFECTS ON THE CRYSTALLINE LENS, CONJUNCTIVAL THICKENING AND OBSTRUCTION OF THE NASOLACRIMAL CANALS WHEN USED AS MIOTIC EYEDROPS.

FIRST AID- IRRIGATE EYES WITH WATER OR SALINE SOLUTION. IF SYMPTOMS OF POISONING OCCUR, TREAT RESPIRATORY DIFFICULTY WITH ARTIFICIAL RESPIRATION AND OXYGEN. OBSERVE PATIENT FOR AT LEAST 24-36 HOURS (GOSSELIN, CLINICAL TOXICOLOGY OF COMMERCIAL PRODUCTS, 5TH ED.). GET MEDICAL ATTENTION IMMEDIATELY. OXYGEN SHOULD BE ADMINISTERED BY QUALIFIED MEDICAL PERSONNEL.

INGESTION: CHLORPYRIFOS: TOXIC. A DOSE OF 0.1 MG/KG INGESTED DAILY FOR FOUR WEEKS PRODUCED SIGNIFICANT CHOLINESTERASE INHIBITION IN SEVERAL HUMAN VOLUNTEERS. IN A DELAYED NEUROTOXICITY STUDY IN HENS, THE RESULTS WERE NEGATIVE. FETOTOXICITY AND FETAL DEVELOPMENTAL ABNORMALITIES WERE OBSERVED IN A CHRONIC INGESTION STUDY OF PREGNANT MICE, BUT THE SAME DOSE PRODUCED SEVERE MATERNAL TOXICITY. SEE INFORMATION ON ORGANOPHOSPHATES.

ORGANOPHOSPHATES: CHOLINESTERASE INHIBITOR. **ACUTE EXPOSURE-** WHEN INGESTED, THE FIRST EFFECTS MAY BE NAUSEA, VOMITING, ANOREXIA, ABDOMINAL CRAMPS AND DIARRHEA. GASTROINTESTINAL ABSORPTION MAY CAUSE THE SYMPTOMS OF CHOLINESTERASE INHIBITION AS DESCRIBED IN ACUTE INHALATION. SYMPTOMS MAY BEGIN WITHIN MINUTES OR BE DELAYED. **CHRONIC EXPOSURE-** REPEATED INGESTION MAY CAUSE EFFECTS AS DESCRIBED IN ACUTE EXPOSURE.

FIRST AID- IF PERSON IS ALERT AND RESPIRATION IS NOT DEPRESSED, GIVE SYRUP OF IPECAC FOLLOWED BY WATER (IF VOMITING OCCURS, KEEP HEAD BELOW HIPS TO PREVENT ASPIRATION). IF CONSCIOUSNESS LEVEL DECLINES OR VOMITING HAS NOT OCCURRED IN 15 MINUTES EMPTY STOMACH BY GASTRIC LAVAGE WITH THE AID OF CUFFED ENDOTRACHEAL TUBE USING ISOTONIC SALINE OR 5% SODIUM BICARBONATE FOLLOW WITH ACTIVATED CHARCOAL. ESTABLISH AND MAINTAIN AIRWAY. TREAT RESPIRATORY DIFFICULTY WITH ARTIFICIAL RESPIRATION AND OXYGEN. DO NOT GIVE MORPHINE, AMINOPHYLLINE, PHENOTHIAZINES, RESERPINE, FUROSEMIDE, OR ETHACRYNIC ACID (MORGAN, RECOGNITION AND MANAGEMENT OF PESTICIDE POISONINGS, 3RD ED.). TREAT SYMPTOMATICALLY AND SUPPORTIVELY. ADMINISTRATION OF OXYGEN AND LAVAGE MUST BE PERFORMED BY QUALIFIED MEDICAL PERSONNEL. GET MEDICAL ATTENTION IMMEDIATELY.

ANTIDOTE: THE FOLLOWING ANTIDOTE(S) HAVE BEEN RECOMMENDED. HOWEVER, THE DECISION AS TO WHETHER THE SEVERITY OF POISONING REQUIRES ADMINISTRATION OF ANY ANTIDOTE AND ACTUAL DOSE REQUIRED SHOULD BE MADE BY QUALIFIED MEDICAL PERSONNEL.

FOR CHOLINESTERASE INHIBITORS: ESTABLISH CLEAR AIRWAY AND TISSUE OXYGENATION BY ASPIRATION OF SECRETIONS, AND IF NECESSARY, BY ASSISTED PULMONARY VENTILATION WITH OXYGEN. IMPROVE TISSUE OXYGENATION AS MUCH AS POSSIBLE BEFORE ADMINISTERING ATROPINE TO MINIMIZE THE RISK OF VENTRICULAR FIBRILLATION. ADMINISTER ATROPINE SULFATE INTRAVENOUSLY, OR INTRAMUSCULARLY IF IV INJECTION IS NOT POSSIBLE. IN MODERATELY SEVERE POISONING ADMINISTER ATROPINE SULFATE, 0.4-2.0 MG REPEATED EVERY 15 MINUTES UNTIL ATROPINIZATION IS ACHIEVED (TACHYCARDIA, FLUSHING, DRY MOUTH, MYDRIASIS). MAINTAIN ATROPINIZATION BY REPEATED DOSES FOR 2-12 HOURS, OR LONGER, DEPENDING ON THE SEVERITY OF POISONING. THE APPEARANCE OF RALES IN THE LUNG BASES, MIOSIS, SALIVATION, NAUSEA, BRADYCARDIA, ARE ALL INDICATIONS OF INADEQUATE ATROPINIZATION. SEVERELY POISONED INDIVIDUALS MAY EXHIBIT REMARKABLE TOLERANCE TO ATROPINE; TWO OR MORE TIMES THE DOSAGES SUGGESTED ABOVE MAY BE NEEDED. PERSONS NOT POISONED OR ONLY SLIGHTLY POISONED, HOWEVER, MAY DEVELOP SIGNS OF ATROPINE TOXICITY FROM SUCH LARGE DOSAGES: FEVER, MUSCLE FIBRILLATIONS, AND DELIRIUM ARE THE MAIN SIGNS OF ATROPINE TOXICITY. IF THESE SIGNS APPEAR WHILE THE PATIENT IS FULLY ATROPINIZED, ATROPINE ADMINISTRATION SHOULD BE DISCONTINUED, AT LEAST TEMPORARILY. OBSERVE TREATED PATIENTS CLOSELY AT LEAST 24 HOURS TO INSURE THAT SYMPTOMS (POSSIBLY PULMONARY EDEMA) DO NOT RECUR AS ATROPINIZATION WEARS OFF. IN VERY SEVERE POISONINGS, METABOLIC DISPOSITION OF TOXICANT MAY REQUIRE SEVERAL HOURS OR DAYS DURING WHICH ATROPINIZATION MUST BE MAINTAINED. MARKEDLY LOWER LEVELS OF URINARY METABOLITES INDICATE THAT ATROPINE DOSAGE CAN BE TAPERED OFF. AS

PROMPTLY (MORGAN, RECOGNITION AND MANAGEMENT OF PESTICIDE POISONINGS, 3RD ED.). ADMINISTRATION OF ANTIDOTE MUST BE PERFORMED BY QUALIFIED MEDICAL PERSONNEL.

IN CASES OF SEVERE POISONING BY ORGANOPHOSPHATE PESTICIDES IN WHICH RESPIRATORY DEPRESSION, MUSCLE WEAKNESS AND TWITCHINGS ARE SEVERE, GIVE PRALIDOXIME (PROTOPAM-AYERST, 2-PAM), 1.0 GRAM INTRAVENOUSLY AT NO MORE THAN 0.5 GRAM PER MINUTE. DOSAGE OF PRALIDOXIME MAY BE REPEATED IN 1-2 HOURS, THEN AT 10-12 HOUR INTERVALS IF NEEDED. IN VERY SEVERE POISONINGS, DOSAGE RATES MAY BE DOUBLED. TREATMENT WITH PRALIDOXIME WILL BE MOST EFFECTIVE IF GIVEN WITHIN THIRTY-SIX HOURS AFTER POISONING (MORGAN, RECOGNITION AND MANAGEMENT OF PESTICIDE POISONINGS, 3RD ED.). ANTIDOTE SHOULD BE ADMINISTERED BY QUALIFIED MEDICAL PERSONNEL.

REACTIVITY

REACTIVITY: MAY UNDERGO VIOLENT EXOTHERMIC DECOMPOSITION ABOVE 130 C (266 F). THE INCREASE IN TEMPERATURE AND PRESSURE MAY RESULT IN THE VIOLENT RUPTURE OF THE CONTAINER.

INCOMPATIBILITIES: CHLORPYRIFOS: ALKALINE CONDITIONS: MAY CAUSE HYDROLYSIS. BRASS: MAY BE CORRODED. COPPER: MAY BE CORRODED.

DECOMPOSITION: THERMAL DECOMPOSITION MAY RELEASE TOXIC AND/OR HAZARDOUS GASES.

POLYMERIZATION: HAZARDOUS POLYMERIZATION HAS NOT BEEN REPORTED TO OCCUR UNDER NORMAL TEMPERATURES AND PRESSURES.

STORAGE AND DISPOSAL

OBSERVE ALL FEDERAL, STATE AND LOCAL REGULATIONS WHEN STORING OR DISPOSING OF THIS SUBSTANCE. FOR ASSISTANCE, CONTACT THE DISTRICT DIRECTOR OF THE ENVIRONMENTAL PROTECTION AGENCY.

STORAGE

STORE IN ACCORDANCE WITH 40 CFR 165 RECOMMENDED PROCEDURES FOR THE DISPOSAL AND STORAGE OF PESTICIDES AND PESTICIDE CONTAINERS.

STORE AWAY FROM INCOMPATIBLE SUBSTANCES.

THRESHOLD PLANNING QUANTITY (TPQ): THE SUPERFUND AMENDMENTS AND REAUTHORIZATION ACT (SARA) SECTION 302 REQUIRES THAT EACH FACILITY WHERE ANY EXTREMELY HAZARDOUS SUBSTANCE IS PRESENT IN A QUANTITY EQUAL TO OR GREATER THAN THE TPQ ESTABLISHED FOR THAT SUBSTANCE NOTIFY THE STATE EMERGENCY RESPONSE COMMISSION FOR THE STATE IN WHICH IT IS LOCATED. SECTION 303 OF SARA REQUIRES THESE FACILITIES TO PARTICIPATE IN LOCAL EMERGENCY RESPONSE PLANNING (40 CFR 355.30).

DISPOSAL

DISPOSAL MUST BE IN ACCORDANCE WITH 40 CFR 165 RECOMMENDED PROCEDURES FOR THE DISPOSAL AND STORAGE OF PESTICIDES AND PESTICIDE CONTAINERS.

CONDITIONS TO AVOID

NONE REPORTED.

SPILL AND LEAK PROCEDURES

SOIL SPILL: DIG HOLDING AREA SUCH AS LAGOON, POND OR PIT FOR CONTAINMENT. USE PROTECTIVE COVER SUCH AS A PLASTIC SHEET TO PREVENT MATERIAL FROM DISSOLVING IN FIRE EXTINGUISHING WATER OR RAIN.

WATER SPILL: TRAP SPILLED MATERIAL AT BOTTOM IN DEEP WATER POCKETS, EXCAVATED HOLDING AREAS OR WITHIN SAND BAG BARRIERS.

USE ACTIVATED CARBON TO ABSORB SPILLED SUBSTANCE THAT IS DISSOLVED.

USE SUCTION HOSES TO REMOVE TRAPPED SPILL MATERIAL.

USE MECHANICAL DREDGES OR LIFTS TO EXTRACT IMMOBILIZED MASSES OF POLLUTION AND PRECIPITATES.

OCCUPATIONAL SPILL: DO NOT TOUCH SPILLED MATERIAL. STOP LEAK IF YOU CAN DO IT WITHOUT RISK. USE WATER SPRAY TO REDUCE VAPORS. FOR SMALL SPILLS, TAKE UP WITH SAND OR OTHER ABSORBENT MATERIAL AND PLACE INTO CONTAINERS FOR LATER DISPOSAL. FOR SMALL DRY SPILLS, WITH A CLEAN SHOVEL PLACE MATERIAL INTO CLEAN, DRY CONTAINERS AND COVER. MOVE CONTAINERS FROM SPILL AREA. FOR LARGER SPILLS, DIKE FAR AHEAD OF SPILL FOR LATER DISPOSAL. KEEP UNNECESSARY PEOPLE AWAY. ISOLATE HAZARD AREA AND DENY ENTRY. VENTILATE CLOSED SPACES BEFORE ENTERING.

REPORTABLE QUANTITY (RQ): 1 POUND THE SUPERFUND AMENDMENTS AND REAUTHORIZATION ACT (SARA) SECTION 304 REQUIRES THAT A RELEASE EQUAL TO OR GREATER THAN THE REPORTABLE QUANTITY FOR THIS SUBSTANCE BE IMMEDIATELY REPORTED TO THE LOCAL EMERGENCY PLANNING COMMITTEE AND THE STATE EMERGENCY RESPONSE COMMISSION (40 CFR 355.40). IF THE RELEASE OF THIS SUBSTANCE IS REPORTABLE UNDER CERCLA SECTION 103, THE NATIONAL RESPONSE CENTER MUST BE NOTIFIED IMMEDIATELY AT (800) 424-8802 OR (202) 426-2675 IN THE METROPOLITAN WASHINGTON, D.C. AREA (40 CFR 302.6).

PROTECTIVE EQUIPMENT

VENTILATION: PROVIDE LOCAL EXHAUST OR PROCESS ENCLOSURE VENTILATION TO MEET PUBLISHED EXPOSURE LIMITS.

RESPIRATOR: THE FOLLOWING RESPIRATORS ARE RECOMMENDED BASED ON INFORMATION FOUND IN THE PHYSICAL DATA, TOXICITY AND HEALTH EFFECTS SECTIONS. THEY ARE RANKED IN ORDER FROM MINIMUM TO MAXIMUM RESPIRATORY PROTECTION. THE SPECIFIC RESPIRATOR SELECTED MUST BE BASED ON CONTAMINATION LEVELS FOUND IN THE WORK PLACE, MUST NOT EXCEED THE WORKING LIMITS OF THE RESPIRATOR AND BE JOINTLY APPROVED BY THE NATIONAL INSTITUTE FOR OCCUPATIONAL SAFETY AND HEALTH AND THE MINE SAFETY AND HEALTH ADMINISTRATION (NIOSH-MSHA).

TYPE 'C' SUPPLIED-AIR RESPIRATOR WITH A FULL FACEPIECE OPERATED IN PRESSURE-DEMAND OR OTHER POSITIVE PRESSURE MODE OR WITH A FULL FACEPIECE, HELMET OR HOOD OPERATED IN CONTINOUS-FLOW MODE.

SELF-CONTAINED BREATHING APPARATUS WITH A FULL FACEPIECE OPERATED IN PRESSURE-DEMAND OR OTHER POSITIVE PRESSURE MODE.

FOR FIREFIGHTING AND OTHER IMMEDIATELY DANGEROUS TO LIFE OR HEALTH CONDITIONS:

SELF-CONTAINED BREATHING APPARATUS WITH FULL FACEPIECE OPERATED IN PRESSURE-DEMAND OR OTHER POSITIVE PRESSURE MODE.

SUPPLIED-AIR RESPIRATOR WITH FULL FACEPIECE AND OPERATED IN PRESSURE-DEMAND OR OTHER POSITIVE PRESSURE MODE IN COMBINATION WITH AN AUXILIARY SELF-CONTAINED BREATHING APPARATUS OPERATED IN PRESSURE-DEMAND OR OTHER POSITIVE PRESSURE MODE.

CLOTHING: EMPLOYEE MUST WEAR APPROPRIATE PROTECTIVE (IMPERVIOUS) CLOTHING AND EQUIPMENT TO PREVENT ANY POSSIBILITY OF SKIN CONTACT WITH THIS SUBSTANCE.

GLOVES: EMPLOYEE MUST WEAR APPROPRIATE PROTECTIVE GLOVES TO PREVENT CONTACT WITH THIS SUBSTANCE.

EYE PROTECTION: EMPLOYEE MUST WEAR SPLASH-PROOF OR DUST-RESISTANT SAFETY GOGGLES AND A FACESHIELD TO PREVENT CONTACT WITH THIS SUBSTANCE.

EMERGENCY WASH FACILITIES: WHERE THERE IS ANY POSSIBILITY THAT AN EMPLOYEE'S EYES AND/OR SKIN MAY BE EXPOSED TO THIS SUBSTANCE, THE EMPLOYER SHOULD PROVIDE AN EYE WASH FOUNTAIN AND QUICK DRENCH SHOWER WITHIN THE IMMEDIATE WORK AREA FOR EMERGENCY USE.

AUTHORIZED BY- OCCUPATIONAL HEALTH SERVICES, INC.

CREATION DATE: 10/04/89 ***REVISION DATE:*** 06/20/90

MATERIAL SAFETY DATA SHEET

OCCUPATIONAL HEALTH SERVICES, INC.
AGRICULTURE AND PESTICIDE DIVISION
450 SEVENTH AVENUE, SUITE 2407
NEW YORK, NEW YORK 10123
1-800-445-MSDS OR (212) 967-1100

EMERGENCY CONTACT:
JOHN S. BRANSFORD, JR. (615) 292-1180

SUBSTANCE IDENTIFICATION

CAS-NUMBER 5598-15-2

SUBSTANCE: **CHLORPYRIFOS OXYGEN ANALOG**

TRADE NAMES/SYNONYMS: PHOSPHORIC ACID, DIETHYL 3,5,6-TRICHLORO-2-PYRIDINYL ESTER; DIETHYL 3,5,6-TRICHLORO-2-PYRIDINYLPHOSPHATE; PHOSPHORIC ACID, DIETHYL 3,5,6-TRICHLORO-2-PYRIDYL ESTER; DIETHYL 3,5,6-TRICHLORO-2-PYRIDYLPHOSPHATE; CHLOROPYRIFOS OXON; CHLORPYRIFOS OXON; CHLORPYRIFOXON; CHLORPYRIPHOXON; DURSBANOXON; DURSBAN OXYGEN ANALOG; FOSPIRATE-ETHYL; DURSBAN OXON; O,O-DIETHYL-3,5,6-TRICHLORO-2-PYRIDYLPHSOPHATE; C9H11CL3NO4P; PST04911

CHEMICAL FAMILY: ORGANOPHOSPHATE

MOLECULAR FORMULA: (C2-H5-O)2-P-(O)-O-C5-N-H-CL3

MOLECULAR WEIGHT: 334.52

CERCLA RATINGS (SCALE 0-3): HEALTH=3 FIRE=1 REACTIVITY=0 PERSISTENCE=0

NFPA RATINGS (SCALE 0-4): HEALTH=U FIRE=1 REACTIVITY=0

COMPONENTS AND CONTAMINANTS

COMPONENT: CHLORPYRIFOS OXYGEN ANALOG ***PERCENT:*** 100.0
CAS# 5598-15-2

OTHER CONTAMINANTS: NONE

EXPOSURE LIMITS: NO OCCUPATIONAL EXPOSURE LIMITS ESTABLISHED BY OSHA, ACGIH, OR NIOSH.

PHYSICAL DATA

DESCRIPTION: WHITE POWDER. ***MELTING POINT:*** 108-109 F (42-43 C)
SPECIFIC GRAVITY: NOT AVAILABLE ***SOLUBILITY IN WATER:*** NOT AVAILABLE

FIRE AND EXPLOSION DATA

FIRE AND EXPLOSION HAZARD: SLIGHT FIRE HAZARD WHEN EXPOSED TO HEAT OR FLAME.

FIREFIGHTING MEDIA: DRY CHEMICAL, CARBON DIOXIDE, HALON, WATER SPRAY OR STANDARD FOAM (1987 EMERGENCY RESPONSE GUIDEBOOK, DOT P 5800.4). FOR LARGER FIRES, USE WATER SPRAY, FOG OR STANDARD FOAM (1987 EMERGENCY RESPONSE GUIDEBOOK, DOT P 5800.4).

FIREFIGHTING: MOVE CONTAINERS FROM FIRE AREA IF POSSIBLE (1987 EMERGENCY RESPONSE GUIDEBOOK, DOT P 5800.4, GUIDE PAGE 53).
EXTINGUISH USING AGENT SUITABLE FOR TYPE OF SURROUNDING FIRE. AVOID BREATHING VAPORS AND DUSTS. KEEP UPWIND.

TOXICITY

CHLORPYRIFOS OXYGEN ANALOG: TOXICITY DATA: 135 MG/KG ORAL-RAT LD50. CARCINOGEN STATUS: NONE. ACUTE TOXICITY LEVEL: TOXIC BY INGESTION. TARGET EFFECTS: CHOLINESTERASE INHIBITOR. POISONING MAY AFFECT THE NERVOUS SYSTEM.* AT INCREASED RISK FROM EXPOSURE: PERSONS WITH RESPIRATORY AILMENTS, RECENT EXPOSURE TO CHOLINESTERASE INHIBITORS OR IMPAIRED CHOLINESTERASE PRODUCTION, OR LIVER MALFUNCTION.* ADDITIONAL DATA: MAY CROSS THE PLACENTA. HIGH ENVIRONMENTAL TEMPERATURES OR EXPOSURE OF THE CHEMICAL TO VISIBLE OR ULTRAVIOLET LIGHT MAY ENHANCE THE TOXICITY. INTERACTIONS WITH MEDICATIONS MAY OCCUR.*
* MAY BE BASED ON GENERAL INFORMATION ON ORGANOPHOSPHATES.

HEALTH EFFECTS AND FIRST AID

INHALATION: CHLORPYRIFOS OXYGEN ANALOG: SEE INFORMATION ON ORGANOPHOSPHATES.
ORGANOPHOSPHATES: CHOLINESTERASE INHIBITOR. **ACUTE EXPOSURE-** WHEN INHALED, THE FIRST EFFECTS OF CHOLINESTERASE INHIBITORS ARE USUALLY RESPIRATORY AND MAY INCLUDE NASAL HYPEREMIA AND WATERY DISCHARGE, COUGH, CHEST DISCOMFORT, DYSPNEA, AND WHEEZING DUE TO INCREASED BRONCHIAL SECRETIONS AND BRONCHOCONSTRICTION. IF SUFFICIENT AMOUNTS ARE ABSORBED, OTHER SYSTEMIC EFFECTS MAY BEGIN WITHIN A FEW MINUTES OR BE DELAYED FOR UP TO 12 HOURS. SYMPTOMS MAY INCLUDE PALLOR, NAUSEA, VOMITING, DIARRHEA, ABDOMINAL CRAMPS, HEADACHE, DIZZINESS, OCULAR PAIN, BLURRED VISION, MIOSIS OR IN SOME CASES, ESPECIALLY INITIALLY, MYDRIASIS, LACRIMATION, SALIVATION, SWEATING, AND CONFUSION. OTHER REPORTED CENTRAL NERVOUS SYSTEM OR NEUROMUSCULAR EFFECTS MAY INCLUDE ATAXIA, SLURRED SPEECH, AREFLEXIA, WEAKNESS, FATIGUE, FASCICULATIONS, TWITCHING, TREMORS POSSIBLY OF THE TONGUE AND EYELIDS, AND EVENTUALLY PARALYSIS OF THE EXTREMITIES AND POSSIBLY OF THE RESPIRATORY MUSCLES. IN SEVERE CASES THERE MAY ALSO BE INVOLUNTARY DEFECATION AND URINATION, CYANOSIS, PSYCHOSIS, HYPERGLYCEMIA, ACUTE PANCREATITIS, CARDIAC IRREGULARITIES, PULMONARY EDEMA, UNCONSCIOUSNESS, CONVULSIONS, AND COMA. DEATH IS PRIMARILY DUE TO RESPIRATORY FAILURE, ALTHOUGH CARDIOVASCULAR EFFECTS INCLUDING CARDIAC ARREST MAY ALSO BE IMPLICATED. LONG TERM SEQUELAE ARE RARE BUT MAY INCLUDE NEUROPSYCHIATRIC DISORDERS AND MYOPATHY WITH MUSCLE TENDERNESS. SOME ORGANOPHOSPHATES MAY CAUSE A DELAYED NEUROPATHY BEGINNING 1-4 WEEKS AFTER AN ACUTE EXPOSURE WHICH MAY OR MAY NOT HAVE CAUSED ACUTE CHOLINERGIC EFFECTS. NUMBNESS, TINGLING, WEAKNESS AND CRAMPING BEGINNING SYMMETRICALLY IN THE LOWER LIMBS MAY PROGRESS TO ATAXIA AND PARALYSIS. IN SEVERE CASES, UPPER LIMB INVOLVEMENT IS POSSIBLE AND FLACCID PARALYSIS MAY PROGRESS TO SPASTIC PARALYSIS WITH EXAGGERATED REFLEXES. IMPROVEMENT MAY OCCUR OVER MONTHS TO YEARS, BUT SOME RESIDUAL IMPAIRMENT USUALLY REMAINS.
CHRONIC EXPOSURE- REPEATED OR PROLONGED EXPOSURE MAY RESULT IN THE EFFECTS OF ACUTE EXPOSURE INCLUDING THE DELAYED NEUROPATHY. OTHER EFFECTS REPORTED IN WORKERS REPEATEDLY EXPOSED INCLUDE IMPAIRED MEMORY AND CONCENTRATION, ACUTE PSYCHOSIS, SEVERE DEPRESSIONS, IRRITABILTY, CONFUSION, APATHY, EMOTIONAL LABILITY, SOCIAL WITHDRAWAL, CONFUSION, HEADACHE, SPEECH DIFFICULTIES, DELAYED REACTION TIMES, SPATIAL DISORIENTATION, NIGHTMARES, SLEEPWALKING, AND DROWSINESS OR INSOMNIA. AN INFLUENZA-LIKE CONDITION WITH HEADACHE, NAUSEA, WEAKNESS, ANOREXIA AND MALAISE HAS ALSO BEEN REPORTED.

FIRST AID- REMOVE FROM EXPOSURE AREA TO FRESH AIR IMMEDIATELY. IF BREATHING HAS STOPPED, GIVE ARTIFICIAL RESPIRATION. MAINTAIN AIRWAY AND BLOOD PRESSURE AND ADMINISTER OXYGEN IF AVAILABLE. KEEP AFFECTED PERSON WARM AND AT REST. TREAT SYMPTOMATICALLY AND SUPPORTIVELY. ADMINISTRATION OF OXYGEN SHOULD BE PERFORMED BY QUALIFIED PERSONNEL. GET MEDICAL ATTENTION IMMEDIATELY.

SKIN CONTACT: CHLORPYRIFOS OXYGEN ANALOG: SEE INFORMATION ON ORGANOPHOSPHATES.
ORGANOPHOSPHATES: CHOLINESTERASE INHIBITOR. **ACUTE EXPOSURE-** LOCALIZED SWEATING AND FASCICULATIONS MAY OCCUR AT THE SITE OF CONTACT. IF SUFFICIENT AMOUNTS ARE ABSORBED, OTHER EFFECTS OF CHOLINESTERASE INHIBITION AS DESCRIBED IN ACUTE INHALATION MAY OCCUR. SYMPTOMS MAY BE DELAYED 2-3 HOURS, BUT USUALLY NO MORE THAN 12 HOURS. THE RATE OF ABSORPTION IS INCREASED BY THE PRESENCE OF DERMATITIS OR HIGH AMBIENT TEMPERATURES. DELAYED NEUROPATHY IS ALSO POSSIBLE. **CHRONIC EXPOSURE-** REPEATED OR PROLONGED EXPOSURE MAY CAUSE EFFECTS AS DESCRIBED IN ACUTE EXPOSURE. SOME ORGANOPHOSPHATES MAY CAUSE SENSITIZATION.

FIRST AID- REMOVE CONTAMINATED CLOTHING IMMEDIATELY. WASH CONTAMINATED AREAS WITH SOAP AND WATER FOLLOWED BY ALCOHOL (ARENA, POISONING, 4TH ED.). EMERGENCY PERSONNEL SHOULD WEAR GLOVES AND AVOID CONTAMINATION. TREAT RESPIRATORY DIFFICULTY WITH ARTIFICIAL RESPIRATION. GET MEDICAL ATTENTION IMMEDIATELY.

EYE CONTACT: CHLORPYRIFOS OXYGEN ANALOG: SEE INFORMATION ON ORGANOPHOSPHATES.
ORGANOPHOSPHATES: CHOLINESTERASE INHIBITOR. **ACUTE EXPOSURE-** DIRECT CONTACT MAY CAUSE PAIN, HYPEREMIA, LACRIMATION, TWITCHING OF THE EYELIDS, MIOSIS, AND CILIARY MUSCLE SPASM WITH LOSS OF ACCOMODATION, BLURRED OR DIMMED VISION AND BROWACHE. SOMETIMES MYDRIASIS MAY OCCUR INSTEAD OF MIOSIS. WITH SUFFICIENT EXPOSURE, OTHER SYMPTOMS OF CHOLINESTERASE INHIBITION AS DESCRIBED IN ACUTE INHALATION MAY OCCUR. **CHRONIC EXPOSURE-** REPEATED OR PROLONGED EXPOSURE MAY CAUSE EFFECTS AS DESCRIBED IN ACUTE EXPOSURE. SOME COMPOUNDS HAVE CAUSED TOXIC EFFECTS ON THE CRYSTALLINE LENS, CONJUNCTIVAL THICKENING AND OBSTRUCTION OF THE NASOLACRIMAL CANALS WHEN USED AS MIOTIC EYEDROPS.

FIRST AID- IRRIGATE EYES WITH WATER OR SALINE SOLUTION. IF SYMPTOMS OF POISONING OCCUR, TREAT RESPIRATORY DIFFICULTY WITH ARTIFICIAL RESPIRATION AND OXYGEN. OBSERVE PATIENT FOR AT LEAST 24-36 HOURS (GOSSELIN, CLINICAL TOXICOLOGY OF COMMERCIAL PRODUCTS, 5TH ED.). GET MEDICAL ATTENTION IMMEDIATELY. OXYGEN SHOULD BE ADMINISTERED BY QUALIFIED MEDICAL PERSONNEL.

INGESTION: CHLORPYRIFOS OXYGEN ANALOG: TOXIC. SEE INFORMATION ON ORGANOPHOSPHATES.
ORGANOPHOSPHATES: CHOLINESTERASE INHIBITOR. **ACUTE EXPOSURE-** WHEN INGESTED, THE FIRST EFFECTS MAY BE NAUSEA, VOMITING, ANOREXIA, ABDOMINAL CRAMPS AND DIARRHEA. GASTROINTESTINAL ABSORPTION MAY CAUSE SYMPTOMS OF CHOLINESTERASE INHIBITION AS DESCRIBED IN ACUTE INHALATION. SYMPTOMS MAY BEGIN WITHIN MINUTES OR BE DELAYED FOR HOURS. DELAYED EFFECTS INCLUDING NEUROPATHY MAY ALSO OCCUR. **CHRONIC EXPOSURE-** REPEATED INGESTION MAY CAUSE EFFECTS AS DESCRIBED IN ACUTE EXPOSURE.

FIRST AID- IF PERSON IS ALERT AND RESPIRATION IS NOT DEPRESSED, GIVE SYRUP OF IPECAC FOLLOWED BY WATER (IF VOMITING OCCURS, KEEP HEAD BELOW HIPS TO PREVENT ASPIRATION). IF CONSCIOUSNESS LEVEL DECLINES OR VOMITING HAS NOT OCCURRED IN 15 MINUTES EMPTY STOMACH BY GASTRIC LAVAGE WITH THE AID OF CUFFED ENDOTRACHEAL TUBE USING ISOTONIC SALINE OR 5% SODIUM BICARBONATE FOLLOW WITH ACTIVATED CHARCOAL. ESTABLISH AND MAINTAIN AIRWAY. TREAT RESPIRATORY DIFFICULTY WITH ARTIFICIAL RESPIRATION AND OXYGEN. DO NOT GIVE MORPHINE, AMINOPHYLLINE, PHENOTHIAZINES, RESERPINE, FUROSEMIDE, OR ETHACRYNIC ACID (MORGAN, RECOGNITION AND MANAGEMENT OF PESTICIDE POISONINGS, 3RD ED.). TREAT SYMPTOMATICALLY AND SUPPORTIVELY. ADMINISTRATION OF OXYGEN AND LAVAGE MUST BE PERFORMED BY QUALIFIED MEDICAL PERSONNEL. GET MEDICAL ATTENTION IMMEDIATELY.

ANTIDOTE: THE FOLLOWING ANTIDOTE(S) HAVE BEEN RECOMMENDED. HOWEVER, THE DECISION AS TO WHETHER THE SEVERITY OF POISONING REQUIRES ADMINISTRATION OF ANY ANTIDOTE AND ACTUAL DOSE REQUIRED SHOULD BE MADE BY QUALIFIED MEDICAL PERSONNEL.
FOR CHOLINESTERASE INHIBITORS: ESTABLISH CLEAR AIRWAY AND TISSUE OXYGENATION BY ASPIRATION OF SECRETIONS, AND IF NECESSARY, BY ASSISTED PULMONARY VENTILATION WITH OXYGEN. IMPROVE TISSUE OXYGENATION AS MUCH AS POSSIBLE BEFORE ADMINISTERING ATROPINE TO MINIMIZE THE RISK OF VENTRICULAR FIBRILLATION. ADMINISTER ATROPINE SULFATE INTRAVENOUSLY, OR INTRAMUSCULARLY IF IV INJECTION IS NOT POSSIBLE. IN MODERATELY SEVERE POISONING ADMINISTER ATROPINE SULFATE, 0.4-2.0 MG REPEATED EVERY 15 MINUTES UNTIL ATROPINIZATION IS ACHIEVED (TACHYCARDIA, FLUSHING, DRY MOUTH, MYDRIASIS). MAINTAIN ATROPINIZATION BY REPEATED DOSES FOR 2-12

HOURS, OR LONGER, DEPENDING ON THE SEVERITY OF POISONING. THE APPEARANCE OF RALES IN THE LUNG BASES, MIOSIS, SALIVATION, NAUSEA, BRADYCARDIA, ARE ALL INDICATIONS OF INADEQUATE ATROPINIZATION. SEVERELY POISONED INDIVIDUALS MAY EXHIBIT REMARKABLE TOLERANCE TO ATROPINE; TWO OR MORE TIMES THE DOSAGES SUGGESTED ABOVE MAY BE NEEDED. PERSONS NOT POISONED OR ONLY SLIGHTLY POISONED, HOWEVER, MAY DEVELOP SIGNS OF ATROPINE TOXICITY FROM SUCH LARGE DOSAGES: FEVER, MUSCLE FIBRILLATIONS, AND DELIRIUM ARE THE MAIN SIGNS OF ATROPINE TOXICITY. IF THESE SIGNS APPEAR WHILE THE PATIENT IS FULLY ATROPINIZED, ATROPINE ADMINISTRATION SHOULD BE DISCONTINUED, AT LEAST TEMPORARILY. OBSERVE TREATED PATIENTS CLOSELY AT LEAST 24 HOURS TO INSURE THAT SYMPTOMS (POSSIBLY PULMONARY EDEMA) DO NOT RECUR AS ATROPINIZATION WEARS OFF. IN VERY SEVERE POISONINGS, METABOLIC DISPOSITION OF TOXICANT MAY REQUIRE SEVERAL HOURS OR DAYS DURING WHICH ATROPINIZATION MUST BE MAINTAINED. MARKEDLY LOWER LEVELS OF URINARY METABOLITES INDICATE THAT ATROPINE DOSAGE CAN BE TAPERED OFF. AS DOSAGE IS REDUCED, CHECK THE LUNG BASES FREQUENTLY FOR RALES. IF RALES ARE HEARD OR OTHER SYMPTOMS RETURN, RE-ESTABLISH ATROPINIZATION PROMPTLY (MORGAN, RECOGNITION AND MANAGEMENT OF PESTICIDE POISONINGS, 3RD ED.). ADMINISTRATION OF ANTIDOTE MUST BE PERFORMED BY QUALIFIED MEDICAL PERSONNEL.

IN CASES OF SEVERE POISONING BY ORGANOPHOSPHATE PESTICIDES IN WHICH RESPIRATORY DEPRESSION, MUSCLE WEAKNESS AND TWITCHINGS ARE SEVERE, GIVE PRALIDOXIME (PROTOPAM-AYERST, 2-PAM), 1.0 GRAM INTRAVENOUSLY AT NO MORE THAN 0.5 GRAM PER MINUTE. DOSAGE OF PRALIDOXIME MAY BE REPEATED IN 1-2 HOURS, THEN AT 10-12 HOUR INTERVALS IF NEEDED. IN VERY SEVERE POISONINGS, DOSAGE RATES MAY BE DOUBLED. TREATMENT WITH PRALIDOXIME WILL BE MOST EFFECTIVE IF GIVEN WITHIN THIRTY-SIX HOURS AFTER POISONING (MORGAN, RECOGNITION AND MANAGEMENT OF PESTICIDE POISONINGS, 3RD ED.). ANTIDOTE SHOULD BE ADMINISTERED BY QUALIFIED MEDICAL PERSONNEL.

REACTIVITY

REACTIVITY: STABLE UNDER NORMAL TEMPERATURES AND PRESSURES.

INCOMPATIBILITIES: CHLORPYRIFOS OXYGEN ANALOG: OXIDIZERS (STRONG): FIRE AND EXPLOSION HAZARD.

DECOMPOSITION: THERMAL DECOMPOSITION PRODUCTS MAY INCLUDE TOXIC AND CORROSIVE FUMES OF CHLORIDES, AND TOXIC OXIDES OF PHOSPHORUS, NITROGEN, AND CARBON.

POLYMERIZATION: HAZARDOUS POLYMERIZATION HAS NOT BEEN REPORTED TO OCCUR UNDER NORMAL TEMPERATURES AND PRESSURES.

STORAGE AND DISPOSAL

OBSERVE ALL FEDERAL, STATE AND LOCAL REGULATIONS WHEN STORING OR DISPOSING OF THIS SUBSTANCE. FOR ASSISTANCE, CONTACT THE DISTRICT DIRECTOR OF THE ENVIRONMENTAL PROTECTION AGENCY.

STORAGE

STORE AWAY FROM INCOMPATIBLE SUBSTANCES.

CONDITIONS TO AVOID

MAY BURN BUT DOES NOT IGNITE READILY.

SPILL AND LEAK PROCEDURES

OCCUPATIONAL SPILL: DO NOT TOUCH SPILLED MATERIAL. STOP LEAK IF YOU CAN DO IT WITHOUT RISK. FOR SMALL SPILLS, TAKE UP WITH SAND OR OTHER ABSORBENT MATERIAL AND PLACE INTO CONTAINERS FOR LATER DISPOSAL. FOR SMALL DRY SPILLS, WITH A CLEAN SHOVEL PLACE MATERIAL INTO CLEAN, DRY CONTAINER AND COVER. MOVE CONTAINERS FROM SPILL AREA. FOR LARGER SPILLS, DIKE FAR AHEAD OF SPILL FOR LATER DISPOSAL. KEEP UNNECESSARY PEOPLE AWAY. ISOLATE HAZARD AREA AND DENY ENTRY.

PROTECTIVE EQUIPMENT

VENTILATION: PROVIDE LOCAL EXHAUST OR PROCESS ENCLOSURE VENTILATION SYSTEM.

RESPIRATOR: THE FOLLOWING RESPIRATORS ARE RECOMMENDED BASED ON INFORMATION FOUND IN THE PHYSICAL DATA, TOXICITY AND HEALTH EFFECTS SECTIONS. THEY ARE RANKED IN ORDER FROM MINIMUM TO MAXIMUM RESPIRATORY PROTECTION. THE SPECIFIC RESPIRATOR SELECTED MUST BE BASED ON CONTAMINATION LEVELS FOUND IN THE WORK PLACE, MUST NOT EXCEED THE WORKING LIMITS OF THE RESPIRATOR AND BE JOINTLY APPROVED BY THE NATIONAL INSTITUTE FOR OCCUPATIONAL SAFETY AND HEALTH AND THE MINE SAFETY AND HEALTH ADMINISTRATION (NIOSH-MSHA).

CHEMICAL CARTRIDGE RESPIRATOR WITH AN ORGANIC VAPOR CARTRIDGE(S) WITH A FULL FACEPIECE AND ORGANIC VAPOR CARTRIDGE(S) IN COMBINATION WITH A DUST AND MIST FILTER.

POWERED AIR-PURIFYING RESPIRATOR WITH A TIGHT-FITTING FACEPIECE AND ORGANIC VAPOR CARTRIDGE(S) IN COMBINATION WITH A HIGH-EFFICIENCY PARTICULATE FILTER.

TYPE 'C' SUPPLIED-AIR RESPIRATOR WITH A FULL FACEPIECE OPERATED IN A PRESSURE-DEMAND OR OTHER POSITIVE PRESSURE MODE.

SELF-CONTAINED BREATHING APPARATUS WITH A FULL FACEPIECE OPERATED IN PRESSURE-DEMAND OR OTHER POSITIVE PRESSURE MODE.

FOR FIREFIGHTING AND OTHER IMMEDIATELY DANGEROUS TO LIFE OR HEALTH CONDITIONS:

SELF-CONTAINED BREATHING APPARATUS WITH FULL FACEPIECE OPERATED IN PRESSURE-DEMAND OR OTHER POSITIVE PRESSURE MODE.

SUPPLIED-AIR RESPIRATOR WITH FULL FACEPIECE AND OPERATED IN PRESSURE-DEMAND OR OTHER POSITIVE PRESSURE MODE IN COMBINATION WITH AN AUXILIARY SELF-CONTAINED BREATHING APPARATUS OPERATED IN PRESSURE-DEMAND OR OTHER POSITIVE PRESSURE MODE.

CLOTHING: EMPLOYEE MUST WEAR APPROPRIATE PROTECTIVE (IMPERVIOUS) CLOTHING AND EQUIPMENT TO PREVENT ANY POSSIBILITY OF SKIN CONTACT WITH THIS SUBSTANCE.

GLOVES: EMPLOYEE MUST WEAR APPROPRIATE PROTECTIVE GLOVES TO PREVENT CONTACT WITH THIS SUBSTANCE.

EYE PROTECTION: EMPLOYEE MUST WEAR SPLASH-PROOF OR DUST-RESISTANT SAFETY GOGGLES AND A FACESHIELD TO PREVENT CONTACT WITH THIS SUBSTANCE.

EMERGENCY WASH FACILITIES: WHERE THERE IS ANY POSSIBILITY THAT AN EMPLOYEE'S EYES AND/OR SKIN MAY BE EXPOSED TO THIS SUBSTANCE, THE EMPLOYER SHOULD PROVIDE AN EYE WASH FOUNTAIN AND QUICK DRENCH SHOWER WITHIN THE IMMEDIATE WORK AREA FOR EMERGENCY USE.

AUTHORIZED BY- OCCUPATIONAL HEALTH SERVICES, INC.

CREATION DATE: 11/17/89 ***REVISION DATE:*** 05/07/90

MATERIAL SAFETY DATA SHEET

OCCUPATIONAL HEALTH SERVICES, INC.
AGRICULTURE AND PESTICIDE DIVISION
450 SEVENTH AVENUE, SUITE 2407
NEW YORK, NEW YORK 10123
1-800-445-MSDS OR (212) 967-1100

EMERGENCY CONTACT:
JOHN S. BRANSFORD, JR. (615) 292-1180

SUBSTANCE IDENTIFICATION

CAS-NUMBER 15545-48-9

SUBSTANCE: CHLOROTOLURON

TRADE NAMES/SYNONYMS: UREA, N'-(3-CHLORO-4-METHYLPHENYL)-N,N-DIMETHYL-; UREA, 3-(3-CHLORO-P-TOLYL)-1,1-DIMETHYL-; 3-(3-CHLORO-P-TOLYL)-1,1-DIMETHYLUREA; N'-(3-CHLORO-4-METHYLPHENYL)-N,N-DIMETHYLUREA; CGA 15646; C 2242; CHLORTOLURON; CLORTOKEM; DICURAN; TOLUREX; C10H13CLN2O; PST04912

CHEMICAL FAMILY: SUBSTITUTED UREA
HALOGEN COMPOUND, AROMATIC

MOLECULAR FORMULA: C-H3-(CL)-C6-H3-N-H-C-O-N-(C-H3)2

MOLECULAR WEIGHT: 212.70

CERCLA RATINGS (SCALE 0-3): HEALTH=2 FIRE=1 REACTIVITY=0 PERSISTENCE=1

NFPA RATINGS (SCALE 0-4): HEALTH=2 FIRE=1 REACTIVITY=0

COMPONENTS AND CONTAMINANTS

COMPONENT: CHLOROTOLURON ***PERCENT:*** 100.0
CAS# 15545-48-9

OTHER CONTAMINANTS: NONE

EXPOSURE LIMITS: NO OCCUPATIONAL EXPOSURE LIMITS ESTABLISHED BY OSHA, ACGIH, OR NIOSH.

PHYSICAL DATA

DESCRIPTION: ODORLESS, COLORLESS CRYSTALLINE SOLID.

MELTING POINT: 297-298 F (147-148 C) ***SPECIFIC GRAVITY:*** 1.40

VAPOR PRESSURE: NEGLIGIBLE ***SOLUBILITY IN WATER:*** 0.007%

SOLVENT SOLUBILITY: SOLUBLE IN ACETONE, BENZENE, ISOPROPANOL, AND DICHLOROMETHANE.

FIRE AND EXPLOSION DATA

FIRE AND EXPLOSION HAZARD: SLIGHT FIRE HAZARD WHEN EXPOSED TO HEAT OR FLAME.

FIREFIGHTING MEDIA: DRY CHEMICAL, CARBON DIOXIDE, HALON, WATER SPRAY OR STANDARD FOAM (1987 EMERGENCY RESPONSE GUIDEBOOK, DOT P 5800.4). FOR LARGER FIRES, USE WATER SPRAY, FOG OR STANDARD FOAM (1987 EMERGENCY RESPONSE GUIDEBOOK, DOT P 5800.4).

FIREFIGHTING: MOVE CONTAINERS FROM FIRE AREA IF POSSIBLE. FIGHT FIRE FROM MAXIMUM DISTANCE. STAY AWAY FROM STORAGE TANK ENDS. DIKE FIRE CONTROL WATER FOR LATER DISPOSAL. DO NOT SCATTER MATERIAL (1987 EMERGENCY RESPONSE GUIDEBOOK, DOT P 5800.4, GUIDE PAGE 55). EXTINGUISH USING AGENT SUITABLE FOR TYPE OF SURROUNDING FIRE. USE WATER IN FLOODING QUANTITIES AS FOG. KEEP SPARKS, FLAMES AND OTHER SOURCES OF IGNITION AWAY. KEEP MATERIAL OUT OF WATER SOURCES AND SEWERS. DO NOT TOUCH MATERIAL AND AVOID BREATHING DUSTS AND FUMES FROM BURNING MATERIAL. KEEP UPWIND.

TRANSPORTATION DATA

DEPARTMENT OF TRANSPORTATION HAZARD CLASSIFICATION 49 CFR 172.101: POISON B

DEPARTMENT OF TRANSPORTATION LABELING REQUIREMENTS 49 CFR 172.101 AND SUBPART E: POISON

DEPARTMENT OF TRANSPORTATION PACKAGING REQUIREMENTS: 49 CFR 173.365 EXCEPTIONS: 49 CFR 173.364

TOXICITY

CHLOROTOLURON: TOXICITY DATA: 1300 MG/M3 INHALATION-RAT LC50; 5800 MG/KG ORAL-RAT LD50; MUTAGENIC DATA (RTECS); REPRODUCTIVE EFFECTS DATA (RTECS). CARCINOGEN STATUS: NONE. ACUTE TOXICITY LEVEL: HIGHLY TOXIC BY INHALATION AND SLIGHTLY TOXIC BY INGESTION. TARGET EFFECTS: NO DATA AVAILABLE.

HEALTH EFFECTS AND FIRST AID

INHALATION: CHLOROTOLURON: TOXIC. **ACUTE EXPOSURE-** A LETHAL CONCENTRATION IN RATS WAS 1300 MG/M3. MANY SUBSTITUTED UREA HERBICIDES ARE MODERATELY IRRITATING TO THE MUCOUS MEMBRANES. **CHRONIC EXPOSURE-** NO DATA AVAILABLE.

FIRST AID- REMOVE FROM EXPOSURE AREA TO FRESH AIR IMMEDIATELY. IF BREATHING HAS STOPPED, PERFORM ARTIFICIAL RESPIRATION. KEEP PERSON WARM AND AT REST. TREAT SYMPTOMATICALLY AND SUPPORTIVELY. GET MEDICAL ATTENTION IMMEDIATELY.

SKIN CONTACT: CHLOROTOLURON: **ACUTE EXPOSURE-** THIS MATERIAL WAS NOT IRRITATING TO RABBIT SKIN. A LETHAL DOSE IN RATS BY DERMAL ABSORPTION WAS GREATER THAN 2000 MG/KG. **CHRONIC EXPOSURE-** NO DATA AVAILABLE.

FIRST AID- REMOVE CONTAMINATED CLOTHING AND SHOES IMMEDIATELY. WASH AFFECTED AREA WITH SOAP OR MILD DETERGENT AND LARGE AMOUNTS OF WATER UNTIL NO EVIDENCE OF CHEMICAL REMAINS (APPROXIMATELY 15-20 MINUTES). GET MEDICAL ATTENTION IMMEDIATELY.

EYE CONTACT: CHLOROTOLURON: **ACUTE EXPOSURE-** THIS MATERIAL WAS NOT IRRITATING TO RABBIT EYES. **CHRONIC EXPOSURE-** NO DATA AVAILABLE.

FIRST AID- WASH EYES IMMEDIATELY WITH LARGE AMOUNTS OF WATER OR NORMAL SALINE, OCCASIONALLY LIFTING UPPER AND LOWER LIDS, UNTIL NO EVIDENCE OF CHEMICAL REMAINS (APPROXIMATELY 15-20 MINUTES). GET MEDICAL ATTENTION IMMEDIATELY.

INGESTION: CHLOROTOLURON: **ACUTE EXPOSURE-** A LETHAL DOSE IN RATS WAS 5800 MG/KG. EFFECTS ON FERTILITY WERE OBSERVED IN A STUDY OF PREGNANT RATS FED 2 GM/KG OF CHLOROTOLURON. **CHRONIC EXPOSURE-** NO OBSERVABLE EFFECTS WERE NOTED IN SUBCHRONIC STUDIES OF RATS FED 52 MG/KG/DAY OR DOGS FED 23 MG/KG/DAY.

FIRST AID- REMOVE BY GASTRIC LAVAGE AND CATHARSIS. MAINTAIN BLOOD PRESSURE AND AIRWAY. GIVE OXYGEN IF RESPIRATION IS DEPRESSED. DO NOT PERFORM GASTRIC LAVAGE IF VICTIM IS UNCONSCIOUS. GET MEDICAL ATTENTION IMMEDIATELY (DREISBACH, HANDBOOK OF POISONING, 12TH ED.). ADMINISTRATION OF LAVAGE OR OXYGEN SHOULD BE PERFORMED BY QUALIFIED MEDICAL PERSONNEL.

ANTIDOTE: NO SPECIFIC ANTIDOTE. TREAT SYMPTOMATICALLY AND SUPPORTIVELY.

REACTIVITY

REACTIVITY: STABLE UNDER NORMAL TEMPERATURES AND PRESSURES.

INCOMPATIBILITIES: CHLOROTOLURON: OXIDIZERS (STRONG): FIRE AND EXPLOSION HAZARD.

DECOMPOSITION: THERMAL DECOMPOSITION PRODUCTS MAY INCLUDE TOXIC OXIDES OF NITROGEN AND CARBON AND TOXIC AND CORROSIVE FUMES OF CHLORIDES.

POLYMERIZATION: HAZARDOUS POLYMERIZATION HAS NOT BEEN REPORTED TO OCCUR UNDER NORMAL TEMPERATURES AND PRESSURES.

STORAGE AND DISPOSAL

OBSERVE ALL FEDERAL, STATE AND LOCAL REGULATIONS WHEN STORING OR DISPOSING OF THIS SUBSTANCE. FOR ASSISTANCE, CONTACT THE DISTRICT DIRECTOR OF THE ENVIRONMENTAL PROTECTION AGENCY.

STORAGE

STORE IN ACCORDANCE WITH 40 CFR 165 RECOMMENDED PROCEDURES FOR THE DISPOSAL AND STORAGE OF PESTICIDES AND PESTICIDE CONTAINERS. STORE AWAY FROM INCOMPATIBLE SUBSTANCES.

DISPOSAL

DISPOSAL MUST BE IN ACCORDANCE WITH 40 CFR 165 RECOMMENDED PROCEDURES FOR THE DISPOSAL AND STORAGE OF PESTICIDES AND PESTICIDE CONTAINERS.

CONDITIONS TO AVOID

MAY BURN BUT DOES NOT IGNITE READILY. CONTAINERS MAY EXPLODE IN HEAT OF FIRE.

SPILL AND LEAK PROCEDURES

OCCUPATIONAL SPILL: DO NOT TOUCH SPILLED MATERIAL. STOP LEAK IF YOU CAN DO IT WITHOUT RISK. USE WATER SPRAY TO REDUCE VAPORS. FOR SMALL SPILLS, TAKE UP WITH SAND OR OTHER ABSORBENT MATERIAL AND PLACE INTO CONTAINERS FOR LATER DISPOSAL. FOR SMALL DRY SPILLS, WITH A CLEAN SHOVEL PLACE MATERIAL INTO CLEAN, DRY CONTAINERS AND COVER. MOVE CONTAINERS FROM SPILL AREA. FOR LARGER SPILLS, DIKE FAR AHEAD OF SPILL FOR LATER DISPOSAL. KEEP UNNECESSARY PEOPLE AWAY. ISOLATE HAZARD AREA AND DENY ENTRY. VENTILATE CLOSED SPACES BEFORE ENTERING.

PROTECTIVE EQUIPMENT

VENTILATION: PROVIDE LOCAL EXHAUST OR PROCESS ENCLOSURE VENTILATION SYSTEM.

RESPIRATOR: THE FOLLOWING RESPIRATORS ARE RECOMMENDED BASED ON INFORMATION FOUND IN THE PHYSICAL DATA, TOXICITY AND HEALTH EFFECTS SECTIONS. THEY ARE RANKED IN ORDER FROM MINIMUM TO MAXIMUM RESPIRATORY PROTECTION. THE SPECIFIC RESPIRATOR SELECTED MUST BE BASED ON CONTAMINATION LEVELS FOUND IN THE WORK PLACE, MUST NOT EXCEED THE WORKING LIMITS OF THE RESPIRATOR AND BE JOINTLY APPROVED BY THE NATIONAL INSTITUTE FOR OCCUPATIONAL SAFETY AND HEALTH AND THE MINE SAFETY AND HEALTH ADMINISTRATION (NIOSH-MSHA).

TYPE 'C' SUPPLIED-AIR RESPIRATOR WITH A FULL FACEPIECE OPERATED IN PRESSURE-DEMAND OR OTHER POSITIVE PRESSURE MODE OR WITH A FULL FACEPIECE, HELMET OR HOOD OPERATED IN CONTINOUS-FLOW MODE.

SELF-CONTAINED BREATHING APPARATUS WITH A FULL FACEPIECE OPERATED IN PRESSURE-DEMAND OR OTHER POSITIVE PRESSURE MODE.

FOR FIREFIGHTING AND OTHER IMMEDIATELY DANGEROUS TO LIFE OR HEALTH CONDITIONS:

SELF-CONTAINED BREATHING APPARATUS WITH FULL FACEPIECE OPERATED IN PRESSURE-DEMAND OR OTHER POSITIVE PRESSURE MODE.

SUPPLIED-AIR RESPIRATOR WITH FULL FACEPIECE AND OPERATED IN PRESSURE-DEMAND OR OTHER POSITIVE PRESSURE MODE IN COMBINATION WITH AN AUXILIARY SELF-CONTAINED BREATHING APPARATUS OPERATED IN PRESSURE-DEMAND OR OTHER POSITIVE PRESSURE MODE.

CLOTHING: EMPLOYEE MUST WEAR APPROPRIATE PROTECTIVE (IMPERVIOUS) CLOTHING AND EQUIPMENT TO PREVENT ANY POSSIBILITY OF SKIN CONTACT WITH THIS SUBSTANCE.

GLOVES: EMPLOYEE MUST WEAR APPROPRIATE PROTECTIVE GLOVES TO PREVENT CONTACT WITH THIS SUBSTANCE.

EYE PROTECTION: EMPLOYEE MUST WEAR SPLASH-PROOF OR DUST-RESISTANT SAFETY GOGGLES WITH OR WITHOUT A FACESHIELD TO PREVENT CONTACT WITH THIS SUBSTANCE.

EMERGENCY EYE WASH: WHERE THERE IS ANY POSSIBILITY THAT AN EMPLOYEE'S EYES MAY BE EXPOSED TO THIS SUBSTANCE, THE EMPLOYER SHOULD PROVIDE AN EYE WASH FOUNTAIN WITHIN THE IMMEDIATE WORK AREA FOR EMERGENCY USE.

AUTHORIZED BY- OCCUPATIONAL HEALTH SERVICES, INC.

CREATION DATE: 10/04/89 ***REVISION DATE:*** 05/09/90

MATERIAL SAFETY DATA SHEET

OCCUPATIONAL HEALTH SERVICES, INC. EMERGENCY CONTACT:

AGRICULTURE AND PESTICIDE DIVISION JOHN S. BRANSFORD, JR. (615) 292-1180
450 SEVENTH AVENUE, SUITE 2407
NEW YORK, NEW YORK 10123
1-800-445-MSDS OR (212) 967-1100

SUBSTANCE IDENTIFICATION

CAS-NUMBER 1861-32-1
***SUBSTANCE:* CHLORTHAL-DIMETHYL**
TRADE NAMES/SYNONYMS: 1,4-BENZENEDICARBOXYLIC ACID, 2,3,5,6-TETRACHLORO-, DIMETHYL ESTER; TEREPHTHALIC ACID, TETRACHLORO-, DIMETHYL ESTER; 2,3,5,6-TETRACHLORO-1,4-BENZENEDICARBOXYLIC ACID DIMETHYL ESTER; TETRACHLOROTEREPHTHALIC ACID DIMETHYL ESTER; DIMETHYL TETRACHLOROTEREPHTHALATE; DIMETHYL 2,3,5,6-TETRACHLORO-1,4-BENZENEDICARBOXYLATE; DIMETHYL 2,3,5,6-TETRACHLOROTEREPHTHALATE; CHLORTHAL DIMETHYL ESTER; CHLORTHAL-METHYL; DAC 893; DCPA; DACTHALOR; DACTHAL; CHLORTHAL DIMETHYL; C10H6CL4O4; PST04913
CHEMICAL FAMILY: CARBOXYLIC ACID, AROMATIC HALOGEN
MOLECULAR FORMULA: C-H3-O-C-(O)-C6-CL4-C-(O)-O-C-H3
MOLECULAR WEIGHT: 331.97
CERCLA RATINGS (SCALE 0-3): HEALTH=3 FIRE=1 REACTIVITY=0 PERSISTENCE=3
NFPA RATINGS (SCALE 0-4): HEALTH=U FIRE=1 REACTIVITY=0

COMPONENTS AND CONTAMINANTS

COMPONENT: CHLORTHAL-DIMETHYL ***PERCENT:*** 100.0
CAS# 1861-32-1
EXPOSURE LIMITS: NO OCCUPATIONAL EXPOSURE LIMITS ESTABLISHED BY OSHA, ACGIH, OR NIOSH.

PHYSICAL DATA

DESCRIPTION: ODORLESS, COLORLESS TO WHITE CRYSTALLINE SOLID.
BOILING POINT: 680-689 F (360-370 C) (DECOMPOSES)
MELTING POINT: 313 F (156C)
SPECIFIC GRAVITY: NOT AVAILABLE ***VAPOR PRESSURE:*** <0.5 MMHG @ 40 C
SOLUBILITY IN WATER: <0.5 PPM @ 25 C
SOLVENT SOLUBILITY: SOLUBLE IN BENZENE, TOLUENE, XYLENE, DIOXANE, ACETONE; MODERATELY SOLUBLE IN CARBON TETRACHLORIDE; SLIGHTLY SOLUBLE IN TETRAHYDROFURAN, CYCLOHEXANONE, AND PETROLEUM SOLVENTS.

FIRE AND EXPLOSION DATA

FIRE AND EXPLOSION HAZARD: SLIGHT FIRE HAZARD WHEN EXPOSED TO HEAT OR FLAME.
DUST-AIR MIXTURES MAY IGNITE OR EXPLODE.
FIREFIGHTING MEDIA: DRY CHEMICAL, CARBON DIOXIDE, HALON, WATER SPRAY OR STANDARD FOAM (1987 EMERGENCY RESPONSE GUIDEBOOK, DOT P 5800.4).
FOR LARGER FIRES, USE WATER SPRAY, FOG OR STANDARD FOAM (1987 EMERGENCY RESPONSE GUIDEBOOK, DOT P 5800.4).
FIREFIGHTING: MOVE CONTAINER FROM FIRE AREA IF POSSIBLE. DO NOT SCATTER SPILLED MATERIAL WITH HIGH PRESSURE WATER STREAMS. DIKE FIRE CONTROL WATER FOR LATER DISPOSAL (1987 EMERGENCY RESPONSE GUIDEBOOK, DOT P 5800.4, GUIDE PAGE 31).
USE AGENTS SUITABLE FOR TYPE OF SURROUNDING FIRE. AVOID BREATHING HAZARDOUS VAPORS, KEEP UPWIND.

TOXICITY

CHLORTHAL-DIMETHYL: TOXICITY DATA: >5700 MG/M3/4 HOURS INHALATION-RAT LC50 (FMCHA2); 10 GM/KG SKIN-RABBIT LD50; 3 GM/KG ORAL-RAT LD50; 320 MG/KG INTRAVENOUS-MOUSE LD50; 3500 MG/KG UNREPORTED-MOUSE LD50. CARCINOGEN STATUS: NONE. ACUTE TOXICITY LEVEL: MODERATELY TOXIC BY INGESTION; SLIGHTLY TOXIC BY DERMAL ABSORPTION. TARGET EFFECTS: NO DATA AVAILABLE.

HEALTH EFFECTS AND FIRST AID

INHALATION: CHLORTHAL-DIMETHYL: **ACUTE EXPOSURE-** THE LC50 REPORTED IN RATS WAS GREATER THAN 5700 MG/M3/4 HOURS. **CHRONIC EXPOSURE-** NO DATA AVAILABLE.
FIRST AID- REMOVE FROM EXPOSURE AREA TO FRESH AIR IMMEDIATELY. IF BREATHING HAS STOPPED, PERFORM ARTIFICIAL RESPIRATION. KEEP PERSON WARM AND AT REST. TREAT SYMPTOMATICALLY AND SUPPORTIVELY. GET MEDICAL ATTENTION IMMEDIATELY.

SKIN CONTACT: CHLORTHAL-DIMETHYL: **ACUTE EXPOSURE-** THIS MATERIAL WAS MILDLY IRRITATING TO RABBIT SKIN. **CHRONIC EXPOSURE-** NO DATA AVAILABLE.
FIRST AID- REMOVE CONTAMINATED CLOTHING AND SHOES IMMEDIATELY. WASH AFFECTED AREA WITH SOAP OR MILD DETERGENT AND LARGE AMOUNTS OF WATER UNTIL NO EVIDENCE OF CHEMICAL REMAINS (APPROXIMATELY 15-20 MINUTES). GET MEDICAL ATTENTION IMMEDIATELY.

EYE CONTACT: CHLORTHAL DIMETHYL: **ACUTE EXPOSURE-** 3 MG APPLIED TO RABBIT EYES WAS MILDLY IRRITATING. **CHRONIC EXPOSURE-** NO DATA AVAILABLE.
FIRST AID- WASH EYES IMMEDIATELY WITH LARGE AMOUNTS OF WATER OR NORMAL SALINE, OCCASIONALLY LIFTING UPPER AND LOWER LIDS, UNTIL NO EVIDENCE OF CHEMICAL REMAINS (APPROXIMATELY 15-20 MINUTES). GET MEDICAL ATTENTION IMMEDIATELY.

INGESTION: CHLORTHAL DIMETHYL: **ACUTE EXPOSURE-** HUMAN VOLUNTEERS HAVE INGESTED 50 MG WITHOUT DETECTABLE EFFECTS. **CHRONIC EXPOSURE-** NO GROSS OR HISTOPATHOLOGIC EFFECTS WERE OBSERVED IN RATS AND DOGS RECEIVING DIETARY LEVELS UP TO 10,000 PPM FOR 2 YEARS.
FIRST AID- IF THE PERSON IS CONSCIOUS AND NOT CONVULSING, REMOVE BY GIVING SYRUP OF IPECAC (IF VOMITING OCCURS, KEEP THE HEAD BELOW THE HIPS TO PREVENT ASPIRATION). GIVE ACTIVATED CHARCOAL FOLLOWED BY GASTRIC LAVAGE. FOLLOW WITH A SALINE CATHARTIC. DO NOT GIVE FATS OR OILS. INTESTINAL LAVAGE WITH 20% MANNITOL (200 ML) BY STOMACH TUBE IS ALSO USEFUL. GIVE ARTIFICIAL RESPIRATION WITH OXYGEN IF RESPIRATION IS DEPRESSED (DREISBACH, HANDBOOK OF POISONING, 12TH ED.). TREAT SYMPTOMATICALLY AND SUPPORTIVELY. LAVAGE AND ADMINISTRATION OF OXYGEN SHOULD BE PERFORMED BY QUALIFIED MEDICAL PERSONNEL. GET MEDICAL ATTENTION IMMEDIATELY.
ANTIDOTE: NO SPECIFIC ANTIDOTE. TREAT SYMPTOMATICALLY AND SUPPORTIVELY.

REACTIVITY

REACTIVITY: STABLE UNDER NORMAL TEMPERATURES AND PRESSURES.
INCOMPATIBILITIES: CHLORTHAL-DIMETHYL: OXIDIZERS (STRONG): FIRE AND EXPLOSION HAZARD.
DECOMPOSITION: THERMAL DECOMPOSITION PRODUCTS MAY INCLUDE TOXIC AND CORROSIVE FUMES OF CHLORIDES AND TOXIC OXIDES OF CARBON.
POLYMERIZATION: HAZARDOUS POLYMERIZATION HAS NOT BEEN REPORTED TO OCCUR UNDER NORMAL TEMPERATURES AND PRESSURES.

STORAGE AND DISPOSAL

OBSERVE ALL FEDERAL, STATE AND LOCAL REGULATIONS WHEN STORING OR DISPOSING OF THIS SUBSTANCE. FOR ASSISTANCE, CONTACT THE DISTRICT DIRECTOR OF THE ENVIRONMENTAL PROTECTION AGENCY.

STORAGE

STORE IN ACCORDANCE WITH 40 CFR 165 RECOMMENDED PROCEDURES FOR THE DISPOSAL AND STORAGE OF PESTICIDES AND PESTICIDE CONTAINERS.
STORE AWAY FROM INCOMPATIBLE SUBSTANCES.

DISPOSAL

DISPOSAL MUST BE IN ACCORDANCE WITH 40 CFR 165 RECOMMENDED PROCEDURES FOR THE DISPOSAL AND STORAGE OF PESTICIDES AND PESTICIDE CONTAINERS.

CONDITIONS TO AVOID

MAY BURN BUT DOES NOT IGNITE READILY. AVOID CONTACT WITH STRONG OXIDIZERS, EXCESSIVE HEAT, SPARKS, OR OPEN FLAME.

SPILL AND LEAK PROCEDURES

OCCUPATIONAL SPILL: SWEEP UP AND PLACE IN SUITABLE CLEAN, DRY CONTAINERS FOR RECLAMATION OR LATER DISPOSAL. DO NOT FLUSH SPILLED MATERIAL INTO SEWER. KEEP UNNECESSARY PEOPLE AWAY.

PROTECTIVE EQUIPMENT

VENTILATION: PROVIDE LOCAL EXHAUST OR GENERAL DILUTION VENTILATION SYSTEM.
RESPIRATOR: THE FOLLOWING RESPIRATORS ARE RECOMMENDED BASED ON INFORMATION FOUND IN THE PHYSICAL DATA, TOXICITY AND HEALTH EFFECTS SECTIONS. THEY ARE RANKED IN ORDER FROM MINIMUM TO MAXIMUM RESPIRATORY PROTECTION. THE SPECIFIC RESPIRATOR SELECTED MUST BE BASED ON CONTAMINATION LEVELS FOUND IN THE WORK PLACE, MUST NOT EXCEED THE WORKING LIMITS OF THE RESPIRATOR AND BE JOINTLY APPROVED BY THE NATIONAL INSTITUTE FOR OCCUPATIONAL SAFETY AND HEALTH AND THE MINE SAFETY AND HEALTH ADMINISTRATION (NIOSH-MSHA).
CHEMICAL CARTRIDGE RESPIRATOR WITH AN ORGANIC VAPOR CARTRIDGE(S) IN COMBINATION WITH A DUST AND MIST FILTER.
GAS MASK WITH ORGANIC VAPOR CANISTER (CHIN-STYLE OR FRONT- OR BACK-MOUNTED CANISTER) WITH A DUST AND MIST FILTER.
GAS MASK WITH ORGANIC VAPOR CANISTER (CHIN-STYLE OR FRONT- OR BACK-MOUNTED CANISTER) WITH A PARTICULATE FILTER.
POWERED AIR-PURIFYING RESPIRATOR WITH A HIGH-EFFICIENCY FILTER.
TYPE 'C' SUPPLIED-AIR RESPIRATOR WITH A FULL FACEPIECE OPERATED IN A

PRESSURE-DEMAND OR OTHER POSITIVE PRESSURE MODE. SELF-CONTAINED BREATHING APPARATUS WITH A FULL FACEPIECE OPERATED IN PRESSURE-DEMAND OR OTHER POSITIVE PRESSURE MODE.

FOR FIREFIGHTING AND OTHER IMMEDIATELY DANGEROUS TO LIFE OR HEALTH CONDITIONS:

SELF-CONTAINED BREATHING APPARATUS WITH FULL FACEPIECE OPERATED IN PRESSURE-DEMAND OR OTHER POSITIVE PRESSURE MODE.

SUPPLIED-AIR RESPIRATOR WITH FULL FACEPIECE AND OPERATED IN PRESSURE-DEMAND OR OTHER POSITIVE PRESSURE MODE IN COMBINATION WITH AN AUXILIARY SELF-CONTAINED BREATHING APPARATUS OPERATED IN PRESSURE-DEMAND OR OTHER POSITIVE PRESSURE MODE.

CLOTHING: EMPLOYEE MUST WEAR APPROPRIATE PROTECTIVE (IMPERVIOUS) CLOTHING AND EQUIPMENT TO PREVENT REPEATED OR PROLONGED SKIN CONTACT WITH THIS SUBSTANCE.

GLOVES: EMPLOYEE MUST WEAR APPROPRIATE PROTECTIVE GLOVES TO PREVENT CONTACT WITH THIS SUBSTANCE.

EYE PROTECTION: EMPLOYEE MUST WEAR SPLASH-PROOF OR DUST-RESISTANT SAFETY GOGGLES TO PREVENT EYE CONTACT WITH THIS SUBSTANCE.

EMERGENCY EYE WASH: WHERE THERE IS ANY POSSIBILITY THAT AN EMPLOYEE'S EYES MAY BE EXPOSED TO THIS SUBSTANCE, THE EMPLOYER SHOULD PROVIDE AN EYE WASH FOUNTAIN WITHIN THE IMMEDIATE WORK AREA FOR EMERGENCY USE.

AUTHORIZED BY- OCCUPATIONAL HEALTH SERVICES, INC.

CREATION DATE: 04/13/90 ***REVISION DATE:*** 05/31/90

MATERIAL SAFETY DATA SHEET

OCCUPATIONAL HEALTH SERVICES, INC.
AGRICULTURE AND PESTICIDE DIVISION
450 SEVENTH AVENUE, SUITE 2407
NEW YORK, NEW YORK 10123
1-800-445-MSDS OR (212) 967-1100

EMERGENCY CONTACT:
JOHN S. BRANSFORD, JR. (615) 292-1180

SUBSTANCE IDENTIFICATION

CAS-NUMBER 7738-94-5

SUBSTANCE: **CHROMIC ACID**

TRADE NAMES/SYNONYMS: CHROMIC ACID, SOLUTION; CHROMIC(VI) ACID; CHROMIUM TRIOXIDE, SOLUTION; TURCOAT ACCELAGOLD PART II (TURCO PRODUCTS, INCORPORATED); STCC 4930206; UN 1755; PST04930

CHEMICAL FAMILY: MIXTURE, AQUEOUS

MOLECULAR FORMULA: CR-H2-O4

MOLECULAR WEIGHT: 117.99

CERCLA RATINGS (SCALE 0-3): HEALTH=3 FIRE=0 REACTIVITY=0 PERSISTENCE=3

NFPA RATINGS (SCALE 0-4): HEALTH=3 FIRE=0 REACTIVITY=0

COMPONENTS AND CONTAMINANTS

COMPONENT: CHROMIC ANHYDRIDE ***PERCENT:*** <67.0
CAS# 1333-82-0

COMPONENT: WATER ***PERCENT:*** >33.0

EXPOSURE LIMITS: CHROMIC ACID AND CHROMATES: 0.1 MG(CRO3)/M3 OSHA CEILING 0.05 MG(CR)/M3 ACGIH TWA 25 UG(CR(VI))/M3 NIOSH RECOMMENDED 10 HOUR TWA; 50 UG(CR(VI))/M3 NIOSH RECOMMENDED 15 MINUTE CEILING

SUBJECT TO SARA SECTION 313 ANNUAL TOXIC CHEMICAL RELEASE REPORTING

SUBJECT TO CALIFORNIA PROPOSITION 65 CANCER AND/OR REPRODUCTIVE TOXICITY WARNING AND RELEASE REQUIREMENTS (HEXAVALENT CHROMIUM COMPOUNDS) (FEBRUARY 27, 1987)

CHROMIC ACID: 1000 POUNDS CERCLA SECTION 103 REPORTABLE QUANTITY

PHYSICAL DATA

DESCRIPTION: DARK RED LIQUID. ***BOILING POINT:*** NOT AVAILABLE

SPECIFIC GRAVITY: 1.67 ***VAPOR PRESSURE:*** NOT AVAILABLE

SOLUBILITY IN WATER: COMPLETE

FIRE AND EXPLOSION DATA

FIRE AND EXPLOSION HAZARD: NEGLIGIBLE FIRE HAZARD WHEN EXPOSED TO HEAT OR FLAME.

OXIDIZER: OXIDIZERS DECOMPOSE, ESPECIALLY WHEN HEATED, TO YIELD OXYGEN OR OTHER GASES WHICH WILL INCREASE THE BURNING RATE OF COMBUSTIBLE MATTER. CONTACT WITH EASILY OXIDIZABLE, ORGANIC, OR OTHER COMBUSTIBLE MATERIALS MAY RESULT IN IGNITION, VIOLENT COMBUSTION OR EXPLOSION.

FIREFIGHTING MEDIA: DRY CHEMICAL, CARBON DIOXIDE, HALON, WATER SPRAY OR STANDARD FOAM (1987 EMERGENCY RESPONSE GUIDEBOOK, DOT P 5800.4).

FOR LARGER FIRES, USE WATER SPRAY, FOG OR STANDARD FOAM (1987 EMERGENCY RESPONSE GUIDEBOOK, DOT P 5800.4).

FIREFIGHTING: MOVE CONTAINERS FROM FIRE AREA IF POSSIBLE. COOL CONTAINERS EXPOSED TO FLAMES WITH WATER FROM SIDE UNTIL WELL AFTER FIRE IS OUT. STAY AWAY FROM STORAGE TANK ENDS (1987 EMERGENCY RESPONSE GUIDEBOOK, DOT P 5800.4, GUIDE PAGE 60).

USE AGENT SUITABLE FOR TYPE OF FIRE; USE WATER IN FLOODING AMOUNTS AS FOG. COOL CONTAINERS WITH FLOODING QUANTITIES OF WATER, APPLY FROM AS FAR A DISTANCE AS POSSIBLE. AVOID BREATHING CORROSIVE VAPORS, KEEP UPWIND.

TRANSPORTATION DATA

DEPARTMENT OF TRANSPORTATION HAZARD CLASSIFICATION 49 CFR 172.101: CORROSIVE MATERIAL

DEPARTMENT OF TRANSPORTATION LABELING REQUIREMENTS 49 CFR 172.101 AND SUBPART E: CORROSIVE

DEPARTMENT OF TRANSPORTATION PACKAGING REQUIREMENTS: 49 CFR 173.164 EXCEPTIONS: 49 CFR 173.153

TOXICITY

CHROMIC ACID: TOXICITY DATA: 320 MG/KG SUBCUTANEOUS-DOG LDLO; MUTAGENIC DATA (RTECS). CARCINOGEN STATUS: KNOWN HUMAN CARCINOGEN (NTP); HUMAN SUFFICIENT EVIDENCE, ANIMAL SUFFICIENT EVIDENCE (IARC GROUP-1 FOR HEXAVALENT CHROMIUM COMPOUNDS). AN INCREASED INCIDENCE OF LUNG CANCER HAS BEEN OBSERVED AMONG WORKERS OCCUPATIONALLY EXPOSED DURING CHROMATE PRODUCTION, PIGMENT MANUFACTURING AND PLATING AND ALLOYING PROCESSES. INCIDENCES OF CANCERS AT OTHER SITES MAY ALSO BE INCREASED IN SUCH PERSONS. HOWEVER, A CLEAR DISTINCTION BETWEEN THE RELATIVE CARCINOGENICITY OF CHROMIUM COMPOUNDS OF DIFFERENT OXIDATION STATES OR SOLUBILITIES HAS BEEN DIFFICULT TO ACHIEVE. LOCAL EFFECTS: CORROSIVE- INHALATION, SKIN, AND EYES. ACUTE TOXICITY LEVEL: INSUFFICIENT DATA. TARGET EFFECTS: SENSITIZER- SKIN. POISONING MAY AFFECT THE LIVER AND KIDNEYS. AT INCREASED RISK FROM EXPOSURE: PERSONS WITH PRE-EXISTING RESPIRATORY, LIVER, KIDNEY, SKIN, OR BLOOD DISORDERS.

HEALTH EFFECTS AND FIRST AID

INHALATION: CHROMIC ANHYDRIDE (CHROMIUM TRIOXIDE):
CORROSIVE/SENSITIZER/CARCINOGEN. 30 MG(CRO3)/M3 IMMEDIATELY DANGEROUS TO LIFE OR HEALTH. **ACUTE EXPOSURE-** DUST OR MIST MAY CAUSE SEVERE IRRITATION OF THE MUCOUS MEMBRANES, COUGHING, SNEEZING, RHINORRHEA, DYSPNEA, BRONCHOSPASM, HEADACHE, PAIN ON DEEP INSPIRATION, FEVER, LOSS OF WEIGHT AND DELAYED PULMONARY EDEMA. TRACHEOBRONCHIAL IRRITATION AND EDEMA MAY PERSIST AFTER OTHER SYMPTOMS SUBSIDE. IN A FEW CASES SENSITIZATION OCCURS, RESULTING IN TYPICAL ASTHMATIC ATTACKS, WHICH RECUR ON SUBSEQUENT EXPOSURE.
CHRONIC EXPOSURE- REPEATED OR PROLONGED EXPOSURE MAY CAUSE IRRITATION OF THE RESPIRATORY SYSTEM, INFLAMMATION, ULCERATION, EDEMA, AND HYPEREMIA OF THE LARYNGEAL MUCOSA, ASTHMATIC BRONCHITIS, COUGHING, DYSPNEA, WHEEZING, PAIN ON INSPIRATION, HEADACHE, LOSS OF SENSE OF SMELL AND TASTE, REDNESS AND IRRITATION OF THE NASAL MUCOSA, PROGRESSING TO ULCERS OF THE NASAL SEPTUM WITH RHINORRHEA, BLEEDING, AND LATER DRYNESS AND SCABING. IF CESSATION OF EXPOSURE IS NOT IMMEDIATE, PERFORATION OF THE NASAL SEPTUM MANIFESTED AS A PAINLESS HOLE SURROUNDED BY A CRUSTED EDGE MAY OCCUR. OTHER SYMPTOMS MAY INCLUDE SORE THROAT, TOOTH EROSION AND DISCOLORATION, PERFORATED EARDRUMS, CHRONIC BRONCHITIS, BRONCHOPNEUMONIA, CENTRAL NERVOUS SYSTEM INVOLVEMENT, AND GASTROINTESTINAL DISORDERS WITH EXCESSIVE INFLAMMATORY AND ULCERATIVE CONDITIONS, AND SPASMS ASSOCIATED WITH FATIGUE, LASSITUDE, AND RHEUMATIC PAIN. DISTURBANCES OF SHORT-TERM MEMORY AND ATTENTION SPAN WERE OBSERVED IN 149 OCCUPATIONALLY EXPOSED WORKERS. PULMONARY SENSITIZATION HAS BEEN REPORTED. NEPHRITIS AND MILD TO MODERATE LIVER DAMAGE WITH OR WITHOUT JAUNDICE HAVE BEEN REPORTED TO OCCUR. OCCUPATIONAL EXPOSURE TO SOME HEXAVALENT CHROMIUM COMPOUNDS HAS BEEN RELATED TO AN INCREASED INCIDENCE OF LUNG CANCER. THE LATENT PERIOD APPEARS TO BE 10-15 YEARS.

FIRST AID- REMOVE FROM EXPOSURE AREA TO FRESH AIR IMMEDIATELY. IF BREATHING HAS STOPPED, GIVE ARTIFICIAL RESPIRATION. MAINTAIN AIRWAY AND BLOOD PRESSURE AND ADMINISTER OXYGEN IF AVAILABLE. KEEP AFFECTED PERSON WARM AND AT REST. TREAT SYMPTOMATICALLY AND SUPPORTIVELY. ADMINISTRATION OF OXYGEN SHOULD BE PERFORMED BY QUALIFIED PERSONNEL. GET MEDICAL ATTENTION IMMEDIATELY.

SKIN CONTACT: CHROMIC ANHYDRIDE (CHROMIUM TRIOXIDE): CORROSIVE/SENSITIZER/NEPHROTOXIN. **ACUTE EXPOSURE-** MAY CAUSE SEVERE IRRITATION, AND SKIN ULCERATION. THE ULCERS MOST COMMONLY OCCUR ON THE HANDS, WRISTS AND FOREARMS, BUT FREQUENTLY ON THE EYELIDS, NECK OR ANY OTHER PART OF THE BODY IN CONTACT WITH THE MIST OR SOLUTION ESPECIALLY IF THE SKIN IS ABRADED OR BROKEN. CHARACTERISTICALLY THE ULCERS ARE SMALL (2-5 MM), PUNCHED OUT, RELATIVELY PAINLESS, AND MAY VARY FROM A DRY ERYTHEMATOUS ERUPTION TO A WEEPING ECZEMATOUS CONDITION WHICH HEALS SLOWLY, AND PRODUCES A DEPRESSED SCAR. SECONDARY BACTERIAL INFECTION IS COMMON. ONE CASE OF FATAL NEPHRITIS HAS BEEN REPORTED FOLLOWING USE TO CAUTERIZE A WOUND. SIMILAR USES HAVE RESULTED IN SEVERAL CASES OF SYSTEMIC POISONING. SENSITIZATION DERMATITIS MAY OCCUR IN PREVIOUSLY EXPOSED PERSONS. **CHRONIC EXPOSURE-** PROLONGED OR REPEATED CONTACT MAY CAUSE IRRITATIVE DERMATITIS AND SLOW HEALING ULCERATION OR SENSITIZATION DERMATITIS. ALLERGIC ERUPTIONS MAY BE OOZING, OR MAY BE DRY, FISSURED, AND LICHENIFIED.

FIRST AID- REMOVE CONTAMINATED CLOTHING AND SHOES IMMEDIATELY. WASH AFFECTED AREA WITH SOAP OR MILD DETERGENT AND LARGE AMOUNTS OF WATER UNTIL NO EVIDENCE OF CHEMICAL REMAINS (APPROXIMATELY 15-20 MINUTES). LESIONS CAN BE SCRUBBED WITH A 20% SOLUTION OF SODIUM HYPOSULFITE OR TREATED WITH CALCIUM DISODIUM EDETATE OINTMENTS. FRESHLY PREPARED AND PROMPTLY APPLIED 10% ASCORBIC ACID SOLUTION MAY SPEED HEALING OF ULCERS (GOSSELIN, CLINICAL TOXICOLOGY OF COMMERCIAL PRODUCTS, 5TH ED.), AS WILL 1% SOLUTION OF ALUMINUM ACETATE WET DRESSING (ARENA, POISONING 4TH ED.).

EYE CONTACT: CHROMIC ANHYDRIDE (CHROMIUM TRIOXIDE): CORROSIVE. **ACUTE EXPOSURE-** DIRECT CONTACT MAY CAUSE IRRITATION, PAIN, BLURRED VISION, SEVERE BURNS, SEVERE CORNEAL INJURY WITH CORNEAL OPACITY AND POSSIBLY LOSS OF VISION. **CHRONIC EXPOSURE-** REPEATED OR PROLONGED EXPOSURE MAY CAUSE CHRONIC CONJUNCTIVITIS, LACRIMATION AND RARELY, BROWN STAINING OF THE CORNEA.

FIRST AID- WASH EYES IMMEDIATELY WITH LARGE AMOUNTS OF WATER, OCCASIONALLY LIFTING UPPER AND LOWER LIDS, UNTIL NO EVIDENCE OF CHEMICAL REMAINS (AT LEAST 15-20 MINUTES). CONTINUE IRRIGATING WITH NORMAL SALINE UNTIL THE PH HAS RETURNED TO NORMAL (30-60 MINUTES). COVER WITH STERILE BANDAGES. GET MEDICAL ATTENTION IMMEDIATELY.

INGESTION: CHROMIC ANHYDRIDE (CHROMIUM TRIOXIDE): CORROSIVE/NEPHROTOXIN/TOXIC. **ACUTE EXPOSURE-** MAY CAUSE YELLOW DISCOLORATION OF THE MOUTH AND PHARYNX, COLD, CLAMMY CYANOTIC SKIN, DYSPHAGIA FROM CORROSION AND EDEMA OF THE POSTERIOR PHARYNX, GLOTTIS, AND ESOPHAGUS, SORE THROAT, ABDOMINAL SPASM, SEVERE GASTRIC BURNING, VOMITING OF YELLOWISH AND GREENISH MATERIAL, FOLLOWED BY WATERY, BLOODY DIARRHEA AND GENERALIZED MYALGIA. OTHER SYMPTOMS MAY INCLUDE INTENSE THIRST, DIZZINESS, OLIGURIA, ANURIA AND SEVERE CIRCULATORY COLLAPSE. DEATH MAY BE DUE TO UREMIA OR HEMORRHAGING. **CHRONIC EXPOSURE-** NO DATA AVAILABLE.

FIRST AID- DO NOT USE GASTRIC LAVAGE OR EMESIS. DILUTE THE ACID IMMEDIATELY BY DRINKING LARGE QUANTITIES OF WATER OR MILK. IF VOMITING PERSISTS, ADMINISTER FLUIDS REPEATEDLY. INGESTED ACID MUST BE DILUTED APPROXIMATELY 100 FOLD TO RENDER IT HARMLESS TO TISSUES. MAINTAIN AIRWAY AND TREAT SHOCK (DREISBACH, HANDBOOK OF POISONING, 12TH ED.). GET MEDICAL ATTENTION IMMEDIATELY. IF VOMITING OCCURS, KEEP HEAD BELOW HIPS TO HELP PREVENT ASPIRATION.

ANTIDOTE: THE FOLLOWING ANTIDOTE HAS BEEN RECOMMENDED. HOWEVER, THE DECISION AS TO WHETHER THE SEVERITY OF POISONING REQUIRES ADMINISTRATION OF ANY ANTIDOTE AND ACTUAL DOSE REQUIRED SHOULD BE MADE BY QUALIFIED MEDICAL PERSONNEL.

CHROMIUM POISONING: USE OF DIMERCAPROL HAS BEEN SUGGESTED ON THE BASIS OF FINDINGS IN ANIMALS. GIVE 3 MG/KG (OR 0.3 ML/10 KG) EVERY 4 HOURS, INTRAMUSCULARLY FOR THE FIRST 2 DAYS AND THEN 2 MG/KG EVERY 12 HOURS FOR A TOTAL OF 10 DAYS (DREISBACH, HANDBOOK OF POISONING, 11TH ED.). ANTIDOTE SHOULD BE ADMINISTERED BY QUALIFIED MEDICAL PERSONNEL.

REACTIVITY

REACTIVITY: STABLE UNDER NORMAL TEMPERATURES AND PRESSURES.

INCOMPATIBILITIES: CHROMIC ANHYDRIDE (CHROMIUM TRIOXIDE): ACETIC ACID: EXPLODES WHEN HEATED. ACETALDEHYDE: EXPLOSION HAZARD. ACETIC ANHYDRIDE: PROBABLE EXPLOSION. ACETIC ANHYDRIDE + 3-METHYLPHENOL: VIOLENT EXOTHEREMIC REACTION. ACETIC ANHYDRIDE + TETRAHYDRONAPHTHALENE: FIRE HAZARD. ACETONE: IGNITES ON CONTACT. ACETYLENE: VIOLENT OXIDATION REACTION. ALCOHOLS: IGNITES. ALKALIES: VIOLENT REACTION. ALUMINUM: VIOLENT REACTION AND POSSIBLE IGNITION. AMMONIA: INCANDESCENT REACTION. ANILINE: FIRE AND EXPLOSION HAZARD. ANTHRACENE: IGNITES ON CONTACT. ARSENIC: INCANDESCENT REACTION. BASES: VIOLENT REACTION. BENZALDEHYDE: VIOLENT REACTION OR IGNITION. BENZENE: IGNITES ON CONTACT. BENZYLETHYLANILINE: VIOLENT REACTION OR IGNITION. BRASS: CORRODES. BROMINE PENTAFLUORIDE: VIOLENT REACTION OR POSSIBLE IGNITION. BUTANOL: IGNITES ON CONTACT. BUTANONE: VIOLENT COMBUSTION. BUTYRALDEHYDE: VIOLENT REACTION OR IGNITION. BUTYRIC ACID: IGNITION (ABOVE 100 C). CAMPHOR: VIOLENT REACTION. CHLORINE TRIFLUORIDE: VIOLENT OR INCANDESCENT REACTION. CHROMIUM(II) SULFIDE: IGNITION REACTION. CLOTH: FIRE AND EXPLOSION HAZARD. COPPER: CORRODES. CYCLOHEXANOL: IGNITION. DIETHYL ETHER: VIOLENT REACTION. DIMETHYLDIOXANE: VIOLENT REACTION OR IGNITION. DIMETHYLFORMAMIDE: IGNITION OR VIOLENT REACTION. 1,3-DIMETHYLHEXAHYDROPYRIMIDONE: EXPLOSIVE REACTION WHICH MAY IGNITE. ETHYL ACETATE: VIOLENT REACTION OR IGNITION. ETHYL ALCOHOL: IGNITES ON CONTACT. ETHYLENE GLYCOL: IGNITES. GLYCEROL: VIOLENT IGNITION REACTION. GREASE: FIRE AND EXPLOSION HAZARD. HEXAMETHYLPHOSPHORIC TRIAMIDE: VIOLENT DECOMPOSITION. HYDRAZINE: EXPLOSIVE DECOMPOSITION. HYDROCARBONS: IGNITES. HYDROGEN SULFIDE: INCANDESCENT REACTION. ISOBUTANOL: IGNITES ON CONTACT. ISOPROPYL ACETATE: VIOLENT REACTION OR IGNITION. ISOPROPYL ALCOHOL: IGNITION. LEATHER: ATTACKS. LITHIUM + NITROGEN: VIOLENT COMBUSTION. METALS: CORRODES. METHANOL: POSSIBLE EXPLOSION. METHYL DIOXANE: VIOLENT REACTION OR IGNITION. NAPHTHALENE: VIOLENT REACTION. ORGANIC MATTER: FIRE AND EXPLOSION HAZARD. PAPER: FIRE AND EXPLOSION HAZARD. PELARGONIC ACID: FIRE AND EXPLOSION HAZARD. PENTYL ACETATE: FIRE AND EXPLOSION HAZARD. PEROXYFORMIC ACID: VIOLENT DECOMPOSITION AND POSSIBLE EXPLOSION. PHOSPHORUS: EXPLOSION. PLASTICS: ATTACKS. POTASSIUM: REACTS WITH INCANDESCENCE. POTASSIUM HEXACYANOFERRATE: IGNITION OR EXPLOSION WHEN HEATED OR GROUND. PROPIONALDEHYDE: FIRE AND EXPLOSION HAZARD. PYRIDINE: FIRE AND EXPLOSION HAZARD. QUINOLINE: FIRE AND EXPLOSION HAZARD. RUBBER: POSSIBLE IGNITION. SELENIUM: VIOLENT REACTION. SODIUM: REACTS WITH INCANDESCENCE. SODIUM AMIDE: VIOLENT REACTION. SULFUR: IGNITES WHEN HEATED. THINNER: FIRE AND EXPLOSION HAZARD. TURPENTINE: VIOLENT REACTION. WOOD: FIRE AND EXPLOSION HAZARD.

DECOMPOSITION: CHROMIC ACID DECOMPOSES UPON HEATING ABOVE 250 C FORMING TRIVALENT CHROMIUM OXIDE(CR2-O3) AND OXYGEN WHICH INCREASES THE FIRE HAZARD.

POLYMERIZATION: HAZARDOUS POLYMERIZATION HAS NOT BEEN REPORTED TO OCCUR UNDER NORMAL TEMPERATURES AND PRESSURES.

STORAGE AND DISPOSAL

OBSERVE ALL FEDERAL, STATE AND LOCAL REGULATIONS WHEN STORING OR DISPOSING OF THIS SUBSTANCE. FOR ASSISTANCE, CONTACT THE DISTRICT DIRECTOR OF THE ENVIRONMENTAL PROTECTION AGENCY.

****STORAGE****

STORE AWAY FROM INCOMPATIBLE SUBSTANCES.

****DISPOSAL****

DISPOSAL MUST BE IN ACCORDANCE WITH STANDARDS APPLICABLE TO GENERATORS OF HAZARDOUS WASTE, 40 CFR 262. EPA HAZARDOUS WASTE NUMBER D002. 100 POUND CERCLA SECTION 103 REPORTABLE QUANTITY. CHROMIUM - REGULATORY LEVEL: 5.0 MG/L MATERIALS WHICH CONTAIN THE ABOVE SUBSTANCE AT OR ABOVE THE REGULATORY LEVEL MEET THE EPA CHARACTERISTIC OF TOXICITY, AND MUST BE DISPOSED OF IN ACCORDANCE WITH 40 CFR PART 262. EPA HAZARDOUS WASTE NUMBER D007.

CONDITIONS TO AVOID

MAY BURN BUT DOES NOT IGNITE READILY. FLAMMABLE, POISONOUS GASES MAY ACCUMULATE IN TANKS AND HOPPER CARS. MAY IGNITE COMBUSTIBLES (WOOD, PAPER, OIL, ETC.).

SPILL AND LEAK PROCEDURES

SOIL SPILL: DIG A HOLDING AREA SUCH AS A PIT, POND OR LAGOON TO CONTAIN SPILL AND DIKE SURFACE FLOW USING BARRIER OF SOIL, SANDBAGS, FOAMED POLYURETHANE OR FOAMED CONCRETE. ABSORB LIQUID MASS WITH FLY ASH OR CEMENT POWDER.

NEUTRALIZE SPILL WITH SLAKED LIME, SODIUM BICARBONATE OR CRUSHED LIMESTONE.

AIR SPILL: APPLY WATER SPRAY TO KNOCK DOWN AND REDUCE VAPORS. KNOCK-DOWN WATER IS CORROSIVE AND TOXIC AND SHOULD BE DIKED FOR CONTAINMENT AND LATER DISPOSAL.

WATER SPILL: NEUTRALIZE WITH AGRICULTURAL LIME, SLAKED LIME, CRUSHED LIMESTONE, OR SODIUM BICARBONATE.

ADD SUITABLE AGENT TO NEUTRALIZE SPILLED MATERIAL TO PH-7.

USE MECHANICAL DREDGES OR LIFTS TO EXTRACT IMMOBILIZED MASSES OF POLLUTION AND PRECIPITATES.

THE CALIFORNIA SAFE DRINKING WATER AND TOXIC ENFORCEMENT ACT OF 1986 (PROPOSITION 65) PROHIBITS CONTAMINATING ANY KNOWN SOURCE OF DRINKING

WATER WITH SUBSTANCES KNOWN TO CAUSE CANCER AND/OR REPRODUCTIVE TOXICITY.

OCCUPATIONAL SPILL: DO NOT TOUCH SPILLED MATERIAL. STOP LEAK IF YOU CAN DO IT WITHOUT RISK. FOR SMALL SPILLS, TAKE UP WITH SAND OR OTHER ABSORBENT MATERIAL AND PLACE INTO CONTAINERS FOR LATER DISPOSAL. FOR SMALL DRY SPILLS, WITH CLEAN SHOVEL PLACE MATERIAL INTO CLEAN, DRY CONTAINER AND COVER. MOVE CONTAINERS FROM SPILL AREA. FOR LARGER SPILLS, DIKE FAR AHEAD OF SPILL FOR LATER DISPOSAL. KEEP UNNECESSARY PEOPLE AWAY. ISOLATE HAZARD AREA AND DENY ENTRY.

REPORTABLE QUANTITY (RQ): 1000 POUNDS THE SUPERFUND AMENDMENTS AND REAUTHORIZATION ACT (SARA) SECTION 304 REQUIRES THAT A RELEASE EQUAL TO OR GREATER THAN THE REPORTABLE QUANTITY FOR THIS SUBSTANCE BE IMMEDIATELY REPORTED TO THE LOCAL EMERGENCY PLANNING COMMITTEE AND THE STATE EMERGENCY RESPONSE COMMISSION (40 CFR 355.40). IF THE RELEASE OF THIS SUBSTANCE IS REPORTABLE UNDER CERCLA SECTION 103, THE NATIONAL RESPONSE CENTER MUST BE NOTIFIED IMMEDIATELY AT (800) 424-8802 OR (202) 426-2675 IN THE METROPOLITAN WASHINGTON, D.C. AREA (40 CFR 302.6).

PROTECTIVE EQUIPMENT

VENTILATION: PROVIDE LOCAL EXHAUST OR PROCESS ENCLOSURE VENTILATION TO MEET PUBLISHED EXPOSURE LIMITS.

RESPIRATOR: THE FOLLOWING RESPIRATORS AND MAXIMUM USE CONCENTRATIONS ARE RECOMMENDATIONS BY THE U.S. DEPARTMENT OF HEALTH AND HUMAN SERVICES, NIOSH POCKET GUIDE TO CHEMICAL HAZARDS; NIOSH CRITERIA DOCUMENTS OR BY THE U.S. DEPARTMENT OF LABOR, 29 CFR 1910 SUBPART Z. THE SPECIFIC RESPIRATOR SELECTED MUST BE BASED ON CONTAMINATION LEVELS FOUND IN THE WORK PLACE, MUST NOT EXCEED THE WORKING LIMITS OF THE RESPIRATOR AND BE JOINTLY APPROVED BY THE NATIONAL INSTITUTE FOR OCCUPATIONAL SAFETY AND HEALTH AND THE MINE SAFETY AND HEALTH ADMINISTRATION (NIOSH-MSHA).

HEXAVALENT CHROMIUM COMPOUNDS:

0.25 MG/M3- ANY SUPPLIED-AIR RESPIRATOR. ANY SELF-CONTAINED BREATHING APPARATUS. ANY DUST AND MIST RESPIRATOR EXCEPT SINGLE-USE AND QUARTER-MASK RESPIRATORS.

0.625 MG/M3- ANY POWERED AIR-PURIFYING RESPIRATOR WITH A HIGH-EFFICIENCY PARTICULATE FILTER. ANY SUPPLIED-AIR RESPIRATOR OPERATED IN A CONTINUOUS FLOW MODE.

1.25 MG/M3- ANY AIR-PURIFYING FULL FACEPIECE RESPIRATOR WITH A HIGH-EFFICIENCY PARTICULATE FILTER. ANY POWERED AIR-PURIFYING RESPIRATOR WITH A TIGHT-FITTING FACEPIECE AND A HIGH-EFFICIENCY PARTICULATE FILTER. ANY SELF-CONTAINED BREATHING APPARATUS WITH A FULL FACEPIECE. ANY SUPPLIED-AIR RESPIRATOR WITH A FULL FACEPIECE.

25 MG/M3- ANY SUPPLIED-AIR RESPIRATOR WITH A HALF-MASK AND OPERATED IN A PRESSURE-DEMAND OR OTHER POSITIVE PRESSURE MODE.

50 MG/M3- ANY SUPPLIED-AIR RESPIRATOR WITH A FULL FACEPIECE AND OPERATED IN A PRESSURE-DEMAND OR OTHER POSITIVE PRESSURE MODE.

ESCAPE- ANY AIR-PURIFYING FULL FACEPIECE RESPIRATOR WITH A HIGH-EFFICIENCY PARTICULATE FILTER. ANY APPROPRIATE ESCAPE-TYPE SELF-CONTAINED BREATHING APPARATUS.

FOR FIREFIGHTING AND OTHER IMMEDIATELY DANGEROUS TO LIFE OR HEALTH CONDITIONS:

SELF-CONTAINED BREATHING APPARATUS WITH FULL FACEPIECE OPERATED IN PRESSURE-DEMAND OR OTHER POSITIVE PRESSURE MODE.

SUPPLIED-AIR RESPIRATOR WITH FULL FACEPIECE AND OPERATED IN PRESSURE-DEMAND OR OTHER POSITIVE PRESSURE MODE IN COMBINATION WITH AN AUXILIARY SELF-CONTAINED BREATHING APPARATUS OPERATED IN PRESSURE-DEMAND OR OTHER POSITIVE PRESSURE MODE.

CLOTHING: EMPLOYEE MUST WEAR APPROPRIATE PROTECTIVE (IMPERVIOUS) CLOTHING AND EQUIPMENT TO PREVENT ANY POSSIBILITY OF SKIN CONTACT WITH THIS SUBSTANCE.

GLOVES: EMPLOYEE MUST WEAR APPROPRIATE PROTECTIVE GLOVES TO PREVENT CONTACT WITH THIS SUBSTANCE.

EYE PROTECTION: EMPLOYEE MUST WEAR SPLASH-PROOF OR DUST-RESISTANT SAFETY GOGGLES AND A FACESHIELD TO PREVENT CONTACT WITH THIS SUBSTANCE.

EMERGENCY WASH FACILITIES: WHERE THERE IS ANY POSSIBILITY THAT AN EMPLOYEE'S EYES AND/OR SKIN MAY BE EXPOSED TO THIS SUBSTANCE, THE EMPLOYER SHOULD PROVIDE AN EYE WASH FOUNTAIN AND QUICK DRENCH SHOWER WITHIN THE IMMEDIATE WORK AREA FOR EMERGENCY USE.

AUTHORIZED BY- OCCUPATIONAL HEALTH SERVICES, INC.

CREATION DATE: 10/04/89 ***REVISION DATE:*** 07/13/90

MATERIAL SAFETY DATA SHEET

OCCUPATIONAL HEALTH SERVICES, INC.
AGRICULTURE AND PESTICIDE DIVISION
450 SEVENTH AVENUE, SUITE 2407
NEW YORK, NEW YORK 10123
1-800-445-MSDS OR (212) 967-1100

EMERGENCY CONTACT:
JOHN S. BRANSFORD, JR. (615) 292-1180

SUBSTANCE IDENTIFICATION

CAS-NUMBER 25402-06-6

***SUBSTANCE:* CINERIN I**

TRADE NAMES/SYNONYMS: CYCLOPROPANECARBOXYLIC ACID, 2,2-DIMETHYL-3-(2-METHYL-1-PROPENYL)-, 3-(2-BUTENYL)-2-METHYL-4-OXO-2-CYCLOPENTEN-1-YL ESTER, (1R-(1ALPHA (S*(Z)),3BETA))-; CYCLOPROPANECARBOXYLIC ACID, 2,2-DIMETHYL-3-(2-METHYLPROPENYL)-, ESTER WITH 2-(2-BUTENYL)-4-HYDROXY-3-METHYL-2-CYCLOPENTEN-1-ONE; (1R-(1ALPHA(S*(Z)),3BETA))-2,2-DIMETHYL-3-(2-METHYL-1-PROPENYL)- CYCLOPROPANECARBOXYLIC ACID, 3-(2-BUTENYL)-2-METHYL-4-OXO-2- CYCLOPENTEN-1-YL ESTER; 2,2-DIMETHYL-3-(2-METHYLPROPENYL)CYCLOPROPANECARBOXYLIC ACID ESTER WITH 2-(2-BUTENYL)-4-HYDROXY-3-METHYL-2-CYCLOPENTEN-1-ONE; CINERIN; PYRETHRIN; C20H28O3; PST05090

CHEMICAL FAMILY: PYRETHRIN (NATURAL)

MOLECULAR FORMULA: C20-H28-O3

MOLECULAR WEIGHT: 316.48

CERCLA RATINGS (SCALE 0-3): HEALTH=U FIRE=2 REACTIVITY=0 PERSISTENCE=1

NFPA RATINGS (SCALE 0-4): HEALTH=U FIRE=2 REACTIVITY=0

COMPONENTS AND CONTAMINANTS

COMPONENT: CINERIN I ***PERCENT:*** 100.0
CAS# 25402-06-6

OTHER CONTAMINANTS: NONE

EXPOSURE LIMITS: PYRETHRUM: 5 MG/M3 OSHA TWA 5 MG/M3 ACGIH TWA
1 POUND CERCLA SECTION 103 REPORTABLE QUANTITY

PHYSICAL DATA

DESCRIPTION: VISCOUS LIQUID. ***BOILING POINT:*** 277-280 F (136-138 C) 0.008 MMHG

SPECIFIC GRAVITY: NOT AVAILABLE ***VAPOR PRESSURE:*** NEGLIGIBLE

SOLUBILITY IN WATER: INSOLUBLE

SOLVENT SOLUBILITY: SOLUBLE IN ALCOHOL, PETROLEUM ETHER, KEROSENE, CARBON TETRACHLORIDE, ETHYLENE DICHLORIDE, NITROMETHANE, AND ORGANIC SOLVENTS.

FIRE AND EXPLOSION DATA

FIRE AND EXPLOSION HAZARD: MODERATE FIRE HAZARD WHEN EXPOSED TO HEAT OR FLAME.

FLASH POINT: 180-190 F (82-88 C) (OC) ***FLAMMABILITY CLASS(OSHA):*** IIIA

FIREFIGHTING MEDIA: DRY CHEMICAL, CARBON DIOXIDE, HALON, WATER SPRAY OR STANDARD FOAM (1987 EMERGENCY RESPONSE GUIDEBOOK, DOT P 5800.4). FOR LARGER FIRES, USE WATER SPRAY, FOG OR STANDARD FOAM (1987 EMERGENCY RESPONSE GUIDEBOOK, DOT P 5800.4).

FIREFIGHTING: MOVE CONTAINER FROM FIRE AREA IF POSSIBLE. COOL FIRE-EXPOSED CONTAINERS WITH WATER FROM SIDE UNTIL WELL AFTER FIRE IS OUT. STAY AWAY FROM STORAGE TANK ENDS. FOR MASSIVE FIRE IN STORAGE AREA, USE UNMANNED HOSE HOLDER OR MONITOR NOZZLES, ELSE WITHDRAW FROM AREA AND LET FIRE BURN. WITHDRAW IMMEDIATELY IN CASE OF RISING SOUND FROM VENTING SAFETY DEVICE OR ANY DISCOLORATION OF STORAGE TANK DUE TO FIRE (1987 EMERGENCY RESPONSE GUIDEBOOK, DOT P 5800.4, GUIDE PAGE 27). EXTINGUISH ONLY IF FLOW CAN BE STOPPED; USE FLOODING AMOUNTS OF WATER AS A FOG, SOLID STREAMS MAY BE INEFFECTIVE. COOL CONTAINERS WITH FLOODING AMOUNTS OF WATER, APPLY FROM AS FAR A DISTANCE AS POSSIBLE. AVOID BREATHING VAPORS, KEEP UPWIND.

TRANSPORTATION DATA

DEPARTMENT OF TRANSPORTATION HAZARD CLASSIFICATION 49 CFR 172.101: COMBUSTIBLE LIQUID

DEPARTMENT OF TRANSPORTATION LABELING REQUIREMENTS 49 CFR 172.101 AND SUBPART E: NONE

DEPARTMENT OF TRANSPORTATION PACKAGING REQUIREMENTS: NONE EXCEPTIONS: 49 CFR 173.118A

TOXICITY

CINERIN I: TOXICITY DATA: 1050 MG/KG UNREPORTED-RAT LD50. CARCINOGEN STATUS: NONE. ACUTE TOXICITY LEVEL: INSUFFICIENT DATA. TARGET EFFECTS:

POISONING MAY AFFECT THE RESPIRATORY AND CENTRAL NERVOUS SYSTEMS.* AT INCREASED RISK FROM EXPOSURE: PERSONS WITH ALLERGIES AND CHRONIC RESPIRATORY AND SKIN DISEASES.* * MAY BE BASED ON GENERAL INFORMATION ON PYRETHRINS.

HEALTH EFFECTS AND FIRST AID

INHALATION: CINERIN I: SEE INFORMATION ON PYRETHRINS.
PYRETHRINS: 5000 MG/M3 IMMEDIATELY DANGEROUS TO LIFE AND HEALTH.
ACUTE EXPOSURE- MAY CAUSE MUCOUS MEMBRANE IRRITATION. NERVOUS IRRITABILITY, TREMORS, AND ATAXIA HAVE RARELY OCCURRED WITH MASSIVE EXPOSURE. SOME PYRETHRINS MAY CAUSE SENSITIZATION REACTIONS IN SUSCEPTIBLE INDIVIDUALS. **CHRONIC EXPOSURE-** PROLONGED OR REPEATED EXPOSURE TO SOME PYRETHRINS MAY RESULT IN SENSITIZATION. EFFECTS MAY INCLUDE SNEEZING, NASAL DISCHARGE AND STUFFINESS, SCRATCHY THROAT, ASTHMA, AND RARELY ANAPHYLACTIC REACTIONS WITH THE POSSIBILITY OF SHOCK AND RESPIRATORY DIFFICULTIES. A CASE OF HYPERSENSITIVITY PNEUMONITIS HAS ALSO BEEN REPORTED.
FIRST AID- REMOVE FROM EXPOSURE AREA TO FRESH AIR IMMEDIATELY. IF BREATHING HAS STOPPED, PERFORM ARTIFICIAL RESPIRATION. KEEP PERSON WARM AND AT REST. TREAT SYMPTOMATICALLY AND SUPPORTIVELY. GET MEDICAL ATTENTION IMMEDIATELY.

SKIN CONTACT: CINERIN I: SEE INFORMATION ON PYRETHRINS.
PYRETHRINS: **ACUTE EXPOSURE-** MAY CAUSE IRRITATION. EXPOSURE TO SOME PYRETHRINS MAY RESULT IN SENSITIZATION REACTIONS IN SUSCEPTIBLE INDIVIDUALS. **CHRONIC EXPOSURE-** PROLONGED OR REPEATED EXPOSURE MAY CAUSE AN ERYTHEMATOUS DERMATITIS WITH VESICLES, PAPULES, ESPECIALLY IN MOIST AREAS, AND INTENSE PRURITIS; TOUGHENING, AND IN SEVERE CASES, EDEMA AND CRACKING OF THE SKIN MAY OCCUR. THE EFFECTS MAY BE ALLERGIC REACTIONS; EOSINOPHILIA MAY ALSO BE PRESENT. EXPOSURE TO THE SUN, WARM WEATHER OR EXCESSIVE PERSPIRATION MAY EXACERBATE THE DERMAL EFFECTS.
FIRST AID- REMOVE CONTAMINATED CLOTHING AND SHOES IMMEDIATELY. WASH AFFECTED AREA WITH SOAP OR MILD DETERGENT AND LARGE AMOUNTS OF WATER UNTIL NO EVIDENCE OF CHEMICAL REMAINS (APPROXIMATELY 15-20 MINUTES). GET MEDICAL ATTENTION IMMEDIATELY.

EYE CONTACT: CINERIN I: SEE INFORMATION ON PYRETHRINS.
PYRETHRINS: **ACUTE EXPOSURE-** MAY CAUSE IRRITATION AND TRANSIENT CONJUNCTIVAL EDEMA AND HYPEREMIA. **CHRONIC EXPOSURE-** NO DATA AVAILABLE.
FIRST AID- WASH EYES IMMEDIATELY WITH LARGE AMOUNTS OF WATER OR NORMAL SALINE, OCCASIONALLY LIFTING UPPER AND LOWER LIDS, UNTIL NO EVIDENCE OF CHEMICAL REMAINS (APPROXIMATELY 15-20 MINUTES). GET MEDICAL ATTENTION IMMEDIATELY.

INGESTION: CINERIN I: SEE INFORMATION ON PYRETHRINS.
PYRETHRINS: **ACUTE EXPOSURE-** LARGE AMOUNTS MAY CAUSE NAUSEA, VOMITING, GASTROENTERITIS WITH DIARRHEA, HYPEREXCITABILITY, INCOORDINATION, TREMORS, MUSCULAR FIBRILLATION, BRADYCARDIA, CONVULSIONS LEADING TO PARALYSIS, AND DEATH DUE TO RESPIRATORY FAILURE. **CHRONIC EXPOSURE-** DOGS FED A DIETARY LEVEL OF 5000 PPM FOR 3 MONTHS EXHIBITED TREMOR, ATAXIA, LABORED RESPIRATION, AND SALIVATION DURING THE FIRST MONTH. SLIGHT LIVER DAMAGE WAS THE ONLY EFFECT REPORTED IN RATS FED DIETARY LEVELS OF 1000 AND 5000 PPM FOR 2 YEARS. AN INCREASED INCIDENCE OF FETAL RESORPTIONS WAS NOTED IN A STUDY OF PREGNANT RATS.
FIRST AID- REMOVE BY GASTRIC LAVAGE AND CATHARSIS. MAINTAIN BLOOD PRESSURE AND AIRWAY. GIVE OXYGEN IF RESPIRATION IS DEPRESSED. DO NOT PERFORM GASTRIC LAVAGE IF VICTIM IS UNCONSCIOUS. GET MEDICAL ATTENTION IMMEDIATELY (DREISBACH, HANDBOOK OF POISONING, 12TH ED.). ADMINISTRATION OF LAVAGE OR OXYGEN SHOULD BE PERFORMED BY QUALIFIED MEDICAL PERSONNEL.
ANTIDOTE: NO SPECIFIC ANTIDOTE. TREAT SYMPTOMATICALLY AND SUPPORTIVELY.

REACTIVITY

REACTIVITY: STABLE UNDER NORMAL TEMPERATURES AND PRESSURES.
INCOMPATIBILITIES: CINERIN I: OXIDIZERS (STRONG): FIRE AND EXPLOSION HAZARD.
DECOMPOSITION: THERMAL DECOMPOSITION PRODUCTS MAY INCLUDE TOXIC OXIDES OF CARBON.
POLYMERIZATION: HAZARDOUS POLYMERIZATION HAS NOT BEEN REPORTED TO OCCUR UNDER NORMAL TEMPERATURES AND PRESSURES.

STORAGE AND DISPOSAL

OBSERVE ALL FEDERAL, STATE AND LOCAL REGULATIONS WHEN STORING OR DISPOSING OF THIS SUBSTANCE. FOR ASSISTANCE, CONTACT THE DISTRICT DIRECTOR OF THE ENVIRONMENTAL PROTECTION AGENCY.

STORAGE

STORE IN ACCORDANCE WITH 29 CFR 1910.106.
STORE IN ACCORDANCE WITH 40 CFR 165 RECOMMENDED PROCEDURES FOR THE DISPOSAL AND STORAGE OF PESTICIDES AND PESTICIDE CONTAINERS. STORE AWAY FROM INCOMPATIBLE SUBSTANCES.
STORE IN A TIGHTLY CLOSED CONTAINER AT TEMPERATURES NOT EXCEEDING 39 F (4 C).

DISPOSAL

DISPOSAL MUST BE IN ACCORDANCE WITH 40 CFR 165 RECOMMENDED PROCEDURES FOR THE DISPOSAL AND STORAGE OF PESTICIDES AND PESTICIDE CONTAINERS.

CONDITIONS TO AVOID

AVOID CONTACT WITH HEAT, SPARKS, FLAMES, OR OTHER SOURCES OF IGNITION. VAPORS MAY BE EXPLOSIVE. AVOID OVERHEATING OF CONTAINERS; CONTAINERS MAY VIOLENTLY RUPTURE IN HEAT OF FIRE. AVOID CONTAMINATION OF WATER SOURCES.

SPILL AND LEAK PROCEDURES

SOIL SPILL: DIG HOLDING AREA SUCH AS LAGOON, POND OR PIT FOR CONTAINMENT. DIKE FLOW OF SPILLED MATERIAL USING SOIL OR SANDBAGS OR FOAMED BARRIERS SUCH AS POLYURETHANE OR CONCRETE.
USE CEMENT POWDER OR FLY ASH TO ABSORB LIQUID MASS.
WATER SPILL: USE ACTIVATED CARBON TO ABSORB SPILLED SUBSTANCE THAT IS DISSOLVED.
USE MECHANICAL DREDGES OR LIFTS TO EXTRACT IMMOBILIZED MASSES OF POLLUTION AND PRECIPITATES.
OCCUPATIONAL SPILL: SHUT OFF IGNITION SOURCES. STOP LEAK IF YOU CAN DO IT WITHOUT RISK. USE WATER SPRAY TO REDUCE VAPORS. FOR SMALL SPILLS, TAKE UP WITH SAND OR OTHER ABSORBENT MATERIAL AND PLACE INTO CONTAINERS FOR LATER DISPOSAL. FOR LARGER SPILLS, DIKE FAR AHEAD OF SPILL FOR LATER DISPOSAL. NO SMOKING, FLAMES OR FLARES IN HAZARD AREA. KEEP UNNECESSARY PEOPLE AWAY; ISOLATE HAZARD AREA AND RESTRICT ENTRY.

PROTECTIVE EQUIPMENT

VENTILATION: PROVIDE LOCAL EXHAUST OR PROCESS ENCLOSURE VENTILATION TO MEET PUBLISHED EXPOSURE LIMITS.
RESPIRATOR: THE FOLLOWING RESPIRATORS AND MAXIMUM USE CONCENTRATIONS ARE RECOMMENDATIONS BY THE U.S. DEPARTMENT OF HEALTH AND HUMAN SERVICES, NIOSH POCKET GUIDE TO CHEMICAL HAZARDS; NIOSH CRITERIA DOCUMENTS OR BY THE U.S. DEPARTMENT OF LABOR, 29 CFR 1910 SUBPART Z. THE SPECIFIC RESPIRATOR SELECTED MUST BE BASED ON CONTAMINATION LEVELS FOUND IN THE WORK PLACE, MUST NOT EXCEED THE WORKING LIMITS OF THE RESPIRATOR AND BE JOINTLY APPROVED BY THE NATIONAL INSTITUTE FOR OCCUPATIONAL SAFETY AND HEALTH AND THE MINE SAFETY AND HEALTH ADMINISTRATION (NIOSH-MSHA).
PYRETHRUM:
50 MG/M3- ANY CHEMICAL CARTRIDGE RESPIRATOR WITH ORGANIC VAPOR CARTRIDGE(S) IN COMBINATION WITH A DUST, MIST, AND FUME FILTER. ANY SUPPLIED-AIR RESPIRATOR. ANY SELF-CONTAINED BREATHING APPARATUS.
125 MG/M3- ANY SUPPLIED-AIR RESPIRATOR OPERATED IN A CONTINUOUS FLOW MODE. ANY POWERED AIR-PURIFYING RESPIRATOR WITH ORGANIC VAPOR CARTRIDGE(S) IN COMBINATION WITH A DUST, MIST, AND FUME FILTER.
250 MG/M3- ANY CHEMICAL CARTRIDGE RESPIRATOR WITH A FULL FACEPIECE AND ORGANIC VAPOR CARTRIDGE(S) IN COMBINATION WITH A HIGH-EFFICIENCY PARTICULATE FILTER. ANY SUPPLIED-AIR RESPIRATOR WITH A FULL FACEPIECE. ANY SELF-CONTAINED BREATHING APPARATUS WITH A FULL FACEPIECE. ANY POWERED AIR-PURIFYING RESPIRATOR WITH A TIGHT-FITTING FACEPIECE AND ORGANIC VAPOR CARTRIDGE(S) IN COMBINATION WITH A HIGH-EFFICIENCY PARTICULATE FILTER.
5000 MG/M3- ANY SUPPLIED-AIR RESPIRATOR WITH A HALF-MASK AND OPERATED IN A PRESSURE-DEMAND OR OTHER POSITIVE PRESSURE MODE.
ESCAPE- ANY AIR-PURIFYING FULL FACEPIECE RESPIRATOR (GAS MASK) WITH A CHIN STYLE OR FRONT- OR BACK-MOUNTED ORGANIC VAPOR CANISTER HAVING A HIGH-EFFICIENCY PARTICULATE FILTER. ANY APPROPRIATE ESCAPE-TYPE SELF-CONTAINED BREATHING APPARATUS.
FOR FIREFIGHTING AND OTHER IMMEDIATELY DANGEROUS TO LIFE OR HEALTH CONDITIONS:
SELF-CONTAINED BREATHING APPARATUS WITH FULL FACEPIECE OPERATED IN PRESSURE-DEMAND OR OTHER POSITIVE PRESSURE MODE.
SUPPLIED-AIR RESPIRATOR WITH FULL FACEPIECE AND OPERATED IN PRESSURE-DEMAND OR OTHER POSITIVE PRESSURE MODE IN COMBINATION WITH AN AUXILIARY SELF-CONTAINED BREATHING APPARATUS OPERATED IN PRESSURE-DEMAND OR OTHER POSITIVE PRESSURE MODE.

CLOTHING: EMPLOYEE MUST WEAR APPROPRIATE PROTECTIVE (IMPERVIOUS) CLOTHING AND EQUIPMENT TO PREVENT REPEATED OR PROLONGED SKIN CONTACT WITH THIS SUBSTANCE.
GLOVES: EMPLOYEE MUST WEAR APPROPRIATE PROTECTIVE GLOVES TO PREVENT CONTACT WITH THIS SUBSTANCE.
EYE PROTECTION: EMPLOYEE MUST WEAR SPLASH-PROOF OR DUST-RESISTANT SAFETY GOGGLES TO PREVENT EYE CONTACT WITH THIS SUBSTANCE.
EMERGENCY EYE WASH: WHERE THERE IS ANY POSSIBILITY THAT AN EMPLOYEE'S EYES MAY BE EXPOSED TO THIS SUBSTANCE, THE EMPLOYER SHOULD PROVIDE AN EYE WASH FOUNTAIN WITHIN THE IMMEDIATE WORK AREA FOR EMERGENCY USE.

AUTHORIZED BY- OCCUPATIONAL HEALTH SERVICES, INC.
CREATION DATE: 10/04/89 ***REVISION DATE:*** 05/11/90

MATERIAL SAFETY DATA SHEET

OCCUPATIONAL HEALTH SERVICES, INC.
AGRICULTURE AND PESTICIDE DIVISION
450 SEVENTH AVENUE, SUITE 2407
NEW YORK, NEW YORK 10123
1-800-445-MSDS OR (212) 967-1100

EMERGENCY CONTACT:
JOHN S. BRANSFORD, JR. (615) 292-1180

SUBSTANCE IDENTIFICATION

CAS-NUMBER 104-55-2
SUBSTANCE: CINNAMALDEHYDE
TRADE NAMES/SYNONYMS: 3-PHENYLACROLEIN; CASSIA ALDEHYDE; CINNAMAL; CINNAMYL ALDEHYDE; ZIMTALDEHYDE; 3-PHENYL-2-PROPENAL; CINNAMIC ALDEHYDE; 0-1980; PST05100
CHEMICAL FAMILY: ALDEHYDE, ALIPHATIC
MOLECULAR FORMULA: C9-H8-O
MOLECULAR WEIGHT: 132.17
CERCLA RATINGS (SCALE 0-3): HEALTH=2 FIRE=0 REACTIVITY=0 PERSISTENCE=0
NFPA RATINGS (SCALE 0-4): HEALTH=2 FIRE=0 REACTIVITY=0

COMPONENTS AND CONTAMINANTS

COMPONENT: CINNAMALDEHYDE ***PERCENT:*** 100
CAS# 104-55-2
OTHER CONTAMINANTS: NONE
EXPOSURE LIMITS: NO OCCUPATIONAL EXPOSURE LIMITS ESTABLISHED BY OSHA, ACGIH, OR NIOSH.

PHYSICAL DATA

DESCRIPTION: YELLOWISH OILY LIQUID, CINNAMIC ODOR AND SWEET TASTE.
BOILING POINT: 455 F (235 C) ***MELTING POINT:*** 19 F (-8 C)
SPECIFIC GRAVITY: 1.05 ***VAPOR PRESSURE:*** 0.40 MMHG @ 60 C
SOLUBILITY IN WATER: PRACT. INSOLUBLE ***VAPOR DENSITY:*** 4.6
SOLVENT SOLUBILITY: ALCOHOL, ETHER AND CHLOROFORM

FIRE AND EXPLOSION DATA

FIRE AND EXPLOSION HAZARD: NEGLIGIBLE FIRE HAZARD WHEN EXPOSED TO HEAT OR FLAME.
FLASH POINT: 232 F (111 C) ***FLAMMABILITY CLASS(OSHA):*** IIIB
FIREFIGHTING MEDIA: DRY CHEMICAL, CARBON DIOXIDE, HALON, WATER SPRAY OR ALCOHOL FOAM (1987 EMERGENCY RESPONSE GUIDEBOOK, DOT P 5800.4).
FOR LARGER FIRES, USE WATER SPRAY, FOG OR ALCOHOL FOAM (1987 EMERGENCY RESPONSE GUIDEBOOK, DOT P 5800.4).
FIREFIGHTING: MOVE CONTAINER FROM FIRE AREA IF POSSIBLE. COOL FIRE-EXPOSED CONTAINERS WITH WATER FROM SIDE UNTIL WELL AFTER FIRE IS OUT. STAY AWAY FROM STORAGE TANK ENDS. FOR MASSIVE FIRE IN STORAGE AREA, USE UNMANNED HOSE HOLDER OR MONITOR NOZZLES, ELSE WITHDRAW FROM AREA AND LET FIRE BURN. WITHDRAW IMMEDIATELY IN CASE OF RISING SOUND FROM VENTING SAFETY DEVICE OR ANY DISCOLORATION OF STORAGE TANK DUE TO FIRE (1987 EMERGENCY RESPONSE GUIDEBOOK, DOT P 5800.4, GUIDE PAGE 26). EXTINGUISH ONLY IF FLOW CAN BE STOPPED; USE FLOODING AMOUNTS OF WATER AS A FOG, SOLID STREAMS MAY BE INEFFECTIVE. COOL CONTAINERS WITH FLOODING AMOUNTS OF WATER, APPLY FROM AS FAR A DISTANCE AS POSSIBLE. AVOID BREATHING VAPORS, KEEP UPWIND.

TOXICITY

CINNAMALDEHYDE: IRRITATION DATA: 40 MG/48 HOURS SKIN-HUMAN SEVERE. TOXICITY DATA: 2220 MG/KG ORAL-RAT LD50; 2225 MG/KG ORAL-MOUSE LD50; 1160 MG/KG ORAL-GUINEA PIG LD50; 75 MG/KG INTRAVENOUS-MOUSE LD50; 200 MG/KG PARENTERAL-MOUSE LDLO; 200 MG/KG INTRAPERITONEAL-MOUSE LD50; MUTAGENIC DATA (RTECS). CARCINOGEN STATUS: NONE. LOCAL EFFECTS: IRRITANT- INHALATION, SKIN, AND EYES. ACUTE TOXICITY LEVEL: MODERATELY TOXIC BY INGESTION. TARGET EFFECTS: SENSITIZER- SKIN.

HEALTH EFFECTS AND FIRST AID

INHALATION: CINNAMALDEHYDE: IRRITANT. **ACUTE EXPOSURE**- INHALATION MAY CAUSE RESPIRATORY IRRITATION, COUGH, SORE THROAT, AND PULMONARY EDEMA. **CHRONIC EXPOSURE**- REPEATED OR PROLONGED EXPOSURE MAY CAUSE MUCOUS MEMBRANE IRRITATION.
FIRST AID- REMOVE FROM EXPOSURE AREA TO FRESH AIR IMMEDIATELY. IF BREATHING HAS STOPPED, PERFORM ARTIFICIAL RESPIRATION. KEEP PERSON WARM AND AT REST. TREAT SYMPTOMATICALLY AND SUPPORTIVELY. GET MEDICAL ATTENTION IMMEDIATELY.

SKIN CONTACT: CINNAMALDEHYDE: IRRITANT/SENSITIZER. **ACUTE EXPOSURE**- MAY CAUSE IRRITATION, PAIN, AND SENSITIZATION DERMATITIS IN PREVIOSLY EXPOSED INDIVIDUALS. **CHRONIC EXPOSURE**- PROLONGED OR REPEATED EXPOSURE MAY CAUSE SENSITIZATION DERMATITIS CHARACTERIZED BY ECZEMA.
FIRST AID- REMOVE CONTAMINATED CLOTHING AND SHOES IMMEDIATELY. WASH AFFECTED AREA WITH SOAP OR MILD DETERGENT AND LARGE AMOUNTS OF WATER UNTIL NO EVIDENCE OF CHEMICAL REMAINS (APPROXIMATELY 15-20 MINUTES). GET MEDICAL ATTENTION IMMEDIATELY.

EYE CONTACT: CINNAMALDEHYDE: IRRITANT. **ACUTE EXPOSURE**- MAY CAUSE IRRITATION, REDNESS, AND PAIN. **CHRONIC EXPOSURE**- REPEATED OR PROLONGED EXPOSURE MAY CAUSE CONJUNCTIVITIS.
FIRST AID- WASH EYES IMMEDIATELY WITH LARGE AMOUNTS OF WATER OR NORMAL SALINE, OCCASIONALLY LIFTING UPPER AND LOWER LIDS, UNTIL NO EVIDENCE OF CHEMICAL REMAINS (APPROXIMATELY 15-20 MINUTES). GET MEDICAL ATTENTION IMMEDIATELY.

INGESTION: CINNAMALDEHYDE: **ACUTE EXPOSURE**- MAY CAUSE NAUSEA, ABDOMINAL PAIN, AND INFLAMMATION AND EROSION OF THE GASTROINTESTINAL TRACT. ANIMAL STUDIES INDICATE THAT SOMNOLENCE, DIARRHEA, ATAXIA, DEPRESSION, SCRAWNY APPEARANCE, RESPIRATORY STIMULATION, CONVULSIONS, AND COMA OCCURRED AFTER INGESTION. DEATH OCCURRED WITHIN 2 TO 3 HOURS FOLLOWING EXPOSURE IN RATS. **CHRONIC EXPOSURE**- NO DATA AVAILABLE.
FIRST AID- IF PERSON IS CONSCIOUS, GIVE LARGE QUANTITIES OF WATER. IF THERE IS NO EVIDENCE OF CORROSION, INDUCE VOMITING. TREAT SYMPTOMATICALLY AND SUPPORTIVELY. DO NOT MAKE AN UNCONSCIOUS PERSON VOMIT OR DRINK ANYTHING. GET MEDICAL ATTENTION. (DREISBACH, HANDBOOK OF POISONING 11TH, ED.)
ANTIDOTE: NO SPECIFIC ANTIDOTE. TREAT SYMPTOMATICALLY AND SUPPORTIVELY.

REACTIVITY

REACTIVITY: STABLE UNDER NORMAL TEMPERATURES AND PRESSURES.
INCOMPATIBILITIES: CINNAMALDEHYDE: SODIUM HYDROXIDE: WHEN HEATED, IT MAY IGNITE AND RELEASE TOXIC PEROXIDES OF HYDROGEN. STRONG OXIDIZERS: VIOLENT REACTION.
DECOMPOSITION: THERMAL DECOMPOSITION PRODUCTS MAY INCLUDE TOXIC OXIDES OF CARBON.
POLYMERIZATION: HAZARDOUS POLYMERIZATION HAS NOT BEEN REPORTED TO OCCUR UNDER NORMAL TEMPERATURES AND PRESSURES.

CONDITIONS TO AVOID

FLAMMABLE, COMBUSTIBLE MATERIAL; MAY BE IGNITED BY HEAT, SPARKS OR FLAMES. VAPORS MAY TRAVEL TO A SOURCE OF IGNITION AND FLASH BACK. CONTAINER MAY EXPLODE IN HEAT OF FIRE. VAPOR EXPLOSION HAZARD INDOORS, OUTDOORS OR IN SEWERS. RUNOFF TO SEWER MAY CREATE FIRE OR EXPLOSION HAZARD.
SUBSTANCE BECOMES VOLATILE WITH STEAM.

SPILL AND LEAK PROCEDURES

SOIL SPILL: DIG HOLDING AREA SUCH AS LAGOON, POND OR PIT FOR CONTAINMENT. DIKE FLOW OF SPILLED MATERIAL USING SOIL OR SANDBAGS OR FOAMED BARRIERS SUCH AS POLYURETHANE OR CONCRETE.
USE CEMENT POWDER OR FLY ASH TO ABSORB LIQUID MASS.
WATER SPILL: IF WATER POLLUTION OCCURS, NOTIFY APPROPRIATE AUTHORITIES.
OCCUPATIONAL SPILL: SHUT OFF IGNITION SOURCES. DO NOT TOUCH SPILLED MATERIAL. STOP LEAK IF YOU CAN DO IT WITHOUT RISK. USE WATER SPRAY TO REDUCE VAPORS. FOR SMALL SPILLS, TAKE UP WITH SAND OR OTHER ABSORBENT

MATERIAL AND PLACE INTO CONTAINERS FOR LATER DISPOSAL. FOR LARGER SPILLS, DIKE FAR AHEAD OF SPILL FOR LATER DISPOSAL. NO SMOKING, FLAMES OR FLARES IN HAZARD AREA! KEEP UNNECESSARY PEOPLE AWAY; ISOLATE HAZARD AREA AND DENY ENTRY.

PROTECTIVE EQUIPMENT

VENTILATION: PROVIDE LOCAL EXHAUST OR GENERAL DILUTION VENTILATION SYSTEM.

RESPIRATOR: THE FOLLOWING RESPIRATORS ARE RECOMMENDED BASED ON INFORMATION FOUND IN THE PHYSICAL DATA, TOXICITY AND HEALTH EFFECTS SECTIONS. THEY ARE RANKED IN ORDER FROM MINIMUM TO MAXIMUM RESPIRATORY PROTECTION. THE SPECIFIC RESPIRATOR SELECTED MUST BE BASED ON CONTAMINATION LEVELS FOUND IN THE WORK PLACE, MUST NOT EXCEED THE WORKING LIMITS OF THE RESPIRATOR AND BE JOINTLY APPROVED BY THE NATIONAL INSTITUTE FOR OCCUPATIONAL SAFETY AND HEALTH AND THE MINE SAFETY AND HEALTH ADMINISTRATION (NIOSH-MSHA).

HIGH LEVELS- SUPPLIED-AIR RESPIRATOR. SELF-CONTAINED BREATHING APPARATUS.

FIREFIGHTING- SELF-CONTAINED BREATHING APPARATUS WITH A FULL FACEPIECE OPERATED IN PRESSURE-DEMAND OR OTHER POSITIVE PRESSURE MODE.

CLOTHING: EMPLOYEE MUST WEAR APPROPRIATE PROTECTIVE (IMPERVIOUS) CLOTHING AND EQUIPMENT TO PREVENT ANY POSSIBILITY OF SKIN CONTACT WITH THIS SUBSTANCE.

GLOVES: EMPLOYEE MUST WEAR APPROPRIATE PROTECTIVE GLOVES TO PREVENT CONTACT WITH THIS SUBSTANCE.

EYE PROTECTION: EMPLOYEE MUST WEAR SPLASH-PROOF OR DUST-RESISTANT SAFETY GOGGLES AND A FACESHIELD TO PREVENT CONTACT WITH THIS SUBSTANCE.

EMERGENCY WASH FACILITIES: WHERE THERE IS ANY POSSIBILITY THAT AN EMPLOYEE'S EYES AND/OR SKIN MAY BE EXPOSED TO THIS SUBSTANCE, THE EMPLOYER SHOULD PROVIDE AN EYE WASH FOUNTAIN AND QUICK DRENCH SHOWER WITHIN THE IMMEDIATE WORK AREA FOR EMERGENCY USE.

AUTHORIZED BY- OCCUPATIONAL HEALTH SERVICES, INC.
CREATION DATE: 10/04/89 ***REVISION DATE:*** 05/07/90

MATERIAL SAFETY DATA SHEET

OCCUPATIONAL HEALTH SERVICES, INC.
AGRICULTURE AND PESTICIDE DIVISION
450 SEVENTH AVENUE, SUITE 2407
NEW YORK, NEW YORK 10123
1-800-445-MSDS OR (212) 967-1100

EMERGENCY CONTACT:
JOHN S. BRANSFORD, JR. (615) 292-1180

SUBSTANCE IDENTIFICATION

CAS-NUMBER 7700-17-6

SUBSTANCE: **CROTOXYPHOS**

TRADE NAMES/SYNONYMS: 2-BUTENOIC ACID, 3-((DIMETHOXYPHOSPHINYL)OXY)-, 1-PHENYLETHYL ESTER, (E)-; CROTONIC ACID, 3-HYDROXY-, ALPHA-METHYLBENZYL ESTER, DIMETHYL PHOSPHATE, (E)-; DIMETHYL (E)-1-METHYL-2-(1-PHENYLETHOXYCARBONYL)VINYL PHOSPHATE; (E)-1-PHENYLETHYL 3-((DIMETHOXYPHOSPHINYL)OXY)-2-BUTENOATE; ALPHA-METHYLBENZYL (E)-3-HYDROXYCROTONATE ESTER WITH DIMETHYL PHOSPHATE; 1-PHENYLETHYL 3-(DIMETHOXYPHOSPHINOYLOXY)ISOCROTONATE; 1-PHENYLETHYL 3-(DIMETHOXYPHOSPHINYLOXY)ISOCROTONATE; ALPHA-METHYLBENZYL 3-(DIMETHOXYPHOSPHINYLOXY)-CIS-CROTONATE; DIMETHYL CIS-1-METHYL-2-(1-PHENYLETHOXYCARBONYL)VINYL PHOSPHATE; DIMETHYL PHOSPHATE OF ALPHA-METHYLBENZYL 3-HYDROXY-CIS-CROTONATE; CIODRIN; CYODRIN; SD 4294; ENT 24,717; PST05115

CHEMICAL FAMILY: ORGANOPHOSPHATE

MOLECULAR FORMULA: C14-H19-O6-P

MOLECULAR WEIGHT: 314.30

CERCLA RATINGS (SCALE 0-3): HEALTH=3 FIRE=0 REACTIVITY=0 PERSISTENCE=1

NFPA RATINGS (SCALE 0-4): HEALTH=3 FIRE=0 REACTIVITY=0

COMPONENTS AND CONTAMINANTS

COMPONENT: CROTOXYPHOS ***PERCENT:*** 100
CAS# 7700-17-6

EXPOSURE LIMITS: NO OCCUPATIONAL EXPOSURE LIMITS ESTABLISHED BY OSHA, ACGIH, OR NIOSH.

PHYSICAL DATA

DESCRIPTION: CLEAR TO LIGHT STRAW-COLORED LIQUID WITH A MILD ESTER ODOR

BOILING POINT: 275 F (135 C) @ 0.03 MMHG ***SPECIFIC GRAVITY:*** 1.19

VAPOR PRESSURE: 0.000014 MMHG @ 20 C ***SOLUBILITY IN WATER:*** 0.1%

SOLVENT SOLUBILITY: SOLUBLE IN ACETONE, CHLOROFORM, ETHANOL, PROPAN-2-OL, XYLENE, AND HIGHLY CHLORINATED HYDROCARBONS; SLIGHTLY SOLUBLE IN KEROSENE AND SATURATED HYDROCARBONS

FIRE AND EXPLOSION DATA

FIRE AND EXPLOSION HAZARD: NEGLIGIBLE FIRE HAZARD WHEN EXPOSED TO HEAT OR FLAME.

FIREFIGHTING MEDIA: DRY CHEMICAL, CARBON DIOXIDE, HALON, WATER SPRAY OR STANDARD FOAM (1987 EMERGENCY RESPONSE GUIDEBOOK, DOT P 5800.4). FOR LARGER FIRES, USE WATER SPRAY, FOG OR STANDARD FOAM (1987 EMERGENCY RESPONSE GUIDEBOOK, DOT P 5800.4).

FIREFIGHTING: MOVE CONTAINERS FROM FIRE AREA IF POSSIBLE. FIGHT FIRE FROM MAXIMUM DISTANCE. STAY AWAY FROM STORAGE TANK ENDS. DIKE FIRE CONTROL WATER FOR LATER DISPOSAL. DO NOT SCATTER MATERIAL (1987 EMERGENCY RESPONSE GUIDEBOOK, DOT P 5800.4, GUIDE PAGE 55). EXTINGUISH USING AGENT SUITABLE FOR TYPE OF SURROUNDING FIRE. AVOID BREATHING VAPORS AND DUSTS. KEEP UPWIND.

TOXICITY

CROTOXYPHOS: TOXICITY DATA: 385 MG/KG SKIN-RABBIT LD50; 202 MG/KG SKIN-RAT LD50; 38400 UG/KG ORAL-RAT LD50; 39800 UG/KG ORAL-MOUSE LD50; 802 MG/KG ORAL-CAT LD50; 47 MG/KG SUBCUTANEOUS-RAT LD50; 15 MG/KG SUBCUTANEOUS-MOUSE LD50; 4500 UG/KG INTRAVENOUS-MOUSE LD50;71 MG/KG INTRAPERITONEAL-MOUSE LD50; 64800 UG/KG UNREPORTED-RAT LD50; 40 MG/KG UNREPORTED-MOUSE LD50; 125 MG/KG UNREPORTED-MAMMAL LD50; MUTAGENIC DATA (RTECS). CARCINOGEN STATUS: NONE. ACUTE TOXICITY LEVEL: HIGHLY TOXIC BY INGESTION AND TOXIC BY DERMAL ABSORPTION. TARGET EFFECTS: CHOLINESTERASE INHIBITOR. POISONING MAY AFFECT THE NERVOUS SYSTEM.* AT INCREASED RISK FROM EXPOSURE: PERSONS WITH RESPIRATORY AILMENTS, RECENT EXPOSURE TO CHOLINESTERASE INHIBITORS OR IMPAIRED CHOLINESTERASE PRODUCTION, OR LIVER MALFUNCTION.* ADDITIONAL DATA: MAY CROSS THE PLACENTA. HIGH ENVIRONMENTAL TEMPERATURES OR EXPOSURE OF THE CHEMICAL TO VISIBLE OR ULTRAVIOLET LIGHT MAY ENHANCE THE TOXICITY. INTERACTIONS WITH MEDICATIONS MAY OCCUR.*

* MAY BE BASED ON GENERAL INFORMATION ON ORGANOPHOSPHATES.

HEALTH EFFECTS AND FIRST AID

INHALATION: CROTOXYPHOS: SEE INFORMATION ON ORGANOPHOSPHATES.

ORGANOPHOSPHATES: CHOLINESTERASE INHIBITOR. **ACUTE EXPOSURE-** WHEN INHALED, THE FIRST EFFECTS OF CHOLINESTERASE INHIBITORS ARE USUALLY RESPIRATORY AND MAY INCLUDE NASAL HYPEREMIA AND WATERY DISCHARGE, COUGH, CHEST DISCOMFORT, DYSPNEA, AND WHEEZING DUE TO INCREASED BRONCHIAL SECRETIONS AND BRONCHOCONSTRICTION. IF SUFFICIENT AMOUNTS ARE ABSORBED, OTHER SYSTEMIC EFFECTS MAY BEGIN WITHIN A FEW MINUTES OR BE DELAYED FOR UP TO 12 HOURS. SYMPTOMS MAY INCLUDE PALLOR, NAUSEA, VOMITING, DIARRHEA, ABDOMINAL CRAMPS, HEADACHE, DIZZINESS, OCULAR PAIN, BLURRED VISION, MIOSIS OR IN SOME CASES, ESPECIALLY INITIALLY, MYDRIASIS, LACRIMATION, SALIVATION, SWEATING, AND CONFUSION. OTHER REPORTED CENTRAL NERVOUS SYSTEM OR NEUROMUSCULAR EFFECTS MAY INCLUDE ATAXIA, SLURRED SPEECH, AREFLEXIA, WEAKNESS, FATIGUE, FASCICULATIONS, TWITCHING, TREMORS POSSIBLY OF THE TONGUE AND EYELIDS, AND EVENTUALLY PARALYSIS OF THE EXTREMITIES AND POSSIBLY OF THE RESPIRATORY MUSCLES. IN SEVERE CASES THERE MAY ALSO BE INVOLUNTARY DEFECATION AND URINATION, CYANOSIS, PSYCHOSIS, HYPERGLYCEMIA, ACUTE PANCREATITIS, CARDIAC IRREGULARITIES, PULMONARY EDEMA, UNCONSCIOUSNESS, CONVULSIONS, AND COMA. DEATH IS PRIMARILY DUE TO RESPIRATORY FAILURE, ALTHOUGH CARDIOVASCULAR EFFECTS INCLUDING CARDIAC ARREST MAY ALSO BE IMPLICATED. LONG TERM SEQUELAE ARE RARE BUT MAY INCLUDE NEUROPSYCHIATRIC DISORDERS AND MYOPATHY WITH MUSCLE TENDERNESS. SOME ORGANOPHOSPHATES MAY CAUSE A DELAYED NEUROPATHY BEGINNING 1-4 WEEKS AFTER AN ACUTE EXPOSURE WHICH MAY OR MAY NOT HAVE CAUSED ACUTE CHOLINERGIC EFFECTS. NUMBNESS, TINGLING, WEAKNESS AND CRAMPING BEGINNING SYMMETRICALLY IN THE LOWER LIMBS MAY PROGRESS TO ATAXIA AND PARALYSIS. IN SEVERE CASES, UPPER LIMB INVOLVEMENT IS POSSIBLE AND FLACCID PARALYSIS MAY PROGRESS TO SPASTIC PARALYSIS WITH EXAGGERATED REFLEXES. IMPROVEMENT MAY OCCUR OVER MONTHS TO YEARS, BUT SOME RESIDUAL IMPAIRMENT USUALLY REMAINS.

CHRONIC EXPOSURE- REPEATED OR PROLONGED EXPOSURE MAY RESULT IN THE EFFECTS OF ACUTE EXPOSURE INCLUDING THE DELAYED NEUROPATHY. OTHER EFFECTS REPORTED IN WORKERS REPEATEDLY EXPOSED INCLUDE IMPAIRED MEMORY AND CONCENTRATION, ACUTE PSYCHOSIS, SEVERE DEPRESSIONS,

IRRITABILTY, CONFUSION, APATHY, EMOTIONAL LABILITY, SOCIAL WITHDRAWAL, CONFUSION, HEADACHE, SPEECH DIFFICULTIES, DELAYED REACTION TIMES, SPATIAL DISORIENTATION, NIGHTMARES, SLEEPWALKING, AND DROWSINESS OR INSOMNIA. AN INFLUENZA-LIKE CONDITION WITH HEADACHE, NAUSEA, WEAKNESS, ANOREXIA AND MALAISE HAS ALSO BEEN REPORTED.

FIRST AID- REMOVE FROM EXPOSURE AREA TO FRESH AIR IMMEDIATELY. IF BREATHING HAS STOPPED, GIVE ARTIFICIAL RESPIRATION. MAINTAIN AIRWAY AND BLOOD PRESSURE AND ADMINISTER OXYGEN IF AVAILABLE. KEEP AFFECTED PERSON WARM AND AT REST. TREAT SYMPTOMATICALLY AND SUPPORTIVELY. ADMINISTRATION OF OXYGEN SHOULD BE PERFORMED BY QUALIFIED PERSONNEL. GET MEDICAL ATTENTION IMMEDIATELY.

SKIN CONTACT: CROTOXYPHOS: TOXIC. SEE INFORMATION ON ORGANOPHOSPHATES.

ORGANOPHOSPHATES: CHOLINESTERASE INHIBITOR. **ACUTE EXPOSURE**- LOCALIZED SWEATING AND FASCICULATIONS MAY OCCUR AT THE SITE OF CONTACT. IF SUFFICIENT AMOUNTS ARE ABSORBED, OTHER EFFECTS OF CHOLINESTERASE INHIBITION AS DESCRIBED IN ACUTE INHALATION MAY OCCUR. SYMPTOMS MAY BE DELAYED 2-3 HOURS, BUT USUALLY NO MORE THAN 12 HOURS. THE RATE OF ABSORPTION IS INCREASED BY THE PRESENCE OF DERMATITIS OR HIGH AMBIENT TEMPERATURES. DELAYED NEUROPATHY IS ALSO POSSIBLE. **CHRONIC EXPOSURE**- REPEATED OR PROLONGED EXPOSURE MAY CAUSE EFFECTS AS DESCRIBED IN ACUTE EXPOSURE. SOME ORGANOPHOSPHATES MAY CAUSE SENSITIZATION.

FIRST AID- REMOVE CONTAMINATED CLOTHING IMMEDIATELY. WASH CONTAMINATED AREAS WITH SOAP AND WATER FOLLOWED BY ALCOHOL (ARENA, POISONING, 4TH ED.). EMERGENCY PERSONNEL SHOULD WEAR GLOVES AND AVOID CONTAMINATION. TREAT RESPIRATORY DIFFICULTY WITH ARTIFICIAL RESPIRATION. GET MEDICAL ATTENTION IMMEDIATELY.

EYE CONTACT: CROTOXYPHOS: SEE INFORMATION ON ORGANOPHOSPHATES.

ORGANOPHOSPHATES: CHOLINESTERASE INHIBITOR. **ACUTE EXPOSURE**- DIRECT CONTACT MAY CAUSE PAIN, HYPEREMIA, LACRIMATION, TWITCHING OF THE EYELIDS, MIOSIS, AND CILIARY MUSCLE SPASM WITH LOSS OF ACCOMODATION, BLURRED OR DIMMED VISION AND BROWACHE. SOMETIMES MYDRIASIS MAY OCCUR INSTEAD OF MIOSIS. WITH SUFFICIENT EXPOSURE, OTHER SYMPTOMS OF CHOLINESTERASE INHIBITION AS DESCRIBED IN ACUTE INHALATION MAY OCCUR. **CHRONIC EXPOSURE**- REPEATED OR PROLONGED EXPOSURE MAY CAUSE EFFECTS AS DESCRIBED IN ACUTE EXPOSURE. SOME COMPOUNDS HAVE CAUSED TOXIC EFFECTS ON THE CRYSTALLINE LENS, CONJUNCTIVAL THICKENING AND OBSTRUCTION OF THE NASOLACRIMAL CANALS WHEN USED AS MIOTIC EYEDROPS.

FIRST AID- IRRIGATE EYES WITH WATER OR SALINE SOLUTION. IF SYMPTOMS OF POISONING OCCUR, TREAT RESPIRATORY DIFFICULTY WITH ARTIFICIAL RESPIRATION AND OXYGEN. OBSERVE PATIENT FOR AT LEAST 24-36 HOURS (GOSSELIN, CLINICAL TOXICOLOGY OF COMMERCIAL PRODUCTS, 5TH ED.). GET MEDICAL ATTENTION IMMEDIATELY. OXYGEN SHOULD BE ADMINISTERED BY QUALIFIED MEDICAL PERSONNEL.

INGESTION: CROTOXYPHOS: HIGHLY TOXIC. SEE INFORMATION ON ORGANOPHOSPHATES.

ORGANOPHOSPHATES: CHOLINESTERASE INHIBITOR. **ACUTE EXPOSURE**- WHEN INGESTED, THE FIRST EFFECTS MAY BE NAUSEA, VOMITING, ANOREXIA, ABDOMINAL CRAMPS AND DIARRHEA. GASTROINTESTINAL ABSORPTION MAY CAUSE SYMPTOMS OF CHOLINESTERASE INHIBITION AS DESCRIBED IN ACUTE INHALATION. SYMPTOMS MAY BEGIN WITHIN MINUTES OR BE DELAYED FOR HOURS. DELAYED EFFECTS INCLUDING NEUROPATHY MAY ALSO OCCUR. **CHRONIC EXPOSURE**- REPEATED INGESTION MAY CAUSE EFFECTS AS DESCRIBED IN ACUTE EXPOSURE.

FIRST AID- IF PERSON IS ALERT AND RESPIRATION IS NOT DEPRESSED, GIVE SYRUP OF IPECAC FOLLOWED BY WATER (IF VOMITING OCCURS, KEEP HEAD BELOW HIPS TO PREVENT ASPIRATION). IF CONSCIOUSNESS LEVEL DECLINES OR VOMITING HAS NOT OCCURRED IN 15 MINUTES EMPTY STOMACH BY GASTRIC LAVAGE WITH THE AID OF CUFFED ENDOTRACHEAL TUBE USING ISOTONIC SALINE OR 5% SODIUM BICARBONATE FOLLOW WITH ACTIVATED CHARCOAL. ESTABLISH AND MAINTAIN AIRWAY. TREAT RESPIRATORY DIFFICULTY WITH ARTIFICIAL RESPIRATION AND OXYGEN. DO NOT GIVE MORPHINE, AMINOPHYLLINE, PHENOTHIAZINES, RESERPINE, FUROSEMIDE, OR ETHACRYNIC ACID (MORGAN, RECOGNITION AND MANAGEMENT OF PESTICIDE POISONINGS, 3RD ED.). TREAT SYMPTOMATICALLY AND SUPPORTIVELY. ADMINISTRATION OF OXYGEN AND LAVAGE MUST BE PERFORMED BY QUALIFIED MEDICAL PERSONNEL. GET MEDICAL ATTENTION IMMEDIATELY.

ANTIDOTE: THE FOLLOWING ANTIDOTE(S) HAVE BEEN RECOMMENDED. HOWEVER, THE DECISION AS TO WHETHER THE SEVERITY OF POISONING REQUIRES ADMINISTRATION OF ANY ANTIDOTE AND ACTUAL DOSE REQUIRED SHOULD BE MADE BY QUALIFIED MEDICAL PERSONNEL.

FOR CHOLINESTERASE INHIBITORS: ESTABLISH CLEAR AIRWAY AND TISSUE OXYGENATION BY ASPIRATION OF SECRETIONS, AND IF NECESSARY, BY ASSISTED PULMONARY VENTILATION WITH OXYGEN. IMPROVE TISSUE OXYGENATION AS MUCH AS POSSIBLE BEFORE ADMINISTERING ATROPINE TO MINIMIZE THE RISK OF VENTRICULAR FIBRILLATION. ADMINISTER ATROPINE SULFATE INTRAVENOUSLY, OR INTRAMUSCULARLY IF IV INJECTION IS NOT POSSIBLE. IN MODERATELY SEVERE POISONING ADMINISTER ATROPINE SULFATE, 0.4-2.0 MG REPEATED EVERY 15 MINUTES UNTIL ATROPINIZATION IS ACHIEVED (TACHYCARDIA, FLUSHING, DRY MOUTH, MYDRIASIS). MAINTAIN ATROPINIZATION BY REPEATED DOSES FOR 2-12 HOURS, OR LONGER, DEPENDING ON THE SEVERITY OF POISONING. THE APPEARANCE OF RALES IN THE LUNG BASES, MIOSIS, SALIVATION, NAUSEA, BRADYCARDIA, ARE ALL INDICATIONS OF INADEQUATE ATROPINIZATION. SEVERELY POISONED INDIVIDUALS MAY EXHIBIT REMARKABLE TOLERANCE TO ATROPINE; TWO OR MORE TIMES THE DOSAGES SUGGESTED ABOVE MAY BE NEEDED. PERSONS NOT POISONED OR ONLY SLIGHTLY POISONED, HOWEVER, MAY DEVELOP SIGNS OF ATROPINE TOXICITY FROM SUCH LARGE DOSAGES: FEVER, MUSCLE FIBRILLATIONS, AND DELIRIUM ARE THE MAIN SIGNS OF ATROPINE TOXICITY. IF THESE SIGNS APPEAR WHILE THE PATIENT IS FULLY ATROPINIZED, ATROPINE ADMINISTRATION SHOULD BE DISCONTINUED, AT LEAST TEMPORARILY. OBSERVE TREATED PATIENTS CLOSELY AT LEAST 24 HOURS TO INSURE THAT SYMPTOMS (POSSIBLY PULMONARY EDEMA) DO NOT RECUR AS ATROPINIZATION WEARS OFF. IN VERY SEVERE POISONINGS, METABOLIC DISPOSITION OF TOXICANT MAY REQUIRE SEVERAL HOURS OR DAYS DURING WHICH ATROPINIZATION MUST BE MAINTAINED. MARKEDLY LOWER LEVELS OF URINARY METABOLITES INDICATE THAT ATROPINE DOSAGE CAN BE TAPERED OFF. AS DOSAGE IS REDUCED, CHECK THE LUNG BASES FREQUENTLY FOR RALES. IF RALES ARE HEARD OR OTHER SYMPTOMS RETURN, RE-ESTABLISH ATROPINIZATION PROMPTLY (MORGAN, RECOGNITION AND MANAGEMENT OF PESTICIDE POISONINGS, 3RD ED.). ADMINISTRATION OF ANTIDOTE MUST BE PERFORMED BY QUALIFIED MEDICAL PERSONNEL.

IN CASES OF SEVERE POISONING BY ORGANOPHOSPHATE PESTICIDES IN WHICH RESPIRATORY DEPRESSION, MUSCLE WEAKNESS AND TWITCHINGS ARE SEVERE, GIVE PRALIDOXIME (PROTOPAM-AYERST, 2-PAM), 1.0 GRAM INTRAVENOUSLY AT NO MORE THAN 0.5 GRAM PER MINUTE. DOSAGE OF PRALIDOXIME MAY BE REPEATED IN 1-2 HOURS, THEN AT 10-12 HOUR INTERVALS IF NEEDED. IN VERY SEVERE POISONINGS, DOSAGE RATES MAY BE DOUBLED. TREATMENT WITH PRALIDOXIME WILL BE MOST EFFECTIVE IF GIVEN WITHIN THIRTY-SIX HOURS AFTER POISONING (MORGAN, RECOGNITION AND MANAGEMENT OF PESTICIDE POISONINGS, 3RD ED.). ANTIDOTE SHOULD BE ADMINISTERED BY QUALIFIED MEDICAL PERSONNEL.

REACTIVITY

REACTIVITY: STABLE UNDER NORMAL TEMPERATURES AND PRESSURES.

INCOMPATIBILITIES: CROTOXYPHOS: COPPER: CORROSIVE. LEAD: CORROSIVE. MILD STEEL: CORROSIVE. MOST MINERAL CARRIERS (EXCEPT SYNTHETIC SILICAS): INCOMPATIBLE. TIN: CORROSIVE. ZINC: CORROSIVE.

DECOMPOSITION: THERMAL DECOMPOSITION MAY RELEASE TOXIC OXIDES OF PHOSPHORUS.

POLYMERIZATION: HAZARDOUS POLYMERIZATION HAS NOT BEEN REPORTED TO OCCUR UNDER NORMAL TEMPERATURES AND PRESSURES.

STORAGE AND DISPOSAL

OBSERVE ALL FEDERAL, STATE AND LOCAL REGULATIONS WHEN STORING OR DISPOSING OF THIS SUBSTANCE. FOR ASSISTANCE, CONTACT THE DISTRICT DIRECTOR OF THE ENVIRONMENTAL PROTECTION AGENCY.

STORAGE

STORE IN ACCORDANCE WITH 40 CFR 165 RECOMMENDED PROCEDURES FOR THE DISPOSAL AND STORAGE OF PESTICIDES AND PESTICIDE CONTAINERS.
STORE AWAY FROM INCOMPATIBLE SUBSTANCES.

DISPOSAL

DISPOSAL MUST BE IN ACCORDANCE WITH 40 CFR 165 RECOMMENDED PROCEDURES FOR THE DISPOSAL AND STORAGE OF PESTICIDES AND PESTICIDE CONTAINERS.

CONDITIONS TO AVOID

KEEP COOL, BUT AVOID FREEZING.

SPILL AND LEAK PROCEDURES

OCCUPATIONAL SPILL: DO NOT TOUCH SPILLED MATERIAL. STOP LEAK IF YOU CAN DO IT WITHOUT RISK. USE WATER SPRAY TO REDUCE VAPORS. FOR SMALL SPILLS, TAKE UP WITH SAND OR OTHER ABSORBENT MATERIAL AND PLACE INTO CONTAINERS FOR LATER DISPOSAL. FOR SMALL DRY SPILLS, WITH A CLEAN SHOVEL PLACE MATERIAL INTO CLEAN, DRY CONTAINERS AND COVER. MOVE CONTAINERS FROM SPILL AREA. FOR LARGER SPILLS, DIKE FAR AHEAD OF SPILL FOR LATER DISPOSAL. KEEP UNNECESSARY PEOPLE AWAY. ISOLATE HAZARD AREA AND DENY ENTRY. VENTILATE CLOSED SPACES BEFORE ENTERING.

PROTECTIVE EQUIPMENT

VENTILATION: PROVIDE LOCAL EXHAUST OR PROCESS ENCLOSURE VENTILATION SYSTEM.

RESPIRATOR: THE FOLLOWING RESPIRATORS ARE RECOMMENDED BASED ON INFORMATION FOUND IN THE PHYSICAL DATA, TOXICITY AND HEALTH EFFECTS SECTIONS. THEY ARE RANKED IN ORDER FROM MINIMUM TO MAXIMUM RESPIRATORY PROTECTION. THE SPECIFIC RESPIRATOR SELECTED MUST BE BASED ON CONTAMINATION LEVELS FOUND IN THE WORK PLACE, MUST NOT EXCEED THE WORKING LIMITS OF THE RESPIRATOR AND BE JOINTLY APPROVED BY THE NATIONAL INSTITUTE FOR OCCUPATIONAL SAFETY AND HEALTH AND THE MINE SAFETY AND HEALTH ADMINISTRATION (NIOSH-MSHA).

TYPE 'C' SUPPLIED-AIR RESPIRATOR WITH A FULL FACEPIECE OPERATED IN PRESSURE-DEMAND OR OTHER POSITIVE PRESSURE MODE OR WITH A FULL FACEPIECE, HELMET OR HOOD OPERATED IN CONTINOUS-FLOW MODE.

SELF-CONTAINED BREATHING APPARATUS WITH A FULL FACEPIECE OPERATED IN PRESSURE-DEMAND OR OTHER POSITIVE PRESSURE MODE.

FOR FIREFIGHTING AND OTHER IMMEDIATELY DANGEROUS TO LIFE OR HEALTH CONDITIONS:

SELF-CONTAINED BREATHING APPARATUS WITH FULL FACEPIECE OPERATED IN PRESSURE-DEMAND OR OTHER POSITIVE PRESSURE MODE.

SUPPLIED-AIR RESPIRATOR WITH FULL FACEPIECE AND OPERATED IN PRESSURE-DEMAND OR OTHER POSITIVE PRESSURE MODE IN COMBINATION WITH AN AUXILIARY SELF-CONTAINED BREATHING APPARATUS OPERATED IN PRESSURE-DEMAND OR OTHER POSITIVE PRESSURE MODE.

CLOTHING: EMPLOYEE MUST WEAR APPROPRIATE PROTECTIVE (IMPERVIOUS) CLOTHING AND EQUIPMENT TO PREVENT ANY POSSIBILITY OF SKIN CONTACT WITH THIS SUBSTANCE.

GLOVES: EMPLOYEE MUST WEAR APPROPRIATE PROTECTIVE GLOVES TO PREVENT CONTACT WITH THIS SUBSTANCE.

EYE PROTECTION: EMPLOYEE MUST WEAR SPLASH-PROOF OR DUST-RESISTANT SAFETY GOGGLES AND A FACESHIELD TO PREVENT CONTACT WITH THIS SUBSTANCE.

EMERGENCY WASH FACILITIES: WHERE THERE IS ANY POSSIBILITY THAT AN EMPLOYEE'S EYES AND/OR SKIN MAY BE EXPOSED TO THIS SUBSTANCE, THE EMPLOYER SHOULD PROVIDE AN EYE WASH FOUNTAIN AND QUICK DRENCH SHOWER WITHIN THE IMMEDIATE WORK AREA FOR EMERGENCY USE.

AUTHORIZED BY- OCCUPATIONAL HEALTH SERVICES, INC.

CREATION DATE: 10/04/89 ***REVISION DATE:*** 05/03/90

MATERIAL SAFETY DATA SHEET

OCCUPATIONAL HEALTH SERVICES, INC.
AGRICULTURE AND PESTICIDE DIVISION
450 SEVENTH AVENUE, SUITE 2407
NEW YORK, NEW YORK 10123
1-800-445-MSDS OR (212) 967-1100

EMERGENCY CONTACT:
JOHN S. BRANSFORD, JR. (615) 292-1180

SUBSTANCE IDENTIFICATION

CAS-NUMBER 27519-02-4

SUBSTANCE: **CIS-9-TRICOSENE**

TRADE NAMES/SYNONYMS: 9-TRICOSENE, (Z)-; MUSCALURE; (Z)-9-TRICOSENE; PST05185

CHEMICAL FAMILY: HYDROCARBON, ALIPHATIC

MOLECULAR FORMULA: C23-H46

MOLECULAR WEIGHT: 322.62

CERCLA RATINGS (SCALE 0-3): HEALTH=U FIRE=1 REACTIVITY=0 PERSISTENCE=1

NFPA RATINGS (SCALE 0-4): HEALTH=U FIRE=1 REACTIVITY=0

COMPONENTS AND CONTAMINANTS

COMPONENT: CIS-9-TRICOSENE ***PERCENT:*** 100.0
CAS# 27519-02-4

EXPOSURE LIMITS: NO OCCUPATIONAL EXPOSURE LIMITS ESTABLISHED BY OSHA, ACGIH, OR NIOSH.

PHYSICAL DATA

DESCRIPTION: COLORLESS TO PALE YELLOW MOBILE LIQUID WITH A FAINT, WAXY ODOR

BOILING POINT: 572-712 F (300-378 C) ***MELTING POINT:*** <32 F (<0 C)

SPECIFIC GRAVITY: 0.807 ***VAPOR PRESSURE:*** 0.000035 MMHG @ 27 C

EVAPORATION RATE: NOT AVAILABLE ***SOLUBILITY IN WATER:*** INSOLUBLE

FIRE AND EXPLOSION DATA

FIRE AND EXPLOSION HAZARD: SLIGHT FIRE HAZARD WHEN EXPOSED TO HEAT OR FLAME.

FLASH POINT: >235 F (>113 C)

FIREFIGHTING MEDIA: DRY CHEMICAL, CARBON DIOXIDE, HALON, WATER SPRAY OR STANDARD FOAM (1987 EMERGENCY RESPONSE GUIDEBOOK, DOT P 5800.4).
FOR LARGER FIRES, USE WATER SPRAY, FOG OR STANDARD FOAM (1987 EMERGENCY RESPONSE GUIDEBOOK, DOT P 5800.4).

FIREFIGHTING: MOVE CONTAINER FROM FIRE AREA IF POSSIBLE. DO NOT SCATTER SPILLED MATERIAL WITH HIGH PRESSURE WATER STREAMS. DIKE FIRE CONTROL WATER FOR LATER DISPOSAL (1987 EMERGENCY RESPONSE GUIDEBOOK, DOT P 5800.4, GUIDE PAGE 31).
USE AGENTS SUITABLE FOR TYPE OF SURROUNDING FIRE. AVOID BREATHING HAZARDOUS VAPORS, KEEP UPWIND.

TOXICITY

CIS-9-TRICOSENE: CARCINOGEN STATUS: NONE. ACUTE TOXICITY LEVEL: NO DATA AVAILABLE. TARGET EFFECTS: NO DATA AVAILABLE.

HEALTH EFFECTS AND FIRST AID

INHALATION: CIS-9-TRICOSENE: **ACUTE EXPOSURE-** NO DATA AVAILABLE. **CHRONIC EXPOSURE-** NO DATA AVAILABLE.

FIRST AID- REMOVE FROM EXPOSURE AREA TO FRESH AIR IMMEDIATELY. IF BREATHING HAS STOPPED, PERFORM ARTIFICIAL RESPIRATION. KEEP PERSON WARM AND AT REST. TREAT SYMPTOMATICALLY AND SUPPORTIVELY. GET MEDICAL ATTENTION IMMEDIATELY.

SKIN CONTACT: CIS-9-TRICOSENE: **ACUTE EXPOSURE-** NO DATA AVAILABLE. **CHRONIC EXPOSURE-** NO DATA AVAILABLE.

FIRST AID- REMOVE CONTAMINATED CLOTHING AND SHOES IMMEDIATELY. WASH AFFECTED AREA WITH SOAP OR MILD DETERGENT AND LARGE AMOUNTS OF WATER UNTIL NO EVIDENCE OF CHEMICAL REMAINS (APPROXIMATELY 15-20 MINUTES). GET MEDICAL ATTENTION IMMEDIATELY.

EYE CONTACT: CIS-9-TRICOSENE: **ACUTE EXPOSURE-** NO DATA AVAILABLE. **CHRONIC EXPOSURE-** NO DATA AVAILABLE.

FIRST AID- WASH EYES IMMEDIATELY WITH LARGE AMOUNTS OF WATER OR NORMAL SALINE, OCCASIONALLY LIFTING UPPER AND LOWER LIDS, UNTIL NO EVIDENCE OF CHEMICAL REMAINS (APPROXIMATELY 15-20 MINUTES). GET MEDICAL ATTENTION IMMEDIATELY.

INGESTION: CIS-9-TRICOSENE: **ACUTE EXPOSURE-** NO DATA AVAILABLE. **CHRONIC EXPOSURE-** NO DATA AVAILABLE.

FIRST AID- TREAT SYMPTOMATICALLY AND SUPPORTIVELY. GET MEDICAL ATTENTION IMMEDIATELY. IF VOMITING OCCURS, KEEP HEAD LOWER THAN HIPS TO PREVENT ASPIRATION.

ANTIDOTE: NO SPECIFIC ANTIDOTE. TREAT SYMPTOMATICALLY AND SUPPORTIVELY.

REACTIVITY

REACTIVITY: STABLE UNDER NORMAL TEMPERATURES AND PRESSURES.

INCOMPATIBILITIES: CIS-9-TRICOSENE: OXIDIZERS (STRONG): INCOMPATIBLE.

DECOMPOSITION: THERMAL DECOMPOSITION PRODUCTS MAY INCLUDE TOXIC OXIDES OF CARBON.

POLYMERIZATION: HAZARDOUS POLYMERIZATION HAS NOT BEEN REPORTED TO OCCUR UNDER NORMAL TEMPERATURES AND PRESSURES.

STORAGE AND DISPOSAL

OBSERVE ALL FEDERAL, STATE AND LOCAL REGULATIONS WHEN STORING OR DISPOSING OF THIS SUBSTANCE. FOR ASSISTANCE, CONTACT THE DISTRICT DIRECTOR OF THE ENVIRONMENTAL PROTECTION AGENCY.

****STORAGE****

STORE AWAY FROM INCOMPATIBLE SUBSTANCES.

CONDITIONS TO AVOID

MAY BURN BUT DOES NOT IGNITE READILY. AVOID CONTACT WITH STRONG OXIDIZERS, EXCESSIVE HEAT, SPARKS, OR OPEN FLAME.

SPILL AND LEAK PROCEDURES

OCCUPATIONAL SPILL: STOP LEAK IF YOU CAN DO IT WITHOUT RISK. FOR SMALL SPILLS, TAKE UP WITH SAND OR OTHER ABSORBENT MATERIAL AND PLACE INTO CLEAN, DRY CONTAINERS FOR LATER DISPOSAL. KEEP UNNECESSARY PEOPLE AWAY. ISOLATE HAZARD AREA AND DENY ENTRY.

PROTECTIVE EQUIPMENT

VENTILATION: PROVIDE LOCAL EXHAUST OR PROCESS ENCLOSURE VENTILATION SYSTEM.

RESPIRATOR: THE FOLLOWING RESPIRATORS ARE RECOMMENDED BASED ON INFORMATION FOUND IN THE PHYSICAL DATA, TOXICITY AND HEALTH EFFECTS SECTIONS. THEY ARE RANKED IN ORDER FROM MINIMUM TO MAXIMUM RESPIRATORY PROTECTION. THE SPECIFIC RESPIRATOR SELECTED MUST BE BASED ON CONTAMINATION LEVELS FOUND IN THE WORK PLACE, MUST NOT EXCEED THE WORKING LIMITS OF THE RESPIRATOR AND BE JOINTLY APPROVED BY THE NATIONAL INSTITUTE FOR OCCUPATIONAL SAFETY AND HEALTH AND THE MINE SAFETY AND HEALTH ADMINISTRATION (NIOSH-MSHA).

CHEMICAL CARTRIDGE RESPIRATOR WITH AN ORGANIC VAPOR CARTRIDGE(S) WITH A FULL FACEPIECE.

GAS MASK WITH ORGANIC VAPOR CANISTER (CHIN-STYLE OR FRONT- OR BACK-MOUNTED CANISTER) WITH A FULL FACEPIECE.

TYPE 'C' SUPPLIED-AIR RESPIRATOR WITH A FULL FACEPIECE OPERATED IN PRESSURE-DEMAND OR OTHER POSITIVE PRESSURE MODE OR WITH A FULL FACEPIECE, HELMET OR HOOD OPERATED IN CONTINUOUS-FLOW MODE.

SELF-CONTAINED BREATHING APPARATUS WITH A FULL FACEPIECE OPERATED IN PRESSURE-DEMAND OR OTHER POSITIVE PRESSURE MODE.

FOR FIREFIGHTING AND OTHER IMMEDIATELY DANGEROUS TO LIFE OR HEALTH CONDITIONS:

SELF-CONTAINED BREATHING APPARATUS WITH FULL FACEPIECE OPERATED IN PRESSURE-DEMAND OR OTHER POSITIVE PRESSURE MODE.

SUPPLIED-AIR RESPIRATOR WITH FULL FACEPIECE AND OPERATED IN PRESSURE-DEMAND OR OTHER POSITIVE PRESSURE MODE IN COMBINATION WITH AN AUXILIARY SELF-CONTAINED BREATHING APPARATUS OPERATED IN PRESSURE-DEMAND OR OTHER POSITIVE PRESSURE MODE.

CLOTHING: EMPLOYEE MUST WEAR APPROPRIATE PROTECTIVE (IMPERVIOUS) CLOTHING AND EQUIPMENT TO PREVENT REPEATED OR PROLONGED SKIN CONTACT WITH THIS SUBSTANCE.

GLOVES: EMPLOYEE MUST WEAR APPROPRIATE PROTECTIVE GLOVES TO PREVENT CONTACT WITH THIS SUBSTANCE.

EYE PROTECTION: EMPLOYEE MUST WEAR SPLASH-PROOF OR DUST-RESISTANT SAFETY GOGGLES TO PREVENT EYE CONTACT WITH THIS SUBSTANCE.

EMERGENCY EYE WASH: WHERE THERE IS ANY POSSIBILITY THAT AN EMPLOYEE'S EYES MAY BE EXPOSED TO THIS SUBSTANCE, THE EMPLOYER SHOULD PROVIDE AN EYE WASH FOUNTAIN WITHIN THE IMMEDIATE WORK AREA FOR EMERGENCY USE.

AUTHORIZED BY- OCCUPATIONAL HEALTH SERVICES, INC.

CREATION DATE: 02/08/90 ***REVISION DATE:*** 06/18/90

MATERIAL SAFETY DATA SHEET

OCCUPATIONAL HEALTH SERVICES, INC.
AGRICULTURE AND PESTICIDE DIVISION
450 SEVENTH AVENUE, SUITE 2407
NEW YORK, NEW YORK 10123
1-800-445-MSDS OR (212) 967-1100

EMERGENCY CONTACT:
JOHN S. BRANSFORD, JR. (615) 292-1180

SUBSTANCE IDENTIFICATION

CAS-NUMBER 77-92-9

SUBSTANCE: CITRIC ACID

TRADE NAMES/SYNONYMS: BETA-HYDROXYTRICARBALLYLIC ACID; ANHYDROUS CITRIC ACID; 1,2,3-PROPANETRICARBOXYLIC ACID, 2-HYDROXY-; 2-HYDROXY-1,2,3-PROPANETRICARBOXYLIC ACID; CITRO; CITRETTEN; HYDROCEROL A; C6H8O7; PST05200

CHEMICAL FAMILY: CARBOXYLIC ACID, ALIPHATIC

MOLECULAR FORMULA: H-O-C-(C-H2-C-O2-H)2-C-O2-H

MOLECULAR WEIGHT: 192.14

CERCLA RATINGS (SCALE 0-3): HEALTH=1 FIRE=1 REACTIVITY=0 PERSISTENCE=0

NFPA RATINGS (SCALE 0-4): HEALTH=1 FIRE=1 REACTIVITY=0

COMPONENTS AND CONTAMINANTS

COMPONENT: CITRIC ACID ***PERCENT:*** 100.0

CAS# 77-92-9

OTHER CONTAMINANTS: NONE

EXPOSURE LIMITS: NO OCCUPATIONAL EXPOSURE LIMITS ESTABLISHED BY OSHA, ACGIH, OR NIOSH.

PHYSICAL DATA

DESCRIPTION: ODORLESS, COLORLESS, TRANSLUCENT CRYSTALS OR POWDER WITH A STRONG ACID TASTE. ***BOILING POINT:*** DECOMPOSES ***MELTING POINT:*** 307 F (153 C)

SPECIFIC GRAVITY: 1.665 ***PH:*** 2.2 @ 0.1 N SOLN

SOLUBILITY IN WATER: 59.2% @ 20 C

SOLVENT SOLUBILITY: SOLUBLE IN ALCOHOL AND ETHER.

FIRE AND EXPLOSION DATA

FIRE AND EXPLOSION HAZARD: SLIGHT FIRE HAZARD WHEN EXPOSED TO HEAT OR FLAME. ***UPPER EXPLOSIVE LIMIT:*** 65 GM/FT3 (OPTIMUM) ***LOWER EXPLOSIVE LIMIT:*** 8 GM/FT3

AUTOIGNITION TEMP.: 1832-1868 F (1000-1020 C) (POWDER)

FIREFIGHTING MEDIA: DRY CHEMICAL, CARBON DIOXIDE, HALON, WATER SPRAY OR STANDARD FOAM (1987 EMERGENCY RESPONSE GUIDEBOOK, DOT P 5800.4).

FOR LARGER FIRES, USE WATER SPRAY, FOG OR STANDARD FOAM (1987 EMERGENCY RESPONSE GUIDEBOOK, DOT P 5800.4).

FIREFIGHTING: MOVE CONTAINER FROM FIRE AREA IF POSSIBLE. DO NOT SCATTER SPILLED MATERIAL WITH HIGH PRESSURE WATER STREAMS. DIKE FIRE CONTROL WATER FOR LATER DISPOSAL (1987 EMERGENCY RESPONSE GUIDEBOOK, DOT P 5800.4, GUIDE PAGE 31).

USE AGENTS SUITABLE FOR TYPE OF SURROUNDING FIRE. AVOID BREATHING HAZARDOUS VAPORS, KEEP UPWIND.

TOXICITY

CITRIC ACID: IRRITATION DATA: ANHYDROUS: 500 MG/24 HOURS SKIN-RABBIT MILD; 750 UG/24 HOURS EYE-RABBIT SEVERE. MONOHYDRATE: 5 MG/30 SECONDS RINSED EYE-RABBIT MILD. TOXICITY DATA: ANHYDROUS: 5040 MG/KG ORAL-MOUSE LD50; 7000 MG/KG ORAL-RABBIT LDLO; 883 MG/KG INTRAPERITONEAL-RAT LD50; 961 MG/KG INTRAPERITONEAL-MOUSE LD50; 42 MG/KG INTRAVENOUS-MOUSE LD50; 330 MG/KG INTRAVENOUS-RABBIT LD50; 5500 MG/KG SUBCUTANEOUS-RAT LD50; 2700 MG/KG SUBCUTANEOUS-MOUSE LD50. MONOHYDRATE: 375 MG/KG INTRAPERITONEAL-RAT LD50. CARCINOGEN STATUS: NONE. LOCAL EFFECTS: CORROSIVE- EYE; IRRITANT- INHALATION, SKIN. ACUTE TOXICITY LEVEL: SLIGHTLY TOXIC BY INGESTION. AT INCREASED RISK FROM EXPOSURE: PERSONS WITH RENAL IMPAIRMENT; ADDISON'S DISEASE; DEHYDRATION; HYPERKALEMIA.

HEALTH EFFECTS AND FIRST AID

INHALATION: CITRIC ACID: IRRITANT. **ACUTE EXPOSURE-** INHALATION MAY CAUSE MUCOUS MEMBRANE IRRITATION WITH SORE THROAT, COUGHING AND SHORTNESS OF BREATH. ALLERGIC REACTIONS MAY OCCUR IN SOME INDIVIDUALS. **CHRONIC EXPOSURE-** LONG-TERM OVEREXPOSURE MAY DAMAGE TOOTH ENAMEL.

FIRST AID- REMOVE FROM EXPOSURE AREA TO FRESH AIR IMMEDIATELY. IF BREATHING HAS STOPPED, PERFORM ARTIFICIAL RESPIRATION. KEEP PERSON WARM AND AT REST. TREAT SYMPTOMATICALLY AND SUPPORTIVELY. GET MEDICAL ATTENTION IMMEDIATELY.

SKIN CONTACT: CITRIC ACID: IRRITANT. **ACUTE EXPOSURE-** CONTACT MAY CAUSE MODERATE IRRITATION WITH REDNESS AND PAIN. ALLERGIC REACTIONS MAY OCCUR IN SOME INDIVIDUALS. **CHRONIC EXPOSURE-** REPEATED OR PROLONGED CONTACT WITH IRRITANTS MAY CAUSE DERMATITIS.

FIRST AID- REMOVE CONTAMINATED CLOTHING AND SHOES IMMEDIATELY. WASH AFFECTED AREA WITH SOAP OR MILD DETERGENT AND LARGE AMOUNTS OF WATER UNTIL NO EVIDENCE OF CHEMICAL REMAINS (APPROXIMATELY 15-20 MINUTES). GET MEDICAL ATTENTION IMMEDIATELY.

EYE CONTACT: CITRIC ACID: CORROSIVE. **ACUTE EXPOSURE-** CONTACT MAY CAUSE SEVERE IRRITATION WITH REDNESS, PAIN AND POSSIBLY BURNS. A LARGE QUANTITY OF SATURATED SOLUTION SPLASHED IN HUMAN EYES PRODUCED A SEVERE CONJUNCTIVAL REACTION AND ULCERATION OF THE CORNEA, RESULTING IN EXTENSIVE ADHERENT LEUKOMA. IRRIGATION WITH A 0.5% SOLUTION FOR 30 MINUTES CAUSED PERMANENT CLOUDINESS OF THE CORNEA IN RABBIT EYES; A 2% SOLUTION CAUSED SEVERE DENSE OPACIFICATION. **CHRONIC EXPOSURE-** EFFECTS ARE DEPENDENT UPON CONCENTRATION AND DURATION OF EXPOSURE. CONJUNCTIVITIS OR EFFECTS SIMILAR TO THOSE AS FOR ACUTE EXPOSURE MAY OCCUR.

FIRST AID- WASH EYES IMMEDIATELY WITH LARGE AMOUNTS OF WATER, OCCASIONALLY LIFTING UPPER AND LOWER LIDS, UNTIL NO EVIDENCE OF CHEMICAL REMAINS (AT LEAST 15-20 MINUTES). CONTINUE IRRIGATING WITH NORMAL SALINE UNTIL THE PH HAS RETURNED TO NORMAL (30-60 MINUTES). COVER WITH STERILE BANDAGES. GET MEDICAL ATTENTION IMMEDIATELY.

INGESTION: CITRIC ACID: **ACUTE EXPOSURE-** INGESTION OF LARGE AMOUNTS MAY CAUSE ACUTE BUT TRANSIENT GASTROINTESTINAL IRRITATION WITH VOMITING AND DIARRHEA. CONCENTRATED SOLUTIONS MAY CAUSE MILD CORROSION OF THE UPPER GASTROINTESTINAL TRACT WITH SORE THROAT, ABDOMINAL PAIN, WRINKLING AND ROUGHENING OF MUCOUS MEMBRANES OF THE MOUTH AND ESOPHAGUS, AND SWELLING AND DISCOLORATION OF THE STOMACH AND INTESTINE. A HUMAN DEATH HAS BEEN REPORTED FOLLOWING INGESTION OF 20-30 GRAMS OF THE PURE ACID. LETHAL DOSES IN RATS PRODUCED METABOLIC ACIDOSIS AND CALCIUM DEFICIENCY. **CHRONIC EXPOSURE-** FREQUENT OR EXCESSIVE INTAKE OF CITRIC ACID MAY CAUSE EROSION OF THE TEETH AND LOCAL IRRITATION. PROLONGED FEEDING STUDIES IN ANIMALS RESULTED ONLY IN A SLIGHT INCREASE IN DENTAL ATTRITION.

FIRST AID- TREAT SYMPTOMATICALLY AND SUPPORTIVELY. GET MEDICAL ATTENTION IMMEDIATELY. IF VOMITING OCCURS, KEEP HEAD LOWER THAN HIPS TO PREVENT ASPIRATION.

ANTIDOTE: NO SPECIFIC ANTIDOTE. TREAT SYMPTOMATICALLY AND SUPPORTIVELY.

REACTIVITY

REACTIVITY: STABLE UNDER NORMAL TEMPERATURES AND PRESSURES.

INCOMPATIBILITIES: CITRIC ACID: BASES: INCOMPATIBLE. METAL NITRATES: POSSIBLE EXPLOSION HAZARD. OXIDIZERS (STRONG): FIRE AND EXPLOSION HAZARD.

DECOMPOSITION: THERMAL DECOMPOSITION PRODUCTS MAY INCLUDE TOXIC OXIDES OF CARBON.

POLYMERIZATION: HAZARDOUS POLYMERIZATION HAS NOT BEEN REPORTED TO OCCUR UNDER NORMAL TEMPERATURES AND PRESSURES.

STORAGE AND DISPOSAL

OBSERVE ALL FEDERAL, STATE AND LOCAL REGULATIONS WHEN STORING OR DISPOSING OF THIS SUBSTANCE. FOR ASSISTANCE, CONTACT THE DISTRICT DIRECTOR OF THE ENVIRONMENTAL PROTECTION AGENCY.

****STORAGE****

STORE AWAY FROM INCOMPATIBLE SUBSTANCES.

KEEP IN A TIGHTLY CLOSED CONTAINER. STORE IN A COOL, DRY, VENTILATED AREA.

CONDITIONS TO AVOID

MAY BURN BUT DOES NOT IGNITE READILY. AVOID CONTACT WITH STRONG OXIDIZERS, EXCESSIVE HEAT, SPARKS, OR OPEN FLAME.

SPILL AND LEAK PROCEDURES

OCCUPATIONAL SPILL: SWEEP UP AND PLACE IN SUITABLE CLEAN, DRY CONTAINERS FOR RECLAMATION OR LATER DISPOSAL. DO NOT FLUSH SPILLED MATERIAL INTO SEWER. KEEP UNNECESSARY PEOPLE AWAY.

PROTECTIVE EQUIPMENT

VENTILATION: PROVIDE LOCAL EXHAUST OR GENERAL DILUTION VENTILATION SYSTEM.

RESPIRATOR: THE FOLLOWING RESPIRATORS ARE RECOMMENDED BASED ON INFORMATION FOUND IN THE PHYSICAL DATA, TOXICITY AND HEALTH EFFECTS SECTIONS. THEY ARE RANKED IN ORDER FROM MINIMUM TO MAXIMUM RESPIRATORY PROTECTION. THE SPECIFIC RESPIRATOR SELECTED MUST BE BASED ON CONTAMINATION LEVELS FOUND IN THE WORK PLACE, MUST NOT EXCEED THE WORKING LIMITS OF THE RESPIRATOR AND BE JOINTLY APPROVED BY THE NATIONAL INSTITUTE FOR OCCUPATIONAL SAFETY AND HEALTH AND THE MINE SAFETY AND HEALTH ADMINISTRATION (NIOSH-MSHA).

DUST AND MIST RESPIRATOR WITH A FULL FACEPIECE. AIR-PURIFYING FULL FACEPIECE RESPIRATOR WITH A HIGH-EFFICIENCY PARTICULATE FILTER.

POWERED AIR-PURIFYING RESPIRATOR WITH A TIGHT-FITTING FACEPIECE AND HIGH-EFFICIENCY PARTICULATE FILTER.

TYPE 'C' SUPPLIED-AIR RESPIRATOR WITH A FULL FACEPIECE OPERATED IN PRESSURE-DEMAND OR OTHER POSITIVE PRESSURE MODE OR WITH A FULL FACEPIECE, HELMET OR HOOD OPERATED IN CONTINUOUS-FLOW MODE.

SELF-CONTAINED BREATHING APPARATUS WITH A FULL FACEPIECE OPERATED IN PRESSURE-DEMAND OR OTHER POSITIVE PRESSURE MODE.

FOR FIREFIGHTING AND OTHER IMMEDIATELY DANGEROUS TO LIFE OR HEALTH CONDITIONS:

SELF-CONTAINED BREATHING APPARATUS WITH FULL FACEPIECE OPERATED IN PRESSURE-DEMAND OR OTHER POSITIVE PRESSURE MODE.

SUPPLIED-AIR RESPIRATOR WITH FULL FACEPIECE AND OPERATED IN PRESSURE-DEMAND OR OTHER POSITIVE PRESSURE MODE IN COMBINATION WITH AN AUXILIARY SELF-CONTAINED BREATHING APPARATUS OPERATED IN PRESSURE-DEMAND OR OTHER POSITIVE PRESSURE MODE.

CLOTHING: EMPLOYEE MUST WEAR APPROPRIATE PROTECTIVE (IMPERVIOUS) CLOTHING AND EQUIPMENT TO PREVENT REPEATED OR PROLONGED SKIN CONTACT WITH THIS SUBSTANCE.

GLOVES: EMPLOYEE MUST WEAR APPROPRIATE PROTECTIVE GLOVES TO PREVENT CONTACT WITH THIS SUBSTANCE.

EYE PROTECTION: EMPLOYEE MUST WEAR SPLASH-PROOF OR DUST-RESISTANT SAFETY GOGGLES AND A FACESHIELD TO PREVENT CONTACT WITH THIS SUBSTANCE.

EMERGENCY WASH FACILITIES: WHERE THERE IS ANY POSSIBILITY THAT AN EMPLOYEE'S EYES AND/OR SKIN MAY BE EXPOSED TO THIS SUBSTANCE, THE EMPLOYER SHOULD PROVIDE AN EYE WASH FOUNTAIN AND QUICK DRENCH SHOWER WITHIN THE IMMEDIATE WORK AREA FOR EMERGENCY USE.

AUTHORIZED BY- OCCUPATIONAL HEALTH SERVICES, INC.

CREATION DATE: 11/15/89 ***REVISION DATE:*** 05/31/90

MATERIAL SAFETY DATA SHEET

OCCUPATIONAL HEALTH SERVICES, INC.
AGRICULTURE AND PESTICIDE DIVISION
450 SEVENTH AVENUE, SUITE 2407
NEW YORK, NEW YORK 10123
1-800-445-MSDS OR (212) 967-1100

EMERGENCY CONTACT:
JOHN S. BRANSFORD, JR. (615) 292-1180

SUBSTANCE IDENTIFICATION

CAS-NUMBER 38083-17-9

SUBSTANCE: **CLIMBAZOLE**

TRADE NAMES/SYNONYMS: 2-BUTANONE, 1-(4-CHLOROPHENOXY)-1-(1H-IMIDAZOL-1-YL)-3,3-DIMETHYL-; 1-(4-CHLOROPHENOXY)-1-(1H-IMIDAZOL-1-YL)-3,3-DIMETHYL-2-BUTANONE; 1-(4-CHLOROPHENOXY)-1-(1H-IMIDAZOL-1-YL)-3,3-DIMETHYLBUTANONE; 1-(4-CHLOROPHENOXY)-1-(IMIDAZOL-1-YL)-3,3-DIMETHYLBUTANONE; 1-(4-CHLOROPHENOXY)-1-(IMIDAZOLE-1-YL)-3,3-DIMETHYLBUTANONE; BAY-E 6975; BAYPIVAL; BAYSAN; CLIMBAZOL; C15H17CLN2O2; PST05208

CHEMICAL FAMILY: IMIDAZOLE
KETONE, ALKYL-ARYL

MOLECULAR FORMULA: CL-C6-H4-O-C-H-N2-C3-C-O-C(C-H3)3

MOLECULAR WEIGHT: 292.76

CERCLA RATINGS (SCALE 0-3): HEALTH=3 FIRE=1 REACTIVITY=0 PERSISTENCE=3

NFPA RATINGS (SCALE 0-4): HEALTH=3 FIRE=1 REACTIVITY=0

COMPONENTS AND CONTAMINANTS

COMPONENT: CLIMBAZOLE ***PERCENT:*** 100
CAS# 38083-17-9

OTHER CONTAMINANTS: NONE

EXPOSURE LIMITS: NO OCCUPATIONAL EXPOSURE LIMITS ESTABLISHED BY OSHA, ACGIH, OR NIOSH.

PHYSICAL DATA

DESCRIPTION: SOLID ***MELTING POINT:*** 205 F (96 C)

SPECIFIC GRAVITY: NOT AVAILABLE ***VAPOR PRESSURE:*** NEGLIGIBLE

SOLUBILITY IN WATER: 5.5 PPM

SOLVENT SOLUBILITY: SOLUBLE IN ISOPROPANOL, CYCLOHEXANONE.

FIRE AND EXPLOSION DATA

FIRE AND EXPLOSION HAZARD: SLIGHT FIRE HAZARD WHEN EXPOSED TO HEAT OR FLAME.

FLASH POINT: 212 F (100 C)

FIREFIGHTING MEDIA: DRY CHEMICAL, CARBON DIOXIDE, HALON, WATER SPRAY OR STANDARD FOAM (1987 EMERGENCY RESPONSE GUIDEBOOK, DOT P 5800.4).

FOR LARGER FIRES, USE WATER SPRAY, FOG OR STANDARD FOAM (1987 EMERGENCY RESPONSE GUIDEBOOK, DOT P 5800.4).

FIREFIGHTING: MOVE CONTAINERS FROM FIRE AREA IF POSSIBLE (1987 EMERGENCY RESPONSE GUIDEBOOK, DOT P 5800.4, GUIDE PAGE 53).

EXTINGUISH FIRE USING AGENTS SUITABLE FOR TYPE OF SURROUNDING FIRE. USE WATER IN FLOODING AMOUNTS AS A FOG. AVOID BREATHING DUSTS AND FUMES FROM BURNING MATERIAL; KEEP UPWIND.

TOXICITY

CLIMBAZOLE: TOXICITY DATA: 400 MG/KG ORAL-RAT LD50. CARCINOGEN STATUS: NONE. ACUTE TOXICITY LEVEL: TOXIC BY INGESTION. TARGET EFFECTS: NO DATA AVAILABLE.

HEALTH EFFECTS AND FIRST AID

INHALATION: CLIMBAZOLE: **ACUTE EXPOSURE-** NO DATA AVAILABLE. **CHRONIC EXPOSURE-** NO DATA AVAILABLE.

FIRST AID- REMOVE FROM EXPOSURE AREA TO FRESH AIR IMMEDIATELY. IF BREATHING HAS STOPPED, PERFORM ARTIFICIAL RESPIRATION. KEEP PERSON WARM AND AT REST. TREAT SYMPTOMATICALLY AND SUPPORTIVELY. GET MEDICAL ATTENTION IMMEDIATELY.

SKIN CONTACT: CLIMBAZOLE: **ACUTE EXPOSURE-** NO DATA AVAILABLE. **CHRONIC EXPOSURE-** NO DATA AVAILABLE.

FIRST AID- REMOVE CONTAMINATED CLOTHING AND SHOES IMMEDIATELY. WASH AFFECTED AREA WITH SOAP OR MILD DETERGENT AND LARGE AMOUNTS OF WATER UNTIL NO EVIDENCE OF CHEMICAL REMAINS (APPROXIMATELY 15-20 MINUTES). GET MEDICAL ATTENTION IMMEDIATELY.

EYE CONTACT: CLIMBAZOLE: **ACUTE EXPOSURE-** NO DATA AVAILABLE. **CHRONIC EXPOSURE-** NO DATA AVAILABLE.

FIRST AID- WASH EYES IMMEDIATELY WITH LARGE AMOUNTS OF WATER OR NORMAL SALINE, OCCASIONALLY LIFTING UPPER AND LOWER LIDS, UNTIL NO EVIDENCE OF CHEMICAL REMAINS (APPROXIMATELY 15-20 MINUTES). GET MEDICAL ATTENTION IMMEDIATELY.

INGESTION: CLIMBAZOLE: TOXIC. **ACUTE EXPOSURE-** A LETHAL DOSE IN RATS WAS 400 MG/KG. **CHRONIC EXPOSURE-** NO DATA AVAILABLE.

FIRST AID- TREAT SYMPTOMATICALLY AND SUPPORTIVELY. GET MEDICAL ATTENTION IMMEDIATELY. IF VOMITING OCCURS, KEEP HEAD LOWER THAN HIPS TO PREVENT ASPIRATION.

ANTIDOTE: NO SPECIFIC ANTIDOTE. TREAT SYMPTOMATICALLY AND SUPPORTIVELY.

REACTIVITY

REACTIVITY: STABLE UNDER NORMAL TEMPERATURES AND PRESSURES.

INCOMPATIBILITIES: CLIMBAZOLE: NO DATA AVAILABLE.

DECOMPOSITION: THERMAL DECOMPOSITION PRODUCTS MAY INCLUDE TOXIC OXIDES OF CARBON AND NITROGEN.

POLYMERIZATION: HAZARDOUS POLYMERIZATION HAS NOT BEEN REPORTED TO OCCUR UNDER NORMAL TEMPERATURES AND PRESSURES.

STORAGE AND DISPOSAL

OBSERVE ALL FEDERAL, STATE AND LOCAL REGULATIONS WHEN STORING OR DISPOSING OF THIS SUBSTANCE. FOR ASSISTANCE, CONTACT THE DISTRICT DIRECTOR OF THE ENVIRONMENTAL PROTECTION AGENCY.

STORAGE

STORE IN ACCORDANCE WITH 40 CFR 165 RECOMMENDED PROCEDURES FOR THE DISPOSAL AND STORAGE OF PESTICIDES AND PESTICIDE CONTAINERS.

DISPOSAL

DISPOSAL MUST BE IN ACCORDANCE WITH 40 CFR 165 RECOMMENDED PROCEDURES FOR THE DISPOSAL AND STORAGE OF PESTICIDES AND PESTICIDE CONTAINERS.

CONDITIONS TO AVOID

MAY BURN BUT DOES NOT IGNITE READILY.

SPILL AND LEAK PROCEDURES

OCCUPATIONAL SPILL: DO NOT TOUCH SPILLED MATERIAL. STOP LEAK IF YOU CAN DO IT WITHOUT RISK. FOR SMALL SPILLS, TAKE UP WITH SAND OR OTHER ABSORBENT MATERIAL AND PLACE INTO CONTAINERS FOR LATER DISPOSAL. FOR SMALL DRY SPILLS, WITH A CLEAN SHOVEL PLACE MATERIAL INTO CLEAN, DRY CONTAINER AND COVER. MOVE CONTAINERS FROM SPILL AREA. FOR LARGER SPILLS, DIKE FAR AHEAD OF SPILL FOR LATER DISPOSAL. KEEP UNNECESSARY PEOPLE AWAY. ISOLATE HAZARD AREA AND DENY ENTRY.

PROTECTIVE EQUIPMENT

VENTILATION: PROVIDE LOCAL EXHAUST OR PROCESS ENCLOSURE VENTILATION SYSTEM.

RESPIRATOR: THE FOLLOWING RESPIRATORS ARE RECOMMENDED BASED ON INFORMATION FOUND IN THE PHYSICAL DATA, TOXICITY AND HEALTH EFFECTS SECTIONS. THEY ARE RANKED IN ORDER FROM MINIMUM TO MAXIMUM RESPIRATORY PROTECTION. THE SPECIFIC RESPIRATOR SELECTED MUST BE BASED ON CONTAMINATION LEVELS FOUND IN THE WORK PLACE, MUST NOT EXCEED THE WORKING LIMITS OF THE RESPIRATOR AND BE JOINTLY APPROVED BY THE NATIONAL INSTITUTE FOR OCCUPATIONAL SAFETY AND HEALTH AND THE MINE SAFETY AND HEALTH ADMINISTRATION (NIOSH-MSHA).

CHEMICAL CARTRIDGE RESPIRATOR WITH AN ORGANIC VAPOR CARTRIDGE(S) WITH A FULL FACEPIECE AND ORGANIC VAPOR CARTRIDGE(S) IN COMBINATION WITH A DUST AND MIST FILTER.

POWERED AIR-PURIFYING RESPIRATOR WITH A TIGHT-FITTING FACEPIECE AND ORGANIC VAPOR CARTRIDGE(S) IN COMBINATION WITH A HIGH-EFFICIENCY PARTICULATE FILTER.

TYPE 'C' SUPPLIED-AIR RESPIRATOR WITH A FULL FACEPIECE OPERATED IN A PRESSURE-DEMAND OR OTHER POSITIVE PRESSURE MODE.

SELF-CONTAINED BREATHING APPARATUS WITH A FULL FACEPIECE OPERATED IN PRESSURE-DEMAND OR OTHER POSITIVE PRESSURE MODE.

FOR FIREFIGHTING AND OTHER IMMEDIATELY DANGEROUS TO LIFE OR HEALTH CONDITIONS:

SELF-CONTAINED BREATHING APPARATUS WITH FULL FACEPIECE OPERATED IN PRESSURE-DEMAND OR OTHER POSITIVE PRESSURE MODE.

SUPPLIED-AIR RESPIRATOR WITH FULL FACEPIECE AND OPERATED IN PRESSURE-DEMAND OR OTHER POSITIVE PRESSURE MODE IN COMBINATION WITH AN AUXILIARY SELF-CONTAINED BREATHING APPARATUS OPERATED IN PRESSURE-DEMAND OR OTHER POSITIVE PRESSURE MODE.

CLOTHING: EMPLOYEE MUST WEAR APPROPRIATE PROTECTIVE (IMPERVIOUS) CLOTHING AND EQUIPMENT TO PREVENT REPEATED OR PROLONGED SKIN CONTACT WITH THIS SUBSTANCE.

GLOVES: EMPLOYEE MUST WEAR APPROPRIATE PROTECTIVE GLOVES TO PREVENT CONTACT WITH THIS SUBSTANCE.

EYE PROTECTION: EMPLOYEE MUST WEAR SPLASH-PROOF OR DUST-RESISTANT SAFETY GOGGLES TO PREVENT EYE CONTACT WITH THIS SUBSTANCE.

EMERGENCY EYE WASH: WHERE THERE IS ANY POSSIBILITY THAT AN EMPLOYEE'S EYES MAY BE EXPOSED TO THIS SUBSTANCE, THE EMPLOYER SHOULD PROVIDE AN EYE WASH FOUNTAIN WITHIN THE IMMEDIATE WORK AREA FOR EMERGENCY USE.

AUTHORIZED BY- OCCUPATIONAL HEALTH SERVICES, INC.
CREATION DATE: 10/04/89 ***REVISION DATE:*** 05/11/90

MATERIAL SAFETY DATA SHEET

OCCUPATIONAL HEALTH SERVICES, INC.
AGRICULTURE AND PESTICIDE DIVISION
450 SEVENTH AVENUE, SUITE 2407
NEW YORK, NEW YORK 10123
1-800-445-MSDS OR (212) 967-1100

EMERGENCY CONTACT:
JOHN S. BRANSFORD, JR. (615) 292-1180

SUBSTANCE IDENTIFICATION

CAS-NUMBER 1702-17-6

SUBSTANCE: **CLOPYRALID**

TRADE NAMES/SYNONYMS: 2-PYRIDINECARBOXYLIC ACID, 3,6-DICHLORO-; 3,6-DICHLORO-2-PYRIDINECARBOXYLIC ACID; PICOLINIC ACID, 3,6-DICHLORO-; 3,6-DICHLOROPICOLINIC ACID; DOWCO 290; LONTREL; C6H3CL2NO2; PST05211

CHEMICAL FAMILY: PYRIDINE
HALOGEN COMPOUND, AROMATIC

MOLECULAR FORMULA: C6-H3-CL2-N-O2

MOLECULAR WEIGHT: 192.0

CERCLA RATINGS (SCALE 0-3): HEALTH=U FIRE=1 REACTIVITY=0 PERSISTENCE=3

NFPA RATINGS (SCALE 0-4): HEALTH=U FIRE=1 REACTIVITY=0

COMPONENTS AND CONTAMINANTS

COMPONENT: CLOPYRALID ***PERCENT:*** 100.0
CAS# 1702-17-6

OTHER CONTAMINANTS: NONE

EXPOSURE LIMITS: NO OCCUPATIONAL EXPOSURE LIMITS ESTABLISHED BY OSHA, ACGIH, OR NIOSH.
CLOPYRALID: 10 MG/M3 DOW CHEMICAL COMPANY RECOMMENDED TWA

PHYSICAL DATA

DESCRIPTION: COLORLESS CRYSTALS. ***MELTING POINT:*** 304-306 F (151-152 C)

SPECIFIC GRAVITY: 0.75 ***VAPOR PRESSURE:*** NEGLIGIBLE ***PH:*** ACIDIC

SOLUBILITY IN WATER: 0.9%

SOLVENT SOLUBILITY: SOLUBLE IN ACETONE AND CYCLOHEXANONE; MODERATELY SOLUBLE IN XYLENE.

FIRE AND EXPLOSION DATA

FIRE AND EXPLOSION HAZARD: SLIGHT FIRE HAZARD WHEN EXPOSED TO HEAT OR FLAME.

FIREFIGHTING MEDIA: DRY CHEMICAL, CARBON DIOXIDE, HALON, WATER SPRAY OR STANDARD FOAM (1987 EMERGENCY RESPONSE GUIDEBOOK, DOT P 5800.4). FOR LARGER FIRES, USE WATER SPRAY, FOG OR STANDARD FOAM (1987 EMERGENCY RESPONSE GUIDEBOOK, DOT P 5800.4).

FIREFIGHTING: MOVE CONTAINER FROM FIRE AREA IF POSSIBLE. DO NOT SCATTER SPILLED MATERIAL WITH HIGH PRESSURE WATER STREAMS. DIKE FIRE CONTROL WATER FOR LATER DISPOSAL (1987 EMERGENCY RESPONSE GUIDEBOOK, DOT P 5800.4, GUIDE PAGE 31).
USE AGENTS SUITABLE FOR TYPE OF SURROUNDING FIRE. AVOID BREATHING HAZARDOUS VAPORS, KEEP UPWIND.

TOXICITY

CLOPYRALID: TOXICITY DATA: 4300 MG/KG ORAL-RAT LD50; >2000 MG/KG SKIN-RABBIT LD50 (DOW MSDS); REPRODUCTIVE EFFECTS DATA (RTECS). CARCINOGEN STATUS: NONE. LOCAL EFFECTS: CORROSIVE- EYES. ACUTE TOXICITY LEVEL: MODERATELY TOXIC BY INGESTION; SLIGHTLY TOXIC BY DERMAL ABSORPTION. TARGET EFFECTS: NO DATA AVAILABLE.

HEALTH EFFECTS AND FIRST AID

INHALATION: CLOPYRALID: **ACUTE EXPOSURE-** NO SPECIFIC DATA AVAILABLE. INHALATION OF HERBICIDES MAY CAUSE RESPIRATORY TRACT IRRITATION.
CHRONIC EXPOSURE- NO DATA AVAILABLE.

FIRST AID- REMOVE FROM EXPOSURE AREA TO FRESH AIR IMMEDIATELY. IF BREATHING HAS STOPPED, PERFORM ARTIFICIAL RESPIRATION. KEEP PERSON WARM AND AT REST. TREAT SYMPTOMATICALLY AND SUPPORTIVELY. GET MEDICAL ATTENTION IMMEDIATELY.

SKIN CONTACT: CLOPYRALID: **ACUTE EXPOSURE-** CONTACT MAY CAUSE IRRITATION.
CHRONIC EXPOSURE- NO DATA AVAILABLE.

FIRST AID- REMOVE CONTAMINATED CLOTHING AND SHOES IMMEDIATELY. WASH AFFECTED AREA WITH SOAP OR MILD DETERGENT AND LARGE AMOUNTS OF WATER UNTIL NO EVIDENCE OF CHEMICAL REMAINS (APPROXIMATELY 15-20 MINUTES). GET MEDICAL ATTENTION IMMEDIATELY.

EYE CONTACT: CLOPYRALID: CORROSIVE. **ACUTE EXPOSURE-** MAY CAUSE SEVERE IRRITATION, CORNEAL DAMAGE, PERMANENT IMPAIRMENT OF VISION, AND POSSIBLY BLINDNESS. CORNEAL DAMAGE IN ANIMALS DID NOT HEAL WITHIN 21 DAYS. **CHRONIC EXPOSURE-** EFFECTS DEPEND ON THE CONCENTRATION AND DURATION OF EXPOSURE. REPEATED OR PROLONGED CONTACT WITH CORROSIVE SUBSTANCES MAY CAUSE CONJUNCTIVITIS OR EFFECTS AS IN ACUTE EXPOSURE.

FIRST AID- WASH EYES IMMEDIATELY WITH LARGE AMOUNTS OF WATER, OCCASIONALLY LIFTING UPPER AND LOWER LIDS, UNTIL NO EVIDENCE OF CHEMICAL REMAINS (AT LEAST 15-20 MINUTES). CONTINUE IRRIGATING WITH NORMAL SALINE UNTIL THE PH HAS RETURNED TO NORMAL (30-60 MINUTES). COVER WITH STERILE BANDAGES. GET MEDICAL ATTENTION IMMEDIATELY.

INGESTION: CLOPYRALID: **ACUTE EXPOSURE-** IN RATS, INGESTION OF EXCESSIVE AMOUNTS HAS BEEN REPORTED TO CAUSE LETHARGY. **CHRONIC EXPOSURE-** REPEATED INGESTION OF LARGE AMOUNTS WAS REPORTED TO HAVE CAUSED LIVER AND KIDNEY DAMAGE IN RATS. REPRODUCTIVE EFFECTS HAVE BEEN REPORTED IN ANIMALS.

FIRST AID- IF THE PERSON IS CONSCIOUS AND NOT CONVULSING, REMOVE BY GIVING SYRUP OF IPECAC (IF VOMITING OCCURS, KEEP THE HEAD BELOW THE HIPS TO PREVENT ASPIRATION). GIVE ACTIVATED CHARCOAL FOLLOWED BY GASTRIC LAVAGE. FOLLOW WITH A SALINE CATHARTIC. DO NOT GIVE FATS OR OILS. INTESTINAL LAVAGE WITH 20% MANNITOL (200 ML) BY STOMACH TUBE IS ALSO USEFUL. GIVE ARTIFICIAL RESPIRATION WITH OXYGEN IF RESPIRATION IS DEPRESSED (DREISBACH, HANDBOOK OF POISONING, 12TH ED.). TREAT SYMPTOMATICALLY AND SUPPORTIVELY. LAVAGE AND ADMINISTRATION OF OXYGEN SHOULD BE PERFORMED BY QUALIFIED MEDICAL PERSONNEL. GET MEDICAL ATTENTION IMMEDIATELY.

ANTIDOTE: NO SPECIFIC ANTIDOTE. TREAT SYMPTOMATICALLY AND SUPPORTIVELY.

REACTIVITY

REACTIVITY: STABLE UNDER NORMAL TEMPERATURES AND PRESSURES.

INCOMPATIBILITIES: CLOPYRALID: ALUMINUM: MAY REACT VIOLENTLY ABOVE 110 C WHEN IN PRESENCE OF WATER. OXIDIZERS (STRONG): FIRE AND EXPLOSION HAZARD. STEEL AND TIN PLATE: MAY CORRODE IN PRESENCE OF MOISTURE.

DECOMPOSITION: THERMAL DECOMPOSITION PRODUCTS MAY INCLUDE TOXIC OXIDES OF NITROGEN AND CARBON AND TOXIC AND CORROSIVE FUMES OF CHLORIDES.

POLYMERIZATION: HAZARDOUS POLYMERIZATION HAS NOT BEEN REPORTED TO OCCUR UNDER NORMAL TEMPERATURES AND PRESSURES.

STORAGE AND DISPOSAL

OBSERVE ALL FEDERAL, STATE AND LOCAL REGULATIONS WHEN STORING OR DISPOSING OF THIS SUBSTANCE. FOR ASSISTANCE, CONTACT THE DISTRICT DIRECTOR OF THE ENVIRONMENTAL PROTECTION AGENCY.

****STORAGE****

STORE IN ACCORDANCE WITH 40 CFR 165 RECOMMENDED PROCEDURES FOR THE DISPOSAL AND STORAGE OF PESTICIDES AND PESTICIDE CONTAINERS.
STORE AWAY FROM INCOMPATIBLE SUBSTANCES.

****DISPOSAL****

DISPOSAL MUST BE IN ACCORDANCE WITH 40 CFR 165 RECOMMENDED PROCEDURES FOR THE DISPOSAL AND STORAGE OF PESTICIDES AND PESTICIDE CONTAINERS.

CONDITIONS TO AVOID

MAY BURN BUT DOES NOT IGNITE READILY. AVOID CONTACT WITH STRONG OXIDIZERS, EXCESSIVE HEAT, SPARKS, OR OPEN FLAME.

SPILL AND LEAK PROCEDURES

OCCUPATIONAL SPILL: STOP LEAK IF YOU CAN DO IT WITHOUT RISK. FOR SMALL SPILLS, TAKE UP WITH SAND OR OTHER ABSORBENT MATERIAL AND PLACE INTO CLEAN, DRY CONTAINERS FOR LATER DISPOSAL. KEEP UNNECESSARY PEOPLE AWAY. ISOLATE HAZARD AREA AND DENY ENTRY.

PROTECTIVE EQUIPMENT

VENTILATION: PROVIDE LOCAL EXHAUST VENTILATION AND/OR GENERAL DILUTION VENTILATION TO MEET PUBLISHED EXPOSURE LIMITS.

RESPIRATOR: THE FOLLOWING RESPIRATORS ARE RECOMMENDED BASED ON INFORMATION FOUND IN THE PHYSICAL DATA, TOXICITY AND HEALTH EFFECTS SECTIONS. THEY ARE RANKED IN ORDER FROM MINIMUM TO MAXIMUM RESPIRATORY PROTECTION. THE SPECIFIC RESPIRATOR SELECTED MUST BE BASED ON CONTAMINATION LEVELS FOUND IN THE WORK PLACE, MUST NOT EXCEED THE WORKING LIMITS OF THE RESPIRATOR AND BE JOINTLY APPROVED BY THE NATIONAL INSTITUTE FOR OCCUPATIONAL SAFETY AND HEALTH AND THE MINE SAFETY AND HEALTH ADMINISTRATION (NIOSH-MSHA).
CHEMICAL CARTRIDGE RESPIRATOR WITH AN ORGANIC VAPOR CARTRIDGE(S) WITH A FULL FACEPIECE AND ORGANIC VAPOR CARTRIDGE(S) IN COMBINATION WITH A DUST AND MIST FILTER.
POWERED AIR-PURIFYING RESPIRATOR WITH A TIGHT-FITTING FACEPIECE AND ORGANIC VAPOR CARTRIDGE(S) IN COMBINATION WITH A HIGH-EFFICIENCY PARTICULATE FILTER.
TYPE 'C' SUPPLIED-AIR RESPIRATOR WITH A FULL FACEPIECE OPERATED IN A PRESSURE-DEMAND OR OTHER POSITIVE PRESSURE MODE.
SELF-CONTAINED BREATHING APPARATUS WITH A FULL FACEPIECE OPERATED IN PRESSURE-DEMAND OR OTHER POSITIVE PRESSURE MODE.
FOR FIREFIGHTING AND OTHER IMMEDIATELY DANGEROUS TO LIFE OR HEALTH CONDITIONS:
SELF-CONTAINED BREATHING APPARATUS WITH FULL FACEPIECE OPERATED IN PRESSURE-DEMAND OR OTHER POSITIVE PRESSURE MODE.
SUPPLIED-AIR RESPIRATOR WITH FULL FACEPIECE AND OPERATED IN PRESSURE-DEMAND OR OTHER POSITIVE PRESSURE MODE IN COMBINATION WITH AN AUXILIARY SELF-CONTAINED BREATHING APPARATUS OPERATED IN PRESSURE-DEMAND OR OTHER POSITIVE PRESSURE MODE.

CLOTHING: EMPLOYEE MUST WEAR APPROPRIATE PROTECTIVE (IMPERVIOUS) CLOTHING AND EQUIPMENT TO PREVENT REPEATED OR PROLONGED SKIN CONTACT WITH THIS SUBSTANCE.

GLOVES: EMPLOYEE MUST WEAR APPROPRIATE PROTECTIVE GLOVES TO PREVENT CONTACT WITH THIS SUBSTANCE.

EYE PROTECTION: EMPLOYEE MUST WEAR SPLASH-PROOF OR DUST-RESISTANT SAFETY GOGGLES TO PREVENT CONTACT WITH THIS SUBSTANCE.
EMERGENCY WASH FACILITIES: WHERE THERE IS ANY POSSIBILITY THAT AN EMPLOYEE'S EYES AND/OR SKIN MAY BE EXPOSED TO THIS SUBSTANCE, THE EMPLOYER SHOULD PROVIDE AN EYE WASH FOUNTAIN AND QUICK DRENCH SHOWER WITHIN THE IMMEDIATE WORK AREA FOR EMERGENCY USE.

AUTHORIZED BY- OCCUPATIONAL HEALTH SERVICES, INC.
CREATION DATE: 10/04/89 ***REVISION DATE:*** 05/07/90

MATERIAL SAFETY DATA SHEET

OCCUPATIONAL HEALTH SERVICES, INC. EMERGENCY CONTACT:

AGRICULTURE AND PESTICIDE DIVISION JOHN S. BRANSFORD, JR. (615) 292-1180
450 SEVENTH AVENUE, SUITE 2407
NEW YORK, NEW YORK 10123
1-800-445-MSDS OR (212) 967-1100

SUBSTANCE IDENTIFICATION

CAS-NUMBER 8001-58-9

SUBSTANCE: **COAL TAR CREOSOTE**

TRADE NAMES/SYNONYMS: BRICK OIL; COAL TAR OIL; LIQUID PITCH OIL; DEAD OIL; NAPHTHALENE OIL; WASH OIL; CREOSOTE; CREOSOTE, COAL TAR; CREOSOTE FROM COAL TAR; CREOSOTUM; CRESYLIC CREOSOTE; HEAVY OIL; TAR OIL; RCRA U051; PST05230

CERCLA RATINGS (SCALE 0-3): HEALTH=3 FIRE=2 REACTIVITY=0 PERSISTENCE=3

NFPA RATINGS (SCALE 0-4): HEALTH=2 FIRE=2 REACTIVITY=0

COMPONENTS AND CONTAMINANTS

COMPONENT: COAL TAR CREOSOTE ***PERCENT:*** 100
CAS# 8001-58-9

OTHER CONTAMINANTS: NONE

EXPOSURE LIMITS: COAL TAR CREOSOTE AS COAL TAR PITCH VOLATILES: 0.2 MG/M3 OSHA TWA (AS BENZENE SOLUBLES) 0.2 MG/M3 ACGIH TWA (AS BENZENE SOLUBLES) ACGIH A1-CONFIRMED HUMAN CARCINOGEN. 0.1 MG/M3 NIOSH RECOMMENDED 10 HOUR TWA (CYCLOHEXANE-EXTRACTABLE FRACTION)
1 POUND CERCLA SECTION 103 REPORTABLE QUANTITY SUBJECT TO SARA SECTION 313 ANNUAL TOXIC CHEMICAL RELEASE REPORTING SUBJECT TO CALIFORNIA PROPOSITION 65 CANCER AND/OR REPRODUCTIVE TOXICITY WARNING AND RELEASE REQUIREMENTS- (FEBRUARY 27, 1987)

PHYSICAL DATA

DESCRIPTION: COLORLESS, YELLOW, OR DARK GREEN-BROWN OILY LIQUID WITH A HEAVY SMOKY ODOR AND A CAUSTIC BURNING TASTE

BOILING POINT: 382-752F (194-400 C)

SPECIFIC GRAVITY: 1.05-1.10 ***VAPOR PRESSURE:*** NOT AVAILABLE

EVAPORATION RATE: NOT AVAILABLE ***SOLUBILITY IN WATER:*** INSOLUBLE

SOLVENT SOLUBILITY: ALCOHOL, BENZENE, TOLUENE, ETHER, FIXED OR VOLATILE OILS, GLYCERIN, SOLUTIONS OF FIXED ALKALI HYDROXIDES

FIRE AND EXPLOSION DATA

FIRE AND EXPLOSION HAZARD: MODERATE FIRE HAZARD WHEN EXPOSED TO HEAT OR FLAME.
VAPOR-AIR MIXTURES ARE EXPLOSIVE ABOVE FLASH POINT.

FLASH POINT: 165 F (74 C) (CC) ***AUTOIGNITION TEMP.:*** 637 F (336 C)

FLAMMABILITY CLASS(OSHA): IIIA

FIREFIGHTING MEDIA: DRY CHEMICAL, CARBON DIOXIDE, HALON, WATER SPRAY OR STANDARD FOAM (1987 EMERGENCY RESPONSE GUIDEBOOK, DOT P 5800.4).
FOR LARGER FIRES, USE WATER SPRAY, FOG OR STANDARD FOAM (1987 EMERGENCY RESPONSE GUIDEBOOK, DOT P 5800.4).

FIREFIGHTING: MOVE CONTAINER FROM FIRE AREA IF POSSIBLE. COOL FIRE-EXPOSED CONTAINERS WITH WATER FROM SIDE UNTIL WELL AFTER FIRE IS OUT. STAY AWAY FROM STORAGE TANK ENDS. FOR MASSIVE FIRE IN STORAGE AREA, USE UNMANNED HOSE HOLDER OR MONITOR NOZZLES, ELSE WITHDRAW FROM AREA AND LET FIRE BURN. WITHDRAW IMMEDIATELY IN CASE OF RISING SOUND FROM VENTING SAFETY DEVICE OR ANY DISCOLORATION OF STORAGE TANK DUE TO FIRE (1987 EMERGENCY RESPONSE GUIDEBOOK, DOT P 5800.4, GUIDE PAGE 27).
EXTINGUISH ONLY IF FLOW CAN BE STOPPED; USE FLOODING AMOUNTS OF WATER AS A FOG, SOLID STREAMS MAY BE INEFFECTIVE. COOL CONTAINERS WITH FLOODING AMOUNTS OF WATER, APPLY FROM AS FAR A DISTANCE AS POSSIBLE. AVOID BREATHING VAPORS, KEEP UPWIND.
WATER MAY BE USED TO BLANKET FIRE (NFPA 325M FIRE HAZARD PROPERTIES OF FLAMMABLE LIQUIDS, GASES, AND VOLATILE SOLIDS, 1984)

TRANSPORTATION DATA

DEPARTMENT OF TRANSPORTATION HAZARD CLASSIFICATION 49 CFR 172.101: COMBUSTIBLE LIQUID
DEPARTMENT OF TRANSPORTATION LABELING REQUIREMENTS 49 CFR 172.101 AND SUBPART E: NONE
DEPARTMENT OF TRANSPORTATION PACKAGING REQUIREMENTS: NONE
EXCEPTIONS: 49 CFR 173.118A

TOXICITY

COAL TAR CREOSOTE: TOXICITY DATA: 725 MG/KG ORAL-RAT LD50; 433 MG/KG ORAL-MOUSE LD50; 600 MG/KG ORAL-DOG LDLO; 600 MG/KG ORAL-RABBIT LDLO; 600 MG/KG ORAL-CAT LDLO; MUTAGENIC DATA (RTECS); REPRODUCTIVE EFFECTS DATA (RTECS); TUMORIGENIC DATA (RTECS). CARCINOGEN STATUS: KNOWN HUMAN CARCINOGEN (NTP) (SOOTS, TARS, MINERAL OILS); HUMAN LIMITED EVIDENCE, ANIMAL SUFFICIENT EVIDENCE (IARC GROUP-2A). THERE IS SUFFICIENT EVIDENCE FOR THE CARCINOGENICITY IN EXPERIMENTAL ANIMALS OF CRESOTE OILS AND LIMITED EVIDENCE THAT COAL-TAR DERIVED CREOSOTES ARE CARCINOGENIC IN HUMANS. LOCAL EFFECTS: CORROSIVE- SKIN AND EYES; IRRITANT- INHALATION. ACUTE TOXICITY LEVEL: MODERATELY TOXIC BY INGESTION. TARGET EFFECTS: NO DATA AVAILABLE.

HEALTH EFFECTS AND FIRST AID

INHALATION: COAL TAR CREOSOTE: IRRITANT. **ACUTE EXPOSURE-** MAY CAUSE MODERATE RESPIRATORY TRACT IRRITATION. IN ONE STUDY OF WORKERS WHO DEVELOPED CREOSOTE BURNS, A SMALL PERCENT ALSO COMPLAINED OF DEPRESSION, WEAKNESS, SEVERE HEADACHE, SLIGHT CONFUSION, VERTIGO, SALIVATION, AND NAUSEA. IT IS UNCLEAR WHETHER THE ROUTE OF EXPOSURE WAS SKIN CONTACT OR INHALATION OR BOTH. **CHRONIC EXPOSURE-** A STUDY OF WORKERS SPRAYING WARMED CREOSOTE WITH CONCENTRATIONS UP TO 0.01 MG/L REPORTED HEADACHES, GIDDINESS, NAUSEA, VOMITING, AND SALIVATION.

FIRST AID- REMOVE FROM EXPOSURE AREA TO FRESH AIR IMMEDIATELY. IF BREATHING HAS STOPPED, GIVE ARTIFICIAL RESPIRATION. MAINTAIN AIRWAY AND BLOOD PRESSURE AND ADMINISTER OXYGEN IF AVAILABLE. KEEP AFFECTED PERSON WARM AND AT REST. TREAT SYMPTOMATICALLY AND SUPPORTIVELY. ADMINISTRATION OF OXYGEN SHOULD BE PERFORMED BY QUALIFIED PERSONNEL. GET MEDICAL ATTENTION IMMEDIATELY.

SKIN CONTACT: COAL TAR CREOSOTE: CORROSIVE/CARCINOGEN. **ACUTE EXPOSURE-** THE LIQUID AND VAPORS ARE STRONG IRRITANTS AND MAY CAUSE A BURNING, ITCHING, LOCAL ERYTHEMA PROGESSING TO A BRONZE PIGMENTATION, PAPULAR AND VESICULAR ERUPTIONS, ULCERATION, AND DESQUAMATION. PHOTOSENSITIZATION OCCURS, ESPECIALLY IN FAIR-SKINNED PERSONS. PROLONGED CONTACT MAY CAUSE BURNS. IT IS READILY ABSORBED THROUGH THE SKIN AND MAY CAUSE SYSTEMIC ILLNESS WITH SALIVATION, NAUSEA, VOMITING, HEADACHE, THREADY PULSE, RESPIRATORY DISTRESS, LOSS OF PUPILLARY REFLEXES, HYPOTHERMIA, MILD CONVULSIONS, AND CYANOSIS. DEPRESSION, WEAKNESS, SLIGHT CONFUSION, NAUSEA, AND VERTIGO WERE ALSO REPORTED FROM ONE STUDY IN WHICH IT WAS NOT CLEAR WHETHER THE ROUTE OF EXPOSURE WAS INHALATION OR SKIN CONTACT OR BOTH. **CHRONIC EXPOSURE-** REPEATED OR PROLONGED EXPOSURE MAY CAUSE DARKENING OF THE SKIN AND DERMATITIS. IF SUFFICIENT AMOUNTS ARE ABSORBED, SYSTEMIC SYMPTOMS AS WITH ACUTE EXPOSURE MAY OCCUR. FIVE CREOSOTES OR CREOSOTE OILS PRODUCED SKIN TUMORS WHEN APPLIED TO THE SKIN OF MICE; ONE ALSO PRODUCED LUNG TUMORS. HUMAN MORTALITY ANALYSIS OF CREOSOTE-EXPOSED BRICKMAKERS INDICATED INCREASED RISK OF MORTALITY FROM SCROTAL CANCER. MALIGNANT EPITHELIOMAS, ABOUT ONE-THIRD OF WHICH WERE SCROTAL, HAVE BEEN REPORTED IN SEVERAL CASE REPORTS OF WORKERS EXPOSED TO CREOSOTE.

FIRST AID- REMOVE CONTAMINATED CLOTHING AND SHOES IMMEDIATELY. WASH AFFECTED AREA WITH SOAP OR MILD DETERGENT AND LARGE AMOUNTS OF WATER UNTIL NO EVIDENCE OF CHEMICAL REMAINS (APPROXIMATELY 15-20 MINUTES). GET MEDICAL ATTENTION IMMEDIATELY.

EYE CONTACT: COAL TAR CREOSOTE: CORROSIVE. **ACUTE EXPOSURE-** LIQUID CONTACT HAS CAUSED PAINFUL PROTRACTED KERATOCONJUNCTIVITIS INVOLVING LOSS OF CORNEAL EPITHELIUM, CLOUDING OF THE CORNEA, MIOSIS AND LONG-LASTING IRRITABILITY AND PHOTOPHOBIA. OTHER SYMPTOMS WHICH HAVE BEEN REPORTED FROM EXPOSURE TO CREOSOTE-TREATED PARTICLES INCLUDE ABRASION OF THE CORNEA WITH SOME PERMANENT SCARRING, HYPEREMIA, AND PRONOUCED SEROUS SECRETION. **CHRONIC EXPOSURE-** REPEATED OR PROLONGED EXPOSURE MAY CAUSE CONJUNCTIVITIS.

FIRST AID- WASH EYES IMMEDIATELY WITH LARGE AMOUNTS OF WATER OR NORMAL SALINE, OCCASIONALLY LIFTING UPPER AND LOWER LIDS, UNTIL NO EVIDENCE OF CHEMICAL REMAINS (APPROXIMATELY 15-20 MINUTES). GET MEDICAL ATTENTION IMMEDIATELY.

INGESTION: COAL TAR CREOSOTE: **ACUTE EXPOSURE-** HAS CAUSED INTENSE IRRITATION AND CONGESTION OF THE ENTIRE GASTROENTERIC TRACT. SALIVATION, NAUSEA, VOMITING, RESPIRATORY DISTRESS, THREADY PULSE, VERTIGO, HEADACHE, LOSS OF PUPILLARY REFLEXES, HYPOTHERMIA, CYANOSIS AND MILD CONVULSIONS MAY ALSO OCCUR. DEATH FROM LARGE DOSES APPEARS LARGELY DUE TO CARDIOVASCULAR COLLAPSE. **CHRONIC EXPOSURE-** REPEATED INGESTION OF SMALL DOSES MAY RESULT IN CHRONIC INTOXICATION CHARACTERIZED BY DISTUBANCES OF VISION AND DIGESTION INCLUDING INCREASED PERISTALSIS AND BLOODY STOOLS. IN ONE CASE, HYPERTENSION AND GENERAL CARDIOVASCULAR COLLAPSE WERE REPORTED. OTHER SYMPTOMS OF ACUTE EXPOSURE ARE ALSO POSSIBLE. PATERNAL REPRODUCTIVE EFFECTS HAVE BEEN REPORTED IN RATS AND MICE FOLLOWING REPEATED EXPOSURES PRIOR TO MATING.

FIRST AID- IF THE PATIENT IS ALERT AND ABLE TO SWALLOW, GIVE A SLURRY OF ACTIVATED CHARCOAL IN WATER. DO NOT GIVE EMETICS. CAREFUL GASTRIC LAVAGE WITH WATER IS RECOMMENDED IF THERE ARE NO DEEP BURNS IN THE MOUTH OR PHARYNX. OLDER RECOMMENDATIONS TO LAVAGE WITH OLIVE OR OTHER VEGETABLE OILS DO NOT APPEAR TO BE SUBSTANTIATED. IN ANY CASE AVOID MINERAL OIL AND ALCOHOL. (GOSSELIN, CLINICAL TOXICOLOGY OF COMMERCIAL PRODUCTS, 5TH ED.). LAVAGE MUST BE PERFORMED BY QUALIFIED MEDICAL PERSONNEL.

ANTIDOTE: NO SPECIFIC ANTIDOTE. TREAT SYMPTOMATICALLY AND SUPPORTIVELY.

REACTIVITY

REACTIVITY: STABLE UNDER NORMAL TEMPERATURES AND PRESSURES.

INCOMPATIBILITIES: COAL TAR CREOSOTE: CHLOROSULFONIC ACID: MIXING IN CLOSED CONTAINER RESULTS IN INCREASED TEMPERATURE AND PRESSURE. STRONG OXIDIZERS: POSSIBLE VIOLENT REACTION.

DECOMPOSITION: THERMAL DECOMPOSITION PRODUCTS MAY INCLUDE TOXIC OXIDES OF CARBON.

POLYMERIZATION: HAZARDOUS POLYMERIZATION HAS NOT BEEN REPORTED TO OCCUR UNDER NORMAL TEMPERATURES AND PRESSURES.

STORAGE AND DISPOSAL

OBSERVE ALL FEDERAL, STATE AND LOCAL REGULATIONS WHEN STORING OR DISPOSING OF THIS SUBSTANCE. FOR ASSISTANCE, CONTACT THE DISTRICT DIRECTOR OF THE ENVIRONMENTAL PROTECTION AGENCY.

****STORAGE****

STORE IN ACCORDANCE WITH 29 CFR 1910.106.

STORE AWAY FROM INCOMPATIBLE SUBSTANCES.

BONDING AND GROUNDING: SUBSTANCES WITH LOW ELECTROCONDUCTIVITY, WHICH MAY BE IGNITED BY ELECTROSTATIC SPARKS, SHOULD BE STORED IN CONTAINERS WHICH MEET THE BONDING AND GROUNDING GUIDELINES SPECIFIED IN NFPA 77-1983, RECOMMENDED PRACTICE ON STATIC ELECTRICITY.

****DISPOSAL****

DISPOSAL MUST BE IN ACCORDANCE WITH STANDARDS APPLICABLE TO GENERATORS OF HAZARDOUS WASTE, 40CFR 262. EPA HAZARDOUS WASTE NUMBER U051.

CONDITIONS TO AVOID

AVOID CONTACT WITH HEAT, SPARKS, FLAMES, OR OTHER SOURCES OF IGNITION. VAPORS MAY BE EXPLOSIVE. AVOID OVERHEATING OF CONTAINERS; CONTAINERS MAY VIOLENTLY RUPTURE IN HEAT OF FIRE. AVOID CONTAMINATION OF WATER SOURCES.

SPILL AND LEAK PROCEDURES

WATER SPILL: THE CALIFORNIA SAFE DRINKING WATER AND TOXIC ENFORCEMENT ACT OF 1986 (PROPOSITION 65) PROHIBITS CONTAMINATING ANY KNOWN SOURCE OF DRINKING WATER WITH SUBSTANCES KNOWN TO CAUSE CANCER AND/OR REPRODUCTIVE TOXICITY.

OCCUPATIONAL SPILL: SHUT OFF IGNITION SOURCES. STOP LEAK IF YOU CAN DO IT WITHOUT RISK. USE WATER SPRAY TO REDUCE VAPORS. FOR SMALL SPILLS, TAKE UP WITH SAND OR OTHER ABSORBENT MATERIAL AND PLACE INTO CONTAINERS FOR LATER DISPOSAL. FOR LARGER SPILLS, DIKE FAR AHEAD OF SPILL FOR LATER DISPOSAL. NO SMOKING, FLAMES OR FLARES IN HAZARD AREA. KEEP UNNECESSARY PEOPLE AWAY; ISOLATE HAZARD AREA AND RESTRICT ENTRY. REPORTABLE QUANTITY (RQ): 1 POUND THE SUPERFUND AMENDMENTS AND REAUTHORIZATION ACT (SARA) SECTION 304 REQUIRES THAT A RELEASE EQUAL TO OR GREATER THAN THE REPORTABLE QUANTITY FOR THIS SUBSTANCE BE IMMEDIATELY REPORTED TO THE LOCAL EMERGENCY PLANNING COMMITTEE AND THE STATE EMERGENCY RESPONSE COMMISSION (40 CFR 355.40). IF THE RELEASE OF THIS SUBSTANCE IS REPORTABLE UNDER CERCLA SECTION 103, THE NATIONAL RESPONSE CENTER MUST BE NOTIFIED IMMEDIATELY AT (800) 424-8802 OR (202) 426-2675 IN THE METROPOLITAN WASHINGTON, D.C. AREA (40 CFR 302.6).

PROTECTIVE EQUIPMENT

VENTILATION: PROVIDE LOCAL EXHAUST VENTILATION SYSTEM TO MEET PUBLISHED EXPOSURE LIMITS.

RESPIRATOR: THE FOLLOWING RESPIRATORS AND MAXIMUM USE CONCENTRATIONS ARE RECOMMENDATIONS BY THE U.S. DEPARTMENT OF HEALTH AND HUMAN SERVICES, NIOSH POCKET GUIDE TO CHEMICAL HAZARDS; NIOSH CRITERIA DOCUMENTS OR BY THE U.S. DEPARTMENT OF LABOR, 29 CFR 1910 SUBPART Z. THE SPECIFIC RESPIRATOR SELECTED MUST BE BASED ON CONTAMINATION LEVELS FOUND IN THE WORK PLACE, MUST NOT EXCEED THE WORKING LIMITS OF THE RESPIRATOR AND BE JOINTLY APPROVED BY THE NATIONAL INSTITUTE FOR OCCUPATIONAL SAFETY AND HEALTH AND THE MINE SAFETY AND HEALTH ADMINISTRATION (NIOSH-MSHA).

AT ANY DETECTABLE CONCENTRATION:

SELF-CONTAINED BREATHING APPARATUS WITH FULL FACEPIECE OPERATED IN PRESSURE-DEMAND OR OTHER POSITIVE PRESSURE MODE. SUPPLIED-AIR RESPIRATOR WITH FULL FACEPIECE OPERATED IN PRESSURE-DEMAND OF OTHER POSITIVE PRESSURE MODE IN COMBINATION WITH AN AUXILIARY SELF-CONTAINED BREATHING APPARATUS OPERATED IN PRESSURE-DEMAND OR OTHER POSITIVE PRESSURE MODE. ESCAPE- AIR-PURIFYING FULL FACEPIECE RESPIRATOR (GAS MASK) WITH A CHIN-STYLE OR FRONT- OR BACK-MOUNTED ORGANIC VAPOR CANISTER HAVING A HIGH-EFFICIENCY PARTICULATE FILTER. ESCAPE-TYPE SELF-CONTAINED BREATHING APPARATUS.

FOR FIREFIGHTING AND OTHER IMMEDIATELY DANGEROUS TO LIFE OR HEALTH CONDITIONS:

SELF-CONTAINED BREATHING APPARATUS WITH FULL FACEPIECE OPERATED IN PRESSURE-DEMAND OR OTHER POSITIVE PRESSURE MODE.

SUPPLIED-AIR RESPIRATOR WITH FULL FACEPIECE AND OPERATED IN PRESSURE-DEMAND OR OTHER POSITIVE PRESSURE MODE IN COMBINATION WITH AN AUXILIARY SELF-CONTAINED BREATHING APPARATUS OPERATED IN PRESSURE-DEMAND OR OTHER POSITIVE PRESSURE MODE.

CLOTHING: EMPLOYEE MUST WEAR APPROPRIATE PROTECTIVE (IMPERVIOUS) CLOTHING AND EQUIPMENT TO PREVENT ANY POSSIBILITY OF SKIN CONTACT WITH THIS SUBSTANCE.

GLOVES: EMPLOYEE MUST WEAR APPROPRIATE PROTECTIVE GLOVES TO PREVENT CONTACT WITH THIS SUBSTANCE.

EYE PROTECTION: EMPLOYEE MUST WEAR SPLASH-PROOF OR DUST-RESISTANT SAFETY GOGGLES AND A FACESHIELD TO PREVENT CONTACT WITH THIS SUBSTANCE.

EMERGENCY WASH FACILITIES: WHERE THERE IS ANY POSSIBILITY THAT AN EMPLOYEE'S EYES AND/OR SKIN MAY BE EXPOSED TO THIS SUBSTANCE, THE EMPLOYER SHOULD PROVIDE AN EYE WASH FOUNTAIN AND QUICK DRENCH SHOWER WITHIN THE IMMEDIATE WORK AREA FOR EMERGENCY USE.

AUTHORIZED BY- OCCUPATIONAL HEALTH SERVICES, INC.

CREATION DATE: 10/04/89 ***REVISION DATE:*** 07/12/90

MATERIAL SAFETY DATA SHEET

OCCUPATIONAL HEALTH SERVICES, INC.	EMERGENCY CONTACT:
AGRICULTURE AND PESTICIDE DIVISION	JOHN S. BRANSFORD, JR. (615) 292-1180
450 SEVENTH AVENUE, SUITE 2407	
NEW YORK, NEW YORK 10123	
1-800-445-MSDS OR (212) 967-1100	

SUBSTANCE IDENTIFICATION

CAS-NUMBER 7440-50-8

SUBSTANCE: COPPER

TRADE NAMES/SYNONYMS: ALLBRI NATURAL COPPER; C.I. PIGMENT METAL 2; COPPER DUST; COPPER FUME; COPPER-AIRBORNE; COPPER-BRONZE; COPPER-MILLED; COPPER SLAG-AIRBORNE; COPPER SLAG-MILLED; GOLD BRONZE; ELECTROLYTIC TOUGH PITCH (EASTERN ROLLING MILLS, INC.); C.I. 77400; CU; PST05430

CHEMICAL FAMILY: METAL

MOLECULAR FORMULA: CU

MOLECULAR WEIGHT: 63.5

CERCLA RATINGS (SCALE 0-3): HEALTH = U FIRE = 3 REACTIVITY = 0 PERSISTENCE = 3

NFPA RATINGS (SCALE 0-4): HEALTH = U FIRE = 3 REACTIVITY = 0

COMPONENTS AND CONTAMINANTS

COMPONENT: COPPER ***PERCENT:*** 100

CAS# 7440-50-8

OTHER CONTAMINANTS: NONE

EXPOSURE LIMITS: COPPER AND COMPOUNDS (AS CU): 0.1 MG/M3 OSHA TWA (FUME); 1 MG/M3 OSHA TWA (DUST AND MISTS) 0.2 MG/M3 ACGIH TWA (FUME); 1 MG/M3 ACGIH TWA (DUST AND MISTS)

SUBJECT TO SARA SECTION 313 ANNUAL TOXIC CHEMICAL RELEASE REPORTING

PHYSICAL DATA

DESCRIPTION: REDDISH, DUCTILE, MALLEABLE, LUSTROUS METAL OR CUBIC CRYSTALS.

BOILING POINT: 4653 F (2567 C) ***MELTING POINT:*** 1946 F (1083 C)

SPECIFIC GRAVITY: 8.92 ***VAPOR PRESSURE:*** 1 MMHG @ 1628 C

SOLUBILITY IN WATER: INSOLUBLE

SOLVENT SOLUBILITY: SOLUBLE IN NITRIC ACID, SULFURIC ACID (HOT), HYDROGEN BROMIDE (HOT); SLIGHTLY SOLUBLE IN HYDROCHLORIC ACID, AMMONIUM HYDROXIDE

FIRE AND EXPLOSION DATA

FIRE AND EXPLOSION HAZARD: NEGLIGIBLE FIRE HAZARD IN METALLIC FORM; HOWEVER, DUST, POWDER, OR FUMES ARE FLAMMABLE OR EXPLOSIVE WHEN EXPOSED TO HEAT OR FLAMES.

FLASH POINT: FLAMMABLE (DUST) ***AUTOIGNITION TEMP.:*** 1292 F (700 C)

FIREFIGHTING MEDIA: USE DRY SAND, DOLOMITE, GRAPHITE, SODIUM CHLORIDE, SODA ASH, OR APPROPRIATE METAL-EXTINGUISHING POWDER. DO NOT APPLY WATER TO BURNING MATERIAL (NFPA FIRE PROTECTION HANDBOOK, 16TH EDITION).

FIREFIGHTING: MOVE CONTAINER FROM FIRE AREA IF POSSIBLE. COOL CONTAINERS EXPOSED TO FLAME WITH WATER FROM SIDE UNTIL WELL AFTER FIRE IS OUT. STAY AWAY FROM STORAGE TANK ENDS. FOR MASSIVE FIRE IN CARGO AREA, USE UNMANNED HOSE HOLDER OR MONITOR NOZZLES; ELSE WITHDRAW AND LET FIRE BURN (1987 EMERGENCY RESPONSE GUIDEBOOK, DOT P 5800.4, GUIDE PAGE 32).

EXTINGUISH USING AGENT FOR TYPE OF FIRE. AVOID BREATHING FUMES FROM BURNING MATERIAL.

TRANSPORTATION DATA

DEPARTMENT OF TRANSPORTATION HAZARD CLASSIFICATION 49 CFR 172.101: *FLAMMABLE SOLID

DEPARTMENT OF TRANSPORTATION LABELING REQUIREMENTS 49 CFR 172.101 AND SUBPART E: *FLAMMABLE SOLID

*HAZARD CLASSIFICATION AND LABEL APPLY TO DUST AND POWDER FORM ONLY.

DEPARTMENT OF TRANSPORTATION PACKAGING REQUIREMENTS: 49 CFR 173.154 EXCEPTIONS: 49 CFR 173.153

TOXICITY

COPPER: TOXICITY DATA: 120 UG/KG ORAL-HUMAN TDLO; 3500 UG/KG INTRAPERITONEAL-MOUSE LD50; REPRODUCTIVE EFFECTS DATA (RTECS); TUMORIGENIC DATA (RTECS). CARCINOGEN STATUS: NONE. LOCAL EFFECTS: IRRITANT- INHALATION, EYE. ACUTE TOXICITY LEVEL: INSUFFICIENT DATA. TARGET EFFECTS: POISONING MAY AFFECT THE LIVER AND KIDNEYS. AT INCREASED RISK FROM EXPOSURE: PERSONS WITH PRE-EXISTING RESPIRATORY, LIVER, KIDNEY, SKIN, AND BLOOD DISORDERS OR WILSON'S DISEASE.

HEALTH EFFECTS AND FIRST AID

INHALATION: COPPER: IRRITANT. **ACUTE EXPOSURE-** POWDERED DUST MAY CAUSE IRRITATION OF THE UPPER RESPIRATORY TRACT AND ULCERATION AND PERFORATION OF THE NASAL SEPTUM. A FEELING OF ILLNESS SIMILAR TO THE COMMON COLD HAS BEEN REPORTED WITH SYMPTOMS OF CHILLS AND STUFFINESS OF THE HEAD. WORKERS EXPOSED TO COPPER DUST IN CONCENTRATIONS OF 0.075 TO 0.120 MG/M3 COMPLAINED OF MILD NASAL DISCOMFORT. EXPOSURE TO COPPER FUME MAY CAUSE IRRITATION TO THE MUCOUS MEMBRANES. FRESHLY FORMED COPPER FUMES MAY CAUSE METAL FUME FEVER. SYMPTOMS MAY INCLUDE A SWEET, METALLIC, OR FOUL TASTE IN THE MOUTH, DRY THROAT, COUGHING, FEVER, CHILLS, MUSCLE ACHES, WEAKNESS, LASSITUDE, NAUSEA, RARELY VOMITING, MILD TO SEVERE HEADACHES, AND SOMETIMES EXAGGERATED MENTAL ACTIVITY. WORKERS EXPOSED TO CONCENTRATIONS OF 1 TO 3 MG/M3 EXPERIENCED AN ALTERED TASTE RESPONSE BUT NO NAUSEA. **CHRONIC EXPOSURE-** PROLONGED INDUSTRIAL EXPOSURE MAY CAUSE A GREEN DISCOLORATION OF THE SKIN, HAIR AND TEETH. WELDERS EXPOSED TO COPPER FUME EXPERIENCED ATROPHIC RHINITIS, METALLIC TASTE, RUNNY NOSE, AND MUCOSAL IRRITATION OF THE MOUTH AND EYES. IT IS INCONCLUSIVE AS TO WHETHER PROLONGED EXPOSURE HAS ANY AFFECT ON THE NERVOUS SYSTEM. A SMALL NUMBER OF STUDIES SUGGEST AN AFFINITY OF COPPER FOR THE SYMPATHETIC SYSTEM, HOWEVER, THERE IS NO PROOF THAT CHRONIC POISONING WILL AFFECT EITHER THE CENTRAL OR PERIPHERAL NERVOUS SYSTEM.

FIRST AID- REMOVE FROM EXPOSURE AREA TO FRESH AIR IMMEDIATELY. IF BREATHING HAS STOPPED, PERFORM ARTIFICIAL RESPIRATION. KEEP PERSON WARM AND AT REST. TREAT SYMPTOMATICALLY AND SUPPORTIVELY. GET MEDICAL ATTENTION IMMEDIATELY.

SKIN CONTACT: COPPER: **ACUTE EXPOSURE-** MAY BE IRRITATING AND CAUSE KERATINIZATION. ALLERGIC DERMATITIS ALTHOUGH RARE, HAS BEEN REPORTED. DERMAL ABSORPTION IS NEGLIGIBLE THROUGH INTACT SKIN. **CHRONIC EXPOSURE-** REPEATED OR PROLONGED CONTACT MAY CAUSE IRRITATION AND DISCOLORATION OF THE SKIN.

FIRST AID- REMOVE CONTAMINATED CLOTHING AND SHOES IMMEDIATELY. WASH AFFECTED AREA WITH SOAP OR MILD DETERGENT AND LARGE AMOUNTS OF WATER UNTIL NO EVIDENCE OF CHEMICAL REMAINS (APPROXIMATELY 15-20 MINUTES). GET MEDICAL ATTENTION IMMEDIATELY.

EYE CONTACT: COPPER: IRRITANT. **ACUTE EXPOSURE-** THE DUST MAY CAUSE IRRITATION WITH REDNESS AND PAIN. COPPER PARTICLES IN THE EYE MAY RESULT IN A FOREIGN BODY RESPONSE WITH CHARACTERISTIC DISCOLORATION OF OCULAR TISSUE, DEGENERATION AND/OR DETACHMENT OF THE RETINA, AND ATROPHY OF THE GLOBE. **CHRONIC EXPOSURE-** REPEATED OR PROLONGED EXPOSURE TO IRRITANTS MAY CAUSE CONJUNCTIVITIS.

FIRST AID- WASH EYES IMMEDIATELY WITH LARGE AMOUNTS OF WATER OR NORMAL SALINE, OCCASIONALLY LIFTING UPPER AND LOWER LIDS, UNTIL NO EVIDENCE OF CHEMICAL REMAINS (APPROXIMATELY 15-20 MINUTES). GET MEDICAL ATTENTION IMMEDIATELY.

INGESTION: COPPER: **ACUTE EXPOSURE-** 120 UG/KG INGESTED BY A HUMAN CAUSED GASTROINTESTINAL DISORDER WITH NAUSEA AND VOMITING. **CHRONIC EXPOSURE-** COPPER IS AN ESSENTIAL ELEMENT AND IS FOUND IN MOST HUMAN DIETS IN MINUTE AMOUNTS. PROLONGED INGESTION THROUGH THE DIET IS NOT KNOWN TO CAUSE TOXIC EFFECTS EXCEPT IN PEOPLE WITH A RECESSIVE GENE DISORDER TERMED WILSON'S DISEASE WHICH CAUSES AN ABNORMALLY HIGH ABSORPTION, RETENTION, AND STORAGE OF COPPER BY THE BODY. THIS DISEASE MAY CAUSE A DYSFUNCTION OF AND STRUCTURAL DAMAGE TO THE LIVER, CENTRAL NERVOUS SYSTEM, KIDNEY, BONES AND EYES. THE DISEASE IS USUALLY PROGRESSIVE AND MAY BE FATAL IF LEFT UNTREATED.

FIRST AID: IF PERSON IS CONSCIOUS, GIVE LARGE AMOUNTS OF WATER IMMEDIATELY. REMOVE BY EMESIS OR GASTRIC LAVAGE. DO NOT MAKE AN UNCONSCIOUS PERSON VOMIT OR DRINK ANYTHING. GIVE ACTIVATED CHARCOAL. GIVE OXYGEN IF RESPIRATION IS DEPRESSED. MAINTAIN AIRWAY AND BLOOD PRESSURE. GET MEDICAL ATTENTION. (DREISBACH, HANDBOOK OF POISONING, 11TH ED.) LAVAGE OR OXYGEN MUST BE ADMINISTERED BY QUALIFIED MEDICAL PERSONNEL.

ANTIDOTE: THE FOLLOWING ANTIDOTE HAS BEEN RECOMMENDED. HOWEVER, THE DECISION AS TO WHETHER THE SEVERITY OF POISONING REQUIRES ADMINISTRATION OF ANY ANTIDOTE AND ACTUAL DOSE REQUIRED SHOULD BE MADE BY QUALIFIED MEDICAL PERSONNEL.

COPPER POISONING: GIVE CALCIUM DISODIUM EDETATE 15-25 MG/KG (0.08-0.125 ML OF 20% SOLUTION PER KILOGRAM BODY WEIGHT) IN 250-500 ML OF 5% DEXTROSE INTRAVENOUSLY OVER A 1 TO 2 HOUR PERIOD TWICE DAILY. THE MAXIMUM DOSE SHOULD NOT EXCEED 50 MG/KG/DAY. THE DRUG SHOULD BE GIVEN IN 5-DAY COURSES WITH A REST PERIOD OF AT LEAST 2 DAYS BETWEEN COURSES. AFTER THE FIRST COURSE, SUBSEQUENT COURSES SHOULD NOT EXCEED 50 MG/KG/DAY. DAILY URINALYSES SHOULD NOT BE DONE DURING THE TREATMENT PERIOD. THE DOSAGE SHOULD BE REDUCED IF ANY UNUSUAL URINARY FINDINGS APPEAR. INTRAVENOUS ADMINISTRATION IS CONTRAINDICATED IN THE PRESENCE OF ELEVATED CEREBROSPINAL FLUID PRESSURE. PENICILLAMINE IS ALSO EFFECTIVE IN COPPER POISONING. GIVE UP TO 100 MG/KG/DAY (MAXIMUM 1 G/DAY) DIVIDED INTO 4 DOSES FOR NO LONGER THAN 1 WEEK. IF A LONGER ADMINISTRATION PERIOD IS WARRANTED, DOSAGE SHOULD NOT EXCEED 40 MG/KG/DAY. GIVE THE DRUG ORALLY, HALF AN HOUR BEFORE MEALS (DREISBACH, HANDBOOK OF POISONING, 12TH ED.). ANTIDOTE SHOULD BE ADMINISTERED BY QUALIFIED MEDICAL PERSONNEL.

REACTIVITY

REACTIVITY: STABLE UNDER NORMAL TEMPERATURES AND PRESSURES.

INCOMPATIBILITIES: COPPER: ACETYLENE: FORMS EXPLOSIVE COPPER ACETYLIDE. ACETYLENIC COMPOUNDS: FORMATION OF EXPLOSIVE ACETYLIDES. ALUMINUM + SULFUR: POSSIBLE EXPLOSION. AMMONIUM NITRATE: VIOLENT OR EXPLOSIVE REACTION. BARIUM BROMATE: EXPLOSIVE REACTION BY HEAT, IMPACT OR FRICTION. BARIUM CHLORATE: EXPLOSIVE REACTION BY HEAT, IMPACT OR FRICTION. BARIUM IODATE: EXPLOSIVE REACTION BY HEAT, IMPACT OR FRICTION. 1-BROMO-2-PROPYNE: FORMATION OF EXPLOSIVE COMPOUND. CALCIUM BROMATE: EXPLOSIVE REACTION BY HEAT, IMPACT OR FRICTION. CALCIUM CHLORATE: EXPLOSIVE REACTION BY HEAT, IMPACT OR FRICTION. CALCIUM IODATE: EXPLOSIVE REACTION BY HEAT, IMPACT OR FRICTION. CHLORATES: EXPLOSIVE REACTION. CHLORINE: IGNITION REACTION. CHLORINE + OXYGEN DIFLUORIDE: EXPLOSIVE REACTION AT -10 C. CHLORINE TRIFLUORIDE: INTENSE REACTION WITH POSSIBLE IGNITION. DIMETHYL SULFOXIDE + TRICHLOROACETIC ACID: POSSIBLE EXPLOSION. ETHYLENE OXIDE: POSSIBLE EXPLOSION. FLUORINE: IGNITION REACTION. HYDRAZINIUM NITRATE: IGNITION REACTION. HYDRAZOIC ACID: POSSIBLE EXPLOSION. HYDROGEN PEROXIDE: VIOLENT DECOMPOSITION. HYDROGEN SULFIDE: INTENSE EXOTHERMIC REACTION WITH POSSIBLE IGNITION. LEAD AZIDE: FORMS EXPLOSIVE COPPER AZIDE. MAGNESIUM BROMATE: EXPLOSIVE REACTION BY HEAT, IMPACT OR FRICTION. MAGNESIUM CHLORATE: EXPLOSIVE REACTION BY HEAT, IMPACT OR FRICTION. MAGNESIUM IODATE: EXPLOSIVE REACTION BY HEAT, IMPACT OR FRICTION. PHOSPHORUS: INCANDESCENT REACTION. POTASSIUM BROMATE: EXPLOSIVE REACTION BY HEAT, IMPACT OR FRICTION. POTASSIUM CHLORATE: EXPLOSIVE REACTION BY

HEAT, IMPACT OR FRICTION. POTASSIUM DIOXIDE: INCANDESCENT REACTION. POTASSIUM IODATE: EXPLOSIVE REACTION BY HEAT, IMPACT OR FRICTION. SODIUM AZIDE: FORMS EXPLOSIVE COMPOUND. SODIUM BROMATE: EXPLOSIVE REACTION BY HEAT, IMPACT OR FRICTION. SODIUM CHLORATE: EXPLOSIVE REACTION BY HEAT, IMPACT OR FRICTION. SODIUM IODATE: EXPLOSIVE REACTION BY HEAT, IMPACT OR FRICTION. SODIUM PEROXIDE: INCANDESCENT REACTION. SULFUR + CHLORATES: SPONTANEOUS EXPLOSION. SULFURIC ACID: INTENSE REACTION. ZINC BROMATE: EXPLOSIVE REACTION BY HEAT, IMPACT OR FRICTION. ZINC CHLORATE: EXPLOSIVE REACTION BY HEAT, IMPACT OR FRICTION. ZINC IODATE: EXPLOSIVE REACTION BY HEAT, IMPACT OR FRICTION.

DECOMPOSITION: THERMAL DECOMPOSITION MAY RELEASE TOXIC AND/OR HAZARDOUS GASES.

POLYMERIZATION: HAZARDOUS POLYMERIZATION HAS NOT BEEN REPORTED TO OCCUR UNDER NORMAL TEMPERATURES AND PRESSURES.

STORAGE AND DISPOSAL

OBSERVE ALL FEDERAL, STATE AND LOCAL REGULATIONS WHEN STORING OR DISPOSING OF THIS SUBSTANCE. FOR ASSISTANCE, CONTACT THE DISTRICT DIRECTOR OF THE ENVIRONMENTAL PROTECTION AGENCY.

STORAGE

STORE AWAY FROM INCOMPATIBLE SUBSTANCES.

CONDITIONS TO AVOID

AVOID DISPERSION OF DUST IN AIR. FINELY DIVIDED PARTICLES, DUST, OR FUMES MAY BE FLAMMABLE OR EXPLOSIVE. KEEP AWAY FROM SPARKS OR IGNITION SOURCES.

SPILL AND LEAK PROCEDURES

SOIL SPILL: DIG HOLDING AREA SUCH AS LAGOON, POND OR PIT FOR CONTAINMENT.

USE CEMENT POWDER OR FLY ASH TO ABSORB LIQUID MASS.

USE PROTECTIVE COVER SUCH AS A PLASTIC SHEET TO PREVENT MATERIAL FROM DISSOLVING IN FIRE EXTINGUISHING WATER OR RAIN.

WATER SPILL: USE ACTIVATED CARBON TO ABSORB SPILLED SUBSTANCE THAT IS DISSOLVED.

USE SUCTION HOSES TO REMOVE TRAPPED SPILL MATERIAL.

USE MECHANICAL DREDGES OR LIFTS TO EXTRACT IMMOBILIZED MASSES OF POLLUTION AND PRECIPITATES.

OCCUPATIONAL SPILL: SHUT OFF IGNITION SOURCES. DO NOT TOUCH SPILLED MATERIAL. FOR SMALL SPILLS, WITH CLEAN SHOVEL, PLACE MATERIAL INTO CLEAN, DRY CONTAINER AND COVER; MOVE CONTAINERS FROM SPILL AREA. FOR LARGER SPILLS, WET DOWN WITH WATER AND DIKE FOR LATER DISPOSAL. NO SMOKING, FLAMES OR FLARES IN HAZARD AREA! KEEP UNNECESSARY PEOPLE AWAY. ISOLATE HAZARD AREA AND DENY ENTRY.

RESIDUE SHOULD BE CLEANED UP USING A HIGH-EFFICIENCY PARTICULATE FILTER VACUUM.

REPORTABLE QUANTITY (RQ): 5000 POUNDS THE SUPERFUND AMENDMENTS AND REAUTHORIZATION ACT (SARA) SECTION 304 REQUIRES THAT A RELEASE EQUAL TO OR GREATER THAN THE REPORTABLE QUANTITY FOR THIS SUBSTANCE BE IMMEDIATELY REPORTED TO THE LOCAL EMERGENCY PLANNING COMMITTEE AND THE STATE EMERGENCY RESPONSE COMMISSION (40 CFR 355.40). IF THE RELEASE OF THIS SUBSTANCE IS REPORTABLE UNDER CERCLA SECTION 103, THE NATIONAL RESPONSE CENTER MUST BE NOTIFIED IMMEDIATELY AT (800) 424-8802 OR (202) 426-2675 IN THE METROPOLITAN WASHINGTON, D.C. AREA (40 CFR 302.6).

PROTECTIVE EQUIPMENT

VENTILATION: PROVIDE LOCAL EXHAUST VENTILATION SYSTEM TO MEET PUBLISHED EXPOSURE LIMITS.

RESPIRATOR: THE FOLLOWING RESPIRATORS AND MAXIMUM USE CONCENTRATIONS ARE RECOMMENDATIONS BY THE U.S. DEPARTMENT OF HEALTH AND HUMAN SERVICES, NIOSH POCKET GUIDE TO CHEMICAL HAZARDS; NIOSH CRITERIA DOCUMENTS OR BY THE U.S. DEPARTMENT OF LABOR, 29 CFR 1910 SUBPART Z. THE SPECIFIC RESPIRATOR SELECTED MUST BE BASED ON CONTAMINATION LEVELS FOUND IN THE WORK PLACE, MUST NOT EXCEED THE WORKING LIMITS OF THE RESPIRATOR AND BE JOINTLY APPROVED BY THE NATIONAL INSTITUTE FOR OCCUPATIONAL SAFETY AND HEALTH AND THE MINE SAFETY AND HEALTH ADMINISTRATION (NIOSH-MSHA).

COPPER (AS CU):

FOR FUME: 1 MG/M3- ANY DUST, MIST, AND FUME RESPIRATOR WITH A FULL FACEPIECE. ANY SUPPLIED-AIR RESPIRATOR. ANY SELF-CONTAINED BREATHING APPARATUS.

2.5 MG/M3- ANY POWERED AIR-PURIFYING RESPIRATOR WITH A DUST, MIST, AND FUME FILTER. ANY SUPPLIED-AIR RESPIRATOR OPERATED IN A CONTINUOUS FLOW MODE.

5 MG/M3- ANY AIR-PURIFYING FULL FACEPIECE RESPIRATOR WITH A HIGH-EFFICIENCY PARTICULATE FILTER. ANY POWERED AIR-PURIFYING RESPIRATOR WITH A TIGHT-FITTING FACEPIECE AND A HIGH EFFICIENCY PARTICULATE FILTER. ANY SELF-CONTAINED BREATHING APPARATUS WITH A FULL FACEPIECE. ANY SUPPLIED-AIR RESPIRATOR WITH A FULL FACEPIECE. ANY SUPPLIED-AIR RESPIRATOR WITH A TIGHT-FITTING FACEPIECE OPERATED IN A CONTINUOUS FLOW MODE.

100 MG/M3- ANY SUPPLIED-AIR RESPIRATOR WITH A HALF-MASK AND OPERATED IN A PRESSURE-DEMAND OR OTHER POSITIVE PRESSURE MODE.

200 MG/M3- ANY SUPPLIED-AIR RESPIRATOR WITH A FULL FACEPIECE AND OPERATED IN A PRESSURE-DEMAND OR OTHER POSITIVE PRESSURE MODE.

ESCAPE- ANY AIR-PURIFYING FULL FACEPIECE RESPIRATOR WITH A HIGH-EFFICIENCY PARTICULATE FILTER. ANY APPROPRIATE ESCAPE-TYPE SELF-CONTAINED BREATHING APPARATUS.

FOR FIREFIGHTING AND OTHER IMMEDIATELY DANGEROUS TO LIFE OR HEALTH CONDITIONS:

SELF-CONTAINED BREATHING APPARATUS WITH FULL FACEPIECE OPERATED IN PRESSURE-DEMAND OR OTHER POSITIVE PRESSURE MODE.

SUPPLIED-AIR RESPIRATOR WITH FULL FACEPIECE AND OPERATED IN PRESSURE-DEMAND OR OTHER POSITIVE PRESSURE MODE IN COMBINATION WITH AN AUXILIARY SELF-CONTAINED BREATHING APPARATUS OPERATED IN PRESSURE-DEMAND OR OTHER POSITIVE PRESSURE MODE.

CLOTHING: EMPLOYEE MUST WEAR APPROPRIATE PROTECTIVE (IMPERVIOUS) CLOTHING AND EQUIPMENT TO PREVENT REPEATED OR PROLONGED SKIN CONTACT WITH THIS SUBSTANCE.

GLOVES: EMPLOYEE MUST WEAR APPROPRIATE PROTECTIVE GLOVES TO PREVENT CONTACT WITH THIS SUBSTANCE.

EYE PROTECTION: EMPLOYEE MUST WEAR SPLASH-PROOF OR DUST-RESISTANT SAFETY GOGGLES TO PREVENT EYE CONTACT WITH THIS SUBSTANCE.

EMERGENCY EYE WASH: WHERE THERE IS ANY POSSIBILITY THAT AN EMPLOYEE'S EYES MAY BE EXPOSED TO THIS SUBSTANCE, THE EMPLOYER SHOULD PROVIDE AN EYE WASH FOUNTAIN WITHIN THE IMMEDIATE WORK AREA FOR EMERGENCY USE.

AUTHORIZED BY- OCCUPATIONAL HEALTH SERVICES, INC.

CREATION DATE: 11/15/89 ***REVISION DATE:*** 04/16/90

MATERIAL SAFETY DATA SHEET

OCCUPATIONAL HEALTH SERVICES, INC.
AGRICULTURE AND PESTICIDE DIVISION
450 SEVENTH AVENUE, SUITE 2407
NEW YORK, NEW YORK 10123
1-800-445-MSDS OR (212) 967-1100

EMERGENCY CONTACT:
JOHN S. BRANSFORD, JR. (615) 292-1180

SUBSTANCE IDENTIFICATION

CAS-NUMBER 1338-02-9

SUBSTANCE: COPPER NAPHTHENATE

TRADE NAMES/SYNONYMS: NAPHTHENIC ACID, COPPER SALT; COPPER UVERSOL; CUPRINOL; WITTOX C; PST05460

CHEMICAL FAMILY: ORGANOMETALLIC

MOLECULAR FORMULA: C14-H10-CU-O4

MOLECULAR WEIGHT: 221.9

CERCLA RATINGS (SCALE 0-3): HEALTH=U FIRE=2 REACTIVITY=0 PERSISTENCE=3

NFPA RATINGS (SCALE 0-4): HEALTH=U FIRE=2 REACTIVITY=0

COMPONENTS AND CONTAMINANTS

COMPONENT: COPPER NAPHTHENATE ***PERCENT:*** 100
CAS# 1338-02-9

EXPOSURE LIMITS: NO OCCUPATIONAL EXPOSURE LIMITS ESTABLISHED BY OSHA, ACGIH, OR NIOSH.

PHYSICAL DATA

DESCRIPTION: GREEN-BLUE SEMI-SOLID WITH A GASOLINE-LIKE ODOR.

BOILING POINT: 302 F (150 C) ***SPECIFIC GRAVITY:*** 1.02

SOLUBILITY IN WATER: INSOLUBLE ***VAPOR DENSITY:*** 3.9

SOLVENT SOLUBILITY: GASOLINE, BENZENE, MINERAL OIL DISTILLATES

FIRE AND EXPLOSION DATA

FIRE AND EXPLOSION HAZARD: MODERATE FIRE HAZARD WHEN EXPOSED TO HEAT OR FLAME.

FLASH POINT: 100 F (38 C) (CC) ***UPPER EXPLOSIVE LIMIT:*** 5.0%

LOWER EXPLOSIVE LIMIT: 0.8% ***FLAMMABILITY CLASS(OSHA):*** II

FIREFIGHTING MEDIA: DRY CHEMICAL, SAND, WATER SPRAY OR FOAM (1987 EMERGENCY RESPONSE GUIDEBOOK, DOT P 5800.4).
FOR LARGER FIRES, USE WATER SPRAY, FOG OR STANDARD FOAM (1987 EMERGENCY RESPONSE GUIDEBOOK, DOT P 5800.4).

FIREFIGHTING: MOVE CONTAINER FROM FIRE AREA IF POSSIBLE. COOL CONTAINERS EXPOSED TO FLAME WITH WATER FROM SIDE UNTIL WELL AFTER FIRE IS OUT. STAY AWAY FROM STORAGE TANK ENDS. FOR MASSIVE FIRE IN CARGO AREA, USE UNMANNED HOSE HOLDER OR MONITOR NOZZLES; ELSE WITHDRAW AND LET FIRE BURN (1987 EMERGENCY RESPONSE GUIDEBOOK, DOT P 5800.4, GUIDE PAGE 32).
EXTINGUISH USING AGENT FOR TYPE OF FIRE. AVOID BREATHING FUMES FROM BURNING MATERIAL.

TRANSPORTATION DATA

DEPARTMENT OF TRANSPORTATION HAZARD CLASSIFICATION 49 CFR 172.101: COMBUSTIBLE LIQUID
DEPARTMENT OF TRANSPORTATION LABELING REQUIREMENTS 49 CFR 172.101 AND SUBPART E: NONE
DEPARTMENT OF TRANSPORTATION PACKAGING REQUIREMENTS: NONE
EXCEPTIONS: 49 CFR 173.118A

TOXICITY

COPPER NAPHTHENATE: TOXICITY DATA: 2 GM/KG ORAL-RAT LD50; 110 MG/KG ORAL-MOUSE LDLO. CARCINOGEN STATUS: NONE. LOCAL EFFECTS: IRRITANT-INHALATION, SKIN, AND EYES. ACUTE TOXICITY DATA: MODERATELY TOXIC BY INGESTION. TARGET EFFECTS: POISONING MAY AFFECT THE CENTRAL NERVOUS SYSTEM.

HEALTH EFFECTS AND FIRST AID

INHALATION: COPPER NAPHTHENATE: IRRITANT/NARCOTIC. **ACUTE EXPOSURE-** VAPORS MAY CAUSE MILD IRRITATION OF THE RESPIRATORY TRACT. **CHRONIC EXPOSURE-** NO DATA AVAILABLE.

FIRST AID- REMOVE FROM EXPOSURE AREA TO FRESH AIR IMMEDIATELY. IF BREATHING HAS STOPPED, PERFORM ARTIFICIAL RESPIRATION. KEEP PERSON WARM AND AT REST. TREAT SYMPTOMATICALLY AND SUPPORTIVELY. GET MEDICAL ATTENTION IMMEDIATELY.

SKIN CONTACT: COPPER NAPHTHENATE: IRRITANT. **ACUTE EXPOSURE-** DIRECT CONTACT MAY CAUSE SKIN IRRITATION WITH REDDENING AND SMARTING. **CHRONIC EXPOSURE-** REPEATED AND PROLONGED CONTACT WITH IRRITANTS MAY CAUSE DERMATITIS.

FIRST AID- REMOVE CONTAMINATED CLOTHING AND SHOES IMMEDIATELY. WASH AFFECTED AREA WITH SOAP OR MILD DETERGENT AND LARGE AMOUNTS OF WATER UNTIL NO EVIDENCE OF CHEMICAL REMAINS (APPROXIMATELY 15-20 MINUTES). GET MEDICAL ATTENTION IMMEDIATELY.

EYE CONTACT: COPPER NAPHTHENATE: IRRITANT. **ACUTE EXPOSURE-** VAPORS MAY CAUSE MILD IRRITATION OF THE EYES. **CHRONIC EXPOSURE-** REPEATED OR PROLONGED EXPOSURE TO IRRITANTS MAY CAUSE CONJUNCTIVITIS.

FIRST AID- WASH EYES IMMEDIATELY WITH LARGE AMOUNTS OF WATER OR NORMAL SALINE, OCCASIONALLY LIFTING UPPER AND LOWER LIDS, UNTIL NO EVIDENCE OF CHEMICAL REMAINS (APPROXIMATELY 15-20 MINUTES). GET MEDICAL ATTENTION IMMEDIATELY.

INGESTION: COPPER NAPHTHENATE: **ACUTE EXPOSURE-** MAY BE IRRITATING TO THE GASTROINTESTINAL TRACT. ASPIRATION MAY CAUSE SEVERE LUNG IRRITATION AND RAPIDLY DEVELOPING PULMONARY EDEMA. THERE MAY ALSO BE CENTRAL NERVOUS SYSTEM EXCITEMENT FOLLOWED BY DEPRESSION. **CHRONIC EXPOSURE-** NO DATA AVAILABLE.

FIRST AID- EXTREME CARE MUST BE TAKEN TO PREVENT ASPIRATION. DILUTE THE POISON IMMEDIATELY WITH WATER OR MILK AND REMOVE BY GASTRIC LAVAGE UNLESS PATIENT IS ALREADY VOMITING. KEEP HEAD LOWER THAN HIPS DURING VOMITING TO PREVENT ASPIRATION. (DREISBACH, HANDBOOK OF POISONING, 11TH ED.) GET MEDICAL ATTENTION IMMEDIATELY. TREATMENT SHOULD ONLY BE PERFORMED BY QUALIFIED MEDICAL PERSONNEL.

ANTIDOTE: NO SPECIFIC ANTIDOTE. TREAT SYMPTOMATICALLY AND SUPPORTIVELY.

REACTIVITY

REACTIVITY: STABLE UNDER NORMAL TEMPERATURES AND PRESSURES.
INCOMPATIBILITIES: COPPER NAPHTHENATE: STRONG OXIDIZERS: INCOMPATIBLE.
DECOMPOSITION: THERMAL DECOMPOSITION MAY RELEASE TOXIC AND/OR HAZARDOUS GASES.
POLYMERIZATION: HAZARDOUS POLYMERIZATION HAS NOT BEEN REPORTED TO OCCUR UNDER NORMAL TEMPERATURES AND PRESSURES.

CONDITIONS TO AVOID

MAY BURN BUT DOES NOT IGNITE READILY. AVOID CONTACT WITH STRONG OXIDIZERS, EXCESSIVE HEAT, SPARKS, OR OPEN FLAME.

SPILL AND LEAK PROCEDURES

OCCUPATIONAL SPILL: STOP LEAK IF YOU CAN DO IT WITHOUT RISK. FOR SMALL SPILLS, TAKE UP WITH SAND OR OTHER ABSORBENT MATERIAL AND PLACE INTO CLEAN, DRY CONTAINERS FOR LATER DISPOSAL. KEEP UNNECESSARY PEOPLE AWAY. ISOLATE HAZARD AREA AND DENY ENTRY.

PROTECTIVE EQUIPMENT

VENTILATION: PROVIDE LOCAL EXHAUST OR PROCESS ENCLOSURE VENTILATION SYSTEM.

RESPIRATOR: THE FOLLOWING RESPIRATORS ARE RECOMMENDED BASED ON INFORMATION FOUND IN THE PHYSICAL DATA, TOXICITY AND HEALTH EFFECTS SECTIONS. THEY ARE RANKED IN ORDER FROM MINIMUM TO MAXIMUM RESPIRATORY PROTECTION. THE SPECIFIC RESPIRATOR SELECTED MUST BE BASED ON CONTAMINATION LEVELS FOUND IN THE WORK PLACE, MUST NOT EXCEED THE WORKING LIMITS OF THE RESPIRATOR AND BE JOINTLY APPROVED BY THE NATIONAL INSTITUTE FOR OCCUPATIONAL SAFETY AND HEALTH AND THE MINE SAFETY AND HEALTH ADMINISTRATION (NIOSH-MSHA).
CHEMICAL CARTRIDGE RESPIRATOR WITH AN ORGANIC VAPOR CARTRIDGE(S) WITH AN ACID GAS CARTRIDGE(S) AND A FULL FACEPIECE.
GAS MASK WITH ORGANIC VAPOR CANISTER (CHIN-STYLE OR FRONT- OR BACK-MOUNTED CANISTER), WITH A FULL FACEPIECE, PROVIDING PROTECTION AGAINST ACID GASES.
TYPE 'C' SUPPLIED-AIR RESPIRATOR WITH A FULL FACEPIECE OPERATED IN PRESSURE-DEMAND OR OTHER POSITIVE PRESSURE MODE OR WITH A FULL FACEPIECE, HELMET OR HOOD OPERATED IN CONTINUOUS-FLOW MODE.
SELF-CONTAINED BREATHING APPARATUS WITH A FULL FACEPIECE OPERATED IN PRESSURE-DEMAND OR OTHER POSITIVE PRESSURE MODE.
FOR FIREFIGHTING AND OTHER IMMEDIATELY DANGEROUS TO LIFE OR HEALTH CONDITIONS:
SELF-CONTAINED BREATHING APPARATUS WITH FULL FACEPIECE OPERATED IN PRESSURE-DEMAND OR OTHER POSITIVE PRESSURE MODE.
SUPPLIED-AIR RESPIRATOR WITH FULL FACEPIECE AND OPERATED IN PRESSURE-DEMAND OR OTHER POSITIVE PRESSURE MODE IN COMBINATION WITH AN AUXILIARY SELF-CONTAINED BREATHING APPARATUS OPERATED IN PRESSURE-DEMAND OR OTHER POSITIVE PRESSURE MODE.

CLOTHING: EMPLOYEE MUST WEAR APPROPRIATE PROTECTIVE (IMPERVIOUS) CLOTHING AND EQUIPMENT TO PREVENT REPEATED OR PROLONGED SKIN CONTACT WITH THIS SUBSTANCE.

GLOVES: EMPLOYEE MUST WEAR APPROPRIATE PROTECTIVE GLOVES TO PREVENT CONTACT WITH THIS SUBSTANCE.

EYE PROTECTION: EMPLOYEE MUST WEAR SPLASH-PROOF OR DUST-RESISTANT SAFETY GOGGLES TO PREVENT EYE CONTACT WITH THIS SUBSTANCE.
EMERGENCY EYE WASH: WHERE THERE IS ANY POSSIBILITY THAT AN EMPLOYEE'S EYES MAY BE EXPOSED TO THIS SUBSTANCE, THE EMPLOYER SHOULD PROVIDE AN EYE WASH FOUNTAIN WITHIN THE IMMEDIATE WORK AREA FOR EMERGENCY USE.

AUTHORIZED BY- OCCUPATIONAL HEALTH SERVICES, INC.
CREATION DATE: 10/04/89 ***REVISION DATE:*** 05/08/90

MATERIAL SAFETY DATA SHEET

OCCUPATIONAL HEALTH SERVICES, INC.
AGRICULTURE AND PESTICIDE DIVISION
450 SEVENTH AVENUE, SUITE 2407
NEW YORK, NEW YORK 10123
1-800-445-MSDS OR (212) 967-1100

EMERGENCY CONTACT:
JOHN S. BRANSFORD, JR. (615) 292-1180

SUBSTANCE IDENTIFICATION

CAS-NUMBER 1317-39-1
SUBSTANCE: **CUPROUS OXIDE**
TRADE NAMES/SYNONYMS: BROWN COPPER OXIDE; COPPER(I) OXIDE; COPPER OXIDE; COPPER(1+) OXIDE; DICOPPER MONOXIDE; YELLOW CUPROCIDE; RED COPPER OXIDE; COPPER NARDOX; COPPER-SANDOZ; COPPER SUBOXIDE; CUPRAMAR; COPOX; CUPROCIDE; FUNGIMAR; KUPRITE; NORDOX; OLEO NORDOX; PERENOX; C-477; PST05470
CHEMICAL FAMILY: METAL OXIDE
MOLECULAR FORMULA: CU2-O

MOLECULAR WEIGHT: 143.08
CERCLA RATINGS (SCALE 0-3): HEALTH=3 FIRE=0 REACTIVITY=0 PERSISTENCE=3
NFPA RATINGS (SCALE 0-4): HEALTH=3 FIRE=0 REACTIVITY=0

COMPONENTS AND CONTAMINANTS

COMPONENT: CUPROUS OXIDE ***PERCENT:*** 100
CAS# 1317-39-1
OTHER CONTAMINANTS: NONE
EXPOSURE LIMITS: COPPER AND COMPOUNDS (AS CU): 0.1 MG/M3 OSHA TWA (FUME); 1 MG/M3 OSHA TWA (DUST AND MISTS) 0.2 MG/M3 ACGIH TWA (FUME); 1 MG/M3 ACGIH TWA (DUST AND MISTS)
SUBJECT TO SARA SECTION 313 ANNUAL TOXIC CHEMICAL RELEASE REPORTING

PHYSICAL DATA

DESCRIPTION: YELLOW TO REDDISH-BROWN OCTAHEDRAL OR CUBIC CRYSTALS OR MICROCRYSTALLINE POWDER. ***BOILING POINT:*** 2372 F (1800 C)
MELTING POINT: 2255 F (1235 C) ***SPECIFIC GRAVITY:*** 6.000
SOLUBILITY IN WATER: INSOLUBLE
SOLVENT SOLUBILITY: HYDROCHLORIC ACID, AMMONIUM CHLORIDE, AMMONIUM HYDROXIDE; INSOLUBLE IN ALCOHOL.

FIRE AND EXPLOSION DATA

FIRE AND EXPLOSION HAZARD: NEGLIGIBLE FIRE HAZARD WHEN EXPOSED TO HEAT OR FLAME.
FIREFIGHTING MEDIA: USE DRY SAND, DOLOMITE, GRAPHITE, SODIUM CHLORIDE, SODA ASH, OR APPROPRIATE METAL-EXTINGUISHING POWDER. DO NOT APPLY WATER TO BURNING MATERIAL (NFPA FIRE PROTECTION HANDBOOK, 16TH EDITION).
FIREFIGHTING: NO ACUTE HAZARD. MOVE CONTAINER FROM FIRE AREA IF POSSIBLE. AVOID BREATHING VAPORS OR DUSTS; KEEP UPWIND.

TOXICITY

CUPROUS OXIDE: TOXICITY DATA: 470 MG/KG ORAL-RAT LD50; REPRODUCTIVE EFFECTS DATA (RTECS). CARCINOGEN STATUS: NONE. LOCAL EFFECTS: IRRITANT-INHALATION, SKIN, AND EYES. ACUTE TOXICITY LEVEL: TOXIC BY INGESTION. TARGET EFFECTS: POISONING MAY AFFECT THE LIVER AND KIDNEYS.

HEALTH EFFECTS AND FIRST AID

INHALATION: CUPROUS OXIDE: IRRITANT. **ACUTE EXPOSURE-** MAY CAUSE METAL FUME FEVER CHARACTERIZED BY CHILLS, FEVER, ACHING MUSCLES, DRYNESS AND OBJECTIONABLE METAL TASTE IN THE MOUTH AND THROAT, HEADACHES, SNEEZING, NAUSEA, AND IRRITATION OF THE NOSE AND TRACHEA. OCCASIONALLY ULCERATION AND PERFORATION OF THE NASAL SEPTUM OCCURS. HIGHER CONCENTRATIONS MAY LEAD TO HEMOLYSIS, JAUNDICE, ANURIA, AND CONVULSIONS. **CHRONIC EXPOSURE-** PROLONGED EXPOSURE MAY LEAD TO KIDNEY AND LIVER DAMAGE. CHRONIC INHALATION STUDIES ON MALE RATS SHOWED ADVERSE EFFECTS ON FERTILITY.
FIRST AID- REMOVE FROM EXPOSURE AREA TO FRESH AIR IMMEDIATELY. IF BREATHING HAS STOPPED, PERFORM ARTIFICIAL RESPIRATION. KEEP PERSON WARM AND AT REST. TREAT SYMPTOMATICALLY AND SUPPORTIVELY. GET MEDICAL ATTENTION IMMEDIATELY.

SKIN CONTACT: CUPROUS OXIDE: IRRITANT. **ACUTE EXPOSURE-** MAY CAUSE IRRITATION PRODUCING ITCHING ECZEMA. **CHRONIC EXPOSURE-** REPEATED OR PROLONGED CONTACT MAY CAUSE DERMATITIS AND DISCOLORATION OF THE SKIN AND HAIR.
FIRST AID- REMOVE CONTAMINATED CLOTHING AND SHOES IMMEDIATELY. WASH AFFECTED AREA WITH SOAP OR MILD DETERGENT AND LARGE AMOUNTS OF WATER UNTIL NO EVIDENCE OF CHEMICAL REMAINS (APPROXIMATELY 15-20 MINUTES). GET MEDICAL ATTENTION IMMEDIATELY.

EYE CONTACT: CUPROUS OXIDE: IRRITANT. **ACUTE EXPOSURE-** MAY CAUSE IRRITATION, REDNESS, PAIN, AND CORNEAL TURBIDITY. **CHRONIC EXPOSURE-** CONJUNCTIVITIS AND CORNEAL DESTRUCTION MAY OCCUR FROM REPEATED OR PROLONGED EXPOSURE.
FIRST AID- WASH EYES IMMEDIATELY WITH LARGE AMOUNTS OF WATER OR NORMAL SALINE, OCCASIONALLY LIFTING UPPER AND LOWER LIDS, UNTIL NO EVIDENCE OF CHEMICAL REMAINS (APPROXIMATELY 15-20 MINUTES). GET MEDICAL ATTENTION IMMEDIATELY.

INGESTION: CUPROUS OXIDE: TOXIC. **ACUTE EXPOSURE-** MAY CAUSE GASTROINTESTINAL IRRITATION CHARACTERIZED BY INFLAMMATION, NAUSEA, VOMITING AND TENESMUS, WEAKNESS AND COLLAPSE. A DOSE OF 470 MG/KG WAS LETHAL TO 50% OF A RAT POPULATION, HOWEVER NO SYMPTOMS WERE REPORTED. **CHRONIC EXPOSURE-** PROLONGED EXPOSURE MAY LEAD TO LIVER AND KIDNEY DAMAGE.
FIRST AID- IF PERSON IS CONSCIOUS, GIVE LARGE QUANTITIES OF WATER OR MILK IMMEDIATELY AND INDUCE VOMITING OR PERFORM GASTRIC LAVAGE. DO NOT MAKE AN UNCONSCIOUS PERSON VOMIT OR DRINK ANYTHING. IRRITATION MAY BE RELIEVED BY MILK OR A STARCH DRINK MADE BY DISSOLVING TEN GRAMS OF CORNSTARCH OR FLOUR IN ONE LITER OF WATER. KEEP AFFECTED PERSON WARM AND AT REST. MAINTAIN BLOOD PRESSURE, AIRWAY, AND GIVE OXYGEN IF RESPIRATION IS DEPRESSED. GET MEDICAL ATTENTION. (DREISBACH, HANDBOOK OF POISONING, 11TH ED.) GASTRIC LAVAGE AND OXYGEN MUST BE ADMINISTERED BY QUALIFIED MEDICAL PERSONNEL.
ANTIDOTE: THE FOLLOWING ANTIDOTE HAS BEEN RECOMMENDED. HOWEVER, THE DECISION AS TO WHETHER THE SEVERITY OF POISONING REQUIRES ADMINISTRATION OF ANY ANTIDOTE AND ACTUAL DOSE REQUIRED SHOULD BE MADE BY QUALIFIED MEDICAL PERSONNEL.
COPPER POISONING: GIVE CALCIUM DISODIUM EDETATE 15-25 MG/KG (0.08-0.125 ML OF 20% SOLUTION PER KILOGRAM BODY WEIGHT) IN 250-500 ML OF 5% DEXTROSE INTRAVENOUSLY OVER A 1 TO 2 HOUR PERIOD TWICE DAILY. THE MAXIMUM DOSE SHOULD NOT EXCEED 50 MG/KG/DAY. THE DRUG SHOULD BE GIVEN IN 5-DAY COURSES WITH A REST PERIOD OF AT LEAST 2 DAYS BETWEEN COURSES. AFTER THE FIRST COURSE, SUBSEQUENT COURSES SHOULD NOT EXCEED 50 MG/KG/DAY. DAILY URINALYSES SHOULD NOT BE DONE DURING THE TREATMENT PERIOD. THE DOSAGE SHOULD BE REDUCED IF ANY UNUSUAL URINARY FINDINGS APPEAR. INTRAVENOUS ADMINISTRATION IS CONTRAINDICATED IN THE PRESENCE OF ELEVATED CEREBROSPINAL FLUID PRESSURE. PENICILLAMINE IS ALSO EFFECTIVE IN COPPER POISONING. GIVE UP TO 100 MG/KG/DAY (MAXIMUM 1 G/DAY) DIVIDED INTO 4 DOSES FOR NO LONGER THAN 1 WEEK. IF A LONGER ADMINISTRATION PERIOD IS WARRANTED, DOSAGE SHOULD NOT EXCEED 40 MG/KG/DAY. GIVE THE DRUG ORALLY, HALF AN HOUR BEFORE MEALS (DREISBACH, HANDBOOK OF POISONING, 12TH ED.). ANTIDOTE SHOULD BE ADMINISTERED BY QUALIFIED MEDICAL PERSONNEL.

REACTIVITY

REACTIVITY: STABLE UNDER NORMAL TEMPERATURES AND PRESSURES.
INCOMPATIBILITIES: CUPROUS OXIDE: LITHIUM NITRIDE: VIOLENT REACTION. PEROXYFORMIC ACID: VIOLENT DECOMPOSITION.
DECOMPOSITION: THERMAL DECOMPOSITION MAY RELEASE TOXIC AND/OR HAZARDOUS GASES.
POLYMERIZATION: HAZARDOUS POLYMERIZATION HAS NOT BEEN REPORTED TO OCCUR UNDER NORMAL TEMPERATURES AND PRESSURES.

CONDITIONS TO AVOID

MAY BURN BUT DOES NOT IGNITE READILY.
AVOID DISPERSION OF DUST IN AIR. FINELY DIVIDED PARTICLES, DUST, OR FUMES MAY BE FLAMMABLE OR EXPLOSIVE. KEEP AWAY FROM SPARKS OR IGNITION SOURCES.

SPILL AND LEAK PROCEDURES

OCCUPATIONAL SPILL: DO NOT TOUCH SPILLED MATERIAL. STOP LEAK IF YOU CAN DO IT WITHOUT RISK. FOR SMALL SPILLS, TAKE UP WITH SAND OR OTHER ABSORBENT MATERIAL AND PLACE INTO CONTAINERS FOR LATER DISPOSAL. FOR SMALL DRY SPILLS, WITH A CLEAN SHOVEL PLACE MATERIAL INTO CLEAN, DRY CONTAINER AND COVER. MOVE CONTAINERS FROM SPILL AREA. FOR LARGER SPILLS, DIKE FAR AHEAD OF SPILL FOR LATER DISPOSAL. KEEP UNNECESSARY PEOPLE AWAY. ISOLATE HAZARD AREA AND DENY ENTRY.
RESIDUE SHOULD BE CLEANED UP USING A HIGH-EFFICIENCY PARTICULATE FILTER VACUUM.

PROTECTIVE EQUIPMENT

VENTILATION: PROVIDE LOCAL EXHAUST OR PROCESS ENCLOSURE VENTILATION TO MEET PUBLISHED EXPOSURE LIMITS.
RESPIRATOR: THE FOLLOWING RESPIRATORS AND MAXIMUM USE CONCENTRATIONS ARE RECOMMENDATIONS BY THE U.S. DEPARTMENT OF HEALTH AND HUMAN SERVICES, NIOSH POCKET GUIDE TO CHEMICAL HAZARDS; NIOSH CRITERIA DOCUMENTS OR BY THE U.S. DEPARTMENT OF LABOR, 29 CFR 1910 SUBPART Z. THE SPECIFIC RESPIRATOR SELECTED MUST BE BASED ON CONTAMINATION LEVELS FOUND IN THE WORK PLACE, MUST NOT EXCEED THE WORKING LIMITS OF THE RESPIRATOR AND BE JOINTLY APPROVED BY THE NATIONAL INSTITUTE FOR OCCUPATIONAL SAFETY AND HEALTH AND THE MINE SAFETY AND HEALTH ADMINISTRATION (NIOSH-MSHA).
COPPER (AS CU):
FOR FUME: 1 MG/M3- ANY DUST, MIST, AND FUME RESPIRATOR WITH A FULL FACEPIECE. ANY SUPPLIED-AIR RESPIRATOR. ANY SELF-CONTAINED BREATHING APPARATUS.
2.5 MG/M3- ANY POWERED AIR-PURIFYING RESPIRATOR WITH A DUST, MIST, AND FUME FILTER. ANY SUPPLIED-AIR RESPIRATOR OPERATED IN A CONTINUOUS FLOW MODE.

5 MG/M3- ANY AIR-PURIFYING FULL FACEPIECE RESPIRATOR WITH A HIGH-EFFICIENCY PARTICULATE FILTER. ANY POWERED AIR-PURIFYING RESPIRATOR WITH A TIGHT-FITTING FACEPIECE AND A HIGH EFFICIENCY PARTICULATE FILTER. ANY SELF-CONTAINED BREATHING APPARATUS WITH A FULL FACEPIECE. ANY SUPPLIED-AIR RESPIRATOR WITH A FULL FACEPIECE. ANY SUPPLIED-AIR RESPIRATOR WITH A TIGHT-FITTING FACEPIECE OPERATED IN A CONTINUOUS FLOW MODE.

100 MG/M3- ANY SUPPLIED-AIR RESPIRATOR WITH A HALF-MASK AND OPERATED IN A PRESSURE-DEMAND OR OTHER POSITIVE PRESSURE MODE.

200 MG/M3- ANY SUPPLIED-AIR RESPIRATOR WITH A FULL FACEPIECE AND OPERATED IN A PRESSURE-DEMAND OR OTHER POSITIVE PRESSURE MODE.

ESCAPE- ANY AIR-PURIFYING FULL FACEPIECE RESPIRATOR WITH A HIGH-EFFICIENCY PARTICULATE FILTER. ANY APPROPRIATE ESCAPE-TYPE SELF-CONTAINED BREATHING APPARATUS.

FOR FIREFIGHTING AND OTHER IMMEDIATELY DANGEROUS TO LIFE OR HEALTH CONDITIONS:

SELF-CONTAINED BREATHING APPARATUS WITH FULL FACEPIECE OPERATED IN PRESSURE-DEMAND OR OTHER POSITIVE PRESSURE MODE.

SUPPLIED-AIR RESPIRATOR WITH FULL FACEPIECE AND OPERATED IN PRESSURE-DEMAND OR OTHER POSITIVE PRESSURE MODE IN COMBINATION WITH AN AUXILIARY SELF-CONTAINED BREATHING APPARATUS OPERATED IN PRESSURE-DEMAND OR OTHER POSITIVE PRESSURE MODE.

CLOTHING: EMPLOYEE MUST WEAR APPROPRIATE PROTECTIVE (IMPERVIOUS) CLOTHING AND EQUIPMENT TO PREVENT ANY POSSIBILITY OF SKIN CONTACT WITH THIS SUBSTANCE.

GLOVES: EMPLOYEE MUST WEAR APPROPRIATE PROTECTIVE GLOVES TO PREVENT CONTACT WITH THIS SUBSTANCE.

EYE PROTECTION: EMPLOYEE MUST WEAR SPLASH-PROOF OR DUST-RESISTANT SAFETY GOGGLES AND A FACESHIELD TO PREVENT CONTACT WITH THIS SUBSTANCE.

EMERGENCY WASH FACILITIES: WHERE THERE IS ANY POSSIBILITY THAT AN EMPLOYEE'S EYES AND/OR SKIN MAY BE EXPOSED TO THIS SUBSTANCE, THE EMPLOYER SHOULD PROVIDE AN EYE WASH FOUNTAIN AND QUICK DRENCH SHOWER WITHIN THE IMMEDIATE WORK AREA FOR EMERGENCY USE.

AUTHORIZED BY- OCCUPATIONAL HEALTH SERVICES, INC.
CREATION DATE: 11/15/89 ***REVISION DATE:*** 05/09/90

MATERIAL SAFETY DATA SHEET

OCCUPATIONAL HEALTH SERVICES, INC.
AGRICULTURE AND PESTICIDE DIVISION
450 SEVENTH AVENUE, SUITE 2407
NEW YORK, NEW YORK 10123
1-800-445-MSDS OR (212) 967-1100

EMERGENCY CONTACT:
JOHN S. BRANSFORD, JR. (615) 292-1180

SUBSTANCE IDENTIFICATION

CAS-NUMBER 8001-29-4

SUBSTANCE: **COTTONSEED OIL**

TRADE NAMES/SYNONYMS: COTTONSEED OIL REFINED; COTTON SEED OIL; COTTON OIL; COTTONSEED OIL (DEODERIZED WINTERIZED); DEODERIZED, WINTERIZED COTTON SEED OIL; FMC 710; 0-63; PST05475

CHEMICAL FAMILY: ESSENTIAL OIL

CERCLA RATINGS (SCALE 0-3): HEALTH=3 FIRE=1 REACTIVITY=0 PERSISTENCE=0

NFPA RATINGS (SCALE 0-4): HEALTH=0 FIRE=1 REACTIVITY=0

COMPONENTS AND CONTAMINANTS

COMPONENT: COTTONSEED OIL ***PERCENT:*** 100.0
CAS# 8001-29-4

OTHER CONTAMINANTS: NONE

EXPOSURE LIMITS: NO OCCUPATIONAL EXPOSURE LIMITS ESTABLISHED BY OSHA, ACGIH, OR NIOSH.

PHYSICAL DATA

DESCRIPTION: NEARLY ODORLESS, OILY, PALE YELLOW LIQUID WITH A BLAND TASTE.

MELTING POINT: 30 F (-1 C) ***SPECIFIC GRAVITY:*** 0.917 @ 25 C

SOLUBILITY IN WATER: INSOLUBLE

SOLVENT SOLUBILITY: SOLUBLE IN CHLOROFORM, ETHER, CARBON DISULFIDE, PETROLEUM ETHER, AND HEXANE; SLIGHTLY SOLUBLE IN ALCOHOL.

FIRE AND EXPLOSION DATA

FIRE AND EXPLOSION HAZARD: SLIGHT FIRE HAZARD WHEN EXPOSED TO HEAT OR FLAME.

FLASH POINT: 486 F (252 C) (CC) ***AUTOIGNITION TEMP.:*** 650 F (343 C)

FLAMMABILITY CLASS(OSHA): IIIB

FIREFIGHTING MEDIA: DRY CHEMICAL, CARBON DIOXIDE, HALON, WATER SPRAY OR STANDARD FOAM (1987 EMERGENCY RESPONSE GUIDEBOOK, DOT P 5800.4). DRY CHEMICAL, CARBON DIOXIDE OR HALON (1987 EMERGENCY RESPONSE GUIDEBOOK, DOT P 5800.4).

FIREFIGHTING: MOVE CONTAINER FROM FIRE AREA IF POSSIBLE. DO NOT SCATTER SPILLED MATERIAL WITH HIGH PRESSURE WATER STREAMS. DIKE FIRE CONTROL WATER FOR LATER DISPOSAL (1987 EMERGENCY RESPONSE GUIDEBOOK, DOT P 5800.4, GUIDE PAGE 31).

USE AGENTS SUITABLE FOR TYPE OF SURROUNDING FIRE. AVOID BREATHING HAZARDOUS VAPORS, KEEP UPWIND.

WATER OR FOAM MAY CAUSE FROTHING (NFPA 325M, FIRE HAZARD PROPERTIES OF FLAMMABLE LIQUIDS, GASES, AND VOLATILE SOLIDS, 1984)

TOXICITY

COTTONSEED OIL: TOXICITY DATA: REPRODUCTIVE EFFECTS DATA (RTECS); TUMORIGENIC DATA (RTECS). CARCINOGEN STATUS: NONE. ACUTE TOXICITY LEVEL: NO DATA AVAILABLE. TARGET EFFECTS: NO DATA AVAILABLE.

HEALTH EFFECTS AND FIRST AID

INHALATION: COTTONSEED OIL: **ACUTE EXPOSURE-** NO DATA AVAILABLE. **CHRONIC EXPOSURE-** NO DATA AVAILABLE.

FIRST AID- REMOVE FROM EXPOSURE AREA TO FRESH AIR IMMEDIATELY. IF BREATHING HAS STOPPED, PERFORM ARTIFICIAL RESPIRATION. KEEP PERSON WARM AND AT REST. TREAT SYMPTOMATICALLY AND SUPPORTIVELY. GET MEDICAL ATTENTION IMMEDIATELY.

SKIN CONTACT: COTTONSEED OIL: **ACUTE EXPOSURE-** NO DATA AVAILABLE. **CHRONIC EXPOSURE-** NO DATA AVAILABLE.

FIRST AID- REMOVE CONTAMINATED CLOTHING AND SHOES IMMEDIATELY. WASH AFFECTED AREA WITH SOAP OR MILD DETERGENT AND LARGE AMOUNTS OF WATER UNTIL NO EVIDENCE OF CHEMICAL REMAINS (APPROXIMATELY 15-20 MINUTES). GET MEDICAL ATTENTION IMMEDIATELY.

EYE CONTACT: COTTONSEED OIL: **ACUTE EXPOSURE-** NO DATA AVAILABLE. **CHRONIC EXPOSURE-** NO DATA AVAILABLE.

FIRST AID- WASH EYES IMMEDIATELY WITH LARGE AMOUNTS OF WATER OR NORMAL SALINE, OCCASIONALLY LIFTING UPPER AND LOWER LIDS, UNTIL NO EVIDENCE OF CHEMICAL REMAINS (APPROXIMATELY 15-20 MINUTES). GET MEDICAL ATTENTION IMMEDIATELY.

INGESTION: COTTONSEED OIL: **ACUTE EXPOSURE-** INGESTION MAY RETARD GASTRIC SECRETION AND MOTILITY; LARGE AMOUNTS MAY PRODUCE A LAXATIVE EFFECT. ASPIRATION MAY RESULT IN LIPOID PNEUMONIA. **CHRONIC EXPOSURE-** NO DATA AVAILABLE.

FIRST AID- TREAT SYMPTOMATICALLY AND SUPPORTIVELY. GET MEDICAL ATTENTION IMMEDIATELY. IF VOMITING OCCURS, KEEP HEAD LOWER THAN HIPS TO PREVENT ASPIRATION.

ANTIDOTE: NO SPECIFIC ANTIDOTE. TREAT SYMPTOMATICALLY AND SUPPORTIVELY.

REACTIVITY

REACTIVITY: STABLE UNDER NORMAL TEMPERATURES AND PRESSURES.

INCOMPATIBILITIES: COTTONSEED OIL: OXIDIZERS (STRONG): FIRE AND EXPLOSION HAZARD.

DECOMPOSITION: THERMAL DECOMPOSITION MAY RELEASE ACRID SMOKE AND IRRITATING FUMES.

POLYMERIZATION: HAZARDOUS POLYMERIZATION HAS NOT BEEN REPORTED TO OCCUR UNDER NORMAL TEMPERATURES AND PRESSURES.

STORAGE AND DISPOSAL

OBSERVE ALL FEDERAL, STATE AND LOCAL REGULATIONS WHEN STORING OR DISPOSING OF THIS SUBSTANCE. FOR ASSISTANCE, CONTACT THE DISTRICT DIRECTOR OF THE ENVIRONMENTAL PROTECTION AGENCY.

****STORAGE****

STORE AWAY FROM INCOMPATIBLE SUBSTANCES.

CONDITIONS TO AVOID

MAY BURN BUT DOES NOT IGNITE READILY. AVOID CONTACT WITH STRONG OXIDIZERS, EXCESSIVE HEAT, SPARKS, OR OPEN FLAME.

SPILL AND LEAK PROCEDURES

OCCUPATIONAL SPILL: STOP LEAK IF YOU CAN DO IT WITHOUT RISK. FOR SMALL SPILLS, TAKE UP WITH SAND OR OTHER ABSORBENT MATERIAL AND PLACE INTO CLEAN, DRY CONTAINERS FOR LATER DISPOSAL. KEEP UNNECESSARY PEOPLE AWAY. ISOLATE HAZARD AREA AND DENY ENTRY.

PROTECTIVE EQUIPMENT

VENTILATION: PROVIDE GENERAL DILUTION VENTILATION.

RESPIRATOR: THE FOLLOWING RESPIRATORS ARE RECOMMENDED BASED ON INFORMATION FOUND IN THE PHYSICAL DATA, TOXICITY AND HEALTH EFFECTS SECTIONS. THEY ARE RANKED IN ORDER FROM MINIMUM TO MAXIMUM RESPIRATORY PROTECTION. THE SPECIFIC RESPIRATOR SELECTED MUST BE BASED ON CONTAMINATION LEVELS FOUND IN THE WORK PLACE, MUST NOT EXCEED THE WORKING LIMITS OF THE RESPIRATOR AND BE JOINTLY APPROVED BY THE NATIONAL INSTITUTE FOR OCCUPATIONAL SAFETY AND HEALTH AND THE MINE SAFETY AND HEALTH ADMINISTRATION (NIOSH-MSHA).

CHEMICAL CARTRIDGE RESPIRATOR WITH AN ORGANIC VAPOR CARTRIDGE(S) WITH A FULL FACEPIECE.

GAS MASK WITH ORGANIC VAPOR CANISTER (CHIN-STYLE OR FRONT- OR BACK-MOUNTED CANISTER) WITH A FULL FACEPIECE.

TYPE 'C' SUPPLIED-AIR RESPIRATOR WITH A FULL FACEPIECE OPERATED IN PRESSURE-DEMAND OR OTHER POSITIVE PRESSURE MODE OR WITH A FULL FACEPIECE, HELMET OR HOOD OPERATED IN CONTINUOUS-FLOW MODE.

SELF-CONTAINED BREATHING APPARATUS WITH A FULL FACEPIECE OPERATED IN PRESSURE-DEMAND OR OTHER POSITIVE PRESSURE MODE.

FOR FIREFIGHTING AND OTHER IMMEDIATELY DANGEROUS TO LIFE OR HEALTH CONDITIONS:

SELF-CONTAINED BREATHING APPARATUS WITH FULL FACEPIECE OPERATED IN PRESSURE-DEMAND OR OTHER POSITIVE PRESSURE MODE.

SUPPLIED-AIR RESPIRATOR WITH FULL FACEPIECE AND OPERATED IN PRESSURE-DEMAND OR OTHER POSITIVE PRESSURE MODE IN COMBINATION WITH AN AUXILIARY SELF-CONTAINED BREATHING APPARATUS OPERATED IN PRESSURE-DEMAND OR OTHER POSITIVE PRESSURE MODE.

CLOTHING: EMPLOYEE MUST WEAR APPROPRIATE PROTECTIVE (IMPERVIOUS) CLOTHING AND EQUIPMENT TO PREVENT REPEATED OR PROLONGED SKIN CONTACT WITH THIS SUBSTANCE.

GLOVES: EMPLOYEE MUST WEAR APPROPRIATE PROTECTIVE GLOVES TO PREVENT CONTACT WITH THIS SUBSTANCE.

EYE PROTECTION: EMPLOYEE MUST WEAR SPLASH-PROOF OR DUST-RESISTANT SAFETY GOGGLES TO PREVENT EYE CONTACT WITH THIS SUBSTANCE.

EMERGENCY EYE WASH: WHERE THERE IS ANY POSSIBILITY THAT AN EMPLOYEE'S EYES MAY BE EXPOSED TO THIS SUBSTANCE, THE EMPLOYER SHOULD PROVIDE AN EYE WASH FOUNTAIN WITHIN THE IMMEDIATE WORK AREA FOR EMERGENCY USE.

AUTHORIZED BY- OCCUPATIONAL HEALTH SERVICES, INC.

CREATION DATE: 02/08/90 ***REVISION DATE:*** 05/18/90

MATERIAL SAFETY DATA SHEET

OCCUPATIONAL HEALTH SERVICES, INC.
AGRICULTURE AND PESTICIDE DIVISION
450 SEVENTH AVENUE, SUITE 2407
NEW YORK, NEW YORK 10123
1-800-445-MSDS OR (212) 967-1100

EMERGENCY CONTACT:
JOHN S. BRANSFORD, JR. (615) 292-1180

SUBSTANCE IDENTIFICATION

CAS-NUMBER 117-52-2

SUBSTANCE: COUMAFURYL

TRADE NAMES/SYNONYMS: 2H-1-BENZOPYRAN-2-ONE, 3-(1-(2-FURANYL)-3-OXOBUTYL)-4-HYDROXY-; COUMARIN, 3-(ALPHA-ACETONYLFURFURYL)-4-HYDROXY-; 3-(1-(2-FURANYL)-3-OXOBUTYL)-4-HYDROXY-2H-1-BENZOPYRAN-2-ONE; 3-(ALPHA-ACETONYLFURFURYL)-4-HYDROXYCOUMARIN; 3-(ALPHA-(2-FURYL)-BETA-ACETYLETHYL)4-HYDROXYCOUMARIN; FUMARIN; RATAFIN; TOMARIN; C17H14O5; PST05476

CHEMICAL FAMILY: COUMARIN

MOLECULAR FORMULA: C17-H14-O5

MOLECULAR WEIGHT: 298.31

CERCLA RATINGS (SCALE 0-3): HEALTH=3 FIRE=1 REACTIVITY=0 PERSISTENCE=2

NFPA RATINGS (SCALE 0-4): HEALTH=U FIRE=1 REACTIVITY=0

COMPONENTS AND CONTAMINANTS

COMPONENT: COUMAFURYL ***PERCENT:*** 100.0

CAS# 117-52-2

OTHER CONTAMINANTS: NONE

EXPOSURE LIMITS: NO OCCUPATIONAL EXPOSURE LIMITS ESTABLISHED BY OSHA, ACGIH, OR NIOSH.

PHYSICAL DATA

DESCRIPTION: ODORLESS, WHITE, CRYSTALLINE SOLID.

MELTING POINT: 255 F (124C)

SPECIFIC GRAVITY: NOT AVAILABLE ***SOLUBILITY IN WATER:*** INSOLUBLE

SOLVENT SOLUBILITY: SOLUBLE IN ALCOHOL.

FIRE AND EXPLOSION DATA

FIRE AND EXPLOSION HAZARD: SLIGHT FIRE HAZARD WHEN EXPOSED TO HEAT OR FLAME.

DUST-AIR MIXTURES MAY IGNITE OR EXPLODE.

FIREFIGHTING MEDIA: DRY CHEMICAL, CARBON DIOXIDE, HALON, WATER SPRAY OR STANDARD FOAM (1987 EMERGENCY RESPONSE GUIDEBOOK, DOT P 5800.4).

FOR LARGER FIRES, USE WATER SPRAY, FOG OR STANDARD FOAM (1987 EMERGENCY RESPONSE GUIDEBOOK, DOT P 5800.4).

FIREFIGHTING: MOVE CONTAINERS FROM FIRE AREA IF POSSIBLE. FIGHT FIRE FROM MAXIMUM DISTANCE. STAY AWAY FROM STORAGE TANK ENDS. DIKE FIRE CONTROL WATER FOR LATER DISPOSAL. DO NOT SCATTER MATERIAL (1987 EMERGENCY RESPONSE GUIDEBOOK, DOT P 5800.4, GUIDE PAGE 55).

EXTINGUISH USING AGENT SUITABLE FOR TYPE OF SURROUNDING FIRE. AVOID BREATHING VAPORS AND DUSTS. KEEP UPWIND.

TRANSPORTATION DATA

DEPARTMENT OF TRANSPORTATION HAZARD CLASSIFICATION 49 CFR 172.101: POISON B

DEPARTMENT OF TRANSPORTATION LABELING REQUIREMENTS 49 CFR 172.101 AND SUBPART E: POISON

DEPARTMENT OF TRANSPORTATION PACKAGING REQUIREMENTS: 49 CFR 173.365 EXCEPTIONS: 49 CFR 173.364

TOXICITY

COUMAFURYL: TOXICITY DATA: 25 MG/KG ORAL-RAT LD50; 14700 UG/KG ORAL-MOUSE LD50. 0.4 MG/KG ORAL-RAT LD50 (HAYES, PESTICIDES STUDIED IN MAN, 1982). CARCINOGEN STATUS: NONE. ACUTE TOXICITY LEVEL: HIGHLY TOXIC BY INGESTION. TARGET EFFECTS: HEMORRHAGIC AGENT. AT INCREASED RISK FROM EXPOSURE: PERSONS WITH SKIN IRRITATION, ASTHMA, INFLAMMATORY OR FIBROTIC PULMONARY DISEASE, BLOOD DYSCARSIAS, BLEEDING TENDENCIES, LIVER OR KIDNEY DISEASE, ULCERS OF THE GASTROINTESTINAL TRACT, OR HYPERTENSION.* ADDITIONAL DATA: INTERACTIONS WITH MEDICATIONS HAVE BEEN REPORTED.*

* MAY BE BASED ON GENERAL INFORMATION ON COUMARIN DERIVATIVES.

HEALTH EFFECTS AND FIRST AID

INHALATION: COUMAFURYL: SEE INFORMATION ON COUMARIN DERIVATIVES.

COUMARIN DERIVATIVES: HEMORRHAGIC AGENT. **ACUTE EXPOSURE-** ABSORPTION BY THE LUNGS MAY RESULT IN HEMORRHAGIC EFFECTS AS DESCRIBED IN CHRONIC EXPOSURE. SEVERE CASES MAY BE FATAL. **CHRONIC EXPOSURE-** REPEATED ABSORPTION MAY CAUSE THE INHIBITION OF PROTHROMBIN SYNTHESIS AND DAMAGE TO CAPILLARY PERMEABILITY RESULTING IN WIDESPREAD INTERNAL HEMORRHAGE WITH ASSOCIATED EFFECTS OF NOSEBLEED, HEMATOMA, HEMATURIA, WIDESPREAD BRUISING, AND ANEMIA.

FIRST AID- REMOVE FROM EXPOSURE AREA TO FRESH AIR IMMEDIATELY. IF BREATHING HAS STOPPED, PERFORM ARTIFICIAL RESPIRATION. KEEP PERSON WARM AND AT REST. TREAT SYMPTOMATICALLY AND SUPPORTIVELY. GET MEDICAL ATTENTION IMMEDIATELY.

SKIN CONTACT: COUMAFURYL: SEE INFORMATION ON COUMARIN DERIVATIVES.

COUMARIN DERIVATIVES: HEMORRHAGIC AGENT. **ACUTE EXPOSURE-** ABSORPTION THROUGH THE SKIN MAY RESULT IN HEMORRHAGIC EFFECTS AS DESCRIBED IN CHRONIC EXPOSURE. SEVERE CASES MAY BE FATAL. **CHRONIC EXPOSURE-** REPEATED ABSORPTION MAY CAUSE THE INHIBITION OF PROTHROMBIN SYNTHESIS AND DAMAGE TO CAPILLARY PERMEABILITY RESULTING IN WIDESPREAD INTERNAL HEMORRHAGE WITH ASSOCIATED EFFECTS OF NOSEBLEED, HEMATOMA, HEMATURIA, WIDESPREAD BRUISING, AND ANEMIA.

FIRST AID- REMOVE CONTAMINATED CLOTHING AND SHOES IMMEDIATELY. WASH AFFECTED AREA WITH SOAP OR MILD DETERGENT AND LARGE AMOUNTS OF WATER UNTIL NO EVIDENCE OF CHEMICAL REMAINS (APPROXIMATELY 15-20 MINUTES). GET MEDICAL ATTENTION IMMEDIATELY.

EYE CONTACT: COUMAFURYL: **ACUTE EXPOSURE**- NO DATA AVAILABLE. **CHRONIC EXPOSURE**- NO DATA AVAILABLE.

FIRST AID- WASH EYES IMMEDIATELY WITH LARGE AMOUNTS OF WATER OR NORMAL SALINE, OCCASIONALLY LIFTING UPPER AND LOWER LIDS, UNTIL NO EVIDENCE OF CHEMICAL REMAINS (APPROXIMATELY 15-20 MINUTES). GET MEDICAL ATTENTION IMMEDIATELY.

INGESTION: COUMAFURYL: HIGHLY TOXIC. SEE INFORMATION ON COUMARIN DERIVATIVES.

COUMARIN DERIVATIVES: HEMORRHAGIC AGENT. **ACUTE EXPOSURE**- MAY BE READILY ABSORBED FROM THE GASTROINTESTINAL TRACT AND CAUSE THE INHIBITION OF PROTHROMBIN SYNTHESIS AND DAMAGE TO CAPILLARY PERMEABILITY RESULTING IN WIDESPREAD INTERNAL HEMORRHAGE ACCOMPANIED BY THE HEMORRHAGIC SYMPTOMS AS DESCRIBED IN CHRONIC EXPOSURE. SEVERE CASES MAY BE FATAL. **CHRONIC EXPOSURE**- REPEATED INGESTION MAY CAUSE NOSEBLEED, BLEEDING GUMS AND PHARYNX, PETECHIAL RASH, WIDESPREAD BRUISING, HEMATOMA, HEMOPTYSIS, HEMATEMESIS, HEMATURIA, BLOODY STOOLS, BLEEDING INTO THE ORGANS, GASTROINTESTINAL TRACT, JOINTS, ABDOMINAL OR RETROPERITONEAL AREA WITH ABDOMINAL, BACK, JOINT AND LIMB PAIN AND CEREBROVASCULAR ACCIDENT. ANEMIA ACCOMPANIED BY WEAKNESS, PALLOR, AND SHOCK MAY OCCUR. SEVERE HEMORRHAGING MAY CAUSE DEATH. THERAPEUTIC USE OF SOME COUMARIN DERIVATIVES HAS INFREQUENTLY PRODUCED GASTROINTESTINAL DISTURBANCES, ELEVATED TRANSAMINASE, URTICARIA, DERMATITIS, LEUKOPENIA, ALOPECIA, FEVER, HYPERSENSITIVITY REACTIONS, AND RARELY SKIN NECROSIS.

FIRST AID- IF ONLY A FEW GRAINS OF ANTICOAGULANT BAIT HAVE BEEN INGESTED BY AN ADULT OR CHILD HAVING NO ANTECEDENT LIVER OR BLOOD CLOTTING DISEASE, TREATMENT IS PROBABLY UNNECESSARY. IF LARGE AMOUNTS OF ANTICOAGULANT WERE INGESTED IN THE PRECEDING 2-3 HOURS, INDUCE VOMITING WITH SYRUP OF IPECAC, FOLLOWED BY 1-2 GLASSES OF WATER. FOLLOWING EMESIS, GIVE ACTIVATED CHARCOAL IN 4-8 OUNCES OF WATER TO LIMIT ABSORPTION OF ANTICOAGULANT REMAINING IN THE GUT. OBSERVE PATIENT 4-5 DAYS AFTER INGESTION. (MORGAN, RECOGNITION AND MANAGEMENT OF PESTICIDE POISONINGS, THIRD EDITION). GET MEDICAL ATTENTION.

ANTIDOTE: THE FOLLOWING ANTIDOTE HAS BEEN RECOMMENDED. HOWEVER, THE DECISION AS TO WHETHER THE SEVERITY OF POISONING REQUIRES ADMINISTRATION OF ANY ANTIDOTE AND ACTUAL DOSE REQUIRED SHOULD BE MADE BY QUALIFIED MEDICAL PERSONNEL.

OVERDOSE OF ANTICOAGULANTS: VITAMIN K IS A SPECIFIC ANTIDOTE. VITAMIN K1 EMULSION IS THE PREFERRED FORM. THE INITIAL SUBCUTANEOUS OR INTRAMUSCULAR DOSE IN ADULTS IS 5 TO 10 MG (UP TO 25 MG), REPEATED ONCE IF NECESSARY. ONLY IN VICTIMS WHO ARE BLEEDING SEVERLY OR OTHERWISE IN SERIOUS DISTRESS SHOULD THE DRUG BE GIVEN INTRAVENOUSLY AND THEN AT A RATE NO FASTER THAN 1 MG/MINUTE. IF NECESSARY, ON SUBSEQUENT DAYS, VITAMIN K1 SHOULD BE CONTINUED AT A REDUCED LEVEL UNTIL THE PROTHROMBIN TIME RETURNS TO NORMAL. VITAMIN K1 IS PREFERABLE TO K1 OXIDE (DOSE 0.5-2.5) AND CERTAINLY PREFERABLE TO MENADIONE OR MENADIONE SODIUM BISULFITE (GOSSELIN, CLINICAL TOXICOLOGY OF COMMERCIAL PRODUCTS, 5TH ED.). ANTIDOTE SHOULD BE ADMINISTERED BY QUALIFIED MEDICAL PERSONNEL.

REACTIVITY

REACTIVITY: STABLE UNDER NORMAL TEMPERATURES AND PRESSURES.

INCOMPATIBILITIES: COUMAFURYL: OXIDIZERS (STRONG): FIRE AND EXPLOSION HAZARD.

DECOMPOSITION: THERMAL DECOMPOSITION PRODUCTS MAY INCLUDE TOXIC OXIDES OF CARBON.

POLYMERIZATION: HAZARDOUS POLYMERIZATION HAS NOT BEEN REPORTED TO OCCUR UNDER NORMAL TEMPERATURES AND PRESSURES.

STORAGE AND DISPOSAL

OBSERVE ALL FEDERAL, STATE AND LOCAL REGULATIONS WHEN STORING OR DISPOSING OF THIS SUBSTANCE. FOR ASSISTANCE, CONTACT THE DISTRICT DIRECTOR OF THE ENVIRONMENTAL PROTECTION AGENCY.

STORAGE

STORE IN ACCORDANCE WITH 40 CFR 165 RECOMMENDED PROCEDURES FOR THE DISPOSAL AND STORAGE OF PESTICIDES AND PESTICIDE CONTAINERS.
STORE AWAY FROM INCOMPATIBLE SUBSTANCES.

DISPOSAL

DISPOSAL MUST BE IN ACCORDANCE WITH 40 CFR 165 RECOMMENDED PROCEDURES FOR THE DISPOSAL AND STORAGE OF PESTICIDES AND PESTICIDE CONTAINERS.

CONDITIONS TO AVOID

MAY BURN BUT DOES NOT IGNITE READILY. CONTAINERS MAY EXPLODE IN HEAT OF FIRE.

SPILL AND LEAK PROCEDURES

OCCUPATIONAL SPILL: DO NOT TOUCH SPILLED MATERIAL. STOP LEAK IF YOU CAN DO IT WITHOUT RISK. USE WATER SPRAY TO REDUCE VAPORS. FOR SMALL SPILLS, TAKE UP WITH SAND OR OTHER ABSORBENT MATERIAL AND PLACE INTO CONTAINERS FOR LATER DISPOSAL. FOR SMALL DRY SPILLS, WITH A CLEAN SHOVEL PLACE MATERIAL INTO CLEAN, DRY CONTAINERS AND COVER. MOVE CONTAINERS FROM SPILL AREA. FOR LARGER SPILLS, DIKE FAR AHEAD OF SPILL FOR LATER DISPOSAL. KEEP UNNECESSARY PEOPLE AWAY. ISOLATE HAZARD AREA AND DENY ENTRY. VENTILATE CLOSED SPACES BEFORE ENTERING.

PROTECTIVE EQUIPMENT

VENTILATION: PROCESS ENCLOSURE RECOMMENDED.

RESPIRATOR: THE FOLLOWING RESPIRATORS ARE RECOMMENDED BASED ON INFORMATION FOUND IN THE PHYSICAL DATA, TOXICITY AND HEALTH EFFECTS SECTIONS. THEY ARE RANKED IN ORDER FROM MINIMUM TO MAXIMUM RESPIRATORY PROTECTION. THE SPECIFIC RESPIRATOR SELECTED MUST BE BASED ON CONTAMINATION LEVELS FOUND IN THE WORK PLACE, MUST NOT EXCEED THE WORKING LIMITS OF THE RESPIRATOR AND BE JOINTLY APPROVED BY THE NATIONAL INSTITUTE FOR OCCUPATIONAL SAFETY AND HEALTH AND THE MINE SAFETY AND HEALTH ADMINISTRATION (NIOSH-MSHA).

TYPE 'C' SUPPLIED-AIR RESPIRATOR WITH A FULL FACEPIECE OPERATED IN PRESSURE-DEMAND OR OTHER POSITIVE PRESSURE MODE OR WITH A FULL FACEPIECE, HELMET OR HOOD OPERATED IN CONTINOUS-FLOW MODE.

SELF-CONTAINED BREATHING APPARATUS WITH A FULL FACEPIECE OPERATED IN PRESSURE-DEMAND OR OTHER POSITIVE PRESSURE MODE.

FOR FIREFIGHTING AND OTHER IMMEDIATELY DANGEROUS TO LIFE OR HEALTH CONDITIONS:

SELF-CONTAINED BREATHING APPARATUS WITH FULL FACEPIECE OPERATED IN PRESSURE-DEMAND OR OTHER POSITIVE PRESSURE MODE.

SUPPLIED-AIR RESPIRATOR WITH FULL FACEPIECE AND OPERATED IN PRESSURE-DEMAND OR OTHER POSITIVE PRESSURE MODE IN COMBINATION WITH AN AUXILIARY SELF-CONTAINED BREATHING APPARATUS OPERATED IN PRESSURE-DEMAND OR OTHER POSITIVE PRESSURE MODE.

CLOTHING: EMPLOYEE MUST WEAR APPROPRIATE PROTECTIVE (IMPERVIOUS) CLOTHING AND EQUIPMENT TO PREVENT ANY POSSIBILITY OF SKIN CONTACT WITH THIS SUBSTANCE.

GLOVES: EMPLOYEE MUST WEAR APPROPRIATE PROTECTIVE GLOVES TO PREVENT CONTACT WITH THIS SUBSTANCE.

EYE PROTECTION: EMPLOYEE MUST WEAR SPLASH-PROOF OR DUST-RESISTANT SAFETY GOGGLES WITH OR WITHOUT A FACESHIELD TO PREVENT CONTACT WITH THIS SUBSTANCE.

EMERGENCY EYE WASH: WHERE THERE IS ANY POSSIBILITY THAT AN EMPLOYEE'S EYES MAY BE EXPOSED TO THIS SUBSTANCE, THE EMPLOYER SHOULD PROVIDE AN EYE WASH FOUNTAIN WITHIN THE IMMEDIATE WORK AREA FOR EMERGENCY USE.

AUTHORIZED BY- OCCUPATIONAL HEALTH SERVICES, INC.

CREATION DATE: 10/04/89 ***REVISION DATE:*** 05/04/90

MATERIAL SAFETY DATA SHEET

OCCUPATIONAL HEALTH SERVICES, INC.
AGRICULTURE AND PESTICIDE DIVISION
450 SEVENTH AVENUE, SUITE 2407
NEW YORK, NEW YORK 10123
1-800-445-MSDS OR (212) 967-1100

EMERGENCY CONTACT:
JOHN S. BRANSFORD, JR. (615) 292-1180

SUBSTANCE IDENTIFICATION

CAS-NUMBER 56-72-4

SUBSTANCE: **COUMAPHOS**

TRADE NAMES/SYNONYMS: PHOSPHOROTHIOIC ACID, O-(3-CHLORO-4-METHYL-2-OXO-2H-1-BENZOPYRAN-7-YL) O,O-DIETHYL ESTER; COUMARIN, 3-CHLORO-7-HYDROXY-4-METHYL-,O-ESTER WITH O,O-DIETHYL PHOSPHOROTHIOATE; O-3-CHLORO-4-METHYL-2-OXO-2H-CHROMEN-7-YL O,O-DIETHYL PHOSPHOROTHIOATE; O-3-CHLORO-4-METHYLCOUMARIN-7-YL O,O-DIETHYL PHOSPHOROTHIOATE; 3-CHLORO-7-DIETHOXYPHOSPHINOTHIOYLOXY-4-METHYLCOUMARIN; O-(3-CHLORO-4-METHYL-2-OXO-2H-1-BENZOPYRAN-7-YL) O,O DIETHYL PHOSPHOROTHIOATE; 3-CHLORO-7-HYDROXY-4-METHYLCOUMARIN O-ESTER WITH O,O DIETHYL PHOSPHOROTHIOATE;

3-CHLORO-4-METHYLCOUMARIN-7-YL DIETHYL PHOSPHOROTHIONATE; 3-CHLORO-7-HYDROXY-4-METHYL-COUMARIN-O,O-DIETHYL PHOSPHOROTHIOATE; O,O DIETHYL O-3-CHLORO-4-METHYL-2-OXO-2H-1-BENZOPYRAN-7-YL PHOSPHOROTHIOATE; CO-RAL; MUSCATOX; ENT 17,957; STCC 4921505; C14H16CLO5PS; PST05490

CHEMICAL FAMILY: ORGANOPHOSPHATE

MOLECULAR FORMULA: C14-H16-CL-O5-P-S

MOLECULAR WEIGHT: 362.78

CERCLA RATINGS (SCALE 0-3): HEALTH=3 FIRE=0 REACTIVITY=0 PERSISTENCE=2

NFPA RATINGS (SCALE 0-4): HEALTH=4 FIRE=0 REACTIVITY=0

COMPONENTS AND CONTAMINANTS

COMPONENT: COUMAPHOS ***PERCENT:*** 100
CAS# 56-72-4

OTHER CONTAMINANTS: NONE

EXPOSURE LIMITS: NO OCCUPATIONAL EXPOSURE LIMITS ESTABLISHED BY OSHA, ACGIH, OR NIOSH.

COUMAPHOS: 100/10,000 POUNDS SARA SECTION 302 THRESHOLD PLANNING QUANTITY 10 POUNDS SARA SECTION 304 REPORTABLE QUANTITY 10 POUNDS CERLCA SECTION 103 REPORTABLE QUANTITY

PHYSICAL DATA

DESCRIPTION: COLORLESS CRYSTALLINE POWDER WITH SLIGHT ODOR OF SULFUR COMPOUNDS

MELTING POINT: 194 F (90 C) ***SPECIFIC GRAVITY:*** 1.474

SOLUBILITY IN WATER: 1.50 PPM ***ODOR THRESHOLD:*** 0.02 PPM

SOLVENT SOLUBILITY: SOLUBLE IN ESTER, KETONES, ALCOHOLS, ACETONE, CORN OIL, CHLOROFORM, AND AROMATIC HYDROCARBONS

FIRE AND EXPLOSION DATA

FIRE AND EXPLOSION HAZARD: NEGLIGIBLE FIRE HAZARD WHEN EXPOSED TO HEAT OR FLAME.

FIREFIGHTING MEDIA: DRY CHEMICAL, CARBON DIOXIDE, HALON, WATER SPRAY OR STANDARD FOAM (1987 EMERGENCY RESPONSE GUIDEBOOK, DOT P 5800.4).
FOR LARGER FIRES, USE WATER SPRAY, FOG OR STANDARD FOAM (1987 EMERGENCY RESPONSE GUIDEBOOK, DOT P 5800.4).

FIREFIGHTING: MOVE CONTAINERS FROM FIRE AREA IF POSSIBLE. FIGHT FIRE FROM MAXIMUM DISTANCE. STAY AWAY FROM STORAGE TANK ENDS. DIKE FIRE CONTROL WATER FOR LATER DISPOSAL. DO NOT SCATTER MATERIAL (1987 EMERGENCY RESPONSE GUIDEBOOK, DOT P 5800.4, GUIDE PAGE 55).
EXTINGUISH ONLY IF FLOW CAN BE STOPPED; USE FLOODING AMOUNTS OF WATER AS FOG, SOLID STREAMS MAY BE INEFFECTIVE. COOL CONTAINERS WITH FLOODING AMOUNTS OF WATER FROM AS FAR A DISTANCE AS POSSIBLE. USE WATER SPRAY TO ABSORB TOXIC VAPORS. AVOID BREATHING TOXIC VAPORS; KEEP UPWIND. CONSIDER EVACUATION OF DOWNWIND AREA IF MATERIAL IS LEAKING.

TRANSPORTATION DATA

DEPARTMENT OF TRANSPORTATION HAZARD CLASSIFICATION 49 CFR 172.101: POISON B

DEPARTMENT OF TRANSPORTATION LABELING REQUIREMENTS 49 CFR 172.101 AND SUBPART E: POISON

DEPARTMENT OF TRANSPORTATION PACKAGING REQUIREMENTS: 49 CFR 173.365 EXCEPTIONS: 49 CFR 173.364

TOXICITY

COUMAPHOS: TOXICITY DATA: 303 MG/M3 INHALATION-RAT LC50; 500 MG/KG SKIN-RABBIT LD50; 860 MG/KG SKIN-RAT LD50; 13 MG/KG ORAL-RAT LD50; 28 MG/KG ORAL-MOUSE LD50; 80 MG/KG ORAL-RABBIT LD50;58 MG/KG ORAL-GUINEA PIG LD50; 22600 UG/KG ORAL-DOMESTIC ANIMAL LD50; 7500 UG/KG INTRAPERITONEAL-RAT LD50; 50 MG/KG INTRAPERITONEAL-MOUSE LD50; 140 MG/KG INTRAPERITONEAL-GUINEA PIG LD50; MUTAGENIC DATA (RTECS). CARCINOGEN STATUS: NONE. ACUTE TOXICITY LEVEL: HIGHLY TOXIC BY INHALATION AND INGESTION; TOXIC BY DERMAL ABSORPTION. TARGET EFFECTS: CHOLINESTERASE INHIBITOR. POISONING MAY AFFECT THE NERVOUS SYSTEM.* AT INCREASED RISK FROM EXPOSURE: PERSONS WITH RESPIRATORY AILMENTS, RECENT EXPOSURE TO CHOLINESTERASE INHIBITORS OR IMPAIRED CHOLINESTERASE PRODUCTION, OR LIVER MALFUNCTION.* ADDITIONAL DATA: MAY CROSS THE PLACENTA. HIGH ENVIRONMENTAL TEMPERATURES OR EXPOSURE OF THE CHEMICAL TO VISIBLE OR ULTRAVIOLET LIGHT MAY ENHANCE THE TOXICITY. INTERACTIONS WITH MEDICATIONS MAY OCCUR.*

* MAY BE BASED ON GENERAL INFORMATION ON ORGANOPHOSPHATES.

HEALTH EFFECTS AND FIRST AID

INHALATION: COUMAPHOS: HIGHLY TOXIC. SEE INFORMATION ON ORGANOPHOSPHATES.

ORGANOPHOSPHATES: CHOLINESTERASE INHIBITOR. **ACUTE EXPOSURE**- WHEN INHALED, THE FIRST EFFECTS OF CHOLINESTERASE INHIBITORS ARE USUALLY RESPIRATORY AND MAY INCLUDE NASAL HYPEREMIA AND WATERY DISCHARGE, COUGH, CHEST DISCOMFORT, DYSPNEA, AND WHEEZING DUE TO INCREASED BRONCHIAL SECRETIONS AND BRONCHOCONSTRICTION. IF SUFFICIENT AMOUNTS ARE ABSORBED, OTHER SYSTEMIC EFFECTS MAY BEGIN WITHIN A FEW MINUTES OR BE DELAYED FOR UP TO 12 HOURS. SYMPTOMS MAY INCLUDE PALLOR, NAUSEA, VOMITING, DIARRHEA, ABDOMINAL CRAMPS, HEADACHE, DIZZINESS, OCULAR PAIN, BLURRED VISION, MIOSIS OR IN SOME CASES, ESPECIALLY INITIALLY, MYDRIASIS, LACRIMATION, SALIVATION, SWEATING, AND CONFUSION. OTHER REPORTED CENTRAL NERVOUS SYSTEM OR NEUROMUSCULAR EFFECTS MAY INCLUDE ATAXIA, SLURRED SPEECH, AREFLEXIA, WEAKNESS, FATIGUE, FASCICULATIONS, TWITCHING, TREMORS POSSIBLY OF THE TONGUE AND EYELIDS, AND EVENTUALLY PARALYSIS OF THE EXTREMITIES AND POSSIBLY OF THE RESPIRATORY MUSCLES. IN SEVERE CASES THERE MAY ALSO BE INVOLUNTARY DEFECATION AND URINATION, CYANOSIS, PSYCHOSIS, HYPERGLYCEMIA, ACUTE PANCREATITIS, CARDIAC IRREGULARITIES, PULMONARY EDEMA, UNCONSCIOUSNESS, CONVULSIONS, AND COMA. DEATH IS PRIMARILY DUE TO RESPIRATORY FAILURE, ALTHOUGH CARDIOVASCULAR EFFECTS INCLUDING CARDIAC ARREST MAY ALSO BE IMPLICATED. LONG TERM SEQUELAE ARE RARE BUT MAY INCLUDE NEUROPSYCHIATRIC DISORDERS AND MYOPATHY WITH MUSCLE TENDERNESS. SOME ORGANOPHOSPHATES MAY CAUSE A DELAYED NEUROPATHY BEGINNING 1-4 WEEKS AFTER AN ACUTE EXPOSURE WHICH MAY OR MAY NOT HAVE CAUSED ACUTE CHOLINERGIC EFFECTS. NUMBNESS, TINGLING, WEAKNESS AND CRAMPING BEGINNING SYMMETRICALLY IN THE LOWER LIMBS MAY PROGRESS TO ATAXIA AND PARALYSIS. IN SEVERE CASES, UPPER LIMB INVOLVEMENT IS POSSIBLE AND FLACCID PARALYSIS MAY PROGRESS TO SPASTIC PARALYSIS WITH EXAGGERATED REFLEXES. IMPROVEMENT MAY OCCUR OVER MONTHS TO YEARS, BUT SOME RESIDUAL IMPAIRMENT USUALLY REMAINS.
CHRONIC EXPOSURE- REPEATED OR PROLONGED EXPOSURE MAY RESULT IN THE EFFECTS OF ACUTE EXPOSURE INCLUDING THE DELAYED NEUROPATHY. OTHER EFFECTS REPORTED IN WORKERS REPEATEDLY EXPOSED INCLUDE IMPAIRED MEMORY AND CONCENTRATION, ACUTE PSYCHOSIS, SEVERE DEPRESSIONS, IRRITABILTY, CONFUSION, APATHY, EMOTIONAL LABILITY, SOCIAL WITHDRAWAL, CONFUSION, HEADACHE, SPEECH DIFFICULTIES, DELAYED REACTION TIMES, SPATIAL DISORIENTATION, NIGHTMARES, SLEEPWALKING, AND DROWSINESS OR INSOMNIA. AN INFLUENZA-LIKE CONDITION WITH HEADACHE, NAUSEA, WEAKNESS, ANOREXIA AND MALAISE HAS ALSO BEEN REPORTED.

FIRST AID- REMOVE FROM EXPOSURE AREA TO FRESH AIR IMMEDIATELY. IF BREATHING HAS STOPPED, GIVE ARTIFICIAL RESPIRATION. MAINTAIN AIRWAY AND BLOOD PRESSURE AND ADMINISTER OXYGEN IF AVAILABLE. KEEP AFFECTED PERSON WARM AND AT REST. TREAT SYMPTOMATICALLY AND SUPPORTIVELY. ADMINISTRATION OF OXYGEN SHOULD BE PERFORMED BY QUALIFIED PERSONNEL. GET MEDICAL ATTENTION IMMEDIATELY.

SKIN CONTACT: COUMAPHOS: TOXIC. SEE INFORMATION ON ORGANOPHOSPHATES.

ORGANOPHOSPHATES: CHOLINESTERASE INHIBITOR. **ACUTE EXPOSURE**- LOCALIZED SWEATING AND FASCICULATIONS MAY OCCUR AT THE SITE OF CONTACT. IF SUFFICIENT AMOUNTS ARE ABSORBED, OTHER EFFECTS OF CHOLINESTERASE INHIBITION AS DESCRIBED IN ACUTE INHALATION MAY OCCUR. SYMPTOMS MAY BE DELAYED 2-3 HOURS, BUT USUALLY NO MORE THAN 12 HOURS. THE RATE OF ABSORPTION IS INCREASED BY THE PRESENCE OF DERMATITIS OR HIGH AMBIENT TEMPERATURES. DELAYED NEUROPATHY IS ALSO POSSIBLE. **CHRONIC EXPOSURE**- REPEATED OR PROLONGED EXPOSURE MAY CAUSE EFFECTS AS DESCRIBED IN ACUTE EXPOSURE. SOME ORGANOPHOSPHATES MAY CAUSE SENSITIZATION.

FIRST AID- REMOVE CONTAMINATED CLOTHING IMMEDIATELY. WASH CONTAMINATED AREAS WITH SOAP AND WATER FOLLOWED BY ALCOHOL (ARENA, POISONING, 4TH ED.). EMERGENCY PERSONNEL SHOULD WEAR GLOVES AND AVOID CONTAMINATION. TREAT RESPIRATORY DIFFICULTY WITH ARTIFICIAL RESPIRATION. GET MEDICAL ATTENTION IMMEDIATELY.

EYE CONTACT: COUMAPHOS: SEE INFORMATION ON ORGANOPHOSPHATES.

ORGANOPHOSPHATES: CHOLINESTERASE INHIBITOR. **ACUTE EXPOSURE**- DIRECT CONTACT MAY CAUSE PAIN, HYPEREMIA, LACRIMATION, TWITCHING OF THE EYELIDS, MIOSIS, AND CILIARY MUSCLE SPASM WITH LOSS OF ACCOMODATION, BLURRED OR DIMMED VISION AND BROWACHE. SOMETIMES MYDRIASIS MAY OCCUR INSTEAD OF MIOSIS. WITH SUFFICIENT EXPOSURE, OTHER SYMPTOMS OF CHOLINESTERASE INHIBITION AS DESCRIBED IN ACUTE INHALATION MAY OCCUR. **CHRONIC EXPOSURE**- REPEATED OR PROLONGED EXPOSURE MAY CAUSE EFFECTS AS DESCRIBED IN ACUTE EXPOSURE. SOME COMPOUNDS HAVE CAUSED TOXIC EFFECTS ON THE CRYSTALLINE LENS, CONJUNCTIVAL THICKENING AND OBSTRUCTION OF THE NASOLACRIMAL CANALS WHEN USED AS MIOTIC EYEDROPS.

FIRST AID- IRRIGATE EYES WITH WATER OR SALINE SOLUTION. IF SYMPTOMS OF POISONING OCCUR, TREAT RESPIRATORY DIFFICULTY WITH ARTIFICIAL RESPIRATION AND OXYGEN. OBSERVE PATIENT FOR AT LEAST 24-36 HOURS (GOSSELIN, CLINICAL TOXICOLOGY OF COMMERCIAL PRODUCTS, 5TH ED.). GET MEDICAL ATTENTION IMMEDIATELY. OXYGEN SHOULD BE ADMINISTERED BY QUALIFIED MEDICAL PERSONNEL.

INGESTION: COUMAPHOS: HIGHLY TOXIC. RATS FED AT LEVELS OF 25 AND 100 PPM FOR TWO YEARS DEVELOPED A SHORTENED LIFE SPAN AND DECREASED LIVER WEIGHT. A DECREASE IN THE NUMBER OF PREGNANCIES, LITTER SIZE, AND SURVIVING OFFSPRING WAS OBSERVED IN A STUDY OF MICE FED COUMAPHOS AT A DIETARY LEVEL OF 100 PPM. NO REPRODUCTIVE EFFECTS WERE OBSERVED IN THREE GENERATIONS OF MICE AT A DIETARY LEVEL OF 25 PPM. SEE INFORMATION ON ORGANOPHOSPHATES.

ORGANOPHOSPHATES: CHOLINESTERASE INHIBITOR. **ACUTE EXPOSURE**- WHEN INGESTED, THE FIRST EFFECTS MAY BE NAUSEA, VOMITING, ANOREXIA, ABDOMINAL CRAMPS AND DIARRHEA. GASTROINTESTINAL ABSORPTION MAY CAUSE SYMPTOMS OF CHOLINESTERASE INHIBITION AS DESCRIBED IN ACUTE INHALATION. SYMPTOMS MAY BEGIN WITHIN MINUTES OR BE DELAYED FOR HOURS. DELAYED EFFECTS INCLUDING NEUROPATHY MAY ALSO OCCUR. **CHRONIC EXPOSURE**- REPEATED INGESTION MAY CAUSE EFFECTS AS DESCRIBED IN ACUTE EXPOSURE.

FIRST AID- IF PERSON IS ALERT AND RESPIRATION IS NOT DEPRESSED, GIVE SYRUP OF IPECAC FOLLOWED BY WATER (IF VOMITING OCCURS, KEEP HEAD BELOW HIPS TO PREVENT ASPIRATION). IF CONSCIOUSNESS LEVEL DECLINES OR VOMITING HAS NOT OCCURRED IN 15 MINUTES EMPTY STOMACH BY GASTRIC LAVAGE WITH THE AID OF CUFFED ENDOTRACHEAL TUBE USING ISOTONIC SALINE OR 5% SODIUM BICARBONATE FOLLOW WITH ACTIVATED CHARCOAL. ESTABLISH AND MAINTAIN AIRWAY. TREAT RESPIRATORY DIFFICULTY WITH ARTIFICIAL RESPIRATION AND OXYGEN. DO NOT GIVE MORPHINE, AMINOPHYLLINE, PHENOTHIAZINES, RESERPINE, FUROSEMIDE, OR ETHACRYNIC ACID (MORGAN, RECOGNITION AND MANAGEMENT OF PESTICIDE POISONINGS, 3RD ED.). TREAT SYMPTOMATICALLY AND SUPPORTIVELY. ADMINISTRATION OF OXYGEN AND LAVAGE MUST BE PERFORMED BY QUALIFIED MEDICAL PERSONNEL. GET MEDICAL ATTENTION IMMEDIATELY.

ANTIDOTE: THE FOLLOWING ANTIDOTE(S) HAVE BEEN RECOMMENDED. HOWEVER, THE DECISION AS TO WHETHER THE SEVERITY OF POISONING REQUIRES ADMINISTRATION OF ANY ANTIDOTE AND ACTUAL DOSE REQUIRED SHOULD BE MADE BY QUALIFIED MEDICAL PERSONNEL.

FOR CHOLINESTERASE INHIBITORS: ESTABLISH CLEAR AIRWAY AND TISSUE OXYGENATION BY ASPIRATION OF SECRETIONS, AND IF NECESSARY, BY ASSISTED PULMONARY VENTILATION WITH OXYGEN. IMPROVE TISSUE OXYGENATION AS MUCH AS POSSIBLE BEFORE ADMINISTERING ATROPINE TO MINIMIZE THE RISK OF VENTRICULAR FIBRILLATION. ADMINISTER ATROPINE SULFATE INTRAVENOUSLY, OR INTRAMUSCULARLY IF IV INJECTION IS NOT POSSIBLE. IN MODERATELY SEVERE POISONING ADMINISTER ATROPINE SULFATE, 0.4-2.0 MG REPEATED EVERY 15 MINUTES UNTIL ATROPINIZATION IS ACHIEVED (TACHYCARDIA, FLUSHING, DRY MOUTH, MYDRIASIS). MAINTAIN ATROPINIZATION BY REPEATED DOSES FOR 2-12 HOURS, OR LONGER, DEPENDING ON THE SEVERITY OF POISONING. THE APPEARANCE OF RALES IN THE LUNG BASES, MIOSIS, SALIVATION, NAUSEA, BRADYCARDIA, ARE ALL INDICATIONS OF INADEQUATE ATROPINIZATION. SEVERELY POISONED INDIVIDUALS MAY EXHIBIT REMARKABLE TOLERANCE TO ATROPINE; TWO OR MORE TIMES THE DOSAGES SUGGESTED ABOVE MAY BE NEEDED. PERSONS NOT POISONED OR ONLY SLIGHTLY POISONED, HOWEVER, MAY DEVELOP SIGNS OF ATROPINE TOXICITY FROM SUCH LARGE DOSAGES: FEVER, MUSCLE FIBRILLATIONS, AND DELIRIUM ARE THE MAIN SIGNS OF ATROPINE TOXICITY. IF THESE SIGNS APPEAR WHILE THE PATIENT IS FULLY ATROPINIZED, ATROPINE ADMINISTRATION SHOULD BE DISCONTINUED, AT LEAST TEMPORARILY. OBSERVE TREATED PATIENTS CLOSELY AT LEAST 24 HOURS TO INSURE THAT SYMPTOMS (POSSIBLY PULMONARY EDEMA) DO NOT RECUR AS ATROPINIZATION WEARS OFF. IN VERY SEVERE POISONINGS, METABOLIC DISPOSITION OF TOXICANT MAY REQUIRE SEVERAL HOURS OR DAYS DURING WHICH ATROPINIZATION MUST BE MAINTAINED. MARKEDLY LOWER LEVELS OF URINARY METABOLITES INDICATE THAT ATROPINE DOSAGE CAN BE TAPERED OFF. AS DOSAGE IS REDUCED, CHECK THE LUNG BASES FREQUENTLY FOR RALES. IF RALES ARE HEARD OR OTHER SYMPTOMS RETURN, RE-ESTABLISH ATROPINIZATION PROMPTLY (MORGAN, RECOGNITION AND MANAGEMENT OF PESTICIDE POISONINGS, 3RD ED.). ADMINISTRATION OF ANTIDOTE MUST BE PERFORMED BY QUALIFIED MEDICAL PERSONNEL.

IN CASES OF SEVERE POISONING BY ORGANOPHOSPHATE PESTICIDES IN WHICH RESPIRATORY DEPRESSION, MUSCLE WEAKNESS AND TWITCHINGS ARE SEVERE, GIVE PRALIDOXIME (PROTOPAM-AYERST, 2-PAM), 1.0 GRAM INTRAVENOUSLY AT NO MORE THAN 0.5 GRAM PER MINUTE. DOSAGE OF PRALIDOXIME MAY BE REPEATED IN 1-2 HOURS, THEN AT 10-12 HOUR INTERVALS IF NEEDED. IN VERY SEVERE POISONINGS, DOSAGE RATES MAY BE DOUBLED. TREATMENT WITH PRALIDOXIME WILL BE MOST EFFECTIVE IF GIVEN WITHIN THIRTY-SIX HOURS AFTER POISONING (MORGAN, RECOGNITION AND MANAGEMENT OF PESTICIDE POISONINGS, 3RD ED.). ANTIDOTE SHOULD BE ADMINISTERED BY QUALIFIED MEDICAL PERSONNEL.

REACTIVITY

REACTIVITY: STABLE UNDER NORMAL TEMPERATURES AND PRESSURES.

INCOMPATIBILITIES: COUMAPHOS: PIPERONYL BUTOXIDE: INCOMPATIBLE. ALKALINE CONDITIONS: SLOWLY HYDROLYZES.

DECOMPOSITION: THERMAL DECOMPOSITION PRODUCTS MAY INCLUDE TOXIC AND HAZARDOUS FUMES OF CHLORINE AND OXIDES OF OXIDES OF SULFUR AND PHOSPHORUS.

POLYMERIZATION: HAZARDOUS POLYMERIZATION HAS NOT BEEN REPORTED TO OCCUR UNDER NORMAL TEMPERATURES AND PRESSURES.

STORAGE AND DISPOSAL

OBSERVE ALL FEDERAL, STATE AND LOCAL REGULATIONS WHEN STORING OR DISPOSING OF THIS SUBSTANCE. FOR ASSISTANCE, CONTACT THE DISTRICT DIRECTOR OF THE ENVIRONMENTAL PROTECTION AGENCY.

****STORAGE****

STORE IN ACCORDANCE WITH 40 CFR 165 RECOMMENDED PROCEDURES FOR THE DISPOSAL AND STORAGE OF PESTICIDES AND PESTICIDE CONTAINERS.

STORE AWAY FROM INCOMPATIBLE SUBSTANCES.

KEEP COOL.

THRESHOLD PLANNING QUANTITY (TPQ): THE SUPERFUND AMENDMENTS AND REAUTHORIZATION ACT (SARA) SECTION 302 REQUIRES THAT EACH FACILITY WHERE ANY EXTREMELY HAZARDOUS SUBSTANCE IS PRESENT IN A QUANTITY EQUAL TO OR GREATER THAN THE TPQ ESTABLISHED FOR THAT SUBSTANCE NOTIFY THE STATE EMERGENCY RESPONSE COMMISSION FOR THE STATE IN WHICH IT IS LOCATED. SECTION 303 OF SARA REQUIRES THESE FACILITIES TO PARTICIPATE IN LOCAL EMERGENCY RESPONSE PLANNING (40 CFR 355.30).

****DISPOSAL****

DISPOSAL MUST BE IN ACCORDANCE WITH 40 CFR 165 RECOMMENDED PROCEDURES FOR THE DISPOSAL AND STORAGE OF PESTICIDES AND PESTICIDE CONTAINERS.

CONDITIONS TO AVOID

NONE REPORTED.

SPILL AND LEAK PROCEDURES

SOIL SPILL: DIG HOLDING AREA SUCH AS LAGOON, POND OR PIT FOR CONTAINMENT. USE PROTECTIVE COVER SUCH AS A PLASTIC SHEET TO PREVENT MATERIAL FROM DISSOLVING IN FIRE EXTINGUISHING WATER OR RAIN.

WATER SPILL: TRAP SPILLED MATERIAL AT BOTTOM IN DEEP WATER POCKETS, EXCAVATED HOLDING AREAS OR WITHIN SAND BAG BARRIERS.

USE ACTIVATED CARBON TO ABSORB SPILLED SUBSTANCE THAT IS DISSOLVED.

USE MECHANICAL DREDGES OR LIFTS TO EXTRACT IMMOBILIZED MASSES OF POLLUTION AND PRECIPITATES.

OCCUPATIONAL SPILL: DO NOT TOUCH SPILLED MATERIAL. STOP LEAK IF YOU CAN DO IT WITHOUT RISK. USE WATER SPRAY TO REDUCE VAPORS. FOR SMALL SPILLS, TAKE UP WITH SAND OR OTHER ABSORBENT MATERIAL AND PLACE INTO CONTAINERS FOR LATER DISPOSAL. FOR SMALL DRY SPILLS, WITH A CLEAN SHOVEL PLACE MATERIAL INTO CLEAN, DRY CONTAINERS AND COVER. MOVE CONTAINERS FROM SPILL AREA. FOR LARGER SPILLS, DIKE FAR AHEAD OF SPILL FOR LATER DISPOSAL. KEEP UNNECESSARY PEOPLE AWAY. ISOLATE HAZARD AREA AND DENY ENTRY. VENTILATE CLOSED SPACES BEFORE ENTERING.

REPORTABLE QUANTITY (RQ): 10 POUNDS THE SUPERFUND AMENDMENTS AND REAUTHORIZATION ACT (SARA) SECTION 304 REQUIRES THAT A RELEASE EQUAL TO OR GREATER THAN THE REPORTABLE QUANTITY FOR THIS SUBSTANCE BE IMMEDIATELY REPORTED TO THE LOCAL EMERGENCY PLANNING COMMITTEE AND THE STATE EMERGENCY RESPONSE COMMISSION (40 CFR 355.40). IF THE RELEASE OF THIS SUBSTANCE IS REPORTABLE UNDER CERCLA SECTION 103, THE NATIONAL RESPONSE CENTER MUST BE NOTIFIED IMMEDIATELY AT (800) 424-8802 OR (202) 426-2675 IN THE METROPOLITAN WASHINGTON, D.C. AREA (40 CFR 302.6).

PROTECTIVE EQUIPMENT

VENTILATION: PROCESS ENCLOSURE RECOMMENDED.

RESPIRATOR: THE FOLLOWING RESPIRATORS ARE RECOMMENDED BASED ON INFORMATION FOUND IN THE PHYSICAL DATA, TOXICITY AND HEALTH EFFECTS SECTIONS. THEY ARE RANKED IN ORDER FROM MINIMUM TO MAXIMUM RESPIRATORY PROTECTION. THE SPECIFIC RESPIRATOR SELECTED MUST BE BASED ON CONTAMINATION LEVELS FOUND IN THE WORK PLACE, MUST NOT EXCEED THE WORKING LIMITS OF THE RESPIRATOR AND BE JOINTLY APPROVED BY THE NATIONAL INSTITUTE FOR OCCUPATIONAL SAFETY AND HEALTH AND THE MINE SAFETY AND HEALTH ADMINISTRATION (NIOSH-MSHA).

TYPE 'C' SUPPLIED-AIR RESPIRATOR WITH A FULL FACEPIECE OPERATED IN PRESSURE-DEMAND OR OTHER POSITIVE PRESSURE MODE OR WITH A FULL FACEPIECE, HELMET OR HOOD OPERATED IN CONTINOUS-FLOW MODE.

SELF-CONTAINED BREATHING APPARATUS WITH A FULL FACEPIECE OPERATED IN PRESSURE-DEMAND OR OTHER POSITIVE PRESSURE MODE.
FOR FIREFIGHTING AND OTHER IMMEDIATELY DANGEROUS TO LIFE OR HEALTH CONDITIONS:
SELF-CONTAINED BREATHING APPARATUS WITH FULL FACEPIECE OPERATED IN PRESSURE-DEMAND OR OTHER POSITIVE PRESSURE MODE.
SUPPLIED-AIR RESPIRATOR WITH FULL FACEPIECE AND OPERATED IN PRESSURE-DEMAND OR OTHER POSITIVE PRESSURE MODE IN COMBINATION WITH AN AUXILIARY SELF-CONTAINED BREATHING APPARATUS OPERATED IN PRESSURE-DEMAND OR OTHER POSITIVE PRESSURE MODE.
CLOTHING: EMPLOYEE MUST WEAR APPROPRIATE PROTECTIVE (IMPERVIOUS) CLOTHING AND EQUIPMENT TO PREVENT ANY POSSIBILITY OF SKIN CONTACT WITH THIS SUBSTANCE.
GLOVES: EMPLOYEE MUST WEAR APPROPRIATE PROTECTIVE GLOVES TO PREVENT CONTACT WITH THIS SUBSTANCE.
EYE PROTECTION: EMPLOYEE MUST WEAR SPLASH-PROOF OR DUST-RESISTANT SAFETY GOGGLES AND A FACESHIELD TO PREVENT CONTACT WITH THIS SUBSTANCE.
EMERGENCY WASH FACILITIES: WHERE THERE IS ANY POSSIBILITY THAT AN EMPLOYEE'S EYES AND/OR SKIN MAY BE EXPOSED TO THIS SUBSTANCE, THE EMPLOYER SHOULD PROVIDE AN EYE WASH FOUNTAIN AND QUICK DRENCH SHOWER WITHIN THE IMMEDIATE WORK AREA FOR EMERGENCY USE.

AUTHORIZED BY- OCCUPATIONAL HEALTH SERVICES, INC.
CREATION DATE: 10/04/89 ***REVISION DATE:*** 04/25/90

MATERIAL SAFETY DATA SHEET

OCCUPATIONAL HEALTH SERVICES, INC.
AGRICULTURE AND PESTICIDE DIVISION
450 SEVENTH AVENUE, SUITE 2407
NEW YORK, NEW YORK 10123
1-800-445-MSDS OR (212) 967-1100

EMERGENCY CONTACT:
JOHN S. BRANSFORD, JR. (615) 292-1180

SUBSTANCE IDENTIFICATION

CAS-NUMBER 5836-29-3
SUBSTANCE: COUMATETRALYL
TRADE NAMES/SYNONYMS: 2H-1-BENZOPYRAN-2-ONE, 4-HYDROXY-3-(1,2,3,4-TETRAHYDRO-1- NAPHTHALENYL)-; COUMARIN, 4-HYDROXY-3-(1,2,3,4-TETRAHYDRO-1-NAPHTHYL)-; 4-HYDROXY-3-(1,2,3,4-TETRAHYDRO-1-NAPHTHALENYL)-2H-1-BENZOPYRAN-2-ONE; 4-HYDROXY-3-(1,2,3,4-TETRAHYDRO-1-NAPHTHYL)COUMARIN; ENDROCIDE; RACUMIN; RODENTIN; C19H16O3; PST05493
CHEMICAL FAMILY: COUMARIN
MOLECULAR FORMULA: C19-H16-O3
MOLECULAR WEIGHT: 292.35
CERCLA RATINGS (SCALE 0-3): HEALTH=3 FIRE=1 REACTIVITY=0 PERSISTENCE=2
NFPA RATINGS (SCALE 0-4): HEALTH=3 FIRE=1 REACTIVITY=0

COMPONENTS AND CONTAMINANTS

COMPONENT: COUMATETRALYL ***PERCENT:*** 100.0
CAS# 5836-29-3
OTHER CONTAMINANTS: NONE
EXPOSURE LIMITS: COUMATETRALYL: NO OCCUPATIONAL EXPOSURE LIMITS ESTABLISHED BY OSHA, ACGIH, OR NIOSH.
500/10,000 POUNDS SARA SECTION 302 THRESHOLD PLANNING QUANTITY 1 POUND SARA SECTION 304 REPORTABLE QUANTITY

PHYSICAL DATA

DESCRIPTION: COLORLESS CRYSTALLINE POWDER. ***MELTING POINT:*** 342-349 F (172-176 C)
SPECIFIC GRAVITY: NOT AVAILABLE ***SOLUBILITY IN WATER:*** 4 PPM @ 20 C
SOLVENT SOLUBILITY: SOLUBLE IN ACETONE AND ALCOHOL; MODERATELY SOLUBLE IN DICHLOROMETHANE AND ISOPROPANOL; SLIGHTLY SOLUBLE IN ETHER AND BENZENE.

FIRE AND EXPLOSION DATA

FIRE AND EXPLOSION HAZARD: SLIGHT FIRE HAZARD WHEN EXPOSED TO HEAT OR FLAME.
FIREFIGHTING MEDIA: DRY CHEMICAL, CARBON DIOXIDE, HALON, WATER SPRAY OR STANDARD FOAM (1987 EMERGENCY RESPONSE GUIDEBOOK, DOT P 5800.4).
FOR LARGER FIRES, USE WATER SPRAY, FOG OR STANDARD FOAM (1987 EMERGENCY RESPONSE GUIDEBOOK, DOT P 5800.4).
FIREFIGHTING: MOVE CONTAINERS FROM FIRE AREA IF POSSIBLE. FIGHT FIRE FROM MAXIMUM DISTANCE. STAY AWAY FROM STORAGE TANK ENDS. DIKE FIRE CONTROL WATER FOR LATER DISPOSAL. DO NOT SCATTER MATERIAL (1987 EMERGENCY RESPONSE GUIDEBOOK, DOT P 5800.4, GUIDE PAGE 55).
EXTINGUISH USING AGENT SUITABLE FOR TYPE OF SURROUNDING FIRE. AVOID BREATHING VAPORS AND DUSTS. KEEP UPWIND.

TRANSPORTATION DATA

DEPARTMENT OF TRANSPORTATION HAZARD CLASSIFICATION 49 CFR 172.101: POISON B
DEPARTMENT OF TRANSPORTATION LABELING REQUIREMENTS 49 CFR 172.101 AND SUBPART E: POISON
DEPARTMENT OF TRANSPORTATION PACKAGING REQUIREMENTS: 49 CFR 173.365 EXCEPTIONS: 49 CFR 173.364

TOXICITY

COUMATETRALYL: TOXICITY DATA: 25 MG/KG ORAL-RAT LD50; 250 MG/KG ORAL-GUINEA PIG LDLO; 20 MG/KG ORAL-CAT LDLO. CARCINOGEN STATUS: NONE. ACUTE TOXICITY LEVEL: HIGHLY TOXIC BY INGESTION. TARGET EFFECTS: HEMORRHAGIC AGENT. AT INCREASED RISK FROM EXPOSURE: PERSONS WITH BLOOD DYSCRASIAS, BLEEDING TENDENCIES, LIVER OR KIDNEY DISEASE, ULCERS OF THE GASTROINTESTINAL TRACT, OR HYPERTENSION.* ADDITIONAL DATA: INTERACTIONS WITH MEDICATIONS HAVE BEEN REPORTED.*
* MAY BE BASED ON GENERAL INFORMATION ON COUMARIN DERIVATIVES.

HEALTH EFFECTS AND FIRST AID

INHALATION: COUMATETRALYL: SEE INFORMATION ON COUMARIN DERIVATIVES.
COUMARIN DERIVATIVES: HEMORRHAGIC AGENT. **ACUTE EXPOSURE-** ABSORPTION BY THE LUNGS MAY RESULT IN HEMORRHAGIC EFFECTS AS DESCRIBED IN CHRONIC EXPOSURE. SEVERE CASES MAY BE FATAL. **CHRONIC EXPOSURE-** REPEATED ABSORPTION MAY CAUSE THE INHIBITION OF PROTHROMBIN SYNTHESIS AND DAMAGE TO CAPILLARY PERMEABILITY RESULTING IN WIDESPREAD INTERNAL HEMORRHAGE WITH ASSOCIATED EFFECTS OF NOSEBLEED, HEMATOMA, HEMATURIA, WIDESPREAD BRUISING, AND ANEMIA.
FIRST AID- REMOVE FROM EXPOSURE AREA TO FRESH AIR IMMEDIATELY. IF BREATHING HAS STOPPED, PERFORM ARTIFICIAL RESPIRATION. KEEP PERSON WARM AND AT REST. TREAT SYMPTOMATICALLY AND SUPPORTIVELY. GET MEDICAL ATTENTION IMMEDIATELY.

SKIN CONTACT: COUMATETRALYL: SEE INFORMATION ON COUMARIN DERIVATIVES.
COUMARIN DERIVATIVES: HEMORRHAGIC AGENT. **ACUTE EXPOSURE-** ABSORPTION THROUGH THE SKIN MAY RESULT IN HEMORRHAGIC EFFECTS AS DESCRIBED IN CHRONIC EXPOSURE. SEVERE CASES MAY BE FATAL. **CHRONIC EXPOSURE-** REPEATED ABSORPTION MAY CAUSE THE INHIBITION OF PROTHROMBIN SYNTHESIS AND DAMAGE TO CAPILLARY PERMEABILITY RESULTING IN WIDESPREAD INTERNAL HEMORRHAGE WITH ASSOCIATED EFFECTS OF NOSEBLEED, HEMATOMA, HEMATURIA, WIDESPREAD BRUISING, AND ANEMIA.
FIRST AID- REMOVE CONTAMINATED CLOTHING AND SHOES IMMEDIATELY. WASH AFFECTED AREA WITH SOAP OR MILD DETERGENT AND LARGE AMOUNTS OF WATER UNTIL NO EVIDENCE OF CHEMICAL REMAINS (APPROXIMATELY 15-20 MINUTES). GET MEDICAL ATTENTION IMMEDIATELY.

EYE CONTACT: COUMATETRALYL: **ACUTE EXPOSURE-** NO DATA AVAILABLE. **CHRONIC EXPOSURE-** NO DATA AVAILABLE.
FIRST AID- WASH EYES IMMEDIATELY WITH LARGE AMOUNTS OF WATER OR NORMAL SALINE, OCCASIONALLY LIFTING UPPER AND LOWER LIDS, UNTIL NO EVIDENCE OF CHEMICAL REMAINS (APPROXIMATELY 15-20 MINUTES). GET MEDICAL ATTENTION IMMEDIATELY.

INGESTION: COUMATETRALYL: HIGHLY TOXIC. SEE INFORMATION ON COUMARIN DERIVATIVES.
COUMARIN DERIVATIVES: HEMORRHAGIC AGENT. **ACUTE EXPOSURE-** MAY BE READILY ABSORBED FROM THE GASTROINTESTINAL TRACT AND CAUSE THE INHIBITION OF PROTHROMBIN SYNTHESIS AND DAMAGE TO CAPILLARY PERMEABILITY RESULTING IN WIDESPREAD INTERNAL HEMORRHAGE ACCOMPANIED BY THE HEMORRHAGIC SYMPTOMS AS DESCRIBED IN CHRONIC EXPOSURE. SEVERE CASES MAY BE FATAL. **CHRONIC EXPOSURE-** REPEATED INGESTION MAY CAUSE NOSEBLEED, BLEEDING GUMS AND PHARYNX, PETECHIAL RASH, WIDESPREAD BRUISING, HEMATOMA, HEMOPTYSIS, HEMATEMESIS, HEMATURIA, BLOODY STOOLS, BLEEDING INTO THE ORGANS, GASTROINTESTINAL TRACT, JOINTS, ABDOMINAL OR RETROPERITONEAL AREA WITH ABDOMINAL, BACK, JOINT AND LIMB PAIN AND CEREBROVASCULAR ACCIDENT. ANEMIA ACCOMPANIED BY WEAKNESS, PALLOR, AND SHOCK MAY OCCUR. SEVERE

HEMORRHAGING MAY CAUSE DEATH. THERAPEUTIC USE OF SOME COUMARIN DERIVATIVES HAS INFREQUENTLY PRODUCED GASTROINTESTINAL DISTURBANCES, ELEVATED TRANSAMINASE, URTICARIA, DERMATITIS, LEUKOPENIA, ALOPECIA, FEVER, HYPERSENSITIVITY REACTIONS, AND RARELY SKIN NECROSIS.

FIRST AID- IF ONLY A FEW GRAINS OF ANTICOAGULANT BAIT HAVE BEEN INGESTED BY AN ADULT OR CHILD HAVING NO ANTECEDENT LIVER OR BLOOD CLOTTING DISEASE, TREATMENT IS PROBABLY UNNECESSARY. IF LARGE AMOUNTS OF ANTICOAGULANT WERE INGESTED IN THE PRECEDING 2-3 HOURS, INDUCE VOMITING WITH SYRUP OF IPECAC, FOLLOWED BY 1-2 GLASSES OF WATER. FOLLOWING EMESIS, GIVE ACTIVATED CHARCOAL IN 4-6 OUNCES OF WATER TO LIMIT ABSORPTION OF ANTICOAGULANT REMAINING IN THE GUT. OBSERVE PATIENT 4-5 DAYS AFTER INGESTION. (MORGAN, RECOGNITION AND MANAGEMENT OF PESTICIDE POISONINGS, THIRD EDITION). GET MEDICAL ATTENTION.

ANTIDOTE: THE FOLLOWING ANTIDOTE HAS BEEN RECOMMENDED. HOWEVER, THE DECISION AS TO WHETHER THE SEVERITY OF POISONING REQUIRES ADMINISTRATION OF ANY ANTIDOTE AND ACTUAL DOSE REQUIRED SHOULD BE MADE BY QUALIFIED MEDICAL PERSONNEL.

OVERDOSE OF ANTICOAGULANTS: VITAMIN K IS A SPECIFIC ANTIDOTE. VITAMIN K1 EMULSION IS THE PREFERRED FORM. THE INITIAL SUBCUTANEOUS OR INTRAMUSCULAR DOSE IN ADULTS IS 5 TO 10 MG (UP TO 25 MG), REPEATED ONCE IF NECESSARY. ONLY IN VICTIMS WHO ARE BLEEDING SEVERLY OR OTHERWISE IN SERIOUS DISTRESS SHOULD THE DRUG BE GIVEN INTRAVENOUSLY AND THEN AT A RATE NO FASTER THAN 1 MG/MINUTE. IF NECESSARY, ON SUBSEQUENT DAYS, VITAMIN K1 SHOULD BE CONTINUED AT A REDUCED LEVEL UNTIL THE PROTHROMBIN TIME RETURNS TO NORMAL. VITAMIN K1 IS PREFERABLE TO K1 OXIDE (DOSE 0.5-2.5) AND CERTAINLY PREFERABLE TO MENADIONE OR MENADIONE SODIUM BISULFITE (GOSSELIN, CLINICAL TOXICOLOGY OF COMMERCIAL PRODUCTS, 5TH ED.). ANTIDOTE SHOULD BE ADMINISTERED BY QUALIFIED MEDICAL PERSONNEL.

REACTIVITY

REACTIVITY: STABLE UNDER NORMAL TEMPERATURES AND PRESSURES.

INCOMPATIBILITIES: COUMATETRALYL: OXIDIZERS (STRONG): FIRE AND EXPLOSION HAZARD.

DECOMPOSITION: THERMAL DECOMPOSITION PRODUCTS MAY INCLUDE TOXIC OXIDES OF CARBON.

POLYMERIZATION: HAZARDOUS POLYMERIZATION HAS NOT BEEN REPORTED TO OCCUR UNDER NORMAL TEMPERATURES AND PRESSURES.

STORAGE AND DISPOSAL

OBSERVE ALL FEDERAL, STATE AND LOCAL REGULATIONS WHEN STORING OR DISPOSING OF THIS SUBSTANCE. FOR ASSISTANCE, CONTACT THE DISTRICT DIRECTOR OF THE ENVIRONMENTAL PROTECTION AGENCY.

STORAGE

STORE IN ACCORDANCE WITH 40 CFR 165 RECOMMENDED PROCEDURES FOR THE DISPOSAL AND STORAGE OF PESTICIDES AND PESTICIDE CONTAINERS.

STORE AWAY FROM INCOMPATIBLE SUBSTANCES.

THRESHOLD PLANNING QUANTITY (TPQ): THE SUPERFUND AMENDMENTS AND REAUTHORIZATION ACT (SARA) SECTION 302 REQUIRES THAT EACH FACILITY WHERE ANY EXTREMELY HAZARDOUS SUBSTANCE IS PRESENT IN A QUANTITY EQUAL TO OR GREATER THAN THE TPQ ESTABLISHED FOR THAT SUBSTANCE NOTIFY THE STATE EMERGENCY RESPONSE COMMISSION FOR THE STATE IN WHICH IT IS LOCATED. SECTION 303 OF SARA REQUIRES THESE FACILITIES TO PARTICIPATE IN LOCAL EMERGENCY RESPONSE PLANNING (40 CFR 355.30).

DISPOSAL

DISPOSAL MUST BE IN ACCORDANCE WITH 40 CFR 165 RECOMMENDED PROCEDURES FOR THE DISPOSAL AND STORAGE OF PESTICIDES AND PESTICIDE CONTAINERS.

CONDITIONS TO AVOID

MAY BURN BUT DOES NOT IGNITE READILY. CONTAINERS MAY EXPLODE IN HEAT OF FIRE.

SPILL AND LEAK PROCEDURES

OCCUPATIONAL SPILL: DO NOT TOUCH SPILLED MATERIAL. STOP LEAK IF YOU CAN DO IT WITHOUT RISK. USE WATER SPRAY TO REDUCE VAPORS. FOR SMALL SPILLS, TAKE UP WITH SAND OR OTHER ABSORBENT MATERIAL AND PLACE INTO CONTAINERS FOR LATER DISPOSAL. FOR SMALL DRY SPILLS, WITH A CLEAN SHOVEL PLACE MATERIAL INTO CLEAN, DRY CONTAINERS AND COVER. MOVE CONTAINERS FROM SPILL AREA. FOR LARGER SPILLS, DIKE FAR AHEAD OF SPILL FOR LATER DISPOSAL. KEEP UNNECESSARY PEOPLE AWAY. ISOLATE HAZARD AREA AND DENY ENTRY. VENTILATE CLOSED SPACES BEFORE ENTERING.

REPORTABLE QUANTITY (RQ): 1 POUND THE SUPERFUND AMENDMENTS AND REAUTHORIZATION ACT (SARA) SECTION 304 REQUIRES THAT A RELEASE EQUAL TO OR GREATER THAN THE REPORTABLE QUANTITY FOR THIS SUBSTANCE BE IMMEDIATELY REPORTED TO THE LOCAL EMERGENCY PLANNING COMMITTEE AND THE STATE EMERGENCY RESPONSE COMMISSION (40 CFR 355.40). IF THE RELEASE OF THIS SUBSTANCE IS REPORTABLE UNDER CERCLA SECTION 103, THE NATIONAL RESPONSE CENTER MUST BE NOTIFIED IMMEDIATELY AT (800) 424-8802 OR (202) 426-2675 IN THE METROPOLITAN WASHINGTON, D.C. AREA (40 CFR 302.6).

PROTECTIVE EQUIPMENT

VENTILATION: PROCESS ENCLOSURE RECOMMENDED.

RESPIRATOR: THE FOLLOWING RESPIRATORS ARE RECOMMENDED BASED ON INFORMATION FOUND IN THE PHYSICAL DATA, TOXICITY AND HEALTH EFFECTS SECTIONS. THEY ARE RANKED IN ORDER FROM MINIMUM TO MAXIMUM RESPIRATORY PROTECTION. THE SPECIFIC RESPIRATOR SELECTED MUST BE BASED ON CONTAMINATION LEVELS FOUND IN THE WORK PLACE, MUST NOT EXCEED THE WORKING LIMITS OF THE RESPIRATOR AND BE JOINTLY APPROVED BY THE NATIONAL INSTITUTE FOR OCCUPATIONAL SAFETY AND HEALTH AND THE MINE SAFETY AND HEALTH ADMINISTRATION (NIOSH-MSHA).

TYPE 'C' SUPPLIED-AIR RESPIRATOR WITH A FULL FACEPIECE OPERATED IN PRESSURE-DEMAND OR OTHER POSITIVE PRESSURE MODE OR WITH A FULL FACEPIECE, HELMET OR HOOD OPERATED IN CONTINOUS-FLOW MODE.

SELF-CONTAINED BREATHING APPARATUS WITH A FULL FACEPIECE OPERATED IN PRESSURE-DEMAND OR OTHER POSITIVE PRESSURE MODE.

FOR FIREFIGHTING AND OTHER IMMEDIATELY DANGEROUS TO LIFE OR HEALTH CONDITIONS:

SELF-CONTAINED BREATHING APPARATUS WITH FULL FACEPIECE OPERATED IN PRESSURE-DEMAND OR OTHER POSITIVE PRESSURE MODE.

SUPPLIED-AIR RESPIRATOR WITH FULL FACEPIECE AND OPERATED IN PRESSURE-DEMAND OR OTHER POSITIVE PRESSURE MODE IN COMBINATION WITH AN AUXILIARY SELF-CONTAINED BREATHING APPARATUS OPERATED IN PRESSURE-DEMAND OR OTHER POSITIVE PRESSURE MODE.

CLOTHING: EMPLOYEE MUST WEAR APPROPRIATE PROTECTIVE (IMPERVIOUS) CLOTHING AND EQUIPMENT TO PREVENT ANY POSSIBILITY OF SKIN CONTACT WITH THIS SUBSTANCE.

GLOVES: EMPLOYEE MUST WEAR APPROPRIATE PROTECTIVE GLOVES TO PREVENT CONTACT WITH THIS SUBSTANCE.

EYE PROTECTION: EMPLOYEE MUST WEAR SPLASH-PROOF OR DUST-RESISTANT SAFETY GOGGLES WITH OR WITHOUT A FACESHIELD TO PREVENT CONTACT WITH THIS SUBSTANCE.

EMERGENCY EYE WASH: WHERE THERE IS ANY POSSIBILITY THAT AN EMPLOYEE'S EYES MAY BE EXPOSED TO THIS SUBSTANCE, THE EMPLOYER SHOULD PROVIDE AN EYE WASH FOUNTAIN WITHIN THE IMMEDIATE WORK AREA FOR EMERGENCY USE.

AUTHORIZED BY- OCCUPATIONAL HEALTH SERVICES, INC.

CREATION DATE: 10/04/89 ***REVISION DATE:*** 05/15/90

MATERIAL SAFETY DATA SHEET

OCCUPATIONAL HEALTH SERVICES, INC.
AGRICULTURE AND PESTICIDE DIVISION
450 SEVENTH AVENUE, SUITE 2407
NEW YORK, NEW YORK 10123
1-800-445-MSDS OR (212) 967-1100

EMERGENCY CONTACT:
JOHN S. BRANSFORD, JR. (615) 292-1180

SUBSTANCE IDENTIFICATION

CAS-NUMBER 136-78-7

SUBSTANCE: **SODIUM 2,4-DICHLOROPHENOXYETHYL SULFATE**

TRADE NAMES/SYNONYMS: 2-(2,4-DICHLOROPHENOXY)ETHANOL HYDROGEN SULFATE, SODIUM SALT; 2,4-DICHLOROPHENOXYETHYL SULFATE, SODIUM SALT; SODIUM 2-(2,4-DICHLOROPHENOXY)ETHYL SULFATE; CRAG HERBICIDE 1; CRAG SESONE; DISUL-SODIUM; EXPERIMENTAL HERBICIDE 1; SES; SESON; SESONE; SES-T; 2,4-DES SODIUM; PST05500

CHEMICAL FAMILY: ORGANIC SULFATE ETHER, AROMATIC

MOLECULAR FORMULA: C8-H7-CL2-O5-S.NA

MOLECULAR WEIGHT: 309.10

CERCLA RATINGS (SCALE 0-3): HEALTH=2 FIRE=0 REACTIVITY=0 PERSISTENCE=3

NFPA RATINGS (SCALE 0-4): HEALTH=2 FIRE=0 REACTIVITY=0

COMPONENTS AND CONTAMINANTS

COMPONENT: SODIUM 2,4 DICHLOROPHENOXYETHYL SULFATE ***PERCENT:*** 100
CAS# 136-78-7

OTHER CONTAMINANTS: NONE

EXPOSURE LIMITS: SODIUM 2,4-DICHLOROPHENOXYETHYL SULFATE: 5 MG/M3 OSHA TWA (RESPIRABLE FRACTION); 10 MG/M3 OSHA TWA (TOTAL DUST) 10 MG/M3 ACGIH TWA

PHYSICAL DATA

DESCRIPTION: ODORLESS, COLORLESS CRYSTALS ***BOILING POINT:*** DECOMPOSES

MELTING POINT: 473 F (245 C) (DECOMPOSES) ***SPECIFIC GRAVITY:*** 1.70 @ 20 C

VAPOR PRESSURE: 1 MMHG @ 20 C ***SOLUBILITY IN WATER:*** 25.5% @ 25 C

SOLVENT SOLUBILITY: INSOLUBLE IN MOST ORGANIC SOLVENTS EXCEPT METHANOL

FIRE AND EXPLOSION DATA

FIRE AND EXPLOSION HAZARD: NEGLIGIBLE FIRE HAZARD WHEN EXPOSED TO HEAT OR FLAME.

FIREFIGHTING MEDIA: DRY CHEMICAL, CARBON DIOXIDE, HALON, WATER SPRAY OR STANDARD FOAM (1987 EMERGENCY RESPONSE GUIDEBOOK, DOT P 5800.4).
FOR LARGER FIRES, USE WATER SPRAY, FOG OR STANDARD FOAM (1987 EMERGENCY RESPONSE GUIDEBOOK, DOT P 5800.4).

FIREFIGHTING: MOVE CONTAINER FROM FIRE AREA IF POSSIBLE. DO NOT SCATTER SPILLED MATERIAL WITH HIGH PRESSURE WATER STREAMS. DIKE FIRE CONTROL WATER FOR LATER DISPOSAL (1987 EMERGENCY RESPONSE GUIDEBOOK, DOT P 5800.4, GUIDE PAGE 31).
USE AGENTS SUITABLE FOR TYPE OF SURROUNDING FIRE. AVOID BREATHING HAZARDOUS VAPORS, KEEP UPWIND.

TOXICITY

SODIUM 2,4-DICHLOROPHENOXYETHYL SULFATE: TOXICITY DATA: 480 MG/KG ORAL-RAT LD50; 1230 MG/KG ORAL-MAMMAL LD50. CARCINOGEN STATUS: HUMAN LIMITED EVIDENCE (IARC GROUP-2B FOR CHLOROPHENOXY HERBICIDES). STUDIES REVEALED A SIGNIFICANT INCREASE IN SOFT-TISSUE SARCOMAS, MALIGNANT LYMPHOMAS AND BRONCHIAL CARCINOMAS IN WORKERS EXPOSED TO CHLOROPHENOXY HERBICIDES. LOCAL EFFECTS: CORROSIVE- SKIN AND EYES. ACUTE TOXICITY LEVEL: TOXIC BY INGESTION. TARGET EFFECTS: POISONING MAY AFFECT THE GASTROINTESTINAL TRACT AND THE CARDIOVASCULAR AND NERVOUS SYSTEMS.* AT INCREASED RISK FROM EXPOSURE: PERSONS WITH SKIN, CARDIOVASCULAR, KIDNEY, LIVER, AND CONVULSIVE DISORDERS. ADDITIONAL DATA: STIMULANTS SUCH AS EPINEPHRINE MAY INDUCE VENTRICULAR FIBRILLATION.*

* MAY BE BASED ON GENERAL INFORMATION ON DICHLOROPHENOXY DERIVATIVES.

HEALTH EFFECTS AND FIRST AID

INHALATION: SODIUM 2,4-DICHLOROPHENOXYETHYL SULFATE: 5000 MG/M3 IMMEDIATELY DANGEROUS TO LIFE OR HEALTH. IN ANIMAL STUDIES, THIS MATERIAL PRODUCED TREMORS, MUSCLE SPASMS, CONVULSIONS, AND CONGESTION OF THE LUNGS, LIVER AND KIDNEYS. SEE INFORMATION ON 2,4-D AND DERIVATIVES.

2,4-D AND DERIVATIVES: **ACUTE EXPOSURE-** EXPOSURE TO 2,4-D AND ITS DERIVATIVES MAY CAUSE IRRITATION WITH SORE THROAT AND BURNING SENSATIONS IN THE NASOPHARYNX AND CHEST, COUGHING, LACRIMATION, RHINITIS, DULLNESS, DIZZINESS, AND ATAXIA. OTHER EFFECTS OF FATIGUE, NAUSEA, VOMITING, DIARRHEA, STOMACH PAINS, MALAISE, HEADACHE, FEVER, TACHYCARDIA, URINARY INCONTINENCE, CONSTIPATION, LEUKOPENIA, MYALGIA, AND TRANSIENT UNCONSCIOUSNESS MAY OCCUR. A DELAYED PERIPHERAL NEUROPATHY MAY DEVELOP CHARACTERIZED BY PARESTHESIAS, SEVERE PAIN, SYMMETRICAL MOTOR AND SENSORY DEFICITS, WEAKNESS, MYOTONIA, FASCICULATIONS, AND IN SOME CASES PARALYSIS OF THE EXTREMITIES. THE DISABILITY MAY BE PROLONGED AND RECOVERY INCOMPLETE. **CHRONIC EXPOSURE-** IN ADDITION TO THE EFFECTS LISTED IN ACUTE EXPOSURE, OCCUPATIONAL EXPOSURE TO 2,4-D AND ITS DERIVATIVES HAS PRODUCED A SWEET TASTE IN THE MOUTH, HYPERACUSIA, LOWERED SENSITIVITY TO TASTE AND SMELL, INCREASED SALIVATION, VERTIGO, SOMNOLENCE, ANOREXIA, HEAVINESS OF THE LEGS. OTHER EFFECTS HAVE INCLUDED HYPOTENSION, BRADYCARDIA AND OTHER CARDIOVASCULAR SYSTEM CHANGES, PAIN IN THE REGION OF THE LIVER AND STOMACH, AND CHANGES IN THE DIGESTIVE FUNCTION, LIVER FUNCTION AND METABOLIC PROCESSES. A CASE REPORT DESCRIBED A CHILD WITH MULTIPLE CONGENITAL ANOMALIES AND SEVERE MENTAL RETARDATION OF UNCERTAIN CAUSE BORN TO PARENTS HEAVILY EXPOSED TO 2,4-D WHILE SPRAYING TREES. AN INCREASED PREVALENCE OF SLOWED NERVE CONDUCTION VELOCITY WITH NO ASSOCIATED SYMPTOMS WAS REPORTED IN A STUDY OF CHEMICAL WORKERS EMPLOYED IN THE PRODUCTION OF 2,4-D AND 2,4,5-T. EPIDEMIOLOGICAL STUDIES REVEALED A SIGNIFICANT INCREASE IN SOFT-TISSUE SARCOMAS, MALIGNANT LYMPHOMAS, AND BRONCHIAL CARCINOMAS IN WORKERS EXPOSED TO CHLOROPHENOXY HERBICIDES INCLUDING 2,4-D.

FIRST AID- REMOVE FROM EXPOSURE AREA TO FRESH AIR IMMEDIATELY. IF BREATHING HAS STOPPED, PERFORM ARTIFICIAL RESPIRATION. KEEP PERSON WARM AND AT REST. TREAT SYMPTOMATICALLY AND SUPPORTIVELY. GET MEDICAL ATTENTION IMMEDIATELY.

SKIN CONTACT: SODIUM 2,4-DICHLOROPHENOXYETHYL SULFATE: CORROSIVE. 0.1 ML OF A 5% SUSPENSION OF THIS MATERIAL APPLIED TO THE SKIN OF RABBITS PRODUCED EDEMA AND NECROSIS. SEE INFORMATION ON 2,4-D AND DERIVATIVES.

2,4-D AND DERIVATIVES: **ACUTE EXPOSURE-** MAY CAUSE IRRITATION. IF SUFFICIENT AMOUNTS ARE ABSORBED THROUGH THE SKIN, EFFECTS, INCLUDING PERIPHERAL NEUROPATHY, AS DESCRIBED IN ACUTE INHALATION MAY OCCUR. **CHRONIC EXPOSURE-** PROLONGED OR REPEATED EXPOSURE MAY CAUSE DERMATITIS AND EFFECTS AS DESCRIBED IN CHRONIC INHALATION.

FIRST AID- REMOVE CONTAMINATED CLOTHING AND SHOES IMMEDIATELY. WASH AFFECTED AREA WITH SOAP OR MILD DETERGENT AND LARGE AMOUNTS OF WATER UNTIL NO EVIDENCE OF CHEMICAL REMAINS (AT LEAST 15-20 MINUTES). IN CASE OF CHEMICAL BURNS, COVER AREA WITH STERILE, DRY DRESSING. BANDAGE SECURELY, BUT NOT TOO TIGHTLY. GET MEDICAL ATTENTION IMMEDIATELY.

EYE CONTACT: SODIUM 2,4-DICHLOROPHENOXYETHYL SULFATE: CORROSIVE. **ACUTE EXPOSURE-** MAY CAUSE SEVERE IRRITATION AND POSSIBLY CORROSIVE EFFECTS. A 5% AQUEOUS SOLUTION APPLIED IN THE EYE OF RABBITS PRODUCED CORNEAL NECROSIS. **CHRONIC EXPOSURE-** DEPENDING ON THE CONCENTRATION AND DURATION OF CONTACT, EFFECTS AS IN ACUTE EXPOSURE MAY OCCUR WITH REPEATED OR PROLONGED EXPOSURE.

FIRST AID- WASH EYES IMMEDIATELY WITH LARGE AMOUNTS OF WATER, OCCASIONALLY LIFTING UPPER AND LOWER LIDS, UNTIL NO EVIDENCE OF CHEMICAL REMAINS (AT LEAST 15-20 MINUTES). CONTINUE IRRIGATING WITH NORMAL SALINE UNTIL THE PH HAS RETURNED TO NORMAL (30-60 MINUTES). COVER WITH STERILE BANDAGES. GET MEDICAL ATTENTION IMMEDIATELY.

INGESTION: SODIUM 2,4-DICHLOROPHENOXYETHYL SULFATE: TOXIC. 20 MG IN THE DIET OF RATS FOR TWO YEARS DID NOT PRODUCED ANY ADVERSE ADVERSE EFFECTS. SEE INFORMATION ON 2,4-D AND DERIVATIVES.

2,4-D AND DERIVATIVES: **ACUTE EXPOSURE-** INGESTION OF 2,4-D AND ITS DERIVATIVES MAY CAUSE IRRITATION OF THE MOUTH, THROAT, AND GASTROINTESTINAL TRACT, NAUSEA, VOMITING, CHEST AND ABDOMINAL PAIN, AND DIARRHEA. INGESTION OF VERY LARGE DOSES MAY PRODUCE METABOLIC ACIDOSIS, FEVER OR SUBNORMAL TEMPERATURES, HYPERVENTILATION, HYPOTENSION, VASODILATION, FLUSHING OF THE SKIN, SWEATING, CARDIAC ARRHYTHMIAS, TACHYCARDIA, LETHARGY, WEAKNESS, INTERCOSTAL PARALYSIS, RENAL AND HEPATIC DYSFUNCTION, MYOTONIA, COMA, AND CONVULSIONS. DAMAGE TO SKELETAL MUSCLE MAY BE MANIFEST BY MUSCLE TWITCHING AND ACHING WITH ELEVATED SERUM ENZYMES AND MYOGLOBIN IN THE BLOOD AND URINE. IMPAIRED MEMORY AND CHANGES IN COLOR VISION WERE REPORTED IN ONE CASE OF POISONING. DEATH MAY BE DUE TO CIRCULATORY COLLAPSE. **CHRONIC EXPOSURE-** NO DATA AVAILABLE.

FIRST AID- IF THE PERSON IS CONSCIOUS AND NOT CONVULSING, INDUCE EMESIS BY GIVING SYRUP OF IPECAC (KEEPING THE HEAD BELOW THE HIPS TO PREVENT ASPIRATION) FOLLOWED BY WATER. REPEAT IN 20 MINUTES IF NOT EFFECTIVE INITIALLY. IN PATIENTS WITH DEPRESSED RESPIRATION OR IF EMESIS IS NOT PRODUCED, PERFORM GASTRIC LAVAGE WITH ACTIVATED CHARCOAL. FOLLOW WITH A SALINE CATHARTIC (DREISBACH, HANDBOOK OF POISONING, 12TH ED.). TREAT SYMPTOMATICALLY AND SUPPORTIVELY. GASTRIC LAVAGE SHOULD BE PERFORMED BY QUALIFIED MEDICAL PERSONNEL. GET MEDICAL ATTENTION IMMEDIATELY.

ANTIDOTE: NO SPECIFIC ANTIDOTE. TREAT SYMPTOMATICALLY AND SUPPORTIVELY.

REACTIVITY

REACTIVITY: STABLE UNDER NORMAL TEMPERATURES AND PRESSURES.

INCOMPATIBILITIES: SODIUM 2,4-DICHLOROPHENOXYETHYL SULFATE: STRONG OXIDIZERS: MAY CAUSE FIRE AND EXPLOSIONS.

DECOMPOSITION: WHEN HEATED TO DECOMPOSITION MAY EMIT TOXIC AND HAZARDOUS FUMES OF HYDROGEN CHLORIDE, OXIDES OF SULFUR, AND OXIDES OF CARBON.

POLYMERIZATION: HAZARDOUS POLYMERIZATION HAS NOT BEEN REPORTED TO OCCUR UNDER NORMAL TEMPERATURES AND PRESSURES.

STORAGE AND DISPOSAL

OBSERVE ALL FEDERAL, STATE AND LOCAL REGULATIONS WHEN STORING OR DISPOSING OF THIS SUBSTANCE. FOR ASSISTANCE, CONTACT THE DISTRICT DIRECTOR OF THE ENVIRONMENTAL PROTECTION AGENCY.

STORAGE

STORE IN ACCORDANCE WITH 40 CFR 165 RECOMMENDED PROCEDURES FOR THE DISPOSAL AND STORAGE OF PESTICIDES AND PESTICIDE CONTAINERS.

DISPOSAL

DISPOSAL MUST BE IN ACCORDANCE WITH 40 CFR 165 RECOMMENDED PROCEDURES FOR THE DISPOSAL AND STORAGE OF PESTICIDES AND PESTICIDE CONTAINERS.

CONDITIONS TO AVOID

MAY BURN BUT DOES NOT IGNITE READILY. AVOID CONTACT WITH STRONG OXIDIZERS, EXCESSIVE HEAT, SPARKS, OR OPEN FLAME.

SPILL AND LEAK PROCEDURES

OCCUPATIONAL SPILL: SWEEP UP AND PLACE IN SUITABLE CLEAN, DRY CONTAINERS FOR RECLAMATION OR LATER DISPOSAL. DO NOT FLUSH SPILLED MATERIAL INTO SEWER. KEEP UNNECESSARY PEOPLE AWAY.

PROTECTIVE EQUIPMENT

VENTILATION: PROVIDE LOCAL EXHAUST VENTILATION AND/OR GENERAL DILUTION VENTILATION TO MEET PUBLISHED EXPOSURE LIMITS.

RESPIRATOR: THE FOLLOWING RESPIRATORS AND MAXIMUM USE CONCENTRATIONS ARE RECOMMENDATIONS BY THE U.S. DEPARTMENT OF HEALTH AND HUMAN SERVICES, NIOSH POCKET GUIDE TO CHEMICAL HAZARDS; NIOSH CRITERIA DOCUMENTS OR BY THE U.S. DEPARTMENT OF LABOR, 29 CFR 1910 SUBPART Z. THE SPECIFIC RESPIRATOR SELECTED MUST BE BASED ON CONTAMINATION LEVELS FOUND IN THE WORK PLACE, MUST NOT EXCEED THE WORKING LIMITS OF THE RESPIRATOR AND BE JOINTLY APPROVED BY THE NATIONAL INSTITUTE FOR OCCUPATIONAL SAFETY AND HEALTH AND THE MINE SAFETY AND HEALTH ADMINISTRATION (NIOSH-MSHA).

SODIUM 2,4-DICHLOROPHENOXYETHYL SULFATE:

50 MG/M3- ANY DUST AND MIST RESPIRATOR EXCEPT SINGLE-USE RESPIRATOR.

100 MG/M3- ANY DUST AND MIST RESPIRATOR EXCEPT SINGLE-USE AND QUARTER MASK RESPIRATOR. ANY SUPPLIED-AIR RESPIRATOR. ANY SELF-CONTAINED BREATHING APPARATUS. 250 MG/M3- ANY POWERED AIR-PURIFYING RESPIRATOR WITH A DUST AND MIST FILTER. ANY SUPPLIED-AIR RESPIRATOR OPERATED IN CONTINUOUS FLOW MODE.

500 MG/M3- ANY AIR-PURIFYING FULL FACEPIECE RESPIRATOR WITH A HIGH-EFFICIENCY PARTICULATE FILTER. ANY SELF-CONTAINED BREATHING APPARATUS WITH A FULL FACEPIECE. ANY SUPPLIED-AIR RESPIRATOR WITH A FULL FACEPIECE. ANY POWERED AIR-PURIFYING RESPIRATOR WITH A TIGHT-FITTING FACEPIECE AND A HIGH-EFFICIENCY PARTICULATE FILTER. ANY SUPPLIED-AIR RESPIRATOR WITH A TIGHT-FITTING FACEPIECE OPERATED IN A CONTINUOUS FLOW MODE.

5000 MG/M3- ANY SUPPLIED-AIR RESPIRATOR WITH A HALF-MASK AND OPERATED IN A PRESSURE-DEMAND OR OTHER POSITIVE PRESSURE MODE.

ESCAPE- ANY AIR-PURIFYING FULL FACEPIECE RESPIRATOR WITH A HIGH-EFFICIENCY PARTICULATE FILTER. ANY APPROPRIATE ESCAPE-TYPE SELF-CONTAINED BREATHING APPARATUS.

FOR FIREFIGHTING AND OTHER IMMEDIATELY DANGEROUS TO LIFE OR HEALTH CONDITIONS:

SELF-CONTAINED BREATHING APPARATUS WITH FULL FACEPIECE OPERATED IN PRESSURE-DEMAND OR OTHER POSITIVE PRESSURE MODE.

SUPPLIED-AIR RESPIRATOR WITH FULL FACEPIECE AND OPERATED IN PRESSURE-DEMAND OR OTHER POSITIVE PRESSURE MODE IN COMBINATION WITH AN AUXILIARY SELF-CONTAINED BREATHING APPARATUS OPERATED IN PRESSURE-DEMAND OR OTHER POSITIVE PRESSURE MODE.

CLOTHING: EMPLOYEE MUST WEAR APPROPRIATE PROTECTIVE (IMPERVIOUS) CLOTHING AND EQUIPMENT TO PREVENT REPEATED OR PROLONGED SKIN CONTACT WITH THIS SUBSTANCE.

GLOVES: EMPLOYEE MUST WEAR APPROPRIATE PROTECTIVE GLOVES TO PREVENT CONTACT WITH THIS SUBSTANCE.

EYE PROTECTION: EMPLOYEE MUST WEAR SPLASH-PROOF OR DUST-RESISTANT SAFETY GOGGLES TO PREVENT EYE CONTACT WITH THIS SUBSTANCE.

EMERGENCY EYE WASH: WHERE THERE IS ANY POSSIBILITY THAT AN EMPLOYEE'S EYES MAY BE EXPOSED TO THIS SUBSTANCE, THE EMPLOYER SHOULD PROVIDE AN EYE WASH FOUNTAIN WITHIN THE IMMEDIATE WORK AREA FOR EMERGENCY USE.

AUTHORIZED BY- OCCUPATIONAL HEALTH SERVICES, INC.

CREATION DATE: 10/05/89 ***REVISION DATE:*** 07/12/90

MATERIAL SAFETY DATA SHEET

OCCUPATIONAL HEALTH SERVICES, INC.
AGRICULTURE AND PESTICIDE DIVISION
450 SEVENTH AVENUE, SUITE 2407
NEW YORK, NEW YORK 10123
1-800-445-MSDS OR (212) 967-1100

EMERGENCY CONTACT:
JOHN S. BRANSFORD, JR. (615) 292-1180

SUBSTANCE IDENTIFICATION

CAS-NUMBER 1319-77-3

SUBSTANCE: CRESOL

TRADE NAMES/SYNONYMS: CRESYLIC ACID; BASCILLOL; TEKRESOL; TRICRESOL; AR-TOLUENOL; PHENOL, METHYL-; STCC 4931417; UN 2076; O-2043; U052; PST05510

CHEMICAL FAMILY: HYDROXYL, AROMATIC

MOLECULAR FORMULA: C7-H8-O

MOLECULAR WEIGHT: 108.15

CERCLA RATINGS (SCALE 0-3): HEALTH=3 FIRE=2 REACTIVITY=0 PERSISTENCE=2

NFPA RATINGS (SCALE 0-4): HEALTH=3 FIRE=2 REACTIVITY=0

COMPONENTS AND CONTAMINANTS

COMPONENT: CRESOL (O,M,P-ISOMERS) ***PERCENT:*** 100
CAS# 1319-77-3

OTHER CONTAMINANTS: NONE

EXPOSURE LIMITS: CRESOL (ALL ISOMERS): 5 PPM (22 MG/M3) OSHA TWA (SKIN) 5 PPM (22 MG/M3) ACGIH TWA (SKIN) 2.3 PPM (10 MG/M3) NIOSH 10 HOUR RECOMMENDED TWA

1000 POUND CERCLA SECTION 103 REPORTABLE QUANTITY SUBJECT TO SARA SECTION 313 ANNUAL TOXIC CHEMICAL RELEASE REPORTING

PHYSICAL DATA

DESCRIPTION: COLORLESS, YELLOW, OR PINK LIQUID WITH A PHENOLIC ODOR.

BOILING POINT: 376-397 F (191-203 C) ***MELTING POINT:*** 52-95 F (11-35 C)

SPECIFIC GRAVITY: 1.03 ***VAPOR PRESSURE:*** 0.1 MMHG @ 25 C

PH: ACIDIC IN SOLUTION

SOLUBILITY IN WATER: SLIGHT ***ODOR THRESHOLD:*** 5PPM

VAPOR DENSITY: > 1

SOLVENT SOLUBILITY: ALCOHOL, GLYCEROL, DILUTE ALKALIES, PETROLEUM ETHER, BENZENE, VEGETABLE OILS, ORGANIC SOLVENTS

FIRE AND EXPLOSION DATA

FIRE AND EXPLOSION HAZARD: MODERATE FIRE HAZARD WHEN EXPOSED TO HEAT OR FLAME.

VAPOR-AIR MIXTURES ARE EXPLOSIVE ABOVE FLASH POINT.

VAPORS ARE HEAVIER THAN AIR AND MAY TRAVEL A CONSIDERABLE DISTANCE TO A SOURCE OF IGNITION AND FLASH BACK.

FLASH POINT: 180 F (82 C) (CC) ***LOWER EXPLOSIVE LIMIT:*** 1.35% @ 300 F

AUTOIGNITION TEMP.: 1038 F (559 C) ***FLAMMABILITY CLASS(OSHA):*** IIIA

FIREFIGHTING MEDIA: DRY CHEMICAL, CARBON DIOXIDE, HALON, WATER SPRAY OR STANDARD FOAM (1987 EMERGENCY RESPONSE GUIDEBOOK, DOT P 5800.4). FOR LARGER FIRES, USE WATER SPRAY, FOG OR STANDARD FOAM (1987 EMERGENCY RESPONSE GUIDEBOOK, DOT P 5800.4).

FIREFIGHTING: MOVE CONTAINERS FROM FIRE AREA IF POSSIBLE. FIGHT FIRE FROM MAXIMUM DISTANCE. STAY AWAY FROM STORAGE TANK ENDS. DIKE FIRE CONTROL WATER FOR LATER DISPOSAL. DO NOT SCATTER MATERIAL (1987 EMERGENCY RESPONSE GUIDEBOOK, DOT P 5800.4, GUIDE PAGE 55).

USE FLOODING AMOUNTS OF WATER AS A FOG; SOLID STREAMS MAY NOT BE EFFECTIVE. COOL CONTANINERS WITH FLOODING QUANTITIES OF WATER, APPLY FROM AS FAR A DISTANCE AS POSSIBLE. AVOID BREATHING CORROSIVE VAPORS, KEEP UPWIND.

FIRE FIGHTING PHASES: USE WATER SPRAY, DRY CHEMICAL, ALCOHOL FOAM OR CARBON DIOXIDE. USE WATER TO KEEP FIRE-EXPOSED CONTAINERS COOL. IF A LEAK OR SPILL HAS NOT IGNITED, USE WATER SPRAY TO DISPERSE THE VAPORS AND TO PROVIDE PROTECTION FOR THE MEN ATTEMPTING TO STOP THE LEAK. WATER SPRAY MAY BE USED TO FLUSH SPILLS AWAY FROM EXPOSURES (NFPA 49, HAZARDOUS CHEMICALS DATA, 1975).

TRANSPORTATION DATA

DEPARTMENT OF TRANSPORTATION HAZARD CLASSIFICATION 49 CFR 172.101: CORROSIVE MATERIAL

DEPARTMENT OF TRANSPORTATION LABELING REQUIREMENTS 49 CFR 172.101 AND SUBPART E: CORROSIVE

DEPARTMENT OF TRANSPORTATION PACKAGING REQUIREMENTS: 49 CFR 173.245 EXCEPTIONS: 49 CFR 173.244

TOXICITY

CRESOL (MIXED ISOMERS): TOXICITY DATA: 2000 MG/KG SKIN-RABBIT LD50; 177 MG/KG ORAL-HUMAN TDLO; 1454 MG/KG ORAL-RAT LD50; 760 MG/KG ORAL-MOUSE LD50. CARCINOGEN STATUS: NONE. LOCAL EFFECTS: CORROSIVE- INHALATION, SKIN, AND EYES. ACUTE TOXICITY LEVEL: MODERATELY TOXIC BY DERMAL ABSORPTION AND INGESTION. TARGET EFFECTS: SENSITIZER- SKIN. CENTRAL NERVOUS SYSTEM DEPRESSANT. POISONING MAY AFFECT THE LIVER, KIDNEYS, RESPIRATORY AND CARDIOVASCULAR SYSTEMS.

HEALTH EFFECTS AND FIRST AID

INHALATION: CRESOL (MIXED ISOMERS): CORROSIVE/NARCOTIC. 250 PPM IMMEDIATELY DANGEROUS TO LIFE OR HEALTH. **ACUTE EXPOSURE-** HUMANS EXPOSED EXPERIMENTALLY TO 6 MG/MG OF THE ORTHO ISOMER REPORTED NASAL CONSTRICTION, THROAT IRRITATION, RESPIRATORY MUCOSA DRYNESS, AND THE SENSATION OF AN UNSPECIFIED TASTE. HOWEVER, INHALATION IS NOT USUALLY AN ACUTE HAZARD DUE TO THE LOW VAPOR PRESSURE AND THE DISAGREEABLE ODOR WHICH IS DETECTABLE EVEN AT LOW CONCENTRATIONS. EXPOSURE TO AEROSOLS OR TO VAPORS PRODUCED BY HIGH TEMPERATURE PROCESSES MAY CAUSE SEVERE RESPIRATORY TRACT IRRITATION AND SYSTEMIC ABSORPTION. THE SYMPTOMS, POSSIBLY DELAYED 20-30 MINUTES, MAY INCLUDE HEADACHE, DIZZINESS, VOMITING, TINNITUS, DIMNESS OF VISION, RAPID, IRREGULAR RESPIRATION, WEAK PULSE, DYSPNEA, PROFOUND MUSCULAR WEAKNESS, AND OCCASIONALLY, MENTAL CONFUSION. IF SUFFICIENT AMOUNTS ARE ABSORBED, VASCULAR COLLAPSE, SHOCK, HYPOTHERMIA, UNCONSCIOUSNESS, RESPIRATORY FAILURE, AND DEATH ARE POSSIBLE. PATHOLOGIC FINDINGS AS DETAILED IN ACUTE SKIN EXPOSURE MAY BE FOUND. **CHRONIC EXPOSURE-** CHRONIC INHALATION OF VAPORS MAY RESULT IN RESPIRATORY TRACT IRRITATION AND DISTURBANCES OF THE NERVOUS, GASTROINTESTINAL AND VASCULAR SYSTEMS. SYMPTOMS MAY INCLUDE HEADACHE, DIZZINESS, FAINTING, FACIAL MUSCLE SPASMS, TREMORS, MENTAL DISTURBANCES, DIFFICULTY IN SWALLOWING, SALIVATION, NAUSEA, VOMITING, DIARRHEA, ANOREXIA, HYPERTENSION, SLIGHTLY ENLARGED HEART, AND SKIN RASH. LIVER AND KIDNEY DAMAGE ARE POSSIBLE AND, IF SEVERE, MAY RESULT IN DEATH.

FIRST AID- REMOVE FROM EXPOSURE AREA TO FRESH AIR IMMEDIATELY. IF BREATHING HAS STOPPED, GIVE ARTIFICIAL RESPIRATION. MAINTAIN AIRWAY AND BLOOD PRESSURE AND ADMINISTER OXYGEN IF AVAILABLE. KEEP AFFECTED PERSON WARM AND AT REST. TREAT SYMPTOMATICALLY AND SUPPORTIVELY. ADMINISTRATION OF OXYGEN SHOULD BE PERFORMED BY QUALIFIED PERSONNEL. GET MEDICAL ATTENTION IMMEDIATELY.

SKIN CONTACT: CRESOL (MIXED ISOMERS): CORROSIVE/NARCOTIC/SENSITIZER. **ACUTE EXPOSURE-** MAY CAUSE SEVERE IRRITATION. PRICKLING AND INTENSE BURNING MAY OCCUR AFTER A FEW MINUTES FOLLOWED BY LOCAL ANETHESIA. AFFECTED TISSUES MAY INITIALLY SHOW WHITE DISCOLORATION, WRINKLING, AND SOFTENING, WHICH SUBSEQUENTLY MAY BECOME GANGRENOUS. SENSITIZATION DERMATITIS MAY OCCUR IN PREVIOUSLY EXPOSED PERSONS. CRESOLS MAY BE READILY ABSORBED BY SKIN TO CAUSE SYSTEMIC EFFECTS WHICH MAY BE DELAYED 20-30 MINUTES. THE SYMPTOMS MAY INCLUDE HEADACHE, DIZZINESS, VOMITING, TINNITUS, DIMNESS OF VISION, IRREGULAR, RAPID RESPIRATION, WEAK PULSE, DYSPNEA, PROFOUND MUSCULAR WEAKNESS, AND OCCASIONALLY, MENTAL CONFUSION. IF SUFFICIENT AMOUNTS ARE ABSORBED, VASCULAR COLLAPSE, SHOCK, HYPOTHERMIA, UNCONSCIOUSNESS, AND DEATH MAY OCCUR. PATHOLOGIC FINDINGS HAVE INCLUDED PULMONARY HYPEREMIA, EMPHYSEMA, AND EDEMA; BRONCHOPNEUMONIA WITH PETECHIAL HEMORRHAGES IN THE PLEURA; AND NODULAR PNEUMONIA. KIDNEYS HAVE SHOWN PARENCHYMATOUS AND HEMORRHAGIC NEPHRITIS AND TUBULE DAMAGE. THE LIVER HAS SHOWN CONGESTION WITH PALLOR AND NECROSIS OF HEPATIC CELLS. DEGENERATED MYOCARDIUM AND SMALL HEMORRHAGES IN THE EPICARDIUM AND ENDOCARDIUM HAVE BEEN SEEN. CONGESTION IN THE BRAIN AND DAMAGE TO THE PANCREAS AND SPLEEN HAVE ALSO BEEN REPORTED. **CHRONIC EXPOSURE-** REPEATED OR PROLONGED EXPOSURE TO LOW CONCENTRATIONS MAY CAUSE DERMATITIS AND EVEN VERY DILUTE SOLUTIONS MAY CAUSE SENSITIZATION. RARELY, PROLONGED CONTACT MAY RESULT IN A PIGMENTORY DISORDER CALLED OCHRONOSIS, WHICH IS A DARKENING OF THE CONJUNCTIVA, SKIN AND CARTILAGE OF THE NOSE AND EARS. REPEATED ABSORPTION MAY RESULT IN DISTURBANCES OF THE NERVOUS, GASTROINTESTINAL AND VASCULAR SYSTEMS. SYMPTOMS MAY INCLUDE HEADACHE, DIZZINESS, FAINTING, FACIAL MUSCLE SPASMS, TREMORS, MENTAL DISTURBANCES, DIFFICULTY IN SWALLOWING, SALIVATION, NAUSEA, VOMITING, DIARRHEA, ANOREXIA, HYPERTENSION, SLIGHTLY ENLARGED HEART, AND SKIN RASH. LIVER AND KIDNEY DAMAGE ARE POSSIBLE AND, IF SEVERE, MAY RESULT IN DEATH.

FIRST AID- REMOVE CONTAMINATED CLOTHING AND SHOES IMMEDIATELY. WASH AFFECTED AREA WITH SOAP OR MILD DETERGENT AND LARGE AMOUNTS OF WATER UNTIL NO EVIDENCE OF CHEMICAL REMAINS (AT LEAST 15-20 MINUTES). IN CASE OF CHEMICAL BURNS, COVER AREA WITH STERILE, DRY DRESSING. BANDAGE SECURELY, BUT NOT TOO TIGHTLY. GET MEDICAL ATTENTION IMMEDIATELY.

EYE CONTACT: CRESOL (MIXED ISOMERS): CORROSIVE. **ACUTE EXPOSURE-** CRESOL SOLUTIONS SPLASHED IN THE EYE MAY CAUSE PERMANENT CORNEAL OPACIFICATION AND VASCULARIZATION, HYPERMIA, AND SWELLING OF THE CONJUCTIVA. INJURY FROM CRESOLS DEPENDS ON THE CONCENTRATION AND THE DURATION OF CONTACT. **CHRONIC EXPOSURE-** REPEATED OR PROLONGED CONTACT MAY CAUSE CONJUNCTIVITIS.

FIRST AID- WASH EYES IMMEDIATELY WITH LARGE AMOUNTS OF WATER, OCCASIONALLY LIFTING UPPER AND LOWER LIDS, UNTIL NO EVIDENCE OF CHEMICAL REMAINS (AT LEAST 15-20 MINUTES). CONTINUE IRRIGATING WITH NORMAL SALINE UNTIL THE PH HAS RETURNED TO NORMAL (30-60 MINUTES). COVER WITH STERILE BANDAGES. GET MEDICAL ATTENTION IMMEDIATELY.

INGESTION: CRESOL (MIXED ISOMERS): CORROSIVE/NARCOTIC. **ACUTE EXPOSURE-** MAY CAUSE SEVERE MUCOSAL IRRITATION WITH INTENSE BURNING IN THE MOUTH AND THROAT FOLLOWED BY MARKED ABDOMINAL PAIN AND DISTRESS, NAUSEA, VOMITING, AND DIARRHEA. IT IS READILY ABSORBED BY THE GASTROINTESTINAL TRACT TO CAUSE SYSTEMIC EFFECTS WHICH MAY BE DELAYED 20-30 MINUTES. THE SYMPTOMS MAY INCLUDE HEADACHE, DIZZINESS, TINNITUS, DIMNESS OF VISION, IRREGULAR, RAPID RESPIRATION, WEAK PULSE, DYSPNEA, PROFOUND MUSCULAR WEAKNESS, AND OCCASIONALLY, MENTAL CONFUSION. OTHER POSSIBLE EFFECTS INCLUDE PULMONARY EDEMA, PNEUMONIA, KIDNEY CONGESTION AND FAILURE, PANCREATITIS, AND DAMAGE TO THE LIVER AND SPLEEN. IF SUFFICIENT AMOUNTS ARE ABSORBED, VASCULAR COLLAPSE, SHOCK, HYPOTHERMIA, UNCONSCIOUSNESS, AND DEATH MAY OCCUR. PATHOLOGIC FINDINGS AS DETAILED IN ACUTE SKIN EXPOSURE MAY BE FOUND. **CHRONIC EXPOSURE-** NO SPECIFIC DATA AVAILABLE. MAY CAUSE SYSTEMIC SYMPTOMS AS DETAILED IN CHRONIC INHALATION.

FIRST AID- IN THE ABSENCE OF CORROSIVE INJURY, REMOVE POISON BY IPECAC EMESIS. ACTIVATED CHARCOAL IS ALSO USEFUL. FOLLOW WITH 240 ML OF MILK. GASTRIC LAVAGE AND EMESIS ARE CONTRAINDICATED IN THE PRESENCE OF ESOPHAGEAL INJURY (DREISBACH, HANDBOOK OF POISONING, 12TH EDITION). GET MEDICAL ATTENTION IMMEDIATELY.

ANTIDOTE: NO SPECIFIC ANTIDOTE. TREAT SYMPTOMATICALLY AND SUPPORTIVELY.

REACTIVITY

REACTIVITY: STABLE UNDER NORMAL TEMPERATURES AND PRESSURES.

INCOMPATIBILITIES: CRESOL (MIXED ISOMERS): ACIDS (STRONG): VIOLENT REACTION. CHLOROSULFONIC ACID: INCREASE IN TEMPERATURE AND PRESSURE WHEN MIXED IN CLOSED CONTAINER. NITRIC ACID: INCREASE IN TEMPERATURE AND PRESSURE WHEN MIXED IN CLOSED CONTAINER. OLEUM: INCREASE IN TEMPERATURE AND PRESSURE WHEN MIXED IN CLOSED CONTAINER. OXIDIZERS (STRONG): FIRE AND EXPLOSION HAZARD.

DECOMPOSITION: THERMAL DECOMPOSITION MAY RELEASE ACRID SMOKE AND IRRITATING FUMES.

POLYMERIZATION: HAZARDOUS POLYMERIZATION HAS NOT BEEN REPORTED TO OCCUR UNDER NORMAL TEMPERATURES AND PRESSURES.

STORAGE AND DISPOSAL

OBSERVE ALL FEDERAL, STATE AND LOCAL REGULATIONS WHEN STORING OR DISPOSING OF THIS SUBSTANCE. FOR ASSISTANCE, CONTACT THE DISTRICT DIRECTOR OF THE ENVIRONMENTAL PROTECTION AGENCY.

STORAGE

STORE IN ACCORDANCE WITH 29 CFR 1910.106.

PROTECT AGAINST PHYSICAL DAMAGE. STORE IN A COOL, DRY, WELL VENTILATED LOCATION, AWAY FROM ANY AREA WHERE THE FIRE HAZARD MAY BE ACUTE. OUTSIDE OR DETACHED STORAGE IS PREFERRED. SEPARATE FROM OXIDIZING MATERIALS (NFPA 49, HAZARDOUS CHEMICALS DATA, 1975).

STORE AWAY FROM INCOMPATIBLE SUBSTANCES.

BONDING AND GROUNDING: SUBSTANCES WITH LOW ELECTROCONDUCTIVITY, WHICH MAY BE IGNITED BY ELECTROSTATIC SPARKS, SHOULD BE STORED IN CONTAINERS WHICH MEET THE BONDING AND GROUNDING GUIDELINES SPECIFIED IN NFPA 77-1983, RECOMMENDED PRACTICE ON STATIC ELECTRICITY.

DISPOSAL

DISPOSAL MUST BE IN ACCORDANCE WITH STANDARDS APPLICABLE TO GENERATORS OF HAZARDOUS WASTE, 40CFR 262. EPA HAZARDOUS WASTE NUMBER U052. CRESOL - REGULATORY LEVEL: 200.0 MG/L MATERIALS WHICH CONTAIN THE ABOVE SUBSTANCE AT OR ABOVE THE REGULATORY LEVEL MEET THE EPA CHARACTERISTIC OF TOXICITY, AND MUST BE DISPOSED OF IN ACCORDANCE WITH 40 CFR PART 262. EPA HAZARDOUS WASTE NUMBER D026.

CONDITIONS TO AVOID

MAY BURN BUT DOES NOT IGNITE READILY. CONTAINERS MAY EXPLODE IN HEAT OF FIRE.

SPILL AND LEAK PROCEDURES

SOIL SPILL: DIG HOLDING AREA SUCH AS LAGOON, POND OR PIT FOR CONTAINMENT. DIKE FLOW OF SPILLED MATERIAL USING SOIL OR SANDBAGS OR FOAMED BARRIERS SUCH AS POLYURETHANE OR CONCRETE.
USE CEMENT POWDER OR FLY ASH TO ABSORB LIQUID MASS.

AIR SPILL: KNOCK DOWN VAPORS WITH WATER SPRAY. KEEP UPWIND.
WATER USED TO KNOCK DOWN VAPORS MAY BECOME CORROSIVE OR TOXIC AND SHOULD BE CONTAINED PROPERLY FOR LATER DISPOSAL.

WATER SPILL: USE ACTIVATED CARBON TO ABSORB SPILLED SUBSTANCE THAT IS DISSOLVED.
USE MECHANICAL DREDGES OR LIFTS TO EXTRACT IMMOBILIZED MASSES OF POLLUTION AND PRECIPITATES.
TRAP SPILLED MATERIAL AT BOTTOM IN DEEP WATER POCKETS, EXCAVATED HOLDING AREAS OR WITHIN SAND BAG BARRIERS.

OCCUPATIONAL SPILL: DO NOT TOUCH SPILLED MATERIAL. STOP LEAK IF YOU CAN DO IT WITHOUT RISK. USE WATER SPRAY TO REDUCE VAPORS. FOR SMALL SPILLS, TAKE UP WITH SAND OR OTHER ABSORBENT MATERIAL AND PLACE INTO CONTAINERS FOR LATER DISPOSAL. FOR SMALL DRY SPILLS, WITH A CLEAN SHOVEL PLACE MATERIAL INTO CLEAN, DRY CONTAINERS AND COVER. MOVE CONTAINERS FROM SPILL AREA. FOR LARGER SPILLS, DIKE FAR AHEAD OF SPILL FOR LATER DISPOSAL. KEEP UNNECESSARY PEOPLE AWAY. ISOLATE HAZARD AREA AND DENY ENTRY. VENTILATE CLOSED SPACES BEFORE ENTERING.
REPORTABLE QUANTITY (RQ): 1000 POUNDS THE SUPERFUND AMENDMENTS AND REAUTHORIZATION ACT (SARA) SECTION 304 REQUIRES THAT A RELEASE EQUAL TO OR GREATER THAN THE REPORTABLE QUANTITY FOR THIS SUBSTANCE BE IMMEDIATELY REPORTED TO THE LOCAL EMERGENCY PLANNING COMMITTEE AND THE STATE EMERGENCY RESPONSE COMMISSION (40 CFR 355.40). IF THE RELEASE OF THIS SUBSTANCE IS REPORTABLE UNDER CERCLA SECTION 103, THE NATIONAL RESPONSE CENTER MUST BE NOTIFIED IMMEDIATELY AT (800) 424-8802 OR (202) 426-2675 IN THE METROPOLITAN WASHINGTON, D.C. AREA (40 CFR 302.6).

PROTECTIVE EQUIPMENT

VENTILATION: PROVIDE LOCAL EXHAUST OR PROCESS ENCLOSURE VENTILATION TO MEET PUBLISHED EXPOSURE LIMITS.

RESPIRATOR: THE FOLLOWING RESPIRATORS AND MAXIMUM USE CONCENTRATIONS ARE RECOMMENDATIONS BY THE U.S. DEPARTMENT OF HEALTH AND HUMAN SERVICES, NIOSH POCKET GUIDE TO CHEMICAL HAZARDS; NIOSH CRITERIA DOCUMENTS OR BY THE U.S. DEPARTMENT OF LABOR, 29 CFR 1910 SUBPART Z. THE SPECIFIC RESPIRATOR SELECTED MUST BE BASED ON CONTAMINATION LEVELS FOUND IN THE WORK PLACE, MUST NOT EXCEED THE WORKING LIMITS OF THE RESPIRATOR AND BE JOINTLY APPROVED BY THE NATIONAL INSTITUTE FOR OCCUPATIONAL SAFETY AND HEALTH AND THE MINE SAFETY AND HEALTH ADMINISTRATION (NIOSH-MSHA).
CRESOL (ALL ISOMERS):
23 PPM- ANY CHEMICAL CARTRIDGE RESPIRATOR WITH ORGANIC VAPOR CARTRIDGE(S) IN COMBINATION WITH A DUST AND MIST FILTER. ANY SUPPLIED-AIR RESPIRATOR. ANY SELF-CONTAINED BREATHING APPARATUS.
57.5 PPM- ANY SUPPLIED-AIR RESPIRATOR OPERATED IN CONTINUOUS FLOW MODE. ANY POWERED AIR-PURIFYING RESPIRATOR WITH ORGANIC VAPOR CARTRIDGE(S) IN COMBINATION WITH A DUST AND MIST FILTER.
115 PPM- ANY CHEMICAL CARTRIDGE RESPIRATOR WITH A FULL FACEPIECE AND ORGANIC VAPOR CARTRIDGE(S) IN COMBINATION WITH A HIGH-EFFICIENCY PARTICULATE FILTER. ANY SUPPLIED-AIR RESPIRATOR WITH A FULL FACEPIECE. ANY SELF-CONTAINED BREATHING APPARATUS WITH A FULL FACEPIECE. ANY AIR-PURIFYING FULL FACEPIECE RESPIRATOR (GAS MASK) WITH A CHIN-STYLE OR FRONT- OR BACK-MOUNTED ORGANIC VAPOR CANISTER HAVING A HIGH-EFFICIENCY PARTICULATE FILTER. ANY POWERED AIR-PURIFYING RESPIRATOR WITH A TIGHT-FITTING FACEPIECE AND A HIGH-EFFICIENCY PARTICULATE FILTER. ANY SUPPLIED-AIR RESPIRATOR WITH A TIGHT-FITTING FACEPIECE OPERATED IN A CONTINUOUS FLOW MODE.
250 PPM- ANY SUPPLIED-AIR RESPIRATOR WITH A FULL FACEPIECE AND OPERATED IN A PRESSURE-DEMAND OR OTHER POSITIVE PRESSURE MODE.
ESCAPE- ANY AIR-PURIFYING FULL FACEPIECE RESPIRATOR (GAS MASK) WITH A CHIN-STYLE OR FRONT- OR BACK-MOUNTED ORGANIC VAPOR CANISTER. HAVING A HIGH-EFFICIENCY PARTICULATE FILTER. ANY APPROPRIATE ESCAPE-TYPE SELF-CONTAINED BREATHING APPARATUS.
FOR FIREFIGHTING AND OTHER IMMEDIATELY DANGEROUS TO LIFE OR HEALTH CONDITIONS:
SELF-CONTAINED BREATHING APPARATUS WITH FULL FACEPIECE OPERATED IN PRESSURE-DEMAND OR OTHER POSITIVE PRESSURE MODE.
SUPPLIED-AIR RESPIRATOR WITH FULL FACEPIECE AND OPERATED IN PRESSURE-DEMAND OR OTHER POSITIVE PRESSURE MODE IN COMBINATION WITH AN AUXILIARY SELF-CONTAINED BREATHING APPARATUS OPERATED IN PRESSURE-DEMAND OR OTHER POSITIVE PRESSURE MODE.

CLOTHING: EMPLOYEE MUST WEAR APPROPRIATE PROTECTIVE (IMPERVIOUS) CLOTHING AND EQUIPMENT TO PREVENT ANY POSSIBILITY OF SKIN CONTACT WITH THIS SUBSTANCE.

GLOVES: EMPLOYEE MUST WEAR APPROPRIATE PROTECTIVE GLOVES TO PREVENT CONTACT WITH THIS SUBSTANCE.

EYE PROTECTION: EMPLOYEE MUST WEAR SPLASH-PROOF OR DUST-RESISTANT SAFETY GOGGLES AND A FACESHIELD TO PREVENT CONTACT WITH THIS SUBSTANCE.
EMERGENCY WASH FACILITIES: WHERE THERE IS ANY POSSIBILITY THAT AN EMPLOYEE'S EYES AND/OR SKIN MAY BE EXPOSED TO THIS SUBSTANCE, THE EMPLOYER SHOULD PROVIDE AN EYE WASH FOUNTAIN AND QUICK DRENCH SHOWER WITHIN THE IMMEDIATE WORK AREA FOR EMERGENCY USE.

AUTHORIZED BY- OCCUPATIONAL HEALTH SERVICES, INC.
CREATION DATE: 10/04/89 ***REVISION DATE:*** 07/13/90

MATERIAL SAFETY DATA SHEET

OCCUPATIONAL HEALTH SERVICES, INC.
AGRICULTURE AND PESTICIDE DIVISION
450 SEVENTH AVENUE, SUITE 2407
NEW YORK, NEW YORK 10123
1-800-445-MSDS OR (212) 967-1100

EMERGENCY CONTACT:
JOHN S. BRANSFORD, JR. (615) 292-1180

SUBSTANCE IDENTIFICATION

CAS-NUMBER 299-86-5

SUBSTANCE: CRUFOMATE

TRADE NAMES/SYNONYMS: PHOSPHORAMIDIC ACID, METHYL-,2-CHLORO-4-(1,1-DIMETHYLETHYL)PHENYL METHYL ESTER; PHOSPHORAMIDIC ACID, METHYL-, 4-TERT-BUTYL-2-CHLOROPHENYL METHYL ESTER; METHYLPHOSPHORAMIDIC ACID 2-CHLORO-4-(1,1-DIMETHYLETHYL)PHENYL METHYL ESTER; METHYLPHOSPHORAMIDIC ACID 4-TERT-BUTYL-2-CHLOROPHENYL METHYL ESTER; 4-TERT-BUTYL-2-CHLOROPHENYL METHYL METHYLPHOSPHORAMIDATE; 2-CHLORO-4-(1,1-DIMETHYLETHYL)PHENYL METHYL METHYLPHOSPHORAMIDATE; 4-TERT-BUTYL-2-CHLOROPHENYL N-METHYL O-METHYLPHOSPHORAMIDATE; 2-CHLORO-4-TERT-BUTYLPHENYL METHYL N-METHYLPHOSPHORAMIDATE; 4-T-BUTYL-2-CHLOROPHENYL METHYL METHYLPHOSPHORAMIDATE; O-METHYL-O-(4-TERT-BUTYL-2-CHLOROPHENYL)METHYLPHOSPHORAMIDATE; AMIDOFOS; AMIDOPHOS; CRUFOMAT; DOWCO 132; MONTREL; RUELENE; ENT 25,602-X; C12H19CLNO3P; PST05550

CHEMICAL FAMILY: ORGANIC PHOSPHATE
AROMATIC
HALOGEN

MOLECULAR FORMULA: C12-H19-CL-N-O3-P

MOLECULAR WEIGHT: 291.71

CERCLA RATINGS (SCALE 0-3): HEALTH=3 FIRE=1 REACTIVITY=0 PERSISTENCE=1

NFPA RATINGS (SCALE 0-4): HEALTH=U FIRE=1 REACTIVITY=0

COMPONENTS AND CONTAMINANTS

COMPONENT: CRUFOMATE ***PERCENT:*** 100
CAS# 299-86-5

OTHER CONTAMINANTS: NONE

EXPOSURE LIMITS: CRUFOMATE: 5 MG/M3 OSHA TWA 5 MG/M3 ACGIH TWA; 20 MG/M3 ACGIH STEL (NOTICE OF INTENDED CHANGES 1988-89)

PHYSICAL DATA

DESCRIPTION: ODORLESS, WHITE CRYSTALLINE POWDER; THE TECHNICAL GRADE IS A YELLOW OIL. ***BOILING POINT:*** 243-244 F (117-118 C) @ 0.01 MMHG

MELTING POINT: 140-142 F (60-61 C) ***SPECIFIC GRAVITY:*** 1.1618

VAPOR PRESSURE: 0.01 MMHG @ 117 C ***SOLUBILITY IN WATER:*** 0.5%

SOLVENT SOLUBILITY: SOLUBLE IN ACETONE, BENZENE, CARBON TETRACHLORIDE, ETHER, METHANOL, CYCLOHEXANE, MOST POLAR SOLVENTS; MODERATELY SOLUBLE IN PARAFFIN SOLVENTS; PRACTICALLY INSOLUBLE IN LIGHT PETROLEUM.

FIRE AND EXPLOSION DATA

FIRE AND EXPLOSION HAZARD: SLIGHT FIRE HAZARD WHEN EXPOSED TO HEAT OR FLAME.

FIREFIGHTING MEDIA: DRY CHEMICAL, CARBON DIOXIDE, HALON, WATER SPRAY OR STANDARD FOAM (1987 EMERGENCY RESPONSE GUIDEBOOK, DOT P 5800.4). FOR LARGER FIRES, USE WATER SPRAY, FOG OR STANDARD FOAM (1987 EMERGENCY RESPONSE GUIDEBOOK, DOT P 5800.4).

FIREFIGHTING: MOVE CONTAINERS FROM FIRE AREA IF POSSIBLE. FIGHT FIRE FROM MAXIMUM DISTANCE. STAY AWAY FROM STORAGE TANK ENDS. DIKE FIRE CONTROL WATER FOR LATER DISPOSAL. DO NOT SCATTER MATERIAL (1987 EMERGENCY RESPONSE GUIDEBOOK, DOT P 5800.4, GUIDE PAGE 55). EXTINGUISH ONLY IF FLOW CAN BE STOPPED. EXTINGUISH USING AGENT INDICATED. USE FLOODING AMOUNTS OF WATER AS A FOG. COOL CONTAINERS WITH FLOODING AMOUNTS OF WATER FROM AS FAR A DISTANCE AS POSSIBLE. AVOID BREATHING POISONOUS VAPORS, KEEP UPWIND. CONSIDER EVACUATION OF DOWNWIND AREA IF MATERIAL IS LEAKING.

TOXICITY

CRUFOMATE: TOXICITY DATA: 12 MG/M3/4 HOURS INHALATION-RAT LCLO; 2000 MG/KG SKIN-RABBIT LD50; 460 MG/KG ORAL-RAT LD50; 400 MG/KG ORAL-RABBIT LD50; 1000 MG/KG ORAL-GUINEA PIG LD50; 251 MG/KG ORAL-MAMMAL LD50; 50 MG/KG SUBCUTANEOUS-GUINEA PIG LDLO; REPRODUCTIVE EFFECTS DATA (RTECS). CARCINOGEN STATUS: NONE. LOCAL EFFECTS: IRRITANT- EYE. ACUTE TOXICITY LEVEL: TOXIC BY INGESTION AND MODERATELY TOXIC BY DERMAL ABSORPTION. TARGET EFFECTS: CHOLINESTERASE INHIBITOR. POISONING MAY AFFECT THE NERVOUS SYSTEM.* AT INCREASED RISK FROM EXPOSURE: PERSONS WITH RESPIRATORY AILMENTS, RECENT EXPOSURE TO CHOLINESTERASE INHIBITORS OR IMPAIRED CHOLINESTERASE PRODUCTION, OR LIVER MALFUNCTION.* ADDITIONAL DATA: MAY CROSS THE PLACENTA. HIGH ENVIRONMENTAL TEMPERATURES OR EXPOSURE OF THE CHEMICAL TO VISIBLE OR ULTRAVIOLET LIGHT MAY ENHANCE THE TOXICITY. INTERACTIONS WITH MEDICATIONS MAY OCCUR.* MALATHION MAY POTENTIATE THE TOXICITY.

* MAY BE BASED ON GENERAL INFORMATION ON ORGANOPHOSPHATES.

HEALTH EFFECTS AND FIRST AID

INHALATION: CRUFOMATE: SEE INFORMATION ON ORGANOPHOSPHATES.

ORGANOPHOSPHATES: CHOLINESTERASE INHIBITOR. **ACUTE EXPOSURE-** WHEN INHALED, THE FIRST EFFECTS OF CHOLINESTERASE INHIBITORS ARE USUALLY RESPIRATORY AND MAY INCLUDE NASAL HYPEREMIA AND WATERY DISCHARGE, COUGH, CHEST DISCOMFORT, DYSPNEA, AND WHEEZING DUE TO INCREASED BRONCHIAL SECRETIONS AND BRONCHOCONSTRICTION. IF SUFFICIENT AMOUNTS ARE ABSORBED, OTHER SYSTEMIC EFFECTS MAY BEGIN WITHIN A FEW MINUTES OR BE DELAYED FOR UP TO 12 HOURS. SYMPTOMS MAY INCLUDE PALLOR, NAUSEA, VOMITING, DIARRHEA, ABDOMINAL CRAMPS, HEADACHE, DIZZINESS, OCULAR PAIN, BLURRED VISION, MIOSIS OR IN SOME CASES, ESPECIALLY INITIALLY, MYDRIASIS, LACRIMATION, SALIVATION, SWEATING, AND CONFUSION. OTHER REPORTED CENTRAL NERVOUS SYSTEM OR NEUROMUSCULAR EFFECTS MAY INCLUDE ATAXIA, SLURRED SPEECH, AREFLEXIA, WEAKNESS, FATIGUE, FASCICULATIONS, TWITCHING, TREMORS POSSIBLY OF THE TONGUE AND EYELIDS, AND EVENTUALLY PARALYSIS OF THE EXTREMITIES AND POSSIBLY OF THE RESPIRATORY MUSCLES. IN SEVERE CASES THERE MAY ALSO BE INVOLUNTARY DEFECATION AND URINATION, CYANOSIS, PSYCHOSIS, HYPERGLYCEMIA, ACUTE PANCREATITIS, CARDIAC IRREGULARITIES, PULMONARY EDEMA, UNCONSCIOUSNESS, CONVULSIONS, AND COMA. DEATH IS PRIMARILY DUE TO RESPIRATORY FAILURE, ALTHOUGH CARDIOVASCULAR EFFECTS INCLUDING CARDIAC ARREST MAY ALSO BE IMPLICATED. LONG TERM SEQUELAE ARE RARE BUT MAY INCLUDE NEUROPSYCHIATRIC DISORDERS AND MYOPATHY WITH MUSCLE TENDERNESS. SOME ORGANOPHOSPHATES MAY CAUSE A DELAYED NEUROPATHY BEGINNING 1-4 WEEKS AFTER AN ACUTE EXPOSURE WHICH MAY OR MAY NOT HAVE CAUSED ACUTE CHOLINERGIC EFFECTS. NUMBNESS, TINGLING, WEAKNESS AND CRAMPING BEGINNING SYMMETRICALLY IN THE LOWER LIMBS MAY PROGRESS TO ATAXIA AND PARALYSIS. IN SEVERE CASES, UPPER LIMB INVOLVEMENT IS POSSIBLE AND FLACCID PARALYSIS MAY PROGRESS TO SPASTIC PARALYSIS WITH EXAGGERATED REFLEXES. IMPROVEMENT MAY OCCUR OVER MONTHS TO YEARS, BUT SOME RESIDUAL IMPAIRMENT USUALLY REMAINS. **CHRONIC EXPOSURE-** REPEATED OR PROLONGED EXPOSURE MAY RESULT IN THE EFFECTS OF ACUTE EXPOSURE INCLUDING THE DELAYED NEUROPATHY. OTHER EFFECTS REPORTED IN WORKERS REPEATEDLY EXPOSED INCLUDE IMPAIRED MEMORY AND CONCENTRATION, ACUTE PSYCHOSIS, SEVERE DEPRESSIONS, IRRITABILTY, CONFUSION, APATHY, EMOTIONAL LABILITY, SOCIAL WITHDRAWAL, CONFUSION, HEADACHE, SPEECH DIFFICULTIES, DELAYED REACTION TIMES, SPATIAL DISORIENTATION, NIGHTMARES, SLEEPWALKING, AND DROWSINESS OR INSOMNIA. AN INFLUENZA-LIKE CONDITION WITH HEADACHE, NAUSEA, WEAKNESS, ANOREXIA AND MALAISE HAS ALSO BEEN REPORTED.

FIRST AID- REMOVE FROM EXPOSURE AREA TO FRESH AIR IMMEDIATELY. IF BREATHING HAS STOPPED, GIVE ARTIFICIAL RESPIRATION. MAINTAIN AIRWAY AND BLOOD PRESSURE AND ADMINISTER OXYGEN IF AVAILABLE. KEEP AFFECTED PERSON WARM AND AT REST. TREAT SYMPTOMATICALLY AND SUPPORTIVELY. ADMINISTRATION OF OXYGEN SHOULD BE PERFORMED BY QUALIFIED PERSONNEL. GET MEDICAL ATTENTION IMMEDIATELY.

SKIN CONTACT: CRUFOMATE: THIS MATERIAL PRODUCED SLIGHT ERYTHEMA WHEN APPLIED UNDILUTED TO THE ABRADED OR INTACT SKIN OF THE RABBIT. ADVERSE EFFECTS ON FERTILITY AND THE OFFSPRING AND MATERNAL EFFECTS WERE REPORTED IN STUDIES OF FEMALE MICE RECEIVING TWO DERMAL APPLICATIONS OF 50 OR 100 MG/KG PRIOR TO MATING. SEE INFORMATION ON ORGANOPHOSPHATES.

ORGANOPHOSPHATES: CHOLINESTERASE INHIBITOR. **ACUTE EXPOSURE-** LOCALIZED SWEATING AND FASCICULATIONS MAY OCCUR AT THE SITE OF CONTACT. IF SUFFICIENT AMOUNTS ARE ABSORBED, OTHER EFFECTS OF CHOLINESTERASE INHIBITION AS DESCRIBED IN ACUTE INHALATION MAY OCCUR. SYMPTOMS MAY BE DELAYED 2-3 HOURS, BUT USUALLY NO MORE THAN 12 HOURS. THE RATE OF ABSORPTION IS INCREASED BY THE PRESENCE OF DERMATITIS OR HIGH AMBIENT TEMPERATURES. DELAYED NEUROPATHY IS ALSO POSSIBLE. **CHRONIC EXPOSURE-** REPEATED OR PROLONGED EXPOSURE MAY CAUSE EFFECTS AS DESCRIBED IN ACUTE EXPOSURE. SOME ORGANOPHOSPHATES MAY CAUSE SENSITIZATION.

FIRST AID- REMOVE CONTAMINATED CLOTHING IMMEDIATELY. WASH CONTAMINATED AREAS WITH SOAP AND WATER FOLLOWED BY ALCOHOL (ARENA, POISONING, 4TH ED.). EMERGENCY PERSONNEL SHOULD WEAR GLOVES AND AVOID CONTAMINATION. TREAT RESPIRATORY DIFFICULTY WITH ARTIFICIAL RESPIRATION. GET MEDICAL ATTENTION IMMEDIATELY.

EYE CONTACT: CRUFOMATE: IRRITANT. THIS MATERIAL PRODUCED CORNEAL CLOUDINESS AND CONJUNCTIVAL IRRITATION, ALONG WITH SLIGHT PAIN WHEN APPLIED UNDILUTED TO THE EYES OF RABBITS. SEE INFORMATION ON ORGANOPHOSPHATES.

ORGANOPHOSPHATES: CHOLINESTERASE INHIBITOR. **ACUTE EXPOSURE-** DIRECT CONTACT MAY CAUSE PAIN, HYPEREMIA, LACRIMATION, TWITCHING OF THE EYELIDS, MIOSIS, AND CILIARY MUSCLE SPASM WITH LOSS OF ACCOMODATION, BLURRED OR DIMMED VISION AND BROWACHE. SOMETIMES MYDRIASIS MAY OCCUR INSTEAD OF MIOSIS. WITH SUFFICIENT EXPOSURE, OTHER SYMPTOMS OF CHOLINESTERASE INHIBITION AS DESCRIBED IN ACUTE INHALATION MAY OCCUR. **CHRONIC EXPOSURE-** REPEATED OR PROLONGED EXPOSURE MAY CAUSE EFFECTS AS DESCRIBED IN ACUTE EXPOSURE. SOME COMPOUNDS HAVE CAUSED TOXIC EFFECTS ON THE CRYSTALLINE LENS, CONJUNCTIVAL THICKENING AND OBSTRUCTION OF THE NASOLACRIMAL CANALS WHEN USED AS MIOTIC EYEDROPS.

FIRST AID- IRRIGATE EYES WITH WATER OR SALINE SOLUTION. IF SYMPTOMS OF POISONING OCCUR, TREAT RESPIRATORY DIFFICULTY WITH ARTIFICIAL RESPIRATION AND OXYGEN. OBSERVE PATIENT FOR AT LEAST 24-36 HOURS (GOSSELIN, CLINICAL TOXICOLOGY OF COMMERCIAL PRODUCTS, 5TH ED.). GET MEDICAL ATTENTION IMMEDIATELY. OXYGEN SHOULD BE ADMINISTERED BY QUALIFIED MEDICAL PERSONNEL.

INGESTION: CRUFOMATE: TOXIC. IN A DEMYELINATION STUDY OF HENS, ATAXIA AND PARALYSIS WERE OBSERVED WITH RECOVERY OCCURRING WITHIN 90 DAYS OF TREATMENT. CHOLINESTERASE INHIBITION AND NEUROTOXIC EFFECTS INVOLVING THE MUSCLES OF THE HINDQUATERS WERE OBSERVED IN A 2-YEAR STUDY OF RATS AND DOGS AT DIETARY LEVELS OF 1000 AND 2000 PPM RESPECTIVELY. OTHER REPORTED EFFECTS INCLUDED DEGENERATION OF TESTES AND SLIGHT DEGENERATION OF SCIATIC NERVE IN RATS AND AN ELEVATION IN SERUM ENZYME ACTIVITIES IN DOGS. SEE INFORMATION ON ORGANOPHOSPHATES.

ORGANOPHOSPHATES: CHOLINESTERASE INHIBITOR. **ACUTE EXPOSURE-** WHEN INGESTED, THE FIRST EFFECTS MAY BE NAUSEA, VOMITING, ANOREXIA, ABDOMINAL CRAMPS AND DIARRHEA. GASTROINTESTINAL ABSORPTION MAY CAUSE SYMPTOMS OF CHOLINESTERASE INHIBITION AS DESCRIBED IN ACUTE INHALATION. SYMPTOMS MAY BEGIN WITHIN MINUTES OR BE DELAYED FOR HOURS. DELAYED EFFECTS INCLUDING NEUROPATHY MAY ALSO OCCUR. **CHRONIC EXPOSURE-** REPEATED INGESTION MAY CAUSE EFFECTS AS DESCRIBED IN ACUTE EXPOSURE.

FIRST AID- IF PERSON IS ALERT AND RESPIRATION IS NOT DEPRESSED, GIVE SYRUP OF IPECAC FOLLOWED BY WATER (IF VOMITING OCCURS, KEEP HEAD BELOW HIPS TO PREVENT ASPIRATION). IF CONSCIOUSNESS LEVEL DECLINES OR VOMITING HAS NOT OCCURRED IN 15 MINUTES EMPTY STOMACH BY GASTRIC LAVAGE WITH THE AID OF CUFFED ENDOTRACHEAL TUBE USING ISOTONIC SALINE OR 5% SODIUM BICARBONATE FOLLOW WITH ACTIVATED CHARCOAL. ESTABLISH AND MAINTAIN AIRWAY. TREAT RESPIRATORY DIFFICULTY WITH ARTIFICIAL RESPIRATION AND OXYGEN. DO NOT GIVE MORPHINE, AMINOPHYLLINE, PHENOTHIAZINES, RESERPINE, FUROSEMIDE, OR ETHACRYNIC ACID (MORGAN, RECOGNITION AND MANAGEMENT OF PESTICIDE POISONINGS, 3RD ED.). TREAT SYMPTOMATICALLY AND SUPPORTIVELY. ADMINISTRATION OF OXYGEN AND LAVAGE MUST BE PERFORMED BY QUALIFIED MEDICAL PERSONNEL. GET MEDICAL ATTENTION IMMEDIATELY.

ANTIDOTE: THE FOLLOWING ANTIDOTE(S) HAVE BEEN RECOMMENDED. HOWEVER, THE DECISION AS TO WHETHER THE SEVERITY OF POISONING REQUIRES ADMINISTRATION OF ANY ANTIDOTE AND ACTUAL DOSE REQUIRED SHOULD BE MADE BY QUALIFIED MEDICAL PERSONNEL.

FOR CHOLINESTERASE INHIBITORS: ESTABLISH CLEAR AIRWAY AND TISSUE OXYGENATION BY ASPIRATION OF SECRETIONS, AND IF NECESSARY, BY ASSISTED PULMONARY VENTILATION WITH OXYGEN. IMPROVE TISSUE OXYGENATION AS MUCH AS POSSIBLE BEFORE ADMINISTERING ATROPINE TO MINIMIZE THE RISK OF VENTRICULAR FIBRILLATION. ADMINISTER ATROPINE SULFATE INTRAVENOUSLY, OR INTRAMUSCULARLY IF IV INJECTION IS NOT POSSIBLE. IN MODERATELY SEVERE POISONING ADMINISTER ATROPINE SULFATE, 0.4-2.0 MG REPEATED EVERY 15 MINUTES UNTIL ATROPINIZATION IS ACHIEVED (TACHYCARDIA, FLUSHING, DRY MOUTH, MYDRIASIS). MAINTAIN ATROPINIZATION BY REPEATED DOSES FOR 2-12 HOURS, OR LONGER, DEPENDING ON THE SEVERITY OF POISONING. THE APPEARANCE OF RALES IN THE LUNG BASES, MIOSIS, SALIVATION, NAUSEA, BRADYCARDIA, ARE ALL INDICATIONS OF INADEQUATE ATROPINIZATION. SEVERELY POISONED INDIVIDUALS MAY EXHIBIT REMARKABLE TOLERANCE TO ATROPINE; TWO OR MORE TIMES THE DOSAGES SUGGESTED ABOVE MAY BE NEEDED. PERSONS NOT POISONED OR ONLY SLIGHTLY POISONED, HOWEVER, MAY DEVELOP SIGNS OF ATROPINE TOXICITY FROM SUCH LARGE DOSAGES: FEVER, MUSCLE FIBRILLATIONS, AND DELIRIUM ARE THE MAIN SIGNS OF ATROPINE TOXICITY. IF THESE SIGNS APPEAR WHILE THE PATIENT IS FULLY ATROPINIZED, ATROPINE ADMINISTRATION SHOULD BE DISCONTINUED, AT LEAST TEMPORARILY. OBSERVE TREATED PATIENTS CLOSELY AT LEAST 24 HOURS TO INSURE THAT SYMPTOMS (POSSIBLY PULMONARY EDEMA) DO NOT RECUR AS ATROPINIZATION WEARS OFF. IN VERY SEVERE POISONINGS, METABOLIC DISPOSITION OF TOXICANT MAY REQUIRE SEVERAL HOURS OR DAYS DURING WHICH ATROPINIZATION MUST BE MAINTAINED. MARKEDLY LOWER LEVELS OF URINARY METABOLITES INDICATE THAT ATROPINE DOSAGE CAN BE TAPERED OFF. AS DOSAGE IS REDUCED, CHECK THE LUNG BASES FREQUENTLY FOR RALES. IF RALES ARE HEARD OR OTHER SYMPTOMS RETURN, RE-ESTABLISH ATROPINIZATION PROMPTLY (MORGAN, RECOGNITION AND MANAGEMENT OF PESTICIDE POISONINGS, 3RD ED.). ADMINISTRATION OF ANTIDOTE MUST BE PERFORMED BY QUALIFIED MEDICAL PERSONNEL.

IN CASES OF SEVERE POISONING BY ORGANOPHOSPHATE PESTICIDES IN WHICH RESPIRATORY DEPRESSION, MUSCLE WEAKNESS AND TWITCHINGS ARE SEVERE, GIVE PRALIDOXIME (PROTOPAM-AYERST, 2-PAM), 1.0 GRAM INTRAVENOUSLY AT NO MORE THAN 0.5 GRAM PER MINUTE. DOSAGE OF PRALIDOXIME MAY BE REPEATED IN 1-2 HOURS, THEN AT 10-12 HOUR INTERVALS IF NEEDED. IN VERY SEVERE POISONINGS, DOSAGE RATES MAY BE DOUBLED. TREATMENT WITH PRALIDOXIME WILL BE MOST EFFECTIVE IF GIVEN WITHIN THIRTY-SIX HOURS AFTER POISONING (MORGAN, RECOGNITION AND MANAGEMENT OF PESTICIDE POISONINGS, 3RD ED.). ANTIDOTE SHOULD BE ADMINISTERED BY QUALIFIED MEDICAL PERSONNEL.

REACTIVITY

REACTIVITY: STABLE UNDER NORMAL TEMPERATURES AND PRESSURES.

INCOMPATIBILITIES: CRUFOMATE: OXIDIZERS (STRONG): FIRE AND EXPLOSION HAZARD.

DECOMPOSITION: THERMAL DECOMPOSITION MAY RELEASE TOXIC OXIDES OF NITROGEN AND PHOSPHORUS AND CORROSIVE HYDROGEN CHLORIDE.

POLYMERIZATION: HAZARDOUS POLYMERIZATION HAS NOT BEEN REPORTED TO OCCUR UNDER NORMAL TEMPERATURES AND PRESSURES.

STORAGE AND DISPOSAL

OBSERVE ALL FEDERAL, STATE AND LOCAL REGULATIONS WHEN STORING OR DISPOSING OF THIS SUBSTANCE. FOR ASSISTANCE, CONTACT THE DISTRICT DIRECTOR OF THE ENVIRONMENTAL PROTECTION AGENCY.

****STORAGE****

STORE IN ACCORDANCE WITH 40 CFR 165 RECOMMENDED PROCEDURES FOR THE DISPOSAL AND STORAGE OF PESTICIDES AND PESTICIDE CONTAINERS.

STORE AWAY FROM INCOMPATIBLE SUBSTANCES.

****DISPOSAL****

DISPOSAL MUST BE IN ACCORDANCE WITH 40 CFR 165 RECOMMENDED PROCEDURES FOR THE DISPOSAL AND STORAGE OF PESTICIDES AND PESTICIDE CONTAINERS.

CONDITIONS TO AVOID

MAY BURN BUT DOES NOT IGNITE READILY. CONTAINERS MAY EXPLODE IN HEAT OF FIRE.

SPILL AND LEAK PROCEDURES

OCCUPATIONAL SPILL: DO NOT TOUCH SPILLED MATERIAL. STOP LEAK IF YOU CAN DO IT WITHOUT RISK. USE WATER SPRAY TO REDUCE VAPORS. FOR SMALL SPILLS, TAKE UP WITH SAND OR OTHER ABSORBENT MATERIAL AND PLACE INTO CONTAINERS FOR LATER DISPOSAL. FOR SMALL DRY SPILLS, WITH A CLEAN SHOVEL PLACE MATERIAL INTO CLEAN, DRY CONTAINERS AND COVER. MOVE CONTAINERS FROM SPILL AREA. FOR LARGER SPILLS, DIKE FAR AHEAD OF SPILL FOR LATER DISPOSAL. KEEP UNNECESSARY PEOPLE AWAY. ISOLATE HAZARD AREA AND DENY ENTRY. VENTILATE CLOSED SPACES BEFORE ENTERING.

PROTECTIVE EQUIPMENT

VENTILATION: PROVIDE LOCAL EXHAUST OR GENERAL DILUTION VENTILATION SYSTEM.

RESPIRATOR: THE FOLLOWING RESPIRATORS ARE RECOMMENDED BASED ON INFORMATION FOUND IN THE PHYSICAL DATA, TOXICITY AND HEALTH EFFECTS SECTIONS. THEY ARE RANKED IN ORDER FROM MINIMUM TO MAXIMUM RESPIRATORY PROTECTION. THE SPECIFIC RESPIRATOR SELECTED MUST BE BASED ON CONTAMINATION LEVELS FOUND IN THE WORK PLACE, MUST NOT EXCEED THE WORKING LIMITS OF THE RESPIRATOR AND BE JOINTLY APPROVED BY THE NATIONAL INSTITUTE FOR OCCUPATIONAL SAFETY AND HEALTH AND THE MINE SAFETY AND HEALTH ADMINISTRATION (NIOSH-MSHA).

CHEMICAL CARTRIDGE RESPIRATOR WITH AN ORGANIC VAPOR CARTRIDGE(S) WITH A FULL FACEPIECE AND ORGANIC VAPOR CARTRIDGE(S) IN COMBINATION WITH A DUST AND MIST FILTER.

POWERED AIR-PURIFYING RESPIRATOR WITH A TIGHT-FITTING FACEPIECE AND ORGANIC VAPOR CARTRIDGE(S) IN COMBINATION WITH A HIGH-EFFICIENCY PARTICULATE FILTER.

TYPE 'C' SUPPLIED-AIR RESPIRATOR WITH A FULL FACEPIECE OPERATED IN A PRESSURE-DEMAND OR OTHER POSITIVE PRESSURE MODE.

SELF-CONTAINED BREATHING APPARATUS WITH A FULL FACEPIECE OPERATED IN PRESSURE-DEMAND OR OTHER POSITIVE PRESSURE MODE.

FOR FIREFIGHTING AND OTHER IMMEDIATELY DANGEROUS TO LIFE OR HEALTH CONDITIONS:

SELF-CONTAINED BREATHING APPARATUS WITH FULL FACEPIECE OPERATED IN PRESSURE-DEMAND OR OTHER POSITIVE PRESSURE MODE.

SUPPLIED-AIR RESPIRATOR WITH FULL FACEPIECE AND OPERATED IN PRESSURE-DEMAND OR OTHER POSITIVE PRESSURE MODE IN COMBINATION WITH AN AUXILIARY SELF-CONTAINED BREATHING APPARATUS OPERATED IN PRESSURE-DEMAND OR OTHER POSITIVE PRESSURE MODE.

CLOTHING: EMPLOYEE MUST WEAR APPROPRIATE PROTECTIVE (IMPERVIOUS) CLOTHING AND EQUIPMENT TO PREVENT REPEATED OR PROLONGED SKIN CONTACT WITH THIS SUBSTANCE.

GLOVES: EMPLOYEE MUST WEAR APPROPRIATE PROTECTIVE GLOVES TO PREVENT CONTACT WITH THIS SUBSTANCE.

EYE PROTECTION: EMPLOYEE MUST WEAR SPLASH-PROOF OR DUST-RESISTANT SAFETY GOGGLES WITH OR WITHOUT A FACESHIELD TO PREVENT CONTACT WITH THIS SUBSTANCE.

EMERGENCY EYE WASH: WHERE THERE IS ANY POSSIBILITY THAT AN EMPLOYEE'S EYES MAY BE EXPOSED TO THIS SUBSTANCE, THE EMPLOYER SHOULD PROVIDE AN EYE WASH FOUNTAIN WITHIN THE IMMEDIATE WORK AREA FOR EMERGENCY USE.

AUTHORIZED BY- OCCUPATIONAL HEALTH SERVICES, INC.

CREATION DATE: 10/04/89 ***REVISION DATE:*** 05/08/90

MATERIAL SAFETY DATA SHEET

OCCUPATIONAL HEALTH SERVICES, INC.
AGRICULTURE AND PESTICIDE DIVISION
450 SEVENTH AVENUE, SUITE 2407
NEW YORK, NEW YORK 10123
1-800-445-MSDS OR (212) 967-1100

EMERGENCY CONTACT:
JOHN S. BRANSFORD, JR. (615) 292-1180

SUBSTANCE IDENTIFICATION

CAS-NUMBER 15096-52-3

SUBSTANCE: **SODIUM FLUOALUMINATE**

TRADE NAMES/SYNONYMS: CRYOLITE; SODIUM HEXAFLUOROALUMINATE; VILLIALUMITE; SODIUM ALUMINOFLUORIDE; SODIUM ALUMINUM FLUORIDE; KRYOCIDE; ICETONE; PST05560

CHEMICAL FAMILY: INORGANIC SALT

MOLECULAR FORMULA: AL-F6-NA3 MOL WT: 209.95

CERCLA RATINGS (SCALE 0-3): HEALTH=3 FIRE=0 REACTIVITY=0 PERSISTENCE=3

NFPA RATINGS (SCALE 0-4): HEALTH=3 FIRE=0 REACTIVITY=0

COMPONENTS AND CONTAMINANTS

COMPONENT: SODIUM FLUOALUMINATE ***PERCENT:*** 100
CAS# 15096-52-3

OTHER CONTAMINANTS: NONE

EXPOSURE LIMITS: SODIUM FLUOALUMINATE: 2.5 MG(F)/M3 OSHA TWA 2.5 MG(F)/M3 ACGIH TWA 2.5 MG(F)/M3 NIOSH RECOMMENDED TWA 2 MG(AL)/M3 ACGIH TWA

PHYSICAL DATA

DESCRIPTION: ODORLESS WHITE TO DARK VITREOUS MASSES.

MELTING POINT: 1832 F (1000 C) ***SPECIFIC GRAVITY:*** 2.95

SOLUBILITY IN WATER: SLIGHTLY SOLUBLE

SOLVENT SOLUBILITY: CONCENTRATED SULFURIC ACID

FIRE AND EXPLOSION DATA

FIRE AND EXPLOSION HAZARD: NEGLIGIBLE FIRE HAZARD WHEN EXPOSED TO HEAT OR FLAME.

FIREFIGHTING MEDIA: DRY CHEMICAL, CARBON DIOXIDE, HALON, WATER SPRAY OR STANDARD FOAM (1987 EMERGENCY RESPONSE GUIDEBOOK, DOT P 5800.4).
FOR LARGER FIRES, USE WATER SPRAY, FOG OR STANDARD FOAM (1987 EMERGENCY RESPONSE GUIDEBOOK, DOT P 5800.4).

FIREFIGHTING: MOVE CONTAINER FROM FIRE AREA IF POSSIBLE. DO NOT SCATTER SPILLED MATERIAL WITH HIGH PRESSURE WATER STREAMS. DIKE FIRE CONTROL WATER FOR LATER DISPOSAL (1987 EMERGENCY RESPONSE GUIDEBOOK, DOT P 5800.4, GUIDE PAGE 31).
USE AGENTS SUITABLE FOR TYPE OF SURROUNDING FIRE. AVOID BREATHING HAZARDOUS VAPORS, KEEP UPWIND.

TOXICITY

SODIUM FLUOALUMINATE: TOXICITY DATA: 200 MG/KG ORAL-RAT LD50; 9 GM/KG ORAL-RABBIT LDLO. CARCINOGEN STATUS: NONE. ACUTE TOXICITY LEVEL: TOXIC BY INGESTION. TARGET EFFECTS: POISONING WITH FLUORIDES MAY AFFECT THE CALCIUM METABOLISM AND ENZYME MECHANISMS.

HEALTH EFFECTS AND FIRST AID

INHALATION: SODIUM FLUOALUMINATE: IRRITANT. 500 MG(F)/M3 IMMEDIATELY DANGEROUS TO LIFE OR HEALTH. **ACUTE EXPOSURE-** DUST MAY CAUSE RESPIRATORY IRRITATION. INHALATION OF FUMES MAY CAUSE COUGHING, CHILLS LASTING 1-2 HOURS AFTER EXPOSURE. FEVER, TIGHTNESS IN THE CHEST, RALES, AND CYANOSIS ARE DELAYED SYMPTOMS AND MAY INDICATE PULMONARY EDEMA. **CHRONIC EXPOSURE-** REPEATED OR PROLONGED EXPOSURE TO DUST MAY CAUSE MUCOUS MEMBRANE IRRITATION. CHRONIC EXPOSURE TO VAPORS MAY CAUSE SYMPTOMS SIMILAR TO THOSE OF ACUTE EXPOSURE.

FIRST AID- REMOVE FROM EXPOSURE AREA TO FRESH AIR IMMEDIATELY. IF BREATHING HAS STOPPED, PERFORM ARTIFICIAL RESPIRATION. KEEP PERSON WARM AND AT REST. TREAT SYMPTOMATICALLY AND SUPPORTIVELY. GET MEDICAL ATTENTION IMMEDIATELY.

SKIN CONTACT: SODIUM FLUOALUMINATE: IRRITANT. **ACUTE EXPOSURE-** CONTACT WITH DUST MAY CAUSE IRRITATION. VAPOR CONTACT MAY CAUSE MORE SEVERE IRRITATION AND BURNS WHICH ARE DEEP AND HEAL SLOWLY. THE EXTENT OF DAMAGE DEPENDS ON THE CONCENTRATION OF HYDROGEN FLUORIDE IN THE VAPOR AND THE DURATION OF CONTACT. **CHRONIC EXPOSURE-** REPEATED OR PROLONGED EXPOSURE MAY CAUSE DERMATITIS OR ULCERATION OF THE SKIN.

FIRST AID- REMOVE CONTAMINATED CLOTHING AND SHOES IMMEDIATELY. WASH AFFECTED AREA WITH SOAP OR MILD DETERGENT AND LARGE AMOUNTS OF WATER UNTIL NO EVIDENCE OF CHEMICAL REMAINS (APPROXIMATELY 15-20 MINUTES). GET MEDICAL ATTENTION IMMEDIATELY.

EYE CONTACT: SODIUM FLUOALUMINATE: IRRITANT. **ACUTE EXPOSURE-** DUST MAY BE IRRITATING. VAPORS MAY CAUSE MORE SEVERE IRRITATION, PAIN, AND BURNS. THE EXTENT OF INJURY DEPENDS ON THE CONCENTRATION OF HYDROGEN FLUORIDE IN THE VAPORS AND THE DURATION OF CONTACT. **CHRONIC EXPOSURE-** REPEATED OR PROLONGED CONTACT MAY CAUSE CONJUNCITIVIS AND POSSIBLE DAMAGE TO THE CORNEA.

FIRST AID- WASH EYES IMMEDIATELY WITH LARGE AMOUNTS OF WATER OR NORMAL SALINE, OCCASIONALLY LIFTING UPPER AND LOWER LIDS, UNTIL NO EVIDENCE OF CHEMICAL REMAINS (APPROXIMATELY 15-20 MINUTES). GET MEDICAL ATTENTION IMMEDIATELY.

INGESTION: SODIUM FLUOALUMINATE: TOXIC. **ACUTE EXPOSURE-** MAY CAUSE NAUSEA, VOMITING, ABDOMINAL PAIN, AND DIARRHEA. LATER, WEAKNESS, TREMORS, SHALLOW RESPIRATION, CARPOPEDAL SPASMS, AND CONVULSIONS MAY OCCUR. JAUNDICE AND OLIGURIA MAY ALSO OCCUR. **CHRONIC EXPOSURE-** INTAKE OF MORE THAN 6 MG OF FLUORINE PER DAY MAY RESULT IN FLUOROSIS WITH ANEMIA, WEIGHT LOSS, BRITTLENESS OF BONES, WEAKNESS, STIFFNESS IN THE JOINTS, AND DISCOLORATION OF THE TEETH WHEN EXPOSURE IS DURING TOOTH FORMATION.

FIRST AID- IF PERSON IS CONSCIOUS, GIVE LARGE QUANTITIES OF WATER. IF THERE IS NO EVIDENCE OF CORROSION, INDUCE VOMITING. TREAT SYMPTOMATICALLY AND SUPPORTIVELY. DO NOT MAKE AN UNCONSCIOUS PERSON VOMIT OR DRINK ANYTHING. GET MEDICAL ATTENTION. (DREISBACH, HANDBOOK OF POISONING 11TH, ED.)

ANTIDOTE: NO SPECIFIC ANTIDOTE. TREAT SYMPTOMATICALLY AND SUPPORTIVELY.

REACTIVITY

REACTIVITY: STABLE UNDER NORMAL TEMPERATURES AND PRESSURES.

INCOMPATIBILITIES: SODIUM FLUOALUMINATE: NO DATA AVAILABLE.

DECOMPOSITION: THERMAL DECOMPOSITION PRODUCTS MAY INCLUDE TOXIC FUMES OF SODIUM OXIDE AND CORROSIVE VAPORS OF HYDROGEN FLUORIDE.

POLYMERIZATION: HAZARDOUS POLYMERIZATION HAS NOT BEEN REPORTED TO OCCUR UNDER NORMAL TEMPERATURES AND PRESSURES.

CONDITIONS TO AVOID

MAY BURN BUT DOES NOT IGNITE READILY. AVOID CONTACT WITH STRONG OXIDIZERS, EXCESSIVE HEAT, SPARKS, OR OPEN FLAME.

SPILL AND LEAK PROCEDURES

OCCUPATIONAL SPILL: STOP LEAK IF YOU CAN DO IT WITHOUT RISK. FOR SMALL SPILLS, TAKE UP WITH SAND OR OTHER ABSORBENT MATERIAL AND PLACE INTO CLEAN, DRY CONTAINERS FOR LATER DISPOSAL. KEEP UNNECESSARY PEOPLE AWAY. ISOLATE HAZARD AREA AND DENY ENTRY.
RESIDUE SHOULD BE CLEANED UP USING A HIGH-EFFICIENCY PARTICULATE FILTER VACUUM.

PROTECTIVE EQUIPMENT

VENTILATION: PROVIDE LOCAL EXHAUST VENTILATION AND/OR GENERAL DILUTION VENTILATION TO MEET PUBLISHED EXPOSURE LIMITS.

RESPIRATOR: THE FOLLOWING RESPIRATORS AND MAXIMUM USE CONCENTRATIONS ARE RECOMMENDATIONS BY THE U.S. DEPARTMENT OF HEALTH AND HUMAN SERVICES, NIOSH POCKET GUIDE TO CHEMICAL HAZARDS; NIOSH CRITERIA DOCUMENTS OR BY THE U.S. DEPARTMENT OF LABOR, 29 CFR 1910 SUBPART Z.
THE SPECIFIC RESPIRATOR SELECTED MUST BE BASED ON CONTAMINATION LEVELS FOUND IN THE WORK PLACE, MUST NOT EXCEED THE WORKING LIMITS OF THE RESPIRATOR AND BE JOINTLY APPROVED BY THE NATIONAL INSTITUTE FOR OCCUPATIONAL SAFETY AND HEALTH AND THE MINE SAFETY AND HEALTH ADMINISTRATION (NIOSH-MSHA).
12.5 MG(F)/M3- DUST MASK.
25 MG(F)/M3- DUST MASK, EXCEPT SINGLE-USE AND QUARTER-MASK RESPIRATORS WITH WITH AN ACID GAS SORBENT. SUPPLIED-AIR RESPIRATOR. SELF-CONTAINED BREATHING APPARATUS.
125 MG(F)/M3- HIGH-EFFICIENCY PARTICULATE RESPIRATOR WITH A FULL FACEPIECE. SUPPLIED-AIR RESPIRATOR WITH A FULL FACEPIECE, HELMET, OR HOOD. SELF-CONTAINED BREATHING APPARATUS WITH A FULL FACEPIECE.
250 MG(F)/M3- POWERED AIR-PURIFYING RESPIRATOR WITH A HIGH-EFFICIENCY FILTER AND A FULL FACEPIECE. TYPE "C" SUPPLIED AIR RESPIRATOR WITH FULL FACEPIECE OPERATED IN PRESSURE-DEMAND OR OTHER POSITIVE PRESSURE MODE OR WITH FULL FACEPIECE, HELMET OR HOOD OPERATED IN CONTINUOUS FLOW MODE.
ESCAPE- GAS MASK WITH ORGANIC VAPOR CANNISTER (CHIN-STYLE OR FRONT- OR BACK-MOUNTED CANNISTER). SELF-CONTAINED BREATHING APPARATUS.
FOR FIREFIGHTING AND OTHER IMMEDIATELY DANGEROUS TO LIFE OR HEALTH CONDITIONS:
SELF-CONTAINED BREATHING APPARATUS WITH FULL FACEPIECE OPERATED IN PRESSURE-DEMAND OR OTHER POSITIVE PRESSURE MODE.
SUPPLIED-AIR RESPIRATOR WITH FULL FACEPIECE AND OPERATED IN PRESSURE-DEMAND OR OTHER POSITIVE PRESSURE MODE IN COMBINATION WITH AN AUXILIARY SELF-CONTAINED BREATHING APPARATUS OPERATED IN PRESSURE-DEMAND OR OTHER POSITIVE PRESSURE MODE.

CLOTHING: EMPLOYEE MUST WEAR APPROPRIATE PROTECTIVE (IMPERVIOUS) CLOTHING AND EQUIPMENT TO PREVENT REPEATED OR PROLONGED SKIN CONTACT WITH THIS SUBSTANCE.

GLOVES: EMPLOYEE MUST WEAR APPROPRIATE PROTECTIVE GLOVES TO PREVENT CONTACT WITH THIS SUBSTANCE.

EYE PROTECTION: EMPLOYEE MUST WEAR SPLASH-PROOF OR DUST-RESISTANT SAFETY GOGGLES AND A FACESHIELD TO PREVENT CONTACT WITH THIS SUBSTANCE.
EMERGENCY WASH FACILITIES: WHERE THERE IS ANY POSSIBILITY THAT AN EMPLOYEE'S EYES AND/OR SKIN MAY BE EXPOSED TO THIS SUBSTANCE, THE EMPLOYER SHOULD PROVIDE AN EYE WASH FOUNTAIN AND QUICK DRENCH SHOWER WITHIN THE IMMEDIATE WORK AREA FOR EMERGENCY USE.

AUTHORIZED BY- OCCUPATIONAL HEALTH SERVICES, INC.

AUTHORIZED BY- OCCUPATIONAL HEALTH SERVICES, INC.
CREATION DATE: 10/05/89 ***REVISION DATE:*** 05/18/90

MATERIAL SAFETY DATA SHEET

OCCUPATIONAL HEALTH SERVICES, INC.
AGRICULTURE AND PESTICIDE DIVISION
450 SEVENTH AVENUE, SUITE 2407
NEW YORK, NEW YORK 10123
1-800-445-MSDS OR (212) 967-1100

EMERGENCY CONTACT:
JOHN S. BRANSFORD, JR. (615) 292-1180

SUBSTANCE IDENTIFICATION

CAS-NUMBER 10125-13-0
SUBSTANCE: CUPRIC CHLORIDE, DIHYDRATE
TRADE NAMES/SYNONYMS: COPPER CHLORIDE DIHYDRATE; COPPER DICHLORIDE DIHYDRATE; COPPER CHLORIDE (CUCL2), DIHYDRATE; CUPRIC CHLORIDE DIHYDRATE; COPPER CHLORIDE (CUCL2.2H2O); STCC 4944173; UN2802; CL2CUH4O2; PST05625
CHEMICAL FAMILY: INORGANIC SALT
MOLECULAR FORMULA: CU-CL2.2H20
MOLECULAR WEIGHT: 170.43
CERCLA RATINGS (SCALE 0-3): HEALTH=3 FIRE=0 REACTIVITY=0 PERSISTENCE=3
NFPA RATINGS (SCALE 0-4): HEALTH=U FIRE=0 REACTIVITY=0

COMPONENTS AND CONTAMINANTS

COMPONENT: CUPRIC CHLORIDE, DIHYDRATE ***PERCENT:*** 100.0
CAS# 10125-13-0
OTHER CONTAMINANTS: NONE
EXPOSURE LIMITS: COPPER DUST AND MIST (AS CU): 1 MG/M3 OSHA TWA 1 MG/M3 ACGIH TWA
SUBJECT TO SARA SECTION 313 ANNUAL TOXIC CHEMICAL RELEASE REPORTING

PHYSICAL DATA

DESCRIPTION: GREEN TO BLUE DELIQUESCENT CRYSTALS OR POWDER.
BOILING POINT: 1819 F (993 C) (DECOMPOSES) ***MELTING POINT:*** 212 F (100 C)
SPECIFIC GRAVITY: 2.54 ***PH:*** 3.6 @ 0.2 M SOLUTION
SOLUBILITY IN WATER: 110% @ 0 C
SOLVENT SOLUBILITY: SOLUBLE IN METHANOL, ETHANOL, AND AMMONIUM HYDROXIDE; MODERATELY SOLUBLE IN ACETONE AND ETHYL ACETATE; SLIGHTLY SOLUBLE IN ETHER.
LOSES WATER OF HYDRATION BETWEEN 158-392 F (70-200 C).

FIRE AND EXPLOSION DATA

FIRE AND EXPLOSION HAZARD: NEGLIGIBLE FIRE HAZARD WHEN EXPOSED TO HEAT OR FLAME.
FIREFIGHTING MEDIA: DRY CHEMICAL, CARBON DIOXIDE, HALON, WATER SPRAY OR STANDARD FOAM (1987 EMERGENCY RESPONSE GUIDEBOOK, DOT P 5800.4).
FOR LARGER FIRES, USE WATER SPRAY, FOG OR STANDARD FOAM (1987 EMERGENCY RESPONSE GUIDEBOOK, DOT P 5800.4).
FIREFIGHTING: MOVE CONTAINERS FROM FIRE AREA IF POSSIBLE. COOL CONTAINERS EXPOSED TO FLAMES WITH WATER FROM SIDE UNTIL WELL AFTER FIRE IS OUT. STAY AWAY FROM STORAGE TANK ENDS (1987 EMERGENCY RESPONSE GUIDEBOOK, DOT P 5800.4, GUIDE PAGE 60).
USE AGENTS SUITABLE FOR TYPE OF FIRE. AVOID BREATHING CORROSIVE VAPORS, KEEP UPWIND.

TRANSPORTATION DATA

DEPARTMENT OF TRANSPORTATION HAZARD CLASSIFICATION 49 CFR 172.101: ORM-B
DEPARTMENT OF TRANSPORTATION LABELING REQUIREMENTS 49 CFR 172.101 AND SUBPART E: NONE
DEPARTMENT OF TRANSPORTATION PACKAGING REQUIREMENTS: 49 CFR 173.800 EXCEPTIONS: 49 CFR 173.505

TOXICITY

CUPRIC CHLORIDE: TOXICITY DATA: ANHYDROUS: 200 MG/KG ORAL-HUMAN LDLO; 140 MG/KG ORAL-RAT LD50; 190 MG/KG ORAL-MOUSE LD50; 31 MG/KG ORAL-GUINEA PIG LD50; 7400 UG/KG INTRAPERITONEAL-MOUSE LD50; 100 MG/KG SUBCUTANEOUS-GUINEA PIG LDLO; 17,500 UG/KG INTRAVENOUS-MOUSE LD50; MUTAGENIC DATA (RTECS); REPRODUCTIVE EFFECTS DATA (RTECS). DIHYDRATE: NO DATA AVAILABLE. CARCINOGEN STATUS: NONE. LOCAL EFFECTS: IRRITANT-EYE, SKIN, AND MUCOUS MEMBRANES. ACUTE TOXICITY EFFECTS: TOXIC BY INGESTION. TARGET EFFECTS: POISONING MAY AFFECT THE LIVER, KIDNEYS AND SPLEEN. AT INCREASED RISK FROM EXPOSURE (TO COPPER SALTS): PERSONS WITH PRE-EXISTING RESPIRATORY, LIVER, SKIN, KIDNEY, HEMATOPOIETIC OR WILSON'S DISEASE.

HEALTH EFFECTS AND FIRST AID

INHALATION: CUPRIC CHLORIDE: IRRITANT. **ACUTE EXPOSURE-** MAY CAUSE IRRITATION OF MUCOUS MEMBRANES, SORE THROAT, COUGHING, AND SHORTNESS OF BREATH. INHALATION OF COPPER DUST MAY CAUSE AN ILLNESS SIMILAR TO THE COMMON COLD WITH SENSATIONS OF CHILLS AND STUFFINESS OF THE HEAD. **CHRONIC EXPOSURE-** PROLONGED INHALATION OF DUST OR MIST OF COPPER SALTS MAY CAUSE CONGESTION OF THE NASAL MUCOUS MEMBRANES, SOMETIMES OF THE PHARNYX, AND ON OCCASIONS ULCERATION AND PERFORATION OF THE NASAL SEPTUM. ATROPHIC CHANGES IN THE MUCOUS MEMBRANES WERE NOTED IN SUBJECTS EXPOSED TO COMPLEX COPPER SALTS FOR LONG PERIODS OF TIME. INHALATION OF COPPER COMPOUNDS HAS CAUSED INJURY TO THE LUNGS AND LIVER WITH HEMOCHROMATOSIS IN ANIMALS. REPRODUCTIVE EFFECTS HAVE BEEN REPORTED IN ANIMALS.
FIRST AID- REMOVE FROM EXPOSURE AREA TO FRESH AIR IMMEDIATELY. IF BREATHING HAS STOPPED, PERFORM ARTIFICIAL RESPIRATION. KEEP PERSON WARM AND AT REST. TREAT SYMPTOMATICALLY AND SUPPORTIVELY. GET MEDICAL ATTENTION IMMEDIATELY.

SKIN CONTACT: CUPRIC CHLORIDE: IRRITANT. **ACUTE EXPOSURE-** DIRECT CONTACT MAY CAUSE REDNESS, PAIN, AND IRRITATION. COPPER SALTS HAVE BEEN REPORTED TO CAUSE AN ITCHING PAPULOVESICULATION, SKIN DISCOLORATION AND ECZEMATOID LESIONS. **CHRONIC EXPOSURE-** REPEATED OR PROLONGED CONTACT WITH SOME COPPER SALTS HAS RESULTED IN IRRITATION, NECROSIS, AND GREENISH SKIN DISCOLORATION. ALLERGIC CONTACT DERMATITIS, ALTHOUGH RARE, HAS BEEN REPORTED.
FIRST AID- REMOVE CONTAMINATED CLOTHING AND SHOES IMMEDIATELY. WASH AFFECTED AREA WITH SOAP OR MILD DETERGENT AND LARGE AMOUNTS OF WATER UNTIL NO EVIDENCE OF CHEMICAL REMAINS (APPROXIMATELY 15-20 MINUTES). GET MEDICAL ATTENTION IMMEDIATELY.

EYE CONTACT: CUPRIC CHLORIDE: IRRITANT. **ACUTE EXPOSURE-** DIRECT CONTACT MAY CAUSE REDNESS, PAIN, AND BLURRED VISION. APPLICATION OF A 0.08 TO 0.16 M SOLUTION OF CUPRIC CHLORIDE TO THE CORNEAS OF RABBITS AFTER THE REMOVAL OF THE EPITHELIUM CAUSED A SEVERE REACTION WITH PERMANENT OPACIFICATION. SOME COPPER SALTS HAVE BEEN REPORTED TO CAUSE CONJUNCTIVITIS, CORNEAL ULCERATION, AND TURBIDITY POSSIBLY WITH PALPEBRAL EDEMA. COPPER PARTICLES EMBEDDED IN THE EYE MAY RESULT IN A PRONOUNCED FOREIGN-BODY RESPONSE WITH CHARACTERISTIC DISCOLORATION OF OCULAR TISSUE. **CHRONIC EXPOSURE-** REPEATED AND PROLONGED CONTACT WITH IRRITANTS MAY CAUSE CONJUNCTIVITIS.
FIRST AID- WASH EYES IMMEDIATELY WITH LARGE AMOUNTS OF WATER OR NORMAL SALINE, OCCASIONALLY LIFTING UPPER AND LOWER LIDS, UNTIL NO EVIDENCE OF CHEMICAL REMAINS (APPROXIMATELY 15-20 MINUTES). GET MEDICAL ATTENTION IMMEDIATELY.

INGESTION: CUPRIC CHLORIDE: TOXIC. **ACUTE EXPOSURE-** THE MEDIAN LETHAL DOSE IN RATS WAS 140 MG/KG. INGESTION MAY CAUSE ABDOMINAL PAIN, VOMITING AND DIARRHEA. INGESTION OF COPPER SALTS MAY CAUSE AN IMMEDIATE METALLIC TASTE, SALIVATION, NAUSEA, EPIGASTRIC BURNING, ULCERS, HEMORRHAGIC GASTRITIS, ANURIA, COMA, CONVULSIONS AND DEATH. **CHRONIC EXPOSURE-** REPEATED AND PROLONGED INGESTION OF COPPER SALTS HAS PRODUCED HEMOLYTIC ANEMIA AND LIVER, KIDNEY, AND SPLEEN DAMAGE IN ANIMALS.
FIRST AID- DILUTE THE POISON IMMEDIATELY WITH LARGE AMOUNTS OF WATER OR MILK AND REMOVE BY GASTRIC LAVAGE UNLESS THE VICTIM IS ALREADY VOMITING. (DREISBACH, HANDBOOK OF POISONING, 12TH ED.) GET MEDICAL ATTENTION IMMEDIATELY. ADMINISTRATION OF GASTRIC LAVAGE SHOULD BE PERFORMED BY QUALIFIED MEDICAL PERSONNEL.
ANTIDOTE: THE FOLLOWING ANTIDOTE HAS BEEN RECOMMENDED. HOWEVER, THE DECISION AS TO WHETHER THE SEVERITY OF POISONING REQUIRES ADMINISTRATION OF ANY ANTIDOTE AND ACTUAL DOSE REQUIRED SHOULD BE MADE BY QUALIFIED MEDICAL PERSONNEL.
COPPER POISONING: GIVE CALCIUM DISODIUM EDETATE 15-25 MG/KG (0.08-0.125 ML OF 20% SOLUTION PER KILOGRAM BODY WEIGHT) IN 250-500 ML OF 5% DEXTROSE INTRAVENOUSLY OVER A 1 TO 2 HOUR PERIOD TWICE DAILY. THE MAXIMUM DOSE SHOULD NOT EXCEED 50 MG/KG/DAY. THE DRUG SHOULD BE GIVEN IN 5-DAY COURSES WITH A REST PERIOD OF AT LEAST 2 DAYS BETWEEN COURSES. AFTER THE FIRST COURSE, SUBSEQUENT COURSES SHOULD NOT

URINARY FINDINGS APPEAR. INTRAVENOUS ADMINISTRATION IS CONTRAINDICATED IN THE PRESENCE OF ELEVATED CEREBROSPINAL FLUID PRESSURE. PENICILLAMINE IS ALSO EFFECTIVE IN COPPER POISONING. GIVE UP TO 100 MG/KG/DAY (MAXIMUM 1 G/DAY) DIVIDED INTO 4 DOSES FOR NO LONGER THAN 1 WEEK. IF A LONGER ADMINISTRATION PERIOD IS WARRANTED, DOSAGE SHOULD NOT EXCEED 40 MG/KG/DAY. GIVE THE DRUG ORALLY, HALF AN HOUR BEFORE MEALS (DREISBACH, HANDBOOK OF POISONING, 12TH ED.). ANTIDOTE SHOULD BE ADMINISTERED BY QUALIFIED MEDICAL PERSONNEL.

REACTIVITY

REACTIVITY: STABLE UNDER NORMAL TEMPERATURES AND PRESSURES.

INCOMPATIBILITIES: CUPRIC CHLORIDE: POTASSIUM: POSSIBLE EXPLOSION ON IMPACT. SODIUM: POSSIBLE EXPLOSION ON IMPACT.

DECOMPOSITION: THERMAL DECOMPOSITION MAY YIELD CORROSIVE FUMES OF HYDROGEN CHLORIDE AND TOXIC OXIDES OF COPPER.

POLYMERIZATION: HAZARDOUS POLYMERIZATION HAS NOT BEEN REPORTED TO OCCUR UNDER NORMAL TEMPERATURES AND PRESSURES.

STORAGE AND DISPOSAL

OBSERVE ALL FEDERAL, STATE AND LOCAL REGULATIONS WHEN STORING OR DISPOSING OF THIS SUBSTANCE. FOR ASSISTANCE, CONTACT THE DISTRICT DIRECTOR OF THE ENVIRONMENTAL PROTECTION AGENCY.

****STORAGE****

STORE AWAY FROM INCOMPATIBLE SUBSTANCES.

CONDITIONS TO AVOID

MAY BURN BUT DOES NOT IGNITE READILY. FLAMMABLE, POISONOUS GASES MAY ACCUMULATE IN TANKS AND HOPPER CARS. MAY IGNITE COMBUSTIBLES (WOOD, PAPER, OIL, ETC.).

PREVENT DISPERSION OF DUST.

SPILL AND LEAK PROCEDURES

SOIL SPILL: DIG HOLDING AREA SUCH AS LAGOON, POND OR PIT FOR CONTAINMENT. USE PROTECTIVE COVER SUCH AS A PLASTIC SHEET TO PREVENT MATERIAL FROM DISSOLVING IN FIRE EXTINGUISHING WATER OR RAIN.

WATER SPILL: USE MECHANICAL DREDGES OR LIFTS TO EXTRACT IMMOBILIZED MASSES OF POLLUTION AND PRECIPITATES.

ADD SUITABLE AGENT TO NEUTRALIZE SPILLED MATERIAL TO PH-7.

OCCUPATIONAL SPILL: DO NOT TOUCH SPILLED MATERIAL. STOP LEAK IF YOU CAN DO IT WITHOUT RISK. FOR SMALL SPILLS, TAKE UP WITH SAND OR OTHER ABSORBENT MATERIAL AND PLACE INTO CONTAINERS FOR LATER DISPOSAL. FOR SMALL DRY SPILLS, WITH CLEAN SHOVEL PLACE MATERIAL INTO CLEAN, DRY CONTAINER AND COVER. MOVE CONTAINERS FROM SPILL AREA. FOR LARGER SPILLS, DIKE FAR AHEAD OF SPILL FOR LATER DISPOSAL. KEEP UNNECESSARY PEOPLE AWAY. ISOLATE HAZARD AREA AND DENY ENTRY.

PROTECTIVE EQUIPMENT

VENTILATION: PROVIDE LOCAL EXHAUST OR PROCESS ENCLOSURE VENTILATION TO MEET PUBLISHED EXPOSURE LIMITS.

RESPIRATOR: THE FOLLOWING RESPIRATORS AND MAXIMUM USE CONCENTRATIONS ARE RECOMMENDATIONS BY THE U.S. DEPARTMENT OF HEALTH AND HUMAN SERVICES, NIOSH POCKET GUIDE TO CHEMICAL HAZARDS; NIOSH CRITERIA DOCUMENTS OR BY THE U.S. DEPARTMENT OF LABOR, 29 CFR 1910 SUBPART Z. THE SPECIFIC RESPIRATOR SELECTED MUST BE BASED ON CONTAMINATION LEVELS FOUND IN THE WORK PLACE, MUST NOT EXCEED THE WORKING LIMITS OF THE RESPIRATOR AND BE JOINTLY APPROVED BY THE NATIONAL INSTITUTE FOR OCCUPATIONAL SAFETY AND HEALTH AND THE MINE SAFETY AND HEALTH ADMINISTRATION (NIOSH-MSHA).

COPPER DUST AND MIST (AS CU):

5 MG/M3- ANY DUST AND MIST RESPIRATOR EXCEPT SINGLE-USE RESPIRATORS.

10 MG/M3- ANY DUST AND MIST RESPIRATOR EXCEPT SINGLE-USE AND QUARTER-MASK RESPIRATORS. ANY SUPPLIED-AIR RESPIRATOR. ANY SELF-CONTAINED BREATHING APPARATUS.

25 MG/M3- ANY POWERED AIR-PURIFYING RESPIRATOR WITH A DUST AND MIST FILTER. ANY SUPPLIED-AIR RESPIRATOR OPERATED IN A CONTINUOUS FLOW MODE.

50 MG/M3- ANY AIR-PURIFYING FULL FACEPIECE RESPIRATOR WITH A HIGH-EFFICIENCY PARTICULATE FILTER. ANY SELF-CONTAINED BREATHING APPARATUS WITH A FULL FACEPIECE. ANY SUPPLIED-AIR RESPIRATOR WITH A FULL FACEPIECE. ANY POWERED AIR-PURIFYING RESPIRATOR WITH A TIGHT-FITTING FACEPIECE AND A HIGH-EFFICIENCY PARTICULATE FILTER.

1000 MG/M3- ANY SUPPLIED-AIR RESPIRATOR WITH A HALF-MASK AND OPERATED IN A PRESSURE-DEMAND OR OTHER POSITIVE PRESSURE MODE.

2000 MG/M3- ANY SUPPLIED-AIR RESPIRATOR WITH A FULL FACEPIECE AND OPERATED IN A PRESSURE-DEMAND OR OTHER POSITIVE PRESSURE MODE.

ESCAPE- ANY AIR-PURIFYING FULL FACEPIECE RESPIRATOR WITH A HIGH-EFFICIENCY PARTICULATE FILTER. ANY APPROPRIATE ESCAPE-TYPE SELF-CONTAINED BREATHING APPARATUS.

FOR FIREFIGHTING AND OTHER IMMEDIATELY DANGEROUS TO LIFE OR HEALTH CONDITIONS:

SELF-CONTAINED BREATHING APPARATUS WITH FULL FACEPIECE OPERATED IN PRESSURE-DEMAND OR OTHER POSITIVE PRESSURE MODE.

SUPPLIED-AIR RESPIRATOR WITH FULL FACEPIECE AND OPERATED IN PRESSURE-DEMAND OR OTHER POSITIVE PRESSURE MODE IN COMBINATION WITH AN AUXILIARY SELF-CONTAINED BREATHING APPARATUS OPERATED IN PRESSURE-DEMAND OR OTHER POSITIVE PRESSURE MODE.

CLOTHING: EMPLOYEE MUST WEAR APPROPRIATE PROTECTIVE (IMPERVIOUS) CLOTHING AND EQUIPMENT TO PREVENT REPEATED OR PROLONGED SKIN CONTACT WITH THIS SUBSTANCE.

GLOVES: EMPLOYEE MUST WEAR APPROPRIATE PROTECTIVE GLOVES TO PREVENT CONTACT WITH THIS SUBSTANCE.

EYE PROTECTION: EMPLOYEE MUST WEAR SPLASH-PROOF OR DUST-RESISTANT SAFETY GOGGLES TO PREVENT EYE CONTACT WITH THIS SUBSTANCE.

EMERGENCY EYE WASH: WHERE THERE IS ANY POSSIBILITY THAT AN EMPLOYEE'S EYES MAY BE EXPOSED TO THIS SUBSTANCE, THE EMPLOYER SHOULD PROVIDE AN EYE WASH FOUNTAIN WITHIN THE IMMEDIATE WORK AREA FOR EMERGENCY USE.

AUTHORIZED BY- OCCUPATIONAL HEALTH SERVICES, INC.

CREATION DATE: 10/04/89 ***REVISION DATE:*** 03/28/90

MATERIAL SAFETY DATA SHEET

OCCUPATIONAL HEALTH SERVICES, INC.
AGRICULTURE AND PESTICIDE DIVISION
450 SEVENTH AVENUE, SUITE 2407
NEW YORK, NEW YORK 10123
1-800-445-MSDS OR (212) 967-1100

EMERGENCY CONTACT:
JOHN S. BRANSFORD, JR. (615) 292-1180

SUBSTANCE IDENTIFICATION

CAS-NUMBER 20427-59-2

SUBSTANCE: CUPRIC HYDROXIDE

TRADE NAMES/SYNONYMS: COPPER HYDROXIDE; COPPER DIHYDROXIDE; COPPER(2+) HYDROXIDE; COPPER(II) HYDROXIDE; PST05640

CHEMICAL FAMILY: METAL

MOLECULAR FORMULA: CU.H2-O2

MOLECULAR WEIGHT: 97.56

CERCLA RATINGS (SCALE 0-3): HEALTH=U FIRE=0 REACTIVITY=0 PERSISTENCE=3

NFPA RATINGS (SCALE 0-4): HEALTH=U FIRE=0 REACTIVITY=0

COMPONENTS AND CONTAMINANTS

COMPONENT: CUPRIC HYDROXIDE ***PERCENT:*** 100
CAS# 20427-59-2

OTHER CONTAMINANTS: NONE

EXPOSURE LIMITS: COPPER AND COMPOUNDS (AS CU): 0.1 MG/M3 OSHA TWA (FUME); 1 MG/M3 OSHA TWA (DUST AND MISTS) 0.2 MG/M3 ACGIH TWA (FUME); 1 MG/M3 ACGIH TWA (DUST AND MISTS)

SUBJECT TO SARA SECTION 313 ANNUAL TOXIC CHEMICAL RELEASE REPORTING

PHYSICAL DATA

DESCRIPTION: LIGHT BLUE AMORPHOUS POWDER WHICH MAY DECOMPOSE TO BLACK COPPER OXIDE ON STANDING OR HEATING

MELTING POINT:DECOMPOSES

SPECIFIC GRAVITY: 3.368

SOLUBILITY IN WATER: INSOLUBLE IN COLD; DECOMPOSES IN HOT

SOLVENT SOLUBILITY: ACIDS, AMMONIUM HYDROXIDE, CONCENTRATED ALKALI, POTASSIUM CYANIDE, ALCOHOL

FIRE AND EXPLOSION DATA

FIRE AND EXPLOSION HAZARD: NEGLIGIBLE FIRE HAZARD WHEN EXPOSED TO HEAT OR FLAME.

FIREFIGHTING MEDIA: DRY CHEMICAL, CARBON DIOXIDE, HALON, WATER SPRAY OR STANDARD FOAM (1987 EMERGENCY RESPONSE GUIDEBOOK, DOT P 5800.4).

FOR LARGER FIRES, USE WATER SPRAY, FOG OR STANDARD FOAM (1987 EMERGENCY RESPONSE GUIDEBOOK, DOT P 5800.4).

FIREFIGHTING: NO ACUTE HAZARD. MOVE CONTAINER FROM FIRE AREA IF POSSIBLE. AVOID BREATHING VAPORS OR DUSTS; KEEP UPWIND.

TOXICITY

CUPRIC HYDROXIDE: TOXICITY DATA: 200 MG/KG ORAL-HUMAN LDLO; 1 GM/KG ORAL-RAT LD50. CARCINOGEN STATUS: NONE. LOCAL EFFECTS: CORROSIVE- EYES; IRRITANT- INHALATION AND SKIN. ACUTE TOXICITY LEVEL: MODERATELY TOXIC BY INGESTION. TARGET EFFECTS: POISONING MAY AFFECT THE LIVER AND KIDNEYS.

HEALTH EFFECTS AND FIRST AID

INHALATION: CUPRIC HYDROXIDE: IRRITANT. **ACUTE EXPOSURE-** MAY CAUSE IRRITATION OF THE MUCOUS MEMBRANES. EXPOSURE TO COPPER FUME MAY RESULT IN METALLIC TASTE, NAUSEA, VOMITING, AND METAL FUME FEVER WITH CHILLS, FEVER, ACHING MUSCLES, DRY THROAT AND HEADACHE. **CHRONIC EXPOSURE-** REPEATED OR PROLONGED INHALATION OF DUST, MIST OF FUMES OF COPPER AND COPPER SALTS MAY CAUSE IRRITATION OF THE UPPER RESPIRATORY TRACT AND OCCASIONALLY ULCERATION AND PERFORATION OF THE NASAL SEPTUM.

FIRST AID- REMOVE FROM EXPOSURE AREA TO FRESH AIR IMMEDIATELY. IF BREATHING HAS STOPPED, PERFORM ARTIFICIAL RESPIRATION. KEEP PERSON WARM AND AT REST. TREAT SYMPTOMATICALLY AND SUPPORTIVELY. GET MEDICAL ATTENTION IMMEDIATELY.

SKIN CONTACT: CUPRIC HYDROXIDE: IRRITANT. **ACUTE EXPOSURE-** MAY CAUSE IRRITATION. MANY COPPER SALTS CAUSE ITCHING, ECZEMA AND, RARELY, SENSITIZATION REACTIONS IN PREVIOUSLY EXPOSED PERSONS. **CHRONIC EXPOSURE-** REPEATED OR PROLONGED EXPOSURE MAY CAUSE DERMATITIS. RARELY, SENSITIZATION TO COPPER MAY OCCUR.

FIRST AID- REMOVE CONTAMINATED CLOTHING AND SHOES IMMEDIATELY. WASH AFFECTED AREA WITH SOAP OR MILD DETERGENT AND LARGE AMOUNTS OF WATER UNTIL NO EVIDENCE OF CHEMICAL REMAINS (APPROXIMATELY 15-20 MINUTES). GET MEDICAL ATTENTION IMMEDIATELY.

EYE CONTACT: CUPRIC HYDROXIDE: CORROSIVE. **ACUTE EXPOSURE-** MAY CAUSE SEVERE IRRITATION WITH POSSIBLE TISSUE DAMAGE AND CORNEAL OPACIFICATION. **CHRONIC EXPOSURE-** DEPENDING ON CONCENTRATION AND DURATION OF CONTACT, REPEATED OR PROLONGED EXPOSURE MAY RESULT IN SYMPTOMS AS IN ACUTE EXPOSURE.

FIRST AID- WASH EYES IMMEDIATELY WITH LARGE AMOUNTS OF WATER, OCCASIONALLY LIFTING UPPER AND LOWER LIDS, UNTIL NO EVIDENCE OF CHEMICAL REMAINS (AT LEAST 15-20 MINUTES). CONTINUE IRRIGATING WITH NORMAL SALINE UNTIL THE PH HAS RETURNED TO NORMAL (30-60 MINUTES). COVER WITH STERILE BANDAGES. GET MEDICAL ATTENTION IMMEDIATELY.

INGESTION: CUPRIC HYDROXIDE: **ACUTE EXPOSURE-** THE LOWEST REPORTED LETHAL DOSE FOR A HUMAN IS 200 MG/KG, HOWEVER THE SYMPTOMS WERE NOT REPORTED. INGESTION OF COPPER SALTS MAY RESULT IN IRRITATION OF THE GASTROINTESTINAL TRACT, NAUSEA, VOMITING, SALIVATION, GASTRIC PAIN, HEMORRHAGIC GASTRITIS, DIARRHEA, CAPILLARY DAMAGE, LIVER AND KIDNEY DAMAGE, AND CENTRAL NERVOUS SYSTEM STIMULATION FOLLOWED BY DEPRESSION. JAUNDICE, PAIN IN THE LIVER, AND HEMOLYTIC ANEMIA HAVE BEEN REPORTED FOLLOWING ACUTE HUMAN POISONINGS. **CHRONIC EXPOSURE-** REPEATED INGESTION OF COPPER SALTS MAY RESULT IN ANEMIA, LIVER AND KIDNEY DAMAGE.

FIRST AID- UNLESS EXTENSIVE VOMITING HAS OCCURRED, EMPTY THE STOMACH BY GASTRIC LAVAGE WITH WATER, MILK, SODIUM BICARBONATE SOLUTION OR A 0.1% SOLUTION OF POTASSIUM FERROCYANIDE. ADMINISTER EGG WHITE AND OTHER DEMULCENTS. GET MEDICAL ATTENTION IMMEDIATELY. (GOSSELIN, CLINICAL TOXICOLOGY OF COMMERCIAL PRODUCTS, 5TH ED.) ADMINISTRATION OF GASTRIC LAVAGE SHOULD BE PERFORMED BY QUALIFIED MEDICAL PERSONNEL.

ANTIDOTE: THE FOLLOWING ANTIDOTE HAS BEEN RECOMMENDED. HOWEVER, THE DECISION AS TO WHETHER THE SEVERITY OF POISONING REQUIRES ADMINISTRATION OF ANY ANTIDOTE AND ACTUAL DOSE REQUIRED SHOULD BE MADE BY QUALIFIED MEDICAL PERSONNEL.

COPPER POISONING: GIVE CALCIUM DISODIUM EDETATE 15-25 MG/KG (0.08-0.125 ML OF 20% SOLUTION PER KILOGRAM BODY WEIGHT) IN 250-500 ML OF 5% DEXTROSE INTRAVENOUSLY OVER A 1 TO 2 HOUR PERIOD TWICE DAILY. THE MAXIMUM DOSE SHOULD NOT EXCEED 50 MG/KG/DAY. THE DRUG SHOULD BE GIVEN IN 5-DAY COURSES WITH A REST PERIOD OF AT LEAST 2 DAYS BETWEEN COURSES. AFTER THE FIRST COURSE, SUBSEQUENT COURSES SHOULD NOT EXCEED 50 MG/KG/DAY. DAILY URINALYSES SHOULD NOT BE DONE DURING THE TREATMENT PERIOD. THE DOSAGE SHOULD BE REDUCED IF ANY UNUSUAL URINARY FINDINGS APPEAR. INTRAVENOUS ADMINISTRATION IS CONTRAINDICATED IN THE PRESENCE OF ELEVATED CEREBROSPINAL FLUID PRESSURE. PENICILLAMINE IS ALSO EFFECTIVE IN COPPER POISONING. GIVE UP TO 100 MG/KG/DAY (MAXIMUM 1 G/DAY) DIVIDED INTO 4 DOSES FOR NO LONGER THAN 1 WEEK. IF A LONGER ADMINISTRATION PERIOD IS WARRANTED, DOSAGE SHOULD NOT EXCEED 40 MG/KG/DAY. GIVE THE DRUG ORALLY, HALF AN HOUR BEFORE MEALS (DREISBACH, HANDBOOK OF POISONING, 12TH ED.). ANTIDOTE SHOULD BE ADMINISTERED BY QUALIFIED MEDICAL PERSONNEL.

REACTIVITY

REACTIVITY: STABLE UNDER NORMAL TEMPERATURES AND PRESSURES.

INCOMPATIBILITIES: CUPRIC HYDROXIDE: NO DATA AVAILABLE.

DECOMPOSITION: THERMAL DECOMPOSITION MAY RELEASE TOXIC AND/OR HAZARDOUS GASES.

POLYMERIZATION: HAZARDOUS POLYMERIZATION HAS NOT BEEN REPORTED TO OCCUR UNDER NORMAL TEMPERATURES AND PRESSURES.

CONDITIONS TO AVOID

NONE REPORTED.

SPILL AND LEAK PROCEDURES

OCCUPATIONAL SPILL: SWEEP UP AND PLACE IN SUITABLE (FIBERBOARD) CONTAINERS FOR RECLAMATION OR LATER DISPOSAL.

PROTECTIVE EQUIPMENT

VENTILATION: PROVIDE LOCAL EXHAUST VENTILATION AND/OR GENERAL DILUTION VENTILATION TO MEET PUBLISHED EXPOSURE LIMITS.

RESPIRATOR: THE FOLLOWING RESPIRATORS AND MAXIMUM USE CONCENTRATIONS ARE RECOMMENDATIONS BY THE U.S. DEPARTMENT OF HEALTH AND HUMAN SERVICES, NIOSH POCKET GUIDE TO CHEMICAL HAZARDS; NIOSH CRITERIA DOCUMENTS OR BY THE U.S. DEPARTMENT OF LABOR, 29 CFR 1910 SUBPART Z. THE SPECIFIC RESPIRATOR SELECTED MUST BE BASED ON CONTAMINATION LEVELS FOUND IN THE WORK PLACE, MUST NOT EXCEED THE WORKING LIMITS OF THE RESPIRATOR AND BE JOINTLY APPROVED BY THE NATIONAL INSTITUTE FOR OCCUPATIONAL SAFETY AND HEALTH AND THE MINE SAFETY AND HEALTH ADMINISTRATION (NIOSH-MSHA).

COPPER (AS CU):

FOR FUME: 1 MG/M3- ANY DUST, MIST, AND FUME RESPIRATOR WITH A FULL FACEPIECE. ANY SUPPLIED-AIR RESPIRATOR. ANY SELF-CONTAINED BREATHING APPARATUS.

2.5 MG/M3- ANY POWERED AIR-PURIFYING RESPIRATOR WITH A DUST, MIST, AND FUME FILTER. ANY SUPPLIED-AIR RESPIRATOR OPERATED IN A CONTINUOUS FLOW MODE.

5 MG/M3- ANY AIR-PURIFYING FULL FACEPIECE RESPIRATOR WITH A HIGH-EFFICIENCY PARTICULATE FILTER. ANY POWERED AIR-PURIFYING RESPIRATOR WITH A TIGHT-FITTING FACEPIECE AND A HIGH EFFICIENCY PARTICULATE FILTER. ANY SELF-CONTAINED BREATHING APPARATUS WITH A FULL FACEPIECE. ANY SUPPLIED-AIR RESPIRATOR WITH A FULL FACEPIECE. ANY SUPPLIED-AIR RESPIRATOR WITH A TIGHT-FITTING FACEPIECE OPERATED IN A CONTINUOUS FLOW MODE.

100 MG/M3- ANY SUPPLIED-AIR RESPIRATOR WITH A HALF-MASK AND OPERATED IN A PRESSURE-DEMAND OR OTHER POSITIVE PRESSURE MODE.

200 MG/M3- ANY SUPPLIED-AIR RESPIRATOR WITH A FULL FACEPIECE AND OPERATED IN A PRESSURE-DEMAND OR OTHER POSITIVE PRESSURE MODE.

ESCAPE- ANY AIR-PURIFYING FULL FACEPIECE RESPIRATOR WITH A HIGH-EFFICIENCY PARTICULATE FILTER. ANY APPROPRIATE ESCAPE-TYPE SELF-CONTAINED BREATHING APPARATUS.

FOR FIREFIGHTING AND OTHER IMMEDIATELY DANGEROUS TO LIFE OR HEALTH CONDITIONS:

SELF-CONTAINED BREATHING APPARATUS WITH FULL FACEPIECE OPERATED IN PRESSURE-DEMAND OR OTHER POSITIVE PRESSURE MODE.

SUPPLIED-AIR RESPIRATOR WITH FULL FACEPIECE AND OPERATED IN PRESSURE-DEMAND OR OTHER POSITIVE PRESSURE MODE IN COMBINATION WITH AN AUXILIARY SELF-CONTAINED BREATHING APPARATUS OPERATED IN PRESSURE-DEMAND OR OTHER POSITIVE PRESSURE MODE.

CLOTHING: EMPLOYEE MUST WEAR APPROPRIATE PROTECTIVE (IMPERVIOUS) CLOTHING AND EQUIPMENT TO PREVENT REPEATED OR PROLONGED SKIN CONTACT WITH THIS SUBSTANCE.

GLOVES: EMPLOYEE MUST WEAR APPROPRIATE PROTECTIVE GLOVES TO PREVENT CONTACT WITH THIS SUBSTANCE.

EYE PROTECTION: EMPLOYEE MUST WEAR SPLASH-PROOF OR DUST-RESISTANT SAFETY GOGGLES TO PREVENT CONTACT WITH THIS SUBSTANCE.

EMERGENCY WASH FACILITIES: WHERE THERE IS ANY POSSIBILITY THAT AN EMPLOYEE'S EYES AND/OR SKIN MAY BE EXPOSED TO THIS SUBSTANCE, THE EMPLOYER SHOULD PROVIDE AN EYE WASH FOUNTAIN AND QUICK DRENCH SHOWER WITHIN THE IMMEDIATE WORK AREA FOR EMERGENCY USE.

AUTHORIZED BY- OCCUPATIONAL HEALTH SERVICES, INC.
CREATION DATE: 10/04/89 ***REVISION DATE:*** 05/11/90

MATERIAL SAFETY DATA SHEET

OCCUPATIONAL HEALTH SERVICES, INC.
AGRICULTURE AND PESTICIDE DIVISION
450 SEVENTH AVENUE, SUITE 2407
NEW YORK, NEW YORK 10123
1-800-445-MSDS OR (212) 967-1100

EMERGENCY CONTACT:
JOHN S. BRANSFORD, JR. (615) 292-1180

SUBSTANCE IDENTIFICATION

CAS-NUMBER 3251-23-8
SUBSTANCE: **CUPRIC NITRATE**
TRADE NAMES/SYNONYMS: COPPER DINITRATE; COPPER(II) NITRATE; COPPER(2+) NITRATE; CUPRIC DINITRATE; NITRIC ACID, COPPER(2+) SALT; STCC 4918744; CUN206; PST05644
CHEMICAL FAMILY: INORGANIC SALT
MOLECULAR FORMULA: CU-(N-O3)2
MOLECULAR WEIGHT: 187.55
CERCLA RATINGS (SCALE 0-3): HEALTH=2 FIRE=0 REACTIVITY=0 PERSISTENCE=3
NFPA RATINGS (SCALE 0-4): HEALTH=0 FIRE=0 REACTIVITY=0

COMPONENTS AND CONTAMINANTS

COMPONENT: CUPRIC NITRATE ***PERCENT:*** 100.0
CAS# 3251-23-8
OTHER CONTAMINANTS: NONE
EXPOSURE LIMITS: COPPER DUST AND MIST (AS CU): 1 MG/M3 OSHA TWA 1 MG/M3 ACGIH TWA
SUBJECT TO SARA SECTION 313 ANNUAL TOXIC CHEMICAL RELEASE REPORTING
CUPRIC NITRATE: 100 POUNDS CERCLA SECTION 103 REPORTABLE QUANTITY.

PHYSICAL DATA

DESCRIPTION: BLUE DELIQUESCENT CRYSTALS.
MELTING POINT: 338 F (170 C) (DECOMPOSES) ***SPECIFIC GRAVITY:*** NOT AVAILABLE
PH: 4.0 @ 0.2 M SOLUTION ***SOLUBILITY IN WATER:*** SOLUBLE
SOLVENT SOLUBILITY: SOLUBLE IN ETHYL ACETATE, DIOXANE.

FIRE AND EXPLOSION DATA

FIRE AND EXPLOSION HAZARD: NEGLIGIBLE FIRE HAZARD WHEN EXPOSED TO HEAT OR FLAME.
OXIDIZER: OXIDIZERS DECOMPOSE, ESPECIALLY WHEN HEATED, TO YIELD OXYGEN OR OTHER GASES WHICH WILL INCREASE THE BURNING RATE OF COMBUSTIBLE MATTER. CONTACT WITH EASILY OXIDIZABLE, ORGANIC, OR OTHER COMBUSTIBLE MATERIALS MAY RESULT IN IGNITION, VIOLENT COMBUSTION OR EXPLOSION.
FIREFIGHTING MEDIA: DRY CHEMICAL, CARBON DIOXIDE, HALON OR WATER SPRAY (1987 EMERGENCY RESPONSE GUIDEBOOK, DOT P 5800.4).
FOR LARGER FIRES, USE WATER SPRAY OR FOG (1987 EMERGENCY RESPONSE GUIDEBOOK, DOT P 5800.4).
FIREFIGHTING: MOVE CONTAINERS FROM FIRE AREA IF POSSIBLE. COOL CONTAINERS EXPOSED TO FLAMES WITH WATER FROM SIDE UNTIL WELL AFTER FIRE IS OUT. STAY AWAY FROM STORAGE TANK ENDS. FOR MASSIVE FIRE IN STORAGE AREA, USE UNMANNED HOSE HOLDER OR MONITOR NOZZLES; ELSE WITHDRAW FROM AREA AND LET FIRE BURN (1987 EMERGENCY RESPONSE GUIDEBOOK, DOT P 5800.4, GUIDE PAGE 35)
FLOOD WITH WATER. COOL CONTAINERS WITH FLOODING AMOUNTS OF WATER FROM AS FAR A DISTANCE AS POSSIBLE. AVOID BREATHING VAPORS OR DUSTS. EVACUATE TO A RADIUS OF 2500 FEET FOR UNCONTROLLABLE FIRES.

TRANSPORTATION DATA

DEPARTMENT OF TRANSPORTATION HAZARD CLASSIFICATION 49 CFR 172.101: OXIDIZER
DEPARTMENT OF TRANSPORTATION LABELING REQUIREMENTS 49 CFR 172.101 AND SUBPART E: OXIDIZER
DEPARTMENT OF TRANSPORTATION PACKAGING REQUIREMENTS: 49 CFR 173.182 EXCEPTIONS: 49 CFR 173.153

TOXICITY

CUPRIC NITRATE: IRRITATION DATA: ANHYDROUS: 500 MG SKIN-RABBIT SEVERE; 100 MG EYE-RABBIT SEVERE; 100 MG/4 SECONDS RINSED EYE-RABBIT SEVERE. TRIHYDRATE: NO DATA AVAILABLE. TOXICITY DATA: ANHYDROUS: 940 MG/KG ORAL-RAT LD50. TRIHYDRATE: 940 MG/KG ORAL-RAT LD50; MUTAGENIC DATA (RTECS). CARCINOGEN STATUS: NONE. LOCAL EFFECTS: CORROSIVE- EYE AND SKIN; IRRITANT- MUCOUS MEMBRANES. ACUTE TOXICITY LEVEL: MODERATELY TOXIC BY INGESTION. TARGET EFFECTS: POISONING BY COPPER COMPOUNDS MAY AFFECT THE RESPIRATORY AND DIGESTIVE SYSTEMS AND THE LIVER AND KIDNEYS. AT INCREASED RISK FROM EXPOSURE: PERSONS WITH PRE-EXISTING SKIN DISORDERS OR IMPAIRED LIVER, KIDNEY, AND PULMONARY FUNCTION OR PRE-EXISTING WILSON'S DISEASE.

HEALTH EFFECTS AND FIRST AID

INHALATION: CUPRIC NITRATE: IRRITANT. **ACUTE EXPOSURE-** MAY CAUSE IRRITATION TO THE UPPER RESPIRATORY TRACT WITH COUGHING, SORE THROAT, AND SHORTNESS OF BREATH. SYMPTOMS SIMILAR TO THE COMMON COLD MAY OCCUR INCLUDING CHILLS AND STUFFINESS OF THE HEAD. **CHRONIC EXPOSURE-** PROLONGED INHALATION OF DUST OR MIST OF COPPER SALTS MAY CAUSE CONGESTION OF THE NASAL MUCOUS MEMBRANES, SOMETIMES OF THE PHARYNX, AND ON OCCASIONS ULCERATION AND PERFORATION OF THE NASAL SEPTUM. ATROPHIC CHANGES IN THE MUCOUS MEMBRANES WERE NOTED IN SUBJECTS EXPOSED TO COMPLEX COPPER SALTS FOR LONG PERIODS OF TIME. INHALATION OF COPPER COMPOUNDS HAS CAUSED INJURY TO THE LUNGS AND LIVER WITH HEMOCHROMATOSIS IN ANIMALS.
FIRST AID- REMOVE FROM EXPOSURE AREA TO FRESH AIR IMMEDIATELY. IF BREATHING HAS STOPPED, GIVE ARTIFICIAL RESPIRATION. MAINTAIN AIRWAY AND BLOOD PRESSURE AND ADMINISTER OXYGEN IF AVAILABLE. KEEP AFFECTED PERSON WARM AND AT REST. TREAT SYMPTOMATICALLY AND SUPPORTIVELY. ADMINISTRATION OF OXYGEN SHOULD BE PERFORMED BY QUALIFIED PERSONNEL. GET MEDICAL ATTENTION IMMEDIATELY.

SKIN CONTACT: CUPRIC NITRATE: CORROSIVE. **ACUTE EXPOSURE-** MAY CAUSE SEVERE IRRITATION, REDNESS, PAIN AND POSSIBLY BURNS. COPPER SALTS HAVE BEEN REPORTED TO CAUSE ITCHING PAPULOVESICULATION, SKIN DISCOLORATION, AND ECZEMATOID LESIONS. **CHRONIC EXPOSURE-** REPEATED OR PROLONGED EXPOSURE MAY CAUSE DERMATITIS OR SYMPTOMS AS DESCRIBED IN ACUTE EXPOSURE. GREENISH SKIN DISCOLORATION AND ALLERGIC CONTACT DERMATITIS, ALTHOUGH RARE, HAS BEEN REPORTED FROM CONTACT WITH COPPER SALTS.
FIRST AID- REMOVE CONTAMINATED CLOTHING AND SHOES IMMEDIATELY. WASH AFFECTED AREA WITH SOAP OR MILD DETERGENT AND LARGE AMOUNTS OF WATER UNTIL NO EVIDENCE OF CHEMICAL REMAINS (AT LEAST 15-20 MINUTES). IN CASE OF CHEMICAL BURNS, COVER AREA WITH STERILE, DRY DRESSING. BANDAGE SECURELY, BUT NOT TOO TIGHTLY. GET MEDICAL ATTENTION IMMEDIATELY.

EYE CONTACT: CUPRIC NITRATE: CORROSIVE. **ACUTE EXPOSURE-** MAY CAUSE SEVERE IRRITATION, REDNESS, PAIN, DISCOLORATION, AND POSSIBLY BURNS. SOME COPPER SALTS HAVE BEEN REPORTED TO CAUSE CORNEAL ULCERATIONS, AND TURBIDITY POSSIBLY WITH PALPEBRAL EDEMA. **CHRONIC EXPOSURE-** REPEATED OR PROLONGED EXPOSURE MAY CAUSE CONJUNCTIVITIS OR SYMPTOMS AS THOSE DESCRIBED IN ACUTE EXPOSURE.
FIRST AID- WASH EYES IMMEDIATELY WITH LARGE AMOUNTS OF WATER, OCCASIONALLY LIFTING UPPER AND LOWER LIDS, UNTIL NO EVIDENCE OF CHEMICAL REMAINS (AT LEAST 15-20 MINUTES). CONTINUE IRRIGATING WITH NORMAL SALINE UNTIL THE PH HAS RETURNED TO NORMAL (30-60 MINUTES). COVER WITH STERILE BANDAGES. GET MEDICAL ATTENTION IMMEDIATELY.

INGESTION: CUPRIC NITRATE: **ACUTE EXPOSURE-** INGESTION OF COPPER SALTS MAY CAUSE AN IMMEDIATE METALLIC TASTE, BURNING PAIN IN THE MOUTH, ESOPHAGUS AND STOMACH, SALIVATION, NAUSEA, VOMITING, DIARRHEA, HEMORRHAGIC GASTRITIS, ULCERS, ANURIA, COMA, AND CONVULSIONS. IF SUFFICIENT VOMITING DOES NOT OCCUR, SOME COPPER SALTS MAY CAUSE SYSTEMIC EFFECTS INCLUDING CAPILLARY DAMAGE, WEAK PULSE, COLD SWEAT, HEADACHE, KIDNEY AND LIVER INJURY, CENTRAL NERVOUS SYSTEM EXCITATION FOLLOWED BY DEPRESSION, AND DEATH FROM SHOCK OR RENAL FAILURE. RARELY, INORGANIC NITRATES MAY BE CONVERTED TO NITRITES BY NITRATE-REDUCING BACTERIA IN THE DIGESTIVE TRACT, RESULTING IN METHEMOGLOBINEMIA. **CHRONIC EXPOSURE-** REPEATED AND PROLONGED INGESTION OF COPPER SALTS HAS PRODUCED HEMOLYTIC ANEMIA AND LIVER, KIDNEY AND SPLEEN DAMAGE IN ANIMALS. REPEATED OR PROLONGED EXPOSURE TO NITRATES MAY CAUSE ANEMIA, NEPHRITIS, AND POSSIBLY METHEMOGLOBINEMIA.

FIRST AID- DO NOT USE GASTRIC LAVAGE OR EMESIS. DILUTE THE ACID IMMEDIATELY BY DRINKING LARGE QUANTITIES OF WATER OR MILK. IF VOMITING PERSISTS, ADMINISTER FLUIDS REPEATEDLY. INGESTED ACID MUST BE DILUTED APPROXIMATELY 100 FOLD TO RENDER IT HARMLESS TO TISSUES. MAINTAIN AIRWAY AND TREAT SHOCK (DREISBACH, HANDBOOK OF POISONING, 12TH ED.). GET MEDICAL ATTENTION IMMEDIATELY. IF VOMITING OCCURS, KEEP HEAD BELOW HIPS TO HELP PREVENT ASPIRATION.

ANTIDOTE: NO SPECIFIC ANTIDOTE. TREAT SYMPTOMATICALLY AND SUPPORTIVELY.

REACTIVITY

REACTIVITY: STABLE UNDER NORMAL TEMPERATURES AND PRESSURES.

INCOMPATIBILITIES: CUPRIC NITRATE: ACETIC ANHYDRIDE: VIOLENT REACTION. ACETYLENE: MAY IGNITE ON CONTACT. AMMONIUM + POTASSIUM AMIDE: FORMS EXPLOSIVE PRODUCT. AMMONIUM HEXACYANOFERRATE(II): POSSIBLE EXPLOSION. COMBUSTIBLE MATERIALS: MAY IGNITE ON CONTACT; FINELY DIVIDED MATERIALS MAY RESULT IN AN EXPLOSION. ETHER: VIOLENT REACTION. HYDRAZINE: MAY IGNITE ON CONTACT. METALS: MAY BE ATTACKED. NITROMETHANE: MAY IGNITE ON CONTACT. ORGANIC MATERIALS: MAY INCREASE THE BURNING RATE, OR CAUSE IGNITION ON CONTACT; FINELY DIVIDED MATERIALS MAY RESULT IN AN EXPLOSION. POTASSIUM HEXACYANOFERRATE(II): EXPLOSIVE REACTION ABOVE 220 C. REDUCING AGENTS: MAY REACT VIOLENTLY. TIN: POSSIBLE IGNITION WITH CONCENTRATED SOLUTIONS. SEE ALSO METAL NITRATES.

METAL NITRATES: CITRIC ACID: POSSIBLE EXPLOSION HAZARD. ESTERS: POSSIBLE EXPLOSION HAZARD. PHOSPHINATES: MAY EXPLODE WHEN HEATED. PHOSPHOROUS: POSSIBLE EXPLOSIVE REACTION. POTASSIUM HEXANITROCOBALTATE(3-): MAY EXPLODE VIOLENTLY. REDUCTANTS: POSSIBLE EXPLOSION HAZARD. TIN(II) CHLORIDE: POSSIBLE EXPLOSIVE HAZARD.

DECOMPOSITION: THERMAL DECOMPOSITION PRODUCTS MAY INCLUDE TOXIC OXIDES OF NITROGEN.

POLYMERIZATION: HAZARDOUS POLYMERIZATION HAS NOT BEEN REPORTED TO OCCUR UNDER NORMAL TEMPERATURES AND PRESSURES.

STORAGE AND DISPOSAL

OBSERVE ALL FEDERAL, STATE AND LOCAL REGULATIONS WHEN STORING OR DISPOSING OF THIS SUBSTANCE. FOR ASSISTANCE, CONTACT THE DISTRICT DIRECTOR OF THE ENVIRONMENTAL PROTECTION AGENCY.

****STORAGE****

CONSULT NFPA PUBLICATION 43A, STORAGE OF LIQUID AND SOLID OXIDIZING MATERIALS, FOR STORAGE REQUIREMENTS.

STORE IN A COOL, DRY PLACE; KEEP CONTAINER TIGHTLY CLOSED WHEN NOT IN USE.

PROTECT AGAINST PHYSICAL DAMAGE. STORE IN A COOL, DRY PLACE; AVOID STORAGE ON WOOD FLOORS. SEPARATE FROM COMBUSTIBLE, ORGANIC, OR OTHER READILY OXIDIZABLE MATERIALS. IMMEDIATELY REMOVE AND DISPOSE OF ANY SPILLED NITRATE (NFPA 49, HAZARDOUS CHEMICALS DATA, 1975).

STORE AWAY FROM INCOMPATIBLE SUBSTANCES.

****DISPOSAL****

DISPOSAL MUST BE IN ACCORDANCE WITH STANDARDS APPLICABLE TO GENERATORS OF HAZARDOUS WASTE, 40 CFR 262. EPA HAZARDOUS WASTE NUMBER D001. 100 POUND CERCLA SECTION 103 REPORTABLE QUANTITY.

CONDITIONS TO AVOID

AVOID CONTACT WITH COMBUSTIBLE MATERIALS (WOOD, PAPER, FUEL, OILS, ETC); IGNITION OR EXPLOSION MAY RESULT. AVOID CONTAMINATION OF WATER SOURCES.

SPILL AND LEAK PROCEDURES

SOIL SPILL: DIG A HOLDING AREA SUCH AS PIT, POND OR LAGOON TO CONTAIN SPILLED MATERIAL. USE PROTECTIVE COVER SUCH AS A PLASTIC SHEET TO PREVENT DISSOLVING IN FIREFIGHTING WATER OR RAIN.

WATER SPILL: NEUTRALIZE WITH AGRICULTURAL LIME, SLAKED LIME, CRUSHED LIMESTONE, OR SODIUM BICARBONATE.

USE MECHANICAL DREDGES OR LIFTS TO EXTRACT IMMOBILIZED MASSES OF POLLUTION AND PRECIPITATES.

OCCUPATIONAL SPILL: KEEP COMBUSTIBLES (WOOD, PAPER, OIL, ETC) AWAY FROM SPILLED MATERIAL. DO NOT TOUCH SPILLED MATERIAL. FOR SMALL DRY SPILLS, WITH CLEAN SHOVEL PLACE MATERIAL INTO CLEAN, DRY CONTAINER AND COVER; MOVE CONTAINERS FROM SPILL AREA. FOR SMALL LIQUID SPILLS, TAKE UP WITH SAND, EARTH OR OTHER ABSORBENT MATERIAL AND PLACE INTO CONTAINERS FOR LATER DISPOSAL. FOR LARGER SPILLS, DIKE FAR AHEAD OF SPILL FOR LATER DISPOSAL. KEEP UNNECESSARY PEOPLE AWAY. ISOLATE HAZARD AREA AND DENY ENTRY.

REPORTABLE QUANTITY (RQ): 100 POUNDS THE SUPERFUND AMENDMENTS AND REAUTHORIZATION ACT (SARA) SECTION 304 REQUIRES THAT A RELEASE EQUAL TO OR GREATER THAN THE REPORTABLE QUANTITY FOR THIS SUBSTANCE BE IMMEDIATELY REPORTED TO THE LOCAL EMERGENCY PLANNING COMMITTEE AND THE STATE EMERGENCY RESPONSE COMMISSION (40 CFR 355.40). IF THE RELEASE OF THIS SUBSTANCE IS REPORTABLE UNDER CERCLA SECTION 103, THE NATIONAL RESPONSE CENTER MUST BE NOTIFIED IMMEDIATELY AT (800) 424-8802 OR (202) 426-2675 IN THE METROPOLITAN WASHINGTON, D.C. AREA (40 CFR 302.6).

PROTECTIVE EQUIPMENT

VENTILATION: PROVIDE LOCAL EXHAUST VENTILATION AND/OR GENERAL DILUTION VENTILATION TO MEET PUBLISHED EXPOSURE LIMITS.

RESPIRATOR: THE FOLLOWING RESPIRATORS AND MAXIMUM USE CONCENTRATIONS ARE RECOMMENDATIONS BY THE U.S. DEPARTMENT OF HEALTH AND HUMAN SERVICES, NIOSH POCKET GUIDE TO CHEMICAL HAZARDS; NIOSH CRITERIA DOCUMENTS OR BY THE U.S. DEPARTMENT OF LABOR, 29 CFR 1910 SUBPART Z. THE SPECIFIC RESPIRATOR SELECTED MUST BE BASED ON CONTAMINATION LEVELS FOUND IN THE WORK PLACE, MUST NOT EXCEED THE WORKING LIMITS OF THE RESPIRATOR AND BE JOINTLY APPROVED BY THE NATIONAL INSTITUTE FOR OCCUPATIONAL SAFETY AND HEALTH AND THE MINE SAFETY AND HEALTH ADMINISTRATION (NIOSH-MSHA).

COPPER DUST AND MIST (AS CU):

5 MG/M3- ANY DUST AND MIST RESPIRATOR EXCEPT SINGLE-USE RESPIRATORS.

10 MG/M3- ANY DUST AND MIST RESPIRATOR EXCEPT SINGLE-USE AND QUARTER-MASK RESPIRATORS. ANY SUPPLIED-AIR RESPIRATOR. ANY SELF-CONTAINED BREATHING APPARATUS.

25 MG/M3- ANY POWERED AIR-PURIFYING RESPIRATOR WITH A DUST AND MIST FILTER. ANY SUPPLIED-AIR RESPIRATOR OPERATED IN A CONTINUOUS FLOW MODE.

50 MG/M3- ANY AIR-PURIFYING FULL FACEPIECE RESPIRATOR WITH A HIGH-EFFICIENCY PARTICULATE FILTER. ANY SELF-CONTAINED BREATHING APPARATUS WITH A FULL FACEPIECE. ANY SUPPLIED-AIR RESPIRATOR WITH A FULL FACEPIECE. ANY POWERED AIR-PURIFYING RESPIRATOR WITH A TIGHT-FITTING FACEPIECE AND A HIGH-EFFICIENCY PARTICULATE FILTER.

1000 MG/M3- ANY SUPPLIED-AIR RESPIRATOR WITH A HALF-MASK AND OPERATED IN A PRESSURE-DEMAND OR OTHER POSITIVE PRESSURE MODE.

2000 MG/M3- ANY SUPPLIED-AIR RESPIRATOR WITH A FULL FACEPIECE AND OPERATED IN A PRESSURE-DEMAND OR OTHER POSITIVE PRESSURE MODE.

ESCAPE- ANY AIR-PURIFYING FULL FACEPIECE RESPIRATOR WITH A HIGH-EFFICIENCY PARTICULATE FILTER. ANY APPROPRIATE ESCAPE-TYPE SELF-CONTAINED BREATHING APPARATUS.

FOR FIREFIGHTING AND OTHER IMMEDIATELY DANGEROUS TO LIFE OR HEALTH CONDITIONS:

SELF-CONTAINED BREATHING APPARATUS WITH FULL FACEPIECE OPERATED IN PRESSURE-DEMAND OR OTHER POSITIVE PRESSURE MODE.

SUPPLIED-AIR RESPIRATOR WITH FULL FACEPIECE AND OPERATED IN PRESSURE-DEMAND OR OTHER POSITIVE PRESSURE MODE IN COMBINATION WITH AN AUXILIARY SELF-CONTAINED BREATHING APPARATUS OPERATED IN PRESSURE-DEMAND OR OTHER POSITIVE PRESSURE MODE.

CLOTHING: EMPLOYEE MUST WEAR APPROPRIATE PROTECTIVE (IMPERVIOUS) CLOTHING AND EQUIPMENT TO PREVENT ANY POSSIBILITY OF SKIN CONTACT WITH THIS SUBSTANCE.

GLOVES: EMPLOYEE MUST WEAR APPROPRIATE PROTECTIVE GLOVES TO PREVENT CONTACT WITH THIS SUBSTANCE.

EYE PROTECTION: EMPLOYEE MUST WEAR SPLASH-PROOF OR DUST-RESISTANT SAFETY GOGGLES AND A FACESHIELD TO PREVENT CONTACT WITH THIS SUBSTANCE.

EMERGENCY WASH FACILITIES: WHERE THERE IS ANY POSSIBILITY THAT AN EMPLOYEE'S EYES AND/OR SKIN MAY BE EXPOSED TO THIS SUBSTANCE, THE EMPLOYER SHOULD PROVIDE AN EYE WASH FOUNTAIN AND QUICK DRENCH SHOWER WITHIN THE IMMEDIATE WORK AREA FOR EMERGENCY USE.

AUTHORIZED BY- OCCUPATIONAL HEALTH SERVICES, INC.

CREATION DATE: 10/04/89 ***REVISION DATE:*** 03/28/90

MATERIAL SAFETY DATA SHEET

OCCUPATIONAL HEALTH SERVICES, INC.
AGRICULTURE AND PESTICIDE DIVISION
450 SEVENTH AVENUE, SUITE 2407
NEW YORK, NEW YORK 10123
1-800-445-MSDS OR (212) 967-1100

EMERGENCY CONTACT:
JOHN S. BRANSFORD, JR. (615) 292-1180

SUBSTANCE IDENTIFICATION

CAS-NUMBER 814-91-5

SUBSTANCE: CUPRIC OXALATE

TRADE NAMES/SYNONYMS: COPPER(II) OXALATE; ETHANEDIOIC ACID, COPPER (2+) SALT (1:1); OXALIC ACID, COPPER; PST05650

CHEMICAL FAMILY: METAL OXALATE

MOLECULAR FORMULA: C2-O4.CU

MOLECULAR WEIGHT: 151.57

CERCLA RATINGS (SCALE 0-3): HEALTH=U FIRE=0 REACTIVITY=0 PERSISTENCE=3

NFPA RATINGS (SCALE 0-4): HEALTH=U FIRE=0 REACTIVITY=0

COMPONENTS AND CONTAMINANTS

COMPONENT: CUPRIC OXALATE ***PERCENT:*** >98 CAS# 814-91-5

EXPOSURE LIMITS: CUPRIC OXALATE: 1 MG(CU)/M3 OSHA TWA 1 MG(CU)/M3 ACGIH TWA

100 POUNDS CERCLA SECTION 103 REPORTABLE QUANTITY SUBJECT TO SARA SECTION 313 ANNUAL TOXIC CHEMICAL RELEASE REPORTING

PHYSICAL DATA

DESCRIPTION: BLUE-WHITE POWDER ***BOILING POINT:*** 590 F (310 C) DECOM.

MELTING POINT: 392 F (200 C) (-H2O) ***SPECIFIC GRAVITY:*** > 1 @ 20 C

SOLUBILITY IN WATER: INSOLUBLE

SOLVENT SOLUBILITY: AMMONIUM HYDROXIDE; INSOLUBLE IN ALCOHOL, ACETIC ACID, AND ETHER

FIRE AND EXPLOSION DATA

FIRE AND EXPLOSION HAZARD: NEGLIGIBLE FIRE HAZARD WHEN EXPOSED TO HEAT OR FLAME.

FIREFIGHTING MEDIA: DRY CHEMICAL, CARBON DIOXIDE, HALON, WATER SPRAY OR STANDARD FOAM (1987 EMERGENCY RESPONSE GUIDEBOOK, DOT P 5800.4).

FOR LARGER FIRES, USE WATER SPRAY, FOG OR STANDARD FOAM (1987 EMERGENCY RESPONSE GUIDEBOOK, DOT P 5800.4).

FIREFIGHTING: MOVE CONTAINERS FROM FIRE AREA IF POSSIBLE (1987 EMERGENCY RESPONSE GUIDEBOOK, DOT P 5800.4, GUIDE PAGE 54).

USE AGENTS SUITABLE FOR TYPE OF FIRE. AVOID BREATHING HAZARDOUS VAPORS AND DUSTS, KEEP UPWIND.

TRANSPORTATION DATA

DEPARTMENT OF TRANSPORTATION HAZARD CLASSIFICATION 49 CFR 172.101: ORM-E

DEPARTMENT OF TRANSPORTATION LABELING REQUIREMENTS 49 CFR 172.101 AND SUBPART E: NONE

DEPARTMENT OF TRANSPORTATION PACKAGING REQUIREMENTS: 49 CFR 173.510 EXCEPTIONS: NONE

TOXICITY

CUPRIC OXALATE: CARCINOGEN STATUS: NONE. LOCAL EFFECTS: IRRITANT-INHALATION, SKIN, AND EYES. ACUTE TOXICITY LEVEL: NO DATA AVAILABLE. TARGET EFFECTS: POISONING MAY AFFECT THE LIVER, KIDNEY, SPLEEN, DIGESTIVE OR RESPIRATORY TRACT. AT INCREASED RISK FROM EXPOSURE: PERSONS WITH PREEXISTING RESPIRATORY, LIVER, SKIN, KIDNEY, HEMATOPOIETIC OR WILSON'S DISEASES.

HEALTH EFFECTS AND FIRST AID

INHALATION: CUPRIC OXALATE: IRRITANT. **ACUTE EXPOSURE-** INHALATION OF COPPER DUST MAY CAUSE IRRITATION OF THE RESPIRATORY TRACT OR AN ILLNESS SIMILAR TO THE COMMON COLD WITH SENSATIONS OF CHILLS AND STUFFINESS OF THE HEAD. **CHRONIC EXPOSURE-** PROLONGED INHALATION OF DUST OR MIST OF COPPER SALTS MAY CAUSE CONGESTION OF THE NASAL MUCOUS MEMBRANES, SOMETIMES OF THE PHARYNX, AND ON OCCASIONS ULCERATION AND PERFORATION OF THE NASAL SEPTUM. ATROPHIC CHANGES IN THE MUCOUS MEMBRANES WERE NOTED IN SUBJECTS EXPOSED FOR LONG PERIODS OF TIME. INHALATION OF COPPER COMPOUNDS HAS CAUSED INJURY TO THE LUNGS WITH HEMOCHROMATOSIS IN ANIMALS.

FIRST AID- REMOVE FROM EXPOSURE AREA TO FRESH AIR IMMEDIATELY. IF BREATHING HAS STOPPED, PERFORM ARTIFICIAL RESPIRATION. KEEP PERSON WARM AND AT REST. TREAT SYMPTOMATICALLY AND SUPPORTIVELY. GET MEDICAL ATTENTION IMMEDIATELY.

SKIN CONTACT: CUPRIC OXALATE: IRRITANT. **ACUTE EXPOSURE-** DIRECT CONTACT MAY CAUSE IRRITATION. COPPER SALTS HAVE BEEN REPORTED TO CAUSE AN ITCHING PAPULOVESICULAR, SKIN DISCOLORATION AND ECZEMATOID LESIONS. **CHRONIC EXPOSURE-** REPEATED OR PROLONGED CONTACT WITH SOME COPPER SALTS HAS RESULTED IN NECROSIS. ALLERGIC CONTACT DERMATITIS, ALTHOUGH RARE, HAS BEEN REPORTED.

FIRST AID- REMOVE CONTAMINATED CLOTHING AND SHOES IMMEDIATELY. WASH AFFECTED AREA WITH SOAP OR MILD DETERGENT AND LARGE AMOUNTS OF WATER UNTIL NO EVIDENCE OF CHEMICAL REMAINS (APPROXIMATELY 15-20 MINUTES). GET MEDICAL ATTENTION IMMEDIATELY.

EYE CONTACT: CUPRIC OXALATE: IRRITANT. **ACUTE EXPOSURE-** CONTACT MAY CAUSE IRRITATION. SOME COPPER SALTS HAVE BEEN REPORTED TO CAUSE CONJUNCTIVITIS, CORNEAL ULCERATIONS, AND TURBIDITY POSSIBLY WITH PALPEBRAL EDEMA. COPPER PARTICLES EMBEDDED IN THE EYE MAY RESULT IN A PRONOUNCED FOREIGN BODY RESPONSE WITH CHARACTERISTIC DISCOLORATION OF OCULAR TISSUE. **CHRONIC EXPOSURE-** REPEATED AND PROLONGED EXPOSURE TO IRRITANTS MAY CAUSE CONJUNCTIVITIS.

FIRST AID- WASH EYES IMMEDIATELY WITH LARGE AMOUNTS OF WATER OR NORMAL SALINE, OCCASIONALLY LIFTING UPPER AND LOWER LIDS, UNTIL NO EVIDENCE OF CHEMICAL REMAINS (APPROXIMATELY 15-20 MINUTES). GET MEDICAL ATTENTION IMMEDIATELY.

INGESTION: CUPRIC OXALATE: **ACUTE EXPOSURE-** INGESTION OF COPPER SALTS MAY CAUSE AN IMMEDIATE METALLIC TASTE, SALIVATION, NAUSEA, EPIGASTRIC BURNING, VOMITING, DIARRHEA, ULCERS, HEMORRHAGIC GASTRITIS AND GASTROINTESTINAL DAMAGE. **CHRONIC EXPOSURE-** REPEATED OR PROLONGED INGESTION OF COPPER SALTS HAS PRODUCED HEMOLYTIC ANEMIA AND LIVER, KIDNEY AND SPLEEN DAMAGE IN ANIMALS.

FIRST AID- DILUTE THE POISON IMMEDIATELY WITH LARGE AMOUNTS OF WATER OR MILK AND REMOVE BY GASTRIC LAVAGE UNLESS THE VICTIM IS ALREADY VOMITING. (DREISBACH, HANDBOOK OF POISONING, 12TH ED.) GET MEDICAL ATTENTION IMMEDIATELY. ADMINISTRATION OF GASTRIC LAVAGE SHOULD BE PERFORMED BY QUALIFIED MEDICAL PERSONNEL.

ANTIDOTE: THE FOLLOWING ANTIDOTE HAS BEEN RECOMMENDED. HOWEVER, THE DECISION AS TO WHETHER THE SEVERITY OF POISONING REQUIRES ADMINISTRATION OF ANY ANTIDOTE AND ACTUAL DOSE REQUIRED SHOULD BE MADE BY QUALIFIED MEDICAL PERSONNEL. COPPER POISONING: GIVE CALCIUM DISODIUM EDETATE 15-25 MG/KG (0.08-0.125 ML OF 20% SOLUTION PER KILOGRAM BODY WEIGHT) IN 250-500 ML OF 5% DEXTROSE INTRAVENOUSLY OVER A 1 TO 2 HOUR PERIOD TWICE DAILY. THE MAXIMUM DOSE SHOULD NOT EXCEED 50 MG/KG/DAY. THE DRUG SHOULD BE GIVEN IN 5-DAY COURSES WITH A REST PERIOD OF AT LEAST 2 DAYS BETWEEN COURSES. AFTER THE FIRST COURSE, SUBSEQUENT COURSES SHOULD NOT EXCEED 50 MG/KG/DAY. DAILY URINALYSES SHOULD NOT BE DONE DURING THE TREATMENT PERIOD. THE DOSAGE SHOULD BE REDUCED IF ANY UNUSUAL URINARY FINDINGS APPEAR. INTRAVENOUS ADMINISTRATION IS CONTRAINDICATED IN THE PRESENCE OF ELEVATED CEREBROSPINAL FLUID PRESSURE. PENICILLAMINE IS ALSO EFFECTIVE IN COPPER POISONING. GIVE UP TO 100 MG/KG/DAY (MAXIMUM 1 G/DAY) DIVIDED INTO 4 DOSES FOR NO LONGER THAN 1 WEEK. IF A LONGER ADMINISTRATION PERIOD IS WARRANTED, DOSAGE SHOULD NOT EXCEED 40 MG/KG/DAY. GIVE THE DRUG ORALLY, HALF AN HOUR BEFORE MEALS (DREISBACH, HANDBOOK OF POISONING, 12TH ED.). ANTIDOTE SHOULD BE ADMINISTERED BY QUALIFIED MEDICAL PERSONNEL.

REACTIVITY

REACTIVITY: STABLE UNDER NORMAL TEMPERATURES AND PRESSURES.

INCOMPATIBILITIES: CUPRIC OXALATE: NO DATA AVAILABLE.

DECOMPOSITION: THERMAL DECOMPOSITION MAY RELEASE TOXIC AND/OR HAZARDOUS GASES.

POLYMERIZATION: HAZARDOUS POLYMERIZATION HAS NOT BEEN REPORTED TO OCCUR UNDER NORMAL TEMPERATURES AND PRESSURES.

CONDITIONS TO AVOID

MAY BURN BUT DOES NOT IGNITE READILY. AVOID CONTACT WITH STRONG OXIDIZERS, EXCESSIVE HEAT, SPARKS, OR OPEN FLAME.

SPILL AND LEAK PROCEDURES

SOIL SPILL: DIG HOLDING AREA SUCH AS LAGOON, POND OR PIT FOR CONTAINMENT. USE PROTECTIVE COVER SUCH AS A PLASTIC SHEET TO PREVENT MATERIAL FROM DISSOLVING IN FIRE EXTINGUISHING WATER OR RAIN.

WATER SPILL: USE ACTIVATED CARBON TO ABSORB SPILLED SUBSTANCE THAT IS DISSOLVED.

USE MECHANICAL DREDGES OR LIFTS TO EXTRACT IMMOBILIZED MASSES OF POLLUTION AND PRECIPITATES.

OCCUPATIONAL SPILL: DO NOT TOUCH SPILLED MATERIAL. STOP LEAK IF YOU CAN DO IT WITHOUT RISK. FOR SMALL SPILLS, TAKE UP WITH SAND OR OTHER ABSORBENT MATERIAL AND PLACE INTO CONTAINERS FOR LATER DISPOSAL. FOR SMALL DRY SPILLS, PLACE MATERIAL INTO A CLEAN, DRY CONTAINER WITH A CLEAN SHOVEL AND COVER. MOVE CONTAINERS FROM SPILL AREA. FOR LARGER

SPILLS, DIKE FAR AHEAD OF SPILL FOR LATER DISPOSAL. KEEP UNNECESSARY PEOPLE AWAY. ISOLATE HAZARD AREA AND DENY ENTRY.
REPORTABLE QUANTITY (RQ): 100 POUNDS THE SUPERFUND AMENDMENTS AND REAUTHORIZATION ACT (SARA) SECTION 304 REQUIRES THAT A RELEASE EQUAL TO OR GREATER THAN THE REPORTABLE QUANTITY FOR THIS SUBSTANCE BE IMMEDIATELY REPORTED TO THE LOCAL EMERGENCY PLANNING COMMITTEE AND THE STATE EMERGENCY RESPONSE COMMISSION (40 CFR 355.40). IF THE RELEASE OF THIS SUBSTANCE IS REPORTABLE UNDER CERCLA SECTION 103, THE NATIONAL RESPONSE CENTER MUST BE NOTIFIED IMMEDIATELY AT (800) 424-8802 OR (202) 426-2675 IN THE METROPOLITAN WASHINGTON, D.C. AREA (40 CFR 302.6).

PROTECTIVE EQUIPMENT

VENTILATION: PROVIDE GENERAL DILUTION VENTILATION.

RESPIRATOR: THE FOLLOWING RESPIRATORS AND MAXIMUM USE CONCENTRATIONS ARE RECOMMENDATIONS BY THE U.S. DEPARTMENT OF HEALTH AND HUMAN SERVICES, NIOSH POCKET GUIDE TO CHEMICAL HAZARDS; NIOSH CRITERIA DOCUMENTS OR BY THE U.S. DEPARTMENT OF LABOR, 29 CFR 1910 SUBPART Z. THE SPECIFIC RESPIRATOR SELECTED MUST BE BASED ON CONTAMINATION LEVELS FOUND IN THE WORK PLACE, MUST NOT EXCEED THE WORKING LIMITS OF THE RESPIRATOR AND BE JOINTLY APPROVED BY THE NATIONAL INSTITUTE FOR OCCUPATIONAL SAFETY AND HEALTH AND THE MINE SAFETY AND HEALTH ADMINISTRATION (NIOSH-MSHA).
COPPER DUST AND MIST (AS CU):
5 MG/M3- ANY DUST AND MIST RESPIRATOR EXCEPT SINGLE-USE RESPIRATORS.
10 MG/M3- ANY DUST AND MIST RESPIRATOR EXCEPT SINGLE-USE AND QUARTER-MASK RESPIRATORS. ANY SUPPLIED-AIR RESPIRATOR. ANY SELF-CONTAINED BREATHING APPARATUS.
25 MG/M3- ANY POWERED AIR-PURIFYING RESPIRATOR WITH A DUST AND MIST FILTER. ANY SUPPLIED-AIR RESPIRATOR OPERATED IN A CONTINUOUS FLOW MODE.
50 MG/M3- ANY AIR-PURIFYING FULL FACEPIECE RESPIRATOR WITH A HIGH-EFFICIENCY PARTICULATE FILTER. ANY SELF-CONTAINED BREATHING APPARATUS WITH A FULL FACEPIECE. ANY SUPPLIED-AIR RESPIRATOR WITH A FULL FACEPIECE. ANY POWERED AIR-PURIFYING RESPIRATOR WITH A TIGHT-FITTING FACEPIECE AND A HIGH-EFFICIENCY PARTICULATE FILTER.
1000 MG/M3- ANY SUPPLIED-AIR RESPIRATOR WITH A HALF-MASK AND OPERATED IN A PRESSURE-DEMAND OR OTHER POSITIVE PRESSURE MODE.
2000 MG/M3- ANY SUPPLIED-AIR RESPIRATOR WITH A FULL FACEPIECE AND OPERATED IN A PRESSURE-DEMAND OR OTHER POSITIVE PRESSURE MODE.
ESCAPE- ANY AIR-PURIFYING FULL FACEPIECE RESPIRATOR WITH A HIGH-EFFICIENCY PARTICULATE FILTER. ANY APPROPRIATE ESCAPE-TYPE SELF-CONTAINED BREATHING APPARATUS. FOR FIREFIGHTING AND OTHER IMMEDIATELY DANGEROUS TO LIFE OR HEALTH CONDITIONS:
SELF-CONTAINED BREATHING APPARATUS WITH FULL FACEPIECE OPERATED IN PRESSURE-DEMAND OR OTHER POSITIVE PRESSURE MODE.
SUPPLIED-AIR RESPIRATOR WITH FULL FACEPIECE AND OPERATED IN PRESSURE-DEMAND OR OTHER POSITIVE PRESSURE MODE IN COMBINATION WITH AN AUXILIARY SELF-CONTAINED BREATHING APPARATUS OPERATED IN PRESSURE-DEMAND OR OTHER POSITIVE PRESSURE MODE.

CLOTHING: EMPLOYEE MUST WEAR APPROPRIATE PROTECTIVE (IMPERVIOUS) CLOTHING AND EQUIPMENT TO PREVENT REPEATED OR PROLONGED SKIN CONTACT WITH THIS SUBSTANCE.

GLOVES: EMPLOYEE MUST WEAR APPROPRIATE PROTECTIVE GLOVES TO PREVENT CONTACT WITH THIS SUBSTANCE.

EYE PROTECTION: EMPLOYEE MUST WEAR SPLASH-PROOF OR DUST-RESISTANT SAFETY GOGGLES TO PREVENT EYE CONTACT WITH THIS SUBSTANCE.
EMERGENCY EYE WASH: WHERE THERE IS ANY POSSIBILITY THAT AN EMPLOYEE'S EYES MAY BE EXPOSED TO THIS SUBSTANCE, THE EMPLOYER SHOULD PROVIDE AN EYE WASH FOUNTAIN WITHIN THE IMMEDIATE WORK AREA FOR EMERGENCY USE.

AUTHORIZED BY- OCCUPATIONAL HEALTH SERVICES, INC.
CREATION DATE: 10/04/89 ***REVISION DATE:*** 05/18/90

MATERIAL SAFETY DATA SHEET

OCCUPATIONAL HEALTH SERVICES, INC.
AGRICULTURE AND PESTICIDE DIVISION
450 SEVENTH AVENUE, SUITE 2407
NEW YORK, NEW YORK 10123
1-800-445-MSDS OR (212) 967-1100

EMERGENCY CONTACT:
JOHN S. BRANSFORD, JR. (615) 292-1180

SUBSTANCE IDENTIFICATION

CAS-NUMBER 1317-38-0

SUBSTANCE: **CUPRIC OXIDE**

TRADE NAMES/SYNONYMS: BLACK COPPER OXIDE; COPPER MONOXIDE; COPPER OXIDE; NATURAL TENORITE; C.I. 77403; C.I. PIGMENT BLACK 15; COPPER BROWN; COPPER(2+) OXIDE; COPPER OXIDE (CUO); COPPER(II) OXIDE(CUO); COPPER(II) OXIDE; C-470,C-472,C-474; CUO; PST05655

CHEMICAL FAMILY: INORGANIC SALT

MOLECULAR FORMULA: CU-O

MOLECULAR WEIGHT: 79.54

CERCLA RATINGS (SCALE 0-3): HEALTH=U FIRE=0 REACTIVITY=0 PERSISTENCE=3

NFPA RATINGS (SCALE 0-4): HEALTH=U FIRE=0 REACTIVITY=0

COMPONENTS AND CONTAMINANTS

COMPONENT: CUPRIC OXIDE ***PERCENT:*** 100
CAS# 1317-38-0

OTHER CONTAMINANTS: NONE

EXPOSURE LIMITS: COPPER DUST AND MIST (AS CU): 1 MG/M3 OSHA TWA 1 MG/M3 ACGIH TWA
SUBJECT TO SARA SECTION 313 ANNUAL TOXIC CHEMICAL RELEASE REPORTING

PHYSICAL DATA

DESCRIPTION: BLACK TO BROWNISH-BLACK CRYSTALS OR POWDER.

MELTING POINT: 2419 F (1326 C) ***SPECIFIC GRAVITY:*** 6.3-6.49

SOLUBILITY IN WATER: INSOLUBLE

SOLVENT SOLUBILITY: SOLUBLE IN ACIDS, AMMONIA, AMMONIUM CARBONATE, AMMONIUM CHLORIDE, POTASSIUM CYANIDE; INSOLUBLE IN ALCOHOL.

FIRE AND EXPLOSION DATA

FIRE AND EXPLOSION HAZARD: NEGLIGIBLE FIRE HAZARD WHEN EXPOSED TO HEAT OR FLAME.

FIREFIGHTING MEDIA: DRY CHEMICAL, CARBON DIOXIDE, WATER SPRAY OR FOAM FOR LARGER FIRES, USE WATER SPRAY, FOG OR ALCOHOL FOAM

FIREFIGHTING: NO ACUTE HAZARD. MOVE CONTAINER FROM FIRE AREA IF POSSIBLE. AVOID BREATHING VAPORS OR DUSTS; KEEP UPWIND.

TOXICITY

CUPRIC OXIDE: TOXICITY DATA: 278 MG/KG INTRATRACHEAL-RAT LDLO. CARCINOGEN STATUS: NONE. LOCAL EFFECTS: IRRITANT- SKIN AND EYES. ACUTE TOXICITY LEVEL: INSUFFICIENT DATA AVAILABLE. TARGET EFFECTS: POISONING MAY AFFECT THE RESPIRATORY TRACT, LIVER, KIDNEY, AND SPLEEN. AT INCREASED RISK FROM EXPOSURE: PERSONS WITH PRE-EXISTING RESPIRATORY, LIVER, SKIN, KIDNEY, HEMATOPOIETIC, OR WILSON'S DISEASE.

HEALTH EFFECTS AND FIRST AID

INHALATION: CUPRIC OXIDE: **ACUTE EXPOSURE-** INHALATION OF COPPER DUST MAY CAUSE IRRITATION OF THE UPPER RESPIRATORY TRACT OR AN ILLNESS SIMILAR TO THE COMMON COLD WITH SENSATIONS OF CHILLS AND STUFFINESS OF THE HEAD. **CHRONIC EXPOSURE-** PROLONGED INHALATION OF DUST OR MIST OF COPPER SALTS MAY CAUSE CONGESTION OF THE NASAL MUCOUS MEMBRANES, SOMETIMES OF THE PHARYNX, AND ON OCCASIONS ULCERATION AND PERFORATION OF THE NASAL SEPTUM. ATROPHIC CHANGES IN THE MUCOUS MEMBRANES WERE NOTED IN SUBJECTS EXPOSED TO COMPLEX COPPER SALTS FOR LONG PERIODS OF TIME. INHALATION OF COPPER COMPOUNDS HAS CAUSED INJURY TO THE LUNGS AND LIVER WITH HEMOCHROMATOSIS IN ANIMALS.

FIRST AID- REMOVE FROM EXPOSURE AREA TO FRESH AIR IMMEDIATELY. IF BREATHING HAS STOPPED, PERFORM ARTIFICIAL RESPIRATION. KEEP PERSON WARM AND AT REST. TREAT SYMPTOMATICALLY AND SUPPORTIVELY. GET MEDICAL ATTENTION IMMEDIATELY.

SKIN CONTACT: CUPRIC OXIDE: IRRITANT. **ACUTE EXPOSURE-** MAY CAUSE IRRITATION. COPPER SALTS HAVE BEEN REPORTED TO CAUSE AN ITCHING PAPULOVESICULAR, SKIN DISCOLORATION, AND ECZEMATOID LESIONS. **CHRONIC EXPOSURE-** REPEATED OR PROLONGED CONTACT WITH SOME COPPER SALTS HAS RESULTED IN IRRITATION, NECROSIS, AND GREENISH SKIN DISCOLORATION. ALLERGIC CONTACT DERMATITIS, ALTHOUGH RARE, HAS BEEN REPORTED.

FIRST AID- REMOVE CONTAMINATED CLOTHING AND SHOES IMMEDIATELY. WASH AFFECTED AREA WITH SOAP OR MILD DETERGENT AND LARGE AMOUNTS OF WATER UNTIL NO EVIDENCE OF CHEMICAL REMAINS (APPROXIMATELY 15-20 MINUTES). GET MEDICAL ATTENTION IMMEDIATELY.

EYE CONTACT: CUPRIC OXIDE: IRRITANT. **ACUTE EXPOSURE-** CONTACT MAY CAUSE IRRITATION. SOME COPPER SALTS HAVE BEEN REPORTED TO CAUSE CONJUNCTIVITIS, CORNEAL ULCERATIONS, AND TURBIDITY POSSIBLY WITH

PALPEBRAL EDEMA. COPPER PARTICLES EMBEDDED IN THE EYE MAY RESULT IN A PRONOUNCED FOREIGN-BODY RESPONSE WITH CHARACTERISTIC DISCOLORATION OF OCULAR TISSUE. **CHRONIC EXPOSURE-** REPEATED AND PROLONGED EXPOSURE TO IRRITANTS MAY CAUSE CONJUNCTIVITIS.

FIRST AID- WASH EYES IMMEDIATELY WITH LARGE AMOUNTS OF WATER OR NORMAL SALINE, OCCASIONALLY LIFTING UPPER AND LOWER LIDS, UNTIL NO EVIDENCE OF CHEMICAL REMAINS (APPROXIMATELY 15-20 MINUTES). GET MEDICAL ATTENTION IMMEDIATELY.

INGESTION: CUPRIC OXIDE: **ACUTE EXPOSURE-** INGESTION OF COPPER SALTS MAY CAUSE AN IMMEDIATE METALLIC TASTE, SALIVATION, NAUSEA, EPIGASTRIC BURNING, VOMITING, DIARRHEA, ULCERS, HEMORRHAGIC GASTRITIS, ANURIA, COMA, CONVULSIONS AND DEATH. **CHRONIC EXPOSURE-** REPEATED OR PROLONGED EXPOSURE TO COPPER SALTS HAS PRODUCED HEMOLYTIC ANEMIA AND LIVER, KIDNEY, AND SPLEEN DAMAGE IN ANIMALS.

FIRST AID- DILUTE THE POISON IMMEDIATELY WITH LARGE AMOUNTS OF WATER OR MILK AND REMOVE BY GASTRIC LAVAGE UNLESS THE VICTIM IS ALREADY VOMITING. (DREISBACH, HANDBOOK OF POISONING, 12TH ED.) GET MEDICAL ATTENTION IMMEDIATELY. ADMINISTRATION OF GASTRIC LAVAGE SHOULD BE PERFORMED BY QUALIFIED MEDICAL PERSONNEL.

ANTIDOTE: THE FOLLOWING ANTIDOTE HAS BEEN RECOMMENDED. HOWEVER, THE DECISION AS TO WHETHER THE SEVERITY OF POISONING REQUIRES ADMINISTRATION OF ANY ANTIDOTE AND ACTUAL DOSE REQUIRED SHOULD BE MADE BY QUALIFIED MEDICAL PERSONNEL.

COPPER POISONING: GIVE CALCIUM DISODIUM EDETATE 15-25 MG/KG (0.08-0.125 ML OF 20% SOLUTION PER KILOGRAM BODY WEIGHT) IN 250-500 ML OF 5% DEXTROSE INTRAVENOUSLY OVER A 1 TO 2 HOUR PERIOD TWICE DAILY. THE MAXIMUM DOSE SHOULD NOT EXCEED 50 MG/KG/DAY. THE DRUG SHOULD BE GIVEN IN 5-DAY COURSES WITH A REST PERIOD OF AT LEAST 2 DAYS BETWEEN COURSES. AFTER THE FIRST COURSE, SUBSEQUENT COURSES SHOULD NOT EXCEED 50 MG/KG/DAY. DAILY URINALYSES SHOULD NOT BE DONE DURING THE TREATMENT PERIOD. THE DOSAGE SHOULD BE REDUCED IF ANY UNUSUAL URINARY FINDINGS APPEAR. INTRAVENOUS ADMINISTRATION IS CONTRAINDICATED IN THE PRESENCE OF ELEVATED CEREBROSPINAL FLUID PRESSURE. PENICILLAMINE IS ALSO EFFECTIVE IN COPPER POISONING. GIVE UP TO 100 MG/KG/DAY (MAXIMUM 1 G/DAY) DIVIDED INTO 4 DOSES FOR NO LONGER THAN 1 WEEK. IF A LONGER ADMINISTRATION PERIOD IS WARRANTED, DOSAGE SHOULD NOT EXCEED 40 MG/KG/DAY. GIVE THE DRUG ORALLY, HALF AN HOUR BEFORE MEALS (DREISBACH, HANDBOOK OF POISONING, 12TH ED.). ANTIDOTE SHOULD BE ADMINISTERED BY QUALIFIED MEDICAL PERSONNEL.

REACTIVITY

REACTIVITY: STABLE UNDER NORMAL TEMPERATURES AND PRESSURES.

INCOMPATIBILITIES: CUPRIC OXIDE: ALUMINUM: POSSIBLE EXPLOSION WHEN HEATED. ANILINIUM PERCHLORATE: POSSIBLE EXPLOSION AND THERMAL DECOMPOSITION. BORON: POSSIBLE VIOLENT EXOTHERMIC REACTION UPON WARMING. CESIUM ACETYLENE CARBIDE: POSSIBLE EXPLOSION AT 350 C. DICHLOROMETHYLSILANE: POSSIBLE IGNITION. HYDRAZINE: VIGOROUS REACTION. HYDROGEN: POSSIBLE EXPLOSION HAZARD. HYDROGEN SULFIDE: HYDROGEN SULFIDE IS READILY OXIDIZED AND MAY IGNITE UPON CONTACT. HYDROGEN TRISULFIDE: MAY CAUSE VIOLENT DECOMPOSITION AND IGNITION. HYDROXYLAMINE: VIGOROUS REACTION. MAGNESIUM: POSSIBLE INCANDESCENCE AND EXPLOSIVE REACTION. PHOSPHAM: MAY DECOMPOSE WITH INCANDESCENCE. PHTHALIC ANHYDRIDE: POSSIBLE VIOLENT EXPLOSION. POTASSIUM: MAY INCANDESCE AND REDUCE TO COPPER METAL. RUBIDIUM ACETYLIDE AND ACETYLENE CARBIDE: INCANDESCENCE AND VIGOROUS REACTION AT 350 C. SODIUM: MAY REDUCE WITH INCANDESCENCE. TITANIUM: MAY REACT VIOLENTLY WHEN HEATED. ZIRCONIUM: POSSIBLE EXPLOSION.

DECOMPOSITION: THERMAL DECOMPOSITION MAY RELEASE TOXIC AND/OR HAZARDOUS GASES.

POLYMERIZATION: HAZARDOUS POLYMERIZATION HAS NOT BEEN REPORTED TO OCCUR UNDER NORMAL TEMPERATURES AND PRESSURES.

STORAGE AND DISPOSAL

OBSERVE ALL FEDERAL, STATE AND LOCAL REGULATIONS WHEN STORING OR DISPOSING OF THIS SUBSTANCE. FOR ASSISTANCE, CONTACT THE DISTRICT DIRECTOR OF THE ENVIRONMENTAL PROTECTION AGENCY.

CONDITIONS TO AVOID

NONE REPORTED.

SPILL AND LEAK PROCEDURES

OCCUPATIONAL SPILL: FOR LARGE SPILLS, SWEEP UP WITH A MINIMUM OF DUSTING AND PLACE INTO SUITABLE CLEAN, DRY CONTAINERS FOR RECLAMATION OR LATER DISPOSAL.

RESIDUE SHOULD BE CLEANED UP USING A HIGH-EFFICIENCY PARTICULATE FILTER VACUUM.

PROTECTIVE EQUIPMENT

VENTILATION: PROVIDE LOCAL EXHAUST OR PROCESS ENCLOSURE VENTILATION TO MEET PUBLISHED EXPOSURE LIMITS.

RESPIRATOR: THE FOLLOWING RESPIRATORS AND MAXIMUM USE CONCENTRATIONS ARE RECOMMENDATIONS BY THE U.S. DEPARTMENT OF HEALTH AND HUMAN SERVICES, NIOSH POCKET GUIDE TO CHEMICAL HAZARDS; NIOSH CRITERIA DOCUMENTS OR BY THE U.S. DEPARTMENT OF LABOR, 29 CFR 1910 SUBPART Z. THE SPECIFIC RESPIRATOR SELECTED MUST BE BASED ON CONTAMINATION LEVELS FOUND IN THE WORK PLACE, MUST NOT EXCEED THE WORKING LIMITS OF THE RESPIRATOR AND BE JOINTLY APPROVED BY THE NATIONAL INSTITUTE FOR OCCUPATIONAL SAFETY AND HEALTH AND THE MINE SAFETY AND HEALTH ADMINISTRATION (NIOSH-MSHA).

COPPER DUST AND MIST (AS CU):

5 MG/M3- ANY DUST AND MIST RESPIRATOR EXCEPT SINGLE-USE RESPIRATORS.

10 MG/M3- ANY DUST AND MIST RESPIRATOR EXCEPT SINGLE-USE AND QUARTER-MASK RESPIRATORS. ANY SUPPLIED-AIR RESPIRATOR. ANY SELF-CONTAINED BREATHING APPARATUS.

25 MG/M3- ANY POWERED AIR-PURIFYING RESPIRATOR WITH A DUST AND MIST FILTER. ANY SUPPLIED-AIR RESPIRATOR OPERATED IN A CONTINUOUS FLOW MODE.

50 MG/M3- ANY AIR-PURIFYING FULL FACEPIECE RESPIRATOR WITH A HIGH-EFFICIENCY PARTICULATE FILTER. ANY SELF-CONTAINED BREATHING APPARATUS WITH A FULL FACEPIECE. ANY SUPPLIED-AIR RESPIRATOR WITH A FULL FACEPIECE. ANY POWERED AIR-PURIFYING RESPIRATOR WITH A TIGHT-FITTING FACEPIECE AND A HIGH-EFFICIENCY PARTICULATE FILTER.

1000 MG/M3- ANY SUPPLIED-AIR RESPIRATOR WITH A HALF-MASK AND OPERATED IN A PRESSURE-DEMAND OR OTHER POSITIVE PRESSURE MODE.

2000 MG/M3- ANY SUPPLIED-AIR RESPIRATOR WITH A FULL FACEPIECE AND OPERATED IN A PRESSURE-DEMAND OR OTHER POSITIVE PRESSURE MODE.

ESCAPE- ANY AIR-PURIFYING FULL FACEPIECE RESPIRATOR WITH A HIGH-EFFICIENCY PARTICULATE FILTER. ANY APPROPRIATE ESCAPE-TYPE SELF-CONTAINED BREATHING APPARATUS.

FOR FIREFIGHTING AND OTHER IMMEDIATELY DANGEROUS TO LIFE OR HEALTH CONDITIONS:

SELF-CONTAINED BREATHING APPARATUS WITH FULL FACEPIECE OPERATED IN PRESSURE-DEMAND OR OTHER POSITIVE PRESSURE MODE.

SUPPLIED-AIR RESPIRATOR WITH FULL FACEPIECE AND OPERATED IN PRESSURE-DEMAND OR OTHER POSITIVE PRESSURE MODE IN COMBINATION WITH AN AUXILIARY SELF-CONTAINED BREATHING APPARATUS OPERATED IN PRESSURE-DEMAND OR OTHER POSITIVE PRESSURE MODE.

CLOTHING: EMPLOYEE MUST WEAR APPROPRIATE PROTECTIVE (IMPERVIOUS) CLOTHING AND EQUIPMENT TO PREVENT REPEATED OR PROLONGED SKIN CONTACT WITH THIS SUBSTANCE.

GLOVES: EMPLOYEE MUST WEAR APPROPRIATE PROTECTIVE GLOVES TO PREVENT CONTACT WITH THIS SUBSTANCE.

EYE PROTECTION: EMPLOYEE MUST WEAR SPLASH-PROOF OR DUST-RESISTANT SAFETY GOGGLES TO PREVENT EYE CONTACT WITH THIS SUBSTANCE.

EMERGENCY EYE WASH: WHERE THERE IS ANY POSSIBILITY THAT AN EMPLOYEE'S EYES MAY BE EXPOSED TO THIS SUBSTANCE, THE EMPLOYER SHOULD PROVIDE AN EYE WASH FOUNTAIN WITHIN THE IMMEDIATE WORK AREA FOR EMERGENCY USE.

AUTHORIZED BY- OCCUPATIONAL HEALTH SERVICES, INC.

CREATION DATE: 11/15/89 ***REVISION DATE:*** 05/11/90

MATERIAL SAFETY DATA SHEET

OCCUPATIONAL HEALTH SERVICES, INC.
AGRICULTURE AND PESTICIDE DIVISION
450 SEVENTH AVENUE, SUITE 2407
NEW YORK, NEW YORK 10123
1-800-445-MSDS OR (212) 967-1100

EMERGENCY CONTACT:
JOHN S. BRANSFORD, JR. (615) 292-1180

SUBSTANCE IDENTIFICATION

CAS-NUMBER 7758-98-7

SUBSTANCE: **CUPRIC SULFATE**

TRADE NAMES/SYNONYMS: CUPRIC SULFATE ANHYDROUS; COPPER(II)SULFATE; COPPER SULFATE; CUPRIC SULPHATE; SULFURIC ACID, COPPER(2+) SALT; ROMAN VITRIOL; BLUE VITRIOL; BLUE COPPER; COPPER MONOSULFATE; COPPER SULFATE

SUPERFINE XTLS (ASHLAND CHEMICAL COMPANY); STCC 4961316; NA 9109; C-495; PST05670

CHEMICAL FAMILY: INORGANIC SALT

MOLECULAR FORMULA: CU-S-O4

MOLECULAR WEIGHT: 159.60

CERCLA RATINGS (SCALE 0-3): HEALTH=3 FIRE=0 REACTIVITY=0 PERSISTENCE=3

NFPA RATINGS (SCALE 0-4): HEALTH=3 FIRE=0 REACTIVITY=0

COMPONENTS AND CONTAMINANTS

COMPONENT: CUPRIC SULFATE ***PERCENT:*** >97
CAS# 7758-98-7

OTHER CONTAMINANTS: CHLORIDE, INSOLUBLE MATTER, ALKALIES AND EARTH, IRON.

EXPOSURE LIMITS: CUPRIC SULFATE: 1 MG(CU)/M3 OSHA TWA (DUST AND MIST) 1 MG(CU)/M3 ACGIH TWA (DUST AND MIST)
10 POUNDS CERCLA SECTION 103 REPORTABLE QUANTITY SUBJECT TO SARA SECTION 313 ANNUAL TOXIC CHEMICAL RELEASE REPORTING

PHYSICAL DATA

DESCRIPTION: GRAYISH-WHITE TO GREENISH-WHITE RHOMBIC CRYSTALS

BOILING POINT: 1202 F (650 C) DECOMPOSES

MELTING POINT: 392 F (200 C) SLIGHT DECOMPOSITION ***SPECIFIC GRAVITY:*** 3.6

SOLUBILITY IN WATER: 14.3% @ 0 C

SOLVENT SOLUBILITY: SOLUBLE WITH METHANOL

FIRE AND EXPLOSION DATA

FIRE AND EXPLOSION HAZARD: NEGLIGIBLE FIRE HAZARD WHEN EXPOSED TO HEAT OR FLAME.

FIREFIGHTING MEDIA: DRY CHEMICAL, CARBON DIOXIDE, HALON, WATER SPRAY OR STANDARD FOAM (1987 EMERGENCY RESPONSE GUIDEBOOK, DOT P 5800.4).
FOR LARGER FIRES, USE WATER SPRAY, FOG OR STANDARD FOAM (1987 EMERGENCY RESPONSE GUIDEBOOK, DOT P 5800.4).

FIREFIGHTING: MOVE CONTAINER FROM FIRE AREA IF POSSIBLE. DO NOT SCATTER SPILLED MATERIAL WITH HIGH PRESSURE WATER STREAMS. DIKE FIRE CONTROL WATER FOR LATER DISPOSAL (1987 EMERGENCY RESPONSE GUIDEBOOK, DOT P 5800.4, GUIDE PAGE 31).
EXTINGUISH USING AGENTS SUITABLE FOR TYPE OF FIRE. AVOID BREATHING VAPORS OR DUSTS.

TRANSPORTATION DATA

DEPARTMENT OF TRANSPORTATION HAZARD CLASSIFICATION 49 CFR 172.101: ORM-E

DEPARTMENT OF TRANSPORTATION LABELING REQUIREMENTS 49 CFR 172.101 AND SUBPART E: NONE

DEPARTMENT OF TRANSPORTATION PACKAGING REQUIREMENTS: 49 CFR 173.510 EXCEPTIONS: NONE

TOXICITY

CUPRIC SULFATE (COPPER SULFATE): TOXICITY DATA: ANHYDROUS: 150 MG/KG ORAL-CHILD TDLO; 11 MG/KG ORAL-HUMAN TDLO; 857 MG/KG ORAL-MAN LDLO; 50 MG/KG ORAL-HUMAN LDLO; 300 MG/KG ORAL-RAT LD50; 43 MG/KG SUBCUTANEOUS-RAT LD50; 520 MG/KG UNREPORTED ROUTE-RAT LD50; 18 MG/KG INTRAPERITONEAL-MOUSE LD50; 500 UG/KG SUBCUTANEOUS-MOUSE LDLO; 50 MG/KG INTRAVENOUS-MOUSE LDLO; 4500 UG/KG INTRAVENOUS-RABBIT LDLO; 2 MG/KG INTRAVENOUS-GUINEA PIG LDLO; MUTAGENIC DATA (RTECS); REPRODUCTIVE EFFECTS DATA (RTECS); TUMORIGENIC DATA (RTECS). MONOHYDRATE: NO DATA AVAILABLE. PENTAHYDRATE: 272 MG/KG ORAL-HUMAN TDLO; 1088 MG/KG ORAL-HUMAN LDLO; 221 MG/KG UNREPORTED ROUTE-MAN LDLO; 300 MG/KG ORAL-RAT LD50; 33 MG/KG INTRAPERITONEAL-MOUSE LD50; 60 MG/KG ORAL-DOG LDLO; 62 MG/KG SUBCUTANEOUS-GUINEA PIG LDLO; MUTAGENIC DATA (RTECS). CARCINOGEN STATUS: NONE. LOCAL EFFECTS: IRRITANT- INHALATION, SKIN, AND EYES. ACUTE TOXICITY LEVEL: TOXIC BY INGESTION. TARGET EFFECTS: POISONING MAY AFFECT THE LIVER, KIDNEYS, AND GASTROINTESTINAL TRACT. AT INCREASED RISK FROM EXPOSURE: PERSONS WITH A HISTORY OF CHRONIC RESPIRATORY OR SKIN DISEASE OR WILSON'S DISEASE.

HEALTH EFFECTS AND FIRST AID

INHALATION: CUPRIC SULFATE (COPPER SULFATE): IRRITANT. **ACUTE EXPOSURE-** INHALATION OF DUSTS AND MIST OF COPPER SALTS MAY CAUSE IRRITATION OF THE UPPER RESPIRATORY TRACT. WORKERS EXPOSED TO COPPER SALTS IN DUST FORM COMPLAINED OF METALLIC TASTE WITH IRRITATION OF NASAL AND ORAL MUCOSA. **CHRONIC EXPOSURE-** REPEATED OR PROLONGED EXPOSURE TO COPPER SALTS MAY PRODUCE SEVERE CONGESTION OF THE NASAL MUCOSA WITH RHINITIS AND POSSIBLE SLOUGHING AND ULCERATION.

FIRST AID- REMOVE FROM EXPOSURE AREA TO FRESH AIR IMMEDIATELY. IF BREATHING HAS STOPPED, PERFORM ARTIFICIAL RESPIRATION. KEEP PERSON WARM AND AT REST. TREAT SYMPTOMATICALLY AND SUPPORTIVELY. GET MEDICAL ATTENTION IMMEDIATELY.

SKIN CONTACT: CUPRIC SULFATE (COPPER SULFATE): IRRITANT. **ACUTE EXPOSURE-** DIRECT CONTACT OF COPPER SALTS WITH THE SKIN MAY GIVE RISE TO AN ITCHING, PAPULOVESICULAR AND ECZEMATOID LESION. **CHRONIC EXPOSURE-** REPEATED OR PROLONGED EXPOSURE TO COPPER SALTS MAY CAUSE SOME DEGREE OF NECROSIS. ALLERGIC CONTACT DERMATITIS, ALTHOUGH RARE, HAS BEEN REPORTED. EFFECTS OF SYSTEMIC POISONING, WHICH HAS FOLLOWED REPEATED APPLICATIONS OF COPPER SULFATE SOLUTION TO EXTENSIVE AREAS OF BURNED SKIN, MAY INCLUDE BLUE DISCOLORATION OF THE GUMS AND TONGUE, HEMOLYTIC ANEMIA, HEMORRHAGIC GASTRITIS, COLIC AND DIARRHEA WITH BLOODY STOOLS. IN SEVERE CASES OF POISONING, LIVER AND KIDNEY DAMAGE WITH SEVERE ANEMIA MAY OCCUR WITH POSSIBLE SOMNOLENCE AND COMA. DEATH MAY OCCUR FROM CIRCULATORY FAILURE. GREENISH DISCOLORATION OF THE SKIN AND HAIR OF SOME COPPER WORKERS HAS BEEN OBSERVED.

FIRST AID- REMOVE CONTAMINATED CLOTHING AND SHOES IMMEDIATELY. WASH AFFECTED AREA WITH SOAP OR MILD DETERGENT AND LARGE AMOUNTS OF WATER UNTIL NO EVIDENCE OF CHEMICAL REMAINS (APPROXIMATELY 15-20 MINUTES). GET MEDICAL ATTENTION IMMEDIATELY.

EYE CONTACT: CUPRIC SULFATE (COPPER SULFATE): IRRITANT. **ACUTE EXPOSURE-** COPPER SALTS SPLASHED IN THE EYES MAY CAUSE CONJUNCTIVITIS, CORNEAL ULCERATION AND TURBIDITY, AND PALPEBRAL EDEMA. COPPER PARTICLES LODGED IN THE EYE MAY RESULT IN PRONOUNCED FOREIGN-BODY REACTION WITH CHARACTERISTIC DISCOLORATION OF OCULAR TISSUE. **CHRONIC EXPOSURE-** REPEATED OR PROLONGED USE OF SOLID COPPER SULFATE FOR TREATMENT OF TRACHOMA PRODUCED INFLAMMATION AND PURULENT REACTION, AND DISCOLORATION OF THE CORNEA. THE DISCOLORATION IN ADVANCED CASES COVERED THE WHOLE CORNEA BUT CAUSED SLIGHT OR NO INTERFERENCE WITH VISION. WHEN A PARTICLE OF COPPER SULFATE WAS LEFT ACCIDENTALLY IN THE CONJUNCTIVAL SAC, IT CAUSED MORE SEVERE LOCAL INFLAMMATION AND NECROSIS, CORNEAL OPACITY, AND SYMBLEPHARON. A VERY LOW CONCENTRATION OF COPPER SULFATE (0.001 M) CAUSED THE PRECORNEAL TEAR FILM TO CURDLE. THERE WAS NO INJURY TO THE CORNEA AND LITTLE DISCOMFORT FELT BY THE HUMAN SUBJECTS EXPOSED TO THIS MATERIAL.

FIRST AID- WASH EYES IMMEDIATELY WITH LARGE AMOUNTS OF WATER OR NORMAL SALINE, OCCASIONALLY LIFTING UPPER AND LOWER LIDS, UNTIL NO EVIDENCE OF CHEMICAL REMAINS (APPROXIMATELY 15-20 MINUTES). GET MEDICAL ATTENTION IMMEDIATELY.

INGESTION: CUPRIC SULFATE (COPPER SULFATE): TOXIC. **ACUTE EXPOSURE-** INGESTION OF A TOXIC DOSE OF COPPER SULFATE MAY CAUSE SALIVATION, NAUSEA, VOMITING, GASTRIC PAIN, AND LOCAL CORROSION AND HEMORRHAGES. OTHER SYMPTOMS OF SYSTEMIC INTOXICATION INCLUDE BLUE DISCOLORATION OF THE GUMS AND TONGUE, HEMOLYTIC ANEMIA, HEMORRHAGIC GASTRITIS, COLIC AND DIARRHEA WITH BLOODY STOOLS. IN SEVERE CASES OF POISONING, LIVER AND KIDNEY DAMAGE WITH SEVERE ANEMIA MAY OCCUR WITH POSSIBLE SOMNOLENCE AND COMA. DEATH MAY OCCUR FROM CIRCULATORY FAILURE. TWO MEN WHO INGESTED 60 AND 80 GRAMS IN SOLUTION DIED IN 6 AND 9 DAYS, RESPECTIVELY. THE MINIMAL LETHAL ORAL DOSE FOR AN ADULT APPEARS TO BE 10 GRAMS. **CHRONIC EXPOSURE-** CHRONIC HUMAN POISONING HAS ONLY BEEN REPORTED IN INDIVIDUALS WITH WILSON'S DISEASE. THIS DISEASE IS A RARE GENETIC CONDITION IN WHICH THERE MAY BE AN ABNORMALLY HIGH ABSORPTION, RETENTION AND STORAGE OF COPPER BY THE BODY. THIS ACCUMULATION HAS BEEN NOTED TO PRECEDE THE DEVELOPMENT OF LIVER PATHOLOGY, WHICH MAY ULTIMATELY PROVE FATAL.

FIRST AID- DILUTE THE POISON IMMEDIATELY WITH LARGE AMOUNTS OF WATER OR MILK AND REMOVE BY GASTRIC LAVAGE UNLESS THE VICTIM IS ALREADY VOMITING. (DREISBACH, HANDBOOK OF POISONING, 12TH ED.) GET MEDICAL ATTENTION IMMEDIATELY. ADMINISTRATION OF GASTRIC LAVAGE SHOULD BE PERFORMED BY QUALIFIED MEDICAL PERSONNEL.

ANTIDOTE: THE FOLLOWING ANTIDOTE HAS BEEN RECOMMENDED. HOWEVER, THE DECISION AS TO WHETHER THE SEVERITY OF POISONING REQUIRES ADMINISTRATION OF ANY ANTIDOTE AND ACTUAL DOSE REQUIRED SHOULD BE MADE BY QUALIFIED MEDICAL PERSONNEL.
COPPER POISONING: GIVE CALCIUM DISODIUM EDETATE 15-25 MG/KG (0.08-0.125 ML OF 20% SOLUTION PER KILOGRAM BODY WEIGHT) IN 250-500 ML OF 5% DEXTROSE INTRAVENOUSLY OVER A 1 TO 2 HOUR PERIOD TWICE DAILY. THE MAXIMUM DOSE SHOULD NOT EXCEED 50 MG/KG/DAY. THE DRUG SHOULD BE GIVEN IN 5-DAY COURSES WITH A REST PERIOD OF AT LEAST 2 DAYS BETWEEN COURSES. AFTER THE FIRST COURSE, SUBSEQUENT COURSES SHOULD NOT EXCEED 50 MG/KG/DAY. DAILY URINALYSES SHOULD NOT BE DONE DURING THE

TREATMENT PERIOD. THE DOSAGE SHOULD BE REDUCED IF ANY UNUSUAL URINARY FINDINGS APPEAR. INTRAVENOUS ADMINISTRATION IS CONTRAINDICATED IN THE PRESENCE OF ELEVATED CEREBROSPINAL FLUID PRESSURE. PENICILLAMINE IS ALSO EFFECTIVE IN COPPER POISONING. GIVE UP TO 100 MG/KG/DAY (MAXIMUM 1 G/DAY) DIVIDED INTO 4 DOSES FOR NO LONGER THAN 1 WEEK. IF A LONGER ADMINISTRATION PERIOD IS WARRANTED, DOSAGE SHOULD NOT EXCEED 40 MG/KG/DAY. GIVE THE DRUG ORALLY, HALF AN HOUR BEFORE MEALS (DREISBACH, HANDBOOK OF POISONING, 12TH ED.). ANTIDOTE SHOULD BE ADMINISTERED BY QUALIFIED MEDICAL PERSONNEL.

REACTIVITY

REACTIVITY: STABLE UNDER NORMAL TEMPERATURES AND PRESSURES.

INCOMPATIBILITIES: CUPRIC SULFATE (COPPER SULFATE): HYDROXYLAMINE: MAY BE IGNITED WHEN MIXED WITH ANHYDROUS COPPER SULFATE. MAGNESIUM: PRODUCES HYDROGEN WHEN MIXED. SODIUM HYPOBROMITE: SOLUTIONS OF SODIUM HYPOBROMITE ARE DECOMPOSED BY POWERFUL CATALYTIC ACTION OF CUPRIC IONS.

DECOMPOSITION: THERMAL DECOMPOSITION MAY RELEASE TOXIC OXIDES OF SULFUR.

POLYMERIZATION: HAZARDOUS POLYMERIZATION HAS NOT BEEN REPORTED TO OCCUR UNDER NORMAL TEMPERATURES AND PRESSURES.

CONDITIONS TO AVOID

MAY BURN BUT DOES NOT IGNITE READILY. AVOID CONTACT WITH STRONG OXIDIZERS, EXCESSIVE HEAT, SPARKS, OR OPEN FLAME.

SPILL AND LEAK PROCEDURES

OCCUPATIONAL SPILL: SWEEP UP AND PLACE IN SUITABLE CLEAN, DRY CONTAINERS FOR RECLAMATION OR LATER DISPOSAL. DO NOT FLUSH SPILLED MATERIAL INTO SEWER. KEEP UNNECESSARY PEOPLE AWAY.

REPORTABLE QUANTITY (RQ): 10 POUNDS THE SUPERFUND AMENDMENTS AND REAUTHORIZATION ACT (SARA) SECTION 304 REQUIRES THAT A RELEASE EQUAL TO OR GREATER THAN THE REPORTABLE QUANTITY FOR THIS SUBSTANCE BE IMMEDIATELY REPORTED TO THE LOCAL EMERGENCY PLANNING COMMITTEE AND THE STATE EMERGENCY RESPONSE COMMISSION (40 CFR 355.40). IF THE RELEASE OF THIS SUBSTANCE IS REPORTABLE UNDER CERCLA SECTION 103, THE NATIONAL RESPONSE CENTER MUST BE NOTIFIED IMMEDIATELY AT (800) 424-8802 OR (202) 426-2675 IN THE METROPOLITAN WASHINGTON, D.C. AREA (40 CFR 302.6).

PROTECTIVE EQUIPMENT

VENTILATION: PROVIDE LOCAL EXHAUST OR PROCESS ENCLOSURE VENTILATION TO MEET PUBLISHED EXPOSURE LIMITS.

RESPIRATOR: THE FOLLOWING RESPIRATORS AND MAXIMUM USE CONCENTRATIONS ARE RECOMMENDATIONS BY THE U.S. DEPARTMENT OF HEALTH AND HUMAN SERVICES, NIOSH POCKET GUIDE TO CHEMICAL HAZARDS; NIOSH CRITERIA DOCUMENTS OR BY THE U.S. DEPARTMENT OF LABOR, 29 CFR 1910 SUBPART Z. THE SPECIFIC RESPIRATOR SELECTED MUST BE BASED ON CONTAMINATION LEVELS FOUND IN THE WORK PLACE, MUST NOT EXCEED THE WORKING LIMITS OF THE RESPIRATOR AND BE JOINTLY APPROVED BY THE NATIONAL INSTITUTE FOR OCCUPATIONAL SAFETY AND HEALTH AND THE MINE SAFETY AND HEALTH ADMINISTRATION (NIOSH-MSHA).

COPPER DUST AND MIST (AS CU):

5 MG/M3- ANY DUST AND MIST RESPIRATOR EXCEPT SINGLE-USE RESPIRATORS.

10 MG/M3- ANY DUST AND MIST RESPIRATOR EXCEPT SINGLE-USE AND QUARTER-MASK RESPIRATORS. ANY SUPPLIED-AIR RESPIRATOR. ANY SELF-CONTAINED BREATHING APPARATUS.

25 MG/M3- ANY POWERED AIR-PURIFYING RESPIRATOR WITH A DUST AND MIST FILTER. ANY SUPPLIED-AIR RESPIRATOR OPERATED IN A CONTINUOUS FLOW MODE.

50 MG/M3- ANY AIR-PURIFYING FULL FACEPIECE RESPIRATOR WITH A HIGH-EFFICIENCY PARTICULATE FILTER. ANY SELF-CONTAINED BREATHING APPARATUS WITH A FULL FACEPIECE. ANY SUPPLIED-AIR RESPIRATOR WITH A FULL FACEPIECE. ANY POWERED AIR-PURIFYING RESPIRATOR WITH A TIGHT-FITTING FACEPIECE AND A HIGH-EFFICIENCY PARTICULATE FILTER.

1000 MG/M3- ANY SUPPLIED-AIR RESPIRATOR WITH A HALF-MASK AND OPERATED IN A PRESSURE-DEMAND OR OTHER POSITIVE PRESSURE MODE.

2000 MG/M3- ANY SUPPLIED-AIR RESPIRATOR WITH A FULL FACEPIECE AND OPERATED IN A PRESSURE-DEMAND OR OTHER POSITIVE PRESSURE MODE.

ESCAPE- ANY AIR-PURIFYING FULL FACEPIECE RESPIRATOR WITH A HIGH-EFFICIENCY PARTICULATE FILTER. ANY APPROPRIATE ESCAPE-TYPE SELF-CONTAINED BREATHING APPARATUS.

FOR FIREFIGHTING AND OTHER IMMEDIATELY DANGEROUS TO LIFE OR HEALTH CONDITIONS:

SELF-CONTAINED BREATHING APPARATUS WITH FULL FACEPIECE OPERATED IN PRESSURE-DEMAND OR OTHER POSITIVE PRESSURE MODE.

SUPPLIED-AIR RESPIRATOR WITH FULL FACEPIECE AND OPERATED IN PRESSURE-DEMAND OR OTHER POSITIVE PRESSURE MODE IN COMBINATION WITH AN AUXILIARY SELF-CONTAINED BREATHING APPARATUS OPERATED IN PRESSURE-DEMAND OR OTHER POSITIVE PRESSURE MODE.

CLOTHING: EMPLOYEE MUST WEAR APPROPRIATE PROTECTIVE (IMPERVIOUS) CLOTHING AND EQUIPMENT TO PREVENT REPEATED OR PROLONGED SKIN CONTACT WITH THIS SUBSTANCE.

GLOVES: EMPLOYEE MUST WEAR APPROPRIATE PROTECTIVE GLOVES TO PREVENT CONTACT WITH THIS SUBSTANCE.

EYE PROTECTION: EMPLOYEE MUST WEAR SPLASH-PROOF OR DUST-RESISTANT SAFETY GOGGLES TO PREVENT EYE CONTACT WITH THIS SUBSTANCE.

EMERGENCY EYE WASH: WHERE THERE IS ANY POSSIBILITY THAT AN EMPLOYEE'S EYES MAY BE EXPOSED TO THIS SUBSTANCE, THE EMPLOYER SHOULD PROVIDE AN EYE WASH FOUNTAIN WITHIN THE IMMEDIATE WORK AREA FOR EMERGENCY USE.

AUTHORIZED BY- OCCUPATIONAL HEALTH SERVICES, INC.

CREATION DATE: 10/04/89 ***REVISION DATE:*** 05/31/90

MATERIAL SAFETY DATA SHEET

OCCUPATIONAL HEALTH SERVICES, INC.	EMERGENCY CONTACT:
AGRICULTURE AND PESTICIDE DIVISION	JOHN S. BRANSFORD, JR. (615) 292-1180
450 SEVENTH AVENUE, SUITE 2407	
NEW YORK, NEW YORK 10123	
1-800-445-MSDS OR (212) 967-1100	

SUBSTANCE IDENTIFICATION

CAS-NUMBER 10257-54-2

SUBSTANCE: <u>CUPRIC SULFATE, MONOHYDRATE</u>

TRADE NAMES/SYNONYMS: SULFURIC ACID COPPER SALT, MONOHYDRATE; COPPER MESOSULFATE; PST05675

CHEMICAL FAMILY: INORGANIC SALT

MOLECULAR FORMULA: CU-S-O4.H2O

MOLECULAR WEIGHT: 177.60

CERCLA RATINGS (SCALE 0-3): HEALTH=U FIRE=0 REACTIVITY=0 PERSISTENCE=3

NFPA RATINGS (SCALE 0-4): HEALTH=U FIRE=0 REACTIVITY=0

COMPONENTS AND CONTAMINANTS

COMPONENT: CUPRIC SULFATE, MONOHYDRATE ***PERCENT:*** 99

CAS# 10257-54-2

OTHER CONTAMINANTS: CHLORIDE, INSOLUBLE MATTER, ALKALIES AND EARTH, IRON.

EXPOSURE LIMITS: CUPRIC SULFATE: 1 MG(CU)/M3 OSHA TWA (DUST AND MIST) 1 MG(CU)/M3 ACGIH TWA (DUST AND MIST)

10 POUNDS CERCLA SECTION 103 REPORTABLE QUANTITY SUBJECT TO SARA SECTION 313 ANNUAL TOXIC CHEMICAL RELEASE REPORTING

PHYSICAL DATA

DESCRIPTION: ALMOST WHITE, HYGROSCOPIC POWDER. ***MELTING POINT:*** NOT AVAILABLE

SPECIFIC GRAVITY: NOT AVAILABLE ***SOLUBILITY IN WATER:*** SOLUBLE

SOLVENT SOLUBILITY: INSOLUBLE IN ALCOHOL.

FIRE AND EXPLOSION DATA

FIRE AND EXPLOSION HAZARD: NEGLIGIBLE FIRE HAZARD WHEN EXPOSED TO HEAT OR FLAME.

FIREFIGHTING MEDIA: DRY CHEMICAL, CARBON DIOXIDE, HALON, WATER SPRAY OR STANDARD FOAM (1987 EMERGENCY RESPONSE GUIDEBOOK, DOT P 5800.4).

FOR LARGER FIRES, USE WATER SPRAY, FOG OR STANDARD FOAM (1987 EMERGENCY RESPONSE GUIDEBOOK, DOT P 5800.4).

FIREFIGHTING: MOVE CONTAINER FROM FIRE AREA IF POSSIBLE. DO NOT SCATTER SPILLED MATERIAL WITH HIGH PRESSURE WATER STREAMS. DIKE FIRE CONTROL WATER FOR LATER DISPOSAL (1987 EMERGENCY RESPONSE GUIDEBOOK, DOT P 5800.4, GUIDE PAGE 31).

EXTINGUISH USING AGENTS SUITABLE FOR TYPE OF FIRE. AVOID BREATHING VAPORS OR DUSTS.

TRANSPORTATION DATA

DEPARTMENT OF TRANSPORTATION HAZARD CLASSIFICATION 49 CFR 172.101: ORM-E

DEPARTMENT OF TRANSPORTATION LABELING REQUIREMENTS 49 CFR 172.101 AND SUBPART E: NONE
DEPARTMENT OF TRANSPORTATION PACKAGING REQUIREMENTS: 49 CFR 173.510 EXCEPTIONS: NONE

TOXICITY

CUPRIC SULFATE (COPPER SULFATE): TOXICITY DATA: ANHYDROUS: 150 MG/KG ORAL-CHILD TDLO; 11 MG/KG ORAL-HUMAN TDLO; 857 MG/KG ORAL-MAN LDLO; 50 MG/KG ORAL-HUMAN LDLO; 300 MG/KG ORAL-RAT LD50; 43 MG/KG SUBCUTANEOUS-RAT LD50; 520 MG/KG UNREPORTED ROUTE-RAT LD50; 18 MG/KG INTRAPERITONEAL-MOUSE LD50; 500 UG/KG SUBCUTANEOUS-MOUSE LDLO; 50 MG/KG INTRAVENOUS-MOUSE LDLO; 4500 UG/KG INTRAVENOUS-RABBIT LDLO; 2 MG/KG INTRAVENOUS-GUINEA PIG LDLO; MUTAGENIC DATA (RTECS); REPRODUCTIVE EFFECTS DATA (RTECS); TUMORIGENIC DATA (RTECS). MONOHYDRATE: NO DATA AVAILABLE. PENTAHYDRATE: 272 MG/KG ORAL-HUMAN TDLO; 1088 MG/KG ORAL-HUMAN LDLO; 221 MG/KG UNREPORTED ROUTE-MAN LDLO; 300 MG/KG ORAL-RAT LD50; 33 MG/KG INTRAPERITONEAL-MOUSE LD50; 60 MG/KG ORAL-DOG LDLO; 62 MG/KG SUBCUTANEOUS-GUINEA PIG LDLO; MUTAGENIC DATA (RTECS). CARCINOGEN STATUS: NONE. LOCAL EFFECTS: IRRITANT- INHALATION, SKIN, AND EYES. ACUTE TOXICITY LEVEL: TOXIC BY INGESTION. TARGET EFFECTS: POISONING MAY AFFECT THE LIVER, KIDNEYS, AND GASTROINTESTINAL TRACT. AT INCREASED RISK FROM EXPOSURE: PERSONS WITH A HISTORY OF CHRONIC RESPIRATORY OR SKIN DISEASE OR WILSON'S DISEASE.

HEALTH EFFECTS AND FIRST AID

INHALATION: CUPRIC SULFATE (COPPER SULFATE): IRRITANT. **ACUTE EXPOSURE-** INHALATION OF DUSTS AND MIST OF COPPER SALTS MAY CAUSE IRRITATION OF THE UPPER RESPIRATORY TRACT. WORKERS EXPOSED TO COPPER SALTS IN DUST FORM COMPLAINED OF METALLIC TASTE WITH IRRITATION OF NASAL AND ORAL MUCOSA. **CHRONIC EXPOSURE-** REPEATED OR PROLONGED EXPOSURE TO COPPER SALTS MAY PRODUCE SEVERE CONGESTION OF THE NASAL MUCOSA WITH RHINITIS AND POSSIBLE SLOUGHING AND ULCERATION.

FIRST AID- REMOVE FROM EXPOSURE AREA TO FRESH AIR IMMEDIATELY. IF BREATHING HAS STOPPED, PERFORM ARTIFICIAL RESPIRATION. KEEP PERSON WARM AND AT REST. TREAT SYMPTOMATICALLY AND SUPPORTIVELY. GET MEDICAL ATTENTION IMMEDIATELY.

SKIN CONTACT: CUPRIC SULFATE (COPPER SULFATE): IRRITANT. **ACUTE EXPOSURE-** DIRECT CONTACT OF COPPER SALTS WITH THE SKIN MAY GIVE RISE TO AN ITCHING, PAPULOVESICULAR AND ECZEMATOID LESION. **CHRONIC EXPOSURE-** REPEATED OR PROLONGED EXPOSURE TO COPPER SALTS MAY CAUSE SOME DEGREE OF NECROSIS. ALLERGIC CONTACT DERMATITIS, ALTHOUGH RARE, HAS BEEN REPORTED. EFFECTS OF SYSTEMIC POISONING, WHICH HAS FOLLOWED REPEATED APPLICATIONS OF COPPER SULFATE SOLUTION TO EXTENSIVE AREAS OF BURNED SKIN, MAY INCLUDE BLUE DISCOLORATION OF THE GUMS AND TONGUE, HEMOLYTIC ANEMIA, HEMORRHAGIC GASTRITIS, COLIC AND DIARRHEA WITH BLOODY STOOLS. IN SEVERE CASES OF POISONING, LIVER AND KIDNEY DAMAGE WITH SEVERE ANEMIA MAY OCCUR WITH POSSIBLE SOMNOLENCE AND COMA. DEATH MAY OCCUR FROM CIRCULATORY FAILURE. GREENISH DISCOLORATION OF THE SKIN AND HAIR OF SOME COPPER WORKERS HAS BEEN OBSERVED.

FIRST AID- REMOVE CONTAMINATED CLOTHING AND SHOES IMMEDIATELY. WASH AFFECTED AREA WITH SOAP OR MILD DETERGENT AND LARGE AMOUNTS OF WATER UNTIL NO EVIDENCE OF CHEMICAL REMAINS (APPROXIMATELY 15-20 MINUTES). GET MEDICAL ATTENTION IMMEDIATELY.

EYE CONTACT: CUPRIC SULFATE (COPPER SULFATE): IRRITANT. **ACUTE EXPOSURE-** COPPER SALTS SPLASHED IN THE EYES MAY CAUSE CONJUNCTIVITIS, CORNEAL ULCERATION AND TURBIDITY, AND PALPEBRAL EDEMA. COPPER PARTICLES LODGED IN THE EYE MAY RESULT IN PRONOUNCED FOREIGN-BODY REACTION WITH CHARACTERISTIC DISCOLORATION OF OCULAR TISSURE. **CHRONIC EXPOSURE-** REPEATED OR PROLONGED USE OF SOLID COPPER SULFATE FOR TREATMENT OF TRACHOMA PRODUCED INFLAMMATION AND PURULENT REACTION, AND DISCOLORATION OF THE CORNEA. THE DISCOLORATION IN ADVANCED CASES COVERED THE WHOLE CORNEA BUT CAUSED SLIGHT OR NO INTERFERENCE WITH VISION. WHEN A PARTICLE OF COPPER SULFATE WAS LEFT ACCIDENTALLY IN THE CONJUNCTIVAL SAC, IT CAUSED MORE SEVERE LOCAL INFLAMMATION AND NECROSIS, CORNEAL OPACITY, AND SYMBLEPHARON. A VERY LOW CONCENTRATION OF COPPER SULFATE (0.001 M) CAUSED THE PRECORNEAL TEAR FILM TO CURDLE. THERE WAS NO INJURY TO THE CORNEA AND LITTLE DISCOMFORT FELT BY THE HUMAN SUBJECTS EXPOSED TO THIS MATERIAL.

FIRST AID- WASH EYES IMMEDIATELY WITH LARGE AMOUNTS OF WATER OR NORMAL SALINE, OCCASIONALLY LIFTING UPPER AND LOWER LIDS, UNTIL NO EVIDENCE OF CHEMICAL REMAINS (APPROXIMATELY 15-20 MINUTES). GET MEDICAL ATTENTION IMMEDIATELY.

INGESTION: CUPRIC SULFATE (COPPER SULFATE): TOXIC. **ACUTE EXPOSURE-** INGESTION OF A TOXIC DOSE OF COPPER SULFATE MAY CAUSE SALIVATION, NAUSEA, VOMITING, GASTRIC PAIN, AND LOCAL CORROSION AND HEMORRHAGES. OTHER SYMPTOMS OF SYSTEMIC INTOXICATION INCLUDE BLUE DISCOLORATION OF THE GUMS AND TONGUE, HEMOLYTIC ANEMIA, HEMORRHAGIC GASTRITIS, COLIC AND DIARRHEA WITH BLOODY STOOLS. IN SEVERE CASES OF POISONING, LIVER AND KIDNEY DAMAGE WITH SEVERE ANEMIA MAY OCCUR WITH POSSIBLE SOMNOLENCE AND COMA. DEATH MAY OCCUR FROM CIRCULATORY FAILURE. TWO MEN WHO INGESTED 60 AND 80 GRAMS IN SOLUTION DIED IN 6 AND 9 DAYS, RESPECTIVELY. THE MINIMAL LETHAL ORAL DOSE FOR AN ADULT APPEARS TO BE 10 GRAMS. **CHRONIC EXPOSURE-** CHRONIC HUMAN POISONING HAS ONLY BEEN REPORTED IN INDIVIDUALS WITH WILSON'S DISEASE. THIS DISEASE IS A RARE GENETIC CONDITION IN WHICH THERE MAY BE AN ABNORMALLY HIGH ABSORPTION, RETENTION AND STORAGE OF COPPER BY THE BODY. THIS ACCUMULATION HAS BEEN NOTED TO PRECEDE THE DEVELOPMENT OF LIVER PATHOLOGY, WHICH MAY ULTIMATELY PROVE FATAL.

FIRST AID- DILUTE THE POISON IMMEDIATELY WITH LARGE AMOUNTS OF WATER OR MILK AND REMOVE BY GASTRIC LAVAGE UNLESS THE VICTIM IS ALREADY VOMITING. (DREISBACH, HANDBOOK OF POISONING, 12TH ED.) GET MEDICAL ATTENTION IMMEDIATELY. ADMINISTRATION OF GASTRIC LAVAGE SHOULD BE PERFORMED BY QUALIFIED MEDICAL PERSONNEL.

ANTIDOTE: THE FOLLOWING ANTIDOTE HAS BEEN RECOMMENDED. HOWEVER, THE DECISION AS TO WHETHER THE SEVERITY OF POISONING REQUIRES ADMINISTRATION OF ANY ANTIDOTE AND ACTUAL DOSE REQUIRED SHOULD BE MADE BY QUALIFIED MEDICAL PERSONNEL.

COPPER POISONING: GIVE CALCIUM DISODIUM EDETATE 15-25 MG/KG (0.08-0.125 ML OF 20% SOLUTION PER KILOGRAM BODY WEIGHT) IN 250-500 ML OF 5% DEXTROSE INTRAVENOUSLY OVER A 1 TO 2 HOUR PERIOD TWICE DAILY. THE MAXIMUM DOSE SHOULD NOT EXCEED 50 MG/KG/DAY. THE DRUG SHOULD BE GIVEN IN 5-DAY COURSES WITH A REST PERIOD OF AT LEAST 2 DAYS BETWEEN COURSES. AFTER THE FIRST COURSE, SUBSEQUENT COURSES SHOULD NOT EXCEED 50 MG/KG/DAY. DAILY URINALYSES SHOULD NOT BE DONE DURING THE TREATMENT PERIOD. THE DOSAGE SHOULD BE REDUCED IF ANY UNUSUAL URINARY FINDINGS APPEAR. INTRAVENOUS ADMINISTRATION IS CONTRAINDICATED IN THE PRESENCE OF ELEVATED CEREBROSPINAL FLUID PRESSURE. PENICILLAMINE IS ALSO EFFECTIVE IN COPPER POISONING. GIVE UP TO 100 MG/KG/DAY (MAXIMUM 1 G/DAY) DIVIDED INTO 4 DOSES FOR NO LONGER THAN 1 WEEK. IF A LONGER ADMINISTRATION PERIOD IS WARRANTED, DOSAGE SHOULD NOT EXCEED 40 MG/KG/DAY. GIVE THE DRUG ORALLY, HALF AN HOUR BEFORE MEALS (DREISBACH, HANDBOOK OF POISONING, 12TH ED.). ANTIDOTE SHOULD BE ADMINISTERED BY QUALIFIED MEDICAL PERSONNEL.

REACTIVITY

REACTIVITY: STABLE UNDER NORMAL TEMPERATURES AND PRESSURES.

INCOMPATIBILITIES: CUPRIC SULFATE (COPPER SULFATE): HYDROXYLAMINE: MAY BE IGNITED WHEN MIXED WITH ANHYDROUS COPPER SULFATE. MAGNESIUM: PRODUCES HYDROGEN WHEN MIXED. SODIUM HYPOBROMITE: SOLUTIONS OF SODIUM HYPOBROMITE ARE DECOMPOSED BY POWERFUL CATALYTIC ACTION OF CUPRIC IONS.

DECOMPOSITION: THERMAL DECOMPOSITION MAY RELEASE TOXIC OXIDES OF SULFUR.

POLYMERIZATION: HAZARDOUS POLYMERIZATION HAS NOT BEEN REPORTED TO OCCUR UNDER NORMAL TEMPERATURES AND PRESSURES.

CONDITIONS TO AVOID

MAY BURN BUT DOES NOT IGNITE READILY. FLAMMABLE, POISONOUS GASES MAY ACCUMULATE IN TANKS AND HOPPER CARS. MAY IGNITE COMBUSTIBLES (WOOD, PAPER, OIL, ETC.).

SPILL AND LEAK PROCEDURES

SOIL SPILL: DIG HOLDING AREA SUCH AS LAGOON, POND OR PIT FOR CONTAINMENT. USE PROTECTIVE COVER SUCH AS A PLASTIC SHEET TO PREVENT MATERIAL FROM DISSOLVING IN FIRE EXTINGUISHING WATER OR RAIN.

WATER SPILL: ADD SUITABLE AGENT TO NEUTRALIZE SPILLED MATERIAL TO PH-7. USE MECHANICAL DREDGES OR LIFTS TO EXTRACT IMMOBILIZED MASSES OF POLLUTION AND PRECIPITATES.

OCCUPATIONAL SPILL: DO NOT TOUCH SPILLED MATERIAL. STOP LEAK IF YOU CAN DO IT WITHOUT RISK. FOR SMALL SPILLS, TAKE UP WITH SAND OR OTHER ABSORBENT MATERIAL AND PLACE INTO CONTAINERS FOR LATER DISPOSAL. FOR SMALL DRY SPILLS, WITH CLEAN SHOVEL PLACE MATERIAL INTO CLEAN, DRY CONTAINER AND COVER. MOVE CONTAINERS FROM SPILL AREA. FOR LARGER SPILLS, DIKE FAR AHEAD OF SPILL FOR LATER DISPOSAL. KEEP UNNECESSARY PEOPLE AWAY. ISOLATE HAZARD AREA AND DENY ENTRY.

REPORTABLE QUANTITY (RQ): 10 POUNDS THE SUPERFUND AMENDMENTS AND REAUTHORIZATION ACT (SARA) SECTION 304 REQUIRES THAT A RELEASE EQUAL

TO OR GREATER THAN THE REPORTABLE QUANTITY FOR THIS SUBSTANCE BE IMMEDIATELY REPORTED TO THE LOCAL EMERGENCY PLANNING COMMITTEE AND THE STATE EMERGENCY RESPONSE COMMISSION (40 CFR 355.40). IF THE RELEASE OF THIS SUBSTANCE IS REPORTABLE UNDER CERCLA SECTION 103, THE NATIONAL RESPONSE CENTER MUST BE NOTIFIED IMMEDIATELY AT (800) 424-8802 OR (202) 426-2675 IN THE METROPOLITAN WASHINGTON, D.C. AREA (40 CFR 302.6).

PROTECTIVE EQUIPMENT

VENTILATION: PROVIDE LOCAL EXHAUST OR PROCESS ENCLOSURE VENTILATION TO MEET PUBLISHED EXPOSURE LIMITS.

RESPIRATOR: THE FOLLOWING RESPIRATORS AND MAXIMUM USE CONCENTRATIONS ARE RECOMMENDATIONS BY THE U.S. DEPARTMENT OF HEALTH AND HUMAN SERVICES, NIOSH POCKET GUIDE TO CHEMICAL HAZARDS; NIOSH CRITERIA DOCUMENTS OR BY THE U.S. DEPARTMENT OF LABOR, 29 CFR 1910 SUBPART Z. THE SPECIFIC RESPIRATOR SELECTED MUST BE BASED ON CONTAMINATION LEVELS FOUND IN THE WORK PLACE, MUST NOT EXCEED THE WORKING LIMITS OF THE RESPIRATOR AND BE JOINTLY APPROVED BY THE NATIONAL INSTITUTE FOR OCCUPATIONAL SAFETY AND HEALTH AND THE MINE SAFETY AND HEALTH ADMINISTRATION (NIOSH-MSHA).

COPPER DUST AND MIST (AS CU):

5 MG/M3- ANY DUST AND MIST RESPIRATOR EXCEPT SINGLE-USE RESPIRATORS.

10 MG/M3- ANY DUST AND MIST RESPIRATOR EXCEPT SINGLE-USE AND QUARTER-MASK RESPIRATORS. ANY SUPPLIED-AIR RESPIRATOR. ANY SELF-CONTAINED BREATHING APPARATUS.

25 MG/M3- ANY POWERED AIR-PURIFYING RESPIRATOR WITH A DUST AND MIST FILTER. ANY SUPPLIED-AIR RESPIRATOR OPERATED IN A CONTINUOUS FLOW MODE.

50 MG/M3- ANY AIR-PURIFYING FULL FACEPIECE RESPIRATOR WITH A HIGH-EFFICIENCY PARTICULATE FILTER. ANY SELF-CONTAINED BREATHING APPARATUS WITH A FULL FACEPIECE. ANY SUPPLIED-AIR RESPIRATOR WITH A FULL FACEPIECE. ANY POWERED AIR-PURIFYING RESPIRATOR WITH A TIGHT-FITTING FACEPIECE AND A HIGH-EFFICIENCY PARTICULATE FILTER.

1000 MG/M3- ANY SUPPLIED-AIR RESPIRATOR WITH A HALF-MASK AND OPERATED IN A PRESSURE-DEMAND OR OTHER POSITIVE PRESSURE MODE.

2000 MG/M3- ANY SUPPLIED-AIR RESPIRATOR WITH A FULL FACEPIECE AND OPERATED IN A PRESSURE-DEMAND OR OTHER POSITIVE PRESSURE MODE.

ESCAPE- ANY AIR-PURIFYING FULL FACEPIECE RESPIRATOR WITH A HIGH-EFFICIENCY PARTICULATE FILTER. ANY APPROPRIATE ESCAPE-TYPE SELF-CONTAINED BREATHING APPARATUS.

FOR FIREFIGHTING AND OTHER IMMEDIATELY DANGEROUS TO LIFE OR HEALTH CONDITIONS:

SELF-CONTAINED BREATHING APPARATUS WITH FULL FACEPIECE OPERATED IN PRESSURE-DEMAND OR OTHER POSITIVE PRESSURE MODE.

SUPPLIED-AIR RESPIRATOR WITH FULL FACEPIECE AND OPERATED IN PRESSURE-DEMAND OR OTHER POSITIVE PRESSURE MODE IN COMBINATION WITH AN AUXILIARY SELF-CONTAINED BREATHING APPARATUS OPERATED IN PRESSURE-DEMAND OR OTHER POSITIVE PRESSURE MODE.

CLOTHING: EMPLOYEE MUST WEAR APPROPRIATE PROTECTIVE (IMPERVIOUS) CLOTHING AND EQUIPMENT TO PREVENT REPEATED OR PROLONGED SKIN CONTACT WITH THIS SUBSTANCE.

GLOVES: EMPLOYEE MUST WEAR APPROPRIATE PROTECTIVE GLOVES TO PREVENT CONTACT WITH THIS SUBSTANCE.

EYE PROTECTION: EMPLOYEE MUST WEAR SPLASH-PROOF OR DUST-RESISTANT SAFETY GOGGLES TO PREVENT EYE CONTACT WITH THIS SUBSTANCE.

EMERGENCY EYE WASH: WHERE THERE IS ANY POSSIBILITY THAT AN EMPLOYEE'S EYES MAY BE EXPOSED TO THIS SUBSTANCE, THE EMPLOYER SHOULD PROVIDE AN EYE WASH FOUNTAIN WITHIN THE IMMEDIATE WORK AREA FOR EMERGENCY USE.

AUTHORIZED BY- OCCUPATIONAL HEALTH SERVICES, INC.

CREATION DATE: 10/04/89 ***REVISION DATE:*** 05/18/90

MATERIAL SAFETY DATA SHEET

OCCUPATIONAL HEALTH SERVICES, INC.
AGRICULTURE AND PESTICIDE DIVISION
450 SEVENTH AVENUE, SUITE 2407
NEW YORK, NEW YORK 10123
1-800-445-MSDS OR (212) 967-1100

EMERGENCY CONTACT:
JOHN S. BRANSFORD, JR. (615) 292-1180

SUBSTANCE IDENTIFICATION

CAS-NUMBER 7758-99-8

SUBSTANCE: CUPRIC SULFATE, PENTAHYDRATE

TRADE NAMES/SYNONYMS: COPPER(II) SULFATE, PENTAHYDRATE; TRIANGLE; BLUESTONE; COPPER(II) SULFATE, PENTAHYDRATE (1:1:5); BLUE COPPER AS; COPPER SULPHATE; COPPER(2+) SULFATE, PENTAHYDRATE; COPPERFINE-ZINC; BLUE VITRIOL; ROMAN VITRIOL; STCC 4961316; NA 9109; PST05690

CHEMICAL FAMILY: INORGANIC SALT

MOLECULAR FORMULA: CU-O4-S.5H2O

MOLECULAR WEIGHT: 249.68

CERCLA RATINGS (SCALE 0-3): HEALTH=3 FIRE=0 REACTIVITY=0 PERSISTENCE=3

NFPA RATINGS (SCALE 0-4): HEALTH=3 FIRE=0 REACTIVITY=0

COMPONENTS AND CONTAMINANTS

COMPONENT: CUPRIC SULFATE, PENTAHYDRATE ***PERCENT:*** 100
CAS# 7758-99-8

OTHER CONTAMINANTS: NONE

EXPOSURE LIMITS: COPPER DUST AND MIST (AS CU): 1 MG/M3 OSHA TWA 1 MG/M3 ACGIH TWA

SUBJECT TO SARA SECTION 313 ANNUAL TOXIC CHEMICAL RELEASE REPORTING

PHYSICAL DATA

DESCRIPTION: BLUE CRYSTALS, GRANULES, OR POWDER

BOILING POINT: 302 F (150 C) -H2O ***MELTING POINT:*** 230 F (110 C) -H2O

SPECIFIC GRAVITY: 2.3 ***SOLUBILITY IN WATER:*** 32%

SOLVENT SOLUBILITY: METHANOL; SLIGHTLY SOLUBLE IN ETHANOL, GLYCEROL

FIRE AND EXPLOSION DATA

FIRE AND EXPLOSION HAZARD: NEGLIGIBLE FIRE HAZARD WHEN EXPOSED TO HEAT OR FLAME.

FIREFIGHTING MEDIA: DRY CHEMICAL, CARBON DIOXIDE, HALON, WATER SPRAY OR STANDARD FOAM (1987 EMERGENCY RESPONSE GUIDEBOOK, DOT P 5800.4).
FOR LARGER FIRES, USE WATER SPRAY, FOG OR STANDARD FOAM (1987 EMERGENCY RESPONSE GUIDEBOOK, DOT P 5800.4).

FIREFIGHTING: MOVE CONTAINER FROM FIRE AREA IF POSSIBLE. DO NOT SCATTER SPILLED MATERIAL WITH HIGH PRESSURE WATER STREAMS. DIKE FIRE CONTROL WATER FOR LATER DISPOSAL (1987 EMERGENCY RESPONSE GUIDEBOOK, DOT P 5800.4, GUIDE PAGE 31).
EXTINGUISH USING AGENTS SUITABLE FOR TYPE OF FIRE. AVOID BREATHING VAPORS OR DUSTS.

TRANSPORTATION DATA

DEPARTMENT OF TRANSPORTATION HAZARD CLASSIFICATION 49 CFR 172.101: ORM-E

DEPARTMENT OF TRANSPORTATION LABELING REQUIREMENTS 49 CFR 172.101 AND SUBPART E: NONE

DEPARTMENT OF TRANSPORTATION PACKAGING REQUIREMENTS: 49 CFR 173.510 EXCEPTIONS: NONE

TOXICITY

CUPRIC SULFATE (COPPER SULFATE): TOXICITY DATA: ANHYDROUS: 150 MG/KG ORAL-CHILD TDLO; 11 MG/KG ORAL-HUMAN TDLO; 857 MG/KG ORAL-MAN LDLO; 50 MG/KG ORAL-HUMAN LDLO; 300 MG/KG ORAL-RAT LD50; 43 MG/KG SUBCUTANEOUS-RAT LD50; 520 MG/KG UNREPORTED ROUTE-RAT LD50; 18 MG/KG INTRAPERITONEAL-MOUSE LD50; 500 UG/KG SUBCUTANEOUS-MOUSE LDLO; 50 MG/KG INTRAVENOUS-MOUSE LDLO; 4500 UG/KG INTRAVENOUS-RABBIT LDLO; 2 MG/KG INTRAVENOUS-GUINEA PIG LDLO; MUTAGENIC DATA (RTECS); REPRODUCTIVE EFFECTS DATA (RTECS); TUMORIGENIC DATA (RTECS). MONOHYDRATE: NO DATA AVAILABLE. PENTAHYDRATE: 272 MG/KG ORAL-HUMAN TDLO; 1088 MG/KG ORAL-HUMAN LDLO; 221 MG/KG UNREPORTED ROUTE-MAN LDLO; 300 MG/KG ORAL-RAT LD50; 33 MG/KG INTRAPERITONEAL-MOUSE LD50; 60 MG/KG ORAL-DOG LDLO; 62 MG/KG SUBCUTANEOUS-GUINEA PIG LDLO; MUTAGENIC DATA (RTECS). CARCINOGEN STATUS: NONE. LOCAL EFFECTS: IRRITANT- INHALATION, SKIN, AND EYES. ACUTE TOXICITY LEVEL: TOXIC BY INGESTION. TARGET EFFECTS: POISONING MAY AFFECT THE LIVER, KIDNEYS, AND GASTROINTESTINAL TRACT. AT INCREASED RISK FROM EXPOSURE: PERSONS WITH A HISTORY OF CHRONIC RESPIRATORY OR SKIN DISEASE OR WILSON'S DISEASE.

HEALTH EFFECTS AND FIRST AID

INHALATION: CUPRIC SULFATE (COPPER SULFATE): IRRITANT. **ACUTE EXPOSURE-** INHALATION OF DUSTS AND MIST OF COPPER SALTS MAY CAUSE IRRITATION OF THE UPPER RESPIRATORY TRACT. WORKERS EXPOSED TO COPPER SALTS IN DUST FORM COMPLAINED OF METALLIC TASTE WITH IRRITATION OF NASAL AND ORAL MUCOSA. **CHRONIC EXPOSURE-** REPEATED OR PROLONGED EXPOSURE TO COPPER SALTS MAY PRODUCE SEVERE CONGESTION OF THE NASAL MUCOSA WITH RHINITIS AND POSSIBLE SLOUGHING AND ULCERATION.

FIRST AID- REMOVE FROM EXPOSURE AREA TO FRESH AIR IMMEDIATELY. IF BREATHING HAS STOPPED, PERFORM ARTIFICIAL RESPIRATION. KEEP PERSON WARM AND AT REST. TREAT SYMPTOMATICALLY AND SUPPORTIVELY. GET MEDICAL ATTENTION IMMEDIATELY.

SKIN CONTACT: CUPRIC SULFATE (COPPER SULFATE): IRRITANT. **ACUTE EXPOSURE**- DIRECT CONTACT OF COPPER SALTS WITH THE SKIN MAY GIVE RISE TO AN ITCHING, PAPULOVESICULAR AND ECZEMATOID LESION. **CHRONIC EXPOSURE**- REPEATED OR PROLONGED EXPOSURE TO COPPER SALTS MAY CAUSE SOME DEGREE OF NECROSIS. ALLERGIC CONTACT DERMATITIS, ALTHOUGH RARE, HAS BEEN REPORTED. EFFECTS OF SYSTEMIC POISONING, WHICH HAS FOLLOWED REPEATED APPLICATIONS OF COPPER SULFATE SOLUTION TO EXTENSIVE AREAS OF BURNED SKIN, MAY INCLUDE BLUE DISCOLORATION OF THE GUMS AND TONGUE, HEMOLYTIC ANEMIA, HEMORRHAGIC GASTRITIS, COLIC AND DIARRHEA WITH BLOODY STOOLS. IN SEVERE CASES OF POISONING, LIVER AND KIDNEY DAMAGE WITH SEVERE ANEMIA MAY OCCUR WITH POSSIBLE SOMNOLENCE AND COMA. DEATH MAY OCCUR FROM CIRCULATORY FAILURE. GREENISH DISCOLORATION OF THE SKIN AND HAIR OF SOME COPPER WORKERS HAS BEEN OBSERVED.

FIRST AID- REMOVE CONTAMINATED CLOTHING AND SHOES IMMEDIATELY. WASH AFFECTED AREA WITH SOAP OR MILD DETERGENT AND LARGE AMOUNTS OF WATER UNTIL NO EVIDENCE OF CHEMICAL REMAINS (APPROXIMATELY 15-20 MINUTES). GET MEDICAL ATTENTION IMMEDIATELY.

EYE CONTACT: CUPRIC SULFATE (COPPER SULFATE): IRRITANT. **ACUTE EXPOSURE**- COPPER SALTS SPLASHED IN THE EYES MAY CAUSE CONJUNCTIVITIS, CORNEAL ULCERATION AND TURBIDITY, AND PALPEBRAL EDEMA. COPPER PARTICLES LODGED IN THE EYE MAY RESULT IN PRONOUNCED FOREIGN-BODY REACTION WITH CHARACTERISTIC DISCOLORATION OF OCULAR TISSUE. **CHRONIC EXPOSURE**- REPEATED OR PROLONGED USE OF SOLID COPPER SULFATE FOR TREATMENT OF TRACHOMA PRODUCED INFLAMMATION AND PURULENT REACTION, AND DISCOLORATION OF THE CORNEA. THE DISCOLORATION IN ADVANCED CASES COVERED THE WHOLE CORNEA BUT CAUSED SLIGHT OR NO INTERFERENCE WITH VISION. WHEN A PARTICLE OF COPPER SULFATE WAS LEFT ACCIDENTALLY IN THE CONJUNCTIVAL SAC, IT CAUSED MORE SEVERE LOCAL INFLAMMATION AND NECROSIS, CORNEAL OPACITY, AND SYMBLEPHARON. A VERY LOW CONCENTRATION OF COPPER SULFATE (0.001 M) CAUSED THE PRECORNEAL TEAR FILM TO CURDLE. THERE WAS NO INJURY TO THE CORNEA AND LITTLE DISCOMFORT FELT BY THE HUMAN SUBJECTS EXPOSED TO THIS MATERIAL.

FIRST AID- WASH EYES IMMEDIATELY WITH LARGE AMOUNTS OF WATER OR NORMAL SALINE, OCCASIONALLY LIFTING UPPER AND LOWER LIDS, UNTIL NO EVIDENCE OF CHEMICAL REMAINS (APPROXIMATELY 15-20 MINUTES). GET MEDICAL ATTENTION IMMEDIATELY.

INGESTION: CUPRIC SULFATE (COPPER SULFATE): TOXIC. **ACUTE EXPOSURE**- INGESTION OF A TOXIC DOSE OF COPPER SULFATE MAY CAUSE SALIVATION, NAUSEA, VOMITING, GASTRIC PAIN, AND LOCAL CORROSION AND HEMORRHAGES. OTHER SYMPTOMS OF SYSTEMIC INTOXICATION INCLUDE BLUE DISCOLORATION OF THE GUMS AND TONGUE, HEMOLYTIC ANEMIA, HEMORRHAGIC GASTRITIS, COLIC AND DIARRHEA WITH BLOODY STOOLS. IN SEVERE CASES OF POISONING, LIVER AND KIDNEY DAMAGE WITH SEVERE ANEMIA MAY OCCUR WITH POSSIBLE SOMNOLENCE AND COMA. DEATH MAY OCCUR FROM CIRCULATORY FAILURE. TWO MEN WHO INGESTED 60 AND 80 GRAMS IN SOLUTION DIED IN 6 AND 9 DAYS, RESPECTIVELY. THE MINIMAL LETHAL ORAL DOSE FOR AN ADULT APPEARS TO BE 10 GRAMS. **CHRONIC EXPOSURE**- CHRONIC HUMAN POISONING HAS ONLY BEEN REPORTED IN INDIVIDUALS WITH WILSON'S DISEASE. THIS DISEASE IS A RARE GENETIC CONDITION IN WHICH THERE MAY BE AN ABNORMALLY HIGH ABSORPTION, RETENTION AND STORAGE OF COPPER BY THE BODY. THIS ACCUMULATION HAS BEEN NOTED TO PRECEDE THE DEVELOPMENT OF LIVER PATHOLOGY, WHICH MAY ULTIMATELY PROVE FATAL.

FIRST AID- DILUTE THE POISON IMMEDIATELY WITH LARGE AMOUNTS OF WATER OR MILK AND REMOVE BY GASTRIC LAVAGE UNLESS THE VICTIM IS ALREADY VOMITING. (DREISBACH, HANDBOOK OF POISONING, 12TH ED.) GET MEDICAL ATTENTION IMMEDIATELY. ADMINISTRATION OF GASTRIC LAVAGE SHOULD BE PERFORMED BY QUALIFIED MEDICAL PERSONNEL.

ANTIDOTE: THE FOLLOWING ANTIDOTE HAS BEEN RECOMMENDED. HOWEVER, THE DECISION AS TO WHETHER THE SEVERITY OF POISONING REQUIRES ADMINISTRATION OF ANY ANTIDOTE AND ACTUAL DOSE REQUIRED SHOULD BE MADE BY QUALIFIED MEDICAL PERSONNEL.

COPPER POISONING: GIVE CALCIUM DISODIUM EDETATE 15-25 MG/KG (0.08-0.125 ML OF 20% SOLUTION PER KILOGRAM BODY WEIGHT) IN 250-500 ML OF 5% DEXTROSE INTRAVENOUSLY OVER A 1 TO 2 HOUR PERIOD TWICE DAILY. THE MAXIMUM DOSE SHOULD NOT EXCEED 50 MG/KG/DAY. THE DRUG SHOULD BE GIVEN IN 5-DAY COURSES WITH A REST PERIOD OF AT LEAST 2 DAYS BETWEEN COURSES. AFTER THE FIRST COURSE, SUBSEQUENT COURSES SHOULD NOT EXCEED 50 MG/KG/DAY. DAILY URINALYSES SHOULD NOT BE DONE DURING THE TREATMENT PERIOD. THE DOSAGE SHOULD BE REDUCED IF ANY UNUSUAL URINARY FINDINGS APPEAR. INTRAVENOUS ADMINISTRATION IS CONTRAINDICATED IN THE PRESENCE OF ELEVATED CEREBROSPINAL FLUID PRESSURE. PENICILLAMINE IS ALSO EFFECTIVE IN COPPER POISONING. GIVE UP TO 100 MG/KG/DAY (MAXIMUM 1 G/DAY) DIVIDED INTO 4 DOSES FOR NO LONGER THAN 1 WEEK. IF A LONGER ADMINISTRATION PERIOD IS WARRANTED, DOSAGE SHOULD NOT EXCEED 40 MG/KG/DAY. GIVE THE DRUG ORALLY, HALF AN HOUR BEFORE MEALS (DREISBACH, HANDBOOK OF POISONING, 12TH ED.). ANTIDOTE SHOULD BE ADMINISTERED BY QUALIFIED MEDICAL PERSONNEL.

REACTIVITY

REACTIVITY: STABLE UNDER NORMAL TEMPERATURES AND PRESSURES.

INCOMPATIBILITIES: CUPRIC SULFATE (COPPER SULFATE): HYDROXYLAMINE: MAY BE IGNITED WHEN MIXED WITH ANHYDROUS COPPER SULFATE. MAGNESIUM: PRODUCES HYDROGEN WHEN MIXED. SODIUM HYPOBROMITE: SOLUTIONS OF SODIUM HYPOBROMITE ARE DECOMPOSED BY POWERFUL CATALYTIC ACTION OF CUPRIC IONS.

DECOMPOSITION: THERMAL DECOMPOSITION MAY RELEASE TOXIC OXIDES OF SULFUR.

POLYMERIZATION: HAZARDOUS POLYMERIZATION HAS NOT BEEN REPORTED TO OCCUR UNDER NORMAL TEMPERATURES AND PRESSURES.

CONDITIONS TO AVOID

NONE REPORTED.

SPILL AND LEAK PROCEDURES

SOIL SPILL: DIG HOLDING AREA SUCH AS LAGOON, POND OR PIT FOR CONTAINMENT. USE PROTECTIVE COVER SUCH AS A PLASTIC SHEET TO PREVENT MATERIAL FROM DISSOLVING IN FIRE EXTINGUISHING WATER OR RAIN.

WATER SPILL: ADD SUITABLE AGENT TO NEUTRALIZE SPILLED MATERIAL TO PH-7. USE MECHANICAL DREDGES OR LIFTS TO EXTRACT IMMOBILIZED MASSES OF POLLUTION AND PRECIPITATES.

OCCUPATIONAL SPILL: STOP LEAK IF YOU CAN DO IT WITHOUT RISK. FOR SMALL SPILLS, TAKE UP WITH SAND OR OTHER ABSORBENT MATERIAL AND PLACE INTO CLEAN, DRY CONTAINERS FOR LATER DISPOSAL. KEEP UNNECESSARY PEOPLE AWAY. ISOLATE HAZARD AREA AND DENY ENTRY.

PROTECTIVE EQUIPMENT

VENTILATION: PROVIDE LOCAL EXHAUST OR PROCESS ENCLOSURE VENTILATION TO MEET PUBLISHED EXPOSURE LIMITS.

RESPIRATOR: THE FOLLOWING RESPIRATORS AND MAXIMUM USE CONCENTRATIONS ARE RECOMMENDATIONS BY THE U.S. DEPARTMENT OF HEALTH AND HUMAN SERVICES, NIOSH POCKET GUIDE TO CHEMICAL HAZARDS; NIOSH CRITERIA DOCUMENTS OR BY THE U.S. DEPARTMENT OF LABOR, 29 CFR 1910 SUBPART Z. THE SPECIFIC RESPIRATOR SELECTED MUST BE BASED ON CONTAMINATION LEVELS FOUND IN THE WORK PLACE, MUST NOT EXCEED THE WORKING LIMITS OF THE RESPIRATOR AND BE JOINTLY APPROVED BY THE NATIONAL INSTITUTE FOR OCCUPATIONAL SAFETY AND HEALTH AND THE MINE SAFETY AND HEALTH ADMINISTRATION (NIOSH-MSHA). COPPER DUST AND MIST (AS CU):

5 MG/M3- ANY DUST AND MIST RESPIRATOR EXCEPT SINGLE-USE RESPIRATORS.

10 MG/M3- ANY DUST AND MIST RESPIRATOR EXCEPT SINGLE-USE AND QUARTER-MASK RESPIRATORS. ANY SUPPLIED-AIR RESPIRATOR. ANY SELF-CONTAINED BREATHING APPARATUS.

25 MG/M3- ANY POWERED AIR-PURIFYING RESPIRATOR WITH A DUST AND MIST FILTER. ANY SUPPLIED-AIR RESPIRATOR OPERATED IN A CONTINUOUS FLOW MODE.

50 MG/M3- ANY AIR-PURIFYING FULL FACEPIECE RESPIRATOR WITH A HIGH-EFFICIENCY PARTICULATE FILTER. ANY SELF-CONTAINED BREATHING APPARATUS WITH A FULL FACEPIECE. ANY SUPPLIED-AIR RESPIRATOR WITH A FULL FACEPIECE. ANY POWERED AIR-PURIFYING RESPIRATOR WITH A TIGHT-FITTING FACEPIECE AND A HIGH-EFFICIENCY PARTICULATE FILTER.

1000 MG/M3- ANY SUPPLIED-AIR RESPIRATOR WITH A HALF-MASK AND OPERATED IN A PRESSURE-DEMAND OR OTHER POSITIVE PRESSURE MODE.

2000 MG/M3- ANY SUPPLIED-AIR RESPIRATOR WITH A FULL FACEPIECE AND OPERATED IN A PRESSURE-DEMAND OR OTHER POSITIVE PRESSURE MODE.

ESCAPE- ANY AIR-PURIFYING FULL FACEPIECE RESPIRATOR WITH A HIGH-EFFICIENCY PARTICULATE FILTER. ANY APPROPRIATE ESCAPE-TYPE SELF-CONTAINED BREATHING APPARATUS.

FOR FIREFIGHTING AND OTHER IMMEDIATELY DANGEROUS TO LIFE OR HEALTH CONDITIONS:

SELF-CONTAINED BREATHING APPARATUS WITH FULL FACEPIECE OPERATED IN PRESSURE-DEMAND OR OTHER POSITIVE PRESSURE MODE.

SUPPLIED-AIR RESPIRATOR WITH FULL FACEPIECE AND OPERATED IN PRESSURE-DEMAND OR OTHER POSITIVE PRESSURE MODE IN COMBINATION WITH AN

AUXILIARY SELF-CONTAINED BREATHING APPARATUS OPERATED IN PRESSURE-DEMAND OR OTHER POSITIVE PRESSURE MODE.

CLOTHING: EMPLOYEE MUST WEAR APPROPRIATE PROTECTIVE (IMPERVIOUS) CLOTHING AND EQUIPMENT TO PREVENT REPEATED OR PROLONGED SKIN CONTACT WITH THIS SUBSTANCE.

GLOVES: EMPLOYEE MUST WEAR APPROPRIATE PROTECTIVE GLOVES TO PREVENT CONTACT WITH THIS SUBSTANCE.

EYE PROTECTION: EMPLOYEE MUST WEAR SPLASH-PROOF OR DUST-RESISTANT SAFETY GOGGLES TO PREVENT EYE CONTACT WITH THIS SUBSTANCE. EMERGENCY EYE WASH: WHERE THERE IS ANY POSSIBILITY THAT AN EMPLOYEE'S EYES MAY BE EXPOSED TO THIS SUBSTANCE, THE EMPLOYER SHOULD PROVIDE AN EYE WASH FOUNTAIN WITHIN THE IMMEDIATE WORK AREA FOR EMERGENCY USE.

AUTHORIZED BY- OCCUPATIONAL HEALTH SERVICES, INC.
CREATION DATE: 10/04/89 ***REVISION DATE:*** 05/18/90

MATERIAL SAFETY DATA SHEET

OCCUPATIONAL HEALTH SERVICES, INC.
AGRICULTURE AND PESTICIDE DIVISION
450 SEVENTH AVENUE, SUITE 2407
NEW YORK, NEW YORK 10123
1-800-445-MSDS OR (212) 967-1100

EMERGENCY CONTACT:
JOHN S. BRANSFORD, JR. (615) 292-1180

SUBSTANCE IDENTIFICATION

CAS-NUMBER 13426-91-0

SUBSTANCE: CUPRIETHYLENEDIAMINE

TRADE NAMES/SYNONYMS: BIS(1,2-ETHANEDIAMINE-N,N')COPPER(2+); BIS(ETHYLENEDIAMINE)COPPER(2+) ION; BIS(ETHYLENEDIAMINE)COPPER(2+); BIS(ETHYLENEDIAMINE)COPPER(II); COPPER(2+), BIS(1,2-ETHANEDIAMINE-N,N')-; BIS(ETHYLENEDIAMINE)COPPER ION; COPPER-ETHYLENEDIAMINE COMPLEX; STCC 4935630; UN 1761; PST05710

CHEMICAL FAMILY: ORGANOMETALLIC

MOLECULAR FORMULA: C4-H8-N4.CU

CERCLA RATINGS (SCALE 0-3): HEALTH=U FIRE=U REACTIVITY=U PERSISTENCE=3

NFPA RATINGS (SCALE 0-4): HEALTH=U FIRE=U REACTIVITY=U

COMPONENTS AND CONTAMINANTS

COMPONENT: CUPRIETHYLENEDIAMINE ***PERCENT:*** 100
CAS# 13426-91-0

OTHER CONTAMINANTS: NONE

EXPOSURE LIMITS: COPPER: 0.1 MG/M3 OSHA TWA (FUME); 1 MG/M3 OSHA TWA (DUST AND MIST) 0.2 MG/M3 ACGIH TWA (FUME); 1 MG/M3 ACGIH TWA (DUST AND MIST)

PHYSICAL DATA

DESCRIPTION: PURPLE LIQUID WITH AMMONIACAL ODOR ***BOILING POINT:*** NOT AVAILABLE

SPECIFIC GRAVITY: NOT AVAILABLE ***EVAPORATION RATE:*** NOT AVAILABLE

PH: STRONG BASE ***SOLUBILITY IN WATER:*** SOLUBLE

FIRE AND EXPLOSION DATA

FIRE AND EXPLOSION HAZARD: UNKNOWN FIRE AND EXPLOSION HAZARD.

FIREFIGHTING MEDIA: DRY CHEMICAL, CARBON DIOXIDE, HALON, WATER SPRAY OR STANDARD FOAM (1987 EMERGENCY RESPONSE GUIDEBOOK, DOT P 5800.4). FOR LARGER FIRES, USE WATER SPRAY, FOG OR STANDARD FOAM (1987 EMERGENCY RESPONSE GUIDEBOOK, DOT P 5800.4).

FIREFIGHTING: MOVE CONTAINERS FROM FIRE AREA IF POSSIBLE. COOL CONTAINERS EXPOSED TO FLAMES WITH WATER FROM SIDE UNTIL WELL AFTER FIRE IS OUT. STAY AWAY FROM STORAGE TANK ENDS (1987 EMERGENCY RESPONSE GUIDEBOOK, DOT P 5800.4, GUIDE PAGE 60). EXTINGUISH ONLY IF FLOW CAN BE STOPPED; USE FLOODING AMOUNTS OF WATER AS A FOG, SOLID STREAMS MAY BE INEFFECTIVE. COOL CONTAINERS WITH FLOODING AMOUNTS OF WATER, APPLY FROM AS FAR A DISTANCE AS POSSIBLE. AVOID BREATHING VAPORS, KEEP UPWIND.

TRANSPORTATION DATA

DEPARTMENT OF TRANSPORTATION HAZARD CLASSIFICATION 49 CFR 172.101: CORROSIVE MATERIAL

DEPARTMENT OF TRANSPORTATION LABELING REQUIREMENTS 49 CFR 172.101 AND SUBPART E: CORROSIVE

DEPARTMENT OF TRANSPORTATION PACKAGING REQUIREMENTS: 49 CFR 173.249 EXCEPTIONS: 49 CFR 173.244

TOXICITY

CUPRIETHYLENEDIAMINE: CARCINOGEN STATUS: NONE. LOCAL EFFECTS: CORROSIVE- INHALATION, SKIN, AND EYES. ACUTE TOXICITY LEVEL: NO DATA AVAILABLE. TARGET EFFECTS: COPPER POISONING MAY AFFECT THE KIDNEYS, LIVER, CENTRAL NERVOUS SYSTEM, AND BLOOD.

HEALTH EFFECTS AND FIRST AID

INHALATION: CUPRIETHYLENEDIAMINE: CORROSIVE. **ACUTE EXPOSURE-** VAPOR MAY BE SEVERELY IRRITATING TO MUCOUS MEMBRANES. IT MAY CAUSE DIFFICULT BREATHING AND ASTHMA. COPPER SALTS MAY CAUSE ULCERATION AND PERFORATION OF THE NASAL SEPTUM. **CHRONIC EXPOSURE-** NO DATA AVAILABLE.

FIRST AID- REMOVE FROM EXPOSURE AREA TO FRESH AIR IMMEDIATELY. IF BREATHING HAS STOPPED, PERFORM ARTIFICIAL RESPIRATION. KEEP PERSON WARM AND AT REST. TREAT SYMPTOMATICALLY AND SUPPORTIVELY. GET MEDICAL ATTENTION IMMEDIATELY.

SKIN CONTACT: CUPRIETHYLENEDIAMINE: CORROSIVE. **ACUTE EXPOSURE-** MAY SEVERELY IRRITATE SKIN. HUMAN CONTACT HAS SHOWN THAT ETHYLENEDIAMINES HAVE SENSITIZING PROPERTIES. HOWEVER, SENSITIZATION HAS USUALLY BEEN ASSOCIATED WITH PHARMACEUTICAL PREPARATIONS. SENSITIZATION USUALLY DOES NOT OCCUR AFTER INDUSTRIAL EXPOSURE BECAUSE CONTACT IS NOT PROLONGED AND THE SKIN IS HEALTHY. **CHRONIC EXPOSURE-** SENSITIZATION DERMATITIS MAY OCCUR IN INDIVIDUALS SENSITIZED TO ETHYLENEDIAMINE.

FIRST AID- REMOVE CONTAMINATED CLOTHING AND SHOES IMMEDIATELY. WASH AFFECTED AREA WITH SOAP OR MILD DETERGENT AND LARGE AMOUNTS OF WATER UNTIL NO EVIDENCE OF CHEMICAL REMAINS (APPROXIMATELY 15-20 MINUTES). GET MEDICAL ATTENTION IMMEDIATELY.

EYE CONTACT: CUPRIETHYLENEDIAMINE: CORROSIVE. **ACUTE EXPOSURE-** MAY SEVERELY IRRITATE EYES WITH POSSIBLE CORNEAL DAMAGE. **CHRONIC EXPOSURE-** NO DATA AVAILABLE.

FIRST AID- WASH EYES IMMEDIATELY WITH LARGE AMOUNTS OF WATER, OCCASIONALLY LIFTING UPPER AND LOWER LIDS, UNTIL NO EVIDENCE OF CHEMICAL REMAINS (AT LEAST 15-20 MINUTES). CONTINUE IRRIGATING WITH NORMAL SALINE UNTIL THE PH HAS RETURNED TO NORMAL (30-60 MINUTES). COVER WITH STERILE BANDAGES. GET MEDICAL ATTENTION IMMEDIATELY.

INGESTION: CUPRIETHYLENEDIAMINE: CORROSIVE. **ACUTE EXPOSURE-** MAY SEVERELY IRRITATE TISSUES. COPPER SALTS MAY CAUSE VOMITING; BURNING PAIN IN MOUTH, ESOPHAGUS, AND STOMACH; METALLIC TASTE IN MOUTH; DIARRHEA; ABDOMINAL PAIN; HEADACHE; COLD SWEAT; AND WEAK PULSE. CAPILLARY DAMAGE, KIDNEY AND LIVER INJURY, AND CENTRAL NERVOUS SYSTEM EXCITATION FOLLOWED BY DEPRESSION MAY OCCUR. SYMPTOMS MAY INCLUDE JAUNDICE, HEMOLYSIS, ANURIA AND OTHER SIGNS OF TUBULAR NECROSIS, CONVULSIONS, PARALYSIS, COMA, AND DEATHS DUE TO HEPATIC OR RENAL FAILURE. **CHRONIC EXPOSURE-** NO DATA AVAILABLE.

FIRST AID- TREAT SYMPTOMATICALLY AND SUPPORTIVELY. GET MEDICAL ATTENTION AND ADVICE IMMEDIATELY ON WHETHER TO USE GASTRIC LAVAGE. GASTRIC LAVAGE PERFORMED BY QUALIFIED MEDICAL PERSONNEL MAY BE SUITABLE IF THERE ARE NO SIGNS OF PERFORATION.

ANTIDOTE: NO SPECIFIC ANTIDOTE. TREAT SYMPTOMATICALLY AND SUPPORTIVELY.

REACTIVITY

REACTIVITY: NO DATA AVAILABLE.

INCOMPATIBILITIES: CUPRIETHYLENEDIAMINE: CELLULOSIC MATERIALS: DISSOLVES. COPPER: CORROSIVE. CUPRIETHYLENEDIAMINE: ALUMINUM: CORROSIVE. CELLULOSIC MATERIALS: DISSOLVES. COPPER: CORROSIVE. TIN: CORROSIVE. ZINC: CORROSIVE.

DECOMPOSITION: THERMAL DECOMPOSITION PRODUCTS MAY INCLUDE TOXIC OXIDES OF NITROGEN.

POLYMERIZATION: HAZARDOUS POLYMERIZATION HAS NOT BEEN REPORTED TO OCCUR UNDER NORMAL TEMPERATURES AND PRESSURES.

STORAGE AND DISPOSAL

OBSERVE ALL FEDERAL, STATE AND LOCAL REGULATIONS WHEN STORING OR DISPOSING OF THIS SUBSTANCE. FOR ASSISTANCE, CONTACT THE DISTRICT DIRECTOR OF THE ENVIRONMENTAL PROTECTION AGENCY.

****STORAGE****

STORE AWAY FROM INCOMPATIBLE SUBSTANCES.

****DISPOSAL****

DISPOSAL MUST BE IN ACCORDANCE WITH STANDARDS APPLICABLE TO GENERATORS OF HAZARDOUS WASTE, 40 CFR 262. EPA HAZARDOUS WASTE NUMBER D002. 100 POUND CERCLA SECTION 103 REPORTABLE QUANTITY.

CONDITIONS TO AVOID

MAY BURN BUT DOES NOT IGNITE READILY. FLAMMABLE, POISONOUS GASES MAY ACCUMULATE IN TANKS AND HOPPER CARS. MAY IGNITE COMBUSTIBLES (WOOD, PAPER, OIL, ETC.).

SPILL AND LEAK PROCEDURES

OCCUPATIONAL SPILL: DO NOT TOUCH SPILLED MATERIAL. STOP LEAK IF YOU CAN DO IT WITHOUT RISK. FOR SMALL SPILLS, TAKE UP WITH SAND OR OTHER ABSORBENT MATERIAL AND PLACE INTO CONTAINERS FOR LATER DISPOSAL. FOR SMALL DRY SPILLS, WITH CLEAN SHOVEL PLACE MATERIAL INTO CLEAN, DRY CONTAINER AND COVER. MOVE CONTAINERS FROM SPILL AREA. FOR LARGER SPILLS, DIKE FAR AHEAD OF SPILL FOR LATER DISPOSAL. KEEP UNNECESSARY PEOPLE AWAY. ISOLATE HAZARD AREA AND DENY ENTRY.

PROTECTIVE EQUIPMENT

VENTILATION: PROVIDE LOCAL EXHAUST OR PROCESS ENCLOSURE VENTILATION. VENTILATION EQUIPMENT MUST BE EXPLOSION-PROOF.

RESPIRATOR: THE FOLLOWING RESPIRATORS ARE RECOMMENDED BASED ON INFORMATION FOUND IN THE PHYSICAL DATA, TOXICITY AND HEALTH EFFECTS SECTIONS. THEY ARE RANKED IN ORDER FROM MINIMUM TO MAXIMUM RESPIRATORY PROTECTION. THE SPECIFIC RESPIRATOR SELECTED MUST BE BASED ON CONTAMINATION LEVELS FOUND IN THE WORK PLACE, MUST NOT EXCEED THE WORKING LIMITS OF THE RESPIRATOR AND BE JOINTLY APPROVED BY THE NATIONAL INSTITUTE FOR OCCUPATIONAL SAFETY AND HEALTH AND THE MINE SAFETY AND HEALTH ADMINISTRATION (NIOSH-MSHA).

CHEMICAL CARTRIDGE RESPIRATOR WITH FULL FACEPIECE.

TYPE 'C' SUPPLIED-AIR RESPIRATOR WITH A FULL FACEPIECE OPERATED IN PRESSURE-DEMAND OR OTHER POSITIVE PRESSURE MODE OR WITH A FULL FACEPIECE, HELMET OR HOOD OPERATED IN CONTINUOUS-FLOW MODE.

SELF-CONTAINED BREATHING APPARATUS WITH A FULL FACEPIECE OPERATED IN PRESSURE-DEMAND OR OTHER POSITIVE PRESSURE MODE.

FOR FIREFIGHTING AND OTHER IMMEDIATELY DANGEROUS TO LIFE OR HEALTH CONDITIONS:

SELF-CONTAINED BREATHING APPARATUS WITH FULL FACEPIECE OPERATED IN PRESSURE-DEMAND OR OTHER POSITIVE PRESSURE MODE.

SUPPLIED-AIR RESPIRATOR WITH FULL FACEPIECE AND OPERATED IN PRESSURE-DEMAND OR OTHER POSITIVE PRESSURE MODE IN COMBINATION WITH AN AUXILIARY SELF-CONTAINED BREATHING APPARATUS OPERATED IN PRESSURE-DEMAND OR OTHER POSITIVE PRESSURE MODE.

CLOTHING: EMPLOYEE MUST WEAR APPROPRIATE PROTECTIVE (IMPERVIOUS) CLOTHING AND EQUIPMENT TO PREVENT ANY POSSIBILITY OF SKIN CONTACT WITH THIS SUBSTANCE.

GLOVES: EMPLOYEE MUST WEAR APPROPRIATE PROTECTIVE GLOVES TO PREVENT CONTACT WITH THIS SUBSTANCE.

EYE PROTECTION: EMPLOYEE MUST WEAR SPLASH-PROOF OR DUST-RESISTANT SAFETY GOGGLES AND A FACESHIELD TO PREVENT CONTACT WITH THIS SUBSTANCE.

EMERGENCY WASH FACILITIES: WHERE THERE IS ANY POSSIBILITY THAT AN EMPLOYEE'S EYES AND/OR SKIN MAY BE EXPOSED TO THIS SUBSTANCE, THE EMPLOYER SHOULD PROVIDE AN EYE WASH FOUNTAIN AND QUICK DRENCH SHOWER WITHIN THE IMMEDIATE WORK AREA FOR EMERGENCY USE.

AUTHORIZED BY- OCCUPATIONAL HEALTH SERVICES, INC.

CREATION DATE: 11/16/89 ***REVISION DATE:*** 05/08/90

MATERIAL SAFETY DATA SHEET

OCCUPATIONAL HEALTH SERVICES, INC.
AGRICULTURE AND PESTICIDE DIVISION
450 SEVENTH AVENUE, SUITE 2407
NEW YORK, NEW YORK 10123
1-800-445-MSDS OR (212) 967-1100

EMERGENCY CONTACT:
JOHN S. BRANSFORD, JR. (615) 292-1180

SUBSTANCE IDENTIFICATION

CAS-NUMBER 420-04-2

SUBSTANCE: CYANAMIDE

TRADE NAMES/SYNONYMS: AMIDOCYANOGEN; CARBAMONITRILE; CARBIMIDE; CYANOGEN NITRIDE; CYANOGENAMIDE; HYDROGEN CYANAMIDE; N-CYANOAMINE; CYANOAMINE; 0-2069; CH2N2; PST05760

CHEMICAL FAMILY: CYANAMIDE

MOLECULAR FORMULA: N-H2-C-N

MOLECULAR WEIGHT: 42.04

CERCLA RATINGS (SCALE 0-3): HEALTH=3 FIRE=1 REACTIVITY=3 PERSISTENCE=0

NFPA RATINGS (SCALE 0-4): HEALTH=4 FIRE=1 REACTIVITY=3

COMPONENTS AND CONTAMINANTS

COMPONENT: CYANAMIDE ***PERCENT:*** 95

CAS# 420-04-2

OTHER CONTAMINANTS: <5% BORIC ACID OR SODIUM DYHYDROGEN PHOSPHATE AS STABILIZERS.

EXPOSURE LIMITS: CYANAMIDE: 2 MG/M3 OSHA TWA 2 MG/M3 ACGIH TWA

PHYSICAL DATA

DESCRIPTION: COLORLESS DELIQUESCENT CRYSTALLINE SOLID.

BOILING POINT: 284 F (140 C) @ 19 MMHG

MELTING POINT: 108-115 F (42-46 C) (DECOMPOSES) ***SPECIFIC GRAVITY:*** 1.282

SOLUBILITY IN WATER: 100% @ 43 C ***VAPOR DENSITY:*** 1.45

SOLVENT SOLUBILITY: SOLUBLE IN ALCOHOLS, ETHERS, ACETONE, BENZENE, BUTANOL, CHLOROFORM, METHYL ETHYL KETONE, ETHYL ACETATE, CYCLOHEXANE, PHENOLS, AMINES, KETONES, POLAR ORGANIC SOLVENTS, HALOGENATED HYDROCARBONS.

FIRE AND EXPLOSION DATA

FIRE AND EXPLOSION HAZARD: SLIGHT FIRE HAZARD WHEN EXPOSED TO HEAT OR FLAME.

FLASH POINT: 286 F (141 C) (CC)

FIREFIGHTING MEDIA: DRY CHEMICAL, CARBON DIOXIDE OR HALON (1987 EMERGENCY RESPONSE GUIDEBOOK, DOT P 5800.4).

FOR LARGER FIRES, USE WATER SPRAY, FOG OR STANDARD FOAM (1987 EMERGENCY RESPONSE GUIDEBOOK, DOT P 5800.4).

FIREFIGHTING: MOVE CONTAINER FROM FIRE AREA IF POSSIBLE. DO NOT SCATTER SPILLED MATERIAL WITH HIGH PRESSURE WATER STREAMS. DIKE FIRE CONTROL WATER FOR LATER DISPOSAL (1987 EMERGENCY RESPONSE GUIDEBOOK, DOT P 5800.4, GUIDE PAGE 31).

USE AGENTS SUITABLE FOR TYPE OF SURROUNDING FIRE. AVOID BREATHING HAZARDOUS VAPORS, KEEP UPWIND.

TOXICITY

CYANAMIDE: TOXICITY DATA: 86 MG/M3/4 HOURS INHALATION-RAT LCLO; 590 MG/KG SKIN-RABBIT LD50; 84 MG/KG SKIN-RAT LD50; 125 MG/KG ORAL-RAT LD50; 388 MG/KG ORAL-MOUSE LD50; 150 MG/KG ORAL-RABBIT LD50; 100 MG/KG ORAL-CAT LD50; 56 MG/KG INTRAVENOUS-RAT LD50; 200 MG/KG INTRAPERITONEAL-RAT LDLO; 200 MG/KG INTRAPERITONEAL-MOUSE LD50; 280 MG/KG UNREPORTED-RAT LD50; REPRODUCTIVE EFFECTS DATA (RTECS). CARCINOGEN STATUS: NONE. LOCAL EFFECTS: CORROSIVE- SKIN, EYE; IRRITANT- INHALATION. ACUTE TOXICITY LEVEL: TOXIC BY DERMAL ABSORPTION AND INGESTION. TARGET EFFECTS: NO DATA AVAILABLE. ADDITIONAL DATA: ALCOHOL MAY ENHANCE THE TOXIC EFFECTS.

HEALTH EFFECTS AND FIRST AID

INHALATION: CYANAMIDE: IRRITANT. **ACUTE EXPOSURE**- MAY BE IRRITATING TO MUCOUS MEMBRANES, POSSIBLY SEVERE. SYMPTOMS THAT MAY OCCUR INCLUDE, HEADACHE, VERTIGO, TRANSITORY REDNESS OF FACE, GASPING, INCREASED RESPIRATIONS, TACHYCARDIA, HYPOTENSION AND POSSIBLY PROFOUND SHOCK. POISONING OF HUMAN BEINGS AND RATS CHARACTERISTICALLY INDUCES PARASYMPATHETIC OVERACTIVITY, CAUSING MIOSIS, SALIVATION, LACRIMATION, AND TWITCHING. INHALATION SYMPTOMS SEEM TO BE INTENSIFIED BY INGESTION OF ALCOHOL. **CHRONIC EXPOSURE**- PROLONGED AND REPEATED EXPOSURE MAY PRODUCE SYMPTOMS SIMILAR TO THOSE OF ACUTE EXPOSURE.

FIRST AID- REMOVE FROM EXPOSURE AREA TO FRESH AIR IMMEDIATELY. IF BREATHING HAS STOPPED, PERFORM ARTIFICIAL RESPIRATION. KEEP PERSON WARM AND AT REST. TREAT SYMPTOMATICALLY AND SUPPORTIVELY. GET MEDICAL ATTENTION IMMEDIATELY.

SKIN CONTACT: CYANAMIDE: CORROSIVE/TOXIC. **ACUTE EXPOSURE**- DIRECT CONTACT MAY CAUSE BURNS, SEVERE DERMATITIS AND ULCERATION, ESPECIALLY ON MOIST SKIN. 590 MG/KG IS THE LETHAL DOSE IN RABBITS. A 25% SOLUTION CAUSED SLIGHT IRRITATION TO RABBIT SKIN. **CHRONIC EXPOSURE**- EFFECTS DEPEND ON CONCENTRATION AND DURATION OF EXPOSURE. REPEATED

OR PROLONGED CONTACT WITH CORROSIVE SUBSTANCES MAY RESULT IN DERMATITIS OR EFFECTS SIMILAR TO ACUTE EXPOSURE.

FIRST AID- REMOVE CONTAMINATED CLOTHING AND SHOES IMMEDIATELY. WASH AFFECTED AREA WITH SOAP OR MILD DETERGENT AND LARGE AMOUNTS OF WATER UNTIL NO EVIDENCE OF CHEMICAL REMAINS (AT LEAST 15-20 MINUTES). IN CASE OF CHEMICAL BURNS, COVER AREA WITH STERILE, DRY DRESSING. BANDAGE SECURELY, BUT NOT TOO TIGHTLY. GET MEDICAL ATTENTION IMMEDIATELY.

EYE CONTACT: CYANAMIDE: CORROSIVE. **ACUTE EXPOSURE-** DIRECT CONTACT MAY CAUSE SEVERE IRRITATION, BURNS, POSSIBLY SEVERE, LACRIMATION AND MIOSIS. A 25% SOLUTION CAUSED SLIGHT IRRITATION IN RABBIT EYES. **CHRONIC EXPOSURE-** EFFECTS DEPEND ON CONCENTRATION AND DURATION OF EXPOSURE. REPEATED OR PROLONGED CONTACT WITH CORROSIVE SUBSTANCES MAY RESULT IN CONJUNCTIVITIS OR EFFECTS AS IN ACUTE EXPOSURE.

FIRST AID- WASH EYES IMMEDIATELY WITH LARGE AMOUNTS OF WATER, OCCASIONALLY LIFTING UPPER AND LOWER LIDS, UNTIL NO EVIDENCE OF CHEMICAL REMAINS (AT LEAST 15-20 MINUTES). CONTINUE IRRIGATING WITH NORMAL SALINE UNTIL THE PH HAS RETURNED TO NORMAL (30-60 MINUTES). COVER WITH STERILE BANDAGES. GET MEDICAL ATTENTION IMMEDIATELY.

INGESTION: CYANAMIDE: TOXIC. **ACUTE EXPOSURE-** MAY CAUSE IRRITATION OF THE MUCOUS MEMBRANES, POSSIBLY SEVERE. SYMPTOMS THAT MAY OCCUR INCLUDE HEADACHE, VERTIGO, TRANSITORY REDNESS OF FACE, GASPING, INCREASED RESPIRATIONS, TACHYCARDIA, HYPOTENSION AND POSSIBLY PROFOUND SHOCK. POISONING OF HUMAN BEINGS AND RATS CHARACTERISTICALLY INDUCES PARASYMPATHETIC OVERACTIVITY, CAUSING MIOSIS, SALIVATION, LACRIMATION, AND TWITCHING. AN ATTACK AFTER A SINGLE ORAL DOSE IS USUALLY TRANSIENT, LASTING 1/2 TO 2 HOURS. A FATAL DOSE IN MAN IS ESTIMATED AT 40 TO 50 GRAMS. SYMPTOMS ARE INTENSIFIED BY CONCOMITANT INGESTION OF ALCOHOL. 125 MG/KG WAS LETHAL TO RATS. **CHRONIC EXPOSURE-** NO DATA AVAILABLE.

FIRST AID- IF EXTENSIVE VOMITING HAS NOT OCCURRED, THE SUBSTANCE SHOULD BE REMOVED BY EMESIS OR GASTRIC LAVAGE PROVIDED THAT THE PATIENT IS CONSCIOUS AND CONVULSIONS ARE NOT PRESENT. KEEP HEAD BELOW HIPS DURING VOMITING TO PREVENT ASPIRATION. DO NOT ATTEMPT TO MAKE AN UNCONSCIOUS PERSON VOMIT. TREAT SYMPTOMATICALLY AND SUPPORTIVELY. GET MEDICAL ATTENTION IMMEDIATELY (DREISBACH, HANDBOOK OF POISONING, 12TH ED.). TREATMENT SHOULD BE PERFORMED BY QUALIFIED MEDICAL PERSONNEL.

ANTIDOTE: NO SPECIFIC ANTIDOTE. TREAT SYMPTOMATICALLY AND SUPPORTIVELY.

REACTIVITY

REACTIVITY: THERMAL DECOMPOSITION IS RAPID AND MAY BECOME VIOLENT AT TEMPERATURES ABOVE 40 C. CONTACT WITH MOISTURE, ACIDS OR ALKALIES ACCELERATES THE RATE OF DECOMPOSITION.

INCOMPATIBILITIES: CYANAMIDE: ACIDS: VIOLENT DECOMPOSITION. ALKALIES: VIOLENT DECOMPOSITION. 1,2-PHENYLENEDIAMINE SALTS: EXPLOSIVE POLYMERIZATION ABOVE 90 C.

DECOMPOSITION: THERMAL DECOMPOSITION MAY RELEASE TOXIC AND/OR HAZARDOUS GASES, INCLUDING TOXIC MAGNESIUM OXIDE AND TOXIC OXIDES OF CARBON. MAY RELEASE CORROSIVE FUMES OF HYDROGEN CHLORIDE AND TOXIC OXIDES OF SULFUR.

POLYMERIZATION: EXPLOSIVE POLYMERIZATION MAY OCCUR IN CONCENTRATED AQUEOUS SOLUTIONS OR UPON STORAGE AT AMBIENT TEMPERATURES.

STORAGE AND DISPOSAL

OBSERVE ALL FEDERAL, STATE AND LOCAL REGULATIONS WHEN STORING OR DISPOSING OF THIS SUBSTANCE. FOR ASSISTANCE, CONTACT THE DISTRICT DIRECTOR OF THE ENVIRONMENTAL PROTECTION AGENCY.

****STORAGE****

STORE AWAY FROM INCOMPATIBLE SUBSTANCES.

STORE IN A COOL, DRY PLACE; KEEP CONTAINER TIGHTLY CLOSED WHEN NOT IN USE.

CONDITIONS TO AVOID

MAY BURN BUT DOES NOT IGNITE READILY. AVOID CONTACT WITH STRONG OXIDIZERS, EXCESSIVE HEAT, SPARKS, OR OPEN FLAME.

SPILL AND LEAK PROCEDURES

OCCUPATIONAL SPILL: SWEEP UP AND PLACE IN SUITABLE CLEAN, DRY CONTAINERS FOR RECLAMATION OR LATER DISPOSAL. DO NOT FLUSH SPILLED MATERIAL INTO SEWER. KEEP UNNECESSARY PEOPLE AWAY.

PROTECTIVE EQUIPMENT

VENTILATION: PROCESS ENCLOSURE RECOMMENDED TO MEET PUBLISHED EXPOSURE LIMITS.

RESPIRATOR: THE FOLLOWING RESPIRATORS ARE RECOMMENDED BASED ON INFORMATION FOUND IN THE PHYSICAL DATA, TOXICITY AND HEALTH EFFECTS SECTIONS. THEY ARE RANKED IN ORDER FROM MINIMUM TO MAXIMUM RESPIRATORY PROTECTION. THE SPECIFIC RESPIRATOR SELECTED MUST BE BASED ON CONTAMINATION LEVELS FOUND IN THE WORK PLACE, MUST NOT EXCEED THE WORKING LIMITS OF THE RESPIRATOR AND BE JOINTLY APPROVED BY THE NATIONAL INSTITUTE FOR OCCUPATIONAL SAFETY AND HEALTH AND THE MINE SAFETY AND HEALTH ADMINISTRATION (NIOSH-MSHA).

DUST AND MIST RESPIRATOR WITH A FULL FACEPIECE.

AIR-PURIFYING FULL FACEPIECE RESPIRATOR WITH A HIGH-EFFICIENCY PARTICULATE FILTER.

POWERED AIR-PURIFYING RESPIRATOR WITH A TIGHT-FITTING FACEPIECE AND HIGH-EFFICIENCY PARTICULATE FILTER.

TYPE 'C' SUPPLIED-AIR RESPIRATOR WITH A FULL FACEPIECE OPERATED IN PRESSURE-DEMAND OR OTHER POSITIVE PRESSURE MODE OR WITH A FULL FACEPIECE, HELMET OR HOOD OPERATED IN CONTINUOUS-FLOW MODE.

SELF-CONTAINED BREATHING APPARATUS WITH A FULL FACEPIECE OPERATED IN PRESSURE-DEMAND OR OTHER POSITIVE PRESSURE MODE.

FOR FIREFIGHTING AND OTHER IMMEDIATELY DANGEROUS TO LIFE OR HEALTH CONDITIONS:

SELF-CONTAINED BREATHING APPARATUS WITH FULL FACEPIECE OPERATED IN PRESSURE-DEMAND OR OTHER POSITIVE PRESSURE MODE.

SUPPLIED-AIR RESPIRATOR WITH FULL FACEPIECE AND OPERATED IN PRESSURE-DEMAND OR OTHER POSITIVE PRESSURE MODE IN COMBINATION WITH AN AUXILIARY SELF-CONTAINED BREATHING APPARATUS OPERATED IN PRESSURE-DEMAND OR OTHER POSITIVE PRESSURE MODE.

CLOTHING: EMPLOYEE MUST WEAR APPROPRIATE PROTECTIVE (IMPERVIOUS) CLOTHING AND EQUIPMENT TO PREVENT ANY POSSIBILITY OF SKIN CONTACT WITH THIS SUBSTANCE.

GLOVES: EMPLOYEE MUST WEAR APPROPRIATE PROTECTIVE GLOVES TO PREVENT CONTACT WITH THIS SUBSTANCE.

EYE PROTECTION: EMPLOYEE MUST WEAR SPLASH-PROOF OR DUST-RESISTANT SAFETY GOGGLES AND A FACESHIELD TO PREVENT CONTACT WITH THIS SUBSTANCE.

EMERGENCY WASH FACILITIES: WHERE THERE IS ANY POSSIBILITY THAT AN EMPLOYEE'S EYES AND/OR SKIN MAY BE EXPOSED TO THIS SUBSTANCE, THE EMPLOYER SHOULD PROVIDE AN EYE WASH FOUNTAIN AND QUICK DRENCH SHOWER WITHIN THE IMMEDIATE WORK AREA FOR EMERGENCY USE.

AUTHORIZED BY- OCCUPATIONAL HEALTH SERVICES, INC.

CREATION DATE: 10/04/89 ***REVISION DATE:*** 05/31/90

MATERIAL SAFETY DATA SHEET

OCCUPATIONAL HEALTH SERVICES, INC.
AGRICULTURE AND PESTICIDE DIVISION
450 SEVENTH AVENUE, SUITE 2407
NEW YORK, NEW YORK 10123
1-800-445-MSDS OR (212) 967-1100

EMERGENCY CONTACT:
JOHN S. BRANSFORD, JR. (615) 292-1180

SUBSTANCE IDENTIFICATION

CAS-NUMBER 21725-46-2

SUBSTANCE: CYANAZINE

TRADE NAMES/SYNONYMS: PROPANENITRILE, 2-((4-CHLORO-6-(ETHYLAMINO)-1,3,5-TRIAZIN-2-YL) AMINO)-2-METHYL-; PROPIONITRILE, 2-((4-CHLORO-6-(ETHYLAMINO)-S-TRIAZIN-2-YL) AMINO)-2-METHYL- 2-((4-CHLORO-6-(ETHYLAMINO)-1,3,5-TRIAZIN-2-YL)AMINO)-2-METHYLPROPANENITRILE; 2-((4-CHLORO-6-(ETHYLAMINO)-S-TRIAZIN-2-YL))AMINO)-2- METHYLPROPIONITRILE; 2-CHLORO-4-(1-CYANO-1-METHYLETHYLAMINO)-6-ETHYLAMINO-1,3,5-TRIAZINE; 2-((4-CHLORO-6-(ETHYLAMINO)-S-TRIAZIN-2-YL)AMINO-2-METHYLPROPIONITRILE; BLADEX; DW3418; FORTROL; SD 15418; WL 19805; C9H13CLN6; PST05762

CHEMICAL FAMILY: S-TRIAZINE

MOLECULAR FORMULA: C9-H13-CL-N6

MOLECULAR WEIGHT: 240.68

CERCLA RATINGS (SCALE 0-3): HEALTH=3 FIRE=1 REACTIVITY=0 PERSISTENCE=3

NFPA RATINGS (SCALE 0-4): HEALTH=3 FIRE=1 REACTIVITY=0

COMPONENTS AND CONTAMINANTS

COMPONENT: CYANAZINE ***PERCENT:*** 100
CAS# 21725-46-2

OTHER CONTAMINANTS: NONE.

EXPOSURE LIMITS: NO OCCUPATIONAL EXPOSURE LIMITS ESTABLISHED BY OSHA, ACGIH, OR NIOSH.
CYANAZINE: SUBJECT TO CALIFORNIA PROPOSTION 65 CANCER AND/OR REPRODUCTIVE TOXICITY WARNING AND RELEASE REQUIREMENTS-(APRIL 1,1990)

PHYSICAL DATA

DESCRIPTION: WHITE CRYSTALLINE SOLID. ***MELTING POINT:*** 334-336 F (168-169 C)

SPECIFIC GRAVITY: NOT AVAILABLE ***VAPOR PRESSURE:*** NEGLIGIBLE

SOLUBILITY IN WATER: 0.0171%

SOLVENT SOLUBILITY: SOLUBLE IN ACETONE, CHLOROFORM; SLIGHTLY SOLUBLE IN HEXANE, CARBON TETRACHLORIDE, BENZENE AND ETHANOL.

FIRE AND EXPLOSION DATA

FIRE AND EXPLOSION HAZARD: SLIGHT FIRE HAZARD WHEN EXPOSED TO HEAT OR FLAME.

FIREFIGHTING MEDIA: DRY CHEMICAL, CARBON DIOXIDE, HALON, WATER SPRAY OR STANDARD FOAM (1987 EMERGENCY RESPONSE GUIDEBOOK, DOT P 5800.4).
FOR LARGER FIRES, USE WATER SPRAY, FOG OR STANDARD FOAM (1987 EMERGENCY RESPONSE GUIDEBOOK, DOT P 5800.4).

FIREFIGHTING: MOVE CONTAINERS FROM FIRE AREA IF POSSIBLE (1987 EMERGENCY RESPONSE GUIDEBOOK, DOT P 5800.4, GUIDE PAGE 53).
EXTINGUISH USING AGENTS SUITABLE FOR SURROUNDING FIRE. USE FLOODING QUANTITIES OF WATER AS A FOG. KEEP MATERIAL OUT OF SEWERS AND WATER SOURCES. DO NOT TOUCH SPILLED MATERIAL. AVOID BREATHING HAZARDOUS FUMES; KEEP UPWIND.

TOXICITY

CYANAZINE: TOXICITY DATA: 2470 MG/M3/4 HOURS INHALATION-MOUSE LC50; 1200 MG/KG SKIN-RAT LD50; 149 MG/KG ORAL-RAT LD50; 380 MG/KG ORAL-MOUSE LD50; 141 MG/KG ORAL-RABBIT LD50; 1738 MG/KG SUBCUTANEOUS-RAT LD50; 3715 MG/KG SUBCUTANEOUS-MOUSE LD50; 112 MG/KG INTRAPERITONEAL-RAT LD50; 174 MG/KG INTRAPERITONEAL-MOUSE LD50; MUTAGENIC DATA (RTECS); REPRODUCTIVE EFFECTS DATA (RTECS). CARCINOGEN STATUS: NONE.
ACUTE TOXICITY LEVEL: TOXIC BY INHALATION AND INGESTION, AND MODERATELY TOXIC BY DERMAL ABSORPTION. TARGET EFFECTS: NO DATA AVAILABLE.

HEALTH EFFECTS AND FIRST AID

INHALATION: CYANAZINE: TOXIC. **ACUTE EXPOSURE-** A LETHAL CONCENTRATION IN MICE WAS 2470 MG/M3/4 HOURS; SYMPTOMS WERE NOT REPORTED. SOME TRIAZINES ARE IRRITATING TO THE UPPER RESPIRATORY TRACT. **CHRONIC EXPOSURE-** NO DATA AVAILABLE.

FIRST AID- REMOVE FROM EXPOSURE AREA TO FRESH AIR IMMEDIATELY. IF BREATHING HAS STOPPED, PERFORM ARTIFICIAL RESPIRATION. KEEP PERSON WARM AND AT REST. TREAT SYMPTOMATICALLY AND SUPPORTIVELY. GET MEDICAL ATTENTION IMMEDIATELY.

SKIN CONTACT: CYANAZINE: **ACUTE EXPOSURE-** A LETHAL DOSE IN RATS BY DERMAL ABSORPTION WAS 1200 MG/KG. A 5% SOLUTION OF CYANAZINE IN DIMETHYLSULFOXIDE WAS NOT IRRITATING TO RABBIT SKIN. **CHRONIC EXPOSURE-** FETAL STRUCTURAL ANOMALIES WERE OBSERVED IN A STUDY OF PREGNANT RABBITS RECEIVING REPEATED DERMAL APPLICATIONS OF CYANAZINE AT DOSES THAT PRODUCED MATERNAL TOXICITY.

FIRST AID- REMOVE CONTAMINATED CLOTHING AND SHOES IMMEDIATELY. WASH AFFECTED AREA WITH SOAP OR MILD DETERGENT AND LARGE AMOUNTS OF WATER UNTIL NO EVIDENCE OF CHEMICAL REMAINS (APPROXIMATELY 15-20 MINUTES). GET MEDICAL ATTENTION IMMEDIATELY.

EYE CONTACT: CYANAZINE: **ACUTE EXPOSURE-** A 5% SOLUTION OF CYANAZINE IN DIMETHYL SULFOXIDE WAS NOT IRRITATING TO RABBIT EYES. **CHRONIC EXPOSURE-** NO DATA AVAILABLE.

FIRST AID- WASH EYES IMMEDIATELY WITH LARGE AMOUNTS OF WATER OR NORMAL SALINE, OCCASIONALLY LIFTING UPPER AND LOWER LIDS, UNTIL NO EVIDENCE OF CHEMICAL REMAINS (APPROXIMATELY 15-20 MINUTES). GET MEDICAL ATTENTION IMMEDIATELY.

INGESTION: CYANAZINE: TOXIC. **ACUTE EXPOSURE-** A LETHAL DOSE IN RATS WAS 149 MG/KG. SYMPTOMS OF POISONING IN RATS INCLUDED LETHARGY, LABORED BREATHING, AND BLOOD-STAINED SALIVA. **CHRONIC EXPOSURE-** FETAL DEVELOPMENTAL EFFECTS OF DILATED BRAIN VENTRICLES, ANOPHTHALMIA/MICROOPHTHALMIA, AND DIAPHRAGMATIC HERNIA WERE OBSERVED IN STUDIES OF PREGNANT RATS AND RABBITS FED CYANAZINE.

FIRST AID- REMOVE BY GASTRIC LAVAGE AND CATHARSIS. MAINTAIN BLOOD PRESSURE AND AIRWAY. GIVE OXYGEN IF RESPIRATION IS DEPRESSED. DO NOT PERFORM GASTRIC LAVAGE IF VICTIM IS UNCONSCIOUS. GET MEDICAL ATTENTION IMMEDIATELY (DREISBACH, HANDBOOK OF POISONING, 12TH ED.).
ADMINISTRATION OF LAVAGE OR OXYGEN SHOULD BE PERFORMED BY QUALIFIED MEDICAL PERSONNEL.

ANTIDOTE: NO SPECIFIC ANTIDOTE. TREAT SYMPTOMATICALLY AND SUPPORTIVELY.

REACTIVITY

REACTIVITY: STABLE UNDER NORMAL TEMPERATURES AND PRESSURES.

INCOMPATIBILITIES: CYANAZINE: METALS: INCOMPATIBLE.

DECOMPOSITION: THERMAL DECOMPOSITION PRODUCTS MAY INCLUDE HIGHLY TOXIC HYDROGEN CYANIDE, TOXIC OXIDES OF NITROGEN AND CARBON, AND TOXIC AND CORROSIVE FUMES OF CHLORIDES.

POLYMERIZATION: HAZARDOUS POLYMERIZATION HAS NOT BEEN REPORTED TO OCCUR UNDER NORMAL TEMPERATURES AND PRESSURES.

STORAGE AND DISPOSAL

OBSERVE ALL FEDERAL, STATE AND LOCAL REGULATIONS WHEN STORING OR DISPOSING OF THIS SUBSTANCE. FOR ASSISTANCE, CONTACT THE DISTRICT DIRECTOR OF THE ENVIRONMENTAL PROTECTION AGENCY.

STORAGE

STORE IN ACCORDANCE WITH 40 CFR 165 RECOMMENDED PROCEDURES FOR THE DISPOSAL AND STORAGE OF PESTICIDES AND PESTICIDE CONTAINERS.
STORE AWAY FROM INCOMPATIBLE SUBSTANCES.

DISPOSAL

DISPOSAL MUST BE IN ACCORDANCE WITH 40 CFR 165 RECOMMENDED PROCEDURES FOR THE DISPOSAL AND STORAGE OF PESTICIDES AND PESTICIDE CONTAINERS.

CONDITIONS TO AVOID

MAY BURN BUT DOES NOT IGNITE READILY.

SPILL AND LEAK PROCEDURES

WATER SPILL: THE CALIFORNIA SAFE DRINKING WATER AND TOXIC ENFORCEMENT ACT OF 1986 (PROPOSITION 65) PROHIBITS CONTAMINATING ANY KNOWN SOURCE OF DRINKING WATER WITH SUBSTANCES KNOWN TO CAUSE CANCER AND/OR REPRODUCTIVE TOXICITY.

OCCUPATIONAL SPILL: DO NOT TOUCH SPILLED MATERIAL. STOP LEAK IF YOU CAN DO IT WITHOUT RISK. FOR SMALL SPILLS, TAKE UP WITH SAND OR OTHER ABSORBENT MATERIAL AND PLACE INTO CONTAINERS FOR LATER DISPOSAL. FOR SMALL DRY SPILLS, WITH A CLEAN SHOVEL PLACE MATERIAL INTO CLEAN, DRY CONTAINER AND COVER. MOVE CONTAINERS FROM SPILL AREA. FOR LARGER SPILLS, DIKE FAR AHEAD OF SPILL FOR LATER DISPOSAL. KEEP UNNECESSARY PEOPLE AWAY. ISOLATE HAZARD AREA AND DENY ENTRY.

PROTECTIVE EQUIPMENT

VENTILATION: PROVIDE LOCAL EXHAUST OR GENERAL DILUTION VENTILATION SYSTEM.

RESPIRATOR: THE FOLLOWING RESPIRATORS ARE RECOMMENDED BASED ON INFORMATION FOUND IN THE PHYSICAL DATA, TOXICITY AND HEALTH EFFECTS SECTIONS. THEY ARE RANKED IN ORDER FROM MINIMUM TO MAXIMUM RESPIRATORY PROTECTION. THE SPECIFIC RESPIRATOR SELECTED MUST BE BASED ON CONTAMINATION LEVELS FOUND IN THE WORK PLACE, MUST NOT EXCEED THE WORKING LIMITS OF THE RESPIRATOR AND BE JOINTLY APPROVED BY THE NATIONAL INSTITUTE FOR OCCUPATIONAL SAFETY AND HEALTH AND THE MINE SAFETY AND HEALTH ADMINISTRATION (NIOSH-MSHA).
TYPE 'C' SUPPLIED-AIR RESPIRATOR WITH A FULL FACEPIECE OPERATED IN PRESSURE-DEMAND OR OTHER POSITIVE PRESSURE MODE OR WITH A FULL FACEPIECE, HELMET OR HOOD OPERATED IN CONTINOUS-FLOW MODE.
SELF-CONTAINED BREATHING APPARATUS WITH A FULL FACEPIECE OPERATED IN PRESSURE-DEMAND OR OTHER POSITIVE PRESSURE MODE.
FOR FIREFIGHTING AND OTHER IMMEDIATELY DANGEROUS TO LIFE OR HEALTH CONDITIONS:
SELF-CONTAINED BREATHING APPARATUS WITH FULL FACEPIECE OPERATED IN PRESSURE-DEMAND OR OTHER POSITIVE PRESSURE MODE.
SUPPLIED-AIR RESPIRATOR WITH FULL FACEPIECE AND OPERATED IN PRESSURE-DEMAND OR OTHER POSITIVE PRESSURE MODE IN COMBINATION WITH AN AUXILIARY SELF-CONTAINED BREATHING APPARATUS OPERATED IN PRESSURE-DEMAND OR OTHER POSITIVE PRESSURE MODE.

CLOTHING: EMPLOYEE MUST WEAR APPROPRIATE PROTECTIVE (IMPERVIOUS) CLOTHING AND EQUIPMENT TO PREVENT REPEATED OR PROLONGED SKIN CONTACT WITH THIS SUBSTANCE.

GLOVES: EMPLOYEE MUST WEAR APPROPRIATE PROTECTIVE GLOVES TO PREVENT CONTACT WITH THIS SUBSTANCE.

EYE PROTECTION: EMPLOYEE MUST WEAR SPLASH-PROOF OR DUST-RESISTANT SAFETY GOGGLES TO PREVENT EYE CONTACT WITH THIS SUBSTANCE. EMERGENCY EYE WASH: WHERE THERE IS ANY POSSIBILITY THAT AN EMPLOYEE'S EYES MAY BE EXPOSED TO THIS SUBSTANCE, THE EMPLOYER SHOULD PROVIDE AN EYE WASH FOUNTAIN WITHIN THE IMMEDIATE WORK AREA FOR EMERGENCY USE.

AUTHORIZED BY- OCCUPATIONAL HEALTH SERVICES, INC.
CREATION DATE: 10/04/89 ***REVISION DATE:*** 07/11/90

MATERIAL SAFETY DATA SHEET

OCCUPATIONAL HEALTH SERVICES, INC.
AGRICULTURE AND PESTICIDE DIVISION
450 SEVENTH AVENUE, SUITE 2407
NEW YORK, NEW YORK 10123
1-800-445-MSDS OR (212) 967-1100

EMERGENCY CONTACT:
JOHN S. BRANSFORD, JR. (615) 292-1180

SUBSTANCE IDENTIFICATION

CAS-NUMBER 13067-93-1

SUBSTANCE: CYANOFENPHOS

TRADE NAMES/SYNONYMS: PHOSPHONOTHIOIC ACID, PHENYL-, O-(4-CYANOPHENYL) O-ETHYL ESTER; PHOSPHONOTHIOIC ACID, PHENYL-, O-ETHYL ESTER, O-ESTER WITH P-HYDROXYBENZONITRILE; PHENYLPHOSPHONOTHIOIC ACID O-(4-CYANOPHENYL) O-ETHYL ESTER; PHENYLPHOSPHONOTHIOIC ACID O-ETHYL ESTER O-ESTER WITH P-HYDROXYBENZONITRILE; 4-CYANOPHENYLETHYLPHENYL PHOSPHONOTHIONATE; O-4-CYANOPHENYL O-ETHYL PHENYLPHOSPHONOTHIOATE; O-ETHYL O-(4-CYANOPHENYL) PHENYLPHOSPHONOTHIOATE; P-CYANOPHENYL ETHYL PHENYLPHOSPHONOTHIONATE; B 10094; CP 19699; CYANOPHENPHOS; CYP; MONSANTO CP-19699; S 4087; SURAZON; SURECIDE; OMS 870; ENT 25,832; PST05805

CHEMICAL FAMILY: ORGANOPHOSPHATE
NITRILE, AROMATIC

MOLECULAR FORMULA: C15-H14-N-O2-P-S

MOLECULAR WEIGHT: 303.32

CERCLA RATINGS (SCALE 0-3): HEALTH=3 FIRE=0 REACTIVITY=U PERSISTENCE=1

NFPA RATINGS (SCALE 0-4): HEALTH=3 FIRE=0 REACTIVITY=U

COMPONENTS AND CONTAMINANTS

COMPONENT: CYANOFENPHOS ***PERCENT:*** 100
CAS# 13067-93-1

OTHER CONTAMINANTS: NONE

EXPOSURE LIMITS: NO OCCUPATIONAL EXPOSURE LIMITS ESTABLISHED BY OSHA, ACGIH, OR NIOSH.

PHYSICAL DATA

DESCRIPTION: WHITE CRYSTALLINE POWDER ***MELTING POINT:*** 181 F (83 C)

VAPOR PRESSURE: 0.0000132 MMHG ***SOLUBILITY IN WATER:*** 6 PPM @ 25 C

SOLVENT SOLUBILITY: MODERATELY SOLUBLE IN KETONES, AROMATIC SOLVENTS

FIRE AND EXPLOSION DATA

FIRE AND EXPLOSION HAZARD: NEGLIGIBLE FIRE HAZARD WHEN EXPOSED TO HEAT OR FLAME.

FIREFIGHTING MEDIA: DRY CHEMICAL, CARBON DIOXIDE, HALON, WATER SPRAY OR STANDARD FOAM (1987 EMERGENCY RESPONSE GUIDEBOOK, DOT P 5800.4). FOR LARGER FIRES, USE WATER SPRAY, FOG OR STANDARD FOAM (1987 EMERGENCY RESPONSE GUIDEBOOK, DOT P 5800.4).

FIREFIGHTING: MOVE CONTAINERS FROM FIRE AREA IF POSSIBLE. FIGHT FIRE FROM MAXIMUM DISTANCE. STAY AWAY FROM STORAGE TANK ENDS. DIKE FIRE CONTROL WATER FOR LATER DISPOSAL. DO NOT SCATTER MATERIAL (1987 EMERGENCY RESPONSE GUIDEBOOK, DOT P 5800.4, GUIDE PAGE 55). EXTINGUISH USING AGENT SUITABLE FOR TYPE OF SURROUNDING FIRE. AVOID BREATHING VAPORS AND DUSTS. KEEP UPWIND.

TOXICITY

CYANOFENPHOS: TOXICITY DATA: 28,500 UG/KG ORAL-RAT LD50; 43,700 UG/KG ORAL-MOUSE LD50; 50 MG/KG ORAL-GUINEA PIG LDLO; 100 MG/KG SUBCUTANEOUS-GUINEA PIG LDLO; 122 MG/KG SUBCUTANEOUS-MOUSE LD50; 45 MG/KG INTRAPERITONEAL-MOUSE LD50. CARCINOGEN STATUS: NONE. ACUTE TOXICITY LEVEL: HIGHLY TOXIC BY INGESTION. TARGET EFFECTS: CHOLINESTERASE INHIBITOR. POISONING MAY AFFECT THE NERVOUS SYSTEM.* AT INCREASED RISK FROM EXPOSURE: PERSONS WITH RESPIRATORY AILMENTS, RECENT EXPOSURE TO CHOLINESTERASE INHIBITORS OR IMPAIRED CHOLINESTERASE PRODUCTION, OR LIVER MALFUNCTION.* ADDITIONAL DATA: MAY CROSS THE PLACENTA. HIGH ENVIRONMENTAL TEMPERATURES OR EXPOSURE OF THE CHEMICAL TO VISIBLE OR ULTRAVIOLET LIGHT MAY ENHANCE THE TOXICITY. INTERACTIONS WITH MEDICATIONS MAY OCCUR.*
* MAY BE BASED ON GENERAL INFORMATION ON ORGANOPHOSPHATES.

HEALTH EFFECTS AND FIRST AID

INHALATION: CYANOFENPHOS: SEE INFORMATION ON ORGANOPHOSPHATES. ORGANOPHOSPHATES: CHOLINESTERASE INHIBITOR. **ACUTE EXPOSURE-** WHEN INHALED, THE FIRST EFFECTS OF CHOLINESTERASE INHIBITORS ARE USUALLY RESPIRATORY AND MAY INCLUDE NASAL HYPEREMIA AND WATERY DISCHARGE, COUGH, CHEST DISCOMFORT, DYSPNEA, AND WHEEZING DUE TO INCREASED BRONCHIAL SECRETIONS AND BRONCHOCONSTRICTION. IF SUFFICIENT AMOUNTS ARE ABSORBED, OTHER SYSTEMIC EFFECTS MAY BEGIN WITHIN A FEW MINUTES OR BE DELAYED FOR UP TO 12 HOURS. SYMPTOMS MAY INCLUDE PALLOR, NAUSEA, VOMITING, DIARRHEA, ABDOMINAL CRAMPS, HEADACHE, DIZZINESS, OCULAR PAIN, BLURRED VISION, MIOSIS OR IN SOME CASES, ESPECIALLY INITIALLY, MYDRIASIS, LACRIMATION, SALIVATION, SWEATING, AND CONFUSION. OTHER REPORTED CENTRAL NERVOUS SYSTEM OR NEUROMUSCULAR EFFECTS MAY INCLUDE ATAXIA, SLURRED SPEECH, AREFLEXIA, WEAKNESS, FATIGUE, FASCICULATIONS, TWITCHING, TREMORS POSSIBLY OF THE TONGUE AND EYELIDS, AND EVENTUALLY PARALYSIS OF THE EXTREMITIES AND POSSIBLY OF THE RESPIRATORY MUSCLES. IN SEVERE CASES THERE MAY ALSO BE INVOLUNTARY DEFECATION AND URINATION, CYANOSIS, PSYCHOSIS, HYPERGLYCEMIA, ACUTE PANCREATITIS, CARDIAC IRREGULARITIES, PULMONARY EDEMA, UNCONSCIOUSNESS, CONVULSIONS, AND COMA. DEATH IS PRIMARILY DUE TO RESPIRATORY FAILURE, ALTHOUGH CARDIOVASCULAR EFFECTS INCLUDING CARDIAC ARREST MAY ALSO BE IMPLICATED. LONG TERM SEQUELAE ARE RARE BUT MAY INCLUDE NEUROPSYCHIATRIC DISORDERS AND MYOPATHY WITH MUSCLE TENDERNESS. SOME ORGANOPHOSPHATES MAY CAUSE A DELAYED NEUROPATHY BEGINNING 1-4 WEEKS AFTER AN ACUTE EXPOSURE WHICH MAY OR MAY NOT HAVE CAUSED ACUTE CHOLINERGIC EFFECTS. NUMBNESS, TINGLING, WEAKNESS AND CRAMPING BEGINNING SYMMETRICALLY IN THE LOWER LIMBS MAY PROGRESS TO ATAXIA AND PARALYSIS. IN SEVERE CASES, UPPER LIMB INVOLVEMENT IS POSSIBLE AND FLACCID PARALYSIS MAY PROGRESS TO SPASTIC PARALYSIS WITH EXAGGERATED REFLEXES. IMPROVEMENT MAY OCCUR OVER MONTHS TO YEARS, BUT SOME RESIDUAL IMPAIRMENT USUALLY REMAINS. **CHRONIC EXPOSURE-** REPEATED OR PROLONGED EXPOSURE MAY RESULT IN THE EFFECTS OF ACUTE EXPOSURE INCLUDING THE DELAYED NEUROPATHY. OTHER EFFECTS REPORTED IN WORKERS REPEATEDLY EXPOSED INCLUDE IMPAIRED MEMORY AND CONCENTRATION, ACUTE PSYCHOSIS, SEVERE DEPRESSIONS, IRRITABILTY, CONFUSION, APATHY, EMOTIONAL LABILITY, SOCIAL WITHDRAWAL, CONFUSION, HEADACHE, SPEECH DIFFICULTIES, DELAYED REACTION TIMES, SPATIAL DISORIENTATION, NIGHTMARES, SLEEPWALKING, AND DROWSINESS OR INSOMNIA. AN INFLUENZA-LIKE CONDITION WITH HEADACHE, NAUSEA, WEAKNESS, ANOREXIA AND MALAISE HAS ALSO BEEN REPORTED.

FIRST AID- REMOVE FROM EXPOSURE AREA TO FRESH AIR IMMEDIATELY. IF BREATHING HAS STOPPED, GIVE ARTIFICIAL RESPIRATION. MAINTAIN AIRWAY AND BLOOD PRESSURE AND ADMINISTER OXYGEN IF AVAILABLE. KEEP AFFECTED PERSON WARM AND AT REST. TREAT SYMPTOMATICALLY AND SUPPORTIVELY. ADMINISTRATION OF OXYGEN SHOULD BE PERFORMED BY QUALIFIED PERSONNEL. GET MEDICAL ATTENTION IMMEDIATELY.

SKIN CONTACT: CYANOFENPHOS: SEE INFORMATION ON ORGANOPHOSPHATES. ORGANOPHOSPHATES: CHOLINESTERASE INHIBITOR. **ACUTE EXPOSURE-** LOCALIZED SWEATING AND FASCICULATIONS MAY OCCUR AT THE SITE OF CONTACT. IF SUFFICIENT AMOUNTS ARE ABSORBED, OTHER EFFECTS OF CHOLINESTERASE INHIBITION AS DESCRIBED IN ACUTE INHALATION MAY OCCUR. SYMPTOMS MAY BE DELAYED 2-3 HOURS, BUT USUALLY NO MORE THAN 12 HOURS. THE RATE OF ABSORPTION IS INCREASED BY THE PRESENCE OF DERMATITIS OR HIGH AMBIENT TEMPERATURES. DELAYED NEUROPATHY IS ALSO POSSIBLE. **CHRONIC EXPOSURE-** REPEATED OR PROLONGED EXPOSURE MAY CAUSE EFFECTS AS DESCRIBED IN ACUTE EXPOSURE. SOME ORGANOPHOSPHATES MAY CAUSE SENSITIZATION.

FIRST AID- REMOVE CONTAMINATED CLOTHING IMMEDIATELY. WASH CONTAMINATED AREAS WITH SOAP AND WATER FOLLOWED BY ALCOHOL (ARENA, POISONING, 4TH ED.). EMERGENCY PERSONNEL SHOULD WEAR GLOVES AND AVOID CONTAMINATION. TREAT RESPIRATORY DIFFICULTY WITH ARTIFICIAL RESPIRATION. GET MEDICAL ATTENTION IMMEDIATELY.

EYE CONTACT: CYANOFENPHOS: SEE INFORMATION ON ORGANOPHOSPHATES. ORGANOPHOSPHATES: CHOLINESTERASE INHIBITOR. **ACUTE EXPOSURE-** DIRECT CONTACT MAY CAUSE PAIN, HYPEREMIA, LACRIMATION, TWITCHING OF THE

EYELIDS, MIOSIS, AND CILIARY MUSCLE SPASM WITH LOSS OF ACCOMODATION, BLURRED OR DIMMED VISION AND BROWACHE. SOMETIMES MYDRIASIS MAY OCCUR INSTEAD OF MIOSIS. WITH SUFFICIENT EXPOSURE, OTHER SYMPTOMS OF CHOLINESTERASE INHIBITION AS DESCRIBED IN ACUTE INHALATION MAY OCCUR. **CHRONIC EXPOSURE-** REPEATED OR PROLONGED EXPOSURE MAY CAUSE EFFECTS AS DESCRIBED IN ACUTE EXPOSURE. SOME COMPOUNDS HAVE CAUSED TOXIC EFFECTS ON THE CRYSTALLINE LENS, CONJUNCTIVAL THICKENING AND OBSTRUCTION OF THE NASOLACRIMAL CANALS WHEN USED AS MIOTIC EYEDROPS.

FIRST AID- IRRIGATE EYES WITH WATER OR SALINE SOLUTION. IF SYMPTOMS OF POISONING OCCUR, TREAT RESPIRATORY DIFFICULTY WITH ARTIFICIAL RESPIRATION AND OXYGEN. OBSERVE PATIENT FOR AT LEAST 24-36 HOURS (GOSSELIN, CLINICAL TOXICOLOGY OF COMMERCIAL PRODUCTS, 5TH ED.). GET MEDICAL ATTENTION IMMEDIATELY. OXYGEN SHOULD BE ADMINISTERED BY QUALIFIED MEDICAL PERSONNEL.

INGESTION: CYANOFENPHOS: HIGHLY TOXIC. REPRODUCTIVE EFFECTS WERE OBSERVED IN BOTH PARENTAL ANIMALS AND PROGENY AT 30 PPM. SEE INFORMATION ON ORGANOPHOSPHATES.

ORGANOPHOSPHATES: CHOLINESTERASE INHIBITOR. **ACUTE EXPOSURE-** WHEN INGESTED, THE FIRST EFFECTS MAY BE NAUSEA, VOMITING, ANOREXIA, ABDOMINAL CRAMPS AND DIARRHEA. GASTROINTESTINAL ABSORPTION MAY CAUSE SYMPTOMS OF CHOLINESTERASE INHIBITION AS DESCRIBED IN ACUTE INHALATION. SYMPTOMS MAY BEGIN WITHIN MINUTES OR BE DELAYED FOR HOURS. DELAYED EFFECTS INCLUDING NEUROPATHY MAY ALSO OCCUR. **CHRONIC EXPOSURE-** REPEATED INGESTION MAY CAUSE EFFECTS AS DESCRIBED IN ACUTE EXPOSURE.

FIRST AID- IF PERSON IS ALERT AND RESPIRATION IS NOT DEPRESSED, GIVE SYRUP OF IPECAC FOLLOWED BY WATER (IF VOMITING OCCURS, KEEP HEAD BELOW HIPS TO PREVENT ASPIRATION). IF CONSCIOUSNESS LEVEL DECLINES OR VOMITING HAS NOT OCCURRED IN 15 MINUTES EMPTY STOMACH BY GASTRIC LAVAGE WITH THE AID OF CUFFED ENDOTRACHEAL TUBE USING ISOTONIC SALINE OR 5% SODIUM BICARBONATE FOLLOW WITH ACTIVATED CHARCOAL. ESTABLISH AND MAINTAIN AIRWAY. TREAT RESPIRATORY DIFFICULTY WITH ARTIFICIAL RESPIRATION AND OXYGEN. DO NOT GIVE MORPHINE, AMINOPHYLLINE, PHENOTHIAZINES, RESERPINE, FUROSEMIDE, OR ETHACRYNIC ACID (MORGAN, RECOGNITION AND MANAGEMENT OF PESTICIDE POISONINGS, 3RD ED.). TREAT SYMPTOMATICALLY AND SUPPORTIVELY. ADMINISTRATION OF OXYGEN AND LAVAGE MUST BE PERFORMED BY QUALIFIED MEDICAL PERSONNEL. GET MEDICAL ATTENTION IMMEDIATELY.

ANTIDOTE: THE FOLLOWING ANTIDOTE(S) HAVE BEEN RECOMMENDED. HOWEVER, THE DECISION AS TO WHETHER THE SEVERITY OF POISONING REQUIRES ADMINISTRATION OF ANY ANTIDOTE AND ACTUAL DOSE REQUIRED SHOULD BE MADE BY QUALIFIED MEDICAL PERSONNEL.

FOR CHOLINESTERASE INHIBITORS: ESTABLISH CLEAR AIRWAY AND TISSUE OXYGENATION BY ASPIRATION OF SECRETIONS, AND IF NECESSARY, BY ASSISTED PULMONARY VENTILATION WITH OXYGEN. IMPROVE TISSUE OXYGENATION AS MUCH AS POSSIBLE BEFORE ADMINISTERING ATROPINE TO MINIMIZE THE RISK OF VENTRICULAR FIBRILLATION. ADMINISTER ATROPINE SULFATE INTRAVENOUSLY, OR INTRAMUSCULARLY IF IV INJECTION IS NOT POSSIBLE. IN MODERATELY SEVERE POISONING ADMINISTER ATROPINE SULFATE, 0.4-2.0 MG REPEATED EVERY 15 MINUTES UNTIL ATROPINIZATION IS ACHIEVED (TACHYCARDIA, FLUSHING, DRY MOUTH, MYDRIASIS). MAINTAIN ATROPINIZATION BY REPEATED DOSES FOR 2-12 HOURS, OR LONGER, DEPENDING ON THE SEVERITY OF POISONING. THE APPEARANCE OF RALES IN THE LUNG BASES, MIOSIS, SALIVATION, NAUSEA, BRADYCARDIA, ARE ALL INDICATIONS OF INADEQUATE ATROPINIZATION.

SEVERELY POISONED INDIVIDUALS MAY EXHIBIT REMARKABLE TOLERANCE TO ATROPINE; TWO OR MORE TIMES THE DOSAGES SUGGESTED ABOVE MAY BE NEEDED. PERSONS NOT POISONED OR ONLY SLIGHTLY POISONED, HOWEVER, MAY DEVELOP SIGNS OF ATROPINE TOXICITY FROM SUCH LARGE DOSAGES: FEVER, MUSCLE FIBRILLATIONS, AND DELIRIUM ARE THE MAIN SIGNS OF ATROPINE TOXICITY. IF THESE SIGNS APPEAR WHILE THE PATIENT IS FULLY ATROPINIZED, ATROPINE ADMINISTRATION SHOULD BE DISCONTINUED, AT LEAST TEMPORARILY.

OBSERVE TREATED PATIENTS CLOSELY AT LEAST 24 HOURS TO INSURE THAT SYMPTOMS (POSSIBLY PULMONARY EDEMA) DO NOT RECUR AS ATROPINIZATION WEARS OFF. IN VERY SEVERE POISONINGS, METABOLIC DISPOSITION OF TOXICANT MAY REQUIRE SEVERAL HOURS OR DAYS DURING WHICH ATROPINIZATION MUST BE MAINTAINED. MARKEDLY LOWER LEVELS OF URINARY METABOLITES INDICATE THAT ATROPINE DOSAGE CAN BE TAPERED OFF. AS DOSAGE IS REDUCED, CHECK THE LUNG BASES FREQUENTLY FOR RALES. IF RALES ARE HEARD OR OTHER SYMPTOMS RETURN, RE-ESTABLISH ATROPINIZATION PROMPTLY (MORGAN, RECOGNITION AND MANAGEMENT OF PESTICIDE POISONINGS, 3RD ED.). ADMINISTRATION OF ANTIDOTE MUST BE PERFORMED BY QUALIFIED MEDICAL PERSONNEL.

IN CASES OF SEVERE POISONING BY ORGANOPHOSPHATE PESTICIDES IN WHICH RESPIRATORY DEPRESSION, MUSCLE WEAKNESS AND TWITCHINGS ARE SEVERE, GIVE PRALIDOXIME (PROTOPAM-AYERST, 2-PAM), 1.0 GRAM INTRAVENOUSLY AT NO MORE THAN 0.5 GRAM PER MINUTE. DOSAGE OF PRALIDOXIME MAY BE REPEATED IN 1-2 HOURS, THEN AT 10-12 HOUR INTERVALS IF NEEDED. IN VERY SEVERE POISONINGS, DOSAGE RATES MAY BE DOUBLED. TREATMENT WITH PRALIDOXIME WILL BE MOST EFFECTIVE IF GIVEN WITHIN THIRTY-SIX HOURS AFTER POISONING (MORGAN, RECOGNITION AND MANAGEMENT OF PESTICIDE POISONINGS, 3RD ED.). ANTIDOTE SHOULD BE ADMINISTERED BY QUALIFIED MEDICAL PERSONNEL.

REACTIVITY

REACTIVITY: NO SPECIFIC DATA AVAILABLE. HOWEVER, A NUMBER OF PHOSPHATE AND THIOPHOSPHATE ESTERS ARE OF LIMITED THERMAL STABILITY AND UNDERGO HIGHLY EXOTHERMIC SELF-ACCELERATING DECOMPOSITION REACTIONS.

INCOMPATIBILITIES: CYANOFENPHOS: NO DATA AVAILABLE.

DECOMPOSITION: THERMAL DECOMPOSITION MAY RELEASE TOXIC AND/OR HAZARDOUS GASES.

POLYMERIZATION: HAZARDOUS POLYMERIZATION HAS NOT BEEN REPORTED TO OCCUR UNDER NORMAL TEMPERATURES AND PRESSURES.

STORAGE AND DISPOSAL

OBSERVE ALL FEDERAL, STATE AND LOCAL REGULATIONS WHEN STORING OR DISPOSING OF THIS SUBSTANCE. FOR ASSISTANCE, CONTACT THE DISTRICT DIRECTOR OF THE ENVIRONMENTAL PROTECTION AGENCY.

****STORAGE****

STORE IN ACCORDANCE WITH 40 CFR 165 RECOMMENDED PROCEDURES FOR THE DISPOSAL AND STORAGE OF PESTICIDES AND PESTICIDE CONTAINERS.

****DISPOSAL****

DISPOSAL MUST BE IN ACCORDANCE WITH 40 CFR 165 RECOMMENDED PROCEDURES FOR THE DISPOSAL AND STORAGE OF PESTICIDES AND PESTICIDE CONTAINERS.

CONDITIONS TO AVOID

NONE REPORTED.

SPILL AND LEAK PROCEDURES

OCCUPATIONAL SPILL: DO NOT TOUCH SPILLED MATERIAL. STOP LEAK IF YOU CAN DO IT WITHOUT RISK. USE WATER SPRAY TO REDUCE VAPORS. FOR SMALL SPILLS, TAKE UP WITH SAND OR OTHER ABSORBENT MATERIAL AND PLACE INTO CONTAINERS FOR LATER DISPOSAL. FOR SMALL DRY SPILLS, WITH A CLEAN SHOVEL PLACE MATERIAL INTO CLEAN, DRY CONTAINERS AND COVER. MOVE CONTAINERS FROM SPILL AREA. FOR LARGER SPILLS, DIKE FAR AHEAD OF SPILL FOR LATER DISPOSAL. KEEP UNNECESSARY PEOPLE AWAY. ISOLATE HAZARD AREA AND DENY ENTRY. VENTILATE CLOSED SPACES BEFORE ENTERING.

PROTECTIVE EQUIPMENT

VENTILATION: PROVIDE LOCAL EXHAUST OR PROCESS ENCLOSURE VENTILATION SYSTEM.

RESPIRATOR: THE FOLLOWING RESPIRATORS ARE RECOMMENDED BASED ON INFORMATION FOUND IN THE PHYSICAL DATA, TOXICITY AND HEALTH EFFECTS SECTIONS. THEY ARE RANKED IN ORDER FROM MINIMUM TO MAXIMUM RESPIRATORY PROTECTION. THE SPECIFIC RESPIRATOR SELECTED MUST BE BASED ON CONTAMINATION LEVELS FOUND IN THE WORK PLACE, MUST NOT EXCEED THE WORKING LIMITS OF THE RESPIRATOR AND BE JOINTLY APPROVED BY THE NATIONAL INSTITUTE FOR OCCUPATIONAL SAFETY AND HEALTH AND THE MINE SAFETY AND HEALTH ADMINISTRATION (NIOSH-MSHA).

CHEMICAL CARTRIDGE RESPIRATOR WITH AN ORGANIC VAPOR CARTRIDGE(S) IN COMBINATION WITH A DUST AND MIST FILTER.

GAS MASK WITH ORGANIC VAPOR CANISTER (CHIN-STYLE OR FRONT- OR BACK-MOUNTED CANISTER) WITH A DUST AND MIST FILTER.

GAS MASK WITH ORGANIC VAPOR CANISTER (CHIN-STYLE OR FRONT- OR BACK-MOUNTED CANISTER) WITH A PARTICULATE FILTER.

POWERED AIR-PURIFYING RESPIRATOR WITH A HIGH-EFFICIENCY FILTER.

TYPE 'C' SUPPLIED-AIR RESPIRATOR WITH A FULL FACEPIECE OPERATED IN A PRESSURE-DEMAND OR OTHER POSITIVE PRESSURE MODE.

SELF-CONTAINED BREATHING APPARATUS WITH A FULL FACEPIECE OPERATED IN PRESSURE-DEMAND OR OTHER POSITIVE PRESSURE MODE.

FOR FIREFIGHTING AND OTHER IMMEDIATELY DANGEROUS TO LIFE OR HEALTH CONDITIONS:

SELF-CONTAINED BREATHING APPARATUS WITH FULL FACEPIECE OPERATED IN PRESSURE-DEMAND OR OTHER POSITIVE PRESSURE MODE.

SUPPLIED-AIR RESPIRATOR WITH FULL FACEPIECE AND OPERATED IN PRESSURE-DEMAND OR OTHER POSITIVE PRESSURE MODE IN COMBINATION WITH AN AUXILIARY SELF-CONTAINED BREATHING APPARATUS OPERATED IN PRESSURE-DEMAND OR OTHER POSITIVE PRESSURE MODE.

CLOTHING: EMPLOYEE MUST WEAR APPROPRIATE PROTECTIVE (IMPERVIOUS) CLOTHING AND EQUIPMENT TO PREVENT REPEATED OR PROLONGED SKIN CONTACT WITH THIS SUBSTANCE.
GLOVES: EMPLOYEE MUST WEAR APPROPRIATE PROTECTIVE GLOVES TO PREVENT CONTACT WITH THIS SUBSTANCE.
EYE PROTECTION: EMPLOYEE MUST WEAR SPLASH-PROOF OR DUST-RESISTANT SAFETY GOGGLES TO PREVENT EYE CONTACT WITH THIS SUBSTANCE.
EMERGENCY EYE WASH: WHERE THERE IS ANY POSSIBILITY THAT AN EMPLOYEE'S EYES MAY BE EXPOSED TO THIS SUBSTANCE, THE EMPLOYER SHOULD PROVIDE AN EYE WASH FOUNTAIN WITHIN THE IMMEDIATE WORK AREA FOR EMERGENCY USE.

AUTHORIZED BY- OCCUPATIONAL HEALTH SERVICES, INC.
CREATION DATE: 10/04/89 ***REVISION DATE:*** 05/07/90

MATERIAL SAFETY DATA SHEET

OCCUPATIONAL HEALTH SERVICES, INC.
AGRICULTURE AND PESTICIDE DIVISION
450 SEVENTH AVENUE, SUITE 2407
NEW YORK, NEW YORK 10123
1-800-445-MSDS OR (212) 967-1100

EMERGENCY CONTACT:
JOHN S. BRANSFORD, JR. (615) 292-1180

SUBSTANCE IDENTIFICATION

CAS-NUMBER 108-94-1
SUBSTANCE: CYCLOHEXANONE
TRADE NAMES/SYNONYMS: ANON; ANONE; HEXANON; HYTROL O; NADONE; PIMELIC KETONE; PIMELIN KETONE; SEXTONE; KETOHEXAMETHYLENE; RCRA U057; STCC 4913179; UN 1915; C-550; O-2109; C6H10O; PST05890
CHEMICAL FAMILY: KETONE, ALICYCLIC
MOLECULAR FORMULA: C6-H10-O
MOLECULAR WEIGHT: 98.2
CERCLA RATINGS (SCALE 0-3): HEALTH=3 FIRE=2 REACTIVITY=0 PERSISTENCE=1
NFPA RATINGS (SCALE 0-4): HEALTH=1 FIRE=2 REACTIVITY=0

COMPONENTS AND CONTAMINANTS

COMPONENT: CYCLOHEXANONE ***PERCENT:*** 100
CAS# 108-94-1
OTHER CONTAMINANTS: NONE
EXPOSURE LIMITS: CYCLOHEXANONE: 25 PPM (100 MG/M3) OSHA TWA (SKIN) 25 PPM (100 MG/M3) ACGIH TWA (SKIN) 25 PPM (100 MG/M3) NIOSH RECOMMENDED TWA
5000 POUNDS CERCLA SECTION 103 REPORTABLE QUANTITY

PHYSICAL DATA

DESCRIPTION: CLEAR, COLORLESS TO PALE YELLOW OILY LIQUID WITH A CHARACTERISTIC, PLEASANT ODOR OF PEPPERMINT AND ACETONE.
BOILING POINT: 313 F (156 C) ***MELTING POINT:*** -53 F (-47 C)
SPECIFIC GRAVITY: 0.948 ***VISCOSITY:*** 2.133 CENTIPOISE @ 70 F
VAPOR PRESSURE: 10 MMHG @ 38.7 C ***EVAPORATION RATE:*** (BUTYL ACETATE = 1) 0.23
SOLUBILITY IN WATER: 15% ***ODOR THRESHOLD:*** 0.12-0.24 PPM
VAPOR DENSITY: 3.4
SOLVENT SOLUBILITY: SOLUBLE IN ACETONE, BENZENE, ETHANOL, ETHER, CHLOROFORM, MOST ORGANIC SOLVENTS

FIRE AND EXPLOSION DATA

FIRE AND EXPLOSION HAZARD: MODERATE FIRE HAZARD WHEN EXPOSED TO HEAT OR FLAME.
SLIGHT EXPLOSION HAZARD WHEN EXPOSED TO HEAT OR FLAME.
VAPORS ARE HEAVIER THAN AIR AND MAY TRAVEL A CONSIDERABLE DISTANCE TO A SOURCE OF IGNITION AND FLASH BACK.
VAPOR-AIR MIXTURES ARE EXPLOSIVE ABOVE FLASH POINT.
FLASH POINT: 111 F (44 C) (CC) ***UPPER EXPLOSIVE LIMIT:*** 9.4%
LOWER EXPLOSIVE LIMIT: 1.1% @ 212 F (100 C) ***AUTOIGNITION TEMP.:*** 788 F (420 C)
FLAMMABILITY CLASS(OSHA): II
FIREFIGHTING MEDIA: DRY CHEMICAL, CARBON DIOXIDE, HALON, WATER SPRAY OR ALCOHOL FOAM (1987 EMERGENCY RESPONSE GUIDEBOOK, DOT P 5800.4).
FOR LARGER FIRES, USE WATER SPRAY, FOG OR ALCOHOL FOAM (1987 EMERGENCY RESPONSE GUIDEBOOK, DOT P 5800.4).
ALCOHOL FOAM (NFPA 325M, FIRE HAZARD PROPERTIES OF FLAMMABLE LIQUIDS, GASES, AND VOLATILE SOLIDS, 1984).
FIREFIGHTING: MOVE CONTAINER FROM FIRE AREA IF POSSIBLE. COOL FIRE-EXPOSED CONTAINERS WITH WATER FROM SIDE UNTIL WELL AFTER FIRE IS OUT. STAY AWAY FROM STORAGE TANK ENDS. FOR MASSIVE FIRE IN STORAGE AREA, USE UNMANNED HOSE HOLDER OR MONITOR NOZZLES, ELSE WITHDRAW FROM AREA AND LET FIRE BURN. WITHDRAW IMMEDIATELY IN CASE OF RISING SOUND FROM VENTING SAFETY DEVICE OR ANY DISCOLORATION OF STORAGE TANK DUE TO FIRE (1987 EMERGENCY RESPONSE GUIDEBOOK, DOT P 5800.4, GUIDE PAGE 26). EXTINGUISH ONLY IF FLOW CAN BE STOPPED; USE FLOODING AMOUNTS OF WATER AS A FOG, SOLID STREAMS MAY BE INEFFECTIVE. COOL CONTAINERS WITH FLOODING AMOUNTS OF WATER, APPLY FROM AS FAR A DISTANCE AS POSSIBLE. AVOID BREATHING VAPORS, KEEP UPWIND.

TRANSPORTATION DATA

DEPARTMENT OF TRANSPORTATION HAZARD CLASSIFICATION 49 CFR 172.101: COMBUSTIBLE LIQUID
DEPARTMENT OF TRANSPORTATION LABELING REQUIREMENTS 49 CFR 172.101 AND SUBPART E: NONE DEPARTMENT OF TRANSPORTATION PACKAGING REQUIREMENTS: NONE EXCEPTIONS: 49 CFR 173.118A

TOXICITY

CYCLOHEXANONE: IRRITATION DATA: 500 MG OPEN SKIN-RABBIT MILD; 75 PPM EYE-HUMAN; 4740 UG EYE-RABBIT SEVERE; 250 UG/24 HOURS EYE-RABBIT SEVERE. TOXICITY DATA: 75 PPM INHALATION-HUMAN TCLO; 8000 PPM/4 HOURS INHALATION-RAT LC50; 19,200 MG/M3/90 MINUTES INHALATION-MOUSE LCLO; 400 PPM/4 HOURS INHALATION-GUINEA PIG TCLO; 948 MG/KG SKIN-RABBIT LD50; 1535 MG/KG ORAL-RAT LD50; 1400 MG/KG ORAL-MOUSE LD50; 1600 MG/KG ORAL-RABBIT LDLO; 2170 MG/KG SUBCUTANEOUS-RAT LD50; 1300 MG/KG SUBCUTANEOUS-MOUSE LDLO; 630 MG/KG INTRAVENOUS-DOG LDLO; 1130 MG/KG INTRAPERITONEAL-RAT LD50; 1230 MG/KG INTRAPERITONEAL-MOUSE LD50; 1540 MG/KG INTRAPERITONEAL-RABBIT LD50; 760 MG/KG INTRAPERITONEAL-GUINEA PIG LDLO; MUTAGENIC DATA (RTECS); REPRODUCTIVE EFFECTS DATA (RTECS). CARCINOGEN STATUS: NONE. LOCAL EFFECTS: IRRITANT- INHALATION, SKIN, EYE. ACUTE TOXICITY LEVEL: TOXIC BY DERMAL ABSORPTION; MODERATELY TOXIC BY INHALATION AND INGESTION. TARGET EFFECTS: CENTRAL NERVOUS SYSTEM DEPRESSANT. POISONING MAY AFFECT THE LIVER AND KIDNEYS. AT INCREASED RISK FROM EXPOSURE: PERSONS WITH A HISTORY OF CHRONIC RESPIRATORY OR SKIN DISEASE. ADDITIONAL DATA: ALCOHOLIC BEVERAGES MAY ENHANCE THE TOXIC EFFECTS.

HEALTH EFFECTS AND FIRST AID

INHALATION: CYCLOHEXANONE: IRRITANT/NARCOTIC. 5000 PPM IMMEDIATELY DANGEROUS TO LIFE OR HEALTH. **ACUTE EXPOSURE-** EXPOSURE TO 25 PPM OF THE VAPOR FOR 5 MINUTES WAS REPORTED TO PRODUCE NO EFFECTS IN HUMANS. EXPOSURE TO 50-75 PPM FOR 5 MINUTES PRODUCED IRRITATION OF THE MUCOUS MEMBRANES. HUMAN SYSTEMIC EFFECTS MAY INCLUDE CHANGES IN THE SENSE OF SMELL, CONJUNCTIVAL IRRITATION, RESPIRATORY SYSTEM CHANGES, AND MILD NARCOSIS. INHALATION OF HIGH CONCENTRATIONS MAY CAUSE CENTRAL NERVOUS SYSTEM DEPRESSION WITH HEADACHE, DIZZINESS, DULLNESS, LETHARGY, AND UNCONSCIOUSNESS. EXPOSURE TO 4000 PPM FOR 6 HOURS PRODUCED SALIVATION, TEARING, CORNEAL CLOUDING, WEAKNESS, INCOORDINATION, NAUSEA, DECREASED BODY TEMPERATURE AND HEART AND RESPIRATION RATES, AND NARCOSIS IN GUINEA PIGS, AND COMA AND DEATH IN RATS. **CHRONIC EXPOSURE-** ANIMAL STUDIES SHOW THAT PROLONGED EXPOSURE RESULTED IN WEIGHT LOSS, INCOORDINATION, DISTENDED EAR VEINS, EXCESS SALIVATION, NARCOSIS, LETHARGY, HYPOTHERMIA, LYMPHOCYTOSIS FOLLOWED BY LYMPHOPENIA, DECREASED LUNG VENTILATION AND OXYGEN CONSUMPTION, AND HEART, LIVER, AND KIDNEY DAMAGE. REPRODUCTIVE EFFECTS HAVE BEEN REPORTED IN ANIMALS.
FIRST AID- REMOVE FROM EXPOSURE AREA TO FRESH AIR IMMEDIATELY. IF BREATHING HAS STOPPED, PERFORM ARTIFICIAL RESPIRATION. KEEP PERSON WARM AND AT REST. TREAT SYMPTOMATICALLY AND SUPPORTIVELY. GET MEDICAL ATTENTION IMMEDIATELY.

SKIN CONTACT: CYCLOHEXANONE: IRRITANT/NARCOTIC/TOXIC. **ACUTE EXPOSURE-** IRRITATION RANGING FROM MILD TO MODERATE HAS BEEN REPORTED IN ANIMALS. FIRST DEGREE BURNS ARE POSSIBLE. A SINGLE APPLICATION PRODUCED LABORED BREATHING, HYPNOTIC SIGNS, AND PERITONEAL AND INTESTINAL CONGESTION IN RATS. **CHRONIC EXPOSURE-** REPEATED OR PROLONGED EXPOSURE TO THE LIQUID MAY CAUSE DEFATTING OF THE SKIN WITH REDNESS AND A DRY, SCALY, FISSURED DERMATITIS. SECONDARY BURNS ARE POSSIBLE. REPEATED DERMAL APPLICATIONS TO GUINEA PIGS RESULTED IN EXTENSIVE LENS CHANGES AND CATARACTS.

FIRST AID- REMOVE CONTAMINATED CLOTHING AND SHOES IMMEDIATELY. WASH AFFECTED AREA WITH SOAP OR MILD DETERGENT AND LARGE AMOUNTS OF WATER UNTIL NO EVIDENCE OF CHEMICAL REMAINS (APPROXIMATELY 15-20 MINUTES). GET MEDICAL ATTENTION IMMEDIATELY.

EYE CONTACT: CYCLOHEXANONE: IRRITANT. **ACUTE EXPOSURE-** CONTACT WITH THE LIQUID OR VAPORS ABOVE 25-75 PPM MAY CAUSE SEVERE IRRITATION WITH PAIN, REDNESS, LACRIMATION, AND CORNEAL INJURY. APPLICATION TO RABBIT EYES CAUSED MODERATE TEMPORARY IRRITATION, GRADED 5 ON A SCALE OF 1-10. **CHRONIC EXPOSURE-** REPEATED OR PROLONGED EXPOSURE MAY CAUSE CONJUNCTIVITIS.

FIRST AID- WASH EYES IMMEDIATELY WITH LARGE AMOUNTS OF WATER OR NORMAL SALINE, OCCASIONALLY LIFTING UPPER AND LOWER LIDS, UNTIL NO EVIDENCE OF CHEMICAL REMAINS (APPROXIMATELY 15-20 MINUTES). GET MEDICAL ATTENTION IMMEDIATELY.

INGESTION: CYCLOHEXANONE: NARCOTIC. **ACUTE EXPOSURE-** INGESTION OF HIGH DOSES MAY CAUSE COUGHING, CENTRAL NERVOUS SYSTEM DEPRESSION, DULLNESS, GASTROINTESTINAL IRRITATION, HEPATIC NECROSIS, UNCONSCIOUSNESS, AND DEATH. **CHRONIC EXPOSURE-** REPEATED OR PROLONGED INGESTION OF CYCLOHEXANONE IN THE DIETS OF MICE REDUCED THE GROWTH RATE IN THE FIRST GENERATION OFFSPRING; HOWEVER, GROWTH OF THE SECOND GENERATION WAS NORMAL. OTHER REPRODUCTIVE EFFECTS HAVE BEEN REPORTED IN ANIMALS.

FIRST AID- IF THE PERSON IS CONSCIOUS AND NOT CONVULSING, INDUCE EMESIS BY GIVING SYRUP OF IPECAC FOLLOWED BY WATER. (IF VOMITING OCCURS KEEP THE HEAD BELOW THE HIPS TO PREVENT ASPIRATION). REPEAT IN 20 MINUTES IF NOT EFFECTIVE INITIALLY. GIVE ACTIVATED CHARCOAL. IN PATIENTS WITH DEPRESSED RESPIRATION OR IF EMESIS IS NOT PRODUCED, PERFORM GASTRIC LAVAGE CAUTIOUSLY (DREISBACH, HANDBOOK OF POISONING, 12TH ED.). TREAT SYMPTOMATICALLY AND SUPPORTIVELY. GASTRIC LAVAGE SHOULD BE PERFORMED BY QUALIFIED MEDICAL PERSONNEL. GET MEDICAL ATTENTION IMMEDIATELY.

ANTIDOTE: NO SPECIFIC ANTIDOTE. TREAT SYMPTOMATICALLY AND SUPPORTIVELY.

REACTIVITY

REACTIVITY: STABLE UNDER NORMAL TEMPERATURES AND PRESSURES.

INCOMPATIBILITIES: CYCLOHEXANONE: HYDROGEN PEROXIDE + NITRIC ACID: MAY FORM OILY, EXPLOSIVE PEROXIDE. NITRIC ACID: VIOLENT REACTION WITH POSSIBLE DETONATION. OXIDIZERS (STRONG): VIOLENT REACTION WITH POSSIBLE IGNITION. PLASTICS: MAY BE ATTACKED. RESINS: MAY BE ATTACKED. RUBBER: MAY BE ATTACKED.

DECOMPOSITION: THERMAL DECOMPOSITION MAY RELEASE ACRID SMOKE AND IRRITATING FUMES.

POLYMERIZATION: HAZARDOUS POLYMERIZATION HAS NOT BEEN REPORTED TO OCCUR UNDER NORMAL TEMPERATURES AND PRESSURES.

STORAGE AND DISPOSAL

OBSERVE ALL FEDERAL, STATE AND LOCAL REGULATIONS WHEN STORING OR DISPOSING OF THIS SUBSTANCE. FOR ASSISTANCE, CONTACT THE DISTRICT DIRECTOR OF THE ENVIRONMENTAL PROTECTION AGENCY.

****STORAGE****

STORE IN ACCORDANCE WITH 29 CFR 1910.106.

BONDING AND GROUNDING: SUBSTANCES WITH LOW ELECTROCONDUCTIVITY, WHICH MAY BE IGNITED BY ELECTROSTATIC SPARKS, SHOULD BE STORED IN CONTAINERS WHICH MEET THE BONDING AND GROUNDING GUIDELINES SPECIFIED IN NFPA 77-1983, RECOMMENDED PRACTICE ON STATIC ELECTRICITY.

STORE AWAY FROM INCOMPATIBLE SUBSTANCES.

****DISPOSAL****

DISPOSAL MUST BE IN ACCORDANCE WITH STANDARDS APPLICABLE TO GENERATORS OF HAZARDOUS WASTE, 40 CFR 262. EPA HAZARDOUS WASTE NUMBER U057.

CONDITIONS TO AVOID

AVOID CONTACT WITH HEAT, SPARKS, FLAMES, OR OTHER SOURCES OF IGNITION. VAPORS MAY BE EXPLOSIVE AND POISONOUS; DO NOT ALLOW UNNECESSARY PERSONNEL IN AREA. DO NOT OVERHEAT CONTAINERS; CONTAINERS MAY VIOLENTLY RUPTURE AND TRAVEL A CONSIDERABLE DISTANCE IN HEAT OF FIRE. WILL ATTACK SOME FORMS OF PLASTICS, RUBBER, AND COATINGS.

SPILL AND LEAK PROCEDURES

OCCUPATIONAL SPILL: SHUT OFF IGNITION SOURCES. STOP LEAK IF YOU CAN DO IT WITHOUT RISK. USE WATER SPRAY TO REDUCE VAPORS. FOR SMALL SPILLS, TAKE UP WITH SAND OR OTHER ABSORBENT MATERIAL AND PLACE INTO CONTAINERS FOR LATER DISPOSAL. FOR LARGER SPILLS, DIKE FAR AHEAD OF SPILL FOR LATER DISPOSAL. NO SMOKING, FLAMES OR FLARES IN HAZARD AREA. KEEP UNNECESSARY PEOPLE AWAY; ISOLATE HAZARD AREA AND DENY ENTRY.

REPORTABLE QUANTITY (RQ): 5000 POUNDS THE SUPERFUND AMENDMENTS AND REAUTHORIZATION ACT (SARA) SECTION 304 REQUIRES THAT A RELEASE EQUAL TO OR GREATER THAN THE REPORTABLE QUANTITY FOR THIS SUBSTANCE BE IMMEDIATELY REPORTED TO THE LOCAL EMERGENCY PLANNING COMMITTEE AND THE STATE EMERGENCY RESPONSE COMMISSION (40 CFR 355.40). IF THE RELEASE OF THIS SUBSTANCE IS REPORTABLE UNDER CERCLA SECTION 103, THE NATIONAL RESPONSE CENTER MUST BE NOTIFIED IMMEDIATELY AT (800) 424-8802 OR (202) 426-2675 IN THE METROPOLITAN WASHINGTON, D.C. AREA (40 CFR 302.6).

PROTECTIVE EQUIPMENT

VENTILATION: PROVIDE LOCAL EXHAUST OR PROCESS ENCLOSURE VENTILATION TO MEET PUBLISHED EXPOSURE LIMITS.

RESPIRATOR: THE FOLLOWING RESPIRATORS AND MAXIMUM USE CONCENTRATIONS ARE RECOMMENDATIONS BY THE U.S. DEPARTMENT OF HEALTH AND HUMAN SERVICES, NIOSH POCKET GUIDE TO CHEMICAL HAZARDS; NIOSH CRITERIA DOCUMENTS OR BY THE U.S. DEPARTMENT OF LABOR, 29 CFR 1910 SUBPART Z. THE SPECIFIC RESPIRATOR SELECTED MUST BE BASED ON CONTAMINATION LEVELS FOUND IN THE WORK PLACE, MUST NOT EXCEED THE WORKING LIMITS OF THE RESPIRATOR AND BE JOINTLY APPROVED BY THE NATIONAL INSTITUTE FOR OCCUPATIONAL SAFETY AND HEALTH AND THE MINE SAFETY AND HEALTH ADMINISTRATION (NIOSH-MSHA).

CYCLOHEXANONE: 625 PPM- ANY SUPPLIED-AIR RESPIRATOR OPERATED IN A CONTINUOUS FLOW MODE. ANY POWERED AIR-PURIFYING RESPIRATOR WITH ORGANIC VAPOR CARTRIDGE(S).

1000 PPM- ANY CHEMICAL CARTRIDGE RESPIRATOR WITH A FULL FACEPIECE AND ORGANIC VAPOR CARTRIDGE(S).

1250 PPM- ANY AIR-PURIFYING FULL FACEPIECE RESPIRATOR (GAS MASK) WITH A CHIN-STYLE OR FRONT- OR BACK-MOUNTED ORGANIC VAPOR CANISTER. ANY SELF-CONTAINED BREATHING APPARATUS WITH A FULL FACEPIECE. ANY SUPPLIED-AIR RESPIRATOR WITH A FULL FACEPIECE.

5000 PPM- ANY SUPPLIED-AIR RESPIRATOR WITH A HALF-MASK AND OPERATED IN A PRESSURE-DEMAND OR OTHER POSITIVE PRESSURE MODE.

ESCAPE- ANY AIR-PURIFYING FULL FACEPIECE RESPIRATOR (GAS MASK) WITH A CHIN-STYLE OR FRONT- OR BACK-MOUNTED ORGANIC VAPOR CANISTER. ANY APPROPRIATE ESCAPE-TYPE SELF-CONTAINED BREATHING APPARATUS.

FOR FIREFIGHTING AND OTHER IMMEDIATELY DANGEROUS TO LIFE OR HEALTH CONDITIONS:

SELF-CONTAINED BREATHING APPARATUS WITH FULL FACEPIECE OPERATED IN PRESSURE-DEMAND OR OTHER POSITIVE PRESSURE MODE.

SUPPLIED-AIR RESPIRATOR WITH FULL FACEPIECE AND OPERATED IN PRESSURE-DEMAND OR OTHER POSITIVE PRESSURE MODE IN COMBINATION WITH AN AUXILIARY SELF-CONTAINED BREATHING APPARATUS OPERATED IN PRESSURE-DEMAND OR OTHER POSITIVE PRESSURE MODE.

CLOTHING: EMPLOYEE MUST WEAR APPROPRIATE PROTECTIVE (IMPERVIOUS) CLOTHING AND EQUIPMENT TO PREVENT REPEATED OR PROLONGED SKIN CONTACT WITH THIS SUBSTANCE.

GLOVES: EMPLOYEE MUST WEAR APPROPRIATE PROTECTIVE GLOVES TO PREVENT CONTACT WITH THIS SUBSTANCE.

EYE PROTECTION: EMPLOYEE MUST WEAR SPLASH-PROOF OR DUST-RESISTANT SAFETY GOGGLES TO PREVENT EYE CONTACT WITH THIS SUBSTANCE.

EMERGENCY EYE WASH: WHERE THERE IS ANY POSSIBILITY THAT AN EMPLOYEE'S EYES MAY BE EXPOSED TO THIS SUBSTANCE, THE EMPLOYER SHOULD PROVIDE AN EYE WASH FOUNTAIN WITHIN THE IMMEDIATE WORK AREA FOR EMERGENCY USE.

AUTHORIZED BY- OCCUPATIONAL HEALTH SERVICES, INC.
CREATION DATE: 02/08/90 ***REVISION DATE:*** 05/24/90

MATERIAL SAFETY DATA SHEET

OCCUPATIONAL HEALTH SERVICES, INC.
AGRICULTURE AND PESTICIDE DIVISION
450 SEVENTH AVENUE, SUITE 2407
NEW YORK, NEW YORK 10123
1-800-445-MSDS OR (212) 967-1100

EMERGENCY CONTACT:
JOHN S. BRANSFORD, JR. (615) 292-1180

SUBSTANCE IDENTIFICATION

CAS-NUMBER 66-81-9
SUBSTANCE: CYCLOHEXIMIDE

TRADE NAMES/SYNONYMS: ACTI-AID; ACTIDION; ACTIODIONE; ACTIDIONE PM; ACTIDONE; ACTIDIONE TGF; ACTISPRAY; HIZAROCIN; KAKEN; NARAMYCIN; NARAMYCIN A; BETA-(2-(3,5-DIMETHYL-2-OXOCYCLOHEXYL)-2-HYDROXYETHYL)GLUTARIMIDE; NEOCYCLOHEXIMIDE; U-4527; PST05930
CHEMICAL FAMILY: HETEROCYCLIC NITROGEN
MOLECULAR FORMULA: C15-H23-N-O4 MOL WT: 281.39
CERCLA RATINGS (SCALE 0-3): HEALTH=3 FIRE=0 REACTIVITY=0 PERSISTENCE=2
NFPA RATINGS (SCALE 0-4): HEALTH=3 FIRE=0 REACTIVITY=0

COMPONENTS AND CONTAMINANTS

COMPONENT: CYCLOHEXIMIDE ***PERCENT:*** 100
CAS# 66-81-9
OTHER CONTAMINANTS: NONE
EXPOSURE LIMITS: NO OCCUPATIONAL EXPOSURE LIMITS ESTABLISHED BY OSHA, ACGIH, OR NIOSH.
CYCLOHEXIMIDE: 100/10,000 POUNDS SARA SECTION 302 THRESHOLD PLANNING QUANTITY 1 POUND SARA SECTION 304 REPORTABLE QUANTITY SUBJECT TO CALIFORNIA PROPOSITION 65 CANCER AND/OR REPRODUCTIVE TOXICITY WARNING AND RELEASE REQUIREMENTS- (JANUARY 1, 1989)

PHYSICAL DATA

DESCRIPTION: CRYSTALS ***MELTING POINT:*** 241 F (116 C)
SOLUBILITY IN WATER: MODERATELY SOLUBLE
SOLVENT SOLUBILITY: CHLOROFORM, ETHER, ACETONE, ALCOHOL

FIRE AND EXPLOSION DATA

FIRE AND EXPLOSION HAZARD: NEGLIGIBLE FIRE HAZARD WHEN EXPOSED TO HEAT OR FLAME.
FIREFIGHTING MEDIA: DRY CHEMICAL, CARBON DIOXIDE, HALON, WATER SPRAY OR STANDARD FOAM (1987 EMERGENCY RESPONSE GUIDEBOOK, DOT P 5800.4).
FOR LARGER FIRES, USE WATER SPRAY, FOG OR STANDARD FOAM (1987 EMERGENCY RESPONSE GUIDEBOOK, DOT P 5800.4).
FIREFIGHTING: MOVE CONTAINER FROM FIRE AREA IF POSSIBLE. DO NOT SCATTER SPILLED MATERIAL WITH HIGH PRESSURE WATER STREAMS. DIKE FIRE CONTROL WATER FOR LATER DISPOSAL (1987 EMERGENCY RESPONSE GUIDEBOOK, DOT P 5800.4, GUIDE PAGE 31).
USE AGENTS SUITABLE FOR TYPE OF SURROUNDING FIRE. AVOID BREATHING HAZARDOUS VAPORS, KEEP UPWIND.

TOXICITY

CYCLOHEXIMIDE: IRRITATION DATA: 5 MG/24 HOURS RINSED SKIN-RABBIT; 1 PPH/24 HOURS SKIN-RABBIT MODERATE. TOXICITY DATA: 2 MG/KG ORAL-RAT LD50; 133 MG/KG ORAL-MOUSE LD50; 65 MG/KG ORAL-DOG LD50; 60 MG/KG ORAL-MONKEY LD50; 65 MG/KG ORAL-GUINEA PIG LD50; 2500 UG/KG SUBCUTANEOUS-RAT LD50; 160 MG/KG SUBCUTANEOUS-MOUSE LD50; 60 MG/KG SUBCUTANEOUS-GUINEA PIG LD50; 2 MG/KG INTRAVENOUS-RAT LD50; 150 MG/KG INTRAVENOUS-MOUSE LD50; 17 MG/KG INTRAVENOUS-RABBIT LD50; 3700 UG/KG INTRAPERITONEAL-RAT LD50; 138 MG/KG INTRAPERITONEAL-MOUSE LD50; 4 MG/KG INTRAPERITONEAL-CAT LD50; 60 MG/KG INTRAPERITONEAL-GUINEA PIG LD50; 40 MG/KG INTRAPERITONEAL-HAMSTER LDLO, 133 MG/KG UNREPORTED-RAT LD50; MUTAGENIC DATA (RTECS); REPRODUCTIVE EFFECTS DATA (RTECS). CARCINOGEN STATUS: NONE. LOCAL EFFECTS: IRRITANT- INHALATION, SKIN, AND EYES. ACUTE TOXICITY LEVEL: HIGHLY TOXIC BY INGESTION. TARGET EFFECTS: CONVULSANT. POISONING MAY AFFECT THE LIVER AND NERVOUS SYSTEM.

HEALTH EFFECTS AND FIRST AID

INHALATION: IRRITANT/CONVULSANT. **ACUTE EXPOSURE-** MAY CAUSE IRRITATION, EXCITEMENT, SALIVATION, TREMORS AND CONVULSIONS OR COMA.
CHRONIC EXPOSURE- NO DATA AVAILABLE.
FIRST AID- REMOVE FROM EXPOSURE AREA TO FRESH AIR IMMEDIATELY. IF BREATHING HAS STOPPED, PERFORM ARTIFICIAL RESPIRATION. KEEP PERSON WARM AND AT REST. TREAT SYMPTOMATICALLY AND SUPPORTIVELY. GET MEDICAL ATTENTION IMMEDIATELY.

SKIN CONTACT: IRRITANT. **ACUTE EXPOSURE-** MAY CAUSE IRRITATION.
CHRONIC EXPOSURE- REPEATED AND PROLONGED CONTACT MAY CAUSE DERMATITIS.
FIRST AID- REMOVE CONTAMINATED CLOTHING AND SHOES IMMEDIATELY. WASH AFFECTED AREA WITH SOAP OR MILD DETERGENT AND LARGE AMOUNTS OF WATER UNTIL NO EVIDENCE OF CHEMICAL REMAINS (APPROXIMATELY 15-20 MINUTES). GET MEDICAL ATTENTION IMMEDIATELY.

EYE CONTACT: IRRITANT. **ACUTE EXPOSURE-** MAY CAUSE IRRITATION.
CHRONIC EXPOSURE- REPEATED AND PROLONGED CONTACT MAY CAUSE CONJUNCTIVITIS.
FIRST AID- WASH EYES IMMEDIATELY WITH LARGE AMOUNTS OF WATER OR NORMAL SALINE, OCCASIONALLY LIFTING UPPER AND LOWER LIDS, UNTIL NO EVIDENCE OF CHEMICAL REMAINS (APPROXIMATELY 15-20 MINUTES). GET MEDICAL ATTENTION IMMEDIATELY.

INGESTION: HIGHLY TOXIC/CONVULSANT. **ACUTE EXPOSURE-** MAY CAUSE DIARRHEA, EXCITEMENT, MELENA, SALIVATION, TREMORS AND CONVULSIONS OR COMA. A DOSE OF ONLY 2 MG/KG WAS LETHAL TO 50% OF THE RATS TESTED.
CHRONIC EXPOSURE- MAY PRODUCE A FATTY LIVER.
FIRST AID- REMOVE BY GASTRIC LAVAGE OR EMESIS. FOLLOW WITH A SALINE CATHARTIC. MAINTAIN BLOOD PRESSURE, AIRWAY, AND GIVE OXYGEN IF RESPIRATION IS DEPRESSED. DO NOT PERFORM GASTRIC LAVAGE OR EMESIS IF VICTIM IS UNCONSCIOUS. GET MEDICAL ATTENTION IMMEDIATELY. (DREISBACH, HANDBOOK OF POISONING, 12TH ED.) ADMINISTRATION OF GASTRIC LAVAGE OR OXYGEN SHOULD BE PERFORMED BY QUALIFIED MEDICAL PERSONNEL.
ANTIDOTE: NO SPECIFIC ANTIDOTE. TREAT SYMPTOMATICALLY AND SUPPORTIVELY.

REACTIVITY

REACTIVITY: STABLE UNDER NORMAL TEMPERATURES AND PRESSURES.
INCOMPATIBILITIES: ALKALIS: INCOMPATIBLE.
DECOMPOSITION: THERMAL DECOMPOSITION PRODUCTS MAY INCLUDE TOXIC OXIDES OF CARBON AND NITROGEN.
POLYMERIZATION: HAZARDOUS POLYMERIZATION HAS NOT BEEN REPORTED TO OCCUR UNDER NORMAL TEMPERATURES AND PRESSURES.

STORAGE AND DISPOSAL

OBSERVE ALL FEDERAL, STATE AND LOCAL REGULATIONS WHEN STORING OR DISPOSING OF THIS SUBSTANCE. FOR ASSISTANCE, CONTACT THE DISTRICT DIRECTOR OF THE ENVIRONMENTAL PROTECTION AGENCY.

****STORAGE****

STORE AWAY FROM INCOMPATIBLE SUBSTANCES.
THRESHOLD PLANNING QUANTITY (TPQ): THE SUPERFUND AMENDMENTS AND REAUTHORIZATION ACT (SARA) SECTION 302 REQUIRES THAT EACH FACILITY WHERE ANY EXTREMELY HAZARDOUS SUBSTANCE IS PRESENT IN A QUANTITY EQUAL TO OR GREATER THAN THE TPQ ESTABLISHED FOR THAT SUBSTANCE NOTIFY THE STATE EMERGENCY RESPONSE COMMISSION FOR THE STATE IN WHICH IT IS LOCATED. SECTION 303 OF SARA REQUIRES THESE FACILITIES TO PARTICIPATE IN LOCAL EMERGENCY RESPONSE PLANNING (40 CFR 355.30).

CONDITIONS TO AVOID

NONE REPORTED.

SPILL AND LEAK PROCEDURES

WATER SPILL: THE CALIFORNIA SAFE DRINKING WATER AND TOXIC ENFORCEMENT ACT OF 1986 (PROPOSITION 65) PROHIBITS CONTAMINATING ANY KNOWN SOURCE OF DRINKING WATER WITH SUBSTANCES KNOWN TO CAUSE CANCER AND/OR REPRODUCTIVE TOXICITY.
OCCUPATIONAL SPILL: SWEEP UP AND PLACE IN SUITABLE CLEAN, DRY CONTAINERS FOR RECLAMATION OR LATER DISPOSAL. DO NOT FLUSH SPILLED MATERIAL INTO SEWER. KEEP UNNECESSARY PEOPLE AWAY.
REPORTABLE QUANTITY (RQ): 1 POUND THE SUPERFUND AMENDMENTS AND REAUTHORIZATION ACT (SARA) SECTION 304 REQUIRES THAT A RELEASE EQUAL TO OR GREATER THAN THE REPORTABLE QUANTITY FOR THIS SUBSTANCE BE IMMEDIATELY REPORTED TO THE LOCAL EMERGENCY PLANNING COMMITTEE AND THE STATE EMERGENCY RESPONSE COMMISSION (40 CFR 355.40). IF THE RELEASE OF THIS SUBSTANCE IS REPORTABLE UNDER CERCLA SECTION 103, THE NATIONAL RESPONSE CENTER MUST BE NOTIFIED IMMEDIATELY AT (800) 424-8802 OR (202) 426-2675 IN THE METROPOLITAN WASHINGTON, D.C. AREA (40 CFR 302.6).

PROTECTIVE EQUIPMENT

VENTILATION: PROVIDE LOCAL EXHAUST OR PROCESS ENCLOSURE VENTILATION SYSTEM.
RESPIRATOR: THE FOLLOWING RESPIRATORS ARE RECOMMENDED BASED ON INFORMATION FOUND IN THE PHYSICAL DATA, TOXICITY AND HEALTH EFFECTS SECTIONS. THEY ARE RANKED IN ORDER FROM MINIMUM TO MAXIMUM RESPIRATORY PROTECTION. THE SPECIFIC RESPIRATOR SELECTED MUST BE BASED ON CONTAMINATION LEVELS FOUND IN THE WORK PLACE, MUST NOT EXCEED THE WORKING LIMITS OF THE RESPIRATOR AND BE JOINTLY APPROVED BY THE NATIONAL INSTITUTE FOR OCCUPATIONAL SAFETY AND HEALTH AND THE MINE SAFETY AND HEALTH ADMINISTRATION (NIOSH-MSHA).
TYPE 'C' SUPPLIED-AIR RESPIRATOR WITH A FULL FACEPIECE OPERATED IN PRESSURE-DEMAND OR OTHER POSITIVE PRESSURE MODE OR WITH A FULL FACEPIECE, HELMET OR HOOD OPERATED IN CONTINOUS-FLOW MODE.
SELF-CONTAINED BREATHING APPARATUS WITH A FULL FACEPIECE OPERATED IN PRESSURE-DEMAND OR OTHER POSITIVE PRESSURE MODE.

FOR FIREFIGHTING AND OTHER IMMEDIATELY DANGEROUS TO LIFE OR HEALTH CONDITIONS:
SELF-CONTAINED BREATHING APPARATUS WITH FULL FACEPIECE OPERATED IN PRESSURE-DEMAND OR OTHER POSITIVE PRESSURE MODE.
SUPPLIED-AIR RESPIRATOR WITH FULL FACEPIECE AND OPERATED IN PRESSURE-DEMAND OR OTHER POSITIVE PRESSURE MODE IN COMBINATION WITH AN AUXILIARY SELF-CONTAINED BREATHING APPARATUS OPERATED IN PRESSURE-DEMAND OR OTHER POSITIVE PRESSURE MODE.
CLOTHING: EMPLOYEE MUST WEAR APPROPRIATE PROTECTIVE (IMPERVIOUS) CLOTHING AND EQUIPMENT TO PREVENT REPEATED OR PROLONGED SKIN CONTACT WITH THIS SUBSTANCE.
GLOVES: EMPLOYEE MUST WEAR APPROPRIATE PROTECTIVE GLOVES TO PREVENT CONTACT WITH THIS SUBSTANCE.
EYE PROTECTION: EMPLOYEE MUST WEAR SPLASH-PROOF OR DUST-RESISTANT SAFETY GOGGLES TO PREVENT EYE CONTACT WITH THIS SUBSTANCE.
EMERGENCY EYE WASH: WHERE THERE IS ANY POSSIBILITY THAT AN EMPLOYEE'S EYES MAY BE EXPOSED TO THIS SUBSTANCE, THE EMPLOYER SHOULD PROVIDE AN EYE WASH FOUNTAIN WITHIN THE IMMEDIATE WORK AREA FOR EMERGENCY USE.

AUTHORIZED BY- OCCUPATIONAL HEALTH SERVICES, INC.
CREATION DATE: 02/08/90 ***REVISION DATE:*** 05/31/90

MATERIAL SAFETY DATA SHEET

OCCUPATIONAL HEALTH SERVICES, INC.
AGRICULTURE AND PESTICIDE DIVISION
450 SEVENTH AVENUE, SUITE 2407
NEW YORK, NEW YORK 10123
1-800-445-MSDS OR (212) 967-1100

EMERGENCY CONTACT:
JOHN S. BRANSFORD, JR. (615) 292-1180

SUBSTANCE IDENTIFICATION

CAS-NUMBER 2163-69-1
SUBSTANCE: **CYCLURON**
TRADE NAMES/SYNONYMS: UREA, N'-CYCLOOCTYL-N,N-DIMETHYL-; UREA, 3-CYCLOOCTYL-1,1-DIMETHYL-; N'-CYCLOOCTYL-N,N-DIMETHYLUREA; 3-CYCLOOCTYL-1,1-DIMETHYLUREA; 3-CYCLO-OCTYL-1,1-DIMETHYLUREA; HS 61; OMU; C11H22N2O; PST05996
CHEMICAL FAMILY: SUBSTITUTED UREA
MOLECULAR FORMULA: C8-H15-N-H-C-O-N-(C-H3)2
MOLECULAR WEIGHT: 198.35
CERCLA RATINGS (SCALE 0-3): HEALTH=3 FIRE=1 REACTIVITY=0 PERSISTENCE=1
NFPA RATINGS (SCALE 0-4): HEALTH=U FIRE=1 REACTIVITY=0

COMPONENTS AND CONTAMINANTS

COMPONENT: CYCLURON ***PERCENT:*** 100.0
CAS# 2163-69-1
OTHER CONTAMINANTS: NONE
EXPOSURE LIMITS: NO OCCUPATIONAL EXPOSURE LIMITS ESTABLISHED BY OSHA, ACGIH, OR NIOSH.

PHYSICAL DATA

DESCRIPTION: WHITE POWDER. ***MELTING POINT:*** 279-280 F (137-138 C)
SPECIFIC GRAVITY: NOT AVAILABLE ***SOLUBILITY IN WATER:*** NOT AVAILABLE
SOLVENT SOLUBILITY: SOLUBLE IN CYCLOHEXANE.

FIRE AND EXPLOSION DATA

FIRE AND EXPLOSION HAZARD: SLIGHT FIRE HAZARD WHEN EXPOSED TO HEAT OR FLAME.
FIREFIGHTING MEDIA: DRY CHEMICAL, CARBON DIOXIDE, HALON, WATER SPRAY OR STANDARD FOAM (1987 EMERGENCY RESPONSE GUIDEBOOK, DOT P 5800.4).
FOR LARGER FIRES, USE WATER SPRAY, FOG OR STANDARD FOAM (1987 EMERGENCY RESPONSE GUIDEBOOK, DOT P 5800.4).
FIREFIGHTING: MOVE CONTAINER FROM FIRE AREA IF POSSIBLE. DO NOT SCATTER SPILLED MATERIAL WITH HIGH PRESSURE WATER STREAMS. DIKE FIRE CONTROL WATER FOR LATER DISPOSAL (1987 EMERGENCY RESPONSE GUIDEBOOK, DOT P 5800.4, GUIDE PAGE 31).
USE AGENTS SUITABLE FOR TYPE OF SURROUNDING FIRE. AVOID BREATHING HAZARDOUS VAPORS, KEEP UPWIND.

TOXICITY

CYCLURON: TOXICITY DATA: 1500 MG/KG ORAL-RAT LD50; 2600 MG/KG ORAL-MAMMAL LD50; 300 MG/KG INTRAPERITONEAL-MOUSE LD50; 1125 MG/KG UNREPORTED-RAT LD50; 300 MG/KG UNREPORTED-MOUSE LD50. CARCINOGEN STATUS: NONE. ACUTE TOXICITY LEVEL: MODERATELY TOXIC BY INGESTION. TARGET EFFECTS: NO DATA AVAILABLE.

HEALTH EFFECTS AND FIRST AID

INHALATION: CYCLURON: **ACUTE EXPOSURE-** MANY SUBSTITUTED UREA HERBICIDES ARE MODERATELY IRRITATING TO THE MUCOUS MEMBRANES. **CHRONIC EXPOSURE-** NO DATA AVAILABLE.
FIRST AID- REMOVE FROM EXPOSURE AREA TO FRESH AIR IMMEDIATELY. IF BREATHING HAS STOPPED, PERFORM ARTIFICIAL RESPIRATION. KEEP PERSON WARM AND AT REST. TREAT SYMPTOMATICALLY AND SUPPORTIVELY. GET MEDICAL ATTENTION IMMEDIATELY.

SKIN CONTACT: CYCLURON: **ACUTE EXPOSURE-** THIS MATERIAL WAS NOT IRRITATING TO RABBIT SKIN. **CHRONIC EXPOSURE-** NO DATA AVAILABLE.
FIRST AID- REMOVE CONTAMINATED CLOTHING AND SHOES IMMEDIATELY. WASH AFFECTED AREA WITH SOAP OR MILD DETERGENT AND LARGE AMOUNTS OF WATER UNTIL NO EVIDENCE OF CHEMICAL REMAINS (APPROXIMATELY 15-20 MINUTES). GET MEDICAL ATTENTION IMMEDIATELY.

EYE CONTACT: CYCLURON: **ACUTE EXPOSURE-** MANY SUBSTITUTED UREA HERBICIDES ARE MODERATELY IRRITATING TO THE EYES. **CHRONIC EXPOSURE-** NO DATA AVAILABLE.
FIRST AID- WASH EYES IMMEDIATELY WITH LARGE AMOUNTS OF WATER OR NORMAL SALINE, OCCASIONALLY LIFTING UPPER AND LOWER LIDS, UNTIL NO EVIDENCE OF CHEMICAL REMAINS (APPROXIMATELY 15-20 MINUTES). GET MEDICAL ATTENTION IMMEDIATELY.

INGESTION: CYCLURON: **ACUTE EXPOSURE-** A LETHAL DOSE IN RATS WAS 1500 MG/KG; SYMPTOMS WERE NOT REPORTED. **CHRONIC EXPOSURE-** NO DATA AVAILABLE.
FIRST AID- TREAT SYMPTOMATICALLY AND SUPPORTIVELY. GET MEDICAL ATTENTION IMMEDIATELY. IF VOMITING OCCURS, KEEP HEAD LOWER THAN HIPS TO PREVENT ASPIRATION.
ANTIDOTE: NO SPECIFIC ANTIDOTE. TREAT SYMPTOMATICALLY AND SUPPORTIVELY.

REACTIVITY

REACTIVITY: STABLE UNDER NORMAL TEMPERATURES AND PRESSURES.
INCOMPATIBILITIES: CYCLURON: OXIDIZERS (STRONG): FIRE AND EXPLOSION HAZARD.
DECOMPOSITION: THERMAL DECOMPOSITION PRODUCTS MAY INCLUDE TOXIC OXIDES OF CARBON AND NITROGEN.
POLYMERIZATION: HAZARDOUS POLYMERIZATION HAS NOT BEEN REPORTED TO OCCUR UNDER NORMAL TEMPERATURES AND PRESSURES.

STORAGE AND DISPOSAL

OBSERVE ALL FEDERAL, STATE AND LOCAL REGULATIONS WHEN STORING OR DISPOSING OF THIS SUBSTANCE. FOR ASSISTANCE, CONTACT THE DISTRICT DIRECTOR OF THE ENVIRONMENTAL PROTECTION AGENCY.

STORAGE

STORE IN ACCORDANCE WITH 40 CFR 165 RECOMMENDED PROCEDURES FOR THE DISPOSAL AND STORAGE OF PESTICIDES AND PESTICIDE CONTAINERS.
STORE AWAY FROM INCOMPATIBLE SUBSTANCES.

DISPOSAL

DISPOSAL MUST BE IN ACCORDANCE WITH 40 CFR 165 RECOMMENDED PROCEDURES FOR THE DISPOSAL AND STORAGE OF PESTICIDES AND PESTICIDE CONTAINERS.

CONDITIONS TO AVOID

MAY BURN BUT DOES NOT IGNITE READILY. AVOID CONTACT WITH STRONG OXIDIZERS, EXCESSIVE HEAT, SPARKS, OR OPEN FLAME.

SPILL AND LEAK PROCEDURES

OCCUPATIONAL SPILL: SWEEP UP AND PLACE IN SUITABLE CLEAN, DRY CONTAINERS FOR RECLAMATION OR LATER DISPOSAL. DO NOT FLUSH SPILLED MATERIAL INTO SEWER. KEEP UNNECESSARY PEOPLE AWAY.

PROTECTIVE EQUIPMENT

VENTILATION: PROVIDE LOCAL EXHAUST OR GENERAL DILUTION VENTILATION SYSTEM.
RESPIRATOR: THE FOLLOWING RESPIRATORS ARE RECOMMENDED BASED ON INFORMATION FOUND IN THE PHYSICAL DATA, TOXICITY AND HEALTH EFFECTS SECTIONS. THEY ARE RANKED IN ORDER FROM MINIMUM TO MAXIMUM

RESPIRATORY PROTECTION. THE SPECIFIC RESPIRATOR SELECTED MUST BE BASED ON CONTAMINATION LEVELS FOUND IN THE WORK PLACE, MUST NOT EXCEED THE WORKING LIMITS OF THE RESPIRATOR AND BE JOINTLY APPROVED BY THE NATIONAL INSTITUTE FOR OCCUPATIONAL SAFETY AND HEALTH AND THE MINE SAFETY AND HEALTH ADMINISTRATION (NIOSH-MSHA).

CHEMICAL CARTRIDGE RESPIRATOR WITH AN ORGANIC VAPOR CARTRIDGE(S) WITH A FULL FACEPIECE AND ORGANIC VAPOR CARTRIDGE(S) IN COMBINATION WITH A DUST AND MIST FILTER.

POWERED AIR-PURIFYING RESPIRATOR WITH A TIGHT-FITTING FACEPIECE AND ORGANIC VAPOR CARTRIDGE(S) IN COMBINATION WITH A HIGH-EFFICIENCY PARTICULATE FILTER.

TYPE 'C' SUPPLIED-AIR RESPIRATOR WITH A FULL FACEPIECE OPERATED IN A PRESSURE-DEMAND OR OTHER POSITIVE PRESSURE MODE.

SELF-CONTAINED BREATHING APPARATUS WITH A FULL FACEPIECE OPERATED IN PRESSURE-DEMAND OR OTHER POSITIVE PRESSURE MODE.

FOR FIREFIGHTING AND OTHER IMMEDIATELY DANGEROUS TO LIFE OR HEALTH CONDITIONS:

SELF-CONTAINED BREATHING APPARATUS WITH FULL FACEPIECE OPERATED IN PRESSURE-DEMAND OR OTHER POSITIVE PRESSURE MODE.

SUPPLIED-AIR RESPIRATOR WITH FULL FACEPIECE AND OPERATED IN PRESSURE-DEMAND OR OTHER POSITIVE PRESSURE MODE IN COMBINATION WITH AN AUXILIARY SELF-CONTAINED BREATHING APPARATUS OPERATED IN PRESSURE-DEMAND OR OTHER POSITIVE PRESSURE MODE.

CLOTHING: EMPLOYEE MUST WEAR APPROPRIATE PROTECTIVE (IMPERVIOUS) CLOTHING AND EQUIPMENT TO PREVENT REPEATED OR PROLONGED SKIN CONTACT WITH THIS SUBSTANCE.

GLOVES: EMPLOYEE MUST WEAR APPROPRIATE PROTECTIVE GLOVES TO PREVENT CONTACT WITH THIS SUBSTANCE.

EYE PROTECTION: EMPLOYEE MUST WEAR SPLASH-PROOF OR DUST-RESISTANT SAFETY GOGGLES TO PREVENT EYE CONTACT WITH THIS SUBSTANCE.

EMERGENCY EYE WASH: WHERE THERE IS ANY POSSIBILITY THAT AN EMPLOYEE'S EYES MAY BE EXPOSED TO THIS SUBSTANCE, THE EMPLOYER SHOULD PROVIDE AN EYE WASH FOUNTAIN WITHIN THE IMMEDIATE WORK AREA FOR EMERGENCY USE.

AUTHORIZED BY- OCCUPATIONAL HEALTH SERVICES, INC.

CREATION DATE: 10/04/89 ***REVISION DATE:*** 05/31/90

MATERIAL SAFETY DATA SHEET

OCCUPATIONAL HEALTH SERVICES, INC.
AGRICULTURE AND PESTICIDE DIVISION
450 SEVENTH AVENUE, SUITE 2407
NEW YORK, NEW YORK 10123
1-800-445-MSDS OR (212) 967-1100

EMERGENCY CONTACT:
JOHN S. BRANSFORD, JR. (615) 292-1180

SUBSTANCE IDENTIFICATION

CAS-NUMBER 13121-70-5

SUBSTANCE: **CYHEXATIN**

TRADE NAMES/SYNONYMS: TRICYCLOHEXYLHYDROXY TIN; TRICYCLOHEXYLHYDROXYSTANNANE; TRICYCLOHEXYLHYDROXYTIN; TRICYCLOHEXYLSTANNOL; TRICYCLOHEXYLTIN HYDROXIDE; HYDROXYTRICYCLOHEXYLSTANNANE; DOWCO 213; M 3180; PLICTRAN; PLYCTRAN; TRICYCLOHEXYLSTANNYL HYDROXIDE; ENT 27395; ENT 27,395-X; PST06110

CHEMICAL FAMILY: ORGANOMETALLIC

MOLECULAR FORMULA: C18-H34-O-SN

MOLECULAR WEIGHT: 385.21

CERCLA RATINGS (SCALE 0-3): HEALTH=3 FIRE=0 REACTIVITY=0 PERSISTENCE=3

NFPA RATINGS (SCALE 0-4): HEALTH=3 FIRE=0 REACTIVITY=0

COMPONENTS AND CONTAMINANTS

COMPONENT: CYHEXATIN ***PERCENT:*** 100
CAS# 13121-70-5

OTHER CONTAMINANTS: NONE

EXPOSURE LIMITS: CYHEXATIN: 5 MG/M3 OSHA TWA 5 MG/M3 ACGIH TWA SUBJECT TO CALIFORNIA PROPOSITION 65 CANCER AND/OR REPRODUCTIVE TOXICITY WARNING AND RELEASE REQUIREMENTS- (JANUARY 1, 1989)

PHYSICAL DATA

DESCRIPTION: WHITISH CRYSTALLINE POWDER WHICH DECOMPOSES WHEN EXPOSED IN THIN LAYERS TO UV LIGHT ***MELTING POINT:*** 383-388 F (195-198 C)

SPECIFIC GRAVITY: NOT AVAILABLE ***SOLUBILITY IN WATER:*** INSOLUBLE

SOLVENT SOLUBILITY: MOST ORGANIC

FIRE AND EXPLOSION DATA

FIRE AND EXPLOSION HAZARD: NEGLIGIBLE FIRE HAZARD WHEN EXPOSED TO HEAT OR FLAME.

FIREFIGHTING MEDIA: DRY CHEMICAL, CARBON DIOXIDE, HALON, WATER SPRAY OR STANDARD FOAM (1987 EMERGENCY RESPONSE GUIDEBOOK, DOT P 5800.4). FOR LARGER FIRES, USE WATER SPRAY, FOG OR STANDARD FOAM (1987 EMERGENCY RESPONSE GUIDEBOOK, DOT P 5800.4).

FIREFIGHTING: NO ACUTE HAZARD. MOVE CONTAINER FROM FIRE AREA IF POSSIBLE. AVOID BREATHING VAPORS OR DUSTS; KEEP UPWIND.

TOXICITY

CYHEXATIN: TOXICITY DATA: 244 MG/M3 INHALATION-RAT LC50; 2422 MG/KG SKIN-RABBIT LD50; 446 MG/KG SKIN-RAT LD50; 180 MG/KG ORAL-RAT LD50; 275 GM/KG ORAL-MOUSE LD50; 458 MG/KG ORAL-RABBIT LD50; 780 MG/KG ORAL-GUINEA PIG LD50; 150 MG/KG ORAL-DOMESTIC ANIMAL LDLO; 13 MG/KG INTRAPERITONEAL-RAT LD50; 780 MG/KG UNREPORTED-MOUSE LD50; REPRODUCTIVE EFFECTS DATA (RTECS). CARCINOGEN STATUS: NONE. LOCAL EFFECTS: IRRITANT- INHALATION, SKIN, AND EYES. ACUTE TOXICITY LEVEL: HIGHLY TOXIC BY INHALATION, TOXIC BY INGESTION, AND SLIGHTLY TOXIC BY DERMAL ABSORPTION. TARGET EFFECTS: POISONING MAY AFFECT THE CENTRAL NERVOUS SYSTEM.

HEALTH EFFECTS AND FIRST AID

INHALATION: CYHEXATIN: IRRITANT. **ACUTE EXPOSURE-** DUST MAY CAUSE IRRITATION OF MUCOUS MEMBRANES. **CHRONIC EXPOSURE-** NO DATA AVAILABLE.

FIRST AID- REMOVE FROM EXPOSURE AREA TO FRESH AIR IMMEDIATELY. IF BREATHING HAS STOPPED, PERFORM ARTIFICIAL RESPIRATION. KEEP PERSON WARM AND AT REST. TREAT SYMPTOMATICALLY AND SUPPORTIVELY. GET MEDICAL ATTENTION IMMEDIATELY.

SKIN CONTACT: CYHEXATIN: IRRITANT. **ACUTE EXPOSURE-** ORGANOTIN COMPOUNDS ARE LIKELY TO CAUSE MILD TO SEVERE IRRITATION. ANIMAL STUDIES INDICATE LETHAL AMOUNTS OF CYHEXATIN CAN BE ABSORBED THROUGH THE SKIN. THE SYMPTOMS WERE NOT REPORTED. **CHRONIC EXPOSURE-** NO DATA AVAILABLE.

FIRST AID- REMOVE CONTAMINATED CLOTHING AND SHOES IMMEDIATELY. WASH AFFECTED AREA WITH SOAP OR MILD DETERGENT AND LARGE AMOUNTS OF WATER UNTIL NO EVIDENCE OF CHEMICAL REMAINS (APPROXIMATELY 15-20 MINUTES). GET MEDICAL ATTENTION IMMEDIATELY.

EYE CONTACT: CYHEXATIN: IRRITANT. **ACUTE EXPOSURE-** ORGANOTIN COMPOUNDS ARE LIKELY TO CAUSE MODERATE TO SEVERE IRRITATION. **CHRONIC EXPOSURE-** NO DATA AVAILABLE.

FIRST AID- WASH EYES IMMEDIATELY WITH LARGE AMOUNTS OF WATER, OCCASIONALLY LIFTING UPPER AND LOWER LIDS, UNTIL NO EVIDENCE OF CHEMICAL REMAINS (AT LEAST 15-20 MINUTES). CONTINUE IRRIGATING WITH NORMAL SALINE UNTIL THE PH HAS RETURNED TO NORMAL (30-60 MINUTES). COVER WITH STERILE BANDAGES. GET MEDICAL ATTENTION IMMEDIATELY.

INGESTION: CYHEXATIN: TOXIC. **ACUTE EXPOSURE-** TRIALKYL TIN DERIVATIVES ARE LIKELY TO AFFECT THE CENTRAL NERVOUS SYSTEM. THEY MAY CAUSE PSYCHIC DISTURBANCES, MUSCULAR WEAKNESS, CONVULSIONS, AND CEREBRAL EDEMA. THE MOST DISTINCTIVE AND DANGEROUS REACTION IS MASSIVE INTERSTITIAL EDEMA IN THE WHITE MATTER OF THE BRAIN. RAT STUDIES INDICATE THAT MILD DEFECTS OF LIVER AND KIDNEY FUNCTION MAY OCCUR. 180 MG/KG KILLED 50% OF RATS TESTED. **CHRONIC EXPOSURE-** ANIMAL STUDIES INDICATE THAT AT LOW LEVELS NO ADVERSE EFFECTS OCCUR. DOGS AND RATS FED UP TO 12 MG/KG PER DAY FOR 2 YEARS EXHIBITED NO TOXICOLOGICAL OR PATHOLOGICAL EFFECTS. MICROSCOPIC CHANGES IN THE LIVER, KIDNEY, AND ADRENAL GLANDS WERE NOTED IN RATS GIVEN 25 MG/KG PER DAY FOR 2 WEEKS. REPRODUCTIVE STUDIES INDICATE THAT ORAL ADMINISTRATION CAUSED REDUCED WEIGHT GAINS IN NEWBORN RATS.

FIRST AID- TREAT SYMPTOMATICALLY AND SUPPORTIVELY. GET MEDICAL ATTENTION IMMEDIATELY. IF VOMITING OCCURS, KEEP HEAD LOWER THAN HIPS TO PREVENT ASPIRATION.

ANTIDOTE: NO SPECIFIC ANTIDOTE. TREAT SYMPTOMATICALLY AND SUPPORTIVELY.

REACTIVITY

REACTIVITY: STABLE UNDER NORMAL TEMPERATURES AND PRESSURES.

INCOMPATIBILITIES: CYHEXATIN: NO DATA AVAILABLE.

DECOMPOSITION: THERMAL DECOMPOSITION MAY RELEASE TOXIC AND/OR HAZARDOUS GASES.

POLYMERIZATION: HAZARDOUS POLYMERIZATION HAS NOT BEEN REPORTED TO OCCUR UNDER NORMAL TEMPERATURES AND PRESSURES.

CONDITIONS TO AVOID

NONE REPORTED.

SPILL AND LEAK PROCEDURES

WATER SPILL: THE CALIFORNIA SAFE DRINKING WATER AND TOXIC ENFORCEMENT ACT OF 1986 (PROPOSITION 65) PROHIBITS CONTAMINATING ANY KNOWN SOURCE OF DRINKING WATER WITH SUBSTANCES KNOWN TO CAUSE CANCER AND/OR REPRODUCTIVE TOXICITY.

OCCUPATIONAL SPILL: NO SPECIAL PRECAUTIONS INDICATED.

PROTECTIVE EQUIPMENT

VENTILATION: PROVIDE LOCAL EXHAUST OR PROCESS ENCLOSURE VENTILATION TO MEET PUBLISHED EXPOSURE LIMITS.

RESPIRATOR: THE FOLLOWING RESPIRATORS ARE RECOMMENDED BASED ON INFORMATION FOUND IN THE PHYSICAL DATA, TOXICITY AND HEALTH EFFECTS SECTIONS. THEY ARE RANKED IN ORDER FROM MINIMUM TO MAXIMUM RESPIRATORY PROTECTION. THE SPECIFIC RESPIRATOR SELECTED MUST BE BASED ON CONTAMINATION LEVELS FOUND IN THE WORK PLACE, MUST NOT EXCEED THE WORKING LIMITS OF THE RESPIRATOR AND BE JOINTLY APPROVED BY THE NATIONAL INSTITUTE FOR OCCUPATIONAL SAFETY AND HEALTH AND THE MINE SAFETY AND HEALTH ADMINISTRATION (NIOSH-MSHA).

TYPE 'C' SUPPLIED-AIR RESPIRATOR WITH A FULL FACEPIECE OPERATED IN PRESSURE-DEMAND OR OTHER POSITIVE PRESSURE MODE OR WITH A FULL FACEPIECE, HELMET OR HOOD OPERATED IN CONTINOUS-FLOW MODE.

SELF-CONTAINED BREATHING APPARATUS WITH A FULL FACEPIECE OPERATED IN PRESSURE-DEMAND OR OTHER POSITIVE PRESSURE MODE.

FOR FIREFIGHTING AND OTHER IMMEDIATELY DANGEROUS TO LIFE OR HEALTH CONDITIONS:

SELF-CONTAINED BREATHING APPARATUS WITH FULL FACEPIECE OPERATED IN PRESSURE-DEMAND OR OTHER POSITIVE PRESSURE MODE.

SUPPLIED-AIR RESPIRATOR WITH FULL FACEPIECE AND OPERATED IN PRESSURE-DEMAND OR OTHER POSITIVE PRESSURE MODE IN COMBINATION WITH AN AUXILIARY SELF-CONTAINED BREATHING APPARATUS OPERATED IN PRESSURE-DEMAND OR OTHER POSITIVE PRESSURE MODE.

CLOTHING: EMPLOYEE MUST WEAR APPROPRIATE PROTECTIVE (IMPERVIOUS) CLOTHING AND EQUIPMENT TO PREVENT REPEATED OR PROLONGED SKIN CONTACT WITH THIS SUBSTANCE.

GLOVES: EMPLOYEE MUST WEAR APPROPRIATE PROTECTIVE GLOVES TO PREVENT CONTACT WITH THIS SUBSTANCE.

EYE PROTECTION: EMPLOYEE MUST WEAR SPLASH-PROOF OR DUST-RESISTANT SAFETY GOGGLES TO PREVENT EYE CONTACT WITH THIS SUBSTANCE.

EMERGENCY EYE WASH: WHERE THERE IS ANY POSSIBILITY THAT AN EMPLOYEE'S EYES MAY BE EXPOSED TO THIS SUBSTANCE, THE EMPLOYER SHOULD PROVIDE AN EYE WASH FOUNTAIN WITHIN THE IMMEDIATE WORK AREA FOR EMERGENCY USE.

AUTHORIZED BY- OCCUPATIONAL HEALTH SERVICES, INC.

CREATION DATE: 10/04/89 ***REVISION DATE:*** 05/09/90

MATERIAL SAFETY DATA SHEET

OCCUPATIONAL HEALTH SERVICES, INC.
AGRICULTURE AND PESTICIDE DIVISION
450 SEVENTH AVENUE, SUITE 2407
NEW YORK, NEW YORK 10123
1-800-445-MSDS OR (212) 967-1100

EMERGENCY CONTACT:
JOHN S. BRANSFORD, JR. (615) 292-1180

SUBSTANCE IDENTIFICATION

CAS-NUMBER 947-02-4

SUBSTANCE: PHOSFOLAN

TRADE NAMES/SYNONYMS: PHOSPHORAMIDIC ACID, 1-3-DITHIOLAN-2-YLIDENE-, DIETHYL ESTER; IMIDOCARBONIC ACID, PHOSPHONODITHIO-,CYCLIC ETHYLENE P,P-DIETHYL ESTER; DIETHYL 1,3-DITHIOLAN-2-YLIDENEPHOSPHORAMIDATE; 2-(DIETHOXYPHOSPHINYLIMINO)-1,3-DITHIOLAN; P,P-DIETHYL CYCLIC ETHYLENE PHOSPHONODITHIOIMIDOCARBONATE; 2-(DIETHOXYPHOSPHINYLIMINO)-1,3-DITHIOLANE; CYOLANE; EI 47031; PHOSPHOLAN; ENT 25,830; PST06115

CHEMICAL FAMILY: ORGANOPHOSPHATE HETEROCYCLIC SULFUR

MOLECULAR FORMULA: C7-H14-N-O3-P-S2

MOLECULAR WEIGHT: 255.31

CERCLA RATINGS (SCALE 0-3): HEALTH=3 FIRE=0 REACTIVITY=0 PERSISTENCE=0

NFPA RATINGS (SCALE 0-4): HEALTH=4 FIRE=0 REACTIVITY=0

COMPONENTS AND CONTAMINANTS

COMPONENT: PHOSFOLAN ***PERCENT:*** 100

CAS# 947-02-4

EXPOSURE LIMITS: PHOSFOLAN: NO OCCUPATIONAL EXPOSURE LIMITS ESTABLISHED BY OSHA, ACGIH, OR NIOSH.

100/10,000 POUNDS SARA SECTION 302 THRESHOLD PLANNING QUANTITY 1 POUND SARA SECTION 304 REPORTABLE QUANTITY

PHYSICAL DATA

DESCRIPTION: COLORLESS TO YELLOW SOLID

BOILING POINT: 239-244 F (115-118 C) @ 0.001 MMHG ***MELTING POINT:*** 99 F (37 C)

SPECIFIC GRAVITY: NOT AVAILABLE ***EVAPORATION RATE:*** NOT AVAILABLE

SOLUBILITY IN WATER: SOLUBLE

SOLVENT SOLUBILITY: SOLUBLE IN ACETONE, BENZENE, ETHANOL, CYCLOHEXANE, TOLUENE; SLIGHTLY SOLUBLE IN ETHER; SPARINGLY SOLUBLE IN HEXANE

FIRE AND EXPLOSION DATA

FIRE AND EXPLOSION HAZARD: NEGLIGIBLE FIRE HAZARD WHEN EXPOSED TO HEAT OR FLAME.

FIREFIGHTING MEDIA: DRY CHEMICAL, CARBON DIOXIDE, HALON, WATER SPRAY OR STANDARD FOAM (1987 EMERGENCY RESPONSE GUIDEBOOK, DOT P 5800.4).

FOR LARGER FIRES, USE WATER SPRAY, FOG OR STANDARD FOAM (1987 EMERGENCY RESPONSE GUIDEBOOK, DOT P 5800.4).

FIREFIGHTING: MOVE CONTAINERS FROM FIRE AREA IF POSSIBLE. FIGHT FIRE FROM MAXIMUM DISTANCE. STAY AWAY FROM STORAGE TANK ENDS. DIKE FIRE CONTROL WATER FOR LATER DISPOSAL. DO NOT SCATTER MATERIAL (1987 EMERGENCY RESPONSE GUIDEBOOK, DOT P 5800.4, GUIDE PAGE 55).

EXTINGUISH ONLY IF FLOW CAN BE STOPPED; USE FLOODING AMOUNTS OF WATER AS FOG, SOLID STREAMS MAY BE INEFFECTIVE. COOL CONTAINERS WITH FLOODING AMOUNTS OF WATER FROM AS FAR A DISTANCE AS POSSIBLE. USE WATER SPRAY TO ABSORB TOXIC VAPORS. AVOID BREATHING TOXIC VAPORS; KEEP UPWIND. CONSIDER EVACUATION OF DOWNWIND AREA IF MATERIAL IS LEAKING.

TRANSPORTATION DATA

DEPARTMENT OF TRANSPORTATION HAZARD CLASSIFICATION 49 CFR 172.101: POISON B

DEPARTMENT OF TRANSPORTATION LABELING REQUIREMENTS 49 CFR 172.101 AND SUBPART E: POISON

DEPARTMENT OF TRANSPORTATION PACKAGING REQUIREMENTS: 49 CFR 173.365 EXCEPTIONS: 49 CFR 173.364

TOXICITY

PHOSFOLAN: TOXICITY DATA: 23 MG/KG SKIN-RABBIT LD50; 54 MG/KG SKIN-GUINEA PIG LD50; 8900 UG/KG ORAL-RAT LD50; 12 MG/KG ORAL-MOUSE LD50. CARCINOGEN STATUS: NONE. ACUTE TOXICITY LEVEL: HIGHLY TOXIC BY INGESTION AND DERMAL ABSORPTION. TARGET EFFECTS: CHOLINESTERASE INHIBITOR. POISONING MAY AFFECT THE NERVOUS SYSTEM.* AT INCREASED RISK FROM EXPOSURE: PERSONS WITH RESPIRATORY AILMENTS, RECENT EXPOSURE TO CHOLINESTERASE INHIBITORS OR IMPAIRED CHOLINESTERASE PRODUCTION, OR LIVER MALFUNCTION.* ADDITIONAL DATA: MAY CROSS THE PLACENTA. HIGH ENVIRONMENTAL TEMPERATURES OR EXPOSURE OF THE CHEMICAL TO VISIBLE OR ULTRAVIOLET LIGHT MAY ENHANCE THE TOXICITY. INTERACTIONS WITH MEDICATIONS MAY OCCUR.*

* MAY BE BASED ON GENERAL INFORMATION ON ORGANOPHOSPHATES.

HEALTH EFFECTS AND FIRST AID

INHALATION: PHOSFOLAN: SEE INFORMATION ON ORGANOPHOSPHATES.

ORGANOPHOSPHATES: CHOLINESTERASE INHIBITOR. ACUTE EXPOSURE- WHEN INHALED, THE FIRST EFFECTS OF CHOLINESTERASE INHIBITORS ARE USUALLY RESPIRATORY AND MAY INCLUDE NASAL HYPEREMIA AND WATERY DISCHARGE, COUGH, CHEST DISCOMFORT, DYSPNEA, AND WHEEZING DUE TO INCREASED BRONCHIAL SECRETIONS AND BRONCHOCONSTRICTION. IF SUFFICIENT AMOUNTS ARE ABSORBED, OTHER SYSTEMIC EFFECTS MAY BEGIN WITHIN A FEW MINUTES OR BE DELAYED FOR UP TO 12 HOURS. SYMPTOMS MAY INCLUDE PALLOR, NAUSEA, VOMITING, DIARRHEA, ABDOMINAL CRAMPS, HEADACHE, DIZZINESS, OCULAR PAIN, BLURRED VISION, MIOSIS OR IN SOME CASES, ESPECIALLY INITIALLY, MYDRIASIS, LACRIMATION, SALIVATION, SWEATING, AND CONFUSION. OTHER REPORTED CENTRAL NERVOUS SYSTEM OR NEUROMUSCULAR EFFECTS MAY INCLUDE ATAXIA, SLURRED SPEECH, AREFLEXIA, WEAKNESS, FATIGUE,

FASCICULATIONS, TWITCHING, TREMORS POSSIBLY OF THE TONGUE AND EYELIDS, AND EVENTUALLY PARALYSIS OF THE EXTREMITIES AND POSSIBLY OF THE RESPIRATORY MUSCLES. IN SEVERE CASES THERE MAY ALSO BE INVOLUNTARY DEFECATION AND URINATION, CYANOSIS, PSYCHOSIS, HYPERGLYCEMIA, ACUTE PANCREATITIS, CARDIAC IRREGULARITIES, PULMONARY EDEMA, UNCONSCIOUSNESS, CONVULSIONS, AND COMA. DEATH IS PRIMARILY DUE TO RESPIRATORY FAILURE, ALTHOUGH CARDIOVASCULAR EFFECTS INCLUDING CARDIAC ARREST MAY ALSO BE IMPLICATED. LONG TERM SEQUELAE ARE RARE BUT MAY INCLUDE NEUROPSYCHIATRIC DISORDERS AND MYOPATHY WITH MUSCLE TENDERNESS. SOME ORGANOPHOSPHATES MAY CAUSE A DELAYED NEUROPATHY BEGINNING 1-4 WEEKS AFTER AN ACUTE EXPOSURE WHICH MAY OR MAY NOT HAVE CAUSED ACUTE CHOLINERGIC EFFECTS. NUMBNESS, TINGLING, WEAKNESS AND CRAMPING BEGINNING SYMMETRICALLY IN THE LOWER LIMBS MAY PROGRESS TO ATAXIA AND PARALYSIS. IN SEVERE CASES, UPPER LIMB INVOLVEMENT IS POSSIBLE AND FLACCID PARALYSIS MAY PROGRESS TO SPASTIC PARALYSIS WITH EXAGGERATED REFLEXES. IMPROVEMENT MAY OCCUR OVER MONTHS TO YEARS, BUT SOME RESIDUAL IMPAIRMENT USUALLY REMAINS. **CHRONIC EXPOSURE-** REPEATED OR PROLONGED EXPOSURE MAY RESULT IN THE EFFECTS OF ACUTE EXPOSURE INCLUDING THE DELAYED NEUROPATHY. OTHER EFFECTS REPORTED IN WORKERS REPEATEDLY EXPOSED INCLUDE IMPAIRED MEMORY AND CONCENTRATION, ACUTE PSYCHOSIS, SEVERE DEPRESSIONS, IRRITABILTY, CONFUSION, APATHY, EMOTIONAL LABILITY, SOCIAL WITHDRAWAL, CONFUSION, HEADACHE, SPEECH DIFFICULTIES, DELAYED REACTION TIMES, SPATIAL DISORIENTATION, NIGHTMARES, SLEEPWALKING, AND DROWSINESS OR INSOMNIA. AN INFLUENZA-LIKE CONDITION WITH HEADACHE, NAUSEA, WEAKNESS, ANOREXIA AND MALAISE HAS ALSO BEEN REPORTED.

FIRST AID- REMOVE FROM EXPOSURE AREA TO FRESH AIR IMMEDIATELY. IF BREATHING HAS STOPPED, GIVE ARTIFICIAL RESPIRATION. MAINTAIN AIRWAY AND BLOOD PRESSURE AND ADMINISTER OXYGEN IF AVAILABLE. KEEP AFFECTED PERSON WARM AND AT REST. TREAT SYMPTOMATICALLY AND SUPPORTIVELY. ADMINISTRATION OF OXYGEN SHOULD BE PERFORMED BY QUALIFIED PERSONNEL. GET MEDICAL ATTENTION IMMEDIATELY.

SKIN CONTACT: PHOSFOLAN: HIGHLY TOXIC. SEE INFORMATION ON ORGANOPHOSPHATES.

ORGANOPHOSPHATES: CHOLINESTERASE INHIBITOR. **ACUTE EXPOSURE-** LOCALIZED SWEATING AND FASCICULATIONS MAY OCCUR AT THE SITE OF CONTACT. IF SUFFICIENT AMOUNTS ARE ABSORBED, OTHER EFFECTS OF CHOLINESTERASE INHIBITION AS DESCRIBED IN ACUTE INHALATION MAY OCCUR. SYMPTOMS MAY BE DELAYED 2-3 HOURS, BUT USUALLY NO MORE THAN 12 HOURS. THE RATE OF ABSORPTION IS INCREASED BY THE PRESENCE OF DERMATITIS OR HIGH AMBIENT TEMPERATURES. DELAYED NEUROPATHY IS ALSO POSSIBLE. **CHRONIC EXPOSURE-** REPEATED OR PROLONGED EXPOSURE MAY CAUSE EFFECTS AS DESCRIBED IN ACUTE EXPOSURE. SOME ORGANOPHOSPHATES MAY CAUSE SENSITIZATION.

FIRST AID- REMOVE CONTAMINATED CLOTHING IMMEDIATELY. WASH CONTAMINATED AREAS WITH SOAP AND WATER FOLLOWED BY ALCOHOL (ARENA, POISONING, 4TH ED.). EMERGENCY PERSONNEL SHOULD WEAR GLOVES AND AVOID CONTAMINATION. TREAT RESPIRATORY DIFFICULTY WITH ARTIFICIAL RESPIRATION. GET MEDICAL ATTENTION IMMEDIATELY.

EYE CONTACT: PHOSFOLAN: SEE INFORMATION ON ORGANOPHOSPHATES.

ORGANOPHOSPHATES: CHOLINESTERASE INHIBITOR. **ACUTE EXPOSURE-** DIRECT CONTACT MAY CAUSE PAIN, HYPEREMIA, LACRIMATION, TWITCHING OF THE EYELIDS, MIOSIS, AND CILIARY MUSCLE SPASM WITH LOSS OF ACCOMODATION, BLURRED OR DIMMED VISION AND BROWACHE. SOMETIMES MYDRIASIS MAY OCCUR INSTEAD OF MIOSIS. WITH SUFFICIENT EXPOSURE, OTHER SYMPTOMS OF CHOLINESTERASE INHIBITION AS DESCRIBED IN ACUTE INHALATION MAY OCCUR. **CHRONIC EXPOSURE-** REPEATED OR PROLONGED EXPOSURE MAY CAUSE EFFECTS AS DESCRIBED IN ACUTE EXPOSURE. SOME COMPOUNDS HAVE CAUSED TOXIC EFFECTS ON THE CRYSTALLINE LENS, CONJUNCTIVAL THICKENING AND OBSTRUCTION OF THE NASOLACRIMAL CANALS WHEN USED AS MIOTIC EYEDROPS.

FIRST AID- IRRIGATE EYES WITH WATER OR SALINE SOLUTION. IF SYMPTOMS OF POISONING OCCUR, TREAT RESPIRATORY DIFFICULTY WITH ARTIFICIAL RESPIRATION AND OXYGEN. OBSERVE PATIENT FOR AT LEAST 24-36 HOURS (GOSSELIN, CLINICAL TOXICOLOGY OF COMMERCIAL PRODUCTS, 5TH ED.). GET MEDICAL ATTENTION IMMEDIATELY. OXYGEN SHOULD BE ADMINISTERED BY QUALIFIED MEDICAL PERSONNEL.

INGESTION: PHOSFOLAN: HIGHLY TOXIC. SEE INFORMATION ON ORGANOPHOSPHATES.

ORGANOPHOSPHATES: CHOLINESTERASE INHIBITOR. **ACUTE EXPOSURE-** WHEN INGESTED, THE FIRST EFFECTS MAY BE NAUSEA, VOMITING, ANOREXIA, ABDOMINAL CRAMPS AND DIARRHEA. GASTROINTESTINAL ABSORPTION MAY CAUSE SYMPTOMS OF CHOLINESTERASE INHIBITION AS DESCRIBED IN ACUTE INHALATION. SYMPTOMS MAY BEGIN WITHIN MINUTES OR BE DELAYED FOR HOURS. DELAYED EFFECTS INCLUDING NEUROPATHY MAY ALSO OCCUR. **CHRONIC EXPOSURE-** REPEATED INGESTION MAY CAUSE EFFECTS AS DESCRIBED IN ACUTE EXPOSURE.

FIRST AID- IF PERSON IS ALERT AND RESPIRATION IS NOT DEPRESSED, GIVE SYRUP OF IPECAC FOLLOWED BY WATER (IF VOMITING OCCURS, KEEP HEAD BELOW HIPS TO PREVENT ASPIRATION). IF CONSCIOUSNESS LEVEL DECLINES OR VOMITING HAS NOT OCCURRED IN 15 MINUTES EMPTY STOMACH BY GASTRIC LAVAGE WITH THE AID OF CUFFED ENDOTRACHEAL TUBE USING ISOTONIC SALINE OR 5% SODIUM BICARBONATE FOLLOW WITH ACTIVATED CHARCOAL. ESTABLISH AND MAINTAIN AIRWAY. TREAT RESPIRATORY DIFFICULTY WITH ARTIFICIAL RESPIRATION AND OXYGEN. DO NOT GIVE MORPHINE, AMINOPHYLLINE, PHENOTHIAZINES, RESERPINE, FUROSEMIDE, OR ETHACRYNIC ACID (MORGAN, RECOGNITION AND MANAGEMENT OF PESTICIDE POISONINGS, 3RD ED.). TREAT SYMPTOMATICALLY AND SUPPORTIVELY. ADMINISTRATION OF OXYGEN AND LAVAGE MUST BE PERFORMED BY QUALIFIED MEDICAL PERSONNEL. GET MEDICAL ATTENTION IMMEDIATELY.

ANTIDOTE: THE FOLLOWING ANTIDOTE(S) HAVE BEEN RECOMMENDED. HOWEVER, THE DECISION AS TO WHETHER THE SEVERITY OF POISONING REQUIRES ADMINISTRATION OF ANY ANTIDOTE AND ACTUAL DOSE REQUIRED SHOULD BE MADE BY QUALIFIED MEDICAL PERSONNEL.

FOR CHOLINESTERASE INHIBITORS: ESTABLISH CLEAR AIRWAY AND TISSUE OXYGENATION BY ASPIRATION OF SECRETIONS, AND IF NECESSARY, BY ASSISTED PULMONARY VENTILATION WITH OXYGEN. IMPROVE TISSUE OXYGENATION AS MUCH AS POSSIBLE BEFORE ADMINISTERING ATROPINE TO MINIMIZE THE RISK OF VENTRICULAR FIBRILLATION. ADMINISTER ATROPINE SULFATE INTRAVENOUSLY, OR INTRAMUSCULARLY IF IV INJECTION IS NOT POSSIBLE. IN MODERATELY SEVERE POISONING ADMINISTER ATROPINE SULFATE, 0.4-2.0 MG REPEATED EVERY 15 MINUTES UNTIL ATROPINIZATION IS ACHIEVED (TACHYCARDIA, FLUSHING, DRY MOUTH, MYDRIASIS). MAINTAIN ATROPINIZATION BY REPEATED DOSES FOR 2-12 HOURS, OR LONGER, DEPENDING ON THE SEVERITY OF POISONING. THE APPEARANCE OF RALES IN THE LUNG BASES, MIOSIS, SALIVATION, NAUSEA, BRADYCARDIA, ARE ALL INDICATIONS OF INADEQUATE ATROPINIZATION. SEVERELY POISONED INDIVIDUALS MAY EXHIBIT REMARKABLE TOLERANCE TO ATROPINE; TWO OR MORE TIMES THE DOSAGES SUGGESTED ABOVE MAY BE NEEDED. PERSONS NOT POISONED OR ONLY SLIGHTLY POISONED, HOWEVER, MAY DEVELOP SIGNS OF ATROPINE TOXICITY FROM SUCH LARGE DOSAGES: FEVER, MUSCLE FIBRILLATIONS, AND DELIRIUM ARE THE MAIN SIGNS OF ATROPINE TOXICITY. IF THESE SIGNS APPEAR WHILE THE PATIENT IS FULLY ATROPINIZED, ATROPINE ADMINISTRATION SHOULD BE DISCONTINUED, AT LEAST TEMPORARILY. OBSERVE TREATED PATIENTS CLOSELY AT LEAST 24 HOURS TO INSURE THAT SYMPTOMS (POSSIBLY PULMONARY EDEMA) DO NOT RECUR AS ATROPINIZATION WEARS OFF. IN VERY SEVERE POISONINGS, METABOLIC DISPOSITION OF TOXICANT MAY REQUIRE SEVERAL HOURS OR DAYS DURING WHICH ATROPINIZATION MUST BE MAINTAINED. MARKEDLY LOWER LEVELS OF URINARY METABOLITES INDICATE THAT ATROPINE DOSAGE CAN BE TAPERED OFF. AS DOSAGE IS REDUCED, CHECK THE LUNG BASES FREQUENTLY FOR RALES. IF RALES ARE HEARD OR OTHER SYMPTOMS RETURN, RE-ESTABLISH ATROPINIZATION PROMPTLY (MORGAN, RECOGNITION AND MANAGEMENT OF PESTICIDE POISONINGS, 3RD ED.). ADMINISTRATION OF ANTIDOTE MUST BE PERFORMED BY QUALIFIED MEDICAL PERSONNEL.

IN CASES OF SEVERE POISONING BY ORGANOPHOSPHATE PESTICIDES IN WHICH RESPIRATORY DEPRESSION, MUSCLE WEAKNESS AND TWITCHINGS ARE SEVERE, GIVE PRALIDOXIME (PROTOPAM-AYERST, 2-PAM), 1.0 GRAM INTRAVENOUSLY AT NO MORE THAN 0.5 GRAM PER MINUTE. DOSAGE OF PRALIDOXIME MAY BE REPEATED IN 1-2 HOURS, THEN AT 10-12 HOUR INTERVALS IF NEEDED. IN VERY SEVERE POISONINGS, DOSAGE RATES MAY BE DOUBLED. TREATMENT WITH PRALIDOXIME WILL BE MOST EFFECTIVE IF GIVEN WITHIN THIRTY-SIX HOURS AFTER POISONING (MORGAN, RECOGNITION AND MANAGEMENT OF PESTICIDE POISONINGS, 3RD ED.). ANTIDOTE SHOULD BE ADMINISTERED BY QUALIFIED MEDICAL PERSONNEL.

REACTIVITY

REACTIVITY: STABLE UNDER NORMAL TEMPERATURES AND PRESSURES.

INCOMPATIBILITIES: PHOSFOLAN: ALKALI: HYDROLYZED.

DECOMPOSITION: THERMAL DECOMPOSITION PRODUCTS MAY INCLUDE TOXIC AND HAZARDOUS FUMES OF SULFUR, NITROGEN AND PHOSPHORUS.

POLYMERIZATION: HAZARDOUS POLYMERIZATION HAS NOT BEEN REPORTED TO OCCUR UNDER NORMAL TEMPERATURES AND PRESSURES.

STORAGE AND DISPOSAL

OBSERVE ALL FEDERAL, STATE AND LOCAL REGULATIONS WHEN STORING OR DISPOSING OF THIS SUBSTANCE. FOR ASSISTANCE, CONTACT THE DISTRICT DIRECTOR OF THE ENVIRONMENTAL PROTECTION AGENCY.

****STORAGE****

STORE IN ACCORDANCE WITH 40 CFR 165 RECOMMENDED PROCEDURES FOR THE DISPOSAL AND STORAGE OF PESTICIDES AND PESTICIDE CONTAINERS.

STORE AWAY FROM INCOMPATIBLE SUBSTANCES.
THRESHOLD PLANNING QUANTITY (TPQ): THE SUPERFUND AMENDMENTS AND REAUTHORIZATION ACT (SARA) SECTION 302 REQUIRES THAT EACH FACILITY WHERE ANY EXTREMELY HAZARDOUS SUBSTANCE IS PRESENT IN A QUANTITY EQUAL TO OR GREATER THAN THE TPQ ESTABLISHED FOR THAT SUBSTANCE NOTIFY THE STATE EMERGENCY RESPONSE COMMISSION FOR THE STATE IN WHICH IT IS LOCATED. SECTION 303 OF SARA REQUIRES THESE FACILITIES TO PARTICIPATE IN LOCAL EMERGENCY RESPONSE PLANNING (40 CFR 355.30).

DISPOSAL

DISPOSAL MUST BE IN ACCORDANCE WITH 40 CFR 165 RECOMMENDED PROCEDURES FOR THE DISPOSAL AND STORAGE OF PESTICIDES AND PESTICIDE CONTAINERS.

CONDITIONS TO AVOID

NONE REPORTED.

SPILL AND LEAK PROCEDURES

OCCUPATIONAL SPILL: DO NOT TOUCH SPILLED MATERIAL. STOP LEAK IF YOU CAN DO IT WITHOUT RISK. USE WATER SPRAY TO REDUCE VAPORS. FOR SMALL SPILLS, TAKE UP WITH SAND OR OTHER ABSORBENT MATERIAL AND PLACE INTO CONTAINERS FOR LATER DISPOSAL. FOR SMALL DRY SPILLS, WITH A CLEAN SHOVEL PLACE MATERIAL INTO CLEAN, DRY CONTAINERS AND COVER. MOVE CONTAINERS FROM SPILL AREA. FOR LARGER SPILLS, DIKE FAR AHEAD OF SPILL FOR LATER DISPOSAL. KEEP UNNECESSARY PEOPLE AWAY. ISOLATE HAZARD AREA AND DENY ENTRY. VENTILATE CLOSED SPACES BEFORE ENTERING.
REPORTABLE QUANTITY (RQ): 1 POUND THE SUPERFUND AMENDMENTS AND REAUTHORIZATION ACT (SARA) SECTION 304 REQUIRES THAT A RELEASE EQUAL TO OR GREATER THAN THE REPORTABLE QUANTITY FOR THIS SUBSTANCE BE IMMEDIATELY REPORTED TO THE LOCAL EMERGENCY PLANNING COMMITTEE AND THE STATE EMERGENCY RESPONSE COMMISSION (40 CFR 355.40). IF THE RELEASE OF THIS SUBSTANCE IS REPORTABLE UNDER CERCLA SECTION 103, THE NATIONAL RESPONSE CENTER MUST BE NOTIFIED IMMEDIATELY AT (800) 424-8802 OR (202) 426-2675 IN THE METROPOLITAN WASHINGTON, D.C. AREA (40 CFR 302.6).

PROTECTIVE EQUIPMENT

VENTILATION: PROCESS ENCLOSURE RECOMMENDED.

RESPIRATOR: THE FOLLOWING RESPIRATORS ARE RECOMMENDED BASED ON INFORMATION FOUND IN THE PHYSICAL DATA, TOXICITY AND HEALTH EFFECTS SECTIONS. THEY ARE RANKED IN ORDER FROM MINIMUM TO MAXIMUM RESPIRATORY PROTECTION. THE SPECIFIC RESPIRATOR SELECTED MUST BE BASED ON CONTAMINATION LEVELS FOUND IN THE WORK PLACE, MUST NOT EXCEED THE WORKING LIMITS OF THE RESPIRATOR AND BE JOINTLY APPROVED BY THE NATIONAL INSTITUTE FOR OCCUPATIONAL SAFETY AND HEALTH AND THE MINE SAFETY AND HEALTH ADMINISTRATION (NIOSH-MSHA).
TYPE 'C' SUPPLIED-AIR RESPIRATOR WITH A FULL FACEPIECE OPERATED IN PRESSURE-DEMAND OR OTHER POSITIVE PRESSURE MODE OR WITH A FULL FACEPIECE, HELMET OR HOOD OPERATED IN CONTINOUS-FLOW MODE.
SELF-CONTAINED BREATHING APPARATUS WITH A FULL FACEPIECE OPERATED IN PRESSURE-DEMAND OR OTHER POSITIVE PRESSURE MODE.
FOR FIREFIGHTING AND OTHER IMMEDIATELY DANGEROUS TO LIFE OR HEALTH CONDITIONS:
SELF-CONTAINED BREATHING APPARATUS WITH FULL FACEPIECE OPERATED IN PRESSURE-DEMAND OR OTHER POSITIVE PRESSURE MODE.
SUPPLIED-AIR RESPIRATOR WITH FULL FACEPIECE AND OPERATED IN PRESSURE-DEMAND OR OTHER POSITIVE PRESSURE MODE IN COMBINATION WITH AN AUXILIARY SELF-CONTAINED BREATHING APPARATUS OPERATED IN PRESSURE-DEMAND OR OTHER POSITIVE PRESSURE MODE.

CLOTHING: EMPLOYEE MUST WEAR APPROPRIATE PROTECTIVE (IMPERVIOUS) CLOTHING AND EQUIPMENT TO PREVENT ANY POSSIBILITY OF SKIN CONTACT WITH THIS SUBSTANCE.

GLOVES: EMPLOYEE MUST WEAR APPROPRIATE PROTECTIVE GLOVES TO PREVENT CONTACT WITH THIS SUBSTANCE.

EYE PROTECTION: EMPLOYEE MUST WEAR SPLASH-PROOF OR DUST-RESISTANT SAFETY GOGGLES AND A FACESHIELD TO PREVENT CONTACT WITH THIS SUBSTANCE.
EMERGENCY WASH FACILITIES: WHERE THERE IS ANY POSSIBILITY THAT AN EMPLOYEE'S EYES AND/OR SKIN MAY BE EXPOSED TO THIS SUBSTANCE, THE EMPLOYER SHOULD PROVIDE AN EYE WASH FOUNTAIN AND QUICK DRENCH SHOWER WITHIN THE IMMEDIATE WORK AREA FOR EMERGENCY USE.

AUTHORIZED BY- OCCUPATIONAL HEALTH SERVICES, INC.
CREATION DATE: 10/04/89 ***REVISION DATE:*** 04/24/90

MATERIAL SAFETY DATA SHEET

OCCUPATIONAL HEALTH SERVICES, INC.
AGRICULTURE AND PESTICIDE DIVISION
450 SEVENTH AVENUE, SUITE 2407
NEW YORK, NEW YORK 10123
1-800-445-MSDS OR (212) 967-1100

EMERGENCY CONTACT:
JOHN S. BRANSFORD, JR. (615) 292-1180

SUBSTANCE IDENTIFICATION

CAS-NUMBER 67375-30-8

SUBSTANCE: **ALPHACYPERMETHRIN**

TRADE NAMES/SYNONYMS: CYCLOPROPANECARBOXYLIC ACID, 3-(2,2-DICHLOROETHENYL)-2,2-DIMETHYL-, CYANO(3-PHENOXYPHENYL)METHYL ESTER, (1ALPHA(S*),3ALPHA)-(+/-)-; (1ALPHA(S*)3ALPHA)-(+/-)-CYANO(3-PHENOXYPHENYL)METHYL 3-(2,2- DICHLOROETHENYL)-2,2-DIMETHYLCYCLOPROPANECARBOXYLATE; (1R CIS S) AND (1S CIS R) ENANTIOMERIC ISOMER PAIR OF ALPHA-CYANO-3- PHENOXYBENZYL-3-(2,2-DICHLOROVINYL)-2,2- DIMETHYLCYCLOPROPANECARBOXYLATE; ALFOXYLATE; ALPHAMETHRIN; WL 85871; FASTAC; CONCORD; FEDONA; RENEGADE; C22H19CL2NO3; PST06118

CHEMICAL FAMILY: PYRETHROID (SYNTHETIC)

MOLECULAR FORMULA: C22-H19-CL2-N-O3

MOLECULAR WEIGHT: 416.32

CERCLA RATINGS (SCALE 0-3): HEALTH=3 FIRE=1 REACTIVITY=0 PERSISTENCE=3

NFPA RATINGS (SCALE 0-4): HEALTH=3 FIRE=1 REACTIVITY=0

COMPONENTS AND CONTAMINANTS

COMPONENT: ALPHACYPERMETHRIN ***PERCENT:*** 100.0
CAS# 67375-30-8

OTHER CONTAMINANTS: NONE

EXPOSURE LIMITS: NO OCCUPATIONAL EXPOSURE LIMITS ESTABLISHED BY OSHA, ACGIH, OR NIOSH.

PHYSICAL DATA

DESCRIPTION: WHITE TO CREAM COLORED CRYSTALLINE SOLID WITH A MILD CHEMICAL ODOR.

BOILING POINT: 392 F (200 C) @ 0.07 MMHG ***MELTING POINT:*** 178 F (81 C)

SPECIFIC GRAVITY: 1.12 ***VAPOR PRESSURE:*** NEGLIGIBLE

SOLUBILITY IN WATER: 0.01 PPM

SOLVENT SOLUBILITY: SOLUBLE IN ACETONE, CYCLOHEXANONE, XYLENE, DICHLOROMETHANE, ETHYL ACETATE, CHLOROBENZENE AND ACETOPHENONE; MODERATELY SOLUBLE IN CORN OIL; SLIGHTLY SOLUBLE IN HEXANE AND ETHYLENE GLYCOL.

FIRE AND EXPLOSION DATA

FIRE AND EXPLOSION HAZARD: SLIGHT FIRE HAZARD WHEN EXPOSED TO HEAT OR FLAME.

FIREFIGHTING MEDIA: DRY CHEMICAL, CARBON DIOXIDE, HALON, WATER SPRAY OR STANDARD FOAM (1987 EMERGENCY RESPONSE GUIDEBOOK, DOT P 5800.4).
FOR LARGER FIRES, USE WATER SPRAY, FOG OR STANDARD FOAM (1987 EMERGENCY RESPONSE GUIDEBOOK, DOT P 5800.4).

FIREFIGHTING: MOVE CONTAINERS FROM FIRE AREA IF POSSIBLE (1987 EMERGENCY RESPONSE GUIDEBOOK, DOT P 5800.4, GUIDE PAGE 53).
EXTINGUISH USING AGENT SUITABLE FOR TYPE OF SURROUNDING FIRE. AVOID BREATHING VAPORS AND DUSTS. KEEP UPWIND.

TOXICITY

ALPHACYPERMETHRIN: TOXICITY DATA: 500 MG/KG SKIN-RAT LD50; 79 MG/KG ORAL-RAT LD50. CARCINOGEN STATUS: NONE. ACUTE TOXICITY LEVEL: TOXIC BY DERMAL ABSORPTION, INGESTION. TARGET EFFECTS: NO DATA AVAILABLE.

HEALTH EFFECTS AND FIRST AID

INHALATION: ALPHACYPERMETHRIN: SEE INFORMATION ON PYRETHROIDS.
PYRETHROIDS: **ACUTE EXPOSURE-** HEAVY EXPOSURE TO A MIST OF SOME PYRETHROIDS HAS PRODUCED HYPERSENSITIVIITY, ATAXIA, AND URINARY INCONTINENCE. CONVULSIONS MAY ALSO BE POSSIBLE. **CHRONIC EXPOSURE-** ANIMALS EXPOSED TO AEROSOLS OF SOME PYRETHROIDS FOR 3-4 HOURS/DAY FOR UP TO 4 WEEKS DID NOT EXHIBIT ANY SIGNIFICANT COMPOUND RELATED FINDINGS.

FIRST AID- REMOVE FROM EXPOSURE AREA TO FRESH AIR IMMEDIATELY. IF BREATHING HAS STOPPED, PERFORM ARTIFICIAL RESPIRATION. KEEP PERSON WARM AND AT REST. TREAT SYMPTOMATICALLY AND SUPPORTIVELY. GET MEDICAL ATTENTION IMMEDIATELY.

SKIN CONTACT: ALPHACYPERMETHRIN: TOXIC. SEE INFORMATION ON PYRETHROIDS. THE TECHNICAL GRADE WAS MINIMALLY IRRITATING TO RABBIT SKIN AND FORMULATIONS CAUSED MILD TO MODERATE IRRITATION. THE LETHAL DOSE REPORTED IN RATS WAS 500 MG/KG. THE SYMPTOMS WERE NOT REPORTED. PYRETHROIDS: **ACUTE EXPOSURE-** BASED ON ANIMAL AND HUMAN STUDIES AND HUMAN EXPERIENCES WITH SOME PYRETHROIDS, PRIMARY IRRITATION IS UNLIKELY. CUTANEOUS PARESTHESIAS MAY OCCUR INCLUDING NUMBNESS, ITCHING, BURNING, TINGLING AND WARMTH WITHOUT SIGNS OF IRRITATION. THESE EFFECTS MAY BE DELAYED FOR 30 MINUTES OR MORE AND LAST LESS THAN 24 HOURS. **CHRONIC EXPOSURE-** TESTS WITH SOME PYRETHROIDS ON HUMANS AND ANIMALS INDICATE SENSITIZATION IS UNLIKELY.

FIRST AID- REMOVE CONTAMINATED CLOTHING AND SHOES IMMEDIATELY. WASH AFFECTED AREA WITH SOAP OR MILD DETERGENT AND LARGE AMOUNTS OF WATER UNTIL NO EVIDENCE OF CHEMICAL REMAINS (APPROXIMATELY 15-20 MINUTES). GET MEDICAL ATTENTION IMMEDIATELY.

EYE CONTACT: ALPHACYPERMETHRIN: SEE INFORMATION ON PYRETHROIDS. THE TECHNICAL GRADE WAS MILDLY IRRITATING TO RABBIT EYES AND FORMULATIONS CAUSED SEVERE IRRITATION.
PYRETHROIDS: **ACUTE EXPOSURE-** MASSIVE INSTILLATION OF SOME PYRETHROIDS INTO RABBIT EYES PRODUCED ONLY A SLIGHT, TRANSIENT CONGESTION OF THE CONJUNCTIVA OR LACRIMATION. **CHRONIC EXPOSURE-** NO DATA AVAILABLE.

FIRST AID- WASH EYES IMMEDIATELY WITH LARGE AMOUNTS OF WATER OR NORMAL SALINE, OCCASIONALLY LIFTING UPPER AND LOWER LIDS, UNTIL NO EVIDENCE OF CHEMICAL REMAINS (APPROXIMATELY 15-20 MINUTES). GET MEDICAL ATTENTION IMMEDIATELY.

INGESTION: ALPHACYPERMETHRIN: TOXIC. SEE INFORMATION ON PYRETHROIDS. THE LETHAL DOSE REPORTED IN RATS WAS 79 MG/KG. THE SYMPTOMS WERE NOT REPORTED. IN 90 DAY FEEDING STUDIES, RATS FED UP TO 60 MG/KG IN THE DIET SHOWED NO MAJOR TOXICOLOGICAL OR PATHOLOGICAL CHANGES.
PYRETHROIDS: **ACUTE EXPOSURE-** SOME PYRETHROIDS HAVE PRODUCED HYPERSENSITIVITY, NERVOUS IRRITABILITY, TREMORS, ATAXIA, AND URINARY INCONTINENCE IN ANIMALS. CONVULSIONS MAY ALSO BE POSSIBLE. **CHRONIC EXPOSURE-** INCREASED KIDNEY AND LIVER WEIGHTS AND HEPATIC HISTOPATHOLOGICAL CHANGES WERE NOTED IN ANIMALS CHRONICALLY FED SOME PYRETHROIDS.

FIRST AID- IF EXTENSIVE VOMITING HAS NOT OCCURRED, THE SUBSTANCE SHOULD BE REMOVED BY EMESIS OR GASTRIC LAVAGE PROVIDED THAT THE PATIENT IS CONSCIOUS AND CONVULSIONS ARE NOT PRESENT. KEEP HEAD BELOW HIPS DURING VOMITING TO PREVENT ASPIRATION. DO NOT ATTEMPT TO MAKE AN UNCONSCIOUS PERSON VOMIT. TREAT SYMPTOMATICALLY AND SUPPORTIVELY. GET MEDICAL ATTENTION IMMEDIATELY (DREISBACH, HANDBOOK OF POISONING, 12TH ED.). TREATMENT SHOULD BE PERFORMED BY QUALIFIED MEDICAL PERSONNEL.

ANTIDOTE: NO SPECIFIC ANTIDOTE. TREAT SYMPTOMATICALLY AND SUPPORTIVELY.

REACTIVITY

REACTIVITY: STABLE UNDER NORMAL TEMPERATURES AND PRESSURES.

INCOMPATIBILITIES: ALPHACYPERMETHRIN: OXIDIZERS (STRONG): FIRE AND EXPLOSION HAZARD.

DECOMPOSITION: THERMAL DECOMPOSITION PRODUCTS MAY INCLUDE HIGHLY TOXIC VAPORS OF HYDROGEN CYANIDE, TOXIC AND CORROSIVE FUMES OF CHLORIDES, AND TOXIC OXIDES OF CARBON AND NITROGEN.

POLYMERIZATION: HAZARDOUS POLYMERIZATION HAS NOT BEEN REPORTED TO OCCUR UNDER NORMAL TEMPERATURES AND PRESSURES.

STORAGE AND DISPOSAL

OBSERVE ALL FEDERAL, STATE AND LOCAL REGULATIONS WHEN STORING OR DISPOSING OF THIS SUBSTANCE. FOR ASSISTANCE, CONTACT THE DISTRICT DIRECTOR OF THE ENVIRONMENTAL PROTECTION AGENCY.

****STORAGE****

STORE IN ACCORDANCE WITH 40 CFR 165 RECOMMENDED PROCEDURES FOR THE DISPOSAL AND STORAGE OF PESTICIDES AND PESTICIDE CONTAINERS.
STORE AWAY FROM INCOMPATIBLE SUBSTANCES.

****DISPOSAL****

DISPOSAL MUST BE IN ACCORDANCE WITH 40 CFR 165 RECOMMENDED PROCEDURES FOR THE DISPOSAL AND STORAGE OF PESTICIDES AND PESTICIDE CONTAINERS.

CONDITIONS TO AVOID

MAY BURN BUT DOES NOT IGNITE READILY.

SPILL AND LEAK PROCEDURES

OCCUPATIONAL SPILL: DO NOT TOUCH SPILLED MATERIAL. STOP LEAK IF YOU CAN DO IT WITHOUT RISK. FOR SMALL SPILLS, TAKE UP WITH SAND OR OTHER ABSORBENT MATERIAL AND PLACE INTO CONTAINERS FOR LATER DISPOSAL. FOR SMALL DRY SPILLS, WITH A CLEAN SHOVEL PLACE MATERIAL INTO CLEAN, DRY CONTAINER AND COVER. MOVE CONTAINERS FROM SPILL AREA. FOR LARGER SPILLS, DIKE FAR AHEAD OF SPILL FOR LATER DISPOSAL. KEEP UNNECESSARY PEOPLE AWAY. ISOLATE HAZARD AREA AND DENY ENTRY.

PROTECTIVE EQUIPMENT

VENTILATION: PROVIDE LOCAL EXHAUST OR PROCESS ENCLOSURE VENTILATION SYSTEM.

RESPIRATOR: THE FOLLOWING RESPIRATORS ARE RECOMMENDED BASED ON INFORMATION FOUND IN THE PHYSICAL DATA, TOXICITY AND HEALTH EFFECTS SECTIONS. THEY ARE RANKED IN ORDER FROM MINIMUM TO MAXIMUM RESPIRATORY PROTECTION. THE SPECIFIC RESPIRATOR SELECTED MUST BE BASED ON CONTAMINATION LEVELS FOUND IN THE WORK PLACE, MUST NOT EXCEED THE WORKING LIMITS OF THE RESPIRATOR AND BE JOINTLY APPROVED BY THE NATIONAL INSTITUTE FOR OCCUPATIONAL SAFETY AND HEALTH AND THE MINE SAFETY AND HEALTH ADMINISTRATION (NIOSH-MSHA).
CHEMICAL CARTRIDGE RESPIRATOR WITH AN ORGANIC VAPOR CARTRIDGE(S) WITH A FULL FACEPIECE AND ORGANIC VAPOR CARTRIDGE(S) IN COMBINATION WITH A DUST AND MIST FILTER.
POWERED AIR-PURIFYING RESPIRATOR WITH A TIGHT-FITTING FACEPIECE AND ORGANIC VAPOR CARTRIDGE(S) IN COMBINATION WITH A HIGH-EFFICIENCY PARTICULATE FILTER.
TYPE 'C' SUPPLIED-AIR RESPIRATOR WITH A FULL FACEPIECE OPERATED IN A PRESSURE-DEMAND OR OTHER POSITIVE PRESSURE MODE.
SELF-CONTAINED BREATHING APPARATUS WITH A FULL FACEPIECE OPERATED IN PRESSURE-DEMAND OR OTHER POSITIVE PRESSURE MODE.
FOR FIREFIGHTING AND OTHER IMMEDIATELY DANGEROUS TO LIFE OR HEALTH CONDITIONS:
SELF-CONTAINED BREATHING APPARATUS WITH FULL FACEPIECE OPERATED IN PRESSURE-DEMAND OR OTHER POSITIVE PRESSURE MODE.
SUPPLIED-AIR RESPIRATOR WITH FULL FACEPIECE AND OPERATED IN PRESSURE-DEMAND OR OTHER POSITIVE PRESSURE MODE IN COMBINATION WITH AN AUXILIARY SELF-CONTAINED BREATHING APPARATUS OPERATED IN PRESSURE-DEMAND OR OTHER POSITIVE PRESSURE MODE.

CLOTHING: EMPLOYEE MUST WEAR APPROPRIATE PROTECTIVE (IMPERVIOUS) CLOTHING AND EQUIPMENT TO PREVENT ANY POSSIBILITY OF SKIN CONTACT WITH THIS SUBSTANCE.

GLOVES: EMPLOYEE MUST WEAR APPROPRIATE PROTECTIVE GLOVES TO PREVENT CONTACT WITH THIS SUBSTANCE.

EYE PROTECTION: EMPLOYEE MUST WEAR SPLASH-PROOF OR DUST-RESISTANT SAFETY GOGGLES WITH OR WITHOUT A FACESHIELD TO PREVENT CONTACT WITH THIS SUBSTANCE.
EMERGENCY EYE WASH: WHERE THERE IS ANY POSSIBILITY THAT AN EMPLOYEE'S EYES MAY BE EXPOSED TO THIS SUBSTANCE, THE EMPLOYER SHOULD PROVIDE AN EYE WASH FOUNTAIN WITHIN THE IMMEDIATE WORK AREA FOR EMERGENCY USE.

AUTHORIZED BY- OCCUPATIONAL HEALTH SERVICES, INC.
CREATION DATE: 02/02/90 ***REVISION DATE:*** 05/07/90

MATERIAL SAFETY DATA SHEET

OCCUPATIONAL HEALTH SERVICES, INC.
AGRICULTURE AND PESTICIDE DIVISION
450 SEVENTH AVENUE, SUITE 2407
NEW YORK, NEW YORK 10123
1-800-445-MSDS OR (212) 967-1100

EMERGENCY CONTACT:
JOHN S. BRANSFORD, JR. (615) 292-1180

SUBSTANCE IDENTIFICATION

CAS-NUMBER 115-93-5

SUBSTANCE: **CYTHIOATE**

TRADE NAMES/SYNONYMS: PHOSPHOROTHIOIC ACID, O-(4-(AMINOSULFONYL)PHENYL) O,O-DIMETHYL ESTER; PHOSPHOROTHIOIC ACID, O,O-DIMETHYL ESTER, O-ESTER WITH P-HYDROXYBENZENESULFONAMIDE; O,O-DIMETHYL O-4-SULPHAMOYLPHENYL PHOSPHOROTHIOATE; O,O-DIMETHYL O-(4-(AMINOSULFONYL)PHENYL) PHOSPHOROTHIOATE; O,O-DIMETHYL PHOSPHOROTHIOATE O-ESTER WITH P-HYDROXYBENZENESULFONAMIDE; O,O-DIMETHYL O-P-SULFAMOYLPHENYLPHOSPHOROTHIOATE; CL 26691; CYFLEE; ENT

25,640; PST06135

CHEMICAL FAMILY: ORGANOPHOSPHATE

MOLECULAR FORMULA: C8-H12-N-O5-P-S2

MOLECULAR WEIGHT: 297.30

CERCLA RATINGS (SCALE 0-3): HEALTH=3 FIRE=0 REACTIVITY=0 PERSISTENCE=1

NFPA RATINGS (SCALE 0-4): HEALTH=3 FIRE=0 REACTIVITY=0

COMPONENTS AND CONTAMINANTS

COMPONENT: CYTHIOATE ***PERCENT:*** 100

CAS# 115-93-5

EXPOSURE LIMITS: NO OCCUPATIONAL EXPOSURE LIMITS ESTABLISHED BY OSHA, ACGIH, OR NIOSH.

PHYSICAL DATA

DESCRIPTION: WHITE CRYSTALLINE SOLID ***MELTING POINT:*** 165 F (74 C)

SOLUBILITY IN WATER: INSOLUBLE

SOLVENT SOLUBILITY: SOLUBLE IN ACETONE, BENZENE, DIETHYL ETHER, ETHANOL; INSOLUBLE IN CARBON TETRACHLORIDE

FIRE AND EXPLOSION DATA

FIRE AND EXPLOSION HAZARD: NEGLIGIBLE FIRE HAZARD WHEN EXPOSED TO HEAT OR FLAME.

FIREFIGHTING MEDIA: DRY CHEMICAL, CARBON DIOXIDE, HALON, WATER SPRAY OR STANDARD FOAM (1987 EMERGENCY RESPONSE GUIDEBOOK, DOT P 5800.4). FOR LARGER FIRES, USE WATER SPRAY, FOG OR STANDARD FOAM (1987 EMERGENCY RESPONSE GUIDEBOOK, DOT P 5800.4).

FIREFIGHTING: MOVE CONTAINERS FROM FIRE AREA IF POSSIBLE. FIGHT FIRE FROM MAXIMUM DISTANCE. STAY AWAY FROM STORAGE TANK ENDS. DIKE FIRE CONTROL WATER FOR LATER DISPOSAL. DO NOT SCATTER MATERIAL (1987 EMERGENCY RESPONSE GUIDEBOOK, DOT P 5800.4, GUIDE PAGE 55). EXTINGUISH USING AGENT SUITABLE FOR TYPE OF SURROUNDING FIRE. AVOID BREATHING VAPORS AND DUSTS. KEEP UPWIND.

TOXICITY

CYTHIOATE: TOXICITY DATA: 160 MG/KG ORAL-RAT LD50; 38 MG/KG ORAL-MOUSE LD50. CARCINOGEN STATUS: NONE. ACUTE TOXICITY LEVEL: TOXIC BY INGESTION. TARGET EFFECTS: CHOLINESTERASE INHIBITOR. POISONING MAY AFFECT THE NERVOUS SYSTEM.* AT INCREASED RISK FROM EXPOSURE: PERSONS WITH RESPIRATORY AILMENTS, RECENT EXPOSURE TO CHOLINESTERASE INHIBITORS OR IMPAIRED CHOLINESTERASE PRODUCTION, OR LIVER MALFUNCTION.* ADDITIONAL DATA: MAY CROSS THE PLACENTA. HIGH ENVIRONMENTAL TEMPERATURES OR EXPOSURE OF THE CHEMICAL TO VISIBLE OR ULTRAVIOLET LIGHT MAY ENHANCE THE TOXICITY. INTERACTIONS WITH MEDICATIONS MAY OCCUR.*

* MAY BE BASED ON GENERAL INFORMATION ON ORGANOPHOSPHATES.

HEALTH EFFECTS AND FIRST AID

INHALATION: CYTHIOATE: SEE INFORMATION ON ORGANOPHOSPHATES.
ORGANOPHOSPHATES: CHOLINESTERASE INHIBITOR. **ACUTE EXPOSURE-** WHEN INHALED, THE FIRST EFFECTS OF CHOLINESTERASE INHIBITORS ARE USUALLY RESPIRATORY AND MAY INCLUDE NASAL HYPEREMIA AND WATERY DISCHARGE, COUGH, CHEST DISCOMFORT, DYSPNEA, AND WHEEZING DUE TO INCREASED BRONCHIAL SECRETIONS AND BRONCHOCONSTRICTION. IF SUFFICIENT AMOUNTS ARE ABSORBED, OTHER SYSTEMIC EFFECTS MAY BEGIN WITHIN A FEW MINUTES OR BE DELAYED FOR UP TO 12 HOURS. SYMPTOMS MAY INCLUDE PALLOR, NAUSEA, VOMITING, DIARRHEA, ABDOMINAL CRAMPS, HEADACHE, DIZZINESS, OCULAR PAIN, BLURRED VISION, MIOSIS OR IN SOME CASES, ESPECIALLY INITIALLY, MYDRIASIS, LACRIMATION, SALIVATION, SWEATING, AND CONFUSION. OTHER REPORTED CENTRAL NERVOUS SYSTEM OR NEUROMUSCULAR EFFECTS MAY INCLUDE ATAXIA, SLURRED SPEECH, AREFLEXIA, WEAKNESS, FATIGUE, FASCICULATIONS, TWITCHING, TREMORS POSSIBLY OF THE TONGUE AND EYELIDS, AND EVENTUALLY PARALYSIS OF THE EXTREMITIES AND POSSIBLY OF THE RESPIRATORY MUSCLES. IN SEVERE CASES THERE MAY ALSO BE INVOLUNTARY DEFECATION AND URINATION, CYANOSIS, PSYCHOSIS, HYPERGLYCEMIA, ACUTE PANCREATITIS, CARDIAC IRREGULARITIES, PULMONARY EDEMA, UNCONSCIOUSNESS, CONVULSIONS, AND COMA. DEATH IS PRIMARILY DUE TO RESPIRATORY FAILURE, ALTHOUGH CARDIOVASCULAR EFFECTS INCLUDING CARDIAC ARREST MAY ALSO BE IMPLICATED. LONG TERM SEQUELAE ARE RARE BUT MAY INCLUDE NEUROPSYCHIATRIC DISORDERS AND MYOPATHY WITH MUSCLE TENDERNESS. SOME ORGANOPHOSPHATES MAY CAUSE A DELAYED NEUROPATHY BEGINNING 1-4 WEEKS AFTER AN ACUTE EXPOSURE WHICH MAY OR MAY NOT HAVE CAUSED ACUTE CHOLINERGIC EFFECTS. NUMBNESS, TINGLING, WEAKNESS AND CRAMPING BEGINNING SYMMETRICALLY IN THE LOWER LIMBS MAY PROGRESS TO ATAXIA AND PARALYSIS. IN SEVERE CASES, UPPER LIMB INVOLVEMENT IS POSSIBLE AND FLACCID PARALYSIS MAY PROGRESS TO SPASTIC PARALYSIS WITH EXAGGERATED REFLEXES. IMPROVEMENT MAY OCCUR OVER MONTHS TO YEARS, BUT SOME RESIDUAL IMPAIRMENT USUALLY REMAINS. **CHRONIC EXPOSURE-** REPEATED OR PROLONGED EXPOSURE MAY RESULT IN THE EFFECTS OF ACUTE EXPOSURE INCLUDING THE DELAYED NEUROPATHY. OTHER EFFECTS REPORTED IN WORKERS REPEATEDLY EXPOSED INCLUDE IMPAIRED MEMORY AND CONCENTRATION, ACUTE PSYCHOSIS, SEVERE DEPRESSIONS, IRRITABILTY, CONFUSION, APATHY, EMOTIONAL LABILITY, SOCIAL WITHDRAWAL, CONFUSION, HEADACHE, SPEECH DIFFICULTIES, DELAYED REACTION TIMES, SPATIAL DISORIENTATION, NIGHTMARES, SLEEPWALKING, AND DROWSINESS OR INSOMNIA. AN INFLUENZA-LIKE CONDITION WITH HEADACHE, NAUSEA, WEAKNESS, ANOREXIA AND MALAISE HAS ALSO BEEN REPORTED.

FIRST AID- REMOVE FROM EXPOSURE AREA TO FRESH AIR IMMEDIATELY. IF BREATHING HAS STOPPED, GIVE ARTIFICIAL RESPIRATION. MAINTAIN AIRWAY AND BLOOD PRESSURE AND ADMINISTER OXYGEN IF AVAILABLE. KEEP AFFECTED PERSON WARM AND AT REST. TREAT SYMPTOMATICALLY AND SUPPORTIVELY. ADMINISTRATION OF OXYGEN SHOULD BE PERFORMED BY QUALIFIED PERSONNEL. GET MEDICAL ATTENTION IMMEDIATELY.

SKIN CONTACT: CYTHIOATE: SEE INFORMATION ON ORGANOPHOSPHATES.
ORGANOPHOSPHATES: CHOLINESTERASE INHIBITOR. **ACUTE EXPOSURE-** LOCALIZED SWEATING AND FASCICULATIONS MAY OCCUR AT THE SITE OF CONTACT. IF SUFFICIENT AMOUNTS ARE ABSORBED, OTHER EFFECTS OF CHOLINESTERASE INHIBITION AS DESCRIBED IN ACUTE INHALATION MAY OCCUR. SYMPTOMS MAY BE DELAYED 2-3 HOURS, BUT USUALLY NO MORE THAN 12 HOURS. THE RATE OF ABSORPTION IS INCREASED BY THE PRESENCE OF DERMATITIS OR HIGH AMBIENT TEMPERATURES. DELAYED NEUROPATHY IS ALSO POSSIBLE. **CHRONIC EXPOSURE-** REPEATED OR PROLONGED EXPOSURE MAY CAUSE EFFECTS AS DESCRIBED IN ACUTE EXPOSURE. SOME ORGANOPHOSPHATES MAY CAUSE SENSITIZATION.

FIRST AID- REMOVE CONTAMINATED CLOTHING IMMEDIATELY. WASH CONTAMINATED AREAS WITH SOAP AND WATER FOLLOWED BY ALCOHOL (ARENA, POISONING, 4TH ED.). EMERGENCY PERSONNEL SHOULD WEAR GLOVES AND AVOID CONTAMINATION. TREAT RESPIRATORY DIFFICULTY WITH ARTIFICIAL RESPIRATION. GET MEDICAL ATTENTION IMMEDIATELY.

EYE CONTACT: CYTHIOATE: SEE INFORMATION ON ORGANOPHOSPHATES.
ORGANOPHOSPHATES: CHOLINESTERASE INHIBITOR. **ACUTE EXPOSURE-** DIRECT CONTACT MAY CAUSE PAIN, HYPEREMIA, LACRIMATION, TWITCHING OF THE EYELIDS, MIOSIS, AND CILIARY MUSCLE SPASM WITH LOSS OF ACCOMODATION, BLURRED OR DIMMED VISION AND BROWACHE. SOMETIMES MYDRIASIS MAY OCCUR INSTEAD OF MIOSIS. WITH SUFFICIENT EXPOSURE, OTHER SYMPTOMS OF CHOLINESTERASE INHIBITION AS DESCRIBED IN ACUTE INHALATION MAY OCCUR. **CHRONIC EXPOSURE-** REPEATED OR PROLONGED EXPOSURE MAY CAUSE EFFECTS AS DESCRIBED IN ACUTE EXPOSURE. SOME COMPOUNDS HAVE CAUSED TOXIC EFFECTS ON THE CRYSTALLINE LENS, CONJUNCTIVAL THICKENING AND OBSTRUCTION OF THE NASOLACRIMAL CANALS WHEN USED AS MIOTIC EYEDROPS.

FIRST AID- IRRIGATE EYES WITH WATER OR SALINE SOLUTION. IF SYMPTOMS OF POISONING OCCUR, TREAT RESPIRATORY DIFFICULTY WITH ARTIFICIAL RESPIRATION AND OXYGEN. OBSERVE PATIENT FOR AT LEAST 24-36 HOURS (GOSSELIN, CLINICAL TOXICOLOGY OF COMMERCIAL PRODUCTS, 5TH ED.). GET MEDICAL ATTENTION IMMEDIATELY. OXYGEN SHOULD BE ADMINISTERED BY QUALIFIED MEDICAL PERSONNEL.

INGESTION: CYTHIOATE: TOXIC. SEE INFORMATION ON ORGANOPHOSPHATES.
ORGANOPHOSPHATES: CHOLINESTERASE INHIBITOR. **ACUTE EXPOSURE-** WHEN INGESTED, THE FIRST EFFECTS MAY BE NAUSEA, VOMITING, ANOREXIA, ABDOMINAL CRAMPS AND DIARRHEA. GASTROINTESTINAL ABSORPTION MAY CAUSE SYMPTOMS OF CHOLINESTERASE INHIBITION AS DESCRIBED IN ACUTE INHALATION. SYMPTOMS MAY BEGIN WITHIN MINUTES OR BE DELAYED FOR HOURS. DELAYED EFFECTS INCLUDING NEUROPATHY MAY ALSO OCCUR. **CHRONIC EXPOSURE-** REPEATED INGESTION MAY CAUSE EFFECTS AS DESCRIBED IN ACUTE EXPOSURE.

FIRST AID- IF PERSON IS ALERT AND RESPIRATION IS NOT DEPRESSED, GIVE SYRUP OF IPECAC FOLLOWED BY WATER (IF VOMITING OCCURS, KEEP HEAD BELOW HIPS TO PREVENT ASPIRATION). IF CONSCIOUSNESS LEVEL DECLINES OR VOMITING HAS NOT OCCURRED IN 15 MINUTES EMPTY STOMACH BY GASTRIC LAVAGE WITH THE AID OF CUFFED ENDOTRACHEAL TUBE USING ISOTONIC SALINE OR 5% SODIUM BICARBONATE FOLLOW WITH ACTIVATED CHARCOAL. ESTABLISH AND MAINTAIN AIRWAY. TREAT RESPIRATORY DIFFICULTY WITH ARTIFICIAL RESPIRATION AND OXYGEN. DO NOT GIVE MORPHINE, AMINOPHYLLINE, PHENOTHIAZINES, RESERPINE, FUROSEMIDE, OR ETHACRYNIC ACID (MORGAN, RECOGNITION AND MANAGEMENT OF PESTICIDE POISONINGS, 3RD ED.). TREAT SYMPTOMATICALLY AND

SUPPORTIVELY. ADMINISTRATION OF OXYGEN AND LAVAGE MUST BE PERFORMED BY QUALIFIED MEDICAL PERSONNEL. GET MEDICAL ATTENTION IMMEDIATELY.

ANTIDOTE: THE FOLLOWING ANTIDOTE(S) HAVE BEEN RECOMMENDED. HOWEVER, THE DECISION AS TO WHETHER THE SEVERITY OF POISONING REQUIRES ADMINISTRATION OF ANY ANTIDOTE AND ACTUAL DOSE REQUIRED SHOULD BE MADE BY QUALIFIED MEDICAL PERSONNEL.

FOR CHOLINESTERASE INHIBITORS: ESTABLISH CLEAR AIRWAY AND TISSUE OXYGENATION BY ASPIRATION OF SECRETIONS, AND IF NECESSARY, BY ASSISTED PULMONARY VENTILATION WITH OXYGEN. IMPROVE TISSUE OXYGENATION AS MUCH AS POSSIBLE BEFORE ADMINISTERING ATROPINE TO MINIMIZE THE RISK OF VENTRICULAR FIBRILLATION. ADMINISTER ATROPINE SULFATE INTRAVENOUSLY, OR INTRAMUSCULARLY IF IV INJECTION IS NOT POSSIBLE. IN MODERATELY SEVERE POISONING ADMINISTER ATROPINE SULFATE, 0.4-2.0 MG REPEATED EVERY 15 MINUTES UNTIL ATROPINIZATION IS ACHIEVED (TACHYCARDIA, FLUSHING, DRY MOUTH, MYDRIASIS). MAINTAIN ATROPINIZATION BY REPEATED DOSES FOR 2-12 HOURS, OR LONGER, DEPENDING ON THE SEVERITY OF POISONING. THE APPEARANCE OF RALES IN THE LUNG BASES, MIOSIS, SALIVATION, NAUSEA, BRADYCARDIA, ARE ALL INDICATIONS OF INADEQUATE ATROPINIZATION. SEVERELY POISONED INDIVIDUALS MAY EXHIBIT REMARKABLE TOLERANCE TO ATROPINE; TWO OR MORE TIMES THE DOSAGES SUGGESTED ABOVE MAY BE NEEDED. PERSONS NOT POISONED OR ONLY SLIGHTLY POISONED, HOWEVER, MAY DEVELOP SIGNS OF ATROPINE TOXICITY FROM SUCH LARGE DOSAGES: FEVER, MUSCLE FIBRILLATIONS, AND DELIRIUM ARE THE MAIN SIGNS OF ATROPINE TOXICITY. IF THESE SIGNS APPEAR WHILE THE PATIENT IS FULLY ATROPINIZED, ATROPINE ADMINISTRATION SHOULD BE DISCONTINUED, AT LEAST TEMPORARILY. OBSERVE TREATED PATIENTS CLOSELY AT LEAST 24 HOURS TO INSURE THAT SYMPTOMS (POSSIBLY PULMONARY EDEMA) DO NOT RECUR AS ATROPINIZATION WEARS OFF. IN VERY SEVERE POISONINGS, METABOLIC DISPOSITION OF TOXICANT MAY REQUIRE SEVERAL HOURS OR DAYS DURING WHICH ATROPINIZATION MUST BE MAINTAINED. MARKEDLY LOWER LEVELS OF URINARY METABOLITES INDICATE THAT ATROPINE DOSAGE CAN BE TAPERED OFF. AS DOSAGE IS REDUCED, CHECK THE LUNG BASES FREQUENTLY FOR RALES. IF RALES ARE HEARD OR OTHER SYMPTOMS RETURN, RE-ESTABLISH ATROPINIZATION PROMPTLY (MORGAN, RECOGNITION AND MANAGEMENT OF PESTICIDE POISONINGS, 3RD ED.). ADMINISTRATION OF ANTIDOTE MUST BE PERFORMED BY QUALIFIED MEDICAL PERSONNEL.

IN CASES OF SEVERE POISONING BY ORGANOPHOSPHATE PESTICIDES IN WHICH RESPIRATORY DEPRESSION, MUSCLE WEAKNESS AND TWITCHINGS ARE SEVERE, GIVE PRALIDOXIME (PROTOPAM-AYERST, 2-PAM), 1.0 GRAM INTRAVENOUSLY AT NO MORE THAN 0.5 GRAM PER MINUTE. DOSAGE OF PRALIDOXIME MAY BE REPEATED IN 1-2 HOURS, THEN AT 10-12 HOUR INTERVALS IF NEEDED. IN VERY SEVERE POISONINGS, DOSAGE RATES MAY BE DOUBLED. TREATMENT WITH PRALIDOXIME WILL BE MOST EFFECTIVE IF GIVEN WITHIN THIRTY-SIX HOURS AFTER POISONING (MORGAN, RECOGNITION AND MANAGEMENT OF PESTICIDE POISONINGS, 3RD ED.). ANTIDOTE SHOULD BE ADMINISTERED BY QUALIFIED MEDICAL PERSONNEL.

REACTIVITY

REACTIVITY: STABLE UNDER NORMAL TEMPERATURES AND PRESSURES.

INCOMPATIBILITIES: CYTHIOATE: NO DATA AVAILABLE.

DECOMPOSITION: THERMAL DECOMPOSITION MAY RELEASE TOXIC AND/OR HAZARDOUS GASES.

POLYMERIZATION: HAZARDOUS POLYMERIZATION HAS NOT BEEN REPORTED TO OCCUR UNDER NORMAL TEMPERATURES AND PRESSURES.

STORAGE AND DISPOSAL

OBSERVE ALL FEDERAL, STATE AND LOCAL REGULATIONS WHEN STORING OR DISPOSING OF THIS SUBSTANCE. FOR ASSISTANCE, CONTACT THE DISTRICT DIRECTOR OF THE ENVIRONMENTAL PROTECTION AGENCY.

****STORAGE****

STORE IN ACCORDANCE WITH 40 CFR 165 RECOMMENDED PROCEDURES FOR THE DISPOSAL AND STORAGE OF PESTICIDES AND PESTICIDE CONTAINERS.

****DISPOSAL****

DISPOSAL MUST BE IN ACCORDANCE WITH 40 CFR 165 RECOMMENDED PROCEDURES FOR THE DISPOSAL AND STORAGE OF PESTICIDES AND PESTICIDE CONTAINERS.

CONDITIONS TO AVOID

NONE REPORTED.

SPILL AND LEAK PROCEDURES

OCCUPATIONAL SPILL: DO NOT TOUCH SPILLED MATERIAL. STOP LEAK IF YOU CAN DO IT WITHOUT RISK. USE WATER SPRAY TO REDUCE VAPORS. FOR SMALL SPILLS, TAKE UP WITH SAND OR OTHER ABSORBENT MATERIAL AND PLACE INTO CONTAINERS FOR LATER DISPOSAL. FOR SMALL DRY SPILLS, WITH A CLEAN SHOVEL PLACE MATERIAL INTO CLEAN, DRY CONTAINERS AND COVER. MOVE CONTAINERS FROM SPILL AREA. FOR LARGER SPILLS, DIKE FAR AHEAD OF SPILL FOR LATER DISPOSAL. KEEP UNNECESSARY PEOPLE AWAY. ISOLATE HAZARD AREA AND DENY ENTRY. VENTILATE CLOSED SPACES BEFORE ENTERING.

PROTECTIVE EQUIPMENT

VENTILATION: PROVIDE LOCAL EXHAUST OR PROCESS ENCLOSURE VENTILATION SYSTEM.

RESPIRATOR: THE FOLLOWING RESPIRATORS ARE RECOMMENDED BASED ON INFORMATION FOUND IN THE PHYSICAL DATA, TOXICITY AND HEALTH EFFECTS SECTIONS. THEY ARE RANKED IN ORDER FROM MINIMUM TO MAXIMUM RESPIRATORY PROTECTION. THE SPECIFIC RESPIRATOR SELECTED MUST BE BASED ON CONTAMINATION LEVELS FOUND IN THE WORK PLACE, MUST NOT EXCEED THE WORKING LIMITS OF THE RESPIRATOR AND BE JOINTLY APPROVED BY THE NATIONAL INSTITUTE FOR OCCUPATIONAL SAFETY AND HEALTH AND THE MINE SAFETY AND HEALTH ADMINISTRATION (NIOSH-MSHA).

TYPE 'C' SUPPLIED-AIR RESPIRATOR WITH A FULL FACEPIECE OPERATED IN PRESSURE-DEMAND OR OTHER POSITIVE PRESSURE MODE OR WITH A FULL FACEPIECE, HELMET OR HOOD OPERATED IN CONTINOUS-FLOW MODE.

SELF-CONTAINED BREATHING APPARATUS WITH A FULL FACEPIECE OPERATED IN PRESSURE-DEMAND OR OTHER POSITIVE PRESSURE MODE.

FOR FIREFIGHTING AND OTHER IMMEDIATELY DANGEROUS TO LIFE OR HEALTH CONDITIONS:

SELF-CONTAINED BREATHING APPARATUS WITH FULL FACEPIECE OPERATED IN PRESSURE-DEMAND OR OTHER POSITIVE PRESSURE MODE.

SUPPLIED-AIR RESPIRATOR WITH FULL FACEPIECE AND OPERATED IN PRESSURE-DEMAND OR OTHER POSITIVE PRESSURE MODE IN COMBINATION WITH AN AUXILIARY SELF-CONTAINED BREATHING APPARATUS OPERATED IN PRESSURE-DEMAND OR OTHER POSITIVE PRESSURE MODE.

CLOTHING: EMPLOYEE MUST WEAR APPROPRIATE PROTECTIVE (IMPERVIOUS) CLOTHING AND EQUIPMENT TO PREVENT REPEATED OR PROLONGED SKIN CONTACT WITH THIS SUBSTANCE.

GLOVES: EMPLOYEE MUST WEAR APPROPRIATE PROTECTIVE GLOVES TO PREVENT CONTACT WITH THIS SUBSTANCE.

EYE PROTECTION: EMPLOYEE MUST WEAR SPLASH-PROOF OR DUST-RESISTANT SAFETY GOGGLES TO PREVENT EYE CONTACT WITH THIS SUBSTANCE.

EMERGENCY EYE WASH: WHERE THERE IS ANY POSSIBILITY THAT AN EMPLOYEE'S EYES MAY BE EXPOSED TO THIS SUBSTANCE, THE EMPLOYER SHOULD PROVIDE AN EYE WASH FOUNTAIN WITHIN THE IMMEDIATE WORK AREA FOR EMERGENCY USE.

AUTHORIZED BY- OCCUPATIONAL HEALTH SERVICES, INC.

CREATION DATE: 10/04/89 ***REVISION DATE:*** 04/25/90

MATERIAL SAFETY DATA SHEET

OCCUPATIONAL HEALTH SERVICES, INC.
AGRICULTURE AND PESTICIDE DIVISION
450 SEVENTH AVENUE, SUITE 2407
NEW YORK, NEW YORK 10123
1-800-445-MSDS OR (212) 967-1100

EMERGENCY CONTACT:
JOHN S. BRANSFORD, JR. (615) 292-1180

SUBSTANCE IDENTIFICATION

CAS-NUMBER 1596-84-5

SUBSTANCE: DAMINOZIDE

TRADE NAMES/SYNONYMS: BUTANEDIOIC ACID, MONO(2,2-DIMETHYLHYDRAZIDE); SUCCINIC ACID, MONO(2,2-DIMETHYLHYDRAZIDE); MONO(2,2-DIMETHLYHYDRAZIDE)SUCCINIC ACID; N-(DIMETHYLAMINO)SUCCINAMIC ACID; N-DIMETHYLAMINOSUCCINAMIC ACID; BUTANEDIOIC ACID MONO(2,2-DIMETHYLHYDRAZIDE); SUCCINIC N',N'-DIMETHYLHYDRAZIDE; ALAR; AMINOZIDE; B-995; B-NINE; DMASA; KYLAR; SUCCINIC ACID, 2,2-DIMETHYL HYDRAZIDE; C6H12N2O3; PST06195

CHEMICAL FAMILY: HYDRAZIDE

MOLECULAR FORMULA: H-O2-C-C-H2-C-(C-H3)2-C-O-N-H-N-H2

MOLECULAR WEIGHT: 160.17

CERCLA RATINGS (SCALE 0-3): HEALTH=3 FIRE=1 REACTIVITY=0 PERSISTENCE=0

NFPA RATINGS (SCALE 0-4): HEALTH=U FIRE=1 REACTIVITY=0

COMPONENTS AND CONTAMINANTS

COMPONENT: DAMINOZIDE ***PERCENT:*** 100.0
CAS# 1596-84-5

OTHER CONTAMINANTS: NONE

EXPOSURE LIMITS: NO OCCUPATIONAL EXPOSURE LIMITS ESTABLISHED BY OSHA, ACGIH, OR NIOSH.
DAMINOZIDE: SUBJECT TO CALIFORNIA PROPOSITION 65 CANCER AND/OR REPRODUCTIVE TOXICITY WARNING AND RELEASE REQUIREMENTS- (JANUARY 1, 1990)

PHYSICAL DATA

DESCRIPTION: COLORLESS TO WHITE CRYSTALLINE SOLID.
MELTING POINT: 309-311 F (154-155 C) ***SPECIFIC GRAVITY:*** NOT AVAILABLE
VAPOR PRESSURE: <0.9975 MMHG @ 20 C ***PH:*** 3.8 @ 0.5% AQ SOLN
SOLUBILITY IN WATER: 10%
SOLVENT SOLUBILITY: SOLUBLE IN METHANOL, ACETONE, POLAR ORGANIC SOLVENTS; MODERATELY SOLUBLE IN METHANOL, ACETONE; PRACTICALLY INSOLUBLE IN AROMATIC AND ALIPHATIC HYDROCARBON SOLVENTS.

FIRE AND EXPLOSION DATA

FIRE AND EXPLOSION HAZARD: SLIGHT FIRE HAZARD WHEN EXPOSED TO HEAT OR FLAME.
FIREFIGHTING MEDIA: DRY CHEMICAL, CARBON DIOXIDE, HALON, WATER SPRAY OR STANDARD FOAM (1987 EMERGENCY RESPONSE GUIDEBOOK, DOT P 5800.4).
FOR LARGER FIRES, USE WATER SPRAY, FOG OR STANDARD FOAM (1987 EMERGENCY RESPONSE GUIDEBOOK, DOT P 5800.4).
FIREFIGHTING: MOVE CONTAINER FROM FIRE AREA IF POSSIBLE. DO NOT SCATTER SPILLED MATERIAL WITH HIGH PRESSURE WATER STREAMS. DIKE FIRE CONTROL WATER FOR LATER DISPOSAL (1987 EMERGENCY RESPONSE GUIDEBOOK, DOT P 5800.4, GUIDE PAGE 31).
USE AGENTS SUITABLE FOR TYPE OF SURROUNDING FIRE. AVOID BREATHING HAZARDOUS VAPORS, KEEP UPWIND.

TOXICITY

DAMINOZIDE: TOXICITY DATA: >147,000 MG/M3 INHALATION-RAT LC50 (PEMNDP); >1600 MG/KG SKIN-RABBIT LD50 (FARM CHEMICALS HANDBOOK); >5000 MG/KG SKIN-RABBIT LD50 (PEMNDP); 8400 MG/KG ORAL-RAT LD50; 6300 MG/KG ORAL-MOUSE LD50; 1325 MG/KG INTRAPERITONEAL-MOUSE LD50; 8400 MG/KG UNREPORTED-MAMMAL LD50; MUTAGENIC DATA (RTECS); TUMORIGENIC DATA (RTECS). CARCINOGEN STATUS: NONE. ACUTE TOXICITY LEVEL: SLIGHTLY TOXIC BY INHALATION AND INGESTION. TARGET EFFECTS: NO DATA AVAILABLE.

HEALTH EFFECTS AND FIRST AID

INHALATION: DAMINOZIDE: **ACUTE EXPOSURE-** THE LD50 FOR RATS WAS >147,000 MG/M3. **CHRONIC EXPOSURE-** NO DATA AVAILABLE.
FIRST AID- REMOVE FROM EXPOSURE AREA TO FRESH AIR IMMEDIATELY. IF BREATHING HAS STOPPED, PERFORM ARTIFICIAL RESPIRATION. KEEP PERSON WARM AND AT REST. TREAT SYMPTOMATICALLY AND SUPPORTIVELY. GET MEDICAL ATTENTION IMMEDIATELY.

SKIN CONTACT: DAMINOZIDE: **ACUTE EXPOSURE-** MAY BE MILDLY IRRITATING. THE LD50 FOR RABBITS WAS >5000 MG/KG. **CHRONIC EXPOSURE-** NO DATA AVAILABLE.
FIRST AID- REMOVE CONTAMINATED CLOTHING AND SHOES IMMEDIATELY. WASH AFFECTED AREA WITH SOAP OR MILD DETERGENT AND LARGE AMOUNTS OF WATER UNTIL NO EVIDENCE OF CHEMICAL REMAINS (APPROXIMATELY 15-20 MINUTES). GET MEDICAL ATTENTION IMMEDIATELY.

EYE CONTACT: DAMINOZIDE: **ACUTE EXPOSURE-** MAY BE MILDLY IRRITATING. **CHRONIC EXPOSURE-** NO DATA AVAILABLE.
FIRST AID- WASH EYES IMMEDIATELY WITH LARGE AMOUNTS OF WATER OR NORMAL SALINE, OCCASIONALLY LIFTING UPPER AND LOWER LIDS, UNTIL NO EVIDENCE OF CHEMICAL REMAINS (APPROXIMATELY 15-20 MINUTES). GET MEDICAL ATTENTION IMMEDIATELY.

INGESTION: DAMINOZIDE: **ACUTE EXPOSURE-** ALTERATIONS IN LIVER FUNCTION OF EXPERIMENTAL ANIMALS GIVEN VERY LARGE DOSES WERE REPORTED. **CHRONIC EXPOSURE-** DIETARY LEVELS OF 5,000 OR 10,000 PPM PRODUCED UTERINE ADENOCARCINOMAS AND LEIOMYOSARCOMAS IN FEMALE RATS. A STATISTICALLY SIGNIFICANT INCREASE IN HEMANGIOSARCOMAS/HEMANGIOMAS WAS OBSERVED IN MICE.
FIRST AID- REMOVE BY GASTRIC LAVAGE AND CATHARSIS. MAINTAIN BLOOD PRESSURE AND AIRWAY. GIVE OXYGEN IF RESPIRATION IS DEPRESSED. DO NOT PERFORM GASTRIC LAVAGE IF VICTIM IS UNCONSCIOUS. GET MEDICAL ATTENTION IMMEDIATELY (DREISBACH, HANDBOOK OF POISONING, 12TH ED.).
ADMINISTRATION OF LAVAGE OR OXYGEN SHOULD BE PERFORMED BY QUALIFIED MEDICAL PERSONNEL.
ANTIDOTE: NO SPECIFIC ANTIDOTE. TREAT SYMPTOMATICALLY AND SUPPORTIVELY.

REACTIVITY

REACTIVITY: STABLE UNDER NORMAL TEMPERATURES AND PRESSURES.
INCOMPATIBILITIES: DAMINOZIDE: OXIDIZERS (STRONG): FIRE AND EXPLOSION HAZARD.
DECOMPOSITION: THERMAL DECOMPOSITION PRODUCTS MAY INCLUDE TOXIC OXIDES OF CARBON AND NITROGEN.
POLYMERIZATION: HAZARDOUS POLYMERIZATION HAS NOT BEEN REPORTED TO OCCUR UNDER NORMAL TEMPERATURES AND PRESSURES.

STORAGE AND DISPOSAL

OBSERVE ALL FEDERAL, STATE AND LOCAL REGULATIONS WHEN STORING OR DISPOSING OF THIS SUBSTANCE. FOR ASSISTANCE, CONTACT THE DISTRICT DIRECTOR OF THE ENVIRONMENTAL PROTECTION AGENCY.

****STORAGE****

STORE IN ACCORDANCE WITH 40 CFR 165 RECOMMENDED PROCEDURES FOR THE DISPOSAL AND STORAGE OF PESTICIDES AND PESTICIDE CONTAINERS.
STORE AWAY FROM INCOMPATIBLE SUBSTANCES.

****DISPOSAL****

DISPOSAL MUST BE IN ACCORDANCE WITH 40 CFR 165 RECOMMENDED PROCEDURES FOR THE DISPOSAL AND STORAGE OF PESTICIDES AND PESTICIDE CONTAINERS.

CONDITIONS TO AVOID

MAY BURN BUT DOES NOT IGNITE READILY. AVOID CONTACT WITH STRONG OXIDIZERS, EXCESSIVE HEAT, SPARKS, OR OPEN FLAME.

SPILL AND LEAK PROCEDURES

WATER SPILL: THE CALIFORNIA SAFE DRINKING WATER AND TOXIC ENFORCEMENT ACT OF 1986 (PROPOSITION 65) PROHIBITS CONTAMINATING ANY KNOWN SOURCE OF DRINKING WATER WITH SUBSTANCES KNOWN TO CAUSE CANCER AND/OR REPRODUCTIVE TOXICITY.
OCCUPATIONAL SPILL: SWEEP UP AND PLACE IN SUITABLE CLEAN, DRY CONTAINERS FOR RECLAMATION OR LATER DISPOSAL. DO NOT FLUSH SPILLED MATERIAL INTO SEWER. KEEP UNNECESSARY PEOPLE AWAY.

PROTECTIVE EQUIPMENT

VENTILATION: PROVIDE LOCAL EXHAUST OR GENERAL DILUTION VENTILATION SYSTEM.
RESPIRATOR: THE FOLLOWING RESPIRATORS ARE RECOMMENDED BASED ON INFORMATION FOUND IN THE PHYSICAL DATA, TOXICITY AND HEALTH EFFECTS SECTIONS. THEY ARE RANKED IN ORDER FROM MINIMUM TO MAXIMUM RESPIRATORY PROTECTION. THE SPECIFIC RESPIRATOR SELECTED MUST BE BASED ON CONTAMINATION LEVELS FOUND IN THE WORK PLACE, MUST NOT EXCEED THE WORKING LIMITS OF THE RESPIRATOR AND BE JOINTLY APPROVED BY THE NATIONAL INSTITUTE FOR OCCUPATIONAL SAFETY AND HEALTH AND THE MINE SAFETY AND HEALTH ADMINISTRATION (NIOSH-MSHA).
CHEMICAL CARTRIDGE RESPIRATOR WITH AN ORGANIC VAPOR CARTRIDGE(S) WITH A FULL FACEPIECE AND ORGANIC VAPOR CARTRIDGE(S) IN COMBINATION WITH A DUST AND MIST FILTER.
POWERED AIR-PURIFYING RESPIRATOR WITH A TIGHT-FITTING FACEPIECE AND ORGANIC VAPOR CARTRIDGE(S) IN COMBINATION WITH A HIGH-EFFICIENCY PARTICULATE FILTER.
TYPE 'C' SUPPLIED-AIR RESPIRATOR WITH A FULL FACEPIECE OPERATED IN A PRESSURE-DEMAND OR OTHER POSITIVE PRESSURE MODE.
SELF-CONTAINED BREATHING APPARATUS WITH A FULL FACEPIECE OPERATED IN PRESSURE-DEMAND OR OTHER POSITIVE PRESSURE MODE.
FOR FIREFIGHTING AND OTHER IMMEDIATELY DANGEROUS TO LIFE OR HEALTH CONDITIONS:
SELF-CONTAINED BREATHING APPARATUS WITH FULL FACEPIECE OPERATED IN PRESSURE-DEMAND OR OTHER POSITIVE PRESSURE MODE.
SUPPLIED-AIR RESPIRATOR WITH FULL FACEPIECE AND OPERATED IN PRESSURE-DEMAND OR OTHER POSITIVE PRESSURE MODE IN COMBINATION WITH AN AUXILIARY SELF-CONTAINED BREATHING APPARATUS OPERATED IN PRESSURE-DEMAND OR OTHER POSITIVE PRESSURE MODE.
CLOTHING: EMPLOYEE MUST WEAR APPROPRIATE PROTECTIVE (IMPERVIOUS) CLOTHING AND EQUIPMENT TO PREVENT REPEATED OR PROLONGED SKIN CONTACT WITH THIS SUBSTANCE.
GLOVES: EMPLOYEE MUST WEAR APPROPRIATE PROTECTIVE GLOVES TO PREVENT CONTACT WITH THIS SUBSTANCE.
EYE PROTECTION: EMPLOYEE MUST WEAR SPLASH-PROOF OR DUST-RESISTANT SAFETY GOGGLES TO PREVENT EYE CONTACT WITH THIS SUBSTANCE.
EMERGENCY EYE WASH: WHERE THERE IS ANY POSSIBILITY THAT AN EMPLOYEE'S EYES MAY BE EXPOSED TO THIS SUBSTANCE, THE EMPLOYER SHOULD PROVIDE AN EYE WASH FOUNTAIN WITHIN THE IMMEDIATE WORK AREA FOR EMERGENCY USE.

AUTHORIZED BY- OCCUPATIONAL HEALTH SERVICES, INC.
CREATION DATE: 10/04/89 ***REVISION DATE:*** 05/31/90

MATERIAL SAFETY DATA SHEET

OCCUPATIONAL HEALTH SERVICES, INC.
AGRICULTURE AND PESTICIDE DIVISION
450 SEVENTH AVENUE, SUITE 2407
NEW YORK, NEW YORK 10123
1-800-445-MSDS OR (212) 967-1100

EMERGENCY CONTACT:
JOHN S. BRANSFORD, JR. (615) 292-1180

SUBSTANCE IDENTIFICATION

CAS-NUMBER 75-99-0
SUBSTANCE: DALAPON
TRADE NAMES/SYNONYMS: 2,2-DICHLOROPROPANOIC ACID; ALATEX; BASINEX P; BASFAPON; BASFAPON B; BASFAPON/BASFAPON N; BH DALAPON; BASINEX; CRISAPON; DALAPON 85; DED-WEED; DEVIPON; ALPHA-DICHLOROPROPIONIC ACID; ALPHA,ALPHA-DICHLOROPROPIONIC ACID; DOWPON; GRAMEVIN; KENAPON; LIROPON; RADAPON; NA 1760; PST06200
CHEMICAL FAMILY: HALOGEN
CARBOXYLIC ACID, ALIPHATIC
MOLECULAR FORMULA: C3-H4-CL2-O2
MOLECULAR WEIGHT: 142.97
CERCLA RATINGS (SCALE 0-3): HEALTH=2 FIRE=0 REACTIVITY=U PERSISTENCE=3
NFPA RATINGS (SCALE 0-4): HEALTH=2 FIRE=0 REACTIVITY=U

COMPONENTS AND CONTAMINANTS

COMPONENT: DALAPON ***PERCENT:*** 100
CAS# 75-99-0
OTHER CONTAMINANTS: NONE
EXPOSURE LIMITS: DALAPON: 1 PPM (6 MG/M3) OSHA TWA 1 PPM (6 MG/M3) ACGIH TWA
5000 POUNDS CERCLA SECTION 103 REPORTABLE QUANTITY

PHYSICAL DATA

DESCRIPTION: COLORLESS LIQUID WITH AN ACRID ODOR.
BOILING POINT: 208-210 F (98-99 C) ***SPECIFIC GRAVITY:*** 1.40
SOLUBILITY IN WATER: SOLUBLE
SOLVENT SOLUBILITY: ALCOHOL, ETHER

FIRE AND EXPLOSION DATA

FIRE AND EXPLOSION HAZARD: NEGLIGIBLE FIRE HAZARD WHEN EXPOSED TO HEAT OR FLAME.
FIREFIGHTING MEDIA: DRY CHEMICAL, CARBON DIOXIDE, HALON, WATER SPRAY OR STANDARD FOAM (1987 EMERGENCY RESPONSE GUIDEBOOK, DOT P 5800.4).
FOR LARGER FIRES, USE WATER SPRAY, FOG OR STANDARD FOAM (1987 EMERGENCY RESPONSE GUIDEBOOK, DOT P 5800.4).
FIREFIGHTING: MOVE CONTAINER FROM FIRE AREA IF POSSIBLE. DO NOT SCATTER SPILLED MATERIAL WITH HIGH PRESSURE WATER STREAMS. DIKE FIRE CONTROL WATER FOR LATER DISPOSAL (1987 EMERGENCY RESPONSE GUIDEBOOK, DOT P 5800.4, GUIDE PAGE 31).
USE AGENTS SUITABLE FOR TYPE OF SURROUNDING FIRE. AVOID BREATHING HAZARDOUS VAPORS, KEEP UPWIND.

TOXICITY

DALAPON: IRRITATION DATA: 100 UG/24 HOURS OPEN SKIN-RABBIT. TOXICITY DATA: 970 MG/KG ORAL-RAT LD50; MUTAGENIC DATA (RTECS). CARCINOGEN STATUS: NONE. LOCAL EFFECTS: CORROSIVE- INHALATION, SKIN, AND EYES. ACUTE TOXICITY LEVEL: MODERATELY TOXIC BY INGESTION. TARGET EFFECTS: NO DATA AVAILABLE.

HEALTH EFFECTS AND FIRST AID

INHALATION: DALAPON: CORROSIVE. **ACUTE EXPOSURE-** VAPORS MAY CAUSE SEVERE IRRITATION TO THE RESPIRATORY TRACT. **CHRONIC EXPOSURE-** NO DATA AVAILABLE. REPEATED OR PROLONGED EXPOSURE MAY CAUSE MUCOUS MEMBRANE IRRITATION.
FIRST AID- REMOVE FROM EXPOSURE AREA TO FRESH AIR IMMEDIATELY. IF BREATHING HAS STOPPED, PERFORM ARTIFICIAL RESPIRATION. KEEP PERSON WARM AND AT REST. TREAT SYMPTOMATICALLY AND SUPPORTIVELY. GET MEDICAL ATTENTION IMMEDIATELY.

SKIN CONTACT: DALAPON: CORROSIVE. **ACUTE EXPOSURE-** DIRECT CONTACT MAY CAUSE SEVERE IRRITATION. BURNS OR A BURNING SENSATION MAY OCCUR ESPECIALLY WHEN SKIN IS MOIST. **CHRONIC EXPOSURE-** MAY CAUSE DERMATITIS AND/OR BURNS AFTER REPEATED OR PROLONGED EXPOSURE.
FIRST AID- REMOVE CONTAMINATED CLOTHING AND SHOES IMMEDIATELY. WASH AFFECTED AREA WITH SOAP OR MILD DETERGENT AND LARGE AMOUNTS OF WATER UNTIL NO EVIDENCE OF CHEMICAL REMAINS (APPROXIMATELY 15-20 MINUTES). GET MEDICAL ATTENTION IMMEDIATELY.

EYE CONTACT: DALAPON: CORROSIVE. **ACUTE EXPOSURE-** MAY CAUSE SEVERE IRRITATION OR BURNS. **CHRONIC EXPOSURE-** VAPORS MAY CAUSE CONJUNCTIVITIS AFTER REPEATED OR PROLONGED EXPOSURE.
FIRST AID- WASH EYES IMMEDIATELY WITH LARGE AMOUNTS OF WATER OR NORMAL SALINE, OCCASIONALLY LIFTING UPPER AND LOWER LIDS, UNTIL NO EVIDENCE OF CHEMICAL REMAINS (APPROXIMATELY 15-20 MINUTES). GET MEDICAL ATTENTION IMMEDIATELY.

INGESTION: DALAPON: CORROSIVE. **ACUTE EXPOSURE-** MAY CAUSE IRRITATION TO THE GASTROINTESTINAL SYSTEM CAUSING NAUSEA, VOMITING, AND DIARRHEA. 970 MG/KG IS THE LETHAL DOSE FOR RATS. **CHRONIC EXPOSURE-** LONG-TERM FEEDING STUDIES IN DOGS AND RATS PRODUCED NO LESIONS EXCEPT INCREASED KIDNEY WEIGHTS IN ANIMALS FED VERY HIGH DAILY DOSES.
FIRST AID- TREAT SYMPTOMATICALLY AND SUPPORTIVELY. GET MEDICAL ATTENTION IMMEDIATELY.
ANTIDOTE: NO SPECIFIC ANTIDOTE. TREAT SYMPTOMATICALLY AND SUPPORTIVELY.

REACTIVITY

REACTIVITY: NO DATA AVAILABLE.
INCOMPATIBILITIES: DALAPON: NO DATA AVAILABLE.
DECOMPOSITION: THERMAL DECOMPOSITION MAY RELEASE TOXIC AND/OR HAZARDOUS GASES.
POLYMERIZATION: NO DATA AVAILABLE.

CONDITIONS TO AVOID

MAY BURN BUT DOES NOT IGNITE READILY. AVOID CONTACT WITH STRONG OXIDIZERS, EXCESSIVE HEAT, SPARKS, OR OPEN FLAME.

SPILL AND LEAK PROCEDURES

OCCUPATIONAL SPILL: STOP LEAK IF YOU CAN DO IT WITHOUT RISK. FOR SMALL SPILLS, TAKE UP WITH SAND OR OTHER ABSORBENT MATERIAL AND PLACE INTO CLEAN, DRY CONTAINERS FOR LATER DISPOSAL. KEEP UNNECESSARY PEOPLE AWAY. ISOLATE HAZARD AREA AND DENY ENTRY.
REPORTABLE QUANTITY (RQ): 5000 POUNDS THE SUPERFUND AMENDMENTS AND REAUTHORIZATION ACT (SARA) SECTION 304 REQUIRES THAT A RELEASE EQUAL TO OR GREATER THAN THE REPORTABLE QUANTITY FOR THIS SUBSTANCE BE IMMEDIATELY REPORTED TO THE LOCAL EMERGENCY PLANNING COMMITTEE AND THE STATE EMERGENCY RESPONSE COMMISSION (40 CFR 355.40). IF THE RELEASE OF THIS SUBSTANCE IS REPORTABLE UNDER CERCLA SECTION 103, THE NATIONAL RESPONSE CENTER MUST BE NOTIFIED IMMEDIATELY AT (800) 424-8802 OR (202) 426-2675 IN THE METROPOLITAN WASHINGTON, D.C. AREA (40 CFR 302.6).

PROTECTIVE EQUIPMENT

VENTILATION: PROVIDE LOCAL EXHAUST OR GENERAL DILUTION VENTILATION SYSTEM.
RESPIRATOR: THE FOLLOWING RESPIRATORS ARE RECOMMENDED BASED ON INFORMATION FOUND IN THE PHYSICAL DATA, TOXICITY AND HEALTH EFFECTS SECTIONS. THEY ARE RANKED IN ORDER FROM MINIMUM TO MAXIMUM RESPIRATORY PROTECTION. THE SPECIFIC RESPIRATOR SELECTED MUST BE BASED ON CONTAMINATION LEVELS FOUND IN THE WORK PLACE, MUST NOT EXCEED THE WORKING LIMITS OF THE RESPIRATOR AND BE JOINTLY APPROVED BY THE NATIONAL INSTITUTE FOR OCCUPATIONAL SAFETY AND HEALTH AND THE MINE SAFETY AND HEALTH ADMINISTRATION (NIOSH-MSHA).
CHEMICAL CARTRIDGE RESPIRATOR WITH FULL FACEPIECE AND PESTICIDE CARTRIDGE.
TYPE 'C' SUPPLIED-AIR RESPIRATOR WITH A FULL FACEPIECE OPERATED IN PRESSURE-DEMAND OR OTHER POSITIVE PRESSURE MODE OR WITH A FULL FACEPIECE, HELMET OR HOOD OPERATED IN CONTINUOUS-FLOW MODE.
SELF-CONTAINED BREATHING APPARATUS OPERATED IN PRESSURE-DEMAND OR OTHER POSITIVE PRESSURE MODE.
FOR FIREFIGHTING AND OTHER IMMEDIATELY DANGEROUS TO LIFE OR HEALTH CONDITIONS:
SELF-CONTAINED BREATHING APPARATUS WITH FULL FACEPIECE OPERATED IN PRESSURE-DEMAND OR OTHER POSITIVE PRESSURE MODE.
SUPPLIED-AIR RESPIRATOR WITH FULL FACEPIECE AND OPERATED IN PRESSURE-DEMAND OR OTHER POSITIVE PRESSURE MODE IN COMBINATION WITH AN

AUXILIARY SELF-CONTAINED BREATHING APPARATUS OPERATED IN PRESSURE-DEMAND OR OTHER POSITIVE PRESSURE MODE.

CLOTHING: EMPLOYEE MUST WEAR APPROPRIATE PROTECTIVE (IMPERVIOUS) CLOTHING AND EQUIPMENT TO PREVENT ANY POSSIBILITY OF SKIN CONTACT WITH THIS SUBSTANCE.

GLOVES: EMPLOYEE MUST WEAR APPROPRIATE PROTECTIVE GLOVES TO PREVENT CONTACT WITH THIS SUBSTANCE.

EYE PROTECTION: EMPLOYEE MUST WEAR SPLASH-PROOF OR DUST-RESISTANT SAFETY GOGGLES AND A FACESHIELD TO PREVENT CONTACT WITH THIS SUBSTANCE.

EMERGENCY WASH FACILITIES: WHERE THERE IS ANY POSSIBILITY THAT AN EMPLOYEE'S EYES AND/OR SKIN MAY BE EXPOSED TO THIS SUBSTANCE, THE EMPLOYER SHOULD PROVIDE AN EYE WASH FOUNTAIN AND QUICK DRENCH SHOWER WITHIN THE IMMEDIATE WORK AREA FOR EMERGENCY USE.

AUTHORIZED BY- OCCUPATIONAL HEALTH SERVICES, INC.

CREATION DATE: 10/04/89 ***REVISION DATE:*** 05/15/90

MATERIAL SAFETY DATA SHEET

OCCUPATIONAL HEALTH SERVICES, INC.
AGRICULTURE AND PESTICIDE DIVISION
450 SEVENTH AVENUE, SUITE 2407
NEW YORK, NEW YORK 10123
1-800-445-MSDS OR (212) 967-1100

EMERGENCY CONTACT:
JOHN S. BRANSFORD, JR. (615) 292-1180

SUBSTANCE IDENTIFICATION

CAS-NUMBER 115-90-2

SUBSTANCE: **FENSULFOTHION**

TRADE NAMES/SYNONYMS: PHOSPHOROTHIOIC ACID, O,O-DIETHYL O-(4-(METHYLSULFINYL)PHENYL) ESTER; PHOSPHOROTHIOIC ACID, O,O-DIETHYL O-(P-(METHYLSULFINYL)PHENYL) ESTER; O,O-DIETHYL O-(4-(METHYLSULFINYL)PHENYL) PHOSPHOROTHIOATE; O,O-DIETHYL O-(P-(METHYLSULFINYL)PHENYL) PHOSPHOROTHIOATE; DASANIT (FORMULATION); BAY 25141; S 767; TERRACUR P (FORMULATION); C11H17O4PS2; PST06210

CHEMICAL FAMILY: ORGANOPHOSPHATE

MOLECULAR FORMULA: C-H3-S-(O)-C6-H4-O-P-(S)-(O-C2H5)2

MOLECULAR WEIGHT: 308.35

CERCLA RATINGS (SCALE 0-3): HEALTH=3 FIRE=U REACTIVITY=0 PERSISTENCE=1

NFPA RATINGS (SCALE 0-4): HEALTH=4 FIRE=U REACTIVITY=0

COMPONENTS AND CONTAMINANTS

COMPONENT: FENSULFOTHION ***PERCENT:*** 100.0
CAS# 115-90-2

OTHER CONTAMINANTS: NONE

EXPOSURE LIMITS: FENSULFOTHION: 0.1 MG/M3 OSHA TWA 0.1 MG/M3 ACGIH TWA 500 POUNDS SARA SECTION 302 THRESHOLD PLANNING QUANTITY 1 POUND SARA SECTION 304 REPORTABLE QUANTITY

PHYSICAL DATA

DESCRIPTION: OILY, YELLOW OR BROWN LIQUID.

BOILING POINT: 280-286 F (138-141 C) @ 0.01 MMHG ***SPECIFIC GRAVITY:*** 1.202 @ 20 C

VAPOR PRESSURE: NOT AVAILABLE ***SOLUBILITY IN WATER:*** 1600 PPM

SOLVENT SOLUBILITY: SOLUBLE IN MOST ORGANIC SOLVENTS, DICHLOROMETHANE, ISOPROPANOL; INSOLUBLE IN ALIPHATIC ORGANIC SOLVENTS.

FIRE AND EXPLOSION DATA

FIRE AND EXPLOSION HAZARD: UNKNOWN FIRE AND EXPLOSION HAZARD.

FLASH POINT: NOT AVAILABLE

FIREFIGHTING MEDIA: DRY CHEMICAL, CARBON DIOXIDE, HALON, WATER SPRAY OR STANDARD FOAM (1987 EMERGENCY RESPONSE GUIDEBOOK, DOT P 5800.4).
FOR LARGER FIRES, USE WATER SPRAY, FOG OR STANDARD FOAM (1987 EMERGENCY RESPONSE GUIDEBOOK, DOT P 5800.4).

FIREFIGHTING: MOVE CONTAINER FROM FIRE AREA IF POSSIBLE. DIKE FIRE CONTROL WATER FOR LATER DISPOSAL; DO NOT SCATTER THE MATERIAL. COOL FIRE-EXPOSED CONTAINERS WITH WATER FROM SIDE UNTIL WELL AFTER FIRE IS OUT. STAY AWAY FROM STORAGE TANK ENDS. WITHDRAW IMMEDIATELY IN CASE OF RISING SOUND FROM VENTING SAFETY DEVICE OR ANY DISCOLORATION OF STORAGE TANK DUE TO FIRE (1987 EMERGENCY RESPONSE GUIDEBOOK, DOT P 5800.4, GUIDE PAGE 28).
EXTINGUISH ONLY IF FLOW CAN BE STOPPED. USE FLOODING AMOUNTS OF WATER AS A FOG; SOLID STREAMS MAY BE INEFFECTIVE. COOL CONTAINERS WITH FLOODING AMOUNTS OF WATER FROM AS FAR A DISTANCE AS POSSIBLE. AVOID BREATHING POISONOUS VAPORS, KEEP UPWIND.

TRANSPORTATION DATA

DEPARTMENT OF TRANSPORTATION HAZARD CLASSIFICATION 49 CFR 172.101: POISON B

DEPARTMENT OF TRANSPORTATION LABELING REQUIREMENTS 49 CFR 172.101 AND SUBPART E: POISON

DEPARTMENT OF TRANSPORTATION PACKAGING REQUIREMENTS: 49 CFR 173.359 EXCEPTIONS: 49 CFR 173.359

TOXICITY

FENSULFOTHION: TOXICITY DATA: 113 MG/M3/1 HOUR INHALATION-RAT LC50 (ACGIH); 3 MG/KG SKIN-RAT LD50; 2 MG/KG ORAL-RAT LD50; 9 MG/KG ORAL-GUINEA PIG LD50; 1500 UG/KG INTRAPERITONEAL-RAT LD50; 7 MG/KG INTRAPERITONEAL-MOUSE LD50; 5400 UG/KG INTRAPERITONEAL-GUINEA PIG LD50; 2 MG/MG INTRACEREBRAL-MOUSE LD50; 11 MG/KG UNREPORTED-RAT LD50. CARCINOGEN STATUS: NONE. ACUTE TOXICITY LEVEL: HIGHLY TOXIC BY INHALATION, DERMAL ABSORPTION, INGESTION. TARGET EFFECTS: CHOLINESTERASE INHIBITOR. POISONING MAY AFFECT THE NERVOUS SYSTEM.* AT INCREASED RISK FROM EXPOSURE: PERSONS WITH RESPIRATORY AILMENTS, RECENT EXPOSURE TO CHOLINESTERASE INHIBITORS OR IMPAIRED CHOLINESTERASE PRODUCTION, OR LIVER MALFUNCTION.* ADDITIONAL DATA: MAY CROSS THE PLACENTA. HIGH ENVIRONMENTAL TEMPERATURES OR EXPOSURE OF THE CHEMICAL TO VISIBLE OR ULTRAVIOLET LIGHT MAY ENHANCE THE TOXICITY. INTERACTIONS WITH MEDICATIONS MAY OCCUR.*

* MAY BE BASED ON GENERAL INFORMATION ON ORGANOPHOSPHATES.

HEALTH EFFECTS AND FIRST AID

INHALATION: FENSULFOTHION: HIGHLY TOXIC. SEE INFORMATION ON ORGANOPHOSPHATES.

ORGANOPHOSPHATES: CHOLINESTERASE INHIBITOR. **ACUTE EXPOSURE-** WHEN INHALED, THE FIRST EFFECTS OF CHOLINESTERASE INHIBITORS ARE USUALLY RESPIRATORY AND MAY INCLUDE NASAL HYPEREMIA AND WATERY DISCHARGE, COUGH, CHEST DISCOMFORT, DYSPNEA, AND WHEEZING DUE TO INCREASED BRONCHIAL SECRETIONS AND BRONCHOCONSTRICTION. IF SUFFICIENT AMOUNTS ARE ABSORBED, OTHER SYSTEMIC EFFECTS MAY BEGIN WITHIN A FEW MINUTES OR BE DELAYED FOR UP TO 12 HOURS. SYMPTOMS MAY INCLUDE PALLOR, NAUSEA, VOMITING, DIARRHEA, ABDOMINAL CRAMPS, HEADACHE, DIZZINESS, OCULAR PAIN, BLURRED VISION, MIOSIS OR IN SOME CASES, ESPECIALLY INITIALLY, MYDRIASIS, LACRIMATION, SALIVATION, SWEATING, AND CONFUSION. OTHER REPORTED CENTRAL NERVOUS SYSTEM OR NEUROMUSCULAR EFFECTS MAY INCLUDE ATAXIA, SLURRED SPEECH, AREFLEXIA, WEAKNESS, FATIGUE, FASCICULATIONS, TWITCHING, TREMORS POSSIBLY OF THE TONGUE AND EYELIDS, AND EVENTUALLY PARALYSIS OF THE EXTREMITIES AND POSSIBLY OF THE RESPIRATORY MUSCLES. IN SEVERE CASES THERE MAY ALSO BE INVOLUNTARY DEFECATION AND URINATION, CYANOSIS, PSYCHOSIS, HYPERGLYCEMIA, ACUTE PANCREATITIS, CARDIAC IRREGULARITIES, PULMONARY EDEMA, UNCONSCIOUSNESS, CONVULSIONS, AND COMA. DEATH IS PRIMARILY DUE TO RESPIRATORY FAILURE, ALTHOUGH CARDIOVASCULAR EFFECTS INCLUDING CARDIAC ARREST MAY ALSO BE IMPLICATED. LONG TERM SEQUELAE ARE RARE BUT MAY INCLUDE NEUROPSYCHIATRIC DISORDERS AND MYOPATHY WITH MUSCLE TENDERNESS. SOME ORGANOPHOSPHATES MAY CAUSE A DELAYED NEUROPATHY BEGINNING 1-4 WEEKS AFTER AN ACUTE EXPOSURE WHICH MAY OR MAY NOT HAVE CAUSED ACUTE CHOLINERGIC EFFECTS. NUMBNESS, TINGLING, WEAKNESS AND CRAMPING BEGINNING SYMMETRICALLY IN THE LOWER LIMBS MAY PROGRESS TO ATAXIA AND PARALYSIS. IN SEVERE CASES, UPPER LIMB INVOLVEMENT IS POSSIBLE AND FLACCID PARALYSIS MAY PROGRESS TO SPASTIC PARALYSIS WITH EXAGGERATED REFLEXES. IMPROVEMENT MAY OCCUR OVER MONTHS TO YEARS, BUT SOME RESIDUAL IMPAIRMENT USUALLY REMAINS.

CHRONIC EXPOSURE- REPEATED OR PROLONGED EXPOSURE MAY RESULT IN THE EFFECTS OF ACUTE EXPOSURE INCLUDING THE DELAYED NEUROPATHY. OTHER EFFECTS REPORTED IN WORKERS REPEATEDLY EXPOSED INCLUDE IMPAIRED MEMORY AND CONCENTRATION, ACUTE PSYCHOSIS, SEVERE DEPRESSIONS, IRRITABILTY, CONFUSION, APATHY, EMOTIONAL LABILITY, SOCIAL WITHDRAWAL, CONFUSION, HEADACHE, SPEECH DIFFICULTIES, DELAYED REACTION TIMES, SPATIAL DISORIENTATION, NIGHTMARES, SLEEPWALKING, AND DROWSINESS OR INSOMNIA. AN INFLUENZA-LIKE CONDITION WITH HEADACHE, NAUSEA, WEAKNESS, ANOREXIA AND MALAISE HAS ALSO BEEN REPORTED.

FIRST AID- REMOVE FROM EXPOSURE AREA TO FRESH AIR IMMEDIATELY. IF BREATHING HAS STOPPED, GIVE ARTIFICIAL RESPIRATION. MAINTAIN AIRWAY AND BLOOD PRESSURE AND ADMINISTER OXYGEN IF AVAILABLE. KEEP AFFECTED PERSON WARM AND AT REST. TREAT SYMPTOMATICALLY AND SUPPORTIVELY.

CHRONIC EXPOSURE- REPEATED OR PROLONGED EXPOSURE MAY RESULT IN THE EFFECTS OF ACUTE EXPOSURE INCLUDING THE DELAYED NEUROPATHY. OTHER EFFECTS REPORTED IN WORKERS REPEATEDLY EXPOSED INCLUDE IMPAIRED MEMORY AND CONCENTRATION, ACUTE PSYCHOSIS, SEVERE DEPRESSIONS, IRRITABILTY, CONFUSION, APATHY, EMOTIONAL LABILITY, SOCIAL WITHDRAWAL, CONFUSION, HEADACHE, SPEECH DIFFICULTIES, DELAYED REACTION TIMES, SPATIAL DISORIENTATION, NIGHTMARES, SLEEPWALKING, AND DROWSINESS OR INSOMNIA. AN INFLUENZA-LIKE CONDITION WITH HEADACHE, NAUSEA, WEAKNESS, ANOREXIA AND MALAISE HAS ALSO BEEN REPORTED.

FIRST AID- REMOVE FROM EXPOSURE AREA TO FRESH AIR IMMEDIATELY. IF BREATHING HAS STOPPED, GIVE ARTIFICIAL RESPIRATION. MAINTAIN AIRWAY AND BLOOD PRESSURE AND ADMINISTER OXYGEN IF AVAILABLE. KEEP AFFECTED PERSON WARM AND AT REST. TREAT SYMPTOMATICALLY AND SUPPORTIVELY. ADMINISTRATION OF OXYGEN SHOULD BE PERFORMED BY QUALIFIED PERSONNEL. GET MEDICAL ATTENTION IMMEDIATELY.

SKIN CONTACT: FENSULFOTHION OXYGEN ANALOG SULFONE: SEE INFORMATION ON ORGANOPHOSPHATES.

ORGANOPHOSPHATES: CHOLINESTERASE INHIBITOR. **ACUTE EXPOSURE-** LOCALIZED SWEATING AND FASCICULATIONS MAY OCCUR AT THE SITE OF CONTACT. IF SUFFICIENT AMOUNTS ARE ABSORBED, OTHER EFFECTS OF CHOLINESTERASE INHIBITION AS DESCRIBED IN ACUTE INHALATION MAY OCCUR. SYMPTOMS MAY BE DELAYED 2-3 HOURS, BUT USUALLY NO MORE THAN 12 HOURS. THE RATE OF ABSORPTION IS INCREASED BY THE PRESENCE OF DERMATITIS OR HIGH AMBIENT TEMPERATURES. DELAYED NEUROPATHY IS ALSO POSSIBLE. **CHRONIC EXPOSURE-** REPEATED OR PROLONGED EXPOSURE MAY CAUSE EFFECTS AS DESCRIBED IN ACUTE EXPOSURE. SOME ORGANOPHOSPHATES MAY CAUSE SENSITIZATION.

FIRST AID- REMOVE CONTAMINATED CLOTHING IMMEDIATELY. WASH CONTAMINATED AREAS WITH SOAP AND WATER FOLLOWED BY ALCOHOL (ARENA, POISONING, 4TH ED.). EMERGENCY PERSONNEL SHOULD WEAR GLOVES AND AVOID CONTAMINATION. TREAT RESPIRATORY DIFFICULTY WITH ARTIFICIAL RESPIRATION. GET MEDICAL ATTENTION IMMEDIATELY.

EYE CONTACT: FENSULFOTHION OXYGEN ANALOG SULFONE: SEE INFORMATION ON ORGANOPHOSPHATES.

ORGANOPHOSPHATES: CHOLINESTERASE INHIBITOR. **ACUTE EXPOSURE-** DIRECT CONTACT MAY CAUSE PAIN, HYPEREMIA, LACRIMATION, TWITCHING OF THE EYELIDS, MIOSIS, AND CILIARY MUSCLE SPASM WITH LOSS OF ACCOMODATION, BLURRED OR DIMMED VISION AND BROWACHE. SOMETIMES MYDRIASIS MAY OCCUR INSTEAD OF MIOSIS. WITH SUFFICIENT EXPOSURE, OTHER SYMPTOMS OF CHOLINESTERASE INHIBITION AS DESCRIBED IN ACUTE INHALATION MAY OCCUR. **CHRONIC EXPOSURE-** REPEATED OR PROLONGED EXPOSURE MAY CAUSE EFFECTS AS DESCRIBED IN ACUTE EXPOSURE. SOME COMPOUNDS HAVE CAUSED TOXIC EFFECTS ON THE CRYSTALLINE LENS, CONJUNCTIVAL THICKENING AND OBSTRUCTION OF THE NASOLACRIMAL CANALS WHEN USED AS MIOTIC EYEDROPS.

FIRST AID- IRRIGATE EYES WITH WATER OR SALINE SOLUTION. IF SYMPTOMS OF POISONING OCCUR, TREAT RESPIRATORY DIFFICULTY WITH ARTIFICIAL RESPIRATION AND OXYGEN. OBSERVE PATIENT FOR AT LEAST 24-36 HOURS (GOSSELIN, CLINICAL TOXICOLOGY OF COMMERCIAL PRODUCTS, 5TH ED.). GET MEDICAL ATTENTION IMMEDIATELY. OXYGEN SHOULD BE ADMINISTERED BY QUALIFIED MEDICAL PERSONNEL.

INGESTION: FENSULFOTHION OXYGEN ANALOG SULFONE: HIGHLY TOXIC. SEE INFORMATION ON ORGANOPHOSPHATES.

ORGANOPHOSPHATES: CHOLINESTERASE INHIBITOR. **ACUTE EXPOSURE-** WHEN INGESTED, THE FIRST EFFECTS MAY BE NAUSEA, VOMITING, ANOREXIA, ABDOMINAL CRAMPS AND DIARRHEA. GASTROINTESTINAL ABSORPTION MAY CAUSE SYMPTOMS OF CHOLINESTERASE INHIBITION AS DESCRIBED IN ACUTE INHALATION. SYMPTOMS MAY BEGIN WITHIN MINUTES OR BE DELAYED FOR HOURS. DELAYED EFFECTS INCLUDING NEUROPATHY MAY ALSO OCCUR. **CHRONIC EXPOSURE-** REPEATED INGESTION MAY CAUSE EFFECTS AS DESCRIBED IN ACUTE EXPOSURE.

FIRST AID- IF PERSON IS ALERT AND RESPIRATION IS NOT DEPRESSED, GIVE SYRUP OF IPECAC FOLLOWED BY WATER (IF VOMITING OCCURS, KEEP HEAD BELOW HIPS TO PREVENT ASPIRATION). IF CONSCIOUSNESS LEVEL DECLINES OR VOMITING HAS NOT OCCURRED IN 15 MINUTES EMPTY STOMACH BY GASTRIC LAVAGE WITH THE AID OF CUFFED ENDOTRACHEAL TUBE USING ISOTONIC SALINE OR 5% SODIUM BICARBONATE FOLLOW WITH ACTIVATED CHARCOAL. ESTABLISH AND MAINTAIN AIRWAY. TREAT RESPIRATORY DIFFICULTY WITH ARTIFICIAL RESPIRATION AND OXYGEN. DO NOT GIVE MORPHINE, AMINOPHYLLINE, PHENOTHIAZINES, RESERPINE, FUROSEMIDE, OR ETHACRYNIC ACID (MORGAN, RECOGNITION AND MANAGEMENT OF PESTICIDE POISONINGS, 3RD ED.). TREAT SYMPTOMATICALLY AND SUPPORTIVELY. ADMINISTRATION OF OXYGEN AND LAVAGE MUST BE PERFORMED BY QUALIFIED MEDICAL PERSONNEL. GET MEDICAL ATTENTION IMMEDIATELY.

ANTIDOTE: THE FOLLOWING ANTIDOTE(S) HAVE BEEN RECOMMENDED. HOWEVER, THE DECISION AS TO WHETHER THE SEVERITY OF POISONING REQUIRES ADMINISTRATION OF ANY ANTIDOTE AND ACTUAL DOSE REQUIRED SHOULD BE MADE BY QUALIFIED MEDICAL PERSONNEL. FOR CHOLINESTERASE INHIBITORS: ESTABLISH CLEAR AIRWAY AND TISSUE OXYGENATION BY ASPIRATION OF SECRETIONS, AND IF NECESSARY, BY ASSISTED PULMONARY VENTILATION WITH OXYGEN. IMPROVE TISSUE OXYGENATION AS MUCH AS POSSIBLE BEFORE ADMINISTERING ATROPINE TO MINIMIZE THE RISK OF VENTRICULAR FIBRILLATION. ADMINISTER ATROPINE SULFATE INTRAVENOUSLY, OR INTRAMUSCULARLY IF IV INJECTION IS NOT POSSIBLE. IN MODERATELY SEVERE POISONING ADMINISTER ATROPINE SULFATE, 0.4-2.0 MG REPEATED EVERY 15 MINUTES UNTIL ATROPINIZATION IS ACHIEVED (TACHYCARDIA, FLUSHING, DRY MOUTH, MYDRIASIS). MAINTAIN ATROPINIZATION BY REPEATED DOSES FOR 2-12 HOURS, OR LONGER, DEPENDING ON THE SEVERITY OF POISONING. THE APPEARANCE OF RALES IN THE LUNG BASES, MIOSIS, SALIVATION, NAUSEA, BRADYCARDIA, ARE ALL INDICATIONS OF INADEQUATE ATROPINIZATION. SEVERELY POISONED INDIVIDUALS MAY EXHIBIT REMARKABLE TOLERANCE TO ATROPINE; TWO OR MORE TIMES THE DOSAGES SUGGESTED ABOVE MAY BE NEEDED. PERSONS NOT POISONED OR ONLY SLIGHTLY POISONED, HOWEVER, MAY DEVELOP SIGNS OF ATROPINE TOXICITY FROM SUCH LARGE DOSAGES: FEVER, MUSCLE FIBRILLATIONS, AND DELIRIUM ARE THE MAIN SIGNS OF ATROPINE TOXICITY. IF THESE SIGNS APPEAR WHILE THE PATIENT IS FULLY ATROPINIZED, ATROPINE ADMINISTRATION SHOULD BE DISCONTINUED, AT LEAST TEMPORARILY. OBSERVE TREATED PATIENTS CLOSELY AT LEAST 24 HOURS TO INSURE THAT SYMPTOMS (POSSIBLY PULMONARY EDEMA) DO NOT RECUR AS ATROPINIZATION WEARS OFF. IN VERY SEVERE POISONINGS, METABOLIC DISPOSITION OF TOXICANT MAY REQUIRE SEVERAL HOURS OR DAYS DURING WHICH ATROPINIZATION MUST BE MAINTAINED. MARKEDLY LOWER LEVELS OF URINARY METABOLITES INDICATE THAT ATROPINE DOSAGE CAN BE TAPERED OFF. AS DOSAGE IS REDUCED, CHECK THE LUNG BASES FREQUENTLY FOR RALES. IF RALES ARE HEARD OR OTHER SYMPTOMS RETURN, RE-ESTABLISH ATROPINIZATION PROMPTLY (MORGAN, RECOGNITION AND MANAGEMENT OF PESTICIDE POISONINGS, 3RD ED.). ADMINISTRATION OF ANTIDOTE MUST BE PERFORMED BY QUALIFIED MEDICAL PERSONNEL.

IN CASES OF SEVERE POISONING BY ORGANOPHOSPHATE PESTICIDES IN WHICH RESPIRATORY DEPRESSION, MUSCLE WEAKNESS AND TWITCHINGS ARE SEVERE, GIVE PRALIDOXIME (PROTOPAM-AYERST, 2-PAM), 1.0 GRAM INTRAVENOUSLY AT NO MORE THAN 0.5 GRAM PER MINUTE. DOSAGE OF PRALIDOXIME MAY BE REPEATED IN 1-2 HOURS, THEN AT 10-12 HOUR INTERVALS IF NEEDED. IN VERY SEVERE POISONINGS, DOSAGE RATES MAY BE DOUBLED. TREATMENT WITH PRALIDOXIME WILL BE MOST EFFECTIVE IF GIVEN WITHIN THIRTY-SIX HOURS AFTER POISONING (MORGAN, RECOGNITION AND MANAGEMENT OF PESTICIDE POISONINGS, 3RD ED.). ANTIDOTE SHOULD BE ADMINISTERED BY QUALIFIED MEDICAL PERSONNEL.

REACTIVITY

REACTIVITY: STABLE UNDER NORMAL TEMPERATURES AND PRESSURES.

INCOMPATIBILITIES: FENSULFOTHION OXYGEN ANALOG SULFONE: OXIDIZERS (STRONG): FIRE AND EXPLOSION HAZARD.

DECOMPOSITION: THERMAL DECOMPOSITION PRODUCTS MAY INCLUDE TOXIC OXIDES OF CARBON, SULFUR, AND PHOSPHORUS.

POLYMERIZATION: HAZARDOUS POLYMERIZATION HAS NOT BEEN REPORTED TO OCCUR UNDER NORMAL TEMPERATURES AND PRESSURES.

STORAGE AND DISPOSAL

OBSERVE ALL FEDERAL, STATE AND LOCAL REGULATIONS WHEN STORING OR DISPOSING OF THIS SUBSTANCE. FOR ASSISTANCE, CONTACT THE DISTRICT DIRECTOR OF THE ENVIRONMENTAL PROTECTION AGENCY.

STORAGE

STORE AWAY FROM INCOMPATIBLE SUBSTANCES.

STORE IN ACCORDANCE WITH 40 CFR 165 RECOMMENDED PROCEDURES FOR THE DISPOSAL AND STORAGE OF PESTICIDES AND PESTICIDE CONTAINERS.

DISPOSAL

DISPOSAL MUST BE IN ACCORDANCE WITH 40 CFR 165 RECOMMENDED PROCEDURES FOR THE DISPOSAL AND STORAGE OF PESTICIDES AND PESTICIDE CONTAINERS.

CONDITIONS TO AVOID

MAY BURN BUT DOES NOT IGNITE READILY.

SPILL AND LEAK PROCEDURES

OCCUPATIONAL SPILL: DO NOT TOUCH SPILLED MATERIAL. STOP LEAK IF YOU CAN DO IT WITHOUT RISK. FOR SMALL SPILLS, TAKE UP WITH SAND OR OTHER ABSORBENT MATERIAL AND PLACE INTO CONTAINERS FOR LATER DISPOSAL. FOR SMALL DRY SPILLS, WITH A CLEAN SHOVEL PLACE MATERIAL INTO CLEAN, DRY CONTAINER AND COVER. MOVE CONTAINERS FROM SPILL AREA. FOR LARGER

SPILLS, DIKE FAR AHEAD OF SPILL FOR LATER DISPOSAL. KEEP UNNECESSARY PEOPLE AWAY. ISOLATE HAZARD AREA AND DENY ENTRY.

PROTECTIVE EQUIPMENT

VENTILATION: PROVIDE LOCAL EXHAUST OR PROCESS ENCLOSURE VENTILATION SYSTEM.

RESPIRATOR: THE FOLLOWING RESPIRATORS ARE RECOMMENDED BASED ON INFORMATION FOUND IN THE PHYSICAL DATA, TOXICITY AND HEALTH EFFECTS SECTIONS. THEY ARE RANKED IN ORDER FROM MINIMUM TO MAXIMUM RESPIRATORY PROTECTION. THE SPECIFIC RESPIRATOR SELECTED MUST BE BASED ON CONTAMINATION LEVELS FOUND IN THE WORK PLACE, MUST NOT EXCEED THE WORKING LIMITS OF THE RESPIRATOR AND BE JOINTLY APPROVED BY THE NATIONAL INSTITUTE FOR OCCUPATIONAL SAFETY AND HEALTH AND THE MINE SAFETY AND HEALTH ADMINISTRATION (NIOSH-MSHA).

CHEMICAL CARTRIDGE RESPIRATOR WITH AN ORGANIC VAPOR CARTRIDGE(S) WITH A FULL FACEPIECE AND ORGANIC VAPOR CARTRIDGE(S) IN COMBINATION WITH A DUST AND MIST FILTER.

POWERED AIR-PURIFYING RESPIRATOR WITH A TIGHT-FITTING FACEPIECE AND ORGANIC VAPOR CARTRIDGE(S) IN COMBINATION WITH A HIGH-EFFICIENCY PARTICULATE FILTER.

TYPE 'C' SUPPLIED-AIR RESPIRATOR WITH A FULL FACEPIECE OPERATED IN A PRESSURE-DEMAND OR OTHER POSITIVE PRESSURE MODE.

SELF-CONTAINED BREATHING APPARATUS WITH A FULL FACEPIECE OPERATED IN PRESSURE-DEMAND OR OTHER POSITIVE PRESSURE MODE.

FOR FIREFIGHTING AND OTHER IMMEDIATELY DANGEROUS TO LIFE OR HEALTH CONDITIONS:

SELF-CONTAINED BREATHING APPARATUS WITH FULL FACEPIECE OPERATED IN PRESSURE-DEMAND OR OTHER POSITIVE PRESSURE MODE.

SUPPLIED-AIR RESPIRATOR WITH FULL FACEPIECE AND OPERATED IN PRESSURE-DEMAND OR OTHER POSITIVE PRESSURE MODE IN COMBINATION WITH AN AUXILIARY SELF-CONTAINED BREATHING APPARATUS OPERATED IN PRESSURE-DEMAND OR OTHER POSITIVE PRESSURE MODE.

CLOTHING: EMPLOYEE MUST WEAR APPROPRIATE PROTECTIVE (IMPERVIOUS) CLOTHING AND EQUIPMENT TO PREVENT ANY POSSIBILITY OF SKIN CONTACT WITH THIS SUBSTANCE.

GLOVES: EMPLOYEE MUST WEAR APPROPRIATE PROTECTIVE GLOVES TO PREVENT CONTACT WITH THIS SUBSTANCE.

EYE PROTECTION: EMPLOYEE MUST WEAR SPLASH-PROOF OR DUST-RESISTANT SAFETY GOGGLES TO PREVENT EYE CONTACT WITH THIS SUBSTANCE.

EMERGENCY EYE WASH: WHERE THERE IS ANY POSSIBILITY THAT AN EMPLOYEE'S EYES MAY BE EXPOSED TO THIS SUBSTANCE, THE EMPLOYER SHOULD PROVIDE AN EYE WASH FOUNTAIN WITHIN THE IMMEDIATE WORK AREA FOR EMERGENCY USE.

AUTHORIZED BY- OCCUPATIONAL HEALTH SERVICES, INC.

CREATION DATE: 10/04/89 ***REVISION DATE:*** 05/07/90

MATERIAL SAFETY DATA SHEET

OCCUPATIONAL HEALTH SERVICES, INC.
AGRICULTURE AND PESTICIDE DIVISION
450 SEVENTH AVENUE, SUITE 2407
NEW YORK, NEW YORK 10123
1-800-445-MSDS OR (212) 967-1100

EMERGENCY CONTACT:
JOHN S. BRANSFORD, JR. (615) 292-1180

SUBSTANCE IDENTIFICATION

CAS-NUMBER 18625-12-2

SUBSTANCE: **2,4-DB METHYL ESTER**

TRADE NAMES/SYNONYMS: BUTANOIC ACID, 4-(2,4-DICHLOROPHENOXY)-, METHYL ESTER; 4-(2,4-DICHLOROPHENOXY)METHYL BUTANOATE; BUTYRIC ACID, 4-(2,4-DICHLOROPHENOXY)-, METHYL ESTER; 4-(2,4-DICHLOROPHENOXY) METHYL BUTYRATE; 4-(2,4-DB) METHYL ESTER; METHYL 4-(2,4-DICHLOROPHENOXY)BUTYRATE; 4-(2,4-DICHLOROPHENOXY)BUTANOIC ACID METHYL ESTER; 4-(2,4-DICHLOROPHENOXY)BUTYRIC ACID METHYL ESTER; C11H12CL2O3; PST06227

CHEMICAL FAMILY: HALOGEN COMPOUND, AROMATIC ESTER, NON-CARBOXYLIC

MOLECULAR FORMULA: C6-H3-(CL)2-O-(C-H2)3-C-(O)-O-C-H3

MOLECULAR WEIGHT: 263.12

CERCLA RATINGS (SCALE 0-3): HEALTH=3 FIRE=1 REACTIVITY=0 PERSISTENCE=2

NFPA RATINGS (SCALE 0-4): HEALTH=U FIRE=1 REACTIVITY=0

COMPONENTS AND CONTAMINANTS

COMPONENT: 2,4-DB METHYL ESTER ***PERCENT:*** 100.0

CAS# 18625-12-2

OTHER CONTAMINANTS: NONE

EXPOSURE LIMITS: NO OCCUPATIONAL EXPOSURE LIMITS ESTABLISHED BY OSHA, ACGIH, OR NIOSH.

PHYSICAL DATA

DESCRIPTION: WHITE POWDER. ***MELTING POINT:*** NOT AVAILABLE

SPECIFIC GRAVITY: NOT AVAILABLE ***SOLUBILITY IN WATER:*** NOT AVAILABLE

FIRE AND EXPLOSION DATA

FIRE AND EXPLOSION HAZARD: SLIGHT FIRE HAZARD WHEN EXPOSED TO HEAT OR FLAME.

DUST-AIR MIXTURES MAY IGNITE OR EXPLODE.

FIREFIGHTING MEDIA: DRY CHEMICAL, CARBON DIOXIDE, HALON, WATER SPRAY OR STANDARD FOAM (1987 EMERGENCY RESPONSE GUIDEBOOK, DOT P 5800.4).

FOR LARGER FIRES, USE WATER SPRAY, FOG OR STANDARD FOAM (1987 EMERGENCY RESPONSE GUIDEBOOK, DOT P 5800.4).

FIREFIGHTING: MOVE CONTAINERS FROM FIRE AREA IF POSSIBLE (1987 EMERGENCY RESPONSE GUIDEBOOK, DOT P 5800.4, GUIDE PAGE 53).

EXTINGUISH USING AGENT SUITABLE FOR TYPE OF SURROUNDING FIRE. AVOID BREATHING VAPORS AND DUSTS. KEEP UPWIND.

TOXICITY

2,4-DB METHYL ESTER: TOXICITY DATA: 400 MG/KG ORAL-RAT LD50 (EPA). CARCINOGEN STATUS: HUMAN LIMITED EVIDENCE (IARC GROUP-2B FOR CHLOROPHENOXY HERBICIDES). STUDIES REVEALED A SIGNIFICANT INCREASE IN SOFT-TISSUE SARCOMAS, MALIGNANT LYMPHOMAS AND BRONCHIAL CARCINOMAS IN WORKERS EXPOSED TO CHLOROPHENOXY HERBICIDES. ACUTE TOXICITY LEVEL: TOXIC BY INGESTION. TARGET EFFECTS: POISONING MAY AFFECT THE GASTROINTESTINAL TRACT AND THE CARDIOVASCULAR AND NERVOUS SYSTEMS.* AT INCREASED RISK FROM EXPOSURE: PERSONS WITH LIVER, KIDNEY, CARDIOVASCULAR, OR SKIN DISEASES, AND CONVULSIVE DISORDERS OR NEUROPATHY.* ADDITIONAL DATA: STIMULANTS SUCH AS EPINEPHRINE MAY INDUCE VENTRICULAR FIBRILLATION. *MAY BE BASED ON GENERAL INFORMATION ON DICHLOROPHENOXY DERIVATIVES.

HEALTH EFFECTS AND FIRST AID

INHALATION: 2,4-DB METHYL ESTER: SEE INFORMATION ON 2,4-D AND DERIVATIVES.

2,4-D AND DERIVATIVES: **ACUTE EXPOSURE-** EXPOSURE TO 2,4-D AND ITS DERIVATIVES MAY CAUSE IRRITATION WITH SORE THROAT AND BURNING SENSATIONS IN THE NASOPHARYNX AND CHEST, COUGHING, LACRIMATION, RHINITIS, DULLNESS, DIZZINESS, AND ATAXIA. OTHER EFFECTS OF FATIGUE, NAUSEA, VOMITING, DIARRHEA, STOMACH PAINS, MALAISE, HEADACHE, FEVER, TACHYCARDIA, URINARY INCONTINENCE, CONSTIPATION, LEUKOPENIA, MYALGIA, AND TRANSIENT UNCONSCIOUSNESS MAY OCCUR. A DELAYED PERIPHERAL NEUROPATHY MAY DEVELOP CHARACTERIZED BY PARESTHESIAS, SEVERE PAIN, SYMMETRICAL MOTOR AND SENSORY DEFICITS, WEAKNESS, MYOTONIA, FASCICULATIONS, AND IN SOME CASES PARALYSIS OF THE EXTREMITIES. THE DISABILITY MAY BE PROLONGED AND RECOVERY INCOMPLETE. **CHRONIC EXPOSURE-** IN ADDITION TO THE EFFECTS LISTED IN ACUTE EXPOSURE, OCCUPATIONAL EXPOSURE TO 2,4-D AND ITS DERIVATIVES HAS PRODUCED A SWEET TASTE IN THE MOUTH, HYPERACUSIA, LOWERED SENSITIVITY TO TASTE AND SMELL, INCREASED SALIVATION, VERTIGO, SOMNOLENCE, ANOREXIA, HEAVINESS OF THE LEGS. OTHER EFFECTS HAVE INCLUDED HYPOTENSION, BRADYCARDIA AND OTHER CARDIOVASCULAR SYSTEM CHANGES, PAIN IN THE REGION OF THE LIVER AND STOMACH, AND CHANGES IN THE DIGESTIVE FUNCTION, LIVER FUNCTION AND METABOLIC PROCESSES. A CASE REPORT DESCRIBED A CHILD WITH MULTIPLE CONGENITAL ANOMALIES AND SEVERE MENTAL RETARDATION OF UNCERTAIN CAUSE BORN TO PARENTS HEAVILY EXPOSED TO 2,4-D WHILE SPRAYING TREES. AN INCREASED PREVALENCE OF SLOWED NERVE CONDUCTION VELOCITY WITH NO ASSOCIATED SYMPTOMS WAS REPORTED IN A STUDY OF CHEMICAL WORKERS EMPLOYED IN THE PRODUCTION OF 2,4-D AND 2,4,5-T. EPIDEMIOLOGICAL STUDIES REVEALED A SIGNIFICANT INCREASE IN SOFT-TISSUE SARCOMAS, MALIGNANT LYMPHOMAS, AND BRONCHIAL CARCINOMAS IN WORKERS EXPOSED TO CHLOROPHENOXY HERBICIDES INCLUDING 2,4-D.

FIRST AID- REMOVE FROM EXPOSURE AREA TO FRESH AIR IMMEDIATELY. IF BREATHING HAS STOPPED, PERFORM ARTIFICIAL RESPIRATION. KEEP PERSON WARM AND AT REST. TREAT SYMPTOMATICALLY AND SUPPORTIVELY. GET MEDICAL ATTENTION IMMEDIATELY.

SKIN CONTACT: 2,4-DB METHYL ESTER: SEE INFORMATION ON 2,4-D AND DERIVATIVES.

2,4-D AND DERIVATIVES: **ACUTE EXPOSURE-** MAY CAUSE IRRITATION. IF SUFFICIENT AMOUNTS ARE ABSORBED THROUGH THE SKIN, EFFECTS, INCLUDING PERIPHERAL NEUROPATHY, AS DESCRIBED IN ACUTE INHALATION MAY OCCUR. **CHRONIC EXPOSURE-** PROLONGED OR REPEATED EXPOSURE MAY CAUSE DERMATITIS AND EFFECTS AS DESCRIBED IN CHRONIC INHALATION.

FIRST AID- REMOVE CONTAMINATED CLOTHING AND SHOES IMMEDIATELY. WASH AFFECTED AREA WITH SOAP OR MILD DETERGENT AND LARGE AMOUNTS OF WATER UNTIL NO EVIDENCE OF CHEMICAL REMAINS (APPROXIMATELY 15-20 MINUTES). GET MEDICAL ATTENTION IMMEDIATELY.

EYE CONTACT: 2,4-DB METHYL ESTER: SEE INFORMATION ON 2,4-D AND DERIVATIVES.

2,4-D AND DERIVATIVES: **ACUTE EXPOSURE-** MAY CAUSE IRRITATION. **CHRONIC EXPOSURE-** NO DATA AVAILABLE.

FIRST AID- WASH EYES IMMEDIATELY WITH LARGE AMOUNTS OF WATER OR NORMAL SALINE, OCCASIONALLY LIFTING UPPER AND LOWER LIDS, UNTIL NO EVIDENCE OF CHEMICAL REMAINS (APPROXIMATELY 15-20 MINUTES). GET MEDICAL ATTENTION IMMEDIATELY.

INGESTION: 2,4-DB METHYL ESTER: TOXIC. SEE INFORMATION ON 2,4-D AND DERIVATIVES.

2,4-D AND DERIVATIVES: **ACUTE EXPOSURE-** INGESTION OF 2,4-D AND ITS DERIVATIVES MAY CAUSE IRRITATION OF THE MOUTH, THROAT, AND GASTROINTESTINAL TRACT, NAUSEA, VOMITING, CHEST AND ABDOMINAL PAIN, AND DIARRHEA. INGESTION OF VERY LARGE DOSES MAY PRODUCE METABOLIC ACIDOSIS, FEVER OR SUBNORMAL TEMPERATURES, HYPERVENTILATION, HYPOTENSION, VASODILATION, FLUSHING OF THE SKIN, SWEATING, CARDIAC ARRHYTHMIAS, TACHYCARDIA, LETHARGY, WEAKNESS, INTERCOSTAL PARALYSIS, RENAL AND HEPATIC DYSFUNCTION, MYOTONIA, COMA, AND CONVULSIONS. DAMAGE TO SKELETAL MUSCLE MAY BE MANIFEST BY MUSCLE TWITCHING AND ACHING WITH ELEVATED SERUM ENZYMES AND MYOGLOBIN IN THE BLOOD AND URINE. IMPAIRED MEMORY AND CHANGES IN COLOR VISION WERE REPORTED IN ONE CASE OF POISONING. DEATH MAY BE DUE TO CIRCULATORY COLLAPSE. **CHRONIC EXPOSURE-** NO DATA AVAILABLE.

FIRST AID- IF THE PERSON IS CONSCIOUS AND NOT CONVULSING, INDUCE EMESIS BY GIVING SYRUP OF IPECAC (KEEPING THE HEAD BELOW THE HIPS TO PREVENT ASPIRATION) FOLLOWED BY WATER. REPEAT IN 20 MINUTES IF NOT EFFECTIVE INITIALLY. IN PATIENTS WITH DEPRESSED RESPIRATION OR IF EMESIS IS NOT PRODUCED, PERFORM GASTRIC LAVAGE WITH ACTIVATED CHARCOAL. FOLLOW WITH A SALINE CATHARTIC (DREISBACH, HANDBOOK OF POISONING, 12TH ED.). TREAT SYMPTOMATICALLY AND SUPPORTIVELY. GASTRIC LAVAGE SHOULD BE PERFORMED BY QUALIFIED MEDICAL PERSONNEL. GET MEDICAL ATTENTION IMMEDIATELY.

ANTIDOTE: NO SPECIFIC ANTIDOTE. TREAT SYMPTOMATICALLY AND SUPPORTIVELY.

REACTIVITY

REACTIVITY: STABLE UNDER NORMAL TEMPERATURES AND PRESSURES.

INCOMPATIBILITIES: 2,4-DB METHYL ESTER: OXIDIZERS (STRONG): FIRE AND EXPLOSION HAZARD.

DECOMPOSITION: THERMAL DECOMPOSITION PRODUCTS MAY INCLUDE TOXIC AND CORROSIVE FUMES OF CHLORIDES AND TOXIC OXIDES OF CARBON.

POLYMERIZATION: HAZARDOUS POLYMERIZATION HAS NOT BEEN REPORTED TO OCCUR UNDER NORMAL TEMPERATURES AND PRESSURES.

STORAGE AND DISPOSAL

OBSERVE ALL FEDERAL, STATE AND LOCAL REGULATIONS WHEN STORING OR DISPOSING OF THIS SUBSTANCE. FOR ASSISTANCE, CONTACT THE DISTRICT DIRECTOR OF THE ENVIRONMENTAL PROTECTION AGENCY.

****STORAGE****

STORE IN ACCORDANCE WITH 40 CFR 165 RECOMMENDED PROCEDURES FOR THE DISPOSAL AND STORAGE OF PESTICIDES AND PESTICIDE CONTAINERS.
STORE AWAY FROM INCOMPATIBLE SUBSTANCES.

****DISPOSAL****

DISPOSAL MUST BE IN ACCORDANCE WITH 40 CFR 165 RECOMMENDED PROCEDURES FOR THE DISPOSAL AND STORAGE OF PESTICIDES AND PESTICIDE CONTAINERS.

CONDITIONS TO AVOID

MAY BURN BUT DOES NOT IGNITE READILY.

SPILL AND LEAK PROCEDURES

OCCUPATIONAL SPILL: DO NOT TOUCH SPILLED MATERIAL. STOP LEAK IF YOU CAN DO IT WITHOUT RISK. FOR SMALL SPILLS, TAKE UP WITH SAND OR OTHER ABSORBENT MATERIAL AND PLACE INTO CONTAINERS FOR LATER DISPOSAL. FOR SMALL DRY SPILLS, WITH A CLEAN SHOVEL PLACE MATERIAL INTO CLEAN, DRY CONTAINER AND COVER. MOVE CONTAINERS FROM SPILL AREA. FOR LARGER SPILLS, DIKE FAR AHEAD OF SPILL FOR LATER DISPOSAL. KEEP UNNECESSARY PEOPLE AWAY. ISOLATE HAZARD AREA AND DENY ENTRY.

PROTECTIVE EQUIPMENT

VENTILATION: PROVIDE LOCAL EXHAUST OR PROCESS ENCLOSURE VENTILATION SYSTEM.

RESPIRATOR: THE FOLLOWING RESPIRATORS ARE RECOMMENDED BASED ON INFORMATION FOUND IN THE PHYSICAL DATA, TOXICITY AND HEALTH EFFECTS SECTIONS. THEY ARE RANKED IN ORDER FROM MINIMUM TO MAXIMUM RESPIRATORY PROTECTION. THE SPECIFIC RESPIRATOR SELECTED MUST BE BASED ON CONTAMINATION LEVELS FOUND IN THE WORK PLACE, MUST NOT EXCEED THE WORKING LIMITS OF THE RESPIRATOR AND BE JOINTLY APPROVED BY THE NATIONAL INSTITUTE FOR OCCUPATIONAL SAFETY AND HEALTH AND THE MINE SAFETY AND HEALTH ADMINISTRATION (NIOSH-MSHA).

TYPE 'C' SUPPLIED-AIR RESPIRATOR WITH A FULL FACEPIECE OPERATED IN PRESSURE-DEMAND OR OTHER POSITIVE PRESSURE MODE OR WITH A FULL FACEPIECE, HELMET OR HOOD OPERATED IN CONTINOUS-FLOW MODE.

SELF-CONTAINED BREATHING APPARATUS WITH A FULL FACEPIECE OPERATED IN PRESSURE-DEMAND OR OTHER POSITIVE PRESSURE MODE.

FOR FIREFIGHTING AND OTHER IMMEDIATELY DANGEROUS TO LIFE OR HEALTH CONDITIONS:

SELF-CONTAINED BREATHING APPARATUS WITH FULL FACEPIECE OPERATED IN PRESSURE-DEMAND OR OTHER POSITIVE PRESSURE MODE.

SUPPLIED-AIR RESPIRATOR WITH FULL FACEPIECE AND OPERATED IN PRESSURE-DEMAND OR OTHER POSITIVE PRESSURE MODE IN COMBINATION WITH AN AUXILIARY SELF-CONTAINED BREATHING APPARATUS OPERATED IN PRESSURE-DEMAND OR OTHER POSITIVE PRESSURE MODE.

CLOTHING: EMPLOYEE MUST WEAR APPROPRIATE PROTECTIVE (IMPERVIOUS) CLOTHING AND EQUIPMENT TO PREVENT REPEATED OR PROLONGED SKIN CONTACT WITH THIS SUBSTANCE.

GLOVES: EMPLOYEE MUST WEAR APPROPRIATE PROTECTIVE GLOVES TO PREVENT CONTACT WITH THIS SUBSTANCE.

EYE PROTECTION: EMPLOYEE MUST WEAR SPLASH-PROOF OR DUST-RESISTANT SAFETY GOGGLES TO PREVENT EYE CONTACT WITH THIS SUBSTANCE.

EMERGENCY EYE WASH: WHERE THERE IS ANY POSSIBILITY THAT AN EMPLOYEE'S EYES MAY BE EXPOSED TO THIS SUBSTANCE, THE EMPLOYER SHOULD PROVIDE AN EYE WASH FOUNTAIN WITHIN THE IMMEDIATE WORK AREA FOR EMERGENCY USE.

AUTHORIZED BY- OCCUPATIONAL HEALTH SERVICES, INC.

CREATION DATE: 05/02/90 ***REVISION DATE:*** 07/12/90

MATERIAL SAFETY DATA SHEET

OCCUPATIONAL HEALTH SERVICES, INC.
AGRICULTURE AND PESTICIDE DIVISION
450 SEVENTH AVENUE, SUITE 2407
NEW YORK, NEW YORK 10123
1-800-445-MSDS OR (212) 967-1100

EMERGENCY CONTACT:
JOHN S. BRANSFORD, JR. (615) 292-1180

SUBSTANCE IDENTIFICATION

CAS-NUMBER 14255-72-2

SUBSTANCE: **FENSULFOTHION SULFONE**

TRADE NAMES/SYNONYMS: PHOSPHOROTHIOIC ACID, O,O-DIETHYL O-(4-(METHYLSULFONYL)PHENYL) ESTER; O,O DIETHYL O-(4-(METHYLSULFONYL)PHENYL PHOSPHOROTHIOATE; PHOSPHOROTHIOIC ACID, O,O-DIETHYL O-(P-(METHYLSULFONYL)PHENYL) ESTER; PHOSPHOROTHIOIC ACID, DIETHYL O-(P-(METHYLSULFONYL)PHENYL) ESTER; O,O-DIETHYL O-(P-METHYLSULFONYL)PHENYL PHOSPHOROTHIOATE; DIETHYL O-(P-(METHYLSULFONYL)PHENYL PHOSPHOROTHIOATE; DASANIT SULPHONE; C11H17O5PS2; PST06228

CHEMICAL FAMILY: PHOSPHOROTHIOATE
SULFONYL

MOLECULAR FORMULA: (C2-H5-O)2-P-(S)-O-C6-H4-S-(O2)-C-H3

MOLECULAR WEIGHT: 324.37

CERCLA RATINGS (SCALE 0-3): HEALTH=U FIRE=1 REACTIVITY=0 PERSISTENCE=0

NFPA RATINGS (SCALE 0-4): HEALTH=U FIRE=1 REACTIVITY=0

COMPONENTS AND CONTAMINANTS

COMPONENT: FENSULFOTHION SULFONE ***PERCENT:*** 100.0
CAS# 14255-72-2

OTHER CONTAMINANTS: NONE

EXPOSURE LIMITS: NO OCCUPATIONAL EXPOSURE LIMITS ESTABLISHED BY OSHA, ACGIH, OR NIOSH.

PHYSICAL DATA

DESCRIPTION: WHITE POWDER. ***MELTING POINT:*** NOT AVAILABLE
SPECIFIC GRAVITY: NOT AVAILABLE ***SOLUBILITY IN WATER:*** NOT AVAILABLE

FIRE AND EXPLOSION DATA

FIRE AND EXPLOSION HAZARD: SLIGHT FIRE HAZARD WHEN EXPOSED TO HEAT OR FLAME.

FIREFIGHTING MEDIA: DRY CHEMICAL, CARBON DIOXIDE, HALON, WATER SPRAY OR STANDARD FOAM (1987 EMERGENCY RESPONSE GUIDEBOOK, DOT P 5800.4).
FOR LARGER FIRES, USE WATER SPRAY, FOG OR STANDARD FOAM (1987 EMERGENCY RESPONSE GUIDEBOOK, DOT P 5800.4).

FIREFIGHTING: MOVE CONTAINERS FROM FIRE AREA IF POSSIBLE (1987 EMERGENCY RESPONSE GUIDEBOOK, DOT P 5800.4, GUIDE PAGE 53).
EXTINGUISH USING AGENT SUITABLE FOR TYPE OF SURROUNDING FIRE. AVOID BREATHING VAPORS AND DUSTS. KEEP UPWIND.

TOXICITY

FENSULFOTHION SULFONE: TOXICITY DATA: 1600 UG/KG INTRAPERITONEAL-RAT LD50; 1700 UG/KG INTRACEREBRAL-MOUSE LD50. CARCINOGEN STATUS: NONE. ACUTE TOXICITY LEVEL: INSUFFICIENT DATA. TARGET EFFECTS: CHOLINESTERASE INHIBITOR. POISONING MAY AFFECT THE NERVOUS SYSTEM.* AT INCREASED RISK FROM EXPOSURE: PERSONS WITH RESPIRATORY AILMENTS, RECENT EXPOSURE TO CHOLINESTERASE INHIBITORS OR IMPAIRED CHOLINESTERASE PRODUCTION, OR LIVER MALFUNCTION.* ADDITIONAL DATA: MAY CROSS THE PLACENTA. HIGH ENVIRONMENTAL TEMPERATURES OR EXPOSURE OF THE CHEMICAL TO VISIBLE OR ULTRAVIOLET LIGHT MAY ENHANCE THE TOXICITY. INTERACTIONS WITH MEDICATIONS MAY OCCUR.*

* MAY BE BASED ON GENERAL INFORMATION ON ORGANOPHOSPHATES.

HEALTH EFFECTS AND FIRST AID

INHALATION: FENSULFOTHION SULFONE: SEE INFORMATION ON ORGANOPHOSPHATES.
ORGANOPHOSPHATES: CHOLINESTERASE INHIBITOR. **ACUTE EXPOSURE-** WHEN INHALED, THE FIRST EFFECTS OF CHOLINESTERASE INHIBITORS ARE USUALLY RESPIRATORY AND MAY INCLUDE NASAL HYPEREMIA AND WATERY DISCHARGE, COUGH, CHEST DISCOMFORT, DYSPNEA, AND WHEEZING DUE TO INCREASED BRONCHIAL SECRETIONS AND BRONCHOCONSTRICTION. IF SUFFICIENT AMOUNTS ARE ABSORBED, OTHER SYSTEMIC EFFECTS MAY BEGIN WITHIN A FEW MINUTES OR BE DELAYED FOR UP TO 12 HOURS. SYMPTOMS MAY INCLUDE PALLOR, NAUSEA, VOMITING, DIARRHEA, ABDOMINAL CRAMPS, HEADACHE, DIZZINESS, OCULAR PAIN, BLURRED VISION, MIOSIS OR IN SOME CASES, ESPECIALLY INITIALLY, MYDRIASIS, LACRIMATION, SALIVATION, SWEATING, AND CONFUSION. OTHER REPORTED CENTRAL NERVOUS SYSTEM OR NEUROMUSCULAR EFFECTS MAY INCLUDE ATAXIA, SLURRED SPEECH, AREFLEXIA, WEAKNESS, FATIGUE, FASCICULATIONS, TWITCHING, TREMORS POSSIBLY OF THE TONGUE AND EYELIDS, AND EVENTUALLY PARALYSIS OF THE EXTREMITIES AND POSSIBLY OF THE RESPIRATORY MUSCLES. IN SEVERE CASES THERE MAY ALSO BE INVOLUNTARY DEFECATION AND URINATION, CYANOSIS, PSYCHOSIS, HYPERGLYCEMIA, ACUTE PANCREATITIS, CARDIAC IRREGULARITIES, PULMONARY EDEMA, UNCONSCIOUSNESS, CONVULSIONS, AND COMA. DEATH IS PRIMARILY DUE TO RESPIRATORY FAILURE, ALTHOUGH CARDIOVASCULAR EFFECTS INCLUDING CARDIAC ARREST MAY ALSO BE IMPLICATED. LONG TERM SEQUELAE ARE RARE BUT MAY INCLUDE NEUROPSYCHIATRIC DISORDERS AND MYOPATHY WITH MUSCLE TENDERNESS. SOME ORGANOPHOSPHATES MAY CAUSE A DELAYED NEUROPATHY BEGINNING 1-4 WEEKS AFTER AN ACUTE EXPOSURE WHICH MAY OR MAY NOT HAVE CAUSED ACUTE CHOLINERGIC EFFECTS. NUMBNESS, TINGLING, WEAKNESS AND CRAMPING BEGINNING SYMMETRICALLY IN THE LOWER LIMBS MAY PROGRESS TO ATAXIA AND PARALYSIS. IN SEVERE CASES, UPPER LIMB INVOLVEMENT IS POSSIBLE AND FLACCID PARALYSIS MAY PROGRESS TO SPASTIC PARALYSIS WITH EXAGGERATED REFLEXES. IMPROVEMENT MAY OCCUR OVER MONTHS TO YEARS, BUT SOME RESIDUAL IMPAIRMENT USUALLY REMAINS. **CHRONIC EXPOSURE-** REPEATED OR PROLONGED EXPOSURE MAY RESULT IN THE EFFECTS OF ACUTE EXPOSURE INCLUDING THE DELAYED NEUROPATHY. OTHER EFFECTS REPORTED IN WORKERS REPEATEDLY EXPOSED INCLUDE IMPAIRED MEMORY AND CONCENTRATION, ACUTE PSYCHOSIS, SEVERE DEPRESSIONS, IRRITABILTY, CONFUSION, APATHY, EMOTIONAL LABILITY, SOCIAL WITHDRAWAL, CONFUSION, HEADACHE, SPEECH DIFFICULTIES, DELAYED REACTION TIMES, SPATIAL DISORIENTATION, NIGHTMARES, SLEEPWALKING, AND DROWSINESS OR INSOMNIA. AN INFLUENZA-LIKE CONDITION WITH HEADACHE, NAUSEA, WEAKNESS, ANOREXIA AND MALAISE HAS ALSO BEEN REPORTED.

FIRST AID- REMOVE FROM EXPOSURE AREA TO FRESH AIR IMMEDIATELY. IF BREATHING HAS STOPPED, GIVE ARTIFICIAL RESPIRATION. MAINTAIN AIRWAY AND BLOOD PRESSURE AND ADMINISTER OXYGEN IF AVAILABLE. KEEP AFFECTED PERSON WARM AND AT REST. TREAT SYMPTOMATICALLY AND SUPPORTIVELY. ADMINISTRATION OF OXYGEN SHOULD BE PERFORMED BY QUALIFIED PERSONNEL. GET MEDICAL ATTENTION IMMEDIATELY.

SKIN CONTACT: FENSULFOTHION SULFONE: SEE INFORMATION ON ORGANOPHOSPHATES.
ORGANOPHOSPHATES: CHOLINESTERASE INHIBITOR. **ACUTE EXPOSURE-** LOCALIZED SWEATING AND FASCICULATIONS MAY OCCUR AT THE SITE OF CONTACT. IF SUFFICIENT AMOUNTS ARE ABSORBED, OTHER EFFECTS OF CHOLINESTERASE INHIBITION AS DESCRIBED IN ACUTE INHALATION MAY OCCUR. SYMPTOMS MAY BE DELAYED 2-3 HOURS, BUT USUALLY NO MORE THAN 12 HOURS. THE RATE OF ABSORPTION IS INCREASED BY THE PRESENCE OF DERMATITIS OR HIGH AMBIENT TEMPERATURES. DELAYED NEUROPATHY IS ALSO POSSIBLE. **CHRONIC EXPOSURE-** REPEATED OR PROLONGED EXPOSURE MAY CAUSE EFFECTS AS DESCRIBED IN ACUTE EXPOSURE. SOME ORGANOPHOSPHATES MAY CAUSE SENSITIZATION.

FIRST AID- REMOVE CONTAMINATED CLOTHING IMMEDIATELY. WASH CONTAMINATED AREAS WITH SOAP AND WATER FOLLOWED BY ALCOHOL (ARENA, POISONING, 4TH ED.). EMERGENCY PERSONNEL SHOULD WEAR GLOVES AND AVOID CONTAMINATION. TREAT RESPIRATORY DIFFICULTY WITH ARTIFICIAL RESPIRATION. GET MEDICAL ATTENTION IMMEDIATELY.

EYE CONTACT: FENSULFOTHION SULFONE: SEE INFORMATION ON ORGANOPHOSPHATES.
ORGANOPHOSPHATES: CHOLINESTERASE INHIBITOR. **ACUTE EXPOSURE-** DIRECT CONTACT MAY CAUSE PAIN, HYPEREMIA, LACRIMATION, TWITCHING OF THE EYELIDS, MIOSIS, AND CILIARY MUSCLE SPASM WITH LOSS OF ACCOMODATION, BLURRED OR DIMMED VISION AND BROWACHE. SOMETIMES MYDRIASIS MAY OCCUR INSTEAD OF MIOSIS. WITH SUFFICIENT EXPOSURE, OTHER SYMPTOMS OF CHOLINESTERASE INHIBITION AS DESCRIBED IN ACUTE INHALATION MAY OCCUR. **CHRONIC EXPOSURE-** REPEATED OR PROLONGED EXPOSURE MAY CAUSE EFFECTS AS DESCRIBED IN ACUTE EXPOSURE. SOME COMPOUNDS HAVE CAUSED TOXIC EFFECTS ON THE CRYSTALLINE LENS, CONJUNCTIVAL THICKENING AND OBSTRUCTION OF THE NASOLACRIMAL CANALS WHEN USED AS MIOTIC EYEDROPS.

FIRST AID- IRRIGATE EYES WITH WATER OR SALINE SOLUTION. IF SYMPTOMS OF POISONING OCCUR, TREAT RESPIRATORY DIFFICULTY WITH ARTIFICIAL RESPIRATION AND OXYGEN. OBSERVE PATIENT FOR AT LEAST 24-36 HOURS (GOSSELIN, CLINICAL TOXICOLOGY OF COMMERCIAL PRODUCTS, 5TH ED.). GET MEDICAL ATTENTION IMMEDIATELY. OXYGEN SHOULD BE ADMINISTERED BY QUALIFIED MEDICAL PERSONNEL.

INGESTION: FENSULFOTHION SULFONE: SEE INFORMATION ON ORGANOPHOSPHATES.
ORGANOPHOSPHATES: CHOLINESTERASE INHIBITOR. **ACUTE EXPOSURE-** WHEN INGESTED, THE FIRST EFFECTS MAY BE NAUSEA, VOMITING, ANOREXIA, ABDOMINAL CRAMPS AND DIARRHEA. GASTROINTESTINAL ABSORPTION MAY CAUSE SYMPTOMS OF CHOLINESTERASE INHIBITION AS DESCRIBED IN ACUTE INHALATION. SYMPTOMS MAY BEGIN WITHIN MINUTES OR BE DELAYED FOR HOURS. DELAYED EFFECTS INCLUDING NEUROPATHY MAY ALSO OCCUR. **CHRONIC EXPOSURE-** REPEATED INGESTION MAY CAUSE EFFECTS AS DESCRIBED IN ACUTE EXPOSURE.

FIRST AID- IF PERSON IS ALERT AND RESPIRATION IS NOT DEPRESSED, GIVE SYRUP OF IPECAC FOLLOWED BY WATER (IF VOMITING OCCURS, KEEP HEAD BELOW HIPS TO PREVENT ASPIRATION). IF CONSCIOUSNESS LEVEL DECLINES OR VOMITING HAS NOT OCCURRED IN 15 MINUTES EMPTY STOMACH BY GASTRIC LAVAGE WITH THE AID OF CUFFED ENDOTRACHEAL TUBE USING ISOTONIC SALINE OR 5% SODIUM BICARBONATE FOLLOW WITH ACTIVATED CHARCOAL. ESTABLISH AND MAINTAIN AIRWAY. TREAT RESPIRATORY DIFFICULTY WITH ARTIFICIAL RESPIRATION AND OXYGEN. DO NOT GIVE MORPHINE, AMINOPHYLLINE, PHENOTHIAZINES, RESERPINE, FUROSEMIDE, OR ETHACRYNIC ACID (MORGAN, RECOGNITION AND MANAGEMENT OF PESTICIDE POISONINGS, 3RD ED.). TREAT SYMPTOMATICALLY AND SUPPORTIVELY. ADMINISTRATION OF OXYGEN AND LAVAGE MUST BE PERFORMED BY QUALIFIED MEDICAL PERSONNEL. GET MEDICAL ATTENTION IMMEDIATELY.

ANTIDOTE: THE FOLLOWING ANTIDOTE(S) HAVE BEEN RECOMMENDED. HOWEVER, THE DECISION AS TO WHETHER THE SEVERITY OF POISONING REQUIRES ADMINISTRATION OF ANY ANTIDOTE AND ACTUAL DOSE REQUIRED SHOULD BE MADE BY QUALIFIED MEDICAL PERSONNEL.
FOR CHOLINESTERASE INHIBITORS: ESTABLISH CLEAR AIRWAY AND TISSUE OXYGENATION BY ASPIRATION OF SECRETIONS, AND IF NECESSARY, BY ASSISTED PULMONARY VENTILATION WITH OXYGEN. IMPROVE TISSUE OXYGENATION AS MUCH AS POSSIBLE BEFORE ADMINISTERING ATROPINE TO MINIMIZE THE RISK OF VENTRICULAR FIBRILLATION. ADMINISTER ATROPINE SULFATE INTRAVENOUSLY,

OR INTRAMUSCULARLY IF IV INJECTION IS NOT POSSIBLE. IN MODERATELY SEVERE POISONING ADMINISTER ATROPINE SULFATE, 0.4-2.0 MG REPEATED EVERY 15 MINUTES UNTIL ATROPINIZATION IS ACHIEVED (TACHYCARDIA, FLUSHING, DRY MOUTH, MYDRIASIS). MAINTAIN ATROPINIZATION BY REPEATED DOSES FOR 2-12 HOURS, OR LONGER, DEPENDING ON THE SEVERITY OF POISONING. THE APPEARANCE OF RALES IN THE LUNG BASES, MIOSIS, SALIVATION, NAUSEA, BRADYCARDIA, ARE ALL INDICATIONS OF INADEQUATE ATROPINIZATION. SEVERELY POISONED INDIVIDUALS MAY EXHIBIT REMARKABLE TOLERANCE TO ATROPINE; TWO OR MORE TIMES THE DOSAGES SUGGESTED ABOVE MAY BE NEEDED. PERSONS NOT POISONED OR ONLY SLIGHTLY POISONED, HOWEVER, MAY DEVELOP SIGNS OF ATROPINE TOXICITY FROM SUCH LARGE DOSAGES: FEVER, MUSCLE FIBRILLATIONS, AND DELIRIUM ARE THE MAIN SIGNS OF ATROPINE TOXICITY. IF THESE SIGNS APPEAR WHILE THE PATIENT IS FULLY ATROPINIZED, ATROPINE ADMINISTRATION SHOULD BE DISCONTINUED, AT LEAST TEMPORARILY. OBSERVE TREATED PATIENTS CLOSELY AT LEAST 24 HOURS TO INSURE THAT SYMPTOMS (POSSIBLY PULMONARY EDEMA) DO NOT RECUR AS ATROPINIZATION WEARS OFF. IN VERY SEVERE POISONINGS, METABOLIC DISPOSITION OF TOXICANT MAY REQUIRE SEVERAL HOURS OR DAYS DURING WHICH ATROPINIZATION MUST BE MAINTAINED. MARKEDLY LOWER LEVELS OF URINARY METABOLITES INDICATE THAT ATROPINE DOSAGE CAN BE TAPERED OFF. AS DOSAGE IS REDUCED, CHECK THE LUNG BASES FREQUENTLY FOR RALES. IF RALES ARE HEARD OR OTHER SYMPTOMS RETURN, RE-ESTABLISH ATROPINIZATION PROMPTLY (MORGAN, RECOGNITION AND MANAGEMENT OF PESTICIDE POISONINGS, 3RD ED.). ADMINISTRATION OF ANTIDOTE MUST BE PERFORMED BY QUALIFIED MEDICAL PERSONNEL.

IN CASES OF SEVERE POISONING BY ORGANOPHOSPHATE PESTICIDES IN WHICH RESPIRATORY DEPRESSION, MUSCLE WEAKNESS AND TWITCHINGS ARE SEVERE, GIVE PRALIDOXIME (PROTOPAM-AYERST, 2-PAM), 1.0 GRAM INTRAVENOUSLY AT NO MORE THAN 0.5 GRAM PER MINUTE. DOSAGE OF PRALIDOXIME MAY BE REPEATED IN 1-2 HOURS, THEN AT 10-12 HOUR INTERVALS IF NEEDED. IN VERY SEVERE POISONINGS, DOSAGE RATES MAY BE DOUBLED. TREATMENT WITH PRALIDOXIME WILL BE MOST EFFECTIVE IF GIVEN WITHIN THIRTY-SIX HOURS AFTER POISONING (MORGAN, RECOGNITION AND MANAGEMENT OF PESTICIDE POISONINGS, 3RD ED.). ANTIDOTE SHOULD BE ADMINISTERED BY QUALIFIED MEDICAL PERSONNEL.

REACTIVITY

REACTIVITY: STABLE UNDER NORMAL TEMPERATURES AND PRESSURES.

INCOMPATIBILITIES: FENSULFOTHION SULFONE: OXIDIZERS (STRONG): FIRE AND EXPLOSION HAZARD.

DECOMPOSITION: THERMAL DECOMPOSITION PRODUCTS MAY INCLUDE TOXIC OXIDES OF CARBON, SULFUR, AND PHOSPHORUS.

POLYMERIZATION: HAZARDOUS POLYMERIZATION HAS NOT BEEN REPORTED TO OCCUR UNDER NORMAL TEMPERATURES AND PRESSURES.

STORAGE AND DISPOSAL

OBSERVE ALL FEDERAL, STATE AND LOCAL REGULATIONS WHEN STORING OR DISPOSING OF THIS SUBSTANCE. FOR ASSISTANCE, CONTACT THE DISTRICT DIRECTOR OF THE ENVIRONMENTAL PROTECTION AGENCY.

****STORAGE****

STORE AWAY FROM INCOMPATIBLE SUBSTANCES.

CONDITIONS TO AVOID

MAY BURN BUT DOES NOT IGNITE READILY.

SPILL AND LEAK PROCEDURES

OCCUPATIONAL SPILL: DO NOT TOUCH SPILLED MATERIAL. STOP LEAK IF YOU CAN DO IT WITHOUT RISK. FOR SMALL SPILLS, TAKE UP WITH SAND OR OTHER ABSORBENT MATERIAL AND PLACE INTO CONTAINERS FOR LATER DISPOSAL. FOR SMALL DRY SPILLS, WITH A CLEAN SHOVEL PLACE MATERIAL INTO CLEAN, DRY CONTAINER AND COVER. MOVE CONTAINERS FROM SPILL AREA. FOR LARGER SPILLS, DIKE FAR AHEAD OF SPILL FOR LATER DISPOSAL. KEEP UNNECESSARY PEOPLE AWAY. ISOLATE HAZARD AREA AND DENY ENTRY.

PROTECTIVE EQUIPMENT

VENTILATION: PROVIDE LOCAL EXHAUST OR PROCESS ENCLOSURE VENTILATION SYSTEM.

RESPIRATOR: THE FOLLOWING RESPIRATORS ARE RECOMMENDED BASED ON INFORMATION FOUND IN THE PHYSICAL DATA, TOXICITY AND HEALTH EFFECTS SECTIONS. THEY ARE RANKED IN ORDER FROM MINIMUM TO MAXIMUM RESPIRATORY PROTECTION. THE SPECIFIC RESPIRATOR SELECTED MUST BE BASED ON CONTAMINATION LEVELS FOUND IN THE WORK PLACE, MUST NOT EXCEED THE WORKING LIMITS OF THE RESPIRATOR AND BE JOINTLY APPROVED BY THE NATIONAL INSTITUTE FOR OCCUPATIONAL SAFETY AND HEALTH AND THE MINE SAFETY AND HEALTH ADMINISTRATION (NIOSH-MSHA).

CHEMICAL CARTRIDGE RESPIRATOR WITH AN ORGANIC VAPOR CARTRIDGE(S) WITH A FULL FACEPIECE AND ORGANIC VAPOR CARTRIDGE(S) IN COMBINATION WITH A DUST AND MIST FILTER.

POWERED AIR-PURIFYING RESPIRATOR WITH A TIGHT-FITTING FACEPIECE AND ORGANIC VAPOR CARTRIDGE(S) IN COMBINATION WITH A HIGH-EFFICIENCY PARTICULATE FILTER.

TYPE 'C' SUPPLIED-AIR RESPIRATOR WITH A FULL FACEPIECE OPERATED IN A PRESSURE-DEMAND OR OTHER POSITIVE PRESSURE MODE.

SELF-CONTAINED BREATHING APPARATUS WITH A FULL FACEPIECE OPERATED IN PRESSURE-DEMAND OR OTHER POSITIVE PRESSURE MODE.

FOR FIREFIGHTING AND OTHER IMMEDIATELY DANGEROUS TO LIFE OR HEALTH CONDITIONS:

SELF-CONTAINED BREATHING APPARATUS WITH FULL FACEPIECE OPERATED IN PRESSURE-DEMAND OR OTHER POSITIVE PRESSURE MODE.

SUPPLIED-AIR RESPIRATOR WITH FULL FACEPIECE AND OPERATED IN PRESSURE-DEMAND OR OTHER POSITIVE PRESSURE MODE IN COMBINATION WITH AN AUXILIARY SELF-CONTAINED BREATHING APPARATUS OPERATED IN PRESSURE-DEMAND OR OTHER POSITIVE PRESSURE MODE.

CLOTHING: EMPLOYEE MUST WEAR APPROPRIATE PROTECTIVE (IMPERVIOUS) CLOTHING AND EQUIPMENT TO PREVENT REPEATED OR PROLONGED SKIN CONTACT WITH THIS SUBSTANCE.

GLOVES: EMPLOYEE MUST WEAR APPROPRIATE PROTECTIVE GLOVES TO PREVENT CONTACT WITH THIS SUBSTANCE.

EYE PROTECTION: EMPLOYEE MUST WEAR SPLASH-PROOF OR DUST-RESISTANT SAFETY GOGGLES TO PREVENT EYE CONTACT WITH THIS SUBSTANCE.

EMERGENCY EYE WASH: WHERE THERE IS ANY POSSIBILITY THAT AN EMPLOYEE'S EYES MAY BE EXPOSED TO THIS SUBSTANCE, THE EMPLOYER SHOULD PROVIDE AN EYE WASH FOUNTAIN WITHIN THE IMMEDIATE WORK AREA FOR EMERGENCY USE.

AUTHORIZED BY- OCCUPATIONAL HEALTH SERVICES, INC.

CREATION DATE: 02/08/90 ***REVISION DATE:*** 05/07/90

MATERIAL SAFETY DATA SHEET

OCCUPATIONAL HEALTH SERVICES, INC.
AGRICULTURE AND PESTICIDE DIVISION
450 SEVENTH AVENUE, SUITE 2407
NEW YORK, NEW YORK 10123
1-800-445-MSDS OR (212) 967-1100

EMERGENCY CONTACT:
JOHN S. BRANSFORD, JR. (615) 292-1180

SUBSTANCE IDENTIFICATION

CAS-NUMBER 533-74-4

SUBSTANCE: DAZOMET

TRADE NAMES/SYNONYMS: 2H-1,3,5-THIADIAZINE-2-THIONEETRAHYDRO-3,5-DIMETHYL; BASAMID (FORMULATION); DIMETHYLFORMOCARBOTHIALDINE; DMTT; MYLONE; NEFUSAN; THIAZON; UCC 974; 3,5-DIMETHYL-1,3,5-THIADIAZINANE-2-THIONE; TETRAHYDRO-3,5-DIMETHYL-2H-1,3,5-THIADIAZINE-2-THIONE; 2-THIO-3,5-DIMETHYLTETRAHYDRO-1,3,5,-THIADIAZINE; 3,5-DIMETHYL-2-THIONOTETRAHYDRO-1,3,5-THIADIAZINE; CRAG 974 (FORMULATION); N-521; SALVO; C5H10N2S2; PST06230

CHEMICAL FAMILY: THIADIAZINE

MOLECULAR FORMULA: C5-H10-N2-S2

MOLECULAR WEIGHT: 162.29

CERCLA RATINGS (SCALE 0-3): HEALTH=3 FIRE=1 REACTIVITY=1 PERSISTENCE=0

NFPA RATINGS (SCALE 0-4): HEALTH=U FIRE=1 REACTIVITY=1

COMPONENTS AND CONTAMINANTS

COMPONENT: DAZOMET ***PERCENT:*** 100.0
CAS# 533-74-4

OTHER CONTAMINANTS: NONE

EXPOSURE LIMITS: NO OCCUPATIONAL EXPOSURE LIMITS ESTABLISHED BY OSHA, ACGIH, OR NIOSH.

PHYSICAL DATA

DESCRIPTION: WHITE TO GRAYISH CRYSTALS WITH A SLIGHT ODOR.

MELTING POINT: 223-224 F (106-107 C) (DECOMPOSES)

SPECIFIC GRAVITY: NOT AVAILABLE ***VAPOR PRESSURE:*** NEGLIGIBLE

SOLUBILITY IN WATER: 0.3% (DECOMPOSES)

SOLVENT SOLUBILITY: SOLUBLE IN ACETONE, CHLOROFORM, CYCLOHEXANE: MODERATELY SOLUBLE IN BENZENE; SLIGHTLY SOLUBLE IN ETHER.

FIRE AND EXPLOSION DATA

FIRE AND EXPLOSION HAZARD: SLIGHT FIRE HAZARD WHEN EXPOSED TO HEAT OR FLAME.

FIREFIGHTING MEDIA: DRY CHEMICAL, CARBON DIOXIDE, HALON, WATER SPRAY OR STANDARD FOAM (1987 EMERGENCY RESPONSE GUIDEBOOK, DOT P 5800.4). FOR LARGER FIRES, USE WATER SPRAY, FOG OR STANDARD FOAM (1987 EMERGENCY RESPONSE GUIDEBOOK, DOT P 5800.4).

FIREFIGHTING: MOVE CONTAINERS FROM FIRE AREA IF POSSIBLE (1987 EMERGENCY RESPONSE GUIDEBOOK, DOT P 5800.4, GUIDE PAGE 53). EXTINGUISH USING AGENT SUITABLE FOR TYPE OF SURROUNDING FIRE. AVOID BREATHING VAPORS AND DUSTS. KEEP UPWIND.

TOXICITY

DAZOMET: IRRITATION DATA: 500 MG/24 HOURS EYE-RABBIT MILD. TOXICITY DATA: 7 GM/KG SKIN-RABBIT LD50; 320 MG/KG ORAL-RAT LD50; 180 MG/KG ORAL-MOUSE LD50; 160 MG/KG ORAL-GUINEA PIG LD50; 120 MG/KG ORAL-RABBIT LD50; 500 MG/KG SUBCUTANEOUS-MOUSE LDLO; 87 MG/KG INTRAPERITONEAL-RAT LD50; 127 MG/KG INTRAPERITONEAL-RABBIT LD50; 50 MG/KG INTRAPERITONEAL-MOUSE LDLO; 47 MG/KG INTRAPERITONEAL-DOG LD50; 650 MG/KG UNREPORTED-MOUSE LD50. CARCINOGEN STATUS: NONE. LOCAL EFFECTS: IRRITANT- SKIN, EYE. ACUTE TOXICITY LEVEL: TOXIC BY INGESTION; SLIGHTLY TOXIC BY DERMAL ABSORPTION. TARGET EFFECTS: SENSITIZER- SKIN. POISONING MAY AFFECT THE CENTRAL NERVOUS SYSTEM, KIDNEYS, AND LIVER.

HEALTH EFFECTS AND FIRST AID

INHALATION: DAZOMET: **ACUTE EXPOSURE-** DUST MAY CAUSE IRRITATION OF THE RESPIRATORY TRACT. CONVULSIONS, COMA, AND DEATH MAY ALSO OCCUR. **CHRONIC EXPOSURE-** NO DATA AVAILABLE.

FIRST AID- REMOVE FROM EXPOSURE AREA TO FRESH AIR IMMEDIATELY. IF BREATHING HAS STOPPED, PERFORM ARTIFICIAL RESPIRATION. KEEP PERSON WARM AND AT REST. TREAT SYMPTOMATICALLY AND SUPPORTIVELY. GET MEDICAL ATTENTION IMMEDIATELY.

SKIN CONTACT: DAZOMET: IRRITANT/SENSITIZER. **ACUTE EXPOSURE-** MAY CAUSE SLIGHT TO MODERATE IRRITATION AND POSSIBLY BLISTERS. MAY CAUSE SENSITIZATION IN PREVIOUSLY EXPOSED INDIVIDUALS. MAY BE ABSORBED THROUGH THE SKIN. **CHRONIC EXPOSURE-** REPEATED OR PROLONGED EXPOSURE MAY CAUSE DERMATITIS DUE TO IRRITATION OR SENSITIZATION.

FIRST AID- REMOVE CONTAMINATED CLOTHING AND SHOES IMMEDIATELY. WASH AFFECTED AREA WITH SOAP OR MILD DETERGENT AND LARGE AMOUNTS OF WATER UNTIL NO EVIDENCE OF CHEMICAL REMAINS (APPROXIMATELY 15-20 MINUTES). GET MEDICAL ATTENTION IMMEDIATELY.

EYE CONTACT: DAZOMET: IRRITANT. **ACUTE EXPOSURE-** MAY CAUSE MODERATE IRRITATION. **CHRONIC EXPOSURE-** REPEATED OR PROLONGED EXPOSURE TO IRRITANTS MAY CAUSE CONJUNCTIVITIS.

FIRST AID- WASH EYES IMMEDIATELY WITH LARGE AMOUNTS OF WATER OR NORMAL SALINE, OCCASIONALLY LIFTING UPPER AND LOWER LIDS, UNTIL NO EVIDENCE OF CHEMICAL REMAINS (APPROXIMATELY 15-20 MINUTES). GET MEDICAL ATTENTION IMMEDIATELY.

INGESTION: DAZOMET: TOXIC. ACUTE- A SINGLE TOXIC DOSE TO RATS CAUSED CLONIC-TONIC CONVULSIONS, COMA, AND DEATH WITHIN 10 MINUTES OR COMPLETE RECOVERY WITHIN 24 HOURS. **CHRONIC EXPOSURE-** ANIMALS FED 10-40 PPM FOR 2 YEARS SHOWED FOCAL NECROSIS OF THE KIDNEYS AND LIVER.

FIRST AID- IF EXTENSIVE VOMITING HAS NOT OCCURRED, THE SUBSTANCE SHOULD BE REMOVED BY EMESIS OR GASTRIC LAVAGE PROVIDED THAT THE PATIENT IS CONSCIOUS AND CONVULSIONS ARE NOT PRESENT. KEEP HEAD BELOW HIPS DURING VOMITING TO PREVENT ASPIRATION. DO NOT ATTEMPT TO MAKE AN UNCONSCIOUS PERSON VOMIT. TREAT SYMPTOMATICALLY AND SUPPORTIVELY. GET MEDICAL ATTENTION IMMEDIATELY (DREISBACH, HANDBOOK OF POISONING, 12TH ED.). TREATMENT SHOULD BE PERFORMED BY QUALIFIED MEDICAL PERSONNEL.

ANTIDOTE: NO SPECIFIC ANTIDOTE. TREAT SYMPTOMATICALLY AND SUPPORTIVELY.

REACTIVITY

REACTIVITY: STABLE UNDER NORMAL TEMPERATURES AND PRESSURES.

INCOMPATIBILITIES: DAZOMET: OXIDIZERS (STRONG): FIRE AND EXPLOSION HAZARD.

DECOMPOSITION: THERMAL DECOMPOSITION PRODUCTS MAY INCLUDE TOXIC OXIDES OF CARBON, NITROGEN, AND SULFUR.

POLYMERIZATION: HAZARDOUS POLYMERIZATION HAS NOT BEEN REPORTED TO OCCUR UNDER NORMAL TEMPERATURES AND PRESSURES.

STORAGE AND DISPOSAL

****STORAGE****

STORE IN ACCORDANCE WITH 40 CFR 165 RECOMMENDED PROCEDURES FOR THE DISPOSAL AND STORAGE OF PESTICIDES AND PESTICIDE CONTAINERS.
KEEP IN A TIGHTLY CLOSED CONTAINER. STORE IN A COOL, DRY, VENTILATED AREA.

****DISPOSAL****

DISPOSAL MUST BE IN ACCORDANCE WITH 40 CFR 165 RECOMMENDED PROCEDURES FOR THE DISPOSAL AND STORAGE OF PESTICIDES AND PESTICIDE CONTAINERS.

CONDITIONS TO AVOID

MAY BURN BUT DOES NOT IGNITE READILY.

SPILL AND LEAK PROCEDURES

OCCUPATIONAL SPILL: DO NOT TOUCH SPILLED MATERIAL. STOP LEAK IF YOU CAN DO IT WITHOUT RISK. FOR SMALL SPILLS, TAKE UP WITH SAND OR OTHER ABSORBENT MATERIAL AND PLACE INTO CONTAINERS FOR LATER DISPOSAL. FOR SMALL DRY SPILLS, WITH A CLEAN SHOVEL PLACE MATERIAL INTO CLEAN, DRY CONTAINER AND COVER. MOVE CONTAINERS FROM SPILL AREA. FOR LARGER SPILLS, DIKE FAR AHEAD OF SPILL FOR LATER DISPOSAL. KEEP UNNECESSARY PEOPLE AWAY. ISOLATE HAZARD AREA AND DENY ENTRY.

PROTECTIVE EQUIPMENT

VENTILATION: PROVIDE LOCAL EXHAUST OR PROCESS ENCLOSURE VENTILATION SYSTEM.

RESPIRATOR: THE FOLLOWING RESPIRATORS ARE RECOMMENDED BASED ON INFORMATION FOUND IN THE PHYSICAL DATA, TOXICITY AND HEALTH EFFECTS SECTIONS. THEY ARE RANKED IN ORDER FROM MINIMUM TO MAXIMUM RESPIRATORY PROTECTION. THE SPECIFIC RESPIRATOR SELECTED MUST BE BASED ON CONTAMINATION LEVELS FOUND IN THE WORK PLACE, MUST NOT EXCEED THE WORKING LIMITS OF THE RESPIRATOR AND BE JOINTLY APPROVED BY THE NATIONAL INSTITUTE FOR OCCUPATIONAL SAFETY AND HEALTH AND THE MINE SAFETY AND HEALTH ADMINISTRATION (NIOSH-MSHA).
CHEMICAL CARTRIDGE RESPIRATOR WITH AN ORGANIC VAPOR CARTRIDGE(S) WITH A FULL FACEPIECE AND ORGANIC VAPOR CARTRIDGE(S) IN COMBINATION WITH A DUST AND MIST FILTER.
POWERED AIR-PURIFYING RESPIRATOR WITH A TIGHT-FITTING FACEPIECE AND ORGANIC VAPOR CARTRIDGE(S) IN COMBINATION WITH A HIGH-EFFICIENCY PARTICULATE FILTER.
TYPE 'C' SUPPLIED-AIR RESPIRATOR WITH A FULL FACEPIECE OPERATED IN A PRESSURE-DEMAND OR OTHER POSITIVE PRESSURE MODE.
SELF-CONTAINED BREATHING APPARATUS WITH A FULL FACEPIECE OPERATED IN PRESSURE-DEMAND OR OTHER POSITIVE PRESSURE MODE.
FOR FIREFIGHTING AND OTHER IMMEDIATELY DANGEROUS TO LIFE OR HEALTH CONDITIONS:
SELF-CONTAINED BREATHING APPARATUS WITH FULL FACEPIECE OPERATED IN PRESSURE-DEMAND OR OTHER POSITIVE PRESSURE MODE.
SUPPLIED-AIR RESPIRATOR WITH FULL FACEPIECE AND OPERATED IN PRESSURE-DEMAND OR OTHER POSITIVE PRESSURE MODE IN COMBINATION WITH AN AUXILIARY SELF-CONTAINED BREATHING APPARATUS OPERATED IN PRESSURE-DEMAND OR OTHER POSITIVE PRESSURE MODE.

CLOTHING: EMPLOYEE MUST WEAR APPROPRIATE PROTECTIVE (IMPERVIOUS) CLOTHING AND EQUIPMENT TO PREVENT ANY POSSIBILITY OF SKIN CONTACT WITH THIS SUBSTANCE.

GLOVES: EMPLOYEE MUST WEAR APPROPRIATE PROTECTIVE GLOVES TO PREVENT CONTACT WITH THIS SUBSTANCE.

EYE PROTECTION: EMPLOYEE MUST WEAR SPLASH-PROOF OR DUST-RESISTANT SAFETY GOGGLES AND A FACESHIELD TO PREVENT CONTACT WITH THIS SUBSTANCE.
EMERGENCY WASH FACILITIES: WHERE THERE IS ANY POSSIBILITY THAT AN EMPLOYEE'S EYES AND/OR SKIN MAY BE EXPOSED TO THIS SUBSTANCE, THE EMPLOYER SHOULD PROVIDE AN EYE WASH FOUNTAIN AND QUICK DRENCH SHOWER WITHIN THE IMMEDIATE WORK AREA FOR EMERGENCY USE.

AUTHORIZED BY- OCCUPATIONAL HEALTH SERVICES, INC.
CREATION DATE: 02/08/90 ***REVISION DATE:*** 05/07/90

MATERIAL SAFETY DATA SHEET

OCCUPATIONAL HEALTH SERVICES, INC.
AGRICULTURE AND PESTICIDE DIVISION
450 SEVENTH AVENUE, SUITE 2407

EMERGENCY CONTACT:
JOHN S. BRANSFORD, JR. (615) 292-1180

NEW YORK, NEW YORK 10123
1-800-445-MSDS OR (212) 967-1100

SUBSTANCE IDENTIFICATION

CAS-NUMBER 83-05-6

SUBSTANCE: **DDA-P,P'**

TRADE NAMES/SYNONYMS: BENZENEACETIC ACID, 4-CHLORO-ALPHA-(4-CHLOROPHENYL)-; ACETIC ACID, BIS(P-CHLOROPHENYL)-; BIS(P-CHLOROPHENYL)ACETIC ACID; BIS(4-CHLOROPHENYL)ACETIC ACID; P,P'-DDA; DDA; DDA (DEGRADATION PRODUCT); DICHLORODIPHENYLACETIC ACID; DI(P-CHLOROPHENYL)ACETIC ACID; 4-CHLORO-ALPHA-(4-CHLOROPHENYL)BENZENEACETIC ACID; C14H10CL2O2; PST06232

CHEMICAL FAMILY: HALOGEN COMPOUND, AROMATIC

MOLECULAR FORMULA: (CL-C6-H4)2-C-H-C-O2-H

MOLECULAR WEIGHT: 281.14

CERCLA RATINGS (SCALE 0-3): HEALTH=2 FIRE=1 REACTIVITY=0 PERSISTENCE=3

NFPA RATINGS (SCALE 0-4): HEALTH=U FIRE=1 REACTIVITY=0

COMPONENTS AND CONTAMINANTS

COMPONENT: DDA-P,P' ***PERCENT:*** 100.0
CAS# 83-05-6

OTHER CONTAMINANTS: NONE

EXPOSURE LIMITS: NO OCCUPATIONAL EXPOSURE LIMITS ESTABLISHED BY OSHA, ACGIH, OR NIOSH.

PHYSICAL DATA

DESCRIPTION: WHITE POWDER. ***MELTING POINT:*** 333-336 F (167-169 C)

SPECIFIC GRAVITY: NOT AVAILABLE ***SOLUBILITY IN WATER:*** NOT AVAILABLE

FIRE AND EXPLOSION DATA

FIRE AND EXPLOSION HAZARD: SLIGHT FIRE HAZARD WHEN EXPOSED TO HEAT OR FLAME.

FIREFIGHTING MEDIA: DRY CHEMICAL, CARBON DIOXIDE, HALON, WATER SPRAY OR STANDARD FOAM (1987 EMERGENCY RESPONSE GUIDEBOOK, DOT P 5800.4).
FOR LARGER FIRES, USE WATER SPRAY, FOG OR STANDARD FOAM (1987 EMERGENCY RESPONSE GUIDEBOOK, DOT P 5800.4).

FIREFIGHTING: MOVE CONTAINER FROM FIRE AREA IF POSSIBLE. DO NOT SCATTER SPILLED MATERIAL WITH HIGH PRESSURE WATER STREAMS. DIKE FIRE CONTROL WATER FOR LATER DISPOSAL (1987 EMERGENCY RESPONSE GUIDEBOOK, DOT P 5800.4, GUIDE PAGE 31).
USE AGENTS SUITABLE FOR TYPE OF SURROUNDING FIRE. AVOID BREATHING HAZARDOUS VAPORS, KEEP UPWIND.

TOXICITY

DDA-P,P': TOXICITY DATA: 590 MG/KG ORAL-MOUSE LD50; MUTAGENIC DATA (RTECS); REPRODUCTIVE EFFECTS DATA (RTECS). CARCINOGEN STATUS: NONE. ACUTE TOXCITY DATA: MODERATELY TOXIC BY INGESTION. TARGET EFFECTS: CONVULSANT. POISONING MAY AFFECT THE LIVER AND KIDNEYS.* ADDITIONAL DATA: DDT METABOLITE. MAY CROSS THE PLACENTA AND BE EXCRETED IN BREAST MILK. MAY IMPAIR FERTILITY. STIMULANTS SUCH AS EPINEPHRINE OR EPHEDRINE MAY INDUCE VENTRICULAR FIBRILLATION.*
* MAY BE BASED ON GENERAL INFORMATION ON ORGANOCHLORINE PESTICIDES.

HEALTH EFFECTS AND FIRST AID

INHALATION: DDA-P,P': **ACUTE EXPOSURE-** EFFECTS AS DESCRIBED FOR ORGANOCHLORINE PESTICIDES IN ACUTE INGESTION MAY OCCUR IF SUFFICIENT AMOUNTS ARE ABSORBED FROM THE LUNGS. **CHRONIC EXPOSURE-** A STUDY OF OCCUPATIONAL EXPOSURE TO DDT REPORTED A HIGHER FREQUENCY OF WHITE BLOOD CELLS WITH CHROMOSOMAL ABNORMALITIES AMONG WORKERS WITH HIGH DDT BLOOD LEVELS; MENSTRUAL IRREGULARITIES AS THE MOST FREQUENT COMPLAINT AMONG MIGRANT FARM WORKERS WERE OBSERVED IN ANOTHER STUDY. PROLONGED OR REPEATED EXPOSURE TO ORGANOCHLORINE PESTICIDES MAY CAUSE EFFECTS AS DESCRIBED IN ACUTE INGESTION.

FIRST AID- REMOVE FROM EXPOSURE AREA TO FRESH AIR IMMEDIATELY. IF BREATHING HAS STOPPED, PERFORM ARTIFICIAL RESPIRATION. KEEP PERSON WARM AND AT REST. TREAT SYMPTOMATICALLY AND SUPPORTIVELY. GET MEDICAL ATTENTION IMMEDIATELY.

SKIN CONTACT: DDA-P,P': **ACUTE EXPOSURE-** EFFECTS AS DESCRIBED FOR ORGANOCHLORINE PESTICIDES IN ACUTE INGESTION MAY OCCUR IF SUFFICIENT AMOUNTS ARE ABSORBED THROUGH THE THE SKIN. **CHRONIC EXPOSURE-** A STUDY OF OCCUPATIONAL EXPOSURE TO DDT REPORTED A HIGHER FREQUENCY OF WHITE BLOOD CELLS WITH CHROMOSOMAL ABNORMALITIES AMONG WORKERS WITH HIGH DDT BLOOD LEVELS; MENSTRUAL IRREGULARITIES AS THE MOST FREQUENT COMPLAINT AMONG MIGRANT FARM WORKERS WERE OBSERVED IN ANOTHER STUDY. PROLONGED OR REPEATED EXPOSURE TO ORGANOCHLORINE PESTICIDES MAY CAUSE EFFECTS AS DESCRIBED IN ACUTE INGESTION. **FIRST AID-** REMOVE CONTAMINATED CLOTHING AND SHOES IMMEDIATELY. WASH AFFECTED AREA WITH SOAP OR MILD DETERGENT AND LARGE AMOUNTS OF WATER UNTIL NO EVIDENCE OF CHEMICAL REMAINS (APPROXIMATELY 15-20 MINUTES). GET MEDICAL ATTENTION IMMEDIATELY.

EYE CONTACT: DDA-P,P': **ACUTE EXPOSURE-** NO DATA AVAILABLE. **CHRONIC EXPOSURE-** NO DATA AVAILABLE.

FIRST AID- WASH EYES IMMEDIATELY WITH LARGE AMOUNTS OF WATER OR NORMAL SALINE, OCCASIONALLY LIFTING UPPER AND LOWER LIDS, UNTIL NO EVIDENCE OF CHEMICAL REMAINS (APPROXIMATELY 15-20 MINUTES). GET MEDICAL ATTENTION IMMEDIATELY.

INGESTION: DDA-P,P': **ACUTE EXPOSURE-** INGESTION OF ORGANOCHLORINE PESTICIDES MAY CAUSE GASTROINTESTINAL EFFECTS OF NAUSEA, VOMITING, DIARRHEA, AND STOMACH PAINS. OTHER SYMPTOMS OF CONFUSION, APPREHENSION, IRRITABILITY, EXCITABILITY, DIZZINESS, HEADACHE, DISORIENTATION, WEAKNESS, PARESTHESIAS, MUSCLE TWITCHING, TREMOR, STUPOR, COMA, AND CONVULSIONS MAY OCCUR. SIGNS OF LIVER AND KIDNEY DAMAGE MAY DEVELOP. DEATH MAY BE DUE TO TO RESPIRATORY FAILURE OR VENTRICULAR FIBRILLATION. SYMPTOMS OF POISONING MAY OCCUR SEVERAL HOURS AFTER INGESTION. **CHRONIC EXPOSURE-** REPRODUCTIVE EFFECTS HAVE BEEN REPORTED IN ANIMALS. REPEATED EXPOSURE TO ORGANOCHLORINE PESTICIDES MAY CAUSE EFFECTS AS DESCRIBED IN ACUTE EXPOSURE.

FIRST AID- IF THE PERSON IS CONSCIOUS AND NOT CONVULSING, REMOVE BY GIVING SYRUP OF IPECAC (IF VOMITING OCCURS, KEEP THE HEAD BELOW THE HIPS TO PREVENT ASPIRATION). GIVE ACTIVATED CHARCOAL FOLLOWED BY GASTRIC LAVAGE. FOLLOW WITH A SALINE CATHARTIC. DO NOT GIVE FATS OR OILS. INTESTINAL LAVAGE WITH 20% MANNITOL (200 ML) BY STOMACH TUBE IS ALSO USEFUL. GIVE ARTIFICIAL RESPIRATION WITH OXYGEN IF RESPIRATION IS DEPRESSED (DREISBACH, HANDBOOK OF POISONING, 12TH ED.). TREAT SYMPTOMATICALLY AND SUPPORTIVELY. LAVAGE AND ADMINISTRATION OF OXYGEN SHOULD BE PERFORMED BY QUALIFIED MEDICAL PERSONNEL. GET MEDICAL ATTENTION IMMEDIATELY.

ANTIDOTE: NO SPECIFIC ANTIDOTE. TREAT SYMPTOMATICALLY AND SUPPORTIVELY.

REACTIVITY

REACTIVITY: STABLE UNDER NORMAL TEMPERATURES AND PRESSURES.

INCOMPATIBILITIES: DDA-P,P': OXIDIZERS (STRONG): FIRE AND EXPLOSION HAZARD.

DECOMPOSITION: THERMAL DECOMPOSITION PRODUCTS MAY INCLUDE TOXIC AND CORROSIVE FUMES OF CHLORIDES AND TOXIC OXIDES OF CARBON.

POLYMERIZATION: HAZARDOUS POLYMERIZATION HAS NOT BEEN REPORTED TO OCCUR UNDER NORMAL TEMPERATURES AND PRESSURES.

STORAGE AND DISPOSAL

OBSERVE ALL FEDERAL, STATE AND LOCAL REGULATIONS WHEN STORING OR DISPOSING OF THIS SUBSTANCE. FOR ASSISTANCE, CONTACT THE DISTRICT DIRECTOR OF THE ENVIRONMENTAL PROTECTION AGENCY.

STORAGE

STORE AWAY FROM INCOMPATIBLE SUBSTANCES.

CONDITIONS TO AVOID

MAY BURN BUT DOES NOT IGNITE READILY. AVOID CONTACT WITH STRONG OXIDIZERS, EXCESSIVE HEAT, SPARKS, OR OPEN FLAME.

SPILL AND LEAK PROCEDURES

OCCUPATIONAL SPILL: SWEEP UP AND PLACE IN SUITABLE CLEAN, DRY CONTAINERS FOR RECLAMATION OR LATER DISPOSAL. DO NOT FLUSH SPILLED MATERIAL INTO SEWER. KEEP UNNECESSARY PEOPLE AWAY.

PROTECTIVE EQUIPMENT

VENTILATION: PROVIDE LOCAL EXHAUST OR GENERAL DILUTION VENTILATION SYSTEM.

RESPIRATOR: THE FOLLOWING RESPIRATORS ARE RECOMMENDED BASED ON INFORMATION FOUND IN THE PHYSICAL DATA, TOXICITY AND HEALTH EFFECTS SECTIONS. THEY ARE RANKED IN ORDER FROM MINIMUM TO MAXIMUM RESPIRATORY PROTECTION. THE SPECIFIC RESPIRATOR SELECTED MUST BE BASED ON CONTAMINATION LEVELS FOUND IN THE WORK PLACE, MUST NOT EXCEED THE WORKING LIMITS OF THE RESPIRATOR AND BE JOINTLY APPROVED BY THE NATIONAL INSTITUTE FOR OCCUPATIONAL SAFETY AND HEALTH AND THE MINE SAFETY AND HEALTH ADMINISTRATION (NIOSH-MSHA).
CHEMICAL CARTRIDGE RESPIRATOR WITH AN ORGANIC VAPOR CARTRIDGE(S) IN COMBINATION WITH A DUST AND MIST FILTER.
GAS MASK WITH ORGANIC VAPOR CANISTER (CHIN-STYLE OR FRONT- OR BACK-MOUNTED CANISTER) WITH A DUST AND MIST FILTER.

GAS MASK WITH ORGANIC VAPOR CANISTER (CHIN-STYLE OR FRONT- OR BACK-MOUNTED CANISTER) WITH A PARTICULATE FILTER.
POWERED AIR-PURIFYING RESPIRATOR WITH A HIGH-EFFICIENCY FILTER.
TYPE 'C' SUPPLIED-AIR RESPIRATOR WITH A FULL FACEPIECE OPERATED IN A PRESSURE-DEMAND OR OTHER POSITIVE PRESSURE MODE.
SELF-CONTAINED BREATHING APPARATUS WITH A FULL FACEPIECE OPERATED IN PRESSURE-DEMAND OR OTHER POSITIVE PRESSURE MODE.
FOR FIREFIGHTING AND OTHER IMMEDIATELY DANGEROUS TO LIFE OR HEALTH CONDITIONS:
SELF-CONTAINED BREATHING APPARATUS WITH FULL FACEPIECE OPERATED IN PRESSURE-DEMAND OR OTHER POSITIVE PRESSURE MODE.
SUPPLIED-AIR RESPIRATOR WITH FULL FACEPIECE AND OPERATED IN PRESSURE-DEMAND OR OTHER POSITIVE PRESSURE MODE IN COMBINATION WITH AN AUXILIARY SELF-CONTAINED BREATHING APPARATUS OPERATED IN PRESSURE-DEMAND OR OTHER POSITIVE PRESSURE MODE.

CLOTHING: EMPLOYEE MUST WEAR APPROPRIATE PROTECTIVE (IMPERVIOUS) CLOTHING AND EQUIPMENT TO PREVENT REPEATED OR PROLONGED SKIN CONTACT WITH THIS SUBSTANCE.

GLOVES: EMPLOYEE MUST WEAR APPROPRIATE PROTECTIVE GLOVES TO PREVENT CONTACT WITH THIS SUBSTANCE.

EYE PROTECTION: EMPLOYEE MUST WEAR SPLASH-PROOF OR DUST-RESISTANT SAFETY GOGGLES AND A FACESHIELD TO PREVENT CONTACT WITH THIS SUBSTANCE.
EMERGENCY WASH FACILITIES: WHERE THERE IS ANY POSSIBILITY THAT AN EMPLOYEE'S EYES AND/OR SKIN MAY BE EXPOSED TO THIS SUBSTANCE, THE EMPLOYER SHOULD PROVIDE AN EYE WASH FOUNTAIN AND QUICK DRENCH SHOWER WITHIN THE IMMEDIATE WORK AREA FOR EMERGENCY USE.

AUTHORIZED BY- OCCUPATIONAL HEALTH SERVICES, INC.
CREATION DATE: 12/18/89 ***REVISION DATE:*** 05/31/90

MATERIAL SAFETY DATA SHEET

OCCUPATIONAL HEALTH SERVICES, INC.
AGRICULTURE AND PESTICIDE DIVISION
450 SEVENTH AVENUE, SUITE 2407
NEW YORK, NEW YORK 10123
1-800-445-MSDS OR (212) 967-1100

EMERGENCY CONTACT:
JOHN S. BRANSFORD, JR. (615) 292-1180

SUBSTANCE IDENTIFICATION

CAS-NUMBER 72-54-8

SUBSTANCE: **1,1-DICHLORO-2,2-BIS(P-CHLOROPHENYL)ETHANE**

TRADE NAMES/SYNONYMS: BENZENE, 1,1'-(2,2-DICHLOROETHYLIDENE)BIS(4-CHLORO-; ETHANE, 1,1-DICHLORO-2,2-BIS(P-CHLOROPHENYL)-; 1,1'-(2,2-DICHLOROETHYLIDENE)BIS(4-CHLOROBENZENE); 1,1'-DICHLORO-2,2-BIS(4-CHLOROPHENYL)ETHANE; 1,1-BIS(4-CHLOROPHENYL)-2,2-DICHLOROETHANE; DICHLORODIPHENYL DICHLOROETHANE; TETRACHLORODIPHENYLETHANE; P,P'-DDD; DDD; 4,4'-DDD; RHOTHANE; P,P'-TDE; TDE; OMS 1078; NCI-C00475; ENT 4225; STCC 4940370; RCRA U060; C14H10CL4; PST06240

CHEMICAL FAMILY: HALOGEN COMPOUND, AROMATIC

MOLECULAR FORMULA: (CL-C6)H4)2-(C-H)2-CL2

MOLECULAR WEIGHT: 320.05

CERCLA RATINGS (SCALE 0-3): HEALTH=3 FIRE=0 REACTIVITY=0 PERSISTENCE=3

NFPA RATINGS (SCALE 0-4): HEALTH=3 FIRE=0 REACTIVITY=0

COMPONENTS AND CONTAMINANTS

COMPONENT: 1,1-DICHLORO-2,2-BIS(P-CHLOROPHENYL)ETHANE ***PERCENT:*** 100
CAS# 72-54-8

OTHER CONTAMINANTS: NONE

EXPOSURE LIMITS: NO OCCUPATIONAL EXPOSURE LIMITS ESTABLISHED BY OSHA, ACGIH, OR NIOSH.
1,1-DICHLORO-2,2-BIS(P-CHLOROPHENYL)ETHANE: 1 POUND CERCLA SECTION 103 REPORTABLE QUANTITY SUBJECT TO CALIFORNIA PROPOSITION 65 CANCER AND/OR REPRODUCTIVE TOXICITY WARNING AND RELEASE REQUIREMENTS- (JANUARY 1, 1989)

PHYSICAL DATA

DESCRIPTION: COLORLESS CRYSTALLINE SOLID.

BOILING POINT: 365-379 F (185-193 C) @ 1 MMHG

MELTING POINT: 228.2-230 F (109-110 C) ***SPECIFIC GRAVITY:*** 1.385

SOLUBILITY IN WATER: ALMOST INSOLUBLE ***VAPOR DENSITY:*** 11

SOLVENT SOLUBILITY: SOLUBLE IN FATS, ORGANIC SOLVENTS.

FIRE AND EXPLOSION DATA

FIRE AND EXPLOSION HAZARD: NEGLIGIBLE FIRE HAZARD WHEN EXPOSED TO HEAT OR FLAME.

FIREFIGHTING MEDIA: DRY CHEMICAL, CARBON DIOXIDE, HALON, WATER SPRAY OR STANDARD FOAM (1987 EMERGENCY RESPONSE GUIDEBOOK, DOT P 5800.4).
FOR LARGER FIRES, USE WATER SPRAY, FOG OR STANDARD FOAM (1987 EMERGENCY RESPONSE GUIDEBOOK, DOT P 5800.4).

FIREFIGHTING: DO NOT TOUCH SPILLED MATERIAL (1987 EMERGENCY RESPONSE GUIDEBOOK, DOT P 5800.4, GUIDE PAGE 58).
EXTINGUISH USING AGENTS INDICATED. USE FLOODING AMOUNTS OF WATER AS A FOG. COOL CONTAINERS WITH FLOODING AMOUNTS OF WATER. USE WATER TO ABSORB VAPORS. AVOID BREATHING IRRITATING VAPORS; KEEP UPWIND.

TRANSPORTATION DATA

DEPARTMENT OF TRANSPORTATION HAZARD CLASSIFICATION 49 CFR 172.101: ORM-A
DEPARTMENT OF TRANSPORTATION LABELING REQUIREMENTS 49 CFR 172.101 AND SUBPART E: NONE
DEPARTMENT OF TRANSPORTATION PACKAGING REQUIREMENTS: 49 CFR 173.510 EXCEPTIONS: 49 CFR 173.505

TOXICITY

1,1-DICHLORO-2,2-BIS(P-CHLOROPHENYL)ETHANE: TOXICITY DATA: 1200 MG/KG SKIN-RABBIT LD50; 113 MG/KG ORAL-RAT LD50; 600 MG/KG ORAL-MOUSE LDLO; MUTAGENIC DATA (RTECS); TUMORIGENIC DATA (RTECS). CARCINOGEN STATUS: NONE. ORAL ADMINISTRATION PRODUCED A SIGNIFICANT INCREASE IN LUNG TUMORS IN MICE (IARC). ACUTE TOXICITY LEVEL: TOXIC BY INGESTION; MODERATELY TOXIC BY DERMAL ABSORPTION. TARGET EFFECTS: CONVULSANT. POISONING MAY DEPRESSES THE FUNCTION OF THE ADRENAL CORTEX AND AFFECT THE LIVER AND KIDNEYS.* ADDITIONAL DATA: DDT METABOLITE. MAY CROSS THE PLACENTA AND BE EXCRETED IN BREAST MILK. MAY IMPAIR FERTILITY. STIMULANTS SUCH AS EPINEPHRINE OR EPHEDRINE MAY INDUCE VENTRICULAR FIBRILLATION.*
* MAY BE BASED ON GROUP INFORMATION ON ORGANOCHLORINE PESTICIDES.

HEALTH EFFECTS AND FIRST AID

INHALATION: 1,1-DICHLORO-2,2-BIS(P-CHLOROPHENYL)ETHANE: **ACUTE EXPOSURE-** MAY CAUSE IRRITATION OF THE MUCOUS MEMBRANES. EFFECTS AS DESCRIBED FOR ORGANOCHLORINE PESTICIDES IN ACUTE INGESTION MAY OCCUR IF SUFFICIENT AMOUNTS ARE ABSORBED THROUGH THE LUNGS. **CHRONIC EXPOSURE-** A STUDY OF OCCUPATIONAL EXPOSURE TO DDT REPORTED A HIGHER FREQUENCY OF WHITE BLOOD CELLS WITH CHROMOSOMAL ABNORMALITIES AMONG WORKERS WITH HIGH DDT BLOOD LEVELS; MENSTRUAL IRREGULARITIES AS THE MOST FREQUENT COMPLAINT AMONG MIGRANT FARM WORKERS WERE OBSERVED IN ANOTHER STUDY. PROLONGED OR REPEATED EXPOSURE TO ORGANOCHLORINE PESTICIDES MAY CAUSE EFFECTS AS DESCRIBED IN ACUTE INGESTION.

FIRST AID- REMOVE FROM EXPOSURE AREA TO FRESH AIR IMMEDIATELY. IF BREATHING HAS STOPPED, PERFORM ARTIFICIAL RESPIRATION. KEEP PERSON WARM AND AT REST. TREAT SYMPTOMATICALLY AND SUPPORTIVELY. GET MEDICAL ATTENTION IMMEDIATELY.

SKIN CONTACT: 1,1-DICHLORO-2,2-BIS(P-CHLOROPHENYL)ETHANE: **ACUTE EXPOSURE-** MAY CAUSE IRRITATION. A LETHAL DOSE IN RABBITS BY DERMAL ABSORPTION WAS 1200 MG/KG; SYMPTOMS OF EXCITEMENT, CONVULSIONS AND IRRITATION WERE REPORTED. **CHRONIC EXPOSURE-** RABBITS WERE MADE SEVERELY ILL BUT DID NOT DIE WHEN TREATED WITH 200 MG/KG/DAY FOR 90 DAYS. HOWEVER, THE RABBITS DIED QUICKLY FROM DERMAL APPLICATIONS OF 400 MG/KG/DAY. A STUDY OF OCCUPATIONAL EXPOSURE TO DDT REPORTED A HIGHER FREQUENCY OF WHITE BLOOD CELLS WITH CHROMOSOMAL ABNORMALITIES AMONG WORKERS WITH HIGH DDT BLOOD LEVELS; MENSTRUAL IRREGULARITIES AS THE MOST FREQUENT COMPLAINT AMONG MIGRANT FARM WORKERS WERE OBSERVED IN ANOTHER STUDY. PROLONGED OR REPEATED EXPOSURE TO ORGANOCHLORINE PESTICIDES MAY CAUSE EFFECTS AS DESCRIBED IN ACUTE INGESTION.

FIRST AID- REMOVE CONTAMINATED CLOTHING AND SHOES IMMEDIATELY. WASH AFFECTED AREA WITH SOAP OR MILD DETERGENT AND LARGE AMOUNTS OF WATER UNTIL NO EVIDENCE OF CHEMICAL REMAINS (APPROXIMATELY 15-20 MINUTES). GET MEDICAL ATTENTION IMMEDIATELY.

EYE CONTACT: 1,1-DICHLORO-2,2-BIS(P-CHLOROPHENYL)ETHANE: **ACUTE EXPOSURE-** MAY CAUSE IRRITATION. **CHRONIC EXPOSURE-** NO DATA AVAILABLE.

FIRST AID- WASH EYES IMMEDIATELY WITH LARGE AMOUNTS OF WATER OR NORMAL SALINE, OCCASIONALLY LIFTING UPPER AND LOWER LIDS, UNTIL NO EVIDENCE OF

CHEMICAL REMAINS (APPROXIMATELY 15-20 MINUTES). GET MEDICAL ATTENTION IMMEDIATELY.

INGESTION: 1,1-DICHLORO-2,2-BIS(P-CHLOROPHENYL)ETHANE: TOXIC. **ACUTE EXPOSURE-** A LETHAL DOSE IN RATS WAS 113 MG/KG. ORGANOCHLORINE PESTICIDES MAY CAUSE GASTROINTESTINAL EFFECTS OF NAUSEA, VOMITING, DIARRHEA, AND STOMACH PAINS. OTHER SYMPTOMS OF CONFUSION, APPREHENSION, IRRITABILITY, EXCITABILITY, DIZZINESS, HEADACHE, DISORIENTATION, WEAKNESS, PARESTHESIAS, MUSCLE TWITCHING, TREMOR, STUPOR, COMA, AND CONVULSION MAY OCCUR. SIGNS OF LIVER AND KIDNEY DAMAGE MAY DEVELOP. DEATH MAY BE DUE TO RESPIRATORY FAILURE OR VENTRICULAR FIBRILLATION. SYMPTOMS OF POISONING MAY OCCUR SEVERAL HOURS AFTER INGESTION. **CHRONIC EXPOSURE-** IN A STUDY OF MICE, 1,1-DICHLORO-2,2-BIS(P-CHLOROPHENYL) ETHANE AT A DIETARY LEVEL OF 250 PPM MODERATELY INCREASED THE INCIDENCE OF LIVER TUMORS IN MALES ONLY AND INCREASED THE INCIDENCE OF LUNG TUMORS IN BOTH SEXES. EFFECTS ON THE ADRENAL GLANDS WERE OBSERVED IN DOGS. THERAPEUTIC ADMINISTRATION OF THE O,P-ISOMER HAS PRODUCED NAUSEA, VOMITING, DIARRHEA, LETHARGY, SOMNOLENCE AND DIZZINESS. GENERALIZED ACHING, HYPERPYREXIA, GYNECOMASTIA, LOWERED PROTEIN BOUND IODINE, AND EFFECTS ON THE EYE, GENITOURINARY AND CARDIOVASCULAR SYSTEMS HAVE ALSO OCCURRED.

FIRST AID- IF THE PERSON IS CONSCIOUS AND NOT CONVULSING, REMOVE BY GIVING SYRUP OF IPECAC (IF VOMITING OCCURS, KEEP THE HEAD BELOW THE HIPS TO PREVENT ASPIRATION). GIVE ACTIVATED CHARCOAL FOLLOWED BY GASTRIC LAVAGE. FOLLOW WITH A SALINE CATHARTIC. DO NOT GIVE FATS OR OILS. INTESTINAL LAVAGE WITH 20% MANNITOL (200 ML) BY STOMACH TUBE IS ALSO USEFUL. GIVE ARTIFICIAL RESPIRATION WITH OXYGEN IF RESPIRATION IS DEPRESSED (DREISBACH, HANDBOOK OF POISONING, 12TH ED.). TREAT SYMPTOMATICALLY AND SUPPORTIVELY. LAVAGE AND ADMINISTRATION OF OXYGEN SHOULD BE PERFORMED BY QUALIFIED MEDICAL PERSONNEL. GET MEDICAL ATTENTION IMMEDIATELY.

ANTIDOTE: NO SPECIFIC ANTIDOTE. TREAT SYMPTOMATICALLY AND SUPPORTIVELY.

REACTIVITY

REACTIVITY: STABLE UNDER NORMAL TEMPERATURES AND PRESSURES.

INCOMPATIBILITIES: 1,1-DICHLORO-2,2-BIS(P-CHLOROPHENYL)ETHANE: OXIDIZERS: FIRE AND EXPLOSION HAZARD.

DECOMPOSITION: THERMAL DECOMPOSITION PRODUCTS MAY INCLUDE TOXIC AND CORROSIVE FUMES OF CHLORIDES AND TOXIC OXIDES OF CARBON.

POLYMERIZATION: HAZARDOUS POLYMERIZATION HAS NOT BEEN REPORTED TO OCCUR UNDER NORMAL TEMPERATURES AND PRESSURES.

STORAGE AND DISPOSAL

OBSERVE ALL FEDERAL, STATE AND LOCAL REGULATIONS WHEN STORING OR DISPOSING OF THIS SUBSTANCE. FOR ASSISTANCE, CONTACT THE DISTRICT DIRECTOR OF THE ENVIRONMENTAL PROTECTION AGENCY.

****STORAGE****

STORE IN ACCORDANCE WITH 40 CFR 165 RECOMMENDED PROCEDURES FOR THE DISPOSAL AND STORAGE OF PESTICIDES AND PESTICIDE CONTAINERS.
STORE AWAY FROM INCOMPATIBLE SUBSTANCES.

****DISPOSAL****

DISPOSAL MUST BE IN ACCORDANCE WITH STANDARDS APPLICABLE TO GENERATORS OF HAZARDOUS WASTE, 40CFR 262. EPA HAZARDOUS WASTE NUMBER U060.

CONDITIONS TO AVOID

MAY BURN BUT DOES NOT IGNITE READILY.

SPILL AND LEAK PROCEDURES

SOIL SPILL: DIG A HOLDING AREA SUCH AS PIT, POND OR LAGOON TO CONTAIN SPILLED MATERIAL. USE PROTECTIVE COVER SUCH AS A PLASTIC SHEET TO PREVENT DISSOLVING IN FIREFIGHTING WATER OR RAIN.

WATER SPILL: USE NATURAL DEEP WATER POCKETS, EXCAVATED LAGOONS, OR SAND BAG BARRIERS TO TRAP MATERIAL AT BOTTOM. USE ACTIVATED CARBON AT 10 TIMES THE SPILLED AMOUNT IF IT IS DISSOLVED AT 10 PPM OR GREATER CONCENTRATION. REMOVE TRAPPED MATERIAL WITH SUCTION HOSES. USE MECHANICAL DREDGES OR LIFTS TO REMOVE IMMOBILIZED MASSES OF POLLUTION AND PRECIPITATES.
THE CALIFORNIA SAFE DRINKING WATER AND TOXIC ENFORCEMENT ACT OF 1986 (PROPOSITION 65) PROHIBITS CONTAMINATING ANY KNOWN SOURCE OF DRINKING WATER WITH SUBSTANCES KNOWN TO CAUSE CANCER AND/OR REPRODUCTIVE TOXICITY.

OCCUPATIONAL SPILL: SWEEP UP AND PLACE IN SUITABLE CLEAN, DRY CONTAINERS FOR RECLAMATION OR LATER DISPOSAL. DO NOT FLUSH SPILLED MATERIAL INTO SEWER. KEEP UNNECESSARY PEOPLE AWAY.

REPORTABLE QUANTITY (RQ): 1 POUND THE SUPERFUND AMENDMENTS AND REAUTHORIZATION ACT (SARA) SECTION 304 REQUIRES THAT A RELEASE EQUAL TO OR GREATER THAN THE REPORTABLE QUANTITY FOR THIS SUBSTANCE BE IMMEDIATELY REPORTED TO THE LOCAL EMERGENCY PLANNING COMMITTEE AND THE STATE EMERGENCY RESPONSE COMMISSION (40 CFR 355.40). IF THE RELEASE OF THIS SUBSTANCE IS REPORTABLE UNDER CERCLA SECTION 103, THE NATIONAL RESPONSE CENTER MUST BE NOTIFIED IMMEDIATELY AT (800) 424-8802 OR (202) 426-2675 IN THE METROPOLITAN WASHINGTON, D.C. AREA (40 CFR 302.6).

PROTECTIVE EQUIPMENT

VENTILATION: PROVIDE LOCAL EXHAUST OR PROCESS ENCLOSURE VENTILATION SYSTEM.

RESPIRATOR: THE FOLLOWING RESPIRATORS ARE RECOMMENDED BASED ON INFORMATION FOUND IN THE PHYSICAL DATA, TOXICITY AND HEALTH EFFECTS SECTIONS. THEY ARE RANKED IN ORDER FROM MINIMUM TO MAXIMUM RESPIRATORY PROTECTION. THE SPECIFIC RESPIRATOR SELECTED MUST BE BASED ON CONTAMINATION LEVELS FOUND IN THE WORK PLACE, MUST NOT EXCEED THE WORKING LIMITS OF THE RESPIRATOR AND BE JOINTLY APPROVED BY THE NATIONAL INSTITUTE FOR OCCUPATIONAL SAFETY AND HEALTH AND THE MINE SAFETY AND HEALTH ADMINISTRATION (NIOSH-MSHA).
TYPE 'C' SUPPLIED-AIR RESPIRATOR WITH A FULL FACEPIECE OPERATED IN PRESSURE-DEMAND OR OTHER POSITIVE PRESSURE MODE OR WITH A FULL FACEPIECE, HELMET OR HOOD OPERATED IN CONTINOUS-FLOW MODE.
SELF-CONTAINED BREATHING APPARATUS WITH A FULL FACEPIECE OPERATED IN PRESSURE-DEMAND OR OTHER POSITIVE PRESSURE MODE.
FOR FIREFIGHTING AND OTHER IMMEDIATELY DANGEROUS TO LIFE OR HEALTH CONDITIONS:
SELF-CONTAINED BREATHING APPARATUS WITH FULL FACEPIECE OPERATED IN PRESSURE-DEMAND OR OTHER POSITIVE PRESSURE MODE.
SUPPLIED-AIR RESPIRATOR WITH FULL FACEPIECE AND OPERATED IN PRESSURE-DEMAND OR OTHER POSITIVE PRESSURE MODE IN COMBINATION WITH AN AUXILIARY SELF-CONTAINED BREATHING APPARATUS OPERATED IN PRESSURE-DEMAND OR OTHER POSITIVE PRESSURE MODE.

CLOTHING: EMPLOYEE MUST WEAR APPROPRIATE PROTECTIVE (IMPERVIOUS) CLOTHING AND EQUIPMENT TO PREVENT REPEATED OR PROLONGED SKIN CONTACT WITH THIS SUBSTANCE.

GLOVES: EMPLOYEE MUST WEAR APPROPRIATE PROTECTIVE GLOVES TO PREVENT CONTACT WITH THIS SUBSTANCE.

EYE PROTECTION: EMPLOYEE MUST WEAR SPLASH-PROOF OR DUST-RESISTANT SAFETY GOGGLES TO PREVENT EYE CONTACT WITH THIS SUBSTANCE.
EMERGENCY EYE WASH: WHERE THERE IS ANY POSSIBILITY THAT AN EMPLOYEE'S EYES MAY BE EXPOSED TO THIS SUBSTANCE, THE EMPLOYER SHOULD PROVIDE AN EYE WASH FOUNTAIN WITHIN THE IMMEDIATE WORK AREA FOR EMERGENCY USE.

AUTHORIZED BY- OCCUPATIONAL HEALTH SERVICES, INC.
CREATION DATE: 10/05/89 ***REVISION DATE:*** 05/31/90

MATERIAL SAFETY DATA SHEET

OCCUPATIONAL HEALTH SERVICES, INC.
AGRICULTURE AND PESTICIDE DIVISION
450 SEVENTH AVENUE, SUITE 2407
NEW YORK, NEW YORK 10123
1-800-445-MSDS OR (212) 967-1100

EMERGENCY CONTACT:
JOHN S. BRANSFORD, JR. (615) 292-1180

SUBSTANCE IDENTIFICATION

CAS-NUMBER 3424-82-6

SUBSTANCE: **2-(2-CHLOROPHENYL)-2-(4-CHLOROPHENYL)-1,1-DICHLOROETHENE**

TRADE NAMES/SYNONYMS: ETHYLENE, 1,1-DICHLORO-2-(O-CHLOROPHENYL)-2-(P-CHLOROPHENYL)-; 1,1-DICHLORO-2,2-BIS(4-CHLOROPHENYL)ETHYLENE; 1,1-DICHLORO-2-(O-CHLOROPHENYL)-2-(P-CHLOROPHENYL)ETHYLENE; DICHLORODIPHENYLDICHLOROETHYLENE; BENZENE, 1-CHLORO-2-(2,2-DICHLORO-1-(4-CHLOROPHENYL)ETHENYL); 1-CHLORO-2-(2,2-DICHLORO-1-(4-CHLOROPHENYL)ETHENYLBENZENE; DDE; 2,4'-DDE; O,P'-DDE; C14H8CL4; PST06245

CHEMICAL FAMILY: HALOGEN COMPOUND, AROMATIC

MOLECULAR FORMULA: CL-C6-H4-C-(C-CL2)-C6-H4-CL

MOLECULAR WEIGHT: 318.03

CERCLA RATINGS (SCALE 0-3): HEALTH=2 FIRE=1 REACTIVITY=0 PERSISTENCE=3
NFPA RATINGS (SCALE 0-4): HEALTH=2 FIRE=1 REACTIVITY=0

COMPONENTS AND CONTAMINANTS

COMPONENT: 2-(2-CHLOROPHENYL)-2-(4-CHLOROPHENYL)-1,1-DICHLOROETHENE ***PERCENT:*** 100
CAS# 3424-82-6

OTHER CONTAMINANTS: NONE

EXPOSURE LIMITS: NO OCCUPATIONAL EXPOSURE LIMITS ESTABLISHED BY OSHA, ACGIH, OR NIOSH.

PHYSICAL DATA

DESCRIPTION: SOLID ***MELTING POINT:*** 169-174 F (76-79 C)
SPECIFIC GRAVITY: NOT AVAILABLE ***SOLUBILITY IN WATER:*** NOT AVAIABLE
SOLVENT SOLUBILITY: SOLUBLE IN ETHANOL, ACETONE, DICHLOROMETHANE.

FIRE AND EXPLOSION DATA

FIRE AND EXPLOSION HAZARD: SLIGHT FIRE HAZARD WHEN EXPOSED TO HEAT OR FLAME.

FIREFIGHTING MEDIA: DRY CHEMICAL, CARBON DIOXIDE, HALON, WATER SPRAY OR STANDARD FOAM (1987 EMERGENCY RESPONSE GUIDEBOOK, DOT P 5800.4). FOR LARGER FIRES, USE WATER SPRAY, FOG OR STANDARD FOAM (1987 EMERGENCY RESPONSE GUIDEBOOK, DOT P 5800.4).

FIREFIGHTING: MOVE CONTAINERS FROM FIRE AREA IF POSSIBLE. FIGHT FIRE FROM MAXIMUM DISTANCE. STAY AWAY FROM STORAGE TANK ENDS. DIKE FIRE CONTROL WATER FOR LATER DISPOSAL. DO NOT SCATTER MATERIAL (1987 EMERGENCY RESPONSE GUIDEBOOK, DOT P 5800.4, GUIDE PAGE 55).
USE AGENTS SUITABLE FOR TYPE OF FIRE. COOL CONTAINERS WITH FLOODING AMOUNTS OF WATER. AVOID BREATHING VAPORS OR DUSTS, KEEP UPWIND.

TOXICITY

2-(2-CHLOROPHENYL)-2-(4-CHLOROPHENYL)-1,1-DICHLOROETHANE (2,4'-DDE): TOXICITY DATA: 880 MG/KG ORAL-RAT LD50; MUTAGENIC DATA (RTECS). CARCINOGEN STATUS: NONE. ACUTE TOXICITY LEVEL: MODERATELY TOXIC BY INGESTION. TARGET EFFECTS: CONVULSANT. POISONING MAY AFFECT THE LIVER AND KIDNEY.* ADDITIONAL DATA: DDT METABOLITE. MAY CROSS THE PLACENTA AND BE EXCRETED IN BREAST MILK. MAY IMPAIR FERTILITY. STIMULANTS SUCH AS EPINEPHRINE OR EPHEDRINE MAY INDUCE VENTRICULAR FIBRILLATION.*
* MAY BE BASED ON GENERAL INFORMATION ON ORGANOCHLORINE COMPOUNDS.

HEALTH EFFECTS AND FIRST AID

INHALATION: 2-(2-CHLOROPHENYL)-2-(4-CHLOROPHENYL)-1,1-DICHLOROETHENE (2,4'-DDE): **ACUTE EXPOSURE-** EFFECTS AS DESCRIBED FOR ORGANOCHLORINE PESTICIDES IN ACUTE INGESTION MAY OCCUR IF SUFFICIENT AMOUNTS ARE ABSORBED FROM THE LUNGS. **CHRONIC EXPOSURE-** A STUDY OF OCCUPATIONAL EXPOSURE TO DDT REPORTED A HIGHER FREQUENCY OF WHITE BLOOD CELLS WITH CHROMOSOMAL ABNORMALITIES AMONG WORKERS WITH HIGH DDT BLOOD LEVELS; ANOTHER STUDY REPORTED MENSTRUAL IRREGULARITIES AS THE MOST FREQUENT COMPLAINT AMONG MIGRANT FARM WORKERS. PROLONGED OR REPEATED EXPOSURE TO ORGANOCHLORINE PESTICIDES MAY CAUSE EFFECTS AS DESCRIBED IN ACUTE INGESTION.

FIRST AID- REMOVE FROM EXPOSURE AREA TO FRESH AIR IMMEDIATELY. IF BREATHING HAS STOPPED, PERFORM ARTIFICIAL RESPIRATION. KEEP PERSON WARM AND AT REST. TREAT SYMPTOMATICALLY AND SUPPORTIVELY. GET MEDICAL ATTENTION IMMEDIATELY.

SKIN CONTACT: 2-(2-CHLOROPHENYL)-2-(4-CHLOROPHENYL)-1,1-DICHLOROETHENE (2,4'-DDE): **ACUTE EXPOSURE-** EFFECTS AS DESCRIBED FOR ORGANOCHLORINE PESTICIDES IN ACUTE INGESTION MAY OCCUR IF SUFFICIENT AMOUNTS ARE ABSORBED THROUGH THE SKIN. **CHRONIC EXPOSURE-** A STUDY OF OCCUPATIONAL EXPOSURE TO DDT REPORTED A HIGHER FREQUENCY OF WHITE BLOOD CELLS WITH CHROMOSOMAL ABNORMALITIES AMONG WORKERS WITH HIGH DDT BLOOD LEVELS; ANOTHER STUDY REPORTED MENSTRUAL IRREGULARITIES AS THE MOST FREQUENT COMPLAINT AMONG MIGRANT FARM WORKERS. PROLONGED OR REPEATED EXPOSURE TO ORGANOCHLORINE PESTICIDES MAY CAUSE EFFECTS AS DESCRIBED IN ACUTE INGESTION.

FIRST AID- REMOVE CONTAMINATED CLOTHING AND SHOES IMMEDIATELY. WASH AFFECTED AREA WITH SOAP OR MILD DETERGENT AND LARGE AMOUNTS OF WATER UNTIL NO EVIDENCE OF CHEMICAL REMAINS (APPROXIMATELY 15-20 MINUTES). GET MEDICAL ATTENTION IMMEDIATELY.

EYE CONTACT: 2-(2-CHLOROPHENYL)-2-(4-CHLOROPHENYL)-1,1-DICHLOROETHENE (2,4'-DDE): **ACUTE EXPOSURE-** NO DATA AVAILABLE. **CHRONIC EXPOSURE-** NO DATA AVAILABLE.

FIRST AID- WASH EYES IMMEDIATELY WITH LARGE AMOUNTS OF WATER OR NORMAL SALINE, OCCASIONALLY LIFTING UPPER AND LOWER LIDS, UNTIL NO EVIDENCE OF CHEMICAL REMAINS (APPROXIMATELY 15-20 MINUTES). GET MEDICAL ATTENTION IMMEDIATELY.

INGESTION: 2-(2-CHLOROPHENYL)-2-(4-CHOROPHENYL)-1,1-DICHLOROETHENE (2,4'-DDE): **ACUTE EXPOSURE-** INGESTION OF ORGANOCHLORINE PESTICIDES MAY CAUSE GASTROINTESTINAL EFFECTS OF NAUSEA, VOMITING, DIARRHEA, AND STOMACH PAINS. OTHER SYMPTOMS OF CONFUSION, APPREHENSION, IRRITABILITY, EXCITABILITY, DIZZINESS, HEADACHE, DISORIENTATION, WEAKNESS, PARESTHESIAS, MUSCLE TWITCHING, TREMOR, STUPOR, COMA, AND CONVULSIONS MAY OCCUR. SIGNS OF LIVER AND KIDNEY DAMAGE MAY DEVELOP. DEATH MAY BE DUE TO RESPIRATORY FAILURE OR VENTRICULAR FIBRILLATION. SYMPTOMS OF POISONING MAY OCCUR SEVERAL HOURS AFTER INGESTION. **CHRONIC EXPOSURE-** REPEATED EXPOSURE TO ORGANOCHLORINE PESTICIDES MAY CAUSE EFFECTS AS DESCRIBED IN ACUTE EXPOSURE.

FIRST AID- IF THE PERSON IS CONSCIOUS AND NOT CONVULSING, REMOVE BY GIVING SYRUP OF IPECAC (IF VOMITING OCCURS, KEEP THE HEAD BELOW THE HIPS TO PREVENT ASPIRATION). GIVE ACTIVATED CHARCOAL FOLLOWED BY GASTRIC LAVAGE. FOLLOW WITH A SALINE CATHARTIC. DO NOT GIVE FATS OR OILS. INTESTINAL LAVAGE WITH 20% MANNITOL (200 ML) BY STOMACH TUBE IS ALSO USEFUL. GIVE ARTIFICIAL RESPIRATION WITH OXYGEN IF RESPIRATION IS DEPRESSED (DREISBACH, HANDBOOK OF POISONING, 12TH ED.). TREAT SYMPTOMATICALLY AND SUPPORTIVELY. LAVAGE AND ADMINISTRATION OF OXYGEN SHOULD BE PERFORMED BY QUALIFIED MEDICAL PERSONNEL. GET MEDICAL ATTENTION IMMEDIATELY.

ANTIDOTE: NO SPECIFIC ANTIDOTE. TREAT SYMPTOMATICALLY AND SUPPORTIVELY.

REACTIVITY

REACTIVITY: STABLE UNDER NORMAL TEMPERATURES AND PRESSURES.

INCOMPATIBILITIES: 2-(2-CHLOROPHENYL)-2-(4-CHLOROPHENYL)-1,1-DICHLOROETHENE (2,4'-DDE): NO DATA AVAILABLE.

DECOMPOSITION: THERMAL DECOMPOSITION PRODUCTS MAY INCLUDE HIGHLY TOXIC FUMES OF PHOSGENE, TOXIC AND CORROSIVE FUMES OF CHLORIDES, AND OXIDES OF CARBON.

POLYMERIZATION: HAZARDOUS POLYMERIZATION HAS NOT BEEN REPORTED TO OCCUR UNDER NORMAL TEMPERATURES AND PRESSURES.

STORAGE AND DISPOSAL

OBSERVE ALL FEDERAL, STATE AND LOCAL REGULATIONS WHEN STORING OR DISPOSING OF THIS SUBSTANCE. FOR ASSISTANCE, CONTACT THE DISTRICT DIRECTOR OF THE ENVIRONMENTAL PROTECTION AGENCY.

CONDITIONS TO AVOID

MAY BURN BUT DOES NOT IGNITE READILY. CONTAINERS MAY EXPLODE IN HEAT OF FIRE.

SPILL AND LEAK PROCEDURES

OCCUPATIONAL SPILL: DO NOT TOUCH SPILLED MATERIAL. STOP LEAK IF YOU CAN DO IT WITHOUT RISK. USE WATER SPRAY TO REDUCE VAPORS. FOR SMALL SPILLS, TAKE UP WITH SAND OR OTHER ABSORBENT MATERIAL AND PLACE INTO CONTAINERS FOR LATER DISPOSAL. FOR SMALL DRY SPILLS, WITH A CLEAN SHOVEL PLACE MATERIAL INTO CLEAN, DRY CONTAINERS AND COVER. MOVE CONTAINERS FROM SPILL AREA. FOR LARGER SPILLS, DIKE FAR AHEAD OF SPILL FOR LATER DISPOSAL. KEEP UNNECESSARY PEOPLE AWAY. ISOLATE HAZARD AREA AND DENY ENTRY. VENTILATE CLOSED SPACES BEFORE ENTERING.

PROTECTIVE EQUIPMENT

VENTILATION: PROVIDE LOCAL EXHAUST OR GENERAL DILUTION VENTILATION SYSTEM.

RESPIRATOR: THE FOLLOWING RESPIRATORS ARE RECOMMENDED BASED ON INFORMATION FOUND IN THE PHYSICAL DATA, TOXICITY AND HEALTH EFFECTS SECTIONS. THEY ARE RANKED IN ORDER FROM MINIMUM TO MAXIMUM RESPIRATORY PROTECTION. THE SPECIFIC RESPIRATOR SELECTED MUST BE BASED ON CONTAMINATION LEVELS FOUND IN THE WORK PLACE, MUST NOT EXCEED THE WORKING LIMITS OF THE RESPIRATOR AND BE JOINTLY APPROVED BY THE NATIONAL INSTITUTE FOR OCCUPATIONAL SAFETY AND HEALTH AND THE MINE SAFETY AND HEALTH ADMINISTRATION (NIOSH-MSHA).
DUST AND MIST RESPIRATOR WITH A FULL FACEPIECE.
AIR-PURIFYING FULL FACEPIECE RESPIRATOR WITH A HIGH-EFFICIENCY PARTICULATE FILTER.
POWERED AIR-PURIFYING RESPIRATOR WITH A TIGHT-FITTING FACEPIECE AND HIGH-EFFICIENCY PARTICULATE FILTER.
TYPE 'C' SUPPLIED-AIR RESPIRATOR WITH A FULL FACEPIECE OPERATED IN PRESSURE-DEMAND OR OTHER POSITIVE PRESSURE MODE OR WITH A FULL FACEPIECE, HELMET OR HOOD OPERATED IN CONTINUOUS-FLOW MODE.

SELF-CONTAINED BREATHING APPARATUS WITH A FULL FACEPIECE OPERATED IN PRESSURE-DEMAND OR OTHER POSITIVE PRESSURE MODE.
FOR FIREFIGHTING AND OTHER IMMEDIATELY DANGEROUS TO LIFE OR HEALTH CONDITIONS:
SELF-CONTAINED BREATHING APPARATUS WITH FULL FACEPIECE OPERATED IN PRESSURE-DEMAND OR OTHER POSITIVE PRESSURE MODE.
SUPPLIED-AIR RESPIRATOR WITH FULL FACEPIECE AND OPERATED IN PRESSURE-DEMAND OR OTHER POSITIVE PRESSURE MODE IN COMBINATION WITH AN AUXILIARY SELF-CONTAINED BREATHING APPARATUS OPERATED IN PRESSURE-DEMAND OR OTHER POSITIVE PRESSURE MODE.

CLOTHING: EMPLOYEE MUST WEAR APPROPRIATE PROTECTIVE (IMPERVIOUS) CLOTHING AND EQUIPMENT TO PREVENT REPEATED OR PROLONGED SKIN CONTACT WITH THIS SUBSTANCE.

GLOVES: EMPLOYEE MUST WEAR APPROPRIATE PROTECTIVE GLOVES TO PREVENT CONTACT WITH THIS SUBSTANCE.

EYE PROTECTION: EMPLOYEE MUST WEAR SPLASH-PROOF OR DUST-RESISTANT SAFETY GOGGLES TO PREVENT EYE CONTACT WITH THIS SUBSTANCE.
EMERGENCY EYE WASH: WHERE THERE IS ANY POSSIBILITY THAT AN EMPLOYEE'S EYES MAY BE EXPOSED TO THIS SUBSTANCE, THE EMPLOYER SHOULD PROVIDE AN EYE WASH FOUNTAIN WITHIN THE IMMEDIATE WORK AREA FOR EMERGENCY USE.

AUTHORIZED BY- OCCUPATIONAL HEALTH SERVICES, INC.
CREATION DATE: 10/05/89 ***REVISION DATE:*** 05/29/90

MATERIAL SAFETY DATA SHEET

OCCUPATIONAL HEALTH SERVICES, INC.
AGRICULTURE AND PESTICIDE DIVISION
450 SEVENTH AVENUE, SUITE 2407
NEW YORK, NEW YORK 10123
1-800-445-MSDS OR (212) 967-1100

EMERGENCY CONTACT:
JOHN S. BRANSFORD, JR. (615) 292-1180

SUBSTANCE IDENTIFICATION

CAS-NUMBER 90-98-2

SUBSTANCE: **4,4'-DICHLOROBENZOPHENONE**

TRADE NAMES/SYNONYMS: 4,4'-DBP; BIS(4-CHLOROPHENYL)METHANONE; P,P'-DICHLOROBENZOPHENONE; BENZOPHENONE,4,4'-DICHLORO-; METHANONE, BIS(4-CHLOROPHENYL)-; BIS(4-CHLOROPHENYL) KETONE; DCBP; DI(P-CHLOROPHENYL)KETONE; C13H8CL2O; PST06246

CHEMICAL FAMILY: HALOGEN COMPOUND, AROMATIC

MOLECULAR FORMULA: CL-C6-H4-C-O-C6-H4-CL

MOLECULAR WEIGHT: 251.11

CERCLA RATINGS (SCALE 0-3): HEALTH=3 FIRE=1 REACTIVITY=0 PERSISTENCE=3

NFPA RATINGS (SCALE 0-4): HEALTH=3 FIRE=1 REACTIVITY=0

COMPONENTS AND CONTAMINANTS

COMPONENT: 4,4'-DICHLOROBENZOPHENONE ***PERCENT:*** 100
CAS# 90-98-2

OTHER CONTAMINANTS: NONE

EXPOSURE LIMITS: NO OCCUPATIONAL EXPOSURE LIMITS ESTABLISHED BY OSHA, ACGIH, OR NIOSH.

PHYSICAL DATA

DESCRIPTION: WHITE POWDER. ***BOILING POINT:*** 667 F (353 C)

MELTING POINT: 291-297 F (144-147 C) ***SOLUBILITY IN WATER:*** ALMOST INSOLUBLE

SOLVENT SOLUBILITY: SOLUBLE IN ACETONE, TOLUENE, METHANOL, ETHANOL, BENZENE.

FIRE AND EXPLOSION DATA

FIRE AND EXPLOSION HAZARD: SLIGHT FIRE HAZARD WHEN EXPOSED TO HEAT OR FLAME.

FIREFIGHTING MEDIA: DRY CHEMICAL, CARBON DIOXIDE, HALON, WATER SPRAY OR STANDARD FOAM (1987 EMERGENCY RESPONSE GUIDEBOOK, DOT P 5800.4).
FOR LARGER FIRES, USE WATER SPRAY, FOG OR STANDARD FOAM (1987 EMERGENCY RESPONSE GUIDEBOOK, DOT P 5800.4).

FIREFIGHTING: MOVE CONTAINERS FROM FIRE AREA IF POSSIBLE. FIGHT FIRE FROM MAXIMUM DISTANCE. STAY AWAY FROM STORAGE TANK ENDS. DIKE FIRE CONTROL WATER FOR LATER DISPOSAL. DO NOT SCATTER MATERIAL (1987 EMERGENCY RESPONSE GUIDEBOOK, DOT P 5800.4, GUIDE PAGE 55).
USE AGENTS SUITABLE FOR TYPE OF FIRE. COOL CONTAINERS WITH FLOODING AMOUNTS OF WATER. AVOID BREATHING VAPORS OR DUSTS, KEEP UPWIND.

TOXICITY

4,4'-DICHLOROBENZOPHENONE: TOXICITY DATA: 200 MG/KG INTRAPERITONEAL-MOUSE LD50. CARCINOGEN STATUS: NONE. ACUTE TOXICITY LEVEL: INSUFFICIENT DATA. TARGET EFFECTS: CONVULSANT. POISONING MAY AFFECT THE LIVER AND KIDNEY.* ADDITIONAL DATA: DDT METABOLITE. MAY CROSS THE PLACENTA AND BE EXCRETED IN BREAST MILK. MAY IMPAIR FERTILITY. STIMULANTS SUCH AS EPINEPHRINE OR EPHEDRINE MAY INDUCE VENTRICULAR FIBRILLATION.*
* MAY BE BASED ON GENERAL INFORMATION ON ORGANOCHLORINE COMPOUNDS.

HEALTH EFFECTS AND FIRST AID

INHALATION: 4,4'-DICHLOROBENZOPHENONE: **ACUTE EXPOSURE-** EFFECTS AS DESCRIBED FOR ORGANOCHLORINE PESTICIDES IN ACUTE INGESTION MAY OCCUR IF SUFFICIENT AMOUNTS ARE ABSORBED FROM THE LUNGS. **CHRONIC EXPOSURE-** A STUDY OF OCCUPATIONAL EXPOSURE TO DDT REPORTED A HIGHER FREQUENCY OF WHITE BLOOD CELLS WITH CHROMOSOMAL ABNORMALITIES AMONG WORKERS WITH HIGH DDT BLOOD LEVELS; ANOTHER STUDY REPORTED MENSTRUAL IRREGULARITIES AS THE MOST FREQUENT COMPLAINT AMONG MIGRANT FARM WORKERS. PROLONGED OR REPEATED EXPOSURE TO ORGANOCHLORINE PESTICIDES MAY CAUSE EFFECTS AS DESCRIBED IN ACUTE INGESTION.

FIRST AID- REMOVE FROM EXPOSURE AREA TO FRESH AIR IMMEDIATELY. IF BREATHING HAS STOPPED, PERFORM ARTIFICIAL RESPIRATION. KEEP PERSON WARM AND AT REST. TREAT SYMPTOMATICALLY AND SUPPORTIVELY. GET MEDICAL ATTENTION IMMEDIATELY.

SKIN CONTACT: 4,4'-DICHLOROBENZOPHENONE: **ACUTE EXPOSURE-** EFFECTS AS DESCRIBED FOR ORGANOCHLORINE PESTICIDES IN ACUTE INGESTION MAY OCCUR IF SUFFICIENT AMOUNTS ARE ABSORBED THROUGH THE SKIN. **CHRONIC EXPOSURE-** A STUDY OF OCCUPATIONAL EXPOSURE TO DDT REPORTED A HIGHER FREQUENCY OF WHITE BLOOD CELLS WITH CHROMOSOMAL ABNORMALITIES AMONG WORKERS WITH HIGH DDT BLOOD LEVELS; ANOTHER STUDY REPORTED MENSTRUAL IRREGULARITIES AS THE MOST FREQUENT COMPLAINT AMONG MIGRANT FARM WORKERS. PROLONGED OR REPEATED EXPOSURE TO ORGANOCHLORINE PESTICIDES MAY CAUSE EFFECTS AS DESCRIBED IN ACUTE INGESTION.

FIRST AID- REMOVE CONTAMINATED CLOTHING AND SHOES IMMEDIATELY. WASH AFFECTED AREA WITH SOAP OR MILD DETERGENT AND LARGE AMOUNTS OF WATER UNTIL NO EVIDENCE OF CHEMICAL REMAINS (APPROXIMATELY 15-20 MINUTES). GET MEDICAL ATTENTION IMMEDIATELY.

EYE CONTACT: 4,4'-DICHLOROBENZOPHENONE: **ACUTE EXPOSURE-** NO DATA AVAILABLE. **CHRONIC EXPOSURE-** NO DATA AVAILABLE.

FIRST AID- WASH EYES IMMEDIATELY WITH LARGE AMOUNTS OF WATER OR NORMAL SALINE, OCCASIONALLY LIFTING UPPER AND LOWER LIDS, UNTIL NO EVIDENCE OF CHEMICAL REMAINS (APPROXIMATELY 15-20 MINUTES). GET MEDICAL ATTENTION IMMEDIATELY.

INGESTION: 4,4'-DICHLOROBENZOPHENONE: **ACUTE EXPOSURE-** INGESTION OF ORGANOCHLORINE PESTICIDES MAY CAUSE GASTROINTESTINAL EFFECTS OF NAUSEA, VOMITING, DIARRHEA, AND STOMACH PAINS. OTHER SYMPTOMS OF CONFUSION, APPREHENSION, IRRITABILITY, EXCITABILITY, DIZZINESS, HEADACHE, DISORIENTATION, WEAKNESS, PARESTHESIAS, MUSCLE TWITCHING, TREMOR, STUPOR, COMA, AND CONVULSIONS MAY OCCUR. SIGNS OF LIVER AND KIDNEY DAMAGE MAY DEVELOP. DEATH MAY BE DUE TO RESPIRATORY FAILURE OR VENTRICULAR FIBRILLATION. SYMPTOMS OF POISONING MAY OCCUR SEVERAL HOURS AFTER INGESTION. **CHRONIC EXPOSURE-** REPEATED EXPOSURE TO ORGANOCHLORINE PESTICIDES MAY CAUSE EFFECTS AS DESCRIBED IN ACUTE EXPOSURE.

FIRST AID- TREAT SYMPTOMATICALLY AND SUPPORTIVELY. GET MEDICAL ATTENTION IMMEDIATELY. IF VOMITING OCCURS, KEEP HEAD LOWER THAN HIPS TO PREVENT ASPIRATION.

ANTIDOTE: NO SPECIFIC ANTIDOTE. TREAT SYMPTOMATICALLY AND SUPPORTIVELY.

REACTIVITY

REACTIVITY: STABLE UNDER NORMAL TEMPERATURES AND PRESSURES.

INCOMPATIBILITIES: 4,4'-DICHLOROBENZOPHENONE: NO DATA AVAILABLE.

DECOMPOSITION: THERMAL DECOMPOSITION PRODUCTS MAY INCLUDE TOXIC AND CORROSIVE FUMES OF CHLORIDES.

POLYMERIZATION: HAZARDOUS POLYMERIZATION HAS NOT BEEN REPORTED TO OCCUR UNDER NORMAL TEMPERATURES AND PRESSURES.

STORAGE AND DISPOSAL

OBSERVE ALL FEDERAL, STATE AND LOCAL REGULATIONS WHEN STORING OR DISPOSING OF THIS SUBSTANCE. FOR ASSISTANCE, CONTACT THE DISTRICT DIRECTOR OF THE ENVIRONMENTAL PROTECTION AGENCY.

CONDITIONS TO AVOID

MAY BURN BUT DOES NOT IGNITE READILY. CONTAINERS MAY EXPLODE IN HEAT OF FIRE.

SPILL AND LEAK PROCEDURES

OCCUPATIONAL SPILL: DO NOT TOUCH SPILLED MATERIAL. STOP LEAK IF YOU CAN DO IT WITHOUT RISK. USE WATER SPRAY TO REDUCE VAPORS. FOR SMALL SPILLS, TAKE UP WITH SAND OR OTHER ABSORBENT MATERIAL AND PLACE INTO CONTAINERS FOR LATER DISPOSAL. FOR SMALL DRY SPILLS, WITH A CLEAN SHOVEL PLACE MATERIAL INTO CLEAN, DRY CONTAINERS AND COVER. MOVE CONTAINERS FROM SPILL AREA. FOR LARGER SPILLS, DIKE FAR AHEAD OF SPILL FOR LATER DISPOSAL. KEEP UNNECESSARY PEOPLE AWAY. ISOLATE HAZARD AREA AND DENY ENTRY. VENTILATE CLOSED SPACES BEFORE ENTERING.

PROTECTIVE EQUIPMENT

VENTILATION: PROVIDE LOCAL EXHAUST OR PROCESS ENCLOSURE VENTILATION SYSTEM.

RESPIRATOR: THE FOLLOWING RESPIRATORS ARE RECOMMENDED BASED ON INFORMATION FOUND IN THE PHYSICAL DATA, TOXICITY AND HEALTH EFFECTS SECTIONS. THEY ARE RANKED IN ORDER FROM MINIMUM TO MAXIMUM RESPIRATORY PROTECTION. THE SPECIFIC RESPIRATOR SELECTED MUST BE BASED ON CONTAMINATION LEVELS FOUND IN THE WORK PLACE, MUST NOT EXCEED THE WORKING LIMITS OF THE RESPIRATOR AND BE JOINTLY APPROVED BY THE NATIONAL INSTITUTE FOR OCCUPATIONAL SAFETY AND HEALTH AND THE MINE SAFETY AND HEALTH ADMINISTRATION (NIOSH-MSHA).

DUST AND MIST RESPIRATOR WITH A FULL FACEPIECE.

AIR-PURIFYING FULL FACEPIECE RESPIRATOR WITH A HIGH-EFFICIENCY PARTICULATE FILTER.

POWERED AIR-PURIFYING RESPIRATOR WITH A TIGHT-FITTING FACEPIECE AND HIGH-EFFICIENCY PARTICULATE FILTER.

TYPE 'C' SUPPLIED-AIR RESPIRATOR WITH A FULL FACEPIECE OPERATED IN PRESSURE-DEMAND OR OTHER POSITIVE PRESSURE MODE OR WITH A FULL FACEPIECE, HELMET OR HOOD OPERATED IN CONTINUOUS-FLOW MODE.

SELF-CONTAINED BREATHING APPARATUS WITH A FULL FACEPIECE OPERATED IN PRESSURE-DEMAND OR OTHER POSITIVE PRESSURE MODE.

FOR FIREFIGHTING AND OTHER IMMEDIATELY DANGEROUS TO LIFE OR HEALTH CONDITIONS:

SELF-CONTAINED BREATHING APPARATUS WITH FULL FACEPIECE OPERATED IN PRESSURE-DEMAND OR OTHER POSITIVE PRESSURE MODE.

SUPPLIED-AIR RESPIRATOR WITH FULL FACEPIECE AND OPERATED IN PRESSURE-DEMAND OR OTHER POSITIVE PRESSURE MODE IN COMBINATION WITH AN AUXILIARY SELF-CONTAINED BREATHING APPARATUS OPERATED IN PRESSURE-DEMAND OR OTHER POSITIVE PRESSURE MODE.

CLOTHING: EMPLOYEE MUST WEAR APPROPRIATE PROTECTIVE (IMPERVIOUS) CLOTHING AND EQUIPMENT TO PREVENT REPEATED OR PROLONGED SKIN CONTACT WITH THIS SUBSTANCE.

GLOVES: EMPLOYEE MUST WEAR APPROPRIATE PROTECTIVE GLOVES TO PREVENT CONTACT WITH THIS SUBSTANCE.

EYE PROTECTION: EMPLOYEE MUST WEAR SPLASH-PROOF OR DUST-RESISTANT SAFETY GOGGLES TO PREVENT EYE CONTACT WITH THIS SUBSTANCE.

EMERGENCY EYE WASH: WHERE THERE IS ANY POSSIBILITY THAT AN EMPLOYEE'S EYES MAY BE EXPOSED TO THIS SUBSTANCE, THE EMPLOYER SHOULD PROVIDE AN EYE WASH FOUNTAIN WITHIN THE IMMEDIATE WORK AREA FOR EMERGENCY USE.

AUTHORIZED BY- OCCUPATIONAL HEALTH SERVICES, INC.

CREATION DATE: 10/05/89 ***REVISION DATE:*** 05/29/90

MATERIAL SAFETY DATA SHEET

OCCUPATIONAL HEALTH SERVICES, INC.
AGRICULTURE AND PESTICIDE DIVISION
450 SEVENTH AVENUE, SUITE 2407
NEW YORK, NEW YORK 10123
1-800-445-MSDS OR (212) 967-1100

EMERGENCY CONTACT:
JOHN S. BRANSFORD, JR. (615) 292-1180

SUBSTANCE IDENTIFICATION

CAS-NUMBER 72-55-9

SUBSTANCE: **2,2-BIS-(4-CHLOROPHENYL)-1,1-DICHLOROETHENE**

TRADE NAMES/SYNONYMS: ETHYLENE, 1,1-DICHLORO-2,2-BIS(P-CHLOROPHENYL)-; 1,1-DICHLORO-2,2-BIS(P-CHLOROPHENYL)ETHYLENE; BENZENE, 1,1'-(DICHLOROETHENYLIDENE)BIS(4-CHLORO-; 1,1'-(DICHLOROETHENYLIDENE)BIS(4-CHLORO-BENZENE); DICHLORODIPHENYLDICHLOROETHYLENE; P,P'-DDE; DDE; 4,4'-DDE; NCI-C00555; C14H8CL4; PST06247

CHEMICAL FAMILY: HALOGEN COMPOUND, AROMATIC

MOLECULAR FORMULA: CL-C6-H4-C-(C-CL2)-C6-H4-CL

MOLECULAR WEIGHT: 318.03

CERCLA RATINGS (SCALE 0-3): HEALTH=3 FIRE=1 REACTIVITY=0 PERSISTENCE=3

NFPA RATINGS (SCALE 0-4): HEALTH=U FIRE=1 REACTIVITY=0

COMPONENTS AND CONTAMINANTS

COMPONENT: 2,2-BIS(4-CHLOROPHENYL)-1,1-DICHLOROETHENE ***PERCENT:*** 100 CAS# 72-55-9

OTHER CONTAMINANTS: NONE

EXPOSURE LIMITS: NO OCCUPATIONAL EXPOSURE LIMITS ESTABLISHED BY OSHA, ACGIH, OR NIOSH.

2,2-BIS-(4-CHLOROPHENYL)-1,1-DICHLOROETHENE (4,4'-DDE): 1 POUND CERCLA SECTION 103 REPORTABLE QUANTITY SUBJECT TO CALIFORNIA PROPOSITION 65 CANCER AND/OR REPRODUCTIVE TOXICITY WARNING AND RELEASE REQUIREMENTS- (JANUARY 1, 1989)

PHYSICAL DATA

DESCRIPTION: WHITE CRYSTALLINE SOLID. ***MELTING POINT:*** 190-194 F (88-90 C)

SPECIFIC GRAVITY: NOT AVAILABLE ***VAPOR PRESSURE:*** NEGLIGIBLE

SOLUBILITY IN WATER: 0.12 PPM @ 25 C

SOLVENT SOLUBILITY: SOLUBLE IN ETHANOL, ACETONE, DICHLOROMETHANE, FAT, AND MOST ORGANIC SOLVENTS

FIRE AND EXPLOSION DATA

FIRE AND EXPLOSION HAZARD: SLIGHT FIRE HAZARD WHEN EXPOSED TO HEAT OR FLAME.

FIREFIGHTING MEDIA: DRY CHEMICAL, CARBON DIOXIDE, HALON, WATER SPRAY OR STANDARD FOAM (1987 EMERGENCY RESPONSE GUIDEBOOK, DOT P 5800.4).

FOR LARGER FIRES, USE WATER SPRAY, FOG OR STANDARD FOAM (1987 EMERGENCY RESPONSE GUIDEBOOK, DOT P 5800.4).

FIREFIGHTING: MOVE CONTAINERS FROM FIRE AREA IF POSSIBLE (1987 EMERGENCY RESPONSE GUIDEBOOK, DOT P 5800.4, GUIDE PAGE 53).

EXTINGUISH USING AGENT SUITABLE FOR TYPE OF SURROUNDING FIRE. AVOID BREATHING VAPORS AND DUSTS. KEEP UPWIND.

TOXICITY

2,2-BIS-(4-CHLOROPHENYL)-1,1-DICHLOROETHENE (4,4'-DDE): TOXICITY DATA: 880 MG/KG ORAL-RAT LD50; 700 MG/KG ORAL-MOUSE LD50; MUTAGENIC DATA (RTECS); REPRODUCTIVE EFFECTS DATA (RTECS); TUMORIGENIC DATA (RTECS). CARCINOGEN STATUS: NONE. A HIGH INCIDENCE OF LIVER-CELL TUMORS WAS OBSERVED IN MICE ADMINISTERED DDE ORALLY (IARC). ACUTE TOXCITY DATA: MODERATELY TOXIC BY INGESTION. TARGET EFFECTS: CONVULSANT. POISONING MAY AFFECT THE LIVER AND KIDNEYS.* ADDITIONAL DATA: DDT METABOLITE. MAY CROSS THE PLACENTA AND BE EXCRETED IN BREAST MILK. MAY IMPAIR FERTILITY. STIMULANTS SUCH AS EPINEPHRINE OR EPHEDRINE MAY INDUCE VENTRICULAR FIBRILLATION.*

* MAY BE BASED ON GENERAL INFORMATION ON ORGANOCHLORINE PESTICIDES.

HEALTH EFFECTS AND FIRST AID

INHALATION: 2,2-BIS-(4-CHLOROPHENYL)-1,1-DICHLOROETHENE (4,4'-DDE): **ACUTE EXPOSURE-** EFFECTS AS DESCRIBED FOR ORGANOCHLORINE PESTICIDES IN ACUTE INGESTION MAY OCCUR IF SUFFICIENT AMOUNTS ARE ABSORBED FROM THE LUNGS. **CHRONIC EXPOSURE-** A STUDY OF OCCUPATIONAL EXPOSURE TO DDT REPORTED A HIGHER FREQUENCY OF WHITE BLOOD CELLS WITH CHROMOSOMAL ABNORMALITIES AMONG WORKERS WITH HIGH DDT BLOOD LEVELS; MENSTRUAL IRREGULARITIES AS THE MOST FREQUENT COMPLAINT AMONG MIGRANT FARM WORKERS WERE OBSERVED IN ANOTHER STUDY. PROLONGED OR REPEATED EXPOSURE TO ORGANOCHLORINE PESTICIDES MAY CAUSE EFFECTS AS DESCRIBED IN ACUTE INGESTION.

FIRST AID- REMOVE FROM EXPOSURE AREA TO FRESH AIR IMMEDIATELY. IF BREATHING HAS STOPPED, PERFORM ARTIFICIAL RESPIRATION. KEEP PERSON WARM AND AT REST. TREAT SYMPTOMATICALLY AND SUPPORTIVELY. GET MEDICAL ATTENTION IMMEDIATELY.

SKIN CONTACT: 2,2-BIS-(4-CHLOROPHENYL)1,1-DICHLOROETHENE (4,4'-DDE): **ACUTE EXPOSURE-** EFFECTS AS DESCRIBED FOR ORGANOCHLORINE PESTICIDES IN ACUTE

INGESTION MAY OCCUR IF SUFFICIENT AMOUNTS ARE ABSORBED THROUGH THE THE SKIN. **CHRONIC EXPOSURE-** A STUDY OF OCCUPATIONAL EXPOSURE TO DDT REPORTED A HIGHER FREQUENCY OF WHITE BLOOD CELLS WITH CHROMOSOMAL ABNORMALITIES AMONG WORKERS WITH HIGH DDT BLOOD LEVELS; MENSTRUAL IRREGULARITIES AS THE MOST FREQUENT COMPLAINT AMONG MIGRANT FARM WORKERS WERE OBSERVED IN ANOTHER STUDY. PROLONGED OR REPEATED EXPOSURE TO ORGANOCHLORINE PESTICIDES MAY CAUSE EFFECTS AS DESCRIBED IN ACUTE INGESTION.

FIRST AID- REMOVE CONTAMINATED CLOTHING AND SHOES IMMEDIATELY. WASH AFFECTED AREA WITH SOAP OR MILD DETERGENT AND LARGE AMOUNTS OF WATER UNTIL NO EVIDENCE OF CHEMICAL REMAINS (APPROXIMATELY 15-20 MINUTES). GET MEDICAL ATTENTION IMMEDIATELY.

EYE CONTACT: 2,2-BIS-(4-CHLOROPHENYL)-1,1-DICHLOROETHENE (4,4'-DDE): **ACUTE EXPOSURE-** NO DATA AVAILABLE. **CHRONIC EXPOSURE-** NO DATA AVAILABLE.

FIRST AID- WASH EYES IMMEDIATELY WITH LARGE AMOUNTS OF WATER OR NORMAL SALINE, OCCASIONALLY LIFTING UPPER AND LOWER LIDS, UNTIL NO EVIDENCE OF CHEMICAL REMAINS (APPROXIMATELY 15-20 MINUTES). GET MEDICAL ATTENTION IMMEDIATELY.

INGESTION: 2,2-BIS-(4-CHLOROPHENYL)-1,1-DICHLOROETHENE (4,4'-DDE): **ACUTE EXPOSURE-** A LETHAL DOSE IN RATS WAS 880 MG/KG. INGESTION OF ORGANOCHLORINE PESTICIDES MAY CAUSE GASTROINTESTINAL EFFECTS OF NAUSEA, VOMITING, DIARRHEA, AND STOMACH PAINS. OTHER SYMPTOMS OF CONFUSION, APPREHENSION, IRRITABILITY, EXCITABILITY, DIZZINESS, HEADACHE, DISORIENTATION, WEAKNESS, PARESTHESIAS, MUSCLE TWITCHING, TREMOR, STUPOR, COMA, AND CONVULSIONS MAY OCCUR. SIGNS OF LIVER AND KIDNEY DAMAGE MAY DEVELOP. DEATH MAY BE DUE TO RESPIRATORY FAILURE OR VENTRICULAR FIBRILLATION. SYMPTOMS OF POISONING MAY OCCUR SEVERAL HOURS AFTER INGESTION. **CHRONIC EXPOSURE-** HEPATIC EFFECTS INCLUDING LIVER NECROSIS HAVE BEEN REPORTED IN EXPERIMENTAL ANIMALS. A HIGH INCIDENCE OF LIVER-CELL TUMORS WERE OBSERVED IN A STUDY OF MICE. REPEATED EXPOSURE TO ORGANOCHLORINE PESTICIDES MAY CAUSE EFFECTS AS DESCRIBED IN ACUTE EXPOSURE.

FIRST AID- IF THE PERSON IS CONSCIOUS AND NOT CONVULSING, REMOVE BY GIVING SYRUP OF IPECAC (IF VOMITING OCCURS, KEEP THE HEAD BELOW THE HIPS TO PREVENT ASPIRATION). GIVE ACTIVATED CHARCOAL FOLLOWED BY GASTRIC LAVAGE. FOLLOW WITH A SALINE CATHARTIC. DO NOT GIVE FATS OR OILS. INTESTINAL LAVAGE WITH 20% MANNITOL (200 ML) BY STOMACH TUBE IS ALSO USEFUL. GIVE ARTIFICIAL RESPIRATION WITH OXYGEN IF RESPIRATION IS DEPRESSED (DREISBACH, HANDBOOK OF POISONING, 12TH ED.). TREAT SYMPTOMATICALLY AND SUPPORTIVELY. LAVAGE AND ADMINISTRATION OF OXYGEN SHOULD BE PERFORMED BY QUALIFIED MEDICAL PERSONNEL. GET MEDICAL ATTENTION IMMEDIATELY.

ANTIDOTE: NO SPECIFIC ANTIDOTE. TREAT SYMPTOMATICALLY AND SUPPORTIVELY.

REACTIVITY

REACTIVITY: STABLE UNDER NORMAL TEMPERATURES AND PRESSURES.

INCOMPATIBILITIES: 2,2-BIS-(4-CHLOROPHENYL)1,1-DICHLOROETHENE (4,4'-DDE): OXIDIZERS (STRONG): FIRE AND EXPLOSION HAZARD.

DECOMPOSITION: THERMAL DECOMPOSITION PRODUCTS MAY INCLUDE TOXIC AND CORROSIVE FUMES OF CHLORIDES AND TOXIC OXIDES OF CARBON.

POLYMERIZATION: HAZARDOUS POLYMERIZATION HAS NOT BEEN REPORTED TO OCCUR UNDER NORMAL TEMPERATURES AND PRESSURES.

STORAGE AND DISPOSAL

OBSERVE ALL FEDERAL, STATE AND LOCAL REGULATIONS WHEN STORING OR DISPOSING OF THIS SUBSTANCE. FOR ASSISTANCE, CONTACT THE DISTRICT DIRECTOR OF THE ENVIRONMENTAL PROTECTION AGENCY.

STORAGE

STORE IN ACCORDANCE WITH 40 CFR 165 RECOMMENDED PROCEDURES FOR THE DISPOSAL AND STORAGE OF PESTICIDES AND PESTICIDE CONTAINERS.

STORE AWAY FROM INCOMPATIBLE SUBSTANCES.

DISPOSAL

DISPOSAL MUST BE IN ACCORDANCE WITH 40 CFR 165 RECOMMENDED PROCEDURES FOR THE DISPOSAL AND STORAGE OF PESTICIDES AND PESTICIDE CONTAINERS.

CONDITIONS TO AVOID

MAY BURN BUT DOES NOT IGNITE READILY.

SPILL AND LEAK PROCEDURES

SOIL SPILL: DIG A HOLDING AREA SUCH AS PIT, POND OR LAGOON TO CONTAIN SPILLED MATERIAL. USE PROTECTIVE COVER SUCH AS A PLASTIC SHEET TO PREVENT DISSOLVING IN FIREFIGHTING WATER OR RAIN.

WATER SPILL: USE NATURAL DEEP WATER POCKETS, EXCAVATED LAGOONS, OR SAND BAG BARRIERS TO TRAP MATERIAL AT BOTTOM. USE ACTIVATED CARBON AT 10 TIMES THE SPILLED AMOUNT IF IT IS DISSOLVED AT 10 PPM OR GREATER CONCENTRATION. REMOVE TRAPPED MATERIAL WITH SUCTION HOSES. USE MECHANICAL DREDGES OR LIFTS TO REMOVE IMMOBILIZED MASSES OF POLLUTION AND PRECIPITATES. THE CALIFORNIA SAFE DRINKING WATER AND TOXIC ENFORCEMENT ACT OF 1986 (PROPOSITION 65) PROHIBITS CONTAMINATING ANY KNOWN SOURCE OF DRINKING WATER WITH SUBSTANCES KNOWN TO CAUSE CANCER AND/OR REPRODUCTIVE TOXICITY.

OCCUPATIONAL SPILL: DO NOT TOUCH SPILLED MATERIAL. STOP LEAK IF YOU CAN DO IT WITHOUT RISK. USE WATER SPRAY TO REDUCE VAPORS. FOR SMALL SPILLS, TAKE UP WITH SAND OR OTHER ABSORBENT MATERIAL AND PLACE INTO CONTAINERS FOR LATER DISPOSAL. FOR SMALL DRY SPILLS, WITH A CLEAN SHOVEL PLACE MATERIAL INTO CLEAN, DRY CONTAINERS AND COVER. MOVE CONTAINERS FROM SPILL AREA. FOR LARGER SPILLS, DIKE FAR AHEAD OF SPILL FOR LATER DISPOSAL. KEEP UNNECESSARY PEOPLE AWAY. ISOLATE HAZARD AREA AND DENY ENTRY. VENTILATE CLOSED SPACES BEFORE ENTERING.

REPORTABLE QUANTITY (RQ): 1 POUND THE SUPERFUND AMENDMENTS AND REAUTHORIZATION ACT (SARA) SECTION 304 REQUIRES THAT A RELEASE EQUAL TO OR GREATER THAN THE REPORTABLE QUANTITY FOR THIS SUBSTANCE BE IMMEDIATELY REPORTED TO THE LOCAL EMERGENCY PLANNING COMMITTEE AND THE STATE EMERGENCY RESPONSE COMMISSION (40 CFR 355.40). IF THE RELEASE OF THIS SUBSTANCE IS REPORTABLE UNDER CERCLA SECTION 103, THE NATIONAL RESPONSE CENTER MUST BE NOTIFIED IMMEDIATELY AT (800) 424-8802 OR (202) 426-2675 IN THE METROPOLITAN WASHINGTON, D.C. AREA (40 CFR 302.6).

PROTECTIVE EQUIPMENT

VENTILATION: PROVIDE LOCAL EXHAUST OR GENERAL DILUTION VENTILATION SYSTEM.

RESPIRATOR: THE FOLLOWING RESPIRATORS ARE RECOMMENDED BASED ON INFORMATION FOUND IN THE PHYSICAL DATA, TOXICITY AND HEALTH EFFECTS SECTIONS. THEY ARE RANKED IN ORDER FROM MINIMUM TO MAXIMUM RESPIRATORY PROTECTION. THE SPECIFIC RESPIRATOR SELECTED MUST BE BASED ON CONTAMINATION LEVELS FOUND IN THE WORK PLACE, MUST NOT EXCEED THE WORKING LIMITS OF THE RESPIRATOR AND BE JOINTLY APPROVED BY THE NATIONAL INSTITUTE FOR OCCUPATIONAL SAFETY AND HEALTH AND THE MINE SAFETY AND HEALTH ADMINISTRATION (NIOSH-MSHA).

CHEMICAL CARTRIDGE RESPIRATOR WITH AN ORGANIC VAPOR CARTRIDGE(S) WITH A HIGH-EFFICIENCY PARTICULATE FILTER AND FULL FACEPIECE.

HIGH-EFFICIENCY PARTICULATE RESPIRATOR WITH A FULL FACEPIECE.

POWERED AIR-PURIFYING RESPIRATOR WITH A HIGH-EFFICIENCY FILTER WITH A FULL FACEPIECE.

TYPE 'C' SUPPLIED-AIR RESPIRATOR WITH A FULL FACEPIECE OPERATED IN PRESSURE-DEMAND OR OTHER POSITIVE PRESSURE MODE OR WITH A FULL FACEPIECE, HELMET OR HOOD OPERATED IN CONTINUOUS-FLOW MODE.

SELF-CONTAINED BREATHING APPARATUS WITH A FULL FACEPIECE OPERATED IN PRESSURE-DEMAND OR OTHER POSITIVE PRESSURE MODE.

FOR FIREFIGHTING AND OTHER IMMEDIATELY DANGEROUS TO LIFE OR HEALTH CONDITIONS:

SELF-CONTAINED BREATHING APPARATUS WITH FULL FACEPIECE OPERATED IN PRESSURE-DEMAND OR OTHER POSITIVE PRESSURE MODE.

SUPPLIED-AIR RESPIRATOR WITH FULL FACEPIECE AND OPERATED IN PRESSURE-DEMAND OR OTHER POSITIVE PRESSURE MODE IN COMBINATION WITH AN AUXILIARY SELF-CONTAINED BREATHING APPARATUS OPERATED IN PRESSURE-DEMAND OR OTHER POSITIVE PRESSURE MODE.

CLOTHING: EMPLOYEE MUST WEAR APPROPRIATE PROTECTIVE (IMPERVIOUS) CLOTHING AND EQUIPMENT TO PREVENT REPEATED OR PROLONGED SKIN CONTACT WITH THIS SUBSTANCE.

GLOVES: EMPLOYEE MUST WEAR APPROPRIATE PROTECTIVE GLOVES TO PREVENT CONTACT WITH THIS SUBSTANCE.

EYE PROTECTION: EMPLOYEE MUST WEAR SPLASH-PROOF OR DUST-RESISTANT SAFETY GOGGLES TO PREVENT EYE CONTACT WITH THIS SUBSTANCE.

EMERGENCY EYE WASH: WHERE THERE IS ANY POSSIBILITY THAT AN EMPLOYEE'S EYES MAY BE EXPOSED TO THIS SUBSTANCE, THE EMPLOYER SHOULD PROVIDE AN EYE WASH FOUNTAIN WITHIN THE IMMEDIATE WORK AREA FOR EMERGENCY USE.

AUTHORIZED BY- OCCUPATIONAL HEALTH SERVICES, INC.

CREATION DATE: 10/11/89 ***REVISION DATE:*** 03/20/90

MATERIAL SAFETY DATA SHEET

OCCUPATIONAL HEALTH SERVICES, INC.
AGRICULTURE AND PESTICIDE DIVISION
450 SEVENTH AVENUE, SUITE 2407
NEW YORK, NEW YORK 10123
1-800-445-MSDS OR (212) 967-1100

EMERGENCY CONTACT:
JOHN S. BRANSFORD, JR. (615) 292-1180

SUBSTANCE IDENTIFICATION

CAS-NUMBER 50-29-3

SUBSTANCE: **DICHLORODIPHENYLTRICHLOROETHANE**

TRADE NAMES/SYNONYMS: BENZENE, 1,1'-(2,2,2-TRICHLOROETHYLIDENE)BIS(4-CHLORO-; ETHANE, 1,1,1-TRICHLORO-2,2-BIS(P-CHLOROPHENY)-; 1,1'-(2,2,2-TRICHLOROETHYLIDENE)BIS(4-CHLOROBENZENE); 1,1,1-TRICHLORO-2,2-BIS(P-CHLOROPHENYL)ETHANE; 1,1,1-TRICHLORO-DI-(4-CHLOROPHENYL)ETHANE; ALPHA, ALPHA-BIS(P-CHLOROPHENYL)-BETA,BETA,BETA-TRICHLOROETHANE; CHLOROPHENOTHANE; DICOPHANE; PENTACHLORIN; DDT; P'P'-DDT; 4,4'-DDT; ARKOTINE; GESAROL; NEOCID; OMS 16; ENT 1506; RCRA U061; STCC 4941129; C14H9CL5; PST06250

CHEMICAL FAMILY: HALOGEN COMPOUND, AROMATIC

MOLECULAR FORMULA: (CL-C6-H4)2-C-H-C-CL3

MOLECULAR WEIGHT: 354.49

CERCLA RATINGS (SCALE 0-3): HEALTH=3 FIRE=1 REACTIVITY=0 PERSISTENCE=3

NFPA RATINGS (SCALE 0-4): HEALTH=3 FIRE=1 REACTIVITY=0

COMPONENTS AND CONTAMINANTS

COMPONENT: DICHLORODIPHENYLTRICHLOROETHANE ***PERCENT:*** 100
CAS# 50-29-3

EXPOSURE LIMITS: DICHLORODIPHENYLTRICHLOROETHANE (DDT): 1 MG/M3 OSHA TWA (SKIN) 1 MG/M3 ACGIH TWA LOWEST DETECTABLE LIMIT NIOSH RECOMMENDED EXPOSURE CRITERA 0.5 MG/M3 TWA BY NIOSH-VALIDATED METHOD
1 POUND CERCLA SECTION 103 REPORTABLE QUANTITY SUBJECT TO CALIFORNIA PROPOSITION 65 CANCER AND/OR REPRODUCTIVE TOXICITY WARNING AND RELEASE REQUIREMENTS- (OCTOBER 1, 1987)

PHYSICAL DATA

DESCRIPTION: TASTELESS, ALMOST ODORLESS, WHITE CRYSTALLINE SOLID.

BOILING POINT: 500 F (260 C) ***MELTING POINT:*** 225-228 F (107-109 C)

SPECIFIC GRAVITY: 1.56 @ 15 C ***VAPOR PRESSURE:*** NEGLIGIBLE

SOLUBILITY IN WATER: PRACTICALLY INSOL.

SOLVENT SOLUBILITY: SOLUBLE IN ACETONE, ETHER, PYRIDINE, KEROSENE, BENZENE, CARBON TETRACHLORIDE, DIOXANE, CHLOROFORM, MOST ORGANIC SOLVENTS; LIMITED SOLUBILITY IN ALIPHATIC OILS; INSOLUBLE IN DILUTE ACIDS, ALKALIES.

FIRE AND EXPLOSION DATA

FIRE AND EXPLOSION HAZARD: SLIGHT FIRE HAZARD WHEN EXPOSED TO HEAT OR FLAME.

FIREFIGHTING MEDIA: DRY CHEMICAL, CARBON DIOXIDE, HALON, WATER SPRAY OR STANDARD FOAM (1987 EMERGENCY RESPONSE GUIDEBOOK, DOT P 5800.4).
FOR LARGER FIRES, USE WATER SPRAY, FOG OR STANDARD FOAM (1987 EMERGENCY RESPONSE GUIDEBOOK, DOT P 5800.4).

FIREFIGHTING: MOVE CONTAINERS FROM FIRE AREA IF POSSIBLE. FIGHT FIRE FROM MAXIMUM DISTANCE. STAY AWAY FROM STORAGE TANK ENDS. DIKE FIRE CONTROL WATER FOR LATER DISPOSAL. DO NOT SCATTER MATERIAL (1987 EMERGENCY RESPONSE GUIDEBOOK, DOT P 5800.4, GUIDE PAGE 55).
USE AGENTS SUITABLE FOR TYPE OF FIRE. COOL CONTAINERS WITH FLOODING AMOUNTS OF WATER. AVOID BREATHING VAPORS OR DUSTS, KEEP UPWIND.

TRANSPORTATION DATA

DEPARTMENT OF TRANSPORTATION HAZARD CLASSIFICATION 49 CFR 172.101: ORM-A

DEPARTMENT OF TRANSPORTATION LABELING REQUIREMENTS 49 CFR 172.101 AND SUBPART E: NONE

DEPARTMENT OF TRANSPORTATION PACKAGING REQUIREMENTS: 49 CFR 173.510 EXCEPTIONS: 49 CFR 173.505

TOXICITY

DICHLORODIPHENYLTRICHLOROETHANE (DDT): TOXICITY DATA: 300 MG/KG SKIN-RABBIT LD50; 1931 MG/KG SKIN-RAT LD50; 1000 MG/KG SKIN-GUINEA PIG LD50; 5 MG/KG ORAL-HUMAN TDLO; 150 MG/KG ORAL-INFANT LDLO; 6 MG/KG ORAL-MAN TDLO; 500 MG/KG ORAL-HUMAN LDLO; 16 MG/KG ORAL-HUMAN TDLO; 87 MG/KG ORAL-RAT LD50; 135 MG/KG ORAL-MOUSE LD50; 150 MG/KG ORAL-DOG LD50; 250 MG/KG ORAL-RABBIT LD50; 150 MG/KG ORAL-GUINEA PIG LD50; 200 MG/KG ORAL-MONKEY LD50; 250 MG/KG ORAL-CAT LDLO; 300 MG/KG ORAL-DOMESTIC ANIMAL LDLO; 1500 MG/KG SUBCUTANEOUS-RAT LD50; 250 MG/KG SUBCUTANEOUS-RABBIT LD50; 900 MG/KG SUBCUTANEOUS-GUINEA PIG LD50; 68 MG/KG INTRAVENOUS-RAT LD50; 68,500 UG/KG INTRAVENOUS-MOUSE LD50; 50 MG/KG INTRAVENOUS-RABBIT LDLO; 50 MG/KG INTRAVENOUS-MONKEY LDLO; 75 MG/KG INTRAVENOUS-DOG LDLO; 9100 UG/KG INTRAPERITONEAL-RAT LD50; 32 MG/KG INTRAPERITONEAL-MOUSE LD50; 221 MG/KG UNREPORTED-MAN LDLO; MUTAGENIC DATA (RTECS); REPRODUCTIVE EFFECTS DATA (RTECS); TUMORIGENIC DATA (RTECS). CARCINOGEN STATUS: ANTICIPATED HUMAN CARCINOGEN (NTP); HUMAN INADEQUATE EVIDENCE, ANIMAL SUFFICIENT EVIDENCE (IARC GROUP-2B). ORAL ADMINISTRATION TO MICE PRODUCED BENIGN AND MALIGNANT LIVER NEOPLASMS AND LYMPHOMAS AND LUNG NEOPLASMS. ORAL ADMINISTRATION TO RATS CAUSED LIVER NEOPLASMS. DDT SLIGHTLY INCREASED THE INCIDENCE OF LIVER NEOPLASMS IN RATS PREVIOUSLY EXPOSED TO N-NITROSODIETHYLAMINE. HUMAN STUDIES WERE TOO LIMITED TO ALLOW ANY CONCLUSIONS TO BE MADE REGARDING CARCINOGENESIS. ACUTE TOXICITY LEVEL: TOXIC BY DERMAL ABSORPTION AND INGESTION. TARGET EFFECTS: CONVULSANT. POISONING MAY AFFECT THE PERIPHERAL NERVOUS SYSTEM AND THE LIVER. AT INCREASED RISK FROM EXPOSURE: PERSONS WITH DISEASES OF THE NERVOUS SYSTEM, LIVER OR BLOOD. ADDITIONAL DATA: ORGANIC SOLVENTS MAY DECREASE THE CONVULSIVE EFFECTS OF DDT AND INCREASE THE TOXICITY. DDT MAY CROSS THE PLACENTA AND BE EXCRETED IN HUMAN MILK. STIMULANTS SUCH AS EPINEPHRINE OR EPHEDRINE MAY INDUCE VENTRICULAR FIBRILLATION.

HEALTH EFFECTS AND FIRST AID

INHALATION: DICHLORODIPHENYLTRICHLOROETHANE (DDT): **ACUTE EXPOSURE-** IF SUFFICIENT AMOUNTS OF DUST AND AEROSOL PARTICLES ARE ABSORBED THROUGH THE LUNGS, SYSTEMIC EFFECTS AS DESCRIBED IN ACUTE INGESTION MAY OCCUR. **CHRONIC EXPOSURE-** REPEATED OR PROLONGED EXPOSURE MAY CAUSE IRRITATION OF THE NOSE, THROAT, AND MUCOUS MEMBRANES. PROLONGED OR REPEATED EXPOSURE MAY CAUSE EFFECTS AS DESCRIBED IN CHRONIC INGESTION. LIVER BIOPSY OF 8 WORKERS EXPOSED TO BHC, DDT OR BOTH FOR 5-13 YEARS REVEALED CHRONIC LIVER DAMAGE INCLUDING CIRRHOSIS AND CHRONIC HEPATITIS.

FIRST AID- REMOVE FROM EXPOSURE AREA TO FRESH AIR IMMEDIATELY. IF BREATHING HAS STOPPED, PERFORM ARTIFICIAL RESPIRATION. KEEP PERSON WARM AND AT REST. TREAT SYMPTOMATICALLY AND SUPPORTIVELY. GET MEDICAL ATTENTION IMMEDIATELY.

SKIN CONTACT: DICHLORODIPHENYLTRICHLOROETHANE (DDT): TOXIC. **ACUTE EXPOSURE-** NO IRRITATION WAS OBSERVED IN SEVERAL STUDIES OF HUMAN DERMAL EXPOSURE TO DDT. THE REPORTS OF IRRITATION AND ALLERGIC DERMATITIS FROM EXPOSURE TO DDT ARE DUE TO THE MATERIALS USED IN THE FORMULATION OF DDT. IF SUFFICIENT AMOUNTS ARE ABSORBED THROUGH THE SKIN, EFFECTS AS DESCRIBED IN ACUTE INGESTION MAY OCCUR. **CHRONIC EXPOSURE-** PROLONGED OR REPEATED EXPOSURE MAY CAUSE EFFECTS AS DESCRIBED IN CHRONIC INGESTION.

FIRST AID- REMOVE CONTAMINATED CLOTHING AND SHOES IMMEDIATELY. WASH AFFECTED AREA WITH SOAP OR MILD DETERGENT AND LARGE AMOUNTS OF WATER UNTIL NO EVIDENCE OF CHEMICAL REMAINS (APPROXIMATELY 15-20 MINUTES). GET MEDICAL ATTENTION IMMEDIATELY.

EYE CONTACT: DICHLORODIPHENYLTRICHLOROETHANE (DDT): **ACUTE EXPOSURE-** A CONCENTRATION OF 0.01% OF DDT DISSOLVED IN KEROSENE DID NOT PRODUCED IRRITATION WHEN APPLIED TO A HUMAN EYE; NO IRRITATION WAS OBSERVED WHEN A CONCENTRATION OF 4% WAS APPLIED TO RABBIT EYES. **CHRONIC EXPOSURE-** EYE IRRITATION WAS EXPERIENCED BY VOLUNTEERS WHO WERE EXPOSED TO 423 MG/M3 FOR ONE HOUR A DAY FOR SIX DAYS.

FIRST AID- WASH EYES IMMEDIATELY WITH LARGE AMOUNTS OF WATER OR NORMAL SALINE, OCCASIONALLY LIFTING UPPER AND LOWER LIDS, UNTIL NO EVIDENCE OF CHEMICAL REMAINS (APPROXIMATELY 15-20 MINUTES). GET MEDICAL ATTENTION IMMEDIATELY.

INGESTION: DICHLORODIPHENYLTRICHLOROETHANE (DDT): CONVULSANT/CARCINOGEN/TOXIC. **ACUTE EXPOSURE-** EFFECTS OF POISONING MAY BE DELAYED FOR SEVERAL HOURS AND ARE CHARACTERIZED BY PARESTHESIAS OF THE TONGUE, LIPS, AND FACE FOLLOWED BY TREMOR, A SENSE OF APPREHENSION, DIZZINESS, CONFUSION, MALAISE, HEADACHE, FATIGUE, WEAKNESS, ATAXIA, NYSTAGMUS, INCREASED RESPIRATION, AND HYPEREXCITABILITY. INGESTION OF VERY LARGE DOSES MAY INDUCE PROMPT VOMITING WITH NAUSEA AND DIARRHEA. CONVULSIONS MAY ALTERNATE WITH PERIODS OF COMA AND PARTIAL PARALYSIS. DEATH IS DUE TO RESPIRATORY FAILURE FROM MEDULLARY PARALYSIS. COMPLETE RECOVERY FROM SUBLETHAL DOSES MAY OCCUR WITHIN 1 TO 3 DAYS, HOWEVER, CASES OF WEAKNESS, PARALYSIS AND ATAXIA WERE REPORTED TO HAVE PERSISTED FOR WEEKS. PALPITATIONS, TACHYCARDIA, AND "IRREGULAR HEART ACTION" HAVE BEEN NOTED IN SOME CASES OF ACUTE POISONING. DDT HAS BEEN IMPLICATED IN THE DEVELOPMENT OF APLASTIC ANEMIA, AGRANULOCYTOSIS, AND THROMBOCYTOPENIA. THE OCCURRENCE OF PULMONARY EDEMA MAY INDICATE

THE INVOLVEMENT OF A SOLVENT. AN ACUTE DOSE OF 50 MG/KG IN MALE RATS PRODUCED ADVERSE EFFECTS ON FERTILITY. **CHRONIC EXPOSURE-** IN ADDITION TO THE SYMPTOMS LISTED ABOVE, CHRONIC INTOXICATION MAY CAUSE LOSS OF WEIGHT, ANOREXIA, MILD ANEMIA, ANXIETY, NERVOUS TENSION, FEAR, AND MYOCLONIC JERKS. CHRONIC ADMINISTRATION TO ANIMALS HAS PRODUCED NECROSIS OF THE LIVER AND CARDIAC AND SKELETAL MUSCLES, DEGENERATION OF THE KIDNEYS, AND EFFECTS ON THE IMMUNE SYSTEM. ORAL ADMINISTRATION TO MICE PRODUCED BENIGN AND MALIGNANT LIVER NEOPLASMS AND LYMPHOMAS AND LUNG NEOPLASMS. ORAL ADMINISTRATION TO RATS CAUSED LIVER NEOPLASMS. IN RATS PREVIOUSLY EXPOSED TO N-NITROSODIETHYLAMINE, DDT SLIGHTLY INCREASED THE INCIDENCE OF LIVER TUMORS. ADVERSE EFFECTS ON THE REPRODUCTIVE SYSTEM, FERTILITY, THE FETUS, AND FETAL DEVELOPMENTAL ABNORMALITIES WERE REPORTED FROM STUDIES OF MALE AND FEMALE RATS.

FIRST AID- IF THE PERSON IS CONSCIOUS AND NOT CONVULSING, REMOVE BY GIVING SYRUP OF IPECAC (IF VOMITING OCCURS, KEEP THE HEAD BELOW THE HIPS TO PREVENT ASPIRATION). GIVE ACTIVATED CHARCOAL FOLLOWED BY GASTRIC LAVAGE. FOLLOW WITH A SALINE CATHARTIC. DO NOT GIVE FATS OR OILS. INTESTINAL LAVAGE WITH 20% MANNITOL (200 ML) BY STOMACH TUBE IS ALSO USEFUL. GIVE ARTIFICIAL RESPIRATION WITH OXYGEN IF RESPIRATION IS DEPRESSED (DREISBACH, HANDBOOK OF POISONING, 12TH ED.). TREAT SYMPTOMATICALLY AND SUPPORTIVELY. LAVAGE AND ADMINISTRATION OF OXYGEN SHOULD BE PERFORMED BY QUALIFIED MEDICAL PERSONNEL. GET MEDICAL ATTENTION IMMEDIATELY.

ANTIDOTE: NO SPECIFIC ANTIDOTE. TREAT SYMPTOMATICALLY AND SUPPORTIVELY.

REACTIVITY

REACTIVITY: STABLE UNDER NORMAL TEMPERATURES AND PRESSURES.

INCOMPATIBILITIES: DICHLORODIPHENYLTRICHLOROETHANE (DDT): ALKALIES: MAY CAUSE DECOMPOSITION. ALKALOID NICOTINE: MAY CAUSE DECOMPOSITION. ALUMINUM SALTS: INCOMPATIBLE. BORDEAU MIXTURE: MAY CAUSE DECOMPOSITION. CLAY: MAY CAUSE DECOMPOSITION. DOLOMITE: MAY CAUSE DECOMPOSITION. FERBAM: MAY CAUSE DECOMPOSITION. IRON: INCOMPATIBLE. OXIDIZER (STRONG): MAY CAUSE FIRE AND EXPLOSION HAZARD.

DECOMPOSITION: THERMAL DECOMPOSITION PRODUCTS MAY INCLUDE TOXIC AND CORROSIVE FUMES OF CHLORIDES AND TOXIC OXIDES OF CARBON.

POLYMERIZATION: HAZARDOUS POLYMERIZATION HAS NOT BEEN REPORTED TO OCCUR UNDER NORMAL TEMPERATURES AND PRESSURES.

STORAGE AND DISPOSAL

OBSERVE ALL FEDERAL, STATE AND LOCAL REGULATIONS WHEN STORING OR DISPOSING OF THIS SUBSTANCE. FOR ASSISTANCE, CONTACT THE DISTRICT DIRECTOR OF THE ENVIRONMENTAL PROTECTION AGENCY.

****STORAGE****

STORE IN ACCORDANCE WITH 40 CFR 165 RECOMMENDED PROCEDURES FOR THE DISPOSAL AND STORAGE OF PESTICIDES AND PESTICIDE CONTAINERS.
STORE AWAY FROM INCOMPATIBLE SUBSTANCES.

****DISPOSAL****

DISPOSAL MUST BE IN ACCORDANCE WITH STANDARDS APPLICABLE TO GENERATORS OF HAZARDOUS WASTE, 40CFR 262. EPA HAZARDOUS WASTE NUMBER U061.

CONDITIONS TO AVOID

MAY BURN BUT DOES NOT IGNITE READILY. CONTAINERS MAY EXPLODE IN HEAT OF FIRE.

SPILL AND LEAK PROCEDURES

SOIL SPILL: DIG HOLDING AREA SUCH AS LAGOON, POND OR PIT FOR CONTAINMENT. USE PROTECTIVE COVER SUCH AS A PLASTIC SHEET TO PREVENT MATERIAL FROM DISSOLVING IN FIRE EXTINGUISHING WATER OR RAIN.

WATER SPILL: TRAP SPILLED MATERIAL AT BOTTOM IN DEEP WATER POCKETS, EXCAVATED HOLDING AREAS OR WITHIN SAND BAG BARRIERS.
USE ACTIVATED CARBON TO ABSORB SPILLED SUBSTANCE THAT IS DISSOLVED.
USE SUCTION HOSES TO REMOVE TRAPPED SPILL MATERIAL.
USE MECHANICAL DREDGES OR LIFTS TO EXTRACT IMMOBILIZED MASSES OF POLLUTION AND PRECIPITATES.
THE CALIFORNIA SAFE DRINKING WATER AND TOXIC ENFORCEMENT ACT OF 1986 (PROPOSITION 65) PROHIBITS CONTAMINATING ANY KNOWN SOURCE OF DRINKING WATER WITH SUBSTANCES KNOWN TO CAUSE CANCER AND/OR REPRODUCTIVE TOXICITY.

OCCUPATIONAL SPILL: DO NOT TOUCH SPILLED MATERIAL. STOP LEAK IF YOU CAN DO IT WITHOUT RISK. USE WATER SPRAY TO REDUCE VAPORS. FOR SMALL SPILLS, TAKE UP WITH SAND OR OTHER ABSORBENT MATERIAL AND PLACE INTO CONTAINERS FOR LATER DISPOSAL. FOR SMALL DRY SPILLS, WITH A CLEAN SHOVEL PLACE MATERIAL INTO CLEAN, DRY CONTAINERS AND COVER. MOVE CONTAINERS FROM SPILL AREA. FOR LARGER SPILLS, DIKE FAR AHEAD OF SPILL FOR LATER DISPOSAL. KEEP UNNECESSARY PEOPLE AWAY. ISOLATE HAZARD AREA AND DENY ENTRY. VENTILATE CLOSED SPACES BEFORE ENTERING.
REPORTABLE QUANTITY (RQ): 1 POUND THE SUPERFUND AMENDMENTS AND REAUTHORIZATION ACT (SARA) SECTION 304 REQUIRES THAT A RELEASE EQUAL TO OR GREATER THAN THE REPORTABLE QUANTITY FOR THIS SUBSTANCE BE IMMEDIATELY REPORTED TO THE LOCAL EMERGENCY PLANNING COMMITTEE AND THE STATE EMERGENCY RESPONSE COMMISSION (40 CFR 355.40). IF THE RELEASE OF THIS SUBSTANCE IS REPORTABLE UNDER CERCLA SECTION 103, THE NATIONAL RESPONSE CENTER MUST BE NOTIFIED IMMEDIATELY AT (800) 424-8802 OR (202) 426-2675 IN THE METROPOLITAN WASHINGTON, D.C. AREA (40 CFR 302.6).

PROTECTIVE EQUIPMENT

VENTILATION: PROVIDE LOCAL EXHAUST OR PROCESS ENCLOSURE VENTILATION TO MEET PUBLISHED EXPOSURE LIMITS.

RESPIRATOR: THE FOLLOWING RESPIRATORS AND MAXIMUM USE CONCENTRATIONS ARE RECOMMENDATIONS BY THE U.S. DEPARTMENT OF HEALTH AND HUMAN SERVICES, NIOSH POCKET GUIDE TO CHEMICAL HAZARDS; NIOSH CRITERIA DOCUMENTS OR BY THE U.S. DEPARTMENT OF LABOR, 29 CFR 1910 SUBPART Z. THE SPECIFIC RESPIRATOR SELECTED MUST BE BASED ON CONTAMINATION LEVELS FOUND IN THE WORK PLACE, MUST NOT EXCEED THE WORKING LIMITS OF THE RESPIRATOR AND BE JOINTLY APPROVED BY THE NATIONAL INSTITUTE FOR OCCUPATIONAL SAFETY AND HEALTH AND THE MINE SAFETY AND HEALTH ADMINISTRATION (NIOSH-MSHA).
DICHLORODIPHENYLTRICHLOROETHANE:
AT ANY DETECTABLE CONCENTRATION:
SELF-CONTAINED BREATHING APPARATUS WITH FULL FACEPIECE OPERATED IN PRESSURE-DEMAND OR OTHER POSITIVE PRESSURE MODE. SUPPLIED-AIR RESPIRATOR WITH FULL FACEPIECE OPERATED IN PRESSURE-DEMAND OR OTHER POSITIVE PRESSURE MODE IN COMBINATION WITH AN AUXILIARY SELF-CONTAINED BREATHING APPARATUS OPERATED IN PRESSURE-DEMAND OR OTHER POSITIVE PRESSURE MODE.
ESCAPE- AIR-PURIFYING FULL FACEPIECE RESPIRATOR (GAS MASK) WITH A CHIN-STYLE OR FRONT- OR BACK- MOUNTED ORGANIC VAPOR CANISTER HAVING A HIGH-EFFICIENCY PARTICULATE FILTER. ESCAPE-TYPE SELF-CONTAINED BREATHING APPARATUS.
FOR FIREFIGHTING AND OTHER IMMEDIATELY DANGEROUS TO LIFE OR HEALTH CONDITIONS:
SELF-CONTAINED BREATHING APPARATUS WITH FULL FACEPIECE OPERATED IN PRESSURE-DEMAND OR OTHER POSITIVE PRESSURE MODE.
SUPPLIED-AIR RESPIRATOR WITH FULL FACEPIECE AND OPERATED IN PRESSURE-DEMAND OR OTHER POSITIVE PRESSURE MODE IN COMBINATION WITH AN AUXILIARY SELF-CONTAINED BREATHING APPARATUS OPERATED IN PRESSURE-DEMAND OR OTHER POSITIVE PRESSURE MODE.

CLOTHING: EMPLOYEE MUST WEAR APPROPRIATE PROTECTIVE (IMPERVIOUS) CLOTHING AND EQUIPMENT TO PREVENT ANY POSSIBILITY OF SKIN CONTACT WITH THIS SUBSTANCE.

GLOVES: EMPLOYEE MUST WEAR APPROPRIATE PROTECTIVE GLOVES TO PREVENT CONTACT WITH THIS SUBSTANCE.

EYE PROTECTION: EMPLOYEE MUST WEAR SPLASH-PROOF OR DUST-RESISTANT SAFETY GOGGLES AND A FACESHIELD TO PREVENT CONTACT WITH THIS SUBSTANCE.
EMERGENCY WASH FACILITIES: WHERE THERE IS ANY POSSIBILITY THAT AN EMPLOYEE'S EYES AND/OR SKIN MAY BE EXPOSED TO THIS SUBSTANCE, THE EMPLOYER SHOULD PROVIDE AN EYE WASH FOUNTAIN AND QUICK DRENCH SHOWER WITHIN THE IMMEDIATE WORK AREA FOR EMERGENCY USE.

AUTHORIZED BY- OCCUPATIONAL HEALTH SERVICES, INC.
CREATION DATE: 10/04/89 ***REVISION DATE:*** 07/12/90

MATERIAL SAFETY DATA SHEET

OCCUPATIONAL HEALTH SERVICES, INC.
AGRICULTURE AND PESTICIDE DIVISION
450 SEVENTH AVENUE, SUITE 2407
NEW YORK, NEW YORK 10123
1-800-445-MSDS OR (212) 967-1100

EMERGENCY CONTACT:
JOHN S. BRANSFORD, JR. (615) 292-1180

SUBSTANCE IDENTIFICATION

CAS-NUMBER 112-30-1
SUBSTANCE: DECYL ALCOHOL

TRADE NAMES/SYNONYMS: 1-DECANOL; ALFOL 10; ANTAK; CAPRIC ALCOHOL; CAPRINIC ALCOHOL; DECANOL; N-DECYL ALCOHOL; EPAL 10; N-DECANOL; NONYLCARBINOL; SIPOL L 10; T 148; AGENT 504; ALCOHOL C-10; C 10 ALCOHOL; N-DECATYL ALCOHOL; DECYLIC ALCOHOL; PRIMARY DECYL ALCOHOL; DYTOL S-91; C10H22O; PST06285
CHEMICAL FAMILY: HYDROXYL, ALIPHATIC
MOLECULAR FORMULA: C-H3-(C-H2)8-C-H2-O-H
MOLECULAR WEIGHT: 158.32
CERCLA RATINGS (SCALE 0-3): HEALTH=3 FIRE=1 REACTIVITY=0 PERSISTENCE=0
NFPA RATINGS (SCALE 0-4): HEALTH=0 FIRE=2 REACTIVITY=0

COMPONENTS AND CONTAMINANTS

COMPONENT: DECYL ALCOHOL ***PERCENT:*** 100
CAS# 112-30-1
OTHER CONTAMINANTS: NONE
EXPOSURE LIMITS: NO OCCUPATIONAL EXPOSURE LIMITS ESTABLISHED BY OSHA, ACGIH, OR NIOSH.

PHYSICAL DATA

DESCRIPTION: COLORLESS, WATER-WHITE LIQUID WITH A SWEET ODOR.
BOILING POINT: 444 F (229 C) ***MELTING POINT:*** 45 F (7 C)
SPECIFIC GRAVITY: 0.8297 ***VAPOR PRESSURE:*** <1 MMHG @ 20 C
EVAPORATION RATE: NOT AVAILABLE ***SOLUBILITY IN WATER:*** INSOLUBLE
VAPOR DENSITY: 5.45
SOLVENT SOLUBILITY: SOLUBLE IN ALCOHOL, ETHER, ACETONE, BENZENE, CHLOROFORM

FIRE AND EXPLOSION DATA

FIRE AND EXPLOSION HAZARD: MODERATE FIRE HAZARD WHEN EXPOSED TO HEAT OR FLAME.
VAPORS ARE HEAVIER THAN AIR AND MAY TRAVEL A CONSIDERABLE DISTANCE TO A SOURCE OF IGNITION AND FLASH BACK.
VAPOR-AIR MIXTURES ARE EXPLOSIVE ABOVE FLASH POINT.
FLASH POINT: 180 F (82 C) (OC) ***UPPER EXPLOSIVE LIMIT:*** 8%
LOWER EXPLOSIVE LIMIT: 1% ***AUTOIGNITION TEMP.:*** 550 F (288 C)
FLAMMABILITY CLASS(OSHA): IIIB
FIREFIGHTING MEDIA: DRY CHEMICAL, CARBON DIOXIDE, HALON, WATER SPRAY OR STANDARD FOAM (1987 EMERGENCY RESPONSE GUIDEBOOK, DOT P 5800.4).
FOR LARGER FIRES, USE WATER SPRAY, FOG OR STANDARD FOAM (1987 EMERGENCY RESPONSE GUIDEBOOK, DOT P 5800.4).
FIREFIGHTING: MOVE CONTAINER FROM FIRE AREA IF POSSIBLE. COOL FIRE-EXPOSED CONTAINERS WITH WATER FROM SIDE UNTIL WELL AFTER FIRE IS OUT. STAY AWAY FROM STORAGE TANK ENDS. FOR MASSIVE FIRE IN STORAGE AREA, USE UNMANNED HOSE HOLDER OR MONITOR NOZZLES, ELSE WITHDRAW FROM AREA AND LET FIRE BURN. WITHDRAW IMMEDIATELY IN CASE OF RISING SOUND FROM VENTING SAFETY DEVICE OR ANY DISCOLORATION OF STORAGE TANK DUE TO FIRE (1987 EMERGENCY RESPONSE GUIDEBOOK, DOT P 5800.4, GUIDE PAGE 27). EXTINGUISH ONLY IF FLOW CAN BE STOPPED; USE FLOODING AMOUNTS OF WATER AS A FOG, SOLID STREAMS MAY BE INEFFECTIVE. COOL CONTAINERS WITH FLOODING AMOUNTS OF WATER, APPLY FROM AS FAR A DISTANCE AS POSSIBLE. AVOID BREATHING VAPORS, KEEP UPWIND.

TOXICITY

DECYL ALCOHOL: IRRITATION DATA: 75 MG/3 DAYS INTERMITTENT SKIN-HUMAN SEVERE; 2600 MG/KG/24 HOURS SKIN-RABBIT MODERATE; 20 MG/24 HOURS SKIN-RABBIT MODERATE; 83 MG EYE-RABBIT SEVERE; 500 MG/24 HOURS EYE-RABBIT MILD. TOXICITY DATA: 3 GM/M3 INHALATION-MAMMAL LC50; 4 GM/M3/2 HOURS INHALATION-MOUSE LC50; 3560 MG/KG SKIN-RABBIT LD50; 4720 MG/KG ORAL-RAT LD50; 6500 MG/KG ORAL-MOUSE LD50; 800 MG/KG INTRAPERITONEAL-RAT LD50; 800 MG/KG INTRAPERITONEAL-MOUSE LD50; 26 MG/KG UNREPORTED-MAMMAL LD50; TUMORIGENIC DATA (RTECS). CARCINOGEN STATUS: NONE. LOCAL EFFECTS: IRRITANT- INHALATION, SKIN, AND EYES. ACUTE TOXICITY LEVEL: TOXIC BY INHALATION; MODERATELY TOXIC BY INGESTION; SLIGHTLY TOXIC BY DERMAL ABSORPTION. TARGET EFFECTS: CENTRAL NERVOUS SYSTEM DEPRESSANT.

HEALTH EFFECTS AND FIRST AID

INHALATION: DECYL ALCOHOL: TOXIC. **ACUTE EXPOSURE-** EXPOSURE TO 95 PPM FOR 6 HOURS RESULTED IN IRRITATION OF THE RESPIRATORY TRACT IN MICE, RATS, AND GUINEA PIGS. INHALATION OF VAPORS OF HIGHER ALCOHOLS MAY CAUSE IRRITATION OF MUCOUS MEMBRANES, COUGH, DYSPNEA, AND PULMONARY INJURY. CENTRAL NERVOUS SYSTEM EFFECTS MAY INCLUDE HEADACHE, SLEEPINESS, MUSCLE WEAKNESS, GIDDINESS, CONFUSION, DELIRIUM, AND COMA. **CHRONIC EXPOSURE-** NO DATA AVAILABLE.
FIRST AID- REMOVE FROM EXPOSURE AREA TO FRESH AIR IMMEDIATELY. IF BREATHING HAS STOPPED, PERFORM ARTIFICIAL RESPIRATION. KEEP PERSON WARM AND AT REST. TREAT SYMPTOMATICALLY AND SUPPORTIVELY. GET MEDICAL ATTENTION IMMEDIATELY.

SKIN CONTACT: DECYL ALCOHOL: **ACUTE EXPOSURE-** DIRECT CONTACT WITH LIQUID MAY CAUSE IRRITATION. EXPOSURE TO 20 MG FOR 24 HOURS RESULTED IN MODERATE IRRITATION IN RABBITS. **CHRONIC EXPOSURE-** REPEATED OR PROLONGED CONTACT MAY CAUSE DEFATTING OF THE SKIN AND DERMATITIS. EXPOSURE TO 75 MG INTERMITTENTLY FOR 3 DAYS RESULTED IN SEVERE IRRITATION IN HUMANS. DECYL ALCOHOL DEMONSTRATED A WEAK TUMOR-PROMOTING ACTIVITY WHEN APPLIED 3 TIMES WEEKLY FOR 60 WEEKS TO THE SKIN OF MICE PREVIOUSLY TREATED WITH DIMETHYLBENZANTHRACENE.
FIRST AID- REMOVE CONTAMINATED CLOTHING AND SHOES IMMEDIATELY. WASH AFFECTED AREA WITH SOAP OR MILD DETERGENT AND LARGE AMOUNTS OF WATER UNTIL NO EVIDENCE OF CHEMICAL REMAINS (APPROXIMATELY 15-20 MINUTES). GET MEDICAL ATTENTION IMMEDIATELY.

EYE CONTACT: DECYL ALCOHOL: **ACUTE EXPOSURE-** DIRECT CONTACT WITH LIQUID MAY CAUSE IRRITATION. EXPOSURE TO 83 MG RESULTED IN SEVERE IRRITATION IN RABBITS. EXPOSURE TO SOME DECYL ALCOHOLS CAUSED SEVERE IRRITATION TO THE CONJUNCTIVAL MEMBRANES WITH CORNEAL INJURY IN RABBITS. **CHRONIC EXPOSURE-** REPEATED OR PROLONGED EXPOSURE MAY CAUSE CONJUNCTIVITIS.
FIRST AID- WASH EYES IMMEDIATELY WITH LARGE AMOUNTS OF WATER OR NORMAL SALINE, OCCASIONALLY LIFTING UPPER AND LOWER LIDS, UNTIL NO EVIDENCE OF CHEMICAL REMAINS (APPROXIMATELY 15-20 MINUTES). GET MEDICAL ATTENTION IMMEDIATELY.

INGESTION: DECYL ALCOHOL: **ACUTE EXPOSURE-** ASPIRATION INTO THE TRACHEOBRONCHIAL TREE OF RATS RESULTED IN RAPID DEATH BY RESPIRATORY ARREST. INGESTION OF SOME HIGHER ALCOHOLS MAY CAUSE GASTROINTESTINAL DISTURBANCES WITH NAUSEA, VOMITING, DIARRHEA, ANOREXIA, AND AN ODOR OF ALCOHOL IN EXCRETA. CENTRAL NERVOUS SYSTEM EFFECTS MAY INCLUDE HEADACHE, MUSCLE WEAKNESS, GIDDINESS, CONFUSION, DELIRIUM, AND COMA. OCCASIONAL COMPLICATIONS MAY INCLUDE PULMONARY EDEMA AND LIVER AND KIDNEY INJURY. DEATH MAY OCCUR DUE TO RESPIRATORY FAILURE OR CARDIAC ARRHYTHMIAS. **CHRONIC EXPOSURE-** NO DATA AVAILABLE.
FIRST AID- REMOVE INGESTED MATERIAL BY GASTRIC LAVAGE OR EMESIS. GIVE ARTIFICIAL RESPIRATION WITH OXYGEN IF RESPIRATION IS DEPRESSED. (DREISBACH HANDBOOK OF POISONING, 11TH ED.). GET MEDICAL ATTENTION IMMEDIATELY. ADMINISTRATION OF GASTRIC LAVAGE SHOULD BE PERFORMED BY QUALIFIED MEDICAL PERSONNEL.
ANTIDOTE: NO SPECIFIC ANTIDOTE. TREAT SYMPTOMATICALLY AND SUPPORTIVELY.

REACTIVITY

REACTIVITY: STABLE UNDER NORMAL TEMPERATURES AND PRESSURES.
INCOMPATIBILITIES: DECYL ALCOHOL: OXIDIZERS (STRONG): POSSIBLE FIRE HAZARD.
DECOMPOSITION: THERMAL DECOMPOSITION PRODUCTS MAY INCLUDE TOXIC OXIDES OF CARBON.
POLYMERIZATION: HAZARDOUS POLYMERIZATION HAS NOT BEEN REPORTED TO OCCUR UNDER NORMAL TEMPERATURES AND PRESSURES.

CONDITIONS TO AVOID

AVOID CONTACT WITH HEAT, SPARKS, FLAMES, OR OTHER SOURCES OF IGNITION. VAPORS MAY BE EXPLOSIVE. AVOID OVERHEATING OF CONTAINERS; CONTAINERS MAY VIOLENTLY RUPTURE IN HEAT OF FIRE. AVOID CONTAMINATION OF WATER SOURCES.

SPILL AND LEAK PROCEDURES

OCCUPATIONAL SPILL: SHUT OFF IGNITION SOURCES. STOP LEAK IF YOU CAN DO IT WITHOUT RISK. USE WATER SPRAY TO REDUCE VAPORS. FOR SMALL SPILLS, TAKE UP WITH SAND OR OTHER ABSORBENT MATERIAL AND PLACE INTO CONTAINERS FOR LATER DISPOSAL. FOR LARGER SPILLS, DIKE FAR AHEAD OF SPILL FOR LATER DISPOSAL. NO SMOKING, FLAMES OR FLARES IN HAZARD AREA. KEEP UNNECESSARY PEOPLE AWAY; ISOLATE HAZARD AREA AND RESTRICT ENTRY.

PROTECTIVE EQUIPMENT

VENTILATION: PROVIDE LOCAL EXHAUST OR GENERAL DILUTION VENTILATION SYSTEM.
RESPIRATOR: THE FOLLOWING RESPIRATORS ARE RECOMMENDED BASED ON INFORMATION FOUND IN THE PHYSICAL DATA, TOXICITY AND HEALTH EFFECTS SECTIONS. THEY ARE RANKED IN ORDER FROM MINIMUM TO MAXIMUM RESPIRATORY PROTECTION. THE SPECIFIC RESPIRATOR SELECTED MUST BE BASED ON CONTAMINATION LEVELS FOUND IN THE WORK PLACE, MUST NOT EXCEED THE WORKING LIMITS OF THE RESPIRATOR AND BE JOINTLY APPROVED BY THE NATIONAL INSTITUTE FOR OCCUPATIONAL SAFETY AND HEALTH AND THE MINE

SAFETY AND HEALTH ADMINISTRATION (NIOSH-MSHA).
CHEMICAL CARTRIDGE RESPIRATOR WITH AN ORGANIC VAPOR CARTRIDGE(S) WITH A FULL FACEPIECE.
GAS MASK WITH ORGANIC VAPOR CANISTER (CHIN-STYLE OR FRONT- OR BACK-MOUNTED CANISTER) WITH A FULL FACEPIECE.
TYPE 'C' SUPPLIED-AIR RESPIRATOR WITH A FULL FACEPIECE OPERATED IN PRESSURE-DEMAND OR OTHER POSITIVE PRESSURE MODE OR WITH A FULL FACEPIECE, HELMET OR HOOD OPERATED IN CONTINUOUS-FLOW MODE.
SELF-CONTAINED BREATHING APPARATUS WITH A FULL FACEPIECE OPERATED IN PRESSURE-DEMAND OR OTHER POSITIVE PRESSURE MODE.
FOR FIREFIGHTING AND OTHER IMMEDIATELY DANGEROUS TO LIFE OR HEALTH CONDITIONS:
SELF-CONTAINED BREATHING APPARATUS WITH FULL FACEPIECE OPERATED IN PRESSURE-DEMAND OR OTHER POSITIVE PRESSURE MODE.
SUPPLIED-AIR RESPIRATOR WITH FULL FACEPIECE AND OPERATED IN PRESSURE-DEMAND OR OTHER POSITIVE PRESSURE MODE IN COMBINATION WITH AN AUXILIARY SELF-CONTAINED BREATHING APPARATUS OPERATED IN PRESSURE-DEMAND OR OTHER POSITIVE PRESSURE MODE.

CLOTHING: EMPLOYEE MUST WEAR APPROPRIATE PROTECTIVE (IMPERVIOUS) CLOTHING AND EQUIPMENT TO PREVENT REPEATED OR PROLONGED SKIN CONTACT WITH THIS SUBSTANCE.

GLOVES: EMPLOYEE MUST WEAR APPROPRIATE PROTECTIVE GLOVES TO PREVENT CONTACT WITH THIS SUBSTANCE.

EYE PROTECTION: EMPLOYEE MUST WEAR SPLASH-PROOF OR DUST-RESISTANT SAFETY GOGGLES TO PREVENT EYE CONTACT WITH THIS SUBSTANCE.
EMERGENCY EYE WASH: WHERE THERE IS ANY POSSIBILITY THAT AN EMPLOYEE'S EYES MAY BE EXPOSED TO THIS SUBSTANCE, THE EMPLOYER SHOULD PROVIDE AN EYE WASH FOUNTAIN WITHIN THE IMMEDIATE WORK AREA FOR EMERGENCY USE.

AUTHORIZED BY- OCCUPATIONAL HEALTH SERVICES, INC.
CREATION DATE: 11/15/89 ***REVISION DATE:*** 05/11/90

MATERIAL SAFETY DATA SHEET

OCCUPATIONAL HEALTH SERVICES, INC.
AGRICULTURE AND PESTICIDE DIVISION
450 SEVENTH AVENUE, SUITE 2407
NEW YORK, NEW YORK 10123
1-800-445-MSDS OR (212) 967-1100

EMERGENCY CONTACT:
JOHN S. BRANSFORD, JR. (615) 292-1180

SUBSTANCE IDENTIFICATION

CAS-NUMBER 78-48-8

SUBSTANCE: DEF

TRADE NAMES/SYNONYMS: PHOSPHOROTRITHIOIC ACID, S,S,S,-TRIBUTYL ESTER; BUTYL PHOSPHOROTRITHIOATE; S,S,S-TRIBUTYL PHOSPHOROTRITHIOATE; S,S,S-TRIBUTYL TRITHIOPHOSPHATE; BUTIFOS; CHEMAGRO B-1776; DEF DEFOLIANT; DE-GREEN; FOSFALL; FOS-FALL A; TBPT; TBTP; PST06300

CHEMICAL FAMILY: ORGANOPHOSPHATE

MOLECULAR FORMULA: C12-H27-O-P-S3

MOLECULAR WEIGHT: 314.54

CERCLA RATINGS (SCALE 0-3): HEALTH=3 FIRE=0 REACTIVITY=0 PERSISTENCE=0

NFPA RATINGS (SCALE 0-4): HEALTH=4 FIRE=0 REACTIVITY=0

COMPONENTS AND CONTAMINANTS

COMPONENT: DEF ***PERCENT:*** 100
CAS# 78-48-8

EXPOSURE LIMITS: NO OCCUPATIONAL EXPOSURE LIMITS ESTABLISHED BY OSHA, ACGIH, OR NIOSH.

PHYSICAL DATA

DESCRIPTION: COLORLESS TO PALE YELLOW CLEAR LIQUID WITH MERCAPTAN-LIKE ODOR

BOILING POINT: 302 F (150 C) @ 0.3 MMHG ***SPECIFIC GRAVITY:*** 1.057

EVAPORATION RATE: NOT AVAILABLE ***SOLUBILITY IN WATER:*** INSOLUBLE

SOLVENT SOLUBILITY: SOLUBLE IN ALIPHATIC, AROMATIC AND CHLORINATED HYDROCARBONS AND ALCOHOL SOLVENTS

FIRE AND EXPLOSION DATA

FIRE AND EXPLOSION HAZARD: NEGLIGIBLE FIRE HAZARD WHEN EXPOSED TO HEAT OR FLAME.

FIREFIGHTING MEDIA: DRY CHEMICAL, CARBON DIOXIDE, HALON, WATER SPRAY OR STANDARD FOAM (1987 EMERGENCY RESPONSE GUIDEBOOK, DOT P 5800.4).
FOR LARGER FIRES, USE WATER SPRAY, FOG OR STANDARD FOAM (1987 EMERGENCY RESPONSE GUIDEBOOK, DOT P 5800.4).

FIREFIGHTING: MOVE CONTAINERS FROM FIRE AREA IF POSSIBLE. FIGHT FIRE FROM MAXIMUM DISTANCE. STAY AWAY FROM STORAGE TANK ENDS. DIKE FIRE CONTROL WATER FOR LATER DISPOSAL. DO NOT SCATTER MATERIAL (1987 EMERGENCY RESPONSE GUIDEBOOK, DOT P 5800.4, GUIDE PAGE 55).
EXTINGUISH ONLY IF FLOW CAN BE STOPPED; USE FLOODING AMOUNTS OF WATER AS FOG, SOLID STREAMS MAY BE INEFFECTIVE. COOL CONTAINERS WITH FLOODING AMOUNTS OF WATER FROM AS FAR A DISTANCE AS POSSIBLE. USE WATER SPRAY TO ABSORB TOXIC VAPORS. AVOID BREATHING TOXIC VAPORS; KEEP UPWIND. CONSIDER EVACUATION OF DOWNWIND AREA IF MATERIAL IS LEAKING.

TRANSPORTATION DATA

DEPARTMENT OF TRANSPORTATION HAZARD CLASSIFICATION 49 CFR 172.101: POISON B
DEPARTMENT OF TRANSPORTATION LABELING REQUIREMENTS 49 CFR 172.101 AND SUBPART E: POISON
DEPARTMENT OF TRANSPORTATION PACKAGING REQUIREMENTS: 49 CFR 173.346 EXCEPTIONS: 49 CFR 173.345

TOXICITY

DEF: TOXICITY DATA: 3804 MG/M3/1 HOUR INHALATION-MOUSE LCLO; 97 MG/KG SKIN-RABBIT LD50; 168 MG/KG SKIN-RAT LD50; 150 MG/KG ORAL-RAT LD50; 77 MG/KG ORAL-MOUSE LD50; 242 MG/KG ORAL-RABBIT LD50; 140 MG/KG ORAL-GUINEA PIG LD50; 210 MG/KG INTRAPERITONEAL-RAT LD50; 285 MG/KG INTRAPERITONEAL-MOUSE LD50; 150 MG/KG INTRAPERITONEAL-GUINEA PIG LD50; 170 MG/KG UNREPORTED-MAMMAL LD50; REPRODUCTIVE EFFECTS DATA (RTECS). CARCINOGEN STATUS: NONE. ACUTE TOXICITY LEVEL: HIGHLY TOXIC BY DERMAL ABSORPTION; TOXIC BY INGESTION. TARGET EFFECTS: CHOLINESTERASE INHIBITOR. POISONING MAY AFFECT THE NERVOUS SYSTEM.* AT INCREASED RISK FROM EXPOSURE: PERSONS WITH RESPIRATORY AILMENTS, RECENT EXPOSURE TO CHOLINESTERASE INHIBITORS OR IMPAIRED CHOLINESTERASE PRODUCTION, OR LIVER MALFUNCTION.* ADDITIONAL DATA: MAY CROSS THE PLACENTA. HIGH ENVIRONMENTAL TEMPERATURES OR EXPOSURE OF THE CHEMICAL TO VISIBLE OR ULTRAVIOLET LIGHT MAY ENHANCE THE TOXICITY. INTERACTIONS WITH MEDICATIONS MAY OCCUR.*
* MAY BE BASED ON GENERAL INFORMATION ON ORGANOPHOSPHATES.

HEALTH EFFECTS AND FIRST AID

INHALATION: DEF: SEE INFORMATION ON ORGANOPHOSPHATES.
ORGANOPHOSPHATES: CHOLINESTERASE INHIBITOR. **ACUTE EXPOSURE**- WHEN INHALED, THE FIRST EFFECTS OF CHOLINESTERASE INHIBITORS ARE USUALLY RESPIRATORY AND MAY INCLUDE NASAL HYPEREMIA AND WATERY DISCHARGE, COUGH, CHEST DISCOMFORT, DYSPNEA, AND WHEEZING DUE TO INCREASED BRONCHIAL SECRETIONS AND BRONCHOCONSTRICTION. IF SUFFICIENT AMOUNTS ARE ABSORBED, OTHER SYSTEMIC EFFECTS MAY BEGIN WITHIN A FEW MINUTES OR BE DELAYED FOR UP TO 12 HOURS. SYMPTOMS MAY INCLUDE PALLOR, NAUSEA, VOMITING, DIARRHEA, ABDOMINAL CRAMPS, HEADACHE, DIZZINESS, OCULAR PAIN, BLURRED VISION, MIOSIS OR IN SOME CASES, ESPECIALLY INITIALLY, MYDRIASIS, LACRIMATION, SALIVATION, SWEATING, AND CONFUSION. OTHER REPORTED CENTRAL NERVOUS SYSTEM OR NEUROMUSCULAR EFFECTS MAY INCLUDE ATAXIA, SLURRED SPEECH, AREFLEXIA, WEAKNESS, FATIGUE, FASCICULATIONS, TWITCHING, TREMORS POSSIBLY OF THE TONGUE AND EYELIDS, AND EVENTUALLY PARALYSIS OF THE EXTREMITIES AND POSSIBLY OF THE RESPIRATORY MUSCLES. IN SEVERE CASES THERE MAY ALSO BE INVOLUNTARY DEFECATION AND URINATION, CYANOSIS, PSYCHOSIS, HYPERGLYCEMIA, ACUTE PANCREATITIS, CARDIAC IRREGULARITIES, PULMONARY EDEMA, UNCONSCIOUSNESS, CONVULSIONS, AND COMA. DEATH IS PRIMARILY DUE TO RESPIRATORY FAILURE, ALTHOUGH CARDIOVASCULAR EFFECTS INCLUDING CARDIAC ARREST MAY ALSO BE IMPLICATED. LONG TERM SEQUELAE ARE RARE BUT MAY INCLUDE NEUROPSYCHIATRIC DISORDERS AND MYOPATHY WITH MUSCLE TENDERNESS. SOME ORGANOPHOSPHATES MAY CAUSE A DELAYED NEUROPATHY BEGINNING 1-4 WEEKS AFTER AN ACUTE EXPOSURE WHICH MAY OR MAY NOT HAVE CAUSED ACUTE CHOLINERGIC EFFECTS. NUMBNESS, TINGLING, WEAKNESS AND CRAMPING BEGINNING SYMMETRICALLY IN THE LOWER LIMBS MAY PROGRESS TO ATAXIA AND PARALYSIS. IN SEVERE CASES, UPPER LIMB INVOLVEMENT IS POSSIBLE AND FLACCID PARALYSIS MAY PROGRESS TO SPASTIC PARALYSIS WITH EXAGGERATED REFLEXES. IMPROVEMENT MAY OCCUR OVER MONTHS TO YEARS, BUT SOME RESIDUAL IMPAIRMENT USUALLY REMAINS.
CHRONIC EXPOSURE- REPEATED OR PROLONGED EXPOSURE MAY RESULT IN THE EFFECTS OF ACUTE EXPOSURE INCLUDING THE DELAYED NEUROPATHY. OTHER EFFECTS REPORTED IN WORKERS REPEATEDLY EXPOSED INCLUDE IMPAIRED

MEMORY AND CONCENTRATION, ACUTE PSYCHOSIS, SEVERE DEPRESSIONS, IRRITABILTY, CONFUSION, APATHY, EMOTIONAL LABILITY, SOCIAL WITHDRAWAL, CONFUSION, HEADACHE, SPEECH DIFFICULTIES, DELAYED REACTION TIMES, SPATIAL DISORIENTATION, NIGHTMARES, SLEEPWALKING, AND DROWSINESS OR INSOMNIA. AN INFLUENZA-LIKE CONDITION WITH HEADACHE, NAUSEA, WEAKNESS, ANOREXIA AND MALAISE HAS ALSO BEEN REPORTED.

FIRST AID- REMOVE FROM EXPOSURE AREA TO FRESH AIR IMMEDIATELY. IF BREATHING HAS STOPPED, GIVE ARTIFICIAL RESPIRATION. MAINTAIN AIRWAY AND BLOOD PRESSURE AND ADMINISTER OXYGEN IF AVAILABLE. KEEP AFFECTED PERSON WARM AND AT REST. TREAT SYMPTOMATICALLY AND SUPPORTIVELY. ADMINISTRATION OF OXYGEN SHOULD BE PERFORMED BY QUALIFIED PERSONNEL. GET MEDICAL ATTENTION IMMEDIATELY.

SKIN CONTACT: DEF: HIGHLY TOXIC. SEE INFORMATION ON ORGANOPHOSPHATES.
ORGANOPHOSPHATES: CHOLINESTERASE INHIBITOR. **ACUTE EXPOSURE-** LOCALIZED SWEATING AND FASCICULATIONS MAY OCCUR AT THE SITE OF CONTACT. IF SUFFICIENT AMOUNTS ARE ABSORBED, OTHER EFFECTS OF CHOLINESTERASE INHIBITION AS DESCRIBED IN ACUTE INHALATION MAY OCCUR. SYMPTOMS MAY BE DELAYED 2-3 HOURS, BUT USUALLY NO MORE THAN 12 HOURS. THE RATE OF ABSORPTION IS INCREASED BY THE PRESENCE OF DERMATITIS OR HIGH AMBIENT TEMPERATURES. DELAYED NEUROPATHY IS ALSO POSSIBLE. **CHRONIC EXPOSURE-** REPEATED OR PROLONGED EXPOSURE MAY CAUSE EFFECTS AS DESCRIBED IN ACUTE EXPOSURE. SOME ORGANOPHOSPHATES MAY CAUSE SENSITIZATION.

FIRST AID- REMOVE CONTAMINATED CLOTHING IMMEDIATELY. WASH CONTAMINATED AREAS WITH SOAP AND WATER FOLLOWED BY ALCOHOL (ARENA, POISONING, 4TH ED.). EMERGENCY PERSONNEL SHOULD WEAR GLOVES AND AVOID CONTAMINATION. TREAT RESPIRATORY DIFFICULTY WITH ARTIFICIAL RESPIRATION. GET MEDICAL ATTENTION IMMEDIATELY.

EYE CONTACT: DEF: SEE INFORMATION ON ORGANOPHOSPHATES.
ORGANOPHOSPHATES: CHOLINESTERASE INHIBITOR. **ACUTE EXPOSURE-** DIRECT CONTACT MAY CAUSE PAIN, HYPEREMIA, LACRIMATION, TWITCHING OF THE EYELIDS, MIOSIS, AND CILIARY MUSCLE SPASM WITH LOSS OF ACCOMODATION, BLURRED OR DIMMED VISION AND BROWACHE. SOMETIMES MYDRIASIS MAY OCCUR INSTEAD OF MIOSIS. WITH SUFFICIENT EXPOSURE, OTHER SYMPTOMS OF CHOLINESTERASE INHIBITION AS DESCRIBED IN ACUTE INHALATION MAY OCCUR. **CHRONIC EXPOSURE-** REPEATED OR PROLONGED EXPOSURE MAY CAUSE EFFECTS AS DESCRIBED IN ACUTE EXPOSURE. SOME COMPOUNDS HAVE CAUSED TOXIC EFFECTS ON THE CRYSTALLINE LENS, CONJUNCTIVAL THICKENING AND OBSTRUCTION OF THE NASOLACRIMAL CANALS WHEN USED AS MIOTIC EYEDROPS.

FIRST AID- IRRIGATE EYES WITH WATER OR SALINE SOLUTION. IF SYMPTOMS OF POISONING OCCUR, TREAT RESPIRATORY DIFFICULTY WITH ARTIFICIAL RESPIRATION AND OXYGEN. OBSERVE PATIENT FOR AT LEAST 24-36 HOURS (GOSSELIN, CLINICAL TOXICOLOGY OF COMMERCIAL PRODUCTS, 5TH ED.). GET MEDICAL ATTENTION IMMEDIATELY. OXYGEN SHOULD BE ADMINISTERED BY QUALIFIED MEDICAL PERSONNEL.

INGESTION: DEF: TOXIC. CHRONIC INGESTION BY RATS RESULTED IN ADVERSE EFFECTS ON THE FEMALE REPRODUCTIVE SYSTEM. IN CHRONIC STUDIES OF HENS, SEVERE ATAXIA AND POSITIVE HISTOPATHOLOGY WERE OBSERVED AT 20 MG/KG AND ABOVE. IN OTHER CHRONIC STUDIES OF HENS, DOSES AS HIGH AS 62.5 MG/KG DID NOT PRODUCE ANY NEUROTOXIC EFFECTS. SEE INFORMATION ON ORGANOPHOSPHATES.
ORGANOPHOSPHATES: CHOLINESTERASE INHIBITOR. **ACUTE EXPOSURE-** WHEN INGESTED, THE FIRST EFFECTS MAY BE NAUSEA, VOMITING, ANOREXIA, ABDOMINAL CRAMPS AND DIARRHEA. GASTROINTESTINAL ABSORPTION MAY CAUSE SYMPTOMS OF CHOLINESTERASE INHIBITION AS DESCRIBED IN ACUTE INHALATION. SYMPTOMS MAY BEGIN WITHIN MINUTES OR BE DELAYED FOR HOURS. DELAYED EFFECTS INCLUDING NEUROPATHY MAY ALSO OCCUR. **CHRONIC EXPOSURE-** REPEATED INGESTION MAY CAUSE EFFECTS AS DESCRIBED IN ACUTE EXPOSURE.

FIRST AID- IF PERSON IS ALERT AND RESPIRATION IS NOT DEPRESSED, GIVE SYRUP OF IPECAC FOLLOWED BY WATER (IF VOMITING OCCURS, KEEP HEAD BELOW HIPS TO PREVENT ASPIRATION). IF CONSCIOUSNESS LEVEL DECLINES OR VOMITING HAS NOT OCCURRED IN 15 MINUTES EMPTY STOMACH BY GASTRIC LAVAGE WITH THE AID OF CUFFED ENDOTRACHEAL TUBE USING ISOTONIC SALINE OR 5% SODIUM BICARBONATE FOLLOW WITH ACTIVATED CHARCOAL. ESTABLISH AND MAINTAIN AIRWAY. TREAT RESPIRATORY DIFFICULTY WITH ARTIFICIAL RESPIRATION AND OXYGEN. DO NOT GIVE MORPHINE, AMINOPHYLLINE, PHENOTHIAZINES, RESERPINE, FUROSEMIDE, OR ETHACRYNIC ACID (MORGAN, RECOGNITION AND MANAGEMENT OF PESTICIDE POISONINGS, 3RD ED.). TREAT SYMPTOMATICALLY AND SUPPORTIVELY. ADMINISTRATION OF OXYGEN AND LAVAGE MUST BE PERFORMED BY QUALIFIED MEDICAL PERSONNEL. GET MEDICAL ATTENTION IMMEDIATELY.

ANTIDOTE: THE FOLLOWING ANTIDOTE(S) HAVE BEEN RECOMMENDED. HOWEVER, THE DECISION AS TO WHETHER THE SEVERITY OF POISONING REQUIRES ADMINISTRATION OF ANY ANTIDOTE AND ACTUAL DOSE REQUIRED SHOULD BE MADE BY QUALIFIED MEDICAL PERSONNEL.
FOR CHOLINESTERASE INHIBITORS: ESTABLISH CLEAR AIRWAY AND TISSUE OXYGENATION BY ASPIRATION OF SECRETIONS, AND IF NECESSARY, BY ASSISTED PULMONARY VENTILATION WITH OXYGEN. IMPROVE TISSUE OXYGENATION AS MUCH AS POSSIBLE BEFORE ADMINISTERING ATROPINE TO MINIMIZE THE RISK OF VENTRICULAR FIBRILLATION. ADMINISTER ATROPINE SULFATE INTRAVENOUSLY, OR INTRAMUSCULARLY IF IV INJECTION IS NOT POSSIBLE. IN MODERATELY SEVERE POISONING ADMINISTER ATROPINE SULFATE, 0.4-2.0 MG REPEATED EVERY 15 MINUTES UNTIL ATROPINIZATION IS ACHIEVED (TACHYCARDIA, FLUSHING, DRY MOUTH, MYDRIASIS). MAINTAIN ATROPINIZATION BY REPEATED DOSES FOR 2-12 HOURS, OR LONGER, DEPENDING ON THE SEVERITY OF POISONING. THE APPEARANCE OF RALES IN THE LUNG BASES, MIOSIS, SALIVATION, NAUSEA, BRADYCARDIA, ARE ALL INDICATIONS OF INADEQUATE ATROPINIZATION. SEVERELY POISONED INDIVIDUALS MAY EXHIBIT REMARKABLE TOLERANCE TO ATROPINE; TWO OR MORE TIMES THE DOSAGES SUGGESTED ABOVE MAY BE NEEDED. PERSONS NOT POISONED OR ONLY SLIGHTLY POISONED, HOWEVER, MAY DEVELOP SIGNS OF ATROPINE TOXICITY FROM SUCH LARGE DOSAGES: FEVER, MUSCLE FIBRILLATIONS, AND DELIRIUM ARE THE MAIN SIGNS OF ATROPINE TOXICITY. IF THESE SIGNS APPEAR WHILE THE PATIENT IS FULLY ATROPINIZED, ATROPINE ADMINISTRATION SHOULD BE DISCONTINUED, AT LEAST TEMPORARILY. OBSERVE TREATED PATIENTS CLOSELY AT LEAST 24 HOURS TO INSURE THAT SYMPTOMS (POSSIBLY PULMONARY EDEMA) DO NOT RECUR AS ATROPINIZATION WEARS OFF. IN VERY SEVERE POISONINGS, METABOLIC DISPOSITION OF TOXICANT MAY REQUIRE SEVERAL HOURS OR DAYS DURING WHICH ATROPINIZATION MUST BE MAINTAINED. MARKEDLY LOWER LEVELS OF URINARY METABOLITES INDICATE THAT ATROPINE DOSAGE CAN BE TAPERED OFF. AS DOSAGE IS REDUCED, CHECK THE LUNG BASES FREQUENTLY FOR RALES. IF RALES ARE HEARD OR OTHER SYMPTOMS RETURN, RE-ESTABLISH ATROPINIZATION PROMPTLY (MORGAN, RECOGNITION AND MANAGEMENT OF PESTICIDE POISONINGS, 3RD ED.). ADMINISTRATION OF ANTIDOTE MUST BE PERFORMED BY QUALIFIED MEDICAL PERSONNEL.
IN CASES OF SEVERE POISONING BY ORGANOPHOSPHATE PESTICIDES IN WHICH RESPIRATORY DEPRESSION, MUSCLE WEAKNESS AND TWITCHINGS ARE SEVERE, GIVE PRALIDOXIME (PROTOPAM-AYERST, 2-PAM), 1.0 GRAM INTRAVENOUSLY AT NO MORE THAN 0.5 GRAM PER MINUTE. DOSAGE OF PRALIDOXIME MAY BE REPEATED IN 1-2 HOURS, THEN AT 10-12 HOUR INTERVALS IF NEEDED. IN VERY SEVERE POISONINGS, DOSAGE RATES MAY BE DOUBLED. TREATMENT WITH PRALIDOXIME WILL BE MOST EFFECTIVE IF GIVEN WITHIN THIRTY-SIX HOURS AFTER POISONING (MORGAN, RECOGNITION AND MANAGEMENT OF PESTICIDE POISONINGS, 3RD ED.). ANTIDOTE SHOULD BE ADMINISTERED BY QUALIFIED MEDICAL PERSONNEL.

REACTIVITY

REACTIVITY: STABLE UNDER NORMAL TEMPERATURES AND PRESSURES.

INCOMPATIBILITIES: DEF: ALKALINE CONDITIONS: MAY CAUSE HYDROLYSIS.

DECOMPOSITION: THERMAL DECOMPOSITION MAY RELEASE TOXIC AND/OR HAZARDOUS GASES.

POLYMERIZATION: HAZARDOUS POLYMERIZATION HAS NOT BEEN REPORTED TO OCCUR UNDER NORMAL TEMPERATURES AND PRESSURES.

STORAGE AND DISPOSAL

OBSERVE ALL FEDERAL, STATE AND LOCAL REGULATIONS WHEN STORING OR DISPOSING OF THIS SUBSTANCE. FOR ASSISTANCE, CONTACT THE DISTRICT DIRECTOR OF THE ENVIRONMENTAL PROTECTION AGENCY.

****STORAGE****

STORE IN ACCORDANCE WITH 40 CFR 165 RECOMMENDED PROCEDURES FOR THE DISPOSAL AND STORAGE OF PESTICIDES AND PESTICIDE CONTAINERS.
STORE AWAY FROM INCOMPATIBLE SUBSTANCES.

****DISPOSAL****

DISPOSAL MUST BE IN ACCORDANCE WITH 40 CFR 165 RECOMMENDED PROCEDURES FOR THE DISPOSAL AND STORAGE OF PESTICIDES AND PESTICIDE CONTAINERS.

CONDITIONS TO AVOID

NONE REPORTED.

SPILL AND LEAK PROCEDURES

OCCUPATIONAL SPILL: DO NOT TOUCH SPILLED MATERIAL. STOP LEAK IF YOU CAN DO IT WITHOUT RISK. USE WATER SPRAY TO REDUCE VAPORS. FOR SMALL SPILLS, TAKE UP WITH SAND OR OTHER ABSORBENT MATERIAL AND PLACE INTO CONTAINERS FOR LATER DISPOSAL. FOR SMALL DRY SPILLS, WITH A CLEAN SHOVEL PLACE MATERIAL INTO CLEAN, DRY CONTAINERS AND COVER. MOVE CONTAINERS FROM SPILL AREA. FOR LARGER SPILLS, DIKE FAR AHEAD OF SPILL

FOR LATER DISPOSAL. KEEP UNNECESSARY PEOPLE AWAY. ISOLATE HAZARD AREA AND DENY ENTRY. VENTILATE CLOSED SPACES BEFORE ENTERING.

PROTECTIVE EQUIPMENT

VENTILATION: PROCESS ENCLOSURE RECOMMENDED.

RESPIRATOR: THE FOLLOWING RESPIRATORS ARE RECOMMENDED BASED ON INFORMATION FOUND IN THE PHYSICAL DATA, TOXICITY AND HEALTH EFFECTS SECTIONS. THEY ARE RANKED IN ORDER FROM MINIMUM TO MAXIMUM RESPIRATORY PROTECTION. THE SPECIFIC RESPIRATOR SELECTED MUST BE BASED ON CONTAMINATION LEVELS FOUND IN THE WORK PLACE, MUST NOT EXCEED THE WORKING LIMITS OF THE RESPIRATOR AND BE JOINTLY APPROVED BY THE NATIONAL INSTITUTE FOR OCCUPATIONAL SAFETY AND HEALTH AND THE MINE SAFETY AND HEALTH ADMINISTRATION (NIOSH-MSHA).

TYPE 'C' SUPPLIED-AIR RESPIRATOR WITH A FULL FACEPIECE OPERATED IN PRESSURE-DEMAND OR OTHER POSITIVE PRESSURE MODE OR WITH A FULL FACEPIECE, HELMET OR HOOD OPERATED IN CONTINOUS-FLOW MODE.

SELF-CONTAINED BREATHING APPARATUS WITH A FULL FACEPIECE OPERATED IN PRESSURE-DEMAND OR OTHER POSITIVE PRESSURE MODE.

FOR FIREFIGHTING AND OTHER IMMEDIATELY DANGEROUS TO LIFE OR HEALTH CONDITIONS:

SELF-CONTAINED BREATHING APPARATUS WITH FULL FACEPIECE OPERATED IN PRESSURE-DEMAND OR OTHER POSITIVE PRESSURE MODE.

SUPPLIED-AIR RESPIRATOR WITH FULL FACEPIECE AND OPERATED IN PRESSURE-DEMAND OR OTHER POSITIVE PRESSURE MODE IN COMBINATION WITH AN AUXILIARY SELF-CONTAINED BREATHING APPARATUS OPERATED IN PRESSURE-DEMAND OR OTHER POSITIVE PRESSURE MODE.

CLOTHING: EMPLOYEE MUST WEAR APPROPRIATE PROTECTIVE (IMPERVIOUS) CLOTHING AND EQUIPMENT TO PREVENT ANY POSSIBILITY OF SKIN CONTACT WITH THIS SUBSTANCE.

GLOVES: EMPLOYEE MUST WEAR APPROPRIATE PROTECTIVE GLOVES TO PREVENT CONTACT WITH THIS SUBSTANCE.

EYE PROTECTION: EMPLOYEE MUST WEAR SPLASH-PROOF OR DUST-RESISTANT SAFETY GOGGLES AND A FACESHIELD TO PREVENT CONTACT WITH THIS SUBSTANCE.

EMERGENCY WASH FACILITIES: WHERE THERE IS ANY POSSIBILITY THAT AN EMPLOYEE'S EYES AND/OR SKIN MAY BE EXPOSED TO THIS SUBSTANCE, THE EMPLOYER SHOULD PROVIDE AN EYE WASH FOUNTAIN AND QUICK DRENCH SHOWER WITHIN THE IMMEDIATE WORK AREA FOR EMERGENCY USE.

AUTHORIZED BY- OCCUPATIONAL HEALTH SERVICES, INC.

CREATION DATE: 10/04/89 ***REVISION DATE:*** 05/04/90

MATERIAL SAFETY DATA SHEET

OCCUPATIONAL HEALTH SERVICES, INC.
AGRICULTURE AND PESTICIDE DIVISION
450 SEVENTH AVENUE, SUITE 2407
NEW YORK, NEW YORK 10123
1-800-445-MSDS OR (212) 967-1100

EMERGENCY CONTACT:
JOHN S. BRANSFORD, JR. (615) 292-1180

SUBSTANCE IDENTIFICATION

CAS-NUMBER 2496-91-5

SUBSTANCE: **DEMETON-S-SULFONE**

TRADE NAMES/SYNONYMS: PHOSPHOROTHIOIC ACID, O,O-DIETHYL S-(2-(ETHYLSULFONYL)ETHYL) ESTER; O,O-DIETHYL S-(2 (ETHYLSULFONYL)ETHYL) ESTER, PHOSPHOROTHIOIC ACID; O,O-DIETHYL S-(2-(ETHYLSULFONYL)ETHYL) PHOSPHOROTHIOATE; SYSTOXTHIOL ISOMER SULFONE; DISULFOTON O.A. SULFONE; DISYSTOX O.A. SULFONE; DEMETON SULFONE; DEMETON THIOL SULFONE; ISOSYSTOX SULFONE; DISULFOTON OXYGEN ANALOG SULFONE; C8H19O5PS2; PST06306

CHEMICAL FAMILY: ORGANOPHOSPHATE SULFONYL

MOLECULAR FORMULA: (C2-H5-O)2-P-(O)-S-(C-H2)2-S-(O2)-C2-H5

MOLECULAR WEIGHT: 290.34

CERCLA RATINGS (SCALE 0-3): HEALTH=3 FIRE=U REACTIVITY=0 PERSISTENCE=0

NFPA RATINGS (SCALE 0-4): HEALTH=4 FIRE=U REACTIVITY=0

COMPONENTS AND CONTAMINANTS

COMPONENT: DEMETON-S-SULFONE ***PERCENT:*** 100.0

CAS# 2496-91-5

OTHER CONTAMINANTS: NONE

EXPOSURE LIMITS: NO OCCUPATIONAL EXPOSURE LIMITS ESTABLISHED BY OSHA, ACGIH, OR NIOSH.

PHYSICAL DATA

DESCRIPTION: CLEAR, THICK LIQUID. ***BOILING POINT:*** NOT AVAILABLE

SPECIFIC GRAVITY: NOT AVAILABLE ***VAPOR PRESSURE:*** NOT AVAILABLE

SOLUBILITY IN WATER: NOT AVAILABLE

FIRE AND EXPLOSION DATA

FIRE AND EXPLOSION HAZARD: UNKNOWN FIRE AND EXPLOSION HAZARD. ***FLASH POINT:*** NOT AVAILABLE

FIREFIGHTING MEDIA: DRY CHEMICAL, CARBON DIOXIDE, HALON, WATER SPRAY OR STANDARD FOAM (1987 EMERGENCY RESPONSE GUIDEBOOK, DOT P 5800.4). FOR LARGER FIRES, USE WATER SPRAY, FOG OR STANDARD FOAM (1987 EMERGENCY RESPONSE GUIDEBOOK, DOT P 5800.4).

FIREFIGHTING: MOVE CONTAINERS FROM FIRE AREA IF POSSIBLE. COOL CONTAINERS EXPOSED TO FLAMES WITH WATER FROM SIDE UNTIL WELL AFTER FIRE IS OUT. FIGHT FIRE FROM MAXIMUM DISTANCE. STAY AWAY FROM STORAGE TANK ENDS. DIKE FIRE CONTROL WATER FOR LATER DISPOSAL. DO NOT SCATTER MATERIAL. (1987 EMERGENCY RESPONSE GUIDEBOOK, DOT P 5800.4, GUIDE PAGE 57). EXTINGUISH ONLY IF FLOW CAN BE STOPPED. USE FLOODING AMOUNTS OF WATER AS A FOG; SOLID STREAMS MAY BE INEFFECTIVE. COOL CONTAINERS WITH FLOODING AMOUNTS OF WATER FROM AS FAR A DISTANCE AS POSSIBLE. AVOID BREATHING POISONOUS VAPORS, KEEP UPWIND.

TRANSPORTATION DATA

DEPARTMENT OF TRANSPORTATION HAZARD CLASSIFICATION 49 CFR 172.101: POISON B

DEPARTMENT OF TRANSPORTATION LABELING REQUIREMENTS 49 CFR 172.101 AND SUBPART E: POISON

DEPARTMENT OF TRANSPORTATION PACKAGING REQUIREMENTS: 49 CFR 173.365 EXCEPTIONS: 49 CFR 173.364

TOXICITY

DEMETON-S-SULFONE: TOXICITY DATA: 1900 UG/KG ORAL-RAT LD50; 1800 UG/KG INTRAPERITONEAL-RAT LD50; 5900 UG/KG INTRAPERITONEAL-MOUSE LD50; 8500 UG/KG INTRAPERITONEAL-GUINEA PIG LD50; 2 MG/KG UNREPORTED-RAT LD50. CARCINOGEN STATUS: NONE. ACUTE TOXICITY LEVEL: HIGHLY TOXIC BY INGESTION. TARGET EFFECTS: CHOLINESTERASE INHIBITOR. POISONING MAY AFFECT THE NERVOUS SYSTEM.* AT INCREASED RISK FROM EXPOSURE: PERSONS WITH RESPIRATORY AILMENTS, RECENT EXPOSURE TO CHOLINESTERASE INHIBITORS OR IMPAIRED CHOLINESTERASE PRODUCTION, OR LIVER MALFUNCTION.* ADDITIONAL DATA: MAY CROSS THE PLACENTA. HIGH ENVIRONMENTAL TEMPERATURES OR EXPOSURE OF THE CHEMICAL TO VISIBLE OR ULTRAVIOLET LIGHT MAY ENHANCE THE TOXICITY. INTERACTIONS WITH MEDICATIONS MAY OCCUR.*

* MAY BE BASED ON GENERAL INFORMATION ON ORGANOPHOSPHATES.

HEALTH EFFECTS AND FIRST AID

INHALATION: DEMETON-S-SULFONE: SEE INFORMATION ON ORGANOPHOSPHATES. ORGANOPHOSPHATES: CHOLINESTERASE INHIBITOR. **ACUTE EXPOSURE-** WHEN INHALED, THE FIRST EFFECTS OF CHOLINESTERASE INHIBITORS ARE USUALLY RESPIRATORY AND MAY INCLUDE NASAL HYPEREMIA AND WATERY DISCHARGE, COUGH, CHEST DISCOMFORT, DYSPNEA, AND WHEEZING DUE TO INCREASED BRONCHIAL SECRETIONS AND BRONCHOCONSTRICTION. IF SUFFICIENT AMOUNTS ARE ABSORBED, OTHER SYSTEMIC EFFECTS MAY BEGIN WITHIN A FEW MINUTES OR BE DELAYED FOR UP TO 12 HOURS. SYMPTOMS MAY INCLUDE PALLOR, NAUSEA, VOMITING, DIARRHEA, ABDOMINAL CRAMPS, HEADACHE, DIZZINESS, OCULAR PAIN, BLURRED VISION, MIOSIS OR IN SOME CASES, ESPECIALLY INITIALLY, MYDRIASIS, LACRIMATION, SALIVATION, SWEATING, AND CONFUSION. OTHER REPORTED CENTRAL NERVOUS SYSTEM OR NEUROMUSCULAR EFFECTS MAY INCLUDE ATAXIA, SLURRED SPEECH, AREFLEXIA, WEAKNESS, FATIGUE, FASCICULATIONS, TWITCHING, TREMORS POSSIBLY OF THE TONGUE AND EYELIDS, AND EVENTUALLY PARALYSIS OF THE EXTREMITIES AND POSSIBLY OF THE RESPIRATORY MUSCLES. IN SEVERE CASES THERE MAY ALSO BE INVOLUNTARY DEFECATION AND URINATION, CYANOSIS, PSYCHOSIS, HYPERGLYCEMIA, ACUTE PANCREATITIS, CARDIAC IRREGULARITIES, PULMONARY EDEMA, UNCONSCIOUSNESS, CONVULSIONS, AND COMA. DEATH IS PRIMARILY DUE TO RESPIRATORY FAILURE, ALTHOUGH CARDIOVASCULAR EFFECTS INCLUDING CARDIAC ARREST MAY ALSO BE IMPLICATED. LONG TERM SEQUELAE ARE RARE BUT MAY INCLUDE NEUROPSYCHIATRIC DISORDERS AND MYOPATHY WITH MUSCLE TENDERNESS. SOME ORGANOPHOSPHATES MAY CAUSE A DELAYED

NEUROPATHY BEGINNING 1-4 WEEKS AFTER AN ACUTE EXPOSURE WHICH MAY OR MAY NOT HAVE CAUSED ACUTE CHOLINERGIC EFFECTS. NUMBNESS, TINGLING, WEAKNESS AND CRAMPING BEGINNING SYMMETRICALLY IN THE LOWER LIMBS MAY PROGRESS TO ATAXIA AND PARALYSIS. IN SEVERE CASES, UPPER LIMB INVOLVEMENT IS POSSIBLE AND FLACCID PARALYSIS MAY PROGRESS TO SPASTIC PARALYSIS WITH EXAGGERATED REFLEXES. IMPROVEMENT MAY OCCUR OVER MONTHS TO YEARS, BUT SOME RESIDUAL IMPAIRMENT USUALLY REMAINS. **CHRONIC EXPOSURE-** REPEATED OR PROLONGED EXPOSURE MAY RESULT IN THE EFFECTS OF ACUTE EXPOSURE INCLUDING THE DELAYED NEUROPATHY. OTHER EFFECTS REPORTED IN WORKERS REPEATEDLY EXPOSED INCLUDE IMPAIRED MEMORY AND CONCENTRATION, ACUTE PSYCHOSIS, SEVERE DEPRESSIONS, IRRITABILTY, CONFUSION, APATHY, EMOTIONAL LABILITY, SOCIAL WITHDRAWAL, CONFUSION, HEADACHE, SPEECH DIFFICULTIES, DELAYED REACTION TIMES, SPATIAL DISORIENTATION, NIGHTMARES, SLEEPWALKING, AND DROWSINESS OR INSOMNIA. AN INFLUENZA-LIKE CONDITION WITH HEADACHE, NAUSEA, WEAKNESS, ANOREXIA AND MALAISE HAS ALSO BEEN REPORTED.

FIRST AID- REMOVE FROM EXPOSURE AREA TO FRESH AIR IMMEDIATELY. IF BREATHING HAS STOPPED, GIVE ARTIFICIAL RESPIRATION. MAINTAIN AIRWAY AND BLOOD PRESSURE AND ADMINISTER OXYGEN IF AVAILABLE. KEEP AFFECTED PERSON WARM AND AT REST. TREAT SYMPTOMATICALLY AND SUPPORTIVELY. ADMINISTRATION OF OXYGEN SHOULD BE PERFORMED BY QUALIFIED PERSONNEL. GET MEDICAL ATTENTION IMMEDIATELY.

SKIN CONTACT: DEMETON-S-SULFONE: SEE INFORMATION ON ORGANOPHOSPHATES. ORGANOPHOSPHATES: CHOLINESTERASE INHIBITOR. **ACUTE EXPOSURE-** LOCALIZED SWEATING AND FASCICULATIONS MAY OCCUR AT THE SITE OF CONTACT. IF SUFFICIENT AMOUNTS ARE ABSORBED, OTHER EFFECTS OF CHOLINESTERASE INHIBITION AS DESCRIBED IN ACUTE INHALATION MAY OCCUR. SYMPTOMS MAY BE DELAYED 2-3 HOURS, BUT USUALLY NO MORE THAN 12 HOURS. THE RATE OF ABSORPTION IS INCREASED BY THE PRESENCE OF DERMATITIS OR HIGH AMBIENT TEMPERATURES. DELAYED NEUROPATHY IS ALSO POSSIBLE. **CHRONIC EXPOSURE-** REPEATED OR PROLONGED EXPOSURE MAY CAUSE EFFECTS AS DESCRIBED IN ACUTE EXPOSURE. SOME ORGANOPHOSPHATES MAY CAUSE SENSITIZATION.

FIRST AID- REMOVE CONTAMINATED CLOTHING IMMEDIATELY. WASH CONTAMINATED AREAS WITH SOAP AND WATER FOLLOWED BY ALCOHOL (ARENA, POISONING, 4TH ED.). EMERGENCY PERSONNEL SHOULD WEAR GLOVES AND AVOID CONTAMINATION. TREAT RESPIRATORY DIFFICULTY WITH ARTIFICIAL RESPIRATION. GET MEDICAL ATTENTION IMMEDIATELY.

EYE CONTACT: DEMETON-S-SULFONE: SEE INFORMATION ON ORGANOPHOSPHATES. ORGANOPHOSPHATES: CHOLINESTERASE INHIBITOR. **ACUTE EXPOSURE-** DIRECT CONTACT MAY CAUSE PAIN, HYPEREMIA, LACRIMATION, TWITCHING OF THE EYELIDS, MIOSIS, AND CILIARY MUSCLE SPASM WITH LOSS OF ACCOMODATION, BLURRED OR DIMMED VISION AND BROWACHE. SOMETIMES MYDRIASIS MAY OCCUR INSTEAD OF MIOSIS. WITH SUFFICIENT EXPOSURE, OTHER SYMPTOMS OF CHOLINESTERASE INHIBITION AS DESCRIBED IN ACUTE INHALATION MAY OCCUR. **CHRONIC EXPOSURE-** REPEATED OR PROLONGED EXPOSURE MAY CAUSE EFFECTS AS DESCRIBED IN ACUTE EXPOSURE. SOME COMPOUNDS HAVE CAUSED TOXIC EFFECTS ON THE CRYSTALLINE LENS, CONJUNCTIVAL THICKENING AND OBSTRUCTION OF THE NASOLACRIMAL CANALS WHEN USED AS MIOTIC EYEDROPS.

FIRST AID- IRRIGATE EYES WITH WATER OR SALINE SOLUTION. IF SYMPTOMS OF POISONING OCCUR, TREAT RESPIRATORY DIFFICULTY WITH ARTIFICIAL RESPIRATION AND OXYGEN. OBSERVE PATIENT FOR AT LEAST 24-36 HOURS (GOSSELIN, CLINICAL TOXICOLOGY OF COMMERCIAL PRODUCTS, 5TH ED.). GET MEDICAL ATTENTION IMMEDIATELY. OXYGEN SHOULD BE ADMINISTERED BY QUALIFIED MEDICAL PERSONNEL.

INGESTION: DEMETON-S-SULFONE: HIGHLY TOXIC. THE LETHAL DOSE REPORTED IN RATS WAS 1900 UG/KG. SEE INFORMATION ON ORGANOPHOSPHATES. ORGANOPHOSPHATES: CHOLINESTERASE INHIBITOR. **ACUTE EXPOSURE-** WHEN INGESTED, THE FIRST EFFECTS MAY BE NAUSEA, VOMITING, ANOREXIA, ABDOMINAL CRAMPS AND DIARRHEA. GASTROINTESTINAL ABSORPTION MAY CAUSE SYMPTOMS OF CHOLINESTERASE INHIBITION AS DESCRIBED IN ACUTE INHALATION. SYMPTOMS MAY BEGIN WITHIN MINUTES OR BE DELAYED FOR HOURS. DELAYED EFFECTS INCLUDING NEUROPATHY MAY ALSO OCCUR. **CHRONIC EXPOSURE-** REPEATED INGESTION MAY CAUSE EFFECTS AS DESCRIBED IN ACUTE EXPOSURE.

FIRST AID- IF PERSON IS ALERT AND RESPIRATION IS NOT DEPRESSED, GIVE SYRUP OF IPECAC FOLLOWED BY WATER (IF VOMITING OCCURS, KEEP HEAD BELOW HIPS TO PREVENT ASPIRATION). IF CONSCIOUSNESS LEVEL DECLINES OR VOMITING HAS NOT OCCURRED IN 15 MINUTES EMPTY STOMACH BY GASTRIC LAVAGE WITH THE AID OF CUFFED ENDOTRACHEAL TUBE USING ISOTONIC SALINE OR 5% SODIUM BICARBONATE FOLLOW WITH ACTIVATED CHARCOAL. ESTABLISH AND MAINTAIN AIRWAY. TREAT RESPIRATORY DIFFICULTY WITH ARTIFICIAL RESPIRATION AND OXYGEN. DO NOT GIVE MORPHINE, AMINOPHYLLINE, PHENOTHIAZINES, RESERPINE, FUROSEMIDE, OR ETHACRYNIC ACID (MORGAN, RECOGNITION AND MANAGEMENT OF PESTICIDE POISONINGS, 3RD ED.). TREAT SYMPTOMATICALLY AND SUPPORTIVELY. ADMINISTRATION OF OXYGEN AND LAVAGE MUST BE PERFORMED BY QUALIFIED MEDICAL PERSONNEL. GET MEDICAL ATTENTION IMMEDIATELY.

ANTIDOTE: THE FOLLOWING ANTIDOTE(S) HAVE BEEN RECOMMENDED. HOWEVER, THE DECISION AS TO WHETHER THE SEVERITY OF POISONING REQUIRES ADMINISTRATION OF ANY ANTIDOTE AND ACTUAL DOSE REQUIRED SHOULD BE MADE BY QUALIFIED MEDICAL PERSONNEL.

FOR CHOLINESTERASE INHIBITORS: ESTABLISH CLEAR AIRWAY AND TISSUE OXYGENATION BY ASPIRATION OF SECRETIONS, AND IF NECESSARY, BY ASSISTED PULMONARY VENTILATION WITH OXYGEN. IMPROVE TISSUE OXYGENATION AS MUCH AS POSSIBLE BEFORE ADMINISTERING ATROPINE TO MINIMIZE THE RISK OF VENTRICULAR FIBRILLATION. ADMINISTER ATROPINE SULFATE INTRAVENOUSLY, OR INTRAMUSCULARLY IF IV INJECTION IS NOT POSSIBLE. IN MODERATELY SEVERE POISONING ADMINISTER ATROPINE SULFATE, 0.4-2.0 MG REPEATED EVERY 15 MINUTES UNTIL ATROPINIZATION IS ACHIEVED (TACHYCARDIA, FLUSHING, DRY MOUTH, MYDRIASIS). MAINTAIN ATROPINIZATION BY REPEATED DOSES FOR 2-12 HOURS, OR LONGER, DEPENDING ON THE SEVERITY OF POISONING. THE APPEARANCE OF RALES IN THE LUNG BASES, MIOSIS, SALIVATION, NAUSEA, BRADYCARDIA, ARE ALL INDICATIONS OF INADEQUATE ATROPINIZATION. SEVERELY POISONED INDIVIDUALS MAY EXHIBIT REMARKABLE TOLERANCE TO ATROPINE; TWO OR MORE TIMES THE DOSAGES SUGGESTED ABOVE MAY BE NEEDED. PERSONS NOT POISONED OR ONLY SLIGHTLY POISONED, HOWEVER, MAY DEVELOP SIGNS OF ATROPINE TOXICITY FROM SUCH LARGE DOSAGES: FEVER, MUSCLE FIBRILLATIONS, AND DELIRIUM ARE THE MAIN SIGNS OF ATROPINE TOXICITY. IF THESE SIGNS APPEAR WHILE THE PATIENT IS FULLY ATROPINIZED, ATROPINE ADMINISTRATION SHOULD BE DISCONTINUED, AT LEAST TEMPORARILY. OBSERVE TREATED PATIENTS CLOSELY AT LEAST 24 HOURS TO INSURE THAT SYMPTOMS (POSSIBLY PULMONARY EDEMA) DO NOT RECUR AS ATROPINIZATION WEARS OFF. IN VERY SEVERE POISONINGS, METABOLIC DISPOSITION OF TOXICANT MAY REQUIRE SEVERAL HOURS OR DAYS DURING WHICH ATROPINIZATION MUST BE MAINTAINED. MARKEDLY LOWER LEVELS OF URINARY METABOLITES INDICATE THAT ATROPINE DOSAGE CAN BE TAPERED OFF. AS DOSAGE IS REDUCED, CHECK THE LUNG BASES FREQUENTLY FOR RALES. IF RALES ARE HEARD OR OTHER SYMPTOMS RETURN, RE-ESTABLISH ATROPINIZATION PROMPTLY (MORGAN, RECOGNITION AND MANAGEMENT OF PESTICIDE POISONINGS, 3RD ED.). ADMINISTRATION OF ANTIDOTE MUST BE PERFORMED BY QUALIFIED MEDICAL PERSONNEL.

IN CASES OF SEVERE POISONING BY ORGANOPHOSPHATE PESTICIDES IN WHICH RESPIRATORY DEPRESSION, MUSCLE WEAKNESS AND TWITCHINGS ARE SEVERE, GIVE PRALIDOXIME (PROTOPAM-AYERST, 2-PAM), 1.0 GRAM INTRAVENOUSLY AT NO MORE THAN 0.5 GRAM PER MINUTE. DOSAGE OF PRALIDOXIME MAY BE REPEATED IN 1-2 HOURS, THEN AT 10-12 HOUR INTERVALS IF NEEDED. IN VERY SEVERE POISONINGS, DOSAGE RATES MAY BE DOUBLED. TREATMENT WITH PRALIDOXIME WILL BE MOST EFFECTIVE IF GIVEN WITHIN THIRTY-SIX HOURS AFTER POISONING (MORGAN, RECOGNITION AND MANAGEMENT OF PESTICIDE POISONINGS, 3RD ED.). ANTIDOTE SHOULD BE ADMINISTERED BY QUALIFIED MEDICAL PERSONNEL.

REACTIVITY

REACTIVITY: STABLE UNDER NORMAL TEMPERATURES AND PRESSURES.

INCOMPATIBILITIES: DEMETON-S-SULFONE: OXIDIZERS (STRONG): FIRE AND EXPLOSION HAZARD.

DECOMPOSITION: THERMAL DECOMPOSITION PRODUCTS MAY INCLUDE TOXIC OXIDES OF CARBON, SULFUR, AND PHOSPHORUS.

POLYMERIZATION: HAZARDOUS POLYMERIZATION HAS NOT BEEN REPORTED TO OCCUR UNDER NORMAL TEMPERATURES AND PRESSURES.

STORAGE AND DISPOSAL

OBSERVE ALL FEDERAL, STATE AND LOCAL REGULATIONS WHEN STORING OR DISPOSING OF THIS SUBSTANCE. FOR ASSISTANCE, CONTACT THE DISTRICT DIRECTOR OF THE ENVIRONMENTAL PROTECTION AGENCY.

STORAGE

STORE IN ACCORDANCE WITH 40 CFR 165 RECOMMENDED PROCEDURES FOR THE DISPOSAL AND STORAGE OF PESTICIDES AND PESTICIDE CONTAINERS. STORE AWAY FROM INCOMPATIBLE SUBSTANCES.

DISPOSAL

DISPOSAL MUST BE IN ACCORDANCE WITH 40 CFR 165 RECOMMENDED PROCEDURES FOR THE DISPOSAL AND STORAGE OF PESTICIDES AND PESTICIDE CONTAINERS.

CONDITIONS TO AVOID

MAY BE IGNITED BY HEAT, SPARKS OR FLAMES. CONTAINER MAY EXPLODE IN HEAT OF FIRE. VAPOR EXPLOSION AND POISON HAZARD INDOORS, OUTDOORS OR IN SEWERS.

MATERIAL SAFETY DATA SHEET

OCCUPATIONAL HEALTH SERVICES, INC.
AGRICULTURE AND PESTICIDE DIVISION
450 SEVENTH AVENUE, SUITE 2407
NEW YORK, NEW YORK 10123
1-800-445-MSDS OR (212) 967-1100

EMERGENCY CONTACT:
JOHN S. BRANSFORD, JR. (615) 292-1180

SUBSTANCE IDENTIFICATION

SUBSTANCE: **DEMETON-O-SULFOXIDE**

TRADE NAMES/SYNONYMS: O,O-DIETHYL O-2 ETHYLSULFINYLETHYL PHOSPHOROTHIOATE; PHOSPHORIC ACID, O,O-DIETHYL O-2 ETHYLSULFINYLETHYL ESTER; THIOL SYSTOX SULFOXIDE; C8H19O4PS2; PST06308

CHEMICAL FAMILY: ORGANOPHOSPHATE

MOLECULAR FORMULA: (C2-H5-O)2-P-(S)-O-(C-H2)2-S-(O)-C2-H5

MOLECULAR WEIGHT: 274.34

CERCLA RATINGS (SCALE 0-3): HEALTH=3 FIRE=U REACTIVITY=0 PERSISTENCE=0

NFPA RATINGS (SCALE 0-4): HEALTH=3 FIRE=U REACTIVITY=0

COMPONENTS AND CONTAMINANTS

COMPONENT: DEMETON-O-SULFOXIDE ***PERCENT:*** 100.0

OTHER CONTAMINANTS: NONE

EXPOSURE LIMITS: NO OCCUPATIONAL EXPOSURE LIMITS ESTABLISHED BY OSHA, ACGIH, OR NIOSH.

PHYSICAL DATA

DESCRIPTION: AMBER LIQUID. ***BOILING POINT:*** NOT AVAILABLE

SPECIFIC GRAVITY: NOT AVAILABLE ***VAPOR PRESSURE:*** NOT AVAILABLE

SOLUBILITY IN WATER: NOT AVAILABLE

FIRE AND EXPLOSION DATA

FIRE AND EXPLOSION HAZARD: UNKNOWN FIRE AND EXPLOSION HAZARD.

FLASH POINT: NOT AVAILABLE

FIREFIGHTING MEDIA: DRY CHEMICAL, CARBON DIOXIDE, HALON, WATER SPRAY OR STANDARD FOAM (1987 EMERGENCY RESPONSE GUIDEBOOK, DOT P 5800.4). FOR LARGER FIRES, USE WATER SPRAY, FOG OR STANDARD FOAM (1987 EMERGENCY RESPONSE GUIDEBOOK, DOT P 5800.4).

FIREFIGHTING: MOVE CONTAINERS FROM FIRE AREA IF POSSIBLE. COOL CONTAINERS EXPOSED TO FLAMES WITH WATER FROM SIDE UNTIL WELL AFTER FIRE IS OUT. FIGHT FIRE FROM MAXIMUM DISTANCE. STAY AWAY FROM STORAGE TANK ENDS. DIKE FIRE CONTROL WATER FOR LATER DISPOSAL. DO NOT SCATTER MATERIAL. (1987 EMERGENCY RESPONSE GUIDEBOOK, DOT P 5800.4, GUIDE PAGE 57). EXTINGUISH ONLY IF FLOW CAN BE STOPPED. USE FLOODING AMOUNTS OF WATER AS A FOG; SOLID STREAMS MAY BE INEFFECTIVE. COOL CONTAINERS WITH FLOODING AMOUNTS OF WATER FROM AS FAR A DISTANCE AS POSSIBLE. AVOID BREATHING POISONOUS VAPORS, KEEP UPWIND.

TRANSPORTATION DATA

DEPARTMENT OF TRANSPORTATION HAZARD CLASSIFICATION 49 CFR 172.101: POISON B

DEPARTMENT OF TRANSPORTATION LABELING REQUIREMENTS 49 CFR 172.101 AND SUBPART E: POISON

DEPARTMENT OF TRANSPORTATION PACKAGING REQUIREMENTS: 49 CFR 173.365 EXCEPTIONS: 49 CFR 173.364

TOXICITY

DEMETON-O-SULFOXIDE: TOXICITY DATA: 7.5 MG/KG ORAL-RAT LD50 (EPA). CARCINOGEN STATUS: NONE. ACUTE TOXICITY LEVEL: HIGHLY TOXIC BY INGESTION. TARGET EFFECTS: CHOLINESTERASE INHIBITOR. POISONING MAY AFFECT THE NERVOUS SYSTEM. AT INCREASED RISK FROM EXPOSURE: PERSONS WITH RESPIRATORY AILMENTS, RECENT EXPOSURE TO CHOLINESTERASE INHIBITORS OR IMPAIRED CHOLINESTERASE PRODUCTION, OR LIVER MALFUNCTION.* ADDITIONAL DATA: MAY CROSS THE PLACENTA. HIGH ENVIRONMENTAL TEMPERATURES OR EXPOSURE OF THE CHEMICAL TO VISIBLE OR ULTRAVIOLET LIGHT MAY ENHANCE THE TOXICITY. INTERACTIONS WITH MEDICATIONS MAY OCCUR.*

* MAY BE BASED ON GENERAL INFORMATION ON ORGANOPHOSPHATES.

HEALTH EFFECTS AND FIRST AID

INHALATION: DEMETON-O-SULFOXIDE: SEE INFORMATION ON ORGANOPHOSPHATES. ORGANOPHOSPHATES: CHOLINESTERASE INHIBITOR. **ACUTE EXPOSURE-** WHEN INHALED, THE FIRST EFFECTS OF CHOLINESTERASE INHIBITORS ARE USUALLY RESPIRATORY AND MAY INCLUDE NASAL HYPEREMIA AND WATERY DISCHARGE, COUGH, CHEST DISCOMFORT, DYSPNEA, AND WHEEZING DUE TO INCREASED BRONCHIAL SECRETIONS AND BRONCHOCONSTRICTION. IF SUFFICIENT AMOUNTS ARE ABSORBED, OTHER SYSTEMIC EFFECTS MAY BEGIN WITHIN A FEW MINUTES OR BE DELAYED FOR UP TO 12 HOURS. SYMPTOMS MAY INCLUDE PALLOR, NAUSEA, VOMITING, DIARRHEA, ABDOMINAL CRAMPS, HEADACHE, DIZZINESS, OCULAR PAIN, BLURRED VISION, MIOSIS OR IN SOME CASES, ESPECIALLY INITIALLY, MYDRIASIS, LACRIMATION, SALIVATION, SWEATING, AND CONFUSION. OTHER REPORTED CENTRAL NERVOUS SYSTEM OR NEUROMUSCULAR EFFECTS MAY INCLUDE ATAXIA, SLURRED SPEECH, AREFLEXIA, WEAKNESS, FATIGUE, FASCICULATIONS, TWITCHING, TREMORS POSSIBLY OF THE TONGUE AND EYELIDS, AND EVENTUALLY PARALYSIS OF THE EXTREMITIES AND POSSIBLY OF THE RESPIRATORY MUSCLES. IN SEVERE CASES THERE MAY ALSO BE INVOLUNTARY DEFECATION AND URINATION, CYANOSIS, PSYCHOSIS, HYPERGLYCEMIA, ACUTE PANCREATITIS, CARDIAC IRREGULARITIES, PULMONARY EDEMA, UNCONSCIOUSNESS, CONVULSIONS, AND COMA. DEATH IS PRIMARILY DUE TO RESPIRATORY FAILURE, ALTHOUGH CARDIOVASCULAR EFFECTS INCLUDING CARDIAC ARREST MAY ALSO BE IMPLICATED. LONG TERM SEQUELAE ARE RARE BUT MAY INCLUDE NEUROPSYCHIATRIC DISORDERS AND MYOPATHY WITH MUSCLE TENDERNESS. SOME ORGANOPHOSPHATES MAY CAUSE A DELAYED NEUROPATHY BEGINNING 1-4 WEEKS AFTER AN ACUTE EXPOSURE WHICH MAY OR MAY NOT HAVE CAUSED ACUTE CHOLINERGIC EFFECTS. NUMBNESS, TINGLING,

SPILL AND LEAK PROCEDURES

OCCUPATIONAL SPILL: SHUT OFF IGNITION SOURCES. DO NOT TOUCH SPILLED MATERIAL. STOP LEAK IF YOU CAN DO IT WITHOUT RISK. USE WATER SPRAY TO REDUCE VAPORS. FOR SMALL SPILLS, TAKE UP WITH SAND OR OTHER ABSORBENT MATERIAL AND PLACE INTO CONTAINERS FOR LATER DISPOSAL. FOR SMALL DRY SPILLS, WITH CLEAN SHOVEL PLACE MATERIAL INTO CLEAN, DRY CONTAINERS AND COVER. MOVE CONTAINERS FROM SPILL AREA. FOR LARGER SPILLS, DIKE FAR AHEAD OF SPILL FOR LATER DISPOSAL. NO SMOKING, FLAMES OR FLARES IN HAZARD AREA! KEEP UNNECESSARY PEOPLE AWAY. ISOLATE HAZARD AREA AND DENY ENTRY. VENTILATE CLOSED SPACES BEFORE ENTERING.

PROTECTIVE EQUIPMENT

VENTILATION: PROCESS ENCLOSURE RECOMMENDED. VENTILATION EQUIPMENT MUST BE EXPLOSION-PROOF.

RESPIRATOR: THE FOLLOWING RESPIRATORS ARE RECOMMENDED BASED ON INFORMATION FOUND IN THE PHYSICAL DATA, TOXICITY AND HEALTH EFFECTS SECTIONS. THEY ARE RANKED IN ORDER FROM MINIMUM TO MAXIMUM RESPIRATORY PROTECTION. THE SPECIFIC RESPIRATOR SELECTED MUST BE BASED ON CONTAMINATION LEVELS FOUND IN THE WORK PLACE, MUST NOT EXCEED THE WORKING LIMITS OF THE RESPIRATOR AND BE JOINTLY APPROVED BY THE NATIONAL INSTITUTE FOR OCCUPATIONAL SAFETY AND HEALTH AND THE MINE SAFETY AND HEALTH ADMINISTRATION (NIOSH-MSHA).

TYPE 'C' SUPPLIED-AIR RESPIRATOR WITH A FULL FACEPIECE OPERATED IN PRESSURE-DEMAND OR OTHER POSITIVE PRESSURE MODE OR WITH A FULL FACEPIECE, HELMET OR HOOD OPERATED IN CONTINOUS-FLOW MODE.

SELF-CONTAINED BREATHING APPARATUS WITH A FULL FACEPIECE OPERATED IN PRESSURE-DEMAND OR OTHER POSITIVE PRESSURE MODE.

FOR FIREFIGHTING AND OTHER IMMEDIATELY DANGEROUS TO LIFE OR HEALTH CONDITIONS:

SELF-CONTAINED BREATHING APPARATUS WITH FULL FACEPIECE OPERATED IN PRESSURE-DEMAND OR OTHER POSITIVE PRESSURE MODE.

SUPPLIED-AIR RESPIRATOR WITH FULL FACEPIECE AND OPERATED IN PRESSURE-DEMAND OR OTHER POSITIVE PRESSURE MODE IN COMBINATION WITH AN AUXILIARY SELF-CONTAINED BREATHING APPARATUS OPERATED IN PRESSURE-DEMAND OR OTHER POSITIVE PRESSURE MODE.

CLOTHING: EMPLOYEE MUST WEAR APPROPRIATE PROTECTIVE (IMPERVIOUS) CLOTHING AND EQUIPMENT TO PREVENT ANY POSSIBILITY OF SKIN CONTACT WITH THIS SUBSTANCE.

GLOVES: EMPLOYEE MUST WEAR APPROPRIATE PROTECTIVE GLOVES TO PREVENT CONTACT WITH THIS SUBSTANCE.

EYE PROTECTION: EMPLOYEE MUST WEAR SPLASH-PROOF OR DUST-RESISTANT SAFETY GOGGLES AND A FACESHIELD TO PREVENT CONTACT WITH THIS SUBSTANCE.

EMERGENCY WASH FACILITIES: WHERE THERE IS ANY POSSIBILITY THAT AN EMPLOYEE'S EYES AND/OR SKIN MAY BE EXPOSED TO THIS SUBSTANCE, THE EMPLOYER SHOULD PROVIDE AN EYE WASH FOUNTAIN AND QUICK DRENCH SHOWER WITHIN THE IMMEDIATE WORK AREA FOR EMERGENCY USE.

AUTHORIZED BY- OCCUPATIONAL HEALTH SERVICES, INC.

CREATION DATE: 06/20/90 ***REVISION DATE:*** 06/20/90

WEAKNESS AND CRAMPING BEGINNING SYMMETRICALLY IN THE LOWER LIMBS MAY PROGRESS TO ATAXIA AND PARALYSIS. IN SEVERE CASES, UPPER LIMB INVOLVEMENT IS POSSIBLE AND FLACCID PARALYSIS MAY PROGRESS TO SPASTIC PARALYSIS WITH EXAGGERATED REFLEXES. IMPROVEMENT MAY OCCUR OVER MONTHS TO YEARS, BUT SOME RESIDUAL IMPAIRMENT USUALLY REMAINS. **CHRONIC EXPOSURE**- REPEATED OR PROLONGED EXPOSURE MAY RESULT IN THE EFFECTS OF ACUTE EXPOSURE INCLUDING THE DELAYED NEUROPATHY. OTHER EFFECTS REPORTED IN WORKERS REPEATEDLY EXPOSED INCLUDE IMPAIRED MEMORY AND CONCENTRATION, ACUTE PSYCHOSIS, SEVERE DEPRESSIONS, IRRITABILTY, CONFUSION, APATHY, EMOTIONAL LABILITY, SOCIAL WITHDRAWAL, CONFUSION, HEADACHE, SPEECH DIFFICULTIES, DELAYED REACTION TIMES, SPATIAL DISORIENTATION, NIGHTMARES, SLEEPWALKING, AND DROWSINESS OR INSOMNIA. AN INFLUENZA-LIKE CONDITION WITH HEADACHE, NAUSEA, WEAKNESS, ANOREXIA AND MALAISE HAS ALSO BEEN REPORTED.

FIRST AID- REMOVE FROM EXPOSURE AREA TO FRESH AIR IMMEDIATELY. IF BREATHING HAS STOPPED, PERFORM ARTIFICIAL RESPIRATION. KEEP PERSON WARM AND AT REST. TREAT SYMPTOMATICALLY AND SUPPORTIVELY. GET MEDICAL ATTENTION IMMEDIATELY.

SKIN CONTACT: DEMETON-O-SULFOXIDE: SEE INFORMATION ON ORGANOPHOSPHATES.

ORGANOPHOSPHATES: CHOLINESTERASE INHIBITOR. **ACUTE EXPOSURE**- LOCALIZED SWEATING AND FASCICULATIONS MAY OCCUR AT THE SITE OF CONTACT. IF SUFFICIENT AMOUNTS ARE ABSORBED, OTHER EFFECTS OF CHOLINESTERASE INHIBITION AS DESCRIBED IN ACUTE INHALATION MAY OCCUR. SYMPTOMS MAY BE DELAYED 2-3 HOURS, BUT USUALLY NO MORE THAN 12 HOURS. THE RATE OF ABSORPTION IS INCREASED BY THE PRESENCE OF DERMATITIS OR HIGH AMBIENT TEMPERATURES. DELAYED NEUROPATHY IS ALSO POSSIBLE. **CHRONIC EXPOSURE**- REPEATED OR PROLONGED EXPOSURE MAY CAUSE EFFECTS AS DESCRIBED IN ACUTE EXPOSURE. SOME ORGANOPHOSPHATES MAY CAUSE SENSITIZATION.

FIRST AID- REMOVE CONTAMINATED CLOTHING IMMEDIATELY. WASH CONTAMINATED AREAS WITH SOAP AND WATER FOLLOWED BY ALCOHOL (ARENA, POISONING, 4TH ED.). EMERGENCY PERSONNEL SHOULD WEAR GLOVES AND AVOID CONTAMINATION. TREAT RESPIRATORY DIFFICULTY WITH ARTIFICIAL RESPIRATION. GET MEDICAL ATTENTION IMMEDIATELY.

EYE CONTACT: DEMETON-O-SULFOXIDE: SEE INFORMATION ON ORGANOPHOSPHATES.

ORGANOPHOSPHATES: CHOLINESTERASE INHIBITOR. **ACUTE EXPOSURE**- DIRECT CONTACT MAY CAUSE PAIN, HYPEREMIA, LACRIMATION, TWITCHING OF THE EYELIDS, MIOSIS, AND CILIARY MUSCLE SPASM WITH LOSS OF ACCOMODATION, BLURRED OR DIMMED VISION AND BROWACHE. SOMETIMES MYDRIASIS MAY OCCUR INSTEAD OF MIOSIS. WITH SUFFICIENT EXPOSURE, OTHER SYMPTOMS OF CHOLINESTERASE INHIBITION AS DESCRIBED IN ACUTE INHALATION MAY OCCUR. **CHRONIC EXPOSURE**- REPEATED OR PROLONGED EXPOSURE MAY CAUSE EFFECTS AS DESCRIBED IN ACUTE EXPOSURE. SOME COMPOUNDS HAVE CAUSED TOXIC EFFECTS ON THE CRYSTALLINE LENS, CONJUNCTIVAL THICKENING AND OBSTRUCTION OF THE NASOLACRIMAL CANALS WHEN USED AS MIOTIC EYEDROPS.

FIRST AID- IRRIGATE EYES WITH WATER OR SALINE SOLUTION. IF SYMPTOMS OF POISONING OCCUR, TREAT RESPIRATORY DIFFICULTY WITH ARTIFICIAL RESPIRATION AND OXYGEN. OBSERVE PATIENT FOR AT LEAST 24-36 HOURS (GOSSELIN, CLINICAL TOXICOLOGY OF COMMERCIAL PRODUCTS, 5TH ED.). GET MEDICAL ATTENTION IMMEDIATELY. OXYGEN SHOULD BE ADMINISTERED BY QUALIFIED MEDICAL PERSONNEL.

INGESTION: DEMETON-O-SULFOXIDE: HIGHLY TOXIC. SEE INFORMATION ON ORGANOPHOSPHATES.

ORGANOPHOSPHATES: CHOLINESTERASE INHIBITOR. **ACUTE EXPOSURE**- WHEN INGESTED, THE FIRST EFFECTS MAY BE NAUSEA, VOMITING, ANOREXIA, ABDOMINAL CRAMPS AND DIARRHEA. GASTROINTESTINAL ABSORPTION MAY CAUSE SYMPTOMS OF CHOLINESTERASE INHIBITION AS DESCRIBED IN ACUTE INHALATION. SYMPTOMS MAY BEGIN WITHIN MINUTES OR BE DELAYED FOR HOURS. DELAYED EFFECTS INCLUDING NEUROPATHY MAY ALSO OCCUR. **CHRONIC EXPOSURE**- REPEATED INGESTION MAY CAUSE EFFECTS AS DESCRIBED IN ACUTE EXPOSURE.

FIRST AID- IF PERSON IS ALERT AND RESPIRATION IS NOT DEPRESSED, GIVE SYRUP OF IPECAC FOLLOWED BY WATER (IF VOMITING OCCURS, KEEP HEAD BELOW HIPS TO PREVENT ASPIRATION). IF CONSCIOUSNESS LEVEL DECLINES OR VOMITING HAS NOT OCCURRED IN 15 MINUTES EMPTY STOMACH BY GASTRIC LAVAGE WITH THE AID OF CUFFED ENDOTRACHEAL TUBE USING ISOTONIC SALINE OR 5% SODIUM BICARBONATE FOLLOW WITH ACTIVATED CHARCOAL. ESTABLISH AND MAINTAIN AIRWAY. TREAT RESPIRATORY DIFFICULTY WITH ARTIFICIAL RESPIRATION AND OXYGEN. DO NOT GIVE MORPHINE, AMINOPHYLLINE, PHENOTHIAZINES, RESERPINE, FUROSEMIDE, OR ETHACRYNIC ACID (MORGAN, RECOGNITION AND MANAGEMENT OF PESTICIDE POISONINGS, 3RD ED.). TREAT SYMPTOMATICALLY AND SUPPORTIVELY. ADMINISTRATION OF OXYGEN AND LAVAGE MUST BE PERFORMED BY QUALIFIED MEDICAL PERSONNEL. GET MEDICAL ATTENTION IMMEDIATELY.

ANTIDOTE: THE FOLLOWING ANTIDOTE(S) HAVE BEEN RECOMMENDED. HOWEVER, THE DECISION AS TO WHETHER THE SEVERITY OF POISONING REQUIRES ADMINISTRATION OF ANY ANTIDOTE AND ACTUAL DOSE REQUIRED SHOULD BE MADE BY QUALIFIED MEDICAL PERSONNEL.

FOR CHOLINESTERASE INHIBITORS: ESTABLISH CLEAR AIRWAY AND TISSUE OXYGENATION BY ASPIRATION OF SECRETIONS, AND IF NECESSARY, BY ASSISTED PULMONARY VENTILATION WITH OXYGEN. IMPROVE TISSUE OXYGENATION AS MUCH AS POSSIBLE BEFORE ADMINISTERING ATROPINE TO MINIMIZE THE RISK OF VENTRICULAR FIBRILLATION. ADMINISTER ATROPINE SULFATE INTRAVENOUSLY, OR INTRAMUSCULARLY IF IV INJECTION IS NOT POSSIBLE. IN MODERATELY SEVERE POISONING ADMINISTER ATROPINE SULFATE, 0.4-2.0 MG REPEATED EVERY 15 MINUTES UNTIL ATROPINIZATION IS ACHIEVED (TACHYCARDIA, FLUSHING, DRY MOUTH, MYDRIASIS). MAINTAIN ATROPINIZATION BY REPEATED DOSES FOR 2-12 HOURS, OR LONGER, DEPENDING ON THE SEVERITY OF POISONING. THE APPEARANCE OF RALES IN THE LUNG BASES, MIOSIS, SALIVATION, NAUSEA, BRADYCARDIA, ARE ALL INDICATIONS OF INADEQUATE ATROPINIZATION. SEVERELY POISONED INDIVIDUALS MAY EXHIBIT REMARKABLE TOLERANCE TO ATROPINE; TWO OR MORE TIMES THE DOSAGES SUGGESTED ABOVE MAY BE NEEDED. PERSONS NOT POISONED OR ONLY SLIGHTLY POISONED, HOWEVER, MAY DEVELOP SIGNS OF ATROPINE TOXICITY FROM SUCH LARGE DOSAGES: FEVER, MUSCLE FIBRILLATIONS, AND DELIRIUM ARE THE MAIN SIGNS OF ATROPINE TOXICITY. IF THESE SIGNS APPEAR WHILE THE PATIENT IS FULLY ATROPINIZED, ATROPINE ADMINISTRATION SHOULD BE DISCONTINUED, AT LEAST TEMPORARILY. OBSERVE TREATED PATIENTS CLOSELY AT LEAST 24 HOURS TO INSURE THAT SYMPTOMS (POSSIBLY PULMONARY EDEMA) DO NOT RECUR AS ATROPINIZATION WEARS OFF. IN VERY SEVERE POISONINGS, METABOLIC DISPOSITION OF TOXICANT MAY REQUIRE SEVERAL HOURS OR DAYS DURING WHICH ATROPINIZATION MUST BE MAINTAINED. MARKEDLY LOWER LEVELS OF URINARY METABOLITES INDICATE THAT ATROPINE DOSAGE CAN BE TAPERED OFF. AS DOSAGE IS REDUCED, CHECK THE LUNG BASES FREQUENTLY FOR RALES. IF RALES ARE HEARD OR OTHER SYMPTOMS RETURN, RE-ESTABLISH ATROPINIZATION PROMPTLY (MORGAN, RECOGNITION AND MANAGEMENT OF PESTICIDE POISONINGS, 3RD ED.). ADMINISTRATION OF ANTIDOTE MUST BE PERFORMED BY QUALIFIED MEDICAL PERSONNEL.

IN CASES OF SEVERE POISONING BY ORGANOPHOSPHATE PESTICIDES IN WHICH RESPIRATORY DEPRESSION, MUSCLE WEAKNESS AND TWITCHINGS ARE SEVERE, GIVE PRALIDOXIME (PROTOPAM-AYERST, 2-PAM), 1.0 GRAM INTRAVENOUSLY AT NO MORE THAN 0.5 GRAM PER MINUTE. DOSAGE OF PRALIDOXIME MAY BE REPEATED IN 1-2 HOURS, THEN AT 10-12 HOUR INTERVALS IF NEEDED. IN VERY SEVERE POISONINGS, DOSAGE RATES MAY BE DOUBLED. TREATMENT WITH PRALIDOXIME WILL BE MOST EFFECTIVE IF GIVEN WITHIN THIRTY-SIX HOURS AFTER POISONING (MORGAN, RECOGNITION AND MANAGEMENT OF PESTICIDE POISONINGS, 3RD ED.). ANTIDOTE SHOULD BE ADMINISTERED BY QUALIFIED MEDICAL PERSONNEL.

REACTIVITY

REACTIVITY: STABLE UNDER NORMAL TEMPERATURES AND PRESSURES.

INCOMPATIBILITIES: DEMETON-O-SULFOXIDE: OXIDIZERS (STRONG): FIRE AND EXPLOSION DATA.

DECOMPOSITION: THERMAL DECOMPOSITION PRODUCTS MAY INCLUDE TOXIC OXIDES OF CARBON, SULFUR, AND PHOSPHORUS.

POLYMERIZATION: HAZARDOUS POLYMERIZATION HAS NOT BEEN REPORTED TO OCCUR UNDER NORMAL TEMPERATURES AND PRESSURES.

STORAGE AND DISPOSAL

OBSERVE ALL FEDERAL, STATE AND LOCAL REGULATIONS WHEN STORING OR DISPOSING OF THIS SUBSTANCE. FOR ASSISTANCE, CONTACT THE DISTRICT DIRECTOR OF THE ENVIRONMENTAL PROTECTION AGENCY.

****STORAGE****

STORE IN ACCORDANCE WITH 40 CFR 165 RECOMMENDED PROCEDURES FOR THE DISPOSAL AND STORAGE OF PESTICIDES AND PESTICIDE CONTAINERS.
STORE AWAY FROM INCOMPATIBLE SUBSTANCES.

****DISPOSAL****

DISPOSAL MUST BE IN ACCORDANCE WITH 40 CFR 165 RECOMMENDED PROCEDURES FOR THE DISPOSAL AND STORAGE OF PESTICIDES AND PESTICIDE CONTAINERS.

CONDITIONS TO AVOID

MAY BE IGNITED BY HEAT, SPARKS OR FLAMES. CONTAINER MAY EXPLODE IN HEAT OF FIRE. VAPOR EXPLOSION AND POISON HAZARD INDOORS, OUTDOORS OR IN SEWERS.

SPILL AND LEAK PROCEDURES

OCCUPATIONAL SPILL: SHUT OFF IGNITION SOURCES. DO NOT TOUCH SPILLED MATERIAL. STOP LEAK IF YOU CAN DO IT WITHOUT RISK. USE WATER SPRAY TO REDUCE VAPORS. FOR SMALL SPILLS, TAKE UP WITH SAND OR OTHER ABSORBENT MATERIAL AND PLACE INTO CONTAINERS FOR LATER DISPOSAL. FOR SMALL DRY SPILLS, WITH CLEAN SHOVEL PLACE MATERIAL INTO CLEAN, DRY CONTAINERS AND COVER. MOVE CONTAINERS FROM SPILL AREA. FOR LARGER SPILLS, DIKE FAR AHEAD OF SPILL FOR LATER DISPOSAL. NO SMOKING, FLAMES OR FLARES IN HAZARD AREA! KEEP UNNECESSARY PEOPLE AWAY. ISOLATE HAZARD AREA AND DENY ENTRY. VENTILATE CLOSED SPACES BEFORE ENTERING.

PROTECTIVE EQUIPMENT

VENTILATION: PROCESS ENCLOSURE RECOMMENDED. VENTILATION EQUIPMENT MUST BE EXPLOSION-PROOF.

RESPIRATOR: THE FOLLOWING RESPIRATORS ARE RECOMMENDED BASED ON INFORMATION FOUND IN THE PHYSICAL DATA, TOXICITY AND HEALTH EFFECTS SECTIONS. THEY ARE RANKED IN ORDER FROM MINIMUM TO MAXIMUM RESPIRATORY PROTECTION. THE SPECIFIC RESPIRATOR SELECTED MUST BE BASED ON CONTAMINATION LEVELS FOUND IN THE WORK PLACE, MUST NOT EXCEED THE WORKING LIMITS OF THE RESPIRATOR AND BE JOINTLY APPROVED BY THE NATIONAL INSTITUTE FOR OCCUPATIONAL SAFETY AND HEALTH AND THE MINE SAFETY AND HEALTH ADMINISTRATION (NIOSH-MSHA).

TYPE 'C' SUPPLIED-AIR RESPIRATOR WITH A FULL FACEPIECE OPERATED IN PRESSURE-DEMAND OR OTHER POSITIVE PRESSURE MODE OR WITH A FULL FACEPIECE, HELMET OR HOOD OPERATED IN CONTINOUS-FLOW MODE.

SELF-CONTAINED BREATHING APPARATUS WITH A FULL FACEPIECE OPERATED IN PRESSURE-DEMAND OR OTHER POSITIVE PRESSURE MODE.

FOR FIREFIGHTING AND OTHER IMMEDIATELY DANGEROUS TO LIFE OR HEALTH CONDITIONS:

SELF-CONTAINED BREATHING APPARATUS WITH FULL FACEPIECE OPERATED IN PRESSURE-DEMAND OR OTHER POSITIVE PRESSURE MODE.

SUPPLIED-AIR RESPIRATOR WITH FULL FACEPIECE AND OPERATED IN PRESSURE-DEMAND OR OTHER POSITIVE PRESSURE MODE IN COMBINATION WITH AN AUXILIARY SELF-CONTAINED BREATHING APPARATUS OPERATED IN PRESSURE-DEMAND OR OTHER POSITIVE PRESSURE MODE.

CLOTHING: EMPLOYEE MUST WEAR APPROPRIATE PROTECTIVE (IMPERVIOUS) CLOTHING AND EQUIPMENT TO PREVENT ANY POSSIBILITY OF SKIN CONTACT WITH THIS SUBSTANCE.

GLOVES: EMPLOYEE MUST WEAR APPROPRIATE PROTECTIVE GLOVES TO PREVENT CONTACT WITH THIS SUBSTANCE.

EYE PROTECTION: EMPLOYEE MUST WEAR SPLASH-PROOF OR DUST-RESISTANT SAFETY GOGGLES WITH OR WITHOUT A FACESHIELD TO PREVENT CONTACT WITH THIS SUBSTANCE.

EMERGENCY EYE WASH: WHERE THERE IS ANY POSSIBILITY THAT AN EMPLOYEE'S EYES MAY BE EXPOSED TO THIS SUBSTANCE, THE EMPLOYER SHOULD PROVIDE AN EYE WASH FOUNTAIN WITHIN THE IMMEDIATE WORK AREA FOR EMERGENCY USE.

AUTHORIZED BY- OCCUPATIONAL HEALTH SERVICES, INC.
CREATION DATE: 05/18/90 ***REVISION DATE:*** 05/18/90

MATERIAL SAFETY DATA SHEET

OCCUPATIONAL HEALTH SERVICES, INC.
AGRICULTURE AND PESTICIDE DIVISION
450 SEVENTH AVENUE, SUITE 2407
NEW YORK, NEW YORK 10123
1-800-445-MSDS OR (212) 967-1100

EMERGENCY CONTACT:
JOHN S. BRANSFORD, JR. (615) 292-1180

SUBSTANCE IDENTIFICATION

CAS-NUMBER 4891-54-7

SUBSTANCE: **DEMETON-O-SULFONE**

TRADE NAMES/SYNONYMS: PHOSPHOROTHIOIC ACID, O,O-DIETHYL O-(2-(ETHYLSULFONYL)ETHYL) ESTER; O,O-DIETHYL O-(2-(ETHYLSULFONYL)ETHYL) PHOSPHOROTHIOATE; PHOSPHOROTHIOIC ACID, O,O-DIETHYL 2-(ETHYLSULFONYL)ETHYL ESTER; O,O-DIETHYL 2-(ETHYLSULFONYL)ETHYL PHOSPHOROTHIOATE; THIONODEMETON SULFONE; O,O-DIETHYL O-2-ETHYL-SULFONYLETHYL PHOSPHOROTHIOATE; THIONO SYSTOX SULFONE; SYSTOX SULFONE; C8H19O5PS2; PST06309

CHEMICAL FAMILY: ORGANOPHOSPHATE

MOLECULAR FORMULA: (C2-H5-O)2-P-(S)-O-(C-H2)2-S-(O)2-C2-H5

MOLECULAR WEIGHT: 290.34

CERCLA RATINGS (SCALE 0-3): HEALTH=3 FIRE=U REACTIVITY=0 PERSISTENCE=0

NFPA RATINGS (SCALE 0-4): HEALTH=3 FIRE=U REACTIVITY=0

COMPONENTS AND CONTAMINANTS

COMPONENT: DEMETON-O-SULFONE ***PERCENT:*** 100.0
CAS# 4891-54-7

OTHER CONTAMINANTS: NONE

EXPOSURE LIMITS: NO OCCUPATIONAL EXPOSURE LIMITS ESTABLISHED BY OSHA, ACGIH, OR NIOSH.

PHYSICAL DATA

DESCRIPTION: AMBER LIQUID. ***BOILING POINT:*** NOT AVAILABLE
SPECIFIC GRAVITY: NOT AVAILABLE ***VAPOR PRESSURE:*** NOT AVAILABLE
SOLUBILITY IN WATER: NOT AVAILABLE

FIRE AND EXPLOSION DATA

FIRE AND EXPLOSION HAZARD: UNKNOWN FIRE AND EXPLOSION HAZARD.

FLASH POINT: NOT AVAILABLE

FIREFIGHTING MEDIA: DRY CHEMICAL, CARBON DIOXIDE, HALON, WATER SPRAY OR STANDARD FOAM (1987 EMERGENCY RESPONSE GUIDEBOOK, DOT P 5800.4). FOR LARGER FIRES, USE WATER SPRAY, FOG OR STANDARD FOAM (1987 EMERGENCY RESPONSE GUIDEBOOK, DOT P 5800.4).

FIREFIGHTING: MOVE CONTAINERS FROM FIRE AREA IF POSSIBLE. COOL CONTAINERS EXPOSED TO FLAMES WITH WATER FROM SIDE UNTIL WELL AFTER FIRE IS OUT. FIGHT FIRE FROM MAXIMUM DISTANCE. STAY AWAY FROM STORAGE TANK ENDS. DIKE FIRE CONTROL WATER FOR LATER DISPOSAL. DO NOT SCATTER MATERIAL. (1987 EMERGENCY RESPONSE GUIDEBOOK, DOT P 5800.4, GUIDE PAGE 57). EXTINGUISH ONLY IF FLOW CAN BE STOPPED. USE FLOODING AMOUNTS OF WATER AS A FOG; SOLID STREAMS MAY BE INEFFECTIVE. COOL CONTAINERS WITH FLOODING AMOUNTS OF WATER FROM AS FAR A DISTANCE AS POSSIBLE. AVOID BREATHING POISONOUS VAPORS, KEEP UPWIND.

TRANSPORTATION DATA

DEPARTMENT OF TRANSPORTATION HAZARD CLASSIFICATION 49 CFR 172.101: POISON B

DEPARTMENT OF TRANSPORTATION LABELING REQUIREMENTS 49 CFR 172.101 AND SUBPART E: POISON

DEPARTMENT OF TRANSPORTATION PACKAGING REQUIREMENTS: 49 CFR 173.365 EXCEPTIONS: 49 CFR 173.364

TOXICITY

DEMETON-O-SULFONE: TOXICITY DATA: 90 MG/KG ORAL-RAT LD50; 7.5 MG/KG ORAL-RAT LD50 (EPA); 30 MG/KG UNREPORTED-RAT LD50. CARCINOGEN STATUS: NONE. ACUTE TOXICITY LEVEL: HIGHLY TOXIC BY INGESTION. TARGET EFFECTS: CHOLINESTERASE INHIBITOR. POISONING MAY AFFECT THE NERVOUS SYSTEM. AT INCREASED RISK FROM EXPOSURE: PERSONS WITH RESPIRATORY AILMENTS, RECENT EXPOSURE TO CHOLINESTERASE INHIBITORS OR IMPAIRED CHOLINESTERASE PRODUCTION, OR LIVER MALFUNCTION.* ADDITIONAL DATA: MAY CROSS THE PLACENTA. HIGH ENVIRONMENTAL TEMPERATURES OR EXPOSURE OF THE CHEMICAL TO VISIBLE OR ULTRAVIOLET LIGHT MAY ENHANCE THE TOXICITY. INTERACTIONS WITH MEDICATIONS MAY OCCUR.*

* MAY BE BASED ON GENERAL INFORMATION ON ORGANOPHOSPHATES.

HEALTH EFFECTS AND FIRST AID

INHALATION: DEMETON-O-SULFONE: SEE INFORMATION ON ORGANOPHOSPHATES. ORGANOPHOSPHATES: CHOLINESTERASE INHIBITOR. **ACUTE EXPOSURE-** WHEN INHALED, THE FIRST EFFECTS OF CHOLINESTERASE INHIBITORS ARE USUALLY RESPIRATORY AND MAY INCLUDE NASAL HYPEREMIA AND WATERY DISCHARGE, COUGH, CHEST DISCOMFORT, DYSPNEA, AND WHEEZING DUE TO INCREASED BRONCHIAL SECRETIONS AND BRONCHOCONSTRICTION. IF SUFFICIENT AMOUNTS ARE ABSORBED, OTHER SYSTEMIC EFFECTS MAY BEGIN WITHIN A FEW MINUTES OR BE DELAYED FOR UP TO 12 HOURS. SYMPTOMS MAY INCLUDE PALLOR, NAUSEA, VOMITING, DIARRHEA, ABDOMINAL CRAMPS, HEADACHE, DIZZINESS, OCULAR PAIN, BLURRED VISION, MIOSIS OR IN SOME CASES, ESPECIALLY INITIALLY, MYDRIASIS, LACRIMATION, SALIVATION, SWEATING, AND CONFUSION. OTHER REPORTED CENTRAL NERVOUS SYSTEM OR NEUROMUSCULAR EFFECTS MAY INCLUDE ATAXIA, SLURRED SPEECH, AREFLEXIA, WEAKNESS, FATIGUE, FASCICULATIONS, TWITCHING, TREMORS POSSIBLY OF THE TONGUE AND EYELIDS, AND EVENTUALLY PARALYSIS OF THE EXTREMITIES AND POSSIBLY OF THE RESPIRATORY MUSCLES. IN SEVERE CASES THERE MAY ALSO BE INVOLUNTARY DEFECATION AND URINATION, CYANOSIS, PSYCHOSIS, HYPERGLYCEMIA, ACUTE PANCREATITIS, CARDIAC IRREGULARITIES, PULMONARY EDEMA, UNCONSCIOUSNESS, CONVULSIONS, AND COMA. DEATH IS PRIMARILY DUE TO RESPIRATORY FAILURE, ALTHOUGH CARDIOVASCULAR EFFECTS INCLUDING

CARDIAC ARREST MAY ALSO BE IMPLICATED. LONG TERM SEQUELAE ARE RARE BUT MAY INCLUDE NEUROPSYCHIATRIC DISORDERS AND MYOPATHY WITH MUSCLE TENDERNESS. SOME ORGANOPHOSPHATES MAY CAUSE A DELAYED NEUROPATHY BEGINNING 1-4 WEEKS AFTER AN ACUTE EXPOSURE WHICH MAY OR MAY NOT HAVE CAUSED ACUTE CHOLINERGIC EFFECTS. NUMBNESS, TINGLING, WEAKNESS AND CRAMPING BEGINNING SYMMETRICALLY IN THE LOWER LIMBS MAY PROGRESS TO ATAXIA AND PARALYSIS. IN SEVERE CASES, UPPER LIMB INVOLVEMENT IS POSSIBLE AND FLACCID PARALYSIS MAY PROGRESS TO SPASTIC PARALYSIS WITH EXAGGERATED REFLEXES. IMPROVEMENT MAY OCCUR OVER MONTHS TO YEARS, BUT SOME RESIDUAL IMPAIRMENT USUALLY REMAINS. **CHRONIC EXPOSURE-** REPEATED OR PROLONGED EXPOSURE MAY RESULT IN THE EFFECTS OF ACUTE EXPOSURE INCLUDING THE DELAYED NEUROPATHY. OTHER EFFECTS REPORTED IN WORKERS REPEATEDLY EXPOSED INCLUDE IMPAIRED MEMORY AND CONCENTRATION, ACUTE PSYCHOSIS, SEVERE DEPRESSIONS, IRRITABILTY, CONFUSION, APATHY, EMOTIONAL LABILITY, SOCIAL WITHDRAWAL, CONFUSION, HEADACHE, SPEECH DIFFICULTIES, DELAYED REACTION TIMES, SPATIAL DISORIENTATION, NIGHTMARES, SLEEPWALKING, AND DROWSINESS OR INSOMNIA. AN INFLUENZA-LIKE CONDITION WITH HEADACHE, NAUSEA, WEAKNESS, ANOREXIA AND MALAISE HAS ALSO BEEN REPORTED.

FIRST AID- REMOVE FROM EXPOSURE AREA TO FRESH AIR IMMEDIATELY. IF BREATHING HAS STOPPED, PERFORM ARTIFICIAL RESPIRATION. KEEP PERSON WARM AND AT REST. TREAT SYMPTOMATICALLY AND SUPPORTIVELY. GET MEDICAL ATTENTION IMMEDIATELY.

SKIN CONTACT: DEMETON-O-SULFONE: SEE INFORMATION ON ORGANOPHOSPHATES. ORGANOPHOSPHATES: CHOLINESTERASE INHIBITOR. **ACUTE EXPOSURE-** LOCALIZED SWEATING AND FASCICULATIONS MAY OCCUR AT THE SITE OF CONTACT. IF SUFFICIENT AMOUNTS ARE ABSORBED, OTHER EFFECTS OF CHOLINESTERASE INHIBITION AS DESCRIBED IN ACUTE INHALATION MAY OCCUR. SYMPTOMS MAY BE DELAYED 2-3 HOURS, BUT USUALLY NO MORE THAN 12 HOURS. THE RATE OF ABSORPTION IS INCREASED BY THE PRESENCE OF DERMATITIS OR HIGH AMBIENT TEMPERATURES. DELAYED NEUROPATHY IS ALSO POSSIBLE. **CHRONIC EXPOSURE-** REPEATED OR PROLONGED EXPOSURE MAY CAUSE EFFECTS AS DESCRIBED IN ACUTE EXPOSURE. SOME ORGANOPHOSPHATES MAY CAUSE SENSITIZATION.

FIRST AID- REMOVE CONTAMINATED CLOTHING IMMEDIATELY. WASH CONTAMINATED AREAS WITH SOAP AND WATER FOLLOWED BY ALCOHOL (ARENA, POISONING, 4TH ED.). EMERGENCY PERSONNEL SHOULD WEAR GLOVES AND AVOID CONTAMINATION. TREAT RESPIRATORY DIFFICULTY WITH ARTIFICIAL RESPIRATION. GET MEDICAL ATTENTION IMMEDIATELY.

EYE CONTACT: DEMETON-O-SULFONE: SEE INFORMATION ON ORGANOPHOSPHATES. ORGANOPHOSPHATES: CHOLINESTERASE INHIBITOR. **ACUTE EXPOSURE-** DIRECT CONTACT MAY CAUSE PAIN, HYPEREMIA, LACRIMATION, TWITCHING OF THE EYELIDS, MIOSIS, AND CILIARY MUSCLE SPASM WITH LOSS OF ACCOMODATION, BLURRED OR DIMMED VISION AND BROWACHE. SOMETIMES MYDRIASIS MAY OCCUR INSTEAD OF MIOSIS. WITH SUFFICIENT EXPOSURE, OTHER SYMPTOMS OF CHOLINESTERASE INHIBITION AS DESCRIBED IN ACUTE INHALATION MAY OCCUR. **CHRONIC EXPOSURE-** REPEATED OR PROLONGED EXPOSURE MAY CAUSE EFFECTS AS DESCRIBED IN ACUTE EXPOSURE. SOME COMPOUNDS HAVE CAUSED TOXIC EFFECTS ON THE CRYSTALLINE LENS, CONJUNCTIVAL THICKENING AND OBSTRUCTION OF THE NASOLACRIMAL CANALS WHEN USED AS MIOTIC EYEDROPS.

FIRST AID- IRRIGATE EYES WITH WATER OR SALINE SOLUTION. IF SYMPTOMS OF POISONING OCCUR, TREAT RESPIRATORY DIFFICULTY WITH ARTIFICIAL RESPIRATION AND OXYGEN. OBSERVE PATIENT FOR AT LEAST 24-36 HOURS (GOSSELIN, CLINICAL TOXICOLOGY OF COMMERCIAL PRODUCTS, 5TH ED.). GET MEDICAL ATTENTION IMMEDIATELY. OXYGEN SHOULD BE ADMINISTERED BY QUALIFIED MEDICAL PERSONNEL.

INGESTION: DEMETON-O-SULFONE: HIGHLY TOXIC. SEE INFORMATION ON ORGANOPHOSPHATES.
ORGANOPHOSPHATES: CHOLINESTERASE INHIBITOR. **ACUTE EXPOSURE-** WHEN INGESTED, THE FIRST EFFECTS MAY BE NAUSEA, VOMITING, ANOREXIA, ABDOMINAL CRAMPS AND DIARRHEA. GASTROINTESTINAL ABSORPTION MAY CAUSE SYMPTOMS OF CHOLINESTERASE INHIBITION AS DESCRIBED IN ACUTE INHALATION. SYMPTOMS MAY BEGIN WITHIN MINUTES OR BE DELAYED FOR HOURS. DELAYED EFFECTS INCLUDING NEUROPATHY MAY ALSO OCCUR. **CHRONIC EXPOSURE-** REPEATED INGESTION MAY CAUSE EFFECTS AS DESCRIBED IN ACUTE EXPOSURE.

FIRST AID- IF PERSON IS ALERT AND RESPIRATION IS NOT DEPRESSED, GIVE SYRUP OF IPECAC FOLLOWED BY WATER (IF VOMITING OCCURS, KEEP HEAD BELOW HIPS TO PREVENT ASPIRATION). IF CONSCIOUSNESS LEVEL DECLINES OR VOMITING HAS NOT OCCURRED IN 15 MINUTES EMPTY STOMACH BY GASTRIC LAVAGE WITH THE AID OF CUFFED ENDOTRACHEAL TUBE USING ISOTONIC SALINE OR 5% SODIUM BICARBONATE FOLLOW WITH ACTIVATED CHARCOAL. ESTABLISH AND MAINTAIN AIRWAY. TREAT RESPIRATORY DIFFICULTY WITH ARTIFICIAL RESPIRATION AND OXYGEN. DO NOT GIVE MORPHINE, AMINOPHYLLINE, PHENOTHIAZINES, RESERPINE, FUROSEMIDE, OR ETHACRYNIC ACID (MORGAN, RECOGNITION AND MANAGEMENT OF PESTICIDE POISONINGS, 3RD ED.). TREAT SYMPTOMATICALLY AND SUPPORTIVELY. ADMINISTRATION OF OXYGEN AND LAVAGE MUST BE PERFORMED BY QUALIFIED MEDICAL PERSONNEL. GET MEDICAL ATTENTION IMMEDIATELY.

ANTIDOTE: THE FOLLOWING ANTIDOTE(S) HAVE BEEN RECOMMENDED. HOWEVER, THE DECISION AS TO WHETHER THE SEVERITY OF POISONING REQUIRES ADMINISTRATION OF ANY ANTIDOTE AND ACTUAL DOSE REQUIRED SHOULD BE MADE BY QUALIFIED MEDICAL PERSONNEL.
FOR CHOLINESTERASE INHIBITORS: ESTABLISH CLEAR AIRWAY AND TISSUE OXYGENATION BY ASPIRATION OF SECRETIONS, AND IF NECESSARY, BY ASSISTED PULMONARY VENTILATION WITH OXYGEN. IMPROVE TISSUE OXYGENATION AS MUCH AS POSSIBLE BEFORE ADMINISTERING ATROPINE TO MINIMIZE THE RISK OF VENTRICULAR FIBRILLATION. ADMINISTER ATROPINE SULFATE INTRAVENOUSLY, OR INTRAMUSCULARLY IF IV INJECTION IS NOT POSSIBLE. IN MODERATELY SEVERE POISONING ADMINISTER ATROPINE SULFATE, 0.4-2.0 MG REPEATED EVERY 15 MINUTES UNTIL ATROPINIZATION IS ACHIEVED (TACHYCARDIA, FLUSHING, DRY MOUTH, MYDRIASIS). MAINTAIN ATROPINIZATION BY REPEATED DOSES FOR 2-12 HOURS, OR LONGER, DEPENDING ON THE SEVERITY OF POISONING. THE APPEARANCE OF RALES IN THE LUNG BASES, MIOSIS, SALIVATION, NAUSEA, BRADYCARDIA, ARE ALL INDICATIONS OF INADEQUATE ATROPINIZATION. SEVERELY POISONED INDIVIDUALS MAY EXHIBIT REMARKABLE TOLERANCE TO ATROPINE; TWO OR MORE TIMES THE DOSAGES SUGGESTED ABOVE MAY BE NEEDED. PERSONS NOT POISONED OR ONLY SLIGHTLY POISONED, HOWEVER, MAY DEVELOP SIGNS OF ATROPINE TOXICITY FROM SUCH LARGE DOSAGES: FEVER, MUSCLE FIBRILLATIONS, AND DELIRIUM ARE THE MAIN SIGNS OF ATROPINE TOXICITY. IF THESE SIGNS APPEAR WHILE THE PATIENT IS FULLY ATROPINIZED, ATROPINE ADMINISTRATION SHOULD BE DISCONTINUED, AT LEAST TEMPORARILY. OBSERVE TREATED PATIENTS CLOSELY AT LEAST 24 HOURS TO INSURE THAT SYMPTOMS (POSSIBLY PULMONARY EDEMA) DO NOT RECUR AS ATROPINIZATION WEARS OFF. IN VERY SEVERE POISONINGS, METABOLIC DISPOSITION OF TOXICANT MAY REQUIRE SEVERAL HOURS OR DAYS DURING WHICH ATROPINIZATION MUST BE MAINTAINED. MARKEDLY LOWER LEVELS OF URINARY METABOLITES INDICATE THAT ATROPINE DOSAGE CAN BE TAPERED OFF. AS DOSAGE IS REDUCED, CHECK THE LUNG BASES FREQUENTLY FOR RALES. IF RALES ARE HEARD OR OTHER SYMPTOMS RETURN, RE-ESTABLISH ATROPINIZATION PROMPTLY (MORGAN, RECOGNITION AND MANAGEMENT OF PESTICIDE POISONINGS, 3RD ED.). ADMINISTRATION OF ANTIDOTE MUST BE PERFORMED BY QUALIFIED MEDICAL PERSONNEL.
IN CASES OF SEVERE POISONING BY ORGANOPHOSPHATE PESTICIDES IN WHICH RESPIRATORY DEPRESSION, MUSCLE WEAKNESS AND TWITCHINGS ARE SEVERE, GIVE PRALIDOXIME (PROTOPAM-AYERST, 2-PAM), 1.0 GRAM INTRAVENOUSLY AT NO MORE THAN 0.5 GRAM PER MINUTE. DOSAGE OF PRALIDOXIME MAY BE REPEATED IN 1-2 HOURS, THEN AT 10-12 HOUR INTERVALS IF NEEDED. IN VERY SEVERE POISONINGS, DOSAGE RATES MAY BE DOUBLED. TREATMENT WITH PRALIDOXIME WILL BE MOST EFFECTIVE IF GIVEN WITHIN THIRTY-SIX HOURS AFTER POISONING (MORGAN, RECOGNITION AND MANAGEMENT OF PESTICIDE POISONINGS, 3RD ED.). ANTIDOTE SHOULD BE ADMINISTERED BY QUALIFIED MEDICAL PERSONNEL.

REACTIVITY

REACTIVITY: STABLE UNDER NORMAL TEMPERATURES AND PRESSURES.

INCOMPATIBILITIES: DEMETON-O-SULFONE: OXIDIZERS (STORNG): FIRE AND EXPLOSION HAZARD.

DECOMPOSITION: THERMAL DECOMPOSITION PRODUCTS MAY INCLUDE TOXIC OXIDES OF CARBON, SULFUR, AND PHOSPHORUS.

POLYMERIZATION: HAZARDOUS POLYMERIZATION HAS NOT BEEN REPORTED TO OCCUR UNDER NORMAL TEMPERATURES AND PRESSURES.

STORAGE AND DISPOSAL

OBSERVE ALL FEDERAL, STATE AND LOCAL REGULATIONS WHEN STORING OR DISPOSING OF THIS SUBSTANCE. FOR ASSISTANCE, CONTACT THE DISTRICT DIRECTOR OF THE ENVIRONMENTAL PROTECTION AGENCY.

STORAGE

STORE IN ACCORDANCE WITH 40 CFR 165 RECOMMENDED PROCEDURES FOR THE DISPOSAL AND STORAGE OF PESTICIDES AND PESTICIDE CONTAINERS.
STORE AWAY FROM INCOMPATIBLE SUBSTANCES.

DISPOSAL

DISPOSAL MUST BE IN ACCORDANCE WITH 40 CFR 165 RECOMMENDED PROCEDURES FOR THE DISPOSAL AND STORAGE OF PESTICIDES AND PESTICIDE CONTAINERS.

CONDITIONS TO AVOID

MAY BE IGNITED BY HEAT, SPARKS OR FLAMES. CONTAINER MAY EXPLODE IN HEAT OF FIRE. VAPOR EXPLOSION AND POISON HAZARD INDOORS, OUTDOORS OR IN SEWERS.

SPILL AND LEAK PROCEDURES

OCCUPATIONAL SPILL: SHUT OFF IGNITION SOURCES. DO NOT TOUCH SPILLED MATERIAL. STOP LEAK IF YOU CAN DO IT WITHOUT RISK. USE WATER SPRAY TO REDUCE VAPORS. FOR SMALL SPILLS, TAKE UP WITH SAND OR OTHER ABSORBENT MATERIAL AND PLACE INTO CONTAINERS FOR LATER DISPOSAL. FOR SMALL DRY SPILLS, WITH CLEAN SHOVEL PLACE MATERIAL INTO CLEAN, DRY CONTAINERS AND COVER. MOVE CONTAINERS FROM SPILL AREA. FOR LARGER SPILLS, DIKE FAR AHEAD OF SPILL FOR LATER DISPOSAL. NO SMOKING, FLAMES OR FLARES IN HAZARD AREA! KEEP UNNECESSARY PEOPLE AWAY. ISOLATE HAZARD AREA AND DENY ENTRY. VENTILATE CLOSED SPACES BEFORE ENTERING.

PROTECTIVE EQUIPMENT

VENTILATION: PROCESS ENCLOSURE RECOMMENDED. VENTILATION EQUIPMENT MUST BE EXPLOSION-PROOF.

RESPIRATOR: THE FOLLOWING RESPIRATORS ARE RECOMMENDED BASED ON INFORMATION FOUND IN THE PHYSICAL DATA, TOXICITY AND HEALTH EFFECTS SECTIONS. THEY ARE RANKED IN ORDER FROM MINIMUM TO MAXIMUM RESPIRATORY PROTECTION. THE SPECIFIC RESPIRATOR SELECTED MUST BE BASED ON CONTAMINATION LEVELS FOUND IN THE WORK PLACE, MUST NOT EXCEED THE WORKING LIMITS OF THE RESPIRATOR AND BE JOINTLY APPROVED BY THE NATIONAL INSTITUTE FOR OCCUPATIONAL SAFETY AND HEALTH AND THE MINE SAFETY AND HEALTH ADMINISTRATION (NIOSH-MSHA).

TYPE 'C' SUPPLIED-AIR RESPIRATOR WITH A FULL FACEPIECE OPERATED IN PRESSURE-DEMAND OR OTHER POSITIVE PRESSURE MODE OR WITH A FULL FACEPIECE, HELMET OR HOOD OPERATED IN CONTINOUS-FLOW MODE.

SELF-CONTAINED BREATHING APPARATUS WITH A FULL FACEPIECE OPERATED IN PRESSURE-DEMAND OR OTHER POSITIVE PRESSURE MODE.

FOR FIREFIGHTING AND OTHER IMMEDIATELY DANGEROUS TO LIFE OR HEALTH CONDITIONS:

SELF-CONTAINED BREATHING APPARATUS WITH FULL FACEPIECE OPERATED IN PRESSURE-DEMAND OR OTHER POSITIVE PRESSURE MODE.

SUPPLIED-AIR RESPIRATOR WITH FULL FACEPIECE AND OPERATED IN PRESSURE-DEMAND OR OTHER POSITIVE PRESSURE MODE IN COMBINATION WITH AN AUXILIARY SELF-CONTAINED BREATHING APPARATUS OPERATED IN PRESSURE-DEMAND OR OTHER POSITIVE PRESSURE MODE.

CLOTHING: EMPLOYEE MUST WEAR APPROPRIATE PROTECTIVE (IMPERVIOUS) CLOTHING AND EQUIPMENT TO PREVENT ANY POSSIBILITY OF SKIN CONTACT WITH THIS SUBSTANCE.

GLOVES: EMPLOYEE MUST WEAR APPROPRIATE PROTECTIVE GLOVES TO PREVENT CONTACT WITH THIS SUBSTANCE.

EYE PROTECTION: EMPLOYEE MUST WEAR SPLASH-PROOF OR DUST-RESISTANT SAFETY GOGGLES WITH OR WITHOUT A FACESHIELD TO PREVENT CONTACT WITH THIS SUBSTANCE.

EMERGENCY EYE WASH: WHERE THERE IS ANY POSSIBILITY THAT AN EMPLOYEE'S EYES MAY BE EXPOSED TO THIS SUBSTANCE, THE EMPLOYER SHOULD PROVIDE AN EYE WASH FOUNTAIN WITHIN THE IMMEDIATE WORK AREA FOR EMERGENCY USE.

AUTHORIZED BY- OCCUPATIONAL HEALTH SERVICES, INC.

CREATION DATE: 05/18/90 ***REVISION DATE:*** 05/18/90

MATERIAL SAFETY DATA SHEET

OCCUPATIONAL HEALTH SERVICES, INC.
AGRICULTURE AND PESTICIDE DIVISION
450 SEVENTH AVENUE, SUITE 2407
NEW YORK, NEW YORK 10123
1-800-445-MSDS OR (212) 967-1100

EMERGENCY CONTACT:
JOHN S. BRANSFORD, JR. (615) 292-1180

SUBSTANCE IDENTIFICATION

CAS-NUMBER 319-86-8

SUBSTANCE: DELTA-HEXACHLOROCYCLOHEXANE

TRADE NAMES/SYNONYMS: CYCLOHEXANE, 1,2,3,4,5,6-HEXACHLORO-, (1ALPHA,2ALPHA,3ALPHA,4BETA, 5ALPHA,6BETA)-; (1ALPHA,2ALPHA,3ALPHA,4BETA,5ALPHA,6BETA)-1,2,3,4,5,6-HEXACHLOROCYCLOHEXANE; CYCLOHEXANE, 1,2,3,4,5,6-HEXACHLORO-, DELTA-; DELTA-1,2,3,4,5,6-HEXACHLOROCYCLOHEXANE; DELTA-BENZENE HEXACHLORIDE; DELTA-BHC; DELTA-HCH; BENZENE HEXACHLORIDE; 1,2,3,4,5,6-HEXACHLOROCYCLOHEXANE; HEXACHLOROCYCLOHEXANE; HCH; BHC; ENT 9,234; DELTA-LINDANE; C6H6CL6; PST06310

CHEMICAL FAMILY: HALOGEN COMPOUND, ALICYCLIC

MOLECULAR FORMULA: C6-H6-CL6

MOLECULAR WEIGHT: 290.83

CERCLA RATINGS (SCALE 0-3): HEALTH=2 FIRE=0 REACTIVITY=0 PERSISTENCE=3

NFPA RATINGS (SCALE 0-4): HEALTH=U FIRE=0 REACTIVITY=0

COMPONENTS AND CONTAMINANTS

COMPONENT: DELTA-HEXACHLOROCYCLOHEXANE ***PERCENT:*** 100.0
CAS# 319-86-8

OTHER CONTAMINANTS: NONE

EXPOSURE LIMITS: NO OCCUPATIONAL EXPOSURE LIMITS ESTABLISHED BY OSHA, ACGIH, OR NIOSH.

DELTA-HEXACHLOROCYCLOHEXANE: 1 POUND CERCLA SECTION 103 REPORTABLE QUANTITY SUBJECT TO CALIFORNIA PROPOSITION 65 CANCER AND/OR REPRODUCTIVE TOXICITY WARNING AND RELEASE REQUIREMENTS- (OCTOBER 1, 1989)

PHYSICAL DATA

DESCRIPTION: COLORLESS PLATES. ***BOILING POINT:*** 140 F (60 C) @ 0.36 MMHG

MELTING POINT: 286-288 F (141-142 C) ***SPECIFIC GRAVITY:*** NOT AVAILABLE

VAPOR PRESSURE: 0.02 MMHG @ 20 C ***SOLUBILITY IN WATER:*** 10 PPM

SOLVENT SOLUBILITY: SOLUBLE IN ACETONE, BENZENE, CHLOROFORM, ETHER, ETHANOL, METHANOL, XYLENE, FATS AND OILS.

FIRE AND EXPLOSION DATA

FIRE AND EXPLOSION HAZARD: NEGLIGIBLE FIRE HAZARD WHEN EXPOSED TO HEAT OR FLAME.

FIREFIGHTING MEDIA: DRY CHEMICAL, CARBON DIOXIDE, HALON, WATER SPRAY OR STANDARD FOAM (1987 EMERGENCY RESPONSE GUIDEBOOK, DOT P 5800.4). FOR LARGER FIRES, USE WATER SPRAY, FOG OR STANDARD FOAM (1987 EMERGENCY RESPONSE GUIDEBOOK, DOT P 5800.4).

FIREFIGHTING: MOVE CONTAINERS FROM FIRE AREA IF POSSIBLE. FIGHT FIRE FROM MAXIMUM DISTANCE. STAY AWAY FROM STORAGE TANK ENDS. DIKE FIRE CONTROL WATER FOR LATER DISPOSAL. DO NOT SCATTER MATERIAL (1987 EMERGENCY RESPONSE GUIDEBOOK, DOT P 5800.4, GUIDE PAGE 55).

USE AGENTS SUITABLE FOR TYPE OF FIRE. COOL CONTAINERS WITH FLOODING AMOUNTS OF WATER. AVOID BREATHING VAPORS OR DUSTS, KEEP UPWIND.

TOXICITY

DELTA-HEXACHLOROCYCLOHEXANE: TOXICITY DATA: 1000 MG/KG ORAL-RAT LD50; 750 MG/KG ORAL-RAT LD50 (IARC, VOLUME 20, 1979). CARCINOGEN STATUS: ANTICIPATED HUMAN CARCINOGEN (NTP); HUMAN INADEQUATE EVIDENCE (IARC GROUP-2B). THE EVIDENCE FOR THE CARCINOGENICITY OF HEXACHLOROCYCLOHEXANES ISOMERS WAS JUDGED AS INADEQUATE. ACUTE TOXICITY LEVEL: MODERATELY TOXIC BY INGESTION. TARGET EFFECTS: POISONING MAY AFFECT THE LIVER. CENTRAL NERVOUS SYSTEM DEPRESSION WAS OBSERVED IN ANIMAL STUDIES. ADDITIONAL DATA: STIMULANTS SUCH AS EPINEPHRINE MAY INDUCE VENTRICULAR FIBRILLATION.

HEALTH EFFECTS AND FIRST AID

INHALATION: DELTA-HEXACHLOROCYCLOHEXANE: **ACUTE EXPOSURE-** MAY CAUSE IRRITATION. **CHRONIC EXPOSURE-** NO DATA AVAILABLE.

FIRST AID- REMOVE FROM EXPOSURE AREA TO FRESH AIR IMMEDIATELY. IF BREATHING HAS STOPPED, PERFORM ARTIFICIAL RESPIRATION. KEEP PERSON WARM AND AT REST. TREAT SYMPTOMATICALLY AND SUPPORTIVELY. GET MEDICAL ATTENTION IMMEDIATELY.

SKIN CONTACT: DELTA-HEXACHLOROCYCLOHEXANE: **ACUTE EXPOSURE-** MAY CAUSE IRRITATION. **CHRONIC EXPOSURE-** NO DATA AVAILABLE.

FIRST AID- REMOVE CONTAMINATED CLOTHING AND SHOES IMMEDIATELY. WASH AFFECTED AREA WITH SOAP OR MILD DETERGENT AND LARGE AMOUNTS OF WATER UNTIL NO EVIDENCE OF CHEMICAL REMAINS (APPROXIMATELY 15-20 MINUTES). GET MEDICAL ATTENTION IMMEDIATELY.

EYE CONTACT: DELTA-HEXACHLOROCYCLOHEXANE: **ACUTE EXPOSURE-** MAY CAUSE IRRITATION. **CHRONIC EXPOSURE-** NO DATA AVAILABLE.

FIRST AID- WASH EYES IMMEDIATELY WITH LARGE AMOUNTS OF WATER OR NORMAL SALINE, OCCASIONALLY LIFTING UPPER AND LOWER LIDS, UNTIL NO EVIDENCE OF CHEMICAL REMAINS (APPROXIMATELY 15-20 MINUTES). GET MEDICAL ATTENTION IMMEDIATELY.

INGESTION: DELTA-HEXACHLOROCYCLOHEXANE: **ACUTE EXPOSURE-** A LETHAL DOSE IN RATS WAS 750 MG/KG; SYMPTOMS WERE NOT REPORTED. **CHRONIC EXPOSURE-** CHANGES HAVE BEEN REPORTED IN THE KIDNEYS, LIVER, PANCREAS, TESTES, LUNGS AND NASAL MUCOUS MEMBRANES OF ANIMALS FOLLOWING SUFFICIENTLY HIGH REPEATED ABSORPTION OF HEXACHLOROCYCLOHEXANE OR ONE OF ITS ISOMERS. A MIXTURE OF THE DELTA ISOMER AND OTHER ISOMERS OF HEXACHLOROCYCLOHEXANE HAVE PRODUCED LIVER TUMORS IN MICE.

FIRST AID- IF THE PERSON IS CONSCIOUS AND NOT CONVULSING, REMOVE BY GIVING SYRUP OF IPECAC (IF VOMITING OCCURS, KEEP THE HEAD BELOW THE HIPS TO PREVENT ASPIRATION). GIVE ACTIVATED CHARCOAL FOLLOWED BY GASTRIC LAVAGE. FOLLOW WITH A SALINE CATHARTIC. DO NOT GIVE FATS OR OILS. INTESTINAL LAVAGE WITH 20% MANNITOL (200 ML) BY STOMACH TUBE IS ALSO USEFUL. GIVE ARTIFICIAL RESPIRATION WITH OXYGEN IF RESPIRATION IS DEPRESSED (DREISBACH, HANDBOOK OF POISONING, 12TH ED.). TREAT SYMPTOMATICALLY AND SUPPORTIVELY. LAVAGE AND ADMINISTRATION OF OXYGEN SHOULD BE PERFORMED BY QUALIFIED MEDICAL PERSONNEL. GET MEDICAL ATTENTION IMMEDIATELY.

REACTIVITY

REACTIVITY: STABLE UNDER NORMAL TEMPERATURES AND PRESSURES.

INCOMPATIBILITIES: 1,2,3,4,5,6-HEXACHLOROCYCLOHEXANE: ALKALIES- MAY DECOMPOSE. ALUMINUM: MAY DECOMPOSE. N,N-DIMETHYLACETAMIDE: EXOTHERMIC, POSSIBLE VIOLENT REACTION. DIMETHYLFORMAMIDE: POSSIBLE DANGEROUS REACTION. IRON: MAY DECOMPOSE. ZINC: MAY DECOMPOSE.

DECOMPOSITION: THERMAL DECOMPOSITION PRODUCTS MAY INCLUDE HIGHLY TOXIC FUMES OF PHOSGENE, TOXIC AND CORROSIVE FUMES OF CHLORIDES, AND OXIDES OF CARBON.

POLYMERIZATION: HAZARDOUS POLYMERIZATION HAS NOT BEEN REPORTED TO OCCUR UNDER NORMAL TEMPERATURES AND PRESSURES.

STORAGE AND DISPOSAL

OBSERVE ALL FEDERAL, STATE AND LOCAL REGULATIONS WHEN STORING OR DISPOSING OF THIS SUBSTANCE. FOR ASSISTANCE, CONTACT THE DISTRICT DIRECTOR OF THE ENVIRONMENTAL PROTECTION AGENCY.

STORAGE

STORE IN ACCORDANCE WITH 40 CFR 165 RECOMMENDED PROCEDURES FOR THE DISPOSAL AND STORAGE OF PESTICIDES AND PESTICIDE CONTAINERS.
STORE AWAY FROM INCOMPATIBLE SUBSTANCES.

DISPOSAL

DISPOSAL MUST BE IN ACCORDANCE WITH 40 CFR 165 RECOMMENDED PROCEDURES FOR THE DISPOSAL AND STORAGE OF PESTICIDES AND PESTICIDE CONTAINERS.

CONDITIONS TO AVOID

MAY BURN BUT DOES NOT IGNITE READILY. CONTAINERS MAY EXPLODE IN HEAT OF FIRE.

SPILL AND LEAK PROCEDURES

WATER SPILL: THE CALIFORNIA SAFE DRINKING WATER AND TOXIC ENFORCEMENT ACT OF 1986 (PROPOSITION 65) PROHIBITS CONTAMINATING ANY KNOWN SOURCE OF DRINKING WATER WITH SUBSTANCES KNOWN TO CAUSE CANCER AND/OR REPRODUCTIVE TOXICITY.

OCCUPATIONAL SPILL: DO NOT TOUCH SPILLED MATERIAL. STOP LEAK IF YOU CAN DO IT WITHOUT RISK. USE WATER SPRAY TO REDUCE VAPORS. FOR SMALL SPILLS, TAKE UP WITH SAND OR OTHER ABSORBENT MATERIAL AND PLACE INTO CONTAINERS FOR LATER DISPOSAL. FOR SMALL DRY SPILLS, WITH A CLEAN SHOVEL PLACE MATERIAL INTO CLEAN, DRY CONTAINERS AND COVER. MOVE CONTAINERS FROM SPILL AREA. FOR LARGER SPILLS, DIKE FAR AHEAD OF SPILL FOR LATER DISPOSAL. KEEP UNNECESSARY PEOPLE AWAY. ISOLATE HAZARD AREA AND DENY ENTRY. VENTILATE CLOSED SPACES BEFORE ENTERING. REPORTABLE QUANTITY (RQ): 1 POUND THE SUPERFUND AMENDMENTS AND REAUTHORIZATION ACT (SARA) SECTION 304 REQUIRES THAT A RELEASE EQUAL TO OR GREATER THAN THE REPORTABLE QUANTITY FOR THIS SUBSTANCE BE IMMEDIATELY REPORTED TO THE LOCAL EMERGENCY PLANNING COMMITTEE AND THE STATE EMERGENCY RESPONSE COMMISSION (40 CFR 355.40). IF THE RELEASE OF THIS SUBSTANCE IS REPORTABLE UNDER CERCLA SECTION 103, THE NATIONAL RESPONSE CENTER MUST BE NOTIFIED IMMEDIATELY AT (800) 424-8802 OR (202) 426-2675 IN THE METROPOLITAN WASHINGTON, D.C. AREA (40 CFR 302.6).

PROTECTIVE EQUIPMENT

VENTILATION: PROVIDE LOCAL EXHAUST OR GENERAL DILUTION VENTILATION SYSTEM.

RESPIRATOR: THE FOLLOWING RESPIRATORS ARE RECOMMENDED BASED ON INFORMATION FOUND IN THE PHYSICAL DATA, TOXICITY AND HEALTH EFFECTS SECTIONS. THEY ARE RANKED IN ORDER FROM MINIMUM TO MAXIMUM RESPIRATORY PROTECTION. THE SPECIFIC RESPIRATOR SELECTED MUST BE BASED ON CONTAMINATION LEVELS FOUND IN THE WORK PLACE, MUST NOT EXCEED THE WORKING LIMITS OF THE RESPIRATOR AND BE JOINTLY APPROVED BY THE NATIONAL INSTITUTE FOR OCCUPATIONAL SAFETY AND HEALTH AND THE MINE SAFETY AND HEALTH ADMINISTRATION (NIOSH-MSHA).
CHEMICAL CARTRIDGE RESPIRATOR WITH AN ORGANIC VAPOR CARTRIDGE(S) WITH A FULL FACEPIECE AND ORGANIC VAPOR CARTRIDGE(S) IN COMBINATION WITH A DUST AND MIST FILTER.
POWERED AIR-PURIFYING RESPIRATOR WITH A TIGHT-FITTING FACEPIECE AND ORGANIC VAPOR CARTRIDGE(S) IN COMBINATION WITH A HIGH-EFFICIENCY PARTICULATE FILTER.
TYPE 'C' SUPPLIED-AIR RESPIRATOR WITH A FULL FACEPIECE OPERATED IN A PRESSURE-DEMAND OR OTHER POSITIVE PRESSURE MODE.
SELF-CONTAINED BREATHING APPARATUS WITH A FULL FACEPIECE OPERATED IN PRESSURE-DEMAND OR OTHER POSITIVE PRESSURE MODE.
FOR FIREFIGHTING AND OTHER IMMEDIATELY DANGEROUS TO LIFE OR HEALTH CONDITIONS:
SELF-CONTAINED BREATHING APPARATUS WITH FULL FACEPIECE OPERATED IN PRESSURE-DEMAND OR OTHER POSITIVE PRESSURE MODE.
SUPPLIED-AIR RESPIRATOR WITH FULL FACEPIECE AND OPERATED IN PRESSURE-DEMAND OR OTHER POSITIVE PRESSURE MODE IN COMBINATION WITH AN AUXILIARY SELF-CONTAINED BREATHING APPARATUS OPERATED IN PRESSURE-DEMAND OR OTHER POSITIVE PRESSURE MODE.

CLOTHING: EMPLOYEE MUST WEAR APPROPRIATE PROTECTIVE (IMPERVIOUS) CLOTHING AND EQUIPMENT TO PREVENT ANY POSSIBILITY OF SKIN CONTACT WITH THIS SUBSTANCE.

GLOVES: EMPLOYEE MUST WEAR APPROPRIATE PROTECTIVE GLOVES TO PREVENT CONTACT WITH THIS SUBSTANCE.

EYE PROTECTION: EMPLOYEE MUST WEAR SPLASH-PROOF OR DUST-RESISTANT SAFETY GOGGLES TO PREVENT EYE CONTACT WITH THIS SUBSTANCE.
EMERGENCY EYE WASH: WHERE THERE IS ANY POSSIBILITY THAT AN EMPLOYEE'S EYES MAY BE EXPOSED TO THIS SUBSTANCE, THE EMPLOYER SHOULD PROVIDE AN EYE WASH FOUNTAIN WITHIN THE IMMEDIATE WORK AREA FOR EMERGENCY USE.

AUTHORIZED BY- OCCUPATIONAL HEALTH SERVICES, INC.
CREATION DATE: 10/04/89 ***REVISION DATE:*** 07/12/90

MATERIAL SAFETY DATA SHEET

OCCUPATIONAL HEALTH SERVICES, INC.
AGRICULTURE AND PESTICIDE DIVISION
450 SEVENTH AVENUE, SUITE 2407
NEW YORK, NEW YORK 10123
1-800-445-MSDS OR (212) 967-1100

EMERGENCY CONTACT:
JOHN S. BRANSFORD, JR. (615) 292-1180

SUBSTANCE IDENTIFICATION

CAS-NUMBER 2496-92-6

SUBSTANCE: **DEMETON-S SULFOXIDE**

TRADE NAMES/SYNONYMS: PHOSPHOROTHIOIC ACID, O,O-DIETHYL S-(2-(ETHYLSULFINYL)ETHYL) ESTER; O,O-DIETHYL S-(2-(ETHYLSULFINYL)ETHYL PHOSPHOROTHIOATE; ISOSYSTOX SULFOXIDE; SYSTOX SULFOXIDE; O,O-DIETHYL S-ETHYLSULFINYLETHYL-PHOSPHOROTHIOATE; C8H19O4PS2; PST06316

CHEMICAL FAMILY: ORGANOPHOSPHATE

MOLECULAR FORMULA: (C2-H5-O)2-P-(O)-S-(C-H2)2-S-(O)-C2-H5

MOLECULAR WEIGHT: 274.34

CERCLA RATINGS (SCALE 0-3): HEALTH=3 FIRE=U REACTIVITY=0 PERSISTENCE=0

NFPA RATINGS (SCALE 0-4): HEALTH=3 FIRE=U REACTIVITY=0

COMPONENTS AND CONTAMINANTS

COMPONENT: DEMETON-S SULFOXIDE ***PERCENT:*** 100.0
CAS# 2496-92-6

OTHER CONTAMINANTS: NONE

EXPOSURE LIMITS: NO OCCUPATIONAL EXPOSURE LIMITS ESTABLISHED BY OSHA, ACGIH, OR NIOSH.

PHYSICAL DATA

DESCRIPTION: CLEAR LIQUID. ***BOILING POINT:*** NOT AVAILABLE
SPECIFIC GRAVITY: NOT AVAILABLE ***VAPOR PRESSURE:*** NOT AVAILABLE
SOLUBILITY IN WATER: NOT AVAILABLE

FIRE AND EXPLOSION DATA

FIRE AND EXPLOSION HAZARD: UNKNOWN FIRE AND EXPLOSION HAZARD.

FLASH POINT: NOT AVAILABLE

FIREFIGHTING MEDIA: DRY CHEMICAL, CARBON DIOXIDE, HALON, WATER SPRAY OR STANDARD FOAM (1987 EMERGENCY RESPONSE GUIDEBOOK, DOT P 5800.4). FOR LARGER FIRES, USE WATER SPRAY, FOG OR STANDARD FOAM (1987 EMERGENCY RESPONSE GUIDEBOOK, DOT P 5800.4).

FIREFIGHTING: MOVE CONTAINERS FROM FIRE AREA IF POSSIBLE. COOL CONTAINERS EXPOSED TO FLAMES WITH WATER FROM SIDE UNTIL WELL AFTER FIRE IS OUT. FIGHT FIRE FROM MAXIMUM DISTANCE. STAY AWAY FROM STORAGE TANK ENDS. DIKE FIRE CONTROL WATER FOR LATER DISPOSAL. DO NOT SCATTER MATERIAL. (1987 EMERGENCY RESPONSE GUIDEBOOK, DOT P 5800.4, GUIDE PAGE 57). EXTINGUISH ONLY IF FLOW CAN BE STOPPED. USE FLOODING AMOUNTS OF WATER AS A FOG; SOLID STREAMS MAY BE INEFFECTIVE. COOL CONTAINERS WITH FLOODING AMOUNTS OF WATER FROM AS FAR A DISTANCE AS POSSIBLE. AVOID BREATHING POISONOUS VAPORS, KEEP UPWIND.

TRANSPORTATION DATA

DEPARTMENT OF TRANSPORTATION HAZARD CLASSIFICATION 49 CFR 172.101: POISON B

DEPARTMENT OF TRANSPORTATION LABELING REQUIREMENTS 49 CFR 172.101 AND SUBPART E: POISON

DEPARTMENT OF TRANSPORTATION PACKAGING REQUIREMENTS: 49 CFR 173.365 EXCEPTIONS: 49 CFR 173.364

TOXICITY

DEMETON-S SULFOXIDE: TOXICITY DATA: 2000 UG/KG ORAL-RAT LD50; 5000 UG/KG INTRAPERITONEAL-GUINEA PIG LD50; 5600 UG/KG INTRAPERITONEAL-MOUSE LD50; 1500 UG/KG INTRAPERITONEAL-RAT LD50. CARCINOGEN STATUS: NONE. ACUTE TOXICITY LEVEL: HIGHLY TOXIC BY INGESTION. TARGET EFFECTS: CHOLINESTERASE INHIBITOR. POISONING MAY AFFECT THE NERVOUS SYSTEM. AT INCREASED RISK FROM EXPOSURE: PERSONS WITH RESPIRATORY AILMENTS, RECENT EXPOSURE TO CHOLINESTERASE INHIBITORS OR IMPAIRED CHOLINESTERASE PRODUCTION, OR LIVER MALFUNCTION.* ADDITIONAL DATA: MAY CROSS THE PLACENTA. HIGH ENVIRONMENTAL TEMPERATURES OR EXPOSURE OF THE CHEMICAL TO VISIBLE OR ULTRAVIOLET LIGHT MAY ENHANCE THE TOXICITY. INTERACTIONS WITH MEDICATIONS MAY OCCUR.*

* MAY BE BASED ON GENERAL INFORMATION ON ORGANOPHOSPHATES.

HEALTH EFFECTS AND FIRST AID

INHALATION: DEMETON-S SULFOXIDE: SEE INFORMATION ON ORGANOPHOSPHATES.

ORGANOPHOSPHATES: CHOLINESTERASE INHIBITOR. **ACUTE EXPOSURE-** WHEN INHALED, THE FIRST EFFECTS OF CHOLINESTERASE INHIBITORS ARE USUALLY RESPIRATORY AND MAY INCLUDE NASAL HYPEREMIA AND WATERY DISCHARGE, COUGH, CHEST DISCOMFORT, DYSPNEA, AND WHEEZING DUE TO INCREASED BRONCHIAL SECRETIONS AND BRONCHOCONSTRICTION. IF SUFFICIENT AMOUNTS ARE ABSORBED, OTHER SYSTEMIC EFFECTS MAY BEGIN WITHIN A FEW MINUTES OR BE DELAYED FOR UP TO 12 HOURS. SYMPTOMS MAY INCLUDE PALLOR, NAUSEA, VOMITING, DIARRHEA, ABDOMINAL CRAMPS, HEADACHE, DIZZINESS, OCULAR PAIN, BLURRED VISION, MIOSIS OR IN SOME CASES, ESPECIALLY INITIALLY, MYDRIASIS, LACRIMATION, SALIVATION, SWEATING, AND CONFUSION. OTHER REPORTED CENTRAL NERVOUS SYSTEM OR NEUROMUSCULAR EFFECTS MAY INCLUDE ATAXIA, SLURRED SPEECH, AREFLEXIA, WEAKNESS, FATIGUE, FASCICULATIONS, TWITCHING, TREMORS POSSIBLY OF THE TONGUE AND EYELIDS, AND EVENTUALLY PARALYSIS OF THE EXTREMITIES AND POSSIBLY OF THE RESPIRATORY MUSCLES. IN SEVERE CASES THERE MAY ALSO BE INVOLUNTARY DEFECATION AND URINATION, CYANOSIS, PSYCHOSIS, HYPERGLYCEMIA, ACUTE PANCREATITIS, CARDIAC IRREGULARITIES, PULMONARY EDEMA, UNCONSCIOUSNESS, CONVULSIONS, AND COMA. DEATH IS PRIMARILY DUE TO RESPIRATORY FAILURE, ALTHOUGH CARDIOVASCULAR EFFECTS INCLUDING CARDIAC ARREST MAY ALSO BE IMPLICATED. LONG TERM SEQUELAE ARE RARE BUT MAY INCLUDE NEUROPSYCHIATRIC DISORDERS AND MYOPATHY WITH MUSCLE TENDERNESS. SOME ORGANOPHOSPHATES MAY CAUSE A DELAYED NEUROPATHY BEGINNING 1-4 WEEKS AFTER AN ACUTE EXPOSURE WHICH MAY OR MAY NOT HAVE CAUSED ACUTE CHOLINERGIC EFFECTS. NUMBNESS, TINGLING, WEAKNESS AND CRAMPING BEGINNING SYMMETRICALLY IN THE LOWER LIMBS MAY PROGRESS TO ATAXIA AND PARALYSIS. IN SEVERE CASES, UPPER LIMB INVOLVEMENT IS POSSIBLE AND FLACCID PARALYSIS MAY PROGRESS TO SPASTIC PARALYSIS WITH EXAGGERATED REFLEXES. IMPROVEMENT MAY OCCUR OVER MONTHS TO YEARS, BUT SOME RESIDUAL IMPAIRMENT USUALLY REMAINS. **CHRONIC EXPOSURE-** REPEATED OR PROLONGED EXPOSURE MAY RESULT IN THE EFFECTS OF ACUTE EXPOSURE INCLUDING THE DELAYED NEUROPATHY. OTHER EFFECTS REPORTED IN WORKERS REPEATEDLY EXPOSED INCLUDE IMPAIRED MEMORY AND CONCENTRATION, ACUTE PSYCHOSIS, SEVERE DEPRESSIONS, IRRITABILTY, CONFUSION, APATHY, EMOTIONAL LABILITY, SOCIAL WITHDRAWAL, CONFUSION, HEADACHE, SPEECH DIFFICULTIES, DELAYED REACTION TIMES, SPATIAL DISORIENTATION, NIGHTMARES, SLEEPWALKING, AND DROWSINESS OR INSOMNIA. AN INFLUENZA-LIKE CONDITION WITH HEADACHE, NAUSEA, WEAKNESS, ANOREXIA AND MALAISE HAS ALSO BEEN REPORTED.

FIRST AID- REMOVE FROM EXPOSURE AREA TO FRESH AIR IMMEDIATELY. IF BREATHING HAS STOPPED, PERFORM ARTIFICIAL RESPIRATION. KEEP PERSON WARM AND AT REST. TREAT SYMPTOMATICALLY AND SUPPORTIVELY. GET MEDICAL ATTENTION IMMEDIATELY.

SKIN CONTACT: DEMETON-S SULFOXIDE: SEE INFORMATION ON ORGANOPHOSPHATES.

ORGANOPHOSPHATES: CHOLINESTERASE INHIBITOR. **ACUTE EXPOSURE-** LOCALIZED SWEATING AND FASCICULATIONS MAY OCCUR AT THE SITE OF CONTACT. IF SUFFICIENT AMOUNTS ARE ABSORBED, OTHER EFFECTS OF CHOLINESTERASE INHIBITION AS DESCRIBED IN ACUTE INHALATION MAY OCCUR. SYMPTOMS MAY BE DELAYED 2-3 HOURS, BUT USUALLY NO MORE THAN 12 HOURS. THE RATE OF ABSORPTION IS INCREASED BY THE PRESENCE OF DERMATITIS OR HIGH AMBIENT TEMPERATURES. DELAYED NEUROPATHY IS ALSO POSSIBLE. **CHRONIC EXPOSURE-** REPEATED OR PROLONGED EXPOSURE MAY CAUSE EFFECTS AS DESCRIBED IN ACUTE EXPOSURE. SOME ORGANOPHOSPHATES MAY CAUSE SENSITIZATION.

FIRST AID- REMOVE CONTAMINATED CLOTHING IMMEDIATELY. WASH CONTAMINATED AREAS WITH SOAP AND WATER FOLLOWED BY ALCOHOL (ARENA, POISONING, 4TH ED.). EMERGENCY PERSONNEL SHOULD WEAR GLOVES AND AVOID CONTAMINATION. TREAT RESPIRATORY DIFFICULTY WITH ARTIFICIAL RESPIRATION. GET MEDICAL ATTENTION IMMEDIATELY.

EYE CONTACT: DEMETON-S SULFOXIDE: SEE INFORMATION ON ORGANOPHOSPHATES.

ORGANOPHOSPHATES: CHOLINESTERASE INHIBITOR. **ACUTE EXPOSURE-** DIRECT CONTACT MAY CAUSE PAIN, HYPEREMIA, LACRIMATION, TWITCHING OF THE EYELIDS, MIOSIS, AND CILIARY MUSCLE SPASM WITH LOSS OF ACCOMODATION, BLURRED OR DIMMED VISION AND BROWACHE. SOMETIMES MYDRIASIS MAY OCCUR INSTEAD OF MIOSIS. WITH SUFFICIENT EXPOSURE, OTHER SYMPTOMS OF CHOLINESTERASE INHIBITION AS DESCRIBED IN ACUTE INHALATION MAY OCCUR. **CHRONIC EXPOSURE-** REPEATED OR PROLONGED EXPOSURE MAY CAUSE EFFECTS AS DESCRIBED IN ACUTE EXPOSURE. SOME COMPOUNDS HAVE CAUSED TOXIC EFFECTS ON THE CRYSTALLINE LENS, CONJUNCTIVAL THICKENING AND OBSTRUCTION OF THE NASOLACRIMAL CANALS WHEN USED AS MIOTIC EYEDROPS.

FIRST AID- IRRIGATE EYES WITH WATER OR SALINE SOLUTION. IF SYMPTOMS OF POISONING OCCUR, TREAT RESPIRATORY DIFFICULTY WITH ARTIFICIAL RESPIRATION AND OXYGEN. OBSERVE PATIENT FOR AT LEAST 24-36 HOURS (GOSSELIN, CLINICAL TOXICOLOGY OF COMMERCIAL PRODUCTS, 5TH ED.). GET MEDICAL ATTENTION IMMEDIATELY. OXYGEN SHOULD BE ADMINISTERED BY QUALIFIED MEDICAL PERSONNEL.

INGESTION: DEMETON-S SULFOXIDE: HIGHLY TOXIC. SEE INFORMATION ON ORGANOPHOSPHATES.

ORGANOPHOSPHATES: CHOLINESTERASE INHIBITOR. **ACUTE EXPOSURE-** WHEN INGESTED, THE FIRST EFFECTS MAY BE NAUSEA, VOMITING, ANOREXIA, ABDOMINAL CRAMPS AND DIARRHEA. GASTROINTESTINAL ABSORPTION MAY CAUSE SYMPTOMS OF CHOLINESTERASE INHIBITION AS DESCRIBED IN ACUTE INHALATION. SYMPTOMS MAY BEGIN WITHIN MINUTES OR BE DELAYED FOR HOURS. DELAYED EFFECTS INCLUDING NEUROPATHY MAY ALSO OCCUR. **CHRONIC EXPOSURE-** REPEATED INGESTION MAY CAUSE EFFECTS AS DESCRIBED IN ACUTE EXPOSURE.

FIRST AID- IF PERSON IS ALERT AND RESPIRATION IS NOT DEPRESSED, GIVE SYRUP OF IPECAC FOLLOWED BY WATER (IF VOMITING OCCURS, KEEP HEAD BELOW HIPS TO PREVENT ASPIRATION). IF CONSCIOUSNESS LEVEL DECLINES OR VOMITING HAS NOT OCCURRED IN 15 MINUTES EMPTY STOMACH BY GASTRIC LAVAGE WITH THE AID OF CUFFED ENDOTRACHEAL TUBE USING ISOTONIC SALINE OR 5% SODIUM BICARBONATE FOLLOW WITH ACTIVATED CHARCOAL. ESTABLISH AND MAINTAIN AIRWAY. TREAT RESPIRATORY DIFFICULTY WITH ARTIFICIAL RESPIRATION AND OXYGEN. DO NOT GIVE MORPHINE, AMINOPHYLLINE, PHENOTHIAZINES, RESERPINE, FUROSEMIDE, OR ETHACRYNIC ACID (MORGAN, RECOGNITION AND MANAGEMENT OF PESTICIDE POISONINGS, 3RD ED.). TREAT SYMPTOMATICALLY AND SUPPORTIVELY. ADMINISTRATION OF OXYGEN AND LAVAGE MUST BE PERFORMED BY QUALIFIED MEDICAL PERSONNEL. GET MEDICAL ATTENTION IMMEDIATELY.

ANTIDOTE: THE FOLLOWING ANTIDOTE(S) HAVE BEEN RECOMMENDED. HOWEVER, THE DECISION AS TO WHETHER THE SEVERITY OF POISONING REQUIRES ADMINISTRATION OF ANY ANTIDOTE AND ACTUAL DOSE REQUIRED SHOULD BE MADE BY QUALIFIED MEDICAL PERSONNEL.

FOR CHOLINESTERASE INHIBITORS: ESTABLISH CLEAR AIRWAY AND TISSUE OXYGENATION BY ASPIRATION OF SECRETIONS, AND IF NECESSARY, BY ASSISTED PULMONARY VENTILATION WITH OXYGEN. IMPROVE TISSUE OXYGENATION AS MUCH AS POSSIBLE BEFORE ADMINISTERING ATROPINE TO MINIMIZE THE RISK OF VENTRICULAR FIBRILLATION. ADMINISTER ATROPINE SULFATE INTRAVENOUSLY,

OR INTRAMUSCULARLY IF IV INJECTION IS NOT POSSIBLE. IN MODERATELY SEVERE POISONING ADMINISTER ATROPINE SULFATE, 0.4-2.0 MG REPEATED EVERY 15 MINUTES UNTIL ATROPINIZATION IS ACHIEVED (TACHYCARDIA, FLUSHING, DRY MOUTH, MYDRIASIS). MAINTAIN ATROPINIZATION BY REPEATED DOSES FOR 2-12 HOURS, OR LONGER, DEPENDING ON THE SEVERITY OF POISONING. THE APPEARANCE OF RALES IN THE LUNG BASES, MIOSIS, SALIVATION, NAUSEA, BRADYCARDIA, ARE ALL INDICATIONS OF INADEQUATE ATROPINIZATION. SEVERELY POISONED INDIVIDUALS MAY EXHIBIT REMARKABLE TOLERANCE TO ATROPINE; TWO OR MORE TIMES THE DOSAGES SUGGESTED ABOVE MAY BE NEEDED. PERSONS NOT POISONED OR ONLY SLIGHTLY POISONED, HOWEVER, MAY DEVELOP SIGNS OF ATROPINE TOXICITY FROM SUCH LARGE DOSAGES: FEVER, MUSCLE FIBRILLATIONS, AND DELIRIUM ARE THE MAIN SIGNS OF ATROPINE TOXICITY. IF THESE SIGNS APPEAR WHILE THE PATIENT IS FULLY ATROPINIZED, ATROPINE ADMINISTRATION SHOULD BE DISCONTINUED, AT LEAST TEMPORARILY. OBSERVE TREATED PATIENTS CLOSELY AT LEAST 24 HOURS TO INSURE THAT SYMPTOMS (POSSIBLY PULMONARY EDEMA) DO NOT RECUR AS ATROPINIZATION WEARS OFF. IN VERY SEVERE POISONINGS, METABOLIC DISPOSITION OF TOXICANT MAY REQUIRE SEVERAL HOURS OR DAYS DURING WHICH ATROPINIZATION MUST BE MAINTAINED. MARKEDLY LOWER LEVELS OF URINARY METABOLITES INDICATE THAT ATROPINE DOSAGE CAN BE TAPERED OFF. AS DOSAGE IS REDUCED, CHECK THE LUNG BASES FREQUENTLY FOR RALES. IF RALES ARE HEARD OR OTHER SYMPTOMS RETURN, RE-ESTABLISH ATROPINIZATION PROMPTLY (MORGAN, RECOGNITION AND MANAGEMENT OF PESTICIDE POISONINGS, 3RD ED.). ADMINISTRATION OF ANTIDOTE MUST BE PERFORMED BY QUALIFIED MEDICAL PERSONNEL.

IN CASES OF SEVERE POISONING BY ORGANOPHOSPHATE PESTICIDES IN WHICH RESPIRATORY DEPRESSION, MUSCLE WEAKNESS AND TWITCHINGS ARE SEVERE, GIVE PRALIDOXIME (PROTOPAM-AYERST, 2-PAM), 1.0 GRAM INTRAVENOUSLY AT NO MORE THAN 0.5 GRAM PER MINUTE. DOSAGE OF PRALIDOXIME MAY BE REPEATED IN 1-2 HOURS, THEN AT 10-12 HOUR INTERVALS IF NEEDED. IN VERY SEVERE POISONINGS, DOSAGE RATES MAY BE DOUBLED. TREATMENT WITH PRALIDOXIME WILL BE MOST EFFECTIVE IF GIVEN WITHIN THIRTY-SIX HOURS AFTER POISONING (MORGAN, RECOGNITION AND MANAGEMENT OF PESTICIDE POISONINGS, 3RD ED.). ANTIDOTE SHOULD BE ADMINISTERED BY QUALIFIED MEDICAL PERSONNEL.

REACTIVITY

REACTIVITY: STABLE UNDER NORMAL TEMPERATURES AND PRESSURES.

INCOMPATIBILITIES: DEMETON-S SULFOXIDE: OXIDIZERS (STRONG): FIRE AND EXPLOSION HAZARD.

DECOMPOSITION: THERMAL DECOMPOSITION PRODUCTS MAY INCLUDE TOXIC OXIDES OF CARBON, SULFUR, AND PHOSPHORUS.

POLYMERIZATION: HAZARDOUS POLYMERIZATION HAS NOT BEEN REPORTED TO OCCUR UNDER NORMAL TEMPERATURES AND PRESSURES.

STORAGE AND DISPOSAL

OBSERVE ALL FEDERAL, STATE AND LOCAL REGULATIONS WHEN STORING OR DISPOSING OF THIS SUBSTANCE. FOR ASSISTANCE, CONTACT THE DISTRICT DIRECTOR OF THE ENVIRONMENTAL PROTECTION AGENCY.

****STORAGE****

STORE IN ACCORDANCE WITH 40 CFR 165 RECOMMENDED PROCEDURES FOR THE DISPOSAL AND STORAGE OF PESTICIDES AND PESTICIDE CONTAINERS.

STORE AWAY FROM INCOMPATIBLE SUBSTANCES.

****DISPOSAL****

DISPOSAL MUST BE IN ACCORDANCE WITH 40 CFR 165 RECOMMENDED PROCEDURES FOR THE DISPOSAL AND STORAGE OF PESTICIDES AND PESTICIDE CONTAINERS.

CONDITIONS TO AVOID

MAY BE IGNITED BY HEAT, SPARKS OR FLAMES. CONTAINER MAY EXPLODE IN HEAT OF FIRE. VAPOR EXPLOSION AND POISON HAZARD INDOORS, OUTDOORS OR IN SEWERS.

SPILL AND LEAK PROCEDURES

OCCUPATIONAL SPILL: SHUT OFF IGNITION SOURCES. DO NOT TOUCH SPILLED MATERIAL. STOP LEAK IF YOU CAN DO IT WITHOUT RISK. USE WATER SPRAY TO REDUCE VAPORS. FOR SMALL SPILLS, TAKE UP WITH SAND OR OTHER ABSORBENT MATERIAL AND PLACE INTO CONTAINERS FOR LATER DISPOSAL. FOR SMALL DRY SPILLS, WITH CLEAN SHOVEL PLACE MATERIAL INTO CLEAN, DRY CONTAINERS AND COVER. MOVE CONTAINERS FROM SPILL AREA. FOR LARGER SPILLS, DIKE FAR AHEAD OF SPILL FOR LATER DISPOSAL. NO SMOKING, FLAMES OR FLARES IN HAZARD AREA! KEEP UNNECESSARY PEOPLE AWAY. ISOLATE HAZARD AREA AND DENY ENTRY. VENTILATE CLOSED SPACES BEFORE ENTERING.

PROTECTIVE EQUIPMENT

VENTILATION: PROCESS ENCLOSURE RECOMMENDED. VENTILATION EQUIPMENT MUST BE EXPLOSION-PROOF.

RESPIRATOR: THE FOLLOWING RESPIRATORS ARE RECOMMENDED BASED ON INFORMATION FOUND IN THE PHYSICAL DATA, TOXICITY AND HEALTH EFFECTS SECTIONS. THEY ARE RANKED IN ORDER FROM MINIMUM TO MAXIMUM RESPIRATORY PROTECTION. THE SPECIFIC RESPIRATOR SELECTED MUST BE BASED ON CONTAMINATION LEVELS FOUND IN THE WORK PLACE, MUST NOT EXCEED THE WORKING LIMITS OF THE RESPIRATOR AND BE JOINTLY APPROVED BY THE NATIONAL INSTITUTE FOR OCCUPATIONAL SAFETY AND HEALTH AND THE MINE SAFETY AND HEALTH ADMINISTRATION (NIOSH-MSHA).

TYPE 'C' SUPPLIED-AIR RESPIRATOR WITH A FULL FACEPIECE OPERATED IN PRESSURE-DEMAND OR OTHER POSITIVE PRESSURE MODE OR WITH A FULL FACEPIECE, HELMET OR HOOD OPERATED IN CONTINOUS-FLOW MODE.

SELF-CONTAINED BREATHING APPARATUS WITH A FULL FACEPIECE OPERATED IN PRESSURE-DEMAND OR OTHER POSITIVE PRESSURE MODE.

FOR FIREFIGHTING AND OTHER IMMEDIATELY DANGEROUS TO LIFE OR HEALTH CONDITIONS:

SELF-CONTAINED BREATHING APPARATUS WITH FULL FACEPIECE OPERATED IN PRESSURE-DEMAND OR OTHER POSITIVE PRESSURE MODE.

SUPPLIED-AIR RESPIRATOR WITH FULL FACEPIECE AND OPERATED IN PRESSURE-DEMAND OR OTHER POSITIVE PRESSURE MODE IN COMBINATION WITH AN AUXILIARY SELF-CONTAINED BREATHING APPARATUS OPERATED IN PRESSURE-DEMAND OR OTHER POSITIVE PRESSURE MODE.

CLOTHING: EMPLOYEE MUST WEAR APPROPRIATE PROTECTIVE (IMPERVIOUS) CLOTHING AND EQUIPMENT TO PREVENT ANY POSSIBILITY OF SKIN CONTACT WITH THIS SUBSTANCE.

GLOVES: EMPLOYEE MUST WEAR APPROPRIATE PROTECTIVE GLOVES TO PREVENT CONTACT WITH THIS SUBSTANCE.

EYE PROTECTION: EMPLOYEE MUST WEAR SPLASH-PROOF OR DUST-RESISTANT SAFETY GOGGLES WITH OR WITHOUT A FACESHIELD TO PREVENT CONTACT WITH THIS SUBSTANCE.

EMERGENCY EYE WASH: WHERE THERE IS ANY POSSIBILITY THAT AN EMPLOYEE'S EYES MAY BE EXPOSED TO THIS SUBSTANCE, THE EMPLOYER SHOULD PROVIDE AN EYE WASH FOUNTAIN WITHIN THE IMMEDIATE WORK AREA FOR EMERGENCY USE.

AUTHORIZED BY- OCCUPATIONAL HEALTH SERVICES, INC.

CREATION DATE: 05/18/90 ***REVISION DATE:*** 05/18/90

MATERIAL SAFETY DATA SHEET

OCCUPATIONAL HEALTH SERVICES, INC.
AGRICULTURE AND PESTICIDE DIVISION
450 SEVENTH AVENUE, SUITE 2407
NEW YORK, NEW YORK 10123
1-800-445-MSDS OR (212) 967-1100

EMERGENCY CONTACT:
JOHN S. BRANSFORD, JR. (615) 292-1180

SUBSTANCE IDENTIFICATION

CAS-NUMBER 23052-51-9

SUBSTANCE: **DEMETON-O OXYGEN ANALOG**

TRADE NAMES/SYNONYMS: PHOSPHORIC ACID, DIETHYL 2-(ETHYLTHIO)ETHYL ESTER; O,O-DIETHYL O-2-ETHYLTHIOETHYL PHOSPHATE; ETHANOL, 2-(ETHYLTHIO)-, DIETHYL PHOSPHATE; DIETHYL 2-(ETHYLTHIO)ETHYL PHOSPHATE; SYSTOX THIONO ISOMER OXYGEN ANALOG; C8H19O4PS; PST06317

CHEMICAL FAMILY: ORGANOPHOSPHATE

MOLECULAR FORMULA: (C2-H5-O)2-P-(O)-O-(C-H2)2-S-C2-H5

MOLECULAR WEIGHT: 242.27

CERCLA RATINGS (SCALE 0-3): HEALTH=3 FIRE=U REACTIVITY=0 PERSISTENCE=0

NFPA RATINGS (SCALE 0-4): HEALTH=U FIRE=U REACTIVITY=0

COMPONENTS AND CONTAMINANTS

COMPONENT: DEMETON-O OXYGEN ANALOG ***PERCENT:*** 100.0
CAS# 23052-51-9

OTHER CONTAMINANTS: NONE

EXPOSURE LIMITS: NO OCCUPATIONAL EXPOSURE LIMITS ESTABLISHED BY OSHA, ACGIH, OR NIOSH.

PHYSICAL DATA

DESCRIPTION: CLEAR LIQUID. ***BOILING POINT:*** 230-237 F (110-117 C)

SPECIFIC GRAVITY: NOT AVAILABLE ***EVAPORATION RATE:*** NOT AVAILABLE

SOLUBILITY IN WATER: NOT AVAILABLE

FIRE AND EXPLOSION DATA

FIRE AND EXPLOSION HAZARD: UNKNOWN FIRE AND EXPLOSION HAZARD.

FIREFIGHTING MEDIA: DRY CHEMICAL, CARBON DIOXIDE, HALON, WATER SPRAY OR STANDARD FOAM (1987 EMERGENCY RESPONSE GUIDEBOOK, DOT P 5800.4). FOR LARGER FIRES, USE WATER SPRAY, FOG OR STANDARD FOAM (1987 EMERGENCY RESPONSE GUIDEBOOK, DOT P 5800.4).

FIREFIGHTING: MOVE CONTAINER FROM FIRE AREA IF POSSIBLE. DIKE FIRE CONTROL WATER FOR LATER DISPOSAL; DO NOT SCATTER THE MATERIAL. COOL FIRE-EXPOSED CONTAINERS WITH WATER FROM SIDE UNTIL WELL AFTER FIRE IS OUT. STAY AWAY FROM STORAGE TANK ENDS. WITHDRAW IMMEDIATELY IN CASE OF RISING SOUND FROM VENTING SAFETY DEVICE OR ANY DISCOLORATION OF STORAGE TANK DUE TO FIRE (1987 EMERGENCY RESPONSE GUIDEBOOK, DOT P 5800.4, GUIDE PAGE 28).
EXTINGUISH ONLY IF FLOW CAN BE STOPPED. USE FLOODING AMOUNTS OF WATER AS A FOG; SOLID STREAMS MAY BE INEFFECTIVE. COOL CONTAINERS WITH FLOODING AMOUNTS OF WATER FROM AS FAR A DISTANCE AS POSSIBLE. AVOID BREATHING POISONOUS VAPORS, KEEP UPWIND.

TOXICITY

DEMETON-O OXYGEN ANALOG: TOXICITY DATA: 175 MG/KG ORAL-RAT LD50 (EPA); 10 MG/KG INTRAVENOUS-MOUSE LD50; 175 MG/KG UNREPORTED-RAT LD50. CARCINOGEN STATUS: NONE. ACUTE TOXICITY LEVEL: TOXIC BY INGESTION. TARGET EFFECTS: CHOLINESTERASE INHIBITOR. POISONING MAY AFFECT THE NERVOUS SYSTEM.* AT INCREASED RISK FROM EXPOSURE: PERSONS WITH RESPIRATORY AILMENTS, RECENT EXPOSURE TO CHOLINESTERASE INHIBITORS OR IMPAIRED CHOLINESTERASE PRODUCTION, OR LIVER MALFUNCTION.* ADDITIONAL DATA: MAY CROSS THE PLACENTA. HIGH ENVIRONMENTAL TEMPERATURES OR EXPOSURE OF THE CHEMICAL TO VISIBLE OR ULTRAVIOLET LIGHT MAY ENHANCE THE TOXICITY. INTERACTIONS WITH MEDICATIONS MAY OCCUR.*
* MAY BE BASED ON GENERAL INFORMATION ON ORGANOPHOSPHATES.

HEALTH EFFECTS AND FIRST AID

INHALATION: DEMETON-O OXYGEN ANALOG: SEE INFORMATION ON ORGANOPHOSPHATES.
ORGANOPHOSPHATES: CHOLINESTERASE INHIBITOR. **ACUTE EXPOSURE**- WHEN INHALED, THE FIRST EFFECTS OF CHOLINESTERASE INHIBITORS ARE USUALLY RESPIRATORY AND MAY INCLUDE NASAL HYPEREMIA AND WATERY DISCHARGE, COUGH, CHEST DISCOMFORT, DYSPNEA, AND WHEEZING DUE TO INCREASED BRONCHIAL SECRETIONS AND BRONCHOCONSTRICTION. IF SUFFICIENT AMOUNTS ARE ABSORBED, OTHER SYSTEMIC EFFECTS MAY BEGIN WITHIN A FEW MINUTES OR BE DELAYED FOR UP TO 12 HOURS. SYMPTOMS MAY INCLUDE PALLOR, NAUSEA, VOMITING, DIARRHEA, ABDOMINAL CRAMPS, HEADACHE, DIZZINESS, OCULAR PAIN, BLURRED VISION, MIOSIS OR IN SOME CASES, ESPECIALLY INITIALLY, MYDRIASIS, LACRIMATION, SALIVATION, SWEATING, AND CONFUSION. OTHER REPORTED CENTRAL NERVOUS SYSTEM OR NEUROMUSCULAR EFFECTS MAY INCLUDE ATAXIA, SLURRED SPEECH, AREFLEXIA, WEAKNESS, FATIGUE, FASCICULATIONS, TWITCHING, TREMORS POSSIBLY OF THE TONGUE AND EYELIDS, AND EVENTUALLY PARALYSIS OF THE EXTREMITIES AND POSSIBLY OF THE RESPIRATORY MUSCLES. IN SEVERE CASES THERE MAY ALSO BE INVOLUNTARY DEFECATION AND URINATION, CYANOSIS, PSYCHOSIS, HYPERGLYCEMIA, ACUTE PANCREATITIS, CARDIAC IRREGULARITIES, PULMONARY EDEMA, UNCONSCIOUSNESS, CONVULSIONS, AND COMA. DEATH IS PRIMARILY DUE TO RESPIRATORY FAILURE, ALTHOUGH CARDIOVASCULAR EFFECTS INCLUDING CARDIAC ARREST MAY ALSO BE IMPLICATED. LONG TERM SEQUELAE ARE RARE BUT MAY INCLUDE NEUROPSYCHIATRIC DISORDERS AND MYOPATHY WITH MUSCLE TENDERNESS. SOME ORGANOPHOSPHATES MAY CAUSE A DELAYED NEUROPATHY BEGINNING 1-4 WEEKS AFTER AN ACUTE EXPOSURE WHICH MAY OR MAY NOT HAVE CAUSED ACUTE CHOLINERGIC EFFECTS. NUMBNESS, TINGLING, WEAKNESS AND CRAMPING BEGINNING SYMMETRICALLY IN THE LOWER LIMBS MAY PROGRESS TO ATAXIA AND PARALYSIS. IN SEVERE CASES, UPPER LIMB INVOLVEMENT IS POSSIBLE AND FLACCID PARALYSIS MAY PROGRESS TO SPASTIC PARALYSIS WITH EXAGGERATED REFLEXES. IMPROVEMENT MAY OCCUR OVER MONTHS TO YEARS, BUT SOME RESIDUAL IMPAIRMENT USUALLY REMAINS. **CHRONIC EXPOSURE**- REPEATED OR PROLONGED EXPOSURE MAY RESULT IN THE EFFECTS OF ACUTE EXPOSURE INCLUDING THE DELAYED NEUROPATHY. OTHER EFFECTS REPORTED IN WORKERS REPEATEDLY EXPOSED INCLUDE IMPAIRED MEMORY AND CONCENTRATION, ACUTE PSYCHOSIS, SEVERE DEPRESSIONS, IRRITABILTY, CONFUSION, APATHY, EMOTIONAL LABILITY, SOCIAL WITHDRAWAL, CONFUSION, HEADACHE, SPEECH DIFFICULTIES, DELAYED REACTION TIMES, SPATIAL DISORIENTATION, NIGHTMARES, SLEEPWALKING, AND DROWSINESS OR INSOMNIA. AN INFLUENZA-LIKE CONDITION WITH HEADACHE, NAUSEA, WEAKNESS, ANOREXIA AND MALAISE HAS ALSO BEEN REPORTED.

FIRST AID- REMOVE FROM EXPOSURE AREA TO FRESH AIR IMMEDIATELY. IF BREATHING HAS STOPPED, GIVE ARTIFICIAL RESPIRATION. MAINTAIN AIRWAY AND BLOOD PRESSURE AND ADMINISTER OXYGEN IF AVAILABLE. KEEP AFFECTED PERSON WARM AND AT REST. TREAT SYMPTOMATICALLY AND SUPPORTIVELY. ADMINISTRATION OF OXYGEN SHOULD BE PERFORMED BY QUALIFIED PERSONNEL. GET MEDICAL ATTENTION IMMEDIATELY.

SKIN CONTACT: DEMETON-O OXYGEN ANALOG: SEE INFORMATION ON ORGANOPHOSPHATES.
ORGANOPHOSPHATES: CHOLINESTERASE INHIBITOR. **ACUTE EXPOSURE**- LOCALIZED SWEATING AND FASCICULATIONS MAY OCCUR AT THE SITE OF CONTACT. IF SUFFICIENT AMOUNTS ARE ABSORBED, OTHER EFFECTS OF CHOLINESTERASE INHIBITION AS DESCRIBED IN ACUTE INHALATION MAY OCCUR. SYMPTOMS MAY BE DELAYED 2-3 HOURS, BUT USUALLY NO MORE THAN 12 HOURS. THE RATE OF ABSORPTION IS INCREASED BY THE PRESENCE OF DERMATITIS OR HIGH AMBIENT TEMPERATURES. DELAYED NEUROPATHY IS ALSO POSSIBLE. **CHRONIC EXPOSURE**- REPEATED OR PROLONGED EXPOSURE MAY CAUSE EFFECTS AS DESCRIBED IN ACUTE EXPOSURE. SOME ORGANOPHOSPHATES MAY CAUSE SENSITIZATION.

FIRST AID- REMOVE CONTAMINATED CLOTHING IMMEDIATELY. WASH CONTAMINATED AREAS WITH SOAP AND WATER FOLLOWED BY ALCOHOL (ARENA, POISONING, 4TH ED.). EMERGENCY PERSONNEL SHOULD WEAR GLOVES AND AVOID CONTAMINATION. TREAT RESPIRATORY DIFFICULTY WITH ARTIFICIAL RESPIRATION. GET MEDICAL ATTENTION IMMEDIATELY.

EYE CONTACT: DEMETON-O OXYGEN ANALOG: SEE INFORMATION ON ORGANOPHOSPHATES.
ORGANOPHOSPHATES: CHOLINESTERASE INHIBITOR. **ACUTE EXPOSURE**- DIRECT CONTACT MAY CAUSE PAIN, HYPEREMIA, LACRIMATION, TWITCHING OF THE EYELIDS, MIOSIS, AND CILIARY MUSCLE SPASM WITH LOSS OF ACCOMODATION, BLURRED OR DIMMED VISION AND BROWACHE. SOMETIMES MYDRIASIS MAY OCCUR INSTEAD OF MIOSIS. WITH SUFFICIENT EXPOSURE, OTHER SYMPTOMS OF CHOLINESTERASE INHIBITION AS DESCRIBED IN ACUTE INHALATION MAY OCCUR. **CHRONIC EXPOSURE**- REPEATED OR PROLONGED EXPOSURE MAY CAUSE EFFECTS AS DESCRIBED IN ACUTE EXPOSURE. SOME COMPOUNDS HAVE CAUSED TOXIC EFFECTS ON THE CRYSTALLINE LENS, CONJUNCTIVAL THICKENING AND OBSTRUCTION OF THE NASOLACRIMAL CANALS WHEN USED AS MIOTIC EYEDROPS.

FIRST AID- IRRIGATE EYES WITH WATER OR SALINE SOLUTION. IF SYMPTOMS OF POISONING OCCUR, TREAT RESPIRATORY DIFFICULTY WITH ARTIFICIAL RESPIRATION AND OXYGEN. OBSERVE PATIENT FOR AT LEAST 24-36 HOURS (GOSSELIN, CLINICAL TOXICOLOGY OF COMMERCIAL PRODUCTS, 5TH ED.). GET MEDICAL ATTENTION IMMEDIATELY. OXYGEN SHOULD BE ADMINISTERED BY QUALIFIED MEDICAL PERSONNEL.

INGESTION: DEMETON-O OXYGEN ANALOG: TOXIC. SEE INFORMATION ON ORGANOPHOSPHATES.
ORGANOPHOSPHATES: CHOLINESTERASE INHIBITOR. **ACUTE EXPOSURE**- WHEN INGESTED, THE FIRST EFFECTS MAY BE NAUSEA, VOMITING, ANOREXIA, ABDOMINAL CRAMPS AND DIARRHEA. GASTROINTESTINAL ABSORPTION MAY CAUSE SYMPTOMS OF CHOLINESTERASE INHIBITION AS DESCRIBED IN ACUTE INHALATION. SYMPTOMS MAY BEGIN WITHIN MINUTES OR BE DELAYED FOR HOURS. DELAYED EFFECTS INCLUDING NEUROPATHY MAY ALSO OCCUR. **CHRONIC EXPOSURE**- REPEATED INGESTION MAY CAUSE EFFECTS AS DESCRIBED IN ACUTE EXPOSURE.

FIRST AID- IF PERSON IS ALERT AND RESPIRATION IS NOT DEPRESSED, GIVE SYRUP OF IPECAC FOLLOWED BY WATER (IF VOMITING OCCURS, KEEP HEAD BELOW HIPS TO PREVENT ASPIRATION). IF CONSCIOUSNESS LEVEL DECLINES OR VOMITING HAS NOT OCCURRED IN 15 MINUTES EMPTY STOMACH BY GASTRIC LAVAGE WITH THE AID OF CUFFED ENDOTRACHEAL TUBE USING ISOTONIC SALINE OR 5% SODIUM BICARBONATE FOLLOW WITH ACTIVATED CHARCOAL. ESTABLISH AND MAINTAIN AIRWAY. TREAT RESPIRATORY DIFFICULTY WITH ARTIFICIAL RESPIRATION AND OXYGEN. DO NOT GIVE MORPHINE, AMINOPHYLLINE, PHENOTHIAZINES, RESERPINE, FUROSEMIDE, OR ETHACRYNIC ACID (MORGAN, RECOGNITION AND MANAGEMENT OF PESTICIDE POISONINGS, 3RD ED.). TREAT SYMPTOMATICALLY AND SUPPORTIVELY. ADMINISTRATION OF OXYGEN AND LAVAGE MUST BE PERFORMED BY QUALIFIED MEDICAL PERSONNEL. GET MEDICAL ATTENTION IMMEDIATELY.

ANTIDOTE: THE FOLLOWING ANTIDOTE(S) HAVE BEEN RECOMMENDED. HOWEVER, THE DECISION AS TO WHETHER THE SEVERITY OF POISONING REQUIRES ADMINISTRATION OF ANY ANTIDOTE AND ACTUAL DOSE REQUIRED SHOULD BE MADE BY QUALIFIED MEDICAL PERSONNEL.
FOR CHOLINESTERASE INHIBITORS: ESTABLISH CLEAR AIRWAY AND TISSUE OXYGENATION BY ASPIRATION OF SECRETIONS, AND IF NECESSARY, BY ASSISTED PULMONARY VENTILATION WITH OXYGEN. IMPROVE TISSUE OXYGENATION AS MUCH AS POSSIBLE BEFORE ADMINISTERING ATROPINE TO MINIMIZE THE RISK OF VENTRICULAR FIBRILLATION. ADMINISTER ATROPINE SULFATE INTRAVENOUSLY, OR INTRAMUSCULARLY IF IV INJECTION IS NOT POSSIBLE. IN MODERATELY SEVERE POISONING ADMINISTER ATROPINE SULFATE, 0.4-2.0 MG REPEATED EVERY

15 MINUTES UNTIL ATROPINIZATION IS ACHIEVED (TACHYCARDIA, FLUSHING, DRY MOUTH, MYDRIASIS). MAINTAIN ATROPINIZATION BY REPEATED DOSES FOR 2-12 HOURS, OR LONGER, DEPENDING ON THE SEVERITY OF POISONING. THE APPEARANCE OF RALES IN THE LUNG BASES, MIOSIS, SALIVATION, NAUSEA, BRADYCARDIA, ARE ALL INDICATIONS OF INADEQUATE ATROPINIZATION. SEVERELY POISONED INDIVIDUALS MAY EXHIBIT REMARKABLE TOLERANCE TO ATROPINE; TWO OR MORE TIMES THE DOSAGES SUGGESTED ABOVE MAY BE NEEDED. PERSONS NOT POISONED OR ONLY SLIGHTLY POISONED, HOWEVER, MAY DEVELOP SIGNS OF ATROPINE TOXICITY FROM SUCH LARGE DOSAGES: FEVER, MUSCLE FIBRILLATIONS, AND DELIRIUM ARE THE MAIN SIGNS OF ATROPINE TOXICITY. IF THESE SIGNS APPEAR WHILE THE PATIENT IS FULLY ATROPINIZED, ATROPINE ADMINISTRATION SHOULD BE DISCONTINUED, AT LEAST TEMPORARILY. OBSERVE TREATED PATIENTS CLOSELY AT LEAST 24 HOURS TO INSURE THAT SYMPTOMS (POSSIBLY PULMONARY EDEMA) DO NOT RECUR AS ATROPINIZATION WEARS OFF. IN VERY SEVERE POISONINGS, METABOLIC DISPOSITION OF TOXICANT MAY REQUIRE SEVERAL HOURS OR DAYS DURING WHICH ATROPINIZATION MUST BE MAINTAINED. MARKEDLY LOWER LEVELS OF URINARY METABOLITES INDICATE THAT ATROPINE DOSAGE CAN BE TAPERED OFF. AS DOSAGE IS REDUCED, CHECK THE LUNG BASES FREQUENTLY FOR RALES. IF RALES ARE HEARD OR OTHER SYMPTOMS RETURN, RE-ESTABLISH ATROPINIZATION PROMPTLY (MORGAN, RECOGNITION AND MANAGEMENT OF PESTICIDE POISONINGS, 3RD ED.). ADMINISTRATION OF ANTIDOTE MUST BE PERFORMED BY QUALIFIED MEDICAL PERSONNEL.

IN CASES OF SEVERE POISONING BY ORGANOPHOSPHATE PESTICIDES IN WHICH RESPIRATORY DEPRESSION, MUSCLE WEAKNESS AND TWITCHINGS ARE SEVERE, GIVE PRALIDOXIME (PROTOPAM-AYERST, 2-PAM), 1.0 GRAM INTRAVENOUSLY AT NO MORE THAN 0.5 GRAM PER MINUTE. DOSAGE OF PRALIDOXIME MAY BE REPEATED IN 1-2 HOURS, THEN AT 10-12 HOUR INTERVALS IF NEEDED. IN VERY SEVERE POISONINGS, DOSAGE RATES MAY BE DOUBLED. TREATMENT WITH PRALIDOXIME WILL BE MOST EFFECTIVE IF GIVEN WITHIN THIRTY-SIX HOURS AFTER POISONING (MORGAN, RECOGNITION AND MANAGEMENT OF PESTICIDE POISONINGS, 3RD ED.). ANTIDOTE SHOULD BE ADMINISTERED BY QUALIFIED MEDICAL PERSONNEL.

REACTIVITY

REACTIVITY: STABLE UNDER NORMAL TEMPERATURES AND PRESSURES.

INCOMPATIBILITIES: DEMETON-O OXYGEN ANALOG: OXIDIZERS (STRONG): FIRE AND EXPLOSION HAZARD.

DECOMPOSITION: THERMAL DECOMPOSITION PRODUCTS MAY INCLUDE TOXIC OXIDES OF CARBON, SULFUR, AND PHOSPHORUS.

POLYMERIZATION: HAZARDOUS POLYMERIZATION WILL NOT OCCUR.

STORAGE AND DISPOSAL

OBSERVE ALL FEDERAL, STATE AND LOCAL REGULATIONS WHEN STORING OR DISPOSING OF THIS SUBSTANCE. FOR ASSISTANCE, CONTACT THE DISTRICT DIRECTOR OF THE ENVIRONMENTAL PROTECTION AGENCY.

STORAGE

STORE AWAY FROM INCOMPATIBLE SUBSTANCES.

CONDITIONS TO AVOID

AVOID CONTACT WITH HEAT, SPARKS, FLAMES OR OTHER IGNITION SOURCES. VAPORS MAY BE EXPLOSIVE. MATERIAL IS POISONOUS; AVOID INHALATION OF VAPORS OR CONTACT WITH SKIN. DO NOT ALLOW MATERIAL TO CONTAMINATE WATER SOURCES.

SPILL AND LEAK PROCEDURES

OCCUPATIONAL SPILL: STOP LEAK IF YOU CAN DO IT WITHOUT RISK. FOR SMALL SPILLS, TAKE UP WITH SAND OR OTHER ABSORBENT MATERIAL AND PLACE INTO CLEAN DRY CONTAINERS FOR LATER DISPOSAL. KEEP UNNECESSARY PEOPLE AWAY. ISOLATE HAZARD AREA AND DENY ENTRY.

PROTECTIVE EQUIPMENT

VENTILATION: PROVIDE LOCAL EXHAUST OR PROCESS ENCLOSURE VENTILATION SYSTEM.

RESPIRATOR: THE FOLLOWING RESPIRATORS ARE RECOMMENDED BASED ON INFORMATION FOUND IN THE PHYSICAL DATA, TOXICITY AND HEALTH EFFECTS SECTIONS. THEY ARE RANKED IN ORDER FROM MINIMUM TO MAXIMUM RESPIRATORY PROTECTION. THE SPECIFIC RESPIRATOR SELECTED MUST BE BASED ON CONTAMINATION LEVELS FOUND IN THE WORK PLACE, MUST NOT EXCEED THE WORKING LIMITS OF THE RESPIRATOR AND BE JOINTLY APPROVED BY THE NATIONAL INSTITUTE FOR OCCUPATIONAL SAFETY AND HEALTH AND THE MINE SAFETY AND HEALTH ADMINISTRATION (NIOSH-MSHA).

TYPE 'C' SUPPLIED-AIR RESPIRATOR WITH A FULL FACEPIECE OPERATED IN PRESSURE-DEMAND OR OTHER POSITIVE PRESSURE MODE OR WITH A FULL FACEPIECE, HELMET OR HOOD OPERATED IN CONTINOUS-FLOW MODE.

SELF-CONTAINED BREATHING APPARATUS WITH A FULL FACEPIECE OPERATED IN PRESSURE-DEMAND OR OTHER POSITIVE PRESSURE MODE.

FOR FIREFIGHTING AND OTHER IMMEDIATELY DANGEROUS TO LIFE OR HEALTH CONDITIONS:

SELF-CONTAINED BREATHING APPARATUS WITH FULL FACEPIECE OPERATED IN PRESSURE-DEMAND OR OTHER POSITIVE PRESSURE MODE.

SUPPLIED-AIR RESPIRATOR WITH FULL FACEPIECE AND OPERATED IN PRESSURE-DEMAND OR OTHER POSITIVE PRESSURE MODE IN COMBINATION WITH AN AUXILIARY SELF-CONTAINED BREATHING APPARATUS OPERATED IN PRESSURE-DEMAND OR OTHER POSITIVE PRESSURE MODE.

CLOTHING: EMPLOYEE MUST WEAR APPROPRIATE PROTECTIVE (IMPERVIOUS) CLOTHING AND EQUIPMENT TO PREVENT ANY POSSIBILITY OF SKIN CONTACT WITH THIS SUBSTANCE.

GLOVES: EMPLOYEE MUST WEAR APPROPRIATE PROTECTIVE GLOVES TO PREVENT CONTACT WITH THIS SUBSTANCE.

EYE PROTECTION: EMPLOYEE MUST WEAR SPLASH-PROOF OR DUST-RESISTANT SAFETY GOGGLES AND A FACESHIELD TO PREVENT CONTACT WITH THIS SUBSTANCE.

EMERGENCY WASH FACILITIES: WHERE THERE IS ANY POSSIBILITY THAT AN EMPLOYEE'S EYES AND/OR SKIN MAY BE EXPOSED TO THIS SUBSTANCE, THE EMPLOYER SHOULD PROVIDE AN EYE WASH FOUNTAIN AND QUICK DRENCH SHOWER WITHIN THE IMMEDIATE WORK AREA FOR EMERGENCY USE.

AUTHORIZED BY- OCCUPATIONAL HEALTH SERVICES, INC.

CREATION DATE: 02/08/90 ***REVISION DATE:*** 04/30/90

MATERIAL SAFETY DATA SHEET

OCCUPATIONAL HEALTH SERVICES, INC.
AGRICULTURE AND PESTICIDE DIVISION
450 SEVENTH AVENUE, SUITE 2407
NEW YORK, NEW YORK 10123
1-800-445-MSDS OR (212) 967-1100

EMERGENCY CONTACT:
JOHN S. BRANSFORD, JR. (615) 292-1180

SUBSTANCE IDENTIFICATION

CAS-NUMBER 17040-19-6

SUBSTANCE: DEMETON-S-METHYL SULFONE

TRADE NAMES/SYNONYMS: PHOSPHOROTHIOIC ACID, S-(2-(ETHYLSULFONYL)ETHYL) O,O-DIMETHYL ESTER; S-(2-(ETHYLSULFONYL)ETHYL) O,O-DIMETHYL PHOSPHOROTHIOATE; DEMETON-S-METHYLSULFONE; METASYSTOX I SULFONE (FORMULATION); METASYSTOX R SULFONE (FORMULATION); OXYDEMETONMETHYL SULFONE; DEMETON-S-METHYL SULPHONE; C6H15O5PS2; PST06319

CHEMICAL FAMILY: ORGANOPHOSPHATE

MOLECULAR FORMULA: C2-H5-S-O2-C2-H4-S-P-(O)-(O-C-H3)2

MOLECULAR WEIGHT: 262.30

CERCLA RATINGS (SCALE 0-3): HEALTH=3 FIRE=1 REACTIVITY=0 PERSISTENCE=1

NFPA RATINGS (SCALE 0-4): HEALTH=4 FIRE=1 REACTIVITY=0

COMPONENTS AND CONTAMINANTS

COMPONENT: DEMETON-S-METHYL SULFONE ***PERCENT:*** 100.0
CAS# 17040-19-6

OTHER CONTAMINANTS: NONE

EXPOSURE LIMITS: NO OCCUPATIONAL EXPOSURE LIMITS ESTABLISHED BY OSHA, ACGIH, OR NIOSH.

PHYSICAL DATA

DESCRIPTION: COLORLESS TO YELLOW CRYSTALLINE SOLID.

BOILING POINT: 248 F (120 C) @ 0.03 MMHG ***MELTING POINT:*** 140 F (60 C)

VAPOR PRESSURE: NEGLIGIBLE ***SOLUBILITY IN WATER:*** 0.33%

SOLVENT SOLUBILITY: SOLUBLE IN METHYLENE CHLORIDE, ALCOHOLS, KETONES AND MOST CHLORINATED HYDROCARBONS; SLIGHTLY SOLUBLE IN TOLUENE.

FIRE AND EXPLOSION DATA

FIRE AND EXPLOSION HAZARD: SLIGHT FIRE HAZARD WHEN EXPOSED TO HEAT OR FLAME.

FIREFIGHTING MEDIA: DRY CHEMICAL, CARBON DIOXIDE, HALON, WATER SPRAY OR STANDARD FOAM (1987 EMERGENCY RESPONSE GUIDEBOOK, DOT P 5800.4).
FOR LARGER FIRES, USE WATER SPRAY, FOG OR STANDARD FOAM (1987 EMERGENCY RESPONSE GUIDEBOOK, DOT P 5800.4).

FIREFIGHTING: MOVE CONTAINERS FROM FIRE AREA IF POSSIBLE (1987 EMERGENCY RESPONSE GUIDEBOOK, DOT P 5800.4, GUIDE PAGE 53).
EXTINGUISH USING AGENT SUITABLE FOR TYPE OF SURROUNDING FIRE. AVOID BREATHING VAPORS AND DUSTS. KEEP UPWIND.

TRANSPORTATION DATA

DEPARTMENT OF TRANSPORTATION HAZARD CLASSIFICATION 49 CFR 172.101: POISON B
DEPARTMENT OF TRANSPORTATION LABELING REQUIREMENTS 49 CFR 172.101 AND SUBPART E: POISON
DEPARTMENT OF TRANSPORTATION PACKAGING REQUIREMENTS: 49 CFR 173.365 EXCEPTIONS: 49 CFR 173.364

TOXICITY

DEMETON-S-METHYL SULFONE: TOXICITY DATA: 195 MG/M3/4 HOURS INHALATION-RAT LC50; 500 MG/KG SKIN-RAT LD50; 32,400 UG/KG ORAL-RAT LD50; 30 MG/KG ORAL-MOUSE LD50; 50 MG/KG ORAL-RABBIT LD50; 120 MG/KG ORAL-GUINEA PIG LD50; 22 MG/KG INTRAVENOUS-RAT LD50; 21 MG/KG INTRAPERITONEAL-RAT LD50; 85 MG/KG INTRAPERITONEAL-GUINEA PIG LD50; 40 MG/KG UNREPORTED-RAT LD50; MUTAGENIC DATA (RTECS). CARCINOGEN STATUS: NONE. ACUTE TOXICITY LEVEL: HIGHLY TOXIC BY INHALATION AND INGESTION; TOXIC BY DERMAL ABSORPTION. TARGET EFFECTS: CHOLINESTERASE INHIBITOR. POISONING MAY AFFECT THE NERVOUS SYSTEM.* AT INCREASED RISK FROM EXPOSURE: PERSONS WITH RESPIRATORY AILMENTS, RECENT EXPOSURE TO CHOLINESTERASE INHIBITORS OR IMPAIRED CHOLINESTERASE PRODUCTION, OR LIVER MALFUNCTION.* ADDITIONAL DATA: MAY CROSS THE PLACENTA. HIGH ENVIRONMENTAL TEMPERATURES OR EXPOSURE OF THE CHEMICAL TO VISIBLE OR ULTRAVIOLET LIGHT MAY ENHANCE THE TOXICITY. INTERACTIONS WITH MEDICATIONS MAY OCCUR.*

* MAY BE BASED ON GENERAL INFORMATION ON ORGANOPHOSPHATES.

HEALTH EFFECTS AND FIRST AID

INHALATION: DEMETON-S-METHYL SULFONE: HIGHLY TOXIC. SEE INFORMATION ON ORGANOPHOSPHATES.

ORGANOPHOSPHATES: CHOLINESTERASE INHIBITOR. **ACUTE EXPOSURE-** WHEN INHALED, THE FIRST EFFECTS OF CHOLINESTERASE INHIBITORS ARE USUALLY RESPIRATORY AND MAY INCLUDE NASAL HYPEREMIA AND WATERY DISCHARGE, COUGH, CHEST DISCOMFORT, DYSPNEA, AND WHEEZING DUE TO INCREASED BRONCHIAL SECRETIONS AND BRONCHOCONSTRICTION. IF SUFFICIENT AMOUNTS ARE ABSORBED, OTHER SYSTEMIC EFFECTS MAY BEGIN WITHIN A FEW MINUTES OR BE DELAYED FOR UP TO 12 HOURS. SYMPTOMS MAY INCLUDE PALLOR, NAUSEA, VOMITING, DIARRHEA, ABDOMINAL CRAMPS, HEADACHE, DIZZINESS, OCULAR PAIN, BLURRED VISION, MIOSIS OR IN SOME CASES, ESPECIALLY INITIALLY, MYDRIASIS, LACRIMATION, SALIVATION, SWEATING, AND CONFUSION. OTHER REPORTED CENTRAL NERVOUS SYSTEM OR NEUROMUSCULAR EFFECTS MAY INCLUDE ATAXIA, SLURRED SPEECH, AREFLEXIA, WEAKNESS, FATIGUE, FASCICULATIONS, TWITCHING, TREMORS POSSIBLY OF THE TONGUE AND EYELIDS, AND EVENTUALLY PARALYSIS OF THE EXTREMITIES AND POSSIBLY OF THE RESPIRATORY MUSCLES. IN SEVERE CASES THERE MAY ALSO BE INVOLUNTARY DEFECATION AND URINATION, CYANOSIS, PSYCHOSIS, HYPERGLYCEMIA, ACUTE PANCREATITIS, CARDIAC IRREGULARITIES, PULMONARY EDEMA, UNCONSCIOUSNESS, CONVULSIONS, AND COMA. DEATH IS PRIMARILY DUE TO RESPIRATORY FAILURE, ALTHOUGH CARDIOVASCULAR EFFECTS INCLUDING CARDIAC ARREST MAY ALSO BE IMPLICATED. LONG TERM SEQUELAE ARE RARE BUT MAY INCLUDE NEUROPSYCHIATRIC DISORDERS AND MYOPATHY WITH MUSCLE TENDERNESS. SOME ORGANOPHOSPHATES MAY CAUSE A DELAYED NEUROPATHY BEGINNING 1-4 WEEKS AFTER AN ACUTE EXPOSURE WHICH MAY OR MAY NOT HAVE CAUSED ACUTE CHOLINERGIC EFFECTS. NUMBNESS, TINGLING, WEAKNESS AND CRAMPING BEGINNING SYMMETRICALLY IN THE LOWER LIMBS MAY PROGRESS TO ATAXIA AND PARALYSIS. IN SEVERE CASES, UPPER LIMB INVOLVEMENT IS POSSIBLE AND FLACCID PARALYSIS MAY PROGRESS TO SPASTIC PARALYSIS WITH EXAGGERATED REFLEXES. IMPROVEMENT MAY OCCUR OVER MONTHS TO YEARS, BUT SOME RESIDUAL IMPAIRMENT USUALLY REMAINS. **CHRONIC EXPOSURE-** REPEATED OR PROLONGED EXPOSURE MAY RESULT IN THE EFFECTS OF ACUTE EXPOSURE INCLUDING THE DELAYED NEUROPATHY. OTHER EFFECTS REPORTED IN WORKERS REPEATEDLY EXPOSED INCLUDE IMPAIRED MEMORY AND CONCENTRATION, ACUTE PSYCHOSIS, SEVERE DEPRESSIONS, IRRITABILTY, CONFUSION, APATHY, EMOTIONAL LABILITY, SOCIAL WITHDRAWAL, CONFUSION, HEADACHE, SPEECH DIFFICULTIES, DELAYED REACTION TIMES, SPATIAL DISORIENTATION, NIGHTMARES, SLEEPWALKING, AND DROWSINESS OR INSOMNIA. AN INFLUENZA-LIKE CONDITION WITH HEADACHE, NAUSEA, WEAKNESS, ANOREXIA AND MALAISE HAS ALSO BEEN REPORTED.

FIRST AID- REMOVE FROM EXPOSURE AREA TO FRESH AIR IMMEDIATELY. IF BREATHING HAS STOPPED, GIVE ARTIFICIAL RESPIRATION. MAINTAIN AIRWAY AND BLOOD PRESSURE AND ADMINISTER OXYGEN IF AVAILABLE. KEEP AFFECTED PERSON WARM AND AT REST. TREAT SYMPTOMATICALLY AND SUPPORTIVELY. ADMINISTRATION OF OXYGEN SHOULD BE PERFORMED BY QUALIFIED PERSONNEL. GET MEDICAL ATTENTION IMMEDIATELY.

SKIN CONTACT: DEMETON-S-METHYL SULFONE: TOXIC. SEE INFORMATION ON ORGANOPHOSPHATES.

ORGANOPHOSPHATES: CHOLINESTERASE INHIBITOR. **ACUTE EXPOSURE-** LOCALIZED SWEATING AND FASCICULATIONS MAY OCCUR AT THE SITE OF CONTACT. IF SUFFICIENT AMOUNTS ARE ABSORBED, OTHER EFFECTS OF CHOLINESTERASE INHIBITION AS DESCRIBED IN ACUTE INHALATION MAY OCCUR. SYMPTOMS MAY BE DELAYED 2-3 HOURS, BUT USUALLY NO MORE THAN 12 HOURS. THE RATE OF ABSORPTION IS INCREASED BY THE PRESENCE OF DERMATITIS OR HIGH AMBIENT TEMPERATURES. DELAYED NEUROPATHY IS ALSO POSSIBLE. **CHRONIC EXPOSURE-** REPEATED OR PROLONGED EXPOSURE MAY CAUSE EFFECTS AS DESCRIBED IN ACUTE EXPOSURE. SOME ORGANOPHOSPHATES MAY CAUSE SENSITIZATION.

FIRST AID- REMOVE CONTAMINATED CLOTHING IMMEDIATELY. WASH CONTAMINATED AREAS WITH SOAP AND WATER FOLLOWED BY ALCOHOL (ARENA, POISONING, 4TH ED.). EMERGENCY PERSONNEL SHOULD WEAR GLOVES AND AVOID CONTAMINATION. TREAT RESPIRATORY DIFFICULTY WITH ARTIFICIAL RESPIRATION. GET MEDICAL ATTENTION IMMEDIATELY.

EYE CONTACT: DEMETON-S-METHYL SULFONE: SEE INFORMATION ON ORGANOPHOSPHATES. MAY BE IRRITATING.

ORGANOPHOSPHATES: CHOLINESTERASE INHIBITOR. **ACUTE EXPOSURE-** DIRECT CONTACT MAY CAUSE PAIN, HYPEREMIA, LACRIMATION, TWITCHING OF THE EYELIDS, MIOSIS, AND CILIARY MUSCLE SPASM WITH LOSS OF ACCOMODATION, BLURRED OR DIMMED VISION AND BROWACHE. SOMETIMES MYDRIASIS MAY OCCUR INSTEAD OF MIOSIS. WITH SUFFICIENT EXPOSURE, OTHER SYMPTOMS OF CHOLINESTERASE INHIBITION AS DESCRIBED IN ACUTE INHALATION MAY OCCUR. **CHRONIC EXPOSURE-** REPEATED OR PROLONGED EXPOSURE MAY CAUSE EFFECTS AS DESCRIBED IN ACUTE EXPOSURE. SOME COMPOUNDS HAVE CAUSED TOXIC EFFECTS ON THE CRYSTALLINE LENS, CONJUNCTIVAL THICKENING AND OBSTRUCTION OF THE NASOLACRIMAL CANALS WHEN USED AS MIOTIC EYEDROPS.

FIRST AID- IRRIGATE EYES WITH WATER OR SALINE SOLUTION. IF SYMPTOMS OF POISONING OCCUR, TREAT RESPIRATORY DIFFICULTY WITH ARTIFICIAL RESPIRATION AND OXYGEN. OBSERVE PATIENT FOR AT LEAST 24-36 HOURS (GOSSELIN, CLINICAL TOXICOLOGY OF COMMERCIAL PRODUCTS, 5TH ED.). GET MEDICAL ATTENTION IMMEDIATELY. OXYGEN SHOULD BE ADMINISTERED BY QUALIFIED MEDICAL PERSONNEL.

INGESTION: DEMETON-S-METHYL SULFONE: HIGHLY TOXIC. SEE INFORMATION ON ORGANOPHOSPHATES.

ORGANOPHOSPHATES: CHOLINESTERASE INHIBITOR. **ACUTE EXPOSURE-** WHEN INGESTED, THE FIRST EFFECTS MAY BE NAUSEA, VOMITING, ANOREXIA, ABDOMINAL CRAMPS AND DIARRHEA. GASTROINTESTINAL ABSORPTION MAY CAUSE SYMPTOMS OF CHOLINESTERASE INHIBITION AS DESCRIBED IN ACUTE INHALATION. SYMPTOMS MAY BEGIN WITHIN MINUTES OR BE DELAYED FOR HOURS. DELAYED EFFECTS INCLUDING NEUROPATHY MAY ALSO OCCUR. **CHRONIC EXPOSURE-** REPEATED INGESTION MAY CAUSE EFFECTS AS DESCRIBED IN ACUTE EXPOSURE.

FIRST AID- IF PERSON IS ALERT AND RESPIRATION IS NOT DEPRESSED, GIVE SYRUP OF IPECAC FOLLOWED BY WATER (IF VOMITING OCCURS, KEEP HEAD BELOW HIPS TO PREVENT ASPIRATION). IF CONSCIOUSNESS LEVEL DECLINES OR VOMITING HAS NOT OCCURRED IN 15 MINUTES EMPTY STOMACH BY GASTRIC LAVAGE WITH THE AID OF CUFFED ENDOTRACHEAL TUBE USING ISOTONIC SALINE OR 5% SODIUM BICARBONATE FOLLOW WITH ACTIVATED CHARCOAL. ESTABLISH AND MAINTAIN AIRWAY. TREAT RESPIRATORY DIFFICULTY WITH ARTIFICIAL RESPIRATION AND OXYGEN. DO NOT GIVE MORPHINE, AMINOPHYLLINE, PHENOTHIAZINES, RESERPINE, FUROSEMIDE, OR ETHACRYNIC ACID (MORGAN, RECOGNITION AND MANAGEMENT OF PESTICIDE POISONINGS, 3RD ED.). TREAT SYMPTOMATICALLY AND SUPPORTIVELY. ADMINISTRATION OF OXYGEN AND LAVAGE MUST BE PERFORMED BY QUALIFIED MEDICAL PERSONNEL. GET MEDICAL ATTENTION IMMEDIATELY.

ANTIDOTE: THE FOLLOWING ANTIDOTE(S) HAVE BEEN RECOMMENDED. HOWEVER, THE DECISION AS TO WHETHER THE SEVERITY OF POISONING REQUIRES ADMINISTRATION OF ANY ANTIDOTE AND ACTUAL DOSE REQUIRED SHOULD BE MADE BY QUALIFIED MEDICAL PERSONNEL.

FOR CHOLINESTERASE INHIBITORS: ESTABLISH CLEAR AIRWAY AND TISSUE OXYGENATION BY ASPIRATION OF SECRETIONS, AND IF NECESSARY, BY ASSISTED PULMONARY VENTILATION WITH OXYGEN. IMPROVE TISSUE OXYGENATION AS MUCH AS POSSIBLE BEFORE ADMINISTERING ATROPINE TO MINIMIZE THE RISK OF VENTRICULAR FIBRILLATION. ADMINISTER ATROPINE SULFATE INTRAVENOUSLY, OR INTRAMUSCULARLY IF IV INJECTION IS NOT POSSIBLE. IN MODERATELY SEVERE POISONING ADMINISTER ATROPINE SULFATE, 0.4-2.0 MG REPEATED EVERY 15 MINUTES UNTIL ATROPINIZATION IS ACHIEVED (TACHYCARDIA, FLUSHING, DRY MOUTH, MYDRIASIS). MAINTAIN ATROPINIZATION BY REPEATED DOSES FOR 2-12 HOURS, OR LONGER, DEPENDING ON THE SEVERITY OF POISONING. THE APPEARANCE OF RALES IN THE LUNG BASES, MIOSIS, SALIVATION, NAUSEA, BRADYCARDIA, ARE ALL INDICATIONS OF INADEQUATE ATROPINIZATION. SEVERELY POISONED INDIVIDUALS MAY EXHIBIT REMARKABLE TOLERANCE TO ATROPINE; TWO OR MORE TIMES THE DOSAGES SUGGESTED ABOVE MAY BE

NEEDED. PERSONS NOT POISONED OR ONLY SLIGHTLY POISONED, HOWEVER, MAY DEVELOP SIGNS OF ATROPINE TOXICITY FROM SUCH LARGE DOSAGES: FEVER, MUSCLE FIBRILLATIONS, AND DELIRIUM ARE THE MAIN SIGNS OF ATROPINE TOXICITY. IF THESE SIGNS APPEAR WHILE THE PATIENT IS FULLY ATROPINIZED, ATROPINE ADMINISTRATION SHOULD BE DISCONTINUED, AT LEAST TEMPORARILY. OBSERVE TREATED PATIENTS CLOSELY AT LEAST 24 HOURS TO INSURE THAT SYMPTOMS (POSSIBLY PULMONARY EDEMA) DO NOT RECUR AS ATROPINIZATION WEARS OFF. IN VERY SEVERE POISONINGS, METABOLIC DISPOSITION OF TOXICANT MAY REQUIRE SEVERAL HOURS OR DAYS DURING WHICH ATROPINIZATION MUST BE MAINTAINED. MARKEDLY LOWER LEVELS OF URINARY METABOLITES INDICATE THAT ATROPINE DOSAGE CAN BE TAPERED OFF. AS DOSAGE IS REDUCED, CHECK THE LUNG BASES FREQUENTLY FOR RALES. IF RALES ARE HEARD OR OTHER SYMPTOMS RETURN, RE-ESTABLISH ATROPINIZATION PROMPTLY (MORGAN, RECOGNITION AND MANAGEMENT OF PESTICIDE POISONINGS, 3RD ED.). ADMINISTRATION OF ANTIDOTE MUST BE PERFORMED BY QUALIFIED MEDICAL PERSONNEL.

IN CASES OF SEVERE POISONING BY ORGANOPHOSPHATE PESTICIDES IN WHICH RESPIRATORY DEPRESSION, MUSCLE WEAKNESS AND TWITCHINGS ARE SEVERE, GIVE PRALIDOXIME (PROTOPAM-AYERST, 2-PAM), 1.0 GRAM INTRAVENOUSLY AT NO MORE THAN 0.5 GRAM PER MINUTE. DOSAGE OF PRALIDOXIME MAY BE REPEATED IN 1-2 HOURS, THEN AT 10-12 HOUR INTERVALS IF NEEDED. IN VERY SEVERE POISONINGS, DOSAGE RATES MAY BE DOUBLED. TREATMENT WITH PRALIDOXIME WILL BE MOST EFFECTIVE IF GIVEN WITHIN THIRTY-SIX HOURS AFTER POISONING (MORGAN, RECOGNITION AND MANAGEMENT OF PESTICIDE POISONINGS, 3RD ED.). ANTIDOTE SHOULD BE ADMINISTERED BY QUALIFIED MEDICAL PERSONNEL.

REACTIVITY

REACTIVITY: STABLE UNDER NORMAL TEMPERATURES AND PRESSURES.
INCOMPATIBILITIES: DEMETON-S-METHYL SULFONE: OXIDIZERS (STRONG): FIRE AND EXPLOSION HAZARD.
DECOMPOSITION: THERMAL DECOMPOSITION PRODUCTS MAY INCLUDE TOXIC OXIDES OF CARBON, SULFUR, AND PHOSPHORUS.
POLYMERIZATION: HAZARDOUS POLYMERIZATION HAS NOT BEEN REPORTED TO OCCUR UNDER NORMAL TEMPERATURES AND PRESSURES.

STORAGE AND DISPOSAL

OBSERVE ALL FEDERAL, STATE AND LOCAL REGULATIONS WHEN STORING OR DISPOSING OF THIS SUBSTANCE. FOR ASSISTANCE, CONTACT THE DISTRICT DIRECTOR OF THE ENVIRONMENTAL PROTECTION AGENCY.

****STORAGE****

STORE IN ACCORDANCE WITH 40 CFR 165 RECOMMENDED PROCEDURES FOR THE DISPOSAL AND STORAGE OF PESTICIDES AND PESTICIDE CONTAINERS.
STORE AWAY FROM INCOMPATIBLE SUBSTANCES.

****DISPOSAL****

DISPOSAL MUST BE IN ACCORDANCE WITH 40 CFR 165 RECOMMENDED PROCEDURES FOR THE DISPOSAL AND STORAGE OF PESTICIDES AND PESTICIDE CONTAINERS.

CONDITIONS TO AVOID

MAY BURN BUT DOES NOT IGNITE READILY.

SPILL AND LEAK PROCEDURES

OCCUPATIONAL SPILL: DO NOT TOUCH SPILLED MATERIAL. STOP LEAK IF YOU CAN DO IT WITHOUT RISK. FOR SMALL SPILLS, TAKE UP WITH SAND OR OTHER ABSORBENT MATERIAL AND PLACE INTO CONTAINERS FOR LATER DISPOSAL. FOR SMALL DRY SPILLS, WITH A CLEAN SHOVEL PLACE MATERIAL INTO CLEAN, DRY CONTAINER AND COVER. MOVE CONTAINERS FROM SPILL AREA. FOR LARGER SPILLS, DIKE FAR AHEAD OF SPILL FOR LATER DISPOSAL. KEEP UNNECESSARY PEOPLE AWAY. ISOLATE HAZARD AREA AND DENY ENTRY.

PROTECTIVE EQUIPMENT

VENTILATION: PROVIDE LOCAL EXHAUST OR PROCESS ENCLOSURE VENTILATION SYSTEM.
RESPIRATOR: THE FOLLOWING RESPIRATORS ARE RECOMMENDED BASED ON INFORMATION FOUND IN THE PHYSICAL DATA, TOXICITY AND HEALTH EFFECTS SECTIONS. THEY ARE RANKED IN ORDER FROM MINIMUM TO MAXIMUM RESPIRATORY PROTECTION. THE SPECIFIC RESPIRATOR SELECTED MUST BE BASED ON CONTAMINATION LEVELS FOUND IN THE WORK PLACE, MUST NOT EXCEED THE WORKING LIMITS OF THE RESPIRATOR AND BE JOINTLY APPROVED BY THE NATIONAL INSTITUTE FOR OCCUPATIONAL SAFETY AND HEALTH AND THE MINE SAFETY AND HEALTH ADMINISTRATION (NIOSH-MSHA).
TYPE 'C' SUPPLIED-AIR RESPIRATOR WITH A FULL FACEPIECE OPERATED IN PRESSURE-DEMAND OR OTHER POSITIVE PRESSURE MODE OR WITH A FULL FACEPIECE, HELMET OR HOOD OPERATED IN CONTINOUS-FLOW MODE.
SELF-CONTAINED BREATHING APPARATUS WITH A FULL FACEPIECE OPERATED IN PRESSURE-DEMAND OR OTHER POSITIVE PRESSURE MODE.
FOR FIREFIGHTING AND OTHER IMMEDIATELY DANGEROUS TO LIFE OR HEALTH CONDITIONS:
SELF-CONTAINED BREATHING APPARATUS WITH FULL FACEPIECE OPERATED IN PRESSURE-DEMAND OR OTHER POSITIVE PRESSURE MODE.
SUPPLIED-AIR RESPIRATOR WITH FULL FACEPIECE AND OPERATED IN PRESSURE-DEMAND OR OTHER POSITIVE PRESSURE MODE IN COMBINATION WITH AN AUXILIARY SELF-CONTAINED BREATHING APPARATUS OPERATED IN PRESSURE-DEMAND OR OTHER POSITIVE PRESSURE MODE.
CLOTHING: EMPLOYEE MUST WEAR APPROPRIATE PROTECTIVE (IMPERVIOUS) CLOTHING AND EQUIPMENT TO PREVENT ANY POSSIBILITY OF SKIN CONTACT WITH THIS SUBSTANCE.
GLOVES: EMPLOYEE MUST WEAR APPROPRIATE PROTECTIVE GLOVES TO PREVENT CONTACT WITH THIS SUBSTANCE.
EYE PROTECTION: EMPLOYEE MUST WEAR SPLASH-PROOF OR DUST-RESISTANT SAFETY GOGGLES AND A FACESHIELD TO PREVENT CONTACT WITH THIS SUBSTANCE.
EMERGENCY WASH FACILITIES: WHERE THERE IS ANY POSSIBILITY THAT AN EMPLOYEE'S EYES AND/OR SKIN MAY BE EXPOSED TO THIS SUBSTANCE, THE EMPLOYER SHOULD PROVIDE AN EYE WASH FOUNTAIN AND QUICK DRENCH SHOWER WITHIN THE IMMEDIATE WORK AREA FOR EMERGENCY USE.

AUTHORIZED BY- OCCUPATIONAL HEALTH SERVICES, INC.
CREATION DATE: 10/04/89 ***REVISION DATE:*** 04/30/90

MATERIAL SAFETY DATA SHEET

OCCUPATIONAL HEALTH SERVICES, INC.
AGRICULTURE AND PESTICIDE DIVISION
450 SEVENTH AVENUE, SUITE 2407
NEW YORK, NEW YORK 10123
1-800-445-MSDS OR (212) 967-1100

EMERGENCY CONTACT:
JOHN S. BRANSFORD, JR. (615) 292-1180

SUBSTANCE IDENTIFICATION

CAS-NUMBER 8065-48-3
SUBSTANCE: DEMETON
TRADE NAMES/SYNONYMS: O,O-DIETHYL 2-ETHYLTHIOETHYL PHOSPHOROTHIOATE; PHOSPHOROTHIOIC ACID, O,O-DIETHYL O-(2-(ETHYLTHIO)ETHYL)ESTER, MIXED WITH O,O-DIETHYL S-(2-(ETHYLTHIO)ETHYL)PHOSPHOROTHIOATE; DIETHOXY THIOPHOSPHORIC ACID ESTER OF 2-ETHYLMERCAPTOETHANOL; O,O-DIETHYL 2-ETHYLMERCAPTOETHYL THIOPHOSPHATE; BAYER 8169; E 1059; ETHYL SYSTOX; MERCAPTOFOS; MERCAPTOPHOS; SEPTOX; SYSTOX; ENT 17,295; PST06320
CHEMICAL FAMILY: ORGANOPHOSPHATE
MOLECULAR FORMULA: C8-H19-O3-P-S2.C8-H19-O3-P-S2
MOLECULAR WEIGHT: 516.72
CERCLA RATINGS (SCALE 0-3): HEALTH=3 FIRE=U REACTIVITY=0 PERSISTENCE=0
NFPA RATINGS (SCALE 0-4): HEALTH=4 FIRE=U REACTIVITY=0

COMPONENTS AND CONTAMINANTS

COMPONENT: O,O-DIETHYL O-(2-ETHYLTHIOETHYL) PHOSPHOROTHIOATE ***PERCENT:*** 70
COMPONENT: O,O-DIETHYL S-(2-ETHYLTHIOETHYL) PHOSPHOROTHIOATE ***PERCENT:*** 30
OTHER CONTAMINANTS: NONE
EXPOSURE LIMITS: DEMETON: 0.1 MG/M3 OSHA TWA (SKIN) 0.01 PPM (0.1 MG/M3) ACGIH TWA (SKIN)
500 POUNDS SARA SECTION 302 THRESHOLD PLANNING QUANTITY 1 POUND SARA SECTION 304 REPORTABLE QUANTITY

PHYSICAL DATA

DESCRIPTION: LIGHT BROWN LIQUID WITH A FAINT SULFUR ODOR.
BOILING POINT: 273 F (134 C) @ 2 MMHG ***MELTING POINT:*** >-13 F (>-25 C)
SPECIFIC GRAVITY: 1.118 ***VAPOR PRESSURE:*** 0.00025 MMHG @ 20 C
SOLUBILITY IN WATER: 0.2%
SOLVENT SOLUBILITY: ETHANOL, PROPYLENE GLYCOL, TOLUENE, AND MOST ORGANIC SOLVENTS

FIRE AND EXPLOSION DATA

FIRE AND EXPLOSION HAZARD: UNKNOWN FIRE AND EXPLOSION HAZARD.

FIREFIGHTING MEDIA: DRY CHEMICAL, CARBON DIOXIDE, HALON, WATER SPRAY OR STANDARD FOAM (1987 EMERGENCY RESPONSE GUIDEBOOK, DOT P 5800.4). FOR LARGER FIRES, USE WATER SPRAY, FOG OR STANDARD FOAM (1987 EMERGENCY RESPONSE GUIDEBOOK, DOT P 5800.4).

FIREFIGHTING: MOVE CONTAINERS FROM FIRE AREA IF POSSIBLE. FIGHT FIRE FROM MAXIMUM DISTANCE. STAY AWAY FROM STORAGE TANK ENDS. DIKE FIRE CONTROL WATER FOR LATER DISPOSAL. DO NOT SCATTER MATERIAL (1987 EMERGENCY RESPONSE GUIDEBOOK, DOT P 5800.4, GUIDE PAGE 55). EXTINGUISH ONLY IF FLOW CAN BE STOPPED; USE FLOODING AMOUNTS OF WATER AS FOG, SOLID STREAMS MAY BE INEFFECTIVE. COOL CONTAINERS WITH FLOODING AMOUNTS OF WATER FROM AS FAR A DISTANCE AS POSSIBLE. USE WATER SPRAY TO ABSORB TOXIC VAPORS. AVOID BREATHING TOXIC VAPORS; KEEP UPWIND. CONSIDER EVACUATION OF DOWNWIND AREA IF MATERIAL IS LEAKING.

TRANSPORTATION DATA

DEPARTMENT OF TRANSPORTATION HAZARD CLASSIFICATION 49 CFR 172.101: POISON B

DEPARTMENT OF TRANSPORTATION LABELING REQUIREMENTS 49 CFR 172.101 AND SUBPART E: POISON

DEPARTMENT OF TRANSPORTATION PACKAGING REQUIREMENTS: 49 CFR 173.346 EXCEPTIONS: 49 CFR 173.345

TOXICITY

DEMETON: TOXICITY DATA: 15 MG/M3/4 HOURS INHALATION-RAT LCLO; 15 MG/M3/4 HOURS INHALATION-CAT LCLO; 24 MG/KG SKIN-RABBIT LD50; 8200 UG/KG SKIN-RAT LD50; 171 UG/KG ORAL-HUMAN LDLO; 144 MG/KG/24 DAYS INTERMITTENT ORAL-MAN TDLO; 1700 UG/KG ORAL-RAT LD50; 7850 UG/KG ORAL-MOUSE LD50; 24 MG/KG SUBCUTANEOUS-RABBIT LD50; 1750 UG/KG INTRAVENOUS-RAT LD50; LD50; 3900 UG/KG INTRAVENOUS-MOUSE LD50; 2500 UG/KG INTRAPERITONEAL-RAT LD50; 4 MG/KG INTRAPERITONEAL-MOUSE LD50; 3250 UG/KG INTRAPERITONEAL-RABBIT LD50; 3 MG/KG INTRAMUSCULAR-RAT LDLO; 3650 UG/KG INTRAMUSCULAR-DOG LD50; 3900 UG/KG INTRAMUSCULAR-CAT LD50; MUTAGENIC DATA (RTECS); REPRODUCTIVE EFFECTS DATA (RTECS). CARCINOGEN STATUS: NONE. ACUTE TOXICITY LEVEL: HIGHLY TOXIC BY DERMAL ABSORPTION AND INGESTION. TARGET EFFECTS: CHOLINESTERASE INHIBITOR. POISONING MAY AFFECT THE NERVOUS SYSTEM.* AT INCREASED RISK FROM EXPOSURE: PERSONS WITH RESPIRATORY AILMENTS, RECENT EXPOSURE TO CHOLINESTERASE INHIBITORS OR IMPAIRED CHOLINESTERASE PRODUCTION, OR LIVER MALFUNCTION.* ADDITIONAL DATA: MAY CROSS THE PLACENTA. HIGH ENVIRONMENTAL TEMPERATURES OR EXPOSURE OF THE CHEMICAL TO VISIBLE OR ULTRAVIOLET LIGHT MAY ENHANCE THE TOXICITY. INTERACTIONS WITH MEDICATIONS MAY OCCUR.*

* MAY BE BASED ON GENERAL INFORMATION ON ORGANOPHOSPHATES.

HEALTH EFFECTS AND FIRST AID

INHALATION: DEMETON: 20 MG/M3 IMMEDIATELY DANGEROUS TO LIFE OR HEALTH. IN AN INCIDENCE OF OCCUPATIONAL EXPOSURE, A YOUNG MAN CONTINUED TO EXPERIENCE SYMPTOMS OF DIFFICULTY IN BREATHING, GENERAL WEAKNESS, AND LACK OF COORDINATION IN WALKING FIVE WEEKS AFTER EXPOSURE. AFTER 3 MONTHS, HE STILL HAD DISTURBANCES OF THE AUTONOMIC NERVOUS SYSTEM. A CONCENTRATION OF 3 MG/M3 FOR TWO HOURS EACH DAY WAS LETHAL ON THE FOURTH EXPOSURE TO 10 OF 17 RATS TESTED. SEE INFORMATION ON ORGANOPHOSPHATES.

ORGANOPHOSPHATES: CHOLINESTERASE INHIBITOR. **ACUTE EXPOSURE-** WHEN INHALED, THE FIRST EFFECTS OF CHOLINESTERASE INHIBITORS ARE USUALLY RESPIRATORY AND MAY INCLUDE NASAL HYPEREMIA AND WATERY DISCHARGE, COUGH, CHEST DISCOMFORT, DYSPNEA, AND WHEEZING DUE TO INCREASED BRONCHIAL SECRETIONS AND BRONCHOCONSTRICTION. IF SUFFICIENT AMOUNTS ARE ABSORBED, OTHER SYSTEMIC EFFECTS MAY BEGIN WITHIN A FEW MINUTES OR BE DELAYED FOR UP TO 12 HOURS. SYMPTOMS MAY INCLUDE PALLOR, NAUSEA, VOMITING, DIARRHEA, ABDOMINAL CRAMPS, HEADACHE, DIZZINESS, OCULAR PAIN, BLURRED VISION, MIOSIS OR IN SOME CASES, ESPECIALLY INITIALLY, MYDRIASIS, LACRIMATION, SALIVATION, SWEATING, AND CONFUSION. OTHER REPORTED CENTRAL NERVOUS SYSTEM OR NEUROMUSCULAR EFFECTS MAY INCLUDE ATAXIA, SLURRED SPEECH, AREFLEXIA, WEAKNESS, FATIGUE, FASCICULATIONS, TWITCHING, TREMORS POSSIBLY OF THE TONGUE AND EYELIDS, AND EVENTUALLY PARALYSIS OF THE EXTREMITIES AND POSSIBLY OF THE RESPIRATORY MUSCLES. IN SEVERE CASES THERE MAY ALSO BE INVOLUNTARY DEFECATION AND URINATION, CYANOSIS, PSYCHOSIS, HYPERGLYCEMIA, ACUTE PANCREATITIS, CARDIAC IRREGULARITIES, PULMONARY EDEMA, UNCONSCIOUSNESS, CONVULSIONS, AND COMA. DEATH IS PRIMARILY DUE TO RESPIRATORY FAILURE, ALTHOUGH CARDIOVASCULAR EFFECTS INCLUDING CARDIAC ARREST MAY ALSO BE IMPLICATED. LONG TERM SEQUELAE ARE RARE BUT MAY INCLUDE NEUROPSYCHIATRIC DISORDERS AND MYOPATHY WITH MUSCLE TENDERNESS. SOME ORGANOPHOSPHATES MAY CAUSE A DELAYED NEUROPATHY BEGINNING 1-4 WEEKS AFTER AN ACUTE EXPOSURE WHICH MAY OR MAY NOT HAVE CAUSED ACUTE CHOLINERGIC EFFECTS. NUMBNESS, TINGLING, WEAKNESS AND CRAMPING BEGINNING SYMMETRICALLY IN THE LOWER LIMBS MAY PROGRESS TO ATAXIA AND PARALYSIS. IN SEVERE CASES, UPPER LIMB INVOLVEMENT IS POSSIBLE AND FLACCID PARALYSIS MAY PROGRESS TO SPASTIC PARALYSIS WITH EXAGGERATED REFLEXES. IMPROVEMENT MAY OCCUR OVER MONTHS TO YEARS, BUT SOME RESIDUAL IMPAIRMENT USUALLY REMAINS. **CHRONIC EXPOSURE-** REPEATED OR PROLONGED EXPOSURE MAY RESULT IN THE EFFECTS OF ACUTE EXPOSURE INCLUDING THE DELAYED NEUROPATHY. OTHER EFFECTS REPORTED IN WORKERS REPEATEDLY EXPOSED INCLUDE IMPAIRED MEMORY AND CONCENTRATION, ACUTE PSYCHOSIS, SEVERE DEPRESSIONS, IRRITABILTY, CONFUSION, APATHY, EMOTIONAL LABILITY, SOCIAL WITHDRAWAL, CONFUSION, HEADACHE, SPEECH DIFFICULTIES, DELAYED REACTION TIMES, SPATIAL DISORIENTATION, NIGHTMARES, SLEEPWALKING, AND DROWSINESS OR INSOMNIA. AN INFLUENZA-LIKE CONDITION WITH HEADACHE, NAUSEA, WEAKNESS, ANOREXIA AND MALAISE HAS ALSO BEEN REPORTED.

FIRST AID- REMOVE FROM EXPOSURE AREA TO FRESH AIR IMMEDIATELY. IF BREATHING HAS STOPPED, GIVE ARTIFICIAL RESPIRATION. MAINTAIN AIRWAY AND BLOOD PRESSURE AND ADMINISTER OXYGEN IF AVAILABLE. KEEP AFFECTED PERSON WARM AND AT REST. TREAT SYMPTOMATICALLY AND SUPPORTIVELY. ADMINISTRATION OF OXYGEN SHOULD BE PERFORMED BY QUALIFIED PERSONNEL. GET MEDICAL ATTENTION IMMEDIATELY.

SKIN CONTACT: DEMETON: HIGHLY TOXIC. SEE INFORMATION ON ORGANOPHOSPHATES.

ORGANOPHOSPHATES: CHOLINESTERASE INHIBITOR. **ACUTE EXPOSURE-** LOCALIZED SWEATING AND FASCICULATIONS MAY OCCUR AT THE SITE OF CONTACT. IF SUFFICIENT AMOUNTS ARE ABSORBED, OTHER EFFECTS OF CHOLINESTERASE INHIBITION AS DESCRIBED IN ACUTE INHALATION MAY OCCUR. SYMPTOMS MAY BE DELAYED 2-3 HOURS, BUT USUALLY NO MORE THAN 12 HOURS. THE RATE OF ABSORPTION IS INCREASED BY THE PRESENCE OF DERMATITIS OR HIGH AMBIENT TEMPERATURES. DELAYED NEUROPATHY IS ALSO POSSIBLE. **CHRONIC EXPOSURE-** REPEATED OR PROLONGED EXPOSURE MAY CAUSE EFFECTS AS DESCRIBED IN ACUTE EXPOSURE. SOME ORGANOPHOSPHATES MAY CAUSE SENSITIZATION.

FIRST AID- REMOVE CONTAMINATED CLOTHING IMMEDIATELY. WASH CONTAMINATED AREAS WITH SOAP AND WATER FOLLOWED BY ALCOHOL (ARENA, POISONING, 4TH ED.). EMERGENCY PERSONNEL SHOULD WEAR GLOVES AND AVOID CONTAMINATION. TREAT RESPIRATORY DIFFICULTY WITH ARTIFICIAL RESPIRATION. GET MEDICAL ATTENTION IMMEDIATELY.

EYE CONTACT: DEMETON: SEE INFORMATION ON ORGANOPHOSPHATES.

ORGANOPHOSPHATES: CHOLINESTERASE INHIBITOR. **ACUTE EXPOSURE-** DIRECT CONTACT MAY CAUSE PAIN, HYPEREMIA, LACRIMATION, TWITCHING OF THE EYELIDS, MIOSIS, AND CILIARY MUSCLE SPASM WITH LOSS OF ACCOMODATION, BLURRED OR DIMMED VISION AND BROWACHE. SOMETIMES MYDRIASIS MAY OCCUR INSTEAD OF MIOSIS. WITH SUFFICIENT EXPOSURE, OTHER SYMPTOMS OF CHOLINESTERASE INHIBITION AS DESCRIBED IN ACUTE INHALATION MAY OCCUR. **CHRONIC EXPOSURE-** REPEATED OR PROLONGED EXPOSURE MAY CAUSE EFFECTS AS DESCRIBED IN ACUTE EXPOSURE. SOME COMPOUNDS HAVE CAUSED TOXIC EFFECTS ON THE CRYSTALLINE LENS, CONJUNCTIVAL THICKENING AND OBSTRUCTION OF THE NASOLACRIMAL CANALS WHEN USED AS MIOTIC EYEDROPS.

FIRST AID- IRRIGATE EYES WITH WATER OR SALINE SOLUTION. IF SYMPTOMS OF POISONING OCCUR, TREAT RESPIRATORY DIFFICULTY WITH ARTIFICIAL RESPIRATION AND OXYGEN. OBSERVE PATIENT FOR AT LEAST 24-36 HOURS (GOSSELIN, CLINICAL TOXICOLOGY OF COMMERCIAL PRODUCTS, 5TH ED.). GET MEDICAL ATTENTION IMMEDIATELY. OXYGEN SHOULD BE ADMINISTERED BY QUALIFIED MEDICAL PERSONNEL.

INGESTION: DEMETON: HIGHLY TOXIC. IN ONE STUDY OF 5 MEN WHO EACH INGESTED 7.125 MG PER DAY FOR 25 DAYS, 39.8% AND 15.9% DEPRESSIONS IN PLASMA AND ERYTHROCYTE CHOLINESTERASE ACTIVITYWERE OBSERVED. IN A 12-WEEK FEEDING STUDY WITH HENS, NO NEUROTOXIC EFFECTS WERE NOTED AT 0.06 MG/KG/DAY. SEE INFORMATION ON ORGANOPHOSPHATES.

ORGANOPHOSPHATES: CHOLINESTERASE INHIBITOR. **ACUTE EXPOSURE-** WHEN INGESTED, THE FIRST EFFECTS MAY BE NAUSEA, VOMITING, ANOREXIA, ABDOMINAL CRAMPS AND DIARRHEA. GASTROINTESTINAL ABSORPTION MAY CAUSE SYMPTOMS OF CHOLINESTERASE INHIBITION AS DESCRIBED IN ACUTE INHALATION. SYMPTOMS MAY BEGIN WITHIN MINUTES OR BE DELAYED FOR HOURS. DELAYED EFFECTS INCLUDING NEUROPATHY MAY ALSO OCCUR. **CHRONIC EXPOSURE-** REPEATED INGESTION MAY CAUSE EFFECTS AS DESCRIBED IN ACUTE EXPOSURE.

FIRST AID- IF PERSON IS ALERT AND RESPIRATION IS NOT DEPRESSED, GIVE SYRUP OF IPECAC FOLLOWED BY WATER (IF VOMITING OCCURS, KEEP HEAD BELOW HIPS TO PREVENT ASPIRATION). IF CONSCIOUSNESS LEVEL DECLINES OR VOMITING HAS

NOT OCCURRED IN 15 MINUTES EMPTY STOMACH BY GASTRIC LAVAGE WITH THE AID OF CUFFED ENDOTRACHEAL TUBE USING ISOTONIC SALINE OR 5% SODIUM BICARBONATE FOLLOW WITH ACTIVATED CHARCOAL. ESTABLISH AND MAINTAIN AIRWAY. TREAT RESPIRATORY DIFFICULTY WITH ARTIFICIAL RESPIRATION AND OXYGEN. DO NOT GIVE MORPHINE, AMINOPHYLLINE, PHENOTHIAZINES, RESERPINE, FUROSEMIDE, OR ETHACRYNIC ACID (MORGAN, RECOGNITION AND MANAGEMENT OF PESTICIDE POISONINGS, 3RD ED.). TREAT SYMPTOMATICALLY AND SUPPORTIVELY. ADMINISTRATION OF OXYGEN AND LAVAGE MUST BE PERFORMED BY QUALIFIED MEDICAL PERSONNEL. GET MEDICAL ATTENTION IMMEDIATELY.

ANTIDOTE: THE FOLLOWING ANTIDOTE(S) HAVE BEEN RECOMMENDED. HOWEVER, THE DECISION AS TO WHETHER THE SEVERITY OF POISONING REQUIRES ADMINISTRATION OF ANY ANTIDOTE AND ACTUAL DOSE REQUIRED SHOULD BE MADE BY QUALIFIED MEDICAL PERSONNEL.

FOR CHOLINESTERASE INHIBITORS: ESTABLISH CLEAR AIRWAY AND TISSUE OXYGENATION BY ASPIRATION OF SECRETIONS, AND IF NECESSARY, BY ASSISTED PULMONARY VENTILATION WITH OXYGEN. IMPROVE TISSUE OXYGENATION AS MUCH AS POSSIBLE BEFORE ADMINISTERING ATROPINE TO MINIMIZE THE RISK OF VENTRICULAR FIBRILLATION. ADMINISTER ATROPINE SULFATE INTRAVENOUSLY, OR INTRAMUSCULARLY IF IV INJECTION IS NOT POSSIBLE. IN MODERATELY SEVERE POISONING ADMINISTER ATROPINE SULFATE, 0.4-2.0 MG REPEATED EVERY 15 MINUTES UNTIL ATROPINIZATION IS ACHIEVED (TACHYCARDIA, FLUSHING, DRY MOUTH, MYDRIASIS). MAINTAIN ATROPINIZATION BY REPEATED DOSES FOR 2-12 HOURS, OR LONGER, DEPENDING ON THE SEVERITY OF POISONING. THE APPEARANCE OF RALES IN THE LUNG BASES, MIOSIS, SALIVATION, NAUSEA, BRADYCARDIA, ARE ALL INDICATIONS OF INADEQUATE ATROPINIZATION. SEVERELY POISONED INDIVIDUALS MAY EXHIBIT REMARKABLE TOLERANCE TO ATROPINE; TWO OR MORE TIMES THE DOSAGES SUGGESTED ABOVE MAY BE NEEDED. PERSONS NOT POISONED OR ONLY SLIGHTLY POISONED, HOWEVER, MAY DEVELOP SIGNS OF ATROPINE TOXICITY FROM SUCH LARGE DOSAGES: FEVER, MUSCLE FIBRILLATIONS, AND DELIRIUM ARE THE MAIN SIGNS OF ATROPINE TOXICITY. IF THESE SIGNS APPEAR WHILE THE PATIENT IS FULLY ATROPINIZED, ATROPINE ADMINISTRATION SHOULD BE DISCONTINUED, AT LEAST TEMPORARILY. OBSERVE TREATED PATIENTS CLOSELY AT LEAST 24 HOURS TO INSURE THAT SYMPTOMS (POSSIBLY PULMONARY EDEMA) DO NOT RECUR AS ATROPINIZATION WEARS OFF. IN VERY SEVERE POISONINGS, METABOLIC DISPOSITION OF TOXICANT MAY REQUIRE SEVERAL HOURS OR DAYS DURING WHICH ATROPINIZATION MUST BE MAINTAINED. MARKEDLY LOWER LEVELS OF URINARY METABOLITES INDICATE THAT ATROPINE DOSAGE CAN BE TAPERED OFF. AS DOSAGE IS REDUCED, CHECK THE LUNG BASES FREQUENTLY FOR RALES. IF RALES ARE HEARD OR OTHER SYMPTOMS RETURN, RE-ESTABLISH ATROPINIZATION PROMPTLY (MORGAN, RECOGNITION AND MANAGEMENT OF PESTICIDE POISONINGS, 3RD ED.). ADMINISTRATION OF ANTIDOTE MUST BE PERFORMED BY QUALIFIED MEDICAL PERSONNEL.

IN CASES OF SEVERE POISONING BY ORGANOPHOSPHATE PESTICIDES IN WHICH RESPIRATORY DEPRESSION, MUSCLE WEAKNESS AND TWITCHINGS ARE SEVERE, GIVE PRALIDOXIME (PROTOPAM-AYERST, 2-PAM), 1.0 GRAM INTRAVENOUSLY AT NO MORE THAN 0.5 GRAM PER MINUTE. DOSAGE OF PRALIDOXIME MAY BE REPEATED IN 1-2 HOURS, THEN AT 10-12 HOUR INTERVALS IF NEEDED. IN VERY SEVERE POISONINGS, DOSAGE RATES MAY BE DOUBLED. TREATMENT WITH PRALIDOXIME WILL BE MOST EFFECTIVE IF GIVEN WITHIN THIRTY-SIX HOURS AFTER POISONING (MORGAN, RECOGNITION AND MANAGEMENT OF PESTICIDE POISONINGS, 3RD ED.). ANTIDOTE SHOULD BE ADMINISTERED BY QUALIFIED MEDICAL PERSONNEL.

REACTIVITY

REACTIVITY: STABLE UNDER NORMAL TEMPERATURES AND PRESSURES; HYDROLYZED BY BOILING WATER.

INCOMPATIBILITIES: DEMETON: ALKALINE CONDITIONS: MAY CAUSE HYDROLYSIS. BORDEAUX:INCOMPATIBLE CALCIUM ARSENATE: INCOMPATIBLE. CYPREX: INCOMPATIBLE. LIME OR LIME SULFUR: INCOMPATIBLE. MERCURY COMPOUNDS (WATER SOLUBLE): INCOMPATIBLE. PARIS GREEN: INCOMPATIBLE PLASTICS, RUBBER, AND COATINGS: SOME FORMS MAY BE ATTACKED. STRONG OXIDIZERS: MAY CAUSE FIRE OR EXPLOSION. UREA: INCOMPATIBLE. ZINC ARSENATE: INCOMPATIBLE.

DECOMPOSITION: THERMAL DECOMPOSITION MAY RELEASE TOXIC OXIDES OF PHOSPHORUS AND SULFUR.

POLYMERIZATION: HAZARDOUS POLYMERIZATION HAS NOT BEEN REPORTED TO OCCUR UNDER NORMAL TEMPERATURES AND PRESSURES.

STORAGE AND DISPOSAL

OBSERVE ALL FEDERAL, STATE AND LOCAL REGULATIONS WHEN STORING OR DISPOSING OF THIS SUBSTANCE. FOR ASSISTANCE, CONTACT THE DISTRICT DIRECTOR OF THE ENVIRONMENTAL PROTECTION AGENCY.

****STORAGE****

STORE IN ACCORDANCE WITH 40 CFR 165 RECOMMENDED PROCEDURES FOR THE DISPOSAL AND STORAGE OF PESTICIDES AND PESTICIDE CONTAINERS. STORE AWAY FROM INCOMPATIBLE SUBSTANCES.

THRESHOLD PLANNING QUANTITY (TPQ): THE SUPERFUND AMENDMENTS AND REAUTHORIZATION ACT (SARA) SECTION 302 REQUIRES THAT EACH FACILITY WHERE ANY EXTREMELY HAZARDOUS SUBSTANCE IS PRESENT IN A QUANTITY EQUAL TO OR GREATER THAN THE TPQ ESTABLISHED FOR THAT SUBSTANCE NOTIFY THE STATE EMERGENCY RESPONSE COMMISSION FOR THE STATE IN WHICH IT IS LOCATED. SECTION 303 OF SARA REQUIRES THESE FACILITIES TO PARTICIPATE IN LOCAL EMERGENCY RESPONSE PLANNING (40 CFR 355.30).

****DISPOSAL****

DISPOSAL MUST BE IN ACCORDANCE WITH 40 CFR 165 RECOMMENDED PROCEDURES FOR THE DISPOSAL AND STORAGE OF PESTICIDES AND PESTICIDE CONTAINERS.

CONDITIONS TO AVOID

NONE REPORTED.

SPILL AND LEAK PROCEDURES

OCCUPATIONAL SPILL: DO NOT TOUCH SPILLED MATERIAL. STOP LEAK IF YOU CAN DO IT WITHOUT RISK. USE WATER SPRAY TO REDUCE VAPORS. FOR SMALL SPILLS, TAKE UP WITH SAND OR OTHER ABSORBENT MATERIAL AND PLACE INTO CONTAINERS FOR LATER DISPOSAL. FOR SMALL DRY SPILLS, WITH A CLEAN SHOVEL PLACE MATERIAL INTO CLEAN, DRY CONTAINERS AND COVER. MOVE CONTAINERS FROM SPILL AREA. FOR LARGER SPILLS, DIKE FAR AHEAD OF SPILL FOR LATER DISPOSAL. KEEP UNNECESSARY PEOPLE AWAY. ISOLATE HAZARD AREA AND DENY ENTRY. VENTILATE CLOSED SPACES BEFORE ENTERING.

REPORTABLE QUANTITY (RQ): 1 POUND THE SUPERFUND AMENDMENTS AND REAUTHORIZATION ACT (SARA) SECTION 304 REQUIRES THAT A RELEASE EQUAL TO OR GREATER THAN THE REPORTABLE QUANTITY FOR THIS SUBSTANCE BE IMMEDIATELY REPORTED TO THE LOCAL EMERGENCY PLANNING COMMITTEE AND THE STATE EMERGENCY RESPONSE COMMISSION (40 CFR 355.40). IF THE RELEASE OF THIS SUBSTANCE IS REPORTABLE UNDER CERCLA SECTION 103, THE NATIONAL RESPONSE CENTER MUST BE NOTIFIED IMMEDIATELY AT (800) 424-8802 OR (202) 426-2675 IN THE METROPOLITAN WASHINGTON, D.C. AREA (40 CFR 302.6).

PROTECTIVE EQUIPMENT

VENTILATION: PROCESS ENCLOSURE RECOMMENDED TO MEET PUBLISHED EXPOSURE LIMITS.

RESPIRATOR: THE FOLLOWING RESPIRATORS AND MAXIMUM USE CONCENTRATIONS ARE RECOMMENDATIONS BY THE U.S. DEPARTMENT OF HEALTH AND HUMAN SERVICES, NIOSH POCKET GUIDE TO CHEMICAL HAZARDS; NIOSH CRITERIA DOCUMENTS OR BY THE U.S. DEPARTMENT OF LABOR, 29 CFR 1910 SUBPART Z. THE SPECIFIC RESPIRATOR SELECTED MUST BE BASED ON CONTAMINATION LEVELS FOUND IN THE WORK PLACE, MUST NOT EXCEED THE WORKING LIMITS OF THE RESPIRATOR AND BE JOINTLY APPROVED BY THE NATIONAL INSTITUTE FOR OCCUPATIONAL SAFETY AND HEALTH AND THE MINE SAFETY AND HEALTH ADMINISTRATION (NIOSH-MSHA).

DEMETON: 1 MG/M3- ANY SUPPLIED-AIR RESPIRATOR. ANY SELF-CONTAINED BREATHING APPARATUS.

2.5 MG/M3- ANY SUPPLIED-AIR RESPIRATOR OPERATED IN A CONTINUOUS FLOW MODE.

5 MG/M3- ANY SELF-CONTAINED BREATHING APPARATUS WITH A FULL FACEPIECE. ANY SUPPLIED-AIR RESPIRATOR WITH A FULL FACEPIECE. ANY SUPPLIED-AIR RESPIRATOR WITH A TIGHT-FITTING FACEPIECE OPERATED IN A CONTINUOUS FLOW MODE.

20 MG/M3- ANY SUPPLIED-AIR RESPIRATOR WITH A HALF-MASK AND OPERATED IN A PRESSURE-DEMAND OR OTHER POSITIVE PRESSURE MODE.

ESCAPE- ANY AIR-PURIFYING FULL FACEPIECE RESPIRATOR (GAS MASK) WITH A CHIN-STYLE OR FRONT- OR BACK-MOUNTED ORGANIC VAPOR CANISTER HAVING A HIGH-EFFICIENCY PARTICULATE FILTER. ANY APPROPRIATE ESCAPE-TYPE SELF-CONTAINED BREATHING APPARATUS.

FOR FIREFIGHTING AND OTHER IMMEDIATELY DANGEROUS TO LIFE OR HEALTH CONDITIONS:

SELF-CONTAINED BREATHING APPARATUS WITH FULL FACEPIECE OPERATED IN PRESSURE-DEMAND OR OTHER POSITIVE PRESSURE MODE.

SUPPLIED-AIR RESPIRATOR WITH FULL FACEPIECE AND OPERATED IN PRESSURE-DEMAND OR OTHER POSITIVE PRESSURE MODE IN COMBINATION WITH AN AUXILIARY SELF-CONTAINED BREATHING APPARATUS OPERATED IN PRESSURE-DEMAND OR OTHER POSITIVE PRESSURE MODE.

CLOTHING: EMPLOYEE MUST WEAR APPROPRIATE PROTECTIVE (IMPERVIOUS) CLOTHING AND EQUIPMENT TO PREVENT ANY POSSIBILITY OF SKIN CONTACT WITH THIS SUBSTANCE.

GLOVES: EMPLOYEE MUST WEAR APPROPRIATE PROTECTIVE GLOVES TO PREVENT CONTACT WITH THIS SUBSTANCE.

EYE PROTECTION: EMPLOYEE MUST WEAR SPLASH-PROOF OR DUST-RESISTANT SAFETY GOGGLES AND A FACESHIELD TO PREVENT CONTACT WITH THIS SUBSTANCE.

EMERGENCY WASH FACILITIES: WHERE THERE IS ANY POSSIBILITY THAT AN EMPLOYEE'S EYES AND/OR SKIN MAY BE EXPOSED TO THIS SUBSTANCE, THE EMPLOYER SHOULD PROVIDE AN EYE WASH FOUNTAIN AND QUICK DRENCH SHOWER WITHIN THE IMMEDIATE WORK AREA FOR EMERGENCY USE.

AUTHORIZED BY- OCCUPATIONAL HEALTH SERVICES, INC.
CREATION DATE: 10/04/89 ***REVISION DATE:*** 05/04/90

MATERIAL SAFETY DATA SHEET

OCCUPATIONAL HEALTH SERVICES, INC.
AGRICULTURE AND PESTICIDE DIVISION
450 SEVENTH AVENUE, SUITE 2407
NEW YORK, NEW YORK 10123
1-800-445-MSDS OR (212) 967-1100

EMERGENCY CONTACT:
JOHN S. BRANSFORD, JR. (615) 292-1180

SUBSTANCE IDENTIFICATION

CAS-NUMBER 101-76-8
SUBSTANCE: **4,4'-DICHLORODIPHENYLMETHANE**
TRADE NAMES/SYNONYMS: BIS-(4-CHLOROPHENYL)-METHANE; BENZENE, 1,1'METHYLENEBIS(4-CHLORO-; METHANE, BIS(P-CHLOROPHENYL)-; BIS(P-CHLOROPHENYL)METHANE; 1,1'-METHYLENEBIS(4-CHLOROBENZENE); DBM; DDM; P,P'-DICHLORODIPHENYLMETHANE; BIS(4-CHLOROPHENYL)METHANE; C13H10CL2; PST06321
CHEMICAL FAMILY: HALOGEN COMPOUND, AROMATIC
MOLECULAR FORMULA: (CL-C6-H4)2-C-H2
MOLECULAR WEIGHT: 237.13
CERCLA RATINGS (SCALE 0-3): HEALTH=2 FIRE=1 REACTIVITY=0 PERSISTENCE=3
NFPA RATINGS (SCALE 0-4): HEALTH=2 FIRE=1 REACTIVITY=0

COMPONENTS AND CONTAMINANTS

COMPONENT: 4,4'-DICHLORODIPHENYLMETHANE ***PERCENT:*** 100
CAS# 101-76-8
OTHER CONTAMINANTS: NONE
EXPOSURE LIMITS: NO OCCUPATIONAL EXPOSURE LIMITS ESTABLISHED BY OSHA, ACGIH, OR NIOSH.

PHYSICAL DATA

DESCRIPTION: SOLID ***BOILING POINT:*** 367-374 F (186-190 C) @ 18 MMHG
MELTING POINT: 131-133 F (55-56 C) ***SPECIFIC GRAVITY:*** 1.365 @ 17 C
SOLUBILITY IN WATER: INSOLUBLE
SOLVENT SOLUBILITY: SOLUBLE IN ETHANOL, ACETONE, DICHLOROMETHANE.

FIRE AND EXPLOSION DATA

FIRE AND EXPLOSION HAZARD: SLIGHT FIRE HAZARD WHEN EXPOSED TO HEAT OR FLAME.
FIREFIGHTING MEDIA: DRY CHEMICAL, CARBON DIOXIDE, HALON, WATER SPRAY OR STANDARD FOAM (1987 EMERGENCY RESPONSE GUIDEBOOK, DOT P 5800.4).
FOR LARGER FIRES, USE WATER SPRAY, FOG OR STANDARD FOAM (1987 EMERGENCY RESPONSE GUIDEBOOK, DOT P 5800.4).
FIREFIGHTING: MOVE CONTAINER FROM FIRE AREA IF POSSIBLE. DO NOT SCATTER SPILLED MATERIAL WITH HIGH PRESSURE WATER STREAMS. DIKE FIRE CONTROL WATER FOR LATER DISPOSAL (1987 EMERGENCY RESPONSE GUIDEBOOK, DOT P 5800.4, GUIDE PAGE 31).
USE AGENTS SUITABLE FOR TYPE OF SURROUNDING FIRE. AVOID BREATHING HAZARDOUS VAPORS, KEEP UPWIND.

TOXICITY

4,4'-DICHLORODIPHENYLMETHANE: TOXICITY DATA: 1000 MG/KG ORAL-RAT LD50; 1500 MG/KG ORAL-MOUSE LDLO. CARCINOGEN STATUS: NONE. ACUTE TOXICITY LEVEL: MODERATELY TOXIC BY INGESTION. TARGET EFFECTS: CONVULSANT. POISONING MAY AFFECT THE LIVER AND KIDNEY.* ADDITIONAL DATA: DDT METABOLITE. MAY CROSS THE PLACENTA AND BE EXCRETED IN BREAST MILK. MAY IMPAIR FERTILITY. STIMULANTS SUCH AS EPINEPHRINE OR EPHEDRINE MAY INDUCE VENTRICULAR FIBRILLATION.*
* MAY BE BASED ON GENERAL INFORMATION ON ORGANOCHLORINE COMPOUNDS.

HEALTH EFFECTS AND FIRST AID

INHALATION: 4,4'-DICHLORODIPHENYLMETHANE: **ACUTE EXPOSURE-** EFFECTS AS DESCRIBED FOR ORGANOCHLORINE PESTICIDES IN ACUTE INGESTION MAY OCCUR IF SUFFICIENT AMOUNTS ARE ABSORBED FROM THE LUNGS. **CHRONIC EXPOSURE-** A STUDY OF OCCUPATIONAL EXPOSURE TO DDT REPORTED A HIGHER FREQUENCY OF WHITE BLOOD CELLS WITH CHROMOSOMAL ABNORMALITIES AMONG WORKERS WITH HIGH DDT BLOOD LEVELS; ANOTHER STUDY REPORTED MENSTRUAL IRREGULARITIES AS THE MOST FREQUENT COMPLAINT AMONG MIGRANT FARM WORKERS. PROLONGED OR REPEATED EXPOSURE TO ORGANOCHLORINE PESTICIDES MAY CAUSE EFFECTS AS DESCRIBED IN ACUTE INGESTION.
FIRST AID- REMOVE FROM EXPOSURE AREA TO FRESH AIR IMMEDIATELY. IF BREATHING HAS STOPPED, PERFORM ARTIFICIAL RESPIRATION. KEEP PERSON WARM AND AT REST. TREAT SYMPTOMATICALLY AND SUPPORTIVELY. GET MEDICAL ATTENTION IMMEDIATELY.

SKIN CONTACT: 4,4'-DICHLORODIPHENYLMETHANE: **ACUTE EXPOSURE-** EFFECTS AS DESCRIBED FOR ORGANOCHLORINE PESTICIDES IN ACUTE INGESTION MAY OCCUR IF SUFFICIENT AMOUNTS ARE ABSORBED THROUGH THE SKIN. **CHRONIC EXPOSURE-** A STUDY OF OCCUPATIONAL EXPOSURE TO DDT REPORTED A HIGHER FREQUENCY OF WHITE BLOOD CELLS WITH CHROMOSOMAL ABNORMALITIES AMONG WORKERS WITH HIGH DDT BLOOD LEVELS; ANOTHER STUDY REPORTED MENSTRUAL IRREGULARITIES AS THE MOST FREQUENT COMPLAINT AMONG MIGRANT FARM WORKERS. PROLONGED OR REPEATED EXPOSURE TO ORGANOCHLORINE PESTICIDES MAY CAUSE EFFECTS AS DESCRIBED IN ACUTE INGESTION. **FIRST AID-** REMOVE CONTAMINATED CLOTHING AND SHOES IMMEDIATELY. WASH AFFECTED AREA WITH SOAP OR MILD DETERGENT AND LARGE AMOUNTS OF WATER UNTIL NO EVIDENCE OF CHEMICAL REMAINS (APPROXIMATELY 15-20 MINUTES). GET MEDICAL ATTENTION IMMEDIATELY.

EYE CONTACT: 4,4'-DICHLORODIPHENYLMETHANE: **ACUTE EXPOSURE-** NO DATA AVAILABLE. **CHRONIC EXPOSURE-** NO DATA AVAILABLE.
FIRST AID- WASH EYES IMMEDIATELY WITH LARGE AMOUNTS OF WATER OR NORMAL SALINE, OCCASIONALLY LIFTING UPPER AND LOWER LIDS, UNTIL NO EVIDENCE OF CHEMICAL REMAINS (APPROXIMATELY 15-20 MINUTES). GET MEDICAL ATTENTION IMMEDIATELY.

INGESTION: 4,4'-DICHLORODIPHENYLMETHANE: **ACUTE EXPOSURE-** INGESTION OF ORGANOCHLORINE PESTICIDES MAY CAUSE GASTROINTESTINAL EFFECTS OF NAUSEA, VOMITING, DIARRHEA, AND STOMACH PAINS. OTHER SYMPTOMS OF CONFUSION, APPREHENSION, IRRITABILITY, EXCITABILITY, DIZZINESS, HEADACHE, DISORIENTATION, WEAKNESS, PARESTHESIAS, MUSCLE TWITCHING, TREMOR, STUPOR, COMA, AND CONVULSIONS MAY OCCUR. SIGNS OF LIVER AND KIDNEY DAMAGE MAY DEVELOP. DEATH MAY BE DUE TO RESPIRATORY FAILURE OR VENTRICULAR FIBRILLATION. SYMPTOMS OF POISONING MAY OCCUR SEVERAL HOURS AFTER INGESTION. **CHRONIC EXPOSURE-** REPEATED EXPOSURE TO ORGANOCHLORINE PESTICIDES MAY CAUSE EFFECTS AS DESCRIBED IN ACUTE EXPOSURE.
FIRST AID- TREAT SYMPTOMATICALLY AND SUPPORTIVELY. GET MEDICAL ATTENTION IMMEDIATELY. IF VOMITING OCCURS, KEEP HEAD LOWER THAN HIPS TO PREVENT ASPIRATION.
ANTIDOTE: NO SPECIFIC ANTIDOTE. TREAT SYMPTOMATICALLY AND SUPPORTIVELY.

REACTIVITY

REACTIVITY: STABLE UNDER NORMAL TEMPERATURES AND PRESSURES.
INCOMPATIBILITIES: 4,4'DICHLORODIPHENYLMETHANE: NO DATA AVAILABLE.
DECOMPOSITION: THERMAL DECOMPOSITION PRODUCTS MAY INCLUDE TOXIC AND CORROSIVE FUMES OF CHLORIDES AND PHOSGENE, AND TOXIC OXIDES OF CARBON.
POLYMERIZATION: HAZARDOUS POLYMERIZATION HAS NOT BEEN REPORTED TO OCCUR UNDER NORMAL TEMPERATURES AND PRESSURES.

STORAGE AND DISPOSAL

OBSERVE ALL FEDERAL, STATE AND LOCAL REGULATIONS WHEN STORING OR DISPOSING OF THIS SUBSTANCE. FOR ASSISTANCE, CONTACT THE DISTRICT DIRECTOR OF THE ENVIRONMENTAL PROTECTION AGENCY.

STORAGE

STORE IN ACCORDANCE WITH 40 CFR 165 RECOMMENDED PROCEDURES FOR THE DISPOSAL AND STORAGE OF PESTICIDES AND PESTICIDE CONTAINERS.

DISPOSAL

DISPOSAL MUST BE IN ACCORDANCE WITH 40 CFR 165 RECOMMENDED PROCEDURES FOR THE DISPOSAL AND STORAGE OF PESTICIDES AND PESTICIDE CONTAINERS.

CONDITIONS TO AVOID

MAY BURN BUT DOES NOT IGNITE READILY. AVOID CONTACT WITH STRONG OXIDIZERS, EXCESSIVE HEAT, SPARKS, OR OPEN FLAME.

SPILL AND LEAK PROCEDURES

OCCUPATIONAL SPILL: SWEEP UP AND PLACE IN SUITABLE CLEAN, DRY CONTAINERS FOR RECLAMATION OR LATER DISPOSAL. DO NOT FLUSH SPILLED MATERIAL INTO SEWER. KEEP UNNECESSARY PEOPLE AWAY.

PROTECTIVE EQUIPMENT

VENTILATION: PROVIDE LOCAL EXHAUST OR GENERAL DILUTION VENTILATION SYSTEM.

RESPIRATOR: THE FOLLOWING RESPIRATORS ARE RECOMMENDED BASED ON INFORMATION FOUND IN THE PHYSICAL DATA, TOXICITY AND HEALTH EFFECTS SECTIONS. THEY ARE RANKED IN ORDER FROM MINIMUM TO MAXIMUM RESPIRATORY PROTECTION. THE SPECIFIC RESPIRATOR SELECTED MUST BE BASED ON CONTAMINATION LEVELS FOUND IN THE WORK PLACE, MUST NOT EXCEED THE WORKING LIMITS OF THE RESPIRATOR AND BE JOINTLY APPROVED BY THE NATIONAL INSTITUTE FOR OCCUPATIONAL SAFETY AND HEALTH AND THE MINE SAFETY AND HEALTH ADMINISTRATION (NIOSH-MSHA).

CHEMICAL CARTRIDGE RESPIRATOR WITH AN ORGANIC VAPOR CARTRIDGE(S) WITH A FULL FACEPIECE AND ORGANIC VAPOR CARTRIDGE(S) IN COMBINATION WITH A DUST AND MIST FILTER.

POWERED AIR-PURIFYING RESPIRATOR WITH A TIGHT-FITTING FACEPIECE AND ORGANIC VAPOR CARTRIDGE(S) IN COMBINATION WITH A HIGH-EFFICIENCY PARTICULATE FILTER.

TYPE 'C' SUPPLIED-AIR RESPIRATOR WITH A FULL FACEPIECE OPERATED IN A PRESSURE-DEMAND OR OTHER POSITIVE PRESSURE MODE.

SELF-CONTAINED BREATHING APPARATUS WITH A FULL FACEPIECE OPERATED IN PRESSURE-DEMAND OR OTHER POSITIVE PRESSURE MODE. FOR FIREFIGHTING AND OTHER IMMEDIATELY DANGEROUS TO LIFE OR HEALTH CONDITIONS:

SELF-CONTAINED BREATHING APPARATUS WITH FULL FACEPIECE OPERATED IN PRESSURE-DEMAND OR OTHER POSITIVE PRESSURE MODE.

SUPPLIED-AIR RESPIRATOR WITH FULL FACEPIECE AND OPERATED IN PRESSURE-DEMAND OR OTHER POSITIVE PRESSURE MODE IN COMBINATION WITH AN AUXILIARY SELF-CONTAINED BREATHING APPARATUS OPERATED IN PRESSURE-DEMAND OR OTHER POSITIVE PRESSURE MODE.

CLOTHING: EMPLOYEE MUST WEAR APPROPRIATE PROTECTIVE (IMPERVIOUS) CLOTHING AND EQUIPMENT TO PREVENT REPEATED OR PROLONGED SKIN CONTACT WITH THIS SUBSTANCE.

GLOVES: EMPLOYEE MUST WEAR APPROPRIATE PROTECTIVE GLOVES TO PREVENT CONTACT WITH THIS SUBSTANCE.

EYE PROTECTION: EMPLOYEE MUST WEAR SPLASH-PROOF OR DUST-RESISTANT SAFETY GOGGLES TO PREVENT EYE CONTACT WITH THIS SUBSTANCE.

EMERGENCY EYE WASH: WHERE THERE IS ANY POSSIBILITY THAT AN EMPLOYEE'S EYES MAY BE EXPOSED TO THIS SUBSTANCE, THE EMPLOYER SHOULD PROVIDE AN EYE WASH FOUNTAIN WITHIN THE IMMEDIATE WORK AREA FOR EMERGENCY USE.

AUTHORIZED BY- OCCUPATIONAL HEALTH SERVICES, INC.

CREATION DATE: 10/05/89 ***REVISION DATE:*** 05/31/90

MATERIAL SAFETY DATA SHEET

OCCUPATIONAL HEALTH SERVICES, INC.
AGRICULTURE AND PESTICIDE DIVISION
450 SEVENTH AVENUE, SUITE 2407
NEW YORK, NEW YORK 10123
1-800-445-MSDS OR (212) 967-1100

EMERGENCY CONTACT:
JOHN S. BRANSFORD, JR. (615) 292-1180

SUBSTANCE IDENTIFICATION

CAS-NUMBER 1022-22-6

SUBSTANCE: **2,2-BIS(4-CHLOROPHENYL)-1-CHLOROETHENE**

TRADE NAMES/SYNONYMS: BENZENE, 1,1'-(CHLOROETHENYLIDENE)BIS(4-CHLORO-; 1,1'-(CHLOROETHENYLIDENE)BIS(4-CHLOROBENZENE); ETHYLENE, 2-CHLORO-1,1-BIS(P-CHLOROPHENYL)-; 2-CHLORO-1,1-BIS(P-CHLOROPHENYL)ETHYLENE; P,P'-DDD OLEFIN; P,P'-DDMU; DDMU; P,P'-DME; P,P'-TDEE; TDEE; P,P'-TDE OLEFIN; 4,4'-DDMU; P,P'-DDM; C14H9CL3; PST06322

CHEMICAL FAMILY: HALOGEN COMPOUND, AROMATIC

MOLECULAR FORMULA: (CL-C6-H4)2-C-C-CL-H

MOLECULAR WEIGHT: 283.58

CERCLA RATINGS (SCALE 0-3): HEALTH=2 FIRE=1 REACTIVITY=0 PERSISTENCE=3

NFPA RATINGS (SCALE 0-4): HEALTH=2 FIRE=1 REACTIVITY=0

COMPONENTS AND CONTAMINANTS

COMPONENT: 2,2-BIS(4-CHLOROPHENYL)-1-CHLOROETHENE ***PERCENT:*** 100
CAS# 1022-22-6

OTHER CONTAMINANTS: NONE

EXPOSURE LIMITS: NO OCCUPATIONAL EXPOSURE LIMITS ESTABLISHED BY OSHA, ACGIH, OR NIOSH.

PHYSICAL DATA

DESCRIPTION: SOLID ***MELTING POINT:*** 147-151 F (64-66 C)

SPECIFIC GRAVITY: NOT AVAILABLE ***SOLUBILITY IN WATER:*** NOT AVAILABLE

SOLVENT SOLUBILITY: SOLUBLE IN ACETONE, ETHANOL, DICHLOROMETHANE.

FIRE AND EXPLOSION DATA

FIRE AND EXPLOSION HAZARD: SLIGHT FIRE HAZARD WHEN EXPOSED TO HEAT OR FLAME.

FIREFIGHTING MEDIA: DRY CHEMICAL, CARBON DIOXIDE, HALON, WATER SPRAY OR STANDARD FOAM (1987 EMERGENCY RESPONSE GUIDEBOOK, DOT P 5800.4).

FOR LARGER FIRES, USE WATER SPRAY, FOG OR STANDARD FOAM (1987 EMERGENCY RESPONSE GUIDEBOOK, DOT P 5800.4).

FIREFIGHTING: MOVE CONTAINER FROM FIRE AREA IF POSSIBLE. DO NOT SCATTER SPILLED MATERIAL WITH HIGH PRESSURE WATER STREAMS. DIKE FIRE CONTROL WATER FOR LATER DISPOSAL (1987 EMERGENCY RESPONSE GUIDEBOOK, DOT P 5800.4, GUIDE PAGE 31).

USE AGENTS SUITABLE FOR TYPE OF SURROUNDING FIRE. AVOID BREATHING HAZARDOUS VAPORS, KEEP UPWIND.

TOXICITY

2,2-BIS-(4-CHLOROPHENYL)-1-CHLOROETHENE: TOXICITY DATA: 2700 MG/KG ORAL-MOUSE LD50. CARCINOGEN STATUS: NONE. ACUTE TOXICITY LEVEL: MODERATELY TOXIC BY INGESTION. TARGET EFFECTS: CONVULSANT. POISONING MAY AFFECT THE LIVER AND KIDNEY.* ADDITIONAL DATA: DDT METABOLITE. MAY CROSS THE PLACENTA AND BE EXCRETED IN BREAST MILK. MAY IMPAIR FERTILITY. STIMULANTS SUCH AS EPINEPHRINE OR EPHEDRINE MAY INDUCE VENTRICULAR FIBRILLATION.*

* MAY BE BASED ON GENERAL INFORMATION ON ORGANOCHLORINE COMPOUNDS.

HEALTH EFFECTS AND FIRST AID

INHALATION: 2,2-BIS-(4-CHLOROPHENYL)-1-CHLOROETHENE: **ACUTE EXPOSURE-** EFFECTS AS DESCRIBED FOR ORGANOCHLORINE PESTICIDES IN ACUTE INGESTION MAY OCCUR IF SUFFICIENT AMOUNTS ARE ABSORBED FROM THE LUNGS. **CHRONIC EXPOSURE-** A STUDY OF OCCUPATIONAL EXPOSURE TO DDT REPORTED A HIGHER FREQUENCY OF WHITE BLOOD CELLS WITH CHROMOSOMAL ABNORMALITIES AMONG WORKERS WITH HIGH DDT BLOOD LEVELS; ANOTHER STUDY REPORTED MENSTRUAL IRREGULARITIES AS THE MOST FREQUENT COMPLAINT AMONG MIGRANT FARM WORKERS. PROLONGED OR REPEATED EXPOSURE TO ORGANOCHLORINE PESTICIDES MAY CAUSE EFFECTS AS DESCRIBED IN ACUTE INGESTION.

FIRST AID- REMOVE FROM EXPOSURE AREA TO FRESH AIR IMMEDIATELY. IF BREATHING HAS STOPPED, PERFORM ARTIFICIAL RESPIRATION. KEEP PERSON WARM AND AT REST. TREAT SYMPTOMATICALLY AND SUPPORTIVELY. GET MEDICAL ATTENTION IMMEDIATELY.

SKIN CONTACT: 2,2-BIS-(4-CHLOROPHENYL)-1-CHLOROETHENE: **ACUTE EXPOSURE-** EFFECTS AS DESCRIBED FOR ORGANOCHLORINE PESTICIDES IN ACUTE INGESTION MAY OCCUR IF SUFFICIENT AMOUNTS ARE ABSORBED THROUGH THE SKIN. **CHRONIC EXPOSURE-** A STUDY OF OCCUPATIONAL EXPOSURE TO DDT REPORTED A HIGHER FREQUENCY OF WHITE BLOOD CELLS WITH CHROMOSOMAL ABNORMALITIES AMONG WORKERS WITH HIGH DDT BLOOD LEVELS; ANOTHER STUDY REPORTED MENSTRUAL IRREGULARITIES AS THE MOST FREQUENT COMPLAINT AMONG MIGRANT FARM WORKERS. PROLONGED OR REPEATED EXPOSURE TO ORGANOCHLORINE PESTICIDES MAY CAUSE EFFECTS AS DESCRIBED IN ACUTE INGESTION. **FIRST AID-** REMOVE CONTAMINATED CLOTHING AND SHOES IMMEDIATELY. WASH AFFECTED AREA WITH SOAP OR MILD DETERGENT AND LARGE AMOUNTS OF WATER UNTIL NO EVIDENCE OF CHEMICAL REMAINS (APPROXIMATELY 15-20 MINUTES). GET MEDICAL ATTENTION IMMEDIATELY.

EYE CONTACT: 2,2-BIS-(4-CHLOROPHENYL)-1-CHLOROETHENE: **ACUTE EXPOSURE-** NO DATA AVAILABLE. **CHRONIC EXPOSURE-** NO DATA AVAILABLE.

FIRST AID- WASH EYES IMMEDIATELY WITH LARGE AMOUNTS OF WATER OR NORMAL SALINE, OCCASIONALLY LIFTING UPPER AND LOWER LIDS, UNTIL NO EVIDENCE OF CHEMICAL REMAINS (APPROXIMATELY 15-20 MINUTES). GET MEDICAL ATTENTION IMMEDIATELY.

INGESTION: 2,2-BIS-(4-CHLOROPHENYL)-1-CHLOROETHENE: **ACUTE EXPOSURE-** INGESTION OF ORGANOCHLORINE PESTICIDES MAY CAUSE GASTROINTESTINAL EFFECTS OF NAUSEA, VOMITING, DIARRHEA, AND STOMACH PAINS. OTHER

SYMPTOMS OF CONFUSION, APPREHENSION, IRRITABILITY, EXCITABILITY, DIZZINESS, HEADACHE, DISORIENTATION, WEAKNESS, PARESTHESIAS, MUSCLE TWITCHING, TREMOR, STUPOR, COMA, AND CONVULSIONS MAY OCCUR. SIGNS OF LIVER AND KIDNEY DAMAGE MAY DEVELOP. DEATH MAY BE DUE TO RESPIRATORY FAILURE OR VENTRICULAR FIBRILLATION. SYMPTOMS OF POISONING MAY OCCUR SEVERAL HOURS AFTER INGESTION. **CHRONIC EXPOSURE-** REPEATED EXPOSURE TO ORGANOCHLORINE PESTICIDES MAY CAUSE EFFECTS AS DESCRIBED IN ACUTE EXPOSURE.

FIRST AID- TREAT SYMPTOMATICALLY AND SUPPORTIVELY. GET MEDICAL ATTENTION IMMEDIATELY. IF VOMITING OCCURS, KEEP HEAD LOWER THAN HIPS TO PREVENT ASPIRATION.

ANTIDOTE: NO SPECIFIC ANTIDOTE. TREAT SYMPTOMATICALLY AND SUPPORTIVELY.

REACTIVITY

REACTIVITY: STABLE UNDER NORMAL TEMPERATURES AND PRESSURES.

INCOMPATIBILITIES: 2,2-BIS(4-CHLOROPHENYL)-1-CHLOROETHENE: NO DATA AVAILABLE.

DECOMPOSITION: THERMAL DECOMPOSITION PRODUCTS MAY INCLUDE HIGHLY TOXIC FUMES OF PHOSGENE, TOXIC AND CORROSIVE FUMES OF CHLORIDES, AND OXIDES OF CARBON.

POLYMERIZATION: HAZARDOUS POLYMERIZATION HAS NOT BEEN REPORTED TO OCCUR UNDER NORMAL TEMPERATURES AND PRESSURES.

STORAGE AND DISPOSAL

OBSERVE ALL FEDERAL, STATE AND LOCAL REGULATIONS WHEN STORING OR DISPOSING OF THIS SUBSTANCE. FOR ASSISTANCE, CONTACT THE DISTRICT DIRECTOR OF THE ENVIRONMENTAL PROTECTION AGENCY.

STORAGE

STORE IN ACCORDANCE WITH 40 CFR 165 RECOMMENDED PROCEDURES FOR THE DISPOSAL AND STORAGE OF PESTICIDES AND PESTICIDE CONTAINERS.

DISPOSAL

DISPOSAL MUST BE IN ACCORDANCE WITH 40 CFR 165 RECOMMENDED PROCEDURES FOR THE DISPOSAL AND STORAGE OF PESTICIDES AND PESTICIDE CONTAINERS.

CONDITIONS TO AVOID

MAY BURN BUT DOES NOT IGNITE READILY. AVOID CONTACT WITH STRONG OXIDIZERS, EXCESSIVE HEAT, SPARKS, OR OPEN FLAME.

SPILL AND LEAK PROCEDURES

OCCUPATIONAL SPILL: SWEEP UP AND PLACE IN SUITABLE CLEAN, DRY CONTAINERS FOR RECLAMATION OR LATER DISPOSAL. DO NOT FLUSH SPILLED MATERIAL INTO SEWER. KEEP UNNECESSARY PEOPLE AWAY.

PROTECTIVE EQUIPMENT

VENTILATION: PROVIDE LOCAL EXHAUST OR GENERAL DILUTION VENTILATION SYSTEM.

RESPIRATOR: THE FOLLOWING RESPIRATORS ARE RECOMMENDED BASED ON INFORMATION FOUND IN THE PHYSICAL DATA, TOXICITY AND HEALTH EFFECTS SECTIONS. THEY ARE RANKED IN ORDER FROM MINIMUM TO MAXIMUM RESPIRATORY PROTECTION. THE SPECIFIC RESPIRATOR SELECTED MUST BE BASED ON CONTAMINATION LEVELS FOUND IN THE WORK PLACE, MUST NOT EXCEED THE WORKING LIMITS OF THE RESPIRATOR AND BE JOINTLY APPROVED BY THE NATIONAL INSTITUTE FOR OCCUPATIONAL SAFETY AND HEALTH AND THE MINE SAFETY AND HEALTH ADMINISTRATION (NIOSH-MSHA).

CHEMICAL CARTRIDGE RESPIRATOR WITH AN ORGANIC VAPOR CARTRIDGE(S) WITH A FULL FACEPIECE AND ORGANIC VAPOR CARTRIDGE(S) IN COMBINATION WITH A DUST AND MIST FILTER.

POWERED AIR-PURIFYING RESPIRATOR WITH A TIGHT-FITTING FACEPIECE AND ORGANIC VAPOR CARTRIDGE(S) IN COMBINATION WITH A HIGH-EFFICIENCY PARTICULATE FILTER.

TYPE 'C' SUPPLIED-AIR RESPIRATOR WITH A FULL FACEPIECE OPERATED IN A PRESSURE-DEMAND OR OTHER POSITIVE PRESSURE MODE.

SELF-CONTAINED BREATHING APPARATUS WITH A FULL FACEPIECE OPERATED IN PRESSURE-DEMAND OR OTHER POSITIVE PRESSURE MODE. FOR FIREFIGHTING AND OTHER IMMEDIATELY DANGEROUS TO LIFE OR HEALTH CONDITIONS:

SELF-CONTAINED BREATHING APPARATUS WITH FULL FACEPIECE OPERATED IN PRESSURE-DEMAND OR OTHER POSITIVE PRESSURE MODE.

SUPPLIED-AIR RESPIRATOR WITH FULL FACEPIECE AND OPERATED IN PRESSURE-DEMAND OR OTHER POSITIVE PRESSURE MODE IN COMBINATION WITH AN AUXILIARY SELF-CONTAINED BREATHING APPARATUS OPERATED IN PRESSURE-DEMAND OR OTHER POSITIVE PRESSURE MODE.

CLOTHING: EMPLOYEE MUST WEAR APPROPRIATE PROTECTIVE (IMPERVIOUS) CLOTHING AND EQUIPMENT TO PREVENT REPEATED OR PROLONGED SKIN CONTACT WITH THIS SUBSTANCE.

GLOVES: EMPLOYEE MUST WEAR APPROPRIATE PROTECTIVE GLOVES TO PREVENT CONTACT WITH THIS SUBSTANCE.

EYE PROTECTION: EMPLOYEE MUST WEAR SPLASH-PROOF OR DUST-RESISTANT SAFETY GOGGLES TO PREVENT EYE CONTACT WITH THIS SUBSTANCE. EMERGENCY EYE WASH: WHERE THERE IS ANY POSSIBILITY THAT AN EMPLOYEE'S EYES MAY BE EXPOSED TO THIS SUBSTANCE, THE EMPLOYER SHOULD PROVIDE AN EYE WASH FOUNTAIN WITHIN THE IMMEDIATE WORK AREA FOR EMERGENCY USE.

AUTHORIZED BY- OCCUPATIONAL HEALTH SERVICES, INC.
CREATION DATE: 10/05/89 ***REVISION DATE:*** 05/31/90

MATERIAL SAFETY DATA SHEET

OCCUPATIONAL HEALTH SERVICES, INC.
AGRICULTURE AND PESTICIDE DIVISION
450 SEVENTH AVENUE, SUITE 2407
NEW YORK, NEW YORK 10123
1-800-445-MSDS OR (212) 967-1100

EMERGENCY CONTACT:
JOHN S. BRANSFORD, JR. (615) 292-1180

SUBSTANCE IDENTIFICATION

CAS-NUMBER 2642-82-2

SUBSTANCE: **2,2-BIS(4-CHLOROPHENYL)ETHANOL**

TRADE NAMES/SYNONYMS: BENZENEETHANOL, 4-CHLORO-BETA-(4-CHLOROPHENYL)-; ETHANOL, 2,2-BIS(P-CHLOROPHENYL)-; 4-CHLORO-BETA-(4-CHLOROPHENYL)BENZENEETHANOL; 2,2-BIS(P-CHLOROPHENYL)ETHANOL; 2,2-BIS-(4-CHLOROPHENYL)-ETHANOL; DDOM; DDOH; P,P'-DDOH; C14H12CL2O; PST06323

CHEMICAL FAMILY: HALOGEN COMPOUND, AROMATIC

MOLECULAR FORMULA: (CL-C6-H4)2-C-H-C-H2-O-H

MOLECULAR WEIGHT: 267.15

CERCLA RATINGS (SCALE 0-3): HEALTH=U FIRE=1 REACTIVITY=0 PERSISTENCE=3

NFPA RATINGS (SCALE 0-4): HEALTH=U FIRE=1 REACTIVITY=0

COMPONENTS AND CONTAMINANTS

COMPONENT: 2,2-BIS(4-CHLOROPHENYL)ETHANOL ***PERCENT:*** 100
CAS# 2642-82-2

OTHER CONTAMINANTS: NONE

EXPOSURE LIMITS: NO OCCUPATIONAL EXPOSURE LIMITS ESTABLISHED BY OSHA, ACGIH, OR NIOSH.

PHYSICAL DATA

DESCRIPTION: SOLID ***MELTING POINT:*** 212-216 F (100-102 C)

SPECIFIC GRAVITY: NOT AVAILABLE ***SOLUBILITY IN WATER:*** INSOLUBLE

FIRE AND EXPLOSION DATA

FIRE AND EXPLOSION HAZARD: SLIGHT FIRE HAZARD WHEN EXPOSED TO HEAT OR FLAME.

FIREFIGHTING MEDIA: DRY CHEMICAL, CARBON DIOXIDE, HALON, WATER SPRAY OR STANDARD FOAM (1987 EMERGENCY RESPONSE GUIDEBOOK, DOT P 5800.4). FOR LARGER FIRES, USE WATER SPRAY, FOG OR STANDARD FOAM (1987 EMERGENCY RESPONSE GUIDEBOOK, DOT P 5800.4).

FIREFIGHTING: MOVE CONTAINER FROM FIRE AREA IF POSSIBLE. DO NOT SCATTER SPILLED MATERIAL WITH HIGH PRESSURE WATER STREAMS. DIKE FIRE CONTROL WATER FOR LATER DISPOSAL (1987 EMERGENCY RESPONSE GUIDEBOOK, DOT P 5800.4, GUIDE PAGE 31).
USE AGENTS SUITABLE FOR TYPE OF SURROUNDING FIRE. AVOID BREATHING HAZARDOUS VAPORS, KEEP UPWIND.

TOXICITY

2,2-BIS(4-CHLOROPHENYL)ETHANOL: CARCINOGEN STATUS: NONE. ACUTE TOXICITY LEVEL: NO DATA AVAILABLE. TARGET EFFECTS: CONVULSANT. POISONING MAY AFFECT THE LIVER AND KIDNEY.* ADDITIONAL DATA: DDT METABOLITE. MAY CROSS THE PLACENTA AND BE EXCRETED IN BREAST MILK. MAY IMPAIR FERTILITY. STIMULANTS SUCH AS EPINEPHRINE OR EPHEDRINE MAY INDUCE VENTRICULAR FIBRILLATION.*

* MAY BE BASED ON GENERAL INFORMATION ON ORGANOCHLORINE COMPOUNDS.

HEALTH EFFECTS AND FIRST AID

INHALATION: 2,2-BIS(4-CHLOROPHENYL)ETHANOL: **ACUTE EXPOSURE-** EFFECTS AS DESCRIBED FOR ORGANOCHLORINE PESTICIDES IN ACUTE INGESTION MAY OCCUR

IF SUFFICIENT AMOUNTS ARE ABSORBED FROM THE LUNGS. **CHRONIC EXPOSURE-** A STUDY OF OCCUPATIONAL EXPOSURE TO DDT REPORTED A HIGHER FREQUENCY OF WHITE BLOOD CELLS WITH CHROMOSOMAL ABNORMALITIES AMONG WORKERS WITH HIGH DDT BLOOD LEVELS; ANOTHER STUDY REPORTED MENSTRUAL IRREGULARITIES AS THE MOST FREQUENT COMPLAINT AMONG MIGRANT FARM WORKERS. PROLONGED OR REPEATED EXPOSURE TO ORGANOCHLORINE PESTICIDES MAY CAUSE EFFECTS AS DESCRIBED IN ACUTE INGESTION.

FIRST AID- REMOVE FROM EXPOSURE AREA TO FRESH AIR IMMEDIATELY. IF BREATHING HAS STOPPED, PERFORM ARTIFICIAL RESPIRATION. KEEP PERSON WARM AND AT REST. TREAT SYMPTOMATICALLY AND SUPPORTIVELY. GET MEDICAL ATTENTION IMMEDIATELY.

SKIN CONTACT: 2,2-BIS(4-CHLOROPHENYL)ETHANOL: **ACUTE EXPOSURE-** EFFECTS AS DESCRIBED FOR ORGANOCHLORINE PESTICIDES IN ACUTE INGESTION MAY OCCUR IF SUFFICIENT AMOUNTS ARE ABSORBED THROUGH THE SKIN. **CHRONIC EXPOSURE-** A STUDY OF OCCUPATIONAL EXPOSURE TO DDT REPORTED A HIGHER FREQUENCY OF WHITE BLOOD CELLS WITH CHROMOSOMAL ABNORMALITIES AMONG WORKERS WITH HIGH DDT BLOOD LEVELS; ANOTHER STUDY REPORTED MENSTRUAL IRREGULARITIES AS THE MOST FREQUENT COMPLAINT OF MIGRANT FARM WORKERS. PROLONGED OR REPEATED EXPOSURE TO ORGANOCHLORINE PESTICIDES MAY CAUSE EFFECTS AS DESCRIBED IN ACUTE INGESTION.

FIRST AID- REMOVE CONTAMINATED CLOTHING AND SHOES IMMEDIATELY. WASH AFFECTED AREA WITH SOAP OR MILD DETERGENT AND LARGE AMOUNTS OF WATER UNTIL NO EVIDENCE OF CHEMICAL REMAINS (APPROXIMATELY 15-20 MINUTES). GET MEDICAL ATTENTION IMMEDIATELY.

EYE CONTACT: 2,2-BIS(4-CHLOROPHENYL)ETHANOL: **ACUTE EXPOSURE-** MAY CAUSE IRRITATION. **CHRONIC EXPOSURE-** NO DATA AVAILABLE.

FIRST AID- WASH EYES IMMEDIATELY WITH LARGE AMOUNTS OF WATER OR NORMAL SALINE, OCCASIONALLY LIFTING UPPER AND LOWER LIDS, UNTIL NO EVIDENCE OF CHEMICAL REMAINS (APPROXIMATELY 15-20 MINUTES). GET MEDICAL ATTENTION IMMEDIATELY.

INGESTION: 2,2-BIS(4-CHLOROPHENYL)ETHANOL: **ACUTE EXPOSURE-** INGESTION OF ORGANOCHLORINE PESTICIDES MAY CAUSE GASTROINTESTINAL EFFECTS OF NAUSEA, VOMITING, DIARRHEA, AND STOMACH PAINS. OTHER SYMPTOMS OF CONFUSION, APPREHENSION, IRRITABILITY, EXCITABILITY, DIZZINESS, HEADACHE, DISORIENTATION, WEAKNESS, PARESTHESIAS, MUSCLE TWITCHING, TREMOR, STUPOR, COMA, AND CONVULSIONS MAY OCCUR. SIGNS OF LIVER AND KIDNEY DAMAGE MAY DEVELOP. DEATH MAY BE DUE TO RESPIRATORY FAILURE OR VENTRICULAR FIBRILLATION. SYMPTOMS OF POISONING MAY OCCUR SEVERAL HOURS AFTER INGESTION. **CHRONIC EXPOSURE-** REPEATED EXPOSURE TO ORGANOCHLORINE PESTICIDES MAY CAUSE EFFECTS AS DESCRIBED IN ACUTE EXPOSURE.

FIRST AID- TREAT SYMPTOMATICALLY AND SUPPORTIVELY. GET MEDICAL ATTENTION IMMEDIATELY. IF VOMITING OCCURS, KEEP HEAD LOWER THAN HIPS TO PREVENT ASPIRATION.

ANTIDOTE: NO SPECIFIC ANTIDOTE. TREAT SYMPTOMATICALLY AND SUPPORTIVELY.

REACTIVITY

REACTIVITY: STABLE UNDER NORMAL TEMPERATURES AND PRESSURES.

INCOMPATIBILITIES: 2,2-BIS(4-CHLOROPHENYL)ETHANOL: NO DATA AVAILABLE.

DECOMPOSITION: THERMAL DECOMPOSITION PRODUCTS MAY INCLUDE HIGHLY TOXIC FUMES OF PHOSGENE, TOXIC AND CORROSIVE FUMES OF CHLORIDES, AND OXIDES OF CARBON.

POLYMERIZATION: HAZARDOUS POLYMERIZATION HAS NOT BEEN REPORTED TO OCCUR UNDER NORMAL TEMPERATURES AND PRESSURES.

STORAGE AND DISPOSAL

OBSERVE ALL FEDERAL, STATE AND LOCAL REGULATIONS WHEN STORING OR DISPOSING OF THIS SUBSTANCE. FOR ASSISTANCE, CONTACT THE DISTRICT DIRECTOR OF THE ENVIRONMENTAL PROTECTION AGENCY.

STORAGE

STORE IN ACCORDANCE WITH 40 CFR 165 RECOMMENDED PROCEDURES FOR THE DISPOSAL AND STORAGE OF PESTICIDES AND PESTICIDE CONTAINERS.

DISPOSAL

DISPOSAL MUST BE IN ACCORDANCE WITH 40 CFR 165 RECOMMENDED PROCEDURES FOR THE DISPOSAL AND STORAGE OF PESTICIDES AND PESTICIDE CONTAINERS.

CONDITIONS TO AVOID

MAY BURN BUT DOES NOT IGNITE READILY. AVOID CONTACT WITH STRONG OXIDIZERS, EXCESSIVE HEAT, SPARKS, OR OPEN FLAME.

SPILL AND LEAK PROCEDURES

OCCUPATIONAL SPILL: SWEEP UP AND PLACE IN SUITABLE CLEAN, DRY CONTAINERS FOR RECLAMATION OR LATER DISPOSAL. DO NOT FLUSH SPILLED MATERIAL INTO SEWER. KEEP UNNECESSARY PEOPLE AWAY.

PROTECTIVE EQUIPMENT

VENTILATION: PROVIDE LOCAL EXHAUST OR GENERAL DILUTION VENTILATION SYSTEM.

RESPIRATOR: THE FOLLOWING RESPIRATORS ARE RECOMMENDED BASED ON INFORMATION FOUND IN THE PHYSICAL DATA, TOXICITY AND HEALTH EFFECTS SECTIONS. THEY ARE RANKED IN ORDER FROM MINIMUM TO MAXIMUM RESPIRATORY PROTECTION. THE SPECIFIC RESPIRATOR SELECTED MUST BE BASED ON CONTAMINATION LEVELS FOUND IN THE WORK PLACE, MUST NOT EXCEED THE WORKING LIMITS OF THE RESPIRATOR AND BE JOINTLY APPROVED BY THE NATIONAL INSTITUTE FOR OCCUPATIONAL SAFETY AND HEALTH AND THE MINE SAFETY AND HEALTH ADMINISTRATION (NIOSH-MSHA).

CHEMICAL CARTRIDGE RESPIRATOR WITH AN ORGANIC VAPOR CARTRIDGE(S) WITH A FULL FACEPIECE AND ORGANIC VAPOR CARTRIDGE(S) IN COMBINATION WITH A DUST AND MIST FILTER.

POWERED AIR-PURIFYING RESPIRATOR WITH A TIGHT-FITTING FACEPIECE AND ORGANIC VAPOR CARTRIDGE(S) IN COMBINATION WITH A HIGH-EFFICIENCY PARTICULATE FILTER.

TYPE 'C' SUPPLIED-AIR RESPIRATOR WITH A FULL FACEPIECE OPERATED IN A PRESSURE-DEMAND OR OTHER POSITIVE PRESSURE MODE.

SELF-CONTAINED BREATHING APPARATUS WITH A FULL FACEPIECE OPERATED IN PRESSURE-DEMAND OR OTHER POSITIVE PRESSURE MODE.

FOR FIREFIGHTING AND OTHER IMMEDIATELY DANGEROUS TO LIFE OR HEALTH CONDITIONS:

SELF-CONTAINED BREATHING APPARATUS WITH FULL FACEPIECE OPERATED IN PRESSURE-DEMAND OR OTHER POSITIVE PRESSURE MODE.

SUPPLIED-AIR RESPIRATOR WITH FULL FACEPIECE AND OPERATED IN PRESSURE-DEMAND OR OTHER POSITIVE PRESSURE MODE IN COMBINATION WITH AN AUXILIARY SELF-CONTAINED BREATHING APPARATUS OPERATED IN PRESSURE-DEMAND OR OTHER POSITIVE PRESSURE MODE.

CLOTHING: EMPLOYEE MUST WEAR APPROPRIATE PROTECTIVE (IMPERVIOUS) CLOTHING AND EQUIPMENT TO PREVENT REPEATED OR PROLONGED SKIN CONTACT WITH THIS SUBSTANCE.

GLOVES: EMPLOYEE MUST WEAR APPROPRIATE PROTECTIVE GLOVES TO PREVENT CONTACT WITH THIS SUBSTANCE.

EYE PROTECTION: EMPLOYEE MUST WEAR SPLASH-PROOF OR DUST-RESISTANT SAFETY GOGGLES TO PREVENT EYE CONTACT WITH THIS SUBSTANCE.

EMERGENCY EYE WASH: WHERE THERE IS ANY POSSIBILITY THAT AN EMPLOYEE'S EYES MAY BE EXPOSED TO THIS SUBSTANCE, THE EMPLOYER SHOULD PROVIDE AN EYE WASH FOUNTAIN WITHIN THE IMMEDIATE WORK AREA FOR EMERGENCY USE.

AUTHORIZED BY- OCCUPATIONAL HEALTH SERVICES, INC.

CREATION DATE: 10/05/89 ***REVISION DATE:*** 05/31/90

MATERIAL SAFETY DATA SHEET

OCCUPATIONAL HEALTH SERVICES, INC.
AGRICULTURE AND PESTICIDE DIVISION
450 SEVENTH AVENUE, SUITE 2407
NEW YORK, NEW YORK 10123
1-800-445-MSDS OR (212) 967-1100

EMERGENCY CONTACT:
JOHN S. BRANSFORD, JR. (615) 292-1180

SUBSTANCE IDENTIFICATION

***SUBSTANCE:* DESMETHYL PIRIMICARB**

TRADE NAMES/SYNONYMS: 5,6-DIMETHYL-2-(METHYLAMINO)-4-PYRIMIDINYL DIMETHYLCARBAMATE; DESMETHYL PIRIMOR; C10H16N4O2; PST06336

CHEMICAL FAMILY: PYRIMIDINE CARBAMATE

MOLECULAR FORMULA: C10-H16-N4-O2

MOLECULAR WEIGHT: 224.27

CERCLA RATINGS (SCALE 0-3): HEALTH=3 FIRE=1 REACTIVITY=0 PERSISTENCE=1

NFPA RATINGS (SCALE 0-4): HEALTH=U FIRE=1 REACTIVITY=0

COMPONENTS AND CONTAMINANTS

COMPONENT: DESMETHYL PIRIMICARB ***PERCENT:*** 100.0

OTHER CONTAMINANTS: NONE

EXPOSURE LIMITS: NO OCCUPATIONAL EXPOSURE LIMITS ESTABLISHED BY OSHA, ACGIH, OR NIOSH.

PHYSICAL DATA

DESCRIPTION: WHITE CRYSTALS. ***MELTING POINT:*** 307-315 F (153-157 C)
SPECIFIC GRAVITY: NOT AVAILABLE ***SOLUBILITY IN WATER:*** NOT AVAILABLE

FIRE AND EXPLOSION DATA

FIRE AND EXPLOSION HAZARD: SLIGHT FIRE HAZARD WHEN EXPOSED TO HEAT OR FLAME.
DUST-AIR MIXTURES MAY IGNITE OR EXPLODE.
FIREFIGHTING MEDIA: DRY CHEMICAL, CARBON DIOXIDE, HALON, WATER SPRAY OR STANDARD FOAM (1987 EMERGENCY RESPONSE GUIDEBOOK, DOT P 5800.4). FOR LARGER FIRES, USE WATER SPRAY, FOG OR STANDARD FOAM (1987 EMERGENCY RESPONSE GUIDEBOOK, DOT P 5800.4).
FIREFIGHTING: MOVE CONTAINERS FROM FIRE AREA IF POSSIBLE (1987 EMERGENCY RESPONSE GUIDEBOOK, DOT P 5800.4, GUIDE PAGE 53).
EXTINGUISH USING AGENT SUITABLE FOR TYPE OF SURROUNDING FIRE. AVOID BREATHING VAPORS AND DUSTS. KEEP UPWIND.

TOXICITY

DESMETHYL PIRIMICARB: TOXICITY DATA: 147 MG/KG ORAL-RAT LD50 (EPA).
CARCINOGEN STATUS: NONE. ACUTE TOXICITY LEVEL: TOXIC BY INGESTION.
TARGET EFFECTS: CHOLINESTERASE INHIBITOR. AT INCREASED RISK FROM EXPOSURE: PERSONS WITH ASTHMA, DIABETES, CARDIOVASCULAR DISEASE, MECHANICAL OBSTRUCTION OF THE GASTROINTESTINAL OR UROGENITAL TRACT, AND THOSE IN VAGOTONIC STATES.*
* MAY BE BASED ON GENERAL INFORMATION ON CARBAMATES.

HEALTH EFFECTS AND FIRST AID

INHALATION: DESMETHYL PIRIMICARB: SEE INFORMATION ON CARBAMATES. CARBAMATES: CHOLINESTERASE INHIBITOR. **ACUTE EXPOSURE-** WHEN INHALED, THE FIRST EFFECTS OF CHOLINESTERASE INHIBITION ARE USUALLY RESPIRATORY AND MAY INCLUDE NASAL HYPEREMIA AND WATERY DISCHARGE, CHEST DISCOMFORT, DYSPNEA, AND WHEEZING DUE TO INCREASED BRONCHIAL SECRETIONS AND BRONCHOCONSTRICTION. OTHER SYSTEMIC EFFECTS MAY BEGIN WITHIN A FEW MINUTES OR SEVERAL HOURS OF EXPOSURE. SYMPTOMS MAY INCLUDE NAUSEA, VOMITING, DIARRHEA, ABDOMINAL CRAMPS, HEADACHE, VERTIGO, OCULAR PAIN, CILIARY MUSCLE SPASM, BLURRING OR DIMNESS OF VISION, MIOSIS, OR IN SOME CASES MYDRIASIS, LACRIMATION, SALIVATION, SWEATING, AND CONFUSION. OTHER REPORTED CENTRAL NERVOUS SYSTEM OR NEUROMUSCULAR EFFECTS INCLUDE ATAXIA, SLURRED SPEECH, AREFLEXIA, WEAKNESS, FATIGUE, TWITCHING, FASCICULATION, TREMOR, AND EVENTUALLY PARALYSIS OF THE EXTREMITIES AND POSSIBLY OF THE RESPIRATORY MUSCLES. IN SEVERE CASES, THERE MAY ALSO BE INVOLUNTARY DEFECATION AND URINATION, BRADYCARDIA, HYPOTENSION, PULMONARY EDEMA, CONVULSIONS, COMA, AND DEATH FROM RESPIRATORY FAILURE OR CARDIAC ARREST. CARBAMATES GENERALLY DO NOT ACCUMULATE IN MAMMALIAN TISSUE AND THE CHOLINESTERASE INHIBITION REVERSES RATHER RAPIDLY. IN NON-FATAL CASES, THE ILLNESS GENERALLY LASTS LESS THAN 24 HOURS. **CHRONIC EXPOSURE-** PROLONGED OR REPEATED EXPOSURE MAY CAUSE EFFECTS AS DESCRIBED IN ACUTE EXPOSURE.
FIRST AID- REMOVE FROM EXPOSURE AREA TO FRESH AIR IMMEDIATELY. IF BREATHING HAS STOPPED, GIVE ARTIFICIAL RESPIRATION. MAINTAIN AIRWAY AND BLOOD PRESSURE AND ADMINISTER OXYGEN IF AVAILABLE. KEEP AFFECTED PERSON WARM AND AT REST. TREAT SYMPTOMATICALLY AND SUPPORTIVELY. ADMINISTRATION OF OXYGEN SHOULD BE PERFORMED BY QUALIFIED PERSONNEL. GET MEDICAL ATTENTION IMMEDIATELY.

SKIN CONTACT: DESMETHYL PIRIMICARB: SEE INFORMATION ON CARBAMATES. CARBAMATES: CHOLINESTERASE INHIBITOR. **ACUTE EXPOSURE-** SOME COMPOUNDS MAY CAUSE IRRITATION. LOCALIZED SWEATING AND FASCICULATIONS MAY OCCUR AT THE SITE OF CONTACT. IF SUFFICIENT AMOUNTS ARE ABSORBED THROUGH THE SKIN, OTHER EFFECTS OF CHOLINESTERASE INHIBITION MAY OCCUR AS DESCRIBED IN ACUTE INHALATION; SYMPTOMS MAY BE DELAYED FOR 2-3 HOURS, USUALLY NO MORE THAN 8 HOURS. **CHRONIC EXPOSURE-** REPEATED OR PROLONGED EXPOSURE MAY CAUSE EFFECTS AS DESCRIBED IN ACUTE EXPOSURE.
FIRST AID- REMOVE CONTAMINATED CLOTHING IMMEDIATELY. WASH CONTAMINATED AREAS WITH SOAP AND WATER FOLLOWED BY ALCOHOL (ARENA, POISONING, 4TH ED.). EMERGENCY PERSONNEL SHOULD WEAR GLOVES AND AVOID CONTAMINATION. TREAT RESPIRATORY DIFFICULTY WITH ARTIFICIAL RESPIRATION. GET MEDICAL ATTENTION IMMEDIATELY.

EYE CONTACT: DESMETHYL PIRIMICARB: SEE INFORMATION ON CARBAMATES. CARBAMATES: CHOLINESTERASE INHIBITOR. **ACUTE EXPOSURE-** DIRECT CONTACT MAY CAUSE PAIN, HYPEREMIA, LACRIMATION, TWITCHING OF THE EYELIDS, MIOSIS, AND CILIARY MUSCLE SPASM WITH LOSS OF ACCOMODATION, BLURRED OR DIMMED VISION AND BROWACHE. SOMETIMES MYDRIASIS MAY OCCUR INSTEAD OF MIOSIS. WITH SUFFICIENT EXPOSURE, OTHER SYMPTOMS OF CHOLINESTERASE INHIBITION MAY OCCUR AS DESCRIBED IN ACUTE INHALATION. **CHRONIC EXPOSURE-** PROLONGED EXPOSURE MAY CAUSE EFFECTS AS DESCRIBED IN ACUTE EXPOSURE. SOME COMPOUNDS HAVE CAUSED TOXIC EFFECTS ON THE CRYSTALLINE LENS, CONJUNCTIVAL THICKENING AND OBSTRUCTION OF NASOLACRIMAL CANALS WHEN USED AS MIOTIC EYE DROPS.
FIRST AID- IRRIGATE EYES WITH WATER OR SALINE SOLUTION. IF SYMPTOMS OF POISONING OCCUR, TREAT RESPIRATORY DIFFICULTY WITH ARTIFICIAL RESPIRATION AND OXYGEN. OBSERVE PATIENT FOR AT LEAST 24-36 HOURS (GOSSELIN, CLINICAL TOXICOLOGY OF COMMERCIAL PRODUCTS, 5TH ED.). GET MEDICAL ATTENTION IMMEDIATELY. OXYGEN SHOULD BE ADMINISTERED BY QUALIFIED MEDICAL PERSONNEL.

INGESTION: DESMETHYL PIRIMICARB: TOXIC. SEE INFORMATION ON CARBAMATES. CARBAMATES: CHOLINESTERASE INHIBITOR. **ACUTE EXPOSURE-** WHEN INGESTED, THE FIRST EFFECTS MAY BE NAUSEA, VOMITING, ANOREXIA, ABDOMINAL CRAMPS, AND DIARRHEA. WITH ABSORPTION FROM THE GASTROINTESTINAL TRACT, THE OTHER EFFECTS OF CHOLINESTERASE INHIBITION AS DESCRIBED IN ACUTE INHALATION MAY OCCUR; SYMPTOMS MAY BEGIN WITHIN MINUTES OR BE DELAYED SEVERAL HOURS. **CHRONIC EXPOSURE-** REPEATED INGESTION MAY CAUSE EFFECTS AS DESCRIBED IN ACUTE EXPOSURE.
FIRST AID- IF PERSON IS ALERT AND RESPIRATION IS NOT DEPRESSED, GIVE SYRUP OF IPECAC FOLLOWED BY WATER (IF VOMITING OCCURS, KEEP HEAD BELOW HIPS TO PREVENT ASPIRATION). IF CONSCIOUSNESS LEVEL DECLINES OR VOMITING HAS NOT OCCURRED IN 15 MINUTES EMPTY STOMACH BY GASTRIC LAVAGE WITH THE AID OF CUFFED ENDOTRACHEAL TUBE USING ISOTONIC SALINE OR 5% SODIUM BICARBONATE FOLLOW WITH ACTIVATED CHARCOAL. ESTABLISH AND MAINTAIN AIRWAY. TREAT RESPIRATORY DIFFICULTY WITH ARTIFICIAL RESPIRATION AND OXYGEN. DO NOT GIVE MORPHINE, AMINOPHYLLINE, PHENOTHIAZINES, RESERPINE, FUROSEMIDE, OR ETHACRYNIC ACID (MORGAN, RECOGNITION AND MANAGEMENT OF PESTICIDE POISONINGS, 3RD ED.). TREAT SYMPTOMATICALLY AND SUPPORTIVELY. ADMINISTRATION OF OXYGEN AND LAVAGE MUST BE PERFORMED BY QUALIFIED MEDICAL PERSONNEL. GET MEDICAL ATTENTION IMMEDIATELY.
ANTIDOTE: THE FOLLOWING ANTIDOTE(S) HAVE BEEN RECOMMENDED. HOWEVER, THE DECISION AS TO WHETHER THE SEVERITY OF POISONING REQUIRES ADMINISTRATION OF ANY ANTIDOTE AND ACTUAL DOSE REQUIRED SHOULD BE MADE BY QUALIFIED MEDICAL PERSONNEL.
FOR CHOLINESTERASE INHIBITORS: ESTABLISH CLEAR AIRWAY AND TISSUE OXYGENATION BY ASPIRATION OF SECRETIONS, AND IF NECESSARY, BY ASSISTED PULMONARY VENTILATION WITH OXYGEN. IMPROVE TISSUE OXYGENATION AS MUCH AS POSSIBLE BEFORE ADMINISTERING ATROPINE TO MINIMIZE THE RISK OF VENTRICULAR FIBRILLATION. ADMINISTER ATROPINE SULFATE INTRAVENOUSLY, OR INTRAMUSCULARLY IF IV INJECTION IS NOT POSSIBLE. IN MODERATELY SEVERE POISONING ADMINISTER ATROPINE SULFATE, 0.4-2.0 MG REPEATED EVERY 15 MINUTES UNTIL ATROPINIZATION IS ACHIEVED (TACHYCARDIA, FLUSHING, DRY MOUTH, MYDRIASIS). MAINTAIN ATROPINIZATION BY REPEATED DOSES FOR 2-12 HOURS, OR LONGER, DEPENDING ON THE SEVERITY OF POISONING. THE APPEARANCE OF RALES IN THE LUNG BASES, MIOSIS, SALIVATION, NAUSEA, BRADYCARDIA, ARE ALL INDICATIONS OF INADEQUATE ATROPINIZATION. SEVERELY POISONED INDIVIDUALS MAY EXHIBIT REMARKABLE TOLERANCE TO ATROPINE; TWO OR MORE TIMES THE DOSAGES SUGGESTED ABOVE MAY BE NEEDED. PERSONS NOT POISONED OR ONLY SLIGHTLY POISONED, HOWEVER, MAY DEVELOP SIGNS OF ATROPINE TOXICITY FROM SUCH LARGE DOSAGES: FEVER, MUSCLE FIBRILLATIONS, AND DELIRIUM ARE THE MAIN SIGNS OF ATROPINE TOXICITY. IF THESE SIGNS APPEAR WHILE THE PATIENT IS FULLY ATROPINIZED, ATROPINE ADMINISTRATION SHOULD BE DISCONTINUED, AT LEAST TEMPORARILY. OBSERVE TREATED PATIENTS CLOSELY AT LEAST 24 HOURS TO INSURE THAT SYMPTOMS (POSSIBLY PULMONARY EDEMA) DO NOT RECUR AS ATROPINIZATION WEARS OFF. IN VERY SEVERE POISONINGS, METABOLIC DISPOSITION OF TOXICANT MAY REQUIRE SEVERAL HOURS OR DAYS DURING WHICH ATROPINIZATION MUST BE MAINTAINED. MARKEDLY LOWER LEVELS OF URINARY METABOLITES INDICATE THAT ATROPINE DOSAGE CAN BE TAPERED OFF. AS DOSAGE IS REDUCED, CHECK THE LUNG BASES FREQUENTLY FOR RALES. IF RALES ARE HEARD OR OTHER SYMPTOMS RETURN, RE-ESTABLISH ATROPINIZATION PROMPTLY (MORGAN, RECOGNITION AND MANAGEMENT OF PESTICIDE POISONINGS, 3RD ED.). ADMINISTRATION OF ANTIDOTE MUST BE PERFORMED BY QUALIFIED MEDICAL PERSONNEL.
PRALIDOXIME (PROTOPAM-AYERST, 2-PAM) IS OF DOUBTFUL VALUE IN POISONINGS BY CARBAMATE INHIBITORS OF CHOLINESTERASE. ATROPINE ALONE IS ALMOST ALWAYS AN ADEQUATE ANTIDOTE. PRALIDOXIME IS PROBABLY CONTRAINDICATED IN POISONING BY CARBARYL SPECIFICALLY, AND OTHER MONOMETHYLATED CARBAMATES. IF A VICTIM OF DIMETHYLCARBAMATE INSECTICIDE POISONING FAILS TO RESPOND PROMPTLY AND ADEQUATELY TO

ATROPINE, OR IF POISONING INVOLVES A COMBINATION OF CARBAMATE AND ORGANOPHOSPHATE, A DILUTE SOLUTION OF PRALIDOXIME (TOTAL DOSE IN 250 ML 5% GLUCOSE SOLUTION) MAY BE GIVEN CAUTIOUSLY INTRAVENOUSLY. ADULT DOSAGE IS 1 GRAM (MORGAN, RECOGNITION AND MANAGEMENT OF PESTICIDE POISONINGS, THIRD EDITION; HAYES, PESTICIDES STUDIED IN MAN, 1982).

REACTIVITY

REACTIVITY: STABLE UNDER NORMAL TEMPERATURES AND PRESSURES.

INCOMPATIBILITIES: DESMETHYL PIRIMICARB: OXIDIZERS (STRONG): FIRE AND EXPLOSION HAZARD.

DECOMPOSITION: THERMAL DECOMPOSITION PRODUCTS MAY INCLUDE TOXIC OXIDES OF CARBON AND NITROGEN.

POLYMERIZATION: HAZARDOUS POLYMERIZATION HAS NOT BEEN REPORTED TO OCCUR UNDER NORMAL TEMPERATURES AND PRESSURES.

STORAGE AND DISPOSAL

OBSERVE ALL FEDERAL, STATE AND LOCAL REGULATIONS WHEN STORING OR DISPOSING OF THIS SUBSTANCE. FOR ASSISTANCE, CONTACT THE DISTRICT DIRECTOR OF THE ENVIRONMENTAL PROTECTION AGENCY.

STORAGE

STORE IN ACCORDANCE WITH 40 CFR 165 RECOMMENDED PROCEDURES FOR THE DISPOSAL AND STORAGE OF PESTICIDES AND PESTICIDE CONTAINERS.
STORE IN A COOL, DRY PLACE PROTECTED AGAINST LIGHT.
STORE AWAY FROM INCOMPATIBLE SUBSTANCES.

DISPOSAL

DISPOSAL MUST BE IN ACCORDANCE WITH 40 CFR 165 RECOMMENDED PROCEDURES FOR THE DISPOSAL AND STORAGE OF PESTICIDES AND PESTICIDE CONTAINERS.

CONDITIONS TO AVOID

MAY BURN BUT DOES NOT IGNITE READILY.

SPILL AND LEAK PROCEDURES

OCCUPATIONAL SPILL: DO NOT TOUCH SPILLED MATERIAL. STOP LEAK IF YOU CAN DO IT WITHOUT RISK. FOR SMALL SPILLS, TAKE UP WITH SAND OR OTHER ABSORBENT MATERIAL AND PLACE INTO CONTAINERS FOR LATER DISPOSAL. FOR SMALL DRY SPILLS, WITH A CLEAN SHOVEL PLACE MATERIAL INTO CLEAN, DRY CONTAINER AND COVER. MOVE CONTAINERS FROM SPILL AREA. FOR LARGER SPILLS, DIKE FAR AHEAD OF SPILL FOR LATER DISPOSAL. KEEP UNNECESSARY PEOPLE AWAY. ISOLATE HAZARD AREA AND DENY ENTRY.

PROTECTIVE EQUIPMENT

VENTILATION: PROVIDE LOCAL EXHAUST OR PROCESS ENCLOSURE VENTILATION SYSTEM.

RESPIRATOR: THE FOLLOWING RESPIRATORS ARE RECOMMENDED BASED ON INFORMATION FOUND IN THE PHYSICAL DATA, TOXICITY AND HEALTH EFFECTS SECTIONS. THEY ARE RANKED IN ORDER FROM MINIMUM TO MAXIMUM RESPIRATORY PROTECTION. THE SPECIFIC RESPIRATOR SELECTED MUST BE BASED ON CONTAMINATION LEVELS FOUND IN THE WORK PLACE, MUST NOT EXCEED THE WORKING LIMITS OF THE RESPIRATOR AND BE JOINTLY APPROVED BY THE NATIONAL INSTITUTE FOR OCCUPATIONAL SAFETY AND HEALTH AND THE MINE SAFETY AND HEALTH ADMINISTRATION (NIOSH-MSHA).
TYPE 'C' SUPPLIED-AIR RESPIRATOR WITH A FULL FACEPIECE OPERATED IN PRESSURE-DEMAND OR OTHER POSITIVE PRESSURE MODE OR WITH A FULL FACEPIECE, HELMET OR HOOD OPERATED IN CONTINOUS-FLOW MODE.
SELF-CONTAINED BREATHING APPARATUS WITH A FULL FACEPIECE OPERATED IN PRESSURE-DEMAND OR OTHER POSITIVE PRESSURE MODE.
FOR FIREFIGHTING AND OTHER IMMEDIATELY DANGEROUS TO LIFE OR HEALTH CONDITIONS:
SELF-CONTAINED BREATHING APPARATUS WITH FULL FACEPIECE OPERATED IN PRESSURE-DEMAND OR OTHER POSITIVE PRESSURE MODE.
SUPPLIED-AIR RESPIRATOR WITH FULL FACEPIECE AND OPERATED IN PRESSURE-DEMAND OR OTHER POSITIVE PRESSURE MODE IN COMBINATION WITH AN AUXILIARY SELF-CONTAINED BREATHING APPARATUS OPERATED IN PRESSURE-DEMAND OR OTHER POSITIVE PRESSURE MODE.

CLOTHING: EMPLOYEE MUST WEAR APPROPRIATE PROTECTIVE (IMPERVIOUS) CLOTHING AND EQUIPMENT TO PREVENT ANY POSSIBILITY OF SKIN CONTACT WITH THIS SUBSTANCE.

GLOVES: EMPLOYEE MUST WEAR APPROPRIATE PROTECTIVE GLOVES TO PREVENT CONTACT WITH THIS SUBSTANCE.

EYE PROTECTION: EMPLOYEE MUST WEAR SPLASH-PROOF OR DUST-RESISTANT SAFETY GOGGLES WITH OR WITHOUT A FACESHIELD TO PREVENT CONTACT WITH THIS SUBSTANCE.
EMERGENCY EYE WASH: WHERE THERE IS ANY POSSIBILITY THAT AN EMPLOYEE'S EYES MAY BE EXPOSED TO THIS SUBSTANCE, THE EMPLOYER SHOULD PROVIDE AN EYE WASH FOUNTAIN WITHIN THE IMMEDIATE WORK AREA FOR EMERGENCY USE.

AUTHORIZED BY- OCCUPATIONAL HEALTH SERVICES, INC.
CREATION DATE: 05/18/90 ***REVISION DATE:*** 06/12/90

MATERIAL SAFETY DATA SHEET

OCCUPATIONAL HEALTH SERVICES, INC.
AGRICULTURE AND PESTICIDE DIVISION
450 SEVENTH AVENUE, SUITE 2407
NEW YORK, NEW YORK 10123
1-800-445-MSDS OR (212) 967-1100

EMERGENCY CONTACT:
JOHN S. BRANSFORD, JR. (615) 292-1180

SUBSTANCE IDENTIFICATION

CAS-NUMBER 1014-69-3

SUBSTANCE: DESMETRYNE

TRADE NAMES/SYNONYMS: 1,3,5-TRIAZINE-2,4-DIAMINE, N-METHYL-N'-(1-METHYLETHYL)-6 -(METHYLTHIO)-; S-TRIAZINE, 2-(ISOPROPYLAMINO)-4-(METHYLAMINO)-6-(METHYLTHIO)-; N-METHYL-N'-(1-METHYLETHYL)-6-(METHYLTHIO)-1,3,5-TRIAZINE-2,4-DIAMINE; 2-(ISOPROPYLAMINO)-4-(METHYLAMINO)-6-(METHYLTHIO)-S-TRIAZINE; 2-ISOPROPYLAMINO-4-METHYLAMINO-6-METHYLTHIO-1,3,5-TRIAZINE; DESMETRYN; G 34360; NORAMETRYNE; SEMERON; TOPUSYN; C8H15N5S; PST06353

CHEMICAL FAMILY: S-TRIAZINE

MOLECULAR FORMULA: C8-H15-N5-S

MOLECULAR WEIGHT: 213.34

CERCLA RATINGS (SCALE 0-3): HEALTH=2 FIRE=1 REACTIVITY=0 PERSISTENCE=2

NFPA RATINGS (SCALE 0-4): HEALTH=2 FIRE=1 REACTIVITY=0

COMPONENTS AND CONTAMINANTS

COMPONENT: DESMETRYNE ***PERCENT:*** 100.0
CAS# 1014-69-3

OTHER CONTAMINANTS: NONE

EXPOSURE LIMITS: NO OCCUPATIONAL EXPOSURE LIMITS ESTABLISHED BY OSHA, ACGIH, OR NIOSH.

PHYSICAL DATA

DESCRIPTION: COLORLESS OR WHITE CRYSTALLINE SOLID.

MELTING POINT: 183-187 F (84-86 C) ***SPECIFIC GRAVITY:*** 1.172

VAPOR PRESSURE: 0.000001 MMHG @ 20 C

SOLUBILITY IN WATER: 580 PPM @ 20C

SOLVENT SOLUBILITY: SOLUBLE IN ACETONE, DICHLOROMETHANE, METHANOL, TOLUENE, OCTAN-1-OL, AND MOST ORGANIC SOLVENTS; SLIGHTLY SOLUBLE IN HEXANE.

FIRE AND EXPLOSION DATA

FIRE AND EXPLOSION HAZARD: SLIGHT FIRE HAZARD WHEN EXPOSED TO HEAT OR FLAME.

FIREFIGHTING MEDIA: DRY CHEMICAL, CARBON DIOXIDE, HALON, WATER SPRAY OR STANDARD FOAM (1987 EMERGENCY RESPONSE GUIDEBOOK, DOT P 5800.4). FOR LARGER FIRES, USE WATER SPRAY, FOG OR STANDARD FOAM (1987 EMERGENCY RESPONSE GUIDEBOOK, DOT P 5800.4).

FIREFIGHTING: MOVE CONTAINERS FROM FIRE AREA IF POSSIBLE (1987 EMERGENCY RESPONSE GUIDEBOOK, DOT P 5800.4, GUIDE PAGE 53).
EXTINGUISH USING AGENTS SUITABLE FOR SURROUNDING FIRE. USE FLOODING QUANTITIES OF WATER AS A FOG. KEEP MATERIAL OUT OF SEWERS AND WATER SOURCES. DO NOT TOUCH SPILLED MATERIAL. AVOID BREATHING HAZARDOUS FUMES; KEEP UPWIND.

TOXICITY

DESMETRYNE: TOXICITY DATA: 1563 GM/M3/1 HOUR INHALATION-RAT LC50; 1390 MG/KG ORAL-RAT LD50; 700 MG/KG ORAL-MOUSE LD50; 1390 MG/KG UNREPORTED-RAT LD50; 2 GM/KG UNREPORTED-MAMMAL LD50; MUTAGENIC DATA (RTECS). CARCINOGEN STATUS: NONE. ACUTE TOXICITY LEVEL: MODERATELY TOXIC BY INGESTION; RELATIVELY NONTOXIC BY INHALATION. TARGET EFFECTS: NO DATA AVAILABLE.

HEALTH EFFECTS AND FIRST AID

INHALATION: DESMETRYNE: **ACUTE EXPOSURE-** SOME TRIAZINES ARE MILDLY IRRITATING TO THE UPPER RESPIRATORY TRACT. **CHRONIC EXPOSURE-** NO DATA AVAILABLE.

FIRST AID- REMOVE FROM EXPOSURE AREA TO FRESH AIR IMMEDIATELY. IF BREATHING HAS STOPPED, PERFORM ARTIFICIAL RESPIRATION. KEEP PERSON WARM AND AT REST. TREAT SYMPTOMATICALLY AND SUPPORTIVELY. GET MEDICAL ATTENTION IMMEDIATELY.

SKIN CONTACT: DESMETRYNE: **ACUTE EXPOSURE-** SOME TRIAZINES ARE MILDLY IRRITATING TO THE SKIN. **CHRONIC EXPOSURE-** NO DATA AVAILABLE.

FIRST AID- REMOVE CONTAMINATED CLOTHING AND SHOES IMMEDIATELY. WASH AFFECTED AREA WITH SOAP OR MILD DETERGENT AND LARGE AMOUNTS OF WATER UNTIL NO EVIDENCE OF CHEMICAL REMAINS (APPROXIMATELY 15-20 MINUTES). GET MEDICAL ATTENTION IMMEDIATELY.

EYE CONTACT: DESMETRYNE: **ACUTE EXPOSURE-** SOME TRIAZINES ARE MILDLY IRRITATING TO THE EYES. **CHRONIC EXPOSURE-** NO DATA AVAILABLE.

FIRST AID- WASH EYES IMMEDIATELY WITH LARGE AMOUNTS OF WATER OR NORMAL SALINE, OCCASIONALLY LIFTING UPPER AND LOWER LIDS, UNTIL NO EVIDENCE OF CHEMICAL REMAINS (APPROXIMATELY 15-20 MINUTES). GET MEDICAL ATTENTION IMMEDIATELY.

INGESTION: DESMETRYNE: **ACUTE EXPOSURE-** A LETHAL DOSE IN RATS WAS 1390 MG/KG; SYMPTOMS WERE NOT REPORTED. **CHRONIC EXPOSURE-** NO ADVERSE EFFECTS WERE NOTED IN A 90-DAY STUDY OF RATS FED 13 MG/KG/DAY AND DOGS FED 6.6 MG/KG/DAY.

FIRST AID- REMOVE BY GASTRIC LAVAGE AND CATHARSIS. MAINTAIN BLOOD PRESSURE AND AIRWAY. GIVE OXYGEN IF RESPIRATION IS DEPRESSED. DO NOT PERFORM GASTRIC LAVAGE IF VICTIM IS UNCONSCIOUS. GET MEDICAL ATTENTION IMMEDIATELY (DREISBACH, HANDBOOK OF POISONING, 12TH ED.). ADMINISTRATION OF LAVAGE OR OXYGEN SHOULD BE PERFORMED BY QUALIFIED MEDICAL PERSONNEL.

ANTIDOTE: NO SPECIFIC ANTIDOTE. TREAT SYMPTOMATICALLY AND SUPPORTIVELY.

REACTIVITY

REACTIVITY: STABLE UNDER NORMAL TEMPERATURES AND PRESSURES.

INCOMPATIBILITIES: DESMETRYNE: NO DATA AVAILABLE.

DECOMPOSITION: THERMAL DECOMPOSITION PRODUCTS MAY INCLUDE TOXIC OXIDES OF CARBON, NITROGEN, AND SULFUR.

POLYMERIZATION: HAZARDOUS POLYMERIZATION HAS NOT BEEN REPORTED TO OCCUR UNDER NORMAL TEMPERATURES AND PRESSURES.

STORAGE AND DISPOSAL

OBSERVE ALL FEDERAL, STATE AND LOCAL REGULATIONS WHEN STORING OR DISPOSING OF THIS SUBSTANCE. FOR ASSISTANCE, CONTACT THE DISTRICT DIRECTOR OF THE ENVIRONMENTAL PROTECTION AGENCY.

****STORAGE****

STORE IN ACCORDANCE WITH 40 CFR 165 RECOMMENDED PROCEDURES FOR THE DISPOSAL AND STORAGE OF PESTICIDES AND PESTICIDE CONTAINERS.

****DISPOSAL****

DISPOSAL MUST BE IN ACCORDANCE WITH 40 CFR 165 RECOMMENDED PROCEDURES FOR THE DISPOSAL AND STORAGE OF PESTICIDES AND PESTICIDE CONTAINERS.

CONDITIONS TO AVOID

MAY BURN BUT DOES NOT IGNITE READILY.

SPILL AND LEAK PROCEDURES

OCCUPATIONAL SPILL: DO NOT TOUCH SPILLED MATERIAL. STOP LEAK IF YOU CAN DO IT WITHOUT RISK. FOR SMALL SPILLS, TAKE UP WITH SAND OR OTHER ABSORBENT MATERIAL AND PLACE INTO CONTAINERS FOR LATER DISPOSAL. FOR SMALL DRY SPILLS, WITH A CLEAN SHOVEL PLACE MATERIAL INTO CLEAN, DRY CONTAINER AND COVER. MOVE CONTAINERS FROM SPILL AREA. FOR LARGER SPILLS, DIKE FAR AHEAD OF SPILL FOR LATER DISPOSAL. KEEP UNNECESSARY PEOPLE AWAY. ISOLATE HAZARD AREA AND DENY ENTRY.

PROTECTIVE EQUIPMENT

VENTILATION: PROVIDE LOCAL EXHAUST OR GENERAL DILUTION VENTILATION SYSTEM.

RESPIRATOR: THE FOLLOWING RESPIRATORS ARE RECOMMENDED BASED ON INFORMATION FOUND IN THE PHYSICAL DATA, TOXICITY AND HEALTH EFFECTS SECTIONS. THEY ARE RANKED IN ORDER FROM MINIMUM TO MAXIMUM RESPIRATORY PROTECTION. THE SPECIFIC RESPIRATOR SELECTED MUST BE BASED ON CONTAMINATION LEVELS FOUND IN THE WORK PLACE, MUST NOT EXCEED THE WORKING LIMITS OF THE RESPIRATOR AND BE JOINTLY APPROVED BY THE NATIONAL INSTITUTE FOR OCCUPATIONAL SAFETY AND HEALTH AND THE MINE SAFETY AND HEALTH ADMINISTRATION (NIOSH-MSHA).

CHEMICAL CARTRIDGE RESPIRATOR WITH AN ORGANIC VAPOR CARTRIDGE(S) WITH A FULL FACEPIECE AND ORGANIC VAPOR CARTRIDGE(S) IN COMBINATION WITH A DUST AND MIST FILTER.

POWERED AIR-PURIFYING RESPIRATOR WITH A TIGHT-FITTING FACEPIECE AND ORGANIC VAPOR CARTRIDGE(S) IN COMBINATION WITH A HIGH-EFFICIENCY PARTICULATE FILTER.

TYPE 'C' SUPPLIED-AIR RESPIRATOR WITH A FULL FACEPIECE OPERATED IN A PRESSURE-DEMAND OR OTHER POSITIVE PRESSURE MODE.

SELF-CONTAINED BREATHING APPARATUS WITH A FULL FACEPIECE OPERATED IN PRESSURE-DEMAND OR OTHER POSITIVE PRESSURE MODE.

FOR FIREFIGHTING AND OTHER IMMEDIATELY DANGEROUS TO LIFE OR HEALTH CONDITIONS:

SELF-CONTAINED BREATHING APPARATUS WITH FULL FACEPIECE OPERATED IN PRESSURE-DEMAND OR OTHER POSITIVE PRESSURE MODE.

SUPPLIED-AIR RESPIRATOR WITH FULL FACEPIECE AND OPERATED IN PRESSURE-DEMAND OR OTHER POSITIVE PRESSURE MODE IN COMBINATION WITH AN AUXILIARY SELF-CONTAINED BREATHING APPARATUS OPERATED IN PRESSURE-DEMAND OR OTHER POSITIVE PRESSURE MODE.

CLOTHING: EMPLOYEE MUST WEAR APPROPRIATE PROTECTIVE (IMPERVIOUS) CLOTHING AND EQUIPMENT TO PREVENT REPEATED OR PROLONGED SKIN CONTACT WITH THIS SUBSTANCE.

GLOVES: EMPLOYEE MUST WEAR APPROPRIATE PROTECTIVE GLOVES TO PREVENT CONTACT WITH THIS SUBSTANCE.

EYE PROTECTION: EMPLOYEE MUST WEAR SPLASH-PROOF OR DUST-RESISTANT SAFETY GOGGLES TO PREVENT EYE CONTACT WITH THIS SUBSTANCE. EMERGENCY EYE WASH: WHERE THERE IS ANY POSSIBILITY THAT AN EMPLOYEE'S EYES MAY BE EXPOSED TO THIS SUBSTANCE, THE EMPLOYER SHOULD PROVIDE AN EYE WASH FOUNTAIN WITHIN THE IMMEDIATE WORK AREA FOR EMERGENCY USE.

AUTHORIZED BY- OCCUPATIONAL HEALTH SERVICES, INC.
CREATION DATE: 10/04/89 ***REVISION DATE:*** 05/07/90

MATERIAL SAFETY DATA SHEET

OCCUPATIONAL HEALTH SERVICES, INC.
AGRICULTURE AND PESTICIDE DIVISION
450 SEVENTH AVENUE, SUITE 2407
NEW YORK, NEW YORK 10123
1-800-445-MSDS OR (212) 967-1100

EMERGENCY CONTACT:
JOHN S. BRANSFORD, JR. (615) 292-1180

SUBSTANCE IDENTIFICATION

CAS-NUMBER 9004-53-9

SUBSTANCE: **DEXTRIN, CORN**

TRADE NAMES/SYNONYMS: DEXTRINS; BRITISH GUM; STARCH GUM; GOMMELIN; LEIOCOM; FORTODEX; NADEX; HYDROLYSED DEXTRIN; TAPIOCA DEXTRIN; PYRODEXTRIN; TORREFACTION DEXTRIN; AMYLIN; D-7; 1297; BP-648; CORN DEXTRIN; DEXTRIN; DEXTRID; DEXTRINE; CODEXTRIN; PST06363

CHEMICAL FAMILY: HYDROXYL, POLYNUCLEAR

MOLECULAR FORMULA: C6-H10-O5

MOLECULAR WEIGHT: (162.14)X

CERCLA RATINGS (SCALE 0-3): HEALTH=U FIRE=0 REACTIVITY=0 PERSISTENCE=0

NFPA RATINGS (SCALE 0-4): HEALTH=U FIRE=0 REACTIVITY=0

COMPONENTS AND CONTAMINANTS

COMPONENT: DEXTRINS ***PERCENT:*** 100
CAS# 9004-53-9

OTHER CONTAMINANTS: NONE

EXPOSURE LIMITS: NO OCCUPATIONAL EXPOSURE LIMITS ESTABLISHED BY OSHA, ACGIH, OR NIOSH.

PHYSICAL DATA

DESCRIPTION: WHITE OR YELLOW, AMORPHOUS POWDER OR GRANULES WITH A SWEETISH TASTE. THE WHITE IS PRACTICALLY ODORLESS; THE YELLOW HAS A CHARACTERISTIC ODOR.

MELTING POINT: DECOMPOSES ***SPECIFIC GRAVITY:*** 1.0384

SOLUBILITY IN WATER: SLIGHTLY SOLUBLE

SOLVENT SOLUBILITY: SOLUBLE IN BOILING WATER; INSOLUBLE IN ALCOHOL AND ETHER.

FIRE AND EXPLOSION DATA

FIRE AND EXPLOSION HAZARD: NEGLIGIBLE FIRE HAZARD WHEN EXPOSED TO HEAT OR FLAME.

FIREFIGHTING MEDIA: DRY CHEMICAL, CARBON DIOXIDE, HALON, WATER SPRAY OR STANDARD FOAM (1987 EMERGENCY RESPONSE GUIDEBOOK, DOT P 5800.4). FOR LARGER FIRES, USE WATER SPRAY, FOG OR STANDARD FOAM (1987 EMERGENCY RESPONSE GUIDEBOOK, DOT P 5800.4).

FIREFIGHTING: NO ACUTE HAZARD. MOVE CONTAINER FROM FIRE AREA IF POSSIBLE. AVOID BREATHING VAPORS OR DUSTS; KEEP UPWIND.

TOXICITY

DEXTRIN, CORN: TOXICITY DATA: 350 MG(FE)/KG INTRAVENOUS-MOUSE LD50. CARCINOGEN STATUS: NONE. ACUTE TOXICITY LEVEL: INSUFFICIENT DATA. TARGET EFFECTS: NO DATA AVAILABLE.

HEALTH EFFECTS AND FIRST AID

INHALATION: DEXTRIN, CORN: **ACUTE EXPOSURE-** NO DATA AVAILABLE. MAY BE IRRITATING TO MUCOUS MEMBRANES. **CHRONIC EXPOSURE-** NO DATA AVAILABLE.

FIRST AID- REMOVE FROM EXPOSURE AREA TO FRESH AIR IMMEDIATELY. IF BREATHING HAS STOPPED, PERFORM ARTIFICIAL RESPIRATION. KEEP PERSON WARM AND AT REST. TREAT SYMPTOMATICALLY AND SUPPORTIVELY. GET MEDICAL ATTENTION IMMEDIATELY.

SKIN CONTACT: DEXTRIN, CORN: **ACUTE EXPOSURE-** NO DATA AVAILABLE. MAY BE IRRITATING TO THE SKIN. **CHRONIC EXPOSURE-** NO DATA AVAILABLE. MAY CAUSE DERMATITIS.

FIRST AID- REMOVE CONTAMINATED CLOTHING AND SHOES IMMEDIATELY. WASH AFFECTED AREA WITH SOAP OR MILD DETERGENT AND LARGE AMOUNTS OF WATER UNTIL NO EVIDENCE OF CHEMICAL REMAINS (APPROXIMATELY 15-20 MINUTES). GET MEDICAL ATTENTION IMMEDIATELY.

EYE CONTACT: DEXTRIN, CORN: **ACUTE EXPOSURE-** NO DATA AVAILABLE. MAY CAUSE IRRITATION. **CHRONIC EXPOSURE-** NO DATA AVAILABLE.

FIRST AID- WASH EYES IMMEDIATELY WITH LARGE AMOUNTS OF WATER OR NORMAL SALINE, OCCASIONALLY LIFTING UPPER AND LOWER LIDS, UNTIL NO EVIDENCE OF CHEMICAL REMAINS (APPROXIMATELY 15-20 MINUTES). GET MEDICAL ATTENTION IMMEDIATELY.

INGESTION: DEXTRIN, CORN: **ACUTE EXPOSURE-** NO HUMAN DATA AVAILABLE. **CHRONIC EXPOSURE-** NO HUMAN DATA AVAILABLE.

FIRST AID- TREAT SYMPTOMATICALLY AND SUPPORTIVELY. GET MEDICAL ATTENTION IMMEDIATELY. IF VOMITING OCCURS, KEEP HEAD LOWER THAN HIPS TO PREVENT ASPIRATION.

ANTIDOTE: NO SPECIFIC ANTIDOTE. TREAT SYMPTOMATICALLY AND SUPPORTIVELY.

REACTIVITY

REACTIVITY: STABLE UNDER NORMAL TEMPERATURES AND PRESSURES.

INCOMPATIBILITIES: DEXTRIN, CORN: NO DATA AVAILABLE.

DECOMPOSITION: THERMAL DECOMPOSITION MAY RELEASE TOXIC AND/OR HAZARDOUS GASES.

POLYMERIZATION: HAZARDOUS POLYMERIZATION HAS NOT BEEN REPORTED TO OCCUR UNDER NORMAL TEMPERATURES AND PRESSURES.

STORAGE AND DISPOSAL

OBSERVE ALL FEDERAL, STATE AND LOCAL REGULATIONS WHEN STORING OR DISPOSING OF THIS SUBSTANCE. FOR ASSISTANCE, CONTACT THE DISTRICT DIRECTOR OF THE ENVIRONMENTAL PROTECTION AGENCY.

CONDITIONS TO AVOID

NONE REPORTED.

SPILL AND LEAK PROCEDURES

OCCUPATIONAL SPILL: NO SPECIAL PRECAUTIONS INDICATED.

PROTECTIVE EQUIPMENT

VENTILATION: PROVIDE GENERAL DILUTION VENTILATION.

RESPIRATOR: THE FOLLOWING RESPIRATORS ARE RECOMMENDED BASED ON INFORMATION FOUND IN THE PHYSICAL DATA, TOXICITY AND HEALTH EFFECTS SECTIONS. THEY ARE RANKED IN ORDER FROM MINIMUM TO MAXIMUM RESPIRATORY PROTECTION. THE SPECIFIC RESPIRATOR SELECTED MUST BE BASED ON CONTAMINATION LEVELS FOUND IN THE WORK PLACE, MUST NOT EXCEED THE WORKING LIMITS OF THE RESPIRATOR AND BE JOINTLY APPROVED BY THE NATIONAL INSTITUTE FOR OCCUPATIONAL SAFETY AND HEALTH AND THE MINE SAFETY AND HEALTH ADMINISTRATION (NIOSH-MSHA).

DUST AND MIST RESPIRATOR WITH A FULL FACEPIECE.

AIR-PURIFYING FULL FACEPIECE RESPIRATOR WITH A HIGH-EFFICIENCY PARTICULATE FILTER.

POWERED AIR-PURIFYING RESPIRATOR WITH A TIGHT-FITTING FACEPIECE AND HIGH-EFFICIENCY PARTICULATE FILTER.

TYPE 'C' SUPPLIED-AIR RESPIRATOR WITH A FULL FACEPIECE OPERATED IN PRESSURE-DEMAND OR OTHER POSITIVE PRESSURE MODE OR WITH A FULL FACEPIECE, HELMET OR HOOD OPERATED IN CONTINUOUS-FLOW MODE.

SELF-CONTAINED BREATHING APPARATUS WITH A FULL FACEPIECE OPERATED IN PRESSURE-DEMAND OR OTHER POSITIVE PRESSURE MODE.

FOR FIREFIGHTING AND OTHER IMMEDIATELY DANGEROUS TO LIFE OR HEALTH CONDITIONS:

SELF-CONTAINED BREATHING APPARATUS WITH FULL FACEPIECE OPERATED IN PRESSURE-DEMAND OR OTHER POSITIVE PRESSURE MODE.

SUPPLIED-AIR RESPIRATOR WITH FULL FACEPIECE AND OPERATED IN PRESSURE-DEMAND OR OTHER POSITIVE PRESSURE MODE IN COMBINATION WITH AN AUXILIARY SELF-CONTAINED BREATHING APPARATUS OPERATED IN PRESSURE-DEMAND OR OTHER POSITIVE PRESSURE MODE.

CLOTHING: EMPLOYEE MUST WEAR APPROPRIATE PROTECTIVE (IMPERVIOUS) CLOTHING AND EQUIPMENT TO PREVENT REPEATED OR PROLONGED SKIN CONTACT WITH THIS SUBSTANCE.

GLOVES: EMPLOYEE MUST WEAR APPROPRIATE PROTECTIVE GLOVES TO PREVENT CONTACT WITH THIS SUBSTANCE.

EYE PROTECTION: EMPLOYEE MUST WEAR SPLASH-PROOF OR DUST-RESISTANT SAFETY GOGGLES TO PREVENT EYE CONTACT WITH THIS SUBSTANCE. EMERGENCY EYE WASH: WHERE THERE IS ANY POSSIBILITY THAT AN EMPLOYEE'S EYES MAY BE EXPOSED TO THIS SUBSTANCE, THE EMPLOYER SHOULD PROVIDE AN EYE WASH FOUNTAIN WITHIN THE IMMEDIATE WORK AREA FOR EMERGENCY USE.

AUTHORIZED BY- OCCUPATIONAL HEALTH SERVICES, INC.
CREATION DATE: 11/16/89 ***REVISION DATE:*** 05/25/90

MATERIAL SAFETY DATA SHEET

OCCUPATIONAL HEALTH SERVICES, INC.
AGRICULTURE AND PESTICIDE DIVISION
450 SEVENTH AVENUE, SUITE 2407
NEW YORK, NEW YORK 10123
1-800-445-MSDS OR (212) 967-1100

EMERGENCY CONTACT:
JOHN S. BRANSFORD, JR. (615) 292-1180

SUBSTANCE IDENTIFICATION

CAS-NUMBER 117-81-7

SUBSTANCE: **DI-(2-ETHYLHEXYL)PHTHALATE**

TRADE NAMES/SYNONYMS: BIS(2-ETHYLHEXYL) PHTHALATE; DI(2-ETHYLHEXYL) PHTHALATE; 1,2-BENZENEDICARBOXYLIC ACID, BIS(2-ETHYLHEXYL)ESTER; DEHP; OCTYL PHTHALATE; ETHYLHEXYL PHTHALATE; BISOFLEX 81; PHTHALIC ACID DIOCTYL ESTER; PHTHALIC ACID, BIS(2-ETHYLHEXYL)ESTER; DIETHYLHEXYLPHTHALATE; DIOCTYL PHTHALATE; DI(ETHYLHEXYL)PHTHALATE; 2-ETHYLHEXYL PHTHALATE; FLEXIMEL; FLEXOL DOP; KODAFLEX DOP; OCTOIL; DOP; RCRA U028; C24H38O4; PST06440

CHEMICAL FAMILY: ESTER, CARBOXYLIC, AROMATIC

MOLECULAR FORMULA: C6-H4(C-O2-C-H2-C-H(C2-H5)C4-H9)2

MOLECULAR WEIGHT: 390.56

CERCLA RATINGS (SCALE 0-3): HEALTH=3 FIRE=1 REACTIVITY=0 PERSISTENCE=2

NFPA RATINGS (SCALE 0-4): HEALTH=0 FIRE=1 REACTIVITY=0

COMPONENTS AND CONTAMINANTS

COMPONENT: DI-(2-ETHYLHEXYL)PHTHALATE ***PERCENT:*** 100
CAS# 117-81-7

OTHER CONTAMINANTS: NONE

EXPOSURE LIMITS: DI-(2-ETHYLHEXYL)PHTHALATE: 5 MG/M3 OSHA TWA; 10 MG/M3 OSHA STEL 5 MG/M3 ACGIH TWA; 10 MG/M3 ACGIH STEL LOWEST FEASIBLE LIMIT NIOSH RECOMMENDED EXPOSURE CRITERIA
100 POUNDS CERCLA SECTION 103 REPORTABLE QUANTITY SUBJECT TO SARA SECTION 313 ANNUAL TOXIC CHEMICAL RELEASE REPORTING SUBJECT TO CALIFORNIA PROPOSITION 65 CANCER AND/OR REPRODUCTIVE TOXICITY WARNING AND RELEASE REQUIREMENTS- (JANUARY 1, 1988)

PHYSICAL DATA

DESCRIPTION: ALMOST ODORLESS, COLORLESS TO PALE YELLOW, OILY LIQUID.
BOILING POINT: 723 F (384 C) ***MELTING POINT:*** -67 F (-55 C)
SPECIFIC GRAVITY: 0.981 ***VISCOSITY:*** 81.4 CP @ 20 C
VAPOR PRESSURE: 1.32 MMHG @ 200 C ***SOLUBILITY IN WATER:*** 0.005% @ 20 C
VAPOR DENSITY: 16
SOLVENT SOLUBILITY: SOLUBLE IN HEXANE, MINERAL OIL.

FIRE AND EXPLOSION DATA

FIRE AND EXPLOSION HAZARD: SLIGHT FIRE HAZARD WHEN EXPOSED TO HEAT OR FLAME.
FLASH POINT: 420 F (215 C) (OC) ***LOWER EXPLOSIVE LIMIT:*** 0.3% @ 474 F (245 C)
AUTOIGNITION TEMP.: 735 F (390 C) ***FLAMMABILITY CLASS(OSHA):*** IIIB
FIREFIGHTING MEDIA: DRY CHEMICAL, CARBON DIOXIDE, HALON, WATER SPRAY OR STANDARD FOAM (1987 EMERGENCY RESPONSE GUIDEBOOK, DOT P 5800.4).
FOR LARGER FIRES, USE WATER SPRAY, FOG OR STANDARD FOAM (1987 EMERGENCY RESPONSE GUIDEBOOK, DOT P 5800.4).
FIREFIGHTING: MOVE CONTAINER FROM FIRE AREA IF POSSIBLE. DO NOT SCATTER SPILLED MATERIAL WITH HIGH PRESSURE WATER STREAMS. DIKE FIRE CONTROL WATER FOR LATER DISPOSAL (1987 EMERGENCY RESPONSE GUIDEBOOK, DOT P 5800.4, GUIDE PAGE 31).
USE AGENTS SUITABLE FOR TYPE OF SURROUNDING FIRE. AVOID BREATHING HAZARDOUS VAPORS, KEEP UPWIND.
WATER OR FOAM MAY CAUSE FROTHING (NFPA 325M, FIRE HAZARD PROPERTIES OF FLAMMABLE LIQUIDS, GASES, AND VOLATILE SOLIDS, 1984)

TOXICITY

DI-(2-ETHYLHEXYL)PHTHALATE: IRRITATION DATA: 500 MG/24 HOURS SKIN-RABBIT MILD; 500 MG EYE-RABBIT; 500 MG/24 HOURS EYE-RABBIT MILD. TOXICITY DATA: 25 GM/KG SKIN-RABBIT LD50; 10 GM/KG SKIN-GUINEA PIG LD50; 143 MG/KG ORAL-MAN TDLO; 30,600 MG/KG ORAL-RAT LD50; 30 GM/KG ORAL-MOUSE LD50; 34 GM/KG ORAL-RABBIT LD50; 26 GM/KG ORAL-GUINEA PIG LD50; 250 MG/KG INTRAVENOUS-RAT LD50; 1060 MG/KG INTRAVENOUS-MOUSE LD50; 30,700 MG/KG INTRAPERITONEAL-RAT LD50; 14 GM/KG INTRAPERITONEAL-MOUSE LD50; MUTAGENIC DATA (RTECS); REPRODUCTIVE EFFECTS DATA (RTECS); TUMORIGENIC DATA (RTECS). CARCINOGEN STATUS: ANTICIPATED HUMAN CARCINOGEN (NTP); ANIMAL SUFFICIENT EVIDENCE (IARC GROUP-2B). ORAL ADMINISTRATION SIGNIFICANTLY INCREASED THE INCIDENCE OF BENIGN AND MALIGNANT LIVER-CELL TUMORS IN MICE AND RATS, AND A DOSE-RESPONSE RELATIONSHIP WAS OBSERVED. ACUTE TOXICITY LEVEL: RELATIVELY NON-TOXIC BY DERMAL ABSORPTION AND INGESTION. TARGET EFFECTS: NO DATA AVAILABLE.

HEALTH EFFECTS AND FIRST AID

INHALATION: DI-(2-ETHYLHEXYL)PHTHALATE: **ACUTE EXPOSURE-** NO ILL EFFECTS HAVE BEEN REPORTED AT ROOM TEMPERATURE. MIST, OR VAPORS FROM HEATED MATERIAL MAY CAUSE IRRITATION WITH COUGHING, SORE THROAT, NAUSEA, STAGGERING AND BRONCHITIS. EXPOSURE TO SATURATED VAPORS PRODUCED NO DEATHS IN RATS AFTER 2 HOURS; ALL ANIMALS DIED WITHIN THE NEXT 2 HOURS. **CHRONIC EXPOSURE-** AFTER EXPOSURE OF 6-7 YEARS, PAIN, NUMBNESS, SPASMS, WEAKNESS IN THE UPPER AND LOWER EXTREMITIES, POLYNEURITIS AND NEUROSOMATIC DYSFUNCTION WAS REPORTED IN WORKERS. INTERMITTENT EXPOSURE OF MICE FOR 12 WEEKS PRODUCED SIGNS OF DIFFUSE CHRONIC LUNG INFLAMMATION, SIMILAR TO A BURN REACTION.
FIRST AID- REMOVE FROM EXPOSURE AREA TO FRESH AIR IMMEDIATELY. IF BREATHING HAS STOPPED, PERFORM ARTIFICIAL RESPIRATION. KEEP PERSON WARM AND AT REST. TREAT SYMPTOMATICALLY AND SUPPORTIVELY. GET MEDICAL ATTENTION IMMEDIATELY.

SKIN CONTACT: DI-(2 ETHYLHEXYL)PHTHALATE: **ACUTE EXPOSURE-** CONTACT MAY CAUSE IRRITATION AND ECZEMA. **CHRONIC EXPOSURE-** NO DATA AVAILABLE.
FIRST AID- REMOVE CONTAMINATED CLOTHING AND SHOES IMMEDIATELY. WASH AFFECTED AREA WITH SOAP OR MILD DETERGENT AND LARGE AMOUNTS OF WATER UNTIL NO EVIDENCE OF CHEMICAL REMAINS (APPROXIMATELY 15-20 MINUTES). GET MEDICAL ATTENTION IMMEDIATELY.

EYE CONTACT: DI-(2-ETHYLHEXYL)PHTHALATE: **ACUTE EXPOSURE-** DIRECT CONTACT MAY CAUSE REDNESS AND IRRITATION. **CHRONIC EXPOSURE-** NO DATA AVAILABLE.
FIRST AID- WASH EYES IMMEDIATELY WITH LARGE AMOUNTS OF WATER OR NORMAL SALINE, OCCASIONALLY LIFTING UPPER AND LOWER LIDS, UNTIL NO EVIDENCE OF CHEMICAL REMAINS (APPROXIMATELY 15-20 MINUTES). GET MEDICAL ATTENTION IMMEDIATELY.

INGESTION: DI-(2-ETHYLHEXYL)PHTHALATE: CARCINOGEN. **ACUTE EXPOSURE-** INGESTION OF 10 GRAMS PRODUCED MILD GASTRIC DISTURBANCES WITH SYMPTOMS OF NAUSEA, ABDOMINAL PAIN, AND DIARRHEA. A SINGLE DOSE ADMINISTERED TO PREGNANT RODENTS PRODUCED FETAL DEATH, AND SPECIFIC DEVELOPMENTAL ABNORMALITIES IN NEWBORNS. **CHRONIC EXPOSURE-** RAT FEEDING STUDIES SHOWED TESTICULAR ATROPHY, HEPATOMEGALY AND PROLIFERATION OF HEPATIC PEROXISOMES. INCREASED RESORPTIONS AND MALFORMED FETUSES WERE PRODUCED WHEN PREGNANT MICE WERE ADMINISTERED 1000 MG/KG. FETAL WEIGHTS WERE ALSO SIGNIFICANTLY SUPPRESSED. ANTERIOR NEURAL TUBE DEFECTS (ANENCEPHALY AND EXENCEPHALY) WERE THE MALFORMATIONS MOST COMMONLY PRODUCED. MATERNAL AND PATERNAL REPRODUCTIVE EFFECTS HAVE BEEN REPORTED FOLLOWING ADMINISTRATION PRIOR TO MATING. HEPATOCELLULAR CARCINOMAS, SOME OF WHICH METASTASIZED, WERE REPORTED IN MICE FOLLOWING REPEATED DIETARY ADMINISTRATION. HEPATOCELLULAR CARCINOMAS AND NEOPLASTIC NODULES WERE REPORTED IN RATS.
FIRST AID- IF THE PERSON IS CONSCIOUS AND NOT CONVULSING, INDUCE EMESIS BY GIVING SYRUP OF IPECAC FOLLOWED BY WATER. (IF VOMITING OCCURS KEEP THE HEAD BELOW THE HIPS TO PREVENT ASPIRATION). REPEAT IN 20 MINUTES IF NOT EFFECTIVE INITIALLY. GIVE ACTIVATED CHARCOAL. IN PATIENTS WITH DEPRESSED RESPIRATION OR IF EMESIS IS NOT PRODUCED, PERFORM GASTRIC LAVAGE CAUTIOUSLY (DREISBACH, HANDBOOK OF POISONING, 12TH ED.). TREAT SYMPTOMATICALLY AND SUPPORTIVELY. GASTRIC LAVAGE SHOULD BE PERFORMED BY QUALIFIED MEDICAL PERSONNEL. GET MEDICAL ATTENTION IMMEDIATELY.
ANTIDOTE: NO SPECIFIC ANTIDOTE. TREAT SYMPTOMATICALLY AND SUPPORTIVELY.

REACTIVITY

REACTIVITY: STABLE UNDER NORMAL TEMPERATURES AND PRESSURES.
INCOMPATIBILITIES: DI-(2-ETHYLHEXYL)PHTHALATE: ACIDS (STRONG): INCOMPATIBLE. ALKALIES (STRONG): INCOMPATIBLE. NITRATES: FIRE AND EXPLOSION HAZARD. OXIDIZERS (STRONG): FIRE AND EXPLOSION HAZARD.
DECOMPOSITION: THERMAL DECOMPOSITION MAY RELEASE TOXIC AND/OR HAZARDOUS GASES.
POLYMERIZATION: HAZARDOUS POLYMERIZATION HAS NOT BEEN REPORTED TO OCCUR UNDER NORMAL TEMPERATURES AND PRESSURES.

STORAGE AND DISPOSAL

OBSERVE ALL FEDERAL, STATE AND LOCAL REGULATIONS WHEN STORING OR DISPOSING OF THIS SUBSTANCE. FOR ASSISTANCE, CONTACT THE DISTRICT DIRECTOR OF THE ENVIRONMENTAL PROTECTION AGENCY.

STORAGE

STORE AWAY FROM INCOMPATIBLE SUBSTANCES.

DISPOSAL

DISPOSAL MUST BE IN ACCORDANCE WITH STANDARDS APPLICABLE TO GENERATORS OF HAZARDOUS WASTE, 40CFR 262. EPA HAZARDOUS WASTE NUMBER U028.

CONDITIONS TO AVOID

MAY BURN BUT DOES NOT IGNITE READILY. AVOID CONTACT WITH STRONG OXIDIZERS, EXCESSIVE HEAT, SPARKS, OR OPEN FLAME.

SPILL AND LEAK PROCEDURES

WATER SPILL: THE CALIFORNIA SAFE DRINKING WATER AND TOXIC ENFORCEMENT ACT OF 1986 (PROPOSITION 65) PROHIBITS CONTAMINATING ANY KNOWN SOURCE OF DRINKING WATER WITH SUBSTANCES KNOWN TO CAUSE CANCER AND/OR REPRODUCTIVE TOXICITY.
OCCUPATIONAL SPILL: STOP LEAK IF YOU CAN DO IT WITHOUT RISK. FOR SMALL SPILLS, TAKE UP WITH SAND OR OTHER ABSORBENT MATERIAL AND PLACE INTO CLEAN, DRY CONTAINERS FOR LATER DISPOSAL. KEEP UNNECESSARY PEOPLE AWAY. ISOLATE HAZARD AREA AND DENY ENTRY.
REPORTABLE QUANTITY (RQ): 100 POUNDS THE SUPERFUND AMENDMENTS AND REAUTHORIZATION ACT (SARA) SECTION 304 REQUIRES THAT A RELEASE EQUAL TO OR GREATER THAN THE REPORTABLE QUANTITY FOR THIS SUBSTANCE BE IMMEDIATELY REPORTED TO THE LOCAL EMERGENCY PLANNING COMMITTEE AND THE STATE EMERGENCY RESPONSE COMMISSION (40 CFR 355.40). IF THE RELEASE OF THIS SUBSTANCE IS REPORTABLE UNDER CERCLA SECTION 103, THE NATIONAL RESPONSE CENTER MUST BE NOTIFIED IMMEDIATELY AT (800) 424-8802 OR (202) 426-2675 IN THE METROPOLITAN WASHINGTON, D.C. AREA (40 CFR 302.6).

PROTECTIVE EQUIPMENT

VENTILATION: PROVIDE GENERAL DILUTION VENTILATION TO MEET PUBLISHED EXPOSURE LIMITS.
RESPIRATOR: THE FOLLOWING RESPIRATORS AND MAXIMUM USE CONCENTRATIONS ARE RECOMMENDATIONS BY THE U.S. DEPARTMENT OF HEALTH AND HUMAN SERVICES, NIOSH POCKET GUIDE TO CHEMICAL HAZARDS; NIOSH CRITERIA DOCUMENTS OR BY THE U.S. DEPARTMENT OF LABOR, 29 CFR 1910 SUBPART Z. THE SPECIFIC RESPIRATOR SELECTED MUST BE BASED ON CONTAMINATION LEVELS FOUND IN THE WORK PLACE, MUST NOT EXCEED THE WORKING LIMITS OF

THE RESPIRATOR AND BE JOINTLY APPROVED BY THE NATIONAL INSTITUTE FOR OCCUPATIONAL SAFETY AND HEALTH AND THE MINE SAFETY AND HEALTH ADMINISTRATION (NIOSH-MSHA).
DI-(2-ETHYLHEXYL)PHTHLATE: AT ANY DETECTABLE CONCENTRATION: ANY SUPPLIED-AIR RESPIRATOR WITH A FULL FACEPIECE AND OPERATED IN A PRESSURE-DEMAND OR OTHER POSITIVE PRESSURE MODE IN COMBINATION WITH AN AUXILIARY SELF-CONTAINED BREATHING APPARATUS OPERATED IN PRESSURE-DEMAND OR OTHER POSITIVE PRESSURE MODE. ANY SELF-CONTAINED BREATHING APPARATUS WITH FULL FACEPIECE AND OPERATED IN A PRESSURE-DEMAND OR OTHER POSITIVE PRESSURE MODE.
ESCAPE: ANY AIR-PURIFYING FULL FACEPIECE RESPIRATOR WITH A HIGH-EFFICIENCY PARTICULATE FILTER AND GAS CARTRIDGE(S). ANY APPROPRIATE ESCAPE-TYPE SELF-CONTAINED BREATHING APPARATUS.
FOR FIREFIGHTING AND OTHER IMMEDIATELY DANGEROUS TO LIFE OR HEALTH CONDITIONS:
SELF-CONTAINED BREATHING APPARATUS WITH FULL FACEPIECE OPERATED IN PRESSURE-DEMAND OR OTHER POSITIVE PRESSURE MODE.
SUPPLIED-AIR RESPIRATOR WITH FULL FACEPIECE AND OPERATED IN PRESSURE-DEMAND OR OTHER POSITIVE PRESSURE MODE IN COMBINATION WITH AN AUXILIARY SELF-CONTAINED BREATHING APPARATUS OPERATED IN PRESSURE-DEMAND OR OTHER POSITIVE PRESSURE MODE.

CLOTHING: EMPLOYEE MUST WEAR APPROPRIATE PROTECTIVE (IMPERVIOUS) CLOTHING AND EQUIPMENT TO PREVENT REPEATED OR PROLONGED SKIN CONTACT WITH THIS SUBSTANCE.

GLOVES: EMPLOYEE MUST WEAR APPROPRIATE PROTECTIVE GLOVES TO PREVENT CONTACT WITH THIS SUBSTANCE.

EYE PROTECTION: EMPLOYEE MUST WEAR SPLASH-PROOF OR DUST-RESISTANT SAFETY GOGGLES TO PREVENT EYE CONTACT WITH THIS SUBSTANCE.
EMERGENCY EYE WASH: WHERE THERE IS ANY POSSIBILITY THAT AN EMPLOYEE'S EYES MAY BE EXPOSED TO THIS SUBSTANCE, THE EMPLOYER SHOULD PROVIDE AN EYE WASH FOUNTAIN WITHIN THE IMMEDIATE WORK AREA FOR EMERGENCY USE.

AUTHORIZED BY- OCCUPATIONAL HEALTH SERVICES, INC.
CREATION DATE: 10/04/89 ***REVISION DATE:*** 07/12/90

MATERIAL SAFETY DATA SHEET

OCCUPATIONAL HEALTH SERVICES, INC.
AGRICULTURE AND PESTICIDE DIVISION
450 SEVENTH AVENUE, SUITE 2407
NEW YORK, NEW YORK 10123
1-800-445-MSDS OR (212) 967-1100

EMERGENCY CONTACT:
JOHN S. BRANSFORD, JR. (615) 292-1180

SUBSTANCE IDENTIFICATION

CAS-NUMBER 2303-16-4

SUBSTANCE: DIALLATE

TRADE NAMES/SYNONYMS: CARBAMOTHIOIC ACID, BIS(1-METHYLETHYL)-, S-(2,3-DICHLORO-2-PROPENYL) ESTER; CARBAMIC ACID, DIISOPROPYLTHIO-, S (2,3-DICHLOROALLYL) ESTER; BIS(1-METHYLETHYL)CARBAMOTHIOIC ACID S-(2,3-DICHLORO-2-PROPENYL) ESTER; DIISOPROPYLTHIOCARBAMIC ACID, S (2,3-DICHLOROALLYL) ESTER; S-2,3-DICHLOROALLYL DIISOPROPYLTHIOCARBAMATE; S-2,3-DICHLOROALLYL DI-ISOPROPYL(THIOCARBAMATE); S-(2,3-DICHLORO-2-PROPENYL) BIS(1-METHYLETHYL)CARBAMOTHIOATE; S-(2,3-DICHLOROALLYL) DIISOPROPYLTHIOCARBAMATE; 5-2,3-DICHLOROALLYL DIISOPROPYLTHIOCARBAMATE; 2,3-DICHLOROALLYL DIISOPROPYLTHIOLCARBAMATE; AVADEX; CP 15336; DATC; 2,3-DCDT; DI-ALLATE; RCRA U062; C10H17CL2NOS; PST06480

CHEMICAL FAMILY: THIOCARBAMATE
HALOGEN

MOLECULAR FORMULA: C10-H17-CL2-N-O-S

MOLECULAR WEIGHT: 270.24

CERCLA RATINGS (SCALE 0-3): HEALTH=3 FIRE=0 REACTIVITY=0 PERSISTENCE=3

NFPA RATINGS (SCALE 0-4): HEALTH=3 FIRE=0 REACTIVITY=0

COMPONENTS AND CONTAMINANTS

COMPONENT: DIALLATE ***PERCENT:*** 100
CAS# 2303-16-4

OTHER CONTAMINANTS: POSSIBLE DIISOPROPYLAMINE

EXPOSURE LIMITS: NO OCCUPATIONAL EXPOSURE LIMITS ESTABLISHED BY OSHA, ACGIH, OR NIOSH.
DIALLATE: 100 POUNDS CERCLA SECTION 103 REPORTABLE QUANTITY SUBJECT TO SARA SECTION 313 ANNUAL TOXIC CHEMICAL RELEASE REPORTING

PHYSICAL DATA

DESCRIPTION: AMBER-COLORED LIQUID ***BOILING POINT:*** 302 F (150 C) @ 9 MMHG
MELTING POINT: 77-86 F (25-30 C) ***SPECIFIC GRAVITY:*** 1.188
VAPOR PRESSURE: 0.00015 MMHG @ 25 C
EVAPORATION RATE: 0.000000001063 MOL/CM2.HR @ 20 C ***SOLUBILITY IN WATER:*** 40 PPM
SOLVENT SOLUBILITY: SOLUBLE IN ACETONE, BENZENE, CHLOROFORM, KEROSENE, XYLENE, HEPTANE, ETHANOL, ETHER, ETHYL ACETATE, PROPAN-2-OL AND MOST ORGANIC SOLVENTS
DECOMPOSES ABOVE 392 F (200 C)

FIRE AND EXPLOSION DATA

FIRE AND EXPLOSION HAZARD: NEGLIGIBLE FIRE HAZARD WHEN EXPOSED TO HEAT OR FLAME.

FIREFIGHTING MEDIA: DRY CHEMICAL, CARBON DIOXIDE, HALON, WATER SPRAY OR STANDARD FOAM (1987 EMERGENCY RESPONSE GUIDEBOOK, DOT P 5800.4).
FOR LARGER FIRES, USE WATER SPRAY, FOG OR STANDARD FOAM (1987 EMERGENCY RESPONSE GUIDEBOOK, DOT P 5800.4).

FIREFIGHTING: MOVE CONTAINER FROM FIRE AREA IF POSSIBLE. DO NOT SCATTER SPILLED MATERIAL WITH HIGH PRESSURE WATER STREAMS. DIKE FIRE CONTROL WATER FOR LATER DISPOSAL (1987 EMERGENCY RESPONSE GUIDEBOOK, DOT P 5800.4, GUIDE PAGE 31).
USE AGENTS SUITABLE FOR TYPE OF SURROUNDING FIRE. AVOID BREATHING HAZARDOUS VAPORS, KEEP UPWIND.

TOXICITY

DIALLATE: TOXICITY DATA: 2000 MG/KG SKIN-RABBIT LD50; 2124 MG/KG SKIN-RAT LD50; 395 MG/KG ORAL-RAT LD50; 420 MG/KG ORAL-GUINEA PIG LD50; 510 MG/KG ORAL-DOG LD50; 393 MG/KG UNREPORTED-RAT LD50; 395 MG/KG UNREPORTED-MAMMAL LD50; MUTAGENIC DATA (RTECS); TUMORIGENIC DATA (RTECS). CARCINOGEN STATUS: ANIMAL LIMITED EVIDENCE (IARC GROUP-3). ORAL ADMINISTRATION OF DIALLATE IN THE DIET OF MICE PRODUCED AN INCREASED INCIDENCE OF HEPATOMAS IN MALE MICE OF TWO STRAINS AND AN INCREASED INCIDENCE OF LUNG ADENOMAS IN MALE MICE OF ONE STRAIN. LOCAL EFFECTS: IRRITANT- INHALATION, SKIN, AND EYES. ACUTE TOXICITY LEVEL: TOXIC BY INGESTION AND MODERATELY TOXIC BY DERMAL ABSORPTION. TARGET EFFECTS: ANIMAL STUDIES INDICATED THAT DIALLATE MAY BE A WEAK CHOLINESTERASE INHIBITOR.

HEALTH EFFECTS AND FIRST AID

INHALATION: DIALLATE: IRRITANT. ACUTE EXPOSURE- MAY CAUSE RESPIRATORY AND MUCOUS MEMBRANE IRRITATION. ANIMAL STUDIES INDICATED THAT DIALLATE MAY BE A WEAK CHOLINESTERASE INHIBITOR. EARLY SYMPTOMS OF CHOLINESTERASE INHIBITION ARE BLURRED VISION, FATIGUE, HEADACHE, VERTIGO, NAUSEA, MIOSIS, ABDOMINAL CRAMPS AND DIARRHEA. SEVERE INHIBITION OF CHOLINESTERASE MAY CAUSE EXCESSIVE SWEATING, TEARING, BRADYCARDIA, GIDDINESS, SLURRED SPEECH, CONFUSION, PULMONARY EDEMA, CONVULSIONS AND COMA. CHRONIC EXPOSURE- NO DATA AVAILABLE.

FIRST AID- REMOVE FROM EXPOSURE AREA TO FRESH AIR IMMEDIATELY. IF BREATHING HAS STOPPED, PERFORM ARTIFICIAL RESPIRATION. KEEP PERSON WARM AND AT REST. TREAT SYMPTOMATICALLY AND SUPPORTIVELY. GET MEDICAL ATTENTION IMMEDIATELY.

SKIN CONTACT: DIALLATE: IRRITANT. ACUTE EXPOSURE- MAY CAUSE IRRITATION. A LETHAL DOSE IN RABBITS BY DERMAL ABSORPTION WAS 2000 MG/KG. ANIMAL STUDIES INDICATED THAT DIALLATE MAY BE A WEAK CHOLINESTERASE INHIBITOR. CHRONIC EXPOSURE- PROLONGED OR REPEATED EXPOSURE TO IRRITANTS MAY CAUSE DERMATITIS. CHRONIC EXPOSURE OF GUINEA PIGS AND RABBITS TO DIALLATE CAUSED LOCAL IRRITATION WHICH WAS FOLLOWED BY LOSS OF WEIGHT, NEUTROPHILE LEUCOCYTOSIS, EOSINOPENIA AND ERYTHROPENIA.

FIRST AID- REMOVE CONTAMINATED CLOTHING AND SHOES IMMEDIATELY. WASH AFFECTED AREA WITH SOAP OR MILD DETERGENT AND LARGE AMOUNTS OF WATER UNTIL NO EVIDENCE OF CHEMICAL REMAINS (APPROXIMATELY 15-20 MINUTES). GET MEDICAL ATTENTION IMMEDIATELY.

EYE CONTACT: DIALLATE: IRRITANT. ACUTE EXPOSURE- MAY CAUSE IRRITATION OF THE EYES. CHRONIC EXPOSURE- CHRONIC EXPOSURE OF GUINEA PIGS AND RABBITS TO DIALLATE CAUSED LOCAL IRRITATION WHICH WAS FOLLOWED BY LOSS OF WEIGHT, NEUTROPHILE LEUCOCYTOSIS, EOSINOPENIA AND ERYTHROPENIA.

FIRST AID- WASH EYES IMMEDIATELY WITH LARGE AMOUNTS OF WATER OR NORMAL SALINE, OCCASIONALLY LIFTING UPPER AND LOWER LIDS, UNTIL NO EVIDENCE OF CHEMICAL REMAINS (APPROXIMATELY 15-20 MINUTES). GET MEDICAL ATTENTION IMMEDIATELY.

INGESTION: DIALLATE: TOXIC/LIMITED ANIMAL CARCINOGEN. **ACUTE EXPOSURE**- A LETHAL DOSE IN RATS WAS 395 MG/KG. REPORTED SYMPTOMS OF POISONING IN RATS WAS TEARING, SALIVATION, PANTING, AND EXCITEMENT FOLLOWED BY DEPRESSION, PARALYSIS, AND CONIC-TONIC CONVULSIONS. **CHRONIC EXPOSURE**- REPEATED ORAL ADMINISTRATION IN GUINEA PIGS AND RABBITS PRODUCED WEIGHT LOSS, LEUCOCYTOSIS AND ANEMIA. NEUROTOXIC EFFECTS WERE EVIDENT IN HENS RECEIVING 3.74 GM/KG OVER A 6 DAY PERIOD. STATISTICALLY SIGNIFICANT INCREASES IN HEPATOMAS AND LUNG ADENOMAS WERE OBSERVED IN A MOUSE STUDY.

FIRST AID- GIVE SYRUP OF IPECAC, FOLLOWED BY 1-2 GLASSES OF WATER, TO INDUCE VOMITING (ADULTS: 30 ML). FOLLOWING EMESIS, ADMINISTER 30-50 GRAMS ACTIVATED CHARCOAL. FOLLOW CHARCOAL WITH SODIUM OR MAGNESIUM SULFATE, 250 MG/KG, TO REMOVE TOXICANT FROM THE GUT BY CATHARSIS (EPA, RECOGNITION AND MANAGEMENT OF PESTICIDE POISONINGS, 3RD ED.). FIRST AID SHOULD BE ADMINISTERED UNDER THE DIRECTION OF QUALIFIED MEDICAL PERSONNEL. GET MEDICAL ATTENTION.

ANTIDOTE: NO SPECIFIC ANTIDOTE. TREAT SYMPTOMATICALLY AND SUPPORTIVELY.

REACTIVITY

REACTIVITY: STABLE UNDER NORMAL TEMPERATURES AND PRESSURES.

INCOMPATIBILITIES: NO DATA AVAILABLE.

DECOMPOSITION: THERMAL DECOMPOSITION PRODUCTS MAY INCLUDE TOXIC AND HAZARDOUS FUMES OF HYDROGEN CHLORIDE AND OXIDES OF SULFUR AND NITROGEN.

POLYMERIZATION: HAZARDOUS POLYMERIZATION HAS NOT BEEN REPORTED TO OCCUR UNDER NORMAL TEMPERATURES AND PRESSURES.

STORAGE AND DISPOSAL

OBSERVE ALL FEDERAL, STATE AND LOCAL REGULATIONS WHEN STORING OR DISPOSING OF THIS SUBSTANCE. FOR ASSISTANCE, CONTACT THE DISTRICT DIRECTOR OF THE ENVIRONMENTAL PROTECTION AGENCY.

****STORAGE****

STORE IN ACCORDANCE WITH 40 CFR 165 RECOMMENDED PROCEDURES FOR THE DISPOSAL AND STORAGE OF PESTICIDES AND PESTICIDE CONTAINERS.
STORE AWAY FROM INCOMPATIBLE SUBSTANCES.

****DISPOSAL****

DISPOSAL MUST BE IN ACCORDANCE WITH 40 CFR 165 RECOMMENDED PROCEDURES FOR THE DISPOSAL AND STORAGE OF PESTICIDES AND PESTICIDE CONTAINERS.

CONDITIONS TO AVOID

MAY BURN BUT DOES NOT IGNITE READILY. AVOID CONTACT WITH STRONG OXIDIZERS, EXCESSIVE HEAT, SPARKS, OR OPEN FLAME.

SPILL AND LEAK PROCEDURES

OCCUPATIONAL SPILL: STOP LEAK IF YOU CAN DO IT WITHOUT RISK. FOR SMALL SPILLS, TAKE UP WITH SAND OR OTHER ABSORBENT MATERIAL AND PLACE INTO CLEAN, DRY CONTAINERS FOR LATER DISPOSAL. KEEP UNNECESSARY PEOPLE AWAY. ISOLATE HAZARD AREA AND DENY ENTRY.
REPORTABLE QUANTITY (RQ): 100 POUNDS THE SUPERFUND AMENDMENTS AND REAUTHORIZATION ACT (SARA) SECTION 304 REQUIRES THAT A RELEASE EQUAL TO OR GREATER THAN THE REPORTABLE QUANTITY FOR THIS SUBSTANCE BE IMMEDIATELY REPORTED TO THE LOCAL EMERGENCY PLANNING COMMITTEE AND THE STATE EMERGENCY RESPONSE COMMISSION (40 CFR 355.40). IF THE RELEASE OF THIS SUBSTANCE IS REPORTABLE UNDER CERCLA SECTION 103, THE NATIONAL RESPONSE CENTER MUST BE NOTIFIED IMMEDIATELY AT (800) 424-8802 OR (202) 426-2675 IN THE METROPOLITAN WASHINGTON, D.C. AREA (40 CFR 302.6).

PROTECTIVE EQUIPMENT

VENTILATION: PROVIDE LOCAL EXHAUST OR PROCESS ENCLOSURE VENTILATION SYSTEM.

RESPIRATOR: THE FOLLOWING RESPIRATORS ARE RECOMMENDED BASED ON INFORMATION FOUND IN THE PHYSICAL DATA, TOXICITY AND HEALTH EFFECTS SECTIONS. THEY ARE RANKED IN ORDER FROM MINIMUM TO MAXIMUM RESPIRATORY PROTECTION. THE SPECIFIC RESPIRATOR SELECTED MUST BE BASED ON CONTAMINATION LEVELS FOUND IN THE WORK PLACE, MUST NOT EXCEED THE WORKING LIMITS OF THE RESPIRATOR AND BE JOINTLY APPROVED BY THE NATIONAL INSTITUTE FOR OCCUPATIONAL SAFETY AND HEALTH AND THE MINE SAFETY AND HEALTH ADMINISTRATION (NIOSH-MSHA).
TYPE 'C' SUPPLIED-AIR RESPIRATOR WITH A FULL FACEPIECE OPERATED IN PRESSURE-DEMAND OR OTHER POSITIVE PRESSURE MODE OR WITH A FULL FACEPIECE, HELMET OR HOOD OPERATED IN CONTINOUS-FLOW MODE.
SELF-CONTAINED BREATHING APPARATUS WITH A FULL FACEPIECE OPERATED IN PRESSURE-DEMAND OR OTHER POSITIVE PRESSURE MODE.
FOR FIREFIGHTING AND OTHER IMMEDIATELY DANGEROUS TO LIFE OR HEALTH CONDITIONS:
SELF-CONTAINED BREATHING APPARATUS WITH FULL FACEPIECE OPERATED IN PRESSURE-DEMAND OR OTHER POSITIVE PRESSURE MODE.
SUPPLIED-AIR RESPIRATOR WITH FULL FACEPIECE AND OPERATED IN PRESSURE-DEMAND OR OTHER POSITIVE PRESSURE MODE IN COMBINATION WITH AN AUXILIARY SELF-CONTAINED BREATHING APPARATUS OPERATED IN PRESSURE-DEMAND OR OTHER POSITIVE PRESSURE MODE.

CLOTHING: EMPLOYEE MUST WEAR APPROPRIATE PROTECTIVE (IMPERVIOUS) CLOTHING AND EQUIPMENT TO PREVENT REPEATED OR PROLONGED SKIN CONTACT WITH THIS SUBSTANCE.

GLOVES: EMPLOYEE MUST WEAR APPROPRIATE PROTECTIVE GLOVES TO PREVENT CONTACT WITH THIS SUBSTANCE.

EYE PROTECTION: EMPLOYEE MUST WEAR SPLASH-PROOF OR DUST-RESISTANT SAFETY GOGGLES TO PREVENT EYE CONTACT WITH THIS SUBSTANCE.
EMERGENCY EYE WASH: WHERE THERE IS ANY POSSIBILITY THAT AN EMPLOYEE'S EYES MAY BE EXPOSED TO THIS SUBSTANCE, THE EMPLOYER SHOULD PROVIDE AN EYE WASH FOUNTAIN WITHIN THE IMMEDIATE WORK AREA FOR EMERGENCY USE.

AUTHORIZED BY- OCCUPATIONAL HEALTH SERVICES, INC.
CREATION DATE: 10/04/89 ***REVISION DATE:*** 07/13/90

MATERIAL SAFETY DATA SHEET

OCCUPATIONAL HEALTH SERVICES, INC.
AGRICULTURE AND PESTICIDE DIVISION
450 SEVENTH AVENUE, SUITE 2407
NEW YORK, NEW YORK 10123
1-800-445-MSDS OR (212) 967-1100

EMERGENCY CONTACT:
JOHN S. BRANSFORD, JR. (615) 292-1180

SUBSTANCE IDENTIFICATION

SUBSTANCE: **2,4-DIAMINO-6-CHLORO-S-TRIAZINE**

TRADE NAMES/SYNONYMS: SIMAZINE, METABOLITE; C3H4CLN5; PST06504

CHEMICAL FAMILY: TRIAZINE
AMINE

MOLECULAR FORMULA: (CL)-C3-N3-(N-H2)2

MOLECULAR WEIGHT: 145.55

CERCLA RATINGS (SCALE 0-3): HEALTH=3 FIRE=1 REACTIVITY=0 PERSISTENCE=2

NFPA RATINGS (SCALE 0-4): HEALTH=U FIRE=1 REACTIVITY=0

COMPONENTS AND CONTAMINANTS

COMPONENT: 2,4-DIAMINO-6-CHLORO-S-TRIAZINE ***PERCENT:*** 100.0

OTHER CONTAMINANTS: NONE

EXPOSURE LIMITS: NO OCCUPATIONAL EXPOSURE LIMITS ESTABLISHED BY OSHA, ACGIH, OR NIOSH.

PHYSICAL DATA

DESCRIPTION: WHITE POWDER. ***MELTING POINT:*** >572 F (>300 C)

SPECIFIC GRAVITY: NOT AVAILABLE ***SOLUBILITY IN WATER:*** NOT AVAILABLE

FIRE AND EXPLOSION DATA

FIRE AND EXPLOSION HAZARD: SLIGHT FIRE HAZARD WHEN EXPOSED TO HEAT OR FLAME.

FIREFIGHTING MEDIA: DRY CHEMICAL, CARBON DIOXIDE, HALON, WATER SPRAY OR STANDARD FOAM (1987 EMERGENCY RESPONSE GUIDEBOOK, DOT P 5800.4).
FOR LARGER FIRES, USE WATER SPRAY, FOG OR STANDARD FOAM (1987 EMERGENCY RESPONSE GUIDEBOOK, DOT P 5800.4).

FIREFIGHTING: MOVE CONTAINERS FROM FIRE AREA IF POSSIBLE (1987 EMERGENCY RESPONSE GUIDEBOOK, DOT P 5800.4, GUIDE PAGE 53).
EXTINGUISH USING AGENT SUITABLE FOR TYPE OF SURROUNDING FIRE. AVOID BREATHING VAPORS AND DUSTS. KEEP UPWIND.

TOXICITY

2,4-DIAMINO-6-CHLORO-S-TRIAZINE. TOXICITY DATA: 75 MG/KG ORAL-RAT LD50 (EPA). CARCINOGEN STATUS: NONE. ACUTE TOXICITY LEVEL: TOXIC BY INGESTION. TARGET EFFECTS: NO DATA AVAILABLE.

HEALTH EFFECTS AND FIRST AID

INHALATION: 2,4-DIAMINO-6-CHLORO-S-TRIAZINE: **ACUTE EXPOSURE-** NO DATA AVAILABLE. **CHRONIC EXPOSURE-** NO DATA AVAILABLE.

FIRST AID- REMOVE FROM EXPOSURE AREA TO FRESH AIR IMMEDIATELY. IF BREATHING HAS STOPPED, PERFORM ARTIFICIAL RESPIRATION. KEEP PERSON WARM AND AT REST. TREAT SYMPTOMATICALLY AND SUPPORTIVELY. GET MEDICAL ATTENTION IMMEDIATELY.

SKIN CONTACT: 2,4-DIAMINO-6-CHLORO-S-TRIAZINE: **ACUTE EXPOSURE-** NO DATA AVAILABLE. **CHRONIC EXPOSURE-** NO DATA AVAILABLE.

FIRST AID- REMOVE CONTAMINATED CLOTHING AND SHOES IMMEDIATELY. WASH AFFECTED AREA WITH SOAP OR MILD DETERGENT AND LARGE AMOUNTS OF WATER UNTIL NO EVIDENCE OF CHEMICAL REMAINS (APPROXIMATELY 15-20 MINUTES). GET MEDICAL ATTENTION IMMEDIATELY.

EYE CONTACT: 2,4-DIAMINO-6-CHLORO-S-TRIAZINE: **ACUTE EXPOSURE-** NO DATA AVAILABLE. **CHRONIC EXPOSURE-** NO DATA AVAILABLE.

FIRST AID- WASH EYES IMMEDIATELY WITH LARGE AMOUNTS OF WATER OR NORMAL SALINE, OCCASIONALLY LIFTING UPPER AND LOWER LIDS, UNTIL NO EVIDENCE OF CHEMICAL REMAINS (APPROXIMATELY 15-20 MINUTES). GET MEDICAL ATTENTION IMMEDIATELY.

INGESTION: 2,4-DIAMINO-6-CHLORO-S-TRIAZINE: TOXIC. **ACUTE EXPOSURE-** A LETHAL DOSE IN RATS WAS 75 MG/KG. THE SYMPTOMS WERE NOT REPORTED. **CHRONIC EXPOSURE-** NO DATA AVAILABLE.

FIRST AID- TREAT SYMPTOMATICALLY AND SUPPORTIVELY. GET MEDICAL ATTENTION IMMEDIATELY. IF VOMITING OCCURS, KEEP HEAD LOWER THAN HIPS TO PREVENT ASPIRATION.

ANTIDOTE: NO SPECIFIC ANTIDOTE. TREAT SYMPTOMATICALLY AND SUPPORTIVELY.

REACTIVITY

REACTIVITY: STABLE UNDER NORMAL TEMPERATURES AND PRESSURES.

INCOMPATIBILITIES: 2,4-DIAMINO-6-CHLORO-S-TRIAZINE: OXIDIZERS (STRONG): FIRE AND EXPLOSION HAZARD.

DECOMPOSITION: THERMAL DECOMPOSITION PRODUCTS MAY INCLUDE TOXIC OXIDES OF NITROGEN AND CARBON AND TOXIC AND CORROSIVE FUMES OF CHLORIDES.

POLYMERIZATION: HAZARDOUS POLYMERIZATION HAS NOT BEEN REPORTED TO OCCUR UNDER NORMAL TEMPERATURES AND PRESSURES.

STORAGE AND DISPOSAL

OBSERVE ALL FEDERAL, STATE AND LOCAL REGULATIONS WHEN STORING OR DISPOSING OF THIS SUBSTANCE. FOR ASSISTANCE, CONTACT THE DISTRICT DIRECTOR OF THE ENVIRONMENTAL PROTECTION AGENCY.

****STORAGE****

STORE AWAY FROM INCOMPATIBLE SUBSTANCES.

CONDITIONS TO AVOID

MAY BURN BUT DOES NOT IGNITE READILY.

SPILL AND LEAK PROCEDURES

OCCUPATIONAL SPILL: DO NOT TOUCH SPILLED MATERIAL. STOP LEAK IF YOU CAN DO IT WITHOUT RISK. FOR SMALL SPILLS, TAKE UP WITH SAND OR OTHER ABSORBENT MATERIAL AND PLACE INTO CONTAINERS FOR LATER DISPOSAL. FOR SMALL DRY SPILLS, WITH A CLEAN SHOVEL PLACE MATERIAL INTO CLEAN, DRY CONTAINER AND COVER. MOVE CONTAINERS FROM SPILL AREA. FOR LARGER SPILLS, DIKE FAR AHEAD OF SPILL FOR LATER DISPOSAL. KEEP UNNECESSARY PEOPLE AWAY. ISOLATE HAZARD AREA AND DENY ENTRY.

PROTECTIVE EQUIPMENT

VENTILATION: PROVIDE LOCAL EXHAUST OR PROCESS ENCLOSURE VENTILATION SYSTEM.

RESPIRATOR: THE FOLLOWING RESPIRATORS ARE RECOMMENDED BASED ON INFORMATION FOUND IN THE PHYSICAL DATA, TOXICITY AND HEALTH EFFECTS SECTIONS. THEY ARE RANKED IN ORDER FROM MINIMUM TO MAXIMUM RESPIRATORY PROTECTION. THE SPECIFIC RESPIRATOR SELECTED MUST BE BASED ON CONTAMINATION LEVELS FOUND IN THE WORK PLACE, MUST NOT EXCEED THE WORKING LIMITS OF THE RESPIRATOR AND BE JOINTLY APPROVED BY THE NATIONAL INSTITUTE FOR OCCUPATIONAL SAFETY AND HEALTH AND THE MINE SAFETY AND HEALTH ADMINISTRATION (NIOSH-MSHA).

DUST AND MIST RESPIRATOR WITH A FULL FACEPIECE.

AIR-PURIFYING FULL FACEPIECE RESPIRATOR WITH A HIGH-EFFICIENCY PARTICULATE FILTER.

POWERED AIR-PURIFYING RESPIRATOR WITH A TIGHT-FITTING FACEPIECE AND HIGH-EFFICIENCY PARTICULATE FILTER.

TYPE 'C' SUPPLIED-AIR RESPIRATOR WITH A FULL FACEPIECE OPERATED IN PRESSURE-DEMAND OR OTHER POSITIVE PRESSURE MODE OR WITH A FULL FACEPIECE, HELMET OR HOOD OPERATED IN CONTINUOUS-FLOW MODE.

SELF-CONTAINED BREATHING APPARATUS WITH A FULL FACEPIECE OPERATED IN PRESSURE-DEMAND OR OTHER POSITIVE PRESSURE MODE.

FOR FIREFIGHTING AND OTHER IMMEDIATELY DANGEROUS TO LIFE OR HEALTH CONDITIONS:

SELF-CONTAINED BREATHING APPARATUS WITH FULL FACEPIECE OPERATED IN PRESSURE-DEMAND OR OTHER POSITIVE PRESSURE MODE.

SUPPLIED-AIR RESPIRATOR WITH FULL FACEPIECE AND OPERATED IN PRESSURE-DEMAND OR OTHER POSITIVE PRESSURE MODE IN COMBINATION WITH AN AUXILIARY SELF-CONTAINED BREATHING APPARATUS OPERATED IN PRESSURE-DEMAND OR OTHER POSITIVE PRESSURE MODE.

CLOTHING: EMPLOYEE MUST WEAR APPROPRIATE PROTECTIVE (IMPERVIOUS) CLOTHING AND EQUIPMENT TO PREVENT REPEATED OR PROLONGED SKIN CONTACT WITH THIS SUBSTANCE.

GLOVES: EMPLOYEE MUST WEAR APPROPRIATE PROTECTIVE GLOVES TO PREVENT CONTACT WITH THIS SUBSTANCE.

EYE PROTECTION: EMPLOYEE MUST WEAR SPLASH-PROOF OR DUST-RESISTANT SAFETY GOGGLES TO PREVENT EYE CONTACT WITH THIS SUBSTANCE.

EMERGENCY EYE WASH: WHERE THERE IS ANY POSSIBILITY THAT AN EMPLOYEE'S EYES MAY BE EXPOSED TO THIS SUBSTANCE, THE EMPLOYER SHOULD PROVIDE AN EYE WASH FOUNTAIN WITHIN THE IMMEDIATE WORK AREA FOR EMERGENCY USE.

AUTHORIZED BY- OCCUPATIONAL HEALTH SERVICES, INC.

CREATION DATE: 10/18/89 ***REVISION DATE:*** 05/25/90

MATERIAL SAFETY DATA SHEET

OCCUPATIONAL HEALTH SERVICES, INC.
AGRICULTURE AND PESTICIDE DIVISION
450 SEVENTH AVENUE, SUITE 2407
NEW YORK, NEW YORK 10123
1-800-445-MSDS OR (212) 967-1100

EMERGENCY CONTACT:
JOHN S. BRANSFORD, JR. (615) 292-1180

SUBSTANCE IDENTIFICATION

CAS-NUMBER 333-41-5

SUBSTANCE: **DIAZINON**

TRADE NAMES/SYNONYMS: PHOSPHOROTHIOIC ACID, O,O-DIETHYL O-(6-METHYL-2-(1-METHYLETHYL)-4- PYRIMIDINYL) ESTER; PHOSPHOROTHIOIC ACID, O,O-DIETHYL O-(2-ISOPROPYL-6-METHYL -4-PYRIMIDINYL) ESTER; PHOSPHOROTHIOIC ACID, O,O-DIETHYL 2-ISOPROPYL-6-METHYL-4-PYRIMIDINYL ESTER; O,O-DIETHYL O-2-ISOPROPYL-6-METHYLPYRIMIDIN-4-YL PHOSPHOROTHIOATE; O,O-DIETHYL O-(6-METHYL-2-(1-METHYLETHYL)-4-PYRIMIDINYL) PHOSPHOROTHIOATE; O,O-DIETHYL O-(2-ISOPROPYL-6-METHYL-4-PYRIMIDINYL)PHOSPHOROTHIOATE; O,O-DIETHYL O-(2-ISOPROPYL-4-METHYL-6-PYRIMIDINYL)PHOSPHOROTHIOATE; O,O-DIETHYL O-2-ISOPROPYL-4-METHYL-6-PYRIMIDINYL THIONOPHOSPHATE; THIOPHOSPHORIC ACID 2-ISOPROPYL-4-METHYL-6-PYRIMIDYL DIETHYL ESTER; DIETHYL 2-ISOPROPYL-4-METHYL-6-PYRIMIDYL THIONOPHOSPHATE; DIAZIDE; SPECTRACIDE; NCI-C08673; STCC 4941141; ENT 19,507; C12H21N2O3PS; PST06540

CHEMICAL FAMILY: ORGANOPHOSPHATE

MOLECULAR FORMULA: ((C-H3)2-C-H-C4-N2-H(C-H3)O)P-S(O-C2-H5)

MOLECULAR WEIGHT: 304.34

CERCLA RATINGS (SCALE 0-3): HEALTH=3 FIRE=0 REACTIVITY=1 PERSISTENCE=0

NFPA RATINGS (SCALE 0-4): HEALTH=4 FIRE=0 REACTIVITY=1

COMPONENTS AND CONTAMINANTS

COMPONENT: DIAZINON ***PERCENT:*** 100.00
CAS# 333-41-5

OTHER CONTAMINANTS: NONE

EXPOSURE LIMITS: DIAZINON: 0.1 MG/M3 OSHA TWA (SKIN) 0.1 MG/M3 ACGIH TWA (SKIN)
1 POUND CERCLA SECTION 103 REPORTABLE QUANTITY

PHYSICAL DATA

DESCRIPTION: COLORLESS LIQUID; TECHNICAL PRODUCT IS PALE TO DARK BROWN LIQUID WITH FAINT ESTER-LIKE ODOR. ***BOILING POINT:*** 181-183 F (83-84 C) @ 0.002 MMHG

SPECIFIC GRAVITY: 1.116-1.118 ***VAPOR PRESSURE:*** 0.00014 MMHG @ 20 C

SOLUBILITY IN WATER: 0.004% @ 20 C

SOLVENT SOLUBILITY: SOLUBLE IN ETHER, ACETONE, XYLENE, PETROLEUM OILS, ALCOHOL, CYCLOHEXANE, BENZENE, DICHLOROMETHANE, DIETHYL ETHER, TOLUENE, AND MOST ORGANIC SOLVENTS

FIRE AND EXPLOSION DATA

FIRE AND EXPLOSION HAZARD: NEGLIGIBLE FIRE HAZARD WHEN EXPOSED TO HEAT OR FLAME.

FIREFIGHTING MEDIA: DRY CHEMICAL, CARBON DIOXIDE, HALON, WATER SPRAY OR STANDARD FOAM (1987 EMERGENCY RESPONSE GUIDEBOOK, DOT P 5800.4). FOR LARGER FIRES, USE WATER SPRAY, FOG OR STANDARD FOAM (1987 EMERGENCY RESPONSE GUIDEBOOK, DOT P 5800.4).

FIREFIGHTING: MOVE CONTAINERS FROM FIRE AREA IF POSSIBLE. FIGHT FIRE FROM MAXIMUM DISTANCE. STAY AWAY FROM STORAGE TANK ENDS. DIKE FIRE CONTROL WATER FOR LATER DISPOSAL. DO NOT SCATTER MATERIAL (1987 EMERGENCY RESPONSE GUIDEBOOK, DOT P 5800.4, GUIDE PAGE 55). EXTINGUISH ONLY IF FLOW CAN BE STOPPED; USE FLOODING AMOUNTS OF WATER AS FOG, SOLID STREAMS MAY BE INEFFECTIVE. COOL CONTAINERS WITH FLOODING AMOUNTS OF WATER FROM AS FAR A DISTANCE AS POSSIBLE. USE WATER SPRAY TO ABSORB TOXIC VAPORS. AVOID BREATHING TOXIC VAPORS; KEEP UPWIND. CONSIDER EVACUATION OF DOWNWIND AREA IF MATERIAL IS LEAKING.

TRANSPORTATION DATA

DEPARTMENT OF TRANSPORTATION HAZARD CLASSIFICATION 49 CFR 172.101: ORM-A

DEPARTMENT OF TRANSPORTATION LABELING REQUIREMENTS 49 CFR 172.101 AND SUBPART E: NONE

DEPARTMENT OF TRANSPORTATION PACKAGING REQUIREMENTS: 49 CFR 173.510 EXCEPTIONS: 49 CFR 173.505

TOXICITY

DIAZINON: IRRITATION DATA: 100 MG EYE-RABBIT SEVERE; 500 MG OPEN SKIN-RABBIT MODERATE. TOXICITY DATA: 3500 MG/M3/4 HOURS INHALATION-RAT LC50; 1600 MG/M3/4 HOURS INHALATION-MOUSE LC50; 5500 MG/M3/4 HOURS INHALATION-GUINEA PIG LC50; 180 MG/KG SKIN-RABBIT LD50; 180 MG/KG SKIN-RAT LD50; 2750 MG/KG SKIN-MOUSE LD50; 633 MG/KG SKIN-PIG LD50; 214 MG/KG ORAL-HUMAN TDLO; 66 MG/KG ORAL-RAT LD50; 143 MG/KG ORAL-RABBIT LD50; 17 MG/KG ORAL-MOUSE LD50; 250 MG/KG ORAL-GUINEA PIG LD50; 320 MG/KG ORAL-PIG LD50; 58 MG/KG SUBCUTANEOUS-MOUSE LD50; 180 MG/KG INTRAVENOUS-MOUSE LD50; 65 MG/KG INTRAPERITONEAL-RAT LD50; 33 MG/KG INTRAPERITONEAL-MOUSE LD50; 76 MG/KG UNREPORTED-MAMMAL LD50; MUTAGENIC DATA (RTECS); REPRODUCTIVE EFFECTS DATA (RTECS). CARCINOGEN STATUS: NONE. LOCAL EFFECTS: IRRITANT- SKIN, EYE. ACUTE TOXICITY DATA: HIGHLY TOXIC BY DERMAL ABSORPTION; TOXIC BY INHALATION AND INGESTION. TARGET EFFECTS: CHOLINESTERASE INHIBITOR. POISONING MAY AFFECT THE NERVOUS SYSTEM.* AT INCREASED RISK FROM EXPOSURE: PERSONS WITH RESPIRATORY AILMENTS, RECENT EXPOSURE TO CHOLINESTERASE INHIBITORS OR IMPAIRED CHOLINESTERASE PRODUCTION, OR LIVER MALFUNCTION.* ADDITIONAL DATA: MAY CROSS THE PLACENTA. HIGH ENVIRONMENTAL TEMPERATURES OR EXPOSURE OF THE CHEMICAL TO VISIBLE OR ULTRAVIOLET LIGHT MAY ENHANCE THE TOXICITIY. INTERACTIONS WITH MEDICATIONS MAY OCCUR.*

* MAY BE BASED ON GENERAL INFORMATION ON ORGANOPHOSPHATES.

HEALTH EFFECTS AND FIRST AID

INHALATION: DIAZINON: TOXIC. SEE INFORMATION ON ORGANOPHOSPHATES. ORGANOPHOSPHATES: CHOLINESTERASE INHIBITOR. **ACUTE EXPOSURE-** WHEN INHALED, THE FIRST EFFECTS OF CHOLINESTERASE INHIBITORS ARE USUALLY RESPIRATORY AND MAY INCLUDE NASAL HYPEREMIA AND WATERY DISCHARGE, COUGH, CHEST DISCOMFORT, DYSPNEA, AND WHEEZING DUE TO INCREASED BRONCHIAL SECRETIONS AND BRONCHOCONSTRICTION. IF SUFFICIENT AMOUNTS ARE ABSORBED, OTHER SYSTEMIC EFFECTS MAY BEGIN WITHIN A FEW MINUTES OR BE DELAYED FOR UP TO 12 HOURS. SYMPTOMS MAY INCLUDE PALLOR, NAUSEA, VOMITING, DIARRHEA, ABDOMINAL CRAMPS, HEADACHE, DIZZINESS, OCULAR PAIN, BLURRED VISION, MIOSIS OR IN SOME CASES, ESPECIALLY INITIALLY, MYDRIASIS, LACRIMATION, SALIVATION, SWEATING, AND CONFUSION. OTHER REPORTED CENTRAL NERVOUS SYSTEM OR NEUROMUSCULAR EFFECTS MAY INCLUDE ATAXIA, SLURRED SPEECH, AREFLEXIA, WEAKNESS, FATIGUE, FASCICULATIONS, TWITCHING, TREMORS POSSIBLY OF THE TONGUE AND EYELIDS, AND EVENTUALLY PARALYSIS OF THE EXTREMITIES AND POSSIBLY OF THE RESPIRATORY MUSCLES. IN SEVERE CASES THERE MAY ALSO BE INVOLUNTARY DEFECATION AND URINATION, CYANOSIS, PSYCHOSIS, HYPERGLYCEMIA, ACUTE PANCREATITIS, CARDIAC IRREGULARITIES, PULMONARY EDEMA, UNCONSCIOUSNESS, CONVULSIONS, AND COMA. DEATH IS PRIMARILY DUE TO RESPIRATORY FAILURE, ALTHOUGH CARDIOVASCULAR EFFECTS INCLUDING CARDIAC ARREST MAY ALSO BE IMPLICATED. LONG TERM SEQUELAE ARE RARE BUT MAY INCLUDE NEUROPSYCHIATRIC DISORDERS AND MYOPATHY WITH MUSCLE TENDERNESS. SOME ORGANOPHOSPHATES MAY CAUSE A DELAYED NEUROPATHY BEGINNING 1-4 WEEKS AFTER AN ACUTE EXPOSURE WHICH MAY OR MAY NOT HAVE CAUSED ACUTE CHOLINERGIC EFFECTS. NUMBNESS, TINGLING, WEAKNESS AND CRAMPING BEGINNING SYMMETRICALLY IN THE LOWER LIMBS MAY PROGRESS TO ATAXIA AND PARALYSIS. IN SEVERE CASES, UPPER LIMB INVOLVEMENT IS POSSIBLE AND FLACCID PARALYSIS MAY PROGRESS TO SPASTIC PARALYSIS WITH EXAGGERATED REFLEXES. IMPROVEMENT MAY OCCUR OVER MONTHS TO YEARS, BUT SOME RESIDUAL IMPAIRMENT USUALLY REMAINS. **CHRONIC EXPOSURE-** REPEATED OR PROLONGED EXPOSURE MAY RESULT IN THE EFFECTS OF ACUTE EXPOSURE INCLUDING THE DELAYED NEUROPATHY. OTHER EFFECTS REPORTED IN WORKERS REPEATEDLY EXPOSED INCLUDE IMPAIRED MEMORY AND CONCENTRATION, ACUTE PSYCHOSIS, SEVERE DEPRESSIONS, IRRITABILTY, CONFUSION, APATHY, EMOTIONAL LABILITY, SOCIAL WITHDRAWAL, CONFUSION, HEADACHE, SPEECH DIFFICULTIES, DELAYED REACTION TIMES, SPATIAL DISORIENTATION, NIGHTMARES, SLEEPWALKING, AND DROWSINESS OR INSOMNIA. AN INFLUENZA-LIKE CONDITION WITH HEADACHE, NAUSEA, WEAKNESS, ANOREXIA AND MALAISE HAS ALSO BEEN REPORTED.

FIRST AID- REMOVE FROM EXPOSURE AREA TO FRESH AIR IMMEDIATELY. IF BREATHING HAS STOPPED, GIVE ARTIFICIAL RESPIRATION. MAINTAIN AIRWAY AND BLOOD PRESSURE AND ADMINISTER OXYGEN IF AVAILABLE. KEEP AFFECTED PERSON WARM AND AT REST. TREAT SYMPTOMATICALLY AND SUPPORTIVELY. ADMINISTRATION OF OXYGEN SHOULD BE PERFORMED BY QUALIFIED PERSONNEL. GET MEDICAL ATTENTION IMMEDIATELY.

SKIN CONTACT: DIAZINON: IRRITANT/HIGHLY TOXIC. 500 MG APPLIED TO OPEN RABBIT SKIN PRODUCED MODERATE IRRITATION. SEE INFORMATION ON ORGANOPHOSPHATES.

ORGANOPHOSPHATES: CHOLINESTERASE INHIBITOR. **ACUTE EXPOSURE-** LOCALIZED SWEATING AND FASCICULATIONS MAY OCCUR AT THE SITE OF CONTACT. IF SUFFICIENT AMOUNTS ARE ABSORBED, OTHER EFFECTS OF CHOLINESTERASE INHIBITION AS DESCRIBED IN ACUTE INHALATION MAY OCCUR. SYMPTOMS MAY BE DELAYED 2-3 HOURS, BUT USUALLY NO MORE THAN 12 HOURS. THE RATE OF ABSORPTION IS INCREASED BY THE PRESENCE OF DERMATITIS OR HIGH AMBIENT TEMPERATURES. DELAYED NEUROPATHY IS ALSO POSSIBLE. **CHRONIC EXPOSURE-** REPEATED OR PROLONGED EXPOSURE MAY CAUSE EFFECTS AS DESCRIBED IN ACUTE EXPOSURE. SOME ORGANOPHOSPHATES MAY CAUSE SENSITIZATION.

FIRST AID- REMOVE CONTAMINATED CLOTHING IMMEDIATELY. WASH CONTAMINATED AREAS WITH SOAP AND WATER FOLLOWED BY ALCOHOL (ARENA, POISONING, 4TH ED.). EMERGENCY PERSONNEL SHOULD WEAR GLOVES AND AVOID CONTAMINATION. TREAT RESPIRATORY DIFFICULTY WITH ARTIFICIAL RESPIRATION. GET MEDICAL ATTENTION IMMEDIATELY.

EYE CONTACT: DIAZINON: IRRITANT. 100 MG APPLIED TO THE EYES OF RABBITS PRODUCED SEVERE IRRITATION. SEE INFORMATION ON ORGANOPHOSPHATES. ORGANOPHOSPHATES: CHOLINESTERASE INHIBITOR. **ACUTE EXPOSURE-** DIRECT CONTACT MAY CAUSE PAIN, HYPEREMIA, LACRIMATION, TWITCHING OF THE EYELIDS, MIOSIS, AND CILIARY MUSCLE SPASM WITH LOSS OF ACCOMODATION, BLURRED OR DIMMED VISION AND BROWACHE. SOMETIMES MYDRIASIS MAY OCCUR INSTEAD OF MIOSIS. WITH SUFFICIENT EXPOSURE, OTHER SYMPTOMS OF CHOLINESTERASE INHIBITION AS DESCRIBED IN ACUTE INHALATION MAY OCCUR. **CHRONIC EXPOSURE-** REPEATED OR PROLONGED EXPOSURE MAY CAUSE EFFECTS AS DESCRIBED IN ACUTE EXPOSURE. SOME COMPOUNDS HAVE CAUSED TOXIC EFFECTS ON THE CRYSTALLINE LENS, CONJUNCTIVAL THICKENING AND OBSTRUCTION OF THE NASOLACRIMAL CANALS WHEN USED AS MIOTIC EYEDROPS.

FIRST AID- IRRIGATE EYES WITH WATER OR SALINE SOLUTION. IF SYMPTOMS OF POISONING OCCUR, TREAT RESPIRATORY DIFFICULTY WITH ARTIFICIAL RESPIRATION AND OXYGEN. OBSERVE PATIENT FOR AT LEAST 24-36 HOURS (GOSSELIN, CLINICAL TOXICOLOGY OF COMMERCIAL PRODUCTS, 5TH ED.). GET MEDICAL ATTENTION IMMEDIATELY. OXYGEN SHOULD BE ADMINISTERED BY QUALIFIED MEDICAL PERSONNEL.

INGESTION: DIAZINON: TOXIC. A DOSE OF 63.5 MG/KG FED TO PREGNANT RATS PRODUCED ADVERSE EFFECTS ON FERTILITY. CHRONIC ADMINISTRATION TO PREGNANT RATS RESULTED IN FETAL DEVELOPMENTAL ABNORMALITIES. IN PREGNANT MICE, CHRONIC INGESTION PRODUCED ADVERSE EFFECTS ON FERTILITY AND THE NEWBORN AND FETAL DEVELOPMENTAL ABNORMALITIES. SEE INFORMATION ON ORGANOPHOSPHATES.

ORGANOPHOSPHATES: CHOLINESTERASE INHIBITOR. **ACUTE EXPOSURE**- WHEN INGESTED, THE FIRST EFFECTS MAY BE NAUSEA, VOMITING, ANOREXIA, ABDOMINAL CRAMPS AND DIARRHEA. GASTROINTESTINAL ABSORPTION MAY CAUSE SYMPTOMS OF CHOLINESTERASE INHIBITION AS DESCRIBED IN ACUTE INHALATION. SYMPTOMS MAY BEGIN WITHIN MINUTES OR BE DELAYED FOR HOURS. DELAYED EFFECTS INCLUDING NEUROPATHY MAY ALSO OCCUR. **CHRONIC EXPOSURE**- REPEATED INGESTION MAY CAUSE EFFECTS AS DESCRIBED IN ACUTE EXPOSURE.

FIRST AID- IF PERSON IS ALERT AND RESPIRATION IS NOT DEPRESSED, GIVE SYRUP OF IPECAC FOLLOWED BY WATER (IF VOMITING OCCURS, KEEP HEAD BELOW HIPS TO PREVENT ASPIRATION). IF CONSCIOUSNESS LEVEL DECLINES OR VOMITING HAS NOT OCCURRED IN 15 MINUTES EMPTY STOMACH BY GASTRIC LAVAGE WITH THE AID OF CUFFED ENDOTRACHEAL TUBE USING ISOTONIC SALINE OR 5% SODIUM BICARBONATE FOLLOW WITH ACTIVATED CHARCOAL. ESTABLISH AND MAINTAIN AIRWAY. TREAT RESPIRATORY DIFFICULTY WITH ARTIFICIAL RESPIRATION AND OXYGEN. DO NOT GIVE MORPHINE, AMINOPHYLLINE, PHENOTHIAZINES, RESERPINE, FUROSEMIDE, OR ETHACRYNIC ACID (MORGAN, RECOGNITION AND MANAGEMENT OF PESTICIDE POISONINGS, 3RD ED.). TREAT SYMPTOMATICALLY AND SUPPORTIVELY. ADMINISTRATION OF OXYGEN AND LAVAGE MUST BE PERFORMED BY QUALIFIED MEDICAL PERSONNEL. GET MEDICAL ATTENTION IMMEDIATELY.

ANTIDOTE: THE FOLLOWING ANTIDOTE(S) HAVE BEEN RECOMMENDED. HOWEVER, THE DECISION AS TO WHETHER THE SEVERITY OF POISONING REQUIRES ADMINISTRATION OF ANY ANTIDOTE AND ACTUAL DOSE REQUIRED SHOULD BE MADE BY QUALIFIED MEDICAL PERSONNEL.

FOR CHOLINESTERASE INHIBITORS: ESTABLISH CLEAR AIRWAY AND TISSUE OXYGENATION BY ASPIRATION OF SECRETIONS, AND IF NECESSARY, BY ASSISTED PULMONARY VENTILATION WITH OXYGEN. IMPROVE TISSUE OXYGENATION AS MUCH AS POSSIBLE BEFORE ADMINISTERING ATROPINE TO MINIMIZE THE RISK OF VENTRICULAR FIBRILLATION. ADMINISTER ATROPINE SULFATE INTRAVENOUSLY, OR INTRAMUSCULARLY IF IV INJECTION IS NOT POSSIBLE. IN MODERATELY SEVERE POISONING ADMINISTER ATROPINE SULFATE, 0.4-2.0 MG REPEATED EVERY 15 MINUTES UNTIL ATROPINIZATION IS ACHIEVED (TACHYCARDIA, FLUSHING, DRY MOUTH, MYDRIASIS). MAINTAIN ATROPINIZATION BY REPEATED DOSES FOR 2-12 HOURS, OR LONGER, DEPENDING ON THE SEVERITY OF POISONING. THE APPEARANCE OF RALES IN THE LUNG BASES, MIOSIS, SALIVATION, NAUSEA, BRADYCARDIA, ARE ALL INDICATIONS OF INADEQUATE ATROPINIZATION.

SEVERELY POISONED INDIVIDUALS MAY EXHIBIT REMARKABLE TOLERANCE TO ATROPINE; TWO OR MORE TIMES THE DOSAGES SUGGESTED ABOVE MAY BE NEEDED. PERSONS NOT POISONED OR ONLY SLIGHTLY POISONED, HOWEVER, MAY DEVELOP SIGNS OF ATROPINE TOXICITY FROM SUCH LARGE DOSAGES: FEVER, MUSCLE FIBRILLATIONS, AND DELIRIUM ARE THE MAIN SIGNS OF ATROPINE TOXICITY. IF THESE SIGNS APPEAR WHILE THE PATIENT IS FULLY ATROPINIZED, ATROPINE ADMINISTRATION SHOULD BE DISCONTINUED, AT LEAST TEMPORARILY. OBSERVE TREATED PATIENTS CLOSELY AT LEAST 24 HOURS TO INSURE THAT SYMPTOMS (POSSIBLY PULMONARY EDEMA) DO NOT RECUR AS ATROPINIZATION WEARS OFF. IN VERY SEVERE POISONINGS, METABOLIC DISPOSITION OF TOXICANT MAY REQUIRE SEVERAL HOURS OR DAYS DURING WHICH ATROPINIZATION MUST BE MAINTAINED. MARKEDLY LOWER LEVELS OF URINARY METABOLITES INDICATE THAT ATROPINE DOSAGE CAN BE TAPERED OFF. AS DOSAGE IS REDUCED, CHECK THE LUNG BASES FREQUENTLY FOR RALES. IF RALES ARE HEARD OR OTHER SYMPTOMS RETURN, RE-ESTABLISH ATROPINIZATION PROMPTLY (MORGAN, RECOGNITION AND MANAGEMENT OF PESTICIDE POISONINGS, 3RD ED.). ADMINISTRATION OF ANTIDOTE MUST BE PERFORMED BY QUALIFIED MEDICAL PERSONNEL.

IN CASES OF SEVERE POISONING BY ORGANOPHOSPHATE PESTICIDES IN WHICH RESPIRATORY DEPRESSION, MUSCLE WEAKNESS AND TWITCHINGS ARE SEVERE, GIVE PRALIDOXIME (PROTOPAM-AYERST, 2-PAM), 1.0 GRAM INTRAVENOUSLY AT NO MORE THAN 0.5 GRAM PER MINUTE. DOSAGE OF PRALIDOXIME MAY BE REPEATED IN 1-2 HOURS, THEN AT 10-12 HOUR INTERVALS IF NEEDED. IN VERY SEVERE POISONINGS, DOSAGE RATES MAY BE DOUBLED. TREATMENT WITH PRALIDOXIME WILL BE MOST EFFECTIVE IF GIVEN WITHIN THIRTY-SIX HOURS AFTER POISONING (MORGAN, RECOGNITION AND MANAGEMENT OF PESTICIDE POISONINGS, 3RD ED.). ANTIDOTE SHOULD BE ADMINISTERED BY QUALIFIED MEDICAL PERSONNEL.

REACTIVITY

REACTIVITY: DECOMPOSES ABOVE 120 C. IF DECOMPOSITION OCCURS IN A CLOSED CONTAINER, THE INCREASE IN TEMPERATURE AND PRESSURE MAY BE SUFFICIENT TO RUPTURE THE CONTAINER.

INCOMPATIBILITIES: DIAZINON: WATER: HYDROLYZE SLOWLY. ACIDS: HYDROLYZE SLOWLY. STRONG ALKALIES: HYDROLYZE.

DECOMPOSITION: THERMAL DECOMPOSITION PRODUCTS MAY INCLUDE TOXIC AND HAZARDOUS FUMES OF SULFUR, NITROGEN AND PHOSPHORUS.

POLYMERIZATION: HAZARDOUS POLYMERIZATION HAS NOT BEEN REPORTED TO OCCUR UNDER NORMAL TEMPERATURES AND PRESSURES.

STORAGE AND DISPOSAL

OBSERVE ALL FEDERAL, STATE AND LOCAL REGULATIONS WHEN STORING OR DISPOSING OF THIS SUBSTANCE. FOR ASSISTANCE, CONTACT THE DISTRICT DIRECTOR OF THE ENVIRONMENTAL PROTECTION AGENCY.

STORAGE

STORE IN ACCORDANCE WITH 40 CFR 165 RECOMMENDED PROCEDURES FOR THE DISPOSAL AND STORAGE OF PESTICIDES AND PESTICIDE CONTAINERS.
STORE AWAY FROM INCOMPATIBLE SUBSTANCES.

DISPOSAL

DISPOSAL MUST BE IN ACCORDANCE WITH 40 CFR 165 RECOMMENDED PROCEDURES FOR THE DISPOSAL AND STORAGE OF PESTICIDES AND PESTICIDE CONTAINERS.

CONDITIONS TO AVOID

MAY BURN BUT DOES NOT IGNITE READILY. CONTAINERS MAY EXPLODE IN HEAT OF FIRE.

SPILL AND LEAK PROCEDURES

SOIL SPILL: DIG A PIT, POND, LAGOON OR HOLDING AREA TO CONTAIN LIQUID OR SOLID MATERIAL. DIKE SURFACE FLOW USING SOIL, SANDBAGS, FOAMED POLYURETHANE OR FOAMED CONCRETE. ABSORB BULK LIQUID WITH FLY ASH OR CEMENT POWDER. ADD CAUSTIC SODA.

WATER SPILL: LIMIT SPILL MOTION AND DISPERSION WITH NATURAL BARRIERS OR OIL SPILL CONTROL BOOMS.

IF DISSOLVED, AT A CONCENTRATION OF 10 PPM OR GREATER, APPLY ACTIVATED CARBON AT TEN TIMES THE AMOUNT THAT HAS BEEN SPILLED.

USE MECHANICAL DREDGES OR LIFTS TO EXTRACT IMMOBILIZED MASSES OF POLLUTION AND PRECIPITATES.

OCCUPATIONAL SPILL: DO NOT TOUCH SPILLED MATERIAL. STOP LEAK IF YOU CAN DO IT WITHOUT RISK. USE WATER SPRAY TO REDUCE VAPORS. FOR SMALL SPILLS, TAKE UP WITH SAND OR OTHER ABSORBENT MATERIAL AND PLACE INTO CONTAINERS FOR LATER DISPOSAL. FOR SMALL DRY SPILLS, WITH A CLEAN SHOVEL PLACE MATERIAL INTO CLEAN, DRY CONTAINERS AND COVER. MOVE CONTAINERS FROM SPILL AREA. FOR LARGER SPILLS, DIKE FAR AHEAD OF SPILL FOR LATER DISPOSAL. KEEP UNNECESSARY PEOPLE AWAY. ISOLATE HAZARD AREA AND DENY ENTRY. VENTILATE CLOSED SPACES BEFORE ENTERING.

REPORTABLE QUANTITY (RQ): 1 POUND THE SUPERFUND AMENDMENTS AND REAUTHORIZATION ACT (SARA) SECTION 304 REQUIRES THAT A RELEASE EQUAL TO OR GREATER THAN THE REPORTABLE QUANTITY FOR THIS SUBSTANCE BE IMMEDIATELY REPORTED TO THE LOCAL EMERGENCY PLANNING COMMITTEE AND THE STATE EMERGENCY RESPONSE COMMISSION (40 CFR 355.40). IF THE RELEASE OF THIS SUBSTANCE IS REPORTABLE UNDER CERCLA SECTION 103, THE NATIONAL RESPONSE CENTER MUST BE NOTIFIED IMMEDIATELY AT (800) 424-8802 OR (202) 426-2675 IN THE METROPOLITAN WASHINGTON, D.C. AREA (40 CFR 302.6).

PROTECTIVE EQUIPMENT

VENTILATION: PROCESS ENCLOSURE RECOMMENDED TO MEET PUBLISHED EXPOSURE LIMITS.

RESPIRATOR: THE FOLLOWING RESPIRATORS ARE RECOMMENDED BASED ON INFORMATION FOUND IN THE PHYSICAL DATA, TOXICITY AND HEALTH EFFECTS SECTIONS. THEY ARE RANKED IN ORDER FROM MINIMUM TO MAXIMUM RESPIRATORY PROTECTION. THE SPECIFIC RESPIRATOR SELECTED MUST BE BASED ON CONTAMINATION LEVELS FOUND IN THE WORK PLACE, MUST NOT EXCEED THE WORKING LIMITS OF THE RESPIRATOR AND BE JOINTLY APPROVED BY THE NATIONAL INSTITUTE FOR OCCUPATIONAL SAFETY AND HEALTH AND THE MINE SAFETY AND HEALTH ADMINISTRATION (NIOSH-MSHA).

TYPE 'C' SUPPLIED-AIR RESPIRATOR WITH A FULL FACEPIECE OPERATED IN PRESSURE-DEMAND OR OTHER POSITIVE PRESSURE MODE OR WITH A FULL FACEPIECE, HELMET OR HOOD OPERATED IN CONTINOUS-FLOW MODE.

SELF-CONTAINED BREATHING APPARATUS WITH A FULL FACEPIECE OPERATED IN PRESSURE-DEMAND OR OTHER POSITIVE PRESSURE MODE.

FOR FIREFIGHTING AND OTHER IMMEDIATELY DANGEROUS TO LIFE OR HEALTH CONDITIONS:

SELF-CONTAINED BREATHING APPARATUS WITH FULL FACEPIECE OPERATED IN PRESSURE-DEMAND OR OTHER POSITIVE PRESSURE MODE.

SUPPLIED-AIR RESPIRATOR WITH FULL FACEPIECE AND OPERATED IN PRESSURE-DEMAND OR OTHER POSITIVE PRESSURE MODE IN COMBINATION WITH AN AUXILIARY SELF-CONTAINED BREATHING APPARATUS OPERATED IN PRESSURE-DEMAND OR OTHER POSITIVE PRESSURE MODE.

CLOTHING: EMPLOYEE MUST WEAR APPROPRIATE PROTECTIVE (IMPERVIOUS) CLOTHING AND EQUIPMENT TO PREVENT ANY POSSIBILITY OF SKIN CONTACT WITH THIS SUBSTANCE.

GLOVES: EMPLOYEE MUST WEAR APPROPRIATE PROTECTIVE GLOVES TO PREVENT CONTACT WITH THIS SUBSTANCE.

EYE PROTECTION: EMPLOYEE MUST WEAR SPLASH-PROOF OR DUST-RESISTANT SAFETY GOGGLES AND A FACESHIELD TO PREVENT CONTACT WITH THIS SUBSTANCE.
EMERGENCY WASH FACILITIES: WHERE THERE IS ANY POSSIBILITY THAT AN EMPLOYEE'S EYES AND/OR SKIN MAY BE EXPOSED TO THIS SUBSTANCE, THE EMPLOYER SHOULD PROVIDE AN EYE WASH FOUNTAIN AND QUICK DRENCH SHOWER WITHIN THE IMMEDIATE WORK AREA FOR EMERGENCY USE.

AUTHORIZED BY- OCCUPATIONAL HEALTH SERVICES, INC.
CREATION DATE: 10/04/89 ***REVISION DATE:*** 04/26/90

MATERIAL SAFETY DATA SHEET

OCCUPATIONAL HEALTH SERVICES, INC.
AGRICULTURE AND PESTICIDE DIVISION
450 SEVENTH AVENUE, SUITE 2407
NEW YORK, NEW YORK 10123
1-800-445-MSDS OR (212) 967-1100

EMERGENCY CONTACT:
JOHN S. BRANSFORD, JR. (615) 292-1180

SUBSTANCE IDENTIFICATION

CAS-NUMBER 962-58-3
SUBSTANCE: DIAZINON OXYGEN ANALOG
TRADE NAMES/SYNONYMS: PHOSPHORIC ACID, DIETHYL 6-METHYL-2-(1-METHYLETHYL)-4-PYRIMIDINYL ESTER; PHOSPHORIC ACID, DIETHYL 2-ISOPROPYL-6-METHYL-4-PYRIMIDINYL ESTER; DIETHYL 6-METHYL-2-(1-METHYLETHYL)-4-PYRIMIDINYL PHOSPHATE; DIETHYL 2-ISOPROPYL-6-METHYL-4-PYRIMIDINYL PHOSPHATE; DIAZINON OXON; DIAZOXON; OXODIAZINON; C12H21N2O4P; PST06541
CHEMICAL FAMILY: ORGANOPHOSPHATE
MOLECULAR FORMULA: C12-H21-O4-N2-P
MOLECULAR WEIGHT: 288.28
CERCLA RATINGS (SCALE 0-3): HEALTH=3 FIRE=U REACTIVITY=0 PERSISTENCE=0
NFPA RATINGS (SCALE 0-4): HEALTH=U FIRE=U REACTIVITY=0

COMPONENTS AND CONTAMINANTS

COMPONENT: DIAZINON OXYGEN ANALOG ***PERCENT:*** 100.0
CAS# 962-58-3
OTHER CONTAMINANTS: NONE
EXPOSURE LIMITS: NO OCCUPATIONAL EXPOSURE LIMITS ESTABLISHED BY OSHA, ACGIH, OR NIOSH.

PHYSICAL DATA

DESCRIPTION: LIGHT AMBER LIQUID. ***BOILING POINT:*** 244-246 F (118-120 C)
SPECIFIC GRAVITY: NOT AVAILABLE ***VAPOR PRESSURE:*** NOT AVAILABLE
SOLUBILITY IN WATER: NOT AVAILABLE

FIRE AND EXPLOSION DATA

FIRE AND EXPLOSION HAZARD: UNKNOWN FIRE AND EXPLOSION HAZARD.
FIREFIGHTING MEDIA: DRY CHEMICAL, CARBON DIOXIDE, HALON, WATER SPRAY OR STANDARD FOAM (1987 EMERGENCY RESPONSE GUIDEBOOK, DOT P 5800.4).
FOR LARGER FIRES, USE WATER SPRAY, FOG OR STANDARD FOAM (1987 EMERGENCY RESPONSE GUIDEBOOK, DOT P 5800.4).
FIREFIGHTING: MOVE CONTAINER FROM FIRE AREA IF POSSIBLE. DIKE FIRE CONTROL WATER FOR LATER DISPOSAL; DO NOT SCATTER THE MATERIAL. COOL FIRE-EXPOSED CONTAINERS WITH WATER FROM SIDE UNTIL WELL AFTER FIRE IS OUT. STAY AWAY FROM STORAGE TANK ENDS. WITHDRAW IMMEDIATELY IN CASE OF RISING SOUND FROM VENTING SAFETY DEVICE OR ANY DISCOLORATION OF STORAGE TANK DUE TO FIRE (1987 EMERGENCY RESPONSE GUIDEBOOK, DOT P 5800.4, GUIDE PAGE 28).
EXTINGUISH ONLY IF FLOW CAN BE STOPPED. USE FLOODING AMOUNTS OF WATER AS A FOG; SOLID STREAMS MAY BE INEFFECTIVE. COOL CONTAINERS WITH FLOODING AMOUNTS OF WATER FROM AS FAR A DISTANCE AS POSSIBLE. AVOID BREATHING POISONOUS VAPORS, KEEP UPWIND.

TOXICITY

DIAZINON OXYGEN ANALOG: TOXICITY DATA: 100 MG/KG ORAL-RAT LD50 (EPA). CARCINOGEN STATUS: NONE. ACUTE TOXICITY DATA: TOXIC BY INGESTION. TARGET EFFECTS: CHOLINESTERASE INHIBITOR. POISONING MAY AFFECT THE NERVOUS SYSTEM.* AT INCREASED RISK FROM EXPOSURE: PERSONS WITH RESPIRATORY AILMENTS, RECENT EXPOSURE TO CHOLINESTERASE INHIBITORS OR IMPAIRED CHOLINESTERASE PRODUCTION, OR LIVER MALFUNCTION.* ADDITIONAL DATA: MAY CROSS THE PLACENTA. HIGH ENVIRONMENTAL TEMPERATURES OR EXPOSURE OF THE CHEMICAL TO VISIBLE OR ULTRAVIOLET LIGHT MAY ENHANCE THE TOXICITY. INTERACTIONS WITH MEDICATIONS MAY OCCUR.*
* MAY BE BASED ON GENERAL INFORMATION ON ORGANOPHOSPHATES.

HEALTH EFFECTS AND FIRST AID

INHALATION: DIAZINON OXYGEN ANALOG: SEE INFORMATION ON ORGANOPHOSPHATES:
ORGANOPHOSPHATES: CHOLINESTERASE INHIBITOR. **ACUTE EXPOSURE-** WHEN INHALED, THE FIRST EFFECTS OF CHOLINESTERASE INHIBITORS ARE USUALLY RESPIRATORY AND MAY INCLUDE NASAL HYPEREMIA AND WATERY DISCHARGE, COUGH, CHEST DISCOMFORT, DYSPNEA, AND WHEEZING DUE TO INCREASED BRONCHIAL SECRETIONS AND BRONCHOCONSTRICTION. IF SUFFICIENT AMOUNTS ARE ABSORBED, OTHER SYSTEMIC EFFECTS MAY BEGIN WITHIN A FEW MINUTES OR BE DELAYED FOR UP TO 12 HOURS. SYMPTOMS MAY INCLUDE PALLOR, NAUSEA, VOMITING, DIARRHEA, ABDOMINAL CRAMPS, HEADACHE, DIZZINESS, OCULAR PAIN, BLURRED VISION, MIOSIS OR IN SOME CASES, ESPECIALLY INITIALLY, MYDRIASIS, LACRIMATION, SALIVATION, SWEATING, AND CONFUSION. OTHER REPORTED CENTRAL NERVOUS SYSTEM OR NEUROMUSCULAR EFFECTS MAY INCLUDE ATAXIA, SLURRED SPEECH, AREFLEXIA, WEAKNESS, FATIGUE, FASCICULATIONS, TWITCHING, TREMORS POSSIBLY OF THE TONGUE AND EYELIDS, AND EVENTUALLY PARALYSIS OF THE EXTREMITIES AND POSSIBLY OF THE RESPIRATORY MUSCLES. IN SEVERE CASES THERE MAY ALSO BE INVOLUNTARY DEFECATION AND URINATION, CYANOSIS, PSYCHOSIS, HYPERGLYCEMIA, ACUTE PANCREATITIS, CARDIAC IRREGULARITIES, PULMONARY EDEMA, UNCONSCIOUSNESS, CONVULSIONS, AND COMA. DEATH IS PRIMARILY DUE TO RESPIRATORY FAILURE, ALTHOUGH CARDIOVASCULAR EFFECTS INCLUDING CARDIAC ARREST MAY ALSO BE IMPLICATED. LONG TERM SEQUELAE ARE RARE BUT MAY INCLUDE NEUROPSYCHIATRIC DISORDERS AND MYOPATHY WITH MUSCLE TENDERNESS. SOME ORGANOPHOSPHATES MAY CAUSE A DELAYED NEUROPATHY BEGINNING 1-4 WEEKS AFTER AN ACUTE EXPOSURE WHICH MAY OR MAY NOT HAVE CAUSED ACUTE CHOLINERGIC EFFECTS. NUMBNESS, TINGLING, WEAKNESS AND CRAMPING BEGINNING SYMMETRICALLY IN THE LOWER LIMBS MAY PROGRESS TO ATAXIA AND PARALYSIS. IN SEVERE CASES, UPPER LIMB INVOLVEMENT IS POSSIBLE AND FLACCID PARALYSIS MAY PROGRESS TO SPASTIC PARALYSIS WITH EXAGGERATED REFLEXES. IMPROVEMENT MAY OCCUR OVER MONTHS TO YEARS, BUT SOME RESIDUAL IMPAIRMENT USUALLY REMAINS.
CHRONIC EXPOSURE- REPEATED OR PROLONGED EXPOSURE MAY RESULT IN THE EFFECTS OF ACUTE EXPOSURE INCLUDING THE DELAYED NEUROPATHY. OTHER EFFECTS REPORTED IN WORKERS REPEATEDLY EXPOSED INCLUDE IMPAIRED MEMORY AND CONCENTRATION, ACUTE PSYCHOSIS, SEVERE DEPRESSIONS, IRRITABILTY, CONFUSION, APATHY, EMOTIONAL LABILITY, SOCIAL WITHDRAWAL, CONFUSION, HEADACHE, SPEECH DIFFICULTIES, DELAYED REACTION TIMES, SPATIAL DISORIENTATION, NIGHTMARES, SLEEPWALKING, AND DROWSINESS OR INSOMNIA. AN INFLUENZA-LIKE CONDITION WITH HEADACHE, NAUSEA, WEAKNESS, ANOREXIA AND MALAISE HAS ALSO BEEN REPORTED.
FIRST AID- REMOVE FROM EXPOSURE AREA TO FRESH AIR IMMEDIATELY. IF BREATHING HAS STOPPED, GIVE ARTIFICIAL RESPIRATION. MAINTAIN AIRWAY AND BLOOD PRESSURE AND ADMINISTER OXYGEN IF AVAILABLE. KEEP AFFECTED PERSON WARM AND AT REST. TREAT SYMPTOMATICALLY AND SUPPORTIVELY. ADMINISTRATION OF OXYGEN SHOULD BE PERFORMED BY QUALIFIED PERSONNEL. GET MEDICAL ATTENTION IMMEDIATELY.

SKIN CONTACT: DIAZINON OXYGEN ANALOG: SEE INFORMATION ON ORGANOPHOSPHATES.
ORGANOPHOSPHATES: CHOLINESTERASE INHIBITOR. **ACUTE EXPOSURE-** LOCALIZED SWEATING AND FASCICULATIONS MAY OCCUR AT THE SITE OF CONTACT. IF SUFFICIENT AMOUNTS ARE ABSORBED, OTHER EFFECTS OF CHOLINESTERASE INHIBITION AS DESCRIBED IN ACUTE INHALATION MAY OCCUR. SYMPTOMS MAY BE DELAYED 2-3 HOURS, BUT USUALLY NO MORE THAN 12 HOURS. THE RATE OF ABSORPTION IS INCREASED BY THE PRESENCE OF DERMATITIS OR HIGH AMBIENT TEMPERATURES. DELAYED NEUROPATHY IS ALSO POSSIBLE. **CHRONIC EXPOSURE-** REPEATED OR PROLONGED EXPOSURE MAY CAUSE EFFECTS AS DESCRIBED IN ACUTE EXPOSURE. SOME ORGANOPHOSPHATES MAY CAUSE SENSITIZATION.
FIRST AID- REMOVE CONTAMINATED CLOTHING IMMEDIATELY. WASH CONTAMINATED AREAS WITH SOAP AND WATER FOLLOWED BY ALCOHOL (ARENA, POISONING, 4TH ED.). EMERGENCY PERSONNEL SHOULD WEAR GLOVES AND AVOID CONTAMINATION. TREAT RESPIRATORY DIFFICULTY WITH ARTIFICIAL RESPIRATION. GET MEDICAL ATTENTION IMMEDIATELY.

EYE CONTACT: DIAZINON OXYGEN ANALOG: SEE INFORMATION ON ORGANOPHOSPHATES.
ORGANOPHOSPHATES: CHOLINESTERASE INHIBITOR. **ACUTE EXPOSURE-** DIRECT CONTACT MAY CAUSE PAIN, HYPEREMIA, LACRIMATION, TWITCHING OF THE

EYELIDS, MIOSIS, AND CILIARY MUSCLE SPASM WITH LOSS OF ACCOMODATION, BLURRED OR DIMMED VISION AND BROWACHE. SOMETIMES MYDRIASIS MAY OCCUR INSTEAD OF MIOSIS. WITH SUFFICIENT EXPOSURE, OTHER SYMPTOMS OF CHOLINESTERASE INHIBITION AS DESCRIBED IN ACUTE INHALATION MAY OCCUR. **CHRONIC EXPOSURE-** REPEATED OR PROLONGED EXPOSURE MAY CAUSE EFFECTS AS DESCRIBED IN ACUTE EXPOSURE. SOME COMPOUNDS HAVE CAUSED TOXIC EFFECTS ON THE CRYSTALLINE LENS, CONJUNCTIVAL THICKENING AND OBSTRUCTION OF THE NASOLACRIMAL CANALS WHEN USED AS MIOTIC EYEDROPS.

FIRST AID- IRRIGATE EYES WITH WATER OR SALINE SOLUTION. IF SYMPTOMS OF POISONING OCCUR, TREAT RESPIRATORY DIFFICULTY WITH ARTIFICIAL RESPIRATION AND OXYGEN. OBSERVE PATIENT FOR AT LEAST 24-36 HOURS (GOSSELIN, CLINICAL TOXICOLOGY OF COMMERCIAL PRODUCTS, 5TH ED.). GET MEDICAL ATTENTION IMMEDIATELY. OXYGEN SHOULD BE ADMINISTERED BY QUALIFIED MEDICAL PERSONNEL.

INGESTION: DIAZINON OXYGEN ANALOG: TOXIC. SEE INFORMATION ON ORGANOPHOSPHATES.

ORGANOPHOSPHATES: CHOLINESTERASE INHIBITOR. **ACUTE EXPOSURE-** WHEN INGESTED, THE FIRST EFFECTS MAY BE NAUSEA, VOMITING, ANOREXIA, ABDOMINAL CRAMPS AND DIARRHEA. GASTROINTESTINAL ABSORPTION MAY CAUSE SYMPTOMS OF CHOLINESTERASE INHIBITION AS DESCRIBED IN ACUTE INHALATION. SYMPTOMS MAY BEGIN WITHIN MINUTES OR BE DELAYED FOR HOURS. DELAYED EFFECTS INCLUDING NEUROPATHY MAY ALSO OCCUR. **CHRONIC EXPOSURE-** REPEATED INGESTION MAY CAUSE EFFECTS AS DESCRIBED IN ACUTE EXPOSURE.

FIRST AID- IF PERSON IS ALERT AND RESPIRATION IS NOT DEPRESSED, GIVE SYRUP OF IPECAC FOLLOWED BY WATER (IF VOMITING OCCURS, KEEP HEAD BELOW HIPS TO PREVENT ASPIRATION). IF CONSCIOUSNESS LEVEL DECLINES OR VOMITING HAS NOT OCCURRED IN 15 MINUTES EMPTY STOMACH BY GASTRIC LAVAGE WITH THE AID OF CUFFED ENDOTRACHEAL TUBE USING ISOTONIC SALINE OR 5% SODIUM BICARBONATE FOLLOW WITH ACTIVATED CHARCOAL. ESTABLISH AND MAINTAIN AIRWAY. TREAT RESPIRATORY DIFFICULTY WITH ARTIFICIAL RESPIRATION AND OXYGEN. DO NOT GIVE MORPHINE, AMINOPHYLLINE, PHENOTHIAZINES, RESERPINE, FUROSEMIDE, OR ETHACRYNIC ACID (MORGAN, RECOGNITION AND MANAGEMENT OF PESTICIDE POISONINGS, 3RD ED.). TREAT SYMPTOMATICALLY AND SUPPORTIVELY. ADMINISTRATION OF OXYGEN AND LAVAGE MUST BE PERFORMED BY QUALIFIED MEDICAL PERSONNEL. GET MEDICAL ATTENTION IMMEDIATELY.

ANTIDOTE: THE FOLLOWING ANTIDOTE(S) HAVE BEEN RECOMMENDED. HOWEVER, THE DECISION AS TO WHETHER THE SEVERITY OF POISONING REQUIRES ADMINISTRATION OF ANY ANTIDOTE AND ACTUAL DOSE REQUIRED SHOULD BE MADE BY QUALIFIED MEDICAL PERSONNEL.

FOR CHOLINESTERASE INHIBITORS: ESTABLISH CLEAR AIRWAY AND TISSUE OXYGENATION BY ASPIRATION OF SECRETIONS, AND IF NECESSARY, BY ASSISTED PULMONARY VENTILATION WITH OXYGEN. IMPROVE TISSUE OXYGENATION AS MUCH AS POSSIBLE BEFORE ADMINISTERING ATROPINE TO MINIMIZE THE RISK OF VENTRICULAR FIBRILLATION. ADMINISTER ATROPINE SULFATE INTRAVENOUSLY, OR INTRAMUSCULARLY IF IV INJECTION IS NOT POSSIBLE. IN MODERATELY SEVERE POISONING ADMINISTER ATROPINE SULFATE, 0.4-2.0 MG REPEATED EVERY 15 MINUTES UNTIL ATROPINIZATION IS ACHIEVED (TACHYCARDIA, FLUSHING, DRY MOUTH, MYDRIASIS). MAINTAIN ATROPINIZATION BY REPEATED DOSES FOR 2-12 HOURS, OR LONGER, DEPENDING ON THE SEVERITY OF POISONING. THE APPEARANCE OF RALES IN THE LUNG BASES, MIOSIS, SALIVATION, NAUSEA, BRADYCARDIA, ARE ALL INDICATIONS OF INADEQUATE ATROPINIZATION. SEVERELY POISONED INDIVIDUALS MAY EXHIBIT REMARKABLE TOLERANCE TO ATROPINE; TWO OR MORE TIMES THE DOSAGES SUGGESTED ABOVE MAY BE NEEDED. PERSONS NOT POISONED OR ONLY SLIGHTLY POISONED, HOWEVER, MAY DEVELOP SIGNS OF ATROPINE TOXICITY FROM SUCH LARGE DOSAGES: FEVER, MUSCLE FIBRILLATIONS, AND DELIRIUM ARE THE MAIN SIGNS OF ATROPINE TOXICITY. IF THESE SIGNS APPEAR WHILE THE PATIENT IS FULLY ATROPINIZED, ATROPINE ADMINISTRATION SHOULD BE DISCONTINUED, AT LEAST TEMPORARILY. OBSERVE TREATED PATIENTS CLOSELY AT LEAST 24 HOURS TO INSURE THAT SYMPTOMS (POSSIBLY PULMONARY EDEMA) DO NOT RECUR AS ATROPINIZATION WEARS OFF. IN VERY SEVERE POISONINGS, METABOLIC DISPOSITION OF TOXICANT MAY REQUIRE SEVERAL HOURS OR DAYS DURING WHICH ATROPINIZATION MUST BE MAINTAINED. MARKEDLY LOWER LEVELS OF URINARY METABOLITES INDICATE THAT ATROPINE DOSAGE CAN BE TAPERED OFF. AS DOSAGE IS REDUCED, CHECK THE LUNG BASES FREQUENTLY FOR RALES. IF RALES ARE HEARD OR OTHER SYMPTOMS RETURN, RE-ESTABLISH ATROPINIZATION PROMPTLY (MORGAN, RECOGNITION AND MANAGEMENT OF PESTICIDE POISONINGS, 3RD ED.). ADMINISTRATION OF ANTIDOTE MUST BE PERFORMED BY QUALIFIED MEDICAL PERSONNEL.

IN CASES OF SEVERE POISONING BY ORGANOPHOSPHATE PESTICIDES IN WHICH RESPIRATORY DEPRESSION, MUSCLE WEAKNESS AND TWITCHINGS ARE SEVERE, GIVE PRALIDOXIME (PROTOPAM-AYERST, 2-PAM), 1.0 GRAM INTRAVENOUSLY AT NO MORE THAN 0.5 GRAM PER MINUTE. DOSAGE OF PRALIDOXIME MAY BE REPEATED IN 1-2 HOURS, THEN AT 10-12 HOUR INTERVALS IF NEEDED. IN VERY SEVERE POISONINGS, DOSAGE RATES MAY BE DOUBLED. TREATMENT WITH PRALIDOXIME WILL BE MOST EFFECTIVE IF GIVEN WITHIN THIRTY-SIX HOURS AFTER POISONING (MORGAN, RECOGNITION AND MANAGEMENT OF PESTICIDE POISONINGS, 3RD ED.). ANTIDOTE SHOULD BE ADMINISTERED BY QUALIFIED MEDICAL PERSONNEL.

REACTIVITY

REACTIVITY: STABLE UNDER NORMAL TEMPERATURES AND PRESSURES.

INCOMPATIBILITIES: DIAZINON OXYGEN ANALOG: OXIDIZERS (STRONG): FIRE AND EXPLOSION HAZARD.

DECOMPOSITION: THERMAL DECOMPOSITION MAY RELEASE TOXIC OXIDES OF NITROGEN, PHOSPHORUS AND CARBON.

POLYMERIZATION: HAZARDOUS POLYMERIZATION HAS NOT BEEN REPORTED TO OCCUR UNDER NORMAL TEMPERATURES AND PRESSURES.

STORAGE AND DISPOSAL

OBSERVE ALL FEDERAL, STATE AND LOCAL REGULATIONS WHEN STORING OR DISPOSING OF THIS SUBSTANCE. FOR ASSISTANCE, CONTACT THE DISTRICT DIRECTOR OF THE ENVIRONMENTAL PROTECTION AGENCY.

****STORAGE****

STORE AWAY FROM INCOMPATIBLE SUBSTANCES.

CONDITIONS TO AVOID

AVOID CONTACT WITH HEAT, SPARKS, FLAMES OR OTHER IGNITION SOURCES. VAPORS MAY BE EXPLOSIVE. MATERIAL IS POISONOUS; AVOID INHALATION OF VAPORS OR CONTACT WITH SKIN. DO NOT ALLOW MATERIAL TO CONTAMINATE WATER SOURCES.

SPILL AND LEAK PROCEDURES

OCCUPATIONAL SPILL: STOP LEAK IF YOU CAN DO IT WITHOUT RISK. FOR SMALL SPILLS, TAKE UP WITH SAND OR OTHER ABSORBENT MATERIAL AND PLACE INTO CLEAN, DRY CONTAINERS FOR LATER DISPOSAL. KEEP UNNECESSARY PEOPLE AWAY. ISOLATE HAZARD AREA AND DENY ENTRY.

PROTECTIVE EQUIPMENT

VENTILATION: PROVIDE LOCAL EXHAUST OR GENERAL DILUTION VENTILATION SYSTEM.

RESPIRATOR: THE FOLLOWING RESPIRATORS ARE RECOMMENDED BASED ON INFORMATION FOUND IN THE PHYSICAL DATA, TOXICITY AND HEALTH EFFECTS SECTIONS. THEY ARE RANKED IN ORDER FROM MINIMUM TO MAXIMUM RESPIRATORY PROTECTION. THE SPECIFIC RESPIRATOR SELECTED MUST BE BASED ON CONTAMINATION LEVELS FOUND IN THE WORK PLACE, MUST NOT EXCEED THE WORKING LIMITS OF THE RESPIRATOR AND BE JOINTLY APPROVED BY THE NATIONAL INSTITUTE FOR OCCUPATIONAL SAFETY AND HEALTH AND THE MINE SAFETY AND HEALTH ADMINISTRATION (NIOSH-MSHA).

CHEMICAL CARTRIDGE RESPIRATOR WITH AN ORGANIC VAPOR CARTRIDGE(S) WITH A FULL FACEPIECE AND ORGANIC VAPOR CARTRIDGE(S) IN COMBINATION WITH A DUST AND MIST FILTER.

POWERED AIR-PURIFYING RESPIRATOR WITH A TIGHT-FITTING FACEPIECE AND ORGANIC VAPOR CARTRIDGE(S) IN COMBINATION WITH A HIGH-EFFICIENCY PARTICULATE FILTER.

TYPE 'C' SUPPLIED-AIR RESPIRATOR WITH A FULL FACEPIECE OPERATED IN A PRESSURE-DEMAND OR OTHER POSITIVE PRESSURE MODE.

SELF-CONTAINED BREATHING APPARATUS WITH A FULL FACEPIECE OPERATED IN PRESSURE-DEMAND OR OTHER POSITIVE PRESSURE MODE.

FOR FIREFIGHTING AND OTHER IMMEDIATELY DANGEROUS TO LIFE OR HEALTH CONDITIONS:

SELF-CONTAINED BREATHING APPARATUS WITH FULL FACEPIECE OPERATED IN PRESSURE-DEMAND OR OTHER POSITIVE PRESSURE MODE.

SUPPLIED-AIR RESPIRATOR WITH FULL FACEPIECE AND OPERATED IN PRESSURE-DEMAND OR OTHER POSITIVE PRESSURE MODE IN COMBINATION WITH AN AUXILIARY SELF-CONTAINED BREATHING APPARATUS OPERATED IN PRESSURE-DEMAND OR OTHER POSITIVE PRESSURE MODE.

CLOTHING: EMPLOYEE MUST WEAR APPROPRIATE PROTECTIVE (IMPERVIOUS) CLOTHING AND EQUIPMENT TO PREVENT ANY POSSIBILITY OF SKIN CONTACT WITH THIS SUBSTANCE.

GLOVES: EMPLOYEE MUST WEAR APPROPRIATE PROTECTIVE GLOVES TO PREVENT CONTACT WITH THIS SUBSTANCE.

EYE PROTECTION: EMPLOYEE MUST WEAR SPLASH-PROOF OR DUST-RESISTANT SAFETY GOGGLES TO PREVENT EYE CONTACT WITH THIS SUBSTANCE.

EMERGENCY EYE WASH: WHERE THERE IS ANY POSSIBILITY THAT AN EMPLOYEE'S EYES MAY BE EXPOSED TO THIS SUBSTANCE, THE EMPLOYER SHOULD PROVIDE AN EYE WASH FOUNTAIN WITHIN THE IMMEDIATE WORK AREA FOR EMERGENCY USE.

AUTHORIZED BY- OCCUPATIONAL HEALTH SERVICES, INC.
CREATION DATE: 11/17/89 ***REVISION DATE:*** 05/07/90

MATERIAL SAFETY DATA SHEET

OCCUPATIONAL HEALTH SERVICES, INC.
AGRICULTURE AND PESTICIDE DIVISION
450 SEVENTH AVENUE, SUITE 2407
NEW YORK, NEW YORK 10123
1-800-445-MSDS OR (212) 967-1100

EMERGENCY CONTACT:
JOHN S. BRANSFORD, JR. (615) 292-1180

SUBSTANCE IDENTIFICATION

CAS-NUMBER 300-76-5
SUBSTANCE: NALED
TRADE NAMES/SYNONYMS: PHOSPHORIC ACID, 1,2-DIBROMO-2,2-DICHLOROETHYL DIMETHYL ESTER; DIMETHYL 1,2-DIBROMO-2,2-DICHLOROETHYL PHOSPHATE; 1,2-DIBROMO-2,2-DICHLOROETHYL DIMETHYL PHOSPHATE; O,O-DIMETHYL-O-1,2-DIBROMO-2,2-DICHLOROETHYL PHOSPHATE; BROMCHLOPHOS; BROMEX; DIBROM; DIBROMFOS; RE 4355; ENT 24988; STCC 4961658; PST06660
CHEMICAL FAMILY: ORGANOPHOSPHATE
MOLECULAR FORMULA: C4-H7-BR2-CL2-O4-P
MOLECULAR WEIGHT: 380.80
CERCLA RATINGS (SCALE 0-3): HEALTH=3 FIRE=0 REACTIVITY=0 PERSISTENCE=2
NFPA RATINGS (SCALE 0-4): HEALTH=4 FIRE=0 REACTIVITY=0

COMPONENTS AND CONTAMINANTS

COMPONENT: NALED ***PERCENT:*** 100
CAS# 300-76-5
EXPOSURE LIMITS: NALED: 3 MG/M3 OSHA TWA; 3 MG/M3 ACGIH TWA (SKIN)

PHYSICAL DATA

DESCRIPTION: WHITE SOLID; THE TECHNICAL MATERIAL FORMS A YELLOW LIQUID WITH A SLIGHT PUNGENT ODOR. ***BOILING POINT:*** 252 F (110 C) @ 0.5 MMHG
MELTING POINT: 81 F (27 C) ***SPECIFIC GRAVITY:*** 1.96 ***VOLATILITY:*** LOW
VAPOR PRESSURE: 0.002 MMHG @ 20 C ***SOLUBILITY IN WATER:*** INSOLUBLE
SOLVENT SOLUBILITY: SOLUBLE IN KETONES, ALCOHOLS, AROMATIC AND CHLORINATED HYDROCARBONS; SPARINGLY SOLUBLE IN PETROLEUM SOLVENTS AND MINERAL OILS

FIRE AND EXPLOSION DATA

FIRE AND EXPLOSION HAZARD: NEGLIGIBLE FIRE HAZARD WHEN EXPOSED TO HEAT OR FLAME.
FIREFIGHTING MEDIA: DRY CHEMICAL, CARBON DIOXIDE, HALON, WATER SPRAY OR STANDARD FOAM (1987 EMERGENCY RESPONSE GUIDEBOOK, DOT P 5800.4). FOR LARGER FIRES, USE WATER SPRAY, FOG OR STANDARD FOAM (1987 EMERGENCY RESPONSE GUIDEBOOK, DOT P 5800.4).
FIREFIGHTING: MOVE CONTAINERS FROM FIRE AREA IF POSSIBLE. FIGHT FIRE FROM MAXIMUM DISTANCE. STAY AWAY FROM STORAGE TANK ENDS. DIKE FIRE CONTROL WATER FOR LATER DISPOSAL. DO NOT SCATTER MATERIAL (1987 EMERGENCY RESPONSE GUIDEBOOK, DOT P 5800.4, GUIDE PAGE 55). EXTINGUISH ONLY IF FLOW CAN BE STOPPED; USE FLOODING AMOUNTS OF WATER AS FOG, SOLID STREAMS MAY BE INEFFECTIVE. COOL CONTAINERS WITH FLOODING AMOUNTS OF WATER FROM AS FAR A DISTANCE AS POSSIBLE. USE WATER SPRAY TO ABSORB TOXIC VAPORS. AVOID BREATHING TOXIC VAPORS; KEEP UPWIND. CONSIDER EVACUATION OF DOWNWIND AREA IF MATERIAL IS LEAKING.

TRANSPORTATION DATA

DEPARTMENT OF TRANSPORTATION HAZARD CLASSIFICATION 49 CFR 172.101: ORM-E
DEPARTMENT OF TRANSPORTATION LABELING REQUIREMENTS 49 CFR 172.101 AND SUBPART E: NONE
DEPARTMENT OF TRANSPORTATION PACKAGING REQUIREMENTS: 49 CFR 173.510 EXCEPTIONS: NONE

TOXICITY

NALED: IRRITATION DATA: 42 MG/21 DAYS-INTERMITTENT OPEN SKIN-MAN IRRITATION; 500 MG/24 HOURS SKIN-RABBIT SEVERE IRRITATION; TOXICITY DATA: 7700 UG/KG INHALATION-RAT LD50; 156 MG/KG INHALATION-MOUSE LD50; 1100 MG/KG SKIN-RABBIT LD50; 800 MG/KG SKIN-RAT LD50; 250 MG/KG ORAL-RAT LD50; 330 MG/KG ORAL-MOUSE LD50;MUTAGENIC DATA (RTECS). CARCINOGEN STATUS: NONE. LOCAL EFFECTS: CORROSIVE- INHALATION, SKIN, EYES. ACUTE TOXICITY LEVEL: TOXIC BY INHALATION AND INGESTION AND MODERATELY TOXIC BY DERMAL ABSORPTION. TARGET EFFECTS: SENSTITIZER- SKIN; CHOLINESTERASE INHIBITOR. POISONING MAY AFFECT THE NERVOUS SYSTEM.* AT INCREASED RISK FROM EXPOSURE: PERSONS WITH RESPIRATORY AILMENTS, RECENT EXPOSURE TO CHOLINESTERASE INHIBITORS OR IMPAIRED CHOLINESTERASE PRODUCTION, OR LIVER MALFUNCTION.* ADDITIONAL DATA: MAY CROSS THE PLACENTA. HIGH ENVIRONMENTAL TEMPERATURES OR EXPOSURE OF THE CHEMICAL TO VISIBLE OR ULTRAVIOLET LIGHT MAY ENHANCE THE TOXICITY. INTERACTIONS WITH MEDICATIONS MAY OCCUR.*
* MAY BE BASED ON GENERAL INFORMATION ON ORGANOPHOSPHATES.

HEALTH EFFECTS AND FIRST AID

INHALATION: NALED: CORROSIVE/HIGHLY TOXIC. 1800 MG/M3 IMMEDIATELY DANGEROUS TO LIFE OR HEALTH. MAY CAUSE SEVERE IRRITATION OF THE MUCOUS MEMBRANES. SEE INFORMATION ON ORGANOPHOSPHATES.
ORGANOPHOSPHATES: CHOLINESTERASE INHIBITOR. **ACUTE EXPOSURE**- WHEN INHALED, THE FIRST EFFECTS OF CHOLINESTERASE INHIBITORS ARE USUALLY RESPIRATORY AND MAY INCLUDE NASAL HYPEREMIA AND WATERY DISCHARGE, COUGH, CHEST DISCOMFORT, DYSPNEA, AND WHEEZING DUE TO INCREASED BRONCHIAL SECRETIONS AND BRONCHOCONSTRICTION. IF SUFFICIENT AMOUNTS ARE ABSORBED, OTHER SYSTEMIC EFFECTS MAY BEGIN WITHIN A FEW MINUTES OR BE DELAYED FOR UP TO 12 HOURS. SYMPTOMS MAY INCLUDE PALLOR, NAUSEA, VOMITING, DIARRHEA, ABDOMINAL CRAMPS, HEADACHE, DIZZINESS, OCULAR PAIN, BLURRED VISION, MIOSIS OR IN SOME CASES, ESPECIALLY INITIALLY, MYDRIASIS, LACRIMATION, SALIVATION, SWEATING, AND CONFUSION. OTHER REPORTED CENTRAL NERVOUS SYSTEM OR NEUROMUSCULAR EFFECTS MAY INCLUDE ATAXIA, SLURRED SPEECH, AREFLEXIA, WEAKNESS, FATIGUE, FASCICULATIONS, TWITCHING, TREMORS POSSIBLY OF THE TONGUE AND EYELIDS, AND EVENTUALLY PARALYSIS OF THE EXTREMITIES AND POSSIBLY OF THE RESPIRATORY MUSCLES. IN SEVERE CASES THERE MAY ALSO BE INVOLUNTARY DEFECATION AND URINATION, CYANOSIS, PSYCHOSIS, HYPERGLYCEMIA, ACUTE PANCREATITIS, CARDIAC IRREGULARITIES, PULMONARY EDEMA, UNCONSCIOUSNESS, CONVULSIONS, AND COMA. DEATH IS PRIMARILY DUE TO RESPIRATORY FAILURE, ALTHOUGH CARDIOVASCULAR EFFECTS INCLUDING CARDIAC ARREST MAY ALSO BE IMPLICATED. LONG TERM SEQUELAE ARE RARE BUT MAY INCLUDE NEUROPSYCHIATRIC DISORDERS AND MYOPATHY WITH MUSCLE TENDERNESS. SOME ORGANOPHOSPHATES MAY CAUSE A DELAYED NEUROPATHY BEGINNING 1-4 WEEKS AFTER AN ACUTE EXPOSURE WHICH MAY OR MAY NOT HAVE CAUSED ACUTE CHOLINERGIC EFFECTS. NUMBNESS, TINGLING, WEAKNESS AND CRAMPING BEGINNING SYMMETRICALLY IN THE LOWER LIMBS MAY PROGRESS TO ATAXIA AND PARALYSIS. IN SEVERE CASES, UPPER LIMB INVOLVEMENT IS POSSIBLE AND FLACCID PARALYSIS MAY PROGRESS TO SPASTIC PARALYSIS WITH EXAGGERATED REFLEXES. IMPROVEMENT MAY OCCUR OVER MONTHS TO YEARS, BUT SOME RESIDUAL IMPAIRMENT USUALLY REMAINS.
CHRONIC EXPOSURE- REPEATED OR PROLONGED EXPOSURE MAY RESULT IN THE EFFECTS OF ACUTE EXPOSURE INCLUDING THE DELAYED NEUROPATHY. OTHER EFFECTS REPORTED IN WORKERS REPEATEDLY EXPOSED INCLUDE IMPAIRED MEMORY AND CONCENTRATION, ACUTE PSYCHOSIS, SEVERE DEPRESSIONS, IRRITABILTY, CONFUSION, APATHY, EMOTIONAL LABILITY, SOCIAL WITHDRAWAL, CONFUSION, HEADACHE, SPEECH DIFFICULTIES, DELAYED REACTION TIMES, SPATIAL DISORIENTATION, NIGHTMARES, SLEEPWALKING, AND DROWSINESS OR INSOMNIA. AN INFLUENZA-LIKE CONDITION WITH HEADACHE, NAUSEA, WEAKNESS, ANOREXIA AND MALAISE HAS ALSO BEEN REPORTED.
FIRST AID- REMOVE FROM EXPOSURE AREA TO FRESH AIR IMMEDIATELY. IF BREATHING HAS STOPPED, GIVE ARTIFICIAL RESPIRATION. MAINTAIN AIRWAY AND BLOOD PRESSURE AND ADMINISTER OXYGEN IF AVAILABLE. KEEP AFFECTED PERSON WARM AND AT REST. TREAT SYMPTOMATICALLY AND SUPPORTIVELY. ADMINISTRATION OF OXYGEN SHOULD BE PERFORMED BY QUALIFIED PERSONNEL. GET MEDICAL ATTENTION IMMEDIATELY.

SKIN CONTACT: NALED: CORROSIVE/SENSITIZER MAY CAUSE SEVERE IRRITATION AND POSSIBLE SKIN DAMAGE. SENSITIZATION MAY OCCUR IN PREVIOUSLY EXPOSED INDIVIDUALS. SKIN CONTACT IN ONE INDIVIDUAL RESULTED IN THE EXPOSED AREA BECOMING ERYTHEMATOUS WITH A BURNING SENSATION FOLLOWED BY EDEMATOUS VESICULATING BLISTERING. PROLONGED OR REPEATED EXPOSUR MAY LEAD TO SENSITIZATION DERMATITIS. 42 MG APPLIED INTERMITTENTLY TO THE SKIN FOR 21 DAYS PRODUCED IRRITATION IN MAN. SEE INFORMATION ON ORGANOPHOSPHATES.
ORGANOPHOSPHATES: CHOLINESTERASE INHIBITOR. **ACUTE EXPOSURE**- LOCALIZED SWEATING AND FASCICULATIONS MAY OCCUR AT THE SITE OF CONTACT. IF SUFFICIENT AMOUNTS ARE ABSORBED, OTHER EFFECTS OF CHOLINESTERASE INHIBITION AS DESCRIBED IN ACUTE INHALATION MAY OCCUR. SYMPTOMS MAY BE DELAYED 2-3 HOURS, BUT USUALLY NO MORE THAN 12 HOURS. THE RATE OF ABSORPTION IS INCREASED BY THE PRESENCE OF

DERMATITIS OR HIGH AMBIENT TEMPERATURES. DELAYED NEUROPATHY IS ALSO POSSIBLE. **CHRONIC EXPOSURE-** REPEATED OR PROLONGED EXPOSURE MAY CAUSE EFFECTS AS DESCRIBED IN ACUTE EXPOSURE. SOME ORGANOPHOSPHATES MAY CAUSE SENSITIZATION.

FIRST AID- REMOVE CONTAMINATED CLOTHING IMMEDIATELY. WASH CONTAMINATED AREAS WITH SOAP AND WATER FOLLOWED BY ALCOHOL (ARENA, POISONING, 4TH ED.). EMERGENCY PERSONNEL SHOULD WEAR GLOVES AND AVOID CONTAMINATION. TREAT RESPIRATORY DIFFICULTY WITH ARTIFICIAL RESPIRATION. GET MEDICAL ATTENTION IMMEDIATELY.

EYE CONTACT: NALED: CORROSIVE MAY CAUSE SEVERE IRRITATION AND EYE DAMAGE. SEE INFORMATION ON ORGANOPHOSPHATES.

ORGANOPHOSPHATES: CHOLINESTERASE INHIBITOR. **ACUTE EXPOSURE-** DIRECT CONTACT MAY CAUSE PAIN, HYPEREMIA, LACRIMATION, TWITCHING OF THE EYELIDS, MIOSIS, AND CILIARY MUSCLE SPASM WITH LOSS OF ACCOMODATION, BLURRED OR DIMMED VISION AND BROWACHE. SOMETIMES MYDRIASIS MAY OCCUR INSTEAD OF MIOSIS. WITH SUFFICIENT EXPOSURE, OTHER SYMPTOMS OF CHOLINESTERASE INHIBITION AS DESCRIBED IN ACUTE INHALATION MAY OCCUR. **CHRONIC EXPOSURE-** REPEATED OR PROLONGED EXPOSURE MAY CAUSE EFFECTS AS DESCRIBED IN ACUTE EXPOSURE. SOME COMPOUNDS HAVE CAUSED TOXIC EFFECTS ON THE CRYSTALLINE LENS, CONJUNCTIVAL THICKENING AND OBSTRUCTION OF THE NASOLACRIMAL CANALS WHEN USED AS MIOTIC EYEDROPS.

FIRST AID- IRRIGATE EYES WITH WATER OR SALINE SOLUTION. IF SYMPTOMS OF POISONING OCCUR, TREAT RESPIRATORY DIFFICULTY WITH ARTIFICIAL RESPIRATION AND OXYGEN. OBSERVE PATIENT FOR AT LEAST 24-36 HOURS (GOSSELIN, CLINICAL TOXICOLOGY OF COMMERCIAL PRODUCTS, 5TH ED.). GET MEDICAL ATTENTION IMMEDIATELY. OXYGEN SHOULD BE ADMINISTERED BY QUALIFIED MEDICAL PERSONNEL.

INGESTION: NALED: TOXIC. SEE INFORMATION ON ORGANOPHOSPHATES.

ORGANOPHOSPHATES: CHOLINESTERASE INHIBITOR. **ACUTE EXPOSURE-** WHEN INGESTED, THE FIRST EFFECTS MAY BE NAUSEA, VOMITING, ANOREXIA, ABDOMINAL CRAMPS AND DIARRHEA. GASTROINTESTINAL ABSORPTION MAY CAUSE SYMPTOMS OF CHOLINESTERASE INHIBITION AS DESCRIBED IN ACUTE INHALATION. SYMPTOMS MAY BEGIN WITHIN MINUTES OR BE DELAYED FOR HOURS. DELAYED EFFECTS INCLUDING NEUROPATHY MAY ALSO OCCUR. **CHRONIC EXPOSURE-** REPEATED INGESTION MAY CAUSE EFFECTS AS DESCRIBED IN ACUTE EXPOSURE.

FIRST AID- IF PERSON IS ALERT AND RESPIRATION IS NOT DEPRESSED, GIVE SYRUP OF IPECAC FOLLOWED BY WATER (IF VOMITING OCCURS, KEEP HEAD BELOW HIPS TO PREVENT ASPIRATION). IF CONSCIOUSNESS LEVEL DECLINES OR VOMITING HAS NOT OCCURRED IN 15 MINUTES EMPTY STOMACH BY GASTRIC LAVAGE WITH THE AID OF CUFFED ENDOTRACHEAL TUBE USING ISOTONIC SALINE OR 5% SODIUM BICARBONATE FOLLOW WITH ACTIVATED CHARCOAL. ESTABLISH AND MAINTAIN AIRWAY. TREAT RESPIRATORY DIFFICULTY WITH ARTIFICIAL RESPIRATION AND OXYGEN. DO NOT GIVE MORPHINE, AMINOPHYLLINE, PHENOTHIAZINES, RESERPINE, FUROSEMIDE, OR ETHACRYNIC ACID (MORGAN, RECOGNITION AND MANAGEMENT OF PESTICIDE POISONINGS, 3RD ED.). TREAT SYMPTOMATICALLY AND SUPPORTIVELY. ADMINISTRATION OF OXYGEN AND LAVAGE MUST BE PERFORMED BY QUALIFIED MEDICAL PERSONNEL. GET MEDICAL ATTENTION IMMEDIATELY.

ANTIDOTE: THE FOLLOWING ANTIDOTE(S) HAVE BEEN RECOMMENDED. HOWEVER, THE DECISION AS TO WHETHER THE SEVERITY OF POISONING REQUIRES ADMINISTRATION OF ANY ANTIDOTE AND ACTUAL DOSE REQUIRED SHOULD BE MADE BY QUALIFIED MEDICAL PERSONNEL.

FOR CHOLINESTERASE INHIBITORS: ESTABLISH CLEAR AIRWAY AND TISSUE OXYGENATION BY ASPIRATION OF SECRETIONS, AND IF NECESSARY, BY ASSISTED PULMONARY VENTILATION WITH OXYGEN. IMPROVE TISSUE OXYGENATION AS MUCH AS POSSIBLE BEFORE ADMINISTERING ATROPINE TO MINIMIZE THE RISK OF VENTRICULAR FIBRILLATION. ADMINISTER ATROPINE SULFATE INTRAVENOUSLY, OR INTRAMUSCULARLY IF IV INJECTION IS NOT POSSIBLE. IN MODERATELY SEVERE POISONING ADMINISTER ATROPINE SULFATE, 0.4-2.0 MG REPEATED EVERY 15 MINUTES UNTIL ATROPINIZATION IS ACHIEVED (TACHYCARDIA, FLUSHING, DRY MOUTH, MYDRIASIS). MAINTAIN ATROPINIZATION BY REPEATED DOSES FOR 2-12 HOURS, OR LONGER, DEPENDING ON THE SEVERITY OF POISONING. THE APPEARANCE OF RALES IN THE LUNG BASES, MIOSIS, SALIVATION, NAUSEA, BRADYCARDIA, ARE ALL INDICATIONS OF INADEQUATE ATROPINIZATION. SEVERELY POISONED INDIVIDUALS MAY EXHIBIT REMARKABLE TOLERANCE TO ATROPINE; TWO OR MORE TIMES THE DOSAGES SUGGESTED ABOVE MAY BE NEEDED. PERSONS NOT POISONED OR ONLY SLIGHTLY POISONED, HOWEVER, MAY DEVELOP SIGNS OF ATROPINE TOXICITY FROM SUCH LARGE DOSAGES: FEVER, MUSCLE FIBRILLATIONS, AND DELIRIUM ARE THE MAIN SIGNS OF ATROPINE TOXICITY. IF THESE SIGNS APPEAR WHILE THE PATIENT IS FULLY ATROPINIZED, ATROPINE ADMINISTRATION SHOULD BE DISCONTINUED, AT LEAST TEMPORARILY. OBSERVE TREATED PATIENTS CLOSELY AT LEAST 24 HOURS TO INSURE THAT SYMPTOMS (POSSIBLY PULMONARY EDEMA) DO NOT RECUR AS ATROPINIZATION WEARS OFF. IN VERY SEVERE POISONINGS, METABOLIC DISPOSITION OF TOXICANT MAY REQUIRE SEVERAL HOURS OR DAYS DURING WHICH ATROPINIZATION MUST BE MAINTAINED. MARKEDLY LOWER LEVELS OF URINARY METABOLITES INDICATE THAT ATROPINE DOSAGE CAN BE TAPERED OFF. AS DOSAGE IS REDUCED, CHECK THE LUNG BASES FREQUENTLY FOR RALES. IF RALES ARE HEARD OR OTHER SYMPTOMS RETURN, RE-ESTABLISH ATROPINIZATION PROMPTLY (MORGAN, RECOGNITION AND MANAGEMENT OF PESTICIDE POISONINGS, 3RD ED.). ADMINISTRATION OF ANTIDOTE MUST BE PERFORMED BY QUALIFIED MEDICAL PERSONNEL.

IN CASES OF SEVERE POISONING BY ORGANOPHOSPHATE PESTICIDES IN WHICH RESPIRATORY DEPRESSION, MUSCLE WEAKNESS AND TWITCHINGS ARE SEVERE, GIVE PRALIDOXIME (PROTOPAM-AYERST, 2-PAM), 1.0 GRAM INTRAVENOUSLY AT NO MORE THAN 0.5 GRAM PER MINUTE. DOSAGE OF PRALIDOXIME MAY BE REPEATED IN 1-2 HOURS, THEN AT 10-12 HOUR INTERVALS IF NEEDED. IN VERY SEVERE POISONINGS, DOSAGE RATES MAY BE DOUBLED. TREATMENT WITH PRALIDOXIME WILL BE MOST EFFECTIVE IF GIVEN WITHIN THIRTY-SIX HOURS AFTER POISONING (MORGAN, RECOGNITION AND MANAGEMENT OF PESTICIDE POISONINGS, 3RD ED.). ANTIDOTE SHOULD BE ADMINISTERED BY QUALIFIED MEDICAL PERSONNEL.

REACTIVITY

REACTIVITY: IS STABLE IN BROWN, CLOSED CONTAINER UNDER NORMAL TEMPERATURES AND PRESSURES. IT IS HYDROLYZED IN WATER WITHIN 2 DAYS AT ROOM TEMPERATURE AND MAY BE DEGRADED BY SUNLIGHT.

INCOMPATIBILITIES: NALED: ALKALI: MAY HYDROLYZE. IRON: UNSTABLE. METALS: MAY RAPIDLY LOSE BROMIDE AND REVERT TO DICHLOROVOS ON CONTACT. OXIDIZERS: MAY CAUSE FIRE AND EXPLOSION HAZARD. PLASTICS, RUBBER, AND COATINGS: SOME FORMS MAY BE ATTACK. REDUCING AGENTS: MAY RAPIDLY LOSE BROMIDE AND REVERT TO DICHLOROVOS ON CONTACT. SULFHYDRYLS: MAY RAPIDLY LOSE BROMIDE AND REVERT TO DICHLOROVOS ON CONTACT.

DECOMPOSITION: THERMAL DECOMPOSITION MAY RELEASE TOXIC OXIDES OF PHOSPHORUS, AND CORROSIVE FUMES OF HYDROGEN BROMIDE AND HYDROGEN CHLORIDE.

POLYMERIZATION: HAZARDOUS POLYMERIZATION HAS NOT BEEN REPORTED TO OCCUR UNDER NORMAL TEMPERATURES AND PRESSURES.

STORAGE AND DISPOSAL

OBSERVE ALL FEDERAL, STATE AND LOCAL REGULATIONS WHEN STORING OR DISPOSING OF THIS SUBSTANCE. FOR ASSISTANCE, CONTACT THE DISTRICT DIRECTOR OF THE ENVIRONMENTAL PROTECTION AGENCY.

****STORAGE****

STORE IN ACCORDANCE WITH 40 CFR 165 RECOMMENDED PROCEDURES FOR THE DISPOSAL AND STORAGE OF PESTICIDES AND PESTICIDE CONTAINERS.
STORE AWAY FROM INCOMPATIBLE SUBSTANCES.

****DISPOSAL****

DISPOSAL MUST BE IN ACCORDANCE WITH 40 CFR 165 RECOMMENDED PROCEDURES FOR THE DISPOSAL AND STORAGE OF PESTICIDES AND PESTICIDE CONTAINERS.

CONDITIONS TO AVOID

NONE REPORTED.

SPILL AND LEAK PROCEDURES

SOIL SPILL: DIG HOLDING AREA SUCH AS LAGOON, POND OR PIT FOR CONTAINMENT. DIKE FLOW OF SPILLED MATERIAL USING SOIL OR SANDBAGS OR FOAMED BARRIERS SUCH AS POLYURETHANE OR CONCRETE.

WATER SPILL: IF DISSOLVED, APPLY ACTIVATED CARBON AT TEN TIMES THE SPILLED AMOUNT IN REGIONS OF 10 PPM OR GREATER CONCENTRATION.
USE MECHANICAL DREDGES OR LIFTS TO EXTRACT IMMOBILIZED MASSES OF POLLUTION AND PRECIPITATES.

OCCUPATIONAL SPILL: DO NOT TOUCH SPILLED MATERIAL. STOP LEAK IF YOU CAN DO IT WITHOUT RISK. USE WATER SPRAY TO REDUCE VAPORS. FOR SMALL SPILLS, TAKE UP WITH SAND OR OTHER ABSORBENT MATERIAL AND PLACE INTO CONTAINERS FOR LATER DISPOSAL. FOR SMALL DRY SPILLS, WITH A CLEAN SHOVEL PLACE MATERIAL INTO CLEAN, DRY CONTAINERS AND COVER. MOVE CONTAINERS FROM SPILL AREA. FOR LARGER SPILLS, DIKE FAR AHEAD OF SPILL FOR LATER DISPOSAL. KEEP UNNECESSARY PEOPLE AWAY. ISOLATE HAZARD AREA AND DENY ENTRY. VENTILATE CLOSED SPACES BEFORE ENTERING.

PROTECTIVE EQUIPMENT

VENTILATION: PROCESS ENCLOSURE RECOMMENDED TO MEET PUBLISHED EXPOSURE LIMITS.

RESPIRATOR: THE FOLLOWING RESPIRATORS AND MAXIMUM USE CONCENTRATIONS ARE RECOMMENDATIONS BY THE U.S. DEPARTMENT OF HEALTH AND HUMAN SERVICES, NIOSH POCKET GUIDE TO CHEMICAL HAZARDS; NIOSH CRITERIA DOCUMENTS OR BY THE U.S. DEPARTMENT OF LABOR, 29 CFR 1910 SUBPART Z.

THE SPECIFIC RESPIRATOR SELECTED MUST BE BASED ON CONTAMINATION LEVELS FOUND IN THE WORK PLACE, MUST NOT EXCEED THE WORKING LIMITS OF THE RESPIRATOR AND BE JOINTLY APPROVED BY THE NATIONAL INSTITUTE FOR OCCUPATIONAL SAFETY AND HEALTH AND THE MINE SAFETY AND HEALTH ADMINISTRATION (NIOSH-MSHA).

30 MG/M3- ANY DUST, MIST AND FUME RESPIRATOR WITH A FULL FACEPIECE. ANY SUPPLIED-AIR RESPIRATOR. ANY AIR-PURIFYING RESPIRATOR WITH A HIGH-EFFICIENCY PARTICULATE FILTER. ANY SELF-CONTAINED BREATHING APPARATUS.

75 MG/M3- ANY POWERED AIR-PURIFYING RESPIRATOR WITH A DUST, MIST AND FUME FILTER. ANY SUPPLIED-AIR RESPIRATOR OPERATED IN A CONTIUOUS FLOW MODE. 150 MG/M3- ANY AIR-PURIFYING FULL FACEPIECE RESPIRATOR WITH A HIGH-EFFICIENCY PARTICULATE FILTER. ANY POWERED AIR-PURIFYING RESPIRATOR WITH A TIGHT-FITTING FACEPIECE AND A HIGH-EFFICIENCY PARTICULATE FILTER. ANY SUPPLIED-AIR RESPIRATOR WITH A TIGHT-FITTING FACEPIECE OPERATED IN A CONTINUOUS FLOW MODE. ANY SELF-CONTAINED BREATHING APPARATUS WITH A FULL FACEPIECE. ANY SUPPLIED-AIR RESPIRATOR WITH A FULL FACEPIECE.

1800 MG/M3- ANY SUPPLIED-AIR RESPIRATOR WITH A HALF-MASK AND OPERATED IN A PRESSURE-DEMAND OR OTHER POSITIVE PRESSURE MODE.

ESCAPE- ANY AIR-PURIFYING FULL FACEPIECE RESPIRATOR WITH A HIGH-EFFICIENCY PARTICULATE FILTER. ANY APPROPRIATE ESCAPE-TYPE SELF-CONTAINED BREATHING APPARATUS.

FOR FIREFIGHTING AND OTHER IMMEDIATELY DANGEROUS TO LIFE OR HEALTH CONDITIONS:

SELF-CONTAINED BREATHING APPARATUS WITH FULL FACEPIECE OPERATED IN PRESSURE-DEMAND OR OTHER POSITIVE PRESSURE MODE.

SUPPLIED-AIR RESPIRATOR WITH FULL FACEPIECE AND OPERATED IN PRESSURE-DEMAND OR OTHER POSITIVE PRESSURE MODE IN COMBINATION WITH AN AUXILIARY SELF-CONTAINED BREATHING APPARATUS OPERATED IN PRESSURE-DEMAND OR OTHER POSITIVE PRESSURE MODE.

CLOTHING: EMPLOYEE MUST WEAR APPROPRIATE PROTECTIVE (IMPERVIOUS) CLOTHING AND EQUIPMENT TO PREVENT ANY POSSIBILITY OF SKIN CONTACT WITH THIS SUBSTANCE.

GLOVES: EMPLOYEE MUST WEAR APPROPRIATE PROTECTIVE GLOVES TO PREVENT CONTACT WITH THIS SUBSTANCE.

EYE PROTECTION: EMPLOYEE MUST WEAR SPLASH-PROOF OR DUST-RESISTANT SAFETY GOGGLES AND A FACESHIELD TO PREVENT CONTACT WITH THIS SUBSTANCE.

EMERGENCY WASH FACILITIES: WHERE THERE IS ANY POSSIBILITY THAT AN EMPLOYEE'S EYES AND/OR SKIN MAY BE EXPOSED TO THIS SUBSTANCE, THE EMPLOYER SHOULD PROVIDE AN EYE WASH FOUNTAIN AND QUICK DRENCH SHOWER WITHIN THE IMMEDIATE WORK AREA FOR EMERGENCY USE.

AUTHORIZED BY- OCCUPATIONAL HEALTH SERVICES, INC.

CREATION DATE: 10/04/89 ***REVISION DATE:*** 04/26/90

MATERIAL SAFETY DATA SHEET

OCCUPATIONAL HEALTH SERVICES, INC.
AGRICULTURE AND PESTICIDE DIVISION
450 SEVENTH AVENUE, SUITE 2407
NEW YORK, NEW YORK 10123
1-800-445-MSDS OR (212) 967-1100

EMERGENCY CONTACT:
JOHN S. BRANSFORD, JR. (615) 292-1180

SUBSTANCE IDENTIFICATION

CAS-NUMBER 84-74-2

SUBSTANCE: **DIBUTYL PHTHALATE**

TRADE NAMES/SYNONYMS: PHTHALIC ACID, DIBUTYL ESTER; DI-N-BUTYL PHTHALATE; DBP; O-BENZENEDICARBOXYLIC ACID, DIBUTYL ESTER; 1,2-BENZENEDICARBOXYLIC ACID, DIBUTYL ESTER; D-29; D-30; RCRA U069; PST06740

CHEMICAL FAMILY: ESTER, CARBOXYLIC, AROMATIC

MOLECULAR FORMULA: C16-H22-O4

MOLECULAR WEIGHT: 278.4

CERCLA RATINGS (SCALE 0-3): HEALTH=1 FIRE=1 REACTIVITY=0 PERSISTENCE=3

NFPA RATINGS (SCALE 0-4): HEALTH=1 FIRE=1 REACTIVITY=0

COMPONENTS AND CONTAMINANTS

COMPONENT: DIBUTYL PHTHALATE ***PERCENT:*** 99
CAS# 84-74-2

EXPOSURE LIMITS: DIBUTYL PHTHALATE: 5 MG/M3 OSHA TWA 5 MG/M3 ACGIH TWA 10 POUNDS CERCLA SECTION 103 REPORTABLE QUANTITY

PHYSICAL DATA

DESCRIPTION: COLORLESS, STABLE, OILY LIQUID WITH A VERY WEAK AROMATIC ODOR.

BOILING POINT: 644 F (340 C) ***MELTING POINT:*** -31 F (-35 C)

SPECIFIC GRAVITY: 1.0 ***VAPOR PRESSURE:*** 0.1 MMHG @ 89 C

SOLUBILITY IN WATER: SLIGHTLY ***VAPOR DENSITY:*** 9.58

SOLVENT SOLUBILITY: ALCOHOL, ETHER, BENZENE, ACETONE

FIRE AND EXPLOSION DATA

FIRE AND EXPLOSION HAZARD: SLIGHT FIRE HAZARD WHEN EXPOSED TO HEAT OR FLAME.

FLASH POINT: 315 F (157 C) (CC) ***UPPER EXPLOSIVE LIMIT:*** 2.5%

LOWER EXPLOSIVE LIMIT: 0.5% @ 255 C ***AUTOIGNITION TEMP.:*** 757 F (402 C)

FLAMMABILITY CLASS(OSHA): IIIB

FIREFIGHTING MEDIA: DRY CHEMICAL, CARBON DIOXIDE, HALON, WATER SPRAY OR STANDARD FOAM (1987 EMERGENCY RESPONSE GUIDEBOOK, DOT P 5800.4). FOR LARGER FIRES, USE WATER SPRAY, FOG OR STANDARD FOAM (1987 EMERGENCY RESPONSE GUIDEBOOK, DOT P 5800.4).

FIREFIGHTING: MOVE CONTAINER FROM FIRE AREA IF POSSIBLE. DO NOT SCATTER SPILLED MATERIAL WITH HIGH PRESSURE WATER STREAMS. DIKE FIRE CONTROL WATER FOR LATER DISPOSAL (1987 EMERGENCY RESPONSE GUIDEBOOK, DOT P 5800.4, GUIDE PAGE 31).

USE AGENTS SUITABLE FOR TYPE OF SURROUNDING FIRE. AVOID BREATHING HAZARDOUS VAPORS, KEEP UPWIND.

WATER OR FOAM MAY CAUSE FROTHING (NFPA 325M, FIRE HAZARD PROPERTIES OF FLAMMABLE LIQUIDS, GASES, AND VOLATILE SOLIDS, 1984)

TOXICITY

DIBUTYL PHTHALATE (N-BUTYL PHTHALATE): TOXICITY DATA: 25 GM/M3/2 HOURS INHALATION-MOUSE LC50; 6 GM/KG SKIN-RAT LDLO; 140 MG/KG ORAL-HUMAN TDLO; 8 GM/KG ORAL-RAT LD50; 5289 MG/KG ORAL-MOUSE LD50; 10 GM/KG ORAL-GUINEA PIG LD50; 720 MG/KG INTRAVENOUS-MOUSE LD50; 3050 MG/KG INTRAPERITONEAL-RAT LD50; 3570 MG/KG INTRAPERITONEAL-MOUSE LD50; MUTAGENIC DATA (RTECS); REPRODUCTIVE EFFECTS DATA (RTECS). CARCINOGEN STATUS: NONE. LOCAL EFFECTS: IRRITANT- EYE. ACUTE TOXICITY LEVEL: MODERATELY TOXIC BY INHALATION; SLIGHTLY TOXIC BY INGESTION. TARGET EFFECTS: POISONING MAY AFFECT THE RESPIRATORY SYSTEM AND THE GASTROINTESTINAL TRACT.

HEALTH EFFECTS AND FIRST AID

INHALATION: DIBUTYL PHTHALATE (N-BUTYL PHTHALATE): 9300 MG/M3 IMMEDIATELY DANGEROUS TO LIFE OR HEALTH. **ACUTE EXPOSURE-** DUE TO LOW VAPOR PRESSURE POISONING BY INHALATION IS UNLIKELY. HOWEVER INHALATION OF SIGNIFICANT AMOUNTS MAY OCCUR BY SPRAY OR MIST EXPOSURE AND MAY CAUSE IRRITATION OF THE MUCOUS MEMBRANES, HEADACHE, DROWSINESS AND CONVULSIONS. ANIMAL STUDIES INDICATE 250 MG/M3 CAUSED IRRITATION OF THE RESPIRATORY SYSTEM, WHILE 25,000 MG/M3 CAUSED LABORED BREATHING, ATAXIA, PARESIS, CONVULSIONS AND DEATH FROM PARALYSIS OF THE RESPIRATORY SYSTEM. **CHRONIC EXPOSURE-** WORKERS IN AN ARTIFICIAL LEATHER INDUSTRY IN WHICH THE DURATION OF EXPOSURE RANGED FROM .5 YEAR TO 19 YEARS AND IN WHICH SEVERAL PHTHALATE PLASTICIZERS WERE USED, (DIBUTYL PHTHALATE MOST FREQUENTLY) SHOWED SIGNS OF POLYNERUITIS WITH PAIN, NUMBNESS AND SPASMS IN THE UPPER AND LOWER EXTREMITIES.

FIRST AID- REMOVE FROM EXPOSURE AREA TO FRESH AIR IMMEDIATELY. IF BREATHING HAS STOPPED, PERFORM ARTIFICIAL RESPIRATION. KEEP PERSON WARM AND AT REST. TREAT SYMPTOMATICALLY AND SUPPORTIVELY. GET MEDICAL ATTENTION IMMEDIATELY.

SKIN CONTACT: DIBUTYL PHTHALATE (N-BUTYL PHTHALATE): **ACUTE EXPOSURE-** MAY CAUSE IRRITATION WITH REDNESS AND PAIN. **CHRONIC EXPOSURE-** NO DATA AVAILABLE.

FIRST AID- REMOVE CONTAMINATED CLOTHING AND SHOES IMMEDIATELY. WASH AFFECTED AREA WITH SOAP OR MILD DETERGENT AND LARGE AMOUNTS OF WATER UNTIL NO EVIDENCE OF CHEMICAL REMAINS (APPROXIMATELY 15-20 MINUTES). GET MEDICAL ATTENTION IMMEDIATELY.

EYE CONTACT: DIBUTYL PHTHALATE (N-BUTYL PHTHALATE): IRRITANT. **ACUTE EXPOSURE-** A SPLASH IN THE EYE MAY CAUSE AN IMMEDIATE SEVERE STINGING PAIN WITH PROFUSE TEARING. **CHRONIC EXPOSURE-** REPEATED OR PROLONGED EXPOSURE TO IRRITANTS MAY CAUSE CONJUNCTIVITIS.

FIRST AID- WASH EYES IMMEDIATELY WITH LARGE AMOUNTS OF WATER OR NORMAL SALINE, OCCASIONALLY LIFTING UPPER AND LOWER LIDS, UNTIL NO EVIDENCE OF CHEMICAL REMAINS (APPROXIMATELY 15-20 MINUTES). GET MEDICAL ATTENTION IMMEDIATELY.

INGESTION: DIBUTYL PHTHALATE (N-BUTYL PHTHALATE): **ACUTE EXPOSURE**- MAY CAUSE GASTROINTESTINAL IRRITATION WITH ABDOMINAL PAIN, NAUSEA, VOMITING AND DIZZINESS. A CHEMICAL WORKER WHO ACCIDENTALLY INGESTED 10 GRAMS EXPERIENCED NAUSEA, VOMITING AND DIZZINESS FOLLOWED LATER BY HEADACHE, PAIN AND IRRITATION IN THE EYES, LACRIMATION, PHOTOPHOBIA AND CONJUNCTIVITIS. DELAYED RENAL INVOLVEMENT OCCURRED WITH COMPLETE RECOVERY IN 2 WEEKS. **CHRONIC EXPOSURE**- RATS GIVEN 1 ML/KG TWICE WEEKLY FOR 6 WEEKS TO 1.5 YEARS SHOWED NO ADVERSE EFFECTS. IN OTHER ANIMAL STUDIES REPRODUCTIVE EFFECTS HAVE BEEN REPORTED FROM PROLONGED OR REPEATED INGESTION. IN MALES LOSS OF TESTICULAR ATROPHY AND LOSS OF TESTICULAR ZINC OCCURRED, WHILE IN PREGNANT ANIMALS EFFECTS ON THE FETUS OR EMBRYO WERE REPORTED.

FIRST AID- TREAT SYMPTOMATICALLY AND SUPPORTIVELY. GET MEDICAL ATTENTION IMMEDIATELY. IF VOMITING OCCURS, KEEP HEAD LOWER THAN HIPS TO PREVENT ASPIRATION.

ANTIDOTE: NO SPECIFIC ANTIDOTE. TREAT SYMPTOMATICALLY AND SUPPORTIVELY.

REACTIVITY

REACTIVITY: STABLE UNDER NORMAL TEMPERATURES AND PRESSURES.

INCOMPATIBILITIES: DIBUTYL PHTHALATE (N-BUTYL PHTHALATE): ACIDS (STRONG): POSSIBLE FIRE AND EXPLOSION HAZARD. ALKALIES (STRONG): POSSIBLE FIRE AND EXPLOSION HAZARD. CHLORINE: POSSIBLE EXPLOSION. NITRATES: POSSIBLE FIRE AND EXPLOSION HAZARD. OXIDIZERS (STRONG): POSSIBLE FIRE AND EXPLOSION HAZARD.

DECOMPOSITION: THERMAL DECOMPOSITION MAY RELEASE ACRID SMOKE AND IRRITATING FUMES.

POLYMERIZATION: HAZARDOUS POLYMERIZATION HAS NOT BEEN REPORTED TO OCCUR UNDER NORMAL TEMPERATURES AND PRESSURES.

STORAGE AND DISPOSAL

OBSERVE ALL FEDERAL, STATE AND LOCAL REGULATIONS WHEN STORING OR DISPOSING OF THIS SUBSTANCE. FOR ASSISTANCE, CONTACT THE DISTRICT DIRECTOR OF THE ENVIRONMENTAL PROTECTION AGENCY.

STORAGE

STORE AWAY FROM INCOMPATIBLE SUBSTANCES.

DISPOSAL

DISPOSAL MUST BE IN ACCORDANCE WITH STANDARDS APPLICABLE TO GENERATORS OF HAZARDOUS WASTE, 40CFR 262. EPA HAZARDOUS WASTE NUMBER U069.

CONDITIONS TO AVOID

MAY BURN BUT DOES NOT IGNITE READILY.

SPILL AND LEAK PROCEDURES

SOIL SPILL: DIG HOLDING AREA SUCH AS LAGOON, POND OR PIT FOR CONTAINMENT. DIKE FLOW OF SPILLED MATERIAL USING SOIL OR SANDBAGS OR FOAMED BARRIERS SUCH AS POLYURETHANE OR CONCRETE.
USE CEMENT POWDER OR FLY ASH TO ABSORB LIQUID MASS.

AIR SPILL: KNOCK DOWN VAPORS WITH WATER SPRAY. KEEP UPWIND.

WATER SPILL: LIMIT SPILL MOTION AND DISPERSION WITH NATURAL BARRIERS OR OIL SPILL CONTROL BOOMS.
APPLY DETERGENTS, SOAPS, ALCOHOLS OR ANOTHER SURFACE ACTIVE AGENT.
APPLY UNIVERSAL GELLING AGENT TO IMMOBILIZE TRAPPED SPILL AND INCREASE EFFICIENCY OF REMOVAL.
USE SUCTION HOSES TO REMOVE TRAPPED SPILL MATERIAL.
USE ACTIVATED CARBON TO ABSORB SPILLED SUBSTANCE THAT IS DISSOLVED.
USE MECHANICAL DREDGES OR LIFTS TO EXTRACT IMMOBILIZED MASSES OF POLLUTION AND PRECIPITATES.

OCCUPATIONAL SPILL: DO NOT TOUCH SPILLED MATERIAL. STOP LEAK IF YOU CAN DO IT WITHOUT RISK. FOR SMALL SPILLS, TAKE UP WITH SAND OR OTHER ABSORBENT MATERIAL AND PLACE INTO CONTAINERS FOR LATER DISPOSAL. FOR LARGER SPILLS, DIKE FAR AHEAD OF SPILL FOR LATER DISPOSAL. KEEP UNNECESSARY PEOPLE AWAY. ISOLATE HAZARD AREA AND DENY ENTRY. VENTILATE CLOSED SPACES BEFORE ENTERING.
REPORTABLE QUANTITY (RQ): 10 POUNDS THE SUPERFUND AMENDMENTS AND REAUTHORIZATION ACT (SARA) SECTION 304 REQUIRES THAT A RELEASE EQUAL TO OR GREATER THAN THE REPORTABLE QUANTITY FOR THIS SUBSTANCE BE IMMEDIATELY REPORTED TO THE LOCAL EMERGENCY PLANNING COMMITTEE AND THE STATE EMERGENCY RESPONSE COMMISSION (40 CFR 355.40). IF THE RELEASE OF THIS SUBSTANCE IS REPORTABLE UNDER CERCLA SECTION 103, THE NATIONAL RESPONSE CENTER MUST BE NOTIFIED IMMEDIATELY AT (800) 424-8802 OR (202) 426-2675 IN THE METROPOLITAN WASHINGTON, D.C. AREA (40 CFR 302.6).

PROTECTIVE EQUIPMENT

VENTILATION: PROVIDE GENERAL DILUTION VENTILATION TO MEET PUBLISHED EXPOSURE LIMITS.

RESPIRATOR: THE FOLLOWING RESPIRATORS AND MAXIMUM USE CONCENTRATIONS ARE RECOMMENDATIONS BY THE U.S. DEPARTMENT OF HEALTH AND HUMAN SERVICES, NIOSH POCKET GUIDE TO CHEMICAL HAZARDS; NIOSH CRITERIA DOCUMENTS OR BY THE U.S. DEPARTMENT OF LABOR, 29 CFR 1910 SUBPART Z.
THE SPECIFIC RESPIRATOR SELECTED MUST BE BASED ON CONTAMINATION LEVELS FOUND IN THE WORK PLACE, MUST NOT EXCEED THE WORKING LIMITS OF THE RESPIRATOR AND BE JOINTLY APPROVED BY THE NATIONAL INSTITUTE FOR OCCUPATIONAL SAFETY AND HEALTH AND THE MINE SAFETY AND HEALTH ADMINISTRATION (NIOSH-MSHA).
50 MG/M3- ANY DUST AND MIST RESPIRATOR WIHT A FULL FACEPIECE.
125 MG/M3- ANY POWERED AIR-PURIFYING RESPIRATOR WITH A DUST AND MIST FILTER. ANY SUPPLIED-AIR RESPIRATOR OPERATED IN A CONTINUOUS FLOW MODE.
250 MG/M3- ANY AIR-PURIFYING FULL FACEPIECE RESPIRATOR WITH A HIGH-EFFICIENCY PARTICULATE FILTER. ANY SELF-CONTAINED BREATHING APPARATUS WIHT A FULL FACEPIECE. ANY SUPPLIED-AIR RESPIRATOR WITH A FULL FACEPIECE.
9300 MG/M3- ANY SUPPLIED-AIR RESPIRATOR WITH A FULL FACEPIECE AND OPERATED IN A PRESSURE-DEMAND OR OTHER POSITIVE PRESSURE MODE.
ESCAPE- ANY AIR-PURIFYING FULL FACEPIECE RESPIRATOR WITH A HIGH-EFFICIENCY PARTICULATE FILTER. ANY APPROPRIATE ESCAPE-TYPE SELF-CONTAINED BREATHING APPARATUS. FOR FIREFIGHTING AND OTHER IMMEDIATELY DANGEROUS TO LIFE OR HEALTH CONDITIONS:
SELF-CONTAINED BREATHING APPARATUS WITH FULL FACEPIECE OPERATED IN PRESSURE-DEMAND OR OTHER POSITIVE PRESSURE MODE.
SUPPLIED-AIR RESPIRATOR WITH FULL FACEPIECE AND OPERATED IN PRESSURE-DEMAND OR OTHER POSITIVE PRESSURE MODE IN COMBINATION WITH AN AUXILIARY SELF-CONTAINED BREATHING APPARATUS OPERATED IN PRESSURE-DEMAND OR OTHER POSITIVE PRESSURE MODE.

CLOTHING: EMPLOYEE MUST WEAR APPROPRIATE PROTECTIVE (IMPERVIOUS) CLOTHING AND EQUIPMENT TO PREVENT REPEATED OR PROLONGED SKIN CONTACT WITH THIS SUBSTANCE.

GLOVES: EMPLOYEE MUST WEAR APPROPRIATE PROTECTIVE GLOVES TO PREVENT CONTACT WITH THIS SUBSTANCE.

EYE PROTECTION: EMPLOYEE MUST WEAR SPLASH-PROOF OR DUST-RESISTANT SAFETY GOGGLES TO PREVENT EYE CONTACT WITH THIS SUBSTANCE.
EMERGENCY EYE WASH: WHERE THERE IS ANY POSSIBILITY THAT AN EMPLOYEE'S EYES MAY BE EXPOSED TO THIS SUBSTANCE, THE EMPLOYER SHOULD PROVIDE AN EYE WASH FOUNTAIN WITHIN THE IMMEDIATE WORK AREA FOR EMERGENCY USE.

AUTHORIZED BY- OCCUPATIONAL HEALTH SERVICES, INC.
CREATION DATE: 10/04/89 ***REVISION DATE:*** 05/17/90

MATERIAL SAFETY DATA SHEET

OCCUPATIONAL HEALTH SERVICES, INC.
AGRICULTURE AND PESTICIDE DIVISION
450 SEVENTH AVENUE, SUITE 2407
NEW YORK, NEW YORK 10123
1-800-445-MSDS OR (212) 967-1100

EMERGENCY CONTACT:
JOHN S. BRANSFORD, JR. (615) 292-1180

SUBSTANCE IDENTIFICATION

CAS-NUMBER 1194-65-6

SUBSTANCE: DICHLOBENIL

TRADE NAMES/SYNONYMS: BENZONITRILE, 2,6-DICHLORO-; 2,6-DICHLOROBENZONITRILE; 2,6-DICHLOROCYANOBENZENE; CASORON; DECABANE; DYCLOMEC; DCB; DBN; 2,6-DBN; H 133; NIA 5996; NIAGARA 5006; NOROSAC; PREFIX D; STCC 4963814; C7H3CL2N; PST06800

CHEMICAL FAMILY: NITRILE, AROMATIC
HALOGEN

MOLECULAR FORMULA: CL2-C6-H3-C-N

MOLECULAR WEIGHT: 172.01

CERCLA RATINGS (SCALE 0-3): HEALTH=2 FIRE=1 REACTIVITY=0 PERSISTENCE=3

NFPA RATINGS (SCALE 0-4): HEALTH=U FIRE=1 REACTIVITY=0

COMPONENTS AND CONTAMINANTS

COMPONENT: DICHLOBENIL ***PERCENT:*** 100.0
CAS# 1194-65-6

EXPOSURE LIMITS: NO OCCUPATIONAL EXPOSURE LIMITS ESTABLISHED BY OSHA, ACGIH, OR NIOSH.
DICHLOBENIL: 100 POUNDS CERCLA SECTION 103 REPORTABLE QUANTITY

PHYSICAL DATA

DESCRIPTION: COLORLESS TO OFF-WHITE CRYSTALLINE SOLID WITH AN AROMATIC ODOR
BOILING POINT: 518 F (270 C) @ 760 MMHG ***MELTING POINT:*** 291-295 F (144-146 C)
SPECIFIC GRAVITY: NOT AVAILABLE ***VAPOR PRESSURE:*** NEGLIGIBLE @ 20 C
SOLUBILITY IN WATER: 18 PPM @ 20 C
SOLVENT SOLUBILITY: SOLUBLE IN DICHLOROMETHANE; MODERATELY SOLUBLE IN ETHANOL, ISOPROPANOL, ACETONE, BENZENE, TOLUENE, XYLENE, AND MOST ORGANIC SOLVENTS; VERY SLIGHTLY SOLUBLE IN CARBON TETRACHLORIDE AND PYRIDINE.

FIRE AND EXPLOSION DATA

FIRE AND EXPLOSION HAZARD: SLIGHT FIRE HAZARD WHEN EXPOSED TO HEAT OR FLAME.
FIREFIGHTING MEDIA: DRY CHEMICAL, CARBON DIOXIDE, HALON, WATER SPRAY OR STANDARD FOAM (1987 EMERGENCY RESPONSE GUIDEBOOK, DOT P 5800.4).
FOR LARGER FIRES, USE WATER SPRAY, FOG OR STANDARD FOAM (1987 EMERGENCY RESPONSE GUIDEBOOK, DOT P 5800.4).
FIREFIGHTING: MOVE CONTAINER FROM FIRE AREA IF POSSIBLE. DO NOT SCATTER SPILLED MATERIAL WITH HIGH PRESSURE WATER STREAMS. DIKE FIRE CONTROL WATER FOR LATER DISPOSAL (1987 EMERGENCY RESPONSE GUIDEBOOK, DOT P 5800.4, GUIDE PAGE 31).
USE AGENTS SUITABLE FOR TYPE OF SURROUNDING FIRE. AVOID BREATHING HAZARDOUS VAPORS, KEEP UPWIND.

TOXICITY

DICHLOBENIL: TOXICITY DATA: 1350 MG/KG SKIN-RABBIT LD50; 2710 MG/KG ORAL-RAT LD50; 2056 MG/KG ORAL-MOUSE LD50; 270 MG/KG ORAL-RABBIT LD50; 681 MG/KG ORAL-GUINEA PIG LD50; 360 MG/KG INTRAPERITONEAL-MOUSE LD50; 500 MG/KG UNREPORTED-RAT LD50; 1000 MG/KG UNREPORTED-MAMMAL LD50; TUMORIGENIC DATA (RTECS). CARCINOGEN STATUS: NONE. ACUTE TOXICITY LEVEL: MODERATELY TOXIC BY DERMAL ABSORPTION AND INGESTION. TARGET EFFECTS: NO DATA AVAILABLE.

HEALTH EFFECTS AND FIRST AID

INHALATION: DICHLOBENIL: **ACUTE EXPOSURE-** MAY BE MODERATELY IRRITATING TO THE RESPIRATORY TRACT. **CHRONIC EXPOSURE-** NO DATA AVAILABLE.
FIRST AID- REMOVE FROM EXPOSURE AREA TO FRESH AIR IMMEDIATELY. IF BREATHING HAS STOPPED, PERFORM ARTIFICIAL RESPIRATION. KEEP PERSON WARM AND AT REST. TREAT SYMPTOMATICALLY AND SUPPORTIVELY. GET MEDICAL ATTENTION IMMEDIATELY.

SKIN CONTACT: DICHLOBENIL: **ACUTE EXPOSURE-** MAY BE MODERATELY IRRITATING TO THE SKIN. HOWEVER, NO IRRITATION WAS REPORTED FROM APPLICATION TO RABBIT SKIN. **CHRONIC EXPOSURE-** DERMATITIS WAS REPORTED FROM OCCUPATIONAL EXPOSURE. CERTAIN MANUFACTURING PROCESSES OF THIS MATERIAL MAY RESULT IN CONTAMINANTS THAT ARE CAPABLE OF CAUSING CHLORACNE.
FIRST AID- REMOVE CONTAMINATED CLOTHING AND SHOES IMMEDIATELY. WASH AFFECTED AREA WITH SOAP OR MILD DETERGENT AND LARGE AMOUNTS OF WATER UNTIL NO EVIDENCE OF CHEMICAL REMAINS (APPROXIMATELY 15-20 MINUTES). GET MEDICAL ATTENTION IMMEDIATELY.

EYE CONTACT: DICHLOBENIL: **ACUTE EXPOSURE-** NO DATA AVAILABLE. **CHRONIC EXPOSURE-** NO DATA AVAILABLE.
FIRST AID- WASH EYES IMMEDIATELY WITH LARGE AMOUNTS OF WATER OR NORMAL SALINE, OCCASIONALLY LIFTING UPPER AND LOWER LIDS, UNTIL NO EVIDENCE OF CHEMICAL REMAINS (APPROXIMATELY 15-20 MINUTES). GET MEDICAL ATTENTION IMMEDIATELY.

INGESTION: DICHLOBENIL: **ACUTE EXPOSURE-** INACTIVITY, ANOREXIA AND SEDATION OCCURRED IN LABORATORY ANIMALS. A LETHAL DOSE PRODUCED LIVER NECROSIS IN RABBITS, BUT NO LIVER DAMAGE WAS OBSERVED FROM SUBLETHAL DOSES. **CHRONIC EXPOSURE-** HEPATIC DEGENERATION AND NEUTROPENIA AND LEUKOPENIA WERE OBSERVED IN RATS AT 3000 PPM AND ABOVE; AT THE 10,000 PPM LEVEL, HEPATIC NECROSIS AND DEATH WERE REPORTED. IN DOGS, CHANGES IN HEPATIC ENZYMES LEVELS WERE NOTED.
FIRST AID- IF THE PERSON IS CONSCIOUS AND NOT CONVULSING, REMOVE BY GASTRIC LAVAGE AND FOLLOW WITH A CATHARTIC (DREISBACH, HANDBOOK OF POISONING, 12TH ED.). TREAT SYMPTOMATICALLY AND SUPPORTIVELY. GASTRIC LAVAGE SHOULD BE PERFORMED BY QUALIFIED MEDICAL PERSONNEL. GET MEDICAL ATTENTION IMMEDIATELY.

ANTIDOTE: NO SPECIFIC ANTIDOTE. TREAT SYMPTOMATICALLY AND SUPPORTIVELY.

REACTIVITY

REACTIVITY: STABLE UNDER NORMAL TEMPERATURES AND PRESSURES.
INCOMPATIBILITIES: DICHLOBENIL: OXIDIZERS (STRONG): FIRE AND EXPLOSION HAZARD.
DECOMPOSITION: THERMAL DECOMPOSITION PRODUCTS MAY INCLUDE HIGHLY TOXIC HYDROGEN CYANIDE, TOXIC OXIDES OF NITROGEN AND CARBON, AND TOXIC AND CORROSIVE FUMES OF CHLORIDES.
POLYMERIZATION: HAZARDOUS POLYMERIZATION HAS NOT BEEN REPORTED TO OCCUR UNDER NORMAL TEMPERATURES AND PRESSURES.

STORAGE AND DISPOSAL

OBSERVE ALL FEDERAL, STATE AND LOCAL REGULATIONS WHEN STORING OR DISPOSING OF THIS SUBSTANCE. FOR ASSISTANCE, CONTACT THE DISTRICT DIRECTOR OF THE ENVIRONMENTAL PROTECTION AGENCY.

****STORAGE****

STORE IN ACCORDANCE WITH 40 CFR 165 RECOMMENDED PROCEDURES FOR THE DISPOSAL AND STORAGE OF PESTICIDES AND PESTICIDE CONTAINERS.
STORE AWAY FROM INCOMPATIBLE SUBSTANCES.

****DISPOSAL****

DISPOSAL MUST BE IN ACCORDANCE WITH 40 CFR 165 RECOMMENDED PROCEDURES FOR THE DISPOSAL AND STORAGE OF PESTICIDES AND PESTICIDE CONTAINERS.

CONDITIONS TO AVOID

MAY BURN BUT DOES NOT IGNITE READILY.

SPILL AND LEAK PROCEDURES

SOIL SPILL: DIG HOLDING AREA SUCH AS LAGOON, POND OR PIT FOR CONTAINMENT.
USE PROTECTIVE COVER SUCH AS A PLASTIC SHEET TO PREVENT MATERIAL FROM DISSOLVING IN FIRE EXTINGUISHING WATER OR RAIN.
WATER SPILL: USE ACTIVATED CARBON TO ABSORB SPILLED SUBSTANCE THAT IS DISSOLVED.
USE MECHANICAL DREDGES OR LIFTS TO EXTRACT IMMOBILIZED MASSES OF POLLUTION AND PRECIPITATES.
OCCUPATIONAL SPILL: DO NOT TOUCH SPILLED MATERIAL. STOP LEAK IF YOU CAN DO IT WITHOUT RISK. FOR SMALL SPILLS, TAKE UP WITH SAND OR OTHER ABSORBENT MATERIAL AND PLACE INTO CONTAINERS FOR LATER DISPOSAL. FOR SMALL DRY SPILLS, WITH A CLEAN SHOVEL PLACE MATERIAL INTO CLEAN, DRY CONTAINER AND COVER. MOVE CONTAINERS FROM SPILL AREA. FOR LARGER SPILLS, DIKE FAR AHEAD OF SPILL FOR LATER DISPOSAL. KEEP UNNECESSARY PEOPLE AWAY. ISOLATE HAZARD AREA AND DENY ENTRY.
REPORTABLE QUANTITY (RQ): 100 POUNDS THE SUPERFUND AMENDMENTS AND REAUTHORIZATION ACT (SARA) SECTION 304 REQUIRES THAT A RELEASE EQUAL TO OR GREATER THAN THE REPORTABLE QUANTITY FOR THIS SUBSTANCE BE IMMEDIATELY REPORTED TO THE LOCAL EMERGENCY PLANNING COMMITTEE AND THE STATE EMERGENCY RESPONSE COMMISSION (40 CFR 355.40). IF THE RELEASE OF THIS SUBSTANCE IS REPORTABLE UNDER CERCLA SECTION 103, THE NATIONAL RESPONSE CENTER MUST BE NOTIFIED IMMEDIATELY AT (800) 424-8802 OR (202) 426-2675 IN THE METROPOLITAN WASHINGTON, D.C. AREA (40 CFR 302.6).

PROTECTIVE EQUIPMENT

VENTILATION: PROVIDE LOCAL EXHAUST OR GENERAL DILUTION VENTILATION SYSTEM.
RESPIRATOR: THE FOLLOWING RESPIRATORS ARE RECOMMENDED BASED ON INFORMATION FOUND IN THE PHYSICAL DATA, TOXICITY AND HEALTH EFFECTS SECTIONS. THEY ARE RANKED IN ORDER FROM MINIMUM TO MAXIMUM RESPIRATORY PROTECTION. THE SPECIFIC RESPIRATOR SELECTED MUST BE BASED ON CONTAMINATION LEVELS FOUND IN THE WORK PLACE, MUST NOT EXCEED THE WORKING LIMITS OF THE RESPIRATOR AND BE JOINTLY APPROVED BY THE NATIONAL INSTITUTE FOR OCCUPATIONAL SAFETY AND HEALTH AND THE MINE SAFETY AND HEALTH ADMINISTRATION (NIOSH-MSHA).
CHEMICAL CARTRIDGE RESPIRATOR WITH AN ORGANIC VAPOR CARTRIDGE(S) WITH A FULL FACEPIECE AND ORGANIC VAPOR CARTRIDGE(S) IN COMBINATION WITH A DUST AND MIST FILTER.
POWERED AIR-PURIFYING RESPIRATOR WITH A TIGHT-FITTING FACEPIECE AND ORGANIC VAPOR CARTRIDGE(S) IN COMBINATION WITH A HIGH-EFFICIENCY PARTICULATE FILTER.
TYPE 'C' SUPPLIED-AIR RESPIRATOR WITH A FULL FACEPIECE OPERATED IN A PRESSURE-DEMAND OR OTHER POSITIVE PRESSURE MODE.
SELF-CONTAINED BREATHING APPARATUS WITH A FULL FACEPIECE OPERATED IN PRESSURE-DEMAND OR OTHER POSITIVE PRESSURE MODE.
FOR FIREFIGHTING AND OTHER IMMEDIATELY DANGEROUS TO LIFE OR HEALTH CONDITIONS:
SELF-CONTAINED BREATHING APPARATUS WITH FULL FACEPIECE OPERATED IN

PRESSURE-DEMAND OR OTHER POSITIVE PRESSURE MODE.
SUPPLIED-AIR RESPIRATOR WITH FULL FACEPIECE AND OPERATED IN PRESSURE-DEMAND OR OTHER POSITIVE PRESSURE MODE IN COMBINATION WITH AN AUXILIARY SELF-CONTAINED BREATHING APPARATUS OPERATED IN PRESSURE-DEMAND OR OTHER POSITIVE PRESSURE MODE.

CLOTHING: EMPLOYEE MUST WEAR APPROPRIATE PROTECTIVE (IMPERVIOUS) CLOTHING AND EQUIPMENT TO PREVENT REPEATED OR PROLONGED SKIN CONTACT WITH THIS SUBSTANCE.

GLOVES: EMPLOYEE MUST WEAR APPROPRIATE PROTECTIVE GLOVES TO PREVENT CONTACT WITH THIS SUBSTANCE.

EYE PROTECTION: EMPLOYEE MUST WEAR SPLASH-PROOF OR DUST-RESISTANT SAFETY GOGGLES TO PREVENT EYE CONTACT WITH THIS SUBSTANCE.
EMERGENCY EYE WASH: WHERE THERE IS ANY POSSIBILITY THAT AN EMPLOYEE'S EYES MAY BE EXPOSED TO THIS SUBSTANCE, THE EMPLOYER SHOULD PROVIDE AN EYE WASH FOUNTAIN WITHIN THE IMMEDIATE WORK AREA FOR EMERGENCY USE.

AUTHORIZED BY- OCCUPATIONAL HEALTH SERVICES, INC.
CREATION DATE: 10/04/89 ***REVISION DATE:*** 06/07/90

MATERIAL SAFETY DATA SHEET

OCCUPATIONAL HEALTH SERVICES, INC.
AGRICULTURE AND PESTICIDE DIVISION
450 SEVENTH AVENUE, SUITE 2407
NEW YORK, NEW YORK 10123
1-800-445-MSDS OR (212) 967-1100

EMERGENCY CONTACT:
JOHN S. BRANSFORD, JR. (615) 292-1180

SUBSTANCE IDENTIFICATION

CAS-NUMBER 97-17-6

SUBSTANCE: **DICHLOFENTHION**

TRADE NAMES/SYNONYMS: PHOSPHOROTHIOIC ACID, O-(2,4-DICHLOROPHENYL) O,O-DIETHYL ESTER; O,2,4-DICHLOROPHENYL O,O-DIETHYLPHOSPHOROTHIOATE; 2,4-DICHLOROPHENYL DIETHYL PHOSPHOROTHIONATE; O,O-DIETHYL O-2,4-DICHLOROPHENYL PHOSPHOROTHIOATE; DICHLOFENTION; DICHLOPHENTHION; HEXANEMA; NEMACIDE; VC 13; ENT 17,470; PST06805

CHEMICAL FAMILY: ORGANOPHOSPHATE

MOLECULAR FORMULA: C10-H13-CL2-O3-P-S

MOLECULAR WEIGHT: 315.16

CERCLA RATINGS (SCALE 0-3): HEALTH=3 FIRE=0 REACTIVITY=0 PERSISTENCE=3

NFPA RATINGS (SCALE 0-4): HEALTH=3 FIRE=0 REACTIVITY=0

COMPONENTS AND CONTAMINANTS

COMPONENT: DICHLOFENTHION ***PERCENT:*** 100
CAS# 97-17-6

EXPOSURE LIMITS: NO OCCUPATIONAL EXPOSURE LIMITS ESTABLISHED BY OSHA, ACGIH, OR NIOSH.

PHYSICAL DATA

DESCRIPTION: COLORLESS LIQUID ***BOILING POINT:*** 248-253 F (120-123 C) @ 0.2 MMHG

SPECIFIC GRAVITY: 1.313 ***EVAPORATION RATE:*** NOT AVAILABLE

SOLUBILITY IN WATER: 245 PPM

SOLVENT SOLUBILITY: SOLUBLE IN MOST ORGANIC SOLVENTS

FIRE AND EXPLOSION DATA

FIRE AND EXPLOSION HAZARD: NEGLIGIBLE FIRE HAZARD WHEN EXPOSED TO HEAT OR FLAME.

FIREFIGHTING MEDIA: DRY CHEMICAL, CARBON DIOXIDE, HALON, WATER SPRAY OR STANDARD FOAM (1987 EMERGENCY RESPONSE GUIDEBOOK, DOT P 5800.4).
FOR LARGER FIRES, USE WATER SPRAY, FOG OR STANDARD FOAM (1987 EMERGENCY RESPONSE GUIDEBOOK, DOT P 5800.4).

FIREFIGHTING: MOVE CONTAINERS FROM FIRE AREA IF POSSIBLE. FIGHT FIRE FROM MAXIMUM DISTANCE. STAY AWAY FROM STORAGE TANK ENDS. DIKE FIRE CONTROL WATER FOR LATER DISPOSAL. DO NOT SCATTER MATERIAL (1987 EMERGENCY RESPONSE GUIDEBOOK, DOT P 5800.4, GUIDE PAGE 55).

TOXICITY

DICHLOFENTHION: TOXICITY DATA: 6 GM/KG SKIN-RABBIT LD50; 355 MG/KG SKIN-RAT LD50; 172 MG/KG ORAL-RAT LD50; MUTAGENIC DATA (RTECS). CARCINOGEN STATUS: NONE. ACUTE TOXICITY LEVEL: TOXIC BY INGESTION; SLIGHTLY TOXIC BY DERMAL ABSORPTION. TARGET EFFECTS: CHOLINESTERASE INHIBITOR. POISONING MAY AFFECT THE NERVOUS SYSTEM.* AT INCREASED RISK FROM EXPOSURE: PERSONS WITH RESPIRATORY AILMENTS, RECENT EXPOSURE TO CHOLINESTERASE INHIBITORS OR IMPAIRED CHOLINESTERASE PRODUCTION, OR LIVER MALFUNCTION.* ADDITIONAL DATA: MAY CROSS THE PLACENTA. HIGH ENVIRONMENTAL TEMPERATURES OR EXPOSURE OF THE CHEMICAL TO VISIBLE OR ULTRAVIOLET LIGHT MAY ENHANCE THE TOXICITY. INTERACTIONS WITH MEDICATIONS MAY OCCUR.*
* MAY BE BASED ON GENERAL INFORMATION ON ORGANOPHOSPHATES.

HEALTH EFFECTS AND FIRST AID

INHALATION: DICHLOFENTHION: SEE INFORMATION ON ORGANOPHOSPHATES.
ORGANOPHOSPHATES: CHOLINESTERASE INHIBITOR. **ACUTE EXPOSURE-** WHEN INHALED, THE FIRST EFFECTS OF CHOLINESTERASE INHIBITORS ARE USUALLY RESPIRATORY AND MAY INCLUDE NASAL HYPEREMIA AND WATERY DISCHARGE, COUGH, CHEST DISCOMFORT, DYSPNEA, AND WHEEZING DUE TO INCREASED BRONCHIAL SECRETIONS AND BRONCHOCONSTRICTION. IF SUFFICIENT AMOUNTS ARE ABSORBED, OTHER SYSTEMIC EFFECTS MAY BEGIN WITHIN A FEW MINUTES OR BE DELAYED FOR UP TO 12 HOURS. SYMPTOMS MAY INCLUDE PALLOR, NAUSEA, VOMITING, DIARRHEA, ABDOMINAL CRAMPS, HEADACHE, DIZZINESS, OCULAR PAIN, BLURRED VISION, MIOSIS OR IN SOME CASES, ESPECIALLY INITIALLY, MYDRIASIS, LACRIMATION, SALIVATION, SWEATING, AND CONFUSION. OTHER REPORTED CENTRAL NERVOUS SYSTEM OR NEUROMUSCULAR EFFECTS MAY INCLUDE ATAXIA, SLURRED SPEECH, AREFLEXIA, WEAKNESS, FATIGUE, FASCICULATIONS, TWITCHING, TREMORS POSSIBLY OF THE TONGUE AND EYELIDS, AND EVENTUALLY PARALYSIS OF THE EXTREMITIES AND POSSIBLY OF THE RESPIRATORY MUSCLES. IN SEVERE CASES THERE MAY ALSO BE INVOLUNTARY DEFECATION AND URINATION, CYANOSIS, PSYCHOSIS, HYPERGLYCEMIA, ACUTE PANCREATITIS, CARDIAC IRREGULARITIES, PULMONARY EDEMA, UNCONSCIOUSNESS, CONVULSIONS, AND COMA. DEATH IS PRIMARILY DUE TO RESPIRATORY FAILURE, ALTHOUGH CARDIOVASCULAR EFFECTS INCLUDING CARDIAC ARREST MAY ALSO BE IMPLICATED. LONG TERM SEQUELAE ARE RARE BUT MAY INCLUDE NEUROPSYCHIATRIC DISORDERS AND MYOPATHY WITH MUSCLE TENDERNESS. SOME ORGANOPHOSPHATES MAY CAUSE A DELAYED NEUROPATHY BEGINNING 1-4 WEEKS AFTER AN ACUTE EXPOSURE WHICH MAY OR MAY NOT HAVE CAUSED ACUTE CHOLINERGIC EFFECTS. NUMBNESS, TINGLING, WEAKNESS AND CRAMPING BEGINNING SYMMETRICALLY IN THE LOWER LIMBS MAY PROGRESS TO ATAXIA AND PARALYSIS. IN SEVERE CASES, UPPER LIMB INVOLVEMENT IS POSSIBLE AND FLACCID PARALYSIS MAY PROGRESS TO SPASTIC PARALYSIS WITH EXAGGERATED REFLEXES. IMPROVEMENT MAY OCCUR OVER MONTHS TO YEARS, BUT SOME RESIDUAL IMPAIRMENT USUALLY REMAINS.
CHRONIC EXPOSURE- REPEATED OR PROLONGED EXPOSURE MAY RESULT IN THE EFFECTS OF ACUTE EXPOSURE INCLUDING THE DELAYED NEUROPATHY. OTHER EFFECTS REPORTED IN WORKERS REPEATEDLY EXPOSED INCLUDE IMPAIRED MEMORY AND CONCENTRATION, ACUTE PSYCHOSIS, SEVERE DEPRESSIONS, IRRITABILTY, CONFUSION, APATHY, EMOTIONAL LABILITY, SOCIAL WITHDRAWAL, CONFUSION, HEADACHE, SPEECH DIFFICULTIES, DELAYED REACTION TIMES, SPATIAL DISORIENTATION, NIGHTMARES, SLEEPWALKING, AND DROWSINESS OR INSOMNIA. AN INFLUENZA-LIKE CONDITION WITH HEADACHE, NAUSEA, WEAKNESS, ANOREXIA AND MALAISE HAS ALSO BEEN REPORTED.

FIRST AID- REMOVE FROM EXPOSURE AREA TO FRESH AIR IMMEDIATELY. IF BREATHING HAS STOPPED, GIVE ARTIFICIAL RESPIRATION. MAINTAIN AIRWAY AND BLOOD PRESSURE AND ADMINISTER OXYGEN IF AVAILABLE. KEEP AFFECTED PERSON WARM AND AT REST. TREAT SYMPTOMATICALLY AND SUPPORTIVELY. ADMINISTRATION OF OXYGEN SHOULD BE PERFORMED BY QUALIFIED PERSONNEL. GET MEDICAL ATTENTION IMMEDIATELY.

SKIN CONTACT: DICHLOFENTHION: SEE INFORMATION ON ORGANOPHOSPHATES.
ORGANOPHOSPHATES: CHOLINESTERASE INHIBITOR. **ACUTE EXPOSURE-** LOCALIZED SWEATING AND FASCICULATIONS MAY OCCUR AT THE SITE OF CONTACT. IF SUFFICIENT AMOUNTS ARE ABSORBED, OTHER EFFECTS OF CHOLINESTERASE INHIBITION AS DESCRIBED IN ACUTE INHALATION MAY OCCUR. SYMPTOMS MAY BE DELAYED 2-3 HOURS, BUT USUALLY NO MORE THAN 12 HOURS. THE RATE OF ABSORPTION IS INCREASED BY THE PRESENCE OF DERMATITIS OR HIGH AMBIENT TEMPERATURES. DELAYED NEUROPATHY IS ALSO POSSIBLE. **CHRONIC EXPOSURE-** REPEATED OR PROLONGED EXPOSURE MAY CAUSE EFFECTS AS DESCRIBED IN ACUTE EXPOSURE. SOME ORGANOPHOSPHATES MAY CAUSE SENSITIZATION.

FIRST AID- REMOVE CONTAMINATED CLOTHING IMMEDIATELY. WASH CONTAMINATED AREAS WITH SOAP AND WATER FOLLOWED BY ALCOHOL (ARENA, POISONING, 4TH ED.). EMERGENCY PERSONNEL SHOULD WEAR GLOVES AND AVOID CONTAMINATION. TREAT RESPIRATORY DIFFICULTY WITH ARTIFICIAL RESPIRATION. GET MEDICAL ATTENTION IMMEDIATELY.

EYE CONTACT: DICHLOFENTHION: SEE INFORMATION ON ORGANOPHOSPHATES. ORGANOPHOSPHATES: CHOLINESTERASE INHIBITOR. **ACUTE EXPOSURE-** DIRECT CONTACT MAY CAUSE PAIN, HYPEREMIA, LACRIMATION, TWITCHING OF THE EYELIDS, MIOSIS, AND CILIARY MUSCLE SPASM WITH LOSS OF ACCOMODATION, BLURRED OR DIMMED VISION AND BROWACHE. SOMETIMES MYDRIASIS MAY OCCUR INSTEAD OF MIOSIS. WITH SUFFICIENT EXPOSURE, OTHER SYMPTOMS OF CHOLINESTERASE INHIBITION AS DESCRIBED IN ACUTE INHALATION MAY OCCUR. **CHRONIC EXPOSURE-** REPEATED OR PROLONGED EXPOSURE MAY CAUSE EFFECTS AS DESCRIBED IN ACUTE EXPOSURE. SOME COMPOUNDS HAVE CAUSED TOXIC EFFECTS ON THE CRYSTALLINE LENS, CONJUNCTIVAL THICKENING AND OBSTRUCTION OF THE NASOLACRIMAL CANALS WHEN USED AS MIOTIC EYEDROPS.

FIRST AID- IRRIGATE EYES WITH WATER OR SALINE SOLUTION. IF SYMPTOMS OF POISONING OCCUR, TREAT RESPIRATORY DIFFICULTY WITH ARTIFICIAL RESPIRATION AND OXYGEN. OBSERVE PATIENT FOR AT LEAST 24-36 HOURS (GOSSELIN, CLINICAL TOXICOLOGY OF COMMERCIAL PRODUCTS, 5TH ED.). GET MEDICAL ATTENTION IMMEDIATELY. OXYGEN SHOULD BE ADMINISTERED BY QUALIFIED MEDICAL PERSONNEL.

INGESTION: DICHLOFENTHION: TOXIC. SEE INFORMATION ON ORGANOPHOSPHATES. ORGANOPHOSPHATES: CHOLINESTERASE INHIBITOR. **ACUTE EXPOSURE-** WHEN INGESTED, THE FIRST EFFECTS MAY BE NAUSEA, VOMITING, ANOREXIA, ABDOMINAL CRAMPS AND DIARRHEA. GASTROINTESTINAL ABSORPTION MAY CAUSE SYMPTOMS OF CHOLINESTERASE INHIBITION AS DESCRIBED IN ACUTE INHALATION. SYMPTOMS MAY BEGIN WITHIN MINUTES OR BE DELAYED FOR HOURS. DELAYED EFFECTS INCLUDING NEUROPATHY MAY ALSO OCCUR. **CHRONIC EXPOSURE-** REPEATED INGESTION MAY CAUSE EFFECTS AS DESCRIBED IN ACUTE EXPOSURE.

FIRST AID- IF PERSON IS ALERT AND RESPIRATION IS NOT DEPRESSED, GIVE SYRUP OF IPECAC FOLLOWED BY WATER (IF VOMITING OCCURS, KEEP HEAD BELOW HIPS TO PREVENT ASPIRATION). IF CONSCIOUSNESS LEVEL DECLINES OR VOMITING HAS NOT OCCURRED IN 15 MINUTES EMPTY STOMACH BY GASTRIC LAVAGE WITH THE AID OF CUFFED ENDOTRACHEAL TUBE USING ISOTONIC SALINE OR 5% SODIUM BICARBONATE FOLLOW WITH ACTIVATED CHARCOAL. ESTABLISH AND MAINTAIN AIRWAY. TREAT RESPIRATORY DIFFICULTY WITH ARTIFICIAL RESPIRATION AND OXYGEN. DO NOT GIVE MORPHINE, AMINOPHYLLINE, PHENOTHIAZINES, RESERPINE, FUROSEMIDE, OR ETHACRYNIC ACID (MORGAN, RECOGNITION AND MANAGEMENT OF PESTICIDE POISONINGS, 3RD ED.). TREAT SYMPTOMATICALLY AND SUPPORTIVELY. ADMINISTRATION OF OXYGEN AND LAVAGE MUST BE PERFORMED BY QUALIFIED MEDICAL PERSONNEL. GET MEDICAL ATTENTION IMMEDIATELY.

ANTIDOTE: THE FOLLOWING ANTIDOTE(S) HAVE BEEN RECOMMENDED. HOWEVER, THE DECISION AS TO WHETHER THE SEVERITY OF POISONING REQUIRES ADMINISTRATION OF ANY ANTIDOTE AND ACTUAL DOSE REQUIRED SHOULD BE MADE BY QUALIFIED MEDICAL PERSONNEL.

FOR CHOLINESTERASE INHIBITORS: ESTABLISH CLEAR AIRWAY AND TISSUE OXYGENATION BY ASPIRATION OF SECRETIONS, AND IF NECESSARY, BY ASSISTED PULMONARY VENTILATION WITH OXYGEN. IMPROVE TISSUE OXYGENATION AS MUCH AS POSSIBLE BEFORE ADMINISTERING ATROPINE TO MINIMIZE THE RISK OF VENTRICULAR FIBRILLATION. ADMINISTER ATROPINE SULFATE INTRAVENOUSLY, OR INTRAMUSCULARLY IF IV INJECTION IS NOT POSSIBLE. IN MODERATELY SEVERE POISONING ADMINISTER ATROPINE SULFATE, 0.4-2.0 MG REPEATED EVERY 15 MINUTES UNTIL ATROPINIZATION IS ACHIEVED (TACHYCARDIA, FLUSHING, DRY MOUTH, MYDRIASIS). MAINTAIN ATROPINIZATION BY REPEATED DOSES FOR 2-12 HOURS, OR LONGER, DEPENDING ON THE SEVERITY OF POISONING. THE APPEARANCE OF RALES IN THE LUNG BASES, MIOSIS, SALIVATION, NAUSEA, BRADYCARDIA, ARE ALL INDICATIONS OF INADEQUATE ATROPINIZATION. SEVERELY POISONED INDIVIDUALS MAY EXHIBIT REMARKABLE TOLERANCE TO ATROPINE; TWO OR MORE TIMES THE DOSAGES SUGGESTED ABOVE MAY BE NEEDED. PERSONS NOT POISONED OR ONLY SLIGHTLY POISONED, HOWEVER, MAY DEVELOP SIGNS OF ATROPINE TOXICITY FROM SUCH LARGE DOSAGES: FEVER, MUSCLE FIBRILLATIONS, AND DELIRIUM ARE THE MAIN SIGNS OF ATROPINE TOXICITY. IF THESE SIGNS APPEAR WHILE THE PATIENT IS FULLY ATROPINIZED, ATROPINE ADMINISTRATION SHOULD BE DISCONTINUED, AT LEAST TEMPORARILY. OBSERVE TREATED PATIENTS CLOSELY AT LEAST 24 HOURS TO INSURE THAT SYMPTOMS (POSSIBLY PULMONARY EDEMA) DO NOT RECUR AS ATROPINIZATION WEARS OFF. IN VERY SEVERE POISONINGS, METABOLIC DISPOSITION OF TOXICANT MAY REQUIRE SEVERAL HOURS OR DAYS DURING WHICH ATROPINIZATION MUST BE MAINTAINED. MARKEDLY LOWER LEVELS OF URINARY METABOLITES INDICATE THAT ATROPINE DOSAGE CAN BE TAPERED OFF. AS DOSAGE IS REDUCED, CHECK THE LUNG BASES FREQUENTLY FOR RALES. IF RALES ARE HEARD OR OTHER SYMPTOMS RETURN, RE-ESTABLISH ATROPINIZATION PROMPTLY (MORGAN, RECOGNITION AND MANAGEMENT OF PESTICIDE POISONINGS, 3RD ED.). ADMINISTRATION OF ANTIDOTE MUST BE PERFORMED BY QUALIFIED MEDICAL PERSONNEL.

IN CASES OF SEVERE POISONING BY ORGANOPHOSPHATE PESTICIDES IN WHICH RESPIRATORY DEPRESSION, MUSCLE WEAKNESS AND TWITCHINGS ARE SEVERE, GIVE PRALIDOXIME (PROTOPAM-AYERST, 2-PAM), 1.0 GRAM INTRAVENOUSLY AT NO MORE THAN 0.5 GRAM PER MINUTE. DOSAGE OF PRALIDOXIME MAY BE REPEATED IN 1-2 HOURS, THEN AT 10-12 HOUR INTERVALS IF NEEDED. IN VERY SEVERE POISONINGS, DOSAGE RATES MAY BE DOUBLED. TREATMENT WITH PRALIDOXIME WILL BE MOST EFFECTIVE IF GIVEN WITHIN THIRTY-SIX HOURS AFTER POISONING (MORGAN, RECOGNITION AND MANAGEMENT OF PESTICIDE POISONINGS, 3RD ED.). ANTIDOTE SHOULD BE ADMINISTERED BY QUALIFIED MEDICAL PERSONNEL.

REACTIVITY

REACTIVITY: STABLE UNDER NORMAL TEMPERATURES AND PRESSURES.

INCOMPATIBILITIES: DICHLOFENTHION: STRONG ALKALINE CONDITIONS: MAY CAUSE HYDROLYSIS.

DECOMPOSITION: THERMAL DECOMPOSITION PRODUCTS MAY INCLUDE TOXIC AND HAZARDOUS FUMES OF SULFUR, NITROGEN AND PHOSPHORUS.

POLYMERIZATION: HAZARDOUS POLYMERIZATION HAS NOT BEEN REPORTED TO OCCUR UNDER NORMAL TEMPERATURES AND PRESSURES.

STORAGE AND DISPOSAL

OBSERVE ALL FEDERAL, STATE AND LOCAL REGULATIONS WHEN STORING OR DISPOSING OF THIS SUBSTANCE. FOR ASSISTANCE, CONTACT THE DISTRICT DIRECTOR OF THE ENVIRONMENTAL PROTECTION AGENCY.

STORAGE

STORE IN ACCORDANCE WITH 40 CFR 165 RECOMMENDED PROCEDURES FOR THE DISPOSAL AND STORAGE OF PESTICIDES AND PESTICIDE CONTAINERS.
STORE AWAY FROM INCOMPATIBLE SUBSTANCES.

DISPOSAL

DISPOSAL MUST BE IN ACCORDANCE WITH 40 CFR 165 RECOMMENDED PROCEDURES FOR THE DISPOSAL AND STORAGE OF PESTICIDES AND PESTICIDE CONTAINERS.

CONDITIONS TO AVOID

NONE REPORTED.

SPILL AND LEAK PROCEDURES

OCCUPATIONAL SPILL: DO NOT TOUCH SPILLED MATERIAL. STOP LEAK IF YOU CAN DO IT WITHOUT RISK. USE WATER SPRAY TO REDUCE VAPORS. FOR SMALL SPILLS, TAKE UP WITH SAND OR OTHER ABSORBENT MATERIAL AND PLACE INTO CONTAINERS FOR LATER DISPOSAL. FOR SMALL DRY SPILLS, WITH A CLEAN SHOVEL PLACE MATERIAL INTO CLEAN, DRY CONTAINERS AND COVER. MOVE CONTAINERS FROM SPILL AREA. FOR LARGER SPILLS, DIKE FAR AHEAD OF SPILL FOR LATER DISPOSAL. KEEP UNNECESSARY PEOPLE AWAY. ISOLATE HAZARD AREA AND DENY ENTRY. VENTILATE CLOSED SPACES BEFORE ENTERING.

PROTECTIVE EQUIPMENT

VENTILATION: PROVIDE LOCAL EXHAUST OR PROCESS ENCLOSURE VENTILATION SYSTEM.

RESPIRATOR: THE FOLLOWING RESPIRATORS ARE RECOMMENDED BASED ON INFORMATION FOUND IN THE PHYSICAL DATA, TOXICITY AND HEALTH EFFECTS SECTIONS. THEY ARE RANKED IN ORDER FROM MINIMUM TO MAXIMUM RESPIRATORY PROTECTION. THE SPECIFIC RESPIRATOR SELECTED MUST BE BASED ON CONTAMINATION LEVELS FOUND IN THE WORK PLACE, MUST NOT EXCEED THE WORKING LIMITS OF THE RESPIRATOR AND BE JOINTLY APPROVED BY THE NATIONAL INSTITUTE FOR OCCUPATIONAL SAFETY AND HEALTH AND THE MINE SAFETY AND HEALTH ADMINISTRATION (NIOSH-MSHA).

TYPE 'C' SUPPLIED-AIR RESPIRATOR WITH A FULL FACEPIECE OPERATED IN PRESSURE-DEMAND OR OTHER POSITIVE PRESSURE MODE OR WITH A FULL FACEPIECE, HELMET OR HOOD OPERATED IN CONTINOUS-FLOW MODE.

SELF-CONTAINED BREATHING APPARATUS WITH A FULL FACEPIECE OPERATED IN PRESSURE-DEMAND OR OTHER POSITIVE PRESSURE MODE.

FOR FIREFIGHTING AND OTHER IMMEDIATELY DANGEROUS TO LIFE OR HEALTH CONDITIONS:

SELF-CONTAINED BREATHING APPARATUS WITH FULL FACEPIECE OPERATED IN PRESSURE-DEMAND OR OTHER POSITIVE PRESSURE MODE.

SUPPLIED-AIR RESPIRATOR WITH FULL FACEPIECE AND OPERATED IN PRESSURE-DEMAND OR OTHER POSITIVE PRESSURE MODE IN COMBINATION WITH AN AUXILIARY SELF-CONTAINED BREATHING APPARATUS OPERATED IN PRESSURE-DEMAND OR OTHER POSITIVE PRESSURE MODE.

CLOTHING: EMPLOYEE MUST WEAR APPROPRIATE PROTECTIVE (IMPERVIOUS) CLOTHING AND EQUIPMENT TO PREVENT REPEATED OR PROLONGED SKIN CONTACT WITH THIS SUBSTANCE.

GLOVES: EMPLOYEE MUST WEAR APPROPRIATE PROTECTIVE GLOVES TO PREVENT CONTACT WITH THIS SUBSTANCE.

EYE PROTECTION: EMPLOYEE MUST WEAR SPLASH-PROOF OR DUST-RESISTANT SAFETY GOGGLES TO PREVENT EYE CONTACT WITH THIS SUBSTANCE.

EMERGENCY EYE WASH: WHERE THERE IS ANY POSSIBILITY THAT AN EMPLOYEE'S

EYES MAY BE EXPOSED TO THIS SUBSTANCE, THE EMPLOYER SHOULD PROVIDE AN EYE WASH FOUNTAIN WITHIN THE IMMEDIATE WORK AREA FOR EMERGENCY USE.

AUTHORIZED BY- OCCUPATIONAL HEALTH SERVICES, INC.
CREATION DATE: 10/04/89 ***REVISION DATE:*** 04/26/90

MATERIAL SAFETY DATA SHEET

OCCUPATIONAL HEALTH SERVICES, INC.
AGRICULTURE AND PESTICIDE DIVISION
450 SEVENTH AVENUE, SUITE 2407
NEW YORK, NEW YORK 10123
1-800-445-MSDS OR (212) 967-1100

EMERGENCY CONTACT:
JOHN S. BRANSFORD, JR. (615) 292-1180

SUBSTANCE IDENTIFICATION

CAS-NUMBER 117-80-6
SUBSTANCE: DICHLONE
TRADE NAMES/SYNONYMS: 2,3-DICHLORO-1,4-NAPHTHALENEDIONE; 2,3-DICHLORO-1,4-NAPHTHOQUINONE; ALGISTAT; COMPOUND 604; DICLONE; PHYGON; PHYGON SEED PROTECTANT; PHYGON XL; SANQUINON; USR 604; PST06810
CHEMICAL FAMILY: HALOGEN AROMATIC
MOLECULAR FORMULA: C10-H4-CL2-O2
MOLECULAR WEIGHT: 227.04
CERCLA RATINGS (SCALE 0-3): HEALTH=3 FIRE=0 REACTIVITY=0 PERSISTENCE=3
NFPA RATINGS (SCALE 0-4): HEALTH=3 FIRE=0 REACTIVITY=0

COMPONENTS AND CONTAMINANTS

COMPONENT: DICHLONE ***PERCENT:*** 100
CAS# 117-80-6
OTHER CONTAMINANTS: NONE
EXPOSURE LIMITS: DICHLONE: NO OCCUPATIONAL EXPOSURE LIMITS ESTABLISHED BY OSHA, ACGIH, OR NIOSH.
1 POUND CERCLA SECTION 103 REPORTABLE QUANTITY SUBJECT TO SARA SECTION 313 ANNUAL TOXIC CHEMICAL RELEASE REPORTING

PHYSICAL DATA

DESCRIPTION: GOLDEN YELLOW NEEDLES OR LEAFLETS WHICH SUBLIME
BOILING POINT: NOT AVAILABLE ***MELTING POINT:*** 381-387 F (194-197 C)
SPECIFIC GRAVITY: NOT AVAILABLE ***SOLUBILITY IN WATER:*** ALMOST INSOLUBLE
SOLVENT SOLUBILITY: XYLENE, ORTHO-DICHLOROBENZENE, ETHYL ALCOHOL, GLACIAL ACETIC ACID, CARBON TETRACHLORIDE, DIOXANE

FIRE AND EXPLOSION DATA

FIRE AND EXPLOSION HAZARD: NEGLIGIBLE FIRE HAZARD WHEN EXPOSED TO HEAT OR FLAME.
FIREFIGHTING MEDIA: DRY CHEMICAL, CARBON DIOXIDE, HALON, WATER SPRAY OR STANDARD FOAM (1987 EMERGENCY RESPONSE GUIDEBOOK, DOT P 5800.4).
FOR LARGER FIRES, USE WATER SPRAY, FOG OR STANDARD FOAM (1987 EMERGENCY RESPONSE GUIDEBOOK, DOT P 5800.4).
FIREFIGHTING: MOVE CONTAINERS FROM FIRE AREA IF POSSIBLE. FIGHT FIRE FROM MAXIMUM DISTANCE. STAY AWAY FROM STORAGE TANK ENDS. DIKE FIRE CONTROL WATER FOR LATER DISPOSAL. DO NOT SCATTER MATERIAL (1987 EMERGENCY RESPONSE GUIDEBOOK, DOT P 5800.4, GUIDE PAGE 55). EXTINGUISH ONLY IF FLOW CAN BE STOPPED. EXTINGUISH USING AGENT INDICATED. USE FLOODING AMOUNTS OF WATER AS A FOG. COOL CONTAINERS WITH FLOODING AMOUNTS OF WATER FROM AS FAR A DISTANCE AS POSSIBLE. AVOID BREATHING POISONOUS VAPORS, KEEP UPWIND. CONSIDER EVACUATION OF DOWNWIND AREA IF MATERIAL IS LEAKING.

TRANSPORTATION DATA

DEPARTMENT OF TRANSPORTATION HAZARD CLASSIFICATION 49 CFR 172.101: ORM-E
DEPARTMENT OF TRANSPORTATION LABELING REQUIREMENTS 49 CFR 172.101 AND SUBPART E: NONE
DEPARTMENT OF TRANSPORTATION PACKAGING REQUIREMENTS: 49 CFR 173.510 EXCEPTIONS: NONE

TOXICITY

DICHLONE: TOXICITY DATA: 5000 MG/KG SKIN-RABBIT LD50; 160 MG/KG ORAL-RAT LD50; 440 MG/KG ORAL-MOUSE LD50; 30 MG/KG INTRAPERITONEAL-MOUSE LD50; TUMORIGENIC DATA (RTEC). CARCINOGEN STATUS: NONE. LOCAL EFFECTS: IRRITANT- INHALATION, SKIN, AND EYES. ACUTE TOXICITY LEVEL: TOXIC BY INGESTION AND SLIGHTLY TOXIC BY DERMAL ABSORPTION. TARGET EFFECTS: CENTRAL NERVOUS SYSTEM DEPRESSANT. POISONING MAY AFFECT THE LIVER AND KIDNEYS.

HEALTH EFFECTS AND FIRST AID

INHALATION: DICHLONE: IRRITANT. **ACUTE EXPOSURE-** MAY CAUSE IRRITATION. **CHRONIC EXPOSURE-** REPEATED OR PROLONGED CONTACT MAY CAUSE IRRITATION TO THE MUCOUS MEMBRANES.
FIRST AID- REMOVE FROM EXPOSURE AREA TO FRESH AIR IMMEDIATELY. IF BREATHING HAS STOPPED, PERFORM ARTIFICIAL RESPIRATION. KEEP PERSON WARM AND AT REST. TREAT SYMPTOMATICALLY AND SUPPORTIVELY. GET MEDICAL ATTENTION IMMEDIATELY.

SKIN CONTACT: DICHLONE: IRRITANT. **ACUTE EXPOSURE-** MAY CAUSE IRRITATION. A LARGE DOSE WAS REQUIRED TO CAUSE DEATH IN RABBITS. **CHRONIC EXPOSURE-** REPEATED OR PROLONGED CONTACT MAY CAUSE DERMATITIS.
FIRST AID- REMOVE CONTAMINATED CLOTHING AND SHOES IMMEDIATELY. WASH AFFECTED AREA WITH SOAP OR MILD DETERGENT AND LARGE AMOUNTS OF WATER UNTIL NO EVIDENCE OF CHEMICAL REMAINS (APPROXIMATELY 15-20 MINUTES). GET MEDICAL ATTENTION IMMEDIATELY.

EYE CONTACT: DICHLONE: IRRITANT. **ACUTE EXPOSURE-** MAY CAUSE IRRITATION. **CHRONIC EXPOSURE-** REPEATED OR PROLONGED CONTACT MAY CAUSE CONJUNCTIVITIS.
FIRST AID- WASH EYES IMMEDIATELY WITH LARGE AMOUNTS OF WATER OR NORMAL SALINE, OCCASIONALLY LIFTING UPPER AND LOWER LIDS, UNTIL NO EVIDENCE OF CHEMICAL REMAINS (APPROXIMATELY 15-20 MINUTES). GET MEDICAL ATTENTION IMMEDIATELY.

INGESTION: DICHLONE: NARCOTIC/TOXIC. **ACUTE EXPOSURE-** MAY CAUSE NAUSEA OR VOMITING AND CENTRAL NERVOUS SYSTEM DEPRESSION WITH DIZZINESS, HEADACHE, WEAKNESS AND LABORED BREATHING. LIVER AND KIDNEY DAMAGE MAY OCCUR. **CHRONIC EXPOSURE-** DOGS GIVEN 500 PPM IN FOOD FOR 1 YEAR SHOWED SLIGHT LIVER DAMAGE. MICE FED A TOTAL DOSE OF 3300 MG/KG FOR 78 WEEKS DEVELOPED TUMORS OF THE LUNGS AND LEUKEMIA.
FIRST AID- REMOVE BY GASTRIC LAVAGE OR EMESIS. MAINTAIN BLOOD PRESSURE AND AIRWAY. DO NOT PERFORM GASTRIC LAVAGE OR EMESIS IF VICTIM IS UNCONSCIOUS. DO NOT GIVE STIMULANTS WHICH MAY INDUCE VENTRICULAR FIBRILLATION. GET MEDICAL ATTENTION IMMEDIATELY. (DREISBACH, HANDBOOK OF POISONING, 11TH EDITION) ADMINISTRATION OF GASTRIC LAVAGE SHOULD BE PERFORMED BY QUALIFIED MEDICAL PERSONNEL.
ANTIDOTE: NO SPECIFIC ANTIDOTE. TREAT SYMPTOMATICALLY AND SUPPORTIVELY.

REACTIVITY

REACTIVITY: STABLE UNDER NORMAL TEMPERATURES AND PRESSURES.
INCOMPATIBILITIES: DICHLONE: NO DATA AVAILABLE.
DECOMPOSITION: THERMAL DECOMPOSITION MAY RELEASE TOXIC AND/OR HAZARDOUS GASES.
POLYMERIZATION: NO DATA AVAILABLE.

CONDITIONS TO AVOID

MAY BURN BUT DOES NOT IGNITE READILY. CONTAINERS MAY EXPLODE IN HEAT OF FIRE.

SPILL AND LEAK PROCEDURES

SOIL SPILL: DIG A PIT, POND, LAGOON OR HOLDING AREA TO CONTAIN LIQUID OR SOLID MATERIAL. COVER SOLIDS WITH A PLASTIC SHEET TO PREVENT DISSOLVING IN RAIN OR FIREFIGHTING WATER.
WATER SPILL: USE NATURAL DEEP WATER POCKETS, EXCAVATED LAGOONS, OR SAND BAG BARRIERS TO TRAP MATERIAL AT BOTTOM. USE ACTIVATED CARBON AT 10 TIMES THE SPILLED AMOUNT IF IT IS DISSOLVED AT 10 PPM OR GREATER CONCENTRATION. REMOVE TRAPPED MATERIAL WITH SUCTION HOSES. USE MECHANICAL DREDGES OR LIFTS TO REMOVE IMMOBILIZED MASSES OF POLLUTION AND PRECIPITATES.
OCCUPATIONAL SPILL: DO NOT TOUCH SPILLED MATERIAL. STOP LEAK IF YOU CAN DO IT WITHOUT RISK. USE WATER SPRAY TO REDUCE VAPORS. FOR SMALL SPILLS, TAKE UP WITH SAND OR OTHER ABSORBENT MATERIAL AND PLACE INTO CONTAINERS FOR LATER DISPOSAL. FOR SMALL DRY SPILLS, WITH A CLEAN SHOVEL PLACE MATERIAL INTO CLEAN, DRY CONTAINERS AND COVER. MOVE CONTAINERS FROM SPILL AREA. FOR LARGER SPILLS, DIKE FAR AHEAD OF SPILL FOR LATER DISPOSAL. KEEP UNNECESSARY PEOPLE AWAY. ISOLATE HAZARD AREA AND DENY ENTRY. VENTILATE CLOSED SPACES BEFORE ENTERING.

REPORTABLE QUANTITY (RQ): 1 POUND THE SUPERFUND AMENDMENTS AND REAUTHORIZATION ACT (SARA) SECTION 304 REQUIRES THAT A RELEASE EQUAL TO OR GREATER THAN THE REPORTABLE QUANTITY FOR THIS SUBSTANCE BE IMMEDIATELY REPORTED TO THE LOCAL EMERGENCY PLANNING COMMITTEE AND THE STATE EMERGENCY RESPONSE COMMISSION (40 CFR 355.40). IF THE RELEASE OF THIS SUBSTANCE IS REPORTABLE UNDER CERCLA SECTION 103, THE NATIONAL RESPONSE CENTER MUST BE NOTIFIED IMMEDIATELY AT (800) 424-8802 OR (202) 426-2675 IN THE METROPOLITAN WASHINGTON, D.C. AREA (40 CFR 302.6).

PROTECTIVE EQUIPMENT

VENTILATION: PROVIDE LOCAL EXHAUST OR PROCESS ENCLOSURE VENTILATION SYSTEM.

RESPIRATOR: THE FOLLOWING RESPIRATORS ARE RECOMMENDED BASED ON INFORMATION FOUND IN THE PHYSICAL DATA, TOXICITY AND HEALTH EFFECTS SECTIONS. THEY ARE RANKED IN ORDER FROM MINIMUM TO MAXIMUM RESPIRATORY PROTECTION. THE SPECIFIC RESPIRATOR SELECTED MUST BE BASED ON CONTAMINATION LEVELS FOUND IN THE WORK PLACE, MUST NOT EXCEED THE WORKING LIMITS OF THE RESPIRATOR AND BE JOINTLY APPROVED BY THE NATIONAL INSTITUTE FOR OCCUPATIONAL SAFETY AND HEALTH AND THE MINE SAFETY AND HEALTH ADMINISTRATION (NIOSH-MSHA).

TYPE 'C' SUPPLIED-AIR RESPIRATOR WITH A FULL FACEPIECE OPERATED IN PRESSURE-DEMAND OR OTHER POSITIVE PRESSURE MODE OR WITH A FULL FACEPIECE, HELMET OR HOOD OPERATED IN CONTINOUS-FLOW MODE.

SELF-CONTAINED BREATHING APPARATUS WITH A FULL FACEPIECE OPERATED IN PRESSURE-DEMAND OR OTHER POSITIVE PRESSURE MODE.

FOR FIREFIGHTING AND OTHER IMMEDIATELY DANGEROUS TO LIFE OR HEALTH CONDITIONS:

SELF-CONTAINED BREATHING APPARATUS WITH FULL FACEPIECE OPERATED IN PRESSURE-DEMAND OR OTHER POSITIVE PRESSURE MODE.

SUPPLIED-AIR RESPIRATOR WITH FULL FACEPIECE AND OPERATED IN PRESSURE-DEMAND OR OTHER POSITIVE PRESSURE MODE IN COMBINATION WITH AN AUXILIARY SELF-CONTAINED BREATHING APPARATUS OPERATED IN PRESSURE-DEMAND OR OTHER POSITIVE PRESSURE MODE.

CLOTHING: EMPLOYEE MUST WEAR APPROPRIATE PROTECTIVE (IMPERVIOUS) CLOTHING AND EQUIPMENT TO PREVENT REPEATED OR PROLONGED SKIN CONTACT WITH THIS SUBSTANCE.

GLOVES: EMPLOYEE MUST WEAR APPROPRIATE PROTECTIVE GLOVES TO PREVENT CONTACT WITH THIS SUBSTANCE.

EYE PROTECTION: EMPLOYEE MUST WEAR SPLASH-PROOF OR DUST-RESISTANT SAFETY GOGGLES TO PREVENT EYE CONTACT WITH THIS SUBSTANCE.

EMERGENCY EYE WASH: WHERE THERE IS ANY POSSIBILITY THAT AN EMPLOYEE'S EYES MAY BE EXPOSED TO THIS SUBSTANCE, THE EMPLOYER SHOULD PROVIDE AN EYE WASH FOUNTAIN WITHIN THE IMMEDIATE WORK AREA FOR EMERGENCY USE.

AUTHORIZED BY- OCCUPATIONAL HEALTH SERVICES, INC.

CREATION DATE: 10/04/89 ***REVISION DATE:*** 05/04/90

MATERIAL SAFETY DATA SHEET

OCCUPATIONAL HEALTH SERVICES, INC.
AGRICULTURE AND PESTICIDE DIVISION
450 SEVENTH AVENUE, SUITE 2407
NEW YORK, NEW YORK 10123
1-800-445-MSDS OR (212) 967-1100

EMERGENCY CONTACT:
JOHN S. BRANSFORD, JR. (615) 292-1180

SUBSTANCE IDENTIFICATION

CAS-NUMBER 116-52-9

SUBSTANCE: **DICHLORALUREA**

TRADE NAMES/SYNONYMS: UREA, N,N'-BIS(2,2,2-TRICHLORO-1-HYDROXYETHYL)-; UREA, 1,3-BIS(2,2,2-TRICHLORO-1-HYDROXYETHYL)-; N,N'-BIS(2,2,2-TRICHLORO-1-HYDROXYETHYL)UREA; 1,3-BIS(2,2,2-TRICHLORO-1-HYDROXYETHYL)UREA; CRAG EXPERIMENTAL HERBICIDE 2; CRAG HERBICIDE 2; DCU; DICHLORAL UREA; DICLORALUREA; DKHM; EH2; EXPERIMENTAL HERBICIDE; RC 9485; C5H6CL6N2O3; PST06817

CHEMICAL FAMILY: SUBSTITUTED UREA
HALOGEN

MOLECULAR FORMULA: (C-CL3-C-H-(O-H)-N-H)2-C-O

MOLECULAR WEIGHT: 354.83

CERCLA RATINGS (SCALE 0-3): HEALTH=1 FIRE=1 REACTIVITY=0
PERSISTENCE=2

NFPA RATINGS (SCALE 0-4): HEALTH=1 FIRE=1 REACTIVITY=0

COMPONENTS AND CONTAMINANTS

COMPONENT: DICHLORALUREA ***PERCENT:*** 100.0
CAS# 116-52-9

OTHER CONTAMINANTS: NONE

EXPOSURE LIMITS: NO OCCUPATIONAL EXPOSURE LIMITS ESTABLISHED BY OSHA, ACGIH, OR NIOSH.

PHYSICAL DATA

DESCRIPTION: SOLID. ***MELTING POINT:*** 385 F (196 C)

SPECIFIC GRAVITY: NOT AVAILABLE ***SOLUBILITY IN WATER:*** NOT AVAILABLE

SOLVENT SOLUBILITY: SOLUBLE IN ALCOHOL AND ACETONE.

FIRE AND EXPLOSION DATA

FIRE AND EXPLOSION HAZARD: SLIGHT FIRE HAZARD WHEN EXPOSED TO HEAT OR FLAME.

FIREFIGHTING MEDIA: DRY CHEMICAL, CARBON DIOXIDE, HALON, WATER SPRAY OR STANDARD FOAM (1987 EMERGENCY RESPONSE GUIDEBOOK, DOT P 5800.4). FOR LARGER FIRES, USE WATER SPRAY, FOG OR STANDARD FOAM (1987 EMERGENCY RESPONSE GUIDEBOOK, DOT P 5800.4).

FIREFIGHTING: MOVE CONTAINERS FROM FIRE AREA IF POSSIBLE. FIGHT FIRE FROM MAXIMUM DISTANCE. STAY AWAY FROM STORAGE TANK ENDS. DIKE FIRE CONTROL WATER FOR LATER DISPOSAL. DO NOT SCATTER MATERIAL (1987 EMERGENCY RESPONSE GUIDEBOOK, DOT P 5800.4, GUIDE PAGE 55). EXTINGUISH USING AGENT SUITABLE FOR TYPE OF SURROUNDING FIRE. USE WATER IN FLOODING QUANTITIES AS FOG. KEEP SPARKS, FLAMES AND OTHER SOURCES OF IGNITION AWAY. KEEP MATERIAL OUT OF WATER SOURCES AND SEWERS. DO NOT TOUCH MATERIAL AND AVOID BREATHING DUSTS AND FUMES FROM BURNING MATERIAL. KEEP UPWIND.

TOXICITY

DICHLORALUREA: IRRITATION DATA: 50 MG OPEN SKIN-RABBIT MILD. TOXICITY DATA: 6680 MG/KG ORAL-RAT LD50; MUTAGENIC DATA (RTECS). CARCINOGEN STATUS: NONE. ACUTE TOXICITY LEVEL: SLIGHTLY TOXIC BY INGESTION. TARGET EFFECTS: NO DATA AVAILABLE.

HEALTH EFFECTS AND FIRST AID

INHALATION: DICHLORALUREA: **ACUTE EXPOSURE**- MANY SUBSTITUTED UREA HERBICIDES ARE MODERATELY IRRITATING TO THE MUCOUS MEMBRANES. **CHRONIC EXPOSURE**- NO DATA AVAILABLE.

FIRST AID- REMOVE FROM EXPOSURE AREA TO FRESH AIR IMMEDIATELY. IF BREATHING HAS STOPPED, PERFORM ARTIFICIAL RESPIRATION. KEEP PERSON WARM AND AT REST. TREAT SYMPTOMATICALLY AND SUPPORTIVELY. GET MEDICAL ATTENTION IMMEDIATELY.

SKIN CONTACT: DICHLORALUREA: **ACUTE EXPOSURE**- 50 MG APPLIED TO OPEN RABBIT SKIN WAS MILDLY IRRITATING. **CHRONIC EXPOSURE**- NO DATA AVAILABLE.

FIRST AID- REMOVE CONTAMINATED CLOTHING AND SHOES IMMEDIATELY. WASH AFFECTED AREA WITH SOAP OR MILD DETERGENT AND LARGE AMOUNTS OF WATER UNTIL NO EVIDENCE OF CHEMICAL REMAINS (APPROXIMATELY 15-20 MINUTES). GET MEDICAL ATTENTION IMMEDIATELY.

EYE CONTACT: DICHLORALUREA: **ACUTE EXPOSURE**- MANY SUBSTITUTED UREA HERBICIDES ARE MODERATELY IRRITATING TO THE EYES. **CHRONIC EXPOSURE**- NO DATA AVAILABLE.

FIRST AID- WASH EYES IMMEDIATELY WITH LARGE AMOUNTS OF WATER OR NORMAL SALINE, OCCASIONALLY LIFTING UPPER AND LOWER LIDS, UNTIL NO EVIDENCE OF CHEMICAL REMAINS (APPROXIMATELY 15-20 MINUTES). GET MEDICAL ATTENTION IMMEDIATELY.

INGESTION: DICHLORALUREA: **ACUTE EXPOSURE**- A LETHAL DOSE IN RATS WAS 6680 MG/KG; SYMPTOMS WERE NOT REPORTED. **CHRONIC EXPOSURE**- CHRONIC FEEDING IN RATS CAUSED FUNCTIONAL ALTERATIONS IN BLOOD, LIVER AND KIDNEY.

FIRST AID- TREAT SYMPTOMATICALLY AND SUPPORTIVELY. GET MEDICAL ATTENTION IMMEDIATELY. IF VOMITING OCCURS, KEEP HEAD LOWER THAN HIPS TO PREVENT ASPIRATION.

REACTIVITY

REACTIVITY: STABLE UNDER NORMAL TEMPERATURES AND PRESSURES.

INCOMPATIBILITIES: DICHLORALUREA: OXIDIZERS (STRONG): FIRE AND EXPLOSION HAZARD.

DECOMPOSITION: THERMAL DECOMPOSITION PRODUCTS MAY INCLUDE TOXIC OXIDES OF NITROGEN AND CARBON AND TOXIC AND CORROSIVE FUMES OF CHLORIDES.
POLYMERIZATION: HAZARDOUS POLYMERIZATION HAS NOT BEEN REPORTED TO OCCUR UNDER NORMAL TEMPERATURES AND PRESSURES.

STORAGE AND DISPOSAL

OBSERVE ALL FEDERAL, STATE AND LOCAL REGULATIONS WHEN STORING OR DISPOSING OF THIS SUBSTANCE. FOR ASSISTANCE, CONTACT THE DISTRICT DIRECTOR OF THE ENVIRONMENTAL PROTECTION AGENCY.

****STORAGE****

STORE IN ACCORDANCE WITH 40 CFR 165 RECOMMENDED PROCEDURES FOR THE DISPOSAL AND STORAGE OF PESTICIDES AND PESTICIDE CONTAINERS.
STORE AWAY FROM INCOMPATIBLE SUBSTANCES.

****DISPOSAL****

DISPOSAL MUST BE IN ACCORDANCE WITH 40 CFR 165 RECOMMENDED PROCEDURES FOR THE DISPOSAL AND STORAGE OF PESTICIDES AND PESTICIDE CONTAINERS.

CONDITIONS TO AVOID

MAY BURN BUT DOES NOT IGNITE READILY. CONTAINERS MAY EXPLODE IN HEAT OF FIRE.

SPILL AND LEAK PROCEDURES

OCCUPATIONAL SPILL: DO NOT TOUCH SPILLED MATERIAL. STOP LEAK IF YOU CAN DO IT WITHOUT RISK. USE WATER SPRAY TO REDUCE VAPORS. FOR SMALL SPILLS, TAKE UP WITH SAND OR OTHER ABSORBENT MATERIAL AND PLACE INTO CONTAINERS FOR LATER DISPOSAL. FOR SMALL DRY SPILLS, WITH A CLEAN SHOVEL PLACE MATERIAL INTO CLEAN, DRY CONTAINERS AND COVER. MOVE CONTAINERS FROM SPILL AREA. FOR LARGER SPILLS, DIKE FAR AHEAD OF SPILL FOR LATER DISPOSAL. KEEP UNNECESSARY PEOPLE AWAY. ISOLATE HAZARD AREA AND DENY ENTRY. VENTILATE CLOSED SPACES BEFORE ENTERING.

PROTECTIVE EQUIPMENT

VENTILATION: PROVIDE GENERAL DILUTION VENTILATION.
RESPIRATOR: THE FOLLOWING RESPIRATORS ARE RECOMMENDED BASED ON INFORMATION FOUND IN THE PHYSICAL DATA, TOXICITY AND HEALTH EFFECTS SECTIONS. THEY ARE RANKED IN ORDER FROM MINIMUM TO MAXIMUM RESPIRATORY PROTECTION. THE SPECIFIC RESPIRATOR SELECTED MUST BE BASED ON CONTAMINATION LEVELS FOUND IN THE WORK PLACE, MUST NOT EXCEED THE WORKING LIMITS OF THE RESPIRATOR AND BE JOINTLY APPROVED BY THE NATIONAL INSTITUTE FOR OCCUPATIONAL SAFETY AND HEALTH AND THE MINE SAFETY AND HEALTH ADMINISTRATION (NIOSH-MSHA).
CHEMICAL CARTRIDGE RESPIRATOR WITH AN ORGANIC VAPOR CARTRIDGE(S) WITH A FULL FACEPIECE AND ORGANIC VAPOR CARTRIDGE(S) IN COMBINATION WITH A DUST AND MIST FILTER.
POWERED AIR-PURIFYING RESPIRATOR WITH A TIGHT-FITTING FACEPIECE AND ORGANIC VAPOR CARTRIDGE(S) IN COMBINATION WITH A HIGH-EFFICIENCY PARTICULATE FILTER.
TYPE 'C' SUPPLIED-AIR RESPIRATOR WITH A FULL FACEPIECE OPERATED IN A PRESSURE-DEMAND OR OTHER POSITIVE PRESSURE MODE.
SELF-CONTAINED BREATHING APPARATUS WITH A FULL FACEPIECE OPERATED IN PRESSURE-DEMAND OR OTHER POSITIVE PRESSURE MODE.
FOR FIREFIGHTING AND OTHER IMMEDIATELY DANGEROUS TO LIFE OR HEALTH CONDITIONS:
SELF-CONTAINED BREATHING APPARATUS WITH FULL FACEPIECE OPERATED IN PRESSURE-DEMAND OR OTHER POSITIVE PRESSURE MODE.
SUPPLIED-AIR RESPIRATOR WITH FULL FACEPIECE AND OPERATED IN PRESSURE-DEMAND OR OTHER POSITIVE PRESSURE MODE IN COMBINATION WITH AN AUXILIARY SELF-CONTAINED BREATHING APPARATUS OPERATED IN PRESSURE-DEMAND OR OTHER POSITIVE PRESSURE MODE.
CLOTHING: EMPLOYEE MUST WEAR APPROPRIATE PROTECTIVE (IMPERVIOUS) CLOTHING AND EQUIPMENT TO PREVENT REPEATED OR PROLONGED SKIN CONTACT WITH THIS SUBSTANCE.
GLOVES: EMPLOYEE MUST WEAR APPROPRIATE PROTECTIVE GLOVES TO PREVENT CONTACT WITH THIS SUBSTANCE.
EYE PROTECTION: EMPLOYEE MUST WEAR SPLASH-PROOF OR DUST-RESISTANT SAFETY GOGGLES TO PREVENT EYE CONTACT WITH THIS SUBSTANCE.
EMERGENCY EYE WASH: WHERE THERE IS ANY POSSIBILITY THAT AN EMPLOYEE'S EYES MAY BE EXPOSED TO THIS SUBSTANCE, THE EMPLOYER SHOULD PROVIDE AN EYE WASH FOUNTAIN WITHIN THE IMMEDIATE WORK AREA FOR EMERGENCY USE.

AUTHORIZED BY- OCCUPATIONAL HEALTH SERVICES, INC.
CREATION DATE: 10/04/89 ***REVISION DATE:*** 05/07/90

MATERIAL SAFETY DATA SHEET

OCCUPATIONAL HEALTH SERVICES, INC.
AGRICULTURE AND PESTICIDE DIVISION
450 SEVENTH AVENUE, SUITE 2407
NEW YORK, NEW YORK 10123
1-800-445-MSDS OR (212) 967-1100

EMERGENCY CONTACT:
JOHN S. BRANSFORD, JR. (615) 292-1180

SUBSTANCE IDENTIFICATION

CAS-NUMBER 75-71-8
SUBSTANCE: **DICHLORODIFLUOROMETHANE**
TRADE NAMES/SYNONYMS: METHANE, DICHLORODIFLUORO-; ALGOGRENE TYPE 2; ARCTON 6; UCON (R) 12 (UNION CARBIDE CORPORATION); CHLOROFLUOROCARBON 12; DICHLORODIFLUOROMETHANE(R-12); DICHLORODIFLUOROMETHANE (CCL2F2); DIFLUORODICHLOROMETHANE; #8668 FREEZE MIST (GC ELECTRONICS); CF 12; FREON 12; FRIGEN 12; GENETRON 12; CFC 12; FALCON DUST OFF II (FALCON SAFETY PRODUCT INC.); R 12 (REFRIGERANT); RCRA U075; STCC 4904516; UN 1028; CCL2F2; PST06880
CHEMICAL FAMILY: HALOGEN COMPOUND, ALIPHATIC
MOLECULAR FORMULA: CL2-C-F2
MOLECULAR WEIGHT: 120.91
CERCLA RATINGS (SCALE 0-3): HEALTH=1 FIRE=0 REACTIVITY=0 PERSISTENCE=3
NFPA RATINGS (SCALE 0-4): HEALTH=1 FIRE=0 REACTIVITY=0

COMPONENTS AND CONTAMINANTS

COMPONENT: DICHLORODIFLUOROMETHANE ***PERCENT:*** 100.0
CAS# 75-71-8
OTHER CONTAMINANTS: NONE
EXPOSURE LIMITS: DICHLORODIFLUOROMETHANE: 1000 PPM (4950 MG/M3) OSHA TWA 1000 PPM (4950 MG/M3) ACGIH TWA
5000 POUNDS CERCLA SECTION 103 REPORTABLE QUANTITY

PHYSICAL DATA

DESCRIPTION: COLORLESS GAS WITH A FAINT ETHER-LIKE ODOR.
BOILING POINT: -22 F (-30 C) ***MELTING POINT:*** -252 F (-158 C)
SPECIFIC GRAVITY: 5.056 G/L @ 20 C ***VOLATILITY:*** 100%
VAPOR PRESSURE: 4393 MMHG @ 21.1 C
EVAPORATION RATE: (BUTYL ACETATE=1) 380
SOLUBILITY IN WATER: 0.028% @ 25 C ***VAPOR DENSITY:*** 4.2
SOLVENT SOLUBILITY: SOLUBLE IN ALCOHOL, ETHER, ACETIC ACID, KETONES, ESTERS, HYDROCARBONS, OIL LUBRICANTS, CHLORINATED SOLVENTS, ORGANIC ACIDS; INSOLUBLE IN GLYCOLS, GLYCERIN, PHENOLS, CASTOR OIL.
VISCOSITY: 0.0117 CPS @ 4.4 C (GAS); 0.398 CPS @ -40 C (LIQUID)

FIRE AND EXPLOSION DATA

FIRE AND EXPLOSION HAZARD: NEGLIGIBLE FIRE HAZARD WHEN EXPOSED TO HEAT OR FLAME.
CYLINDER MAY EXPLODE IN HEAT OF FIRE.
FIREFIGHTING MEDIA: DRY CHEMICAL, CARBON DIOXIDE OR HALON (1987 EMERGENCY RESPONSE GUIDEBOOK, DOT P 5800.4).
FOR LARGER FIRES, USE WATER SPRAY, FOG OR STANDARD FOAM (1987 EMERGENCY RESPONSE GUIDEBOOK, DOT P 5800.4).
FIREFIGHTING: MOVE CONTAINER FROM FIRE AREA IF POSSIBLE. STAY AWAY FROM STORAGE TANK ENDS. COOL FIRE-EXPOSED CONTAINERS WITH WATER FROM THE SIDE UNTIL WELL AFTER THE FIRE IS OUT. WITHDRAW IMMEDIATELY IF RISING SOUND FROM VENTING SAFETY DEVICE OR ANY DISCOLORATION OF STORAGE TANKS DUE TO FIRE (1987 EMERGENCY RESPONSE GUIDEBOOK, DOT P 5800.4, GUIDE PAGE 12).
EXTINGUISH USING AGENT INDICATED. COOL CYLINDERS WITH FLOODING AMOUNTS OF WATER FROM AS FAR A DISTANCE AS POSSIBLE. DO NOT USE WATER DIRECTLY ON MATERIAL. USE WATER SPRAY TO ABSORB VAPORS. AVOID BREATHING VAPORS; KEEP UPWIND. CONSIDER EVACUATION OF DOWNWIND AREA IF MATERIAL IS LEAKING.

TRANSPORTATION DATA

DEPARTMENT OF TRANSPORTATION HAZARD CLASSIFICATION 49 CFR 172.101: NONFLAMMABLE GAS
DEPARTMENT OF TRANSPORTATION LABELING REQUIREMENTS 49 CFR 172.101 AND SUBPART E: NONFLAMMABLE GAS

DEPARTMENT OF TRANSPORTATION PACKAGING REQUIREMENTS: 49 CFR 173.304; 49 CFR 173.314 AND 49 CFR 173.315 EXCEPTIONS: 49 CFR 173.306

TOXICITY

DICHLORODIFLUOROMETHANE: TOXICITY DATA: 200,000 PPM/30 MINUTES INHALATION-HUMAN TCLO; 76 PPH/30 MINUTES INHALATION-MOUSE LC50; 80 PPH/30 MINUTES INHALATION-RABBIT LC50; 80 PPH/30 MINUTES INHALATION-GUINEA PIG LC50. CARCINOGEN STATUS: NONE. ACUTE TOXICITY LEVEL: RELATIVELY NON-TOXIC BY INHALATION. TARGET EFFECTS: CENTRAL NERVOUS SYSTEM DEPRESSANT; SIMPLE ASPHYXIANT. POISONING MAY ALSO AFFECT THE RESPIRATORY AND CARDIOVASCULAR SYSTEM. AT INCREASED RISK FROM EXPOSURE: PERSONS WITH CHRONIC CARDIOVASCULAR DISEASE. ADDITIONAL DATA: USE OF STIMULANTS SUCH AS EPINEPHRINE MAY INDUCE VENTRICULAR FIBRILLATION.

HEALTH EFFECTS AND FIRST AID

INHALATION: DICHLORODIFLUOROMETHANE: NARCOTIC. 50,000 PPM IMMEDIATELY DANGEROUS TO LIFE OR HEALTH EXPOSURE TO HIGH CONCENTRATIONS OF GAS MAY CAUSE CENTRAL NERVOUS SYSTEM DEPRESSION. SNIFFING AEROSOLS OF FLUOROCHLORINATED HYDROCARBONS HAS CAUSED SUDDEN DEATH BY CARDIAC ARREST, PROBABLY DUE TO SENSITIZATION OF THE MYOCARDIUM. A GROUP OF WORKERS WITH INTERMITTENT FLUOROCARBON EXPOSURE REPORTED AN INCREASED INCIDENCE OF PALPITATIONS AND LIGHTHEADEDNESS. ANIMALS EXPOSED TO 20% 40 HOURS WEEKLY FOR 10-12 WEEKS SHOWED GENERALIZED TREMORS AND OTHER SIGNS OF MILD NARCOSIS, AS WELL AS SLIGHT BLOOD CHANGES, BUT NO PATHOLOGICAL EFFECTS. IN ANOTHER ANIMAL STUDY, 40% FOR 30 MINUTES PER DAY FOR 3-6 WEEKS RESULTED IN SOME RESPIRATORY PATHOLOGY. SEE INFORMATION ON SIMPLE ASPHYXIANTS.

SIMPLE ASPHYXIANTS: **ACUTE EXPOSURE**- THE SYMPTOMS OF ASPHYXIA DEPEND ON THE RAPIDITY WITH WHICH THE OXYGEN DEFICIENCY DEVELOPS AND HOW LONG IT CONTINUES. IN SUDDEN ACUTE ASPHYXIA, UNCONSCIOUSNESS MAY BE IMMEDIATE. WITH SLOW DEVELOPMENT THERE MAY BE RAPID RESPIRATION AND PULSE, AIR HUNGER, DIZZINESS, REDUCED AWARENESS, TIGHTNESS IN THE HEAD, TINGLING SENSATIONS, INCOORDINATION, FAULTY JUDGEMENT, EMOTIONAL INSTABILITY, AND RAPID FATIGUE. AS THE ASPHYXIA PROGRESSES, NAUSEA, VOMITING, COLLAPSE, UNCONSCIOUSNESS, CONVULSIONS, DEEP COMA AND DEATH ARE POSSIBLE. **CHRONIC EXPOSURE**- NO DATA AVAILABLE.

FIRST AID- REMOVE FROM EXPOSURE AREA TO FRESH AIR IMMEDIATELY. IF BREATHING HAS STOPPED, GIVE ARTIFICIAL RESPIRATION. MAINTAIN AIRWAY AND BLOOD PRESSURE AND ADMINISTER OXYGEN IF AVAILABLE. KEEP AFFECTED PERSON WARM AND AT REST. TREAT SYMPTOMATICALLY AND SUPPORTIVELY. ADMINISTRATION OF OXYGEN SHOULD BE PERFORMED BY QUALIFIED PERSONNEL. GET MEDICAL ATTENTION IMMEDIATELY.

SKIN CONTACT: DICHLORODIFLUOROMETHANE: **ACUTE EXPOSURE**- NO ADVERSE EFFECTS HAVE BEEN REPORTED FROM THE GAS. DUE TO RAPID EVAPORATION, THE LIQUID MAY CAUSE FROSTBITE WITH REDNESS, TINGLING AND PAIN OR NUMBNESS. IN MORE SEVERE CASES, THE SKIN MAY BECOME HARD AND WHITE AND DEVELOP BLISTERS. **CHRONIC EXPOSURE**- NO DATA AVAILABLE.

FIRST AID- IT IS UNLIKELY THAT EMERGENCY TREATMENT WILL BE REQUIRED. IF ADVERSE EFFECTS OCCUR, GET MEDICAL ATTENTION. IN CASE OF FROSTBITE, WARM AFFECTED SKIN IN WARM WATER AT A TEMPERATURE OF 107 F. IF WARM WATER IS NOT AVAILABLE OR IMPRACTICAL TO USE, GENTLY WRAP AFFECTED PART IN BLANKETS. ENCOURAGE VICTIM TO EXERCISE AFFECTED PART WHILE IT IS BEING WARMED. ALLOW CIRCULATION TO RETURN NATURALLY (MATHESON GAS, 6TH ED.). GET MEDICAL ATTENTION IMMEDIATELY.

EYE CONTACT: DICHLORODIFLUOROMETHANE: **ACUTE EXPOSURE**- ORDINARY OCCUPATIONAL AND DOMESTIC EXPOSURE TO THE GAS IS NOT EXPECTED TO CAUSE OCULAR IRRITATION. HOWEVER, 200,000 PPM FOR 30 MINUTES HAS BEEN REPORTED TO CAUSE IRRITATION. RAPID EVAPORATION OF THE LIQUIFIED GAS MAY CAUSE FROSTBITE, REDNESS, PAIN, AND BLURRED VISION. SPRAYING OF RABBIT EYES WITH THE LIQUID FOR FIVE TO TEN SECONDS CAUSED DAMAGE OF THE CORNEAL ENDOTHELIUM WITH SWELLING OF THE STROMA. RECOVERY WAS GRADUAL OVER A PERIOD OF SIX WEEKS. MORE SEVERE CORNEAL DAMAGE OCCURRED WHEN THE EYES WERE SPRAYED CONTINUOUSLY FOR THIRTY SECONDS. **CHRONIC EXPOSURE**- NO DATA AVAILABLE.

FIRST AID- IT IS UNLIKELY THAT CONTACT WITH THE GAS FORM WILL REQUIRE EMERGENCY TREATMENT. IF CONTACT WITH LIQUIFIED OR COMPRESSED GAS OCCURS, WASH WITH LARGE AMOUNTS OF WARM WATER UNTIL NO EVIDENCE OF CHEMICAL REMAINS (APPROXIMATELY 15-20 MINUTES). GET MEDICAL ATTENTION IMMEDIATELY.

INGESTION: DICHLORODIFLUOROMETHANE: **ACUTE EXPOSURE**- INGESTION OF A GAS IS UNLIKELY. IF THE LIQUID IS SWALLOWED, FROSTBITE DAMAGE TO THE LIPS, MOUTH AND MUCOUS MEMBRANES MAY OCCUR. **CHRONIC EXPOSURE**- 0.3% HAS BEEN EVALUATED AS THE DIETARY LEVEL CAUSING NO TOXICOLOGICAL EFFECT IN ANIMALS.

FIRST AID- IT IS UNLIKELY THAT EMERGENCY TREATMENT WILL BE REQUIRED. IF ADVERSE EFFECTS OCCUR, TREAT SYMPTOMATICALLY AND SUPPORTIVELY AND GET MEDICAL ATTENTION.

ANTIDOTE: NO SPECIFIC ANTIDOTE. TREAT SYMPTOMATICALLY AND SUPPORTIVELY.

REACTIVITY

REACTIVITY: STABLE UNDER NORMAL TEMPERATURES AND PRESSURES.

INCOMPATIBILITIES: DICHLORODIFLUOROMETHANE: ALUMINUM: VIGOROUS EXOTHERMIC REACTION. CALCIUM: EXOTHERMIC REACTION. MAGNESIUM: EXOTHERMIC REACTION. METALS: MAY REACT EXOTHERMICALLY AT ELEVATED TEMPERATURES. PLASTICS, RUBBER, AND COATINGS: MAY BE ATTACKED. POTASSIUM: EXOTHERMIC REACTION. SODIUM: EXOTHERMIC REACTION. ZINC: EXOTHERMIC REACTION.

DECOMPOSITION: THERMAL DECOMPOSITION PRODUCTS MAY INCLUDE TOXIC FUMES OF PHOSGENE AND CARBONYL HALIDES AND TOXIC AND CORROSIVE FUMES OF CHLORIDES AND FLUORIDES.

POLYMERIZATION: HAZARDOUS POLYMERIZATION HAS NOT BEEN REPORTED TO OCCUR UNDER NORMAL TEMPERATURES AND PRESSURES.

STORAGE AND DISPOSAL

OBSERVE ALL FEDERAL, STATE AND LOCAL REGULATIONS WHEN STORING OR DISPOSING OF THIS SUBSTANCE. FOR ASSISTANCE, CONTACT THE DISTRICT DIRECTOR OF THE ENVIRONMENTAL PROTECTION AGENCY.

****STORAGE****

STORE IN ACCORDANCE WITH 29 CFR 1910.101.
STORE AWAY FROM INCOMPATIBLE SUBSTANCES.

****DISPOSAL****

DISPOSAL MUST BE IN ACCORDANCE WITH STANDARDS APPLICABLE TO GENERATORS OF HAZARDOUS WASTE, 40CFR 262. EPA HAZARDOUS WASTE NUMBER U075.

CONDITIONS TO AVOID

DO NOT PERMIT PHYSICAL DAMAGE OR OVERHEATING OF CONTAINERS. CONTENTS ARE UNDER PRESSURE; CONTAINERS MAY VIOLENTLY RUPTURE AND TRAVEL A CONSIDERABLE DISTANCE.

SPILL AND LEAK PROCEDURES

OCCUPATIONAL SPILL: STOP LEAK IF YOU CAN DO IT WITHOUT RISK. KEEP UNNECESSARY PEOPLE AWAY; ISOLATE HAZARD AREA AND DENY ENTRY. REPORTABLE QUANTITY (RQ): 5000 POUNDS THE SUPERFUND AMENDMENTS AND REAUTHORIZATION ACT (SARA) SECTION 304 REQUIRES THAT A RELEASE EQUAL TO OR GREATER THAN THE REPORTABLE QUANTITY FOR THIS SUBSTANCE BE IMMEDIATELY REPORTED TO THE LOCAL EMERGENCY PLANNING COMMITTEE AND THE STATE EMERGENCY RESPONSE COMMISSION (40 CFR 355.40). IF THE RELEASE OF THIS SUBSTANCE IS REPORTABLE UNDER CERCLA SECTION 103, THE NATIONAL RESPONSE CENTER MUST BE NOTIFIED IMMEDIATELY AT (800) 424-8802 OR (202) 426-2675 IN THE METROPOLITAN WASHINGTON, D.C. AREA (40 CFR 302.6).

PROTECTIVE EQUIPMENT

VENTILATION: PROVIDE GENERAL DILUTION VENTILATION TO MEET PUBLISHED EXPOSURE LIMITS.

RESPIRATOR: THE FOLLOWING RESPIRATORS AND MAXIMUM USE CONCENTRATIONS ARE RECOMMENDATIONS BY THE U.S. DEPARTMENT OF HEALTH AND HUMAN SERVICES, NIOSH POCKET GUIDE TO CHEMICAL HAZARDS; NIOSH CRITERIA DOCUMENTS OR BY THE U.S. DEPARTMENT OF LABOR, 29 CFR 1910 SUBPART Z. THE SPECIFIC RESPIRATOR SELECTED MUST BE BASED ON CONTAMINATION LEVELS FOUND IN THE WORK PLACE, MUST NOT EXCEED THE WORKING LIMITS OF THE RESPIRATOR AND BE JOINTLY APPROVED BY THE NATIONAL INSTITUTE FOR OCCUPATIONAL SAFETY AND HEALTH AND THE MINE SAFETY AND HEALTH ADMINISTRATION (NIOSH-MSHA).

DICHLORODIFLUOROMETHANE:

10,000 PPM- ANY SUPPLIED-AIR RESPIRATOR. ANY SELF-CONTAINED BREATHING APPARATUS.

25,000 PPM- ANY SUPPLIED-AIR RESPIRATOR OPERATED IN A CONTINUOUS FLOW MODE.

50,000 PPM- ANY SELF-CONTAINED BREATHING APPARATUS WITH A FULL FACEPIECE. ANY SUPPLIED-AIR RESPIRATOR WITH A FULL FACEPIECE.

ESCAPE- ANY AIR-PURIFYING FULL FACEPIECE RESPIRATOR (GAS MASK) WITH A CHIN-STYLE OR FRONT- OR BACK-MOUNTED ORGANIC VAPOR CANISTER. ANY APPROPRIATE ESCAPE-TYPE SELF-CONTAINED BREATHING APPARATUS.

FOR FIREFIGHTING AND OTHER IMMEDIATELY DANGEROUS TO LIFE OR HEALTH CONDITIONS:

SELF-CONTAINED BREATHING APPARATUS WITH FULL FACEPIECE OPERATED IN PRESSURE-DEMAND OR OTHER POSITIVE PRESSURE MODE.

SUPPLIED-AIR RESPIRATOR WITH FULL FACEPIECE AND OPERATED IN PRESSURE-DEMAND OR OTHER POSITIVE PRESSURE MODE IN COMBINATION WITH AN AUXILIARY SELF-CONTAINED BREATHING APPARATUS OPERATED IN PRESSURE-DEMAND OR OTHER POSITIVE PRESSURE MODE.

CLOTHING: FOR THE GAS FORM, PROTECTIVE CLOTHING NOT REQUIRED. IF CONTACT WITH THE LIQUID FORM IS POSSIBLE, EMPLOYEE MUST WEAR APPROPRIATE PROTECTIVE CLOTHING AND EQUIPMENT TO PREVENT SKIN FROM FREEZING.

GLOVES: WEAR FULL PROTECTIVE, COLD INSULATING GLOVES.

EYE PROTECTION: EMPLOYEE MUST WEAR SPLASH-PROOF OR DUST-RESISTANT SAFETY GOGGLES AND A FACESHIELD TO PREVENT CONTACT WITH THIS SUBSTANCE.

EMERGENCY WASH FACILITIES: WHERE THERE IS ANY POSSIBILITY THAT AN EMPLOYEE'S EYES AND/OR SKIN MAY BE EXPOSED TO THIS SUBSTANCE, THE EMPLOYER SHOULD PROVIDE AN EYE WASH FOUNTAIN AND QUICK DRENCH SHOWER WITHIN THE IMMEDIATE WORK AREA FOR EMERGENCY USE.

AUTHORIZED BY- OCCUPATIONAL HEALTH SERVICES, INC.

CREATION DATE: 11/16/89 ***REVISION DATE:*** 06/28/90

MATERIAL SAFETY DATA SHEET

OCCUPATIONAL HEALTH SERVICES, INC.
AGRICULTURE AND PESTICIDE DIVISION
450 SEVENTH AVENUE, SUITE 2407
NEW YORK, NEW YORK 10123
1-800-445-MSDS OR (212) 967-1100

EMERGENCY CONTACT:
JOHN S. BRANSFORD, JR. (615) 292-1180

SUBSTANCE IDENTIFICATION

CAS-NUMBER 120-67-2

SUBSTANCE: **2,4-DICHLOROPHENOXY ETHANOL**

TRADE NAMES/SYNONYMS: ETHANOL, 2-(2,4-DICHLOROPHENOXY)-; O,P-DICHLOROPHENOXYETHANOL; 2,4-D ALCOHOL; 2-(2,4-DICHLOROPHENOXY)ETHANOL; C8H8CL2O2; PST06915

CHEMICAL FAMILY: ETHER, ALKYL-ARYL
HYDROXYL
HALOGEN

MOLECULAR FORMULA: CL2-C6-H3-O-(C-H2)2-O-H

MOLECULAR WEIGHT: 207.05

CERCLA RATINGS (SCALE 0-3): HEALTH=3 FIRE=U REACTIVITY=0 PERSISTENCE=2

NFPA RATINGS (SCALE 0-4): HEALTH=U FIRE=U REACTIVITY=0

COMPONENTS AND CONTAMINANTS

COMPONENT: 2,4-DICHLOROPHENOXY ETHANOL ***PERCENT:*** 100.0
CAS# 120-67-2

OTHER CONTAMINANTS: NONE

EXPOSURE LIMITS: NO OCCUPATIONAL EXPOSURE LIMITS ESTABLISHED BY OSHA, ACGIH, OR NIOSH.

PHYSICAL DATA

DESCRIPTION: VISCOUS AMBER LIQUID. ***BOILING POINT:*** NOT AVAILABLE

SPECIFIC GRAVITY: NOT AVAILABLE ***VAPOR PRESSURE:*** NOT AVAILABLE

SOLUBILITY IN WATER: NOT AVAILABLE

FIRE AND EXPLOSION DATA

FIRE AND EXPLOSION HAZARD: UNKNOWN FIRE AND EXPLOSION HAZARD.

FLASH POINT: NOT AVAILABLE

FIREFIGHTING MEDIA: DRY CHEMICAL, CARBON DIOXIDE, HALON, WATER SPRAY OR ALCOHOL FOAM (1987 EMERGENCY RESPONSE GUIDEBOOK, DOT P 5800.4). FOR LARGER FIRES, USE WATER SPRAY, FOG OR ALCOHOL FOAM (1987 EMERGENCY RESPONSE GUIDEBOOK, DOT P 5800.4).

FIREFIGHTING: MOVE CONTAINER FROM FIRE AREA IF POSSIBLE. COOL FIRE-EXPOSED CONTAINERS WITH WATER FROM SIDE UNTIL WELL AFTER FIRE IS OUT. STAY AWAY FROM STORAGE TANK ENDS. FOR MASSIVE FIRE IN STORAGE AREA, USE UNMANNED HOSE HOLDER OR MONITOR NOZZLES, ELSE WITHDRAW FROM AREA AND LET FIRE BURN. WITHDRAW IMMEDIATELY IN CASE OF RISING SOUND FROM VENTING SAFETY DEVICE OR ANY DISCOLORATION OF STORAGE TANK DUE TO FIRE (1987 EMERGENCY RESPONSE GUIDEBOOK, DOT P 5800.4, GUIDE PAGE 26). EXTINGUISH ONLY IF FLOW CAN BE STOPPED. USE FLOODING AMOUNTS OF WATER AS FOG; SOLID STREAMS MAY BE INEFFECTIVE. COOL CONTAINERS WITH FLOODING AMOUNTS OF WATER FROM AS FAR A DISTANCE AS POSSIBLE. AVOID BREATHING VAPORS; KEEP UPWIND.

TOXICITY

2,4-DICHLOROPHENOXY ETHANOL: IRRITATION DATA: 500 MG/24 HOURS SKIN-RABBIT MILD; 50 UG/24 HOURS EYE-RABBIT SEVERE. TOXICITY DATA: 1250 MG/KG SKIN-RABBIT LD50; 1410 MG/KG ORAL-RAT LD50. CARCINOGEN STATUS: HUMAN LIMITED EVIDENCE (IARC GROUP-2B FOR CHLOROPHENOXY HERBICIDES). STUDIES REVEALED A SIGNIFICANT INCREASE IN SOFT-TISSUE SARCOMAS, MALIGNANT LYMPHOMAS AND BRONCHIAL CARCINOMAS IN WORKERS EXPOSED TO CHLOROPHENOXY HERBICIDES. LOCAL EFFECTS: IRRITANT- EYES. ACUTE TOXICITY LEVEL: MODERATELY TOXIC BY DERMAL ABSORPTION AND INGESTION. TARGET EFFECTS: POISONING MAY AFFECT THE GASTROINTESTINAL TRACT AND THE CARDIOVASCULAR AND NERVOUS SYSTEMS.* AT INCREASED RISK FROM EXPOSURE: PERSONS WITH LIVER, KIDNEY, CARDIOVASCULAR, OR SKIN DISEASES, AND CONVULSIVE DISORDERS OR NEUROPATHY.*

* MAY BE BASED ON GENERAL INFORMATION ON DICHLOROPHENOXY DERIVATIVES.

HEALTH EFFECTS AND FIRST AID

INHALATION: 2,4-DICHLOROPHENOXY ETHANOL: SEE INFORMATION ON 2,4-D AND DERIVATIVES.

2,4-D AND DERIVATIVES: **ACUTE EXPOSURE-** EXPOSURE TO 2,4-D AND ITS DERIVATIVES MAY CAUSE IRRITATION WITH SORE THROAT AND BURNING SENSATIONS IN THE NASOPHARYNX AND CHEST, COUGHING, LACRIMATION, RHINITIS, DULLNESS, DIZZINESS, AND ATAXIA. OTHER EFFECTS OF FATIGUE, NAUSEA, VOMITING, DIARRHEA, STOMACH PAINS, MALAISE, HEADACHE, FEVER, TACHYCARDIA, URINARY INCONTINENCE, CONSTIPATION, LEUKOPENIA, MYALGIA, AND TRANSIENT UNCONSCIOUSNESS MAY OCCUR. A DELAYED PERIPHERAL NEUROPATHY MAY DEVELOP CHARACTERIZED BY PARESTHESIAS, SEVERE PAIN, SYMMETRICAL MOTOR AND SENSORY DEFICITS, WEAKNESS, MYOTONIA, FASCICULATIONS, AND IN SOME CASES PARALYSIS OF THE EXTREMITIES. THE DISABILITY MAY BE PROLONGED AND RECOVERY INCOMPLETE. **CHRONIC EXPOSURE-** IN ADDITION TO THE EFFECTS LISTED IN ACUTE EXPOSURE, OCCUPATIONAL EXPOSURE TO 2,4-D AND ITS DERIVATIVES HAS PRODUCED A SWEET TASTE IN THE MOUTH, HYPERACUSIA, LOWERED SENSITIVITY TO TASTE AND SMELL, INCREASED SALIVATION, VERTIGO, SOMNOLENCE, ANOREXIA, HEAVINESS OF THE LEGS. OTHER EFFECTS HAVE INCLUDED HYPOTENSION, BRADYCARDIA AND OTHER CARDIOVASCULAR SYSTEM CHANGES, PAIN IN THE REGION OF THE LIVER AND STOMACH, AND CHANGES IN THE DIGESTIVE FUNCTION, LIVER FUNCTION AND METABOLIC PROCESSES. A CASE REPORT DESCRIBED A CHILD WITH MULTIPLE CONGENITAL ANOMALIES AND SEVERE MENTAL RETARDATION OF UNCERTAIN CAUSE BORN TO PARENTS HEAVILY EXPOSED TO 2,4-D WHILE SPRAYING TREES. AN INCREASED PREVALENCE OF SLOWED NERVE CONDUCTION VELOCITY WITH NO ASSOCIATED SYMPTOMS WAS REPORTED IN A STUDY OF CHEMICAL WORKERS EMPLOYED IN THE PRODUCTION OF 2,4-D AND 2,4,5-T. EPIDEMIOLOGICAL STUDIES REVEALED A SIGNIFICANT INCREASE IN SOFT-TISSUE SARCOMAS, MALIGNANT LYMPHOMAS, AND BRONCHIAL CARCINOMAS IN WORKERS EXPOSED TO CHLOROPHENOXY HERBICIDES INCLUDING 2,4-D.

FIRST AID- REMOVE FROM EXPOSURE AREA TO FRESH AIR IMMEDIATELY. IF BREATHING HAS STOPPED, PERFORM ARTIFICIAL RESPIRATION. KEEP PERSON WARM AND AT REST. TREAT SYMPTOMATICALLY AND SUPPORTIVELY. GET MEDICAL ATTENTION IMMEDIATELY.

SKIN CONTACT: 2,4-DICHLOROPHENOXY ETHANOL: SEE INFORMATION ON 2,4-D AND DERIVATIVES.

2,4-D AND DERIVATIVES: **ACUTE EXPOSURE-** MAY CAUSE IRRITATION. IF SUFFICIENT AMOUNTS ARE ABSORBED THROUGH THE SKIN, EFFECTS, INCLUDING PERIPHERAL NEUROPATHY, AS DESCRIBED IN ACUTE INHALATION MAY OCCUR. **CHRONIC EXPOSURE-** PROLONGED OR REPEATED EXPOSURE MAY CAUSE DERMATITIS AND EFFECTS AS DESCRIBED IN CHRONIC INHALATION.

FIRST AID- REMOVE CONTAMINATED CLOTHING AND SHOES IMMEDIATELY. WASH AFFECTED AREA WITH SOAP OR MILD DETERGENT AND LARGE AMOUNTS OF WATER UNTIL NO EVIDENCE OF CHEMICAL REMAINS (APPROXIMATELY 15-20 MINUTES). GET MEDICAL ATTENTION IMMEDIATELY.

EYE CONTACT: 2,4-DICHLOROPHENOXY ETHANOL: IRRITANT. **ACUTE EXPOSURE-** 50 UG WAS SEVERELY IRRITATING TO RABBIT EYES. **CHRONIC EXPOSURE-** REPEATED OR PROLONGED EXPOSURE TO IRRITANTS MAY CAUSE CONJUNCTIVITIS.

FIRST AID- WASH EYES IMMEDIATELY WITH LARGE AMOUNTS OF WATER OR NORMAL SALINE, OCCASIONALLY LIFTING UPPER AND LOWER LIDS, UNTIL NO EVIDENCE OF CHEMICAL REMAINS (APPROXIMATELY 15-20 MINUTES). GET MEDICAL ATTENTION IMMEDIATELY.

INGESTION: 2,4-DICHLOROPHENOXY ETHANOL: SEE INFORMATION ON 2,4-D AND DERIVATIVES.

2,4-D AND DERIVATIVES: **ACUTE EXPOSURE-** INGESTION OF 2,4-D AND ITS DERIVATIVES MAY CAUSE IRRITATION OF THE MOUTH, THROAT, AND GASTROINTESTINAL TRACT, NAUSEA, VOMITING, CHEST AND ABDOMINAL PAIN, AND DIARRHEA. INGESTION OF VERY LARGE DOSES MAY PRODUCE METABOLIC ACIDOSIS, FEVER OR SUBNORMAL TEMPERATURES, HYPER VENTILATION, HYPOTENSION, VASODILATION, FLUSHING OF THE SKIN, SWEATING, CARDIAC ARRHYTHMIAS, TACHYCARDIA, LETHARGY, WEAKNESS, INTERCOSTAL PARALYSIS, RENAL AND HEPATIC DYSFUNCTION, MYOTONIA, COMA, AND CONVULSIONS. DAMAGE TO SKELETAL MUSCLE MAY BE MANIFEST BY MUSCLE TWITCHING AND ACHING WITH ELEVATED SERUM ENZYMES AND MYOGLOBIN IN THE BLOOD AND URINE. IMPAIRED MEMORY AND CHANGES IN COLOR VISION WERE REPORTED IN ONE CASE OF POISONING. DEATH MAY BE DUE TO CIRCULATORY COLLAPSE. **CHRONIC EXPOSURE-** NO DATA AVAILABLE.

FIRST AID- IF THE PERSON IS CONSCIOUS AND NOT CONVULSING, INDUCE EMESIS BY GIVING SYRUP OF IPECAC (KEEPING THE HEAD BELOW THE HIPS TO PREVENT ASPIRATION) FOLLOWED BY WATER. REPEAT IN 20 MINUTES IF NOT EFFECTIVE INITIALLY. IN PATIENTS WITH DEPRESSED RESPIRATION OR IF EMESIS IS NOT PRODUCED, PERFORM GASTRIC LAVAGE WITH ACTIVATED CHARCOAL. FOLLOW WITH A SALINE CATHARTIC (DREISBACH, HANDBOOK OF POISONING, 12TH ED.). TREAT SYMPTOMATICALLY AND SUPPORTIVELY. GASTRIC LAVAGE SHOULD BE PERFORMED BY QUALIFIED MEDICAL PERSONNEL. GET MEDICAL ATTENTION IMMEDIATELY.

ANTIDOTE: NO SPECIFIC ANTIDOTE. TREAT SYMPTOMATICALLY AND SUPPORTIVELY.

REACTIVITY

REACTIVITY: STABLE UNDER NORMAL TEMPERATURES AND PRESSURES.

INCOMPATIBILITIES: 2,4-DICHLOROPHENOXY ETHANOL: OXIDIZERS (STRONG): FIRE AND EXPLOSION HAZARD.

DECOMPOSITION: THERMAL DECOMPOSITION PRODUCTS MAY INCLUDE TOXIC AND CORROSIVE FUMES OF CHLORIDES AND TOXIC OXIDES OF CARBON.

POLYMERIZATION: HAZARDOUS POLYMERIZATION HAS NOT BEEN REPORTED TO OCCUR UNDER NORMAL TEMPERATURES AND PRESSURES.

STORAGE AND DISPOSAL

OBSERVE ALL FEDERAL, STATE AND LOCAL REGULATIONS WHEN STORING OR DISPOSING OF THIS SUBSTANCE. FOR ASSISTANCE, CONTACT THE DISTRICT DIRECTOR OF THE ENVIRONMENTAL PROTECTION AGENCY.

****STORAGE****

STORE AWAY FROM INCOMPATIBLE SUBSTANCES.

CONDITIONS TO AVOID

AVOID CONTACT WITH HEAT, SPARKS, FLAMES, OR OTHER SOURCES OF IGNITION. VAPORS MAY BE EXPLOSIVE AND POISONOUS; DO NOT ALLOW UNNECESSARY PERSONNEL IN AREA. DO NOT OVERHEAT CONTAINERS; CONTAINERS MAY VIOLENTLY RUPTURE AND TRAVEL A CONSIDERABLE DISTANCE IN HEAT OF FIRE.

SPILL AND LEAK PROCEDURES

OCCUPATIONAL SPILL: SHUT OFF IGNITION SOURCES. STOP LEAK IF YOU CAN DO IT WITHOUT RISK. USE WATER SPRAY TO REDUCE VAPORS. FOR SMALL SPILLS, TAKE UP WITH SAND OR OTHER ABSORBENT MATERIAL AND PLACE INTO CONTAINERS FOR LATER DISPOSAL. FOR LARGER SPILLS, DIKE FAR AHEAD OF SPILL FOR LATER DISPOSAL. NO SMOKING, FLAMES OR FLARES IN HAZARD AREA. KEEP UNNECESSARY PEOPLE AWAY; ISOLATE HAZARD AREA AND DENY ENTRY.

PROTECTIVE EQUIPMENT

VENTILATION: PROVIDE LOCAL EXHAUST OR PROCESS ENCLOSURE VENTILATION SYSTEM.

RESPIRATOR: THE FOLLOWING RESPIRATORS ARE RECOMMENDED BASED ON INFORMATION FOUND IN THE PHYSICAL DATA, TOXICITY AND HEALTH EFFECTS SECTIONS. THEY ARE RANKED IN ORDER FROM MINIMUM TO MAXIMUM RESPIRATORY PROTECTION. THE SPECIFIC RESPIRATOR SELECTED MUST BE BASED ON CONTAMINATION LEVELS FOUND IN THE WORK PLACE, MUST NOT EXCEED THE WORKING LIMITS OF THE RESPIRATOR AND BE JOINTLY APPROVED BY THE NATIONAL INSTITUTE FOR OCCUPATIONAL SAFETY AND HEALTH AND THE MINE SAFETY AND HEALTH ADMINISTRATION (NIOSH-MSHA).

CHEMICAL CARTRIDGE RESPIRATOR WITH FULL FACEPIECE AND PESTICIDE CARTRIDGE.

TYPE 'C' SUPPLIED-AIR RESPIRATOR WITH A FULL FACEPIECE OPERATED IN PRESSURE-DEMAND OR OTHER POSITIVE PRESSURE MODE OR WITH A FULL FACEPIECE, HELMET OR HOOD OPERATED IN CONTINUOUS-FLOW MODE.

SELF-CONTAINED BREATHING APPARATUS OPERATED IN PRESSURE-DEMAND OR OTHER POSITIVE PRESSURE MODE.

FOR FIREFIGHTING AND OTHER IMMEDIATELY DANGEROUS TO LIFE OR HEALTH CONDITIONS:

SELF-CONTAINED BREATHING APPARATUS WITH FULL FACEPIECE OPERATED IN PRESSURE-DEMAND OR OTHER POSITIVE PRESSURE MODE.

SUPPLIED-AIR RESPIRATOR WITH FULL FACEPIECE AND OPERATED IN PRESSURE-DEMAND OR OTHER POSITIVE PRESSURE MODE IN COMBINATION WITH AN AUXILIARY SELF-CONTAINED BREATHING APPARATUS OPERATED IN PRESSURE-DEMAND OR OTHER POSITIVE PRESSURE MODE.

CLOTHING: EMPLOYEE MUST WEAR APPROPRIATE PROTECTIVE (IMPERVIOUS) CLOTHING AND EQUIPMENT TO PREVENT REPEATED OR PROLONGED SKIN CONTACT WITH THIS SUBSTANCE.

GLOVES: EMPLOYEE MUST WEAR APPROPRIATE PROTECTIVE GLOVES TO PREVENT CONTACT WITH THIS SUBSTANCE.

EYE PROTECTION: EMPLOYEE MUST WEAR SPLASH-PROOF OR DUST-RESISTANT SAFETY GOGGLES TO PREVENT EYE CONTACT WITH THIS SUBSTANCE.

EMERGENCY EYE WASH: WHERE THERE IS ANY POSSIBILITY THAT AN EMPLOYEE'S EYES MAY BE EXPOSED TO THIS SUBSTANCE, THE EMPLOYER SHOULD PROVIDE AN EYE WASH FOUNTAIN WITHIN THE IMMEDIATE WORK AREA FOR EMERGENCY USE.

AUTHORIZED BY- OCCUPATIONAL HEALTH SERVICES, INC.

CREATION DATE: 04/09/90 ***REVISION DATE:*** 07/12/90

MATERIAL SAFETY DATA SHEET

OCCUPATIONAL HEALTH SERVICES, INC.
AGRICULTURE AND PESTICIDE DIVISION
450 SEVENTH AVENUE, SUITE 2407
NEW YORK, NEW YORK 10123
1-800-445-MSDS OR (212) 967-1100

EMERGENCY CONTACT:
JOHN S. BRANSFORD, JR. (615) 292-1180

SUBSTANCE IDENTIFICATION

CAS-NUMBER 2782-57-2

SUBSTANCE: **DICHLORO-S-TRIAZINE TRIONE**

TRADE NAMES/SYNONYMS: ACL-59; ACL-70; DICHLOROISOCYANURIC ACID; TROCLOSENE; DICHLORO-S-TRIAZINE-2,4,6-TRIONE; 1,3-DICHLORO-S-TRIAZINE-2,4,6,(1H,3H,5H) -TRIONE; UN 2465; PST06975

CHEMICAL FAMILY: ISOCYANATE

MOLECULAR FORMULA: C3-H2-CL2-N3-O3

MOLECULAR WEIGHT: 198.98

CERCLA RATINGS (SCALE 0-3): HEALTH = 2 FIRE = 0 REACTIVITY = 2 PERSISTENCE = 2

NFPA RATINGS (SCALE 0-4): HEALTH = 3 FIRE = 0 REACTIVITY = 2

COMPONENTS AND CONTAMINANTS

COMPONENT: DICHLORO-S-TRIAZINE TRIONE ***PERCENT:*** 100

CAS# 2782-57-2

OTHER CONTAMINANTS: NONE

EXPOSURE LIMITS: NO OCCUPATIONAL EXPOSURE LIMITS ESTABLISHED BY OSHA, ACGIH, OR NIOSH.

PHYSICAL DATA

DESCRIPTION: WHITE CRYSTALLINE SOLID WITH A STRONG CHLORINE-LIKE ODOR

MELTING POINT: 437 F (225 C) ***SPECIFIC GRAVITY:*** NOT AVAILABLE

SOLUBILITY IN WATER: MODERATELY SOLUBLE

FIRE AND EXPLOSION DATA

FIRE AND EXPLOSION HAZARD: NEGLIGIBLE FIRE HAZARD WHEN EXPOSED TO HEAT OR FLAME.

OXIDIZER: OXIDIZERS DECOMPOSE, ESPECIALLY WHEN HEATED, TO YIELD OXYGEN OR OTHER GASES WHICH WILL INCREASE THE BURNING RATE OF COMBUSTIBLE MATTER. CONTACT WITH EASILY OXIDIZABLE, ORGANIC, OR OTHER COMBUSTIBLE MATERIALS MAY RESULT IN IGNITION, VIOLENT COMBUSTION OR EXPLOSION.

FIREFIGHTING MEDIA: DRY CHEMICAL, CARBON DIOXIDE, HALON OR WATER SPRAY (1987 EMERGENCY RESPONSE GUIDEBOOK, DOT P 5800.4).

FOR LARGER FIRES, USE WATER SPRAY OR FOG (1987 EMERGENCY RESPONSE GUIDEBOOK, DOT P 5800.4).

FIREFIGHTING: MOVE CONTAINERS FROM FIRE AREA IF POSSIBLE. COOL CONTAINERS EXPOSED TO FLAME WITH WATER FROM SIDE UNTIL WELL AFTER FIRE IS OUT. KEEP AWAY FROM STORAGE TANK ENDS. FOR MASSIVE FIRE IN STORAGE AREA, USE UNMANNED HOSE HOLDER OR MONITOR NOZZLES (1987 EMERGENCY RESPONSE GUIDEBOOK, DOT 5800.4, GUIDE PAGE 42).

FLOOD WITH WATER. COOL CONTAINERS WITH FLOODING AMOUNTS OF WATER FROM AS FAR A DISTANCE AS POSSIBLE. AVOID BREATHING VAPORS OR DUSTS. EVACUATE TO A RADIUS OF 2500 FEET FOR UNCONTROLLABLE FIRES.

TRANSPORTATION DATA

DEPARTMENT OF TRANSPORTATION HAZARD CLASSIFICATION 49 CFR 172.101: OXIDIZER
DEPARTMENT OF TRANSPORTATION LABELING REQUIREMENTS 49 CFR 172.101 AND SUBPART E: OXIDIZER
DEPARTMENT OF TRANSPORTATION PACKAGING REQUIREMENTS: 49 CFR 173.154 EXCEPTIONS: 49 CFR 173.153

TOXICITY

DICHLORO-S-TRIAZINE TRIONE: IRRITATION DATA: 500 MG SKIN-RABBIT SEVERE. TOXICITY DATA: 3570 MG/KG ORAL-HUMAN LDLO; 1173 MG/KG ORAL-RAT LD50. CARCINOGEN STATUS: NONE. LOCAL EFFECTS: IRRITANT- INHALATION, SKIN, AND EYES. ACUTE TOXICITY LEVEL: MODERATELY TOXIC BY INGESTION. TARGET EFFECTS: NO DATA AVAILABLE.

HEALTH EFFECTS AND FIRST AID

INHALATION: DICHLORO-S-TRIAZINE TRIONE: IRRITANT. **ACUTE EXPOSURE-** MAY BE IRRITATING TO THE MUCOUS MEMBRANES AND THE RESPIRATORY TRACT WITH SYMPTOMS OF SORE THROAT, AND COUGHING. IN SOME INDIVIDUALS BRONCHOSPASM MAY RESULT FROM BREATHING THE DUST. **CHRONIC EXPOSURE-** NO DATA AVAILABLE.
FIRST AID- REMOVE FROM EXPOSURE AREA TO FRESH AIR IMMEDIATELY. IF BREATHING HAS STOPPED, PERFORM ARTIFICIAL RESPIRATION. KEEP PERSON WARM AND AT REST. TREAT SYMPTOMATICALLY AND SUPPORTIVELY. GET MEDICAL ATTENTION IMMEDIATELY.

SKIN CONTACT: DICHLORO-S-TRIAZINE TRIONE: IRRITANT. **ACUTE EXPOSURE-** MAY BE IRRITATING TO THE SKIN WITH SYMPTOMS OF REDNESS AND PAIN. **CHRONIC EXPOSURE-** PROLONGED OR REPEATED EXPOSURE MAY CAUSE DERMATITIS.
FIRST AID- REMOVE CONTAMINATED CLOTHING AND SHOES IMMEDIATELY. WASH AFFECTED AREA WITH SOAP OR MILD DETERGENT AND LARGE AMOUNTS OF WATER UNTIL NO EVIDENCE OF CHEMICAL REMAINS (APPROXIMATELY 15-20 MINUTES). GET MEDICAL ATTENTION IMMEDIATELY.

EYE CONTACT: DICHLORO-S-TRIAZINE TRIONE: IRRITANT. **ACUTE EXPOSURE-** CONTACT WITH THE DUST MAY BE IRRITATING TO THE EYES WITH REDNESS AND PAIN. IN STRONG SOLUTIONS, IT MAY DECOMPOSE TO NITROGEN TRICHLORIDE WHICH IS A STRONG LACRIMATOR. **CHRONIC EXPOSURE-** PROLONGED OR REPEATED EXPOSURE MAY CAUSE CONJUNCTIVITIS.
FIRST AID- WASH EYES IMMEDIATELY WITH LARGE AMOUNTS OF WATER OR NORMAL SALINE, OCCASIONALLY LIFTING UPPER AND LOWER LIDS, UNTIL NO EVIDENCE OF CHEMICAL REMAINS (APPROXIMATELY 15-20 MINUTES). GET MEDICAL ATTENTION IMMEDIATELY.

INGESTION: DICHLORO-S-TRIAZINE TRIONE: CORROSIVE. **ACUTE EXPOSURE-** MAY BE IRRITATING AND DAMAGING TO THE ALIMENTARY SYSTEM WITH SYMPTOMS OF SORE THROAT, ABDOMINAL PAIN AND VOMITING. **CHRONIC EXPOSURE-** NO DATA AVAILABLE.
FIRST AID- REMOVE BY GASTRIC LAVAGE OR EMESIS. MAINTAIN BLOOD PRESSURE AND AIRWAY. GIVE OXYGEN IF RESPIRATION IS DEPRESSED. DO NOT PERFORM GASTRIC LAVAGE OR EMESIS IF VICTIM IS UNCONSCIOUS. GET MEDICAL ATTENTION IMMEDIATELY (DREISBACH, HANDBOOK OF POISONING, 11TH ED.). ADMINISTRATION OF GASTRIC LAVAGE OR OXYGEN SHOULD BE PERFORMED BY QUALIFIED MEDICAL PERSONNEL.
ANTIDOTE: NO SPECIFIC ANTIDOTE. TREAT SYMPTOMATICALLY AND SUPPORTIVELY.

REACTIVITY

REACTIVITY: HIGHLY REACTIVE OXIDIZING AND CHLORINATING AGENT THAT MAY CAUSE IGNITION BY CONTACT WITH MOST COMBUSTIBLE AND REDUCING MATERIALS. REACTS WITH WATER TO RELEASE CHLORINE AND OTHER TOXIC GASES.
INCOMPATIBILITIES: DICHLORO-S-TRIAZINE TRIONE: AMMONIA: FORMS EXPLOSIVE NITROGEN TRICHLORIDE WHEN MIXED. AMINE: FORMS EXPLOSIVE NITROGEN TRICHLORIDE WHEN MIXED. UREA: FORMS EXPLOSIVE NITROGEN TRICHLORIDE WHEN MIXED. NITROGEN CONTAINING COMPOUNDS: FORMS EXPLOSIVE NITROGEN TRICHLORIDE WHEN MIXED. PAPER, WOOD AND OTHER ORGANIC AND COMBUSTIBLE MATERIALS: REACT VIOLENTLY OR MAY CAUSE IGNITION ON CONTACT. REDUCING MATERIALS: REACTS VIOLENTLY OR MAY CAUSE IGNITION ON CONTACT. WATER: REACTS TO FORM CHLORINE AND OTHER TOXIC GASES.
DECOMPOSITION: THERMAL DECOMPOSITION MAY EMIT TOXIC FUMES OF CHLORINE, OXIDES OF CARBON AND NITROGEN.
POLYMERIZATION: HAZARDOUS POLYMERIZATION HAS NOT BEEN REPORTED TO OCCUR UNDER NORMAL TEMPERATURES AND PRESSURES.

CONDITIONS TO AVOID

AVOID CONTACT WITH OTHER COMBUSTIBLE MATERIALS (WOOD, PAPER, OIL, ETC.). AVOID CONTACT WITH EYES AND SKIN; MATERIAL MAY BE POISONOUS OR CORROSIVE.

SPILL AND LEAK PROCEDURES

OCCUPATIONAL SPILL: KEEP COMBUSTIBLES (WOOD, PAPER, OIL, ETC.) AWAY FROM SPILLED MATERIAL. DO NOT TOUCH SPILLED MATERIAL. FOR SMALL DRY SPILLS, WITH CLEAN SHOVEL PLACE MATERIAL INTO CLEAN, DRY CONTAINER AND COVER; MOVE CONTAINERS FROM SPILL AREA. FOR LARGER SPILLS, DIKE FAR AHEAD OF SPILL FOR LATER DISPOSAL. KEEP UNNECESSARY PEOPLE AWAY. ISOLATE HAZARD AREA AND DENY ENTRY.

PROTECTIVE EQUIPMENT

VENTILATION: PROVIDE LOCAL EXHAUST OR PROCESS ENCLOSURE VENTILATION SYSTEM.
RESPIRATOR: THE FOLLOWING RESPIRATORS ARE RECOMMENDED BASED ON INFORMATION FOUND IN THE PHYSICAL DATA, TOXICITY AND HEALTH EFFECTS SECTIONS. THEY ARE RANKED IN ORDER FROM MINIMUM TO MAXIMUM RESPIRATORY PROTECTION. THE SPECIFIC RESPIRATOR SELECTED MUST BE BASED ON CONTAMINATION LEVELS FOUND IN THE WORK PLACE, MUST NOT EXCEED THE WORKING LIMITS OF THE RESPIRATOR AND BE JOINTLY APPROVED BY THE NATIONAL INSTITUTE FOR OCCUPATIONAL SAFETY AND HEALTH AND THE MINE SAFETY AND HEALTH ADMINISTRATION (NIOSH-MSHA).
DUST AND MIST RESPIRATOR WITH A FULL FACEPIECE.
AIR-PURIFYING FULL FACEPIECE RESPIRATOR WITH A HIGH-EFFICIENCY PARTICULATE FILTER.
POWERED AIR-PURIFYING RESPIRATOR WITH A TIGHT-FITTING FACEPIECE AND HIGH-EFFICIENCY PARTICULATE FILTER.
TYPE 'C' SUPPLIED-AIR RESPIRATOR WITH A FULL FACEPIECE OPERATED IN PRESSURE-DEMAND OR OTHER POSITIVE PRESSURE MODE OR WITH A FULL FACEPIECE, HELMET OR HOOD OPERATED IN CONTINUOUS-FLOW MODE.
SELF-CONTAINED BREATHING APPARATUS WITH A FULL FACEPIECE OPERATED IN PRESSURE-DEMAND OR OTHER POSITIVE PRESSURE MODE.
FOR FIREFIGHTING AND OTHER IMMEDIATELY DANGEROUS TO LIFE OR HEALTH CONDITIONS:
SELF-CONTAINED BREATHING APPARATUS WITH FULL FACEPIECE OPERATED IN PRESSURE-DEMAND OR OTHER POSITIVE PRESSURE MODE.
SUPPLIED-AIR RESPIRATOR WITH FULL FACEPIECE AND OPERATED IN PRESSURE-DEMAND OR OTHER POSITIVE PRESSURE MODE IN COMBINATION WITH AN AUXILIARY SELF-CONTAINED BREATHING APPARATUS OPERATED IN PRESSURE-DEMAND OR OTHER POSITIVE PRESSURE MODE.
CLOTHING: EMPLOYEE MUST WEAR APPROPRIATE PROTECTIVE (IMPERVIOUS) CLOTHING AND EQUIPMENT TO PREVENT REPEATED OR PROLONGED SKIN CONTACT WITH THIS SUBSTANCE.
GLOVES: EMPLOYEE MUST WEAR APPROPRIATE PROTECTIVE GLOVES TO PREVENT CONTACT WITH THIS SUBSTANCE.
EYE PROTECTION: EMPLOYEE MUST WEAR SPLASH-PROOF OR DUST-RESISTANT SAFETY GOGGLES AND A FACESHIELD TO PREVENT CONTACT WITH THIS SUBSTANCE.
EMERGENCY WASH FACILITIES: WHERE THERE IS ANY POSSIBILITY THAT AN EMPLOYEE'S EYES AND/OR SKIN MAY BE EXPOSED TO THIS SUBSTANCE, THE EMPLOYER SHOULD PROVIDE AN EYE WASH FOUNTAIN AND QUICK DRENCH SHOWER WITHIN THE IMMEDIATE WORK AREA FOR EMERGENCY USE.

AUTHORIZED BY- OCCUPATIONAL HEALTH SERVICES, INC.
CREATION DATE: 10/04/89 ***REVISION DATE:*** 05/25/90

MATERIAL SAFETY DATA SHEET

OCCUPATIONAL HEALTH SERVICES, INC.
AGRICULTURE AND PESTICIDE DIVISION
450 SEVENTH AVENUE, SUITE 2407
NEW YORK, NEW YORK 10123
1-800-445-MSDS OR (212) 967-1100

EMERGENCY CONTACT:
JOHN S. BRANSFORD, JR. (615) 292-1180

SUBSTANCE IDENTIFICATION

CAS-NUMBER 62-73-7
SUBSTANCE: **DICHLORVOS**
TRADE NAMES/SYNONYMS: PHOSPHORIC ACID, 2,2-DICHLOROETHENYL DIMETHYL ESTER; PHOSPHORIC ACID, 2,2-DICHLOROVINYL DIMETHYL ESTER; O,O-DIMETHYL O-(2,2-DICHLOROVINYL) PHOSPHATE; 2,2-DICHLOROVINYL DIMETHYL PHOSPHATE;

2,2-DICHLOROETHENYL DIMETHYL PHOSPHATE; DIMETHYL 2,2-DICHLOROVINYL PHOSPHATE; ATGARD; DDVP; DEDEVAP; DICHLORMAN; DICHLOROVOS; DIVIPAN; EQUIGARD; NUVAN; SD 1750; VAPONA; ENT 20738; NCI-C00113; STCC 4921534; C4H7CL2O4P; PST07000

CHEMICAL FAMILY: ORGANOPHOSPHATE

MOLECULAR FORMULA: C4-H7-CL2-O4-P

MOLECULAR WEIGHT: 220.98

CERCLA RATINGS (SCALE 0-3): HEALTH=3 FIRE=2 REACTIVITY=0 PERSISTENCE=0

NFPA RATINGS (SCALE 0-4): HEALTH=4 FIRE=2 REACTIVITY=0

COMPONENTS AND CONTAMINANTS

COMPONENT: DICHLORVOS ***PERCENT:*** 100
CAS# 62-73-7

OTHER CONTAMINANTS: NONE

EXPOSURE LIMITS: DICHLORVOS: 1 MG/M3 OSHA TWA (SKIN) 0.1 PPM (1.0 MG/M3) ACGIH TWA (SKIN)
1000 POUNDS SARA SECTION 302 THRESHOLD PLANNING QUANTITY 10 POUNDS SARA SECTION 304 REPORTABLE QUANTITY 10 POUNDS CERCLA SECTION 103 REPORTABLE QUANTITY SUBJECT TO SARA SECTION 313 ANNUAL TOXIC CHEMICAL RELEASE REPORTING SUBJECT TO CALIFORNIA PROPOSITION 65 CANCER AND/OR REPRODUCTIVE TOXICITY WARNING AND RELEASE REQUIREMENTS- (JANUARY 1, 1989)

PHYSICAL DATA

DESCRIPTION: COLORLESS TO AMBER LIQUID WITH A PLEASANT ODOR.

BOILING POINT: 183 F (84 C) @ 1 MMHG ***MELTING POINT:*** NOT AVAILABLE

SPECIFIC GRAVITY: 1.415 @ 25 C ***VAPOR PRESSURE:*** 0.012 MMHG @ 20 C

EVAPORATION RATE: (BUTYL ACETATE=1) 0.05 ***SOLUBILITY IN WATER:*** 1%

VAPOR DENSITY: 15.3

SOLVENT SOLUBILITY: SOLUBLE IN ALCOHOLS, KEROSENE, MINERAL OILS, DIESEL OIL AEROSOL PROPELLANTS, AROMATIC AND CHLORINATED SOLVENTS, NON-POLAR SOLVENTS, AND MOST OTHER ORGANIC SOLVENTS; SLIGHTLY SOLUBLE IN GLYCERINE.

FIRE AND EXPLOSION DATA

FIRE AND EXPLOSION HAZARD: MODERATE FIRE HAZARD WHEN EXPOSED TO HEAT OR FLAME.

FLASH POINT: >176 F (>80 C) ***FLAMMABILITY CLASS(OSHA):*** IIIA

FIREFIGHTING MEDIA: DRY CHEMICAL, CARBON DIOXIDE, HALON, WATER SPRAY OR STANDARD FOAM (1987 EMERGENCY RESPONSE GUIDEBOOK, DOT P 5800.4). FOR LARGER FIRES, USE WATER SPRAY, FOG OR STANDARD FOAM (1987 EMERGENCY RESPONSE GUIDEBOOK, DOT P 5800.4).

FIREFIGHTING: MOVE CONTAINERS FROM FIRE AREA IF POSSIBLE. FIGHT FIRE FROM MAXIMUM DISTANCE. STAY AWAY FROM STORAGE TANK ENDS. DIKE FIRE CONTROL WATER FOR LATER DISPOSAL. DO NOT SCATTER MATERIAL (1987 EMERGENCY RESPONSE GUIDEBOOK, DOT P 5800.4, GUIDE PAGE 55). EXTINGUISH ONLY IF FLOW CAN BE STOPPED; USE FLOODING AMOUNTS OF WATER AS FOG, SOLID STREAMS MAY BE INEFFECTIVE. COOL CONTAINERS WITH FLOODING AMOUNTS OF WATER FROM AS FAR A DISTANCE AS POSSIBLE. USE WATER SPRAY TO ABSORB TOXIC VAPORS. AVOID BREATHING TOXIC VAPORS; KEEP UPWIND. CONSIDER EVACUATION OF DOWNWIND AREA IF MATERIAL IS LEAKING.

TRANSPORTATION DATA

DEPARTMENT OF TRANSPORTATION HAZARD CLASSIFICATION 49 CFR 172.101: POISON B

DEPARTMENT OF TRANSPORTATION LABELING REQUIREMENTS 49 CFR 172.101 AND SUBPART E: POISON

DEPARTMENT OF TRANSPORTATION PACKAGING REQUIREMENTS: 49 CFR 173.346 EXCEPTIONS: 49 CFR 173.345

TOXICITY

DICHLORVOS: TOXICITY DATA: 15 MG/M3/4 HOURS INHALATION-RAT LC50; 13 MG/M3/4 HOURS INHALATION-MOUSE LC50; 70400 UG/KG SKIN-RAT LD50; 107 MG/KG SKIN-RABBIT LD50; 206 MG/KG SKIN-MOUSE LD50; 25 MG/KG ORAL-RAT LD50; 61 MG/KG ORAL-MOUSE LD50; 10 MG/KG ORAL-RABBIT LD50; 100 MG/KG ORAL-DOG LD50; 157 MG/KG ORAL-PIG LD50; 10800 UG/KG SUBCUTANEOUS-RAT LD50; 24 MG/KG SUBCUTANEOUS-MOUSE LD50; 18 MG/KG INTRAVENOUS-MOUSE LD50; 2200 UG/KG INTRAVENOUS-DOG LDLO; 40 MG/KG INTRAPERITONEAL-RAT LDLO; 23300 UG/MG INTRAPERITONEAL-RAT LD50; 22 MG/KG INTRAPERITONEAL-MOUSE LD50; 30 MG/KG INTRAPERITONEAL-HAMSTER LD50; MUTAGENIC DATA (RTECS); REPRODUCTIVE EFFECTS DATA (RTECS). CARCINOGEN STATUS: ANIMAL INADEQUATE EVIDENCE (IARC GROUP 3). WHEN TESTED IN ONE EXPERIMENT IN MICE AND IN RATS BY ORAL ADMINISTRATION, NO STATISTICALLY SIGNIFICANT EXCESS OF TUMORS WAS OBSERVED. HOWEVER, IN MICE, A FEW ESOPHAGEAL TUMORS, RARELY SEEN IN UNTREATED ANIMALS, WERE FOUND. IN TWO-YEAR GAVAGE STUDIES, CLEAR EVIDENCE OF CARCINOGENIC ACTIVITY WAS OBSERVED AS INDICATED BY INCREASED INCIDENCES OF PANCREATIC ADENOMAS AND MONONUCLEAR CELL LEUKEMIA IN MALE RATS. SOME EVIDENCE OF CARCINOGENIC ACTIVITY WAS REPORTED IN FEMALE RATS WITH INCREASED INCIDENCES OF PANCREATIC ADENOMAS AND MAMMARY GLAND FIBROADENOMAS AND IN MICE WITH INCREASED INCIDENCES OF FORESTOMACH SQUAMOUS CELL PAPILLOMAS (NTP TR 342). ACUTE TOXICITY LEVEL: HIGHLY TOXIC BY INHALATION, DERMAL ABSORPTION, AND INGESTION. TARGET EFFECTS: CHOLINESTERASE INHIBITOR. POISONING MAY AFFECT THE NERVOUS SYSTEM.* AT INCREASED RISK FROM EXPOSURE: PERSONS WITH REDUCED PULMONARY FUNCTION, CONVULSIVE DISORDERS, HEPATIC INSUFFICIENCY, OR RECENT EXPOSURE TO ANTICHOLINESTERASE AGENTS. ADDITIONAL DATA: ALCOHOLIC BEVERAGES MAY ENHANCE THE TOXIC EFFECTS. MAY CROSS THE PLACENTA. HIGH ENVIRONMENTAL TEMPERATURES OR EXPOSURE OF THE CHEMICAL TO VISIBLE OR ULTRAVIOLET LIGHT MAY ENHANCE THE TOXICITY. INTERACTIONS WITH MEDICATIONS MAY OCCUR.*

* MAY BE BASED ON GENERAL INFORMATION ON ORGANOPHOSPHATES.

HEALTH EFFECTS AND FIRST AID

INHALATION: DICHLORVOS: HIGHLY TOXIC. 200 MG/M3 IMMEDIATELY DANGEROUS TO LIFE OR HEALTH. REPRODUCTIVE EFFECTS HAVE BEEN REPORTED IN ANIMALS. SEE INFORMATION ON ORGANOPHOSPHATES.
ORGANOPHOSPHATES: CHOLINESTERASE INHIBITOR. **ACUTE EXPOSURE-** WHEN INHALED, THE FIRST EFFECTS OF CHOLINESTERASE INHIBITORS ARE USUALLY RESPIRATORY AND MAY INCLUDE NASAL HYPEREMIA AND WATERY DISCHARGE, COUGH, CHEST DISCOMFORT, DYSPNEA, AND WHEEZING DUE TO INCREASED BRONCHIAL SECRETIONS AND BRONCHOCONSTRICTION. IF SUFFICIENT AMOUNTS ARE ABSORBED, OTHER SYSTEMIC EFFECTS MAY BEGIN WITHIN A FEW MINUTES OR BE DELAYED FOR UP TO 12 HOURS. SYMPTOMS MAY INCLUDE PALLOR, NAUSEA, VOMITING, DIARRHEA, ABDOMINAL CRAMPS, HEADACHE, DIZZINESS, OCULAR PAIN, BLURRED VISION, MIOSIS OR IN SOME CASES, ESPECIALLY INITIALLY, MYDRIASIS, LACRIMATION, SALIVATION, SWEATING, AND CONFUSION. OTHER REPORTED CENTRAL NERVOUS SYSTEM OR NEUROMUSCULAR EFFECTS MAY INCLUDE ATAXIA, SLURRED SPEECH, AREFLEXIA, WEAKNESS, FATIGUE, FASCICULATIONS, TWITCHING, TREMORS POSSIBLY OF THE TONGUE AND EYELIDS, AND EVENTUALLY PARALYSIS OF THE EXTREMITIES AND POSSIBLY OF THE RESPIRATORY MUSCLES. IN SEVERE CASES THERE MAY ALSO BE INVOLUNTARY DEFECATION AND URINATION, CYANOSIS, PSYCHOSIS, HYPERGLYCEMIA, ACUTE PANCREATITIS, CARDIAC IRREGULARITIES, PULMONARY EDEMA, UNCONSCIOUSNESS, CONVULSIONS, AND COMA. DEATH IS PRIMARILY DUE TO RESPIRATORY FAILURE, ALTHOUGH CARDIOVASCULAR EFFECTS INCLUDING CARDIAC ARREST MAY ALSO BE IMPLICATED. LONG TERM SEQUELAE ARE RARE BUT MAY INCLUDE NEUROPSYCHIATRIC DISORDERS AND MYOPATHY WITH MUSCLE TENDERNESS. SOME ORGANOPHOSPHATES MAY CAUSE A DELAYED NEUROPATHY BEGINNING 1-4 WEEKS AFTER AN ACUTE EXPOSURE WHICH MAY OR MAY NOT HAVE CAUSED ACUTE CHOLINERGIC EFFECTS. NUMBNESS, TINGLING, WEAKNESS AND CRAMPING BEGINNING SYMMETRICALLY IN THE LOWER LIMBS MAY PROGRESS TO ATAXIA AND PARALYSIS. IN SEVERE CASES, UPPER LIMB INVOLVEMENT IS POSSIBLE AND FLACCID PARALYSIS MAY PROGRESS TO SPASTIC PARALYSIS WITH EXAGGERATED REFLEXES. IMPROVEMENT MAY OCCUR OVER MONTHS TO YEARS, BUT SOME RESIDUAL IMPAIRMENT USUALLY REMAINS.
CHRONIC EXPOSURE- REPEATED OR PROLONGED EXPOSURE MAY RESULT IN THE EFFECTS OF ACUTE EXPOSURE INCLUDING THE DELAYED NEUROPATHY. OTHER EFFECTS REPORTED IN WORKERS REPEATEDLY EXPOSED INCLUDE IMPAIRED MEMORY AND CONCENTRATION, ACUTE PSYCHOSIS, SEVERE DEPRESSIONS, IRRITABILTY, CONFUSION, APATHY, EMOTIONAL LABILITY, SOCIAL WITHDRAWAL, CONFUSION, HEADACHE, SPEECH DIFFICULTIES, DELAYED REACTION TIMES, SPATIAL DISORIENTATION, NIGHTMARES, SLEEPWALKING, AND DROWSINESS OR INSOMNIA. AN INFLUENZA-LIKE CONDITION WITH HEADACHE, NAUSEA, WEAKNESS, ANOREXIA AND MALAISE HAS ALSO BEEN REPORTED.

FIRST AID- REMOVE FROM EXPOSURE AREA TO FRESH AIR IMMEDIATELY. IF BREATHING HAS STOPPED, GIVE ARTIFICIAL RESPIRATION. MAINTAIN AIRWAY AND BLOOD PRESSURE AND ADMINISTER OXYGEN IF AVAILABLE. KEEP AFFECTED PERSON WARM AND AT REST. TREAT SYMPTOMATICALLY AND SUPPORTIVELY. ADMINISTRATION OF OXYGEN SHOULD BE PERFORMED BY QUALIFIED PERSONNEL. GET MEDICAL ATTENTION IMMEDIATELY.

SKIN CONTACT: DICHLORVOS: HIGHLY TOXIC. APPLICATION TO RABBIT SKIN PRODUCED MILD IRRITATION. SEE INFORMATION ON ORGANOPHOSPHATES.
ORGANOPHOSPHATES: CHOLINESTERASE INHIBITOR. **ACUTE EXPOSURE-** LOCALIZED SWEATING AND FASCICULATIONS MAY OCCUR AT THE SITE OF CONTACT. IF SUFFICIENT AMOUNTS ARE ABSORBED, OTHER EFFECTS OF CHOLINESTERASE INHIBITION AS DESCRIBED IN ACUTE INHALATION MAY OCCUR. SYMPTOMS MAY BE DELAYED 2-3 HOURS, BUT USUALLY NO MORE THAN 12 HOURS. THE RATE OF ABSORPTION IS INCREASED BY THE PRESENCE OF

DERMATITIS OR HIGH AMBIENT TEMPERATURES. DELAYED NEUROPATHY IS ALSO POSSIBLE. **CHRONIC EXPOSURE**- REPEATED OR PROLONGED EXPOSURE MAY CAUSE EFFECTS AS DESCRIBED IN ACUTE EXPOSURE. SOME ORGANOPHOSPHATES MAY CAUSE SENSITIZATION.

FIRST AID- REMOVE CONTAMINATED CLOTHING IMMEDIATELY. WASH CONTAMINATED AREAS WITH SOAP AND WATER FOLLOWED BY ALCOHOL (ARENA, POISONING, 4TH ED.). EMERGENCY PERSONNEL SHOULD WEAR GLOVES AND AVOID CONTAMINATION. TREAT RESPIRATORY DIFFICULTY WITH ARTIFICIAL RESPIRATION. GET MEDICAL ATTENTION IMMEDIATELY.

EYE CONTACT: DICHLORVOS: APPLICATION OF 1.67 MG/KG IN RABBITS' EYES PRODUCED MILD REDNESS AND CHEMOSIS, BUT NO CORNEAL INJURY WAS OBSERVED. SEE INFORMATION ON ORGANOPHOSPHATES.

ORGANOPHOSPHATES: CHOLINESTERASE INHIBITOR. **ACUTE EXPOSURE**- DIRECT CONTACT MAY CAUSE PAIN, HYPEREMIA, LACRIMATION, TWITCHING OF THE EYELIDS, MIOSIS, AND CILIARY MUSCLE SPASM WITH LOSS OF ACCOMODATION, BLURRED OR DIMMED VISION AND BROWACHE. SOMETIMES MYDRIASIS MAY OCCUR INSTEAD OF MIOSIS. WITH SUFFICIENT EXPOSURE, OTHER SYMPTOMS OF CHOLINESTERASE INHIBITION AS DESCRIBED IN ACUTE INHALATION MAY OCCUR. **CHRONIC EXPOSURE**- REPEATED OR PROLONGED EXPOSURE MAY CAUSE EFFECTS AS DESCRIBED IN ACUTE EXPOSURE. SOME COMPOUNDS HAVE CAUSED TOXIC EFFECTS ON THE CRYSTALLINE LENS, CONJUNCTIVAL THICKENING AND OBSTRUCTION OF THE NASOLACRIMAL CANALS WHEN USED AS MIOTIC EYEDROPS.

FIRST AID- IRRIGATE EYES WITH WATER OR SALINE SOLUTION. IF SYMPTOMS OF POISONING OCCUR, TREAT RESPIRATORY DIFFICULTY WITH ARTIFICIAL RESPIRATION AND OXYGEN. OBSERVE PATIENT FOR AT LEAST 24-36 HOURS (GOSSELIN, CLINICAL TOXICOLOGY OF COMMERCIAL PRODUCTS, 5TH ED.). GET MEDICAL ATTENTION IMMEDIATELY. OXYGEN SHOULD BE ADMINISTERED BY QUALIFIED MEDICAL PERSONNEL.

INGESTION: DICHLORVOS: HIGHLY TOXIC. A SINGLE ORAL DOSE OF 40 UG/KG PRODUCED DEPLETION OF TESTICULAR GERMINAL EPITHELIUM IN MICE. IN MALE RATS, REPEATED ADMINISTRATION PRODUCED AGGREGATES OF ALVEOLAR MACROPHAGES IN THE LUNGS, INTERSTITIAL FIBROSIS OF THE MYOCARDIUM, FOCAL FOLLICULAR-CELL HYPERPLASIA OF THE THYROID, FOCAL HEPATOCYTOMEGALY AND CHRONIC NEPHRITIS. LIVER EFFECTS WERE ALSO OBSERVED IN DOGS AND PIGS. CHRONIC GAVAGE STUDIES REPORTED INCREASED INCIDENCES OF PANCREATIC ADENOMAS AND MONONUCLEAR CELL LEUKEMIA IN MALE RATS; PANCREATIC ADENOMAS AND MAMMARY GLAND FIBROADENOMAS IN FEMALE RATS; AND FORESTOMACH SQUAMOUS CELL PAPILLOMAS IN MALE AND FEMALE MICE. REPRODUCTIVE EFFECTS HAVE BEEN REPORTED IN ANIMALS. SEE INFORMATION ON ORGANOPHOSPHATES.

ORGANOPHOSPHATES: CHOLINESTERASE INHIBITOR. **ACUTE EXPOSURE**- WHEN INGESTED, THE FIRST EFFECTS MAY BE NAUSEA, VOMITING, ANOREXIA, ABDOMINAL CRAMPS AND DIARRHEA. GASTROINTESTINAL ABSORPTION MAY CAUSE SYMPTOMS OF CHOLINESTERASE INHIBITION AS DESCRIBED IN ACUTE INHALATION. SYMPTOMS MAY BEGIN WITHIN MINUTES OR BE DELAYED FOR HOURS. DELAYED EFFECTS INCLUDING NEUROPATHY MAY ALSO OCCUR. **CHRONIC EXPOSURE**- REPEATED INGESTION MAY CAUSE EFFECTS AS DESCRIBED IN ACUTE EXPOSURE.

FIRST AID- IF PERSON IS ALERT AND RESPIRATION IS NOT DEPRESSED, GIVE SYRUP OF IPECAC FOLLOWED BY WATER (IF VOMITING OCCURS, KEEP HEAD BELOW HIPS TO PREVENT ASPIRATION). IF CONSCIOUSNESS LEVEL DECLINES OR VOMITING HAS NOT OCCURRED IN 15 MINUTES EMPTY STOMACH BY GASTRIC LAVAGE WITH THE AID OF CUFFED ENDOTRACHEAL TUBE USING ISOTONIC SALINE OR 5% SODIUM BICARBONATE FOLLOW WITH ACTIVATED CHARCOAL. ESTABLISH AND MAINTAIN AIRWAY. TREAT RESPIRATORY DIFFICULTY WITH ARTIFICIAL RESPIRATION AND OXYGEN. DO NOT GIVE MORPHINE, AMINOPHYLLINE, PHENOTHIAZINES, RESERPINE, FUROSEMIDE, OR ETHACRYNIC ACID (MORGAN, RECOGNITION AND MANAGEMENT OF PESTICIDE POISONINGS, 3RD ED.). TREAT SYMPTOMATICALLY AND SUPPORTIVELY. ADMINISTRATION OF OXYGEN AND LAVAGE MUST BE PERFORMED BY QUALIFIED MEDICAL PERSONNEL. GET MEDICAL ATTENTION IMMEDIATELY.

ANTIDOTE: THE FOLLOWING ANTIDOTE(S) HAVE BEEN RECOMMENDED. HOWEVER, THE DECISION AS TO WHETHER THE SEVERITY OF POISONING REQUIRES ADMINISTRATION OF ANY ANTIDOTE AND ACTUAL DOSE REQUIRED SHOULD BE MADE BY QUALIFIED MEDICAL PERSONNEL.

FOR CHOLINESTERASE INHIBITORS: ESTABLISH CLEAR AIRWAY AND TISSUE OXYGENATION BY ASPIRATION OF SECRETIONS, AND IF NECESSARY, BY ASSISTED PULMONARY VENTILATION WITH OXYGEN. IMPROVE TISSUE OXYGENATION AS MUCH AS POSSIBLE BEFORE ADMINISTERING ATROPINE TO MINIMIZE THE RISK OF VENTRICULAR FIBRILLATION. ADMINISTER ATROPINE SULFATE INTRAVENOUSLY, OR INTRAMUSCULARLY IF IV INJECTION IS NOT POSSIBLE. IN MODERATELY SEVERE POISONING ADMINISTER ATROPINE SULFATE, 0.4-2.0 MG REPEATED EVERY 15 MINUTES UNTIL ATROPINIZATION IS ACHIEVED (TACHYCARDIA, FLUSHING, DRY MOUTH, MYDRIASIS). MAINTAIN ATROPINIZATION BY REPEATED DOSES FOR 2-12 HOURS, OR LONGER, DEPENDING ON THE SEVERITY OF POISONING. THE APPEARANCE OF RALES IN THE LUNG BASES, MIOSIS, SALIVATION, NAUSEA, BRADYCARDIA, ARE ALL INDICATIONS OF INADEQUATE ATROPINIZATION. SEVERELY POISONED INDIVIDUALS MAY EXHIBIT REMARKABLE TOLERANCE TO ATROPINE; TWO OR MORE TIMES THE DOSAGES SUGGESTED ABOVE MAY BE NEEDED. PERSONS NOT POISONED OR ONLY SLIGHTLY POISONED, HOWEVER, MAY DEVELOP SIGNS OF ATROPINE TOXICITY FROM SUCH LARGE DOSAGES: FEVER, MUSCLE FIBRILLATIONS, AND DELIRIUM ARE THE MAIN SIGNS OF ATROPINE TOXICITY. IF THESE SIGNS APPEAR WHILE THE PATIENT IS FULLY ATROPINIZED, ATROPINE ADMINISTRATION SHOULD BE DISCONTINUED, AT LEAST TEMPORARILY. OBSERVE TREATED PATIENTS CLOSELY AT LEAST 24 HOURS TO INSURE THAT SYMPTOMS (POSSIBLY PULMONARY EDEMA) DO NOT RECUR AS ATROPINIZATION WEARS OFF. IN VERY SEVERE POISONINGS, METABOLIC DISPOSITION OF TOXICANT MAY REQUIRE SEVERAL HOURS OR DAYS DURING WHICH ATROPINIZATION MUST BE MAINTAINED. MARKEDLY LOWER LEVELS OF URINARY METABOLITES INDICATE THAT ATROPINE DOSAGE CAN BE TAPERED OFF. AS DOSAGE IS REDUCED, CHECK THE LUNG BASES FREQUENTLY FOR RALES. IF RALES ARE HEARD OR OTHER SYMPTOMS RETURN, RE-ESTABLISH ATROPINIZATION PROMPTLY (MORGAN, RECOGNITION AND MANAGEMENT OF PESTICIDE POISONINGS, 3RD ED.). ADMINISTRATION OF ANTIDOTE MUST BE PERFORMED BY QUALIFIED MEDICAL PERSONNEL.

IN CASES OF SEVERE POISONING BY ORGANOPHOSPHATE PESTICIDES IN WHICH RESPIRATORY DEPRESSION, MUSCLE WEAKNESS AND TWITCHINGS ARE SEVERE, GIVE PRALIDOXIME (PROTOPAM-AYERST, 2-PAM), 1.0 GRAM INTRAVENOUSLY AT NO MORE THAN 0.5 GRAM PER MINUTE. DOSAGE OF PRALIDOXIME MAY BE REPEATED IN 1-2 HOURS, THEN AT 10-12 HOUR INTERVALS IF NEEDED. IN VERY SEVERE POISONINGS, DOSAGE RATES MAY BE DOUBLED. TREATMENT WITH PRALIDOXIME WILL BE MOST EFFECTIVE IF GIVEN WITHIN THIRTY-SIX HOURS AFTER POISONING (MORGAN, RECOGNITION AND MANAGEMENT OF PESTICIDE POISONINGS, 3RD ED.). ANTIDOTE SHOULD BE ADMINISTERED BY QUALIFIED MEDICAL PERSONNEL.

REACTIVITY

REACTIVITY: STABLE UNDER NORMAL TEMPERATURES AND PRESSURES IN A CLOSED CONTAINER; MAY HYDROLYZE ON CONTACT WITH MOISTURE.

INCOMPATIBILITIES: DICHLORVOS: ACIDS (STRONG): DECOMPOSITION. BASES (STRONG): DECOMPOSITION. IRON: MAY CORRODE. PLASTICS, RUBBER, COATINGS: MAY BE ATTACKED. STEEL: MAY CORRODE.

DECOMPOSITION: THERMAL DECOMPOSITION MAY RELEASE TOXIC OXIDES OF PHOSPHORUS AND CARBON, TOXIC AND CORROSIVE CHLORIDES, AND TOXIC PHOSGENE GAS.

POLYMERIZATION: HAZARDOUS POLYMERIZATION HAS NOT BEEN REPORTED TO OCCUR UNDER NORMAL TEMPERATURES AND PRESSURES.

STORAGE AND DISPOSAL

OBSERVE ALL FEDERAL, STATE AND LOCAL REGULATIONS WHEN STORING OR DISPOSING OF THIS SUBSTANCE. FOR ASSISTANCE, CONTACT THE DISTRICT DIRECTOR OF THE ENVIRONMENTAL PROTECTION AGENCY.

STORAGE

STORE IN ACCORDANCE WITH 40 CFR 165 RECOMMENDED PROCEDURES FOR THE DISPOSAL AND STORAGE OF PESTICIDES AND PESTICIDE CONTAINERS.

STORE AWAY FROM INCOMPATIBLE SUBSTANCES.

THRESHOLD PLANNING QUANTITY (TPQ): THE SUPERFUND AMENDMENTS AND REAUTHORIZATION ACT (SARA) SECTION 302 REQUIRES THAT EACH FACILITY WHERE ANY EXTREMELY HAZARDOUS SUBSTANCE IS PRESENT IN A QUANTITY EQUAL TO OR GREATER THAN THE TPQ ESTABLISHED FOR THAT SUBSTANCE NOTIFY THE STATE EMERGENCY RESPONSE COMMISSION FOR THE STATE IN WHICH IT IS LOCATED. SECTION 303 OF SARA REQUIRES THESE FACILITIES TO PARTICIPATE IN LOCAL EMERGENCY RESPONSE PLANNING (40 CFR 355.30).

DISPOSAL

DISPOSAL MUST BE IN ACCORDANCE WITH 40 CFR 165 RECOMMENDED PROCEDURES FOR THE DISPOSAL AND STORAGE OF PESTICIDES AND PESTICIDE CONTAINERS.

CONDITIONS TO AVOID

MAY BURN BUT DOES NOT IGNITE READILY. CONTAINERS MAY EXPLODE IN HEAT OF FIRE.

SPILL AND LEAK PROCEDURES

SOIL SPILL: DIG HOLDING AREA SUCH AS LAGOON, POND OR PIT FOR CONTAINMENT. DIKE FLOW OF SPILLED MATERIAL USING SOIL OR SANDBAGS OR FOAMED BARRIERS SUCH AS POLYURETHANE OR CONCRETE.

USE CEMENT POWDER OR FLY ASH TO ABSORB LIQUID MASS.

AIR SPILL: KNOCK DOWN VAPORS WITH WATER SPRAY. KEEP UPWIND.

WATER SPILL: USE ACTIVATED CARBON TO ABSORB SPILLED SUBSTANCE THAT IS DISSOLVED. USE MECHANICAL DREDGES OR LIFTS TO EXTRACT IMMOBILIZED MASSES OF POLLUTION AND PRECIPITATES.
THE CALIFORNIA SAFE DRINKING WATER AND TOXIC ENFORCEMENT ACT OF 1986 (PROPOSITION 65) PROHIBITS CONTAMINATING ANY KNOWN SOURCE OF DRINKING WATER WITH SUBSTANCES KNOWN TO CAUSE CANCER AND/OR REPRODUCTIVE TOXICITY.

OCCUPATIONAL SPILL: DO NOT TOUCH SPILLED MATERIAL. STOP LEAK IF YOU CAN DO IT WITHOUT RISK. USE WATER SPRAY TO REDUCE VAPORS. FOR SMALL SPILLS, TAKE UP WITH SAND OR OTHER ABSORBENT MATERIAL AND PLACE INTO CONTAINERS FOR LATER DISPOSAL. FOR SMALL DRY SPILLS, WITH A CLEAN SHOVEL PLACE MATERIAL INTO CLEAN, DRY CONTAINERS AND COVER. MOVE CONTAINERS FROM SPILL AREA. FOR LARGER SPILLS, DIKE FAR AHEAD OF SPILL FOR LATER DISPOSAL. KEEP UNNECESSARY PEOPLE AWAY. ISOLATE HAZARD AREA AND DENY ENTRY. VENTILATE CLOSED SPACES BEFORE ENTERING.
REPORTABLE QUANTITY (RQ): 10 POUNDS THE SUPERFUND AMENDMENTS AND REAUTHORIZATION ACT (SARA) SECTION 304 REQUIRES THAT A RELEASE EQUAL TO OR GREATER THAN THE REPORTABLE QUANTITY FOR THIS SUBSTANCE BE IMMEDIATELY REPORTED TO THE LOCAL EMERGENCY PLANNING COMMITTEE AND THE STATE EMERGENCY RESPONSE COMMISSION (40 CFR 355.40). IF THE RELEASE OF THIS SUBSTANCE IS REPORTABLE UNDER CERCLA SECTION 103, THE NATIONAL RESPONSE CENTER MUST BE NOTIFIED IMMEDIATELY AT (800) 424-8802 OR (202) 426-2675 IN THE METROPOLITAN WASHINGTON, D.C. AREA (40 CFR 302.6).

PROTECTIVE EQUIPMENT

VENTILATION: PROCESS ENCLOSURE RECOMMENDED TO MEET PUBLISHED EXPOSURE LIMITS.

RESPIRATOR: THE FOLLOWING RESPIRATORS AND MAXIMUM USE CONCENTRATIONS ARE RECOMMENDATIONS BY THE U.S. DEPARTMENT OF HEALTH AND HUMAN SERVICES, NIOSH POCKET GUIDE TO CHEMICAL HAZARDS; NIOSH CRITERIA DOCUMENTS OR BY THE U.S. DEPARTMENT OF LABOR, 29 CFR 1910 SUBPART Z.
THE SPECIFIC RESPIRATOR SELECTED MUST BE BASED ON CONTAMINATION LEVELS FOUND IN THE WORK PLACE, MUST NOT EXCEED THE WORKING LIMITS OF THE RESPIRATOR AND BE JOINTLY APPROVED BY THE NATIONAL INSTITUTE FOR OCCUPATIONAL SAFETY AND HEALTH AND THE MINE SAFETY AND HEALTH ADMINISTRATION (NIOSH-MSHA).
DICHLORVOS:
10 MG/M3- ANY SUPPLIED-AIR RESPIRATOR. ANY SELF-CONTAINED BREATHING APPARATUS.
25 MG/M3- ANY SUPPLIED-AIR RESPIRATOR OPERATED IN A CONTINOUS FLOW MODE.
50 MG/M3- ANY SUPPLIED-AIR RESPIRATOR WITH A FULL FACEPIECE. ANY SELF-CONTAINED BREATHING APPARATUS WITH A FULL FACEPIECE. ANY SUPPLIED-AIR RESPIRATOR WITH A TIGHT-FITTING FACEPIECE OPERATED IN A CONTINUOUS FLOW MODE.
200 MG/M3- ANY SUPPLIED-AIR RESPIRATOR WITH A HALF-MASK AND OPERATED IN A PRESSURE-DEMAND OR OTHER POSITIVE PRESSURE MODE.
ESCAPE- ANY AIR-PURIFYING FULL FACEPIECE RESPIRATOR (GAS MASK) WITH A CHIN-STYLE OR FRONT- OR BACK-MOUNTED ORGANIC VAPOR CANISTER HAVING A HIGH-EFFICIENCY PARTICULATE FILTER. ANY APPROPRIATE ESCAPE-TYPE SELF-CONTAINED BREATHING APPARATUS.
FOR FIREFIGHTING AND OTHER IMMEDIATELY DANGEROUS TO LIFE OR HEALTH CONDITIONS:
SELF-CONTAINED BREATHING APPARATUS WITH FULL FACEPIECE OPERATED IN PRESSURE-DEMAND OR OTHER POSITIVE PRESSURE MODE.
SUPPLIED-AIR RESPIRATOR WITH FULL FACEPIECE AND OPERATED IN PRESSURE-DEMAND OR OTHER POSITIVE PRESSURE MODE IN COMBINATION WITH AN AUXILIARY SELF-CONTAINED BREATHING APPARATUS OPERATED IN PRESSURE-DEMAND OR OTHER POSITIVE PRESSURE MODE.

CLOTHING: EMPLOYEE MUST WEAR APPROPRIATE PROTECTIVE (IMPERVIOUS) CLOTHING AND EQUIPMENT TO PREVENT ANY POSSIBILITY OF SKIN CONTACT WITH THIS SUBSTANCE.

GLOVES: EMPLOYEE MUST WEAR APPROPRIATE PROTECTIVE GLOVES TO PREVENT CONTACT WITH THIS SUBSTANCE.

EYE PROTECTION: EMPLOYEE MUST WEAR SPLASH-PROOF OR DUST-RESISTANT SAFETY GOGGLES WITH OR WITHOUT A FACESHIELD TO PREVENT CONTACT WITH THIS SUBSTANCE.
EMERGENCY EYE WASH: WHERE THERE IS ANY POSSIBILITY THAT AN EMPLOYEE'S EYES MAY BE EXPOSED TO THIS SUBSTANCE, THE EMPLOYER SHOULD PROVIDE AN EYE WASH FOUNTAIN WITHIN THE IMMEDIATE WORK AREA FOR EMERGENCY USE.

AUTHORIZED BY- OCCUPATIONAL HEALTH SERVICES, INC.
CREATION DATE: 10/04/89 ***REVISION DATE:*** 07/12/90

MATERIAL SAFETY DATA SHEET

OCCUPATIONAL HEALTH SERVICES, INC.
AGRICULTURE AND PESTICIDE DIVISION
450 SEVENTH AVENUE, SUITE 2407
NEW YORK, NEW YORK 10123
1-800-445-MSDS OR (212) 967-1100

EMERGENCY CONTACT:
JOHN S. BRANSFORD, JR. (615) 292-1180

SUBSTANCE IDENTIFICATION

CAS-NUMBER 75736-33-3

SUBSTANCE: DICLOBUTRAZOL

TRADE NAMES/SYNONYMS: 1H-1,2,4-TRIAZOLE-1-ETHANOL, BETA-((2,4-DICHLOROPHENYL)METHYL)-ALPHA- (1,1-DIMETHYLETHYL)-, (R*,R*)-(+/-)'; 1-(2,4-DICHLOROPHENYL)-4,4-DIMETHYL-2-(1,2,4-TRIAZOL-1-YL)PENTAN-3-OL; DICHLOBUTRAZOL; VIGIL; PP 296; (R*,R*)-(+/-)-DETA-((2,4-DICHLOROPHENYL)METHYL)-ALPHA-(1,1- DIMETHYLETHYL)-1H-1,2,4-TRIAZOLE-1-EHANOL; C15H19CL2N3O; PST07005

CHEMICAL FAMILY: TRIAZOLE
HYDROXYL, ALIPHATIC

MOLECULAR FORMULA: C15-H19-CL2-N3-O

MOLECULAR WEIGHT: 328.24

CERCLA RATINGS (SCALE 0-3): HEALTH=U FIRE=1 REACTIVITY=0 PERSISTENCE=2

NFPA RATINGS (SCALE 0-4): HEALTH=U FIRE=1 REACTIVITY=0

COMPONENTS AND CONTAMINANTS

COMPONENT: DICLOBUTRAZOL ***PERCENT:*** 100.0
CAS# 75736-33-3

OTHER CONTAMINANTS: NONE

EXPOSURE LIMITS: NO OCCUPATIONAL EXPOSURE LIMITS ESTABLISHED BY OSHA, ACGIH, OR NIOSH.

PHYSICAL DATA

DESCRIPTION: OFF-WHITE CRYSTALLINE SOLID. ***MELTING POINT:*** 297-298 F (147-149 C)

SPECIFIC GRAVITY: NOT AVAILABLE ***VAPOR PRESSURE:*** NEGLIGIBLE

SOLUBILITY IN WATER: 9 PPM

SOLVENT SOLUBILITY: MODERATELY SOLUBLE IN 2-BUTOXYETHANOL, CYCLOHEXANONE, DIMETHYLFORMAMIDE, GLYCOL ETHERS, ACETONE, CHLOROFORM, ETHANOL, AND METHANOL; SLIGHTLY SOLUBLE IN XYLENE.

FIRE AND EXPLOSION DATA

FIRE AND EXPLOSION HAZARD: SLIGHT FIRE HAZARD WHEN EXPOSED TO HEAT OR FLAME.

FIREFIGHTING MEDIA: DRY CHEMICAL, CARBON DIOXIDE, HALON, WATER SPRAY OR STANDARD FOAM (1987 EMERGENCY RESPONSE GUIDEBOOK, DOT P 5800.4).
FOR LARGER FIRES, USE WATER SPRAY, FOG OR STANDARD FOAM (1987 EMERGENCY RESPONSE GUIDEBOOK, DOT P 5800.4).

FIREFIGHTING: MOVE CONTAINER FROM FIRE AREA IF POSSIBLE. DO NOT SCATTER SPILLED MATERIAL WITH HIGH PRESSURE WATER STREAMS. DIKE FIRE CONTROL WATER FOR LATER DISPOSAL (1987 EMERGENCY RESPONSE GUIDEBOOK, DOT P 5800.4, GUIDE PAGE 31).
USE AGENTS SUITABLE FOR TYPE OF SURROUNDING FIRE. AVOID BREATHING HAZARDOUS VAPORS, KEEP UPWIND.

TOXICITY

DICHLOBUTRAZOL: TOXICITY DATA: >1000 MG/KG SKIN-RABBIT LD50 (PEMNDP); >1000 MG/KG SKIN-RAT LD50 (PEMNDP); 4 GM/KG ORAL-RAT LD50; 4 GM/KG ORAL-GUINEA PIG LD50; 4 GM/KG ORAL-RABBIT LD50; 500 MG/KG INTRAPERITONEAL-RAT LD50. CARCINOGEN STATUS: NONE. ACUTE TOXICITY LEVEL: MODERATELY TOXIC BY DERMAL ABSORPTION AND INGESTION. TARGET EFFECTS: NO DATA AVAILABLE.

HEALTH EFFECTS AND FIRST AID

INHALATION: DICLOBUTRAZOL: **ACUTE EXPOSURE-** NO DATA AVAILABLE. **CHRONIC EXPOSURE-** NO DATA AVAILABLE.

FIRST AID- REMOVE FROM EXPOSURE AREA TO FRESH AIR IMMEDIATELY. IF BREATHING HAS STOPPED, PERFORM ARTIFICIAL RESPIRATION. KEEP PERSON WARM AND AT REST. TREAT SYMPTOMATICALLY AND SUPPORTIVELY. GET MEDICAL ATTENTION IMMEDIATELY.

SKIN CONTACT: DICLOBUTRAZOL: **ACUTE EXPOSURE-** APPLICATION TO RABBIT SKIN CAUSED MILD IRRITATION. **CHRONIC EXPOSURE-** NO DATA AVAILABLE.

FIRST AID- REMOVE CONTAMINATED CLOTHING AND SHOES IMMEDIATELY. WASH AFFECTED AREA WITH SOAP OR MILD DETERGENT AND LARGE AMOUNTS OF WATER UNTIL NO EVIDENCE OF CHEMICAL REMAINS (APPROXIMATELY 15-20 MINUTES). GET MEDICAL ATTENTION IMMEDIATELY.

EYE CONTACT: DICLOBUTRAZOL: **ACUTE EXPOSURE-** APPLICATION TO RABBIT EYES CAUSED MILD IRRITATION. **CHRONIC EXPOSURE-** NO DATA AVAILABLE.

FIRST AID- WASH EYES IMMEDIATELY WITH LARGE AMOUNTS OF WATER OR NORMAL SALINE, OCCASIONALLY LIFTING UPPER AND LOWER LIDS, UNTIL NO EVIDENCE OF CHEMICAL REMAINS (APPROXIMATELY 15-20 MINUTES). GET MEDICAL ATTENTION IMMEDIATELY.

INGESTION: DICLOBUTRAZOL: **ACUTE EXPOSURE-** NO DATA AVAILABLE. **CHRONIC EXPOSURE-** FEEDING DOGS 15 MG/KG/DAY FOR 6 MONTHS OR RATS 2.5 MG/KG/DAY FOR 90 DAYS CAUSED NO OBSERVABLE EFFECTS.

FIRST AID- IF THE PERSON IS CONSCIOUS AND NOT CONVULSING, REMOVE BY GASTRIC LAVAGE AND FOLLOW WITH A CATHARTIC (DREISBACH, HANDBOOK OF POISONING, 12TH ED.). TREAT SYMPTOMATICALLY AND SUPPORTIVELY. GASTRIC LAVAGE SHOULD BE PERFORMED BY QUALIFIED MEDICAL PERSONNEL. GET MEDICAL ATTENTION IMMEDIATELY.

ANTIDOTE: NO SPECIFIC ANTIDOTE. TREAT SYMPTOMATICALLY AND SUPPORTIVELY.

REACTIVITY

REACTIVITY: STABLE UNDER NORMAL TEMPERATURES AND PRESSURES.

INCOMPATIBILITIES: DICLOBUTRAZOL: OXIDIZERS (STRONG): FIRE AND EXPLOSION HAZARD.

DECOMPOSITION: THERMAL DECOMPOSITION PRODUCTS MAY INCLUDE TOXIC OXIDES OF NITROGEN AND CARBON AND TOXIC AND CORROSIVE FUMES OF CHLORIDES.

POLYMERIZATION: HAZARDOUS POLYMERIZATION HAS NOT BEEN REPORTED TO OCCUR UNDER NORMAL TEMPERATURES AND PRESSURES.

STORAGE AND DISPOSAL

OBSERVE ALL FEDERAL, STATE AND LOCAL REGULATIONS WHEN STORING OR DISPOSING OF THIS SUBSTANCE. FOR ASSISTANCE, CONTACT THE DISTRICT DIRECTOR OF THE ENVIRONMENTAL PROTECTION AGENCY.

STORAGE

STORE IN ACCORDANCE WITH 40 CFR 165 RECOMMENDED PROCEDURES FOR THE DISPOSAL AND STORAGE OF PESTICIDES AND PESTICIDE CONTAINERS.
STORE AWAY FROM INCOMPATIBLE SUBSTANCES.

DISPOSAL

DISPOSAL MUST BE IN ACCORDANCE WITH 40 CFR 165 RECOMMENDED PROCEDURES FOR THE DISPOSAL AND STORAGE OF PESTICIDES AND PESTICIDE CONTAINERS.

CONDITIONS TO AVOID

MAY BURN BUT DOES NOT IGNITE READILY. AVOID CONTACT WITH STRONG OXIDIZERS, EXCESSIVE HEAT, SPARKS, OR OPEN FLAME.

SPILL AND LEAK PROCEDURES

OCCUPATIONAL SPILL: SWEEP UP AND PLACE IN SUITABLE CLEAN, DRY CONTAINERS FOR RECLAMATION OR LATER DISPOSAL. DO NOT FLUSH SPILLED MATERIAL INTO SEWER. KEEP UNNECESSARY PEOPLE AWAY.

PROTECTIVE EQUIPMENT

VENTILATION: PROVIDE LOCAL EXHAUST OR GENERAL DILUTION VENTILATION SYSTEM.

RESPIRATOR: THE FOLLOWING RESPIRATORS ARE RECOMMENDED BASED ON INFORMATION FOUND IN THE PHYSICAL DATA, TOXICITY AND HEALTH EFFECTS SECTIONS. THEY ARE RANKED IN ORDER FROM MINIMUM TO MAXIMUM RESPIRATORY PROTECTION. THE SPECIFIC RESPIRATOR SELECTED MUST BE BASED ON CONTAMINATION LEVELS FOUND IN THE WORK PLACE, MUST NOT EXCEED THE WORKING LIMITS OF THE RESPIRATOR AND BE JOINTLY APPROVED BY THE NATIONAL INSTITUTE FOR OCCUPATIONAL SAFETY AND HEALTH AND THE MINE SAFETY AND HEALTH ADMINISTRATION (NIOSH-MSHA).
CHEMICAL CARTRIDGE RESPIRATOR WITH AN ORGANIC VAPOR CARTRIDGE(S) IN COMBINATION WITH A DUST AND MIST FILTER.
GAS MASK WITH ORGANIC VAPOR CANISTER (CHIN-STYLE OR FRONT- OR BACK-MOUNTED CANISTER) WITH A DUST AND MIST FILTER.
GAS MASK WITH ORGANIC VAPOR CANISTER (CHIN-STYLE OR FRONT- OR BACK-MOUNTED CANISTER) WITH A PARTICULATE FILTER.
POWERED AIR-PURIFYING RESPIRATOR WITH A HIGH-EFFICIENCY FILTER.
TYPE 'C' SUPPLIED-AIR RESPIRATOR WITH A FULL FACEPIECE OPERATED IN A PRESSURE-DEMAND OR OTHER POSITIVE PRESSURE MODE.
SELF-CONTAINED BREATHING APPARATUS WITH A FULL FACEPIECE OPERATED IN PRESSURE-DEMAND OR OTHER POSITIVE PRESSURE MODE.
FOR FIREFIGHTING AND OTHER IMMEDIATELY DANGEROUS TO LIFE OR HEALTH CONDITIONS:
SELF-CONTAINED BREATHING APPARATUS WITH FULL FACEPIECE OPERATED IN PRESSURE-DEMAND OR OTHER POSITIVE PRESSURE MODE.
SUPPLIED-AIR RESPIRATOR WITH FULL FACEPIECE AND OPERATED IN PRESSURE-DEMAND OR OTHER POSITIVE PRESSURE MODE IN COMBINATION WITH AN AUXILIARY SELF-CONTAINED BREATHING APPARATUS OPERATED IN PRESSURE-DEMAND OR OTHER POSITIVE PRESSURE MODE.

CLOTHING: EMPLOYEE MUST WEAR APPROPRIATE PROTECTIVE (IMPERVIOUS) CLOTHING AND EQUIPMENT TO PREVENT REPEATED OR PROLONGED SKIN CONTACT WITH THIS SUBSTANCE.

GLOVES: EMPLOYEE MUST WEAR APPROPRIATE PROTECTIVE GLOVES TO PREVENT CONTACT WITH THIS SUBSTANCE.

EYE PROTECTION: EMPLOYEE MUST WEAR SPLASH-PROOF OR DUST-RESISTANT SAFETY GOGGLES TO PREVENT EYE CONTACT WITH THIS SUBSTANCE.
EMERGENCY EYE WASH: WHERE THERE IS ANY POSSIBILITY THAT AN EMPLOYEE'S EYES MAY BE EXPOSED TO THIS SUBSTANCE, THE EMPLOYER SHOULD PROVIDE AN EYE WASH FOUNTAIN WITHIN THE IMMEDIATE WORK AREA FOR EMERGENCY USE.

AUTHORIZED BY- OCCUPATIONAL HEALTH SERVICES, INC.
CREATION DATE: 10/20/89 **REVISION DATE:** 05/31/90

MATERIAL SAFETY DATA SHEET

OCCUPATIONAL HEALTH SERVICES, INC.
AGRICULTURE AND PESTICIDE DIVISION
450 SEVENTH AVENUE, SUITE 2407
NEW YORK, NEW YORK 10123
1-800-445-MSDS OR (212) 967-1100

EMERGENCY CONTACT:
JOHN S. BRANSFORD, JR. (615) 292-1180

SUBSTANCE IDENTIFICATION

CAS-NUMBER 115-32-2

SUBSTANCE: DICOFOL

TRADE NAMES/SYNONYMS: BENZENEMETHANOL, 4-CHLORO-ALPHA-(4-CHLOROPHENYL)-ALPHA -(TRICHLOROMETHYL)-; BENZHYDROL, 4,4'-DICHLORO-ALPHA-(TRICHLOROMETHYL)-; 4-CHLORO-ALPHA-(4-CHLOROPHENYL)-ALPHA(TRICHLOROMETHYL)BENZENEMETHANOL; 4,4'-DICHLORO-ALPHA-(TRICHLOROMETHYL)BENZHYDROL; 1,1-BIS(P-CHLOROPHENYL)-2,2,2-TRICHLOROETHANOL; DI(P-CHLOROPHENYL)TRICHLOROMETHYLCARBINOL; 2,2,2-TRICHLORO-1,1-BIS(4-CHLOROPHENYL)ETHANOL; 2,2,2-TRICHLORO-1,1-DI-(4-CHLOROPHENYL)ETHANOL; 4,4'-DICHLORO-ALPHA(TRICHLOROMETHYL)BENZHYDROL; ACARIN; CPCA; DECOFOL; DICHLOROKELTHANE; DTMC761; KELTHANE; NCI-COO486; ENT 23648; STCC 4966940; C14H9CL5O; PST07010

CHEMICAL FAMILY: HALOGEN COMPOUND, AROMATIC

MOLECULAR FORMULA: (CL-C6-H4)2-C-(O-H)-C-CL3

MOLECULAR WEIGHT: 370.49

CERCLA RATINGS (SCALE 0-3): HEALTH=3 FIRE=2 REACTIVITY=0 PERSISTENCE=3

NFPA RATINGS (SCALE 0-4): HEALTH=3 FIRE=2 REACTIVITY=0

COMPONENTS AND CONTAMINANTS

COMPONENT: DICOFOL **PERCENT:** 100
CAS# 115-32-2

OTHER CONTAMINANTS: NONE

EXPOSURE LIMITS: NO OCCUPATIONAL EXPOSURE LIMITS ESTABLISHED BY OSHA, ACGIH, OR NIOSH.
DICOFOL: 10 POUNDS CERCLA SECTION 103 REPORTABLE QUANTITY SUBJECT TO SARA SECTION 313 ANNUAL TOXIC CHEMICAL RELEASE REPORTING

PHYSICAL DATA

DESCRIPTION: COLORLESS CRYSTALLINE SOLID. **BOILING POINT:** 437 F (225 C)

MELTING POINT: 173-175 F (79-80 C) **SPECIFIC GRAVITY:** 1.45

SOLUBILITY IN WATER: ALMOST INSOLUBLE

SOLVENT SOLUBILITY: SOLUBLE IN DIMETHYL SULFOXIDE, ETHANOL, ACETONE, MOST ALIPHATIC AND AROMATIC SOLVENTS

FIRE AND EXPLOSION DATA

FIRE AND EXPLOSION HAZARD: MODERATE FIRE HAZARD WHEN EXPOSED TO HEAT OR FLAME.

FLASH POINT: 120 F (49 C) (CC)

FIREFIGHTING MEDIA: DRY CHEMICAL, CARBON DIOXIDE, HALON, WATER SPRAY OR STANDARD FOAM (1987 EMERGENCY RESPONSE GUIDEBOOK, DOT P 5800.4). FOR LARGER FIRES, USE WATER SPRAY, FOG OR STANDARD FOAM (1987 EMERGENCY RESPONSE GUIDEBOOK, DOT P 5800.4).

FIREFIGHTING: MOVE CONTAINERS FROM FIRE AREA IF POSSIBLE. FIGHT FIRE FROM MAXIMUM DISTANCE. STAY AWAY FROM STORAGE TANK ENDS. DIKE FIRE CONTROL WATER FOR LATER DISPOSAL. DO NOT SCATTER MATERIAL (1987 EMERGENCY RESPONSE GUIDEBOOK, DOT P 5800.4, GUIDE PAGE 55).
USE AGENTS SUITABLE FOR TYPE OF FIRE. COOL CONTAINERS WITH FLOODING AMOUNTS OF WATER. AVOID BREATHING VAPORS OR DUSTS, KEEP UPWIND.

TOXICITY

DICOFOL: TOXICITY DATA: 1870 MG/KG SKIN-RABBIT LD50; 100 MG/KG SKIN-RAT LD50; 575 MG/KG ORAL-RAT LD50; 1810 MG/KG ORAL-RABBIT LD50; 420 MG/KG ORAL-MOUSE LD50; 1810 MG/KG ORAL-GUINEA PIG LD50; 1150 MG/KG INTRAPERITONEAL-RAT LD50; MUTAGENIC DATA (RTECS); REPRODUCTIVE EFFECTS DATA (RTECS); TUMORIGENIC DATA (RTECS). CARCINOGEN STATUS: ANIMAL LIMITED EVIDENCE (IARC GROUP-3). AN INCREASED INCIDENCE OF HEPATOCELLULAR CARACINOMAS WAS OBSERVED IN MALE MICE FED DICOFOL. LOCAL EFFECTS: IRRITANT- SKIN. ACUTE TOXICITY LEVEL: MODERATELY TOXIC BY DERMAL ABSORPTION AND INGESTION. TARGET EFFECTS: POISONING MAY AFFECT THE LIVER, KIDNEYS, AND THE CENTRAL NERVOUS SYSTEM. ADDITION DATA: MAY BE STORED IN THE ADIPOSE TISSUES; INTENSE ACTIVITY AND STARVATION MAY MOBILIZED THE PESTICIDE RESULTING IN THE REAPPEARANCE OF TOXIC SYMPTOMS. MAY BE EXCRETED IN BREAST MILK. STIMULANTS SUCH AS EPINEPHRINE MAY INDUCE VENTRICULAR FIBRILLATION.

HEALTH EFFECTS AND FIRST AID

INHALATION: DICOFOL: **ACUTE EXPOSURE-** DICOFOL IS AN ORGANOCHLORINE PESTICIDE. THESE PESTICIDES HAVE DIRECT ACTION ON THE CENTRAL NERVOUS SYSTEM PRODUCING SYMPTOMS OF APPREHENSION, EXCITABILITY, DIZZINESS, HEADACHE, DISORIENTATION, WEAKNESS, PARESTHESIAS, MUSCLE TWITCHING, TREMORS, AND CONVULSIONS. SYMPTOMS MAY OCCUR WITHIN SEVERAL HOURS AFTER EXPOSURE. **CHRONIC EXPOSURE-** PROLONGED OR REPEATED EXPOSURE TO ORGANOCHLORINE PESTICIDES MAY PRODUCE EFFECTS AS DESCRIBED IN ACUTE EXPOSURE.

FIRST AID- REMOVE FROM EXPOSURE AREA TO FRESH AIR IMMEDIATELY. IF BREATHING HAS STOPPED, PERFORM ARTIFICIAL RESPIRATION. KEEP PERSON WARM AND AT REST. TREAT SYMPTOMATICALLY AND SUPPORTIVELY. GET MEDICAL ATTENTION IMMEDIATELY.

SKIN CONTACT: DICOFOL: IRRITANT. **ACUTE EXPOSURE-** A WATER-DISPERSIBLE POWDER OF DICOFOL WAS ONLY MILDLY IRRITATING TO THE SKIN OF RABBITS. SOLUTIONS OF DICOFOL IN DIMETHYL PHTHALATE WERE MORE IRRITATING, CAUSING ERYTHEMA AND SUPERFICIAL DESTRUCTION OF THE SKIN OF RABBITS; EMULSIONS PRODUCED MARKED TISSUE DESTRUCTION. A LETHAL DOSE IN RABBITS BY DERMAL ABSORPTION WAS 1870 MG/KG. ORGANOCHLORINE PESTICIDES ARE ABSORBED THROUGH THE SKIN AND PRODUCE SYMPTOMS OF APPREHENSION, EXCITABILITY, DIZZINESS, HEADACHE, DISORIENTATION, WEAKNESS, PARESTHESIAS, MUSCLE TWITCHING, TREMORS, AND CONVULSIONS. **CHRONIC EXPOSURE-** REPEATED APPLICATIONS OF 500 MG/KG OF WATER-DISPERSIBLE POWDER WAS LETHAL TO RABBITS; REPEATED APPLICATION OF EMULSIONS AND SOLUTIONS CONTAINING DIMETHYL PHTHALATE WAS ALSO LETHAL TO RABBITS.

FIRST AID- REMOVE CONTAMINATED CLOTHING AND SHOES IMMEDIATELY. WASH AFFECTED AREA WITH SOAP OR MILD DETERGENT AND LARGE AMOUNTS OF WATER UNTIL NO EVIDENCE OF CHEMICAL REMAINS (APPROXIMATELY 15-20 MINUTES). GET MEDICAL ATTENTION IMMEDIATELY.

EYE CONTACT: DICOFOL: **ACUTE EXPOSURE-** NO DATA AVAILABLE. MAY CAUSE IRRITATION. **CHRONIC EXPOSURE-** NO DATA AVAILABLE.

FIRST AID- WASH EYES IMMEDIATELY WITH LARGE AMOUNTS OF WATER OR NORMAL SALINE, OCCASIONALLY LIFTING UPPER AND LOWER LIDS, UNTIL NO EVIDENCE OF CHEMICAL REMAINS (APPROXIMATELY 15-20 MINUTES). GET MEDICAL ATTENTION IMMEDIATELY.

INGESTION: DICOFOL: LIMITED ANIMAL CARCINOGEN. **ACUTE EXPOSURE-** A LETHAL DOSE IN RATS WAS 575 MG/KG. AT HIGH LEVELS, ANIMALS SHOWED GENERAL WEAKNESS AND COMA PRIOR TO DEATH; TREMORS WERE NOT OBSERVED. INGESTION OF ORGANOCHLORINE PESTICIDES MAY CAUSE GASTROINTESTINAL EFFECTS OF NAUSEA, VOMITING, DIARRHEA, AND STOMACH PAINS. OTHER SYMPTOMS OF APPREHENSION, EXCITABILITY, DIZZINESS, HEADACHE, DISORIENTATION, WEAKNESS, PARESTHESIAS, MUSCLE TWITCHING, TREMOR, AND CONVULSIONS MAY OCCUR. DEATH MAY BE DUE TO RESPIRATORY FAILURE OR VENTRICULAR FIBRILLATION. SYMPTOMS MAY OCCUR WITHIN HOURS OF EXPOSURE. DICOFOL IS EXCRETED RAPIDLY BY HUMANS, USUALLY WITHIN 3-4 DAYS OF INGESTION. **CHRONIC EXPOSURE-** DOGS FED A DIET CONTAINING 300 PPM FOR 1 YEAR SHOWED NO EFFECT WHILE 900 PPM CAUSED DEATH IN 2 OF 4 ANIMALS. 250 PPM OR HIGHER IN THE DIET OF RATS FOR TWO YEARS PRODUCED DEPRESSION OF GROWTH AND SKIN CHANGES OF ERYTHEMA AND SUPERFICIAL NECROSIS. HEPATOCELLULAR CARCINOMAS WAS OBSERVED IN ONE STUDY OF MALE MICE FED TECHNICAL GRADE DICOFOL; HOWEVER, NO EVIDENCE OF CARCINOGENICITY WAS OBSERVED IN RATS OF EITHER SEX OR IN FEMALE MICE.

FIRST AID- IF THE PERSON IS CONSCIOUS AND NOT CONVULSING, REMOVE BY GIVING SYRUP OF IPECAC (IF VOMITING OCCURS, KEEP THE HEAD BELOW THE HIPS TO PREVENT ASPIRATION). GIVE ACTIVATED CHARCOAL FOLLOWED BY GASTRIC LAVAGE. FOLLOW WITH A SALINE CATHARTIC. DO NOT GIVE FATS OR OILS. INTESTINAL LAVAGE WITH 20% MANNITOL (200 ML) BY STOMACH TUBE IS ALSO USEFUL. GIVE ARTIFICIAL RESPIRATION WITH OXYGEN IF RESPIRATION IS DEPRESSED (DREISBACH, HANDBOOK OF POISONING, 12TH ED.). TREAT SYMPTOMATICALLY AND SUPPORTIVELY. LAVAGE AND ADMINISTRATION OF OXYGEN SHOULD BE PERFORMED BY QUALIFIED MEDICAL PERSONNEL. GET MEDICAL ATTENTION IMMEDIATELY.

ANTIDOTE: NO SPECIFIC ANTIDOTE. TREAT SYMPTOMATICALLY AND SUPPORTIVELY.

REACTIVITY

REACTIVITY: STABLE UNDER NORMAL TEMPERATURES AND PRESSURES.

INCOMPATIBILITIES: DICOFOL: ALKALIES: MAY CAUSE HYDROLYSIS.

DECOMPOSITION: THERMAL DECOMPOSITION PRODUCTS MAY INCLUDE TOXIC AND CORROSIVE FUMES OF CHLORIDES AND TOXIC OXIDES OF CARBON.

POLYMERIZATION: HAZARDOUS POLYMERIZATION HAS NOT BEEN REPORTED TO OCCUR UNDER NORMAL TEMPERATURES AND PRESSURES.

STORAGE AND DISPOSAL

OBSERVE ALL FEDERAL, STATE AND LOCAL REGULATIONS WHEN STORING OR DISPOSING OF THIS SUBSTANCE. FOR ASSISTANCE, CONTACT THE DISTRICT DIRECTOR OF THE ENVIRONMENTAL PROTECTION AGENCY.

****STORAGE****

STORE IN ACCORDANCE WITH 29 CFR 1910.106.
STORE IN ACCORDANCE WITH 40 CFR 165 RECOMMENDED PROCEDURES FOR THE DISPOSAL AND STORAGE OF PESTICIDES AND PESTICIDE CONTAINERS.
BONDING AND GROUNDING: SUBSTANCES WITH LOW ELECTROCONDUCTIVITY, WHICH MAY BE IGNITED BY ELECTROSTATIC SPARKS, SHOULD BE STORED IN CONTAINERS WHICH MEET THE BONDING AND GROUNDING GUIDELINES SPECIFIED IN NFPA 77-1983, RECOMMENDED PRACTICE ON STATIC ELECTRICITY.
STORE AWAY FROM INCOMPATIBLE SUBSTANCES.

****DISPOSAL****

DISPOSAL MUST BE IN ACCORDANCE WITH STANDARDS APPLICABLE TO GENERATORS OF HAZARDOUS WASTE, 40 CFR 262. EPA HAZARDOUS WASTE NUMBER D001. 100 POUND CERCLA SECTION 103 REPORTABLE QUANTITY.
DISPOSAL MUST BE IN ACCORDANCE WITH 40 CFR 165 RECOMMENDED PROCEDURES FOR THE DISPOSAL AND STORAGE OF PESTICIDES AND PESTICIDE CONTAINERS.

CONDITIONS TO AVOID

MAY BURN BUT DOES NOT IGNITE READILY. CONTAINERS MAY EXPLODE IN HEAT OF FIRE.

SPILL AND LEAK PROCEDURES

OCCUPATIONAL SPILL: DO NOT TOUCH SPILLED MATERIAL. STOP LEAK IF YOU CAN DO IT WITHOUT RISK. USE WATER SPRAY TO REDUCE VAPORS. FOR SMALL SPILLS, TAKE UP WITH SAND OR OTHER ABSORBENT MATERIAL AND PLACE INTO CONTAINERS FOR LATER DISPOSAL. FOR SMALL DRY SPILLS, WITH A CLEAN SHOVEL PLACE MATERIAL INTO CLEAN, DRY CONTAINERS AND COVER. MOVE CONTAINERS FROM SPILL AREA. FOR LARGER SPILLS, DIKE FAR AHEAD OF SPILL FOR LATER DISPOSAL. KEEP UNNECESSARY PEOPLE AWAY. ISOLATE HAZARD AREA AND DENY ENTRY. VENTILATE CLOSED SPACES BEFORE ENTERING.
REPORTABLE QUANTITY (RQ): 10 POUNDS THE SUPERFUND AMENDMENTS AND REAUTHORIZATION ACT (SARA) SECTION 304 REQUIRES THAT A RELEASE EQUAL TO OR GREATER THAN THE REPORTABLE QUANTITY FOR THIS SUBSTANCE BE IMMEDIATELY REPORTED TO THE LOCAL EMERGENCY PLANNING COMMITTEE AND THE STATE EMERGENCY RESPONSE COMMISSION (40 CFR 355.40). IF THE RELEASE OF THIS SUBSTANCE IS REPORTABLE UNDER CERCLA SECTION 103, THE NATIONAL RESPONSE CENTER MUST BE NOTIFIED IMMEDIATELY AT (800) 424-8802 OR (202) 426-2675 IN THE METROPOLITAN WASHINGTON, D.C. AREA (40 CFR 302.6).

PROTECTIVE EQUIPMENT

VENTILATION: PROVIDE LOCAL EXHAUST OR PROCESS ENCLOSURE VENTILATION SYSTEM.

RESPIRATOR: THE FOLLOWING RESPIRATORS ARE RECOMMENDED BASED ON INFORMATION FOUND IN THE PHYSICAL DATA, TOXICITY AND HEALTH EFFECTS SECTIONS. THEY ARE RANKED IN ORDER FROM MINIMUM TO MAXIMUM RESPIRATORY PROTECTION. THE SPECIFIC RESPIRATOR SELECTED MUST BE BASED ON CONTAMINATION LEVELS FOUND IN THE WORK PLACE, MUST NOT EXCEED THE WORKING LIMITS OF THE RESPIRATOR AND BE JOINTLY APPROVED BY THE NATIONAL INSTITUTE FOR OCCUPATIONAL SAFETY AND HEALTH AND THE MINE SAFETY AND HEALTH ADMINISTRATION (NIOSH-MSHA).
TYPE 'C' SUPPLIED-AIR RESPIRATOR WITH A FULL FACEPIECE OPERATED IN PRESSURE-DEMAND OR OTHER POSITIVE PRESSURE MODE OR WITH A FULL FACEPIECE, HELMET OR HOOD OPERATED IN CONTINOUS-FLOW MODE.
SELF-CONTAINED BREATHING APPARATUS WITH A FULL FACEPIECE OPERATED IN PRESSURE-DEMAND OR OTHER POSITIVE PRESSURE MODE.
FOR FIREFIGHTING AND OTHER IMMEDIATELY DANGEROUS TO LIFE OR HEALTH CONDITIONS: SELF-CONTAINED BREATHING APPARATUS WITH FULL FACEPIECE OPERATED IN PRESSURE-DEMAND OR OTHER POSITIVE PRESSURE MODE.
SUPPLIED-AIR RESPIRATOR WITH FULL FACEPIECE AND OPERATED IN PRESSURE-DEMAND OR OTHER POSITIVE PRESSURE MODE IN COMBINATION WITH AN AUXILIARY SELF-CONTAINED BREATHING APPARATUS OPERATED IN PRESSURE-DEMAND OR OTHER POSITIVE PRESSURE MODE.

CLOTHING: EMPLOYEE MUST WEAR APPROPRIATE PROTECTIVE (IMPERVIOUS) CLOTHING AND EQUIPMENT TO PREVENT REPEATED OR PROLONGED SKIN CONTACT WITH THIS SUBSTANCE.

GLOVES: EMPLOYEE MUST WEAR APPROPRIATE PROTECTIVE GLOVES TO PREVENT CONTACT WITH THIS SUBSTANCE.

EYE PROTECTION: EMPLOYEE MUST WEAR SPLASH-PROOF OR DUST-RESISTANT SAFETY GOGGLES TO PREVENT EYE CONTACT WITH THIS SUBSTANCE.
EMERGENCY EYE WASH: WHERE THERE IS ANY POSSIBILITY THAT AN EMPLOYEE'S EYES MAY BE EXPOSED TO THIS SUBSTANCE, THE EMPLOYER SHOULD PROVIDE AN EYE WASH FOUNTAIN WITHIN THE IMMEDIATE WORK AREA FOR EMERGENCY USE.

AUTHORIZED BY- OCCUPATIONAL HEALTH SERVICES, INC.
CREATION DATE: 10/04/89 ***REVISION DATE:*** 07/13/90

MATERIAL SAFETY DATA SHEET

OCCUPATIONAL HEALTH SERVICES, INC.
AGRICULTURE AND PESTICIDE DIVISION
450 SEVENTH AVENUE, SUITE 2407
NEW YORK, NEW YORK 10123
1-800-445-MSDS OR (212) 967-1100

EMERGENCY CONTACT:
JOHN S. BRANSFORD, JR. (615) 292-1180

SUBSTANCE IDENTIFICATION

CAS-NUMBER 60-57-1

SUBSTANCE: <u>DIELDRIN</u>

TRADE NAMES/SYNONYMS: (1A ALPHA, 2 BETA, 2A ALPHA, 3 BETA, 6 BETA, 6A ALPHA, 7 BETA, 7A ALPHA)-3,4,5,6,9,9-HEXACHLORO-1A,2,2A,3,6,6A,7,7A-OCTAHYDRO-2,7:3,6 -DIMETHANONAPHTH(2,3-B)OXIRENE; 1,2,3,4,10,10-HEXACHLORO-6,7-EPOXY-1,4,4A,5,6,7,8,8A-OCTAHYDRO-1, 4-ENDO-EXO-5,8-DIMETHANONAPHTHALENE; 1,2,3,4,10,10-HEXACHLORO-6,7-EPOXY-1,4,4A,5,6,7,8,8A-OCTAHYDRO-ENDO -1,4-EXO-5,8-DIMETHANONAPHTHALENE; (1R,4S,4AS,5R,6R,7S,8S,8AR)-1,2,3,4,10,10-HEXACHLORO-1,4,4A,5,6,7,8,8A -OCTAHYDRO-6,7-EPOXY-1,4:5,8-DIMETHANONAPHTHALENE; ENDO,EXO-1,2,3,4,10,10-HEXACHLORO-6,7-EPOXY-1,4,4A5,6,7,8,8A-OCTAHYDRO 1,4:5,8-DIMETHANONAPHTHALENE; 2,7:3,6-DIMETHANONAPHTH(2,3-B)OXIRENE, 3,4,5,6,9,9-HEXACHLORO-1A,2,2A, 3,6,6A,7,7A-OCTAHYDRO-, (1A ALPHA, 2 BETA, 2A ALPHA, 3 BETA, 6 BETA, 6A ALPHA, 7 BETA, 7A ALPHA)-; 1,4:5,8-DIMETHANONAPHTHALENE, 1,2,3,4,10,10,10-HEXACHLORO-6,7-EPOXY-1, 4,4A,5,6,7,8,8A-OCTAHYDRO-,ENDO, EXO-; ENT 16255; STCC 4941133; RCRA P037; C12H8CL6O; PST07080

CHEMICAL FAMILY: HYDROCARBON, POLYNUCLEAR

MOLECULAR FORMULA: C12-H8-CL6-O

MOLECULAR WEIGHT: 380.90

CERCLA RATINGS (SCALE 0-3): HEALTH=3 FIRE=0 REACTIVITY=0 PERSISTENCE=3

NFPA RATINGS (SCALE 0-4): HEALTH=3 FIRE=0 REACTIVITY=0

COMPONENTS AND CONTAMINANTS

COMPONENT: DIELDRIN ***PERCENT:*** 100
CAS# 60-57-1

OTHER CONTAMINANTS: NONE

EXPOSURE LIMITS: DIELDRIN: 0.25 MG/M3 OSHA TWA (SKIN) 0.25 MG/M3 ACGIH TWA (SKIN) LOWEST DETECTABLE LIMIT NIOSH RECOMMENDED EXPOSURE CRITERIA (0.15 MG/M3 TWA BY NIOSH VALIDATED METHOD)
1 POUND CERCLA SECTION 103 REPORTABLE QUANTITY SUBJECT TO CALIFORNIA PROPOSITION 65 CANCER AND/OR REPRODUCTIVE TOXICITY WARNING AND RELEASE REQUIREMENTS- (JULY 1, 1988)

PHYSICAL DATA

DESCRIPTION: ODORLESS, WHITE CRYSTALLINE SOLID ***BOILING POINT:*** DECOMPOSES

MELTING POINT: 349-351 F (176-177 C) ***SPECIFIC GRAVITY:*** 1.70 @ 20 C

VAPOR PRESSURE: 0.0000002 MMHG @ 25C ***SOLUBILITY IN WATER:*** INSOLUBLE

ODOR THRESHOLD: 0.041 PPM ***VAPOR DENSITY:*** 13.2

SOLVENT SOLUBILITY: SOLUBLE IN ACETONE, BENZENE, AROMATIC AND HALOGENATED SOLVENTS; SLIGHTLY SOLUBLE IN MINERAL OIL, ALCOHOL, AND ALIPHATIC HYDROCARBONS

FIRE AND EXPLOSION DATA

FIRE AND EXPLOSION HAZARD: NEGLIGIBLE FIRE HAZARD WHEN EXPOSED TO HEAT OR FLAME.

FIREFIGHTING MEDIA: DRY CHEMICAL, CARBON DIOXIDE, HALON, WATER SPRAY OR STANDARD FOAM (1987 EMERGENCY RESPONSE GUIDEBOOK, DOT P 5800.4).
FOR LARGER FIRES, USE WATER SPRAY, FOG OR STANDARD FOAM (1987 EMERGENCY RESPONSE GUIDEBOOK, DOT P 5800.4).

FIREFIGHTING: MOVE CONTAINERS FROM FIRE AREA IF POSSIBLE. FIGHT FIRE FROM MAXIMUM DISTANCE. STAY AWAY FROM STORAGE TANK ENDS. DIKE FIRE CONTROL WATER FOR LATER DISPOSAL. DO NOT SCATTER MATERIAL (1987 EMERGENCY RESPONSE GUIDEBOOK, DOT P 5800.4, GUIDE PAGE 55).
USE AGENTS SUITABLE FOR TYPE OF FIRE. COOL CONTAINERS WITH FLOODING AMOUNTS OF WATER. AVOID BREATHING VAPORS OR DUSTS, KEEP UPWIND.

TRANSPORTATION DATA

DEPARTMENT OF TRANSPORTATION HAZARD CLASSIFICATION 49 CFR 172.101: ORM-A
DEPARTMENT OF TRANSPORTATION LABELING REQUIREMENTS 49 CFR 172.101 AND SUBPART E: NONE
DEPARTMENT OF TRANSPORTATION PACKAGING REQUIREMENTS: 49 CFR 173.510 EXCEPTIONS: 49 CFR 173.505

TOXICITY

DIELDRIN: TOXICITY DATA: 13 MG/M3/4 HOURS INHALATION-RAT LC50; 80 MG/M3/4 HOURS INHALATION-CAT LC50; 250 MG/KG SKIN-RABBIT LD50; 56 MG/KG SKIN-RAT LD50; 750 MG/KG SKIN-CAT LDLO; 65 MG/KG ORAL-MAN LDLO; 500 MG/KG ORAL-CAT LDLO; 38300 UG/KG ORAL-RAT LD50; 38 MG/KG ORAL-MOUSE LD50; 65 MG/KG ORAL-DOG LD50; 3 MG/KG ORAL-MONKEY LD50; 45 MG/KG ORAL-RABBIT LD50; 60 MG/KG ORAL-HAMSTER LD50; 49 MG/KG ORAL-GUINEA PIG LD50; 38 MG/KG ORAL-PIG LD50; 49 MG/KG SUBCUTANEOUS-RAT LD50; 9 MG/KG INTRAVENOUS-RAT LD50; 26 MG/KG INTRAPERITONEAL-MOUSE LDLO; 150 MG/KG SUBCUTANEOUS-RABBIT LDLO; 10500 UG/KG INTRAVENOUS-MOUSE LD50; 35 MG/KG INTRAPERITONEAL-RAT LD50; 28 MG/KG UNREPORTED-HUMAN LDLO; MUTAGENIC DATA (RTECS); REPRODUCTIVE EFFECTS DATA (RTECS); TUMORIGENIC DATA (RTECS). CARCINOGEN STATUS: HUMAN INADEQUATE EVIDENCE, ANIMAL LIMITED EVIDENCE (IARC GROUP-3). DIELDRIN IS CARCINOGENIC TO MICE, PRODUCING BENIGN AND MALIGNANT LIVER NEOPLASMS FOLLOWING ITS ORAL ADMINISTRATION. ACUTE TOXICITY LEVEL: HIGHLY TOXIC BY INHALATION AND INGESTION; TOXIC BY DERMAL ABSORPTION. TARGET EFFECTS: CONVULSANT. POISONING MAY AFFECT THE LIVER. AT INCREASED RISK FROM EXPOSURE: PERSONS WITH SKIN OR LIVER DISEASES. ADDITIONAL DATA: DIELDRIN MAY BE STORED IN THE ADIPOSE TISSUE FOR WEEKS TO SEVERAL MONTHS BEFORE IT IS EXCRETED FROM THE BODY. INTENSE ACTIVITY AND STARVATION MAY MOBILIZE THE PESTICIDE RESULTING IN THE REAPPEARANCE OF TOXIC SYMPTOMS. DIELDRIN MAY BE EXCRETED IN THE MILK OF LACTATING WOMEN AND IS TRANSFERRED TRANSPLACENTALLY TO THE FETUS. STIMULANTS SUCH AS EPINEPHRINE MAY INDUCE VENTRICULAR FIBRILLATION.

HEALTH EFFECTS AND FIRST AID

INHALATION: DIELDRIN: CONVULSANT/HIGHLY TOXIC. <u>ACUTE EXPOSURE</u>- A LETHAL CONCENTRATION IN RATS WAS 13 MG/M3/4 HOURS. DIELDRIN MAY CAUSE CENTRAL NERVOUS SYSTEM STIMULATION WITH SYMPTOMS OF HEADACHE, DIZZINESS, VISUAL DISTURBANCES, MALAISE, SWEATING, MILD CHRONIC JERKING, NAUSEA, AND VOMITING. ONE OR MORE EPILEPTIFORM CONVULSIONS

MAY OCCUR FOLLOWED BY POSSIBLE UNCONSCIOUSNESS AND COMA. SOMETIMES CONVULSIONS WILL OCCUR WITHOUT ANY PRECEDING SYMPTOMS. SOMETIMES DELAYED AND SUDDEN APPEARANCES OF SYMPTOMS OF POISONING MAY APPEAR WEEKS OR MONTHS AFTER LAST EXPOSURE. OTHER SYMPTOMS OF INCOORDINATION, HYPERIRRITABILITY, BEHAVIORAL CHANGES, NYSTAGMUS, AND TACHYCARDIA MAY ALSO DEVELOP IN SOME CASES OF POISONING. **CHRONIC EXPOSURE-** PROLONGED OR REPEATED EXPOSURE MAY RESULT IN THE ACCUMULATION OF THE PESTICIDE IN THE BLOOD RESULTING IN A PROGRESSION OF THE SYMPTOMS LISTED ABOVE OR IN A SUDDEN ONSET OF SYMPTOMS AFTER AN ACUTE EXPOSURE. IN ADDITION TO SYMPTOMS LISTED ABOVE, DROWSINESS AND ANOREXIA MAY OCCUR.

FIRST AID- REMOVE FROM EXPOSURE AREA TO FRESH AIR IMMEDIATELY. IF BREATHING HAS STOPPED, PERFORM ARTIFICIAL RESPIRATION. KEEP PERSON WARM AND AT REST. TREAT SYMPTOMATICALLY AND SUPPORTIVELY. GET MEDICAL ATTENTION IMMEDIATELY.

SKIN CONTACT: DIELDRIN: CONVULSANT/TOXIC. **ACUTE EXPOSURE-** A LETHAL DOSE IN RABBITS BY DERMAL ABSORPTION WAS 250 MG/KG. DERMAL ABSORPTION OF DIELDRIN MAY RESULT IN CENTRAL NERVOUS SYSTEM STIMULATION WITH SYMPTOMS OF HEADACHE, DIZZINESS, VISUAL DISTURBANCES, MALAISE, SWEATING, MILD CHRONIC JERKING, NAUSEA, AND VOMITING. ONE OR MORE EPILEPTIFORM CONVULSIONS MAY OCCUR FOLLOWED BY POSSIBLE UNCONSCIOUSNESS AND COMA. SOMETIMES CONVULSIONS WILL OCCUR WITHOUT ANY PRECEDING SYMPTOMS. SOMETIMES DELAYED AND SUDDEN APPEARANCES OF SYMPTOMS OF POISONING MAY APPEAR WEEKS OR MONTHS AFTER LAST EXPOSURE. OTHER SYMPTOMS OF INCOORDINATION, HYPERIRRITABILITY, BEHAVIORAL CHANGES, NYSTAGMUS, AND TACHYCARDIA MAY ALSO DEVELOP IN SOME CASES OF POISONING. SKIN DISEASES, SUCH AS SCLERODERMA, MAY FACILITATE DERMAL ABSORPTION. **CHRONIC EXPOSURE-** PROLONGED OR REPEATED EXPOSURE MAY RESULT IN THE ACCUMULATION OF THE PESTICIDE IN THE BLOOD RESULTING IN A PROGRESSION OF THE SYMPTOMS LISTED ABOVE OR IN A SUDDEN ONSET OF SYMPTOMS AFTER AN ACUTE EXPOSURE.

FIRST AID- REMOVE CONTAMINATED CLOTHING AND SHOES IMMEDIATELY. WASH AFFECTED AREA WITH SOAP OR MILD DETERGENT AND LARGE AMOUNTS OF WATER UNTIL NO EVIDENCE OF CHEMICAL REMAINS (APPROXIMATELY 15-20 MINUTES). GET MEDICAL ATTENTION IMMEDIATELY.

EYE CONTACT: DIELDRIN: **ACUTE EXPOSURE-** MAY BE IRRITATING. **CHRONIC EXPOSURE-** NO DATA AVAILABLE.

FIRST AID- WASH EYES IMMEDIATELY WITH LARGE AMOUNTS OF WATER OR NORMAL SALINE, OCCASIONALLY LIFTING UPPER AND LOWER LIDS, UNTIL NO EVIDENCE OF CHEMICAL REMAINS (APPROXIMATELY 15-20 MINUTES). GET MEDICAL ATTENTION IMMEDIATELY.

INGESTION: DIELDRIN: CONVULSANT/HIGHLY TOXIC/LIMITED ANIMAL CARCINOGEN. **ACUTE EXPOSURE-** A LETHAL DOSE IN RATS WAS 38300 UG/KG. DIELDRIN MAY CAUSE CENTRAL NERVOUS SYSTEM STIMULATION WITH SYMPTOMS OF HEADACHE, DIZZINESS, VISUAL DISTURBANCES, MALAISE, SWEATING, MILD CHRONIC JERKING, NAUSEA, AND VOMITING. ONE OR MORE EPILEPTIFORM CONVULSIONS MAY OCCUR FOLLOWED BY POSSIBLE UNCONSCIOUSNESS AND COMA. SOMETIMES CONVULSIONS WILL OCCUR WITHOUT ANY PRECEDING SYMPTOMS. OTHER SYMPTOMS OF INCOORDINATION, HYPERIRRITABILITY, BEHAVIORAL CHANGES, NYSTAGMUS, TACHYCARDIA, AND EEG CHANGES MAY ALSO DEVELOP. MILD TRANSIENT INJURIES OF THE KIDNEY AND LIVER HAVE OCCURRED IN SUBLETHAL POISONING IN MAN. AN ESTIMATED LETHAL DOSE IN MAN IS 5 GRAMS. DEATH MAY BE DUE TO RESPIRATORY ARREST. INGESTION BY A PREGNANT WOMAN RESULTED IN FETAL DEATH. A DOSE OF 30 MG/KG FED TO PREGNANT GOLDEN HAMSTERS PRODUCED A HIGH INCIDENCE OF FETAL DEATHS, CONGENITAL ANOMALIES, AND GROWTH RETARDATION; 15 MG/KG FED TO PREGNANT MICE PRODUCED A HIGH INCIDENCE OF CONGENITAL ANOMALIES. **CHRONIC EXPOSURE-** REPEATED EXPOSURE MAY CAUSE EFFECTS AS DESCRIBED IN ACUTE EXPOSURE. REPEATED ADMINISTRATION CAUSED NEURONAL NECROSIS IN RATS AND IMMUNOSUPPRESSION IN MICE. SIGNIFICANT DEPRESSION OF THE ESTRUS CYCLE AND AN INCREASE IN NONSPECIFIC ESTERASE ACTIVITY WERE OBSERVED IN RATS FED 50 PPM IN THEIR DIET FOR 57 WEEKS. EFFECTS ON THE MALE REPRODUCTIVE SYSTEM WERE REPORTED FROM STUDIES OF RATS AND MICE. EFFECTS ON FERTILITY AND THE FETUS AND FETAL DEVELOPMENTAL ABNORMALITIES WERE NOTED IN STUDIES OF PREGNANT MICE FED DIELDRIN. BENIGN AND MALIGNANT LIVER NEOPLASMS WERE OBSERVED IN STUDIES OF MICE. NO CARCINOGENIC EFFECT WAS OBSERVED IN FEEDING STUDIES IN RATS, TROUT, OR HAMSTERS.

FIRST AID- IF THE PERSON IS CONSCIOUS AND NOT CONVULSING, REMOVE BY GIVING SYRUP OF IPECAC (IF VOMITING OCCURS, KEEP THE HEAD BELOW THE HIPS TO PREVENT ASPIRATION). GIVE ACTIVATED CHARCOAL FOLLOWED BY GASTRIC LAVAGE. FOLLOW WITH A SALINE CATHARTIC. DO NOT GIVE FATS OR OILS. INTESTINAL LAVAGE WITH 20% MANNITOL (200 ML) BY STOMACH TUBE IS ALSO USEFUL. GIVE ARTIFICIAL RESPIRATION WITH OXYGEN IF RESPIRATION IS DEPRESSED (DREISBACH, HANDBOOK OF POISONING, 12TH ED.). TREAT SYMPTOMATICALLY AND SUPPORTIVELY. LAVAGE AND ADMINISTRATION OF OXYGEN SHOULD BE PERFORMED BY QUALIFIED MEDICAL PERSONNEL. GET MEDICAL ATTENTION IMMEDIATELY.

ANTIDOTE: NO SPECIFIC ANTIDOTE. TREAT SYMPTOMATICALLY AND SUPPORTIVELY.

REACTIVITY

REACTIVITY: STABLE UNDER NORMAL TEMPERATURES AND PRESSURES.

INCOMPATIBILITIES: DIELDRIN: ACID CATALYSTS: MAY REACT. ACID OXIDIZING AGENTS: MAY REACT. ACTIVE METALS: MAY REACT. HYDROGEN BROMIDE: MAY REACT TO GIVE BROMOHYDRIN. MINERAL ACIDS (CONCENTRATED): MAY REACT. OXIDIZERS (STRONG): INCOMPATIBLE. PHENOLS: MAY REACT.

DECOMPOSITION: THERMAL DECOMPOSITION MAY RELEASE CORROSIVE FUMES OF HYDROGEN CHLORIDE.

POLYMERIZATION: HAZARDOUS POLYMERIZATION HAS NOT BEEN REPORTED TO OCCUR UNDER NORMAL TEMPERATURES AND PRESSURES.

STORAGE AND DISPOSAL

OBSERVE ALL FEDERAL, STATE AND LOCAL REGULATIONS WHEN STORING OR DISPOSING OF THIS SUBSTANCE. FOR ASSISTANCE, CONTACT THE DISTRICT DIRECTOR OF THE ENVIRONMENTAL PROTECTION AGENCY.

STORAGE

STORE IN ACCORDANCE WITH 40 CFR 165 RECOMMENDED PROCEDURES FOR THE DISPOSAL AND STORAGE OF PESTICIDES AND PESTICIDE CONTAINERS.
STORE AWAY FROM INCOMPATIBLE SUBSTANCES.

DISPOSAL

DISPOSAL MUST BE IN ACCORDANCE WITH STANDARDS APPLICABLE TO GENERATORS OF HAZARDOUS WASTE, 40CFR 262. EPA HAZARDOUS WASTE NUMBER P037.

CONDITIONS TO AVOID

MAY BURN BUT DOES NOT IGNITE READILY. CONTAINERS MAY EXPLODE IN HEAT OF FIRE.

SPILL AND LEAK PROCEDURES

SOIL SPILL: DIKE FLOW OF SPILLED MATERIAL USING SOIL OR SANDBAGS OR FOAMED BARRIERS SUCH AS POLYURETHANE OR CONCRETE.
USE PROTECTIVE COVER SUCH AS A PLASTIC SHEET TO PREVENT MATERIAL FROM DISSOLVING IN FIRE EXTINGUISHING WATER OR RAIN.

WATER SPILL: TRAP SPILLED MATERIAL AT BOTTOM IN DEEP WATER POCKETS, EXCAVATED HOLDING AREAS OR WITHIN SAND BAG BARRIERS.
USE ACTIVATED CARBON TO ABSORB SPILLED SUBSTANCE THAT IS DISSOLVED.
USE SUCTION HOSES TO REMOVE TRAPPED SPILL MATERIAL.
USE MECHANICAL DREDGES OR LIFTS TO EXTRACT IMMOBILIZED MASSES OF POLLUTION AND PRECIPITATES.

OCCUPATIONAL SPILL: DO NOT TOUCH SPILLED MATERIAL. STOP LEAK IF YOU CAN DO IT WITHOUT RISK. USE WATER SPRAY TO REDUCE VAPORS. FOR SMALL SPILLS, TAKE UP WITH SAND OR OTHER ABSORBENT MATERIAL AND PLACE INTO CONTAINERS FOR LATER DISPOSAL. FOR SMALL DRY SPILLS, WITH A CLEAN SHOVEL PLACE MATERIAL INTO CLEAN, DRY CONTAINERS AND COVER. MOVE CONTAINERS FROM SPILL AREA. FOR LARGER SPILLS, DIKE FAR AHEAD OF SPILL FOR LATER DISPOSAL. KEEP UNNECESSARY PEOPLE AWAY. ISOLATE HAZARD AREA AND DENY ENTRY. VENTILATE CLOSED SPACES BEFORE ENTERING.
REPORTABLE QUANTITY (RQ): 1 POUND THE SUPERFUND AMENDMENTS AND REAUTHORIZATION ACT (SARA) SECTION 304 REQUIRES THAT A RELEASE EQUAL TO OR GREATER THAN THE REPORTABLE QUANTITY FOR THIS SUBSTANCE BE IMMEDIATELY REPORTED TO THE LOCAL EMERGENCY PLANNING COMMITTEE AND THE STATE EMERGENCY RESPONSE COMMISSION (40 CFR 355.40). IF THE RELEASE OF THIS SUBSTANCE IS REPORTABLE UNDER CERCLA SECTION 103, THE NATIONAL RESPONSE CENTER MUST BE NOTIFIED IMMEDIATELY AT (800) 424-8802 OR (202) 426-2675 IN THE METROPOLITAN WASHINGTON, D.C. AREA (40 CFR 302.6).

PROTECTIVE EQUIPMENT

VENTILATION: PROCESS ENCLOSURE RECOMMENDED TO MEET PUBLISHED EXPOSURE LIMITS.

RESPIRATOR: THE FOLLOWING RESPIRATORS AND MAXIMUM USE CONCENTRATIONS ARE RECOMMENDATIONS BY THE U.S. DEPARTMENT OF HEALTH AND HUMAN SERVICES, NIOSH POCKET GUIDE TO CHEMICAL HAZARDS; NIOSH CRITERIA DOCUMENTS OR BY THE U.S. DEPARTMENT OF LABOR, 29 CFR 1910 SUBPART Z. THE SPECIFIC RESPIRATOR SELECTED MUST BE BASED ON CONTAMINATION LEVELS FOUND IN THE WORK PLACE, MUST NOT EXCEED THE WORKING LIMITS OF THE RESPIRATOR AND BE JOINTLY APPROVED BY THE NATIONAL INSTITUTE FOR OCCUPATIONAL SAFETY AND HEALTH AND THE MINE SAFETY AND HEALTH ADMINISTRATION (NIOSH-MSHA).

DIELDRIN: AT ANY DETECTABLE CONCENTRATION:
SELF-CONTAINED BREATHING APPARATUS WITH FULL FACEPIECE AND OPERATED IN PRESSURE-DEMAND OR OTHER POSITIVE PRESSURE MODE. SUPPLIED-AIR RESPIRATOR WITH FULL FACEPIECE OPERATED IN PRESSURE-DEMAND OR OTHER POSITIVE PRESSURE MODE IN COMBINATION WITH AN AUXILIARY SELF-CONTAINED BREATHING APPARATUS OPERATED IN PRESSURE-DEMAND OR OTHER POSITIVE PRESSURE MODE.
ESCAPE- AIR-PURIFYING FULL FACEPIECE RESPIRATOR (GAS MASK) WITH A CHIN-STYLE OR FRONT- OR BACK-MOUNTED ORGANIC VAPOR AND ACID GAS CANISTER HAVING A HIGH-EFFICIENCY PARTICULATE FILTER. ANY ESCAPE-TYPE SELF-CONTAINED BREATHING APPARATUS.
FOR FIREFIGHTING AND OTHER IMMEDIATELY DANGEROUS TO LIFE OR HEALTH CONDITIONS:
SELF-CONTAINED BREATHING APPARATUS WITH FULL FACEPIECE OPERATED IN PRESSURE-DEMAND OR OTHER POSITIVE PRESSURE MODE.
SUPPLIED-AIR RESPIRATOR WITH FULL FACEPIECE AND OPERATED IN PRESSURE-DEMAND OR OTHER POSITIVE PRESSURE MODE IN COMBINATION WITH AN AUXILIARY SELF-CONTAINED BREATHING APPARATUS OPERATED IN PRESSURE-DEMAND OR OTHER POSITIVE PRESSURE MODE.

CLOTHING: EMPLOYEE MUST WEAR APPROPRIATE PROTECTIVE (IMPERVIOUS) CLOTHING AND EQUIPMENT TO PREVENT ANY POSSIBILITY OF SKIN CONTACT WITH THIS SUBSTANCE.

GLOVES: EMPLOYEE MUST WEAR APPROPRIATE PROTECTIVE GLOVES TO PREVENT CONTACT WITH THIS SUBSTANCE.

EYE PROTECTION: EMPLOYEE MUST WEAR SPLASH-PROOF OR DUST-RESISTANT SAFETY GOGGLES AND A FACESHIELD TO PREVENT CONTACT WITH THIS SUBSTANCE.
EMERGENCY WASH FACILITIES: WHERE THERE IS ANY POSSIBILITY THAT AN EMPLOYEE'S EYES AND/OR SKIN MAY BE EXPOSED TO THIS SUBSTANCE, THE EMPLOYER SHOULD PROVIDE AN EYE WASH FOUNTAIN AND QUICK DRENCH SHOWER WITHIN THE IMMEDIATE WORK AREA FOR EMERGENCY USE.

AUTHORIZED BY- OCCUPATIONAL HEALTH SERVICES, INC.
CREATION DATE: 10/04/89 ***REVISION DATE:*** 07/13/90

MATERIAL SAFETY DATA SHEET

OCCUPATIONAL HEALTH SERVICES, INC.
AGRICULTURE AND PESTICIDE DIVISION
450 SEVENTH AVENUE, SUITE 2407
NEW YORK, NEW YORK 10123
1-800-445-MSDS OR (212) 967-1100

EMERGENCY CONTACT:
JOHN S. BRANSFORD, JR. (615) 292-1180

SUBSTANCE IDENTIFICATION

CAS-NUMBER 311-45-5

SUBSTANCE: **DIETHYL P-NITROPHENYL PHOSPHATE**

TRADE NAMES/SYNONYMS: PHOSPHORIC ACID, DIETHYL 4-NITROPHENYL ESTER; PHOSPHORIC ACID, DIETHYL P-NITROPHENYL ESTER; DIETHYLPHOSPHORIC ACID 4-NITROPHENYL ESTER; DIETHYL PHOSPHORIC ACID P-NITROPHENYL ESTER; DIETHYL 4-NITROPHENYL PHOSPHATE; P-NITROPHENYL DIETHYL PHOSPHATE; CHINORTO; E 600; ESTER 25; ETHYL PARAOXON; ETICOL; FOSFAKOL; HC 2072; MINTACOL; MIOTISAL; OXYPARATHION; PARAOXON; PHOSPHACHOLE; PHOSPHACOL; PHOSPHAKOL; RCRA P041; PST07200

CHEMICAL FAMILY: NITRO
AROMATIC
ORGANOPHOSPHATE

MOLECULAR FORMULA: C10-H14-N-O6-P

MOLECULAR WEIGHT: 275.22

CERCLA RATINGS (SCALE 0-3): HEALTH=3 FIRE=0 REACTIVITY=2 PERSISTENCE=2

NFPA RATINGS (SCALE 0-4): HEALTH=4 FIRE=0 REACTIVITY=2

COMPONENTS AND CONTAMINANTS

COMPONENT: DIETHYL P-NITROPHENYL PHOSPHATE ***PERCENT:*** 100
CAS# 311-45-5

OTHER CONTAMINANTS: NONE

EXPOSURE LIMITS: DIETHYL P-NITROPHENYL PHOSPHATE: NO OCCUPATIONAL EXPOSURE LIMITS ESTABLISHED BY OSHA, ACGIH, OR NIOSH.
100 POUNDS CERCLA SECTION 103 REPORTABLE QUANTITY

PHYSICAL DATA

DESCRIPTION: OILY LIQUID WITH A SLIGHT ODOR

BOILING POINT: 336-338 F (169-170 C) @ 1 MMHG ***SPECIFIC GRAVITY:*** 1.2683

EVAPORATION RATE: NOT AVAILABLE ***SOLUBILITY IN WATER:*** 2.4 MG/ML

SOLVENT SOLUBILITY: ETHER, OTHER ORGANIC SOLVENTS

FIRE AND EXPLOSION DATA

FIRE AND EXPLOSION HAZARD: NEGLIGIBLE FIRE HAZARD WHEN EXPOSED TO HEAT OR FLAME.

FIREFIGHTING MEDIA: DRY CHEMICAL, CARBON DIOXIDE, HALON, WATER SPRAY OR STANDARD FOAM (1987 EMERGENCY RESPONSE GUIDEBOOK, DOT P 5800.4). FOR LARGER FIRES, USE WATER SPRAY, FOG OR STANDARD FOAM (1987 EMERGENCY RESPONSE GUIDEBOOK, DOT P 5800.4).

FIREFIGHTING: MOVE CONTAINERS FROM FIRE AREA IF POSSIBLE. FIGHT FIRE FROM MAXIMUM DISTANCE. STAY AWAY FROM STORAGE TANK ENDS. DIKE FIRE CONTROL WATER FOR LATER DISPOSAL. DO NOT SCATTER MATERIAL (1987 EMERGENCY RESPONSE GUIDEBOOK, DOT P 5800.4, GUIDE PAGE 55). EXTINGUISH ONLY IF FLOW CAN BE STOPPED; USE FLOODING AMOUNTS OF WATER AS FOG, SOLID STREAMS MAY BE INEFFECTIVE. COOL CONTAINERS WITH FLOODING AMOUNTS OF WATER FROM AS FAR A DISTANCE AS POSSIBLE. USE WATER SPRAY TO ABSORB TOXIC VAPORS. AVOID BREATHING TOXIC VAPORS; KEEP UPWIND. CONSIDER EVACUATION OF DOWNWIND AREA IF MATERIAL IS LEAKING.

TRANSPORTATION DATA

DEPARTMENT OF TRANSPORTATION HAZARD CLASSIFICATION 49 CFR 172.101: POISON B
DEPARTMENT OF TRANSPORTATION LABELING REQUIREMENTS 49 CFR 172.101 AND SUBPART E: POISON
DEPARTMENT OF TRANSPORTATION PACKAGING REQUIREMENTS: 49 CFR 173.346
EXCEPTIONS: 49 CFR 173.345

TOXICITY

DIETHYL P-NITROPHENYL PHOSPHATE: TOXICITY DATA: 5 MG/KG SKIN-RABBIT LD50; 14 MG/KG ORAL-MAN TDLO; 1800 UG/KG ORAL-RAT LD50; 760 UG/KG ORAL-MOUSE LD50; 230 UG/KG SUBCUTANEOUS-RABBIT LD50; 426 UG/KG SUBCUTANEOUS-RAT LD50; 270 UG/KG SUBCUTANEOUS-MOUSE LD50; 240 UG/KG INTRAVENOUS-RAT LD50; 520 UG/KG INTRAVENOUS-MOUSE LD50; 716 UG/KG INTRAPERITONEAL-RAT LD50; 330 UG/KG INTRAPERITONEAL-MOUSE LD50; 446 UG/KG INTRAMUSCULAR-RAT LD50; 710 UG/KG INTRAMUSCULAR-MOUSE LD50; 600 UG/KG PARENTERAL-MOUSE LDLO; MUTAGENIC DATA (RTECS). CARCINOGEN STATUS: NONE. ACUTE TOXICITY LEVEL: HIGHLY TOXIC BY INGESTION AND DERMAL ABSORPTION. TARGET EFFECTS: CHOLINESTERASE INHIBITOR. POISONING MAY AFFECT THE NERVOUS SYSTEM.* AT INCREASED RISK FROM EXPOSURE: PERSONS WITH RESPIRATORY AILMENTS, RECENT EXPOSURE TO CHOLINESTERASE INHIBITORS OR IMPAIRED CHOLINESTERASE PRODUCTION, OR LIVER MALFUNCTION.* ADDITIONAL DATA: MAY CROSS THE PLACENTA. HIGH ENVIRONMENTAL TEMPERATURES OR EXPOSURE OF THE CHEMICAL TO VISIBLE OR ULTRAVIOLET LIGHT MAY ENHANCE THE TOXICITY. INTERACTIONS WITH MEDICATIONS MAY OCCUR.*
* MAY BE BASED ON GENERAL INFORMATION ON ORGANOPHOSPHATES.

HEALTH EFFECTS AND FIRST AID

INHALATION: DIETHYL P-NITROPHENYL PHOSPHATE: SEE INFORMATION ON ORGANOPHOSPHATES.
ORGANOPHOSPHATES: CHOLINESTERASE INHIBITOR. **ACUTE EXPOSURE-** WHEN INHALED, THE FIRST EFFECTS OF CHOLINESTERASE INHIBITORS ARE USUALLY RESPIRATORY AND MAY INCLUDE NASAL HYPEREMIA AND WATERY DISCHARGE, COUGH, CHEST DISCOMFORT, DYSPNEA, AND WHEEZING DUE TO INCREASED BRONCHIAL SECRETIONS AND BRONCHOCONSTRICTION. IF SUFFICIENT AMOUNTS ARE ABSORBED, OTHER SYSTEMIC EFFECTS MAY BEGIN WITHIN A FEW MINUTES OR BE DELAYED FOR UP TO 12 HOURS. SYMPTOMS MAY INCLUDE PALLOR, NAUSEA, VOMITING, DIARRHEA, ABDOMINAL CRAMPS, HEADACHE, DIZZINESS, OCULAR PAIN, BLURRED VISION, MIOSIS OR IN SOME CASES, ESPECIALLY INITIALLY, MYDRIASIS, LACRIMATION, SALIVATION, SWEATING, AND CONFUSION. OTHER REPORTED CENTRAL NERVOUS SYSTEM OR NEUROMUSCULAR EFFECTS MAY INCLUDE ATAXIA, SLURRED SPEECH, AREFLEXIA, WEAKNESS, FATIGUE, FASCICULATIONS, TWITCHING, TREMORS POSSIBLY OF THE TONGUE AND EYELIDS, AND EVENTUALLY PARALYSIS OF THE EXTREMITIES AND POSSIBLY OF THE RESPIRATORY MUSCLES. IN SEVERE CASES THERE MAY ALSO BE INVOLUNTARY DEFECATION AND URINATION, CYANOSIS, PSYCHOSIS, HYPERGLYCEMIA, ACUTE PANCREATITIS, CARDIAC IRREGULARITIES, PULMONARY EDEMA, UNCONSCIOUSNESS, CONVULSIONS, AND COMA. DEATH IS PRIMARILY DUE TO RESPIRATORY FAILURE, ALTHOUGH CARDIOVASCULAR EFFECTS INCLUDING CARDIAC ARREST MAY ALSO BE IMPLICATED. LONG TERM SEQUELAE ARE RARE

BUT MAY INCLUDE NEUROPSYCHIATRIC DISORDERS AND MYOPATHY WITH MUSCLE TENDERNESS. SOME ORGANOPHOSPHATES MAY CAUSE A DELAYED NEUROPATHY BEGINNING 1-4 WEEKS AFTER AN ACUTE EXPOSURE WHICH MAY OR MAY NOT HAVE CAUSED ACUTE CHOLINERGIC EFFECTS. NUMBNESS, TINGLING, WEAKNESS AND CRAMPING BEGINNING SYMMETRICALLY IN THE LOWER LIMBS MAY PROGRESS TO ATAXIA AND PARALYSIS. IN SEVERE CASES, UPPER LIMB INVOLVEMENT IS POSSIBLE AND FLACCID PARALYSIS MAY PROGRESS TO SPASTIC PARALYSIS WITH EXAGGERATED REFLEXES. IMPROVEMENT MAY OCCUR OVER MONTHS TO YEARS, BUT SOME RESIDUAL IMPAIRMENT USUALLY REMAINS.

CHRONIC EXPOSURE- REPEATED OR PROLONGED EXPOSURE MAY RESULT IN THE EFFECTS OF ACUTE EXPOSURE INCLUDING THE DELAYED NEUROPATHY. OTHER EFFECTS REPORTED IN WORKERS REPEATEDLY EXPOSED INCLUDE IMPAIRED MEMORY AND CONCENTRATION, ACUTE PSYCHOSIS, SEVERE DEPRESSIONS, IRRITABILTY, CONFUSION, APATHY, EMOTIONAL LABILITY, SOCIAL WITHDRAWAL, CONFUSION, HEADACHE, SPEECH DIFFICULTIES, DELAYED REACTION TIMES, SPATIAL DISORIENTATION, NIGHTMARES, SLEEPWALKING, AND DROWSINESS OR INSOMNIA. AN INFLUENZA-LIKE CONDITION WITH HEADACHE, NAUSEA, WEAKNESS, ANOREXIA AND MALAISE HAS ALSO BEEN REPORTED.

FIRST AID- REMOVE FROM EXPOSURE AREA TO FRESH AIR IMMEDIATELY. IF BREATHING HAS STOPPED, GIVE ARTIFICIAL RESPIRATION. MAINTAIN AIRWAY AND BLOOD PRESSURE AND ADMINISTER OXYGEN IF AVAILABLE. KEEP AFFECTED PERSON WARM AND AT REST. TREAT SYMPTOMATICALLY AND SUPPORTIVELY. ADMINISTRATION OF OXYGEN SHOULD BE PERFORMED BY QUALIFIED PERSONNEL. GET MEDICAL ATTENTION IMMEDIATELY.

SKIN CONTACT: DIETHYL P-NITROPHENYL PHOSPHATE: HIGHLY TOXIC. SEE INFORMATION ON ORGANOPHOSPHATES.

ORGANOPHOSPHATES: CHOLINESTERASE INHIBITOR. **ACUTE EXPOSURE-** LOCALIZED SWEATING AND FASCICULATIONS MAY OCCUR AT THE SITE OF CONTACT. IF SUFFICIENT AMOUNTS ARE ABSORBED, OTHER EFFECTS OF CHOLINESTERASE INHIBITION AS DESCRIBED IN ACUTE INHALATION MAY OCCUR. SYMPTOMS MAY BE DELAYED 2-3 HOURS, BUT USUALLY NO MORE THAN 12 HOURS. THE RATE OF ABSORPTION IS INCREASED BY THE PRESENCE OF DERMATITIS OR HIGH AMBIENT TEMPERATURES. DELAYED NEUROPATHY IS ALSO POSSIBLE. **CHRONIC EXPOSURE-** REPEATED OR PROLONGED EXPOSURE MAY CAUSE EFFECTS AS DESCRIBED IN ACUTE EXPOSURE. SOME ORGANOPHOSPHATES MAY CAUSE SENSITIZATION.

FIRST AID- REMOVE CONTAMINATED CLOTHING IMMEDIATELY. WASH CONTAMINATED AREAS WITH SOAP AND WATER FOLLOWED BY ALCOHOL (ARENA, POISONING, 4TH ED.). EMERGENCY PERSONNEL SHOULD WEAR GLOVES AND AVOID CONTAMINATION. TREAT RESPIRATORY DIFFICULTY WITH ARTIFICIAL RESPIRATION. GET MEDICAL ATTENTION IMMEDIATELY.

EYE CONTACT: DIETHYL P-NITROPHENYL PHOSPHATE: SEE INFORMATION ON ORGANOPHOSPHATES.

ORGANOPHOSPHATES: CHOLINESTERASE INHIBITOR. **ACUTE EXPOSURE-** DIRECT CONTACT MAY CAUSE PAIN, HYPEREMIA, LACRIMATION, TWITCHING OF THE EYELIDS, MIOSIS, AND CILIARY MUSCLE SPASM WITH LOSS OF ACCOMODATION, BLURRED OR DIMMED VISION AND BROWACHE. SOMETIMES MYDRIASIS MAY OCCUR INSTEAD OF MIOSIS. WITH SUFFICIENT EXPOSURE, OTHER SYMPTOMS OF CHOLINESTERASE INHIBITION AS DESCRIBED IN ACUTE INHALATION MAY OCCUR. **CHRONIC EXPOSURE-** REPEATED OR PROLONGED EXPOSURE MAY CAUSE EFFECTS AS DESCRIBED IN ACUTE EXPOSURE. SOME COMPOUNDS HAVE CAUSED TOXIC EFFECTS ON THE CRYSTALLINE LENS, CONJUNCTIVAL THICKENING AND OBSTRUCTION OF THE NASOLACRIMAL CANALS WHEN USED AS MIOTIC EYEDROPS.

FIRST AID- IRRIGATE EYES WITH WATER OR SALINE SOLUTION. IF SYMPTOMS OF POISONING OCCUR, TREAT RESPIRATORY DIFFICULTY WITH ARTIFICIAL RESPIRATION AND OXYGEN. OBSERVE PATIENT FOR AT LEAST 24-36 HOURS (GOSSELIN, CLINICAL TOXICOLOGY OF COMMERCIAL PRODUCTS, 5TH ED.). GET MEDICAL ATTENTION IMMEDIATELY. OXYGEN SHOULD BE ADMINISTERED BY QUALIFIED MEDICAL PERSONNEL.

INGESTION: DIETHYL P-NITROPHENYL PHOSPHATE: HIGHLY TOXIC. SEE INFORMATION ON ORGANOPHOSPHATES.

ORGANOPHOSPHATES: CHOLINESTERASE INHIBITOR. **ACUTE EXPOSURE-** WHEN INGESTED, THE FIRST EFFECTS MAY BE NAUSEA, VOMITING, ANOREXIA, ABDOMINAL CRAMPS AND DIARRHEA. GASTROINTESTINAL ABSORPTION MAY CAUSE SYMPTOMS OF CHOLINESTERASE INHIBITION AS DESCRIBED IN ACUTE INHALATION. SYMPTOMS MAY BEGIN WITHIN MINUTES OR BE DELAYED FOR HOURS. DELAYED EFFECTS INCLUDING NEUROPATHY MAY ALSO OCCUR. **CHRONIC EXPOSURE-** REPEATED INGESTION MAY CAUSE EFFECTS AS DESCRIBED IN ACUTE EXPOSURE.

FIRST AID- IF PERSON IS ALERT AND RESPIRATION IS NOT DEPRESSED, GIVE SYRUP OF IPECAC FOLLOWED BY WATER (IF VOMITING OCCURS, KEEP HEAD BELOW HIPS TO PREVENT ASPIRATION). IF CONSCIOUSNESS LEVEL DECLINES OR VOMITING HAS NOT OCCURRED IN 15 MINUTES EMPTY STOMACH BY GASTRIC LAVAGE WITH THE AID OF CUFFED ENDOTRACHEAL TUBE USING ISOTONIC SALINE OR 5% SODIUM BICARBONATE FOLLOW WITH ACTIVATED CHARCOAL. ESTABLISH AND MAINTAIN AIRWAY. TREAT RESPIRATORY DIFFICULTY WITH ARTIFICIAL RESPIRATION AND OXYGEN. DO NOT GIVE MORPHINE, AMINOPHYLLINE, PHENOTHIAZINES, RESERPINE, FUROSEMIDE, OR ETHACRYNIC ACID (MORGAN, RECOGNITION AND MANAGEMENT OF PESTICIDE POISONINGS, 3RD ED.). TREAT SYMPTOMATICALLY AND SUPPORTIVELY. ADMINISTRATION OF OXYGEN AND LAVAGE MUST BE PERFORMED BY QUALIFIED MEDICAL PERSONNEL. GET MEDICAL ATTENTION IMMEDIATELY.

ANTIDOTE: THE FOLLOWING ANTIDOTE(S) HAVE BEEN RECOMMENDED. HOWEVER, THE DECISION AS TO WHETHER THE SEVERITY OF POISONING REQUIRES ADMINISTRATION OF ANY ANTIDOTE AND ACTUAL DOSE REQUIRED SHOULD BE MADE BY QUALIFIED MEDICAL PERSONNEL.

FOR CHOLINESTERASE INHIBITORS: ESTABLISH CLEAR AIRWAY AND TISSUE OXYGENATION BY ASPIRATION OF SECRETIONS, AND IF NECESSARY, BY ASSISTED PULMONARY VENTILATION WITH OXYGEN. IMPROVE TISSUE OXYGENATION AS MUCH AS POSSIBLE BEFORE ADMINISTERING ATROPINE TO MINIMIZE THE RISK OF VENTRICULAR FIBRILLATION. ADMINISTER ATROPINE SULFATE INTRAVENOUSLY, OR INTRAMUSCULARLY IF IV INJECTION IS NOT POSSIBLE. IN MODERATELY SEVERE POISONING ADMINISTER ATROPINE SULFATE, 0.4-2.0 MG REPEATED EVERY 15 MINUTES UNTIL ATROPINIZATION IS ACHIEVED (TACHYCARDIA, FLUSHING, DRY MOUTH, MYDRIASIS). MAINTAIN ATROPINIZATION BY REPEATED DOSES FOR 2-12 HOURS, OR LONGER, DEPENDING ON THE SEVERITY OF POISONING. THE APPEARANCE OF RALES IN THE LUNG BASES, MIOSIS, SALIVATION, NAUSEA, BRADYCARDIA, ARE ALL INDICATIONS OF INADEQUATE ATROPINIZATION. SEVERELY POISONED INDIVIDUALS MAY EXHIBIT REMARKABLE TOLERANCE TO ATROPINE; TWO OR MORE TIMES THE DOSAGES SUGGESTED ABOVE MAY BE NEEDED. PERSONS NOT POISONED OR ONLY SLIGHTLY POISONED, HOWEVER, MAY DEVELOP SIGNS OF ATROPINE TOXICITY FROM SUCH LARGE DOSAGES: FEVER, MUSCLE FIBRILLATIONS, AND DELIRIUM ARE THE MAIN SIGNS OF ATROPINE TOXICITY. IF THESE SIGNS APPEAR WHILE THE PATIENT IS FULLY ATROPINIZED, ATROPINE ADMINISTRATION SHOULD BE DISCONTINUED, AT LEAST TEMPORARILY. OBSERVE TREATED PATIENTS CLOSELY AT LEAST 24 HOURS TO INSURE THAT SYMPTOMS (POSSIBLY PULMONARY EDEMA) DO NOT RECUR AS ATROPINIZATION WEARS OFF. IN VERY SEVERE POISONINGS, METABOLIC DISPOSITION OF TOXICANT MAY REQUIRE SEVERAL HOURS OR DAYS DURING WHICH ATROPINIZATION MUST BE MAINTAINED. MARKEDLY LOWER LEVELS OF URINARY METABOLITES INDICATE THAT ATROPINE DOSAGE CAN BE TAPERED OFF. AS DOSAGE IS REDUCED, CHECK THE LUNG BASES FREQUENTLY FOR RALES. IF RALES ARE HEARD OR OTHER SYMPTOMS RETURN, RE-ESTABLISH ATROPINIZATION PROMPTLY (MORGAN, RECOGNITION AND MANAGEMENT OF PESTICIDE POISONINGS, 3RD ED.). ADMINISTRATION OF ANTIDOTE MUST BE PERFORMED BY QUALIFIED MEDICAL PERSONNEL.

IN CASES OF SEVERE POISONING BY ORGANOPHOSPHATE PESTICIDES IN WHICH RESPIRATORY DEPRESSION, MUSCLE WEAKNESS AND TWITCHINGS ARE SEVERE, GIVE PRALIDOXIME (PROTOPAM-AYERST, 2-PAM), 1.0 GRAM INTRAVENOUSLY AT NO MORE THAN 0.5 GRAM PER MINUTE. DOSAGE OF PRALIDOXIME MAY BE REPEATED IN 1-2 HOURS, THEN AT 10-12 HOUR INTERVALS IF NEEDED. IN VERY SEVERE POISONINGS, DOSAGE RATES MAY BE DOUBLED. TREATMENT WITH PRALIDOXIME WILL BE MOST EFFECTIVE IF GIVEN WITHIN THIRTY-SIX HOURS AFTER POISONING (MORGAN, RECOGNITION AND MANAGEMENT OF PESTICIDE POISONINGS, 3RD ED.). ANTIDOTE SHOULD BE ADMINISTERED BY QUALIFIED MEDICAL PERSONNEL.

REACTIVITY

REACTIVITY: MAY DECOMPOSE AT ELEVATED TEMPERATURES AND DEVELOP SUFFICIENT PRESSURE TO CAUSE THE CONTAINER TO RUPTURE VIOLENTLY.

INCOMPATIBILITIES: DIETHYL P-NITROPHENYL PHOSPHATE: NO DATA AVAILABLE.

DECOMPOSITION: THERMAL DECOMPOSITION MAY RELEASE TOXIC OXIDES OF PHOSPHORUS AND NITROGEN.

POLYMERIZATION: HAZARDOUS POLYMERIZATION HAS NOT BEEN REPORTED TO OCCUR UNDER NORMAL TEMPERATURES AND PRESSURES.

STORAGE AND DISPOSAL

OBSERVE ALL FEDERAL, STATE AND LOCAL REGULATIONS WHEN STORING OR DISPOSING OF THIS SUBSTANCE. FOR ASSISTANCE, CONTACT THE DISTRICT DIRECTOR OF THE ENVIRONMENTAL PROTECTION AGENCY.

CONDITIONS TO AVOID

MAY BURN BUT DOES NOT IGNITE READILY. CONTAINERS MAY EXPLODE IN HEAT OF FIRE.

SPILL AND LEAK PROCEDURES

OCCUPATIONAL SPILL: DO NOT TOUCH SPILLED MATERIAL. STOP LEAK IF YOU CAN DO IT WITHOUT RISK. USE WATER SPRAY TO REDUCE VAPORS. FOR SMALL SPILLS, TAKE UP WITH SAND OR OTHER ABSORBENT MATERIAL AND PLACE INTO CONTAINERS FOR LATER DISPOSAL. FOR SMALL DRY SPILLS, WITH A CLEAN SHOVEL PLACE MATERIAL INTO CLEAN, DRY CONTAINERS AND COVER. MOVE CONTAINERS FROM SPILL AREA. FOR LARGER SPILLS, DIKE FAR AHEAD OF SPILL FOR LATER DISPOSAL. KEEP UNNECESSARY PEOPLE AWAY. ISOLATE HAZARD AREA AND DENY ENTRY. VENTILATE CLOSED SPACES BEFORE ENTERING. REPORTABLE QUANTITY (RQ): 100 POUNDS THE SUPERFUND AMENDMENTS AND REAUTHORIZATION ACT (SARA) SECTION 304 REQUIRES THAT A RELEASE EQUAL TO OR GREATER THAN THE REPORTABLE QUANTITY FOR THIS SUBSTANCE BE IMMEDIATELY REPORTED TO THE LOCAL EMERGENCY PLANNING COMMITTEE AND THE STATE EMERGENCY RESPONSE COMMISSION (40 CFR 355.40). IF THE RELEASE OF THIS SUBSTANCE IS REPORTABLE UNDER CERCLA SECTION 103, THE NATIONAL RESPONSE CENTER MUST BE NOTIFIED IMMEDIATELY AT (800) 424-8802 OR (202) 426-2675 IN THE METROPOLITAN WASHINGTON, D.C. AREA (40 CFR 302.6).

PROTECTIVE EQUIPMENT

VENTILATION: PROCESS ENCLOSURE RECOMMENDED.

RESPIRATOR: THE FOLLOWING RESPIRATORS ARE RECOMMENDED BASED ON INFORMATION FOUND IN THE PHYSICAL DATA, TOXICITY AND HEALTH EFFECTS SECTIONS. THEY ARE RANKED IN ORDER FROM MINIMUM TO MAXIMUM RESPIRATORY PROTECTION. THE SPECIFIC RESPIRATOR SELECTED MUST BE BASED ON CONTAMINATION LEVELS FOUND IN THE WORK PLACE, MUST NOT EXCEED THE WORKING LIMITS OF THE RESPIRATOR AND BE JOINTLY APPROVED BY THE NATIONAL INSTITUTE FOR OCCUPATIONAL SAFETY AND HEALTH AND THE MINE SAFETY AND HEALTH ADMINISTRATION (NIOSH-MSHA).

TYPE 'C' SUPPLIED-AIR RESPIRATOR WITH A FULL FACEPIECE OPERATED IN PRESSURE-DEMAND OR OTHER POSITIVE PRESSURE MODE OR WITH A FULL FACEPIECE, HELMET OR HOOD OPERATED IN CONTINOUS-FLOW MODE.

SELF-CONTAINED BREATHING APPARATUS WITH A FULL FACEPIECE OPERATED IN PRESSURE-DEMAND OR OTHER POSITIVE PRESSURE MODE.

FOR FIREFIGHTING AND OTHER IMMEDIATELY DANGEROUS TO LIFE OR HEALTH CONDITIONS:

SELF-CONTAINED BREATHING APPARATUS WITH FULL FACEPIECE OPERATED IN PRESSURE-DEMAND OR OTHER POSITIVE PRESSURE MODE.

SUPPLIED-AIR RESPIRATOR WITH FULL FACEPIECE AND OPERATED IN PRESSURE-DEMAND OR OTHER POSITIVE PRESSURE MODE IN COMBINATION WITH AN AUXILIARY SELF-CONTAINED BREATHING APPARATUS OPERATED IN PRESSURE-DEMAND OR OTHER POSITIVE PRESSURE MODE.

CLOTHING: EMPLOYEE MUST WEAR APPROPRIATE PROTECTIVE (IMPERVIOUS) CLOTHING AND EQUIPMENT TO PREVENT ANY POSSIBILITY OF SKIN CONTACT WITH THIS SUBSTANCE.

GLOVES: EMPLOYEE MUST WEAR APPROPRIATE PROTECTIVE GLOVES TO PREVENT CONTACT WITH THIS SUBSTANCE.

EYE PROTECTION: EMPLOYEE MUST WEAR SPLASH-PROOF OR DUST-RESISTANT SAFETY GOGGLES AND A FACESHIELD TO PREVENT CONTACT WITH THIS SUBSTANCE.

EMERGENCY WASH FACILITIES: WHERE THERE IS ANY POSSIBILITY THAT AN EMPLOYEE'S EYES AND/OR SKIN MAY BE EXPOSED TO THIS SUBSTANCE, THE EMPLOYER SHOULD PROVIDE AN EYE WASH FOUNTAIN AND QUICK DRENCH SHOWER WITHIN THE IMMEDIATE WORK AREA FOR EMERGENCY USE.

AUTHORIZED BY- OCCUPATIONAL HEALTH SERVICES, INC.

CREATION DATE: 10/04/89 ***REVISION DATE:*** 04/26/90

MATERIAL SAFETY DATA SHEET

OCCUPATIONAL HEALTH SERVICES, INC.
AGRICULTURE AND PESTICIDE DIVISION
450 SEVENTH AVENUE, SUITE 2407
NEW YORK, NEW YORK 10123
1-800-445-MSDS OR (212) 967-1100

EMERGENCY CONTACT:
JOHN S. BRANSFORD, JR. (615) 292-1180

SUBSTANCE IDENTIFICATION

CAS-NUMBER 84-66-2

SUBSTANCE: DIETHYL PHTHALATE

TRADE NAMES/SYNONYMS: ANOZOL; ETHYL PHTHALATE; NEANTINE; SOLVANOL; PALATINOL; O-BENZENEDICARBOXYLIC ACID DIETHYL ESTHER; PLACID E; 1,2-BENZENEDICARBOXYLIC ACID, DIETHYL ESTER; PHTHALIC ACID, DIETHYL ESTER; PHTHALOL; PLACIDOLE E; NCI-C60048; U088; E-162; PST07210

CHEMICAL FAMILY: ESTER, CARBOXYLIC, AROMATIC

MOLECULAR FORMULA: C12-H14-O4

MOLECULAR WEIGHT: 222.26

CERCLA RATINGS (SCALE 0-3): HEALTH=3 FIRE=1 REACTIVITY=0 PERSISTENCE=2

NFPA RATINGS (SCALE 0-4): HEALTH=0 FIRE=1 REACTIVITY=0

COMPONENTS AND CONTAMINANTS

COMPONENT: DIETHYL PHTHALATE ***PERCENT:*** 100

CAS# 84-66-2

EXPOSURE LIMITS: DIETHYL PHTHALATE: 5 MG/M3 OSHA TWA 5 MG/M3 ACGIH TWA 1000 POUNDS CERCLA SECTION 103 REPORTABLE QUANTITY SUBJECT TO SARA SECTION 313 ANNUAL TOXIC CHEMICAL RELEASE REPORTING

PHYSICAL DATA

DESCRIPTION: ODORLESS, CLEAR, COLORLESS LIQUID WITH A BITTER DISAGREEABLE TASTE.

BOILING POINT: 565 F (296 C) ***MELTING POINT:*** -40 F (-40 C)

SPECIFIC GRAVITY: 1.120 ***VISCOSITY:*** 31.3 CST @ 0 C

VAPOR PRESSURE: 14 MMHG @ 325 F ***SOLUBILITY IN WATER:*** INSOLUBLE

VAPOR DENSITY: 7.66

SOLVENT SOLUBILITY: ALCOHOL, ETHER, ACETONE, BENZENE, KETONES, ESTERS, AROMATIC HYDROCARBONS

FIRE AND EXPLOSION DATA

FIRE AND EXPLOSION HAZARD: SLIGHT FIRE HAZARD WHEN EXPOSED TO HEAT OR FLAME.

VAPORS ARE HEAVIER THAN AIR AND MAY TRAVEL A CONSIDERABLE DISTANCE TO A SOURCE OF IGNITION AND FLASH BACK.

FLASH POINT: 322 F (161 C) (OC) ***UPPER EXPLOSIVE LIMIT:*** NOT AVAILABLE

LOWER EXPLOSIVE LIMIT: 0.7% @ 368 F ***AUTOIGNITION TEMP.:*** 855 F (457 C)

FLAMMABILITY CLASS(OSHA): IIIB

FIREFIGHTING MEDIA: DRY CHEMICAL, CARBON DIOXIDE, HALON, WATER SPRAY OR STANDARD FOAM (1987 EMERGENCY RESPONSE GUIDEBOOK, DOT P 5800.4).

FOR LARGER FIRES, USE WATER SPRAY, FOG OR STANDARD FOAM (1987 EMERGENCY RESPONSE GUIDEBOOK, DOT P 5800.4).

FIREFIGHTING: MOVE CONTAINERS FROM FIRE AREA IF POSSIBLE (1987 EMERGENCY RESPONSE GUIDEBOOK, DOT P 5800.4, GUIDE PAGE 53).

EXTINGUISH ONLY IF FLOW CAN BE STOPPED. EXTINGUISH USING AGENT INDICATED. USE FLOODING AMOUNTS OF WATER AS A FOG. COOL CONTAINERS WITH FLOODING AMOUNTS OF WATER FROM AS FAR A DISTANCE AS POSSIBLE. AVOID BREATHING POISONOUS VAPORS, KEEP UPWIND. CONSIDER EVACUATION OF DOWNWIND AREA IF MATERIAL IS LEAKING.

TOXICITY

DIETHYL PHTHALATE (ETHYL PHTHALATE): IRRITATION DATA: 112 MG EYE-RABBIT. TOXICITY DATA: 1000 MG/M3 INHALATION-HUMAN TCLO; >20 ML/KG SKIN-GUINEA PIG LD50 (KODAK MSDS); 8600 MG/KG ORAL-RAT LD50; 6172 MG/KG ORAL-MOUSE LD50; 1000 MG/KG ORAL-RABBIT LDLO; 8600 MG/KG ORAL-GUINEA PIG LD50; 3000 MG/KG SUBCUTANEOUS-GUINEA PIG LDLO; 100 MG/KG INTRAVENOUS-RABBIT LDLO; 5058 MG/KG INTRAPERITONEAL-RAT LD50; 2749 MG/KG INTRAPERITONEAL-MOUSE LD50; MUTAGENIC DATA (RTECS); REPRODUCTIVE EFFECTS DATA (RTECS). CARCINOGEN STATUS: NONE. ACUTE TOXICITY LEVEL: SLIGHTLY TOXIC BY INGESTION; RELATIVELY NON-TOXIC BY DERMAL ABSORPTION. TARGET EFFECTS: CENTRAL NERVOUS SYSTEM DEPRESSANT. ADDITIONAL DATA: MAY CROSS THE PLACENTA.

HEALTH EFFECTS AND FIRST AID

INHALATION: DIETHYL PHTHALATE (ETHYL PHTHALATE): NARCOTIC. **ACUTE EXPOSURE**- MAY CAUSE IRRITATION OF THE NOSE AND THROAT WITH COUGHING, DIFFICULTY BREATHING, AND CHEST DISCOMFORT. HIGH CONCENTRATIONS MAY CAUSE CENTRAL NERVOUS SYSTEM DEPRESSION. EXPOSURE TO 511 PPM FOR 6 HOURS CAUSED NO DEATHS AMONG THE 3 RATS TESTED. HOWEVER, VASODILATION OF THE EARS AND FEET OCCURRED. **CHRONIC EXPOSURE**- CHRONIC ADMINISTRATION TO ANIMALS RESULTED IN A BRIEF PERIOD OF IRRITATION FOLLOWED BY SLOWING DOWN, SLUGGISHNESS, STRENGTH LOSS, AND WEIGHT LOSS. PARESIS AND PARALYSIS OF THE HIND EXTREMITIES AND CHANGES IN TOTAL SUBTHRESHOLD IMPULSES OCCURRED IN SOME ANIMALS. BRAIN EDEMA, CHROMATOLYSIS, VACUOLIZATION OF NERVE CELL CYTOPLASM, REDUCTION OF HEART RATE AND CHANGES IN BLOOD CELL MORPHOLOGY, AND RESPIRATORY, LIVER, GONAD, AND KIDNEY FUNCTIONS WERE OBSERVED.

FIRST AID- REMOVE FROM EXPOSURE AREA TO FRESH AIR IMMEDIATELY. IF BREATHING HAS STOPPED, PERFORM ARTIFICIAL RESPIRATION. KEEP PERSON WARM AND AT REST. TREAT SYMPTOMATICALLY AND SUPPORTIVELY. GET MEDICAL ATTENTION IMMEDIATELY.

SKIN CONTACT: DIETHYL PHTHALATE (ETHYL PHTHALATE): **ACUTE EXPOSURE**- MAY CAUSE IRRITATION AND MAY BE ABSORBED THROUGH THE SKIN. **CHRONIC EXPOSURE**- REPRODUCTIVE EFFECTS HAVE BEEN REPORTED IN ANIMALS.

FIRST AID- REMOVE CONTAMINATED CLOTHING AND SHOES IMMEDIATELY. WASH AFFECTED AREA WITH SOAP OR MILD DETERGENT AND LARGE AMOUNTS OF WATER UNTIL NO EVIDENCE OF CHEMICAL REMAINS (APPROXIMATELY 15-20 MINUTES). GET MEDICAL ATTENTION IMMEDIATELY.

EYE CONTACT: DIETHYL PHTHALATE (ETHYL PHTHALATE): **ACUTE EXPOSURE**- LIQUID OR MIST MAY CAUSE IRRITATION WITH REDNESS AND TEARING. **CHRONIC EXPOSURE**- NO DATA AVAILABLE.

FIRST AID- WASH EYES IMMEDIATELY WITH LARGE AMOUNTS OF WATER OR NORMAL SALINE, OCCASIONALLY LIFTING UPPER AND LOWER LIDS, UNTIL NO EVIDENCE OF CHEMICAL REMAINS (APPROXIMATELY 15-20 MINUTES). GET MEDICAL ATTENTION IMMEDIATELY.

INGESTION: DIETHYL PHTHALATE (ETHYL PHTHALATE): NARCOTIC. **ACUTE EXPOSURE**- MAY CAUSE A BURNING-LIKE IRRITATION OF THE MUCOUS MEMBRANES. ADDITIONAL EFFECTS MAY INCLUDE CENTRAL NERVOUS SYSTEM DEPRESSION, HEADACHE, DIZZINESS, NAUSEA, AND VOMITING. **CHRONIC EXPOSURE**- RATS AND DOGS FED 1.2-2.5 MG/KG FOR 6 OR MORE WEEKS OF DIETHYL PHTHALATE SHOWED NO ADVERSE EFFECTS. CHRONIC FEEDING OF DIETHYL PHTHALATE TO MICE CAUSED DECREASED BODY WEIGHT BUT DID NOT AFFECT REPRODUCTION IN THE FIRST GENERATION. HOWEVER, IT WAS ASSOCIATED WITH DECREASED LITTER SIZE IN THE SECOND GENERATION. OTHER REPRODUCTIVE EFFECTS HAVE BEEN REPORTED IN ANIMALS.

FIRST AID- IF THE PERSON IS CONSCIOUS AND NOT CONVULSING, INDUCE EMESIS BY GIVING SYRUP OF IPECAC FOLLOWED BY WATER. (IF VOMITING OCCURS KEEP THE HEAD BELOW THE HIPS TO PREVENT ASPIRATION). REPEAT IN 20 MINUTES IF NOT EFFECTIVE INITIALLY. GIVE ACTIVATED CHARCOAL. IN PATIENTS WITH DEPRESSED RESPIRATION OR IF EMESIS IS NOT PRODUCED, PERFORM GASTRIC LAVAGE CAUTIOUSLY (DREISBACH, HANDBOOK OF POISONING, 12TH ED.). TREAT SYMPTOMATICALLY AND SUPPORTIVELY. GASTRIC LAVAGE SHOULD BE PERFORMED BY QUALIFIED MEDICAL PERSONNEL. GET MEDICAL ATTENTION IMMEDIATELY. ***ANTIDOTE:*** NO SPECIFIC ANTIDOTE. TREAT SYMPTOMATICALLY AND SUPPORTIVELY.

REACTIVITY

REACTIVITY: STABLE UNDER NORMAL TEMPERATURES AND PRESSURES.

INCOMPATIBILITIES: DIETHYL PHTHALATE (ETHYL PHTHALATE): ACIDS (STRONG): INCOMPATIBLE. ALKALIS (STRONG): INCOMPATIBLE. OXIDIZERS (STRONG): FIRE AND EXPLOSION HAZARD. PERMANGANATES: INCOMPATIBLE.

DECOMPOSITION: THERMAL DECOMPOSITION MAY RELEASE TOXIC AND/OR HAZARDOUS GASES.

POLYMERIZATION: HAZARDOUS POLYMERIZATION HAS NOT BEEN REPORTED TO OCCUR UNDER NORMAL TEMPERATURES AND PRESSURES.

STORAGE AND DISPOSAL

OBSERVE ALL FEDERAL, STATE AND LOCAL REGULATIONS WHEN STORING OR DISPOSING OF THIS SUBSTANCE. FOR ASSISTANCE, CONTACT THE DISTRICT DIRECTOR OF THE ENVIRONMENTAL PROTECTION AGENCY.

****DISPOSAL****

DISPOSAL MUST BE IN ACCORDANCE WITH STANDARDS APPLICABLE TO GENERATORS OF HAZARDOUS WASTE, 40CFR 262. EPA HAZARDOUS WASTE NUMBER U088.

CONDITIONS TO AVOID

MAY BURN BUT DOES NOT IGNITE READILY. AVOID CONTACT WITH STRONG OXIDIZERS, EXCESSIVE HEAT, SPARKS, OR OPEN FLAME.

SPILL AND LEAK PROCEDURES

OCCUPATIONAL SPILL: STOP LEAK IF YOU CAN DO IT WITHOUT RISK. FOR SMALL SPILLS, TAKE UP WITH SAND OR OTHER ABSORBENT MATERIAL AND PLACE INTO CLEAN, DRY CONTAINERS FOR LATER DISPOSAL. KEEP UNNECESSARY PEOPLE AWAY. ISOLATE HAZARD AREA AND DENY ENTRY.

REPORTABLE QUANTITY (RQ): 1000 POUNDS THE SUPERFUND AMENDMENTS AND REAUTHORIZATION ACT (SARA) SECTION 304 REQUIRES THAT A RELEASE EQUAL TO OR GREATER THAN THE REPORTABLE QUANTITY FOR THIS SUBSTANCE BE IMMEDIATELY REPORTED TO THE LOCAL EMERGENCY PLANNING COMMITTEE AND THE STATE EMERGENCY RESPONSE COMMISSION (40 CFR 355.40). IF THE RELEASE OF THIS SUBSTANCE IS REPORTABLE UNDER CERCLA SECTION 103, THE NATIONAL RESPONSE CENTER MUST BE NOTIFIED IMMEDIATELY AT (800) 424-8802 OR (202) 426-2675 IN THE METROPOLITAN WASHINGTON, D.C. AREA (40 CFR 302.6).

PROTECTIVE EQUIPMENT

VENTILATION: PROVIDE LOCAL EXHAUST OR PROCESS ENCLOSURE VENTILATION TO MEET PUBLISHED EXPOSURE LIMITS.

RESPIRATOR: THE FOLLOWING RESPIRATORS ARE RECOMMENDED BASED ON INFORMATION FOUND IN THE PHYSICAL DATA, TOXICITY AND HEALTH EFFECTS SECTIONS. THEY ARE RANKED IN ORDER FROM MINIMUM TO MAXIMUM RESPIRATORY PROTECTION. THE SPECIFIC RESPIRATOR SELECTED MUST BE BASED ON CONTAMINATION LEVELS FOUND IN THE WORK PLACE, MUST NOT EXCEED THE WORKING LIMITS OF THE RESPIRATOR AND BE JOINTLY APPROVED BY THE NATIONAL INSTITUTE FOR OCCUPATIONAL SAFETY AND HEALTH AND THE MINE SAFETY AND HEALTH ADMINISTRATION (NIOSH-MSHA).

CHEMICAL CARTRIDGE RESPIRATOR WITH AN ORGANIC VAPOR CARTRIDGE(S) WITH A FULL FACEPIECE.

GAS MASK WITH ORGANIC VAPOR CANISTER (CHIN-STYLE OR FRONT- OR BACK-MOUNTED CANISTER) WITH A FULL FACEPIECE.

TYPE 'C' SUPPLIED-AIR RESPIRATOR WITH A FULL FACEPIECE OPERATED IN PRESSURE-DEMAND OR OTHER POSITIVE PRESSURE MODE OR WITH A FULL FACEPIECE, HELMET OR HOOD OPERATED IN CONTINUOUS-FLOW MODE.

SELF-CONTAINED BREATHING APPARATUS WITH A FULL FACEPIECE OPERATED IN PRESSURE-DEMAND OR OTHER POSITIVE PRESSURE MODE.

FOR FIREFIGHTING AND OTHER IMMEDIATELY DANGEROUS TO LIFE OR HEALTH CONDITIONS:

SELF-CONTAINED BREATHING APPARATUS WITH FULL FACEPIECE OPERATED IN PRESSURE-DEMAND OR OTHER POSITIVE PRESSURE MODE.

SUPPLIED-AIR RESPIRATOR WITH FULL FACEPIECE AND OPERATED IN PRESSURE-DEMAND OR OTHER POSITIVE PRESSURE MODE IN COMBINATION WITH AN AUXILIARY SELF-CONTAINED BREATHING APPARATUS OPERATED IN PRESSURE-DEMAND OR OTHER POSITIVE PRESSURE MODE.

CLOTHING: EMPLOYEE MUST WEAR APPROPRIATE PROTECTIVE (IMPERVIOUS) CLOTHING AND EQUIPMENT TO PREVENT REPEATED OR PROLONGED SKIN CONTACT WITH THIS SUBSTANCE.

GLOVES: EMPLOYEE MUST WEAR APPROPRIATE PROTECTIVE GLOVES TO PREVENT CONTACT WITH THIS SUBSTANCE.

EYE PROTECTION: EMPLOYEE MUST WEAR SPLASH-PROOF OR DUST-RESISTANT SAFETY GOGGLES TO PREVENT EYE CONTACT WITH THIS SUBSTANCE.

EMERGENCY EYE WASH: WHERE THERE IS ANY POSSIBILITY THAT AN EMPLOYEE'S EYES MAY BE EXPOSED TO THIS SUBSTANCE, THE EMPLOYER SHOULD PROVIDE AN EYE WASH FOUNTAIN WITHIN THE IMMEDIATE WORK AREA FOR EMERGENCY USE.

AUTHORIZED BY- OCCUPATIONAL HEALTH SERVICES, INC.

CREATION DATE: 10/04/89 ***REVISION DATE:*** 07/03/90

MATERIAL SAFETY DATA SHEET

OCCUPATIONAL HEALTH SERVICES, INC.
AGRICULTURE AND PESTICIDE DIVISION
450 SEVENTH AVENUE, SUITE 2407
NEW YORK, NEW YORK 10123
1-800-445-MSDS OR (212) 967-1100

EMERGENCY CONTACT:
JOHN S. BRANSFORD, JR. (615) 292-1180

SUBSTANCE IDENTIFICATION

CAS-NUMBER 56073-07-5

SUBSTANCE: **DIFENACOUM**

TRADE NAMES/SYNONYMS: 2H-1-BENZOPYRAN-2-ONE, 3-(3-(1,1'-BIPHENYL)-4-YL-1,2,3,4-TETRAHYDRO- 1-NAPHTHALENYL)-4-HYDROXY-; 3-(3-(1,1'-BIPHENYL)-4-YL-1,2,3,4-TETRAHYDRO-1-NAPHTHALENYL)-4- HYDROXY-2H-1-BENZOPYRAN-2-ONE; 3-(3-BIPHENYL-4-YL-1,2,3,4-TETRAHYDRO-1-NAPHTHYL)-4-HYDROXYCOUMARIN; DIPHENACOUM; NEOSOREXA; RATAK; C31H24O3; PST07385

CHEMICAL FAMILY: COUMARIN

MOLECULAR FORMULA: C31-H24-O3

MOLECULAR WEIGHT: 444.55

CERCLA RATINGS (SCALE 0-3): HEALTH=3 FIRE=1 REACTIVITY=0 PERSISTENCE=2

NFPA RATINGS (SCALE 0-4): HEALTH=4 FIRE=1 REACTIVITY=0

COMPONENTS AND CONTAMINANTS

COMPONENT: DIFENACOUM ***PERCENT:*** 100.0
CAS# 56073-07-5

EXPOSURE LIMITS: NO OCCUPATIONAL EXPOSURE LIMITS ESTABLISHED BY OSHA, ACGIH, OR NIOSH.

PHYSICAL DATA

DESCRIPTION: OFF-WHITE POWDER. ***MELTING POINT:*** 419-426 F (215-219 C)
SPECIFIC GRAVITY: NOT AVAILABLE ***VAPOR PRESSURE:*** NEGLIGIBLE
SOLUBILITY IN WATER: < 10 PPM @ PH 7
SOLVENT SOLUBILITY: SOLUBLE IN BENZENE AND CHLOROFORM; MODERATELY SOLUBLE IN ACETONE AND ETHANOL; PRACTICALLY INSOLUBLE IN PETROLEUM ETHER.

FIRE AND EXPLOSION DATA

FIRE AND EXPLOSION HAZARD: SLIGHT FIRE HAZARD WHEN EXPOSED TO HEAT OR FLAME.

FIREFIGHTING MEDIA: DRY CHEMICAL, CARBON DIOXIDE, HALON, WATER SPRAY OR STANDARD FOAM (1987 EMERGENCY RESPONSE GUIDEBOOK, DOT P 5800.4). FOR LARGER FIRES, USE WATER SPRAY, FOG OR STANDARD FOAM (1987 EMERGENCY RESPONSE GUIDEBOOK, DOT P 5800.4).

FIREFIGHTING: MOVE CONTAINERS FROM FIRE AREA IF POSSIBLE. FIGHT FIRE FROM MAXIMUM DISTANCE. STAY AWAY FROM STORAGE TANK ENDS. DIKE FIRE CONTROL WATER FOR LATER DISPOSAL. DO NOT SCATTER MATERIAL (1987 EMERGENCY RESPONSE GUIDEBOOK, DOT P 5800.4, GUIDE PAGE 55). EXTINGUISH USING AGENT SUITABLE FOR TYPE OF SURROUNDING FIRE. AVOID BREATHING VAPORS AND DUSTS. KEEP UPWIND.

TRANSPORTATION DATA

DEPARTMENT OF TRANSPORTATION HAZARD CLASSIFICATION 49 CFR 172.101: POISON B

DEPARTMENT OF TRANSPORTATION LABELING REQUIREMENTS 49 CFR 172.101 AND SUBPART E: POISON

DEPARTMENT OF TRANSPORTATION PACKAGING REQUIREMENTS: 49 CFR 173.365 EXCEPTIONS: 49 CFR 173.364

TOXICITY

DIFENACOUM: TOXICITY DATA: 1 GM/KG SKIN-RABBIT LD50; 680 UG/KG ORAL-RAT LD50; 800 UG/KG ORAL-MOUSE LD50; 50 MG/KG ORAL-GUINEA PIG LD50; 2 GM/KG ORAL-RABBIT LD50; 50 MG/KG ORAL-DOG LD50; 100 MG/KG ORAL-CAT LD50; 80 MG/KG ORAL-PIG LD50. CARCINOGEN STATUS: NONE. ACUTE TOXICITY LEVEL: HIGHLY TOXIC BY INGESTION; TOXIC BY DERMAL ABSORPTION. TARGET EFFECTS: HEMORRHAGIC AGENT. AT INCREASED RISK FROM EXPOSURE: PERSONS WITH BLOOD DYSCRASIAS WITH BLEEDING TENDENCIES, LIVER OR KIDNEY DISEASE, ULCERS OF THE GASTROINTESTINAL TRACT, OR HYPERTENSION.* ADDITIONAL DATA: INTERACTIONS WITH MEDICATIONS HAVE BEEN REPORTED.*

*MAY BE BASED ON GENERAL INFORMATION ON COUMARIN DERIVATIVES.

HEALTH EFFECTS AND FIRST AID

INHALATION: DIFENACOUM: SEE INFORMATION ON COUMARIN DERIVATIVES.
COUMARIN DERIVATIVES: HEMORRHAGIC AGENT. **ACUTE EXPOSURE-** ABSORPTION BY THE LUNGS MAY RESULT IN HEMORRHAGIC EFFECTS AS DESCRIBED IN CHRONIC EXPOSURE. SEVERE CASES MAY BE FATAL. **CHRONIC EXPOSURE-** REPEATED ABSORPTION MAY CAUSE THE INHIBITION OF PROTHROMBIN SYNTHESIS AND DAMAGE TO CAPILLARY PERMEABILITY RESULTING IN WIDESPREAD INTERNAL HEMORRHAGE WITH ASSOCIATED EFFECTS OF NOSEBLEED, HEMATOMA, HEMATURIA, WIDESPREAD BRUISING, AND ANEMIA.

FIRST AID- REMOVE FROM EXPOSURE AREA TO FRESH AIR IMMEDIATELY. IF BREATHING HAS STOPPED, PERFORM ARTIFICIAL RESPIRATION. KEEP PERSON WARM AND AT REST. TREAT SYMPTOMATICALLY AND SUPPORTIVELY. GET MEDICAL ATTENTION IMMEDIATELY.

SKIN CONTACT: DIFENACOUM: TOXIC. SEE INFORMATION ON COUMARIN DERIVATIVES.
COUMARIN DERIVATIVES: HEMORRHAGIC AGENT. **ACUTE EXPOSURE-** ABSORPTION THROUGH THE SKIN MAY RESULT IN HEMORRHAGIC EFFECTS AS DESCRIBED IN CHRONIC EXPOSURE. SEVERE CASES MAY BE FATAL. **CHRONIC EXPOSURE-** REPEATED ABSORPTION MAY CAUSE THE INHIBITION OF PROTHROMBIN SYNTHESIS AND DAMAGE TO CAPILLARY PERMEABILITY RESULTING IN WIDESPREAD INTERNAL HEMORRHAGE WITH ASSOCIATED EFFECTS OF NOSEBLEED, HEMATOMA, HEMATURIA, WIDESPREAD BRUISING, AND ANEMIA.

FIRST AID- REMOVE CONTAMINATED CLOTHING AND SHOES IMMEDIATELY. WASH AFFECTED AREA WITH SOAP OR MILD DETERGENT AND LARGE AMOUNTS OF WATER UNTIL NO EVIDENCE OF CHEMICAL REMAINS (APPROXIMATELY 15-20 MINUTES). GET MEDICAL ATTENTION IMMEDIATELY.

EYE CONTACT: DIFENACOUM: **ACUTE EXPOSURE-** NO DATA AVAILABLE. **CHRONIC EXPOSURE-** NO DATA AVAILABLE.

FIRST AID- WASH EYES IMMEDIATELY WITH LARGE AMOUNTS OF WATER OR NORMAL SALINE, OCCASIONALLY LIFTING UPPER AND LOWER LIDS, UNTIL NO EVIDENCE OF CHEMICAL REMAINS (APPROXIMATELY 15-20 MINUTES). GET MEDICAL ATTENTION IMMEDIATELY.

INGESTION: DIFENACOUM: HIGHLY TOXIC. SEE INFORMATION ON COUMARIN DERIVATIVES.
COUMARIN DERIVATIVES: HEMORRHAGIC AGENT. **ACUTE EXPOSURE-** MAY BE READILY ABSORBED FROM THE GASTROINTESTINAL TRACT AND CAUSE THE INHIBITION OF PROTHROMBIN SYNTHESIS AND DAMAGE TO CAPILLARY PERMEABILITY RESULTING IN WIDESPREAD INTERNAL HEMORRHAGE ACCOMPANIED BY THE HEMORRHAGIC SYMPTOMS AS DESCRIBED IN CHRONIC EXPOSURE. SEVERE CASES MAY BE FATAL. **CHRONIC EXPOSURE-** REPEATED INGESTION MAY CAUSE NOSEBLEED, BLEEDING GUMS AND PHARYNX, PETECHIAL RASH, WIDESPREAD BRUISING, HEMATOMA, HEMOPTYSIS, HEMATEMESIS, HEMATURIA, BLOODY STOOLS, BLEEDING INTO THE ORGANS, GASTROINTESTINAL TRACT, JOINTS, ABDOMINAL OR RETROPERITONEAL AREA WITH ABDOMINAL, BACK, JOINT AND LIMB PAIN AND CEREBROVASCULAR ACCIDENT. ANEMIA ACCOMPANIED BY WEAKNESS, PALLOR, AND SHOCK MAY OCCUR. SEVERE HEMORRHAGING MAY CAUSE DEATH. THERAPEUTIC USE OF SOME COUMARIN DERIVATIVES HAS INFREQUENTLY PRODUCED GASTROINTESTINAL DISTURBANCES, ELEVATED TRANSAMINASE, URTICARIA, DERMATITIS, LEUKOPENIA, ALOPECIA, FEVER, HYPERSENSITIVITY REACTIONS, AND RARELY SKIN NECROSIS.

FIRST AID- IF ONLY A FEW GRAINS OF ANTICOAGULANT BAIT HAVE BEEN INGESTED BY AN ADULT OR CHILD HAVING NO ANTECEDENT LIVER OR BLOOD CLOTTING DISEASE, TREATMENT IS PROBABLY UNNECESSARY. IF LARGE AMOUNTS OF ANTICOAGULANT WERE INGESTED IN THE PRECEDING 2-3 HOURS, INDUCE VOMITING WITH SYRUP OF IPECAC, FOLLOWED BY 1-2 GLASSES OF WATER. FOLLOWING EMESIS, GIVE ACTIVATED CHARCOAL IN 4-6 OUNCES OF WATER TO LIMIT ABSORPTION OF ANTICOAGULANT REMAINING IN THE GUT. OBSERVE PATIENT 4-5 DAYS AFTER INGESTION. (MORGAN, RECOGNITION AND MANAGEMENT OF PESTICIDE POISONINGS, THIRD EDITION). GET MEDICAL ATTENTION.

ANTIDOTE: THE FOLLOWING ANTIDOTE HAS BEEN RECOMMENDED. HOWEVER, THE DECISION AS TO WHETHER THE SEVERITY OF POISONING REQUIRES ADMINISTRATION OF ANY ANTIDOTE AND ACTUAL DOSE REQUIRED SHOULD BE MADE BY QUALIFIED MEDICAL PERSONNEL.
OVERDOSE OF ANTICOAGULANTS: VITAMIN K IS A SPECIFIC ANTIDOTE. VITAMIN K1 EMULSION IS THE PREFERRED FORM. THE INITIAL SUBCUTANEOUS OR INTRAMUSCULAR DOSE IN ADULTS IS 5 TO 10 MG (UP TO 25 MG), REPEATED ONCE IF NECESSARY. ONLY IN VICTIMS WHO ARE BLEEDING SEVERLY OR OTHERWISE IN SERIOUS DISTRESS SHOULD THE DRUG BE GIVEN INTRAVENOUSLY AND THEN AT A RATE NO FASTER THAN 1 MG/MINUTE. IF NECESSARY, ON SUBSEQUENT DAYS, VITAMIN K1 SHOULD BE CONTINUED AT A REDUCED LEVEL UNTIL THE PROTHROMBIN TIME RETURNS TO NORMAL. VITAMIN K1 IS PREFERABLE TO K1 OXIDE (DOSE 0.5-2.5) AND CERTAINLY PREFERABLE TO MENADIONE OR MENADIONE SODIUM BISULFITE (GOSSELIN, CLINICAL TOXICOLOGY OF COMMERCIAL PRODUCTS, 5TH ED.). ANTIDOTE SHOULD BE ADMINISTERED BY QUALIFIED MEDICAL PERSONNEL.

REACTIVITY

REACTIVITY: STABLE UNDER NORMAL TEMPERATURES AND PRESSURES.
INCOMPATIBILITIES: DIFENACOUM: OXIDIZERS (STRONG): FIRE AND EXPLOSION HAZARD.
DECOMPOSITION: THERMAL DECOMPOSITION PRODUCTS MAY INCLUDE TOXIC OXIDES OF CARBON.
POLYMERIZATION: HAZARDOUS POLYMERIZATION HAS NOT BEEN REPORTED TO OCCUR UNDER NORMAL TEMPERATURES AND PRESSURES.

STORAGE AND DISPOSAL

OBSERVE ALL FEDERAL, STATE AND LOCAL REGULATIONS WHEN STORING OR DISPOSING OF THIS SUBSTANCE. FOR ASSISTANCE, CONTACT THE DISTRICT DIRECTOR OF THE ENVIRONMENTAL PROTECTION AGENCY.

STORAGE

STORE IN ACCORDANCE WITH 40 CFR 165 RECOMMENDED PROCEDURES FOR THE DISPOSAL AND STORAGE OF PESTICIDES AND PESTICIDE CONTAINERS. STORE AWAY FROM INCOMPATIBLE SUBSTANCES.

DISPOSAL

DISPOSAL MUST BE IN ACCORDANCE WITH 40 CFR 165 RECOMMENDED PROCEDURES FOR THE DISPOSAL AND STORAGE OF PESTICIDES AND PESTICIDE CONTAINERS.

CONDITIONS TO AVOID

MAY BURN BUT DOES NOT IGNITE READILY. CONTAINERS MAY EXPLODE IN HEAT OF FIRE.

SPILL AND LEAK PROCEDURES

OCCUPATIONAL SPILL: DO NOT TOUCH SPILLED MATERIAL. STOP LEAK IF YOU CAN DO IT WITHOUT RISK. USE WATER SPRAY TO REDUCE VAPORS. FOR SMALL SPILLS, TAKE UP WITH SAND OR OTHER ABSORBENT MATERIAL AND PLACE INTO

CONTAINERS FOR LATER DISPOSAL. FOR SMALL DRY SPILLS, WITH A CLEAN SHOVEL PLACE MATERIAL INTO CLEAN, DRY CONTAINERS AND COVER. MOVE CONTAINERS FROM SPILL AREA. FOR LARGER SPILLS, DIKE FAR AHEAD OF SPILL FOR LATER DISPOSAL. KEEP UNNECESSARY PEOPLE AWAY. ISOLATE HAZARD AREA AND DENY ENTRY. VENTILATE CLOSED SPACES BEFORE ENTERING.

PROTECTIVE EQUIPMENT

VENTILATION: PROVIDE LOCAL EXHAUST OR PROCESS ENCLOSURE VENTILATION SYSTEM.

RESPIRATOR: THE FOLLOWING RESPIRATORS ARE RECOMMENDED BASED ON INFORMATION FOUND IN THE PHYSICAL DATA, TOXICITY AND HEALTH EFFECTS SECTIONS. THEY ARE RANKED IN ORDER FROM MINIMUM TO MAXIMUM RESPIRATORY PROTECTION. THE SPECIFIC RESPIRATOR SELECTED MUST BE BASED ON CONTAMINATION LEVELS FOUND IN THE WORK PLACE, MUST NOT EXCEED THE WORKING LIMITS OF THE RESPIRATOR AND BE JOINTLY APPROVED BY THE NATIONAL INSTITUTE FOR OCCUPATIONAL SAFETY AND HEALTH AND THE MINE SAFETY AND HEALTH ADMINISTRATION (NIOSH-MSHA).

TYPE 'C' SUPPLIED-AIR RESPIRATOR WITH A FULL FACEPIECE OPERATED IN PRESSURE-DEMAND OR OTHER POSITIVE PRESSURE MODE OR WITH A FULL FACEPIECE, HELMET OR HOOD OPERATED IN CONTINOUS-FLOW MODE.

SELF-CONTAINED BREATHING APPARATUS WITH A FULL FACEPIECE OPERATED IN PRESSURE-DEMAND OR OTHER POSITIVE PRESSURE MODE.

FOR FIREFIGHTING AND OTHER IMMEDIATELY DANGEROUS TO LIFE OR HEALTH CONDITIONS:

SELF-CONTAINED BREATHING APPARATUS WITH FULL FACEPIECE OPERATED IN PRESSURE-DEMAND OR OTHER POSITIVE PRESSURE MODE.

SUPPLIED-AIR RESPIRATOR WITH FULL FACEPIECE AND OPERATED IN PRESSURE-DEMAND OR OTHER POSITIVE PRESSURE MODE IN COMBINATION WITH AN AUXILIARY SELF-CONTAINED BREATHING APPARATUS OPERATED IN PRESSURE-DEMAND OR OTHER POSITIVE PRESSURE MODE.

CLOTHING: EMPLOYEE MUST WEAR APPROPRIATE PROTECTIVE (IMPERVIOUS) CLOTHING AND EQUIPMENT TO PREVENT ANY POSSIBILITY OF SKIN CONTACT WITH THIS SUBSTANCE.

GLOVES: EMPLOYEE MUST WEAR APPROPRIATE PROTECTIVE GLOVES TO PREVENT CONTACT WITH THIS SUBSTANCE.

EYE PROTECTION: EMPLOYEE MUST WEAR SPLASH-PROOF OR DUST-RESISTANT SAFETY GOGGLES WITH OR WITHOUT A FACESHIELD TO PREVENT CONTACT WITH THIS SUBSTANCE.

EMERGENCY EYE WASH: WHERE THERE IS ANY POSSIBILITY THAT AN EMPLOYEE'S EYES MAY BE EXPOSED TO THIS SUBSTANCE, THE EMPLOYER SHOULD PROVIDE AN EYE WASH FOUNTAIN WITHIN THE IMMEDIATE WORK AREA FOR EMERGENCY USE.

AUTHORIZED BY- OCCUPATIONAL HEALTH SERVICES, INC.

CREATION DATE: 10/04/89 ***REVISION DATE:*** 04/04/90

MATERIAL SAFETY DATA SHEET

OCCUPATIONAL HEALTH SERVICES, INC.	EMERGENCY CONTACT:
AGRICULTURE AND PESTICIDE DIVISION	JOHN S. BRANSFORD, JR. (615) 292-1180
450 SEVENTH AVENUE, SUITE 2407	
NEW YORK, NEW YORK 10123	
1-800-445-MSDS OR (212) 967-1100	

SUBSTANCE IDENTIFICATION

CAS-NUMBER 14214-32-5

SUBSTANCE: DIFENOXURON

TRADE NAMES/SYNONYMS: UREA, N'-(4-(4-METHOXYPHENOXY)PHENYL)-N,N-DIMETHYL-,; N'-(4-(4-METHOXYPHENOXY)PHENYL)-N,N-DIMETHYLUREA; UREA, 3-(P-(P-METHOXYPHENOXY)PHENYL-1,1-DIMETHYL-,; 3-(P-(P-METHOXYPHENOXY)PHENYL)-1,1-DIMETHYLUREA; 3-(4-(4-METHOXYPHENOXY)PHENYL)-1,1-DIMETHYLUREA; N-4(P-METHOXY-PHENOXY)-PHENY-N',N'-DIMETHYLUREA; 1,1-DIMETHYL-3-(4-(4-METHOXYPHENOXY)-PHENYL)-UREA; DIPHENOXURON; LIRONION; C16H18N2O3; PST07386

CHEMICAL FAMILY: UREA

MOLECULAR FORMULA: (C-H3)2-N-C-O-N-H-C6-H4-O-C6-H4-O-C-H3

MOLECULAR WEIGHT: 286.33

CERCLA RATINGS (SCALE 0-3): HEALTH=2 FIRE=1 REACTIVITY=0 PERSISTENCE=3

NFPA RATINGS (SCALE 0-4): HEALTH=2 FIRE=1 REACTIVITY=0

COMPONENTS AND CONTAMINANTS

COMPONENT: DIFENOXURON ***PERCENT:*** 100
CAS# 14214-32-5

OTHER CONTAMINANTS: NONE

EXPOSURE LIMITS: NO OCCUPATIONAL EXPOSURE LIMITS ESTABLISHED BY OSHA, ACGIH, OR NIOSH.

PHYSICAL DATA

DESCRIPTION: COLORLESS CRYSTALS ***MELTING POINT:*** 280-282 F (138-139 C)

SPECIFIC GRAVITY: 1.3 ***VAPOR PRESSURE:*** NEGLIGIBLE

SOLUBILITY IN WATER: 20 PPM

SOLVENT SOLUBILITY: SOLUBLE IN METHYLENE CHLORIDE, ACETONE, HEXANE; SLIGHTLY SOLUBLE IN ISOPROPANOL, BENZENE.

FIRE AND EXPLOSION DATA

FIRE AND EXPLOSION HAZARD: SLIGHT FIRE HAZARD WHEN EXPOSED TO HEAT OR FLAME.

FIREFIGHTING MEDIA: DRY CHEMICAL, CARBON DIOXIDE, HALON, WATER SPRAY OR STANDARD FOAM (1987 EMERGENCY RESPONSE GUIDEBOOK, DOT P 5800.4).
FOR LARGER FIRES, USE WATER SPRAY, FOG OR STANDARD FOAM (1987 EMERGENCY RESPONSE GUIDEBOOK, DOT P 5800.4).

FIREFIGHTING: MOVE CONTAINERS FROM FIRE AREA IF POSSIBLE (1987 EMERGENCY RESPONSE GUIDEBOOK, DOT P 5800.4, GUIDE PAGE 53).
EXTINGUISH FIRE USING AGENTS SUITABLE FOR TYPE OF SURROUNDING FIRE. USE WATER IN FLOODING AMOUNTS AS A FOG. AVOID BREATHING DUSTS AND FUMES FROM BURNING MATERIAL; KEEP UPWIND.

TOXICITY

DIFENOXURON: TOXICITY DATA: 1000 MG/KG ORAL-RAT LD50. CARCINOGEN STATUS: NONE. ACUTE TOXICITY LEVEL: MODERATELY TOXIC BY INGESTION. TARGET EFFECTS: NO DATA AVAILABLE.

HEALTH EFFECTS AND FIRST AID

INHALATION: DIFENOXURON: **ACUTE EXPOSURE-** A LETHAL CONCENTRATION IN RATS IS GREATER THAN 660 MG/M3/6 HOURS. **CHRONIC EXPOSURE-** NO DATA AVAILABLE.

FIRST AID- REMOVE FROM EXPOSURE AREA TO FRESH AIR IMMEDIATELY. IF BREATHING HAS STOPPED, PERFORM ARTIFICIAL RESPIRATION. KEEP PERSON WARM AND AT REST. TREAT SYMPTOMATICALLY AND SUPPORTIVELY. GET MEDICAL ATTENTION IMMEDIATELY.

SKIN CONTACT: DIFENOXURON: **ACUTE EXPOSURE-** THIS MATERIAL WAS NOT AN IRRITANT OF RABBIT SKIN. A LETHAL DOSE IN RATS BY DERMAL ABSORPTION WAS GREATER THAN 2150 MG/KG. **CHRONIC EXPOSURE-** NO DATA AVAILABLE.

FIRST AID- REMOVE CONTAMINATED CLOTHING AND SHOES IMMEDIATELY. WASH AFFECTED AREA WITH SOAP OR MILD DETERGENT AND LARGE AMOUNTS OF WATER UNTIL NO EVIDENCE OF CHEMICAL REMAINS (APPROXIMATELY 15-20 MINUTES). GET MEDICAL ATTENTION IMMEDIATELY.

EYE CONTACT: DIFENOXURON: **ACUTE EXPOSURE-** THIS MATERIAL WAS NOT AN IRRITANT OF RABBIT EYES. **CHRONIC EXPOSURE-** NO DATA AVAILABLE.

FIRST AID- WASH EYES IMMEDIATELY WITH LARGE AMOUNTS OF WATER OR NORMAL SALINE, OCCASIONALLY LIFTING UPPER AND LOWER LIDS, UNTIL NO EVIDENCE OF CHEMICAL REMAINS (APPROXIMATELY 15-20 MINUTES). GET MEDICAL ATTENTION IMMEDIATELY.

INGESTION: DIFENOXURON: **ACUTE EXPOSURE-** A LETHAL DOSE IN RATS WAS 1000 MG/KG. **CHRONIC EXPOSURE-** NO ADVERSE EFFECTS WERE OBSERVED IN A 90-DAY STUDY OF RATS FED 50 MG/KG/DAY OR DOGS FED 200 MG/KG/DAY.

FIRST AID- REMOVE BY GASTRIC LAVAGE AND CATHARSIS. MAINTAIN BLOOD PRESSURE AND AIRWAY. GIVE OXYGEN IF RESPIRATION IS DEPRESSED. DO NOT PERFORM GASTRIC LAVAGE IF VICTIM IS UNCONSCIOUS. GET MEDICAL ATTENTION IMMEDIATELY (DREISBACH, HANDBOOK OF POISONING, 12TH ED.).
ADMINISTRATION OF LAVAGE OR OXYGEN SHOULD BE PERFORMED BY QUALIFIED MEDICAL PERSONNEL.

ANTIDOTE: NO SPECIFIC ANTIDOTE. TREAT SYMPTOMATICALLY AND SUPPORTIVELY.

REACTIVITY

REACTIVITY: STABLE UNDER NORMAL TEMPERATURES AND PRESSURES.

INCOMPATIBILITIES: DIFENOXURON: NO DATA AVAILABLE.

DECOMPOSITION: THERMAL DECOMPOSITION PRODUCTS MAY INCLUDE TOXIC OXIDES OF CARBON AND NITROGEN.

POLYMERIZATION: HAZARDOUS POLYMERIZATION HAS NOT BEEN REPORTED TO OCCUR UNDER NORMAL TEMPERATURES AND PRESSURES.

STORAGE AND DISPOSAL

OBSERVE ALL FEDERAL, STATE AND LOCAL REGULATIONS WHEN STORING OR DISPOSING OF THIS SUBSTANCE. FOR ASSISTANCE, CONTACT THE DISTRICT DIRECTOR OF THE ENVIRONMENTAL PROTECTION AGENCY.

STORAGE

STORE IN ACCORDANCE WITH 40 CFR 165 RECOMMENDED PROCEDURES FOR THE DISPOSAL AND STORAGE OF PESTICIDES AND PESTICIDE CONTAINERS.

DISPOSAL

DISPOSAL MUST BE IN ACCORDANCE WITH 40 CFR 165 RECOMMENDED PROCEDURES FOR THE DISPOSAL AND STORAGE OF PESTICIDES AND PESTICIDE CONTAINERS.

CONDITIONS TO AVOID

MAY BURN BUT DOES NOT IGNITE READILY.

SPILL AND LEAK PROCEDURES

OCCUPATIONAL SPILL: DO NOT TOUCH SPILLED MATERIAL. STOP LEAK IF YOU CAN DO IT WITHOUT RISK. FOR SMALL SPILLS, TAKE UP WITH SAND OR OTHER ABSORBENT MATERIAL AND PLACE INTO CONTAINERS FOR LATER DISPOSAL. FOR SMALL DRY SPILLS, WITH A CLEAN SHOVEL PLACE MATERIAL INTO CLEAN, DRY CONTAINER AND COVER. MOVE CONTAINERS FROM SPILL AREA. FOR LARGER SPILLS, DIKE FAR AHEAD OF SPILL FOR LATER DISPOSAL. KEEP UNNECESSARY PEOPLE AWAY. ISOLATE HAZARD AREA AND DENY ENTRY.

PROTECTIVE EQUIPMENT

VENTILATION: PROVIDE LOCAL EXHAUST OR GENERAL DILUTION VENTILATION SYSTEM.

RESPIRATOR: THE FOLLOWING RESPIRATORS ARE RECOMMENDED BASED ON INFORMATION FOUND IN THE PHYSICAL DATA, TOXICITY AND HEALTH EFFECTS SECTIONS. THEY ARE RANKED IN ORDER FROM MINIMUM TO MAXIMUM RESPIRATORY PROTECTION. THE SPECIFIC RESPIRATOR SELECTED MUST BE BASED ON CONTAMINATION LEVELS FOUND IN THE WORK PLACE, MUST NOT EXCEED THE WORKING LIMITS OF THE RESPIRATOR AND BE JOINTLY APPROVED BY THE NATIONAL INSTITUTE FOR OCCUPATIONAL SAFETY AND HEALTH AND THE MINE SAFETY AND HEALTH ADMINISTRATION (NIOSH-MSHA).

CHEMICAL CARTRIDGE RESPIRATOR WITH AN ORGANIC VAPOR CARTRIDGE(S) IN COMBINATION WITH A DUST AND MIST FILTER.

GAS MASK WITH ORGANIC VAPOR CANISTER (CHIN-STYLE OR FRONT- OR BACK-MOUNTED CANISTER) WITH A DUST AND MIST FILTER.

GAS MASK WITH ORGANIC VAPOR CANISTER (CHIN-STYLE OR FRONT- OR BACK-MOUNTED CANISTER) WITH A PARTICULATE FILTER.

POWERED AIR-PURIFYING RESPIRATOR WITH A HIGH-EFFICIENCY FILTER.

TYPE 'C' SUPPLIED-AIR RESPIRATOR WITH A FULL FACEPIECE OPERATED IN A PRESSURE-DEMAND OR OTHER POSITIVE PRESSURE MODE.

SELF-CONTAINED BREATHING APPARATUS WITH A FULL FACEPIECE OPERATED IN PRESSURE-DEMAND OR OTHER POSITIVE PRESSURE MODE.

FOR FIREFIGHTING AND OTHER IMMEDIATELY DANGEROUS TO LIFE OR HEALTH CONDITIONS:

SELF-CONTAINED BREATHING APPARATUS WITH FULL FACEPIECE OPERATED IN PRESSURE-DEMAND OR OTHER POSITIVE PRESSURE MODE.

SUPPLIED-AIR RESPIRATOR WITH FULL FACEPIECE AND OPERATED IN PRESSURE-DEMAND OR OTHER POSITIVE PRESSURE MODE IN COMBINATION WITH AN AUXILIARY SELF-CONTAINED BREATHING APPARATUS OPERATED IN PRESSURE-DEMAND OR OTHER POSITIVE PRESSURE MODE.

CLOTHING: EMPLOYEE MUST WEAR APPROPRIATE PROTECTIVE (IMPERVIOUS) CLOTHING AND EQUIPMENT TO PREVENT REPEATED OR PROLONGED SKIN CONTACT WITH THIS SUBSTANCE.

GLOVES: EMPLOYEE MUST WEAR APPROPRIATE PROTECTIVE GLOVES TO PREVENT CONTACT WITH THIS SUBSTANCE.

EYE PROTECTION: EMPLOYEE MUST WEAR SPLASH-PROOF OR DUST-RESISTANT SAFETY GOGGLES TO PREVENT EYE CONTACT WITH THIS SUBSTANCE.

EMERGENCY EYE WASH: WHERE THERE IS ANY POSSIBILITY THAT AN EMPLOYEE'S EYES MAY BE EXPOSED TO THIS SUBSTANCE, THE EMPLOYER SHOULD PROVIDE AN EYE WASH FOUNTAIN WITHIN THE IMMEDIATE WORK AREA FOR EMERGENCY USE.

AUTHORIZED BY- OCCUPATIONAL HEALTH SERVICES, INC.

CREATION DATE: 10/04/89 ***REVISION DATE:*** 05/08/90

MATERIAL SAFETY DATA SHEET

OCCUPATIONAL HEALTH SERVICES, INC.
AGRICULTURE AND PESTICIDE DIVISION
450 SEVENTH AVENUE, SUITE 2407
NEW YORK, NEW YORK 10123
1-800-445-MSDS OR (212) 967-1100

EMERGENCY CONTACT:
JOHN S. BRANSFORD, JR. (615) 292-1180

SUBSTANCE IDENTIFICATION

CAS-NUMBER 35367-38-5

SUBSTANCE: **DIFLUBENZURON**

TRADE NAMES/SYNONYMS: BENZAMIDE, N-(((4-CHLOROPHENYL)AMINO)CARBONYL)-2,6-DIFLUORO; N-(((4-CHLOROPHENYL)AMINO)CARBONYL)-2,6-DIFLUOROBENZAMIDE; 1-(4-CHLOROPHENYL)-3-(2,6-DIFLUOROBENZOYL)UREA; AI 3-29054; DIFLURON; DIMILIN; DUPHAR PH 60-40; LARVAKIL; PH 6040; PH 60-40; TH 6040; THOMPSON-HAYWARD 6040; OMS 1804; ENT 29054; C14H9CLF2N2O2; PST07388

CHEMICAL FAMILY: SUBSTITUTED UREA
HALOGEN COMPOUND, AROMATIC

MOLECULAR FORMULA: C14-H9-CL-F2-N2-O2

MOLECULAR WEIGHT: 310.70

CERCLA RATINGS (SCALE 0-3): HEALTH=2 FIRE=1 REACTIVITY=0 PERSISTENCE=3

NFPA RATINGS (SCALE 0-4): HEALTH=2 FIRE=1 REACTIVITY=0

COMPONENTS AND CONTAMINANTS

COMPONENT: DIFLUBENZURON ***PERCENT:*** 100.0
CAS# 35367-38-5

OTHER CONTAMINANTS: NONE

EXPOSURE LIMITS: NO OCCUPATIONAL EXPOSURE LIMITS ESTABLISHED BY OSHA, ACGIH, OR NIOSH.

PHYSICAL DATA

DESCRIPTION: OFF-WHITE TO YELLOW CRYSTALLINE SOLID.

MELTING POINT: 446-450 F (230-232 C) ***SPECIFIC GRAVITY:*** NOT AVAILABLE

VAPOR PRESSURE: NEGLIGIBLE ***SOLUBILITY IN WATER:*** 0.1 PPM

SOLVENT SOLUBILITY: SOLUBLE IN ACETONE, DIMETHYLFORMAMIDE; SLIGHTLY SOLUBLE IN ACETONE, DIOXANE AND MOST POLAR SOLVENTS; ALMOST INSOLUBLE IN NONPOLAR SOLVENTS.

FIRE AND EXPLOSION DATA

FIRE AND EXPLOSION HAZARD: SLIGHT FIRE HAZARD WHEN EXPOSED TO HEAT OR FLAME.

FIREFIGHTING MEDIA: DRY CHEMICAL, CARBON DIOXIDE, HALON, WATER SPRAY OR STANDARD FOAM (1987 EMERGENCY RESPONSE GUIDEBOOK, DOT P 5800.4). FOR LARGER FIRES, USE WATER SPRAY, FOG OR STANDARD FOAM (1987 EMERGENCY RESPONSE GUIDEBOOK, DOT P 5800.4).

FIREFIGHTING: MOVE CONTAINERS FROM FIRE AREA IF POSSIBLE. FIGHT FIRE FROM MAXIMUM DISTANCE. STAY AWAY FROM STORAGE TANK ENDS. DIKE FIRE CONTROL WATER FOR LATER DISPOSAL. DO NOT SCATTER MATERIAL (1987 EMERGENCY RESPONSE GUIDEBOOK, DOT P 5800.4, GUIDE PAGE 55). EXTINGUISH USING AGENT SUITABLE FOR TYPE OF SURROUNDING FIRE. USE WATER IN FLOODING QUANTITIES AS FOG. KEEP SPARKS, FLAMES AND OTHER SOURCES OF IGNITION AWAY. KEEP MATERIAL OUT OF WATER SOURCES AND SEWERS. DO NOT TOUCH MATERIAL AND AVOID BREATHING DUSTS AND FUMES FROM BURNING MATERIAL. KEEP UPWIND.

TOXICITY

DIFLUBENZURON: TOXICITY DATA: 2000 MG/KG SKIN-RABBIT LD50; 4640 MG/KG ORAL-RAT LD50; 4640 MG/KG ORAL-MOUSE LD50; 2150 MG/KG INTRAPERITONEAL-MOUSE LD50; 4600 MG/KG UNREPORTED-MOUSE LD50; MUTAGENIC DATA (RTECS). CARCINOGEN STATUS: NONE. ACUTE TOXICITY LEVEL: MODERATELY TOXIC BY DERMAL ABSORPTION AND INGESTION. TARGET EFFECTS: NO DATA AVAILABLE.

HEALTH EFFECTS AND FIRST AID

INHALATION: DIFLUBENZURON: **ACUTE EXPOSURE-** METHEMOGLOBINEMIA WAS DETECTED IN RATS EXPOSED TO A CONCENTRATION OF 100 MG/M3. MANY SUBSTITUTED UREAS ARE MODERATELY IRRITATING TO THE MUCOUS MEMBRANES. **CHRONIC EXPOSURE-** NO DATA AVAILABLE.

FIRST AID- REMOVE FROM EXPOSURE AREA TO FRESH AIR IMMEDIATELY. IF BREATHING HAS STOPPED, PERFORM ARTIFICIAL RESPIRATION. KEEP PERSON WARM AND AT REST. TREAT SYMPTOMATICALLY AND SUPPORTIVELY. GET MEDICAL ATTENTION IMMEDIATELY.

SKIN CONTACT: DIFLUBENZURON: **ACUTE EXPOSURE-** 69 MG/KG OF THIS MATERIAL APPLIED TO RABBIT SKIN PRODUCED METHEMOGLOBINEMIA. MANY SUBSTITUTED

UREA HERBICIDES ARE MODERATELY IRRITATING TO THE SKIN. **CHRONIC EXPOSURE-** NO DATA AVAILABLE.
FIRST AID- REMOVE CONTAMINATED CLOTHING AND SHOES IMMEDIATELY. WASH AFFECTED AREA WITH SOAP OR MILD DETERGENT AND LARGE AMOUNTS OF WATER UNTIL NO EVIDENCE OF CHEMICAL REMAINS (APPROXIMATELY 15-20 MINUTES). GET MEDICAL ATTENTION IMMEDIATELY.

EYE CONTACT: DIFLUBENZURON: **ACUTE EXPOSURE-** MANY SUBSTITUTED UREA HERBICIDES ARE MODERATELY IRRITATING TO THE EYES. **CHRONIC EXPOSURE-** NO DATA AVAILABLE.
FIRST AID- WASH EYES IMMEDIATELY WITH LARGE AMOUNTS OF WATER OR NORMAL SALINE, OCCASIONALLY LIFTING UPPER AND LOWER LIDS, UNTIL NO EVIDENCE OF CHEMICAL REMAINS (APPROXIMATELY 15-20 MINUTES). GET MEDICAL ATTENTION IMMEDIATELY.

INGESTION: DIFLUBENZURON: **ACUTE EXPOSURE-** A LETHAL DOSE IN RATS WAS 4640 MG/KG. METHEMOGLOBINEMIA AND SULFHEMOGLOBINEMIA WERE DETECTED IN RABBITS FED 19.2 MG/KG. **CHRONIC EXPOSURE-** AN INCREASE OF LYMPHORETICULAR TUMORS IN FEMALES SUGGESTING A POSITIVE ONCOGENIC EFFECT WAS OBSERVED IN A STUDY OF MICE. EFFECTS ON HEMOGLOBIN HAVE BEEN REPORTED FOLLOWING REPEATED ADMINISTRATION IN SEVERAL SPECIES.
FIRST AID- REMOVE BY GASTRIC LAVAGE AND CATHARSIS. MAINTAIN BLOOD PRESSURE AND AIRWAY. GIVE OXYGEN IF RESPIRATION IS DEPRESSED. DO NOT PERFORM GASTRIC LAVAGE IF VICTIM IS UNCONSCIOUS. GET MEDICAL ATTENTION IMMEDIATELY (DREISBACH, HANDBOOK OF POISONING, 12TH ED.).
ADMINISTRATION OF LAVAGE OR OXYGEN SHOULD BE PERFORMED BY QUALIFIED MEDICAL PERSONNEL.
ANTIDOTE: NO SPECIFIC ANTIDOTE. TREAT SYMPTOMATICALLY AND SUPPORTIVELY.

REACTIVITY

REACTIVITY: STABLE UNDER NORMAL TEMPERATURES AND PRESSURES.
INCOMPATIBILITIES: DIFLUBENZURON: BASIC SOLUTIONS (STRONG): UNSTABLE. OXIDIZERS (STRONG): FIRE AND EXPLOSION HAZARD.
DECOMPOSITION: THERMAL DECOMPOSITION PRODUCTS MAY INCLUDE TOXIC AND CORROSIVE FUMES OF CHLORIDES AND FLUORIDES AND TOXIC OXIDES OF NITROGEN.
POLYMERIZATION: HAZARDOUS POLYMERIZATION HAS NOT BEEN REPORTED TO OCCUR UNDER NORMAL TEMPERATURES AND PRESSURES.

STORAGE AND DISPOSAL

OBSERVE ALL FEDERAL, STATE AND LOCAL REGULATIONS WHEN STORING OR DISPOSING OF THIS SUBSTANCE. FOR ASSISTANCE, CONTACT THE DISTRICT DIRECTOR OF THE ENVIRONMENTAL PROTECTION AGENCY.

STORAGE

STORE IN ACCORDANCE WITH 40 CFR 165 RECOMMENDED PROCEDURES FOR THE DISPOSAL AND STORAGE OF PESTICIDES AND PESTICIDE CONTAINERS.
STORE AWAY FROM INCOMPATIBLE SUBSTANCES.

DISPOSAL

DISPOSAL MUST BE IN ACCORDANCE WITH 40 CFR 165 RECOMMENDED PROCEDURES FOR THE DISPOSAL AND STORAGE OF PESTICIDES AND PESTICIDE CONTAINERS.

CONDITIONS TO AVOID

MAY BURN BUT DOES NOT IGNITE READILY. CONTAINERS MAY EXPLODE IN HEAT OF FIRE.

SPILL AND LEAK PROCEDURES

OCCUPATIONAL SPILL: DO NOT TOUCH SPILLED MATERIAL. STOP LEAK IF YOU CAN DO IT WITHOUT RISK. USE WATER SPRAY TO REDUCE VAPORS. FOR SMALL SPILLS, TAKE UP WITH SAND OR OTHER ABSORBENT MATERIAL AND PLACE INTO CONTAINERS FOR LATER DISPOSAL. FOR SMALL DRY SPILLS, WITH A CLEAN SHOVEL PLACE MATERIAL INTO CLEAN, DRY CONTAINERS AND COVER. MOVE CONTAINERS FROM SPILL AREA. FOR LARGER SPILLS, DIKE FAR AHEAD OF SPILL FOR LATER DISPOSAL. KEEP UNNECESSARY PEOPLE AWAY. ISOLATE HAZARD AREA AND DENY ENTRY. VENTILATE CLOSED SPACES BEFORE ENTERING.

PROTECTIVE EQUIPMENT

VENTILATION: PROVIDE LOCAL EXHAUST OR GENERAL DILUTION VENTILATION SYSTEM.
RESPIRATOR: THE FOLLOWING RESPIRATORS ARE RECOMMENDED BASED ON INFORMATION FOUND IN THE PHYSICAL DATA, TOXICITY AND HEALTH EFFECTS SECTIONS. THEY ARE RANKED IN ORDER FROM MINIMUM TO MAXIMUM RESPIRATORY PROTECTION. THE SPECIFIC RESPIRATOR SELECTED MUST BE BASED ON CONTAMINATION LEVELS FOUND IN THE WORK PLACE, MUST NOT EXCEED THE WORKING LIMITS OF THE RESPIRATOR AND BE JOINTLY APPROVED BY THE NATIONAL INSTITUTE FOR OCCUPATIONAL SAFETY AND HEALTH AND THE MINE SAFETY AND HEALTH ADMINISTRATION (NIOSH-MSHA).
CHEMICAL CARTRIDGE RESPIRATOR WITH AN ORGANIC VAPOR CARTRIDGE(S) WITH A FULL FACEPIECE AND ORGANIC VAPOR CARTRIDGE(S) IN COMBINATION WITH A DUST AND MIST FILTER.
POWERED AIR-PURIFYING RESPIRATOR WITH A TIGHT-FITTING FACEPIECE AND ORGANIC VAPOR CARTRIDGE(S) IN COMBINATION WITH A HIGH-EFFICIENCY PARTICULATE FILTER.
TYPE 'C' SUPPLIED-AIR RESPIRATOR WITH A FULL FACEPIECE OPERATED IN A PRESSURE-DEMAND OR OTHER POSITIVE PRESSURE MODE.
SELF-CONTAINED BREATHING APPARATUS WITH A FULL FACEPIECE OPERATED IN PRESSURE-DEMAND OR OTHER POSITIVE PRESSURE MODE.
FOR FIREFIGHTING AND OTHER IMMEDIATELY DANGEROUS TO LIFE OR HEALTH CONDITIONS:
SELF-CONTAINED BREATHING APPARATUS WITH FULL FACEPIECE OPERATED IN PRESSURE-DEMAND OR OTHER POSITIVE PRESSURE MODE.
SUPPLIED-AIR RESPIRATOR WITH FULL FACEPIECE AND OPERATED IN PRESSURE-DEMAND OR OTHER POSITIVE PRESSURE MODE IN COMBINATION WITH AN AUXILIARY SELF-CONTAINED BREATHING APPARATUS OPERATED IN PRESSURE-DEMAND OR OTHER POSITIVE PRESSURE MODE.
CLOTHING: EMPLOYEE MUST WEAR APPROPRIATE PROTECTIVE (IMPERVIOUS) CLOTHING AND EQUIPMENT TO PREVENT REPEATED OR PROLONGED SKIN CONTACT WITH THIS SUBSTANCE.
GLOVES: EMPLOYEE MUST WEAR APPROPRIATE PROTECTIVE GLOVES TO PREVENT CONTACT WITH THIS SUBSTANCE.
EYE PROTECTION: EMPLOYEE MUST WEAR SPLASH-PROOF OR DUST-RESISTANT SAFETY GOGGLES TO PREVENT EYE CONTACT WITH THIS SUBSTANCE.
EMERGENCY EYE WASH: WHERE THERE IS ANY POSSIBILITY THAT AN EMPLOYEE'S EYES MAY BE EXPOSED TO THIS SUBSTANCE, THE EMPLOYER SHOULD PROVIDE AN EYE WASH FOUNTAIN WITHIN THE IMMEDIATE WORK AREA FOR EMERGENCY USE.

AUTHORIZED BY- OCCUPATIONAL HEALTH SERVICES, INC.
CREATION DATE: 10/04/89 ***REVISION DATE:*** 05/11/90

MATERIAL SAFETY DATA SHEET

OCCUPATIONAL HEALTH SERVICES, INC.
AGRICULTURE AND PESTICIDE DIVISION
450 SEVENTH AVENUE, SUITE 2407
NEW YORK, NEW YORK 10123
1-800-445-MSDS OR (212) 967-1100

EMERGENCY CONTACT:
JOHN S. BRANSFORD, JR. (615) 292-1180

SUBSTANCE IDENTIFICATION

CAS-NUMBER 108-83-8
SUBSTANCE: **DIISOBUTYL KETONE**
TRADE NAMES/SYNONYMS: 2,6-DIMETHYL-4-HEPTANONE; SYM-DIISOPROPYL-ACETONE; ISOVALERONE; ISOBUTYL KETONE; 2,6-DIMETHYL-HEPT-4-ONE; S-DIISOPROPYLACETONE; VALERONE; STCC 4913140; UN 1157; PST07500
CHEMICAL FAMILY: KETONE, ALIPHATIC
MOLECULAR FORMULA: C9-H18-O MOL WT: 142.27
CERCLA RATINGS (SCALE 0-3): HEALTH=1 FIRE=2 REACTIVITY=0 PERSISTENCE=0
NFPA RATINGS (SCALE 0-4): HEALTH=1 FIRE=2 REACTIVITY=0

COMPONENTS AND CONTAMINANTS

COMPONENT: DIISOBUTYL KETONE ***PERCENT:*** 100
CAS# 108-83-8
OTHER CONTAMINANTS: NONE
EXPOSURE LIMITS: NO OCCUPATIONAL EXPOSURE LIMITS ESTABLISHED BY OSHA, ACGIH, OR NIOSH.

PHYSICAL DATA

DESCRIPTION: COLORLESS LIQUID WITH A MILD KETONE ODOR.
BOILING POINT: 335 F (168 C) ***MELTING POINT:*** -43 F (-42 C)
SPECIFIC GRAVITY: 0.8 ***VAPOR PRESSURE:*** 1.7 MMHG @ 20 C
SOLUBILITY IN WATER: INSOLUBLE ***ODOR THRESHOLD:*** <0.11 PPM
VAPOR DENSITY: 4.9
SOLVENT SOLUBILITY: MISCIBLE WITH MOST ORGANIC LIQUIDS

FIRE AND EXPLOSION DATA

FIRE AND EXPLOSION HAZARD: MODERATE FIRE HAZARD WHEN EXPOSED TO HEAT OR FLAME.
VAPOR-AIR MIXTURES ARE EXPLOSIVE ABOVE FLASH POINT.
VAPORS ARE HEAVIER THAN AIR AND MAY TRAVEL A CONSIDERABLE DISTANCE TO A SOURCE OF IGNITION AND FLASH BACK.

FLASH POINT: 120 F (49 C) (CC) ***UPPER EXPLOSIVE LIMIT:*** 7.1% @ 93 C
LOWER EXPLOSIVE LIMIT: 0.8% @ 93 C ***AUTOIGNITION TEMP.:*** 745 F (396 C)
FLAMMABILITY CLASS(OSHA): II

FIREFIGHTING MEDIA: DRY CHEMICAL, CARBON DIOXIDE, HALON, WATER SPRAY OR ALCOHOL FOAM (1987 EMERGENCY RESPONSE GUIDEBOOK, DOT P 5800.4).
FOR LARGER FIRES, USE WATER SPRAY, FOG OR ALCOHOL FOAM (1987 EMERGENCY RESPONSE GUIDEBOOK, DOT P 5800.4).

FIREFIGHTING: MOVE CONTAINER FROM FIRE AREA IF POSSIBLE. COOL FIRE-EXPOSED CONTAINERS WITH WATER FROM SIDE UNTIL WELL AFTER FIRE IS OUT. STAY AWAY FROM STORAGE TANK ENDS. FOR MASSIVE FIRE IN STORAGE AREA, USE UNMANNED HOSE HOLDER OR MONITOR NOZZLES, ELSE WITHDRAW FROM AREA AND LET FIRE BURN. WITHDRAW IMMEDIATELY IN CASE OF RISING SOUND FROM VENTING SAFETY DEVICE OR ANY DISCOLORATION OF STORAGE TANK DUE TO FIRE (1987 EMERGENCY RESPONSE GUIDEBOOK, DOT P 5800.4, GUIDE PAGE 26).
EXTINGUISH ONLY IF FLOW CAN BE STOPPED; USE WATER IN FLOODING QUANTITIES AS A FOG, SOLID STREAMS MAY SPREAD FIRE. COOL CONTAINERS WITH FLOODING AMOUNTS OF WATER, APPLY FROM AS FAR A DISTANCE AS POSSIBLE. AVOID BREATHING TOXIC VAPORS, KEEP UPWIND.

TRANSPORTATION DATA

DEPARTMENT OF TRANSPORTATION HAZARD CLASSIFICATION 49 CFR 172.101: COMBUSTIBLE LIQUID
DEPARTMENT OF TRANSPORTATION LABELING REQUIREMENTS 49 CFR 172.101 AND SUBPART E: NONE
DEPARTMENT OF TRANSPORTATION PACKAGING REQUIREMENTS: NONE EXCEPTIONS: 49 CFR 173.118A

TOXICITY

DIISOBUTYL KETONE: IRRITATION DATA: 25 PPM/15 MINUTES EYE-HUMAN MILD; 10 MG/24 HOURS SKIN-RABBIT MILD; 500 MG OPEN SKIN-RABBIT MILD; 500 MG EYE-RABBIT. TOXICITY DATA: 50 PPM INHALATION-HUMAN TCLO; 2000 PPM/4 HOURS INHALATION-RAT LCLO; 16 GM/KG SKIN-RABBIT LD50; 5750 MG/KG ORAL-RAT LD50; 1416 MG/KG ORAL-MOUSE LD50. CARCINOGEN STATUS: NONE. LOCAL EFFECTS: IRRITANT- INHALATION, SKIN, AND EYES. ACUTE TOXICITY LEVEL: SLIGHTLY TOXIC BY DERMAL ABSORPTION AND INGESTION. TARGET EFFECTS: MAY AFFECT THE CENTRAL NERVOUS SYSTEM. AT INCREASED RISK FROM EXPOSURE: PERSONS WITH CHRONIC SKIN OR RESPIRATORY DISEASES.

HEALTH EFFECTS AND FIRST AID

INHALATION: DIISOBUTYL KETONE: IRRITANT/NARCOTIC. 2000 PPM IMMEDIATELY DANGEROUS TO LIFE OR HEALTH. **ACUTE EXPOSURE-** VAPORS MAY CAUSE IRRITATION AND AFFECT THE CENTRAL NERVOUS SYSTEM WITH HEADACHE, DIZZINESS, DROWSINESS, NAUSEA, VOMITING, ATAXIA, NARCOSIS, PULMONARY EDEMA, AND UNCONSCIOUSNESS. **CHRONIC EXPOSURE-** REPEATED OR PROLONGED CONTACT MAY CAUSE MUCOUS MEMBRANE IRRITATION. ANIMAL STUDIES INDICATE LUNG, LIVER AND KIDNEY DAMAGE MAY OCCUR.

FIRST AID- REMOVE FROM EXPOSURE AREA TO FRESH AIR IMMEDIATELY. IF BREATHING HAS STOPPED, PERFORM ARTIFICIAL RESPIRATION. KEEP PERSON WARM AND AT REST. TREAT SYMPTOMATICALLY AND SUPPORTIVELY. GET MEDICAL ATTENTION IMMEDIATELY.

SKIN CONTACT: DIISOBUTYL KETONE: IRRITANT. **ACUTE EXPOSURE-** CONTACT WITH VAPORS OR LIQUID MAY CAUSE IRRITATION AND PAIN. CHEMICAL DEFATS THE SKIN AND MAY BE ABSORBED. **CHRONIC EXPOSURE-** REPEATED OR PROLONGED CONTACT MAY CAUSE DERMATITIS.

FIRST AID- REMOVE CONTAMINATED CLOTHING AND SHOES IMMEDIATELY. WASH AFFECTED AREA WITH SOAP OR MILD DETERGENT AND LARGE AMOUNTS OF WATER UNTIL NO EVIDENCE OF CHEMICAL REMAINS (APPROXIMATELY 15-20 MINUTES). GET MEDICAL ATTENTION IMMEDIATELY.

EYE CONTACT: DIISOBUTYL KETONE: IRRITANT. **ACUTE EXPOSURE-** VAPORS MAY IRRITATE THE EYES. DIRECT CONTACT MAY CAUSE PAIN AND IRRITATION. **CHRONIC EXPOSURE-** REPEATED OR PROLONGED CONTACT MAY CAUSE CONJUNCTIVITIS.

FIRST AID- WASH EYES IMMEDIATELY WITH LARGE AMOUNTS OF WATER OR NORMAL SALINE, OCCASIONALLY LIFTING UPPER AND LOWER LIDS, UNTIL NO EVIDENCE OF CHEMICAL REMAINS (APPROXIMATELY 15-20 MINUTES). GET MEDICAL ATTENTION IMMEDIATELY.

INGESTION: DIISOBUTYL KETONE: NARCOTIC. **ACUTE EXPOSURE-** MAY IRRITATE THE MOUTH, THROAT, AND ABDOMEN. LARGE AMOUNTS MAY CAUSE NAUSEA, CENTRAL NERVOUS SYSTEM DEPRESSION WITH DROWSINESS, DIZZINESS, HEADACHE, AND UNCONSCIOUSNESS. **CHRONIC EXPOSURE-** ANIMAL STUDIES INDICATE PULMONARY CONGESTION AND EDEMA, DEHYDRATION, AND LIVER AND KIDNEY DAMAGE ARE POSSIBLE.

FIRST AID- IF THE PERSON IS CONSCIOUS AND NOT CONVULSING, INDUCE EMESIS BY GIVING SYRUP OF IPECAC FOLLOWED BY WATER. (IF VOMITING OCCURS KEEP THE HEAD BELOW THE HIPS TO PREVENT ASPIRATION). REPEAT IN 20 MINUTES IF NOT EFFECTIVE INITIALLY. GIVE ACTIVATED CHARCOAL. IN PATIENTS WITH DEPRESSED RESPIRATION OR IF EMESIS IS NOT PRODUCED, PERFORM GASTRIC LAVAGE CAUTIOUSLY (DREISBACH, HANDBOOK OF POISONING, 12TH ED.). TREAT SYMPTOMATICALLY AND SUPPORTIVELY. GASTRIC LAVAGE SHOULD BE PERFORMED BY QUALIFIED MEDICAL PERSONNEL. GET MEDICAL ATTENTION IMMEDIATELY.

ANTIDOTE: NO SPECIFIC ANTIDOTE. TREAT SYMPTOMATICALLY AND SUPPORTIVELY.

REACTIVITY

REACTIVITY: STABLE UNDER NORMAL TEMPERATURES AND PRESSURES.
INCOMPATIBILITIES: DIISOBUTYL KETONE: STRONG OXIDANTS: VIGOROUS REACTION.
DECOMPOSITION: THERMAL DECOMPOSITION PRODUCTS MAY INCLUDE TOXIC OXIDES OF CARBON.
POLYMERIZATION: HAZARDOUS POLYMERIZATION HAS NOT BEEN REPORTED TO OCCUR UNDER NORMAL TEMPERATURES AND PRESSURES.

CONDITIONS TO AVOID

AVOID CONTACT WITH HEAT, SPARKS, FLAMES, OR OTHER SOURCES OF IGNITION. VAPORS MAY BE EXPLOSIVE AND POISONOUS; DO NOT ALLOW UNNECESSARY PERSONNEL IN AREA. DO NOT OVERHEAT CONTAINERS; CONTAINERS MAY VIOLENTLY RUPTURE AND TRAVEL A CONSIDERABLE DISTANCE IN HEAT OF FIRE.

SPILL AND LEAK PROCEDURES

OCCUPATIONAL SPILL: SHUT OFF IGNITION SOURCES. STOP LEAK IF YOU CAN DO IT WITHOUT RISK. USE WATER SPRAY TO REDUCE VAPORS. FOR SMALL SPILLS, TAKE UP WITH SAND OR OTHER ABSORBENT MATERIAL AND PLACE INTO CONTAINERS FOR LATER DISPOSAL. FOR LARGER SPILLS, DIKE FAR AHEAD OF SPILL FOR LATER DISPOSAL. NO SMOKING, FLAMES OR FLARES IN HAZARD AREA. KEEP UNNECESSARY PEOPLE AWAY; ISOLATE HAZARD AREA AND DENY ENTRY.

PROTECTIVE EQUIPMENT

VENTILATION: PROVIDE LOCAL EXHAUST VENTILATION AND/OR GENERAL DILUTION VENTILATION TO MEET PUBLISHED EXPOSURE LIMITS.

RESPIRATOR: THE FOLLOWING RESPIRATORS AND MAXIMUM USE CONCENTRATIONS ARE RECOMMENDATIONS BY THE U.S. DEPARTMENT OF HEALTH AND HUMAN SERVICES, NIOSH POCKET GUIDE TO CHEMICAL HAZARDS; NIOSH CRITERIA DOCUMENTS OR BY THE U.S. DEPARTMENT OF LABOR, 29 CFR 1910 SUBPART Z. THE SPECIFIC RESPIRATOR SELECTED MUST BE BASED ON CONTAMINATION LEVELS FOUND IN THE WORK PLACE, MUST NOT EXCEED THE WORKING LIMITS OF THE RESPIRATOR AND BE JOINTLY APPROVED BY THE NATIONAL INSTITUTE FOR OCCUPATIONAL SAFETY AND HEALTH AND THE MINE SAFETY AND HEALTH ADMINISTRATION (NIOSH-MSHA).
DIISOBUTYL KETONE: 625 PPM- SUPPLIED-AIR RESPIRATOR OPERATED IN CONTINUOUS-FLOW MODE. POWERED AIR-PURIFYING RESPIRATOR WITH ORGANIC VAPOR CARTRIDGE(S).
1000 PPM- CHEMICAL CARTRIDGE RESPIRATOR WITH AN ORGANIC VAPOR CARTRIDGE AND A FULL FACEPIECE.
1250 PPM- AIR-PURIFYING FULL FACEPIECE RESPIRATOR (GAS MASK) WITH CHIN-STYLE OR FRONT- OR BACK-MOUNTED ORGANIC VAPOR CANISTER. SELF-CONTAINED BREATHING APPARATUS WITH FULL FACEPIECE. SUPPLIED-AIR RESPIRATOR WITH FULL FACEPIECE.
2000 PPM- SUPPLIED-AIR RESPIRATOR WITH FULL FACEPIECE AND OPERATED IN PRESSURE-DEMAND OR OTHER POSITIVE PRESSURE MODE.
ESCAPE- AIR-PURIFYING FULL FACEPIECE RESPIRATOR (GAS MASK) WITH CHIN-STYLE OR FRONT- OR BACK-MOUNTED ORGANIC VAPOR CANISTER. ESCAPE-TYPE SELF-CONTAINED BREATHING APPARATUS.
FOR FIREFIGHTING AND OTHER IMMEDIATELY DANGEROUS TO LIFE OR HEALTH CONDITIONS:
SELF-CONTAINED BREATHING APPARATUS WITH FULL FACEPIECE OPERATED IN PRESSURE-DEMAND OR OTHER POSITIVE PRESSURE MODE.
SUPPLIED-AIR RESPIRATOR WITH FULL FACEPIECE AND OPERATED IN PRESSURE-DEMAND OR OTHER POSITIVE PRESSURE MODE IN COMBINATION WITH AN AUXILIARY SELF-CONTAINED BREATHING APPARATUS OPERATED IN PRESSURE-DEMAND OR OTHER POSITIVE PRESSURE MODE.

CLOTHING: EMPLOYEE MUST WEAR APPROPRIATE PROTECTIVE (IMPERVIOUS) CLOTHING AND EQUIPMENT TO PREVENT REPEATED OR PROLONGED SKIN CONTACT WITH THIS SUBSTANCE.

GLOVES: EMPLOYEE MUST WEAR APPROPRIATE PROTECTIVE GLOVES TO PREVENT CONTACT WITH THIS SUBSTANCE.

EYE PROTECTION: EMPLOYEE MUST WEAR SPLASH-PROOF OR DUST-RESISTANT SAFETY GOGGLES AND A FACESHIELD TO PREVENT CONTACT WITH THIS SUBSTANCE.

EMERGENCY WASH FACILITIES: WHERE THERE IS ANY POSSIBILITY THAT AN EMPLOYEE'S EYES AND/OR SKIN MAY BE EXPOSED TO THIS SUBSTANCE, THE EMPLOYER SHOULD PROVIDE AN EYE WASH FOUNTAIN AND QUICK DRENCH SHOWER WITHIN THE IMMEDIATE WORK AREA FOR EMERGENCY USE.

AUTHORIZED BY- OCCUPATIONAL HEALTH SERVICES, INC.
CREATION DATE: 11/17/89 ***REVISION DATE:*** 05/11/90

MATERIAL SAFETY DATA SHEET

OCCUPATIONAL HEALTH SERVICES, INC.
AGRICULTURE AND PESTICIDE DIVISION
450 SEVENTH AVENUE, SUITE 2407
NEW YORK, NEW YORK 10123
1-800-445-MSDS OR (212) 967-1100

EMERGENCY CONTACT:
JOHN S. BRANSFORD, JR. (615) 292-1180

SUBSTANCE IDENTIFICATION

CAS-NUMBER 55-91-4

SUBSTANCE: **ISOFLUROPHATE**

TRADE NAMES/SYNONYMS: PHOSPHOROFLUORIDIC ACID, BIS(1-METHYLETHYL) ESTER; PHOSPHOROFLUORIDIC ACID, DIISOPROPYL ESTER; DIISOPROPOXYPHOSPHORYL FLUORIDE; DIISOPROPYL FLUOROPHOSPHATE; DIISOPROPYL PHOSPHOFLUORIDATE; DIISOPROPYL PHOSPHOROFLUORIDATE; FLUORODIISOPROPYL PHOSPHATE; ISOPROPYL FLUOPHOSPHATE; ISOPROPYL PHOSPHOROFLUORIDATE; DFP; DYFLOS; DIFLUOROPHATE; FLUOSTIGMINE; NEOGLAUCIT; DIFLUPYL; RCRA P043; C6H14FO3P; PST07590

CHEMICAL FAMILY: ORGANOPHOSPHATE

MOLECULAR FORMULA: C6-H14-F-O3-P

MOLECULAR WEIGHT: 184.17

CERCLA RATINGS (SCALE 0-3): HEALTH=3 FIRE=U REACTIVITY=U PERSISTENCE=0

NFPA RATINGS (SCALE 0-4): HEALTH=4 FIRE=U REACTIVITY=U

COMPONENTS AND CONTAMINANTS

COMPONENT: ISOFLUROPHATE ***PERCENT:*** 100
CAS# 55-91-4

EXPOSURE LIMITS: NO OCCUPATIONAL EXPOSURE LIMITS ESTABLISHED BY OSHA, ACGIH, OR NIOSH.

ISOFLUORPHATE: 100 POUNDS SARA SECTION 302 THRESHOLD PLANNING QUANTITY 100 POUNDS SARA SECTION 304 REPORTABLE QUANTITY 100 POUNDS CERCLA SECTION 103 REPORTABLE QUANTITY

PHYSICAL DATA

DESCRIPTION: LIQUID ***BOILING POINT:*** 361 F (183 C)

MELTING POINT: -121 F (-85 C) ***SPECIFIC GRAVITY:*** 1.055

VAPOR PRESSURE: 0.579 @ 20 C ***SOLUBILITY IN WATER:*** 1.5% @ 25 C

SOLVENT SOLUBILITY: SOLUBLE IN VEGETABLE OILS

FIRE AND EXPLOSION DATA

FIRE AND EXPLOSION HAZARD: UNKNOWN FIRE AND EXPLOSION HAZARD.

FIREFIGHTING MEDIA: DRY CHEMICAL, CARBON DIOXIDE, HALON, WATER SPRAY OR STANDARD FOAM (1987 EMERGENCY RESPONSE GUIDEBOOK, DOT P 5800.4).
FOR LARGER FIRES, USE WATER SPRAY, FOG OR STANDARD FOAM (1987 EMERGENCY RESPONSE GUIDEBOOK, DOT P 5800.4).

FIREFIGHTING: MOVE CONTAINERS FROM FIRE AREA IF POSSIBLE. FIGHT FIRE FROM MAXIMUM DISTANCE. STAY AWAY FROM STORAGE TANK ENDS. DIKE FIRE CONTROL WATER FOR LATER DISPOSAL. DO NOT SCATTER MATERIAL (1987 EMERGENCY RESPONSE GUIDEBOOK, DOT P 5800.4, GUIDE PAGE 55).

TRANSPORTATION DATA

DEPARTMENT OF TRANSPORTATION HAZARD CLASSIFICATION 49 CFR 172.101: POISON B

DEPARTMENT OF TRANSPORTATION LABELING REQUIREMENTS 49 CFR 172.101 AND SUBPART E: POISON

DEPARTMENT OF TRANSPORTATION PACKAGING REQUIREMENTS: 49 CFR 173.346 EXCEPTIONS: 49 CFR 173.345

TOXICITY

ISOFLUROPHATE: TOXICITY DATA: 8200 UG/M3/10 MINUTES INHALATION-HUMAN TCLO; 360 MG/M3/10 MINUTES INHALATION-RAT LC50; 8 GM/M3/10 MINUTES INHALATION-RABBIT LC50; 440 MG/M3/10 MINUTES INHALATION-MOUSE LC50; 500 MG/M3/2 MINUTES INHALATION-MONKEY LC50; 5 GM/M3/10 MINUTES INHALATION-DOG LC50; 6 GM/M3/10 MINUTES INHALATION-DOMESTIC ANIMAL LC50; 72 MG/KG SKIN-MOUSE LD50; 1150 UG/KG OCULAR-RABBIT LD50; 5 MG/KG ORAL-RAT LD50; 2 MG/KG ORAL-MOUSE LD50; 4 MG/KG ORAL-RABBIT LD50; 1600 MG/KG ORAL-CAT LD50; 1750 UG/KG SUBCUTANEOUS-RAT LD50; 3 MG/KG SUBCUTANEOUS-MOUSE LD50; 1 MG/KG SUBCUTANEOUS-RABBIT LD50; 1 MG/KG SUBCUTANEOUS-MONKEY LD50; 3200 UG/KG INTRAVENOUS-MOUSE LD50; 300 UG/KG INTRAVENOUS-RABBIT LD50; 100 UG/KG INTRAVENOUS-MONKEY LD50; 1280 UG/KG INTRAPERITONEAL-RAT LD50; 2450 UG/KG INTRAPERITONEAL-MOUSE LD50; 1800 UG/KG INTRAMUSCULAR-RAT LD50; 750 UG/KG INTRAMUSCULAR-RABBIT LD50; REPRODUCTIVE EFFECTS DATA (RTECS). CARCINOGEN STATUS: NONE. ACUTE TOXICITY LEVEL: HIGHLY TOXIC BY INHALATION, DERMAL ABSORPTION AND INGESTION. TARGET EFFECTS: CHOLINESTERASE INHIBITOR; NEUROTOXIN. AT INCREASED RISK FROM EXPOSURE: PERSONS WITH RESPIRATORY AILMENTS, RECENT EXPOSURE TO CHOLINESTERASE INHIBITORS OR IMPAIRED CHOLINESTERASE PRODUCTION, OR LIVER MALFUNCTION.* ADDITIONAL DATA: MAY CROSS THE PLACENTA. HIGH ENVIRONMENTAL TEMPERATURES OR EXPOSURE OF THE CHEMICAL TO VISIBLE OR ULTRAVIOLET LIGHT MAY ENHANCE THE TOXICITY. INTERACTIONS WITH MEDICATIONS MAY OCCUR.*

* MAY BE BASED ON GENERAL INFORMATION ON ORGANOPHOSPHATES.

HEALTH EFFECTS AND FIRST AID

INHALATION: ISOFLUROPHATE: HIGHLY TOXIC. A CONCENTRATION OF 8200 UG/M3 FOR 10 MINUTES PRODUCED SYMPTOMS OF CHOLINESTERASE INHIBITION IN HUMANS. SEE INFORMATION ON ORGANOPHOSPHATES.

ORGANOPHOSPHATES: CHOLINESTERASE INHIBITOR. **ACUTE EXPOSURE-** WHEN INHALED, THE FIRST EFFECTS OF CHOLINESTERASE INHIBITORS ARE USUALLY RESPIRATORY AND MAY INCLUDE NASAL HYPEREMIA AND WATERY DISCHARGE, COUGH, CHEST DISCOMFORT, DYSPNEA, AND WHEEZING DUE TO INCREASED BRONCHIAL SECRETIONS AND BRONCHOCONSTRICTION. IF SUFFICIENT AMOUNTS ARE ABSORBED, OTHER SYSTEMIC EFFECTS MAY BEGIN WITHIN A FEW MINUTES OR BE DELAYED FOR UP TO 12 HOURS. SYMPTOMS MAY INCLUDE PALLOR, NAUSEA, VOMITING, DIARRHEA, ABDOMINAL CRAMPS, HEADACHE, DIZZINESS, OCULAR PAIN, BLURRED VISION, MIOSIS OR IN SOME CASES, ESPECIALLY INITIALLY, MYDRIASIS, LACRIMATION, SALIVATION, SWEATING, AND CONFUSION. OTHER REPORTED CENTRAL NERVOUS SYSTEM OR NEUROMUSCULAR EFFECTS MAY INCLUDE ATAXIA, SLURRED SPEECH, AREFLEXIA, WEAKNESS, FATIGUE, FASCICULATIONS, TWITCHING, TREMORS POSSIBLY OF THE TONGUE AND EYELIDS, AND EVENTUALLY PARALYSIS OF THE EXTREMITIES AND POSSIBLY OF THE RESPIRATORY MUSCLES. IN SEVERE CASES THERE MAY ALSO BE INVOLUNTARY DEFECATION AND URINATION, CYANOSIS, PSYCHOSIS, HYPERGLYCEMIA, ACUTE PANCREATITIS, CARDIAC IRREGULARITIES, PULMONARY EDEMA, UNCONSCIOUSNESS, CONVULSIONS, AND COMA. DEATH IS PRIMARILY DUE TO RESPIRATORY FAILURE, ALTHOUGH CARDIOVASCULAR EFFECTS INCLUDING CARDIAC ARREST MAY ALSO BE IMPLICATED. LONG TERM SEQUELAE ARE RARE BUT MAY INCLUDE NEUROPSYCHIATRIC DISORDERS AND MYOPATHY WITH MUSCLE TENDERNESS. SOME ORGANOPHOSPHATES MAY CAUSE A DELAYED NEUROPATHY BEGINNING 1-4 WEEKS AFTER AN ACUTE EXPOSURE WHICH MAY OR MAY NOT HAVE CAUSED ACUTE CHOLINERGIC EFFECTS. NUMBNESS, TINGLING, WEAKNESS AND CRAMPING BEGINNING SYMMETRICALLY IN THE LOWER LIMBS MAY PROGRESS TO ATAXIA AND PARALYSIS. IN SEVERE CASES, UPPER LIMB INVOLVEMENT IS POSSIBLE AND FLACCID PARALYSIS MAY PROGRESS TO SPASTIC PARALYSIS WITH EXAGGERATED REFLEXES. IMPROVEMENT MAY OCCUR OVER MONTHS TO YEARS, BUT SOME RESIDUAL IMPAIRMENT USUALLY REMAINS.

CHRONIC EXPOSURE- REPEATED OR PROLONGED EXPOSURE MAY RESULT IN THE EFFECTS OF ACUTE EXPOSURE INCLUDING THE DELAYED NEUROPATHY. OTHER EFFECTS REPORTED IN WORKERS REPEATEDLY EXPOSED INCLUDE IMPAIRED MEMORY AND CONCENTRATION, ACUTE PSYCHOSIS, SEVERE DEPRESSIONS, IRRITABILTY, CONFUSION, APATHY, EMOTIONAL LABILITY, SOCIAL WITHDRAWAL, CONFUSION, HEADACHE, SPEECH DIFFICULTIES, DELAYED REACTION TIMES, SPATIAL DISORIENTATION, NIGHTMARES, SLEEPWALKING, AND DROWSINESS OR INSOMNIA. AN INFLUENZA-LIKE CONDITION WITH HEADACHE, NAUSEA, WEAKNESS, ANOREXIA AND MALAISE HAS ALSO BEEN REPORTED.

FIRST AID- REMOVE FROM EXPOSURE AREA TO FRESH AIR IMMEDIATELY. IF BREATHING HAS STOPPED, GIVE ARTIFICIAL RESPIRATION. MAINTAIN AIRWAY AND BLOOD PRESSURE AND ADMINISTER OXYGEN IF AVAILABLE. KEEP AFFECTED PERSON WARM AND AT REST. TREAT SYMPTOMATICALLY AND SUPPORTIVELY. ADMINISTRATION OF OXYGEN SHOULD BE PERFORMED BY QUALIFIED PERSONNEL. GET MEDICAL ATTENTION IMMEDIATELY.

SKIN CONTACT: ISOFLUROPHATE: HIGHLY TOXIC. SEE INFORMATION ON ORGANOPHOSPHATES.
ORGANOPHOSPHATES: CHOLINESTERASE INHIBITOR. **ACUTE EXPOSURE-** LOCALIZED SWEATING AND FASCICULATIONS MAY OCCUR AT THE SITE OF CONTACT. IF SUFFICIENT AMOUNTS ARE ABSORBED, OTHER EFFECTS OF CHOLINESTERASE INHIBITION AS DESCRIBED IN ACUTE INHALATION MAY OCCUR. SYMPTOMS MAY BE DELAYED 2-3 HOURS, BUT USUALLY NO MORE THAN 12 HOURS. THE RATE OF ABSORPTION IS INCREASED BY THE PRESENCE OF DERMATITIS OR HIGH AMBIENT TEMPERATURES. DELAYED NEUROPATHY IS ALSO POSSIBLE. **CHRONIC EXPOSURE-** REPEATED OR PROLONGED EXPOSURE MAY CAUSE EFFECTS AS DESCRIBED IN ACUTE EXPOSURE. SOME ORGANOPHOSPHATES MAY CAUSE SENSITIZATION.
FIRST AID- REMOVE CONTAMINATED CLOTHING IMMEDIATELY. WASH CONTAMINATED AREAS WITH SOAP AND WATER FOLLOWED BY ALCOHOL (ARENA, POISONING, 4TH ED.). EMERGENCY PERSONNEL SHOULD WEAR GLOVES AND AVOID CONTAMINATION. TREAT RESPIRATORY DIFFICULTY WITH ARTIFICIAL RESPIRATION. GET MEDICAL ATTENTION IMMEDIATELY.

EYE CONTACT: ISOFLUROPHATE: HIGHLY TOXIC. SEE INFORMATION ON ORGANOPHOSPHATES.
ORGANOPHOSPHATES: CHOLINESTERASE INHIBITOR. **ACUTE EXPOSURE-** DIRECT CONTACT MAY CAUSE PAIN, HYPEREMIA, LACRIMATION, TWITCHING OF THE EYELIDS, MIOSIS, AND CILIARY MUSCLE SPASM WITH LOSS OF ACCOMODATION, BLURRED OR DIMMED VISION AND BROWACHE. SOMETIMES MYDRIASIS MAY OCCUR INSTEAD OF MIOSIS. WITH SUFFICIENT EXPOSURE, OTHER SYMPTOMS OF CHOLINESTERASE INHIBITION AS DESCRIBED IN ACUTE INHALATION MAY OCCUR. **CHRONIC EXPOSURE-** REPEATED OR PROLONGED EXPOSURE MAY CAUSE EFFECTS AS DESCRIBED IN ACUTE EXPOSURE. SOME COMPOUNDS HAVE CAUSED TOXIC EFFECTS ON THE CRYSTALLINE LENS, CONJUNCTIVAL THICKENING AND OBSTRUCTION OF THE NASOLACRIMAL CANALS WHEN USED AS MIOTIC EYEDROPS.
FIRST AID- IRRIGATE EYES WITH WATER OR SALINE SOLUTION. IF SYMPTOMS OF POISONING OCCUR, TREAT RESPIRATORY DIFFICULTY WITH ARTIFICIAL RESPIRATION AND OXYGEN. OBSERVE PATIENT FOR AT LEAST 24-36 HOURS (GOSSELIN, CLINICAL TOXICOLOGY OF COMMERCIAL PRODUCTS, 5TH ED.). GET MEDICAL ATTENTION IMMEDIATELY. OXYGEN SHOULD BE ADMINISTERED BY QUALIFIED MEDICAL PERSONNEL.

INGESTION: ISOFLUROPHATE: NEUROTOXIN/HIGHLY TOXIC. IN HENS, CHRONIC EXPOSURE PRODUCED PARALYSIS DUE TO THE DEMYELINATION OF PERIPHERAL NERVES. SEE INFORMATION ON ORGANOPHOSPHATES.
ORGANOPHOSPHATES: CHOLINESTERASE INHIBITOR. **ACUTE EXPOSURE-** WHEN INGESTED, THE FIRST EFFECTS MAY BE NAUSEA, VOMITING, ANOREXIA, ABDOMINAL CRAMPS AND DIARRHEA. GASTROINTESTINAL ABSORPTION MAY CAUSE SYMPTOMS OF CHOLINESTERASE INHIBITION AS DESCRIBED IN ACUTE INHALATION. SYMPTOMS MAY BEGIN WITHIN MINUTES OR BE DELAYED FOR HOURS. DELAYED EFFECTS INCLUDING NEUROPATHY MAY ALSO OCCUR. **CHRONIC EXPOSURE-** REPEATED INGESTION MAY CAUSE EFFECTS AS DESCRIBED IN ACUTE EXPOSURE.
FIRST AID- IF PERSON IS ALERT AND RESPIRATION IS NOT DEPRESSED, GIVE SYRUP OF IPECAC FOLLOWED BY WATER (IF VOMITING OCCURS, KEEP HEAD BELOW HIPS TO PREVENT ASPIRATION). IF CONSCIOUSNESS LEVEL DECLINES OR VOMITING HAS NOT OCCURRED IN 15 MINUTES EMPTY STOMACH BY GASTRIC LAVAGE WITH THE AID OF CUFFED ENDOTRACHEAL TUBE USING ISOTONIC SALINE OR 5% SODIUM BICARBONATE FOLLOW WITH ACTIVATED CHARCOAL. ESTABLISH AND MAINTAIN AIRWAY. TREAT RESPIRATORY DIFFICULTY WITH ARTIFICIAL RESPIRATION AND OXYGEN. DO NOT GIVE MORPHINE, AMINOPHYLLINE, PHENOTHIAZINES, RESERPINE, FUROSEMIDE, OR ETHACRYNIC ACID (MORGAN, RECOGNITION AND MANAGEMENT OF PESTICIDE POISONINGS, 3RD ED.). TREAT SYMPTOMATICALLY AND SUPPORTIVELY. ADMINISTRATION OF OXYGEN AND LAVAGE MUST BE PERFORMED BY QUALIFIED MEDICAL PERSONNEL. GET MEDICAL ATTENTION IMMEDIATELY.
ANTIDOTE: THE FOLLOWING ANTIDOTE(S) HAVE BEEN RECOMMENDED. HOWEVER, THE DECISION AS TO WHETHER THE SEVERITY OF POISONING REQUIRES ADMINISTRATION OF ANY ANTIDOTE AND ACTUAL DOSE REQUIRED SHOULD BE MADE BY QUALIFIED MEDICAL PERSONNEL.
FOR CHOLINESTERASE INHIBITORS: ESTABLISH CLEAR AIRWAY AND TISSUE OXYGENATION BY ASPIRATION OF SECRETIONS, AND IF NECESSARY, BY ASSISTED PULMONARY VENTILATION WITH OXYGEN. IMPROVE TISSUE OXYGENATION AS MUCH AS POSSIBLE BEFORE ADMINISTERING ATROPINE TO MINIMIZE THE RISK OF VENTRICULAR FIBRILLATION. ADMINISTER ATROPINE SULFATE INTRAVENOUSLY, OR INTRAMUSCULARLY IF IV INJECTION IS NOT POSSIBLE. IN MODERATELY SEVERE POISONING ADMINISTER ATROPINE SULFATE, 0.4-2.0 MG REPEATED EVERY 15 MINUTES UNTIL ATROPINIZATION IS ACHIEVED (TACHYCARDIA, FLUSHING, DRY MOUTH, MYDRIASIS). MAINTAIN ATROPINIZATION BY REPEATED DOSES FOR 2-12 HOURS, OR LONGER, DEPENDING ON THE SEVERITY OF POISONING. THE APPEARANCE OF RALES IN THE LUNG BASES, MIOSIS, SALIVATION, NAUSEA, BRADYCARDIA, ARE ALL INDICATIONS OF INADEQUATE ATROPINIZATION. SEVERELY POISONED INDIVIDUALS MAY EXHIBIT REMARKABLE TOLERANCE TO ATROPINE; TWO OR MORE TIMES THE DOSAGES SUGGESTED ABOVE MAY BE NEEDED. PERSONS NOT POISONED OR ONLY SLIGHTLY POISONED, HOWEVER, MAY DEVELOP SIGNS OF ATROPINE TOXICITY FROM SUCH LARGE DOSAGES: FEVER, MUSCLE FIBRILLATIONS, AND DELIRIUM ARE THE MAIN SIGNS OF ATROPINE TOXICITY. IF THESE SIGNS APPEAR WHILE THE PATIENT IS FULLY ATROPINIZED, ATROPINE ADMINISTRATION SHOULD BE DISCONTINUED, AT LEAST TEMPORARILY. OBSERVE TREATED PATIENTS CLOSELY AT LEAST 24 HOURS TO INSURE THAT SYMPTOMS (POSSIBLY PULMONARY EDEMA) DO NOT RECUR AS ATROPINIZATION WEARS OFF. IN VERY SEVERE POISONINGS, METABOLIC DISPOSITION OF TOXICANT MAY REQUIRE SEVERAL HOURS OR DAYS DURING WHICH ATROPINIZATION MUST BE MAINTAINED. MARKEDLY LOWER LEVELS OF URINARY METABOLITES INDICATE THAT ATROPINE DOSAGE CAN BE TAPERED OFF. AS DOSAGE IS REDUCED, CHECK THE LUNG BASES FREQUENTLY FOR RALES. IF RALES ARE HEARD OR OTHER SYMPTOMS RETURN, RE-ESTABLISH ATROPINIZATION PROMPTLY (MORGAN, RECOGNITION AND MANAGEMENT OF PESTICIDE POISONINGS, 3RD ED.). ADMINISTRATION OF ANTIDOTE MUST BE PERFORMED BY QUALIFIED MEDICAL PERSONNEL.
IN CASES OF SEVERE POISONING BY ORGANOPHOSPHATE PESTICIDES IN WHICH RESPIRATORY DEPRESSION, MUSCLE WEAKNESS AND TWITCHINGS ARE SEVERE, GIVE PRALIDOXIME (PROTOPAM-AYERST, 2-PAM), 1.0 GRAM INTRAVENOUSLY AT NO MORE THAN 0.5 GRAM PER MINUTE. DOSAGE OF PRALIDOXIME MAY BE REPEATED IN 1-2 HOURS, THEN AT 10-12 HOUR INTERVALS IF NEEDED. IN VERY SEVERE POISONINGS, DOSAGE RATES MAY BE DOUBLED. TREATMENT WITH PRALIDOXIME WILL BE MOST EFFECTIVE IF GIVEN WITHIN THIRTY-SIX HOURS AFTER POISONING (MORGAN, RECOGNITION AND MANAGEMENT OF PESTICIDE POISONINGS, 3RD ED.). ANTIDOTE SHOULD BE ADMINISTERED BY QUALIFIED MEDICAL PERSONNEL.

REACTIVITY

REACTIVITY: FORMS CORROSIVE HYDROGEN FLUORIDE IN THE PRESENCE OF MOISTURE.
INCOMPATIBILITIES: ISOFLUROPHATE: NO DATA AVAILABLE.
DECOMPOSITION: THERMAL DECOMPOSITION MAY RELEASE TOXIC AND/OR HAZARDOUS GASES. CONTACT WITH MOISTURE MAY RELEASE CORROSIVE HYDROGEN FLUORIDE.
POLYMERIZATION: HAZARDOUS POLYMERIZATION HAS NOT BEEN REPORTED TO OCCUR UNDER NORMAL TEMPERATURES AND PRESSURES.

STORAGE AND DISPOSAL

OBSERVE ALL FEDERAL, STATE AND LOCAL REGULATIONS WHEN STORING OR DISPOSING OF THIS SUBSTANCE. FOR ASSISTANCE, CONTACT THE DISTRICT DIRECTOR OF THE ENVIRONMENTAL PROTECTION AGENCY.

****STORAGE****

THRESHOLD PLANNING QUANTITY (TPQ): THE SUPERFUND AMENDMENTS AND REAUTHORIZATION ACT (SARA) SECTION 302 REQUIRES THAT EACH FACILITY WHERE ANY EXTREMELY HAZARDOUS SUBSTANCE IS PRESENT IN A QUANTITY EQUAL TO OR GREATER THAN THE TPQ ESTABLISHED FOR THAT SUBSTANCE NOTIFY THE STATE EMERGENCY RESPONSE COMMISSION FOR THE STATE IN WHICH IT IS LOCATED. SECTION 303 OF SARA REQUIRES THESE FACILITIES TO PARTICIPATE IN LOCAL EMERGENCY RESPONSE PLANNING (40 CFR 355.30).

CONDITIONS TO AVOID

MAY BURN BUT DOES NOT IGNITE READILY. CONTAINERS MAY EXPLODE IN HEAT OF FIRE.

SPILL AND LEAK PROCEDURES

OCCUPATIONAL SPILL: DO NOT TOUCH SPILLED MATERIAL. STOP LEAK IF YOU CAN DO IT WITHOUT RISK. USE WATER SPRAY TO REDUCE VAPORS. FOR SMALL SPILLS, TAKE UP WITH SAND OR OTHER ABSORBENT MATERIAL AND PLACE INTO CONTAINERS FOR LATER DISPOSAL. FOR SMALL DRY SPILLS, WITH A CLEAN SHOVEL PLACE MATERIAL INTO CLEAN, DRY CONTAINERS AND COVER. MOVE CONTAINERS FROM SPILL AREA. FOR LARGER SPILLS, DIKE FAR AHEAD OF SPILL FOR LATER DISPOSAL. KEEP UNNECESSARY PEOPLE AWAY. ISOLATE HAZARD AREA AND DENY ENTRY. VENTILATE CLOSED SPACES BEFORE ENTERING.
REPORTABLE QUANTITY (RQ): 100 POUNDS THE SUPERFUND AMENDMENTS AND REAUTHORIZATION ACT (SARA) SECTION 304 REQUIRES THAT A RELEASE EQUAL TO OR GREATER THAN THE REPORTABLE QUANTITY FOR THIS SUBSTANCE BE IMMEDIATELY REPORTED TO THE LOCAL EMERGENCY PLANNING COMMITTEE AND THE STATE EMERGENCY RESPONSE COMMISSION (40 CFR 355.40). IF THE RELEASE OF THIS SUBSTANCE IS REPORTABLE UNDER CERCLA SECTION 103, THE NATIONAL RESPONSE CENTER MUST BE NOTIFIED IMMEDIATELY AT (800) 424-8802 OR (202) 426-2675 IN THE METROPOLITAN WASHINGTON, D.C. AREA (40 CFR 302.6).

PROTECTIVE EQUIPMENT

VENTILATION: PROCESS ENCLOSURE RECOMMENDED.

RESPIRATOR: THE FOLLOWING RESPIRATORS ARE RECOMMENDED BASED ON INFORMATION FOUND IN THE PHYSICAL DATA, TOXICITY AND HEALTH EFFECTS SECTIONS. THEY ARE RANKED IN ORDER FROM MINIMUM TO MAXIMUM RESPIRATORY PROTECTION. THE SPECIFIC RESPIRATOR SELECTED MUST BE BASED ON CONTAMINATION LEVELS FOUND IN THE WORK PLACE, MUST NOT EXCEED THE WORKING LIMITS OF THE RESPIRATOR AND BE JOINTLY APPROVED BY THE NATIONAL INSTITUTE FOR OCCUPATIONAL SAFETY AND HEALTH AND THE MINE SAFETY AND HEALTH ADMINISTRATION (NIOSH-MSHA).
TYPE 'C' SUPPLIED-AIR RESPIRATOR WITH A FULL FACEPIECE OPERATED IN PRESSURE-DEMAND OR OTHER POSITIVE PRESSURE MODE OR WITH A FULL FACEPIECE, HELMET OR HOOD OPERATED IN CONTINOUS-FLOW MODE.
SELF-CONTAINED BREATHING APPARATUS WITH A FULL FACEPIECE OPERATED IN PRESSURE-DEMAND OR OTHER POSITIVE PRESSURE MODE.
FOR FIREFIGHTING AND OTHER IMMEDIATELY DANGEROUS TO LIFE OR HEALTH CONDITIONS:
SELF-CONTAINED BREATHING APPARATUS WITH FULL FACEPIECE OPERATED IN PRESSURE-DEMAND OR OTHER POSITIVE PRESSURE MODE.
SUPPLIED-AIR RESPIRATOR WITH FULL FACEPIECE AND OPERATED IN PRESSURE-DEMAND OR OTHER POSITIVE PRESSURE MODE IN COMBINATION WITH AN AUXILIARY SELF-CONTAINED BREATHING APPARATUS OPERATED IN PRESSURE-DEMAND OR OTHER POSITIVE PRESSURE MODE.

CLOTHING: EMPLOYEE MUST WEAR APPROPRIATE PROTECTIVE (IMPERVIOUS) CLOTHING AND EQUIPMENT TO PREVENT ANY POSSIBILITY OF SKIN CONTACT WITH THIS SUBSTANCE.

GLOVES: EMPLOYEE MUST WEAR APPROPRIATE PROTECTIVE GLOVES TO PREVENT CONTACT WITH THIS SUBSTANCE.

EYE PROTECTION: EMPLOYEE MUST WEAR SPLASH-PROOF OR DUST-RESISTANT SAFETY GOGGLES WITH OR WITHOUT A FACESHIELD TO PREVENT CONTACT WITH THIS SUBSTANCE.
EMERGENCY EYE WASH: WHERE THERE IS ANY POSSIBILITY THAT AN EMPLOYEE'S EYES MAY BE EXPOSED TO THIS SUBSTANCE, THE EMPLOYER SHOULD PROVIDE AN EYE WASH FOUNTAIN WITHIN THE IMMEDIATE WORK AREA FOR EMERGENCY USE.

AUTHORIZED BY- OCCUPATIONAL HEALTH SERVICES, INC.
CREATION DATE: 10/04/89 ***REVISION DATE:*** 05/07/90

MATERIAL SAFETY DATA SHEET

OCCUPATIONAL HEALTH SERVICES, INC.
AGRICULTURE AND PESTICIDE DIVISION
450 SEVENTH AVENUE, SUITE 2407
NEW YORK, NEW YORK 10123
1-800-445-MSDS OR (212) 967-1100

EMERGENCY CONTACT:
JOHN S. BRANSFORD, JR. (615) 292-1180

SUBSTANCE IDENTIFICATION

CAS-NUMBER 115-26-4

SUBSTANCE: DIMEFOX

TRADE NAMES/SYNONYMS: TETRAMETHYLPHOSPHORODIAMIDIC FLUORIDE; BIS(DIMETHYLAMIDO)FLUOROPHOSPHATE; BIS(DIMETHYLAMINO)FLUOROPHOSPHINE OXIDE; N,N,N',N'-TETRAMETHYLPHOSPHORODIAMIDIC FLUORIDE; BFPO; DIFO; HANANE; PESTOX 14; TETRA-SYSTAM; CR 409; ENT 19,109; PST07655

CHEMICAL FAMILY: ORGANOPHOSPHATE

MOLECULAR FORMULA: C4-H12-F-N2-O-P

MOLECULAR WEIGHT: 154.15

CERCLA RATINGS (SCALE 0-3): HEALTH=3 FIRE=0 REACTIVITY=0 PERSISTENCE=0

NFPA RATINGS (SCALE 0-4): HEALTH=4 FIRE=0 REACTIVITY=0

COMPONENTS AND CONTAMINANTS

COMPONENT: DIMEFOX ***PERCENT:*** 100
CAS# 115-26-4

EXPOSURE LIMITS: NO OCCUPATIONAL EXPOSURE LIMITS ESTABLISHED BY OSHA, ACGIH, OR NIOSH.
DIMEFOX: 500 POUNDS SARA SECTION 302 THRESHOLD PLANNING QUANTITY 1 POUND SARA SECTION 304 REPORTABLE QUANTITY

PHYSICAL DATA

DESCRIPTION: COLORLESS LIQUID WITH FISHY ODOR

BOILING POINT: 153 F (67 C) 4 MMHG ***SPECIFIC GRAVITY:*** 1.1151

VAPOR PRESSURE: 0.36 MMHG @ 25 C ***EVAPORATION RATE:*** NOT AVAILABLE

SOLUBILITY IN WATER: MISCIBLE

SOLVENT SOLUBILITY: SOLUBLE IN BENZENE, ETHER, MOST ORGANIC SOLVENTS

FIRE AND EXPLOSION DATA

FIRE AND EXPLOSION HAZARD: NEGLIGIBLE FIRE HAZARD WHEN EXPOSED TO HEAT OR FLAME.

FIREFIGHTING MEDIA: DRY CHEMICAL, CARBON DIOXIDE, HALON, WATER SPRAY OR STANDARD FOAM (1987 EMERGENCY RESPONSE GUIDEBOOK, DOT P 5800.4).
FOR LARGER FIRES, USE WATER SPRAY, FOG OR STANDARD FOAM (1987 EMERGENCY RESPONSE GUIDEBOOK, DOT P 5800.4).

FIREFIGHTING: MOVE CONTAINERS FROM FIRE AREA IF POSSIBLE. FIGHT FIRE FROM MAXIMUM DISTANCE. STAY AWAY FROM STORAGE TANK ENDS. DIKE FIRE CONTROL WATER FOR LATER DISPOSAL. DO NOT SCATTER MATERIAL (1987 EMERGENCY RESPONSE GUIDEBOOK, DOT P 5800.4, GUIDE PAGE 55).

TRANSPORTATION DATA

DEPARTMENT OF TRANSPORTATION HAZARD CLASSIFICATION 49 CFR 172.101: POISON B
DEPARTMENT OF TRANSPORTATION LABELING REQUIREMENTS 49 CFR 172.101 AND SUBPART E: POISON
DEPARTMENT OF TRANSPORTATION PACKAGING REQUIREMENTS: 49 CFR 173.346 EXCEPTIONS: 49 CFR 173.345

TOXICITY

DIMEFOX: TOXICITY DATA: 2 GM/M3/10 MINUTES INHALATION-RAT LC50; 950 MG/M3/10 MINUTES INHALATION-MOUSE LC50; 2 MG/KG SKIN-RAT LD50; 1 MG/KG ORAL-RAT LD50; 2 MG/KG ORAL-MOUSE LD50; 3 MG/KG ORAL-RABBIT LD50; 2 MG/KG ORAL-MONKEY LD50; 2 MG/KG ORAL-CAT LD50; 4 MG/KG ORAL-GUINEA PIG LD50; 300 UG/KG SUBCUTANEOUS-RAT LD50; 6 MG/KG SUBCUTANEOUS-RABBIT LD50; 1 MG/KG SUBCUTANEOUS-MOUSE LD50; 2 MG/KG SUBCUTANEOUS-GUINEA PIG LD50; 2 MG/KG SUBCUTANEOUS-DOMESTIC ANIMAL LD50; 5 MG/KG INTRAVENOUS-DOG LD50; 3 MG/KG INTRAVENOUS-RABBIT LD50; 5 MG/KG INTRAPERITONEAL-RAT LD50; 1350 UG/KG INTRAPERITONEAL-MOUSE LD50; 2500 UG/KG INTRAPERITONEAL-GUINEA PIG LD50. CARCINOGEN STATUS: NONE. ACUTE TOXICITY LEVEL: HIGHLY TOXIC BY INHALATION, INGESTION, AND DERMAL ABSORPTION. TARGET EFFECTS: CHOLINESTERASE INHIBITOR. POISONING MAY AFFECT THE NERVOUS SYSTEM.* AT INCREASED RISK FROM EXPOSURE: PERSONS WITH RESPIRATORY AILMENTS, RECENT EXPOSURE TO CHOLINESTERASE INHIBITORS OR IMPAIRED CHOLINESTERASE PRODUCTION, OR LIVER MALFUNCTION.* ADDITIONAL DATA: MAY CROSS THE PLACENTA. HIGH ENVIRONMENTAL TEMPERATURES OR EXPOSURE OF THE CHEMICAL TO VISIBLE OR ULTRAVIOLET LIGHT MAY ENHANCE THE TOXICITY. INTERACTIONS WITH MEDICATIONS MAY OCCUR.* * MAY BE BASED ON GENERAL INFORMATION ON ORGANOPHOSPHATES.

HEALTH EFFECTS AND FIRST AID

INHALATION: DIMEFOX: HIGHLY TOXIC. SEE INFORMATION ON ORGANOPHOSPHATES.
ORGANOPHOSPHATES: CHOLINESTERASE INHIBITOR. **ACUTE EXPOSURE-** WHEN INHALED, THE FIRST EFFECTS OF CHOLINESTERASE INHIBITORS ARE USUALLY RESPIRATORY AND MAY INCLUDE NASAL HYPEREMIA AND WATERY DISCHARGE, COUGH, CHEST DISCOMFORT, DYSPNEA, AND WHEEZING DUE TO INCREASED BRONCHIAL SECRETIONS AND BRONCHOCONSTRICTION. IF SUFFICIENT AMOUNTS ARE ABSORBED, OTHER SYSTEMIC EFFECTS MAY BEGIN WITHIN A FEW MINUTES OR BE DELAYED FOR UP TO 12 HOURS. SYMPTOMS MAY INCLUDE PALLOR, NAUSEA, VOMITING, DIARRHEA, ABDOMINAL CRAMPS, HEADACHE, DIZZINESS, OCULAR PAIN, BLURRED VISION, MIOSIS OR IN SOME CASES, ESPECIALLY INITIALLY, MYDRIASIS, LACRIMATION, SALIVATION, SWEATING, AND CONFUSION. OTHER REPORTED CENTRAL NERVOUS SYSTEM OR NEUROMUSCULAR EFFECTS MAY INCLUDE ATAXIA, SLURRED SPEECH, AREFLEXIA, WEAKNESS, FATIGUE, FASCICULATIONS, TWITCHING, TREMORS POSSIBLY OF THE TONGUE AND EYELIDS, AND EVENTUALLY PARALYSIS OF THE EXTREMITIES AND POSSIBLY OF THE RESPIRATORY MUSCLES. IN SEVERE CASES THERE MAY ALSO BE INVOLUNTARY DEFECATION AND URINATION, CYANOSIS, PSYCHOSIS, HYPERGLYCEMIA, ACUTE PANCREATITIS, CARDIAC IRREGULARITIES, PULMONARY EDEMA, UNCONSCIOUSNESS, CONVULSIONS, AND COMA. DEATH IS PRIMARILY DUE TO RESPIRATORY FAILURE, ALTHOUGH CARDIOVASCULAR EFFECTS INCLUDING CARDIAC ARREST MAY ALSO BE IMPLICATED. LONG TERM SEQUELAE ARE RARE BUT MAY INCLUDE NEUROPSYCHIATRIC DISORDERS AND MYOPATHY WITH MUSCLE TENDERNESS. SOME ORGANOPHOSPHATES MAY CAUSE A DELAYED NEUROPATHY BEGINNING 1-4 WEEKS AFTER AN ACUTE EXPOSURE WHICH MAY OR MAY NOT HAVE CAUSED ACUTE CHOLINERGIC EFFECTS. NUMBNESS, TINGLING, WEAKNESS AND CRAMPING BEGINNING SYMMETRICALLY IN THE LOWER LIMBS MAY PROGRESS TO ATAXIA AND PARALYSIS. IN SEVERE CASES, UPPER LIMB

INVOLVEMENT IS POSSIBLE AND FLACCID PARALYSIS MAY PROGRESS TO SPASTIC PARALYSIS WITH EXAGGERATED REFLEXES. IMPROVEMENT MAY OCCUR OVER MONTHS TO YEARS, BUT SOME RESIDUAL IMPAIRMENT USUALLY REMAINS. **CHRONIC EXPOSURE**- REPEATED OR PROLONGED EXPOSURE MAY RESULT IN THE EFFECTS OF ACUTE EXPOSURE INCLUDING THE DELAYED NEUROPATHY. OTHER EFFECTS REPORTED IN WORKERS REPEATEDLY EXPOSED INCLUDE IMPAIRED MEMORY AND CONCENTRATION, ACUTE PSYCHOSIS, SEVERE DEPRESSIONS, IRRITABILTY, CONFUSION, APATHY, EMOTIONAL LABILITY, SOCIAL WITHDRAWAL, CONFUSION, HEADACHE, SPEECH DIFFICULTIES, DELAYED REACTION TIMES, SPATIAL DISORIENTATION, NIGHTMARES, SLEEPWALKING, AND DROWSINESS OR INSOMNIA. AN INFLUENZA-LIKE CONDITION WITH HEADACHE, NAUSEA, WEAKNESS, ANOREXIA AND MALAISE HAS ALSO BEEN REPORTED.

FIRST AID- REMOVE FROM EXPOSURE AREA TO FRESH AIR IMMEDIATELY. IF BREATHING HAS STOPPED, GIVE ARTIFICIAL RESPIRATION. MAINTAIN AIRWAY AND BLOOD PRESSURE AND ADMINISTER OXYGEN IF AVAILABLE. KEEP AFFECTED PERSON WARM AND AT REST. TREAT SYMPTOMATICALLY AND SUPPORTIVELY. ADMINISTRATION OF OXYGEN SHOULD BE PERFORMED BY QUALIFIED PERSONNEL. GET MEDICAL ATTENTION IMMEDIATELY.

SKIN CONTACT: DIMEFOX: HIGHLY TOXIC. SEE INFORMATION ON ORGANOPHOSPHATES.

ORGANOPHOSPHATES: CHOLINESTERASE INHIBITOR. **ACUTE EXPOSURE**- LOCALIZED SWEATING AND FASCICULATIONS MAY OCCUR AT THE SITE OF CONTACT. IF SUFFICIENT AMOUNTS ARE ABSORBED, OTHER EFFECTS OF CHOLINESTERASE INHIBITION AS DESCRIBED IN ACUTE INHALATION MAY OCCUR. SYMPTOMS MAY BE DELAYED 2-3 HOURS, BUT USUALLY NO MORE THAN 12 HOURS. THE RATE OF ABSORPTION IS INCREASED BY THE PRESENCE OF DERMATITIS OR HIGH AMBIENT TEMPERATURES. DELAYED NEUROPATHY IS ALSO POSSIBLE. **CHRONIC EXPOSURE**- REPEATED OR PROLONGED EXPOSURE MAY CAUSE EFFECTS AS DESCRIBED IN ACUTE EXPOSURE. SOME ORGANOPHOSPHATES MAY CAUSE SENSITIZATION.

FIRST AID- REMOVE CONTAMINATED CLOTHING IMMEDIATELY. WASH CONTAMINATED AREAS WITH SOAP AND WATER FOLLOWED BY ALCOHOL (ARENA, POISONING, 4TH ED.). EMERGENCY PERSONNEL SHOULD WEAR GLOVES AND AVOID CONTAMINATION. TREAT RESPIRATORY DIFFICULTY WITH ARTIFICIAL RESPIRATION. GET MEDICAL ATTENTION IMMEDIATELY.

EYE CONTACT: DIMEFOX: SEE INFORMATION ON ORGANOPHOSPHATES.

ORGANOPHOSPHATES: CHOLINESTERASE INHIBITOR. **ACUTE EXPOSURE**- DIRECT CONTACT MAY CAUSE PAIN, HYPEREMIA, LACRIMATION, TWITCHING OF THE EYELIDS, MIOSIS, AND CILIARY MUSCLE SPASM WITH LOSS OF ACCOMODATION, BLURRED OR DIMMED VISION AND BROWACHE. SOMETIMES MYDRIASIS MAY OCCUR INSTEAD OF MIOSIS. WITH SUFFICIENT EXPOSURE, OTHER SYMPTOMS OF CHOLINESTERASE INHIBITION AS DESCRIBED IN ACUTE INHALATION MAY OCCUR. **CHRONIC EXPOSURE**- REPEATED OR PROLONGED EXPOSURE MAY CAUSE EFFECTS AS DESCRIBED IN ACUTE EXPOSURE. SOME COMPOUNDS HAVE CAUSED TOXIC EFFECTS ON THE CRYSTALLINE LENS, CONJUNCTIVAL THICKENING AND OBSTRUCTION OF THE NASOLACRIMAL CANALS WHEN USED AS MIOTIC EYEDROPS.

FIRST AID- IRRIGATE EYES WITH WATER OR SALINE SOLUTION. IF SYMPTOMS OF POISONING OCCUR, TREAT RESPIRATORY DIFFICULTY WITH ARTIFICIAL RESPIRATION AND OXYGEN. OBSERVE PATIENT FOR AT LEAST 24-36 HOURS (GOSSELIN, CLINICAL TOXICOLOGY OF COMMERCIAL PRODUCTS, 5TH ED.). GET MEDICAL ATTENTION IMMEDIATELY. OXYGEN SHOULD BE ADMINISTERED BY QUALIFIED MEDICAL PERSONNEL.

INGESTION: DIMEFOX: HIGHLY TOXIC. SEE INFORMATION ON ORGANOPHOSPHATES.

ORGANOPHOSPHATES: CHOLINESTERASE INHIBITOR. **ACUTE EXPOSURE**- WHEN INGESTED, THE FIRST EFFECTS MAY BE NAUSEA, VOMITING, ANOREXIA, ABDOMINAL CRAMPS AND DIARRHEA. GASTROINTESTINAL ABSORPTION MAY CAUSE SYMPTOMS OF CHOLINESTERASE INHIBITION AS DESCRIBED IN ACUTE INHALATION. SYMPTOMS MAY BEGIN WITHIN MINUTES OR BE DELAYED FOR HOURS. DELAYED EFFECTS INCLUDING NEUROPATHY MAY ALSO OCCUR. **CHRONIC EXPOSURE**- REPEATED INGESTION MAY CAUSE EFFECTS AS DESCRIBED IN ACUTE EXPOSURE.

FIRST AID- IF PERSON IS ALERT AND RESPIRATION IS NOT DEPRESSED, GIVE SYRUP OF IPECAC FOLLOWED BY WATER (IF VOMITING OCCURS, KEEP HEAD BELOW HIPS TO PREVENT ASPIRATION). IF CONSCIOUSNESS LEVEL DECLINES OR VOMITING HAS NOT OCCURRED IN 15 MINUTES EMPTY STOMACH BY GASTRIC LAVAGE WITH THE AID OF CUFFED ENDOTRACHEAL TUBE USING ISOTONIC SALINE OR 5% SODIUM BICARBONATE FOLLOW WITH ACTIVATED CHARCOAL. ESTABLISH AND MAINTAIN AIRWAY. TREAT RESPIRATORY DIFFICULTY WITH ARTIFICIAL RESPIRATION AND OXYGEN. DO NOT GIVE MORPHINE, AMINOPHYLLINE, PHENOTHIAZINES, RESERPINE, FUROSEMIDE, OR ETHACRYNIC ACID (MORGAN, RECOGNITION AND MANAGEMENT OF PESTICIDE POISONINGS, 3RD ED.). TREAT SYMPTOMATICALLY AND SUPPORTIVELY. ADMINISTRATION OF OXYGEN AND LAVAGE MUST BE PERFORMED BY QUALIFIED MEDICAL PERSONNEL. GET MEDICAL ATTENTION IMMEDIATELY.

ANTIDOTE: THE FOLLOWING ANTIDOTE(S) HAVE BEEN RECOMMENDED. HOWEVER, THE DECISION AS TO WHETHER THE SEVERITY OF POISONING REQUIRES ADMINISTRATION OF ANY ANTIDOTE AND ACTUAL DOSE REQUIRED SHOULD BE MADE BY QUALIFIED MEDICAL PERSONNEL.

FOR CHOLINESTERASE INHIBITORS: ESTABLISH CLEAR AIRWAY AND TISSUE OXYGENATION BY ASPIRATION OF SECRETIONS, AND IF NECESSARY, BY ASSISTED PULMONARY VENTILATION WITH OXYGEN. IMPROVE TISSUE OXYGENATION AS MUCH AS POSSIBLE BEFORE ADMINISTERING ATROPINE TO MINIMIZE THE RISK OF VENTRICULAR FIBRILLATION. ADMINISTER ATROPINE SULFATE INTRAVENOUSLY, OR INTRAMUSCULARLY IF IV INJECTION IS NOT POSSIBLE. IN MODERATELY SEVERE POISONING ADMINISTER ATROPINE SULFATE, 0.4-2.0 MG REPEATED EVERY 15 MINUTES UNTIL ATROPINIZATION IS ACHIEVED (TACHYCARDIA, FLUSHING, DRY MOUTH, MYDRIASIS). MAINTAIN ATROPINIZATION BY REPEATED DOSES FOR 2-12 HOURS, OR LONGER, DEPENDING ON THE SEVERITY OF POISONING. THE APPEARANCE OF RALES IN THE LUNG BASES, MIOSIS, SALIVATION, NAUSEA, BRADYCARDIA, ARE ALL INDICATIONS OF INADEQUATE ATROPINIZATION. SEVERELY POISONED INDIVIDUALS MAY EXHIBIT REMARKABLE TOLERANCE TO ATROPINE; TWO OR MORE TIMES THE DOSAGES SUGGESTED ABOVE MAY BE NEEDED. PERSONS NOT POISONED OR ONLY SLIGHTLY POISONED, HOWEVER, MAY DEVELOP SIGNS OF ATROPINE TOXICITY FROM SUCH LARGE DOSAGES: FEVER, MUSCLE FIBRILLATIONS, AND DELIRIUM ARE THE MAIN SIGNS OF ATROPINE TOXICITY. IF THESE SIGNS APPEAR WHILE THE PATIENT IS FULLY ATROPINIZED, ATROPINE ADMINISTRATION SHOULD BE DISCONTINUED, AT LEAST TEMPORARILY. OBSERVE TREATED PATIENTS CLOSELY AT LEAST 24 HOURS TO INSURE THAT SYMPTOMS (POSSIBLY PULMONARY EDEMA) DO NOT RECUR AS ATROPINIZATION WEARS OFF. IN VERY SEVERE POISONINGS, METABOLIC DISPOSITION OF TOXICANT MAY REQUIRE SEVERAL HOURS OR DAYS DURING WHICH ATROPINIZATION MUST BE MAINTAINED. MARKEDLY LOWER LEVELS OF URINARY METABOLITES INDICATE THAT ATROPINE DOSAGE CAN BE TAPERED OFF. AS DOSAGE IS REDUCED, CHECK THE LUNG BASES FREQUENTLY FOR RALES. IF RALES ARE HEARD OR OTHER SYMPTOMS RETURN, RE-ESTABLISH ATROPINIZATION PROMPTLY (MORGAN, RECOGNITION AND MANAGEMENT OF PESTICIDE POISONINGS, 3RD ED.). ADMINISTRATION OF ANTIDOTE MUST BE PERFORMED BY QUALIFIED MEDICAL PERSONNEL.

IN CASES OF SEVERE POISONING BY ORGANOPHOSPHATE PESTICIDES IN WHICH RESPIRATORY DEPRESSION, MUSCLE WEAKNESS AND TWITCHINGS ARE SEVERE, GIVE PRALIDOXIME (PROTOPAM-AYERST, 2-PAM), 1.0 GRAM INTRAVENOUSLY AT NO MORE THAN 0.5 GRAM PER MINUTE. DOSAGE OF PRALIDOXIME MAY BE REPEATED IN 1-2 HOURS, THEN AT 10-12 HOUR INTERVALS IF NEEDED. IN VERY SEVERE POISONINGS, DOSAGE RATES MAY BE DOUBLED. TREATMENT WITH PRALIDOXIME WILL BE MOST EFFECTIVE IF GIVEN WITHIN THIRTY-SIX HOURS AFTER POISONING (MORGAN, RECOGNITION AND MANAGEMENT OF PESTICIDE POISONINGS, 3RD ED.). ANTIDOTE SHOULD BE ADMINISTERED BY QUALIFIED MEDICAL PERSONNEL.

REACTIVITY

REACTIVITY: STABLE UNDER NORMAL TEMPERATURES AND PRESSURES.

INCOMPATIBILITIES: DIMEFOX: ACIDS: MAY CAUSE HYDROLYSIS. CHLORINE: MAY CAUSE OXIDATION. OXIDIZERS (STRONG): FIRE AND EXPLOSION HAZARD.

DECOMPOSITION: THERMAL DECOMPOSITION MAY RELEASE TOXIC AND/OR HAZARDOUS GASES.

POLYMERIZATION: HAZARDOUS POLYMERIZATION HAS NOT BEEN REPORTED TO OCCUR UNDER NORMAL TEMPERATURES AND PRESSURES.

STORAGE AND DISPOSAL

OBSERVE ALL FEDERAL, STATE AND LOCAL REGULATIONS WHEN STORING OR DISPOSING OF THIS SUBSTANCE. FOR ASSISTANCE, CONTACT THE DISTRICT DIRECTOR OF THE ENVIRONMENTAL PROTECTION AGENCY.

****STORAGE****

STORE IN ACCORDANCE WITH 40 CFR 165 RECOMMENDED PROCEDURES FOR THE DISPOSAL AND STORAGE OF PESTICIDES AND PESTICIDE CONTAINERS.

STORE AWAY FROM INCOMPATIBLE SUBSTANCES.

THRESHOLD PLANNING QUANTITY (TPQ): THE SUPERFUND AMENDMENTS AND REAUTHORIZATION ACT (SARA) SECTION 302 REQUIRES THAT EACH FACILITY WHERE ANY EXTREMELY HAZARDOUS SUBSTANCE IS PRESENT IN A QUANTITY EQUAL TO OR GREATER THAN THE TPQ ESTABLISHED FOR THAT SUBSTANCE NOTIFY THE STATE EMERGENCY RESPONSE COMMISSION FOR THE STATE IN WHICH IT IS LOCATED. SECTION 303 OF SARA REQUIRES THESE FACILITIES TO PARTICIPATE IN LOCAL EMERGENCY RESPONSE PLANNING (40 CFR 355.30).

****DISPOSAL****

DISPOSAL MUST BE IN ACCORDANCE WITH 40 CFR 165 RECOMMENDED PROCEDURES FOR THE DISPOSAL AND STORAGE OF PESTICIDES AND PESTICIDE CONTAINERS.

CONDITIONS TO AVOID

NONE REPORTED.

SPILL AND LEAK PROCEDURES

OCCUPATIONAL SPILL: DO NOT TOUCH SPILLED MATERIAL. STOP LEAK IF YOU CAN DO IT WITHOUT RISK. USE WATER SPRAY TO REDUCE VAPORS. FOR SMALL SPILLS, TAKE UP WITH SAND OR OTHER ABSORBENT MATERIAL AND PLACE INTO CONTAINERS FOR LATER DISPOSAL. FOR SMALL DRY SPILLS, WITH A CLEAN SHOVEL PLACE MATERIAL INTO CLEAN, DRY CONTAINERS AND COVER. MOVE CONTAINERS FROM SPILL AREA. FOR LARGER SPILLS, DIKE FAR AHEAD OF SPILL FOR LATER DISPOSAL. KEEP UNNECESSARY PEOPLE AWAY. ISOLATE HAZARD AREA AND DENY ENTRY. VENTILATE CLOSED SPACES BEFORE ENTERING.
REPORTABLE QUANTITY (RQ): 1 POUND THE SUPERFUND AMENDMENTS AND REAUTHORIZATION ACT (SARA) SECTION 304 REQUIRES THAT A RELEASE EQUAL TO OR GREATER THAN THE REPORTABLE QUANTITY FOR THIS SUBSTANCE BE IMMEDIATELY REPORTED TO THE LOCAL EMERGENCY PLANNING COMMITTEE AND THE STATE EMERGENCY RESPONSE COMMISSION (40 CFR 355.40). IF THE RELEASE OF THIS SUBSTANCE IS REPORTABLE UNDER CERCLA SECTION 103, THE NATIONAL RESPONSE CENTER MUST BE NOTIFIED IMMEDIATELY AT (800) 424-8802 OR (202) 426-2675 IN THE METROPOLITAN WASHINGTON, D.C. AREA (40 CFR 302.6).

PROTECTIVE EQUIPMENT

VENTILATION: PROCESS ENCLOSURE RECOMMENDED.

RESPIRATOR: THE FOLLOWING RESPIRATORS AND MAXIMUM USE CONCENTRATIONS ARE RECOMMENDATIONS BY THE U.S. DEPARTMENT OF HEALTH AND HUMAN SERVICES, NIOSH POCKET GUIDE TO CHEMICAL HAZARDS; NIOSH CRITERIA DOCUMENTS OR BY THE U.S. DEPARTMENT OF LABOR, 29 CFR 1910 SUBPART Z.
THE SPECIFIC RESPIRATOR SELECTED MUST BE BASED ON CONTAMINATION LEVELS FOUND IN THE WORK PLACE, MUST NOT EXCEED THE WORKING LIMITS OF THE RESPIRATOR AND BE JOINTLY APPROVED BY THE NATIONAL INSTITUTE FOR OCCUPATIONAL SAFETY AND HEALTH AND THE MINE SAFETY AND HEALTH ADMINISTRATION (NIOSH-MSHA).
FLUORIDES (AS F):
12.5 MG/M3- ANY DUST AND MIST RESPIRATOR EXCEPT SINGLE-USE RESPIRATORS.
25 MG/M3- ANY DUST AND MIST RESPIRATOR EXCEPT SINGLE-USE AND QUARTER-MASK RESPIRATORS. ANY SUPPLIED AIR RESPIRATOR. ANY SELF-CONTAINED BREATHING APPARATUS.
62.5 MG/M3- ANY POWERED AIR-PURIFYING RESPIRATOR WITH A DUST AND MIST FILTER. (MAY NEED ACID GAS SORBENT) ANY SUPPLIED-AIR RESPIRATOR OPERATED IN A CONTINUOUS FLOW MODE.
125 MG/M3- ANY SELF-CONTAINED BREATHING APPARATUS WITH A FULL FACEPIECE. ANY AIR-PURIFYING FULL FACEPIECE RESPIRATOR WITH A HIGH-EFFICIENCY PARTICULATE FILTER. (MAY NEED ACID GAS SORBENT) ANY SUPPLIED-AIR RESPIRATOR WITH A FULL FACEPIECE.
500 MG/M3- ANY SUPPLIED-AIR RESPIRATOR WITH A FULL FACEPIECE AND OPERATED IN A PRESSURE-DEMAND OR OTHER POSITIVE PRESSURE MODE.
ESCAPE- ANY AIR-PURIFYING FULL FACEPIECE RESPIRATOR (GAS MASK) WITH A CHIN-STYLE OR FRONT- OR BACK-MOUNTED ACID GAS CANISTER HAVING A HIGH-EFFICIENCY PARTICULATE FILTER. ANY APPROPRIATE ESCAPE-TYPE SELF-CONTAINED BREATHING APPARATUS.
FOR FIREFIGHTING AND OTHER IMMEDIATELY DANGEROUS TO LIFE OR HEALTH CONDITIONS:
SELF-CONTAINED BREATHING APPARATUS WITH FULL FACEPIECE OPERATED IN PRESSURE-DEMAND OR OTHER POSITIVE PRESSURE MODE.
SUPPLIED-AIR RESPIRATOR WITH FULL FACEPIECE AND OPERATED IN PRESSURE-DEMAND OR OTHER POSITIVE PRESSURE MODE IN COMBINATION WITH AN AUXILIARY SELF-CONTAINED BREATHING APPARATUS OPERATED IN PRESSURE-DEMAND OR OTHER POSITIVE PRESSURE MODE.

CLOTHING: EMPLOYEE MUST WEAR APPROPRIATE PROTECTIVE (IMPERVIOUS) CLOTHING AND EQUIPMENT TO PREVENT ANY POSSIBILITY OF SKIN CONTACT WITH THIS SUBSTANCE.

GLOVES: EMPLOYEE MUST WEAR APPROPRIATE PROTECTIVE GLOVES TO PREVENT CONTACT WITH THIS SUBSTANCE.

EYE PROTECTION: EMPLOYEE MUST WEAR SPLASH-PROOF OR DUST-RESISTANT SAFETY GOGGLES AND A FACESHIELD TO PREVENT CONTACT WITH THIS SUBSTANCE.
EMERGENCY WASH FACILITIES: WHERE THERE IS ANY POSSIBILITY THAT AN EMPLOYEE'S EYES AND/OR SKIN MAY BE EXPOSED TO THIS SUBSTANCE, THE EMPLOYER SHOULD PROVIDE AN EYE WASH FOUNTAIN AND QUICK DRENCH SHOWER WITHIN THE IMMEDIATE WORK AREA FOR EMERGENCY USE.

AUTHORIZED BY- OCCUPATIONAL HEALTH SERVICES, INC.
CREATION DATE: 10/04/89 ***REVISION DATE:*** 04/26/90

MATERIAL SAFETY DATA SHEET

OCCUPATIONAL HEALTH SERVICES, INC.
AGRICULTURE AND PESTICIDE DIVISION
450 SEVENTH AVENUE, SUITE 2407
NEW YORK, NEW YORK 10123
1-800-445-MSDS OR (212) 967-1100

EMERGENCY CONTACT:
JOHN S. BRANSFORD, JR. (615) 292-1180

SUBSTANCE IDENTIFICATION

CAS-NUMBER 60-51-5

SUBSTANCE: DIMETHOATE

TRADE NAMES/SYNONYMS: PHOSPHORODITHIOIC ACID, O,O-DIMETHYL S-(2-(METHYLAMINO)-2-OXOETHYL ESTER; PHOSPHRODITHIOIC ACID, O,O-DIMETHYL ESTER, S-ESTER WITH 2-MERCAPTO-N -METHYLACETAMIDE; PHOSPHORODITHIOIC ACID, O,O-DIMETHYL S-(METHYLCARBAMOYLMETHYL)ESTER; O,O-DIMETHYL S-METHYLCARBAMOYLMETHYL PHOSPHORODITHIOATE; 2-DIMETHOXYPHOSPHINOTHIOYLTHIO-N-METHYLACETAMIDE; O,O-DIMETHYL S-(2-(METHYLAMINO)-2-OXOETHYL)PHOSPHORODITHIOATE; O,O-DIEMTHYL PHOSPHORODITHIOATE S-ESTER WITH 2-MERCAPTO-N -METHYLACETAMIDE; PHOSPHAMIDE; FOSFAMID; CYGON; DEFENDION; ROGOR; ENT 24,650; RCRA P044; PST07670

CHEMICAL FAMILY: ORGANOPHOSPHATE

MOLECULAR FORMULA: C5-H12-N-O3-P-S2

MOLECULAR WEIGHT: 229.27

CERCLA RATINGS (SCALE 0-3): HEALTH=3 FIRE=1 REACTIVITY=U PERSISTENCE=0

NFPA RATINGS (SCALE 0-4): HEALTH=3 FIRE=1 REACTIVITY=U

COMPONENTS AND CONTAMINANTS

COMPONENT: DIMETHOATE ***PERCENT:*** 100
CAS# 60-51-5

EXPOSURE LIMITS: NO OCCUPATIONAL EXPOSURE LIMITS ESTABLISHED BY OSHA, ACGIH, OR NIOSH.
DIMETHOATE: 500/10,000 POUNDS SARA SECTION 302 THRESHOLD PLANNING QUANTITY 10 POUNDS SARA SECTION 304 REPORTABLE QUANTITY 10 POUNDS CERCLA SECTION 103 REPORTABLE QUANTITY

PHYSICAL DATA

DESCRIPTION: COLORLESS CRYSTALLINE SOLID WITH A CAMPHOR-LIKE ODOR

BOILING POINT: 225 F (107 C) @ 0.05 MMHG ***MELTING POINT:*** 124-126 F (51-52 C)

SPECIFIC GRAVITY: 1.277 @ 20 C ***VAPOR PRESSURE:*** 0.000009 MMHG @ 25 C

SOLUBILITY IN WATER: 2.5% @ 21 C

SOLVENT SOLUBILITY: SOLUBLE IN ALCOHOLS, BENZENE, CHLOROFORM, KETONES DICHLOROMETHANE, TOLUENE, ESTERS, AND CHLORINATED HYDROCARBONS; SLIGHTLY SOLUBLE IN AROMATIC HYDROCARBONS; ALMOST INSOLUBLE IN ALIPHATIC HYDROCARBONS

FIRE AND EXPLOSION DATA

FIRE AND EXPLOSION HAZARD: SLIGHT FIRE HAZARD WHEN EXPOSED TO HEAT OR FLAME.

FLASH POINT: 266 F (130 C) ***FLAMMABILITY CLASS(OSHA):*** IIIB

FIREFIGHTING MEDIA: DRY CHEMICAL, CARBON DIOXIDE, HALON, WATER SPRAY OR STANDARD FOAM (1987 EMERGENCY RESPONSE GUIDEBOOK, DOT P 5800.4).
FOR LARGER FIRES, USE WATER SPRAY, FOG OR STANDARD FOAM (1987 EMERGENCY RESPONSE GUIDEBOOK, DOT P 5800.4).

FIREFIGHTING: MOVE CONTAINERS FROM FIRE AREA IF POSSIBLE (1987 EMERGENCY RESPONSE GUIDEBOOK, DOT P 5800.4, GUIDE PAGE 53).
EXTINGUISH USING AGENT SUITABLE FOR TYPE OF SURROUNDING FIRE. AVOID BREATHING VAPORS AND DUSTS. KEEP UPWIND.

TOXICITY

DIMETHOATE: TOXICITY DATA: 1 GM/KG SKIN-RABBIT LD50; 353 MG/KG SKIN-RAT LD50; 286 MG/KG ORAL-MAN TDLO; 300 MG/KG ORAL-MAN TDLO; 30 MG/KG ORAL-HUMAN LD50; 60 MG/KG ORAL-RAT LD50; 60 MG/KG ORAL-MOUSE LD50; 400 MG/KG ORAL-DOG LD50; 200 MG/KG ORAL-HAMSTER LD50; 300 MG/KG ORAL-RABBIT LD50; 350 MG/KG ORAL-GUINEA PIG LD50; 100 MG/KG ORAL-CAT LD50; 60 MG/KG SUBCUTANEOUS-HAMSTER LD50; 450 MG/KG INTRAVENOUS-RAT LD50; 100 MG/KG INTRAPERITONEAL-RAT LD50; 45 MG/KG INTRAPERITONEAL-MOUSE LD50; 160 MG/KG INTRAPERITONEAL-HAMSTER LD50; 750 MG/KG INTRAPERITONEAL-GUINEA PIG LDLO; 215 MG/KG UNREPORTED-RAT LD50; MUTAGENIC DATA (RTECS); REPRODUCTIVE EFFECTS DATA (RTECS); TUMORIGENIC DATA (RTECS). CARCINOGEN STATUS: NONE. ACUTE TOXICITY LEVEL: TOXIC BY

INGESTION AND DERMAL ABSORPTION. TARGET EFFECTS: CHOLINESTERASE INHIBITOR. POISONING MAY AFFECT THE NERVOUS SYSTEM.* AT INCREASED RISK FROM EXPOSURE: PERSONS WITH RESPIRATORY AILMENTS, RECENT EXPOSURE TO CHOLINESTERASE INHIBITORS OR IMPAIRED CHOLINESTERASE PRODUCTION, OR LIVER MALFUNCTION.* ADDITIONAL DATA: MAY CROSS THE PLACENTA. HIGH ENVIRONMENTAL TEMPERATURES OR EXPOSURE OF THE CHEMICAL TO VISIBLE OR ULTRAVIOLET LIGHT MAY ENHANCE THE TOXICITY. INTERACTIONS WITH MEDICATIONS MAY OCCUR.*

* MAY BE BASED ON GENERAL INFORMATION ON ORGANOPHOSPHATES.

HEALTH EFFECTS AND FIRST AID

INHALATION: DIMETHOATE: SEE INFORMATION ON ORGANOPHOSPHATES. ORGANOPHOSPHATES: CHOLINESTERASE INHIBITOR. **ACUTE EXPOSURE**- WHEN INHALED, THE FIRST EFFECTS OF CHOLINESTERASE INHIBITORS ARE USUALLY RESPIRATORY AND MAY INCLUDE NASAL HYPEREMIA AND WATERY DISCHARGE, COUGH, CHEST DISCOMFORT, DYSPNEA, AND WHEEZING DUE TO INCREASED BRONCHIAL SECRETIONS AND BRONCHOCONSTRICTION. IF SUFFICIENT AMOUNTS ARE ABSORBED, OTHER SYSTEMIC EFFECTS MAY BEGIN WITHIN A FEW MINUTES OR BE DELAYED FOR UP TO 12 HOURS. SYMPTOMS MAY INCLUDE PALLOR, NAUSEA, VOMITING, DIARRHEA, ABDOMINAL CRAMPS, HEADACHE, DIZZINESS, OCULAR PAIN, BLURRED VISION, MIOSIS OR IN SOME CASES, ESPECIALLY INITIALLY, MYDRIASIS, LACRIMATION, SALIVATION, SWEATING, AND CONFUSION. OTHER REPORTED CENTRAL NERVOUS SYSTEM OR NEUROMUSCULAR EFFECTS MAY INCLUDE ATAXIA, SLURRED SPEECH, AREFLEXIA, WEAKNESS, FATIGUE, FASCICULATIONS, TWITCHING, TREMORS POSSIBLY OF THE TONGUE AND EYELIDS, AND EVENTUALLY PARALYSIS OF THE EXTREMITIES AND POSSIBLY OF THE RESPIRATORY MUSCLES. IN SEVERE CASES THERE MAY ALSO BE INVOLUNTARY DEFECATION AND URINATION, CYANOSIS, PSYCHOSIS, HYPERGLYCEMIA, ACUTE PANCREATITIS, CARDIAC IRREGULARITIES, PULMONARY EDEMA, UNCONSCIOUSNESS, CONVULSIONS, AND COMA. DEATH IS PRIMARILY DUE TO RESPIRATORY FAILURE, ALTHOUGH CARDIOVASCULAR EFFECTS INCLUDING CARDIAC ARREST MAY ALSO BE IMPLICATED. LONG TERM SEQUELAE ARE RARE BUT MAY INCLUDE NEUROPSYCHIATRIC DISORDERS AND MYOPATHY WITH MUSCLE TENDERNESS. SOME ORGANOPHOSPHATES MAY CAUSE A DELAYED NEUROPATHY BEGINNING 1-4 WEEKS AFTER AN ACUTE EXPOSURE WHICH MAY OR MAY NOT HAVE CAUSED ACUTE CHOLINERGIC EFFECTS. NUMBNESS, TINGLING, WEAKNESS AND CRAMPING BEGINNING SYMMETRICALLY IN THE LOWER LIMBS MAY PROGRESS TO ATAXIA AND PARALYSIS. IN SEVERE CASES, UPPER LIMB INVOLVEMENT IS POSSIBLE AND FLACCID PARALYSIS MAY PROGRESS TO SPASTIC PARALYSIS WITH EXAGGERATED REFLEXES. IMPROVEMENT MAY OCCUR OVER MONTHS TO YEARS, BUT SOME RESIDUAL IMPAIRMENT USUALLY REMAINS. **CHRONIC EXPOSURE**- REPEATED OR PROLONGED EXPOSURE MAY RESULT IN THE EFFECTS OF ACUTE EXPOSURE INCLUDING THE DELAYED NEUROPATHY. OTHER EFFECTS REPORTED IN WORKERS REPEATEDLY EXPOSED INCLUDE IMPAIRED MEMORY AND CONCENTRATION, ACUTE PSYCHOSIS, SEVERE DEPRESSIONS, IRRITABILTY, CONFUSION, APATHY, EMOTIONAL LABILITY, SOCIAL WITHDRAWAL, CONFUSION, HEADACHE, SPEECH DIFFICULTIES, DELAYED REACTION TIMES, SPATIAL DISORIENTATION, NIGHTMARES, SLEEPWALKING, AND DROWSINESS OR INSOMNIA. AN INFLUENZA-LIKE CONDITION WITH HEADACHE, NAUSEA, WEAKNESS, ANOREXIA AND MALAISE HAS ALSO BEEN REPORTED.

FIRST AID- REMOVE FROM EXPOSURE AREA TO FRESH AIR IMMEDIATELY. IF BREATHING HAS STOPPED, GIVE ARTIFICIAL RESPIRATION. MAINTAIN AIRWAY AND BLOOD PRESSURE AND ADMINISTER OXYGEN IF AVAILABLE. KEEP AFFECTED PERSON WARM AND AT REST. TREAT SYMPTOMATICALLY AND SUPPORTIVELY. ADMINISTRATION OF OXYGEN SHOULD BE PERFORMED BY QUALIFIED PERSONNEL. GET MEDICAL ATTENTION IMMEDIATELY.

SKIN CONTACT: DIMETHOATE: TOXIC. SEE INFORMATION ON ORGANOPHOSPHATES. ORGANOPHOSPHATES: CHOLINESTERASE INHIBITOR. **ACUTE EXPOSURE**- LOCALIZED SWEATING AND FASCICULATIONS MAY OCCUR AT THE SITE OF CONTACT. IF SUFFICIENT AMOUNTS ARE ABSORBED, OTHER EFFECTS OF CHOLINESTERASE INHIBITION AS DESCRIBED IN ACUTE INHALATION MAY OCCUR. SYMPTOMS MAY BE DELAYED 2-3 HOURS, BUT USUALLY NO MORE THAN 12 HOURS. THE RATE OF ABSORPTION IS INCREASED BY THE PRESENCE OF DERMATITIS OR HIGH AMBIENT TEMPERATURES. DELAYED NEUROPATHY IS ALSO POSSIBLE. **CHRONIC EXPOSURE**- REPEATED OR PROLONGED EXPOSURE MAY CAUSE EFFECTS AS DESCRIBED IN ACUTE EXPOSURE. SOME ORGANOPHOSPHATES MAY CAUSE SENSITIZATION.

FIRST AID- REMOVE CONTAMINATED CLOTHING IMMEDIATELY. WASH CONTAMINATED AREAS WITH SOAP AND WATER FOLLOWED BY ALCOHOL (ARENA, POISONING, 4TH ED.). EMERGENCY PERSONNEL SHOULD WEAR GLOVES AND AVOID CONTAMINATION. TREAT RESPIRATORY DIFFICULTY WITH ARTIFICIAL RESPIRATION. GET MEDICAL ATTENTION IMMEDIATELY.

EYE CONTACT: DIMETHOATE: SEE INFORMATION ON ORGANOPHOSPHATES. ORGANOPHOSPHATES: CHOLINESTERASE INHIBITOR. **ACUTE EXPOSURE**- DIRECT CONTACT MAY CAUSE PAIN, HYPEREMIA, LACRIMATION, TWITCHING OF THE EYELIDS, MIOSIS, AND CILIARY MUSCLE SPASM WITH LOSS OF ACCOMODATION, BLURRED OR DIMMED VISION AND BROWACHE. SOMETIMES MYDRIASIS MAY OCCUR INSTEAD OF MIOSIS. WITH SUFFICIENT EXPOSURE, OTHER SYMPTOMS OF CHOLINESTERASE INHIBITION AS DESCRIBED IN ACUTE INHALATION MAY OCCUR. **CHRONIC EXPOSURE**- REPEATED OR PROLONGED EXPOSURE MAY CAUSE EFFECTS AS DESCRIBED IN ACUTE EXPOSURE. SOME COMPOUNDS HAVE CAUSED TOXIC EFFECTS ON THE CRYSTALLINE LENS, CONJUNCTIVAL THICKENING AND OBSTRUCTION OF THE NASOLACRIMAL CANALS WHEN USED AS MIOTIC EYEDROPS.

FIRST AID- IRRIGATE EYES WITH WATER OR SALINE SOLUTION. IF SYMPTOMS OF POISONING OCCUR, TREAT RESPIRATORY DIFFICULTY WITH ARTIFICIAL RESPIRATION AND OXYGEN. OBSERVE PATIENT FOR AT LEAST 24-36 HOURS (GOSSELIN, CLINICAL TOXICOLOGY OF COMMERCIAL PRODUCTS, 5TH ED.). GET MEDICAL ATTENTION IMMEDIATELY. OXYGEN SHOULD BE ADMINISTERED BY QUALIFIED MEDICAL PERSONNEL.

INGESTION: DIMETHOATE: TOXIC. THERE IS INSUFFICIENT EVIDENCE TO DETERMINE WHETHER DIMETHOATE CAN INDUCE DELAYED NEUROTOXICITY. A STATISTICALLY SIGNIFICANT INCREASE IN MALIGNANT TUMORS WAS OBSERVED IN ONE CHRONIC FEEDING STUDY WITH RATS. FETAL DEVELOPMENTAL ABNORMALITIES WERE REPORTED FROM CHRONIC FEEDING STUDIES IN CATS AND RATS. ADVERSE EFFECTS ON FERTILITY AND THE NEWBORN WERE OBSERVED IN A MULTIGENERATION STUDY OF MICE. SEE INFORMATION ON ORGANOPHOSPHATES. ORGANOPHOSPHATES: CHOLINESTERASE INHIBITOR. **ACUTE EXPOSURE**- WHEN INGESTED, THE FIRST EFFECTS MAY BE NAUSEA, VOMITING, ANOREXIA, ABDOMINAL CRAMPS AND DIARRHEA. GASTROINTESTINAL ABSORPTION MAY CAUSE SYMPTOMS OF CHOLINESTERASE INHIBITION AS DESCRIBED IN ACUTE INHALATION. SYMPTOMS MAY BEGIN WITHIN MINUTES OR BE DELAYED FOR HOURS. DELAYED EFFECTS INCLUDING NEUROPATHY MAY ALSO OCCUR. **CHRONIC EXPOSURE**- REPEATED INGESTION MAY CAUSE EFFECTS AS DESCRIBED IN ACUTE EXPOSURE.

FIRST AID- IF PERSON IS ALERT AND RESPIRATION IS NOT DEPRESSED, GIVE SYRUP OF IPECAC FOLLOWED BY WATER (IF VOMITING OCCURS, KEEP HEAD BELOW HIPS TO PREVENT ASPIRATION). IF CONSCIOUSNESS LEVEL DECLINES OR VOMITING HAS NOT OCCURRED IN 15 MINUTES EMPTY STOMACH BY GASTRIC LAVAGE WITH THE AID OF CUFFED ENDOTRACHEAL TUBE USING ISOTONIC SALINE OR 5% SODIUM BICARBONATE FOLLOW WITH ACTIVATED CHARCOAL. ESTABLISH AND MAINTAIN AIRWAY. TREAT RESPIRATORY DIFFICULTY WITH ARTIFICIAL RESPIRATION AND OXYGEN. DO NOT GIVE MORPHINE, AMINOPHYLLINE, PHENOTHIAZINES, RESERPINE, FUROSEMIDE, OR ETHACRYNIC ACID (MORGAN, RECOGNITION AND MANAGEMENT OF PESTICIDE POISONINGS, 3RD ED.). TREAT SYMPTOMATICALLY AND SUPPORTIVELY. ADMINISTRATION OF OXYGEN AND LAVAGE MUST BE PERFORMED BY QUALIFIED MEDICAL PERSONNEL. GET MEDICAL ATTENTION IMMEDIATELY.

ANTIDOTE: THE FOLLOWING ANTIDOTE(S) HAVE BEEN RECOMMENDED. HOWEVER, THE DECISION AS TO WHETHER THE SEVERITY OF POISONING REQUIRES ADMINISTRATION OF ANY ANTIDOTE AND ACTUAL DOSE REQUIRED SHOULD BE MADE BY QUALIFIED MEDICAL PERSONNEL.

FOR CHOLINESTERASE INHIBITORS: ESTABLISH CLEAR AIRWAY AND TISSUE OXYGENATION BY ASPIRATION OF SECRETIONS, AND IF NECESSARY, BY ASSISTED PULMONARY VENTILATION WITH OXYGEN. IMPROVE TISSUE OXYGENATION AS MUCH AS POSSIBLE BEFORE ADMINISTERING ATROPINE TO MINIMIZE THE RISK OF VENTRICULAR FIBRILLATION. ADMINISTER ATROPINE SULFATE INTRAVENOUSLY, OR INTRAMUSCULARLY IF IV INJECTION IS NOT POSSIBLE. IN MODERATELY SEVERE POISONING ADMINISTER ATROPINE SULFATE, 0.4-2.0 MG REPEATED EVERY 15 MINUTES UNTIL ATROPINIZATION IS ACHIEVED (TACHYCARDIA, FLUSHING, DRY MOUTH, MYDRIASIS). MAINTAIN ATROPINIZATION BY REPEATED DOSES FOR 2-12 HOURS, OR LONGER, DEPENDING ON THE SEVERITY OF POISONING. THE APPEARANCE OF RALES IN THE LUNG BASES, MIOSIS, SALIVATION, NAUSEA, BRADYCARDIA, ARE ALL INDICATIONS OF INADEQUATE ATROPINIZATION. SEVERELY POISONED INDIVIDUALS MAY EXHIBIT REMARKABLE TOLERANCE TO ATROPINE; TWO OR MORE TIMES THE DOSAGES SUGGESTED ABOVE MAY BE NEEDED. PERSONS NOT POISONED OR ONLY SLIGHTLY POISONED, HOWEVER, MAY DEVELOP SIGNS OF ATROPINE TOXICITY FROM SUCH LARGE DOSAGES: FEVER, MUSCLE FIBRILLATIONS, AND DELIRIUM ARE THE MAIN SIGNS OF ATROPINE TOXICITY. IF THESE SIGNS APPEAR WHILE THE PATIENT IS FULLY ATROPINIZED, ATROPINE ADMINISTRATION SHOULD BE DISCONTINUED, AT LEAST TEMPORARILY. OBSERVE TREATED PATIENTS CLOSELY AT LEAST 24 HOURS TO INSURE THAT SYMPTOMS (POSSIBLY PULMONARY EDEMA) DO NOT RECUR AS ATROPINIZATION WEARS OFF. IN VERY SEVERE POISONINGS, METABOLIC DISPOSITION OF TOXICANT MAY REQUIRE SEVERAL HOURS OR DAYS DURING WHICH ATROPINIZATION MUST BE MAINTAINED. MARKEDLY LOWER LEVELS OF URINARY METABOLITES INDICATE THAT ATROPINE DOSAGE CAN BE TAPERED OFF. AS DOSAGE IS REDUCED, CHECK THE LUNG BASES FREQUENTLY FOR RALES. IF RALES ARE HEARD OR OTHER SYMPTOMS RETURN, RE-ESTABLISH ATROPINIZATION PROMPTLY (MORGAN, RECOGNITION AND MANAGEMENT OF PESTICIDE

SUBSTANCE IDENTIFICATION

CAS-NUMBER 50563-36-5
SUBSTANCE: DIMETHACHLOR
TRADE NAMES/SYNONYMS: ACETAMIDE, 2-CHLORO-N-(2,6-DIMETHYLPHENYL)-N-(2-METHOXYETHYL)-; 2-CHLORO-N-(2,6-DIMETHYLPHENYL)-N-(2-METHOXYETHYL))ACETAMIDE; 2-CHLORO-N-(2-METHOXYETHYL)ACET-2',6'-XYLIDIDE; 2-CHLORO-N-(2,6-DIMETHYLPHENYL)-N-(2-METHOXYETHYL)ACETAMIDE; 2,6-DIMETHYL-N-(2-METHOXYETHYL)CHLOROACETANILIDE; CGA 17020; DIMETHACHLORO; TERIDOX; C13H18CLNO2; PST07677
CHEMICAL FAMILY: HALOGENATED ACETAMIDE
MOLECULAR FORMULA: C13H18CLNO2
MOLECULAR WEIGHT: 255.74
CERCLA RATINGS (SCALE 0-3): HEALTH=2 FIRE=1 REACTIVITY=0 PERSISTENCE=2
NFPA RATINGS (SCALE 0-4): HEALTH=2 FIRE=1 REACTIVITY=0

COMPONENTS AND CONTAMINANTS

COMPONENT: DIMETHACHLOR ***PERCENT:*** 100
CAS# 50563-36-5
OTHER CONTAMINANTS: NONE
EXPOSURE LIMITS: NO OCCUPATIONAL EXPOSURE LIMITS ESTABLISHED BY OSHA, ACGIH, OR NIOSH.

PHYSICAL DATA

DESCRIPTION: COLORLESS CRYSTALS ***MELTING POINT:*** 117 F (47 C)
SPECIFIC GRAVITY: 1.21 ***VAPOR PRESSURE:*** 0.000016 MMHG @ 20 C
SOLUBILITY IN WATER: 0.21%
SOLVENT SOLUBILITY: SOLUBLE IN BENZENE, DICHLOROMETHANE, METHANOL, ISOOCTANOL, ACETONE, OCTANOL.

FIRE AND EXPLOSION DATA

FIRE AND EXPLOSION HAZARD: SLIGHT FIRE HAZARD WHEN EXPOSED TO HEAT OR FLAME.
FIREFIGHTING MEDIA: DRY CHEMICAL, CARBON DIOXIDE, HALON, WATER SPRAY OR STANDARD FOAM (1987 EMERGENCY RESPONSE GUIDEBOOK, DOT P 5800.4).
FOR LARGER FIRES, USE WATER SPRAY, FOG OR STANDARD FOAM (1987 EMERGENCY RESPONSE GUIDEBOOK, DOT P 5800.4).
FIREFIGHTING: MOVE CONTAINERS FROM FIRE AREA IF POSSIBLE (1987 EMERGENCY RESPONSE GUIDEBOOK, DOT P 5800.4, GUIDE PAGE 53).
EXTINGUISH FIRE USING AGENTS SUITABLE FOR TYPE OF SURROUNDING FIRE. USE WATER IN FLOODING AMOUNTS AS A FOG. AVOID BREATHING DUSTS AND FUMES FROM BURNING MATERIAL; KEEP UPWIND.

TOXICITY

DIMETHACHLOR: TOXICITY DATA: 1600 MG/KG ORAL-RAT LD50. CARCINOGEN STATUS: NONE. ACUTE TOXICITY LEVEL: MODERATELY TOXIC BY INGESTION. TARGET EFFECTS: NO DATA AVAILABLE.

HEALTH EFFECTS AND FIRST AID

INHALATION: DIMETHACHLOR: **ACUTE EXPOSURE-** NO DATA AVAILABLE. **CHRONIC EXPOSURE-** NO DATA AVAILABLE.
FIRST AID- REMOVE FROM EXPOSURE AREA TO FRESH AIR IMMEDIATELY. IF BREATHING HAS STOPPED, PERFORM ARTIFICIAL RESPIRATION. KEEP PERSON WARM AND AT REST. TREAT SYMPTOMATICALLY AND SUPPORTIVELY. GET MEDICAL ATTENTION IMMEDIATELY.

SKIN CONTACT: DIMETHACHLOR: **ACUTE EXPOSURE-** THIS MATERIAL WAS SLIGHTLY IRRITATING TO THE SKIN OF RABBITS. A LETHAL DOSE IN RATS BY DERMAL ABSORPTION IS GREATER THAN 3170 MG/KG. **CHRONIC EXPOSURE-** NO DATA AVAILABLE.
FIRST AID- REMOVE CONTAMINATED CLOTHING AND SHOES IMMEDIATELY. WASH AFFECTED AREA WITH SOAP OR MILD DETERGENT AND LARGE AMOUNTS OF WATER UNTIL NO EVIDENCE OF CHEMICAL REMAINS (APPROXIMATELY 15-20 MINUTES). GET MEDICAL ATTENTION IMMEDIATELY.

EYE CONTACT: DIMETHACHLOR: **ACUTE EXPOSURE-** THIS MATERIAL WAS SLIGHTLY IRRITATING TO RABBIT EYES. **CHRONIC EXPOSURE-** NO DATA AVAILABLE.
FIRST AID- WASH EYES IMMEDIATELY WITH LARGE AMOUNTS OF WATER OR NORMAL SALINE, OCCASIONALLY LIFTING UPPER AND LOWER LIDS, UNTIL NO EVIDENCE OF CHEMICAL REMAINS (APPROXIMATELY 15-20 MINUTES). GET MEDICAL ATTENTION IMMEDIATELY.

INGESTION: DIMETHACHLOR: **ACUTE EXPOSURE-** A LETHAL DOSE IN RATS WAS 1600 MG/KG. **CHRONIC EXPOSURE-** NO EFFECTS WERE OBSERVED IN RATS FED 47 MG/KG/DAY FOR 90 DAYS.
FIRST AID- TREAT SYMPTOMATICALLY AND SUPPORTIVELY. GET MEDICAL ATTENTION IMMEDIATELY. IF VOMITING OCCURS, KEEP HEAD LOWER THAN HIPS TO PREVENT ASPIRATION.
ANTIDOTE: NO SPECIFIC ANTIDOTE. TREAT SYMPTOMATICALLY AND SUPPORTIVELY.

REACTIVITY

REACTIVITY: STABLE UNDER NORMAL TEMPERATURES AND PRESSURES.
INCOMPATIBILITIES: DIMETHACHLOR: NO DATA AVAILABLE.
DECOMPOSITION: THERMAL DECOMPOSITION PRODUCTS MAY INCLUDE HIGHLY TOXIC FUMES OF PHOSGENE, TOXIC AND CORROSIVE FUMES OF CHLORIDES, AND OXIDES OF CARBON.
POLYMERIZATION: HAZARDOUS POLYMERIZATION HAS NOT BEEN REPORTED TO OCCUR UNDER NORMAL TEMPERATURES AND PRESSURES.

STORAGE AND DISPOSAL

OBSERVE ALL FEDERAL, STATE AND LOCAL REGULATIONS WHEN STORING OR DISPOSING OF THIS SUBSTANCE. FOR ASSISTANCE, CONTACT THE DISTRICT DIRECTOR OF THE ENVIRONMENTAL PROTECTION AGENCY.

****STORAGE****

STORE IN ACCORDANCE WITH 40 CFR 165 RECOMMENDED PROCEDURES FOR THE DISPOSAL AND STORAGE OF PESTICIDES AND PESTICIDE CONTAINERS.

****DISPOSAL****

DISPOSAL MUST BE IN ACCORDANCE WITH 40 CFR 165 RECOMMENDED PROCEDURES FOR THE DISPOSAL AND STORAGE OF PESTICIDES AND PESTICIDE CONTAINERS.

CONDITIONS TO AVOID

MAY BURN BUT DOES NOT IGNITE READILY.

SPILL AND LEAK PROCEDURES

OCCUPATIONAL SPILL: DO NOT TOUCH SPILLED MATERIAL. STOP LEAK IF YOU CAN DO IT WITHOUT RISK. FOR SMALL SPILLS, TAKE UP WITH SAND OR OTHER ABSORBENT MATERIAL AND PLACE INTO CONTAINERS FOR LATER DISPOSAL. FOR SMALL DRY SPILLS, WITH A CLEAN SHOVEL PLACE MATERIAL INTO CLEAN, DRY CONTAINER AND COVER. MOVE CONTAINERS FROM SPILL AREA. FOR LARGER SPILLS, DIKE FAR AHEAD OF SPILL FOR LATER DISPOSAL. KEEP UNNECESSARY PEOPLE AWAY. ISOLATE HAZARD AREA AND DENY ENTRY.

PROTECTIVE EQUIPMENT

VENTILATION: PROVIDE LOCAL EXHAUST OR GENERAL DILUTION VENTILATION SYSTEM.
RESPIRATOR: THE FOLLOWING RESPIRATORS ARE RECOMMENDED BASED ON INFORMATION FOUND IN THE PHYSICAL DATA, TOXICITY AND HEALTH EFFECTS SECTIONS. THEY ARE RANKED IN ORDER FROM MINIMUM TO MAXIMUM RESPIRATORY PROTECTION. THE SPECIFIC RESPIRATOR SELECTED MUST BE BASED ON CONTAMINATION LEVELS FOUND IN THE WORK PLACE, MUST NOT EXCEED THE WORKING LIMITS OF THE RESPIRATOR AND BE JOINTLY APPROVED BY THE NATIONAL INSTITUTE FOR OCCUPATIONAL SAFETY AND HEALTH AND THE MINE SAFETY AND HEALTH ADMINISTRATION (NIOSH-MSHA).
CHEMICAL CARTRIDGE RESPIRATOR WITH AN ORGANIC VAPOR CARTRIDGE(S) WITH A FULL FACEPIECE AND ORGANIC VAPOR CARTRIDGE(S) IN COMBINATION WITH A DUST AND MIST FILTER.
POWERED AIR-PURIFYING RESPIRATOR WITH A TIGHT-FITTING FACEPIECE AND ORGANIC VAPOR CARTRIDGE(S) IN COMBINATION WITH A HIGH-EFFICIENCY PARTICULATE FILTER.
TYPE 'C' SUPPLIED-AIR RESPIRATOR WITH A FULL FACEPIECE OPERATED IN A PRESSURE-DEMAND OR OTHER POSITIVE PRESSURE MODE.
SELF-CONTAINED BREATHING APPARATUS WITH A FULL FACEPIECE OPERATED IN PRESSURE-DEMAND OR OTHER POSITIVE PRESSURE MODE.
FOR FIREFIGHTING AND OTHER IMMEDIATELY DANGEROUS TO LIFE OR HEALTH CONDITIONS:
SELF-CONTAINED BREATHING APPARATUS WITH FULL FACEPIECE OPERATED IN PRESSURE-DEMAND OR OTHER POSITIVE PRESSURE MODE.
SUPPLIED-AIR RESPIRATOR WITH FULL FACEPIECE AND OPERATED IN PRESSURE-DEMAND OR OTHER POSITIVE PRESSURE MODE IN COMBINATION WITH AN AUXILIARY SELF-CONTAINED BREATHING APPARATUS OPERATED IN PRESSURE-DEMAND OR OTHER POSITIVE PRESSURE MODE.
CLOTHING: EMPLOYEE MUST WEAR APPROPRIATE PROTECTIVE (IMPERVIOUS) CLOTHING AND EQUIPMENT TO PREVENT REPEATED OR PROLONGED SKIN CONTACT WITH THIS SUBSTANCE.
GLOVES: EMPLOYEE MUST WEAR APPROPRIATE PROTECTIVE GLOVES TO PREVENT CONTACT WITH THIS SUBSTANCE.
EYE PROTECTION: EMPLOYEE MUST WEAR SPLASH-PROOF OR DUST-RESISTANT SAFETY GOGGLES TO PREVENT EYE CONTACT WITH THIS SUBSTANCE.
EMERGENCY EYE WASH: WHERE THERE IS ANY POSSIBILITY THAT AN EMPLOYEE'S EYES MAY BE EXPOSED TO THIS SUBSTANCE, THE EMPLOYER SHOULD PROVIDE

AN EYE WASH FOUNTAIN WITHIN THE IMMEDIATE WORK AREA FOR EMERGENCY USE.

AUTHORIZED BY- OCCUPATIONAL HEALTH SERVICES, INC.
CREATION DATE: 10/04/89 ***REVISION DATE:*** 05/14/90

MATERIAL SAFETY DATA SHEET

OCCUPATIONAL HEALTH SERVICES, INC.
AGRICULTURE AND PESTICIDE DIVISION
450 SEVENTH AVENUE, SUITE 2407
NEW YORK, NEW YORK 10123
1-800-445-MSDS OR (212) 967-1100

EMERGENCY CONTACT:
JOHN S. BRANSFORD, JR. (615) 292-1180

SUBSTANCE IDENTIFICATION

CAS-NUMBER 131-11-3
SUBSTANCE: DIMETHYL PHTHALATE
TRADE NAMES/SYNONYMS: 1,2-BENZENEDICARBOXYLIC ACID, DIMETHYL ESTER; PHTHALIC ACID, DIMETHYL ESTER; DIMETHYL 1,2-BENZENEDICARBOXYLATE; DIMETHYL O-PHTHALATE; AVOLIN; DMP; FERMINE; PALITINOL M; UNIMOLL DM; RCRA U102; C10H10O4; PST07740
CHEMICAL FAMILY: ESTER, CARBOXYLIC, AROMATIC PHTHALATE
MOLECULAR FORMULA: C6-H4-(C-O2-C-H3)2
MOLECULAR WEIGHT: 194.19
CERCLA RATINGS (SCALE 0-3): HEALTH=3 FIRE=1 REACTIVITY=0 PERSISTENCE=2
NFPA RATINGS (SCALE 0-4): HEALTH=0 FIRE=1 REACTIVITY=0

COMPONENTS AND CONTAMINANTS

COMPONENT: DIMETHYL PHTHALATE ***PERCENT:*** 100.0
CAS# 131-11-3
OTHER CONTAMINANTS: NONE
EXPOSURE LIMITS: DIMETHYL PHTHALATE: 5 MG/M3 OSHA TWA 5 MG/M3 ACGIH TWA
5000 POUNDS CERCLA SECTION 103 REPORTABLE QUANTITY SUBJECT TO SARA SECTION 313 ANNUAL TOXIC CHEMICAL RELEASE REPORTING

PHYSICAL DATA

DESCRIPTION: COLORLESS TO PALE YELLOW OILY LIQUID WITH A SLIGHT AROMATIC ODOR.
BOILING POINT: 543 F (284 C) ***MELTING POINT:*** 32-36 F (0-2 C)
SPECIFIC GRAVITY: 1.1905 ***VISCOSITY:*** 17.2 CPS @ 25 C ***VOLATILITY:*** 100%
VAPOR PRESSURE: <0.01 MMHG @ 20 C
EVAPORATION RATE: (METHYL ACETATE=1) ALMOST ZERO ***SOLUBILITY IN WATER:*** 0.43%
VAPOR DENSITY: 6.69
SOLVENT SOLUBILITY: SOLUBLE IN BENZENE, ALCOHOL, ETHER, CHLOROFORM; SLIGHTLY SOLUBLE IN MINERAL OIL; PRACTICALLY INSOLUBLE IN PETROLEUM ETHER AND OTHER PARAFFIN HYDROCARBONS.

FIRE AND EXPLOSION DATA

FIRE AND EXPLOSION HAZARD: SLIGHT FIRE HAZARD WHEN EXPOSED TO HEAT OR FLAME.
FLASH POINT: 295 F (146 C) (CC) ***LOWER EXPLOSIVE LIMIT:*** 0.9% @ 358 F (180 C)
AUTOIGNITION TEMP.: 915 F (490 C) ***FLAMMABILITY CLASS(OSHA):*** IIIB
FIREFIGHTING MEDIA: DRY CHEMICAL, CARBON DIOXIDE, HALON, WATER SPRAY OR STANDARD FOAM (1987 EMERGENCY RESPONSE GUIDEBOOK, DOT P 5800.4).
FOR LARGER FIRES, USE WATER SPRAY, FOG OR STANDARD FOAM (1987 EMERGENCY RESPONSE GUIDEBOOK, DOT P 5800.4).
FIREFIGHTING: MOVE CONTAINER FROM FIRE AREA IF POSSIBLE. DO NOT SCATTER SPILLED MATERIAL WITH HIGH PRESSURE WATER STREAMS. DIKE FIRE CONTROL WATER FOR LATER DISPOSAL (1987 EMERGENCY RESPONSE GUIDEBOOK, DOT P 5800.4, GUIDE PAGE 31).
USE AGENTS SUITABLE FOR TYPE OF SURROUNDING FIRE. AVOID BREATHING HAZARDOUS VAPORS, KEEP UPWIND.
WATER OR FOAM MAY CAUSE FROTHING (NFPA 325M, FIRE HAZARD PROPERTIES OF FLAMMABLE LIQUIDS, GASES, AND VOLATILE SOLIDS, 1984)

TOXICITY

DIMETHYL PHTHALATE: IRRITATION DATA: 119 MG EYE-RABBIT. TOXICITY DATA: 9630 MG/M3/6 HOURS INHALATION-CAT LCLO; 6800 MG/KG ORAL-RAT LD50; 6800 MG/KG ORAL-MOUSE LD50; 4400 MG/KG ORAL-RABBIT LD50; 2400 MG/KG ORAL-GUINEA PIG LD50; 6500 MG/KG SUBCUTANEOUS-MOUSE LDLO; 3375 MG/KG INTRAPERITONEAL-RAT LD50; 1380 MG/KG INTRAPERITONEAL-MOUSE LD50; MUTAGENIC DATA (RTECS); REPRODUCTIVE EFFECTS DATA (RTECS). CARCINOGEN STATUS: NONE. ACUTE TOXICITY LEVEL: SLIGHTLY TOXIC BY INGESTION. TARGET EFFECTS: CENTRAL NERVOUS SYSTEM DEPRESSANT.

HEALTH EFFECTS AND FIRST AID

INHALATION: DIMETHYL PHTHALATE: NARCOTIC. 9300 MG/M3 IMMEDIATELY DANGEROUS TO LIFE OR HEALTH. **ACUTE EXPOSURE-** VAPOR OR MIST MAY CAUSE IRRITATION OF THE UPPER RESPIRATORY TRACT WITH COUGHING, SORE THROAT AND DIFFICULTY IN BREATHING. CENTRAL NERVOUS SYSTEM DEPRESSION MAY ALSO OCCUR. **CHRONIC EXPOSURE-** PROLONGED EXPOSURE MAY RESULT IN IRRITATION.
FIRST AID- REMOVE FROM EXPOSURE AREA TO FRESH AIR IMMEDIATELY. IF BREATHING HAS STOPPED, PERFORM ARTIFICIAL RESPIRATION. KEEP PERSON WARM AND AT REST. TREAT SYMPTOMATICALLY AND SUPPORTIVELY. GET MEDICAL ATTENTION IMMEDIATELY.

SKIN CONTACT: DIMETHYL PHTHALATE: **ACUTE EXPOSURE-** USE IN INSECT REPELLANT FORMULATIONS HAS RESULTED IN VERY LITTLE IRRITANCY FOR HUMANS. ANIMAL STUDIES INDICATE THAT ABSORPTION THROUGH THE SKIN IS NOT LIKELY TO RESULT IN ACUTE TOXIC EFFECTS. **CHRONIC EXPOSURE-** THE 90 DAY LD50 BY REPEATED SKIN APPLICATION IN RABBITS WAS GREATER THAN 4 ML/KG. SYMPTOMS INCLUDED PULMONARY EDEMA AND SLIGHT RENAL DAMAGE. THERE WAS NO IRRITATION OR SENSITIZATION REPORTED.
FIRST AID- REMOVE CONTAMINATED CLOTHING AND SHOES IMMEDIATELY. WASH AFFECTED AREA WITH SOAP OR MILD DETERGENT AND LARGE AMOUNTS OF WATER UNTIL NO EVIDENCE OF CHEMICAL REMAINS (APPROXIMATELY 15-20 MINUTES). GET MEDICAL ATTENTION IMMEDIATELY.

EYE CONTACT: DIMETHYL PHTHALATE: **ACUTE EXPOSURE-** CONTACT WITH THE EYES MAY CAUSE SMARTING AND CONSIDERABLE PAIN, BUT NO DAMAGE OR ONLY SLIGHT REVERSIBLE DISTURBANCE OF THE EPITHELIUM. **CHRONIC EXPOSURE-** REPEATED OR PROLONGED EXPOSURE MAY CAUSE CONJUNCTIVITIS.
FIRST AID- WASH EYES IMMEDIATELY WITH LARGE AMOUNTS OF WATER OR NORMAL SALINE, OCCASIONALLY LIFTING UPPER AND LOWER LIDS, UNTIL NO EVIDENCE OF CHEMICAL REMAINS (APPROXIMATELY 15-20 MINUTES). GET MEDICAL ATTENTION IMMEDIATELY.

INGESTION: DIMETHYL PHTHALATE: NARCOTIC. **ACUTE EXPOSURE-** MAY CAUSE A BURNING SENSATION OF THE LIPS, TONGUE AND MOUTH, AND ABDOMINAL PAIN WITH NAUSEA, VOMITING, AND DIARRHEA. CENTRAL NERVOUS SYSTEM DEPRESSION MAY OCCUR WITH DIZZINESS, HYPOTENSION, UNCONSCIOUSNESS, AND COMA. **CHRONIC EXPOSURE-** RATS FED DIETARY LEVELS OF UP TO 8% FOR 2 YEARS SHOWED GROWTH EFFECTS AND CHRONIC NEPHRITIC CHANGES.
FIRST AID- REMOVE BY GASTRIC LAVAGE AND CATHARSIS. MAINTAIN BLOOD PRESSURE AND AIRWAY. GIVE OXYGEN IF RESPIRATION IS DEPRESSED. DO NOT PERFORM GASTRIC LAVAGE IF VICTIM IS UNCONSCIOUS. GET MEDICAL ATTENTION IMMEDIATELY (DREISBACH, HANDBOOK OF POISONING, 12TH ED.).
ADMINISTRATION OF LAVAGE OR OXYGEN SHOULD BE PERFORMED BY QUALIFIED MEDICAL PERSONNEL.
ANTIDOTE: NO SPECIFIC ANTIDOTE. TREAT SYMPTOMATICALLY AND SUPPORTIVELY.

REACTIVITY

REACTIVITY: STABLE UNDER NORMAL TEMPERATURES AND PRESSURES.
INCOMPATIBILITIES: DIMETHYL PHTHALATE: ACIDS (STRONG): FIRE AND EXPLOSION HAZARD. ALKALIES (STRONG): FIRE AND EXPLOSION HAZARD. NITRATES: FIRE AND EXPLOSION HAZARD. OXIDIZERS (STRONG): FIRE AND EXPLOSION HAZARD.
DECOMPOSITION: THERMAL DECOMPOSITION PRODUCTS MAY INCLUDE TOXIC OXIDES OF CARBON.
POLYMERIZATION: HAZARDOUS POLYMERIZATION HAS NOT BEEN REPORTED TO OCCUR UNDER NORMAL TEMPERATURES AND PRESSURES.

STORAGE AND DISPOSAL

OBSERVE ALL FEDERAL, STATE AND LOCAL REGULATIONS WHEN STORING OR DISPOSING OF THIS SUBSTANCE. FOR ASSISTANCE, CONTACT THE DISTRICT DIRECTOR OF THE ENVIRONMENTAL PROTECTION AGENCY.

STORAGE

STORE AWAY FROM INCOMPATIBLE SUBSTANCES.

DISPOSAL

DISPOSAL MUST BE IN ACCORDANCE WITH STANDARDS APPLICABLE TO GENERATORS OF HAZARDOUS WASTE, 40CFR 262. EPA HAZARDOUS WASTE NUMBER U102.

CONDITIONS TO AVOID

MAY BURN BUT DOES NOT IGNITE READILY. AVOID CONTACT WITH STRONG OXIDIZERS, EXCESSIVE HEAT, SPARKS, OR OPEN FLAME.

SPILL AND LEAK PROCEDURES

OCCUPATIONAL SPILL: STOP LEAK IF YOU CAN DO IT WITHOUT RISK. FOR SMALL SPILLS, TAKE UP WITH SAND OR OTHER ABSORBENT MATERIAL AND PLACE INTO CLEAN, DRY CONTAINERS FOR LATER DISPOSAL. KEEP UNNECESSARY PEOPLE AWAY. ISOLATE HAZARD AREA AND DENY ENTRY.

REPORTABLE QUANTITY (RQ): 5000 POUNDS THE SUPERFUND AMENDMENTS AND REAUTHORIZATION ACT (SARA) SECTION 304 REQUIRES THAT A RELEASE EQUAL TO OR GREATER THAN THE REPORTABLE QUANTITY FOR THIS SUBSTANCE BE IMMEDIATELY REPORTED TO THE LOCAL EMERGENCY PLANNING COMMITTEE AND THE STATE EMERGENCY RESPONSE COMMISSION (40 CFR 355.40). IF THE RELEASE OF THIS SUBSTANCE IS REPORTABLE UNDER CERCLA SECTION 103, THE NATIONAL RESPONSE CENTER MUST BE NOTIFIED IMMEDIATELY AT (800) 424-8802 OR (202) 426-2675 IN THE METROPOLITAN WASHINGTON, D.C. AREA (40 CFR 302.6).

PROTECTIVE EQUIPMENT

VENTILATION: PROVIDE LOCAL EXHAUST VENTILATION AND/OR GENERAL DILUTION VENTILATION TO MEET PUBLISHED EXPOSURE LIMITS.

RESPIRATOR: THE FOLLOWING RESPIRATORS AND MAXIMUM USE CONCENTRATIONS ARE RECOMMENDATIONS BY THE U.S. DEPARTMENT OF HEALTH AND HUMAN SERVICES, NIOSH POCKET GUIDE TO CHEMICAL HAZARDS; NIOSH CRITERIA DOCUMENTS OR BY THE U.S. DEPARTMENT OF LABOR, 29 CFR 1910 SUBPART Z. THE SPECIFIC RESPIRATOR SELECTED MUST BE BASED ON CONTAMINATION LEVELS FOUND IN THE WORK PLACE, MUST NOT EXCEED THE WORKING LIMITS OF THE RESPIRATOR AND BE JOINTLY APPROVED BY THE NATIONAL INSTITUTE FOR OCCUPATIONAL SAFETY AND HEALTH AND THE MINE SAFETY AND HEALTH ADMINISTRATION (NIOSH-MSHA).

DIMETHYL PHTHALATE:

50 MG/M3- ANY DUST AND MIST RESPIRATOR WITH A FULL FACEPIECE.

125 MG/M3- ANY POWERED AIR-PURIFYING RESPIRATOR WITH A DUST AND MIST FILTER. ANY SUPPLIED-AIR RESPIRATOR OPERATED IN A CONTINUOUS FLOW MODE.

250 MG/M3- ANY AIR-PURIFYING FULL FACEPIECE RESPIRATOR WITH A HIGH-EFFICIENCY PARTICULATE FILTER. ANY SELF-CONTAINED BREATHING APPARATUS WITH A FULL FACEPIECE. ANY SUPPLIED-AIR RESPIRATOR WITH A FULL FACEPIECE.

9300 MG/M3- ANY SUPPLIED-AIR RESPIRATOR WITH A HALF-MASK AND OPERATED IN A PRESSURE-DEMAND OR OTHER POSITIVE PRESSURE MODE.

ESCAPE- ANY AIR-PURIFYING FULL FACEPIECE RESPIRATOR WITH A HIGH-EFFICIENCY PARTICULATE FILTER. ANY APPROPRIATE ESCAPE-TYPE SELF-CONTAINED BREATHING APPARATUS.

FOR FIREFIGHTING AND OTHER IMMEDIATELY DANGEROUS TO LIFE OR HEALTH CONDITIONS:

SELF-CONTAINED BREATHING APPARATUS WITH FULL FACEPIECE OPERATED IN PRESSURE-DEMAND OR OTHER POSITIVE PRESSURE MODE.

SUPPLIED-AIR RESPIRATOR WITH FULL FACEPIECE AND OPERATED IN PRESSURE-DEMAND OR OTHER POSITIVE PRESSURE MODE IN COMBINATION WITH AN AUXILIARY SELF-CONTAINED BREATHING APPARATUS OPERATED IN PRESSURE-DEMAND OR OTHER POSITIVE PRESSURE MODE.

CLOTHING: EMPLOYEE MUST WEAR APPROPRIATE PROTECTIVE (IMPERVIOUS) CLOTHING AND EQUIPMENT TO PREVENT REPEATED OR PROLONGED SKIN CONTACT WITH THIS SUBSTANCE.

GLOVES: EMPLOYEE MUST WEAR APPROPRIATE PROTECTIVE GLOVES TO PREVENT CONTACT WITH THIS SUBSTANCE.

EYE PROTECTION: EMPLOYEE MUST WEAR SPLASH-PROOF OR DUST-RESISTANT SAFETY GOGGLES TO PREVENT EYE CONTACT WITH THIS SUBSTANCE.

EMERGENCY EYE WASH: WHERE THERE IS ANY POSSIBILITY THAT AN EMPLOYEE'S EYES MAY BE EXPOSED TO THIS SUBSTANCE, THE EMPLOYER SHOULD PROVIDE AN EYE WASH FOUNTAIN WITHIN THE IMMEDIATE WORK AREA FOR EMERGENCY USE.

AUTHORIZED BY- OCCUPATIONAL HEALTH SERVICES, INC.

CREATION DATE: 10/04/89 ***REVISION DATE:*** 05/08/90

MATERIAL SAFETY DATA SHEET

OCCUPATIONAL HEALTH SERVICES, INC.
AGRICULTURE AND PESTICIDE DIVISION
450 SEVENTH AVENUE, SUITE 2407
NEW YORK, NEW YORK 10123
1-800-445-MSDS OR (212) 967-1100

EMERGENCY CONTACT:
JOHN S. BRANSFORD, JR. (615) 292-1180

SUBSTANCE IDENTIFICATION

CAS-NUMBER 813-78-5

SUBSTANCE: DIMETHYL PHOSPHATE

TRADE NAMES/SYNONYMS: PHOSPHORIC ACID, DIMETHYL ESTER; DIMETHYL HYDROGEN PHOSPHATE; O,O-DIMETHYL HYDROGEN PHOSPHATE; O,O-DIMETHYL PHOSPHATE; DMP; C2H7O4P; PST07882

CHEMICAL FAMILY: ORGANOPHOSPHATE

MOLECULAR FORMULA: (C-H3-O)2-P-(O)-O-H

MOLECULAR WEIGHT: 126.05

CERCLA RATINGS (SCALE 0-3): HEALTH=U FIRE=1 REACTIVITY=0 PERSISTENCE=0

NFPA RATINGS (SCALE 0-4): HEALTH=U FIRE=1 REACTIVITY=0

COMPONENTS AND CONTAMINANTS

COMPONENT: DIMETHYL PHOSPHATE ***PERCENT:*** 100.0
CAS# 813-78-5

OTHER CONTAMINANTS: NONE

EXPOSURE LIMITS: NO OCCUPATIONAL EXPOSURE LIMITS ESTABLISHED BY OSHA, ACGIH, OR NIOSH.

PHYSICAL DATA

DESCRIPTION: WHITE POWDER. ***BOILING POINT:*** 342-349 F (172-176 C) (DECOMPOSES)

MELTING POINT: NOT AVAILABLE ***SPECIFIC GRAVITY:*** 1.335 @ 25 C

SOLUBILITY IN WATER: SOLUBLE

SOLVENT SOLUBILITY: SOLUBLE IN ALCOHOL AND ACETONE.

FIRE AND EXPLOSION DATA

FIRE AND EXPLOSION HAZARD: SLIGHT FIRE HAZARD WHEN EXPOSED TO HEAT OR FLAME.

FIREFIGHTING MEDIA: DRY CHEMICAL, CARBON DIOXIDE, HALON, WATER SPRAY OR STANDARD FOAM (1987 EMERGENCY RESPONSE GUIDEBOOK, DOT P 5800.4).

FOR LARGER FIRES, USE WATER SPRAY, FOG OR STANDARD FOAM (1987 EMERGENCY RESPONSE GUIDEBOOK, DOT P 5800.4).

FIREFIGHTING: MOVE CONTAINER FROM FIRE AREA IF POSSIBLE. DO NOT SCATTER SPILLED MATERIAL WITH HIGH PRESSURE WATER STREAMS. DIKE FIRE CONTROL WATER FOR LATER DISPOSAL (1987 EMERGENCY RESPONSE GUIDEBOOK, DOT P 5800.4, GUIDE PAGE 31).

USE AGENTS SUITABLE FOR TYPE OF SURROUNDING FIRE. AVOID BREATHING HAZARDOUS VAPORS, KEEP UPWIND.

TOXICITY

DIMETHYL PHOSPHATE: TOXICITY DATA: 8714 MG/KG UNREPORTED-RAT LD50. CARCINOGEN STATUS: NONE. ACUTE TOXCITY LEVEL: INSUFFICIENT DATA. TARGET EFFECTS: NO DATA AVAILABLE. ADDITIONAL DATA: THE TOXIC EFFECTS PRODUCED BY ALKYL PHOSPHATES RANGE FROM SEVERE TO NONE AND INCLUDE IRRITATION, NEUROTOXICITY, AND ANTICHOLINESTERASE ACTIVITY.

HEALTH EFFECTS AND FIRST AID

INHALATION: DIMETHYL PHOSPHATE: **ACUTE EXPOSURE**- NO DATA AVAILABLE.
CHRONIC EXPOSURE- NO DATA AVAILABLE.

FIRST AID- REMOVE FROM EXPOSURE AREA TO FRESH AIR IMMEDIATELY. IF BREATHING HAS STOPPED, PERFORM ARTIFICIAL RESPIRATION. KEEP PERSON WARM AND AT REST. TREAT SYMPTOMATICALLY AND SUPPORTIVELY. GET MEDICAL ATTENTION IMMEDIATELY.

SKIN CONTACT: DIMETHYL PHOSPHATE: **ACUTE EXPOSURE**- NO DATA AVAILABLE.
CHRONIC EXPOSURE- NO DATA AVAILABLE.

FIRST AID- REMOVE CONTAMINATED CLOTHING AND SHOES IMMEDIATELY. WASH AFFECTED AREA WITH SOAP OR MILD DETERGENT AND LARGE AMOUNTS OF WATER UNTIL NO EVIDENCE OF CHEMICAL REMAINS (APPROXIMATELY 15-20 MINUTES). GET MEDICAL ATTENTION IMMEDIATELY.

EYE CONTACT: DIMETHYL PHOSPHATE: **ACUTE EXPOSURE**- NO DATA AVAILABLE.
CHRONIC EXPOSURE- NO DATA AVAILABLE.

FIRST AID- WASH EYES IMMEDIATELY WITH LARGE AMOUNTS OF WATER OR NORMAL SALINE, OCCASIONALLY LIFTING UPPER AND LOWER LIDS, UNTIL NO EVIDENCE OF CHEMICAL REMAINS (APPROXIMATELY 15-20 MINUTES). GET MEDICAL ATTENTION IMMEDIATELY.

INGESTION: DIMETHYL PHOSPHATE: **ACUTE EXPOSURE**- NO DATA AVAILABLE.
CHRONIC EXPOSURE- NO DATA AVAILABLE.

FIRST AID- TREAT SYMPTOMATICALLY AND SUPPORTIVELY. GET MEDICAL ATTENTION IMMEDIATELY. IF VOMITING OCCURS, KEEP HEAD LOWER THAN HIPS TO PREVENT ASPIRATION.
ANTIDOTE: NO SPECIFIC ANTIDOTE. TREAT SYMPTOMATICALLY AND SUPPORTIVELY.

REACTIVITY

REACTIVITY: STABLE UNDER NORMAL TEMPERATURES AND PRESSURES.
INCOMPATIBILITIES: DIMETHYL PHOSPHATE: OXIDIZERS (STRONG): FIRE AND EXPLOSION HAZARD.
DECOMPOSITION: THERMAL DECOMPOSITION PRODUCTS MAY INCLUDE TOXIC AND HAZARDOUS OXIDES OF PHOSPHORUS AND CARBON.
POLYMERIZATION: HAZARDOUS POLYMERIZATION HAS NOT BEEN REPORTED TO OCCUR UNDER NORMAL TEMPERATURES AND PRESSURES.

STORAGE AND DISPOSAL

OBSERVE ALL FEDERAL, STATE AND LOCAL REGULATIONS WHEN STORING OR DISPOSING OF THIS SUBSTANCE. FOR ASSISTANCE, CONTACT THE DISTRICT DIRECTOR OF THE ENVIRONMENTAL PROTECTION AGENCY.

STORAGE

STORE AWAY FROM INCOMPATIBLE SUBSTANCES.

CONDITIONS TO AVOID

MAY BURN BUT DOES NOT IGNITE READILY. AVOID CONTACT WITH STRONG OXIDIZERS, EXCESSIVE HEAT, SPARKS, OR OPEN FLAME.

SPILL AND LEAK PROCEDURES

OCCUPATIONAL SPILL: SWEEP UP AND PLACE IN SUITABLE CLEAN, DRY CONTAINERS FOR RECLAMATION OR LATER DISPOSAL. DO NOT FLUSH SPILLED MATERIAL INTO SEWER. KEEP UNNECESSARY PEOPLE AWAY.

PROTECTIVE EQUIPMENT

VENTILATION: PROVIDE LOCAL EXHAUST OR PROCESS ENCLOSURE VENTILATION SYSTEM.
RESPIRATOR: THE FOLLOWING RESPIRATORS ARE RECOMMENDED BASED ON INFORMATION FOUND IN THE PHYSICAL DATA, TOXICITY AND HEALTH EFFECTS SECTIONS. THEY ARE RANKED IN ORDER FROM MINIMUM TO MAXIMUM RESPIRATORY PROTECTION. THE SPECIFIC RESPIRATOR SELECTED MUST BE BASED ON CONTAMINATION LEVELS FOUND IN THE WORK PLACE, MUST NOT EXCEED THE WORKING LIMITS OF THE RESPIRATOR AND BE JOINTLY APPROVED BY THE NATIONAL INSTITUTE FOR OCCUPATIONAL SAFETY AND HEALTH AND THE MINE SAFETY AND HEALTH ADMINISTRATION (NIOSH-MSHA).
DUST AND MIST RESPIRATOR WITH A FULL FACEPIECE.
AIR-PURIFYING FULL FACEPIECE RESPIRATOR WITH A HIGH-EFFICIENCY PARTICULATE FILTER.
POWERED AIR-PURIFYING RESPIRATOR WITH A TIGHT-FITTING FACEPIECE AND HIGH-EFFICIENCY PARTICULATE FILTER.
TYPE 'C' SUPPLIED-AIR RESPIRATOR WITH A FULL FACEPIECE OPERATED IN PRESSURE-DEMAND OR OTHER POSITIVE PRESSURE MODE OR WITH A FULL FACEPIECE, HELMET OR HOOD OPERATED IN CONTINUOUS-FLOW MODE.
SELF-CONTAINED BREATHING APPARATUS WITH A FULL FACEPIECE OPERATED IN PRESSURE-DEMAND OR OTHER POSITIVE PRESSURE MODE.
FOR FIREFIGHTING AND OTHER IMMEDIATELY DANGEROUS TO LIFE OR HEALTH CONDITIONS:
SELF-CONTAINED BREATHING APPARATUS WITH FULL FACEPIECE OPERATED IN PRESSURE-DEMAND OR OTHER POSITIVE PRESSURE MODE.
SUPPLIED-AIR RESPIRATOR WITH FULL FACEPIECE AND OPERATED IN PRESSURE-DEMAND OR OTHER POSITIVE PRESSURE MODE IN COMBINATION WITH AN AUXILIARY SELF-CONTAINED BREATHING APPARATUS OPERATED IN PRESSURE-DEMAND OR OTHER POSITIVE PRESSURE MODE.
CLOTHING: EMPLOYEE MUST WEAR APPROPRIATE PROTECTIVE (IMPERVIOUS) CLOTHING AND EQUIPMENT TO PREVENT REPEATED OR PROLONGED SKIN CONTACT WITH THIS SUBSTANCE.
GLOVES: EMPLOYEE MUST WEAR APPROPRIATE PROTECTIVE GLOVES TO PREVENT CONTACT WITH THIS SUBSTANCE.
EYE PROTECTION: EMPLOYEE MUST WEAR SPLASH-PROOF OR DUST-RESISTANT SAFETY GOGGLES TO PREVENT EYE CONTACT WITH THIS SUBSTANCE.
EMERGENCY EYE WASH: WHERE THERE IS ANY POSSIBILITY THAT AN EMPLOYEE'S EYES MAY BE EXPOSED TO THIS SUBSTANCE, THE EMPLOYER SHOULD PROVIDE AN EYE WASH FOUNTAIN WITHIN THE IMMEDIATE WORK AREA FOR EMERGENCY USE.

AUTHORIZED BY- OCCUPATIONAL HEALTH SERVICES, INC.
CREATION DATE: 12/14/89 ***REVISION DATE:*** 05/31/90

MATERIAL SAFETY DATA SHEET

OCCUPATIONAL HEALTH SERVICES, INC.
AGRICULTURE AND PESTICIDE DIVISION
450 SEVENTH AVENUE, SUITE 2407
NEW YORK, NEW YORK 10123
1-800-445-MSDS OR (212) 967-1100

EMERGENCY CONTACT:
JOHN S. BRANSFORD, JR. (615) 292-1180

SUBSTANCE IDENTIFICATION

CAS-NUMBER 534-52-1
SUBSTANCE: DINITRO-ORTHO-CRESOL
TRADE NAMES/SYNONYMS: PHENOL, 2-METHYL-4,6-DINITRO-; O-CRESOL, 4,6-DINITRO-; 2-METHYL-4,6-DINITROPHENOL; 4,6-DINITRO-O-CRESOL; 4,6-DINITRO-2-METHYPHENOL; 3,5-DINITRO-2-HYDROXYTOLUENE; DINITROCRESOL; DINITRO-O-CRESOL; DNOC; DNC; DEKRYSIL; DETAL; DINITROL; NITRADOR; SELINON; SINOX; ENT 154; RCRA P047; UN 1598; C7H6N2O5; PST07910
CHEMICAL FAMILY: NITRO CRESOL
MOLECULAR FORMULA: (N-O2)2-C-H3-C6-H2-O-H
MOLECULAR WEIGHT: 198.14
CERCLA RATINGS (SCALE 0-3): HEALTH=3 FIRE=1 REACTIVITY=3 PERSISTENCE=1
NFPA RATINGS (SCALE 0-4): HEALTH=3 FIRE=1 REACTIVITY=4

COMPONENTS AND CONTAMINANTS

COMPONENT: DINITRO-ORTHO-CRESOL ***PERCENT:*** 100.0
CAS# 534-52-1
OTHER CONTAMINANTS: MAY CONTAIN UP TO 10% WATER TO REDUCE DETONATION SENSITIVITY.
EXPOSURE LIMITS: DINITRO-ORTHO-CRESOL: 0.2 MG/M3 OSHA TWA (SKIN) 0.2 MG/M3 ACGIH TWA (SKIN) 0.2 MG/M3 NIOSH RECOMMENDED 10 HOUR TWA 10/10,000 POUNDS SARA SECTION 302 THRESHOLD PLANNING QUANTITY 10 POUNDS SARA SECTION 304 REPORTABLE QUANTITY 10 POUNDS CERCLA SECTION 103 REPORTABLE QUANTITY SUBJECT TO SARA SECTION 313 ANNUAL TOXIC CHEMICAL RELEASE REPORTING

PHYSICAL DATA

DESCRIPTION: ODORLESS, YELLOW, CRYSTALLINE SOLID. ***BOILING POINT:*** 595 F (312 C)
MELTING POINT: 188 F (87) ***SPECIFIC GRAVITY:*** >1.1 @ 20 C
VAPOR PRESSURE: NEGLIGIBLE ***SOLUBILITY IN WATER:*** 0.013% @ 15 C
VAPOR DENSITY: 6.84
SOLVENT SOLUBILITY: SOLUBLE IN ALCOHOL, ACETONE, ETHER, ALKALINE SOLUTIONS; ACETIC ACID, CHLOROFORM, AND MOST ORGANIC SOLVENTS; SLIGHTLY SOLUBLE IN CARBON TETRACHLORIDE; SPARINGLY SOLUBLE IN PETROLEUM ETHER.

FIRE AND EXPLOSION DATA

FIRE AND EXPLOSION HAZARD: SLIGHT FIRE HAZARD WHEN EXPOSED TO HEAT OR FLAME.
MODERATE EXPLOSION HAZARD WHEN EXPOSED TO HEAT OR FLAME.
DUST-AIR MIXTURES MAY IGNITE OR EXPLODE.
LOWER EXPLOSIVE LIMIT: 30 GM/M3 ***AUTOIGNITION TEMP.:*** 644 F (340 C)
FIREFIGHTING MEDIA: DRY CHEMICAL, CARBON DIOXIDE, HALON, WATER SPRAY OR STANDARD FOAM (1987 EMERGENCY RESPONSE GUIDEBOOK, DOT P 5800.4).
FOR LARGER FIRES, USE WATER SPRAY, FOG OR STANDARD FOAM (1987 EMERGENCY RESPONSE GUIDEBOOK, DOT P 5800.4).
FIREFIGHTING: MOVE CONTAINERS FROM FIRE AREA IF POSSIBLE. COOL CONTAINERS EXPOSED TO FLAMES WITH WATER FROM SIDE UNTIL WELL AFTER FIRE IS OUT. STAY AWAY FROM STORAGE TANK ENDS. FOR MASSIVE FIRE IN STORAGE AREA, USE UNMANNED HOSE HOLDER OR MONITOR NOZZLES; ELSE WITHDRAW FROM AREA AND LET FIRE BURN (1987 EMERGENCY RESPONSE GUIDEBOOK, DOT P 5800.4, GUIDE PAGE 56).
EXTINGUISH ONLY IF FLOW CAN BE STOPPED. USE WATER IN FLOODING AMOUNTS AS A FOG; SOLID STREAMS MAY NOT BE EFFECTIVE. COOL CONTAINERS WITH FLOODING QUANTITIES OF WATER APPLIED FROM AS FAR A DISTANCE AS POSSIBLE. AVOID BREATHING TOXIC VAPORS, KEEP UPWIND.

TRANSPORTATION DATA

DEPARTMENT OF TRANSPORTATION HAZARD CLASSIFICATION 49 CFR 172.101: POISON B
DEPARTMENT OF TRANSPORTATION LABELING REQUIREMENTS 49 CFR 172.101 AND SUBPART E: POISON

DEPARTMENT OF TRANSPORTATION PACKAGING REQUIREMENTS: 49 CFR 173.365 EXCEPTIONS: 49 CFR 173.364

TOXICITY

DINITRO-ORTHO-CRESOL: IRRITATION DATA: 20 MG/24 HOURS EYE-RABBIT MODERATE; 105 MG/9 DAYS INTERMITTENT SKIN-RABBIT MILD. TOXICITY DATA: 1 MG/M3 INHALATION-HUMAN TCLO; 40 MG/M3/4 HOURS INHALATION-CAT LCLO; 100 MG/M3 INHALATION-MAMMAL LC30; 500 MG/KG SKIN-CHILD LDLO; 1 GM/KG SKIN-RABBIT LD50; 200 MG/KG SKIN-RAT LD50; 500 MG/KG SKIN-GUINEA PIG LDLO; 7500 UG/KG/7 DAYS ORAL-MAN TDLO; 10 MG/KG ORAL-RAT LD50; 21 MG/KG ORAL-MOUSE LD50; 50 MG/KG ORAL-CAT LD50; 100 MG/KG ORAL-DOMESTIC ANIMAL LD50; 25600 UG/KG SUBCUTANEOUS-RAT LD50; 28 MG/KG INTRAPERITONEAL-RAT LDLO; 23500 UG/KG INTRAPERITONEAL-RABBIT LD50; 19 MG/KG INTRAPERITONEAL-MOUSE LD50; 22500 UG/KG INTRAPERITONEAL-GUINEA PIG LD50; 15 MG/KG INTRAVENOUS-DOG LDLO; 29 MG/KG UNREPORTED-MAN LDLO; 85 MG/KG UNREPORTED-RAT LD50; 40 MG/KG UNREPORTED-MOUSE LD50; MUTAGENIC DATA (RTECS). CARCINOGEN STATUS: NONE. ACUTE TOXICITY LEVEL: HIGHLY TOXIC BY INGESTION; TOXIC BY DERMAL ABSORPTION. TARGET EFFECTS: POISONING MAY INCREASE THE METABOLIC RATE AND AFFECT THE NERVOUS SYSTEM, LIVER, AND KIDNEY. AT INCREASED RISK FROM EXPOSURE: ALCOHOLICS AND PERSONS WITH RENAL OR HEPATIC DISEASES. ADDITIONAL DATA: HOT ENVIRONMENTS MAY ENHANCE ABSORPTION AND THE TOXIC EFFECTS.

HEALTH EFFECTS AND FIRST AID

INHALATION: DINITRO-ORTHO-CRESOL: 5 MG/M3 IMMEDIATELY DANGEROUS TO LIFE OR HEALTH. SEE INFORMATION ON DINITROPHENOL DERIVATIVES.
DINITROPHENOL DERIVATIVES: **ACUTE EXPOSURE-** MAY BE ABSORBED WITH SYMPTOMS OCCURRING SUDDENLY AND UP TO 2 DAYS AFTER CESSATION OF EXPOSURE. SYMPTOMS MAY INCLUDE FATIGUE, WEAKNESS, FEVER, THIRST, NAUSEA, VOMITING, HEADACHES, FLUSHED SKIN, PROSTRATION, EXCESSIVE PERSPIRATION, TACHYCARDIA, TACHYPNEA, AND DYSPNEA. APPREHENSION, RESTLESSNESS, ANXIETY, MANIC BEHAVIOR, OR UNCONSCIOUSNESS MAY INDICATE CEREBRAL INJURY. CONVULSIONS MAY OCCUR IN THE MOST SEVERE POISONINGS. ANOXIA WITH CYANOSIS, LIVIDITY AND METABOLIC ACIDOSIS, SEVERE HYPERPYREXIA, DEHYDRATION, AND MUSCULAR TREMORS MAY BE FOLLOWED BY CIRCULATORY OR RESPIRATORY COLLAPSE AND COMA. DEGENERATIVE CHANGES IN THE HEART, RENAL TUBULES AND LIVER PARENCHYMA MAY OCCUR. THERE MAY BE ALBUMINURIA, PYURIA, HEMATURIA, JAUNDICE, AND INCREASED BUN. THE EFFECTS FROM POISONING ARE RAPID AND DEATH OR RECOVERY GENERALLY OCCURS WITHIN 24 TO 48 HOURS. FATAL DINITROPHENOL POISONING IS FOLLOWED BY INSTANTANEOUS RIGOR MORTIS.
CHRONIC EXPOSURE- IN ADDITION TO THE SYMPTOMS OF ACUTE EXPOSURE, PROLONGED OR REPEATED EXPOSURE MAY CAUSE WEIGHT LOSS, CATARACT FORMATION, AND LIVER AND KIDNEY DAMAGE. YELLOW STAINING OF THE SCLERAE AND URINE INDICATES ABSORPTION OF POTENTIALLY TOXIC AMOUNTS.
FIRST AID- REMOVE FROM EXPOSURE AREA TO FRESH AIR IMMEDIATELY. IF BREATHING HAS STOPPED, PERFORM ARTIFICIAL RESPIRATION. ADMINISTER OXYGEN. TREAT SYMPTOMATICALLY AND SUPPORTIVELY. GET MEDICAL ATTENTION IMMEDIATELY.

SKIN CONTACT: DINITRO-ORTHO-CRESOL: TOXIC. NAIL DAMAGE HAS OCCURRED FROM REPEATED EXPOSURE. SEE INFORMATION ON DINITROPHENOL DERIVATIVES.
DINITROPHENOL DERIVATIVES: **ACUTE EXPOSURE-** MAY CAUSE IRRITATION. CONTACT MAY RESULT IN YELLOW STAINING OF THE SKIN AHD HAIR. SOME DERIVATIVES MAY BE ABSORBED THROUGH THE SKIN WITH SYMPTOMS OCCURRING SUDDENLY AND UP TO 2 DAYS AFTER CESSATION OF EXPOSURE AND PRODUCE EFFECTS ON THE METABOLIC RATE, CENTRAL NERVOUS SYSTEM AND LIVER AND KIDNEY RESULTING IN SIGNS AND SYMPTOMS AS DESCRIBED IN ACUTE INHALATION. **CHRONIC EXPOSURE-** REPEATED OR PROLONGED CONTACT MAY RESULT IN DERMATITIS DUE TO IRRITATION OR ALLERGIC SENSITIVITY. IN ADDITION TO THE SYMPTOMS OF ACUTE EXPOSURE, CHRONIC ABSORPTION MAY CAUSE FATIGUE, WEIGHT LOSS, CATARACT FORMATION AND LIVER AND KIDNEY DAMAGE. YELLOW STAINING OF THE SCLERAE AND URINE INDICATES ABSORPTION OF POTENTIALLY TOXIC AMOUNTS.
FIRST AID- REMOVE CONTAMINATED CLOTHING AND SHOES IMMEDIATELY. THEN REMOVE SKIN AND HAIR CONTAMINATION BY SCRUBBING WITH SOAP AND WATER. IF BODY TEMPERATURE IS ELEVATED, REDUCE TO 37 C BY SPONGE BATH, IMMERSION IN COOL WATER OR BY APPLYING COOLING BLANKET. IF BODY TEMPERATURE IS ABOVE 40 C, ICE WATER IS NECESSARY (DREISBACH, HANDBOOK OF POISONING, 12TH EDITION; MORGAN, EPA RECOGNITION AND MANAGEMENT OF PESTICIDE POISONINGS, 3RD EDITION). GET MEDICAL ATTENTION IMMEDIATELY.

EYE CONTACT: DINITRO-ORTHO-CRESOL: **ACUTE EXPOSURE-** MAY CAUSE IRRITATION.
CHRONIC EXPOSURE- NO DATA AVAILABLE.
FIRST AID- WASH EYES IMMEDIATELY WITH LARGE AMOUNTS OF WATER OR NORMAL SALINE, OCCASIONALLY LIFTING UPPER AND LOWER LIDS, UNTIL NO EVIDENCE OF CHEMICAL REMAINS (APPROXIMATELY 15-20 MINUTES). GET MEDICAL ATTENTION IMMEDIATELY.

INGESTION: DINITRO-ORTHO-CRESOL: HIGHLY TOXIC. SEE INFORMATION ON DINITROPHENOL DERIVATIVES.
DINITROPHENOL DERIVATIVES: **ACUTE EXPOSURE-** MAY CAUSE EFFECTS ON THE METABOLIC RATE, CENTRAL NERVOUS SYSTEM AND LIVER AND KIDNEY RESULTING IN SIGNS AND SYMPTOMS AS DESCRIBED IN ACUTE INHALATION.
CHRONIC EXPOSURE- IN ADDITION TO THE SYMPTOMS OF ACUTE EXPOSURE, REPEATED INGESTION MAY CAUSE AN INITIAL SENSE OF WELL-BEING THEN ANOREXIA, DIARRHEA, DIZZINESS, RESTLESSNESS, FATIGUE, WEIGHT LOSS, SKIN ERUPTIONS, PERIPHERAL NEURITIS, LIVER AND KIDNEY DAMAGE, CARDIOVASCULAR COMPLICATIONS, GRANULOCYTOPENIA, AND CATARACT FORMATION. YELLOW STAINING OF THE SCLERAE AND URINE INDICATES ABSORPTION OF POTENTIALLY TOXIC AMOUNTS.
FIRST AID- REMOVE INGESTED POISON BY THOROUGH GASTRIC LAVAGE WITH SATURATED BICARBONATE SOLUTION. IF GASTRIC LAVAGE CANNOT BE ACCOMPLISHED IMMEDIATELY, GIVE SYRUP OF IPECAC TO INDUCE EMESIS AND FOLLOW WITH SALINE CATHARTIC. IF BODY TEMPERATURE IS ELEVATED, REDUCE TO 37 C BY IMMERSION IN COOL WATER OR BY APPLYING COOLING BLANKET. IF BODY TEMPERATURE IS ABOVE 40 C, ICE WATER IS NECESSARY (DREISBACH, HANDBOOK OF POISONING, 12TH ED.). ADMINISTRATION OF GASTRIC LAVAGE SHOULD BE PERFORMED BY QUALIFIED MEDICAL PERSONNEL. GET MEDICAL ATTENTION IMMEDIATELY.
ANTIDOTE: NO SPECIFIC ANTIDOTE. TREAT SYMPTOMATICALLY AND SUPPORTIVELY.

REACTIVITY

REACTIVITY: DINITRO-ORTHO-CRESOL: DRY MATERIAL MAY DETONATE ON EXPOSURE TO HEAT OR SHOCK. MATERIAL MAY BE WET WITH WATER FOR STABILITY DURING STORAGE AND TRANSPORT.
INCOMPATIBILITIES: DINITRO-ORTHO-CRESOL: METALS: MAY BE CORRODED. OXIDIZERS (STRONG): FIRE AND EXPLOSION HAZARD. STEEL: MAY BE CORRODED IN THE PRESENCE OF MOISTURE.
DECOMPOSITION: THERMAL DECOMPOSITION PRODUCTS MAY INCLUDE TOXIC OXIDES OF CARBON AND NITROGEN.
POLYMERIZATION: HAZARDOUS POLYMERIZATION HAS NOT BEEN REPORTED TO OCCUR UNDER NORMAL TEMPERATURES AND PRESSURES.

STORAGE AND DISPOSAL

OBSERVE ALL FEDERAL, STATE AND LOCAL REGULATIONS WHEN STORING OR DISPOSING OF THIS SUBSTANCE. FOR ASSISTANCE, CONTACT THE DISTRICT DIRECTOR OF THE ENVIRONMENTAL PROTECTION AGENCY.

STORAGE

THRESHOLD PLANNING QUANTITY (TPQ): THE SUPERFUND AMENDMENTS AND REAUTHORIZATION ACT (SARA) SECTION 302 REQUIRES THAT EACH FACILITY WHERE ANY EXTREMELY HAZARDOUS SUBSTANCE IS PRESENT IN A QUANTITY EQUAL TO OR GREATER THAN THE TPQ ESTABLISHED FOR THAT SUBSTANCE NOTIFY THE STATE EMERGENCY RESPONSE COMMISSION FOR THE STATE IN WHICH IT IS LOCATED. SECTION 303 OF SARA REQUIRES THESE FACILITIES TO PARTICIPATE IN LOCAL EMERGENCY RESPONSE PLANNING (40 CFR 355.30). STORE AWAY FROM INCOMPATIBLE SUBSTANCES.

DISPOSAL

DISPOSAL MUST BE IN ACCORDANCE WITH STANDARDS APPLICABLE TO GENERATORS OF HAZARDOUS WASTE, 40 CFR 262. EPA HAZARDOUS WASTE NUMBER P047

CONDITIONS TO AVOID

MAY BURN BUT DOES NOT IGNITE READILY. MAY EXPLODE FROM FRICTION, HEAT OR CONTAMINATION.

SPILL AND LEAK PROCEDURES

OCCUPATIONAL SPILL: DO NOT TOUCH SPILLED MATERIAL. STOP LEAK IF YOU CAN DO IT WITHOUT RISK. USE WATER SPRAY TO REDUCE VAPORS. FOR SMALL SPILLS, TAKE UP WITH SAND OR OTHER ABSORBENT MATERIAL AND PLACE INTO CONTAINERS FOR LATER DISPOSAL. FOR SMALL DRY SPILLS, WITH CLEAN SHOVEL PLACE MATERIAL INTO CLEAN, DRY CONTAINERS AND COVER. MOVE CONTAINERS FROM SPILL AREA. FOR LARGER SPILLS, DIKE FAR AHEAD OF SPILL FOR LATER DISPOSAL. KEEP UNNECESSARY PEOPLE AWAY. ISOLATE HAZARD AREA AND DENY ENTRY. VENTILATE CLOSED SPACES BEFORE ENTERING.
REPORTABLE QUANTITY (RQ): 10 POUNDS THE SUPERFUND AMENDMENTS AND REAUTHORIZATION ACT (SARA) SECTION 304 REQUIRES THAT A RELEASE EQUAL TO OR GREATER THAN THE REPORTABLE QUANTITY FOR THIS SUBSTANCE BE IMMEDIATELY REPORTED TO THE LOCAL EMERGENCY PLANNING COMMITTEE AND THE STATE EMERGENCY RESPONSE COMMISSION (40 CFR 355.40). IF THE RELEASE OF THIS SUBSTANCE IS REPORTABLE UNDER CERCLA SECTION 103, THE NATIONAL

RESPONSE CENTER MUST BE NOTIFIED IMMEDIATELY AT (800) 424-8802 OR (202) 426-2675 IN THE METROPOLITAN WASHINGTON, D.C. AREA (40 CFR 302.6).

PROTECTIVE EQUIPMENT

VENTILATION: PROVIDE LOCAL EXHAUST OR PROCESS ENCLOSURE VENTILATION TO MEET THE PUBLISHED EXPOSURE LIMITS. VENTILATION EQUIPMENT MUST BE EXPLOSION-PROOF.

RESPIRATOR: THE FOLLOWING RESPIRATORS AND MAXIMUM USE CONCENTRATIONS ARE RECOMMENDATIONS BY THE U.S. DEPARTMENT OF HEALTH AND HUMAN SERVICES, NIOSH POCKET GUIDE TO CHEMICAL HAZARDS; NIOSH CRITERIA DOCUMENTS OR BY THE U.S. DEPARTMENT OF LABOR, 29 CFR 1910 SUBPART Z. THE SPECIFIC RESPIRATOR SELECTED MUST BE BASED ON CONTAMINATION LEVELS FOUND IN THE WORK PLACE, MUST NOT EXCEED THE WORKING LIMITS OF THE RESPIRATOR AND BE JOINTLY APPROVED BY THE NATIONAL INSTITUTE FOR OCCUPATIONAL SAFETY AND HEALTH AND THE MINE SAFETY AND HEALTH ADMINISTRATION (NIOSH-MSHA).

DINITRO-ORTHO-CRESOL:

2 MG/M3- ANY DUST AND MIST RESPIRATOR WITH A FULL FACEPIECE.

5 MG/M3- ANY POWERED AIR-PURIFYING RESPIRATOR WITH A DUST AND MIST FILTER. ANY SUPPLIED-AIR RESPIRATOR OPERATED IN A CONTINUOUS FLOW MODE. ANY AIR-PURIFYING FULL FACEPIECE RESPIRATOR WITH A HIGH-EFFICIENCY PARTICULATE FILTER. ANY SUPPLIED-AIR RESPIRATOR WITH A FULL FACEPIECE. ANY SELF-CONTAINED BREATHING APPARATUS WITH A FULL FACEPIECE.

ESCAPE- ANY AIR-PURIFYING FULL FACEPIECE RESPIRATOR WITH A HIGH-EFFICIENCY PARTICULATE FILTER. ANY APPROPRIATE ESCAPE-TYPE SELF-CONTAINED BREATHING APPARATUS.

FOR FIREFIGHTING AND OTHER IMMEDIATELY DANGEROUS TO LIFE OR HEALTH CONDITIONS:

SELF-CONTAINED BREATHING APPARATUS WITH FULL FACEPIECE OPERATED IN PRESSURE-DEMAND OR OTHER POSITIVE PRESSURE MODE.

SUPPLIED-AIR RESPIRATOR WITH FULL FACEPIECE AND OPERATED IN PRESSURE-DEMAND OR OTHER POSITIVE PRESSURE MODE IN COMBINATION WITH AN AUXILIARY SELF-CONTAINED BREATHING APPARATUS OPERATED IN PRESSURE-DEMAND OR OTHER POSITIVE PRESSURE MODE.

CLOTHING: EMPLOYEE MUST WEAR APPROPRIATE PROTECTIVE (IMPERVIOUS) CLOTHING AND EQUIPMENT TO PREVENT ANY POSSIBILITY OF SKIN CONTACT WITH THIS SUBSTANCE.

GLOVES: EMPLOYEE MUST WEAR APPROPRIATE PROTECTIVE GLOVES TO PREVENT CONTACT WITH THIS SUBSTANCE.

EYE PROTECTION: EMPLOYEE MUST WEAR SPLASH-PROOF OR DUST-RESISTANT SAFETY GOGGLES AND A FACESHIELD TO PREVENT CONTACT WITH THIS SUBSTANCE.

EMERGENCY WASH FACILITIES: WHERE THERE IS ANY POSSIBILITY THAT AN EMPLOYEE'S EYES AND/OR SKIN MAY BE EXPOSED TO THIS SUBSTANCE, THE EMPLOYER SHOULD PROVIDE AN EYE WASH FOUNTAIN AND QUICK DRENCH SHOWER WITHIN THE IMMEDIATE WORK AREA FOR EMERGENCY USE.

AUTHORIZED BY- OCCUPATIONAL HEALTH SERVICES, INC.

CREATION DATE: 10/04/89 ***REVISION DATE:*** 04/26/90

MATERIAL SAFETY DATA SHEET

OCCUPATIONAL HEALTH SERVICES, INC.
AGRICULTURE AND PESTICIDE DIVISION
450 SEVENTH AVENUE, SUITE 2407
NEW YORK, NEW YORK 10123
1-800-445-MSDS OR (212) 967-1100

EMERGENCY CONTACT:
JOHN S. BRANSFORD, JR. (615) 292-1180

SUBSTANCE IDENTIFICATION

CAS-NUMBER 973-21-7

SUBSTANCE: DINOBUTON

TRADE NAMES/SYNONYMS: CARBONIC ACID, 1-METHYLETHYL 2-(1-METHYLPROPYL)-4,6-DINITROPHENYL ESTER; CARBONIC ACID, 2-SEC-BUTYL-4,6-DINITROPHENYL ISOPROPYL ESTER; CARBONIC ACID 1-METHYLETHYL 2-(1-METHYLPROPYL)-4,6-DINITROPHENYL ESTER; CARBONIC ACID 2-SEC-BUTYL-4,6-DINITROPHENYL ISOPROPYL ESTER; 2-SEC-BUTYL-4,6-DINITROPHENYL ISOPROPYL CARBONATE; ISOPROPYL 2,4-DINITRO-6-SEC-BUTYLPHENYL CARBONATE; DINTRO-SEC-BUTYLPHENYL ISOPROPYL CARBONATE;
1-METHYLETHYL-2-(1-METHYLPROPYL)-4,6-DINITROPHENYL CARBONATE; ACREX; DESSIN; DINOFEN; MC 1053; SYSTASOL; TALAN; OMS 1056; ENT 27244; C14H18N2O7; PST07990

CHEMICAL FAMILY: ESTER, CARBOXYLIC, AROMATIC NITRO

MOLECULAR FORMULA: C14-H18-N2-O7

MOLECULAR WEIGHT: 326.30

CERCLA RATINGS (SCALE 0-3): HEALTH=3 FIRE=1 REACTIVITY=0 PERSISTENCE=1

NFPA RATINGS (SCALE 0-4): HEALTH=4 FIRE=1 REACTIVITY=0

COMPONENTS AND CONTAMINANTS

COMPONENT: DINOBUTON ***PERCENT:*** 100.0

CAS# 973-21-7

OTHER CONTAMINANTS: NONE

EXPOSURE LIMITS: NO OCCUPATIONAL EXPOSURE LIMITS ESTABLISHED BY OSHA, ACGIH, OR NIOSH.

PHYSICAL DATA

DESCRIPTION: PALE YELLOW, CRYSTALLINE SOLID. ***MELTING POINT:*** 142-144 F (61-62 C)

SPECIFIC GRAVITY: NOT AVAILABLE ***VAPOR PRESSURE:*** NEGLIGIBLE

SOLUBILITY IN WATER: 1 PPM @ 20 C

SOLVENT SOLUBILITY: SOLUBLE IN ACETONE, LOWER ALIPHATIC KETONES, XYLENE, FATTY OILS, AROMATIC AND ALIPHATIC HYDROCARBONS; MODERATELY SOLUBLE IN ETHANOL, N-HEXANE.

FIRE AND EXPLOSION DATA

FIRE AND EXPLOSION HAZARD: SLIGHT FIRE HAZARD WHEN EXPOSED TO HEAT OR FLAME.

DUST-AIR MIXTURES MAY IGNITE OR EXPLODE.

FIREFIGHTING MEDIA: DRY CHEMICAL, CARBON DIOXIDE, HALON, WATER SPRAY OR STANDARD FOAM (1987 EMERGENCY RESPONSE GUIDEBOOK, DOT P 5800.4).

FOR LARGER FIRES, USE WATER SPRAY, FOG OR STANDARD FOAM (1987 EMERGENCY RESPONSE GUIDEBOOK, DOT P 5800.4).

FIREFIGHTING: MOVE CONTAINERS FROM FIRE AREA IF POSSIBLE (1987 EMERGENCY RESPONSE GUIDEBOOK, DOT P 5800.4, GUIDE PAGE 53).

USE AGENTS SUITABLE FOR TYPE OF SURROUNDING FIRE. AVOID BREATHING HAZARDOUS VAPORS, KEEP UPWIND.

TRANSPORTATION DATA

DEPARTMENT OF TRANSPORTATION HAZARD CLASSIFICATION 49 CFR 172.101: POISON B

DEPARTMENT OF TRANSPORTATION LABELING REQUIREMENTS 49 CFR 172.101 AND SUBPART E: POISON

DEPARTMENT OF TRANSPORTATION PACKAGING REQUIREMENTS: 49 CFR 173.365 EXCEPTIONS: 49 CFR 173.364

TOXICITY

DINOBUTON: TOXICITY DATA: 0.08 MG/L/4 HOURS INHALATION-RAT LC50 (85JFAN); 4850 UG/M3/4 HOURS INHALATION-RAT LCLO; 3200 MG/KG SKIN-RABBIT LD50; 1500 MG/KG SKIN-RAT LDLO; 59 MG/KG ORAL-RAT LD50; 170 MG/KG ORAL-MOUSE LD50; 125 MG/KG INTRAPERITONEAL-MOUSE LD50; 140 MG/KG UNREPORTED-RAT LD50; 2540 MG/KG UNREPORTED-MOUSE LD50; MUTAGENIC DATA (RTECS). CARCINOGEN STATUS: NONE. ACUTE TOXICITY LEVEL: HIGHLY TOXIC BY INHALATION; TOXIC BY INGESTION; SLIGHTLY TOXIC BY DERMAL ABSORPTION. TARGET EFFECTS: POISONING MAY INCREASE THE METABOLIC RATE AND AFFECT THE NERVOUS SYSTEM, LIVER, AND KIDNEYS.* AT INCREASED RISK FROM EXPOSURE: ALCOHOLICS AND PERSONS WITH RENAL OR HEPATIC DISEASES.* ADDITIONAL DATA: HOT ENVIRONMENTS MAY ENHANCE ABSORPTION AND THE TOXIC EFFECTS.* * MAY BE BASED ON INFORMATION ON DINITROPHENOL DERIVATIVES.

HEALTH EFFECTS AND FIRST AID

INHALATION: DINOBUTON: HIGHLY TOXIC. SEE INFORMATION ON DINITROPHENOL DERIVATIVES.

DINITROPHENOL DERIVATIVES: ACUTE EXPOSURE- MAY BE ABSORBED WITH SYMPTOMS OCCURRING SUDDENLY AND UP TO 2 DAYS AFTER CESSATION OF EXPOSURE. SYMPTOMS MAY INCLUDE FATIGUE, WEAKNESS, FEVER, THIRST, NAUSEA, VOMITING, HEADACHES, FLUSHED SKIN, PROSTRATION, EXCESSIVE PERSPIRATION, TACHYCARDIA, TACHYPNEA, AND DYSPNEA. APPREHENSION, RESTLESSNESS, ANXIETY, MANIC BEHAVIOR, OR UNCONSCIOUSNESS MAY INDICATE CEREBRAL INJURY. CONVULSIONS MAY OCCUR IN THE MOST SEVERE POISONINGS. ANOXIA WITH CYANOSIS, LIVIDITY AND METABOLIC ACIDOSIS, SEVERE HYPERPYREXIA, DEHYDRATION, AND MUSCULAR TREMORS MAY BE FOLLOWED BY CIRCULATORY OR RESPIRATORY COLLAPSE AND COMA. DEGENERATIVE CHANGES IN THE HEART, RENAL TUBULES AND LIVER PARENCHYMA MAY OCCUR. THERE MAY BE ALBUMINURIA, PYURIA, HEMATURIA, JAUNDICE, AND INCREASED BUN. THE EFFECTS FROM POISONING ARE RAPID AND

DEATH OR RECOVERY GENERALLY OCCURS WITHIN 24 TO 48 HOURS. FATAL DINITROPHENOL POISONING IS FOLLOWED BY INSTANTANEOUS RIGOR MORTIS. **CHRONIC EXPOSURE-** IN ADDITION TO THE SYMPTOMS OF ACUTE EXPOSURE, PROLONGED OR REPEATED EXPOSURE MAY CAUSE WEIGHT LOSS, CATARACT FORMATION, AND LIVER AND KIDNEY DAMAGE. YELLOW STAINING OF THE SCLERAE AND URINE INDICATES ABSORPTION OF POTENTIALLY TOXIC AMOUNTS.

FIRST AID- REMOVE FROM EXPOSURE AREA TO FRESH AIR IMMEDIATELY. IF BREATHING HAS STOPPED, PERFORM ARTIFICIAL RESPIRATION. ADMINISTER OXYGEN. TREAT SYMPTOMATICALLY AND SUPPORTIVELY. GET MEDICAL ATTENTION IMMEDIATELY.

SKIN CONTACT: DINOBUTON: PROLONGED OR REPEATED EXPOSURE MAY RESULT IN SENSITIZATION DERMATITIS. SEE INFORMATION ON DINITROPHENOL DERIVATIVES. DINITROPHENOL DERIVATIVES: **ACUTE EXPOSURE-** MAY CAUSE IRRITATION. CONTACT MAY RESULT IN YELLOW STAINING OF THE SKIN AHD HAIR. SOME DERIVATIVES MAY BE ABSORBED THROUGH THE SKIN WITH SYMPTOMS OCCURRING SUDDENLY AND UP TO 2 DAYS AFTER CESSATION OF EXPOSURE AND PRODUCE EFFECTS ON THE METABOLIC RATE, CENTRAL NERVOUS SYSTEM AND LIVER AND KIDNEY RESULTING IN SIGNS AND SYMPTOMS AS DESCRIBED IN ACUTE INHALATION. **CHRONIC EXPOSURE-** REPEATED OR PROLONGED CONTACT MAY RESULT IN DERMATITIS DUE TO IRRITATION OR ALLERGIC SENSITIVITY. IN ADDITION TO THE SYMPTOMS OF ACUTE EXPOSURE, CHRONIC ABSORPTION MAY CAUSE FATIGUE, WEIGHT LOSS, CATARACT FORMATION AND LIVER AND KIDNEY DAMAGE. YELLOW STAINING OF THE SCLERAE AND URINE INDICATES ABSORPTION OF POTENTIALLY TOXIC AMOUNTS.

FIRST AID- REMOVE CONTAMINATED CLOTHING AND SHOES IMMEDIATELY. THEN REMOVE SKIN AND HAIR CONTAMINATION BY SCRUBBING WITH SOAP AND WATER. IF BODY TEMPERATURE IS ELEVATED, REDUCE TO 37 C BY SPONGE BATH, IMMERSION IN COOL WATER OR BY APPLYING COOLING BLANKET. IF BODY TEMPERATURE IS ABOVE 40 C, ICE WATER IS NECESSARY (DREISBACH, HANDBOOK OF POISONING, 12TH EDITION; MORGAN, EPA RECOGNITION AND MANAGEMENT OF PESTICIDE POISONINGS, 3RD EDITION). GET MEDICAL ATTENTION IMMEDIATELY.

EYE CONTACT: DINOBUTON: **ACUTE EXPOSURE-** NO DATA AVAILABLE. **CHRONIC EXPOSURE-** NO DATA AVAILABLE.

FIRST AID- WASH EYES IMMEDIATELY WITH LARGE AMOUNTS OF WATER OR NORMAL SALINE, OCCASIONALLY LIFTING UPPER AND LOWER LIDS, UNTIL NO EVIDENCE OF CHEMICAL REMAINS (APPROXIMATELY 15-20 MINUTES). GET MEDICAL ATTENTION IMMEDIATELY.

INGESTION: DINOBUTON: TOXIC. SEE INFORMATION ON DINITROPHENOL DERIVATIVES.

DINITROPHENOL DERIVATIVES: **ACUTE EXPOSURE-** MAY CAUSE EFFECTS ON THE METABOLIC RATE, CENTRAL NERVOUS SYSTEM AND LIVER AND KIDNEY RESULTING IN SIGNS AND SYMPTOMS AS DESCRIBED IN ACUTE INHALATION. **CHRONIC EXPOSURE-** IN ADDITION TO THE SYMPTOMS OF ACUTE EXPOSURE, REPEATED INGESTION MAY CAUSE AN INITIAL SENSE OF WELL-BEING THEN ANOREXIA, DIARRHEA, DIZZINESS, RESTLESSNESS, FATIGUE, WEIGHT LOSS, SKIN ERUPTIONS, PERIPHERAL NEURITIS, LIVER AND KIDNEY DAMAGE, CARDIOVASCULAR COMPLICATIONS, GRANULOCYTOPENIA, AND CATARACT FORMATION. YELLOW STAINING OF THE SCLERAE AND URINE INDICATES ABSORPTION OF POTENTIALLY TOXIC AMOUNTS.

FIRST AID- REMOVE INGESTED POISON BY THOROUGH GASTRIC LAVAGE WITH SATURATED BICARBONATE SOLUTION. IF GASTRIC LAVAGE CANNOT BE ACCOMPLISHED IMMEDIATELY, GIVE SYRUP OF IPECAC TO INDUCE EMESIS AND FOLLOW WITH SALINE CATHARTIC. IF BODY TEMPERATURE IS ELEVATED, REDUCE TO 37 C BY IMMERSION IN COOL WATER OR BY APPLYING COOLING BLANKET. IF BODY TEMPERATURE IS ABOVE 40 C, ICE WATER IS NECESSARY (DREISBACH, HANDBOOK OF POISONING, 12TH ED.). ADMINISTRATION OF GASTRIC LAVAGE SHOULD BE PERFORMED BY QUALIFIED MEDICAL PERSONNEL. GET MEDICAL ATTENTION IMMEDIATELY.

ANTIDOTE: NO SPECIFIC ANTIDOTE. TREAT SYMPTOMATICALLY AND SUPPORTIVELY.

REACTIVITY

REACTIVITY: STABLE UNDER NORMAL TEMPERATURES AND PRESSURES.

INCOMPATIBILITIES: DINOBUTON: OXIDIZERS (STRONG): FIRE AND EXPLOSION HAZARD.

DECOMPOSITION: THERMAL DECOMPOSITION PRODUCTS MAY INCLUDE TOXIC OXIDES OF CARBON AND NITROGEN.

POLYMERIZATION: HAZARDOUS POLYMERIZATION HAS NOT BEEN REPORTED TO OCCUR UNDER NORMAL TEMPERATURES AND PRESSURES.

STORAGE AND DISPOSAL

OBSERVE ALL FEDERAL, STATE AND LOCAL REGULATIONS WHEN STORING OR DISPOSING OF THIS SUBSTANCE. FOR ASSISTANCE, CONTACT THE DISTRICT DIRECTOR OF THE ENVIRONMENTAL PROTECTION AGENCY.

STORAGE

STORE IN ACCORDANCE WITH 40 CFR 165 RECOMMENDED PROCEDURES FOR THE DISPOSAL AND STORAGE OF PESTICIDES AND PESTICIDE CONTAINERS.
STORE AWAY FROM INCOMPATIBLE SUBSTANCES.

DISPOSAL

DISPOSAL MUST BE IN ACCORDANCE WITH 40 CFR 165 RECOMMENDED PROCEDURES FOR THE DISPOSAL AND STORAGE OF PESTICIDES AND PESTICIDE CONTAINERS.

CONDITIONS TO AVOID

MAY BURN BUT DOES NOT IGNITE READILY.

SPILL AND LEAK PROCEDURES

OCCUPATIONAL SPILL: DO NOT TOUCH SPILLED MATERIAL. STOP LEAK IF YOU CAN DO IT WITHOUT RISK. FOR SMALL SPILLS, TAKE UP WITH SAND OR OTHER ABSORBENT MATERIAL AND PLACE INTO CONTAINERS FOR LATER DISPOSAL. FOR SMALL DRY SPILLS, WITH A CLEAN SHOVEL PLACE MATERIAL INTO CLEAN, DRY CONTAINER AND COVER. MOVE CONTAINERS FROM SPILL AREA. FOR LARGER SPILLS, DIKE FAR AHEAD OF SPILL FOR LATER DISPOSAL. KEEP UNNECESSARY PEOPLE AWAY. ISOLATE HAZARD AREA AND DENY ENTRY.

PROTECTIVE EQUIPMENT

VENTILATION: PROVIDE LOCAL EXHAUST OR PROCESS ENCLOSURE VENTILATION SYSTEM.

RESPIRATOR: THE FOLLOWING RESPIRATORS ARE RECOMMENDED BASED ON INFORMATION FOUND IN THE PHYSICAL DATA, TOXICITY AND HEALTH EFFECTS SECTIONS. THEY ARE RANKED IN ORDER FROM MINIMUM TO MAXIMUM RESPIRATORY PROTECTION. THE SPECIFIC RESPIRATOR SELECTED MUST BE BASED ON CONTAMINATION LEVELS FOUND IN THE WORK PLACE, MUST NOT EXCEED THE WORKING LIMITS OF THE RESPIRATOR AND BE JOINTLY APPROVED BY THE NATIONAL INSTITUTE FOR OCCUPATIONAL SAFETY AND HEALTH AND THE MINE SAFETY AND HEALTH ADMINISTRATION (NIOSH-MSHA).

TYPE 'C' SUPPLIED-AIR RESPIRATOR WITH A FULL FACEPIECE OPERATED IN PRESSURE-DEMAND OR OTHER POSITIVE PRESSURE MODE OR WITH A FULL FACEPIECE, HELMET OR HOOD OPERATED IN CONTINOUS-FLOW MODE.

SELF-CONTAINED BREATHING APPARATUS WITH A FULL FACEPIECE OPERATED IN PRESSURE-DEMAND OR OTHER POSITIVE PRESSURE MODE.

FOR FIREFIGHTING AND OTHER IMMEDIATELY DANGEROUS TO LIFE OR HEALTH CONDITIONS:

SELF-CONTAINED BREATHING APPARATUS WITH FULL FACEPIECE OPERATED IN PRESSURE-DEMAND OR OTHER POSITIVE PRESSURE MODE.

SUPPLIED-AIR RESPIRATOR WITH FULL FACEPIECE AND OPERATED IN PRESSURE-DEMAND OR OTHER POSITIVE PRESSURE MODE IN COMBINATION WITH AN AUXILIARY SELF-CONTAINED BREATHING APPARATUS OPERATED IN PRESSURE-DEMAND OR OTHER POSITIVE PRESSURE MODE.

CLOTHING: EMPLOYEE MUST WEAR APPROPRIATE PROTECTIVE (IMPERVIOUS) CLOTHING AND EQUIPMENT TO PREVENT REPEATED OR PROLONGED SKIN CONTACT WITH THIS SUBSTANCE.

GLOVES: EMPLOYEE MUST WEAR APPROPRIATE PROTECTIVE GLOVES TO PREVENT CONTACT WITH THIS SUBSTANCE.

EYE PROTECTION: EMPLOYEE MUST WEAR SPLASH-PROOF OR DUST-RESISTANT SAFETY GOGGLES TO PREVENT EYE CONTACT WITH THIS SUBSTANCE.

EMERGENCY EYE WASH: WHERE THERE IS ANY POSSIBILITY THAT AN EMPLOYEE'S EYES MAY BE EXPOSED TO THIS SUBSTANCE, THE EMPLOYER SHOULD PROVIDE AN EYE WASH FOUNTAIN WITHIN THE IMMEDIATE WORK AREA FOR EMERGENCY USE.

AUTHORIZED BY- OCCUPATIONAL HEALTH SERVICES, INC.

CREATION DATE: 04/16/90 ***REVISION DATE:*** 04/18/90

MATERIAL SAFETY DATA SHEET

OCCUPATIONAL HEALTH SERVICES, INC.
AGRICULTURE AND PESTICIDE DIVISION
450 SEVENTH AVENUE, SUITE 2407
NEW YORK, NEW YORK 10123
1-800-445-MSDS OR (212) 967-1100

EMERGENCY CONTACT:
JOHN S. BRANSFORD, JR. (615) 292-1180

SUBSTANCE IDENTIFICATION

CAS-NUMBER 88-85-7

***SUBSTANCE:* DINOSEB**

TRADE NAMES/SYNONYMS: PHENOL, 2-(1-METHYLPROPYL)-4,6-DINITRO-; PHENOL, 2-SEC-BUTYL-4,6-DINITRO-; 2-(1-METHYLPROPYL)-4,6-DINITROPHENOL; 2-SEC-BUTYL-4,6-DINITROPHENOL; CHEMOX; CALDON; GEBUTOX; DN 289; DNBP; PREMERGE (FORMULATION); ENT 1,122; RCRA P020; C10H12N2O5; PST08020

CHEMICAL FAMILY: NITRO PHENOL

MOLECULAR FORMULA: C10-H12-N2-O5

MOLECULAR WEIGHT: 240.29

CERCLA RATINGS (SCALE 0-3): HEALTH=3 FIRE=1 REACTIVITY=0 PERSISTENCE=1

NFPA RATINGS (SCALE 0-4): HEALTH=4 FIRE=1 REACTIVITY=0

COMPONENTS AND CONTAMINANTS

COMPONENT: DINOSEB ***PERCENT:*** 100.0
CAS# 88-85-7

EXPOSURE LIMITS: NO OCCUPATIONAL EXPOSURE LIMITS ESTABLISHED BY OSHA, ACGIH, OR NIOSH.
DINOSEB: 100/10,000 POUNDS SARA SECTION 302 THRESHOLD PLANNING QUANTITY 1000 POUNDS SARA SECTION 304 REPORTABLE QUANTITY 1000 POUNDS CERCLA SECTION 103 REPORTABLE QUANTITY SUBJECT TO CALIFORNIA PROPOSITION 65 CANCER AND/OR REPRODUCTIVE TOXICITY WARNING AND RELEASE REQUIREMENTS- (JANUARY 1, 1989)

PHYSICAL DATA

DESCRIPTION: YELLOW-ORANGE, WAXY, CRYSTALLINE SOLID WITH PUNGENT ODOR.

MELTING POINT: 100-108 F (38-42 C) ***SPECIFIC GRAVITY:*** 1.265 @ 45 C

VISCOSITY: 25 CPS @ 45 C ***VAPOR PRESSURE:*** 1 MMHG @ 151.9 C ***PH:*** ACIDIC

SOLUBILITY IN WATER: 0.01%

SOLVENT SOLUBILITY: SOLUBLE IN ETHANOL, ALCOHOL, ETHER, TOLUENE, XYLENE, N-HEPTANE, PETROLEUM OILS AND MOST ORGANIC SOLVENTS.

FIRE AND EXPLOSION DATA

FIRE AND EXPLOSION HAZARD: SLIGHT FIRE HAZARD WHEN EXPOSED TO HEAT OR FLAME.

FLASH POINT: 351 F (177 C) ***FLAMMABILITY CLASS(OSHA):*** IIIB

FIREFIGHTING MEDIA: DRY CHEMICAL, CARBON DIOXIDE, HALON, WATER SPRAY OR STANDARD FOAM (1987 EMERGENCY RESPONSE GUIDEBOOK, DOT P 5800.4).
FOR LARGER FIRES, USE WATER SPRAY, FOG OR STANDARD FOAM (1987 EMERGENCY RESPONSE GUIDEBOOK, DOT P 5800.4).

FIREFIGHTING: MOVE CONTAINERS FROM FIRE AREA IF POSSIBLE (1987 EMERGENCY RESPONSE GUIDEBOOK, DOT P 5800.4, GUIDE PAGE 53).
EXTINGUISH USING AGENT SUITABLE FOR TYPE OF SURROUNDING FIRE. AVOID BREATHING VAPORS AND DUSTS. KEEP UPWIND.

TRANSPORTATION DATA

DEPARTMENT OF TRANSPORTATION HAZARD CLASSIFICATION 49 CFR 172.101: POISON B
DEPARTMENT OF TRANSPORTATION LABELING REQUIREMENTS 49 CFR 172.101 AND SUBPART E: POISON
DEPARTMENT OF TRANSPORTATION PACKAGING REQUIREMENTS: 49 CFR 173.365 EXCEPTIONS: 49 CFR 173.364

TOXICITY

DINOSEB: IRRITATION DATA: 50 UG/24 HOURS EYE-RABBIT SEVERE. TOXICITY DATA: 45 MG/M3/3 HOURS INHALATION-CAT LCLO; 80 MG/KG SKIN-RABBIT LD50; 80 MG/KG SKIN-RAT LD50; 500 MG/KG SKIN-GUINEA PIG LDLO; 25 MG/KG ORAL-RAT LD50; 16 MG/KG ORAL-MOUSE LD50; 20 MG/KG ORAL-GUINEA PIG LD50; 20368 MG/KG SUBCUTANEOUS-RAT LD50; 10 MG/KG INTRAPERITONEAL-MOUSE LD50; MUTAGENIC DATA (RTECS); REPRODUCTIVE EFFECTS DATA (RTECS); TUMORIGENIC DATA (RTECS). CARCINOGEN STATUS: NONE. LOCAL EFFECTS: IRRITANT- EYE. ACUTE TOXICITY LEVEL: HIGHLY TOXIC BY DERMAL ABSORPTION AND INGESTION. TARGET EFFECTS: POISONING MAY INCREASE THE METABOLIC RATE AND AFFECT THE NERVOUS SYSTEM, LIVER, AND KIDNEYS.* AT INCREASED RISK FROM EXPOSURE: ALCOHOLICS AND PERSONS WITH RENAL OR HEPATIC DISEASES.* ADDITIONAL DATA: EPA HAS DETERMINED THAT AN ADEQUATE MARGIN OF SAFETY DOES NOT EXIST BETWEEN THE USE OF DINOSEB AND POTENTIAL EFFECTS OF INDUCING BIRTH DEFECTS OR PRODUCING STERILITY IN MAN. STUDIES IN LABORATORY ANIMALS SUGGEST THAT DINOSEB HAS THE POTENTIAL TO AFFECT THE IMMUNOLOGICAL SYSTEM. LIVER TUMORS IN FEMALE MICE WERE REPORTED IN A LONG-TERM STUDY OF DINOSEB. HOT ENVIRONMENTS MAY ENHANCE ABSORPTION AND THE TOXIC EFFECTS.
* MAY BE BASED ON INFORMATION ON DINITROPHENOL DERIVATIVES.

HEALTH EFFECTS AND FIRST AID

INHALATION: DINOSEB: SEE INFORMATION ON DINITROPHENOL DERIVATIVES.
DINITROPHENOL DERIVATIVES: **ACUTE EXPOSURE-** MAY BE ABSORBED WITH SYMPTOMS OCCURRING SUDDENLY AND UP TO 2 DAYS AFTER CESSATION OF EXPOSURE. SYMPTOMS MAY INCLUDE FATIGUE, WEAKNESS, FEVER, THIRST, NAUSEA, VOMITING, HEADACHES, FLUSHED SKIN, PROSTRATION, EXCESSIVE PERSPIRATION, TACHYCARDIA, TACHYPNEA, AND DYSPNEA. APPREHENSION, RESTLESSNESS, ANXIETY, MANIC BEHAVIOR, OR UNCONSCIOUSNESS MAY INDICATE CEREBRAL INJURY. CONVULSIONS MAY OCCUR IN THE MOST SEVERE POISONINGS. ANOXIA WITH CYANOSIS, LIVIDITY AND METABOLIC ACIDOSIS, SEVERE HYPERPYREXIA, DEHYDRATION, AND MUSCULAR TREMORS MAY BE FOLLOWED BY CIRCULATORY OR RESPIRATORY COLLAPSE AND COMA. DEGENERATIVE CHANGES IN THE HEART, RENAL TUBULES AND LIVER PARENCHYMA MAY OCCUR. THERE MAY BE ALBUMINURIA, PYURIA, HEMATURIA, JAUNDICE, AND INCREASED BUN. THE EFFECTS FROM POISONING ARE RAPID AND DEATH OR RECOVERY GENERALLY OCCURS WITHIN 24 TO 48 HOURS. FATAL DINITROPHENOL POISONING IS FOLLOWED BY INSTANTANEOUS RIGOR MORTIS.
CHRONIC EXPOSURE- IN ADDITION TO THE SYMPTOMS OF ACUTE EXPOSURE, PROLONGED OR REPEATED EXPOSURE MAY CAUSE WEIGHT LOSS, CATARACT FORMATION, AND LIVER AND KIDNEY DAMAGE. YELLOW STAINING OF THE SCLERAE AND URINE INDICATES ABSORPTION OF POTENTIALLY TOXIC AMOUNTS.

FIRST AID- REMOVE FROM EXPOSURE AREA TO FRESH AIR IMMEDIATELY. IF BREATHING HAS STOPPED, PERFORM ARTIFICIAL RESPIRATION. ADMINISTER OXYGEN. TREAT SYMPTOMATICALLY AND SUPPORTIVELY. GET MEDICAL ATTENTION IMMEDIATELY.

SKIN CONTACT: DINOSEB: HIGHLY TOXIC. SEE INFORMATION ON DINITROPHENOL DERIVATIVES.
DINITROPHENOL DERIVATIVES: **ACUTE EXPOSURE-** MAY CAUSE IRRITATION. CONTACT MAY RESULT IN YELLOW STAINING OF THE SKIN AHD HAIR. SOME DERIVATIVES MAY BE ABSORBED THROUGH THE SKIN WITH SYMPTOMS OCCURRING SUDDENLY AND UP TO 2 DAYS AFTER CESSATION OF EXPOSURE AND PRODUCE EFFECTS ON THE METABOLIC RATE, CENTRAL NERVOUS SYSTEM AND LIVER AND KIDNEY RESULTING IN SIGNS AND SYMPTOMS AS DESCRIBED IN ACUTE INHALATION. **CHRONIC EXPOSURE-** REPEATED OR PROLONGED CONTACT MAY RESULT IN DERMATITIS DUE TO IRRITATION OR ALLERGIC SENSITIVITY. IN ADDITION TO THE SYMPTOMS OF ACUTE EXPOSURE, CHRONIC ABSORPTION MAY CAUSE FATIGUE, WEIGHT LOSS, CATARACT FORMATION AND LIVER AND KIDNEY DAMAGE. YELLOW STAINING OF THE SCLERAE AND URINE INDICATES ABSORPTION OF POTENTIALLY TOXIC AMOUNTS.

FIRST AID- REMOVE CONTAMINATED CLOTHING AND SHOES IMMEDIATELY. THEN REMOVE SKIN AND HAIR CONTAMINATION BY SCRUBBING WITH SOAP AND WATER. IF BODY TEMPERATURE IS ELEVATED, REDUCE TO 37 C BY SPONGE BATH, IMMERSION IN COOL WATER OR BY APPLYING COOLING BLANKET. IF BODY TEMPERATURE IS ABOVE 40 C, ICE WATER IS NECESSARY (DREISBACH, HANDBOOK OF POISONING, 12TH EDITION; MORGAN, EPA RECOGNITION AND MANAGEMENT OF PESTICIDE POISONINGS, 3RD EDITION). GET MEDICAL ATTENTION IMMEDIATELY.

EYE CONTACT: DINOSEB: IRRITANT. **ACUTE EXPOSURE-** EYE CONTACT WITH A DILUTE FORM OF THIS MATERIAL PRODUCED PAIN, SWELLING OF THE EYE, AND IMPAIRED VISION THAT LASTED FOR 3 DAYS FOLLOWED BY COMPLETE RECOVERY. 50 UG APPLIED TO RABBIT EYES PRODUCED SEVERE IRRITATION. **CHRONIC EXPOSURE-** PROLONGED OR REPEATED EXPOSURE TO IRRITANTS MAY CAUSE CONJUNCTIVITIS.

FIRST AID- WASH EYES IMMEDIATELY WITH LARGE AMOUNTS OF WATER OR NORMAL SALINE, OCCASIONALLY LIFTING UPPER AND LOWER LIDS, UNTIL NO EVIDENCE OF CHEMICAL REMAINS (APPROXIMATELY 15-20 MINUTES). GET MEDICAL ATTENTION IMMEDIATELY.

INGESTION: DINOSEB: HIGHLY TOXIC. ADVERSE DEVELOPMENT EFFECTS INCLUDING ANOMALIES OF THE NEUROLOGICAL AND SKELETAL SYSTEMS AND ADVERSE MALE REPRODUCTIVE EFFECTS INCLUDING TESTICULAR EFFECTS AND DECREASED REPRODUCTIVE PERFORMANCE AND FETAL VIABILITY WERE OBSERVED IN LABORATORY ANIMALS. SEE INFORMATION ON DINITROPHENOL DERIVATIVES.
DINITROPHENOL DERIVATIVES: **ACUTE EXPOSURE-** MAY CAUSE EFFECTS ON THE METABOLIC RATE, CENTRAL NERVOUS SYSTEM AND LIVER AND KIDNEY RESULTING IN SIGNS AND SYMPTOMS AS DESCRIBED IN ACUTE INHALATION.
CHRONIC EXPOSURE- IN ADDITION TO THE SYMPTOMS OF ACUTE EXPOSURE, REPEATED INGESTION MAY CAUSE AN INITIAL SENSE OF WELL-BEING THEN ANOREXIA, DIARRHEA, DIZZINESS, RESTLESSNESS, FATIGUE, WEIGHT LOSS, SKIN ERUPTIONS, PERIPHERAL NEURITIS, LIVER AND KIDNEY DAMAGE, CARDIOVASCULAR COMPLICATIONS, GRANULOCYTOPENIA, AND CATARACT FORMATION. YELLOW STAINING OF THE SCLERAE AND URINE INDICATES ABSORPTION OF POTENTIALLY TOXIC AMOUNTS.

FIRST AID- REMOVE INGESTED POISON BY THOROUGH GASTRIC LAVAGE WITH SATURATED BICARBONATE SOLUTION. IF GASTRIC LAVAGE CANNOT BE ACCOMPLISHED IMMEDIATELY, GIVE SYRUP OF IPECAC TO INDUCE EMESIS AND FOLLOW WITH SALINE CATHARTIC. IF BODY TEMPERATURE IS ELEVATED, REDUCE TO 37 C BY IMMERSION IN COOL WATER OR BY APPLYING COOLING BLANKET. IF BODY TEMPERATURE IS ABOVE 40 C, ICE WATER IS NECESSARY (DREISBACH, HANDBOOK OF POISONING, 12TH ED.). ADMINISTRATION OF GASTRIC LAVAGE SHOULD BE PERFORMED BY QUALIFIED MEDICAL PERSONNEL. GET MEDICAL ATTENTION IMMEDIATELY.

ANTIDOTE: NO SPECIFIC ANTIDOTE. TREAT SYMPTOMATICALLY AND SUPPORTIVELY.

REACTIVITY

REACTIVITY: STABLE UNDER NORMAL TEMPERATURES AND PRESSURES.
THIS MATERIAL MAY UNDERGO RAPID EXOTHERMIC DECOMPOSITION ABOVE 374F (190 C). MAY EXPLODE IF HEATED UNDER CONFINEMENT.

INCOMPATIBILITIES: DINOSEB: OXIDIZERS (STRONG): FIRE AND EXPLOSION HAZARD.
STEEL: MAY BE CORROSIVE IN THE PRESENCE OF MOISTURE.

DECOMPOSITION: THERMAL DECOMPOSITION PRODUCTS MAY INCLUDE TOXIC OXIDES OF CARBON AND NITROGEN.

POLYMERIZATION: HAZARDOUS POLYMERIZATION HAS NOT BEEN REPORTED TO OCCUR UNDER NORMAL TEMPERATURES AND PRESSURES.

STORAGE AND DISPOSAL

OBSERVE ALL FEDERAL, STATE AND LOCAL REGULATIONS WHEN STORING OR DISPOSING OF THIS SUBSTANCE. FOR ASSISTANCE, CONTACT THE DISTRICT DIRECTOR OF THE ENVIRONMENTAL PROTECTION AGENCY.

STORAGE

STORE IN ACCORDANCE WITH 40 CFR 165 RECOMMENDED PROCEDURES FOR THE DISPOSAL AND STORAGE OF PESTICIDES AND PESTICIDE CONTAINERS.
STORE AWAY FROM INCOMPATIBLE SUBSTANCES.
THRESHOLD PLANNING QUANTITY (TPQ): THE SUPERFUND AMENDMENTS AND REAUTHORIZATION ACT (SARA) SECTION 302 REQUIRES THAT EACH FACILITY WHERE ANY EXTREMELY HAZARDOUS SUBSTANCE IS PRESENT IN A QUANTITY EQUAL TO OR GREATER THAN THE TPQ ESTABLISHED FOR THAT SUBSTANCE NOTIFY THE STATE EMERGENCY RESPONSE COMMISSION FOR THE STATE IN WHICH IT IS LOCATED. SECTION 303 OF SARA REQUIRES THESE FACILITIES TO PARTICIPATE IN LOCAL EMERGENCY RESPONSE PLANNING (40 CFR 355.30).

DISPOSAL

DISPOSAL MUST BE IN ACCORDANCE WITH STANDARDS APPLICABLE TO GENERATORS OF HAZARDOUS WASTE, 40CFR 262. EPA HAZARDOUS WASTE NUMBER P020.
DISPOSAL MUST BE IN ACCORDANCE WITH 40 CFR 165 RECOMMENDED PROCEDURES FOR THE DISPOSAL AND STORAGE OF PESTICIDES AND PESTICIDE CONTAINERS.

CONDITIONS TO AVOID

MAY BURN BUT DOES NOT IGNITE READILY.

SPILL AND LEAK PROCEDURES

WATER SPILL: THE CALIFORNIA SAFE DRINKING WATER AND TOXIC ENFORCEMENT ACT OF 1986 (PROPOSITION 65) PROHIBITS CONTAMINATING ANY KNOWN SOURCE OF DRINKING WATER WITH SUBSTANCES KNOWN TO CAUSE CANCER AND/OR REPRODUCTIVE TOXICITY.

OCCUPATIONAL SPILL: DO NOT TOUCH SPILLED MATERIAL. STOP LEAK IF YOU CAN DO IT WITHOUT RISK. FOR SMALL SPILLS, TAKE UP WITH SAND OR OTHER ABSORBENT MATERIAL AND PLACE INTO CONTAINERS FOR LATER DISPOSAL. FOR SMALL DRY SPILLS, WITH A CLEAN SHOVEL PLACE MATERIAL INTO CLEAN, DRY CONTAINER AND COVER. MOVE CONTAINERS FROM SPILL AREA. FOR LARGER SPILLS, DIKE FAR AHEAD OF SPILL FOR LATER DISPOSAL. KEEP UNNECESSARY PEOPLE AWAY. ISOLATE HAZARD AREA AND DENY ENTRY.
REPORTABLE QUANTITY (RQ): 1000 POUNDS THE SUPERFUND AMENDMENTS AND REAUTHORIZATION ACT (SARA) SECTION 304 REQUIRES THAT A RELEASE EQUAL TO OR GREATER THAN THE REPORTABLE QUANTITY FOR THIS SUBSTANCE BE IMMEDIATELY REPORTED TO THE LOCAL EMERGENCY PLANNING COMMITTEE AND THE STATE EMERGENCY RESPONSE COMMISSION (40 CFR 355.40). IF THE RELEASE OF THIS SUBSTANCE IS REPORTABLE UNDER CERCLA SECTION 103, THE NATIONAL RESPONSE CENTER MUST BE NOTIFIED IMMEDIATELY AT (800) 424-8802 OR (202) 426-2675 IN THE METROPOLITAN WASHINGTON, D.C. AREA (40 CFR 302.6).

PROTECTIVE EQUIPMENT

VENTILATION: PROVIDE LOCAL EXHAUST OR PROCESS ENCLOSURE VENTILATION SYSTEM.

RESPIRATOR: THE FOLLOWING RESPIRATORS ARE RECOMMENDED BASED ON INFORMATION FOUND IN THE PHYSICAL DATA, TOXICITY AND HEALTH EFFECTS SECTIONS. THEY ARE RANKED IN ORDER FROM MINIMUM TO MAXIMUM RESPIRATORY PROTECTION. THE SPECIFIC RESPIRATOR SELECTED MUST BE BASED ON CONTAMINATION LEVELS FOUND IN THE WORK PLACE, MUST NOT EXCEED THE WORKING LIMITS OF THE RESPIRATOR AND BE JOINTLY APPROVED BY THE NATIONAL INSTITUTE FOR OCCUPATIONAL SAFETY AND HEALTH AND THE MINE SAFETY AND HEALTH ADMINISTRATION (NIOSH-MSHA).
TYPE 'C' SUPPLIED-AIR RESPIRATOR WITH A FULL FACEPIECE OPERATED IN PRESSURE-DEMAND OR OTHER POSITIVE PRESSURE MODE OR WITH A FULL FACEPIECE, HELMET OR HOOD OPERATED IN CONTINOUS-FLOW MODE.
SELF-CONTAINED BREATHING APPARATUS WITH A FULL FACEPIECE OPERATED IN PRESSURE-DEMAND OR OTHER POSITIVE PRESSURE MODE.
FOR FIREFIGHTING AND OTHER IMMEDIATELY DANGEROUS TO LIFE OR HEALTH CONDITIONS:
SELF-CONTAINED BREATHING APPARATUS WITH FULL FACEPIECE OPERATED IN PRESSURE-DEMAND OR OTHER POSITIVE PRESSURE MODE.
SUPPLIED-AIR RESPIRATOR WITH FULL FACEPIECE AND OPERATED IN PRESSURE-DEMAND OR OTHER POSITIVE PRESSURE MODE IN COMBINATION WITH AN AUXILIARY SELF-CONTAINED BREATHING APPARATUS OPERATED IN PRESSURE-DEMAND OR OTHER POSITIVE PRESSURE MODE.

CLOTHING: EMPLOYEE MUST WEAR APPROPRIATE PROTECTIVE (IMPERVIOUS) CLOTHING AND EQUIPMENT TO PREVENT ANY POSSIBILITY OF SKIN CONTACT WITH THIS SUBSTANCE.

GLOVES: EMPLOYEE MUST WEAR APPROPRIATE PROTECTIVE GLOVES TO PREVENT CONTACT WITH THIS SUBSTANCE.

EYE PROTECTION: EMPLOYEE MUST WEAR SPLASH-PROOF OR DUST-RESISTANT SAFETY GOGGLES AND A FACESHIELD TO PREVENT CONTACT WITH THIS SUBSTANCE.
EMERGENCY WASH FACILITIES: WHERE THERE IS ANY POSSIBILITY THAT AN EMPLOYEE'S EYES AND/OR SKIN MAY BE EXPOSED TO THIS SUBSTANCE, THE EMPLOYER SHOULD PROVIDE AN EYE WASH FOUNTAIN AND QUICK DRENCH SHOWER WITHIN THE IMMEDIATE WORK AREA FOR EMERGENCY USE.

AUTHORIZED BY- OCCUPATIONAL HEALTH SERVICES, INC.
CREATION DATE: 10/04/89 ***REVISION DATE:*** 05/09/90

MATERIAL SAFETY DATA SHEET

OCCUPATIONAL HEALTH SERVICES, INC.	EMERGENCY CONTACT:
AGRICULTURE AND PESTICIDE DIVISION	JOHN S. BRANSFORD, JR. (615) 292-1180
450 SEVENTH AVENUE, SUITE 2407	
NEW YORK, NEW YORK 10123	
1-800-445-MSDS OR (212) 967-1100	

SUBSTANCE IDENTIFICATION

CAS-NUMBER 2813-95-8

SUBSTANCE: DINOSEB ACETATE

TRADE NAMES/SYNONYMS: PHENOL, 2-(1-METHYLPROPYL)-4,6-DINITRO-, ACETATE (ESTER); PHENOL, 2-SEC-BUTYL-4,6-DINITRO-, ACETATE (ESTER); PHENO, 2-SEC-BUTYL-4,6-DINITRO, ACETATE; 2-(1-METHYLPROPYL)-4,6-DINITROPHENOL ACETATE (ESTER); 2-SEC-BUTYL-4,6-DINITROPHENOL ACETATE (ESTER); 2-SEC-BUTYL-4,6-DINITROPHENOL ACETATE; 2-(1-METHYLPROPYL)4,6-DINITROPHENYL ACETATE; DINITROBUTYLPHENYLACETATE; O-ACETYL-2-SEC-BUTYL-4,6-DINITROPHENOL; ARETIT; IVOSIT; C12H14N2O6; PST08021

CHEMICAL FAMILY: ESTER, CARBOXYLIC, AROMATIC NITRO

MOLECULAR FORMULA: C12-H14-N2-O6

MOLECULAR WEIGHT: 282.28

CERCLA RATINGS (SCALE 0-3): HEALTH=3 FIRE=U REACTIVITY=0 PERSISTENCE=1

NFPA RATINGS (SCALE 0-4): HEALTH=4 FIRE=U REACTIVITY=0

COMPONENTS AND CONTAMINANTS

COMPONENT: DINOSEB ACETATE ***PERCENT:*** 100.0
CAS# 2813-95-8

EXPOSURE LIMITS: NO OCCUPATIONAL EXPOSURE LIMITS ESTABLISHED BY OSHA, ACGIH, OR NIOSH.

PHYSICAL DATA

DESCRIPTION: VISCOUS BROWN OIL WITH AN AROMATIC VINEGAR-LIKE ODOR.

BOILING POINT: 338 F (170 C) @ 4 MMHG ***MELTING POINT:*** 79-81 F (26-27 C)
SPECIFIC GRAVITY: NOT AVAILABLE ***VAPOR PRESSURE:*** 0.0006 MMHG @ 20 C
SOLUBILITY IN WATER: 0.16%
SOLVENT SOLUBILITY: SOLUBLE IN AROMATIC SOLVENTS.

FIRE AND EXPLOSION DATA

FIRE AND EXPLOSION HAZARD: UNKNOWN FIRE AND EXPLOSION HAZARD.

FIREFIGHTING MEDIA: DRY CHEMICAL, CARBON DIOXIDE, HALON, WATER SPRAY OR STANDARD FOAM (1987 EMERGENCY RESPONSE GUIDEBOOK, DOT P 5800.4).
FOR LARGER FIRES, USE WATER SPRAY, FOG OR STANDARD FOAM (1987 EMERGENCY RESPONSE GUIDEBOOK, DOT P 5800.4).

FIREFIGHTING: MOVE CONTAINER FROM FIRE AREA IF POSSIBLE. DIKE FIRE CONTROL WATER FOR LATER DISPOSAL; DO NOT SCATTER THE MATERIAL. COOL FIRE-EXPOSED CONTAINERS WITH WATER FROM SIDE UNTIL WELL AFTER FIRE IS OUT. STAY AWAY FROM STORAGE TANK ENDS. WITHDRAW IMMEDIATELY IN CASE OF RISING SOUND FROM VENTING SAFETY DEVICE OR ANY DISCOLORATION OF STORAGE TANK DUE TO FIRE (1987 EMERGENCY RESPONSE GUIDEBOOK, DOT P 5800.4, GUIDE PAGE 28).
EXTINGUISH ONLY IF FLOW CAN BE STOPPED. USE FLOODING AMOUNTS OF WATER AS A FOG; SOLID STREAMS MAY BE INEFFECTIVE. COOL CONTAINERS WITH FLOODING AMOUNTS OF WATER FROM AS FAR A DISTANCE AS POSSIBLE. AVOID BREATHING POISONOUS VAPORS, KEEP UPWIND.

TRANSPORTATION DATA

DEPARTMENT OF TRANSPORTATION HAZARD CLASSIFICATION 49 CFR 172.101: POISON B
DEPARTMENT OF TRANSPORTATION LABELING REQUIREMENTS 49 CFR 172.101 AND SUBPART E: POISON
DEPARTMENT OF TRANSPORTATION PACKAGING REQUIREMENTS: 49 CFR 173.346 EXCEPTIONS: 49 CFR 173.345

TOXICITY

DINOSEB ACETATE: IRRITATION DATA: 500 MG/24 HOURS EYE-RABBIT MILD; 500 MG/24 HOURS SKIN-RABBIT MILD. TOXICITY DATA: 1.3 MG/L/4 HOURS INHALATION-RAT LC50 (85JFAN); 60 MG/KG ORAL-RAT LD50. CARCINOGEN STATUS: NONE. ACUTE TOXICITY LEVEL: HIGHLY TOXIC BY INHALATION; TOXIC BY INGESTION. TARGET EFFECTS: POISONING MAY INCREASE THE METABOLIC RATE AND AFFECT THE NERVOUS SYSTEM, LIVER, AND KIDNEYS.* AT INCREASED RISK FROM EXPOSURE: ALCOHOLICS AND PERSONS WITH RENAL OR HEPATIC DISEASES.* ADDITIONAL DATA: EPA HAS DETERMINED THAT AN ADEQUATE MARGIN OF SAFETY DOES NOT EXIST BETWEEN THE USE OF DINOSEB AND POTENTIAL EFFECTS OF INDUCING BIRTH DEFECTS OR PRODUCING STERILITY IN MAN. HOT ENVIRONMENTS MAY ENHANCE ABSORPTION AND THE TOXIC EFFECTS.*
* MAY BE BASED ON INFORMATION ON DINITROPHENOL DERIVATIVES.

HEALTH EFFECTS AND FIRST AID

INHALATION: DINOSEB ACETATE: HIGHLY TOXIC. SEE INFORMATION ON DINITROPHENOL DERIVATIVES.
DINITROPHENOL DERIVATIVES: **ACUTE EXPOSURE-** MAY BE ABSORBED WITH SYMPTOMS OCCURRING SUDDENLY AND UP TO 2 DAYS AFTER CESSATION OF EXPOSURE. SYMPTOMS MAY INCLUDE FATIGUE, WEAKNESS, FEVER, THIRST, NAUSEA, VOMITING, HEADACHES, FLUSHED SKIN, PROSTRATION, EXCESSIVE PERSPIRATION, TACHYCARDIA, TACHYPNEA, AND DYSPNEA. APPREHENSION, RESTLESSNESS, ANXIETY, MANIC BEHAVIOR, OR UNCONSCIOUSNESS MAY INDICATE CEREBRAL INJURY. CONVULSIONS MAY OCCUR IN THE MOST SEVERE POISONINGS. ANOXIA WITH CYANOSIS, LIVIDITY AND METABOLIC ACIDOSIS, SEVERE HYPERPYREXIA, DEHYDRATION, AND MUSCULAR TREMORS MAY BE FOLLOWED BY CIRCULATORY OR RESPIRATORY COLLAPSE AND COMA. DEGENERATIVE CHANGES IN THE HEART, RENAL TUBULES AND LIVER PARENCHYMA MAY OCCUR. THERE MAY BE ALBUMINURIA, PYURIA, HEMATURIA, JAUNDICE, AND INCREASED BUN. THE EFFECTS FROM POISONING ARE RAPID AND DEATH OR RECOVERY GENERALLY OCCURS WITHIN 24 TO 48 HOURS. FATAL DINITROPHENOL POISONING IS FOLLOWED BY INSTANTANEOUS RIGOR MORTIS. **CHRONIC EXPOSURE-** IN ADDITION TO THE SYMPTOMS OF ACUTE EXPOSURE, PROLONGED OR REPEATED EXPOSURE MAY CAUSE WEIGHT LOSS, CATARACT FORMATION, AND LIVER AND KIDNEY DAMAGE. YELLOW STAINING OF THE SCLERAE AND URINE INDICATES ABSORPTION OF POTENTIALLY TOXIC AMOUNTS.

FIRST AID- REMOVE FROM EXPOSURE AREA TO FRESH AIR IMMEDIATELY. IF BREATHING HAS STOPPED, PERFORM ARTIFICIAL RESPIRATION. ADMINISTER OXYGEN. TREAT SYMPTOMATICALLY AND SUPPORTIVELY. GET MEDICAL ATTENTION IMMEDIATELY.

SKIN CONTACT: DINOSEB ACETATE: SEE INFORMATION ON DINITROPHENOL DERIVATIVES.
DINITROPHENOL DERIVATIVES: **ACUTE EXPOSURE-** MAY CAUSE IRRITATION. CONTACT MAY RESULT IN YELLOW STAINING OF THE SKIN AHD HAIR. SOME DERIVATIVES MAY BE ABSORBED THROUGH THE SKIN WITH SYMPTOMS OCCURRING SUDDENLY AND UP TO 2 DAYS AFTER CESSATION OF EXPOSURE AND PRODUCE EFFECTS ON THE METABOLIC RATE, CENTRAL NERVOUS SYSTEM AND LIVER AND KIDNEY RESULTING IN SIGNS AND SYMPTOMS AS DESCRIBED IN ACUTE INHALATION. **CHRONIC EXPOSURE-** REPEATED OR PROLONGED CONTACT MAY RESULT IN DERMATITIS DUE TO IRRITATION OR ALLERGIC SENSITIVITY. IN ADDITION TO THE SYMPTOMS OF ACUTE EXPOSURE, CHRONIC ABSORPTION MAY CAUSE FATIGUE, WEIGHT LOSS, CATARACT FORMATION AND LIVER AND KIDNEY DAMAGE. YELLOW STAINING OF THE SCLERAE AND URINE INDICATES ABSORPTION OF POTENTIALLY TOXIC AMOUNTS.

FIRST AID- REMOVE CONTAMINATED CLOTHING AND SHOES IMMEDIATELY. THEN REMOVE SKIN AND HAIR CONTAMINATION BY SCRUBBING WITH SOAP AND WATER. IF BODY TEMPERATURE IS ELEVATED, REDUCE TO 37 C BY SPONGE BATH, IMMERSION IN COOL WATER OR BY APPLYING COOLING BLANKET. IF BODY TEMPERATURE IS ABOVE 40 C, ICE WATER IS NECESSARY (DREISBACH, HANDBOOK OF POISONING, 12TH EDITION; MORGAN, EPA RECOGNITION AND MANAGEMENT OF PESTICIDE POISONINGS, 3RD EDITION). GET MEDICAL ATTENTION IMMEDIATELY.

EYE CONTACT: DINOSEB ACETATE: **ACUTE EXPOSURE-** 500 MG APPLIED TO RABBIT EYES WERE MILDLY IRRITATING. **CHRONIC EXPOSURE-** NO DATA AVAILABLE.

FIRST AID- WASH EYES IMMEDIATELY WITH LARGE AMOUNTS OF WATER OR NORMAL SALINE, OCCASIONALLY LIFTING UPPER AND LOWER LIDS, UNTIL NO EVIDENCE OF CHEMICAL REMAINS (APPROXIMATELY 15-20 MINUTES). GET MEDICAL ATTENTION IMMEDIATELY.

INGESTION: DINOSEB ACETATE: TOXIC. ADVERSE DEVELOPMENTAL EFFECTS AND ADVERSE MALE REPRODUCTIVE EFFECTS WERE OBSERVED IN LABORATORY ANIMALS REPEATEDLY EXPOSED TO DINOSEB. SEE INFORMATION ON DINITROPHENOL DERIVATIVES.
DINITROPHENOL DERIVATIVES: **ACUTE EXPOSURE-** MAY CAUSE EFFECTS ON THE METABOLIC RATE, CENTRAL NERVOUS SYSTEM AND LIVER AND KIDNEY RESULTING IN SIGNS AND SYMPTOMS AS DESCRIBED IN ACUTE INHALATION. **CHRONIC EXPOSURE-** IN ADDITION TO THE SYMPTOMS OF ACUTE EXPOSURE, REPEATED INGESTION MAY CAUSE AN INITIAL SENSE OF WELL-BEING THEN ANOREXIA, DIARRHEA, DIZZINESS, RESTLESSNESS, FATIGUE, WEIGHT LOSS, SKIN ERUPTIONS, PERIPHERAL NEURITIS, LIVER AND KIDNEY DAMAGE, CARDIOVASCULAR COMPLICATIONS, GRANULOCYTOPENIA, AND CATARACT FORMATION. YELLOW STAINING OF THE SCLERAE AND URINE INDICATES ABSORPTION OF POTENTIALLY TOXIC AMOUNTS.

FIRST AID- REMOVE INGESTED POISON BY THOROUGH GASTRIC LAVAGE WITH SATURATED BICARBONATE SOLUTION. IF GASTRIC LAVAGE CANNOT BE ACCOMPLISHED IMMEDIATELY, GIVE SYRUP OF IPECAC TO INDUCE EMESIS AND FOLLOW WITH SALINE CATHARTIC. IF BODY TEMPERATURE IS ELEVATED, REDUCE TO 37 C BY IMMERSION IN COOL WATER OR BY APPLYING COOLING BLANKET. IF BODY TEMPERATURE IS ABOVE 40 C, ICE WATER IS NECESSARY (DREISBACH, HANDBOOK OF POISONING, 12TH ED.). ADMINISTRATION OF GASTRIC LAVAGE SHOULD BE PERFORMED BY QUALIFIED MEDICAL PERSONNEL. GET MEDICAL ATTENTION IMMEDIATELY.

ANTIDOTE: NO SPECIFIC ANTIDOTE. TREAT SYMPTOMATICALLY AND SUPPORTIVELY.

REACTIVITY

REACTIVITY: DINOSEB ACETATE: STABLE UNDER NORMAL TEMPERATURES AND PRESSURES. MAY SLOWLY HYDROLYSE IN THE PRESENCE OF WATER.

INCOMPATIBILITIES: DINOSEB ACETATE: METALS: MAY BE CORRODED. OXIDIZERS (STRONG): FIRE AND EXPLOSION HAZARD.

DECOMPOSITION: THERMAL DECOMPOSITION PRODUCTS MAY INCLUDE TOXIC OXIDES OF CARBON AND NITROGEN.

POLYMERIZATION: HAZARDOUS POLYMERIZATION HAS NOT BEEN REPORTED TO OCCUR UNDER NORMAL TEMPERATURES AND PRESSURES.

STORAGE AND DISPOSAL

OBSERVE ALL FEDERAL, STATE AND LOCAL REGULATIONS WHEN STORING OR DISPOSING OF THIS SUBSTANCE. FOR ASSISTANCE, CONTACT THE DISTRICT DIRECTOR OF THE ENVIRONMENTAL PROTECTION AGENCY.

STORAGE

STORE IN ACCORDANCE WITH 40 CFR 165 RECOMMENDED PROCEDURES FOR THE DISPOSAL AND STORAGE OF PESTICIDES AND PESTICIDE CONTAINERS.
STORE AWAY FROM INCOMPATIBLE SUBSTANCES.

DISPOSAL

DISPOSAL MUST BE IN ACCORDANCE WITH 40 CFR 165 RECOMMENDED PROCEDURES FOR THE DISPOSAL AND STORAGE OF PESTICIDES AND PESTICIDE CONTAINERS.

CONDITIONS TO AVOID

AVOID CONTACT WITH HEAT, SPARKS, FLAMES OR OTHER IGNITION SOURCES. VAPORS MAY BE EXPLOSIVE. MATERIAL IS POISONOUS; AVOID INHALATION OF VAPORS OR CONTACT WITH SKIN. DO NOT ALLOW MATERIAL TO CONTAMINATE WATER SOURCES.

SPILL AND LEAK PROCEDURES

OCCUPATIONAL SPILL: SHUT OFF IGNITION SOURCES. DO NOT TOUCH SPILLED MATERIAL. STOP LEAK IF YOU CAN DO IT WITHOUT RISK. USE WATER SPRAY TO REDUCE VAPORS. FOR SMALL SPILLS, TAKE UP WITH SAND OR OTHER ABSORBENT MATERIAL AND PLACE INTO CONTAINERS FOR LATER DISPOSAL. FOR LARGER SPILLS, DIKE FAR AHEAD OF SPILL FOR LATER DISPOSAL. NO SMOKING, FLAMES OR FLARES IN HAZARD AREA! KEEP UNNECESSARY PEOPLE AWAY; ISOLATE HAZARD AREA AND DENY ENTRY.

PROTECTIVE EQUIPMENT

VENTILATION: PROVIDE LOCAL EXHAUST OR PROCESS ENCLOSURE VENTILATION SYSTEM.

RESPIRATOR: THE FOLLOWING RESPIRATORS ARE RECOMMENDED BASED ON INFORMATION FOUND IN THE PHYSICAL DATA, TOXICITY AND HEALTH EFFECTS SECTIONS. THEY ARE RANKED IN ORDER FROM MINIMUM TO MAXIMUM RESPIRATORY PROTECTION. THE SPECIFIC RESPIRATOR SELECTED MUST BE BASED ON CONTAMINATION LEVELS FOUND IN THE WORK PLACE, MUST NOT EXCEED THE WORKING LIMITS OF THE RESPIRATOR AND BE JOINTLY APPROVED BY THE NATIONAL INSTITUTE FOR OCCUPATIONAL SAFETY AND HEALTH AND THE MINE SAFETY AND HEALTH ADMINISTRATION (NIOSH-MSHA).

TYPE 'C' SUPPLIED-AIR RESPIRATOR WITH A FULL FACEPIECE OPERATED IN PRESSURE-DEMAND OR OTHER POSITIVE PRESSURE MODE OR WITH A FULL FACEPIECE, HELMET OR HOOD OPERATED IN CONTINOUS-FLOW MODE.

SELF-CONTAINED BREATHING APPARATUS WITH A FULL FACEPIECE OPERATED IN PRESSURE-DEMAND OR OTHER POSITIVE PRESSURE MODE.

FOR FIREFIGHTING AND OTHER IMMEDIATELY DANGEROUS TO LIFE OR HEALTH CONDITIONS:

SELF-CONTAINED BREATHING APPARATUS WITH FULL FACEPIECE OPERATED IN PRESSURE-DEMAND OR OTHER POSITIVE PRESSURE MODE.

SUPPLIED-AIR RESPIRATOR WITH FULL FACEPIECE AND OPERATED IN PRESSURE-DEMAND OR OTHER POSITIVE PRESSURE MODE IN COMBINATION WITH AN AUXILIARY SELF-CONTAINED BREATHING APPARATUS OPERATED IN PRESSURE-DEMAND OR OTHER POSITIVE PRESSURE MODE.

CLOTHING: EMPLOYEE MUST WEAR APPROPRIATE PROTECTIVE (IMPERVIOUS) CLOTHING AND EQUIPMENT TO PREVENT ANY POSSIBILITY OF SKIN CONTACT WITH THIS SUBSTANCE.

GLOVES: EMPLOYEE MUST WEAR APPROPRIATE PROTECTIVE GLOVES TO PREVENT CONTACT WITH THIS SUBSTANCE.

EYE PROTECTION: EMPLOYEE MUST WEAR SPLASH-PROOF OR DUST-RESISTANT SAFETY GOGGLES AND A FACESHIELD TO PREVENT CONTACT WITH THIS SUBSTANCE.

EMERGENCY WASH FACILITIES: WHERE THERE IS ANY POSSIBILITY THAT AN EMPLOYEE'S EYES AND/OR SKIN MAY BE EXPOSED TO THIS SUBSTANCE, THE EMPLOYER SHOULD PROVIDE AN EYE WASH FOUNTAIN AND QUICK DRENCH SHOWER WITHIN THE IMMEDIATE WORK AREA FOR EMERGENCY USE.

AUTHORIZED BY- OCCUPATIONAL HEALTH SERVICES, INC.

CREATION DATE: 04/16/90 ***REVISION DATE:*** 04/18/90

MATERIAL SAFETY DATA SHEET

OCCUPATIONAL HEALTH SERVICES, INC.
AGRICULTURE AND PESTICIDE DIVISION
450 SEVENTH AVENUE, SUITE 2407
NEW YORK, NEW YORK 10123
1-800-445-MSDS OR (212) 967-1100

EMERGENCY CONTACT:
JOHN S. BRANSFORD, JR. (615) 292-1180

SUBSTANCE IDENTIFICATION

CAS-NUMBER 6099-79-2

SUBSTANCE: **DINOSEB METHYL ETHER**

TRADE NAMES/SYNONYMS: BENZENE, 2-METHOXY-1-(1-METHYLPROPYL)-3,5-DINITRO-; 2-METHOXY-1-(1-METHYLPROPYL)-3,5-DINITROBENZENE; ANISOLE, 2-SEC-BUTYL-4,6-DINITRO-; 2-SEC-BUTYL-4,6-DINITROANISOLE; DNBP; C11H14N2O5; PST08022

CHEMICAL FAMILY: NITRO ETHER, AROMATIC

MOLECULAR FORMULA: (N-O2)2-C6-H2-(O-C-H3)-C-H-(C-H3)-C2-H5

MOLECULAR WEIGHT: 254.24

CERCLA RATINGS (SCALE 0-3): HEALTH=U FIRE=U REACTIVITY=0 PERSISTENCE=1

NFPA RATINGS (SCALE 0-4): HEALTH=U FIRE=U REACTIVITY=0

COMPONENTS AND CONTAMINANTS

COMPONENT: DINOSEB METHYL ETHER ***PERCENT:*** 100.0
CAS# 6099-79-2

OTHER CONTAMINANTS: NONE

EXPOSURE LIMITS: NO OCCUPATIONAL EXPOSURE LIMITS ESTABLISHED BY OSHA, ACGIH, OR NIOSH.

PHYSICAL DATA

DESCRIPTION: AMBER LIQUID. ***BOILING POINT:*** NOT AVAILABLE

SPECIFIC GRAVITY: NOT AVAILABLE ***VAPOR PRESSURE:*** NOT AVAILABLE

SOLUBILITY IN WATER: NOT AVAILABLE

FIRE AND EXPLOSION DATA

FIRE AND EXPLOSION HAZARD: UNKNOWN FIRE AND EXPLOSION HAZARD.

FLASH POINT: NOT AVAILABLE

FIREFIGHTING MEDIA: DRY CHEMICAL, CARBON DIOXIDE, HALON, WATER SPRAY OR STANDARD FOAM (1987 EMERGENCY RESPONSE GUIDEBOOK, DOT P 5800.4). FOR LARGER FIRES, USE WATER SPRAY, FOG OR STANDARD FOAM (1987 EMERGENCY RESPONSE GUIDEBOOK, DOT P 5800.4).

FIREFIGHTING: MOVE CONTAINER FROM FIRE AREA IF POSSIBLE. COOL FIRE-EXPOSED CONTAINERS WITH WATER FROM SIDE UNTIL WELL AFTER FIRE IS OUT. STAY AWAY FROM STORAGE TANK ENDS. FOR MASSIVE FIRE IN STORAGE AREA, USE UNMANNED HOSE HOLDER OR MONITOR NOZZLES, ELSE WITHDRAW FROM AREA AND LET FIRE BURN. WITHDRAW IMMEDIATELY IN CASE OF RISING SOUND FROM VENTING SAFETY DEVICE OR ANY DISCOLORATION OF STORAGE TANK DUE TO FIRE (1987 EMERGENCY RESPONSE GUIDEBOOK, DOT P 5800.4, GUIDE PAGE 27). EXTINGUISH ONLY IF FLOW CAN BE STOPPED; USE FLOODING AMOUNTS OF WATER AS A FOG, SOLID STREAMS MAY BE INEFFECTIVE. COOL CONTAINERS WITH FLOODING AMOUNTS OF WATER, APPLY FROM AS FAR A DISTANCE AS POSSIBLE. AVOID BREATHING VAPORS, KEEP UPWIND.

TOXICITY

DINOSEB METHYL ETHER: TOXICITY DATA: >50 MG/KG ORAL-RAT LD50 (EPA). CARCINOGEN STATUS: NONE. ACUTE TOXICITY LEVEL: INSUFFICIENT DATA. TARGET EFFECTS: POISONING MAY INCREASE THE METABOLIC RATE AND AFFECT THE NERVOUS SYSTEM, LIVER, AND KIDNEYS.* AT INCREASED RISK FROM EXPOSURE: ALCOHOLICS AND PERSONS WITH RENAL OR HEPATIC DISEASES.* ADDITIONAL DATA: EPA HAS DETERMINED THAT AN ADEQUATE MARGIN OF SAFETY DOES NOT EXIST BETWEEN THE USE OF DINOSEB AND POTENTIAL EFFECTS OF INDUCING BIRTH DEFECTS OR PRODUCING STERILITY IN MAN. HOT ENVIRONMENTS MAY ENHANCE ABSORPTION AND THE TOXIC EFFECTS.*

* MAY BE BASED ON INFORMATION ON DINITROPHENOL DERIVATIVES.

HEALTH EFFECTS AND FIRST AID

INHALATION: DINOSEB METHYL ETHER: SEE INFORMATION ON DINITROPHENOL DERIVATIVES.

DINITROPHENOL DERIVATIVES: <u>ACUTE EXPOSURE</u>- MAY BE ABSORBED WITH SYMPTOMS OCCURRING SUDDENLY AND UP TO 2 DAYS AFTER CESSATION OF EXPOSURE. SYMPTOMS MAY INCLUDE FATIGUE, WEAKNESS, FEVER, THIRST, NAUSEA, VOMITING, HEADACHES, FLUSHED SKIN, PROSTRATION, EXCESSIVE PERSPIRATION, TACHYCARDIA, TACHYPNEA, AND DYSPNEA. APPREHENSION, RESTLESSNESS, ANXIETY, MANIC BEHAVIOR, OR UNCONSCIOUSNESS MAY INDICATE CEREBRAL INJURY. CONVULSIONS MAY OCCUR IN THE MOST SEVERE POISONINGS. ANOXIA WITH CYANOSIS, LIVIDITY AND METABOLIC ACIDOSIS, SEVERE HYPERPYREXIA, DEHYDRATION, AND MUSCULAR TREMORS MAY BE FOLLOWED BY CIRCULATORY OR RESPIRATORY COLLAPSE AND COMA. DEGENERATIVE CHANGES IN THE HEART, RENAL TUBULES AND LIVER PARENCHYMA MAY OCCUR. THERE MAY BE ALBUMINURIA, PYURIA, HEMATURIA, JAUNDICE, AND INCREASED BUN. THE EFFECTS FROM POISONING ARE RAPID AND DEATH OR RECOVERY GENERALLY OCCURS WITHIN 24 TO 48 HOURS. FATAL DINITROPHENOL POISONING IS FOLLOWED BY INSTANTANEOUS RIGOR MORTIS.

<u>CHRONIC EXPOSURE</u>- IN ADDITION TO THE SYMPTOMS OF ACUTE EXPOSURE, PROLONGED OR REPEATED EXPOSURE MAY CAUSE WEIGHT LOSS, CATARACT FORMATION, AND LIVER AND KIDNEY DAMAGE. YELLOW STAINING OF THE SCLERAE AND URINE INDICATES ABSORPTION OF POTENTIALLY TOXIC AMOUNTS.

FIRST AID- REMOVE FROM EXPOSURE AREA TO FRESH AIR IMMEDIATELY. IF BREATHING HAS STOPPED, PERFORM ARTIFICIAL RESPIRATION. ADMINISTER OXYGEN. TREAT SYMPTOMATICALLY AND SUPPORTIVELY. GET MEDICAL ATTENTION IMMEDIATELY.

SKIN CONTACT: DINOSEB METHYL ETHER: SEE INFORMATION ON DINITROPHENOL DERIVATIVES.

DINITROPHENOL DERIVATIVES: **ACUTE EXPOSURE-** MAY CAUSE IRRITATION. CONTACT MAY RESULT IN YELLOW STAINING OF THE SKIN AHD HAIR. SOME DERIVATIVES MAY BE ABSORBED THROUGH THE SKIN WITH SYMPTOMS OCCURRING SUDDENLY AND UP TO 2 DAYS AFTER CESSATION OF EXPOSURE AND PRODUCE EFFECTS ON THE METABOLIC RATE, CENTRAL NERVOUS SYSTEM AND LIVER AND KIDNEY RESULTING IN SIGNS AND SYMPTOMS AS DESCRIBED IN ACUTE INHALATION. **CHRONIC EXPOSURE-** REPEATED OR PROLONGED CONTACT MAY RESULT IN DERMATITIS DUE TO IRRITATION OR ALLERGIC SENSITIVITY. IN ADDITION TO THE SYMPTOMS OF ACUTE EXPOSURE, CHRONIC ABSORPTION MAY CAUSE FATIGUE, WEIGHT LOSS, CATARACT FORMATION AND LIVER AND KIDNEY DAMAGE. YELLOW STAINING OF THE SCLERAE AND URINE INDICATES ABSORPTION OF POTENTIALLY TOXIC AMOUNTS.

FIRST AID- REMOVE CONTAMINATED CLOTHING AND SHOES IMMEDIATELY. THEN REMOVE SKIN AND HAIR CONTAMINATION BY SCRUBBING WITH SOAP AND WATER. IF BODY TEMPERATURE IS ELEVATED, REDUCE TO 37 C BY SPONGE BATH, IMMERSION IN COOL WATER OR BY APPLYING COOLING BLANKET. IF BODY TEMPERATURE IS ABOVE 40 C, ICE WATER IS NECESSARY (DREISBACH, HANDBOOK OF POISONING, 12TH EDITION; MORGAN, EPA RECOGNITION AND MANAGEMENT OF PESTICIDE POISONINGS, 3RD EDITION). GET MEDICAL ATTENTION IMMEDIATELY.

EYE CONTACT: DINOSEB METHYL ETHER: **ACUTE EXPOSURE-** NO DATA AVAILABLE. **CHRONIC EXPOSURE-** NO DATA AVAILABLE.

FIRST AID- WASH EYES IMMEDIATELY WITH LARGE AMOUNTS OF WATER OR NORMAL SALINE, OCCASIONALLY LIFTING UPPER AND LOWER LIDS, UNTIL NO EVIDENCE OF CHEMICAL REMAINS (APPROXIMATELY 15-20 MINUTES). GET MEDICAL ATTENTION IMMEDIATELY.

INGESTION: DINOSEB METHYL ETHER: SEE INFORMATION ON DINITROPHENOL DERIVATIVES.

DINITROPHENOL DERIVATIVES: **ACUTE EXPOSURE-** MAY CAUSE EFFECTS ON THE METABOLIC RATE, CENTRAL NERVOUS SYSTEM AND LIVER AND KIDNEY RESULTING IN SIGNS AND SYMPTOMS AS DESCRIBED IN ACUTE INHALATION. **CHRONIC EXPOSURE-** IN ADDITION TO THE SYMPTOMS OF ACUTE EXPOSURE, REPEATED INGESTION MAY CAUSE AN INITIAL SENSE OF WELL-BEING THEN ANOREXIA, DIARRHEA, DIZZINESS, RESTLESSNESS, FATIGUE, WEIGHT LOSS, SKIN ERUPTIONS, PERIPHERAL NEURITIS, LIVER AND KIDNEY DAMAGE, CARDIOVASCULAR COMPLICATIONS, GRANULOCYTOPENIA, AND CATARACT FORMATION. YELLOW STAINING OF THE SCLERAE AND URINE INDICATES ABSORPTION OF POTENTIALLY TOXIC AMOUNTS.

FIRST AID- REMOVE INGESTED POISON BY THOROUGH GASTRIC LAVAGE WITH SATURATED BICARBONATE SOLUTION. IF GASTRIC LAVAGE CANNOT BE ACCOMPLISHED IMMEDIATELY, GIVE SYRUP OF IPECAC TO INDUCE EMESIS AND FOLLOW WITH SALINE CATHARTIC. IF BODY TEMPERATURE IS ELEVATED, REDUCE TO 37 C BY IMMERSION IN COOL WATER OR BY APPLYING COOLING BLANKET. IF BODY TEMPERATURE IS ABOVE 40 C, ICE WATER IS NECESSARY (DREISBACH, HANDBOOK OF POISONING, 12TH ED.). ADMINISTRATION OF GASTRIC LAVAGE SHOULD BE PERFORMED BY QUALIFIED MEDICAL PERSONNEL. GET MEDICAL ATTENTION IMMEDIATELY.

ANTIDOTE: NO SPECIFIC ANTIDOTE. TREAT SYMPTOMATICALLY AND SUPPORTIVELY.

REACTIVITY

REACTIVITY: STABLE UNDER NORMAL TEMPERATURES AND PRESSURES.

INCOMPATIBILITIES: DINOSEB METHYL ETHER: OXIDIZERS (STRONG): FIRE AND EXPLOSION HAZARD.

DECOMPOSITION: THERMAL DECOMPOSITION PRODUCTS MAY INCLUDE TOXIC OXIDES OF CARBON AND NITROGEN.

POLYMERIZATION: HAZARDOUS POLYMERIZATION HAS NOT BEEN REPORTED TO OCCUR UNDER NORMAL TEMPERATURES AND PRESSURES.

STORAGE AND DISPOSAL

OBSERVE ALL FEDERAL, STATE AND LOCAL REGULATIONS WHEN STORING OR DISPOSING OF THIS SUBSTANCE. FOR ASSISTANCE, CONTACT THE DISTRICT DIRECTOR OF THE ENVIRONMENTAL PROTECTION AGENCY.

STORAGE

STORE IN ACCORDANCE WITH 40 CFR 165 RECOMMENDED PROCEDURES FOR THE DISPOSAL AND STORAGE OF PESTICIDES AND PESTICIDE CONTAINERS.

STORE AWAY FROM INCOMPATIBLE SUBSTANCES.

DISPOSAL

DISPOSAL MUST BE IN ACCORDANCE WITH 40 CFR 165 RECOMMENDED PROCEDURES FOR THE DISPOSAL AND STORAGE OF PESTICIDES AND PESTICIDE CONTAINERS.

CONDITIONS TO AVOID

AVOID CONTACT WITH HEAT, SPARKS, FLAMES, OR OTHER SOURCES OF IGNITION. VAPORS MAY BE EXPLOSIVE. AVOID OVERHEATING OF CONTAINERS; CONTAINERS MAY VIOLENTLY RUPTURE IN HEAT OF FIRE. AVOID CONTAMINATION OF WATER SOURCES.

SPILL AND LEAK PROCEDURES

OCCUPATIONAL SPILL: SHUT OFF IGNITION SOURCES. STOP LEAK IF YOU CAN DO IT WITHOUT RISK. USE WATER SPRAY TO REDUCE VAPORS. FOR SMALL SPILLS, TAKE UP WITH SAND OR OTHER ABSORBENT MATERIAL AND PLACE INTO CONTAINERS FOR LATER DISPOSAL. FOR LARGER SPILLS, DIKE FAR AHEAD OF SPILL FOR LATER DISPOSAL. NO SMOKING, FLAMES OR FLARES IN HAZARD AREA. KEEP UNNECESSARY PEOPLE AWAY; ISOLATE HAZARD AREA AND RESTRICT ENTRY.

PROTECTIVE EQUIPMENT

VENTILATION: PROVIDE LOCAL EXHAUST OR PROCESS ENCLOSURE VENTILATION SYSTEM.

RESPIRATOR: THE FOLLOWING RESPIRATORS ARE RECOMMENDED BASED ON INFORMATION FOUND IN THE PHYSICAL DATA, TOXICITY AND HEALTH EFFECTS SECTIONS. THEY ARE RANKED IN ORDER FROM MINIMUM TO MAXIMUM RESPIRATORY PROTECTION. THE SPECIFIC RESPIRATOR SELECTED MUST BE BASED ON CONTAMINATION LEVELS FOUND IN THE WORK PLACE, MUST NOT EXCEED THE WORKING LIMITS OF THE RESPIRATOR AND BE JOINTLY APPROVED BY THE NATIONAL INSTITUTE FOR OCCUPATIONAL SAFETY AND HEALTH AND THE MINE SAFETY AND HEALTH ADMINISTRATION (NIOSH-MSHA).

TYPE 'C' SUPPLIED-AIR RESPIRATOR WITH A FULL FACEPIECE OPERATED IN PRESSURE-DEMAND OR OTHER POSITIVE PRESSURE MODE OR WITH A FULL FACEPIECE, HELMET OR HOOD OPERATED IN CONTINOUS-FLOW MODE.

SELF-CONTAINED BREATHING APPARATUS WITH A FULL FACEPIECE OPERATED IN PRESSURE-DEMAND OR OTHER POSITIVE PRESSURE MODE.

FOR FIREFIGHTING AND OTHER IMMEDIATELY DANGEROUS TO LIFE OR HEALTH CONDITIONS:

SELF-CONTAINED BREATHING APPARATUS WITH FULL FACEPIECE OPERATED IN PRESSURE-DEMAND OR OTHER POSITIVE PRESSURE MODE.

SUPPLIED-AIR RESPIRATOR WITH FULL FACEPIECE AND OPERATED IN PRESSURE-DEMAND OR OTHER POSITIVE PRESSURE MODE IN COMBINATION WITH AN AUXILIARY SELF-CONTAINED BREATHING APPARATUS OPERATED IN PRESSURE-DEMAND OR OTHER POSITIVE PRESSURE MODE.

CLOTHING: EMPLOYEE MUST WEAR APPROPRIATE PROTECTIVE (IMPERVIOUS) CLOTHING AND EQUIPMENT TO PREVENT ANY POSSIBILITY OF SKIN CONTACT WITH THIS SUBSTANCE.

GLOVES: EMPLOYEE MUST WEAR APPROPRIATE PROTECTIVE GLOVES TO PREVENT CONTACT WITH THIS SUBSTANCE.

EYE PROTECTION: EMPLOYEE MUST WEAR SPLASH-PROOF OR DUST-RESISTANT SAFETY GOGGLES AND A FACESHIELD TO PREVENT CONTACT WITH THIS SUBSTANCE.

EMERGENCY WASH FACILITIES: WHERE THERE IS ANY POSSIBILITY THAT AN EMPLOYEE'S EYES AND/OR SKIN MAY BE EXPOSED TO THIS SUBSTANCE, THE EMPLOYER SHOULD PROVIDE AN EYE WASH FOUNTAIN AND QUICK DRENCH SHOWER WITHIN THE IMMEDIATE WORK AREA FOR EMERGENCY USE.

AUTHORIZED BY- OCCUPATIONAL HEALTH SERVICES, INC.

CREATION DATE: 05/07/90 ***REVISION DATE:*** 05/07/90

MATERIAL SAFETY DATA SHEET

OCCUPATIONAL HEALTH SERVICES, INC.
AGRICULTURE AND PESTICIDE DIVISION
450 SEVENTH AVENUE, SUITE 2407
NEW YORK, NEW YORK 10123
1-800-445-MSDS OR (212) 967-1100

EMERGENCY CONTACT:
JOHN S. BRANSFORD, JR. (615) 292-1180

SUBSTANCE IDENTIFICATION

CAS-NUMBER 117-84-0

SUBSTANCE: **DIOCTYL PHTHALATE**

TRADE NAMES/SYNONYMS: PHTHALIC ACID, DIOCTYL ESTER; O-BENZENEDICARBOXYLIC ACID, DIOCTYL ESTER; 1,2-BENZENEDICARBOXYLIC ACID, DIOCTYL ESTER; DNOP; DINOPOL NOP; DI-N-OCTYL PHTHALATE; DIOCTYL O-PHTHALATE; OCTYL PHTHALATE; N-OCTYL PHTHALATE; VINICIZER 85; RCRA U107; C24H38O4; PST08040

CHEMICAL FAMILY: ESTER, CARBOXYLIC, AROMATIC

MOLECULAR FORMULA: C6-H4-(C-O2-(C-H2)7-C-H3)2

MOLECULAR WEIGHT: 390.62
CERCLA RATINGS (SCALE 0-3): HEALTH=1 FIRE=1 REACTIVITY=0 PERSISTENCE=3
NFPA RATINGS (SCALE 0-4): HEALTH=1 FIRE=1 REACTIVITY=0

COMPONENTS AND CONTAMINANTS

COMPONENT: DIOCTYL PHTHALATE ***PERCENT:*** 100
CAS# 117-84-0
OTHER CONTAMINANTS: NONE
EXPOSURE LIMITS: DIOCTYL PHTHALATE: NO OCCUPATIONAL EXPOSURE LIMITS ESTABLISHED BY OSHA, ACGIH, OR NIOSH.
5000 POUNDS CERCLA SECTION 103 REPORTABLE QUANTITY SUBJECT TO SARA SECTION 313 ANNUAL TOXIC CHEMICAL RELEASE REPORTING

PHYSICAL DATA

DESCRIPTION: LIGHT-COLORED, ODORLESS LIQUID
BOILING POINT: 428 F (220 C) AT 5 MMHG ***MELTING POINT:*** -22 F (-30 C)
SPECIFIC GRAVITY: 0.9861 ***VAPOR PRESSURE:*** <0.2 MMHG AT 150 C
SOLUBILITY IN WATER: INSOLUBLE ***VAPOR DENSITY:*** 16
SOLVENT SOLUBILITY: MINERAL OIL, DIMETHYL SULFOXIDE, ETHANOL, BENZENE

FIRE AND EXPLOSION DATA

FIRE AND EXPLOSION HAZARD: SLIGHT FIRE HAZARD WHEN EXPOSED TO HEAT OR FLAME.
FLASH POINT: 426 F (219 C)
FIREFIGHTING MEDIA: DRY CHEMICAL, CARBON DIOXIDE, HALON, WATER SPRAY OR STANDARD FOAM (1987 EMERGENCY RESPONSE GUIDEBOOK, DOT P 5800.4).
FOR LARGER FIRES, USE WATER SPRAY, FOG OR STANDARD FOAM (1987 EMERGENCY RESPONSE GUIDEBOOK, DOT P 5800.4).
FIREFIGHTING: MOVE CONTAINER FROM FIRE AREA IF POSSIBLE. DO NOT SCATTER SPILLED MATERIAL WITH HIGH PRESSURE WATER STREAMS. DIKE FIRE CONTROL WATER FOR LATER DISPOSAL (1987 EMERGENCY RESPONSE GUIDEBOOK, DOT P 5800.4, GUIDE PAGE 31).
USE AGENTS SUITABLE FOR TYPE OF SURROUNDING FIRE. AVOID BREATHING HAZARDOUS VAPORS, KEEP UPWIND.
WATER OR FOAM MAY CAUSE FROTHING (NFPA 325M, FIRE HAZARD PROPERTIES OF FLAMMABLE LIQUIDS, GASES, AND VOLATILE SOLIDS, 1984)

TOXICITY

DIOCTYL PHTHALATE: IRRITATION DATA: 500 MG/24 HOURS SKIN-RABBIT MILD; 5 MG EYE-RABBIT SEVERE; 500 MG/24 HOURS EYE-RABBIT MILD. TOXICITY DATA: 6513 MG/KG ORAL-MOUSE LD50; 65 GM/KG INTRAPERITONEAL-MOUSE LD50; REPRODUCTIVE EFFECTS DATA (RTECS). CARCINOGEN STATUS: NONE. LOCAL EFFECTS: CORROSIVE- EYE; IRRITANT-INHALATION AND SKIN. ACUTE TOXICITY LEVEL: SLIGHTLY TOXIC BY INGESTION. TARGET EFFECTS: CENTRAL NERVOUS SYSTEM DEPRESSANT.

HEALTH EFFECTS AND FIRST AID

INHALATION: DIOCTYL PHTHALATE: IRRITANT. **ACUTE EXPOSURE-** MOST PHTHALATE ESTERS HAVE A LOW VOLATILITY AND THUS INHALATION OF THESE AGENTS GENERALLY DOES NOT PRESENT PROBLEMS OF AN ACUTE NATURE. INHALATION OF SUFFICIENT QUANTITIES MAY CAUSE IRRITATION. **CHRONIC EXPOSURE-** NO DATA AVAILABLE.
FIRST AID- REMOVE FROM EXPOSURE AREA TO FRESH AIR IMMEDIATELY. IF BREATHING HAS STOPPED, PERFORM ARTIFICIAL RESPIRATION. KEEP PERSON WARM AND AT REST. TREAT SYMPTOMATICALLY AND SUPPORTIVELY. GET MEDICAL ATTENTION IMMEDIATELY.

SKIN CONTACT: DIOCTYL PHTHALATE: IRRITANT. **ACUTE EXPOSURE-** MAY CAUSE IRRITATION. **CHRONIC EXPOSURE-** REPEATED OR PROLONGED CONTACT MAY CAUSE DERMATITIS.
FIRST AID- REMOVE CONTAMINATED CLOTHING AND SHOES IMMEDIATELY. WASH AFFECTED AREA WITH SOAP OR MILD DETERGENT AND LARGE AMOUNTS OF WATER UNTIL NO EVIDENCE OF CHEMICAL REMAINS (APPROXIMATELY 15-20 MINUTES). GET MEDICAL ATTENTION IMMEDIATELY.

EYE CONTACT: DIOCTYL PHTHALATE: CORROSIVE. **ACUTE EXPOSURE-** MAY CAUSE SEVERE IRRITATION AND POSSIBLE CORNEAL DAMAGE. **CHRONIC EXPOSURE-** NO DATA AVAILABLE.
FIRST AID- WASH EYES IMMEDIATELY WITH LARGE AMOUNTS OF WATER, OCCASIONALLY LIFTING UPPER AND LOWER LIDS, UNTIL NO EVIDENCE OF CHEMICAL REMAINS (AT LEAST 15-20 MINUTES). CONTINUE IRRIGATING WITH NORMAL SALINE UNTIL THE PH HAS RETURNED TO NORMAL (30-60 MINUTES). COVER WITH STERILE BANDAGES. GET MEDICAL ATTENTION IMMEDIATELY.

INGESTION: DIOCTYL PHTHALATE: NARCOTIC. **ACUTE EXPOSURE-** MAY CAUSE CENTRAL NERVOUS SYSTEM DEPRESSION WITH NAUSEA, VOMITING, DIZZINESS, WEAKNESS, HEADACHE, AND DIFFICULT RESPIRATION. A LARGE DOSE WAS REQUIRED TO CAUSE DEATH IN ANIMALS. **CHRONIC EXPOSURE-** NO DATA AVAILABLE.
FIRST AID- TREAT SYMPTOMATICALLY AND SUPPORTIVELY. GET MEDICAL ADVICE IMMEDIATELY AS TO WHETHER TO INDUCE VOMITING.
ANTIDOTE: NO SPECIFIC ANTIDOTE. TREAT SYMPTOMATICALLY AND SUPPORTIVELY.

REACTIVITY

REACTIVITY: STABLE UNDER NORMAL TEMPERATURES AND PRESSURES.
INCOMPATIBILITIES: DIOCTYL PHTHALATE: NO DATA AVAILABLE
DECOMPOSITION: THERMAL DECOMPOSITION MAY RELEASE TOXIC AND/OR HAZARDOUS GASES.
POLYMERIZATION: NO DATA AVAILABLE.

STORAGE AND DISPOSAL

OBSERVE ALL FEDERAL, STATE AND LOCAL REGULATIONS WHEN STORING OR DISPOSING OF THIS SUBSTANCE. FOR ASSISTANCE, CONTACT THE DISTRICT DIRECTOR OF THE ENVIRONMENTAL PROTECTION AGENCY.

****DISPOSAL****

DISPOSAL MUST BE IN ACCORDANCE WITH STANDARDS APPLICABLE TO GENERATORS OF HAZARDOUS WASTE, 40CFR 262. EPA HAZARDOUS WASTE NUMBER U107.

CONDITIONS TO AVOID

AVOID HEATING TO THE FLASH POINT, 118 F (TYPE II) AND <100 F FOR TYPE LC. AVOID CONTACT WITH OR STORAGE WITH INCOMPATIBLE MATERIALS INCLUDING THOSE LISTED IN THE REACTIVITY SECTION.

SPILL AND LEAK PROCEDURES

OCCUPATIONAL SPILL: SHUT OFF IGNITION SOURCES. PROVIDE VENTILATION. WEAR PERSONAL PROTECTIVE EQUIPMENT. USE WATER SPRAY TO REDUCE VAPORS. FOR SMALL SPILLS, TAKE UP WITH SAND OR OTHER INCOMBUSTIBLE ABSORBENT MATERIAL AND PLACE INTO CONTAINERS FOR LATER DISPOSAL. CLOSE TIGHTLY AND LABEL FLAMMABLE OR COMBUSTIBLE. NO SMOKING, FLAMES OR FLARES IN HAZARD AREA. KEEP UNNECESSARY PEOPLE AWAY; ISOLATE AREA AND DENY ENTRY. KEEP OUT OF SEWERS, WATER WAYS AND OTHER WATER SOURCES.
REPORTABLE QUANTITY (RQ): 5000 POUNDS THE SUPERFUND AMENDMENTS AND REAUTHORIZATION ACT (SARA) SECTION 304 REQUIRES THAT A RELEASE EQUAL TO OR GREATER THAN THE REPORTABLE QUANTITY FOR THIS SUBSTANCE BE IMMEDIATELY REPORTED TO THE LOCAL EMERGENCY PLANNING COMMITTEE AND THE STATE EMERGENCY RESPONSE COMMISSION (40 CFR 355.40). IF THE RELEASE OF THIS SUBSTANCE IS REPORTABLE UNDER CERCLA SECTION 103, THE NATIONAL RESPONSE CENTER MUST BE NOTIFIED IMMEDIATELY AT (800) 424-8802 OR (202) 426-2675 IN THE METROPOLITAN WASHINGTON, D.C. AREA (40 CFR 302.6).

PROTECTIVE EQUIPMENT

VENTILATION: PROVIDE GENERAL DILUTION VENTILATION.
RESPIRATOR: THE FOLLOWING RESPIRATORS ARE RECOMMENDED BASED ON INFORMATION FOUND IN THE PHYSICAL DATA, TOXICITY AND HEALTH EFFECTS SECTIONS. THEY ARE RANKED IN ORDER FROM MINIMUM TO MAXIMUM RESPIRATORY PROTECTION. THE SPECIFIC RESPIRATOR SELECTED MUST BE BASED ON CONTAMINATION LEVELS FOUND IN THE WORK PLACE, MUST NOT EXCEED THE WORKING LIMITS OF THE RESPIRATOR AND BE JOINTLY APPROVED BY THE NATIONAL INSTITUTE FOR OCCUPATIONAL SAFETY AND HEALTH AND THE MINE SAFETY AND HEALTH ADMINISTRATION (NIOSH-MSHA).
CHEMICAL CARTRIDGE RESPIRATOR WITH AN ORGANIC VAPOR CARTRIDGE(S) WITH A FULL FACEPIECE.
GAS MASK WITH ORGANIC VAPOR CANISTER (CHIN-STYLE OR FRONT- OR BACK-MOUNTED CANISTER) WITH A FULL FACEPIECE.
TYPE 'C' SUPPLIED-AIR RESPIRATOR WITH A FULL FACEPIECE OPERATED IN PRESSURE-DEMAND OR OTHER POSITIVE PRESSURE MODE OR WITH A FULL FACEPIECE, HELMET OR HOOD OPERATED IN CONTINUOUS-FLOW MODE.
SELF-CONTAINED BREATHING APPARATUS WITH A FULL FACEPIECE OPERATED IN PRESSURE-DEMAND OR OTHER POSITIVE PRESSURE MODE.
FOR FIREFIGHTING AND OTHER IMMEDIATELY DANGEROUS TO LIFE OR HEALTH CONDITIONS:
SELF-CONTAINED BREATHING APPARATUS WITH FULL FACEPIECE OPERATED IN PRESSURE-DEMAND OR OTHER POSITIVE PRESSURE MODE.
SUPPLIED-AIR RESPIRATOR WITH FULL FACEPIECE AND OPERATED IN PRESSURE-DEMAND OR OTHER POSITIVE PRESSURE MODE IN COMBINATION WITH AN AUXILIARY SELF-CONTAINED BREATHING APPARATUS OPERATED IN PRESSURE-DEMAND OR OTHER POSITIVE PRESSURE MODE.
CLOTHING: EMPLOYEE MUST WEAR APPROPRIATE PROTECTIVE (IMPERVIOUS) CLOTHING AND EQUIPMENT TO PREVENT REPEATED OR PROLONGED SKIN CONTACT WITH THIS SUBSTANCE.

GLOVES: EMPLOYEE MUST WEAR APPROPRIATE PROTECTIVE GLOVES TO PREVENT CONTACT WITH THIS SUBSTANCE.

EYE PROTECTION: EMPLOYEE MUST WEAR SPLASH-PROOF OR DUST-RESISTANT SAFETY GOGGLES TO PREVENT EYE CONTACT WITH THIS SUBSTANCE.
EMERGENCY EYE WASH: WHERE THERE IS ANY POSSIBILITY THAT AN EMPLOYEE'S EYES MAY BE EXPOSED TO THIS SUBSTANCE, THE EMPLOYER SHOULD PROVIDE AN EYE WASH FOUNTAIN WITHIN THE IMMEDIATE WORK AREA FOR EMERGENCY USE.

AUTHORIZED BY- OCCUPATIONAL HEALTH SERVICES, INC.
CREATION DATE: 10/04/89 ***REVISION DATE:*** 05/04/90

MATERIAL SAFETY DATA SHEET

OCCUPATIONAL HEALTH SERVICES, INC.
AGRICULTURE AND PESTICIDE DIVISION
450 SEVENTH AVENUE, SUITE 2407
NEW YORK, NEW YORK 10123
1-800-445-MSDS OR (212) 967-1100

EMERGENCY CONTACT:
JOHN S. BRANSFORD, JR. (615) 292-1180

SUBSTANCE IDENTIFICATION

CAS-NUMBER 5221-49-8
SUBSTANCE: **DIOTHYL**
TRADE NAMES/SYNONYMS: PHOSPHOROTHIOIC ACID, O-(2-(DIMETHYLAMINO)-6-METHYL-4-PYRIDINYL) O,O-DIETHYL ESTER; ICI 29661; PYRIMITAL; PYRIMITHATE; O,O-DIETHYL-O-(2-DIMETHYLAMINO)-6-METHYL-4-PYRIMIDINYL PHOSPHOROTHIOATE; C11H20N3O3PS; PST08049
CHEMICAL FAMILY: ORGANOPHOSPHATE
PYRIMIDINE
MOLECULAR FORMULA: C11-H20-N3-O3-P-S
MOLECULAR WEIGHT: 305.35
CERCLA RATINGS (SCALE 0-3): HEALTH=3 FIRE=U REACTIVITY=0
PERSISTENCE=1
NFPA RATINGS (SCALE 0-4): HEALTH=U FIRE=U REACTIVITY=0

COMPONENTS AND CONTAMINANTS

COMPONENT: DIOTHYL ***PERCENT:*** 100.0
CAS# 5221-49-8
OTHER CONTAMINANTS: NONE
EXPOSURE LIMITS: NO OCCUPATIONAL EXPOSURE LIMITS ESTABLISHED BY OSHA, ACGIH, OR NIOSH.

PHYSICAL DATA

DESCRIPTION: COLORLESS LIQUID. ***BOILING POINT:*** 262-270 F (128-132 C) @ 0.04 MMHG
SPECIFIC GRAVITY: 1.165 ***SOLUBILITY IN WATER:*** INSOLUBLE
SOLVENT SOLUBILITY: SOLUBLE IN ALCOHOLS, ACETONE, BENZENE, AND SOLVENT NAPTHA.

FIRE AND EXPLOSION DATA

FIRE AND EXPLOSION HAZARD: UNKNOWN FIRE AND EXPLOSION HAZARD.
FLASH POINT: NOT AVAILABLE
FIREFIGHTING MEDIA: DRY CHEMICAL, CARBON DIOXIDE, HALON, WATER SPRAY OR STANDARD FOAM (1987 EMERGENCY RESPONSE GUIDEBOOK, DOT P 5800.4).
FOR LARGER FIRES, USE WATER SPRAY, FOG OR STANDARD FOAM (1987 EMERGENCY RESPONSE GUIDEBOOK, DOT P 5800.4).
FIREFIGHTING: MOVE CONTAINER FROM FIRE AREA IF POSSIBLE. DIKE FIRE CONTROL WATER FOR LATER DISPOSAL; DO NOT SCATTER THE MATERIAL. COOL FIRE-EXPOSED CONTAINERS WITH WATER FROM SIDE UNTIL WELL AFTER FIRE IS OUT. STAY AWAY FROM STORAGE TANK ENDS. WITHDRAW IMMEDIATELY IN CASE OF RISING SOUND FROM VENTING SAFETY DEVICE OR ANY DISCOLORATION OF STORAGE TANK DUE TO FIRE (1987 EMERGENCY RESPONSE GUIDEBOOK, DOT P 5800.4, GUIDE PAGE 28).
EXTINGUISH ONLY IF FLOW CAN BE STOPPED. USE FLOODING AMOUNTS OF WATER AS A FOG; SOLID STREAMS MAY BE INEFFECTIVE. COOL CONTAINERS WITH FLOODING AMOUNTS OF WATER FROM AS FAR A DISTANCE AS POSSIBLE. AVOID BREATHING POISONOUS VAPORS, KEEP UPWIND.

TOXICITY

DIOTHYL: TOXICITY DATA: 125 MG/KG ORAL-RAT LD50. CARCINOGEN STATUS: NONE. ACUTE TOXICITY LEVEL: TOXIC BY INGESTION. TARGET EFFECTS: CHOLINESTERASE INHIBITOR. POISONING MAY AFFECT THE NERVOUS SYSTEM.* AT INCREASED RISK FROM EXPOSURE: PERSONS WITH RESPIRATORY AILMENTS, RECENT EXPOSURE TO CHOLINESTERASE INHIBITORS OR IMPAIRED CHOLINESTERASE PRODUCTION, OR LIVER MALFUNCTION.* ADDITIONAL DATA: MAY CROSS THE PLACENTA. HIGH ENVIRONMENTAL TEMPERATURES OR EXPOSURE OF THE CHEMICAL TO VISIBLE OR ULTRAVIOLET LIGHT MAY ENHANCE THE TOXICITY. INTERACTIONS WITH MEDICATIONS MAY OCCUR.*
* MAY BE BASED ON GENERAL INFORMATION ON ORGANOPHOSPHATES.

HEALTH EFFECTS AND FIRST AID

INHALATION: DIOTHYL: NO SPECIFIC DATA AVAILABLE. DIOTHYL IS AN ORGANOPHOSPHATE INSECTICIDE AND ACARICIDE. SEE INFORMATION ON ORGANOPHOSPHATES.
ORGANOPHOSPHATES: CHOLINESTERASE INHIBITOR. **ACUTE EXPOSURE-** WHEN INHALED, THE FIRST EFFECTS OF CHOLINESTERASE INHIBITORS ARE USUALLY RESPIRATORY AND MAY INCLUDE NASAL HYPEREMIA AND WATERY DISCHARGE, COUGH, CHEST DISCOMFORT, DYSPNEA, AND WHEEZING DUE TO INCREASED BRONCHIAL SECRETIONS AND BRONCHOCONSTRICTION. IF SUFFICIENT AMOUNTS ARE ABSORBED, OTHER SYSTEMIC EFFECTS MAY BEGIN WITHIN A FEW MINUTES OR BE DELAYED FOR UP TO 12 HOURS. SYMPTOMS MAY INCLUDE PALLOR, NAUSEA, VOMITING, DIARRHEA, ABDOMINAL CRAMPS, HEADACHE, DIZZINESS, OCULAR PAIN, BLURRED VISION, MIOSIS OR IN SOME CASES, ESPECIALLY INITIALLY, MYDRIASIS, LACRIMATION, SALIVATION, SWEATING, AND CONFUSION. OTHER REPORTED CENTRAL NERVOUS SYSTEM OR NEUROMUSCULAR EFFECTS MAY INCLUDE ATAXIA, SLURRED SPEECH, AREFLEXIA, WEAKNESS, FATIGUE, FASCICULATIONS, TWITCHING, TREMORS POSSIBLY OF THE TONGUE AND EYELIDS, AND EVENTUALLY PARALYSIS OF THE EXTREMITIES AND POSSIBLY OF THE RESPIRATORY MUSCLES. IN SEVERE CASES THERE MAY ALSO BE INVOLUNTARY DEFECATION AND URINATION, CYANOSIS, PSYCHOSIS, HYPERGLYCEMIA, ACUTE PANCREATITIS, CARDIAC IRREGULARITIES, PULMONARY EDEMA, UNCONSCIOUSNESS, CONVULSIONS, AND COMA. DEATH IS PRIMARILY DUE TO RESPIRATORY FAILURE, ALTHOUGH CARDIOVASCULAR EFFECTS INCLUDING CARDIAC ARREST MAY ALSO BE IMPLICATED. LONG TERM SEQUELAE ARE RARE BUT MAY INCLUDE NEUROPSYCHIATRIC DISORDERS AND MYOPATHY WITH MUSCLE TENDERNESS. SOME ORGANOPHOSPHATES MAY CAUSE A DELAYED NEUROPATHY BEGINNING 1-4 WEEKS AFTER AN ACUTE EXPOSURE WHICH MAY OR MAY NOT HAVE CAUSED ACUTE CHOLINERGIC EFFECTS. NUMBNESS, TINGLING, WEAKNESS AND CRAMPING BEGINNING SYMMETRICALLY IN THE LOWER LIMBS MAY PROGRESS TO ATAXIA AND PARALYSIS. IN SEVERE CASES, UPPER LIMB INVOLVEMENT IS POSSIBLE AND FLACCID PARALYSIS MAY PROGRESS TO SPASTIC PARALYSIS WITH EXAGGERATED REFLEXES. IMPROVEMENT MAY OCCUR OVER MONTHS TO YEARS, BUT SOME RESIDUAL IMPAIRMENT USUALLY REMAINS.
CHRONIC EXPOSURE- REPEATED OR PROLONGED EXPOSURE MAY RESULT IN THE EFFECTS OF ACUTE EXPOSURE INCLUDING THE DELAYED NEUROPATHY. OTHER EFFECTS REPORTED IN WORKERS REPEATEDLY EXPOSED INCLUDE IMPAIRED MEMORY AND CONCENTRATION, ACUTE PSYCHOSIS, SEVERE DEPRESSIONS, IRRITABILTY, CONFUSION, APATHY, EMOTIONAL LABILITY, SOCIAL WITHDRAWAL, CONFUSION, HEADACHE, SPEECH DIFFICULTIES, DELAYED REACTION TIMES, SPATIAL DISORIENTATION, NIGHTMARES, SLEEPWALKING, AND DROWSINESS OR INSOMNIA. AN INFLUENZA-LIKE CONDITION WITH HEADACHE, NAUSEA, WEAKNESS, ANOREXIA AND MALAISE HAS ALSO BEEN REPORTED.
FIRST AID- REMOVE FROM EXPOSURE AREA TO FRESH AIR IMMEDIATELY. IF BREATHING HAS STOPPED, PERFORM ARTIFICIAL RESPIRATION. KEEP PERSON WARM AND AT REST. TREAT SYMPTOMATICALLY AND SUPPORTIVELY. GET MEDICAL ATTENTION IMMEDIATELY.

SKIN CONTACT: DIOTHYL: NO SPECIFIC DATA AVAILABLE. SEE INFORMATION ON ORGANOPHOSPHATES.
ORGANOPHOSPHATES: CHOLINESTERASE INHIBITOR. **ACUTE EXPOSURE-** LOCALIZED SWEATING AND FASCICULATIONS MAY OCCUR AT THE SITE OF CONTACT. IF SUFFICIENT AMOUNTS ARE ABSORBED, OTHER EFFECTS OF CHOLINESTERASE INHIBITION AS DESCRIBED IN ACUTE INHALATION MAY OCCUR. SYMPTOMS MAY BE DELAYED 2-3 HOURS, BUT USUALLY NO MORE THAN 12 HOURS. THE RATE OF ABSORPTION IS INCREASED BY THE PRESENCE OF DERMATITIS OR HIGH AMBIENT TEMPERATURES. DELAYED NEUROPATHY IS ALSO POSSIBLE. **CHRONIC EXPOSURE-** REPEATED OR PROLONGED EXPOSURE MAY CAUSE EFFECTS AS DESCRIBED IN ACUTE EXPOSURE. SOME ORGANOPHOSPHATES MAY CAUSE SENSITIZATION.
FIRST AID- REMOVE CONTAMINATED CLOTHING IMMEDIATELY. WASH CONTAMINATED AREAS WITH SOAP AND WATER FOLLOWED BY ALCOHOL (ARENA, POISONING, 4TH ED.). EMERGENCY PERSONNEL SHOULD WEAR GLOVES AND AVOID CONTAMINATION. TREAT RESPIRATORY DIFFICULTY WITH ARTIFICIAL RESPIRATION. GET MEDICAL ATTENTION IMMEDIATELY.

EYE CONTACT: DIOTHYL: NO SPECIFIC DATA AVAILABLE. SEE INFORMATION ON ORGANOPHOSPHATES.

ORGANOPHOSPHATES: CHOLINESTERASE INHIBITOR. **ACUTE EXPOSURE-** DIRECT CONTACT MAY CAUSE PAIN, HYPEREMIA, LACRIMATION, TWITCHING OF THE EYELIDS, MIOSIS, AND CILIARY MUSCLE SPASM WITH LOSS OF ACCOMODATION, BLURRED OR DIMMED VISION AND BROWACHE. SOMETIMES MYDRIASIS MAY OCCUR INSTEAD OF MIOSIS. WITH SUFFICIENT EXPOSURE, OTHER SYMPTOMS OF CHOLINESTERASE INHIBITION AS DESCRIBED IN ACUTE INHALATION MAY OCCUR. **CHRONIC EXPOSURE-** REPEATED OR PROLONGED EXPOSURE MAY CAUSE EFFECTS AS DESCRIBED IN ACUTE EXPOSURE. SOME COMPOUNDS HAVE CAUSED TOXIC EFFECTS ON THE CRYSTALLINE LENS, CONJUNCTIVAL THICKENING AND OBSTRUCTION OF THE NASOLACRIMAL CANALS WHEN USED AS MIOTIC EYEDROPS.

FIRST AID- IRRIGATE EYES WITH WATER OR SALINE SOLUTION. IF SYMPTOMS OF POISONING OCCUR, TREAT RESPIRATORY DIFFICULTY WITH ARTIFICIAL RESPIRATION AND OXYGEN. OBSERVE PATIENT FOR AT LEAST 24-36 HOURS (GOSSELIN, CLINICAL TOXICOLOGY OF COMMERCIAL PRODUCTS, 5TH ED.). GET MEDICAL ATTENTION IMMEDIATELY. OXYGEN SHOULD BE ADMINISTERED BY QUALIFIED MEDICAL PERSONNEL.

INGESTION: DIOTHYL: TOXIC. SEE INFORMATION ON ORGANOPHOSPHATES. ORGANOPHOSPHATES: CHOLINESTERASE INHIBITOR. **ACUTE EXPOSURE-** WHEN INGESTED, THE FIRST EFFECTS MAY BE NAUSEA, VOMITING, ANOREXIA, ABDOMINAL CRAMPS AND DIARRHEA. GASTROINTESTINAL ABSORPTION MAY CAUSE SYMPTOMS OF CHOLINESTERASE INHIBITION AS DESCRIBED IN ACUTE INHALATION. SYMPTOMS MAY BEGIN WITHIN MINUTES OR BE DELAYED FOR HOURS. DELAYED EFFECTS INCLUDING NEUROPATHY MAY ALSO OCCUR. **CHRONIC EXPOSURE-** REPEATED INGESTION MAY CAUSE EFFECTS AS DESCRIBED IN ACUTE EXPOSURE.

FIRST AID- IF PERSON IS ALERT AND RESPIRATION IS NOT DEPRESSED, GIVE SYRUP OF IPECAC FOLLOWED BY WATER (IF VOMITING OCCURS, KEEP HEAD BELOW HIPS TO PREVENT ASPIRATION). IF CONSCIOUSNESS LEVEL DECLINES OR VOMITING HAS NOT OCCURRED IN 15 MINUTES EMPTY STOMACH BY GASTRIC LAVAGE WITH THE AID OF CUFFED ENDOTRACHEAL TUBE USING ISOTONIC SALINE OR 5% SODIUM BICARBONATE FOLLOW WITH ACTIVATED CHARCOAL. ESTABLISH AND MAINTAIN AIRWAY. TREAT RESPIRATORY DIFFICULTY WITH ARTIFICIAL RESPIRATION AND OXYGEN. DO NOT GIVE MORPHINE, AMINOPHYLLINE, PHENOTHIAZINES, RESERPINE, FUROSEMIDE, OR ETHACRYNIC ACID (MORGAN, RECOGNITION AND MANAGEMENT OF PESTICIDE POISONINGS, 3RD ED.). TREAT SYMPTOMATICALLY AND SUPPORTIVELY. ADMINISTRATION OF OXYGEN AND LAVAGE MUST BE PERFORMED BY QUALIFIED MEDICAL PERSONNEL. GET MEDICAL ATTENTION IMMEDIATELY.

ANTIDOTE: THE FOLLOWING ANTIDOTE HAS BEEN RECOMMENDED. HOWEVER, THE DECISION AS TO WHETHER THE SEVERITY OF POISONING REQUIRES ADMINISTRATION OF ANY ANTIDOTE AND ACTUAL DOSE REQUIRED SHOULD BE MADE BY QUALIFIED MEDICAL PERSONNEL.

FOR CHOLINESTERASE INHIBITORS: ESTABLISH CLEAR AIRWAY AND TISSUE OXYGENATION BY ASPIRATION OF SECRETIONS, AND IF NECESSARY, BY ASSISTED PULMONARY VENTILATION WITH OXYGEN. IMPROVE TISSUE OXYGENATION AS MUCH AS POSSIBLE BEFORE ADMINISTERING ATROPINE TO MINIMIZE THE RISK OF VENTRICULAR FIBRILLATION. ADMINISTER ATROPINE SULFATE INTRAVENOUSLY, OR INTRAMUSCULARLY IF IV INJECTION IS NOT POSSIBLE. IN MODERATELY SEVERE POISONING ADMINISTER ATROPINE SULFATE, 0.4-2.0 MG REPEATED EVERY 15 MINUTES UNTIL ATROPINIZATION IS ACHIEVED (TACHYCARDIA, FLUSHING, DRY MOUTH, MYDRIASIS). MAINTAIN ATROPINIZATION BY REPEATED DOSES FOR 2-12 HOURS, OR LONGER, DEPENDING ON THE SEVERITY OF POISONING. THE APPEARANCE OF RALES IN THE LUNG BASES, MIOSIS, SALIVATION, NAUSEA, BRADYCARDIA, ARE ALL INDICATIONS OF INADEQUATE ATROPINIZATION. SEVERELY POISONED INDIVIDUALS MAY EXHIBIT REMARKABLE TOLERANCE TO ATROPINE; TWO OR MORE TIMES THE DOSAGES SUGGESTED ABOVE MAY BE NEEDED. PERSONS NOT POISONED OR ONLY SLIGHTLY POISONED, HOWEVER, MAY DEVELOP SIGNS OF ATROPINE TOXICITY FROM SUCH LARGE DOSAGES: FEVER, MUSCLE FIBRILLATIONS, AND DELIRIUM ARE THE MAIN SIGNS OF ATROPINE TOXICITY. IF THESE SIGNS APPEAR WHILE THE PATIENT IS FULLY ATROPINIZED, ATROPINE ADMINISTRATION SHOULD BE DISCONTINUED, AT LEAST TEMPORARILY. OBSERVE TREATED PATIENTS CLOSELY AT LEAST 24 HOURS TO INSURE THAT SYMPTOMS (POSSIBLY PULMONARY EDEMA) DO NOT RECUR AS ATROPINIZATION WEARS OFF. IN VERY SEVERE POISONINGS, METABOLIC DISPOSITION OF TOXICANT MAY REQUIRE SEVERAL HOURS OR DAYS DURING WHICH ATROPINIZATION MUST BE MAINTAINED. MARKEDLY LOWER LEVELS OF URINARY METABOLITES INDICATE THAT ATROPINE DOSAGE CAN BE TAPERED OFF. AS DOSAGE IS REDUCED, CHECK THE LUNG BASES FREQUENTLY FOR RALES. IF RALES ARE HEARD OR OTHER SYMPTOMS RETURN, RE-ESTABLISH ATROPINIZATION PROMPTLY (MORGAN, RECOGNITION AND MANAGEMENT OF PESTICIDE POISONINGS, 3RD ED.). ADMINISTRATION OF ANTIDOTE MUST BE PERFORMED BY QUALIFIED MEDICAL PERSONNEL.

REACTIVITY

REACTIVITY: STABLE UNDER NORMAL TEMPERATURES AND PRESSURES.

INCOMPATIBILITIES: DIOTHYL: OXIDIZERS (STRONG): FIRE AND EXPLOSION HAZARD.

DECOMPOSITION: THERMAL DECOMPOSITION MAY RELEASE TOXIC AND/OR HAZARDOUS GASES.

POLYMERIZATION: HAZARDOUS POLYMERIZATION HAS NOT BEEN REPORTED TO OCCUR UNDER NORMAL TEMPERATURES AND PRESSURES.

STORAGE AND DISPOSAL

OBSERVE ALL FEDERAL, STATE AND LOCAL REGULATIONS WHEN STORING OR DISPOSING OF THIS SUBSTANCE. FOR ASSISTANCE, CONTACT THE DISTRICT DIRECTOR OF THE ENVIRONMENTAL PROTECTION AGENCY.

STORAGE

STORE IN ACCORDANCE WITH 40 CFR 165 RECOMMENDED PROCEDURES FOR THE DISPOSAL AND STORAGE OF PESTICIDES AND PESTICIDE CONTAINERS.
STORE AWAY FROM INCOMPATIBLE SUBSTANCES.

DISPOSAL

DISPOSAL MUST BE IN ACCORDANCE WITH 40 CFR 165 RECOMMENDED PROCEDURES FOR THE DISPOSAL AND STORAGE OF PESTICIDES AND PESTICIDE CONTAINERS.

CONDITIONS TO AVOID

AVOID CONTACT WITH HEAT, SPARKS, FLAMES OR OTHER IGNITION SOURCES. VAPORS MAY BE EXPLOSIVE. MATERIAL IS POISONOUS; AVOID INHALATION OF VAPORS OR CONTACT WITH SKIN. DO NOT ALLOW MATERIAL TO CONTAMINATE WATER SOURCES.

SPILL AND LEAK PROCEDURES

OCCUPATIONAL SPILL: SHUT OFF IGNITION SOURCES. DO NOT TOUCH SPILLED MATERIAL. STOP LEAK IF YOU CAN DO IT WITHOUT RISK. USE WATER SPRAY TO REDUCE VAPORS. FOR SMALL SPILLS, TAKE UP WITH SAND OR OTHER ABSORBENT MATERIAL AND PLACE INTO CONTAINERS FOR LATER DISPOSAL. FOR LARGER SPILLS, DIKE FAR AHEAD OF SPILL FOR LATER DISPOSAL. NO SMOKING, FLAMES OR FLARES IN HAZARD AREA! KEEP UNNECESSARY PEOPLE AWAY; ISOLATE HAZARD AREA AND DENY ENTRY.

PROTECTIVE EQUIPMENT

VENTILATION: PROVIDE LOCAL EXHAUST OR GENERAL DILUTION VENTILATION SYSTEM.

RESPIRATOR: THE FOLLOWING RESPIRATORS ARE RECOMMENDED BASED ON INFORMATION FOUND IN THE PHYSICAL DATA, TOXICITY AND HEALTH EFFECTS SECTIONS. THEY ARE RANKED IN ORDER FROM MINIMUM TO MAXIMUM RESPIRATORY PROTECTION. THE SPECIFIC RESPIRATOR SELECTED MUST BE BASED ON CONTAMINATION LEVELS FOUND IN THE WORK PLACE, MUST NOT EXCEED THE WORKING LIMITS OF THE RESPIRATOR AND BE JOINTLY APPROVED BY THE NATIONAL INSTITUTE FOR OCCUPATIONAL SAFETY AND HEALTH AND THE MINE SAFETY AND HEALTH ADMINISTRATION (NIOSH-MSHA).

TYPE 'C' SUPPLIED-AIR RESPIRATOR WITH A FULL FACEPIECE OPERATED IN PRESSURE-DEMAND OR OTHER POSITIVE PRESSURE MODE OR WITH A FULL FACEPIECE, HELMET OR HOOD OPERATED IN CONTINOUS-FLOW MODE.

SELF-CONTAINED BREATHING APPARATUS WITH A FULL FACEPIECE OPERATED IN PRESSURE-DEMAND OR OTHER POSITIVE PRESSURE MODE.

FOR FIREFIGHTING AND OTHER IMMEDIATELY DANGEROUS TO LIFE OR HEALTH CONDITIONS:

SELF-CONTAINED BREATHING APPARATUS WITH FULL FACEPIECE OPERATED IN PRESSURE-DEMAND OR OTHER POSITIVE PRESSURE MODE.

SUPPLIED-AIR RESPIRATOR WITH FULL FACEPIECE AND OPERATED IN PRESSURE-DEMAND OR OTHER POSITIVE PRESSURE MODE IN COMBINATION WITH AN AUXILIARY SELF-CONTAINED BREATHING APPARATUS OPERATED IN PRESSURE-DEMAND OR OTHER POSITIVE PRESSURE MODE.

CLOTHING: EMPLOYEE MUST WEAR APPROPRIATE PROTECTIVE (IMPERVIOUS) CLOTHING AND EQUIPMENT TO PREVENT ANY POSSIBILITY OF SKIN CONTACT WITH THIS SUBSTANCE.

GLOVES: EMPLOYEE MUST WEAR APPROPRIATE PROTECTIVE GLOVES TO PREVENT CONTACT WITH THIS SUBSTANCE.

EYE PROTECTION: EMPLOYEE MUST WEAR SPLASH-PROOF OR DUST-RESISTANT SAFETY GOGGLES TO PREVENT EYE CONTACT WITH THIS SUBSTANCE.

EMERGENCY EYE WASH: WHERE THERE IS ANY POSSIBILITY THAT AN EMPLOYEE'S EYES MAY BE EXPOSED TO THIS SUBSTANCE, THE EMPLOYER SHOULD PROVIDE AN EYE WASH FOUNTAIN WITHIN THE IMMEDIATE WORK AREA FOR EMERGENCY USE.

AUTHORIZED BY- OCCUPATIONAL HEALTH SERVICES, INC.

CREATION DATE: 05/18/90 ***REVISION DATE:*** 05/18/90

MATERIAL SAFETY DATA SHEET

OCCUPATIONAL HEALTH SERVICES, INC.
AGRICULTURE AND PESTICIDE DIVISION
450 SEVENTH AVENUE, SUITE 2407
NEW YORK, NEW YORK 10123
1-800-445-MSDS OR (212) 967-1100

EMERGENCY CONTACT:
JOHN S. BRANSFORD, JR. (615) 292-1180

SUBSTANCE IDENTIFICATION

CAS-NUMBER 78-34-2

SUBSTANCE: **DIOXATHION**

TRADE NAMES/SYNONYMS: PHOSPHORODITHIOIC ACID, S,S'-1,4-DIOXANE-2,3-DIYL O,O,O',O'-TETRAETHYL ESTHER; PHOSPHORODITHIOIC ACID, S,S'-PARA-DIOXANE-2,3-DIYL O,O,O',O' -TETRAETHYL ESTER; S,S'-(1,4-DIOXANE-2,3-DIYL) O,O,O',O'-TETRAETHYL BIS(PHOSPHORODITHIOATE); 1,4-DIOXAN-2,3-DIYL S,S-DI(O,O-DIETHYL PHOSPHORODITHIOATE); S,S'-PARA-DIOXANE-2,3-DIYL BIS(O,O-DIETHYL PHOSPHORODITHIOATE); S,S'-1,4-DIOXANE,2,3-DIYL BIS(O,O-DIETHYL PHOSPHORODITHIOATE); S,S-BIS(O,O-DIETHYL PHOSPHORODITHIOATE); AC 528; DELNATEX; DELNAV; HERCULES AC528; KAVADEL; NAVADEL; ENT 22879; C12H26O6P2S4; PST08050

CHEMICAL FAMILY: ORGANOPHOSPHATE ETHER, HETEROCYCLIC

MOLECULAR FORMULA: C12-H26-O6-P2-S4

MOLECULAR WEIGHT: 456.56

CERCLA RATINGS (SCALE 0-3): HEALTH=3 FIRE=0 REACTIVITY=0 PERSISTENCE=0

NFPA RATINGS (SCALE 0-4): HEALTH=4 FIRE=0 REACTIVITY=0

COMPONENTS AND CONTAMINANTS

COMPONENT: DIOXATHION ***PERCENT:*** 100
CAS# 78-34-2

EXPOSURE LIMITS: DIOXATHION: 0.2 MG/M3 OSHA TWA (SKIN) 0.2 MG/M3 ACGIH TWA (SKIN)
500 POUNDS SARA SECTION 302 THRESHOLD PLANNING QUANTITY 1 POUND SARA SECTION 304 THRESHOLD PLANNING QUANTITY

PHYSICAL DATA

DESCRIPTION: TAN LIQUID ***BOILING POINT:*** NOT AVAILABLE
MELTING POINT: -4 F (-20 C) ***SPECIFIC GRAVITY:*** 1.257 @ 26 C
VISCOSITY: 117 CENTIPOISES @ 25 C ***EVAPORATION RATE:*** NOT AVAILABLE
SOLUBILITY IN WATER: INSOLUBLE
SOLVENT SOLUBILITY: SOLUBLE IN AROMATIC HYDROCARBON, ETHERS, ESTERS, KETONES; PARTIALLY SOLUBLE IN HEXANE AND KEROSENE

FIRE AND EXPLOSION DATA

FIRE AND EXPLOSION HAZARD: NEGLIGIBLE FIRE HAZARD WHEN EXPOSED TO HEAT OR FLAME.

FIREFIGHTING MEDIA: DRY CHEMICAL, CARBON DIOXIDE, HALON, WATER SPRAY OR STANDARD FOAM (1987 EMERGENCY RESPONSE GUIDEBOOK, DOT P 5800.4). FOR LARGER FIRES, USE WATER SPRAY, FOG OR STANDARD FOAM (1987 EMERGENCY RESPONSE GUIDEBOOK, DOT P 5800.4).

FIREFIGHTING: MOVE CONTAINERS FROM FIRE AREA IF POSSIBLE. FIGHT FIRE FROM MAXIMUM DISTANCE. STAY AWAY FROM STORAGE TANK ENDS. DIKE FIRE CONTROL WATER FOR LATER DISPOSAL. DO NOT SCATTER MATERIAL (1987 EMERGENCY RESPONSE GUIDEBOOK, DOT P 5800.4, GUIDE PAGE 55). EXTINGUISH ONLY IF FLOW CAN BE STOPPED; USE FLOODING AMOUNTS OF WATER AS FOG, SOLID STREAMS MAY BE INEFFECTIVE. COOL CONTAINERS WITH FLOODING AMOUNTS OF WATER FROM AS FAR A DISTANCE AS POSSIBLE. USE WATER SPRAY TO ABSORB TOXIC VAPORS. AVOID BREATHING TOXIC VAPORS; KEEP UPWIND. CONSIDER EVACUATION OF DOWNWIND AREA IF MATERIAL IS LEAKING.

TRANSPORTATION DATA

DEPARTMENT OF TRANSPORTATION HAZARD CLASSIFICATION 49 CFR 172.101: POISON B
DEPARTMENT OF TRANSPORTATION LABELING REQUIREMENTS 49 CFR 172.101 AND SUBPART E: POISON
DEPARTMENT OF TRANSPORTATION PACKAGING REQUIREMENTS: 49 CFR 173.346 EXCEPTIONS: 49 CFR 173.345

TOXICITY

DIOXATHION: TOXICITY DATA: 1398 MG/M3/1 HOUR INHALATION-RAT LC50; 340 MG/M3/1 HOUR INHALATION-MOUSE LC50; 85 MG/KG SKIN-RABBIT LD50; 63 MG/KG SKIN-RAT LD50; 9 MG/KG/60 DAYS ORAL-HUMAN TDLO; 20 MG/KG ORAL-RAT LD50; 176 MG/KG ORAL-MOUSE LD50; 10 MG/KG ORAL-DOG LD50; 30 MG/KG INTRAPERITONEAL-RAT LD50; 33 MG/KG INTRAPERITONEAL-MOUSE LD50; MUTAGENIC DATA (RTECS). CARCINOGEN STATUS: NONE. ACUTE TOXICITY LEVEL: HIGHLY TOXIC BY INHALATION, DERMAL ABSORPTION, AND INGESTION. TARGET EFFECTS: CHOLINESTERASE INHIBITOR. AT INCREASED RISK FROM EXPOSURE: PERSONS WITH RESPIRATORY AILMENTS, RECENT EXPOSURE TO CHOLINESTERASE INHIBITORS OR IMPAIRED CHOLINESTERASE PRODUCTION, OR LIVER MALFUNCTION.* ADDITIONAL DATA: MAY CROSS THE PLACENTA. HIGH ENVIRONMENTAL TEMPERATURES OR EXPOSURE OF THE CHEMICAL TO VISIBLE OR ULTRAVIOLET LIGHT MAY ENHANCE THE TOXICITY. INTERACTIONS WITH MEDICATIONS MAY OCCUR.*
* MAY BE BASED ON GENERAL INFORMATION ON ORGANOPHOSPHATES.

HEALTH EFFECTS AND FIRST AID

INHALATION: DIOXATHION: HIGHLY TOXIC. SEE INFORMATION ON ORGANOPHOSPHATES.
ORGANOPHOSPHATES: CHOLINESTERASE INHIBITOR. **ACUTE EXPOSURE**- WHEN INHALED, THE FIRST EFFECTS OF CHOLINESTERASE INHIBITORS ARE USUALLY RESPIRATORY AND MAY INCLUDE NASAL HYPEREMIA AND WATERY DISCHARGE, COUGH, CHEST DISCOMFORT, DYSPNEA, AND WHEEZING DUE TO INCREASED BRONCHIAL SECRETIONS AND BRONCHOCONSTRICTION. IF SUFFICIENT AMOUNTS ARE ABSORBED, OTHER SYSTEMIC EFFECTS MAY BEGIN WITHIN A FEW MINUTES OR BE DELAYED FOR UP TO 12 HOURS. SYMPTOMS MAY INCLUDE PALLOR, NAUSEA, VOMITING, DIARRHEA, ABDOMINAL CRAMPS, HEADACHE, DIZZINESS, OCULAR PAIN, BLURRED VISION, MIOSIS OR IN SOME CASES, ESPECIALLY INITIALLY, MYDRIASIS, LACRIMATION, SALIVATION, SWEATING, AND CONFUSION. OTHER REPORTED CENTRAL NERVOUS SYSTEM OR NEUROMUSCULAR EFFECTS MAY INCLUDE ATAXIA, SLURRED SPEECH, AREFLEXIA, WEAKNESS, FATIGUE, FASCICULATIONS, TWITCHING, TREMORS POSSIBLY OF THE TONGUE AND EYELIDS, AND EVENTUALLY PARALYSIS OF THE EXTREMITIES AND POSSIBLY OF THE RESPIRATORY MUSCLES. IN SEVERE CASES THERE MAY ALSO BE INVOLUNTARY DEFECATION AND URINATION, CYANOSIS, PSYCHOSIS, HYPERGLYCEMIA, ACUTE PANCREATITIS, CARDIAC IRREGULARITIES, PULMONARY EDEMA, UNCONSCIOUSNESS, CONVULSIONS, AND COMA. DEATH IS PRIMARILY DUE TO RESPIRATORY FAILURE, ALTHOUGH CARDIOVASCULAR EFFECTS INCLUDING CARDIAC ARREST MAY ALSO BE IMPLICATED. LONG TERM SEQUELAE ARE RARE BUT MAY INCLUDE NEUROPSYCHIATRIC DISORDERS AND MYOPATHY WITH MUSCLE TENDERNESS. **CHRONIC EXPOSURE**- REPEATED OR PROLONGED EXPOSURE MAY RESULT IN THE EFFECTS OF ACUTE EXPOSURE. OTHER EFFECTS REPORTED IN WORKERS REPEATEDLY EXPOSED INCLUDE IMPAIRED MEMORY AND CONCENTRATION, ACUTE PSYCHOSIS, SEVERE DEPRESSIONS, IRRITABILTY, CONFUSION, APATHY, EMOTIONAL LABILITY, SOCIAL WITHDRAWAL, CONFUSION, HEADACHE, SPEECH DIFFICULTIES, DELAYED REACTION TIMES, SPATIAL DISORIENTATION, NIGHTMARES, SLEEPWALKING, AND DROWSINESS OR INSOMNIA. AN INFLUENZA-LIKE CONDITION WITH HEADACHE, NAUSEA, WEAKNESS, ANOREXIA AND MALAISE HAS ALSO BEEN REPORTED.

FIRST AID- REMOVE FROM EXPOSURE AREA TO FRESH AIR IMMEDIATELY. IF BREATHING HAS STOPPED, GIVE ARTIFICIAL RESPIRATION. MAINTAIN AIRWAY AND BLOOD PRESSURE AND ADMINISTER OXYGEN IF AVAILABLE. KEEP AFFECTED PERSON WARM AND AT REST. TREAT SYMPTOMATICALLY AND SUPPORTIVELY. ADMINISTRATION OF OXYGEN SHOULD BE PERFORMED BY QUALIFIED PERSONNEL. GET MEDICAL ATTENTION IMMEDIATELY.

SKIN CONTACT: DIOXATHION: HIGHLY TOXIC. SEE INFORMATION ON ORGANOPHOSPHATES.
ORGANOPHOSPHATES: CHOLINESTERASE INHIBITOR. **ACUTE EXPOSURE**- LOCALIZED SWEATING AND FASCICULATIONS MAY OCCUR AT THE SITE OF CONTACT. IF SUFFICIENT AMOUNTS ARE ABSORBED, OTHER EFFECTS OF CHOLINESTERASE INHIBITION AS DESCRIBED IN ACUTE INHALATION MAY OCCUR. SYMPTOMS MAY BE DELAYED 2-3 HOURS, BUT USUALLY NO MORE THAN 12 HOURS. THE RATE OF ABSORPTION IS INCREASED BY THE PRESENCE OF DERMATITIS OR HIGH AMBIENT TEMPERATURES. **CHRONIC EXPOSURE**- REPEATED OR PROLONGED EXPOSURE MAY CAUSE EFFECTS AS DESCRIBED IN ACUTE EXPOSURE. SOME ORGANOPHOSPHATES MAY CAUSE SENSITIZATION.

FIRST AID- REMOVE CONTAMINATED CLOTHING IMMEDIATELY. WASH CONTAMINATED AREAS WITH SOAP AND WATER FOLLOWED BY ALCOHOL (ARENA, POISONING, 4TH ED.). EMERGENCY PERSONNEL SHOULD WEAR GLOVES AND AVOID CONTAMINATION. TREAT RESPIRATORY DIFFICULTY WITH ARTIFICIAL RESPIRATION. GET MEDICAL ATTENTION IMMEDIATELY.

EYE CONTACT: DIOXATHION: 0.1 ML OF DIOXATHION INSTILLED IN THE EYES OF RABBITS PRODUCED MILD TRANSIENT CONJUNCTIVITIS BUT NO PERMANENT CORNEAL DAMAGE. SEE INFORMATION ON ORGANOPHOSPHATES.
ORGANOPHOSPHATES: CHOLINESTERASE INHIBITOR. **ACUTE EXPOSURE**- DIRECT CONTACT MAY CAUSE PAIN, HYPEREMIA, LACRIMATION, TWITCHING OF THE

EYELIDS, MIOSIS, AND CILIARY MUSCLE SPASM WITH LOSS OF ACCOMODATION, BLURRED OR DIMMED VISION AND BROWACHE. SOMETIMES MYDRIASIS MAY OCCUR INSTEAD OF MIOSIS. WITH SUFFICIENT EXPOSURE, OTHER SYMPTOMS OF CHOLINESTERASE INHIBITION AS DESCRIBED IN ACUTE INHALATION MAY OCCUR. **CHRONIC EXPOSURE-** REPEATED OR PROLONGED EXPOSURE MAY CAUSE EFFECTS AS DESCRIBED IN ACUTE EXPOSURE. SOME COMPOUNDS HAVE CAUSED TOXIC EFFECTS ON THE CRYSTALLINE LENS, CONJUNCTIVAL THICKENING AND OBSTRUCTION OF THE NASOLACRIMAL CANALS WHEN USED AS MIOTIC EYEDROPS.

FIRST AID- IRRIGATE EYES WITH WATER OR SALINE SOLUTION. IF SYMPTOMS OF POISONING OCCUR, TREAT RESPIRATORY DIFFICULTY WITH ARTIFICIAL RESPIRATION AND OXYGEN. OBSERVE PATIENT FOR AT LEAST 24-36 HOURS (GOSSELIN, CLINICAL TOXICOLOGY OF COMMERCIAL PRODUCTS, 5TH ED.). GET MEDICAL ATTENTION IMMEDIATELY. OXYGEN SHOULD BE ADMINISTERED BY QUALIFIED MEDICAL PERSONNEL.

INGESTION: DIOXATHION: HIGHLY TOXIC. ACUTE DOSES OF DIOXATHION DID NOT PRODUCE DELAYED NEUROTOXICITY IN HENS. SEE INFORMATION ON ORGANOPHOSPHATES.

ORGANOPHOSPHATES: CHOLINESTERASE INHIBITOR. **ACUTE EXPOSURE-** WHEN INGESTED, THE FIRST EFFECTS MAY BE NAUSEA, VOMITING, ANOREXIA, ABDOMINAL CRAMPS AND DIARRHEA. GASTROINTESTINAL ABSORPTION MAY CAUSE THE SYMPTOMS OF CHOLINESTERASE INHIBITION AS DESCRIBED IN ACUTE INHALATION. SYMPTOMS MAY BEGIN WITHIN MINUTES OR BE DELAYED. **CHRONIC EXPOSURE-** REPEATED INGESTION MAY CAUSE EFFECTS AS DESCRIBED IN ACUTE EXPOSURE.

FIRST AID- IF PERSON IS ALERT AND RESPIRATION IS NOT DEPRESSED, GIVE SYRUP OF IPECAC FOLLOWED BY WATER (IF VOMITING OCCURS, KEEP HEAD BELOW HIPS TO PREVENT ASPIRATION). IF CONSCIOUSNESS LEVEL DECLINES OR VOMITING HAS NOT OCCURRED IN 15 MINUTES EMPTY STOMACH BY GASTRIC LAVAGE WITH THE AID OF CUFFED ENDOTRACHEAL TUBE USING ISOTONIC SALINE OR 5% SODIUM BICARBONATE FOLLOW WITH ACTIVATED CHARCOAL. ESTABLISH AND MAINTAIN AIRWAY. TREAT RESPIRATORY DIFFICULTY WITH ARTIFICIAL RESPIRATION AND OXYGEN. DO NOT GIVE MORPHINE, AMINOPHYLLINE, PHENOTHIAZINES, RESERPINE, FUROSEMIDE, OR ETHACRYNIC ACID (MORGAN, RECOGNITION AND MANAGEMENT OF PESTICIDE POISONINGS, 3RD ED.). TREAT SYMPTOMATICALLY AND SUPPORTIVELY. ADMINISTRATION OF OXYGEN AND LAVAGE MUST BE PERFORMED BY QUALIFIED MEDICAL PERSONNEL. GET MEDICAL ATTENTION IMMEDIATELY.

ANTIDOTE: THE FOLLOWING ANTIDOTE(S) HAVE BEEN RECOMMENDED. HOWEVER, THE DECISION AS TO WHETHER THE SEVERITY OF POISONING REQUIRES ADMINISTRATION OF ANY ANTIDOTE AND ACTUAL DOSE REQUIRED SHOULD BE MADE BY QUALIFIED MEDICAL PERSONNEL.

FOR CHOLINESTERASE INHIBITORS: ESTABLISH CLEAR AIRWAY AND TISSUE OXYGENATION BY ASPIRATION OF SECRETIONS, AND IF NECESSARY, BY ASSISTED PULMONARY VENTILATION WITH OXYGEN. IMPROVE TISSUE OXYGENATION AS MUCH AS POSSIBLE BEFORE ADMINISTERING ATROPINE TO MINIMIZE THE RISK OF VENTRICULAR FIBRILLATION. ADMINISTER ATROPINE SULFATE INTRAVENOUSLY, OR INTRAMUSCULARLY IF IV INJECTION IS NOT POSSIBLE. IN MODERATELY SEVERE POISONING ADMINISTER ATROPINE SULFATE, 0.4-2.0 MG REPEATED EVERY 15 MINUTES UNTIL ATROPINIZATION IS ACHIEVED (TACHYCARDIA, FLUSHING, DRY MOUTH, MYDRIASIS). MAINTAIN ATROPINIZATION BY REPEATED DOSES FOR 2-12 HOURS, OR LONGER, DEPENDING ON THE SEVERITY OF POISONING. THE APPEARANCE OF RALES IN THE LUNG BASES, MIOSIS, SALIVATION, NAUSEA, BRADYCARDIA, ARE ALL INDICATIONS OF INADEQUATE ATROPINIZATION. SEVERELY POISONED INDIVIDUALS MAY EXHIBIT REMARKABLE TOLERANCE TO ATROPINE; TWO OR MORE TIMES THE DOSAGES SUGGESTED ABOVE MAY BE NEEDED. PERSONS NOT POISONED OR ONLY SLIGHTLY POISONED, HOWEVER, MAY DEVELOP SIGNS OF ATROPINE TOXICITY FROM SUCH LARGE DOSAGES: FEVER, MUSCLE FIBRILLATIONS, AND DELIRIUM ARE THE MAIN SIGNS OF ATROPINE TOXICITY. IF THESE SIGNS APPEAR WHILE THE PATIENT IS FULLY ATROPINIZED, ATROPINE ADMINISTRATION SHOULD BE DISCONTINUED, AT LEAST TEMPORARILY. OBSERVE TREATED PATIENTS CLOSELY AT LEAST 24 HOURS TO INSURE THAT SYMPTOMS (POSSIBLY PULMONARY EDEMA) DO NOT RECUR AS ATROPINIZATION WEARS OFF. IN VERY SEVERE POISONINGS, METABOLIC DISPOSITION OF TOXICANT MAY REQUIRE SEVERAL HOURS OR DAYS DURING WHICH ATROPINIZATION MUST BE MAINTAINED. MARKEDLY LOWER LEVELS OF URINARY METABOLITES INDICATE THAT ATROPINE DOSAGE CAN BE TAPERED OFF. AS DOSAGE IS REDUCED, CHECK THE LUNG BASES FREQUENTLY FOR RALES. IF RALES ARE HEARD OR OTHER SYMPTOMS RETURN, RE-ESTABLISH ATROPINIZATION PROMPTLY (MORGAN, RECOGNITION AND MANAGEMENT OF PESTICIDE POISONINGS, 3RD ED.). ADMINISTRATION OF ANTIDOTE MUST BE PERFORMED BY QUALIFIED MEDICAL PERSONNEL.

IN CASES OF SEVERE POISONING BY ORGANOPHOSPHATE PESTICIDES IN WHICH RESPIRATORY DEPRESSION, MUSCLE WEAKNESS AND TWITCHINGS ARE SEVERE, GIVE PRALIDOXIME (PROTOPAM-AYERST, 2-PAM), 1.0 GRAM INTRAVENOUSLY AT NO MORE THAN 0.5 GRAM PER MINUTE. DOSAGE OF PRALIDOXIME MAY BE REPEATED IN 1-2 HOURS, THEN AT 10-12 HOUR INTERVALS IF NEEDED. IN VERY SEVERE POISONINGS, DOSAGE RATES MAY BE DOUBLED. TREATMENT WITH PRALIDOXIME WILL BE MOST EFFECTIVE IF GIVEN WITHIN THIRTY-SIX HOURS AFTER POISONING (MORGAN, RECOGNITION AND MANAGEMENT OF PESTICIDE POISONINGS, 3RD ED.). ANTIDOTE SHOULD BE ADMINISTERED BY QUALIFIED MEDICAL PERSONNEL.

REACTIVITY

REACTIVITY: MAY DECOMPOSE ON HEATING.

INCOMPATIBILITIES: DIXOATHION: ALKALI: MAY CAUSE HYDROLYSIS. IRON: MAY REACT. TIN: MAY REACT.

DECOMPOSITION: THERMAL DECOMPOSITION MAY RELEASE TOXIC OXIDES OF PHOSPHORUS AND SULFUR.

POLYMERIZATION: HAZARDOUS POLYMERIZATION HAS NOT BEEN REPORTED TO OCCUR UNDER NORMAL TEMPERATURES AND PRESSURES.

STORAGE AND DISPOSAL

OBSERVE ALL FEDERAL, STATE AND LOCAL REGULATIONS WHEN STORING OR DISPOSING OF THIS SUBSTANCE. FOR ASSISTANCE, CONTACT THE DISTRICT DIRECTOR OF THE ENVIRONMENTAL PROTECTION AGENCY.

****STORAGE****

STORE IN ACCORDANCE WITH 40 CFR 165 RECOMMENDED PROCEDURES FOR THE DISPOSAL AND STORAGE OF PESTICIDES AND PESTICIDE CONTAINERS.

STORE AWAY FROM INCOMPATIBLE SUBSTANCES.

THRESHOLD PLANNING QUANTITY (TPQ): THE SUPERFUND AMENDMENTS AND REAUTHORIZATION ACT (SARA) SECTION 302 REQUIRES THAT EACH FACILITY WHERE ANY EXTREMELY HAZARDOUS SUBSTANCE IS PRESENT IN A QUANTITY EQUAL TO OR GREATER THAN THE TPQ ESTABLISHED FOR THAT SUBSTANCE NOTIFY THE STATE EMERGENCY RESPONSE COMMISSION FOR THE STATE IN WHICH IT IS LOCATED. SECTION 303 OF SARA REQUIRES THESE FACILITIES TO PARTICIPATE IN LOCAL EMERGENCY RESPONSE PLANNING (40 CFR 355.30).

****DISPOSAL****

DISPOSAL MUST BE IN ACCORDANCE WITH 40 CFR 165 RECOMMENDED PROCEDURES FOR THE DISPOSAL AND STORAGE OF PESTICIDES AND PESTICIDE CONTAINERS.

CONDITIONS TO AVOID

NONE REPORTED.

SPILL AND LEAK PROCEDURES

OCCUPATIONAL SPILL: DO NOT TOUCH SPILLED MATERIAL. STOP LEAK IF YOU CAN DO IT WITHOUT RISK. USE WATER SPRAY TO REDUCE VAPORS. FOR SMALL SPILLS, TAKE UP WITH SAND OR OTHER ABSORBENT MATERIAL AND PLACE INTO CONTAINERS FOR LATER DISPOSAL. FOR SMALL DRY SPILLS, WITH A CLEAN SHOVEL PLACE MATERIAL INTO CLEAN, DRY CONTAINERS AND COVER. MOVE CONTAINERS FROM SPILL AREA. FOR LARGER SPILLS, DIKE FAR AHEAD OF SPILL FOR LATER DISPOSAL. KEEP UNNECESSARY PEOPLE AWAY. ISOLATE HAZARD AREA AND DENY ENTRY. VENTILATE CLOSED SPACES BEFORE ENTERING.

REPORTABLE QUANTITY (RQ): 1 POUND THE SUPERFUND AMENDMENTS AND REAUTHORIZATION ACT (SARA) SECTION 304 REQUIRES THAT A RELEASE EQUAL TO OR GREATER THAN THE REPORTABLE QUANTITY FOR THIS SUBSTANCE BE IMMEDIATELY REPORTED TO THE LOCAL EMERGENCY PLANNING COMMITTEE AND THE STATE EMERGENCY RESPONSE COMMISSION (40 CFR 355.40). IF THE RELEASE OF THIS SUBSTANCE IS REPORTABLE UNDER CERCLA SECTION 103, THE NATIONAL RESPONSE CENTER MUST BE NOTIFIED IMMEDIATELY AT (800) 424-8802 OR (202) 426-2675 IN THE METROPOLITAN WASHINGTON, D.C. AREA (40 CFR 302.6).

PROTECTIVE EQUIPMENT

VENTILATION: PROCESS ENCLOSURE RECOMMENDED TO MEET PUBLISHED EXPOSURE LIMITS.

RESPIRATOR: THE FOLLOWING RESPIRATORS ARE RECOMMENDED BASED ON INFORMATION FOUND IN THE PHYSICAL DATA, TOXICITY AND HEALTH EFFECTS SECTIONS. THEY ARE RANKED IN ORDER FROM MINIMUM TO MAXIMUM RESPIRATORY PROTECTION. THE SPECIFIC RESPIRATOR SELECTED MUST BE BASED ON CONTAMINATION LEVELS FOUND IN THE WORK PLACE, MUST NOT EXCEED THE WORKING LIMITS OF THE RESPIRATOR AND BE JOINTLY APPROVED BY THE NATIONAL INSTITUTE FOR OCCUPATIONAL SAFETY AND HEALTH AND THE MINE SAFETY AND HEALTH ADMINISTRATION (NIOSH-MSHA).

TYPE 'C' SUPPLIED-AIR RESPIRATOR WITH A FULL FACEPIECE OPERATED IN PRESSURE-DEMAND OR OTHER POSITIVE PRESSURE MODE OR WITH A FULL FACEPIECE, HELMET OR HOOD OPERATED IN CONTINOUS-FLOW MODE.

SELF-CONTAINED BREATHING APPARATUS WITH A FULL FACEPIECE OPERATED IN PRESSURE-DEMAND OR OTHER POSITIVE PRESSURE MODE.

FOR FIREFIGHTING AND OTHER IMMEDIATELY DANGEROUS TO LIFE OR HEALTH CONDITIONS:

SELF-CONTAINED BREATHING APPARATUS WITH FULL FACEPIECE OPERATED IN

PRESSURE-DEMAND OR OTHER POSITIVE PRESSURE MODE.
SUPPLIED-AIR RESPIRATOR WITH FULL FACEPIECE AND OPERATED IN PRESSURE-DEMAND OR OTHER POSITIVE PRESSURE MODE IN COMBINATION WITH AN AUXILIARY SELF-CONTAINED BREATHING APPARATUS OPERATED IN PRESSURE-DEMAND OR OTHER POSITIVE PRESSURE MODE.

CLOTHING: EMPLOYEE MUST WEAR APPROPRIATE PROTECTIVE (IMPERVIOUS) CLOTHING AND EQUIPMENT TO PREVENT ANY POSSIBILITY OF SKIN CONTACT WITH THIS SUBSTANCE.

GLOVES: EMPLOYEE MUST WEAR APPROPRIATE PROTECTIVE GLOVES TO PREVENT CONTACT WITH THIS SUBSTANCE.

EYE PROTECTION: EMPLOYEE MUST WEAR SPLASH-PROOF OR DUST-RESISTANT SAFETY GOGGLES AND A FACESHIELD TO PREVENT CONTACT WITH THIS SUBSTANCE.
EMERGENCY WASH FACILITIES: WHERE THERE IS ANY POSSIBILITY THAT AN EMPLOYEE'S EYES AND/OR SKIN MAY BE EXPOSED TO THIS SUBSTANCE, THE EMPLOYER SHOULD PROVIDE AN EYE WASH FOUNTAIN AND QUICK DRENCH SHOWER WITHIN THE IMMEDIATE WORK AREA FOR EMERGENCY USE.

AUTHORIZED BY- OCCUPATIONAL HEALTH SERVICES, INC.
CREATION DATE: 10/04/89 ***REVISION DATE:*** 06/20/90

MATERIAL SAFETY DATA SHEET

OCCUPATIONAL HEALTH SERVICES, INC.
AGRICULTURE AND PESTICIDE DIVISION
450 SEVENTH AVENUE, SUITE 2407
NEW YORK, NEW YORK 10123
1-800-445-MSDS OR (212) 967-1100

EMERGENCY CONTACT:
JOHN S. BRANSFORD, JR. (615) 292-1180

SUBSTANCE IDENTIFICATION

CAS-NUMBER 1746-01-6

SUBSTANCE: **2,3,7,8-TETRACHLORODIBENZO-P-DIOXIN**

TRADE NAMES/SYNONYMS: DIBENZO(B,E)(1,4)DIOXIN, 2,3,7,8-TETRACHLORO-; DIBENZO-P-DIOXIN, 2,3,7,8-TETRACHLORO-; 2,3,7,8-TETRACHLORODIBENZO(B,E)(1,4)DIOXIN; DIOXIN; TCDD; 2,3,7,8-TCDD; TCDBD; 2,3,7,8-TETRACHLORODIBENZODIOXIN; 2,3,7,8-TETRACHLORODIBENZO(1,4)DIOXIN; TETRACHLORODIBENZODIOXIN; C12H4CL4O2; PST08060

CHEMICAL FAMILY: HALOGEN COMPOUND, AROMATIC

MOLECULAR FORMULA: CL2-C6-H2-O2-C6-H2-CL2

MOLECULAR WEIGHT: 321.96

CERCLA RATINGS (SCALE 0-3): HEALTH=3 FIRE=1 REACTIVITY=0 PERSISTENCE=3

NFPA RATINGS (SCALE 0-4): HEALTH=4 FIRE=1 REACTIVITY=0

COMPONENTS AND CONTAMINANTS

COMPONENT: 2,3,7,8-TETRACHLORODIBENZO-P-DIOXIN ***PERCENT:*** 100.0
CAS# 1746-01-6

OTHER CONTAMINANTS: NONE

EXPOSURE LIMITS: DIOXIN: LOWEST FEASIBLE LIMIT NIOSH RECOMMENDED EXPOSURE CRITERIA
1 POUND CERCLA SECTION 103 REPORTABLE QUANTITY SUBJECT TO CALIFORNIA PROPOSITION 65 CANCER AND/OR REPRODUCTIVE TOXICITY WARNING AND RELEASE REQUIREMENTS- (JANUARY 1, 1988)

PHYSICAL DATA

DESCRIPTION: COLORLESS TO WHITE NEEDLES. ***MELTING POINT:*** 581-583 F (305-306 C)

SPECIFIC GRAVITY: NOT AVAILABLE ***SOLUBILITY IN WATER:*** 0.0002 PPM
DECOMPOSES ABOVE 1292 F (700 C)

FIRE AND EXPLOSION DATA

FIRE AND EXPLOSION HAZARD: SLIGHT FIRE HAZARD WHEN EXPOSED TO HEAT OR FLAME.

FIREFIGHTING MEDIA: DRY CHEMICAL, CARBON DIOXIDE, HALON, WATER SPRAY OR STANDARD FOAM (1987 EMERGENCY RESPONSE GUIDEBOOK, DOT P 5800.4).
FOR LARGER FIRES, USE WATER SPRAY, FOG OR STANDARD FOAM (1987 EMERGENCY RESPONSE GUIDEBOOK, DOT P 5800.4).

FIREFIGHTING: MOVE CONTAINERS FROM FIRE AREA IF POSSIBLE (1987 EMERGENCY RESPONSE GUIDEBOOK, DOT P 5800.4, GUIDE PAGE 53).
EXTINGUISH USING AGENT SUITABLE FOR TYPE OF SURROUNDING FIRE. AVOID BREATHING VAPORS AND DUSTS. KEEP UPWIND.

TRANSPORTATION DATA

DEPARTMENT OF TRANSPORTATION HAZARD CLASSIFICATION 49 CFR 172.101: POISON B
DEPARTMENT OF TRANSPORTATION LABELING REQUIREMENTS 49 CFR 172.101 AND SUBPART E: POISON
DEPARTMENT OF TRANSPORTATION PACKAGING REQUIREMENTS: 49 CFR 173.365 EXCEPTIONS: 49 CFR 173.364

TOXICITY

2,3,7,8-TETRACHLORODIBENZO-P-DIOXIN: IRRITATION DATA: 2 MG EYE-RABBIT MODERATE. TOXICITY DATA: 107 UG/KG SKIN-HUMAN TDLO; 275 UG/KG SKIN-RABBIT LD50; 80 UG/KG SKIN-MOUSE LDLO; 20 UG/KG ORAL-RAT LD50; 114 UG/KG ORAL-MOUSE LD50; 1157 UG/KG ORAL-HAMSTER LD50; 500 NG/KG ORAL-GUINEA PIG LD50; 2 UG/KG ORAL-MONKEY LD50; 1 UG/KG ORAL-DOG LD50; 4200 NG/KG ORAL-MAMMAL LD50; 60 UG/KG INTRAPERITONEAL-RAT LD50; 252 UG/KG INTRAPERITONEAL-RABBIT LD50; 120 UG/KG INTRAPERITONEAL-MOUSE LD50; 3 MG/KG INTRAPERITONEAL-HAMSTER LD50; 200 UG/KG UNREPORTED-MOUSE LDLO; MUTAGENIC DATA (RTECS); REPRODUCTIVE EFFECTS DATA (RTECS); TUMORIGENIC DATA (RTECS). CARCINOGEN STATUS: ANTICIPATED HUMAN CARCINOGEN (NTP). HUMAN INADEQUATE EVIDENCE, ANIMALS SUFFICIENT EVIDENCE (IARC GROUP-2B) AN INCREASED INCIDENCE OF LIVER CANCERS AND CANCERS OF THE LUNGS, NOSE, OR MOUTH WERE OBSERVED IN RATS MAINTAINED ON DIETS CONTAINING THIS CHEMICAL. IN OTHER GAVAGE STUDIES, THYROID NEOPLASMS WERE OBSERVED IN RATS, LIVER CANCERS IN MICE, LIVER NEOPLASMS IN FEMALE RATS AND MICE, AND TUMORS IN A VARIETY OF ORGANS IN RATS. THIS MATERIAL APPLIED TO THE SKIN OF MICE PRODUCED INTEGUMENTARY SYSTEM FIBROSARCOMAS IN FEMALES. IN OTHER TWO-STAGE SKIN TUMORIGENESIS ASSAYS, THIS MATERIAL DISPLAYED ACTIVITIES OF A TUMOR PROMOTER AND OF A TUMOR INITIATOR. LOCAL EFFECTS: IRRITANT- EYE. ACUTE TOXICITY LEVEL: HIGHLY TOXIC BY DERMAL ABSORPTION AND INGESTION. TARGET EFFECTS: POISONING MAY AFFECT THE SKIN, LIVER, AND NERVOUS, IMMUNE, AND REPRODUCTIVE SYSTEMS. ADDITIONAL DATA: THE RATE OF SKIN ABSORPTION MAY BE INFLUENCED BY THE DOSE AND AGE OF THE INDIVIDUAL EXPOSED. THE LOWER THE DOSE, THE MORE EASILY DIOXINS TEND TO PENETRATE THE SKIN.

HEALTH EFFECTS AND FIRST AID

INHALATION: 2,3,7,8-TETRACHLORODIBENZO-P-DIOXIN: **ACUTE EXPOSURE-** MAY CAUSE RESPIRATORY TRACT IRRITATION, HEADACHE, DIZZINESS, NAUSEA, AND VOMITING. CHLORACNE MAY APPEAR A FEW WEEKS TO SEVERAL MONTHS AFTER EXPOSURE AND IS CHARACTERIZED BY INCLUSION CYSTS, COMEDONES AND PUSTULES, WITH EVENTUAL SCARING OF THE SKIN. THESE LESIONS INVOLVE THE FACE, THE NECK, TORSO, THIGHS, AND GENITALS. SOMETIMES THE CHLORACNE IS PRECEDED BY ERYTHEMATOUS AND EDEMATOUS SKIN LESIONS. SOME INDIVIDUALS HAVE EXPERIENCED BLEPHAROCONJUNCTIVITIS AND IRRITATION OF OTHER MUCOUS MEMBRANES. CHLORACNE MAY LAST FOR MANY YEARS AFTER EXPOSURE. EFFECTS ON THE CENTRAL NERVOUS SYSTEM AND LIVER MAY OCCUR AS DESCRIBED IN CHRONIC INHALATION. **CHRONIC EXPOSURE-** IN ADDITION TO CHLORACNE, SYSTEMIC EFFECTS FROM EXPOSURE MAY INCLUDE FATIGUE, HEADACHE, INSOMNIA, DECREASED LIBIDO, LOSS OF APPETITE AND WEIGHT, SENSORIAL IMPAIRMENTS, AND INTOLERANCE TO COLD. NEUROMUSCULAR SYMPTOMS MAY OCCUR WITH MUSCULAR WEAKNESS, ACHES AND PAINS WITH NERVE CONDUCTION ABNORMALITIES. IRRITABILITY AND PSYCHOPATHOLOGICAL CHANGES MAY BE OBSERVED. ALTERED PORPHYRIN METABOLISM (PORPHYRIA CUTANEA TARDA) CHARACTERIZED BY HIRSUTISM, ATROPHIC SKIN CHANGES, PHOTOSENSITIVITY, SLATE GRAY SKIN PIGMENTATION, EASY FRIABILITY AND VESICLE FORMATION, ELEVATED UROPORPHYRIN LEVELS IS ANOTHER EFFECT ASSOCIATED WITH EXPOSURE. OTHER EFFECTS MAY INCLUDE HYPERLIPIDEMIA, HYPERCHOLESTEROLEMIA, MYOCARDIAL CHANGES, AND ENLARGED LIVER AND IMPAIRMENT OF LIVER FUNCTIONS. DEPRESSION OF CELL-MEDIATED IMMUNITY, AS DEMONSTRATED BY AN INCREASED INCIDENCE OF ANERGY, WAS REPORTED FROM A STUDY OF INDIVIDUALS EXPOSED TO DUST CONTAMINATED WITH DIOXIN. CONFLICTING RESULTS WERE OBTAINED FROM DIFFERENT EPIDEMIOLOGIC STUDIES CONCERNING THE RELATIONSHIP OF EXPOSURE TO THIS MATERIAL AND INCREASE INCIDENCES OF REPRODUCTIVE EFFECTS. THE RESULTS FROM EPIDEMIOLOGIC STUDIES ARE SUGGESTIVE OF AN ASSOCIATION BETWEEN EXPOSURE TO PHENOXYACETIC HERBICIDES CONTAMINATED WITH 2,3,7,8-TETRACHLORODIBENZO-P-DIOXIN AND EXCESS LYMPHOMA AND STOMACH CANCER.

FIRST AID- REMOVE FROM EXPOSURE AREA TO FRESH AIR IMMEDIATELY. IF BREATHING HAS STOPPED, PERFORM ARTIFICIAL RESPIRATION. KEEP PERSON WARM AND AT REST. TREAT SYMPTOMATICALLY AND SUPPORTIVELY. GET MEDICAL ATTENTION IMMEDIATELY.

SKIN CONTACT: 2,3,7,8-TETRACHLORODIBENZO-P-DIOXIN: HIGHLY TOXIC. **ACUTE EXPOSURE-** A LETHAL DOSE IN RABBITS BY DERMAL ABSORPTION WAS 275

UG/KG. CHLORACNE, A SKIN CONDITION, MAY OCCUR AS A LOCAL EFFECT DUE TO DIRECT SKIN CONTACT OR AS A SYSTEMIC EFFECT DUE TO SKIN ABSORPTION. CHLORACNE IS CHARACTERIZED BY INCLUSION CYSTS, COMEDONES AND PUSTULES, WITH EVENTUAL SCARING OF THE SKIN. THESE LESIONS INVOLVE THE FACE, NECK, TORSO, THIGHS, AND GENITALS. SOMETIMES THE CHLORACNE IS PRECEDED BY ERYTHEMATOUS AND EDEMATOUS SKIN LESIONS. EFFECTS ON THE CENTRAL NERVOUS SYSTEM AND LIVER MAY OCCUR AS DESCRIBED IN CHRONIC INHALATION. **CHRONIC EXPOSURE-** IN ADDITION TO CHLORACNE, PROLONGED OR REPEATED EXPOSURE MAY PRODUCE EFFECTS AS DESCRIBED IN CHRONIC INHALATION. SMALL DOSES TEND TO PENETRATE THE SKIN MORE READILY THAN LARGER DOSES. THUS, CHRONIC LOW-DOSE EXPOSURE MAY HAVE A SIGNIFICANT EFFECT ON TOTAL BODY BURDEN.

FIRST AID- REMOVE CONTAMINATED CLOTHING AND SHOES IMMEDIATELY. WASH AFFECTED AREA WITH SOAP OR MILD DETERGENT AND LARGE AMOUNTS OF WATER UNTIL NO EVIDENCE OF CHEMICAL REMAINS (APPROXIMATELY 15-20 MINUTES). GET MEDICAL ATTENTION IMMEDIATELY.

EYE CONTACT: 2,3,7,8-TETRACHLORODIBENZO-P-DIOXIN: IRRITANT. **ACUTE EXPOSURE-** 2 MG APPLIED TO THE EYE OF A RABBIT WAS MODERATELY IRRITATING. **CHRONIC EXPOSURE-** PROLONGED OR REPEATED EXPOSURE TO IRRITANTS MAY CAUSE CONJUNCTIVITIS.

FIRST AID- WASH EYES IMMEDIATELY WITH LARGE AMOUNTS OF WATER OR NORMAL SALINE, OCCASIONALLY LIFTING UPPER AND LOWER LIDS, UNTIL NO EVIDENCE OF CHEMICAL REMAINS (APPROXIMATELY 15-20 MINUTES). GET MEDICAL ATTENTION IMMEDIATELY.

INGESTION: 2,3,7,8-TETRACHLORODIBENZO-P-DIOXIN: HIGHLY TOXIC/CARCINOGEN. **ACUTE EXPOSURE-** A LETHAL DOSE IN RATS WAS 20 UG/KG. EFFECTS OF POISONING IN RATS WERE RUFFLED HAIR COAT, HUNCHED POSTURE, INACTIVITY AND JAUNDICE, AND IN MICE WERE ASCITES. ANOREXIA, DEHYDRATION, DEPRESSION, EMACIATION, INTESTINAL HEMORRHAGE AND ALOPECIA WERE OBSERVED IN DOGS. SIGNS OF POISONING IN MONKEYS INCLUDED BLEPHARITIS, LOSS OF FINGERNAILS AND EYELASHES, FACIAL ALOPECIA WITH ACNEFORM ERUPTIONS, MILD ANEMIA, NEUTROPHILIA, LYMPHOPENIA, DECREASED SERUM CHOLESTEROL LEVELS, INCREASE IN SERUM TRIGLYCERIDE CONCENTRATIONS, AND AN INCREASE IN LIVER, ADRENAL GLAND, AND KIDNEY WEIGHTS. ANIMALS GIVEN ACUTE DOSES SUFFERED SEVERE WEIGHT LOSS WITH DEATH DELAYED ONE TO SEVERAL WEEKS. AN ALMOST COMPLETE LOSS OF ADIPOSE TISSUE WAS OBSERVED AT NECROPSY. ATROPHY OF THE THYMUS WAS DISPLAYED IN MICE, RATS, GUINEA PIGS, AND MONKEYS; LIVER DAMAGE WAS OBSERVED IN RATS, MICE AND RABBITS. SINGLE DOSES OF AS LITTLE AS 1-10 UG/KG PRODUCED INCREASED FREQUENCY OF CLEFT PALATE IN THE MOUSE FETUS. KIDNEY ABNORMALITIES WERE OBSERVED IN THE FETUSES OF RATS AND MICE GIVEN ACUTE DOSES. **CHRONIC EXPOSURE-** ONE MONKEY THAT RECEIVED A DIETARY LEVEL OF 0.02 PPM PER DAY BECAME LETHARGIC AFTER 3 DAYS AND DIED ON THE 12TH DAY WITH A 30% WEIGHT LOSS. CELL-MEDIATED IMMUNITY WAS SUPPRESSED IN GUINEA PIGS AND MICE FROM SUBLETHAL DOSE LEVELS. THROMBOCYTOPENIA AND OTHER EFFECTS ON THE BLOOD WERE PRODUCED IN RATS AND MAY HAVE BEEN RESPONSIBLE FOR THE PRODUCTION OF HEMORRHAGES THAT OCCURRED IN RATS. CHROMOSOME ABNORMALITIES WERE NOTED IN MALE AND FEMALE RATS DOSED TWICE WEEKLY AT 4 UG/KG FOR 13 WEEKS. REPEATED DOSES FED TO MICE AND RATS PRODUCED FETOTOXIC EFFECTS AS LISTED IN ACUTE INGESTION. OTHER EFFECTS REPORTED IN FETUSES OF PREGNANT RATS REPEATEDLY FED 0.125 TO 2 UG/KG INCLUDED DEPRESSED WEIGHT, INTERNAL HEMORRHAGES, AND LOWERED SURVIVAL. REPEATED DOSES ALSO PRODUCED FETAL ABNORMALITIES IN RABBITS, FERRETS, AND CHICKENS. A DECREASE IN SPERMATOGENESIS CHARACTERIZED BY THE ABSENCE OF SPERMATIDS OR MATURE SPERMATOZOA WAS REPORTED FROM A STUDY OF MALE RHESUS MONKEYS; SPONTANEOUS MISCARRIAGES OCCURRED IN FEMALE MONKEYS. AN INCREASED INCIDENCE OF LIVER CANCERS AND CANCERS OF THE LUNGS, NOSE, OR MOUTH WAS OBSERVED IN RATS MAINTAINED ON DIETS CONTAINING THIS MATERIAL. IN OTHER STUDIES, THYROID NEOPLASMS WERE OBSERVED IN RATS; LIVER CANCERS IN MICE; LIVER NEOPLASMS IN FEMALE RATS AND MICE, AND TUMORS IN A VARIETY OF ORGANS IN RATS.

FIRST AID- REMOVE BY EMESIS WITH SYRUP OF IPECAC. AFTER EMESIS, PERFORM GASTRIC LAVAGE WITH ACTIVATED CHARCOAL AND FOLLOW WITH A SALINE CATHARTIC. (DREISBACH - HANDBOOK OF POISONING, 11TH ED.) TREATMENT SHOULD BE PERFORMED BY QUALIFIED MEDICAL PERSONNEL.

ANTIDOTE: NO SPECIFIC ANTIDOTE. TREAT SYMPTOMATICALLY AND SUPPORTIVELY.

REACTIVITY

REACTIVITY: STABLE UNDER NORMAL TEMPERATURES AND PRESSURES.

INCOMPATIBILITIES: 2,3,7,8-TETRACHLORODIBENZO-P-DIOXIN: NO DATA AVAILABLE.

DECOMPOSITION: THERMAL DECOMPOSITION PRODUCTS MAY INCLUDE TOXIC AND CORROSIVE FUMES OF CHLORIDES AND PHOSGENE, AND TOXIC OXIDES OF CARBON.

POLYMERIZATION: HAZARDOUS POLYMERIZATION HAS NOT BEEN REPORTED TO OCCUR UNDER NORMAL TEMPERATURES AND PRESSURES.

STORAGE AND DISPOSAL

OBSERVE ALL FEDERAL, STATE AND LOCAL REGULATIONS WHEN STORING OR DISPOSING OF THIS SUBSTANCE. FOR ASSISTANCE, CONTACT THE DISTRICT DIRECTOR OF THE ENVIRONMENTAL PROTECTION AGENCY.

CONDITIONS TO AVOID

MAY BURN BUT DOES NOT IGNITE READILY.

SPILL AND LEAK PROCEDURES

WATER SPILL: THE CALIFORNIA SAFE DRINKING WATER AND TOXIC ENFORCEMENT ACT OF 1986 (PROPOSITION 65) PROHIBITS CONTAMINATING ANY KNOWN SOURCE OF DRINKING WATER WITH SUBSTANCES KNOWN TO CAUSE CANCER AND/OR REPRODUCTIVE TOXICITY.

OCCUPATIONAL SPILL: DO NOT TOUCH SPILLED MATERIAL. STOP LEAK IF YOU CAN DO IT WITHOUT RISK. FOR SMALL SPILLS, TAKE UP WITH SAND OR OTHER ABSORBENT MATERIAL AND PLACE INTO CONTAINERS FOR LATER DISPOSAL. FOR SMALL DRY SPILLS, WITH A CLEAN SHOVEL PLACE MATERIAL INTO CLEAN, DRY CONTAINER AND COVER. MOVE CONTAINERS FROM SPILL AREA. FOR LARGER SPILLS, DIKE FAR AHEAD OF SPILL FOR LATER DISPOSAL. KEEP UNNECESSARY PEOPLE AWAY. ISOLATE HAZARD AREA AND DENY ENTRY.

REPORTABLE QUANTITY (RQ): 1 POUND THE SUPERFUND AMENDMENTS AND REAUTHORIZATION ACT (SARA) SECTION 304 REQUIRES THAT A RELEASE EQUAL TO OR GREATER THAN THE REPORTABLE QUANTITY FOR THIS SUBSTANCE BE IMMEDIATELY REPORTED TO THE LOCAL EMERGENCY PLANNING COMMITTEE AND THE STATE EMERGENCY RESPONSE COMMISSION (40 CFR 355.40). IF THE RELEASE OF THIS SUBSTANCE IS REPORTABLE UNDER CERCLA SECTION 103, THE NATIONAL RESPONSE CENTER MUST BE NOTIFIED IMMEDIATELY AT (800) 424-8802 OR (202) 426-2675 IN THE METROPOLITAN WASHINGTON, D.C. AREA (40 CFR 302.6).

PROTECTIVE EQUIPMENT

VENTILATION: PROCESS ENCLOSURE RECOMMENDED.

RESPIRATOR: THE FOLLOWING RESPIRATORS ARE RECOMMENDED BASED ON INFORMATION FOUND IN THE PHYSICAL DATA, TOXICITY AND HEALTH EFFECTS SECTIONS. THEY ARE RANKED IN ORDER FROM MINIMUM TO MAXIMUM RESPIRATORY PROTECTION. THE SPECIFIC RESPIRATOR SELECTED MUST BE BASED ON CONTAMINATION LEVELS FOUND IN THE WORK PLACE, MUST NOT EXCEED THE WORKING LIMITS OF THE RESPIRATOR AND BE JOINTLY APPROVED BY THE NATIONAL INSTITUTE FOR OCCUPATIONAL SAFETY AND HEALTH AND THE MINE SAFETY AND HEALTH ADMINISTRATION (NIOSH-MSHA).

TYPE 'C' SUPPLIED-AIR RESPIRATOR WITH A FULL FACEPIECE OPERATED IN PRESSURE-DEMAND OR OTHER POSITIVE PRESSURE MODE OR WITH A FULL FACEPIECE, HELMET OR HOOD OPERATED IN CONTINOUS-FLOW MODE.

SELF-CONTAINED BREATHING APPARATUS WITH A FULL FACEPIECE OPERATED IN PRESSURE-DEMAND OR OTHER POSITIVE PRESSURE MODE.

FOR FIREFIGHTING AND OTHER IMMEDIATELY DANGEROUS TO LIFE OR HEALTH CONDITIONS:

SELF-CONTAINED BREATHING APPARATUS WITH FULL FACEPIECE OPERATED IN PRESSURE-DEMAND OR OTHER POSITIVE PRESSURE MODE.

SUPPLIED-AIR RESPIRATOR WITH FULL FACEPIECE AND OPERATED IN PRESSURE-DEMAND OR OTHER POSITIVE PRESSURE MODE IN COMBINATION WITH AN AUXILIARY SELF-CONTAINED BREATHING APPARATUS OPERATED IN PRESSURE-DEMAND OR OTHER POSITIVE PRESSURE MODE.

CLOTHING: EMPLOYEE MUST WEAR APPROPRIATE PROTECTIVE (IMPERVIOUS) CLOTHING AND EQUIPMENT TO PREVENT ANY POSSIBILITY OF SKIN CONTACT WITH THIS SUBSTANCE.

GLOVES: EMPLOYEE MUST WEAR APPROPRIATE PROTECTIVE GLOVES TO PREVENT CONTACT WITH THIS SUBSTANCE.

EYE PROTECTION: EMPLOYEE MUST WEAR SPLASH-PROOF OR DUST-RESISTANT SAFETY GOGGLES AND A FACESHIELD TO PREVENT CONTACT WITH THIS SUBSTANCE.

EMERGENCY WASH FACILITIES: WHERE THERE IS ANY POSSIBILITY THAT AN EMPLOYEE'S EYES AND/OR SKIN MAY BE EXPOSED TO THIS SUBSTANCE, THE EMPLOYER SHOULD PROVIDE AN EYE WASH FOUNTAIN AND QUICK DRENCH SHOWER WITHIN THE IMMEDIATE WORK AREA FOR EMERGENCY USE.

AUTHORIZED BY- OCCUPATIONAL HEALTH SERVICES, INC.

CREATION DATE: 10/05/89 ***REVISION DATE:*** 07/12/90

MATERIAL SAFETY DATA SHEET

OCCUPATIONAL HEALTH SERVICES, INC.
AGRICULTURE AND PESTICIDE DIVISION
450 SEVENTH AVENUE, SUITE 2407
NEW YORK, NEW YORK 10123
1-800-445-MSDS OR (212) 967-1100

EMERGENCY CONTACT:
JOHN S. BRANSFORD, JR. (615) 292-1180

SUBSTANCE IDENTIFICATION

CAS-NUMBER 82-66-6

SUBSTANCE: DIPHACINONE

TRADE NAMES/SYNONYMS: 2-(DIPHENYLACETYL)-1H-INDEND-1,3(2H)-DIONE; 2-(DIPHENYLACETYL)-1,3-INDANDIONE; DIDANDIN; DIDION; DIPAXIN; DIPHACIN; DIPHACINON; DIPHENACIN; DIPHENADION; DIPHENADIONE; ORAGULANT; RATINDAN; SOLVAN; PST08068

CHEMICAL FAMILY: INDENE KETONE

MOLECULAR FORMULA: C23-H16-O3

MOLECULAR WEIGHT: 340.38

CERCLA RATINGS (SCALE 0-3): HEALTH=3 FIRE=U REACTIVITY=0 PERSISTENCE=1

NFPA RATINGS (SCALE 0-4): HEALTH=4 FIRE=U REACTIVITY=0

COMPONENTS AND CONTAMINANTS

COMPONENT: DIPHACINONE ***PERCENT:*** 100
CAS# 82-66-6

OTHER CONTAMINANTS: NONE

EXPOSURE LIMITS: DIPHACINONE: NO OCCUPATIONAL EXPOSURE LIMITS ESTABLISHED BY OSHA, ACGIH, OR NIOSH.
10/10,000 POUNDS SARA SECTION 302 THRESHOLD PLANNING QUANTITY 1 POUND SARA SECTION 304 REPORTABLE QUANTITY

PHYSICAL DATA

DESCRIPTION: ODORLESS, PALE YELLOW CRYSTALS

MELTING POINT: 295-297 F (146-147 C) ***SPECIFIC GRAVITY:*** NOT AVAILABLE

SOLUBILITY IN WATER: ALMOST INSOLUBLE

SOLVENT SOLUBILITY: ACETONE, ACETIC ACID; SLIGHTLY SOLUBLE IN BENZENE, HOT ETHANOL

FIRE AND EXPLOSION DATA

FIRE AND EXPLOSION HAZARD: UNKNOWN FIRE AND EXPLOSION HAZARD.

FIREFIGHTING MEDIA: DRY CHEMICAL, CARBON DIOXIDE, HALON, WATER SPRAY OR STANDARD FOAM (1987 EMERGENCY RESPONSE GUIDEBOOK, DOT P 5800.4).
FOR LARGER FIRES, USE WATER SPRAY, FOG OR STANDARD FOAM (1987 EMERGENCY RESPONSE GUIDEBOOK, DOT P 5800.4).

FIREFIGHTING: MOVE CONTAINERS FROM FIRE AREA IF POSSIBLE (1987 EMERGENCY RESPONSE GUIDEBOOK, DOT P 5800.4, GUIDE PAGE 53).
EXTINGUISH USING AGENT SUITABLE FOR TYPE OF SURROUNDING FIRE. AVOID BREATHING VAPORS AND DUSTS. KEEP UPWIND.

TRANSPORTATION DATA

DEPARTMENT OF TRANSPORTATION HAZARD CLASSIFICATION 49 CFR 172.101: POISON B
DEPARTMENT OF TRANSPORTATION LABELING REQUIREMENTS 49 CFR 172.101 AND SUBPART E: POISON
DEPARTMENT OF TRANSPORTATION PACKAGING REQUIREMENTS: 49 CFR 173.365 EXCEPTIONS: 49 CFR 173.364

TOXICITY

DIPHACINONE: TOXICITY DATA: 2 GM/M3/4 HOURS INHALATION-RAT LC50; 200 MG/KG SKIN-RAT LD50; 1500 UG/KG ORAL-RAT LD50; 300 MG/KG ORAL-MOUSE LD50; 3 MG/KG ORAL-DOG LD50; 15 MG/KG ORAL-CAT LD50; 35 MG/KG ORAL-RABBIT LD50; 150 MG/KG ORAL-PIG LD50; 910 UG/KG ORAL-MAMMAL LD50; 11 MG/KG UNREPORTED-RAT LD50. CARCINOGEN STATUS: NONE. ACUTE TOXICITY LEVEL: HIGHLY TOXIC BY INHALATION, DERMAL ABSORPTION AND INGESTION. TARGET EFFECTS: HEMORRHAGIC AGENT. POISONING MAY AFFECT THE HEART AND GASTROINTESTINAL SYSTEM.

HEALTH EFFECTS AND FIRST AID

INHALATION: DIPHACINONE: HIGHLY TOXIC. **ACUTE EXPOSURE-** THE LETHAL CONCENTRATION REPORTED IN RATS WAS 2 GM/M3/4 HOURS. **CHRONIC EXPOSURE-** NO DATA AVAILABLE. **FIRST AID-** REMOVE FROM EXPOSURE AREA TO FRESH AIR IMMEDIATELY. IF BREATHING HAS STOPPED, PERFORM ARTIFICIAL RESPIRATION. KEEP PERSON WARM AND AT REST. TREAT SYMPTOMATICALLY AND SUPPORTIVELY. GET MEDICAL ATTENTION IMMEDIATELY.

SKIN CONTACT: DIPHACINONE: HIGHLY TOXIC. **ACUTE EXPOSURE-** THE LETHAL DOSE REPORTED IN RATS WAS 200 MG/KG; THE SYMPTOMS WERE NOT REPORTED. **CHRONIC EXPOSURE-** NO DATA AVAILABLE.

FIRST AID- REMOVE CONTAMINATED CLOTHING AND SHOES IMMEDIATELY. WASH AFFECTED AREA WITH SOAP OR MILD DETERGENT AND LARGE AMOUNTS OF WATER UNTIL NO EVIDENCE OF CHEMICAL REMAINS (APPROXIMATELY 15-20 MINUTES). GET MEDICAL ATTENTION IMMEDIATELY.

EYE CONTACT: DIPHACINONE: **ACUTE EXPOSURE-** NO DATA AVAILABLE. **CHRONIC EXPOSURE-** NO DATA AVAILABLE.

FIRST AID- WASH EYES IMMEDIATELY WITH LARGE AMOUNTS OF WATER OR NORMAL SALINE, OCCASIONALLY LIFTING UPPER AND LOWER LIDS, UNTIL NO EVIDENCE OF CHEMICAL REMAINS (APPROXIMATELY 15-20 MINUTES). GET MEDICAL ATTENTION IMMEDIATELY.

INGESTION: DIPHACINONE: HEMORRHAGIC AGENT/HIGHLY TOXIC. **ACUTE EXPOSURE-** THE ONLY TOXIC SIDE EFFECT REPORTED IN MAN IS A MILD GASTROINTESTINAL DISORDER. VERY SMALL AMOUNTS WERE REQUIRED TO CAUSE DEATH IN EXPERIMENTAL ANIMALS. ANIMALS RECEIVING LETHAL DOSES OF SUBSTITUTED INDANDIONES EXHIBITED LABORED BREATHING, PROGRESSIVE MUSCULAR WEAKNESS, HYPEREXCITABILITY, PULMONARY CONGESTION, VENOUS ENGORGEMENT AND CARDIAC STANDSTILL IN SYSTOLE. IF THE DOSE RECEIVED IS NOT IMMEDIATELY LETHAL, DEATH TENDS TO BE DELAYED AND DUE TO MASSIVE HEMORRHAGE. SIGNS OF POISONING MAY INCLUDE HEMOPTYSIS, HEMATURIA, BLOODY STOOLS, HEMORRHAGES IN ORGANS, WIDESPREAD BRUISING AND BLEEDING INTO JOINT SPACES. **CHRONIC EXPOSURE-** DIPHACINONE IS A CUMULATIVE POISON AND ITS EFFECTS MAY BE INCREASED BY REPEATED DOSES. RARELY, NECROSIS OF THE SKIN IS A POSSIBLE COMPLICATION.

FIRST AID- REMOVE INGESTED POISON WITH SYRUP OF IPECAC AND/OR GASTRIC LAVAGE WITH TAP WATER IF POSSIBLE WITHIN A FEW HOURS OF A SINGLE LARGE DOSE. (GOSSELIN, CLINICAL TOXICOLOGY OF COMMERICAL PRODUCTS, 5TH ED). GET MEDICAL ATTENTION IMMEDIATELY. TREATMENT MUST BE PERFORMED BY QUALIFIED MEDICAL PERSONNEL.

ANTIDOTE: NO SPECIFIC ANTIDOTE. TREAT SYMPTOMATICALLY AND SUPPORTIVELY.

REACTIVITY

REACTIVITY: STABLE UNDER NORMAL TEMPERATURES AND PRESSURES.

INCOMPATIBILITIES: DIPHACINONE: NO DATA AVAILABLE.

DECOMPOSITION: THERMAL DECOMPOSITION MAY RELEASE TOXIC AND/OR HAZARDOUS GASES.

POLYMERIZATION: HAZARDOUS POLYMERIZATION HAS NOT BEEN REPORTED TO OCCUR UNDER NORMAL TEMPERATURES AND PRESSURES.

STORAGE AND DISPOSAL

OBSERVE ALL FEDERAL, STATE AND LOCAL REGULATIONS WHEN STORING OR DISPOSING OF THIS SUBSTANCE. FOR ASSISTANCE, CONTACT THE DISTRICT DIRECTOR OF THE ENVIRONMENTAL PROTECTION AGENCY.

STORAGE

THRESHOLD PLANNING QUANTITY (TPQ): THE SUPERFUND AMENDMENTS AND REAUTHORIZATION ACT (SARA) SECTION 302 REQUIRES THAT EACH FACILITY WHERE ANY EXTREMELY HAZARDOUS SUBSTANCE IS PRESENT IN A QUANTITY EQUAL TO OR GREATER THAN THE TPQ ESTABLISHED FOR THAT SUBSTANCE NOTIFY THE STATE EMERGENCY RESPONSE COMMISSION FOR THE STATE IN WHICH IT IS LOCATED. SECTION 303 OF SARA REQUIRES THESE FACILITIES TO PARTICIPATE IN LOCAL EMERGENCY RESPONSE PLANNING (40 CFR 355.30).

CONDITIONS TO AVOID

MAY BURN BUT DOES NOT IGNITE READILY.

SPILL AND LEAK PROCEDURES

OCCUPATIONAL SPILL: DO NOT TOUCH SPILLED MATERIAL. STOP LEAK IF YOU CAN DO IT WITHOUT RISK. FOR SMALL SPILLS, TAKE UP WITH SAND OR OTHER ABSORBENT MATERIAL AND PLACE INTO CONTAINERS FOR LATER DISPOSAL. FOR SMALL DRY SPILLS, WITH A CLEAN SHOVEL PLACE MATERIAL INTO CLEAN, DRY CONTAINER AND COVER. MOVE CONTAINERS FROM SPILL AREA. FOR LARGER SPILLS, DIKE FAR AHEAD OF SPILL FOR LATER DISPOSAL. KEEP UNNECESSARY PEOPLE AWAY. ISOLATE HAZARD AREA AND DENY ENTRY.
REPORTABLE QUANTITY (RQ): 1 POUND THE SUPERFUND AMENDMENTS AND REAUTHORIZATION ACT (SARA) SECTION 304 REQUIRES THAT A RELEASE EQUAL TO OR GREATER THAN THE REPORTABLE QUANTITY FOR THIS SUBSTANCE BE IMMEDIATELY REPORTED TO THE LOCAL EMERGENCY PLANNING COMMITTEE AND THE STATE EMERGENCY RESPONSE COMMISSION (40 CFR 355.40). IF THE RELEASE OF THIS SUBSTANCE IS REPORTABLE UNDER CERCLA SECTION 103, THE NATIONAL RESPONSE CENTER MUST BE NOTIFIED IMMEDIATELY AT (800) 424-8802 OR (202) 426-2675 IN THE METROPOLITAN WASHINGTON, D.C. AREA (40 CFR 302.6).

PROTECTIVE EQUIPMENT

VENTILATION: PROVIDE LOCAL EXHAUST OR PROCESS ENCLOSURE VENTILATION. VENTILATION EQUIPMENT MUST BE EXPLOSION-PROOF.

RESPIRATOR: THE FOLLOWING RESPIRATORS ARE RECOMMENDED BASED ON INFORMATION FOUND IN THE PHYSICAL DATA, TOXICITY AND HEALTH EFFECTS SECTIONS. THEY ARE RANKED IN ORDER FROM MINIMUM TO MAXIMUM RESPIRATORY PROTECTION. THE SPECIFIC RESPIRATOR SELECTED MUST BE BASED ON CONTAMINATION LEVELS FOUND IN THE WORK PLACE, MUST NOT EXCEED THE WORKING LIMITS OF THE RESPIRATOR AND BE JOINTLY APPROVED BY THE NATIONAL INSTITUTE FOR OCCUPATIONAL SAFETY AND HEALTH AND THE MINE SAFETY AND HEALTH ADMINISTRATION (NIOSH-MSHA).

TYPE 'C' SUPPLIED-AIR RESPIRATOR WITH A FULL FACEPIECE OPERATED IN PRESSURE-DEMAND OR OTHER POSITIVE PRESSURE MODE OR WITH A FULL FACEPIECE, HELMET OR HOOD OPERATED IN CONTINOUS-FLOW MODE.

SELF-CONTAINED BREATHING APPARATUS WITH A FULL FACEPIECE OPERATED IN PRESSURE-DEMAND OR OTHER POSITIVE PRESSURE MODE.

FOR FIREFIGHTING AND OTHER IMMEDIATELY DANGEROUS TO LIFE OR HEALTH CONDITIONS:

SELF-CONTAINED BREATHING APPARATUS WITH FULL FACEPIECE OPERATED IN PRESSURE-DEMAND OR OTHER POSITIVE PRESSURE MODE.

SUPPLIED-AIR RESPIRATOR WITH FULL FACEPIECE AND OPERATED IN PRESSURE-DEMAND OR OTHER POSITIVE PRESSURE MODE IN COMBINATION WITH AN AUXILIARY SELF-CONTAINED BREATHING APPARATUS OPERATED IN PRESSURE-DEMAND OR OTHER POSITIVE PRESSURE MODE.

CLOTHING: EMPLOYEE MUST WEAR APPROPRIATE PROTECTIVE (IMPERVIOUS) CLOTHING AND EQUIPMENT TO PREVENT REPEATED OR PROLONGED SKIN CONTACT WITH THIS SUBSTANCE.

GLOVES: EMPLOYEE MUST WEAR APPROPRIATE PROTECTIVE GLOVES TO PREVENT CONTACT WITH THIS SUBSTANCE.

EYE PROTECTION: EMPLOYEE MUST WEAR SPLASH-PROOF OR DUST-RESISTANT SAFETY GOGGLES TO PREVENT EYE CONTACT WITH THIS SUBSTANCE.

EMERGENCY EYE WASH: WHERE THERE IS ANY POSSIBILITY THAT AN EMPLOYEE'S EYES MAY BE EXPOSED TO THIS SUBSTANCE, THE EMPLOYER SHOULD PROVIDE AN EYE WASH FOUNTAIN WITHIN THE IMMEDIATE WORK AREA FOR EMERGENCY USE.

AUTHORIZED BY- OCCUPATIONAL HEALTH SERVICES, INC.

CREATION DATE: 10/04/89 ***REVISION DATE:*** 05/18/90

MATERIAL SAFETY DATA SHEET

OCCUPATIONAL HEALTH SERVICES, INC.
AGRICULTURE AND PESTICIDE DIVISION
450 SEVENTH AVENUE, SUITE 2407
NEW YORK, NEW YORK 10123
1-800-445-MSDS OR (212) 967-1100

EMERGENCY CONTACT:
JOHN S. BRANSFORD, JR. (615) 292-1180

SUBSTANCE IDENTIFICATION

CAS-NUMBER 84-62-8

SUBSTANCE: DIPHENYL PHTHALATE

TRADE NAMES/SYNONYMS: 1,2-BENZENEDICARBOXYLIC ACID, DIPHENYL ESTER; PHTHALIC ACID, DIPHENYL ESTER; PHENYL PHTHALATE; C20H14O4; PST08095

CHEMICAL FAMILY: PHTHALATE

MOLECULAR FORMULA: C6-H4-(C-O-O-C6-H5)2

MOLECULAR WEIGHT: 318.33

CERCLA RATINGS (SCALE 0-3): HEALTH=U FIRE=1 REACTIVITY=0 PERSISTENCE=0

NFPA RATINGS (SCALE 0-4): HEALTH=0 FIRE=1 REACTIVITY=0

COMPONENTS AND CONTAMINANTS

COMPONENT: DIPHENYL PHTHALATE ***PERCENT:*** 100.0
CAS# 84-62-8

OTHER CONTAMINANTS: NONE

EXPOSURE LIMITS: NO OCCUPATIONAL EXPOSURE LIMITS ESTABLISHED BY OSHA, ACGIH, OR NIOSH.

PHYSICAL DATA

DESCRIPTION: ODORLESS, WHITE TO YELLOW-WHITE CRYSTALS OR POWDER.

BOILING POINT: 482-495 F (250-257 C) @ 14 MMHG (SUBL)

MELTING POINT: 158-163 F (70-73 C) ***SPECIFIC GRAVITY:*** 1.572 @ 74 C

SOLUBILITY IN WATER: INSOLUBLE

SOLVENT SOLUBILITY: SOLUBLE IN ACETONE AND OTHER KETONES, LIQUID ESTERS, AND CHLORINATED HYDROCARBONS.

FIRE AND EXPLOSION DATA

FIRE AND EXPLOSION HAZARD: SLIGHT FIRE HAZARD WHEN EXPOSED TO HEAT OR FLAME.

FLASH POINT: 435 F (224 C) (CC) ***FLAMMABILITY CLASS(OSHA):*** IIIB

FIREFIGHTING MEDIA: DRY CHEMICAL, CARBON DIOXIDE, HALON, WATER SPRAY OR STANDARD FOAM (1987 EMERGENCY RESPONSE GUIDEBOOK, DOT P 5800.4). FOR LARGER FIRES, USE WATER SPRAY, FOG OR STANDARD FOAM (1987 EMERGENCY RESPONSE GUIDEBOOK, DOT P 5800.4).

FIREFIGHTING: MOVE CONTAINER FROM FIRE AREA IF POSSIBLE. DO NOT SCATTER SPILLED MATERIAL WITH HIGH PRESSURE WATER STREAMS. DIKE FIRE CONTROL WATER FOR LATER DISPOSAL (1987 EMERGENCY RESPONSE GUIDEBOOK, DOT P 5800.4, GUIDE PAGE 31).

USE AGENTS SUITABLE FOR TYPE OF SURROUNDING FIRE. AVOID BREATHING HAZARDOUS VAPORS, KEEP UPWIND.

WATER OR FOAM MAY CAUSE FROTHING (NFPA 325M, FIRE HAZARD PROPERTIES OF FLAMMABLE LIQUIDS, GASES, AND VOLATILE SOLIDS, 1984)

TOXICITY

DIPHENYL PHTHALATE: TOXICITY DATA: 8 GM/KG ORAL-RAT LD50. CARCINOGEN STATUS: NONE. ACUTE TOXICITY LEVEL: SLIGHTLY TOXIC BY INGESTION. TARGET EFFECTS: NO DATA AVAILABLE.

HEALTH EFFECTS AND FIRST AID

INHALATION: DIPHENYL PHTHALATE: **ACUTE EXPOSURE-** NO SPECIFIC DATA AVAILABLE. IN GENERAL PHTHALATE ESTERS HAVE A LOW ORDER OF TOXICITY AND THEREFORE ARE EXPECTED TO BE ONLY A SLIGHT RISK BY INHALATION. IRRITATION OF THE UPPER RESPIRATORY TRACT AND CENTRAL NERVOUS SYSTEM EFFECTS MAY OCCUR WITH SOME PHTHALATE ESTERS. **CHRONIC EXPOSURE-** NO SPECIFIC DATA AVAILABLE. ONE STUDY REPORTED THAT WORKERS EXPOSED TO PHTHALATE ESTER VAPORS FOR A PERIOD OF SIX TO TEN YEARS SHOWED NEUROLOGICAL EFFECTS THAT INCLUDED TOXIC POLYNEURITIS AND INCREASED EXCITABILITY OF VESTIBULAR AND OLFACTORY RECEPTORS.

FIRST AID- REMOVE FROM EXPOSURE AREA TO FRESH AIR IMMEDIATELY. IF BREATHING HAS STOPPED, PERFORM ARTIFICIAL RESPIRATION. KEEP PERSON WARM AND AT REST. TREAT SYMPTOMATICALLY AND SUPPORTIVELY. GET MEDICAL ATTENTION IMMEDIATELY.

SKIN CONTACT: DIPHENYL PHTHALATE: **ACUTE EXPOSURE-** NO SPECIFIC DATA AVAILABLE. PHTHALATE ESTERS IN GENERAL ARE NOT SKIN IRRITANTS OR SENSITIZERS AND ARE NOT APPRECIABLY ABSORBED THROUGH THE SKIN. **CHRONIC EXPOSURE-** NO DATA AVAILABLE.

FIRST AID- REMOVE CONTAMINATED CLOTHING AND SHOES IMMEDIATELY. WASH AFFECTED AREA WITH SOAP OR MILD DETERGENT AND LARGE AMOUNTS OF WATER UNTIL NO EVIDENCE OF CHEMICAL REMAINS (APPROXIMATELY 15-20 MINUTES). GET MEDICAL ATTENTION IMMEDIATELY.

EYE CONTACT: DIPHENYL PHTHALATE: **ACUTE EXPOSURE-** NO DATA AVAILABLE. MAY BE IRRITATING. **CHRONIC EXPOSURE-** NO DATA AVAILABLE.

FIRST AID- WASH EYES IMMEDIATELY WITH LARGE AMOUNTS OF WATER OR NORMAL SALINE, OCCASIONALLY LIFTING UPPER AND LOWER LIDS, UNTIL NO EVIDENCE OF CHEMICAL REMAINS (APPROXIMATELY 15-20 MINUTES). GET MEDICAL ATTENTION IMMEDIATELY.

INGESTION: DIPHENYL PHTHALATE: **ACUTE EXPOSURE-** IN GENERAL PHTHALATE ESTERS HAVE A LOW ORDER OF TOXICITY. SOME MAY CAUSE MILD GASTRIC DISORDERS AFTER INGESTION OF LARGE DOSES. **CHRONIC EXPOSURE-** NO SPECIFIC DATA AVAILABLE. IN ANIMAL STUDIES PROLONGED INGESTION OF SOME PHTHALATE ESTERS CAUSED RETARDATION OF WEIGHT INCREASE, LIVER AND KIDNEY CHANGES, DEGENERATION OF TESTICLES, AND AN INCREASE OF HEPATOCELLULAR CARCINOMAS.

FIRST AID- TREAT SYMPTOMATICALLY AND SUPPORTIVELY. GET MEDICAL ATTENTION IMMEDIATELY. IF VOMITING OCCURS, KEEP HEAD LOWER THAN HIPS TO PREVENT ASPIRATION.

ANTIDOTE: NO SPECIFIC ANTIDOTE. TREAT SYMPTOMATICALLY AND SUPPORTIVELY.

REACTIVITY

REACTIVITY: STABLE UNDER NORMAL TEMPERATURES AND PRESSURES.

INCOMPATIBILITIES: DIPHENYL PHTHALATE: OXIDIZERS (STRONG): FIRE AND EXPLOSION HAZARD.

DECOMPOSITION: THERMAL DECOMPOSITION PRODUCTS MAY INCLUDE TOXIC OXIDES OF CARBON.

POLYMERIZATION: HAZARDOUS POLYMERIZATION HAS NOT BEEN REPORTED TO OCCUR UNDER NORMAL TEMPERATURES AND PRESSURES.

STORAGE AND DISPOSAL

OBSERVE ALL FEDERAL, STATE AND LOCAL REGULATIONS WHEN STORING OR DISPOSING OF THIS SUBSTANCE. FOR ASSISTANCE, CONTACT THE DISTRICT DIRECTOR OF THE ENVIRONMENTAL PROTECTION AGENCY.

STORAGE

STORE AWAY FROM INCOMPATIBLE SUBSTANCES.

CONDITIONS TO AVOID

MAY BURN BUT DOES NOT IGNITE READILY. AVOID CONTACT WITH STRONG OXIDIZERS, EXCESSIVE HEAT, SPARKS, OR OPEN FLAME.

SPILL AND LEAK PROCEDURES

OCCUPATIONAL SPILL: SWEEP UP AND PLACE IN SUITABLE CLEAN, DRY CONTAINERS FOR RECLAMATION OR LATER DISPOSAL. DO NOT FLUSH SPILLED MATERIAL INTO SEWER. KEEP UNNECESSARY PEOPLE AWAY.

PROTECTIVE EQUIPMENT

VENTILATION: PROVIDE GENERAL DILUTION VENTILATION.

RESPIRATOR: THE FOLLOWING RESPIRATORS ARE RECOMMENDED BASED ON INFORMATION FOUND IN THE PHYSICAL DATA, TOXICITY AND HEALTH EFFECTS SECTIONS. THEY ARE RANKED IN ORDER FROM MINIMUM TO MAXIMUM RESPIRATORY PROTECTION. THE SPECIFIC RESPIRATOR SELECTED MUST BE BASED ON CONTAMINATION LEVELS FOUND IN THE WORK PLACE, MUST NOT EXCEED THE WORKING LIMITS OF THE RESPIRATOR AND BE JOINTLY APPROVED BY THE NATIONAL INSTITUTE FOR OCCUPATIONAL SAFETY AND HEALTH AND THE MINE SAFETY AND HEALTH ADMINISTRATION (NIOSH-MSHA).

DUST AND MIST RESPIRATOR.

AIR-PURIFYING RESPIRATOR WITH A HIGH-EFFICIENCY PARTICULATE FILTER.

POWERED AIR-PURIFYING RESPIRATOR WITH A DUST AND MIST FILTER.

POWERED AIR-PURIFYING RESPIRATOR WITH A HIGH-EFFICIENCY PARTICULATE FILTER.

TYPE 'C' SUPPLIED-AIR RESPIRATOR OPERATED IN THE PRESSURE-DEMAND OR OTHER POSITIVE PRESSURE OR CONTINUOUS-FLOW MODE.

SELF-CONTAINED BREATHING APPARATUS.

FOR FIREFIGHTING AND OTHER IMMEDIATELY DANGEROUS TO LIFE OR HEALTH CONDITIONS:

SELF-CONTAINED BREATHING APPARATUS WITH FULL FACEPIECE OPERATED IN PRESSURE-DEMAND OR OTHER POSITIVE PRESSURE MODE.

SUPPLIED-AIR RESPIRATOR WITH FULL FACEPIECE AND OPERATED IN PRESSURE-DEMAND OR OTHER POSITIVE PRESSURE MODE IN COMBINATION WITH AN AUXILIARY SELF-CONTAINED BREATHING APPARATUS OPERATED IN PRESSURE-DEMAND OR OTHER POSITIVE PRESSURE MODE.

CLOTHING: PROTECTIVE CLOTHING NOT REQUIRED. AVOID REPEATED OR PROLONGED CONTACT WITH THIS SUBSTANCE.

GLOVES: PROTECTIVE GLOVES ARE NOT REQUIRED BUT RECOMMENDED.

EYE PROTECTION: EMPLOYEE MUST WEAR SPLASH-PROOF OR DUST-RESISTANT SAFETY GOGGLES TO PREVENT EYE CONTACT WITH THIS SUBSTANCE.

EMERGENCY EYE WASH: WHERE THERE IS ANY POSSIBILITY THAT AN EMPLOYEE'S EYES MAY BE EXPOSED TO THIS SUBSTANCE, THE EMPLOYER SHOULD PROVIDE AN EYE WASH FOUNTAIN WITHIN THE IMMEDIATE WORK AREA FOR EMERGENCY USE.

AUTHORIZED BY- OCCUPATIONAL HEALTH SERVICES, INC.

CREATION DATE: 10/04/89 ***REVISION DATE:*** 05/31/90

MATERIAL SAFETY DATA SHEET

OCCUPATIONAL HEALTH SERVICES, INC.
AGRICULTURE AND PESTICIDE DIVISION
450 SEVENTH AVENUE, SUITE 2407
NEW YORK, NEW YORK 10123
1-800-445-MSDS OR (212) 967-1100

EMERGENCY CONTACT:
JOHN S. BRANSFORD, JR. (615) 292-1180

SUBSTANCE IDENTIFICATION

CAS-NUMBER 122-39-4

SUBSTANCE: **DIPHENYLAMINE**

TRADE NAMES/SYNONYMS: N-DIPHENYLANILINE; ANILINOBENZENE; PHENYLANILINE; BENZENAMINE, N-PHENYL-; N,N-DIPHENYLAMINE; N-PHENYLBENZENAMINE; (PHENYLAMINO)BENZENE; DPA; N-PHENYLANILINE; C12H11N; PST08100

CHEMICAL FAMILY: AMINE, AROMATIC

MOLECULAR FORMULA: (C6-H5)2-N-H

MOLECULAR WEIGHT: 169.23

CERCLA RATINGS (SCALE 0-3): HEALTH=3 FIRE=1 REACTIVITY=0 PERSISTENCE=2

NFPA RATINGS (SCALE 0-4): HEALTH=3 FIRE=1 REACTIVITY=0

COMPONENTS AND CONTAMINANTS

COMPONENT: DIPHENYLAMINE ***PERCENT:*** 100.0
CAS# 122-39-4

OTHER CONTAMINANTS: NONE

EXPOSURE LIMITS: DIPHENYLAMINE: 10 MG/M3 OSHA TWA 10 MG/M3 ACGIH TWA

PHYSICAL DATA

DESCRIPTION: COLORLESS TO GRAYISH, MONOCLINIC LEAFLETS WITH A FLORAL ODOR WHICH MAY DARKEN ON EXPOSURE TO LIGHT.

BOILING POINT: 576 F (302C)

MELTING POINT: 129-131 F (54-55 C) ***SPECIFIC GRAVITY:*** 1.160 @ 22 C

VAPOR PRESSURE: 1 MMHG @ 108 C ***SOLUBILITY IN WATER:*** 0.03%

ODOR THRESHOLD: 0.05 PPM ***VAPOR DENSITY:*** 5.82

SOLVENT SOLUBILITY: SOLUBLE IN ALCOHOL, ETHER, ACETONE, BENZENE, CARBON DISULFIDE, GLACIAL ACETIC ACID, ETHYL ACETATE, CARBON TETRACHLORIDE, PYRIDINE, PROPYL ALCOHOL, AQUEOUS MINERAL ACID SOLUTION.

FIRE AND EXPLOSION DATA

FIRE AND EXPLOSION HAZARD: SLIGHT FIRE HAZARD WHEN EXPOSED TO HEAT OR FLAME.

DUST-AIR MIXTURES MAY IGNITE OR EXPLODE.

FLASH POINT: 307 F (153 C) (CC) ***AUTOIGNITION TEMP.:*** 1173 F (634 C)

FIREFIGHTING MEDIA: DRY CHEMICAL, CARBON DIOXIDE, HALON, WATER SPRAY OR STANDARD FOAM (1987 EMERGENCY RESPONSE GUIDEBOOK, DOT P 5800.4).

FOR LARGER FIRES, USE WATER SPRAY, FOG OR STANDARD FOAM (1987 EMERGENCY RESPONSE GUIDEBOOK, DOT P 5800.4).

FIREFIGHTING: MOVE CONTAINER FROM FIRE AREA IF POSSIBLE. DO NOT SCATTER SPILLED MATERIAL WITH HIGH PRESSURE WATER STREAMS. DIKE FIRE CONTROL WATER FOR LATER DISPOSAL (1987 EMERGENCY RESPONSE GUIDEBOOK, DOT P 5800.4, GUIDE PAGE 31).

USE AGENTS SUITABLE FOR TYPE OF SURROUNDING FIRE. AVOID BREATHING HAZARDOUS VAPORS, KEEP UPWIND.

WATER OR FOAM MAY CAUSE FROTHING (NFPA 325M, FIRE HAZARD PROPERTIES OF FLAMMABLE LIQUIDS, GASES, AND VOLATILE SOLIDS, 1984)

TOXICITY

DIPHENYLAMINE. TOXICITY DATA: 2000 MG/KG ORAL-RAT LD50 (HAZARDOUS CHEMICAL DATA BOOK); 3000 MG/KG ORAL-RAT LDLO; 3200 MG/KG ORAL-MAMMAL LD50; 300 ORAL-GUINEA PIG LD50; REPRODUCTIVE EFFECTS DATA (RTECS). CARCINOGEN STATUS: NONE. LOCAL EFFECTS: IRRITANT- INHALATION, SKIN, EYE. ACUTE TOXICITY LEVEL: MODERATELY TOXIC BY INGESTION. TARGET EFFECTS: POISONING MAY AFFECT THE BLADDER, LIVER, KIDNEYS, HEART, AND SPLEEN. ADDITIONAL DATA: TRANSIENT METHEMOGLOBINEMIA HAS BEEN INDUCED IN CATS.

HEALTH EFFECTS AND FIRST AID

INHALATION: DIPHENYLAMINE: IRRITANT. **ACUTE EXPOSURE-** EXPOSURE TO DUST MAY CAUSE IRRITATION OF THE RESPIRATORY TRACT AND SHALLOW RESPIRATION. SYSTEMIC EFFECTS MAY OCCUR AS DESCRIBED IN ACUTE INGESTION. **CHRONIC EXPOSURE-** INDUSTRIAL POISONING RESULTED IN BLADDER SYMPTOMS, TACHYCARDIA, AND HYPERTENSION. IN ADDITION, CHRONIC EXPOSURE MAY CAUSE WEIGHT LOSS, ANEMIA, WEAKNESS, IRRITABILITY, AND DAMAGE TO THE NERVOUS SYSTEM AND BONE MARROW. CHANGES IN THE LIVER, SPLEEN, AND KIDNEYS HAVE BEEN REPORTED IN ANIMALS.

FIRST AID- REMOVE FROM EXPOSURE AREA TO FRESH AIR IMMEDIATELY. IF BREATHING HAS STOPPED, PERFORM ARTIFICIAL RESPIRATION. KEEP PERSON WARM AND AT REST. TREAT SYMPTOMATICALLY AND SUPPORTIVELY. GET MEDICAL ATTENTION IMMEDIATELY.

SKIN CONTACT: DIPHENYLAMINE: IRRITANT. **ACUTE EXPOSURE-** MAY CAUSE IRRITATION WITH ECZEMA. MAY BE ABSORBED THROUGH THE SKIN AND RESULT IN SYSTEMIC TOXICITY AS DETAILED IN ACUTE INGESTION. **CHRONIC EXPOSURE-** REPEATED OR PROLONGED EXPOSURE TO IRRITANTS MAY CAUSE DERMATITIS. SYSTEMIC EFFECTS MAY OCCUR AS DESCRIBED IN CHRONIC INHALATION.

FIRST AID- REMOVE CONTAMINATED CLOTHING AND SHOES IMMEDIATELY. WASH AFFECTED AREA WITH SOAP OR MILD DETERGENT AND LARGE AMOUNTS OF WATER UNTIL NO EVIDENCE OF CHEMICAL REMAINS (APPROXIMATELY 15-20 MINUTES). GET MEDICAL ATTENTION IMMEDIATELY.

EYE CONTACT: DIPHENYLAMINE: IRRITANT. **ACUTE EXPOSURE-** CONTACT WITH DUST MAY PRODUCE IRRITATION AND POSSIBLY CORNEAL DAMAGE. **CHRONIC EXPOSURE-** REPEATED OR PROLONGED CONTACT MAY CAUSE CONJUNCTIVITIS AND POSSIBLY CORNEAL DAMAGE.

FIRST AID- WASH EYES IMMEDIATELY WITH LARGE AMOUNTS OF WATER OR NORMAL SALINE, OCCASIONALLY LIFTING UPPER AND LOWER LIDS, UNTIL NO EVIDENCE OF CHEMICAL REMAINS (APPROXIMATELY 15-20 MINUTES). GET MEDICAL ATTENTION IMMEDIATELY.

INGESTION: DIPHENYLAMINE: **ACUTE EXPOSURE-** MAY CAUSE NAUSEA, VOMITING, SHALLOW RESPIRATION, DIZZINESS, HEADACHE, TACHYCARDIA, HYPERTENSION, BLADDER SYMPTOMS, AND CENTRAL NERVOUS SYSTEM DEPRESSION. ORAL ADMINISTRATION TO ANIMALS RESULTED IN PERSISTENT ANOREXIA, HYPOTHERMIA, DIARRHEA, EMACIATION, GENERAL DEBILITY, PRESUMABLY FROM PROTRACTED GASTROENTERITIS, AND RENAL CHANGES. DEATHS FROM A SINGLE LETHAL DOSE WERE DELAYED TWO TO THREE WEEKS. **CHRONIC EXPOSURE-** REPEATED INGESTION MAY CAUSE EFFECTS AS DESCRIBED IN ACUTE INGESTION. ANEMIA AND EFFECTS ON THE LIVER, KIDNEYS, HEART, AND SPLEEN HAVE BEEN REPORTED IN ANIMALS. ADMINISTRATION TO PREGNANT RATS PRODUCED A POLYCYSTIC KIDNEY IN OFFSPRING. THERE IS EVIDENCE THAT PURIFIED DIPHENYLAMINE IS NOT THE NEPHROTOXIC COMPONENT OF COMMERCIAL DIPHENYLAMINE, BUT RATHER THAT A CONTAMINANT IS THE CHEMICAL RESPONSIBLE FOR THESE EFFECTS. AN INCREASE IN HEINZ BODY FORMATION HAS RESULTED FROM FEEDING RATS AND MICE HIGH DOSES OF DIPHENYLAMINE.

FIRST AID- IF THE PERSON IS CONSCIOUS AND NOT CONVULSING, INDUCE EMESIS BY GIVING SYRUP OF IPECAC FOLLOWED BY WATER. (IF VOMITING OCCURS KEEP THE HEAD BELOW THE HIPS TO PREVENT ASPIRATION). REPEAT IN 20 MINUTES IF NOT EFFECTIVE INITIALLY. GIVE ACTIVATED CHARCOAL. IN PATIENTS WITH DEPRESSED RESPIRATION OR IF EMESIS IS NOT PRODUCED, PERFORM GASTRIC LAVAGE CAUTIOUSLY (DREISBACH, HANDBOOK OF POISONING, 12TH ED.). TREAT SYMPTOMATICALLY AND SUPPORTIVELY. GASTRIC LAVAGE SHOULD BE PERFORMED BY QUALIFIED MEDICAL PERSONNEL. GET MEDICAL ATTENTION IMMEDIATELY.

ANTIDOTE: NO SPECIFIC ANTIDOTE. TREAT SYMPTOMATICALLY AND SUPPORTIVELY.

REACTIVITY

REACTIVITY: STABLE UNDER NORMAL TEMPERATURES AND PRESSURES.

INCOMPATIBILITIES: DIPHENYLAMINE: HEXACHLOROMELAMINE: VIOLENT REACTION WITH POSSIBLE IGNITION. OXIDIZERS (STRONG): FIRE AND EXPLOSION HAZARD. TRICHLOROMELAMINE: VIOLENT REACTION WITH POSSIBLE IGNITION. SEE ALSO AMINES.

AMINES: ACROLEIN: EXOTHERMIC POLYMERIZATION. CALCIUM HYPOCHLORITE: FORMATION OF EXPLOSIVE CHLOROAMINE. MALEIC ANHYDRIDE: EXPLOSIVE DECOMPOSITION. NITROSYL PERCHLORATE: EXPLOSIVE REACTION. SODIUM HYPOCHLORITE: FORMATION OF EXPLOSIVE CHLOROAMINE. TRI-ISO-BUTYL ALUMINUM: VIOLENT REACTION.

DECOMPOSITION: THERMAL DECOMPOSITION PRODUCTS MAY INCLUDE TOXIC OXIDES OF CARBON AND NITROGEN.

POLYMERIZATION: HAZARDOUS POLYMERIZATION HAS NOT BEEN REPORTED TO OCCUR UNDER NORMAL TEMPERATURES AND PRESSURES.

STORAGE AND DISPOSAL

OBSERVE ALL FEDERAL, STATE AND LOCAL REGULATIONS WHEN STORING OR DISPOSING OF THIS SUBSTANCE. FOR ASSISTANCE, CONTACT THE DISTRICT DIRECTOR OF THE ENVIRONMENTAL PROTECTION AGENCY.

****STORAGE****

STORE IN A COOL, DRY PLACE PROTECTED AGAINST LIGHT.
STORE AWAY FROM INCOMPATIBLE SUBSTANCES.

CONDITIONS TO AVOID

MAY BURN BUT DOES NOT IGNITE READILY. AVOID CONTACT WITH STRONG OXIDIZERS, EXCESSIVE HEAT, SPARKS, OR OPEN FLAME.

SPILL AND LEAK PROCEDURES

OCCUPATIONAL SPILL: STOP LEAK IF YOU CAN DO IT WITHOUT RISK. FOR SMALL SPILLS, TAKE UP WITH SAND OR OTHER ABSORBENT MATERIAL AND PLACE INTO CLEAN, DRY CONTAINERS FOR LATER DISPOSAL. KEEP UNNECESSARY PEOPLE AWAY. ISOLATE HAZARD AREA AND DENY ENTRY.

PROTECTIVE EQUIPMENT

VENTILATION: PROVIDE LOCAL EXHAUST VENTILATION AND/OR GENERAL DILUTION VENTILATION TO MEET PUBLISHED EXPOSURE LIMITS.

RESPIRATOR: THE FOLLOWING RESPIRATORS ARE RECOMMENDED BASED ON INFORMATION FOUND IN THE PHYSICAL DATA, TOXICITY AND HEALTH EFFECTS SECTIONS. THEY ARE RANKED IN ORDER FROM MINIMUM TO MAXIMUM RESPIRATORY PROTECTION. THE SPECIFIC RESPIRATOR SELECTED MUST BE BASED ON CONTAMINATION LEVELS FOUND IN THE WORK PLACE, MUST NOT EXCEED THE WORKING LIMITS OF THE RESPIRATOR AND BE JOINTLY APPROVED BY THE NATIONAL INSTITUTE FOR OCCUPATIONAL SAFETY AND HEALTH AND THE MINE SAFETY AND HEALTH ADMINISTRATION (NIOSH-MSHA).

CHEMICAL CARTRIDGE RESPIRATOR WITH FULL FACEPIECE AND ORGANIC VAPOR CARTRIDGE(S) IN COMBINATION WITH A DUST AND MIST FILTER.

CHEMICAL CARTRIDGE RESPIRATOR WITH FULL FACEPIECE AND ORGANIC VAPOR CARTRIDGE(S) IN COMBINATION WITH A HIGH-EFFICIENCY PARTICULATE FILTER.

GAS MASK WITH ORGANIC VAPOR CANISTER (CHIN-STYLE OR FRONT- OR BACK-MOUNTED CANISTER) WITH A FULL FACEPIECE AND A HIGH-EFFICIENCY PARTICULATE FILTER.

POWERED AIR-PURIFYING RESPIRATOR WITH TIGHT-FITTING FACEPIECE AND ORGANIC VAPOR CARTRIDGE(S) IN COMBINATION WITH A HIGH-EFFICIENCY PARTICULATE FILTER.

TYPE 'C' SUPPLIED-AIR RESPIRATOR WITH A FULL FACEPIECE OPERATED IN PRESSURE-DEMAND OR OTHER POSITIVE PRESSURE MODE OR WITH A FULL FACEPIECE, HELMET OR HOOD OPERATED IN CONTINUOUS-FLOW MODE.

SELF-CONTAINED BREATHING APPARATUS WITH A FULL FACEPIECE OPERATED IN PRESSURE-DEMAND OR OTHER POSITIVE PRESSURE MODE.

FOR FIREFIGHTING AND OTHER IMMEDIATELY DANGEROUS TO LIFE OR HEALTH CONDITIONS:

SELF-CONTAINED BREATHING APPARATUS WITH FULL FACEPIECE OPERATED IN PRESSURE-DEMAND OR OTHER POSITIVE PRESSURE MODE.

SUPPLIED-AIR RESPIRATOR WITH FULL FACEPIECE AND OPERATED IN PRESSURE-DEMAND OR OTHER POSITIVE PRESSURE MODE IN COMBINATION WITH AN AUXILIARY SELF-CONTAINED BREATHING APPARATUS OPERATED IN PRESSURE-DEMAND OR OTHER POSITIVE PRESSURE MODE.

CLOTHING: EMPLOYEE MUST WEAR APPROPRIATE PROTECTIVE (IMPERVIOUS) CLOTHING AND EQUIPMENT TO PREVENT REPEATED OR PROLONGED SKIN CONTACT WITH THIS SUBSTANCE.

GLOVES: EMPLOYEE MUST WEAR APPROPRIATE PROTECTIVE GLOVES TO PREVENT CONTACT WITH THIS SUBSTANCE.

EYE PROTECTION: EMPLOYEE MUST WEAR SPLASH-PROOF OR DUST-RESISTANT SAFETY GOGGLES TO PREVENT EYE CONTACT WITH THIS SUBSTANCE.

EMERGENCY EYE WASH: WHERE THERE IS ANY POSSIBILITY THAT AN EMPLOYEE'S EYES MAY BE EXPOSED TO THIS SUBSTANCE, THE EMPLOYER SHOULD PROVIDE AN EYE WASH FOUNTAIN WITHIN THE IMMEDIATE WORK AREA FOR EMERGENCY USE.

AUTHORIZED BY- OCCUPATIONAL HEALTH SERVICES, INC.
CREATION DATE: 10/04/89 ***REVISION DATE:*** 05/07/90

MATERIAL SAFETY DATA SHEET

OCCUPATIONAL HEALTH SERVICES, INC.
AGRICULTURE AND PESTICIDE DIVISION
450 SEVENTH AVENUE, SUITE 2407
NEW YORK, NEW YORK 10123
1-800-445-MSDS OR (212) 967-1100

EMERGENCY CONTACT:
JOHN S. BRANSFORD, JR. (615) 292-1180

SUBSTANCE IDENTIFICATION

CAS-NUMBER 85-00-7

SUBSTANCE: **DIQUAT**

TRADE NAMES/SYNONYMS: DIPYRIDO(1,2-A:2',1'-C)PYRAZINEDIIUM, 6,7-DIHYDRO-, DIBROMIDE; 6,7-DIHYDRODIPYRIDO(1,2-A:2',1'-C)PYRAZINEDIIUM DIBROMIDE; 6,7-DIHYDRODIPYRIDOL(1,2-A:2',1'-C)PYRAZIDIINIUM DIBROMIDE; 1,1'-ETHYLENE-2,2'-DIPYRIDYLIUM DIBROMIDE; 1,1-ETHYLENE-2,2-DIPYRIDINIUM DIBROMIDE; DIQUAT DIBROMIDE; AQUACIDE; DEIQUAT; FB/2; ORTHO DIQUAT; REGLOX; REGLON; REGLONE; STCC 4963344; C12H12N2.2BR; PST08250

CHEMICAL FAMILY: BIPYRIDYL COMPOUND SALT

MOLECULAR FORMULA: C12-H12-N2.2BR

MOLECULAR WEIGHT: 344.07

CERCLA RATINGS (SCALE 0-3): HEALTH=3 FIRE=0 REACTIVITY=0 PERSISTENCE=3

NFPA RATINGS (SCALE 0-4): HEALTH=3 FIRE=0 REACTIVITY=0

COMPONENTS AND CONTAMINANTS

COMPONENT: DIQUAT ***PERCENT:*** 100.0
CAS# 85-00-7

OTHER CONTAMINANTS: NONE

EXPOSURE LIMITS: DIQUAT: 0.5 MG/M3 OSHA TWA 0.5 MG/M3 ACGIH TWA
1000 POUNDS CERCLA SECTION 103 REPORTABLE QUANTITY

PHYSICAL DATA

DESCRIPTION: PALE YELLOW CRYSTALS. ***MELTING POINT:*** >572 F (>300 C) DECOMPOSES

SPECIFIC GRAVITY: 1.22-1.27 ***SOLUBILITY IN WATER:*** 70%

SOLVENT SOLUBILITY: SLIGHTLY SOLUBLE IN ALCOHOL AND HYDROXYLIC SOLVENTS; PRACTICALLY INSOLUBLE IN NONPOLAR SOLVENTS.

FIRE AND EXPLOSION DATA

FIRE AND EXPLOSION HAZARD: NEGLIGIBLE FIRE HAZARD WHEN EXPOSED TO HEAT OR FLAME.

FIREFIGHTING MEDIA: DRY CHEMICAL, CARBON DIOXIDE, HALON, WATER SPRAY OR STANDARD FOAM (1987 EMERGENCY RESPONSE GUIDEBOOK, DOT P 5800.4). FOR LARGER FIRES, USE WATER SPRAY, FOG OR STANDARD FOAM (1987 EMERGENCY RESPONSE GUIDEBOOK, DOT P 5800.4).

FIREFIGHTING: MOVE CONTAINERS FROM FIRE AREA IF POSSIBLE. FIGHT FIRE FROM MAXIMUM DISTANCE. STAY AWAY FROM STORAGE TANK ENDS. DIKE FIRE CONTROL WATER FOR LATER DISPOSAL. DO NOT SCATTER MATERIAL (1987 EMERGENCY RESPONSE GUIDEBOOK, DOT P 5800.4, GUIDE PAGE 55).
USE AGENTS SUITABLE FOR TYPE OF FIRE. USE WATER IN FLOODING AMOUNTS AS FOG.

TRANSPORTATION DATA

DEPARTMENT OF TRANSPORTATION HAZARD CLASSIFICATION 49 CFR 172.101: ORM-E

DEPARTMENT OF TRANSPORTATION LABELING REQUIREMENTS 49 CFR 172.101 AND SUBPART E: NONE

DEPARTMENT OF TRANSPORTATION PACKAGING REQUIREMENTS: 49 CFR 173.510 EXCEPTIONS: NONE

TOXICITY

DIQUAT: IRRITATION DATA: 400 MG/KG/20 DAYS SKIN-RABBIT MILD; 10 MG EYE-RABBIT MILD. TOXICITY DATA: 433 MG/KG SKIN-RAT LD50; 120 MG/KG ORAL-RAT LD50; 233 MG/KG ORAL-MOUSE LD50; 188 MG/KG ORAL-RABBIT LD50; 187 MG/KG ORAL-GUINEA PIG LD50; 187 MG/KG ORAL-DOG LD50; 56 MG/KG ORAL-CATTLE LD50; 30 MG/KG ORAL-DOMESTIC ANIMAL LD50; 20 MG/KG SUBCUTANEOUS-RAT LD50; 14 MG/KG INTRAVENOUS-RAT LDLO; 500 MG/KG INTRAPERITONEAL-RAT LDLO; MUTAGENIC DATA (RTECS); REPRODUCTIVE EFFECTS DATA (RTECS). CARCINOGEN STATUS: NONE. LOCAL EFFECTS: IRRITANT- INHALATION, SKIN, AND EYE. ACUTE TOXICITY LEVEL: TOXIC BY DERMAL ABSORPTION AND INGESTION. TARGET EFFECTS: POISONING MAY AFFECT THE KIDNEY AND LIVER.

HEALTH EFFECTS AND FIRST AID

INHALATION: DIQUAT: IRRITANT. **ACUTE EXPOSURE-** DUST OR MIST MAY CAUSE IRRITATION OF THE MOUTH AND UPPER RESPIRATORY TRACT, COUGH, CHEST PAINS, AND NASAL BLEEDING. **CHRONIC EXPOSURE-** REPEATED EXPOSURE OF RATS TO CONCENTRATIONS OF 1.9 MG/M3 PRODUCED EFFECTS OF INFLAMMATORY CHANGES IN THE PERIBRONCHIAL AND PERIVASCULAR CONNECTIVE TISSUES, DYSTROPHIC CHANGES IN THE KIDNEY AND OCCASIONALLY THE HEART, ABNORMAL LEVELS OF SEVERAL LIVER ENZYMES, LEUKOPENIA, POLYCYTHEMIA, AND DEPRESSED CHOLINESTERASE ACTIVITY.

FIRST AID- REMOVE FROM EXPOSURE AREA TO FRESH AIR IMMEDIATELY. IF BREATHING HAS STOPPED, PERFORM ARTIFICIAL RESPIRATION. KEEP PERSON WARM AND AT REST. TREAT SYMPTOMATICALLY AND SUPPORTIVELY. GET MEDICAL ATTENTION IMMEDIATELY.

SKIN CONTACT: DIQUAT: IRRITANT/TOXIC. **ACUTE EXPOSURE-** CONTACT WITH THE DILUTE LIQUID OR DUST FORMULATIONS MAY RESULT IN REVERSIBLE SKIN IRRITATION. CONCENTRATED SOLUTIONS MAY CAUSE SEVERE IRRITATION AND BURNING OF THE SKIN AND A COLOR CHANGE AND SOFTENING OF THE FINGERNAILS. CONCENTRATED SOLUTIONS MAY ALSO DELAY THE HEALING OF SUPERFICIAL CUTS AND INTERFERE WITH NAIL GROWTH. THE LETHAL DOSE IN RATS BY DERMAL ABSORPTION WAS 433 MG/KG. THE SYMPTOMS WERE NOT REPORTED. **CHRONIC EXPOSURE-** DAILY APPLICATION OF 20 MG/KG TO RABBIT SKIN PRODUCED ERYTHEMA, THICKENING, AND SCABBING. A DOSE OF 40 MG/KG APPLIED TO RABBIT SKIN WAS LETHAL TO 4 OF 6 RABBITS AFTER 8 TO 20 APPLICATIONS; EFFECTS OF WEIGHT LOSS, UNSTEADINESS, AND MUSCULAR WEAKNESS WERE REPORTED.

FIRST AID- REMOVE CONTAMINATED CLOTHING AND SHOES IMMEDIATELY. WASH AFFECTED AREA WITH SOAP OR MILD DETERGENT AND LARGE AMOUNTS OF WATER UNTIL NO EVIDENCE OF CHEMICAL REMAINS (APPROXIMATELY 15-20 MINUTES). GET MEDICAL ATTENTION IMMEDIATELY.

EYE CONTACT: DIQUAT: IRRITANT. **ACUTE EXPOSURE-** DILUTE LIQUID OR DUST FORMULATIONS MAY CAUSE IRRITATION. A 20% SOLUTION PRODUCED SLIGHT IRRITATION AND HYPEREMIA OF THE LIDS AND CONJUNCTIVA IN RABBIT EYES THAT PERSISTED FOR TWO DAYS. **CHRONIC EXPOSURE-** REPEATED OR PROLONGED EXPOSURE TO IRRITANTS MAY CAUSE CONJUNCTIVITIS.

FIRST AID- WASH EYES IMMEDIATELY WITH LARGE AMOUNTS OF WATER OR NORMAL SALINE, OCCASIONALLY LIFTING UPPER AND LOWER LIDS, UNTIL NO EVIDENCE OF CHEMICAL REMAINS (APPROXIMATELY 15-20 MINUTES). GET MEDICAL ATTENTION IMMEDIATELY.

INGESTION: DIQUAT: TOXIC. **ACUTE EXPOSURE-** CONCENTRATED SOLUTIONS MAY CAUSE SEVERE IRRITATION OF THE MUCOUS MEMBRANES OF THE MOUTH, PHARYNX, ESOPHAGUS AND STOMACH FOLLOWED BY NAUSEA, VOMITING, DIARRHEA AND ABDOMINAL PAINS. DAMAGE TO INTESTINAL LINING MAY OCCUR RESULTING IN DEHYDRATION, HEMATEMESIS AND BLOODY STOOLS. ACUTE TUBULAR NECROSIS MAY DEVELOP ACCOMPANIED BY ANURIA AND INCREASED SERUM BUN AND CREATININE LEVELS. INJURY TO THE PARENCHYMAL CELLS OF THE LIVER IS INDICATED BY ELEVATED LEVELS OF SERUM GOT, GPT, AND LDH AND ALKALINE PHOSPHATASE. CENTRAL NERVOUS SYSTEM EFFECTS INCLUDE COMA AND CONVULSIONS AND MAY BE THE RESULT OF BLEEDING INTO THE BRAIN STEM. MYOCARDIAL NECROSIS AND VENTRICULAR DYSRHYTHMIAS MAY OCCUR IN SEVERE POISONING. A LETHAL DOSE IN RATS WAS 120 MG/KG. THE SYMPTOMS WERE NOT REPORTED. **CHRONIC EXPOSURE-** REPEATED FEEDING OF RATS AND DOGS WITH DIQUAT FOR PROLONGED PERIODS RESULTED IN THE DEVELOPMENT OF CATARACTS. IN RATS, THE DEVELOPMENT OF CATARACT WAS FOLLOWED BY SECONDARY CHANGES, INCLUDING ANTERIOR AND POSTERIOR SYNECHIAE, HEMORRHAGE INTO THE VITREOUS HUMOR, AND DETACHMENT OF THE RETINA.

FIRST AID- INTUBATE THE STOMACH, ASPIRATE CONTENTS, THEN LAVAGE WITH AT LEAST TWO LITERS OF A SLURRY OF ADSORBENT IN NORMAL SALINE. THEN, SLOWLY INSTILL SEVERAL HUNDRED ADDITIONAL ML OF ADSORBENT SLURRY, ALLOWING THE STOMACH AND INTESTINE TO ACCOMMODATE THIS VOLUME WITHOUT OVERDISTENSION AND VOMITING. THE IDEAL ADSORBENT IS BENTONITE. IF NOT IMMEDIATELY AVAILABLE, USE ACTIVATED CHARCOAL. AS SOON AS BENTONITE HAS BEEN OBTAINED, ADMINISTER IT AS RAPIDLY AS THE PATIENT WILL TOLERATE IT. IF PATIENT CANNOT SWALLOW BENTONITE, ADMINISTER IT BY STOMACH TUBE AT THE HIGHEST CONCENTRATION THAT WILL FLOW THROUGH THE TUBE. INITIATE SALINE CATHARSIS. GIVE SODIUM SULFATE AND REPEAT IN TWO HOURS IF NO BOWEL MOVEMENT HAS OCCURRED. MAGNESIUM SALTS ARE PROBABLY CONTRAINDICATED, BECAUSE OF THE RISK OF MAGNESIUM RETENTION IN THE PRESENCE OF IMPAIRED RENAL FUNCTION. CONTINUE ADMINISTERING BENTONITE SUSPENSION AND SODIUM SULFATE UNTIL THE GUT HAS BEEN THOROUGHLY FLUSHED. HEMODIALYSIS AND/OR HEMOPERFUSION OVER SPECIALLY COATED CHARCOAL IS AN EFFECTIVE PROCEDURE FOR REMOVING POISONING FROM THE BLOOD. OXYGEN THERAPY MAY ENHANCE THE TOXICITY. (MORGAN, RECOGNITION AND MANAGEMENT OF PESTICIDE POISONINGS, THIRD EDITION). TREATMENT SHOULD BE PERFORMED BY QUALIFIED MEDICAL PERSONNEL. GET MEDICAL ATTENTION IMMEDIATELY.

ANTIDOTE: NO SPECIFIC ANTIDOTE. TREAT SYMPTOMATICALLY AND SUPPORTIVELY.

REACTIVITY

REACTIVITY: STABLE UNDER NORMAL TEMPERATURES AND PRESSURES.

INCOMPATIBILITIES: DIQUAT: ALKALINE SOLUTIONS: DECOMPOSE. ALUMINUM: MAY CORRODE. ANIONIC SURFACTANTS: INACTIVATE. CLAYS (INERT): INACTIVATE. METALS: MAY CORRODE. OXIDIZERS (STRONG): FIRE AND EXPLOSION HAZARD. ZINC: MAY CORRODE.

DECOMPOSITION: THERMAL DECOMPOSITION PRODUCTS INCLUDE TOXIC/HAZARDOUS VAPORS OF BROMINE, HYDROGEN BROMIDE, OXIDES OF NITROGEN, AND OXIDES OF CARBON.

POLYMERIZATION: HAZARDOUS POLYMERIZATION HAS NOT BEEN REPORTED TO OCCUR UNDER NORMAL TEMPERATURES AND PRESSURES.

STORAGE AND DISPOSAL

OBSERVE ALL FEDERAL, STATE AND LOCAL REGULATIONS WHEN STORING OR DISPOSING OF THIS SUBSTANCE. FOR ASSISTANCE, CONTACT THE DISTRICT DIRECTOR OF THE ENVIRONMENTAL PROTECTION AGENCY.

****STORAGE****

STORE IN ACCORDANCE WITH 40 CFR 165 RECOMMENDED PROCEDURES FOR THE DISPOSAL AND STORAGE OF PESTICIDES AND PESTICIDE CONTAINERS.
STORE AWAY FROM INCOMPATIBLE SUBSTANCES.

****DISPOSAL****

DISPOSAL MUST BE IN ACCORDANCE WITH 40 CFR 165 RECOMMENDED PROCEDURES FOR THE DISPOSAL AND STORAGE OF PESTICIDES AND PESTICIDE CONTAINERS.

CONDITIONS TO AVOID

MAY BURN BUT DOES NOT IGNITE READILY. CONTAINERS MAY EXPLODE IN HEAT OF FIRE.

SPILL AND LEAK PROCEDURES

SOIL SPILL: DIG HOLDING AREA SUCH AS LAGOON, POND OR PIT FOR CONTAINMENT. USE PROTECTIVE COVER SUCH AS A PLASTIC SHEET TO PREVENT MATERIAL FROM DISSOLVING IN FIRE EXTINGUISHING WATER OR RAIN.

WATER SPILL: USE ACTIVATED CARBON TO ABSORB SPILLED SUBSTANCE THAT IS DISSOLVED.
USE MECHANICAL DREDGES OR LIFTS TO EXTRACT IMMOBILIZED MASSES OF POLLUTION AND PRECIPITATES.

OCCUPATIONAL SPILL: DO NOT TOUCH SPILLED MATERIAL. STOP LEAK IF YOU CAN DO IT WITHOUT RISK. USE WATER SPRAY TO REDUCE VAPORS. FOR SMALL SPILLS, TAKE UP WITH SAND OR OTHER ABSORBENT MATERIAL AND PLACE INTO CONTAINERS FOR LATER DISPOSAL. FOR SMALL DRY SPILLS, WITH A CLEAN SHOVEL PLACE MATERIAL INTO CLEAN, DRY CONTAINERS AND COVER. MOVE CONTAINERS FROM SPILL AREA. FOR LARGER SPILLS, DIKE FAR AHEAD OF SPILL FOR LATER DISPOSAL. KEEP UNNECESSARY PEOPLE AWAY. ISOLATE HAZARD AREA AND DENY ENTRY. VENTILATE CLOSED SPACES BEFORE ENTERING.
REPORTABLE QUANTITY (RQ): 1000 POUNDS THE SUPERFUND AMENDMENTS AND REAUTHORIZATION ACT (SARA) SECTION 304 REQUIRES THAT A RELEASE EQUAL TO OR GREATER THAN THE REPORTABLE QUANTITY FOR THIS SUBSTANCE BE IMMEDIATELY REPORTED TO THE LOCAL EMERGENCY PLANNING COMMITTEE AND THE STATE EMERGENCY RESPONSE COMMISSION (40 CFR 355.40). IF THE RELEASE OF THIS SUBSTANCE IS REPORTABLE UNDER CERCLA SECTION 103, THE NATIONAL RESPONSE CENTER MUST BE NOTIFIED IMMEDIATELY AT (800) 424-8802 OR (202) 426-2675 IN THE METROPOLITAN WASHINGTON, D.C. AREA (40 CFR 302.6).

PROTECTIVE EQUIPMENT

VENTILATION: PROVIDE LOCAL EXHAUST OR PROCESS ENCLOSURE VENTILATION TO MEET PUBLISHED EXPOSURE LIMITS.

RESPIRATOR: THE FOLLOWING RESPIRATORS ARE RECOMMENDED BASED ON INFORMATION FOUND IN THE PHYSICAL DATA, TOXICITY AND HEALTH EFFECTS SECTIONS. THEY ARE RANKED IN ORDER FROM MINIMUM TO MAXIMUM RESPIRATORY PROTECTION. THE SPECIFIC RESPIRATOR SELECTED MUST BE BASED ON CONTAMINATION LEVELS FOUND IN THE WORK PLACE, MUST NOT EXCEED THE WORKING LIMITS OF THE RESPIRATOR AND BE JOINTLY APPROVED BY THE NATIONAL INSTITUTE FOR OCCUPATIONAL SAFETY AND HEALTH AND THE MINE SAFETY AND HEALTH ADMINISTRATION (NIOSH-MSHA).
TYPE 'C' SUPPLIED-AIR RESPIRATOR WITH A FULL FACEPIECE OPERATED IN PRESSURE-DEMAND OR OTHER POSITIVE PRESSURE MODE OR WITH A FULL FACEPIECE, HELMET OR HOOD OPERATED IN CONTINOUS-FLOW MODE.
SELF-CONTAINED BREATHING APPARATUS WITH A FULL FACEPIECE OPERATED IN PRESSURE-DEMAND OR OTHER POSITIVE PRESSURE MODE.
FOR FIREFIGHTING AND OTHER IMMEDIATELY DANGEROUS TO LIFE OR HEALTH CONDITIONS:
SELF-CONTAINED BREATHING APPARATUS WITH FULL FACEPIECE OPERATED IN PRESSURE-DEMAND OR OTHER POSITIVE PRESSURE MODE.
SUPPLIED-AIR RESPIRATOR WITH FULL FACEPIECE AND OPERATED IN PRESSURE-DEMAND OR OTHER POSITIVE PRESSURE MODE IN COMBINATION WITH AN AUXILIARY SELF-CONTAINED BREATHING APPARATUS OPERATED IN PRESSURE-DEMAND OR OTHER POSITIVE PRESSURE MODE.

CLOTHING: EMPLOYEE MUST WEAR APPROPRIATE PROTECTIVE (IMPERVIOUS) CLOTHING AND EQUIPMENT TO PREVENT ANY POSSIBILITY OF SKIN CONTACT WITH THIS SUBSTANCE.

GLOVES: EMPLOYEE MUST WEAR APPROPRIATE PROTECTIVE GLOVES TO PREVENT CONTACT WITH THIS SUBSTANCE.

EYE PROTECTION: EMPLOYEE MUST WEAR SPLASH-PROOF OR DUST-RESISTANT SAFETY GOGGLES WITH OR WITHOUT A FACESHIELD TO PREVENT CONTACT WITH THIS SUBSTANCE.
EMERGENCY EYE WASH: WHERE THERE IS ANY POSSIBILITY THAT AN EMPLOYEE'S EYES MAY BE EXPOSED TO THIS SUBSTANCE, THE EMPLOYER SHOULD PROVIDE AN EYE WASH FOUNTAIN WITHIN THE IMMEDIATE WORK AREA FOR EMERGENCY USE.

AUTHORIZED BY- OCCUPATIONAL HEALTH SERVICES, INC.
CREATION DATE: 10/04/89 ***REVISION DATE:*** 03/28/90

MATERIAL SAFETY DATA SHEET

OCCUPATIONAL HEALTH SERVICES, INC.
AGRICULTURE AND PESTICIDE DIVISION
450 SEVENTH AVENUE, SUITE 2407
NEW YORK, NEW YORK 10123
1-800-445-MSDS OR (212) 967-1100

EMERGENCY CONTACT:
JOHN S. BRANSFORD, JR. (615) 292-1180

SUBSTANCE IDENTIFICATION

CAS-NUMBER 2650-18-2

SUBSTANCE: **<u>ACID BLUE 9 (DIAMMONIUM SALT)</u>**

TRADE NAMES/SYNONYMS: N-ETHYL-N-(4((4-ETHYL((3-SULFOPHENYL)METHYL)AMINO)PHENYL)(2- SULFOPHENYL)METHYLENE)-2,5-CYCLOHEXADIEN-1-YLIDENE)-3-SULFOBENZENE METHANAMINIUM HYDROXIDE INNER SALT, DIAMMONIUM SALT; C.I. 42090; ATLANTIC ALPHAZURINE BLUE FGND CONCENTRATE; ERIOGLAUCINE; ALPHAZURINE FG; C.I. ACID BLUE 9, DIAMMONIUM SALT; A.F.BLUE NO. 1; ALPHAZURINE; BRILLIANT BLUE; D AND C BLUE NO. 1; WATER BLUE 9; DISULPHINE LAKE BLUE EG; KITON BLUE AR; NEPTUNE BLUE BRA; PEACOCK BLUE X 1756; TRIANTINE LIGHT BROWN; XYLENE BLUE VSG; BRILLIANT BLUE FCF, DIAMMONIUM SALT; PST08277

CHEMICAL FAMILY: SULFONATE
AMINE, AROMATIC
SALT

MOLECULAR FORMULA: C37-H34-N2-O9-S3.2N-H4

MOLECULAR WEIGHT: 782.8

CERCLA RATINGS (SCALE 0-3): HEALTH=U FIRE=U REACTIVITY=0 PERSISTENCE=3

NFPA RATINGS (SCALE 0-4): HEALTH=U FIRE=U REACTIVITY=0

COMPONENTS AND CONTAMINANTS

COMPONENT: ACID BLUE 9 (DIAMMONIUM SALT) ***PERCENT:*** 100
CAS# 2650-18-2

EXPOSURE LIMITS: NO OCCUPATIONAL EXPOSURE LIMITS ESTABLISHED BY OSHA, ACGIH, OR NIOSH.

PHYSICAL DATA

DESCRIPTION: DARK RED TO REDDISH-VIOLET POWDER OR GRANULES WITH A SLIGHT ODOR.

MELTING POINT: 541 F (283 C) DECOMPOSES ***SPECIFIC GRAVITY:*** 0.64-0.66

SOLUBILITY IN WATER: 12.4% @ 25 C

SOLVENT SOLUBILITY: SOLUBLE IN ETHANOL; INSOLUBLE IN VEGETABLE OILS.

FIRE AND EXPLOSION DATA

FIRE AND EXPLOSION HAZARD: UNKNOWN FIRE AND EXPLOSION HAZARD.

FIREFIGHTING MEDIA: DRY CHEMICAL, CARBON DIOXIDE, WATER SPRAY OR FOAM FOR LARGER FIRES, USE WATER SPRAY, FOG OR ALCOHOL FOAM

FIREFIGHTING: NO ACUTE HAZARD. MOVE CONTAINER FROM FIRE AREA IF POSSIBLE. AVOID BREATHING VAPORS OR DUSTS; KEEP UPWIND.

TOXICITY

ACID BLUE 9 (DIAMMONIUM SALT): TOXICITY DATA: 33 UG/KG INTRAVENOUS-HUMAN LDLO; MUTAGENIC DATA (RTECS); TUMORIGENIC DATA (RTECS). CARCINOGEN STATUS: LIMITED ANIMAL EVIDENCE (IARC GROUP-3). BRILLIANT BLUE FCF, DISODIUM SALT IS CARCINOGENIC IN RATS AFTER ITS SUBCUTAENOUS INJECTIONS. IT ALSO PRODUCED AN INCREASED INCIDENCE OF KIDNEY TUMORS IN MICE AFTER ITS ORAL ADMINISTRATION. ACUTE TOXICITY LEVEL: INSUFFICIENT DATA. TARGET EFFECTS: NO DATA AVAILABLE.

HEALTH EFFECTS AND FIRST AID

INHALATION: ACID BLUE 9 (DIAMMONIUM SALT): **<u>ACUTE EXPOSURE</u>**- NO DATA AVAILABLE. DUST MAY BE IRRITATING TO THE MUCOUS MEMBRANES. **<u>CHRONIC EXPOSURE</u>**- NO DATA AVAILABLE.

FIRST AID- REMOVE FROM EXPOSURE AREA TO FRESH AIR IMMEDIATELY. IF BREATHING HAS STOPPED, PERFORM ARTIFICIAL RESPIRATION. KEEP PERSON WARM AND AT REST. TREAT SYMPTOMATICALLY AND SUPPORTIVELY. GET MEDICAL ATTENTION IMMEDIATELY.

SKIN CONTACT: ACID BLUE 9 (DIAMMONIUM SALT): **<u>ACUTE EXPOSURE</u>**- NO DATA AVAILABLE. MAY BE IRRITATING TO THE SKIN. **<u>CHRONIC EXPOSURE</u>**- NO DATA AVAILABLE.

FIRST AID- REMOVE CONTAMINATED CLOTHING AND SHOES IMMEDIATELY. WASH AFFECTED AREA WITH SOAP OR MILD DETERGENT AND LARGE AMOUNTS OF WATER UNTIL NO EVIDENCE OF CHEMICAL REMAINS (APPROXIMATELY 15-20 MINUTES). GET MEDICAL ATTENTION IMMEDIATELY.

EYE CONTACT: ACID BLUE 9 (DIAMMONIUM SALT): **<u>ACUTE EXPOSURE</u>**- MAY CAUSE SLIGHT TRANSIENT IRRITATION BUT IS NOT DAMAGING TO RABBITS EYES. **<u>CHRONIC EXPOSURE</u>**- NO DATA AVAILABLE.

FIRST AID- WASH EYES IMMEDIATELY WITH LARGE AMOUNTS OF WATER OR NORMAL SALINE, OCCASIONALLY LIFTING UPPER AND LOWER LIDS, UNTIL NO EVIDENCE OF

CHEMICAL REMAINS (APPROXIMATELY 15-20 MINUTES). GET MEDICAL ATTENTION IMMEDIATELY.

INGESTION: ACID BLUE 9 (DIAMMONIUM SALT): **ACUTE EXPOSURE-** NO DATA AVAILABLE. **CHRONIC EXPOSURE-** NO DATA AVAILABLE. PROLONGED ADMINISTRATION TO MICE RESULTED IN AN INCREASED INCIDENCE OF KIDNEY TUMORS.

FIRST AID- TREAT SYMPTOMATICALLY AND SUPPORTIVELY. GET MEDICAL ATTENTION IMMEDIATELY. IF VOMITING OCCURS, KEEP HEAD LOWER THAN HIPS TO PREVENT ASPIRATION.

ANTIDOTE: NO SPECIFIC ANTIDOTE. TREAT SYMPTOMATICALLY AND SUPPORTIVELY.

REACTIVITY

REACTIVITY: STABLE UNDER NORMAL TEMPERATURES AND PRESSURES.

INCOMPATIBILITIES: ACID BLUE 9 (DIAMMONIUM SALT): NO DATA AVAILABLE.

DECOMPOSITION: THERMAL DECOMPOSITION MAY RELEASE TOXIC AND/OR HAZARDOUS GASES.

POLYMERIZATION: HAZARDOUS POLYMERIZATION HAS NOT BEEN REPORTED TO OCCUR UNDER NORMAL TEMPERATURES AND PRESSURES.

CONDITIONS TO AVOID

NONE REPORTED.

SPILL AND LEAK PROCEDURES

OCCUPATIONAL SPILL: NO SPECIAL PRECAUTIONS INDICATED.

PROTECTIVE EQUIPMENT

VENTILATION: PROVIDE LOCAL EXHAUST OR PROCESS ENCLOSURE VENTILATION. VENTILATION EQUIPMENT MUST BE EXPLOSION-PROOF.

RESPIRATOR: THE FOLLOWING RESPIRATORS ARE RECOMMENDED BASED ON INFORMATION FOUND IN THE PHYSICAL DATA, TOXICITY AND HEALTH EFFECTS SECTIONS. THEY ARE RANKED IN ORDER FROM MINIMUM TO MAXIMUM RESPIRATORY PROTECTION. THE SPECIFIC RESPIRATOR SELECTED MUST BE BASED ON CONTAMINATION LEVELS FOUND IN THE WORK PLACE, MUST NOT EXCEED THE WORKING LIMITS OF THE RESPIRATOR AND BE JOINTLY APPROVED BY THE NATIONAL INSTITUTE FOR OCCUPATIONAL SAFETY AND HEALTH AND THE MINE SAFETY AND HEALTH ADMINISTRATION (NIOSH-MSHA).

DUST AND MIST RESPIRATOR WITH A FULL FACEPIECE.

AIR-PURIFYING FULL FACEPIECE RESPIRATOR WITH A HIGH-EFFICIENCY PARTICULATE FILTER.

POWERED AIR-PURIFYING RESPIRATOR WITH A TIGHT-FITTING FACEPIECE AND HIGH-EFFICIENCY PARTICULATE FILTER.

TYPE 'C' SUPPLIED-AIR RESPIRATOR WITH A FULL FACEPIECE OPERATED IN PRESSURE-DEMAND OR OTHER POSITIVE PRESSURE MODE OR WITH A FULL FACEPIECE, HELMET OR HOOD OPERATED IN CONTINUOUS-FLOW MODE.

SELF-CONTAINED BREATHING APPARATUS WITH A FULL FACEPIECE OPERATED IN PRESSURE-DEMAND OR OTHER POSITIVE PRESSURE MODE.

FOR FIREFIGHTING AND OTHER IMMEDIATELY DANGEROUS TO LIFE OR HEALTH CONDITIONS:

SELF-CONTAINED BREATHING APPARATUS WITH FULL FACEPIECE OPERATED IN PRESSURE-DEMAND OR OTHER POSITIVE PRESSURE MODE.

SUPPLIED-AIR RESPIRATOR WITH FULL FACEPIECE AND OPERATED IN PRESSURE-DEMAND OR OTHER POSITIVE PRESSURE MODE IN COMBINATION WITH AN AUXILIARY SELF-CONTAINED BREATHING APPARATUS OPERATED IN PRESSURE-DEMAND OR OTHER POSITIVE PRESSURE MODE.

CLOTHING: EMPLOYEE MUST WEAR APPROPRIATE PROTECTIVE (IMPERVIOUS) CLOTHING AND EQUIPMENT TO PREVENT REPEATED OR PROLONGED SKIN CONTACT WITH THIS SUBSTANCE.

GLOVES: EMPLOYEE MUST WEAR APPROPRIATE PROTECTIVE GLOVES TO PREVENT CONTACT WITH THIS SUBSTANCE.

EYE PROTECTION: EMPLOYEE MUST WEAR SPLASH-PROOF OR DUST-RESISTANT SAFETY GOGGLES TO PREVENT EYE CONTACT WITH THIS SUBSTANCE.

EMERGENCY EYE WASH: WHERE THERE IS ANY POSSIBILITY THAT AN EMPLOYEE'S EYES MAY BE EXPOSED TO THIS SUBSTANCE, THE EMPLOYER SHOULD PROVIDE AN EYE WASH FOUNTAIN WITHIN THE IMMEDIATE WORK AREA FOR EMERGENCY USE.

AUTHORIZED BY- OCCUPATIONAL HEALTH SERVICES, INC.

CREATION DATE: 11/15/89 ***REVISION DATE:*** 06/27/90

MATERIAL SAFETY DATA SHEET

OCCUPATIONAL HEALTH SERVICES, INC.
AGRICULTURE AND PESTICIDE DIVISION
450 SEVENTH AVENUE, SUITE 2407
NEW YORK, NEW YORK 10123
1-800-445-MSDS OR (212) 967-1100

EMERGENCY CONTACT:
JOHN S. BRANSFORD, JR. (615) 292-1180

SUBSTANCE IDENTIFICATION

CAS-NUMBER 139-33-3

***SUBSTANCE:* <u>ETHYLENEDIAMINETETRAACETIC ACID, DISODIUM SALT</u>**

TRADE NAMES/SYNONYMS: EDTA, DISODIUM SALT; DISODIUM ETHYLENEDIAMINE TETRAACETATE; TETRACEMATE DISODIUM; DISODIUM VERSENE; DISODIUM VERSENATE; DISODIUM EDETATE; EDETATE DISODIUM; GLYCINE, N,N'-1,2-ETHYLENEDIYLBIS(N-(CARBOXYMETHYL)-, DISODIUM SALT; N,N'-1,2-ETHYLENEDIYLBIS(N-(CARBOXYMETHYL)GLYCINE, DISODIUM SALT; ACETIC ACID, (ETHYLENEDINITRILO)TETRA-, DISODIUM SALT; (ETHYLENEDIAMINETETRAACETIC ACID), DISODIUM SALT; CHELAPLEX; DISODIUM EDTA; DISODIUM SEQUESTRENE; EDTA DISODIUM SALT; ENDRATE DISODIUM; SODIUM (DI) ETHYLENEDIAMINE TETRAACETATE; SELEKTON B2; S-311; O-2793; C10H14N2NA2O8; PST08305

CHEMICAL FAMILY: EDETATE

MOLECULAR FORMULA: C10-H14-O8-N2.2 NA

MOLECULAR WEIGHT: 336.21

CERCLA RATINGS (SCALE 0-3): HEALTH=3 FIRE=1 REACTIVITY=0 PERSISTENCE=1

NFPA RATINGS (SCALE 0-4): HEALTH=U FIRE=1 REACTIVITY=0

COMPONENTS AND CONTAMINANTS

COMPONENT: ETHYLENEDIAMINETETRAACETIC ACID, DISODIUM SALT ***PERCENT:*** 100.0

CAS# 139-33-3

OTHER CONTAMINANTS: NONE

EXPOSURE LIMITS: NO OCCUPATIONAL EXPOSURE LIMITS ESTABLISHED BY OSHA, ACGIH, OR NIOSH.

PHYSICAL DATA

DESCRIPTION: HYGROSCOPIC, WHITE CRYSTALLINE POWDER.

MELTING POINT: 482 F (250 C) (DECOMPOSES) ***SPECIFIC GRAVITY:*** NOT AVAILABLE

VAPOR PRESSURE: NEGLIGIBLE ***PH:*** 4.0-6.0 @ 5% SOLN

SOLUBILITY IN WATER: SOLUBLE

FIRE AND EXPLOSION DATA

FIRE AND EXPLOSION HAZARD: SLIGHT FIRE HAZARD WHEN EXPOSED TO HEAT OR FLAME.

FIREFIGHTING MEDIA: DRY CHEMICAL, CARBON DIOXIDE, HALON, WATER SPRAY OR STANDARD FOAM (1987 EMERGENCY RESPONSE GUIDEBOOK, DOT P 5800.4). FOR LARGER FIRES, USE WATER SPRAY, FOG OR STANDARD FOAM (1987 EMERGENCY RESPONSE GUIDEBOOK, DOT P 5800.4).

FIREFIGHTING: MOVE CONTAINER FROM FIRE AREA IF POSSIBLE. DO NOT SCATTER SPILLED MATERIAL WITH HIGH PRESSURE WATER STREAMS. DIKE FIRE CONTROL WATER FOR LATER DISPOSAL (1987 EMERGENCY RESPONSE GUIDEBOOK, DOT P 5800.4, GUIDE PAGE 31).

USE AGENTS SUITABLE FOR TYPE OF SURROUNDING FIRE. AVOID BREATHING CORROSIVE DUSTS OR VAPORS, KEEP UPWIND.

TOXICITY

ETHYLENEDIAMINETETRAACETIC ACID, DISODIUM SALT: TOXICITY DATA: ANHYDROUS: 2000 MG/KG ORAL-RAT LD50; 2300 MG/KG ORAL-RABBIT LD50; 2050 MG/KG ORAL-MOUSE LD50; 56 MG/KG INTRAVENOUS-MOUSE LD50; 47 MG/KG INTRAVENOUS-RABBIT LD50; 260 MG/KG INTRAPERITONEAL-MOUSE LD50; MUTAGENIC DATA (RTECS); REPRODUCTIVE EFFECTS DATA (RTECS). DIHYDRATE: 2 GM/KG ORAL-RAT LD50 (TXAPA9); MUTAGENIC DATA (RTECS). CARCINOGEN STATUS: NONE. ACUTE TOXICITY LEVEL: MODERATELY TOXIC BY INGESTION. TARGET EFFECTS: POISONING MAY AFFECT THE KIDNEYS. AT INCREASED RISK FROM EXPOSURE: PERSONS WITH RENAL OR HEART DISEASE; A HISTORY OF SEIZURES OR INTRACRANIAL LESIONS; POTASSIUM DEFICIENCY; OR INSULIN-DEPENDENT DIABETES. ADDITIONAL DATA: PARENTERAL ADMINISTRATION OF EDTA OR ITS SALTS IN HIGH DOSES MAY CAUSE SEVERE RENAL LESIONS AND TUBULAR NECROSIS, INTERNAL HEMORRHAGE, LIFE-THREATENING HYPOCALCEMIA, AND DEATH. PROLONGED PARENTERAL ADMINISTRATION MAY LEAD TO ELECTROLYTE IMBALANCE, AND CARDIAC ARRHYTHMIAS.

HEALTH EFFECTS AND FIRST AID

INHALATION: ETHYLENEDIAMINETETRAACETIC ACID, DISODIUM SALT: **ACUTE EXPOSURE-** NO SPECIFIC DATA AVAILABLE. INHALATION OF DUSTS OR MISTS OF EDTA SALTS MAY CAUSE MUCOUS MEMBRANE IRRITATION WITH SORE THROAT AND COUGHING. **CHRONIC EXPOSURE-** NO DATA AVAILABLE.

FIRST AID- REMOVE FROM EXPOSURE AREA TO FRESH AIR IMMEDIATELY. IF BREATHING HAS STOPPED, PERFORM ARTIFICIAL RESPIRATION. KEEP PERSON WARM AND AT REST. TREAT SYMPTOMATICALLY AND SUPPORTIVELY. GET MEDICAL ATTENTION IMMEDIATELY.

SKIN CONTACT: ETHYLENEDIAMINETETRAACETIC ACID, DISODIUM SALT: **ACUTE EXPOSURE**- NO SPECIFIC DATA AVAILABLE. EDTA SALTS MAY CAUSE IRRITATION WITH REDNESS AND PAIN. **CHRONIC EXPOSURE**- REPEATED OR PROLONGED CONTACT WITH EDTA SALTS MAY CAUSE MODERATE IRRITATION AND POSSIBLY A MILD BURN.
FIRST AID- REMOVE CONTAMINATED CLOTHING AND SHOES IMMEDIATELY. WASH AFFECTED AREA WITH SOAP OR MILD DETERGENT AND LARGE AMOUNTS OF WATER UNTIL NO EVIDENCE OF CHEMICAL REMAINS (APPROXIMATELY 15-20 MINUTES). GET MEDICAL ATTENTION IMMEDIATELY.

EYE CONTACT: ETHYLENEDIAMINETETRAACETIC ACID, DISODIUM SALT: IRRITANT. **ACUTE EXPOSURE**- CONTACT WITH EDTA SALTS MAY CAUSE IRRITATION WITH REDNESS, PAIN, AND SOME TRANSIENT CORNEAL INJURY. **CHRONIC EXPOSURE**- REPEATED OR PROLONGED CONTACT WITH EDTA SALTS MAY CAUSE CONJUNCTIVITIS.
FIRST AID- WASH EYES IMMEDIATELY WITH LARGE AMOUNTS OF WATER OR NORMAL SALINE, OCCASIONALLY LIFTING UPPER AND LOWER LIDS, UNTIL NO EVIDENCE OF CHEMICAL REMAINS (APPROXIMATELY 15-20 MINUTES). GET MEDICAL ATTENTION IMMEDIATELY.

INGESTION: ETHYLENEDIAMINETETRAACETIC ACID, DISODIUM SALT: **ACUTE EXPOSURE**- SOLUTIONS OF THE SALTS OF EDTA ARE EXTREMELY IRRITATING TO THE GASTROINTESTINAL SYSTEM. ALTHOUGH POORLY ABSORBED, IF SUFFICIENT AMOUNTS ARE INGESTED SYSTEMIC TOXICITY MAY RESULT. EDTA AND ITS SALTS MAY CHELATE LEAD, MAGNESIUM, ZINC, AND TRACE METALS IF THEY ARE PRESENT IN THE INTESTINE, POSSIBLY CAUSING THEIR INCREASED ABSORPTION AND THEREBY INCREASING TOTAL BODY STORES OF THESE METALS. **CHRONIC EXPOSURE**- IN FEEDING STUDIES, RATS FED A DIET OF 5 AND 10% EDTA DISODIUM SALTS FOR UP TO 13 WEEKS SHOWED DECREASED FOOD CONSUMPTION AND WEIGHT GAIN WHEN COMPARED TO CONTROLS. THESE RATS ALSO SUFFERED FROM DIARRHEA AND PRIAPISM. A 60% MORTALITY OCCURRED IN THE 10% DIET GROUP, AND 20% MORTALITY IN THE 5% GROUP. REPRODUCTIVE EFFECTS HAVE BEEN REPORTED IN ANIMAL STUDIES.
FIRST AID- TREAT SYMPTOMATICALLY AND SUPPORTIVELY. GET MEDICAL ATTENTION IMMEDIATELY. IF VOMITING OCCURS, KEEP HEAD LOWER THAN HIPS TO PREVENT ASPIRATION.
ANTIDOTE: NO SPECIFIC ANTIDOTE. TREAT SYMPTOMATICALLY AND SUPPORTIVELY.

REACTIVITY

REACTIVITY: STABLE UNDER NORMAL TEMPERATURES AND PRESSURES.
INCOMPATIBILITIES: ETHYLENEDIAMINETETRAACETIC ACID, TETRASODIUM SALT: ACIDS: INCOMPATIBLE. ALUMINUM: MAY FORM FLAMMABLE HYDROGEN GAS. METALS: MAY FORM FLAMMABLE HYDROGEN GAS. OXIDIZERS (STRONG): FIRE AND EXPLOSION HAZARD.
DECOMPOSITION: THERMAL DECOMPOSITION PRODUCTS MAY INCLUDE TOXIC AND HAZARDOUS OXIDES OF CARBON, NITROGEN, AND SODIUM.
POLYMERIZATION: HAZARDOUS POLYMERIZATION HAS NOT BEEN REPORTED TO OCCUR UNDER NORMAL TEMPERATURES AND PRESSURES.

STORAGE AND DISPOSAL

OBSERVE ALL FEDERAL, STATE AND LOCAL REGULATIONS WHEN STORING OR DISPOSING OF THIS SUBSTANCE. FOR ASSISTANCE, CONTACT THE DISTRICT DIRECTOR OF THE ENVIRONMENTAL PROTECTION AGENCY.

****STORAGE****

STORE AWAY FROM INCOMPATIBLE SUBSTANCES.
KEEP IN A TIGHTLY CLOSED CONTAINER. STORE IN A COOL, DRY, VENTILATED AREA.

CONDITIONS TO AVOID

MAY BURN BUT DOES NOT IGNITE READILY. AVOID CONTACT WITH STRONG OXIDIZERS, EXCESSIVE HEAT, SPARKS, OR OPEN FLAME.
PREVENT DISPERSION OF DUST IN AIR.

SPILL AND LEAK PROCEDURES

OCCUPATIONAL SPILL: SWEEP UP AND PLACE IN SUITABLE CLEAN, DRY CONTAINERS FOR RECLAMATION OR LATER DISPOSAL. DO NOT FLUSH SPILLED MATERIAL INTO SEWER. KEEP UNNECESSARY PEOPLE AWAY.

PROTECTIVE EQUIPMENT

VENTILATION: PROVIDE LOCAL EXHAUST OR GENERAL DILUTION VENTILATION SYSTEM.
RESPIRATOR: THE FOLLOWING RESPIRATORS ARE RECOMMENDED BASED ON INFORMATION FOUND IN THE PHYSICAL DATA, TOXICITY AND HEALTH EFFECTS SECTIONS. THEY ARE RANKED IN ORDER FROM MINIMUM TO MAXIMUM RESPIRATORY PROTECTION. THE SPECIFIC RESPIRATOR SELECTED MUST BE BASED ON CONTAMINATION LEVELS FOUND IN THE WORK PLACE, MUST NOT EXCEED THE WORKING LIMITS OF THE RESPIRATOR AND BE JOINTLY APPROVED BY THE NATIONAL INSTITUTE FOR OCCUPATIONAL SAFETY AND HEALTH AND THE MINE SAFETY AND HEALTH ADMINISTRATION (NIOSH-MSHA).
DUST AND MIST RESPIRATOR WITH A FULL FACEPIECE.
AIR-PURIFYING FULL FACEPIECE RESPIRATOR WITH A HIGH-EFFICIENCY PARTICULATE FILTER.
POWERED AIR-PURIFYING RESPIRATOR WITH A TIGHT-FITTING FACEPIECE AND HIGH-EFFICIENCY PARTICULATE FILTER.
TYPE 'C' SUPPLIED-AIR RESPIRATOR WITH A FULL FACEPIECE OPERATED IN PRESSURE-DEMAND OR OTHER POSITIVE PRESSURE MODE OR WITH A FULL FACEPIECE, HELMET OR HOOD OPERATED IN CONTINUOUS-FLOW MODE.
SELF-CONTAINED BREATHING APPARATUS WITH A FULL FACEPIECE OPERATED IN PRESSURE-DEMAND OR OTHER POSITIVE PRESSURE MODE.
FOR FIREFIGHTING AND OTHER IMMEDIATELY DANGEROUS TO LIFE OR HEALTH CONDITIONS:
SELF-CONTAINED BREATHING APPARATUS WITH FULL FACEPIECE OPERATED IN PRESSURE-DEMAND OR OTHER POSITIVE PRESSURE MODE.
SUPPLIED-AIR RESPIRATOR WITH FULL FACEPIECE AND OPERATED IN PRESSURE-DEMAND OR OTHER POSITIVE PRESSURE MODE IN COMBINATION WITH AN AUXILIARY SELF-CONTAINED BREATHING APPARATUS OPERATED IN PRESSURE-DEMAND OR OTHER POSITIVE PRESSURE MODE.
CLOTHING: EMPLOYEE MUST WEAR APPROPRIATE PROTECTIVE (IMPERVIOUS) CLOTHING AND EQUIPMENT TO PREVENT REPEATED OR PROLONGED SKIN CONTACT WITH THIS SUBSTANCE.
GLOVES: EMPLOYEE MUST WEAR APPROPRIATE PROTECTIVE GLOVES TO PREVENT CONTACT WITH THIS SUBSTANCE.
EYE PROTECTION: EMPLOYEE MUST WEAR SPLASH-PROOF OR DUST-RESISTANT SAFETY GOGGLES TO PREVENT EYE CONTACT WITH THIS SUBSTANCE.
EMERGENCY EYE WASH: WHERE THERE IS ANY POSSIBILITY THAT AN EMPLOYEE'S EYES MAY BE EXPOSED TO THIS SUBSTANCE, THE EMPLOYER SHOULD PROVIDE AN EYE WASH FOUNTAIN WITHIN THE IMMEDIATE WORK AREA FOR EMERGENCY USE.

AUTHORIZED BY- OCCUPATIONAL HEALTH SERVICES, INC.
CREATION DATE: 11/16/89 ***REVISION DATE:*** 05/31/90

MATERIAL SAFETY DATA SHEET

OCCUPATIONAL HEALTH SERVICES, INC.
AGRICULTURE AND PESTICIDE DIVISION
450 SEVENTH AVENUE, SUITE 2407
NEW YORK, NEW YORK 10123
1-800-445-MSDS OR (212) 967-1100

EMERGENCY CONTACT:
JOHN S. BRANSFORD, JR. (615) 292-1180

SUBSTANCE IDENTIFICATION

CAS-NUMBER 7558-79-4
SUBSTANCE: **SODIUM PHOSPHATE, DIBASIC**
TRADE NAMES/SYNONYMS: DISODIUM PHOSPHATE; DISODIUM HYDROGEN PHOSPHATE; DISODIUM ACID ORTHOPHOSPHATE; SODA PHOSPHATE; DISODIUM PHOSPHORIC ACID; DISODIUM MONOHYDROGEN PHOSPHATE; MONOHYDROGEN DISODIUM PHOSPHATE; DSP; SODIUM PHOSPHATE; SODIUM PHOSPHATE (NA2HPO4); EXSICCATED SODIUM PHOSPHATE; HYDROGEN DISODIUM PHOSPHATE; PHOSPHORIC ACID, DISODIUM SALT; SODIUM MONOHYDROGEN PHOSPHATE; ANHYDROUS SODIUM ACID PHOSPHATE; DISODIUM ACID PHOSPHATE; DISODIUM ORTHOPHOSPHATE; STCC 4966380; NA 9147; HNA2O4P; PST08330
CHEMICAL FAMILY: INORGANIC SALT
MOLECULAR FORMULA: NA2-H-P-O4
MOLECULAR WEIGHT: 141.96
CERCLA RATINGS (SCALE 0-3): HEALTH=3 FIRE=0 REACTIVITY=0 PERSISTENCE=0
NFPA RATINGS (SCALE 0-4): HEALTH=U FIRE=0 REACTIVITY=0

COMPONENTS AND CONTAMINANTS

COMPONENT: SODIUM PHOSPHATE, DIBASIC ***PERCENT:*** 100.0
CAS# 7558-79-4

OTHER CONTAMINANTS: NONE

EXPOSURE LIMITS: NO OCCUPATIONAL EXPOSURE LIMITS ESTABLISHED BY OSHA, ACGIH, OR NIOSH.

SODIUM PHOSPHATE, DIBASIC, ANHYDROUS: 5000 POUNDS CERCLA SECTION 103 REPORTABLE QUANTITY

PHYSICAL DATA

DESCRIPTION: ODORLESS, HYGROSCOPIC, COLORLESS TRANSLUCENT CRYSTALS OR WHITE POWDER WITH A SALTY TASTE. ***MELTING POINT:*** NOT AVAILABLE

SPECIFIC GRAVITY: 2.066 @ 16 C (2H2O) ***PH:*** 9.1 @ 1% SOLUTION

SOLUBILITY IN WATER: 12.5%

SOLVENT SOLUBILITY: VERY SLIGHTLY SOLUBLE IN ALCOHOL.

FORMS PYROPHOSPHATE AT 464 F (240 C).

FIRE AND EXPLOSION DATA

FIRE AND EXPLOSION HAZARD: NEGLIGIBLE FIRE HAZARD WHEN EXPOSED TO HEAT OR FLAME.

FIREFIGHTING MEDIA: DRY CHEMICAL, CARBON DIOXIDE, HALON, WATER SPRAY OR STANDARD FOAM (1987 EMERGENCY RESPONSE GUIDEBOOK, DOT P 5800.4).

FOR LARGER FIRES, USE WATER SPRAY, FOG OR STANDARD FOAM (1987 EMERGENCY RESPONSE GUIDEBOOK, DOT P 5800.4).

FIREFIGHTING: MOVE CONTAINER FROM FIRE AREA IF POSSIBLE. DO NOT SCATTER SPILLED MATERIAL WITH HIGH PRESSURE WATER STREAMS. DIKE FIRE CONTROL WATER FOR LATER DISPOSAL (1987 EMERGENCY RESPONSE GUIDEBOOK, DOT P 5800.4, GUIDE PAGE 31).

USE AGENTS SUITABLE FOR TYPE OF SURROUNDING FIRE. AVOID BREATHING HAZARDOUS VAPORS, KEEP UPWIND.

TOXICITY

SODIUM PHOSPHATE, DIBASIC: IRRITATION DATA: ANHYDROUS: 500 MG/24 HOURS SKIN-RABBIT MILD; 500 MG/24 HOURS EYE-RABBIT MILD. TOXICITY DATA: ANHYDROUS: 17 GM/KG ORAL-RAT LD50; 1000 MG/KG SUBCUTANEOUS-RAT LDLO; 298 MG/KG INTRAVENOUS-DOG LDLO; 1075 MG/KG INTRAVENOUS-RABBIT LDLO; 1000 MG/KG INTRAPERITONEAL-RAT LDLO; 1000 MG/KG INTRAMUSCULAR-RAT LDLO. HEPTAHYDRATE: 12930 MG/KG ORAL-RAT LD50. CARCINOGEN STATUS: NONE. ACUTE TOXICITY LEVEL: SLIGHTLY TOXIC BY INGESTION (HEPTAHYDRATE); RELATIVELY NONTOXIC BY INGESTION (ANHYDROUS). TARGET EFFECTS: POISONING MAY AFFECT CALCIUM METABOLISM.

HEALTH EFFECTS AND FIRST AID

INHALATION: SODIUM PHOSPHATE, DIBASIC: **ACUTE EXPOSURE-** INHALATION OF DUSTS MAY CAUSE MILD IRRITATION OF MUCOUS MEMBRANES WITH SORE THROAT, COUGHING, CHOKING, AND DIFFICULTY BREATHING. **CHRONIC EXPOSURE-** NO DATA AVAILABLE.

FIRST AID- REMOVE FROM EXPOSURE AREA TO FRESH AIR IMMEDIATELY. IF BREATHING HAS STOPPED, PERFORM ARTIFICIAL RESPIRATION. KEEP PERSON WARM AND AT REST. TREAT SYMPTOMATICALLY AND SUPPORTIVELY. GET MEDICAL ATTENTION IMMEDIATELY.

SKIN CONTACT: SODIUM PHOSPHATE, DIBASIC: **ACUTE EXPOSURE-** CONTACT MAY PRODUCE MILD IRRITATION AND REDNESS. **CHRONIC EXPOSURE-** REPEATED OR PROLONGED EXPOSURE MAY CAUSE DERMATITIS.

FIRST AID- REMOVE CONTAMINATED CLOTHING AND SHOES IMMEDIATELY. WASH AFFECTED AREA WITH SOAP OR MILD DETERGENT AND LARGE AMOUNTS OF WATER UNTIL NO EVIDENCE OF CHEMICAL REMAINS (APPROXIMATELY 15-20 MINUTES). GET MEDICAL ATTENTION IMMEDIATELY.

EYE CONTACT: SODIUM PHOSPHATE, DIBASIC: **ACUTE EXPOSURE-** DUSTS MAY CAUSE MILD IRRITATION WITH REDNESS AND PAIN. **CHRONIC EXPOSURE-** NO DATA AVAILABLE.

FIRST AID- WASH EYES IMMEDIATELY WITH LARGE AMOUNTS OF WATER OR NORMAL SALINE, OCCASIONALLY LIFTING UPPER AND LOWER LIDS, UNTIL NO EVIDENCE OF CHEMICAL REMAINS (APPROXIMATELY 15-20 MINUTES). GET MEDICAL ATTENTION IMMEDIATELY.

INGESTION: SODIUM PHOSPHATE, DIBASIC: **ACUTE EXPOSURE-** INGESTION MAY RESULT IN PAIN AND BURNING IN THE MOUTH, ABDOMINAL PAIN, NAUSEA, VOMITING, DIARRHEA, AND CRAMPS. PHOSPHATES MAY CAUSE A SHOCKLIKE STATE, FALL OF BLOOD PRESSURE, SLOW PULSE, CYANOSIS, COMA, AND SOMETIMES TETANY AS A RESULT OF REDUCTION IN IONIC CALCIUM. **CHRONIC EXPOSURE-** ANIMALS FED SODIUM PHOSPHATE DIBASIC AND POTASSIUM DIHYDROGEN PHOSPHATE HAD A GREATER DEGREE OF BONE POROSITY THAN CONTROLS IN BOTH SHORT AND LONG TERM STUDIES. THERE WAS ALSO EVIDENCE OF HYPERPARATHYROIDISM AND SOFT TISSUE CALCIFICATION.

FIRST AID- DILUTE THE ALKALI BY GIVING WATER OR MILK IMMEDIATELY AND ALLOW VOMITING TO OCCUR. AVOID GASTRIC LAVAGE OR EMETICS. ESOPHAGOSCOPY IS THE ONLY WAY TO EXCLUDE THE POSSIBLITY OF CORROSION IN THE UPPER GASTROINTESTINAL TRACT; IF CORROSION IS SUSPECTED, ESOPHAGOSCOPY SHOULD USUALLY BE PERFORMED WITHIN 24 HOURS (DREISBACH, HANDBOOK OF POISONING, 12TH ED.). MAINTAIN AIRWAY AND TREAT SHOCK. IF VOMITING OCCURS, KEEP HEAD BELOW HIPS TO HELP PREVENT ASPIRATION. GET MEDICAL ATTENTION IMMEDIATELY.

ANTIDOTE: THE FOLLOWING ANTIDOTE HAS BEEN RECOMMENDED. HOWEVER, THE DECISION AS TO WHETHER THE SEVERITY OF POISONING REQUIRES ADMINISTRATION OF ANY ANTIDOTE AND ACTUAL DOSE REQUIRED SHOULD BE MADE BY QUALIFIED MEDICAL PERSONNEL.

PHOSPHATES: FOR HYPOCALCEMIA, AFTER PHOSPHATE INGESTION, GIVE CALCIUM GLUCONATE, 5 ML OF 10% SOLUTION SLOWLY INTRAVENOUSLY, TO RESTORE IONIC CALCIUM TO NORMAL LEVEL (DREISBACH, HANDBOOK OF POISONING, 12TH ED.). ANTIDOTE SHOULD BE ADMINISTERED BY QUALIFIED MEDICAL PERSONNEL.

REACTIVITY

REACTIVITY: STABLE UNDER NORMAL TEMPERATURES AND PRESSURES.

INCOMPATIBILITIES: SODIUM PHOSPHATE, DIBASIC: ACIDS (STRONG): POSSIBLE VIOLENT REACTION. ALUMINUM: MAY CORRODE. STEEL: MAY CORRODE.

DECOMPOSITION: THERMAL DECOMPOSITION PRODUCTS MAY INCLUDE TOXIC AND HAZARDOUS SODIUM OXIDE AND OXIDES OF PHOSPHORUS.

POLYMERIZATION: HAZARDOUS POLYMERIZATION HAS NOT BEEN REPORTED TO OCCUR UNDER NORMAL TEMPERATURES AND PRESSURES.

STORAGE AND DISPOSAL

OBSERVE ALL FEDERAL, STATE AND LOCAL REGULATIONS WHEN STORING OR DISPOSING OF THIS SUBSTANCE. FOR ASSISTANCE, CONTACT THE DISTRICT DIRECTOR OF THE ENVIRONMENTAL PROTECTION AGENCY.

STORAGE

KEEP WELL CLOSED (MERCK INDEX, 10TH ED.).

STORE AWAY FROM INCOMPATIBLE SUBSTANCES.

CONDITIONS TO AVOID

MAY BURN BUT DOES NOT IGNITE READILY. AVOID CONTACT WITH STRONG OXIDIZERS, EXCESSIVE HEAT, SPARKS, OR OPEN FLAME.

SPILL AND LEAK PROCEDURES

SOIL SPILL: DIG A HOLDING AREA SUCH AS PIT, POND OR LAGOON TO CONTAIN SPILLED MATERIAL. USE PROTECTIVE COVER SUCH AS A PLASTIC SHEET TO PREVENT DISSOLVING IN FIREFIGHTING WATER OR RAIN.

WATER SPILL: NEUTRALIZE WITH AGRICULTURAL LIME, SLAKED LIME, CRUSHED LIMESTONE, OR SODIUM BICARBONATE.

USE MECHANICAL DREDGES OR LIFTS TO EXTRACT IMMOBILIZED MASSES OF POLLUTION AND PRECIPITATES.

OCCUPATIONAL SPILL: STOP LEAK IF YOU CAN DO IT WITHOUT RISK. FOR SMALL SPILLS, TAKE UP WITH SAND OR OTHER ABSORBENT MATERIAL AND PLACE INTO CLEAN, DRY CONTAINERS FOR LATER DISPOSAL. KEEP UNNECESSARY PEOPLE AWAY. ISOLATE HAZARD AREA AND DENY ENTRY.

REPORTABLE QUANTITY (RQ): 5000 POUNDS THE SUPERFUND AMENDMENTS AND REAUTHORIZATION ACT (SARA) SECTION 304 REQUIRES THAT A RELEASE EQUAL TO OR GREATER THAN THE REPORTABLE QUANTITY FOR THIS SUBSTANCE BE IMMEDIATELY REPORTED TO THE LOCAL EMERGENCY PLANNING COMMITTEE AND THE STATE EMERGENCY RESPONSE COMMISSION (40 CFR 355.40). IF THE RELEASE OF THIS SUBSTANCE IS REPORTABLE UNDER CERCLA SECTION 103, THE NATIONAL RESPONSE CENTER MUST BE NOTIFIED IMMEDIATELY AT (800) 424-8802 OR (202) 426-2675 IN THE METROPOLITAN WASHINGTON, D.C. AREA (40 CFR 302.6).

PROTECTIVE EQUIPMENT

VENTILATION: PROVIDE GENERAL DILUTION VENTILATION.

RESPIRATOR: THE FOLLOWING RESPIRATORS ARE RECOMMENDED BASED ON INFORMATION FOUND IN THE PHYSICAL DATA, TOXICITY AND HEALTH EFFECTS SECTIONS. THEY ARE RANKED IN ORDER FROM MINIMUM TO MAXIMUM RESPIRATORY PROTECTION. THE SPECIFIC RESPIRATOR SELECTED MUST BE BASED ON CONTAMINATION LEVELS FOUND IN THE WORK PLACE, MUST NOT EXCEED THE WORKING LIMITS OF THE RESPIRATOR AND BE JOINTLY APPROVED BY THE NATIONAL INSTITUTE FOR OCCUPATIONAL SAFETY AND HEALTH AND THE MINE SAFETY AND HEALTH ADMINISTRATION (NIOSH-MSHA).

DUST AND MIST RESPIRATOR WITH A FULL FACEPIECE.

AIR-PURIFYING FULL FACEPIECE RESPIRATOR WITH A HIGH-EFFICIENCY PARTICULATE FILTER.

POWERED AIR-PURIFYING RESPIRATOR WITH A TIGHT-FITTING FACEPIECE AND HIGH-EFFICIENCY PARTICULATE FILTER.

TYPE 'C' SUPPLIED-AIR RESPIRATOR WITH A FULL FACEPIECE OPERATED IN PRESSURE-DEMAND OR OTHER POSITIVE PRESSURE MODE OR WITH A FULL FACEPIECE, HELMET OR HOOD OPERATED IN CONTINUOUS-FLOW MODE.

SELF-CONTAINED BREATHING APPARATUS WITH A FULL FACEPIECE OPERATED IN PRESSURE-DEMAND OR OTHER POSITIVE PRESSURE MODE.
FOR FIREFIGHTING AND OTHER IMMEDIATELY DANGEROUS TO LIFE OR HEALTH CONDITIONS:
SELF-CONTAINED BREATHING APPARATUS WITH FULL FACEPIECE OPERATED IN PRESSURE-DEMAND OR OTHER POSITIVE PRESSURE MODE.
SUPPLIED-AIR RESPIRATOR WITH FULL FACEPIECE AND OPERATED IN PRESSURE-DEMAND OR OTHER POSITIVE PRESSURE MODE IN COMBINATION WITH AN AUXILIARY SELF-CONTAINED BREATHING APPARATUS OPERATED IN PRESSURE-DEMAND OR OTHER POSITIVE PRESSURE MODE.

CLOTHING: PROTECTIVE CLOTHING NOT REQUIRED. AVOID REPEATED OR PROLONGED CONTACT WITH THIS SUBSTANCE.

GLOVES: PROTECTIVE GLOVES ARE NOT REQUIRED BUT RECOMMENDED.

EYE PROTECTION: EYE PROTECTION NOT REQUIRED, BUT ADVISABLE.

AUTHORIZED BY- OCCUPATIONAL HEALTH SERVICES, INC.
CREATION DATE: 11/16/89 ***REVISION DATE:*** 11/16/89

MATERIAL SAFETY DATA SHEET

OCCUPATIONAL HEALTH SERVICES, INC.
AGRICULTURE AND PESTICIDE DIVISION
450 SEVENTH AVENUE, SUITE 2407
NEW YORK, NEW YORK 10123
1-800-445-MSDS OR (212) 967-1100

EMERGENCY CONTACT:
JOHN S. BRANSFORD, JR. (615) 292-1180

SUBSTANCE IDENTIFICATION

CAS-NUMBER 97-77-8

SUBSTANCE: DISULFIRAM

TRADE NAMES/SYNONYMS: TETRAETHYL THIURAM; ETHYL THIURAM; ABSTINIL; CONTRALIN; DISULFAN; NOXAL; ANTABUSE; BIS-DIETHYLCARAMOYL DISULFIDE; TATD; DIS(DIETHYLAMINO)THIOXOMETHYL DISULFIDE; BIS(DIETHYLTHIOCARBAMOYL)DISULFIDE; BIS(N,N-DIETHYLTHIOCARBAMOYL)DISULFIDE; TETRAETHYLTHIOPEROXYDICARBONIC DIAMIDE OHS08370; PST08370

CHEMICAL FAMILY: CARBAMATE
ORGANIC SULFIDE

MOLECULAR FORMULA: C10-H20-N2-S4

MOLECULAR WEIGHT: 296.56

CERCLA RATINGS (SCALE 0-3): HEALTH=3 FIRE=0 REACTIVITY=0 PERSISTENCE=1

NFPA RATINGS (SCALE 0-4): HEALTH=3 FIRE=0 REACTIVITY=0

COMPONENTS AND CONTAMINANTS

COMPONENT: DISULFIRAM ***PERCENT:*** 100%
CAS# 97-77-8

OTHER CONTAMINANTS: NONE.

EXPOSURE LIMITS: DISULFIRAM: 2 MG/M3 OSHA TWA 2 MG/M3 ACGIH TWA

PHYSICAL DATA

DESCRIPTION: COLORLESS, YELLOW, OR PALE GREY POWDER, SLIGHT ODOR.

BOILING POINT: 196 F @ 17 MMHG ***MELTING POINT:*** 160 F (71 C)

SPECIFIC GRAVITY: 1.27 ***SOLUBILITY IN WATER:*** 0.02% @ 25 C

SOLVENT SOLUBILITY: ACETONE, BENZENE, CARBON TETRACHLORIDE, ALCOHOL, CARBON DISULFIDE

FIRE AND EXPLOSION DATA

FIRE AND EXPLOSION HAZARD: NEGLIGIBLE FIRE HAZARD WHEN EXPOSED TO HEAT OR FLAME.
DUST-AIR MIXTURES MAY IGNITE OR EXPLODE.

FIREFIGHTING MEDIA: DRY CHEMICAL, CARBON DIOXIDE, HALON, WATER SPRAY OR STANDARD FOAM (1987 EMERGENCY RESPONSE GUIDEBOOK, DOT P 5800.4).
FOR LARGER FIRES, USE WATER SPRAY, FOG OR STANDARD FOAM (1987 EMERGENCY RESPONSE GUIDEBOOK, DOT P 5800.4).

FIREFIGHTING: MOVE CONTAINER FROM FIRE AREA IF POSSIBLE. DO NOT SCATTER SPILLED MATERIAL WITH HIGH PRESSURE WATER STREAMS. DIKE FIRE CONTROL WATER FOR LATER DISPOSAL (1987 EMERGENCY RESPONSE GUIDEBOOK, DOT P 5800.4, GUIDE PAGE 31).
USE AGENTS SUITABLE FOR TYPE OF SURROUNDING FIRE. AVOID BREATHING HAZARDOUS VAPORS, KEEP UPWIND.

TOXICITY

DISULFIRAM: IRRITATION DATA: 100 MG EYE-RABBIT MILD. TOXICITY DATA: 150 MG/KG/6 WEEKS-INTERMITTENT ORAL-MAN LDLO; 160 MG/KG ORAL-HUMAN LDLO; 150 MG/KG ORAL-CHILD TDLO; 150 MG/KG/6 WEEKS-INTERMITTENT ORAL-MAN TDLO; 90 MG/KG/18 DAYS-INTERMITTENT ORAL-WOMAN TDLO; 500 MG/KG ORAL-RAT LD50; 1980 MG/KG ORAL-MOUSE LD50; 2050 MG/KG ORAL-RABBIT LD50; 2050 MG/KG SUBCUTANEOUS-RABBIT LD50; 75 MG/KG INTRAPERITONEAL-MOUSE LD50; 248 MG/KG INTRAPERITONEAL-RAT LD50; MUTAGENIC DATA (RTECS); REPRODUCTIVE EFFECTS DATA (RTECS); TUMORIGENIC DATA (RTECS).
CARCINOGEN STATUS: ANIMAL INADEQUATE EVIDENCE (IARC GROUP-3) IN MALE MICE, REPEATED ORAL ADMINISTRATION RESULTED IN AN INCREASED INCIDENCE OF LIVER CELL TUMORS AND A SLIGHT INCREASE IN THE NUMBER OF LUNG TUMORS IN ONE OF THE TWO STRAINS TESTED. THE LIMITED DATA AVAILABLE DO NOT ALLOW AN EVALUATION OF THE CARCINOGENICITY TO BE MADE. DISULFIRAM CAN REACT WITH NITRITE UNDER MILDLY ACID CONDITIONS, SIMULATING THOSE IN THE HUMAN STOMACH, TO FORM N-NITROSDIETHYLAMINE, WHICH HAS BEEN SHOWN TO BE CARCINOGENIC IN 10 ANIMAL SPECIES. LOCAL EFFECTS: IRRITANT-INHALATION, SKIN, AND EYES. ACUTE TOXICITY LEVEL: TOXIC BY INGESTION. TARGET EFFECTS: POISONING MAY AFFECT THE CENTRAL NERVOUS SYSTEM, THE LIVER, AND BLOOD. ADDITIONAL DATA: INTERACTIONS WITH ALCOHOL MAY OCCUR.

HEALTH EFFECTS AND FIRST AID

INHALATION: IRRITANT. **ACUTE EXPOSURE-** DUST MAY BE IRRITATING. NO DATA AVAILABLE FOR SYMPTOMS WITHOUT ALCOHOL. WITH THE INHALATION OF AS LITTLE AS 10 ML OF ETHANOL, DISULFIRAM CAUSES FLUSHING, SWEATING, TACHYCARDIA, BREATHLESSNESS, HYPERVENTILATION, FALLING BLOOD PRESSURE, NAUSEA AND VOMITING, DROWSINESS, CARDIAC ARRYTHMIAS, AIR HUNGER, AND CHEST PAIN OR CARDIAC INFARCTION. **CHRONIC EXPOSURE-** NO DATA AVAILABLE. MAY BE IRRITATING.

FIRST AID- REMOVE FROM EXPOSURE AREA TO FRESH AIR IMMEDIATELY. IF BREATHING HAS STOPPED, PERFORM ARTIFICIAL RESPIRATION. KEEP PERSON WARM AND AT REST. TREAT SYMPTOMATICALLY AND SUPPORTIVELY. GET MEDICAL ATTENTION IMMEDIATELY.

SKIN CONTACT: IRRITANT. **ACUTE EXPOSURE-** MAY CAUSE IRRITATION AND DERMATITIS. **CHRONIC EXPOSURE-** MAY CAUSE DERMATITIS.

FIRST AID- REMOVE CONTAMINATED CLOTHING AND SHOES IMMEDIATELY. WASH AFFECTED AREA WITH SOAP OR MILD DETERGENT AND LARGE AMOUNTS OF WATER UNTIL NO EVIDENCE OF CHEMICAL REMAINS (APPROXIMATELY 15-20 MINUTES). GET MEDICAL ATTENTION IMMEDIATELY.

EYE CONTACT: IRRITANT. **ACUTE EXPOSURE-** 100 MG OF DISULFIRAM CAUSED MILD IRRITATION IN RABBIT EYES. SYSTEMIC EFFECTS FROM INGESTION MAY CAUSE EYE DISORDERS. **CHRONIC EXPOSURE-** MAY CAUSE CONJUNCTIVITIS. SYSTEMIC EFFECTS FROM INGESTION MAY CAUSE EYE DISORDERS.

FIRST AID- WASH EYES IMMEDIATELY WITH LARGE AMOUNTS OF WATER OR NORMAL SALINE, OCCASIONALLY LIFTING UPPER AND LOWER LIDS, UNTIL NO EVIDENCE OF CHEMICAL REMAINS (APPROXIMATELY 15-20 MINUTES). GET MEDICAL ATTENTION IMMEDIATELY.

INGESTION: DISULFIRAM: TOXIC. **ACUTE EXPOSURE-** IN THE ABSENCE OF ALCOHOL, ACNEFORM ERUPTIONS, ALLERGIC DERMATITIS, URTICARIA, LASSITUDE, FATIGUE, TREMOR, RESTLESSNESS, REDUCED SEXUAL POTENCY, A GARLIC-LIKE OR METALLIC TASTE, AND MILD GASTROINTESTINAL DISTURBANCES MAY OCCUR. IN RARE CASES, DISULFIRAM CAN CAUSE HEPATOTOXICITY EVEN WHEN ALCOHOL PRESUMABLY IS NOT INVOLVED. IN THE PRESENCE OF ALCOHOL THERE HAS BEEN DESCRIBED IN THE EYE A COMPLETE CIRCULATORY ARREST IN SOME OF THE RETINAL ARTERIOLES, WITH FALL IN RETINAL DIASTOLIC PRESSURE, AND SUBSEQUENT ELEVATION OF THE PRESSURE TO A LEVEL WHICH THE OBSERVER THOUGHT TO BE DANGEROUS. BILATERAL RETROBULBAR NEURITIS HAS BEEN CAUSED IN SEVERAL CASES. THERAPEUTIC DOSE OF THIS DRUG INTERFERES WITH THE METABOLISM OF ETHYL ALCOHOL RESULTING IN AN INCREASED PRODUCTION AND RETENTION OF ACETALDEHYDE. FATALITIES MAY OCCUR AT BLOOD ETHANOL LEVELS OF 1 MG/ML AFTER THE INGESTION OF AS LITTLE AS 0.5-1 GM OF DISULFIRAM. AFTER ALCOHOL CONSUMPTION RESPIRATORY DEPRESSION, CARDIOVASCULAR COLLAPSE, CARDIAC ARRYTHMIAS, MYOCARDIAL INFARCTION, ACUTE CONGESTIVE HEART FAILURE, UNCONSCIOUSNESS, CONVULSIONS, AND SUDDEN AND UNEXPLAINED FATALITIES HAVE OCCURRED. ANIMAL EXPERIMENTS WITHOUT THE PRESENCE OF ALCOHOL INDICATE THAT INGESTION BY AN ADULT OF 30 GM OF DISULFIRAM AS A SINGLE DOSE WOULD BE EXPECTED TO PRODUCE SERIOUS TOXIC EFFECTS. IN A PATIENT RECEIVING DISULFIRAM THERAPY, SUDDEN DEATH MAY OCCUR UP TO 24 HOURS AFTER INGESTING ETHANOL. **CHRONIC EXPOSURE-** FATIGUE, WEAKNESS, IMPOTENCE, AND HEADACHES MAY OCCUR BUT DISAPPEAR WITH CONTINUED USE. TOXIC PSYCHOSIS, HEPATITIS , AND CENTRAL NERVOUS SYSTEM DEPRESSION HAVE BEEN REPORTED WITHOUT THE

CONSUMPTION OF ALCOHOL. A CASE STUDY INDICATES THAT AFTER SEVERAL MONTHS OF REGULAR DOSAGE OF DISULFIRAM, WITH ALCOHOL INTAKE STOPPED, BUT USUALLY WITH MUCH TOBACCO SMOKING CONTINUING, VISUAL ACUITY WAS GREATLY DECREASED DUE TO CENTRAL OR CECOCENTRAL SCOTOMA. COLOR SENSE IS THEN ABNORMAL. RETROBULBAR NEURITIS GENERALLY IMPROVES WHEN DISULFIRAM IS DISCONTINUED. RECOVERY OF VISION IS USUALLY COMPLETE, BUT IN EXCEPTIONAL CASES SLIGHT IMPAIRMENT HAS PERSISTED, ASSOCIATED WITH PALLOR OF THE NERVEHEAD. A CASE REPORTS TREATMENT OF A PATIENT WHO WAS A HEAVY DRINKER BUT CONSUMED NO ALCOHOL OVER THE TREATMENT PERIOD OF 1 GM/DAY FOR 7 MONTHS. THE PATIENT DEVELOPED A CHANGE IN GAIT, SYMPTOMS OF SEVERE PERIPHERAL NEUROPATHY, WITH PARALYTIC FOOTDROP, CLUMSY HANDS, NUMBNESS, AND PARESTHESIA EXTENDING TO THE ELBOWS AND ABOVE THE KNEES. HE RECOVERED SLOWLY AFTER DISCONTINUED USE OF DISULFIRAM. DISULFIRAM IS ABSORBED SLOWLY, REACHING A PEAK 24 HOURS AFTER A SINGLE DOSE. EXCRETION IS SLOW SINCE ONLY ABOUT 50% OF THE DRUG IN THE BODY IS EXCRETED IN 1 WEEK. THUS, A SEVERE REACTION TO ETHANOL MAY OCCUR SEVERAL WEEKS AFTER DISCONTINUATION OF DISULFIRAM. IN MALE MICE, REPEATED ORAL ADMINISTRATION RESULTED IN AN INCREASED INCIDENCE OF LIVER CELL TUMORS AND A SLIGHT INCREASE IN THE NUMBER OF LUNG TUMORS IN ONE OF THE TWO STRAINS TESTED. INGESTION OF 5 MG/KG BY PREGNANT RATS INCREASED THE OCCURRENCE OF POST-IMPLANTATION MORTALITY AND FETOTOXICITY.

FIRST AID- GIVE ARTIFICIAL RESPIRATION AND OXYGEN AND MAINTAIN BLOOD PRESSURE. ASCORBIC ACID ADMINISTRATION HAS BEEN REPORTED TO IMPROVE DISULFIRAM-ETHANOL REACTION; THE SUGGESTED DOSE IS 0.1-1 GM. ADMINISTRATION OF OXYGEN SHOULD BE PERFORMED BY QUALIFIED MEDICAL PERSONNEL. GET MEDICAL ATTENTION IMMEDIATELY. (DREISBACH, HANDBOOK OF POISONING, 11TH ED.) ALTERNATIVELY: GIVE LARGE QUANTITIES OF WATER. AFTER WATER HAS BEEN SWALLOWED, GET PERSON TO VOMIT BY HAVING HIM TOUCH THE BACK OF HIS THROAT WITH HIS FINGER. DO NOT MAKE AN UNCONSCIOUS PERSON VOMIT. GET MEDICAL ATTENTION IMMEDIATELY. (NIOSH/OSHA DHHS81-123).

REACTIVITY

REACTIVITY: STABLE UNDER NORMAL TEMPERATURES AND PRESSURES.

INCOMPATIBILITIES: OXIDIZERS: INCOMPATIBLE.

DECOMPOSITION: THERMAL DECOMPOSITION MAY RELEASE TOXIC OXIDES OF SULFUR.

POLYMERIZATION: HAZARDOUS POLYMERIZATION HAS NOT BEEN REPORTED TO OCCUR UNDER NORMAL TEMPERATURES AND PRESSURES.

CONDITIONS TO AVOID

MAY BURN BUT DOES NOT IGNITE READILY. AVOID CONTACT WITH STRONG OXIDIZERS, EXCESSIVE HEAT, SPARKS, OR OPEN FLAME.

SPILL AND LEAK PROCEDURES

OCCUPATIONAL SPILL: SWEEP UP AND PLACE IN SUITABLE CLEAN, DRY CONTAINERS FOR RECLAMATION OR LATER DISPOSAL. DO NOT FLUSH SPILLED MATERIAL INTO SEWER. KEEP UNNECESSARY PEOPLE AWAY.

PROTECTIVE EQUIPMENT

VENTILATION: PROVIDE LOCAL EXHAUST OR PROCESS ENCLOSURE VENTILATION TO MEET PUBLISHED EXPOSURE LIMITS.

RESPIRATOR: HIGH LEVELS- HIGH-EFFICIENCY PARTICULATE RESPIRATOR WITH A FULL FACEPIECE. SUPPLIED-AIR RESPIRATOR WITH A FULL FACEPIECE, HELMET, OR HOOD. SELF-CONTAINED BREATHING APPARATUS WITH A FULL FACEPIECE.
FIRE FIGHTING- SELF-CONTAINED BREATHING APPARATUS WITH A FULL FACEPIECE, OPERATED IN PRESSURE-DEMAND OR OTHER POSITIVE PRESSURE MODE.

CLOTHING: EMPLOYEE MUST WEAR APPROPRIATE PROTECTIVE (IMPERVIOUS) CLOTHING AND EQUIPMENT TO PREVENT REPEATED OR PROLONGED SKIN CONTACT WITH THIS SUBSTANCE.

GLOVES: EMPLOYEE MUST WEAR APPROPRIATE PROTECTIVE GLOVES TO PREVENT CONTACT WITH THIS SUBSTANCE.

EYE PROTECTION: EMPLOYEE MUST WEAR SPLASH-PROOF OR DUST-RESISTANT SAFETY GOGGLES AND A FACESHIELD TO PREVENT CONTACT WITH THIS SUBSTANCE.
EMERGENCY WASH FACILITIES: WHERE THERE IS ANY POSSIBILITY THAT AN EMPLOYEE'S EYES AND/OR SKIN MAY BE EXPOSED TO THIS SUBSTANCE, THE EMPLOYER SHOULD PROVIDE AN EYE WASH FOUNTAIN AND QUICK DRENCH SHOWER WITHIN THE IMMEDIATE WORK AREA FOR EMERGENCY USE.

AUTHORIZED BY- OCCUPATIONAL HEALTH SERVICES, INC.
CREATION DATE: 10/04/89 ***REVISION DATE:*** 07/12/90

MATERIAL SAFETY DATA SHEET

OCCUPATIONAL HEALTH SERVICES, INC.
AGRICULTURE AND PESTICIDE DIVISION
450 SEVENTH AVENUE, SUITE 2407
NEW YORK, NEW YORK 10123
1-800-445-MSDS OR (212) 967-1100

EMERGENCY CONTACT:
JOHN S. BRANSFORD, JR. (615) 292-1180

SUBSTANCE IDENTIFICATION

CAS-NUMBER 298-04-4

***SUBSTANCE:* DISULFOTON**

TRADE NAMES/SYNONYMS: PHOSPHORODITHIOIC ACID, O,O-DIETHYL S-(2-(ETHYLTHIO)ETHYL)ESTER; O,O-DIETHYL S-2-ETHYLTHIOETHYL PHOSPHORODITHIOATE; DIETHYL S-(2-ETHYLTHIOETHYL)PHOSPHOROTHIOLOTHIONATE; THIODEMETON; DITHIOSYSTOX; ETHYLTHIODEMETON; DI-SYSTON; BAYER 19639; FRUMIN-AL; SOLVIREX; ENT 23,347; RCRA P039; STCC 4921613; PST08380

CHEMICAL FAMILY: ORGANOPHOSPHATE

MOLECULAR FORMULA: C8-H19-O2-P-S2

MOLECULAR WEIGHT: 274.42

CERCLA RATINGS (SCALE 0-3): HEALTH=3 FIRE=0 REACTIVITY=0 PERSISTENCE=0

NFPA RATINGS (SCALE 0-4): HEALTH=3 FIRE=0 REACTIVITY=0

COMPONENTS AND CONTAMINANTS

COMPONENT: DISULFOTON ***PERCENT:*** 100
CAS# 298-04-4

EXPOSURE LIMITS: DISULFOTON: 0.1 MG/M3 OSHA TWA (SKIN) 0.1 MG/M3 ACGIH TWA (SKIN)
500 POUNDS SARA SECTION 302 THRESHOLD PLANNING QUANTITY 1 POUND SARA SECTION 304 REPORTABLE QUANTITY 1 POUND CERCLA SECTION 103 REPORTABLE QUANTITY

PHYSICAL DATA

DESCRIPTION: COLORLESS OILY LIQUID ***BOILING POINT:*** 144 F (62 C) @ 0.01 MMHG

SPECIFIC GRAVITY: 1.144 ***VAPOR PRESSURE:*** 0.00018 @ 20 C

SOLUBILITY IN WATER: 25 PPM

SOLVENT SOLUBILITY: SOLUBLE IN MOST ORGANIC SOLVENTS

FIRE AND EXPLOSION DATA

FIRE AND EXPLOSION HAZARD: NEGLIGIBLE FIRE HAZARD WHEN EXPOSED TO HEAT OR FLAME.

FIREFIGHTING MEDIA: DRY CHEMICAL, CARBON DIOXIDE, HALON, WATER SPRAY OR STANDARD FOAM (1987 EMERGENCY RESPONSE GUIDEBOOK, DOT P 5800.4). FOR LARGER FIRES, USE WATER SPRAY, FOG OR STANDARD FOAM (1987 EMERGENCY RESPONSE GUIDEBOOK, DOT P 5800.4).

FIREFIGHTING: MOVE CONTAINERS FROM FIRE AREA IF POSSIBLE. FIGHT FIRE FROM MAXIMUM DISTANCE. STAY AWAY FROM STORAGE TANK ENDS. DIKE FIRE CONTROL WATER FOR LATER DISPOSAL. DO NOT SCATTER MATERIAL (1987 EMERGENCY RESPONSE GUIDEBOOK, DOT P 5800.4, GUIDE PAGE 55). EXTINGUISH ONLY IF FLOW CAN BE STOPPED; USE FLOODING AMOUNTS OF WATER AS FOG, SOLID STREAMS MAY BE INEFFECTIVE. COOL CONTAINERS WITH FLOODING AMOUNTS OF WATER FROM AS FAR A DISTANCE AS POSSIBLE. USE WATER SPRAY TO ABSORB TOXIC VAPORS. AVOID BREATHING TOXIC VAPORS; KEEP UPWIND. CONSIDER EVACUATION OF DOWNWIND AREA IF MATERIAL IS LEAKING.

TRANSPORTATION DATA

DEPARTMENT OF TRANSPORTATION HAZARD CLASSIFICATION 49 CFR 172.101: POISON B
DEPARTMENT OF TRANSPORTATION LABELING REQUIREMENTS 49 CFR 172.101 AND SUBPART E: POISON
DEPARTMENT OF TRANSPORTATION PACKAGING REQUIREMENTS: 49 CFR 173.346 EXCEPTIONS: 49 CFR 173.345

TOXICITY

DISULFOTON: TOXICITY DATA: 200 MG/M3 INHALATION-RAT LC50; 10 MG/M3/4 HOURS INHALATION-CAT LCLO; 6 MG/KG SKIN-RAT LD50; 2 MG/KG ORAL-RAT LD50; 4800 UG/KG ORAL-MOUSE LD50; 10,800 UG/KG ORAL-GUINEA PIG LD50; 5500 UG/KG INTRAVENOUS-RAT LD50; 2 MG/KG INTRAPERITONEAL-RAT LD50; 7 MG/KG INTRAPERITONEAL-GUINEA PIG LD50; 5500 UG/KG INTRAPERITONEAL-

MOUSE LD50; 2500 UG/KG UNREPORTED-RAT LD50; MUTAGENIC DATA (RTECS). CARCINOGEN STATUS: NONE. ACUTE TOXICITY LEVEL: HIGHLY TOXIC BY INHALATION, DERMAL ABSORPTION, AND INGESTION. TARGET EFFECTS: CHOLINESTERASE INHIBITOR. AT INCREASED RISK FROM EXPOSURE: PERSONS WITH RESPIRATORY AILMENTS, RECENT EXPOSURE TO CHOLINESTERASE INHIBITORS OR IMPAIRED CHOLINESTERASE PRODUCTION, OR LIVER MALFUNCTION.* ADDITIONAL DATA: MAY CROSS THE PLACENTA. HIGH ENVIRONMENTAL TEMPERATURES OR EXPOSURE OF THE CHEMICAL TO VISIBLE OR ULTRAVIOLET LIGHT MAY ENHANCE THE TOXICITY. INTERACTIONS WITH MEDICATIONS MAY OCCUR.*

* MAY BE BASED ON GENERAL INFORMATION ON ORGANOPHOSPHATES.

HEALTH EFFECTS AND FIRST AID

INHALATION: DISULFOTON: HIGHLY TOXIC. SEE INFORMATION ON ORGANOPHOSPHATES.

ORGANOPHOSPHATES: CHOLINESTERASE INHIBITOR. **ACUTE EXPOSURE-** WHEN INHALED, THE FIRST EFFECTS OF CHOLINESTERASE INHIBITORS ARE USUALLY RESPIRATORY AND MAY INCLUDE NASAL HYPEREMIA AND WATERY DISCHARGE, COUGH, CHEST DISCOMFORT, DYSPNEA, AND WHEEZING DUE TO INCREASED BRONCHIAL SECRETIONS AND BRONCHOCONSTRICTION. IF SUFFICIENT AMOUNTS ARE ABSORBED, OTHER SYSTEMIC EFFECTS MAY BEGIN WITHIN A FEW MINUTES OR BE DELAYED FOR UP TO 12 HOURS. SYMPTOMS MAY INCLUDE PALLOR, NAUSEA, VOMITING, DIARRHEA, ABDOMINAL CRAMPS, HEADACHE, DIZZINESS, OCULAR PAIN, BLURRED VISION, MIOSIS OR IN SOME CASES, ESPECIALLY INITIALLY, MYDRIASIS, LACRIMATION, SALIVATION, SWEATING, AND CONFUSION. OTHER REPORTED CENTRAL NERVOUS SYSTEM OR NEUROMUSCULAR EFFECTS MAY INCLUDE ATAXIA, SLURRED SPEECH, AREFLEXIA, WEAKNESS, FATIGUE, FASCICULATIONS, TWITCHING, TREMORS POSSIBLY OF THE TONGUE AND EYELIDS, AND EVENTUALLY PARALYSIS OF THE EXTREMITIES AND POSSIBLY OF THE RESPIRATORY MUSCLES. IN SEVERE CASES THERE MAY ALSO BE INVOLUNTARY DEFECATION AND URINATION, CYANOSIS, PSYCHOSIS, HYPERGLYCEMIA, ACUTE PANCREATITIS, CARDIAC IRREGULARITIES, PULMONARY EDEMA, UNCONSCIOUSNESS, CONVULSIONS, AND COMA. DEATH IS PRIMARILY DUE TO RESPIRATORY FAILURE, ALTHOUGH CARDIOVASCULAR EFFECTS INCLUDING CARDIAC ARREST MAY ALSO BE IMPLICATED. LONG TERM SEQUELAE ARE RARE BUT MAY INCLUDE NEUROPSYCHIATRIC DISORDERS AND MYOPATHY WITH MUSCLE TENDERNESS. **CHRONIC EXPOSURE-** REPEATED OR PROLONGED EXPOSURE MAY RESULT IN THE EFFECTS OF ACUTE EXPOSURE. OTHER EFFECTS REPORTED IN WORKERS REPEATEDLY EXPOSED INCLUDE IMPAIRED MEMORY AND CONCENTRATION, ACUTE PSYCHOSIS, SEVERE DEPRESSIONS, IRRITABILTY, CONFUSION, APATHY, EMOTIONAL LABILITY, SOCIAL WITHDRAWAL, CONFUSION, HEADACHE, SPEECH DIFFICULTIES, DELAYED REACTION TIMES, SPATIAL DISORIENTATION, NIGHTMARES, SLEEPWALKING, AND DROWSINESS OR INSOMNIA. AN INFLUENZA-LIKE CONDITION WITH HEADACHE, NAUSEA, WEAKNESS, ANOREXIA AND MALAISE HAS ALSO BEEN REPORTED.

FIRST AID- REMOVE FROM EXPOSURE AREA TO FRESH AIR IMMEDIATELY. IF BREATHING HAS STOPPED, GIVE ARTIFICIAL RESPIRATION. MAINTAIN AIRWAY AND BLOOD PRESSURE AND ADMINISTER OXYGEN IF AVAILABLE. KEEP AFFECTED PERSON WARM AND AT REST. TREAT SYMPTOMATICALLY AND SUPPORTIVELY. ADMINISTRATION OF OXYGEN SHOULD BE PERFORMED BY QUALIFIED PERSONNEL. GET MEDICAL ATTENTION IMMEDIATELY.

SKIN CONTACT: DISULFOTON: HIGHLY TOXIC. SEE INFORMATION ON ORGANOPHOSPHATES.

ORGANOPHOSPHATES: CHOLINESTERASE INHIBITOR. **ACUTE EXPOSURE-** LOCALIZED SWEATING AND FASCICULATIONS MAY OCCUR AT THE SITE OF CONTACT. IF SUFFICIENT AMOUNTS ARE ABSORBED, OTHER EFFECTS OF CHOLINESTERASE INHIBITION AS DESCRIBED IN ACUTE INHALATION MAY OCCUR. SYMPTOMS MAY BE DELAYED 2-3 HOURS, BUT USUALLY NO MORE THAN 12 HOURS. THE RATE OF ABSORPTION IS INCREASED BY THE PRESENCE OF DERMATITIS OR HIGH AMBIENT TEMPERATURES. **CHRONIC EXPOSURE-** REPEATED OR PROLONGED EXPOSURE MAY CAUSE EFFECTS AS DESCRIBED IN ACUTE EXPOSURE. SOME ORGANOPHOSPHATES MAY CAUSE SENSITIZATION.

FIRST AID- REMOVE CONTAMINATED CLOTHING IMMEDIATELY. WASH CONTAMINATED AREAS WITH SOAP AND WATER FOLLOWED BY ALCOHOL (ARENA, POISONING, 4TH ED.). EMERGENCY PERSONNEL SHOULD WEAR GLOVES AND AVOID CONTAMINATION. TREAT RESPIRATORY DIFFICULTY WITH ARTIFICIAL RESPIRATION. GET MEDICAL ATTENTION IMMEDIATELY.

EYE CONTACT: DISULFOTON: SEE INFORMATION ON ORGANOPHOSPHATES.

ORGANOPHOSPHATES: CHOLINESTERASE INHIBITOR. **ACUTE EXPOSURE-** DIRECT CONTACT MAY CAUSE PAIN, HYPEREMIA, LACRIMATION, TWITCHING OF THE EYELIDS, MIOSIS, AND CILIARY MUSCLE SPASM WITH LOSS OF ACCOMODATION, BLURRED OR DIMMED VISION AND BROWACHE. SOMETIMES MYDRIASIS MAY OCCUR INSTEAD OF MIOSIS. WITH SUFFICIENT EXPOSURE, OTHER SYMPTOMS OF CHOLINESTERASE INHIBITION AS DESCRIBED IN ACUTE INHALATION MAY OCCUR. **CHRONIC EXPOSURE-** REPEATED OR PROLONGED EXPOSURE MAY CAUSE EFFECTS AS DESCRIBED IN ACUTE EXPOSURE. SOME COMPOUNDS HAVE CAUSED TOXIC EFFECTS ON THE CRYSTALLINE LENS, CONJUNCTIVAL THICKENING AND OBSTRUCTION OF THE NASOLACRIMAL CANALS WHEN USED AS MIOTIC EYEDROPS.

FIRST AID- IRRIGATE EYES WITH WATER OR SALINE SOLUTION. IF SYMPTOMS OF POISONING OCCUR, TREAT RESPIRATORY DIFFICULTY WITH ARTIFICIAL RESPIRATION AND OXYGEN. OBSERVE PATIENT FOR AT LEAST 24-36 HOURS (GOSSELIN, CLINICAL TOXICOLOGY OF COMMERCIAL PRODUCTS, 5TH ED.). GET MEDICAL ATTENTION IMMEDIATELY. OXYGEN SHOULD BE ADMINISTERED BY QUALIFIED MEDICAL PERSONNEL.

INGESTION: DISULFOTON: HIGHLY TOXIC. THE RESULTS FROM A CHRONIC INGESTION STUDY OF HENS FOR DELAYED NEUROTOXICITY WERE NEGATIVE. SEE INFORMATION ON ORGANOPHOSPHATES.

ORGANOPHOSPHATES: CHOLINESTERASE INHIBITOR. **ACUTE EXPOSURE-** WHEN INGESTED, THE FIRST EFFECTS MAY BE NAUSEA, VOMITING, ANOREXIA, ABDOMINAL CRAMPS AND DIARRHEA. GASTROINTESTINAL ABSORPTION MAY CAUSE THE SYMPTOMS OF CHOLINESTERASE INHIBITION AS DESCRIBED IN ACUTE INHALATION. SYMPTOMS MAY BEGIN WITHIN MINUTES OR BE DELAYED. **CHRONIC EXPOSURE-** REPEATED INGESTION MAY CAUSE EFFECTS AS DESCRIBED IN ACUTE EXPOSURE.

FIRST AID- IF PERSON IS ALERT AND RESPIRATION IS NOT DEPRESSED, GIVE SYRUP OF IPECAC FOLLOWED BY WATER (IF VOMITING OCCURS, KEEP HEAD BELOW HIPS TO PREVENT ASPIRATION). IF CONSCIOUSNESS LEVEL DECLINES OR VOMITING HAS NOT OCCURRED IN 15 MINUTES EMPTY STOMACH BY GASTRIC LAVAGE WITH THE AID OF CUFFED ENDOTRACHEAL TUBE USING ISOTONIC SALINE OR 5% SODIUM BICARBONATE FOLLOW WITH ACTIVATED CHARCOAL. ESTABLISH AND MAINTAIN AIRWAY. TREAT RESPIRATORY DIFFICULTY WITH ARTIFICIAL RESPIRATION AND OXYGEN. DO NOT GIVE MORPHINE, AMINOPHYLLINE, PHENOTHIAZINES, RESERPINE, FUROSEMIDE, OR ETHACRYNIC ACID (MORGAN, RECOGNITION AND MANAGEMENT OF PESTICIDE POISONINGS, 3RD ED.). TREAT SYMPTOMATICALLY AND SUPPORTIVELY. ADMINISTRATION OF OXYGEN AND LAVAGE MUST BE PERFORMED BY QUALIFIED MEDICAL PERSONNEL. GET MEDICAL ATTENTION IMMEDIATELY.

ANTIDOTE: THE FOLLOWING ANTIDOTE(S) HAVE BEEN RECOMMENDED. HOWEVER, THE DECISION AS TO WHETHER THE SEVERITY OF POISONING REQUIRES ADMINISTRATION OF ANY ANTIDOTE AND ACTUAL DOSE REQUIRED SHOULD BE MADE BY QUALIFIED MEDICAL PERSONNEL.

FOR CHOLINESTERASE INHIBITORS: ESTABLISH CLEAR AIRWAY AND TISSUE OXYGENATION BY ASPIRATION OF SECRETIONS, AND IF NECESSARY, BY ASSISTED PULMONARY VENTILATION WITH OXYGEN. IMPROVE TISSUE OXYGENATION AS MUCH AS POSSIBLE BEFORE ADMINISTERING ATROPINE TO MINIMIZE THE RISK OF VENTRICULAR FIBRILLATION. ADMINISTER ATROPINE SULFATE INTRAVENOUSLY, OR INTRAMUSCULARLY IF IV INJECTION IS NOT POSSIBLE. IN MODERATELY SEVERE POISONING ADMINISTER ATROPINE SULFATE, 0.4-2.0 MG REPEATED EVERY 15 MINUTES UNTIL ATROPINIZATION IS ACHIEVED (TACHYCARDIA, FLUSHING, DRY MOUTH, MYDRIASIS). MAINTAIN ATROPINIZATION BY REPEATED DOSES FOR 2-12 HOURS, OR LONGER, DEPENDING ON THE SEVERITY OF POISONING. THE APPEARANCE OF RALES IN THE LUNG BASES, MIOSIS, SALIVATION, NAUSEA, BRADYCARDIA, ARE ALL INDICATIONS OF INADEQUATE ATROPINIZATION. SEVERELY POISONED INDIVIDUALS MAY EXHIBIT REMARKABLE TOLERANCE TO ATROPINE; TWO OR MORE TIMES THE DOSAGES SUGGESTED ABOVE MAY BE NEEDED. PERSONS NOT POISONED OR ONLY SLIGHTLY POISONED, HOWEVER, MAY DEVELOP SIGNS OF ATROPINE TOXICITY FROM SUCH LARGE DOSAGES: FEVER, MUSCLE FIBRILLATIONS, AND DELIRIUM ARE THE MAIN SIGNS OF ATROPINE TOXICITY. IF THESE SIGNS APPEAR WHILE THE PATIENT IS FULLY ATROPINIZED, ATROPINE ADMINISTRATION SHOULD BE DISCONTINUED, AT LEAST TEMPORARILY. OBSERVE TREATED PATIENTS CLOSELY AT LEAST 24 HOURS TO INSURE THAT SYMPTOMS (POSSIBLY PULMONARY EDEMA) DO NOT RECUR AS ATROPINIZATION WEARS OFF. IN VERY SEVERE POISONINGS, METABOLIC DISPOSITION OF TOXICANT MAY REQUIRE SEVERAL HOURS OR DAYS DURING WHICH ATROPINIZATION MUST BE MAINTAINED. MARKEDLY LOWER LEVELS OF URINARY METABOLITES INDICATE THAT ATROPINE DOSAGE CAN BE TAPERED OFF. AS DOSAGE IS REDUCED, CHECK THE LUNG BASES FREQUENTLY FOR RALES. IF RALES ARE HEARD OR OTHER SYMPTOMS RETURN, RE-ESTABLISH ATROPINIZATION PROMPTLY (MORGAN, RECOGNITION AND MANAGEMENT OF PESTICIDE POISONINGS, 3RD ED.). ADMINISTRATION OF ANTIDOTE MUST BE PERFORMED BY QUALIFIED MEDICAL PERSONNEL.

IN CASES OF SEVERE POISONING BY ORGANOPHOSPHATE PESTICIDES IN WHICH RESPIRATORY DEPRESSION, MUSCLE WEAKNESS AND TWITCHINGS ARE SEVERE, GIVE PRALIDOXIME (PROTOPAM-AYERST, 2-PAM), 1.0 GRAM INTRAVENOUSLY AT NO MORE THAN 0.5 GRAM PER MINUTE. DOSAGE OF PRALIDOXIME MAY BE REPEATED IN 1-2 HOURS, THEN AT 10-12 HOUR INTERVALS IF NEEDED. IN VERY SEVERE POISONINGS, DOSAGE RATES MAY BE DOUBLED. TREATMENT WITH PRALIDOXIME WILL BE MOST EFFECTIVE IF GIVEN WITHIN THIRTY-SIX HOURS AFTER POISONING (MORGAN, RECOGNITION AND MANAGEMENT OF PESTICIDE

POISONINGS, 3RD ED.). ANTIDOTE SHOULD BE ADMINISTERED BY QUALIFIED MEDICAL PERSONNEL.

REACTIVITY

REACTIVITY: STABLE UNDER NORMAL TEMPERATURES AND PRESSURES.
INCOMPATIBILITIES: DISULFOTON: ALKALINE CONDITIONS: MAY CAUSE HYDROLYSIS.
DECOMPOSITION: THERMAL DECOMPOSITION MAY RELEASE TOXIC AND/OR HAZARDOUS GASES.
POLYMERIZATION: HAZARDOUS POLYMERIZATION HAS NOT BEEN REPORTED TO OCCUR UNDER NORMAL TEMPERATURES AND PRESSURES.

STORAGE AND DISPOSAL

OBSERVE ALL FEDERAL, STATE AND LOCAL REGULATIONS WHEN STORING OR DISPOSING OF THIS SUBSTANCE. FOR ASSISTANCE, CONTACT THE DISTRICT DIRECTOR OF THE ENVIRONMENTAL PROTECTION AGENCY.

STORAGE

STORE IN ACCORDANCE WITH 40 CFR 165 RECOMMENDED PROCEDURES FOR THE DISPOSAL AND STORAGE OF PESTICIDES AND PESTICIDE CONTAINERS.
STORE AWAY FROM INCOMPATIBLE SUBSTANCES.
THRESHOLD PLANNING QUANTITY (TPQ): THE SUPERFUND AMENDMENTS AND REAUTHORIZATION ACT (SARA) SECTION 302 REQUIRES THAT EACH FACILITY WHERE ANY EXTREMELY HAZARDOUS SUBSTANCE IS PRESENT IN A QUANTITY EQUAL TO OR GREATER THAN THE TPQ ESTABLISHED FOR THAT SUBSTANCE NOTIFY THE STATE EMERGENCY RESPONSE COMMISSION FOR THE STATE IN WHICH IT IS LOCATED. SECTION 303 OF SARA REQUIRES THESE FACILITIES TO PARTICIPATE IN LOCAL EMERGENCY RESPONSE PLANNING (40 CFR 355.30).

DISPOSAL

DISPOSAL MUST BE IN ACCORDANCE WITH 40 CFR 165 RECOMMENDED PROCEDURES FOR THE DISPOSAL AND STORAGE OF PESTICIDES AND PESTICIDE CONTAINERS.

CONDITIONS TO AVOID

NONE REPORTED.

SPILL AND LEAK PROCEDURES

SOIL SPILL: DIG A HOLDING AREA SUCH AS A PIT, POND OR LAGOON TO CONTAIN SPILL AND DIKE SURFACE FLOW USING BARRIER OF SOIL, SANDBAGS, FOAMED POLYURETHANE OR FOAMED CONCRETE. ABSORB LIQUID MASS WITH FLY ASH OR CEMENT POWDER.
WATER SPILL: USE NATURAL DEEP WATER POCKETS, EXCAVATED LAGOONS, OR SAND BAG BARRIERS TO TRAP MATERIAL AT BOTTOM. IF DISSOLVED, APPLY ACTIVATED CARBON AT 10 TIMES SPILLED AMOUNT AT 10 PPM OR GREATER CONCENTRATION. USE MECHANICAL DREDGES OR LIFTS TO REMOVE IMMOBILIZED MASSES OF POLLUTION AND PRECIPITATES. ***OCCUPATIONAL SPILL:*** DO NOT TOUCH SPILLED MATERIAL. STOP LEAK IF YOU CAN DO IT WITHOUT RISK. USE WATER SPRAY TO REDUCE VAPORS. FOR SMALL SPILLS, TAKE UP WITH SAND OR OTHER ABSORBENT MATERIAL AND PLACE INTO CONTAINERS FOR LATER DISPOSAL. FOR SMALL DRY SPILLS, WITH A CLEAN SHOVEL PLACE MATERIAL INTO CLEAN, DRY CONTAINERS AND COVER. MOVE CONTAINERS FROM SPILL AREA. FOR LARGER SPILLS, DIKE FAR AHEAD OF SPILL FOR LATER DISPOSAL. KEEP UNNECESSARY PEOPLE AWAY. ISOLATE HAZARD AREA AND DENY ENTRY. VENTILATE CLOSED SPACES BEFORE ENTERING.
REPORTABLE QUANTITY (RQ): 1 POUND THE SUPERFUND AMENDMENTS AND REAUTHORIZATION ACT (SARA) SECTION 304 REQUIRES THAT A RELEASE EQUAL TO OR GREATER THAN THE REPORTABLE QUANTITY FOR THIS SUBSTANCE BE IMMEDIATELY REPORTED TO THE LOCAL EMERGENCY PLANNING COMMITTEE AND THE STATE EMERGENCY RESPONSE COMMISSION (40 CFR 355.40). IF THE RELEASE OF THIS SUBSTANCE IS REPORTABLE UNDER CERCLA SECTION 103, THE NATIONAL RESPONSE CENTER MUST BE NOTIFIED IMMEDIATELY AT (800) 424-8802 OR (202) 426-2675 IN THE METROPOLITAN WASHINGTON, D.C. AREA (40 CFR 302.6).

PROTECTIVE EQUIPMENT

VENTILATION: PROCESS ENCLOSURE RECOMMENDED TO MEET PUBLISHED EXPOSURE LIMITS.
RESPIRATOR: THE FOLLOWING RESPIRATORS ARE RECOMMENDED BASED ON INFORMATION FOUND IN THE PHYSICAL DATA, TOXICITY AND HEALTH EFFECTS SECTIONS. THEY ARE RANKED IN ORDER FROM MINIMUM TO MAXIMUM RESPIRATORY PROTECTION. THE SPECIFIC RESPIRATOR SELECTED MUST BE BASED ON CONTAMINATION LEVELS FOUND IN THE WORK PLACE, MUST NOT EXCEED THE WORKING LIMITS OF THE RESPIRATOR AND BE JOINTLY APPROVED BY THE NATIONAL INSTITUTE FOR OCCUPATIONAL SAFETY AND HEALTH AND THE MINE SAFETY AND HEALTH ADMINISTRATION (NIOSH-MSHA).
TYPE 'C' SUPPLIED-AIR RESPIRATOR WITH A FULL FACEPIECE OPERATED IN PRESSURE-DEMAND OR OTHER POSITIVE PRESSURE MODE OR WITH A FULL FACEPIECE, HELMET OR HOOD OPERATED IN CONTINOUS-FLOW MODE.
SELF-CONTAINED BREATHING APPARATUS WITH A FULL FACEPIECE OPERATED IN PRESSURE-DEMAND OR OTHER POSITIVE PRESSURE MODE.
FOR FIREFIGHTING AND OTHER IMMEDIATELY DANGEROUS TO LIFE OR HEALTH CONDITIONS:
SELF-CONTAINED BREATHING APPARATUS WITH FULL FACEPIECE OPERATED IN PRESSURE-DEMAND OR OTHER POSITIVE PRESSURE MODE.
SUPPLIED-AIR RESPIRATOR WITH FULL FACEPIECE AND OPERATED IN PRESSURE-DEMAND OR OTHER POSITIVE PRESSURE MODE IN COMBINATION WITH AN AUXILIARY SELF-CONTAINED BREATHING APPARATUS OPERATED IN PRESSURE-DEMAND OR OTHER POSITIVE PRESSURE MODE.
CLOTHING: EMPLOYEE MUST WEAR APPROPRIATE PROTECTIVE (IMPERVIOUS) CLOTHING AND EQUIPMENT TO PREVENT ANY POSSIBILITY OF SKIN CONTACT WITH THIS SUBSTANCE.
GLOVES: EMPLOYEE MUST WEAR APPROPRIATE PROTECTIVE GLOVES TO PREVENT CONTACT WITH THIS SUBSTANCE.
EYE PROTECTION: EMPLOYEE MUST WEAR SPLASH-PROOF OR DUST-RESISTANT SAFETY GOGGLES AND A FACESHIELD TO PREVENT CONTACT WITH THIS SUBSTANCE.
EMERGENCY WASH FACILITIES: WHERE THERE IS ANY POSSIBILITY THAT AN EMPLOYEE'S EYES AND/OR SKIN MAY BE EXPOSED TO THIS SUBSTANCE, THE EMPLOYER SHOULD PROVIDE AN EYE WASH FOUNTAIN AND QUICK DRENCH SHOWER WITHIN THE IMMEDIATE WORK AREA FOR EMERGENCY USE.

AUTHORIZED BY- OCCUPATIONAL HEALTH SERVICES, INC.
CREATION DATE: 10/04/89 ***REVISION DATE:*** 06/20/90

MATERIAL SAFETY DATA SHEET

OCCUPATIONAL HEALTH SERVICES, INC.
AGRICULTURE AND PESTICIDE DIVISION
450 SEVENTH AVENUE, SUITE 2407
NEW YORK, NEW YORK 10123
1-800-445-MSDS OR (212) 967-1100

EMERGENCY CONTACT:
JOHN S. BRANSFORD, JR. (615) 292-1180

SUBSTANCE IDENTIFICATION

CAS-NUMBER 2497-06-5
SUBSTANCE: DISULFOTON SULFONE
TRADE NAMES/SYNONYMS: PHOSPHORODITHIOIC ACID, O,O-DIETHYL-S-(2-(ETHYLSULFONYL)ETHYL)ESTER; O,O-DIETHYL-S-(2-(ETHYLSULFONYL)ETHYL)PHOSPHOROTHIOATE; DISULFOTON DIOXIDE; DISYSTON SULFONE; C8H19O4PS3; PST08381
CHEMICAL FAMILY: PHOSPHOROTHIOATE SULFONYL
MOLECULAR FORMULA: (C2-H5-O)2-P-(S)-S-C2-H4-S-(O)2-C2-H5
MOLECULAR WEIGHT: 306.40
CERCLA RATINGS (SCALE 0-3): HEALTH=3 FIRE=U REACTIVITY=0 PERSISTENCE=1
NFPA RATINGS (SCALE 0-4): HEALTH=3 FIRE=U REACTIVITY=0

COMPONENTS AND CONTAMINANTS

COMPONENT: DISULFOTON SULFONE ***PERCENT:*** 100.0
CAS# 2497-06-5
OTHER CONTAMINANTS: NONE
EXPOSURE LIMITS: NO OCCUPATIONAL EXPOSURE LIMITS ESTABLISHED BY OSHA, ACGIH, OR NIOSH.

PHYSICAL DATA

DESCRIPTION: CLEAR LIQUID. ***BOILING POINT:*** NOT AVAILABLE
SPECIFIC GRAVITY: NOT AVAILABLE ***VAPOR PRESSURE:*** NOT AVAILABLE
SOLUBILITY IN WATER: NOT AVAILABLE

FIRE AND EXPLOSION DATA

FIRE AND EXPLOSION HAZARD: UNKNOWN FIRE AND EXPLOSION HAZARD.
FLASH POINT: NOT AVAILABLE
FIREFIGHTING MEDIA: DRY CHEMICAL, CARBON DIOXIDE, HALON, WATER SPRAY OR STANDARD FOAM (1987 EMERGENCY RESPONSE GUIDEBOOK, DOT P 5800.4). FOR LARGER FIRES, USE WATER SPRAY, FOG OR STANDARD FOAM (1987 EMERGENCY RESPONSE GUIDEBOOK, DOT P 5800.4).
FIREFIGHTING: MOVE CONTAINERS FROM FIRE AREA IF POSSIBLE. COOL CONTAINERS EXPOSED TO FLAMES WITH WATER FROM SIDE UNTIL WELL AFTER FIRE IS OUT. FIGHT FIRE FROM MAXIMUM DISTANCE. STAY AWAY FROM STORAGE TANK ENDS. DIKE FIRE CONTROL WATER FOR LATER DISPOSAL. DO NOT SCATTER MATERIAL.

(1987 EMERGENCY RESPONSE GUIDEBOOK, DOT P 5800.4, GUIDE PAGE 57). EXTINGUISH ONLY IF FLOW CAN BE STOPPED. USE FLOODING AMOUNTS OF WATER AS A FOG; SOLID STREAMS MAY BE INEFFECTIVE. COOL CONTAINERS WITH FLOODING AMOUNTS OF WATER FROM AS FAR A DISTANCE AS POSSIBLE. AVOID BREATHING POISONOUS VAPORS, KEEP UPWIND.

TRANSPORTATION DATA

DEPARTMENT OF TRANSPORTATION HAZARD CLASSIFICATION 49 CFR 172.101: POISON B

DEPARTMENT OF TRANSPORTATION LABELING REQUIREMENTS 49 CFR 172.101 AND SUBPART E: POISON

DEPARTMENT OF TRANSPORTATION PACKAGING REQUIREMENTS: 49 CFR 173.346 EXCEPTIONS: 49 CFR 173.345

TOXICITY

DISULFOTON SULFONE: TOXICITY DATA: 7500 UG/KG ORAL-RAT LD50. CARCINOGEN STATUS: NONE ACUTE TOXICITY LEVEL: HIGHLY TOXIC BY INGESTION. TARGET EFFECTS: CHOLINESTERASE INHIBITOR. POISONING MAY AFFECT THE NERVOUS SYSTEM.* AT INCREASED RISK FROM EXPOSURE: PERSONS WITH RESPIRATORY AILMENTS, RECENT EXPOSURE TO CHOLINESTERASE INHIBITORS OR IMPAIRED CHOLINESTERASE PRODUCTION, OR LIVER MALFUNCTION.* ADDITIONAL DATA: MAY CROSS THE PLACENTA. HIGH ENVIRONMENTAL TEMPERATURES OR EXPOSURE OF THE CHEMICAL TO VISIBLE OR ULTRAVIOLET LIGHT MAY ENHANCE THE TOXICITY. INTERACTIONS WITH MEDICATIONS MAY OCCUR.*

* MAY BE BASED ON GENERAL INFORMATION ON ORGANOPHOSPHATES.

HEALTH EFFECTS AND FIRST AID

INHALATION: DISULFOTON SULFONE: SEE INFORMATION ON ORGANOPHOSPHATES. ORGANOPHOSPHATES: CHOLINESTERASE INHIBITOR. **ACUTE EXPOSURE-** WHEN INHALED, THE FIRST EFFECTS OF CHOLINESTERASE INHIBITORS ARE USUALLY RESPIRATORY AND MAY INCLUDE NASAL HYPEREMIA AND WATERY DISCHARGE, COUGH, CHEST DISCOMFORT, DYSPNEA, AND WHEEZING DUE TO INCREASED BRONCHIAL SECRETIONS AND BRONCHOCONSTRICTION. IF SUFFICIENT AMOUNTS ARE ABSORBED, OTHER SYSTEMIC EFFECTS MAY BEGIN WITHIN A FEW MINUTES OR BE DELAYED FOR UP TO 12 HOURS. SYMPTOMS MAY INCLUDE PALLOR, NAUSEA, VOMITING, DIARRHEA, ABDOMINAL CRAMPS, HEADACHE, DIZZINESS, OCULAR PAIN, BLURRED VISION, MIOSIS OR IN SOME CASES, ESPECIALLY INITIALLY, MYDRIASIS, LACRIMATION, SALIVATION, SWEATING, AND CONFUSION. OTHER REPORTED CENTRAL NERVOUS SYSTEM OR NEUROMUSCULAR EFFECTS MAY INCLUDE ATAXIA, SLURRED SPEECH, AREFLEXIA, WEAKNESS, FATIGUE, FASCICULATIONS, TWITCHING, TREMORS POSSIBLY OF THE TONGUE AND EYELIDS, AND EVENTUALLY PARALYSIS OF THE EXTREMITIES AND POSSIBLY OF THE RESPIRATORY MUSCLES. IN SEVERE CASES THERE MAY ALSO BE INVOLUNTARY DEFECATION AND URINATION, CYANOSIS, PSYCHOSIS, HYPERGLYCEMIA, ACUTE PANCREATITIS, CARDIAC IRREGULARITIES, PULMONARY EDEMA, UNCONSCIOUSNESS, CONVULSIONS, AND COMA. DEATH IS PRIMARILY DUE TO RESPIRATORY FAILURE, ALTHOUGH CARDIOVASCULAR EFFECTS INCLUDING CARDIAC ARREST MAY ALSO BE IMPLICATED. LONG TERM SEQUELAE ARE RARE BUT MAY INCLUDE NEUROPSYCHIATRIC DISORDERS AND MYOPATHY WITH MUSCLE TENDERNESS. SOME ORGANOPHOSPHATES MAY CAUSE A DELAYED NEUROPATHY BEGINNING 1-4 WEEKS AFTER AN ACUTE EXPOSURE WHICH MAY OR MAY NOT HAVE CAUSED ACUTE CHOLINERGIC EFFECTS. NUMBNESS, TINGLING, WEAKNESS AND CRAMPING BEGINNING SYMMETRICALLY IN THE LOWER LIMBS MAY PROGRESS TO ATAXIA AND PARALYSIS. IN SEVERE CASES, UPPER LIMB INVOLVEMENT IS POSSIBLE AND FLACCID PARALYSIS MAY PROGRESS TO SPASTIC PARALYSIS WITH EXAGGERATED REFLEXES. IMPROVEMENT MAY OCCUR OVER MONTHS TO YEARS, BUT SOME RESIDUAL IMPAIRMENT USUALLY REMAINS. **CHRONIC EXPOSURE-** REPEATED OR PROLONGED EXPOSURE MAY RESULT IN THE EFFECTS OF ACUTE EXPOSURE INCLUDING THE DELAYED NEUROPATHY. OTHER EFFECTS REPORTED IN WORKERS REPEATEDLY EXPOSED INCLUDE IMPAIRED MEMORY AND CONCENTRATION, ACUTE PSYCHOSIS, SEVERE DEPRESSIONS, IRRITABILTY, CONFUSION, APATHY, EMOTIONAL LABILITY, SOCIAL WITHDRAWAL, CONFUSION, HEADACHE, SPEECH DIFFICULTIES, DELAYED REACTION TIMES, SPATIAL DISORIENTATION, NIGHTMARES, SLEEPWALKING, AND DROWSINESS OR INSOMNIA. AN INFLUENZA-LIKE CONDITION WITH HEADACHE, NAUSEA, WEAKNESS, ANOREXIA AND MALAISE HAS ALSO BEEN REPORTED.

FIRST AID- REMOVE FROM EXPOSURE AREA TO FRESH AIR IMMEDIATELY. IF BREATHING HAS STOPPED, GIVE ARTIFICIAL RESPIRATION. MAINTAIN AIRWAY AND BLOOD PRESSURE AND ADMINISTER OXYGEN IF AVAILABLE. KEEP AFFECTED PERSON WARM AND AT REST. TREAT SYMPTOMATICALLY AND SUPPORTIVELY. ADMINISTRATION OF OXYGEN SHOULD BE PERFORMED BY QUALIFIED PERSONNEL. GET MEDICAL ATTENTION IMMEDIATELY.

SKIN CONTACT: DISULFOTON SULFONE: SEE INFORMATION ON ORGANOPHOSPHATES. ORGANOPHOSPHATES: CHOLINESTERASE INHIBITOR. **ACUTE EXPOSURE-** LOCALIZED SWEATING AND FASCICULATIONS MAY OCCUR AT THE SITE OF CONTACT. IF SUFFICIENT AMOUNTS ARE ABSORBED, OTHER EFFECTS OF CHOLINESTERASE INHIBITION AS DESCRIBED IN ACUTE INHALATION MAY OCCUR. SYMPTOMS MAY BE DELAYED 2-3 HOURS, BUT USUALLY NO MORE THAN 12 HOURS. THE RATE OF ABSORPTION IS INCREASED BY THE PRESENCE OF DERMATITIS OR HIGH AMBIENT TEMPERATURES. DELAYED NEUROPATHY IS ALSO POSSIBLE. **CHRONIC EXPOSURE-** REPEATED OR PROLONGED EXPOSURE MAY CAUSE EFFECTS AS DESCRIBED IN ACUTE EXPOSURE. SOME ORGANOPHOSPHATES MAY CAUSE SENSITIZATION.

FIRST AID- REMOVE CONTAMINATED CLOTHING IMMEDIATELY. WASH CONTAMINATED AREAS WITH SOAP AND WATER FOLLOWED BY ALCOHOL (ARENA, POISONING, 4TH ED.). EMERGENCY PERSONNEL SHOULD WEAR GLOVES AND AVOID CONTAMINATION. TREAT RESPIRATORY DIFFICULTY WITH ARTIFICIAL RESPIRATION. GET MEDICAL ATTENTION IMMEDIATELY.

EYE CONTACT: DISULFOTON SULFONE: SEE INFORMATION ON ORGANOPHOSPHATES. ORGANOPHOSPHATES: CHOLINESTERASE INHIBITOR. **ACUTE EXPOSURE-** DIRECT CONTACT MAY CAUSE PAIN, HYPEREMIA, LACRIMATION, TWITCHING OF THE EYELIDS, MIOSIS, AND CILIARY MUSCLE SPASM WITH LOSS OF ACCOMODATION, BLURRED OR DIMMED VISION AND BROWACHE. SOMETIMES MYDRIASIS MAY OCCUR INSTEAD OF MIOSIS. WITH SUFFICIENT EXPOSURE, OTHER SYMPTOMS OF CHOLINESTERASE INHIBITION AS DESCRIBED IN ACUTE INHALATION MAY OCCUR. **CHRONIC EXPOSURE-** REPEATED OR PROLONGED EXPOSURE MAY CAUSE EFFECTS AS DESCRIBED IN ACUTE EXPOSURE. SOME COMPOUNDS HAVE CAUSED TOXIC EFFECTS ON THE CRYSTALLINE LENS, CONJUNCTIVAL THICKENING AND OBSTRUCTION OF THE NASOLACRIMAL CANALS WHEN USED AS MIOTIC EYEDROPS.

FIRST AID- IRRIGATE EYES WITH WATER OR SALINE SOLUTION. IF SYMPTOMS OF POISONING OCCUR, TREAT RESPIRATORY DIFFICULTY WITH ARTIFICIAL RESPIRATION AND OXYGEN. OBSERVE PATIENT FOR AT LEAST 24-36 HOURS (GOSSELIN, CLINICAL TOXICOLOGY OF COMMERCIAL PRODUCTS, 5TH ED.). GET MEDICAL ATTENTION IMMEDIATELY. OXYGEN SHOULD BE ADMINISTERED BY QUALIFIED MEDICAL PERSONNEL.

INGESTION: DISULFOTON SULFONE: HIGHLY TOXIC. THE LETHAL DOSE REPORTED IN RATS WAS 7500 UG/KG. SEE INFORMATION ON ORGANOPHOSPHATES. ORGANOPHOSPHATES: CHOLINESTERASE INHIBITOR. **ACUTE EXPOSURE-** WHEN INGESTED, THE FIRST EFFECTS MAY BE NAUSEA, VOMITING, ANOREXIA, ABDOMINAL CRAMPS AND DIARRHEA. GASTROINTESTINAL ABSORPTION MAY CAUSE SYMPTOMS OF CHOLINESTERASE INHIBITION AS DESCRIBED IN ACUTE INHALATION. SYMPTOMS MAY BEGIN WITHIN MINUTES OR BE DELAYED FOR HOURS. DELAYED EFFECTS INCLUDING NEUROPATHY MAY ALSO OCCUR. **CHRONIC EXPOSURE-** REPEATED INGESTION MAY CAUSE EFFECTS AS DESCRIBED IN ACUTE EXPOSURE.

FIRST AID- IF PERSON IS ALERT AND RESPIRATION IS NOT DEPRESSED, GIVE SYRUP OF IPECAC FOLLOWED BY WATER (IF VOMITING OCCURS, KEEP HEAD BELOW HIPS TO PREVENT ASPIRATION). IF CONSCIOUSNESS LEVEL DECLINES OR VOMITING HAS NOT OCCURRED IN 15 MINUTES EMPTY STOMACH BY GASTRIC LAVAGE WITH THE AID OF CUFFED ENDOTRACHEAL TUBE USING ISOTONIC SALINE OR 5% SODIUM BICARBONATE FOLLOW WITH ACTIVATED CHARCOAL. ESTABLISH AND MAINTAIN AIRWAY. TREAT RESPIRATORY DIFFICULTY WITH ARTIFICIAL RESPIRATION AND OXYGEN. DO NOT GIVE MORPHINE, AMINOPHYLLINE, PHENOTHIAZINES, RESERPINE, FUROSEMIDE, OR ETHACRYNIC ACID (MORGAN, RECOGNITION AND MANAGEMENT OF PESTICIDE POISONINGS, 3RD ED.). TREAT SYMPTOMATICALLY AND SUPPORTIVELY. ADMINISTRATION OF OXYGEN AND LAVAGE MUST BE PERFORMED BY QUALIFIED MEDICAL PERSONNEL. GET MEDICAL ATTENTION IMMEDIATELY.

ANTIDOTE: THE FOLLOWING ANTIDOTE(S) HAVE BEEN RECOMMENDED. HOWEVER, THE DECISION AS TO WHETHER THE SEVERITY OF POISONING REQUIRES ADMINISTRATION OF ANY ANTIDOTE AND ACTUAL DOSE REQUIRED SHOULD BE MADE BY QUALIFIED MEDICAL PERSONNEL.

FOR CHOLINESTERASE INHIBITORS: ESTABLISH CLEAR AIRWAY AND TISSUE OXYGENATION BY ASPIRATION OF SECRETIONS, AND IF NECESSARY, BY ASSISTED PULMONARY VENTILATION WITH OXYGEN. IMPROVE TISSUE OXYGENATION AS MUCH AS POSSIBLE BEFORE ADMINISTERING ATROPINE TO MINIMIZE THE RISK OF VENTRICULAR FIBRILLATION. ADMINISTER ATROPINE SULFATE INTRAVENOUSLY, OR INTRAMUSCULARLY IF IV INJECTION IS NOT POSSIBLE. IN MODERATELY SEVERE POISONING ADMINISTER ATROPINE SULFATE, 0.4-2.0 MG REPEATED EVERY 15 MINUTES UNTIL ATROPINIZATION IS ACHIEVED (TACHYCARDIA, FLUSHING, DRY MOUTH, MYDRIASIS). MAINTAIN ATROPINIZATION BY REPEATED DOSES FOR 2-12 HOURS, OR LONGER, DEPENDING ON THE SEVERITY OF POISONING. THE APPEARANCE OF RALES IN THE LUNG BASES, MIOSIS, SALIVATION, NAUSEA, BRADYCARDIA, ARE ALL INDICATIONS OF INADEQUATE ATROPINIZATION. SEVERELY POISONED INDIVIDUALS MAY EXHIBIT REMARKABLE TOLERANCE TO ATROPINE; TWO OR MORE TIMES THE DOSAGES SUGGESTED ABOVE MAY BE NEEDED. PERSONS NOT POISONED OR ONLY SLIGHTLY POISONED, HOWEVER, MAY

DEVELOP SIGNS OF ATROPINE TOXICITY FROM SUCH LARGE DOSAGES: FEVER, MUSCLE FIBRILLATIONS, AND DELIRIUM ARE THE MAIN SIGNS OF ATROPINE TOXICITY. IF THESE SIGNS APPEAR WHILE THE PATIENT IS FULLY ATROPINIZED, ATROPINE ADMINISTRATION SHOULD BE DISCONTINUED, AT LEAST TEMPORARILY. OBSERVE TREATED PATIENTS CLOSELY AT LEAST 24 HOURS TO INSURE THAT SYMPTOMS (POSSIBLY PULMONARY EDEMA) DO NOT RECUR AS ATROPINIZATION WEARS OFF. IN VERY SEVERE POISONINGS, METABOLIC DISPOSITION OF TOXICANT MAY REQUIRE SEVERAL HOURS OR DAYS DURING WHICH ATROPINIZATION MUST BE MAINTAINED. MARKEDLY LOWER LEVELS OF URINARY METABOLITES INDICATE THAT ATROPINE DOSAGE CAN BE TAPERED OFF. AS DOSAGE IS REDUCED, CHECK THE LUNG BASES FREQUENTLY FOR RALES. IF RALES ARE HEARD OR OTHER SYMPTOMS RETURN, RE-ESTABLISH ATROPINIZATION PROMPTLY (MORGAN, RECOGNITION AND MANAGEMENT OF PESTICIDE POISONINGS, 3RD ED.). ADMINISTRATION OF ANTIDOTE MUST BE PERFORMED BY QUALIFIED MEDICAL PERSONNEL.

IN CASES OF SEVERE POISONING BY ORGANOPHOSPHATE PESTICIDES IN WHICH RESPIRATORY DEPRESSION, MUSCLE WEAKNESS AND TWITCHINGS ARE SEVERE, GIVE PRALIDOXIME (PROTOPAM-AYERST, 2-PAM), 1.0 GRAM INTRAVENOUSLY AT NO MORE THAN 0.5 GRAM PER MINUTE. DOSAGE OF PRALIDOXIME MAY BE REPEATED IN 1-2 HOURS, THEN AT 10-12 HOUR INTERVALS IF NEEDED. IN VERY SEVERE POISONINGS, DOSAGE RATES MAY BE DOUBLED. TREATMENT WITH PRALIDOXIME WILL BE MOST EFFECTIVE IF GIVEN WITHIN THIRTY-SIX HOURS AFTER POISONING (MORGAN, RECOGNITION AND MANAGEMENT OF PESTICIDE POISONINGS, 3RD ED.). ANTIDOTE SHOULD BE ADMINISTERED BY QUALIFIED MEDICAL PERSONNEL.

REACTIVITY

REACTIVITY: STABLE UNDER NORMAL TEMPERATURES AND PRESSURES.

INCOMPATIBILITIES: DISULFOTON SULFONE: OXIDIZERS (STRONG): FIRE AND EXPLOSION HAZARD.

DECOMPOSITION: THERMAL DECOMPOSITION PRODUCTS MAY INCLUDE TOXIC OXIDES OF CARBON, SULFUR, AND PHOSPHORUS.

POLYMERIZATION: HAZARDOUS POLYMERIZATION HAS NOT BEEN REPORTED TO OCCUR UNDER NORMAL TEMPERATURES AND PRESSURES.

STORAGE AND DISPOSAL

OBSERVE ALL FEDERAL, STATE AND LOCAL REGULATIONS WHEN STORING OR DISPOSING OF THIS SUBSTANCE. FOR ASSISTANCE, CONTACT THE DISTRICT DIRECTOR OF THE ENVIRONMENTAL PROTECTION AGENCY.

STORAGE

STORE IN ACCORDANCE WITH 40 CFR 165 RECOMMENDED PROCEDURES FOR THE DISPOSAL AND STORAGE OF PESTICIDES AND PESTICIDE CONTAINERS.

STORE AWAY FROM INCOMPATIBLE SUBSTANCES.

DISPOSAL

DISPOSAL MUST BE IN ACCORDANCE WITH 40 CFR 165 RECOMMENDED PROCEDURES FOR THE DISPOSAL AND STORAGE OF PESTICIDES AND PESTICIDE CONTAINERS.

CONDITIONS TO AVOID

MAY BE IGNITED BY HEAT, SPARKS OR FLAMES. CONTAINER MAY EXPLODE IN HEAT OF FIRE. VAPOR EXPLOSION AND POISON HAZARD INDOORS, OUTDOORS OR IN SEWERS.

SPILL AND LEAK PROCEDURES

OCCUPATIONAL SPILL: SHUT OFF IGNITION SOURCES. DO NOT TOUCH SPILLED MATERIAL. STOP LEAK IF YOU CAN DO IT WITHOUT RISK. USE WATER SPRAY TO REDUCE VAPORS. FOR SMALL SPILLS, TAKE UP WITH SAND OR OTHER ABSORBENT MATERIAL AND PLACE INTO CONTAINERS FOR LATER DISPOSAL. FOR SMALL DRY SPILLS, WITH CLEAN SHOVEL PLACE MATERIAL INTO CLEAN, DRY CONTAINERS AND COVER. MOVE CONTAINERS FROM SPILL AREA. FOR LARGER SPILLS, DIKE FAR AHEAD OF SPILL FOR LATER DISPOSAL. NO SMOKING, FLAMES OR FLARES IN HAZARD AREA! KEEP UNNECESSARY PEOPLE AWAY. ISOLATE HAZARD AREA AND DENY ENTRY. VENTILATE CLOSED SPACES BEFORE ENTERING.

PROTECTIVE EQUIPMENT

VENTILATION: PROCESS ENCLOSURE RECOMMENDED.

RESPIRATOR: THE FOLLOWING RESPIRATORS ARE RECOMMENDED BASED ON INFORMATION FOUND IN THE PHYSICAL DATA, TOXICITY AND HEALTH EFFECTS SECTIONS. THEY ARE RANKED IN ORDER FROM MINIMUM TO MAXIMUM RESPIRATORY PROTECTION. THE SPECIFIC RESPIRATOR SELECTED MUST BE BASED ON CONTAMINATION LEVELS FOUND IN THE WORK PLACE, MUST NOT EXCEED THE WORKING LIMITS OF THE RESPIRATOR AND BE JOINTLY APPROVED BY THE NATIONAL INSTITUTE FOR OCCUPATIONAL SAFETY AND HEALTH AND THE MINE SAFETY AND HEALTH ADMINISTRATION (NIOSH-MSHA).

TYPE 'C' SUPPLIED-AIR RESPIRATOR WITH A FULL FACEPIECE OPERATED IN PRESSURE-DEMAND OR OTHER POSITIVE PRESSURE MODE OR WITH A FULL FACEPIECE, HELMET OR HOOD OPERATED IN CONTINOUS-FLOW MODE.

SELF-CONTAINED BREATHING APPARATUS WITH A FULL FACEPIECE OPERATED IN PRESSURE-DEMAND OR OTHER POSITIVE PRESSURE MODE.

FOR FIREFIGHTING AND OTHER IMMEDIATELY DANGEROUS TO LIFE OR HEALTH CONDITIONS:

SELF-CONTAINED BREATHING APPARATUS WITH FULL FACEPIECE OPERATED IN PRESSURE-DEMAND OR OTHER POSITIVE PRESSURE MODE.

SUPPLIED-AIR RESPIRATOR WITH FULL FACEPIECE AND OPERATED IN PRESSURE-DEMAND OR OTHER POSITIVE PRESSURE MODE IN COMBINATION WITH AN AUXILIARY SELF-CONTAINED BREATHING APPARATUS OPERATED IN PRESSURE-DEMAND OR OTHER POSITIVE PRESSURE MODE.

CLOTHING: EMPLOYEE MUST WEAR APPROPRIATE PROTECTIVE (IMPERVIOUS) CLOTHING AND EQUIPMENT TO PREVENT ANY POSSIBILITY OF SKIN CONTACT WITH THIS SUBSTANCE.

GLOVES: EMPLOYEE MUST WEAR APPROPRIATE PROTECTIVE GLOVES TO PREVENT CONTACT WITH THIS SUBSTANCE.

EYE PROTECTION: EMPLOYEE MUST WEAR SPLASH-PROOF OR DUST-RESISTANT SAFETY GOGGLES AND A FACESHIELD TO PREVENT CONTACT WITH THIS SUBSTANCE.

EMERGENCY WASH FACILITIES: WHERE THERE IS ANY POSSIBILITY THAT AN EMPLOYEE'S EYES AND/OR SKIN MAY BE EXPOSED TO THIS SUBSTANCE, THE EMPLOYER SHOULD PROVIDE AN EYE WASH FOUNTAIN AND QUICK DRENCH SHOWER WITHIN THE IMMEDIATE WORK AREA FOR EMERGENCY USE.

AUTHORIZED BY- OCCUPATIONAL HEALTH SERVICES, INC.

CREATION DATE: 05/04/90 ***REVISION DATE:*** 05/04/90

MATERIAL SAFETY DATA SHEET

OCCUPATIONAL HEALTH SERVICES, INC.
AGRICULTURE AND PESTICIDE DIVISION
450 SEVENTH AVENUE, SUITE 2407
NEW YORK, NEW YORK 10123
1-800-445-MSDS OR (212) 967-1100

EMERGENCY CONTACT:
JOHN S. BRANSFORD, JR. (615) 292-1180

SUBSTANCE IDENTIFICATION

SUBSTANCE: DITHANE Z-78

TRADE NAMES/SYNONYMS: PST08396

CHEMICAL FAMILY: ORGANOMETALLIC

CERCLA RATINGS (SCALE 0-3): HEALTH=3 FIRE=1 REACTIVITY=0 PERSISTENCE=3

NFPA RATINGS (SCALE 0-4): HEALTH=3 FIRE=1 REACTIVITY=0

COMPONENTS AND CONTAMINANTS

COMPONENT: MANGANESE-ETHYLENE-BIS-DITHIOCARBAMATE, ZINC COMPLEX ***PERCENT:*** 75.0-90.0

COMPONENT: ETHYLENE THIOUREA ***PERCENT:*** 25.0-10.0
CAS# 96-45-7

EXPOSURE LIMITS: DITHANE Z-78: 0.1 MG/M3 ROHM AND HAAS RECOMMENDED 8 HOUR TWA AS A DUST

PHYSICAL DATA

DESCRIPTION: GRAY-WHITE POWDER WITH SLIGHT SULFUR ODOR

BOILING POINT: DECOMPOSES ***MELTING POINT:*** 315 F (157 C)DECOMP.

SPECIFIC GRAVITY: NOT AVAILABLE ***SOLUBILITY IN WATER:*** NEGLIGIBLE

SOLVENT SOLUBILITY: CARBON DISULFIDE, PYRIDINE, ALCOHOL

FIRE AND EXPLOSION DATA

FIRE AND EXPLOSION HAZARD: SLIGHT FIRE HAZARD WHEN EXPOSED TO HEAT OR FLAME.

FLASH POINT: 200 F (93 C)

FIREFIGHTING MEDIA: DRY CHEMICAL, CARBON DIOXIDE, HALON, WATER SPRAY OR STANDARD FOAM (1987 EMERGENCY RESPONSE GUIDEBOOK, DOT P 5800.4).

FOR LARGER FIRES, USE WATER SPRAY, FOG OR STANDARD FOAM (1987 EMERGENCY RESPONSE GUIDEBOOK, DOT P 5800.4).

FIREFIGHTING: MOVE CONTAINER FROM FIRE AREA IF POSSIBLE. DO NOT SCATTER SPILLED MATERIAL WITH HIGH PRESSURE WATER STREAMS. DIKE FIRE CONTROL WATER FOR LATER DISPOSAL (1987 EMERGENCY RESPONSE GUIDEBOOK, DOT P 5800.4, GUIDE PAGE 31).
USE AGENTS SUITABLE FOR TYPE OF SURROUNDING FIRE. AVOID BREATHING HAZARDOUS VAPORS, KEEP UPWIND.

TOXICITY

DITHANE Z-78 (CONTAINS MANGANESE ETHYLENE-BIS-DITHIOCARBAMATE, ZINC COMPLEX AND ETHYLENE THIOUREA):
MANGANESE ETHYLENE-BIS-DITHIOCARBAMATE, ZINC COMPLEX: NO DATA AVAILABLE. DATA FOR SIMILAR COMPOUND- ZINC ETHYLENEBISDITHIOCARBAMATE: TOXICITY DATA: 5200 MG/KG ORAL-RAT LD50; 7600 MG/KG ORAL-MOUSE LD50; 600 MG/KG ORAL-RABBIT LDLO; MUTAGENIC DATA (RTECS); REPRODUCTIVE EFFECTS DATA (RTECS); TUMORIGENIC DATA (RTECS). CARCINOGEN STATUS: ANIMAL INADEQUATE EVIDENCE (IARC); INSUFFICIENT DATA EXIST TO EVALUATE THE CARCINOGENICITY. LOCAL EFFECTS: IRRITANT- INHALATION, SKIN, AND EYES. ACUTE TOXICITY LEVEL: SLIGHTLY TOXIC BY INGESTION. TARGET EFFECTS: NO DATA AVAILABLE.
ETHYLENE THIOUREA: 500 MG/24 HOURS EYE-RABBIT MILD IRRITATION; 265 MG/KG ORAL-RAT LD50; 3000 MG/KG ORAL-MOUSE LD50; 200 MG/KG INTRAPERITONEAL-MOUSE LD50; MUTAGENIC DATA (RTECS); REPRODUCTIVE EFFECTS DATA (RTECS); TUMORIGENIC DATA (RTECS). CARCINOGEN STATUS: ANTICIPATED HUMAN CARCINOGEN (NTP); HUMAN INADEQUATE EVIDENCE, ANIMAL SUFFICIENT EVIDENCE (IARC GROUP-2B). ORAL ADMINISTRATION PRODUCED THYROID CANCER IN RATS AND LIVER-CELL TUMORS IN MICE. NIOSH RECOMMENDS THAT ETHYLENE THIOUREA BE HANDLED AS IF IT WERE A HUMAN CARCINOGEN AND TERATOGEN. ETHYLENE THIOUREA IS A SKIN, EYE AND MUCOUS MEMBRANE IRRITANT, A GOITROGEN, AND A TERATOGEN.

HEALTH EFFECTS AND FIRST AID

INHALATION: MANGANESE-ETHYLENE-BIS-DITHIOCARBAMATE, ZINC COMPLEX: IRRITANT. **ACUTE EXPOSURE-** MAY CAUSE IRRITATION OF THE MUCOUS MEMBRANES. **CHRONIC EXPOSURE-** NO DATA AVAILABLE FOR THIS COMPOUND. PROLONGED OR REPEATED EXPOSURE MAY CAUSE IRRITATION OF THE MUCOUS MEMBRANES. REPEATED EXPOSURE TO MANGANESE COMPOUNDS FOR 3 MONTHS TO 2 YEARS MAY CAUSE CHRONIC MANGANESE POISONING. SOME EARLY SYMPTOMS INCLUDE APATHY, ANOREXIA, HEADACHE, HYPERSOMNIA, SPASMS, AND IRRITABILITY. IN THE ADVANCED STAGE OF MANGANESE POISONING, NEUROLOGICAL DISTURBANCES DEVELOP THAT SIMULATE PARKINSON'S DISEASE.
ETHYLENE THIOUREA: IRRITANT/TERATOGEN. **ACUTE EXPOSURE-** MAY CAUSE IRRITATION OF THE MUCOUS MEMBRANES. **CHRONIC EXPOSURE-** PROLONGED AND REPEATED EXPOSURE MAY CAUSE IRRITATION AND MAY RESULT IN DECREASED THYROID HORMONE OUTPUT AND OTHER EFFECTS ON THE THYROID. EXPOSURE OF PREGNANT RATS TO 27.2 MG/M3 FOR 3 HOURS/DAY FOR 8 DAYS PRODUCED FETAL MUSCULOSKELETAL ABNORMALITIES; EXPOSURE TO 120 MG/M3 PRODUCED FETOTOXICITY AND FETAL DEATH.
FIRST AID- REMOVE FROM EXPOSURE AREA TO FRESH AIR IMMEDIATELY. IF BREATHING HAS STOPPED, PERFORM ARTIFICIAL RESPIRATION. KEEP PERSON WARM AND AT REST. TREAT SYMPTOMATICALLY AND SUPPORTIVELY. GET MEDICAL ATTENTION IMMEDIATELY.

SKIN CONTACT: MANGANESE-ETHYLENE-BIS-DITHIOCARBAMATE, ZINC COMPLEX: IRRITANT: **ACUTE EXPOSURE-** MAY CAUSE IRRITATION. **CHRONIC EXPOSURE-** PROLONGED OR REPEATED EXPOSURE MAY CAUSE IRRITATION.
ETHYLENE THIOUREA: IRRITANT/TERATOGEN. **ACUTE EXPOSURE-** MAY CAUSE IRRITATION. APPLICATION OF 50 MG/KG ON SKIN OF PREGNANT RATS ON DAY 12 OR 13 OF GESTATION RESULTED IN MALFORMATIONS IN ALL FETUSES; APPLICATION OF 50 MG/KG ON DAY 10 OR 11 OF GESTATION RESULTED IN ONLY A SMALL NUMBER OF FETAL ABNORMALITIES, INDICATING THAT DOSE AND DAY OF GESTATION ARE CRITICAL FACTORS. FETAL MALFORMATIONS INCLUDED MUSCULOSKELETAL AND CRANIOFACIAL ABNORMALITIES. **CHRONIC EXPOSURE-** PROLONGED EXPOSURE MAY CAUSE IRRITATION.
FIRST AID- REMOVE CONTAMINATED CLOTHING AND SHOES IMMEDIATELY. WASH AFFECTED AREA WITH SOAP OR MILD DETERGENT AND LARGE AMOUNTS OF WATER UNTIL NO EVIDENCE OF CHEMICAL REMAINS (APPROXIMATELY 15-20 MINUTES). GET MEDICAL ATTENTION IMMEDIATELY.

EYE CONTACT: MANGANESE-ETHYLENE-BIS-DITHIOCARBAMATE, ZINC COMPLEX: IRRITANT. **ACUTE EXPOSURE-** MAY CAUSE IRRITATION. **CHRONIC EXPOSURE-** PROLONGED CONTACT MAY CAUSE INFLAMMATION OF THE RETINA.
ETHYLENE THIOUREA: IRRITANT. **ACUTE EXPOSURE-** MAY CAUSE IRRITATION. 500 MG APPLIED TO RABBIT EYES PRODUCED MILD IRRITATION. **CHRONIC EXPOSURE-** PROLONGED EXPOSURE MAY CAUSE IRRITATION.
FIRST AID- WASH EYES IMMEDIATELY WITH LARGE AMOUNTS OF WATER OR NORMAL SALINE, OCCASIONALLY LIFTING UPPER AND LOWER LIDS, UNTIL NO EVIDENCE OF CHEMICAL REMAINS (APPROXIMATELY 15-20 MINUTES). GET MEDICAL ATTENTION IMMEDIATELY.

INGESTION: MANGANESE-ETHYLENE-BIS-DITHIOCARBAMATE, ZINC COMPLEX: **ACUTE EXPOSURE-** MAY CAUSE GASTROINTESTINAL DISTURBANCES. **CHRONIC EXPOSURE-** NO DATA AVAILABLE.
ETHYLENE THIOUREA: TERATOGEN/CARCINOGEN/TOXIC. **ACUTE EXPOSURE-** ANIMAL STUDIES INDICATE RAPID ABSORPTION AND DISSEMINATION THROUGHOUT THE BODY. IT MAY ACCUMULATE HEAVILY IN THYROID TISSUE AND BE SLOWLY RELEASED AND EXCRETED UNCHANGED IN URINE. IN ACUTELY POISONED RATS, DEATH IS DUE TO LUNG EDEMA. ANIMAL STUDIES INDICATE THAT ETHYLENE THIOUREA CROSSES THE PLACENTA AND CAUSES FETAL MALFORMATIONS. AN ORAL DOSE OF 60 MG/KG ADMINISTERED TO PREGNANT RATS ON DAY 13 OF GESTATION CAUSED FETAL ABNORMALITIES OF THE UROGENITAL SYSTEM AND CRANIOFACIAL AREA. A DOSE OF 2 GM/KG ADMINISTERED TO PREGNANT MICE PRODUCED FETOTOXICITY, FETAL MUSCULOSKELETAL ABNORMALITIES, AND FETAL DEATH. **CHRONIC EXPOSURE-** REPEATED SUBLETHAL DOSES PRODUCED HYPOTHYROIDISM IN RATS. HYPERPLASTIC GOITER DEVELOPED IN RATS FOLLOWING DIETARY EXPOSURE FOR 18 MONTHS.
FIRST AID- GIVE SYRUP OF IPECAC, FOLLOWED BY 1-2 GLASSES OF WATER, TO INDUCE VOMITING (ADULTS: 30 ML; CHILDREN UNDER 12 YEARS: 15 ML). FOLLOWING EMESIS, ADMINISTER 30-50 GM ACTIVATED CHARCOAL. FOLLOW CHARCOAL WITH SODIUM OR MAGNESIUM SULFATE, 250 MG/KG, AND REMOVE BY CATHARSIS. (EPA, RECOGNITION AND MANAGEMENT OF PESTICIDE POISONINGS, 3RD EDITION). CATHARSIS SHOULD BE PERFORMED BY QUALIFIED MEDICAL PERSONNEL.
ANTIDOTE: NO SPECIFIC ANTIDOTE. TREAT SYMPTOMATICALLY AND SUPPORTIVELY.

REACTIVITY

REACTIVITY: STABLE UNDER NORMAL TEMPERATURES AND PRESSURES.
INCOMPATIBILITIES: MANGANESE-ETHYLENE-BIS-DITHIOCARBAMATE, ZINC COMPLEX: OXIDIZING MATERIALS: INCOMPATIBLE. ACIDS: INCOMPATIBLE. MOISTURE: MAY DECOMPOSE.
ETHYLENE THIOUREA: STRONG OXIDIZERS: FIRE AND EXPLOSION HAZARD.
DECOMPOSITION: THERMAL DECOMPOSITION PRODUCTS MAY INCLUDE HAZARDOUS FUMES OF HYDROGEN SULFIDE AND CARBON DISULFIDE AND OXIDES OF CARBON, NITROGEN AND SULFUR.
POLYMERIZATION: HAZARDOUS POLYMERIZATION HAS NOT BEEN REPORTED TO OCCUR UNDER NORMAL TEMPERATURES AND PRESSURES.

CONDITIONS TO AVOID

MAY BURN BUT DOES NOT IGNITE READILY. AVOID CONTACT WITH STRONG OXIDIZERS, EXCESSIVE HEAT, SPARKS, OR OPEN FLAME.

SPILL AND LEAK PROCEDURES

OCCUPATIONAL SPILL: SWEEP UP AND PLACE IN SUITABLE CLEAN, DRY CONTAINERS FOR RECLAMATION OR LATER DISPOSAL. DO NOT FLUSH SPILLED MATERIAL INTO SEWER. KEEP UNNECESSARY PEOPLE AWAY.

PROTECTIVE EQUIPMENT

VENTILATION: PROVIDE LOCAL EXHAUST OR PROCESS ENCLOSURE VENTILATION TO MEET PUBLISHED EXPOSURE LIMITS.
RESPIRATOR: THE FOLLOWING RESPIRATORS ARE RECOMMENDED BASED ON INFORMATION FOUND IN THE PHYSICAL DATA, TOXICITY AND HEALTH EFFECTS SECTIONS. THEY ARE RANKED IN ORDER FROM MINIMUM TO MAXIMUM RESPIRATORY PROTECTION. THE SPECIFIC RESPIRATOR SELECTED MUST BE BASED ON CONTAMINATION LEVELS FOUND IN THE WORK PLACE, MUST NOT EXCEED THE WORKING LIMITS OF THE RESPIRATOR AND BE JOINTLY APPROVED BY THE NATIONAL INSTITUTE FOR OCCUPATIONAL SAFETY AND HEALTH AND THE MINE SAFETY AND HEALTH ADMINISTRATION (NIOSH-MSHA).
TYPE 'C' SUPPLIED-AIR RESPIRATOR WITH A FULL FACEPIECE OPERATED IN PRESSURE-DEMAND OR OTHER POSITIVE PRESSURE MODE OR WITH A FULL FACEPIECE, HELMET OR HOOD OPERATED IN CONTINOUS-FLOW MODE.
SELF-CONTAINED BREATHING APPARATUS WITH A FULL FACEPIECE OPERATED IN PRESSURE-DEMAND OR OTHER POSITIVE PRESSURE MODE.
FOR FIREFIGHTING AND OTHER IMMEDIATELY DANGEROUS TO LIFE OR HEALTH CONDITIONS:
SELF-CONTAINED BREATHING APPARATUS WITH FULL FACEPIECE OPERATED IN PRESSURE-DEMAND OR OTHER POSITIVE PRESSURE MODE.
SUPPLIED-AIR RESPIRATOR WITH FULL FACEPIECE AND OPERATED IN PRESSURE-DEMAND OR OTHER POSITIVE PRESSURE MODE IN COMBINATION WITH AN AUXILIARY SELF-CONTAINED BREATHING APPARATUS OPERATED IN PRESSURE-DEMAND OR OTHER POSITIVE PRESSURE MODE.

CLOTHING: EMPLOYEE MUST WEAR APPROPRIATE PROTECTIVE (IMPERVIOUS) CLOTHING AND EQUIPMENT TO PREVENT REPEATED OR PROLONGED SKIN CONTACT WITH THIS SUBSTANCE.

GLOVES: EMPLOYEE MUST WEAR APPROPRIATE PROTECTIVE GLOVES TO PREVENT CONTACT WITH THIS SUBSTANCE.

EYE PROTECTION: EMPLOYEE MUST WEAR SPLASH-PROOF OR DUST-RESISTANT SAFETY GOGGLES AND A FACESHIELD TO PREVENT CONTACT WITH THIS SUBSTANCE.

EMERGENCY WASH FACILITIES: WHERE THERE IS ANY POSSIBILITY THAT AN EMPLOYEE'S EYES AND/OR SKIN MAY BE EXPOSED TO THIS SUBSTANCE, THE EMPLOYER SHOULD PROVIDE AN EYE WASH FOUNTAIN AND QUICK DRENCH SHOWER WITHIN THE IMMEDIATE WORK AREA FOR EMERGENCY USE.

AUTHORIZED BY- OCCUPATIONAL HEALTH SERVICES, INC.
CREATION DATE: 10/04/89 ***REVISION DATE:*** 07/12/90

MATERIAL SAFETY DATA SHEET

OCCUPATIONAL HEALTH SERVICES, INC.
AGRICULTURE AND PESTICIDE DIVISION
450 SEVENTH AVENUE, SUITE 2407
NEW YORK, NEW YORK 10123
1-800-445-MSDS OR (212) 967-1100

EMERGENCY CONTACT:
JOHN S. BRANSFORD, JR. (615) 292-1180

SUBSTANCE IDENTIFICATION

CAS-NUMBER 330-54-1

SUBSTANCE: **DIURON**

TRADE NAMES/SYNONYMS: UREA, N'-(3,4-DICHLOROPHENYL)-N,N-DIMETHYL-; UREA, 3-(3,4-DICHLOROPHENYL)-1,1-DIMETHYL-; N'-(3,4-DICHLOROPHENYL)-N,N-DIMETHYLUREA; 3-(3,4-DICHLOROPHENYL)-1,1-DIMETHYLUREA; 1,1-DIMETHYL-3-(3,4-DICHLOROPHENYL)UREA; DCMU; DMU; DIUREX; DAILON; DICHLORFENIDIM; DI-ON; DYNEX; HERBATOX; KARMEX; MARMER; TELVAR DIURON WEED KILLER; VONDURON; STCC 4962621; C9H10CL2N2O; PST08420

CHEMICAL FAMILY: SUBSTITUTED UREA
HALOGEN COMPOUND, AROMATIC

MOLECULAR FORMULA: (C6-H3-CL2)-N-H-C-O-N-(C-H3)2

MOLECULAR WEIGHT: 233.10

CERCLA RATINGS (SCALE 0-3): HEALTH=2 FIRE=1 REACTIVITY=0 PERSISTENCE=3

NFPA RATINGS (SCALE 0-4): HEALTH=2 FIRE=1 REACTIVITY=0

COMPONENTS AND CONTAMINANTS

COMPONENT: DIURON ***PERCENT:*** 100
CAS# 330-54-1

OTHER CONTAMINANTS: NONE

EXPOSURE LIMITS: DIURON: 10 MG/M3 OSHA TWA 10 MG/M3 ACGIH TWA
100 POUNDS CERCLA SECTION 103 REPORTABLE QUANTITY

PHYSICAL DATA

DESCRIPTION: ODORLESS, WHITE CRYSTALLINE SOLID.

MELTING POINT: 316-318 F (158-159 C) ***SPECIFIC GRAVITY:*** NOT AVAILABLE

VAPOR PRESSURE: NEGLIGIBLE ***SOLUBILITY IN WATER:*** 0.0042% @ 25 C

SOLVENT SOLUBILITY: SOLUBLE IN ACETONE, DIOXANE, ETHYL ACETATE, ETHANOL, HOT BENZENE; SLIGHTLY SOLUBLE IN HYDROCARBON SOLVENTS.
DECOMPOSES @ 356-374 F (180-190 C)

FIRE AND EXPLOSION DATA

FIRE AND EXPLOSION HAZARD: SLIGHT FIRE HAZARD WHEN EXPOSED TO HEAT OR FLAME.

FIREFIGHTING MEDIA: DRY CHEMICAL, CARBON DIOXIDE, HALON, WATER SPRAY OR STANDARD FOAM (1987 EMERGENCY RESPONSE GUIDEBOOK, DOT P 5800.4). FOR LARGER FIRES, USE WATER SPRAY, FOG OR STANDARD FOAM (1987 EMERGENCY RESPONSE GUIDEBOOK, DOT P 5800.4).

FIREFIGHTING: MOVE CONTAINERS FROM FIRE AREA IF POSSIBLE. FIGHT FIRE FROM MAXIMUM DISTANCE. STAY AWAY FROM STORAGE TANK ENDS. DIKE FIRE CONTROL WATER FOR LATER DISPOSAL. DO NOT SCATTER MATERIAL (1987 EMERGENCY RESPONSE GUIDEBOOK, DOT P 5800.4, GUIDE PAGE 55). EXTINGUISH USING AGENT SUITABLE FOR TYPE OF SURROUNDING FIRE. USE WATER IN FLOODING QUANTITIES AS FOG. KEEP SPARKS, FLAMES AND OTHER SOURCES OF IGNITION AWAY. KEEP MATERIAL OUT OF WATER SOURCES AND SEWERS. DO NOT TOUCH MATERIAL AND AVOID BREATHING DUSTS AND FUMES FROM BURNING MATERIAL. KEEP UPWIND.

TOXICITY

DIURON: TOXICITY DATA: 1017 MG/KG ORAL-RAT LD50; 500 MG/KG INTRAPERITONEAL-MOUSE LD50; 3400 MG/KG UNREPORTED-RAT LD50; MUTAGENIC DATA (RTECS); REPRODUCTIVE EFFECTS DATA (RTECS); TUMORIGENIC DATA (RTECS). CARCINOGEN STATUS: NONE. ACUTE TOXICITY LEVEL: MODERATELY TOXIC BY INGESTION. TARGET EFFECTS: NO DATA AVAILABLE.

HEALTH EFFECTS AND FIRST AID

INHALATION: DIURON: **ACUTE EXPOSURE**- MANY UREA DERIVATIVE HERBICIDES ARE MODERATELY IRRITATING TO THE MUCOUS MEMBRANES. **CHRONIC EXPOSURE**- NO DATA AVAILABLE.

FIRST AID- REMOVE FROM EXPOSURE AREA TO FRESH AIR IMMEDIATELY. IF BREATHING HAS STOPPED, PERFORM ARTIFICIAL RESPIRATION. KEEP PERSON WARM AND AT REST. TREAT SYMPTOMATICALLY AND SUPPORTIVELY. GET MEDICAL ATTENTION IMMEDIATELY.

SKIN CONTACT: DIURON: **ACUTE EXPOSURE**- MAY CAUSE IRRITATION. **CHRONIC EXPOSURE**- NO DATA AVAILABLE.

FIRST AID- REMOVE CONTAMINATED CLOTHING AND SHOES IMMEDIATELY. WASH AFFECTED AREA WITH SOAP OR MILD DETERGENT AND LARGE AMOUNTS OF WATER UNTIL NO EVIDENCE OF CHEMICAL REMAINS (APPROXIMATELY 15-20 MINUTES). GET MEDICAL ATTENTION IMMEDIATELY.

EYE CONTACT: DIURON: **ACUTE EXPOSURE**- MAY CAUSE IRRITATION. **CHRONIC EXPOSURE**- NO DATA AVAILABLE.

FIRST AID- WASH EYES IMMEDIATELY WITH LARGE AMOUNTS OF WATER OR NORMAL SALINE, OCCASIONALLY LIFTING UPPER AND LOWER LIDS, UNTIL NO EVIDENCE OF CHEMICAL REMAINS (APPROXIMATELY 15-20 MINUTES). GET MEDICAL ATTENTION IMMEDIATELY.

INGESTION: DIURON: **ACUTE EXPOSURE**- IN RATS, AN ORAL DOSE IN THE LD50 RANGE PRODUCED ATAXIA, DROWSINESS, HYPERREFLEXIA, IRRITABILITY, DIARRHEA, DIURESIS, HYPOTHERMIA, AND WEIGHT LOSS, ACCOMPANIED BY GLYCOSURIA, PROTEINURIA, AND ACIDURIA. DEATH WAS DUE TO RESPIRATORY FAILURE.
CHRONIC EXPOSURE- RATS AND DOGS GIVEN 2500 PPM FOR 2 YEARS SHOWED GROWTH RETARDATION, SLIGHT ANEMIA, PRESENCE OF ABNORMAL PIGMENT, AND INCREASED ERYTHROPOIESIS. SOME RATS SHOWED SPLENIC ENLARGEMENT AND DOGS SHOWED LIVER ENLARGEMENT. ONE RUSSIAN STUDY REPORTED GASTRIC CARCINOMAS, HEPATOMAS AND PANCREATIC TUMORS IN RATS AFTER REPEATED DOSES OF 450 MG/KG. MINOR VARIATIONS IN THE RATE OF BONE DEVELOPMENT, INCLUDING WAVY RIBS, WERE OBSERVED IN THE OFFSPRING OF PREGNANT RATS FED DIURON AT A RATE OF 250 MG/KG/DAY. DECREASED OFFSPRING WEIGHTS WERE NOTED IN THE SECOND AND THIRD GENERATIONS IN A MULTIGENERATION REPRODUCTION STUDY OF RATS.

FIRST AID- REMOVE BY GASTRIC LAVAGE AND CATHARSIS. MAINTAIN BLOOD PRESSURE AND AIRWAY. GIVE OXYGEN IF RESPIRATION IS DEPRESSED. DO NOT PERFORM GASTRIC LAVAGE IF VICTIM IS UNCONSCIOUS. GET MEDICAL ATTENTION IMMEDIATELY (DREISBACH, HANDBOOK OF POISONING, 12TH ED.).
ADMINISTRATION OF LAVAGE OR OXYGEN SHOULD BE PERFORMED BY QUALIFIED MEDICAL PERSONNEL.

ANTIDOTE: NO SPECIFIC ANTIDOTE. TREAT SYMPTOMATICALLY AND SUPPORTIVELY.

REACTIVITY

REACTIVITY: STABLE UNDER NORMAL TEMPERATURES AND PRESSURES.
DECOMPOSES ABOVE 356 F (180 C)

INCOMPATIBILITIES: DIURON: ACIDS: HYDROLYSIS MAY OCCUR ALKALI: HYDROLYSIS MAY OCCUR

DECOMPOSITION: THERMAL DECOMPOSITION PRODUCTS MAY INCLUDE TOXIC OXIDES OF NITROGEN AND CARBON AND TOXIC AND CORROSIVE FUMES OF CHLORIDES.

POLYMERIZATION: HAZARDOUS POLYMERIZATION HAS NOT BEEN REPORTED TO OCCUR UNDER NORMAL TEMPERATURES AND PRESSURES.

STORAGE AND DISPOSAL

OBSERVE ALL FEDERAL, STATE AND LOCAL REGULATIONS WHEN STORING OR DISPOSING OF THIS SUBSTANCE. FOR ASSISTANCE, CONTACT THE DISTRICT DIRECTOR OF THE ENVIRONMENTAL PROTECTION AGENCY.

STORAGE

STORE IN ACCORDANCE WITH 40 CFR 165 RECOMMENDED PROCEDURES FOR THE DISPOSAL AND STORAGE OF PESTICIDES AND PESTICIDE CONTAINERS.
STORE AWAY FROM INCOMPATIBLE SUBSTANCES.

DISPOSAL

DISPOSAL MUST BE IN ACCORDANCE WITH 40 CFR 165 RECOMMENDED PROCEDURES FOR THE DISPOSAL AND STORAGE OF PESTICIDES AND PESTICIDE CONTAINERS.

CONDITIONS TO AVOID

MAY BURN BUT DOES NOT IGNITE READILY. CONTAINERS MAY EXPLODE IN HEAT OF FIRE.

SPILL AND LEAK PROCEDURES

SOIL SPILL: DIG HOLDING AREA SUCH AS LAGOON, POND OR PIT FOR CONTAINMENT. DIKE FLOW OF SPILLED MATERIAL USING SOIL OR SANDBAGS OR FOAMED BARRIERS SUCH AS POLYURETHANE OR CONCRETE.

WATER SPILL: USE ACTIVATED CARBON TO ABSORB SPILLED SUBSTANCE THAT IS DISSOLVED.
USE MECHANICAL DREDGES OR LIFTS TO EXTRACT IMMOBILIZED MASSES OF POLLUTION AND PRECIPITATES.

OCCUPATIONAL SPILL: DO NOT TOUCH SPILLED MATERIAL. STOP LEAK IF YOU CAN DO IT WITHOUT RISK. USE WATER SPRAY TO REDUCE VAPORS. FOR SMALL SPILLS, TAKE UP WITH SAND OR OTHER ABSORBENT MATERIAL AND PLACE INTO CONTAINERS FOR LATER DISPOSAL. FOR SMALL DRY SPILLS, WITH A CLEAN SHOVEL PLACE MATERIAL INTO CLEAN, DRY CONTAINERS AND COVER. MOVE CONTAINERS FROM SPILL AREA. FOR LARGER SPILLS, DIKE FAR AHEAD OF SPILL FOR LATER DISPOSAL. KEEP UNNECESSARY PEOPLE AWAY. ISOLATE HAZARD AREA AND DENY ENTRY. VENTILATE CLOSED SPACES BEFORE ENTERING.
REPORTABLE QUANTITY (RQ): 100 POUNDS THE SUPERFUND AMENDMENTS AND REAUTHORIZATION ACT (SARA) SECTION 304 REQUIRES THAT A RELEASE EQUAL TO OR GREATER THAN THE REPORTABLE QUANTITY FOR THIS SUBSTANCE BE IMMEDIATELY REPORTED TO THE LOCAL EMERGENCY PLANNING COMMITTEE AND THE STATE EMERGENCY RESPONSE COMMISSION (40 CFR 355.40). IF THE RELEASE OF THIS SUBSTANCE IS REPORTABLE UNDER CERCLA SECTION 103, THE NATIONAL RESPONSE CENTER MUST BE NOTIFIED IMMEDIATELY AT (800) 424-8802 OR (202) 426-2675 IN THE METROPOLITAN WASHINGTON, D.C. AREA (40 CFR 302.6).

PROTECTIVE EQUIPMENT

VENTILATION: PROVIDE LOCAL EXHAUST VENTILATION AND/OR GENERAL DILUTION VENTILATION TO MEET PUBLISHED EXPOSURE LIMITS.

RESPIRATOR: THE FOLLOWING RESPIRATORS ARE RECOMMENDED BASED ON INFORMATION FOUND IN THE PHYSICAL DATA, TOXICITY AND HEALTH EFFECTS SECTIONS. THEY ARE RANKED IN ORDER FROM MINIMUM TO MAXIMUM RESPIRATORY PROTECTION. THE SPECIFIC RESPIRATOR SELECTED MUST BE BASED ON CONTAMINATION LEVELS FOUND IN THE WORK PLACE, MUST NOT EXCEED THE WORKING LIMITS OF THE RESPIRATOR AND BE JOINTLY APPROVED BY THE NATIONAL INSTITUTE FOR OCCUPATIONAL SAFETY AND HEALTH AND THE MINE SAFETY AND HEALTH ADMINISTRATION (NIOSH-MSHA).
CHEMICAL CARTRIDGE RESPIRATOR WITH AN ORGANIC VAPOR CARTRIDGE(S) WITH A FULL FACEPIECE AND ORGANIC VAPOR CARTRIDGE(S) IN COMBINATION WITH A DUST AND MIST FILTER.
POWERED AIR-PURIFYING RESPIRATOR WITH A TIGHT-FITTING FACEPIECE AND ORGANIC VAPOR CARTRIDGE(S) IN COMBINATION WITH A HIGH-EFFICIENCY PARTICULATE FILTER.
TYPE 'C' SUPPLIED-AIR RESPIRATOR WITH A FULL FACEPIECE OPERATED IN A PRESSURE-DEMAND OR OTHER POSITIVE PRESSURE MODE.
SELF-CONTAINED BREATHING APPARATUS WITH A FULL FACEPIECE OPERATED IN PRESSURE-DEMAND OR OTHER POSITIVE PRESSURE MODE.
FOR FIREFIGHTING AND OTHER IMMEDIATELY DANGEROUS TO LIFE OR HEALTH CONDITIONS:
SELF-CONTAINED BREATHING APPARATUS WITH FULL FACEPIECE OPERATED IN PRESSURE-DEMAND OR OTHER POSITIVE PRESSURE MODE.
SUPPLIED-AIR RESPIRATOR WITH FULL FACEPIECE AND OPERATED IN PRESSURE-DEMAND OR OTHER POSITIVE PRESSURE MODE IN COMBINATION WITH AN AUXILIARY SELF-CONTAINED BREATHING APPARATUS OPERATED IN PRESSURE-DEMAND OR OTHER POSITIVE PRESSURE MODE.

CLOTHING: EMPLOYEE MUST WEAR APPROPRIATE PROTECTIVE (IMPERVIOUS) CLOTHING AND EQUIPMENT TO PREVENT REPEATED OR PROLONGED SKIN CONTACT WITH THIS SUBSTANCE.

GLOVES: EMPLOYEE MUST WEAR APPROPRIATE PROTECTIVE GLOVES TO PREVENT CONTACT WITH THIS SUBSTANCE.

EYE PROTECTION: EMPLOYEE MUST WEAR SPLASH-PROOF OR DUST-RESISTANT SAFETY GOGGLES TO PREVENT EYE CONTACT WITH THIS SUBSTANCE.
EMERGENCY EYE WASH: WHERE THERE IS ANY POSSIBILITY THAT AN EMPLOYEE'S EYES MAY BE EXPOSED TO THIS SUBSTANCE, THE EMPLOYER SHOULD PROVIDE AN EYE WASH FOUNTAIN WITHIN THE IMMEDIATE WORK AREA FOR EMERGENCY USE.

AUTHORIZED BY- OCCUPATIONAL HEALTH SERVICES, INC.

CREATION DATE: 10/04/89 ***REVISION DATE:*** 05/11/90

MATERIAL SAFETY DATA SHEET

OCCUPATIONAL HEALTH SERVICES, INC.
AGRICULTURE AND PESTICIDE DIVISION
450 SEVENTH AVENUE, SUITE 2407
NEW YORK, NEW YORK 10123
1-800-445-MSDS OR (212) 967-1100

EMERGENCY CONTACT:
JOHN S. BRANSFORD, JR. (615) 292-1180

SUBSTANCE IDENTIFICATION

CAS-NUMBER 27176-87-0

SUBSTANCE: **DODECYLBENZENESULFONIC ACID**

TRADE NAMES/SYNONYMS: N-DODECYLBENZENESULFONIC ACID; LAURYLBENZENESULFONIC ACID; LAURYLBENZENESULFONATE; NANSA SSA; DDBSA; NACCONOL 98 SA; RICHONIC ACID; SULFRAMIN ACID 1298; DODANIC ACID 83; DODECYLBENZENESULPHONIC ACID; E 7256; ELFAN WA SULPHONIC ACID; CALSOFT LAS 99; PST08480

CHEMICAL FAMILY: SULFONIC ACID

MOLECULAR FORMULA: C18-H30-O3-S

MOLECULAR WEIGHT: 326.49

CERCLA RATINGS (SCALE 0-3): HEALTH=U FIRE=U REACTIVITY=0 PERSISTENCE=2

NFPA RATINGS (SCALE 0-4): HEALTH=U FIRE=U REACTIVITY=0

COMPONENTS AND CONTAMINANTS

COMPONENT: DODECYLBENZENESULFONIC ACID ***PERCENT:*** 100
CAS# 27176-87-0

EXPOSURE LIMITS: DODECYLBENZENESULFONIC ACID: 1000 POUNDS CERCLA SECTION 103 REPORTABLE QUANTITY

PHYSICAL DATA

DESCRIPTION: COLORLESS LIQUID. ***MELTING POINT:*** NOT AVAILABLE
SPECIFIC GRAVITY: NOT AVAILABLE ***SOLUBILITY IN WATER:*** SOLUBLE

FIRE AND EXPLOSION DATA

FIRE AND EXPLOSION HAZARD: UNKNOWN FIRE AND EXPLOSION HAZARD.

FIREFIGHTING MEDIA: DRY CHEMICAL, CARBON DIOXIDE, HALON, WATER SPRAY OR STANDARD FOAM (1987 EMERGENCY RESPONSE GUIDEBOOK, DOT P 5800.4).
FOR LARGER FIRES, USE WATER SPRAY, FOG OR STANDARD FOAM (1987 EMERGENCY RESPONSE GUIDEBOOK, DOT P 5800.4).

FIREFIGHTING: MOVE CONTAINERS FROM FIRE AREA IF POSSIBLE. COOL CONTAINERS EXPOSED TO FLAMES WITH WATER FROM SIDE UNTIL WELL AFTER FIRE IS OUT. STAY AWAY FROM STORAGE TANK ENDS (1987 EMERGENCY RESPONSE GUIDEBOOK, DOT P 5800.4, GUIDE PAGE 60).
USE FLOODING AMOUNTS OF WATER AS FOG; SOLID STREAMS MAY NOT BE EFFECTIVE. COOL CONTAINERS WITH FLOODING QUANTITIES OF WATER, APPLY FROM AS FAR A DISTANCE AS POSSIBLE. AVOID BREATHING TOXIC VAPORS, KEEP UPWIND.

TRANSPORTATION DATA

DEPARTMENT OF TRANSPORTATION HAZARD CLASSIFICATION 49 CFR 172.101: CORROSIVE MATERIAL
DEPARTMENT OF TRANSPORTATION LABELING REQUIREMENTS 49 CFR 172.101 AND SUBPART E: CORROSIVE
DEPARTMENT OF TRANSPORTATION PACKAGING REQUIREMENTS: 49 CFR 173.245 EXCEPTIONS: 49 CFR 173.244

TOXICITY

DODECYLBENZENESULFONIC ACID: TOXICITY DATA: 650 MG/KG ORAL-RAT LD50. CARCINOGEN STATUS: NONE. LOCAL EFFECTS: CORROSIVE- INHALATION, SKIN, EYE, INGESTION. ACUTE TOXICITY LEVEL: MODERATELY TOXIC BY INGESTION. TARGET EFFECTS: NO DATA AVAILABLE.

HEALTH EFFECTS AND FIRST AID

INHALATION: DODECYLBENZENESULFONIC ACID: CORROSIVE. **ACUTE EXPOSURE-** INHALATION OF ACIDIC SUBSTANCES MAY CAUSE SYMPTOMS OF SEVERE RESPIRATORY TRACT IRRITATION POSSIBLY INCLUDING COUGHING, CHOKING, PAIN IN THE NOSE, MOUTH AND THROAT AND BURNS OF THE MUCOUS MEMBRANES. IF SUFFICIENT QUANTITIES ARE INHALED, PULMONARY EDEMA MAY DEVELOP, OFTEN WITH A LATENT PERIOD OF 5-72 HOURS. THE SYMPTOMS MAY

INCLUDE TIGHTNESS IN THE CHEST, DYSPNEA, FROTHY SPUTUM, CYANOSIS, AND DIZZINESS. PHYSICAL FINDINGS MAY INCLUDE WEAK, RAPID PULSE, HYPOTENSION, MOIST RALES, AND HEMOCONCENTRATION. RECOVERY MAY BE PROLONGED AND RELAPSES ARE POSSIBLE. IN SEVERE EXPOSURES, DEATH DUE TO ANOXIA MAY OCCUR WITHIN A FEW HOURS AFTER ONSET OF PULMONARY EDEMA SYMPTOMS OR FOLLOWING A RELAPSE. **CHRONIC EXPOSURE-** DEPENDING ON THE CONCENTRATION AND DURATION OF EXPOSURE, REPEATED OR PROLONGED EXPOSURE TO ACIDIC SUBSTANCES MAY CAUSE EROSION OF THE TEETH AND INFLAMMATORY AND ULCERATIVE CHANGES IN THE MOUTH. BRONCHIAL AND GASTROINTESTINAL DISTURBANCES ARE ALSO POSSIBLE.

FIRST AID- REMOVE FROM EXPOSURE AREA TO FRESH AIR IMMEDIATELY. IF BREATHING HAS STOPPED, GIVE ARTIFICIAL RESPIRATION. MAINTAIN AIRWAY AND BLOOD PRESSURE AND ADMINISTER OXYGEN IF AVAILABLE. KEEP AFFECTED PERSON WARM AND AT REST. TREAT SYMPTOMATICALLY AND SUPPORTIVELY. ADMINISTRATION OF OXYGEN SHOULD BE PERFORMED BY QUALIFIED PERSONNEL. GET MEDICAL ATTENTION IMMEDIATELY.

SKIN CONTACT: DODECYLBENZENESULFONIC ACID: CORROSIVE. **ACUTE EXPOSURE-** DIRECT CONTACT WITH CORROSIVE SUBSTANCES MAY CAUSE SEVERE IRRITATION, PAIN AND POSSIBLY BURNS. **CHRONIC EXPOSURE-** EFFECTS DEPEND ON CONCENTRATION AND DURATION OF EXPOSURE. REPEATED OR PROLONGED CONTACT WITH CORROSIVE SUBSTANCES MAY RESULT IN DERMATITIS OR EFFECT SIMILAR TO ACUTE EXPOSURE.

FIRST AID- REMOVE CONTAMINATED CLOTHING AND SHOES IMMEDIATELY. WASH AFFECTED AREA WITH SOAP OR MILD DETERGENT AND LARGE AMOUNTS OF WATER UNTIL NO EVIDENCE OF CHEMICAL REMAINS (AT LEAST 15-20 MINUTES). IN CASE OF CHEMICAL BURNS, COVER AREA WITH STERILE, DRY DRESSING. BANDAGE SECURELY, BUT NOT TOO TIGHTLY. GET MEDICAL ATTENTION IMMEDIATELY.

EYE CONTACT: DODECYLBENZENESULFONIC ACID: CORROSIVE. **ACUTE EXPOSURE-** DIRECT CONTACT WITH CORROSIVE SUBSTANCES MAY CAUSE SEVERE IRRITATION, PAIN, AND BURNS, POSSIBLY SEVERE. THE DEGREE OF INJURY DEPENDS ON THE CONCENTRATION AND DURATION OF CONTACT. THE FULL EXTENT OF THE INJURY MAY NOT BE IMMEDIATELY APPARENT. **CHRONIC EXPOSURE-** EFFECTS DEPEND ON CONCENTRATION AND DURATION OF EXPOSURE. REPEATED OR PROLONGED CONTACT WITH CORROSIVE SUBSTANCES MAY RESULT IN CONJUNCTIVITIS OR EFFECT AS IN ACUTE EXPOSURE.

FIRST AID- WASH EYES IMMEDIATELY WITH LARGE AMOUNTS OF WATER, OCCASIONALLY LIFTING UPPER AND LOWER LIDS, UNTIL NO EVIDENCE OF CHEMICAL REMAINS (AT LEAST 15-20 MINUTES). CONTINUE IRRIGATING WITH NORMAL SALINE UNTIL THE PH HAS RETURNED TO NORMAL (30-60 MINUTES). COVER WITH STERILE BANDAGES. GET MEDICAL ATTENTION IMMEDIATELY.

INGESTION: DODECYLBENZENESULFONIC ACID: CORROSIVE. **ACUTE EXPOSURE-** CORROSIVE SUBSTANCES MAY CAUSE IMMEDIATE PAIN AND SEVERE BURNS OF THE MUCOUS MEMBRANES. THERE MAY BE DISCOLORATION OF THE TISSUES. SWALLOWING AND SPEECH MAY BE DIFFICULT AT FIRST AND THEN ALMOST IMPOSSIBLE. THE EFFECTS ON THE ESOPHAGUS AND GASTROINTESTINAL TRACT MAY RANGE FROM IRRITATION TO SEVERE CORROSION. EDEMA OF THE EPIGLOTTIS AND SHOCK MAY OCCUR. **CHRONIC EXPOSURE-** DEPENDING ON THE CONCENTRATION, REPEATED INGESTION OF CORROSIVE SUBSTANCES MAY RESULT IN EFFECTS AS WITH ACUTE INGESTION.

FIRST AID- TREAT SYMPTOMATICALLY AND SUPPORTIVELY. IF PERSON IS CONSCIOUS AND ABLE TO SWALLOW, GIVE LARGE AMOUNTS OF WATER OR MILK TO DILUTE SUBSTANCE. GET MEDICAL ATTENTION IMMEDIATELY. GASTRIC LAVAGE PERFORMED BY QUALIFIED MEDICAL PERSONNEL MIGHT BE ADVISABLE IF THERE ARE NO SIGNS OF PERFORATION FROM THE INGESTION OF A CORROSIVE SUBSTANCE. IF VOMITING OCCURS, KEEP HEAD BELOW HIPS TO HELP PREVENT ASPIRATION.

ANTIDOTE: NO SPECIFIC ANTIDOTE. TREAT SYMPTOMATICALLY AND SUPPORTIVELY.

REACTIVITY

REACTIVITY: STABLE UNDER NORMAL TEMPERATURES AND PRESSURES.

INCOMPATIBILITIES: DODECYLBENZENESULFONIC ACID: OXIDIZERS (STRONG): FIRE AND EXPLOSION HAZARD.

DECOMPOSITION: THERMAL DECOMPOSITION MAY RELEASE TOXIC OXIDES OF SULFUR.

POLYMERIZATION: HAZARDOUS POLYMERIZATION HAS NOT BEEN REPORTED TO OCCUR UNDER NORMAL TEMPERATURES AND PRESSURES.

STORAGE AND DISPOSAL

OBSERVE ALL FEDERAL, STATE AND LOCAL REGULATIONS WHEN STORING OR DISPOSING OF THIS SUBSTANCE. FOR ASSISTANCE, CONTACT THE DISTRICT DIRECTOR OF THE ENVIRONMENTAL PROTECTION AGENCY.

****DISPOSAL****

DISPOSAL MUST BE IN ACCORDANCE WITH STANDARDS APPLICABLE TO GENERATORS OF HAZARDOUS WASTE, 40 CFR 262. EPA HAZARDOUS WASTE NUMBER D002. 100 POUND CERCLA SECTION 103 REPORTABLE QUANTITY.

CONDITIONS TO AVOID

MAY BURN BUT DOES NOT IGNITE READILY. FLAMMABLE, POISONOUS GASES MAY ACCUMULATE IN TANKS AND HOPPER CARS. MAY IGNITE COMBUSTIBLES (WOOD, PAPER, OIL, ETC.).

SPILL AND LEAK PROCEDURES

SOIL SPILL: DIG HOLDING AREA SUCH AS LAGOON, POND OR PIT FOR CONTAINMENT. USE PROTECTIVE COVER SUCH AS A PLASTIC SHEET TO PREVENT MATERIAL FROM DISSOLVING IN FIRE EXTINGUISHING WATER OR RAIN.

WATER SPILL: NEUTRALIZE WITH AGRICULTURAL LIME, SLAKED LIME, CRUSHED LIMESTONE, OR SODIUM BICARBONATE.

USE ACTIVATED CARBON TO ABSORB SPILLED SUBSTANCE THAT IS DISSOLVED.

USE MECHANICAL DREDGES OR LIFTS TO EXTRACT IMMOBILIZED MASSES OF POLLUTION AND PRECIPITATES.

OCCUPATIONAL SPILL: DO NOT TOUCH SPILLED MATERIAL. STOP LEAK IF YOU CAN DO IT WITHOUT RISK. FOR SMALL SPILLS, TAKE UP WITH SAND OR OTHER ABSORBENT MATERIAL AND PLACE INTO CONTAINERS FOR LATER DISPOSAL. FOR SMALL DRY SPILLS, WITH CLEAN SHOVEL PLACE MATERIAL INTO CLEAN, DRY CONTAINER AND COVER. MOVE CONTAINERS FROM SPILL AREA. FOR LARGER SPILLS, DIKE FAR AHEAD OF SPILL FOR LATER DISPOSAL. KEEP UNNECESSARY PEOPLE AWAY. ISOLATE HAZARD AREA AND DENY ENTRY.

REPORTABLE QUANTITY (RQ): 1000 POUNDS THE SUPERFUND AMENDMENTS AND REAUTHORIZATION ACT (SARA) SECTION 304 REQUIRES THAT A RELEASE EQUAL TO OR GREATER THAN THE REPORTABLE QUANTITY FOR THIS SUBSTANCE BE IMMEDIATELY REPORTED TO THE LOCAL EMERGENCY PLANNING COMMITTEE AND THE STATE EMERGENCY RESPONSE COMMISSION (40 CFR 355.40). IF THE RELEASE OF THIS SUBSTANCE IS REPORTABLE UNDER CERCLA SECTION 103, THE NATIONAL RESPONSE CENTER MUST BE NOTIFIED IMMEDIATELY AT (800) 424-8802 OR (202) 426-2675 IN THE METROPOLITAN WASHINGTON, D.C. AREA (40 CFR 302.6).

PROTECTIVE EQUIPMENT

VENTILATION: PROVIDE LOCAL EXHAUST OR PROCESS ENCLOSURE VENTILATION. VENTILATION EQUIPMENT MUST BE EXPLOSION-PROOF.

RESPIRATOR: THE FOLLOWING RESPIRATORS ARE RECOMMENDED BASED ON INFORMATION FOUND IN THE PHYSICAL DATA, TOXICITY AND HEALTH EFFECTS SECTIONS. THEY ARE RANKED IN ORDER FROM MINIMUM TO MAXIMUM RESPIRATORY PROTECTION. THE SPECIFIC RESPIRATOR SELECTED MUST BE BASED ON CONTAMINATION LEVELS FOUND IN THE WORK PLACE, MUST NOT EXCEED THE WORKING LIMITS OF THE RESPIRATOR AND BE JOINTLY APPROVED BY THE NATIONAL INSTITUTE FOR OCCUPATIONAL SAFETY AND HEALTH AND THE MINE SAFETY AND HEALTH ADMINISTRATION (NIOSH-MSHA).

CHEMICAL CARTRIDGE RESPIRATOR WITH AN ORGANIC VAPOR CARTRIDGE(S) WITH AN ACID GAS CARTRIDGE(S) AND A FULL FACEPIECE.

GAS MASK WITH ORGANIC VAPOR CANISTER (CHIN-STYLE OR FRONT- OR BACK-MOUNTED CANISTER), WITH A FULL FACEPIECE, PROVIDING PROTECTION AGAINST ACID GASES.

TYPE 'C' SUPPLIED-AIR RESPIRATOR WITH A FULL FACEPIECE OPERATED IN PRESSURE-DEMAND OR OTHER POSITIVE PRESSURE MODE OR WITH A FULL FACEPIECE, HELMET OR HOOD OPERATED IN CONTINUOUS-FLOW MODE.

SELF-CONTAINED BREATHING APPARATUS WITH A FULL FACEPIECE OPERATED IN PRESSURE-DEMAND OR OTHER POSITIVE PRESSURE MODE.

FOR FIREFIGHTING AND OTHER IMMEDIATELY DANGEROUS TO LIFE OR HEALTH CONDITIONS:

SELF-CONTAINED BREATHING APPARATUS WITH FULL FACEPIECE OPERATED IN PRESSURE-DEMAND OR OTHER POSITIVE PRESSURE MODE.

SUPPLIED-AIR RESPIRATOR WITH FULL FACEPIECE AND OPERATED IN PRESSURE-DEMAND OR OTHER POSITIVE PRESSURE MODE IN COMBINATION WITH AN AUXILIARY SELF-CONTAINED BREATHING APPARATUS OPERATED IN PRESSURE-DEMAND OR OTHER POSITIVE PRESSURE MODE.

CLOTHING: EMPLOYEE MUST WEAR APPROPRIATE PROTECTIVE (IMPERVIOUS) CLOTHING AND EQUIPMENT TO PREVENT ANY POSSIBILITY OF SKIN CONTACT WITH THIS SUBSTANCE.

GLOVES: EMPLOYEE MUST WEAR APPROPRIATE PROTECTIVE GLOVES TO PREVENT CONTACT WITH THIS SUBSTANCE.

EYE PROTECTION: EMPLOYEE MUST WEAR SPLASH-PROOF OR DUST-RESISTANT SAFETY GOGGLES AND A FACESHIELD TO PREVENT CONTACT WITH THIS SUBSTANCE.

EMERGENCY WASH FACILITIES: WHERE THERE IS ANY POSSIBILITY THAT AN EMPLOYEE'S EYES AND/OR SKIN MAY BE EXPOSED TO THIS SUBSTANCE, THE EMPLOYER SHOULD PROVIDE AN EYE WASH FOUNTAIN AND QUICK DRENCH SHOWER WITHIN THE IMMEDIATE WORK AREA FOR EMERGENCY USE.

AUTHORIZED BY- OCCUPATIONAL HEALTH SERVICES, INC.
CREATION DATE: 11/15/89 ***REVISION DATE:*** 03/28/90

MATERIAL SAFETY DATA SHEET

OCCUPATIONAL HEALTH SERVICES, INC.
AGRICULTURE AND PESTICIDE DIVISION
450 SEVENTH AVENUE, SUITE 2407
NEW YORK, NEW YORK 10123
1-800-445-MSDS OR (212) 967-1100

EMERGENCY CONTACT:
JOHN S. BRANSFORD, JR. (615) 292-1180

SUBSTANCE IDENTIFICATION

CAS-NUMBER 151-21-3
SUBSTANCE: DODECYL SODIUM SULFATE
TRADE NAMES/SYNONYMS: SDS; SODIUM LAURYL SULFATE; SLS; SODIUM DOCECYL SULFATE; SODIUM N-DODECYL SULFATE; SODIUM DODECYL SULPHATE; DODECYL SULFATE, SODIUM SALT; SODIUM LAURYL SULPHATE; SODIUM MONOLAURYL SULFATE; N-DODECYL SULFATE SODIUM; LAURYL SODIUM SULFATE; LAURYL SULFATE SODIUM; LAURYL SULFATE SODIUM SALT; MONODODECYL SODIUM SULFATE; SODIUM DODECYLSULFATE; SULFURIC ACID, MONODODECYL ESTER, SODIUM SALT; SODIUM MONODODECYL SULFATE; DUPONOL; DREFT; C12H25NAO4S; PST08485
CHEMICAL FAMILY: ORGANIC SULFATE
MOLECULAR FORMULA: C-H3-(C-H2)10-C-H2-O-S-O3.NA
MOLECULAR WEIGHT: 288.38
CERCLA RATINGS (SCALE 0-3): HEALTH=3 FIRE=1 REACTIVITY=0 PERSISTENCE=1
NFPA RATINGS (SCALE 0-4): HEALTH=U FIRE=1 REACTIVITY=0

COMPONENTS AND CONTAMINANTS

COMPONENT: DODECYL SODIUM SULFATE ***PERCENT:*** 100.0
CAS# 151-21-3
OTHER CONTAMINANTS: NONE
EXPOSURE LIMITS: NO OCCUPATIONAL EXPOSURE LIMITS ESTABLISHED BY OSHA, ACGIH, OR NIOSH.

PHYSICAL DATA

DESCRIPTION: WHITE TO CREAM-COLORED CRYSTALS, FLAKES OR POWDER WITH A MILD ODOR.
MELTING POINT: 399-405 F (204-207 C) ***SPECIFIC GRAVITY:*** >1.1
SOLUBILITY IN WATER: 10%

FIRE AND EXPLOSION DATA

FIRE AND EXPLOSION HAZARD: SLIGHT FIRE HAZARD WHEN EXPOSED TO HEAT OR FLAME.
FIREFIGHTING MEDIA: DRY CHEMICAL, CARBON DIOXIDE, HALON, WATER SPRAY OR STANDARD FOAM (1987 EMERGENCY RESPONSE GUIDEBOOK, DOT P 5800.4).
FOR LARGER FIRES, USE WATER SPRAY, FOG OR STANDARD FOAM (1987 EMERGENCY RESPONSE GUIDEBOOK, DOT P 5800.4).
FIREFIGHTING: MOVE CONTAINER FROM FIRE AREA IF POSSIBLE. DO NOT SCATTER SPILLED MATERIAL WITH HIGH PRESSURE WATER STREAMS. DIKE FIRE CONTROL WATER FOR LATER DISPOSAL (1987 EMERGENCY RESPONSE GUIDEBOOK, DOT P 5800.4, GUIDE PAGE 31).
USE AGENTS SUITABLE FOR TYPE OF SURROUNDING FIRE. AVOID BREATHING HAZARDOUS VAPORS, KEEP UPWIND.

TOXICITY

DODECYL SODIUM SULFATE (SODIUM LAURYL SULFATE): IRRITATION DATA: 250 MG/24 HOURS SKIN-HUMAN MILD; 25 MG/24 HOURS SKIN-HUMAN MILD; 50 MG/24 HOURS SKIN-RABBIT SEVERE; 25 MG/24 HOURS SKIN-RABBIT MODERATE; 250 MG/24 HOURS SKIN-RABBIT MODERATE; 10 MG/24 HOURS SKIN-RABBIT; 50 MG/24 HOURS SKIN-RABBIT MILD; 25 MG/24 HOURS SKIN-MOUSE MODERATE; 25 MG/24 HOURS SKIN-DOG MILD; 25 MG/24 HOURS SKIN-GUINEA PIG MILD; 25 MG/24 HOURS SKIN-PIG MILD; 100 MG/24 HOURS EYE-RABBIT MODERATE; 250 UG EYE-RABBIT MILD; 2 MG EYE-RABBIT; 10 MG EYE-RABBIT MODERATE. TOXICITY DATA: 1288 MG/KG ORAL-RAT LD50; 118 MG/KG INTRAVENOUS-RAT LD50; 118 MG/KG INTRAVENOUS-MOUSE LD50; 210 MG/KG INTRAPERITONEAL-RAT LD50; 250 MG/KG INTRAPERITONEAL-MOUSE LD50; MUTAGENIC DATA (RTECS); REPRODUCTIVE EFFECTS DATA (RTECS). CARCINOGEN STATUS: NONE. LOCAL EFFECTS: IRRITANT-SKIN, EYE. ACUTE TOXICITY LEVEL: MODERATELY TOXIC BY INGESTION. TARGET EFFECTS: NO DATA AVAILABLE.

HEALTH EFFECTS AND FIRST AID

INHALATION: DODECYL SODIUM SULFATE (SODIUM LAURYL SULFATE): **ACUTE EXPOSURE**- INHALATION OF DUST MAY CAUSE IRRITATION, RESULTING IN COUGHING AND SNEEZING. **CHRONIC EXPOSURE**- NO DATA AVAILABLE.
FIRST AID- REMOVE FROM EXPOSURE AREA TO FRESH AIR IMMEDIATELY. IF BREATHING HAS STOPPED, PERFORM ARTIFICIAL RESPIRATION. KEEP PERSON WARM AND AT REST. TREAT SYMPTOMATICALLY AND SUPPORTIVELY. GET MEDICAL ATTENTION IMMEDIATELY.

SKIN CONTACT: DODECYL SODIUM SULFATE (SODIUM LAURYL SULFATE): IRRITANT. **ACUTE EXPOSURE**- MAY CAUSE IRRITATION. SOLUTIONS MAY CAUSE DEVELOPMENT OF CONTACT DERMATITIS IN SOME INDIVIDUALS, WITH BURNING, REDNESS, TIGHTENING OF THE SKIN, LEATHERY TEXTURE, PAINFUL FISSURES, AND LAMELLAR EXFOLIATION. **CHRONIC EXPOSURE**- REPEATED OR PROLONGED EXPOSURE MAY CAUSE DERMATITIS, AND COMEDONES. REPRODUCTIVE EFFECTS HAVE BEEN REPORTED IN ANIMALS.
FIRST AID- REMOVE CONTAMINATED CLOTHING AND SHOES IMMEDIATELY. WASH AFFECTED AREA WITH SOAP OR MILD DETERGENT AND LARGE AMOUNTS OF WATER UNTIL NO EVIDENCE OF CHEMICAL REMAINS (APPROXIMATELY 15-20 MINUTES). GET MEDICAL ATTENTION IMMEDIATELY.

EYE CONTACT: DODECYL SODIUM SULFATE (SODIUM LAURYL SULFATE): IRRITANT. **ACUTE EXPOSURE**- DUST MAY CAUSE IRRITATION, AND POSSIBLY BURNS. EXPERIMENTS INDICATE THAT IT IS MORE IRRITATING TO RABBITS EYES THAN TO MONKEYS OR HUMANS. **CHRONIC EXPOSURE**- REPEATED OR PROLONGED EXPOSURE TO IRRITANTS MAY CAUSE CONJUNTIVITIS.
FIRST AID- WASH EYES IMMEDIATELY WITH LARGE AMOUNTS OF WATER OR NORMAL SALINE, OCCASIONALLY LIFTING UPPER AND LOWER LIDS, UNTIL NO EVIDENCE OF CHEMICAL REMAINS (APPROXIMATELY 15-20 MINUTES). GET MEDICAL ATTENTION IMMEDIATELY.

INGESTION: DODECYL SODIUM SULFATE (SODIUM LAURYL SULFATE): **ACUTE EXPOSURE**- INGESTION OF LARGE DOSES MAY CAUSE STOMACH IRRITATION, NAUSEA, AND VOMITING. **CHRONIC EXPOSURE**- REPEATED ADMINISTRATION PRODUCED DIARRHEA, BLOATING, AND SOME DEATHS IN ANIMALS.
FIRST AID- TREAT SYMPTOMATICALLY AND SUPPORTIVELY. GET MEDICAL ATTENTION IMMEDIATELY. IF VOMITING OCCURS, KEEP HEAD LOWER THAN HIPS TO PREVENT ASPIRATION.
ANTIDOTE: NO SPECIFIC ANTIDOTE. TREAT SYMPTOMATICALLY AND SUPPORTIVELY.

REACTIVITY

REACTIVITY: STABLE UNDER NORMAL TEMPERATURES AND PRESSURES.
INCOMPATIBILITIES: DODECYL SODIUM SULFATE (SODIUM LAURYL SULFATE): OXIDIZERS (STRONG): FIRE AND EXPLOSION HAZARD.
DECOMPOSITION: THERMAL DECOMPOSITION MAY RELEASE TOXIC AND/OR HAZARDOUS GASES.
POLYMERIZATION: HAZARDOUS POLYMERIZATION HAS NOT BEEN REPORTED TO OCCUR UNDER NORMAL TEMPERATURES AND PRESSURES.

STORAGE AND DISPOSAL

OBSERVE ALL FEDERAL, STATE AND LOCAL REGULATIONS WHEN STORING OR DISPOSING OF THIS SUBSTANCE. FOR ASSISTANCE, CONTACT THE DISTRICT DIRECTOR OF THE ENVIRONMENTAL PROTECTION AGENCY.

****STORAGE****

STORE AWAY FROM INCOMPATIBLE SUBSTANCES.
STORE IN A TIGHTLY CLOSED CONTAINER.

CONDITIONS TO AVOID

MAY BURN BUT DOES NOT IGNITE READILY. AVOID CONTACT WITH STRONG OXIDIZERS, EXCESSIVE HEAT, SPARKS, OR OPEN FLAME.

SPILL AND LEAK PROCEDURES

OCCUPATIONAL SPILL: SWEEP UP AND PLACE IN SUITABLE CLEAN, DRY CONTAINERS FOR RECLAMATION OR LATER DISPOSAL. DO NOT FLUSH SPILLED MATERIAL INTO SEWER. KEEP UNNECESSARY PEOPLE AWAY.

PROTECTIVE EQUIPMENT

VENTILATION: PROVIDE LOCAL EXHAUST OR GENERAL DILUTION VENTILATION SYSTEM.
RESPIRATOR: THE FOLLOWING RESPIRATORS ARE RECOMMENDED BASED ON INFORMATION FOUND IN THE PHYSICAL DATA, TOXICITY AND HEALTH EFFECTS SECTIONS. THEY ARE RANKED IN ORDER FROM MINIMUM TO MAXIMUM RESPIRATORY PROTECTION. THE SPECIFIC RESPIRATOR SELECTED MUST BE BASED ON CONTAMINATION LEVELS FOUND IN THE WORK PLACE, MUST NOT EXCEED THE

WORKING LIMITS OF THE RESPIRATOR AND BE JOINTLY APPROVED BY THE NATIONAL INSTITUTE FOR OCCUPATIONAL SAFETY AND HEALTH AND THE MINE SAFETY AND HEALTH ADMINISTRATION (NIOSH-MSHA).
DUST AND MIST RESPIRATOR WITH A FULL FACEPIECE.
AIR-PURIFYING FULL FACEPIECE RESPIRATOR WITH A HIGH-EFFICIENCY PARTICULATE FILTER.
POWERED AIR-PURIFYING RESPIRATOR WITH A TIGHT-FITTING FACEPIECE AND HIGH-EFFICIENCY PARTICULATE FILTER.
TYPE 'C' SUPPLIED-AIR RESPIRATOR WITH A FULL FACEPIECE OPERATED IN PRESSURE-DEMAND OR OTHER POSITIVE PRESSURE MODE OR WITH A FULL FACEPIECE, HELMET OR HOOD OPERATED IN CONTINUOUS-FLOW MODE.
SELF-CONTAINED BREATHING APPARATUS WITH A FULL FACEPIECE OPERATED IN PRESSURE-DEMAND OR OTHER POSITIVE PRESSURE MODE.
FOR FIREFIGHTING AND OTHER IMMEDIATELY DANGEROUS TO LIFE OR HEALTH CONDITIONS:
SELF-CONTAINED BREATHING APPARATUS WITH FULL FACEPIECE OPERATED IN PRESSURE-DEMAND OR OTHER POSITIVE PRESSURE MODE.
SUPPLIED-AIR RESPIRATOR WITH FULL FACEPIECE AND OPERATED IN PRESSURE-DEMAND OR OTHER POSITIVE PRESSURE MODE IN COMBINATION WITH AN AUXILIARY SELF-CONTAINED BREATHING APPARATUS OPERATED IN PRESSURE-DEMAND OR OTHER POSITIVE PRESSURE MODE.

CLOTHING: EMPLOYEE MUST WEAR APPROPRIATE PROTECTIVE (IMPERVIOUS) CLOTHING AND EQUIPMENT TO PREVENT REPEATED OR PROLONGED SKIN CONTACT WITH THIS SUBSTANCE.

GLOVES: EMPLOYEE MUST WEAR APPROPRIATE PROTECTIVE GLOVES TO PREVENT CONTACT WITH THIS SUBSTANCE.

EYE PROTECTION: EMPLOYEE MUST WEAR SPLASH-PROOF OR DUST-RESISTANT SAFETY GOGGLES TO PREVENT EYE CONTACT WITH THIS SUBSTANCE.
EMERGENCY EYE WASH: WHERE THERE IS ANY POSSIBILITY THAT AN EMPLOYEE'S EYES MAY BE EXPOSED TO THIS SUBSTANCE, THE EMPLOYER SHOULD PROVIDE AN EYE WASH FOUNTAIN WITHIN THE IMMEDIATE WORK AREA FOR EMERGENCY USE.

AUTHORIZED BY- OCCUPATIONAL HEALTH SERVICES, INC.
CREATION DATE: 11/17/89 ***REVISION DATE:*** 05/31/90

MATERIAL SAFETY DATA SHEET

OCCUPATIONAL HEALTH SERVICES, INC.
AGRICULTURE AND PESTICIDE DIVISION
450 SEVENTH AVENUE, SUITE 2407
NEW YORK, NEW YORK 10123
1-800-445-MSDS OR (212) 967-1100

EMERGENCY CONTACT:
JOHN S. BRANSFORD, JR. (615) 292-1180

SUBSTANCE IDENTIFICATION

CAS-NUMBER 132-27-4

SUBSTANCE: **DOWICIDE A**

TRADE NAMES/SYNONYMS: (1,1'-BIPHENYL)-2-OL, SODIUM SALT; 2-BIPHENYLOL,SODIUM SALT; 2-HYDROXYBIPHENYL SODIUM SALT; 2-HYDROXYDIPHENYL SODIUM SALT; O-PHENYL-PHENOL SODIUM SALT; 2-PHENYLPHENOL SODIUM SALT; SODIUM-2-BIPHENOLATE; STOPMOLD B; TOPANE; MYSTOX WFA; O-PHENYLPHENATE, SODIUM; PST08500

MOLECULAR FORMULA: C12-H9-O-NA MOL. WT.: 192.2

CERCLA RATINGS (SCALE 0-3): HEALTH=3 FIRE=0 REACTIVITY=0 PERSISTENCE=3

NFPA RATINGS (SCALE 0-4): HEALTH=3 FIRE=0 REACTIVITY=0

COMPONENTS AND CONTAMINANTS

COMPONENT: DOWICIDE A ***PERCENT:*** 100.0
CAS# 132-27-4

OTHER CONTAMINANTS: NONE

EXPOSURE LIMITS: NO OCCUPATIONAL EXPOSURE LIMITS ESTABLISHED BY OSHA, ACGIH, OR NIOSH.
DOWICIDE A (O-PHENYLPHENATE, SODIUM); SUBJECT TO CALIFORNIA PROPOSITION 65 CANCER AND/OR REPRODUCTIVE TOXICITY WARNING AND RELEASE REQUIREMENTS- (JANUARY 1, 1990)

PHYSICAL DATA

DESCRIPTION: WHITE SOLID ***BOILING POINT:*** DECOMPOSES

FIRE AND EXPLOSION DATA

FIRE AND EXPLOSION HAZARD: NEGLIGIBLE FIRE HAZARD WHEN EXPOSED TO HEAT OR FLAME.

FIREFIGHTING MEDIA: DRY CHEMICAL, CARBON DIOXIDE, HALON, WATER SPRAY OR STANDARD FOAM (1987 EMERGENCY RESPONSE GUIDEBOOK, DOT P 5800.4).
FOR LARGER FIRES, USE WATER SPRAY, FOG OR STANDARD FOAM (1987 EMERGENCY RESPONSE GUIDEBOOK, DOT P 5800.4).

FIREFIGHTING: MOVE CONTAINER FROM FIRE AREA IF POSSIBLE. DO NOT SCATTER SPILLED MATERIAL WITH HIGH PRESSURE WATER STREAMS. DIKE FIRE CONTROL WATER FOR LATER DISPOSAL (1987 EMERGENCY RESPONSE GUIDEBOOK, DOT P 5800.4, GUIDE PAGE 31).
USE AGENTS SUITABLE FOR TYPE OF SURROUNDING FIRE. AVOID BREATHING HAZARDOUS VAPORS, KEEP UPWIND.

TOXICITY

DOWICIDE A: IRRITATION DATA: 1 MG SKIN-HUMAN; 25 MG/24 HOURS SKIN-RABBIT MILD; 50 MG/24 HOURS SKIN-RABBIT SEVERE. TOXICITY DATA: 656 MG/KG ORAL-RAT LD50; 683 MG/KG ORAL-MOUSE LD50; 500 MG/KG ORAL-CAT LD50; MUTAGENIC DATA (RTECS); REPRODUCTIVE EFFECTS DATA (RTECS); TUMORIGENIC DATA (RTECS). CARCINOGEN STATUS: ANIMAL SUFFICIENT EVIDENCE (IARC GROUP-2B). ADMINISTRATION IN THE DIET PRODUCED BOTH BENIGN AND MALIGNANT TUMORS OF THE URINARY TRACT OF RATS. LOCAL EFFECTS: IRRITANT- INHALATION, SKIN, AND EYES. ACUTE TOXICITY DATA: MODERATELY TOXIC BY INGESTION. TARGET EFFECTS: NO DATA AVAILABLE.

HEALTH EFFECTS AND FIRST AID

INHALATION: DOWICIDE A: IRRITANT. **ACUTE EXPOSURE-** INHALATION OF HIGH CONCENTRATIONS OF THIS SUBSTANCE MAY RESULT IN PULMONARY EDEMA. LOWER CONCENTRATIONS MAY CAUSE IRRITATION. **CHRONIC EXPOSURE-** REPEATED OR PROLONGED EXPOSURE MAY CAUSE IRRITATION.

FIRST AID- REMOVE FROM EXPOSURE AREA TO FRESH AIR IMMEDIATELY. IF BREATHING HAS STOPPED, PERFORM ARTIFICIAL RESPIRATION. KEEP PERSON WARM AND AT REST. TREAT SYMPTOMATICALLY AND SUPPORTIVELY. GET MEDICAL ATTENTION IMMEDIATELY.

SKIN CONTACT: DOWICIDE A: IRRITANT. **ACUTE EXPOSURE-** THIS SUBSTANCE IS NOT ABSORBED IN ACUTELY TOXIC AMOUNTS THROUGH INTACT SKIN. A 0.1% AQUEOUS SOLUTION FAILED TO CAUSE SKIN IRRITATION OR SENSITIZATION IN 200 HUMAN TEST SUBJECTS. **CHRONIC EXPOSURE-** REPEATED OR PROLONGED EXPOSURE MAY CAUSE DERMATITIS.

FIRST AID- REMOVE CONTAMINATED CLOTHING AND SHOES IMMEDIATELY. WASH AFFECTED AREA WITH SOAP OR MILD DETERGENT AND LARGE AMOUNTS OF WATER UNTIL NO EVIDENCE OF CHEMICAL REMAINS (APPROXIMATELY 15-20 MINUTES). GET MEDICAL ATTENTION IMMEDIATELY.

EYE CONTACT: DOWICIDE A: CORROSIVE. **ACUTE EXPOSURE-** DIRECT CONTACT MAY CAUSE CORNEAL NECROSIS. CONTACT WITH THE VAPOR MAY CAUSE IRRITATION. **CHRONIC EXPOSURE-** REPEATED OR PROLONGED EXPOSURE MAY CAUSE CONJUNCTIVITIS.

FIRST AID- WASH EYES IMMEDIATELY WITH LARGE AMOUNTS OF WATER OR NORMAL SALINE, OCCASIONALLY LIFTING UPPER AND LOWER LIDS, UNTIL NO EVIDENCE OF CHEMICAL REMAINS (APPROXIMATELY 15-20 MINUTES). GET MEDICAL ATTENTION IMMEDIATELY.

INGESTION: DOWICIDE A: CARCINOGEN. **ACUTE EXPOSURE-**INGESTION MAY CAUSE ABDOMINAL PAIN, NAUSEA AND VOMITING. HEMORRHAGIC GASTROENTESTINITIS AND HEMORRHAGE IN THE LIVER AND MYOCARDIUM MAY OCCUR. IF THE VOMITUS IS INHALED PULMONARY EDEMA MAY RESULT. **CHRONIC EXPOSURE-** ORAL ADMINISTRATION PRODUCED URINARY BLADDER CARCINOMAS IN RATS, AND INCREASED THE INCIDENCE OF HAEMANGIOSARCOMAS OF THE LIVER, AND HEPATOCELLULAR CARCINOMAS IN MICE.

FIRST AID- IN THE ABSENCE OF CORROSIVE INJURY, REMOVE BY IPECAC EMESIS. ACTIVATED CHARCOAL IS ALSO USEFUL. FOLLOW WITH 60 ML OF CASTOR OIL, WHICH DISSOLVES THE PHENOLS, RETARDS ABSORPTION AND HASTENS REMOVAL. FOLLOW CASTOR OIL BY GIVING 30-60 ML OF FLEET'S PHOSPHO-SODA DILUTED 1:4 IN WATER. GASTRIC LAVAGE AND EMESIS ARE CONTRAINDICATED IN THE PRESENCE OF ESOPHAGEAL INJURY. DO NOT PERFORM GASTRIC LAVAGE OR EMESIS ON AN UNCONSCIOUS VICTIM. GET MEDICAL ATTENTION IMMEDIATELY. (DREISBACH, HANDBOOK OF POISONING, 11 TH.ED.). ADMINISTRATION OF GASTRIC LAVEGE OR EMETICS SHOULD BE PERFORMED BY QUALIFIED MEDICAL PERSONNEL.

ANTIDOTE: NO SPECIFIC ANTIDOTE. TREAT SYMPTOMATICALLY AND SUPPORTIVELY.

REACTIVITY

REACTIVITY: STABLE UNDER NORMAL TEMPERATURES AND PRESSURES.

INCOMPATIBILITIES: NONE KNOWN.

DECOMPOSITION: THERMAL DECOMPOSITION MAY RELEASE TOXIC OXIDES OF CARBON AND SODIUM.

POLYMERIZATION: HAZARDOUS POLYMERIZATION HAS NOT BEEN REPORTED TO OCCUR UNDER NORMAL TEMPERATURES AND PRESSURES.

CONDITIONS TO AVOID

NONE REPORTED.

SPILL AND LEAK PROCEDURES

WATER SPILL: THE CALIFORNIA SAFE DRINKING WATER AND TOXIC ENFORCEMENT ACT OF 1986 (PROPOSITION 65) PROHIBITS CONTAMINATING ANY KNOWN SOURCE OF DRINKING WATER WITH SUBSTANCES KNOWN TO CAUSE CANCER AND/OR REPRODUCTIVE TOXICITY.

OCCUPATIONAL SPILL: SWEEP UP AND PLACE IN SUITABLE CLEAN, DRY CONTAINERS FOR RECLAMATION OR LATER DISPOSAL. DO NOT FLUSH SPILLED MATERIAL INTO SEWER. KEEP UNNECESSARY PEOPLE AWAY.

PROTECTIVE EQUIPMENT

VENTILATION: PROCESS ENCLOSURE RECOMMENDED.

RESPIRATOR: HIGH LEVELS- SUPPLIED-AIR RESPIRATOR WITH A FULL FACEPIECE, HELMET, OR HOOD. SELF-CONTAINED BREATHING APPARATUS WITH A FULL FACEPIECE.

FIREFIGHTING- SELF-CONTAINED BREATHING APPARATUS WITH A FULL FACEPIECE OPERATED IN PRESSURE-DEMAND OR OTHER POSITIVE PRESSURE MODE.

CLOTHING: EMPLOYEE MUST WEAR APPROPRIATE PROTECTIVE (IMPERVIOUS) CLOTHING AND EQUIPMENT TO PREVENT REPEATED OR PROLONGED SKIN CONTACT WITH THIS SUBSTANCE.

GLOVES: EMPLOYEE MUST WEAR APPROPRIATE PROTECTIVE GLOVES TO PREVENT CONTACT WITH THIS SUBSTANCE.

EYE PROTECTION: EMPLOYEE MUST WEAR SPLASH-PROOF OR DUST-RESISTANT SAFETY GOGGLES AND A FACESHIELD TO PREVENT CONTACT WITH THIS SUBSTANCE.

EMERGENCY WASH FACILITIES: WHERE THERE IS ANY POSSIBILITY THAT AN EMPLOYEE'S EYES AND/OR SKIN MAY BE EXPOSED TO THIS SUBSTANCE, THE EMPLOYER SHOULD PROVIDE AN EYE WASH FOUNTAIN AND QUICK DRENCH SHOWER WITHIN THE IMMEDIATE WORK AREA FOR EMERGENCY USE.

AUTHORIZED BY- OCCUPATIONAL HEALTH SERVICES, INC.
CREATION DATE: 10/04/89 ***REVISION DATE:*** 07/12/90

MATERIAL SAFETY DATA SHEET

OCCUPATIONAL HEALTH SERVICES, INC.
AGRICULTURE AND PESTICIDE DIVISION
450 SEVENTH AVENUE, SUITE 2407
NEW YORK, NEW YORK 10123
1-800-445-MSDS OR (212) 967-1100

EMERGENCY CONTACT:
JOHN S. BRANSFORD, JR. (615) 292-1180

SUBSTANCE IDENTIFICATION

CAS-NUMBER 131-52-2

SUBSTANCE: **SODIUM PENTACHLOROPHENATE**

TRADE NAMES/SYNONYMS: PHENOL, PENTACHLORO-, SODIUM SALT; PENTACHLOROPHENATE SODIUM; PENTACHLOROPHENOL SODIUM SALT; PENTACHLOROPHENOXY SODIUM; SODIUM PCP; SODIUM PENTACHLOROPHENOL; SODIUM PENTACHLOROPHENOLATE; SODIUM PENTACHLOROPHENOXIDE; PCP-SODIUM; PCP SODIUM SALT; DOWICIDE G; MITROL G-ST; SANTOBRITE; STCC 4941177; UN 2567; C6CL5ONA; PST08506

CHEMICAL FAMILY: HALOGEN COMPOUND, AROMATIC SALT

MOLECULAR FORMULA: C6-CL5-O.NA

MOLECULAR WEIGHT: 288.30

CERCLA RATINGS (SCALE 0-3): HEALTH=3 FIRE=1 REACTIVITY=0 PERSISTENCE=2

NFPA RATINGS (SCALE 0-4): HEALTH=4 FIRE=1 REACTIVITY=0

COMPONENTS AND CONTAMINANTS

COMPONENT: SODIUM PENTACHLOROPHENATE ***PERCENT:*** 100.0
CAS# 131-52-2

EXPOSURE LIMITS: NO OCCUPATIONAL EXPOSURE LIMITS ESTABLISHED BY OSHA, ACGIH, OR NIOSH.

PHYSICAL DATA

DESCRIPTION: WHITE OR TAN POWDER WITH PHENOLIC ODOR. ***MELTING POINT:*** DECOMPOSES

SOLUBILITY IN WATER: 29% @ 40 C

SOLVENT SOLUBILITY: SOLUBLE IN ETHANOL, ACETONE, AND POLAR ORGANIC SOLVENTS; INSOLUBLE IN BENZENE AND PETROLEUM OILS.

FIRE AND EXPLOSION DATA

FIRE AND EXPLOSION HAZARD: SLIGHT FIRE HAZARD WHEN EXPOSED TO HEAT OR FLAME.

FIREFIGHTING MEDIA: DRY CHEMICAL, CARBON DIOXIDE, HALON, WATER SPRAY OR STANDARD FOAM (1987 EMERGENCY RESPONSE GUIDEBOOK, DOT P 5800.4). FOR LARGER FIRES, USE WATER SPRAY, FOG OR STANDARD FOAM (1987 EMERGENCY RESPONSE GUIDEBOOK, DOT P 5800.4).

FIREFIGHTING: MOVE CONTAINERS FROM FIRE AREA IF POSSIBLE (1987 EMERGENCY RESPONSE GUIDEBOOK, DOT P 5800.4, GUIDE PAGE 53).
EXTINGUISH ONLY IF FLOW CAN BE STOPPED. EXTINGUISH USING AGENT INDICATED. USE FLOODING AMOUNTS OF WATER AS A FOG. COOL CONTAINERS WITH FLOODING AMOUNTS OF WATER FROM AS FAR A DISTANCE AS POSSIBLE. AVOID BREATHING POISONOUS VAPORS, KEEP UPWIND. CONSIDER EVACUATION OF DOWNWIND AREA IF MATERIAL IS LEAKING.

TRANSPORTATION DATA

DEPARTMENT OF TRANSPORTATION HAZARD CLASSIFICATION 49 CFR 172.101: ORM-A

DEPARTMENT OF TRANSPORTATION LABELING REQUIREMENTS 49 CFR 172.101 AND SUBPART E: NONE

DEPARTMENT OF TRANSPORTATION PACKAGING REQUIREMENTS: 49 CFR 173.510 EXCEPTIONS: 49 CFR 173.505

TOXICITY

SODIUM PENTACHLOROPHENATE: TOXICITY DATA: 11700 UG/KG INHALATION-RAT LD50; 240 MG/M3/2 HOURS INHALATION-MOUSE LC50; 341 MG/M3/2 HOURS INHALATION-GUINEA PIG LC50; 250 MG/KG SKIN-RABBIT LDLO; 124 MG/KG SKIN-MOUSE LD50; 266 MG/KG SKIN-GUINEA PIG LDLO; 126 MG/KG ORAL-RAT LD50; 197 MG/KG ORAL-MOUSE LD50; 328 MG/KG ORAL-RABBIT LD50; 250 MG/KG ORAL-GUINEA PIG LDLO; 146 MG/KG INTRATRACHEAL-RAT LDLO; 164 MG/KG INTRATRACHEAL-MOUSE LDLO; 120 MG/KG INTRATRACHEAL-GUINEA PIG LDLO; 66 MG/KG SUBCUTANEOUS-RAT LD50; 56 MG/KG SUBCUTANEOUS-MOUSE LDLO; 100 MG/KG SUBCUTANEOUS-RABBIT LDLO; 135 MG/KG SUBCUTANEOUS-DOG LDLO; 22 MG/KG INTRAVENOUS-RABBIT LDLO; 50 MG/KG INTRAPERITONEAL-RABBIT LDLO; 63700 UG/KG INTRAPERITONEAL-MOUSE LD50; MUTAGENIC DATA (RTECS); REPRODUCTIVE EFFECTS DATA (RTECS). CARCINOGEN STATUS: HUMAN LIMITED EVIDENCE (IARC GROUP-2B FOR CHLOROPHENOLS). STUDIES REVEALED A SIGNIFICANT INCREASE IN SOFT-TISSUE SARCOMA AND LUNG, NASAL AND NASOPHARYNGEAL CANCER IN WORKERS EXPOSED TO CHLOROPHENOLS. LOCAL EFFECTS: IRRITANT- SKIN AND INHALATION; CORROSIVE- EYE. ACUTE TOXICITY LEVEL: HIGHLY TOXIC BY INHALATION AND DERMAL ABSORPTION; TOXIC BY INGESTION. TARGET EFFECTS: POISONING MAY INCREASE THE METABOLIC RATE AND AFFECT THE CARDIOVASCULAR AND NERVOUS SYSTEMS, LIVER, AND KIDNEYS. AT INCREASED RISK FROM EXPOSURE: PERSONS WITH RENAL OR HEPATIC DISEASES. ADDITIONAL DATA: HOT ENVIRONMENTS MAY ENHANCE ABSORPTION AND THE TOXIC EFFECTS.

HEALTH EFFECTS AND FIRST AID

INHALATION: SODIUM PENTACHLOROPHENATE: IRRITANT/HIGHLY TOXIC. **ACUTE EXPOSURE-** MAY CAUSE IRRITATION OF THE UPPER RESPIRATORY TRACT AND PAIN IN THE NOSE AND THROAT, VIOLENT SNEEZING, AND COUGH. SYMPTOMS OF SYSTEMIC POISONING MAY INCLUDE HEADACHE, FEVER, INTENSE THIRST, EXCESSIVE PERSPIRATION, GENERALIZED WEAKNESS, DIZZINESS, TACHYCARDIA, TACHYPNEA, DYSPNEA, CHEST PAIN, PAIN IN THE EXTREMITIES, ANOREXIA, METABOLIC ACIDOSIS, AND GASTROINTESTINAL UPSET WITH NAUSEA, VOMITING, AND ABDOMINAL PAIN. IN SEVERE POISONINGS, THESE EFFECTS MAY PROGRESS TO MUSCLE SPASMS, DEHYDRATION, HYPERPYREXIA, ANESTHESIA, LEUKOCYTOSIS, HYPERGLYCEMIA, EDEMA AND HEMORRHAGE IN THE LUNGS, CEREBRAL EDEMA, STUPOR, CONVULSIONS, AND COMA. LIVER AND KIDNEY DAMAGE MAY OCCUR. DEATH MAY BE DUE TO VASCULAR COLLAPSE AND HEART FAILURE AND MAY OCCUR WITHIN HOURS OF THE ONSET OF SYMPTOMS FOLLOWED RAPIDLY BY RIGOR MORTIS. IMPAIRMENT OF AUTONOMIC FUNCTION AND CIRCULATION AND VISUAL DAMAGE WERE OBSERVED IN SOME SERIOUS CASES OF POISONING. **CHRONIC EXPOSURE-** REPEATED EXPOSURE TO LOW-LEVELS MAY CAUSE IRRITATION OF THE NOSE, THROAT, AND LUNGS LEADING TO BRONCHITIS AND SINUSITIS. IN ADDITION TO THE SYSTEMIC EFFECTS LISTED ABOVE, REPEATED OR PROLONGED EXPOSURE HAS BEEN ASSOCIATED WITH THE DEVELOPMENT OF ACUTE PANCREATITIS, LEUKOPENIA, IMMUNOLOGICAL CHANGES, APLASTIC ANEMIA, INTRAVASCULAR HEMOLYSIS, AND POLYNEURITIS.

FIRST AID- REMOVE FROM EXPOSURE AREA TO FRESH AIR IMMEDIATELY. IF BREATHING HAS STOPPED, PERFORM ARTIFICIAL RESPIRATION. ADMINISTER OXYGEN. TREAT SYMPTOMATICALLY AND SUPPORTIVELY. GET MEDICAL ATTENTION IMMEDIATELY.

SKIN CONTACT: SODIUM PENTACHLOROPHENATE: IRRITANT/HIGHLY TOXIC. **ACUTE EXPOSURE**- PREPARATIONS STRONGER THAN 1% MAY CAUSE IRRITATION TO THE SKIN WHILE SOLIDS AND CONCENTRATED SOLUTIONS MAY POSSIBLY PRODUCE SKIN BURNS. THIS MATERIAL MAY BE ABSORBED THROUGH THE SKIN IN FATAL AMOUNTS AND PRODUCE SYSTEMIC EFFECTS AS DESCRIBED IN INHALATION. **CHRONIC EXPOSURE**- PROLONGED OR REPEATED EXPOSURE MAY CAUSE DERMATITIS AND A RARE ALLERGIC SKIN RESPONSE; SOLUTIONS STRONGER THAN 1% MAY CAUSE IRRITATION. REPEATED ABSORPTION MAY RESULT IN SYSTEMIC EFFECTS AS DESCRIBED IN INHALATION. CHLORACNE AND DISORDERS OF THE NERVOUS SYSTEM, LIVER, AND PORPHYRIA MAY OCCUR DUE TO THE PRESENCE OF CHLORINATED DIBENZODIOXINS.

FIRST AID- REMOVE CONTAMINATED CLOTHING AND SHOES IMMEDIATELY. THEN REMOVE SKIN AND HAIR CONTAMINATION BY SCRUBBING WITH SOAP AND WATER. IF BODY TEMPERATURE IS ELEVATED, REDUCE TO 37 C BY SPONGE BATH, IMMERSION IN COOL WATER OR BY APPLYING COOLING BLANKET. IF BODY TEMPERATURE IS ABOVE 40 C, ICE WATER IS NECESSARY (DREISBACH, HANDBOOK OF POISONING, 12TH EDITION; MORGAN, EPA RECOGNITION AND MANAGEMENT OF PESTICIDE POISONINGS, 3RD EDITION). GET MEDICAL ATTENTION IMMEDIATELY.

EYE CONTACT: SODIUM PENTACHLOROPHENATE: CORROSIVE. **ACUTE EXPOSURE**- BRIEF CONTACT WITH VAPORS MAY BE SEVERELY IRRITATING. BRIEF CONTACT WITH THE LIQUID OR MIST MAY SEVERELY DAMAGE THE EYES. **CHRONIC EXPOSURE**- PROLONGED CONTACT MAY CAUSE PERMANENT EYE INJURY WHICH MAY BE FOLLOWED BY BLINDNESS.

FIRST AID- WASH EYES IMMEDIATELY WITH LARGE AMOUNTS OF WATER, OCCASIONALLY LIFTING UPPER AND LOWER LIDS, UNTIL NO EVIDENCE OF CHEMICAL REMAINS (AT LEAST 15-20 MINUTES). CONTINUE IRRIGATING WITH NORMAL SALINE UNTIL THE PH HAS RETURNED TO NORMAL (30-60 MINUTES). COVER WITH STERILE BANDAGES. GET MEDICAL ATTENTION IMMEDIATELY.

INGESTION: SODIUM PENTACHLOROPHENATE: TOXIC. **ACUTE EXPOSURE**- MAY CAUSE SEVERE IRRITATION OF THE GASTROINTESTINAL TRACT AND SYSTEMIC EFFECTS AS DESCRIBED IN INHALATION. **CHRONIC EXPOSURE**- MAY CAUSE EFFECTS AS DESCRIBED IN INHALATION. REPRODUCTIVE EFFECTS WERE REPORTED IN ANIMALS STUDIES. ADVERSE HEPATIC EFFECTS WERE OBSERVED IN RATS REPEATEDLY FED PENTACHLOROPHENOL. INCREASED INCIDENCES OF ADRENAL MEDULLARY, HEPATOCELLULAR NEOPLASMS, AND HEMANGIOSARCOMAS WERE OBSERVED IN A STUDY OF MICE RECEIVING PENTACHLOROPHENOL.

FIRST AID- IF VICTIM IS ALERT AND RESPIRATION IS NOT DEPRESSED, INDUCE EMESIS WITH SYRUP OF IPECAC. IF VICTIM IS NOT FULLY ALERT, EMPTY THE STOMACH IMMEDIATELY BY INTUBATION, ASPIRATION, AND LAVAGE, USING ISOTONIC SALINE OR 5% SODIUM BICARBONATE. FOLLOW EMESIS OR LAVAGE WITH ACTIVATED CHARCOAL. GIVE SODIUM SULFATE AS A CATHARTIC. REDUCE ELEVATED BODY TEMPERATURE TO 37 C BY SPONGE BATHS, IMMERSION IN COOL WATER OR BY APPLYING COOLING BLANKET. (MORGAN, EPA RECOGNITION AND MANAGEMENT OF PESTICIDE POISONINGS, THIRD EDITION). GET MEDICAL ATTENTION.

ANTIDOTE: NO SPECIFIC ANTIDOTE. TREAT SYMPTOMATICALLY AND SUPPORTIVELY.

REACTIVITY

REACTIVITY: STABLE UNDER NORMAL TEMPERATURES AND PRESSURES.

INCOMPATIBILITIES: SODIUM PENTACHLOROPHENATE: OXIDIZERS (STRONG): FIRE AND EXPLOSION HAZARD.

DECOMPOSITION: THERMAL DECOMPOSITION PRODUCTS MAY INCLUDE TOXIC AND CORROSIVE CHLORIDES, AND OXIDES OF SODIUM.

POLYMERIZATION: HAZARDOUS POLYMERIZATION HAS NOT BEEN REPORTED TO OCCUR UNDER NORMAL TEMPERATURES AND PRESSURES.

STORAGE AND DISPOSAL

OBSERVE ALL FEDERAL, STATE AND LOCAL REGULATIONS WHEN STORING OR DISPOSING OF THIS SUBSTANCE. FOR ASSISTANCE, CONTACT THE DISTRICT DIRECTOR OF THE ENVIRONMENTAL PROTECTION AGENCY.

STORAGE

STORE AWAY FROM INCOMPATIBLE SUBSTANCES.

CONDITIONS TO AVOID

MAY BURN BUT DOES NOT IGNITE READILY.

SPILL AND LEAK PROCEDURES

OCCUPATIONAL SPILL: DO NOT TOUCH SPILLED MATERIAL. STOP LEAK IF YOU CAN DO IT WITHOUT RISK. FOR SMALL SPILLS, TAKE UP WITH SAND OR OTHER ABSORBENT MATERIAL AND PLACE INTO CONTAINERS FOR LATER DISPOSAL. FOR SMALL DRY SPILLS, WITH A CLEAN SHOVEL PLACE MATERIAL INTO CLEAN, DRY CONTAINER AND COVER. MOVE CONTAINERS FROM SPILL AREA. FOR LARGER SPILLS, DIKE FAR AHEAD OF SPILL FOR LATER DISPOSAL. KEEP UNNECESSARY PEOPLE AWAY. ISOLATE HAZARD AREA AND DENY ENTRY.

PROTECTIVE EQUIPMENT

VENTILATION: PROCESS ENCLOSURE RECOMMENDED.

RESPIRATOR: THE FOLLOWING RESPIRATORS ARE RECOMMENDED BASED ON INFORMATION FOUND IN THE PHYSICAL DATA, TOXICITY AND HEALTH EFFECTS SECTIONS. THEY ARE RANKED IN ORDER FROM MINIMUM TO MAXIMUM RESPIRATORY PROTECTION. THE SPECIFIC RESPIRATOR SELECTED MUST BE BASED ON CONTAMINATION LEVELS FOUND IN THE WORK PLACE, MUST NOT EXCEED THE WORKING LIMITS OF THE RESPIRATOR AND BE JOINTLY APPROVED BY THE NATIONAL INSTITUTE FOR OCCUPATIONAL SAFETY AND HEALTH AND THE MINE SAFETY AND HEALTH ADMINISTRATION (NIOSH-MSHA).

TYPE 'C' SUPPLIED-AIR RESPIRATOR WITH A FULL FACEPIECE OPERATED IN PRESSURE-DEMAND OR OTHER POSITIVE PRESSURE MODE OR WITH A FULL FACEPIECE, HELMET OR HOOD OPERATED IN CONTINOUS-FLOW MODE.

SELF-CONTAINED BREATHING APPARATUS WITH A FULL FACEPIECE OPERATED IN PRESSURE-DEMAND OR OTHER POSITIVE PRESSURE MODE.

FOR FIREFIGHTING AND OTHER IMMEDIATELY DANGEROUS TO LIFE OR HEALTH CONDITIONS:

SELF-CONTAINED BREATHING APPARATUS WITH FULL FACEPIECE OPERATED IN PRESSURE-DEMAND OR OTHER POSITIVE PRESSURE MODE.

SUPPLIED-AIR RESPIRATOR WITH FULL FACEPIECE AND OPERATED IN PRESSURE-DEMAND OR OTHER POSITIVE PRESSURE MODE IN COMBINATION WITH AN AUXILIARY SELF-CONTAINED BREATHING APPARATUS OPERATED IN PRESSURE-DEMAND OR OTHER POSITIVE PRESSURE MODE.

CLOTHING: EMPLOYEE MUST WEAR APPROPRIATE PROTECTIVE (IMPERVIOUS) CLOTHING AND EQUIPMENT TO PREVENT ANY POSSIBILITY OF SKIN CONTACT WITH THIS SUBSTANCE.

GLOVES: EMPLOYEE MUST WEAR APPROPRIATE PROTECTIVE GLOVES TO PREVENT CONTACT WITH THIS SUBSTANCE.

EYE PROTECTION: EMPLOYEE MUST WEAR SPLASH-PROOF OR DUST-RESISTANT SAFETY GOGGLES AND A FACESHIELD TO PREVENT CONTACT WITH THIS SUBSTANCE.

EMERGENCY WASH FACILITIES: WHERE THERE IS ANY POSSIBILITY THAT AN EMPLOYEE'S EYES AND/OR SKIN MAY BE EXPOSED TO THIS SUBSTANCE, THE EMPLOYER SHOULD PROVIDE AN EYE WASH FOUNTAIN AND QUICK DRENCH SHOWER WITHIN THE IMMEDIATE WORK AREA FOR EMERGENCY USE.

AUTHORIZED BY- OCCUPATIONAL HEALTH SERVICES, INC.

CREATION DATE: 10/05/89 ***REVISION DATE:*** 07/12/90

MATERIAL SAFETY DATA SHEET

OCCUPATIONAL HEALTH SERVICES, INC.
AGRICULTURE AND PESTICIDE DIVISION
450 SEVENTH AVENUE, SUITE 2407
NEW YORK, NEW YORK 10123
1-800-445-MSDS OR (212) 967-1100

EMERGENCY CONTACT:
JOHN S. BRANSFORD, JR. (615) 292-1180

SUBSTANCE IDENTIFICATION

SUBSTANCE: **DURSBAN (R) 4E INSECTICIDE**

TRADE NAMES/SYNONYMS: DURSBAN 4E INSECTICIDE; DURSBAN 4E EMULSIFIABLE INSECTICIDE; DOW DURSBAN 4E INSECTICIDE; NSN 6840-00-402-5411; EPA REG. NO. 464-360; PST08521

CHEMICAL FAMILY: MIXTURE, PESTICIDE FORMULATION ORGANOPHOSPHATE

CERCLA RATINGS (SCALE 0-3): HEALTH=3 FIRE=2 REACTIVITY=1 PERSISTENCE=1

NFPA RATINGS (SCALE 0-4): HEALTH=3 FIRE=2 REACTIVITY=1

COMPONENTS AND CONTAMINANTS

COMPONENT: XYLENE RANGE AROMATIC SOLVENT ***PERCENT:*** 47.7
CAS# 64742-95-6

COMPONENT: CHLORPYRIFOS ***PERCENT:*** 44.4
CAS# 2921-88-2

COMPONENT: PROPRIETARY EMULSIFIERS ***PERCENT:*** 7.8

EXPOSURE LIMITS: XYLENE: 100 PPM (435 MG/M3) OSHA TWA; 150 PPM (655 MG/M3) OSHA STEL 100 PPM (435 MG/M3) ACGIH TWA; 150 PPM (655 MG/M3) ACGIH STEL 100 PPM (435 MG/M3) NIOSH RECOMMENDED 10 HOUR TWA; 200 PPM (870 MG/M3) NIOSH RECOMMENDED 10 MINUTE CEILING
1000 POUNDS CERCLA SECTION 103 REPORTABLE QUANTITY SUBJECT TO SARA SECTION 313 ANNUAL TOXIC CHEMICAL RELEASE REPORTING
CHLORPYRIFOS: 0.2 MG/M3 OSHA TWA (SKIN) 0.2 MG/M3 ACGIH TWA (SKIN); 0.6 MG/M3 ACGIH STEL (NOTICE OF INTENDED CHANGES 1988-89)
1 POUND CERCLA SECTION 103 REPORTABLE QUANTITY

PHYSICAL DATA

DESCRIPTION: YELLOW LIQUID WITH A MERCAPTAN-TYPE ODOR
BOILING POINT: 290 F (143 C) ***SPECIFIC GRAVITY:*** 1.079
VAPOR PRESSURE: >10 MMHG @ 25 C ***EVAPORATION RATE:*** NOT AVAILABLE
SOLUBILITY IN WATER: EMULSIFIABLE ***VAPOR DENSITY:*** NOT AVAILABLE

FIRE AND EXPLOSION DATA

FIRE AND EXPLOSION HAZARD: MODERATE FIRE HAZARD WHEN EXPOSED TO HEAT OR FLAME.
FLASH POINT: 106 F (41 C) (CC) ***UPPER EXPLOSIVE LIMIT:*** 6% (SOLVENT)
LOWER EXPLOSIVE LIMIT: 1% (SOLVENT) ***FLAMMABILITY CLASS(OSHA):*** II
FIREFIGHTING MEDIA: DRY CHEMICAL, CARBON DIOXIDE, HALON, WATER SPRAY OR STANDARD FOAM (1987 EMERGENCY RESPONSE GUIDEBOOK, DOT P 5800.4).
FOR LARGER FIRES, USE WATER SPRAY, FOG OR STANDARD FOAM (1987 EMERGENCY RESPONSE GUIDEBOOK, DOT P 5800.4).
FIREFIGHTING: MOVE CONTAINER FROM FIRE AREA IF POSSIBLE. DIKE FIRE CONTROL WATER FOR LATER DISPOSAL; DO NOT SCATTER THE MATERIAL. COOL FIRE-EXPOSED CONTAINERS WITH WATER FROM SIDE UNTIL WELL AFTER FIRE IS OUT. STAY AWAY FROM STORAGE TANK ENDS. WITHDRAW IMMEDIATELY IN CASE OF RISING SOUND FROM VENTING SAFETY DEVICE OR ANY DISCOLORATION OF STORAGE TANK DUE TO FIRE (1987 EMERGENCY RESPONSE GUIDEBOOK, DOT P 5800.4, GUIDE PAGE 28).
EXTINGUISH ONLY IF FLOW CAN BE STOPPED. USE FLOODING AMOUNTS OF WATER AS A FOG; SOLID STREAMS MAY BE INEFFECTIVE. COOL CONTAINERS WITH FLOODING AMOUNTS OF WATER FROM AS FAR A DISTANCE AS POSSIBLE. AVOID BREATHING POISONOUS VAPORS, KEEP UPWIND.

TRANSPORTATION DATA

DEPARTMENT OF TRANSPORTATION HAZARD CLASSIFICATION 49 CFR 172.101: COMBUSTIBLE LIQUID
DEPARTMENT OF TRANSPORTATION LABELING REQUIREMENTS 49 CFR 172.101 AND SUBPART E: NONE
DEPARTMENT OF TRANSPORTATION PACKAGING REQUIREMENTS: NONE EXCEPTIONS: 49 CFR 173.118A

TOXICITY

DURSBAN 4E INSECTICIDE. TOXICITY DATA: 2200 MG/M3/4 HOURS INHALATION-RAT LC50 (DOW MSDS); 916 MG/KG SKIN-RABBIT LD50 (DOW MSDS); 530-940 MG/KG ORAL-RAT LD50 (DOW MSDS). CARCINOGEN STATUS: NONE. ACUTE TOXICITY LEVEL: TOXIC BY INHALATION AND DERMAL ABSORPTION, AND MODERATELY TOXIC BY INGESTION. CHLORPYRIFOS: TOXICITY DATA: 78 MG/KG INHALATION-RAT LD50; 94 MG/KG INHALATION-MOUSE LD50; 2000 MG/KG SKIN-RABBIT LD50; 202 MG/KG SKIN-RAT LD50; 300 MG/KG ORAL-MAN TDLO; 82 MG/KG ORAL-RAT LD50; 60 MG/KG ORAL-MOUSE LD50; 1000 MG/KG ORAL-RABBIT LD50; 504 MG/KG ORAL-GUINEA PIG LD50; 100 MG/KG SUBCUTANEOUS-GUINEA PIG LDLO; 192 MG/KG INTRAPERITONEAL-MOUSE LD50; 150 MG/KG UNREPORTED-RAT LD50; 163 MG/KG UNREPORTED-MAMMAL LD50; MUTAGENIC DATA (RTECS); REPRODUCTIVE EFFECTS DATA (RTECS). CARCINOGEN STATUS: NONE. LOCAL EFFECTS: IRRITANT- SKIN, EYE. ACUTE TOXICITY LEVEL: TOXIC BY INGESTION; MODERATELY TOXIC BY DERMAL ABSORPTION. TARGET EFFECTS: CHOLINESTERASE INHIBITOR. AT INCREASED RISK FROM EXPOSURE: PERSONS WITH RESPIRATORY AILMENTS, RECENT EXPOSURE TO CHOLINESTERASE INHIBITORS OR IMPAIRED CHOLINESTERASE PRODUCTION, OR LIVER MALFUNCTION.* ADDITIONAL DATA: MAY CROSS THE PLACENTA. HIGH ENVIRONMENTAL TEMPERATURES OR EXPOSURE OF THE CHEMICAL TO VISIBLE OR ULTRAVIOLET LIGHT MAY ENHANCE THE TOXICITY. INTERACTIONS WITH MEDICATIONS MAY OCCUR.*
* MAY BE BASED ON GENERAL INFORMATION ON ORGANOPHOSPHATES.
XYLENE: IRRITATION DATA: 200 PPM EYE-HUMAN; 87 MG EYE-RABBIT MILD; 5 MG/24 HOURS EYE-RABBIT SEVERE; 100% SKIN-RABBIT MODERATE; 500 MG/24 HOURS SKIN-RABBIT MODERATE. TOXICITY DATA: 10000 PPM/6 HOURS INHALATION-MAN LCLO; 200 PPM INHALATION-HUMAN TCLO; 5000 PPM/4 HOURS INHALATION-RAT LC50; 450 PPM INHALATION-GUINEA PIG LCLO; 50 MG/KG ORAL-HUMAN LDLO; 4300 MG/KG ORAL-RAT LD50; 1700 MG/KG SUBCUTANEOUS-RAT LD50; 129 MG/KG INTRAVENOUS-RABBIT LDLO; 2 GM/KG INTRAPERITONEAL-MAMMAL LDLO; 2459 MG/KG INTRAPERITONEAL-RAT LD50; 1548 MG/KG INTRAPERITONEAL-MOUSE LD50; 2000 MG/KG INTRAPERITONEAL-GUINEA PIG LDLO; REPRODUCTIVE EFFECTS DATA (RTECS). CARCINOGEN STATUS: NONE. LOCAL EFFECTS: IRRITANT- INHALATION, SKIN, EYE. ACUTE TOXICITY LEVEL: MODERATELY TOXIC BY INHALATION, INGESTION. TARGET EFFECTS: CENTRAL NERVOUS SYSTEM DEPRESSANT. POISONING MAY ALSO AFFECT THE NERVOUS SYSTEM, LIVER AND KIDNEYS. AT INCREASED RISK FROM EXPOSURE: PREGNANT WOMEN. ADDITIONAL INFORMATION: CONSUMPTION OF ALCOHOLIC BEVERAGES MAY ENHANCE THE TOXIC EFFECTS. STIMULANTS SUCH AS EPINEPHRINE OR EPHEDRINE MAY INDUCE VENTRICULAR FIBRILLATION.

HEALTH EFFECTS AND FIRST AID

INHALATION: DURSBAN 4E INSECTICIDE: TOXIC. EXPOSURE TO THIS MATERIAL MAY CAUSE IRRITATION OF THE UPPER RESPIRATORY TRACT AND CENTRAL NERVOUS SYSTEM DEPRESSION DUE TO THE AROMATIC SOLVENT INVOLVED. SYMPTOMS INCLUDE HEADACHE, DIZZINESS, WEAKNESS, DROWSINESS, INCOORDINATION, NAUSEA, FATIGUE, AND UNCONSCIOUSNESS. WOMEN MAY DEVELOP MENSTRUAL DISORDERS, SUCH AS MENORRHAGIA OR METRORRHAGIA, INFERTILITY, AND PATHOLOGICAL PREGNANCY CONDITIONS INCLUDING TOXICOSIS, DANGER OF MISCARRIAGE, AND HEMORRHAGING DURING DELIVERY. CLINICALLY, MODERATE LIVER ENLARGEMENT, NECROSIS, NEPHROSIS, AND BONE MARROW HYPERPLASIA MAY OCCUR. CHRONIC INHALATION EXPOSURE OF PREGNANT RATS AND MICE TO XYLENE HAVE RESULTED IN EFFECTS ON THE FETUS AND FERTILITY, AND SPECIFIC FETAL DEVELOPMENTAL ABNORMALITIES. SEE INFORMATION ON ORGANOPHOSPHATES.
ORGANOPHOSPHATES: CHOLINESTERASE INHIBITOR. **ACUTE EXPOSURE**- WHEN INHALED, THE FIRST EFFECTS OF CHOLINESTERASE INHIBITORS ARE USUALLY RESPIRATORY AND MAY INCLUDE NASAL HYPEREMIA AND WATERY DISCHARGE, COUGH, CHEST DISCOMFORT, DYSPNEA, AND WHEEZING DUE TO INCREASED BRONCHIAL SECRETIONS AND BRONCHOCONSTRICTION. IF SUFFICIENT AMOUNTS ARE ABSORBED, OTHER SYSTEMIC EFFECTS MAY BEGIN WITHIN A FEW MINUTES OR BE DELAYED FOR UP TO 12 HOURS. SYMPTOMS MAY INCLUDE PALLOR, NAUSEA, VOMITING, DIARRHEA, ABDOMINAL CRAMPS, HEADACHE, DIZZINESS, OCULAR PAIN, BLURRED VISION, MIOSIS OR IN SOME CASES, ESPECIALLY INITIALLY, MYDRIASIS, LACRIMATION, SALIVATION, SWEATING, AND CONFUSION. OTHER REPORTED CENTRAL NERVOUS SYSTEM OR NEUROMUSCULAR EFFECTS MAY INCLUDE ATAXIA, SLURRED SPEECH, AREFLEXIA, WEAKNESS, FATIGUE, FASCICULATIONS, TWITCHING, TREMORS POSSIBLY OF THE TONGUE AND EYELIDS, AND EVENTUALLY PARALYSIS OF THE EXTREMITIES AND POSSIBLY OF THE RESPIRATORY MUSCLES. IN SEVERE CASES THERE MAY ALSO BE INVOLUNTARY DEFECATION AND URINATION, CYANOSIS, PSYCHOSIS, HYPERGLYCEMIA, ACUTE PANCREATITIS, CARDIAC IRREGULARITIES, PULMONARY EDEMA, UNCONSCIOUSNESS, CONVULSIONS, AND COMA. DEATH IS PRIMARILY DUE TO RESPIRATORY FAILURE, ALTHOUGH CARDIOVASCULAR EFFECTS INCLUDING CARDIAC ARREST MAY ALSO BE IMPLICATED. LONG TERM SEQUELAE ARE RARE BUT MAY INCLUDE NEUROPSYCHIATRIC DISORDERS AND MYOPATHY WITH MUSCLE TENDERNESS. **CHRONIC EXPOSURE**- REPEATED OR PROLONGED EXPOSURE MAY RESULT IN THE EFFECTS OF ACUTE EXPOSURE. OTHER EFFECTS REPORTED IN WORKERS REPEATEDLY EXPOSED INCLUDE IMPAIRED MEMORY AND CONCENTRATION, ACUTE PSYCHOSIS, SEVERE DEPRESSIONS, IRRITABILTY, CONFUSION, APATHY, EMOTIONAL LABILITY, SOCIAL WITHDRAWAL, CONFUSION, HEADACHE, SPEECH DIFFICULTIES, DELAYED REACTION TIMES, SPATIAL DISORIENTATION, NIGHTMARES, SLEEPWALKING, AND DROWSINESS OR INSOMNIA. AN INFLUENZA-LIKE CONDITION WITH HEADACHE, NAUSEA, WEAKNESS, ANOREXIA AND MALAISE HAS ALSO BEEN REPORTED.
FIRST AID- REMOVE FROM EXPOSURE AREA TO FRESH AIR IMMEDIATELY. IF BREATHING HAS STOPPED, GIVE ARTIFICIAL RESPIRATION. MAINTAIN AIRWAY AND BLOOD PRESSURE AND ADMINISTER OXYGEN IF AVAILABLE. KEEP AFFECTED PERSON WARM AND AT REST. TREAT SYMPTOMATICALLY AND SUPPORTIVELY. ADMINISTRATION OF OXYGEN SHOULD BE PERFORMED BY QUALIFIED PERSONNEL. GET MEDICAL ATTENTION IMMEDIATELY.

SKIN CONTACT: DURSBAN 4E INSECTICIDE: TOXIC. A TEST IN GUINEA PIGS INDICATED THAT THIS PRODUCT MAY HAVE WEAK SKIN SENSITIZATION POTENTIAL. PROLONGED OR REPEATED EXPOSURE MAY CAUSE SEVERE IRRITATION AND POSSIBLE BURNS. SEE INFORMATION ON ORGANOPHOSPHATES.
ORGANOPHOSPHATES: CHOLINESTERASE INHIBITOR. **ACUTE EXPOSURE**- LOCALIZED SWEATING AND FASCICULATIONS MAY OCCUR AT THE SITE OF CONTACT. IF SUFFICIENT AMOUNTS ARE ABSORBED, OTHER EFFECTS OF CHOLINESTERASE INHIBITION AS DESCRIBED IN ACUTE INHALATION MAY OCCUR. SYMPTOMS MAY BE DELAYED 2-3 HOURS, BUT USUALLY NO MORE THAN 12 HOURS. THE RATE OF ABSORPTION IS INCREASED BY THE PRESENCE OF DERMATITIS OR HIGH AMBIENT TEMPERATURES. **CHRONIC EXPOSURE**- REPEATED OR PROLONGED EXPOSURE MAY CAUSE EFFECTS AS DESCRIBED IN ACUTE EXPOSURE. SOME ORGANOPHOSPHATES MAY CAUSE SENSITIZATION.
FIRST AID- REMOVE CONTAMINATED CLOTHING IMMEDIATELY. WASH CONTAMINATED AREAS WITH SOAP AND WATER FOLLOWED BY ALCOHOL (ARENA,

POISONING, 4TH ED.). EMERGENCY PERSONNEL SHOULD WEAR GLOVES AND AVOID CONTAMINATION. TREAT RESPIRATORY DIFFICULTY WITH ARTIFICIAL RESPIRATION. GET MEDICAL ATTENTION IMMEDIATELY.

EYE CONTACT: DURSBAN 4E INSECTICIDE: MAY CAUSE MODERATE EYE IRRITATION WITH MODERATE CORNEAL INJURY. SEE INFORMATION ON ORGANOPHOSPHATES. ORGANOPHOSPHATES: CHOLINESTERASE INHIBITOR. **ACUTE EXPOSURE-** DIRECT CONTACT MAY CAUSE PAIN, HYPEREMIA, LACRIMATION, TWITCHING OF THE EYELIDS, MIOSIS, AND CILIARY MUSCLE SPASM WITH LOSS OF ACCOMODATION, BLURRED OR DIMMED VISION AND BROWACHE. SOMETIMES MYDRIASIS MAY OCCUR INSTEAD OF MIOSIS. WITH SUFFICIENT EXPOSURE, OTHER SYMPTOMS OF CHOLINESTERASE INHIBITION AS DESCRIBED IN ACUTE INHALATION MAY OCCUR. **CHRONIC EXPOSURE-** REPEATED OR PROLONGED EXPOSURE MAY CAUSE EFFECTS AS DESCRIBED IN ACUTE EXPOSURE. SOME COMPOUNDS HAVE CAUSED TOXIC EFFECTS ON THE CRYSTALLINE LENS, CONJUNCTIVAL THICKENING AND OBSTRUCTION OF THE NASOLACRIMAL CANALS WHEN USED AS MIOTIC EYEDROPS.

FIRST AID- IRRIGATE EYES WITH WATER OR SALINE SOLUTION. IF SYMPTOMS OF POISONING OCCUR, TREAT RESPIRATORY DIFFICULTY WITH ARTIFICIAL RESPIRATION AND OXYGEN. OBSERVE PATIENT FOR AT LEAST 24-36 HOURS (GOSSELIN, CLINICAL TOXICOLOGY OF COMMERCIAL PRODUCTS, 5TH ED.). GET MEDICAL ATTENTION IMMEDIATELY. OXYGEN SHOULD BE ADMINISTERED BY QUALIFIED MEDICAL PERSONNEL.

INGESTION: DURSBAN 4E INSECTICIDE: NARCOTIC. INGESTION OF AROMATIC SOLVENTS MAY CAUSE SEVERE GASTROINTESTINAL DISTRESS WITH NAUSEA AND VOMITING, AND CENTRAL NERVOUS SYSTEM DEPRESSION. POISONING MAY CAUSE LIVER AND KIDNEY DAMAGE. IF ASPIRATION INTO THE LUNGS OCCURS, SEVERE COUGHING, DISTRESS, CHEMICAL PNEUMONITIS, RAPIDLY DEVELOPING PULMONARY EDEMA, AND HEMORRHAGE MAY OCCUR. NEGATIVE RESULTS WERE REPORTED FROM A DELAYED NEUROTOXICITY STUDY OF CHLORPYRIFOS IN HENS. SEE INFORMATION ON ORGANOPHOSPHATES.
ORGANOPHOSPHATES: CHOLINESTERASE INHIBITOR. **ACUTE EXPOSURE-** WHEN INGESTED, THE FIRST EFFECTS MAY BE NAUSEA, VOMITING, ANOREXIA, ABDOMINAL CRAMPS AND DIARRHEA. GASTROINTESTINAL ABSORPTION MAY CAUSE THE SYMPTOMS OF CHOLINESTERASE INHIBITION AS DESCRIBED IN ACUTE INHALATION. SYMPTOMS MAY BEGIN WITHIN MINUTES OR BE DELAYED. **CHRONIC EXPOSURE-** REPEATED INGESTION MAY CAUSE EFFECTS AS DESCRIBED IN ACUTE EXPOSURE.

FIRST AID- IF PERSON IS ALERT AND RESPIRATION IS NOT DEPRESSED, GIVE SYRUP OF IPECAC FOLLOWED BY WATER (IF VOMITING OCCURS, KEEP HEAD BELOW HIPS TO PREVENT ASPIRATION). IF CONSCIOUSNESS LEVEL DECLINES OR VOMITING HAS NOT OCCURRED IN 15 MINUTES EMPTY STOMACH BY GASTRIC LAVAGE WITH THE AID OF CUFFED ENDOTRACHEAL TUBE USING ISOTONIC SALINE OR 5% SODIUM BICARBONATE FOLLOW WITH ACTIVATED CHARCOAL. ESTABLISH AND MAINTAIN AIRWAY. TREAT RESPIRATORY DIFFICULTY WITH ARTIFICIAL RESPIRATION AND OXYGEN. DO NOT GIVE MORPHINE, AMINOPHYLLINE, PHENOTHIAZINES, RESERPINE, FUROSEMIDE, OR ETHACRYNIC ACID (MORGAN, RECOGNITION AND MANAGEMENT OF PESTICIDE POISONINGS, 3RD ED.). TREAT SYMPTOMATICALLY AND SUPPORTIVELY. ADMINISTRATION OF OXYGEN AND LAVAGE MUST BE PERFORMED BY QUALIFIED MEDICAL PERSONNEL. GET MEDICAL ATTENTION IMMEDIATELY.

ANTIDOTE: BECAUSE IT IS DIFFICULT TO DETERMINE HOW CHEMICALS WILL INTERACT ONCE COMBINED IN A MIXTURE, AN ANTIDOTE IS NOT NORMALLY LISTED. HOWEVER DUE TO THE SEVERE POISONING POTENTIAL OF CHLORPYRIFOS, THE ANTIDOTE IS MENTIONED MERELY AS A POSSIBLE AID TO A QUALIFIED MEDICAL PERSON TO DETERMINE IF THE SYMPTOMS DISPLAYED BY THE POISONED VICTIM MERIT THE USE OF THE ANTIDOTE.
FOR CHOLINESTERASE INHIBITORS: ESTABLISH CLEAR AIRWAY AND TISSUE OXYGENATION BY ASPIRATION OF SECRETIONS, AND IF NECESSARY, BY ASSISTED PULMONARY VENTILATION WITH OXYGEN. IMPROVE TISSUE OXYGENATION AS MUCH AS POSSIBLE BEFORE ADMINISTERING ATROPINE TO MINIMIZE THE RISK OF VENTRICULAR FIBRILLATION. ADMINISTER ATROPINE SULFATE INTRAVENOUSLY, OR INTRAMUSCULARLY IF IV INJECTION IS NOT POSSIBLE. IN MODERATELY SEVERE POISONING ADMINISTER ATROPINE SULFATE, 0.4-2.0 MG REPEATED EVERY 15 MINUTES UNTIL ATROPINIZATION IS ACHIEVED (TACHYCARDIA, FLUSHING, DRY MOUTH, MYDRIASIS). MAINTAIN ATROPINIZATION BY REPEATED DOSES FOR 2-12 HOURS, OR LONGER, DEPENDING ON THE SEVERITY OF POISONING. THE APPEARANCE OF RALES IN THE LUNG BASES, MIOSIS, SALIVATION, NAUSEA, BRADYCARDIA, ARE ALL INDICATIONS OF INADEQUATE ATROPINIZATION.
SEVERELY POISONED INDIVIDUALS MAY EXHIBIT REMARKABLE TOLERANCE TO ATROPINE; TWO OR MORE TIMES THE DOSAGES SUGGESTED ABOVE MAY BE NEEDED. PERSONS NOT POISONED OR ONLY SLIGHTLY POISONED, HOWEVER, MAY DEVELOP SIGNS OF ATROPINE TOXICITY FROM SUCH LARGE DOSAGES: FEVER, MUSCLE FIBRILLATIONS, AND DELIRIUM ARE THE MAIN SIGNS OF ATROPINE TOXICITY. IF THESE SIGNS APPEAR WHILE THE PATIENT IS FULLY ATROPINIZED, ATROPINE ADMINISTRATION SHOULD BE DISCONTINUED, AT LEAST TEMPORARILY.
OBSERVE TREATED PATIENTS CLOSELY AT LEAST 24 HOURS TO INSURE THAT SYMPTOMS (POSSIBLY PULMONARY EDEMA) DO NOT RECUR AS ATROPINIZATION WEARS OFF. IN VERY SEVERE POISONINGS, METABOLIC DISPOSITION OF TOXICANT MAY REQUIRE SEVERAL HOURS OR DAYS DURING WHICH ATROPINIZATION MUST BE MAINTAINED. MARKEDLY LOWER LEVELS OF URINARY METABOLITES INDICATE THAT ATROPINE DOSAGE CAN BE TAPERED OFF. AS DOSAGE IS REDUCED, CHECK THE LUNG BASES FREQUENTLY FOR RALES. IF RALES ARE HEARD OR OTHER SYMPTOMS RETURN, RE-ESTABLISH ATROPINIZATION PROMPTLY (MORGAN, RECOGNITION AND MANAGEMENT OF PESTICIDE POISONINGS, 3RD ED.). ADMINISTRATION OF ANTIDOTE MUST BE PERFORMED BY QUALIFIED MEDICAL PERSONNEL.
IN CASES OF SEVERE POISONING BY ORGANOPHOSPHATE PESTICIDES IN WHICH RESPIRATORY DEPRESSION, MUSCLE WEAKNESS AND TWITCHINGS ARE SEVERE, GIVE PRALIDOXIME (PROTOPAM-AYERST, 2-PAM), 1.0 GRAM INTRAVENOUSLY AT NO MORE THAN 0.5 GRAM PER MINUTE. DOSAGE OF PRALIDOXIME MAY BE REPEATED IN 1-2 HOURS, THEN AT 10-12 HOUR INTERVALS IF NEEDED. IN VERY SEVERE POISONINGS, DOSAGE RATES MAY BE DOUBLED. TREATMENT WITH PRALIDOXIME WILL BE MOST EFFECTIVE IF GIVEN WITHIN THIRTY-SIX HOURS AFTER POISONING (MORGAN, RECOGNITION AND MANAGEMENT OF PESTICIDE POISONINGS, 3RD ED.). ANTIDOTE SHOULD BE ADMINISTERED BY QUALIFIED MEDICAL PERSONNEL.

REACTIVITY

REACTIVITY: MAY UNDERGO VIOLENT EXOTHERMIC DECOMPOSITION ABOVE 130 C (266 F). THE INCREASE IN TEMPERATURE AND PRESSURE MAY RESULT IN THE VIOLENT RUPTURE OF THE CONTAINER.

INCOMPATIBILITIES: DURSBAN (R) 4E INSECTICIDE: ALKALIS: INCOMPATIBLE. OXIDIZERS (STRONG): FIRE AND EXPLOSION HAZARD.

DECOMPOSITION: THERMAL DECOMPOSITION MAY RELEASE TOXIC AND/OR HAZARDOUS GASES.

POLYMERIZATION: HAZARDOUS POLYMERIZATION HAS NOT BEEN REPORTED TO OCCUR UNDER NORMAL TEMPERATURES AND PRESSURES.

STORAGE AND DISPOSAL

OBSERVE ALL FEDERAL, STATE AND LOCAL REGULATIONS WHEN STORING OR DISPOSING OF THIS SUBSTANCE. FOR ASSISTANCE, CONTACT THE DISTRICT DIRECTOR OF THE ENVIRONMENTAL PROTECTION AGENCY.

****STORAGE****

STORE IN ACCORDANCE WITH 29 CFR 1910.106.
BONDING AND GROUNDING: SUBSTANCES WITH LOW ELECTROCONDUCTIVITY, WHICH MAY BE IGNITED BY ELECTROSTATIC SPARKS, SHOULD BE STORED IN CONTAINERS WHICH MEET THE BONDING AND GROUNDING GUIDELINES SPECIFIED IN NFPA 77-1983, RECOMMENDED PRACTICE ON STATIC ELECTRICITY.
STORE AWAY FROM INCOMPATIBLE SUBSTANCES.

****DISPOSAL****

DISPOSAL MUST BE IN ACCORDANCE WITH STANDARDS APPLICABLE TO GENERATORS OF HAZARDOUS WASTE, 40 CFR 262. EPA HAZARDOUS WASTE NUMBER D001. 100 POUND CERCLA SECTION 103 REPORTABLE QUANTITY.

CONDITIONS TO AVOID

AVOID CONTACT WITH HEAT, SPARKS, FLAMES OR OTHER IGNITION SOURCES. VAPORS MAY BE EXPLOSIVE. MATERIAL IS POISONOUS; AVOID INHALATION OF VAPORS OR CONTACT WITH SKIN. DO NOT ALLOW MATERIAL TO CONTAMINATE WATER SOURCES.

SPILL AND LEAK PROCEDURES

OCCUPATIONAL SPILL: SHUT OFF IGNITION SOURCES. DO NOT TOUCH SPILLED MATERIAL. STOP LEAK IF YOU CAN DO IT WITHOUT RISK. USE WATER SPRAY TO REDUCE VAPORS. FOR SMALL SPILLS, TAKE UP WITH SAND OR OTHER ABSORBENT MATERIAL AND PLACE INTO CONTAINERS FOR LATER DISPOSAL. FOR LARGER SPILLS, DIKE FAR AHEAD OF SPILL FOR LATER DISPOSAL. NO SMOKING, FLAMES OR FLARES IN HAZARD AREA! KEEP UNNECESSARY PEOPLE AWAY; ISOLATE HAZARD AREA AND DENY ENTRY.
REPORTABLE QUANTITY (RQ): THE SUPERFUND AMENDMENTS AND REAUTHORIZATION ACT (SARA) SECTION 304 REQUIRES THAT A RELEASE EQUAL TO OR GREATER THAN THE REPORTABLE QUANTITY ESTABLISHED FOR THAT SUBSTANCE BE IMMEDIATELY REPORTED TO THE LOCAL EMERGENCY PLANNING COMMITTEE AND THE STATE EMERGENCY RESPONSE COMMISSION (40 CFR 355.40). IF THE RELEASE OF THIS SUBSTANCE IS REPORTABLE UNDER CERCLA SECTION 103, THE NATIONAL RESPONSE CENTER MUST BE NOTIFIED IMMEDIATELY AT (800) 424-8802 OR (202) 426-2675 IN THE METROPOLITAN WASHINGTON, D.C. AREA (40 CFR 302.6).

PROTECTIVE EQUIPMENT

VENTILATION: PROVIDE LOCAL EXHAUST OR PROCESS ENCLOSURE VENTILATION TO MEET PUBLISHED EXPOSURE LIMITS.

RESPIRATOR: THE FOLLOWING RESPIRATORS ARE RECOMMENDED BASED ON INFORMATION FOUND IN THE PHYSICAL DATA, TOXICITY AND HEALTH EFFECTS SECTIONS. THEY ARE RANKED IN ORDER FROM MINIMUM TO MAXIMUM RESPIRATORY PROTECTION. THE SPECIFIC RESPIRATOR SELECTED MUST BE BASED ON CONTAMINATION LEVELS FOUND IN THE WORK PLACE, MUST NOT EXCEED THE WORKING LIMITS OF THE RESPIRATOR AND BE JOINTLY APPROVED BY THE NATIONAL INSTITUTE FOR OCCUPATIONAL SAFETY AND HEALTH AND THE MINE SAFETY AND HEALTH ADMINISTRATION (NIOSH-MSHA).
TYPE 'C' SUPPLIED-AIR RESPIRATOR WITH A FULL FACEPIECE OPERATED IN PRESSURE-DEMAND OR OTHER POSITIVE PRESSURE MODE OR WITH A FULL FACEPIECE, HELMET OR HOOD OPERATED IN CONTINOUS-FLOW MODE.
SELF-CONTAINED BREATHING APPARATUS WITH A FULL FACEPIECE OPERATED IN PRESSURE-DEMAND OR OTHER POSITIVE PRESSURE MODE.
FOR FIREFIGHTING AND OTHER IMMEDIATELY DANGEROUS TO LIFE OR HEALTH CONDITIONS:
SELF-CONTAINED BREATHING APPARATUS WITH FULL FACEPIECE OPERATED IN PRESSURE-DEMAND OR OTHER POSITIVE PRESSURE MODE.
SUPPLIED-AIR RESPIRATOR WITH FULL FACEPIECE AND OPERATED IN PRESSURE-DEMAND OR OTHER POSITIVE PRESSURE MODE IN COMBINATION WITH AN AUXILIARY SELF-CONTAINED BREATHING APPARATUS OPERATED IN PRESSURE-DEMAND OR OTHER POSITIVE PRESSURE MODE.

CLOTHING: EMPLOYEE MUST WEAR APPROPRIATE PROTECTIVE (IMPERVIOUS) CLOTHING AND EQUIPMENT TO PREVENT ANY POSSIBILITY OF SKIN CONTACT WITH THIS SUBSTANCE.

GLOVES: EMPLOYEE MUST WEAR APPROPRIATE PROTECTIVE GLOVES TO PREVENT CONTACT WITH THIS SUBSTANCE.

EYE PROTECTION: EMPLOYEE MUST WEAR SPLASH-PROOF OR DUST-RESISTANT SAFETY GOGGLES AND A FACESHIELD TO PREVENT CONTACT WITH THIS SUBSTANCE.
EMERGENCY WASH FACILITIES: WHERE THERE IS ANY POSSIBILITY THAT AN EMPLOYEE'S EYES AND/OR SKIN MAY BE EXPOSED TO THIS SUBSTANCE, THE EMPLOYER SHOULD PROVIDE AN EYE WASH FOUNTAIN AND QUICK DRENCH SHOWER WITHIN THE IMMEDIATE WORK AREA FOR EMERGENCY USE.

AUTHORIZED BY- OCCUPATIONAL HEALTH SERVICES, INC.
CREATION DATE: 10/04/89 ***REVISION DATE:*** 06/20/90

MATERIAL SAFETY DATA SHEET

OCCUPATIONAL HEALTH SERVICES, INC.
AGRICULTURE AND PESTICIDE DIVISION
450 SEVENTH AVENUE, SUITE 2407
NEW YORK, NEW YORK 10123
1-800-445-MSDS OR (212) 967-1100

EMERGENCY CONTACT:
JOHN S. BRANSFORD, JR. (615) 292-1180

SUBSTANCE IDENTIFICATION

SUBSTANCE: **DURSBAN (R) L.O. INSECTICIDE**

TRADE NAMES/SYNONYMS: DURSBAN L.O. INSECTICIDE; DOW DURSBAN L.O. INSECTICIDE; EPA REG. NO. 464-571; PST08522

CHEMICAL FAMILY: MIXTURE, PESTICIDE FORMULATION ORGANOPHOSPHATE

CERCLA RATINGS (SCALE 0-3): HEALTH=3 FIRE=2 REACTIVITY=1 PERSISTENCE=1

NFPA RATINGS (SCALE 0-4): HEALTH=3 FIRE=2 REACTIVITY=1

COMPONENTS AND CONTAMINANTS

COMPONENT: XYLENE RANGE AROMATIC SOLVENT ***PERCENT:*** 11.5
CAS# 64742-95-6

COMPONENT: CHLORPYRIFOS ***PERCENT:*** 41.5
CAS# 2921-88-2

COMPONENT: PROPRIETARY EMULSIFIERS ***PERCENT:*** 47.0

EXPOSURE LIMITS: XYLENE: 100 PPM (435 MG/M3) OSHA TWA; 150 PPM (655 MG/M3) OSHA STEL 100 PPM (435 MG/M3) ACGIH TWA; 150 PPM (655 MG/M3) ACGIH STEL 100 PPM (435 MG/M3) NIOSH RECOMMENDED 10 HOUR TWA; 200 PPM (870 MG/M3) NIOSH RECOMMENDED 10 MINUTE CEILING
1000 POUNDS CERCLA SECTION 103 REPORTABLE QUANTITY SUBJECT TO SARA SECTION 313 ANNUAL TOXIC CHEMICAL RELEASE REPORTING
CHLORPYRIFOS: 0.2 MG/M3 OSHA TWA (SKIN) 0.2 MG/M3 ACGIH TWA (SKIN); 0.6 MG/M3 ACGIH STEL (NOTICE OF INTENDED CHANGES 1988-89)
1 POUND CERCLA SECTION 103 REPORTABLE QUANTITY

PHYSICAL DATA

DESCRIPTION: CLEAR LIQUID WITH A MERCAPTAN-TYPE ODOR
BOILING POINT: 290 F (143 C) ***SPECIFIC GRAVITY:*** 1.16
VAPOR PRESSURE: <10 MMHG @ 25 C ***EVAPORATION RATE:*** NOT AVAILABLE
SOLUBILITY IN WATER: EMULSIFIABLE ***VAPOR DENSITY:*** NOT AVAILABLE

FIRE AND EXPLOSION DATA

FIRE AND EXPLOSION HAZARD: MODERATE FIRE HAZARD WHEN EXPOSED TO HEAT OR FLAME.

FLASH POINT: 122 F (50 C) (CC) ***UPPER EXPLOSIVE LIMIT:*** 6% (SOLVENT)
LOWER EXPLOSIVE LIMIT: 1% (SOLVENT) ***FLAMMABILITY CLASS(OSHA):*** II

FIREFIGHTING MEDIA: DRY CHEMICAL, CARBON DIOXIDE, HALON, WATER SPRAY OR STANDARD FOAM (1987 EMERGENCY RESPONSE GUIDEBOOK, DOT P 5800.4).
FOR LARGER FIRES, USE WATER SPRAY, FOG OR STANDARD FOAM (1987 EMERGENCY RESPONSE GUIDEBOOK, DOT P 5800.4).

FIREFIGHTING: MOVE CONTAINER FROM FIRE AREA IF POSSIBLE. DIKE FIRE CONTROL WATER FOR LATER DISPOSAL; DO NOT SCATTER THE MATERIAL. COOL FIRE-EXPOSED CONTAINERS WITH WATER FROM SIDE UNTIL WELL AFTER FIRE IS OUT. STAY AWAY FROM STORAGE TANK ENDS. WITHDRAW IMMEDIATELY IN CASE OF RISING SOUND FROM VENTING SAFETY DEVICE OR ANY DISCOLORATION OF STORAGE TANK DUE TO FIRE (1987 EMERGENCY RESPONSE GUIDEBOOK, DOT P 5800.4, GUIDE PAGE 28).
EXTINGUISH ONLY IF FLOW CAN BE STOPPED. USE FLOODING AMOUNTS OF WATER AS A FOG; SOLID STREAMS MAY BE INEFFECTIVE. COOL CONTAINERS WITH FLOODING AMOUNTS OF WATER FROM AS FAR A DISTANCE AS POSSIBLE. AVOID BREATHING POISONOUS VAPORS, KEEP UPWIND.

TRANSPORTATION DATA

DEPARTMENT OF TRANSPORTATION HAZARD CLASSIFICATION 49 CFR 172.101: COMBUSTIBLE LIQUID
DEPARTMENT OF TRANSPORTATION LABELING REQUIREMENTS 49 CFR 172.101 AND SUBPART E: NONE
DEPARTMENT OF TRANSPORTATION PACKAGING REQUIREMENTS: NONE EXCEPTIONS: 49 CFR 173.118A

TOXICITY

DURSBAN L.O. INSECTICIDE: TOXICITY DATA: 2600-3600 MG/M3/4 HOURS INHALATION-RAT LC50 (DOW MSDS); 930-1265 MG/KG SKIN-RABBIT LD50 (DOW MSDS); 226 MG/KG ORAL-RAT LD50 (DOW MSDS). CARCINOGEN STATUS: NONE. ACUTE TOXICITY LEVEL: TOXIC BY INHALATION, DERMAL ABSORPTION, AND INGESTION.
CHLORPYRIFOS: TOXICITY DATA: 78 MG/KG INHALATION-RAT LD50; 94 MG/KG INHALATION-MOUSE LD50; 2000 MG/KG SKIN-RABBIT LD50; 202 MG/KG SKIN-RAT LD50; 300 MG/KG ORAL-MAN TDLO; 82 MG/KG ORAL-RAT LD50; 60 MG/KG ORAL-MOUSE LD50; 1000 MG/KG ORAL-RABBIT LD50; 504 MG/KG ORAL-GUINEA PIG LD50; 100 MG/KG SUBCUTANEOUS-GUINEA PIG LDLO; 192 MG/KG INTRAPERITONEAL-MOUSE LD50; 150 MG/KG UNREPORTED-RAT LD50; 163 MG/KG UNREPORTED-MAMMAL LD50; MUTAGENIC DATA (RTECS); REPRODUCTIVE EFFECTS DATA (RTECS). CARCINOGEN STATUS: NONE. LOCAL EFFECTS: IRRITANT-SKIN, EYE. ACUTE TOXICITY LEVEL: TOXIC BY INGESTION; MODERATELY TOXIC BY DERMAL ABSORPTION. TARGET EFFECTS: CHOLINESTERASE INHIBITOR. AT INCREASED RISK FROM EXPOSURE: PERSONS WITH RESPIRATORY AILMENTS, RECENT EXPOSURE TO CHOLINESTERASE INHIBITORS OR IMPAIRED CHOLINESTERASE PRODUCTION, OR LIVER MALFUNCTION.* ADDITIONAL DATA: MAY CROSS THE PLACENTA. HIGH ENVIRONMENTAL TEMPERATURES OR EXPOSURE OF THE CHEMICAL TO VISIBLE OR ULTRAVIOLET LIGHT MAY ENHANCE THE TOXICITY. INTERACTIONS WITH MEDICATIONS MAY OCCUR.*
* MAY BE BASED ON GENERAL INFORMATION ON ORGANOPHOSPHATES.
XYLENE: IRRITATION DATA: 200 PPM EYE-HUMAN; 87 MG EYE-RABBIT MILD; 5 MG/24 HOURS EYE-RABBIT SEVERE; 100% SKIN-RABBIT MODERATE; 500 MG/24 HOURS SKIN-RABBIT MODERATE. TOXICITY DATA: 10000 PPM/6 HOURS INHALATION-MAN LCLO; 200 PPM INHALATION-HUMAN TCLO; 5000 PPM/4 HOURS INHALATION-RAT LC50; 450 PPM INHALATION-GUINEA PIG LCLO; 50 MG/KG ORAL-HUMAN LDLO; 4300 MG/KG ORAL-RAT LD50; 1700 MG/KG SUBCUTANEOUS-RAT LD50; 129 MG/KG INTRAVENOUS-RABBIT LDLO; 2 GM/KG INTRAPERITONEAL-MAMMAL LDLO; 2459 MG/KG INTRAPERITONEAL-RAT LD50; 1548 MG/KG INTRAPERITONEAL-MOUSE LD50; 2000 MG/KG INTRAPERITONEAL-GUINEA PIG LDLO; REPRODUCTIVE EFFECTS DATA (RTECS). CARCINOGEN STATUS: NONE. LOCAL EFFECTS: IRRITANT- INHALATION, SKIN, EYE. ACUTE TOXICITY LEVEL: MODERATELY TOXIC BY INHALATION, INGESTION. TARGET EFFECTS: CENTRAL NERVOUS SYSTEM DEPRESSANT. POISONING MAY ALSO AFFECT THE NERVOUS SYSTEM, LIVER AND KIDNEYS. AT INCREASED RISK FROM EXPOSURE: PREGNANT WOMEN. ADDITIONAL INFORMATION: CONSUMPTION OF ALCOHOLIC BEVERAGES MAY ENHANCE THE TOXIC EFFECTS. STIMULANTS SUCH AS EPINEPHRINE OR EPHEDRINE MAY INDUCE VENTRICULAR FIBRILLATION.

HEALTH EFFECTS AND FIRST AID

INHALATION: DURSBAN L.O. INSECTICIDE: TOXIC. EXPOSURE TO THIS MATERIAL MAY CAUSE IRRITATION OF THE UPPER RESPIRATORY TRACT AND CENTRAL NERVOUS SYSTEM DEPRESSION DUE TO THE AROMATIC SOLVENT INVOLVED. SYMPTOMS INCLUDE HEADACHE, DIZZINESS, WEAKNESS, DROWSINESS, INCOORDINATION, NAUSEA, FATIGUE, AND UNCONSCIOUSNESS. PROLONGED OR REPEATED EXPOSURE TO XYLENE RANGE SOLVENTS MAY CAUSE EFFECTS OF CENTRAL NERVOUS SYSTEM DEPRESSION. WOMEN MAY DEVELOP MENSTRUAL DISORDERS, SUCH AS MENORRHAGIA OR METRORRHAGIA, INFERTILITY, AND PATHOLOGICAL PREGNANCY CONDITIONS INCLUDING TOXICOSIS, DANGER OF MISCARRIAGE, AND HEMORRHAGING DURING DELIVERY. CLINICALLY, MODERATE LIVER ENLARGEMENT, NECROSIS, NEPHROSIS, AND BONE MARROW HYPERPLASIA MAY OCCUR. CHRONIC INHALATION EXPOSURE OF PREGNANT RATS AND MICE TO XYLENE HAVE RESULTED IN EFFECTS ON THE FETUS AND FERTILITY, AND SPECIFIC FETAL DEVELOPMENTAL ABNORMALITIES. SEE INFORMATION ON ORGANOPHOSPHATES.
ORGANOPHOSPHATES: CHOLINESTERASE INHIBITOR. **ACUTE EXPOSURE-** WHEN INHALED, THE FIRST EFFECTS OF CHOLINESTERASE INHIBITORS ARE USUALLY RESPIRATORY AND MAY INCLUDE NASAL HYPEREMIA AND WATERY DISCHARGE, COUGH, CHEST DISCOMFORT, DYSPNEA, AND WHEEZING DUE TO INCREASED BRONCHIAL SECRETIONS AND BRONCHOCONSTRICTION. IF SUFFICIENT AMOUNTS ARE ABSORBED, OTHER SYSTEMIC EFFECTS MAY BEGIN WITHIN A FEW MINUTES OR BE DELAYED FOR UP TO 12 HOURS. SYMPTOMS MAY INCLUDE PALLOR, NAUSEA, VOMITING, DIARRHEA, ABDOMINAL CRAMPS, HEADACHE, DIZZINESS, OCULAR PAIN, BLURRED VISION, MIOSIS OR IN SOME CASES, ESPECIALLY INITIALLY, MYDRIASIS, LACRIMATION, SALIVATION, SWEATING, AND CONFUSION. OTHER REPORTED CENTRAL NERVOUS SYSTEM OR NEUROMUSCULAR EFFECTS MAY INCLUDE ATAXIA, SLURRED SPEECH, AREFLEXIA, WEAKNESS, FATIGUE, FASCICULATIONS, TWITCHING, TREMORS POSSIBLY OF THE TONGUE AND EYELIDS, AND EVENTUALLY PARALYSIS OF THE EXTREMITIES AND POSSIBLY OF THE RESPIRATORY MUSCLES. IN SEVERE CASES THERE MAY ALSO BE INVOLUNTARY DEFECATION AND URINATION, CYANOSIS, PSYCHOSIS, HYPERGLYCEMIA, ACUTE PANCREATITIS, CARDIAC IRREGULARITIES, PULMONARY EDEMA, UNCONSCIOUSNESS, CONVULSIONS, AND COMA. DEATH IS PRIMARILY DUE TO RESPIRATORY FAILURE, ALTHOUGH CARDIOVASCULAR EFFECTS INCLUDING CARDIAC ARREST MAY ALSO BE IMPLICATED. LONG TERM SEQUELAE ARE RARE BUT MAY INCLUDE NEUROPSYCHIATRIC DISORDERS AND MYOPATHY WITH MUSCLE TENDERNESS. **CHRONIC EXPOSURE-** REPEATED OR PROLONGED EXPOSURE MAY RESULT IN THE EFFECTS OF ACUTE EXPOSURE. OTHER EFFECTS REPORTED IN WORKERS REPEATEDLY EXPOSED INCLUDE IMPAIRED MEMORY AND CONCENTRATION, ACUTE PSYCHOSIS, SEVERE DEPRESSIONS, IRRITABILTY, CONFUSION, APATHY, EMOTIONAL LABILITY, SOCIAL WITHDRAWAL, CONFUSION, HEADACHE, SPEECH DIFFICULTIES, DELAYED REACTION TIMES, SPATIAL DISORIENTATION, NIGHTMARES, SLEEPWALKING, AND DROWSINESS OR INSOMNIA. AN INFLUENZA-LIKE CONDITION WITH HEADACHE, NAUSEA, WEAKNESS, ANOREXIA AND MALAISE HAS ALSO BEEN REPORTED.

FIRST AID- REMOVE FROM EXPOSURE AREA TO FRESH AIR IMMEDIATELY. IF BREATHING HAS STOPPED, GIVE ARTIFICIAL RESPIRATION. MAINTAIN AIRWAY AND BLOOD PRESSURE AND ADMINISTER OXYGEN IF AVAILABLE. KEEP AFFECTED PERSON WARM AND AT REST. TREAT SYMPTOMATICALLY AND SUPPORTIVELY. ADMINISTRATION OF OXYGEN SHOULD BE PERFORMED BY QUALIFIED PERSONNEL. GET MEDICAL ATTENTION IMMEDIATELY.

SKIN CONTACT: DURSBAN L.O. INSECTICIDE: TOXIC. A TEST IN GUINEA PIGS INDICATED THAT THIS PRODUCT MAY HAVE WEAK SKIN SENSITIZATION POTENTIAL. PROLONGED OR REPEATED EXPOSURE MAY CAUSE IRRITATION. SEE INFORMATION ON ORGANOPHOSPHATES.
ORGANOPHOSPHATES: CHOLINESTERASE INHIBITOR. **ACUTE EXPOSURE-** LOCALIZED SWEATING AND FASCICULATIONS MAY OCCUR AT THE SITE OF CONTACT. IF SUFFICIENT AMOUNTS ARE ABSORBED, OTHER EFFECTS OF CHOLINESTERASE INHIBITION AS DESCRIBED IN ACUTE INHALATION MAY OCCUR. SYMPTOMS MAY BE DELAYED 2-3 HOURS, BUT USUALLY NO MORE THAN 12 HOURS. THE RATE OF ABSORPTION IS INCREASED BY THE PRESENCE OF DERMATITIS OR HIGH AMBIENT TEMPERATURES. **CHRONIC EXPOSURE-** REPEATED OR PROLONGED EXPOSURE MAY CAUSE EFFECTS AS DESCRIBED IN ACUTE EXPOSURE. SOME ORGANOPHOSPHATES MAY CAUSE SENSITIZATION.

FIRST AID- REMOVE CONTAMINATED CLOTHING IMMEDIATELY. WASH CONTAMINATED AREAS WITH SOAP AND WATER FOLLOWED BY ALCOHOL (ARENA, POISONING, 4TH ED.). EMERGENCY PERSONNEL SHOULD WEAR GLOVES AND AVOID CONTAMINATION. TREAT RESPIRATORY DIFFICULTY WITH ARTIFICIAL RESPIRATION. GET MEDICAL ATTENTION IMMEDIATELY.

EYE CONTACT: DURSBAN L.O. INSECTICIDE: MAY CAUSE MODERATE EYE IRRITATION WITH SLIGHT CORNEAL INJURY THAT MAY BE SLOW TO HEAL. SEE INFORMATION ON ORGANOPHOSPHATES.
ORGANOPHOSPHATES: CHOLINESTERASE INHIBITOR. **ACUTE EXPOSURE-** DIRECT CONTACT MAY CAUSE PAIN, HYPEREMIA, LACRIMATION, TWITCHING OF THE EYELIDS, MIOSIS, AND CILIARY MUSCLE SPASM WITH LOSS OF ACCOMODATION, BLURRED OR DIMMED VISION AND BROWACHE. SOMETIMES MYDRIASIS MAY OCCUR INSTEAD OF MIOSIS. WITH SUFFICIENT EXPOSURE, OTHER SYMPTOMS OF CHOLINESTERASE INHIBITION AS DESCRIBED IN ACUTE INHALATION MAY OCCUR. **CHRONIC EXPOSURE-** REPEATED OR PROLONGED EXPOSURE MAY CAUSE EFFECTS AS DESCRIBED IN ACUTE EXPOSURE. SOME COMPOUNDS HAVE CAUSED TOXIC EFFECTS ON THE CRYSTALLINE LENS, CONJUNCTIVAL THICKENING AND OBSTRUCTION OF THE NASOLACRIMAL CANALS WHEN USED AS MIOTIC EYEDROPS.

FIRST AID- IRRIGATE EYES WITH WATER OR SALINE SOLUTION. IF SYMPTOMS OF POISONING OCCUR, TREAT RESPIRATORY DIFFICULTY WITH ARTIFICIAL RESPIRATION AND OXYGEN. OBSERVE PATIENT FOR AT LEAST 24-36 HOURS (GOSSELIN, CLINICAL TOXICOLOGY OF COMMERCIAL PRODUCTS, 5TH ED.). GET MEDICAL ATTENTION IMMEDIATELY. OXYGEN SHOULD BE ADMINISTERED BY QUALIFIED MEDICAL PERSONNEL.

INGESTION: DURSBAN L.O. INSECTICIDE: NARCOTIC. INGESTION OF AROMATIC SOLVENTS MAY CAUSE SEVERE GASTROINTESTINAL DISTRESS WITH NAUSEA AND VOMITING, AND CENTRAL NERVOUS SYSTEM DEPRESSION WITH EFFECTS AS DESCRIBED IN INHALATION. POISONING MAY CAUSE LIVER AND KIDNEY DAMAGE. IF ASPIRATION INTO THE LUNGS OCCURS, SEVERE COUGHING, DISTRESS, CHEMICAL PNEUMONITIS, RAPIDLY DEVELOPING PULMONARY EDEMA, AND HEMORRHAGE MAY OCCUR. NEGATIVE RESULTS WERE REPORTED FROM A DELAYED NEUROTOXICITY STUDY OF CHLORPYRIFOS IN HENS. SEE INFORMATION ON ORGANOPHOSPHATES.
ORGANOPHOSPHATES: CHOLINESTERASE INHIBITOR. **ACUTE EXPOSURE-** WHEN INGESTED, THE FIRST EFFECTS MAY BE NAUSEA, VOMITING, ANOREXIA, ABDOMINAL CRAMPS AND DIARRHEA. GASTROINTESTINAL ABSORPTION MAY CAUSE THE SYMPTOMS OF CHOLINESTERASE INHIBITION AS DESCRIBED IN ACUTE INHALATION. SYMPTOMS MAY BEGIN WITHIN MINUTES OR BE DELAYED. **CHRONIC EXPOSURE-** REPEATED INGESTION MAY CAUSE EFFECTS AS DESCRIBED IN ACUTE EXPOSURE.

FIRST AID- IF PERSON IS ALERT AND RESPIRATION IS NOT DEPRESSED, GIVE SYRUP OF IPECAC FOLLOWED BY WATER (IF VOMITING OCCURS, KEEP HEAD BELOW HIPS TO PREVENT ASPIRATION). IF CONSCIOUSNESS LEVEL DECLINES OR VOMITING HAS NOT OCCURRED IN 15 MINUTES EMPTY STOMACH BY GASTRIC LAVAGE WITH THE AID OF CUFFED ENDOTRACHEAL TUBE USING ISOTONIC SALINE OR 5% SODIUM BICARBONATE FOLLOW WITH ACTIVATED CHARCOAL. ESTABLISH AND MAINTAIN AIRWAY. TREAT RESPIRATORY DIFFICULTY WITH ARTIFICIAL RESPIRATION AND OXYGEN. DO NOT GIVE MORPHINE, AMINOPHYLLINE, PHENOTHIAZINES, RESERPINE, FUROSEMIDE, OR ETHACRYNIC ACID (MORGAN, RECOGNITION AND MANAGEMENT OF PESTICIDE POISONINGS, 3RD ED.). TREAT SYMPTOMATICALLY AND SUPPORTIVELY. ADMINISTRATION OF OXYGEN AND LAVAGE MUST BE PERFORMED BY QUALIFIED MEDICAL PERSONNEL. GET MEDICAL ATTENTION IMMEDIATELY.

ANTIDOTE: BECAUSE IT IS DIFFICULT TO DETERMINE HOW CHEMICALS WILL INTERACT ONCE COMBINED IN A MIXTURE, AN ANTIDOTE IS NOT NORMALLY LISTED. HOWEVER DUE TO THE SEVERE POISONING POTENTIAL OF CHLORPYRIFOS, THE ANTIDOTE IS MENTIONED MERELY AS A POSSIBLE AID TO A QUALIFIED MEDICAL PERSON TO DETERMINE IF THE SYMPTOMS DISPLAYED BY THE POISONED VICTIM MERIT THE USE OF THE ANTIDOTE.
FOR CHOLINESTERASE INHIBITORS: ESTABLISH CLEAR AIRWAY AND TISSUE OXYGENATION BY ASPIRATION OF SECRETIONS, AND IF NECESSARY, BY ASSISTED PULMONARY VENTILATION WITH OXYGEN. IMPROVE TISSUE OXYGENATION AS MUCH AS POSSIBLE BEFORE ADMINISTERING ATROPINE TO MINIMIZE THE RISK OF VENTRICULAR FIBRILLATION. ADMINISTER ATROPINE SULFATE INTRAVENOUSLY, OR INTRAMUSCULARLY IF IV INJECTION IS NOT POSSIBLE. IN MODERATELY SEVERE POISONING ADMINISTER ATROPINE SULFATE, 0.4-2.0 MG REPEATED EVERY 15 MINUTES UNTIL ATROPINIZATION IS ACHIEVED (TACHYCARDIA, FLUSHING, DRY MOUTH, MYDRIASIS). MAINTAIN ATROPINIZATION BY REPEATED DOSES FOR 2-12 HOURS, OR LONGER, DEPENDING ON THE SEVERITY OF POISONING. THE APPEARANCE OF RALES IN THE LUNG BASES, MIOSIS, SALIVATION, NAUSEA, BRADYCARDIA, ARE ALL INDICATIONS OF INADEQUATE ATROPINIZATION. SEVERELY POISONED INDIVIDUALS MAY EXHIBIT REMARKABLE TOLERANCE TO ATROPINE; TWO OR MORE TIMES THE DOSAGES SUGGESTED ABOVE MAY BE NEEDED. PERSONS NOT POISONED OR ONLY SLIGHTLY POISONED, HOWEVER, MAY DEVELOP SIGNS OF ATROPINE TOXICITY FROM SUCH LARGE DOSAGES: FEVER, MUSCLE FIBRILLATIONS, AND DELIRIUM ARE THE MAIN SIGNS OF ATROPINE TOXICITY. IF THESE SIGNS APPEAR WHILE THE PATIENT IS FULLY ATROPINIZED, ATROPINE ADMINISTRATION SHOULD BE DISCONTINUED, AT LEAST TEMPORARILY. OBSERVE TREATED PATIENTS CLOSELY AT LEAST 24 HOURS TO INSURE THAT SYMPTOMS (POSSIBLY PULMONARY EDEMA) DO NOT RECUR AS ATROPINIZATION WEARS OFF. IN VERY SEVERE POISONINGS, METABOLIC DISPOSITION OF TOXICANT MAY REQUIRE SEVERAL HOURS OR DAYS DURING WHICH ATROPINIZATION MUST BE MAINTAINED. MARKEDLY LOWER LEVELS OF URINARY METABOLITES INDICATE THAT ATROPINE DOSAGE CAN BE TAPERED OFF. AS DOSAGE IS REDUCED, CHECK THE LUNG BASES FREQUENTLY FOR RALES. IF RALES

ARE HEARD OR OTHER SYMPTOMS RETURN, RE-ESTABLISH ATROPINIZATION PROMPTLY (MORGAN, RECOGNITION AND MANAGEMENT OF PESTICIDE POISONINGS, 3RD ED.). ADMINISTRATION OF ANTIDOTE MUST BE PERFORMED BY QUALIFIED MEDICAL PERSONNEL.

IN CASES OF SEVERE POISONING BY ORGANOPHOSPHATE PESTICIDES IN WHICH RESPIRATORY DEPRESSION, MUSCLE WEAKNESS AND TWITCHINGS ARE SEVERE, GIVE PRALIDOXIME (PROTOPAM-AYERST, 2-PAM), 1.0 GRAM INTRAVENOUSLY AT NO MORE THAN 0.5 GRAM PER MINUTE. DOSAGE OF PRALIDOXIME MAY BE REPEATED IN 1-2 HOURS, THEN AT 10-12 HOUR INTERVALS IF NEEDED. IN VERY SEVERE POISONINGS, DOSAGE RATES MAY BE DOUBLED. TREATMENT WITH PRALIDOXIME WILL BE MOST EFFECTIVE IF GIVEN WITHIN THIRTY-SIX HOURS AFTER POISONING (MORGAN, RECOGNITION AND MANAGEMENT OF PESTICIDE POISONINGS, 3RD ED.). ANTIDOTE SHOULD BE ADMINISTERED BY QUALIFIED MEDICAL PERSONNEL.

REACTIVITY

REACTIVITY: MAY UNDERGO VIOLENT EXOTHERMIC DECOMPOSITION ABOVE 130 C (266 F). THE INCREASE IN TEMPERATURE AND PRESSURE MAY RESULT IN THE VIOLENT RUPTURE OF THE CONTAINER.

INCOMPATIBILITIES: DURSBAN (R) L.O. INSECTICIDE: ALKALIS: INCOMPATIBLE. OXIDIZERS (STRONG): FIRE AND EXPLOSION HAZARD.

DECOMPOSITION: THERMAL DECOMPOSITION MAY RELEASE TOXIC AND/OR HAZARDOUS GASES.

POLYMERIZATION: HAZARDOUS POLYMERIZATION HAS NOT BEEN REPORTED TO OCCUR UNDER NORMAL TEMPERATURES AND PRESSURES.

STORAGE AND DISPOSAL

OBSERVE ALL FEDERAL, STATE AND LOCAL REGULATIONS WHEN STORING OR DISPOSING OF THIS SUBSTANCE. FOR ASSISTANCE, CONTACT THE DISTRICT DIRECTOR OF THE ENVIRONMENTAL PROTECTION AGENCY.

STORAGE

STORE IN ACCORDANCE WITH 29 CFR 1910.106.

BONDING AND GROUNDING: SUBSTANCES WITH LOW ELECTROCONDUCTIVITY, WHICH MAY BE IGNITED BY ELECTROSTATIC SPARKS, SHOULD BE STORED IN CONTAINERS WHICH MEET THE BONDING AND GROUNDING GUIDELINES SPECIFIED IN NFPA 77-1983, RECOMMENDED PRACTICE ON STATIC ELECTRICITY.

STORE AWAY FROM INCOMPATIBLE SUBSTANCES.

DISPOSAL

DISPOSAL MUST BE IN ACCORDANCE WITH STANDARDS APPLICABLE TO GENERATORS OF HAZARDOUS WASTE, 40 CFR 262. EPA HAZARDOUS WASTE NUMBER D001. 100 POUND CERCLA SECTION 103 REPORTABLE QUANTITY.

CONDITIONS TO AVOID

AVOID CONTACT WITH HEAT, SPARKS, FLAMES OR OTHER IGNITION SOURCES. VAPORS MAY BE EXPLOSIVE. MATERIAL IS POISONOUS; AVOID INHALATION OF VAPORS OR CONTACT WITH SKIN. DO NOT ALLOW MATERIAL TO CONTAMINATE WATER SOURCES.

SPILL AND LEAK PROCEDURES

OCCUPATIONAL SPILL: SHUT OFF IGNITION SOURCES. DO NOT TOUCH SPILLED MATERIAL. STOP LEAK IF YOU CAN DO IT WITHOUT RISK. USE WATER SPRAY TO REDUCE VAPORS. FOR SMALL SPILLS, TAKE UP WITH SAND OR OTHER ABSORBENT MATERIAL AND PLACE INTO CONTAINERS FOR LATER DISPOSAL. FOR LARGER SPILLS, DIKE FAR AHEAD OF SPILL FOR LATER DISPOSAL. NO SMOKING, FLAMES OR FLARES IN HAZARD AREA! KEEP UNNECESSARY PEOPLE AWAY; ISOLATE HAZARD AREA AND DENY ENTRY.

REPORTABLE QUANTITY (RQ): THE SUPERFUND AMENDMENTS AND REAUTHORIZATION ACT (SARA) SECTION 304 REQUIRES THAT A RELEASE EQUAL TO OR GREATER THAN THE REPORTABLE QUANTITY ESTABLISHED FOR THAT SUBSTANCE BE IMMEDIATELY REPORTED TO THE LOCAL EMERGENCY PLANNING COMMITTEE AND THE STATE EMERGENCY RESPONSE COMMISSION (40 CFR 355.40). IF THE RELEASE OF THIS SUBSTANCE IS REPORTABLE UNDER CERCLA SECTION 103, THE NATIONAL RESPONSE CENTER MUST BE NOTIFIED IMMEDIATELY AT (800) 424-8802 OR (202) 426-2675 IN THE METROPOLITAN WASHINGTON, D.C. AREA (40 CFR 302.6).

PROTECTIVE EQUIPMENT

VENTILATION: PROVIDE LOCAL EXHAUST OR PROCESS ENCLOSURE VENTILATION TO MEET PUBLISHED EXPOSURE LIMITS.

RESPIRATOR: THE FOLLOWING RESPIRATORS ARE RECOMMENDED BASED ON INFORMATION FOUND IN THE PHYSICAL DATA, TOXICITY AND HEALTH EFFECTS SECTIONS. THEY ARE RANKED IN ORDER FROM MINIMUM TO MAXIMUM RESPIRATORY PROTECTION. THE SPECIFIC RESPIRATOR SELECTED MUST BE BASED ON CONTAMINATION LEVELS FOUND IN THE WORK PLACE, MUST NOT EXCEED THE WORKING LIMITS OF THE RESPIRATOR AND BE JOINTLY APPROVED BY THE NATIONAL INSTITUTE FOR OCCUPATIONAL SAFETY AND HEALTH AND THE MINE SAFETY AND HEALTH ADMINISTRATION (NIOSH-MSHA).

TYPE 'C' SUPPLIED-AIR RESPIRATOR WITH A FULL FACEPIECE OPERATED IN PRESSURE-DEMAND OR OTHER POSITIVE PRESSURE MODE OR WITH A FULL FACEPIECE, HELMET OR HOOD OPERATED IN CONTINOUS-FLOW MODE.

SELF-CONTAINED BREATHING APPARATUS WITH A FULL FACEPIECE OPERATED IN PRESSURE-DEMAND OR OTHER POSITIVE PRESSURE MODE.

FOR FIREFIGHTING AND OTHER IMMEDIATELY DANGEROUS TO LIFE OR HEALTH CONDITIONS:

SELF-CONTAINED BREATHING APPARATUS WITH FULL FACEPIECE OPERATED IN PRESSURE-DEMAND OR OTHER POSITIVE PRESSURE MODE.

SUPPLIED-AIR RESPIRATOR WITH FULL FACEPIECE AND OPERATED IN PRESSURE-DEMAND OR OTHER POSITIVE PRESSURE MODE IN COMBINATION WITH AN AUXILIARY SELF-CONTAINED BREATHING APPARATUS OPERATED IN PRESSURE-DEMAND OR OTHER POSITIVE PRESSURE MODE.

CLOTHING: EMPLOYEE MUST WEAR APPROPRIATE PROTECTIVE (IMPERVIOUS) CLOTHING AND EQUIPMENT TO PREVENT ANY POSSIBILITY OF SKIN CONTACT WITH THIS SUBSTANCE.

GLOVES: EMPLOYEE MUST WEAR APPROPRIATE PROTECTIVE GLOVES TO PREVENT CONTACT WITH THIS SUBSTANCE.

EYE PROTECTION: EMPLOYEE MUST WEAR SPLASH-PROOF OR DUST-RESISTANT SAFETY GOGGLES AND A FACESHIELD TO PREVENT CONTACT WITH THIS SUBSTANCE.

EMERGENCY WASH FACILITIES: WHERE THERE IS ANY POSSIBILITY THAT AN EMPLOYEE'S EYES AND/OR SKIN MAY BE EXPOSED TO THIS SUBSTANCE, THE EMPLOYER SHOULD PROVIDE AN EYE WASH FOUNTAIN AND QUICK DRENCH SHOWER WITHIN THE IMMEDIATE WORK AREA FOR EMERGENCY USE.

AUTHORIZED BY- OCCUPATIONAL HEALTH SERVICES, INC.

CREATION DATE: 10/04/89 ***REVISION DATE:*** 06/20/90

MATERIAL SAFETY DATA SHEET

OCCUPATIONAL HEALTH SERVICES, INC.
AGRICULTURE AND PESTICIDE DIVISION
450 SEVENTH AVENUE, SUITE 2407
NEW YORK, NEW YORK 10123
1-800-445-MSDS OR (212) 967-1100

EMERGENCY CONTACT:
JOHN S. BRANSFORD, JR. (615) 292-1180

SUBSTANCE IDENTIFICATION

CAS-NUMBER 17109-49-8

SUBSTANCE: EDIFENPHOS

TRADE NAMES/SYNONYMS: O-ETHYL S,S-DIPHENYL ESTER PHOSPHORODITHIOIC ACID; O-ETHYL S,S-DIPHENYL PHOSPHORODITHIOATE; BAY 78418; BAYER 78418; EDIPHENPHOS; HINOSAN; PST08555

CHEMICAL FAMILY: ORGANOPHOSPHATE

MOLECULAR FORMULA: C14-H15-O2-P-S2

MOLECULAR WEIGHT: 310.38

CERCLA RATINGS (SCALE 0-3): HEALTH=3 FIRE=0 REACTIVITY=0 PERSISTENCE=1

NFPA RATINGS (SCALE 0-4): HEALTH=3 FIRE=0 REACTIVITY=0

COMPONENTS AND CONTAMINANTS

COMPONENT: EDIFENPHOS ***PERCENT:*** 100
CAS# 17109-49-8

EXPOSURE LIMITS: NO OCCUPATIONAL EXPOSURE LIMITS ESTABLISHED BY OSHA, ACGIH, OR NIOSH.

PHYSICAL DATA

DESCRIPTION: CLEAR YELLOW TO LIGHT BROWN LIQUID WITH THIOPHENOL-LIKE ODOR

BOILING POINT: 309 F (154 C) @ 0.01 MMHG ***SPECIFIC GRAVITY:*** 1.23

SOLUBILITY IN WATER: PRACTICALLY INSOLU.

SOLVENT SOLUBILITY: SOLUBLE IN ACETONE, XYLENE

FIRE AND EXPLOSION DATA

FIRE AND EXPLOSION HAZARD: NEGLIGIBLE FIRE HAZARD WHEN EXPOSED TO HEAT OR FLAME.

FIREFIGHTING MEDIA: DRY CHEMICAL, CARBON DIOXIDE, HALON, WATER SPRAY OR STANDARD FOAM (1987 EMERGENCY RESPONSE GUIDEBOOK, DOT P 5800.4).

FOR LARGER FIRES, USE WATER SPRAY, FOG OR STANDARD FOAM (1987 EMERGENCY RESPONSE GUIDEBOOK, DOT P 5800.4).

FIREFIGHTING: MOVE CONTAINERS FROM FIRE AREA IF POSSIBLE. FIGHT FIRE FROM MAXIMUM DISTANCE. STAY AWAY FROM STORAGE TANK ENDS. DIKE FIRE CONTROL WATER FOR LATER DISPOSAL. DO NOT SCATTER MATERIAL (1987 EMERGENCY RESPONSE GUIDEBOOK, DOT P 5800.4, GUIDE PAGE 55).

TOXICITY

EIDFENPHOS: TOXICITY DATA: 100 MG/KG ORAL-RAT LD50; 143 MG/KG ORAL-MOUSE LD50; 350 MG/KG ORAL-RABBIT LD50; 350 MG/KG ORAL-GUINEA PIG LD50; 350 MG/KG ORAL-DOG LD50; 45 MG/KG ORAL-DOMESTIC ANIMAL LDLO; 26 MG/KG INTRAPERITONEAL-RAT LD50; 212 MG/KG UNREPORTED-RAT LD50; MUTAGENIC DATA (RTECS). CARCINOGEN STATUS: NONE. ACUTE TOXICITY LEVEL: TOXIC BY INGESTION. TARGET EFFECTS: CHOLINESTERASE INHIBITOR. POISONING MAY AFFECT THE NERVOUS SYSTEM.* AT INCREASED RISK FROM EXPOSURE: PERSONS WITH RESPIRATORY AILMENTS, RECENT EXPOSURE TO CHOLINESTERASE INHIBITORS OR IMPAIRED CHOLINESTERASE PRODUCTION, OR LIVER MALFUNCTION.* ADDITIONAL DATA: MAY CROSS THE PLACENTA. HIGH ENVIRONMENTAL TEMPERATURES OR EXPOSURE OF THE CHEMICAL TO VISIBLE OR ULTRAVIOLET LIGHT MAY ENHANCE THE TOXICITY. INTERACTIONS WITH MEDICATIONS MAY OCCUR.*

* MAY BE BASED ON GENERAL INFORMATION ON ORGANOPHOSPHATES.

HEALTH EFFECTS AND FIRST AID

INHALATION: EDIFENPHOS: SEE INFORMATION ON ORGANOPHOSPHATES. ORGANOPHOSPHATES: CHOLINESTERASE INHIBITOR. **ACUTE EXPOSURE-** WHEN INHALED, THE FIRST EFFECTS OF CHOLINESTERASE INHIBITORS ARE USUALLY RESPIRATORY AND MAY INCLUDE NASAL HYPEREMIA AND WATERY DISCHARGE, COUGH, CHEST DISCOMFORT, DYSPNEA, AND WHEEZING DUE TO INCREASED BRONCHIAL SECRETIONS AND BRONCHOCONSTRICTION. IF SUFFICIENT AMOUNTS ARE ABSORBED, OTHER SYSTEMIC EFFECTS MAY BEGIN WITHIN A FEW MINUTES OR BE DELAYED FOR UP TO 12 HOURS. SYMPTOMS MAY INCLUDE PALLOR, NAUSEA, VOMITING, DIARRHEA, ABDOMINAL CRAMPS, HEADACHE, DIZZINESS, OCULAR PAIN, BLURRED VISION, MIOSIS OR IN SOME CASES, ESPECIALLY INITIALLY, MYDRIASIS, LACRIMATION, SALIVATION, SWEATING, AND CONFUSION. OTHER REPORTED CENTRAL NERVOUS SYSTEM OR NEUROMUSCULAR EFFECTS MAY INCLUDE ATAXIA, SLURRED SPEECH, AREFLEXIA, WEAKNESS, FATIGUE, FASCICULATIONS, TWITCHING, TREMORS POSSIBLY OF THE TONGUE AND EYELIDS, AND EVENTUALLY PARALYSIS OF THE EXTREMITIES AND POSSIBLY OF THE RESPIRATORY MUSCLES. IN SEVERE CASES THERE MAY ALSO BE INVOLUNTARY DEFECATION AND URINATION, CYANOSIS, PSYCHOSIS, HYPERGLYCEMIA, ACUTE PANCREATITIS, CARDIAC IRREGULARITIES, PULMONARY EDEMA, UNCONSCIOUSNESS, CONVULSIONS, AND COMA. DEATH IS PRIMARILY DUE TO RESPIRATORY FAILURE, ALTHOUGH CARDIOVASCULAR EFFECTS INCLUDING CARDIAC ARREST MAY ALSO BE IMPLICATED. LONG TERM SEQUELAE ARE RARE BUT MAY INCLUDE NEUROPSYCHIATRIC DISORDERS AND MYOPATHY WITH MUSCLE TENDERNESS. SOME ORGANOPHOSPHATES MAY CAUSE A DELAYED NEUROPATHY BEGINNING 1-4 WEEKS AFTER AN ACUTE EXPOSURE WHICH MAY OR MAY NOT HAVE CAUSED ACUTE CHOLINERGIC EFFECTS. NUMBNESS, TINGLING, WEAKNESS AND CRAMPING BEGINNING SYMMETRICALLY IN THE LOWER LIMBS MAY PROGRESS TO ATAXIA AND PARALYSIS. IN SEVERE CASES, UPPER LIMB INVOLVEMENT IS POSSIBLE AND FLACCID PARALYSIS MAY PROGRESS TO SPASTIC PARALYSIS WITH EXAGGERATED REFLEXES. IMPROVEMENT MAY OCCUR OVER MONTHS TO YEARS, BUT SOME RESIDUAL IMPAIRMENT USUALLY REMAINS. **CHRONIC EXPOSURE-** REPEATED OR PROLONGED EXPOSURE MAY RESULT IN THE EFFECTS OF ACUTE EXPOSURE INCLUDING THE DELAYED NEUROPATHY. OTHER EFFECTS REPORTED IN WORKERS REPEATEDLY EXPOSED INCLUDE IMPAIRED MEMORY AND CONCENTRATION, ACUTE PSYCHOSIS, SEVERE DEPRESSIONS, IRRITABILTY, CONFUSION, APATHY, EMOTIONAL LABILITY, SOCIAL WITHDRAWAL, CONFUSION, HEADACHE, SPEECH DIFFICULTIES, DELAYED REACTION TIMES, SPATIAL DISORIENTATION, NIGHTMARES, SLEEPWALKING, AND DROWSINESS OR INSOMNIA. AN INFLUENZA-LIKE CONDITION WITH HEADACHE, NAUSEA, WEAKNESS, ANOREXIA AND MALAISE HAS ALSO BEEN REPORTED.

FIRST AID- REMOVE FROM EXPOSURE AREA TO FRESH AIR IMMEDIATELY. IF BREATHING HAS STOPPED, GIVE ARTIFICIAL RESPIRATION. MAINTAIN AIRWAY AND BLOOD PRESSURE AND ADMINISTER OXYGEN IF AVAILABLE. KEEP AFFECTED PERSON WARM AND AT REST. TREAT SYMPTOMATICALLY AND SUPPORTIVELY. ADMINISTRATION OF OXYGEN SHOULD BE PERFORMED BY QUALIFIED PERSONNEL. GET MEDICAL ATTENTION IMMEDIATELY.

SKIN CONTACT: EDIFENPHOS: SEE INFORMATION ON ORGANOPHOSPHATES. ORGANOPHOSPHATES: CHOLINESTERASE INHIBITOR. **ACUTE EXPOSURE-** LOCALIZED SWEATING AND FASCICULATIONS MAY OCCUR AT THE SITE OF CONTACT. IF SUFFICIENT AMOUNTS ARE ABSORBED, OTHER EFFECTS OF CHOLINESTERASE INHIBITION AS DESCRIBED IN ACUTE INHALATION MAY OCCUR. SYMPTOMS MAY BE DELAYED 2-3 HOURS, BUT USUALLY NO MORE THAN 12 HOURS. THE RATE OF ABSORPTION IS INCREASED BY THE PRESENCE OF DERMATITIS OR HIGH AMBIENT TEMPERATURES. DELAYED NEUROPATHY IS ALSO POSSIBLE. **CHRONIC EXPOSURE-** REPEATED OR PROLONGED EXPOSURE MAY CAUSE EFFECTS AS DESCRIBED IN ACUTE EXPOSURE. SOME ORGANOPHOSPHATES MAY CAUSE SENSITIZATION.

FIRST AID- REMOVE CONTAMINATED CLOTHING IMMEDIATELY. WASH CONTAMINATED AREAS WITH SOAP AND WATER FOLLOWED BY ALCOHOL (ARENA, POISONING, 4TH ED.). EMERGENCY PERSONNEL SHOULD WEAR GLOVES AND AVOID CONTAMINATION. TREAT RESPIRATORY DIFFICULTY WITH ARTIFICIAL RESPIRATION. GET MEDICAL ATTENTION IMMEDIATELY.

EYE CONTACT: EDIFENPHOS: SEE INFORMATION ON ORGANOPHOSPHATES. ORGANOPHOSPHATES: CHOLINESTERASE INHIBITOR. **ACUTE EXPOSURE-** DIRECT CONTACT MAY CAUSE PAIN, HYPEREMIA, LACRIMATION, TWITCHING OF THE EYELIDS, MIOSIS, AND CILIARY MUSCLE SPASM WITH LOSS OF ACCOMODATION, BLURRED OR DIMMED VISION AND BROWACHE. SOMETIMES MYDRIASIS MAY OCCUR INSTEAD OF MIOSIS. WITH SUFFICIENT EXPOSURE, OTHER SYMPTOMS OF CHOLINESTERASE INHIBITION AS DESCRIBED IN ACUTE INHALATION MAY OCCUR. **CHRONIC EXPOSURE-** REPEATED OR PROLONGED EXPOSURE MAY CAUSE EFFECTS AS DESCRIBED IN ACUTE EXPOSURE. SOME COMPOUNDS HAVE CAUSED TOXIC EFFECTS ON THE CRYSTALLINE LENS, CONJUNCTIVAL THICKENING AND OBSTRUCTION OF THE NASOLACRIMAL CANALS WHEN USED AS MIOTIC EYEDROPS.

FIRST AID- IRRIGATE EYES WITH WATER OR SALINE SOLUTION. IF SYMPTOMS OF POISONING OCCUR, TREAT RESPIRATORY DIFFICULTY WITH ARTIFICIAL RESPIRATION AND OXYGEN. OBSERVE PATIENT FOR AT LEAST 24-36 HOURS (GOSSELIN, CLINICAL TOXICOLOGY OF COMMERCIAL PRODUCTS, 5TH ED.). GET MEDICAL ATTENTION IMMEDIATELY. OXYGEN SHOULD BE ADMINISTERED BY QUALIFIED MEDICAL PERSONNEL.

INGESTION: EDIFENPHOS: TOXIC. SEE INFORMATION ON ORGANOPHOSPHATES. ORGANOPHOSPHATES: CHOLINESTERASE INHIBITOR. **ACUTE EXPOSURE-** WHEN INGESTED, THE FIRST EFFECTS MAY BE NAUSEA, VOMITING, ANOREXIA, ABDOMINAL CRAMPS AND DIARRHEA. GASTROINTESTINAL ABSORPTION MAY CAUSE SYMPTOMS OF CHOLINESTERASE INHIBITION AS DESCRIBED IN ACUTE INHALATION. SYMPTOMS MAY BEGIN WITHIN MINUTES OR BE DELAYED FOR HOURS. DELAYED EFFECTS INCLUDING NEUROPATHY MAY ALSO OCCUR. **CHRONIC EXPOSURE-** REPEATED INGESTION MAY CAUSE EFFECTS AS DESCRIBED IN ACUTE EXPOSURE.

FIRST AID- IF PERSON IS ALERT AND RESPIRATION IS NOT DEPRESSED, GIVE SYRUP OF IPECAC FOLLOWED BY WATER (IF VOMITING OCCURS, KEEP HEAD BELOW HIPS TO PREVENT ASPIRATION). IF CONSCIOUSNESS LEVEL DECLINES OR VOMITING HAS NOT OCCURRED IN 15 MINUTES EMPTY STOMACH BY GASTRIC LAVAGE WITH THE AID OF CUFFED ENDOTRACHEAL TUBE USING ISOTONIC SALINE OR 5% SODIUM BICARBONATE FOLLOW WITH ACTIVATED CHARCOAL. ESTABLISH AND MAINTAIN AIRWAY. TREAT RESPIRATORY DIFFICULTY WITH ARTIFICIAL RESPIRATION AND OXYGEN. DO NOT GIVE MORPHINE, AMINOPHYLLINE, PHENOTHIAZINES, RESERPINE, FUROSEMIDE, OR ETHACRYNIC ACID (MORGAN, RECOGNITION AND MANAGEMENT OF PESTICIDE POISONINGS, 3RD ED.). TREAT SYMPTOMATICALLY AND SUPPORTIVELY. ADMINISTRATION OF OXYGEN AND LAVAGE MUST BE PERFORMED BY QUALIFIED MEDICAL PERSONNEL. GET MEDICAL ATTENTION IMMEDIATELY.

ANTIDOTE: THE FOLLOWING ANTIDOTE(S) HAVE BEEN RECOMMENDED. HOWEVER, THE DECISION AS TO WHETHER THE SEVERITY OF POISONING REQUIRES ADMINISTRATION OF ANY ANTIDOTE AND ACTUAL DOSE REQUIRED SHOULD BE MADE BY QUALIFIED MEDICAL PERSONNEL.

FOR CHOLINESTERASE INHIBITORS: ESTABLISH CLEAR AIRWAY AND TISSUE OXYGENATION BY ASPIRATION OF SECRETIONS, AND IF NECESSARY, BY ASSISTED PULMONARY VENTILATION WITH OXYGEN. IMPROVE TISSUE OXYGENATION AS MUCH AS POSSIBLE BEFORE ADMINISTERING ATROPINE TO MINIMIZE THE RISK OF VENTRICULAR FIBRILLATION. ADMINISTER ATROPINE SULFATE INTRAVENOUSLY, OR INTRAMUSCULARLY IF IV INJECTION IS NOT POSSIBLE. IN MODERATELY SEVERE POISONING ADMINISTER ATROPINE SULFATE, 0.4-2.0 MG REPEATED EVERY 15 MINUTES UNTIL ATROPINIZATION IS ACHIEVED (TACHYCARDIA, FLUSHING, DRY MOUTH, MYDRIASIS). MAINTAIN ATROPINIZATION BY REPEATED DOSES FOR 2-12 HOURS, OR LONGER, DEPENDING ON THE SEVERITY OF POISONING. THE APPEARANCE OF RALES IN THE LUNG BASES, MIOSIS, SALIVATION, NAUSEA, BRADYCARDIA, ARE ALL INDICATIONS OF INADEQUATE ATROPINIZATION. SEVERELY POISONED INDIVIDUALS MAY EXHIBIT REMARKABLE TOLERANCE TO ATROPINE; TWO OR MORE TIMES THE DOSAGES SUGGESTED ABOVE MAY BE NEEDED. PERSONS NOT POISONED OR ONLY SLIGHTLY POISONED, HOWEVER, MAY DEVELOP SIGNS OF ATROPINE TOXICITY FROM SUCH LARGE DOSAGES: FEVER, MUSCLE FIBRILLATIONS, AND DELIRIUM ARE THE MAIN SIGNS OF ATROPINE TOXICITY. IF THESE SIGNS APPEAR WHILE THE PATIENT IS FULLY ATROPINIZED, ATROPINE ADMINISTRATION SHOULD BE DISCONTINUED, AT LEAST TEMPORARILY. OBSERVE TREATED PATIENTS CLOSELY AT LEAST 24 HOURS TO INSURE THAT SYMPTOMS (POSSIBLY PULMONARY EDEMA) DO NOT RECUR AS ATROPINIZATION WEARS OFF. IN VERY SEVERE POISONINGS, METABOLIC DISPOSITION OF TOXICANT MAY REQUIRE SEVERAL HOURS OR DAYS DURING WHICH

ATROPINIZATION MUST BE MAINTAINED. MARKEDLY LOWER LEVELS OF URINARY METABOLITES INDICATE THAT ATROPINE DOSAGE CAN BE TAPERED OFF. AS DOSAGE IS REDUCED, CHECK THE LUNG BASES FREQUENTLY FOR RALES. IF RALES ARE HEARD OR OTHER SYMPTOMS RETURN, RE-ESTABLISH ATROPINIZATION PROMPTLY (MORGAN, RECOGNITION AND MANAGEMENT OF PESTICIDE POISONINGS, 3RD ED.). ADMINISTRATION OF ANTIDOTE MUST BE PERFORMED BY QUALIFIED MEDICAL PERSONNEL.

IN CASES OF SEVERE POISONING BY ORGANOPHOSPHATE PESTICIDES IN WHICH RESPIRATORY DEPRESSION, MUSCLE WEAKNESS AND TWITCHINGS ARE SEVERE, GIVE PRALIDOXIME (PROTOPAM-AYERST, 2-PAM), 1.0 GRAM INTRAVENOUSLY AT NO MORE THAN 0.5 GRAM PER MINUTE. DOSAGE OF PRALIDOXIME MAY BE REPEATED IN 1-2 HOURS, THEN AT 10-12 HOUR INTERVALS IF NEEDED. IN VERY SEVERE POISONINGS, DOSAGE RATES MAY BE DOUBLED. TREATMENT WITH PRALIDOXIME WILL BE MOST EFFECTIVE IF GIVEN WITHIN THIRTY-SIX HOURS AFTER POISONING (MORGAN, RECOGNITION AND MANAGEMENT OF PESTICIDE POISONINGS, 3RD ED.). ANTIDOTE SHOULD BE ADMINISTERED BY QUALIFIED MEDICAL PERSONNEL.

REACTIVITY

REACTIVITY: STABLE UNDER NORMAL TEMPERATURES AND PRESSURES.

INCOMPATIBILITIES: EDIFENPHOS: NO DATA AVAILABLE.

DECOMPOSITION: THERMAL DECOMPOSITION MAY RELEASE TOXIC OXIDES OF PHOSPHORUS AND SULFUR.

POLYMERIZATION: HAZARDOUS POLYMERIZATION HAS NOT BEEN REPORTED TO OCCUR UNDER NORMAL TEMPERATURES AND PRESSURES.

STORAGE AND DISPOSAL

OBSERVE ALL FEDERAL, STATE AND LOCAL REGULATIONS WHEN STORING OR DISPOSING OF THIS SUBSTANCE. FOR ASSISTANCE, CONTACT THE DISTRICT DIRECTOR OF THE ENVIRONMENTAL PROTECTION AGENCY.

****STORAGE****

STORE IN ACCORDANCE WITH 40 CFR 165 RECOMMENDED PROCEDURES FOR THE DISPOSAL AND STORAGE OF PESTICIDES AND PESTICIDE CONTAINERS.

****DISPOSAL****

DISPOSAL MUST BE IN ACCORDANCE WITH 40 CFR 165 RECOMMENDED PROCEDURES FOR THE DISPOSAL AND STORAGE OF PESTICIDES AND PESTICIDE CONTAINERS.

CONDITIONS TO AVOID

NONE REPORTED.

SPILL AND LEAK PROCEDURES

OCCUPATIONAL SPILL: DO NOT TOUCH SPILLED MATERIAL. STOP LEAK IF YOU CAN DO IT WITHOUT RISK. USE WATER SPRAY TO REDUCE VAPORS. FOR SMALL SPILLS, TAKE UP WITH SAND OR OTHER ABSORBENT MATERIAL AND PLACE INTO CONTAINERS FOR LATER DISPOSAL. FOR SMALL DRY SPILLS, WITH A CLEAN SHOVEL PLACE MATERIAL INTO CLEAN, DRY CONTAINERS AND COVER. MOVE CONTAINERS FROM SPILL AREA. FOR LARGER SPILLS, DIKE FAR AHEAD OF SPILL FOR LATER DISPOSAL. KEEP UNNECESSARY PEOPLE AWAY. ISOLATE HAZARD AREA AND DENY ENTRY. VENTILATE CLOSED SPACES BEFORE ENTERING.

PROTECTIVE EQUIPMENT

VENTILATION: PROVIDE LOCAL EXHAUST OR PROCESS ENCLOSURE VENTILATION SYSTEM.

RESPIRATOR: THE FOLLOWING RESPIRATORS ARE RECOMMENDED BASED ON INFORMATION FOUND IN THE PHYSICAL DATA, TOXICITY AND HEALTH EFFECTS SECTIONS. THEY ARE RANKED IN ORDER FROM MINIMUM TO MAXIMUM RESPIRATORY PROTECTION. THE SPECIFIC RESPIRATOR SELECTED MUST BE BASED ON CONTAMINATION LEVELS FOUND IN THE WORK PLACE, MUST NOT EXCEED THE WORKING LIMITS OF THE RESPIRATOR AND BE JOINTLY APPROVED BY THE NATIONAL INSTITUTE FOR OCCUPATIONAL SAFETY AND HEALTH AND THE MINE SAFETY AND HEALTH ADMINISTRATION (NIOSH-MSHA).

TYPE 'C' SUPPLIED-AIR RESPIRATOR WITH A FULL FACEPIECE OPERATED IN PRESSURE-DEMAND OR OTHER POSITIVE PRESSURE MODE OR WITH A FULL FACEPIECE, HELMET OR HOOD OPERATED IN CONTINOUS-FLOW MODE.

SELF-CONTAINED BREATHING APPARATUS WITH A FULL FACEPIECE OPERATED IN PRESSURE-DEMAND OR OTHER POSITIVE PRESSURE MODE.

FOR FIREFIGHTING AND OTHER IMMEDIATELY DANGEROUS TO LIFE OR HEALTH CONDITIONS:

SELF-CONTAINED BREATHING APPARATUS WITH FULL FACEPIECE OPERATED IN PRESSURE-DEMAND OR OTHER POSITIVE PRESSURE MODE.

SUPPLIED-AIR RESPIRATOR WITH FULL FACEPIECE AND OPERATED IN PRESSURE-DEMAND OR OTHER POSITIVE PRESSURE MODE IN COMBINATION WITH AN AUXILIARY SELF-CONTAINED BREATHING APPARATUS OPERATED IN PRESSURE-DEMAND OR OTHER POSITIVE PRESSURE MODE.

CLOTHING: EMPLOYEE MUST WEAR APPROPRIATE PROTECTIVE (IMPERVIOUS) CLOTHING AND EQUIPMENT TO PREVENT ANY POSSIBILITY OF SKIN CONTACT WITH THIS SUBSTANCE.

GLOVES: EMPLOYEE MUST WEAR APPROPRIATE PROTECTIVE GLOVES TO PREVENT CONTACT WITH THIS SUBSTANCE.

EYE PROTECTION: EMPLOYEE MUST WEAR SPLASH-PROOF OR DUST-RESISTANT SAFETY GOGGLES AND A FACESHIELD TO PREVENT CONTACT WITH THIS SUBSTANCE.

EMERGENCY WASH FACILITIES: WHERE THERE IS ANY POSSIBILITY THAT AN EMPLOYEE'S EYES AND/OR SKIN MAY BE EXPOSED TO THIS SUBSTANCE, THE EMPLOYER SHOULD PROVIDE AN EYE WASH FOUNTAIN AND QUICK DRENCH SHOWER WITHIN THE IMMEDIATE WORK AREA FOR EMERGENCY USE.

AUTHORIZED BY- OCCUPATIONAL HEALTH SERVICES, INC.

CREATION DATE: 10/04/89 ***REVISION DATE:*** 05/01/90

MATERIAL SAFETY DATA SHEET

OCCUPATIONAL HEALTH SERVICES, INC.
AGRICULTURE AND PESTICIDE DIVISION
450 SEVENTH AVENUE, SUITE 2407
NEW YORK, NEW YORK 10123
1-800-445-MSDS OR (212) 967-1100

EMERGENCY CONTACT:
JOHN S. BRANSFORD, JR. (615) 292-1180

SUBSTANCE IDENTIFICATION

CAS-NUMBER 115-29-7

SUBSTANCE: **ENDOSULFAN**

TRADE NAMES/SYNONYMS: 6,9-METHANO-2,4,3-BENZODIOXATHIEPIN, 6, 7,8,9,10,10-HEXACHLORO-1,5, 5A,6,9,9A-HEXAHYDRO-,3-OXIDE; 5-NORBORNENE-2,3-DIMETHANOL, 1,4,5,6,7,7-HEXACHLORO-, CYCLIC SULFITE; 6,7,8,9,10,10-HEXACHLORO-1,5,5A,6,9,9A-HEXAHYDRO-6,9-METHANO-2,4, 3-BENZODIOXATHIEPIN 3-OXIDE; 1,4,5,6,7,7-HEXACHLORO-5-NORBORENE-2,3-DIMETHANOL CYCLIC SULFITE; 1,2,3,4,7,7-HEXACHLOROBICYCLO(2.2.1)-2-HEPTENE-5,6-BISOXYMETHYLENE SULFITE; (1,4,5,6,7,7-HEXACHLORO-8,9,10-TRINORBORN-5-EN-2,3-YLENEBISMETHYLENE) SULPHITE; (1,4,5,6,7,7-HEXACHLORO-8,9,10-TRINORBORN-5-EN-2,3-YLENEBISMETHYLENE) SULFITE; C,C'-(1,4,5,6,7,7-HEXACHLORO-8,9-10-TRINORBORN-5-EN-2,3-YLENE) (DIMETHYL SULFITE); THIODAN; BENZOEPIN; ENT 23,979; RCRA P050; STCC 4921522; C9H6CL6O3S; PST08560

CHEMICAL FAMILY: HALOGEN COMPOUND, ALICYCLIC ORGANIC SULFITE

MOLECULAR FORMULA: C9-H6-CL6-O3-S

MOLECULAR WEIGHT: 406.95

CERCLA RATINGS (SCALE 0-3): HEALTH=3 FIRE=0 REACTIVITY=0 PERSISTENCE=3

NFPA RATINGS (SCALE 0-4): HEALTH=4 FIRE=0 REACTIVITY=0

COMPONENTS AND CONTAMINANTS

COMPONENT: ENDOSULFAN ***PERCENT:*** 100.00

CAS# 115-29-7

EXPOSURE LIMITS: ENDOSULFAN (THIODAN): 0.1 MG/M3 OSHA TWA (SKIN) 0.1 MG/M3 ACGIH TWA (SKIN)

10/10,000 POUNDS SARA SECTION 302 THRESHOLD PLANNING QUANTITY 1 POUND SARA SECTION 304 REPORTABLE QUANTITY 1 POUND CERCLA SECTION 103 REPORTABLE QUANTITY

PHYSICAL DATA

DESCRIPTION: COLORLESS TO WHITE CRYSTALLINE SOLID

BOILING POINT: 250 F (121 C) DECOMPOSES ***MELTING POINT:*** 223 F (106 C)

SPECIFIC GRAVITY: 1.745 ***VAPOR PRESSURE:*** 0.009 MMHG @ 80 C

SOLUBILITY IN WATER: 0.6 PPM

SOLVENT SOLUBILITY: SOLUBLE IN ACETONE, XYLENE, ALCOHOL, KEROSENE, CHLOROFORM, CARBON TETRACHLORIDE, TOLUENE, AMYL ACETATE, HEPTANE, CHLOROBENZENE, DIOXANE, ACETIC ACID, BENZENE, AND MOST ORGANIC SOLVENTS

FIRE AND EXPLOSION DATA

FIRE AND EXPLOSION HAZARD: NEGLIGIBLE FIRE HAZARD WHEN EXPOSED TO HEAT OR FLAME.

FIREFIGHTING MEDIA: DRY CHEMICAL, CARBON DIOXIDE, HALON, WATER SPRAY OR STANDARD FOAM (1987 EMERGENCY RESPONSE GUIDEBOOK, DOT P 5800.4).

FOR LARGER FIRES, USE WATER SPRAY, FOG OR STANDARD FOAM (1987 EMERGENCY RESPONSE GUIDEBOOK, DOT P 5800.4).

FIREFIGHTING: MOVE CONTAINERS FROM FIRE AREA IF POSSIBLE. FIGHT FIRE FROM MAXIMUM DISTANCE. STAY AWAY FROM STORAGE TANK ENDS. DIKE FIRE CONTROL WATER FOR LATER DISPOSAL. DO NOT SCATTER MATERIAL (1987 EMERGENCY RESPONSE GUIDEBOOK, DOT P 5800.4, GUIDE PAGE 55).
USE AGENTS SUITABLE FOR TYPE OF FIRE. COOL CONTAINERS WITH FLOODING AMOUNTS OF WATER. AVOID BREATHING VAPORS OR DUSTS, KEEP UPWIND.

TRANSPORTATION DATA

DEPARTMENT OF TRANSPORTATION HAZARD CLASSIFICATION 49 CFR 172.101: POISON B
DEPARTMENT OF TRANSPORTATION LABELING REQUIREMENTS 49 CFR 172.101 AND SUBPART E: POISON
DEPARTMENT OF TRANSPORTATION PACKAGING REQUIREMENTS: 49 CFR 173.365 EXCEPTIONS: 49 CFR 173.364

TOXICITY

ENDOSULFAN (THIODAN): TOXICITY DATA: 80 MG/M3/4 HOURS INHALATION-RAT LC50; 90 MG/M3/4 HOURS INHALATION-CAT LC50; 90 MG/KG SKIN-RABBIT LD50; 34 MG/KG SKIN-RAT LD50; 147 MG/KG SKIN-MAMMAL LD50; 18 MG/KG ORAL-RAT LD50; 7360 UG/KG ORAL-MOUSE LD50; 28 MG/KG ORAL-RABBIT LD50; 118 MG/KG ORAL-HAMSTER LD50; 2 MG/KG ORAL-CAT LD50; 76700 UG/KG ORAL-DOG LD50; 26 MG/KG ORAL-DOMESTIC ANIMAL LD50; 360 MG/KG SUBCUTANEOUS-RABBIT LD50; 80 MG/KG INTRAPERITONEAL-HAMSTER LD50; 7 MG/KG INTRAPERITONEAL-MOUSE LD50; 8 MG/KG INTRAPERITONEAL-RAT LD50; 32 MG/KG UNREPORTED-MOUSE LD50; 40 MG/KG UNREPORTED-RAT LD50; MUTAGENIC DATA (RTECS); REPRODUCTIVE EFFECTS DATA (RTECS); TUMORIGENIC DATA (RTECS).
CARCINOGEN STATUS: NONE. ACUTE TOXICITY: HIGHLY TOXIC BY INHALATION, DERMAL ABSORPTION, AND INGESTION. TARGET EFFECTS: CONVULSANT.

HEALTH EFFECTS AND FIRST AID

INHALATION: ENDOSULFAN (THIODAN): CONVULSANT/HIGHLY TOXIC. **ACUTE EXPOSURE-** A LETHAL CONCENTRATION IN RATS WAS 80 MG/M3/4 HOURS. ENDOSULFAN MAY BE ABSORBED FROM THE LUNGS AND PRODUCE CENTRAL NERVOUS SYSTEM STIMULATION WITH SYMPTOMS OF HEADACHE, RESTLESSNESS, IRRITABILITY, CONFUSION, MALAISE, DIZZINESS, WEAKNESS, NAUSEA, VOMITING, AND FLUSHING AND DRY MOUTH. FAINTING, EPILEPTIC CONVULSIONS AND ALTERED EEG PATTERNS MAY OCCUR. SOME OF THESE SYMPTOMS MAY BE DELAYED FOR SEVERAL HOURS AFTER EXPOSURE. ABSORPTION IS NORMALLY SLOW BUT IS INCREASED WHEN IN SOLUTION WITH ALCOHOLS, OILS AND EMULSIFIERS. IT DOES NOT ACCUMULATE SIGNIFICANTLY IN HUMAN TISSUE. **CHRONIC EXPOSURE-** PROLONGED OR REPEATED EXPOSURE MAY CAUSE EFFECTS AS DESCRIBED IN ACUTE EXPOSURE. ONE INDIVIDUAL EXPERIENCED FAINTING AND CONVULSIONS WHILE ASSIGNED TO CLEANING VATS CONTAINING RESIDUES OF ENDOSULFAN. TWO YEARS AFTER EXPOSURE, THIS PERSON HAD COGNITIVE AND EMOTIONAL DETERIORATION, SEVERE IMPAIRMENT OF MEMORY, GROSS IMPAIRMENT OF VISUAL MOTOR COORDINATION, AND INABILITY TO PERFORM ANY BUT THE SIMPLEST TASKS.

FIRST AID- REMOVE FROM EXPOSURE AREA TO FRESH AIR IMMEDIATELY. IF BREATHING HAS STOPPED, PERFORM ARTIFICIAL RESPIRATION. KEEP PERSON WARM AND AT REST. TREAT SYMPTOMATICALLY AND SUPPORTIVELY. GET MEDICAL ATTENTION IMMEDIATELY.

SKIN CONTACT: ENDOSULFAN (THIODAN): CONVULSANT/HIGHLY TOXIC. **ACUTE EXPOSURE-** A LETHAL DOSE IN RABBITS BY DERMAL ABSORPTION WAS 90 MG/KG. ENDOSULFAN MAY BE ABSORBED FROM THE SKIN AND PRODUCE CENTRAL NERVOUS SYSTEM STIMULATION WITH SYMPTOMS OF HEADACHE, RESTLESSNESS, IRRITABILITY, CONFUSION, MALAISE, DIZZINESS, WEAKNESS, NAUSEA, VOMITING, AND FLUSHING AND DRY MOUTH. FAINTING, EPILEPTIC CONVULSIONS AND ALTERED EEG PATTERNS MAY OCCUR. SOME OF THESE SYMPTOMS MAY BE DELAYED FOR SEVERAL HOURS AFTER EXPOSURE. ABSORPTION IS NORMALLY SLOW BUT IS INCREASED WHEN IN SOLUTION WITH ALCOHOLS, OILS, AND EMULSIFIERS. IT DOES NOT ACCUMULATE SIGNIFICANTLY IN HUMAN TISSUE. SOME FORMULATIONS MAY BE IRRITATING. **CHRONIC EXPOSURE-** PROLONGED OR REPEATED EXPOSURE MAY CAUSE EFFECTS AS DESCRIBED IN ACUTE EXPOSURE.

FIRST AID- REMOVE CONTAMINATED CLOTHING AND SHOES IMMEDIATELY. WASH AFFECTED AREA WITH SOAP OR MILD DETERGENT AND LARGE AMOUNTS OF WATER UNTIL NO EVIDENCE OF CHEMICAL REMAINS (APPROXIMATELY 15-20 MINUTES). GET MEDICAL ATTENTION IMMEDIATELY.

EYE CONTACT: ENDOSULFAN (THIODAN): **ACUTE EXPOSURE-** 83 MG APPLIED TO THE EYES OF RABBITS PRODUCED SLIGHT CONJUNCTIVITIS WHICH CLEARED WITHIN 72 HOURS OF APPLICATION. **CHRONIC EXPOSURE-** NO DATA AVAILABLE.

FIRST AID- WASH EYES IMMEDIATELY WITH LARGE AMOUNTS OF WATER OR NORMAL SALINE, OCCASIONALLY LIFTING UPPER AND LOWER LIDS, UNTIL NO EVIDENCE OF CHEMICAL REMAINS (APPROXIMATELY 15-20 MINUTES). GET MEDICAL ATTENTION IMMEDIATELY.

INGESTION: ENDOSULFAN (THIODAN): CONVULSANT/HIGHLY TOXIC. **ACUTE EXPOSURE-** A LETHAL DOSE IN RATS WAS 18 MG/KG. INGESTION OF THIS MATERIAL MAY CAUSE GAGGING, VOMITING, DIARRHEA, AGITATION, TONIC-CLONIC CONVULSIONS, FOAMING AT THE MOUTH, DYSPNEA, APNEA, CYANOSIS, AND LOSS OF CONSCIOUSNESS. ONE 70-YEAR-OLD WOMAN DIED THREE HOURS AFTER TAKING ONLY "DROPS" OF AN ENDOSULFAN FORMULATION. PERSONS WHO TOOK LARGER DOSES DIED QUICKER, SOME IN LESS THAN AN HOUR. **CHRONIC EXPOSURE-** REPEATED DOSES OF 5 MG/KG/DAY AND GREATER ON DAYS 6 TO 14 OF GESTATION INCREASED THE MORTALITY OF FEMALE RATS AND INCREASED THE RATES OF RESORPTION AND SKELETAL ABNORMALITY IN THEIR FETUSES. ADVERSE EFFECTS ON THE MALE REPRODUCTIVE SYSTEM WERE OBSERVED IN A STUDY OF RATS. HISTOPATHOLOGICAL EXAMINATIONS OF THE LIVER AND KIDNEYS OF RATS FED A DAILY DIET UP TO 10 MG/KG FOR 15 DAYS REVEALED DILATION OF SINUSOID AROUND CENTRAL VEINS, AREAS OF FOCAL NECROSIS AND DEGENERATION OF HEPATOCYTES AND MONONUCLEAR MONOLUCOCYTES, PROLIFERATION IN THE BILE DUCT, AND DEGENERATIVE ALTERATIONS IN THE EPITHELIAL LINING OF KIDNEY TUBULES. OTHER EFFECTS INCLUDED KUPFFER CELL HYPERPLASIA, INFLAMMATORY AREAS IN THE SUBPLEURAL OF THE LUNGS AND DILATION OF THE ALVEOLI, AND SEVERE DEGENERATION OF THE SEMINIFEROUS EPITHELIUM. AS EVALUATED BY RTECS, ORAL ADMINISTRATION TO RATS RESULTED IN A STATISTICALLY SIGNIFICANT INCREASE IN THE INCIDENCE OF NEOPLASTIC TUMORS OF THE RESPIRATORY SYSTEM.

FIRST AID- IF THE PERSON IS CONSCIOUS AND NOT CONVULSING, REMOVE BY GIVING SYRUP OF IPECAC (IF VOMITING OCCURS, KEEP THE HEAD BELOW THE HIPS TO PREVENT ASPIRATION). GIVE ACTIVATED CHARCOAL FOLLOWED BY GASTRIC LAVAGE. FOLLOW WITH A SALINE CATHARTIC. DO NOT GIVE FATS OR OILS. INTESTINAL LAVAGE WITH 20% MANNITOL (200 ML) BY STOMACH TUBE IS ALSO USEFUL. GIVE ARTIFICIAL RESPIRATION WITH OXYGEN IF RESPIRATION IS DEPRESSED (DREISBACH, HANDBOOK OF POISONING, 12TH ED.). TREAT SYMPTOMATICALLY AND SUPPORTIVELY. LAVAGE AND ADMINISTRATION OF OXYGEN SHOULD BE PERFORMED BY QUALIFIED MEDICAL PERSONNEL. GET MEDICAL ATTENTION IMMEDIATELY.

ANTIDOTE: NO SPECIFIC ANTIDOTE. TREAT SYMPTOMATICALLY AND SUPPORTIVELY.

REACTIVITY

REACTIVITY: STABLE UNDER NORMAL TEMPERATURES AND PRESSURES IN AN ENCLOSED CONTAINER. CONTACT WITH MOISTURE MAY CAUSE DECOMPOSITION PRODUCING SULFUR DIOXIDE AND ENDOSULFAN ALCOHOL.

INCOMPATIBILITIES: ENDOSULFAN (THIODAN): ACIDS: MAY CAUSE DECOMPOSITION PRODUCING SULFUR DIOXIDE AND ENDOSULFAN ALCOHOL. BASES: MAY CAUSE DECOMPOSITION PRODUCING SULFUR DIOXIDE AND ENDOSULFAN ALCOHOL. BORDEAUX MIXTURE: INCOMPATIBLE. CALCIUM ARSENATE: INCOMPATIBLE. IRON: MAY BE CORRODED. LIME: INCOMPATIBLE. ZINC SULFATE WITH LIME: INCOMPATIBLE.

DECOMPOSITION: THERMAL DECOMPOSITION PRODUCTS MAY INCLUDE TOXIC OXIDES OF SULFUR AND TOXIC AND CORROSIVE FUMES OF CHLORIDES.

POLYMERIZATION: HAZARDOUS POLYMERIZATION HAS NOT BEEN REPORTED TO OCCUR UNDER NORMAL TEMPERATURES AND PRESSURES.

STORAGE AND DISPOSAL

OBSERVE ALL FEDERAL, STATE AND LOCAL REGULATIONS WHEN STORING OR DISPOSING OF THIS SUBSTANCE. FOR ASSISTANCE, CONTACT THE DISTRICT DIRECTOR OF THE ENVIRONMENTAL PROTECTION AGENCY.

STORAGE

STORE IN ACCORDANCE WITH 40 CFR 165 RECOMMENDED PROCEDURES FOR THE DISPOSAL AND STORAGE OF PESTICIDES AND PESTICIDE CONTAINERS.
STORE AWAY FROM INCOMPATIBLE SUBSTANCES.
THRESHOLD PLANNING QUANTITY (TPQ): THE SUPERFUND AMENDMENTS AND REAUTHORIZATION ACT (SARA) SECTION 302 REQUIRES THAT EACH FACILITY WHERE ANY EXTREMELY HAZARDOUS SUBSTANCE IS PRESENT IN A QUANTITY EQUAL TO OR GREATER THAN THE TPQ ESTABLISHED FOR THAT SUBSTANCE NOTIFY THE STATE EMERGENCY RESPONSE COMMISSION FOR THE STATE IN WHICH IT IS LOCATED. SECTION 303 OF SARA REQUIRES THESE FACILITIES TO PARTICIPATE IN LOCAL EMERGENCY RESPONSE PLANNING (40 CFR 355.30).

DISPOSAL

DISPOSAL MUST BE IN ACCORDANCE WITH STANDARDS APPLICABLE TO GENERATORS OF HAZARDOUS WASTE, 40CFR 262. EPA HAZARDOUS WASTE NUMBER P050.

CONDITIONS TO AVOID

MAY BURN BUT DOES NOT IGNITE READILY. CONTAINERS MAY EXPLODE IN HEAT OF FIRE.

SPILL AND LEAK PROCEDURES

SOIL SPILL: DIG HOLDING AREA SUCH AS LAGOON, POND OR PIT FOR CONTAINMENT. USE PROTECTIVE COVER SUCH AS A PLASTIC SHEET TO PREVENT MATERIAL FROM DISSOLVING IN FIRE EXTINGUISHING WATER OR RAIN.

WATER SPILL: TRAP SPILLED MATERIAL AT BOTTOM IN DEEP WATER POCKETS, EXCAVATED HOLDING AREAS OR WITHIN SAND BAG BARRIERS.
USE ACTIVATED CARBON TO ABSORB SPILLED SUBSTANCE THAT IS DISSOLVED.
USE MECHANICAL DREDGES OR LIFTS TO EXTRACT IMMOBILIZED MASSES OF POLLUTION AND PRECIPITATES.

OCCUPATIONAL SPILL: DO NOT TOUCH SPILLED MATERIAL. STOP LEAK IF YOU CAN DO IT WITHOUT RISK. USE WATER SPRAY TO REDUCE VAPORS. FOR SMALL SPILLS, TAKE UP WITH SAND OR OTHER ABSORBENT MATERIAL AND PLACE INTO CONTAINERS FOR LATER DISPOSAL. FOR SMALL DRY SPILLS, WITH A CLEAN SHOVEL PLACE MATERIAL INTO CLEAN, DRY CONTAINERS AND COVER. MOVE CONTAINERS FROM SPILL AREA. FOR LARGER SPILLS, DIKE FAR AHEAD OF SPILL FOR LATER DISPOSAL. KEEP UNNECESSARY PEOPLE AWAY. ISOLATE HAZARD AREA AND DENY ENTRY. VENTILATE CLOSED SPACES BEFORE ENTERING.
REPORTABLE QUANTITY (RQ): 1 POUND THE SUPERFUND AMENDMENTS AND REAUTHORIZATION ACT (SARA) SECTION 304 REQUIRES THAT A RELEASE EQUAL TO OR GREATER THAN THE REPORTABLE QUANTITY FOR THIS SUBSTANCE BE IMMEDIATELY REPORTED TO THE LOCAL EMERGENCY PLANNING COMMITTEE AND THE STATE EMERGENCY RESPONSE COMMISSION (40 CFR 355.40). IF THE RELEASE OF THIS SUBSTANCE IS REPORTABLE UNDER CERCLA SECTION 103, THE NATIONAL RESPONSE CENTER MUST BE NOTIFIED IMMEDIATELY AT (800) 424-8802 OR (202) 426-2675 IN THE METROPOLITAN WASHINGTON, D.C. AREA (40 CFR 302.6).

PROTECTIVE EQUIPMENT

VENTILATION: PROCESS ENCLOSURE RECOMMENDED TO MEET PUBLISHED EXPOSURE LIMITS.

RESPIRATOR: THE FOLLOWING RESPIRATORS ARE RECOMMENDED BASED ON INFORMATION FOUND IN THE PHYSICAL DATA, TOXICITY AND HEALTH EFFECTS SECTIONS. THEY ARE RANKED IN ORDER FROM MINIMUM TO MAXIMUM RESPIRATORY PROTECTION. THE SPECIFIC RESPIRATOR SELECTED MUST BE BASED ON CONTAMINATION LEVELS FOUND IN THE WORK PLACE, MUST NOT EXCEED THE WORKING LIMITS OF THE RESPIRATOR AND BE JOINTLY APPROVED BY THE NATIONAL INSTITUTE FOR OCCUPATIONAL SAFETY AND HEALTH AND THE MINE SAFETY AND HEALTH ADMINISTRATION (NIOSH-MSHA).
TYPE 'C' SUPPLIED-AIR RESPIRATOR WITH A FULL FACEPIECE OPERATED IN PRESSURE-DEMAND OR OTHER POSITIVE PRESSURE MODE OR WITH A FULL FACEPIECE, HELMET OR HOOD OPERATED IN CONTINOUS-FLOW MODE.
SELF-CONTAINED BREATHING APPARATUS WITH A FULL FACEPIECE OPERATED IN PRESSURE-DEMAND OR OTHER POSITIVE PRESSURE MODE.
FOR FIREFIGHTING AND OTHER IMMEDIATELY DANGEROUS TO LIFE OR HEALTH CONDITIONS:
SELF-CONTAINED BREATHING APPARATUS WITH FULL FACEPIECE OPERATED IN PRESSURE-DEMAND OR OTHER POSITIVE PRESSURE MODE.
SUPPLIED-AIR RESPIRATOR WITH FULL FACEPIECE AND OPERATED IN PRESSURE-DEMAND OR OTHER POSITIVE PRESSURE MODE IN COMBINATION WITH AN AUXILIARY SELF-CONTAINED BREATHING APPARATUS OPERATED IN PRESSURE-DEMAND OR OTHER POSITIVE PRESSURE MODE.

CLOTHING: EMPLOYEE MUST WEAR APPROPRIATE PROTECTIVE (IMPERVIOUS) CLOTHING AND EQUIPMENT TO PREVENT ANY POSSIBILITY OF SKIN CONTACT WITH THIS SUBSTANCE.

GLOVES: EMPLOYEE MUST WEAR APPROPRIATE PROTECTIVE GLOVES TO PREVENT CONTACT WITH THIS SUBSTANCE.

EYE PROTECTION: EMPLOYEE MUST WEAR SPLASH-PROOF OR DUST-RESISTANT SAFETY GOGGLES AND A FACESHIELD TO PREVENT CONTACT WITH THIS SUBSTANCE.
EMERGENCY WASH FACILITIES: WHERE THERE IS ANY POSSIBILITY THAT AN EMPLOYEE'S EYES AND/OR SKIN MAY BE EXPOSED TO THIS SUBSTANCE, THE EMPLOYER SHOULD PROVIDE AN EYE WASH FOUNTAIN AND QUICK DRENCH SHOWER WITHIN THE IMMEDIATE WORK AREA FOR EMERGENCY USE.

AUTHORIZED BY- OCCUPATIONAL HEALTH SERVICES, INC.

CREATION DATE: 10/04/89 ***REVISION DATE:*** 05/07/90

MATERIAL SAFETY DATA SHEET

OCCUPATIONAL HEALTH SERVICES, INC.
AGRICULTURE AND PESTICIDE DIVISION
450 SEVENTH AVENUE, SUITE 2407
NEW YORK, NEW YORK 10123
1-800-445-MSDS OR (212) 967-1100

EMERGENCY CONTACT:
JOHN S. BRANSFORD, JR. (615) 292-1180

SUBSTANCE IDENTIFICATION

CAS-NUMBER 145-73-3

SUBSTANCE: ENDOTHALL

TRADE NAMES/SYNONYMS: 7-OXABICYCLO(2.2.1)HEPTANE-2,3-DICARBOXYLIC ACID; 3,6-ENDOXOHEXAHYDROPHTHALIC ACID; 3,6-ENDOOXOHEXAHYDROPHTHALIC ACID; 3,6-EPOXYCYCLOHEXANE-1,2-DICARBOXYLIC ACID; 1,2-DICARBOXY 3,6-ENDOXOCYCLOHEXANE; ENDOTHAL; HYDOUT; RCRA P088; C8H10O5; PST08580

CHEMICAL FAMILY: CARBOXYLIC ACID, ALICYCLIC

MOLECULAR FORMULA: C8-H10-O5

MOLECULAR WEIGHT: 186.16

CERCLA RATINGS (SCALE 0-3): HEALTH=3 FIRE=1 REACTIVITY=0 PERSISTENCE=1

NFPA RATINGS (SCALE 0-4): HEALTH=4 FIRE=1 REACTIVITY=0

COMPONENTS AND CONTAMINANTS

COMPONENT: ENDOTHALL ***PERCENT:*** 100.0
CAS# 145-73-3

EXPOSURE LIMITS: NO OCCUPATIONAL EXPOSURE LIMITS ESTABLISHED BY OSHA, ACGIH, OR NIOSH.
ENDOTHALL: 1000 POUNDS CERCLA SECTION 103 REPORTABLE QUANTITY

PHYSICAL DATA

DESCRIPTION: COLORLESS TO WHITE CRYSTALLINE SOLID. ***MELTING POINT:*** 291 F (144 C)

SPECIFIC GRAVITY: 1.431 @ 20 C ***VAPOR PRESSURE:*** NEGLIGIBLE

SOLUBILITY IN WATER: 10% @ 25 C

SOLVENT SOLUBILITY: SOLUBLE IN METHANOL; MODERATELY SOLUBLE IN DIOXANE, ACETONE, ISOPROPANOL; SLIGHTLY SOLUBLE IN ETHER; VERY SLIGHTLY SOLUBLE IN BENZENE.
DECOMPOSES @ 194 F (90 C) TO ANHYDRIDE

FIRE AND EXPLOSION DATA

FIRE AND EXPLOSION HAZARD: SLIGHT FIRE HAZARD WHEN EXPOSED TO HEAT OR FLAME.

FIREFIGHTING MEDIA: DRY CHEMICAL, CARBON DIOXIDE, HALON, WATER SPRAY OR STANDARD FOAM (1987 EMERGENCY RESPONSE GUIDEBOOK, DOT P 5800.4).
FOR LARGER FIRES, USE WATER SPRAY, FOG OR STANDARD FOAM (1987 EMERGENCY RESPONSE GUIDEBOOK, DOT P 5800.4).

FIREFIGHTING: MOVE CONTAINERS FROM FIRE AREA IF POSSIBLE (1987 EMERGENCY RESPONSE GUIDEBOOK, DOT P 5800.4, GUIDE PAGE 53).
EXTINGUISH USING AGENT SUITABLE FOR TYPE OF SURROUNDING FIRE. AVOID BREATHING VAPORS AND DUSTS. KEEP UPWIND.

TRANSPORTATION DATA

DEPARTMENT OF TRANSPORTATION HAZARD CLASSIFICATION 49 CFR 172.101: POISON B
DEPARTMENT OF TRANSPORTATION LABELING REQUIREMENTS 49 CFR 172.101 AND SUBPART E: POISON
DEPARTMENT OF TRANSPORTATION PACKAGING REQUIREMENTS: 49 CFR 173.365 EXCEPTIONS: 49 CFR 173.364

TOXICITY

ENDOTHALL: TOXICITY DATA: 200 MG/KG SKIN-RABBIT LD100 (EPA, ENDOTHALL HEALTH ADVISORY, 1988); 38 MG/KG ORAL-RAT LD50; 14 MG/KG INTRAPERITONEAL-MOUSE LD50. CARCINOGEN STATUS: NONE. LOCAL EFFECTS: IRRITANT- INHALATION, SKIN, EYE. ACUTE TOXICITY LEVEL: HIGHLY TOXIC BY DERMAL ABSORPTION AND INGESTION. TARGET EFFECTS: POISONING MAY AFFECT THE CENTRAL NERVOUS SYSTEM.

HEALTH EFFECTS AND FIRST AID

INHALATION: ENDOTHALL: IRRITANT. **ACUTE EXPOSURE-** MAY CAUSE IRRITATION. **CHRONIC EXPOSURE-** PROLONGED OR REPEATED EXPOSURE MAY CAUSE IRRITATION OF THE MUCOUS MEMBRANES.

FIRST AID- REMOVE FROM EXPOSURE AREA TO FRESH AIR IMMEDIATELY. IF BREATHING HAS STOPPED, PERFORM ARTIFICIAL RESPIRATION. KEEP PERSON WARM AND AT REST. TREAT SYMPTOMATICALLY AND SUPPORTIVELY. GET MEDICAL ATTENTION IMMEDIATELY.

SKIN CONTACT: ENDOTHALL: IRRITANT/HIGHLY TOXIC. **ACUTE EXPOSURE-** APPLICATIONS OF PURE POWDERED MATERIAL OR TEN TO TWENTY PERCENT SOLUTIONS TO INTACT OR SCARIFIED RABBIT SKIN PRODUCED DAMAGE INCLUDING NECROSIS AND DEATH FROM SYSTEMIC ABSORPTION. NO

SENSITIZATION WAS OBSERVED IN ANIMAL STUDIES. **CHRONIC EXPOSURE-** REPEATED AND PROLONGED CONTACT TO IRRITANTS MAY CAUSE DERMATITIS.

FIRST AID- REMOVE CONTAMINATED CLOTHING AND SHOES IMMEDIATELY. WASH AFFECTED AREA WITH SOAP OR MILD DETERGENT AND LARGE AMOUNTS OF WATER UNTIL NO EVIDENCE OF CHEMICAL REMAINS (APPROXIMATELY 15-20 MINUTES). GET MEDICAL ATTENTION IMMEDIATELY.

EYE CONTACT: ENDOTHALL: IRRITANT. **ACUTE EXPOSURE-** ENDOTHALL PRODUCED SEVERE IRRITATION WITH EFFECTS OF CORNEAL OPACITY, CONJUNCTIVAL IRRITATION AND IRIDIC CONGESTION WHEN APPLIED TO RABBIT EYES; THESE EFFECTS WERE REVERSED IN 7 DAYS. DEATH WAS OBSERVED IN SOME RABBITS FROM EYE ABSORPTION. **CHRONIC EXPOSURE-** REPEATED AND PROLONGED CONTACT TO IRRITANTS MAY CAUSE CONJUNCTIVITIS.

FIRST AID- WASH EYES IMMEDIATELY WITH LARGE AMOUNTS OF WATER OR NORMAL SALINE, OCCASIONALLY LIFTING UPPER AND LOWER LIDS, UNTIL NO EVIDENCE OF CHEMICAL REMAINS (APPROXIMATELY 15-20 MINUTES). GET MEDICAL ATTENTION IMMEDIATELY.

INGESTION: ENDOTHALL: HIGHLY TOXIC. **ACUTE EXPOSURE-** THE LD50 REPORTED IN RATS WAS 38 MG/KG. REPEATED VOMITING WAS OBSERVED IN AN INDIVIDUAL WHO INGESTED A FATAL DOSE ESTIMATED TO BE 7 TO 8 GRAMS OF THE SODIUM SALT OF ENDOTHALL. AUTOPSY REVEALED FOCAL HEMORRHAGES AND EDEMA IN LUNGS AND GROSS HEMORRHAGE OF THE GASTROINTESTINAL TRACT. DISORDERS OF GAIT AND CONVULSIONS WERE REPORTED IN RATS. **CHRONIC EXPOSURE-** EFFECTS OF VOMITING, DIARRHEA, SEVERE GASTROINTESTINAL INFLAMMATION WITH EROSION, SLIGHT LIVER DEGENERATION, AND FOCAL HEMORRHAGIC AREAS IN THE KIDNEY WERE OBSERVED IN ANIMALS REPEATEDLY FED THE SODIUM SALT OF ENDOTHALL. IN A THREE-GENERATION STUDY, THE OFFSPRING OF RATS RECEIVING 100 MG/KG/DAY OF THE SODIUM SALT DID NOT SURVIVE MORE THAN 1 WEEK.

FIRST AID- IF THE PERSON IS CONSCIOUS AND NOT CONVULSING, REMOVE BY GASTRIC LAVAGE AND FOLLOW WITH A CATHARTIC (DREISBACH, HANDBOOK OF POISONING, 12TH ED.). TREAT SYMPTOMATICALLY AND SUPPORTIVELY. GASTRIC LAVAGE SHOULD BE PERFORMED BY QUALIFIED MEDICAL PERSONNEL. GET MEDICAL ATTENTION IMMEDIATELY.

ANTIDOTE: NO SPECIFIC ANTIDOTE. TREAT SYMPTOMATICALLY AND SUPPORTIVELY.

REACTIVITY

REACTIVITY: STABLE UNDER NORMAL TEMPERATURES AND PRESSURES.

INCOMPATIBILITIES: ENDOTHALL: OXIDIZERS (STRONG): FIRE AND EXPLOSION HAZARD.

DECOMPOSITION: THERMAL DECOMPOSITION PRODUCTS MAY INCLUDE TOXIC OXIDES OF CARBON.

POLYMERIZATION: HAZARDOUS POLYMERIZATION HAS NOT BEEN REPORTED TO OCCUR UNDER NORMAL TEMPERATURES AND PRESSURES.

STORAGE AND DISPOSAL

OBSERVE ALL FEDERAL, STATE AND LOCAL REGULATIONS WHEN STORING OR DISPOSING OF THIS SUBSTANCE. FOR ASSISTANCE, CONTACT THE DISTRICT DIRECTOR OF THE ENVIRONMENTAL PROTECTION AGENCY.

STORAGE

STORE IN ACCORDANCE WITH 40 CFR 165 RECOMMENDED PROCEDURES FOR THE DISPOSAL AND STORAGE OF PESTICIDES AND PESTICIDE CONTAINERS.

STORE AWAY FROM INCOMPATIBLE SUBSTANCES.

DISPOSAL

DISPOSAL MUST BE IN ACCORDANCE WITH STANDARDS APPLICABLE TO GENERATORS OF HAZARDOUS WASTE, 40CFR 262. EPA HAZARDOUS WASTE NUMBER P088.

DISPOSAL MUST BE IN ACCORDANCE WITH 40 CFR 165 RECOMMENDED PROCEDURES FOR THE DISPOSAL AND STORAGE OF PESTICIDES AND PESTICIDE CONTAINERS.

CONDITIONS TO AVOID

MAY BURN BUT DOES NOT IGNITE READILY.

SPILL AND LEAK PROCEDURES

OCCUPATIONAL SPILL: DO NOT TOUCH SPILLED MATERIAL. STOP LEAK IF YOU CAN DO IT WITHOUT RISK. FOR SMALL SPILLS, TAKE UP WITH SAND OR OTHER ABSORBENT MATERIAL AND PLACE INTO CONTAINERS FOR LATER DISPOSAL. FOR SMALL DRY SPILLS, WITH A CLEAN SHOVEL PLACE MATERIAL INTO CLEAN, DRY CONTAINER AND COVER. MOVE CONTAINERS FROM SPILL AREA. FOR LARGER SPILLS, DIKE FAR AHEAD OF SPILL FOR LATER DISPOSAL. KEEP UNNECESSARY PEOPLE AWAY. ISOLATE HAZARD AREA AND DENY ENTRY.

REPORTABLE QUANTITY (RQ): 1000 POUNDS THE SUPERFUND AMENDMENTS AND REAUTHORIZATION ACT (SARA) SECTION 304 REQUIRES THAT A RELEASE EQUAL TO OR GREATER THAN THE REPORTABLE QUANTITY FOR THIS SUBSTANCE BE IMMEDIATELY REPORTED TO THE LOCAL EMERGENCY PLANNING COMMITTEE AND THE STATE EMERGENCY RESPONSE COMMISSION (40 CFR 355.40). IF THE RELEASE OF THIS SUBSTANCE IS REPORTABLE UNDER CERCLA SECTION 103, THE NATIONAL RESPONSE CENTER MUST BE NOTIFIED IMMEDIATELY AT (800) 424-8802 OR (202) 426-2675 IN THE METROPOLITAN WASHINGTON, D.C. AREA (40 CFR 302.6).

PROTECTIVE EQUIPMENT

VENTILATION: PROVIDE LOCAL EXHAUST OR PROCESS ENCLOSURE VENTILATION SYSTEM.

RESPIRATOR: THE FOLLOWING RESPIRATORS ARE RECOMMENDED BASED ON INFORMATION FOUND IN THE PHYSICAL DATA, TOXICITY AND HEALTH EFFECTS SECTIONS. THEY ARE RANKED IN ORDER FROM MINIMUM TO MAXIMUM RESPIRATORY PROTECTION. THE SPECIFIC RESPIRATOR SELECTED MUST BE BASED ON CONTAMINATION LEVELS FOUND IN THE WORK PLACE, MUST NOT EXCEED THE WORKING LIMITS OF THE RESPIRATOR AND BE JOINTLY APPROVED BY THE NATIONAL INSTITUTE FOR OCCUPATIONAL SAFETY AND HEALTH AND THE MINE SAFETY AND HEALTH ADMINISTRATION (NIOSH-MSHA).

TYPE 'C' SUPPLIED-AIR RESPIRATOR WITH A FULL FACEPIECE OPERATED IN PRESSURE-DEMAND OR OTHER POSITIVE PRESSURE MODE OR WITH A FULL FACEPIECE, HELMET OR HOOD OPERATED IN CONTINOUS-FLOW MODE.

SELF-CONTAINED BREATHING APPARATUS WITH A FULL FACEPIECE OPERATED IN PRESSURE-DEMAND OR OTHER POSITIVE PRESSURE MODE.

FOR FIREFIGHTING AND OTHER IMMEDIATELY DANGEROUS TO LIFE OR HEALTH CONDITIONS:

SELF-CONTAINED BREATHING APPARATUS WITH FULL FACEPIECE OPERATED IN PRESSURE-DEMAND OR OTHER POSITIVE PRESSURE MODE.

SUPPLIED-AIR RESPIRATOR WITH FULL FACEPIECE AND OPERATED IN PRESSURE-DEMAND OR OTHER POSITIVE PRESSURE MODE IN COMBINATION WITH AN AUXILIARY SELF-CONTAINED BREATHING APPARATUS OPERATED IN PRESSURE-DEMAND OR OTHER POSITIVE PRESSURE MODE.

CLOTHING: EMPLOYEE MUST WEAR APPROPRIATE PROTECTIVE (IMPERVIOUS) CLOTHING AND EQUIPMENT TO PREVENT ANY POSSIBILITY OF SKIN CONTACT WITH THIS SUBSTANCE.

GLOVES: EMPLOYEE MUST WEAR APPROPRIATE PROTECTIVE GLOVES TO PREVENT CONTACT WITH THIS SUBSTANCE.

EYE PROTECTION: EMPLOYEE MUST WEAR SPLASH-PROOF OR DUST-RESISTANT SAFETY GOGGLES AND A FACESHIELD TO PREVENT CONTACT WITH THIS SUBSTANCE.

EMERGENCY WASH FACILITIES: WHERE THERE IS ANY POSSIBILITY THAT AN EMPLOYEE'S EYES AND/OR SKIN MAY BE EXPOSED TO THIS SUBSTANCE, THE EMPLOYER SHOULD PROVIDE AN EYE WASH FOUNTAIN AND QUICK DRENCH SHOWER WITHIN THE IMMEDIATE WORK AREA FOR EMERGENCY USE.

AUTHORIZED BY- OCCUPATIONAL HEALTH SERVICES, INC.
CREATION DATE: 10/04/89 ***REVISION DATE:*** 05/07/90

MATERIAL SAFETY DATA SHEET

OCCUPATIONAL HEALTH SERVICES, INC.
AGRICULTURE AND PESTICIDE DIVISION
450 SEVENTH AVENUE, SUITE 2407
NEW YORK, NEW YORK 10123
1-800-445-MSDS OR (212) 967-1100

EMERGENCY CONTACT:
JOHN S. BRANSFORD, JR. (615) 292-1180

SUBSTANCE IDENTIFICATION

CAS-NUMBER 129-67-9

SUBSTANCE: **ENDOTHALL-SODIUM**

TRADE NAMES/SYNONYMS: 7-OXABICYCLO(2.2.1)HEPTANE-2,3-DICARBOSYLIC ACID, DISODIUM SALT; DISODIUM 3,6-ENDOXOHEXAHYDROPHTHALATE; DISODIUM 3,6-EPOXYCYCLOHEXANE-1,2-DICARBOXYLATE; DISODIUM-7-OXABICYCLO(2.2.1)HEPTANE-2,3-DICARBOXYLIC ACID; DISODIUM-7-OXABICYCLO(2.2.1)HEPTANE-2,3-DICARBOXYLATE; 3,6-ENDOXOHEXAHYDROPHTHALIC ACID DISODIUM SALT; ENDOTHAL-SODIUM; ENDOTHAL DISODIUM SALT; ENDOTHALL DISODIUM SALT; AGUATHOL; C8H8NA2O5; PST08590

CHEMICAL FAMILY: CARBOXYLIC ACID, ALICYCLIC SALT

MOLECULAR FORMULA: C8-H8-O5.2NA

MOLECULAR WEIGHT: 230.14

CERCLA RATINGS (SCALE 0-3): HEALTH=3 FIRE=1 REACTIVITY=0 PERSISTENCE=1

NFPA RATINGS (SCALE 0-4): HEALTH=4 FIRE=1 REACTIVITY=0

COMPONENTS AND CONTAMINANTS

COMPONENT: ENDOTHALL-SODIUM ***PERCENT:*** 100.0
CAS# 129-67-9

EXPOSURE LIMITS: NO OCCUPATIONAL EXPOSURE LIMITS ESTABLISHED BY OSHA, ACGIH, OR NIOSH.

PHYSICAL DATA

DESCRIPTION: SOLID. ***MELTING POINT:*** 291 F (144 C)
SPECIFIC GRAVITY: NOT AVAILABLE ***SOLUBILITY IN WATER:*** SOLUBLE

FIRE AND EXPLOSION DATA

FIRE AND EXPLOSION HAZARD: SLIGHT FIRE HAZARD WHEN EXPOSED TO HEAT OR FLAME.

FIREFIGHTING MEDIA: DRY CHEMICAL, CARBON DIOXIDE, HALON, WATER SPRAY OR STANDARD FOAM (1987 EMERGENCY RESPONSE GUIDEBOOK, DOT P 5800.4).
FOR LARGER FIRES, USE WATER SPRAY, FOG OR STANDARD FOAM (1987 EMERGENCY RESPONSE GUIDEBOOK, DOT P 5800.4).

FIREFIGHTING: MOVE CONTAINERS FROM FIRE AREA IF POSSIBLE (1987 EMERGENCY RESPONSE GUIDEBOOK, DOT P 5800.4, GUIDE PAGE 53).
EXTINGUISH USING AGENT SUITABLE FOR TYPE OF SURROUNDING FIRE. AVOID BREATHING VAPORS AND DUSTS. KEEP UPWIND.

TRANSPORTATION DATA

DEPARTMENT OF TRANSPORTATION HAZARD CLASSIFICATION 49 CFR 172.101: POISON B
DEPARTMENT OF TRANSPORTATION LABELING REQUIREMENTS 49 CFR 172.101 AND SUBPART E: POISON
DEPARTMENT OF TRANSPORTATION PACKAGING REQUIREMENTS: 49 CFR 173.365 EXCEPTIONS: 49 CFR 173.364

TOXICITY

ENDOTHALL-SODIUM: TOXICITY DATA: 100 MG/KG SKIN-RABBIT LD50; 750 MG/KG SKIN-RAT LD50; 51 MG/KG ORAL-RAT LD50; 250 MG/KG ORAL-GUINEA PIG LDLO; 5 MG/KG INTRAVENOUS-RABBIT LDLO; 5 MG/KG INTRAVENOUS-DOG LDLO.
CARCINOGEN STATUS: NONE. LOCAL EFFECTS: IRRITANT- INHALATION, SKIN, EYE. ACUTE TOXICITY LEVEL: HIGHLY TOXIC BY DERMAL ABSORPTION; TOXIC BY INGESTION. TARGET EFFECTS: MAY AFFECT THE CENTRAL NERVOUS SYSTEM.

HEALTH EFFECTS AND FIRST AID

INHALATION: ENDOTHALL-SODIUM: IRRITANT. **ACUTE EXPOSURE-** MAY CAUSE IRRITATION. **CHRONIC EXPOSURE-** PROLONGED OR REPEATED EXPOSURE MAY CAUSE IRRITATION OF THE MUCOUS MEMBRANES.

FIRST AID- REMOVE FROM EXPOSURE AREA TO FRESH AIR IMMEDIATELY. IF BREATHING HAS STOPPED, PERFORM ARTIFICIAL RESPIRATION. KEEP PERSON WARM AND AT REST. TREAT SYMPTOMATICALLY AND SUPPORTIVELY. GET MEDICAL ATTENTION IMMEDIATELY.

SKIN CONTACT: ENDOTHALL-SODIUM: IRRITANT/HIGHLY TOXIC. **ACUTE EXPOSURE-** IRRITATION INCLUDING NECROSIS WAS OBSERVED FROM APPLICATION TO RABBIT SKIN. A LETHAL DOSE IN RABBITS BY DERMAL ABSORPTION WAS 100 MG/KG. **CHRONIC EXPOSURE-** REPEATED AND PROLONGED CONTACT TO IRRITANTS MAY CAUSE DERMATITIS.

FIRST AID- REMOVE CONTAMINATED CLOTHING AND SHOES IMMEDIATELY. WASH AFFECTED AREA WITH SOAP OR MILD DETERGENT AND LARGE AMOUNTS OF WATER UNTIL NO EVIDENCE OF CHEMICAL REMAINS (APPROXIMATELY 15-20 MINUTES). GET MEDICAL ATTENTION IMMEDIATELY.

EYE CONTACT: ENDOTHALL-SODIUM: IRRITANT. **ACUTE EXPOSURE-** MAY CAUSE IRRITATION. DEATH WAS OBSERVED IN RABBITS FROM EYE ABSORPTION OF ENDOTHALL. **CHRONIC EXPOSURE-** REPEATED AND PROLONGED CONTACT WITH IRRITANTS MAY CAUSE CONJUNCTIVITIS.

FIRST AID- WASH EYES IMMEDIATELY WITH LARGE AMOUNTS OF WATER OR NORMAL SALINE, OCCASIONALLY LIFTING UPPER AND LOWER LIDS, UNTIL NO EVIDENCE OF CHEMICAL REMAINS (APPROXIMATELY 15-20 MINUTES). GET MEDICAL ATTENTION IMMEDIATELY.

INGESTION: ENDOTHALL-SODIUM: TOXIC. **ACUTE EXPOSURE-** REPEATED VOMITING WAS OBSERVED IN AN INDIVIDUAL WHO INGESTED A FATAL DOSE ESTIMATED TO BE 7 TO 8 GRAMS. AUTOPSY REVEALED FOCAL HEMORRHAGES AND EDEMA IN LUNGS AND GROSS HEMORRHAGE OF THE GASTROINTESTINAL TRACT. DISORDERS OF GAIT AND CONVULSIONS WERE REPORTED IN RATS. **CHRONIC EXPOSURE-** EFFECTS OF VOMITING, DIARRHEA, SEVERE GASTROINTESTINAL INFLAMMATION WITH EROSION, SLIGHT LIVER DEGENERATION, AND FOCAL HEMORRHAGIC AREAS IN THE KIDNEY WERE OBSERVED IN ANIMALS REPEATEDLY FED THIS MATERIAL. IN A THREE-GENERATION STUDY, THE OFFSPRING OF RATS RECEIVING 100 MG/KG/DAY DID NOT SURVIVE MORE THAN 1 WEEK.

FIRST AID- IF THE PERSON IS CONSCIOUS AND NOT CONVULSING, REMOVE BY GASTRIC LAVAGE AND FOLLOW WITH A CATHARTIC (DREISBACH, HANDBOOK OF POISONING, 12TH ED.). TREAT SYMPTOMATICALLY AND SUPPORTIVELY. GASTRIC LAVAGE SHOULD BE PERFORMED BY QUALIFIED MEDICAL PERSONNEL. GET MEDICAL ATTENTION IMMEDIATELY.

ANTIDOTE: NO SPECIFIC ANTIDOTE. TREAT SYMPTOMATICALLY AND SUPPORTIVELY.

REACTIVITY

REACTIVITY: STABLE UNDER NORMAL TEMPERATURES AND PRESSURES.

INCOMPATIBILITIES: ENDOTHALL-SODIUM: OXIDIZERS (STRONG): FIRE AND EXPLOSION HAZARD.

DECOMPOSITION: THERMAL DECOMPOSITION MAY RELEASE CAUSTIC FUMES OF SODIUM AND TOXIC OXIDES OF CARBON.

POLYMERIZATION: HAZARDOUS POLYMERIZATION HAS NOT BEEN REPORTED TO OCCUR UNDER NORMAL TEMPERATURES AND PRESSURES.

STORAGE AND DISPOSAL

OBSERVE ALL FEDERAL, STATE AND LOCAL REGULATIONS WHEN STORING OR DISPOSING OF THIS SUBSTANCE. FOR ASSISTANCE, CONTACT THE DISTRICT DIRECTOR OF THE ENVIRONMENTAL PROTECTION AGENCY.

STORAGE

STORE IN ACCORDANCE WITH 40 CFR 165 RECOMMENDED PROCEDURES FOR THE DISPOSAL AND STORAGE OF PESTICIDES AND PESTICIDE CONTAINERS.
STORE AWAY FROM INCOMPATIBLE SUBSTANCES.

DISPOSAL

DISPOSAL MUST BE IN ACCORDANCE WITH 40 CFR 165 RECOMMENDED PROCEDURES FOR THE DISPOSAL AND STORAGE OF PESTICIDES AND PESTICIDE CONTAINERS.

CONDITIONS TO AVOID

MAY BURN BUT DOES NOT IGNITE READILY.

SPILL AND LEAK PROCEDURES

OCCUPATIONAL SPILL: DO NOT TOUCH SPILLED MATERIAL. STOP LEAK IF YOU CAN DO IT WITHOUT RISK. FOR SMALL SPILLS, TAKE UP WITH SAND OR OTHER ABSORBENT MATERIAL AND PLACE INTO CONTAINERS FOR LATER DISPOSAL. FOR SMALL DRY SPILLS, WITH A CLEAN SHOVEL PLACE MATERIAL INTO CLEAN, DRY CONTAINER AND COVER. MOVE CONTAINERS FROM SPILL AREA. FOR LARGER SPILLS, DIKE FAR AHEAD OF SPILL FOR LATER DISPOSAL. KEEP UNNECESSARY PEOPLE AWAY. ISOLATE HAZARD AREA AND DENY ENTRY.

PROTECTIVE EQUIPMENT

VENTILATION: PROVIDE LOCAL EXHAUST OR PROCESS ENCLOSURE VENTILATION SYSTEM.

RESPIRATOR: THE FOLLOWING RESPIRATORS ARE RECOMMENDED BASED ON INFORMATION FOUND IN THE PHYSICAL DATA, TOXICITY AND HEALTH EFFECTS SECTIONS. THEY ARE RANKED IN ORDER FROM MINIMUM TO MAXIMUM RESPIRATORY PROTECTION. THE SPECIFIC RESPIRATOR SELECTED MUST BE BASED ON CONTAMINATION LEVELS FOUND IN THE WORK PLACE, MUST NOT EXCEED THE WORKING LIMITS OF THE RESPIRATOR AND BE JOINTLY APPROVED BY THE NATIONAL INSTITUTE FOR OCCUPATIONAL SAFETY AND HEALTH AND THE MINE SAFETY AND HEALTH ADMINISTRATION (NIOSH-MSHA).
TYPE 'C' SUPPLIED-AIR RESPIRATOR WITH A FULL FACEPIECE OPERATED IN PRESSURE-DEMAND OR OTHER POSITIVE PRESSURE MODE OR WITH A FULL FACEPIECE, HELMET OR HOOD OPERATED IN CONTINOUS-FLOW MODE.
SELF-CONTAINED BREATHING APPARATUS WITH A FULL FACEPIECE OPERATED IN PRESSURE-DEMAND OR OTHER POSITIVE PRESSURE MODE.
FOR FIREFIGHTING AND OTHER IMMEDIATELY DANGEROUS TO LIFE OR HEALTH CONDITIONS:
SELF-CONTAINED BREATHING APPARATUS WITH FULL FACEPIECE OPERATED IN PRESSURE-DEMAND OR OTHER POSITIVE PRESSURE MODE.
SUPPLIED-AIR RESPIRATOR WITH FULL FACEPIECE AND OPERATED IN PRESSURE-DEMAND OR OTHER POSITIVE PRESSURE MODE IN COMBINATION WITH AN AUXILIARY SELF-CONTAINED BREATHING APPARATUS OPERATED IN PRESSURE-DEMAND OR OTHER POSITIVE PRESSURE MODE.

CLOTHING: EMPLOYEE MUST WEAR APPROPRIATE PROTECTIVE (IMPERVIOUS) CLOTHING AND EQUIPMENT TO PREVENT ANY POSSIBILITY OF SKIN CONTACT WITH THIS SUBSTANCE.

GLOVES: EMPLOYEE MUST WEAR APPROPRIATE PROTECTIVE GLOVES TO PREVENT CONTACT WITH THIS SUBSTANCE.

EYE PROTECTION: EMPLOYEE MUST WEAR SPLASH-PROOF OR DUST-RESISTANT SAFETY GOGGLES AND A FACESHIELD TO PREVENT CONTACT WITH THIS SUBSTANCE.

EMERGENCY WASH FACILITIES: WHERE THERE IS ANY POSSIBILITY THAT AN EMPLOYEE'S EYES AND/OR SKIN MAY BE EXPOSED TO THIS SUBSTANCE, THE EMPLOYER SHOULD PROVIDE AN EYE WASH FOUNTAIN AND QUICK DRENCH SHOWER WITHIN THE IMMEDIATE WORK AREA FOR EMERGENCY USE.

AUTHORIZED BY- OCCUPATIONAL HEALTH SERVICES, INC.
CREATION DATE: 10/04/89 ***REVISION DATE:*** 03/28/90

MATERIAL SAFETY DATA SHEET

OCCUPATIONAL HEALTH SERVICES, INC.
AGRICULTURE AND PESTICIDE DIVISION
450 SEVENTH AVENUE, SUITE 2407
NEW YORK, NEW YORK 10123
1-800-445-MSDS OR (212) 967-1100

EMERGENCY CONTACT:
JOHN S. BRANSFORD, JR. (615) 292-1180

SUBSTANCE IDENTIFICATION

CAS-NUMBER 72-20-8
SUBSTANCE: **ENDRIN**
TRADE NAMES/SYNONYMS: 2,7:3,6-DIMETHANONAPHTH(2,3-B)OXIRENE, 3,4,5,6,9,9-HEXACHLORO-1A, 2, 2A,3,6,6A,7,7A-OCTAHYDRO-, (1A ALPHA, 2 BETA, 2A BETA, 3 ALPHA, 6 ALPHA, 6A BETA, 7 BETA, 7A ALPHA); 1,4:5,8-DIMETHANONAPHTHALENE, 1,2,3,4,10,10-HEXACHLORO-6,7,-EPOXY-1,4 4A,5,6A,7,8,8A-OCTAHYDRO-, ENDO, ENDO-; (14,4S,4AS,5S,6S,7R,8R,8AR)-1,2,3,4,10,10-HEXACHLORO-1,4,4A,5,6,7,8, 8A-OCTAHYDRO-6,7-EPOXY-1,4:5,8-DIMETHANONAPHTHALENE; 1,2,3,4,10,10-HEXACHLORO-6,7-EPOXY-1,4,4A,5,6,7,8,8A-OCTAHYDRO-ENDO ENDO-1,4:5,8-DIMETHANONAPHTHALENE; (1A ALPHA, 2 BETA, 2A BETA, 3 ALPHA, 6 ALPHA, 6A BETA, 7 BETA, 7A ALPHA)-3,4,5,6,9,9-HEXACHLORO-1A,2,2A,3,6,6A,7,7A-OCTAHYDRO-2,7:3,6 -DIMETHANONAPHTH(2,3-B)OXIRENE; ENDO,ENDO-1,2,3,4,10,10-HEXACHLORO-6,7-EPOXY-1,4,4A,5,6,7,8,8A- -OCTAHYDRO-1,4:5,8-DIMETHANONAPHTHALENE; EXPERIMENTAL INSECTICIDE 269; OMS 197; ENT 17,251; RCRA P051; STCC 4921523; C12H8CL6O; PST08600
CHEMICAL FAMILY: HALOGEN NAPHTHALENE
MOLECULAR FORMULA: C12-H8-CL6-O
MOLECULAR WEIGHT: 380.93
CERCLA RATINGS (SCALE 0-3): HEALTH=3 FIRE=0 REACTIVITY=0 PERSISTENCE=3
NFPA RATINGS (SCALE 0-4): HEALTH=2 FIRE=0 REACTIVITY=0

COMPONENTS AND CONTAMINANTS

COMPONENT: ENDRIN ***PERCENT:*** 100
CAS# 72-20-8
OTHER CONTAMINANTS: NONE
EXPOSURE LIMITS: ENDRIN: 0.1 MG/M3 OSHA TWA (SKIN) 0.1 MG/M3 ACGIH TWA (SKIN)
500/10,000 POUNDS SARA SECTION 302 THRESHOLD PLANNING QUANTITY 1 POUND SARA SECTION 304 REPORTABLE QUANTITY 1 POUND CERCLA SECTION 103 REPORTABLE QUANTITY

PHYSICAL DATA

DESCRIPTION: WHITE CRYSTALLINE POWDER ***BOILING POINT:*** DECOMPOSES
MELTING POINT: 392 F (200 C) DECOMPOSES ***SPECIFIC GRAVITY:*** 1.70 @ 20 C
VAPOR PRESSURE: 0.0000002 MMHG @ 25C ***SOLUBILITY IN WATER:*** 0.23 PPM
SOLVENT SOLUBILITY: SOLUBLE IN ACETONE, BENZENE, CARBON TETRACHLORIDE, HEXANE, XYLENE, ESTERS, KETONES, AROMATIC HYDROCARBONS; SPARINGLY SOLUBLE IN ALCOHOLS, PETROLEUM DISTILLATES

FIRE AND EXPLOSION DATA

FIRE AND EXPLOSION HAZARD: NEGLIGIBLE FIRE HAZARD WHEN EXPOSED TO HEAT OR FLAME.
FIREFIGHTING MEDIA: DRY CHEMICAL, CARBON DIOXIDE, HALON, WATER SPRAY OR STANDARD FOAM (1987 EMERGENCY RESPONSE GUIDEBOOK, DOT P 5800.4). FOR LARGER FIRES, USE WATER SPRAY, FOG OR STANDARD FOAM (1987 EMERGENCY RESPONSE GUIDEBOOK, DOT P 5800.4).
FIREFIGHTING: MOVE CONTAINERS FROM FIRE AREA IF POSSIBLE. FIGHT FIRE FROM MAXIMUM DISTANCE. STAY AWAY FROM STORAGE TANK ENDS. DIKE FIRE CONTROL WATER FOR LATER DISPOSAL. DO NOT SCATTER MATERIAL (1987 EMERGENCY RESPONSE GUIDEBOOK, DOT P 5800.4, GUIDE PAGE 55).
USE AGENTS SUITABLE FOR TYPE OF FIRE. COOL CONTAINERS WITH FLOODING AMOUNTS OF WATER. AVOID BREATHING VAPORS OR DUSTS, KEEP UPWIND.
FIRE FIGHTING PHASES: FOR SOLUTIONS USE WATER SPRAY, DRY CHEMICAL, FOAM, OR CARBON DIOXIDE. USE WATER TO KEEP FIRE-EXPOSED CONTAINERS COOL. IF A LEAK OR SPILL HAS NOT IGNITED, USE WATER SPRAY TO DISPERSE THE VAPORS AND TO PROVIDE PROTECTION FOR MEN ATTEMPTING TO STOP A LEAK. WATER SPRAY MAY BE USED TO FLUSH SPILLS AWAY FROM EXPOSURES (NFPA 49, HAZARDOUS CHEMICALS DATA, 1975).

TRANSPORTATION DATA

DEPARTMENT OF TRANSPORTATION HAZARD CLASSIFICATION 49 CFR 172.101: POISON B
DEPARTMENT OF TRANSPORTATION LABELING REQUIREMENTS 49 CFR 172.101 AND SUBPART E: POISON
DEPARTMENT OF TRANSPORTATION PACKAGING REQUIREMENTS: 49 CFR 173.365 EXCEPTIONS: 49 CFR 173.364

TOXICITY

ENDRIN: TOXICITY DATA: 60 MG/KG SKIN-RABBIT LD50; 12 MG/KG SKIN-RAT LD50; 171 MG/KG ORAL-MAN LDLO; 3 MG/KG ORAL-RAT LD50; 7 MG/KG ORAL-RABBIT LD50; 1370 UG/KG ORAL-MOUSE LD50; 16 MG/KG ORAL-GUINEA PIG LD50; 10 MG/KG ORAL-HAMSTER LD50; 5 MG/KG ORAL-CAT LDLO; 3 MG/KG ORAL-MONKEY LD50; 2300 UG/KG INTRAVENOUS-MOUSE LD50; MUTAGENIC DATA (RTECS); REPRODUCTIVE EFFECTS DATA (RTECS). CARCINOGEN STATUS: ANIMAL INADEQUATE EVIDENCE (IARC GROUP-3). ACUTE TOXICITY LEVEL: HIGHLY TOXIC BY DERMAL ABSORPTION AND INGESTION. TARGET EFFECTS: CONVULSANT. ADDITIONAL DATA: STIMULANTS SUCH AS EPINEPHRINE MAY INDUCE VENTRICULAR FIBRILLATION.

HEALTH EFFECTS AND FIRST AID

INHALATION: ENDRIN: CONVULSANT. 200 MG/M3 IMMEDIATELY DANGEROUS TO LIFE OR HEALTH **ACUTE EXPOSURE-** APPROXIMATELY 2000 MG/M3 FOR 1 HOUR WAS LETHAL TO 3 OF 10 RATS EXPOSED. OTHER STUDIES OF MIST AND DUST EXPOSURE REPORTED SIMILAR RESULTS. ENDRIN IS A CHLORINATED CYCLODIENE PESTICIDE. THESE PESTICIDES ARE ABSORBED FROM THE LUNGS AND MAY PRODUCE CENTRAL NERVOUS SYSTEM EFFECTS WITH SYMPTOMS OF MOTOR HYPEREXCITABILITY THAT MAY INCLUDE MUSCLE TWITCHING, MYOCLONIC JERKING, AND CONVULSIVE SEIZURES. THE CONVULSIONS MAY OCCUR WITH PERIODS OF UNCONSCIOUSNESS. OTHER SYMPTOMS MAY INCLUDE HEADACHE, NAUSEA, VOMITING, MALAISE, AND DIZZINESS. IN CASES OF GROSS OVEREXPOSURE, CONVULSIONS MAY OCCUR WITHOUT ANY PRIOR SYMPTOMS. ABNORMAL EEG PATTERNS MAY BE OBSERVED; THESE CHANGES IN EEG PATTERNS MAY PERSIST FOR WEEKS OR MONTHS WHILE NO OTHER OBSERVABLE SIGNS OF POISONING MAY EXIST. **CHRONIC EXPOSURE-** IN ADDITION TO THE EFFECTS DESCRIBED IN ACUTE INHALATION, PROLONGED OR REPEATED EXPOSURE MAY CAUSE HYPERIRRITABILITY, DROWSINESS, AND ANOREXIA. NO OBSERVABLE EFFECTS WERE REPORTED FROM A STUDY OF INDUSTRIAL WORKERS WITH LONG-TERM INTENSIVE WORK WITH ENDRIN. CHRONIC INHALATION OF 15 MG/M3 FOR 7 HOURS PER DAY PER 4 DAYS A WEEK FOR 26 WEEKS PRODUCED NO ADVERSE EFFECTS IN RATS AND MICE; 2 OF 4 RABBITS FAILED TO SURVIVE SIMILAR CONDITIONS.
FIRST AID- REMOVE FROM EXPOSURE AREA TO FRESH AIR IMMEDIATELY. IF BREATHING HAS STOPPED, PERFORM ARTIFICIAL RESPIRATION. KEEP PERSON WARM AND AT REST. TREAT SYMPTOMATICALLY AND SUPPORTIVELY. GET MEDICAL ATTENTION IMMEDIATELY..

SKIN CONTACT: ENDRIN: CONVULSANT/HIGHLY TOXIC. **ACUTE EXPOSURE-** MAY CAUSE IRRITATION TO THE SKIN. A LETHAL DOSE IN RABBITS BY DERMAL ABSORPTION WAS 60 MG/KG. CHLORINATED CYCLODIENE PESTICIDES ARE ABSORBED FROM THE SKIN AND MAY PRODUCE CENTRAL NERVOUS SYSTEM EFFECTS WITH SYMPTOMS OF MOTOR HYPEREXCITABILITY THAT MAY INCLUDE MUSCLE TWITCHING, MYOCLONIC JERKING, AND CONVULSIVE SEIZURES. THE CONVULSIONS MAY OCCUR WITH PERIODS OF UNCONSCIOUSNESS. OTHER SYMPTOMS MAY INCLUDE HEADACHE, NAUSEA, VOMITING, MALAISE, AND DIZZINESS. IN CASES OF GROSS OVEREXPOSURE, CONVULSIONS MAY OCCUR WITHOUT ANY PRIOR SYMPTOMS. ABNORMAL EEG PATTERNS MAY BE OBSERVED; THESE CHANGES IN EEG PATTERNS MAY PERSIST FOR WEEKS OR MONTHS WHILE NO OTHER OBSERVABLE SIGNS OF POISONING MAY EXIST. TWO FATALITIES HAVE OCCURRED AS A RESULT OF OVEREXPOSURE TO ENDRIN. **CHRONIC EXPOSURE-** IN ADDITION TO THE EFFECTS DESCRIBED IN ACUTE EXPOSURE, PROLONGED OR REPEATED EXPOSURE MAY PRODUCE HYPERIRRITABILITY, DROWSINESS, AND ANOREXIA. NO OBSERVABLE EFFECTS WERE REPORTED IN ONE STUDY OF INDUSTRIAL WORKERS WITH LONG-TERM INTENSIVE WORK WITH ENDRIN.
FIRST AID- REMOVE CONTAMINATED CLOTHING AND SHOES IMMEDIATELY. WASH AFFECTED AREA WITH SOAP OR MILD DETERGENT AND LARGE AMOUNTS OF WATER UNTIL NO EVIDENCE OF CHEMICAL REMAINS (APPROXIMATELY 15-20 MINUTES). GET MEDICAL ATTENTION IMMEDIATELY.

EYE CONTACT: ENDRIN: **ACUTE EXPOSURE-** NO DATA AVAILABLE. **CHRONIC EXPOSURE-** NO DATA AVAILABLE.

FIRST AID- WASH EYES IMMEDIATELY WITH LARGE AMOUNTS OF WATER OR NORMAL SALINE, OCCASIONALLY LIFTING UPPER AND LOWER LIDS, UNTIL NO EVIDENCE OF CHEMICAL REMAINS (APPROXIMATELY 15-20 MINUTES). GET MEDICAL ATTENTION IMMEDIATELY.

INGESTION: ENDRIN: CONVULSANT/HIGHLY TOXIC. **ACUTE EXPOSURE-** IN SEVERE POISONING, REPEATED, VIOLENT, EPILEPTIFORM CONVULSIONS MAY OCCUR FOLLOWED BY SEMICONSCIOUSNESS OR COMA. RESPIRATORY FAILURE MAY LEAD TO DEATH. IN NONFATAL CASES, HEADACHE, DIZZINESS, LETHARGY, WEAKNESS, AND ANOREXIA MAY PERSIST FOR TWO TO FOUR WEEKS AFTER POISONING. ADDITIONAL EFFECTS, THAT MAY OCCUR IN LESS SEVERE POISONING, INCLUDE ABDOMINAL DISCOMFORT, NAUSEA, INSOMNIA, AGITATION, AND OCCASIONALLY, SLIGHT MENTAL CONFUSION MAY OCCUR. OTHER SYMPTOMS MAY INCLUDE HIGH FEVER AND TEMPORARY DEAFNESS. A DOSE IN THE RANGE OF 0.2 TO 0.25 MG/KG PRODUCES CONVULSIONS IN MAN; A DOSE OF 1.0 MG/KG MAY RESULT IN REPEATED FITS. A VERY LOW DOSE WAS LETHAL IN ANIMALS. THIS MATERIAL FED TO PREGNANT MICE AND HAMSTERS PRODUCED A HIGH INCIDENCE OF FETAL DEATHS AND CONGENITAL ANOMALIES. **CHRONIC EXPOSURE-** RATS FED A DIET OF 50 OR 100 PPM ENDRIN FOR 2 YEARS DEVELOPED DEGENERATIVE CHANGES IN THE LIVER. ADVERSE EFFECTS OF HYPERSENSITIVITY, AUDIOGENIC SEIZURES, SWELLING OF THE SUBCUTANEOUS TISSUES OF THE HEAD, STARING EYES, BLOODY INCRUSTATIONS OVER THE EYELIDS, CONVULSIONS, AND DEATH WERE REPORTED AT LEVELS OF 25 TO 100 PPM IN ANOTHER CHRONIC INGESTION STUDY OF RATS. MULTIPLE DOSES AS HIGH AS 3.5 MG/KG/DAY FED TO PREGNANT HAMSTERS FOR 10 DAYS PRODUCED FETAL MORTALITY, AND MATERNAL WEIGHT LOSS AND MORTALITY. REPRODUCTIVE EFFECTS HAVE ALSO BEEN REPORTED IN OTHER LABORATORY ANIMALS.

FIRST AID- IF THE PERSON IS CONSCIOUS AND NOT CONVULSING, REMOVE BY GIVING SYRUP OF IPECAC (IF VOMITING OCCURS, KEEP THE HEAD BELOW THE HIPS TO PREVENT ASPIRATION). GIVE ACTIVATED CHARCOAL FOLLOWED BY GASTRIC LAVAGE. FOLLOW WITH A SALINE CATHARTIC. DO NOT GIVE FATS OR OILS. INTESTINAL LAVAGE WITH 20% MANNITOL (200 ML) BY STOMACH TUBE IS ALSO USEFUL. GIVE ARTIFICIAL RESPIRATION WITH OXYGEN IF RESPIRATION IS DEPRESSED (DREISBACH, HANDBOOK OF POISONING, 12TH ED.). TREAT SYMPTOMATICALLY AND SUPPORTIVELY. LAVAGE AND ADMINISTRATION OF OXYGEN SHOULD BE PERFORMED BY QUALIFIED MEDICAL PERSONNEL. GET MEDICAL ATTENTION IMMEDIATELY. ***ANTIDOTE:*** NO SPECIFIC ANTIDOTE. TREAT SYMPTOMATICALLY AND SUPPORTIVELY.

REACTIVITY

REACTIVITY: STABLE UNDER NORMAL TEMPERATURES AND PRESSURES.

INCOMPATIBILITIES: ENDRIN: ACIDS (STRONG): MAY CAUSE EVOLUTION OF HEAT AND FORMATION OF EXPLOSIVE SOLVENT VAPORS. CATALYTICALLY ACTIVE CARRIERS: MAY CAUSE DECOMPOSITION. METAL SALTS: MAY CAUSE DECOMPOSITION. OXIDIZERS (STRONG): MAY CAUSE FIRE AND EXPLOSIONS. PARATHION AND PETROLEUM SOLVENT: MECHANICAL AGITATION OF THE MIXTURE CAUSED SOME VAPORIZATION OF THE SOLVENT; THE SOLVENT VAPOR-AIR MIXTURE EXPLODED.

DECOMPOSITION: WHEN HEATED TO DECOMPOSITION, TOXIC GASES AND VAPORS SUCH AS HYDROGEN CHLORIDE, OTHER VOLATILE CHLORINATED COMPOUNDS AND CARBON MONOXIDE MAY BE RELEASED.

POLYMERIZATION: HAZARDOUS POLYMERIZATION HAS NOT BEEN REPORTED TO OCCUR UNDER NORMAL TEMPERATURES AND PRESSURES.

STORAGE AND DISPOSAL

OBSERVE ALL FEDERAL, STATE AND LOCAL REGULATIONS WHEN STORING OR DISPOSING OF THIS SUBSTANCE. FOR ASSISTANCE, CONTACT THE DISTRICT DIRECTOR OF THE ENVIRONMENTAL PROTECTION AGENCY.

****STORAGE****

STORE IN ACCORDANCE WITH 40 CFR 165 RECOMMENDED PROCEDURES FOR THE DISPOSAL AND STORAGE OF PESTICIDES AND PESTICIDE CONTAINERS.

STORE AWAY FROM INCOMPATIBLE SUBSTANCES.

PROTECT AGAINST PHYSICAL DAMAGE. OUTSIDE OR DETACHED STORAGE IS PREFERRED. INSIDE STORAGE OF SOLUTIONS WITH FLASH POINTS AT OR BELOW 140 F SHOULD BE IN A STANDARD FLAMMABLE LIQUIDS STORAGE ROOM. STORE SOLUTIONS WITH FLASH POINTS ABOVE 140 F IN A COOL, DRY, WELL-VENTILATED LOCATION, AWAY FROM ANY AREA WHERE THE FIRE HAZARD MAY BE ACUTE. SEPARATE FROM OTHER STORAGE. (NFPA 49, HAZARDOUS CHEMICALS DATA, 1975).

THRESHOLD PLANNING QUANTITY (TPQ): THE SUPERFUND AMENDMENTS AND REAUTHORIZATION ACT (SARA) SECTION 302 REQUIRES THAT EACH FACILITY WHERE ANY EXTREMELY HAZARDOUS SUBSTANCE IS PRESENT IN A QUANTITY EQUAL TO OR GREATER THAN THE TPQ ESTABLISHED FOR THAT SUBSTANCE NOTIFY THE STATE EMERGENCY RESPONSE COMMISSION FOR THE STATE IN WHICH IT IS LOCATED. SECTION 303 OF SARA REQUIRES THESE FACILITIES TO PARTICIPATE IN LOCAL EMERGENCY RESPONSE PLANNING (40 CFR 355.30).

****DISPOSAL****

DISPOSAL MUST BE IN ACCORDANCE WITH STANDARDS APPLICABLE TO GENERATORS OF HAZARDOUS WASTE, 40CFR 262. EPA HAZARDOUS WASTE NUMBER P051.

ENDRIN - REGULATORY LEVEL: 0.02 MG/L MATERIALS WHICH CONTAIN THE ABOVE SUBSTANCE AT OR ABOVE THE REGULATORY LEVEL MEET THE EPA CHARACTERISTIC OF TOXICITY, AND MUST BE DISPOSED OF IN ACCORDANCE WITH 40 CFR PART 262. EPA HAZARDOUS WASTE NUMBER D012.

CONDITIONS TO AVOID

MAY BURN BUT DOES NOT IGNITE READILY. CONTAINERS MAY EXPLODE IN HEAT OF FIRE.

SPILL AND LEAK PROCEDURES

SOIL SPILL: DIG HOLDING AREA SUCH AS LAGOON, POND OR PIT FOR CONTAINMENT. DIKE FLOW OF SPILLED MATERIAL USING SOIL OR SANDBAGS OR FOAMED BARRIERS SUCH AS POLYURETHANE OR CONCRETE.

USE CEMENT POWDER OR FLY ASH TO ABSORB LIQUID MASS.

AIR SPILL: KNOCK DOWN VAPORS WITH WATER SPRAY. KEEP UPWIND.

WATER SPILL: USE ACTIVATED CARBON TO ABSORB SPILLED SUBSTANCE THAT IS DISSOLVED.

USE MECHANICAL DREDGES OR LIFTS TO EXTRACT IMMOBILIZED MASSES OF POLLUTION AND PRECIPITATES.

OCCUPATIONAL SPILL: DO NOT TOUCH SPILLED MATERIAL. STOP LEAK IF YOU CAN DO IT WITHOUT RISK. USE WATER SPRAY TO REDUCE VAPORS. FOR SMALL SPILLS, TAKE UP WITH SAND OR OTHER ABSORBENT MATERIAL AND PLACE INTO CONTAINERS FOR LATER DISPOSAL. FOR SMALL DRY SPILLS, WITH A CLEAN SHOVEL PLACE MATERIAL INTO CLEAN, DRY CONTAINERS AND COVER. MOVE CONTAINERS FROM SPILL AREA. FOR LARGER SPILLS, DIKE FAR AHEAD OF SPILL FOR LATER DISPOSAL. KEEP UNNECESSARY PEOPLE AWAY. ISOLATE HAZARD AREA AND DENY ENTRY. VENTILATE CLOSED SPACES BEFORE ENTERING.

REPORTABLE QUANTITY (RQ): 1 POUND THE SUPERFUND AMENDMENTS AND REAUTHORIZATION ACT (SARA) SECTION 304 REQUIRES THAT A RELEASE EQUAL TO OR GREATER THAN THE REPORTABLE QUANTITY FOR THIS SUBSTANCE BE IMMEDIATELY REPORTED TO THE LOCAL EMERGENCY PLANNING COMMITTEE AND THE STATE EMERGENCY RESPONSE COMMISSION (40 CFR 355.40). IF THE RELEASE OF THIS SUBSTANCE IS REPORTABLE UNDER CERCLA SECTION 103, THE NATIONAL RESPONSE CENTER MUST BE NOTIFIED IMMEDIATELY AT (800) 424-8802 OR (202) 426-2675 IN THE METROPOLITAN WASHINGTON, D.C. AREA (40 CFR 302.6).

PROTECTIVE EQUIPMENT

VENTILATION: PROCESS ENCLOSURE RECOMMENDED TO MEET PUBLISHED EXPOSURE LIMITS.

RESPIRATOR: THE FOLLOWING RESPIRATORS AND MAXIMUM USE CONCENTRATIONS ARE RECOMMENDATIONS BY THE U.S. DEPARTMENT OF HEALTH AND HUMAN SERVICES, NIOSH POCKET GUIDE TO CHEMICAL HAZARDS; NIOSH CRITERIA DOCUMENTS OR BY THE U.S. DEPARTMENT OF LABOR, 29 CFR 1910 SUBPART Z. THE SPECIFIC RESPIRATOR SELECTED MUST BE BASED ON CONTAMINATION LEVELS FOUND IN THE WORK PLACE, MUST NOT EXCEED THE WORKING LIMITS OF THE RESPIRATOR AND BE JOINTLY APPROVED BY THE NATIONAL INSTITUTE FOR OCCUPATIONAL SAFETY AND HEALTH AND THE MINE SAFETY AND HEALTH ADMINISTRATION (NIOSH-MSHA).

ENDRIN:

1 MG/M3- ANY CHEMICAL CARTRIDGE RESPIRATOR WITH ORGANIC VAPOR CARTRIDGE(S) IN COMBINATION WITH A DUST, MIST, AND FUME FILTER. ANY SUPPLIED-AIR RESPIRATOR. ANY SELF-CONTAINED BREATHING APPARATUS.

2.5 MG/M3- ANY SUPPLIED-AIR RESPIRATOR OPERATED IN A CONTINUOUS FLOW MODE. ANY POWERED AIR-PURIFYING RESPIRATOR WITH ORGANIC VAPOR CARTRIDGE(S) IN COMBINATION WITH A DUST, MIST AND FUME FILTER.

5 MG/M3- ANY CHEMICAL CARTRIDGE RESPIRATOR WITH A FULL FACEPIECE AND ORGANIC VAPOR CARTRIDGE(S) IN COMBINATION WITH A HIGH-EFFICIENCY PARTICULATE FILTER. ANY SUPPLIED-AIR RESPIRATOR WITH A FULL FACEPIECE. ANY SELF-CONTAINED BREATHING APPARATUS WITH A FULL FACEPIECE. ANY AIR-PURIFYING FULL FACEPIECE RESPRIATOR (GAS MASK) WITH A CHIN-SYLE OR FRONT- OR BACK- MOUNTED ORGANIC VAPOR CANISTER HAVING A HIGH-EFFICIENCY PARTICULATE FILTER. ANY POWERED AIR-PURIFYING RESPIRATOR WITH A TIGHT-FITTING FACEPIECE AND ORGANIC VAPOR CARTRIDGE(S) IN COMBINATION WITH A HIGH-EFFICIENCY PARTICULATE FILTER ANY SUPPLIED-AIR RESPIRATOR WITH A TIGHT-FITTING FACEPIECE OPERATED IN A CONTINUOUS FLOW MODE.

100 MG/M3- ANY SUPPLIED-AIR RESPIRATOR WITH A HALF-MASK AND OPERATED IN A PRESSURE-DEMAND OR OTHER POSITIVE PRESSURE MODE.

200 MG/M3- ANY SUPPLIED-AIR RESPIRATOR WITH A FULL FACEPIECE AND OPERATED IN A PRESSURE-DEMAND OR OTHER POSITIVE PRESSURE MODE.

ESCAPE- ANY AIR-PURIFYING FULL FACEPIECE RESPIRATOR (GAS MASK) WITH A

CHIN-STYLE OR FRONT- OR BACK- MOUNTED ORGANIC VAPOR CANISTER HAVING A HIGH-EFFICIENCY PARTICULATE FILTER. ANY APPROPRIATE ESCAPE-TYPE SELF-CONTAINED BREATHING APPARATUS.
FOR FIREFIGHTING AND OTHER IMMEDIATELY DANGEROUS TO LIFE OR HEALTH CONDITIONS:
SELF-CONTAINED BREATHING APPARATUS WITH FULL FACEPIECE OPERATED IN PRESSURE-DEMAND OR OTHER POSITIVE PRESSURE MODE.
SUPPLIED-AIR RESPIRATOR WITH FULL FACEPIECE AND OPERATED IN PRESSURE-DEMAND OR OTHER POSITIVE PRESSURE MODE IN COMBINATION WITH AN AUXILIARY SELF-CONTAINED BREATHING APPARATUS OPERATED IN PRESSURE-DEMAND OR OTHER POSITIVE PRESSURE MODE.

CLOTHING: EMPLOYEE MUST WEAR APPROPRIATE PROTECTIVE (IMPERVIOUS) CLOTHING AND EQUIPMENT TO PREVENT ANY POSSIBILITY OF SKIN CONTACT WITH THIS SUBSTANCE.

GLOVES: EMPLOYEE MUST WEAR APPROPRIATE PROTECTIVE GLOVES TO PREVENT CONTACT WITH THIS SUBSTANCE.

EYE PROTECTION: EMPLOYEE MUST WEAR SPLASH-PROOF OR DUST-RESISTANT SAFETY GOGGLES AND A FACESHIELD TO PREVENT CONTACT WITH THIS SUBSTANCE.
EMERGENCY WASH FACILITIES: WHERE THERE IS ANY POSSIBILITY THAT AN EMPLOYEE'S EYES AND/OR SKIN MAY BE EXPOSED TO THIS SUBSTANCE, THE EMPLOYER SHOULD PROVIDE AN EYE WASH FOUNTAIN AND QUICK DRENCH SHOWER WITHIN THE IMMEDIATE WORK AREA FOR EMERGENCY USE.

AUTHORIZED BY- OCCUPATIONAL HEALTH SERVICES, INC.
CREATION DATE: 10/04/89 ***REVISION DATE:*** 07/13/90

MATERIAL SAFETY DATA SHEET

OCCUPATIONAL HEALTH SERVICES, INC.
AGRICULTURE AND PESTICIDE DIVISION
450 SEVENTH AVENUE, SUITE 2407
NEW YORK, NEW YORK 10123
1-800-445-MSDS OR (212) 967-1100

EMERGENCY CONTACT:
JOHN S. BRANSFORD, JR. (615) 292-1180

SUBSTANCE IDENTIFICATION

SUBSTANCE: DIPEL 2X
TRADE NAMES/SYNONYMS: PST08603
CERCLA RATINGS (SCALE 0-3): HEALTH=1 FIRE=0 REACTIVITY=0 PERSISTENCE=0
NFPA RATINGS (SCALE 0-4): HEALTH=1 FIRE=0 REACTIVITY=0

COMPONENTS AND CONTAMINANTS

COMPONENT: BACILLUS THURINGIENSIS BERLINER, VAR. KURSTAKI ***PERCENT:*** 6.4%
CAS# 68038-71-1
COMPONENT: TRADE SECRET COMPONENTS ***PERCENT:*** 93.6%
EXPOSURE LIMITS: NO OCCUPATIONAL EXPOSURE LIMITS ESTABLISHED BY OSHA, ACGIH, OR NIOSH.

PHYSICAL DATA

DESCRIPTION: FINE TAN POWDER WITH CHARACTERISTIC ODOR
SPECIFIC GRAVITY: NOT AVAILABLE ***PH:*** 4-6.5 IN 10% SLURRY
SOLUBILITY IN WATER: SLIGHTLY SOLUBLE

FIRE AND EXPLOSION DATA

FIRE AND EXPLOSION HAZARD: NEGLIGIBLE FIRE HAZARD WHEN EXPOSED TO HEAT OR FLAME.

FIREFIGHTING MEDIA: DRY CHEMICAL, CARBON DIOXIDE, HALON, WATER SPRAY OR STANDARD FOAM (1987 EMERGENCY RESPONSE GUIDEBOOK, DOT P 5800.4).
FOR LARGER FIRES, USE WATER SPRAY, FOG OR STANDARD FOAM (1987 EMERGENCY RESPONSE GUIDEBOOK, DOT P 5800.4).

FIREFIGHTING: MOVE CONTAINER FROM FIRE AREA IF POSSIBLE. DO NOT SCATTER SPILLED MATERIAL WITH HIGH PRESSURE WATER STREAMS. DIKE FIRE CONTROL WATER FOR LATER DISPOSAL (1987 EMERGENCY RESPONSE GUIDEBOOK, DOT P 5800.4, GUIDE PAGE 31).
USE AGENTS SUITABLE FOR TYPE OF SURROUNDING FIRE. AVOID BREATHING HAZARDOUS VAPORS, KEEP UPWIND.

TOXICITY

DIPEL 2X: TOXICITY DATA: >10.0 G/KG ORAL-MICE LD50 (ABBOTT LABORATORIES MSDS). CARCINOGEN STATUS: NONE. ACUTE TOXICITY DATA: HIGHLY TOXIC BY INGESTION. TARGET EFFECTS: NO DATA AVAILABLE.

HEALTH EFFECTS AND FIRST AID

INHALATION: DIPEL: IRRITANT. **ACUTE EXPOSURE-** THE BACTERIAL SPORES OF BACILLUS THURINGIENSIS, BERLINER, VARIETY KURSTAKI, ARE CONSIDERED TO BE RELATIVELY NONTOXIC TO HUMANS AND ANIMALS. MICE SURVIVED ONE OR MORE 1-HOUR RESPIRATORY EXPOSURES TO A MIST CONTAINING AS MANY AS 60 BILLION SPORES/M3. INHALATION OF A LARGE CONCENTRATION OF THIS MATERIAL MAY CAUSE IRRITATION OF THE MUCOUS MEMBRANES DUE TO THE PRODUCTS USED AS A CARRIER FOR THE SPORE. **CHRONIC EXPOSURE-** PROLONGED EXPOSURE MAY CAUSE IRRITATION DUE TO THE PRODUCTS USED AS A CARRIER FOR THE SPORES. FIVE VOLUNTEERS INHALED 100 MG OF A POWDERED COMMERICAL PREPARATION CONTAINING APPROXIMATELY 300,000,000 SPORES DAILY FOR 5 DAYS WITHOUT ANY TOXIC EFFECTS.

FIRST AID- REMOVE FROM EXPOSURE AREA TO FRESH AIR IMMEDIATELY. IF BREATHING HAS STOPPED, PERFORM ARTIFICIAL RESPIRATION. KEEP PERSON WARM AND AT REST. TREAT SYMPTOMATICALLY AND SUPPORTIVELY. GET MEDICAL ATTENTION IMMEDIATELY.

SKIN CONTACT: DIPEL: **ACUTE EXPOSURE-** THE BACTERIAL SPORES OF BACILLUS THURINGIENSIS BERLINER, VARIETY KURSTAKI, ARE CONSIDERED RELATIVELY NONTOXIC TO MAN AND ANIMALS. THERE ARE NO DATA AVAILABLE ON SYSTEMIC POISONING BY DERMAL ABSORPTION. EXPOSURE TO A LARGE CONCENTRATION OF THE DUST MAY CAUSE IRRITATION DUE TO THE PRODUCTS USED AS A CARRIER FOR THE SPORE. **CHRONIC EXPOSURE-** PROLONGED EXPOSURE TO A LARGE CONCENTRATION OF DUST MAY CAUSE IRRITATION DUE TO THE PRODUCTS USED AS A CARRIER FOR THE SPORE.

FIRST AID- REMOVE CONTAMINATED CLOTHING AND SHOES IMMEDIATELY. WASH AFFECTED AREA WITH SOAP OR MILD DETERGENT AND LARGE AMOUNTS OF WATER UNTIL NO EVIDENCE OF CHEMICAL REMAINS (APPROXIMATELY 15-20 MINUTES). GET MEDICAL ATTENTION IMMEDIATELY.

EYE CONTACT: DIPEL 2X: **ACUTE EXPOSURE-** MAY CAUSE IRRITATION. **CHRONIC EXPOSURE-** PROLONGED EXPOSURE MAY CAUSE IRRITATION.

FIRST AID- WASH EYES IMMEDIATELY WITH LARGE AMOUNTS OF WATER OR NORMAL SALINE, OCCASIONALLY LIFTING UPPER AND LOWER LIDS, UNTIL NO EVIDENCE OF CHEMICAL REMAINS (APPROXIMATELY 15-20 MINUTES). GET MEDICAL ATTENTION IMMEDIATELY.

INGESTION: DIPEL 2X: **ACUTE EXPOSURE-** THE BACTERIAL SPORES OF BACILLUS THURINGIENSIS BERLINER, VARIETY KURSTAKI, ARE CONSIDERED RELATIVELY NONTOXIC TO MAN AND ANIMALS. HOWEVER, ANOTHER VARIETY OF BACILLUS THURINGIENSIS, GALLERIAE, PRODUCED NAUSEA, VOMITING, DIARRHEA, TENESMUS, COLIC-LIKE PAINS IN THE ABDOMEN, AND FEVER IN THREE OUT OF FOUR PEOPLE WHEN THEY INGESTED CONTAMINATED FOOD CONTAINING CONCENTRATIONS BETWEEN ONE HUNDRED THOUSAND TO ONE BILLION CELLS PER GRAM. THE INCUBATION PERIOD WAS 8 HOURS. INGESTION OF A LARGE CONCENTRATION OF THIS PRODUCT MAY CAUSE NAUSEA AND OTHER GASTROINTESTINAL DISTURBANCES DUE TO THE PRODUCTS USE AS AN CARRIER FOR THE SPORES. **CHRONIC EXPOSURE-** 18 PEOPLE INGESTED 1 GRAM OF A COMMERCIAL PREPARATION CONTAINING APPROXIMATELY 3 BILLION SPORES DAILY FOR 5 DAYS ON ALTERNATE DAYS WITHOUT ANY TOXIC EFFECTS.

FIRST AID- GIVE WATER OR FLUIDS. EMESIS IS NOT NECESSARY. TREAT SUPPORTIVELY AND SYMPTOMATICALLY. IF IRRITATION OR DIGESTIVE UPSET OCCURS, GET MEDICAL ATTENTION.

ANTIDOTE: NO SPECIFIC ANTIDOTE. TREAT SYMPTOMATICALLY AND SUPPORTIVELY.

REACTIVITY

REACTIVITY: STABLE UNDER NORMAL TEMPERATURES AND PRESSURES.
INCOMPATIBILITIES: DIPEL 2X: ALKALINITY: INACTIVATE.
DECOMPOSITION: NO DATA AVAILABLE.
POLYMERIZATION: HAZARDOUS POLYMERIZATION HAS NOT BEEN REPORTED TO OCCUR UNDER NORMAL TEMPERATURES AND PRESSURES.

CONDITIONS TO AVOID

MAY BURN BUT DOES NOT IGNITE READILY. AVOID CONTACT WITH STRONG OXIDIZERS, EXCESSIVE HEAT, SPARKS, OR OPEN FLAME.

SPILL AND LEAK PROCEDURES

OCCUPATIONAL SPILL: STOP LEAK IF YOU CAN DO IT WITHOUT RISK. FOR SMALL SPILLS, TAKE UP WITH SAND OR OTHER ABSORBENT MATERIAL AND PLACE INTO CLEAN, DRY CONTAINERS FOR LATER DISPOSAL. KEEP UNNECESSARY PEOPLE AWAY. ISOLATE HAZARD AREA AND DENY ENTRY.

PROTECTIVE EQUIPMENT

VENTILATION: PROVIDE GENERAL DILUTION VENTILATION.

RESPIRATOR: THE FOLLOWING RESPIRATORS ARE RECOMMENDED BASED ON INFORMATION FOUND IN THE PHYSICAL DATA, TOXICITY AND HEALTH EFFECTS SECTIONS. THEY ARE RANKED IN ORDER FROM MINIMUM TO MAXIMUM RESPIRATORY PROTECTION. THE SPECIFIC RESPIRATOR SELECTED MUST BE BASED ON CONTAMINATION LEVELS FOUND IN THE WORK PLACE, MUST NOT EXCEED THE WORKING LIMITS OF THE RESPIRATOR AND BE JOINTLY APPROVED BY THE NATIONAL INSTITUTE FOR OCCUPATIONAL SAFETY AND HEALTH AND THE MINE SAFETY AND HEALTH ADMINISTRATION (NIOSH-MSHA).

CHEMICAL CARTRIDGE RESPIRATOR WITH AN ORGANIC VAPOR CARTRIDGE(S) WITH A FULL FACEPIECE AND ORGANIC VAPOR CARTRIDGE(S) IN COMBINATION WITH A DUST AND MIST FILTER.

POWERED AIR-PURIFYING RESPIRATOR WITH A TIGHT-FITTING FACEPIECE AND ORGANIC VAPOR CARTRIDGE(S) IN COMBINATION WITH A HIGH-EFFICIENCY PARTICULATE FILTER.

TYPE 'C' SUPPLIED-AIR RESPIRATOR WITH A FULL FACEPIECE OPERATED IN A PRESSURE-DEMAND OR OTHER POSITIVE PRESSURE MODE.

SELF-CONTAINED BREATHING APPARATUS WITH A FULL FACEPIECE OPERATED IN PRESSURE-DEMAND OR OTHER POSITIVE PRESSURE MODE.

FOR FIREFIGHTING AND OTHER IMMEDIATELY DANGEROUS TO LIFE OR HEALTH CONDITIONS:

SELF-CONTAINED BREATHING APPARATUS WITH FULL FACEPIECE OPERATED IN PRESSURE-DEMAND OR OTHER POSITIVE PRESSURE MODE.

SUPPLIED-AIR RESPIRATOR WITH FULL FACEPIECE AND OPERATED IN PRESSURE-DEMAND OR OTHER POSITIVE PRESSURE MODE IN COMBINATION WITH AN AUXILIARY SELF-CONTAINED BREATHING APPARATUS OPERATED IN PRESSURE-DEMAND OR OTHER POSITIVE PRESSURE MODE.

CLOTHING: EMPLOYEE MUST WEAR APPROPRIATE PROTECTIVE (IMPERVIOUS) CLOTHING AND EQUIPMENT TO PREVENT REPEATED OR PROLONGED SKIN CONTACT WITH THIS SUBSTANCE.

GLOVES: EMPLOYEE MUST WEAR APPROPRIATE PROTECTIVE GLOVES TO PREVENT CONTACT WITH THIS SUBSTANCE.

EYE PROTECTION: EMPLOYEE MUST WEAR SPLASH-PROOF OR DUST-RESISTANT SAFETY GOGGLES TO PREVENT EYE CONTACT WITH THIS SUBSTANCE.

EMERGENCY EYE WASH: WHERE THERE IS ANY POSSIBILITY THAT AN EMPLOYEE'S EYES MAY BE EXPOSED TO THIS SUBSTANCE, THE EMPLOYER SHOULD PROVIDE AN EYE WASH FOUNTAIN WITHIN THE IMMEDIATE WORK AREA FOR EMERGENCY USE.

AUTHORIZED BY- OCCUPATIONAL HEALTH SERVICES, INC.

CREATION DATE: 10/04/89 ***REVISION DATE:*** 05/18/90

MATERIAL SAFETY DATA SHEET

OCCUPATIONAL HEALTH SERVICES, INC.
AGRICULTURE AND PESTICIDE DIVISION
450 SEVENTH AVENUE, SUITE 2407
NEW YORK, NEW YORK 10123
1-800-445-MSDS OR (212) 967-1100

EMERGENCY CONTACT:
JOHN S. BRANSFORD, JR. (615) 292-1180

SUBSTANCE IDENTIFICATION

CAS-NUMBER 2104-64-5

SUBSTANCE: EPN

TRADE NAMES/SYNONYMS: PHOSPHONOTHIOIC ACID, PHENYL-, O-ETHYL O-(4-NITROPHENYL)ESTER; PHOSPHONOTHIOIC ACID, PHENYL-, O-ETHYL O-(P-NITROPHENYL)ESTER; PHOSPHONOTHIOIC ACID, PHENYL ETHYL P-NITROPHENYL ESTER; PHENYL PHOSPHONOTHIOIC ACID, O-ETHYL O-(4-NITROPHENYL)ESTER; PHENYLPHOSPHONOTHIOIC ACID, O-ETHYL O-(P-NITROPHENYL)ESTER; PHENYLPHOSPHONOTHIOIC ACID, ETHYL P-NITROPHENYL ESTER; O-ETHYL O-P-NITOPHENYL PHENYLPHOSPHONOTHIOATE; ETHYL P-NITOPHENYL BENZENETHIOPHOSPHONATE; O-4-NITROPHENYL PHENYLPHOSPHONOTHIOATE; O-ETHYL O-(4-NITROPHENYL)PHENYLPHOSPHONOTHIOATE; O-ETHYL O-(P-NITROPHENYL) PHENYLPHOSPHONOTHIOATE; ENT 17 298; C14H14NO4PS; PST08650

CHEMICAL FAMILY: ORGANOPHOSPHATE

MOLECULAR FORMULA: C14-H14-N-O4-P-S

MOLECULAR WEIGHT: 323.32

CERCLA RATINGS (SCALE 0-3): HEALTH=3 FIRE=0 REACTIVITY=0 PERSISTENCE=2

NFPA RATINGS (SCALE 0-4): HEALTH=4 FIRE=0 REACTIVITY=0

COMPONENTS AND CONTAMINANTS

COMPONENT: EPN ***PERCENT:*** 100
CAS# 2104-64-5

EXPOSURE LIMITS: EPN: 0.5 MG/M3 OSHA TWA (SKIN) 0.5 MG/M3 ACGIH TWA (SKIN) 100/10,000 POUNDS SARA SECTION 302 THRESHOLD PLANNING QUANTITY 1 POUND SARA SECTION 304 REPORTABLE QUANTITY

PHYSICAL DATA

DESCRIPTION: LIGHT YELLOW CRYSTALLINE POWDER

BOILING POINT: 419 F (215 C) 5 MMHG ***MELTING POINT:*** 98 F (36 C)

SPECIFIC GRAVITY: 1.268 ***VAPOR PRESSURE:*** 0.0003 MMHG @ 100 C

SOLUBILITY IN WATER: PRACTICALLY INSOL

SOLVENT SOLUBILITY: SOLUBLE IN BENZENE, ACETONE, KETONES, TOLUENE, XYLENE, ISOPROPANOL, METHANOL

FIRE AND EXPLOSION DATA

FIRE AND EXPLOSION HAZARD: NEGLIGIBLE FIRE HAZARD WHEN EXPOSED TO HEAT OR FLAME.

FIREFIGHTING MEDIA: DRY CHEMICAL, CARBON DIOXIDE, HALON, WATER SPRAY OR STANDARD FOAM (1987 EMERGENCY RESPONSE GUIDEBOOK, DOT P 5800.4). FOR LARGER FIRES, USE WATER SPRAY, FOG OR STANDARD FOAM (1987 EMERGENCY RESPONSE GUIDEBOOK, DOT P 5800.4).

FIREFIGHTING: MOVE CONTAINERS FROM FIRE AREA IF POSSIBLE. FIGHT FIRE FROM MAXIMUM DISTANCE. STAY AWAY FROM STORAGE TANK ENDS. DIKE FIRE CONTROL WATER FOR LATER DISPOSAL. DO NOT SCATTER MATERIAL (1987 EMERGENCY RESPONSE GUIDEBOOK, DOT P 5800.4, GUIDE PAGE 55). EXTINGUISH USING AGENT SUITABLE FOR TYPE OF SURROUNDING FIRE. AVOID BREATHING VAPORS AND DUSTS. KEEP UPWIND.

TRANSPORTATION DATA

DEPARTMENT OF TRANSPORTATION HAZARD CLASSIFICATION 49 CFR 172.101: POISON B

DEPARTMENT OF TRANSPORTATION LABELING REQUIREMENTS 49 CFR 172.101 AND SUBPART E: POISON

DEPARTMENT OF TRANSPORTATION PACKAGING REQUIREMENTS: 49 CFR 173.365 EXCEPTIONS: 49 CFR 173.364

TOXICITY

EPN: TOXICITY DATA: 30 MG/KG SKIN-RABBIT LD50; 25 MG/KG SKIN-RAT LD50; 45 MG/KG SKIN-CAT LD50; 348 MG/KG SKIN-MOUSE LD50; 7 MG/KG ORAL-RAT LD50; 12200 UG/KG ORAL-MOUSE LD50; 20 MG/KG ORAL-DOG LD50; 22900 UG/KG SUBCUTANEOUS-MOUSE LD50; 20 MG/KG INTRAPERITONEAL-GUINEA PIG LDLO; 7200 UG/KG INTRAPERITONEAL-RAT LD50; 8400 UG/KG INTRAPERITONEAL-MOUSE LD50; 20 MG/KG INTRAPERITONEAL-RABBIT LDLO; 35 MG/KG INTRAPERITONEAL-DOG LDLO; REPRODUCTIVE EFFECTS DATA (RTECS). CARCINOGEN STATUS: NONE. ACUTE TOXICITY LEVEL: HIGHLY TOXIC BY DERMAL ABSORPTION AND INGESTION. TARGET EFFECTS: CHOLINESTERASE INHIBITOR; NEUROTOXIN. AT INCREASED RISK FROM EXPOSURE: PERSONS WITH RESPIRATORY AILMENTS, RECENT EXPOSURE TO CHOLINESTERASE INHIBITORS OR IMPAIRED CHOLINESTERASE PRODUCTION, OR LIVER MALFUNCTION.* ADDITIONAL DATA: EPN POTENTIATES THE TOXICITY OF THE INSECTICIDE, MALATHION. MAY CROSS THE PLACENTA. HIGH ENVIRONMENTAL TEMPERATURES OR EXPOSURE OF THE CHEMICAL TO VISIBLE OR ULTRAVIOLET LIGHT MAY ENHANCE THE TOXICITY. INTERACTIONS WITH MEDICATIONS MAY OCCUR.*

* MAY BE BASED ON GENERAL INFORMATION ON ORGANOPHOSPHATES.

HEALTH EFFECTS AND FIRST AID

INHALATION: EPN: 50 MG/M3 IMMEDIATELY DANGEROUS TO LIFE OR HEALTH. SEE INFORMATION ON ORGANOPHOSPHATES.

ORGANOPHOSPHATES: CHOLINESTERASE INHIBITOR. ACUTE EXPOSURE- WHEN INHALED, THE FIRST EFFECTS OF CHOLINESTERASE INHIBITORS ARE USUALLY RESPIRATORY AND MAY INCLUDE NASAL HYPEREMIA AND WATERY DISCHARGE, COUGH, CHEST DISCOMFORT, DYSPNEA, AND WHEEZING DUE TO INCREASED BRONCHIAL SECRETIONS AND BRONCHOCONSTRICTION. IF SUFFICIENT AMOUNTS ARE ABSORBED, OTHER SYSTEMIC EFFECTS MAY BEGIN WITHIN A FEW MINUTES OR BE DELAYED FOR UP TO 12 HOURS. SYMPTOMS MAY INCLUDE PALLOR, NAUSEA, VOMITING, DIARRHEA, ABDOMINAL CRAMPS, HEADACHE, DIZZINESS, OCULAR PAIN, BLURRED VISION, MIOSIS OR IN SOME CASES, ESPECIALLY INITIALLY, MYDRIASIS, LACRIMATION, SALIVATION, SWEATING, AND CONFUSION. OTHER REPORTED CENTRAL NERVOUS SYSTEM OR NEUROMUSCULAR EFFECTS MAY INCLUDE ATAXIA, SLURRED SPEECH, AREFLEXIA, WEAKNESS, FATIGUE, FASCICULATIONS, TWITCHING, TREMORS POSSIBLY OF THE TONGUE AND EYELIDS, AND EVENTUALLY PARALYSIS OF THE EXTREMITIES AND POSSIBLY OF THE RESPIRATORY MUSCLES. IN SEVERE CASES THERE MAY ALSO BE INVOLUNTARY DEFECATION AND URINATION, CYANOSIS, PSYCHOSIS, HYPERGLYCEMIA, ACUTE

PANCREATITIS, CARDIAC IRREGULARITIES, PULMONARY EDEMA, UNCONSCIOUSNESS, CONVULSIONS, AND COMA. DEATH IS PRIMARILY DUE TO RESPIRATORY FAILURE, ALTHOUGH CARDIOVASCULAR EFFECTS INCLUDING CARDIAC ARREST MAY ALSO BE IMPLICATED. LONG TERM SEQUELAE ARE RARE BUT MAY INCLUDE NEUROPSYCHIATRIC DISORDERS AND MYOPATHY WITH MUSCLE TENDERNESS. SOME ORGANOPHOSPHATES MAY CAUSE A DELAYED NEUROPATHY BEGINNING 1-4 WEEKS AFTER AN ACUTE EXPOSURE WHICH MAY OR MAY NOT HAVE CAUSED ACUTE CHOLINERGIC EFFECTS. NUMBNESS, TINGLING, WEAKNESS AND CRAMPING BEGINNING SYMMETRICALLY IN THE LOWER LIMBS MAY PROGRESS TO ATAXIA AND PARALYSIS. IN SEVERE CASES, UPPER LIMB INVOLVEMENT IS POSSIBLE AND FLACCID PARALYSIS MAY PROGRESS TO SPASTIC PARALYSIS WITH EXAGGERATED REFLEXES. IMPROVEMENT MAY OCCUR OVER MONTHS TO YEARS, BUT SOME RESIDUAL IMPAIRMENT USUALLY REMAINS. **CHRONIC EXPOSURE-** REPEATED OR PROLONGED EXPOSURE MAY RESULT IN THE EFFECTS OF ACUTE EXPOSURE INCLUDING THE DELAYED NEUROPATHY. OTHER EFFECTS REPORTED IN WORKERS REPEATEDLY EXPOSED INCLUDE IMPAIRED MEMORY AND CONCENTRATION, ACUTE PSYCHOSIS, SEVERE DEPRESSIONS, IRRITABILTY, CONFUSION, APATHY, EMOTIONAL LABILITY, SOCIAL WITHDRAWAL, CONFUSION, HEADACHE, SPEECH DIFFICULTIES, DELAYED REACTION TIMES, SPATIAL DISORIENTATION, NIGHTMARES, SLEEPWALKING, AND DROWSINESS OR INSOMNIA. AN INFLUENZA-LIKE CONDITION WITH HEADACHE, NAUSEA, WEAKNESS, ANOREXIA AND MALAISE HAS ALSO BEEN REPORTED.

FIRST AID- REMOVE FROM EXPOSURE AREA TO FRESH AIR IMMEDIATELY. IF BREATHING HAS STOPPED, GIVE ARTIFICIAL RESPIRATION. MAINTAIN AIRWAY AND BLOOD PRESSURE AND ADMINISTER OXYGEN IF AVAILABLE. KEEP AFFECTED PERSON WARM AND AT REST. TREAT SYMPTOMATICALLY AND SUPPORTIVELY. ADMINISTRATION OF OXYGEN SHOULD BE PERFORMED BY QUALIFIED PERSONNEL. GET MEDICAL ATTENTION IMMEDIATELY.

SKIN CONTACT: EPN: HIGHLY TOXIC. SEE INFORMATION ON ORGANOPHOSPHATES. ORGANOPHOSPHATES: CHOLINESTERASE INHIBITOR. **ACUTE EXPOSURE-** LOCALIZED SWEATING AND FASCICULATIONS MAY OCCUR AT THE SITE OF CONTACT. IF SUFFICIENT AMOUNTS ARE ABSORBED, OTHER EFFECTS OF CHOLINESTERASE INHIBITION AS DESCRIBED IN ACUTE INHALATION MAY OCCUR. SYMPTOMS MAY BE DELAYED 2-3 HOURS, BUT USUALLY NO MORE THAN 12 HOURS. THE RATE OF ABSORPTION IS INCREASED BY THE PRESENCE OF DERMATITIS OR HIGH AMBIENT TEMPERATURES. DELAYED NEUROPATHY IS ALSO POSSIBLE. **CHRONIC EXPOSURE-** REPEATED OR PROLONGED EXPOSURE MAY CAUSE EFFECTS AS DESCRIBED IN ACUTE EXPOSURE. SOME ORGANOPHOSPHATES MAY CAUSE SENSITIZATION.

FIRST AID- REMOVE CONTAMINATED CLOTHING IMMEDIATELY. WASH CONTAMINATED AREAS WITH SOAP AND WATER FOLLOWED BY ALCOHOL (ARENA, POISONING, 4TH ED.). EMERGENCY PERSONNEL SHOULD WEAR GLOVES AND AVOID CONTAMINATION. TREAT RESPIRATORY DIFFICULTY WITH ARTIFICIAL RESPIRATION. GET MEDICAL ATTENTION IMMEDIATELY.

EYE CONTACT: EPN: SEE INFORMATION ON ORGANOPHOSPHATES. ORGANOPHOSPHATES: CHOLINESTERASE INHIBITOR. **ACUTE EXPOSURE-** DIRECT CONTACT MAY CAUSE PAIN, HYPEREMIA, LACRIMATION, TWITCHING OF THE EYELIDS, MIOSIS, AND CILIARY MUSCLE SPASM WITH LOSS OF ACCOMODATION, BLURRED OR DIMMED VISION AND BROWACHE. SOMETIMES MYDRIASIS MAY OCCUR INSTEAD OF MIOSIS. WITH SUFFICIENT EXPOSURE, OTHER SYMPTOMS OF CHOLINESTERASE INHIBITION AS DESCRIBED IN ACUTE INHALATION MAY OCCUR. **CHRONIC EXPOSURE-** REPEATED OR PROLONGED EXPOSURE MAY CAUSE EFFECTS AS DESCRIBED IN ACUTE EXPOSURE. SOME COMPOUNDS HAVE CAUSED TOXIC EFFECTS ON THE CRYSTALLINE LENS, CONJUNCTIVAL THICKENING AND OBSTRUCTION OF THE NASOLACRIMAL CANALS WHEN USED AS MIOTIC EYEDROPS.

FIRST AID- IRRIGATE EYES WITH WATER OR SALINE SOLUTION. IF SYMPTOMS OF POISONING OCCUR, TREAT RESPIRATORY DIFFICULTY WITH ARTIFICIAL RESPIRATION AND OXYGEN. OBSERVE PATIENT FOR AT LEAST 24-36 HOURS (GOSSELIN, CLINICAL TOXICOLOGY OF COMMERCIAL PRODUCTS, 5TH ED.). GET MEDICAL ATTENTION IMMEDIATELY. OXYGEN SHOULD BE ADMINISTERED BY QUALIFIED MEDICAL PERSONNEL.

INGESTION: EPN: NEUROTOXIN/HIGHLY TOXIC. SINGLE ORAL DOSES AS LOW AS 25 MG/KG WERE NEUROTOXIC TO HENS. CHRONIC ORAL DOSES OF 0.1 TO 10 MG/KG/DAY PRODUCED DELAYED NEUROTOXICITY IN HENS. SEE INFORMATION ON ORGANOPHOSPHATES. ORGANOPHOSPHATES: CHOLINESTERASE INHIBITOR. **ACUTE EXPOSURE-** WHEN INGESTED, THE FIRST EFFECTS MAY BE NAUSEA, VOMITING, ANOREXIA, ABDOMINAL CRAMPS AND DIARRHEA. GASTROINTESTINAL ABSORPTION MAY CAUSE SYMPTOMS OF CHOLINESTERASE INHIBITION AS DESCRIBED IN ACUTE INHALATION. SYMPTOMS MAY BEGIN WITHIN MINUTES OR BE DELAYED FOR HOURS. DELAYED EFFECTS INCLUDING NEUROPATHY MAY ALSO OCCUR. **CHRONIC EXPOSURE-** REPEATED INGESTION MAY CAUSE EFFECTS AS DESCRIBED IN ACUTE EXPOSURE.

FIRST AID- IF PERSON IS ALERT AND RESPIRATION IS NOT DEPRESSED, GIVE SYRUP OF IPECAC FOLLOWED BY WATER (IF VOMITING OCCURS, KEEP HEAD BELOW HIPS TO PREVENT ASPIRATION). IF CONSCIOUSNESS LEVEL DECLINES OR VOMITING HAS NOT OCCURRED IN 15 MINUTES EMPTY STOMACH BY GASTRIC LAVAGE WITH THE AID OF CUFFED ENDOTRACHEAL TUBE USING ISOTONIC SALINE OR 5% SODIUM BICARBONATE FOLLOW WITH ACTIVATED CHARCOAL. ESTABLISH AND MAINTAIN AIRWAY. TREAT RESPIRATORY DIFFICULTY WITH ARTIFICIAL RESPIRATION AND OXYGEN. DO NOT GIVE MORPHINE, AMINOPHYLLINE, PHENOTHIAZINES, RESERPINE, FUROSEMIDE, OR ETHACRYNIC ACID (MORGAN, RECOGNITION AND MANAGEMENT OF PESTICIDE POISONINGS, 3RD ED.). TREAT SYMPTOMATICALLY AND SUPPORTIVELY. ADMINISTRATION OF OXYGEN AND LAVAGE MUST BE PERFORMED BY QUALIFIED MEDICAL PERSONNEL. GET MEDICAL ATTENTION IMMEDIATELY.

ANTIDOTE: THE FOLLOWING ANTIDOTE(S) HAVE BEEN RECOMMENDED. HOWEVER, THE DECISION AS TO WHETHER THE SEVERITY OF POISONING REQUIRES ADMINISTRATION OF ANY ANTIDOTE AND ACTUAL DOSE REQUIRED SHOULD BE MADE BY QUALIFIED MEDICAL PERSONNEL.

FOR CHOLINESTERASE INHIBITORS: ESTABLISH CLEAR AIRWAY AND TISSUE OXYGENATION BY ASPIRATION OF SECRETIONS, AND IF NECESSARY, BY ASSISTED PULMONARY VENTILATION WITH OXYGEN. IMPROVE TISSUE OXYGENATION AS MUCH AS POSSIBLE BEFORE ADMINISTERING ATROPINE TO MINIMIZE THE RISK OF VENTRICULAR FIBRILLATION. ADMINISTER ATROPINE SULFATE INTRAVENOUSLY, OR INTRAMUSCULARLY IF IV INJECTION IS NOT POSSIBLE. IN MODERATELY SEVERE POISONING ADMINISTER ATROPINE SULFATE, 0.4-2.0 MG REPEATED EVERY 15 MINUTES UNTIL ATROPINIZATION IS ACHIEVED (TACHYCARDIA, FLUSHING, DRY MOUTH, MYDRIASIS). MAINTAIN ATROPINIZATION BY REPEATED DOSES FOR 2-12 HOURS, OR LONGER, DEPENDING ON THE SEVERITY OF POISONING. THE APPEARANCE OF RALES IN THE LUNG BASES, MIOSIS, SALIVATION, NAUSEA, BRADYCARDIA, ARE ALL INDICATIONS OF INADEQUATE ATROPINIZATION. SEVERELY POISONED INDIVIDUALS MAY EXHIBIT REMARKABLE TOLERANCE TO ATROPINE; TWO OR MORE TIMES THE DOSAGES SUGGESTED ABOVE MAY BE NEEDED. PERSONS NOT POISONED OR ONLY SLIGHTLY POISONED, HOWEVER, MAY DEVELOP SIGNS OF ATROPINE TOXICITY FROM SUCH LARGE DOSAGES: FEVER, MUSCLE FIBRILLATIONS, AND DELIRIUM ARE THE MAIN SIGNS OF ATROPINE TOXICITY. IF THESE SIGNS APPEAR WHILE THE PATIENT IS FULLY ATROPINIZED, ATROPINE ADMINISTRATION SHOULD BE DISCONTINUED, AT LEAST TEMPORARILY. OBSERVE TREATED PATIENTS CLOSELY AT LEAST 24 HOURS TO INSURE THAT SYMPTOMS (POSSIBLY PULMONARY EDEMA) DO NOT RECUR AS ATROPINIZATION WEARS OFF. IN VERY SEVERE POISONINGS, METABOLIC DISPOSITION OF TOXICANT MAY REQUIRE SEVERAL HOURS OR DAYS DURING WHICH ATROPINIZATION MUST BE MAINTAINED. MARKEDLY LOWER LEVELS OF URINARY METABOLITES INDICATE THAT ATROPINE DOSAGE CAN BE TAPERED OFF. AS DOSAGE IS REDUCED, CHECK THE LUNG BASES FREQUENTLY FOR RALES. IF RALES ARE HEARD OR OTHER SYMPTOMS RETURN, RE-ESTABLISH ATROPINIZATION PROMPTLY (MORGAN, RECOGNITION AND MANAGEMENT OF PESTICIDE POISONINGS, 3RD ED.). ADMINISTRATION OF ANTIDOTE MUST BE PERFORMED BY QUALIFIED MEDICAL PERSONNEL.

IN CASES OF SEVERE POISONING BY ORGANOPHOSPHATE PESTICIDES IN WHICH RESPIRATORY DEPRESSION, MUSCLE WEAKNESS AND TWITCHINGS ARE SEVERE, GIVE PRALIDOXIME (PROTOPAM-AYERST, 2-PAM), 1.0 GRAM INTRAVENOUSLY AT NO MORE THAN 0.5 GRAM PER MINUTE. DOSAGE OF PRALIDOXIME MAY BE REPEATED IN 1-2 HOURS, THEN AT 10-12 HOUR INTERVALS IF NEEDED. IN VERY SEVERE POISONINGS, DOSAGE RATES MAY BE DOUBLED. TREATMENT WITH PRALIDOXIME WILL BE MOST EFFECTIVE IF GIVEN WITHIN THIRTY-SIX HOURS AFTER POISONING (MORGAN, RECOGNITION AND MANAGEMENT OF PESTICIDE POISONINGS, 3RD ED.). ANTIDOTE SHOULD BE ADMINISTERED BY QUALIFIED MEDICAL PERSONNEL.

REACTIVITY

REACTIVITY: STABLE UNDER NORMAL TEMPERATURES AND PRESSURES.

INCOMPATIBILITIES: EPN: SOME FORMS OF PLASTICS, RUBBER AND COATINGS: MAY ATTACK. STRONG OXIDIZERS: MAY CAUSE FIRE AND EXPLOSION. ALKALINE CONDITION: MAY CAUSE HYDROLYSIS.

DECOMPOSITION: THERMAL DECOMPOSITION MAY RELEASE TOXIC OXIDES OF NITROGEN, PHOSPHORUS, SULFUR AND CARBON.

POLYMERIZATION: HAZARDOUS POLYMERIZATION HAS NOT BEEN REPORTED TO OCCUR UNDER NORMAL TEMPERATURES AND PRESSURES.

STORAGE AND DISPOSAL

OBSERVE ALL FEDERAL, STATE AND LOCAL REGULATIONS WHEN STORING OR DISPOSING OF THIS SUBSTANCE. FOR ASSISTANCE, CONTACT THE DISTRICT DIRECTOR OF THE ENVIRONMENTAL PROTECTION AGENCY.

****STORAGE****

STORE IN ACCORDANCE WITH 40 CFR 165 RECOMMENDED PROCEDURES FOR THE DISPOSAL AND STORAGE OF PESTICIDES AND PESTICIDE CONTAINERS.
STORE AWAY FROM INCOMPATIBLE SUBSTANCES.
STORE AT 65-100 F (18-38 C).

THRESHOLD PLANNING QUANTITY (TPQ): THE SUPERFUND AMENDMENTS AND REAUTHORIZATION ACT (SARA) SECTION 302 REQUIRES THAT EACH FACILITY WHERE ANY EXTREMELY HAZARDOUS SUBSTANCE IS PRESENT IN A QUANTITY EQUAL TO OR GREATER THAN THE TPQ ESTABLISHED FOR THAT SUBSTANCE NOTIFY THE STATE EMERGENCY RESPONSE COMMISSION FOR THE STATE IN WHICH IT IS LOCATED. SECTION 303 OF SARA REQUIRES THESE FACILITIES TO PARTICIPATE IN LOCAL EMERGENCY RESPONSE PLANNING (40 CFR 355.30).

DISPOSAL

DISPOSAL MUST BE IN ACCORDANCE WITH 40 CFR 165 RECOMMENDED PROCEDURES FOR THE DISPOSAL AND STORAGE OF PESTICIDES AND PESTICIDE CONTAINERS.

CONDITIONS TO AVOID

NONE REPORTED.

SPILL AND LEAK PROCEDURES

OCCUPATIONAL SPILL: DO NOT TOUCH SPILLED MATERIAL. STOP LEAK IF YOU CAN DO IT WITHOUT RISK. USE WATER SPRAY TO REDUCE VAPORS. FOR SMALL SPILLS, TAKE UP WITH SAND OR OTHER ABSORBENT MATERIAL AND PLACE INTO CONTAINERS FOR LATER DISPOSAL. FOR SMALL DRY SPILLS, WITH A CLEAN SHOVEL PLACE MATERIAL INTO CLEAN, DRY CONTAINERS AND COVER. MOVE CONTAINERS FROM SPILL AREA. FOR LARGER SPILLS, DIKE FAR AHEAD OF SPILL FOR LATER DISPOSAL. KEEP UNNECESSARY PEOPLE AWAY. ISOLATE HAZARD AREA AND DENY ENTRY. VENTILATE CLOSED SPACES BEFORE ENTERING.
REPORTABLE QUANTITY (RQ): 1 POUND THE SUPERFUND AMENDMENTS AND REAUTHORIZATION ACT (SARA) SECTION 304 REQUIRES THAT A RELEASE EQUAL TO OR GREATER THAN THE REPORTABLE QUANTITY FOR THIS SUBSTANCE BE IMMEDIATELY REPORTED TO THE LOCAL EMERGENCY PLANNING COMMITTEE AND THE STATE EMERGENCY RESPONSE COMMISSION (40 CFR 355.40). IF THE RELEASE OF THIS SUBSTANCE IS REPORTABLE UNDER CERCLA SECTION 103, THE NATIONAL RESPONSE CENTER MUST BE NOTIFIED IMMEDIATELY AT (800) 424-8802 OR (202) 426-2675 IN THE METROPOLITAN WASHINGTON, D.C. AREA (40 CFR 302.6).

PROTECTIVE EQUIPMENT

VENTILATION: PROCESS ENCLOSURE RECOMMENDED TO MEET PUBLISHED EXPOSURE LIMITS.

RESPIRATOR: THE FOLLOWING RESPIRATORS AND MAXIMUM USE CONCENTRATIONS ARE RECOMMENDATIONS BY THE U.S. DEPARTMENT OF HEALTH AND HUMAN SERVICES, NIOSH POCKET GUIDE TO CHEMICAL HAZARDS; NIOSH CRITERIA DOCUMENTS OR BY THE U.S. DEPARTMENT OF LABOR, 29 CFR 1910 SUBPART Z. THE SPECIFIC RESPIRATOR SELECTED MUST BE BASED ON CONTAMINATION LEVELS FOUND IN THE WORK PLACE, MUST NOT EXCEED THE WORKING LIMITS OF THE RESPIRATOR AND BE JOINTLY APPROVED BY THE NATIONAL INSTITUTE FOR OCCUPATIONAL SAFETY AND HEALTH AND THE MINE SAFETY AND HEALTH ADMINISTRATION (NIOSH-MSHA).
5 MG/M3- ANY SUPPLIED-AIR RESPIRATOR. ANY SELF-CONTAINED BREATHING APPARATUS.
12.5 MG/M3- ANY SUPPLIED-AIR RESPIRATOR OPERATED IN A CONTINUOUS FLOW MODE.
25 MG/M3- ANY SELF-CONTAINED BREATHING APPARATUS WITH A FULL FACEPIECE. ANY SUPPLIED-AIR RESPIRATOR WITH A FULL FACEPIECE. ANY SUPPLIED-AIR RESPIRATOR WITH A TIGHT-FITTING FACEPIECE OPERATED IN A CONTINUOUS FLOW MODE.
50 MG/M3- ANY SUPPLIED-AIR RESPIRATOR WITH A HALF-MASK AND OPERATED IN A PRESSURE-DEMAND OR OTHER POSITIVE PRESSURE MODE.
ESCAPE- ANY AIR-PURIFYING FULL FACEPIECE RESPIRATOR (GAS MASK) WITH A CHIN-STYLE OR FRONT- OR BACK-MOUNTED ORGANIC VAPOR CANISTER HAVING A HIGH-EFFICIENCY PARTICULATE FILTER. ANY APPROPRIATE ESCAPE-TYPE SELF-CONTAINED BREATHING APPARATUS.
FOR FIREFIGHTING AND OTHER IMMEDIATELY DANGEROUS TO LIFE OR HEALTH CONDITIONS:
SELF-CONTAINED BREATHING APPARATUS WITH FULL FACEPIECE OPERATED IN PRESSURE-DEMAND OR OTHER POSITIVE PRESSURE MODE.
SUPPLIED-AIR RESPIRATOR WITH FULL FACEPIECE AND OPERATED IN PRESSURE-DEMAND OR OTHER POSITIVE PRESSURE MODE IN COMBINATION WITH AN AUXILIARY SELF-CONTAINED BREATHING APPARATUS OPERATED IN PRESSURE-DEMAND OR OTHER POSITIVE PRESSURE MODE.

CLOTHING: EMPLOYEE MUST WEAR APPROPRIATE PROTECTIVE (IMPERVIOUS) CLOTHING AND EQUIPMENT TO PREVENT ANY POSSIBILITY OF SKIN CONTACT WITH THIS SUBSTANCE.

GLOVES: EMPLOYEE MUST WEAR APPROPRIATE PROTECTIVE GLOVES TO PREVENT CONTACT WITH THIS SUBSTANCE.

EYE PROTECTION: EMPLOYEE MUST WEAR SPLASH-PROOF OR DUST-RESISTANT SAFETY GOGGLES AND A FACESHIELD TO PREVENT CONTACT WITH THIS SUBSTANCE.
EMERGENCY WASH FACILITIES: WHERE THERE IS ANY POSSIBILITY THAT AN EMPLOYEE'S EYES AND/OR SKIN MAY BE EXPOSED TO THIS SUBSTANCE, THE EMPLOYER SHOULD PROVIDE AN EYE WASH FOUNTAIN AND QUICK DRENCH SHOWER WITHIN THE IMMEDIATE WORK AREA FOR EMERGENCY USE.

AUTHORIZED BY- OCCUPATIONAL HEALTH SERVICES, INC.
CREATION DATE: 10/04/89 ***REVISION DATE:*** 05/09/90

MATERIAL SAFETY DATA SHEET

OCCUPATIONAL HEALTH SERVICES, INC.
AGRICULTURE AND PESTICIDE DIVISION
450 SEVENTH AVENUE, SUITE 2407
NEW YORK, NEW YORK 10123
1-800-445-MSDS OR (212) 967-1100

EMERGENCY CONTACT:
JOHN S. BRANSFORD, JR. (615) 292-1180

SUBSTANCE IDENTIFICATION

CAS-NUMBER 16423-68-0

SUBSTANCE: ERYTHROSIN B

TRADE NAMES/SYNONYMS: 3',6'-DIHYDROXY-2',4',5',7'-TETRAIODOSPIRO(ISOBENZOFURAN -1(3H),9'- (9H)XANTHEN)-3-ONE; C.I. 45430; C.I. ACID RED 51; ERYTHROSINE B (BIOLOGICAL STAIN); TETRAIODOFLUORESCEIN SODIUM SALT; 2',4',5',7'-TETRA IODO FLUORESCEIN-DISODIUM SALT; C.I. FOOD RED 14; ERYTHROSINE BLUISH; FD AND C RED NO. 3; E-513; PST08685

CHEMICAL FAMILY: ORGANOMETALLIC

MOLECULAR FORMULA: NA2-C20-H6-I4-O5

MOLECULAR WEIGHT: 879.84

CERCLA RATINGS (SCALE 0-3): HEALTH=3 FIRE=0 REACTIVITY=0 PERSISTENCE=2

NFPA RATINGS (SCALE 0-4): HEALTH=3 FIRE=0 REACTIVITY=0

COMPONENTS AND CONTAMINANTS

COMPONENT: ERYTHROSIN B ***PERCENT:*** 100
CAS# 16423-68-0

OTHER CONTAMINANTS: NONE

EXPOSURE LIMITS: NO OCCUPATIONAL EXPOSURE LIMITS ESTABLISHED BY OSHA, ACGIH, OR NIOSH.

PHYSICAL DATA

DESCRIPTION: BROWN POWDER WHICH FORMS A RED SOLUTION IN WATER.

MELTING POINT: NOT AVAILABLE ***SPECIFIC GRAVITY:*** NOT AVAILABLE

SOLUBILITY IN WATER: SOLUBLE

SOLVENT SOLUBILITY: ALCOHOL

FIRE AND EXPLOSION DATA

FIRE AND EXPLOSION HAZARD: NEGLIGIBLE FIRE HAZARD WHEN EXPOSED TO HEAT OR FLAME.

FIREFIGHTING MEDIA: DRY CHEMICAL, CARBON DIOXIDE OR HALON (1987 EMERGENCY RESPONSE GUIDEBOOK, DOT P 5800.4).
FOR LARGER FIRES, USE WATER SPRAY, FOG OR STANDARD FOAM (1987 EMERGENCY RESPONSE GUIDEBOOK, DOT P 5800.4).

FIREFIGHTING: NO ACUTE HAZARD. MOVE CONTAINER FROM FIRE AREA IF POSSIBLE. AVOID BREATHING VAPORS OR DUSTS; KEEP UPWIND.

TOXICITY

ERYTHROSIN B: TOXICITY DATA: 1840 MG/KG ORAL-RAT LD50; 1264 MG/KG ORAL-MOUSE LD50; 1930 MG/KG ORAL-GERBIL LD50; 200 MG/KG INTRAVENOUS-RAT LD50; 370 MG/KG INTRAVENOUS-MOUSE LD50; 200 MG/KG INTRAVENOUS-RABBIT LD50; 300 MG/KG INTRAPERITONEAL-RAT LD50; 1895 MG/KG UNREPORTED-RAT LD50; MUTAGENIC DATA (RTECS); TUMORIGENIC DATA (RTECS). CARCINOGEN STATUS: NONE. LOCAL EFFECTS: IRRITANT- INHALATION, SKIN. ACUTE TOXICITY LEVEL: MODERATELY TOXIC BY INGESTION. TARGET EFFECTS: POISONING MAY AFFECT THE CENTRAL NERVOUS SYSTEM.

HEALTH EFFECTS AND FIRST AID

INHALATION: ERYTHROSIN B: IRRITANT. <u>ACUTE EXPOSURE</u>- MAY IRRITATE MUCOUS MEMBRANES. MAY BE HARMFUL IF INHALED. <u>CHRONIC EXPOSURE</u>- NO DATA HAS BEEN REPORTED IN HUMANS.

FIRST AID- REMOVE FROM EXPOSURE AREA TO FRESH AIR IMMEDIATELY. IF BREATHING HAS STOPPED, PERFORM ARTIFICIAL RESPIRATION. KEEP PERSON WARM AND AT REST. TREAT SYMPTOMATICALLY AND SUPPORTIVELY. GET MEDICAL ATTENTION IMMEDIATELY.

SKIN CONTACT: ERYTHROSIN B: IRRITANT. **ACUTE EXPOSURE-** MAY CAUSE IRRITATION AND PAIN. **CHRONIC EXPOSURE-** REPEATED OR PROLONGED CONTACT MAY CAUSE DERMATITIS.

FIRST AID- REMOVE CONTAMINATED CLOTHING AND SHOES IMMEDIATELY. WASH AFFECTED AREA WITH SOAP OR MILD DETERGENT AND LARGE AMOUNTS OF WATER UNTIL NO EVIDENCE OF CHEMICAL REMAINS (APPROXIMATELY 15-20 MINUTES). GET MEDICAL ATTENTION IMMEDIATELY.

EYE CONTACT: ERYTHROSIN B: **ACUTE EXPOSURE-** MAY CAUSE IRRITATION. NO EFFECTS REPORTED IN HUMANS. **CHRONIC EXPOSURE-** NO DATA AVAILABLE.

FIRST AID- WASH EYES IMMEDIATELY WITH LARGE AMOUNTS OF WATER OR NORMAL SALINE, OCCASIONALLY LIFTING UPPER AND LOWER LIDS, UNTIL NO EVIDENCE OF CHEMICAL REMAINS (APPROXIMATELY 15-20 MINUTES). GET MEDICAL ATTENTION IMMEDIATELY.

INGESTION: ERYTHROSIN B: **ACUTE EXPOSURE-** HAS CAUSED RESPIRATORY DEPRESSION, DECREASED MOTOR ACTIVITY, ATAXIA, AND CENTRAL NERVOUS SYSTEM DEPRESSION IN EXPERIMENTAL ANIMALS. NO HEALTH EFFECTS HAVE BEEN REPORTED IN HUMANS. **CHRONIC EXPOSURE-** NO HEALTH EFFECTS HAVE BEEN REPORTED IN HUMANS.

FIRST AID- TREAT SYMPTOMATICALLY AND SUPPORTIVELY. GET MEDICAL ATTENTION IMMEDIATELY. IF VOMITING OCCURS, KEEP HEAD LOWER THAN HIPS TO PREVENT ASPIRATION.

ANTIDOTE: NO SPECIFIC ANTIDOTE. TREAT SYMPTOMATICALLY AND SUPPORTIVELY.

REACTIVITY

REACTIVITY: STABLE UNDER NORMAL TEMPERATURES AND PRESSURES.

INCOMPATIBILITIES: ERYTHROSIN B: STRONG OXIDANTS: MAY IGNITE.

DECOMPOSITION: THERMAL DECOMPOSITION RELEASES TOXIC FUMES OF IODIDES AND SODIUM OXIDE.

POLYMERIZATION: HAZARDOUS POLYMERIZATION HAS NOT BEEN REPORTED TO OCCUR UNDER NORMAL TEMPERATURES AND PRESSURES.

CONDITIONS TO AVOID

NONE REPORTED.

SPILL AND LEAK PROCEDURES

OCCUPATIONAL SPILL: NO SPECIAL PRECAUTIONS INDICATED.

PROTECTIVE EQUIPMENT

VENTILATION: PROVIDE LOCAL EXHAUST OR PROCESS ENCLOSURE VENTILATION SYSTEM.

RESPIRATOR: THE FOLLOWING RESPIRATORS ARE RECOMMENDED BASED ON INFORMATION FOUND IN THE PHYSICAL DATA, TOXICITY AND HEALTH EFFECTS SECTIONS. THEY ARE RANKED IN ORDER FROM MINIMUM TO MAXIMUM RESPIRATORY PROTECTION. THE SPECIFIC RESPIRATOR SELECTED MUST BE BASED ON CONTAMINATION LEVELS FOUND IN THE WORK PLACE, MUST NOT EXCEED THE WORKING LIMITS OF THE RESPIRATOR AND BE JOINTLY APPROVED BY THE NATIONAL INSTITUTE FOR OCCUPATIONAL SAFETY AND HEALTH AND THE MINE SAFETY AND HEALTH ADMINISTRATION (NIOSH-MSHA).

TYPE 'C' SUPPLIED-AIR RESPIRATOR WITH A FULL FACEPIECE OPERATED IN PRESSURE-DEMAND OR OTHER POSITIVE PRESSURE MODE OR WITH A FULL FACEPIECE, HELMET OR HOOD OPERATED IN CONTINOUS-FLOW MODE.

SELF-CONTAINED BREATHING APPARATUS WITH A FULL FACEPIECE OPERATED IN PRESSURE-DEMAND OR OTHER POSITIVE PRESSURE MODE.

CLOTHING: EMPLOYEE MUST WEAR APPROPRIATE PROTECTIVE (IMPERVIOUS) CLOTHING AND EQUIPMENT TO PREVENT ANY POSSIBILITY OF SKIN CONTACT WITH THIS SUBSTANCE.

GLOVES: EMPLOYEE MUST WEAR APPROPRIATE PROTECTIVE GLOVES TO PREVENT CONTACT WITH THIS SUBSTANCE.

EYE PROTECTION: EMPLOYEE MUST WEAR SPLASH-PROOF OR DUST-RESISTANT SAFETY GOGGLES AND A FACESHIELD TO PREVENT CONTACT WITH THIS SUBSTANCE.

EMERGENCY WASH FACILITIES: WHERE THERE IS ANY POSSIBILITY THAT AN EMPLOYEE'S EYES AND/OR SKIN MAY BE EXPOSED TO THIS SUBSTANCE, THE EMPLOYER SHOULD PROVIDE AN EYE WASH FOUNTAIN AND QUICK DRENCH SHOWER WITHIN THE IMMEDIATE WORK AREA FOR EMERGENCY USE.

AUTHORIZED BY- OCCUPATIONAL HEALTH SERVICES, INC.

CREATION DATE: 02/08/90 ***REVISION DATE:*** 02/08/90

MATERIAL SAFETY DATA SHEET

OCCUPATIONAL HEALTH SERVICES, INC.
AGRICULTURE AND PESTICIDE DIVISION
450 SEVENTH AVENUE, SUITE 2407
NEW YORK, NEW YORK 10123
1-800-445-MSDS OR (212) 967-1100

EMERGENCY CONTACT:
JOHN S. BRANSFORD, JR. (615) 292-1180

SUBSTANCE IDENTIFICATION

CAS-NUMBER 64-17-5

SUBSTANCE: **ETHYL ALCOHOL**

TRADE NAMES/SYNONYMS: ETHANOL; ETHYL ALCOHOL, 100%; ALCOHOL; ALCOHOL ANHYDROUS; ALGRAIN; ANHYDROL; ETHYL HYDRATE; ETHYL HYDROXIDE; JAYSOL; TECSOL; PL-1075 RINSE (HITACHI CHEMICAL COMPANY, LTD. YAMAZAKI WORKS); STCC 4909159; UN 1170; C2H6O; PST08700

CHEMICAL FAMILY: ALCOHOL, ALIPHATIC

MOLECULAR FORMULA: C-H3-C-H2-O-H

MOLECULAR WEIGHT: 46.07

CERCLA RATINGS (SCALE 0-3): HEALTH=3 FIRE=3 REACTIVITY=0 PERSISTENCE=0

NFPA RATINGS (SCALE 0-4): HEALTH=0 FIRE=3 REACTIVITY=0

COMPONENTS AND CONTAMINANTS

COMPONENT: ETHYL ALCOHOL ***PERCENT:*** 100.0
CAS# 64-17-5

OTHER CONTAMINANTS: NONE

EXPOSURE LIMITS: ETHYL ALCOHOL (ETHANOL): 1000 PPM (1900 MG/M3) OSHA TWA
1000 PPM (1900 MG/M3) ACGIH TWA
SUBJECT TO CALIFORNIA PROPOSITION 65 CANCER AND/OR REPRODUCTIVE TOXICITY WARNING AND RELEASE REQUIREMENTS (ALCOHOLIC BEVERAGES)-(OCTOBER 1, 1987)

PHYSICAL DATA

DESCRIPTION: A CLEAR, COLORLESS, VOLATILE LIQUID WITH A PLEASANT ODOR AND A BURNING TASTE. ***BOILING POINT:*** 173 F (78 C)

MELTING POINT: -179 F (-117 C) ***SPECIFIC GRAVITY:*** 0.7893

VISCOSITY: 1.22 CPS @ 20 C ***VOLATILITY:*** 100%

VAPOR PRESSURE: 40 MMHG @ 19 C ***EVAPORATION RATE:*** (CARBON TETRACHLORIDE=1) 1.4

SOLUBILITY IN WATER: COMPLETE ***ODOR THRESHOLD:*** 5-10 PPM

VAPOR DENSITY: 1.59

SOLVENT SOLUBILITY: SOLUBLE IN BENZENE, ETHER, ACETONE, CHLOROFORM, METHANOL, MANY ORGANIC LIQUIDS

FIRE AND EXPLOSION DATA

FIRE AND EXPLOSION HAZARD: DANGEROUS FIRE HAZARD WHEN EXPOSED TO HEAT OR FLAME.

VAPORS ARE HEAVIER THAN AIR AND MAY TRAVEL A CONSIDERABLE DISTANCE TO A SOURCE OF IGNITION AND FLASH BACK.

VAPOR-AIR MIXTURES ARE EXPLOSIVE.

FLASH POINT: 55 F (13 C) (TCC) ***UPPER EXPLOSIVE LIMIT:*** 19%

LOWER EXPLOSIVE LIMIT: 3.3% ***AUTOIGNITION TEMP.:*** 685 F (363 C)

FLAMMABILITY CLASS(OSHA): IB

FIREFIGHTING MEDIA: DRY CHEMICAL, CARBON DIOXIDE, HALON, WATER SPRAY OR ALCOHOL FOAM (1987 EMERGENCY RESPONSE GUIDEBOOK, DOT P 5800.4).

FOR LARGER FIRES, USE WATER SPRAY, FOG OR ALCOHOL FOAM (1987 EMERGENCY RESPONSE GUIDEBOOK, DOT P 5800.4).

ALCOHOL FOAM (NFPA 325M, FIRE HAZARD PROPERTIES OF FLAMMABLE LIQUIDS, GASES, AND VOLATILE SOLIDS, 1984).

FIREFIGHTING: MOVE CONTAINER FROM FIRE AREA IF POSSIBLE. COOL FIRE-EXPOSED CONTAINERS WITH WATER FROM SIDE UNTIL WELL AFTER FIRE IS OUT. STAY AWAY FROM STORAGE TANK ENDS. FOR MASSIVE FIRE IN STORAGE AREA, USE UNMANNED HOSE HOLDER OR MONITOR NOZZLES, ELSE WITHDRAW FROM AREA AND LET FIRE BURN. WITHDRAW IMMEDIATELY IN CASE OF RISING SOUND FROM VENTING SAFETY DEVICE OR ANY DISCOLORATION OF STORAGE TANK DUE TO FIRE (1987 EMERGENCY RESPONSE GUIDEBOOK, DOT P 5800.4, GUIDE PAGE 26).

EXTINGUISH ONLY IF FLOW CAN BE STOPPED; USE WATER IN FLOODING AMOUNTS AS FOG, SOLID STREAMS MAY NOT BE EFFECTIVE. COOL CONTAINERS WITH FLOODING AMOUNTS OF WATER, APPLY FROM AS FAR A DISTANCE AS POSSIBLE. AVOID BREATHING VAPORS, KEEP UPWIND.

WATER MAY BE INEFFECTIVE (NFPA 325M, FIRE HAZARD PROPERTIES OF FLAMMABLE LIQUIDS, GASES, AND VOLATILE SOLIDS, 1984)

TRANSPORTATION DATA

DEPARTMENT OF TRANSPORTATION HAZARD CLASSIFICATION 49 CFR 172.101: FLAMMABLE LIQUID

DEPARTMENT OF TRANSPORTATION LABELING REQUIREMENTS 49 CFR 172.101 AND SUBPART E: FLAMMABLE LIQUID

DEPARTMENT OF TRANSPORTATION PACKAGING REQUIREMENTS: 49 CFR 173.125 EXCEPTIONS: 49 CFR 173.118

TOXICITY

ETHYL ALCOHOL (ETHANOL): IRRITATION DATA: 400 MG OPEN SKIN-RABBIT MILD; 20 MG/24 HOURS SKIN-RABBIT MODERATE; 500 MG/24 HOURS EYE-RABBIT MILD; 79 MG EYE-RABBIT; 100 MG/4 SECONDS RINSED EYE-RABBIT MODERATE. TOXICITY DATA: 20,000 PPM/10 HOURS INHALATION-RAT LC50; 39 GM/M3/4 HOURS INHALATION-MOUSE LC50; 21,900 PPM INHALATION-GUINEA PIG LCLO; 20 GM/KG SKIN-RABBIT LDLO; 700 MG/KG ORAL-MAN TDLO; 2000 MG/KG ORAL-CHILD LDLO; 14,400 MG/KG/30 MINUTES INTERMITTENT ORAL-CHILD TDLO; 50 MG/KG ORAL-MAN TDLO; 1430 UG/KG ORAL-MAN TDLO; 256 GM/KG/12 WEEKS ORAL-WOMAN TDLO; 1400 MG/KG ORAL-HUMAN LDLO; 7060 MG/KG ORAL-RAT LD50; 3450 MG/KG ORAL-MOUSE LD50; 6000 MG/KG ORAL-CAT LDLO; 5500 MG/KG ORAL-DOG LDLO; 6300 MG/KG ORAL-RABBIT LD50; 5560 MG/KG ORAL-GUINEA PIG LD50; 19,440 MG/KG SUBCUTANEOUS-INFANT LDLO; 8285 MG/KG SUBCUTANEOUS-MOUSE LD50; 1440 MG/KG INTRAVENOUS-RAT LD50; 3945 MG/KG INTRAVENOUS-CAT LDLO; 1600 MG/KG INTRAVENOUS-DOG LDLO; 1973 MG/KG INTRAVENOUS-MOUSE LD50; 2374 MG/KG INTRAVENOUS-RABBIT LD50; 4300 MG/KG INTRAPERITONEAL-MAMMAL LD50; 3000 MG/KG INTRAPERITONEAL-DOG LDLO; 3600 UG/KG INTRAPERITONEAL-RAT LD50; 933 MG/KG INTRAPERITONEAL-MOUSE LD50; 963 MG/KG INTRAPERITONEAL-RABBIT LD50; 3414 MG/KG INTRAPERITONEAL-GUINEA PIG LD50; MUTAGENIC DATA (RTECS); REPRODUCTIVE EFFECTS DATA (RTECS); TUMORIGENIC DATA (RTECS). CARCINOGEN STATUS: NONE. LOCAL EFFECTS: IRRITANT- INHALATION, SKIN, EYE. ACUTE TOXICITY LEVEL: SLIGHTLY TOXIC BY INHALATION, INGESTION. TARGET EFFECTS: CENTRAL NERVOUS SYSTEM DEPRESSANT; HEPATOTOXIN. AT INCREASED RISK FROM EXPOSURE: PERSONS WITH LIVER DISEASE. ADDITIONAL DATA: ALLERGIC REACTIONS TO ALCOHOLS HAVE BEEN REPORTED.

HEALTH EFFECTS AND FIRST AID

INHALATION: ETHYL ALCOHOL (ETHANOL): IRRITANT/NARCOTIC. **ACUTE EXPOSURE-** EXPOSURE OF HUMANS TO 1000-10,000 PPM HAS CAUSED TEMPORARY IRRITATION OF THE UPPER RESPIRATORY TRACT AND COUGHING; AND IF CONTINUED, CENTRAL NERVOUS SYSTEM DEPRESSION WITH HEADACHE, STUPOR, FATIGUE, DIZZINESS, DROWSINESS, DULLNESS, LASSITUDE AND LOSS OF APPETITE MAY OCCUR. A LEVEL OF 20,000 PPM WAS CONSIDERED JUST TOLERABLE, AND ABOVE THIS LEVEL, THE ATMOSPHERE WAS DESCRIBED AS INTOLERABLE AND SUFFOCATING ON EVEN BRIEF EXPOSURES. ADDITIONALLY, EXPOSURE OF ANIMALS TO VARIOUS CONCENTRATIONS HAS RESULTED IN EXCITATION FOLLOWED BY ATAXIA, INCOORDINATION, PROSTRATION, TWITCHING, GENERAL PARALYSIS, DYSPNEA, AND OCCASIONALLY DEATH DUE TO RESPIRATORY FAILURE. **CHRONIC EXPOSURE-** REPEATED OR PROLONGED INHALATION OF VAPORS MAY CAUSE IRRITATION OF THE MUCOUS MEMBRANES, HEADACHE, DIZZINESS, NERVOUSNESS, TREMORS, FATIGUE, NAUSEA, NARCOSIS, LACK OF CONCENTRATION, AND SOMNOLENCE. TOLERANCE MAY BE A FACTOR IN INDIVIDUAL RESPONSE TO A GIVEN AIR CONCENTRATION. REPRODUCTIVE EFFECTS HAVE BEEN REPORTED IN ANIMALS.

FIRST AID- REMOVE FROM EXPOSURE AREA TO FRESH AIR IMMEDIATELY. IF BREATHING HAS STOPPED, PERFORM ARTIFICIAL RESPIRATION. KEEP PERSON WARM AND AT REST. TREAT SYMPTOMATICALLY AND SUPPORTIVELY. GET MEDICAL ATTENTION IMMEDIATELY.

SKIN CONTACT: ETHYL ALCOHOL (ETHANOL): IRRITANT. **ACUTE EXPOSURE-** DIRECT CONTACT MAY CAUSE MILD REDNESS AND BURNING. SENSITIZATION HAS OCCASIONALLY BEEN REPORTED TO OCCUR IN SOME INDIVIDUALS RESULTING IN ALLERGIC CONTACT DERMATITIS IN THE FORM OF ECZEMATOUS ERUPTIONS OR, RARELY, ERYTHEMATOUS FLUSH OR CONTACT URTICARIA AT THE EXPOSED SITE. ANIMAL STUDIES INDICATE THAT, DEPENDING ON CONCENTRATION AND DURATION OF EXPOSURE, VARYING DEGREES OF IRRITATION MAY OCCUR RANGING FROM MILD TO SEVERE. SKIN ABSORPTION MAY ALSO OCCUR. **CHRONIC EXPOSURE-** REPEATED OR PROLONGED CONTACT WITH THE LIQUID CAN CAUSE DEFATTING OF THE SKIN, PRODUCING A DRY, FISSURED DERMATITIS, OR OTHER SYMPTOMS AS IN ACUTE EXPOSURE. A 21-DAY MODIFIED DRAIZE OPEN TEST STUDY RESULTED IN NO IRRITATION IN MEN, WHEREAS AN OCCLUSIVE TEST RESULTED IN ERYTHEMA AND INDURATION TOWARD THE END OF THE EXPOSURE PERIOD.

FIRST AID- REMOVE CONTAMINATED CLOTHING AND SHOES IMMEDIATELY. WASH AFFECTED AREA WITH SOAP OR MILD DETERGENT AND LARGE AMOUNTS OF WATER UNTIL NO EVIDENCE OF CHEMICAL REMAINS (APPROXIMATELY 15-20 MINUTES). GET MEDICAL ATTENTION IMMEDIATELY.

EYE CONTACT: ETHYL ALCOHOL (ETHANOL): IRRITANT. **ACUTE EXPOSURE-** VAPOR CONCENTRATIONS OF 1,000-10,000 PPM MAY CAUSE TEMPORARY EYE IRRITATION, WITH 15,000 PPM CAUSING CONTINUOUS TEARING. DIRECT CONTACT WITH THE LIQUID MAY CAUSE IMMEDIATE BURNING AND STINGING, WITH REFLEX CLOSURE OF THE LIDS, TEARING, TEMPORARY INJURY OF THE CORNEAL EPITHELIUM, AND HYPEREMIA OF THE CONJUNCTIVA. HEALING IS USUALLY SPONTANEOUS AND COMPLETE. DEPENDING ON THE CONCENTRATION, CONTACT WITH RABBIT EYES CAUSES A RESPONSE RANGING FROM MILD IRRITATION TO SEVERE INJURY. IRRIGATION OF RABBIT EYES WITH A 10% SOLUTION FOR SEVERAL MINUTES CAUSED NO SERIOUS DISTURBANCES. **CHRONIC EXPOSURE-** REPEATED APPLICATION TO RABBIT EYES OF 40-80% SOLUTIONS CAUSED CORNEAL CLOUDINESS, CONJUNCTIVAL NECROSIS, AND LOSS OF CORNEAL EPITHELIUM AND ENDOTHELIUM, FOLLOWED BY CONJUNCTIVAL HEMORRHAGING AND EDEMA, AND INFILTRATION AND VASCULARIZATION OF THE CORNEAL STROMA.

FIRST AID- WASH EYES IMMEDIATELY WITH LARGE AMOUNTS OF WATER OR NORMAL SALINE, OCCASIONALLY LIFTING UPPER AND LOWER LIDS, UNTIL NO EVIDENCE OF CHEMICAL REMAINS (APPROXIMATELY 15-20 MINUTES). GET MEDICAL ATTENTION IMMEDIATELY.

INGESTION: ETHYL ALCOHOL (ETHANOL): NARCOTIC/HEPATOTOXIN. **ACUTE EXPOSURE-** INGESTION MAY CAUSE EMOTIONAL LABILITY AND DECREASED INHIBITIONS, WITH EXHILARATION, BOASTFULNESS, TALKATIVENESS, REMORSE, AND BELLIGERENCY; FOLLOWED BY GRADUAL VISUAL IMPAIRMENT, MUSCULAR INCOORDINATION, SLOWING OF REACTION TIME, SENSORY DISTURBANCES, AND SLURRING OF SPEECH. OTHER SYMPTOMS MAY INCLUDE FLUSHING OF THE FACE, DILATED PUPILS, RAPID PULSE, NAUSEA, VOMITING, SWEATING, AND DIURESIS. INGESTION OF LARGE AMOUNTS MAY CAUSE CONFUSION, DISORIENTATION, LOSS OF MOTOR NERVE CONTROL, SHALLOW RESPIRATION, INVOLUNTARY DEFECATION AND URINATION, DROWSINESS, STUPOR, AND POSSIBLY COMA. CONVULSIONS DUE TO HYPOGLYCEMIA AND SHOCK WITH HYPOTENSION, TACHYCARDIA, COLD PALE SKIN, HYPOTHERMIA, RESPIRATORY DEPRESSION, AND DECREASED REFLEXES MAY OCCUR. DEATH MAY OCCUR FROM RESPIRATORY OR CIRCULATORY FAILURE OR LATER FROM ASPIRATION PNEUMONITIS OR PULMONARY EDEMA. RECOVERY MAY BE ACCOMPANIED BY HEADACHE, INSOMNIA, GASTRITIS, INFECTION, RESTLESSNESS, PSYCHOSES WITH UNCONTROLLABLE FEAR, AND VISUAL, AUDITORY, OR GUSTATORY HALLUCINATIONS, EXAGGERATED REFLEXES, TACHYCARDIA, AND CONVULSIONS. SOME INDIVIDUALS SENSITIZED BY EXTERNAL CONTACT MAY SUFFER FROM A GENERALIZED ERYTHEMA, STOMATITIS, URTICARIA, ANGIOEDEMA, MORBILLIFORM ERUPTIONS, OR ECZEMATOUS DERMATITIS AT SITES PREVIOUSLY AFFECTED BY EXTERNAL CONTACT. REPRODUCTIVE EFFECTS HAVE BEEN REPORTED IN ANIMALS. **CHRONIC EXPOSURE-** CHRONIC INTOXICATION MAY RESULT IN WEIGHT LOSS, DEGENERATIVE CHANGES IN THE LIVER, KIDNEYS, AND BRAIN, GASTROENTERITIS WITH ANOREXIA AND DIARRHEA, AND CIRRHOSIS OF THE LIVER. POLYNEURITIS WITH PAIN, MOTOR AND SENSORY LOSS IN THE EXTREMITIES, AND OPTIC ATROPHY MAY OCCUR. AMNESIA, TREMORS, CONFUSION, IMPAIRED JUDGEMENT, AND LOSS OR IMPAIRMENT OF MENTAL ABILITIES ARE POSSIBLE. MANY YEARS OF CHRONIC INGESTION HAVE CAUSED ACUTE MYOPATHY WITH TENDERNESS, ACHING, EDEMA, AND DEGENERATION OF THE MUSCLES. THE HEART MAY BE AFFECTED, CAUSING PALPITATIONS, EXTRASYSTOLE, TACHYCARDIA, OR OTHER ARRHYTHMIAS, WHICH MAY PROGRESS TO IRREVERSIBLE MYOCARDIAL FIBROSIS AND CIRCULATORY FAILURE. ETHYL ALCOHOL HAS BEEN CLEARLY DEMONSTRATED TO CAUSE REPRODUCTIVE EFFECTS. THE NEWBORNS OF ALCOHOLIC MOTHERS MAY EXHIBIT FETAL ALCOHOL SYNDROME WITH LOW BIRTH WEIGHTS, PROMINENCE OF THE FOREHEAD AND MANDIBLE, CLEFT PALATE, MAXILLARY HYPOPLASIA, SHORT PALPEBRAL FISSURES, MICROPHTHALMIA, EPICANTHAL FOLDS, SEVERE GROWTH RETARDATION, MENTAL RETARDATION, MICROCEPHALY, CARDIAC ANOMALIES, AND POSSIBLY MALORIENTATION OF THE BRAIN. 9 NEWBORNS OF A HIGH RISK GROUP, THAT IS WOMEN WHO DRINK MORE THAN 2 OUNCES PER DAY, SHOWED INCREASED TREMORS AND NON-ALERT WAKE STATES AND DECREASED VIGOROUS ACTIVITY. REPRODUCTIVE EFFECTS HAVE ALSO BEEN REPORTED IN ANIMALS.

FIRST AID- IF THE PERSON IS CONSCIOUS AND NOT CONVULSING, REMOVE BY THOROUGH GASTRIC LAVAGE. IF IMMEDIATE GASTRIC LAVAGE CANNOT BE ACCOMPLISHED, INDUCE EMESIS WITH SYRUP OF IPECAC (KEEPING THE HEAD BELOW THE HIPS TO PREVENT ASPIRATION). TREAT SYMPTOMATICALLY AND SUPPORTIVELY. GASTRIC LAVAGE SHOULD BE PERFORMED BY QUALIFIED MEDICAL PERSONNEL. GET MEDICAL ATTENTION IMMEDIATELY.

ANTIDOTE: THE FOLLOWING ANTIDOTE HAS BEEN RECOMMENDED. HOWEVER, THE DECISION AS TO WHETHER THE SEVERITY OF POISONING REQUIRES ADMINISTRATION OF ANY ANTIDOTE AND ACTUAL DOSE REQUIRED SHOULD BE MADE BY QUALIFIED MEDICAL PERSONNEL.

ETHANOL POISONING: NALOXONE, 0.01 MG/KG, INTRAVENOUSLY, HAS AN

AROUSAL EFFECT IN ACUTE ALCOHOLIC COMA (DREISBACH, HANDBOOK OF POISONING, 11TH ED.). ANTIDOTE SHOULD BE ADMINISTERED BY QUALIFIED MEDICAL PERSONNEL.

REACTIVITY

REACTIVITY: STABLE UNDER NORMAL TEMPERATURES AND PRESSURES.

INCOMPATIBILITIES: ETHYL ALCOHOL (ETHANOL): ACETIC ANHYDRIDE AND SODIUM HYDROGEN SULFATE: POSSIBLE EXPLOSION. ACETYL CHLORIDE: VIOLENT REACTION. ACETYL BROMIDE: VIOLENT REACTION. ALKALI METALS: LIBERATES FLAMMABLE HYDROGEN GAS. ALUMINUM SESQUIBROMIDE ETHYLATE: EXPLOSION. AMMONIUM HYDROXIDE AND SILVER (I) OXIDE: FORMATION OF EXPLOSIVE SILVER NITRIDE. BARIUM PERCHLORATE: FORMATION OF EXPLOSIVE COMPOUND. BROMINE PENTAFLUORIDE: IGNITION AND EXPLOSIONS ARE POSSIBLE. CALCIUM HYPOCHLORITE: POSSIBLE EXPLOSION. CHLORINE TRIOXIDE: VIOLENT REACTION. CHLORYL PERCHLORATE: POSSIBLE IGNITION. CHROMIC ANHYDRIDE: IGNITION. CHROMIUM TRIOXIDE: POSSIBLE IGNITION. CHROMYL CHLORIDE: IGNITION. DIOXYGEN DIFLUORIDE: POSSIBLE EXPLOSION. DISULFURIC ACID AND NITRIC ACID: POSSIBLE IGNITION. DISULFURYL DIFLUORIDE: VIOLENT REACTION. FLUORINE NITRATE: EXPLOSION. HYDROGEN PEROXIDE: FORMATION OF HIGHLY EXPLOSIVE SHOCK-SENSITIVE COMPOUND. HYDROGEN PEROXIDE-SULFURIC ACID MIXTURE: EXPLOSION. IODINE HEPTAFLUORIDE: IGNITION. IODINE-MERCURIC OXIDE-METHYL ALCOHOL MIXTURE: POSSIBLE EXPLOSION. IODINE AND PHOSPHORUS: FORMATION OF EXPLOSIVE ETHANE IODIDE. MANGANESE PERCHLORATE AND 2,2-DIMETHOXY PROPANE: POSSIBLE EXPLOSION. MERCURIC NITRATE: FORMATION OF EXPLOSIVE COMPOUND. NITRIC ACID: VIOLENT REACTION. NITROSYL PERCHLORATE: POSSIBLE EXPLOSION. OXIDIZERS (STRONG): FIRE AND EXPLOSION HAZARD. PERCHLORATES: MAY FORM EXPLOSIVE COMPOUND WHEN MIXED. PERCHLORIC ACID: EXPLOSION. PERMANGANIC ACID: IGNITION OR EXPLOSION. PERMANGANATES AND SULFURIC ACID: EXPLOSION. PEROXYDISULFURIC ACID: POSSIBLE EXPLOSION. PHOSPHORUS(III) OXIDE: IGNITION. PLATINUM: IGNITION. POTASSIUM: VIOLENT REACTION. POTASSIUM DIOXIDE: VIOLENT REACTION, POSSIBLE EXPLOSION. POTASSIUM PERCHLORATE: POSSIBLE EXPLOSION. POTASSIUM PERMANGANATE: POSSIBLE EXPLOSION. POTASSIUM TERT-BUTOXIDE: IGNITION. RUTHENIUM(VIII) OXIDE: FORMATION OF EXPLOSIVE COMPOUND. SILVER AND NITRIC ACID: FORMATION OF EXPLOSIVE COMPOUND. SILVER NITRATE: FORMATION OF EXPLOSIVE COMPOUND. SILVER PERCHLORATE: MAY FORM EXPLOSIVE COMPOUND WHEN MIXED. SODIUM-AIR: POSSIBLE EXPLOSION. SODIUM HYDRAZIDE: MAY CAUSE VIOLENT EXPLOSION ON CONTACT. SODIUM PEROXIDE: VIOLENT REACTION. SULFURIC ACID AND SODIUM DICHROMATE: POSSIBLE EXPLOSION. TETRACHLOROSILANE: VIOLENT REACTION. URANIUM HEXAFLUORIDE: VIOLENT REACTION. URANYL PERCHLORATE: MAY FORM EXPLOSIVE COMPOUND WHEN MIXED. SEE ALSO ALCOHOLS.

ALCOHOLS: ACETALDEHYDE: VIOLENT CONDENSATION REACTION. BARIUM PERCHLORATE: FORMATION OF HIGHLY EXPLOSIVE PERCHLORIC ESTER ON REFLUXING. CHLORINE: FORMATION OF HIGHLY EXPLOSIVE ALKYL HYPOCHLORITES. DIETHYL ALUMINUM BROMIDE: SPONTANEOUS IGNITION. ETHYLENE OXIDE: POSSIBLE EXPLOSION. HEXAMETHYLENE DIISOCYANATE: POSSIBLE EXPLOSION IN ABSENCE OF SOLVENT. HYDROGEN PEROXIDE + SULFURIC ACID: POSSIBLE EXPLOSION. HYPOCHLOROUS ACID: FORMATION OF HIGHLY EXPLOSIVE ALKYL HYPOCHLORITES. ISOCYANATES: POSSIBLE EXPLOSION IN ABSENCE OF SOLVENT. LITHIUM ALUMINUM HYDRIDE: VIGOROUS REACTION. NITROGEN TETROXIDE: POSSIBLE EXPLOSION. PERCHLORIC ACID (HOT): DANGEROUS INTERACTION. PERMONOSULFURIC ACID: POSSIBLE EXPLOSION ON CONTACT WITH PRIMARY OR SECONDARY ALCOHOLS. TRI-ISO-BUTYL ALUMINUM: VIOLENT REACTION.

DECOMPOSITION: THERMAL DECOMPOSITION PRODUCTS MAY INCLUDE TOXIC OXIDES OF CARBON.

POLYMERIZATION: HAZARDOUS POLYMERIZATION HAS NOT BEEN REPORTED TO OCCUR UNDER NORMAL TEMPERATURES AND PRESSURES.

STORAGE AND DISPOSAL

OBSERVE ALL FEDERAL, STATE AND LOCAL REGULATIONS WHEN STORING OR DISPOSING OF THIS SUBSTANCE. FOR ASSISTANCE, CONTACT THE DISTRICT DIRECTOR OF THE ENVIRONMENTAL PROTECTION AGENCY.

STORAGE

STORE IN ACCORDANCE WITH 29 CFR 1910.106.

BONDING AND GROUNDING: SUBSTANCES WITH LOW ELECTROCONDUCTIVITY, WHICH MAY BE IGNITED BY ELECTROSTATIC SPARKS, SHOULD BE STORED IN CONTAINERS WHICH MEET THE BONDING AND GROUNDING GUIDELINES SPECIFIED IN NFPA 77-1983, RECOMMENDED PRACTICE ON STATIC ELECTRICITY.

STORE AWAY FROM INCOMPATIBLE SUBSTANCES.

DISPOSAL

DISPOSAL MUST BE IN ACCORDANCE WITH STANDARDS APPLICABLE TO GENERATORS OF HAZARDOUS WASTE, 40 CFR 262. EPA HAZARDOUS WASTE NUMBER D001. 100 POUND CERCLA SECTION 103 REPORTABLE QUANTITY.

CONDITIONS TO AVOID

AVOID CONTACT WITH HEAT, SPARKS, FLAMES, OR OTHER SOURCES OF IGNITION. VAPORS MAY BE EXPLOSIVE AND POISONOUS; DO NOT ALLOW UNNECESSARY PERSONNEL IN AREA. DO NOT OVERHEAT CONTAINERS; CONTAINERS MAY VIOLENTLY RUPTURE AND TRAVEL A CONSIDERABLE DISTANCE IN HEAT OF FIRE.

SPILL AND LEAK PROCEDURES

WATER SPILL: THE CALIFORNIA SAFE DRINKING WATER AND TOXIC ENFORCEMENT ACT OF 1986 (PROPOSITION 65) PROHIBITS CONTAMINATING ANY KNOWN SOURCE OF DRINKING WATER WITH SUBSTANCES KNOWN TO CAUSE CANCER AND/OR REPRODUCTIVE TOXICITY.

OCCUPATIONAL SPILL: SHUT OFF IGNITION SOURCES. STOP LEAK IF YOU CAN DO IT WITHOUT RISK. USE WATER SPRAY TO REDUCE VAPORS. FOR SMALL SPILLS, TAKE UP WITH SAND OR OTHER ABSORBENT MATERIAL AND PLACE INTO CONTAINERS FOR LATER DISPOSAL. FOR LARGER SPILLS, DIKE FAR AHEAD OF SPILL FOR LATER DISPOSAL. NO SMOKING, FLAMES OR FLARES IN HAZARD AREA. KEEP UNNECESSARY PEOPLE AWAY; ISOLATE HAZARD AREA AND DENY ENTRY.

PROTECTIVE EQUIPMENT

VENTILATION: PROVIDE LOCAL EXHAUST OR GENERAL DILUTION VENTILATION TO MEET PUBLISHED EXPOSURE LIMITS. VENTILATION EQUIPMENT MUST BE EXPLOSION-PROOF.

RESPIRATOR: THE FOLLOWING RESPIRATORS AND MAXIMUM USE CONCENTRATIONS ARE RECOMMENDATIONS BY THE U.S. DEPARTMENT OF HEALTH AND HUMAN SERVICES, NIOSH POCKET GUIDE TO CHEMICAL HAZARDS; NIOSH CRITERIA DOCUMENTS OR BY THE U.S. DEPARTMENT OF LABOR, 29 CFR 1910 SUBPART Z. THE SPECIFIC RESPIRATOR SELECTED MUST BE BASED ON CONTAMINATION LEVELS FOUND IN THE WORK PLACE, MUST NOT EXCEED THE WORKING LIMITS OF THE RESPIRATOR AND BE JOINTLY APPROVED BY THE NATIONAL INSTITUTE FOR OCCUPATIONAL SAFETY AND HEALTH AND THE MINE SAFETY AND HEALTH ADMINISTRATION (NIOSH-MSHA).

ETHYL ALCOHOL (ETHANOL):

1000 PPM- ANY SUPPLIED-AIR RESPIRATOR.

ESCAPE- ANY APPROPRIATE ESCAPE-TYPE SELF-CONTAINED BREATHING APPARATUS.

FOR FIREFIGHTING AND OTHER IMMEDIATELY DANGEROUS TO LIFE OR HEALTH CONDITIONS:

SELF-CONTAINED BREATHING APPARATUS WITH FULL FACEPIECE OPERATED IN PRESSURE-DEMAND OR OTHER POSITIVE PRESSURE MODE.

SUPPLIED-AIR RESPIRATOR WITH FULL FACEPIECE AND OPERATED IN PRESSURE-DEMAND OR OTHER POSITIVE PRESSURE MODE IN COMBINATION WITH AN AUXILIARY SELF-CONTAINED BREATHING APPARATUS OPERATED IN PRESSURE-DEMAND OR OTHER POSITIVE PRESSURE MODE.

CLOTHING: EMPLOYEE MUST WEAR APPROPRIATE PROTECTIVE (IMPERVIOUS) CLOTHING AND EQUIPMENT TO PREVENT REPEATED OR PROLONGED SKIN CONTACT WITH THIS SUBSTANCE.

GLOVES: EMPLOYEE MUST WEAR APPROPRIATE PROTECTIVE GLOVES TO PREVENT CONTACT WITH THIS SUBSTANCE.

EYE PROTECTION: EMPLOYEE MUST WEAR SPLASH-PROOF OR DUST-RESISTANT SAFETY GOGGLES TO PREVENT EYE CONTACT WITH THIS SUBSTANCE.

EMERGENCY EYE WASH: WHERE THERE IS ANY POSSIBILITY THAT AN EMPLOYEE'S EYES MAY BE EXPOSED TO THIS SUBSTANCE, THE EMPLOYER SHOULD PROVIDE AN EYE WASH FOUNTAIN WITHIN THE IMMEDIATE WORK AREA FOR EMERGENCY USE.

AUTHORIZED BY- OCCUPATIONAL HEALTH SERVICES, INC.

CREATION DATE: 11/15/89 ***REVISION DATE:*** 05/15/90

MATERIAL SAFETY DATA SHEET

OCCUPATIONAL HEALTH SERVICES, INC.
AGRICULTURE AND PESTICIDE DIVISION
450 SEVENTH AVENUE, SUITE 2407
NEW YORK, NEW YORK 10123
1-800-445-MSDS OR (212) 967-1100

EMERGENCY CONTACT:
JOHN S. BRANSFORD, JR. (615) 292-1180

SUBSTANCE IDENTIFICATION

CAS-NUMBER 141-43-5

SUBSTANCE: **ETHANOLAMINE**

TRADE NAMES/SYNONYMS: ETHANOL, 2-AMINO-; AMINOETHANOL; BETA-AMINOETHANOL; 2-AMINOETHANOL; BETA-AMINOETHYL ALCOHOL; COLAMINE; BETA-ETHANOLAMINE; 2-ETHANOLAMINE; ETHYLOLAMINE; GLYCINOL; 2-

HYDROXYETHANAMINE; BETA-HYDROXYETHYLAMINE; 2-HYDROXYETHYLAMINE; MEA; MONOETHANOLAMINE; M-251; STCC 4935665; UN 2491; C2H7NO; PST08710

CHEMICAL FAMILY: ALCOHOL, ALIPHATIC AMINE

MOLECULAR FORMULA: H2-N-C-H2-C-H2-O-H

MOLECULAR WEIGHT: 61.08

CERCLA RATINGS (SCALE 0-3): HEALTH=3 FIRE=2 REACTIVITY=0 PERSISTENCE=0

NFPA RATINGS (SCALE 0-4): HEALTH=2 FIRE=2 REACTIVITY=0

COMPONENTS AND CONTAMINANTS

COMPONENT: ETHANOLAMINE ***PERCENT:*** 100
CAS# 141-43-5

OTHER CONTAMINANTS: NONE

EXPOSURE LIMITS: ETHANOLAMINE: 3 PPM (8 MG/M3) OSHA TWA; 6 PPM (15 MG/M3) OSHA STEL 3 PPM (8 MG/M3) ACGIH TWA; 6 PPM (15 MG/M3) ACGIH STEL

PHYSICAL DATA

DESCRIPTION: COLORLESS, VISCOUS, HYGROSCOPIC LIQUID WITH AN AMMONIA-LIKE ODOR.

BOILING POINT: 338 F (170 C) ***MELTING POINT:*** 51 F (10 C)

SPECIFIC GRAVITY: 1.0180 ***VISCOSITY:*** 19 CPS @ 20 C

VAPOR PRESSURE: 0.48 MMHG @ 20 C ***EVAPORATION RATE:*** (BUTYL ACETATE=1) >1

PH: 11.5 @ 1% SOLUTION ***SOLUBILITY IN WATER:*** COMPLETE

ODOR THRESHOLD: 3 PPM ***VAPOR DENSITY:*** 2.1

SOLVENT SOLUBILITY: SOLUBLE IN ALCOHOL, CHLOROFORM, ACETONE AND METHANOL; SLIGHTLY SOLUBLE IN BENZENE, ETHER. ALMOST INSOLUBLE IN CARBON TETRACHLORIDE, N-HEPTANE.

FIRE AND EXPLOSION DATA

FIRE AND EXPLOSION HAZARD: MODERATE FIRE HAZARD WHEN EXPOSED TO HEAT OR FLAME.

FLASH POINT: 186 F (86 C) (CC) ***UPPER EXPLOSIVE LIMIT:*** 23.5% @ 140 C

LOWER EXPLOSIVE LIMIT: 3.0% ***AUTOIGNITION TEMP.:*** 770 F (410 C)

FLAMMABILITY CLASS(OSHA): IIIA

FIREFIGHTING MEDIA: DRY CHEMICAL, CARBON DIOXIDE, HALON, WATER SPRAY OR ALCOHOL FOAM (1987 EMERGENCY RESPONSE GUIDEBOOK, DOT P 5800.4).
FOR LARGER FIRES, USE WATER SPRAY, FOG OR ALCOHOL FOAM (1987 EMERGENCY RESPONSE GUIDEBOOK, DOT P 5800.4).
ALCOHOL FOAM (NFPA 325M, FIRE HAZARD PROPERTIES OF FLAMMABLE LIQUIDS, GASES, AND VOLATILE SOLIDS, 1984).

FIREFIGHTING: MOVE CONTAINERS FROM FIRE AREA IF POSSIBLE. COOL CONTAINERS EXPOSED TO FLAMES WITH WATER FROM SIDE UNTIL WELL AFTER FIRE IS OUT. STAY AWAY FROM STORAGE TANK ENDS (1987 EMERGENCY RESPONSE GUIDEBOOK, DOT P 5800.4, GUIDE PAGE 60).
EXTINGUISH ONLY IF FLOW CAN BE STOPPED; USE FLOODING AMOUNTS OF WATER AS FOG, SOLID STREAMS MAY NOT BE EFFECTIVE. COOL CONTAINERS WITH FLOODING AMOUNTS OF WATER, APPLY FROM AS FAR A DISTANCE AS POSSIBLE. AVOID BREATHING CORROSIVE VAPORS, KEEP UPWIND.

TRANSPORTATION DATA

DEPARTMENT OF TRANSPORTATION HAZARD CLASSIFICATION 49 CFR 172.101: CORROSIVE MATERIAL
DEPARTMENT OF TRANSPORTATION LABELING REQUIREMENTS 49 CFR 172.101 AND SUBPART E: CORROSIVE
DEPARTMENT OF TRANSPORTATION PACKAGING REQUIREMENTS: 49 CFR 173.245 EXCEPTIONS: 49 CFR 173.244

TOXICITY

ETHANOLAMINE: IRRITATION DATA: 505 MG OPEN SKIN-RABBIT MODERATE; 763 UG EYE-RABBIT SEVERE. TOXICITY DATA: 0.58 MG/L/1 HOUR (580 MG/M3) INHALATION-GUINEA PIG LCLO (38MKAJ); 1000 MG/KG SKIN-RABBIT LD50; 2050 MG/KG ORAL-RAT LD50; 700 MG/KG ORAL-MOUSE LD50; 620 MG/KG ORAL-GUINEA PIG LD50; 1000 MG/KG ORAL-RABBIT LD50; 1500 MG/KG SUBCUTANEOUS-RAT LD50; 225 MG/KG INTRAVENOUSE-RAT LD50; 67 MG/KG INTRAPERITONEAL-RAT LD50; 50 MG/KG INTRAPERITONEAL-MOUSE LD50; 1750 MG/KG INTRAMUSCULAR-RAT LD50; MUTAGENIC DATA (RTECS); REPRODUCTIVE EFFECTS DATA (RTECS). CARCINOGEN STATUS: NONE. LOCAL EFFECTS: CORROSIVE- INHALATION, SKIN, AND EYES. ACUTE TOXICITY LEVEL: TOXIC BY DERMAL ABSORPTION; MODERATELY TOXIC BY INGESTION. TARGET EFFECTS: POISONING MAY AFFECT THE CENTRAL NERVOUS SYSTEM, LIVER, AND KIDNEYS. AT INCREASED RISK FROM EXPOSURE: PERSONS WITH PRE-EXISTING LIVER, KIDNEY, SKIN OR RESPIRATORY DISEASE.

HEALTH EFFECTS AND FIRST AID

INHALATION: ETHANOLAMINE: CORROSIVE. 1000 PPM IMMEDIATELY DANGEROUS TO LIFE OR HEALTH. **ACUTE EXPOSURE-** MAY CAUSE SEVERE RESPIRATORY TRACT IRRITATION POSSIBLY INCLUDING CHOUGHING, SORE THROAT, CHOKING, SHORTNESS OF BREATH, HEADACHE, PAIN IN THE NOSE, MOUTH AND THROAT AND BURNS OF THE MUCOUS MEMBRANES. IF SUFFICIENT QUANTITIES OF A CORROSIVE SUBSTANCE ARE INHALED, PULMONARY EDEMA MAY DEVELOP, OFTEN WITH A LATENT PERIOD OF 5-72 HOURS. THE SYMPTOMS MAY INCLUDE TIGHTNESS IN THE CHEST, DYSPNEA, FROTHY SPUTUM, CYANOSIS, AND DIZZINESS. PHYSICAL FINDINGS MAY INCLUDE WEAK, RAPID PULSE, HYPOTENSION, HEMOCONCENTRATION AND MOIST RALES. ANIMAL EXPOSURE RESULTED IN CENTRAL NERVOUS SYSTEM STIMULATION AND DEPRESSION. FOUR OUT OF SIX GUINEA PIGS DIED AFTER BEING EXPOSED TO 0.58 MG/K FOR 1 HOUR. PATHOLOGIC FINDINGS INCLUDED PULMONARY IRRITATION, AND DEGENERATIVE LIVER AND KIDNEY DAMAGE. **CHRONIC EXPOSURE-** DEPENDING ON THE CONCENTRATION AND DURATION OF EXPOSURE, REPEATED OR PROLONGED EXPOSURE TO CORROSIVE SUBSTANCES MAY CAUSE INFLAMMATORY AND ULCERATIVE CHANGES IN THE MOUTH AND POSSIBLY BRONCHIAL AND GASTROINTESTINAL DISTURBANCES. CHRONIC EXPOSURE OF ANIMALS RESULTED IN LETHARGY, APATHY, POOR APPETITE, DECREASED ALERTNESS AND CHANGES IN THE LUNGS, LIVER AND KIDNEYS.

FIRST AID- REMOVE FROM EXPOSURE AREA TO FRESH AIR IMMEDIATELY. IF BREATHING HAS STOPPED, GIVE ARTIFICIAL RESPIRATION. MAINTAIN AIRWAY AND BLOOD PRESSURE AND ADMINISTER OXYGEN IF AVAILABLE. KEEP AFFECTED PERSON WARM AND AT REST. TREAT SYMPTOMATICALLY AND SUPPORTIVELY. ADMINISTRATION OF OXYGEN SHOULD BE PERFORMED BY QUALIFIED PERSONNEL. GET MEDICAL ATTENTION IMMEDIATELY.

SKIN CONTACT: ETHANOLAMINE: CORROSIVE/TOXIC. **ACUTE EXPOSURE-** THE VAPOR MAY BE IRRITATING. CONTACT WITH THE UNDILUTED MATERIAL MAY CAUSE SEVERE IRRITATION WITH ERYTHEMA AND BLISTERING. WHEN APPLIED TO HUMAN SKIN FOR 1.5 HOURS REDNESS AND INFILTRATION OF THE SKIN OCCURRED. 1000 MG/KG WAS LETHAL TO ANIMALS TESTED BUT SYMPTOMS WERE NOT REPORTED. **CHRONIC EXPOSURE-** EFFECTS DEPEND ON CONCENTRATION AND DURATION OF EXPOSURE. REPEATED OR PROLONGED CONTACT WITH CORROSIVE SUBSTANCES MAY RESULT IN DERMATITIS OR EFFECTS SIMILAR TO ACUTE EXPOSURE.

FIRST AID- REMOVE CONTAMINATED CLOTHING AND SHOES IMMEDIATELY. WASH AFFECTED AREA WITH SOAP OR MILD DETERGENT AND LARGE AMOUNTS OF WATER UNTIL NO EVIDENCE OF CHEMICAL REMAINS (AT LEAST 15-20 MINUTES). IN CASE OF CHEMICAL BURNS, COVER AREA WITH STERILE, DRY DRESSING. BANDAGE SECURELY, BUT NOT TOO TIGHTLY. GET MEDICAL ATTENTION IMMEDIATELY.

EYE CONTACT: ETHANOLAMINE: CORROSIVE. **ACUTE EXPOSURE-** DIRECT CONTACT WITH CORROSIVE SUBSTANCES MAY CAUSE SEVERE IRRITATION, PAIN, AND BURNS, POSSIBLY SEVERE. THE DEGREE OF INJURY DEPENDS ON THE CONCENTRATION AND DURATION OF CONTACT. THE FULL EXTENT OF THE INJURY MAY NOT BE IMMEDIATELY APPARENT. **CHRONIC EXPOSURE-** EFFECTS DEPEND ON CONCENTRATION AND DURATION OF EXPOSURE. REPEATED OR PROLONGED CONTACT WITH CORROSIVE SUBSTANCES MAY RESULT IN CONJUNCTIVITIS OR EFFECTS AS IN ACUTE EXPOSURE.

FIRST AID- WASH EYES IMMEDIATELY WITH LARGE AMOUNTS OF WATER, OCCASIONALLY LIFTING UPPER AND LOWER LIDS, UNTIL NO EVIDENCE OF CHEMICAL REMAINS (AT LEAST 15-20 MINUTES). CONTINUE IRRIGATING WITH NORMAL SALINE UNTIL THE PH HAS RETURNED TO NORMAL (30-60 MINUTES). COVER WITH STERILE BANDAGES. GET MEDICAL ATTENTION IMMEDIATELY.

INGESTION: ETHANOLAMINE: CORROSIVE. **ACUTE EXPOSURE-** MAY CAUSE ABDOMINAL PAIN, NAUSEA, VOMITING AND MUCOSAL BURNS OF THE MOUTH AND ESOPHAGUS. THERE MAY BE DISCOLORATION OF THE TISSUES. SWALLOWING AND SPEECH MAY BE DIFFICULT AT FIRST AND THEN ALMOST IMPOSSIBLE. THE EFFECTS ON THE ESOPHAGUS AND GASTROINTESTINAL TRACT MAY RANGE FROM IRRITATION TO SEVERE CORROSION. EDEMA OF THE EPIGLOTTIS AND SHOCK MAY OCCUR. **CHRONIC EXPOSURE-** DEPENDING ON THE CONCENTRATION, REPEATED INGESTION OF CORROSIVE SUBSTANCES MAY RESULT IN EFFECTS AS WITH ACUTE INGESTION. DOSE DEPENDENT INCREASES IN EMBRYOTOXICITY AND LETHALITY (MALFORMATION, INTRAUTERINE DEATHS, AND INTRAUTERINE GROWTH RETARDATION) OCCURRED WHEN PREGNANT RATS WERE GIVEN 500, 300, OR 50 MG/KG PER DAY OF ORGANOGENESIS.

FIRST AID- DILUTE THE ALKALI BY GIVING WATER OR MILK IMMEDIATELY AND ALLOW VOMITING TO OCCUR. AVOID GASTRIC LAVAGE OR EMETICS. ESOPHAGOSCOPY IS THE ONLY WAY TO EXCLUDE THE POSSIBLITY OF CORROSION IN THE UPPER GASTROINTESTINAL TRACT; IF CORROSION IS SUSPECTED, ESOPHAGOSCOPY SHOULD USUALLY BE PERFORMED WITHIN 24 HOURS (DREISBACH, HANDBOOK OF POISONING, 12TH ED.). MAINTAIN AIRWAY AND TREAT SHOCK. IF VOMITING

OCCURS, KEEP HEAD BELOW HIPS TO HELP PREVENT ASPIRATION. GET MEDICAL ATTENTION IMMEDIATELY.

ANTIDOTE: NO SPECIFIC ANTIDOTE. TREAT SYMPTOMATICALLY AND SUPPORTIVELY.

REACTIVITY

REACTIVITY: STABLE UNDER NORMAL TEMPERATURES AND PRESSURES.

INCOMPATIBILITIES: ETHANOLAMINE: ACETIC ACID: TEMPERATURE AND PRESSURE INCREASE IN CLOSED CONTAINER. ACETIC ANHYDRIDE: TEMPERATURE AND PRESSURE INCREASE IN CLOSED CONTAINER. ACIDS: TEMPERATURE AND PRESSURE INCREASE IN CLOSED CONTAINER. ACROLEIN: TEMPERATURE AND PRESSURE INCREASE IN CLOSED CONTAINER. ACRYLIC ACID: TEMPERATURE AND PRESSURE INCREASE IN CLOSED CONTAINER. ACRYLONITRILE: TEMPERATURE AND PRESSURE INCREASE IN CLOSED CONTAINER. ALUMINUM: CORRODES ABOVE 100 C. CELLULOSE NITRATE: IGNITES ON CONTACT. CHLOROSULFONIC ACID: TEMPERATURE AND PRESSURE INCREASE IN CLOSED CONTAINER. COPPER, COPPER COMPOUNDS, COPPER ALLOYS: CORRODES. N,N'-DIMETHYL-N,N'DINITROSOTEREPTHALAMIDE: IGNITION. EPICHLOROHYDRIN: TEMPERATURE AND PRESSURE INCREASE IN CLOSED CONTAINER. HYDROCHLORIC ACID: TEMPERATURE AND PRESSURE INCREASE IN CLOSED CONTAINER. HYDROFLUORIC ACID: TEMPERATURE AND PRESSURE INCREASE IN CLOSED CONTAINER. IRON (GALVANIZED): CORRODES. MESITYL OXIDE: TEMPERATURE AND PRESSURE INCREASE IN CLOSED CONTAINER. NITRIC ACID: TEMPERATURE AND PRESSURE INCREASE IN CLOSED CONTAINER. OLEUM: TEMPERATURE AND PRESSURE INCREASE IN CLOSED CONTAINER. OXIDIZERS: FIRE AND EXPLOSION HAZARD. PLASTICS: CORRODES. BETA-PROPIOLACTONE: TEMPERATURE AND PRESSURE INCREASE IN CLOSED CONTAINER. RUBBER: CORRODES. SULFURIC ACID: TEMPERATURE AND PRESSURE INCREASE IN CLOSED CONTAINER. VINYL ACETATE: TEMPERATURE AND PRESSURE INCREASE IN CLOSED CONTAINER. SEE ALSO AMINES.

AMINES: ACROLEIN: EXOTHERMIC POLYMERIZATION. CALCIUM HYPOCHLORITE: FORMATION OF EXPLOSIVE CHLOROAMINE. MALEIC ANHYDRIDE: EXPLOSIVE DECOMPOSITION. NITROSYL PERCHLORATE: EXPLOSIVE REACTION. SODIUM HYPOCHLORITE: FORMATION OF EXPLOSIVE CHLOROAMINE. TRI-ISO-BUTYL ALUMINUM: VIOLENT REACTION.

DECOMPOSITION: THERMAL DECOMPOSITION PRODUCTS MAY INCLUDE TOXIC OXIDES OF CARBON AND NITROGEN.

POLYMERIZATION: HAZARDOUS POLYMERIZATION HAS NOT BEEN REPORTED TO OCCUR UNDER NORMAL TEMPERATURES AND PRESSURES.

STORAGE AND DISPOSAL

OBSERVE ALL FEDERAL, STATE AND LOCAL REGULATIONS WHEN STORING OR DISPOSING OF THIS SUBSTANCE. FOR ASSISTANCE, CONTACT THE DISTRICT DIRECTOR OF THE ENVIRONMENTAL PROTECTION AGENCY.

STORAGE

PROTECT AGAINST PHYSICAL DAMAGE. STORE IN WELL-VENTILATED AREA FREE OF SOURCES OF IGNITION. SEPARATE FROM OXIDIZING MATERIALS (NFPA 49, HAZARDOUS CHEMICALS DATA).
STORE AWAY FROM INCOMPATIBLE SUBSTANCES.

DISPOSAL

DISPOSAL MUST BE IN ACCORDANCE WITH STANDARDS APPLICABLE TO GENERATORS OF HAZARDOUS WASTE, 40 CFR 262. EPA HAZARDOUS WASTE NUMBER D002. 100 POUND CERCLA SECTION 103 REPORTABLE QUANTITY.

CONDITIONS TO AVOID

MAY BURN BUT DOES NOT IGNITE READILY. FLAMMABLE, POISONOUS GASES MAY ACCUMULATE IN TANKS AND HOPPER CARS. MAY IGNITE COMBUSTIBLES (WOOD, PAPER, OIL, ETC.).

SPILL AND LEAK PROCEDURES

OCCUPATIONAL SPILL: DO NOT TOUCH SPILLED MATERIAL. STOP LEAK IF YOU CAN DO IT WITHOUT RISK. FOR SMALL SPILLS, TAKE UP WITH SAND OR OTHER ABSORBENT MATERIAL AND PLACE INTO CONTAINERS FOR LATER DISPOSAL. FOR SMALL DRY SPILLS, WITH CLEAN SHOVEL PLACE MATERIAL INTO CLEAN, DRY CONTAINER AND COVER. MOVE CONTAINERS FROM SPILL AREA. FOR LARGER SPILLS, DIKE FAR AHEAD OF SPILL FOR LATER DISPOSAL. KEEP UNNECESSARY PEOPLE AWAY. ISOLATE HAZARD AREA AND DENY ENTRY.

PROTECTIVE EQUIPMENT

VENTILATION: PROVIDE LOCAL EXHAUST OR PROCESS ENCLOSURE VENTILATION TO MEET PUBLISHED EXPOSURE LIMITS.

RESPIRATOR: THE FOLLOWING RESPIRATORS AND MAXIMUM USE CONCENTRATIONS ARE RECOMMENDATIONS BY THE U.S. DEPARTMENT OF HEALTH AND HUMAN SERVICES, NIOSH POCKET GUIDE TO CHEMICAL HAZARDS; NIOSH CRITERIA DOCUMENTS OR BY THE U.S. DEPARTMENT OF LABOR, 29 CFR 1910 SUBPART Z. THE SPECIFIC RESPIRATOR SELECTED MUST BE BASED ON CONTAMINATION LEVELS FOUND IN THE WORK PLACE, MUST NOT EXCEED THE WORKING LIMITS OF THE RESPIRATOR AND BE JOINTLY APPROVED BY THE NATIONAL INSTITUTE FOR OCCUPATIONAL SAFETY AND HEALTH AND THE MINE SAFETY AND HEALTH ADMINISTRATION (NIOSH-MSHA).

ETHANOLAMINE:

30 PPM- ANY SUPPLIED-AIR RESPIRATOR. ANY SELF-CONTAINED BREATHING APPARATUS. ANY CHEMICAL CARTRIDGE RESPIRATOR WITH CARTRIDGE(S) PROVIDING PROTECTION AGAINST ETHANOLAMINE.

75 PPM- ANY SUPPLIED-AIR RESPIRATOR OPERATED IN A CONTINUOUS FLOW MODE. ANY POWERED AIR-PURIFYING RESPIRATOR WITH CARTRIDGE(S) PROVIDING PROTECTION AGAINST ETHANOLAMINE.

150 PPM- ANY CHEMICAL CARTRIDGE RESPIRATOR WITH A FULL FACEPIECE AND CARTRIDGE(S) PROVIDING PROTECTION AGAINST ETHANOLAMINE. ANY AIR-PURIFYING FULL FACEPIECE RESPIRATOR (GAS MASK) WITH A CHIN-STYLE OR FRONT- OR BACK-MOUNTED CANISTER PROVIDING PROTECTION AGAINST ETHANOLAMINE. ANY SUPPLIED-AIR RESPIRATOR WITH A FULL FACEPIECE. ANY SELF-CONTAINED BREATHING APPARATUS WITH A FULL FACEPIECE.

1000 PPM- ANY SUPPLIED-AIR RESPIRATOR WITH A FULL FACEPIECE AND OPERATED IN A PRESSURE-DEMAND OR OTHER POSITIVE PRESSURE MODE.

ESCAPE- ANY AIR-PURIFYING FULL FACEPIECE RESPIRATOR (GAS MASK) WITH A CHIN-STYLE OR FRONT- OR BACK-MOUNTED CANISTER PROVIDING PROTECTION AGAINST ETHANOLAMINE. ANY APPROPRIATE ESCAPE-TYPE SELF-CONTAINED BREATHING APPARATUS.

FOR FIREFIGHTING AND OTHER IMMEDIATELY DANGEROUS TO LIFE OR HEALTH CONDITIONS:

SELF-CONTAINED BREATHING APPARATUS WITH FULL FACEPIECE OPERATED IN PRESSURE-DEMAND OR OTHER POSITIVE PRESSURE MODE.

SUPPLIED-AIR RESPIRATOR WITH FULL FACEPIECE AND OPERATED IN PRESSURE-DEMAND OR OTHER POSITIVE PRESSURE MODE IN COMBINATION WITH AN AUXILIARY SELF-CONTAINED BREATHING APPARATUS OPERATED IN PRESSURE-DEMAND OR OTHER POSITIVE PRESSURE MODE.

CLOTHING: EMPLOYEE MUST WEAR APPROPRIATE PROTECTIVE (IMPERVIOUS) CLOTHING AND EQUIPMENT TO PREVENT ANY POSSIBILITY OF SKIN CONTACT WITH THIS SUBSTANCE.

GLOVES: EMPLOYEE MUST WEAR APPROPRIATE PROTECTIVE GLOVES TO PREVENT CONTACT WITH THIS SUBSTANCE.

EYE PROTECTION: EMPLOYEE MUST WEAR SPLASH-PROOF OR DUST-RESISTANT SAFETY GOGGLES AND A FACESHIELD TO PREVENT CONTACT WITH THIS SUBSTANCE.

EMERGENCY WASH FACILITIES: WHERE THERE IS ANY POSSIBILITY THAT AN EMPLOYEE'S EYES AND/OR SKIN MAY BE EXPOSED TO THIS SUBSTANCE, THE EMPLOYER SHOULD PROVIDE AN EYE WASH FOUNTAIN AND QUICK DRENCH SHOWER WITHIN THE IMMEDIATE WORK AREA FOR EMERGENCY USE.

AUTHORIZED BY- OCCUPATIONAL HEALTH SERVICES, INC.
CREATION DATE: 11/16/89 ***REVISION DATE:*** 05/29/90

MATERIAL SAFETY DATA SHEET

OCCUPATIONAL HEALTH SERVICES, INC.
AGRICULTURE AND PESTICIDE DIVISION
450 SEVENTH AVENUE, SUITE 2407
NEW YORK, NEW YORK 10123
1-800-445-MSDS OR (212) 967-1100

EMERGENCY CONTACT:
JOHN S. BRANSFORD, JR. (615) 292-1180

SUBSTANCE IDENTIFICATION

CAS-NUMBER 563-12-2

SUBSTANCE: <u>ETHION</u>

TRADE NAMES/SYNONYMS: PHOSPHORODITHIOIC ACID, S,S'-METHYLENE O,O,O',O'-TETRAETHYL ESTER; O,O,O',O'-TETRAETHYL S,S'-METHYLENE BIS(PHOSPHORODITHIOATE); S,S'-METHYLENE BIS (O,O-DIETHYL PHOSPHORODITHIOATE); S,S'-METHYLENE O,O,O',O'-TETRAETHYL DI(PHOSPHORODITHIOATE); ETHYL METHYLENE PHOSPHORODITHIOATE (((ETO)2P(S)S)2CH2); TETRAETHYL S,S'-METHYLENE BIS(PHOSPHOROTHIOLOTHIONATE); O,O,O',O'-TETRAETHYL S,S'-METHYLENE BISPHOSPHORODITHIOATE; O,O,O',O'-TETRAETHYL-S,S'-METHYLENE DI(PHOSPHORODITHIOATE); ENT 24,105; STCC 4921567; PST08720

CHEMICAL FAMILY: ORGANOPHOSPHATE

MOLECULAR FORMULA: C9-H22-O4-P2-S2

MOLECULAR WEIGHT: 384.48

CERCLA RATINGS (SCALE 0-3): HEALTH=3 FIRE=1 REACTIVITY=0 PERSISTENCE=1
NFPA RATINGS (SCALE 0-4): HEALTH=4 FIRE=1 REACTIVITY=0

COMPONENTS AND CONTAMINANTS

COMPONENT: ETHION ***PERCENT:*** 100
CAS# 563-12-2

EXPOSURE LIMITS: ETHION: 0.4 MG/M3 OSHA TWA (SKIN) 0.4 MG/M3 ACGIH TWA (SKIN)
1000 POUNDS SARA SECTION 302 THRESHOLD PLANNING QUANTITY 10 POUNDS SARA SECTION 304 REPORTABLE QUANTITY 10 POUNDS CERCLA SECTION 103 REPORTABLE QUANTITY

PHYSICAL DATA

DESCRIPTION: ODORLESS, COLORLESS LIQUID; TECHNICAL GRADE HAS A VERY DISAGREEABLE ODOR. ***BOILING POINT:*** 302 F (150 C) DECOMPOSES
MELTING POINT: 10 F (-12 C) ***SPECIFIC GRAVITY:*** 1.220 @ 20 C
VAPOR PRESSURE: 0.0000015 MMHG @ 25C ***SOLUBILITY IN WATER:*** SLIGHTLY SOLUBLE
SOLVENT SOLUBILITY: ACETONE, XYLENE, CHLOROFORM, METHYLATED NAPHTHALENE, KEROSENE, PETROLEUM OILS, ETHANOL, METHANOL, 1% METHYL ETHYL KETONE, 1% BENZENE, MOST ORGANIC SOLVENTS

FIRE AND EXPLOSION DATA

FIRE AND EXPLOSION HAZARD: SLIGHT FIRE HAZARD WHEN EXPOSED TO HEAT OR FLAME.
FIREFIGHTING MEDIA: DRY CHEMICAL, CARBON DIOXIDE, HALON, WATER SPRAY OR STANDARD FOAM (1987 EMERGENCY RESPONSE GUIDEBOOK, DOT P 5800.4). FOR LARGER FIRES, USE WATER SPRAY, FOG OR STANDARD FOAM (1987 EMERGENCY RESPONSE GUIDEBOOK, DOT P 5800.4).
FIREFIGHTING: MOVE CONTAINERS FROM FIRE AREA IF POSSIBLE. FIGHT FIRE FROM MAXIMUM DISTANCE. STAY AWAY FROM STORAGE TANK ENDS. DIKE FIRE CONTROL WATER FOR LATER DISPOSAL. DO NOT SCATTER MATERIAL (1987 EMERGENCY RESPONSE GUIDEBOOK, DOT P 5800.4, GUIDE PAGE 55). EXTINGUISH ONLY IF FLOW CAN BE STOPPED; USE FLOODING AMOUNTS OF WATER AS FOG, SOLID STREAMS MAY BE INEFFECTIVE. COOL CONTAINERS WITH FLOODING AMOUNTS OF WATER FROM AS FAR A DISTANCE AS POSSIBLE. USE WATER SPRAY TO ABSORB TOXIC VAPORS. AVOID BREATHING TOXIC VAPORS; KEEP UPWIND. CONSIDER EVACUATION OF DOWNWIND AREA IF MATERIAL IS LEAKING.

TRANSPORTATION DATA

DEPARTMENT OF TRANSPORTATION HAZARD CLASSIFICATION 49 CFR 172.101: POISON B
DEPARTMENT OF TRANSPORTATION LABELING REQUIREMENTS 49 CFR 172.101 AND SUBPART E: POISON
DEPARTMENT OF TRANSPORTATION PACKAGING REQUIREMENTS: 49 CFR 173.346 EXCEPTIONS: 49 CFR 173.345

TOXICITY

ETHION: TOXICITY DATA: 864 MG/M3 INHALATION-RAT LC50; 890 MG/KG SKIN-RABBIT LD50; 62 MG/KG SKIN-RAT LD50; 915 MG/KG SKIN-GUINEA PIG LD50; 100 UG/KG ORAL-HUMAN TDLO; 15,700 UG/KG ORAL-INFANT TDLO; 13 MG/KG ORAL-RAT LD50; 40 MG/KG ORAL-MOUSE LD50; 40 MG/KG ORAL-GUINEA PIG LD50; 26 MG/KG INTRAPERITONEAL-RAT LD50; 35 MG/KG INTRAPERITONEAL-MOUSE LD50; 55 MG/KG UNREPORTED-RAT LD50. CARCINOGEN STATUS: NONE. ACUTE TOXICITY LEVEL: HIGHLY TOXIC BY INHALATION AND INGESTION; TOXIC BY DERMAL ABSORPTION. TARGET EFFECTS: CHOLINESTERASE INHIBITOR. POISONING MAY AFFECT THE NERVOUS SYSTEM.* AT INCREASED RISK FROM EXPOSURE: PERSONS WITH RESPIRATORY AILMENTS, RECENT EXPOSURE TO CHOLINESTERASE INHIBITORS OR IMPAIRED CHOLINESTERASE PRODUCTION, OR LIVER MALFUNCTION.* ADDITIONAL DATA: MAY CROSS THE PLACENTA. HIGH ENVIRONMENTAL TEMPERATURES OR EXPOSURE OF THE CHEMICAL TO VISIBLE OR ULTRAVIOLET LIGHT MAY ENHANCE THE TOXICITY. INTERACTIONS WITH MEDICATIONS MAY OCCUR.*
* MAY BE BASED ON GENERAL INFORMATION ON ORGANOPHOSPHATES.

HEALTH EFFECTS AND FIRST AID

INHALATION: ETHION: HIGHLY TOXIC. SEE INFORMATION ON ORGANOPHOSPHATES. ORGANOPHOSPHATES: CHOLINESTERASE INHIBITOR. **ACUTE EXPOSURE-** WHEN INHALED, THE FIRST EFFECTS OF CHOLINESTERASE INHIBITORS ARE USUALLY RESPIRATORY AND MAY INCLUDE NASAL HYPEREMIA AND WATERY DISCHARGE, COUGH, CHEST DISCOMFORT, DYSPNEA, AND WHEEZING DUE TO INCREASED BRONCHIAL SECRETIONS AND BRONCHOCONSTRICTION. IF SUFFICIENT AMOUNTS ARE ABSORBED, OTHER SYSTEMIC EFFECTS MAY BEGIN WITHIN A FEW MINUTES OR BE DELAYED FOR UP TO 12 HOURS. SYMPTOMS MAY INCLUDE PALLOR, NAUSEA, VOMITING, DIARRHEA, ABDOMINAL CRAMPS, HEADACHE, DIZZINESS, OCULAR PAIN, BLURRED VISION, MIOSIS OR IN SOME CASES, ESPECIALLY INITIALLY, MYDRIASIS, LACRIMATION, SALIVATION, SWEATING, AND CONFUSION. OTHER REPORTED CENTRAL NERVOUS SYSTEM OR NEUROMUSCULAR EFFECTS MAY INCLUDE ATAXIA, SLURRED SPEECH, AREFLEXIA, WEAKNESS, FATIGUE, FASCICULATIONS, TWITCHING, TREMORS POSSIBLY OF THE TONGUE AND EYELIDS, AND EVENTUALLY PARALYSIS OF THE EXTREMITIES AND POSSIBLY OF THE RESPIRATORY MUSCLES. IN SEVERE CASES THERE MAY ALSO BE INVOLUNTARY DEFECATION AND URINATION, CYANOSIS, PSYCHOSIS, HYPERGLYCEMIA, ACUTE PANCREATITIS, CARDIAC IRREGULARITIES, PULMONARY EDEMA, UNCONSCIOUSNESS, CONVULSIONS, AND COMA. DEATH IS PRIMARILY DUE TO RESPIRATORY FAILURE, ALTHOUGH CARDIOVASCULAR EFFECTS INCLUDING CARDIAC ARREST MAY ALSO BE IMPLICATED. LONG TERM SEQUELAE ARE RARE BUT MAY INCLUDE NEUROPSYCHIATRIC DISORDERS AND MYOPATHY WITH MUSCLE TENDERNESS. SOME ORGANOPHOSPHATES MAY CAUSE A DELAYED NEUROPATHY BEGINNING 1-4 WEEKS AFTER AN ACUTE EXPOSURE WHICH MAY OR MAY NOT HAVE CAUSED ACUTE CHOLINERGIC EFFECTS. NUMBNESS, TINGLING, WEAKNESS AND CRAMPING BEGINNING SYMMETRICALLY IN THE LOWER LIMBS MAY PROGRESS TO ATAXIA AND PARALYSIS. IN SEVERE CASES, UPPER LIMB INVOLVEMENT IS POSSIBLE AND FLACCID PARALYSIS MAY PROGRESS TO SPASTIC PARALYSIS WITH EXAGGERATED REFLEXES. IMPROVEMENT MAY OCCUR OVER MONTHS TO YEARS, BUT SOME RESIDUAL IMPAIRMENT USUALLY REMAINS. **CHRONIC EXPOSURE-** REPEATED OR PROLONGED EXPOSURE MAY RESULT IN THE EFFECTS OF ACUTE EXPOSURE INCLUDING THE DELAYED NEUROPATHY. OTHER EFFECTS REPORTED IN WORKERS REPEATEDLY EXPOSED INCLUDE IMPAIRED MEMORY AND CONCENTRATION, ACUTE PSYCHOSIS, SEVERE DEPRESSIONS, IRRITABILTY, CONFUSION, APATHY, EMOTIONAL LABILITY, SOCIAL WITHDRAWAL, CONFUSION, HEADACHE, SPEECH DIFFICULTIES, DELAYED REACTION TIMES, SPATIAL DISORIENTATION, NIGHTMARES, SLEEPWALKING, AND DROWSINESS OR INSOMNIA. AN INFLUENZA-LIKE CONDITION WITH HEADACHE, NAUSEA, WEAKNESS, ANOREXIA AND MALAISE HAS ALSO BEEN REPORTED.
FIRST AID- REMOVE FROM EXPOSURE AREA TO FRESH AIR IMMEDIATELY. IF BREATHING HAS STOPPED, GIVE ARTIFICIAL RESPIRATION. MAINTAIN AIRWAY AND BLOOD PRESSURE AND ADMINISTER OXYGEN IF AVAILABLE. KEEP AFFECTED PERSON WARM AND AT REST. TREAT SYMPTOMATICALLY AND SUPPORTIVELY. ADMINISTRATION OF OXYGEN SHOULD BE PERFORMED BY QUALIFIED PERSONNEL. GET MEDICAL ATTENTION IMMEDIATELY.

SKIN CONTACT: ETHION: TOXIC. SEE INFORMATION ON ORGANOPHOSPHATES. ORGANOPHOSPHATES: CHOLINESTERASE INHIBITOR. **ACUTE EXPOSURE-** LOCALIZED SWEATING AND FASCICULATIONS MAY OCCUR AT THE SITE OF CONTACT. IF SUFFICIENT AMOUNTS ARE ABSORBED, OTHER EFFECTS OF CHOLINESTERASE INHIBITION AS DESCRIBED IN ACUTE INHALATION MAY OCCUR. SYMPTOMS MAY BE DELAYED 2-3 HOURS, BUT USUALLY NO MORE THAN 12 HOURS. THE RATE OF ABSORPTION IS INCREASED BY THE PRESENCE OF DERMATITIS OR HIGH AMBIENT TEMPERATURES. DELAYED NEUROPATHY IS ALSO POSSIBLE. **CHRONIC EXPOSURE-** REPEATED OR PROLONGED EXPOSURE MAY CAUSE EFFECTS AS DESCRIBED IN ACUTE EXPOSURE. SOME ORGANOPHOSPHATES MAY CAUSE SENSITIZATION.
FIRST AID- REMOVE CONTAMINATED CLOTHING IMMEDIATELY. WASH CONTAMINATED AREAS WITH SOAP AND WATER FOLLOWED BY ALCOHOL (ARENA, POISONING, 4TH ED.). EMERGENCY PERSONNEL SHOULD WEAR GLOVES AND AVOID CONTAMINATION. TREAT RESPIRATORY DIFFICULTY WITH ARTIFICIAL RESPIRATION. GET MEDICAL ATTENTION IMMEDIATELY.

EYE CONTACT: ETHION: SEE INFORMATION ON ORGANOPHOSPHATES. ORGANOPHOSPHATES: CHOLINESTERASE INHIBITOR. **ACUTE EXPOSURE-** DIRECT CONTACT MAY CAUSE PAIN, HYPEREMIA, LACRIMATION, TWITCHING OF THE EYELIDS, MIOSIS, AND CILIARY MUSCLE SPASM WITH LOSS OF ACCOMODATION, BLURRED OR DIMMED VISION AND BROWACHE. SOMETIMES MYDRIASIS MAY OCCUR INSTEAD OF MIOSIS. WITH SUFFICIENT EXPOSURE, OTHER SYMPTOMS OF CHOLINESTERASE INHIBITION AS DESCRIBED IN ACUTE INHALATION MAY OCCUR. **CHRONIC EXPOSURE-** REPEATED OR PROLONGED EXPOSURE MAY CAUSE EFFECTS AS DESCRIBED IN ACUTE EXPOSURE. SOME COMPOUNDS HAVE CAUSED TOXIC EFFECTS ON THE CRYSTALLINE LENS, CONJUNCTIVAL THICKENING AND OBSTRUCTION OF THE NASOLACRIMAL CANALS WHEN USED AS MIOTIC EYEDROPS.
FIRST AID- IRRIGATE EYES WITH WATER OR SALINE SOLUTION. IF SYMPTOMS OF POISONING OCCUR, TREAT RESPIRATORY DIFFICULTY WITH ARTIFICIAL RESPIRATION AND OXYGEN. OBSERVE PATIENT FOR AT LEAST 24-36 HOURS (GOSSELIN, CLINICAL TOXICOLOGY OF COMMERCIAL PRODUCTS, 5TH ED.). GET MEDICAL ATTENTION IMMEDIATELY. OXYGEN SHOULD BE ADMINISTERED BY QUALIFIED MEDICAL PERSONNEL.

INGESTION: ETHION: HIGHLY TOXIC. SEE INFORMATION ON ORGANOPHOSPHATES. ORGANOPHOSPHATES: CHOLINESTERASE INHIBITOR. **ACUTE EXPOSURE-** WHEN

INGESTED, THE FIRST EFFECTS MAY BE NAUSEA, VOMITING, ANOREXIA, ABDOMINAL CRAMPS AND DIARRHEA. GASTROINTESTINAL ABSORPTION MAY CAUSE SYMPTOMS OF CHOLINESTERASE INHIBITION AS DESCRIBED IN ACUTE INHALATION. SYMPTOMS MAY BEGIN WITHIN MINUTES OR BE DELAYED FOR HOURS. DELAYED EFFECTS INCLUDING NEUROPATHY MAY ALSO OCCUR. **CHRONIC EXPOSURE-** REPEATED INGESTION MAY CAUSE EFFECTS AS DESCRIBED IN ACUTE EXPOSURE.

FIRST AID- IF PERSON IS ALERT AND RESPIRATION IS NOT DEPRESSED, GIVE SYRUP OF IPECAC FOLLOWED BY WATER (IF VOMITING OCCURS, KEEP HEAD BELOW HIPS TO PREVENT ASPIRATION). IF CONSCIOUSNESS LEVEL DECLINES OR VOMITING HAS NOT OCCURRED IN 15 MINUTES EMPTY STOMACH BY GASTRIC LAVAGE WITH THE AID OF CUFFED ENDOTRACHEAL TUBE USING ISOTONIC SALINE OR 5% SODIUM BICARBONATE FOLLOW WITH ACTIVATED CHARCOAL. ESTABLISH AND MAINTAIN AIRWAY. TREAT RESPIRATORY DIFFICULTY WITH ARTIFICIAL RESPIRATION AND OXYGEN. DO NOT GIVE MORPHINE, AMINOPHYLLINE, PHENOTHIAZINES, RESERPINE, FUROSEMIDE, OR ETHACRYNIC ACID (MORGAN, RECOGNITION AND MANAGEMENT OF PESTICIDE POISONINGS, 3RD ED.). TREAT SYMPTOMATICALLY AND SUPPORTIVELY. ADMINISTRATION OF OXYGEN AND LAVAGE MUST BE PERFORMED BY QUALIFIED MEDICAL PERSONNEL. GET MEDICAL ATTENTION IMMEDIATELY.

ANTIDOTE: THE FOLLOWING ANTIDOTE(S) HAVE BEEN RECOMMENDED. HOWEVER, THE DECISION AS TO WHETHER THE SEVERITY OF POISONING REQUIRES ADMINISTRATION OF ANY ANTIDOTE AND ACTUAL DOSE REQUIRED SHOULD BE MADE BY QUALIFIED MEDICAL PERSONNEL.

FOR CHOLINESTERASE INHIBITORS: ESTABLISH CLEAR AIRWAY AND TISSUE OXYGENATION BY ASPIRATION OF SECRETIONS, AND IF NECESSARY, BY ASSISTED PULMONARY VENTILATION WITH OXYGEN. IMPROVE TISSUE OXYGENATION AS MUCH AS POSSIBLE BEFORE ADMINISTERING ATROPINE TO MINIMIZE THE RISK OF VENTRICULAR FIBRILLATION. ADMINISTER ATROPINE SULFATE INTRAVENOUSLY, OR INTRAMUSCULARLY IF IV INJECTION IS NOT POSSIBLE. IN MODERATELY SEVERE POISONING ADMINISTER ATROPINE SULFATE, 0.4-2.0 MG REPEATED EVERY 15 MINUTES UNTIL ATROPINIZATION IS ACHIEVED (TACHYCARDIA, FLUSHING, DRY MOUTH, MYDRIASIS). MAINTAIN ATROPINIZATION BY REPEATED DOSES FOR 2-12 HOURS, OR LONGER, DEPENDING ON THE SEVERITY OF POISONING. THE APPEARANCE OF RALES IN THE LUNG BASES, MIOSIS, SALIVATION, NAUSEA, BRADYCARDIA, ARE ALL INDICATIONS OF INADEQUATE ATROPINIZATION. SEVERELY POISONED INDIVIDUALS MAY EXHIBIT REMARKABLE TOLERANCE TO ATROPINE; TWO OR MORE TIMES THE DOSAGES SUGGESTED ABOVE MAY BE NEEDED. PERSONS NOT POISONED OR ONLY SLIGHTLY POISONED, HOWEVER, MAY DEVELOP SIGNS OF ATROPINE TOXICITY FROM SUCH LARGE DOSAGES: FEVER, MUSCLE FIBRILLATIONS, AND DELIRIUM ARE THE MAIN SIGNS OF ATROPINE TOXICITY. IF THESE SIGNS APPEAR WHILE THE PATIENT IS FULLY ATROPINIZED, ATROPINE ADMINISTRATION SHOULD BE DISCONTINUED, AT LEAST TEMPORARILY. OBSERVE TREATED PATIENTS CLOSELY AT LEAST 24 HOURS TO INSURE THAT SYMPTOMS (POSSIBLY PULMONARY EDEMA) DO NOT RECUR AS ATROPINIZATION WEARS OFF. IN VERY SEVERE POISONINGS, METABOLIC DISPOSITION OF TOXICANT MAY REQUIRE SEVERAL HOURS OR DAYS DURING WHICH ATROPINIZATION MUST BE MAINTAINED. MARKEDLY LOWER LEVELS OF URINARY METABOLITES INDICATE THAT ATROPINE DOSAGE CAN BE TAPERED OFF. AS DOSAGE IS REDUCED, CHECK THE LUNG BASES FREQUENTLY FOR RALES. IF RALES ARE HEARD OR OTHER SYMPTOMS RETURN, RE-ESTABLISH ATROPINIZATION PROMPTLY (MORGAN, RECOGNITION AND MANAGEMENT OF PESTICIDE POISONINGS, 3RD ED.). ADMINISTRATION OF ANTIDOTE MUST BE PERFORMED BY QUALIFIED MEDICAL PERSONNEL.

IN CASES OF SEVERE POISONING BY ORGANOPHOSPHATE PESTICIDES IN WHICH RESPIRATORY DEPRESSION, MUSCLE WEAKNESS AND TWITCHINGS ARE SEVERE, GIVE PRALIDOXIME (PROTOPAM-AYERST, 2-PAM), 1.0 GRAM INTRAVENOUSLY AT NO MORE THAN 0.5 GRAM PER MINUTE. DOSAGE OF PRALIDOXIME MAY BE REPEATED IN 1-2 HOURS, THEN AT 10-12 HOUR INTERVALS IF NEEDED. IN VERY SEVERE POISONINGS, DOSAGE RATES MAY BE DOUBLED. TREATMENT WITH PRALIDOXIME WILL BE MOST EFFECTIVE IF GIVEN WITHIN THIRTY-SIX HOURS AFTER POISONING (MORGAN, RECOGNITION AND MANAGEMENT OF PESTICIDE POISONINGS, 3RD ED.). ANTIDOTE SHOULD BE ADMINISTERED BY QUALIFIED MEDICAL PERSONNEL.

REACTIVITY

REACTIVITY: STABLE UNDER NORMAL TEMPERATURES AND PRESSURES IN A CLOSED CONTAINER. MAY SLOWLY UNDERGO OXIDATION WHEN EXPOSED TO AIR.

INCOMPATIBILITIES: ETHION: BASES: MAY HYDROLYZE. LIME: MAY HYDROLYZE. ACID: MAY HYDROLYZE.

DECOMPOSITION: THERMAL DECOMPOSITION MAY RELEASE TOXIC OXIDES OF PHOSPHORUS AND SULFUR.

POLYMERIZATION: HAZARDOUS POLYMERIZATION HAS NOT BEEN REPORTED TO OCCUR UNDER NORMAL TEMPERATURES AND PRESSURES.

STORAGE AND DISPOSAL

OBSERVE ALL FEDERAL, STATE AND LOCAL REGULATIONS WHEN STORING OR DISPOSING OF THIS SUBSTANCE. FOR ASSISTANCE, CONTACT THE DISTRICT DIRECTOR OF THE ENVIRONMENTAL PROTECTION AGENCY.

****STORAGE****

STORE IN ACCORDANCE WITH 40 CFR 165 RECOMMENDED PROCEDURES FOR THE DISPOSAL AND STORAGE OF PESTICIDES AND PESTICIDE CONTAINERS.

STORE AWAY FROM INCOMPATIBLE SUBSTANCES.

THRESHOLD PLANNING QUANTITY (TPQ): THE SUPERFUND AMENDMENTS AND REAUTHORIZATION ACT (SARA) SECTION 302 REQUIRES THAT EACH FACILITY WHERE ANY EXTREMELY HAZARDOUS SUBSTANCE IS PRESENT IN A QUANTITY EQUAL TO OR GREATER THAN THE TPQ ESTABLISHED FOR THAT SUBSTANCE NOTIFY THE STATE EMERGENCY RESPONSE COMMISSION FOR THE STATE IN WHICH IT IS LOCATED. SECTION 303 OF SARA REQUIRES THESE FACILITIES TO PARTICIPATE IN LOCAL EMERGENCY RESPONSE PLANNING (40 CFR 355.30).

****DISPOSAL****

DISPOSAL MUST BE IN ACCORDANCE WITH 40 CFR 165 RECOMMENDED PROCEDURES FOR THE DISPOSAL AND STORAGE OF PESTICIDES AND PESTICIDE CONTAINERS.

CONDITIONS TO AVOID

MAY BURN BUT DOES NOT IGNITE READILY. CONTAINERS MAY EXPLODE IN HEAT OF FIRE.

SPILL AND LEAK PROCEDURES

SOIL SPILL: DIG A HOLDING AREA SUCH AS A PIT, POND OR LAGOON TO CONTAIN SPILL AND DIKE SURFACE FLOW USING BARRIER OF SOIL, SANDBAGS, FOAMED POLYURETHANE OR FOAMED CONCRETE. ABSORB LIQUID MASS WITH FLY ASH OR CEMENT POWDER.

AIR SPILL: KNOCK DOWN VAPORS WITH WATER SPRAY. KEEP UPWIND.

WATER SPILL: IF DISSOLVED, AT A CONCENTRATION OF 10 PPM OR GREATER, APPLY ACTIVATED CARBON AT TEN TIMES THE AMOUNT THAT HAS BEEN SPILLED.
USE MECHANICAL DREDGES OR LIFTS TO EXTRACT IMMOBILIZED MASSES OF POLLUTION AND PRECIPITATES.

OCCUPATIONAL SPILL: DO NOT TOUCH SPILLED MATERIAL. STOP LEAK IF YOU CAN DO IT WITHOUT RISK. USE WATER SPRAY TO REDUCE VAPORS. FOR SMALL SPILLS, TAKE UP WITH SAND OR OTHER ABSORBENT MATERIAL AND PLACE INTO CONTAINERS FOR LATER DISPOSAL. FOR SMALL DRY SPILLS, WITH A CLEAN SHOVEL PLACE MATERIAL INTO CLEAN, DRY CONTAINERS AND COVER. MOVE CONTAINERS FROM SPILL AREA. FOR LARGER SPILLS, DIKE FAR AHEAD OF SPILL FOR LATER DISPOSAL. KEEP UNNECESSARY PEOPLE AWAY. ISOLATE HAZARD AREA AND DENY ENTRY. VENTILATE CLOSED SPACES BEFORE ENTERING.
REPORTABLE QUANTITY (RQ): 10 POUNDS THE SUPERFUND AMENDMENTS AND REAUTHORIZATION ACT (SARA) SECTION 304 REQUIRES THAT A RELEASE EQUAL TO OR GREATER THAN THE REPORTABLE QUANTITY FOR THIS SUBSTANCE BE IMMEDIATELY REPORTED TO THE LOCAL EMERGENCY PLANNING COMMITTEE AND THE STATE EMERGENCY RESPONSE COMMISSION (40 CFR 355.40). IF THE RELEASE OF THIS SUBSTANCE IS REPORTABLE UNDER CERCLA SECTION 103, THE NATIONAL RESPONSE CENTER MUST BE NOTIFIED IMMEDIATELY AT (800) 424-8802 OR (202) 426-2675 IN THE METROPOLITAN WASHINGTON, D.C. AREA (40 CFR 302.6).

PROTECTIVE EQUIPMENT

VENTILATION: PROVIDE LOCAL EXHAUST OR PROCESS ENCLOSURE VENTILATION SYSTEM.

RESPIRATOR: THE FOLLOWING RESPIRATORS ARE RECOMMENDED BASED ON INFORMATION FOUND IN THE PHYSICAL DATA, TOXICITY AND HEALTH EFFECTS SECTIONS. THEY ARE RANKED IN ORDER FROM MINIMUM TO MAXIMUM RESPIRATORY PROTECTION. THE SPECIFIC RESPIRATOR SELECTED MUST BE BASED ON CONTAMINATION LEVELS FOUND IN THE WORK PLACE, MUST NOT EXCEED THE WORKING LIMITS OF THE RESPIRATOR AND BE JOINTLY APPROVED BY THE NATIONAL INSTITUTE FOR OCCUPATIONAL SAFETY AND HEALTH AND THE MINE SAFETY AND HEALTH ADMINISTRATION (NIOSH-MSHA).

TYPE 'C' SUPPLIED-AIR RESPIRATOR WITH A FULL FACEPIECE OPERATED IN PRESSURE-DEMAND OR OTHER POSITIVE PRESSURE MODE OR WITH A FULL FACEPIECE, HELMET OR HOOD OPERATED IN CONTINOUS-FLOW MODE.

SELF-CONTAINED BREATHING APPARATUS WITH A FULL FACEPIECE OPERATED IN PRESSURE-DEMAND OR OTHER POSITIVE PRESSURE MODE.

FOR FIREFIGHTING AND OTHER IMMEDIATELY DANGEROUS TO LIFE OR HEALTH CONDITIONS:

SELF-CONTAINED BREATHING APPARATUS WITH FULL FACEPIECE OPERATED IN PRESSURE-DEMAND OR OTHER POSITIVE PRESSURE MODE.

SUPPLIED-AIR RESPIRATOR WITH FULL FACEPIECE AND OPERATED IN PRESSURE-DEMAND OR OTHER POSITIVE PRESSURE MODE IN COMBINATION WITH AN AUXILIARY SELF-CONTAINED BREATHING APPARATUS OPERATED IN PRESSURE-DEMAND OR OTHER POSITIVE PRESSURE MODE.

CLOTHING: EMPLOYEE MUST WEAR APPROPRIATE PROTECTIVE (IMPERVIOUS) CLOTHING AND EQUIPMENT TO PREVENT ANY POSSIBILITY OF SKIN CONTACT WITH THIS SUBSTANCE.

GLOVES: EMPLOYEE MUST WEAR APPROPRIATE PROTECTIVE GLOVES TO PREVENT CONTACT WITH THIS SUBSTANCE.

EYE PROTECTION: EMPLOYEE MUST WEAR SPLASH-PROOF OR DUST-RESISTANT SAFETY GOGGLES AND A FACESHIELD TO PREVENT CONTACT WITH THIS SUBSTANCE.

EMERGENCY WASH FACILITIES: WHERE THERE IS ANY POSSIBILITY THAT AN EMPLOYEE'S EYES AND/OR SKIN MAY BE EXPOSED TO THIS SUBSTANCE, THE EMPLOYER SHOULD PROVIDE AN EYE WASH FOUNTAIN AND QUICK DRENCH SHOWER WITHIN THE IMMEDIATE WORK AREA FOR EMERGENCY USE.

AUTHORIZED BY- OCCUPATIONAL HEALTH SERVICES, INC.
CREATION DATE: 10/04/89 ***REVISION DATE:*** 05/14/90

MATERIAL SAFETY DATA SHEET

OCCUPATIONAL HEALTH SERVICES, INC.
AGRICULTURE AND PESTICIDE DIVISION
450 SEVENTH AVENUE, SUITE 2407
NEW YORK, NEW YORK 10123
1-800-445-MSDS OR (212) 967-1100

EMERGENCY CONTACT:
JOHN S. BRANSFORD, JR. (615) 292-1180

SUBSTANCE IDENTIFICATION

CAS-NUMBER 23947-60-6

SUBSTANCE: ETHIRIMOL

TRADE NAMES/SYNONYMS: 4(1H)-PYRIMIDINONE, 5-BUTYL-2-(ETHYLAMINO)-6-METHYL-; 5-BUTYL-2-(ETHYLAMINO)-6-METHYL-4(1H)-PYRIMIDINONE; 4(3H)-PYRIMIDINONE, 5-BUTYL-2-(ETHYLAMINO)-6-METHYL-; 5-BUTYL-2-(ETHYLAMINO)-6-METHYL-4(3H)-PYRIMIDINONE; MILGO; MILSTEM; MILCURB SUPER; C11H19N3O; PST08721

CHEMICAL FAMILY: PYRIMIDINE

MOLECULAR FORMULA: C11-H19-N3-O

MOLECULAR WEIGHT: 209.29

CERCLA RATINGS (SCALE 0-3): HEALTH=2 FIRE=1 REACTIVITY=0 PERSISTENCE=2

NFPA RATINGS (SCALE 0-4): HEALTH=U FIRE=1 REACTIVITY=0

COMPONENTS AND CONTAMINANTS

COMPONENT: ETHIRIMOL ***PERCENT:*** 100.0
CAS# 23947-60-6

OTHER CONTAMINANTS: NONE

EXPOSURE LIMITS: NO OCCUPATIONAL EXPOSURE LIMITS ESTABLISHED BY OSHA, ACGIH, OR NIOSH.

PHYSICAL DATA

DESCRIPTION: COLORLESS TO WHITE CRYSTALLINE SOLID.

MELTING POINT: 318-320 F (159-160 C) ***SPECIFIC GRAVITY:*** NOT AVAILABLE

VAPOR PRESSURE: NEGLIGIBLE ***SOLUBILITY IN WATER:*** 0.02% @ 25 C

SOLVENT SOLUBILITY: SOLUBLE IN CHLOROFORM, TRICHLOROETHYLENE, AND AQUEOUS SOLUTIONS OF STRONG ACIDS AND BASES; SLIGHTLY SOLUBLE IN ETHANOL AND 4-HYDROXY-4-METHYLPENTANE-2-ONE; SPARINGLY SOLUBLE IN ACETONE.

FIRE AND EXPLOSION DATA

FIRE AND EXPLOSION HAZARD: SLIGHT FIRE HAZARD WHEN EXPOSED TO HEAT OR FLAME.

FIREFIGHTING MEDIA: DRY CHEMICAL, CARBON DIOXIDE, HALON, WATER SPRAY OR STANDARD FOAM (1987 EMERGENCY RESPONSE GUIDEBOOK, DOT P 5800.4). FOR LARGER FIRES, USE WATER SPRAY, FOG OR STANDARD FOAM (1987 EMERGENCY RESPONSE GUIDEBOOK, DOT P 5800.4).

FIREFIGHTING: MOVE CONTAINER FROM FIRE AREA IF POSSIBLE. DO NOT SCATTER SPILLED MATERIAL WITH HIGH PRESSURE WATER STREAMS. DIKE FIRE CONTROL WATER FOR LATER DISPOSAL (1987 EMERGENCY RESPONSE GUIDEBOOK, DOT P 5800.4, GUIDE PAGE 31).
USE AGENTS SUITABLE FOR TYPE OF SURROUNDING FIRE. AVOID BREATHING HAZARDOUS VAPORS, KEEP UPWIND.

TOXICITY

ETHIRIMOL: TOXICITY DATA: 4000 MG/KG ORAL-RAT LD50; 1000 MG/KG ORAL-RABBIT LD50; 1000 MG/KG ORAL-CAT LD50; 800 MG/KG INTRAVENOUS-MOUSE LD50; 4 GM/KG UNREPORTED-MOUSE LD50; MUTAGENIC DATA (RTECS). CARCINOGEN STATUS: NONE. ACUTE TOXICITY LEVEL: MODERATELY TOXIC BY INGESTION. TARGET EFFECTS: NO DATA AVAILABLE.

HEALTH EFFECTS AND FIRST AID

INHALATION: ETHIRIMOL: **ACUTE EXPOSURE-** NO DATA AVAILABLE. **CHRONIC EXPOSURE-** NO DATA AVAILABLE.

FIRST AID- REMOVE FROM EXPOSURE AREA TO FRESH AIR IMMEDIATELY. IF BREATHING HAS STOPPED, PERFORM ARTIFICIAL RESPIRATION. KEEP PERSON WARM AND AT REST. TREAT SYMPTOMATICALLY AND SUPPORTIVELY. GET MEDICAL ATTENTION IMMEDIATELY.

SKIN CONTACT: ETHIRIMOL: **ACUTE EXPOSURE-** NO DATA AVAILABLE. **CHRONIC EXPOSURE-** NO DATA AVAILABLE.

FIRST AID- REMOVE CONTAMINATED CLOTHING AND SHOES IMMEDIATELY. WASH AFFECTED AREA WITH SOAP OR MILD DETERGENT AND LARGE AMOUNTS OF WATER UNTIL NO EVIDENCE OF CHEMICAL REMAINS (APPROXIMATELY 15-20 MINUTES). GET MEDICAL ATTENTION IMMEDIATELY.

EYE CONTACT: ETHIRIMOL: **ACUTE EXPOSURE-** NO DATA AVAILABLE. **CHRONIC EXPOSURE-** NO DATA AVAILABLE. **FIRST AID-** WASH EYES IMMEDIATELY WITH LARGE AMOUNTS OF WATER OR NORMAL SALINE, OCCASIONALLY LIFTING UPPER AND LOWER LIDS, UNTIL NO EVIDENCE OF CHEMICAL REMAINS (APPROXIMATELY 15-20 MINUTES). GET MEDICAL ATTENTION IMMEDIATELY.

INGESTION: ETHIRIMOL: **ACUTE EXPOSURE-** THE LETHAL DOSE REPORTED IN RATS WAS 4000 MG/KG. **CHRONIC EXPOSURE-** NO DATA AVAILABLE.

FIRST AID- IF THE PERSON IS CONSCIOUS AND NOT CONVULSING, REMOVE BY GASTRIC LAVAGE AND FOLLOW WITH A CATHARTIC (DREISBACH, HANDBOOK OF POISONING, 12TH ED.). TREAT SYMPTOMATICALLY AND SUPPORTIVELY. GASTRIC LAVAGE SHOULD BE PERFORMED BY QUALIFIED MEDICAL PERSONNEL. GET MEDICAL ATTENTION IMMEDIATELY.

ANTIDOTE: NO SPECIFIC ANTIDOTE. TREAT SYMPTOMATICALLY AND SUPPORTIVELY.

REACTIVITY

REACTIVITY: STABLE UNDER NORMAL TEMPERATURES AND PRESSURES.

INCOMPATIBILITIES: ETHIRIMOL: OXIDIZERS (STRONG): FIRE AND EXPLOSION HAZARD.

DECOMPOSITION: THERMAL DECOMPOSITION PRODUCTS MAY INCLUDE TOXIC OXIDES OF CARBON AND NITROGEN.

POLYMERIZATION: HAZARDOUS POLYMERIZATION HAS NOT BEEN REPORTED TO OCCUR UNDER NORMAL TEMPERATURES AND PRESSURES.

STORAGE AND DISPOSAL

OBSERVE ALL FEDERAL, STATE AND LOCAL REGULATIONS WHEN STORING OR DISPOSING OF THIS SUBSTANCE. FOR ASSISTANCE, CONTACT THE DISTRICT DIRECTOR OF THE ENVIRONMENTAL PROTECTION AGENCY.

STORAGE

STORE IN ACCORDANCE WITH 40 CFR 165 RECOMMENDED PROCEDURES FOR THE DISPOSAL AND STORAGE OF PESTICIDES AND PESTICIDE CONTAINERS.
STORE AWAY FROM INCOMPATIBLE SUBSTANCES.

DISPOSAL

DISPOSAL MUST BE IN ACCORDANCE WITH 40 CFR 165 RECOMMENDED PROCEDURES FOR THE DISPOSAL AND STORAGE OF PESTICIDES AND PESTICIDE CONTAINERS.

CONDITIONS TO AVOID

MAY BURN BUT DOES NOT IGNITE READILY. AVOID CONTACT WITH STRONG OXIDIZERS, EXCESSIVE HEAT, SPARKS, OR OPEN FLAME.

SPILL AND LEAK PROCEDURES

OCCUPATIONAL SPILL: STOP LEAK IF YOU CAN DO IT WITHOUT RISK. FOR SMALL SPILLS, TAKE UP WITH SAND OR OTHER ABSORBENT MATERIAL AND PLACE INTO CLEAN, DRY CONTAINERS FOR LATER DISPOSAL. KEEP UNNECESSARY PEOPLE AWAY. ISOLATE HAZARD AREA AND DENY ENTRY.

PROTECTIVE EQUIPMENT

VENTILATION: PROVIDE LOCAL EXHAUST OR GENERAL DILUTION VENTILATION SYSTEM.

RESPIRATOR: THE FOLLOWING RESPIRATORS ARE RECOMMENDED BASED ON INFORMATION FOUND IN THE PHYSICAL DATA, TOXICITY AND HEALTH EFFECTS SECTIONS. THEY ARE RANKED IN ORDER FROM MINIMUM TO MAXIMUM RESPIRATORY PROTECTION. THE SPECIFIC RESPIRATOR SELECTED MUST BE BASED ON CONTAMINATION LEVELS FOUND IN THE WORK PLACE, MUST NOT EXCEED THE WORKING LIMITS OF THE RESPIRATOR AND BE JOINTLY APPROVED BY THE NATIONAL INSTITUTE FOR OCCUPATIONAL SAFETY AND HEALTH AND THE MINE SAFETY AND HEALTH ADMINISTRATION (NIOSH-MSHA).
CHEMICAL CARTRIDGE RESPIRATOR WITH AN ORGANIC VAPOR CARTRIDGE(S) WITH A FULL FACEPIECE AND ORGANIC VAPOR CARTRIDGE(S) IN COMBINATION

WITH A DUST AND MIST FILTER.
POWERED AIR-PURIFYING RESPIRATOR WITH A TIGHT-FITTING FACEPIECE AND ORGANIC VAPOR CARTRIDGE(S) IN COMBINATION WITH A HIGH-EFFICIENCY PARTICULATE FILTER.
TYPE 'C' SUPPLIED-AIR RESPIRATOR WITH A FULL FACEPIECE OPERATED IN A PRESSURE-DEMAND OR OTHER POSITIVE PRESSURE MODE.
SELF-CONTAINED BREATHING APPARATUS WITH A FULL FACEPIECE OPERATED IN PRESSURE-DEMAND OR OTHER POSITIVE PRESSURE MODE.
FOR FIREFIGHTING AND OTHER IMMEDIATELY DANGEROUS TO LIFE OR HEALTH CONDITIONS:
SELF-CONTAINED BREATHING APPARATUS WITH FULL FACEPIECE OPERATED IN PRESSURE-DEMAND OR OTHER POSITIVE PRESSURE MODE.
SUPPLIED-AIR RESPIRATOR WITH FULL FACEPIECE AND OPERATED IN PRESSURE-DEMAND OR OTHER POSITIVE PRESSURE MODE IN COMBINATION WITH AN AUXILIARY SELF-CONTAINED BREATHING APPARATUS OPERATED IN PRESSURE-DEMAND OR OTHER POSITIVE PRESSURE MODE.

CLOTHING: EMPLOYEE MUST WEAR APPROPRIATE PROTECTIVE (IMPERVIOUS) CLOTHING AND EQUIPMENT TO PREVENT REPEATED OR PROLONGED SKIN CONTACT WITH THIS SUBSTANCE.

GLOVES: EMPLOYEE MUST WEAR APPROPRIATE PROTECTIVE GLOVES TO PREVENT CONTACT WITH THIS SUBSTANCE.

EYE PROTECTION: EMPLOYEE MUST WEAR SPLASH-PROOF OR DUST-RESISTANT SAFETY GOGGLES TO PREVENT EYE CONTACT WITH THIS SUBSTANCE.
EMERGENCY EYE WASH: WHERE THERE IS ANY POSSIBILITY THAT AN EMPLOYEE'S EYES MAY BE EXPOSED TO THIS SUBSTANCE, THE EMPLOYER SHOULD PROVIDE AN EYE WASH FOUNTAIN WITHIN THE IMMEDIATE WORK AREA FOR EMERGENCY USE.

AUTHORIZED BY- OCCUPATIONAL HEALTH SERVICES, INC.
CREATION DATE: 10/04/89 ***REVISION DATE:*** 05/07/90

MATERIAL SAFETY DATA SHEET

OCCUPATIONAL HEALTH SERVICES, INC.
AGRICULTURE AND PESTICIDE DIVISION
450 SEVENTH AVENUE, SUITE 2407
NEW YORK, NEW YORK 10123
1-800-445-MSDS OR (212) 967-1100

EMERGENCY CONTACT:
JOHN S. BRANSFORD, JR. (615) 292-1180

SUBSTANCE IDENTIFICATION

CAS-NUMBER 116-01-8

SUBSTANCE: **ETHOATE-METHYL**

TRADE NAMES/SYNONYMS: S-(2-(ETHYLAMINO)-2-OXOETHYL) O,O-DIMETHYL ESTER PHOSPHORODITHIOIC ACID; O,O-DIMETHYL ESTER PHOSPHORODITHIOIC ACID S-ESTER WITH N-ETHYL-2 -MERCAPTOACDTAMIDE; S-ETHYLCARBAMOYLMETHYL O,O-DIMETHYL PHOSPHORODITHIOATE; 2-DIMETHOXYPHOSPHINOTHIOYLTHIO-N-ETHYLACETAMIDE; S-(2-(ETHYLAMINO)-2-OXOETHYL) O,O-DIMETHYL PHOSPHORODITHIOATE; O,O-DIMETHYL PHOSPHORODITHIOATE S-ESTER WITH N-ETHYL- 2-MERCAPTOACETAMIDE; N-ETHYLAMIDE OF O,O-DIMETHYL DITHIOPHOSPHORYLACETIC ACID; DIMETHYL S-(N-ETHYLCARBAMOYLMETHYL)PHOSPHOROTHIOLOTHIONATE; DIMETHOATE-ETHYL; FITIOS B/77; FITIOS; ENT 25,506; PST08723

CHEMICAL FAMILY: ORGANOPHOSPHATE

MOLECULAR FORMULA: C6-H14-N-O3-P-S2

MOLECULAR WEIGHT: 243.30

CERCLA RATINGS (SCALE 0-3): HEALTH=3 FIRE=U REACTIVITY=0 PERSISTENCE=0

NFPA RATINGS (SCALE 0-4): HEALTH=3 FIRE=U REACTIVITY=0

COMPONENTS AND CONTAMINANTS

COMPONENT: ETHOATE-METHYL ***PERCENT:*** 100
CAS# 116-01-8

EXPOSURE LIMITS: NO OCCUPATIONAL EXPOSURE LIMITS ESTABLISHED BY OSHA, ACGIH, OR NIOSH.

PHYSICAL DATA

DESCRIPTION: SOLID ***MELTING POINT:*** 153-154 F (67-68 C)

SPECIFIC GRAVITY: 1.167 @ 70/4 C ***SOLUBILITY IN WATER:*** .85

SOLVENT SOLUBILITY: SOLUBLE IN MOST POLAR SOLVENTS

FIRE AND EXPLOSION DATA

FIRE AND EXPLOSION HAZARD: UNKNOWN FIRE AND EXPLOSION HAZARD.

FIREFIGHTING MEDIA: DRY CHEMICAL, CARBON DIOXIDE, HALON, WATER SPRAY OR STANDARD FOAM (1987 EMERGENCY RESPONSE GUIDEBOOK, DOT P 5800.4). FOR LARGER FIRES, USE WATER SPRAY, FOG OR STANDARD FOAM (1987 EMERGENCY RESPONSE GUIDEBOOK, DOT P 5800.4).

FIREFIGHTING: MOVE CONTAINERS FROM FIRE AREA IF POSSIBLE. FIGHT FIRE FROM MAXIMUM DISTANCE. STAY AWAY FROM STORAGE TANK ENDS. DIKE FIRE CONTROL WATER FOR LATER DISPOSAL. DO NOT SCATTER MATERIAL (1987 EMERGENCY RESPONSE GUIDEBOOK, DOT P 5800.4, GUIDE PAGE 55).

TOXICITY

ETHIOATE-METHYL: TOXICITY DATA: 2000 MG/KG SKIN-RAT LD50; 125 MG/KG ORAL-RAT LD50; 350 MG/KG ORAL-MOUSE LD50; 240 MG/KG INTRAPERITONEAL-MOUSE LD50; 250 MG/KG INTRAMUSCULAR-RAT LD50; 350 MG/KG UNREPORTED-MOUSE LD50. CARCINOGEN STATUS: NONE. ACUTE TOXICITY LEVEL: TOXIC BY INGESTION; MODERATELY TOXIC BY DERMAL ABSORPTION. TARGET EFFECTS: CHOLINESTERASE INHIBITOR. POISONING MAY AFFECT THE NERVOUS SYSTEM.* AT INCREASED RISK FROM EXPOSURE: PERSONS WITH RESPIRATORY AILMENTS, RECENT EXPOSURE TO CHOLINESTERASE INHIBITORS OR IMPAIRED CHOLINESTERASE PRODUCTION, OR LIVER MALFUNCTION.* ADDITIONAL DATA: MAY CROSS THE PLACENTA. HIGH ENVIRONMENTAL TEMPERATURES OR EXPOSURE OF THE CHEMICAL TO VISIBLE OR ULTRAVIOLET LIGHT MAY ENHANCE THE TOXICITY. INTERACTIONS WITH MEDICATIONS MAY OCCUR.*
* MAY BE BASED ON GENERAL INFORMATION ON ORGANOPHOSPHATES.

HEALTH EFFECTS AND FIRST AID

INHALATION: ETHOATE-METHYL: SEE INFORMATION ON ORGANOPHOSPHATES.
ORGANOPHOSPHATES: CHOLINESTERASE INHIBITOR. **ACUTE EXPOSURE-** WHEN INHALED, THE FIRST EFFECTS OF CHOLINESTERASE INHIBITORS ARE USUALLY RESPIRATORY AND MAY INCLUDE NASAL HYPEREMIA AND WATERY DISCHARGE, COUGH, CHEST DISCOMFORT, DYSPNEA, AND WHEEZING DUE TO INCREASED BRONCHIAL SECRETIONS AND BRONCHOCONSTRICTION. IF SUFFICIENT AMOUNTS ARE ABSORBED, OTHER SYSTEMIC EFFECTS MAY BEGIN WITHIN A FEW MINUTES OR BE DELAYED FOR UP TO 12 HOURS. SYMPTOMS MAY INCLUDE PALLOR, NAUSEA, VOMITING, DIARRHEA, ABDOMINAL CRAMPS, HEADACHE, DIZZINESS, OCULAR PAIN, BLURRED VISION, MIOSIS OR IN SOME CASES, ESPECIALLY INITIALLY, MYDRIASIS, LACRIMATION, SALIVATION, SWEATING, AND CONFUSION. OTHER REPORTED CENTRAL NERVOUS SYSTEM OR NEUROMUSCULAR EFFECTS MAY INCLUDE ATAXIA, SLURRED SPEECH, AREFLEXIA, WEAKNESS, FATIGUE, FASCICULATIONS, TWITCHING, TREMORS POSSIBLY OF THE TONGUE AND EYELIDS, AND EVENTUALLY PARALYSIS OF THE EXTREMITIES AND POSSIBLY OF THE RESPIRATORY MUSCLES. IN SEVERE CASES THERE MAY ALSO BE INVOLUNTARY DEFECATION AND URINATION, CYANOSIS, PSYCHOSIS, HYPERGLYCEMIA, ACUTE PANCREATITIS, CARDIAC IRREGULARITIES, PULMONARY EDEMA, UNCONSCIOUSNESS, CONVULSIONS, AND COMA. DEATH IS PRIMARILY DUE TO RESPIRATORY FAILURE, ALTHOUGH CARDIOVASCULAR EFFECTS INCLUDING CARDIAC ARREST MAY ALSO BE IMPLICATED. LONG TERM SEQUELAE ARE RARE BUT MAY INCLUDE NEUROPSYCHIATRIC DISORDERS AND MYOPATHY WITH MUSCLE TENDERNESS. SOME ORGANOPHOSPHATES MAY CAUSE A DELAYED NEUROPATHY BEGINNING 1-4 WEEKS AFTER AN ACUTE EXPOSURE WHICH MAY OR MAY NOT HAVE CAUSED ACUTE CHOLINERGIC EFFECTS. NUMBNESS, TINGLING, WEAKNESS AND CRAMPING BEGINNING SYMMETRICALLY IN THE LOWER LIMBS MAY PROGRESS TO ATAXIA AND PARALYSIS. IN SEVERE CASES, UPPER LIMB INVOLVEMENT IS POSSIBLE AND FLACCID PARALYSIS MAY PROGRESS TO SPASTIC PARALYSIS WITH EXAGGERATED REFLEXES. IMPROVEMENT MAY OCCUR OVER MONTHS TO YEARS, BUT SOME RESIDUAL IMPAIRMENT USUALLY REMAINS.
CHRONIC EXPOSURE- REPEATED OR PROLONGED EXPOSURE MAY RESULT IN THE EFFECTS OF ACUTE EXPOSURE INCLUDING THE DELAYED NEUROPATHY. OTHER EFFECTS REPORTED IN WORKERS REPEATEDLY EXPOSED INCLUDE IMPAIRED MEMORY AND CONCENTRATION, ACUTE PSYCHOSIS, SEVERE DEPRESSIONS, IRRITABILTY, CONFUSION, APATHY, EMOTIONAL LABILITY, SOCIAL WITHDRAWAL, CONFUSION, HEADACHE, SPEECH DIFFICULTIES, DELAYED REACTION TIMES, SPATIAL DISORIENTATION, NIGHTMARES, SLEEPWALKING, AND DROWSINESS OR INSOMNIA. AN INFLUENZA-LIKE CONDITION WITH HEADACHE, NAUSEA, WEAKNESS, ANOREXIA AND MALAISE HAS ALSO BEEN REPORTED.

FIRST AID- REMOVE FROM EXPOSURE AREA TO FRESH AIR IMMEDIATELY. IF BREATHING HAS STOPPED, GIVE ARTIFICIAL RESPIRATION. MAINTAIN AIRWAY AND BLOOD PRESSURE AND ADMINISTER OXYGEN IF AVAILABLE. KEEP AFFECTED PERSON WARM AND AT REST. TREAT SYMPTOMATICALLY AND SUPPORTIVELY. ADMINISTRATION OF OXYGEN SHOULD BE PERFORMED BY QUALIFIED PERSONNEL. GET MEDICAL ATTENTION IMMEDIATELY.

SKIN CONTACT: ETHOATE-METHYL: SEE INFORMATION ON ORGANOPHOSPHATES.
ORGANOPHOSPHATES: CHOLINESTERASE INHIBITOR. **ACUTE EXPOSURE-** LOCALIZED SWEATING AND FASCICULATIONS MAY OCCUR AT THE SITE OF CONTACT. IF SUFFICIENT AMOUNTS ARE ABSORBED, OTHER EFFECTS OF

CHOLINESTERASE INHIBITION AS DESCRIBED IN ACUTE INHALATION MAY OCCUR. SYMPTOMS MAY BE DELAYED 2-3 HOURS, BUT USUALLY NO MORE THAN 12 HOURS. THE RATE OF ABSORPTION IS INCREASED BY THE PRESENCE OF DERMATITIS OR HIGH AMBIENT TEMPERATURES. DELAYED NEUROPATHY IS ALSO POSSIBLE. **CHRONIC EXPOSURE-** REPEATED OR PROLONGED EXPOSURE MAY CAUSE EFFECTS AS DESCRIBED IN ACUTE EXPOSURE. SOME ORGANOPHOSPHATES MAY CAUSE SENSITIZATION.

FIRST AID- REMOVE CONTAMINATED CLOTHING IMMEDIATELY. WASH CONTAMINATED AREAS WITH SOAP AND WATER FOLLOWED BY ALCOHOL (ARENA, POISONING, 4TH ED.). EMERGENCY PERSONNEL SHOULD WEAR GLOVES AND AVOID CONTAMINATION. TREAT RESPIRATORY DIFFICULTY WITH ARTIFICIAL RESPIRATION. GET MEDICAL ATTENTION IMMEDIATELY.

EYE CONTACT: ETHOATE-METHYL: SEE INFORMATION ON ORGANOPHOSPHATES. ORGANOPHOSPHATES: CHOLINESTERASE INHIBITOR. **ACUTE EXPOSURE-** DIRECT CONTACT MAY CAUSE PAIN, HYPEREMIA, LACRIMATION, TWITCHING OF THE EYELIDS, MIOSIS, AND CILIARY MUSCLE SPASM WITH LOSS OF ACCOMODATION, BLURRED OR DIMMED VISION AND BROWACHE. SOMETIMES MYDRIASIS MAY OCCUR INSTEAD OF MIOSIS. WITH SUFFICIENT EXPOSURE, OTHER SYMPTOMS OF CHOLINESTERASE INHIBITION AS DESCRIBED IN ACUTE INHALATION MAY OCCUR. **CHRONIC EXPOSURE-** REPEATED OR PROLONGED EXPOSURE MAY CAUSE EFFECTS AS DESCRIBED IN ACUTE EXPOSURE. SOME COMPOUNDS HAVE CAUSED TOXIC EFFECTS ON THE CRYSTALLINE LENS, CONJUNCTIVAL THICKENING AND OBSTRUCTION OF THE NASOLACRIMAL CANALS WHEN USED AS MIOTIC EYEDROPS.

FIRST AID- IRRIGATE EYES WITH WATER OR SALINE SOLUTION. IF SYMPTOMS OF POISONING OCCUR, TREAT RESPIRATORY DIFFICULTY WITH ARTIFICIAL RESPIRATION AND OXYGEN. OBSERVE PATIENT FOR AT LEAST 24-36 HOURS (GOSSELIN, CLINICAL TOXICOLOGY OF COMMERCIAL PRODUCTS, 5TH ED.). GET MEDICAL ATTENTION IMMEDIATELY. OXYGEN SHOULD BE ADMINISTERED BY QUALIFIED MEDICAL PERSONNEL.

INGESTION: ETHOATE-METHYL: TOXIC. SEE INFORMATION ON ORGANOPHOSPHATES. ORGANOPHOSPHATES: CHOLINESTERASE INHIBITOR. **ACUTE EXPOSURE-** WHEN INGESTED, THE FIRST EFFECTS MAY BE NAUSEA, VOMITING, ANOREXIA, ABDOMINAL CRAMPS AND DIARRHEA. GASTROINTESTINAL ABSORPTION MAY CAUSE SYMPTOMS OF CHOLINESTERASE INHIBITION AS DESCRIBED IN ACUTE INHALATION. SYMPTOMS MAY BEGIN WITHIN MINUTES OR BE DELAYED FOR HOURS. DELAYED EFFECTS INCLUDING NEUROPATHY MAY ALSO OCCUR. **CHRONIC EXPOSURE-** REPEATED INGESTION MAY CAUSE EFFECTS AS DESCRIBED IN ACUTE EXPOSURE.

FIRST AID- IF PERSON IS ALERT AND RESPIRATION IS NOT DEPRESSED, GIVE SYRUP OF IPECAC FOLLOWED BY WATER (IF VOMITING OCCURS, KEEP HEAD BELOW HIPS TO PREVENT ASPIRATION). IF CONSCIOUSNESS LEVEL DECLINES OR VOMITING HAS NOT OCCURRED IN 15 MINUTES EMPTY STOMACH BY GASTRIC LAVAGE WITH THE AID OF CUFFED ENDOTRACHEAL TUBE USING ISOTONIC SALINE OR 5% SODIUM BICARBONATE FOLLOW WITH ACTIVATED CHARCOAL. ESTABLISH AND MAINTAIN AIRWAY. TREAT RESPIRATORY DIFFICULTY WITH ARTIFICIAL RESPIRATION AND OXYGEN. DO NOT GIVE MORPHINE, AMINOPHYLLINE, PHENOTHIAZINES, RESERPINE, FUROSEMIDE, OR ETHACRYNIC ACID (MORGAN, RECOGNITION AND MANAGEMENT OF PESTICIDE POISONINGS, 3RD ED.). TREAT SYMPTOMATICALLY AND SUPPORTIVELY. ADMINISTRATION OF OXYGEN AND LAVAGE MUST BE PERFORMED BY QUALIFIED MEDICAL PERSONNEL. GET MEDICAL ATTENTION IMMEDIATELY.

ANTIDOTE: THE FOLLOWING ANTIDOTE(S) HAVE BEEN RECOMMENDED. HOWEVER, THE DECISION AS TO WHETHER THE SEVERITY OF POISONING REQUIRES ADMINISTRATION OF ANY ANTIDOTE AND ACTUAL DOSE REQUIRED SHOULD BE MADE BY QUALIFIED MEDICAL PERSONNEL.

FOR CHOLINESTERASE INHIBITORS: ESTABLISH CLEAR AIRWAY AND TISSUE OXYGENATION BY ASPIRATION OF SECRETIONS, AND IF NECESSARY, BY ASSISTED PULMONARY VENTILATION WITH OXYGEN. IMPROVE TISSUE OXYGENATION AS MUCH AS POSSIBLE BEFORE ADMINISTERING ATROPINE TO MINIMIZE THE RISK OF VENTRICULAR FIBRILLATION. ADMINISTER ATROPINE SULFATE INTRAVENOUSLY, OR INTRAMUSCULARLY IF IV INJECTION IS NOT POSSIBLE. IN MODERATELY SEVERE POISONING ADMINISTER ATROPINE SULFATE, 0.4-2.0 MG REPEATED EVERY 15 MINUTES UNTIL ATROPINIZATION IS ACHIEVED (TACHYCARDIA, FLUSHING, DRY MOUTH, MYDRIASIS). MAINTAIN ATROPINIZATION BY REPEATED DOSES FOR 2-12 HOURS, OR LONGER, DEPENDING ON THE SEVERITY OF POISONING. THE APPEARANCE OF RALES IN THE LUNG BASES, MIOSIS, SALIVATION, NAUSEA, BRADYCARDIA, ARE ALL INDICATIONS OF INADEQUATE ATROPINIZATION. SEVERELY POISONED INDIVIDUALS MAY EXHIBIT REMARKABLE TOLERANCE TO ATROPINE; TWO OR MORE TIMES THE DOSAGES SUGGESTED ABOVE MAY BE NEEDED. PERSONS NOT POISONED OR ONLY SLIGHTLY POISONED, HOWEVER, MAY DEVELOP SIGNS OF ATROPINE TOXICITY FROM SUCH LARGE DOSAGES: FEVER, MUSCLE FIBRILLATIONS, AND DELIRIUM ARE THE MAIN SIGNS OF ATROPINE TOXICITY. IF THESE SIGNS APPEAR WHILE THE PATIENT IS FULLY ATROPINIZED, ATROPINE ADMINISTRATION SHOULD BE DISCONTINUED, AT LEAST TEMPORARILY. OBSERVE TREATED PATIENTS CLOSELY AT LEAST 24 HOURS TO INSURE THAT SYMPTOMS (POSSIBLY PULMONARY EDEMA) DO NOT RECUR AS ATROPINIZATION WEARS OFF. IN VERY SEVERE POISONINGS, METABOLIC DISPOSITION OF TOXICANT MAY REQUIRE SEVERAL HOURS OR DAYS DURING WHICH ATROPINIZATION MUST BE MAINTAINED. MARKEDLY LOWER LEVELS OF URINARY METABOLITES INDICATE THAT ATROPINE DOSAGE CAN BE TAPERED OFF. AS DOSAGE IS REDUCED, CHECK THE LUNG BASES FREQUENTLY FOR RALES. IF RALES ARE HEARD OR OTHER SYMPTOMS RETURN, RE-ESTABLISH ATROPINIZATION PROMPTLY (MORGAN, RECOGNITION AND MANAGEMENT OF PESTICIDE POISONINGS, 3RD ED.). ADMINISTRATION OF ANTIDOTE MUST BE PERFORMED BY QUALIFIED MEDICAL PERSONNEL.

IN CASES OF SEVERE POISONING BY ORGANOPHOSPHATE PESTICIDES IN WHICH RESPIRATORY DEPRESSION, MUSCLE WEAKNESS AND TWITCHINGS ARE SEVERE, GIVE PRALIDOXIME (PROTOPAM-AYERST, 2-PAM), 1.0 GRAM INTRAVENOUSLY AT NO MORE THAN 0.5 GRAM PER MINUTE. DOSAGE OF PRALIDOXIME MAY BE REPEATED IN 1-2 HOURS, THEN AT 10-12 HOUR INTERVALS IF NEEDED. IN VERY SEVERE POISONINGS, DOSAGE RATES MAY BE DOUBLED. TREATMENT WITH PRALIDOXIME WILL BE MOST EFFECTIVE IF GIVEN WITHIN THIRTY-SIX HOURS AFTER POISONING (MORGAN, RECOGNITION AND MANAGEMENT OF PESTICIDE POISONINGS, 3RD ED.). ANTIDOTE SHOULD BE ADMINISTERED BY QUALIFIED MEDICAL PERSONNEL.

REACTIVITY

REACTIVITY: STABLE UNDER NORMAL TEMPERATURES AND PRESSURES.

INCOMPATIBILITIES: ETHOATE-METHYL: NO DATA AVAILABLE.

DECOMPOSITION: THERMAL DECOMPOSITION MAY RELEASE TOXIC AND/OR HAZARDOUS GASES.

POLYMERIZATION: HAZARDOUS POLYMERIZATION HAS NOT BEEN REPORTED TO OCCUR UNDER NORMAL TEMPERATURES AND PRESSURES.

STORAGE AND DISPOSAL

OBSERVE ALL FEDERAL, STATE AND LOCAL REGULATIONS WHEN STORING OR DISPOSING OF THIS SUBSTANCE. FOR ASSISTANCE, CONTACT THE DISTRICT DIRECTOR OF THE ENVIRONMENTAL PROTECTION AGENCY.

****STORAGE****

STORE IN ACCORDANCE WITH 40 CFR 165 RECOMMENDED PROCEDURES FOR THE DISPOSAL AND STORAGE OF PESTICIDES AND PESTICIDE CONTAINERS.

****DISPOSAL****

DISPOSAL MUST BE IN ACCORDANCE WITH 40 CFR 165 RECOMMENDED PROCEDURES FOR THE DISPOSAL AND STORAGE OF PESTICIDES AND PESTICIDE CONTAINERS.

CONDITIONS TO AVOID

NONE REPORTED.

SPILL AND LEAK PROCEDURES

OCCUPATIONAL SPILL: DO NOT TOUCH SPILLED MATERIAL. STOP LEAK IF YOU CAN DO IT WITHOUT RISK. USE WATER SPRAY TO REDUCE VAPORS. FOR SMALL SPILLS, TAKE UP WITH SAND OR OTHER ABSORBENT MATERIAL AND PLACE INTO CONTAINERS FOR LATER DISPOSAL. FOR SMALL DRY SPILLS, WITH A CLEAN SHOVEL PLACE MATERIAL INTO CLEAN, DRY CONTAINERS AND COVER. MOVE CONTAINERS FROM SPILL AREA. FOR LARGER SPILLS, DIKE FAR AHEAD OF SPILL FOR LATER DISPOSAL. KEEP UNNECESSARY PEOPLE AWAY. ISOLATE HAZARD AREA AND DENY ENTRY. VENTILATE CLOSED SPACES BEFORE ENTERING.

PROTECTIVE EQUIPMENT

VENTILATION: PROVIDE LOCAL EXHAUST OR PROCESS ENCLOSURE VENTILATION SYSTEM.

RESPIRATOR: THE FOLLOWING RESPIRATORS ARE RECOMMENDED BASED ON INFORMATION FOUND IN THE PHYSICAL DATA, TOXICITY AND HEALTH EFFECTS SECTIONS. THEY ARE RANKED IN ORDER FROM MINIMUM TO MAXIMUM RESPIRATORY PROTECTION. THE SPECIFIC RESPIRATOR SELECTED MUST BE BASED ON CONTAMINATION LEVELS FOUND IN THE WORK PLACE, MUST NOT EXCEED THE WORKING LIMITS OF THE RESPIRATOR AND BE JOINTLY APPROVED BY THE NATIONAL INSTITUTE FOR OCCUPATIONAL SAFETY AND HEALTH AND THE MINE SAFETY AND HEALTH ADMINISTRATION (NIOSH-MSHA).

TYPE 'C' SUPPLIED-AIR RESPIRATOR WITH A FULL FACEPIECE OPERATED IN PRESSURE-DEMAND OR OTHER POSITIVE PRESSURE MODE OR WITH A FULL FACEPIECE, HELMET OR HOOD OPERATED IN CONTINOUS-FLOW MODE.

SELF-CONTAINED BREATHING APPARATUS WITH A FULL FACEPIECE OPERATED IN PRESSURE-DEMAND OR OTHER POSITIVE PRESSURE MODE.

FOR FIREFIGHTING AND OTHER IMMEDIATELY DANGEROUS TO LIFE OR HEALTH CONDITIONS:

SELF-CONTAINED BREATHING APPARATUS WITH FULL FACEPIECE OPERATED IN PRESSURE-DEMAND OR OTHER POSITIVE PRESSURE MODE.

SUPPLIED-AIR RESPIRATOR WITH FULL FACEPIECE AND OPERATED IN PRESSURE-

DEMAND OR OTHER POSITIVE PRESSURE MODE IN COMBINATION WITH AN AUXILIARY SELF-CONTAINED BREATHING APPARATUS OPERATED IN PRESSURE-DEMAND OR OTHER POSITIVE PRESSURE MODE.

CLOTHING: EMPLOYEE MUST WEAR APPROPRIATE PROTECTIVE (IMPERVIOUS) CLOTHING AND EQUIPMENT TO PREVENT REPEATED OR PROLONGED SKIN CONTACT WITH THIS SUBSTANCE.

GLOVES: EMPLOYEE MUST WEAR APPROPRIATE PROTECTIVE GLOVES TO PREVENT CONTACT WITH THIS SUBSTANCE.

EYE PROTECTION: EMPLOYEE MUST WEAR SPLASH-PROOF OR DUST-RESISTANT SAFETY GOGGLES TO PREVENT EYE CONTACT WITH THIS SUBSTANCE. EMERGENCY EYE WASH: WHERE THERE IS ANY POSSIBILITY THAT AN EMPLOYEE'S EYES MAY BE EXPOSED TO THIS SUBSTANCE, THE EMPLOYER SHOULD PROVIDE AN EYE WASH FOUNTAIN WITHIN THE IMMEDIATE WORK AREA FOR EMERGENCY USE.

AUTHORIZED BY- OCCUPATIONAL HEALTH SERVICES, INC.

CREATION DATE: 10/04/89 ***REVISION DATE:*** 05/07/90

MATERIAL SAFETY DATA SHEET

OCCUPATIONAL HEALTH SERVICES, INC.
AGRICULTURE AND PESTICIDE DIVISION
450 SEVENTH AVENUE, SUITE 2407
NEW YORK, NEW YORK 10123
1-800-445-MSDS OR (212) 967-1100

EMERGENCY CONTACT:
JOHN S. BRANSFORD, JR. (615) 292-1180

SUBSTANCE IDENTIFICATION

CAS-NUMBER 91-53-2

SUBSTANCE: ETHOXYQUIN

TRADE NAMES/SYNONYMS: QUINOLINE, 6-ETHOXY-1,2-DIHYDRO-2,2,4-TRIMETHYL; 6-ETHOXY-1,2-DIHYDRO-2,2,4-TRIMETHYLQUINOLINE; 1,2-DIHYDRO-6-ETHOXY-2,2,4-TRIMETHYLQUINOLINE; AMEA 100; ANTIOXIDANT EC; ETHOXYQUINE; NIFLEX N; NOCRACK AW; SANTOFLEX AW; SANTOQUIN; STOP-SCALD; C14H19NO; PST08740

CHEMICAL FAMILY: QUINOLINE

MOLECULAR FORMULA: C14-H19-N-O

MOLECULAR WEIGHT: 217.31

CERCLA RATINGS (SCALE 0-3): HEALTH=2 FIRE=1 REACTIVITY=0 PERSISTENCE=2

NFPA RATINGS (SCALE 0-4): HEALTH=2 FIRE=1 REACTIVITY=0

COMPONENTS AND CONTAMINANTS

COMPONENT: ETHOXYQUIN ***PERCENT:*** 100
CAS# 91-53-2

OTHER CONTAMINANTS: NONE

EXPOSURE LIMITS: NO OCCUPATIONAL EXPOSURE LIMITS ESTABLISHED BY OSHA, ACGIH, OR NIOSH.

PHYSICAL DATA

DESCRIPTION: CLEAR, LIGHT YELLOW TO DARK BROWN, VISCOUS LIQUID

BOILING POINT: 253-257 F (123-125 C) @ 2 MMHG ***MELTING POINT:*** <32 F (<0 C)

SPECIFIC GRAVITY: 1.029 @ 25 C ***EVAPORATION RATE:*** NOT AVAILABLE

SOLUBILITY IN WATER: INSOLUBLE ***VAPOR DENSITY:*** 7.48

SOLVENT SOLUBILITY: SOLUBLE IN ACETONE, METHANOL, METHYLENE CHLORIDE.

FIRE AND EXPLOSION DATA

FIRE AND EXPLOSION HAZARD: SLIGHT FIRE HAZARD WHEN EXPOSED TO HEAT OR FLAME.

FLASH POINT: 250 F (121 C) (OC) ***FLAMMABILITY CLASS(OSHA):*** IIIB

FIREFIGHTING MEDIA: DRY CHEMICAL, CARBON DIOXIDE, HALON, WATER SPRAY OR STANDARD FOAM (1987 EMERGENCY RESPONSE GUIDEBOOK, DOT P 5800.4). FOR LARGER FIRES, USE WATER SPRAY, FOG OR STANDARD FOAM (1987 EMERGENCY RESPONSE GUIDEBOOK, DOT P 5800.4).

FIREFIGHTING: MOVE CONTAINERS FROM FIRE AREA IF POSSIBLE. FIGHT FIRE FROM MAXIMUM DISTANCE. STAY AWAY FROM STORAGE TANK ENDS. DIKE FIRE CONTROL WATER FOR LATER DISPOSAL. DO NOT SCATTER MATERIAL (1987 EMERGENCY RESPONSE GUIDEBOOK, DOT P 5800.4, GUIDE PAGE 55). EXTINGUISH ONLY IF FLOW CAN BE STOPPED; USE FLOODING AMOUNTS OF WATER AS FOG, SOLID STREAMS MAY BE INEFFECTIVE. COOL CONTAINERS WITH FLOODING AMOUNTS OF WATER, APPLY FROM AS FAR A DISTANCE AS POSSIBLE. USE ALCOHOL FOAM, CARBON DIOXIDE OR DRY CHEMICAL. AVOID BREATHING TOXIC VAPORS, KEEP UPWIND.

TOXICITY

ETHOXYQUIN: TOXICITY DATA: 5010 MG/KG SKIN-RABBIT LD50 (NUTT, TOXIC HAZARDS OF RUBBER CHEMICALS, 1984); 800 MG/KG ORAL-RAT LD50; 1730 MG/KG ORAL-MOUSE LD50; 178 MG/KG INTRAVENOUS-MOUSE LD50; 200 MG/KG INTRAPERITONEAL-MOUSE LD50; MUTAGENIC DATA (RTECS). CARCINOGEN STATUS: NONE. LOCAL EFFECTS: IRRITANT- SKIN. ACUTE TOXICITY LEVEL: MODERATELY TOXIC BY INGESTION AND SLIGHTLY TOXIC BY DERMAL ABSORPTION. TARGET EFFECTS: SENSITIZER- SKIN.

HEALTH EFFECTS AND FIRST AID

INHALATION: ETHOXYQUIN: **ACUTE EXPOSURE-** NO DATA AVAILABLE. **CHRONIC EXPOSURE-** NO MORTALITIES WERE OBSERVED IN RABBITS EXPOSED TO A CONCENTRATION OF 195 MG/M3/5-6 HOURS/DAY FOR 3 DAYS.

FIRST AID- REMOVE FROM EXPOSURE AREA TO FRESH AIR IMMEDIATELY. IF BREATHING HAS STOPPED, PERFORM ARTIFICIAL RESPIRATION. KEEP PERSON WARM AND AT REST. TREAT SYMPTOMATICALLY AND SUPPORTIVELY. GET MEDICAL ATTENTION IMMEDIATELY.

SKIN CONTACT: ETHOXYQUIN: IRRITANT/SENSITIZER. **ACUTE EXPOSURE-** MAY CAUSE IRRITATION. SENSITIZATION MAY OCCUR IN PERSONS PREVIOUSLY EXPOSED. **CHRONIC EXPOSURE-** PROLONGED OR REPEATED EXPOSURE MAY CAUSE SENSITIZATION DERMATITIS.

FIRST AID- REMOVE CONTAMINATED CLOTHING AND SHOES IMMEDIATELY. WASH AFFECTED AREA WITH SOAP OR MILD DETERGENT AND LARGE AMOUNTS OF WATER UNTIL NO EVIDENCE OF CHEMICAL REMAINS (APPROXIMATELY 15-20 MINUTES). GET MEDICAL ATTENTION IMMEDIATELY.

EYE CONTACT: ETHOXYQUIN: **ACUTE EXPOSURE-** THIS MATERIAL WAS NOT IRRITATING TO RABBIT EYES. **CHRONIC EXPOSURE-** MILD LACHRYMATION WAS OBSERVED IN RABBITS REPEATEDLY EXPOSED TO THE VAPORS.

FIRST AID- WASH EYES IMMEDIATELY WITH LARGE AMOUNTS OF WATER OR NORMAL SALINE, OCCASIONALLY LIFTING UPPER AND LOWER LIDS, UNTIL NO EVIDENCE OF CHEMICAL REMAINS (APPROXIMATELY 15-20 MINUTES). GET MEDICAL ATTENTION IMMEDIATELY.

INGESTION: ETHOXYQUIN: **ACUTE EXPOSURE-** IN LABORATORY ANIMALS, ORAL DOSES PRODUCED A SLOW DEVELOPING DEPRESSION LASTING 4 TO 6 DAYS. A LETHAL DOSE IN RATS WAS 800 MG/KG. **CHRONIC EXPOSURE-** AN INCREASE IN THE NUMBER OF STILLBIRTHS, A DECREASE IN THE LITTER SIZE AND IN THE INCIDENCE OF SURVIVAL-TO-WEANING WAS REPORTED IN RATS FED 1125 PPM. DIETARY LEVELS OF 250 PPM IN RATS AND 10 MG/KG/DAY IN DOGS ARE REPORTED TO PRODUCE ADVERSE EFFECTS UPON THE LIVER AND KIDNEY. IN A STUDY OF RATS THAT LASTED UP TO 715 DAYS, A DOSE-RELATED OCCURRENCE OF LESIONS IN KIDNEYS, LIVERS, AND THYROIDS WERE SEEN IN MALE BUT NOT IN FEMALES.

FIRST AID- TREAT SYMPTOMATICALLY AND SUPPORTIVELY. GET MEDICAL ATTENTION IMMEDIATELY. IF VOMITING OCCURS, KEEP HEAD LOWER THAN HIPS TO PREVENT ASPIRATION.

ANTIDOTE: NO SPECIFIC ANTIDOTE. TREAT SYMPTOMATICALLY AND SUPPORTIVELY.

REACTIVITY

REACTIVITY: STABLE UNDER NORMAL TEMPERATURES AND PRESSURES.

INCOMPATIBILITIES: ETHOXYQUIN: OXIDIZERS (STRONG): FIRE AND EXPLOSION HAZARD.

DECOMPOSITION: THERMAL DECOMPOSITION PRODUCTS MAY INCLUDE TOXIC OXIDES OF CARBON AND NITROGEN.

POLYMERIZATION: HAZARDOUS POLYMERIZATION HAS NOT BEEN REPORTED TO OCCUR UNDER NORMAL TEMPERATURES AND PRESSURES.

STORAGE AND DISPOSAL

OBSERVE ALL FEDERAL, STATE AND LOCAL REGULATIONS WHEN STORING OR DISPOSING OF THIS SUBSTANCE. FOR ASSISTANCE, CONTACT THE DISTRICT DIRECTOR OF THE ENVIRONMENTAL PROTECTION AGENCY.

****STORAGE****

STORE IN ACCORDANCE WITH 40 CFR 165 RECOMMENDED PROCEDURES FOR THE DISPOSAL AND STORAGE OF PESTICIDES AND PESTICIDE CONTAINERS. STORE AWAY FROM INCOMPATIBLE SUBSTANCES.

****DISPOSAL****

DISPOSAL MUST BE IN ACCORDANCE WITH 40 CFR 165 RECOMMENDED PROCEDURES FOR THE DISPOSAL AND STORAGE OF PESTICIDES AND PESTICIDE CONTAINERS.

CONDITIONS TO AVOID

MAY BURN BUT DOES NOT IGNITE READILY. CONTAINERS MAY EXPLODE IN HEAT OF FIRE.

SPILL AND LEAK PROCEDURES

OCCUPATIONAL SPILL: DO NOT TOUCH SPILLED MATERIAL. STOP LEAK IF YOU CAN DO IT WITHOUT RISK. USE WATER SPRAY TO REDUCE VAPORS. FOR SMALL SPILLS, TAKE UP WITH SAND OR OTHER ABSORBENT MATERIAL AND PLACE INTO CONTAINERS FOR LATER DISPOSAL. FOR SMALL DRY SPILLS, WITH A CLEAN SHOVEL PLACE MATERIAL INTO CLEAN, DRY CONTAINERS AND COVER. MOVE CONTAINERS FROM SPILL AREA. FOR LARGER SPILLS, DIKE FAR AHEAD OF SPILL FOR LATER DISPOSAL. KEEP UNNECESSARY PEOPLE AWAY. ISOLATE HAZARD AREA AND DENY ENTRY. VENTILATE CLOSED SPACES BEFORE ENTERING.

PROTECTIVE EQUIPMENT

VENTILATION: PROVIDE LOCAL EXHAUST OR GENERAL DILUTION VENTILATION SYSTEM.

RESPIRATOR: THE FOLLOWING RESPIRATORS ARE RECOMMENDED BASED ON INFORMATION FOUND IN THE PHYSICAL DATA, TOXICITY AND HEALTH EFFECTS SECTIONS. THEY ARE RANKED IN ORDER FROM MINIMUM TO MAXIMUM RESPIRATORY PROTECTION. THE SPECIFIC RESPIRATOR SELECTED MUST BE BASED ON CONTAMINATION LEVELS FOUND IN THE WORK PLACE, MUST NOT EXCEED THE WORKING LIMITS OF THE RESPIRATOR AND BE JOINTLY APPROVED BY THE NATIONAL INSTITUTE FOR OCCUPATIONAL SAFETY AND HEALTH AND THE MINE SAFETY AND HEALTH ADMINISTRATION (NIOSH-MSHA).

CHEMICAL CARTRIDGE RESPIRATOR WITH AN ORGANIC VAPOR CARTRIDGE(S) WITH A FULL FACEPIECE AND ORGANIC VAPOR CARTRIDGE(S) IN COMBINATION WITH A DUST AND MIST FILTER.

POWERED AIR-PURIFYING RESPIRATOR WITH A TIGHT-FITTING FACEPIECE AND ORGANIC VAPOR CARTRIDGE(S) IN COMBINATION WITH A HIGH-EFFICIENCY PARTICULATE FILTER.

TYPE 'C' SUPPLIED-AIR RESPIRATOR WITH A FULL FACEPIECE OPERATED IN A PRESSURE-DEMAND OR OTHER POSITIVE PRESSURE MODE.

SELF-CONTAINED BREATHING APPARATUS WITH A FULL FACEPIECE OPERATED IN PRESSURE-DEMAND OR OTHER POSITIVE PRESSURE MODE.

FOR FIREFIGHTING AND OTHER IMMEDIATELY DANGEROUS TO LIFE OR HEALTH CONDITIONS:

SELF-CONTAINED BREATHING APPARATUS WITH FULL FACEPIECE OPERATED IN PRESSURE-DEMAND OR OTHER POSITIVE PRESSURE MODE.

SUPPLIED-AIR RESPIRATOR WITH FULL FACEPIECE AND OPERATED IN PRESSURE-DEMAND OR OTHER POSITIVE PRESSURE MODE IN COMBINATION WITH AN AUXILIARY SELF-CONTAINED BREATHING APPARATUS OPERATED IN PRESSURE-DEMAND OR OTHER POSITIVE PRESSURE MODE.

CLOTHING: EMPLOYEE MUST WEAR APPROPRIATE PROTECTIVE (IMPERVIOUS) CLOTHING AND EQUIPMENT TO PREVENT REPEATED OR PROLONGED SKIN CONTACT WITH THIS SUBSTANCE.

GLOVES: EMPLOYEE MUST WEAR APPROPRIATE PROTECTIVE GLOVES TO PREVENT CONTACT WITH THIS SUBSTANCE.

EYE PROTECTION: EMPLOYEE MUST WEAR SPLASH-PROOF OR DUST-RESISTANT SAFETY GOGGLES TO PREVENT EYE CONTACT WITH THIS SUBSTANCE.

EMERGENCY EYE WASH: WHERE THERE IS ANY POSSIBILITY THAT AN EMPLOYEE'S EYES MAY BE EXPOSED TO THIS SUBSTANCE, THE EMPLOYER SHOULD PROVIDE AN EYE WASH FOUNTAIN WITHIN THE IMMEDIATE WORK AREA FOR EMERGENCY USE.

AUTHORIZED BY- OCCUPATIONAL HEALTH SERVICES, INC.

CREATION DATE: 10/04/89 ***REVISION DATE:*** 05/17/90

MATERIAL SAFETY DATA SHEET

OCCUPATIONAL HEALTH SERVICES, INC.
AGRICULTURE AND PESTICIDE DIVISION
450 SEVENTH AVENUE, SUITE 2407
NEW YORK, NEW YORK 10123
1-800-445-MSDS OR (212) 967-1100

EMERGENCY CONTACT:
JOHN S. BRANSFORD, JR. (615) 292-1180

SUBSTANCE IDENTIFICATION

CAS-NUMBER 61790-81-6

SUBSTANCE: **ETHOXYLAN 1685**

TRADE NAMES/SYNONYMS: ETHOXYLAN 1685 PEG (75) LANOLIN; POLYOXYETHYLENE (75) LANOLIN; ETHOXYLATED LANOLIN; ALCOHOLS, LANOLIN, ETHOXYLATED; ETHOXYLATED LANOLIN ALCOHOLS; WOOL WAX ALCOHOLS, ETHOXYLATED; ETHOXYLATED WOOL WAX ALCOHOLS; PST08741

CHEMICAL FAMILY: ETHOXYLATED FATTY ACID

CERCLA RATINGS (SCALE 0-3): HEALTH=1 FIRE=1 REACTIVITY=0
PERSISTENCE=1

NFPA RATINGS (SCALE 0-4): HEALTH=1 FIRE=1 REACTIVITY=0

COMPONENTS AND CONTAMINANTS

COMPONENT: ETHOXYLATED LANOLIN ***PERCENT:*** >99
CAS# 61790-81-6

EXPOSURE LIMITS: NO OCCUPATIONAL EXPOSURE LIMITS ESTABLISHED BY OSHA, ACGIH, OR NIOSH.

PHYSICAL DATA

DESCRIPTION: DARK AMBER TO BROWN WAXY SOLID.

BOILING POINT: 350 F (177 C) DECOMPOSES ***MELTING POINT:*** 106-113 F (41-45 C)

SPECIFIC GRAVITY: 1.15 ***SOLUBILITY IN WATER:*** SOLUBLE ***VAPOR DENSITY:*** >1

FIRE AND EXPLOSION DATA

FIRE AND EXPLOSION HAZARD: SLIGHT FIRE HAZARD WHEN EXPOSED TO HEAT OR FLAME.

FLASH POINT: 530 F (276 C) (COC) ***FLAMMABILITY CLASS(OSHA):*** IIIB

FIREFIGHTING MEDIA: DRY CHEMICAL, CARBON DIOXIDE, HALON, WATER SPRAY OR STANDARD FOAM (1987 EMERGENCY RESPONSE GUIDEBOOK, DOT P 5800.4). FOR LARGER FIRES, USE WATER SPRAY, FOG OR STANDARD FOAM (1987 EMERGENCY RESPONSE GUIDEBOOK, DOT P 5800.4).

FIREFIGHTING: MOVE CONTAINER FROM FIRE AREA IF POSSIBLE. DO NOT SCATTER SPILLED MATERIAL WITH HIGH PRESSURE WATER STREAMS. DIKE FIRE CONTROL WATER FOR LATER DISPOSAL (1987 EMERGENCY RESPONSE GUIDEBOOK, DOT P 5800.4, GUIDE PAGE 31).

USE AGENTS SUITABLE FOR TYPE OF SURROUNDING FIRE. AVOID BREATHING HAZARDOUS VAPORS, KEEP UPWIND.

TOXICITY

ETHOXYLATED LANOLIN: TOXICITY DATA: >21.3 GM/KG ORAL-RAT LD50 (EMERY CHEMICAL COMPANY MSDS). CARCINOGEN STATUS: NONE. ACUTE TOXICITY LEVEL: NO DATA AVAILABLE. TARGET EFFECTS: NO DATA AVAILABLE.

HEALTH EFFECTS AND FIRST AID

INHALATION: ETHOXYLATED LANOLIN: **ACUTE EXPOSURE-** NO DATA AVAILABLE. MAY BE IRRITATING TO THE MUCOUS MEMBRANES. **CHRONIC EXPOSURE-** NO DATA AVAILABLE.

FIRST AID- REMOVE FROM EXPOSURE AREA TO FRESH AIR IMMEDIATELY. IF BREATHING HAS STOPPED, PERFORM ARTIFICIAL RESPIRATION. KEEP PERSON WARM AND AT REST. TREAT SYMPTOMATICALLY AND SUPPORTIVELY. GET MEDICAL ATTENTION IMMEDIATELY.

SKIN CONTACT: ETHOXYLATED LANOLIN: **ACUTE EXPOSURE-** ANIMAL STUDIES INDICATE THIS MATERIAL IS NON-IRRITATING WHEN APPLIED TO THE SKIN OF RABBITS. **CHRONIC EXPOSURE-** NO DATA AVAILABLE.

FIRST AID- REMOVE CONTAMINATED CLOTHING AND SHOES IMMEDIATELY. WASH AFFECTED AREA WITH SOAP OR MILD DETERGENT AND LARGE AMOUNTS OF WATER UNTIL NO EVIDENCE OF CHEMICAL REMAINS (APPROXIMATELY 15-20 MINUTES). GET MEDICAL ATTENTION IMMEDIATELY.

EYE CONTACT: ETHOXYLATED LANOLIN: **ACUTE EXPOSURE-** ANIMAL STUDIES INDICATE THIS MATERIAL IS NON-IRRITATING WHEN APPLIED TO THE EYES OF RABBITS. **CHRONIC EXPOSURE-** NO DATA AVAILABLE.

FIRST AID- WASH EYES IMMEDIATELY WITH LARGE AMOUNTS OF WATER OR NORMAL SALINE, OCCASIONALLY LIFTING UPPER AND LOWER LIDS, UNTIL NO EVIDENCE OF CHEMICAL REMAINS (APPROXIMATELY 15-20 MINUTES). GET MEDICAL ATTENTION IMMEDIATELY.

INGESTION: ETHOXYLATED LANOLIN: **ACUTE EXPOSURE-** THE ESTIMATED LETHAL DOSE IN RATS IS ESTIMATED TO BE GREATER THAN 21.3 GM/KG. SYMPTOMS OF POISONING HAVE NOT BEEN REPORTED. **CHRONIC EXPOSURE-** NO DATA AVAILABLE.

FIRST AID- TREAT SYMPTOMATICALLY AND SUPPORTIVELY. GET MEDICAL ATTENTION IMMEDIATELY. IF VOMITING OCCURS, KEEP HEAD LOWER THAN HIPS TO PREVENT ASPIRATION.

ANTIDOTE: NO SPECIFIC ANTIDOTE. TREAT SYMPTOMATICALLY AND SUPPORTIVELY.

REACTIVITY

REACTIVITY: STABLE UNDER NORMAL TEMPERATURES AND PRESSURES.

INCOMPATIBILITIES: ETHOXYLATED LANOLIN: OXIDIZERS (STRONG): FIRE AND EXPLOSION HAZARD.

DECOMPOSITION: THERMAL DECOMPOSITION PRODUCTS MAY INCLUDE TOXIC OXIDES OF CARBON.

POLYMERIZATION: HAZARDOUS POLYMERIZATION HAS NOT BEEN REPORTED TO OCCUR UNDER NORMAL TEMPERATURES AND PRESSURES.

STORAGE AND DISPOSAL

OBSERVE ALL FEDERAL, STATE AND LOCAL REGULATIONS WHEN STORING OR DISPOSING OF THIS SUBSTANCE. FOR ASSISTANCE, CONTACT THE DISTRICT DIRECTOR OF THE ENVIRONMENTAL PROTECTION AGENCY.

STORAGE

STORE AWAY FROM INCOMPATIBLE SUBSTANCES.

CONDITIONS TO AVOID

MAY BURN BUT DOES NOT IGNITE READILY. AVOID CONTACT WITH STRONG OXIDIZERS, EXCESSIVE HEAT, SPARKS, OR OPEN FLAME.

SPILL AND LEAK PROCEDURES

OCCUPATIONAL SPILL: NO SPECIAL PRECAUTIONS INDICATED.

PROTECTIVE EQUIPMENT

VENTILATION: PROVIDE GENERAL DILUTION VENTILATION.

RESPIRATOR: THE FOLLOWING RESPIRATORS ARE RECOMMENDED BASED ON INFORMATION FOUND IN THE PHYSICAL DATA, TOXICITY AND HEALTH EFFECTS SECTIONS. THEY ARE RANKED IN ORDER FROM MINIMUM TO MAXIMUM RESPIRATORY PROTECTION. THE SPECIFIC RESPIRATOR SELECTED MUST BE BASED ON CONTAMINATION LEVELS FOUND IN THE WORK PLACE, MUST NOT EXCEED THE WORKING LIMITS OF THE RESPIRATOR AND BE JOINTLY APPROVED BY THE NATIONAL INSTITUTE FOR OCCUPATIONAL SAFETY AND HEALTH AND THE MINE SAFETY AND HEALTH ADMINISTRATION (NIOSH-MSHA).

DUST AND MIST RESPIRATOR.

AIR-PURIFYING RESPIRATOR WITH A HIGH-EFFICIENCY PARTICULATE FILTER.

POWERED AIR-PURIFYING RESPIRATOR WITH A DUST AND MIST FILTER.

POWERED AIR-PURIFYING RESPIRATOR WITH A HIGH-EFFICIENCY PARTICULATE FILTER.

TYPE 'C' SUPPLIED-AIR RESPIRATOR OPERATED IN THE PRESSURE-DEMAND OR OTHER POSITIVE PRESSURE OR CONTINUOUS-FLOW MODE.

SELF-CONTAINED BREATHING APPARATUS.

FOR FIREFIGHTING AND OTHER IMMEDIATELY DANGEROUS TO LIFE OR HEALTH CONDITIONS:

SELF-CONTAINED BREATHING APPARATUS WITH FULL FACEPIECE OPERATED IN PRESSURE-DEMAND OR OTHER POSITIVE PRESSURE MODE.

SUPPLIED-AIR RESPIRATOR WITH FULL FACEPIECE AND OPERATED IN PRESSURE-DEMAND OR OTHER POSITIVE PRESSURE MODE IN COMBINATION WITH AN AUXILIARY SELF-CONTAINED BREATHING APPARATUS OPERATED IN PRESSURE-DEMAND OR OTHER POSITIVE PRESSURE MODE.

CLOTHING: PROTECTIVE CLOTHING NOT REQUIRED. AVOID REPEATED OR PROLONGED CONTACT WITH THIS SUBSTANCE.

GLOVES: PROTECTIVE GLOVES ARE NOT REQUIRED BUT RECOMMENDED.

EYE PROTECTION: EMPLOYEE MUST WEAR SPLASH-PROOF OR DUST-RESISTANT SAFETY GOGGLES TO PREVENT EYE CONTACT WITH THIS SUBSTANCE.

EMERGENCY EYE WASH: WHERE THERE IS ANY POSSIBILITY THAT AN EMPLOYEE'S EYES MAY BE EXPOSED TO THIS SUBSTANCE, THE EMPLOYER SHOULD PROVIDE AN EYE WASH FOUNTAIN WITHIN THE IMMEDIATE WORK AREA FOR EMERGENCY USE.

AUTHORIZED BY- OCCUPATIONAL HEALTH SERVICES, INC.

CREATION DATE: 11/17/89 ***REVISION DATE:*** 05/24/90

MATERIAL SAFETY DATA SHEET

OCCUPATIONAL HEALTH SERVICES, INC.
AGRICULTURE AND PESTICIDE DIVISION
450 SEVENTH AVENUE, SUITE 2407
NEW YORK, NEW YORK 10123
1-800-445-MSDS OR (212) 967-1100

EMERGENCY CONTACT:
JOHN S. BRANSFORD, JR. (615) 292-1180

SUBSTANCE IDENTIFICATION

CAS-NUMBER 141-78-6

SUBSTANCE: ETHYL ACETATE

TRADE NAMES/SYNONYMS: ACETIC ACID ETHYL ESTER; ACETIC ETHER; ACETIDIN; ACETOXYETHANE; ETHYL ETHANOATE; VINEGAR NAPHTHA; ACETIC ESTER; RCRA U112; STCC 4909160; UN 1173; C4H8O2; PST08750

CHEMICAL FAMILY: ESTER, CARBOXYLIC, ALIPHATIC

MOLECULAR FORMULA: C-H3-C-O2-C2-H5

MOLECULAR WEIGHT: 88.11

CERCLA RATINGS (SCALE 0-3): HEALTH=1 FIRE=3 REACTIVITY=0 PERSISTENCE=0

NFPA RATINGS (SCALE 0-4): HEALTH=1 FIRE=3 REACTIVITY=0

COMPONENTS AND CONTAMINANTS

COMPONENT: ETHYL ACETATE ***PERCENT:*** 100.0

CAS# 141-78-6

OTHER CONTAMINANTS: NONE

EXPOSURE LIMITS: ETHYL ACETATE: 400 PPM (1440 MG/M3) OSHA TWA 400 PPM (1440 MG/M3) ACGIH TWA

5000 POUNDS CERCLA SECTION 103 REPORTABLE QUANTITY

PHYSICAL DATA

DESCRIPTION: TRANSPARENT, COLORLESS, VOLATILE LIQUID HAVING A FRAGRANT, SLIGHTLY FRUITY ODOR AND A PECULIAR, FRUITY, BURNING TASTE.

BOILING POINT: 171 F (77 C) ***MELTING POINT:*** -119 F (-84 C)

SPECIFIC GRAVITY: 0.9003 ***VOLATILITY:*** 100% ***VAPOR PRESSURE:*** 73 MMHG @ 20 C

EVAPORATION RATE: (BUTYL ACETATE=1) 6.2 ***PH:*** NEUTRAL

SOLUBILITY IN WATER: 8.7% ***ODOR THRESHOLD:*** 50 PPM ***VAPOR DENSITY:*** 3.04

SOLVENT SOLUBILITY: SOLUBLE IN ALCOHOL, BENZENE, ETHER, ACETONE, AND CHLOROFORM.

FIRE AND EXPLOSION DATA

FIRE AND EXPLOSION HAZARD: DANGEROUS FIRE HAZARD WHEN EXPOSED TO HEAT OR FLAME.

VAPORS ARE HEAVIER THAN AIR AND MAY TRAVEL A CONSIDERABLE DISTANCE TO A SOURCE OF IGNITION AND FLASH BACK.

VAPOR-AIR MIXTURES ARE EXPLOSIVE ABOVE FLASH POINT.

FLASH POINT: 24 F (-4 C) (CC) ***UPPER EXPLOSIVE LIMIT:*** 11.5%

LOWER EXPLOSIVE LIMIT: 2.0% ***AUTOIGNITION TEMP.:*** 800 F (426 C)

FLAMMABILITY CLASS(OSHA): IB

FIREFIGHTING MEDIA: DRY CHEMICAL, CARBON DIOXIDE, HALON, WATER SPRAY OR ALCOHOL FOAM (1987 EMERGENCY RESPONSE GUIDEBOOK, DOT P 5800.4).

FOR LARGER FIRES, USE WATER SPRAY, FOG OR ALCOHOL FOAM (1987 EMERGENCY RESPONSE GUIDEBOOK, DOT P 5800.4).

ALCOHOL FOAM (NFPA 325M, FIRE HAZARD PROPERTIES OF FLAMMABLE LIQUIDS, GASES, AND VOLATILE SOLIDS, 1984).

FIREFIGHTING: MOVE CONTAINER FROM FIRE AREA IF POSSIBLE. COOL FIRE-EXPOSED CONTAINERS WITH WATER FROM SIDE UNTIL WELL AFTER FIRE IS OUT. STAY AWAY FROM STORAGE TANK ENDS. FOR MASSIVE FIRE IN STORAGE AREA, USE UNMANNED HOSE HOLDER OR MONITOR NOZZLES, ELSE WITHDRAW FROM AREA AND LET FIRE BURN. WITHDRAW IMMEDIATELY IN CASE OF RISING SOUND FROM VENTING SAFETY DEVICE OR ANY DISCOLORATION OF STORAGE TANK DUE TO FIRE (1987 EMERGENCY RESPONSE GUIDEBOOK, DOT P 5800.4, GUIDE PAGE 26). EXTINGUISH ONLY IF FLOW CAN BE STOPPED; USE WATER IN FLOODING AMOUNTS AS FOG, SOLID STREAMS MAY NOT BE EFFECTIVE. COOL CONTAINERS WITH FLOODING AMOUNTS OF WATER, APPLY FROM AS FAR A DISTANCE AS POSSIBLE. AVOID BREATHING VAPORS, KEEP UPWIND.

WATER MAY BE INEFFECTIVE (NFPA 325M, FIRE HAZARD PROPERTIES OF FLAMMABLE LIQUIDS, GASES, AND VOLATILE SOLIDS, 1984)

TRANSPORTATION DATA

DEPARTMENT OF TRANSPORTATION HAZARD CLASSIFICATION 49 CFR 172.101: FLAMMABLE LIQUID

DEPARTMENT OF TRANSPORTATION LABELING REQUIREMENTS 49 CFR 172.101 AND SUBPART E: FLAMMABLE LIQUID

DEPARTMENT OF TRANSPORTATION PACKAGING REQUIREMENTS: 49 CFR 173.119 EXCEPTIONS: 49 CFR 173.118

TOXICITY

ETHYL ACETATE: IRRITATION DATA: 400 PPM EYE-HUMAN. TOXICITY DATA: 400 PPM INHALATION-HUMAN TCLO; 1600 PPM/8 HOURS INHALATION-RAT LC50; 45 GM/M3/2 HOURS INHALATION-MOUSE LC50; 77 MG/M3/1 HOUR INHALATION-GUINEA PIG LCLO; 61 GM/M3 INHALATION-CAT LCLO; 5620 MG/KG ORAL-RAT LD50; 4100 MG/KG ORAL-MOUSE LD50; 4935 MG/KG ORAL-RABBIT LD50; 5500 MG/KG ORAL-GUINEA PIG LD50; 5000 MG/KG SUBCUTANEOUS-RAT LDLO; 3000 MG/KG SUBCUTANEOUS-GUINEA PIG LD50; 3000 MG/KG SUBCUTANEOUS-CAT LD50; 709 MG/KG INTRAPERITONEAL-MOUSE LD50; MUTAGENIC DATA (RTECS). CARCINOGEN STATUS: NONE. LOCAL EFFECTS: IRRITANT- INHALATION, SKIN, EYE. ACUTE TOXICITY LEVEL: MODERATELY TOXIC BY INHALATION; SLIGHTLY TOXIC BY INGESTION. TARGET EFFECTS: CENTRAL NERVOUS SYSTEM DEPRESSANT. POISONING MAY ALSO AFFECT THE LIVER AND KIDNEYS. AT INCREASED RISK FROM EXPOSURE: PERSONS WITH CHRONIC RESPIRATORY DISEASE, SKIN DISEASE OR ANEMIA.

HEALTH EFFECTS AND FIRST AID

INHALATION: ETHYL ACETATE: IRRITANT/NARCOTIC. 10,000 PPM IMMEDIATELY DANGEROUS TO LIFE OR HEALTH. **ACUTE EXPOSURE-** INHALATION OF 400 PPM FOR 3-5 MINUTES HAS CAUSED RESPIRATORY TRACT IRRITATION IN HUMANS. LOW VAPOR CONCENTRATIONS MAY ALSO CAUSE HEADACHE, COUGHING, DIZZINESS, DROWSINESS, AND SHORTNESS OF BREATH. HIGH CONCENTRATIONS MAY CAUSE NARCOTIC EFFECTS WITH ANESTHESIA AND UNCONSCIOUSNESS AND RENAL AND HEPATIC DAMAGE. PATHOLOGIC FINDINGS HAVE INCLUDED MARKED HYPEREMIA OF THE RESPIRATORY TRACT, PULMONARY EDEMA, HEMORRHAGIC GASTRITIS, AND HYPEREMIA OF THE SPLEEN AND KIDNEYS. **CHRONIC EXPOSURE-** NO ADVERSE SYMPTOMS WERE OBSERVED IN WORKERS EXPOSED TO 375-1500 PPM FOR SEVERAL MONTHS. ANIMAL STUDIES INDICATE THAT 4450 PPM FOR 1 HOUR DAILY FOR 40 DAYS CAUSED SECONDARY ANEMIA, LEUKOCYTOSIS, AND LIVER AND KIDNEY DAMAGE. IN RARE INSTANCES, REPEATED EXPOSURE MAY RESULT IN SENSITIZATION WITH MUCOUS MEMBRANE IRRITATION AND ECZEMATOUS ERUPTIONS.

FIRST AID- REMOVE FROM EXPOSURE AREA TO FRESH AIR IMMEDIATELY. IF BREATHING HAS STOPPED, PERFORM ARTIFICIAL RESPIRATION. KEEP PERSON WARM AND AT REST. TREAT SYMPTOMATICALLY AND SUPPORTIVELY. GET MEDICAL ATTENTION IMMEDIATELY.

SKIN CONTACT: ETHYL ACETATE: IRRITANT. **ACUTE EXPOSURE-** DIRECT CONTACT WITH THE LIQUID MAY CAUSE IRRITATION WITH REDNESS AND DEFATTING ACTION ON THE SKIN. **CHRONIC EXPOSURE-** REPEATED OR PROLONGED EXPOSURE MAY CAUSE DEFATTING DERMATITIS. IN RARE INSTANCES, REPEATED EXPOSURE MAY RESULT IN SENSITIZATION WITH ECZEMATOUS ERUPTIONS.

FIRST AID- REMOVE CONTAMINATED CLOTHING AND SHOES IMMEDIATELY. WASH AFFECTED AREA WITH SOAP OR MILD DETERGENT AND LARGE AMOUNTS OF WATER UNTIL NO EVIDENCE OF CHEMICAL REMAINS (APPROXIMATELY 15-20 MINUTES). GET MEDICAL ATTENTION IMMEDIATELY.

EYE CONTACT: ETHYL ACETATE: IRRITANT. **ACUTE EXPOSURE-** DIRECT CONTACT WITH THE LIQUID MAY CAUSE IRRITATION, WITH REDNESS, PAIN, AND LACRIMATION. EXPOSURE TO 400 PPM MAY CAUSE A SENSATION OF IRRITATION IN HUMANS. APPLICATION OF 2 DROPS TO RABBIT CORNEAS, FOLLOWED 2 MINUTES LATER BY RINSING WITH WATER, CAUSED IMMEDIATE FINE OPTICAL IRREGULARITY OF THE CORNEAL EPITHELIUM, WHICH RETURNED TO NORMAL IN 2 DAYS. **CHRONIC EXPOSURE-** REPEATED OR PROLONGED EXPOSURE MAY CAUSE CONJUNCTIVITIS AND CORNEA CLOUDING. RABBITS EXPOSED TO THE VAPOR AT LEVELS WHICH WOULD BE SCARCELY TOLERABLE TO HUMANS CAUSED NO CORNEAL DAMAGE DESPITE BEING EXPOSED FOR 8 HOURS/DAY FOR 5 DAYS/WEEK FOR UP TO 7 WEEKS.

FIRST AID- WASH EYES IMMEDIATELY WITH LARGE AMOUNTS OF WATER OR NORMAL SALINE, OCCASIONALLY LIFTING UPPER AND LOWER LIDS, UNTIL NO EVIDENCE OF CHEMICAL REMAINS (APPROXIMATELY 15-20 MINUTES). GET MEDICAL ATTENTION IMMEDIATELY.

INGESTION: ETHYL ACETATE: NARCOTIC. **ACUTE EXPOSURE-** INGESTION OF SMALL AMOUNTS MAY CAUSE SORE THROAT, ABDOMINAL PAIN, AND DIARRHEA. LARGE AMOUNTS MAY CAUSE CENTRAL NERVOUS SYSTEM DEPRESSION, WITH DIZZINESS, HEADACHE, WEAKNESS, FATIGUE, DROWSINESS, AND UNCONSCIOUSNESS. POISONING MAY CAUSE CONGESTION OF THE LIVER AND KIDNEYS. **CHRONIC EXPOSURE-** ANIMALS FED 1000 MG/KG FOR 1 MONTH SHOWED NO EFFECTS.

FIRST AID- REMOVE BY GASTRIC LAVAGE OR EMESIS, USING ACTIVATED CHARCOAL. MAINTAIN AIRWAY AND BLOOD PRESSURE. GIVE OXYGEN IF RESPIRATION IS DEPRESSED (DREISBACH HANDBOOK OF POISONING, 11TH EDITION). GASTRIC LAVAGE OR EMESIS SHOULD NOT BE PERFORMED ON AN UNCONSCIOUS PERSON. LAVAGE SHOULD BE PERFORMED BY QUALIFIED MEDICAL PERSONNEL. GET MEDICAL ATTENTION IMMEDIATELY.

ANTIDOTE: NO SPECIFIC ANTIDOTE. TREAT SYMPTOMATICALLY AND SUPPORTIVELY.

REACTIVITY

REACTIVITY: STABLE UNDER NORMAL TEMPERATURES AND PRESSURES.

INCOMPATIBILITIES: ETHYL ACETATE: ACIDS (STRONG): EXOTHERMIC DECOMPOSITION. BASES (STRONG): EXOTHERMIC DECOMPOSITION. CHLOROSULFONIC ACID: EXOTHERMIC DECOMPOSITION. LITHIUM TETRAHYDROALUMINATE: POSSIBLE EXPLOSION. NITRATES: FIRE AND EXPLOSION HAZARD. OLEUM: EXOTHERMIC DECOMPOSITION. OXIDIZERS (STRONG): FIRE AND EXPLOSION HAZARD. POTASSIUM TERT-BUTOXIDE: POSSIBLE IGNITION.

DECOMPOSITION: THERMAL DECOMPOSITION PRODUCTS MAY INCLUDE TOXIC OXIDES OF CARBON.

POLYMERIZATION: HAZARDOUS POLYMERIZATION HAS NOT BEEN REPORTED TO OCCUR UNDER NORMAL TEMPERATURES AND PRESSURES.

STORAGE AND DISPOSAL

OBSERVE ALL FEDERAL, STATE AND LOCAL REGULATIONS WHEN STORING OR DISPOSING OF THIS SUBSTANCE. FOR ASSISTANCE, CONTACT THE DISTRICT DIRECTOR OF THE ENVIRONMENTAL PROTECTION AGENCY.

STORAGE

STORE IN ACCORDANCE WITH 29 CFR 1910.106.

BONDING AND GROUNDING: SUBSTANCES WITH LOW ELECTROCONDUCTIVITY, WHICH MAY BE IGNITED BY ELECTROSTATIC SPARKS, SHOULD BE STORED IN CONTAINERS WHICH MEET THE BONDING AND GROUNDING GUIDELINES SPECIFIED IN NFPA 77-1983, RECOMMENDED PRACTICE ON STATIC ELECTRICITY.

STORE AWAY FROM INCOMPATIBLE SUBSTANCES.

DISPOSAL

DISPOSAL MUST BE IN ACCORDANCE WITH STANDARDS APPLICABLE TO GENERATORS OF HAZARDOUS WASTE, 40CFR 262. EPA HAZARDOUS WASTE NUMBER U112.

CONDITIONS TO AVOID

AVOID CONTACT WITH HEAT, SPARKS, FLAMES, OR OTHER SOURCES OF IGNITION. VAPORS MAY BE EXPLOSIVE AND POISONOUS; DO NOT ALLOW UNNECESSARY PERSONNEL IN AREA. DO NOT OVERHEAT CONTAINERS; CONTAINERS MAY VIOLENTLY RUPTURE AND TRAVEL A CONSIDERABLE DISTANCE IN HEAT OF FIRE.

SPILL AND LEAK PROCEDURES

OCCUPATIONAL SPILL: SHUT OFF IGNITION SOURCES. STOP LEAK IF YOU CAN DO IT WITHOUT RISK. USE WATER SPRAY TO REDUCE VAPORS. FOR SMALL SPILLS, TAKE UP WITH SAND OR OTHER ABSORBENT MATERIAL AND PLACE INTO CONTAINERS FOR LATER DISPOSAL. FOR LARGER SPILLS, DIKE FAR AHEAD OF SPILL FOR LATER DISPOSAL. NO SMOKING, FLAMES OR FLARES IN HAZARD AREA. KEEP UNNECESSARY PEOPLE AWAY; ISOLATE HAZARD AREA AND DENY ENTRY.

REPORTABLE QUANTITY (RQ): 5000 POUNDS THE SUPERFUND AMENDMENTS AND REAUTHORIZATION ACT (SARA) SECTION 304 REQUIRES THAT A RELEASE EQUAL TO OR GREATER THAN THE REPORTABLE QUANTITY FOR THIS SUBSTANCE BE IMMEDIATELY REPORTED TO THE LOCAL EMERGENCY PLANNING COMMITTEE AND THE STATE EMERGENCY RESPONSE COMMISSION (40 CFR 355.40). IF THE RELEASE OF THIS SUBSTANCE IS REPORTABLE UNDER CERCLA SECTION 103, THE NATIONAL RESPONSE CENTER MUST BE NOTIFIED IMMEDIATELY AT (800) 424-8802 OR (202) 426-2675 IN THE METROPOLITAN WASHINGTON, D.C. AREA (40 CFR 302.6).

PROTECTIVE EQUIPMENT

VENTILATION: PROVIDE GENERAL DILUTION VENTILATION TO MEET PUBLISHED EXPOSURE LIMITS.

RESPIRATOR: THE FOLLOWING RESPIRATORS AND MAXIMUM USE CONCENTRATIONS ARE RECOMMENDATIONS BY THE U.S. DEPARTMENT OF HEALTH AND HUMAN SERVICES, NIOSH POCKET GUIDE TO CHEMICAL HAZARDS; NIOSH CRITERIA DOCUMENTS OR BY THE U.S. DEPARTMENT OF LABOR, 29 CFR 1910 SUBPART Z. THE SPECIFIC RESPIRATOR SELECTED MUST BE BASED ON CONTAMINATION LEVELS FOUND IN THE WORK PLACE, MUST NOT EXCEED THE WORKING LIMITS OF THE RESPIRATOR AND BE JOINTLY APPROVED BY THE NATIONAL INSTITUTE FOR OCCUPATIONAL SAFETY AND HEALTH AND THE MINE SAFETY AND HEALTH ADMINISTRATION (NIOSH-MSHA).

ETHYL ACETATE:

1000 PPM: ANY CHEMICAL CARTRIDGE RESPIRATOR WITH A FULL FACEPIECE AND ORGANIC BAPOR CARTRIDGES. ANY POWERED AIR-PURIFYING RESPIRATOR WITH ORGANIC VAPOR CARTRIDGES.

10,000 PPM: ANY AIR-PURIFYING FULL FACEPIECE RESPIRATOR (GAS MASK) WITH A CHIN-STYLE OR FRONT- OR BACK-MOUNTED ORGANIC VAPOR CANISTER. ANY SUPPLIED-AIR RESPIRATOR WITH A FULL FACEPIECE. ANY SELF-CONTAINED BREATHING APPARATUS WITH AFULL FACEPIECE. ANY SUPPLIED-AIR RESPIRATOR OPERATED IN A CONTINUOUS FLOW MODE.

ESCAPE: ANY AIR-PURIFYING FULL FACEPIECE RESPIRATOR (GAS MASK) WITH A CHIN-STYLE OR FRONT- OR BACK-MOUNTED ORGANIC VAPOR CANISTER. ANY APPROPRIATE ESCAPE-TYPE SELF-CONTAINED BREATHING APPARATUS.

FOR FIREFIGHTING AND OTHER IMMEDIATELY DANGEROUS TO LIFE OR HEALTH CONDITIONS:

SELF-CONTAINED BREATHING APPARATUS WITH FULL FACEPIECE OPERATED IN PRESSURE-DEMAND OR OTHER POSITIVE PRESSURE MODE.

SUPPLIED-AIR RESPIRATOR WITH FULL FACEPIECE AND OPERATED IN PRESSURE-DEMAND OR OTHER POSITIVE PRESSURE MODE IN COMBINATION WITH AN AUXILIARY SELF-CONTAINED BREATHING APPARATUS OPERATED IN PRESSURE-DEMAND OR OTHER POSITIVE PRESSURE MODE.

CLOTHING: EMPLOYEE MUST WEAR APPROPRIATE PROTECTIVE (IMPERVIOUS) CLOTHING AND EQUIPMENT TO PREVENT REPEATED OR PROLONGED SKIN CONTACT WITH THIS SUBSTANCE.

GLOVES: EMPLOYEE MUST WEAR APPROPRIATE PROTECTIVE GLOVES TO PREVENT CONTACT WITH THIS SUBSTANCE.

EYE PROTECTION: EMPLOYEE MUST WEAR SPLASH-PROOF OR DUST-RESISTANT SAFETY GOGGLES TO PREVENT EYE CONTACT WITH THIS SUBSTANCE.

EMERGENCY EYE WASH: WHERE THERE IS ANY POSSIBILITY THAT AN EMPLOYEE'S EYES MAY BE EXPOSED TO THIS SUBSTANCE, THE EMPLOYER SHOULD PROVIDE AN EYE WASH FOUNTAIN WITHIN THE IMMEDIATE WORK AREA FOR EMERGENCY USE.

AUTHORIZED BY- OCCUPATIONAL HEALTH SERVICES, INC.
CREATION DATE: 11/15/89 ***REVISION DATE:*** 05/25/90

MATERIAL SAFETY DATA SHEET

OCCUPATIONAL HEALTH SERVICES, INC.
AGRICULTURE AND PESTICIDE DIVISION
450 SEVENTH AVENUE, SUITE 2407
NEW YORK, NEW YORK 10123
1-800-445-MSDS OR (212) 967-1100

EMERGENCY CONTACT:
JOHN S. BRANSFORD, JR. (615) 292-1180

SUBSTANCE IDENTIFICATION

CAS-NUMBER 64529-56-2
SUBSTANCE: ETHYL METRIBUZIN
TRADE NAMES/SYNONYMS: 1,2,4-TRIAZIN-5(4H)-ONE, 4-AMINO-6-(1,1-DIMETHYLETHYL)-3-(ETHYLTHIO)-; 4-AMINO-6-(1,1-DIMETHYLETHYL)-3-(ETHYLTHIO)-1,2,4-TRIAZIN-5(4H)-ONE; 3-ETHYLTHIO-4-AMINO-6-TERT-BUTYL-1,2,4-TRIAZINE-5-ONE; BAY-SYM 1500; ETHIOZIN; SMY 1500; TYCOR; C9H16N4OS; PST09111
CHEMICAL FAMILY: TRIAZINE
THIO
AMINE
MOLECULAR FORMULA: C3-N3-(O)-(C-(C-H3)3)-(S-(C2-H5))-(N-H2)
MOLECULAR WEIGHT: 228.31
CERCLA RATINGS (SCALE 0-3): HEALTH=2 FIRE=1 REACTIVITY=0 PERSISTENCE=2
NFPA RATINGS (SCALE 0-4): HEALTH=1 FIRE=1 REACTIVITY=0

COMPONENTS AND CONTAMINANTS

COMPONENT: ETHYL METRIBUZIN ***PERCENT:*** 100.0
CAS# 64529-56-2
OTHER CONTAMINANTS: NONE
EXPOSURE LIMITS: NO OCCUPATIONAL EXPOSURE LIMITS ESTABLISHED BY OSHA, ACGIH, OR NIOSH.

PHYSICAL DATA

DESCRIPTION: CRYSTALLINE SOLID. ***MELTING POINT:*** 203 F (95 C)
SPECIFIC GRAVITY: 1.14 ***VAPOR PRESSURE:*** NEGLIGIBLE
SOLUBILITY IN WATER: 0.04%
SOLVENT SOLUBILITY: SOLUBLE IN DICHLOROMETHANE, TOLUOL, 2-PROPANOL; SLIGHTLY SOLUBLE IN HEXANE AND OTHER AROMATIC SOLVENTS.

FIRE AND EXPLOSION DATA

FIRE AND EXPLOSION HAZARD: SLIGHT FIRE HAZARD WHEN EXPOSED TO HEAT OR FLAME.
DUST-AIR MIXTURES MAY IGNITE OR EXPLODE.
FIREFIGHTING MEDIA: DRY CHEMICAL, CARBON DIOXIDE, HALON, WATER SPRAY OR STANDARD FOAM (1987 EMERGENCY RESPONSE GUIDEBOOK, DOT P 5800.4).
FOR LARGER FIRES, USE WATER SPRAY, FOG OR STANDARD FOAM (1987 EMERGENCY RESPONSE GUIDEBOOK, DOT P 5800.4).
FIREFIGHTING: MOVE CONTAINER FROM FIRE AREA IF POSSIBLE. DO NOT SCATTER SPILLED MATERIAL WITH HIGH PRESSURE WATER STREAMS. DIKE FIRE CONTROL WATER FOR LATER DISPOSAL (1987 EMERGENCY RESPONSE GUIDEBOOK, DOT P 5800.4, GUIDE PAGE 31).
USE AGENTS SUITABLE FOR TYPE OF SURROUNDING FIRE. AVOID BREATHING HAZARDOUS VAPORS, KEEP UPWIND.

TOXICITY

ETHYL METRIBUZIN: TOXICITY DATA: >20.8 MG/L/1 HOUR INHALATION-RAT LC50 (MOBAY MSDS); >2000 MG/KG SKIN-RABBIT LD50 (MOBAY MSDS); 599 MG/KG ORAL-RAT LD50 (MOBAY MSDS); 2000 MG/KG ORAL-RAT LD50. CARCINOGEN STATUS: NONE. ACUTE TOXICITY LEVEL: MODERATELY TOXIC BY INHALATION AND INGESTION; SLIGHTLY TOXIC BY DERMAL ABSORPTION. TARGET EFFECTS: NO DATA AVAILABLE.

HEALTH EFFECTS AND FIRST AID

INHALATION: ETHYL METRIBUZIN: **ACUTE EXPOSURE-** SOME TRIAZINES ARE MILDLY IRRITATING TO THE UPPER RESPIRATORY TRACT. **CHRONIC EXPOSURE-** NO OBSERVABLE EFFECTS WERE NOTED IN RATS EXPOSED TO 0.032 MG/L/6 HOURS FOR 3 WEEKS.
FIRST AID- REMOVE FROM EXPOSURE AREA TO FRESH AIR IMMEDIATELY. IF BREATHING HAS STOPPED, PERFORM ARTIFICIAL RESPIRATION. KEEP PERSON WARM AND AT REST. TREAT SYMPTOMATICALLY AND SUPPORTIVELY. GET MEDICAL ATTENTION IMMEDIATELY.

SKIN CONTACT: ETHYL METRIBUZIN: **ACUTE EXPOSURE-** THIS MATERIAL WAS NOT AN IRRITANT OF RABBIT SKIN OR A SENSITIZER OF GUINEA PIG SKIN. **CHRONIC EXPOSURE-** NO OBSERVABLE EFFECTS WERE NOTED IN A 21-DAY STUDY OF RATS EXPOSED TO CONCENTRATIONS UP TO AND INCLUDING 1000 MG/KG.
FIRST AID- REMOVE CONTAMINATED CLOTHING AND SHOES IMMEDIATELY. WASH AFFECTED AREA WITH SOAP OR MILD DETERGENT AND LARGE AMOUNTS OF WATER UNTIL NO EVIDENCE OF CHEMICAL REMAINS (APPROXIMATELY 15-20 MINUTES). GET MEDICAL ATTENTION IMMEDIATELY.

EYE CONTACT: ETHYL METRIBUZIN: **ACUTE EXPOSURE-** MAY BE MILDLY IRRITATING. **CHRONIC EXPOSURE-** NO DATA AVAILABLE.
FIRST AID- WASH EYES IMMEDIATELY WITH LARGE AMOUNTS OF WATER OR NORMAL SALINE, OCCASIONALLY LIFTING UPPER AND LOWER LIDS, UNTIL NO EVIDENCE OF CHEMICAL REMAINS (APPROXIMATELY 15-20 MINUTES). GET MEDICAL ATTENTION IMMEDIATELY.

INGESTION: ETHYL METRIBUZIN: **ACUTE EXPOSURE-** EFFECTS OF STAGGERING, TREMORS, DISTURBED MOBILITY AND RESPIRATION WERE NOTED IN ANIMAL STUDIES. **CHRONIC EXPOSURE-** INCREASED THYROXINE VALUES WERE OBSERVED IN ANIMAL STUDIES. INCREASED FOLLICULAR CELL NEOPLASIA WAS PRODUCED IN RATS RECEIVING A DIETARY LEVEL OF 1600 PPM; THE NO-OBSERVABLE-EFFECTS LEVEL FOR ONCOGENIC EFFECTS WAS FOUND TO BE 400 PPM. FETOTOXICITY IN ASSOCIATION WITH MATERNAL TOXICITY WAS NOTED IN RAT STUDIES AT 300 MG/KG. DEVELOPMENTAL EFFECTS OF DECREASED FETAL AND PLACENTAL WEIGHTS, INCREASED NUMBER OF RUNTS AND DELAYED OSSIFICATION OCCURING WITH TERATA AND MATERNAL EFFECTS INCLUDING INCREASED ABORTIONS AND RESORPTIONS WERE OBSERVED IN RABBITS AT 175 MG/KG; THE NO-OBSERVABLE-EFFECTS LEVEL FOR BOTH DEVELOPMENTAL AND MATERNAL TOXICITY WAS 70 MG/KG.
FIRST AID- TREAT SYMPTOMATICALLY AND SUPPORTIVELY. GET MEDICAL ATTENTION IMMEDIATELY. IF VOMITING OCCURS, KEEP HEAD LOWER THAN HIPS TO PREVENT ASPIRATION.
ANTIDOTE: NO SPECIFIC ANTIDOTE. TREAT SYMPTOMATICALLY AND SUPPORTIVELY.

REACTIVITY

REACTIVITY: STABLE UNDER NORMAL TEMPERATURES AND PRESSURES.
INCOMPATIBILITIES: ETHYL METRIBUZIN: OXIDIZERS (STRONG): FIRE AND EXPLOSION HAZARD.
DECOMPOSITION: THERMAL DECOMPOSITION PRODUCTS MAY INCLUDE TOXIC OXIDES OF CARBON, NITROGEN, AND SULFUR.
POLYMERIZATION: HAZARDOUS POLYMERIZATION HAS NOT BEEN REPORTED TO OCCUR UNDER NORMAL TEMPERATURES AND PRESSURES.

STORAGE AND DISPOSAL

OBSERVE ALL FEDERAL, STATE AND LOCAL REGULATIONS WHEN STORING OR DISPOSING OF THIS SUBSTANCE. FOR ASSISTANCE, CONTACT THE DISTRICT DIRECTOR OF THE ENVIRONMENTAL PROTECTION AGENCY.

STORAGE

STORE IN ACCORDANCE WITH 40 CFR 165 RECOMMENDED PROCEDURES FOR THE DISPOSAL AND STORAGE OF PESTICIDES AND PESTICIDE CONTAINERS.
STORE AWAY FROM INCOMPATIBLE SUBSTANCES.

DISPOSAL

DISPOSAL MUST BE IN ACCORDANCE WITH 40 CFR 165 RECOMMENDED PROCEDURES FOR THE DISPOSAL AND STORAGE OF PESTICIDES AND PESTICIDE CONTAINERS.

CONDITIONS TO AVOID

MAY BURN BUT DOES NOT IGNITE READILY. AVOID CONTACT WITH STRONG OXIDIZERS, EXCESSIVE HEAT, SPARKS, OR OPEN FLAME.

SPILL AND LEAK PROCEDURES

OCCUPATIONAL SPILL: SWEEP UP AND PLACE IN SUITABLE CLEAN, DRY CONTAINERS FOR RECLAMATION OR LATER DISPOSAL. DO NOT FLUSH SPILLED MATERIAL INTO SEWER. KEEP UNNECESSARY PEOPLE AWAY.

PROTECTIVE EQUIPMENT

VENTILATION: PROVIDE LOCAL EXHAUST OR GENERAL DILUTION VENTILATION SYSTEM.

RESPIRATOR: THE FOLLOWING RESPIRATORS ARE RECOMMENDED BASED ON INFORMATION FOUND IN THE PHYSICAL DATA, TOXICITY AND HEALTH EFFECTS SECTIONS. THEY ARE RANKED IN ORDER FROM MINIMUM TO MAXIMUM RESPIRATORY PROTECTION. THE SPECIFIC RESPIRATOR SELECTED MUST BE BASED ON CONTAMINATION LEVELS FOUND IN THE WORK PLACE, MUST NOT EXCEED THE WORKING LIMITS OF THE RESPIRATOR AND BE JOINTLY APPROVED BY THE NATIONAL INSTITUTE FOR OCCUPATIONAL SAFETY AND HEALTH AND THE MINE SAFETY AND HEALTH ADMINISTRATION (NIOSH-MSHA).

DUST AND MIST RESPIRATOR.

CHEMICAL CARTRIDGE RESPIRATOR WITH ORGANIC VAPOR CARTRIDGE(S) WITH A DUST AND MIST FILTER.

CHEMICAL CARTRIDGE RESPIRATOR WITH ORGANIC VAPOR CARTRIDGE(S) IN COMBINATION WITH A HIGH-EFFICIENCY PARTICULATE FILTER. GAS MASK WITH ORGANIC VAPOR CANISTER (CHIN STYLE OR FRONT- OR BACK-MOUNTED CANISTER) WITH A DUST AND MIST FILTER.

POWERED AIR-PURIFYING RESPIRATOR WITH HIGH-EFFICIENCY PARTICULATE FILTER.

TYPE 'C' SUPPLIED-AIR RESPIRATOR OPERATED IN THE PRESSURE-DEMAND OR OTHER POSITIVE PRESSURE OR CONTINUOUS-FLOW MODE.

SELF-CONTAINED BREATHING APPARATUS.

FOR FIREFIGHTING AND OTHER IMMEDIATELY DANGEROUS TO LIFE OR HEALTH CONDITIONS:

SELF-CONTAINED BREATHING APPARATUS WITH FULL FACEPIECE OPERATED IN PRESSURE-DEMAND OR OTHER POSITIVE PRESSURE MODE.

SUPPLIED-AIR RESPIRATOR WITH FULL FACEPIECE AND OPERATED IN PRESSURE-DEMAND OR OTHER POSITIVE PRESSURE MODE IN COMBINATION WITH AN AUXILIARY SELF-CONTAINED BREATHING APPARATUS OPERATED IN PRESSURE-DEMAND OR OTHER POSITIVE PRESSURE MODE.

CLOTHING: EMPLOYEE MUST WEAR APPROPRIATE PROTECTIVE (IMPERVIOUS) CLOTHING AND EQUIPMENT TO PREVENT REPEATED OR PROLONGED SKIN CONTACT WITH THIS SUBSTANCE.

GLOVES: EMPLOYEE MUST WEAR APPROPRIATE PROTECTIVE GLOVES TO PREVENT CONTACT WITH THIS SUBSTANCE.

EYE PROTECTION: EMPLOYEE MUST WEAR SPLASH-PROOF OR DUST-RESISTANT SAFETY GOGGLES TO PREVENT EYE CONTACT WITH THIS SUBSTANCE.

EMERGENCY EYE WASH: WHERE THERE IS ANY POSSIBILITY THAT AN EMPLOYEE'S EYES MAY BE EXPOSED TO THIS SUBSTANCE, THE EMPLOYER SHOULD PROVIDE AN EYE WASH FOUNTAIN WITHIN THE IMMEDIATE WORK AREA FOR EMERGENCY USE.

AUTHORIZED BY- OCCUPATIONAL HEALTH SERVICES, INC.

CREATION DATE: 06/28/90 ***REVISION DATE:*** 06/29/90

MATERIAL SAFETY DATA SHEET

OCCUPATIONAL HEALTH SERVICES, INC.
AGRICULTURE AND PESTICIDE DIVISION
450 SEVENTH AVENUE, SUITE 2407
NEW YORK, NEW YORK 10123
1-800-445-MSDS OR (212) 967-1100

EMERGENCY CONTACT:
JOHN S. BRANSFORD, JR. (615) 292-1180

SUBSTANCE IDENTIFICATION

CAS-NUMBER 74-85-1

SUBSTANCE: **ETHYLENE**

TRADE NAMES/SYNONYMS: ACETENE; ETHENE; ETHYLENE, COMPRESSED GAS; OLEFIANT GAS; BICARBURETTED HYDROGEN; STCC 4905734; UN 1962; C2H4; PST09330

CHEMICAL FAMILY: HYDROCARBON, ALIPHATIC

MOLECULAR FORMULA: C-H2-C-H2

MOLECULAR WEIGHT: 28.05

CERCLA RATINGS (SCALE 0-3): HEALTH=1 FIRE=3 REACTIVITY=2 PERSISTENCE=0

NFPA RATINGS (SCALE 0-4): HEALTH=1 FIRE=4 REACTIVITY=2

COMPONENTS AND CONTAMINANTS

COMPONENT: ETHYLENE ***PERCENT:*** 100.0

CAS# 74-85-1

OTHER CONTAMINANTS: NONE

EXPOSURE LIMITS: NO OCCUPATIONAL EXPOSURE LIMITS ESTABLISHED BY OSHA, ACGIH, OR NIOSH.

ETHYLENE: SUBJECT TO SARA SECTION 313 ANNUAL TOXIC CHEMICAL RELEASE REPORTING

PHYSICAL DATA

DESCRIPTION: COLORLESS COMPRESSED GAS WITH A SWEET ODOR AND TASTE.

BOILING POINT: -155 F (-104 C) ***MELTING POINT:*** -272 F (-169 C)

SPECIFIC GRAVITY: 1.261 G/L @ 0 C ***VISCOSITY:*** 0.0093 CPS @ 0 C

VOLATILITY: 100% ***VAPOR PRESSURE:*** 760 MMHG @ -104 C

SOLUBILITY IN WATER: 22.6% ***VAPOR DENSITY:*** 1.0

SOLVENT SOLUBILITY: SOLUBLE IN ALCOHOL, ETHER, ACETONE, BENZENE.

FIRE AND EXPLOSION DATA

FIRE AND EXPLOSION HAZARD: DANGEROUS FIRE HAZARD WHEN EXPOSED TO HEAT OR FLAME.

DANGEROUS EXPLOSION HAZARD WHEN EXPOSED TO HEAT OR FLAME.

CYLINDER MAY EXPLODE IN HEAT OF FIRE.

DUE TO LOW ELECTROCONDUCTIVITY OF THE SUBSTANCE, FLOW OR AGITATION MAY GENERATE ELECTROSTATIC CHARGES RESULTING IN SPARKS WITH POSSIBLE IGNITION.

UPPER EXPLOSIVE LIMIT: 36% ***LOWER EXPLOSIVE LIMIT:*** 2.7%

AUTOIGNITION TEMP.: 842 F (450 C)

FIREFIGHTING MEDIA: DRY CHEMICAL, CARBON DIOXIDE OR HALON (1987 EMERGENCY RESPONSE GUIDEBOOK, DOT P 5800.4).

FOR LARGER FIRES, USE WATER SPRAY OR FOG (1987 EMERGENCY RESPONSE GUIDEBOOK, DOT P 5800.4).

FIREFIGHTING: MOVE CONTAINER FROM FIRE AREA IF POSSIBLE. STAY AWAY FROM STORAGE TANK ENDS. COOL FIRE-EXPOSED CONTAINERS WITH WATER FROM SIDE UNTIL WELL AFTER FIRE IS OUT. FOR MASSIVE FIRE IN STORAGE AREA, USE UNMANNED HOSE HOLDER OR MONITOR NOZZLES, ELSE WITHDRAW FROM AREA AND LET BURN. WITHDRAW IMMEDIATELY IN CASE OF RISING SOUND FROM VENTING SAFETY DEVICE OR ANY DISCOLORATION OF STORAGE TANK DUE TO FIRE. LET STORAGE TANK BURN UNLESS LEAK CAN BE STOPPED; WITH SMALLER TANKS OR CYLINDERS, EXTINGUISH/ISOLATE FROM OTHER FLAMMABLE MATERIALS. (1987 EMERGENCY RESPONSE GUIDEBOOK, DOT P 5800.4, GUIDE PAGE 22).

EXTINGUISH ONLY IF FLOW CAN BE STOPPED; USE WATER IN FLOODING AMOUNTS AS FOG. COOL CONTAINERS WITH FLOODING QUANTITIES OF WATER, APPLY FROM AS FAR A DISTANCE AS POSSIBLE. AVOID BREATHING TOXIC VAPORS, KEEP UPWIND. EVACUATE TO A RADIUS OF 1500 FEET FOR UNCONTROLLABLE FIRES. CONSIDER EVACUATION OF DOWNWIND AREA IF MATERIAL IS LEAKING.

STOP FLOW OF GAS (NFPA 325M, FIRE HAZARD PROPERTIES OF FLAMMABLE LIQUIDS, GASES, AND VOLATILE SOLIDS, 1984).

TRANSPORTATION DATA

DEPARTMENT OF TRANSPORTATION HAZARD CLASSIFICATION 49 CFR 172.101: FLAMMABLE GAS

DEPARTMENT OF TRANSPORTATION LABELING REQUIREMENTS 49 CFR 172.101 AND SUBPART E: FLAMMABLE GAS

DEPARTMENT OF TRANSPORTATION PACKAGING REQUIREMENTS: 49 CFR 173.304 EXCEPTIONS: 49 CFR 173.306

TOXICITY

ETHYLENE: TOXICITY DATA: 950,000 PPM/5 MINUTES INHALATION-MAMMAL LCLO. CARCINOGEN STATUS: NONE (IARC GROUP-3). ACUTE TOXICITY DATA: INSUFFICIENT DATA. TARGET EFFECTS: CENTRAL NERVOUS SYSTEM DEPRESSANT; SIMPLE ASPHYXIANT. ADDITIONAL DATA: INTERACTIONS WITH MEDICATIONS HAVE BEEN REPORTED.

HEALTH EFFECTS AND FIRST AID

INHALATION: ETHYLENE: SIMPLE ASPHYXIANT. HIGH CONCENTRATIONS MAY CAUSE NARCOSIS. RATS EXPOSED TO 95% ETHYLENE, AND 5% OXYGEN FALL INTO DEEP ANESTHESIA ACCOMPANIED BY MARKED CYANOSIS AND DEPRESSION WITH A SLOW FALL IN BLOOD PRESSURE. OTHER STUDIES REPORTED SOME EFFECTS ON THE LIVER IN EXPOSED RATS. MICE EXPOSED TO 3 MG/M3 FOR 90 DAYS EXHIBITED CHOLINESTERASE ACTIVITY BUT NO HEMATOLOGIC CHANGES. SEE INFORMATION ON SIMPLE ASPHYXIANTS.

SIMPLE ASPHYXIANTS: **ACUTE EXPOSURE-** THE SYMPTOMS OF ASPHYXIA DEPEND ON THE RAPIDITY WITH WHICH THE OXYGEN DEFICIENCY DEVELOPS AND HOW LONG IT CONTINUES. IN SUDDEN ACUTE ASPHYXIA, UNCONSCIOUSNESS MAY BE IMMEDIATE. WITH SLOW DEVELOPMENT THERE MAY BE RAPID RESPIRATION AND PULSE, AIR HUNGER, DIZZINESS, REDUCED AWARENESS, TIGHTNESS IN THE HEAD, TINGLING SENSATIONS, INCOORDINATION, FAULTY JUDGEMENT, EMOTIONAL INSTABILITY, AND RAPID FATIGUE. AS THE ASPHYXIA PROGRESSES, NAUSEA,

VOMITING, COLLAPSE, UNCONSCIOUSNESS, CONVULSIONS, DEEP COMA AND DEATH ARE POSSIBLE. **CHRONIC EXPOSURE-** NO DATA AVAILABLE.

FIRST AID- REMOVE FROM EXPOSURE AREA TO FRESH AIR IMMEDIATELY. IF BREATHING HAS STOPPED, GIVE ARTIFICIAL RESPIRATION. MAINTAIN AIRWAY AND BLOOD PRESSURE AND ADMINISTER OXYGEN IF AVAILABLE. KEEP AFFECTED PERSON WARM AND AT REST. TREAT SYMPTOMATICALLY AND SUPPORTIVELY. ADMINISTRATION OF OXYGEN SHOULD BE PERFORMED BY QUALIFIED PERSONNEL. GET MEDICAL ATTENTION IMMEDIATELY.

SKIN CONTACT: ETHYLENE: **ACUTE EXPOSURE-** NO ADVERSE EFFECTS HAVE BEEN REPORTED FROM THE GAS. DUE TO RAPID EVAPORATION, THE LIQUID MAY CAUSE FROSTBITE WITH REDNESS, TINGLING AND PAIN OR NUMBNESS. IN MORE SEVERE CASES, THE SKIN MAY BECOME HARD AND WHITE AND DEVELOP BLISTERS. **CHRONIC EXPOSURE-** NO DATA AVAILABLE.

FIRST AID- IT IS UNLIKELY THAT EMERGENCY TREATMENT WILL BE REQUIRED. IF ADVERSE EFFECTS OCCUR, GET MEDICAL ATTENTION. IN CASE OF FROSTBITE, WARM AFFECTED SKIN IN WARM WATER AT A TEMPERATURE OF 107 F. IF WARM WATER IS NOT AVAILABLE OR IMPRACTICAL TO USE, GENTLY WRAP AFFECTED PART IN BLANKETS. ENCOURAGE VICTIM TO EXERCISE AFFECTED PART WHILE IT IS BEING WARMED. ALLOW CIRCULATION TO RETURN NATURALLY (MATHESON GAS, 6TH ED.). GET MEDICAL ATTENTION IMMEDIATELY.

EYE CONTACT: ETHYLENE: **ACUTE EXPOSURE-** NO ADVERSE EFFECTS HAVE BEEN REPORTED FROM GAS. DUE TO RAPID EVAPORATION, THE LIQUID MAY CAUSE FROSTBITE WITH REDNESS, PAIN, AND BLURRED VISION. **CHRONIC EXPOSURE-** NO DATA AVAILABLE.

FIRST AID- IT IS UNLIKELY THAT CONTACT WITH THE GAS FORM WILL REQUIRE EMERGENCY TREATMENT. IF CONTACT WITH LIQUIFIED OR COMPRESSED GAS OCCURS, WASH WITH LARGE AMOUNTS OF WARM WATER UNTIL NO EVIDENCE OF CHEMICAL REMAINS (APPROXIMATELY 15-20 MINUTES). GET MEDICAL ATTENTION IMMEDIATELY.

INGESTION: ETHYLENE: **ACUTE EXPOSURE-** INGESTION OF A GAS IS UNLIKELY. IF LIQUID IS SWALLOWED, FROSTBITE DAMAGE TO THE LIPS, MOUTH AND MUCOUS MEMBRANES MAY OCCUR. **CHRONIC EXPOSURE-** NO DATA AVAILABLE.

FIRST AID- IT IS UNLIKELY THAT EMERGENCY TREATMENT WILL BE REQUIRED. IF ADVERSE EFFECTS OCCUR, TREAT SYMPTOMATICALLY AND SUPPORTIVELY AND GET MEDICAL ATTENTION.

ANTIDOTE: NO SPECIFIC ANTIDOTE. TREAT SYMPTOMATICALLY AND SUPPORTIVELY.

REACTIVITY

REACTIVITY: MAY POLYMERIZE AT ELEVATED TEMPERATURES AND PRESSURES.

INCOMPATIBILITIES: ETHYLENE: ACIDS: VIOLENT REACTION. ALUMINUM CHLORIDE: EXPLOSIVE REACTION IN PRESENCE OF CATALYST. BROMOTRICHLOROMETHANE: POSSIBLE EXPLOSION AT ELEVATED PRESSURES. CARBON TETRACHLORIDE: EXPLOSIVE REACTION AT ELEVATED PRESSURES. CHLORINE: EXPLOSIVE REACTION ON CONTACT WITH SUNLIGHT OR METAL OXIDE CATALYSTS. CHLORINE DIOXIDE: SPONTANEOUS EXPLOSION. CHLOROTRIFLUOROETHYLENE: POSSIBLE EXPLOSION HAZARD. COPPER: VIOLENT POLYMERIZATION AT ELEVATED PRESSURES. LITHIUM (HEATED): INCANDESCENT REACTION. NITROGEN OXIDES: FORMATION OF EXPLOSIVE COMPOUNDS. ORGANIC PEROXIDES: MAY INITIATE VIOLENT, EXOTHERMIC POLYMERIZATION. OXIDIZERS (STRONG): FIRE AND EXPLOSION HAZARD. OZONE: FORMATION OF EXPLOSIVE OZONIDE. TETRAFLUOROETHYLENE: POSSIBLE EXPLOSION AT ELEVATED PRESSURE. TRIFLUOROMETHYL HYPOFLUORITE: EXPLOSION HAZARD.

DECOMPOSITION: THERMAL DECOMPOSITION PRODUCTS MAY INCLUDE TOXIC OXIDES OF CARBON.

POLYMERIZATION: MAY UNDERGO EXOTHERMIC POLYMERIZATION AT ELEVATED TEMPERATURES AND PRESSURES OR IN THE PRESENCE OF APPROPRIATE CATALYSTS. IF POLYMERIZATION OCCURS IN A CLOSED CONTAINER, THE INCREASE IN TEMPERATURE AND PRESSURE MAY RUPTURE THE CONTAINER.

STORAGE AND DISPOSAL

OBSERVE ALL FEDERAL, STATE AND LOCAL REGULATIONS WHEN STORING OR DISPOSING OF THIS SUBSTANCE. FOR ASSISTANCE, CONTACT THE DISTRICT DIRECTOR OF THE ENVIRONMENTAL PROTECTION AGENCY.

****STORAGE****

STORE IN ACCORDANCE WITH 29 CFR 1910.101.

BONDING AND GROUNDING: SUBSTANCES WITH LOW ELECTROCONDUCTIVITY, WHICH MAY BE IGNITED BY ELECTROSTATIC SPARKS, SHOULD BE STORED IN CONTAINERS WHICH MEET THE BONDING AND GROUNDING GUIDELINES SPECIFIED IN NFPA 77-1983, RECOMMENDED PRACTICE ON STATIC ELECTRICITY.

PROTECT AGAINST PHYSICAL DAMAGE. ISOLATE FROM OXYGEN, CHLORINE, COMBUSTIBLE, ORGANIC AND OXIDIZING MATERIALS. STORE IN COOL, WELL VENTILATED AREA, OF NONCOMBUSTIBLE CONSTRUCTION, AWAY FROM POSSIBLE SOURCES OF IGNITION. PROTECT AGAINST STATIC ELECTRICITY AND LIGHTNING. OUTSIDE OR DETACHED STORAGE IS PREFERRED (NFPA 49, HAZARDOUS CHEMICALS DATA, 1975).

STORE AWAY FROM INCOMPATIBLE SUBSTANCES.

****DISPOSAL****

DISPOSAL MUST BE IN ACCORDANCE WITH STANDARDS APPLICABLE TO GENERATORS OF HAZARDOUS WASTE, 40 CFR 262. EPA HAZARDOUS WASTE NUMBER D001. 100 POUND CERCLA SECTION 103 REPORTABLE QUANTITY.

CONDITIONS TO AVOID

AVOID CONTACT WITH HEAT, SPARKS, FLAMES OR OTHER IGNITION SOURCES. VAPORS MAY BE EXPLOSIVE. DO NOT ALLOW CONTACT WITH SKIN; MATERIAL MAY CAUSE FROSTBITE. CONTENTS ARE UNDER PRESSURE; CONTAINERS MAY RUPTURE VIOLENTLY AND TRAVEL A CONSIDERABLE DISTANCE.

SPILL AND LEAK PROCEDURES

OCCUPATIONAL SPILL: SHUT OFF IGNITION SOURCES. DO NOT TOUCH SPILLED MATERIAL. STOP LEAK IF YOU CAN DO IT WITHOUT RISK. USE WATER SPRAY TO REDUCE VAPORS. ISOLATE AREA UNTIL GAS HAS DISPERSED. NO SMOKING, FLAMES OR FLARES IN HAZARD AREA! KEEP UNNECESSARY PEOPLE AWAY; ISOLATE HAZARD AREA AND DENY ENTRY. VENTILATE CLOSED SPACES BEFORE ENTERING.

PROTECTIVE EQUIPMENT

VENTILATION: PROVIDE LOCAL EXHAUST OR GENERAL DILUTION VENTILATION. VENTILATION EQUIPMENT MUST BE EXPLOSION-PROOF.

RESPIRATOR: THE FOLLOWING RESPIRATORS ARE RECOMMENDED BASED ON INFORMATION FOUND IN THE PHYSICAL DATA, TOXICITY AND HEALTH EFFECTS SECTIONS. THEY ARE RANKED IN ORDER FROM MINIMUM TO MAXIMUM RESPIRATORY PROTECTION. THE SPECIFIC RESPIRATOR SELECTED MUST BE BASED ON CONTAMINATION LEVELS FOUND IN THE WORK PLACE, MUST NOT EXCEED THE WORKING LIMITS OF THE RESPIRATOR AND BE JOINTLY APPROVED BY THE NATIONAL INSTITUTE FOR OCCUPATIONAL SAFETY AND HEALTH AND THE MINE SAFETY AND HEALTH ADMINISTRATION (NIOSH-MSHA).

ANY SUPPLIED-AIR RESPIRATOR OPERATED IN PRESSURE-DEMAND OR OTHER POSITIVE PRESSURE MODE.

ANY SELF-CONTAINED BREATHING APPARATUS.

FOR FIREFIGHTING AND OTHER IMMEDIATELY DANGEROUS TO LIFE OR HEALTH CONDITIONS:

SELF-CONTAINED BREATHING APPARATUS WITH FULL FACEPIECE OPERATED IN PRESSURE-DEMAND OR OTHER POSITIVE PRESSURE MODE.

SUPPLIED-AIR RESPIRATOR WITH FULL FACEPIECE AND OPERATED IN PRESSURE-DEMAND OR OTHER POSITIVE PRESSURE MODE IN COMBINATION WITH AN AUXILIARY SELF-CONTAINED BREATHING APPARATUS OPERATED IN PRESSURE-DEMAND OR OTHER POSITIVE PRESSURE MODE.

CLOTHING: FOR THE GAS FORM, PROTECTIVE CLOTHING NOT REQUIRED. IF CONTACT WITH THE LIQUID FORM IS POSSIBLE, EMPLOYEE MUST WEAR APPROPRIATE PROTECTIVE CLOTHING AND EQUIPMENT TO PREVENT SKIN FROM FREEZING.

GLOVES: WEAR FULL PROTECTIVE, COLD INSULATING GLOVES.

EYE PROTECTION: FOR THE GAS FORM EYE PROTECTION IS NOT REQUIRED BUT RECOMMENDED. WHERE THERE IS ANY POSSIBILITY OF CONTACT WITH THE LIQUID FORM, EMPLOYEE MUST WEAR SPLASH-PROOF SAFETY GOGGLES AND A FACESHIELD TO PREVENT CONTACT WITH THIS SUBSTANCE. CONTACT LENSES SHOULD NOT BE WORN.

EMERGENCY WASH FACILITIES: WHERE THERE IS ANY POSSIBILITY THAT AN EMPLOYEE'S EYES AND/OR SKIN MAY BE EXPOSED TO THE LIQUID FORM OF THIS SUBSTANCE, THE EMPLOYER SHOULD PROVIDE AN EYE WASH FOUNTAIN AND QUICK DRENCH SHOWER WITHIN THE IMMEDIATE WORK AREA FOR EMERGENCY USE.

AUTHORIZED BY- OCCUPATIONAL HEALTH SERVICES, INC.

CREATION DATE: 10/04/89 ***REVISION DATE:*** 07/12/90

MATERIAL SAFETY DATA SHEET

OCCUPATIONAL HEALTH SERVICES, INC.
AGRICULTURE AND PESTICIDE DIVISION
450 SEVENTH AVENUE, SUITE 2407
NEW YORK, NEW YORK 10123
1-800-445-MSDS OR (212) 967-1100

EMERGENCY CONTACT:
JOHN S. BRANSFORD, JR. (615) 292-1180

SUBSTANCE IDENTIFICATION

CAS-NUMBER 106-93-4
SUBSTANCE: ETHYLENE DIBROMIDE
TRADE NAMES/SYNONYMS: ETHANE, 1,2-DIBROMO-; 1,2-DIBROMOETHANE; SYM-DIBROMOETHANE; ALPHA,BETA-DIBROMOETHANE; 1,2-ETHYLENE DIBROMIDE; ETHYLENE BROMIDE; GLYCOL DIBROMIDE; EDB; BROMOFUME (FORMULATION); DOWFUME W 85 (FORMULATION); RCRA U067; ENT 15,349; STCC 4921497; UN 1605; C2H4BR2; PST09380
CHEMICAL FAMILY: HALOGEN COMPOUND, ALIPHATIC
MOLECULAR FORMULA: BR-C-H2-C-H2-BR
MOLECULAR WEIGHT: 187.86
CERCLA RATINGS (SCALE 0-3): HEALTH=3 FIRE=0 REACTIVITY=0 PERSISTENCE=2
NFPA RATINGS (SCALE 0-4): HEALTH=3 FIRE=0 REACTIVITY=0

COMPONENTS AND CONTAMINANTS

COMPONENT: ETHYLENE DIBROMIDE ***PERCENT:*** 100
CAS# 106-93-4
OTHER CONTAMINANTS: NONE
EXPOSURE LIMITS: ETHYLENE DIBROMIDE: 20 PPM OSHA TWA; 30 PPM OSHA CEILING; 50 PPM/5 MINUTES OSHA PEAK ACGIH A2-SUSPECTED HUMAN CARCINOGEN (SKIN). 0.045 PPM (0.38 MG/M3) NIOSH RECOMMENDED 8 HOUR TWA 0.13 PPM (1.0 MG/M3) NIOSH RECOMMENDED 15 MINUTE CEILING LOWEST FEASIBLE LIMIT NIOSH RECOMMENDED EXPOSURE CRITERIA
1 POUND CERCLA SECTION 103 REPORTABLE QUANTITY SUBJECT TO SARA SECTION 313 ANNUAL TOXIC CHEMICAL RELEASE REPORTING SUBJECT TO CALIFORNIA PROPOSITION 65 CANCER AND/OR REPRODUCTIVE TOXICITY WARNING AND RELEASE REQUIREMENTS- (JULY, 1987)

PHYSICAL DATA

DESCRIPTION: HEAVY, COLORLESS LIQUID WITH A MILD SWEET ODOR WHICH TURNS BROWN ON EXPOSURE TO LIGHT. ***BOILING POINT:*** 268 F (131 C)
MELTING POINT: 50 F (10 C) ***SPECIFIC GRAVITY:*** 2.1792 @ 25 C
VISCOSITY: 38.5 CENTISTOKES @ 20 C ***VAPOR PRESSURE:*** 11 MMHG @ 25 C
SOLUBILITY IN WATER: 0.4% ***ODOR THRESHOLD:*** 10-25 PPM ***VAPOR DENSITY:*** 6.48
SOLVENT SOLUBILITY: SOLUBLE IN ETHER, ALCOHOL, BENZENE, ACETONE, AND MOST ORGANIC SOLVENTS AND THINNERS.

FIRE AND EXPLOSION DATA

FIRE AND EXPLOSION HAZARD: NEGLIGIBLE FIRE HAZARD WHEN EXPOSED TO HEAT OR FLAME.
FIREFIGHTING MEDIA: DRY CHEMICAL, CARBON DIOXIDE, HALON, WATER SPRAY OR STANDARD FOAM (1987 EMERGENCY RESPONSE GUIDEBOOK, DOT P 5800.4).
FOR LARGER FIRES, USE WATER SPRAY, FOG OR STANDARD FOAM (1987 EMERGENCY RESPONSE GUIDEBOOK, DOT P 5800.4).
FIREFIGHTING: MOVE CONTAINERS FROM FIRE AREA IF POSSIBLE. FIGHT FIRE FROM MAXIMUM DISTANCE. STAY AWAY FROM STORAGE TANK ENDS. DIKE FIRE CONTROL WATER FOR LATER DISPOSAL. DO NOT SCATTER MATERIAL (1987 EMERGENCY RESPONSE GUIDEBOOK, DOT P 5800.4, GUIDE PAGE 55).
USE AGENTS SUITABLE FOR TYPE OF SURROUNDING FIRE. AVOID BREATHING VAPORS OR DUSTS, KEEP UPWIND.
FIRE FIGHTING PHASES: USE WATER SPRAY, DRY CHEMICAL, FOAM, OR CARBON DIOXIDE FOR FIGHTING FIRES IN AREAS WHERE DIBROMOEHTANE IS STORED. USE WATER TO KEEP FIRE-EXPOSED CONTAINERS COOL. USE WATER TO DISPERSE THE VAPORS AND TO PROVIDE PROTECTION FOR THE MEN ATTEMPTING TO STOP A LEAK. WATER SPRAY MAY BE USED TO FLUSH SPILLS AWAY FROM EXPOSURES (NFPA 49, HAZARDOUS CHEMICALS DATA, 1975).

TRANSPORTATION DATA

DEPARTMENT OF TRANSPORTATION HAZARD CLASSIFICATION 49 CFR 172.101: POISON B
DEPARTMENT OF TRANSPORTATION LABELING REQUIREMENTS 49 CFR 172.101 AND SUBPART E: POISON
DEPARTMENT OF TRANSPORTATION PACKAGING REQUIREMENTS: 49 CFR 173.346 EXCEPTIONS: 49 CFR 173.345

TOXICITY

ETHYLENE DIBROMIDE (ETHYLENE BROMIDE): IRRITATION DATA: 1538 MG/2 HOURS SKIN-HUMAN SEVERE; 1%/14 DAYS SKIN-RABBIT SEVERE; 1% EYE-RABBIT. TOXICITY DATA: 14,300 MG/M3/30 MINUTES INHALATION-RAT LC50; 400 PPM/3 HOURS INHALATION-GUINEA PIG LCLO; 300 MG/KG SKIN-RABBIT LD50; 300 MG/KG SKIN-RAT LD50; 90 MG/KG ORAL-WOMAN LDLO; 108 MG/KG ORAL-RAT LD50; 250 MG/KG ORAL-MOUSE LDLO; 110 MG/KG ORAL-GUINEA PIG LD50; 55 MG/KG ORAL-RABBIT LD50; 220 MG/KG INTRAPERITONEAL-MOUSE LD50; 2500 MG/KG RECTAL-RABBIT LDLO; 146 MG/KG UNREPORTED-MOUSE LD50; MUTAGENIC DATA (RTECS); REPRODUCTIVE EFFECTS DATA (RTECS); TUMORIGENIC DATA (RTECS).
CARCINOGEN STATUS: ANTICIPATED HUMAN CARCINOGEN (NTP); HUMAN INADEQUATE EVIDENCE, ANIMAL SUFFICIENT EVIDENCE (IARC GROUP-2A). ETHYLENE DIBROMIDE IS CARCINOGENIC TO RATS PRODUCING SQUAMOUS-CELL CARCINOMAS OF THE FORESTOMACH, HEPATOCELLULAR CARCINOMAS IN FEMALES, AND HEMANGIOSARCOMAS IN MALES AND TO MICE PRODUCING SQUAMOUS-CELL CARCINOMAS OF THE FORESTOMACH AND ALVEOLAR/BRONCHIOLAR ADENOMAS. WHEN INHALED, ETHYLENE DIBROMIDE INCREASED THE INCIDENCE OF NASAL CAVITY TUMORS AND TUMORS OF THE CIRCULATORY SYSTEM IN RATS AND LUNGS TUMORS IN MICE. IT PRODUCED SKIN, LUNG AND FORESTOMACH TUMORS IN MICE AFTER TOPICAL ADMINISTRATION. LOCAL EFFECTS: CORROSIVE- INHALATION, SKIN, EYES. ACUTE TOXICITY LEVEL: TOXIC BY INHALATION, SKIN ABSORPTION, INGESTION. TARGET EFFECTS: CENTRAL NERVOUS SYSTEM DEPRESSANT; NEPHROTOXIN; HEPATOTOXIN. POISONING MAY AFFECT THE LUNGS AND HEART. AT INCREASED RISK FROM EXPOSURE: PERSONS WITH SKIN, LUNG, CARDIOVASCULAR, KIDNEY OR LIVER DISEASES. ADDITIONAL DATA: ANIMAL STUDIES INDICATE THAT THE RISK OF CANCER MAY BE INCREASED WHEN THE EXPOSURE TO ETHYLENE DIBROMIDE IS IN COMBINATION WITH DISULFIRAM (ANTABUSE) OR THIRAM. STIMULANTS SUCH AS EPINEPHRINE MAY INDUCE VENTRICULAR FIBRILLATION.

HEALTH EFFECTS AND FIRST AID

INHALATION: ETHYLENE DIBROMIDE (ETHYLENE BROMIDE): CORROSIVE/NARCOTIC/NEPHROTOXIN/HEPATOTOXIN/CARCINOGEN/TOXIC. 400 PPM IMMEDIATELY DANGEROUS TO LIFE OR HEALTH. **ACUTE EXPOSURE-** INHALATION OF VAPORS MAY CAUSE SEVERE IRRITATION AND DAMAGE TO THE UPPER RESPIRATORY TRACT RESULTING IN LUNG CONGESTION, PULMONARY EDEMA AND PNEUMONIA. HEADACHE, NAUSEA, VOMITING, ABDOMINAL PAIN, DIARRHEA, AND OTHER SIGNS AND SYMPTOMS OF CENTRAL NERVOUS SYSTEM DEPRESSION MAY OCCUR. IN SEVERE EXPOSURE, EXTENSIVE AND GENERALIZED NECROSIS OF THE HEART, SKELETAL MUSCLE, LIVER, AND KIDNEYS MAY OCCUR AND RESULT IN A PROGRESSIVE METABOLIC ACIDOSIS, AS WELL AS CARDIAC, RENAL, AND HEPATIC FAILURE. ADVERSE EFFECTS ON THE SPLEEN HAVE ALSO BEEN REPORTED IN ANIMALS. A LETHAL CONCENTRATION IN RATS WAS 14300 MG/M3/30 MINUTES. **CHRONIC EXPOSURE-** CHRONIC EXPOSURE OVER A LONG PERIOD TO LEVELS ABOVE THE THRESHOLD MAY RESULT IN EFFECTS AS DESCRIBED IN ACUTE EXPOSURE. ADVERSE REPRODUCTIVE EFFECTS INVOLVING SPERM COUNT MOBILITY, VIABILITY, AND MORPHOLOGY WERE REPORTED IN ONE STUDY OF 46 MEN EXPOSED TO AN AVERAGE CONCENTRATION OF 0.088 PPM FOR 5 YEARS. MINOR FETAL SKELETAL ANOMALIES WERE OBSERVED IN A STUDY OF RATS AND MICE CONTINUOUSLY EXPOSED DURING GESTATION TO 32 PPM. ETHYLENE DIBROMIDE, WHEN INHALED, INCREASED THE INCIDENCE OF NASAL CAVITY TUMORS AND TUMORS OF THE CIRCULATORY SYSTEM IN RATS AND LUNGS TUMORS IN MICE. THE MORTALITY RATE AND INCIDENCE OF TUMORS INCREASED IN RATS UPON EXPOSURE TO 20 PPM BY INHALATION WHILE RECEIVING A DIET CONTAINING 0.5% DISULFIRAM. TESTICULAR ATROPHY WAS OBSERVED IN 90% OF THE MALE RATS IN THIS STUDY.
FIRST AID- REMOVE FROM EXPOSURE AREA TO FRESH AIR IMMEDIATELY. IF BREATHING HAS STOPPED, GIVE ARTIFICIAL RESPIRATION. MAINTAIN AIRWAY AND BLOOD PRESSURE AND ADMINISTER OXYGEN IF AVAILABLE. KEEP AFFECTED PERSON WARM AND AT REST. TREAT SYMPTOMATICALLY AND SUPPORTIVELY. ADMINISTRATION OF OXYGEN SHOULD BE PERFORMED BY QUALIFIED PERSONNEL. GET MEDICAL ATTENTION IMMEDIATELY.

SKIN CONTACT: ETHYLENE DIBROMIDE (ETHYLENE BROMIDE): CORROSIVE/NARCOTIC/NEPHROTOXIN/HEPATOTOXIN/CARCINOGEN/TOXIC. **ACUTE EXPOSURE-** MAY CAUSE SEVERE IRRITATION WITH BURNING, ITCHING, REDNESS, BLISTERING AND SWELLING. FAILURE TO REMOVE THIS MATERIAL PROMPTLY FROM THE SKIN MAY LEAD TO CHEMICAL BURNS. THIS MATERIAL MAY BE ABSORBED THROUGH THE SKIN AND CAUSE SYSTEMIC EFFECTS AS DESCRIBED IN ACUTE INHALATION. A LETHAL DOSE IN RABBITS BY DERMAL ABSORPTION WAS 300 MG/KG. **CHRONIC EXPOSURE-** PROLONGED OR REPEATED CONTACT MAY CAUSE EFFECTS AS DESCRIBED IN ACUTE EXPOSURE. REPEATED CONTACT WITH THE LIQUID MAY RESULT IN SENSITIZATION. ETHYLENE DIBROMIDE APPLIED TO THE SKIN OF MICE PRODUCED TUMORS OF THE SKIN, LUNG AND FORESTOMACH.
FIRST AID- REMOVE CONTAMINATED CLOTHING AND SHOES IMMEDIATELY. WASH AFFECTED AREA WITH SOAP OR MILD DETERGENT AND LARGE AMOUNTS OF WATER UNTIL NO EVIDENCE OF CHEMICAL REMAINS (AT LEAST 15-20 MINUTES). IN CASE OF CHEMICAL BURNS, COVER AREA WITH STERILE, DRY DRESSING. BANDAGE SECURELY, BUT NOT TOO TIGHTLY. GET MEDICAL ATTENTION IMMEDIATELY.

EYE CONTACT: ETHYLENE DIBROMIDE (ETHYLENE BROMIDE): CORROSIVE. **ACUTE EXPOSURE-** EXPOSURE TO THE VAPOR OR LIQUID MAY CAUSE SEVERE IRRITATION. IN RABBIT EYES, UNDILUTED ETHYLENE DIBROMIDE PRODUCED OBVIOUS PAIN AND CONJUNCTIVAL IRRITATION THAT CLEARED IN 48 HOURS WITH ONLY VERY SLIGHT

SUPERFICIAL CORNEAL NECROSIS WHICH HEALED COMPLETELY. SIMILAR ADVERSE OCULAR EFFECTS WERE ALSO OBSERVED IN RABBITS EYES FOR CONCENTRATIONS OF 1 AND 10%. CHRONIC EXPOSURE- PROLONGED OR REPEATED EXPOSURE TO THE VAPOR MAY CAUSE CONJUNCTIVITIS.

FIRST AID- WASH EYES IMMEDIATELY WITH LARGE AMOUNTS OF WATER, OCCASIONALLY LIFTING UPPER AND LOWER LIDS, UNTIL NO EVIDENCE OF CHEMICAL REMAINS (AT LEAST 15-20 MINUTES). CONTINUE IRRIGATING WITH NORMAL SALINE UNTIL THE PH HAS RETURNED TO NORMAL (30-60 MINUTES). COVER WITH STERILE BANDAGES. GET MEDICAL ATTENTION IMMEDIATELY.

INGESTION: ETHYLENE DIBROMIDE (ETHYLENE BROMIDE): NARCOTIC/NEPHROTOXIN/HEPATOTOXIN/CARCINOGEN/TOXIC. **ACUTE EXPOSURE**- INGESTION MAY CAUSE SEVERE AND PROTRACTED VOMITING, HEADACHE, GENERALIZED WEAKNESS, EXCITEMENT, TINNITUS, AND OTHER SYMPTOMS OF CENTRAL NERVOUS SYSTEM DEPRESSION. DAMAGE TO THE LIVER AND KIDNEYS MAY OCCUR. ONE WOMAN WHO INGESTED A FATAL DOSE OF 4.5 ML, EXPERIENCED VOMITING, DIARRHEA, TACHYPNEA, AND AGITATION. LUNG CONGESTION AND EDEMA, MASSIVE CENTROLOBULAR NECROSIS OF THE LIVER AND PROXIMAL TUBULAR DAMAGE IN THE KIDNEY WERE OBSERVED AT AUTOPSY. **CHRONIC EXPOSURE**- REPEATED INGESTION OF 2 MG/KG/DAY BY BULLS RESULTED IN IMPAIRED SPERMATOGENESIS WITHIN TWO WEEKS. THIS MATERIAL IS CARCINOGENIC IN RATS PRODUCING SQUAMOUS-CELL CARCINOMAS OF THE FORESTOMACH, HEPATOCELLULAR CARCINOMAS IN FEMALES, AND HEMANGIOSARCOMAS IN MALES AND IN MICE PRODUCING SQUAMOUS-CELL CARCINOMAS OF THE FORESTOMACH AND ALEVEOLAR/BRONCHIOLAR ADENOMAS.

FIRST AID- REMOVE BY GASTRIC LAVAGE OR EMESIS. MAINTAIN BLOOD PRESSURE AND AIRWAY. GIVE OXYGEN IF RESPIRATION IS DEPRESSED. DO NOT PERFORM GASTRIC LAVAGE OR EMESIS IF VICTIM IS UNCONSCIOUS. GET MEDICAL ATTENTION IMMEDIATELY (DREISBACH, HANDBOOK OF POISONING, 11TH ED.). ADMINISTRATION OF GASTRIC LAVAGE OR OXYGEN SHOULD BE PERFORMED BY QUALIFIED MEDICAL PERSONNEL.

ANTIDOTE: NO SPECIFIC ANTIDOTE. TREAT SYMPTOMATICALLY AND SUPPORTIVELY.

REACTIVITY

REACTIVITY: STABLE UNDER NORMAL TEMPERATURES AND PRESSURES.

INCOMPATIBILITIES: ETHYLENE DIBROMIDE (ETHYLENE BROMIDE): ALKALIES (STRONG): MAY CAUSE VIGOROUS REACTION. ALUMINUM (POWDERED): MAY CAUSE VIOLENT REACTION. AMMONIA: MAY CAUSE VIGOROUS REACTION. CALCIUM: MAY CAUSE VIOLENT REACTION. GREASES: MAY BE ATTACKED. MAGNESIUM: MAY CAUSE VIOLENT REACTION. METALS: MAY CAUSE VIOLENT REACTION. OXIDIZERS (STRONG): MAY CAUSE VIGOROUS REACTION. PLASTICS, RUBBER, AND COATINGS: MAY ATTACK SOME FORMS. POTASSIUM: MAY CAUSE VIOLENT REACTION. SODIUM: MAY CAUSE VIOLENT REACTION. ZINC: MAY CAUSE VIOLENT REACTION.

DECOMPOSITION: THERMAL DECOMPOSITION PRODUCTS INCLUDE TOXIC AND HAZARDOUS VAPORS OF BROMINE, HYDROGEN BROMIDE, AND CARBON MONOXIDE.

POLYMERIZATION: HAZARDOUS POLYMERIZATION HAS NOT BEEN REPORTED TO OCCUR UNDER NORMAL TEMPERATURES AND PRESSURES.

STORAGE AND DISPOSAL

OBSERVE ALL FEDERAL, STATE AND LOCAL REGULATIONS WHEN STORING OR DISPOSING OF THIS SUBSTANCE. FOR ASSISTANCE, CONTACT THE DISTRICT DIRECTOR OF THE ENVIRONMENTAL PROTECTION AGENCY.

****STORAGE****

PROTECT AGAINST PHYSICAL DAMAGE. STORE IN COOL, DRY, WELL-VENTILATED LOCATION, AWAY FROM ANY AREA WHERE THE FIRE HAZARD MAY BE ACUTE (NFPA 49, HAZARDOUS CHEMICALS DATA, 1975).

STORE AWAY FROM INCOMPATIBLE SUBSTANCES.

****DISPOSAL****

DISPOSAL MUST BE IN ACCORDANCE WITH STANDARDS APPLICABLE TO GENERATORS OF HAZARDOUS WASTE, 40CFR 262. EPA HAZARDOUS WASTE NUMBER U067.

CONDITIONS TO AVOID

MAY BURN BUT DOES NOT IGNITE READILY. CONTAINERS MAY EXPLODE IN HEAT OF FIRE.

SPILL AND LEAK PROCEDURES

SOIL SPILL: DIG HOLDING AREA SUCH AS LAGOON, POND OR PIT FOR CONTAINMENT.

DIKE FLOW OF SPILLED MATERIAL USING SOIL OR SANDBAGS OR FOAMED BARRIERS SUCH AS POLYURETHANE OR CONCRETE.

USE CEMENT POWDER OR FLY ASH TO ABSORB LIQUID MASS.

IMMOBILIZE SPILL WITH UNIVERSAL GELLING AGENT.

WATER SPILL: TRAP SPILLED MATERIAL AT BOTTOM IN DEEP WATER POCKETS, EXCAVATED HOLDING AREAS OR WITHIN SAND BAG BARRIERS.

USE ACTIVATED CARBON TO ABSORB SPILLED SUBSTANCE THAT IS DISSOLVED.

USE SUCTION HOSES TO REMOVE TRAPPED SPILL MATERIAL.

USE MECHANICAL DREDGES OR LIFTS TO EXTRACT IMMOBILIZED MASSES OF POLLUTION AND PRECIPITATES.

THE CALIFORNIA SAFE DRINKING WATER AND TOXIC ENFORCEMENT ACT OF 1986 (PROPOSITION 65) PROHIBITS CONTAMINATING ANY KNOWN SOURCE OF DRINKING WATER WITH SUBSTANCES KNOWN TO CAUSE CANCER AND/OR REPRODUCTIVE TOXICITY.

OCCUPATIONAL SPILL: DO NOT TOUCH SPILLED MATERIAL. STOP LEAK IF YOU CAN DO IT WITHOUT RISK. USE WATER SPRAY TO REDUCE VAPORS. FOR SMALL SPILLS, TAKE UP WITH SAND OR OTHER ABSORBENT MATERIAL AND PLACE INTO CONTAINERS FOR LATER DISPOSAL. FOR SMALL DRY SPILLS, WITH A CLEAN SHOVEL PLACE MATERIAL INTO CLEAN, DRY CONTAINERS AND COVER. MOVE CONTAINERS FROM SPILL AREA. FOR LARGER SPILLS, DIKE FAR AHEAD OF SPILL FOR LATER DISPOSAL. KEEP UNNECESSARY PEOPLE AWAY. ISOLATE HAZARD AREA AND DENY ENTRY. VENTILATE CLOSED SPACES BEFORE ENTERING.

REPORTABLE QUANTITY (RQ): 1 POUND THE SUPERFUND AMENDMENTS AND REAUTHORIZATION ACT (SARA) SECTION 304 REQUIRES THAT A RELEASE EQUAL TO OR GREATER THAN THE REPORTABLE QUANTITY FOR THIS SUBSTANCE BE IMMEDIATELY REPORTED TO THE LOCAL EMERGENCY PLANNING COMMITTEE AND THE STATE EMERGENCY RESPONSE COMMISSION (40 CFR 355.40). IF THE RELEASE OF THIS SUBSTANCE IS REPORTABLE UNDER CERCLA SECTION 103, THE NATIONAL RESPONSE CENTER MUST BE NOTIFIED IMMEDIATELY AT (800) 424-8802 OR (202) 426-2675 IN THE METROPOLITAN WASHINGTON, D.C. AREA (40 CFR 302.6).

PROTECTIVE EQUIPMENT

VENTILATION: PROVIDE LOCAL EXHAUST OR PROCESS ENCLOSURE VENTILATION TO MEET PUBLISHED EXPOSURE LIMITS.

RESPIRATOR: THE FOLLOWING RESPIRATORS AND MAXIMUM USE CONCENTRATIONS ARE RECOMMENDATIONS BY THE U.S. DEPARTMENT OF HEALTH AND HUMAN SERVICES, NIOSH POCKET GUIDE TO CHEMICAL HAZARDS; NIOSH CRITERIA DOCUMENTS OR BY THE U.S. DEPARTMENT OF LABOR, 29 CFR 1910 SUBPART Z. THE SPECIFIC RESPIRATOR SELECTED MUST BE BASED ON CONTAMINATION LEVELS FOUND IN THE WORK PLACE, MUST NOT EXCEED THE WORKING LIMITS OF THE RESPIRATOR AND BE JOINTLY APPROVED BY THE NATIONAL INSTITUTE FOR OCCUPATIONAL SAFETY AND HEALTH AND THE MINE SAFETY AND HEALTH ADMINISTRATION (NIOSH-MSHA).

AT ANY DETECTABLE CONCENTRATION:

SELF-CONTAINED BREATHING APPARATUS WITH FULL FACEPIECE OPERATED IN PRESSURE-DEMAND OR OTHER POSITIVE PRESSURE MODE. SUPPLIED-AIR RESPIRATOR WITH FULL FACEPIECE OPERATED IN PRESSURE-DEMAND OR OTHER POSITIVE PRESSURE MODE IN COMBINATION WITH AN AUXILIARY SELF-CONTAINED BREATHING APPARATUS OPERATED IN PRESSURE-DEMAND OR OTHER POSITIVE PRESSURE MODE.

ESCAPE- AIR-PURIFYING FULL FACEPIECE RESPIRATOR (GAS MASK) WITH A CHIN-STYLE OR FRONT- OR BACK-MOUNTED ORGANIC VAPOR CANISTER. ESCAPE-TYPE SELF-CONTAINED BREATHING APPARATUS.

FOR FIREFIGHTING AND OTHER IMMEDIATELY DANGEROUS TO LIFE OR HEALTH CONDITIONS:

SELF-CONTAINED BREATHING APPARATUS WITH FULL FACEPIECE OPERATED IN PRESSURE-DEMAND OR OTHER POSITIVE PRESSURE MODE.

SUPPLIED-AIR RESPIRATOR WITH FULL FACEPIECE AND OPERATED IN PRESSURE-DEMAND OR OTHER POSITIVE PRESSURE MODE IN COMBINATION WITH AN AUXILIARY SELF-CONTAINED BREATHING APPARATUS OPERATED IN PRESSURE-DEMAND OR OTHER POSITIVE PRESSURE MODE.

CLOTHING: EMPLOYEE MUST WEAR APPROPRIATE PROTECTIVE (IMPERVIOUS) CLOTHING AND EQUIPMENT TO PREVENT ANY POSSIBILITY OF SKIN CONTACT WITH THIS SUBSTANCE.

GLOVES: EMPLOYFF MUST WEAR APPROPRIATE PROTECTIVE GLOVES TO PREVENT CONTACT WITH THIS SUBSTANCE.

EYE PROTECTION: EMPLOYEE MUST WEAR SPLASH-PROOF OR DUST-RESISTANT SAFETY GOGGLES AND A FACESHIELD TO PREVENT CONTACT WITH THIS SUBSTANCE.

EMERGENCY WASH FACILITIES: WHERE THERE IS ANY POSSIBILITY THAT AN EMPLOYEE'S EYES AND/OR SKIN MAY BE EXPOSED TO THIS SUBSTANCE, THE EMPLOYER SHOULD PROVIDE AN EYE WASH FOUNTAIN AND QUICK DRENCH SHOWER WITHIN THE IMMEDIATE WORK AREA FOR EMERGENCY USE.

AUTHORIZED BY- OCCUPATIONAL HEALTH SERVICES, INC.

CREATION DATE: 10/04/89 ***REVISION DATE:*** 07/12/90

MATERIAL SAFETY DATA SHEET

OCCUPATIONAL HEALTH SERVICES, INC.
AGRICULTURE AND PESTICIDE DIVISION
450 SEVENTH AVENUE, SUITE 2407
NEW YORK, NEW YORK 10123
1-800-445-MSDS OR (212) 967-1100

EMERGENCY CONTACT:
JOHN S. BRANSFORD, JR. (615) 292-1180

SUBSTANCE IDENTIFICATION

CAS-NUMBER 107-06-2

SUBSTANCE: **ETHYLENE DICHLORIDE**

TRADE NAMES/SYNONYMS: ETHANE, 1,2-DICHLORO-; 1,2-BICHLOROETHANE; 1,2-DICHLOROETHANE; SYM-DICHLOROETHANE; ALPHA, BETA-DICHLOROETHANE; 1,2-DICHLORETHANE; DUTCH LIQUID; EDC; ETHYLENE CHLORIDE; GLYCOL DICHLORIDE; RCRA U077; STCC 4909166; UN 1184; E-175; C2H4CL2; PST09390

CHEMICAL FAMILY: HALOGEN COMPOUND, ALIPHATIC

MOLECULAR FORMULA: CL-C-H2-C-H2-CL

MOLECULAR WEIGHT: 98.96

CERCLA RATINGS (SCALE 0-3): HEALTH = 3 FIRE = 3 REACTIVITY = 0 PERSISTENCE = 1

NFPA RATINGS (SCALE 0-4): HEALTH = 2 FIRE = 3 REACTIVITY = 0

COMPONENTS AND CONTAMINANTS

COMPONENT: ETHYLENE DICHLORIDE (1,2-DICHLOROETHANE) ***PERCENT:*** 100.0
CAS# 107-06-2

OTHER CONTAMINANTS: NONE

EXPOSURE LIMITS: ETHYLENE DICHLORIDE (1,2-DICHLOROETHANE): 1 PPM (4 MG/M3) OSHA TWA; 2 PPM (8 MG/M3) OSHA STEL 10 PPM (40 MG/M3) ACGIH TWA 1 PPM NIOSH RECOMMENDED 10 HOUR TWA; 2 PPM NIOSH RECOMMENDED 15 MINUTE CEILING

100 POUNDS CERCLA SECTION 103 REPORTABLE QUANTITY SUBJECT TO SARA SECTION 313 ANNUAL TOXIC CHEMICAL RELEASE REPORTING SUBJECT TO CALIFORNIA PROPOSITION 65 CANCER AND/OR REPRODUCTIVE TOXICITY WARNING AND RELEASE REQUIREMENTS- (JANUARY 1, 1987)

PHYSICAL DATA

DESCRIPTION: CLEAR, COLORLESS, OILY LIQUID WITH A PLEASANT CHLOROFORM-LIKE ODOR AND SWEET TASTE. ***BOILING POINT:*** 183 F (84 C)

MELTING POINT: -32 F (-36 C) ***SPECIFIC GRAVITY:*** 1.2351

VISCOSITY: 0.81 CPS @ 21 C ***VAPOR PRESSURE:*** 87 MMHG @ 25 C

EVAPORATION RATE: (BUTYL ACETATE = 1) 6.4 ***SOLUBILITY IN WATER:*** 0.87% @ 20 C

ODOR THRESHOLD: 40 PPM ***VAPOR DENSITY:*** 3.4

SOLVENT SOLUBILITY: SOLUBLE IN ALCOHOL, ETHER, ACETONE, BENZENE, FATS, RESINS, RUBBERS, CHLOROFORM, CARBON TETRACHLORIDE, ORGANIC SOLVENTS.

FIRE AND EXPLOSION DATA

FIRE AND EXPLOSION HAZARD: DANGEROUS FIRE HAZARD WHEN EXPOSED TO HEAT, FLAME, OR OXIDIZERS.

VAPOR-AIR MIXTURES ARE EXPLOSIVE ABOVE FLASH POINT.

VAPORS ARE HEAVIER THAN AIR AND MAY TRAVEL A CONSIDERABLE DISTANCE TO A SOURCE OF IGNITION AND FLASH BACK.

FLASH POINT: 56 F (13 C) (CC) ***UPPER EXPLOSIVE LIMIT:*** 16%

LOWER EXPLOSIVE LIMIT: 6.2% ***AUTOIGNITION TEMP.:*** 775 F (413 C)

FLAMMABILITY CLASS(OSHA): IB

FIREFIGHTING MEDIA: DRY CHEMICAL, CARBON DIOXIDE, HALON, WATER SPRAY OR ALCOHOL FOAM (1987 EMERGENCY RESPONSE GUIDEBOOK, DOT P 5800.4).
FOR LARGER FIRES, USE WATER SPRAY, FOG OR ALCOHOL FOAM (1987 EMERGENCY RESPONSE GUIDEBOOK, DOT P 5800.4).

FIREFIGHTING: MOVE CONTAINER FROM FIRE AREA IF POSSIBLE. COOL FIRE-EXPOSED CONTAINERS WITH WATER FROM SIDE UNTIL WELL AFTER FIRE IS OUT. STAY AWAY FROM STORAGE TANK ENDS. FOR MASSIVE FIRE IN STORAGE AREA, USE UNMANNED HOSE HOLDER OR MONITOR NOZZLES, ELSE WITHDRAW FROM AREA AND LET FIRE BURN. WITHDRAW IMMEDIATELY IN CASE OF RISING SOUND FROM VENTING SAFETY DEVICE OR ANY DISCOLORATION OF STORAGE TANK DUE TO FIRE (1987 EMERGENCY RESPONSE GUIDEBOOK, DOT P 5800.4, GUIDE PAGE 26). EXTINGUISH ONLY IF FLOW CAN BE STOPPED; USE WATER IN FLOODING AMOUNTS AS FOG, SOLID STREAMS MAY NOT BE EFFECTIVE. COOL CONTAINERS WITH FLOODING AMOUNTS OF WATER, APPLY FROM AS FAR A DISTANCE AS POSSIBLE. AVOID BREATHING VAPORS, KEEP UPWIND.
WATER MAY BE INEFFECTIVE EXCEPT AS A BLANKET (NFPA 325M, FIRE HAZARD PROPERTIES OF FLAMMABLE LIQUIDS, GASES, AND VOLATILE SOLIDS, 1984)

TRANSPORTATION DATA

DEPARTMENT OF TRANSPORTATION HAZARD CLASSIFICATION 49 CFR 172.101: FLAMMABLE LIQUID

DEPARTMENT OF TRANSPORTATION LABELING REQUIREMENTS 49 CFR 172.101 AND SUBPART E: FLAMMABLE LIQUID

DEPARTMENT OF TRANSPORTATION PACKAGING REQUIREMENTS: 49 CFR 173.119 EXCEPTIONS: 49 CFR 173.118

TOXICITY

ETHYLENE DICHLORIDE (1,2-DICHLOROETHANE): IRRITATION DATA: 625 MG OPEN SKIN-RABBIT MILD; 500 MG/24 HOURS SKIN-RABBIT MILD; 63 MG EYE-RABBIT SEVERE; 500 MG/24 HOURS EYE-RABBIT MILD. TOXICITY DATA: 4000 PPM/1 HOUR INHALATION-MAN TCLO; 1000 PPM/7 HOURS INHALATION-RAT LC50; 3000 PPM/7 HOURS INHALATION-RABBIT LCLO; 5 GM/M3/2 HOURS INHALATION-MOUSE LCLO; 3000 PPM/7 HOURS INHALATION-MONKEY LC50; 1500 PPM/7 HOURS INHALATION-GUINEA PIG LCLO; 3000 PPM/7 HOURS INHALATION-PIG LCLO; 2800 MG/KG SKIN-RABBIT LD50; 714 MG/KG ORAL-MAN LDLO; 892 MG/KG ORAL-MAN TDLO; 428 MG/KG ORAL-HUMAN TDLO; 286 MG/KG ORAL-HUMAN LDLO; 670 MG/KG ORAL-RAT LD50; 489 MG/KG ORAL-MOUSE LD50; 860 MG/KG ORAL-RABBIT LD50; 5700 MG/KG ORAL-DOG LD50; 1 GM/KG SUBCUTANEOUS-RAT LD50; 380 MG/KG SUBCUTANEOUS-MOUSE LDLO; 1200 MG/KG SUBCUTANEOUS-RABBIT LDLO; 175 MG/KG INTRAVENOUS-DOG LDLO; 807 MG/KG INTRAPERITONEAL-RAT LD50; 470 MG/KG INTRAPERITONEAL-MOUSE LD50; 600 MG/KG INTRAPERITONEAL-GUINEA PIG LDLO; MUTAGENIC DATA (RTECS); REPRODUCTIVE EFFECTS DATA (RTECS); TUMORIGENIC DATA (RTECS). CARCINOGEN STATUS: ANTICIPATED HUMAN CARCINOGEN (NTP); ANIMAL SUFFICIENT EVIDENCE (IARC GROUP-2B). ORAL ADMINISTRATION OF ETHYLENE DICHLORIDE TO MICE AND RATS RESULTED IN A SIGNIFICANT INCREASE IN TUMORS AT VARIOUS SITES IN BOTH SPECIES. IN ABSENCE OF ADEQUATE DATA IN HUMANS, IARC SUGGESTS THAT IT IS REASONABLE FOR PRACTICAL PURPOSES, TO REGARD ETHYLENE DICHLORIDE AS IF IT PRESENTED A CARCINOGENIC RISK TO HUMANS. LOCAL EFFECTS: IRRITANT-INHALATION, SKIN, EYE. ACUTE TOXICITY LEVEL: TOXIC BY INHALATION; MODERATELY TOXIC BY INGESTION; SLIGHTLY TOXIC BY DERMAL ABSORPTION. TARGET EFFECTS: CENTRAL NERVOUS SYSTEM DEPRESSANT; HEPATOTOXIN; NEPHROTOXIN. POISONING MAY ALSO AFFECT THE CARDIOVASCULAR SYSTEM, RESPIRATORY SYSTEM AND THE ADRENAL GLANDS. ADDITIONAL INFORMATION: THE USE OF ALCOHOLIC BEVERAGES MAY ENHANCE THE TOXIC EFFECTS. MAY CROSS THE PLACENTA AND BE EXCRETED IN HUMAN MILK.

HEALTH EFFECTS AND FIRST AID

INHALATION: ETHYLENE DICHLORIDE (1,2-DICHLOROETHANE): IRRITANT/NARCOTIC/HEPATOTOXIN/NEPHROTOXIN/TOXIC. **ACUTE EXPOSURE-** MAY CAUSE IRRITATION OF THE MUCOUS MEMBRANES OF THE UPPER RESPIRATORY TRACT, HEADACHE, NAUSEA AND VOMITING, DIARRHEA, AND INTESTINAL CRAMPS. CENTRAL NERVOUS SYSTEM EFFECTS INCLUDING LIGHTHEADEDNESS, WEAKNESS, STUPOR, DYSEQUILIBRIUM, TREMBLING, ANXIETY, DROWSINESS, DELIRIUM, PARTIAL PARALYSIS, COLLAPSE, AND COMA MAY APPEAR WITHIN SEVERAL HOURS AFTER EXPOSURE. THERE MAY BE A QUIESCENT PERIOD AND THEN, IF THE INDIVIDUAL SURVIVES, OLIGURIA, JAUNDICE, AND ANEMIA MAY RESULT. OVER THE NEXT SEVERAL DAYS HEPATORENAL FAILURE MAY OCCUR AND MAY BE COMPLICATED BY GASTROINTESTINAL BLEEDING, HYPOGLYCEMIA, HYPERCALCEMIA, HYPOPROTHROMBINEMIA, REDUCED CLOTTING FACTORS, AND CEREBRAL SWELLING AND HEMORRHAGE. OTHER SYMPTOMS MAY INCLUDE CYANOSIS, FALL OF BLOOD PRESSURE, WEAK, RAPID PULSE, RESPIRATORY DIFFICULTIES, PULMONARY EDEMA, BRONCHITIS, SUB-NORMAL TEMPERATURE, AND CARDIAC ARRHYTHMIAS. DEATH MAY OCCUR FROM RESPIRATORY OR CARDIAC ARREST. PATHOLOGIC FINDINGS MAY INCLUDE CONGESTON OF THE LUNGS, DEGENERATIVE CHANGES IN THE MYOCARDIUM, NECROSIS OF THE ADRENAL GLANDS, LIVER NECROSIS, KIDNEY TUBULAR NECROSIS, AND SHRUNKEN NERVE CELLS IN THE BRAIN. **CHRONIC EXPOSURE-** CHRONIC EXPOSURE TO 10-37 PPM HAS CAUSED NAUSEA, VOMITING, DIZZINESS, AND ADVERSE NERVOUS SYSTEM AND LIVER EFFECTS. CHARACTERISTIC SYMPTOMS OF ACUTE EXPOSURE MAY DEVELOP FROM REPEATED EXPOSURES TO 75-125 PPM. REPEATED OR PROLONGED EXPOSURE MAY ALSO RESULT IN IRRITATION OF THE MUCOUS MEMBRANES, ACUTE BRONCHIAL INFLAMMATION, LOSS OF APPETITE, WEIGHT LOSS, ANEMIA, CONSTIPATION, INSOMNIA, EPIGASTRIC DISTRESS, NYSTAGMUS, LIVER AND KIDNEY DAMAGE, ELEVATED UROBILINOGEN, AND CARDIAC PAIN. NEUROLOGIC EFFECTS INCLUDING RESTLESSNESS, IRRITABILITY, NERVOUSNESS, DECREASED MUSCLE TONE, DIFFICULTY WALKING, TREMBLING HANDS, LOSS OF REFLEXES, POSITIVE ROMBERG SIGN, HYPERHIDEROSIS, FATIGUE, AND DEAFNESS MAY OCCUR. DEATH MAY RESULT FROM RESPIRATORY, CIRCULATORY, HEPATIC, OR RENAL FAILURE. AN INCREASE IN INFANT DEATHS AMONG THE OFFSPRING OF WORKERS EXPOSED TO HALOGENATED HYDROCARBONS HAS BEEN REPORTED. INCREASED MORTALITY, PRECEDED BY LOSS OF WEIGHT, PULMONARY CONGESTION, AND LIVER CHANGES, WERE REPORTED IN 5 SPECIES OF ANIMALS EXPOSED TO 200 PPM FOR UP TO 7 HOURS A DAY FOR SEVERAL WEEKS. REPRODUCTIVE EFFECTS HAVE BEEN REPORTED IN ANIMALS.

FIRST AID- REMOVE FROM EXPOSURE AREA TO FRESH AIR IMMEDIATELY. IF

BREATHING HAS STOPPED, PERFORM ARTIFICIAL RESPIRATION. KEEP PERSON WARM AND AT REST. TREAT SYMPTOMATICALLY AND SUPPORTIVELY. GET MEDICAL ATTENTION IMMEDIATELY.

SKIN CONTACT: ETHYLENE DICHLORIDE (1,2-DICHLOROETHANE): IRRITANT/NARCOTIC/HEPATOTOXIN/NEPHROTOXIN. **ACUTE EXPOSURE-** DIRECT CONTACT WITH THE LIQUID MAY CAUSE IRRITATION. PROLONGED CONTACT MAY RESULT IN SEVERE IRRITATION, MODERATE EDEMA, AND NECROSIS. MAY BE ABSORBED THROUGH THE SKIN AND CAUSE SYSTEMIC TOXICITY AS DETAILED IN ACUTE INHALATION. **CHRONIC EXPOSURE-** REPEATED OR PROLONGED CONTACT TO THE LIQUID CAN PRODUCE A DRY, SCALY, FISSURED DERMATITIS DUE TO THE DEFATTING ACTION ON THE SKIN. SYSTEMIC EFFECTS, AS IN ACUTE EXPOSURE, MAY ENSUE.

FIRST AID- REMOVE CONTAMINATED CLOTHING AND SHOES IMMEDIATELY. WASH AFFECTED AREA WITH SOAP OR MILD DETERGENT AND LARGE AMOUNTS OF WATER UNTIL NO EVIDENCE OF CHEMICAL REMAINS (APPROXIMATELY 15-20 MINUTES). GET MEDICAL ATTENTION IMMEDIATELY.

EYE CONTACT: ETHYLENE DICHLORIDE (1,2-DICHLOROETHANE): IRRITANT. **ACUTE EXPOSURE-** EXPOSURE TO HIGH VAPOR CONCENTRATIONS OR TO THE LIQUID MAY CAUSE IMMEDIATE DISCOMFORT, LACRIMATION, HYPEREMIA OF THE CONJUNCTIVA, AND CORNEAL INJURY, WHICH MAY RETURN TO NORMAL WITHIN A DAY OR TWO. EXPOSURE TO 63 MG CAUSED SEVERE IRRITATION IN RABBIT EYES. APPLICATION OF A DROP OF THE LIQUID TO RABBIT EYES WAS GRADED 3 ON A SCALE OF 10 AFTER 24 HOURS. **CHRONIC EXPOSURE-** REPEATED OR PROLONGED CONTACT MAY CAUSE CONJUNCTIVITIS.

FIRST AID- WASH EYES IMMEDIATELY WITH LARGE AMOUNTS OF WATER OR NORMAL SALINE, OCCASIONALLY LIFTING UPPER AND LOWER LIDS, UNTIL NO EVIDENCE OF CHEMICAL REMAINS (APPROXIMATELY 15-20 MINUTES). GET MEDICAL ATTENTION IMMEDIATELY.

INGESTION: ETHYLENE DICHLORIDE (1,2-DICHLOROETHANE): NARCOTIC/HEPATOTOXIN/NEPHROTOXIN/CARCINOGEN. **ACUTE EXPOSURE-** INGESTION MAY CAUSE A BURNING SENSATION IN THE MOUTH, THROAT, AND STOMACH. SYSTEMIC TOXICITY, INCLUDING CENTRAL NERVOUS SYSTEM DEPRESSION, HEPATOTOXICITY, AND NEPHROTOXICITY, MAY OCCUR AS DETAILED IN ACUTE INHALATION. THE INGESTION OF 5 ML MAY BE LETHAL TO MAN. **CHRONIC EXPOSURE-** MAY CAUSE SYSTEMIC EFFECTS AS DETAILED IN CHRONIC INHALATION. IN MICE, IT PRODUCED BENIGN AND MALIGNANT TUMORS OF THE LUNG AND MALIGNANT LYMPHOMAS IN ANIMALS OF BOTH SEXES; HEPATOCELLULAR CARCINOMAS IN MALES AND MAMMARY AND UTERINE ADENOCARCINOMAS IN FEMALES. IN RATS, IT PRODUCED CARCINOMAS OF THE FORESTOMACH IN MALES, BENIGN AND MALIGNANT MAMMARY TUMORS IN FEMALES, AND HEMANGIOSARCOMAS IN ANIMALS OF BOTH SEXES. TOTAL DOSES RANGED FROM 18 TO 72 GM/KG INTERMITTENTLY FOR 78 WEEKS.

FIRST AID- IF EXTENSIVE VOMITING HAS NOT OCCURRED, THE SUBSTANCE SHOULD BE REMOVED BY EMESIS OR GASTRIC LAVAGE PROVIDED THAT THE PATIENT IS CONSCIOUS AND CONVULSIONS ARE NOT PRESENT. KEEP HEAD BELOW HIPS DURING VOMITING TO PREVENT ASPIRATION. DO NOT ATTEMPT TO MAKE AN UNCONSCIOUS PERSON VOMIT. TREAT SYMPTOMATICALLY AND SUPPORTIVELY. GET MEDICAL ATTENTION IMMEDIATELY (DREISBACH, HANDBOOK OF POISONING, 12TH ED.). TREATMENT SHOULD BE PERFORMED BY QUALIFIED MEDICAL PERSONNEL.

ANTIDOTE: NO SPECIFIC ANTIDOTE. TREAT SYMPTOMATICALLY AND SUPPORTIVELY.

REACTIVITY

REACTIVITY: STABLE UNDER NORMAL TEMPERATURES AND PRESSURES.

INCOMPATIBILITIES: ETHYLENE DICHLORIDE: (1,2-DICHLOROETHANE): ALUMINUM: FORMATION OF A SHOCK-SENSITIVE COMPOUND. AMMONIA (LIQUID): POSSIBLE VIOLENT EXPLOSION. CAUSTICS (STRONG): FIRE AND EXPLOSION HAZARD. DIMETHYLAMINOPROPYLAMINE: POSSIBLE VIOLENT EXPLOSION. DINITROGEN TETROXIDE: FORMATION OF A SHOCK-SENSITIVE COMPOUND. MAGNESIUM: FIRE AND EXPLOSION HAZARD. METALS (ACTIVE): FIRE AND EXPLOSION HAZARD. METALS: MAY BE CORROSIVE IN THE PRESENCE OF MOISTURE. NITRIC ACID: MIXTURES ARE EASILY DETONATED BY HEAT, IMPACT, OR FRICTION. OXIDIZERS (STRONG): FIRE AND EXPLOSION HAZARD. PLASTICS, RUBBER, AND COATINGS: MAY BE ATTACKED. POTASSIUM: FORMS SHOCK-SENSITIVE COMPOUND. SODIUM: FIRE AND EXPLOSION HAZARD.

DECOMPOSITION: THERMAL DECOMPOSITION PRODUCTS MAY INCLUDE HIGHLY TOXIC FUMES OF PHOSGENE, TOXIC AND CORROSIVE FUMES OF CHLORIDES, AND OXIDES OF CARBON.

POLYMERIZATION: HAZARDOUS POLYMERIZATION HAS NOT BEEN REPORTED TO OCCUR UNDER NORMAL TEMPERATURES AND PRESSURES.

STORAGE AND DISPOSAL

OBSERVE ALL FEDERAL, STATE AND LOCAL REGULATIONS WHEN STORING OR DISPOSING OF THIS SUBSTANCE. FOR ASSISTANCE, CONTACT THE DISTRICT DIRECTOR OF THE ENVIRONMENTAL PROTECTION AGENCY.

****STORAGE****

STORE IN ACCORDANCE WITH 29 CFR 1910.106.

BONDING AND GROUNDING: SUBSTANCES WITH LOW ELECTROCONDUCTIVITY, WHICH MAY BE IGNITED BY ELECTROSTATIC SPARKS, SHOULD BE STORED IN CONTAINERS WHICH MEET THE BONDING AND GROUNDING GUIDELINES SPECIFIED IN NFPA 77-1983, RECOMMENDED PRACTICE ON STATIC ELECTRICITY.

PROTECT AGAINST PHYSICAL DAMAGE. OUTSIDE OR DETACHED STORAGE IS PREFERABLE. INSIDE STORAGE SHOULD BE IN A STANDARD FLAMMABLE LIQUIDS STORAGE ROOM OR CABINET. SEPARATE FROM OXIDIZING MATERIALS. (NFPA 49, HAZARDOUS MATERIALS DATA, 1975).

STORE AWAY FROM INCOMPATIBLE SUBSTANCES.

****DISPOSAL****

DISPOSAL MUST BE IN ACCORDANCE WITH STANDARDS APPLICABLE TO GENERATORS OF HAZARDOUS WASTE, 40CFR 262. EPA HAZARDOUS WASTE NUMBER U077.

1,2-DICHLOROETHANE - REGULATORY LEVEL: 0.5 MG/L MATERIALS WHICH CONTAIN THE ABOVE SUBSTANCE AT OR ABOVE THE REGULATORY LEVEL MEET THE EPA CHARACTERISTIC OF TOXICITY, AND MUST BE DISPOSED OF IN ACCORDANCE WITH 40 CFR PART 262. EPA HAZARDOUS WASTE NUMBER D028.

CONDITIONS TO AVOID

AVOID CONTACT WITH HEAT, SPARKS, FLAMES, OR OTHER SOURCES OF IGNITION. VAPORS MAY BE EXPLOSIVE AND POISONOUS; DO NOT ALLOW UNNECESSARY PERSONNEL IN AREA. DO NOT OVERHEAT CONTAINERS; CONTAINERS MAY VIOLENTLY RUPTURE AND TRAVEL A CONSIDERABLE DISTANCE IN HEAT OF FIRE.

SPILL AND LEAK PROCEDURES

SOIL SPILL: DIG HOLDING AREA SUCH AS LAGOON, POND OR PIT FOR CONTAINMENT. DIKE FLOW OF SPILLED MATERIAL USING SOIL OR SANDBAGS OR FOAMED BARRIERS SUCH AS POLYURETHANE OR CONCRETE.

USE CEMENT POWDER OR FLY ASH TO ABSORB LIQUID MASS.

IMMOBILIZE SPILL WITH UNIVERSAL GELLING AGENT.

REDUCE VAPOR AND FIRE HAZARD WITH APPROPRIATE FOAM.

AIR SPILL: KNOCK DOWN VAPORS WITH WATER SPRAY. KEEP UPWIND. COMBUSTION PRODUCTS INCLUDE CORROSIVE OR TOXIC VAPORS.

WATER SPILL: TRAP SPILLED MATERIAL AT BOTTOM IN DEEP WATER POCKETS, EXCAVATED HOLDING AREAS OR WITHIN SAND BAG BARRIERS.

USE ACTIVATED CARBON TO ABSORB SPILLED SUBSTANCE THAT IS DISSOLVED.

USE SUCTION HOSES TO REMOVE TRAPPED SPILL MATERIAL.

USE MECHANICAL DREDGES OR LIFTS TO EXTRACT IMMOBILIZED MASSES OF POLLUTION AND PRECIPITATES.

THE CALIFORNIA SAFE DRINKING WATER AND TOXIC ENFORCEMENT ACT OF 1986 (PROPOSITION 65) PROHIBITS CONTAMINATING ANY KNOWN SOURCE OF DRINKING WATER WITH SUBSTANCES KNOWN TO CAUSE CANCER AND/OR REPRODUCTIVE TOXICITY.

OCCUPATIONAL SPILL: SHUT OFF IGNITION SOURCES. STOP LEAK IF YOU CAN DO IT WITHOUT RISK. USE WATER SPRAY TO REDUCE VAPORS. FOR SMALL SPILLS, TAKE UP WITH SAND OR OTHER ABSORBENT MATERIAL AND PLACE INTO CONTAINERS FOR LATER DISPOSAL. FOR LARGER SPILLS, DIKE FAR AHEAD OF SPILL FOR LATER DISPOSAL. NO SMOKING, FLAMES OR FLARES IN HAZARD AREA. KEEP UNNECESSARY PEOPLE AWAY; ISOLATE HAZARD AREA AND DENY ENTRY.

REPORTABLE QUANTITY (RQ): 100 POUNDS THE SUPERFUND AMENDMENTS AND REAUTHORIZATION ACT (SARA) SECTION 304 REQUIRES THAT A RELEASE EQUAL TO OR GREATER THAN THE REPORTABLE QUANTITY FOR THIS SUBSTANCE BE IMMEDIATELY REPORTED TO THE LOCAL EMERGENCY PLANNING COMMITTEE AND THE STATE EMERGENCY RESPONSE COMMISSION (40 CFR 355.40). IF THE RELEASE OF THIS SUBSTANCE IS REPORTABLE UNDER CERCLA SECTION 103, THE NATIONAL RESPONSE CENTER MUST BE NOTIFIED IMMEDIATELY AT (800) 424-8802 OR (202) 426-2675 IN THE METROPOLITAN WASHINGTON, D.C. AREA (40 CFR 302.6).

PROTECTIVE EQUIPMENT

VENTILATION: PROVIDE LOCAL EXHAUST OR PROCESS ENCLOSURE VENTILATION TO MEET THE PUBLISHED EXPOSURE LIMITS. VENTILATION EQUIPMENT MUST BE EXPLOSION-PROOF.

RESPIRATOR: THE FOLLOWING RESPIRATORS AND MAXIMUM USE CONCENTRATIONS ARE RECOMMENDATIONS BY THE U.S. DEPARTMENT OF HEALTH AND HUMAN SERVICES, NIOSH POCKET GUIDE TO CHEMICAL HAZARDS; NIOSH CRITERIA DOCUMENTS OR BY THE U.S. DEPARTMENT OF LABOR, 29 CFR 1910 SUBPART Z. THE SPECIFIC RESPIRATOR SELECTED MUST BE BASED ON CONTAMINATION LEVELS FOUND IN THE WORK PLACE, MUST NOT EXCEED THE WORKING LIMITS OF THE RESPIRATOR AND BE JOINTLY APPROVED BY THE NATIONAL INSTITUTE FOR OCCUPATIONAL SAFETY AND HEALTH AND THE MINE SAFETY AND HEALTH ADMINISTRATION (NIOSH-MSHA).

ETHYLENE DICHLORIDE (1,2-DICHLOROETHANE):

AT ANY DETECTABLE CONCENTRATION:
ANY SELF-CONTAINED BREATHING APPARATUS WITH FULL FACEPIECE OPERATED PRESSURE-DEMAND OR OTHER POSITIVE PRESSURE MODE. ANY SUPPLIED-AIR RESPIRATOR WITH FULL FACEPIECE OPERATED IN PRESSURE-DEMAND OR OTHER POSITIVE PRESSURE MODE IN COMBINATION WITH AN AUXILIARY SELF-CONTAINED BREATHING APPARATUS OPERATED IN PRESSURE-DEMAND OR OTHER POSITIVE MODE.
ESCAPE- ANY AIR-PURIFYING FULL FACEPIECE RESPIRATOR (GAS MASK) WITH CHIN-STYLE OR FRONT- OR BACK-MOUNTED ORGANIC VAPOR CANISTER. ANY APPROPRIATE ESCAPE-TYPE SELF-CONTAINED BREATHING APPARATUS.
FOR FIREFIGHTING AND OTHER IMMEDIATELY DANGEROUS TO LIFE OR HEALTH CONDITIONS:
SELF-CONTAINED BREATHING APPARATUS WITH FULL FACEPIECE OPERATED IN PRESSURE-DEMAND OR OTHER POSITIVE PRESSURE MODE.
SUPPLIED-AIR RESPIRATOR WITH FULL FACEPIECE AND OPERATED IN PRESSURE-DEMAND OR OTHER POSITIVE PRESSURE MODE IN COMBINATION WITH AN AUXILIARY SELF-CONTAINED BREATHING APPARATUS OPERATED IN PRESSURE-DEMAND OR OTHER POSITIVE PRESSURE MODE.

CLOTHING: EMPLOYEE MUST WEAR APPROPRIATE PROTECTIVE (IMPERVIOUS) CLOTHING AND EQUIPMENT TO PREVENT REPEATED OR PROLONGED SKIN CONTACT WITH THIS SUBSTANCE.

GLOVES: EMPLOYEE MUST WEAR APPROPRIATE PROTECTIVE GLOVES TO PREVENT CONTACT WITH THIS SUBSTANCE.

EYE PROTECTION: EMPLOYEE MUST WEAR SPLASH-PROOF OR DUST-RESISTANT SAFETY GOGGLES TO PREVENT CONTACT WITH THIS SUBSTANCE.
EMERGENCY WASH FACILITIES: WHERE THERE IS ANY POSSIBILITY THAT AN EMPLOYEE'S EYES AND/OR SKIN MAY BE EXPOSED TO THIS SUBSTANCE, THE EMPLOYER SHOULD PROVIDE AN EYE WASH FOUNTAIN AND QUICK DRENCH SHOWER WITHIN THE IMMEDIATE WORK AREA FOR EMERGENCY USE.

AUTHORIZED BY- OCCUPATIONAL HEALTH SERVICES, INC.
CREATION DATE: 10/04/89 ***REVISION DATE:*** 07/13/90

MATERIAL SAFETY DATA SHEET

OCCUPATIONAL HEALTH SERVICES, INC.
AGRICULTURE AND PESTICIDE DIVISION
450 SEVENTH AVENUE, SUITE 2407
NEW YORK, NEW YORK 10123
1-800-445-MSDS OR (212) 967-1100

EMERGENCY CONTACT:
JOHN S. BRANSFORD, JR. (615) 292-1180

SUBSTANCE IDENTIFICATION

CAS-NUMBER 107-21-1
SUBSTANCE: ETHYLENE GLYCOL
TRADE NAMES/SYNONYMS: 1,2-DIHYDROXYETHANE; 1,2-ETHANEDIOL; ETHYLENE ALCOHOL; GLYCOL; GLYCOL ALCOHOL; MONOETHYLENE GLYCOL; DOWTHERM SR 1; ETHANE-1,2-DIOL; LUTROL-9; MACROGOL 400 BPC; M.E.G.; TESCOL; 2-HYDROXYETHANOL; ETHYLENE DIHYDRATE; DOWTHERM SR; C2H6O2; PST09400
CHEMICAL FAMILY: GLYCOL
MOLECULAR FORMULA: H-O-C-H2-C-H2-O-H
MOLECULAR WEIGHT: 62.07
CERCLA RATINGS (SCALE 0-3): HEALTH=2 FIRE=1 REACTIVITY=0 PERSISTENCE=0
NFPA RATINGS (SCALE 0-4): HEALTH=1 FIRE=1 REACTIVITY=0

COMPONENTS AND CONTAMINANTS

COMPONENT: ETHYLENE GLYCOL ***PERCENT:*** 100
CAS# 107-21-1
OTHER CONTAMINANTS: NONE
EXPOSURE LIMITS: ETHYLENE GLYCOL: 50 PPM (125 MG/M3) OSHA CEILING 50 PPM (125 MG/M3) ACGIH CEILING (VAPOR AND MIST)
SUBJECT TO SARA SECTION 313 ANNUAL TOXIC CHEMICAL RELEASE REPORTING

PHYSICAL DATA

DESCRIPTION: ODORLESS, COLORLESS, HYGROSCOPIC LIQUID WITH A SWEET TASTE.
BOILING POINT: 388 F (198 C) ***MELTING POINT:*** 10 F (-12 C)
SPECIFIC GRAVITY: 1.1088 ***VISCOSITY:*** 21 CPS @ 15 C
VAPOR PRESSURE: 0.05 MMHG @ 20 C ***SOLUBILITY IN WATER:*** SOLUBLE
VAPOR DENSITY: 2.14
SOLVENT SOLUBILITY: SOLUBLE IN ALCOHOL, ACETONE, GLYCEROL, ACETIC ACID, ALDEHYDES, KETONES, PYRIDINE; SLIGHTLY SOLUBLE IN ETHER; PRACTICALLY INSOLUBLE IN BENZENE, PETROLEUM ETHER, OILS, CHLORINATED HYDROCARBONS.

FIRE AND EXPLOSION DATA

FIRE AND EXPLOSION HAZARD: SLIGHT FIRE HAZARD WHEN EXPOSED TO HEAT OR FLAME.
FLASH POINT: 232 F (111 C) (CC) ***UPPER EXPLOSIVE LIMIT:*** 5%
LOWER EXPLOSIVE LIMIT: 3.2% ***AUTOIGNITION TEMP.:*** 748 F (398 C)
FLAMMABILITY CLASS(OSHA): IIIB
FIREFIGHTING MEDIA: DRY CHEMICAL, CARBON DIOXIDE, HALON, WATER SPRAY OR ALCOHOL FOAM (1987 EMERGENCY RESPONSE GUIDEBOOK, DOT P 5800.4).
FOR LARGER FIRES, USE WATER SPRAY, FOG OR ALCOHOL FOAM (1987 EMERGENCY RESPONSE GUIDEBOOK, DOT P 5800.4).
ALCOHOL FOAM (NFPA 325M, FIRE HAZARD PROPERTIES OF FLAMMABLE LIQUIDS, GASES, AND VOLATILE SOLIDS, 1984).
FIREFIGHTING: MOVE CONTAINER FROM FIRE AREA IF POSSIBLE. DO NOT SCATTER SPILLED MATERIAL WITH HIGH PRESSURE WATER STREAMS. DIKE FIRE CONTROL WATER FOR LATER DISPOSAL (1987 EMERGENCY RESPONSE GUIDEBOOK, DOT P 5800.4, GUIDE PAGE 31).
USE AGENTS SUITABLE FOR TYPE OF SURROUNDING FIRE. AVOID BREATHING HAZARDOUS VAPORS, KEEP UPWIND.
WATER OR FOAM MAY CAUSE FROTHING (NFPA 325M, FIRE HAZARD PROPERTIES OF FLAMMABLE LIQUIDS, GASES, AND VOLATILE SOLIDS, 1984)

TOXICITY

ETHYLENE GLYCOL: IRRITATION DATA: 555 MG OPEN SKIN-RABBIT MILD; 12 MG/M3/3 DAYS EYE-RAT; 100 MG/1 HOUR EYE-RABBIT MILD; 500 MG/24 HOURS EYE-RABBIT MILD; 12 MG/M3/3 DAYS EYE-RABBIT; 1440 MG/6 HOURS EYE-RABBIT MODERATE. TOXICITY DATA: 10000 MG/M3 INHALATION-HUMAN TCLO; 9530 MG/KG SKIN-RABBIT LD50; 5500 MG/KG ORAL-CHILD TDLO; 786 MG/KG ORAL-HUMAN LDLO; 398 MG/KG ORAL-HUMAN LDLO; 4700 MG/KG ORAL-RAT LD50; 7500 MG/KG ORAL-MOUSE LD50; 6610 MG/KG ORAL-GUINEA PIG LD50; 5500 MG/KG ORAL-DOG LD50; 1650 MG/KG ORAL-CAT LD50; 2800 MG/KG SUBCUTANEOUS-RAT LD50; 2700 MG/KG SUBCUTANEOUS-MOUSE LDLO; 5000 MG/KG SUBCUTANEOUS-GUINEA PIG LDLO; 2000 MG/KG SUBCUTANEOUS-CAT LDLO; 3260 MG/KG INTRAVENOUS-RAT LD50; 3000 MG/KG INTRAVENOUS-MOUSE LD50; 5 GM/KG INTRAVENOUS-RABBIT LDLO; 5010 MG/KG INTRAPERITONEAL-RAT LD50; 5614 MG/KG INTRAPERITONEAL-MOUSE LD50; 1000 MG/KG INTRAPERITONEAL-RABBIT LDLO; 3300 MG/KG INTRAMUSCULAR-RAT LDLO; 5500 MG/KG INTRAMUSCULAR-RABBIT LDLO; 1637 MG/KG UNREPORTED ROUTE-MAN LDLO; MUTAGENIC DATA (RTECS); REPRODUCTIVE EFFECTS DATA (RTECS).
CARCINOGEN STATUS: NONE. LOCAL EFFECTS: IRRITANT- INHALATION, SKIN, EYE. ACUTE TOXICITY LEVEL: MODERATELY TOXIC BY INGESTION; SLIGHTLY TOXIC BY DERMAL ABSORPTION. TARGET EFFECTS: CENTRAL NERVOUS SYSTEM DEPRESSANT; NEPHROTOXIN; NEUROTOXIN. POISONING MAY AFFECT THE LUNGS, HEART, BLOOD, BRAIN AND LIVER.

HEALTH EFFECTS AND FIRST AID

INHALATION: ETHYLENE GLYCOL: IRRITANT. **ACUTE EXPOSURE-** INHALATION IS UNLIKELY AT ROOM TEMPERATURE, DUE TO THE LOW VAPOR PRESSURE. AEROSOLS AT 140 MG/M3 WERE IRRITATING, AND 200 MG/M3 WERE INTOLERABLE CAUSING A BURNING SENSATION OF THROAT AND COUGHING. EXPOSURE TO HIGH CONCENTRATIONS OF MISTS OR AEROSOLS MAY RESULT IN EFFECTS ON THE HEMATOPOIETIC SYSTEM AND CENTRAL NERVOUS SYSTEM WITH HEADACHE, DIZZINESS AND DROWSINESS. **CHRONIC EXPOSURE-** HUMANS EXPOSED TO AEROSOLS FROM 3-67 MG/M3 CONTINUOUSLY FOR 1 MONTH REPORTED IRRITATION OF THE RESPIRATORY TRACT, OCCASIONALLY SLIGHT HEADACHE AND LOW BACKACHE, BUT NO OTHER SIGNIFICANT ADVERSE EFFECTS. CONTINUED EXPOSURE TO VAPORS FROM A PROCESS UTILIZING A MIXTURE OF ETHYLENE GLYCOL, BORIC ACID AND AMMONIA HEATED ABOVE 100 C RESULTED IN NYSTAGMUS, LYMPHOCYTOSIS AND SUDDEN LOSS OF CONSCIOUSNESS FOR 5-10 MINUTES. NYSTAGMUS OCCURRED 2-3 TIMES WEEKLY UNTIL EXPOSURE CEASED. REPEATED EXPOSURE TO SATURATED ETHYLENE GLYCOL VAPORS PRODUCED SLIGHT NARCOSIS IN RATS. EFFECTS ON THE FETUS HAVE BEEN REPORTED IN RATS AND MICE FOLLOWING EXPOSURE DURING GESTATION. THERE WAS A LIKELIHOOD THAT AT LEAST A PORTION OF THE EFFECTS RESULTED FROM INGESTION SINCE ANIMALS GROOMED CONSTANTLY BEFORE AND AFTER EXPOSURE.

FIRST AID- REMOVE FROM EXPOSURE AREA TO FRESH AIR IMMEDIATELY. IF BREATHING HAS STOPPED, PERFORM ARTIFICIAL RESPIRATION. KEEP PERSON WARM AND AT REST. TREAT SYMPTOMATICALLY AND SUPPORTIVELY. GET MEDICAL ATTENTION IMMEDIATELY.

SKIN CONTACT: ETHYLENE GLYCOL: IRRITANT. **ACUTE EXPOSURE-** LIQUID MAY DEFAT THE SKIN AND CAUSE MINOR IRRITATION. ANIMAL STUDIES INDICATE THAT LETHAL AMOUNTS MAY BE ABSORBED THROUGH INTACT SKIN. ONE CASE HAS BEEN REPORTED OF COMA ACCOMPANIED BY MIOSIS AND SLOWED PULSE 4

HOURS AFTER MASSIVE APPLICATION OF AN ECZEMA REMEDY CONTAINING ETHYLENE GLYCOL. SENSITIZATION REACTIONS MAY OCCUR IN PREVIOUSLY EXPOSED PERSONS. **CHRONIC EXPOSURE-** A SLIGHT MACERATING ACTION ON THE SKIN MAY RESULT FROM VERY SEVERE, PROLONGED EXPOSURE. REPEATED OR PROLONGED CONTACT MAY RESULT IN SENSITIZATION.

FIRST AID- REMOVE CONTAMINATED CLOTHING AND SHOES IMMEDIATELY. WASH AFFECTED AREA WITH SOAP OR MILD DETERGENT AND LARGE AMOUNTS OF WATER UNTIL NO EVIDENCE OF CHEMICAL REMAINS (APPROXIMATELY 15-20 MINUTES). GET MEDICAL ATTENTION IMMEDIATELY.

EYE CONTACT: ETHYLENE GLYCOL: IRRITANT. **ACUTE EXPOSURE-** VAPORS MAY CAUSE REDNESS, AND CONTACT WITH THE LIQUID MAY CAUSE CONJUNCTIVITIS AND IRIDOCYCLITIS, BUT NO PERMANENT DAMAGE. **CHRONIC EXPOSURE-** VAPOR OR SPRAY AT 17 MG/M3/4 WEEKS PRODUCED NO ILL EFFECTS IN HUMANS. RATS EXPOSED CONTINUOUSLY TO 12 MG/M3 FOR SEVERAL DAYS SOMETIMES SHOWED SEVERE EYE IRRITATION, EDEMA OF THE EYELIDS, CORNEAL OPACITY AND APPARENT BLINDNESS, WITHOUT SIGNS OF SYSTEMIC INTOXICATION.

FIRST AID- WASH EYES IMMEDIATELY WITH LARGE AMOUNTS OF WATER OR NORMAL SALINE, OCCASIONALLY LIFTING UPPER AND LOWER LIDS, UNTIL NO EVIDENCE OF CHEMICAL REMAINS (APPROXIMATELY 15-20 MINUTES). GET MEDICAL ATTENTION IMMEDIATELY.

INGESTION: ETHYLENE GLYCOL: NARCOTIC/NEPHROTOXIN/NEUROTOXIN. **ACUTE EXPOSURE-** THE ESTIMATED LETHAL DOSE FOR ADULTS IS 100 MILLILITERS. THERE ARE THREE STAGES OF INTOXICATION FOLLOWING INGESTION OF ETHYLENE GLYCOL: CENTRAL NERVOUS SYSTEM STIMULATION FOLLOWED BY DEPRESSION; CARDIORESPIRATORY FAILURE; AND RENAL FAILURE. AN ACUTE CENTRAL NERVOUS SYSTEM STAGE MAY FOLLOW SHORTLY AFTER INGESTION AND LAST SEVERAL HOURS WITH SYMPTOMS OF NAUSEA, VOMITING, ABDOMINAL PAIN, DEHYDRATION, VISUAL DIFFICULTY, CONFUSION, PERSONALITY CHANGES, HALLUCINATIONS, CONVULSIONS, COMA, MENINGISM, MYOCLONUS, FIXED PUPILS, DECREASED OR LOSS OF VISION, LOSS OF ACCOMMODATION, PAPILLEDEMA, DIPLOPIA, NYSTAGMUS, STRABISMUS, ABNORMAL EYE MOVEMENTS, OPTIC NERVE ATROPHY, CRANIAL NERVE PALSIES, ATAXIA, TREMORS, MYOSITIS, MUSCLE TWITCHING, TETANY, HYPERREFLEXIA, AND AREFLEXIA. LIFE-THREATENING COMPLICATIONS WHICH MAY OCCUR IN THIS PERIOD INCLUDE RESPIRATORY FAILURE, SECONDARY TO CENTRAL NERVOUS SYSTEM DEPRESSION, CARDIOVASCULAR COLLAPSE, PULMONARY EDEMA AND SEVERE METABOLIC ACIDOSIS. WITHOUT TREATMENT, DEATH MAY OCCUR IN 8-24 HOURS. IF DEATH DOES NOT OCCUR EARLY, LUMBAR PAIN, ALBUMINURIA, HEMATURIA AND OLIGURIA PROGRESSING TO ANURIA ARE PROBABLE. ACUTE RENAL FAILURE WITH UREMIA, PERIPHERAL EDEMA, ASCITES, PULMONARY EDEMA, DROWSINESS, CYANOSIS, COMA AND DEATH IN 7-10 DAYS IS POSSIBLE. METABOLISM TO OXALIC ACID RESULTS IN PRECIPITATION OF CALCIUM OXALATE CRYSTALS IN SOFT TISSUES. CAPILLARY DAMAGE MAY RESULT IN EXUDATIVE, CONGESTIVE OR HEMORRHAGIC DAMAGE TO THE BRAIN, PERICARDIUM AND LIVER. MILDER INTOXICATION MAY RESULT IN INEBRIATION FOLLOWED BY AN ASYMPTOMATIC PERIOD OF SEVERAL DAYS BEFORE THE ONSET OF RENAL FAILURE. OLIGURIA MAY BE PERSISTENT, BUT EVENTUAL IMPROVEMENT IN RENAL FUNCTION IS ANTICIPATED IN SURVIVORS. PERMANENT CEREBRAL DAMAGE MAY OCCUR IN SURVIVORS OF PROLONGED COMA OR CONVULSIONS. **CHRONIC EXPOSURE-** REPEATED DAILY INGESTION OF 15-30 ML MAY CAUSE OLIGURIA WITHIN 24-72 HOURS, WHICH MAY PROGRESS RAPIDLY TO ANURIA AND UREMIA. REPEATED ADMINISTRATION TO ANIMALS RESULTED IN SHORTENED LIFE SPAN, CALCIUM OXALATE BLADDER STONES, SEVERE RENAL INJURY, PARTICULARLY OF THE TUBULES, AND CENTRILOBULAR DEGENERATION OF THE LIVER. MATERNAL EFFECTS, EFFECTS ON FERTILITY, FETAL DEVELOPMENTAL ABNORMALITIES AND EFFECTS ON THE EMBRYO AND FETUS HAVE BEEN REPORTED FROM REPEATED ADMINISTRATION TO RATS AND MICE DURING GESTATION; ADMINISTRATION TO LACTATING MICE PRODUCED DELAYED EFFECTS ON THE NEWBORN.

FIRST AID- REMOVE INGESTED MATERIAL BY GASTRIC LAVAGE OR EMESIS. GIVE ARTIFICIAL RESPIRATION WITH OXYGEN IF RESPIRATION IS DEPRESSED. (DREISBACH HANDBOOK OF POISONING, 11TH ED.). GET MEDICAL ATTENTION IMMEDIATELY. ADMINISTRATION OF GASTRIC LAVAGE SHOULD BE PERFORMED BY QUALIFIED MEDICAL PERSONNEL.

ANTIDOTE: THE FOLLOWING ANTIDOTE(S) HAVE BEEN RECOMMENDED. HOWEVER, THE DECISION AS TO WHETHER THE SEVERITY OF POISONING REQUIRES ADMINISTRATION OF ANY ANTIDOTE AND ACTUAL DOSE REQUIRED SHOULD BE MADE BY QUALIFIED MEDICAL PERSONNEL. ETHYLENE GLYCOL POISONING: GIVE ETHANOL, 50% (100 PROOF), 1.5 ML/KG ORALLY INITIALLY, DILUTED TO NOT MORE THAN 5% SOLUTION, FOLLOWED BY 0.5-1.0 ML/KG EVERY 2 HOURS ORALLY OR INTRAVENOUSLY FOR 4 DAYS TO PREVENT METABOLISM OF INGESTED ETHYLENE GLYCOL TO OXALATE. BLOOD ETHANOL LEVEL SHOULD BE IN THE RANGE 1-1.5 MG/ML. GIVE CALCIUM GLUCONATE, 10 ML OF 10% SOLUTION DILUTED IN 1 LITER OF 5% GLUCOSE, INTRAVENOUSLY AS NECESSARY TO MAINTAIN NORMAL SERUM CALCIUM LEVELS. CALCIUM ADMINISTRATION MAY CAUSE ANURIA DUE TO PRECIPITATION OF CALCIUM OXALATE IN THE KIDNEYS (DREISBACH, HANDBOOK OF POISONING, 11TH ED.). IN THE ABSENCE OF RENAL IMPAIRMENT, FORCE FLUIDS TO 4 LITERS DAILY TO INCREASE EXCRETION OR PERFORM HEMODIALYSIS. ANTIDOTE SHOULD BE ADMINISTERED BY QUALIFIED MEDICAL PERSONNEL.

ORAL OR INTRAVENOUS ADMINISTRATION OF 4-METHYLPYRAZOLE INHIBITS ALCOHOL DEHYDROGENASE AND HAS BEEN USED EFFECTIVELY AS AN ANTIDOTE FOR METHANOL OR ETHYLENE GLYCOL POISONING (ELLENHORN AND BARCELOUX, MEDICAL TOXICOLOGY).

REACTIVITY

REACTIVITY: STABLE UNDER NORMAL TEMPERATURES AND PRESSURES.

INCOMPATIBILITIES: ETHYLENE GLYCOL: AMMONIUM DICHROMATE: IGNITES @ 100 C. CHLOROSULFONIC ACID: TEMPERATURE AND PRESSURE INCREASE IN CLOSED CONTAINER. CHROMIUM TRIOXIDE: IGNITES ON CONTACT. DIMETHYL TEREPHTHALATE + TITANIUM BUTOXIDE: POSSIBLE IGNITION. OLEUM: TEMPERATURE AND PRESSURE INCREASE IN CLOSED CONTAINER. OXIDIZERS (STRONG): FIRE AND EXPLOSION HAZARD. PERCHLORIC ACID: VIOLENT DECOMPOSITION. PHOSPHORUS(V) SULFIDE: EXPLOSIVE REACTION ON HEATING. POTASSIUM DICHROMATE: VIGOROUS EXOTHERMIC REACTION @ 100 C. POTASSIUM PERMANGANATE: IGNITES ON CONTACT. SILVER CHLORATE: IGNITES @ 100 C. SILVERED COPPER WIRE: IGNITES. SODIUM CHLORITE: IGNITES @ 100 C. SODIUM HYDROXIDE: EXPLOSION HAZARD. SODIUM PEROXIDE: IGNITES ON CONTACT. SULFURIC ACID: TEMPERATURE AND PRESSURE INCREASE IN CLOSED CONTAINER. URANYL NITRATE: IGNITES @ 100 C.

DECOMPOSITION: THERMAL DECOMPOSITION PRODUCTS MAY INCLUDE TOXIC OXIDES OF CARBON.

POLYMERIZATION: HAZARDOUS POLYMERIZATION HAS NOT BEEN REPORTED TO OCCUR UNDER NORMAL TEMPERATURES AND PRESSURES.

STORAGE AND DISPOSAL

OBSERVE ALL FEDERAL, STATE AND LOCAL REGULATIONS WHEN STORING OR DISPOSING OF THIS SUBSTANCE. FOR ASSISTANCE, CONTACT THE DISTRICT DIRECTOR OF THE ENVIRONMENTAL PROTECTION AGENCY.

STORAGE

STORE AWAY FROM INCOMPATIBLE SUBSTANCES.

CONDITIONS TO AVOID

MAY BURN BUT DOES NOT IGNITE READILY. AVOID CONTACT WITH STRONG OXIDIZERS, EXCESSIVE HEAT, SPARKS, OR OPEN FLAME.

SPILL AND LEAK PROCEDURES

WATER SPILL: THE CALIFORNIA SAFE DRINKING WATER AND TOXIC ENFORCEMENT ACT OF 1986 (PROPOSITION 65) PROHIBITS CONTAMINATING ANY KNOWN SOURCE OF DRINKING WATER WITH SUBSTANCES KNOWN TO CAUSE CANCER AND/OR REPRODUCTIVE TOXICITY.

OCCUPATIONAL SPILL: STOP LEAK IF YOU CAN DO IT WITHOUT RISK. FOR SMALL SPILLS, TAKE UP WITH SAND OR OTHER ABSORBENT MATERIAL AND PLACE INTO CLEAN, DRY CONTAINERS FOR LATER DISPOSAL. KEEP UNNECESSARY PEOPLE AWAY. ISOLATE HAZARD AREA AND DENY ENTRY.

PROTECTIVE EQUIPMENT

VENTILATION: PROVIDE LOCAL EXHAUST VENTILATION AND/OR GENERAL DILUTION VENTILATION TO MEET PUBLISHED EXPOSURE LIMITS.

RESPIRATOR: THE FOLLOWING RESPIRATORS ARE RECOMMENDED BASED ON INFORMATION FOUND IN THE PHYSICAL DATA, TOXICITY AND HEALTH EFFECTS SECTIONS. THEY ARE RANKED IN ORDER FROM MINIMUM TO MAXIMUM RESPIRATORY PROTECTION. THE SPECIFIC RESPIRATOR SELECTED MUST BE BASED ON CONTAMINATION LEVELS FOUND IN THE WORK PLACE, MUST NOT EXCEED THE WORKING LIMITS OF THE RESPIRATOR AND BE JOINTLY APPROVED BY THE NATIONAL INSTITUTE FOR OCCUPATIONAL SAFETY AND HEALTH AND THE MINE SAFETY AND HEALTH ADMINISTRATION (NIOSH-MSHA).

CHEMICAL CARTRIDGE RESPIRATOR WITH AN ORGANIC VAPOR CARTRIDGE(S) WITH A FULL FACEPIECE.

GAS MASK WITH ORGANIC VAPOR CANISTER (CHIN-STYLE OR FRONT- OR BACK-MOUNTED CANISTER) WITH A FULL FACEPIECE.

TYPE 'C' SUPPLIED-AIR RESPIRATOR WITH A FULL FACEPIECE OPERATED IN PRESSURE-DEMAND OR OTHER POSITIVE PRESSURE MODE OR WITH A FULL FACEPIECE, HELMET OR HOOD OPERATED IN CONTINUOUS-FLOW MODE.

SELF-CONTAINED BREATHING APPARATUS WITH A FULL FACEPIECE OPERATED IN PRESSURE-DEMAND OR OTHER POSITIVE PRESSURE MODE.

FOR FIREFIGHTING AND OTHER IMMEDIATELY DANGEROUS TO LIFE OR HEALTH CONDITIONS:

SELF-CONTAINED BREATHING APPARATUS WITH FULL FACEPIECE OPERATED IN PRESSURE-DEMAND OR OTHER POSITIVE PRESSURE MODE. SUPPLIED-AIR

RESPIRATOR WITH FULL FACEPIECE AND OPERATED IN PRESSURE-DEMAND OR OTHER POSITIVE PRESSURE MODE IN COMBINATION WITH AN AUXILIARY SELF-CONTAINED BREATHING APPARATUS OPERATED IN PRESSURE-DEMAND OR OTHER POSITIVE PRESSURE MODE.

CLOTHING: EMPLOYEE MUST WEAR APPROPRIATE PROTECTIVE (IMPERVIOUS) CLOTHING AND EQUIPMENT TO PREVENT REPEATED OR PROLONGED SKIN CONTACT WITH THIS SUBSTANCE.

GLOVES: EMPLOYEE MUST WEAR APPROPRIATE PROTECTIVE GLOVES TO PREVENT CONTACT WITH THIS SUBSTANCE.

EYE PROTECTION: EMPLOYEE MUST WEAR SPLASH-PROOF OR DUST-RESISTANT SAFETY GOGGLES TO PREVENT EYE CONTACT WITH THIS SUBSTANCE. EMERGENCY EYE WASH: WHERE THERE IS ANY POSSIBILITY THAT AN EMPLOYEE'S EYES MAY BE EXPOSED TO THIS SUBSTANCE, THE EMPLOYER SHOULD PROVIDE AN EYE WASH FOUNTAIN WITHIN THE IMMEDIATE WORK AREA FOR EMERGENCY USE.

AUTHORIZED BY- OCCUPATIONAL HEALTH SERVICES, INC.

CREATION DATE: 11/16/89 ***REVISION DATE:*** 05/07/90

MATERIAL SAFETY DATA SHEET

OCCUPATIONAL HEALTH SERVICES, INC.
AGRICULTURE AND PESTICIDE DIVISION
450 SEVENTH AVENUE, SUITE 2407
NEW YORK, NEW YORK 10123
1-800-445-MSDS OR (212) 967-1100

EMERGENCY CONTACT:
JOHN S. BRANSFORD, JR. (615) 292-1180

SUBSTANCE IDENTIFICATION

CAS-NUMBER 75-21-8

SUBSTANCE: <u>ETHYLENE OXIDE</u>

TRADE NAMES/SYNONYMS: OXIRANE; DIHYDROOXIRENE; DIMETHYLENE OXIDE; EPOXYETHANE; 1,2-EPOXYETHANE; ETHENE OXIDE; ETO; EO; OXACYCLOPROPANE; OXANE; OXIDOETHANE; ALPHA,BETA-OXIDOETHANE; OXIRAN; RCRA U115; STCC 4906610; UN 1040; C2H4O; PST09520

CHEMICAL FAMILY: EPOXY

MOLECULAR FORMULA: (C-H2)2-O

MOLECULAR WEIGHT: 44.06

CERCLA RATINGS (SCALE 0-3): HEALTH=3 FIRE=3 REACTIVITY=3 PERSISTENCE=0

NFPA RATINGS (SCALE 0-4): HEALTH=2 FIRE=4 REACTIVITY=3

COMPONENTS AND CONTAMINANTS

COMPONENT: ETHYLENE OXIDE ***PERCENT:*** 99.7
CAS# 75-21-8

OTHER CONTAMINANTS: WATER, ACETALDEHYDE, ACETIC ACID

EXPOSURE LIMITS: ETHYLENE OXIDE: 1 PPM OSHA TWA; 5 PPM OSHA 15 MINUTE EXCURSION LIMIT; 0.5 PPM OSHA TWA ACTION LEVEL 1 PPM ACGIH TWA ACGIH A2-SUSPECTED HUMAN CARCINOGEN. NOT TO EXCEED 0.1 PPM NIOSH RECOMMENDED 8 HOUR TWA; 5 PPM NIOSH RECOMMENDED 10 MINUTE CEILING 1000 POUNDS SARA SECTION 302 THRESHOLD PLANNING QUANTITY 1 POUND SARA SECTION 304 REPORTABLE QUANTITY 10 POUNDS CERCLA SECTION 103 REPORTABLE QUANTITY SUBJECT TO SARA SECTION 313 ANNUAL TOXIC CHEMICAL RELEASE REPORTING SUBJECT TO CALIFORNIA PROPOSITION 65 CANCER AND/OR REPRODUCTIVE TOXICITY WARNING AND RELEASE REQUIREMENTS- (FEBRUARY 27, 1987)

PHYSICAL DATA

DESCRIPTION: COLORLESS LIQUID OR GAS WITH AN ETHER-LIKE ODOR.

BOILING POINT: 55 F (13 C) ***MELTING POINT:*** -168 F (-111 C)

SPECIFIC GRAVITY: 0.8824 @ 10 C ***VOLATILITY:*** 100%

VAPOR PRESSURE: 1095 MMHG @ 20 C ***SOLUBILITY IN WATER:*** COMPLETE

ODOR THRESHOLD: 500 PPM ***VAPOR DENSITY:*** 1.5

SOLVENT SOLUBILITY: SOLUBLE IN ALCOHOL, ETHER, ACETONE, BENZENE, CARBON TETRACHLORIDE, ORGANIC SOLVENTS.

VISCOSITY: 0.0095 CPS @ 25 C (GAS); 0.310 CPS @ 0 C (LIQUID)

FIRE AND EXPLOSION DATA

FIRE AND EXPLOSION HAZARD: DANGEROUS FIRE HAZARD WHEN EXPOSED TO HEAT OR FLAME.
VAPORS ARE HEAVIER THAN AIR AND MAY TRAVEL A CONSIDERABLE DISTANCE TO A SOURCE OF IGNITION AND FLASH BACK.
VAPOR-AIR MIXTURES ARE EXPLOSIVE.

FLASH POINT: -20 F (-29 C) (CC) ***UPPER EXPLOSIVE LIMIT:*** 100%

LOWER EXPLOSIVE LIMIT: 3% ***AUTOIGNITION TEMP.:*** 804 F (429 C)

FLAMMABILITY CLASS(OSHA): IA

FIREFIGHTING MEDIA: DRY CHEMICAL, CARBON DIOXIDE, HALON, WATER SPRAY OR ALCOHOL FOAM (1987 EMERGENCY RESPONSE GUIDEBOOK, DOT P 5800.4). FOR LARGER FIRES, USE WATER SPRAY, FOG OR ALCOHOL FOAM (1987 EMERGENCY RESPONSE GUIDEBOOK, DOT P 5800.4).

FIREFIGHTING: LET BURN UNLESS LEAK CAN BE STOPPED IMMEDIATELY. MOVE CONTAINER FROM FIRE AREA IF POSSIBLE. STAY AWAY FROM STORAGE TANK ENDS. FIGHT FIRE FROM MAXIMUM DISTANCE. FOR MASSIVE FIRE IN STORAGE AREA, USE UNMANNED HOSE HOLDER OR MONITOR NOZZLES; ELSE WITHDRAW FROM AREA AND LET FIRE BURN. WITHDRAW IMMEDIATELY IN CASE OF RISING SOUND FROM VENTING SAFETY DEVICE OR ANY DISCOLORATION OF TANK DUE TO FIRE (1987 EMERGENCY RESPONSE GUIDEBOOK, DOT P 5800.4, GUIDE PAGE 69). EXTINGUISH ONLY IF FLOW CAN BE STOPPED; USE WATER IN FLOODING AMOUNTS AS A FOG, SOLID STREAMS MAY NOT BE EFFECTIVE. APPLY WATER FROM AS FAR A DISTANCE AS POSSIBLE. COOL CONTAINERS WITH FLOODING QUANTITIES OF WATER. AVOID BREATHING CORROSIVE VAPORS, KEEP UPWIND. EVACUATE TO A RADIUS OF 5000 FEET IF FIRE IS PROLONGED AND MATERIAL IS CONFINED IN THE CONTAINERS. EVACUATE TO A RADIUS OF 5000 FEET FOR UNCONTROLLABLE FIRE. WATER MAY BE INEFFECTIVE (NFPA 325M, FIRE HAZARD PROPERTIES OF FLAMMABLE LIQUIDS, GASES, AND VOLATILE SOLIDS, 1984)

TRANSPORTATION DATA

DEPARTMENT OF TRANSPORTATION HAZARD CLASSIFICATION 49 CFR 172.101: FLAMMABLE LIQUID
DEPARTMENT OF TRANSPORTATION LABELING REQUIREMENTS 49 CFR 172.101 AND SUBPART E: FLAMMABLE LIQUID
DEPARTMENT OF TRANSPORTATION PACKAGING REQUIREMENTS: 49 CFR 173.124 EXCEPTIONS: NONE

TOXICITY

ETHYLENE OXIDE: IRRITATION DATA: 1%/7 SECONDS SKIN-HUMAN; 18 MG/6 HOURS EYE-RABBIT MODERATE. TOXICITY DATA: 12500 PPM/10 SECONDS INHALATION-HUMAN TCLO; 500 PPM/2 MINUTES INHALATION-WOMAN TCLO; 800 PPM/4 HOURS INHALATION-RAT LC50; 72 MG/KG ORAL-RAT LD50; 836 PPM/4 HOURS INHALATION-MOUSE LC50; 175 MG/KG INTRAVENOUS-RABBIT LDLO; 960 PPM/4 HOURS INHALATION-DOG LC50; 1500 MG/M3/4 HOURS INHALATION-GUINEA PIG LC50; 270 MG/KG ORAL-GUINEA PIG LD50; 290 MG/KG INTRAVENOUS-MOUSE LD50; 175 MG/KG INTRAPERITONEAL-MOUSE LD50; 187 MG/KG SUBCUTANEOUS-RAT LD50; 100 MG/KG SUBCUTANEOUS-CAT LDLO; 200 MG/KG UNREPORTED ROUTE-RAT LDLO; 330 MG/KG INTRAVENOUS-DOG LD50; MUTAGENIC DATA (RTECS); REPRODUCTIVE EFFECTS DATA (RTECS); TUMORIGENIC DATA (RTECS). CARCINOGEN STATUS: OSHA CARCINOGEN; ANTICIPATED HUMAN CARCINOGEN (NTP); HUMAN LIMITED EVIDENCE, ANIMAL SUFFICIENT EVIDENCE (IARC GROUP-2A). SEVERAL EPIDEMIOLOGICAL STUDIES INDICATE THERE IS A CAUSAL RELATIONSHIP BETWEEN EXPOSURE TO ETHYLENE OXIDE AND AN INCREASED INCIDENCE OF LEUKEMIA. HOWEVER THESE STUDIES SUFFER FROM DISADVANTAGES, ESPECIALLY CONFOUNDING EXPOSURES, WHICH MAKE THEIR INTERPRETATION DIFFICULT. IN RATS GASTRIC INTUBATION PRODUCED DOSE-DEPENDENT LOCAL TUMORS, MAINLY SQUAMOUS-CELL CARCINOMAS OF THE FORESTOMACH. INHALATION EXPOSURE PRODUCED AN INCREASED INCIDENCE OF MONONUCLEAR-CELL LEUKEMIA IN BOTH SEXES OF RATS AND PERITONEAL MESOTHELIOMAS, GLIOMAS OF THE BRAIN, AND A HIGH INCIDENCE OF PROLIFERATIVE LESIONS OF THE ADRENAL CORTEX IN MALES. SUBCUTANEOUS INJECTION IN MICE PRODUCED LOCAL TUMORS IN A DOSE-DEPENDENT MANNER. NTP TR-326 REPORTS CLEAR EVIDENCE OF CARCINOGENIC ACTIVITY FOR MICE AS INDICATED BY DOSE-RELATED INCREASED INCIDENCES OF BENIGN OR MALIGNANT NEOPLASMS OF THE LUNGS IN BOTH SEXES OF MICE FOLLOWING INHALATION EXPOSURE. ADDITIONALLY, MALIGNANT NEOPLASMS OF THE UTERUS, MAMMARY GLAND, AND HEMATOPOIETIC SYSTEM (LYMPHOMA) WERE REPORTED IN FEMALES. LOCAL EFFECTS: IRRITANT- MUCOUS MEMBRANES; CORROSIVE- SKIN, EYES. ACUTE TOXICITY LEVEL: TOXIC BY INHALATION AND INGESTION. TARGET EFFECTS: CENTRAL NERVOUS SYSTEM DEPRESSANT; SENSITIZER- SKIN; POISONING MAY AFFECT THE LIVER, KIDNEYS, BLOOD, RESPIRATORY SYSTEM AND REPRODUCTIVE SYSTEM. ADDITIONAL DATA: ALCOHOL MAY ENHANCE THE TOXIC EFFECTS.

HEALTH EFFECTS AND FIRST AID

INHALATION: ETHYLENE OXIDE: IRRITANT/NARCOTIC/CARCINOGEN/TOXIC. <u>ACUTE EXPOSURE</u>- HIGH LEVELS MAY CAUSE ANOSMIA, MUCOUS MEMBRANE IRRITATION LEADING TO EMPHYSEMA AND BRONCHITIS, SEVERE COUGH, AND A SWEETISH TASTE IN THE MOUTH. VOMITING, RECURRING PERIODICALLY FOR HOURS, ACCOMPANIED BY NAUSEA AND HEADACHE IS COMMON. DELAYED CENTRAL NERVOUS SYSTEM DEPRESSION MAY OCCUR WITH DYSPNEA, CYANOSIS,

DROWSINESS, WEAKNESS, INCOORDINATION, DISORIENTATION AND UNCONSCIOUSNESS. BRADYCARDIA, APHONIA, KIDNEY DAMAGE, PULMONARY EDEMA AND DEATH MAY ALSO OCCUR. STUDIES SUGGEST THAT BLOOD CELL CHANGES, AN INCREASE IN CHROMOSOMAL ABERRATIONS, AND SPONTANEOUS ABORTION MAY ALSO BE CAUSALLY RELATED TO ACUTE OVEREXPOSURE TO ETHYLENE OXIDE. EXPOSURE OF ANIMALS TO GREATER THAN 1000 PPM/2 HOURS CAUSED LACRIMATION AND NASAL DISCHARGE, FOLLOWED BY GASPING AND LABORED BREATHING. DELAYED EFFECTS WERE VOMITING, DIARRHEA, DYSPNEA, PULMONARY EDEMA, PARALYSIS OF HIND QUARTERS, CONVULSIONS AND DEATH. AUTOPSY REVEALED INJURY TO LUNGS, LIVER AND KIDNEYS. PROMPT DEATHS WERE DUE TO EDEMA, WHILE DELAYED DEATHS RESULTED FROM SECONDARY INFECTION OF THE LUNGS. A STATISTICALLY SIGNIFICANT INCREASE IN EMBRYOLETHALITY, DUE TO DOMINANT LETHAL EFFECTS, WAS REPORTED IN MICE FOLLOWING A SINGLE EXPOSURE OF MALES PRIOR TO MATING. **CHRONIC EXPOSURE-** WORKERS EXPOSED TO GREATER THAN 700 PPM INTERMITTENTLY FOR 2 MONTHS REPORTED MUCOSAL IRRITATION, TRANSIENT BLUNTING OF THE SENSES OF SMELL AND TASTE, HEADACHE, NAUSEA, VOMITING, LETHARGY, NUMBNESS AND WEAKNESS IN THE EXTREMITIES, MEMORY/THINKING DISTURBANCES, SLURRED SPEECH, DIFFICULTY SWALLOWING, FACIAL WEAKNESS, AND RECURRENT MAJOR MOTOR SEIZURES. NEUROLOGICAL EXAMINATION RESULTS WERE CONSISTENT WITH SENSORIMOTOR NEUROPATHY. IMPROVEMENT OCCURRED 2 WEEKS AFTER REMOVAL FROM EXPOSURE. AN INCREASE IN SISTER CHROMATID EXCHANGES, CHROMOSOMAL ABERRATIONS OF PERIPHERAL LYMPHOCYTES, REDUCED HEMOGLOBIN AND ELEVATED LYMPHOCYTES HAVE BEEN REPORTED IN PRODUCTION PLANT WORKERS. A FINNISH STUDY SUGGESTS EXPOSURE TO ETHYLENE OXIDE MAY BE RELATED TO AN INCREASE IN SPONTANEOUS ABORTIONS AMONG HOSPITAL STERILIZING STAFF. STUDIES OF PRODUCTION WORKERS EXPOSED TO ETHYLENE OXIDE AND OTHER CHEMICALS INDICATE A SIGNIFICANT EXCESS OF MORTALITY AND CANCER THAT INCLUDED LEUKEMIA, HODGKINS DISEASE, AND GASTROINTESTINAL AND UROGENITAL TRACT MALIGNANCIES AS WELL AS AN INCREASE IN DISEASES OF THE CIRCULATORY SYSTEM. CHRONIC EXPOSURE OF TEST ANIMALS TO 100 PPM RESULTED IN A LONGER GESTATION PERIOD, REDUCED FERTILITY INDEX, AND FEWER PUPS. OTHER ANIMAL STUDIES REPORT DOMINANT LETHAL EFFECTS, AND VARIABLE EFFECTS ON THE TESTES INCLUDING SLIGHT DECREASE IN WEIGHT, APPRECIABLE DEGENERATION AND REPLACEMENT FIBROSIS. INHALATION STUDIES IN RATS SHOWED EXPOSURE CAUSED AN INCREASED INCIDENCE OF MONONUCLEAR-CELL LEUKEMIA IN BOTH SEXES AND PERITONEAL MESOTHELIOMAS, GLIOMAS OF THE BRAIN, AND A HIGH INCIDENCE OF PROLIFERATIVE LESIONS OF THE ADRENAL CORTEX IN THE MALES. DOSE-RELATED INCREASED INCIDENCES OF BENIGN OR MALIGNANT NEOPLASMS OF THE LUNG AND BENIGN NEOPLASMS OF THE HARDERIAN GLAND IN MICE WERE REPORTED FOLLOWING EXPOSURE FOR TWO YEARS TO 5 AND 100 PPM ETHYLENE OXIDE. IN FEMALE MICE ADDITIONAL MALIGNANT NEOPLASMS OF THE UTERUS, MAMMARY GLAND AND HEMATOPOIETIC SYSTEM WERE REPORTED. OTHER EFFECTS REPORTED IN ANIMAL STUDIES INCLUDE GROWTH DEPRESSION, NASAL DISCHARGE, DIARRHEA, RESPIRATORY IRRITATION, FLACCID PARALYSIS OF HINDQUARTERS ACCOMPANIED BY SEVERE ATROPHY OF THE MUSCULATURE OF THE HIND LEGS AND BACK.

FIRST AID- REMOVE FROM EXPOSURE AREA TO FRESH AIR IMMEDIATELY. IF BREATHING HAS STOPPED, GIVE ARTIFICIAL RESPIRATION. MAINTAIN AIRWAY AND BLOOD PRESSURE AND ADMINISTER OXYGEN IF AVAILABLE. KEEP AFFECTED PERSON WARM AND AT REST. TREAT SYMPTOMATICALLY AND SUPPORTIVELY. ADMINISTRATION OF OXYGEN SHOULD BE PERFORMED BY QUALIFIED PERSONNEL. GET MEDICAL ATTENTION IMMEDIATELY.

SKIN CONTACT: ETHYLENE OXIDE: CORROSIVE/SENSITIZER. **ACUTE EXPOSURE-** DIRECT CONTACT MAY CAUSE MILD TO SEVERE IRRITATION DEPENDING ON THE CIRCUMSTANCES. SMALL AMOUNTS OF FULL CONCENTRATION WHICH ARE ALLOWED TO EVAPORATE MAY CAUSE NO ADVERSE EFFECTS, WHILE SMALL DILUTE AMOUNTS CONFINED TO THE SKIN BY WAY OF CLOTHING, GLOVES, OR SHOES HAVE BEEN REPORTED TO CAUSE EDEMA AND ERYTHEMA IN 1-6 HOURS, PROGRESSING TO VESICULATION WITH A TENDENCY TO COALESCE INTO BLEBS AND DESQUAMATION. THESE EFFECTS SEEM TO BE REVERSIBLE AND RECOVERY MAY BE COMPLETE WITHIN 3 WEEKS WITH ONLY RESIDUAL BROWN PIGMENTATION. LARGE AMOUNTS WHICH ARE SPILLED ON THE SKIN AND ALLOWED TO EVAPORATE RAPIDLY MAY CAUSE FROSTBITE. SENSITIZATION DERMATITIS MAY OCCUR IN PREVIOUSLY EXPOSED INDIVIDUALS. **CHRONIC EXPOSURE-** MAY CAUSE DERMATITIS OR EFFECTS SIMILAR TO THOSE IN ACUTE EXPOSURE. SKIN SENSITIZATION HAS BEEN ASSOCIATED WITH REPEATED DERMAL CONTACT.

FIRST AID- REMOVE CONTAMINATED CLOTHING AND SHOES IMMEDIATELY. WASH AFFECTED AREA WITH SOAP OR MILD DETERGENT AND LARGE AMOUNTS OF WATER UNTIL NO EVIDENCE OF CHEMICAL REMAINS. IN CASE OF FROSTBITE, WARM AFFECTED SKIN IN WARM WATER AT A TEMPERATURE OF 107 F. IF WARM WATER IS NOT AVAILABLE OR IMPRACTICAL TO USE, GENTLY WRAP AFFECTED PART IN BLANKETS. ENCOURAGE VICTIM TO EXCERCISE AFFECTED PART WHILE IT IS BEING WARMED. ALLOW CIRCULATION TO RETURN NATURALLY (MATHESON GAS, 6TH ED.). GET MEDICAL ATTENTION IMMEDIATELY.

EYE CONTACT: ETHYLENE OXIDE: CORROSIVE. **ACUTE EXPOSURE-** HIGH VAPOR CONCENTRATIONS MAY CAUSE IRRITATION, LACRIMATION, AND CLOUDING OF THE CORNEA. DIRECT CONTACT WITH LIQUID MAY CAUSE BURNS. FROSTBITE MAY OCCUR DUE TO RAPID EVAPORATION. **CHRONIC EXPOSURE-** MAY CAUSE CONJUNCTIVITIS OR EFFECTS SIMILAR TO THOSE IN ACUTE EXPOSURE.

FIRST AID- IMMEDIATELY WASH THE EYES WITH LARGE AMOUNTS OF WATER, OCCASIONALLY LIFTING UPPER AND LOWER LIDS, UNTIL NO EVIDENCE OF CHEMICAL REMAINS (APPROXIMATELY 15-20 MINUTES). IF FROSTBITE IS PRESENT, WARM WATER MAY BE PREFERRED. GET MEDICAL ATTENTION IMMEDIATELY.

INGESTION: ETHYLENE OXIDE: NARCOTIC/TOXIC/CARCINOGEN. **ACUTE EXPOSURE-** MAY CAUSE SORE THROAT, ABDOMINAL PAIN, PAIN IN THE CHEST, HEADACHE, DIZZINESS, NAUSEA, VOMITING, DIARRHEA, BURNS, CYANOSIS, DROWSINESS, WEAKNESS, INCOORDINATION, UNCONSCIOUSNESS AND POSSIBLY DEATH. FROSTBITE DAMAGE TO THE LIPS, MOUTH, AND MUCOUS MEMBRANES MAY ALSO OCCUR. THE LETHAL DOSE IN RATS WAS 72 MG/KG. **CHRONIC EXPOSURE-** IN ANIMALS PROLONGED INGESTION CAUSED LOSS OF BODY WEIGHT, GASTRIC IRRITATION, AND SLIGHT LIVER DAMAGE. RATS ADMINISTERED ETHYLENE OXIDE BY GASTRIC INTUBATION HAVE SHOWN AN INCREASED INCIDENCE OF SQUAMOUS-CELL CARCINOMAS OF THE FORESTOMACH, IN A DOSE-DEPENDENT MANNER. WHEN RATS WERE FED DIETS FUMIGATED WITH ETHYLENE OXIDE, NO INCREASED INCIDENCE OF TUMORS WAS OBSERVED.

FIRST AID- IF THE PERSON IS CONSCIOUS AND NOT CONVULSING, INDUCE EMESIS BY GIVING SYRUP OF IPECAC FOLLOWED BY WATER. (IF VOMITING OCCURS KEEP THE HEAD BELOW THE HIPS TO PREVENT ASPIRATION). REPEAT IN 20 MINUTES IF NOT EFFECTIVE INITIALLY. GIVE ACTIVATED CHARCOAL. IN PATIENTS WITH DEPRESSED RESPIRATION OR IF EMESIS IS NOT PRODUCED, PERFORM GASTRIC LAVAGE CAUTIOUSLY (DREISBACH, HANDBOOK OF POISONING, 12TH ED.). TREAT SYMPTOMATICALLY AND SUPPORTIVELY. GASTRIC LAVAGE SHOULD BE PERFORMED BY QUALIFIED MEDICAL PERSONNEL. GET MEDICAL ATTENTION IMMEDIATELY.

ANTIDOTE: NO SPECIFIC ANTIDOTE. TREAT SYMPTOMATICALLY AND SUPPORTIVELY.

REACTIVITY

REACTIVITY: ETHYLENE OXIDE: DECOMPOSES VIOLENTLY ABOVE 800 F, AND MAY BE READILY INITIATED INTO EXPLOSIVE DECOMPOSITION IN ABSENCE OF AIR.

INCOMPATIBILITIES: ETHYLENE OXIDE: ACIDS: EXOTHERIC POLYMERIZATION. ALCOHOLS: POSSIBLE EXPLOSION. ALKALI METAL HYDROXIDES: VIOLENT POLYMERIZATION REACTION. ALKANETHIOLS: MAY REACT VIOLENTLY UNDER PRESSURE. ALUMINUM CHLORIDE: EXOTHERMIC POLYMERIZATION. ALUMINUM OXIDE: VIOLENT POLYMERIZATION. AMINES: POSSIBLE EXPLOSIVE POLYMERIZATION. AMMONIA: VIOLENT POLYMERIZATION. BROMOETHANE: INCOMPATIBLE. COPPER AND ALLOYS: POSSIBLE EXPLOSION IF TRACES OF ACETYLENE ARE PRESENT. GLYCEROL: VIOLENT CONDENSATION. IRON CHLORIDES: VIOLENT POLYMERIZATION. IRON(III) HEXACYANOFERRATE(4-)("IRON BLUE PIGMENT"): EXOTHERMIC REACTION YIELDING SPONTANEOUSLY COMBUSTIBLE PRODUCT. IRON OXIDES: VIOLENT POLYMERIZATION. MAGNESIUM: POSSIBLE EXPLOSION IF TRACES OF ACETYLENE ARE PRESENT. MAGNESIUM PERCHLORATE: POSSIBLE EXPLOSION. MERCAPTANS: POSSIBLE EXPLOSION. MERCURY AND ALLOYS: POSSIBLE EXPLOSION IF TRACES OF ACETYLENE ARE PRESENT. M-NITROANILINE: POSSIBLE EXPLOSION ON HEATING. OXIDIZERS (STRONG): FIRE AND EXPLOSION HAZARD. OXYGEN: POSSIBLE IGNITION IF RAPIDLY COMPRESSED. PLASTICS, RUBBER, COATINGS: MAY BE ATTACKED. POTASSIUM: EXPLOSIVE REACTION. RUST: EXPLOSIVE POLYMERIZATION. SILVER AND ALLOYS: POSSIBLE EXPLOSION IF TRACES OF ACETYLENE ARE PRESENT. SODIUM HYDROXIDE: EXOTHERMIC POLYMERIZATION. SUCROGLYCERIDE: EXOTHERMIC REACTION WHEN HEATED. TIN CHLORIDES: VIOLENT POLYMERIZATION. TRIMETHYLAMINE: EXOTHERMIC POLYMERIZATION.

DECOMPOSITION: THERMAL DECOMPOSITION PRODUCTS MAY INCLUDE TOXIC OXIDES OF CARBON.

POLYMERIZATION: ETHYLENE OXIDE: MAY POLYMERIZE VIOLENTLY WHEN EXPOSED TO HEAT OR FLAME, OR WHEN CATALYZED BY ACIDS, ALKALIES, METAL OXIDES, METAL CHLORIDES OR SOME ACTIVE METALS.

STORAGE AND DISPOSAL

OBSERVE ALL FEDERAL, STATE AND LOCAL REGULATIONS WHEN STORING OR DISPOSING OF THIS SUBSTANCE. FOR ASSISTANCE, CONTACT THE DISTRICT DIRECTOR OF THE ENVIRONMENTAL PROTECTION AGENCY.

STORAGE

STORE IN ACCORDANCE WITH 29 CFR 1910.106.
PROTECT AGAINST PHYSICAL DAMAGE. SHOULD BE KEPT COOL, BELOW 86 F. SHOULD BE STORED OUTSIDE, AWAY FROM BUILDINGS AND OTHER MATERIALS, IN

INSULATED TANKS OR CONTAINERS, SHIELDED FROM SUN-HEAT, PROVIDED WITH COOLING FACILITIES AND PROTECTED BY A PROPERLY DESIGNED WATER-SPRAY SYSTEM. ADEQUATE DIKING AND DRAINAGE SHOULD BE PROVIDED IN TANK AREA TO CONFINE AND DISPOSE OF LIQUID IN CASE OF TANK RUPTURE. AVOID PITS AND DEPRESSIONS. INSIDE STORAGE SHOULD BE HELD TO A MINIMUM AND CONFINED TO A STANDARD FIRE-RESISTIVE FLAMMABLE LIQUIDS STORAGE ROOM, PROVIDED WITH CONTINUOUS VENTILATION AND FREE OF SOURCES OF IGNITION. DO NOT PERMIT CHLORIDES, OXIDES, ACIDS, ORGANIC BASES, ALKALI METAL HYDROXIDES, METALLIC POTASSIUM OR OTHER COMBUSTIBLE MATERIALS IN STORAGE ROOM (NFPA 49, HAZARDOUS CHEMICALS DATA, 1975).

BONDING AND GROUNDING: SUBSTANCES WITH LOW ELECTROCONDUCTIVITY, WHICH MAY BE IGNITED BY ELECTROSTATIC SPARKS, SHOULD BE STORED IN CONTAINERS WHICH MEET THE BONDING AND GROUNDING GUIDELINES SPECIFIED IN NFPA 77-1983, RECOMMENDED PRACTICE ON STATIC ELECTRICITY.

STORE AWAY FROM INCOMPATIBLE SUBSTANCES.

THRESHOLD PLANNING QUANTITY (TPQ): THE SUPERFUND AMENDMENTS AND REAUTHORIZATION ACT (SARA) SECTION 302 REQUIRES THAT EACH FACILITY WHERE ANY EXTREMELY HAZARDOUS SUBSTANCE IS PRESENT IN A QUANTITY EQUAL TO OR GREATER THAN THE TPQ ESTABLISHED FOR THAT SUBSTANCE NOTIFY THE STATE EMERGENCY RESPONSE COMMISSION FOR THE STATE IN WHICH IT IS LOCATED. SECTION 303 OF SARA REQUIRES THESE FACILITIES TO PARTICIPATE IN LOCAL EMERGENCY RESPONSE PLANNING (40 CFR 355.30).

****DISPOSAL****

DISPOSAL MUST BE IN ACCORDANCE WITH STANDARDS APPLICABLE TO GENERATORS OF HAZARDOUS WASTE, 40CFR 262. EPA HAZARDOUS WASTE NUMBER U115.

CONDITIONS TO AVOID

EXTREMELY FLAMMABLE; MAY BE IGNITED BY HEAT, SPARKS OR FLAMES. VAPORS MAY TRAVEL TO A SOURCE OF IGNITION AND FLASH BACK. CONTAINER MAY EXPLODE IN HEAT OF FIRE.

SPILL AND LEAK PROCEDURES

WATER SPILL: THE CALIFORNIA SAFE DRINKING WATER AND TOXIC ENFORCEMENT ACT OF 1986 (PROPOSITION 65) PROHIBITS CONTAMINATING ANY KNOWN SOURCE OF DRINKING WATER WITH SUBSTANCES KNOWN TO CAUSE CANCER AND/OR REPRODUCTIVE TOXICITY.

OCCUPATIONAL SPILL: SHUT OFF IGNITION SOURCES. STOP LEAK IF YOU CAN DO IT WITHOUT RISK. USE WATER SPRAY TO REDUCE VAPORS. DO NOT GET WATER INSIDE CONTAINER. FOR SMALL SPILLS, FLUSH AREA WITH FLOODING AMOUNTS OF WATER. FOR LARGER SPILLS, DIKE SPILL FOR DISPOSAL. NO SMOKING, FLAMES OR FLARES IN HAZARD AREA! KEEP UNNECESSARY PEOPLE AWAY; ISOLATE HAZARD AREA AND DENY ENTRY. EVACUATE AREA ENDANGERED BY GAS.

REPORTABLE QUANTITY (RQ): THE SUPERFUND AMENDMENTS AND REAUTHORIZATION ACT (SARA) SECTION 304 REQUIRES THAT A RELEASE EQUAL TO OR GREATER THAN THE REPORTABLE QUANTITY ESTABLISHED FOR THAT SUBSTANCE BE IMMEDIATELY REPORTED TO THE LOCAL EMERGENCY PLANNING COMMITTEE AND THE STATE EMERGENCY RESPONSE COMMISSION (40 CFR 355.40). IF THE RELEASE OF THIS SUBSTANCE IS REPORTABLE UNDER CERCLA SECTION 103, THE NATIONAL RESPONSE CENTER MUST BE NOTIFIED IMMEDIATELY AT (800) 424-8802 OR (202) 426-2675 IN THE METROPOLITAN WASHINGTON, D.C. AREA (40 CFR 302.6).

PROTECTIVE EQUIPMENT

VENTILATION: PROVIDE LOCAL EXHAUST OR PROCESS ENCLOSURE VENTILATION TO MEET PUBLISHED EXPOSURE LIMITS.

ETHYLENE OXIDE: VENTILATION SHOULD MEET THE REQUIREMENTS IN 29 CFR 1910.1047(F).

RESPIRATOR: THE FOLLOWING RESPIRATORS ARE THE MINIMUM LEGAL REQUIREMENTS AS SET FORTH BY THE OCCUPATIONAL SAFETY AND HEALTH ADMINISTRATION FOUND IN 29 CFR 1910, SUBPART Z.

MINIMUM REQUIREMENTS FOR RESPIRATORY PROTECTION FOR AIRBORNE ETHYLENE OXIDE (ETO)

CONDITION OF USE OR CONCENTRATION OF RESPIRATOR ETO (PPM) — MINIMUM REQUIRED

EQUAL TO OR LESS THAN 50 — FULL FACEPIECE RESPIRATOR WITH ETO APPROVED CANISTER, FRONT OR BACK-MOUNTED.

EQUAL TO OR LESS THAN 2000 — POSITIVE-PRESSURE SUPPLIED AIR RESPIRATOR, EQUIPPED WITH FULL FACEPIECE, HELMET OR HOOD; OR CONTINUOUS FLOW SUPPLIED-AIR RESPIRATOR (POSITIVE PRESSURE) EQUIPPED WITH FULL FACEPIECE, HELMET OR HOOD; OR CONTINUOUS FLOW SUPPLIED-AIR RESPIRATOR (POSITIVE PRESSURE) EQUIPPED WITH HELMET, HOOD OR SUIT.

CONCENTRATIONS ABOVE 2000 OR UNKNOWN CONTAINED CONCENTRATIONS (SUCH AS IN EMERGENCIES). — POSITIVE PRESSURE SELF-CONTAINED BREATHING APPARATUS EQUIPPED WITH A FULL FACEPIECE; OR POSITIVE-PRESSURE FULL FACEPIECE SUPPLIED AIR RESPIRATOR EQUIPPED WITH AN AUXILIARY POSITIVE PRESSURE SELF-CONTAINED BREATHING APPARATUS.

FIREFIGHTING — POSITIVE PRESSURE SELF-CONTAINED BREATHING APPARATUS WITH A FULL FACEPIECE.

ESCAPE — ANY RESPIRATOR DESCRIBED ABOVE.

(RESPIRATORS APPROVED FOR USE IN HIGHER CONCENTRATIONS ARE PERMITTED TO BE USED IN LOWER CONCENTRATIONS).

THE FOLLOWING RESPIRATORS AND MAXIMUM USE CONCENTRATIONS ARE RECOMMENDATIONS BY THE U.S. DEPARTMENT OF HEALTH AND HUMAN SERVICES, NIOSH POCKET GUIDE TO CHEMICAL HAZARDS OR NIOSH CRITERIA DOCUMENTS. THE SPECIFIC RESPIRATOR SELECTED MUST BE BASED ON CONTAMINATION LEVELS FOUND IN THE WORK PLACE AND BE JOINTLY APPROVED BY THE NATIONAL INSTITUTE OF OCCUPATIONAL SAFETY AND HEALTH AND THE MINE SAFETY AND HEALTH ADMINISTRATION.

ETHYLENE OXIDE (AT ANY DETECTABLE CONCENTRATION):

SELF-CONTAINED BREATHING APPARATUS WITH FULL FACEPIECE OPERATED IN PRESSURE-DEMAND OR OTHER POSITIVE PRESSURE MODE. SUPPLIED-AIR RESPIRATOR WITH FULL FACEPIECE OPERATED IN PRESSURE-DEMAND OR OTHER POSITIVE PRESSURE MODE IN COMBINATION WITH AN AUXILIARY SELF-CONTAINED BREATHING APPARATUS OPERATED IN PRESSURE-DEMAND OR OTHER POSITIVE PRESSURE MODE.

ESCAPE- AIR-PURIFYING FULL FACEPIECE RESPIRATOR (GAS MASK) WITH A CHIN-STYLE OR FRONT- OR BACK-MOUNTED CANISTER PROVIDING PROTECTION AGAINST ETHYLENE OXIDE. ESCAPE-TYPE SELF-CONTAINED BREATHING APPARATUS.

FOR FIREFIGHTING AND OTHER IMMEDIATELY DANGEROUS TO LIFE OR HEALTH CONDITIONS:

SELF-CONTAINED BREATHING APPARATUS WITH FULL FACEPIECE OPERATED IN PRESSURE-DEMAND OR OTHER POSITIVE PRESSURE MODE.

SUPPLIED-AIR RESPIRATOR WITH FULL FACEPIECE AND OPERATED IN PRESSURE-DEMAND OR OTHER POSITIVE PRESSURE MODE IN COMBINATION WITH AN AUXILIARY SELF-CONTAINED BREATHING APPARATUS OPERATED IN PRESSURE-DEMAND OR OTHER POSITIVE PRESSURE MODE.

CLOTHING: WEAR IMPERVIOUS CLOTHING TO PREVENT CONTACT WITH THE GAS FORM. IF CONTACT WITH THE LIQUIFIED GAS IS POSSIBLE, EMPLOYEE MUST WEAR APPROPRIATE PROTECTIVE CLOTHING AND EQUIPMENT TO PREVENT SKIN FROM FREEZING.

AVOID ANY POSSIBILITY OF SKIN CONTACT WITH LIQUID ETHYLENE OXIDE OR SOLUTIONS OF ETHYLENE OXIDE.

ETHYLENE OXIDE: PROTECTIVE CLOTHING SHOULD MEET THE REQUIREMENTS FOR PERSONAL PROTECTIVE EQUIPMENT IN 29 CFR 1910.1047(G).

GLOVES: FOR GAS: WEAR IMPERVIOUS GLOVES. SPECIFIC TYPE OF GLOVE MAY BE TESTED AND/OR RECOMMENDED BY MANUFACTURER.

FOR COMPRESSED LIQUID: WEAR FULL PROTECTIVE, COLD INSULATING GLOVES.

ETHYLENE OXIDE: PROTECTIVE GLOVES SHOULD MEET THE REQUIREMENTS FOR PERSONAL PROTECTIVE EQUIPMENT IN 29 CFR 1910.1047(G)(4).

EYE PROTECTION: EMPLOYEE MUST WEAR SPLASH-PROOF OR DUST-RESISTANT SAFETY GOGGLES AND A FACESHIELD TO PREVENT CONTACT WITH THIS SUBSTANCE.

EMERGENCY WASH FACILITIES: WHERE THERE IS ANY POSSIBILITY THAT AN EMPLOYEE'S EYES AND/OR SKIN MAY BE EXPOSED TO THIS SUBSTANCE, THE EMPLOYER SHOULD PROVIDE AN EYE WASH FOUNTAIN AND QUICK DRENCH SHOWER WITHIN THE IMMEDIATE WORK AREA FOR EMERGENCY USE.

ETHYLENE OXIDE: PROTECTIVE EYE EQUIPMENT SHOULD MEET THE REQUIREMENTS FOR PROTECTIVE CLOTHING AND EQUIPMENT IN 29 CFR 1910.1047(G).

AUTHORIZED BY- OCCUPATIONAL HEALTH SERVICES, INC.

CREATION DATE: 10/04/89 ***REVISION DATE:*** 07/12/90

MATERIAL SAFETY DATA SHEET

OCCUPATIONAL HEALTH SERVICES, INC.
AGRICULTURE AND PESTICIDE DIVISION
450 SEVENTH AVENUE, SUITE 2407
NEW YORK, NEW YORK 10123
1-800-445-MSDS OR (212) 967-1100

EMERGENCY CONTACT:
JOHN S. BRANSFORD, JR. (615) 292-1180

SUBSTANCE IDENTIFICATION

CAS-NUMBER 107-15-3

***SUBSTANCE:* <u>ETHYLENEDIAMINE</u>**

TRADE NAMES/SYNONYMS: 1,2-DIAMINOETHANE; 1,2-ETHYLENEDIAMINE; DIAMINOETHANE; ETHYLENDIAMINE; BETA-AMINOETHYLAMINE; DIMETHYLENEDIAMINE; 1,2-ETHANEDIAMINE; STCC 4935628; UN 1604; C2H8N2; PST09560

CHEMICAL FAMILY: AMINE, ALIPHATIC

MOLECULAR FORMULA: H2-N-C-H2-C-H2-N-H2

MOLECULAR WEIGHT: 60.10

CERCLA RATINGS (SCALE 0-3): HEALTH=3 FIRE=3 REACTIVITY=0 PERSISTENCE=0

NFPA RATINGS (SCALE 0-4): HEALTH=3 FIRE=2 REACTIVITY=0

COMPONENTS AND CONTAMINANTS

COMPONENT: ETHYLENEDIAMINE ***PERCENT:*** 100.0

CAS# 107-15-3

OTHER CONTAMINANTS: NONE.

EXPOSURE LIMITS: ETHYLENEDIAMINE: 10 PPM (25 MG/M3) OSHA TWA 10 PPM ACGIH TWA

10,000 POUNDS SARA SECTION 302 THRESHOLD PLANNING QUANTITY 5000 POUNDS SARA SECTION 304 REPORTABLE QUANTITY 5000 POUNDS CERCLA SECTION 103 REPORTABLE QUANTITY

PHYSICAL DATA

DESCRIPTION: COLORLESS TO YELLOW, VOLATILE, VISCOUS, HYGROSCOPIC LIQUID WITH AN AMMONIA LIKE ODOR. ***BOILING POINT:*** 243 F (117 C) ***MELTING POINT:*** 48 F (9 C)

SPECIFIC GRAVITY: 0.8995 ***VOLATILITY:*** 100% ***VAPOR PRESSURE:*** 10 MM @ 20 C

EVAPORATION RATE: (BUTYL ACETATE=1) 0.91 ***PH:*** 11.9 @ 25% SOLUTION

SOLUBILITY IN WATER: SOLUBLE ***ODOR THRESHOLD:*** 10 PPM ***VAPOR DENSITY:*** 2.07

SOLVENT SOLUBILITY: SOLUBLE IN ALCOHOL; SLIGHTLY SOLUBLE IN ETHER. INSOLUBLE IN BENZENE.

FIRE AND EXPLOSION DATA

FIRE AND EXPLOSION HAZARD: DANGEROUS FIRE HAZARD WHEN EXPOSED TO HEAT OR FLAME.

VAPORS ARE HEAVIER THAN AIR AND MAY TRAVEL A CONSIDERABLE DISTANCE TO A SOURCE OF IGNITION AND FLASH BACK.

VAPOR-AIR MIXTURES ARE EXPLOSIVE ABOVE FLASH POINT.

FLASH POINT: 104 F (40 C) ***UPPER EXPLOSIVE LIMIT:*** 12.0% @ 100 C

LOWER EXPLOSIVE LIMIT: 2.5% ***AUTOIGNITION TEMP.:*** 725 F (385 C)

FLAMMABILITY CLASS(OSHA): II

FIREFIGHTING MEDIA: DRY CHEMICAL, CARBON DIOXIDE, HALON, WATER SPRAY OR STANDARD FOAM (1987 EMERGENCY RESPONSE GUIDEBOOK, DOT P 5800.4).

FOR LARGER FIRES, USE WATER SPRAY, FOG OR STANDARD FOAM (1987 EMERGENCY RESPONSE GUIDEBOOK, DOT P 5800.4).

ALCOHOL FOAM (NFPA 325M, FIRE HAZARD PROPERTIES OF FLAMMABLE LIQUIDS, GASES, AND VOLATILE SOLIDS, 1984).

FIREFIGHTING: MOVE CONTAINER FROM FIRE AREA IF POSSIBLE. DO NOT GET WATER INSIDE CONTAINER. COOL FIRE-EXPOSED CONTAINERS WITH WATER FROM SIDE UNTIL WELL AFTER FIRE IS OUT. STAY AWAY FROM STORAGE TANK ENDS.

WITHDRAW IMMEDIATELY IN CASE OF RISING SOUND FROM VENTING SAFETY DEVICE OR ANY DISCOLORATION OF STORAGE TANK DUE TO FIRE (1987 EMERGENCY RESPONSE GUIDEBOOK, DOT P 5800.4, GUIDE PAGE 29).

EXTINGUISH ONLY IF FLOW CAN BE STOPPED. USE FLOODING QUANTITIES OF WATER AS A FOG; SOLID STREAMS MAY BE INEFFECTIVE. COOL FIRE-EXPOSED CONTAINERS WITH FLOODING AMOUNTS OF WATER APPLIED FROM AS FAR A DISTANCE AS POSSIBLE. AVOID BREATHING VAPORS; KEEP UPWIND.

TRANSPORTATION DATA

DEPARTMENT OF TRANSPORTATION HAZARD CLASSIFICATION 49 CFR 172.101: CORROSIVE MATERIAL

DEPARTMENT OF TRANSPORTATION LABELING REQUIREMENTS 49 CFR 172.101 AND SUBPART E: CORROSIVE

DEPARTMENT OF TRANSPORTATION PACKAGING REQUIREMENTS: 49 CFR 173.245 EXCEPTIONS: 49 CFR 173.244

TOXICITY

ETHYLENEDIAMINE: IRRITATION DATA: 450 MG OPEN SKIN-RABBIT MODERATE; 10 MG/24 HOURS OPEN SKIN-RABBIT SEVERE; 675 UG EYE-RABBIT SEVERE; 750 UG/24 HOURS EYE-RABBIT SEVERE. TOXICITY DATA: 200 PPM INHALATION-HUMAN TCLO; 300 MG/M3 INHALATION-MOUSE LC50; 4000 PPM/8 HOURS INHALATION-RAT LC100 (AMIHBC); 4000 PPM/8 HOURS INHALATION-RAT LCLO; 730 MG/KG SKIN-RABBIT LD50; 500 MG/KG ORAL-RAT LD50; 470 MG/KG ORAL-GUINEA PIG LD50; 500 MG/KG SUBCUTANEOUS-RABBIT LDLO; 300 MG/KG SUBCUTANEOUS-RAT LD50; 100 MG/KG INTRAVENOUS-DOG LDLO; 76 MG/KG 76 MG/KG INTRAPERITONEAL-RAT LD50; 200 MG/KG INTRAPERITONEAL-MOUSE LD50; MUTAGENIC DATA (RTECS); REPRODUCTIVE EFFECTS DATA (RTECS). CARCINOGEN STATUS: NONE. LOCAL EFFECTS: CORROSIVE- INHALATION, SKIN, EYE, INGESTION. ACUTE TOXICITY LEVEL: HIGHLY TOXIC BY INHALATION; TOXIC BY DERMAL ABSORPTION AND INGESTION. TARGET EFFECTS: SENSITIZER- RESPIRATORY, SKIN. POISONING MAY AFFECT THE LUNGS, LIVER, AND KIDNEYS. AT INCREASED RISK FROM EXPOSURE: PERSONS WITH PREEXISTING ASTHMA OR ALLERGIES. ADDITIONAL DATA: CROSS-SENSITIZATION MAY OCCUR WITH OTHER ETHYLENEAMINES, SOME POLYAMINES, AND WITH HYDRAZINE AND PIPERAZINE ANTIHISTAMINES.

HEALTH EFFECTS AND FIRST AID

INHALATION: ETHYLENEDIAMINE: CORROSIVE/SENSITIZER/HIGHLY TOXIC. 2000 PPM IMMEDIATELY DANGEROUS TO LIFE OR HEALTH. **<u>ACUTE EXPOSURE</u>-** HUMAN EXPOSURE TO 200 PPM FOR 5-10 SECONDS CAUSED FACIAL TINGLING AND SLIGHT NASAL IRRITATION; 400 PPM CAUSED INTOLERABLE NASAL IRRITATION. OTHER SYMPTOMS MAY INCLUDE RESPIRATORY TRACT IRRITATION, COUGH, DYSPNEA, VOMITING, NAUSEA AND PULMONARY EDEMA. PULMONARY SENSITIZATION, MANIFESTED BY ASTHMATIC BREATHING, MAY OCCUR IN PREVIOUSLY EXPOSED PERSONS. RATS EXPOSED TO 4000 PPM FOR 8 HOURS DIED FROM KIDNEY DAMAGE. **<u>CHRONIC EXPOSURE</u>-** PROLONGED OR REPEATED EXPOSURE TO NON-IRRITATING LEVELS MAY RESULT IN PULMONARY SENSITIZATION WITH BRONCHIAL ASTHMA. CHRONIC BRONCHITIS HAS ALSO BEEN REPORTED. SYMPTOMS MAY INCLUDE EOSINOPHILIA, WHEEZING, CHEST TIGHTNESS, COUGHING DYSPNEA, SNEEZING, NASAL DISCHARGE, SWEATING, HEADACHES, MALAISE, AND TACHYCARDIA. EXPOSURE TO 484 PPM FOR 20 DAYS CAUSED DEPILATION AND LUNG, KIDNEY AND LIVER DAMAGE, AND DEATH IN RATS.

FIRST AID- REMOVE FROM EXPOSURE AREA TO FRESH AIR IMMEDIATELY. IF BREATHING HAS STOPPED, GIVE ARTIFICIAL RESPIRATION. MAINTAIN AIRWAY AND BLOOD PRESSURE AND ADMINISTER OXYGEN IF AVAILABLE. KEEP AFFECTED PERSON WARM AND AT REST. TREAT SYMPTOMATICALLY AND SUPPORTIVELY. ADMINISTRATION OF OXYGEN SHOULD BE PERFORMED BY QUALIFIED PERSONNEL. GET MEDICAL ATTENTION IMMEDIATELY.

SKIN CONTACT: ETHYLENEDIAMINE: CORROSIVE/SENSITIZER/TOXIC. **<u>ACUTE EXPOSURE</u>-** DIRECT CONTACT WITH AQUEOUS SOLUTIONS MAY CAUSE SEVERE IRRITATION; UNDILUTED LIQUID MAY CAUSE BURNS. BLISTERING MAY OCCUR AND BE PARTLY DUE TO SENSITIZATION IN PREVIOUSLY EXPOSED PERSONS. ANIMAL STUDIES INDICATE FATAL AMOUNTS MAY BE ABSORBED THROUGH INTACT SKIN. SKIN ABSORPTION IS ENHANCED BY TISSUE DAMAGE. **<u>CHRONIC EXPOSURE</u>-** REPEATED OR PROLONGED EXPOSURE MAY CAUSE DERMATITIS DUE EITHER TO IRRITATION OR SENSITIZATION. SENSITIZATION IS MORE LIKELY TO OCCUR WHEN THE SKIN IS DAMAGED.

FIRST AID- REMOVE CONTAMINATED CLOTHING AND SHOES IMMEDIATELY. WASH AFFECTED AREA WITH SOAP OR MILD DETERGENT AND LARGE AMOUNTS OF WATER UNTIL NO EVIDENCE OF CHEMICAL REMAINS (AT LEAST 15-20 MINUTES). IN CASE OF CHEMICAL BURNS, COVER AREA WITH STERILE, DRY DRESSING. BANDAGE SECURELY, BUT NOT TOO TIGHTLY. GET MEDICAL ATTENTION IMMEDIATELY.

EYE CONTACT: ETHYLENEDIAMINE: CORROSIVE. **<u>ACUTE EXPOSURE</u>-** LOW VAPOR CONCENTRATIONS MAY CAUSE SOME BLURRING OF VISION AND HALOES AROUND OBJECTS. HIGH CONCENTRATIONS MAY CAUSE ACUTE PAIN AND SEVERE IRRITATION. BURNS, CORNEAL DESTRUCTION, AND BLINDNESS MAY RESULTED FROM THE LIQUID. AN AQUEOUS 15% SOLUTION CAUSED SERIOUS CORNEAL DAMAGE TO RABBIT EYES; A 5% SOLUTION CAUSED PARTIAL CORNEAL OPACITY. **<u>CHRONIC EXPOSURE</u>-** EFFECTS DEPEND ON CONCENTRATION AND DURATION OF EXPOSURE. REPEATED OR PROLONGED CONTACT WITH CORROSIVE SUBSTANCES MAY RESULT IN CONJUNCTIVITIS OR EFFECTS AS IN ACUTE EXPOSURE.

FIRST AID- WASH EYES IMMEDIATELY WITH LARGE AMOUNTS OF WATER, OCCASIONALLY LIFTING UPPER AND LOWER LIDS, UNTIL NO EVIDENCE OF CHEMICAL REMAINS (AT LEAST 15-20 MINUTES). CONTINUE IRRIGATING WITH NORMAL SALINE UNTIL THE PH HAS RETURNED TO NORMAL (30-60 MINUTES). COVER WITH STERILE BANDAGES. GET MEDICAL ATTENTION IMMEDIATELY.

INGESTION: ETHYLENEDIAMINE: CORROSIVE/TOXIC. **<u>ACUTE EXPOSURE</u>-** INGESTION MAY CAUSE BURNS OF THE MOUTH AND THROAT, ABDOMINAL PAIN, NAUSEA, AND VOMITING. THE REPORTED LETHAL DOSE IN RATS WAS 500 MG/KG; THE SYMPTOMS WERE NOT REPORTED. **<u>CHRONIC EXPOSURE</u>-** THERAPEUTIC USE HAS RESULTED IN SEVERE EXFOLIATIVE DERMATITIS. REPRODUCTIVE EFFECTS HAVE BEEN REPORTED IN ANIMALS. DEPENDING ON THE CONCENTRATIONS, REPEATED INGESTION OF CORROSIVE SUBSTANCES MAY RESULT IN EFFECTS AS WITH ACUTE INGESTION.

FIRST AID: TREAT SYMPTOMATICALLY AND SUPPORTIVELY. IF PERSON IS CONSCIOUS AND ABLE TO SWALLOW, GIVE LARGE AMOUNTS OF WATER OR MILK TO DILUTE SUBSTANCE. GET MEDICAL ATTENTION IMMEDIATELY. GASTRIC LAVAGE PERFORMED BY QUALIFIED MEDICAL PERSONNEL MIGHT BE ADVISABLE IF THERE ARE NO SIGNS OF PERFORATION FROM THE INGESTION OF A CORROSIVE SUBSTANCE. IF VOMITING OCCURS, KEEP HEAD BELOW HIPS TO HELP PREVENT ASPIRATION.

ANTIDOTE: NO SPECIFIC ANTIDOTE. TREAT SYMPTOMATICALLY AND SUPPORTIVELY.

REACTIVITY

REACTIVITY: STABLE UNDER NORMAL TEMPERATURES AND PRESSURES.

INCOMPATIBILITIES: ETHYLENEDIAMINE: ACETIC ACID: TEMPERATURE AND PRESSURE INCREASE IN A CLOSED CONTAINER. ACETIC ANHYDRIDE: TEMPERATURE AND PRESSURE INCREASE IN A CLOSED CONTAINER.

ACIDS (STRONG): FIRE AND EXPLOSION HAZARD. ACROLEIN: TEMPERATURE AND PRESSURE INCREASE IN A CLOSED CONTAINER. ACRYLIC ACID: TEMPERATURE AND PRESSURE INCREASE IN A CLOSED CONTAINER. ACRYLONITRILE: TEMPERATURE AND PRESSURE INCREASE IN A CLOSED CONTAINER. ALLYL CHLORIDE: TEMPERATURE AND PRESSURE INCREASE IN A CLOSED CONTAINER. ALUMINUM: MAY BE CORROSIVE. CARBON DISULFIDE: TEMPERATURE AND PRESSURE INCREASE IN A CLOSED CONTAINER. CELLULOSE NITRATE: IGNITES SPONTANEOUSLY. CHLORINATED HYDROCARBONS: VIOLENT REACTION. CHLOROSULFONIC ACID: TEMPERATURE AND PRESSURE INCREASE IN A CLOSED CONTAINER. DIISOPROPYLPEROXYDICARBONATE: SPONTANEOUS DECOMPOSITION. EPICHLOROHYDRIN: TEMPERATURE AND PRESSURE INCREASE IN A CLOSED CONTAINER. ETHYLENE CHLOROHYDRIN: TEMPERATURE AND PRESSURE INCREASE IN A CLOSED CONTAINER. HYDROCHLORIC ACID: TEMPERATURE AND PRESSURE INCREASE IN A CLOSED CONTAINER. MESITYL OXIDE: TEMPERATURE AND PRESSURE INCREASE IN A CLOSED CONTAINER. NITRIC ACID: TEMPERATURE AND PRESSURE INCREASE IN A CLOSED CONTAINER. NITROMETHANE: INCREASED SENSITIVITY TOWARD DETONATION. OLEUM: TEMPERATURE AND PRESSURE INCREASE IN A CLOSED CONTAINER. OXIDIZERS (STRONG): FIRE AND EXPLOSION HAZARD. BETA-PROPIOLACTONE: TEMPERATURE AND PRESSURE INCREASE IN A CLOSED CONTAINER. SILVER PERCHLORATE: EXPLOSIVE REACTION. SULFURIC ACID: TEMPERATURE AND PRESSURE INCREASE IN A CLOSED CONTAINER. VINYL ACETATE: TEMPERATURE AND PRESSURE INCREASE IN A CLOSED CONTAINER. ZINC: MAY BE CORROSIVE.

DECOMPOSITION: THERMAL DECOMPOSITION PRODUCTS MAY INCLUDE CORROSIVE FUMES OF AMMONIA, AND TOXIC OXIDES OF NITROGEN AND CARBON.

POLYMERIZATION: HAZARDOUS POLYMERIZATION HAS NOT BEEN REPORTED TO OCCUR UNDER NORMAL TEMPERATURES AND PRESSURES.

STORAGE AND DISPOSAL

OBSERVE ALL FEDERAL, STATE AND LOCAL REGULATIONS WHEN STORING OR DISPOSING OF THIS SUBSTANCE. FOR ASSISTANCE, CONTACT THE DISTRICT DIRECTOR OF THE ENVIRONMENTAL PROTECTION AGENCY.

STORAGE

STORE IN ACCORDANCE WITH 29 CFR 1910.106.

BONDING AND GROUNDING: SUBSTANCES WITH LOW ELECTROCONDUCTIVITY, WHICH MAY BE IGNITED BY ELECTROSTATIC SPARKS, SHOULD BE STORED IN CONTAINERS WHICH MEET THE BONDING AND GROUNDING GUIDELINES SPECIFIED IN NFPA 77-1983, RECOMMENDED PRACTICE ON STATIC ELECTRICITY.

STORE AWAY FROM INCOMPATIBLE SUBSTANCES.

THRESHOLD PLANNING QUANTITY (TPQ): THE SUPERFUND AMENDMENTS AND REAUTHORIZATION ACT (SARA) SECTION 302 REQUIRES THAT EACH FACILITY WHERE ANY EXTREMELY HAZARDOUS SUBSTANCE IS PRESENT IN A QUANTITY EQUAL TO OR GREATER THAN THE TPQ ESTABLISHED FOR THAT SUBSTANCE NOTIFY THE STATE EMERGENCY RESPONSE COMMISSION FOR THE STATE IN WHICH IT IS LOCATED. SECTION 303 OF SARA REQUIRES THESE FACILITIES TO PARTICIPATE IN LOCAL EMERGENCY RESPONSE PLANNING (40 CFR 355.30).

KEEP IN A TIGHTLY CLOSED CONTAINER. STORE IN A COOL, DRY, VENTILATED AREA.

PROTECT FROM PHYSICAL DAMAGE. STORE IN A COOL, DRY, WELL VENTILATED AREA AWAY FROM ANY AREA WHERE FIRE HAZARD MAY BE ACUTE. OUTSIDE OR DETACHED STORAGE IS PREFERRED. INSIDE STORAGE SHOULD BE IN A STANDARD FLAMMABLE LIQUIDS STORAGE ROOM. SEPARATE FROM OXIDIZING MATERIALS. COPPER OR COPPER-BEARING ALLOYS SHOULD NOT BE USED FOR STORAGE OR HANDLING (NFPA 49, HAZARDOUS CHEMICALS DATA, 1975).

DISPOSAL

DISPOSAL MUST BE IN ACCORDANCE WITH STANDARDS APPLICABLE TO GENERATORS OF HAZARDOUS WASTE, 40 CFR 262. EPA HAZARDOUS WASTE NUMBER D001. 100 POUND CERCLA SECTION 103 REPORTABLE QUANTITY.

CONDITIONS TO AVOID

AVOID CONTACT WITH HEAT, SPARKS, FLAMES OR OTHER IGNITION SOURCES. VAPORS MAY BE EXPLOSIVE. MATERIAL IS CORROSIVE; AVOID CONTACT WITH SKIN OR EYES. DO NOT ALLOW CONTAMINATION OF WATER SOURCES.

SPILL AND LEAK PROCEDURES

SOIL SPILL: DIG A HOLDING AREA SUCH AS A PIT, POND OR LAGOON TO CONTAIN SPILL AND DIKE SURFACE FLOW USING BARRIER OF SOIL, SANDBAGS, FOAMED POLYURETHANE OR FOAMED CONCRETE. ABSORB LIQUID MASS WITH FLY ASH OR CEMENT POWDER.

USE SODIUM BISULFATE (NA-H-SO4) TO NEUTRALIZE SPILL.

AIR SPILL: APPLY WATER SPRAY TO KNOCK DOWN AND REDUCE VAPORS. KNOCK-DOWN WATER IS CORROSIVE AND TOXIC AND SHOULD BE DIKED FOR CONTAINMENT.

WATER SPILL: LIMIT SPILL MOTION AND DISPERSION WITH NATURAL BARRIERS OR OIL SPILL CONTROL BOOMS.

APPLY DETERGENTS, SOAPS, ALCOHOLS OR ANOTHER SURFACE ACTIVE AGENT.

APPLY UNIVERSAL GELLING AGENT TO IMMOBILIZE TRAPPED SPILL AND INCREASE EFFICIENCY OF REMOVAL.

ADD SODIUM BISULFITE.

IF DISSOLVED, AT A CONCENTRATION OF 10 PPM OR GREATER, APPLY ACTIVATED CARBON AT TEN TIMES THE AMOUNT THAT HAS BEEN SPILLED.

USE MECHANICAL DREDGES OR LIFTS TO EXTRACT IMMOBILIZED MASSES OF POLLUTION AND PRECIPITATES.

OCCUPATIONAL SPILL: SHUT OFF IGNITION SOURCES. DO NOT TOUCH SPILLED MATERIAL. STOP LEAK IF YOU CAN DO IT WITHOUT RISK. USE WATER SPRAY TO REDUCE VAPORS. DO NOT GET WATER INSIDE CONTAINER. FOR SMALL SPILLS, TAKE UP WITH SAND OR OTHER ABSORBENT MATERIAL AND PLACE INTO CONTAINERS FOR LATER DISPOSAL. FOR LARGER SPILLS, DIKE FAR AHEAD OF SPILL FOR LATER DISPOSAL. NO SMOKING, FLAMES OR FLARES IN HAZARD AREA. KEEP UNNECESSARY PEOPLE AWAY; ISOLATE HAZARD AREA AND DENY ENTRY.

REPORTABLE QUANTITY (RQ): 5000 POUNDS THE SUPERFUND AMENDMENTS AND REAUTHORIZATION ACT (SARA) SECTION 304 REQUIRES THAT A RELEASE EQUAL TO OR GREATER THAN THE REPORTABLE QUANTITY FOR THIS SUBSTANCE BE IMMEDIATELY REPORTED TO THE LOCAL EMERGENCY PLANNING COMMITTEE AND THE STATE EMERGENCY RESPONSE COMMISSION (40 CFR 355.40). IF THE RELEASE OF THIS SUBSTANCE IS REPORTABLE UNDER CERCLA SECTION 103, THE NATIONAL RESPONSE CENTER MUST BE NOTIFIED IMMEDIATELY AT (800) 424-8802 OR (202) 426-2675 IN THE METROPOLITAN WASHINGTON, D.C. AREA (40 CFR 302.6).

PROTECTIVE EQUIPMENT

VENTILATION: PROVIDE LOCAL EXHAUST OR PROCESS ENCLOSURE VENTILATION TO MEET PUBLISHED EXPOSURE LIMITS.

RESPIRATOR: THE FOLLOWING RESPIRATORS AND MAXIMUM USE CONCENTRATIONS ARE RECOMMENDATIONS BY THE U.S. DEPARTMENT OF HEALTH AND HUMAN SERVICES, NIOSH POCKET GUIDE TO CHEMICAL HAZARDS; NIOSH CRITERIA DOCUMENTS OR BY THE U.S. DEPARTMENT OF LABOR, 29 CFR 1910 SUBPART Z. THE SPECIFIC RESPIRATOR SELECTED MUST BE BASED ON CONTAMINATION LEVELS FOUND IN THE WORK PLACE, MUST NOT EXCEED THE WORKING LIMITS OF THE RESPIRATOR AND BE JOINTLY APPROVED BY THE NATIONAL INSTITUTE FOR OCCUPATIONAL SAFETY AND HEALTH AND THE MINE SAFETY AND HEALTH ADMINISTRATION (NIOSH-MSHA).

ETHYLENEDIAMINE:

250 PPM- ANY SUPPLIED-AIR RESPIRATOR OPERATED IN A CONTINUOUS FLOW MODE. ANY POWERED AIR-PURIFYING RESPIRATOR WITH CARTRIDGE(S) PROVIDING PROTECTION AGAINST ETHYLENEDIAMINE.

500 PPM- ANY CHEMICAL CARTRIDGE RESPIRATOR WITH A FULL FACEPIECE AND CARTRIDGE(S) PROVIDING PROTECTION AGAINST ETHYLENEDIAMINE.. ANY AIR-PURIFYING FULL FACEPIECE RESPIRATOR (GAS MASK) WITH A CHIN-STYLE OR FRONT- OR BACK- MOUNTED CANISTER PROVIDING PROTECTION AGAINST ETHYLENEDIAMINE. ANY SELF-CONTAINED BREATHING APPARATUS WITH A FULL FACEPIECE. ANY SUPPLIED-AIR RESPIRATOR WITH A FULL FACEPIECE.

2000 PPM- ANY SUPPLIED-AIR RESPIRATOR WITH A FULL FACEPIECE AND OPERATED IN PRESSURE-DEMAND OR OTHER POSITIVE PRESSURE MODE. ESCAPE-ANY AIR-PURIFYING FULL FACEPIECE RESPIRATOR (GAS MASK) WITH A CHIN-SYYLE OR FRONT- OR BACK-MOUNTED CANISTER PROVIDING PROTECTION AGAINST ETHYLENEDIAMINE. ANY APPROPRIATE ESCAPE-TYPE SELF-CONTAINED BREATHING APPARATUS.

FOR FIREFIGHTING AND OTHER IMMEDIATELY DANGEROUS TO LIFE OR HEALTH CONDITIONS:

SELF-CONTAINED BREATHING APPARATUS WITH FULL FACEPIECE OPERATED IN PRESSURE-DEMAND OR OTHER POSITIVE PRESSURE MODE.

SUPPLIED-AIR RESPIRATOR WITH FULL FACEPIECE AND OPERATED IN PRESSURE-DEMAND OR OTHER POSITIVE PRESSURE MODE IN COMBINATION WITH AN AUXILIARY SELF-CONTAINED BREATHING APPARATUS OPERATED IN PRESSURE-DEMAND OR OTHER POSITIVE PRESSURE MODE.

CLOTHING: EMPLOYEE MUST WEAR APPROPRIATE PROTECTIVE (IMPERVIOUS) CLOTHING AND EQUIPMENT TO PREVENT ANY POSSIBILITY OF SKIN CONTACT WITH THIS SUBSTANCE.

GLOVES: EMPLOYEE MUST WEAR APPROPRIATE PROTECTIVE GLOVES TO PREVENT CONTACT WITH THIS SUBSTANCE.

EYE PROTECTION: EMPLOYEE MUST WEAR SPLASH-PROOF OR DUST-RESISTANT SAFETY GOGGLES AND A FACESHIELD TO PREVENT CONTACT WITH THIS SUBSTANCE.

EMERGENCY WASH FACILITIES: WHERE THERE IS ANY POSSIBILITY THAT AN EMPLOYEE'S EYES AND/OR SKIN MAY BE EXPOSED TO THIS SUBSTANCE, THE EMPLOYER SHOULD PROVIDE AN EYE WASH FOUNTAIN AND QUICK DRENCH SHOWER WITHIN THE IMMEDIATE WORK AREA FOR EMERGENCY USE.

AUTHORIZED BY- OCCUPATIONAL HEALTH SERVICES, INC.

CREATION DATE: 11/16/89 ***REVISION DATE:*** 05/29/90

MATERIAL SAFETY DATA SHEET

OCCUPATIONAL HEALTH SERVICES, INC.
AGRICULTURE AND PESTICIDE DIVISION
450 SEVENTH AVENUE, SUITE 2407
NEW YORK, NEW YORK 10123
1-800-445-MSDS OR (212) 967-1100

EMERGENCY CONTACT:
JOHN S. BRANSFORD, JR. (615) 292-1180

SUBSTANCE IDENTIFICATION

CAS-NUMBER 60-00-4

SUBSTANCE: ETHYLENEDIAMINETETRAACETIC ACID

TRADE NAMES/SYNONYMS: GLYCINE, N,N'-1,2-ETHANEDIYLBIS(N-(CARBOXYMETHYL)-; N,N'-1,2-ETHANEDIYLBIS(N-(CARBOXYMETHYL)GLYCINE; ACETIC ACID, (ETHYLENEDINITRILO)TETRA-; (ETHYLENEDINITRILO)TETRAACETIC ACID; CELON ATH; CHEELOX; CHEMCOLOX 340; CLEWAT; EDETIC ACID; EDTA; EDTA (CHELATING AGENT); ETHYLENEDINITRILOTETRAACETIC ACID; HAVIDOTE; METAQUEST; NULLAPON; PERMA KLEER ACID; SEQUESTRENE AA; VERSENE ACID; C10H16N2O8; PST09570

CHEMICAL FAMILY: AMINE, ALIPHATIC
CARBOXYLIC ACID

MOLECULAR FORMULA: ((H-O2-C-C-H2)2-N-C-H2)2

MOLECULAR WEIGHT: 292.25

CERCLA RATINGS (SCALE 0-3): HEALTH=3 FIRE=1 REACTIVITY=0 PERSISTENCE=1

NFPA RATINGS (SCALE 0-4): HEALTH=U FIRE=1 REACTIVITY=0

COMPONENTS AND CONTAMINANTS

COMPONENT: ETHYLENEDIAMINETETRAACETIC ACID ***PERCENT:*** 100.0
CAS# 60-00-4

OTHER CONTAMINANTS: NONE

EXPOSURE LIMITS: NO OCCUPATIONAL EXPOSURE LIMITS ESTABLISHED BY OSHA, ACGIH, OR NIOSH.
ETHYLENEDIAMINETETRAACETIC ACID: 5000 POUNDS CERCLA SECTION 103 REPORTABLE QUANTITY

PHYSICAL DATA

DESCRIPTION: ODORLESS, COLORLESS OR WHITE CRYSTALLINE SOLID.

MELTING POINT: 473 F (245 C) (DECOMPOSES) ***SPECIFIC GRAVITY:*** 0.86 @ 20 C

SOLUBILITY IN WATER: 0.05% @ 25 C

SOLVENT SOLUBILITY: SOLUBLE IN DILUTE AMMONIUM HYDROXIDE; INSOLUBLE IN ORGANIC SOLVENTS.

FIRE AND EXPLOSION DATA

FIRE AND EXPLOSION HAZARD: SLIGHT FIRE HAZARD WHEN EXPOSED TO HEAT OR FLAME.
DUST-AIR MIXTURES MAY IGNITE OR EXPLODE.

FIREFIGHTING MEDIA: DRY CHEMICAL, CARBON DIOXIDE, HALON, WATER SPRAY OR STANDARD FOAM (1987 EMERGENCY RESPONSE GUIDEBOOK, DOT P 5800.4).
FOR LARGER FIRES, USE WATER SPRAY, FOG OR STANDARD FOAM (1987 EMERGENCY RESPONSE GUIDEBOOK, DOT P 5800.4).

FIREFIGHTING: MOVE CONTAINER FROM FIRE AREA IF POSSIBLE. DO NOT SCATTER SPILLED MATERIAL WITH HIGH PRESSURE WATER STREAMS. DIKE FIRE CONTROL WATER FOR LATER DISPOSAL (1987 EMERGENCY RESPONSE GUIDEBOOK, DOT P 5800.4, GUIDE PAGE 31).
USE AGENTS SUITABLE FOR TYPE OF SURROUNDING FIRE. AVOID BREATHING CORROSIVE DUSTS OR VAPORS, KEEP UPWIND.

TOXICITY

ETHYLENEDIAMINETETRAACETIC ACID: TOXICITY DATA: 2000 MG/KG ORAL-RAT LD50 (DPIRDU); 397 MG/KG INTRAPERITONEAL-RAT LD50; 250 MG/KG INTRAPERITONEAL-MOUSE LD50; MUTAGENIC DATA (RTECS); REPRODUCTIVE EFFECTS DATA (RTECS). CARCINOGEN STATUS: NONE. LOCAL EFFECTS: IRRITANT-INHALATION, SKIN, EYES. ACUTE TOXICITY LEVEL: MODERATELY TOXIC BY INGESTION. TARGET EFFECTS: POISONING MAY AFFECT THE KIDNEYS. AT INCREASED RISK FROM EXPOSURE: PERSONS WITH RENAL OR HEART DISEASE; A HISTORY OF SEIZURES OR INTRACRANIAL LESIONS; POTASSIUM DEFICIENCY; OR INSULIN-DEPENDENT DIABETES. ADDITIONAL DATA: PARENTERAL ADMINISTRATION OF EDTA OR ITS SALTS IN HIGH DOSES MAY CAUSE SEVERE RENAL LESIONS AND TUBULAR NECROSIS, INTERNAL HEMORRHAGE, LIFE-THREATENING HYPOCALCEMIA, AND DEATH. PROLONGED PARENTERAL ADMINISTRATION MAY LEAD TO ELECTROLYTE IMBALANCE AND CARDIAC ARRHYTHMIAS.

HEALTH EFFECTS AND FIRST AID

INHALATION: ETHYLENEDIAMINETETRAACETIC ACID: IRRITANT. **ACUTE EXPOSURE-** INHALATION MAY CAUSE MUCOUS MEMBRANE IRRITATION WITH SORE THROAT AND COUGHING. **CHRONIC EXPOSURE-** NO DATA AVAILABLE.

FIRST AID- REMOVE FROM EXPOSURE AREA TO FRESH AIR IMMEDIATELY. IF BREATHING HAS STOPPED, PERFORM ARTIFICIAL RESPIRATION. KEEP PERSON WARM AND AT REST. TREAT SYMPTOMATICALLY AND SUPPORTIVELY. GET MEDICAL ATTENTION IMMEDIATELY.

SKIN CONTACT: ETHYLENEDIAMINETETRAACETIC ACID: IRRITANT. **ACUTE EXPOSURE-** CONTACT MAY CAUSE IRRITATION WITH REDNESS AND PAIN. **CHRONIC EXPOSURE-** REPEATED OR PROLONGED CONTACT WITH MOIST SKIN MAY CAUSE MODERATE IRRITATION AND POSSIBLY A MILD BURN.

FIRST AID- REMOVE CONTAMINATED CLOTHING AND SHOES IMMEDIATELY. WASH AFFECTED AREA WITH SOAP OR MILD DETERGENT AND LARGE AMOUNTS OF WATER UNTIL NO EVIDENCE OF CHEMICAL REMAINS (APPROXIMATELY 15-20 MINUTES). GET MEDICAL ATTENTION IMMEDIATELY.

EYE CONTACT: ETHYLENEDIAMINETETRAACETIC ACID: IRRITANT. **ACUTE EXPOSURE-** CONTACT MAY CAUSE IRRITATION WITH REDNESS AND PAIN. MAY CAUSE SOME TRANSIENT CORNEAL INJURY OR BURNS. **CHRONIC EXPOSURE-** REPEATED OR PROLONGED CONTACT WITH IRRITANTS MAY CAUSE CONJUNCTIVITIS.

FIRST AID- WASH EYES IMMEDIATELY WITH LARGE AMOUNTS OF WATER OR NORMAL SALINE, OCCASIONALLY LIFTING UPPER AND LOWER LIDS, UNTIL NO EVIDENCE OF CHEMICAL REMAINS (APPROXIMATELY 15-20 MINUTES). GET MEDICAL ATTENTION IMMEDIATELY.

INGESTION: ETHYLENEDIAMINETETRAACETIC ACID: **ACUTE EXPOSURE-** ALTHOUGH POORLY ABSORBED FROM THE GASTROINTESTINAL TRACT, IF SUFFICIENT AMOUNTS ARE INGESTED SYSTEMIC TOXICITY MAY RESULT. MAY CHELATE LEAD, MAGNESIUM, ZINC OR TRACE METALS IF THEY ARE PRESENT IN THE INTESTINE, POSSIBLY CAUSING THEIR INCREASED ABSORPTION AND THEREBY INCREASING TOTAL BODY STORES OF THESE METALS. **CHRONIC EXPOSURE-** REPRODUCTIVE EFFECTS HAVE BEEN REPORTED IN ANIMAL STUDIES.

FIRST AID- TREAT SYMPTOMATICALLY AND SUPPORTIVELY. GET MEDICAL ATTENTION IMMEDIATELY. IF VOMITING OCCURS, KEEP HEAD LOWER THAN HIPS TO PREVENT ASPIRATION.

ANTIDOTE: NO SPECIFIC ANTIDOTE. TREAT SYMPTOMATICALLY AND SUPPORTIVELY.

REACTIVITY

REACTIVITY: STABLE UNDER NORMAL TEMPERATURES AND PRESSURES.

INCOMPATIBILITIES: ETHYLENEDIAMINETETRAACETIC ACID: ALUMINUM: LIBERATES FLAMMABLE HYDROGEN GAS. COPPER AND ALLOYS: MAY CORRODE. NICKEL: MAY CORRODE. OXIDIZERS (STRONG): FIRE AND EXPLOSION HAZARD.

DECOMPOSITION: THERMAL DECOMPOSITION PRODUCTS MAY INCLUDE TOXIC OXIDES OF CARBON AND NITROGEN.

POLYMERIZATION: HAZARDOUS POLYMERIZATION HAS NOT BEEN REPORTED TO OCCUR UNDER NORMAL TEMPERATURES AND PRESSURES.

STORAGE AND DISPOSAL

OBSERVE ALL FEDERAL, STATE AND LOCAL REGULATIONS WHEN STORING OR DISPOSING OF THIS SUBSTANCE. FOR ASSISTANCE, CONTACT THE DISTRICT DIRECTOR OF THE ENVIRONMENTAL PROTECTION AGENCY.

****STORAGE****

STORE AWAY FROM INCOMPATIBLE SUBSTANCES.
STORE IN A TIGHTLY CLOSED CONTAINER.

CONDITIONS TO AVOID

MAY BURN BUT DOES NOT IGNITE READILY. AVOID CONTACT WITH STRONG OXIDIZERS, EXCESSIVE HEAT, SPARKS, OR OPEN FLAME.
PREVENT DISPERSION OF DUST IN AIR.

SPILL AND LEAK PROCEDURES

SOIL SPILL: DIG A PIT, POND, LAGOON OR HOLDING AREA TO CONTAIN LIQUID OR SOLID MATERIAL. COVER SOLIDS WITH A PLASTIC SHEET TO PREVENT DISSOLVING IN RAIN OR FIREFIGHTING WATER.

WATER SPILL: NEUTRALIZE WITH CAUSTIC SODA.
ADD SUITABLE AGENT TO NEUTRALIZE SPILLED MATERIAL TO PH-7.
USE MECHANICAL DREDGES OR LIFTS TO EXTRACT IMMOBILIZED MASSES OF POLLUTION AND PRECIPITATES.

OCCUPATIONAL SPILL: SWEEP UP AND PLACE IN SUITABLE CLEAN, DRY CONTAINERS FOR RECLAMATION OR LATER DISPOSAL. DO NOT FLUSH SPILLED MATERIAL INTO SEWER. KEEP UNNECESSARY PEOPLE AWAY.
REPORTABLE QUANTITY (RQ): 5000 POUNDS THE SUPERFUND AMENDMENTS AND REAUTHORIZATION ACT (SARA) SECTION 304 REQUIRES THAT A RELEASE EQUAL TO OR GREATER THAN THE REPORTABLE QUANTITY FOR THIS SUBSTANCE BE IMMEDIATELY REPORTED TO THE LOCAL EMERGENCY PLANNING COMMITTEE AND THE STATE EMERGENCY RESPONSE COMMISSION (40 CFR 355.40). IF THE RELEASE OF THIS SUBSTANCE IS REPORTABLE UNDER CERCLA SECTION 103, THE NATIONAL RESPONSE CENTER MUST BE NOTIFIED IMMEDIATELY AT (800) 424-8802 OR (202) 426-2675 IN THE METROPOLITAN WASHINGTON, D.C. AREA (40 CFR 302.6).

PROTECTIVE EQUIPMENT

VENTILATION: PROVIDE LOCAL EXHAUST OR GENERAL DILUTION VENTILATION SYSTEM.

RESPIRATOR: THE FOLLOWING RESPIRATORS ARE RECOMMENDED BASED ON INFORMATION FOUND IN THE PHYSICAL DATA, TOXICITY AND HEALTH EFFECTS SECTIONS. THEY ARE RANKED IN ORDER FROM MINIMUM TO MAXIMUM RESPIRATORY PROTECTION. THE SPECIFIC RESPIRATOR SELECTED MUST BE BASED ON CONTAMINATION LEVELS FOUND IN THE WORK PLACE, MUST NOT EXCEED THE WORKING LIMITS OF THE RESPIRATOR AND BE JOINTLY APPROVED BY THE NATIONAL INSTITUTE FOR OCCUPATIONAL SAFETY AND HEALTH AND THE MINE SAFETY AND HEALTH ADMINISTRATION (NIOSH-MSHA).
DUST AND MIST RESPIRATOR WITH A FULL FACEPIECE.
AIR-PURIFYING FULL FACEPIECE RESPIRATOR WITH A HIGH-EFFICIENCY PARTICULATE FILTER.
POWERED AIR-PURIFYING RESPIRATOR WITH A TIGHT-FITTING FACEPIECE AND HIGH-EFFICIENCY PARTICULATE FILTER.
TYPE 'C' SUPPLIED-AIR RESPIRATOR WITH A FULL FACEPIECE OPERATED IN PRESSURE-DEMAND OR OTHER POSITIVE PRESSURE MODE OR WITH A FULL FACEPIECE, HELMET OR HOOD OPERATED IN CONTINUOUS-FLOW MODE.
SELF-CONTAINED BREATHING APPARATUS WITH A FULL FACEPIECE OPERATED IN PRESSURE-DEMAND OR OTHER POSITIVE PRESSURE MODE.
FOR FIREFIGHTING AND OTHER IMMEDIATELY DANGEROUS TO LIFE OR HEALTH CONDITIONS:
SELF-CONTAINED BREATHING APPARATUS WITH FULL FACEPIECE OPERATED IN PRESSURE-DEMAND OR OTHER POSITIVE PRESSURE MODE.
SUPPLIED-AIR RESPIRATOR WITH FULL FACEPIECE AND OPERATED IN PRESSURE-DEMAND OR OTHER POSITIVE PRESSURE MODE IN COMBINATION WITH AN AUXILIARY SELF-CONTAINED BREATHING APPARATUS OPERATED IN PRESSURE-DEMAND OR OTHER POSITIVE PRESSURE MODE.

CLOTHING: EMPLOYEE MUST WEAR APPROPRIATE PROTECTIVE (IMPERVIOUS) CLOTHING AND EQUIPMENT TO PREVENT REPEATED OR PROLONGED SKIN CONTACT WITH THIS SUBSTANCE.

GLOVES: EMPLOYEE MUST WEAR APPROPRIATE PROTECTIVE GLOVES TO PREVENT CONTACT WITH THIS SUBSTANCE.

EYE PROTECTION: EMPLOYEE MUST WEAR SPLASH-PROOF OR DUST-RESISTANT SAFETY GOGGLES TO PREVENT EYE CONTACT WITH THIS SUBSTANCE.
EMERGENCY EYE WASH: WHERE THERE IS ANY POSSIBILITY THAT AN EMPLOYEE'S EYES MAY BE EXPOSED TO THIS SUBSTANCE, THE EMPLOYER SHOULD PROVIDE AN EYE WASH FOUNTAIN WITHIN THE IMMEDIATE WORK AREA FOR EMERGENCY USE.

AUTHORIZED BY- OCCUPATIONAL HEALTH SERVICES, INC.
CREATION DATE: 11/16/89 ***REVISION DATE:*** 05/31/90

MATERIAL SAFETY DATA SHEET

OCCUPATIONAL HEALTH SERVICES, INC.
AGRICULTURE AND PESTICIDE DIVISION
450 SEVENTH AVENUE, SUITE 2407
NEW YORK, NEW YORK 10123

EMERGENCY CONTACT:
JOHN S. BRANSFORD, JR. (615) 292-1180
1-800-445-MSDS OR (212) 967-1100

SUBSTANCE IDENTIFICATION

CAS-NUMBER 107-27-7

SUBSTANCE: **ETHYLMERCURIC CHLORIDE**

TRADE NAMES/SYNONYMS: MERCURY, CHLOROETHYL-; CHLOROETHYLMERCURY; CRYPTODINE; ETHYLMERCURY CHLORIDE; ETHYL MERCURIC CHLORIDE; ETHYL MERCURY CHLORIDE; C2H5CLHG; PST09620

CHEMICAL FAMILY: ORGANOMETALLIC
SALT

MOLECULAR FORMULA: C-H3-C-H2-HG-CL

MOLECULAR WEIGHT: 265.11

CERCLA RATINGS (SCALE 0-3): HEALTH=3 FIRE=1 REACTIVITY=0 PERSISTENCE=3

NFPA RATINGS (SCALE 0-4): HEALTH=4 FIRE=1 REACTIVITY=0

COMPONENTS AND CONTAMINANTS

COMPONENT: ETHYLMERCURIC CHLORIDE ***PERCENT:*** 100.0
CAS# 107-27-7

OTHER CONTAMINANTS: NONE

EXPOSURE LIMITS: ORGANO(ALKYL)MERCURY COMPOUNDS, AS HG: 0.01 MG/M3 OSHA TWA (SKIN); 0.03 MG/M3 OSHA STEL 0.01 MG/M3 ACGIH TWA (SKIN); 0.03 MG/M3 ACGIH STEL
SUBJECT TO SARA SECTION 313 ANNUAL TOXIC CHEMICAL RELEASE REPORTING
SUBJECT TO CALIFORNIA PROPOSITION 65 CANCER AND/OR REPRODUCTIVE TOXICITY WARNING AND RELEASE REQUIREMENTS- (JULY 1, 1990)

PHYSICAL DATA

DESCRIPTION: WHITE, SILVERY IRIDESCENT LEAFLETS. ***MELTING POINT:*** 379 F (193 C)

SPECIFIC GRAVITY: 3.482 ***VAPOR PRESSURE:*** <1 MMHG @ 20 C

SOLUBILITY IN WATER: 1.4 PPM ***VAPOR DENSITY:*** 9.2

SOLVENT SOLUBILITY: SOLUBLE IN CHLOROFORM, HOT ALCOHOL; SLIGHTLY SOLUBLE IN ETHER.

FIRE AND EXPLOSION DATA

FIRE AND EXPLOSION HAZARD: SLIGHT FIRE HAZARD WHEN EXPOSED TO HEAT OR FLAME.

FIREFIGHTING MEDIA: DRY CHEMICAL, CARBON DIOXIDE, HALON, WATER SPRAY OR STANDARD FOAM (1987 EMERGENCY RESPONSE GUIDEBOOK, DOT P 5800.4).
FOR LARGER FIRES, USE WATER SPRAY, FOG OR STANDARD FOAM (1987 EMERGENCY RESPONSE GUIDEBOOK, DOT P 5800.4).

FIREFIGHTING: MOVE CONTAINERS FROM FIRE AREA IF POSSIBLE (1987 EMERGENCY RESPONSE GUIDEBOOK, DOT P 5800.4, GUIDE PAGE 53).
EXTINGUISH USING AGENT SUITABLE FOR TYPE OF SURROUNDING FIRE. AVOID BREATHING VAPORS AND DUSTS. KEEP UPWIND.

TRANSPORTATION DATA

DEPARTMENT OF TRANSPORTATION HAZARD CLASSIFICATION 49 CFR 172.101: POISON B
DEPARTMENT OF TRANSPORTATION LABELING REQUIREMENTS 49 CFR 172.101 AND SUBPART E: POISON
DEPARTMENT OF TRANSPORTATION PACKAGING REQUIREMENTS: 49 CFR 173.365 EXCEPTIONS: 49 CFR 173.364

TOXICITY

ETHYLMERCURIC CHLORIDE: TOXICITY DATA: 5 MG/M3 INHALATION-MOUSE LC50; 200 MG/KG SKIN-RAT LD50; 40 MG/KG ORAL-RAT LD50; 56 MG/KG ORAL-MOUSE LD50; 66 MG/KG SUBCUTANEOUS-RAT LD50; 16 MG/KG INTRAPERITONEAL-MOUSE LD50; 18 MG/KG UNREPORTED-MAMMAL LD50; MUTAGENIC DATA (RTECS); REPRODUCTIVE EFFECTS DATA (RTECS). CARCINOGEN STATUS: NONE. LOCAL EFFECTS: IRRITANT- INHALATION, SKIN, EYE. ACUTE TOXICITY LEVEL: HIGHLY TOXIC BY INHALATION, DERMAL ABSORPTION AND INGESTION. TARGET EFFECTS: NEUROTOXIN; TERATOGEN. POISONING MAY ALSO AFFECT THE BRAIN, SKIN, LIVER, KIDNEY AND THE GASTROINTESTINAL AND CARDIOVASCULAR SYSTEMS.* AT INCREASED RISK FROM EXPOSURE: PERSONS WITH PRE-EXISTING DISORDERS OF THE CENTRAL NERVOUS SYSTEM, KIDNEYS, EYES OR SKIN.*
* MAY BE BASED ON INFORMATION ON ALKYL MERCURY COMPOUNDS.

HEALTH EFFECTS AND FIRST AID

INHALATION: ETHYLMERCURIC CHLORIDE: IRRITANT/HIGHLY TOXIC. SEE INFORMATION ON ALKYL MERCURY COMPOUNDS.
ALKYL MERCURY COMPOUNDS: NEUROTOXIN. 10 MG(HG)/M3 IMMEDIATELY DANGEROUS TO LIFE OR HEALTH. **ACUTE EXPOSURE**- DUST OR VAPORS MAY BE

IRRITATING TO THE RESPIRATORY TRACT. SYSTEMIC POISONING AND DEATH, AS DESCRIBED IN CHRONIC INHALATION, MAY OCCUR. **CHRONIC EXPOSURE-** REPEATED OR PROLONGED EXPOSURE MAY CAUSE RESPIRATORY TRACT IRRITATION. SYSTEMIC SYMPTOMS, OFTEN INSIDIOUS, MAY BEGIN AFTER A LATENCY PERIOD, DEPENDING ON THE SEVERITY OF EXPOSURE, RANGING FROM WEEKS TO YEARS AFTER THE INITIAL EXPOSURE. THE ONSET MAY BEGIN WITH FATIGUE, HEADACHE, PARESTHESIAS OF THE TONGUE, AROUND THE LIPS, AND OF THE HANDS AND FEET, ATAXIA OF THE ARMS AND LEGS, FINE TREMORS IN THE HANDS, ARMS, AND FEET WHICH MAY BECOME CONVULSIVE, ATHETOSIS, ARTHRALGIA, AND AN UNSTEADY GAIT WHICH IS SPASTIC IN NATURE. VISUAL EFFECTS MAY INCLUDE TUNNEL VISION, SCOTOMATA, AND BLINDNESS WITH OPTIC NERVE ATROPHY. SLURRED SPEECH WITH DIFFICULT PRONUNCIATION AND IMPAIRED HEARING ARE ALSO COMMON. GASTROINTESTINAL DISTURBANCES MAY OCCUR WITH NAUSEA, VOMITING, DIARRHEA OR CONSTIPATION, COLIC, EPIGASTRIC PAIN, CATARRHAL GINGIVITIS, BLUE LINE ON THE GUM, AND APHTHOUS STOMATITIS. EMOTIONAL INSTABILITY, MEMORY LOSS, LOSS OF LIBIDO, DEPRESSION, HALLUCINATIONS, IRRITABILITY, ANXIETY, CONFUSION, INSOMNIA, EXCITATION, AND BOUTS OF GROANING, MOANING, SHOUTING, OR CRYING MAY OCCUR. MENTAL DETERIORATION MAY PROGRESS TO STUPOR AND COMA. OTHER EFFECTS MAY INCLUDE DIZZINESS, LACRIMATION, HYPERSALIVATION, ECZEMA, PRURITIS, EXFOLIATIVE DERMATITIS, RENAL DAMAGE, INCONTINENCE, POLYURIA, OLIGURIA, POLYDYPSIA, DEHYDRATION, WEIGHT LOSS, LIVER DAMAGE, BRADYCARDIA AND OTHER SIGNS OF CARDIAC INVOLVEMENT. WITH SEVERE INTOXICATION, CLONIC SEIZURES, PARALYSIS, COMA AND DEATH MAY OCCUR. THE DURATION OF ILLNESS IN FATAL CASES HAS RANGED FROM 1 MONTH TO 15 YEARS, WITH INFECTION, ASPIRATION PNEUMONIA OR INANITION AS THE CAUSE OF DEATH IN PROTRACTED CASES. IN MILD POISONING, SYMPTOMS MAY ALSO PERSIST FOR YEARS. REPRODUCTIVE EFFECTS MAY OCCUR AS DESCRIBED IN CHRONIC INGESTION.

FIRST AID- REMOVE FROM EXPOSURE AREA TO FRESH AIR IMMEDIATELY. IF BREATHING HAS STOPPED, PERFORM ARTIFICIAL RESPIRATION. KEEP PERSON WARM AND AT REST. TREAT SYMPTOMATICALLY AND SUPPORTIVELY. GET MEDICAL ATTENTION IMMEDIATELY.

SKIN CONTACT: ETHYLMERCURIC CHLORIDE: IRRITANT/HIGHLY TOXIC. SEE INFORMATION ON ALKYL MERCURY COMPOUNDS.

ALKYL MERCURY COMPOUNDS: NEUROTOXIN. **ACUTE EXPOSURE-** SYMPTOMS OF SKIN CONTACT MAY BE DELAYED FOR SEVERAL HOURS AND THEN BEGIN WITH A SENSATION OF WARMTH AND REDNESS WHICH MAY PROGRESS TO BURNS AND BLISTERING. HEALING MAY TAKE SEVERAL WEEKS. SYSTEMIC POISONING AND DEATH, AS DESCRIBED IN CHRONIC INHALATION, MAY OCCUR DUE TO SKIN ABSORPTION. **CHRONIC EXPOSURE-** REPEATED OR PROLONGED CONTACT MAY RESULT IN DERMATITIS OR EFFECTS AS DESCRIBED IN ACUTE EXPOSURE. SKIN SENSITIZATION HAS BEEN REPORTED FROM CONTACT WITH SOME ALKYL MERCURY COMPOUNDS.

FIRST AID- REMOVE CONTAMINATED CLOTHING AND SHOES IMMEDIATELY. WASH AFFECTED AREA WITH SOAP OR MILD DETERGENT AND LARGE AMOUNTS OF WATER UNTIL NO EVIDENCE OF CHEMICAL REMAINS (AT LEAST 15-20 MINUTES). IN CASE OF CHEMICAL BURNS, COVER AREA WITH STERILE, DRY DRESSING. BANDAGE SECURELY, BUT NOT TOO TIGHTLY. GET MEDICAL ATTENTION IMMEDIATELY.

EYE CONTACT: ETHYLMERCURIC CHLORIDE: IRRITANT. SEE INFORMATION OF ALKYL MERCURY COMPOUNDS.

ALKYL MERCURY COMPOUNDS: **ACUTE EXPOSURE-** DUSTS OR VAPORS MAY CAUSE IRRITATION. **CHRONIC EXPOSURE-** NO DATA AVAILABLE.

FIRST AID- WASH EYES IMMEDIATELY WITH LARGE AMOUNTS OF WATER OR NORMAL SALINE, OCCASIONALLY LIFTING UPPER AND LOWER LIDS, UNTIL NO EVIDENCE OF CHEMICAL REMAINS (APPROXIMATELY 15-20 MINUTES). GET MEDICAL ATTENTION IMMEDIATELY.

INGESTION: ETHYLMERCURIC CHLORIDE: HIGHLY TOXIC. RATS GIVEN ABOUT 5.6 MG/KG/DAY SHOWED TYPICAL SIGNS OF POISONING IN 34-38 DAYS. REPRODUCTIVE EFFECTS HAVE BEEN REPORTED IN ANIMALS. SEE INFORMATION ON ALKYL MERCURY COMPOUNDS.

ALKYL MERCURY COMPOUNDS: NEUROTOXIN/TERATOGEN. **ACUTE EXPOSURE-** IF A TOXIC DOSE HAS BEEN ABSORBED AND RETAINED FOR A PERIOD OF TIME, SYSTEMIC POISONING AND DEATH AS DESCRIBED IN CHRONIC INHALATION MAY OCCUR. **CHRONIC EXPOSURE-** REPEATED OR PROLONGED EXPOSURE MAY RESULT IN POISONING AS DESCRIBED IN CHRONIC INHALATION. WOMEN EXPOSED TO SOME ALKYL MERCURY COMPOUNDS WHILE PREGNANT OR PERHAPS SEVERAL YEARS BEFORE PREGNANCY HAVE HAD CHILDREN WITH IMPAIRMENT OF MOTOR AND MENTAL DEVELOPMENT OF VARIOUS DEGREES WITH FRETFULLNESS, IRRITABILITY, EXCESSIVE CRYING, DECREASED BIRTH WEIGHT AND MUSCLE TONE, CEREBRAL PALSY, DEAFNESS, BLINDNESS, MICROCEPHALY, AND MENTAL RETARDATION. POSTNATAL EXPOSURE THROUGH BREAST MILK MAY ALSO OCCUR.

FIRST AID- IF THE PERSON IS CONSCIOUS AND NOT CONVULSING, INDUCE EMESIS BY GIVING SYRUP OF IPECAC (KEEPING THE HEAD BELOW THE HIPS TO PREVENT ASPIRATION), FOLLOWED BY WATER. REPEAT IN 20 MINUTES IF NOT EFFECTIVE INITIALLY. IN PATIENTS WITH DEPRESSED RESPIRATION OR IF EMESIS IS NOT PRODUCED, PERFORM GASTRIC LAVAGE CAUTIOUSLY. FOLLOW WITH A CATHARTIC. TREAT SYMPTOMATICALLY AND SUPPORTIVELY. GASTRIC LAVAGE SHOULD BE PERFORMED BY QUALIFIED MEDICAL PERSONNEL. GET MEDICAL ATTENTION IMMEDIATELY.

ANTIDOTE: THE FOLLOWING ANTIDOTE HAS BEEN RECOMMENDED. HOWEVER, THE DECISION AS TO WHETHER THE SEVERITY OF POISONING REQUIRES ADMINISTRATION OF ANY ANTIDOTE AND ACTUAL DOSE REQUIRED SHOULD BE MADE BY QUALIFIED MEDICAL PERSONNEL.

POISONING FROM ORGANIC MERCURY COMPOUNDS: GIVE N-ACETYL-D,L-PENICILLAMINE (OR IF NOT AVAILABLE D-PENICILLAMINE) BY MOUTH, 250 MG, 4 TIMES DAILY FOR 5-10 DAYS. DIMERCAPROL IS LESS EFFECTIVE AND MAY BE CONTRAINDICATED (GOSSELIN, CLINICAL TOXICOLOGY OF COMMERCIAL PRODUCTS, 5TH EDITION). ANTIDOTE SHOULD BE ADMINISTERED BY QUALIFIED MEDICAL PERSONNEL.

REACTIVITY

REACTIVITY: STABLE UNDER NORMAL TEMPERATURES AND PRESSURES.

INCOMPATIBILITIES: ETHYLMERCURIC CHLORIDE: OXIDIZERS (STRONG): FIRE AND EXPLOSION HAZARD. SEE ALSO MERCURY SALTS.

MERCURY SALTS: ACETYLENE: FORMS SHOCK-SENSITIVE ACETYLIDES. BUTYNEDIOL + ACIDS: VIOLENT DECOMPOSITION. NITROMETHANE: FORMS EXPLOSIVE COMPOUND.

DECOMPOSITION: THERMAL DECOMPOSITION PRODUCTS MAY INCLUDE TOXIC AND CORROSIVE FUMES OF CHLORIDES, AND TOXIC MERCURY VAPORS.

POLYMERIZATION: HAZARDOUS POLYMERIZATION HAS NOT BEEN REPORTED TO OCCUR UNDER NORMAL TEMPERATURES AND PRESSURES.

STORAGE AND DISPOSAL

OBSERVE ALL FEDERAL, STATE AND LOCAL REGULATIONS WHEN STORING OR DISPOSING OF THIS SUBSTANCE. FOR ASSISTANCE, CONTACT THE DISTRICT DIRECTOR OF THE ENVIRONMENTAL PROTECTION AGENCY.

STORAGE

STORE IN ACCORDANCE WITH 40 CFR 165 RECOMMENDED PROCEDURES FOR THE DISPOSAL AND STORAGE OF PESTICIDES AND PESTICIDE CONTAINERS. STORE AWAY FROM INCOMPATIBLE SUBSTANCES.

DISPOSAL

DISPOSAL MUST BE IN ACCORDANCE WITH 40 CFR 165 RECOMMENDED PROCEDURES FOR THE DISPOSAL AND STORAGE OF PESTICIDES AND PESTICIDE CONTAINERS.

MERCURY - REGULATORY LEVEL: 0.2 MG/L MATERIALS WHICH CONTAIN THE ABOVE SUBSTANCE AT OR ABOVE THE REGULATORY LEVEL MEET THE EPA CHARACTERISTIC OF TOXICITY, AND MUST BE DISPOSED OF IN ACCORDANCE WITH 40 CFR PART 262. EPA HAZARDOUS WASTE NUMBER D009.

CONDITIONS TO AVOID

MAY BURN BUT DOES NOT IGNITE READILY.

SPILL AND LEAK PROCEDURES

WATER SPILL: THE CALIFORNIA SAFE DRINKING WATER AND TOXIC ENFORCEMENT ACT OF 1986 (PROPOSITION 65) PROHIBITS CONTAMINATING ANY KNOWN SOURCE OF DRINKING WATER WITH SUBSTANCES KNOWN TO CAUSE CANCER AND/OR REPRODUCTIVE TOXICITY.

OCCUPATIONAL SPILL: DO NOT TOUCH SPILLED MATERIAL. STOP LEAK IF YOU CAN DO IT WITHOUT RISK. FOR SMALL SPILLS, TAKE UP WITH SAND OR OTHER ABSORBENT MATERIAL AND PLACE INTO CONTAINERS FOR LATER DISPOSAL. FOR SMALL DRY SPILLS, WITH A CLEAN SHOVEL PLACE MATERIAL INTO CLEAN, DRY CONTAINER AND COVER. MOVE CONTAINERS FROM SPILL AREA. FOR LARGER SPILLS, DIKE FAR AHEAD OF SPILL FOR LATER DISPOSAL. KEEP UNNECESSARY PEOPLE AWAY. ISOLATE HAZARD AREA AND DENY ENTRY.

PROTECTIVE EQUIPMENT

VENTILATION: PROCESS ENCLOSURE RECOMMENDED TO MEET PUBLISHED EXPOSURE LIMITS.

RESPIRATOR: THE FOLLOWING RESPIRATORS AND MAXIMUM USE CONCENTRATIONS ARE RECOMMENDATIONS BY THE U.S. DEPARTMENT OF HEALTH AND HUMAN SERVICES, NIOSH POCKET GUIDE TO CHEMICAL HAZARDS; NIOSH CRITERIA DOCUMENTS OR BY THE U.S. DEPARTMENT OF LABOR, 29 CFR 1910 SUBPART Z. THE SPECIFIC RESPIRATOR SELECTED MUST BE BASED ON CONTAMINATION LEVELS FOUND IN THE WORK PLACE, MUST NOT EXCEED THE WORKING LIMITS OF THE RESPIRATOR AND BE JOINTLY APPROVED BY THE NATIONAL INSTITUTE FOR OCCUPATIONAL SAFETY AND HEALTH AND THE MINE SAFETY AND HEALTH

ADMINISTRATION (NIOSH-MSHA).
MERCURY, (ORGANO) ALKYL COMPOUNDS (AS HG):
0.1 MG/M3- ANY SUPPLIED-AIR RESPIRATOR. ANY SELF-CONTAINED BREATHING APPARATUS.
0.25 MG/M3- ANY SUPPLIED-AIR RESPIRATOR OPERATED IN A CONTINUOUS FLOW MODE.
0.5 MG/M3- ANY SUPPLIED-AIR RESPIRATOR WITH A FULL FACEPIECE. ANY SELF-CONTAINED BREATHING APPARATUS WITH A FULL FACEPIECE. ANY SUPPLIED-AIR RESPIRATOR WITH A TIGHT-FITTING FACEPIECE OPERATED IN A CONTINUOUS FLOW MODE.
10 MG/M3- ANY SUPPLIED-AIR RESPIRATOR WITH A HALF-MASK AND OPERATED IN A PRESSURE-DEMAND OR OTHER POSITIVE PRESSURE MODE.
ESCAPE- ANY APPROPRIATE ESCAPE-TYPE SELF-CONTAINED BREATHING APPARATUS.
FOR FIREFIGHTING AND OTHER IMMEDIATELY DANGEROUS TO LIFE OR HEALTH CONDITIONS:
SELF-CONTAINED BREATHING APPARATUS WITH FULL FACEPIECE OPERATED IN PRESSURE-DEMAND OR OTHER POSITIVE PRESSURE MODE.
SUPPLIED-AIR RESPIRATOR WITH FULL FACEPIECE AND OPERATED IN PRESSURE-DEMAND OR OTHER POSITIVE PRESSURE MODE IN COMBINATION WITH AN AUXILIARY SELF-CONTAINED BREATHING APPARATUS OPERATED IN PRESSURE-DEMAND OR OTHER POSITIVE PRESSURE MODE.

CLOTHING: EMPLOYEE MUST WEAR APPROPRIATE PROTECTIVE (IMPERVIOUS) CLOTHING AND EQUIPMENT TO PREVENT ANY POSSIBILITY OF SKIN CONTACT WITH THIS SUBSTANCE.

GLOVES: EMPLOYEE MUST WEAR APPROPRIATE PROTECTIVE GLOVES TO PREVENT CONTACT WITH THIS SUBSTANCE.

EYE PROTECTION: EMPLOYEE MUST WEAR SPLASH-PROOF OR DUST-RESISTANT SAFETY GOGGLES AND A FACESHIELD TO PREVENT CONTACT WITH THIS SUBSTANCE.
EMERGENCY WASH FACILITIES: WHERE THERE IS ANY POSSIBILITY THAT AN EMPLOYEE'S EYES AND/OR SKIN MAY BE EXPOSED TO THIS SUBSTANCE, THE EMPLOYER SHOULD PROVIDE AN EYE WASH FOUNTAIN AND QUICK DRENCH SHOWER WITHIN THE IMMEDIATE WORK AREA FOR EMERGENCY USE.

AUTHORIZED BY- OCCUPATIONAL HEALTH SERVICES, INC.
CREATION DATE: 10/04/89 ***REVISION DATE:*** 07/13/90

MATERIAL SAFETY DATA SHEET

OCCUPATIONAL HEALTH SERVICES, INC.
AGRICULTURE AND PESTICIDE DIVISION
450 SEVENTH AVENUE, SUITE 2407
NEW YORK, NEW YORK 10123
1-800-445-MSDS OR (212) 967-1100

EMERGENCY CONTACT:
JOHN S. BRANSFORD, JR. (615) 292-1180

SUBSTANCE IDENTIFICATION

SUBSTANCE: **ETRIMFOS OXYGEN ANALOG**

TRADE NAMES/SYNONYMS: ETRIMPHOS OXON; C10H17N2O5P; PST09666

CHEMICAL FAMILY: ORGANOPHOSPHATE

MOLECULAR FORMULA: C10-H17-N2-O5-P

MOLECULAR WEIGHT: 276.23

CERCLA RATINGS (SCALE 0-3): HEALTH = U FIRE = U REACTIVITY = 0 PERSISTENCE = 0

NFPA RATINGS (SCALE 0-4): HEALTH = U FIRE = U REACTIVITY = 0

COMPONENTS AND CONTAMINANTS

COMPONENT: ETRIMFOS OXYGEN ANALOG ***PERCENT:*** 100.0

OTHER CONTAMINANTS: NONE

EXPOSURE LIMITS: NO OCCUPATIONAL EXPOSURE LIMITS ESTABLISHED BY OSHA, ACGIH, OR NIOSH.

PHYSICAL DATA

DESCRIPTION: CLEAR LIQUID. ***BOILING POINT:*** NOT AVAILABLE

SPECIFIC GRAVITY: NOT AVAILABLE ***VAPOR PRESSURE:*** NOT AVAILABLE

SOLUBILITY IN WATER: NOT AVAILABLE

FIRE AND EXPLOSION DATA

FIRE AND EXPLOSION HAZARD: UNKNOWN FIRE AND EXPLOSION HAZARD.

FLASH POINT: NOT AVAILABLE

FIREFIGHTING MEDIA: DRY CHEMICAL, CARBON DIOXIDE, HALON, WATER SPRAY OR STANDARD FOAM (1987 EMERGENCY RESPONSE GUIDEBOOK, DOT P 5800.4). FOR LARGER FIRES, USE WATER SPRAY, FOG OR STANDARD FOAM (1987 EMERGENCY RESPONSE GUIDEBOOK, DOT P 5800.4). ***FIREFIGHTING:*** MOVE CONTAINER FROM FIRE AREA IF POSSIBLE. DIKE FIRE CONTROL WATER FOR LATER DISPOSAL; DO NOT SCATTER THE MATERIAL. COOL FIRE-EXPOSED CONTAINERS WITH WATER FROM SIDE UNTIL WELL AFTER FIRE IS OUT. STAY AWAY FROM STORAGE TANK ENDS. WITHDRAW IMMEDIATELY IN CASE OF RISING SOUND FROM VENTING SAFETY DEVICE OR ANY DISCOLORATION OF STORAGE TANK DUE TO FIRE (1987 EMERGENCY RESPONSE GUIDEBOOK, DOT P 5800.4, GUIDE PAGE 28). EXTINGUISH ONLY IF FLOW CAN BE STOPPED. USE FLOODING AMOUNTS OF WATER AS A FOG; SOLID STREAMS MAY BE INEFFECTIVE. COOL CONTAINERS WITH FLOODING AMOUNTS OF WATER FROM AS FAR A DISTANCE AS POSSIBLE. AVOID BREATHING POISONOUS VAPORS, KEEP UPWIND.

TOXICITY

ETRIMFOS OXYGEN ANALOG: CARCINOGEN STATUS: NONE. ACUTE TOXICITY LEVEL: NO DATA AVAILABLE. TARGET EFFECTS: CHOLINESTERASE INHIBITOR. POISONING MAY AFFECT THE NERVOUS SYSTEM.* AT INCREASED RISK FROM EXPOSURE: PERSONS WITH RESPIRATORY AILMENTS, RECENT EXPOSURE TO CHOLINESTERASE INHIBITORS OR IMPAIRED CHOLINESTERASE PRODUCTION, OR LIVER MALFUNCTION.* ADDITIONAL DATA: MAY CROSS THE PLACENTA. HIGH ENVIRONMENTAL TEMPERATURES OR EXPOSURE OF THE CHEMICAL TO VISIBLE OR ULTRAVIOLET LIGHT MAY ENHANCE THE TOXICITY. INTERACTIONS WITH MEDICATIONS MAY OCCUR.*
* MAY BE BASED ON GENERAL INFORMATION ON ORGANOPHOSPHATES.

HEALTH EFFECTS AND FIRST AID

INHALATION: ETRIMFOS OXYGEN ANALOG: NO SPECIFIC DATA AVAILABLE. THE PARENT COMPOUND, ETRIMFOS, IS AN ORGANOPHOPHATE CHOLINESTERASE INHIBITOR. SEE INFORMATION ON ORGANOPHOSPHATES.
ORGANOPHOSPHATES: CHOLINESTERASE INHIBITOR. **ACUTE EXPOSURE-** WHEN INHALED, THE FIRST EFFECTS OF CHOLINESTERASE INHIBITORS ARE USUALLY RESPIRATORY AND MAY INCLUDE NASAL HYPEREMIA AND WATERY DISCHARGE, COUGH, CHEST DISCOMFORT, DYSPNEA, AND WHEEZING DUE TO INCREASED BRONCHIAL SECRETIONS AND BRONCHOCONSTRICTION. IF SUFFICIENT AMOUNTS ARE ABSORBED, OTHER SYSTEMIC EFFECTS MAY BEGIN WITHIN A FEW MINUTES OR BE DELAYED FOR UP TO 12 HOURS. SYMPTOMS MAY INCLUDE PALLOR, NAUSEA, VOMITING, DIARRHEA, ABDOMINAL CRAMPS, HEADACHE, DIZZINESS, OCULAR PAIN, BLURRED VISION, MIOSIS OR IN SOME CASES, ESPECIALLY INITIALLY, MYDRIASIS, LACRIMATION, SALIVATION, SWEATING, AND CONFUSION. OTHER REPORTED CENTRAL NERVOUS SYSTEM OR NEUROMUSCULAR EFFECTS MAY INCLUDE ATAXIA, SLURRED SPEECH, AREFLEXIA, WEAKNESS, FATIGUE, FASCICULATIONS, TWITCHING, TREMORS POSSIBLY OF THE TONGUE AND EYELIDS, AND EVENTUALLY PARALYSIS OF THE EXTREMITIES AND POSSIBLY OF THE RESPIRATORY MUSCLES. IN SEVERE CASES THERE MAY ALSO BE INVOLUNTARY DEFECATION AND URINATION, CYANOSIS, PSYCHOSIS, HYPERGLYCEMIA, ACUTE PANCREATITIS, CARDIAC IRREGULARITIES, PULMONARY EDEMA, UNCONSCIOUSNESS, CONVULSIONS, AND COMA. DEATH IS PRIMARILY DUE TO RESPIRATORY FAILURE, ALTHOUGH CARDIOVASCULAR EFFECTS INCLUDING CARDIAC ARREST MAY ALSO BE IMPLICATED. LONG TERM SEQUELAE ARE RARE BUT MAY INCLUDE NEUROPSYCHIATRIC DISORDERS AND MYOPATHY WITH MUSCLE TENDERNESS. SOME ORGANOPHOSPHATES MAY CAUSE A DELAYED NEUROPATHY BEGINNING 1-4 WEEKS AFTER AN ACUTE EXPOSURE WHICH MAY OR MAY NOT HAVE CAUSED ACUTE CHOLINERGIC EFFECTS. NUMBNESS, TINGLING, WEAKNESS AND CRAMPING BEGINNING SYMMETRICALLY IN THE LOWER LIMBS MAY PROGRESS TO ATAXIA AND PARALYSIS. IN SEVERE CASES, UPPER LIMB INVOLVEMENT IS POSSIBLE AND FLACCID PARALYSIS MAY PROGRESS TO SPASTIC PARALYSIS WITH EXAGGERATED REFLEXES. IMPROVEMENT MAY OCCUR OVER MONTHS TO YEARS, BUT SOME RESIDUAL IMPAIRMENT USUALLY REMAINS.
CHRONIC EXPOSURE- REPEATED OR PROLONGED EXPOSURE MAY RESULT IN THE EFFECTS OF ACUTE EXPOSURE INCLUDING THE DELAYED NEUROPATHY. OTHER EFFECTS REPORTED IN WORKERS REPEATEDLY EXPOSED INCLUDE IMPAIRED MEMORY AND CONCENTRATION, ACUTE PSYCHOSIS, SEVERE DEPRESSIONS, IRRITABILTY, CONFUSION, APATHY, EMOTIONAL LABILITY, SOCIAL WITHDRAWAL, CONFUSION, HEADACHE, SPEECH DIFFICULTIES, DELAYED REACTION TIMES, SPATIAL DISORIENTATION, NIGHTMARES, SLEEPWALKING, AND DROWSINESS OR INSOMNIA. AN INFLUENZA-LIKE CONDITION WITH HEADACHE, NAUSEA, WEAKNESS, ANOREXIA AND MALAISE HAS ALSO BEEN REPORTED.

FIRST AID- REMOVE FROM EXPOSURE AREA TO FRESH AIR IMMEDIATELY. IF BREATHING HAS STOPPED, GIVE ARTIFICIAL RESPIRATION. MAINTAIN AIRWAY AND BLOOD PRESSURE AND ADMINISTER OXYGEN IF AVAILABLE. KEEP AFFECTED PERSON WARM AND AT REST. TREAT SYMPTOMATICALLY AND SUPPORTIVELY. ADMINISTRATION OF OXYGEN SHOULD BE PERFORMED BY QUALIFIED PERSONNEL. GET MEDICAL ATTENTION IMMEDIATELY.

SKIN CONTACT: ETRIMFOS OXYGEN ANALOG: NO SPECIFIC DATA AVAILABLE. THE PARENT COMPOUND, ETRIMFOS, IS AN ORGANOPHOSPHATE CHOLINESTERASE

INHIBITOR. SEE INFORMATION ON ORGANOPHOSPHATES.
ORGANOPHOSPHATES: CHOLINESTERASE INHIBITOR. **ACUTE EXPOSURE-** LOCALIZED SWEATING AND FASCICULATIONS MAY OCCUR AT THE SITE OF CONTACT. IF SUFFICIENT AMOUNTS ARE ABSORBED, OTHER EFFECTS OF CHOLINESTERASE INHIBITION AS DESCRIBED IN ACUTE INHALATION MAY OCCUR. SYMPTOMS MAY BE DELAYED 2-3 HOURS, BUT USUALLY NO MORE THAN 12 HOURS. THE RATE OF ABSORPTION IS INCREASED BY THE PRESENCE OF DERMATITIS OR HIGH AMBIENT TEMPERATURES. DELAYED NEUROPATHY IS ALSO POSSIBLE. **CHRONIC EXPOSURE-** REPEATED OR PROLONGED EXPOSURE MAY CAUSE EFFECTS AS DESCRIBED IN ACUTE EXPOSURE. SOME ORGANOPHOSPHATES MAY CAUSE SENSITIZATION.

FIRST AID- REMOVE CONTAMINATED CLOTHING IMMEDIATELY. WASH CONTAMINATED AREAS WITH SOAP AND WATER FOLLOWED BY ALCOHOL (ARENA, POISONING, 4TH ED.). EMERGENCY PERSONNEL SHOULD WEAR GLOVES AND AVOID CONTAMINATION. TREAT RESPIRATORY DIFFICULTY WITH ARTIFICIAL RESPIRATION. GET MEDICAL ATTENTION IMMEDIATELY.

EYE CONTACT: ETRIMFOS OXYGEN ANALOG: NO SPECIFIC DATA AVAILABLE. THE PARENT COMPOUND, ETRIMFOS, IS AN ORGANOPHOSPHATE CHOLINESTERASE INHIBITOR. SEE INFORMATION ON ORGANOPHOSPHATES. ORGANOPHOSPHATES: CHOLINESTERASE INHIBITOR. **ACUTE EXPOSURE-** DIRECT CONTACT MAY CAUSE PAIN, HYPEREMIA, LACRIMATION, TWITCHING OF THE EYELIDS, MIOSIS, AND CILIARY MUSCLE SPASM WITH LOSS OF ACCOMODATION, BLURRED OR DIMMED VISION AND BROWACHE. SOMETIMES MYDRIASIS MAY OCCUR INSTEAD OF MIOSIS. WITH SUFFICIENT EXPOSURE, OTHER SYMPTOMS OF CHOLINESTERASE INHIBITION AS DESCRIBED IN ACUTE INHALATION MAY OCCUR. **CHRONIC EXPOSURE-** REPEATED OR PROLONGED EXPOSURE MAY CAUSE EFFECTS AS DESCRIBED IN ACUTE EXPOSURE. SOME COMPOUNDS HAVE CAUSED TOXIC EFFECTS ON THE CRYSTALLINE LENS, CONJUNCTIVAL THICKENING AND OBSTRUCTION OF THE NASOLACRIMAL CANALS WHEN USED AS MIOTIC EYEDROPS.

FIRST AID- IRRIGATE EYES WITH WATER OR SALINE SOLUTION. IF SYMPTOMS OF POISONING OCCUR, TREAT RESPIRATORY DIFFICULTY WITH ARTIFICIAL RESPIRATION AND OXYGEN. OBSERVE PATIENT FOR AT LEAST 24-36 HOURS (GOSSELIN, CLINICAL TOXICOLOGY OF COMMERCIAL PRODUCTS, 5TH ED.). GET MEDICAL ATTENTION IMMEDIATELY. OXYGEN SHOULD BE ADMINISTERED BY QUALIFIED MEDICAL PERSONNEL.

INGESTION: ETRIMFOS OXYGEN ANALOG: NO SPECIFIC DATA AVAILABLE. THE PARENT COMPOUND, ETRIMFOS, IS AN ORGANOPHOSPHATE CHOLINESTERASE INHIBITOR. SEE INFORMATION ON ORGANOPHOSPHATES.
ORGANOPHOSPHATES: CHOLINESTERASE INHIBITOR. **ACUTE EXPOSURE-** WHEN INGESTED, THE FIRST EFFECTS MAY BE NAUSEA, VOMITING, ANOREXIA, ABDOMINAL CRAMPS AND DIARRHEA. GASTROINTESTINAL ABSORPTION MAY CAUSE SYMPTOMS OF CHOLINESTERASE INHIBITION AS DESCRIBED IN ACUTE INHALATION. SYMPTOMS MAY BEGIN WITHIN MINUTES OR BE DELAYED FOR HOURS. DELAYED EFFECTS INCLUDING NEUROPATHY MAY ALSO OCCUR. **CHRONIC EXPOSURE-** REPEATED INGESTION MAY CAUSE EFFECTS AS DESCRIBED IN ACUTE EXPOSURE.

FIRST AID- IF PERSON IS ALERT AND RESPIRATION IS NOT DEPRESSED, GIVE SYRUP OF IPECAC FOLLOWED BY WATER (IF VOMITING OCCURS, KEEP HEAD BELOW HIPS TO PREVENT ASPIRATION). IF CONSCIOUSNESS LEVEL DECLINES OR VOMITING HAS NOT OCCURRED IN 15 MINUTES EMPTY STOMACH BY GASTRIC LAVAGE WITH THE AID OF CUFFED ENDOTRACHEAL TUBE USING ISOTONIC SALINE OR 5% SODIUM BICARBONATE FOLLOW WITH ACTIVATED CHARCOAL. ESTABLISH AND MAINTAIN AIRWAY. TREAT RESPIRATORY DIFFICULTY WITH ARTIFICIAL RESPIRATION AND OXYGEN. DO NOT GIVE MORPHINE, AMINOPHYLLINE, PHENOTHIAZINES, RESERPINE, FUROSEMIDE, OR ETHACRYNIC ACID (MORGAN, RECOGNITION AND MANAGEMENT OF PESTICIDE POISONINGS, 3RD ED.). TREAT SYMPTOMATICALLY AND SUPPORTIVELY. ADMINISTRATION OF OXYGEN AND LAVAGE MUST BE PERFORMED BY QUALIFIED MEDICAL PERSONNEL. GET MEDICAL ATTENTION IMMEDIATELY.

ANTIDOTE: THE FOLLOWING ANTIDOTE(S) HAVE BEEN RECOMMENDED. HOWEVER, THE DECISION AS TO WHETHER THE SEVERITY OF POISONING REQUIRES ADMINISTRATION OF ANY ANTIDOTE AND ACTUAL DOSE REQUIRED SHOULD BE MADE BY QUALIFIED MEDICAL PERSONNEL.
FOR CHOLINESTERASE INHIBITORS: ESTABLISH CLEAR AIRWAY AND TISSUE OXYGENATION BY ASPIRATION OF SECRETIONS, AND IF NECESSARY, BY ASSISTED PULMONARY VENTILATION WITH OXYGEN. IMPROVE TISSUE OXYGENATION AS MUCH AS POSSIBLE BEFORE ADMINISTERING ATROPINE TO MINIMIZE THE RISK OF VENTRICULAR FIBRILLATION. ADMINISTER ATROPINE SULFATE INTRAVENOUSLY, OR INTRAMUSCULARLY IF IV INJECTION IS NOT POSSIBLE. IN MODERATELY SEVERE POISONING ADMINISTER ATROPINE SULFATE, 0.4-2.0 MG REPEATED EVERY 15 MINUTES UNTIL ATROPINIZATION IS ACHIEVED (TACHYCARDIA, FLUSHING, DRY MOUTH, MYDRIASIS). MAINTAIN ATROPINIZATION BY REPEATED DOSES FOR 2-12 HOURS, OR LONGER, DEPENDING ON THE SEVERITY OF POISONING. THE APPEARANCE OF RALES IN THE LUNG BASES, MIOSIS, SALIVATION, NAUSEA, BRADYCARDIA, ARE ALL INDICATIONS OF INADEQUATE ATROPINIZATION. SEVERELY POISONED INDIVIDUALS MAY EXHIBIT REMARKABLE TOLERANCE TO ATROPINE; TWO OR MORE TIMES THE DOSAGES SUGGESTED ABOVE MAY BE NEEDED. PERSONS NOT POISONED OR ONLY SLIGHTLY POISONED, HOWEVER, MAY DEVELOP SIGNS OF ATROPINE TOXICITY FROM SUCH LARGE DOSAGES: FEVER, MUSCLE FIBRILLATIONS, AND DELIRIUM ARE THE MAIN SIGNS OF ATROPINE TOXICITY. IF THESE SIGNS APPEAR WHILE THE PATIENT IS FULLY ATROPINIZED, ATROPINE ADMINISTRATION SHOULD BE DISCONTINUED, AT LEAST TEMPORARILY. OBSERVE TREATED PATIENTS CLOSELY AT LEAST 24 HOURS TO INSURE THAT SYMPTOMS (POSSIBLY PULMONARY EDEMA) DO NOT RECUR AS ATROPINIZATION WEARS OFF. IN VERY SEVERE POISONINGS, METABOLIC DISPOSITION OF TOXICANT MAY REQUIRE SEVERAL HOURS OR DAYS DURING WHICH ATROPINIZATION MUST BE MAINTAINED. MARKEDLY LOWER LEVELS OF URINARY METABOLITES INDICATE THAT ATROPINE DOSAGE CAN BE TAPERED OFF. AS DOSAGE IS REDUCED, CHECK THE LUNG BASES FREQUENTLY FOR RALES. IF RALES ARE HEARD OR OTHER SYMPTOMS RETURN, RE-ESTABLISH ATROPINIZATION PROMPTLY (MORGAN, RECOGNITION AND MANAGEMENT OF PESTICIDE POISONINGS, 3RD ED.). ADMINISTRATION OF ANTIDOTE MUST BE PERFORMED BY QUALIFIED MEDICAL PERSONNEL.
IN CASES OF SEVERE POISONING BY ORGANOPHOSPHATE PESTICIDES IN WHICH RESPIRATORY DEPRESSION, MUSCLE WEAKNESS AND TWITCHINGS ARE SEVERE, GIVE PRALIDOXIME (PROTOPAM-AYERST, 2-PAM), 1.0 GRAM INTRAVENOUSLY AT NO MORE THAN 0.5 GRAM PER MINUTE. DOSAGE OF PRALIDOXIME MAY BE REPEATED IN 1-2 HOURS, THEN AT 10-12 HOUR INTERVALS IF NEEDED. IN VERY SEVERE POISONINGS, DOSAGE RATES MAY BE DOUBLED. TREATMENT WITH PRALIDOXIME WILL BE MOST EFFECTIVE IF GIVEN WITHIN THIRTY-SIX HOURS AFTER POISONING (MORGAN, RECOGNITION AND MANAGEMENT OF PESTICIDE POISONINGS, 3RD ED.). ANTIDOTE SHOULD BE ADMINISTERED BY QUALIFIED MEDICAL PERSONNEL.

REACTIVITY

REACTIVITY: STABLE UNDER NORMAL TEMPERATURES AND PRESSURES.

INCOMPATIBILITIES: ETRIMFOS OXYGEN ANALOG: OXIDIZERS (STRONG): FIRE AND EXPLOSION HAZARD.

DECOMPOSITION: THERMAL DECOMPOSITION MAY RELEASE TOXIC OXIDES OF NITROGEN, PHOSPHORUS AND CARBON.

POLYMERIZATION: HAZARDOUS POLYMERIZATION HAS NOT BEEN REPORTED TO OCCUR UNDER NORMAL TEMPERATURES AND PRESSURES.

STORAGE AND DISPOSAL

OBSERVE ALL FEDERAL, STATE AND LOCAL REGULATIONS WHEN STORING OR DISPOSING OF THIS SUBSTANCE. FOR ASSISTANCE, CONTACT THE DISTRICT DIRECTOR OF THE ENVIRONMENTAL PROTECTION AGENCY.

****STORAGE****

STORE AWAY FROM INCOMPATIBLE SUBSTANCES.
STORE IN ACCORDANCE WITH 40 CFR 165 RECOMMENDED PROCEDURES FOR THE DISPOSAL AND STORAGE OF PESTICIDES AND PESTICIDE CONTAINERS.

****DISPOSAL****

DISPOSAL MUST BE IN ACCORDANCE WITH 40 CFR 165 RECOMMENDED PROCEDURES FOR THE DISPOSAL AND STORAGE OF PESTICIDES AND PESTICIDE CONTAINERS.

CONDITIONS TO AVOID

AVOID CONTACT WITH HEAT, SPARKS, FLAMES OR OTHER IGNITION SOURCES. VAPORS MAY BE EXPLOSIVE. MATERIAL IS POISONOUS; AVOID INHALATION OF VAPORS OR CONTACT WITH SKIN. DO NOT ALLOW MATERIAL TO CONTAMINATE WATER SOURCES.

SPILL AND LEAK PROCEDURES

OCCUPATIONAL SPILL: SHUT OFF IGNITION SOURCES. DO NOT TOUCH SPILLED MATERIAL. STOP LEAK IF YOU CAN DO IT WITHOUT RISK. USE WATER SPRAY TO REDUCE VAPORS. FOR SMALL SPILLS, TAKE UP WITH SAND OR OTHER ABSORBENT MATERIAL AND PLACE INTO CONTAINERS FOR LATER DISPOSAL. FOR LARGER SPILLS, DIKE FAR AHEAD OF SPILL FOR LATER DISPOSAL. NO SMOKING, FLAMES OR FLARES IN HAZARD AREA! KEEP UNNECESSARY PEOPLE AWAY; ISOLATE HAZARD AREA AND DENY ENTRY.

PROTECTIVE EQUIPMENT

VENTILATION: PROVIDE LOCAL EXHAUST OR GENERAL DILUTION VENTILATION SYSTEM.

RESPIRATOR: THE FOLLOWING RESPIRATORS ARE RECOMMENDED BASED ON INFORMATION FOUND IN THE PHYSICAL DATA, TOXICITY AND HEALTH EFFECTS SECTIONS. THEY ARE RANKED IN ORDER FROM MINIMUM TO MAXIMUM RESPIRATORY PROTECTION. THE SPECIFIC RESPIRATOR SELECTED MUST BE BASED ON CONTAMINATION LEVELS FOUND IN THE WORK PLACE, MUST NOT EXCEED THE

WORKING LIMITS OF THE RESPIRATOR AND BE JOINTLY APPROVED BY THE NATIONAL INSTITUTE FOR OCCUPATIONAL SAFETY AND HEALTH AND THE MINE SAFETY AND HEALTH ADMINISTRATION (NIOSH-MSHA).
CHEMICAL CARTRIDGE RESPIRATOR WITH FULL FACEPIECE AND PESTICIDE CARTRIDGE.
TYPE 'C' SUPPLIED-AIR RESPIRATOR WITH A FULL FACEPIECE OPERATED IN PRESSURE-DEMAND OR OTHER POSITIVE PRESSURE MODE OR WITH A FULL FACEPIECE, HELMET OR HOOD OPERATED IN CONTINUOUS-FLOW MODE.
SELF-CONTAINED BREATHING APPARATUS OPERATED IN PRESSURE-DEMAND OR OTHER POSITIVE PRESSURE MODE.
FOR FIREFIGHTING AND OTHER IMMEDIATELY DANGEROUS TO LIFE OR HEALTH CONDITIONS:
SELF-CONTAINED BREATHING APPARATUS WITH FULL FACEPIECE OPERATED IN PRESSURE-DEMAND OR OTHER POSITIVE PRESSURE MODE.
SUPPLIED-AIR RESPIRATOR WITH FULL FACEPIECE AND OPERATED IN PRESSURE-DEMAND OR OTHER POSITIVE PRESSURE MODE IN COMBINATION WITH AN AUXILIARY SELF-CONTAINED BREATHING APPARATUS OPERATED IN PRESSURE-DEMAND OR OTHER POSITIVE PRESSURE MODE.

CLOTHING: EMPLOYEE MUST WEAR APPROPRIATE PROTECTIVE (IMPERVIOUS) CLOTHING AND EQUIPMENT TO PREVENT REPEATED OR PROLONGED SKIN CONTACT WITH THIS SUBSTANCE.

GLOVES: EMPLOYEE MUST WEAR APPROPRIATE PROTECTIVE GLOVES TO PREVENT CONTACT WITH THIS SUBSTANCE.

EYE PROTECTION: EMPLOYEE MUST WEAR SPLASH-PROOF OR DUST-RESISTANT SAFETY GOGGLES TO PREVENT EYE CONTACT WITH THIS SUBSTANCE.
EMERGENCY EYE WASH: WHERE THERE IS ANY POSSIBILITY THAT AN EMPLOYEE'S EYES MAY BE EXPOSED TO THIS SUBSTANCE, THE EMPLOYER SHOULD PROVIDE AN EYE WASH FOUNTAIN WITHIN THE IMMEDIATE WORK AREA FOR EMERGENCY USE.

AUTHORIZED BY- OCCUPATIONAL HEALTH SERVICES, INC.
CREATION DATE: 10/04/89 ***REVISION DATE:*** 04/24/90

MATERIAL SAFETY DATA SHEET

OCCUPATIONAL HEALTH SERVICES, INC.
AGRICULTURE AND PESTICIDE DIVISION
450 SEVENTH AVENUE, SUITE 2407
NEW YORK, NEW YORK 10123
1-800-445-MSDS OR (212) 967-1100

EMERGENCY CONTACT:
JOHN S. BRANSFORD, JR. (615) 292-1180

SUBSTANCE IDENTIFICATION

CAS-NUMBER 52-85-7

SUBSTANCE: FAMPHUR

TRADE NAMES/SYNONYMS: PHOSPHOROTHIOIC ACID, O-(4-((DIMETHYLAMINO)SULFONYL)PHENYL) O,O-DIMETHYL ESTER; PHOSPHOROTHIOIC ACID, O,O-DIMETHYL ESTER, O-ESTER WITH PARA-HYDROXY -N,N-DIMETHYLBENZENESULFONAMIDE; PHOSPHOROTHIOIC ACID, O-(PARA-(DIMETHYLSULFAMOYL)PHENYL) O,O-DIMETHYL ESTER; O-4-DIMETHYLSULPHAMOYLPHENYL O,O-DIMETHYL PHOSPHOROTHIOATE; O-4-DIMETHYLSULFAMOYLPHENYL O,O-DIMETHYL PHOSPHOROTHIOATE; O-(4-((DIMETHYLAMINO)SULFONYL)PHENYL) O,O-DIMETHYL PHOSPHOROTHIOATE; O,O-DIMETHYL PHOSPHOROTHIOATE O-ESTER WITH P-HYDROXY-N,N DIMETHYLBENZENESULFONAMIDE; O,O-DIMETHYL-O-(PARA-(DIMETHYLSULFAMOYL)PHENYL)PHOSPHOROTHIOATE; O,O-DIMETHYL-O-(PARA-(N,N-DIMETHYLSULFAMOYL)PHENYL)PHOSPHOROTHIOATE; DIMETHYL PARA-(DIMETHYLSULFAMOYL)PHENYL PHOSPHOROTHIONATE; FAMOPHOS; FAMPHOS; WARBEX; RCRA P097; ENT 25,644; C10H16NO5PS2; PST09675

CHEMICAL FAMILY: ORGANOPHOSPHATE

MOLECULAR FORMULA: C10-H16-N-O5-P-S2

MOLECULAR WEIGHT: 325.36

CERCLA RATINGS (SCALE 0-3): HEALTH=3 FIRE=0 REACTIVITY=0 PERSISTENCE=1

NFPA RATINGS (SCALE 0-4): HEALTH=3 FIRE=0 REACTIVITY=0

COMPONENTS AND CONTAMINANTS

COMPONENT: FAMPHUR ***PERCENT:*** 100
CAS# 52-85-7

EXPOSURE LIMITS: FAMPHUR: NO OCCUPATIONAL EXPOSURE LIMITS ESTABLISHED BY OSHA, ACGIH, OR NIOSH.
1000 POUNDS CERCLA SECTION 103 REPORTABLE QUANTITY

PHYSICAL DATA

DESCRIPTION: COLORLESS TO WHITE CRYSTALLINE POWDER ***MELTING POINT:*** 127 F (53 C)

SPECIFIC GRAVITY: NOT AVAILABLE ***SOLUBILITY IN WATER:*** SLIGHTLY SOLUBLE

SOLVENT SOLUBILITY: SOLUBLE IN ACETONE, CARBON TETRACHLORIDE, CHLOROFORM, CYCLOHEXANONE, DICHLOROMETHANE, TOLUENE, XYLENE, CHLORINATED HYDROCARBONS; SLIGHTLY SOLUBLE IN POLAR SOLVENTS; INSOLUBLE IN ALIPHATIC HYDROCARBONS

FIRE AND EXPLOSION DATA

FIRE AND EXPLOSION HAZARD: NEGLIGIBLE FIRE HAZARD WHEN EXPOSED TO HEAT OR FLAME.

FIREFIGHTING MEDIA: DRY CHEMICAL, CARBON DIOXIDE, HALON, WATER SPRAY OR STANDARD FOAM (1987 EMERGENCY RESPONSE GUIDEBOOK, DOT P 5800.4).
FOR LARGER FIRES, USE WATER SPRAY, FOG OR STANDARD FOAM (1987 EMERGENCY RESPONSE GUIDEBOOK, DOT P 5800.4).

FIREFIGHTING: MOVE CONTAINERS FROM FIRE AREA IF POSSIBLE. FIGHT FIRE FROM MAXIMUM DISTANCE. STAY AWAY FROM STORAGE TANK ENDS. DIKE FIRE CONTROL WATER FOR LATER DISPOSAL. DO NOT SCATTER MATERIAL (1987 EMERGENCY RESPONSE GUIDEBOOK, DOT P 5800.4, GUIDE PAGE 55).
EXTINGUISH ONLY IF FLOW CAN BE STOPPED; USE FLOODING AMOUNTS OF WATER AS FOG, SOLID STREAMS MAY BE INEFFECTIVE. COOL CONTAINERS WITH FLOODING AMOUNTS OF WATER FROM AS FAR A DISTANCE AS POSSIBLE. USE WATER SPRAY TO ABSORB TOXIC VAPORS. AVOID BREATHING TOXIC VAPORS; KEEP UPWIND. CONSIDER EVACUATION OF DOWNWIND AREA IF MATERIAL IS LEAKING.

TRANSPORTATION DATA

DEPARTMENT OF TRANSPORTATION HAZARD CLASSIFICATION 49 CFR 172.101: POISON B
DEPARTMENT OF TRANSPORTATION LABELING REQUIREMENTS 49 CFR 172.101 AND SUBPART E: POISON
DEPARTMENT OF TRANSPORTATION PACKAGING REQUIREMENTS: 49 CFR 173.365
EXCEPTIONS: 49 CFR 173.364

TOXICITY

FAMPHUR: TOXICITY DATA: 1460 MG/KG SKIN-RABBIT LD50; 400 MG/KG SKIN-RAT LD50; 28 MG/KG ORAL-RAT LD50; 9500 UG/KG ORAL-MOUSE LD50; 400 MG/KG ORAL-DOMESTIC ANIMAL LD50; 11,600 UG/KG INTRAPERITONEAL-MOUSE LD50; 64 MG/KG INTRAMUSCULAR-MAMMAL LD50; 59 MG/KG INTRAMUSCULAR-DOMESTIC ANIMAL LD50. CARCINOGEN STATUS: NONE. ACUTE TOXICITY LEVEL: HIGHLY TOXIC BY INGESTION; MODERATELY TOXIC BY DERMAL ABSORPTION. TARGET EFFECTS: CHOLINESTERASE INHIBITOR. POISONING MAY AFFECT THE NERVOUS SYSTEM.* AT INCREASED RISK FROM EXPOSURE: PERSONS WITH RESPIRATORY AILMENTS, RECENT EXPOSURE TO CHOLINESTERASE INHIBITORS OR IMPAIRED CHOLINESTERASE PRODUCTION, OR LIVER MALFUNCTION.* ADDITIONAL DATA: MAY CROSS THE PLACENTA. HIGH ENVIRONMENTAL TEMPERATURES OR EXPOSURE OF THE CHEMICAL TO VISIBLE OR ULTRAVIOLET LIGHT MAY ENHANCE THE TOXICITY. INTERACTIONS WITH MEDICATIONS MAY OCCUR.*
* MAY BE BASED ON GENERAL INFORMATION ON ORGANOPHOSPHATES.

HEALTH EFFECTS AND FIRST AID

INHALATION: FAMPHUR: SEE INFORMATION ON ORGANOPHOSPHATES.
ORGANOPHOSPHATES: CHOLINESTERASE INHIBITOR. ACUTE EXPOSURE- WHEN INHALED, THE FIRST EFFECTS OF CHOLINESTERASE INHIBITORS ARE USUALLY RESPIRATORY AND MAY INCLUDE NASAL HYPEREMIA AND WATERY DISCHARGE, COUGH, CHEST DISCOMFORT, DYSPNEA, AND WHEEZING DUE TO INCREASED BRONCHIAL SECRETIONS AND BRONCHOCONSTRICTION. IF SUFFICIENT AMOUNTS ARE ABSORBED, OTHER SYSTEMIC EFFECTS MAY BEGIN WITHIN A FEW MINUTES OR BE DELAYED FOR UP TO 12 HOURS. SYMPTOMS MAY INCLUDE PALLOR, NAUSEA, VOMITING, DIARRHEA, ABDOMINAL CRAMPS, HEADACHE, DIZZINESS, OCULAR PAIN, BLURRED VISION, MIOSIS OR IN SOME CASES, ESPECIALLY INITIALLY, MYDRIASIS, LACRIMATION, SALIVATION, SWEATING, AND CONFUSION. OTHER REPORTED CENTRAL NERVOUS SYSTEM OR NEUROMUSCULAR EFFECTS MAY INCLUDE ATAXIA, SLURRED SPEECH, AREFLEXIA, WEAKNESS, FATIGUE, FASCICULATIONS, TWITCHING, TREMORS POSSIBLY OF THE TONGUE AND EYELIDS, AND EVENTUALLY PARALYSIS OF THE EXTREMITIES AND POSSIBLY OF THE RESPIRATORY MUSCLES. IN SEVERE CASES THERE MAY ALSO BE INVOLUNTARY DEFECATION AND URINATION, CYANOSIS, PSYCHOSIS, HYPERGLYCEMIA, ACUTE PANCREATITIS, CARDIAC IRREGULARITIES, PULMONARY EDEMA, UNCONSCIOUSNESS, CONVULSIONS, AND COMA. DEATH IS PRIMARILY DUE TO RESPIRATORY FAILURE, ALTHOUGH CARDIOVASCULAR EFFECTS INCLUDING CARDIAC ARREST MAY ALSO BE IMPLICATED. LONG TERM SEQUELAE ARE RARE BUT MAY INCLUDE NEUROPSYCHIATRIC DISORDERS AND MYOPATHY WITH MUSCLE TENDERNESS. SOME ORGANOPHOSPHATES MAY CAUSE A DELAYED

NEUROPATHY BEGINNING 1-4 WEEKS AFTER AN ACUTE EXPOSURE WHICH MAY OR MAY NOT HAVE CAUSED ACUTE CHOLINERGIC EFFECTS. NUMBNESS, TINGLING, WEAKNESS AND CRAMPING BEGINNING SYMMETRICALLY IN THE LOWER LIMBS MAY PROGRESS TO ATAXIA AND PARALYSIS. IN SEVERE CASES, UPPER LIMB INVOLVEMENT IS POSSIBLE AND FLACCID PARALYSIS MAY PROGRESS TO SPASTIC PARALYSIS WITH EXAGGERATED REFLEXES. IMPROVEMENT MAY OCCUR OVER MONTHS TO YEARS, BUT SOME RESIDUAL IMPAIRMENT USUALLY REMAINS. **CHRONIC EXPOSURE-** REPEATED OR PROLONGED EXPOSURE MAY RESULT IN THE EFFECTS OF ACUTE EXPOSURE INCLUDING THE DELAYED NEUROPATHY. OTHER EFFECTS REPORTED IN WORKERS REPEATEDLY EXPOSED INCLUDE IMPAIRED MEMORY AND CONCENTRATION, ACUTE PSYCHOSIS, SEVERE DEPRESSIONS, IRRITABILTY, CONFUSION, APATHY, EMOTIONAL LABILITY, SOCIAL WITHDRAWAL, CONFUSION, HEADACHE, SPEECH DIFFICULTIES, DELAYED REACTION TIMES, SPATIAL DISORIENTATION, NIGHTMARES, SLEEPWALKING, AND DROWSINESS OR INSOMNIA. AN INFLUENZA-LIKE CONDITION WITH HEADACHE, NAUSEA, WEAKNESS, ANOREXIA AND MALAISE HAS ALSO BEEN REPORTED.

FIRST AID- REMOVE FROM EXPOSURE AREA TO FRESH AIR IMMEDIATELY. IF BREATHING HAS STOPPED, GIVE ARTIFICIAL RESPIRATION. MAINTAIN AIRWAY AND BLOOD PRESSURE AND ADMINISTER OXYGEN IF AVAILABLE. KEEP AFFECTED PERSON WARM AND AT REST. TREAT SYMPTOMATICALLY AND SUPPORTIVELY. ADMINISTRATION OF OXYGEN SHOULD BE PERFORMED BY QUALIFIED PERSONNEL. GET MEDICAL ATTENTION IMMEDIATELY.

SKIN CONTACT: FAMPHUR: SEE INFORMATION ON ORGANOPHOSPHATES. ORGANOPHOSPHATES: CHOLINESTERASE INHIBITOR. **ACUTE EXPOSURE-** LOCALIZED SWEATING AND FASCICULATIONS MAY OCCUR AT THE SITE OF CONTACT. IF SUFFICIENT AMOUNTS ARE ABSORBED, OTHER EFFECTS OF CHOLINESTERASE INHIBITION AS DESCRIBED IN ACUTE INHALATION MAY OCCUR. SYMPTOMS MAY BE DELAYED 2-3 HOURS, BUT USUALLY NO MORE THAN 12 HOURS. THE RATE OF ABSORPTION IS INCREASED BY THE PRESENCE OF DERMATITIS OR HIGH AMBIENT TEMPERATURES. DELAYED NEUROPATHY IS ALSO POSSIBLE. **CHRONIC EXPOSURE-** REPEATED OR PROLONGED EXPOSURE MAY CAUSE EFFECTS AS DESCRIBED IN ACUTE EXPOSURE. SOME ORGANOPHOSPHATES MAY CAUSE SENSITIZATION.

FIRST AID- REMOVE CONTAMINATED CLOTHING IMMEDIATELY. WASH CONTAMINATED AREAS WITH SOAP AND WATER FOLLOWED BY ALCOHOL (ARENA, POISONING, 4TH ED.). EMERGENCY PERSONNEL SHOULD WEAR GLOVES AND AVOID CONTAMINATION. TREAT RESPIRATORY DIFFICULTY WITH ARTIFICIAL RESPIRATION. GET MEDICAL ATTENTION IMMEDIATELY.

EYE CONTACT: FAMPHUR: SEE INFORMATION ON ORGANOPHOSPHATES. ORGANOPHOSPHATES: CHOLINESTERASE INHIBITOR. **ACUTE EXPOSURE-** DIRECT CONTACT MAY CAUSE PAIN, HYPEREMIA, LACRIMATION, TWITCHING OF THE EYELIDS, MIOSIS, AND CILIARY MUSCLE SPASM WITH LOSS OF ACCOMODATION, BLURRED OR DIMMED VISION AND BROWACHE. SOMETIMES MYDRIASIS MAY OCCUR INSTEAD OF MIOSIS. WITH SUFFICIENT EXPOSURE, OTHER SYMPTOMS OF CHOLINESTERASE INHIBITION AS DESCRIBED IN ACUTE INHALATION MAY OCCUR. **CHRONIC EXPOSURE-** REPEATED OR PROLONGED EXPOSURE MAY CAUSE EFFECTS AS DESCRIBED IN ACUTE EXPOSURE. SOME COMPOUNDS HAVE CAUSED TOXIC EFFECTS ON THE CRYSTALLINE LENS, CONJUNCTIVAL THICKENING AND OBSTRUCTION OF THE NASOLACRIMAL CANALS WHEN USED AS MIOTIC EYEDROPS.

FIRST AID- IRRIGATE EYES WITH WATER OR SALINE SOLUTION. IF SYMPTOMS OF POISONING OCCUR, TREAT RESPIRATORY DIFFICULTY WITH ARTIFICIAL RESPIRATION AND OXYGEN. OBSERVE PATIENT FOR AT LEAST 24-36 HOURS (GOSSELIN, CLINICAL TOXICOLOGY OF COMMERCIAL PRODUCTS, 5TH ED.). GET MEDICAL ATTENTION IMMEDIATELY. OXYGEN SHOULD BE ADMINISTERED BY QUALIFIED MEDICAL PERSONNEL.

INGESTION: FAMPHUR: HIGHLY TOXIC. SEE INFORMATION ON ORGANOPHOSPHATES. ORGANOPHOSPHATES: CHOLINESTERASE INHIBITOR. **ACUTE EXPOSURE-** WHEN INGESTED, THE FIRST EFFECTS MAY BE NAUSEA, VOMITING, ANOREXIA, ABDOMINAL CRAMPS AND DIARRHEA. GASTROINTESTINAL ABSORPTION MAY CAUSE SYMPTOMS OF CHOLINESTERASE INHIBITION AS DESCRIBED IN ACUTE INHALATION. SYMPTOMS MAY BEGIN WITHIN MINUTES OR BE DELAYED FOR HOURS. DELAYED EFFECTS INCLUDING NEUROPATHY MAY ALSO OCCUR. **CHRONIC EXPOSURE-** REPEATED INGESTION MAY CAUSE EFFECTS AS DESCRIBED IN ACUTE EXPOSURE.

FIRST AID- IF PERSON IS ALERT AND RESPIRATION IS NOT DEPRESSED, GIVE SYRUP OF IPECAC FOLLOWED BY WATER (IF VOMITING OCCURS, KEEP HEAD BELOW HIPS TO PREVENT ASPIRATION). IF CONSCIOUSNESS LEVEL DECLINES OR VOMITING HAS NOT OCCURRED IN 15 MINUTES EMPTY STOMACH BY GASTRIC LAVAGE WITH THE AID OF CUFFED ENDOTRACHEAL TUBE USING ISOTONIC SALINE OR 5% SODIUM BICARBONATE FOLLOW WITH ACTIVATED CHARCOAL. ESTABLISH AND MAINTAIN AIRWAY. TREAT RESPIRATORY DIFFICULTY WITH ARTIFICIAL RESPIRATION AND OXYGEN. DO NOT GIVE MORPHINE, AMINOPHYLLINE, PHENOTHIAZINES, RESERPINE, FUROSEMIDE, OR ETHACRYNIC ACID (MORGAN, RECOGNITION AND MANAGEMENT OF PESTICIDE POISONINGS, 3RD ED.). TREAT SYMPTOMATICALLY AND SUPPORTIVELY. ADMINISTRATION OF OXYGEN AND LAVAGE MUST BE PERFORMED BY QUALIFIED MEDICAL PERSONNEL. GET MEDICAL ATTENTION IMMEDIATELY.

ANTIDOTE: THE FOLLOWING ANTIDOTE(S) HAVE BEEN RECOMMENDED. HOWEVER, THE DECISION AS TO WHETHER THE SEVERITY OF POISONING REQUIRES ADMINISTRATION OF ANY ANTIDOTE AND ACTUAL DOSE REQUIRED SHOULD BE MADE BY QUALIFIED MEDICAL PERSONNEL.

FOR CHOLINESTERASE INHIBITORS: ESTABLISH CLEAR AIRWAY AND TISSUE OXYGENATION BY ASPIRATION OF SECRETIONS, AND IF NECESSARY, BY ASSISTED PULMONARY VENTILATION WITH OXYGEN. IMPROVE TISSUE OXYGENATION AS MUCH AS POSSIBLE BEFORE ADMINISTERING ATROPINE TO MINIMIZE THE RISK OF VENTRICULAR FIBRILLATION. ADMINISTER ATROPINE SULFATE INTRAVENOUSLY, OR INTRAMUSCULARLY IF IV INJECTION IS NOT POSSIBLE. IN MODERATELY SEVERE POISONING ADMINISTER ATROPINE SULFATE, 0.4-2.0 MG REPEATED EVERY 15 MINUTES UNTIL ATROPINIZATION IS ACHIEVED (TACHYCARDIA, FLUSHING, DRY MOUTH, MYDRIASIS). MAINTAIN ATROPINIZATION BY REPEATED DOSES FOR 2-12 HOURS, OR LONGER, DEPENDING ON THE SEVERITY OF POISONING. THE APPEARANCE OF RALES IN THE LUNG BASES, MIOSIS, SALIVATION, NAUSEA, BRADYCARDIA, ARE ALL INDICATIONS OF INADEQUATE ATROPINIZATION. SEVERELY POISONED INDIVIDUALS MAY EXHIBIT REMARKABLE TOLERANCE TO ATROPINE; TWO OR MORE TIMES THE DOSAGES SUGGESTED ABOVE MAY BE NEEDED. PERSONS NOT POISONED OR ONLY SLIGHTLY POISONED, HOWEVER, MAY DEVELOP SIGNS OF ATROPINE TOXICITY FROM SUCH LARGE DOSAGES: FEVER, MUSCLE FIBRILLATIONS, AND DELIRIUM ARE THE MAIN SIGNS OF ATROPINE TOXICITY. IF THESE SIGNS APPEAR WHILE THE PATIENT IS FULLY ATROPINIZED, ATROPINE ADMINISTRATION SHOULD BE DISCONTINUED, AT LEAST TEMPORARILY. OBSERVE TREATED PATIENTS CLOSELY AT LEAST 24 HOURS TO INSURE THAT SYMPTOMS (POSSIBLY PULMONARY EDEMA) DO NOT RECUR AS ATROPINIZATION WEARS OFF. IN VERY SEVERE POISONINGS, METABOLIC DISPOSITION OF TOXICANT MAY REQUIRE SEVERAL HOURS OR DAYS DURING WHICH ATROPINIZATION MUST BE MAINTAINED. MARKEDLY LOWER LEVELS OF URINARY METABOLITES INDICATE THAT ATROPINE DOSAGE CAN BE TAPERED OFF. AS DOSAGE IS REDUCED, CHECK THE LUNG BASES FREQUENTLY FOR RALES. IF RALES ARE HEARD OR OTHER SYMPTOMS RETURN, RE-ESTABLISH ATROPINIZATION PROMPTLY (MORGAN, RECOGNITION AND MANAGEMENT OF PESTICIDE POISONINGS, 3RD ED.). ADMINISTRATION OF ANTIDOTE MUST BE PERFORMED BY QUALIFIED MEDICAL PERSONNEL.

IN CASES OF SEVERE POISONING BY ORGANOPHOSPHATE PESTICIDES IN WHICH RESPIRATORY DEPRESSION, MUSCLE WEAKNESS AND TWITCHINGS ARE SEVERE, GIVE PRALIDOXIME (PROTOPAM-AYERST, 2-PAM), 1.0 GRAM INTRAVENOUSLY AT NO MORE THAN 0.5 GRAM PER MINUTE. DOSAGE OF PRALIDOXIME MAY BE REPEATED IN 1-2 HOURS, THEN AT 10-12 HOUR INTERVALS IF NEEDED. IN VERY SEVERE POISONINGS, DOSAGE RATES MAY BE DOUBLED. TREATMENT WITH PRALIDOXIME WILL BE MOST EFFECTIVE IF GIVEN WITHIN THIRTY-SIX HOURS AFTER POISONING (MORGAN, RECOGNITION AND MANAGEMENT OF PESTICIDE POISONINGS, 3RD ED.). ANTIDOTE SHOULD BE ADMINISTERED BY QUALIFIED MEDICAL PERSONNEL.

REACTIVITY

REACTIVITY: STABLE UNDER NORMAL TEMPERATURES AND PRESSURES.

INCOMPATIBILITIES: FAMPHUR: NO DATA AVAILABLE.

DECOMPOSITION: THERMAL DECOMPOSITION MAY RELEASE TOXIC OXIDES OF NITROGEN AND SULFUR.

POLYMERIZATION: HAZARDOUS POLYMERIZATION HAS NOT BEEN REPORTED TO OCCUR UNDER NORMAL TEMPERATURES AND PRESSURES.

STORAGE AND DISPOSAL

OBSERVE ALL FEDERAL, STATE AND LOCAL REGULATIONS WHEN STORING OR DISPOSING OF THIS SUBSTANCE. FOR ASSISTANCE, CONTACT THE DISTRICT DIRECTOR OF THE ENVIRONMENTAL PROTECTION AGENCY.

STORAGE

STORE IN ACCORDANCE WITH 40 CFR 165 RECOMMENDED PROCEDURES FOR THE DISPOSAL AND STORAGE OF PESTICIDES AND PESTICIDE CONTAINERS.

DISPOSAL

DISPOSAL MUST BE IN ACCORDANCE WITH STANDARDS APPLICABLE TO GENERATORS OF HAZARDOUS WASTE, 40CFR 262. EPA HAZARDOUS WASTE NUMBER P097

CONDITIONS TO AVOID

NONE REPORTED.

SPILL AND LEAK PROCEDURES

OCCUPATIONAL SPILL: DO NOT TOUCH SPILLED MATERIAL. STOP LEAK IF YOU CAN DO IT WITHOUT RISK. USE WATER SPRAY TO REDUCE VAPORS. FOR SMALL SPILLS, TAKE UP WITH SAND OR OTHER ABSORBENT MATERIAL AND PLACE INTO CONTAINERS FOR LATER DISPOSAL. FOR SMALL DRY SPILLS, WITH A CLEAN SHOVEL PLACE MATERIAL INTO CLEAN, DRY CONTAINERS AND COVER. MOVE CONTAINERS FROM SPILL AREA. FOR LARGER SPILLS, DIKE FAR AHEAD OF SPILL FOR LATER DISPOSAL. KEEP UNNECESSARY PEOPLE AWAY. ISOLATE HAZARD AREA AND DENY ENTRY. VENTILATE CLOSED SPACES BEFORE ENTERING.
REPORTABLE QUANTITY (RQ): 1000 POUNDS THE SUPERFUND AMENDMENTS AND REAUTHORIZATION ACT (SARA) SECTION 304 REQUIRES THAT A RELEASE EQUAL TO OR GREATER THAN THE REPORTABLE QUANTITY FOR THIS SUBSTANCE BE IMMEDIATELY REPORTED TO THE LOCAL EMERGENCY PLANNING COMMITTEE AND THE STATE EMERGENCY RESPONSE COMMISSION (40 CFR 355.40). IF THE RELEASE OF THIS SUBSTANCE IS REPORTABLE UNDER CERCLA SECTION 103, THE NATIONAL RESPONSE CENTER MUST BE NOTIFIED IMMEDIATELY AT (800) 424-8802 OR (202) 426-2675 IN THE METROPOLITAN WASHINGTON, D.C. AREA (40 CFR 302.6).

PROTECTIVE EQUIPMENT

VENTILATION: PROVIDE LOCAL EXHAUST OR GENERAL DILUTION VENTILATION SYSTEM.

RESPIRATOR: THE FOLLOWING RESPIRATORS ARE RECOMMENDED BASED ON INFORMATION FOUND IN THE PHYSICAL DATA, TOXICITY AND HEALTH EFFECTS SECTIONS. THEY ARE RANKED IN ORDER FROM MINIMUM TO MAXIMUM RESPIRATORY PROTECTION. THE SPECIFIC RESPIRATOR SELECTED MUST BE BASED ON CONTAMINATION LEVELS FOUND IN THE WORK PLACE, MUST NOT EXCEED THE WORKING LIMITS OF THE RESPIRATOR AND BE JOINTLY APPROVED BY THE NATIONAL INSTITUTE FOR OCCUPATIONAL SAFETY AND HEALTH AND THE MINE SAFETY AND HEALTH ADMINISTRATION (NIOSH-MSHA).
CHEMICAL CARTRIDGE RESPIRATOR WITH AN ORGANIC VAPOR CARTRIDGE(S) IN COMBINATION WITH A DUST AND MIST FILTER.
GAS MASK WITH ORGANIC VAPOR CANISTER (CHIN-STYLE OR FRONT- OR BACK-MOUNTED CANISTER) WITH A DUST AND MIST FILTER.
GAS MASK WITH ORGANIC VAPOR CANISTER (CHIN-STYLE OR FRONT- OR BACK-MOUNTED CANISTER) WITH A PARTICULATE FILTER.
POWERED AIR-PURIFYING RESPIRATOR WITH A HIGH-EFFICIENCY FILTER.
TYPE 'C' SUPPLIED-AIR RESPIRATOR WITH A FULL FACEPIECE OPERATED IN A PRESSURE-DEMAND OR OTHER POSITIVE PRESSURE MODE.
SELF-CONTAINED BREATHING APPARATUS WITH A FULL FACEPIECE OPERATED IN PRESSURE-DEMAND OR OTHER POSITIVE PRESSURE MODE.
FOR FIREFIGHTING AND OTHER IMMEDIATELY DANGEROUS TO LIFE OR HEALTH CONDITIONS:
SELF-CONTAINED BREATHING APPARATUS WITH FULL FACEPIECE OPERATED IN PRESSURE-DEMAND OR OTHER POSITIVE PRESSURE MODE.
SUPPLIED-AIR RESPIRATOR WITH FULL FACEPIECE AND OPERATED IN PRESSURE-DEMAND OR OTHER POSITIVE PRESSURE MODE IN COMBINATION WITH AN AUXILIARY SELF-CONTAINED BREATHING APPARATUS OPERATED IN PRESSURE-DEMAND OR OTHER POSITIVE PRESSURE MODE.

CLOTHING: EMPLOYEE MUST WEAR APPROPRIATE PROTECTIVE (IMPERVIOUS) CLOTHING AND EQUIPMENT TO PREVENT REPEATED OR PROLONGED SKIN CONTACT WITH THIS SUBSTANCE.

GLOVES: EMPLOYEE MUST WEAR APPROPRIATE PROTECTIVE GLOVES TO PREVENT CONTACT WITH THIS SUBSTANCE.

EYE PROTECTION: EMPLOYEE MUST WEAR SPLASH-PROOF OR DUST-RESISTANT SAFETY GOGGLES TO PREVENT EYE CONTACT WITH THIS SUBSTANCE.
EMERGENCY EYE WASH: WHERE THERE IS ANY POSSIBILITY THAT AN EMPLOYEE'S EYES MAY BE EXPOSED TO THIS SUBSTANCE, THE EMPLOYER SHOULD PROVIDE AN EYE WASH FOUNTAIN WITHIN THE IMMEDIATE WORK AREA FOR EMERGENCY USE.

AUTHORIZED BY- OCCUPATIONAL HEALTH SERVICES, INC.
CREATION DATE: 10/04/89 ***REVISION DATE:*** 05/07/90

MATERIAL SAFETY DATA SHEET

OCCUPATIONAL HEALTH SERVICES, INC.
AGRICULTURE AND PESTICIDE DIVISION
450 SEVENTH AVENUE, SUITE 2407
NEW YORK, NEW YORK 10123
1-800-445-MSDS OR (212) 967-1100

EMERGENCY CONTACT:
JOHN S. BRANSFORD, JR. (615) 292-1180

SUBSTANCE IDENTIFICATION

CAS-NUMBER 80-38-6
SUBSTANCE: **FENSON**
TRADE NAMES/SYNONYMS: BENZENESULFONIC ACID, 4-CHLOROPHENYL ESTER; 4-CHLOROPHENYL BENZENESULFONIC ACID ESTER; BENZENESULFONIC ACID, P-CHLOROPHENYL ESTER; P-CHLOROPHENYL BENZENESULFONIC ACID ESTER; P-CHLOROPHENYL BENZENESULFONATE; 4-CHLOROPHENYL BENZENESULFONATE; 4-CHLOROPHENYL BENZENESULPHONATE; FENSONE; MURVESCO; PCI; CPBS; PCPBS; C12H9CLO3S; PST09677
CHEMICAL FAMILY: SULFONATE
HALOGEN COMPOUND, AROMATIC
MOLECULAR FORMULA: C6-H5-S-O3-C6-H4-CL
MOLECULAR WEIGHT: 268.71
CERCLA RATINGS (SCALE 0-3): HEALTH=2 FIRE=1 REACTIVITY=0 PERSISTENCE=3
NFPA RATINGS (SCALE 0-4): HEALTH=2 FIRE=1 REACTIVITY=0

COMPONENTS AND CONTAMINANTS

COMPONENT: FENSON ***PERCENT:*** 100
CAS# 80-38-6
OTHER CONTAMINANTS: NONE
EXPOSURE LIMITS: NO OCCUPATIONAL EXPOSURE LIMITS ESTABLISHED BY OSHA, ACGIH, OR NIOSH.

PHYSICAL DATA

DESCRIPTION: COLORLESS CRYSTALS. ***MELTING POINT:*** 136-142 F (59-61 C)
SPECIFIC GRAVITY: NOT AVAILABLE. ***SOLUBILITY IN WATER:*** VERY SLIGHTLY
SOLVENT SOLUBILITY: SOLUBLE IN ACETONE, METHANOL, TOLUENE, METHYLENE CHLORIDE

FIRE AND EXPLOSION DATA

FIRE AND EXPLOSION HAZARD: SLIGHT FIRE HAZARD WHEN EXPOSED TO HEAT OR FLAME.

FIREFIGHTING MEDIA: DRY CHEMICAL, CARBON DIOXIDE, HALON, WATER SPRAY OR STANDARD FOAM (1987 EMERGENCY RESPONSE GUIDEBOOK, DOT P 5800.4).
FOR LARGER FIRES, USE WATER SPRAY, FOG OR STANDARD FOAM (1987 EMERGENCY RESPONSE GUIDEBOOK, DOT P 5800.4).

FIREFIGHTING: MOVE CONTAINERS FROM FIRE AREA IF POSSIBLE (1987 EMERGENCY RESPONSE GUIDEBOOK, DOT P 5800.4, GUIDE PAGE 53).
EXTINGUISH FIRE USING AGENTS SUITABLE FOR TYPE OF SURROUNDING FIRE. USE WATER IN FLOODING AMOUNTS AS A FOG. AVOID BREATHING DUSTS AND FUMES FROM BURNING MATERIAL; KEEP UPWIND.

TOXICITY

FENSON: IRRITATION DATA: 500 MG/24 HOURS SKIN-RABBIT MILD; 100 MG/24 HOURS EYE-RABBIT MODERATE. TOXICITY DATA: 1350 MG/KG ORAL-RAT LD50; 1300 MG/KG UNREPORTED-MAMMAL LD50. CARCINOGEN STATUS: NONE. ACUTE TOXICITY LEVEL: MODERATELY TOXIC BY INGESTION. TARGET EFFECTS: NO DATA AVAILABLE.

HEALTH EFFECTS AND FIRST AID

INHALATION: FENSON: **ACUTE EXPOSURE-** NO DATA AVAILABLE. **CHRONIC EXPOSURE-** NO DATA AVAILABLE.
FIRST AID- REMOVE FROM EXPOSURE AREA TO FRESH AIR IMMEDIATELY. IF BREATHING HAS STOPPED, PERFORM ARTIFICIAL RESPIRATION. KEEP PERSON WARM AND AT REST. TREAT SYMPTOMATICALLY AND SUPPORTIVELY. GET MEDICAL ATTENTION IMMEDIATELY.

SKIN CONTACT: FENSON: **ACUTE EXPOSURE-** 500 MG APPLIED TO RABBIT SKIN WAS MILDLY IRRITATING. A LETHAL DOSE IN RABBITS AND RATS WAS GREATER THAN 2000 MG/KG. **CHRONIC EXPOSURE-** NO DATA AVAILABLE.
FIRST AID- REMOVE CONTAMINATED CLOTHING AND SHOES IMMEDIATELY. WASH AFFECTED AREA WITH SOAP OR MILD DETERGENT AND LARGE AMOUNTS OF WATER UNTIL NO EVIDENCE OF CHEMICAL REMAINS (APPROXIMATELY 15-20 MINUTES). GET MEDICAL ATTENTION IMMEDIATELY.

EYE CONTACT: FENSON: **ACUTE EXPOSURE-** A 100 MG APPLIED TO THE EYES OF RABBITS WAS MODERATELY IRRITATING. **CHRONIC EXPOSURE-** NO DATA AVAILABLE.
FIRST AID- WASH EYES IMMEDIATELY WITH LARGE AMOUNTS OF WATER OR NORMAL SALINE, OCCASIONALLY LIFTING UPPER AND LOWER LIDS, UNTIL NO EVIDENCE OF CHEMICAL REMAINS (APPROXIMATELY 15-20 MINUTES). GET MEDICAL ATTENTION IMMEDIATELY.

INGESTION: FENSON: **ACUTE EXPOSURE-** A LETHAL DOSE IN RATS WAS 1350 MG/KG. **CHRONIC EXPOSURE-** NO DATA AVAILABLE.

FIRST AID- TREAT SYMPTOMATICALLY AND SUPPORTIVELY. GET MEDICAL ATTENTION IMMEDIATELY. IF VOMITING OCCURS, KEEP HEAD LOWER THAN HIPS TO PREVENT ASPIRATION.
ANTIDOTE: NO SPECIFIC ANTIDOTE. TREAT SYMPTOMATICALLY AND SUPPORTIVELY.

REACTIVITY

REACTIVITY: STABLE UNDER NORMAL TEMPERATURES AND PRESSURES.
INCOMPATIBILITIES: FENSON: ACIDS: MAY YIELD HIGHLY TOXIC FUMES OF CHLORIDE OR SULFUR OXIDES. ALKALIES: HYDROLYZES WITH RELEASE OF TOXIC FUMES OF CHLORIDE OR SULFUR OXIDES.
DECOMPOSITION: THERMAL DECOMPOSITION MAY YIELD HIGHLY TOXIC OXIDES OF SULFUR, CHLORIDE FUMES, AND PHOSGENE.
POLYMERIZATION: HAZARDOUS POLYMERIZATION HAS NOT BEEN REPORTED TO OCCUR UNDER NORMAL TEMPERATURES AND PRESSURES.

STORAGE AND DISPOSAL

OBSERVE ALL FEDERAL, STATE AND LOCAL REGULATIONS WHEN STORING OR DISPOSING OF THIS SUBSTANCE. FOR ASSISTANCE, CONTACT THE DISTRICT DIRECTOR OF THE ENVIRONMENTAL PROTECTION AGENCY.

STORAGE

STORE IN ACCORDANCE WITH 40 CFR 165 RECOMMENDED PROCEDURES FOR THE DISPOSAL AND STORAGE OF PESTICIDES AND PESTICIDE CONTAINERS.
STORE AWAY FROM INCOMPATIBLE SUBSTANCES.

DISPOSAL

DISPOSAL MUST BE IN ACCORDANCE WITH 40 CFR 165 RECOMMENDED PROCEDURES FOR THE DISPOSAL AND STORAGE OF PESTICIDES AND PESTICIDE CONTAINERS.

CONDITIONS TO AVOID

MAY BURN BUT DOES NOT IGNITE READILY.

SPILL AND LEAK PROCEDURES

OCCUPATIONAL SPILL: DO NOT TOUCH SPILLED MATERIAL. STOP LEAK IF YOU CAN DO IT WITHOUT RISK. FOR SMALL SPILLS, TAKE UP WITH SAND OR OTHER ABSORBENT MATERIAL AND PLACE INTO CONTAINERS FOR LATER DISPOSAL. FOR SMALL DRY SPILLS, WITH A CLEAN SHOVEL PLACE MATERIAL INTO CLEAN, DRY CONTAINER AND COVER. MOVE CONTAINERS FROM SPILL AREA. FOR LARGER SPILLS, DIKE FAR AHEAD OF SPILL FOR LATER DISPOSAL. KEEP UNNECESSARY PEOPLE AWAY. ISOLATE HAZARD AREA AND DENY ENTRY.

PROTECTIVE EQUIPMENT

VENTILATION: PROVIDE LOCAL EXHAUST OR GENERAL DILUTION VENTILATION SYSTEM.
RESPIRATOR: THE FOLLOWING RESPIRATORS ARE RECOMMENDED BASED ON INFORMATION FOUND IN THE PHYSICAL DATA, TOXICITY AND HEALTH EFFECTS SECTIONS. THEY ARE RANKED IN ORDER FROM MINIMUM TO MAXIMUM RESPIRATORY PROTECTION. THE SPECIFIC RESPIRATOR SELECTED MUST BE BASED ON CONTAMINATION LEVELS FOUND IN THE WORK PLACE, MUST NOT EXCEED THE WORKING LIMITS OF THE RESPIRATOR AND BE JOINTLY APPROVED BY THE NATIONAL INSTITUTE FOR OCCUPATIONAL SAFETY AND HEALTH AND THE MINE SAFETY AND HEALTH ADMINISTRATION (NIOSH-MSHA).
CHEMICAL CARTRIDGE RESPIRATOR WITH AN ORGANIC VAPOR CARTRIDGE(S) WITH A FULL FACEPIECE AND ORGANIC VAPOR CARTRIDGE(S) IN COMBINATION WITH A DUST AND MIST FILTER.
POWERED AIR-PURIFYING RESPIRATOR WITH A TIGHT-FITTING FACEPIECE AND ORGANIC VAPOR CARTRIDGE(S) IN COMBINATION WITH A HIGH-EFFICIENCY PARTICULATE FILTER.
TYPE 'C' SUPPLIED-AIR RESPIRATOR WITH A FULL FACEPIECE OPERATED IN A PRESSURE-DEMAND OR OTHER POSITIVE PRESSURE MODE.
SELF-CONTAINED BREATHING APPARATUS WITH A FULL FACEPIECE OPERATED IN PRESSURE-DEMAND OR OTHER POSITIVE PRESSURE MODE.
FOR FIREFIGHTING AND OTHER IMMEDIATELY DANGEROUS TO LIFE OR HEALTH CONDITIONS:
SELF-CONTAINED BREATHING APPARATUS WITH FULL FACEPIECE OPERATED IN PRESSURE-DEMAND OR OTHER POSITIVE PRESSURE MODE.
SUPPLIED-AIR RESPIRATOR WITH FULL FACEPIECE AND OPERATED IN PRESSURE-DEMAND OR OTHER POSITIVE PRESSURE MODE IN COMBINATION WITH AN AUXILIARY SELF-CONTAINED BREATHING APPARATUS OPERATED IN PRESSURE-DEMAND OR OTHER POSITIVE PRESSURE MODE.
CLOTHING: EMPLOYEE MUST WEAR APPROPRIATE PROTECTIVE (IMPERVIOUS) CLOTHING AND EQUIPMENT TO PREVENT REPEATED OR PROLONGED SKIN CONTACT WITH THIS SUBSTANCE.
GLOVES: EMPLOYEE MUST WEAR APPROPRIATE PROTECTIVE GLOVES TO PREVENT CONTACT WITH THIS SUBSTANCE.
EYE PROTECTION: EMPLOYEE MUST WEAR SPLASH-PROOF OR DUST-RESISTANT SAFETY GOGGLES TO PREVENT EYE CONTACT WITH THIS SUBSTANCE.
EMERGENCY EYE WASH: WHERE THERE IS ANY POSSIBILITY THAT AN EMPLOYEE'S EYES MAY BE EXPOSED TO THIS SUBSTANCE, THE EMPLOYER SHOULD PROVIDE AN EYE WASH FOUNTAIN WITHIN THE IMMEDIATE WORK AREA FOR EMERGENCY USE.

AUTHORIZED BY- OCCUPATIONAL HEALTH SERVICES, INC.
CREATION DATE: 10/04/89 ***REVISION DATE:*** 05/16/90

MATERIAL SAFETY DATA SHEET

OCCUPATIONAL HEALTH SERVICES, INC.
AGRICULTURE AND PESTICIDE DIVISION
450 SEVENTH AVENUE, SUITE 2407
NEW YORK, NEW YORK 10123
1-800-445-MSDS OR (212) 967-1100

EMERGENCY CONTACT:
JOHN S. BRANSFORD, JR. (615) 292-1180

SUBSTANCE IDENTIFICATION

CAS-NUMBER 122-14-5
SUBSTANCE: FENITROTHION
TRADE NAMES/SYNONYMS: PHOSPHOROTHIOIC ACID, O,O-DIMETHYL O-(3-METHYL-4-NITROPHENYL)ESTER; PHOSPHOROTHIOIC ACID, O,O-DIMETHYL O-(4-NITRO-M-TOLYL)ESTER; O,O-DIMETHYL O-4-NITRO-M-TOLYL PHOSPHOROTHIOATE; O,O-DIMETHYL O-(3-METHYL-4-NITROPHENYL)PHOSPHOROTHIOATE; O,O-DIMETHYL O-(4-NITRO-M-TOLYL)PHOSPHOROTHIOATE; DIMETHYL 3-METHYL-4-NITROPHENYL PHOSPHOROTHIONATE; ACCOTHION; AGROTHION; BAY 41831; FOLITHION; MEP; METATHION; METATHIONE; NITROPHOS; NUVANOL; S 5660; SUMITHION; VERTHION; OMS 43; ENT 25,715; PST09678
CHEMICAL FAMILY: ORGANOPHOSPHATE
MOLECULAR FORMULA: C9-H12-N-O5-P-S
MOLECULAR WEIGHT: 277.25
CERCLA RATINGS (SCALE 0-3): HEALTH=3 FIRE=U REACTIVITY=0 PERSISTENCE=2
NFPA RATINGS (SCALE 0-4): HEALTH=4 FIRE=U REACTIVITY=0

COMPONENTS AND CONTAMINANTS

COMPONENT: FENITROTHION ***PERCENT:*** 100
CAS# 122-14-5
EXPOSURE LIMITS: NO OCCUPATIONAL EXPOSURE LIMITS ESTABLISHED BY OSHA, ACGIH, OR NIOSH.
FENITROTHION: 500 POUNDS SARA SECTION 302 THRESHOLD PLANNING QUANTITY 1 POUND SARA SECTION 304 REPORTABLE QUANTITY

PHYSICAL DATA

DESCRIPTION: YELLOW OILY LIQUID ***BOILING POINT:*** 244 F (118 C) @ 0.05 MMHG
SPECIFIC GRAVITY: 1.3227 ***VAPOR PRESSURE:*** 0.000006 MMHG @ 20 C
SOLUBILITY IN WATER: 30 PPM
SOLVENT SOLUBILITY: SOLUBLE IN ALCOHOLS, ETHERS, DICHLOROMETHANE, METHANOL, XYLENE, HEXANE, PROPAN-2-OL, KETONES, ESTERS, AND AROMATIC HYDROCARBONS; LOW SOLUBILITY IN ALIPHATIC HYDROCARBONS

FIRE AND EXPLOSION DATA

FIRE AND EXPLOSION HAZARD: UNKNOWN FIRE AND EXPLOSION HAZARD.
FIREFIGHTING MEDIA: DRY CHEMICAL, CARBON DIOXIDE, HALON, WATER SPRAY OR STANDARD FOAM (1987 EMERGENCY RESPONSE GUIDEBOOK, DOT P 5800.4). FOR LARGER FIRES, USE WATER SPRAY, FOG OR STANDARD FOAM (1987 EMERGENCY RESPONSE GUIDEBOOK, DOT P 5800.4).
FIREFIGHTING: MOVE CONTAINERS FROM FIRE AREA IF POSSIBLE. FIGHT FIRE FROM MAXIMUM DISTANCE. STAY AWAY FROM STORAGE TANK ENDS. DIKE FIRE CONTROL WATER FOR LATER DISPOSAL. DO NOT SCATTER MATERIAL (1987 EMERGENCY RESPONSE GUIDEBOOK, DOT P 5800.4, GUIDE PAGE 55). EXTINGUISH ONLY IF FLOW CAN BE STOPPED; USE FLOODING AMOUNTS OF WATER AS FOG, SOLID STREAMS MAY BE INEFFECTIVE. COOL CONTAINERS WITH FLOODING AMOUNTS OF WATER FROM AS FAR A DISTANCE AS POSSIBLE. USE WATER SPRAY TO ABSORB TOXIC VAPORS. AVOID BREATHING TOXIC VAPORS; KEEP UPWIND. CONSIDER EVACUATION OF DOWNWIND AREA IF MATERIAL IS LEAKING.

TRANSPORTATION DATA

DEPARTMENT OF TRANSPORTATION HAZARD CLASSIFICATION 49 CFR 172.101: POISON B

DEPARTMENT OF TRANSPORTATION LABELING REQUIREMENTS 49 CFR 172.101 AND SUBPART E: POISON

TOXICITY

FENITROTHION: TOXICITY DATA: 378 MG/M3/4 HOURS INHALATION-RAT LC50; 890 MG/KG SKIN-RAT LD50; 2500 MG/KG SKIN-MOUSE LD50; 800 MG/KG ORAL-WOMAN TDLO; 250 MG/KG ORAL-RAT LD50; 229 MG/KG ORAL-MOUSE LD50; 500 MG/KG ORAL-GUINEA PIG LD50; 142 MG/KG ORAL-CAT LD50; 950 MG/KG INTRATRACHEAL-RAT LD50; 1000 MG/KG SUBCUTANEOUS-MOUSE LD50; 33 MG/KG INTRAVENOUS-RAT LD50; 112 MG/KG INTRAVENOUS-GUINEA PIG LD50; 300 MG/KG INTRAPERITONEAL-RAT LD50; 280 MG/KG INTRAPERITONEAL-MOUSE LD50; 1 GM/KG INTRACEREBRAL-MOUSE LD50; 290 MG/KG UNREPORTED-RAT LD50; 217 MG/KG UNREPORTED-CATTLE LD50; 142 MG/KG UNREPORTED-MAMMAL LD50; 1250 MG/KG UNREPORTED-MOUSE LD50; MUTAGENIC DATA (RTECS). CARCINOGEN STATUS: NONE. ACUTE TOXICITY LEVEL: HIGHLY TOXIC BY INHALATION; TOXIC BY DERMAL ABSORPTION AND INGESTION. TARGET EFFECTS: CHOLINESTERASE INHIBITOR. AT INCREASED RISK FROM EXPOSURE: PERSONS WITH RESPIRATORY AILMENTS, RECENT EXPOSURE TO CHOLINESTERASE INHIBITORS OR IMPAIRED CHOLINESTERASE PRODUCTION, OR LIVER MALFUNCTION.* ADDITIONAL DATA: MAY CROSS THE PLACENTA. HIGH ENVIRONMENTAL TEMPERATURES OR EXPOSURE OF THE CHEMICAL TO VISIBLE OR ULTRAVIOLET LIGHT MAY ENHANCE THE TOXICITY. INTERACTIONS WITH MEDICATIONS MAY OCCUR.*

* MAY BE BASED ON GENERAL INFORMATION ON ORGANOPHOSPHATES.

HEALTH EFFECTS AND FIRST AID

INHALATION: FENITROTHION: HIGHLY TOXIC. CHOLINESTERASE INHIBITION WAS OBSERVED IN RATS EXPOSED TO 3.030 TO 4.890 MG/M3 FOR 1 HOUR. SEE INFORMATION ON ORGANOPHOSPHATES.

ORGANOPHOSPHATES: CHOLINESTERASE INHIBITOR. **ACUTE EXPOSURE-** WHEN INHALED, THE FIRST EFFECTS OF CHOLINESTERASE INHIBITORS ARE USUALLY RESPIRATORY AND MAY INCLUDE NASAL HYPEREMIA AND WATERY DISCHARGE, COUGH, CHEST DISCOMFORT, DYSPNEA, AND WHEEZING DUE TO INCREASED BRONCHIAL SECRETIONS AND BRONCHOCONSTRICTION. IF SUFFICIENT AMOUNTS ARE ABSORBED, OTHER SYSTEMIC EFFECTS MAY BEGIN WITHIN A FEW MINUTES OR BE DELAYED FOR UP TO 12 HOURS. SYMPTOMS MAY INCLUDE PALLOR, NAUSEA, VOMITING, DIARRHEA, ABDOMINAL CRAMPS, HEADACHE, DIZZINESS, OCULAR PAIN, BLURRED VISION, MIOSIS OR IN SOME CASES, ESPECIALLY INITIALLY, MYDRIASIS, LACRIMATION, SALIVATION, SWEATING, AND CONFUSION. OTHER REPORTED CENTRAL NERVOUS SYSTEM OR NEUROMUSCULAR EFFECTS MAY INCLUDE ATAXIA, SLURRED SPEECH, AREFLEXIA, WEAKNESS, FATIGUE, FASCICULATIONS, TWITCHING, TREMORS POSSIBLY OF THE TONGUE AND EYELIDS, AND EVENTUALLY PARALYSIS OF THE EXTREMITIES AND POSSIBLY OF THE RESPIRATORY MUSCLES. IN SEVERE CASES THERE MAY ALSO BE INVOLUNTARY DEFECATION AND URINATION, CYANOSIS, PSYCHOSIS, HYPERGLYCEMIA, ACUTE PANCREATITIS, CARDIAC IRREGULARITIES, PULMONARY EDEMA, UNCONSCIOUSNESS, CONVULSIONS, AND COMA. DEATH IS PRIMARILY DUE TO RESPIRATORY FAILURE, ALTHOUGH CARDIOVASCULAR EFFECTS INCLUDING CARDIAC ARREST MAY ALSO BE IMPLICATED. LONG TERM SEQUELAE ARE RARE BUT MAY INCLUDE NEUROPSYCHIATRIC DISORDERS AND MYOPATHY WITH MUSCLE TENDERNESS. **CHRONIC EXPOSURE-** REPEATED OR PROLONGED EXPOSURE MAY RESULT IN THE EFFECTS OF ACUTE EXPOSURE. OTHER EFFECTS REPORTED IN WORKERS REPEATEDLY EXPOSED INCLUDE IMPAIRED MEMORY AND CONCENTRATION, ACUTE PSYCHOSIS, SEVERE DEPRESSIONS, IRRITABILTY, CONFUSION, APATHY, EMOTIONAL LABILITY, SOCIAL WITHDRAWAL, CONFUSION, HEADACHE, SPEECH DIFFICULTIES, DELAYED REACTION TIMES, SPATIAL DISORIENTATION, NIGHTMARES, SLEEPWALKING, AND DROWSINESS OR INSOMNIA. AN INFLUENZA-LIKE CONDITION WITH HEADACHE, NAUSEA, WEAKNESS, ANOREXIA AND MALAISE HAS ALSO BEEN REPORTED.

FIRST AID- REMOVE FROM EXPOSURE AREA TO FRESH AIR IMMEDIATELY. IF BREATHING HAS STOPPED, GIVE ARTIFICIAL RESPIRATION. MAINTAIN AIRWAY AND BLOOD PRESSURE AND ADMINISTER OXYGEN IF AVAILABLE. KEEP AFFECTED PERSON WARM AND AT REST. TREAT SYMPTOMATICALLY AND SUPPORTIVELY. ADMINISTRATION OF OXYGEN SHOULD BE PERFORMED BY QUALIFIED PERSONNEL. GET MEDICAL ATTENTION IMMEDIATELY.

SKIN CONTACT: FENITROTHION: TOXIC. SEE INFORMATION ON ORGANOPHOSPHATES.

ORGANOPHOSPHATES: CHOLINESTERASE INHIBITOR. **ACUTE EXPOSURE-** LOCALIZED SWEATING AND FASCICULATIONS MAY OCCUR AT THE SITE OF CONTACT. IF SUFFICIENT AMOUNTS ARE ABSORBED, OTHER EFFECTS OF CHOLINESTERASE INHIBITION AS DESCRIBED IN ACUTE INHALATION MAY OCCUR. SYMPTOMS MAY BE DELAYED 2-3 HOURS, BUT USUALLY NO MORE THAN 12 HOURS. THE RATE OF ABSORPTION IS INCREASED BY THE PRESENCE OF DERMATITIS OR HIGH AMBIENT TEMPERATURES. **CHRONIC EXPOSURE-** REPEATED OR PROLONGED EXPOSURE MAY CAUSE EFFECTS AS DESCRIBED IN ACUTE EXPOSURE. SOME ORGANOPHOSPHATES MAY CAUSE SENSITIZATION.

FIRST AID- REMOVE CONTAMINATED CLOTHING IMMEDIATELY. WASH CONTAMINATED AREAS WITH SOAP AND WATER FOLLOWED BY ALCOHOL (ARENA, POISONING, 4TH ED.). EMERGENCY PERSONNEL SHOULD WEAR GLOVES AND AVOID CONTAMINATION. TREAT RESPIRATORY DIFFICULTY WITH ARTIFICIAL RESPIRATION. GET MEDICAL ATTENTION IMMEDIATELY.

EYE CONTACT: FENITROTHION: SEE INFORMATION ON ORGANOPHOSPHATES.

ORGANOPHOSPHATES: CHOLINESTERASE INHIBITOR. **ACUTE EXPOSURE-** DIRECT CONTACT MAY CAUSE PAIN, HYPEREMIA, LACRIMATION, TWITCHING OF THE EYELIDS, MIOSIS, AND CILIARY MUSCLE SPASM WITH LOSS OF ACCOMODATION, BLURRED OR DIMMED VISION AND BROWACHE. SOMETIMES MYDRIASIS MAY OCCUR INSTEAD OF MIOSIS. WITH SUFFICIENT EXPOSURE, OTHER SYMPTOMS OF CHOLINESTERASE INHIBITION AS DESCRIBED IN ACUTE INHALATION MAY OCCUR. **CHRONIC EXPOSURE-** REPEATED OR PROLONGED EXPOSURE MAY CAUSE EFFECTS AS DESCRIBED IN ACUTE EXPOSURE. SOME COMPOUNDS HAVE CAUSED TOXIC EFFECTS ON THE CRYSTALLINE LENS, CONJUNCTIVAL THICKENING AND OBSTRUCTION OF THE NASOLACRIMAL CANALS WHEN USED AS MIOTIC EYEDROPS.

FIRST AID- IRRIGATE EYES WITH WATER OR SALINE SOLUTION. IF SYMPTOMS OF POISONING OCCUR, TREAT RESPIRATORY DIFFICULTY WITH ARTIFICIAL RESPIRATION AND OXYGEN. OBSERVE PATIENT FOR AT LEAST 24-36 HOURS (GOSSELIN, CLINICAL TOXICOLOGY OF COMMERCIAL PRODUCTS, 5TH ED.). GET MEDICAL ATTENTION IMMEDIATELY. OXYGEN SHOULD BE ADMINISTERED BY QUALIFIED MEDICAL PERSONNEL.

INGESTION: FENITROTHION: TOXIC. DAILY DOSES OF 2.5 AND 5 MG/MAN FOR 5 DAYS WERE EXCRETED WITHIN 12 HOURS. NEGATIVE RESULTS WERE OBSERVED IN STUDIES ON DELAYED NEUROTOXICITY IN HENS. SEE INFORMATION ON ORGANOPHOSPHATES.

ORGANOPHOSPHATES: CHOLINESTERASE INHIBITOR. **ACUTE EXPOSURE-** WHEN INGESTED, THE FIRST EFFECTS MAY BE NAUSEA, VOMITING, ANOREXIA, ABDOMINAL CRAMPS AND DIARRHEA. GASTROINTESTINAL ABSORPTION MAY CAUSE THE SYMPTOMS OF CHOLINESTERASE INHIBITION AS DESCRIBED IN ACUTE INHALATION. SYMPTOMS MAY BEGIN WITHIN MINUTES OR BE DELAYED. **CHRONIC EXPOSURE-** REPEATED INGESTION MAY CAUSE EFFECTS AS DESCRIBED IN ACUTE EXPOSURE.

FIRST AID- IF PERSON IS ALERT AND RESPIRATION IS NOT DEPRESSED, GIVE SYRUP OF IPECAC FOLLOWED BY WATER (IF VOMITING OCCURS, KEEP HEAD BELOW HIPS TO PREVENT ASPIRATION). IF CONSCIOUSNESS LEVEL DECLINES OR VOMITING HAS NOT OCCURRED IN 15 MINUTES EMPTY STOMACH BY GASTRIC LAVAGE WITH THE AID OF CUFFED ENDOTRACHEAL TUBE USING ISOTONIC SALINE OR 5% SODIUM BICARBONATE FOLLOW WITH ACTIVATED CHARCOAL. ESTABLISH AND MAINTAIN AIRWAY. TREAT RESPIRATORY DIFFICULTY WITH ARTIFICIAL RESPIRATION AND OXYGEN. DO NOT GIVE MORPHINE, AMINOPHYLLINE, PHENOTHIAZINES, RESERPINE, FUROSEMIDE, OR ETHACRYNIC ACID (MORGAN, RECOGNITION AND MANAGEMENT OF PESTICIDE POISONINGS, 3RD ED.). TREAT SYMPTOMATICALLY AND SUPPORTIVELY. ADMINISTRATION OF OXYGEN AND LAVAGE MUST BE PERFORMED BY QUALIFIED MEDICAL PERSONNEL. GET MEDICAL ATTENTION IMMEDIATELY.

ANTIDOTE: THE FOLLOWING ANTIDOTE(S) HAVE BEEN RECOMMENDED. HOWEVER, THE DECISION AS TO WHETHER THE SEVERITY OF POISONING REQUIRES ADMINISTRATION OF ANY ANTIDOTE AND ACTUAL DOSE REQUIRED SHOULD BE MADE BY QUALIFIED MEDICAL PERSONNEL.

FOR CHOLINESTERASE INHIBITORS: ESTABLISH CLEAR AIRWAY AND TISSUE OXYGENATION BY ASPIRATION OF SECRETIONS, AND IF NECESSARY, BY ASSISTED PULMONARY VENTILATION WITH OXYGEN. IMPROVE TISSUE OXYGENATION AS MUCH AS POSSIBLE BEFORE ADMINISTERING ATROPINE TO MINIMIZE THE RISK OF VENTRICULAR FIBRILLATION. ADMINISTER ATROPINE SULFATE INTRAVENOUSLY, OR INTRAMUSCULARLY IF IV INJECTION IS NOT POSSIBLE. IN MODERATELY SEVERE POISONING ADMINISTER ATROPINE SULFATE, 0.4-2.0 MG REPEATED EVERY 15 MINUTES UNTIL ATROPINIZATION IS ACHIEVED (TACHYCARDIA, FLUSHING, DRY MOUTH, MYDRIASIS). MAINTAIN ATROPINIZATION BY REPEATED DOSES FOR 2-12 HOURS, OR LONGER, DEPENDING ON THE SEVERITY OF POISONING. THE APPEARANCE OF RALES IN THE LUNG BASES, MIOSIS, SALIVATION, NAUSEA, BRADYCARDIA, ARE ALL INDICATIONS OF INADEQUATE ATROPINIZATION. SEVERELY POISONED INDIVIDUALS MAY EXHIBIT REMARKABLE TOLERANCE TO ATROPINE; TWO OR MORE TIMES THE DOSAGES SUGGESTED ABOVE MAY BE NEEDED. PERSONS NOT POISONED OR ONLY SLIGHTLY POISONED, HOWEVER, MAY DEVELOP SIGNS OF ATROPINE TOXICITY FROM SUCH LARGE DOSAGES: FEVER, MUSCLE FIBRILLATIONS, AND DELIRIUM ARE THE MAIN SIGNS OF ATROPINE TOXICITY. IF THESE SIGNS APPEAR WHILE THE PATIENT IS FULLY ATROPINIZED, ATROPINE ADMINISTRATION SHOULD BE DISCONTINUED, AT LEAST TEMPORARILY. OBSERVE TREATED PATIENTS CLOSELY AT LEAST 24 HOURS TO INSURE THAT SYMPTOMS (POSSIBLY PULMONARY EDEMA) DO NOT RECUR AS ATROPINIZATION WEARS OFF. IN VERY SEVERE POISONINGS, METABOLIC DISPOSITION OF TOXICANT MAY REQUIRE SEVERAL HOURS OR DAYS DURING WHICH ATROPINIZATION MUST BE MAINTAINED. MARKEDLY LOWER LEVELS OF URINARY

METABOLITES INDICATE THAT ATROPINE DOSAGE CAN BE TAPERED OFF. AS DOSAGE IS REDUCED, CHECK THE LUNG BASES FREQUENTLY FOR RALES. IF RALES ARE HEARD OR OTHER SYMPTOMS RETURN, RE-ESTABLISH ATROPINIZATION PROMPTLY (MORGAN, RECOGNITION AND MANAGEMENT OF PESTICIDE POISONINGS, 3RD ED.). ADMINISTRATION OF ANTIDOTE MUST BE PERFORMED BY QUALIFIED MEDICAL PERSONNEL.

IN CASES OF SEVERE POISONING BY ORGANOPHOSPHATE PESTICIDES IN WHICH RESPIRATORY DEPRESSION, MUSCLE WEAKNESS AND TWITCHINGS ARE SEVERE, GIVE PRALIDOXIME (PROTOPAM-AYERST, 2-PAM), 1.0 GRAM INTRAVENOUSLY AT NO MORE THAN 0.5 GRAM PER MINUTE. DOSAGE OF PRALIDOXIME MAY BE REPEATED IN 1-2 HOURS, THEN AT 10-12 HOUR INTERVALS IF NEEDED. IN VERY SEVERE POISONINGS, DOSAGE RATES MAY BE DOUBLED. TREATMENT WITH PRALIDOXIME WILL BE MOST EFFECTIVE IF GIVEN WITHIN THIRTY-SIX HOURS AFTER POISONING (MORGAN, RECOGNITION AND MANAGEMENT OF PESTICIDE POISONINGS, 3RD ED.). ANTIDOTE SHOULD BE ADMINISTERED BY QUALIFIED MEDICAL PERSONNEL.

REACTIVITY

REACTIVITY: STABLE UNDER NORMAL TEMPERATURES AND PRESSURES.

INCOMPATIBILITIES: FENITROTHION: ALKALINE CONDITIONS: MAY CAUSE HYDROLYSIS. IRON: MAY CAUSE DECOMPOSITION. OXIDIZERS (STRONG): FIRE AND EXPLOSION HAZARD.

DECOMPOSITION: THERMAL DECOMPOSITION PRODUCTS MAY INCLUDE TOXIC AND HAZARDOUS FUMES OF SULFUR, NITROGEN AND PHOSPHORUS.

POLYMERIZATION: HAZARDOUS POLYMERIZATION HAS NOT BEEN REPORTED TO OCCUR UNDER NORMAL TEMPERATURES AND PRESSURES.

STORAGE AND DISPOSAL

OBSERVE ALL FEDERAL, STATE AND LOCAL REGULATIONS WHEN STORING OR DISPOSING OF THIS SUBSTANCE. FOR ASSISTANCE, CONTACT THE DISTRICT DIRECTOR OF THE ENVIRONMENTAL PROTECTION AGENCY.

STORAGE

STORE IN ACCORDANCE WITH 40 CFR 165 RECOMMENDED PROCEDURES FOR THE DISPOSAL AND STORAGE OF PESTICIDES AND PESTICIDE CONTAINERS.

STORE AWAY FROM INCOMPATIBLE SUBSTANCES.

THRESHOLD PLANNING QUANTITY (TPQ): THE SUPERFUND AMENDMENTS AND REAUTHORIZATION ACT (SARA) SECTION 302 REQUIRES THAT EACH FACILITY WHERE ANY EXTREMELY HAZARDOUS SUBSTANCE IS PRESENT IN A QUANTITY EQUAL TO OR GREATER THAN THE TPQ ESTABLISHED FOR THAT SUBSTANCE NOTIFY THE STATE EMERGENCY RESPONSE COMMISSION FOR THE STATE IN WHICH IT IS LOCATED. SECTION 303 OF SARA REQUIRES THESE FACILITIES TO PARTICIPATE IN LOCAL EMERGENCY RESPONSE PLANNING (40 CFR 355.30).

DISPOSAL

DISPOSAL MUST BE IN ACCORDANCE WITH 40 CFR 165 RECOMMENDED PROCEDURES FOR THE DISPOSAL AND STORAGE OF PESTICIDES AND PESTICIDE CONTAINERS.

CONDITIONS TO AVOID

NONE REPORTED.

SPILL AND LEAK PROCEDURES

OCCUPATIONAL SPILL: DO NOT TOUCH SPILLED MATERIAL. STOP LEAK IF YOU CAN DO IT WITHOUT RISK. USE WATER SPRAY TO REDUCE VAPORS. FOR SMALL SPILLS, TAKE UP WITH SAND OR OTHER ABSORBENT MATERIAL AND PLACE INTO CONTAINERS FOR LATER DISPOSAL. FOR SMALL DRY SPILLS, WITH A CLEAN SHOVEL PLACE MATERIAL INTO CLEAN, DRY CONTAINERS AND COVER. MOVE CONTAINERS FROM SPILL AREA. FOR LARGER SPILLS, DIKE FAR AHEAD OF SPILL FOR LATER DISPOSAL. KEEP UNNECESSARY PEOPLE AWAY. ISOLATE HAZARD AREA AND DENY ENTRY. VENTILATE CLOSED SPACES BEFORE ENTERING.

REPORTABLE QUANTITY (RQ): 1 POUND THE SUPERFUND AMENDMENTS AND REAUTHORIZATION ACT (SARA) SECTION 304 REQUIRES THAT A RELEASE EQUAL TO OR GREATER THAN THE REPORTABLE QUANTITY FOR THIS SUBSTANCE BE IMMEDIATELY REPORTED TO THE LOCAL EMERGENCY PLANNING COMMITTEE AND THE STATE EMERGENCY RESPONSE COMMISSION (40 CFR 355.40). IF THE RELEASE OF THIS SUBSTANCE IS REPORTABLE UNDER CERCLA SECTION 103, THE NATIONAL RESPONSE CENTER MUST BE NOTIFIED IMMEDIATELY AT (800) 424-8802 OR (202) 426-2675 IN THE METROPOLITAN WASHINGTON, D.C. AREA (40 CFR 302.6).

PROTECTIVE EQUIPMENT

VENTILATION: PROCESS ENCLOSURE RECOMMENDED.

RESPIRATOR: THE FOLLOWING RESPIRATORS ARE RECOMMENDED BASED ON INFORMATION FOUND IN THE PHYSICAL DATA, TOXICITY AND HEALTH EFFECTS SECTIONS. THEY ARE RANKED IN ORDER FROM MINIMUM TO MAXIMUM RESPIRATORY PROTECTION. THE SPECIFIC RESPIRATOR SELECTED MUST BE BASED ON CONTAMINATION LEVELS FOUND IN THE WORK PLACE, MUST NOT EXCEED THE WORKING LIMITS OF THE RESPIRATOR AND BE JOINTLY APPROVED BY THE NATIONAL INSTITUTE FOR OCCUPATIONAL SAFETY AND HEALTH AND THE MINE SAFETY AND HEALTH ADMINISTRATION (NIOSH-MSHA).

TYPE 'C' SUPPLIED-AIR RESPIRATOR WITH A FULL FACEPIECE OPERATED IN PRESSURE-DEMAND OR OTHER POSITIVE PRESSURE MODE OR WITH A FULL FACEPIECE, HELMET OR HOOD OPERATED IN CONTINOUS-FLOW MODE.

SELF-CONTAINED BREATHING APPARATUS WITH A FULL FACEPIECE OPERATED IN PRESSURE-DEMAND OR OTHER POSITIVE PRESSURE MODE.

FOR FIREFIGHTING AND OTHER IMMEDIATELY DANGEROUS TO LIFE OR HEALTH CONDITIONS:

SELF-CONTAINED BREATHING APPARATUS WITH FULL FACEPIECE OPERATED IN PRESSURE-DEMAND OR OTHER POSITIVE PRESSURE MODE.

SUPPLIED-AIR RESPIRATOR WITH FULL FACEPIECE AND OPERATED IN PRESSURE-DEMAND OR OTHER POSITIVE PRESSURE MODE IN COMBINATION WITH AN AUXILIARY SELF-CONTAINED BREATHING APPARATUS OPERATED IN PRESSURE-DEMAND OR OTHER POSITIVE PRESSURE MODE.

CLOTHING: EMPLOYEE MUST WEAR APPROPRIATE PROTECTIVE (IMPERVIOUS) CLOTHING AND EQUIPMENT TO PREVENT ANY POSSIBILITY OF SKIN CONTACT WITH THIS SUBSTANCE.

GLOVES: EMPLOYEE MUST WEAR APPROPRIATE PROTECTIVE GLOVES TO PREVENT CONTACT WITH THIS SUBSTANCE.

EYE PROTECTION: EMPLOYEE MUST WEAR SPLASH-PROOF OR DUST-RESISTANT SAFETY GOGGLES AND A FACESHIELD TO PREVENT CONTACT WITH THIS SUBSTANCE.

EMERGENCY WASH FACILITIES: WHERE THERE IS ANY POSSIBILITY THAT AN EMPLOYEE'S EYES AND/OR SKIN MAY BE EXPOSED TO THIS SUBSTANCE, THE EMPLOYER SHOULD PROVIDE AN EYE WASH FOUNTAIN AND QUICK DRENCH SHOWER WITHIN THE IMMEDIATE WORK AREA FOR EMERGENCY USE.

AUTHORIZED BY- OCCUPATIONAL HEALTH SERVICES, INC.

CREATION DATE: 10/04/89 ***REVISION DATE:*** 06/20/90

MATERIAL SAFETY DATA SHEET

OCCUPATIONAL HEALTH SERVICES, INC.
AGRICULTURE AND PESTICIDE DIVISION
450 SEVENTH AVENUE, SUITE 2407
NEW YORK, NEW YORK 10123
1-800-445-MSDS OR (212) 967-1100

EMERGENCY CONTACT:
JOHN S. BRANSFORD, JR. (615) 292-1180

SUBSTANCE IDENTIFICATION

CAS-NUMBER 101-42-8

SUBSTANCE: **FENURON**

TRADE NAMES/SYNONYMS: UREA, N,N-DIMETHYL-N'-PHENYL-; UREA, 1,1-DIMETHYL-3-PHENYL-; N,N-DIMETHYL-N'-PHENYLUREA; 1,1-DIMETHYL-3-PHENYLUREA; N-PHENYL-N',N'-DIMETHYLUREA; 3-PHENYL-1,1-DIMETHYLUREA; DIBAR; DYBAR; FALISILVAN; FENULON; FENIDIM; BEET-KLEEN; PDU; C9H12N2O; PST09679

CHEMICAL FAMILY: SUBSTITUTED UREA

MOLECULAR FORMULA: C6-H5-N-H-C-O-N-(C-H3)2

MOLECULAR WEIGHT: 164.20

CERCLA RATINGS (SCALE 0-3): HEALTH=1 FIRE=1 REACTIVITY=0 PERSISTENCE=0

NFPA RATINGS (SCALE 0-4): HEALTH=1 FIRE=1 REACTIVITY=0

COMPONENTS AND CONTAMINANTS

COMPONENT: FENURON ***PERCENT:*** 100

CAS# 101-42-8

OTHER CONTAMINANTS: NONE

EXPOSURE LIMITS: NO OCCUPATIONAL EXPOSURE LIMITS ESTABLISHED BY OSHA, ACGIH, OR NIOSH.

PHYSICAL DATA

DESCRIPTION: COLORLESS TO WHITE CRYSTALLINE SOLID.

MELTING POINT: 268-271 F (131-133 C) ***SPECIFIC GRAVITY:*** 1.08 @ 25 C

VAPOR PRESSURE: NEGLIGIBLE ***SOLUBILITY IN WATER:*** 0.385% @ 25 C

SOLVENT SOLUBILITY: SOLUBLE IN 1,2-DICHLOROETHANE AND TRICHLOROETHYLENE; SLIGHTLY SOLUBLE IN HYDROCARBONS.

FIRE AND EXPLOSION DATA

FIRE AND EXPLOSION HAZARD: SLIGHT FIRE HAZARD WHEN EXPOSED TO HEAT OR FLAME.

FIREFIGHTING MEDIA: DRY CHEMICAL, CARBON DIOXIDE, HALON, WATER SPRAY OR STANDARD FOAM (1987 EMERGENCY RESPONSE GUIDEBOOK, DOT P 5800.4). FOR LARGER FIRES, USE WATER SPRAY, FOG OR STANDARD FOAM (1987 EMERGENCY RESPONSE GUIDEBOOK, DOT P 5800.4).

FIREFIGHTING: MOVE CONTAINERS FROM FIRE AREA IF POSSIBLE. FIGHT FIRE FROM MAXIMUM DISTANCE. STAY AWAY FROM STORAGE TANK ENDS. DIKE FIRE CONTROL WATER FOR LATER DISPOSAL. DO NOT SCATTER MATERIAL (1987 EMERGENCY RESPONSE GUIDEBOOK, DOT P 5800.4, GUIDE PAGE 55). EXTINGUISH USING AGENT SUITABLE FOR TYPE OF SURROUNDING FIRE. USE WATER IN FLOODING QUANTITIES AS FOG. KEEP SPARKS, FLAMES AND OTHER SOURCES OF IGNITION AWAY. KEEP MATERIAL OUT OF WATER SOURCES AND SEWERS. DO NOT TOUCH MATERIAL AND AVOID BREATHING DUSTS AND FUMES FROM BURNING MATERIAL. KEEP UPWIND.

TOXICITY

FENURON: TOXICITY DATA: 6400 MG/KG ORAL-RAT LD50; 4700 MG/KG ORAL-MOUSE LD50; 4700 MG/KG ORAL-RABBIT LD50; 3200 MG/KG ORAL-GUINEA PIG LD50; MUTAGENIC DATA (RTECS). CARCINOGEN STATUS: NONE. ACUTE TOXICITY LEVEL: SLIGHTLY TOXIC BY INGESTION. TARGET EFFECTS: NO DATA AVAILABLE.

HEALTH EFFECTS AND FIRST AID

INHALATION: FENURON: **ACUTE EXPOSURE**- MANY SUBSTITUTED UREA HERBICIDES ARE MODERATELY IRRITATING TO THE MUCOUS MEMBRANES. **CHRONIC EXPOSURE**- NO DATA AVAILABLE.

FIRST AID- REMOVE FROM EXPOSURE AREA TO FRESH AIR IMMEDIATELY. IF BREATHING HAS STOPPED, PERFORM ARTIFICIAL RESPIRATION. KEEP PERSON WARM AND AT REST. TREAT SYMPTOMATICALLY AND SUPPORTIVELY. GET MEDICAL ATTENTION IMMEDIATELY.

SKIN CONTACT: FENURON: **ACUTE EXPOSURE**- A 33% AQUEOUS PASTE WAS PRACTICALLY NONIRRITATING TO THE INTACT SKIN OF GUINEA-PIGS; HOWEVER THIS MATERIAL WAS MODERATELY IRRITATING TO ABRADED SKIN OF GUINEA PIGS. **CHRONIC EXPOSURE**- NO DATA AVAILABLE.

FIRST AID- REMOVE CONTAMINATED CLOTHING AND SHOES IMMEDIATELY. WASH AFFECTED AREA WITH SOAP OR MILD DETERGENT AND LARGE AMOUNTS OF WATER UNTIL NO EVIDENCE OF CHEMICAL REMAINS (APPROXIMATELY 15-20 MINUTES). GET MEDICAL ATTENTION IMMEDIATELY.

EYE CONTACT: FENURON: **ACUTE EXPOSURE**- MANY SUBSTITUTED UREA HERBICIDES ARE MODERATELY IRRITATING TO THE EYES. **CHRONIC EXPOSURE**- NO DATA AVAILABLE.

FIRST AID- WASH EYES IMMEDIATELY WITH LARGE AMOUNTS OF WATER OR NORMAL SALINE, OCCASIONALLY LIFTING UPPER AND LOWER LIDS, UNTIL NO EVIDENCE OF CHEMICAL REMAINS (APPROXIMATELY 15-20 MINUTES). GET MEDICAL ATTENTION IMMEDIATELY.

INGESTION: FENURON: **ACUTE EXPOSURE**- A LETHAL DOSE IN RATS WAS 6400 MG/KG; NO SYMPTOMS WERE REPORTED **CHRONIC EXPOSURE**- ANEMIA, HYPOTHYROIDISM AND STRUCTURAL ALTERATIONS IN THE LIVER, KIDNEY, SPLEEN AND MYOCARDIUM WERE OBSERVED IN GUINEA PIGS FED 15 TO 150 MG/KG/DAY FOR 10 MONTHS. ANOREXIA AND INCOORDINATION PROGRESSING TO DEATH WERE PRODUCED IN COWS AND SHEEP RECEIVING 2 TO 5 DAILY DOSES OF 500 MG/KG. NECROPSY REVEALED CONGESTION OF LUNGS AND MYOCARDIAL HEMORRHAGES. RECOVERY WAS EXTREMELY SLOW FOR SURVIVING ANIMALS.

FIRST AID- REMOVE BY GASTRIC LAVAGE AND CATHARSIS. MAINTAIN BLOOD PRESSURE AND AIRWAY. GIVE OXYGEN IF RESPIRATION IS DEPRESSED. DO NOT PERFORM GASTRIC LAVAGE IF VICTIM IS UNCONSCIOUS. GET MEDICAL ATTENTION IMMEDIATELY (DREISBACH, HANDBOOK OF POISONING, 12TH ED.). ADMINISTRATION OF LAVAGE OR OXYGEN SHOULD BE PERFORMED BY QUALIFIED MEDICAL PERSONNEL.

ANTIDOTE: NO SPECIFIC ANTIDOTE. TREAT SYMPTOMATICALLY AND SUPPORTIVELY.

REACTIVITY

REACTIVITY: STABLE UNDER NORMAL TEMPERATURES AND PRESSURES.

INCOMPATIBILITIES: FENURON: ACIDS (STRONG): HYDROLYZES. ALKALIES (STRONG): HYDROLYZES. OXIDIZERS (STRONG): FIRE AND EXPLOSION HAZARD.

DECOMPOSITION: THERMAL DECOMPOSITION PRODUCTS MAY INCLUDE TOXIC OXIDES OF CARBON AND NITROGEN.

POLYMERIZATION: HAZARDOUS POLYMERIZATION HAS NOT BEEN REPORTED TO OCCUR UNDER NORMAL TEMPERATURES AND PRESSURES.

STORAGE AND DISPOSAL

OBSERVE ALL FEDERAL, STATE AND LOCAL REGULATIONS WHEN STORING OR DISPOSING OF THIS SUBSTANCE. FOR ASSISTANCE, CONTACT THE DISTRICT DIRECTOR OF THE ENVIRONMENTAL PROTECTION AGENCY.

****STORAGE****

STORE IN ACCORDANCE WITH 40 CFR 165 RECOMMENDED PROCEDURES FOR THE DISPOSAL AND STORAGE OF PESTICIDES AND PESTICIDE CONTAINERS. STORE AWAY FROM INCOMPATIBLE SUBSTANCES.

****DISPOSAL****

DISPOSAL MUST BE IN ACCORDANCE WITH 40 CFR 165 RECOMMENDED PROCEDURES FOR THE DISPOSAL AND STORAGE OF PESTICIDES AND PESTICIDE CONTAINERS.

CONDITIONS TO AVOID

MAY BURN BUT DOES NOT IGNITE READILY. CONTAINERS MAY EXPLODE IN HEAT OF FIRE.

SPILL AND LEAK PROCEDURES

OCCUPATIONAL SPILL: DO NOT TOUCH SPILLED MATERIAL. STOP LEAK IF YOU CAN DO IT WITHOUT RISK. USE WATER SPRAY TO REDUCE VAPORS. FOR SMALL SPILLS, TAKE UP WITH SAND OR OTHER ABSORBENT MATERIAL AND PLACE INTO CONTAINERS FOR LATER DISPOSAL. FOR SMALL DRY SPILLS, WITH A CLEAN SHOVEL PLACE MATERIAL INTO CLEAN, DRY CONTAINERS AND COVER. MOVE CONTAINERS FROM SPILL AREA. FOR LARGER SPILLS, DIKE FAR AHEAD OF SPILL FOR LATER DISPOSAL. KEEP UNNECESSARY PEOPLE AWAY. ISOLATE HAZARD AREA AND DENY ENTRY. VENTILATE CLOSED SPACES BEFORE ENTERING.

PROTECTIVE EQUIPMENT

VENTILATION: PROVIDE GENERAL DILUTION VENTILATION.

RESPIRATOR: THE FOLLOWING RESPIRATORS ARE RECOMMENDED BASED ON INFORMATION FOUND IN THE PHYSICAL DATA, TOXICITY AND HEALTH EFFECTS SECTIONS. THEY ARE RANKED IN ORDER FROM MINIMUM TO MAXIMUM RESPIRATORY PROTECTION. THE SPECIFIC RESPIRATOR SELECTED MUST BE BASED ON CONTAMINATION LEVELS FOUND IN THE WORK PLACE, MUST NOT EXCEED THE WORKING LIMITS OF THE RESPIRATOR AND BE JOINTLY APPROVED BY THE NATIONAL INSTITUTE FOR OCCUPATIONAL SAFETY AND HEALTH AND THE MINE SAFETY AND HEALTH ADMINISTRATION (NIOSH-MSHA).

CHEMICAL CARTRIDGE RESPIRATOR WITH AN ORGANIC VAPOR CARTRIDGE(S) WITH A FULL FACEPIECE AND ORGANIC VAPOR CARTRIDGE(S) IN COMBINATION WITH A DUST AND MIST FILTER.

POWERED AIR-PURIFYING RESPIRATOR WITH A TIGHT-FITTING FACEPIECE AND ORGANIC VAPOR CARTRIDGE(S) IN COMBINATION WITH A HIGH-EFFICIENCY PARTICULATE FILTER.

TYPE 'C' SUPPLIED-AIR RESPIRATOR WITH A FULL FACEPIECE OPERATED IN A PRESSURE-DEMAND OR OTHER POSITIVE PRESSURE MODE.

SELF-CONTAINED BREATHING APPARATUS WITH A FULL FACEPIECE OPERATED IN PRESSURE-DEMAND OR OTHER POSITIVE PRESSURE MODE.

FOR FIREFIGHTING AND OTHER IMMEDIATELY DANGEROUS TO LIFE OR HEALTH CONDITIONS:

SELF-CONTAINED BREATHING APPARATUS WITH FULL FACEPIECE OPERATED IN PRESSURE-DEMAND OR OTHER POSITIVE PRESSURE MODE.

SUPPLIED-AIR RESPIRATOR WITH FULL FACEPIECE AND OPERATED IN PRESSURE-DEMAND OR OTHER POSITIVE PRESSURE MODE IN COMBINATION WITH AN AUXILIARY SELF-CONTAINED BREATHING APPARATUS OPERATED IN PRESSURE-DEMAND OR OTHER POSITIVE PRESSURE MODE.

CLOTHING: EMPLOYEE MUST WEAR APPROPRIATE PROTECTIVE (IMPERVIOUS) CLOTHING AND EQUIPMENT TO PREVENT REPEATED OR PROLONGED SKIN CONTACT WITH THIS SUBSTANCE.

GLOVES: EMPLOYEE MUST WEAR APPROPRIATE PROTECTIVE GLOVES TO PREVENT CONTACT WITH THIS SUBSTANCE.

EYE PROTECTION: EMPLOYEE MUST WEAR SPLASH-PROOF OR DUST-RESISTANT SAFETY GOGGLES TO PREVENT EYE CONTACT WITH THIS SUBSTANCE.

EMERGENCY EYE WASH: WHERE THERE IS ANY POSSIBILITY THAT AN EMPLOYEE'S EYES MAY BE EXPOSED TO THIS SUBSTANCE, THE EMPLOYER SHOULD PROVIDE AN EYE WASH FOUNTAIN WITHIN THE IMMEDIATE WORK AREA FOR EMERGENCY USE.

AUTHORIZED BY- OCCUPATIONAL HEALTH SERVICES, INC.

CREATION DATE: 10/04/89 ***REVISION DATE:*** 05/07/90

MATERIAL SAFETY DATA SHEET

OCCUPATIONAL HEALTH SERVICES, INC.
AGRICULTURE AND PESTICIDE DIVISION
450 SEVENTH AVENUE, SUITE 2407

EMERGENCY CONTACT:
JOHN S. BRANSFORD, JR. (615) 292-1180

NEW YORK, NEW YORK 10123
1-800-445-MSDS OR (212) 967-1100

SUBSTANCE IDENTIFICATION

CAS-NUMBER 14484-64-1
SUBSTANCE: **FERBAM**
TRADE NAMES/SYNONYMS: TRIS(DIMETHYLDITHIOCARBAMATO) IRON; IRON TRIS(DIMETHYLDITHIOCARBAMATE); IRON (III) DIMETHYLDITHIOCARBAMATE; FERRIC DIMETHYLDITHIOCARBAMATE; (OC-6-11)-TRIS(DIMETHYLCARBAMODITHIOATO-S,S')IRON; FERRIC N,N-DIMETHYLDITHIOCARBAMATE; FERMATE; FERRADOW; FERBERK; FUKLASIN ULTRA; HEXAFERB; KARBAM BLACK; STAUFFER FERBAM; ENT 14,689; PST09680
CHEMICAL FAMILY: THIOCARBAMATE ORGANOMETALLIC
MOLECULAR FORMULA: C9-H18-N3-S6.FE
MOLECULAR WEIGHT: 416.51
CERCLA RATINGS (SCALE 0-3): HEALTH=2 FIRE=1 REACTIVITY=0 PERSISTENCE=3
NFPA RATINGS (SCALE 0-4): HEALTH=2 FIRE=1 REACTIVITY=0

COMPONENTS AND CONTAMINANTS

COMPONENT: FERBAM ***PERCENT:*** 100
CAS# 14484-64-1
OTHER CONTAMINANTS: NONE
EXPOSURE LIMITS: FERBAM: 10 MG/M3 OSHA TWA (TOTAL DUST) 10 MG/M3 ACGIH TWA

PHYSICAL DATA

DESCRIPTION: ODORLESS, BLACK OR DARK COLORED FLUFFY POWDER
BOILING POINT: DECOMPOSES ***MELTING POINT:*** 356 F (180 C) DECOM
SPECIFIC GRAVITY: >1 ***VAPOR PRESSURE:*** NEGLIGIBLE ***PH:*** 5.0 SATURATED SOL
SOLUBILITY IN WATER: 0.01%
SOLVENT SOLUBILITY: SOLUBLE IN ACETONE, ACETONITRILE, CHLOROFORM, PYRIDINE; INSOLUBLE IN ETHANOL

FIRE AND EXPLOSION DATA

FIRE AND EXPLOSION HAZARD: SLIGHT FIRE HAZARD WHEN EXPOSED TO HEAT OR FLAME.
LOWER EXPLOSIVE LIMIT: 0.55 G/L (DUST) ***AUTOIGNITION TEMP.:*** 302 F (150 C) LAYER
FIREFIGHTING MEDIA: DRY CHEMICAL, CARBON DIOXIDE, HALON, WATER SPRAY OR STANDARD FOAM (1987 EMERGENCY RESPONSE GUIDEBOOK, DOT P 5800.4).
FOR LARGER FIRES, USE WATER SPRAY, FOG OR STANDARD FOAM (1987 EMERGENCY RESPONSE GUIDEBOOK, DOT P 5800.4).
FIREFIGHTING: MOVE CONTAINER FROM FIRE AREA IF POSSIBLE. DO NOT SCATTER SPILLED MATERIAL WITH HIGH PRESSURE WATER STREAMS. DIKE FIRE CONTROL WATER FOR LATER DISPOSAL (1987 EMERGENCY RESPONSE GUIDEBOOK, DOT P 5800.4, GUIDE PAGE 31).
USE AGENTS SUITABLE FOR TYPE OF SURROUNDING FIRE. AVOID BREATHING HAZARDOUS VAPORS, KEEP UPWIND.

TOXICITY

FERBAM: TOXICITY DATA: 1130 MG/KG ORAL-RAT LD50; 3400 MG/KG ORAL-MOUSE LD50; 3 GM/KG ORAL-RABBIT LDLO; 2 GM/KG ORAL-GUINEA PIG LDLO; 2700 MG/KG INTRAPERITONEAL-RAT LD50; 3 GM/KG INTRAPERITONEAL-MOUSE LD50; 1500 MG/KG INTRAPERITONEAL-RABBIT LDLO; 2300 MG/KG INTRAPERITONEAL-GUINEA PIG LDLO; MUTAGENIC DATA (RTECS); REPRODUCTIVE EFFECTS DATA (RTECS); TUMORIGENIC DATA (RTECS). CARCINOGEN STATUS: ANIMAL INADEQUATE EVIDENCE (IARC GROUP-3). AN EVALUATION OF THE CARCINOGENICITY OF THIS COMPOUND WAS NOT MADE DUE TO THE INSUFFICIENT DATA THAT WAS AVAILABLE. FERBAN REACTS WITH NITRITE UNDER MILDLY ACID CONDITIONS TO FORM N-NITROSODIMETHYLAMINE, WHICH HAS BEEN SHOWN TO BE CARCINOGENIC IN SEVEN ANIMAL SPECIES. LOCAL EFFECTS: IRRITANT- INHALATION, SKIN AND EYES. ACUTE TOXICITY LEVEL: MODERATELY TOXIC BY INGESTION. TARGET EFFECTS: NO DATA AVAILABLE. ADDITONAL DATA: INTERACTIONS WITH ALCOHOL MAY OCCUR.

HEALTH EFFECTS AND FIRST AID

INHALATION: FERBAM: IRRITANT. **ACUTE EXPOSURE-** MAY CAUSE IRRITATION OF THE UPPER RESPIRATORY TRACT WITH NASAL STUFFINESS, HOARSENESS AND COUGH. **CHRONIC EXPOSURE-** PROLONGED OR REPEATED EXPOSURE MAY CAUSE IRRITATION.
FIRST AID- REMOVE FROM EXPOSURE AREA TO FRESH AIR IMMEDIATELY. IF BREATHING HAS STOPPED, PERFORM ARTIFICIAL RESPIRATION. KEEP PERSON WARM AND AT REST. TREAT SYMPTOMATICALLY AND SUPPORTIVELY. GET MEDICAL ATTENTION IMMEDIATELY.

SKIN CONTACT: FERBAM: IRRITANT. **ACUTE EXPOSURE-** MAY CAUSE IRRITATION. PERSONS WHO HAVE ALLERGIC REACTIONS TO SULFUR COMPOUNDS MAY DEVELOP ITCHING, REDNESS, AND ECZEMATOID DERMATITIS. **CHRONIC EXPOSURE-** PROLONGED OR REPEATED EXPOSURE MAY CAUSE DERMATITIS.
FIRST AID- REMOVE CONTAMINATED CLOTHING AND SHOES IMMEDIATELY. WASH AFFECTED AREA WITH SOAP OR MILD DETERGENT AND LARGE AMOUNTS OF WATER UNTIL NO EVIDENCE OF CHEMICAL REMAINS (APPROXIMATELY 15-20 MINUTES). GET MEDICAL ATTENTION IMMEDIATELY.

EYE CONTACT: FERBAM: IRRITANT. **ACUTE EXPOSURE-** MAY CAUSE IRRITATION. **CHRONIC EXPOSURE-** PROLONGED OR REPEATED EXPOSURE MAY CAUSE CONJUNCTIVITIS.
FIRST AID- WASH EYES IMMEDIATELY WITH LARGE AMOUNTS OF WATER OR NORMAL SALINE, OCCASIONALLY LIFTING UPPER AND LOWER LIDS, UNTIL NO EVIDENCE OF CHEMICAL REMAINS (APPROXIMATELY 15-20 MINUTES). GET MEDICAL ATTENTION IMMEDIATELY.

INGESTION: FERBAM: **ACUTE EXPOSURE-** MAY CAUSE NAUSEA, VOMITING, DIARRHEA AND OTHER GASTROINTESTINAL DISTURBANCES. **CHRONIC EXPOSURE-** ADVERSE EFFECTS ON FERTILITY, THE NEWBORN, AND THE FETUS WAS OBSERVED IN CHRONIC INGESTION STUDIES OF PREGNANT RATS. FEMALE RATS FED 96 MG/KG/DAY DEVELOPED ATAXIA WHICH LED TO A PARALYSIS OF THE THE HINDLIMBS. 0.5% OF FERBAN IN THE DIET OF 20 RATS FOR 30 DAYS WAS LETHAL IN HALF OF THE RATS; SYMPTOMS OF ANEMIA AND MINOR ABNORMALITIES OF THE LUNG, LIVER, KIDNEY, AND BONE MARROW WERE REPORTED.
FIRST AID- IF VIGOROUS EMESIS HAS NOT ALREADY OCCURRED AND VICTIM IS FULLY ALERT, GIVE SYRUP OF IPECAC, FOLLOWED BY 1-2 GLASSES OF WATER TO INDUCE VOMITING (ADULTS, 12 YEARS AND OLDER: 30 ML; CHILDREN UNDER 12: 15 ML). IF CONSCIOUSNESS LEVEL DECLINES OR VOMITING HAS NOT OCCURRED IN 15 MINUTES, EMPTY THE STOMACH BY INTUBATION, ASPIRATION, AND LAVAGE, USING ALL AVAILABLE MEANS TO AVOID ASPIRATION OF VOMITUS. AFTER ASPIRATION OF THE STOMACH AND WASHING WITH ISOTONIC SALINE OR SODIUM BICARBONATE, INSTILL 30-50 GM OF ACTIVATED CHARCOAL IN 3-4 OUNCES OF WATER THROUGH THE STOMACH TUBE TO LIMIT ABSORPTION OF REMAINING TOXICANT. IF THE IRRITANT PROPERTIES OF THE TOXICANT FAIL TO PRODUCE A BOWEL MOVEMENT IN 4 HOURS, ADMINISTER SODIUM OR MAGNESIUM SULFATE AS A CATHARTIC: 0.25 GM/KG BODY WEIGHT IN 1-6 OUNCES OF WATER. ADMINISTER GLUCOSE-CONTAINING FLUIDS INTRAVENOUSLY TO ACCELERATE EXCRETION OF TOXICANT. (MORGAN, RECOGNITION AND MANAGEMENT OF PESTICIDE POISONINGS, THIRD EDITION) GET MEDICAL ATTENTION. TREATMENT SHOULD BE BE ADMINISTERED BY QUALIFIED MEDICAL PERSONNEL.
ANTIDOTE: NO SPECIFIC ANTIDOTE. TREAT SYMPTOMATICALLY AND SUPPORTIVELY.

REACTIVITY

REACTIVITY: STABLE UNDER COLD TEMPERATURES; TENDS TO DECOMPOSE ON PROLONGED STORAGE OR EXPOSURE TO MOISTURE AND HEAT.
INCOMPATIBILITIES: FERBAM: ALKALINE PESTICIDES: INCOMPATIBLE. COPPER: INCOMPATIBLE. LIME: INCOMPATIBLE. MERCURY: INCOMPATIBLE. OXIDIZING AGENTS: MAY CAUSE FIRE AND EXPLOSION HAZARD.
DECOMPOSITION: THERMAL DECOMPOSITION PRODUCTS MAY INCLUDE TOXIC OXIDES OF NITROGEN, SULFUR AND CARBON.
POLYMERIZATION: HAZARDOUS POLYMERIZATION HAS NOT BEEN REPORTED TO OCCUR UNDER NORMAL TEMPERATURES AND PRESSURES.

STORAGE AND DISPOSAL

OBSERVE ALL FEDERAL, STATE AND LOCAL REGULATIONS WHEN STORING OR DISPOSING OF THIS SUBSTANCE. FOR ASSISTANCE, CONTACT THE DISTRICT DIRECTOR OF THE ENVIRONMENTAL PROTECTION AGENCY.

STORAGE

STORE IN ACCORDANCE WITH 40 CFR 165 RECOMMENDED PROCEDURES FOR THE DISPOSAL AND STORAGE OF PESTICIDES AND PESTICIDE CONTAINERS.
STORE AWAY FROM INCOMPATIBLE SUBSTANCES.
STORE AWAY FROM HEAT, MOISTURE, AND IGNITION SOURCES; THE DECOMPOSITION PRODUCTS ARE FLAMMABLE.

DISPOSAL

DISPOSAL MUST BE IN ACCORDANCE WITH 40 CFR 165 RECOMMENDED PROCEDURES FOR THE DISPOSAL AND STORAGE OF PESTICIDES AND PESTICIDE CONTAINERS.

CONDITIONS TO AVOID

MAY BURN BUT DOES NOT IGNITE READILY. AVOID CONTACT WITH STRONG OXIDIZERS, EXCESSIVE HEAT, SPARKS, OR OPEN FLAME.

SPILL AND LEAK PROCEDURES

OCCUPATIONAL SPILL: STOP LEAK IF YOU CAN DO IT WITHOUT RISK. FOR SMALL SPILLS, TAKE UP WITH SAND OR OTHER ABSORBENT MATERIAL AND PLACE INTO CLEAN, DRY CONTAINERS FOR LATER DISPOSAL. KEEP UNNECESSARY PEOPLE AWAY. ISOLATE HAZARD AREA AND DENY ENTRY.

PROTECTIVE EQUIPMENT

VENTILATION: PROVIDE LOCAL EXHAUST VENTILATION AND/OR GENERAL DILUTION VENTILATION TO MEET PUBLISHED EXPOSURE LIMITS.

RESPIRATOR: THE FOLLOWING RESPIRATORS AND MAXIMUM USE CONCENTRATIONS ARE RECOMMENDATIONS BY THE U.S. DEPARTMENT OF HEALTH AND HUMAN SERVICES, NIOSH POCKET GUIDE TO CHEMICAL HAZARDS; NIOSH CRITERIA DOCUMENTS OR BY THE U.S. DEPARTMENT OF LABOR, 29 CFR 1910 SUBPART Z. THE SPECIFIC RESPIRATOR SELECTED MUST BE BASED ON CONTAMINATION LEVELS FOUND IN THE WORK PLACE, MUST NOT EXCEED THE WORKING LIMITS OF THE RESPIRATOR AND BE JOINTLY APPROVED BY THE NATIONAL INSTITUTE FOR OCCUPATIONAL SAFETY AND HEALTH AND THE MINE SAFETY AND HEALTH ADMINISTRATION (NIOSH-MSHA).

FERBAM:

50 MG/M3- ANY DUST RESPIRATOR EXCEPT SINGLE-USE RESPIRATOR.

100 MG/M3- ANY DUST RESPIRATOR EXCEPT SINGLE-USE AND QUARTER MASK RESPIRATORS. ANY SUPPLIED-AIR RESPIRATOR. ANY SELF-CONTAINED BREATHING APPARATUS. ANY AIR-PURIFYING FULL FACEPIECE RESPIRATOR WITH A HIGH-EFFICIENCY PARTICULATE FILTER.

250 MG/M3- ANY POWERED AIR-PURIFYING RESPIRATOR WITH A DUST FILTER. ANY SUPPLIED-AIR RESPIRATOR OPERATED IN CONTINUOUS FLOW MODE.

500 MG/M3- ANY AIR-PURIFYING FULL FACEPIECE RESPIRATOR WITH A HIGH-EFFICIENCY PARTICULATE FILTER. ANY SELF-CONTAINED BREATHING APPARATUS WITH A FULL FACEPIECE. ANY SUPPLIED-AIR RESPIRATOR WITH A FULL FACEPIECE. ANY POWERED AIR-PURIFYING RESPIRATOR WITH A TIGHT-FITTING FACEPIECE AND A HIGH-EFFICIENCY PARTICULATE FILTER. ANY SUPPLIED-AIR RESPIRATOR WITH A TIGHT-FITTING FACEPIECE OPERATED IN A CONTINUOUS FLOW MODE.

7500 MG/M3- ANY SUPPLIED-AIR RESPIRATOR WITH A HALF-MASK AND OPERATED IN A PRESSURE-DEMAND OR OTHER POSITIVE PRESSURE MODE.

ESCAPE- ANY AIR-PURIFYING FULL FACEPIECE RESPIRATOR WITH A HIGH-EFFICIENCY PARTICULATE FILTER. ANY APPROPRIATE ESCAPE-TYPE SELF-CONTAINED BREATHING APPARATUS.

FOR FIREFIGHTING AND OTHER IMMEDIATELY DANGEROUS TO LIFE OR HEALTH CONDITIONS:

SELF-CONTAINED BREATHING APPARATUS WITH FULL FACEPIECE OPERATED IN PRESSURE-DEMAND OR OTHER POSITIVE PRESSURE MODE.

SUPPLIED-AIR RESPIRATOR WITH FULL FACEPIECE AND OPERATED IN PRESSURE-DEMAND OR OTHER POSITIVE PRESSURE MODE IN COMBINATION WITH AN AUXILIARY SELF-CONTAINED BREATHING APPARATUS OPERATED IN PRESSURE-DEMAND OR OTHER POSITIVE PRESSURE MODE.

CLOTHING: EMPLOYEE MUST WEAR APPROPRIATE PROTECTIVE (IMPERVIOUS) CLOTHING AND EQUIPMENT TO PREVENT REPEATED OR PROLONGED SKIN CONTACT WITH THIS SUBSTANCE.

GLOVES: EMPLOYEE MUST WEAR APPROPRIATE PROTECTIVE GLOVES TO PREVENT CONTACT WITH THIS SUBSTANCE.

EYE PROTECTION: EMPLOYEE MUST WEAR SPLASH-PROOF OR DUST-RESISTANT SAFETY GOGGLES TO PREVENT EYE CONTACT WITH THIS SUBSTANCE.

EMERGENCY EYE WASH: WHERE THERE IS ANY POSSIBILITY THAT AN EMPLOYEE'S EYES MAY BE EXPOSED TO THIS SUBSTANCE, THE EMPLOYER SHOULD PROVIDE AN EYE WASH FOUNTAIN WITHIN THE IMMEDIATE WORK AREA FOR EMERGENCY USE.

AUTHORIZED BY- OCCUPATIONAL HEALTH SERVICES, INC.

CREATION DATE: 10/04/89 ***REVISION DATE:*** 07/12/90

MATERIAL SAFETY DATA SHEET

OCCUPATIONAL HEALTH SERVICES, INC.
AGRICULTURE AND PESTICIDE DIVISION
450 SEVENTH AVENUE, SUITE 2407
NEW YORK, NEW YORK 10123
1-800-445-MSDS OR (212) 967-1100

EMERGENCY CONTACT:
JOHN S. BRANSFORD, JR. (615) 292-1180

SUBSTANCE IDENTIFICATION

CAS-NUMBER 6552-21-2

SUBSTANCE: FENSULFOTHION OXYGEN ANALOG

TRADE NAMES/SYNONYMS: PHOSPHORIC ACID, DIETHYL 4-(METHYLSULFINYL)PHENYL ESTER; DIETHYL 4-(METHYLSULFINYL)PHENYL PHOSPHATE; PHOSPHORIC ACID, DIETHYL P-(METHYLSULFINYL)PHENYL ESTER; DIETHYL P-(METHYLSULFINYL)PHENYL PHOSPHATE; DASANIT OXYGEN ANALOG; FENSULFOTHION OXON; DASANIT O; DASANIT O ANALOG; C11H17O5PS; PST09684

CHEMICAL FAMILY: ESTER
ORGANOPHOSPHATE
SULFINYL

MOLECULAR FORMULA: C11-H17-O5-P-S

MOLECULAR WEIGHT: 292.29

CERCLA RATINGS (SCALE 0-3): HEALTH=3 FIRE=1 REACTIVITY=0 PERSISTENCE=0

NFPA RATINGS (SCALE 0-4): HEALTH=U FIRE=1 REACTIVITY=0

COMPONENTS AND CONTAMINANTS

COMPONENT: FENSULFOTHION OXYGEN ANALOG ***PERCENT:*** 100.0
CAS# 6552-21-2

OTHER CONTAMINANTS: NONE

EXPOSURE LIMITS: NO OCCUPATIONAL EXPOSURE LIMITS ESTABLISHED BY OSHA, ACGIH, OR NIOSH.

PHYSICAL DATA

DESCRIPTION: TAN CRYSTALS. ***MELTING POINT:*** NOT AVAILABLE

SPECIFIC GRAVITY: NOT AVAILABLE ***SOLUBILITY IN WATER:*** NOT AVAILABLE

FIRE AND EXPLOSION DATA

FIRE AND EXPLOSION HAZARD: SLIGHT FIRE HAZARD WHEN EXPOSED TO HEAT OR FLAME.

DUST-AIR MIXTURES MAY IGNITE OR EXPLODE.

FIREFIGHTING MEDIA: DRY CHEMICAL, CARBON DIOXIDE, HALON, WATER SPRAY OR STANDARD FOAM (1987 EMERGENCY RESPONSE GUIDEBOOK, DOT P 5800.4).

FOR LARGER FIRES, USE WATER SPRAY, FOG OR STANDARD FOAM (1987 EMERGENCY RESPONSE GUIDEBOOK, DOT P 5800.4).

FIREFIGHTING: MOVE CONTAINERS FROM FIRE AREA IF POSSIBLE (1987 EMERGENCY RESPONSE GUIDEBOOK, DOT P 5800.4, GUIDE PAGE 53).

EXTINGUISH USING AGENT SUITABLE FOR TYPE OF SURROUNDING FIRE. AVOID BREATHING VAPORS AND DUSTS. KEEP UPWIND.

TOXICITY

FENSULFOTHION OXYGEN ANALOG: TOXICITY DATA: 1200 UG/KG INTRAPERITONEAL-RAT LD50; 4200 UG/KG INTRACEREBRAL-MOUSE LD50. CARCINOGEN STATUS: NONE. ACUTE TOXICITY LEVEL: INSUFFICIENT DATA. TARGET EFFECTS: CHOLINESTERASE INHIBITOR. AT INCREASED RISK FROM EXPOSURE: PERSONS WITH RESPIRATORY AILMENTS, RECENT EXPOSURE TO CHOLINESTERASE INHIBITORS OR IMPAIRED CHOLINESTERASE PRODUCTION, OR LIVER MALFUNCTION.* ADDITIONAL DATA: MAY CROSS THE PLACENTA. HIGH ENVIRONMENTAL TEMPERATURES OR EXPOSURE OF THE CHEMICAL TO VISIBLE OR ULTRAVIOLET LIGHT MAY ENHANCE THE TOXICITY. INTERACTIONS WITH MEDICATIONS MAY OCCUR.*

* MAY BE BASED ON GENERAL INFORMATION ON ORGANOPHOSPHATES.

HEALTH EFFECTS AND FIRST AID

INHALATION: FENSULFOTHION OXYGEN ANALOG: SEE INFORMATION ON ORGANOPHOSPHATES.

ORGANOPHOSPHATES: CHOLINESTERASE INHIBITOR. **ACUTE EXPOSURE**- WHEN INHALED, THE FIRST EFFECTS OF CHOLINESTERASE INHIBITORS ARE USUALLY RESPIRATORY AND MAY INCLUDE NASAL HYPEREMIA AND WATERY DISCHARGE, COUGH, CHEST DISCOMFORT, DYSPNEA, AND WHEEZING DUE TO INCREASED BRONCHIAL SECRETIONS AND BRONCHOCONSTRICTION. IF SUFFICIENT AMOUNTS ARE ABSORBED, OTHER SYSTEMIC EFFECTS MAY BEGIN WITHIN A FEW MINUTES OR BE DELAYED FOR UP TO 12 HOURS. SYMPTOMS MAY INCLUDE PALLOR, NAUSEA, VOMITING, DIARRHEA, ABDOMINAL CRAMPS, HEADACHE, DIZZINESS, OCULAR PAIN, BLURRED VISION, MIOSIS OR IN SOME CASES, ESPECIALLY INITIALLY, MYDRIASIS, LACRIMATION, SALIVATION, SWEATING, AND CONFUSION. OTHER REPORTED CENTRAL NERVOUS SYSTEM OR NEUROMUSCULAR EFFECTS MAY INCLUDE ATAXIA, SLURRED SPEECH, AREFLEXIA, WEAKNESS, FATIGUE, FASCICULATIONS, TWITCHING, TREMORS POSSIBLY OF THE TONGUE AND EYELIDS, AND EVENTUALLY PARALYSIS OF THE EXTREMITIES AND POSSIBLY OF THE RESPIRATORY MUSCLES. IN SEVERE CASES THERE MAY ALSO BE INVOLUNTARY DEFECATION AND URINATION, CYANOSIS, PSYCHOSIS, HYPERGLYCEMIA, ACUTE PANCREATITIS, CARDIAC IRREGULARITIES, PULMONARY EDEMA, UNCONSCIOUSNESS, CONVULSIONS, AND COMA. DEATH IS PRIMARILY DUE TO RESPIRATORY FAILURE, ALTHOUGH CARDIOVASCULAR EFFECTS INCLUDING CARDIAC ARREST MAY ALSO BE IMPLICATED. LONG TERM SEQUELAE ARE RARE BUT MAY INCLUDE NEUROPSYCHIATRIC DISORDERS AND MYOPATHY WITH

MUSCLE TENDERNESS. **CHRONIC EXPOSURE-** REPEATED OR PROLONGED EXPOSURE MAY RESULT IN THE EFFECTS OF ACUTE EXPOSURE. OTHER EFFECTS REPORTED IN WORKERS REPEATEDLY EXPOSED INCLUDE IMPAIRED MEMORY AND CONCENTRATION, ACUTE PSYCHOSIS, SEVERE DEPRESSIONS, IRRITABILTY, CONFUSION, APATHY, EMOTIONAL LABILITY, SOCIAL WITHDRAWAL, CONFUSION, HEADACHE, SPEECH DIFFICULTIES, DELAYED REACTION TIMES, SPATIAL DISORIENTATION, NIGHTMARES, SLEEPWALKING, AND DROWSINESS OR INSOMNIA. AN INFLUENZA-LIKE CONDITION WITH HEADACHE, NAUSEA, WEAKNESS, ANOREXIA AND MALAISE HAS ALSO BEEN REPORTED.

FIRST AID- REMOVE FROM EXPOSURE AREA TO FRESH AIR IMMEDIATELY. IF BREATHING HAS STOPPED, PERFORM ARTIFICIAL RESPIRATION. KEEP PERSON WARM AND AT REST. TREAT SYMPTOMATICALLY AND SUPPORTIVELY. GET MEDICAL ATTENTION IMMEDIATELY.

SKIN CONTACT: FENSULFOTHION OXYGEN ANALOG: SEE INFORMATION ON ORGANOPHOSPHATES.
ORGANOPHOSPHATES: CHOLINESTERASE INHIBITOR. **ACUTE EXPOSURE-** LOCALIZED SWEATING AND FASCICULATIONS MAY OCCUR AT THE SITE OF CONTACT. IF SUFFICIENT AMOUNTS ARE ABSORBED, OTHER EFFECTS OF CHOLINESTERASE INHIBITION AS DESCRIBED IN ACUTE INHALATION MAY OCCUR. SYMPTOMS MAY BE DELAYED 2-3 HOURS, BUT USUALLY NO MORE THAN 12 HOURS. THE RATE OF ABSORPTION IS INCREASED BY THE PRESENCE OF DERMATITIS OR HIGH AMBIENT TEMPERATURES. **CHRONIC EXPOSURE-** REPEATED OR PROLONGED EXPOSURE MAY CAUSE EFFECTS AS DESCRIBED IN ACUTE EXPOSURE. SOME ORGANOPHOSPHATES MAY CAUSE SENSITIZATION.

FIRST AID- REMOVE CONTAMINATED CLOTHING IMMEDIATELY. WASH CONTAMINATED AREAS WITH SOAP AND WATER FOLLOWED BY ALCOHOL (ARENA, POISONING, 4TH ED.). EMERGENCY PERSONNEL SHOULD WEAR GLOVES AND AVOID CONTAMINATION. TREAT RESPIRATORY DIFFICULTY WITH ARTIFICIAL RESPIRATION. GET MEDICAL ATTENTION IMMEDIATELY.

EYE CONTACT: FENSULFOTHION OXYGEN ANALOG: SEE INFORMATION ON ORGANOPHOSPHATES.
ORGANOPHOSPHATES: CHOLINESTERASE INHIBITOR. **ACUTE EXPOSURE-** DIRECT CONTACT MAY CAUSE PAIN, HYPEREMIA, LACRIMATION, TWITCHING OF THE EYELIDS, MIOSIS, AND CILIARY MUSCLE SPASM WITH LOSS OF ACCOMODATION, BLURRED OR DIMMED VISION AND BROWACHE. SOMETIMES MYDRIASIS MAY OCCUR INSTEAD OF MIOSIS. WITH SUFFICIENT EXPOSURE, OTHER SYMPTOMS OF CHOLINESTERASE INHIBITION AS DESCRIBED IN ACUTE INHALATION MAY OCCUR. **CHRONIC EXPOSURE-** REPEATED OR PROLONGED EXPOSURE MAY CAUSE EFFECTS AS DESCRIBED IN ACUTE EXPOSURE. SOME COMPOUNDS HAVE CAUSED TOXIC EFFECTS ON THE CRYSTALLINE LENS, CONJUNCTIVAL THICKENING AND OBSTRUCTION OF THE NASOLACRIMAL CANALS WHEN USED AS MIOTIC EYEDROPS.

FIRST AID- IRRIGATE EYES WITH WATER OR SALINE SOLUTION. IF SYMPTOMS OF POISONING OCCUR, TREAT RESPIRATORY DIFFICULTY WITH ARTIFICIAL RESPIRATION AND OXYGEN. OBSERVE PATIENT FOR AT LEAST 24-36 HOURS (GOSSELIN, CLINICAL TOXICOLOGY OF COMMERCIAL PRODUCTS, 5TH ED.). GET MEDICAL ATTENTION IMMEDIATELY. OXYGEN SHOULD BE ADMINISTERED BY QUALIFIED MEDICAL PERSONNEL.

INGESTION: FENSULFOTHION OXYGEN ANALOG: NO DELAYED NEUROTOXIC RESPONSE WAS OBSERVED IN A STUDY OF FENSULFOTHION. SEE INFORMATION ON ORGANOPHOSPHATES.
ORGANOPHOSPHATES: CHOLINESTERASE INHIBITOR. **ACUTE EXPOSURE-** WHEN INGESTED, THE FIRST EFFECTS MAY BE NAUSEA, VOMITING, ANOREXIA, ABDOMINAL CRAMPS AND DIARRHEA. GASTROINTESTINAL ABSORPTION MAY CAUSE THE SYMPTOMS OF CHOLINESTERASE INHIBITION AS DESCRIBED IN ACUTE INHALATION. SYMPTOMS MAY BEGIN WITHIN MINUTES OR BE DELAYED. **CHRONIC EXPOSURE-** REPEATED INGESTION MAY CAUSE EFFECTS AS DESCRIBED IN ACUTE EXPOSURE.

FIRST AID- IF PERSON IS ALERT AND RESPIRATION IS NOT DEPRESSED, GIVE SYRUP OF IPECAC FOLLOWED BY WATER (IF VOMITING OCCURS, KEEP HEAD BELOW HIPS TO PREVENT ASPIRATION). IF CONSCIOUSNESS LEVEL DECLINES OR VOMITING HAS NOT OCCURRED IN 15 MINUTES EMPTY STOMACH BY GASTRIC LAVAGE WITH THE AID OF CUFFED ENDOTRACHEAL TUBE USING ISOTONIC SALINE OR 5% SODIUM BICARBONATE FOLLOW WITH ACTIVATED CHARCOAL. ESTABLISH AND MAINTAIN AIRWAY. TREAT RESPIRATORY DIFFICULTY WITH ARTIFICIAL RESPIRATION AND OXYGEN. DO NOT GIVE MORPHINE, AMINOPHYLLINE, PHENOTHIAZINES, RESERPINE, FUROSEMIDE, OR ETHACRYNIC ACID (MORGAN, RECOGNITION AND MANAGEMENT OF PESTICIDE POISONINGS, 3RD ED.). TREAT SYMPTOMATICALLY AND SUPPORTIVELY. ADMINISTRATION OF OXYGEN AND LAVAGE MUST BE PERFORMED BY QUALIFIED MEDICAL PERSONNEL. GET MEDICAL ATTENTION IMMEDIATELY.

ANTIDOTE: THE FOLLOWING ANTIDOTE(S) HAVE BEEN RECOMMENDED. HOWEVER, THE DECISION AS TO WHETHER THE SEVERITY OF POISONING REQUIRES ADMINISTRATION OF ANY ANTIDOTE AND ACTUAL DOSE REQUIRED SHOULD BE MADE BY QUALIFIED MEDICAL PERSONNEL.
FOR CHOLINESTERASE INHIBITORS: ESTABLISH CLEAR AIRWAY AND TISSUE OXYGENATION BY ASPIRATION OF SECRETIONS, AND IF NECESSARY, BY ASSISTED PULMONARY VENTILATION WITH OXYGEN. IMPROVE TISSUE OXYGENATION AS MUCH AS POSSIBLE BEFORE ADMINISTERING ATROPINE TO MINIMIZE THE RISK OF VENTRICULAR FIBRILLATION. ADMINISTER ATROPINE SULFATE INTRAVENOUSLY, OR INTRAMUSCULARLY IF IV INJECTION IS NOT POSSIBLE. IN MODERATELY SEVERE POISONING ADMINISTER ATROPINE SULFATE, 0.4-2.0 MG REPEATED EVERY 15 MINUTES UNTIL ATROPINIZATION IS ACHIEVED (TACHYCARDIA, FLUSHING, DRY MOUTH, MYDRIASIS). MAINTAIN ATROPINIZATION BY REPEATED DOSES FOR 2-12 HOURS, OR LONGER, DEPENDING ON THE SEVERITY OF POISONING. THE APPEARANCE OF RALES IN THE LUNG BASES, MIOSIS, SALIVATION, NAUSEA, BRADYCARDIA, ARE ALL INDICATIONS OF INADEQUATE ATROPINIZATION. SEVERELY POISONED INDIVIDUALS MAY EXHIBIT REMARKABLE TOLERANCE TO ATROPINE; TWO OR MORE TIMES THE DOSAGES SUGGESTED ABOVE MAY BE NEEDED. PERSONS NOT POISONED OR ONLY SLIGHTLY POISONED, HOWEVER, MAY DEVELOP SIGNS OF ATROPINE TOXICITY FROM SUCH LARGE DOSAGES: FEVER, MUSCLE FIBRILLATIONS, AND DELIRIUM ARE THE MAIN SIGNS OF ATROPINE TOXICITY. IF THESE SIGNS APPEAR WHILE THE PATIENT IS FULLY ATROPINIZED, ATROPINE ADMINISTRATION SHOULD BE DISCONTINUED, AT LEAST TEMPORARILY. OBSERVE TREATED PATIENTS CLOSELY AT LEAST 24 HOURS TO INSURE THAT SYMPTOMS (POSSIBLY PULMONARY EDEMA) DO NOT RECUR AS ATROPINIZATION WEARS OFF. IN VERY SEVERE POISONINGS, METABOLIC DISPOSITION OF TOXICANT MAY REQUIRE SEVERAL HOURS OR DAYS DURING WHICH ATROPINIZATION MUST BE MAINTAINED. MARKEDLY LOWER LEVELS OF URINARY METABOLITES INDICATE THAT ATROPINE DOSAGE CAN BE TAPERED OFF. AS DOSAGE IS REDUCED, CHECK THE LUNG BASES FREQUENTLY FOR RALES. IF RALES ARE HEARD OR OTHER SYMPTOMS RETURN, RE-ESTABLISH ATROPINIZATION PROMPTLY (MORGAN, RECOGNITION AND MANAGEMENT OF PESTICIDE POISONINGS, 3RD ED.). ADMINISTRATION OF ANTIDOTE MUST BE PERFORMED BY QUALIFIED MEDICAL PERSONNEL.
IN CASES OF SEVERE POISONING BY ORGANOPHOSPHATE PESTICIDES IN WHICH RESPIRATORY DEPRESSION, MUSCLE WEAKNESS AND TWITCHINGS ARE SEVERE, GIVE PRALIDOXIME (PROTOPAM-AYERST, 2-PAM), 1.0 GRAM INTRAVENOUSLY AT NO MORE THAN 0.5 GRAM PER MINUTE. DOSAGE OF PRALIDOXIME MAY BE REPEATED IN 1-2 HOURS, THEN AT 10-12 HOUR INTERVALS IF NEEDED. IN VERY SEVERE POISONINGS, DOSAGE RATES MAY BE DOUBLED. TREATMENT WITH PRALIDOXIME WILL BE MOST EFFECTIVE IF GIVEN WITHIN THIRTY-SIX HOURS AFTER POISONING (MORGAN, RECOGNITION AND MANAGEMENT OF PESTICIDE POISONINGS, 3RD ED.). ANTIDOTE SHOULD BE ADMINISTERED BY QUALIFIED MEDICAL PERSONNEL.

REACTIVITY

REACTIVITY: STABLE UNDER NORMAL TEMPERATURES AND PRESSURES.

INCOMPATIBILITIES: FENSULFOTHION OXYGEN ANALOG: OXIDIZERS (STRONG): FIRE AND EXPLOSION HAZARD.

DECOMPOSITION: THERMAL DECOMPOSITION PRODUCTS MAY INCLUDE TOXIC OXIDES OF CARBON, SULFUR, AND PHOSPHORUS.

POLYMERIZATION: HAZARDOUS POLYMERIZATION HAS NOT BEEN REPORTED TO OCCUR UNDER NORMAL TEMPERATURES AND PRESSURES.

STORAGE AND DISPOSAL

OBSERVE ALL FEDERAL, STATE AND LOCAL REGULATIONS WHEN STORING OR DISPOSING OF THIS SUBSTANCE. FOR ASSISTANCE, CONTACT THE DISTRICT DIRECTOR OF THE ENVIRONMENTAL PROTECTION AGENCY.

****STORAGE****

STORE IN ACCORDANCE WITH 40 CFR 165 RECOMMENDED PROCEDURES FOR THE DISPOSAL AND STORAGE OF PESTICIDES AND PESTICIDE CONTAINERS.
STORE AWAY FROM INCOMPATIBLE SUBSTANCES.

****DISPOSAL****

DISPOSAL MUST BE IN ACCORDANCE WITH 40 CFR 165 RECOMMENDED PROCEDURES FOR THE DISPOSAL AND STORAGE OF PESTICIDES AND PESTICIDE CONTAINERS.

CONDITIONS TO AVOID

MAY BURN BUT DOES NOT IGNITE READILY.

SPILL AND LEAK PROCEDURES

OCCUPATIONAL SPILL: DO NOT TOUCH SPILLED MATERIAL. STOP LEAK IF YOU CAN DO IT WITHOUT RISK. FOR SMALL SPILLS, TAKE UP WITH SAND OR OTHER ABSORBENT MATERIAL AND PLACE INTO CONTAINERS FOR LATER DISPOSAL. FOR SMALL DRY SPILLS, WITH A CLEAN SHOVEL PLACE MATERIAL INTO CLEAN, DRY CONTAINER AND COVER. MOVE CONTAINERS FROM SPILL AREA. FOR LARGER SPILLS, DIKE FAR AHEAD OF SPILL FOR LATER DISPOSAL. KEEP UNNECESSARY PEOPLE AWAY. ISOLATE HAZARD AREA AND DENY ENTRY.

PROTECTIVE EQUIPMENT

VENTILATION: PROVIDE LOCAL EXHAUST OR PROCESS ENCLOSURE VENTILATION SYSTEM.

RESPIRATOR: THE FOLLOWING RESPIRATORS ARE RECOMMENDED BASED ON INFORMATION FOUND IN THE PHYSICAL DATA, TOXICITY AND HEALTH EFFECTS SECTIONS. THEY ARE RANKED IN ORDER FROM MINIMUM TO MAXIMUM RESPIRATORY PROTECTION. THE SPECIFIC RESPIRATOR SELECTED MUST BE BASED ON CONTAMINATION LEVELS FOUND IN THE WORK PLACE, MUST NOT EXCEED THE WORKING LIMITS OF THE RESPIRATOR AND BE JOINTLY APPROVED BY THE NATIONAL INSTITUTE FOR OCCUPATIONAL SAFETY AND HEALTH AND THE MINE SAFETY AND HEALTH ADMINISTRATION (NIOSH-MSHA).

TYPE 'C' SUPPLIED-AIR RESPIRATOR WITH A FULL FACEPIECE OPERATED IN PRESSURE-DEMAND OR OTHER POSITIVE PRESSURE MODE OR WITH A FULL FACEPIECE, HELMET OR HOOD OPERATED IN CONTINOUS-FLOW MODE.

SELF-CONTAINED BREATHING APPARATUS WITH A FULL FACEPIECE OPERATED IN PRESSURE-DEMAND OR OTHER POSITIVE PRESSURE MODE.

FOR FIREFIGHTING AND OTHER IMMEDIATELY DANGEROUS TO LIFE OR HEALTH CONDITIONS:

SELF-CONTAINED BREATHING APPARATUS WITH FULL FACEPIECE OPERATED IN PRESSURE-DEMAND OR OTHER POSITIVE PRESSURE MODE.

SUPPLIED-AIR RESPIRATOR WITH FULL FACEPIECE AND OPERATED IN PRESSURE-DEMAND OR OTHER POSITIVE PRESSURE MODE IN COMBINATION WITH AN AUXILIARY SELF-CONTAINED BREATHING APPARATUS OPERATED IN PRESSURE-DEMAND OR OTHER POSITIVE PRESSURE MODE.

CLOTHING: EMPLOYEE MUST WEAR APPROPRIATE PROTECTIVE (IMPERVIOUS) CLOTHING AND EQUIPMENT TO PREVENT ANY POSSIBILITY OF SKIN CONTACT WITH THIS SUBSTANCE.

GLOVES: EMPLOYEE MUST WEAR APPROPRIATE PROTECTIVE GLOVES TO PREVENT CONTACT WITH THIS SUBSTANCE.

EYE PROTECTION: EMPLOYEE MUST WEAR SPLASH-PROOF OR DUST-RESISTANT SAFETY GOGGLES AND A FACESHIELD TO PREVENT CONTACT WITH THIS SUBSTANCE.

EMERGENCY WASH FACILITIES: WHERE THERE IS ANY POSSIBILITY THAT AN EMPLOYEE'S EYES AND/OR SKIN MAY BE EXPOSED TO THIS SUBSTANCE, THE EMPLOYER SHOULD PROVIDE AN EYE WASH FOUNTAIN AND QUICK DRENCH SHOWER WITHIN THE IMMEDIATE WORK AREA FOR EMERGENCY USE.

AUTHORIZED BY- OCCUPATIONAL HEALTH SERVICES, INC.

CREATION DATE: 06/21/90 ***REVISION DATE:*** 06/21/90

MATERIAL SAFETY DATA SHEET

OCCUPATIONAL HEALTH SERVICES, INC.
AGRICULTURE AND PESTICIDE DIVISION
450 SEVENTH AVENUE, SUITE 2407
NEW YORK, NEW YORK 10123
1-800-445-MSDS OR (212) 967-1100

EMERGENCY CONTACT:
JOHN S. BRANSFORD, JR. (615) 292-1180

SUBSTANCE IDENTIFICATION

CAS-NUMBER 2385-85-5

SUBSTANCE: **MIREX**

TRADE NAMES/SYNONYMS: 1,3,4-METHENO-1H-CYCLOBUTA(CD)PENTALENE, 1,1A,2,2,3,3A,4,5,5,5A,5B,6 -DODECACHLOROOCTAHYDRO-; 1,3,4,-METHENO-1H-CYCLOBUTA(CD)PENTALENE, DODECACHLOROOCTAHYDRO-; 1,1A,2,2,3,3A,4,5,5,5A,5B,6-DODECACHLOROOCTAHYDRO-1,3,4-METHENO-1H -CYCLOBUTA(CD)PENTALENE; DODECACHLOROOCTAHYDRO-1,3,4-METHENO-1H-CYCLOBUTA(CD)PENTALENE; HEXACHLOROCYCLOPENTADIENE DIMER; DECHLORANE; GC 1283; PARAMEX PERCHLORODIHOMOCUBANE; PERCHLOROPENTACYCLODECANE; DODECACHLOROPENTACYCLODECANE; ENT 25719; C10CL12; PST09690

CHEMICAL FAMILY: HALOGEN COMPOUND, ALICYCLIC

MOLECULAR FORMULA: C10-CL12

MOLECULAR WEIGHT: 545.59

CERCLA RATINGS (SCALE 0-3): HEALTH=3 FIRE=0 REACTIVITY=0 PERSISTENCE=3

NFPA RATINGS (SCALE 0-4): HEALTH=3 FIRE=0 REACTIVITY=0

COMPONENTS AND CONTAMINANTS

COMPONENT: MIREX ***PERCENT:*** 100.0

CAS# 2385-85-5

OTHER CONTAMINANTS: NONE

EXPOSURE LIMITS: MIREX: SUBJECT TO CALIFORNIA PROPOSITION 65 CANCER AND/OR REPRODUCTIVE TOXICITY WARNING AND RELEASE REQUIREMENTS-(JANUARY 1, 1988)

PHYSICAL DATA

DESCRIPTION: ODORLESS, SNOW-WHITE CRYSTALLINE SOLID.

MELTING POINT: 905 F (485 C) DECOMPOSES ***SPECIFIC GRAVITY:*** NOT AVAILABLE

VAPOR PRESSURE: 0.0000003 MMHG @ 25C ***SOLUBILITY IN WATER:*** INSOLUBLE

SOLVENT SOLUBILITY: SOLUBLE IN BENZENE, ETHANOL, DIMETHYLSULFOXIDE, DIOXANE, CARBON TETRACHLORIDE, METHYL ETHYL KETONE, XYLENE,

---

FIRE AND EXPLOSION DATA

FIRE AND EXPLOSION HAZARD: NEGLIGIBLE FIRE HAZARD WHEN EXPOSED TO HEAT OR FLAME.

FIREFIGHTING MEDIA: DRY CHEMICAL, CARBON DIOXIDE, HALON, WATER SPRAY OR STANDARD FOAM (1987 EMERGENCY RESPONSE GUIDEBOOK, DOT P 5800.4).

FOR LARGER FIRES, USE WATER SPRAY, FOG OR STANDARD FOAM (1987 EMERGENCY RESPONSE GUIDEBOOK, DOT P 5800.4).

FIREFIGHTING: MOVE CONTAINERS FROM FIRE AREA IF POSSIBLE. FIGHT FIRE FROM MAXIMUM DISTANCE. STAY AWAY FROM STORAGE TANK ENDS. DIKE FIRE CONTROL WATER FOR LATER DISPOSAL. DO NOT SCATTER MATERIAL (1987 EMERGENCY RESPONSE GUIDEBOOK, DOT P 5800.4, GUIDE PAGE 55).

USE AGENTS SUITABLE FOR TYPE OF FIRE. COOL CONTAINERS WITH FLOODING AMOUNTS OF WATER. AVOID BREATHING VAPORS OR DUSTS, KEEP UPWIND.

TOXICITY

MIREX: TOXICITY DATA: 1400 PPM INHALATION-DOMESTIC BIRD LC50; 800 MG/KG SKIN-RABBIT LD50; 235 MG/KG ORAL-RAT LD50; 125 MG/KG ORAL-HAMSTER LD50; 6 MG/KG/DAY ORAL-RAT 90-DAY LD50 (AEHLAU); MUTAGENIC DATA (RTECS); REPRODUCTIVE EFFECTS DATA (RTECS); TUMORIGENIC DATA (RTECS). CARCINOGEN STATUS: ANTICIPATED HUMAN CARCINOGEN (NTP); ANIMAL SUFFICIENT EVIDENCE (IARC GROUP 2B). IN ORAL ADMINISTRATION STUDIES, MIREX PRODUCED BENIGN AND MALIGNANT LIVER TUMORS IN MICE AND RATS OF BOTH SEXES. AN EXCESS OF LIVER TUMORS AND A SUGGESTIVE PRODUCTION OF RETICULUM-CELL SARCOMAS WERE NOTED IN MALE MICE FOLLOWING A SINGLE SUBCUTANEOUS INJECTION. INCREASED INCIDENCES OF PHEOCHROMOCYTOMAS OF THE ADRENAL GLAND, TRANSITIONAL CELL PAPILLOMAS OF THE KIDNEY, AND MONONUCLEAR CELL LEUKEMIA WERE REPORTED IN RATS (NTP TR 313). ACUTE TOXICITY LEVEL: TOXIC BY DERMAL ABSORPTION, INGESTION. TARGET EFFECTS: HEPATOTOXIN/NEPHROTOXIN. POISONING MAY AFFECT THE CENTRAL NERVOUS SYSTEM.* ADDITIONAL DATA: MAY BE STORED IN THE ADIPOSE TISSUES FOR MONTHS OR YEARS BEFORE BEING ELIMINATED FROM THE BODY. INTENSE ACTIVITY AND STARVATION MAY MOBILIZED THE PESTICIDE RESULTING IN THE REAPPEARANCE OF TOXIC SYMPTOMS. MAY CROSS THE PLACENTA AND BE EXCRETED IN BREAST MILK. STIMULANTS SUCH AS EPINEPHRINE OR EPHEDRINE MAY INDUCE VENTRICULAR FIBRILLATION.*

* MAY BE BASED ON GENERAL INFORMATION ON CHLORINATED HYDROCARBON PESTICIDES.

HEALTH EFFECTS AND FIRST AID

INHALATION: MIREX: **ACUTE EXPOSURE-** EFFECTS ON THE CENTRAL NERVOUS SYSTEM MAY OCCUR AS DESCRIBED IN ACUTE INGESTION IF SUFFICIENT AMOUNTS ARE ABSORBED THROUGH THE LUNGS. **CHRONIC EXPOSURE-** PROLONGED OR REPEATED EXPOSURE TO CHLORINATED HYDROCARBON PESTICIDES MAY CAUSE EFFECTS AS DESCRIBED IN ACUTE INGESTION.

FIRST AID- REMOVE FROM EXPOSURE AREA TO FRESH AIR IMMEDIATELY. IF BREATHING HAS STOPPED, PERFORM ARTIFICIAL RESPIRATION. KEEP PERSON WARM AND AT REST. TREAT SYMPTOMATICALLY AND SUPPORTIVELY. GET MEDICAL ATTENTION IMMEDIATELY.

SKIN CONTACT: MIREX: TOXIC. **ACUTE EXPOSURE-** A LETHAL DOSE IN RABBITS BY DERMAL ABSORPTION WAS 800 MG/KG. EFFECTS ON THE CENTRAL NERVOUS SYSTEM MAY OCCUR AS DESCRIBED IN ACUTE INGESTION IF SUFFICIENT AMOUNTS ARE ABSORBED THROUGH THE SKIN. **CHRONIC EXPOSURE-** PROLONGED OR REPEATED EXPOSURE TO CHLORINATED HYDROCARBON PESTICIDES MAY CAUSE EFFECTS AS DESCRIBED IN ACUTE INGESTION.

FIRST AID- REMOVE CONTAMINATED CLOTHING AND SHOES IMMEDIATELY. WASH AFFECTED AREA WITH SOAP OR MILD DETERGENT AND LARGE AMOUNTS OF WATER UNTIL NO EVIDENCE OF CHEMICAL REMAINS (APPROXIMATELY 15-20 MINUTES). GET MEDICAL ATTENTION IMMEDIATELY.

EYE CONTACT: MIREX: **ACUTE EXPOSURE-** NO DATA AVAILABLE. **CHRONIC EXPOSURE-** NO DATA AVAILABLE.

FIRST AID- WASH EYES IMMEDIATELY WITH LARGE AMOUNTS OF WATER OR NORMAL SALINE, OCCASIONALLY LIFTING UPPER AND LOWER LIDS, UNTIL NO EVIDENCE OF

CHEMICAL REMAINS (APPROXIMATELY 15-20 MINUTES). GET MEDICAL ATTENTION IMMEDIATELY.

INGESTION: MIREX: HEPATOTOXIN/NEPHROTOXIN/CARCINOGEN/TOXIC. **ACUTE EXPOSURE-** A LETHAL DOSE IN RATS WAS 235 MG/KG. INGESTION OF CHLORINATED HYDROCARBON PESTICIDES MAY CAUSE GASTROINTESTINAL EFFECTS OF NAUSEA, VOMITING, DIARRHEA, AND STOMACH PAINS. OTHER SYMPTOMS OF MALAISE, APPREHENSION, EXCITABILITY, DIZZINESS, HEADACHE, DISORIENTATION, ATAXIA, WEAKNESS, PARESTHESIAS, MUSCLE TWITCHING, TREMOR, CONVULSIONS, AND COMA MAY OCCUR. DEATH MAY BE DUE TO RESPIRATORY FAILURE OR VENTRICULAR FIBRILLATION. SYMPTOMS OF POISONING MAY OCCUR SEVERAL HOURS AFTER INGESTION. HYPERTROPHY OF THE LIVER WAS REPORTED IN ANIMALS. **CHRONIC EXPOSURE-** ADVERSE EFFECTS OBSERVED IN EXPERIMENTAL ANIMALS INCLUDED POOR GROWTH, HYPEREXCITABILITY, DEPRESSED HEMOGLOBIN, TREMORS, CONVULSIONS, CHRONIC MYOCARDITIS, CALCIUM DEPOSITS IN LUNGS, AORTA AND OTHER ORGANS, AND HISTOLOGIC CHANGES IN THYROID, PARATHYROID, AND TESTES. CHRONIC NEPHRITIS, HYPERPLASTIC CHANGES IN THE KIDNEY AND SEVERE NECROSIS AND DEGENERATION OF TUBULAR CELLS RESULTING IN DEATH WERE OBSERVED. FUNCTIONAL AND STRUCTURAL CHANGES IN THE LIVER INCLUDING SEVERE NECROSIS WHICH MAY HAVE BEEN FATAL WERE REPORTED; SIGNIFICANT PATHOLOGICAL CHANGES IN THE LIVER WERE OBSERVED AT DOSES AS LITTLE AS 5 PPM PER DAY. EFFECTS OF MATERNAL TOXICITY, FAILURE OF PREGNANCY, DECREASE IN FETAL SURVIVAL, REDUCED FETAL WEIGHT, AND AN INCREASED INCIDENCE OF VISCERAL AND SKELETAL ANOMALIES WERE OBSERVED IN ANIMALS STUDIES. CATARACTS WERE PRODUCED IN THE OFFSPRING OF RATS AND MICE FED MIREX. IN ORAL ADMINISTRATION STUDIES, MIREX PRODUCED BENIGN AND LIVER TUMORS IN MICE AND RATS OF BOTH SEXES. INCREASED INCIDENCES OF PHEOCHROMOCYTOMAS OF THE ADRENAL GLAND AND TRANSITIONAL CELL PAPILLOMAS OF THE KIDNEY IN MALES AND AN INCREASED INCIDENCE OF MONONUCLEAR CELL LEUKEMIA IN FEMALES WERE REPORTED IN RATS.

FIRST AID- IF VICTIM IS ALERT AND GAG REFLEX IS NOT DEPRESSED, GIVE SYRUP OF IPECAC TO INDUCE VOMITING (ADULTS AND CHILDREN 12 YEARS AND OLDER: 30 ML; CHILDREN UNDER 12: 15 ML), FOLLOWED BY 1-2 GLASSES OF WATER. OBSERVE THE VICTIM CLOSELY AFTER ADMINISTERING IPECAC. IF CONSCIOUSNESS LEVEL DECLINES, OR IF VOMITING HAS NOT OCCURRED IN 15 MINUTES, PROCEED IMMEDIATELY TO INTUBATE STOMACH. FOLLOWING EMESIS, HAVE VICTIM DRINK A SUSPENSION OF 30-50 GRAMS OF ACTIVATED CHARCOAL IN 3-4 OUNCES OF WATER TO LIMIT ABSORPTION OF TOXICANT REMAINING IN THE GUT. IF THE VICTIM IS NOT FULLY ALERT, EMPTY THE STOMACH IMMEDIATELY BY INTUBATION, ASPIRATION, AND LAVAGE, USING ISOTONIC SALINE OR 5% SODIUM BICARBONATE. AFTER ASPIRATION OF GASTRIC CONTENTS AND WASHING OF STOMACH, INSTILL 30-50 GRAMS OF ACTIVATED CHARCOAL IN 3-4 OUNCES OF WATER THROUGH STOMACH TUBE TO LIMIT ABSORPTION OF REMAINING TOXICANT. DO NOT INSTILL MILK, CREAM, OR OTHER SUBSTANCES CONTAINING VEGETABLE OR ANIMAL FATS, WHICH ENHANCE ABSORPTION OF CHLORINATED HYDROCARBONS. (EPA, RECOGNITION AND MANAGEMENT OF PESTICIDE POISONINGS, THIRD EDITION) GASTRIC LAVAGE SHOULD BE ADMINISTERED BY QUALIFIED MEDICAL PERSONNEL. SEEK MEDICAL ATTENTION IMMEDIATELY.

ANTIDOTE: NO SPECIFIC ANTIDOTE. TREAT SYMPTOMATICALLY AND SUPPORTIVELY.

REACTIVITY

REACTIVITY: STABLE UNDER NORMAL TEMPERATURES AND PRESSURES.

INCOMPATIBILITIES: MIREX: OXIDIZERS (STRONG): MAY CAUSE FIRE AND EXPLOSION HAZARD.

DECOMPOSITION: THERMAL DECOMPOSITION MAY RELEASE TOXIC AND HAZARDOUS GASES. ABOVE 500 C MAY EMIT TOXIC AND HAZARDOUS HEXACHLOROBENZENE, HEXACHLOROPENTADIENE, CARBON MONOXIDE, CARBON DIOXIDE, CARBON TETRACHLORIDE, AND PHOSGENE.

POLYMERIZATION: HAZARDOUS POLYMERIZATION HAS NOT BEEN REPORTED TO OCCUR UNDER NORMAL TEMPERATURES AND PRESSURES.

STORAGE AND DISPOSAL

OBSERVE ALL FEDERAL, STATE AND LOCAL REGULATIONS WHEN STORING OR DISPOSING OF THIS SUBSTANCE. FOR ASSISTANCE, CONTACT THE DISTRICT DIRECTOR OF THE ENVIRONMENTAL PROTECTION AGENCY.

STORAGE

STORE IN ACCORDANCE WITH 40 CFR 165 RECOMMENDED PROCEDURES FOR THE DISPOSAL AND STORAGE OF PESTICIDES AND PESTICIDE CONTAINERS.

DISPOSAL

DISPOSAL MUST BE IN ACCORDANCE WITH 40 CFR 165 RECOMMENDED PROCEDURES FOR THE DISPOSAL AND STORAGE OF PESTICIDES AND PESTICIDE CONTAINERS.

CONDITIONS TO AVOID

MAY BURN BUT DOES NOT IGNITE READILY. CONTAINERS MAY EXPLODE IN HEAT OF FIRE.

SPILL AND LEAK PROCEDURES

WATER SPILL: THE CALIFORNIA SAFE DRINKING WATER AND TOXIC ENFORCEMENT ACT OF 1986 (PROPOSITION 65) PROHIBITS CONTAMINATING ANY KNOWN SOURCE OF DRINKING WATER WITH SUBSTANCES KNOWN TO CAUSE CANCER AND/OR REPRODUCTIVE TOXICITY.

OCCUPATIONAL SPILL: DO NOT TOUCH SPILLED MATERIAL. STOP LEAK IF YOU CAN DO IT WITHOUT RISK. USE WATER SPRAY TO REDUCE VAPORS. FOR SMALL SPILLS, TAKE UP WITH SAND OR OTHER ABSORBENT MATERIAL AND PLACE INTO CONTAINERS FOR LATER DISPOSAL. FOR SMALL DRY SPILLS, WITH A CLEAN SHOVEL PLACE MATERIAL INTO CLEAN, DRY CONTAINERS AND COVER. MOVE CONTAINERS FROM SPILL AREA. FOR LARGER SPILLS, DIKE FAR AHEAD OF SPILL FOR LATER DISPOSAL. KEEP UNNECESSARY PEOPLE AWAY. ISOLATE HAZARD AREA AND DENY ENTRY. VENTILATE CLOSED SPACES BEFORE ENTERING.

PROTECTIVE EQUIPMENT

VENTILATION: PROVIDE LOCAL EXHAUST OR PROCESS ENCLOSURE VENTILATION SYSTEM.

RESPIRATOR: THE FOLLOWING RESPIRATORS ARE RECOMMENDED BASED ON INFORMATION FOUND IN THE PHYSICAL DATA, TOXICITY AND HEALTH EFFECTS SECTIONS. THEY ARE RANKED IN ORDER FROM MINIMUM TO MAXIMUM RESPIRATORY PROTECTION. THE SPECIFIC RESPIRATOR SELECTED MUST BE BASED ON CONTAMINATION LEVELS FOUND IN THE WORK PLACE, MUST NOT EXCEED THE WORKING LIMITS OF THE RESPIRATOR AND BE JOINTLY APPROVED BY THE NATIONAL INSTITUTE FOR OCCUPATIONAL SAFETY AND HEALTH AND THE MINE SAFETY AND HEALTH ADMINISTRATION (NIOSH-MSHA).

TYPE 'C' SUPPLIED-AIR RESPIRATOR WITH A FULL FACEPIECE OPERATED IN PRESSURE-DEMAND OR OTHER POSITIVE PRESSURE MODE OR WITH A FULL FACEPIECE, HELMET OR HOOD OPERATED IN CONTINOUS-FLOW MODE.

SELF-CONTAINED BREATHING APPARATUS WITH A FULL FACEPIECE OPERATED IN PRESSURE-DEMAND OR OTHER POSITIVE PRESSURE MODE.

FOR FIREFIGHTING AND OTHER IMMEDIATELY DANGEROUS TO LIFE OR HEALTH CONDITIONS:

SELF-CONTAINED BREATHING APPARATUS WITH FULL FACEPIECE OPERATED IN PRESSURE-DEMAND OR OTHER POSITIVE PRESSURE MODE.

SUPPLIED-AIR RESPIRATOR WITH FULL FACEPIECE AND OPERATED IN PRESSURE-DEMAND OR OTHER POSITIVE PRESSURE MODE IN COMBINATION WITH AN AUXILIARY SELF-CONTAINED BREATHING APPARATUS OPERATED IN PRESSURE-DEMAND OR OTHER POSITIVE PRESSURE MODE.

CLOTHING: EMPLOYEE MUST WEAR APPROPRIATE PROTECTIVE (IMPERVIOUS) CLOTHING AND EQUIPMENT TO PREVENT ANY POSSIBILITY OF SKIN CONTACT WITH THIS SUBSTANCE.

GLOVES: EMPLOYEE MUST WEAR APPROPRIATE PROTECTIVE GLOVES TO PREVENT CONTACT WITH THIS SUBSTANCE.

EYE PROTECTION: EMPLOYEE MUST WEAR SPLASH-PROOF OR DUST-RESISTANT SAFETY GOGGLES WITH OR WITHOUT A FACESHIELD TO PREVENT CONTACT WITH THIS SUBSTANCE.

EMERGENCY EYE WASH: WHERE THERE IS ANY POSSIBILITY THAT AN EMPLOYEE'S EYES MAY BE EXPOSED TO THIS SUBSTANCE, THE EMPLOYER SHOULD PROVIDE AN EYE WASH FOUNTAIN WITHIN THE IMMEDIATE WORK AREA FOR EMERGENCY USE.

AUTHORIZED BY- OCCUPATIONAL HEALTH SERVICES, INC.

CREATION DATE: 10/04/89 ***REVISION DATE:*** 07/12/90

MATERIAL SAFETY DATA SHEET

OCCUPATIONAL HEALTH SERVICES, INC.
AGRICULTURE AND PESTICIDE DIVISION
450 SEVENTH AVENUE, SUITE 2407
NEW YORK, NEW YORK 10123
1-800-445-MSDS OR (212) 967-1100

EMERGENCY CONTACT:
JOHN S. BRANSFORD, JR. (615) 292-1180

SUBSTANCE IDENTIFICATION

CAS-NUMBER 10028-22-5

SUBSTANCE: **FERRIC SULFATE**

TRADE NAMES/SYNONYMS: DIIRON TRISULFATE; IRON PERSULFATE; IRON SESQUISULFATE; IRON SULFATE (2:3); IRON(3+) SULFATE; IRON TERSULFATE; SULFURIC ACID, IRON(3+) SALT (3:2); STCC 4963818; NA 9121; PST09790

CHEMICAL FAMILY: INORGANIC SALT

MOLECULAR FORMULA: FE2-O12-S3
MOLECULAR WEIGHT: 399.88
CERCLA RATINGS (SCALE 0-3): HEALTH=U FIRE=0 REACTIVITY=0
PERSISTENCE=3
NFPA RATINGS (SCALE 0-4): HEALTH=U FIRE=0 REACTIVITY=0

COMPONENTS AND CONTAMINANTS

COMPONENT: FERRIC SULFATE ***PERCENT:*** 100
CAS# 10028-22-5
OTHER CONTAMINANTS: NONE
EXPOSURE LIMITS: FERRIC SULFATE: 1 MG(FE)/M3 ACGIH TWA

PHYSICAL DATA

DESCRIPTION: YELLOW CRYSTALS OR GRAYISH-WHITE POWDER, HYGROSCOPIC.
MELTING POINT: 896 F (480 C) ***SPECIFIC GRAVITY:*** 3.1
PH: ACIDIC IN SOLUTION ***SOLUBILITY IN WATER:*** SLIGHTLY SOLUBLE
SOLVENT SOLUBILITY: INSOLUBLE IN SULFURIC ACID AND AMMONIA

FIRE AND EXPLOSION DATA

FIRE AND EXPLOSION HAZARD: NEGLIGIBLE FIRE HAZARD WHEN EXPOSED TO HEAT OR FLAME.
FIREFIGHTING MEDIA: DRY CHEMICAL, CARBON DIOXIDE, HALON, WATER SPRAY OR STANDARD FOAM (1987 EMERGENCY RESPONSE GUIDEBOOK, DOT P 5800.4).
FOR LARGER FIRES, USE WATER SPRAY, FOG OR STANDARD FOAM (1987 EMERGENCY RESPONSE GUIDEBOOK, DOT P 5800.4).
FIREFIGHTING: MOVE CONTAINER FROM FIRE AREA IF POSSIBLE. DO NOT SCATTER SPILLED MATERIAL WITH HIGH PRESSURE WATER STREAMS. DIKE FIRE CONTROL WATER FOR LATER DISPOSAL (1987 EMERGENCY RESPONSE GUIDEBOOK, DOT P 5800.4, GUIDE PAGE 31).
USE AGENTS SUITABLE FOR TYPE OF FIRE. AVOID BREATHING HAZARDOUS VAPORS OR DUSTS, KEEP UPWIND.

TRANSPORTATION DATA

DEPARTMENT OF TRANSPORTATION HAZARD CLASSIFICATION 49 CFR 172.101: ORM-E
DEPARTMENT OF TRANSPORTATION LABELING REQUIREMENTS 49 CFR 172.101 AND SUBPART E: NONE
DEPARTMENT OF TRANSPORTATION PACKAGING REQUIREMENTS: 49 CFR 173.510 EXCEPTIONS: NONE

TOXICITY

FERRIC SULFATE: TOXICITY DATA: 601 MG/KG INTRAPERITONEAL-MOUSE LD50; MUTAGENIC DATA (RTECS). CARCINOGEN STATUS: NONE. LOCAL EFFECTS: IRRITANT- INHALATION, SKIN, AND EYES. ACUTE TOXICITY LEVEL: INSUFFICIENT DATA. TARGET EFFECTS: POISONING MAY AFFECT THE LIVER AND KIDNEYS.

HEALTH EFFECTS AND FIRST AID

INHALATION: FERRIC SULFATE: IRRITANT. **ACUTE EXPOSURE-** MAY CAUSE IRRITATION. **CHRONIC EXPOSURE-** NO DATA AVAILABLE.
FIRST AID- REMOVE FROM EXPOSURE AREA TO FRESH AIR IMMEDIATELY. IF BREATHING HAS STOPPED, PERFORM ARTIFICIAL RESPIRATION. KEEP PERSON WARM AND AT REST. TREAT SYMPTOMATICALLY AND SUPPORTIVELY. GET MEDICAL ATTENTION IMMEDIATELY.

SKIN CONTACT: FERRIC SULFATE: IRRITANT. **ACUTE EXPOSURE-** MAY CAUSE IRRITATION. **CHRONIC EXPOSURE-** REPEATED OR PROLONGED CONTACT MAY CAUSE DERMATITIS.
FIRST AID- REMOVE CONTAMINATED CLOTHING AND SHOES IMMEDIATELY. WASH AFFECTED AREA WITH SOAP OR MILD DETERGENT AND LARGE AMOUNTS OF WATER UNTIL NO EVIDENCE OF CHEMICAL REMAINS (APPROXIMATELY 15-20 MINUTES). GET MEDICAL ATTENTION IMMEDIATELY.

EYE CONTACT: FERRIC SULFATE: IRRITANT. **ACUTE EXPOSURE-** MAY CAUSE EYE IRRITATION. **CHRONIC EXPOSURE-** REPEATED OR PROLONGED CONTACT MAY CAUSE CONJUNCTIVITIS.
FIRST AID- WASH EYES IMMEDIATELY WITH LARGE AMOUNTS OF WATER OR NORMAL SALINE, OCCASIONALLY LIFTING UPPER AND LOWER LIDS, UNTIL NO EVIDENCE OF CHEMICAL REMAINS (APPROXIMATELY 15-20 MINUTES). GET MEDICAL ATTENTION IMMEDIATELY.

INGESTION: FERRIC SULFATE: CORROSIVE. **ACUTE EXPOSURE-** MAY CAUSE SEVERE GASTROINTESTINAL TRACT IRRITATION. INGESTION OF SOME SOLUBLE IRON COMPOUNDS MAY CAUSE LETHARGY, NAUSEA OR VOMITING, TARRY STOOLS, DIARRHEA, FAST AND WEAK PULSE, HYPOTENSION, DEHYDRATION, ACIDOSIS AND COMA. IF POISONING IS NOT IMMEDIATELY FATAL, THE PATIENT MAY BE ASYMPTOMATIC FOR 24 HOURS, AFTER WHICH SYMPTOMS MAY RETURN CYANOSIS, PULMONARY EDEMA, SHOCK, CONVULSIONS, ACIDOSIS, ANURIA, HYPERTHEMIA AND DEATH IN COMA WITHIN 24-48 HOURS. LIVER NECROSIS MAY OCCUR WITHIN 2 DAYS AFTER INGESTION. **CHRONIC EXPOSURE-** NO DATA AVAILABLE.
FIRST AID- IN PATIENTS NOT IN SHOCK OR COMA, INDUCE EMESIS WITH SYRUP OF IPECAC IF VOMITING HAS NOT OCCURRED. FOLLOW WITH GASTRIC LAVAGE USING DEFEROXAMINE, 2 GRAMS IN 1 LITER OF WATER CONTAINING SODIUM BICARBONATE, 20 GM/L. LEAVE 10 GRAMS OF DEFEROXAMINE IN 50 ML OF 5% SODIUM BICARBONATE IN THE STOMACH. MAINTAIN AIRWAY, BLOOD PRESSURE AND RESPIRATION. TREAT SYMPTOMATICALLY AND SUPPORTIVELY. (DREISBACH, HANDBOOK OF POISONING, 11TH ED.) GET MEDICAL ATTENTION IMMEDIATELY. TREATMENT SHOULD BE ADMINISTERED BY QUALIFIED MEDICAL PERSONNEL.
ANTIDOTE: THE FOLLOWING ANTIDOTE HAS BEEN RECOMMENDED. HOWEVER, THE DECISION AS TO WHETHER THE SEVERITY OF POISONING REQUIRES ADMINISTRATION OF ANY ANTIDOTE AND ACTUAL DOSE REQUIRED SHOULD BE MADE BY QUALIFIED MEDICAL PERSONNEL.
IRON SALT POISONING: GIVE DEFEROXAMINE, 15 MG/KG/HOUR BY CONTINUOUS INTRAVENOUS INFUSION TO A MAXIMUM OF 80 MG/KG IN EACH 12-HOUR PERIOD. MONITOR THE BLOOD PRESSURE DURING ADMINISTRATION OF DEFEROXAMINE AND REDUCE THE RATE OF ADMINISTRATION IF THE BLOOD PRESSURE FALLS. SINGLE DOSES SHOULD NOT EXCEED 1 GRAM AND THE MAXIMUM IN 24 HOURS SHOULD NOT EXCEED 6 GRAMS. DEFEROXAMINE IS HAZARDOUS IN PATIENTS WITH SEVERE RENAL DISEASE OR ANURIA, AND DIALYSIS IS NECESSARY. INJECTED DEFEROXAMINE IS ASSOCIATED WITH A HIGH RISK AND SHOULD BE RESERVED FOR SERIOUS POISONING. CONTINUE DEFEROXAMINE THERAPY UNTIL THE PATIENT IS FREE OF SYMPTOMS AND SIGNS FOR 24 HOURS (DREISBACH, HANDBOOK OF POISONING, 11TH ED.). ANTIDOTE SHOULD BE ADMINISTERED BY QUALIFIED MEDICAL PERSONNEL.

REACTIVITY

REACTIVITY: STABLE UNDER NORMAL TEMPERATURES AND PRESSURES.
INCOMPATIBILITIES: FERRIC SULFATE: COPPER: CORROSIVE COPPOR ALLOYS: CORROSIVE MILD STEEL: CORROSIVE GALVANIZED STEEL: CORROSIVE
DECOMPOSITION: THERMAL DECOMPOSITION PRODUCTS MAY INCLUDE TOXIC AND HAZARDOUS OXIDES OF IRON AND SULFUR.
POLYMERIZATION: HAZARDOUS POLYMERIZATION HAS NOT BEEN REPORTED TO OCCUR UNDER NORMAL TEMPERATURES AND PRESSURES.

CONDITIONS TO AVOID

MAY BURN BUT DOES NOT IGNITE READILY. AVOID CONTACT WITH STRONG OXIDIZERS, EXCESSIVE HEAT, SPARKS, OR OPEN FLAME.

SPILL AND LEAK PROCEDURES

OCCUPATIONAL SPILL: STOP LEAK IF YOU CAN DO IT WITHOUT RISK. FOR SMALL SPILLS, TAKE UP WITH SAND OR OTHER ABSORBENT MATERIAL AND PLACE INTO CLEAN, DRY CONTAINERS FOR LATER DISPOSAL. KEEP UNNECESSARY PEOPLE AWAY. ISOLATE HAZARD AREA AND DENY ENTRY.
REPORTABLE QUANTITY (RQ): 1000 POUNDS THE SUPERFUND AMENDMENTS AND REAUTHORIZATION ACT (SARA) SECTION 304 REQUIRES THAT A RELEASE EQUAL TO OR GREATER THAN THE REPORTABLE QUANTITY FOR THIS SUBSTANCE BE IMMEDIATELY REPORTED TO THE LOCAL EMERGENCY PLANNING COMMITTEE AND THE STATE EMERGENCY RESPONSE COMMISSION (40 CFR 355.40). IF THE RELEASE OF THIS SUBSTANCE IS REPORTABLE UNDER CERCLA SECTION 103, THE NATIONAL RESPONSE CENTER MUST BE NOTIFIED IMMEDIATELY AT (800) 424-8802 OR (202) 426-2675 IN THE METROPOLITAN WASHINGTON, D.C. AREA (40 CFR 302.6).

PROTECTIVE EQUIPMENT

VENTILATION: PROVIDE LOCAL EXHAUST VENTILATION AND/OR GENERAL DILUTION VENTILATION TO MEET PUBLISHED EXPOSURE LIMITS.
RESPIRATOR: THE FOLLOWING RESPIRATORS ARE RECOMMENDED BASED ON INFORMATION FOUND IN THE PHYSICAL DATA, TOXICITY AND HEALTH EFFECTS SECTIONS. THEY ARE RANKED IN ORDER FROM MINIMUM TO MAXIMUM RESPIRATORY PROTECTION. THE SPECIFIC RESPIRATOR SELECTED MUST BE BASED ON CONTAMINATION LEVELS FOUND IN THE WORK PLACE, MUST NOT EXCEED THE WORKING LIMITS OF THE RESPIRATOR AND BE JOINTLY APPROVED BY THE NATIONAL INSTITUTE FOR OCCUPATIONAL SAFETY AND HEALTH AND THE MINE SAFETY AND HEALTH ADMINISTRATION (NIOSH-MSHA).
DUST AND MIST RESPIRATOR WITH A FULL FACEPIECE.
AIR-PURIFYING FULL FACEPIECE RESPIRATOR WITH A HIGH-EFFICIENCY PARTICULATE FILTER.
POWERED AIR-PURIFYING RESPIRATOR WITH A TIGHT-FITTING FACEPIECE AND HIGH-EFFICIENCY PARTICULATE FILTER.
TYPE 'C' SUPPLIED-AIR RESPIRATOR WITH A FULL FACEPIECE OPERATED IN PRESSURE-DEMAND OR OTHER POSITIVE PRESSURE MODE OR WITH A FULL FACEPIECE, HELMET OR HOOD OPERATED IN CONTINUOUS-FLOW MODE.
SELF-CONTAINED BREATHING APPARATUS WITH A FULL FACEPIECE OPERATED IN

PRESSURE-DEMAND OR OTHER POSITIVE PRESSURE MODE.
FOR FIREFIGHTING AND OTHER IMMEDIATELY DANGEROUS TO LIFE OR HEALTH CONDITIONS:
SELF-CONTAINED BREATHING APPARATUS WITH FULL FACEPIECE OPERATED IN PRESSURE-DEMAND OR OTHER POSITIVE PRESSURE MODE.
SUPPLIED-AIR RESPIRATOR WITH FULL FACEPIECE AND OPERATED IN PRESSURE-DEMAND OR OTHER POSITIVE PRESSURE MODE IN COMBINATION WITH AN AUXILIARY SELF-CONTAINED BREATHING APPARATUS OPERATED IN PRESSURE-DEMAND OR OTHER POSITIVE PRESSURE MODE.

CLOTHING: PROTECTIVE CLOTHING NOT REQUIRED. AVOID REPEATED OR PROLONGED CONTACT WITH THIS SUBSTANCE.

GLOVES: PROTECTIVE GLOVES ARE NOT REQUIRED BUT RECOMMENDED.

EYE PROTECTION: EMPLOYEE MUST WEAR SPLASH-PROOF OR DUST-RESISTANT SAFETY GOGGLES TO PREVENT EYE CONTACT WITH THIS SUBSTANCE.
EMERGENCY EYE WASH: WHERE THERE IS ANY POSSIBILITY THAT AN EMPLOYEE'S EYES MAY BE EXPOSED TO THIS SUBSTANCE, THE EMPLOYER SHOULD PROVIDE AN EYE WASH FOUNTAIN WITHIN THE IMMEDIATE WORK AREA FOR EMERGENCY USE.

AUTHORIZED BY- OCCUPATIONAL HEALTH SERVICES, INC.
CREATION DATE: 11/17/89 ***REVISION DATE:*** 04/25/90

MATERIAL SAFETY DATA SHEET

OCCUPATIONAL HEALTH SERVICES, INC.
AGRICULTURE AND PESTICIDE DIVISION
450 SEVENTH AVENUE, SUITE 2407
NEW YORK, NEW YORK 10123
1-800-445-MSDS OR (212) 967-1100

EMERGENCY CONTACT:
JOHN S. BRANSFORD, JR. (615) 292-1180

SUBSTANCE IDENTIFICATION

CAS-NUMBER 10045-89-3

SUBSTANCE: **FERROUS AMMONIUM SULFATE**

TRADE NAMES/SYNONYMS: AMMONIUM FERROUS SULFATE; IRON AMMONIUM SULFATE; SULFURIC ACID, AMMONIUM IRON(2+) SALT; MOHR'S SALT; SULFURIC ACID, AMMONIUM IRON(2+) SALT (2:2:1); AMMONIUM IRON(II) SULFATE (2:1:2); FERROUS DIAMMONIUM SULFATE; STCC 4963354; NA 9122; PST09820

CHEMICAL FAMILY: INORGANIC SALT

MOLECULAR FORMULA: H8-N2.FE.2S-O4

MOLECULAR WEIGHT: 284.1

CERCLA RATINGS (SCALE 0-3): HEALTH=2 FIRE=0 REACTIVITY=0 PERSISTENCE=3

NFPA RATINGS (SCALE 0-4): HEALTH=2 FIRE=0 REACTIVITY=0

COMPONENTS AND CONTAMINANTS

COMPONENT: FERROUS AMMONIUM SULFATE ***PERCENT:*** 100
CAS# 10045-89-3

OTHER CONTAMINANTS: NONE

EXPOSURE LIMITS: FERROUS AMMONIUM SULFATE: 1 MG(FE)/M3 ACGIH TWA
1000 POUNDS CERCLA SECTION 103 REPORTABLE QUANTITY

PHYSICAL DATA

DESCRIPTION: PALE BLUE-GREEN ODORLESS CRYSTALS OR CRYSTALLINE POWDER

MELTING POINT: NOT AVAILABLE ***SPECIFIC GRAVITY:*** NOT AVAILABLE

PH: 3.0-5.0 @ 5% ***SOLUBILITY IN WATER:*** SOLUBLE

SOLVENT SOLUBILITY: INSOLUBLE IN ALCOHOL

FIRE AND EXPLOSION DATA

FIRE AND EXPLOSION HAZARD: NEGLIGIBLE FIRE HAZARD WHEN EXPOSED TO HEAT OR FLAME.

FIREFIGHTING MEDIA: DRY CHEMICAL, CARBON DIOXIDE, HALON, WATER SPRAY OR STANDARD FOAM (1987 EMERGENCY RESPONSE GUIDEBOOK, DOT P 5800.4).
FOR LARGER FIRES, USE WATER SPRAY, FOG OR STANDARD FOAM (1987 EMERGENCY RESPONSE GUIDEBOOK, DOT P 5800.4).

FIREFIGHTING: MOVE CONTAINER FROM FIRE AREA IF POSSIBLE. DO NOT SCATTER SPILLED MATERIAL WITH HIGH PRESSURE WATER STREAMS. DIKE FIRE CONTROL WATER FOR LATER DISPOSAL (1987 EMERGENCY RESPONSE GUIDEBOOK, DOT P 5800.4, GUIDE PAGE 31).
USE AGENTS SUITABLE FOR TYPE OF FIRE. AVOID BREATHING HAZARDOUS VAPORS OR DUSTS, KEEP UPWIND.

TRANSPORTATION DATA

DEPARTMENT OF TRANSPORTATION HAZARD CLASSIFICATION 49 CFR 172.101: ORM-E
DEPARTMENT OF TRANSPORTATION LABELING REQUIREMENTS 49 CFR 172.101 AND SUBPART E: NONE
DEPARTMENT OF TRANSPORTATION PACKAGING REQUIREMENTS: 49 CFR 173.510 EXCEPTIONS: NONE

TOXICITY

FERROUS AMMONIUM SULFATE: TOXICITY DATA: ANHYDROUS: NO DATA AVAILABLE. HEXAHYDRATE: 3250 MG/KG ORAL-RAT LD50. CARCINOGEN STATUS: NONE. LOCAL EFFECTS: IRRITANT- INHALATION, SKIN, AND EYES. ACUTE TOXICITY LEVEL: MODERATE TOXIC BY INGESTION. TARGET EFFECTS: IRON POISONING MAY AFFECT THE LIVER, KIDNEYS, AND CARDIOVASCULAR, RESPIRATORY, DIGESTIVE, AND CENTRAL NERVOUS SYSTEMS.

HEALTH EFFECTS AND FIRST AID

INHALATION: FERROUS AMMONIUM SULFATE: IRRITANT. **ACUTE EXPOSURE-** INHALATION OF DUST MAY IRRITATE NOSE AND THROAT AND CAUSE COUGHING OR DIFFICULT BREATHING. **CHRONIC EXPOSURE-** NO DATA AVAILABLE.

FIRST AID- REMOVE FROM EXPOSURE AREA TO FRESH AIR IMMEDIATELY. IF BREATHING HAS STOPPED, PERFORM ARTIFICIAL RESPIRATION. KEEP PERSON WARM AND AT REST. TREAT SYMPTOMATICALLY AND SUPPORTIVELY. GET MEDICAL ATTENTION IMMEDIATELY.

SKIN CONTACT: AMMONIUM FERROUS SULFATE: IRRITANT. **ACUTE EXPOSURE-** IT MAY IRRITATE THE SKIN. **CHRONIC EXPOSURE-** NO DATA AVAILABLE.

FIRST AID- REMOVE CONTAMINATED CLOTHING AND SHOES IMMEDIATELY. WASH AFFECTED AREA WITH SOAP OR MILD DETERGENT AND LARGE AMOUNTS OF WATER UNTIL NO EVIDENCE OF CHEMICAL REMAINS (APPROXIMATELY 15-20 MINUTES). GET MEDICAL ATTENTION IMMEDIATELY.

EYE CONTACT: AMMONIUM FERROUS SULFATE: IRRITANT. **ACUTE EXPOSURE-** THE CHEMICAL MAY CAUSE EYE IRRITATION. SIMILAR CHEMICALS HAVE CAUSED EYE DEGENERATION IN RABBITS. **CHRONIC EXPOSURE-** NO DATA AVAILABLE.

FIRST AID- WASH EYES IMMEDIATELY WITH LARGE AMOUNTS OF WATER OR NORMAL SALINE, OCCASIONALLY LIFTING UPPER AND LOWER LIDS, UNTIL NO EVIDENCE OF CHEMICAL REMAINS (APPROXIMATELY 15-20 MINUTES). GET MEDICAL ATTENTION IMMEDIATELY.

INGESTION: FERROUS AMMONIUM SULFATE: **ACUTE EXPOSURE-** ABDOMINAL PAIN, RETCHING AND PROLONGED VOMITING MAY BEGIN 10-60 MINUTES AFTER EXCESSIVE INGESTION OF SOLUBLE IRON SALTS. HEMATEMESIS, WATERY AND THEN TARRY DIARRHEA, INTENSE DEHYDRATION, SHOCK, PALLOR, CYANOSIS, HYPOTHERMIA, RAPID, WEAK OR IMPERCEPTIBLE PULSE, HYPOTENSION, RAPID RESPIRATION, ACIDOSIS, COAGULATION DEFECTS, DROWSINESS, HYPOREFLEXIA, VASOMOTOR INSTABILITY, DILATED PUPILS AND COMA MAY FOLLOW. DEATH FROM SHOCK MAY OCCUR WITHIN 4-8 HOURS. IF DEATH IS NOT IMMEDIATE, THE VICTIM MAY IMPROVE, BUT CYANOSIS, PULMONARY EDEMA, PNEUMONITIS FROM ASPIRATION OF VOMITUS, HYPERTHERMIA, ACIDOSIS, ANURIA, SHOCK, CONVULSIONS, COMA AND DEATH MAY OCCUR 1-3 DAYS LATER. AFTER 2 DAYS, SURVIVORS MAY DEVELOP HEMORRHAGIC HEPATIC NECROSIS, WHICH IS USUALLY REVERSIBLE. GASTRIC SCARRING AND CONTRACTURE AND PYLORIC OBSTRUCTION MAY OCCUR AFTER 4 WEEKS. PYLORIC STENOSIS AND MILD HEPATIC CIRRHOSIS MAY PERSIST. **CHRONIC EXPOSURE-** REPEATED DOSAGE OF SOLUBLE IRON COMPOUNDS MAY CAUSE HEMOSIDEROSIS WITH POSSIBLE DAMAGE TO THE LIVER AND PANCREAS.

FIRST AID- MAINTAIN OPEN AIRWAY. GET MEDICAL ATTENTION. TREAT SHOCK. IF CONSCIOUS, USE GASTRIC LAVAGE WITH A CONCENTRATED SOLUTION OF SODIUM BICARBONATE, OR 5% DISODIUM PHOSPHATE DIHYDRATE, OR MILK. AFTER LAVAGE, RETAIN 100-300 MILLILITERS OF SOLUTION IN STOMACH TO FORM POORLY ABSORBED IRON COMPOUNDS. ADMINISTER RECTAL LAVAGE WITH ONE OF THE ABOVE SOLUTIONS, IF THERE IS DIARRHEA, HYPERPERISTALSIS OF INTESTINAL TRACT, OR 3 OR MORE HOUR LAPSE SINCE INGESTION.IN CRITICAL CASES, ADMINISTER CHELATING AGENT SUCH AS EDETATE OR DIETHYLENETRIAMINE-PENTA-ACETIC ACID, OR DEFEROXAMINE MESYLATE (ARENA, POISONING, 4TH EDITION, 1979).

ANTIDOTE: THE FOLLOWING ANTIDOTE HAS BEEN RECOMMENDED. HOWEVER, THE DECISION AS TO WHETHER THE SEVERITY OF POISONING REQUIRES ADMINISTRATION OF ANY ANTIDOTE AND ACTUAL DOSE REQUIRED SHOULD BE MADE BY QUALIFIED MEDICAL PERSONNEL.
IRON SALT POISONING: GIVE DEFEROXAMINE, 15 MG/KG/HOUR BY CONTINUOUS INTRAVENOUS INFUSION TO A MAXIMUM OF 80 MG/KG IN EACH 12-HOUR PERIOD. MONITOR THE BLOOD PRESSURE DURING ADMINISTRATION OF DEFEROXAMINE AND REDUCE THE RATE OF ADMINISTRATION IF THE BLOOD PRESSURE FALLS. SINGLE DOSES SHOULD NOT EXCEED 1 GRAM AND THE MAXIMUM IN 24 HOURS

SHOULD NOT EXCEED 6 GRAMS. DEFEROXAMINE IS HAZARDOUS IN PATIENTS WITH SEVERE RENAL DISEASE OR ANURIA, AND DIALYSIS IS NECESSARY. INJECTED DEFEROXAMINE IS ASSOCIATED WITH A HIGH RISK AND SHOULD BE RESERVED FOR SERIOUS POISONING. CONTINUE DEFEROXAMINE THERAPY UNTIL THE PATIENT IS FREE OF SYMPTOMS AND SIGNS FOR 24 HOURS (DREISBACH, HANDBOOK OF POISONING, 11TH ED.). ANTIDOTE SHOULD BE ADMINISTERED BY QUALIFIED MEDICAL PERSONNEL.

REACTIVITY

REACTIVITY: STABLE UNDER NORMAL TEMPERATURES AND PRESSURES. SLOWLY OXIDIZES AND EFFLORESCES IN AIR.

INCOMPATIBILITIES: FERROUS AMMONIUM SULFATE: NO DATA AVAILABLE.

DECOMPOSITION: THERMAL DECOMPOSITION MAY RELEASE CORROSIVE FUMES OF AMMONIA AND TOXIC OXIDES OF NITROGEN.

POLYMERIZATION: HAZARDOUS POLYMERIZATION HAS NOT BEEN REPORTED TO OCCUR UNDER NORMAL TEMPERATURES AND PRESSURES.

CONDITIONS TO AVOID

MAY BURN BUT DOES NOT IGNITE READILY. AVOID CONTACT WITH STRONG OXIDIZERS, EXCESSIVE HEAT, SPARKS, OR OPEN FLAME.

SPILL AND LEAK PROCEDURES

SOIL SPILL: DIG HOLDING AREA SUCH AS LAGOON, POND OR PIT FOR CONTAINMENT. USE PROTECTIVE COVER SUCH AS A PLASTIC SHEET TO PREVENT MATERIAL FROM DISSOLVING IN FIRE EXTINGUISHING WATER OR RAIN.

WATER SPILL: ALLOW SPILLED MATERIAL TO AERATE.

NEUTRALIZE WITH AGRICULTURAL LIME, SLAKED LIME, CRUSHED LIMESTONE, OR SODIUM BICARBONATE.

ADD SUITABLE AGENT TO NEUTRALIZE SPILLED MATERIAL TO PH-7.

USE MECHANICAL DREDGES OR LIFTS TO EXTRACT IMMOBILIZED MASSES OF POLLUTION AND PRECIPITATES.

OCCUPATIONAL SPILL: STOP LEAK IF YOU CAN DO IT WITHOUT RISK. FOR SMALL SPILLS, TAKE UP WITH SAND OR OTHER ABSORBENT MATERIAL AND PLACE INTO CLEAN, DRY CONTAINERS FOR LATER DISPOSAL. KEEP UNNECESSARY PEOPLE AWAY. ISOLATE HAZARD AREA AND DENY ENTRY.

REPORTABLE QUANTITY (RQ): 1000 POUNDS THE SUPERFUND AMENDMENTS AND REAUTHORIZATION ACT (SARA) SECTION 304 REQUIRES THAT A RELEASE EQUAL TO OR GREATER THAN THE REPORTABLE QUANTITY FOR THIS SUBSTANCE BE IMMEDIATELY REPORTED TO THE LOCAL EMERGENCY PLANNING COMMITTEE AND THE STATE EMERGENCY RESPONSE COMMISSION (40 CFR 355.40). IF THE RELEASE OF THIS SUBSTANCE IS REPORTABLE UNDER CERCLA SECTION 103, THE NATIONAL RESPONSE CENTER MUST BE NOTIFIED IMMEDIATELY AT (800) 424-8802 OR (202) 426-2675 IN THE METROPOLITAN WASHINGTON, D.C. AREA (40 CFR 302.6).

PROTECTIVE EQUIPMENT

VENTILATION: PROVIDE LOCAL EXHAUST VENTILATION AND/OR GENERAL DILUTION VENTILATION TO MEET PUBLISHED EXPOSURE LIMITS.

RESPIRATOR: THE FOLLOWING RESPIRATORS ARE RECOMMENDED BASED ON INFORMATION FOUND IN THE PHYSICAL DATA, TOXICITY AND HEALTH EFFECTS SECTIONS. THEY ARE RANKED IN ORDER FROM MINIMUM TO MAXIMUM RESPIRATORY PROTECTION. THE SPECIFIC RESPIRATOR SELECTED MUST BE BASED ON CONTAMINATION LEVELS FOUND IN THE WORK PLACE, MUST NOT EXCEED THE WORKING LIMITS OF THE RESPIRATOR AND BE JOINTLY APPROVED BY THE NATIONAL INSTITUTE FOR OCCUPATIONAL SAFETY AND HEALTH AND THE MINE SAFETY AND HEALTH ADMINISTRATION (NIOSH-MSHA).

DUST AND MIST RESPIRATOR WITH A FULL FACEPIECE.

AIR-PURIFYING FULL FACEPIECE RESPIRATOR WITH A HIGH-EFFICIENCY PARTICULATE FILTER.

POWERED AIR-PURIFYING RESPIRATOR WITH A TIGHT-FITTING FACEPIECE AND HIGH-EFFICIENCY PARTICULATE FILTER.

TYPE 'C' SUPPLIED-AIR RESPIRATOR WITH A FULL FACEPIECE OPERATED IN PRESSURE-DEMAND OR OTHER POSITIVE PRESSURE MODE OR WITH A FULL FACEPIECE, HELMET OR HOOD OPERATED IN CONTINUOUS-FLOW MODE.

SELF-CONTAINED BREATHING APPARATUS WITH A FULL FACEPIECE OPERATED IN PRESSURE-DEMAND OR OTHER POSITIVE PRESSURE MODE.

FOR FIREFIGHTING AND OTHER IMMEDIATELY DANGEROUS TO LIFE OR HEALTH CONDITIONS:

SELF-CONTAINED BREATHING APPARATUS WITH FULL FACEPIECE OPERATED IN PRESSURE-DEMAND OR OTHER POSITIVE PRESSURE MODE.

SUPPLIED-AIR RESPIRATOR WITH FULL FACEPIECE AND OPERATED IN PRESSURE-DEMAND OR OTHER POSITIVE PRESSURE MODE IN COMBINATION WITH AN AUXILIARY SELF-CONTAINED BREATHING APPARATUS OPERATED IN PRESSURE-DEMAND OR OTHER POSITIVE PRESSURE MODE.

CLOTHING: EMPLOYEE MUST WEAR APPROPRIATE PROTECTIVE (IMPERVIOUS) CLOTHING AND EQUIPMENT TO PREVENT REPEATED OR PROLONGED SKIN CONTACT WITH THIS SUBSTANCE.

GLOVES: EMPLOYEE MUST WEAR APPROPRIATE PROTECTIVE GLOVES TO PREVENT CONTACT WITH THIS SUBSTANCE.

EYE PROTECTION: EMPLOYEE MUST WEAR SPLASH-PROOF OR DUST-RESISTANT SAFETY GOGGLES TO PREVENT EYE CONTACT WITH THIS SUBSTANCE.

EMERGENCY EYE WASH: WHERE THERE IS ANY POSSIBILITY THAT AN EMPLOYEE'S EYES MAY BE EXPOSED TO THIS SUBSTANCE, THE EMPLOYER SHOULD PROVIDE AN EYE WASH FOUNTAIN WITHIN THE IMMEDIATE WORK AREA FOR EMERGENCY USE.

AUTHORIZED BY- OCCUPATIONAL HEALTH SERVICES, INC.

CREATION DATE: 11/17/89 ***REVISION DATE:*** 05/21/90

MATERIAL SAFETY DATA SHEET

OCCUPATIONAL HEALTH SERVICES, INC.
AGRICULTURE AND PESTICIDE DIVISION
450 SEVENTH AVENUE, SUITE 2407
NEW YORK, NEW YORK 10123
1-800-445-MSDS OR (212) 967-1100

EMERGENCY CONTACT:
JOHN S. BRANSFORD, JR. (615) 292-1180

SUBSTANCE IDENTIFICATION

CAS-NUMBER 7782-63-0

SUBSTANCE: FERROUS SULFATE, HEPTAHYDRATE

TRADE NAMES/SYNONYMS: IRON(II) SULFATE; FERROUS SULFATE HEPTAHYDRATE; IRON(2+) SULFATE HEPTAHYDRATE; IRON(II) SULFATE (1:1), HEPTAHYDRATE; FERROUS SULFATE; SULFURIC ACID, IRON(2+) SALT (1:1), HEPTAHYDRATE; IRON SULFATE; COPPERAS; GREEN VITRIOL; STCC 4963841; UN 9125; FEH7O11S; PST09870

CHEMICAL FAMILY: INORGANIC SALT

MOLECULAR FORMULA: FE-S-O4.7(H2-O)

MOLECULAR WEIGHT: 278.01

CERCLA RATINGS (SCALE 0-3): HEALTH=3 FIRE=0 REACTIVITY=0 PERSISTENCE=3

NFPA RATINGS (SCALE 0-4): HEALTH=U FIRE=0 REACTIVITY=0

COMPONENTS AND CONTAMINANTS

COMPONENT: FERROUS SULFATE, HEPTAHYDRATE ***PERCENT:*** 100.0
CAS# 7782-63-0

EXPOSURE LIMITS: IRON SALTS, SOLUBLE, AS FE: 1 MG/M3 OSHA TWA 1 MG/M3 ACGIH TWA

FERROUS SULFATE: 1000 POUNDS CERCLA SECTION 103 REPORTABLE QUANTITY

PHYSICAL DATA

DESCRIPTION: ODORLESS, HYGROSCOPIC, BLUE-GREEN, MONOCLINIC CRYSTALS.

MELTING POINT: DECOMPOSES ***SPECIFIC GRAVITY:*** 1.898 ***PH:*** 3.7 @ 10% SOLUTION

SOLUBILITY IN WATER: 15.65% @ 20 C

SOLVENT SOLUBILITY: SOLUBLE IN ABSOLUTE METHANOL; SLIGHTLY SOLUBLE IN ETHANOL.

LOSES WATER OF HYDRATION TO FORM MONOHYDRATE ABOVE 147 F (64 C) AND ANHYDROUS SALT ABOVE 572 F (300 C).

FIRE AND EXPLOSION DATA

FIRE AND EXPLOSION HAZARD: NEGLIGIBLE FIRE HAZARD WHEN EXPOSED TO HEAT OR FLAME.

FIREFIGHTING MEDIA: DRY CHEMICAL, CARBON DIOXIDE, HALON, WATER SPRAY OR STANDARD FOAM (1987 EMERGENCY RESPONSE GUIDEBOOK, DOT P 5800.4).

FOR LARGER FIRES, USE WATER SPRAY, FOG OR STANDARD FOAM (1987 EMERGENCY RESPONSE GUIDEBOOK, DOT P 5800.4).

FIREFIGHTING: MOVE CONTAINER FROM FIRE AREA IF POSSIBLE. DO NOT SCATTER SPILLED MATERIAL WITH HIGH PRESSURE WATER STREAMS. DIKE FIRE CONTROL WATER FOR LATER DISPOSAL (1987 EMERGENCY RESPONSE GUIDEBOOK, DOT P 5800.4, GUIDE PAGE 31).

USE AGENTS SUITABLE FOR TYPE OF SURROUNDING FIRE. AVOID BREATHING HAZARDOUS VAPORS, KEEP UPWIND.

TOXICITY

FERROUS SULFATE: TOXICITY DATA: ANHYDROUS: 390 MG/KG ORAL-CHILD LDLO; 20 MG/KG ORAL-CHILD TDLO; 150 MG/KG ORAL-CHILD TDLO; 10,560 UG/KG ORAL-WOMAN TDLO; 600 MG/KG ORAL-WOMAN TDLO; 319 MG/KG ORAL-RAT LD50; 680 MG/KG ORAL-MOUSE LD50; 1200 MG/KG ORAL-GUINEA PIG LD50; 155 MG/KG SUBCUTANEOUS-RAT LD50; 60,300 UG/KG SUBCUTANEOUS-MOUSE LD50; 112

MG/KG INTRAVENOUS-MOUSE LD50; 79 MG/KG INTRAVENOUS-DOG LD50; 289 MG/KG INTRAPERITONEAL- MOUSE LD50; 200 MG/KG INTRADUODENAL-RABBIT LDLO; 441 MG/KG UNREPORTED-MAN LDLO; MUTAGENIC DATA (RTECS); REPRODUCTIVE EFFECTS DATA (RTECS); TUMORIGENIC DATA (RTECS). MONOHYDRATE: NO DATA AVAILABLE. HEPTAHYDRATE: 1389 MG/KG ORAL-RAT LDLO; 1520 MG/KG ORAL-MOUSE LD50; 2778 MG/KG ORAL-RABBIT LDLO; 279 MG/KG SUBCUTANEOUS-RABBIT LDLO; 51 MG/KG INTRAVENOUS-MOUSE LD50; 99 MG/KG INTRAVENOUS-RABBIT LDLO; 245 MG/KG INTRAPERITONEAL-MOUSE LD50; 697 MG/KG RECTAL-RAT LDLO; MUTAGENIC DATA (RTECS). CARCINOGEN STATUS: NONE. LOCAL EFFECTS: CORROSIVE-EYE, INGESTION; IRRITANT-SKIN, MUCOUS MEMBRANES. ACUTE TOXICITY LEVEL: TOXIC BY INGESTION (ANHYDROUS); MODERATELY TOXIC BY INGESTION (HEPTAHYDRATE). TARGET EFFECTS: POISONING MAY AFFECT THE LIVER, KIDNEYS, CIRCULATORY, CARDIOVASCULAR AND CENTRAL NERVOUS SYSTEMS. ADDITIONAL DATA: INTERACTIONS WITH MEDICATION MAY CAUSE ADVERSE EFFECTS.

HEALTH EFFECTS AND FIRST AID

INHALATION: FERROUS SULFATE: IRRITANT. **ACUTE EXPOSURE-** MAY CAUSE IRRITATION OF THE RESPIRATORY TRACT. **CHRONIC EXPOSURE-** NO DATA AVAILABLE.

FIRST AID- REMOVE FROM EXPOSURE AREA TO FRESH AIR IMMEDIATELY. IF BREATHING HAS STOPPED, PERFORM ARTIFICIAL RESPIRATION. KEEP PERSON WARM AND AT REST. TREAT SYMPTOMATICALLY AND SUPPORTIVELY. GET MEDICAL ATTENTION IMMEDIATELY.

SKIN CONTACT: FERROUS SULFATE: IRRITANT. **ACUTE EXPOSURE-** MAY CAUSE IRRITATION. **CHRONIC EXPOSURE-** REPEATED OR PROLONGED EXPOSURE TO IRRITANTS MAY CAUSE DERMATITIS.

FIRST AID- REMOVE CONTAMINATED CLOTHING AND SHOES IMMEDIATELY. WASH AFFECTED AREA WITH SOAP OR MILD DETERGENT AND LARGE AMOUNTS OF WATER UNTIL NO EVIDENCE OF CHEMICAL REMAINS (APPROXIMATELY 15-20 MINUTES). GET MEDICAL ATTENTION IMMEDIATELY.

EYE CONTACT: FERROUS SULFATE: CORROSIVE. **ACUTE EXPOSURE-** CONTACT WITH THE EYE MAY CAUSE SEVERE IRRITATION AND CORROSIVE ACTION DUE TO THE ACIDITY OF THE SOLUTION. **CHRONIC EXPOSURE-** EFFECTS DEPEND ON CONCENTRATION AND DURATION OF EXPOSURE. REPEATED OR PROLONGED CONTACT WITH CORROSIVE SUBSTANCES MAY RESULT IN CONJUNCTIVITIS OR EFFECTS AS IN ACUTE EXPOSURE.

FIRST AID- WASH EYES IMMEDIATELY WITH LARGE AMOUNTS OF WATER, OCCASIONALLY LIFTING UPPER AND LOWER LIDS, UNTIL NO EVIDENCE OF CHEMICAL REMAINS (AT LEAST 15-20 MINUTES). CONTINUE IRRIGATING WITH NORMAL SALINE UNTIL THE PH HAS RETURNED TO NORMAL (30-60 MINUTES). COVER WITH STERILE BANDAGES. GET MEDICAL ATTENTION IMMEDIATELY.

INGESTION: FERROUS SULFATE: CORROSIVE/TOXIC. **ACUTE EXPOSURE-** SIDE EFFECTS OF INGESTION OF IRON SALTS MAY INCLUDE HEARTBURN, METALLIC TASTE IN THE MOUTH, NAUSEA, UPPER GASTRIC DISCOMFORT, AND CONSTIPATION OR DIARRHEA. SYMPTOMS OF SEVERE POISONING MAY OCCUR WITHIN 30 MINUTES OR BE DELAYED FOR SEVERAL HOURS. SEVERE HEMORRHAGIC GASTRITIS WITH ABDOMINAL PAIN, RETCHING, VIOLENT DIARRHEA AND VOMITING MAY OCCUR. THE VOMITUS MAY BE BLOODY. DEHYDRATION MAY BECOME INTENSE. THE CIRCULATORY SYSTEM MAY BE AFFECTED WITH SYMPTOMS OF SHOCK, PALLOR, CYANOSIS AND COLDNESS, RAPID, WEAK OR IMPERCEPTIBLE PULSE, SEVERE HYPOTENSION AND PULMONARY CHANGES WITH DYSPNEA, FOCAL ATELECTASIS AND EMPHYSEMA MAY OCCUR. OTHER SYMPTOMS MAY INCLUDE HEMOCONCENTRATION, TACHYCARDIA, LETHARGY, DROWSINESS, MENTAL CONFUSION, HYPOTONIA AND HYPERGLYCEMIA. IF POISONING IS NOT IMMEDIATELY FATAL, THE PATIENT MAY BE ASYMPTOMATIC FOR 24 HOURS, AFTER WHICH SYMTPOMS MAY RETURN WITH CYANOSIS, CONVULSIONS, CIRCULATORY COLLAPSE, MASSIVE HEPATIC FAILURE WITH JAUNDICE, SEVERE BLEEDING WITH ALTERED CLOTTING AND BLEEDING PARAMETERS, SEVERE RENAL IMPAIRMENT OR FAILURE, DIFFUSE VASCULAR CONGESTION, PULMONARY EDEMA AND PULMONARY HEMORRHAGE, ACIDOSIS, ANURIA, HYPERTHERMIA, COMA AND DEATH WITHIN 24-48 HOURS. DEATH IS ALWAYS PRECEDED BY SHOCK. IF THE VICTIM SURVIVES, LATE COMPLICATIONS DUE TO PYLORIC, ANTRAL OR INTESTINAL OBSTRUCTION, HEPATIC CIRRHOSIS WITH FINE DIFFUSE FIBROTIC CHANGES WITH FATTY DEGENERATION AND CENTRAL NERVOUS DAMAGE MAY OCCUR 2 TO 5 WEEKS AFTER INGESTION. DEGENERATIVE CHANGES OF THE PANCREAS, LYMPH NODES, AND HEART ARE ALSO POSSIBLE. THE AVERAGE HUMAN LETHAL DOSE OF IRON IS ABOUT 200 TO 250 MG PER KG OF BODY WEIGHT. **CHRONIC EXPOSURE-** REPRODUCTIVE EFFECTS HAVE BEEN REPORTED IN ANIMALS.

FIRST AID- IN PATIENTS NOT IN SHOCK OR COMA, INDUCE EMESIS WITH SYRUP OF IPECAC IF VOMITING HAS NOT OCCURRED. FOLLOW WITH GASTRIC LAVAGE USING DEFEROXAMINE, 2 GRAMS IN 1 LITER OF WATER CONTAINING SODIUM BICARBONATE, 20 GM/L. LEAVE 10 GRAMS OF DEFEROXAMINE IN 50 ML OF 5% SODIUM BICARBONATE IN THE STOMACH. MAINTAIN AIRWAY, BLOOD PRESSURE AND RESPIRATION. TREAT SYMPTOMATICALLY AND SUPPORTIVELY. (DREISBACH, HANDBOOK OF POISONING, 11TH ED.) GET MEDICAL ATTENTION IMMEDIATELY. TREATMENT SHOULD BE ADMINISTERED BY QUALIFIED MEDICAL PERSONNEL.

ANTIDOTE: THE FOLLOWING ANTIDOTE HAS BEEN RECOMMENDED. HOWEVER, THE DECISION AS TO WHETHER THE SEVERITY OF POISONING REQUIRES ADMINISTRATION OF ANY ANTIDOTE AND ACTUAL DOSE REQUIRED SHOULD BE MADE BY QUALIFIED MEDICAL PERSONNEL.

IRON SALT POISONING: GIVE DEFEROXAMINE, 15 MG/KG/HOUR BY CONTINUOUS INTRAVENOUS INFUSION TO A MAXIMUM OF 80 MG/KG IN EACH 12-HOUR PERIOD. MONITOR THE BLOOD PRESSURE DURING ADMINISTRATION OF DEFEROXAMINE AND REDUCE THE RATE OF ADMINISTRATION IF THE BLOOD PRESSURE FALLS. SINGLE DOSES SHOULD NOT EXCEED 1 GRAM AND THE MAXIMUM IN 24 HOURS SHOULD NOT EXCEED 6 GRAMS. DEFEROXAMINE IS HAZARDOUS IN PATIENTS WITH SEVERE RENAL DISEASE OR ANURIA, AND DIALYSIS IS NECESSARY. INJECTED DEFEROXAMINE IS ASSOCIATED WITH A HIGH RISK AND SHOULD BE RESERVED FOR SERIOUS POISONING. CONTINUE DEFEROXAMINE THERAPY UNTIL THE PATIENT IS FREE OF SYMPTOMS AND SIGNS FOR 24 HOURS (DREISBACH, HANDBOOK OF POISONING, 11TH ED.). ANTIDOTE SHOULD BE ADMINISTERED BY QUALIFIED MEDICAL PERSONNEL.

REACTIVITY

REACTIVITY: STABLE UNDER NORMAL TEMPERATURES AND PRESSURES.

INCOMPATIBILITIES: FERROUS SULFATE: ALKALIES: INCOMPATIBLE. ARSENIC TRIOXIDE + SODIUM NITRATE: SPONTANEOUSLY COMBUSTIBLE MIXTURE. METHYL ISOCYANOACETATE: MAY DECOMPOSE EXPLOSIVELY AT 25 C. OXIDIZERS: FIRE AND EXPLOSION HAZARD.

DECOMPOSITION: THERMAL DECOMPOSITION PRODUCTS MAY INCLUDE TOXIC OXIDES OF SULFUR.

POLYMERIZATION: HAZARDOUS POLYMERIZATION HAS NOT BEEN REPORTED TO OCCUR UNDER NORMAL TEMPERATURES AND PRESSURES.

STORAGE AND DISPOSAL

OBSERVE ALL FEDERAL, STATE AND LOCAL REGULATIONS WHEN STORING OR DISPOSING OF THIS SUBSTANCE. FOR ASSISTANCE, CONTACT THE DISTRICT DIRECTOR OF THE ENVIRONMENTAL PROTECTION AGENCY.

STORAGE

STORE AWAY FROM INCOMPATIBLE SUBSTANCES.

CONDITIONS TO AVOID

PREVENT DISPERSION OF DUST IN AIR.

SPILL AND LEAK PROCEDURES

SOIL SPILL: DIG A HOLDING AREA SUCH AS A PIT, POND OR LAGOON TO CONTAIN SPILL AND DIKE SURFACE FLOW USING BARRIER OF SOIL, SANDBAGS, FOAMED POLYURETHANE OR FOAMED CONCRETE. ABSORB LIQUID MASS WITH FLY ASH OR CEMENT POWDER.

NEUTRALIZE SPILL WITH SLAKED LIME, SODIUM BICARBONATE OR CRUSHED LIMESTONE.

WATER SPILL: ALLOW SPILLED MATERIAL TO AERATE.

NEUTRALIZE WITH AGRICULTURAL LIME, SLAKED LIME, CRUSHED LIMESTONE, OR SODIUM BICARBONATE.

USE MECHANICAL DREDGES OR LIFTS TO EXTRACT IMMOBILIZED MASSES OF POLLUTION AND PRECIPITATES.

OCCUPATIONAL SPILL: SWEEP UP AND PLACE IN SUITABLE CLEAN, DRY CONTAINERS FOR RECLAMATION OR LATER DISPOSAL. DO NOT FLUSH SPILLED MATERIAL INTO SEWER. KEEP UNNECESSARY PEOPLE AWAY.

REPORTABLE QUANTITY (RQ): 1000 POUNDS THE SUPERFUND AMENDMENTS AND REAUTHORIZATION ACT (SARA) SECTION 304 REQUIRES THAT A RELEASE EQUAL TO OR GREATER THAN THE REPORTABLE QUANTITY FOR THIS SUBSTANCE BE IMMEDIATELY REPORTED TO THE LOCAL EMERGENCY PLANNING COMMITTEE AND THE STATE EMERGENCY RESPONSE COMMISSION (40 CFR 355.40). IF THE RELEASE OF THIS SUBSTANCE IS REPORTABLE UNDER CERCLA SECTION 103, THE NATIONAL RESPONSE CENTER MUST BE NOTIFIED IMMEDIATELY AT (800) 424-8802 OR (202) 426-2675 IN THE METROPOLITAN WASHINGTON, D.C. AREA (40 CFR 302.6).

PROTECTIVE EQUIPMENT

VENTILATION: PROVIDE LOCAL EXHAUST OR PROCESS ENCLOSURE VENTILATION TO MEET PUBLISHED EXPOSURE LIMITS.

RESPIRATOR: THE FOLLOWING RESPIRATORS ARE RECOMMENDED BASED ON INFORMATION FOUND IN THE PHYSICAL DATA, TOXICITY AND HEALTH EFFECTS SECTIONS. THEY ARE RANKED IN ORDER FROM MINIMUM TO MAXIMUM RESPIRATORY PROTECTION. THE SPECIFIC RESPIRATOR SELECTED MUST BE BASED ON CONTAMINATION LEVELS FOUND IN THE WORK PLACE, MUST NOT EXCEED THE

WORKING LIMITS OF THE RESPIRATOR AND BE JOINTLY APPROVED BY THE NATIONAL INSTITUTE FOR OCCUPATIONAL SAFETY AND HEALTH AND THE MINE SAFETY AND HEALTH ADMINISTRATION (NIOSH-MSHA).
TYPE 'C' SUPPLIED-AIR RESPIRATOR WITH A FULL FACEPIECE OPERATED IN PRESSURE-DEMAND OR OTHER POSITIVE PRESSURE MODE OR WITH A FULL FACEPIECE, HELMET OR HOOD OPERATED IN CONTINOUS-FLOW MODE.
SELF-CONTAINED BREATHING APPARATUS WITH A FULL FACEPIECE OPERATED IN PRESSURE-DEMAND OR OTHER POSITIVE PRESSURE MODE.
FOR FIREFIGHTING AND OTHER IMMEDIATELY DANGEROUS TO LIFE OR HEALTH CONDITIONS:
SELF-CONTAINED BREATHING APPARATUS WITH FULL FACEPIECE OPERATED IN PRESSURE-DEMAND OR OTHER POSITIVE PRESSURE MODE.
SUPPLIED-AIR RESPIRATOR WITH FULL FACEPIECE AND OPERATED IN PRESSURE-DEMAND OR OTHER POSITIVE PRESSURE MODE IN COMBINATION WITH AN AUXILIARY SELF-CONTAINED BREATHING APPARATUS OPERATED IN PRESSURE-DEMAND OR OTHER POSITIVE PRESSURE MODE.

CLOTHING: EMPLOYEE MUST WEAR APPROPRIATE PROTECTIVE (IMPERVIOUS) CLOTHING AND EQUIPMENT TO PREVENT REPEATED OR PROLONGED SKIN CONTACT WITH THIS SUBSTANCE.

GLOVES: EMPLOYEE MUST WEAR APPROPRIATE PROTECTIVE GLOVES TO PREVENT CONTACT WITH THIS SUBSTANCE.

EYE PROTECTION: EMPLOYEE MUST WEAR SPLASH-PROOF OR DUST-RESISTANT SAFETY GOGGLES AND A FACESHIELD TO PREVENT CONTACT WITH THIS SUBSTANCE.
EMERGENCY WASH FACILITIES: WHERE THERE IS ANY POSSIBILITY THAT AN EMPLOYEE'S EYES AND/OR SKIN MAY BE EXPOSED TO THIS SUBSTANCE, THE EMPLOYER SHOULD PROVIDE AN EYE WASH FOUNTAIN AND QUICK DRENCH SHOWER WITHIN THE IMMEDIATE WORK AREA FOR EMERGENCY USE.

AUTHORIZED BY- OCCUPATIONAL HEALTH SERVICES, INC.
CREATION DATE: 11/17/89 ***REVISION DATE:*** 05/31/90

MATERIAL SAFETY DATA SHEET

OCCUPATIONAL HEALTH SERVICES, INC.
AGRICULTURE AND PESTICIDE DIVISION
450 SEVENTH AVENUE, SUITE 2407
NEW YORK, NEW YORK 10123
1-800-445-MSDS OR (212) 967-1100

EMERGENCY CONTACT:
JOHN S. BRANSFORD, JR. (615) 292-1180

SUBSTANCE IDENTIFICATION

CAS-NUMBER 2164-17-2

***SUBSTANCE:* FLUOMETURON**

TRADE NAMES/SYNONYMS: UREA, N,N-DIMETHYL-N'-(3-(TRIFLUOROMETHYL)PHENYL)-; UREA, 1,1-DIMETHYL-3-(ALPHA, ALPHA, ALPHA-TRIFLUORO-M-TOLYL)-; N,N-DIMETHYL-N'-(3-(TRIFLUOROMETHYL)PHENYL)UREA; 1,1-DIMETHYL-3-(ALPHA, ALPHA, ALPHA-TRIFLUORO-M-TOLYL)UREA; N-(3-TRIFLUOROMETHYLPHENYL)-N',N'-DIMETHYLUREA; C 2059; CIBA 2059; COTORAN; COTTONEX; LANEX; PAKHTARAN; C10H11F3N2O; PST09907

CHEMICAL FAMILY: SUBSTITUTED UREA
HALOGEN COMPOUND, AROMATIC

MOLECULAR FORMULA: F3-C-C6-H4-N-H-C-O-N-(C-H3)2

MOLECULAR WEIGHT: 232.21

CERCLA RATINGS (SCALE 0-3): HEALTH=3 FIRE=1 REACTIVITY=0 PERSISTENCE=2

NFPA RATINGS (SCALE 0-4): HEALTH=3 FIRE=1 REACTIVITY=0

COMPONENTS AND CONTAMINANTS

COMPONENT: FLUORMETURON ***PERCENT:*** 100
CAS# 2164-17-2

OTHER CONTAMINANTS: NONE

EXPOSURE LIMITS: NO OCCUPATIONAL EXPOSURE LIMITS ESTABLISHED BY OSHA, ACGIH, OR NIOSH.
FLUOMETURON: SUBJECT TO SARA SECTION 313 ANNUAL TOXIC CHEMICAL RELEASE REPORTING.

PHYSICAL DATA

DESCRIPTION: COLORLESS TO WHITE CRYSTALLINE SOLID WITH AN AMINE-LIKE ODOR.

MELTING POINT: 325-329 F (163-165 C) ***SPECIFIC GRAVITY:*** 1.39

VAPOR PRESSURE: NEGLIGIBLE ***SOLUBILITY IN WATER:*** 0.0105% @ 20 C

SOLVENT SOLUBILITY: SOLUBLE IN ACETONE, ETHANOL, ISOPROPANOL, METHANOL, DIMETHYLFORMAMIDE, DICHLOROMETHANE, 1-OCTANOL, AND MOST ORGANIC SOLVENTS; SLIGHTLY SOLUBLE IN HEXANE.

FIRE AND EXPLOSION DATA

FIRE AND EXPLOSION HAZARD: SLIGHT FIRE HAZARD WHEN EXPOSED TO HEAT OR FLAME.

FIREFIGHTING MEDIA: DRY CHEMICAL, CARBON DIOXIDE, HALON, WATER SPRAY OR STANDARD FOAM (1987 EMERGENCY RESPONSE GUIDEBOOK, DOT P 5800.4).
FOR LARGER FIRES, USE WATER SPRAY, FOG OR STANDARD FOAM (1987 EMERGENCY RESPONSE GUIDEBOOK, DOT P 5800.4).

FIREFIGHTING: MOVE CONTAINERS FROM FIRE AREA IF POSSIBLE. FIGHT FIRE FROM MAXIMUM DISTANCE. STAY AWAY FROM STORAGE TANK ENDS. DIKE FIRE CONTROL WATER FOR LATER DISPOSAL. DO NOT SCATTER MATERIAL (1987 EMERGENCY RESPONSE GUIDEBOOK, DOT P 5800.4, GUIDE PAGE 55).
EXTINGUISH USING AGENT SUITABLE FOR TYPE OF SURROUNDING FIRE. USE WATER IN FLOODING QUANTITIES AS FOG. KEEP SPARKS, FLAMES AND OTHER SOURCES OF IGNITION AWAY. KEEP MATERIAL OUT OF WATER SOURCES AND SEWERS. DO NOT TOUCH MATERIAL AND AVOID BREATHING DUSTS AND FUMES FROM BURNING MATERIAL. KEEP UPWIND.

TOXICITY

FLUOMETURON: TOXICITY DATA: 3.03 GM/KG SKIN-RABBIT LD50 (EPA, PESTICIDE FACT SHEET NUMBER 88: FLUOMETURON, 1986); 1515 MG/KG ORAL-RAT LD50; 900 MG/KG ORAL-MOUSE LD50; 2500 MG/KG ORAL-RABBIT LD50; 810 MG/KG ORAL-GUINEA PIG LD50; 685 MG/KG INTRAPERITONEAL-RAT LD50; 552 MG/KG INTRAPERITONEAL-MOUSE LD50; 850 MG/KG UNREPORTED-MOUSE LD50; MUTAGENIC DATA (RTECS); TUMORIGENIC DATA (RTECS). CARCINOGEN STATUS: ANIMAL INADEQUATE EVIDENCE (IARC GROUP-3). LOCAL EFFECTS: IRRITANT- SKIN AND EYES. ACUTE TOXICITY LEVEL: MODERATELY TOXIC BY INGESTION AND SLIGHTLY TOXIC BY DERMAL ABSORPTION. TARGET EFFECTS: SENSITIZER- SKIN.

HEALTH EFFECTS AND FIRST AID

INHALATION: FLUOMETURON: **ACUTE EXPOSURE-** CHOLINESTERASE INHIBITION WAS OBSERVED IN GUINEA PIGS EXPOSED TO 588 MG/M3/2 HOURS. MANY UREA DERIVATIVE HERBICIDES ARE MODERATELY IRRITATING TO THE MUCOUS MEMBRANES. **CHRONIC EXPOSURE-** EFFECTS OF CHOLINESTERASE INHIBITION AND AN INCREASE IN THE LEUKOCYTE COUNT IN CIRCULATING BLOOD WERE REPORTED IN ONE STUDY OF AGRICULTURAL WORKERS.

FIRST AID- REMOVE FROM EXPOSURE AREA TO FRESH AIR IMMEDIATELY. IF BREATHING HAS STOPPED, PERFORM ARTIFICIAL RESPIRATION. KEEP PERSON WARM AND AT REST. TREAT SYMPTOMATICALLY AND SUPPORTIVELY. GET MEDICAL ATTENTION IMMEDIATELY.

SKIN CONTACT: FLUOMETURON: IRRITANT/SENSITIZER. **ACUTE EXPOSURE-** THIS MATERIAL MAY CAUSE SEVERE IRRITATION. A LETHAL DOSE IN RABBITS BY DERMAL ABSORPTION WAS 3.03 GM/KG. THIS MATERIAL WAS A MODERATE SKIN SENSITIZER IN GUINEA PIGS AND MEN. **CHRONIC EXPOSURE-** EFFECTS OF CHOLINESTERASE INHIBITION AND AN INCREASED LEUKOCYTE COUNT IN CIRCULATING BLOOD WERE OBSERVED IN A STUDY OF EXPOSED AGRICULTURAL WORKERS.

FIRST AID- REMOVE CONTAMINATED CLOTHING AND SHOES IMMEDIATELY. WASH AFFECTED AREA WITH SOAP OR MILD DETERGENT AND LARGE AMOUNTS OF WATER UNTIL NO EVIDENCE OF CHEMICAL REMAINS (APPROXIMATELY 15-20 MINUTES). GET MEDICAL ATTENTION IMMEDIATELY.

EYE CONTACT: FLUOMETURON: IRRITANT. **ACUTE EXPOSURE-** THIS MATERIAL MAY CAUSE SEVERE IRRITATION AND CORNEAL OPACITY. **CHRONIC EXPOSURE-** PROLONGED OR REPEATED EXPOSURE TO IRRITANTS MAY CAUSE CONJUNCTIVITIS.

FIRST AID- WASH EYES IMMEDIATELY WITH LARGE AMOUNTS OF WATER OR NORMAL SALINE, OCCASIONALLY LIFTING UPPER AND LOWER LIDS, UNTIL NO EVIDENCE OF CHEMICAL REMAINS (APPROXIMATELY 15-20 MINUTES). GET MEDICAL ATTENTION IMMEDIATELY.

INGESTION: FLUOMETURON: **ACUTE EXPOSURE-** A LETHAL DOSE IN RATS WAS 1515 MG/KG. **CHRONIC EXPOSURE-** AN INCREASED IN SPLEEN WEIGHT AND IN THE INCIDENCE OF RED-BLOOD CELLS WITH POLYCHROMASIA AND ANISOCYTOSIS AND DECREASE WEIGHT GAIN IN FEMALES WERE OBSERVED IN A 90-DAY STUDY OF RATS. AN INCREASED INCIDENCE OF LIVER-CELL TUMORS IN MALE MICE WAS NOTED IN A STUDY OF RATS AND MICE; CARCINOGENIC EFFECTS WERE NOT INDICATED BY THE RESULTS IN THE FEMALE MICE AND RATS OF BOTH SEXES.

FIRST AID- REMOVE BY GASTRIC LAVAGE AND CATHARSIS. MAINTAIN BLOOD PRESSURE AND AIRWAY. GIVE OXYGEN IF RESPIRATION IS DEPRESSED. DO NOT PERFORM GASTRIC LAVAGE IF VICTIM IS UNCONSCIOUS. GET MEDICAL ATTENTION IMMEDIATELY (DREISBACH, HANDBOOK OF POISONING, 12TH ED.).

ADMINISTRATION OF LAVAGE OR OXYGEN SHOULD BE PERFORMED BY QUALIFIED MEDICAL PERSONNEL.
ANTIDOTE: NO SPECIFIC ANTIDOTE. TREAT SYMPTOMATICALLY AND SUPPORTIVELY.

REACTIVITY

REACTIVITY: STABLE UNDER NORMAL TEMPERATURES AND PRESSURES.
INCOMPATIBILITIES: FLUOMETURON: ACIDS: MAY DECOMPOSE AT ELEVATED TEMPERATURES. ALKALI: MAY DECOMPOSE AT ELEVATED TEMPERATURES. OXIDIZERS (STRONG): FIRE AND EXPLOSION HAZARD.
DECOMPOSITION: THERMAL DECOMPOSITION PRODUCTS MAY INCLUDE HIGHLY TOXIC FUMES OF FLUORIDES AND OXIDES OF NITROGEN AND CARBON.
POLYMERIZATION: HAZARDOUS POLYMERIZATION HAS NOT BEEN REPORTED TO OCCUR UNDER NORMAL TEMPERATURES AND PRESSURES.

STORAGE AND DISPOSAL

OBSERVE ALL FEDERAL, STATE AND LOCAL REGULATIONS WHEN STORING OR DISPOSING OF THIS SUBSTANCE. FOR ASSISTANCE, CONTACT THE DISTRICT DIRECTOR OF THE ENVIRONMENTAL PROTECTION AGENCY.

STORAGE

STORE IN ACCORDANCE WITH 40 CFR 165 RECOMMENDED PROCEDURES FOR THE DISPOSAL AND STORAGE OF PESTICIDES AND PESTICIDE CONTAINERS.
STORE AWAY FROM INCOMPATIBLE SUBSTANCES.

DISPOSAL

DISPOSAL MUST BE IN ACCORDANCE WITH 40 CFR 165 RECOMMENDED PROCEDURES FOR THE DISPOSAL AND STORAGE OF PESTICIDES AND PESTICIDE CONTAINERS.

CONDITIONS TO AVOID

MAY BURN BUT DOES NOT IGNITE READILY. CONTAINERS MAY EXPLODE IN HEAT OF FIRE.

SPILL AND LEAK PROCEDURES

OCCUPATIONAL SPILL: DO NOT TOUCH SPILLED MATERIAL. STOP LEAK IF YOU CAN DO IT WITHOUT RISK. USE WATER SPRAY TO REDUCE VAPORS. FOR SMALL SPILLS, TAKE UP WITH SAND OR OTHER ABSORBENT MATERIAL AND PLACE INTO CONTAINERS FOR LATER DISPOSAL. FOR SMALL DRY SPILLS, WITH A CLEAN SHOVEL PLACE MATERIAL INTO CLEAN, DRY CONTAINERS AND COVER. MOVE CONTAINERS FROM SPILL AREA. FOR LARGER SPILLS, DIKE FAR AHEAD OF SPILL FOR LATER DISPOSAL. KEEP UNNECESSARY PEOPLE AWAY. ISOLATE HAZARD AREA AND DENY ENTRY. VENTILATE CLOSED SPACES BEFORE ENTERING.

PROTECTIVE EQUIPMENT

VENTILATION: PROVIDE LOCAL EXHAUST OR PROCESS ENCLOSURE VENTILATION SYSTEM.
RESPIRATOR: THE FOLLOWING RESPIRATORS ARE RECOMMENDED BASED ON INFORMATION FOUND IN THE PHYSICAL DATA, TOXICITY AND HEALTH EFFECTS SECTIONS. THEY ARE RANKED IN ORDER FROM MINIMUM TO MAXIMUM RESPIRATORY PROTECTION. THE SPECIFIC RESPIRATOR SELECTED MUST BE BASED ON CONTAMINATION LEVELS FOUND IN THE WORK PLACE, MUST NOT EXCEED THE WORKING LIMITS OF THE RESPIRATOR AND BE JOINTLY APPROVED BY THE NATIONAL INSTITUTE FOR OCCUPATIONAL SAFETY AND HEALTH AND THE MINE SAFETY AND HEALTH ADMINISTRATION (NIOSH-MSHA).
CHEMICAL CARTRIDGE RESPIRATOR WITH AN ORGANIC VAPOR CARTRIDGE(S) WITH A FULL FACEPIECE AND ORGANIC VAPOR CARTRIDGE(S) IN COMBINATION WITH A DUST AND MIST FILTER.
POWERED AIR-PURIFYING RESPIRATOR WITH A TIGHT-FITTING FACEPIECE AND ORGANIC VAPOR CARTRIDGE(S) IN COMBINATION WITH A HIGH-EFFICIENCY PARTICULATE FILTER.
TYPE 'C' SUPPLIED-AIR RESPIRATOR WITH A FULL FACEPIECE OPERATED IN A PRESSURE-DEMAND OR OTHER POSITIVE PRESSURE MODE.
SELF-CONTAINED BREATHING APPARATUS WITH A FULL FACEPIECE OPERATED IN PRESSURE-DEMAND OR OTHER POSITIVE PRESSURE MODE.
FOR FIREFIGHTING AND OTHER IMMEDIATELY DANGEROUS TO LIFE OR HEALTH CONDITIONS:
SELF-CONTAINED BREATHING APPARATUS WITH FULL FACEPIECE OPERATED IN PRESSURE-DEMAND OR OTHER POSITIVE PRESSURE MODE.
SUPPLIED-AIR RESPIRATOR WITH FULL FACEPIECE AND OPERATED IN PRESSURE-DEMAND OR OTHER POSITIVE PRESSURE MODE IN COMBINATION WITH AN AUXILIARY SELF-CONTAINED BREATHING APPARATUS OPERATED IN PRESSURE-DEMAND OR OTHER POSITIVE PRESSURE MODE.
CLOTHING: EMPLOYEE MUST WEAR APPROPRIATE PROTECTIVE (IMPERVIOUS) CLOTHING AND EQUIPMENT TO PREVENT REPEATED OR PROLONGED SKIN CONTACT WITH THIS SUBSTANCE.
GLOVES: EMPLOYEE MUST WEAR APPROPRIATE PROTECTIVE GLOVES TO PREVENT CONTACT WITH THIS SUBSTANCE.
EYE PROTECTION: EMPLOYEE MUST WEAR SPLASH-PROOF OR DUST-RESISTANT SAFETY GOGGLES TO PREVENT EYE CONTACT WITH THIS SUBSTANCE.
EMERGENCY EYE WASH: WHERE THERE IS ANY POSSIBILITY THAT AN EMPLOYEE'S EYES MAY BE EXPOSED TO THIS SUBSTANCE, THE EMPLOYER SHOULD PROVIDE AN EYE WASH FOUNTAIN WITHIN THE IMMEDIATE WORK AREA FOR EMERGENCY USE.

AUTHORIZED BY- OCCUPATIONAL HEALTH SERVICES, INC.
CREATION DATE: 10/04/89 ***REVISION DATE:*** 07/12/90

MATERIAL SAFETY DATA SHEET

OCCUPATIONAL HEALTH SERVICES, INC.
AGRICULTURE AND PESTICIDE DIVISION
450 SEVENTH AVENUE, SUITE 2407
NEW YORK, NEW YORK 10123
1-800-445-MSDS OR (212) 967-1100

EMERGENCY CONTACT:
JOHN S. BRANSFORD, JR. (615) 292-1180

SUBSTANCE IDENTIFICATION

CAS-NUMBER 640-19-7
SUBSTANCE: FLUOROACETAMIDE
TRADE NAMES/SYNONYMS: 2-FLUOROACETAMIDE; NAVRON; RODEX; YANOCK; MEGATOX; FUSSOL; FLUOROACETIC ACID AMIDE; FLUORAKIL 100; AFL 1081; COMPOUND 1081; 2-MONOFLUOROACETAMIDE; FAA; RCRA P057; PST09930
CHEMICAL FAMILY: ACID HALIDE, CARBOXYLIC, ALIPHATIC AMIDE
MOLECULAR FORMULA: C2-H4-F-N-O MOL WT: 77.07
CERCLA RATINGS (SCALE 0-3): HEALTH=3 FIRE=0 REACTIVITY=0 PERSISTENCE=0
NFPA RATINGS (SCALE 0-4): HEALTH=4 FIRE=0 REACTIVITY=0

COMPONENTS AND CONTAMINANTS

COMPONENT: FLUOROACETAMIDE ***PERCENT:*** 100
CAS# 640-19-7
OTHER CONTAMINANTS: NONE
EXPOSURE LIMITS: NO OCCUPATIONAL EXPOSURE LIMITS ESTABLISHED BY OSHA, ACGIH, OR NIOSH.
FLUOROACETAMIDE: 100/10,000 POUNDS SARA SECTION 302 THRESHOLD PLANNING QUANTITY 100 POUNDS SARA SECTION 304 REPORTABLE QUANTITY 100 POUNDS CERCLA SECTION 103 REPORTABLE QUANTITY

PHYSICAL DATA

DESCRIPTION: CRYSTALS. ***MELTING POINT:*** SUBLIMES
VAPOR PRESSURE: 0.875 MMHG @ 25 C ***SOLUBILITY IN WATER:*** SOLUBLE
SOLVENT SOLUBILITY: ACETONE, CHLOROFORM

FIRE AND EXPLOSION DATA

FIRE AND EXPLOSION HAZARD: NEGLIGIBLE FIRE HAZARD WHEN EXPOSED TO HEAT OR FLAME.
FIREFIGHTING MEDIA: DRY CHEMICAL, CARBON DIOXIDE, HALON, WATER SPRAY OR STANDARD FOAM (1987 EMERGENCY RESPONSE GUIDEBOOK, DOT P 5800.4).
FOR LARGER FIRES, USE WATER SPRAY, FOG OR STANDARD FOAM (1987 EMERGENCY RESPONSE GUIDEBOOK, DOT P 5800.4).
FIREFIGHTING: MOVE CONTAINERS FROM FIRE AREA IF POSSIBLE (1987 EMERGENCY RESPONSE GUIDEBOOK, DOT P 5800.4, GUIDE PAGE 53).
EXTINGUISH USING AGENT SUITABLE FOR TYPE OF SURROUNDING FIRE. AVOID BREATHING VAPORS AND DUSTS. KEEP UPWIND.

TRANSPORTATION DATA

DEPARTMENT OF TRANSPORTATION HAZARD CLASSIFICATION 49 CFR 172.101: POISON B
DEPARTMENT OF TRANSPORTATION LABELING REQUIREMENTS 49 CFR 172.101 AND SUBPART E: POISON
DEPARTMENT OF TRANSPORTATION PACKAGING REQUIREMENTS: 49 CFR 173.365 EXCEPTIONS: 49 CFR 173.364

TOXICITY

FLUOROACETAMIDE: TOXICITY DATA: 80 MG/KG SKIN-RAT LD50; 34 MG/KG SKIN-MOUSE LD50; 2 MG/KG ORAL-HUMAN LDLO; 5750 UG/KG ORAL-RAT LD50; 31 MG/KG ORAL-MOUSE LD50; 34 MG/KG SUBCUTANEOUS-MOUSE LD50; 5 MG/KG INTRAVENOUS-MONKEY LD50; 250 UG/KG INTRAVENOUS-RABBIT LD50; 12 MG/KG INTRAPERITONEAL-RAT LD50; 85 MG/KG INTRAPERITONEAL-MOUSE LD50; 4 MG/KG

UNREPORTED-MAMMAL LD50; 5 MG/KG UNREPORTED-HUMAN LDLO; MUTATION DATA (RTECS); REPRODUCTIVE EFFECTS DATA (RTECS). CARCINOGEN STATUS: NONE. ACUTE TOXICITY LEVEL: HIGHLY TOXIC BY DERMAL ABSORPTION AND INGESTION. TARGET EFFECTS: CONVULSANT. POISONING MAY AFFECT THE CARDIOVASCULAR AND CENTRAL NERVOUS SYSTEM. ADDITIONAL DATA: MAY BE METABOLIZED TO FLUORACETATE WHICH IS CONVERTED TO FLUOROCITRATE WHICH BLOCKS THE KREBS CYCLE.

HEALTH EFFECTS AND FIRST AID

INHALATION: CONVULSANT. **ACUTE EXPOSURE-** MAY CAUSE NAUSEA, VOMITING, NERVOUS SYSTEM AGITATION, DEPRESSED CONSCIOUSNESS, SEIZURES AND EVENTUALLY COMA, CARDIAC IRREGULARITIES AND DEATH FROM FIBRILLATION OR RESPIRATORY FAILURE. A DROP OR TWO OF THE POISON BY ALMOST ANY ROUTE OF ADMINISTRATION MAY BE FATAL. CLINICAL EFFECTS MAY BE NOTED AS SOON AS 30 MINUTES FOLLOWING EXPOSURE BUT MAY BE DELAYED AS LONG AS 20 HOURS.

CHRONIC EXPOSURE- NO DATA AVAILABLE.

FIRST AID- REMOVE FROM EXPOSURE AREA TO FRESH AIR IMMEDIATELY. IF BREATHING HAS STOPPED, PERFORM ARTIFICIAL RESPIRATION. KEEP PERSON WARM AND AT REST. TREAT SYMPTOMATICALLY AND SUPPORTIVELY. GET MEDICAL ATTENTION IMMEDIATELY.

SKIN CONTACT: CONVULSANT/HIGHLY TOXIC. **ACUTE EXPOSURE-** MAY BE ABSORBED THROUGH THE SKIN AND CAUSE NAUSEA, VOMITING, NERVOUS SYSTEM AGITATION, DEPRESSED CONSCIOUSNESS, SEIZURES, AND EVENTUALLY COMA, CARDIAC IRREGULARITIES AND DEATH FROM FIBRILLATION OR RESPIRATORY FAILURE.A DROP OR TWO OF THE POISON BY ALMOST ANY ROUTE OF ADMINISTRATION MAY BE FATAL. CLINICAL EFFECTS MAY BE NOTED AS SOON AS 30 MINUTES FOLLOWING EXPOSURE BUT MAY BE DELAYED AS LONG AS 20 HOURS.

CHRONIC EXPOSURE- NO DATA AVAILABLE.

FIRST AID- REMOVE CONTAMINATED CLOTHING AND SHOES IMMEDIATELY. WASH AFFECTED AREA WITH SOAP OR MILD DETERGENT AND LARGE AMOUNTS OF WATER UNTIL NO EVIDENCE OF CHEMICAL REMAINS (APPROXIMATELY 15-20 MINUTES). GET MEDICAL ATTENTION IMMEDIATELY.

EYE CONTACT:

ACUTE EXPOSURE- NO DATA AVAILABLE, HOWEVER POISONING FROM SODIUM FLUOROACETATE, A SIMILAR COMPOUND, MAY CAUSE TRANSIENT DISTURBANCE OF VISION, & BLURRED VISION. A MAN WHO WAS WORKING WITH SODIUM FLUOROACETATE ACCIDENTALLY INHALED SOME DUST WHICH CAUSED BLURRED VISION WITH AN ABILITY TO FOCUS ON OBJECTS. SEVERELY POISONED CATTLE HAVE BEEN REPORTED TO HAVE IMPAIRED VISION CAUSING THE ANIMALS NOT TO AVOID OBJECTS, BUT TO WALK INTO THEM. **CHRONIC EXPOSURE-** NO DATA AVAILABLE.

FIRST AID- WASH EYES IMMEDIATELY WITH LARGE AMOUNTS OF WATER OR NORMAL SALINE, OCCASIONALLY LIFTING UPPER AND LOWER LIDS, UNTIL NO EVIDENCE OF CHEMICAL REMAINS (APPROXIMATELY 15-20 MINUTES). GET MEDICAL ATTENTION IMMEDIATELY.

INGESTION: CONVULSANT/HIGHLY TOXIC. **ACUTE EXPOSURE-** MAY CAUSE NAUSEA, VOMITING, CENTRAL NERVOUS SYSTEM AGITATION, DEPRESSED CONSCIOUSNESS, SEIZURES AND EVENTUALLY COMA, CARDIAC IRREGULARITIES AND DEATH FROM FIBRILLATION OR RESPIRATORY FAILURE. A DROP OR TWO OF THE POISON BY ALMOST ANY ROUTE OF ADMINISTRATION MAY BE FATAL. CLINICAL EFFECTS MAY BE NOTED AS SOON AS 30 MINUTES FOLLOWING EXPOSURE BUT MAY BE DELAYED AS LONG AS 20 HOURS. A YOUNG CHILD INGESTED 300 MG OF THE POISON AND DEATH DID NOT OCCUR UNTIL 96 HOURS AFTER EXPOSURE. THE FATAL POISONING OF THREE OTHER CHILDREN WAS TRACED TO FLUOROACETAMIDE ALSO. **CHRONIC EXPOSURE-** NO HUMAN DATA AVAILABLE. MALE RATS THAT RECEIVED DIETARY LEVELS OF 50 PPM (3.4 MG/KG/DAY) SHOWED MARKED MORPHOLOGICAL CHANGES IN THE NUCLEUS OF STEP-13 SPERMATIDS WITHIN 24 HOURS. EFFECTS BECAME MORE PRONOUNCED AND THE ENTIRE CELL BECAME DISTORTED IN FIVE DAYS. SUBLETHAL DOSES IN MICE REDUCED FERTILITY, INCREASED PRE-NATAL MORTALITY AND CAUSED ABNORMAL NEONATAL DEVELOPMENT WHEN GIVEN DURING PREGNANCY.

FIRST AID- IMMEDIATE EMESIS AND GASTRIC LAVAGE FOLLOWED BY ORAL DOSES OF MAGNESIUM SULFATE ARE USEFUL. OILY CATHARTICS AND EPINEPHRINE SHOULD NOT BE USED. COMPLETE QUIET AND REST ARE INDICATED. (ARENA, POISONING, FOURTH EDITION) DO NOT PERFORM GASTRIC LAVAGE OR EMESIS IF VICTIM IS UNCONSCIOUS. GASTRIC LAVAGE SHOULD BE PERFORMED BY QUALIFIED MEDICAL PERSONNEL. GET MEDICAL ATTENTION IMMEDIATELY.

ANTIDOTE: THE FOLLOWING ANTIDOTE HAS BEEN RECOMMENDED. HOWEVER, THE DECISION AS TO WHETHER THE SEVERITY OF POISONING REQUIRES ADMINISTRATION OF ANY ANTIDOTE AND ACTUAL DOSE REQUIRED SHOULD BE MADE BY QUALIFIED MEDICAL PERSONNEL.

FOR FLUOROACETATE AND FLUOROACETAMIDE POISONING: ADMINISTRATION OF CERTAIN COMPOUNDS CAPABLE OF SUPPLYING ACETATE IONS HAS SHOWN ANTIDOTAL EFFECTS IN ANIMALS, INCLUDING MONKEYS. THE CHOICE DRUGS ARE MONOACETIN (GLYCERYL MONOACETATE 0.24 GM/KG) AND A COMBINATION OF SODIUM ACETATE AND ETHANOL (0.12 GM/KG OF EACH), BUT REPORTS OF THEIR USE IN HUMANS HAVE RARELY APPEARED IN LITERATURE. IF PARENTERAL ADMINISTRATION IS NOT FEASIBLE, A MIXTURE OF 100 ML OF UNDILUTED MONOACETIN IN 500 ML OF WATER CAN BE GIVEN ORALLY AND REPEATED IN AN HOUR. A SINGLE DOSE OF MAGNESIUM SULFATE (800 MG/KG) GIVEN INTRAMUSCULARLY AS A 50% SOLUTION HAS PROVED SUCCESSFUL IN ANIMALS DOSED WITH LETHAL AMOUNTS OF SODIUM FLUOROACETATE (ARENA, POISONING, 4TH ED.). ANTIDOTE SHOULD BE ADMINISTERED BY QUALIFIED MEDICAL PERSONNEL.

REACTIVITY

REACTIVITY: STABLE UNDER NORMAL TEMPERATURES AND PRESSURES.

INCOMPATIBILITIES: NONE KNOWN.

DECOMPOSITION: THERMAL DECOMPOSITION PRODUCTS MAY INCLUDE TOXIC AND HAZARDOUS FUMES OF HYDROGEN FLUORIDE AND OXIDES OF CARBON AND NITROGEN.

POLYMERIZATION: HAZARDOUS POLYMERIZATION HAS NOT BEEN REPORTED TO OCCUR UNDER NORMAL TEMPERATURES AND PRESSURES.

STORAGE AND DISPOSAL

OBSERVE ALL FEDERAL, STATE AND LOCAL REGULATIONS WHEN STORING OR DISPOSING OF THIS SUBSTANCE. FOR ASSISTANCE, CONTACT THE DISTRICT DIRECTOR OF THE ENVIRONMENTAL PROTECTION AGENCY.

****STORAGE****

THRESHOLD PLANNING QUANTITY (TPQ): THE SUPERFUND AMENDMENTS AND REAUTHORIZATION ACT (SARA) SECTION 302 REQUIRES THAT EACH FACILITY WHERE ANY EXTREMELY HAZARDOUS SUBSTANCE IS PRESENT IN A QUANTITY EQUAL TO OR GREATER THAN THE TPQ ESTABLISHED FOR THAT SUBSTANCE NOTIFY THE STATE EMERGENCY RESPONSE COMMISSION FOR THE STATE IN WHICH IT IS LOCATED. SECTION 303 OF SARA REQUIRES THESE FACILITIES TO PARTICIPATE IN LOCAL EMERGENCY RESPONSE PLANNING (40 CFR 355.30).

CONDITIONS TO AVOID

NONE REPORTED.

SPILL AND LEAK PROCEDURES

OCCUPATIONAL SPILL: DO NOT TOUCH SPILLED MATERIAL. STOP LEAK IF YOU CAN DO IT WITHOUT RISK. FOR SMALL SPILLS, TAKE UP WITH SAND OR OTHER ABSORBENT MATERIAL AND PLACE INTO CONTAINERS FOR LATER DISPOSAL. FOR SMALL DRY SPILLS, WITH A CLEAN SHOVEL PLACE MATERIAL INTO CLEAN, DRY CONTAINER AND COVER. MOVE CONTAINERS FROM SPILL AREA. FOR LARGER SPILLS, DIKE FAR AHEAD OF SPILL FOR LATER DISPOSAL. KEEP UNNECESSARY PEOPLE AWAY. ISOLATE HAZARD AREA AND DENY ENTRY.

REPORTABLE QUANTITY (RQ): 100 POUNDS THE SUPERFUND AMENDMENTS AND REAUTHORIZATION ACT (SARA) SECTION 304 REQUIRES THAT A RELEASE EQUAL TO OR GREATER THAN THE REPORTABLE QUANTITY FOR THIS SUBSTANCE BE IMMEDIATELY REPORTED TO THE LOCAL EMERGENCY PLANNING COMMITTEE AND THE STATE EMERGENCY RESPONSE COMMISSION (40 CFR 355.40). IF THE RELEASE OF THIS SUBSTANCE IS REPORTABLE UNDER CERCLA SECTION 103, THE NATIONAL RESPONSE CENTER MUST BE NOTIFIED IMMEDIATELY AT (800) 424-8802 OR (202) 426-2675 IN THE METROPOLITAN WASHINGTON, D.C. AREA (40 CFR 302.6).

PROTECTIVE EQUIPMENT

VENTILATION: PROCESS ENCLOSURE RECOMMENDED.

RESPIRATOR: THE FOLLOWING RESPIRATORS ARE RECOMMENDED BASED ON INFORMATION FOUND IN THE PHYSICAL DATA, TOXICITY AND HEALTH EFFECTS SECTIONS. THEY ARE RANKED IN ORDER FROM MINIMUM TO MAXIMUM RESPIRATORY PROTECTION. THE SPECIFIC RESPIRATOR SELECTED MUST BE BASED ON CONTAMINATION LEVELS FOUND IN THE WORK PLACE, MUST NOT EXCEED THE WORKING LIMITS OF THE RESPIRATOR AND BE JOINTLY APPROVED BY THE NATIONAL INSTITUTE FOR OCCUPATIONAL SAFETY AND HEALTH AND THE MINE SAFETY AND HEALTH ADMINISTRATION (NIOSH-MSHA).

CHEMICAL CARTRIDGE RESPIRATOR WITH AN ORGANIC VAPOR CARTRIDGE(S) IN COMBINATION WITH A DUST AND MIST FILTER.

GAS MASK WITH ORGANIC VAPOR CANISTER (CHIN-STYLE OR FRONT- OR BACK-MOUNTED CANISTER) WITH A DUST AND MIST FILTER.

GAS MASK WITH ORGANIC VAPOR CANISTER (CHIN-STYLE OR FRONT- OR BACK-MOUNTED CANISTER) WITH A PARTICULATE FILTER.

POWERED AIR-PURIFYING RESPIRATOR WITH A HIGH-EFFICIENCY FILTER.

TYPE 'C' SUPPLIED-AIR RESPIRATOR WITH A FULL FACEPIECE OPERATED IN A PRESSURE-DEMAND OR OTHER POSITIVE PRESSURE MODE.

SELF-CONTAINED BREATHING APPARATUS WITH A FULL FACEPIECE OPERATED IN PRESSURE-DEMAND OR OTHER POSITIVE PRESSURE MODE.
FOR FIREFIGHTING AND OTHER IMMEDIATELY DANGEROUS TO LIFE OR HEALTH CONDITIONS:
SELF-CONTAINED BREATHING APPARATUS WITH FULL FACEPIECE OPERATED IN PRESSURE-DEMAND OR OTHER POSITIVE PRESSURE MODE.
SUPPLIED-AIR RESPIRATOR WITH FULL FACEPIECE AND OPERATED IN PRESSURE-DEMAND OR OTHER POSITIVE PRESSURE MODE IN COMBINATION WITH AN AUXILIARY SELF-CONTAINED BREATHING APPARATUS OPERATED IN PRESSURE-DEMAND OR OTHER POSITIVE PRESSURE MODE.

CLOTHING: EMPLOYEE MUST WEAR APPROPRIATE PROTECTIVE (IMPERVIOUS) CLOTHING AND EQUIPMENT TO PREVENT ANY POSSIBILITY OF SKIN CONTACT WITH THIS SUBSTANCE.

GLOVES: EMPLOYEE MUST WEAR APPROPRIATE PROTECTIVE GLOVES TO PREVENT CONTACT WITH THIS SUBSTANCE.

EYE PROTECTION: EMPLOYEE MUST WEAR SPLASH-PROOF OR DUST-RESISTANT SAFETY GOGGLES AND A FACESHIELD TO PREVENT CONTACT WITH THIS SUBSTANCE.
EMERGENCY WASH FACILITIES: WHERE THERE IS ANY POSSIBILITY THAT AN EMPLOYEE'S EYES AND/OR SKIN MAY BE EXPOSED TO THIS SUBSTANCE, THE EMPLOYER SHOULD PROVIDE AN EYE WASH FOUNTAIN AND QUICK DRENCH SHOWER WITHIN THE IMMEDIATE WORK AREA FOR EMERGENCY USE.

AUTHORIZED BY- OCCUPATIONAL HEALTH SERVICES, INC.
CREATION DATE: 10/04/89 ***REVISION DATE:*** 05/18/90

MATERIAL SAFETY DATA SHEET

OCCUPATIONAL HEALTH SERVICES, INC.
AGRICULTURE AND PESTICIDE DIVISION
450 SEVENTH AVENUE, SUITE 2407
NEW YORK, NEW YORK 10123
1-800-445-MSDS OR (212) 967-1100

EMERGENCY CONTACT:
JOHN S. BRANSFORD, JR. (615) 292-1180

SUBSTANCE IDENTIFICATION

CAS-NUMBER 75-69-4

SUBSTANCE: FLUOROTRICHLOROMETHANE

TRADE NAMES/SYNONYMS: FREON 11; REFRIGERANT 11; TRICHLOROFLUOROMETHANE; F 11; FC 11; FRIGEN 11; TRICHLOROMONOFLUOROMETHANE; ISOTRON 11; METHANE, TRICHLOROFLUORO-; MONOFLUOROTRICHLOROMETHANE; TRICHLOROFLUOROCARBON; FLUOROCHLOROFORM; GENETRON 11; CFC 11; RCRA U121; CCL3F; PST09990

CHEMICAL FAMILY: HALOGEN COMPOUND, ALIPHATIC

MOLECULAR FORMULA: C-CL3-F

MOLECULAR WEIGHT: 137.37

CERCLA RATINGS (SCALE 0-3): HEALTH=2 FIRE=0 REACTIVITY=0 PERSISTENCE=3

NFPA RATINGS (SCALE 0-4): HEALTH=U FIRE=0 REACTIVITY=0

COMPONENTS AND CONTAMINANTS

COMPONENT: FLUOROTRICHLOROMETHANE ***PERCENT:*** 100.0
CAS# 75-69-4

OTHER CONTAMINANTS: NONE

EXPOSURE LIMITS: FLUOROTRICHLOROMETHANE: 1000 PPM (5600 MG/M3) OSHA CEILING 1000 PPM (5600 MG/M3) ACGIH CEILING
5000 POUNDS CERCLA SECTION 103 REPORTABLE QUANTITY

PHYSICAL DATA

DESCRIPTION: COLORLESS, VOLATILE LIQUID OR GAS WITH A FAINT ETHEREAL ODOR.

BOILING POINT: 75 F (24 C) ***MELTING POINT:*** -168 F (-111 C)

SPECIFIC GRAVITY: 1.494 @ 17 C ***VISCOSITY:*** 0.43 CPS @ 20 C

VOLATILITY: 100% ***VAPOR PRESSURE:*** 690 MMHG @ 20 C

EVAPORATION RATE: (BUTYL ACETATE=1) 0.63 ***SOLUBILITY IN WATER:*** 0.11% @ 20 C

ODOR THRESHOLD: 200,000 PPM ***VAPOR DENSITY:*** 4.7

SOLVENT SOLUBILITY: SOLUBLE IN ALCOHOL, ETHER, OTHER ORGANIC SOLVENTS.

FIRE AND EXPLOSION DATA

FIRE AND EXPLOSION HAZARD: NEGLIGIBLE FIRE HAZARD WHEN EXPOSED TO HEAT OR FLAME.

FIREFIGHTING MEDIA: DRY CHEMICAL, CARBON DIOXIDE OR HALON (1987 EMERGENCY RESPONSE GUIDEBOOK, DOT P 5800.4).
FOR LARGER FIRES, USE WATER SPRAY, FOG OR STANDARD FOAM (1987 EMERGENCY RESPONSE GUIDEBOOK, DOT P 5800.4).

FIREFIGHTING: MOVE CONTAINER FROM FIRE AREA IF POSSIBLE. STAY AWAY FROM STORAGE TANK ENDS. COOL FIRE-EXPOSED CONTAINERS WITH WATER FROM THE SIDE UNTIL WELL AFTER THE FIRE IS OUT. WITHDRAW IMMEDIATELY IF RISING SOUND FROM VENTING SAFETY DEVICE OR ANY DISCOLORATION OF STORAGE TANKS DUE TO FIRE (1987 EMERGENCY RESPONSE GUIDEBOOK, DOT P 5800.4, GUIDE PAGE 12).
EXTINGUISH USING AGENT INDICATED. COOL CYLINDERS WITH FLOODING AMOUNTS OF WATER FROM AS FAR A DISTANCE AS POSSIBLE. DO NOT USE WATER DIRECTLY ON MATERIAL. USE WATER SPRAY TO ABSORB VAPORS. AVOID BREATHING VAPORS; KEEP UPWIND. CONSIDER EVACUATION OF DOWNWIND AREA IF MATERIAL IS LEAKING.

TOXICITY

FLUOROTRICHLOROMETHANE: TOXICITY DATA: 50000 PPM/30 MINUTES INHALATION-HUMAN TCLO; 10 PPH/30 MINUTES INHALATION-MOUSE LC50; 25 PPH/30 MINUTES INHALATION-RABBIT LC50; 25 PPH/30 MINUTES INHALATION-GUINEA PIG LC50; 13 PPH/15 MINUTES INHALATION-RAT LC50; 1743 MG/KG INTRAPERITONEAL-MOUSE LD50. CARCINOGEN STATUS: NONE. ACUTE TOXICITY LEVEL: RELATIVELY NON-TOXIC BY INHALATION. TARGET EFFECTS: CENTRAL NERVOUS SYSTEM DEPRESSANT. POISONING MAY ALSO AFFECT THE CARDIOVASCULAR SYSTEM. AT INCREASED RISK FROM EXPOSURE: PERSONS WITH CARDIOVASCULAR DISEASES. ADDITIONAL DATA: STIMULANTS SUCH AS EPINEPHRINE MAY CAUSE VENTRICULAR FIBRILLATION. CROSS REACTIONS WITH ETHYL CHLORIDE MAY OCCUR.

HEALTH EFFECTS AND FIRST AID

INHALATION: FLUOROTRICHLOROMETHANE NARCOTIC. 10,000 PPM IMMEDIATELY DANGEROUS TO LIFE OR HEALTH. **ACUTE EXPOSURE-** MAY CAUSE IRRITATION OF THE NOSE, THROAT, AND UPPER RESPIRATORY TRACT, BRONCHOSPASMS, AND REDUCED VENTILATION CAPACITY OF THE LUNGS. HIGH CONCENTRATIONS MAY CAUSE CENTRAL NERVOUS SYSTEM DEPRESSION WITH LIGHTHEADEDNESS, HEADACHE, GIDDINESS, INCOORDINATION, DIZZINESS, DROWSINESS, TINNITUS, AND TREMORS. SEVERE EXPOSURE MAY CAUSE NAUSEA, VOMITING, UNCONSCIOUSNESS, AND, RARELY, COMA. SUDDEN DEATH MAY OCCUR FROM CARDIAC ARRYTHMIAS DUE TO SENSITIZATION OF THE MYOCARDIUM TO EPINEPHRINE. A HUMAN EXPOSED TO 50000 PPM FOR 30 MINUTES DEVELOPED FIBROSING ALVEOLITIS AND LIVER CHANGES. ANIMALS EXPOSED TO SUBLETHAL LEVELS DEVELOPED RAPID, LABORED RESPIRATION AND HYPERACTIVITY; LETHAL LEVELS CAUSED TREMORS, INACTIVITY, IRREGULAR RESPIRATION, AND DEATH. VERY HIGH CONCENTRATIONS MAY CAUSE SIMPLE ASPHYXIATION. **CHRONIC EXPOSURE-** VOLUNTEERS EXPOSED TO 1000 PPM FOR 6 HOURS A DAY FOR 20 DAYS SHOWED AN INSIGNIFICANT DECREMENT IN PERFORMANCE ON COGNITIVE TESTS. RATS EXPOSED TO 5600 MG/M3 FOR 90 DAYS EXHIBITED LUNG AND LIVER CHANGES.

FIRST AID- REMOVE FROM EXPOSURE AREA TO FRESH AIR IMMEDIATELY. IF BREATHING HAS STOPPED, PERFORM ARTIFICIAL RESPIRATION. KEEP PERSON WARM AND AT REST. TREAT SYMPTOMATICALLY AND SUPPORTIVELY. GET MEDICAL ATTENTION IMMEDIATELY.

SKIN CONTACT: FLUOROTRICHLOROMETHANE **ACUTE EXPOSURE-** NO ADVERSE EFFECTS HAVE BEEN REPORTED FROM THE GAS. DUE TO RAPID EVAPORATION, THE LIQUID MAY CAUSE FROSTBITE WITH REDNESS, TINGLING, PAIN, AND NUMBNESS. IN MORE SEVERE CASES, THE SKIN MAY BECOME HARD AND WHITE AND DEVELOP BLISTERS. MILD, REVERSIBLE IRRITATION OCCURS IN ANIMALS. **CHRONIC EXPOSURE-** REPEATED OR PROLONGED CONTACT MAY CAUSE DERMATITIS WITH IRRITATION, REDDENING, DRYING, AND CRACKING.

FIRST AID- IT IS UNLIKELY THAT EMERGENCY TREATMENT WILL BE REQUIRED. IF ADVERSE EFFECTS OCCUR, GET MEDICAL ATTENTION. IN CASE OF FROSTBITE, WARM AFFECTED SKIN IN WARM WATER AT A TEMPERATURE OF 107 F. IF WARM WATER IS NOT AVAILABLE OR IMPRACTICAL TO USE, GENTLY WRAP AFFECTED PART IN BLANKETS. ENCOURAGE VICTIM TO EXERCISE AFFECTED PART WHILE IT IS BEING WARMED. ALLOW CIRCULATION TO RETURN NATURALLY (MATHESON GAS, 6TH ED.). GET MEDICAL ATTENTION IMMEDIATELY.

EYE CONTACT: FLUOROTRICHLOROMETHANE **ACUTE EXPOSURE-** VAPORS OR LIQUID MAY CAUSE MILD IRRITATION. DUE TO RAPID EVAPORATION, THE LIQUID MAY CAUSE FROSTBITE WITH REDNESS, PAIN, AND BLURRED VISION. **CHRONIC EXPOSURE-** 9 APPLICATIONS OF 0.1 ML OVER AN 11 DAY PERIOD CAUSED NO HARMFUL EFFECTS TO RABBIT EYES. IN RABBITS, A 5 SECOND SPRAY FROM A DISTANCE OF 20 CM 5 DAYS A WEEK FOR 1 MONTH PRODUCED HYPEREMIA OF THE EYE LASTING SEVERAL HOURS AND MILD INFLAMMATION OF THE EYELIDS.

FIRST AID- IT IS UNLIKELY THAT CONTACT WITH THE GAS FORM WILL REQUIRE EMERGENCY TREATMENT. IF CONTACT WITH LIQUIFIED OR COMPRESSED GAS

OCCURS, WASH WITH LARGE AMOUNTS OF WARM WATER UNTIL NO EVIDENCE OF CHEMICAL REMAINS (APPROXIMATELY 15-20 MINUTES). GET MEDICAL ATTENTION IMMEDIATELY.

INGESTION: FLUOROTRICHLOROMETHANE **ACUTE EXPOSURE-** MAY CAUSE CENTRAL NERVOUS SYSTEM DEPRESSION AS DISCUSSED IN ACUTE INHALATION. MAY ALSO CAUSE FROSTBITE OF THE LIPS, MOUTH, AND THROAT. AN ACCIDENTAL CASE OF INGESTION RESULTED IN NECROSIS AND MULTIPLE PERFORATIONS OF THE STOMACH. **CHRONIC EXPOSURE-** REPEATED APPLICATION TO ORAL MUCOSA PRODUCED IRRITATION, EDEMA, AND INFLAMMATION IN RATS. **FIRST AID-** TREAT SYMPTOMATICALLY AND SUPPORTIVELY. GET MEDICAL ATTENTION IMMEDIATELY. IF VOMITING OCCURS, KEEP HEAD LOWER THAN HIPS TO PREVENT ASPIRATION.

ANTIDOTE: NO SPECIFIC ANTIDOTE. TREAT SYMPTOMATICALLY AND SUPPORTIVELY.

REACTIVITY

REACTIVITY: STABLE UNDER NORMAL TEMPERATURES AND PRESSURES.

INCOMPATIBILITIES: FLUOROTRICHLOROMETHANE: ALUMINUM: POSSIBLE EXPLOSION HAZARD. BARIUM: MAY DETONATE. LITHIUM: FORMS IMPACT-SENSITIVE MIXTURE. MAGNESIUM AND ALLOYS: MAY BE ATTACKED. METALS: POSSIBLE VIOLENT REACTION. PLASTICS: MAY BE ATTACKED. POTASSIUM: MAY FORM IGNITABLE OR EXPLOSIVE COMPOUND. RUBBER: MAY BE ATTACKED. SODIUM: MAY FORM IGNITABLE OR EXPLOSIVE COMPOUND.

DECOMPOSITION: THERMAL DECOMPOSITION PRODUCTS MAY INCLUDE TOXIC AND CORROSIVE FUMES OF CHLORIDES AND FLUORIDES, AND TOXIC OXIDES OF CARBON.

POLYMERIZATION: HAZARDOUS POLYMERIZATION HAS NOT BEEN REPORTED TO OCCUR UNDER NORMAL TEMPERATURES AND PRESSURES.

STORAGE AND DISPOSAL

OBSERVE ALL FEDERAL, STATE AND LOCAL REGULATIONS WHEN STORING OR DISPOSING OF THIS SUBSTANCE. FOR ASSISTANCE, CONTACT THE DISTRICT DIRECTOR OF THE ENVIRONMENTAL PROTECTION AGENCY.

****STORAGE****

STORE AWAY FROM INCOMPATIBLE SUBSTANCES.

****DISPOSAL****

DISPOSAL MUST BE IN ACCORDANCE WITH STANDARDS APPLICABLE TO GENERATORS OF HAZARDOUS WASTE, 40CFR 262. EPA HAZARDOUS WASTE NUMBER U121.

CONDITIONS TO AVOID

DO NOT PERMIT PHYSICAL DAMAGE OR OVERHEATING OF CONTAINERS. CONTENTS ARE UNDER PRESSURE; CONTAINERS MAY VIOLENTLY RUPTURE AND TRAVEL A CONSIDERABLE DISTANCE.

SPILL AND LEAK PROCEDURES

OCCUPATIONAL SPILL: STOP LEAK IF YOU CAN DO IT WITHOUT RISK. KEEP UNNECESSARY PEOPLE AWAY; ISOLATE HAZARD AREA AND DENY ENTRY. REPORTABLE QUANTITY (RQ): 5000 POUNDS THE SUPERFUND AMENDMENTS AND REAUTHORIZATION ACT (SARA) SECTION 304 REQUIRES THAT A RELEASE EQUAL TO OR GREATER THAN THE REPORTABLE QUANTITY FOR THIS SUBSTANCE BE IMMEDIATELY REPORTED TO THE LOCAL EMERGENCY PLANNING COMMITTEE AND THE STATE EMERGENCY RESPONSE COMMISSION (40 CFR 355.40). IF THE RELEASE OF THIS SUBSTANCE IS REPORTABLE UNDER CERCLA SECTION 103, THE NATIONAL RESPONSE CENTER MUST BE NOTIFIED IMMEDIATELY AT (800) 424-8802 OR (202) 426-2675 IN THE METROPOLITAN WASHINGTON, D.C. AREA (40 CFR 302.6).

PROTECTIVE EQUIPMENT

VENTILATION: PROVIDE GENERAL DILUTION VENTILATION TO MEET PUBLISHED EXPOSURE LIMITS.

RESPIRATOR: THE FOLLOWING RESPIRATORS AND MAXIMUM USE CONCENTRATIONS ARE RECOMMENDATIONS BY THE U.S. DEPARTMENT OF HEALTH AND HUMAN SERVICES, NIOSH POCKET GUIDE TO CHEMICAL HAZARDS; NIOSH CRITERIA DOCUMENTS OR BY THE U.S. DEPARTMENT OF LABOR, 29 CFR 1910 SUBPART Z. THE SPECIFIC RESPIRATOR SELECTED MUST BE BASED ON CONTAMINATION LEVELS FOUND IN THE WORK PLACE, MUST NOT EXCEED THE WORKING LIMITS OF THE RESPIRATOR AND BE JOINTLY APPROVED BY THE NATIONAL INSTITUTE FOR OCCUPATIONAL SAFETY AND HEALTH AND THE MINE SAFETY AND HEALTH ADMINISTRATION (NIOSH-MSHA).

FLUOROTRICHLOROMETHANE:

10,000 PPM- ANY SUPPLIED-AIR RESPIRATOR. ANY SELF-CONTAINED BREATHING APPARATUS.

ESCAPE- ANY AIR-PURIFYING FULL FACEPIECE RESPIRATOR (GAS MASK) WITH A CHIN-STYLE OR FRONT- OR BACK-MOUNTED ORGANIC VAPOR CANISTER. ANY APPROPRIATE ESCAPE-TYPE SELF-CONTAINED BREATHING APPARATUS.

FOR FIREFIGHTING AND OTHER IMMEDIATELY DANGEROUS TO LIFE OR HEALTH CONDITIONS:

SELF-CONTAINED BREATHING APPARATUS WITH FULL FACEPIECE OPERATED IN PRESSURE-DEMAND OR OTHER POSITIVE PRESSURE MODE.

SUPPLIED-AIR RESPIRATOR WITH FULL FACEPIECE AND OPERATED IN PRESSURE-DEMAND OR OTHER POSITIVE PRESSURE MODE IN COMBINATION WITH AN AUXILIARY SELF-CONTAINED BREATHING APPARATUS OPERATED IN PRESSURE-DEMAND OR OTHER POSITIVE PRESSURE MODE.

CLOTHING: FOR THE GAS FORM, PROTECTIVE CLOTHING NOT REQUIRED. IF CONTACT WITH THE LIQUID FORM IS POSSIBLE, EMPLOYEE MUST WEAR APPROPRIATE PROTECTIVE CLOTHING AND EQUIPMENT TO PREVENT SKIN FROM FREEZING.

GLOVES: WEAR FULL PROTECTIVE, COLD INSULATING GLOVES.

EYE PROTECTION: FOR THE GAS FORM EYE PROTECTION IS NOT REQUIRED BUT RECOMMENDED. WHERE THERE IS ANY POSSIBILITY OF CONTACT WITH THE LIQUID FORM, EMPLOYEE MUST WEAR SPLASH-PROOF SAFETY GOGGLES AND A FACESHIELD TO PREVENT CONTACT WITH THIS SUBSTANCE. CONTACT LENSES SHOULD NOT BE WORN.

EMERGENCY WASH FACILITIES: WHERE THERE IS ANY POSSIBILITY THAT AN EMPLOYEE'S EYES AND/OR SKIN MAY BE EXPOSED TO THE LIQUID FORM OF THIS SUBSTANCE, THE EMPLOYER SHOULD PROVIDE AN EYE WASH FOUNTAIN AND QUICK DRENCH SHOWER WITHIN THE IMMEDIATE WORK AREA FOR EMERGENCY USE.

AUTHORIZED BY- OCCUPATIONAL HEALTH SERVICES, INC.

CREATION DATE: 11/16/89 ***REVISION DATE:*** 05/16/90

MATERIAL SAFETY DATA SHEET

OCCUPATIONAL HEALTH SERVICES, INC.	EMERGENCY CONTACT:
AGRICULTURE AND PESTICIDE DIVISION	JOHN S. BRANSFORD, JR. (615) 292-1180
450 SEVENTH AVENUE, SUITE 2407	
NEW YORK, NEW YORK 10123	
1-800-445-MSDS OR (212) 967-1100	

SUBSTANCE IDENTIFICATION

CAS-NUMBER 150-50-5

SUBSTANCE: MERPHOS

TRADE NAMES/SYNONYMS: TRIBUTYL ESTER PHOSPHOROTRITHIOUS ACID; BUTYL PHOSPHOROTRITHIOITE; TRIBUTYL PHOSPHOROTRITHIOITE; TRIBUTYL TRITHIOPHOSPHITE; TRIS(BUTYLTHIO)PHOSPHINE; S,S,S-TRIBUTYL PHOSPHOROTRITHIOITE; FOLEX; PST10010

CHEMICAL FAMILY: ORGANOPHOSPHATE

MOLECULAR FORMULA: C12-H27-P-S3

MOLECULAR WEIGHT: 298.54

CERCLA RATINGS (SCALE 0-3): HEALTH=3 FIRE=0 REACTIVITY=U PERSISTENCE=0

NFPA RATINGS (SCALE 0-4): HEALTH=3 FIRE=0 REACTIVITY=U

COMPONENTS AND CONTAMINANTS

COMPONENT: MERPHOS ***PERCENT:*** 100

CAS# 150-50-5

EXPOSURE LIMITS: NO OCCUPATIONAL EXPOSURE LIMITS ESTABLISHED BY OSHA, ACGIH, OR NIOSH.

PHYSICAL DATA

DESCRIPTION: COLORLESS TO PALE YELLOW LIQUID

BOILING POINT: 239-273 F (115-134 F) @ 0.08 MMHG ***SPECIFIC GRAVITY:*** 0.99-1.01

EVAPORATION RATE: NOT AVAILABLE ***SOLUBILITY IN WATER:*** SPARINGLY SOLUBLE

SOLVENT SOLUBILITY: SOLUBLE IN ACETONE, ETHANOL, BENZENE, HEXANE, KEROSENE, DIESEL OIL, HEAVY AROMATIC NAPHTHAS, XYLENE, AND METHYLATED NAPHTHALENES

FIRE AND EXPLOSION DATA

FIRE AND EXPLOSION HAZARD: NEGLIGIBLE FIRE HAZARD WHEN EXPOSED TO HEAT OR FLAME.

FIREFIGHTING MEDIA: DRY CHEMICAL, CARBON DIOXIDE, HALON, WATER SPRAY OR STANDARD FOAM (1987 EMERGENCY RESPONSE GUIDEBOOK, DOT P 5800.4). FOR LARGER FIRES, USE WATER SPRAY, FOG OR STANDARD FOAM (1987 EMERGENCY RESPONSE GUIDEBOOK, DOT P 5800.4).

FIREFIGHTING: MOVE CONTAINERS FROM FIRE AREA IF POSSIBLE. FIGHT FIRE FROM MAXIMUM DISTANCE. STAY AWAY FROM STORAGE TANK ENDS. DIKE FIRE CONTROL WATER FOR LATER DISPOSAL. DO NOT SCATTER MATERIAL (1987 EMERGENCY RESPONSE GUIDEBOOK, DOT P 5800.4, GUIDE PAGE 55).

TOXICITY

MERPHOS: TOXICITY DATA: 615 MG/KG SKIN-RAT LD50; 910 MG/KG ORAL-RAT LD50; 70 MG/KG INTRAPERITONEAL-RAT LD50; 1400 MG/KG INTRAPERITONEAL-MOUSE LD50; 350 MG/KG UNREPORTED-RAT LD50. CARCINOGEN STATUS: NONE. LOCAL EFFECTS: IRRITANT-INHALATION, SKIN, EYE. ACUTE TOXICITY LEVEL: TOXIC BY DERMAL ABSORPTION AND MODERATELY TOXIC BY INGESTION. TARGET EFFECTS: CHOLINESTERASE INHIBITOR. NEUROTOXIN. AT INCREASED RISK FROM EXPOSURE: PERSONS WITH RESPIRATORY AILMENTS, RECENT EXPOSURE TO CHOLINESTERASE INHIBITORS OR IMPAIRED CHOLINESTERASE PRODUCTION, OR LIVER MALFUNCTION.* ADDITIONAL DATA: THE CHOLINESTERASE-INHIBITING EFFECT OF MERPHOS IS POTENTIATED BY MALATHION, RONNEL, AZINPHOS, AND METHYL PARATHION. MAY CROSS THE PLACENTA. HIGH ENVIRONMENTAL TEMPERATURES OR EXPOSURE OF THE CHEMICAL TO VISIBLE OR ULTRAVIOLET LIGHT MAY ENHANCE THE TOXICITY. INTERACTIONS WITH MEDICATIONS MAY OCCUR.*

* MAY BE BASED ON GENERAL INFORMATION ON ORGANOPHOSPHATES.

HEALTH EFFECTS AND FIRST AID

INHALATION: MERPHOS: IRRITANT. MAY CAUSE IRRITATION OF THE MUCOUS MEMBRANES AND IS A WEAK CHOLINESTERASE INHIBITOR. SEE INFORMATION ON ORGANOPHOSPHATES.

ORGANOPHOSPHATES: CHOLINESTERASE INHIBITOR. **ACUTE EXPOSURE-** WHEN INHALED, THE FIRST EFFECTS OF CHOLINESTERASE INHIBITORS ARE USUALLY RESPIRATORY AND MAY INCLUDE NASAL HYPEREMIA AND WATERY DISCHARGE, COUGH, CHEST DISCOMFORT, DYSPNEA, AND WHEEZING DUE TO INCREASED BRONCHIAL SECRETIONS AND BRONCHOCONSTRICTION. IF SUFFICIENT AMOUNTS ARE ABSORBED, OTHER SYSTEMIC EFFECTS MAY BEGIN WITHIN A FEW MINUTES OR BE DELAYED FOR UP TO 12 HOURS. SYMPTOMS MAY INCLUDE PALLOR, NAUSEA, VOMITING, DIARRHEA, ABDOMINAL CRAMPS, HEADACHE, DIZZINESS, OCULAR PAIN, BLURRED VISION, MIOSIS OR IN SOME CASES, ESPECIALLY INITIALLY, MYDRIASIS, LACRIMATION, SALIVATION, SWEATING, AND CONFUSION. OTHER REPORTED CENTRAL NERVOUS SYSTEM OR NEUROMUSCULAR EFFECTS MAY INCLUDE ATAXIA, SLURRED SPEECH, AREFLEXIA, WEAKNESS, FATIGUE, FASCICULATIONS, TWITCHING, TREMORS POSSIBLY OF THE TONGUE AND EYELIDS, AND EVENTUALLY PARALYSIS OF THE EXTREMITIES AND POSSIBLY OF THE RESPIRATORY MUSCLES. IN SEVERE CASES THERE MAY ALSO BE INVOLUNTARY DEFECATION AND URINATION, CYANOSIS, PSYCHOSIS, HYPERGLYCEMIA, ACUTE PANCREATITIS, CARDIAC IRREGULARITIES, PULMONARY EDEMA, UNCONSCIOUSNESS, CONVULSIONS, AND COMA. DEATH IS PRIMARILY DUE TO RESPIRATORY FAILURE, ALTHOUGH CARDIOVASCULAR EFFECTS INCLUDING CARDIAC ARREST MAY ALSO BE IMPLICATED. LONG TERM SEQUELAE ARE RARE BUT MAY INCLUDE NEUROPSYCHIATRIC DISORDERS AND MYOPATHY WITH MUSCLE TENDERNESS. SOME ORGANOPHOSPHATES MAY CAUSE A DELAYED NEUROPATHY BEGINNING 1-4 WEEKS AFTER AN ACUTE EXPOSURE WHICH MAY OR MAY NOT HAVE CAUSED ACUTE CHOLINERGIC EFFECTS. NUMBNESS, TINGLING, WEAKNESS AND CRAMPING BEGINNING SYMMETRICALLY IN THE LOWER LIMBS MAY PROGRESS TO ATAXIA AND PARALYSIS. IN SEVERE CASES, UPPER LIMB INVOLVEMENT IS POSSIBLE AND FLACCID PARALYSIS MAY PROGRESS TO SPASTIC PARALYSIS WITH EXAGGERATED REFLEXES. IMPROVEMENT MAY OCCUR OVER MONTHS TO YEARS, BUT SOME RESIDUAL IMPAIRMENT USUALLY REMAINS. **CHRONIC EXPOSURE-** REPEATED OR PROLONGED EXPOSURE MAY RESULT IN THE EFFECTS OF ACUTE EXPOSURE INCLUDING THE DELAYED NEUROPATHY. OTHER EFFECTS REPORTED IN WORKERS REPEATEDLY EXPOSED INCLUDE IMPAIRED MEMORY AND CONCENTRATION, ACUTE PSYCHOSIS, SEVERE DEPRESSIONS, IRRITABILTY, CONFUSION, APATHY, EMOTIONAL LABILITY, SOCIAL WITHDRAWAL, CONFUSION, HEADACHE, SPEECH DIFFICULTIES, DELAYED REACTION TIMES, SPATIAL DISORIENTATION, NIGHTMARES, SLEEPWALKING, AND DROWSINESS OR INSOMNIA. AN INFLUENZA-LIKE CONDITION WITH HEADACHE, NAUSEA, WEAKNESS, ANOREXIA AND MALAISE HAS ALSO BEEN REPORTED.

FIRST AID- REMOVE FROM EXPOSURE AREA TO FRESH AIR IMMEDIATELY. IF BREATHING HAS STOPPED, GIVE ARTIFICIAL RESPIRATION. MAINTAIN AIRWAY AND BLOOD PRESSURE AND ADMINISTER OXYGEN IF AVAILABLE. KEEP AFFECTED PERSON WARM AND AT REST. TREAT SYMPTOMATICALLY AND SUPPORTIVELY. ADMINISTRATION OF OXYGEN SHOULD BE PERFORMED BY QUALIFIED PERSONNEL. GET MEDICAL ATTENTION IMMEDIATELY.

SKIN CONTACT: MERPHOS: IRRITANT/NEUROTOXIN/TOXIC. MAY CAUSE IRRITATION. A SINGLE DERMAL APPLICATION OF 1,000 MG/KG PRODUCED DELAYED NEUROTOXICITY IN HENS. PROLONGED OR REPEATED EXPOSURE MAY CAUSE DERMATITIS. ONE INCIDENT OF ACCIDENTAL POISONING RESULTED IN POLYNEUROPATHY WITH WEAKNESS IN THE EXTREMITIES THAT LASTED FOR 20 WEEKS. DELAYED NEUROTOXICITY WAS OBSERVED IN HENS AFTER REPEATED APPLICATION OF MERPHOS. SEE INFORMATION ON ORGANOPHOSPHATES.

ORGANOPHOSPHATES: CHOLINESTERASE INHIBITOR. **ACUTE EXPOSURE-** LOCALIZED SWEATING AND FASCICULATIONS MAY OCCUR AT THE SITE OF CONTACT. IF SUFFICIENT AMOUNTS ARE ABSORBED, OTHER EFFECTS OF CHOLINESTERASE INHIBITION AS DESCRIBED IN ACUTE INHALATION MAY OCCUR. SYMPTOMS MAY BE DELAYED 2-3 HOURS, BUT USUALLY NO MORE THAN 12 HOURS. THE RATE OF ABSORPTION IS INCREASED BY THE PRESENCE OF DERMATITIS OR HIGH AMBIENT TEMPERATURES. DELAYED NEUROPATHY IS ALSO POSSIBLE. **CHRONIC EXPOSURE-** REPEATED OR PROLONGED EXPOSURE MAY CAUSE EFFECTS AS DESCRIBED IN ACUTE EXPOSURE. SOME ORGANOPHOSPHATES MAY CAUSE SENSITIZATION.

FIRST AID- REMOVE CONTAMINATED CLOTHING IMMEDIATELY. WASH CONTAMINATED AREAS WITH SOAP AND WATER FOLLOWED BY ALCOHOL (ARENA, POISONING, 4TH ED.). EMERGENCY PERSONNEL SHOULD WEAR GLOVES AND AVOID CONTAMINATION. TREAT RESPIRATORY DIFFICULTY WITH ARTIFICIAL RESPIRATION. GET MEDICAL ATTENTION IMMEDIATELY.

EYE CONTACT: MERPHOS: IRRITANT. MAY CAUSE IRRITATION. PROLONGED OR REPEATED EXPOSURE MAY CAUSE CONJUNCTIVITIS. SEE INFORMATION ON ORGANOPHOSPHATES.

ORGANOPHOSPHATES: CHOLINESTERASE INHIBITOR. **ACUTE EXPOSURE-** DIRECT CONTACT MAY CAUSE PAIN, HYPEREMIA, LACRIMATION, TWITCHING OF THE EYELIDS, MIOSIS, AND CILIARY MUSCLE SPASM WITH LOSS OF ACCOMODATION, BLURRED OR DIMMED VISION AND BROWACHE. SOMETIMES MYDRIASIS MAY OCCUR INSTEAD OF MIOSIS. WITH SUFFICIENT EXPOSURE, OTHER SYMPTOMS OF CHOLINESTERASE INHIBITION AS DESCRIBED IN ACUTE INHALATION MAY OCCUR. **CHRONIC EXPOSURE-** REPEATED OR PROLONGED EXPOSURE MAY CAUSE EFFECTS AS DESCRIBED IN ACUTE EXPOSURE. SOME COMPOUNDS HAVE CAUSED TOXIC EFFECTS ON THE CRYSTALLINE LENS, CONJUNCTIVAL THICKENING AND OBSTRUCTION OF THE NASOLACRIMAL CANALS WHEN USED AS MIOTIC EYEDROPS.

FIRST AID- IRRIGATE EYES WITH WATER OR SALINE SOLUTION. IF SYMPTOMS OF POISONING OCCUR, TREAT RESPIRATORY DIFFICULTY WITH ARTIFICIAL RESPIRATION AND OXYGEN. OBSERVE PATIENT FOR AT LEAST 24-36 HOURS (GOSSELIN, CLINICAL TOXICOLOGY OF COMMERCIAL PRODUCTS, 5TH ED.). GET MEDICAL ATTENTION IMMEDIATELY. OXYGEN SHOULD BE ADMINISTERED BY QUALIFIED MEDICAL PERSONNEL.

INGESTION: MERPHOS: NEUROTOXIN. DELAYED NEUROTOXICITY WAS OBSERVED IN HENS FED REPEATED DOSES OF MERPHOS. SEE INFORMATION ON ORGANOPHOSPHATES.

ORGANOPHOSPHATES: CHOLINESTERASE INHIBITOR. **ACUTE EXPOSURE-** WHEN INGESTED, THE FIRST EFFECTS MAY BE NAUSEA, VOMITING, ANOREXIA, ABDOMINAL CRAMPS AND DIARRHEA. GASTROINTESTINAL ABSORPTION MAY CAUSE SYMPTOMS OF CHOLINESTERASE INHIBITION AS DESCRIBED IN ACUTE INHALATION. SYMPTOMS MAY BEGIN WITHIN MINUTES OR BE DELAYED FOR HOURS. DELAYED EFFECTS INCLUDING NEUROPATHY MAY ALSO OCCUR. **CHRONIC EXPOSURE-** REPEATED INGESTION MAY CAUSE EFFECTS AS DESCRIBED IN ACUTE EXPOSURE.

FIRST AID- IF PERSON IS ALERT AND RESPIRATION IS NOT DEPRESSED, GIVE SYRUP OF IPECAC FOLLOWED BY WATER (IF VOMITING OCCURS, KEEP HEAD BELOW HIPS TO PREVENT ASPIRATION). IF CONSCIOUSNESS LEVEL DECLINES OR VOMITING HAS NOT OCCURRED IN 15 MINUTES EMPTY STOMACH BY GASTRIC LAVAGE WITH THE AID OF CUFFED ENDOTRACHEAL TUBE USING ISOTONIC SALINE OR 5% SODIUM BICARBONATE FOLLOW WITH ACTIVATED CHARCOAL. ESTABLISH AND MAINTAIN AIRWAY. TREAT RESPIRATORY DIFFICULTY WITH ARTIFICIAL RESPIRATION AND OXYGEN. DO NOT GIVE MORPHINE, AMINOPHYLLINE, PHENOTHIAZINES, RESERPINE, FUROSEMIDE, OR ETHACRYNIC ACID (MORGAN, RECOGNITION AND MANAGEMENT OF PESTICIDE POISONINGS, 3RD ED.). TREAT SYMPTOMATICALLY AND SUPPORTIVELY. ADMINISTRATION OF OXYGEN AND LAVAGE MUST BE PERFORMED BY QUALIFIED MEDICAL PERSONNEL. GET MEDICAL ATTENTION IMMEDIATELY.

ANTIDOTE: THE FOLLOWING ANTIDOTE(S) HAVE BEEN RECOMMENDED. HOWEVER, THE DECISION AS TO WHETHER THE SEVERITY OF POISONING REQUIRES ADMINISTRATION OF ANY ANTIDOTE AND ACTUAL DOSE REQUIRED SHOULD BE MADE BY QUALIFIED MEDICAL PERSONNEL.

FOR CHOLINESTERASE INHIBITORS: ESTABLISH CLEAR AIRWAY AND TISSUE OXYGENATION BY ASPIRATION OF SECRETIONS, AND IF NECESSARY, BY ASSISTED PULMONARY VENTILATION WITH OXYGEN. IMPROVE TISSUE OXYGENATION AS MUCH AS POSSIBLE BEFORE ADMINISTERING ATROPINE TO MINIMIZE THE RISK OF VENTRICULAR FIBRILLATION. ADMINISTER ATROPINE SULFATE INTRAVENOUSLY, OR INTRAMUSCULARLY IF IV INJECTION IS NOT POSSIBLE. IN MODERATELY SEVERE POISONING ADMINISTER ATROPINE SULFATE, 0.4-2.0 MG REPEATED EVERY 15 MINUTES UNTIL ATROPINIZATION IS ACHIEVED (TACHYCARDIA, FLUSHING, DRY MOUTH, MYDRIASIS). MAINTAIN ATROPINIZATION BY REPEATED DOSES FOR 2-12 HOURS, OR LONGER, DEPENDING ON THE SEVERITY OF POISONING. THE APPEARANCE OF RALES IN THE LUNG BASES, MIOSIS, SALIVATION, NAUSEA, BRADYCARDIA, ARE ALL INDICATIONS OF INADEQUATE ATROPINIZATION. SEVERELY POISONED INDIVIDUALS MAY EXHIBIT REMARKABLE TOLERANCE TO ATROPINE; TWO OR MORE TIMES THE DOSAGES SUGGESTED ABOVE MAY BE

NEEDED. PERSONS NOT POISONED OR ONLY SLIGHTLY POISONED, HOWEVER, MAY DEVELOP SIGNS OF ATROPINE TOXICITY FROM SUCH LARGE DOSAGES: FEVER, MUSCLE FIBRILLATIONS, AND DELIRIUM ARE THE MAIN SIGNS OF ATROPINE TOXICITY. IF THESE SIGNS APPEAR WHILE THE PATIENT IS FULLY ATROPINIZED, ATROPINE ADMINISTRATION SHOULD BE DISCONTINUED, AT LEAST TEMPORARILY. OBSERVE TREATED PATIENTS CLOSELY AT LEAST 24 HOURS TO INSURE THAT SYMPTOMS (POSSIBLY PULMONARY EDEMA) DO NOT RECUR AS ATROPINIZATION WEARS OFF. IN VERY SEVERE POISONINGS, METABOLIC DISPOSITION OF TOXICANT MAY REQUIRE SEVERAL HOURS OR DAYS DURING WHICH ATROPINIZATION MUST BE MAINTAINED. MARKEDLY LOWER LEVELS OF URINARY METABOLITES INDICATE THAT ATROPINE DOSAGE CAN BE TAPERED OFF. AS DOSAGE IS REDUCED, CHECK THE LUNG BASES FREQUENTLY FOR RALES. IF RALES ARE HEARD OR OTHER SYMPTOMS RETURN, RE-ESTABLISH ATROPINIZATION PROMPTLY (MORGAN, RECOGNITION AND MANAGEMENT OF PESTICIDE POISONINGS, 3RD ED.). ADMINISTRATION OF ANTIDOTE MUST BE PERFORMED BY QUALIFIED MEDICAL PERSONNEL.

IN CASES OF SEVERE POISONING BY ORGANOPHOSPHATE PESTICIDES IN WHICH RESPIRATORY DEPRESSION, MUSCLE WEAKNESS AND TWITCHINGS ARE SEVERE, GIVE PRALIDOXIME (PROTOPAM-AYERST, 2-PAM), 1.0 GRAM INTRAVENOUSLY AT NO MORE THAN 0.5 GRAM PER MINUTE. DOSAGE OF PRALIDOXIME MAY BE REPEATED IN 1-2 HOURS, THEN AT 10-12 HOUR INTERVALS IF NEEDED. IN VERY SEVERE POISONINGS, DOSAGE RATES MAY BE DOUBLED. TREATMENT WITH PRALIDOXIME WILL BE MOST EFFECTIVE IF GIVEN WITHIN THIRTY-SIX HOURS AFTER POISONING (MORGAN, RECOGNITION AND MANAGEMENT OF PESTICIDE POISONINGS, 3RD ED.). ANTIDOTE SHOULD BE ADMINISTERED BY QUALIFIED MEDICAL PERSONNEL.

REACTIVITY

REACTIVITY: READILY OXIDIZED BY AIR TO S,S,S-TRIBUTYL PHOSPHOROTRITHIOATE.

INCOMPATIBILITIES: MERPHOS: NO DATA AVAILABLE.

DECOMPOSITION: THERMAL DECOMPOSITION MAY RELEASE TOXIC OXIDES OF PHOSPHORUS AND SULFUR.

POLYMERIZATION: HAZARDOUS POLYMERIZATION HAS NOT BEEN REPORTED TO OCCUR UNDER NORMAL TEMPERATURES AND PRESSURES.

STORAGE AND DISPOSAL

OBSERVE ALL FEDERAL, STATE AND LOCAL REGULATIONS WHEN STORING OR DISPOSING OF THIS SUBSTANCE. FOR ASSISTANCE, CONTACT THE DISTRICT DIRECTOR OF THE ENVIRONMENTAL PROTECTION AGENCY.

STORAGE

STORE IN ACCORDANCE WITH 40 CFR 165 RECOMMENDED PROCEDURES FOR THE DISPOSAL AND STORAGE OF PESTICIDES AND PESTICIDE CONTAINERS.

DISPOSAL

DISPOSAL MUST BE IN ACCORDANCE WITH 40 CFR 165 RECOMMENDED PROCEDURES FOR THE DISPOSAL AND STORAGE OF PESTICIDES AND PESTICIDE CONTAINERS.

CONDITIONS TO AVOID

NONE REPORTED.

SPILL AND LEAK PROCEDURES

OCCUPATIONAL SPILL: DO NOT TOUCH SPILLED MATERIAL. STOP LEAK IF YOU CAN DO IT WITHOUT RISK. USE WATER SPRAY TO REDUCE VAPORS. FOR SMALL SPILLS, TAKE UP WITH SAND OR OTHER ABSORBENT MATERIAL AND PLACE INTO CONTAINERS FOR LATER DISPOSAL. FOR SMALL DRY SPILLS, WITH A CLEAN SHOVEL PLACE MATERIAL INTO CLEAN, DRY CONTAINERS AND COVER. MOVE CONTAINERS FROM SPILL AREA. FOR LARGER SPILLS, DIKE FAR AHEAD OF SPILL FOR LATER DISPOSAL. KEEP UNNECESSARY PEOPLE AWAY. ISOLATE HAZARD AREA AND DENY ENTRY. VENTILATE CLOSED SPACES BEFORE ENTERING.

PROTECTIVE EQUIPMENT

VENTILATION: PROVIDE LOCAL EXHAUST OR PROCESS ENCLOSURE VENTILATION SYSTEM.

RESPIRATOR: THE FOLLOWING RESPIRATORS ARE RECOMMENDED BASED ON INFORMATION FOUND IN THE PHYSICAL DATA, TOXICITY AND HEALTH EFFECTS SECTIONS. THEY ARE RANKED IN ORDER FROM MINIMUM TO MAXIMUM RESPIRATORY PROTECTION. THE SPECIFIC RESPIRATOR SELECTED MUST BE BASED ON CONTAMINATION LEVELS FOUND IN THE WORK PLACE, MUST NOT EXCEED THE WORKING LIMITS OF THE RESPIRATOR AND BE JOINTLY APPROVED BY THE NATIONAL INSTITUTE FOR OCCUPATIONAL SAFETY AND HEALTH AND THE MINE SAFETY AND HEALTH ADMINISTRATION (NIOSH-MSHA).

TYPE 'C' SUPPLIED-AIR RESPIRATOR WITH A FULL FACEPIECE OPERATED IN PRESSURE-DEMAND OR OTHER POSITIVE PRESSURE MODE OR WITH A FULL FACEPIECE, HELMET OR HOOD OPERATED IN CONTINOUS-FLOW MODE.

SELF-CONTAINED BREATHING APPARATUS WITH A FULL FACEPIECE OPERATED IN PRESSURE-DEMAND OR OTHER POSITIVE PRESSURE MODE.

FOR FIREFIGHTING AND OTHER IMMEDIATELY DANGEROUS TO LIFE OR HEALTH CONDITIONS:

SELF-CONTAINED BREATHING APPARATUS WITH FULL FACEPIECE OPERATED IN PRESSURE-DEMAND OR OTHER POSITIVE PRESSURE MODE.

SUPPLIED-AIR RESPIRATOR WITH FULL FACEPIECE AND OPERATED IN PRESSURE-DEMAND OR OTHER POSITIVE PRESSURE MODE IN COMBINATION WITH AN AUXILIARY SELF-CONTAINED BREATHING APPARATUS OPERATED IN PRESSURE-DEMAND OR OTHER POSITIVE PRESSURE MODE.

CLOTHING: EMPLOYEE MUST WEAR APPROPRIATE PROTECTIVE (IMPERVIOUS) CLOTHING AND EQUIPMENT TO PREVENT ANY POSSIBILITY OF SKIN CONTACT WITH THIS SUBSTANCE.

GLOVES: EMPLOYEE MUST WEAR APPROPRIATE PROTECTIVE GLOVES TO PREVENT CONTACT WITH THIS SUBSTANCE.

EYE PROTECTION: EMPLOYEE MUST WEAR SPLASH-PROOF OR DUST-RESISTANT SAFETY GOGGLES AND A FACESHIELD TO PREVENT CONTACT WITH THIS SUBSTANCE.

EMERGENCY WASH FACILITIES: WHERE THERE IS ANY POSSIBILITY THAT AN EMPLOYEE'S EYES AND/OR SKIN MAY BE EXPOSED TO THIS SUBSTANCE, THE EMPLOYER SHOULD PROVIDE AN EYE WASH FOUNTAIN AND QUICK DRENCH SHOWER WITHIN THE IMMEDIATE WORK AREA FOR EMERGENCY USE.

AUTHORIZED BY- OCCUPATIONAL HEALTH SERVICES, INC.

CREATION DATE: 10/04/89 ***REVISION DATE:*** 05/09/90

MATERIAL SAFETY DATA SHEET

OCCUPATIONAL HEALTH SERVICES, INC.
AGRICULTURE AND PESTICIDE DIVISION
450 SEVENTH AVENUE, SUITE 2407
NEW YORK, NEW YORK 10123
1-800-445-MSDS OR (212) 967-1100

EMERGENCY CONTACT:
JOHN S. BRANSFORD, JR. (615) 292-1180

SUBSTANCE IDENTIFICATION

CAS-NUMBER 133-07-3

SUBSTANCE: FOLPET

TRADE NAMES/SYNONYMS: 2-((TRICHLOROMETHYL)THIO)-1H-ISOINDOLE-1,3(2H)-DIONE; N-((TRICHLOROMETHYL)THIO)-PHTHALIMIDE; N-(TRICHLOROMETHYLMERCAPTO)PHTHALIMIDE; N-(TRICHLOROMETHYLTHIO)PHTHALIMIDE; COSAN T; FALTAN; FOLNIT; FOLPAN; FOLPEL; FTALAN; FUNGITROL 11; INTERCIDE TMP; ORTHORALTAN 50; ORTHOPHALTAN; PHALTAN; PHTHALTAN; SANFOL; SPOLACID; TRIFOL; VINICOIL; PST10012

CHEMICAL FAMILY: HALOGEN COMPOUND, AROMATIC

MOLECULAR FORMULA: C9-H4-CL3-N-O2-S

MOLECULAR WEIGHT: 296.55

CERCLA RATINGS (SCALE 0-3): HEALTH=1 FIRE=U REACTIVITY=0 PERSISTENCE=3

NFPA RATINGS (SCALE 0-4): HEALTH=1 FIRE=U REACTIVITY=0

COMPONENTS AND CONTAMINANTS

FOLPET CAS# 133-07-3

OTHER CONTAMINANTS: NONE

EXPOSURE LIMITS: NO OCCUPATIONAL EXPOSURE LIMITS ESTABLISHED BY OSHA, ACGIH, OR NIOSH.

FOLMET: SUBJECT TO CALIFORNIA PROPOSITION 65 CANCER AND/OR REPRODUCTIVE TOXICITY WARNING AND RELEASE REQUIREMENTS- (JANUARY 1, 1989)

PHYSICAL DATA

DESCRIPTION: WHITE CRYSTALS OR LIGHT COLORED POWDER

MELTING POINT: 351 F (177 C) ***SPECIFIC GRAVITY:*** NOT AVAILABLE

SOLUBILITY IN WATER: INSOLUBLE

SOLVENT SOLUBILITY: SLIGHTLY SOLUBLE IN ORGANIC SOLVENTS

FIRE AND EXPLOSION DATA

FIRE AND EXPLOSION HAZARD: UNKNOWN FIRE AND EXPLOSION HAZARD.

FIREFIGHTING MEDIA: DRY CHEMICAL, CARBON DIOXIDE, WATER SPRAY OR FOAM FOR LARGER FIRES, USE WATER SPRAY, FOG OR ALCOHOL FOAM

FIREFIGHTING: MOVE CONTAINER FROM FIRE AREA IF POSSIBLE. DO NOT SCATTER SPILLED MATERIAL WITH HIGH PRESSURE WATER STREAMS. DIKE FIRE CONTROL WATER FOR LATER DISPOSAL (1987 EMERGENCY RESPONSE GUIDEBOOK, DOT P 5800.4, GUIDE PAGE 31).

USE AGENTS SUITABLE FOR TYPE OF SURROUNDING FIRE. AVOID BREATHING HAZARDOUS VAPORS, KEEP UPWIND.

TOXICITY

FOLPET: TOXICITY DATA: 7540 MG/KG ORAL-RAT LD50; 1546 MG/KG ORAL-MOUSE LD50; 1115 MG/KG ORAL-RABBIT LD50; 68400 UG/KG INTRAPERITONEAL-RAT LD50; 750 MG/KG UNREPORTED-MOUSE LD50; 80 MG/KG INTRAPERITONEAL-MOUSE LD50; MUTAGENIC DATA (RTECS); REPRODUCTIVE EFFECTS DATA (RTECS); TUMORIGENIC DATA (RTECS). CARCINOGEN STATUS: NONE. ACUTE TOXICITY LEVEL: SLIGHTLY TOXIC BY INGESTION. TARGET EFFECTS: NO DATA AVAILABLE.

HEALTH EFFECTS AND FIRST AID

INHALATION: FOLPET: **ACUTE EXPOSURE-** MAY CAUSE IRRITATION OF THE MUCOUS MEMBRANES. **CHRONIC EXPOSURE-** A INCREASED OF FETAL MORTALITY WAS OBSERVED IN A INHALATION STUDY OF PREGNANT MICE EXPOSED TO 491 MG/M3/4 HOURS FOR 8 DAYS.

FIRST AID- REMOVE FROM EXPOSURE AREA TO FRESH AIR IMMEDIATELY. IF BREATHING HAS STOPPED, PERFORM ARTIFICIAL RESPIRATION. KEEP PERSON WARM AND AT REST. TREAT SYMPTOMATICALLY AND SUPPORTIVELY. GET MEDICAL ATTENTION IMMEDIATELY.

SKIN CONTACT: FOLPET: **ACUTE EXPOSURE-** MAY CAUSE IRRITATION. **CHRONIC EXPOSURE-** PROLONGED OR REPEATED EXPOSURE MAY CAUSE DERMATITIS.

FIRST AID- REMOVE CONTAMINATED CLOTHING AND SHOES IMMEDIATELY. WASH AFFECTED AREA WITH SOAP OR MILD DETERGENT AND LARGE AMOUNTS OF WATER UNTIL NO EVIDENCE OF CHEMICAL REMAINS (APPROXIMATELY 15-20 MINUTES). GET MEDICAL ATTENTION IMMEDIATELY.

EYE CONTACT: FOLPET: **ACUTE EXPOSURE-** MAY CAUSE IRRITATION. **CHRONIC EXPOSURE-** PROLONGED OR REPEATED EXPOSURE MAY CAUSE CONJUNCTITIVITIS.

FIRST AID- WASH EYES IMMEDIATELY WITH LARGE AMOUNTS OF WATER OR NORMAL SALINE, OCCASIONALLY LIFTING UPPER AND LOWER LIDS, UNTIL NO EVIDENCE OF CHEMICAL REMAINS (APPROXIMATELY 15-20 MINUTES). GET MEDICAL ATTENTION IMMEDIATELY.

INGESTION: FOLPET: **ACUTE EXPOSURE-** A HIGH DOSE WAS LETHAL IN RATS; NO SYMPTOMS WAS REPORTED. THE RESULT FROM ONE STUDY OF PREGNANT HAMSTERS GIVEN A SINGLE DOSE OF BETWEEN 500 AND 900 MG/KG ON DAYS SEVEN OR EIGHT OF GESTATION WAS AN INCREASE OF FETAL MORTALITY AND THE PRODUCTION OF SOME ABNORMAL FETUSES. **CHRONIC EXPOSURE-** A CUMULATIVE DOSE OF 10,000 PPM FED TO DOG AND RATS FOR 17 MONTHS PRODUCED NO ADVERSE EFFECTS ON THE MAJOR ORGANS. CHRONIC ADMINISTRATION TO PREGNANT RABBITS OF A CUMULATIVE DOSE OF 488 MG/KG FOR 13 DAYS PRODUCED ADVERSE EFFECTS ON FERTILITY.

FIRST AID- TREAT SYMPTOMATICALLY AND SUPPORTIVELY. GET MEDICAL ATTENTION IMMEDIATELY. IF VOMITING OCCURS, KEEP HEAD LOWER THAN HIPS TO PREVENT ASPIRATION.

ANTIDOTE: NO SPECIFIC ANTIDOTE. TREAT SYMPTOMATICALLY AND SUPPORTIVELY.

REACTIVITY

REACTIVITY: STABLE UNDER NORMAL TEMPERATURES AND PRESSURES.

INCOMPATIBILITIES: FOLPET: ALKALINE CONDITIONS: HYDROLYZES. WATER: HYDROLYZES.

DECOMPOSITION: THERMAL DECOMPOSITION MAY RELEASE TOXIC OXIDES OF NITROGEN AND SULFUR.

POLYMERIZATION: HAZARDOUS POLYMERIZATION HAS NOT BEEN REPORTED TO OCCUR UNDER NORMAL TEMPERATURES AND PRESSURES.

CONDITIONS TO AVOID

NONE REPORTED.

SPILL AND LEAK PROCEDURES

WATER SPILL: THE CALIFORNIA SAFE DRINKING WATER AND TOXIC ENFORCEMENT ACT OF 1986 (PROPOSITION 65) PROHIBITS CONTAMINATING ANY KNOWN SOURCE OF DRINKING WATER WITH SUBSTANCES KNOWN TO CAUSE CANCER AND/OR REPRODUCTIVE TOXICITY. ***OCCUPATIONAL SPILL:*** SWEEP UP AND PLACE IN SUITABLE CLEAN, DRY CONTAINERS FOR RECLAMATION OR LATER DISPOSAL. DO NOT FLUSH SPILLED MATERIAL INTO SEWER. KEEP UNNECESSARY PEOPLE AWAY.

PROTECTIVE EQUIPMENT

VENTILATION: PROVIDE LOCAL EXHAUST OR GENERAL DILUTION VENTILATION SYSTEM.

RESPIRATOR: THE FOLLOWING RESPIRATORS ARE RECOMMENDED BASED ON INFORMATION FOUND IN THE PHYSICAL DATA, TOXICITY AND HEALTH EFFECTS SECTIONS. THEY ARE RANKED IN ORDER FROM MINIMUM TO MAXIMUM RESPIRATORY PROTECTION. THE SPECIFIC RESPIRATOR SELECTED MUST BE BASED ON CONTAMINATION LEVELS FOUND IN THE WORK PLACE, MUST NOT EXCEED THE WORKING LIMITS OF THE RESPIRATOR AND BE JOINTLY APPROVED BY THE NATIONAL INSTITUTE FOR OCCUPATIONAL SAFETY AND HEALTH AND THE MINE SAFETY AND HEALTH ADMINISTRATION (NIOSH-MSHA).

CHEMICAL CARTRIDGE RESPIRATOR WITH AN ORGANIC VAPOR CARTRIDGE(S) WITH A FULL FACEPIECE AND ORGANIC VAPOR CARTRIDGE(S) IN COMBINATION WITH A DUST AND MIST FILTER.

POWERED AIR-PURIFYING RESPIRATOR WITH A TIGHT-FITTING FACEPIECE AND ORGANIC VAPOR CARTRIDGE(S) IN COMBINATION WITH A HIGH-EFFICIENCY PARTICULATE FILTER.

TYPE 'C' SUPPLIED-AIR RESPIRATOR WITH A FULL FACEPIECE OPERATED IN A PRESSURE-DEMAND OR OTHER POSITIVE PRESSURE MODE.

SELF-CONTAINED BREATHING APPARATUS WITH A FULL FACEPIECE OPERATED IN PRESSURE-DEMAND OR OTHER POSITIVE PRESSURE MODE.

FOR FIREFIGHTING AND OTHER IMMEDIATELY DANGEROUS TO LIFE OR HEALTH CONDITIONS:

SELF-CONTAINED BREATHING APPARATUS WITH FULL FACEPIECE OPERATED IN PRESSURE-DEMAND OR OTHER POSITIVE PRESSURE MODE.

SUPPLIED-AIR RESPIRATOR WITH FULL FACEPIECE AND OPERATED IN PRESSURE-DEMAND OR OTHER POSITIVE PRESSURE MODE IN COMBINATION WITH AN AUXILIARY SELF-CONTAINED BREATHING APPARATUS OPERATED IN PRESSURE-DEMAND OR OTHER POSITIVE PRESSURE MODE.

CLOTHING: EMPLOYEE MUST WEAR APPROPRIATE PROTECTIVE (IMPERVIOUS) CLOTHING AND EQUIPMENT TO PREVENT REPEATED OR PROLONGED SKIN CONTACT WITH THIS SUBSTANCE.

GLOVES: EMPLOYEE MUST WEAR APPROPRIATE PROTECTIVE GLOVES TO PREVENT CONTACT WITH THIS SUBSTANCE.

EYE PROTECTION: EMPLOYEE MUST WEAR SPLASH-PROOF OR DUST-RESISTANT SAFETY GOGGLES TO PREVENT EYE CONTACT WITH THIS SUBSTANCE.

EMERGENCY EYE WASH: WHERE THERE IS ANY POSSIBILITY THAT AN EMPLOYEE'S EYES MAY BE EXPOSED TO THIS SUBSTANCE, THE EMPLOYER SHOULD PROVIDE AN EYE WASH FOUNTAIN WITHIN THE IMMEDIATE WORK AREA FOR EMERGENCY USE.

AUTHORIZED BY- OCCUPATIONAL HEALTH SERVICES, INC.

CREATION DATE: 10/04/89 ***REVISION DATE:*** 05/31/90

MATERIAL SAFETY DATA SHEET

OCCUPATIONAL HEALTH SERVICES, INC.
AGRICULTURE AND PESTICIDE DIVISION
450 SEVENTH AVENUE, SUITE 2407
NEW YORK, NEW YORK 10123
1-800-445-MSDS OR (212) 967-1100

EMERGENCY CONTACT:
JOHN S. BRANSFORD, JR. (615) 292-1180

SUBSTANCE IDENTIFICATION

CAS-NUMBER 944-22-9

SUBSTANCE: **FONOFOS**

TRADE NAMES/SYNONYMS: PHOSPHONODITHIOIC ACID, ETHYL-, O-ETHYL S-PHENYL ESTER; ETHYLPHOSPHONODITHIOIC ACID O-ETHYL S-PHENYL ESTER; O-ETHYL S-PHENYL (RS)-ETHYLPHOSPHONODITHIOATE; O-ETHYL S-PHENYL ETHYLPHOSPHONOTHIOLOTHIONATE; ETHYL S-PHENYL ETHYLPHOSPHONOTHIOLOTHIONATE; DIFONATE; DIFONATUL; DYFONAT; DYFONATE; N 2790; STAUFFER N 2790; PST10020

CHEMICAL FAMILY: ORGANOPHOSPHATE

MOLECULAR FORMULA: C10-H15-O-P-S2

MOLECULAR WEIGHT: 246.32

CERCLA RATINGS (SCALE 0-3): HEALTH=3 FIRE=1 REACTIVITY=0 PERSISTENCE=1

NFPA RATINGS (SCALE 0-4): HEALTH=4 FIRE=1 REACTIVITY=0

COMPONENTS AND CONTAMINANTS

COMPONENT: FONOFOS ***PERCENT:*** 100
CAS# 944-22-9

OTHER CONTAMINANTS: NONE

EXPOSURE LIMITS: FONOFOS: 0.1 MG/M3 OSHA TWA (SKIN) 0.1 MG/M3 ACGIH TWA (SKIN)

500 POUNDS SARA SECTION 302 THRESHOLD PLANNING QUANTITY 1 POUND SARA SECTION 304 REPORTABLE QUANTITY

PHYSICAL DATA

DESCRIPTION: CLEAR COLORLESS LIQUID WITH AN AROMATIC ODOR

BOILING POINT: 266 F (130 C) @ 0.01 MMHG ***SPECIFIC GRAVITY:*** 1.154

VAPOR PRESSURE: 0.00021 ***SOLUBILITY IN WATER:*** 13 PPM

SOLVENT SOLUBILITY: SOLUBLE IN ACETONE, ETHANOL, KEROSENE, XYLENE, 4-METHYLPENTAN-2-ONE, ISOBUTYL METHYL KETONE AND MOST ORGANIC SOLVENTS

FIRE AND EXPLOSION DATA

FIRE AND EXPLOSION HAZARD: SLIGHT FIRE HAZARD WHEN EXPOSED TO HEAT OR FLAME.

FLASH POINT: >200 F (>93 C)

FIREFIGHTING MEDIA: DRY CHEMICAL, CARBON DIOXIDE, HALON, WATER SPRAY OR STANDARD FOAM (1987 EMERGENCY RESPONSE GUIDEBOOK, DOT P 5800.4). FOR LARGER FIRES, USE WATER SPRAY, FOG OR STANDARD FOAM (1987 EMERGENCY RESPONSE GUIDEBOOK, DOT P 5800.4).

FIREFIGHTING: MOVE CONTAINERS FROM FIRE AREA IF POSSIBLE. FIGHT FIRE FROM MAXIMUM DISTANCE. STAY AWAY FROM STORAGE TANK ENDS. DIKE FIRE CONTROL WATER FOR LATER DISPOSAL. DO NOT SCATTER MATERIAL (1987 EMERGENCY RESPONSE GUIDEBOOK, DOT P 5800.4, GUIDE PAGE 55). EXTINGUISH ONLY IF FLOW CAN BE STOPPED; USE FLOODING AMOUNTS OF WATER AS FOG, SOLID STREAMS MAY BE INEFFECTIVE. COOL CONTAINERS WITH FLOODING AMOUNTS OF WATER FROM AS FAR A DISTANCE AS POSSIBLE. USE WATER SPRAY TO ABSORB TOXIC VAPORS. AVOID BREATHING TOXIC VAPORS; KEEP UPWIND. CONSIDER EVACUATION OF DOWNWIND AREA IF MATERIAL IS LEAKING.

TRANSPORTATION DATA

DEPARTMENT OF TRANSPORTATION HAZARD CLASSIFICATION 49 CFR 172.101: POISON B

DEPARTMENT OF TRANSPORTATION LABELING REQUIREMENTS 49 CFR 172.101 AND SUBPART E: POISON

DEPARTMENT OF TRANSPORTATION PACKAGING REQUIREMENTS: 49 CFR 173.346 EXCEPTIONS: 49 CFR 173.345

TOXICITY

FONOFOS: TOXICITY DATA: 1900 MG/M3/1 HOUR INHALATION-RAT LC50; 900 MG/M3/1 HOUR INHALATION-RAT LC50 (85HOA6); 25 MG/KG SKIN-RABBIT LD50; 147 MG/KG SKIN-RAT LD50; 278 MG/KG SKIN-GUINEA PIG LD50; 3 MG/KG ORAL-RAT LD50; 1300 UG/KG ORAL-DOMESTIC ANIMAL LD50; 17 MG/KG UNREPORTED-MAMMAL LD50. CARCINOGEN STATUS: NONE. ACUTE TOXICITY LEVEL: HIGHLY TOXIC BY INHALATION, INGESTION, AND DERMAL ABSORPTION. TARGET EFFECTS: CHOLINESTERASE INHIBITOR. POISONING MAY AFFECT THE NERVOUS SYSTEM.* AT INCREASED RISK FROM EXPOSURE: PERSONS WITH RESPIRATORY AILMENTS, RECENT EXPOSURE TO CHOLINESTERASE INHIBITORS OR IMPAIRED CHOLINESTERASE PRODUCTION, OR LIVER MALFUNCTION.* ADDITIONAL DATA: MAY CROSS THE PLACENTA. HIGH ENVIRONMENTAL TEMPERATURES OR EXPOSURE OF THE CHEMICAL TO VISIBLE OR ULTRAVIOLET LIGHT MAY ENHANCE THE TOXICITY. INTERACTIONS WITH MEDICATIONS MAY OCCUR.*

* MAY BE BASED ON GENERAL INFORMATION ON ORGANOPHOSPHATES.

HEALTH EFFECTS AND FIRST AID

INHALATION: FONOFOS: HIGHLY TOXIC. SEE INFORMATION ON ORGANOPHOSPHATES.

ORGANOPHOSPHATES: CHOLINESTERASE INHIBITOR. **ACUTE EXPOSURE-** WHEN INHALED, THE FIRST EFFECTS OF CHOLINESTERASE INHIBITORS ARE USUALLY RESPIRATORY AND MAY INCLUDE NASAL HYPEREMIA AND WATERY DISCHARGE, COUGH, CHEST DISCOMFORT, DYSPNEA, AND WHEEZING DUE TO INCREASED BRONCHIAL SECRETIONS AND BRONCHOCONSTRICTION. IF SUFFICIENT AMOUNTS ARE ABSORBED, OTHER SYSTEMIC EFFECTS MAY BEGIN WITHIN A FEW MINUTES OR BE DELAYED FOR UP TO 12 HOURS. SYMPTOMS MAY INCLUDE PALLOR, NAUSEA, VOMITING, DIARRHEA, ABDOMINAL CRAMPS, HEADACHE, DIZZINESS, OCULAR PAIN, BLURRED VISION, MIOSIS OR IN SOME CASES, ESPECIALLY INITIALLY, MYDRIASIS, LACRIMATION, SALIVATION, SWEATING, AND CONFUSION. OTHER REPORTED CENTRAL NERVOUS SYSTEM OR NEUROMUSCULAR EFFECTS MAY INCLUDE ATAXIA, SLURRED SPEECH, AREFLEXIA, WEAKNESS, FATIGUE, FASCICULATIONS, TWITCHING, TREMORS POSSIBLY OF THE TONGUE AND EYELIDS, AND EVENTUALLY PARALYSIS OF THE EXTREMITIES AND POSSIBLY OF THE RESPIRATORY MUSCLES. IN SEVERE CASES THERE MAY ALSO BE INVOLUNTARY DEFECATION AND URINATION, CYANOSIS, PSYCHOSIS, HYPERGLYCEMIA, ACUTE PANCREATITIS, CARDIAC IRREGULARITIES, PULMONARY EDEMA, UNCONSCIOUSNESS, CONVULSIONS, AND COMA. DEATH IS PRIMARILY DUE TO RESPIRATORY FAILURE, ALTHOUGH CARDIOVASCULAR EFFECTS INCLUDING CARDIAC ARREST MAY ALSO BE IMPLICATED. LONG TERM SEQUELAE ARE RARE BUT MAY INCLUDE NEUROPSYCHIATRIC DISORDERS AND MYOPATHY WITH MUSCLE TENDERNESS. SOME ORGANOPHOSPHATES MAY CAUSE A DELAYED NEUROPATHY BEGINNING 1-4 WEEKS AFTER AN ACUTE EXPOSURE WHICH MAY OR MAY NOT HAVE CAUSED ACUTE CHOLINERGIC EFFECTS. NUMBNESS, TINGLING, WEAKNESS AND CRAMPING BEGINNING SYMMETRICALLY IN THE LOWER LIMBS MAY PROGRESS TO ATAXIA AND PARALYSIS. IN SEVERE CASES, UPPER LIMB INVOLVEMENT IS POSSIBLE AND FLACCID PARALYSIS MAY PROGRESS TO SPASTIC PARALYSIS WITH EXAGGERATED REFLEXES. IMPROVEMENT MAY OCCUR OVER MONTHS TO YEARS, BUT SOME RESIDUAL IMPAIRMENT USUALLY REMAINS. **CHRONIC EXPOSURE-** REPEATED OR PROLONGED EXPOSURE MAY RESULT IN THE EFFECTS OF ACUTE EXPOSURE INCLUDING THE DELAYED NEUROPATHY. OTHER EFFECTS REPORTED IN WORKERS REPEATEDLY EXPOSED INCLUDE IMPAIRED MEMORY AND CONCENTRATION, ACUTE PSYCHOSIS, SEVERE DEPRESSIONS, IRRITABILTY, CONFUSION, APATHY, EMOTIONAL LABILITY, SOCIAL WITHDRAWAL, CONFUSION, HEADACHE, SPEECH DIFFICULTIES, DELAYED REACTION TIMES, SPATIAL DISORIENTATION, NIGHTMARES, SLEEPWALKING, AND DROWSINESS OR INSOMNIA. AN INFLUENZA-LIKE CONDITION WITH HEADACHE, NAUSEA, WEAKNESS, ANOREXIA AND MALAISE HAS ALSO BEEN REPORTED.

FIRST AID- REMOVE FROM EXPOSURE AREA TO FRESH AIR IMMEDIATELY. IF BREATHING HAS STOPPED, GIVE ARTIFICIAL RESPIRATION. MAINTAIN AIRWAY AND BLOOD PRESSURE AND ADMINISTER OXYGEN IF AVAILABLE. KEEP AFFECTED PERSON WARM AND AT REST. TREAT SYMPTOMATICALLY AND SUPPORTIVELY. ADMINISTRATION OF OXYGEN SHOULD BE PERFORMED BY QUALIFIED PERSONNEL. GET MEDICAL ATTENTION IMMEDIATELY.

SKIN CONTACT: FONOFOS: HIGHLY TOXIC. SEE INFORMATION ON ORGANOPHOSPHATES.

ORGANOPHOSPHATES: CHOLINESTERASE INHIBITOR. **ACUTE EXPOSURE-** LOCALIZED SWEATING AND FASCICULATIONS MAY OCCUR AT THE SITE OF CONTACT. IF SUFFICIENT AMOUNTS ARE ABSORBED, OTHER EFFECTS OF CHOLINESTERASE INHIBITION AS DESCRIBED IN ACUTE INHALATION MAY OCCUR. SYMPTOMS MAY BE DELAYED 2-3 HOURS, BUT USUALLY NO MORE THAN 12 HOURS. THE RATE OF ABSORPTION IS INCREASED BY THE PRESENCE OF DERMATITIS OR HIGH AMBIENT TEMPERATURES. DELAYED NEUROPATHY IS ALSO POSSIBLE. **CHRONIC EXPOSURE-** REPEATED OR PROLONGED EXPOSURE MAY CAUSE EFFECTS AS DESCRIBED IN ACUTE EXPOSURE. SOME ORGANOPHOSPHATES MAY CAUSE SENSITIZATION.

FIRST AID- REMOVE CONTAMINATED CLOTHING IMMEDIATELY. WASH CONTAMINATED AREAS WITH SOAP AND WATER FOLLOWED BY ALCOHOL (ARENA, POISONING, 4TH ED.). EMERGENCY PERSONNEL SHOULD WEAR GLOVES AND AVOID CONTAMINATION. TREAT RESPIRATORY DIFFICULTY WITH ARTIFICIAL RESPIRATION. GET MEDICAL ATTENTION IMMEDIATELY.

EYE CONTACT: FONOFOS: SEE INFORMATION ON ORGANOPHOSPHATES.

ORGANOPHOSPHATES: CHOLINESTERASE INHIBITOR. **ACUTE EXPOSURE-** DIRECT CONTACT MAY CAUSE PAIN, HYPEREMIA, LACRIMATION, TWITCHING OF THE EYELIDS, MIOSIS, AND CILIARY MUSCLE SPASM WITH LOSS OF ACCOMODATION, BLURRED OR DIMMED VISION AND BROWACHE. SOMETIMES MYDRIASIS MAY OCCUR INSTEAD OF MIOSIS. WITH SUFFICIENT EXPOSURE, OTHER SYMPTOMS OF CHOLINESTERASE INHIBITION AS DESCRIBED IN ACUTE INHALATION MAY OCCUR. **CHRONIC EXPOSURE-** REPEATED OR PROLONGED EXPOSURE MAY CAUSE EFFECTS AS DESCRIBED IN ACUTE EXPOSURE. SOME COMPOUNDS HAVE CAUSED TOXIC EFFECTS ON THE CRYSTALLINE LENS, CONJUNCTIVAL THICKENING AND OBSTRUCTION OF THE NASOLACRIMAL CANALS WHEN USED AS MIOTIC EYEDROPS.

FIRST AID- IRRIGATE EYES WITH WATER OR SALINE SOLUTION. IF SYMPTOMS OF POISONING OCCUR, TREAT RESPIRATORY DIFFICULTY WITH ARTIFICIAL RESPIRATION AND OXYGEN. OBSERVE PATIENT FOR AT LEAST 24-36 HOURS (GOSSELIN, CLINICAL TOXICOLOGY OF COMMERCIAL PRODUCTS, 5TH ED.). GET MEDICAL ATTENTION IMMEDIATELY. OXYGEN SHOULD BE ADMINISTERED BY QUALIFIED MEDICAL PERSONNEL.

INGESTION: FONOFOS: HIGHLY TOXIC. IN RATS, A DIETARY LEVEL OF 31.6 AND 100 PPM FOR 2 YEARS PRODUCED CHOLINESTERASE INHIBITION, NERVOUS BEHAVIOR, AND TREMORS. IN 2-YEAR DOG STUDIES WITH DAILY INGESTION OF 0.4 TO 6.0 MG/KG, EFFECTS OF CHOLINESTERASE INHIBITION, INCREASED LIVER WEIGHT, CONGESTION OF THE SMALL INTESTINE, DECREASED WEIGHT GAIN, SOFT STOOLS, ALOPECIA, INCREASED NASAL, SALIVARY, AND LACRIMAL SECRETIONS, NERVOUS BEHAVIOR, TREMORS, INCREASED SERUM ALKALINE PHOSPHATASE, AND LIVER MORPHOLOGY WERE REPORTED. SEE INFORMATION ON ORGANOPHOSPHATES.

ORGANOPHOSPHATES: CHOLINESTERASE INHIBITOR. **ACUTE EXPOSURE-** WHEN INGESTED, THE FIRST EFFECTS MAY BE NAUSEA, VOMITING, ANOREXIA, ABDOMINAL CRAMPS AND DIARRHEA. GASTROINTESTINAL ABSORPTION MAY

CAUSE SYMPTOMS OF CHOLINESTERASE INHIBITION AS DESCRIBED IN ACUTE INHALATION. SYMPTOMS MAY BEGIN WITHIN MINUTES OR BE DELAYED FOR HOURS. DELAYED EFFECTS INCLUDING NEUROPATHY MAY ALSO OCCUR. **CHRONIC EXPOSURE-** REPEATED INGESTION MAY CAUSE EFFECTS AS DESCRIBED IN ACUTE EXPOSURE.

FIRST AID- IF PERSON IS ALERT AND RESPIRATION IS NOT DEPRESSED, GIVE SYRUP OF IPECAC FOLLOWED BY WATER (IF VOMITING OCCURS, KEEP HEAD BELOW HIPS TO PREVENT ASPIRATION). IF CONSCIOUSNESS LEVEL DECLINES OR VOMITING HAS NOT OCCURRED IN 15 MINUTES EMPTY STOMACH BY GASTRIC LAVAGE WITH THE AID OF CUFFED ENDOTRACHEAL TUBE USING ISOTONIC SALINE OR 5% SODIUM BICARBONATE FOLLOW WITH ACTIVATED CHARCOAL. ESTABLISH AND MAINTAIN AIRWAY. TREAT RESPIRATORY DIFFICULTY WITH ARTIFICIAL RESPIRATION AND OXYGEN. DO NOT GIVE MORPHINE, AMINOPHYLLINE, PHENOTHIAZINES, RESERPINE, FUROSEMIDE, OR ETHACRYNIC ACID (MORGAN, RECOGNITION AND MANAGEMENT OF PESTICIDE POISONINGS, 3RD ED.). TREAT SYMPTOMATICALLY AND SUPPORTIVELY. ADMINISTRATION OF OXYGEN AND LAVAGE MUST BE PERFORMED BY QUALIFIED MEDICAL PERSONNEL. GET MEDICAL ATTENTION IMMEDIATELY.

ANTIDOTE: THE FOLLOWING ANTIDOTE(S) HAVE BEEN RECOMMENDED. HOWEVER, THE DECISION AS TO WHETHER THE SEVERITY OF POISONING REQUIRES ADMINISTRATION OF ANY ANTIDOTE AND ACTUAL DOSE REQUIRED SHOULD BE MADE BY QUALIFIED MEDICAL PERSONNEL.

FOR CHOLINESTERASE INHIBITORS: ESTABLISH CLEAR AIRWAY AND TISSUE OXYGENATION BY ASPIRATION OF SECRETIONS, AND IF NECESSARY, BY ASSISTED PULMONARY VENTILATION WITH OXYGEN. IMPROVE TISSUE OXYGENATION AS MUCH AS POSSIBLE BEFORE ADMINISTERING ATROPINE TO MINIMIZE THE RISK OF VENTRICULAR FIBRILLATION. ADMINISTER ATROPINE SULFATE INTRAVENOUSLY, OR INTRAMUSCULARLY IF IV INJECTION IS NOT POSSIBLE. IN MODERATELY SEVERE POISONING ADMINISTER ATROPINE SULFATE, 0.4-2.0 MG REPEATED EVERY 15 MINUTES UNTIL ATROPINIZATION IS ACHIEVED (TACHYCARDIA, FLUSHING, DRY MOUTH, MYDRIASIS). MAINTAIN ATROPINIZATION BY REPEATED DOSES FOR 2-12 HOURS, OR LONGER, DEPENDING ON THE SEVERITY OF POISONING. THE APPEARANCE OF RALES IN THE LUNG BASES, MIOSIS, SALIVATION, NAUSEA, BRADYCARDIA, ARE ALL INDICATIONS OF INADEQUATE ATROPINIZATION. SEVERELY POISONED INDIVIDUALS MAY EXHIBIT REMARKABLE TOLERANCE TO ATROPINE; TWO OR MORE TIMES THE DOSAGES SUGGESTED ABOVE MAY BE NEEDED. PERSONS NOT POISONED OR ONLY SLIGHTLY POISONED, HOWEVER, MAY DEVELOP SIGNS OF ATROPINE TOXICITY FROM SUCH LARGE DOSAGES: FEVER, MUSCLE FIBRILLATIONS, AND DELIRIUM ARE THE MAIN SIGNS OF ATROPINE TOXICITY. IF THESE SIGNS APPEAR WHILE THE PATIENT IS FULLY ATROPINIZED, ATROPINE ADMINISTRATION SHOULD BE DISCONTINUED, AT LEAST TEMPORARILY. OBSERVE TREATED PATIENTS CLOSELY AT LEAST 24 HOURS TO INSURE THAT SYMPTOMS (POSSIBLY PULMONARY EDEMA) DO NOT RECUR AS ATROPINIZATION WEARS OFF. IN VERY SEVERE POISONINGS, METABOLIC DISPOSITION OF TOXICANT MAY REQUIRE SEVERAL HOURS OR DAYS DURING WHICH ATROPINIZATION MUST BE MAINTAINED. MARKEDLY LOWER LEVELS OF URINARY METABOLITES INDICATE THAT ATROPINE DOSAGE CAN BE TAPERED OFF. AS DOSAGE IS REDUCED, CHECK THE LUNG BASES FREQUENTLY FOR RALES. IF RALES ARE HEARD OR OTHER SYMPTOMS RETURN, RE-ESTABLISH ATROPINIZATION PROMPTLY (MORGAN, RECOGNITION AND MANAGEMENT OF PESTICIDE POISONINGS, 3RD ED.). ADMINISTRATION OF ANTIDOTE MUST BE PERFORMED BY QUALIFIED MEDICAL PERSONNEL.

IN CASES OF SEVERE POISONING BY ORGANOPHOSPHATE PESTICIDES IN WHICH RESPIRATORY DEPRESSION, MUSCLE WEAKNESS AND TWITCHINGS ARE SEVERE, GIVE PRALIDOXIME (PROTOPAM-AYERST, 2-PAM), 1.0 GRAM INTRAVENOUSLY AT NO MORE THAN 0.5 GRAM PER MINUTE. DOSAGE OF PRALIDOXIME MAY BE REPEATED IN 1-2 HOURS, THEN AT 10-12 HOUR INTERVALS IF NEEDED. IN VERY SEVERE POISONINGS, DOSAGE RATES MAY BE DOUBLED. TREATMENT WITH PRALIDOXIME WILL BE MOST EFFECTIVE IF GIVEN WITHIN THIRTY-SIX HOURS AFTER POISONING (MORGAN, RECOGNITION AND MANAGEMENT OF PESTICIDE POISONINGS, 3RD ED.). ANTIDOTE SHOULD BE ADMINISTERED BY QUALIFIED MEDICAL PERSONNEL.

REACTIVITY

REACTIVITY: STABLE UNDER NORMAL TEMPERATURES AND PRESSURES.

INCOMPATIBILITIES: FONOFOS: NO DATA AVAILABLE.

DECOMPOSITION: THERMAL DECOMPOSITION MAY RELEASE TOXIC OXIDES OF PHOSPHORUS AND SULFUR.

POLYMERIZATION: HAZARDOUS POLYMERIZATION HAS NOT BEEN REPORTED TO OCCUR UNDER NORMAL TEMPERATURES AND PRESSURES.

STORAGE AND DISPOSAL

OBSERVE ALL FEDERAL, STATE AND LOCAL REGULATIONS WHEN STORING OR DISPOSING OF THIS SUBSTANCE. FOR ASSISTANCE, CONTACT THE DISTRICT DIRECTOR OF THE ENVIRONMENTAL PROTECTION AGENCY.

STORAGE

STORE IN ACCORDANCE WITH 40 CFR 165 RECOMMENDED PROCEDURES FOR THE DISPOSAL AND STORAGE OF PESTICIDES AND PESTICIDE CONTAINERS.

THRESHOLD PLANNING QUANTITY (TPQ): THE SUPERFUND AMENDMENTS AND REAUTHORIZATION ACT (SARA) SECTION 302 REQUIRES THAT EACH FACILITY WHERE ANY EXTREMELY HAZARDOUS SUBSTANCE IS PRESENT IN A QUANTITY EQUAL TO OR GREATER THAN THE TPQ ESTABLISHED FOR THAT SUBSTANCE NOTIFY THE STATE EMERGENCY RESPONSE COMMISSION FOR THE STATE IN WHICH IT IS LOCATED. SECTION 303 OF SARA REQUIRES THESE FACILITIES TO PARTICIPATE IN LOCAL EMERGENCY RESPONSE PLANNING (40 CFR 355.30).

DISPOSAL

DISPOSAL MUST BE IN ACCORDANCE WITH 40 CFR 165 RECOMMENDED PROCEDURES FOR THE DISPOSAL AND STORAGE OF PESTICIDES AND PESTICIDE CONTAINERS.

CONDITIONS TO AVOID

MAY BURN BUT DOES NOT IGNITE READILY. CONTAINERS MAY EXPLODE IN HEAT OF FIRE.

SPILL AND LEAK PROCEDURES

OCCUPATIONAL SPILL: DO NOT TOUCH SPILLED MATERIAL. STOP LEAK IF YOU CAN DO IT WITHOUT RISK. USE WATER SPRAY TO REDUCE VAPORS. FOR SMALL SPILLS, TAKE UP WITH SAND OR OTHER ABSORBENT MATERIAL AND PLACE INTO CONTAINERS FOR LATER DISPOSAL. FOR SMALL DRY SPILLS, WITH A CLEAN SHOVEL PLACE MATERIAL INTO CLEAN, DRY CONTAINERS AND COVER. MOVE CONTAINERS FROM SPILL AREA. FOR LARGER SPILLS, DIKE FAR AHEAD OF SPILL FOR LATER DISPOSAL. KEEP UNNECESSARY PEOPLE AWAY. ISOLATE HAZARD AREA AND DENY ENTRY. VENTILATE CLOSED SPACES BEFORE ENTERING.

REPORTABLE QUANTITY (RQ): 1 POUND THE SUPERFUND AMENDMENTS AND REAUTHORIZATION ACT (SARA) SECTION 304 REQUIRES THAT A RELEASE EQUAL TO OR GREATER THAN THE REPORTABLE QUANTITY FOR THIS SUBSTANCE BE IMMEDIATELY REPORTED TO THE LOCAL EMERGENCY PLANNING COMMITTEE AND THE STATE EMERGENCY RESPONSE COMMISSION (40 CFR 355.40). IF THE RELEASE OF THIS SUBSTANCE IS REPORTABLE UNDER CERCLA SECTION 103, THE NATIONAL RESPONSE CENTER MUST BE NOTIFIED IMMEDIATELY AT (800) 424-8802 OR (202) 426-2675 IN THE METROPOLITAN WASHINGTON, D.C. AREA (40 CFR 302.6).

PROTECTIVE EQUIPMENT

VENTILATION: PROCESS ENCLOSURE RECOMMENDED TO MEET PUBLISHED EXPOSURE LIMITS.

RESPIRATOR: THE FOLLOWING RESPIRATORS ARE RECOMMENDED BASED ON INFORMATION FOUND IN THE PHYSICAL DATA, TOXICITY AND HEALTH EFFECTS SECTIONS. THEY ARE RANKED IN ORDER FROM MINIMUM TO MAXIMUM RESPIRATORY PROTECTION. THE SPECIFIC RESPIRATOR SELECTED MUST BE BASED ON CONTAMINATION LEVELS FOUND IN THE WORK PLACE, MUST NOT EXCEED THE WORKING LIMITS OF THE RESPIRATOR AND BE JOINTLY APPROVED BY THE NATIONAL INSTITUTE FOR OCCUPATIONAL SAFETY AND HEALTH AND THE MINE SAFETY AND HEALTH ADMINISTRATION (NIOSH-MSHA).

TYPE 'C' SUPPLIED-AIR RESPIRATOR WITH A FULL FACEPIECE OPERATED IN PRESSURE-DEMAND OR OTHER POSITIVE PRESSURE MODE OR WITH A FULL FACEPIECE, HELMET OR HOOD OPERATED IN CONTINOUS-FLOW MODE.

SELF-CONTAINED BREATHING APPARATUS WITH A FULL FACEPIECE OPERATED IN PRESSURE-DEMAND OR OTHER POSITIVE PRESSURE MODE.

FOR FIREFIGHTING AND OTHER IMMEDIATELY DANGEROUS TO LIFE OR HEALTH CONDITIONS:

SELF-CONTAINED BREATHING APPARATUS WITH FULL FACEPIECE OPERATED IN PRESSURE-DEMAND OR OTHER POSITIVE PRESSURE MODE.

SUPPLIED-AIR RESPIRATOR WITH FULL FACEPIECE AND OPERATED IN PRESSURE-DEMAND OR OTHER POSITIVE PRESSURE MODE IN COMBINATION WITH AN AUXILIARY SELF-CONTAINED BREATHING APPARATUS OPERATED IN PRESSURE-DEMAND OR OTHER POSITIVE PRESSURE MODE.

CLOTHING: EMPLOYEE MUST WEAR APPROPRIATE PROTECTIVE (IMPERVIOUS) CLOTHING AND EQUIPMENT TO PREVENT ANY POSSIBILITY OF SKIN CONTACT WITH THIS SUBSTANCE.

GLOVES: EMPLOYEE MUST WEAR APPROPRIATE PROTECTIVE GLOVES TO PREVENT CONTACT WITH THIS SUBSTANCE.

EYE PROTECTION: EMPLOYEE MUST WEAR SPLASH-PROOF OR DUST-RESISTANT SAFETY GOGGLES AND A FACESHIELD TO PREVENT CONTACT WITH THIS SUBSTANCE.

EMERGENCY WASH FACILITIES: WHERE THERE IS ANY POSSIBILITY THAT AN EMPLOYEE'S EYES AND/OR SKIN MAY BE EXPOSED TO THIS SUBSTANCE, THE EMPLOYER SHOULD PROVIDE AN EYE WASH FOUNTAIN AND QUICK DRENCH SHOWER WITHIN THE IMMEDIATE WORK AREA FOR EMERGENCY USE.

AUTHORIZED BY- OCCUPATIONAL HEALTH SERVICES, INC.

CREATION DATE: 10/04/89 ***REVISION DATE:*** 04/26/90

MATERIAL SAFETY DATA SHEET

OCCUPATIONAL HEALTH SERVICES, INC.
AGRICULTURE AND PESTICIDE DIVISION
450 SEVENTH AVENUE, SUITE 2407
NEW YORK, NEW YORK 10123
1-800-445-MSDS OR (212) 967-1100

EMERGENCY CONTACT:
JOHN S. BRANSFORD, JR. (615) 292-1180

SUBSTANCE IDENTIFICATION

CAS-NUMBER 23422-53-9

SUBSTANCE: **FORMETANATE HYDROCHLORIDE**

TRADE NAMES/SYNONYMS: METHANIMIDAMIDE, N,N-DIMETHYL-N'-(3-(((METHYLAMINO)CARBONYL)OXY) PHENYL)-, MONOHYDROCHLORIDE; CARBAMIC ACID, METHYL-, ESTER WITH N'-(M-HYDROXYPHENYL) -N,N-DIMETHYLFORMAMIDINE, MONOHYDROCHLORIDE; N,N-DIMETHYL-N'-(3-(((METHYLAMINO)CARBONYL)OXY)PHENYL)METHANIMIDAMIDE MONOHYDROCHLORIDE; METHYLCARBAMIC ACID ESTER WITH N'-(M-HYDROXYPHENYL)-N,N- DIMETHYLFORMAMIDINE, MONOHYDROCHLORIDE; M-((DIMETHYLAMINO)METHYLENE)AMINO)PHENYL METHYLCARBAMATE HYDROCHLORIDE; (3-DIMETHYLAMINO-(METHYLENEIMINO PHENYL))-N-METHYLCARBAMATE HYDROCHLORIDE; CARZOL; DICARZOL; EP 332; FORMETANATE MONOHYDROCHLORIDE; ENT 27 566; C11H15N3O2.CLH; PST10050

CHEMICAL FAMILY: CARBAMATE

MOLECULAR FORMULA: C11-H15-N3-O2.CL-H

MOLECULAR WEIGHT: 257.75

CERCLA RATINGS (SCALE 0-3): HEALTH=3 FIRE=U REACTIVITY=0 PERSISTENCE=2

NFPA RATINGS (SCALE 0-4): HEALTH=3 FIRE=U REACTIVITY=0

COMPONENTS AND CONTAMINANTS

COMPONENT: FORMETANATE HYDROCHLORIDE ***PERCENT:*** 100
CAS# 23422-53-9

OTHER CONTAMINANTS: NONE

EXPOSURE LIMITS: FORMETANATE HYDROCHLORIDE: NO OCCUPATIONAL EXPOSURE LIMITS ESTABLISHED BY OSHA, ACGIH, OR NIOSH.
500/10,000 POUNDS SARA SECTION 302 THRESHOLD PLANNING QUANTITY 1 POUND SARA SECTION 304 REPORTABLE QUANTITY

PHYSICAL DATA

DESCRIPTION: WHITE POWDER WITH A FAINT ODOR

MELTING POINT: 392-396 F (200-202 C) DECOMPOSES ***SPECIFIC GRAVITY:*** NOT AVAILABLE

VAPOR PRESSURE: <0.00000008 ***SOLUBILITY IN WATER:*** >50%

SOLVENT SOLUBILITY: SOLUBLE IN METHANOL; SLIGHTLY SOLUBLE IN ACETONE, CHLOROFORM, HEXANE AND OTHER ORGANIC SOLVENTS

FIRE AND EXPLOSION DATA

FIRE AND EXPLOSION HAZARD: UNKNOWN FIRE AND EXPLOSION HAZARD.

FIREFIGHTING MEDIA: DRY CHEMICAL, CARBON DIOXIDE, HALON, WATER SPRAY OR STANDARD FOAM (1987 EMERGENCY RESPONSE GUIDEBOOK, DOT P 5800.4).
FOR LARGER FIRES, USE WATER SPRAY, FOG OR STANDARD FOAM (1987 EMERGENCY RESPONSE GUIDEBOOK, DOT P 5800.4).

FIREFIGHTING: MOVE CONTAINERS FROM FIRE AREA IF POSSIBLE (1987 EMERGENCY RESPONSE GUIDEBOOK, DOT P 5800.4, GUIDE PAGE 53).
EXTINGUISH USING AGENT SUITABLE FOR TYPE OF SURROUNDING FIRE. AVOID BREATHING VAPORS AND DUSTS. KEEP UPWIND.

TRANSPORTATION DATA

DEPARTMENT OF TRANSPORTATION HAZARD CLASSIFICATION 49 CFR 172.101: POISON B
DEPARTMENT OF TRANSPORTATION LABELING REQUIREMENTS 49 CFR 172.101 AND SUBPART E: POISON
DEPARTMENT OF TRANSPORTATION PACKAGING REQUIREMENTS: 49 CFR 173.365 EXCEPTIONS: 49 CFR 173.364

TOXICITY

FORMETANATE HYDROCHLORIDE: TOXICITY DATA: 10200 MG/KG SKIN-RABBIT LD50; 21 MG/KG ORAL-RAT LD50; 18 MG/KG ORAL-MOUSE LD50; 19 MG/KG ORAL-DOG LD50; 4700 UG/KG INTRAPERITONEAL-RAT LD50. CARCINOGEN STATUS: NONE. LOCAL EFFECTS: IRRITANT- EYE. ACUTE TOXICITY LEVEL: HIGHLY TOXIC BY INGESTION; SLIGHTLY TOXIC BY DERMAL ABSORPTION. TARGET EFFECTS: CHOLINESTERASE INHIBITOR. AT INCREASED RISK FROM EXPOSURE: PERSONS WITH ASTHMA, DIABETES, CARDIOVASCULAR DISEASE, MECHANICAL OBSTRUCTION OF THE GASTROINTESTINAL OR UROGENITAL TRACT, AND THOSE IN VAGOTONIC STATES.*
* MAY BE BASED ON GENERAL INFORMATION ON CARBAMATES.

HEALTH EFFECTS AND FIRST AID

INHALATION: FORMETANATE HYDROCHLORIDE: SEE INFORMATION ON CARBAMATES.
CARBAMATES: CHOLINESTERASE INHIBITOR. **ACUTE EXPOSURE-** WHEN INHALED, THE FIRST EFFECTS OF CHOLINESTERASE INHIBITION ARE USUALLY RESPIRATORY AND MAY INCLUDE NASAL HYPEREMIA AND WATERY DISCHARGE, CHEST DISCOMFORT, DYSPNEA, AND WHEEZING DUE TO INCREASED BRONCHIAL SECRETIONS AND BRONCHOCONSTRICTION. OTHER SYSTEMIC EFFECTS MAY BEGIN WITHIN A FEW MINUTES OR SEVERAL HOURS OF EXPOSURE. SYMPTOMS MAY INCLUDE NAUSEA, VOMITING, DIARRHEA, ABDOMINAL CRAMPS, HEADACHE, VERTIGO, OCULAR PAIN, CILIARY MUSCLE SPASM, BLURRING OR DIMNESS OF VISION, MIOSIS, OR IN SOME CASES MYDRIASIS, LACRIMATION, SALIVATION, SWEATING, AND CONFUSION. OTHER REPORTED CENTRAL NERVOUS SYSTEM OR NEUROMUSCULAR EFFECTS INCLUDE ATAXIA, SLURRED SPEECH, AREFLEXIA, WEAKNESS, FATIGUE, TWITCHING, FASCICULATION, TREMOR, AND EVENTUALLY PARALYSIS OF THE EXTREMITIES AND POSSIBLY OF THE RESPIRATORY MUSCLES. IN SEVERE CASES, THERE MAY ALSO BE INVOLUNTARY DEFECATION AND URINATION, BRADYCARDIA, HYPOTENSION, PULMONARY EDEMA, CONVULSIONS, COMA, AND DEATH FROM RESPIRATORY FAILURE OR CARDIAC ARREST. CARBAMATES GENERALLY DO NOT ACCUMULATE IN MAMMALIAN TISSUE AND THE CHOLINESTERASE INHIBITION REVERSES RATHER RAPIDLY. IN NON-FATAL CASES, THE ILLNESS GENERALLY LASTS LESS THAN 24 HOURS. **CHRONIC EXPOSURE-** PROLONGED OR REPEATED EXPOSURE MAY CAUSE EFFECTS AS DESCRIBED IN ACUTE EXPOSURE.

FIRST AID- REMOVE FROM EXPOSURE AREA TO FRESH AIR IMMEDIATELY. IF BREATHING HAS STOPPED, GIVE ARTIFICIAL RESPIRATION. MAINTAIN AIRWAY AND BLOOD PRESSURE AND ADMINISTER OXYGEN IF AVAILABLE. KEEP AFFECTED PERSON WARM AND AT REST. TREAT SYMPTOMATICALLY AND SUPPORTIVELY. ADMINISTRATION OF OXYGEN SHOULD BE PERFORMED BY QUALIFIED PERSONNEL. GET MEDICAL ATTENTION IMMEDIATELY.

SKIN CONTACT: FORMETANATE HYDROCHLORIDE: **ACUTE EXPOSURE-** NO DATA AVAILABLE. **CHRONIC EXPOSURE-** NO DATA AVAILABLE.

FIRST AID- REMOVE CONTAMINATED CLOTHING AND SHOES IMMEDIATELY. WASH AFFECTED AREA WITH SOAP OR MILD DETERGENT AND LARGE AMOUNTS OF WATER UNTIL NO EVIDENCE OF CHEMICAL REMAINS (APPROXIMATELY 15-20 MINUTES). GET MEDICAL ATTENTION IMMEDIATELY.

EYE CONTACT: FORMETANATE HYDROCHLORIDE: IRRITANT. MAY CAUSE IRRITATION OF THE EYES. SEE INFORMATION ON CARBAMATES.
CARBAMATES: CHOLINESTERASE INHIBITOR. **ACUTE EXPOSURE-** DIRECT CONTACT MAY CAUSE PAIN, HYPEREMIA, LACRIMATION, TWITCHING OF THE EYELIDS, MIOSIS, AND CILIARY MUSCLE SPASM WITH LOSS OF ACCOMODATION, BLURRED OR DIMMED VISION AND BROWACHE. SOMETIMES MYDRIASIS MAY OCCUR INSTEAD OF MIOSIS. WITH SUFFICIENT EXPOSURE, OTHER SYMPTOMS OF CHOLINESTERASE INHIBITION MAY OCCUR AS DESCRIBED IN ACUTE INHALATION. **CHRONIC EXPOSURE-** PROLONGED EXPOSURE MAY CAUSE EFFECTS AS DESCRIBED IN ACUTE EXPOSURE. SOME COMPOUNDS HAVE CAUSED TOXIC EFFECTS ON THE CRYSTALLINE LENS, CONJUNCTIVAL THICKENING AND OBSTRUCTION OF NASOLACRIMAL CANALS WHEN USED AS MIOTIC EYE DROPS.

FIRST AID- IRRIGATE EYES WITH WATER OR SALINE SOLUTION. IF SYMPTOMS OF POISONING OCCUR, TREAT RESPIRATORY DIFFICULTY WITH ARTIFICIAL RESPIRATION AND OXYGEN. OBSERVE PATIENT FOR AT LEAST 24-36 HOURS (GOSSELIN, CLINICAL TOXICOLOGY OF COMMERCIAL PRODUCTS, 5TH ED.). GET MEDICAL ATTENTION IMMEDIATELY. OXYGEN SHOULD BE ADMINISTERED BY QUALIFIED MEDICAL PERSONNEL.

INGESTION: FORMETANATE HYDROCHLORIDE: HIGHLY TOXIC. DECREASED WEIGHT GAIN AND AN INCREASE IN THE NUMBER OF FETAL ABSORPTIONS WERE OBSERVED IN A STUDY OF PREGNANT RABBITS FED THIS MATERIAL. SEE INFORMATION ON CARBAMATES.
CARBAMATES: CHOLINESTERASE INHIBITOR. **ACUTE EXPOSURE-** WHEN INGESTED, THE FIRST EFFECTS MAY BE NAUSEA, VOMITING, ANOREXIA, ABDOMINAL CRAMPS, AND DIARRHEA. WITH ABSORPTION FROM THE GASTROINTESTINAL TRACT, THE OTHER EFFECTS OF CHOLINESTERASE INHIBITION AS DESCRIBED IN ACUTE INHALATION MAY OCCUR; SYMPTOMS MAY BEGIN WITHIN MINUTES OR BE DELAYED SEVERAL HOURS. **CHRONIC EXPOSURE-** REPEATED INGESTION MAY CAUSE EFFECTS AS DESCRIBED IN ACUTE EXPOSURE.

FIRST AID- IF PERSON IS ALERT AND RESPIRATION IS NOT DEPRESSED, GIVE SYRUP OF IPECAC FOLLOWED BY WATER (IF VOMITING OCCURS, KEEP HEAD BELOW HIPS TO PREVENT ASPIRATION). IF CONSCIOUSNESS LEVEL DECLINES OR VOMITING HAS NOT OCCURRED IN 15 MINUTES EMPTY STOMACH BY GASTRIC LAVAGE WITH THE

AID OF CUFFED ENDOTRACHEAL TUBE USING ISOTONIC SALINE OR 5% SODIUM BICARBONATE FOLLOW WITH ACTIVATED CHARCOAL. ESTABLISH AND MAINTAIN AIRWAY. TREAT RESPIRATORY DIFFICULTY WITH ARTIFICIAL RESPIRATION AND OXYGEN. DO NOT GIVE MORPHINE, AMINOPHYLLINE, PHENOTHIAZINES, RESERPINE, FUROSEMIDE, OR ETHACRYNIC ACID (MORGAN, RECOGNITION AND MANAGEMENT OF PESTICIDE POISONINGS, 3RD ED.). TREAT SYMPTOMATICALLY AND SUPPORTIVELY. ADMINISTRATION OF OXYGEN AND LAVAGE MUST BE PERFORMED BY QUALIFIED MEDICAL PERSONNEL. GET MEDICAL ATTENTION IMMEDIATELY.

ANTIDOTE: THE FOLLOWING ANTIDOTE HAS BEEN RECOMMENDED. HOWEVER, THE DECISION AS TO WHETHER THE SEVERITY OF POISONING REQUIRES ADMINISTRATION OF ANY ANTIDOTE AND ACTUAL DOSE REQUIRED SHOULD BE MADE BY QUALIFIED MEDICAL PERSONNEL.

FOR CHOLINESTERASE INHIBITORS: ESTABLISH CLEAR AIRWAY AND TISSUE OXYGENATION BY ASPIRATION OF SECRETIONS, AND IF NECESSARY, BY ASSISTED PULMONARY VENTILATION WITH OXYGEN. IMPROVE TISSUE OXYGENATION AS MUCH AS POSSIBLE BEFORE ADMINISTERING ATROPINE TO MINIMIZE THE RISK OF VENTRICULAR FIBRILLATION. ADMINISTER ATROPINE SULFATE INTRAVENOUSLY, OR INTRAMUSCULARLY IF IV INJECTION IS NOT POSSIBLE. IN MODERATELY SEVERE POISONING ADMINISTER ATROPINE SULFATE, 0.4-2.0 MG REPEATED EVERY 15 MINUTES UNTIL ATROPINIZATION IS ACHIEVED (TACHYCARDIA, FLUSHING, DRY MOUTH, MYDRIASIS). MAINTAIN ATROPINIZATION BY REPEATED DOSES FOR 2-12 HOURS, OR LONGER, DEPENDING ON THE SEVERITY OF POISONING. THE APPEARANCE OF RALES IN THE LUNG BASES, MIOSIS, SALIVATION, NAUSEA, BRADYCARDIA, ARE ALL INDICATIONS OF INADEQUATE ATROPINIZATION. SEVERELY POISONED INDIVIDUALS MAY EXHIBIT REMARKABLE TOLERANCE TO ATROPINE; TWO OR MORE TIMES THE DOSAGES SUGGESTED ABOVE MAY BE NEEDED. PERSONS NOT POISONED OR ONLY SLIGHTLY POISONED, HOWEVER, MAY DEVELOP SIGNS OF ATROPINE TOXICITY FROM SUCH LARGE DOSAGES: FEVER, MUSCLE FIBRILLATIONS, AND DELIRIUM ARE THE MAIN SIGNS OF ATROPINE TOXICITY. IF THESE SIGNS APPEAR WHILE THE PATIENT IS FULLY ATROPINIZED, ATROPINE ADMINISTRATION SHOULD BE DISCONTINUED, AT LEAST TEMPORARILY. OBSERVE TREATED PATIENTS CLOSELY AT LEAST 24 HOURS TO INSURE THAT SYMPTOMS (POSSIBLY PULMONARY EDEMA) DO NOT RECUR AS ATROPINIZATION WEARS OFF. IN VERY SEVERE POISONINGS, METABOLIC DISPOSITION OF TOXICANT MAY REQUIRE SEVERAL HOURS OR DAYS DURING WHICH ATROPINIZATION MUST BE MAINTAINED. MARKEDLY LOWER LEVELS OF URINARY METABOLITES INDICATE THAT ATROPINE DOSAGE CAN BE TAPERED OFF. AS DOSAGE IS REDUCED, CHECK THE LUNG BASES FREQUENTLY FOR RALES. IF RALES ARE HEARD OR OTHER SYMPTOMS RETURN, RE-ESTABLISH ATROPINIZATION PROMPTLY (MORGAN, RECOGNITION AND MANAGEMENT OF PESTICIDE POISONINGS, 3RD ED.). ADMINISTRATION OF ANTIDOTE MUST BE PERFORMED BY QUALIFIED MEDICAL PERSONNEL.

REACTIVITY

REACTIVITY: STABLE UNDER NORMAL TEMPERATURES AND PRESSURES.

INCOMPATIBILITIES: FORMETANATE HYDROCHLORIDE: ALKALINE SOLUTIONS: HYDROLYSIS. OXIDIZERS: FIRE AND EXPLOSION HAZARD.

DECOMPOSITION: THERMAL DECOMPOSITION MAY RELEASE TOXIC AND/OR HAZARDOUS GASES.

POLYMERIZATION: HAZARDOUS POLYMERIZATION HAS NOT BEEN REPORTED TO OCCUR UNDER NORMAL TEMPERATURES AND PRESSURES.

STORAGE AND DISPOSAL

OBSERVE ALL FEDERAL, STATE AND LOCAL REGULATIONS WHEN STORING OR DISPOSING OF THIS SUBSTANCE. FOR ASSISTANCE, CONTACT THE DISTRICT DIRECTOR OF THE ENVIRONMENTAL PROTECTION AGENCY.

STORAGE

STORE IN ACCORDANCE WITH 40 CFR 165 RECOMMENDED PROCEDURES FOR THE DISPOSAL AND STORAGE OF PESTICIDES AND PESTICIDE CONTAINERS.

STORE AWAY FROM INCOMPATIBLE SUBSTANCES.

THRESHOLD PLANNING QUANTITY (TPQ): THE SUPERFUND AMENDMENTS AND REAUTHORIZATION ACT (SARA) SECTION 302 REQUIRES THAT EACH FACILITY WHERE ANY EXTREMELY HAZARDOUS SUBSTANCE IS PRESENT IN A QUANTITY EQUAL TO OR GREATER THAN THE TPQ ESTABLISHED FOR THAT SUBSTANCE NOTIFY THE STATE EMERGENCY RESPONSE COMMISSION FOR THE STATE IN WHICH IT IS LOCATED. SECTION 303 OF SARA REQUIRES THESE FACILITIES TO PARTICIPATE IN LOCAL EMERGENCY RESPONSE PLANNING (40 CFR 355.30).

DISPOSAL

DISPOSAL MUST BE IN ACCORDANCE WITH 40 CFR 165 RECOMMENDED PROCEDURES FOR THE DISPOSAL AND STORAGE OF PESTICIDES AND PESTICIDE CONTAINERS.

CONDITIONS TO AVOID

NONE REPORTED.

SPILL AND LEAK PROCEDURES

OCCUPATIONAL SPILL: DO NOT TOUCH SPILLED MATERIAL. STOP LEAK IF YOU CAN DO IT WITHOUT RISK. FOR SMALL SPILLS, TAKE UP WITH SAND OR OTHER ABSORBENT MATERIAL AND PLACE INTO CONTAINERS FOR LATER DISPOSAL. FOR SMALL DRY SPILLS, WITH A CLEAN SHOVEL PLACE MATERIAL INTO CLEAN, DRY CONTAINER AND COVER. MOVE CONTAINERS FROM SPILL AREA. FOR LARGER SPILLS, DIKE FAR AHEAD OF SPILL FOR LATER DISPOSAL. KEEP UNNECESSARY PEOPLE AWAY. ISOLATE HAZARD AREA AND DENY ENTRY.

REPORTABLE QUANTITY (RQ): 1 POUND THE SUPERFUND AMENDMENTS AND REAUTHORIZATION ACT (SARA) SECTION 304 REQUIRES THAT A RELEASE EQUAL TO OR GREATER THAN THE REPORTABLE QUANTITY FOR THIS SUBSTANCE BE IMMEDIATELY REPORTED TO THE LOCAL EMERGENCY PLANNING COMMITTEE AND THE STATE EMERGENCY RESPONSE COMMISSION (40 CFR 355.40). IF THE RELEASE OF THIS SUBSTANCE IS REPORTABLE UNDER CERCLA SECTION 103, THE NATIONAL RESPONSE CENTER MUST BE NOTIFIED IMMEDIATELY AT (800) 424-8802 OR (202) 426-2675 IN THE METROPOLITAN WASHINGTON, D.C. AREA (40 CFR 302.6).

PROTECTIVE EQUIPMENT

VENTILATION: PROVIDE LOCAL EXHAUST OR GENERAL DILUTION VENTILATION SYSTEM.

RESPIRATOR: THE FOLLOWING RESPIRATORS ARE RECOMMENDED BASED ON INFORMATION FOUND IN THE PHYSICAL DATA, TOXICITY AND HEALTH EFFECTS SECTIONS. THEY ARE RANKED IN ORDER FROM MINIMUM TO MAXIMUM RESPIRATORY PROTECTION. THE SPECIFIC RESPIRATOR SELECTED MUST BE BASED ON CONTAMINATION LEVELS FOUND IN THE WORK PLACE, MUST NOT EXCEED THE WORKING LIMITS OF THE RESPIRATOR AND BE JOINTLY APPROVED BY THE NATIONAL INSTITUTE FOR OCCUPATIONAL SAFETY AND HEALTH AND THE MINE SAFETY AND HEALTH ADMINISTRATION (NIOSH-MSHA).

TYPE 'C' SUPPLIED-AIR RESPIRATOR WITH A FULL FACEPIECE OPERATED IN PRESSURE-DEMAND OR OTHER POSITIVE PRESSURE MODE OR WITH A FULL FACEPIECE, HELMET OR HOOD OPERATED IN CONTINOUS-FLOW MODE.

SELF-CONTAINED BREATHING APPARATUS WITH A FULL FACEPIECE OPERATED IN PRESSURE-DEMAND OR OTHER POSITIVE PRESSURE MODE.

FOR FIREFIGHTING AND OTHER IMMEDIATELY DANGEROUS TO LIFE OR HEALTH CONDITIONS: SELF-CONTAINED BREATHING APPARATUS WITH FULL FACEPIECE OPERATED IN PRESSURE-DEMAND OR OTHER POSITIVE PRESSURE MODE.

SUPPLIED-AIR RESPIRATOR WITH FULL FACEPIECE AND OPERATED IN PRESSURE-DEMAND OR OTHER POSITIVE PRESSURE MODE IN COMBINATION WITH AN AUXILIARY SELF-CONTAINED BREATHING APPARATUS OPERATED IN PRESSURE-DEMAND OR OTHER POSITIVE PRESSURE MODE.

CLOTHING: EMPLOYEE MUST WEAR APPROPRIATE PROTECTIVE (IMPERVIOUS) CLOTHING AND EQUIPMENT TO PREVENT REPEATED OR PROLONGED SKIN CONTACT WITH THIS SUBSTANCE.

GLOVES: EMPLOYEE MUST WEAR APPROPRIATE PROTECTIVE GLOVES TO PREVENT CONTACT WITH THIS SUBSTANCE.

EYE PROTECTION: EMPLOYEE MUST WEAR SPLASH-PROOF OR DUST-RESISTANT SAFETY GOGGLES TO PREVENT EYE CONTACT WITH THIS SUBSTANCE.

EMERGENCY EYE WASH: WHERE THERE IS ANY POSSIBILITY THAT AN EMPLOYEE'S EYES MAY BE EXPOSED TO THIS SUBSTANCE, THE EMPLOYER SHOULD PROVIDE AN EYE WASH FOUNTAIN WITHIN THE IMMEDIATE WORK AREA FOR EMERGENCY USE.

AUTHORIZED BY- OCCUPATIONAL HEALTH SERVICES, INC.

CREATION DATE: 10/04/89 ***REVISION DATE:*** 06/12/90

MATERIAL SAFETY DATA SHEET

OCCUPATIONAL HEALTH SERVICES, INC.	EMERGENCY CONTACT:
AGRICULTURE AND PESTICIDE DIVISION	JOHN S. BRANSFORD, JR. (615) 292-1180
450 SEVENTH AVENUE, SUITE 2407	
NEW YORK, NEW YORK 10123	
1-800-445-MSDS OR (212) 967-1100	

SUBSTANCE IDENTIFICATION

CAS-NUMBER 2540-82-1

SUBSTANCE: **FORMOTHION**

TRADE NAMES/SYNONYMS: PHOSPHORODITHIOIC ACID, S-(2-(FORMYLMETHYLAMINO)-2-OXOETHYL) O,O-DIMETHYL ESTER; PHOSPHORODITHIOIC ACID, O,O-DIMETHYL ESTER, S-ESTER WITH N-FORMYL -2-MERCAPTO-N-METHYLACETAMIDE; S-(FORMYL(METHYL)CARBAMOYLMETHYL) O,O-DIMETHYL PHOSPHORODITHIOATE; S-(N-FORMYL-N-METHYLCARBAMOYLMETHYL) O,O-DIMETHYL PHOSPHORODITHOATE; 2-

DIMETHOXYPHOSPHINOTHIOYLTHIO-N-FORMYL-N-METHYLACETAMIDE; S-(2-(FORMYLMETHYLAMINO)-2-OXOETHYL) O,O-DIMETHYL PHOSPHORODITHIOATE; O,O-DIMETHYL PHOSPHORODITHOATE S-ESTER WITH N-FORMYL-2-MERCAPTO -N-METHYLACETAMIDE; O,O-DIMETHYL-S-(N-FORMYL-N-METHYLCARBAMOYLMETHYL)PHOSPHORODITHIOATE; O,O-DIMETHYL-S-(N-METHYL-N-FORMYLCARBAMOYLMETHYL)PHOSPHORODITHIOATE; DIMETHYL S-(N-FORMYL-N-METHYLCARBAMOYLEMETHYL) PHOSPHOROTHIOLOTHIONATE; AFLIX; ANTHIO; CP 53926; S 6900; TOPROSE; ENT 27257; PST10081

CHEMICAL FAMILY: ORGANOPHOSPHATE

MOLECULAR FORMULA: C6-H12-N-O4-P-S2

MOLECULAR WEIGHT: 257.28

CERCLA RATINGS (SCALE 0-3): HEALTH=3 FIRE=U REACTIVITY=U PERSISTENCE=0

NFPA RATINGS (SCALE 0-4): HEALTH=4 FIRE=U REACTIVITY=U

COMPONENTS AND CONTAMINANTS

COMPONENT: FORMOTHON ***PERCENT:*** 100
CAS# 2540-82-1

EXPOSURE LIMITS: FORMOTHION: NO OCCUPATIONAL EXPOSURE LIMITS ESTABLISHED BY OSHA, ACGIH, OR NIOSH.
100 POUNDS SARA SECTION 302 THRESHOLD PLANNING QUANTITY 1 POUND SARA SECTION 304 REPORTABLE QUANTITY

PHYSICAL DATA

DESCRIPTION: ODORLESS, YELLOWISH VISCOUS OIL OR CRYSTALLINE MASS

BOILING POINT: DECOMPOSES ***MELTING POINT:*** 77 F (25 C)

SPECIFIC GRAVITY: 1.361 ***VAPOR PRESSURE:*** 0.0000008 MMHG @ 20C

EVAPORATION RATE: NOT AVAILABLE ***SOLUBILITY IN WATER:*** 2600 PPM

SOLVENT SOLUBILITY: SOLUBLE IN ALCOHOLS, ETHER, CHLOROFORM, KETONES, AND AROMATIC SOLVENTS; INSOLUBLE IN PARAFFIN SOLVENTS

FIRE AND EXPLOSION DATA

FIRE AND EXPLOSION HAZARD: UNKNOWN FIRE AND EXPLOSION HAZARD.

FIREFIGHTING MEDIA: DRY CHEMICAL, CARBON DIOXIDE, HALON, WATER SPRAY OR STANDARD FOAM (1987 EMERGENCY RESPONSE GUIDEBOOK, DOT P 5800.4). FOR LARGER FIRES, USE WATER SPRAY, FOG OR STANDARD FOAM (1987 EMERGENCY RESPONSE GUIDEBOOK, DOT P 5800.4).

FIREFIGHTING: MOVE CONTAINERS FROM FIRE AREA IF POSSIBLE. FIGHT FIRE FROM MAXIMUM DISTANCE. STAY AWAY FROM STORAGE TANK ENDS. DIKE FIRE CONTROL WATER FOR LATER DISPOSAL. DO NOT SCATTER MATERIAL (1987 EMERGENCY RESPONSE GUIDEBOOK, DOT P 5800.4, GUIDE PAGE 55). EXTINGUISH USING AGENT SUITABLE FOR TYPE OF SURROUNDING FIRE. AVOID BREATHING VAPORS AND DUSTS. KEEP UPWIND.

TOXICITY

FORMOTHION: TOXICITY DATA: 27 MG/M3 INHALATION-MOUSE LC50; 400 MG/KG SKIN-MOUSE LD50; 353 MG/KG SKIN-RAT LD50; 250 MG/KG ORAL-RAT LD50; 150 MG/KG ORAL-GUINEA PIG LD50; 90 MG/KG ORAL-MOUSE LD50; 420 MG/KG ORAL-RABBIT LD50; 210 MG/KG ORAL-CAT LD50; 35 MG/KG INTRAVENOUS-RAT LD50; MUTAGENIC DATA (RTECS). CARCINOGEN STATUS: NONE. ACUTE TOXICITY LEVEL: HIGHLY TOXIC BY INHALATION; TOXIC BY INGESTION AND DERMAL ABSORPTION. TARGET EFFECTS: CHOLINESTERASE INHIBITOR. POISONING MAY AFFECT THE NERVOUS SYSTEM.* AT INCREASED RISK FROM EXPOSURE: PERSONS WITH RESPIRATORY AILMENTS, RECENT EXPOSURE TO CHOLINESTERASE INHIBITORS OR IMPAIRED CHOLINESTERASE PRODUCTION, OR LIVER MALFUNCTION.* ADDITIONAL DATA: MAY CROSS THE PLACENTA. HIGH ENVIRONMENTAL TEMPERATURES OR EXPOSURE OF THE CHEMICAL TO VISIBLE OR ULTRAVIOLET LIGHT MAY ENHANCE THE TOXICITY. INTERACTIONS WITH MEDICATIONS MAY OCCUR.*
* MAY BE BASED ON GENERAL INFORMATION ON ORGANOPHOSPHATES.

HEALTH EFFECTS AND FIRST AID

INHALATION: FORMOTHION: HIGHLY TOXIC. SEE INFORMATION ON ORGANOPHOSPHATES.
ORGANOPHOSPHATES: CHOLINESTERASE INHIBITOR. **ACUTE EXPOSURE**- WHEN INHALED, THE FIRST EFFECTS OF CHOLINESTERASE INHIBITORS ARE USUALLY RESPIRATORY AND MAY INCLUDE NASAL HYPEREMIA AND WATERY DISCHARGE, COUGH, CHEST DISCOMFORT, DYSPNEA, AND WHEEZING DUE TO INCREASED BRONCHIAL SECRETIONS AND BRONCHOCONSTRICTION. IF SUFFICIENT AMOUNTS ARE ABSORBED, OTHER SYSTEMIC EFFECTS MAY BEGIN WITHIN A FEW MINUTES OR BE DELAYED FOR UP TO 12 HOURS. SYMPTOMS MAY INCLUDE PALLOR, NAUSEA, VOMITING, DIARRHEA, ABDOMINAL CRAMPS, HEADACHE, DIZZINESS, OCULAR PAIN, BLURRED VISION, MIOSIS OR IN SOME CASES, ESPECIALLY INITIALLY, MYDRIASIS, LACRIMATION, SALIVATION, SWEATING, AND CONFUSION. OTHER REPORTED CENTRAL NERVOUS SYSTEM OR NEUROMUSCULAR EFFECTS MAY INCLUDE ATAXIA, SLURRED SPEECH, AREFLEXIA, WEAKNESS, FATIGUE, FASCICULATIONS, TWITCHING, TREMORS POSSIBLY OF THE TONGUE AND EYELIDS, AND EVENTUALLY PARALYSIS OF THE EXTREMITIES AND POSSIBLY OF THE RESPIRATORY MUSCLES. IN SEVERE CASES THERE MAY ALSO BE INVOLUNTARY DEFECATION AND URINATION, CYANOSIS, PSYCHOSIS, HYPERGLYCEMIA, ACUTE PANCREATITIS, CARDIAC IRREGULARITIES, PULMONARY EDEMA, UNCONSCIOUSNESS, CONVULSIONS, AND COMA. DEATH IS PRIMARILY DUE TO RESPIRATORY FAILURE, ALTHOUGH CARDIOVASCULAR EFFECTS INCLUDING CARDIAC ARREST MAY ALSO BE IMPLICATED. LONG TERM SEQUELAE ARE RARE BUT MAY INCLUDE NEUROPSYCHIATRIC DISORDERS AND MYOPATHY WITH MUSCLE TENDERNESS. SOME ORGANOPHOSPHATES MAY CAUSE A DELAYED NEUROPATHY BEGINNING 1-4 WEEKS AFTER AN ACUTE EXPOSURE WHICH MAY OR MAY NOT HAVE CAUSED ACUTE CHOLINERGIC EFFECTS. NUMBNESS, TINGLING, WEAKNESS AND CRAMPING BEGINNING SYMMETRICALLY IN THE LOWER LIMBS MAY PROGRESS TO ATAXIA AND PARALYSIS. IN SEVERE CASES, UPPER LIMB INVOLVEMENT IS POSSIBLE AND FLACCID PARALYSIS MAY PROGRESS TO SPASTIC PARALYSIS WITH EXAGGERATED REFLEXES. IMPROVEMENT MAY OCCUR OVER MONTHS TO YEARS, BUT SOME RESIDUAL IMPAIRMENT USUALLY REMAINS.
CHRONIC EXPOSURE- REPEATED OR PROLONGED EXPOSURE MAY RESULT IN THE EFFECTS OF ACUTE EXPOSURE INCLUDING THE DELAYED NEUROPATHY. OTHER EFFECTS REPORTED IN WORKERS REPEATEDLY EXPOSED INCLUDE IMPAIRED MEMORY AND CONCENTRATION, ACUTE PSYCHOSIS, SEVERE DEPRESSIONS, IRRITABILTY, CONFUSION, APATHY, EMOTIONAL LABILITY, SOCIAL WITHDRAWAL, CONFUSION, HEADACHE, SPEECH DIFFICULTIES, DELAYED REACTION TIMES, SPATIAL DISORIENTATION, NIGHTMARES, SLEEPWALKING, AND DROWSINESS OR INSOMNIA. AN INFLUENZA-LIKE CONDITION WITH HEADACHE, NAUSEA, WEAKNESS, ANOREXIA AND MALAISE HAS ALSO BEEN REPORTED.

FIRST AID- REMOVE FROM EXPOSURE AREA TO FRESH AIR IMMEDIATELY. IF BREATHING HAS STOPPED, GIVE ARTIFICIAL RESPIRATION. MAINTAIN AIRWAY AND BLOOD PRESSURE AND ADMINISTER OXYGEN IF AVAILABLE. KEEP AFFECTED PERSON WARM AND AT REST. TREAT SYMPTOMATICALLY AND SUPPORTIVELY. ADMINISTRATION OF OXYGEN SHOULD BE PERFORMED BY QUALIFIED PERSONNEL. GET MEDICAL ATTENTION IMMEDIATELY.

SKIN CONTACT: FORMOTHION: TOXIC. SEE INFORMATION ON ORGANOPHOSPHATES.
ORGANOPHOSPHATES: CHOLINESTERASE INHIBITOR. **ACUTE EXPOSURE**- LOCALIZED SWEATING AND FASCICULATIONS MAY OCCUR AT THE SITE OF CONTACT. IF SUFFICIENT AMOUNTS ARE ABSORBED, OTHER EFFECTS OF CHOLINESTERASE INHIBITION AS DESCRIBED IN ACUTE INHALATION MAY OCCUR. SYMPTOMS MAY BE DELAYED 2-3 HOURS, BUT USUALLY NO MORE THAN 12 HOURS. THE RATE OF ABSORPTION IS INCREASED BY THE PRESENCE OF DERMATITIS OR HIGH AMBIENT TEMPERATURES. DELAYED NEUROPATHY IS ALSO POSSIBLE. **CHRONIC EXPOSURE**- REPEATED OR PROLONGED EXPOSURE MAY CAUSE EFFECTS AS DESCRIBED IN ACUTE EXPOSURE. SOME ORGANOPHOSPHATES MAY CAUSE SENSITIZATION.

FIRST AID- REMOVE CONTAMINATED CLOTHING IMMEDIATELY. WASH CONTAMINATED AREAS WITH SOAP AND WATER FOLLOWED BY ALCOHOL (ARENA, POISONING, 4TH ED.). EMERGENCY PERSONNEL SHOULD WEAR GLOVES AND AVOID CONTAMINATION. TREAT RESPIRATORY DIFFICULTY WITH ARTIFICIAL RESPIRATION. GET MEDICAL ATTENTION IMMEDIATELY.

EYE CONTACT: FORMOTHION: SEE INFORMATION ON ORGANOPHOSPHATES.
ORGANOPHOSPHATES: CHOLINESTERASE INHIBITOR. **ACUTE EXPOSURE**- DIRECT CONTACT MAY CAUSE PAIN, HYPEREMIA, LACRIMATION, TWITCHING OF THE EYELIDS, MIOSIS, AND CILIARY MUSCLE SPASM WITH LOSS OF ACCOMODATION, BLURRED OR DIMMED VISION AND BROWACHE. SOMETIMES MYDRIASIS MAY OCCUR INSTEAD OF MIOSIS. WITH SUFFICIENT EXPOSURE, OTHER SYMPTOMS OF CHOLINESTERASE INHIBITION AS DESCRIBED IN ACUTE INHALATION MAY OCCUR. **CHRONIC EXPOSURE**- REPEATED OR PROLONGED EXPOSURE MAY CAUSE EFFECTS AS DESCRIBED IN ACUTE EXPOSURE. SOME COMPOUNDS HAVE CAUSED TOXIC EFFECTS ON THE CRYSTALLINE LENS, CONJUNCTIVAL THICKENING AND OBSTRUCTION OF THE NASOLACRIMAL CANALS WHEN USED AS MIOTIC EYEDROPS.

FIRST AID- IRRIGATE EYES WITH WATER OR SALINE SOLUTION. IF SYMPTOMS OF POISONING OCCUR, TREAT RESPIRATORY DIFFICULTY WITH ARTIFICIAL RESPIRATION AND OXYGEN. OBSERVE PATIENT FOR AT LEAST 24-36 HOURS (GOSSELIN, CLINICAL TOXICOLOGY OF COMMERCIAL PRODUCTS, 5TH ED.). GET MEDICAL ATTENTION IMMEDIATELY. OXYGEN SHOULD BE ADMINISTERED BY QUALIFIED MEDICAL PERSONNEL.

INGESTION: FORMOTHION: TOXIC. SEE INFORMATION ON ORGANOPHOSPHATES.
ORGANOPHOSPHATES: CHOLINESTERASE INHIBITOR. **ACUTE EXPOSURE**- WHEN INGESTED, THE FIRST EFFECTS MAY BE NAUSEA, VOMITING, ANOREXIA, ABDOMINAL CRAMPS AND DIARRHEA. GASTROINTESTINAL ABSORPTION MAY CAUSE SYMPTOMS OF CHOLINESTERASE INHIBITION AS DESCRIBED IN ACUTE INHALATION. SYMPTOMS MAY BEGIN WITHIN MINUTES OR BE DELAYED FOR

HOURS. DELAYED EFFECTS INCLUDING NEUROPATHY MAY ALSO OCCUR. **CHRONIC EXPOSURE-** REPEATED INGESTION MAY CAUSE EFFECTS AS DESCRIBED IN ACUTE EXPOSURE.

FIRST AID- IF PERSON IS ALERT AND RESPIRATION IS NOT DEPRESSED, GIVE SYRUP OF IPECAC FOLLOWED BY WATER (IF VOMITING OCCURS, KEEP HEAD BELOW HIPS TO PREVENT ASPIRATION). IF CONSCIOUSNESS LEVEL DECLINES OR VOMITING HAS NOT OCCURRED IN 15 MINUTES EMPTY STOMACH BY GASTRIC LAVAGE WITH THE AID OF CUFFED ENDOTRACHEAL TUBE USING ISOTONIC SALINE OR 5% SODIUM BICARBONATE FOLLOW WITH ACTIVATED CHARCOAL. ESTABLISH AND MAINTAIN AIRWAY. TREAT RESPIRATORY DIFFICULTY WITH ARTIFICIAL RESPIRATION AND OXYGEN. DO NOT GIVE MORPHINE, AMINOPHYLLINE, PHENOTHIAZINES, RESERPINE, FUROSEMIDE, OR ETHACRYNIC ACID (MORGAN, RECOGNITION AND MANAGEMENT OF PESTICIDE POISONINGS, 3RD ED.). TREAT SYMPTOMATICALLY AND SUPPORTIVELY. ADMINISTRATION OF OXYGEN AND LAVAGE MUST BE PERFORMED BY QUALIFIED MEDICAL PERSONNEL. GET MEDICAL ATTENTION IMMEDIATELY.

ANTIDOTE: THE FOLLOWING ANTIDOTE(S) HAVE BEEN RECOMMENDED. HOWEVER, THE DECISION AS TO WHETHER THE SEVERITY OF POISONING REQUIRES ADMINISTRATION OF ANY ANTIDOTE AND ACTUAL DOSE REQUIRED SHOULD BE MADE BY QUALIFIED MEDICAL PERSONNEL.

FOR CHOLINESTERASE INHIBITORS: ESTABLISH CLEAR AIRWAY AND TISSUE OXYGENATION BY ASPIRATION OF SECRETIONS, AND IF NECESSARY, BY ASSISTED PULMONARY VENTILATION WITH OXYGEN. IMPROVE TISSUE OXYGENATION AS MUCH AS POSSIBLE BEFORE ADMINISTERING ATROPINE TO MINIMIZE THE RISK OF VENTRICULAR FIBRILLATION. ADMINISTER ATROPINE SULFATE INTRAVENOUSLY, OR INTRAMUSCULARLY IF IV INJECTION IS NOT POSSIBLE. IN MODERATELY SEVERE POISONING ADMINISTER ATROPINE SULFATE, 0.4-2.0 MG REPEATED EVERY 15 MINUTES UNTIL ATROPINIZATION IS ACHIEVED (TACHYCARDIA, FLUSHING, DRY MOUTH, MYDRIASIS). MAINTAIN ATROPINIZATION BY REPEATED DOSES FOR 2-12 HOURS, OR LONGER, DEPENDING ON THE SEVERITY OF POISONING. THE APPEARANCE OF RALES IN THE LUNG BASES, MIOSIS, SALIVATION, NAUSEA, BRADYCARDIA, ARE ALL INDICATIONS OF INADEQUATE ATROPINIZATION. SEVERELY POISONED INDIVIDUALS MAY EXHIBIT REMARKABLE TOLERANCE TO ATROPINE; TWO OR MORE TIMES THE DOSAGES SUGGESTED ABOVE MAY BE NEEDED. PERSONS NOT POISONED OR ONLY SLIGHTLY POISONED, HOWEVER, MAY DEVELOP SIGNS OF ATROPINE TOXICITY FROM SUCH LARGE DOSAGES: FEVER, MUSCLE FIBRILLATIONS, AND DELIRIUM ARE THE MAIN SIGNS OF ATROPINE TOXICITY. IF THESE SIGNS APPEAR WHILE THE PATIENT IS FULLY ATROPINIZED, ATROPINE ADMINISTRATION SHOULD BE DISCONTINUED, AT LEAST TEMPORARILY. OBSERVE TREATED PATIENTS CLOSELY AT LEAST 24 HOURS TO INSURE THAT SYMPTOMS (POSSIBLY PULMONARY EDEMA) DO NOT RECUR AS ATROPINIZATION WEARS OFF. IN VERY SEVERE POISONINGS, METABOLIC DISPOSITION OF TOXICANT MAY REQUIRE SEVERAL HOURS OR DAYS DURING WHICH ATROPINIZATION MUST BE MAINTAINED. MARKEDLY LOWER LEVELS OF URINARY METABOLITES INDICATE THAT ATROPINE DOSAGE CAN BE TAPERED OFF. AS DOSAGE IS REDUCED, CHECK THE LUNG BASES FREQUENTLY FOR RALES. IF RALES ARE HEARD OR OTHER SYMPTOMS RETURN, RE-ESTABLISH ATROPINIZATION PROMPTLY (MORGAN, RECOGNITION AND MANAGEMENT OF PESTICIDE POISONINGS, 3RD ED.). ADMINISTRATION OF ANTIDOTE MUST BE PERFORMED BY QUALIFIED MEDICAL PERSONNEL.

IN CASES OF SEVERE POISONING BY ORGANOPHOSPHATE PESTICIDES IN WHICH RESPIRATORY DEPRESSION, MUSCLE WEAKNESS AND TWITCHINGS ARE SEVERE, GIVE PRALIDOXIME (PROTOPAM-AYERST, 2-PAM), 1.0 GRAM INTRAVENOUSLY AT NO MORE THAN 0.5 GRAM PER MINUTE. DOSAGE OF PRALIDOXIME MAY BE REPEATED IN 1-2 HOURS, THEN AT 10-12 HOUR INTERVALS IF NEEDED. IN VERY SEVERE POISONINGS, DOSAGE RATES MAY BE DOUBLED. TREATMENT WITH PRALIDOXIME WILL BE MOST EFFECTIVE IF GIVEN WITHIN THIRTY-SIX HOURS AFTER POISONING (MORGAN, RECOGNITION AND MANAGEMENT OF PESTICIDE POISONINGS, 3RD ED.). ANTIDOTE SHOULD BE ADMINISTERED BY QUALIFIED MEDICAL PERSONNEL.

REACTIVITY

REACTIVITY: MAY HYDROLYZE IN THE PRESENCE OF WATER, ESPECIALLY UNDER ALKALINE CONDITIONS.

INCOMPATIBILITIES: FORMOTHION: ALKALINE CONDITIONS: MAY CAUSE HYDROLYSIS.

DECOMPOSITION: THERMAL DECOMPOSITION MAY RELEASE TOXIC AND/OR HAZARDOUS GASES.

POLYMERIZATION: HAZARDOUS POLYMERIZATION HAS NOT BEEN REPORTED TO OCCUR UNDER NORMAL TEMPERATURES AND PRESSURES.

STORAGE AND DISPOSAL

OBSERVE ALL FEDERAL, STATE AND LOCAL REGULATIONS WHEN STORING OR DISPOSING OF THIS SUBSTANCE. FOR ASSISTANCE, CONTACT THE DISTRICT DIRECTOR OF THE ENVIRONMENTAL PROTECTION AGENCY.

****STORAGE****

STORE IN ACCORDANCE WITH 40 CFR 165 RECOMMENDED PROCEDURES FOR THE DISPOSAL AND STORAGE OF PESTICIDES AND PESTICIDE CONTAINERS. STORE AWAY FROM INCOMPATIBLE SUBSTANCES.

THRESHOLD PLANNING QUANTITY (TPQ): THE SUPERFUND AMENDMENTS AND REAUTHORIZATION ACT (SARA) SECTION 302 REQUIRES THAT EACH FACILITY WHERE ANY EXTREMELY HAZARDOUS SUBSTANCE IS PRESENT IN A QUANTITY EQUAL TO OR GREATER THAN THE TPQ ESTABLISHED FOR THAT SUBSTANCE NOTIFY THE STATE EMERGENCY RESPONSE COMMISSION FOR THE STATE IN WHICH IT IS LOCATED. SECTION 303 OF SARA REQUIRES THESE FACILITIES TO PARTICIPATE IN LOCAL EMERGENCY RESPONSE PLANNING (40 CFR 355.30).

****DISPOSAL****

DISPOSAL MUST BE IN ACCORDANCE WITH 40 CFR 165 RECOMMENDED PROCEDURES FOR THE DISPOSAL AND STORAGE OF PESTICIDES AND PESTICIDE CONTAINERS.

CONDITIONS TO AVOID

NONE REPORTED.

SPILL AND LEAK PROCEDURES

OCCUPATIONAL SPILL: DO NOT TOUCH SPILLED MATERIAL. STOP LEAK IF YOU CAN DO IT WITHOUT RISK. USE WATER SPRAY TO REDUCE VAPORS. FOR SMALL SPILLS, TAKE UP WITH SAND OR OTHER ABSORBENT MATERIAL AND PLACE INTO CONTAINERS FOR LATER DISPOSAL. FOR SMALL DRY SPILLS, WITH A CLEAN SHOVEL PLACE MATERIAL INTO CLEAN, DRY CONTAINERS AND COVER. MOVE CONTAINERS FROM SPILL AREA. FOR LARGER SPILLS, DIKE FAR AHEAD OF SPILL FOR LATER DISPOSAL. KEEP UNNECESSARY PEOPLE AWAY. ISOLATE HAZARD AREA AND DENY ENTRY. VENTILATE CLOSED SPACES BEFORE ENTERING.

REPORTABLE QUANTITY (RQ): 1 POUND THE SUPERFUND AMENDMENTS AND REAUTHORIZATION ACT (SARA) SECTION 304 REQUIRES THAT A RELEASE EQUAL TO OR GREATER THAN THE REPORTABLE QUANTITY FOR THIS SUBSTANCE BE IMMEDIATELY REPORTED TO THE LOCAL EMERGENCY PLANNING COMMITTEE AND THE STATE EMERGENCY RESPONSE COMMISSION (40 CFR 355.40). IF THE RELEASE OF THIS SUBSTANCE IS REPORTABLE UNDER CERCLA SECTION 103, THE NATIONAL RESPONSE CENTER MUST BE NOTIFIED IMMEDIATELY AT (800) 424-8802 OR (202) 426-2675 IN THE METROPOLITAN WASHINGTON, D.C. AREA (40 CFR 302.6).

PROTECTIVE EQUIPMENT

VENTILATION: PROVIDE LOCAL EXHAUST OR PROCESS ENCLOSURE VENTILATION SYSTEM.

RESPIRATOR: THE FOLLOWING RESPIRATORS ARE RECOMMENDED BASED ON INFORMATION FOUND IN THE PHYSICAL DATA, TOXICITY AND HEALTH EFFECTS SECTIONS. THEY ARE RANKED IN ORDER FROM MINIMUM TO MAXIMUM RESPIRATORY PROTECTION. THE SPECIFIC RESPIRATOR SELECTED MUST BE BASED ON CONTAMINATION LEVELS FOUND IN THE WORK PLACE, MUST NOT EXCEED THE WORKING LIMITS OF THE RESPIRATOR AND BE JOINTLY APPROVED BY THE NATIONAL INSTITUTE FOR OCCUPATIONAL SAFETY AND HEALTH AND THE MINE SAFETY AND HEALTH ADMINISTRATION (NIOSH-MSHA).

TYPE 'C' SUPPLIED-AIR RESPIRATOR WITH A FULL FACEPIECE OPERATED IN PRESSURE-DEMAND OR OTHER POSITIVE PRESSURE MODE OR WITH A FULL FACEPIECE, HELMET OR HOOD OPERATED IN CONTINOUS-FLOW MODE.

SELF-CONTAINED BREATHING APPARATUS WITH A FULL FACEPIECE OPERATED IN PRESSURE-DEMAND OR OTHER POSITIVE PRESSURE MODE.

FOR FIREFIGHTING AND OTHER IMMEDIATELY DANGEROUS TO LIFE OR HEALTH CONDITIONS:

SELF-CONTAINED BREATHING APPARATUS WITH FULL FACEPIECE OPERATED IN PRESSURE-DEMAND OR OTHER POSITIVE PRESSURE MODE.

SUPPLIED-AIR RESPIRATOR WITH FULL FACEPIECE AND OPERATED IN PRESSURE-DEMAND OR OTHER POSITIVE PRESSURE MODE IN COMBINATION WITH AN AUXILIARY SELF-CONTAINED BREATHING APPARATUS OPERATED IN PRESSURE-DEMAND OR OTHER POSITIVE PRESSURE MODE.

CLOTHING: EMPLOYEE MUST WEAR APPROPRIATE PROTECTIVE (IMPERVIOUS) CLOTHING AND EQUIPMENT TO PREVENT ANY POSSIBILITY OF SKIN CONTACT WITH THIS SUBSTANCE.

GLOVES: EMPLOYEE MUST WEAR APPROPRIATE PROTECTIVE GLOVES TO PREVENT CONTACT WITH THIS SUBSTANCE.

EYE PROTECTION: EMPLOYEE MUST WEAR SPLASH-PROOF OR DUST-RESISTANT SAFETY GOGGLES AND A FACESHIELD TO PREVENT CONTACT WITH THIS SUBSTANCE.

EMERGENCY WASH FACILITIES: WHERE THERE IS ANY POSSIBILITY THAT AN EMPLOYEE'S EYES AND/OR SKIN MAY BE EXPOSED TO THIS SUBSTANCE, THE EMPLOYER SHOULD PROVIDE AN EYE WASH FOUNTAIN AND QUICK DRENCH SHOWER WITHIN THE IMMEDIATE WORK AREA FOR EMERGENCY USE.

AUTHORIZED BY- OCCUPATIONAL HEALTH SERVICES, INC.

CREATION DATE: 10/04/89 ***REVISION DATE:*** 04/26/90

MATERIAL SAFETY DATA SHEET

OCCUPATIONAL HEALTH SERVICES, INC.
AGRICULTURE AND PESTICIDE DIVISION
450 SEVENTH AVENUE, SUITE 2407
NEW YORK, NEW YORK 10123
1-800-445-MSDS OR (212) 967-1100

EMERGENCY CONTACT:
JOHN S. BRANSFORD, JR. (615) 292-1180

SUBSTANCE IDENTIFICATION

CAS-NUMBER 8008-20-6

SUBSTANCE: **KEROSENE**

TRADE NAMES/SYNONYMS: FUEL OIL NO. 1; COAL OIL; RANGE OIL; KEROSINE; MOBILE KEROSINE (MOBILE OIL CORP.); STCC 4915171; UN 1223; K-10; PST10090

CHEMICAL FAMILY: PETROLEUM HYDROCARBON

CERCLA RATINGS (SCALE 0-3): HEALTH = 3 FIRE = 2 REACTIVITY = 0 PERSISTENCE = 1

NFPA RATINGS (SCALE 0-4): HEALTH = 0 FIRE = 2 REACTIVITY = 0

COMPONENTS AND CONTAMINANTS

COMPONENT: KEROSENE ***PERCENT:*** >99.0
CAS# 8008-20-6

OTHER CONTAMINANTS: MAY CONTAIN TRACES OF SULFUR AND BENZENE.

EXPOSURE LIMITS: KEROSENE (FUEL OIL NO. 1): 100 MG/M3 (14 PPM) NIOSH RECOMMENDED 10 HOUR TWA

PHYSICAL DATA

DESCRIPTION: COLORLESS TO LIGHT-BROWN, MOBILE, OILY LIQUID WITH A MILD PETROLEUM ODOR. ***BOILING POINT:*** 304-574 F (151-301 C)

MELTING POINT: 0 F (-18 C) ***SPECIFIC GRAVITY:*** 0.8

VISCOSITY: >1.3 CST @ 40 C ***VAPOR PRESSURE:*** 5 MMHG @ 38 C

SOLUBILITY IN WATER: INSOLUBLE ***ODOR THRESHOLD:*** 0.09 PPM (0.6 MG/M3)

VAPOR DENSITY: 4.5

FIRE AND EXPLOSION DATA

FIRE AND EXPLOSION HAZARD: MODERATE FIRE HAZARD WHEN EXPOSED TO HEAT OR FLAME.
VAPOR-AIR MIXTURES ARE EXPLOSIVE ABOVE FLASH POINT.
VAPORS ARE HEAVIER THAN AIR AND MAY TRAVEL A CONSIDERABLE DISTANCE TO A SOURCE OF IGNITION AND FLASH BACK.
DUE TO LOW ELECTROCONDUCTIVITY OF THE SUBSTANCE, FLOW OR AGITATION MAY GENERATE ELECTROSTATIC CHARGES RESULTING IN SPARKS WITH POSSIBLE IGNITION.

FLASH POINT: >100 F (>43 C) (CC) ***UPPER EXPLOSIVE LIMIT:*** 5.0%

LOWER EXPLOSIVE LIMIT: 0.7% ***AUTOIGNITION TEMP.:*** 410 F (210 C)

FLAMMABILITY CLASS(OSHA): II

FIREFIGHTING MEDIA: DRY CHEMICAL, CARBON DIOXIDE, HALON, WATER SPRAY OR STANDARD FOAM (1987 EMERGENCY RESPONSE GUIDEBOOK, DOT P 5800.4).
FOR LARGER FIRES, USE WATER SPRAY, FOG OR STANDARD FOAM (1987 EMERGENCY RESPONSE GUIDEBOOK, DOT P 5800.4).

FIREFIGHTING: MOVE CONTAINER FROM FIRE AREA IF POSSIBLE. COOL FIRE-EXPOSED CONTAINERS WITH WATER FROM SIDE UNTIL WELL AFTER FIRE IS OUT. STAY AWAY FROM STORAGE TANK ENDS. FOR MASSIVE FIRE IN STORAGE AREA, USE UNMANNED HOSE HOLDER OR MONITOR NOZZLES, ELSE WITHDRAW FROM AREA AND LET FIRE BURN. WITHDRAW IMMEDIATELY IN CASE OF RISING SOUND FROM VENTING SAFETY DEVICE OR ANY DISCOLORATION OF STORAGE TANK DUE TO FIRE (1987 EMERGENCY RESPONSE GUIDEBOOK, DOT P 5800.4, GUIDE PAGE 27).
EXTINGUISH ONLY IF FLOW CAN BE STOPPED; USE FLOODING AMOUNTS OF WATER AS A FOG, SOLID STREAMS MAY BE INEFFECTIVE. COOL CONTAINERS WITH FLOODING AMOUNTS OF WATER, APPLY FROM AS FAR A DISTANCE AS POSSIBLE. AVOID BREATHING VAPORS, KEEP UPWIND.
FIRE FIGHTING PHASES: USE WATER SPRAY, DRY CHEMICAL, FOAM, OR CARBON DIOXIDE. USE WATER TO KEEP FIRE-EXPOSED CONTAINERS COOL. IF A LEAK HAS NOT IGNITED, USE WATER SPRAY TO DISPERSE THE VAPORS AND TO PROTECT PERSONS ATTEMPTING TO STOP A LEAK. WATER SPRAY MAY BE USED TO FLUSH SPILLS AWAY FROM EXPOSURES (NFPA 49, HAZARDOUS CHEMICALS DATA, 1975).

TRANSPORTATION DATA

DEPARTMENT OF TRANSPORTATION HAZARD CLASSIFICATION 49 CFR 172.101: COMBUSTIBLE LIQUID
DEPARTMENT OF TRANSPORTATION LABELING REQUIREMENTS 49 CFR 172.101 AND SUBPART E: NONE
DEPARTMENT OF TRANSPORTATION PACKAGING REQUIREMENTS: NONE
EXCEPTIONS: 49 CFR 173.118A

TOXICITY

KEROSENE (FUEL OIL NO. 1): TOXICITY DATA: 3570 MG/KG ORAL-MAN TDLO; 500 MG/KG ORAL-MAN LDLO; 36 GM/KG ORAL-RAT LD50; 4 GM/KG ORAL-DOG LDLO; 7072 MG/KG ORAL-RABBIT LD50; 20 GM/KG ORAL-GUINEA PIG LD50; 800 MG/KG INTRATRACHEAL-DOG LDLO; 800 MG/KG INTRATRACHEAL-RAT LDLO; 200 MG/KG INTRATRACHEAL-RABBIT LD50; 403 MG/KG INTRAVENOUS-MAN TDLO; 200 MG/KG INTRAVENOUS-DOG LDLO; 180 MG/KG INTRAVENOUS-RABBIT LD50; 10700 MG/KG INTRAPERITONEAL-RAT LDLO; 6600 MG/KG INTRAPERITONEAL-RABBIT LD50; 1176 MG/KG UNREPORTED-MAN LDLO MUTAGENIC DATA (RTECS). CARCINOGEN STATUS: HUMAN INADEQUATE EVIDENCE (IARC GROUP-3). LOCAL EFFECTS: IRRITANT- MUCOUS MEMBRANE, SKIN. ACUTE TOXICITY: RELATIVELY NONTOXIC BY INGESTION. TARGET EFFECTS: CENTRAL NERVOUS SYSTEM DEPRESSANT. ADDITIONAL DATA: USE OF EPINEPHRINE OR SIMILAR STIMULANTS MAY INDUCE VENTRICULAR FIBRILLATION.

HEALTH EFFECTS AND FIRST AID

INHALATION: KEROSENE (FUEL OIL NO. 1): IRRITANT/NARCOTIC. **ACUTE EXPOSURE-** INHALATION HAZARD IS LOW DUE TO THE LOW VAPOR PRESSURE. ONE STUDY CONCLUDED THAT THERE IS NO INDICATION OF TOXICITY AT CONCENTRATIONS OF 100 MG/M3 OR BELOW. HIGH CONCENTRATIONS OF MIST OR VAPOR MAY CAUSE MUCOUS MEMBRANE IRRITATION, A BURNING SENSATION IN THE CHEST, AN ODOR OF KEROSENE ON THE BREATH, AND CHEMICAL PNEUMONITIS. THERE MAY BE TRANSIENT EUPHORIA AND EXCITEMENT FOLLOWED BY SYMPTOMS OF CENTRAL NERVOUS SYSTEM DEPRESSION WHICH MAY INCLUDE HEADACHE, NAUSEA, DIZZINESS, WEAKNESS, ATAXIA, RESTLESSNESS, AND RINGING IN THE EARS. DISORIENTATION AND CONFUSION MAY PROGRESS TO DROWSINESS AND COMA, SOMETIMES WITH CONVULSIONS. VASOMOTOR DISTURBANCES, POSSIBLY WITH CYANOSIS OF THE EXTREMITIES MAY OCCUR. DEATH IS USUALLY DUE TO RESPIRATORY ARREST, BUT RARELY SUDDEN DEATH MAY OCCUR, PRESUMABLY DUE TO VENTRICULAR FIBRILLATION. **CHRONIC EXPOSURE-** REPEATED OR PROLONGED EXPOSURE TO KEROSENE MIST MAY CAUSE MUCOUS MEMBRANE IRRITATION AND POLYEMIA. AEROSOL EXPOSURE AT 500-12000 MG/M3 FOR 2 HOURS/DAY FOR 2-4 WEEKS CAUSED LEUKOCYTOSIS, TRACHEITIS, BRONCHITIS, AND PNEUMONIA. MALAISE, WEAKNESS, TREMOR, TWITCHING, VERTIGO, AND PAIN IN THE EXTREMITIES HAVE ALSO BEEN REPORTED. DOGS AND RATS EXPOSED TO 100 MG/M3 OF DEODORIZED KEROSENE FOR 6 HOURS/DAY, 5 DAYS/WEEK FOR 67 DAYS SHOWED NO TOXIC EFFECTS.

FIRST AID- REMOVE FROM EXPOSURE AREA TO FRESH AIR IMMEDIATELY. IF BREATHING HAS STOPPED, GIVE ARTIFICIAL RESPIRATION. MAINTAIN AIRWAY AND BLOOD PRESSURE AND ADMINISTER OXYGEN IF AVAILABLE. KEEP AFFECTED PERSON WARM AND AT REST. TREAT SYMPTOMATICALLY AND SUPPORTIVELY. ADMINISTRATION OF OXYGEN SHOULD BE PERFORMED BY QUALIFIED PERSONNEL. GET MEDICAL ATTENTION IMMEDIATELY.

SKIN CONTACT: KEROSENE (FUEL OIL NO. 1): IRRITANT. **ACUTE EXPOSURE-** DIRECT CONTACT MAY CAUSE DEFATTING WITH DRYNESS, IRRITATION, DERMATITIS, AND EDEMA. SECONDARY INFECTIONS ARE POSSIBLE. IN ONE STUDY, SKIN DEVELOPED A BURNING SENSATION DURING THE FIRST HOUR OF EXPOSURE, ERYTHEMA BY THE SECOND, AND BLISTER FORMATION BY THE TWELFTH. ALTHOUGH ABSORPTION THROUGH INTACT SKIN IS SLIGHT, IT MAY BE MODERATE THROUGH INJURED SKIN. KEROSENE MAY INCREASE THE TOXICITY OF SKIN-SENSITIZING AGENTS. **CHRONIC EXPOSURE-** REPEATED OR PROLONGED EXPOSURE MAY CAUSE DEFATTING AND DERMATITIS. SEVERAL CASES HAVE BEEN REPORTED IN HUMANS WHERE MISUSE OF KEROSENE TO MASSAGE EXTREMITIES RESULTED IN APLASTIC ANEMIA AND DEATH, PROBABLY DUE TO ABSORPTION OF BENZENE. RABBITS TREATED FOR 3 DAYS WITH 3 ML/KG/DAY EXPERIENCED HAIR LOSS, SCALING, CRACKING OF THE EPIDERMIS, BUT NO SYSTEMIC TOXICITY.

FIRST AID- REMOVE CONTAMINATED CLOTHING AND SHOES IMMEDIATELY. WASH AFFECTED AREA WITH SOAP OR MILD DETERGENT AND LARGE AMOUNTS OF WATER UNTIL NO EVIDENCE OF CHEMICAL REMAINS (APPROXIMATELY 15-20 MINUTES). GET MEDICAL ATTENTION IMMEDIATELY.

EYE CONTACT: KEROSENE (FUEL OIL NO. 1): **ACUTE EXPOSURE-** APPLICATION TO THE HUMAN EYE IS REPORTED TO CAUSE NO DISCOMFORT OR INJURY. **CHRONIC EXPOSURE-** NO DATA AVAILABLE.

FIRST AID- WASH EYES IMMEDIATELY WITH LARGE AMOUNTS OF WATER OR NORMAL SALINE, OCCASIONALLY LIFTING UPPER AND LOWER LIDS, UNTIL NO EVIDENCE OF CHEMICAL REMAINS (APPROXIMATELY 15-20 MINUTES). GET MEDICAL ATTENTION IMMEDIATELY.

INGESTION: KEROSENE (FUEL OIL NO. 1): NARCOTIC. **ACUTE EXPOSURE-** MAY CAUSE LOCAL IRRITATION WITH A BURNING SENSATION IN THE MOUTH, ESOPHAGUS, AND STOMACH; AND VOMITING, BELCHING, AND DIARRHEA WITH BLOOD-TINGED FECES. ASPIRATION INTO THE LUNGS MAY OCCUR READILY DURING INGESTION OR SUBSEQUENT VOMITING OR BELCHING. EVEN SMALL AMOUNTS MAY CAUSE

CHEMICAL PNEUMONITIS WITH PULMONARY EDEMA AND HEMORRHAGE AND MAY POSSIBLY BE COMPLICATED BY SECONDARY BACTERIAL PNEUMONIA. SIGNS OF LUNG INVOLVEMENT ARE SUDDEN DEVELOPMENT OF RAPID, LABORED BREATHING, DISTRESS, CYANOSIS WITH RALES, FEVER, AND TACHYCARDIA. IF SUFFICIENT AMOUNTS ARE INGESTED AND RETAINED, SYMPTOMS OF CENTRAL NERVOUS SYSTEM DEPRESSION MAY OCCUR AS DETAILED IN ACUTE INHALATION; DROWSINESS MAY PROGRESS TO COMA, SOMETIMES WITH CONVULSIONS. SEVERE CASES MAY BE FATAL. VENTICULLAR FIBRILLATION IS POSSIBLE. **CHRONIC EXPOSURE-** REPEATED DOSING OF RATS AND RABBITS BY GASTRIC INTUBATION DID NOT RESULT IN PULMONARY INJURY.

FIRST AID- EXTREME CARE MUST BE USED TO PREVENT ASPIRATION. USE GASTRIC LAVAGE WITH ACTIVATED CHARCOAL AND A CUFFED ENDOTRACHEAL TUBE WITHIN 15 MINUTES. IN THE ABSENCE OF DEPRESSION OR CONVULSIONS OR IMPAIRED GAG REFLEX, IPECAC EMESIS CAN BE DONE. WHEN VOMITING BEGINS, KEEP HEAD BELOW THE HIPS TO PREVENT ASPIRATION. AFTER VOMITING STOPS, GIVE 30-60 MILLILITERS OF FLEET'S PHOSPHO-SODA DILUTED 1:4 IN WATER. MAINTAIN AIRWAY, BLOOD PRESSURE AND RESPIRATION. (DREISBACH, HANDBOOK OF POISONING, 11TH ED.) GET MEDICAL ATTENTION. TREATMENT MUST BE ADMINISTERED BY QUALIFIED MEDICAL PERSONNEL.

ANTIDOTE: NO SPECIFIC ANTIDOTE. TREAT SYMPTOMATICALLY AND SUPPORTIVELY.

REACTIVITY

REACTIVITY: STABLE UNDER NORMAL TEMPERATURES AND PRESSURES.

INCOMPATIBILITIES: KEROSENE (FUEL OIL NO. 1): OXIDIZERS: POSSIBLE VIOLENT REACTION OR IGNITION. NITROGEN TETROXIDE: POSSIBLE EXPLOSION. CHLORINE: VIGOROUS REACTION OR POSSIBLE IGNITION OR EXPLOSION. FLUORINE: POSSIBLE IGNITION OR EXPLOSION. MAGNESIUM PERCHLORATE: POSSIBLE EXPLOSION ON HEATING.

DECOMPOSITION: THERMAL DECOMPOSITION PRODUCTS MAY INCLUDE TOXIC OXIDES OF CARBON.

POLYMERIZATION: HAZARDOUS POLYMERIZATION HAS NOT BEEN REPORTED TO OCCUR UNDER NORMAL TEMPERATURES AND PRESSURES.

STORAGE AND DISPOSAL

OBSERVE ALL FEDERAL, STATE AND LOCAL REGULATIONS WHEN STORING OR DISPOSING OF THIS SUBSTANCE. FOR ASSISTANCE, CONTACT THE DISTRICT DIRECTOR OF THE ENVIRONMENTAL PROTECTION AGENCY.

STORAGE

STORE IN ACCORDANCE WITH 29 CFR 1910.106.
STORE AWAY FROM INCOMPATIBLE SUBSTANCES.

DISPOSAL

DISPOSAL MUST BE IN ACCORDANCE WITH STANDARDS APPLICABLE TO GENERATORS OF HAZARDOUS WASTE, 40 CFR 262. EPA HAZARDOUS WASTE NUMBER D001. 100 POUND CERCLA SECTION 103 REPORTABLE QUANTITY.

CONDITIONS TO AVOID

AVOID CONTACT WITH HEAT, SPARKS, FLAMES, OR OTHER SOURCES OF IGNITION. VAPORS MAY BE EXPLOSIVE. AVOID OVERHEATING OF CONTAINERS; CONTAINERS MAY VIOLENTLY RUPTURE IN HEAT OF FIRE. AVOID CONTAMINATION OF WATER SOURCES.

SPILL AND LEAK PROCEDURES

OCCUPATIONAL SPILL: SHUT OFF IGNITION SOURCES. STOP LEAK IF YOU CAN DO IT WITHOUT RISK. USE WATER SPRAY TO REDUCE VAPORS. FOR SMALL SPILLS, TAKE UP WITH SAND OR OTHER ABSORBENT MATERIAL AND PLACE INTO CONTAINERS FOR LATER DISPOSAL. FOR LARGER SPILLS, DIKE FAR AHEAD OF SPILL FOR LATER DISPOSAL. NO SMOKING, FLAMES OR FLARES IN HAZARD AREA. KEEP UNNECESSARY PEOPLE AWAY; ISOLATE HAZARD AREA AND RESTRICT ENTRY.

PROTECTIVE EQUIPMENT

VENTILATION: PROVIDE LOCAL EXHAUST VENTILATION AND/OR GENERAL DILUTION VENTILATION TO MEET PUBLISHED EXPOSURE LIMITS.

RESPIRATOR: THE FOLLOWING RESPIRATORS ARE RECOMMENDED BASED ON INFORMATION FOUND IN THE PHYSICAL DATA, TOXICITY AND HEALTH EFFECTS SECTIONS. THEY ARE RANKED IN ORDER FROM MINIMUM TO MAXIMUM RESPIRATORY PROTECTION. THE SPECIFIC RESPIRATOR SELECTED MUST BE BASED ON CONTAMINATION LEVELS FOUND IN THE WORK PLACE, MUST NOT EXCEED THE WORKING LIMITS OF THE RESPIRATOR AND BE JOINTLY APPROVED BY THE NATIONAL INSTITUTE FOR OCCUPATIONAL SAFETY AND HEALTH AND THE MINE SAFETY AND HEALTH ADMINISTRATION (NIOSH-MSHA).

TYPE 'C' SUPPLIED-AIR RESPIRATOR WITH A FULL FACEPIECE OPERATED IN PRESSURE-DEMAND OR OTHER POSITIVE PRESSURE MODE OR WITH A FULL FACEPIECE, HELMET OR HOOD OPERATED IN CONTINOUS-FLOW MODE.

SELF-CONTAINED BREATHING APPARATUS WITH A FULL FACEPIECE OPERATED IN PRESSURE-DEMAND OR OTHER POSITIVE PRESSURE MODE.

FOR FIREFIGHTING AND OTHER IMMEDIATELY DANGEROUS TO LIFE OR HEALTH CONDITIONS:

SELF-CONTAINED BREATHING APPARATUS WITH FULL FACEPIECE OPERATED IN PRESSURE-DEMAND OR OTHER POSITIVE PRESSURE MODE.

SUPPLIED-AIR RESPIRATOR WITH FULL FACEPIECE AND OPERATED IN PRESSURE-DEMAND OR OTHER POSITIVE PRESSURE MODE IN COMBINATION WITH AN AUXILIARY SELF-CONTAINED BREATHING APPARATUS OPERATED IN PRESSURE-DEMAND OR OTHER POSITIVE PRESSURE MODE.

CLOTHING: EMPLOYEE MUST WEAR APPROPRIATE PROTECTIVE (IMPERVIOUS) CLOTHING AND EQUIPMENT TO PREVENT REPEATED OR PROLONGED SKIN CONTACT WITH THIS SUBSTANCE.

GLOVES: EMPLOYEE MUST WEAR APPROPRIATE PROTECTIVE GLOVES TO PREVENT CONTACT WITH THIS SUBSTANCE.

EYE PROTECTION: EMPLOYEE MUST WEAR SPLASH-PROOF OR DUST-RESISTANT SAFETY GOGGLES TO PREVENT EYE CONTACT WITH THIS SUBSTANCE.

EMERGENCY EYE WASH: WHERE THERE IS ANY POSSIBILITY THAT AN EMPLOYEE'S EYES MAY BE EXPOSED TO THIS SUBSTANCE, THE EMPLOYER SHOULD PROVIDE AN EYE WASH FOUNTAIN WITHIN THE IMMEDIATE WORK AREA FOR EMERGENCY USE.

AUTHORIZED BY- OCCUPATIONAL HEALTH SERVICES, INC.

CREATION DATE: 10/04/89 ***REVISION DATE:*** 05/17/90

MATERIAL SAFETY DATA SHEET

OCCUPATIONAL HEALTH SERVICES, INC.
AGRICULTURE AND PESTICIDE DIVISION
450 SEVENTH AVENUE, SUITE 2407
NEW YORK, NEW YORK 10123
1-800-445-MSDS OR (212) 967-1100

EMERGENCY CONTACT:
JOHN S. BRANSFORD, JR. (615) 292-1180

SUBSTANCE IDENTIFICATION

CAS-NUMBER 17080-02-3

SUBSTANCE: FURETHRIN

TRADE NAMES/SYNONYMS: 2,2-DIMETHYL-3-(2-METHYL-1-PROPENYL)-CYCLOPROPANECARBOXYLIC ACID, 3- (2-FURANYLMETHYL)-2-METHYL-4-OXO-2-CYLCOPENTEN-1-YL ESTER; 2,2-DIMETHYL-3-(2-METHYLPROPENYL)-CYCLOPROPANECARBOXYLIC ACID, ESTER WITH 2-FURFURYL-4-HYDROXY-3-METHYL-2-CYCLOPENTEN-1-ONE; 3-(2-FURANYLMETHYL)-2-METHYL-4-OXO-2-CYCLOPENTEN-1-YL 2,2-DIMETHYL -3-(2-METHYL-1-PROPENYL)CYCLOPROPANECARBOXYLATE; 3-FURFURYL-2-METHYL-4-OXO-2-CYCLOPENTEN-1-YL CHRYSANTHEMUMATE; DL-3-(2-FURFURYL)-4-HYDROXY-2-METHYL-2-CYCLOPENTEN-1-ONE ESTER OF DL-CIS-TRANS-CHRYSANTHEMUM MONOCARBOXYLIC ACID; PST10175

CHEMICAL FAMILY: PYRETHROID (SYNTHETIC)

MOLECULAR FORMULA: C21-H26-O4

MOLECULAR WEIGHT: 342.47

CERCLA RATINGS (SCALE 0-3): HEALTH=U FIRE=U REACTIVITY=0 PERSISTENCE=2

NFPA RATINGS (SCALE 0-4): HEALTH=U FIRE=U REACTIVITY=0

COMPONENTS AND CONTAMINANTS

COMPONENT: FURETHRIN ***PERCENT:*** 100.0
CAS# 17080-02-3

OTHER CONTAMINANTS: NONE

EXPOSURE LIMITS: NO OCCUPATIONAL EXPOSURE LIMITS ESTABLISHED BY OSHA, ACGIH, OR NIOSH.

PHYSICAL DATA

DESCRIPTION: YELLOW LIQUID ***BOILING POINT:*** 369-370 F (187-188 C) @ 0.4 MMHG

SPECIFIC GRAVITY: NOT AVAILABLE ***EVAPORATION RATE:*** NOT AVAILABLE

SOLUBILITY IN WATER: INSOLUBLE

SOLVENT SOLUBILITY: LIGHT OILS

FIRE AND EXPLOSION DATA

FIRE AND EXPLOSION HAZARD: UNKNOWN FIRE AND EXPLOSION HAZARD.

FIREFIGHTING MEDIA: DRY CHEMICAL, CARBON DIOXIDE, HALON, WATER SPRAY OR STANDARD FOAM (1987 EMERGENCY RESPONSE GUIDEBOOK, DOT P 5800.4). FOR LARGER FIRES, USE WATER SPRAY, FOG OR STANDARD FOAM (1987 EMERGENCY RESPONSE GUIDEBOOK, DOT P 5800.4).

FIREFIGHTING: MOVE CONTAINER FROM FIRE AREA IF POSSIBLE. DO NOT SCATTER SPILLED MATERIAL WITH HIGH PRESSURE WATER STREAMS. DIKE FIRE CONTROL

WATER FOR LATER DISPOSAL (1987 EMERGENCY RESPONSE GUIDEBOOK, DOT P 5800.4, GUIDE PAGE 31).
USE AGENTS SUITABLE FOR TYPE OF SURROUNDING FIRE. AVOID BREATHING HAZARDOUS VAPORS, KEEP UPWIND.

TOXICITY

FURETHRIN: TOXICITY DATA: 700 MG/KG UNREPORTED-RAT LD50. CARCINOGEN STATUS: NONE. ACUTE TOXICITY LEVEL: INSUFFICIENT DATA. TARGET EFFECTS: POISONING MAY AFFECT THE CENTRAL NERVOUS SYSTEM.

HEALTH EFFECTS AND FIRST AID

INHALATION: FURETHRIN: **ACUTE EXPOSURE-** FURETHRIN IS A SYNTHETIC PYRETHRIN. SYNTHETIC PYRETHRINS, LIKE THE NATURAL PYRETHRINS, PRODUCE CENTRAL NERVOUS SYSTEM STIMULATION IN ANIMALS WITH SYMPTOMS OF NAUSEA, VOMITING, GASTROENTERITIS WITH DIARRHEA, HYPERSENSITIVITY, INCOORDINATION, TREMORS, MUSCULAR PARALYSIS, CONVULSION, COMA, AND DEATH DUE TO RESPIRATORY FAILURE. UNLIKE NATURAL PYRETHRINS, SYNTHETIC PYRETHRINS NORMALLY DO NOT PRODUCE ALLERGIC REACTIONS IN HUMANS. **CHRONIC EXPOSURE-** NO DATA AVAILABLE.

FIRST AID- REMOVE FROM EXPOSURE AREA TO FRESH AIR IMMEDIATELY. IF BREATHING HAS STOPPED, PERFORM ARTIFICIAL RESPIRATION. KEEP PERSON WARM AND AT REST. TREAT SYMPTOMATICALLY AND SUPPORTIVELY. GET MEDICAL ATTENTION IMMEDIATELY.

SKIN CONTACT: FURETHRIN: **ACUTE EXPOSURE-** FURETHRIN IS A SYNTHETIC PYRETHRIN. SYNTHETIC PYRETHRINS ARE NOT IRRITANTS TO RABBIT SKIN AND THE TOXICITY FROM DERMAL ABSORPTION IS USUALLY MODERATE TO LOW. UNLIKE NATURAL PYRETHRINS, SYNTHETIC PYRETHRINS NORMALLY DO NOT PRODUCE ALLERGIC REACTIONS IN HUMANS. HOWEVER, THERE HAVE BEEN SOME REPORTS OF CUTANEOUS PARESTHESIAS AMONG OCCUPATIONALLY EXPOSED INDIVIDUALS. THESE INDIVIDUALS COMPLAINED OF TINGLING, BURNING AND STINGING SENSATIONS ON THE EXPOSED SURFACE OF THE SKIN, BEGINNING FROM 30 MINUTES TO 3 HOURS AFTER EXPOSURE. THE DURATION OF SYMPTOMS VARIED FROM 30 MINUTES TO 8 HOURS. **CHRONIC EXPOSURE-** NO DATA AVAILABLE.

FIRST AID- REMOVE CONTAMINATED CLOTHING AND SHOES IMMEDIATELY. WASH AFFECTED AREA WITH SOAP OR MILD DETERGENT AND LARGE AMOUNTS OF WATER UNTIL NO EVIDENCE OF CHEMICAL REMAINS (APPROXIMATELY 15-20 MINUTES). GET MEDICAL ATTENTION IMMEDIATELY.

EYE CONTACT: FURETHRIN: **ACUTE EXPOSURE-** SYNTHETIC PYRETHRINS ARE NOT IRRITANTS OF RABBIT EYES. **CHRONIC EXPOSURE-** NO DATA AVAILABLE.

FIRST AID- WASH EYES IMMEDIATELY WITH LARGE AMOUNTS OF WATER OR NORMAL SALINE, OCCASIONALLY LIFTING UPPER AND LOWER LIDS, UNTIL NO EVIDENCE OF CHEMICAL REMAINS (APPROXIMATELY 15-20 MINUTES). GET MEDICAL ATTENTION IMMEDIATELY.

INGESTION: FURETHRIN: **ACUTE EXPOSURE-** FURETHRIN IS A SYNTHETIC PYRETHRIN. SYNTHETIC PYRETHRINS, LIKE THE NATURAL PYRETHRINS, PRODUCE CENTRAL NERVOUS SYSTEM STIMULATION IN ANIMALS WITH SYMPTOMS OF NAUSEA, VOMITING, GASTROENTERITIS WITH DIARRHEA, HYPERSENSITIVITY, INCOORDINATION, TREMORS, MUSCULAR PARALYSIS, CONVULSION, COMA, AND DEATH DUE TO RESPIRATORY FAILURE. **CHRONIC EXPOSURE-** NO DATA AVAILABLE.

FIRST AID- TREAT SYMPTOMATICALLY AND SUPPORTIVELY. GET MEDICAL ATTENTION IMMEDIATELY. IF VOMITING OCCURS, KEEP HEAD LOWER THAN HIPS TO PREVENT ASPIRATION.

ANTIDOTE: NO SPECIFIC ANTIDOTE. TREAT SYMPTOMATICALLY AND SUPPORTIVELY.

REACTIVITY

REACTIVITY: MAY DECOMPOSE UPON EXPOSURE TO HEAT OR LIGHT.
INCOMPATIBILITIES: FURETHRIN: NO DATA AVAILABLE.
DECOMPOSITION: THERMAL DECOMPOSITION MAY RELEASE TOXIC AND/OR HAZARDOUS GASES.
POLYMERIZATION: HAZARDOUS POLYMERIZATION HAS NOT BEEN REPORTED TO OCCUR UNDER NORMAL TEMPERATURES AND PRESSURES.

STORAGE AND DISPOSAL

OBSERVE ALL FEDERAL, STATE AND LOCAL REGULATIONS WHEN STORING OR DISPOSING OF THIS SUBSTANCE. FOR ASSISTANCE, CONTACT THE DISTRICT DIRECTOR OF THE ENVIRONMENTAL PROTECTION AGENCY.

****STORAGE****

STORE IN ACCORDANCE WITH 40 CFR 165 RECOMMENDED PROCEDURES FOR THE DISPOSAL AND STORAGE OF PESTICIDES AND PESTICIDE CONTAINERS.

****DISPOSAL****

DISPOSAL MUST BE IN ACCORDANCE WITH 40 CFR 165 RECOMMENDED PROCEDURES FOR THE DISPOSAL AND STORAGE OF PESTICIDES AND PESTICIDE CONTAINERS.

CONDITIONS TO AVOID

MAY BURN BUT DOES NOT IGNITE READILY. AVOID CONTACT WITH STRONG OXIDIZERS, EXCESSIVE HEAT, SPARKS, OR OPEN FLAME.

SPILL AND LEAK PROCEDURES

OCCUPATIONAL SPILL: STOP LEAK IF YOU CAN DO IT WITHOUT RISK. FOR SMALL SPILLS, TAKE UP WITH SAND OR OTHER ABSORBENT MATERIAL AND PLACE INTO CLEAN, DRY CONTAINERS FOR LATER DISPOSAL. KEEP UNNECESSARY PEOPLE AWAY. ISOLATE HAZARD AREA AND DENY ENTRY.

PROTECTIVE EQUIPMENT

VENTILATION: PROVIDE LOCAL EXHAUST OR GENERAL DILUTION VENTILATION SYSTEM.

RESPIRATOR: THE FOLLOWING RESPIRATORS ARE RECOMMENDED BASED ON INFORMATION FOUND IN THE PHYSICAL DATA, TOXICITY AND HEALTH EFFECTS SECTIONS. THEY ARE RANKED IN ORDER FROM MINIMUM TO MAXIMUM RESPIRATORY PROTECTION. THE SPECIFIC RESPIRATOR SELECTED MUST BE BASED ON CONTAMINATION LEVELS FOUND IN THE WORK PLACE, MUST NOT EXCEED THE WORKING LIMITS OF THE RESPIRATOR AND BE JOINTLY APPROVED BY THE NATIONAL INSTITUTE FOR OCCUPATIONAL SAFETY AND HEALTH AND THE MINE SAFETY AND HEALTH ADMINISTRATION (NIOSH-MSHA).
CHEMICAL CARTRIDGE RESPIRATOR WITH PESTICIDE CARTRIDGE.
GAS MASK WITH A PESTICIDE CANISTER (CHIN-STYLE OR FRONT- OR BACK-MOUNTED CANISTER).
TYPE 'C' SUPPLIED-AIR RESPIRATOR OPERATED IN THE PRESSURE-DEMAND OR OTHER POSITIVE PRESSURE OR CONTINUOUS-FLOW MODE.
SELF-CONTAINED BREATHING APPARATUS.
FOR FIREFIGHTING AND OTHER IMMEDIATELY DANGEROUS TO LIFE OR HEALTH CONDITIONS:
SELF-CONTAINED BREATHING APPARATUS WITH FULL FACEPIECE OPERATED IN PRESSURE-DEMAND OR OTHER POSITIVE PRESSURE MODE. SUPPLIED-AIR RESPIRATOR WITH FULL FACEPIECE AND OPERATED IN PRESSURE-DEMAND OR OTHER POSITIVE PRESSURE MODE IN COMBINATION WITH AN AUXILIARY SELF-CONTAINED BREATHING APPARATUS OPERATED IN PRESSURE-DEMAND OR OTHER POSITIVE PRESSURE MODE.

CLOTHING: EMPLOYEE MUST WEAR APPROPRIATE PROTECTIVE (IMPERVIOUS) CLOTHING AND EQUIPMENT TO PREVENT REPEATED OR PROLONGED SKIN CONTACT WITH THIS SUBSTANCE.

GLOVES: EMPLOYEE MUST WEAR APPROPRIATE PROTECTIVE GLOVES TO PREVENT CONTACT WITH THIS SUBSTANCE.

EYE PROTECTION: EMPLOYEE MUST WEAR SPLASH-PROOF OR DUST-RESISTANT SAFETY GOGGLES TO PREVENT EYE CONTACT WITH THIS SUBSTANCE.
EMERGENCY EYE WASH: WHERE THERE IS ANY POSSIBILITY THAT AN EMPLOYEE'S EYES MAY BE EXPOSED TO THIS SUBSTANCE, THE EMPLOYER SHOULD PROVIDE AN EYE WASH FOUNTAIN WITHIN THE IMMEDIATE WORK AREA FOR EMERGENCY USE.

AUTHORIZED BY- OCCUPATIONAL HEALTH SERVICES, INC.
CREATION DATE: 10/04/89 ***REVISION DATE:*** 05/09/90

MATERIAL SAFETY DATA SHEET

OCCUPATIONAL HEALTH SERVICES, INC.
AGRICULTURE AND PESTICIDE DIVISION
450 SEVENTH AVENUE, SUITE 2407
NEW YORK, NEW YORK 10123
1-800-445-MSDS OR (212) 967-1100

EMERGENCY CONTACT:
JOHN S. BRANSFORD, JR. (615) 292-1180

SUBSTANCE IDENTIFICATION

CAS-NUMBER 98-01-1
SUBSTANCE: **FURFURAL**
TRADE NAMES/SYNONYMS: 2-FURALDEHYDE; FURAL; ARTIFICIAL ANT OIL; FURALE; 2-FURANALDEHYDE; 2-FURANCARBONAL; 2-FURANCARBOXALDEHYDE; 2-FURFURAL; FURFUROL; FURFUROLE; ALPHA-FUROLE; 2-FURYL-METHANOAL; PYROMURIC ALDEHYDE; FURFURALDEHYDE; RCRA U125; STCC 4913146; UN 1199; C5H4O2; PST10180
CHEMICAL FAMILY: ALDEHYDE, ALIPHATIC
MOLECULAR FORMULA: C5-H4-O2
MOLECULAR WEIGHT: 96.09

CERCLA RATINGS (SCALE 0-3): HEALTH = 3 FIRE = 2 REACTIVITY = 0 PERSISTENCE = 1

NFPA RATINGS (SCALE 0-4): HEALTH = 2 FIRE = 2 REACTIVITY = 0

COMPONENTS AND CONTAMINANTS

COMPONENT: FURFURAL ***PERCENT:*** 100
CAS# 98-01-1

OTHER CONTAMINANTS: NONE

EXPOSURE LIMITS: FURFURAL: 2 PPM (8 MG/M3) OSHA TWA (SKIN) 2 PPM (8 MG/M3) ACGIH TWA (SKIN)
5000 POUNDS CERCLA SECTION 103 REPORTABLE QUANTITY

PHYSICAL DATA

DESCRIPTION: COLORLESS LIQUID WHEN VERY PURE; BECOMES REDDISH-BROWN ON EXPOSURE TO LIGHT AND AIR WITH A PENETRATING ODOR OF ALMONDS.

BOILING POINT: 323 F (162 C) ***MELTING POINT:*** -38 F (-39 C)

SPECIFIC GRAVITY: 1.16 ***VAPOR PRESSURE:*** 2 MMHG @ 20 C

SOLUBILITY IN WATER: 8.3% ***ODOR THRESHOLD:*** 0.2 PPM ***VAPOR DENSITY:*** 3.0

SOLVENT SOLUBILITY: ALCOHOL, ETHER, ACETONE, BENZENE, CHLOROFORM

FIRE AND EXPLOSION DATA

FIRE AND EXPLOSION HAZARD: MODERATE FIRE HAZARD WHEN EXPOSED TO HEAT OR FLAME.
VAPORS ARE HEAVIER THAN AIR AND MAY TRAVEL A CONSIDERABLE DISTANCE TO A SOURCE OF IGNITION AND FLASH BACK.
VAPOR-AIR MIXTURES ARE EXPLOSIVE ABOVE FLASH POINT.

FLASH POINT: 140 F (60 C) (CC) ***UPPER EXPLOSIVE LIMIT:*** 19.3%

LOWER EXPLOSIVE LIMIT: 2.1% ***AUTOIGNITION TEMP.:*** 797 F (392 C)

FLAMMABILITY CLASS(OSHA): IIIA

FIREFIGHTING MEDIA: DRY CHEMICAL, CARBON DIOXIDE, HALON, WATER SPRAY OR STANDARD FOAM (1987 EMERGENCY RESPONSE GUIDEBOOK, DOT P 5800.4).
FOR LARGER FIRES, USE WATER SPRAY, FOG OR STANDARD FOAM (1987 EMERGENCY RESPONSE GUIDEBOOK, DOT P 5800.4).
ALCOHOL FOAM (NFPA 325M, FIRE HAZARD PROPERTIES OF FLAMMABLE LIQUIDS, GASES, AND VOLATILE SOLIDS, 1984).

FIREFIGHTING: MOVE CONTAINER FROM FIRE AREA IF POSSIBLE. DO NOT GET WATER INSIDE CONTAINER. COOL FIRE-EXPOSED CONTAINERS WITH WATER FROM SIDE UNTIL WELL AFTER FIRE IS OUT. STAY AWAY FROM STORAGE TANK ENDS. WITHDRAW IMMEDIATELY IN CASE OF RISING SOUND FROM VENTING SAFETY DEVICE OR ANY DISCOLORATION OF STORAGE TANK DUE TO FIRE (1987 EMERGENCY RESPONSE GUIDEBOOK, DOT P 5800.4, GUIDE PAGE 29).
EXTINGUISH ONLY IF FLOW CAN BE STOPPED; USE WATER IN FLOODING AMOUNTS AS FOG, SOLID STREAMS MAY NOT BE EFFECTIVE. COOL CONTAINERS WITH FLOODING QUANTITIES OF WATER, APPLY FROM AS FAR A DISTANCE AS POSSIBLE. AVOID BREATHING TOXIC VAPORS, KEEP UPWIND.
FIRE FIGHTING PHASES: USE WATER SPRAY, DRY CHEMICAL, ALCOHOL FOAM, OR CARBON DIOXIDE. WATER OR FOAM MAY CAUSE FROTHING. USE WATER TO KEEP FIRE-EXPOSED CONTAINERS COOL. WATER SPRAY MAY BE USED TO FLUSH SPILLS AWAY FROM EXPOSURES AND TO DILUTE SPILLS TO NONFLAMMABLE MIXTURES (NFPA 49, HAZARDOUS CHEMICALS DATA, 1975).

TRANSPORTATION DATA

DEPARTMENT OF TRANSPORTATION HAZARD CLASSIFICATION 49 CFR 172.101: COMBUSTIBLE LIQUID
DEPARTMENT OF TRANSPORTATION LABELING REQUIREMENTS 49 CFR 172.101 AND SUBPART E: NONE
DEPARTMENT OF TRANSPORTATION PACKAGING REQUIREMENTS: NONE
EXCEPTIONS: 49 CFR 173.118A

TOXICITY

FURFURAL: IRRITATION DATA: 20 MG/24 HOURS SKIN-RABBIT MODERATE; 500 MG/24 HOURS SKIN-RABBIT MILD; 100 MG/24 HOURS EYE-RABBIT MODERATE. TOXICITY DATA: 310 UG/M3 INHALATION-HUMAN TCLO; 370 PPM/6 HOURS INHALATION-DOG LC50; 370 PPM/6 HOURS INHALATION-MOUSE LCLO; 260 PPM/6 HOURS INHALATION-RAT LCLO; 620 MG/KG SKIN-RABBIT LDLO; 65 MG/KG ORAL-RAT LD50; 400 MG/KG ORAL-MOUSE LD50; 950 MG/KG ORAL-DOG LD50; 800 MG/KG ORAL-RABBIT LDLO; 541 MG/KG ORAL-GUINEA PIG LD50; 148 MG/KG SUBCUTANEOUS-RAT LD50; 119 MG/KG SUBCUTANEOUS-MOUSE LD50; 214 MG/KG SUBCUTANEOUS-DOG LD50; 100 MG/KG SUBCUTANEOUS-GUINEA PIG LDLO; 78 MG/KG INTRAMUSCULAR-RABBIT LD50; 102 MG/KG INTRAPERITONEAL-MOUSE LD50; 20 MG/KG INTRAPERITONEAL-RAT LD50; 152 MG/KG INTRAVENOUS-MOUSE LD50; 250 MG/KG INTRAVENOUS-DOG LD50; 23 GM/KG PARENTERAL-FROG LDLO; MUTAGENIC DATA (RTECS). CARCINOGEN STATUS: NONE. LOCAL EFFECTS: IRRITANT- INHALATION, SKIN, EYES. ACUTE TOXICITY LEVEL: TOXIC BY INHALATION, INGESTION. TARGET EFFECTS: SENSITIZER- SKIN. AT INCREASED RISK FROM EXPOSURE: PERSONS WITH A HISTORY OF CHRONIC RESPIRATORY OR SKIN DISEASE AND IMPAIRED RENAL FUNCTION.*
* MAY BE BASED ON GENERAL INFORMATION ON FURAN DERIVATIVES.

HEALTH EFFECTS AND FIRST AID

INHALATION: IRRITANT. 250 PPM IMMEDIATELY DANGEROUS TO LIFE AND HEALTH CONCENTRATIONS. **ACUTE EXPOSURE-** THE VAPOR IS A POTENT IRRITANT. LEVELS OF 1.9 TO 14 PPM HAVE CAUSED COMPLAINTS OF EYE AND THROAT IRRITATION AND HEADACHE. SEVERE EXPOSURES MAY RESULT IN DELAYED PULMONARY EDEMA, LIVER AND KIDNEY INJURY, AND DEATH. 100% OF THE RATS TESTED WERE KILLED AFTER ONE 6-HOUR EXPOSURE AT 96 PPM. 100% OF THE MICE TESTED DIED AFTER ONE 6-HOUR EXPOSURE AT 260 PPM. ALSO 50% OF THE DOGS TESTED DIED AFTER BEING EXPOSED TO 370 PPM FOR 6 HOURS.
CHRONIC EXPOSURE- NO DATA AVAILABLE.

FIRST AID- REMOVE FROM EXPOSURE AREA TO FRESH AIR IMMEDIATELY. IF BREATHING HAS STOPPED, PERFORM ARTIFICIAL RESPIRATION. KEEP PERSON WARM AND AT REST. TREAT SYMPTOMATICALLY AND SUPPORTIVELY. GET MEDICAL ATTENTION IMMEDIATELY.

SKIN CONTACT: IRRITANT/SENSITIZER. **ACUTE EXPOSURE-** CONTACT WITH THE CHEMICAL MAY CAUSE IRRITATION AND SWELLING. SENSITIZATION DERMATITIS MAY OCCUR IN PERSONS PREVIOUSLY EXPOSED. **CHRONIC EXPOSURE-** REPEATED OR PROLONGED CONTACT MAY LEAD TO SENSITIZATION DERMATITIS.

FIRST AID- REMOVE CONTAMINATED CLOTHING AND SHOES IMMEDIATELY. WASH AFFECTED AREA WITH SOAP OR MILD DETERGENT AND LARGE AMOUNTS OF WATER UNTIL NO EVIDENCE OF CHEMICAL REMAINS (APPROXIMATELY 15-20 MINUTES). GET MEDICAL ATTENTION IMMEDIATELY.

EYE CONTACT: IRRITANT. **ACUTE EXPOSURE-** CONTACT WITH THE EYE MAY CAUSE IRRITATION, LACRIMATION, AND POSSIBLE CORNEAL INJURY. ONE DROP APPLIED DIRECTLY TO RABBIT EYES CAUSED SLIGHT EDEMA OF CONJUNCTIVA AND LARGER QUANTITIES CAUSE CORNEA OPACITY. **CHRONIC EXPOSURE-** MAY CAUSE CONJUNCTIVITIS.

FIRST AID- WASH EYES IMMEDIATELY WITH LARGE AMOUNTS OF WATER OR NORMAL SALINE, OCCASIONALLY LIFTING UPPER AND LOWER LIDS, UNTIL NO EVIDENCE OF CHEMICAL REMAINS (APPROXIMATELY 15-20 MINUTES). GET MEDICAL ATTENTION IMMEDIATELY.

INGESTION: FURFURAL: TOXIC. **ACUTE EXPOSURE-** ORAL ADMINISTRATION CAUSED MUSCLE INCOORDINATION, MARKED RETCHING, VOMITING, OCCASIONAL CONVULSIONS, AND DEATH IN DOGS. OTHER ANIMAL STUDIES REPORTED DEPRESSION AND PORPHYRIN-LIKE DEPOSITS AROUND THE EYES AND NOSE. HIGHER DOSES CAUSE LUNG HEMORRHAGE. **CHRONIC EXPOSURE-** REPEATED ORAL ADDMINISTRATION CAUSED CIRRHOSIS IN RATS.

FIRST AID- IF VICTIM IS CONSCIOUS, REMOVE INGESTED POISON BY GASTRIC LAVAGE OR EMESIS. ACTIVATED CHARCOAL IS USEFUL. MAINTAIN AIRWAY AND RESPIRATION. GIVE OXYGEN IF RESPIRATION IS DEPRESSED. GET MEDICAL ATTENTION IMMEDIATELY. (DREISBACH, HANDBOOK OF POISONING, 11TH ED.) ADMINISTRATION OF GASTRIC LAVAGE SHOULD BE PERFORMED BY QUALIFIED MEDICAL PERSONNEL.

ANTIDOTE: NO SPECIFIC ANTIDOTE. TREAT SYMPTOMATICALLY AND SUPPORTIVELY.

REACTIVITY

REACTIVITY: AT ROOM TEMPERATURE, THE SUBSTANCE WILL REACT WITH OXYGEN FROM THE AIR TO CAUSE DARKENING OF THE LIQUID TO A RED-BROWN COLOR. THIS INDICATES PARTIAL OXIDATION AND POLYMERIZATION.

INCOMPATIBILITIES: STRONG ACIDS: MAY REACT VIOLENTLY. STRONG BASES: MAY REACT VIOLENTLY. STRONG OXIDIZERS: MAY REACT VIOLENTLY. PLASTICS: FURFURAL ATTACKS MANY PLASTICS. MINERAL ACIDS: FURFURAL MAY POLYMERIZE VIOLENTLY.

DECOMPOSITION: THERMAL DECOMPOSITION PRODUCTS MAY INCLUDE TOXIC OXIDES OF CARBON.

POLYMERIZATION: CAN UNDERGO HAZARDOUS POLYMERIZATION WHEN CATALYZED AND HEATED OR IN REACTIONS WITH MINERAL ACIDS OR ALKALI.

STORAGE AND DISPOSAL

STORAGE: PROTECT AGAINST PHYSICAL DAMAGE. STORE IN A COOL, DRY, WELL VENTILATED LOCATION, AWAY FROM ANY AREA WHERE THE FIRE HAZARD MAY BE ACUTE. OUTSIDE OR DETACHED STORAGE IS PREFERRED. STORE APART FROM OXIDIZING MATERIALS AND STRONG ACIDS (NFPA 49, HAZARDOUS CHEMICALS DATA, 1975).

CONDITIONS TO AVOID

AVOID CONTACT WITH HEAT, SPARKS, FLAMES OR OTHER IGNITION SOURCES. VAPORS MAY BE EXPLOSIVE. MATERIAL IS CORROSIVE; AVOID CONTACT WITH SKIN OR EYES. DO NOT ALLOW CONTAMINATION OF WATER SOURCES.

SPILL AND LEAK PROCEDURES

SOIL SPILL: DIG HOLDING AREA SUCH AS LAGOON, POND OR PIT FOR CONTAINMENT. DIKE FLOW OF SPILLED MATERIAL USING SOIL OR SANDBAGS OR FOAMED BARRIERS SUCH AS POLYURETHANE OR CONCRETE.
USE CEMENT POWDER OR FLY ASH TO ABSORB LIQUID MASS.
USE SODIUM BISULFITE (NA-H-SO3) TO NEUTRALIZE SPILLED MATERIAL.
AIR SPILL: KNOCK DOWN VAPORS WITH WATER SPRAY. KEEP UPWIND.
COMBUSTION PRODUCTS INCLUDE CORROSIVE OR TOXIC VAPORS.
WATER SPILL: TRAP SPILLED MATERIAL AT BOTTOM IN DEEP WATER POCKETS, EXCAVATED HOLDING AREAS OR WITHIN SAND BAG BARRIERS.
APPLY UNIVERSAL GELLING AGENT TO IMMOBILIZE TRAPPED SPILL AND INCREASE EFFICIENCY OF REMOVAL.
USE ACTIVATED CARBON TO ABSORB SPILLED SUBSTANCE THAT IS DISSOLVED.
USE MECHANICAL DREDGES OR LIFTS TO EXTRACT IMMOBILIZED MASSES OF POLLUTION AND PRECIPITATES.
OCCUPATIONAL SPILL: SHUT OFF IGNITION SOURCES. DO NOT TOUCH SPILLED MATERIAL. STOP LEAK IF YOU CAN DO IT WITHOUT RISK. USE WATER SPRAY TO REDUCE VAPORS. DO NOT GET WATER INSIDE CONTAINER. FOR SMALL SPILLS, TAKE UP WITH SAND OR OTHER ABSORBENT MATERIAL AND PLACE INTO CONTAINERS FOR LATER DISPOSAL. FOR LARGER SPILLS, DIKE FAR AHEAD OF SPILL FOR LATER DISPOSAL. NO SMOKING, FLAMES OR FLARES IN HAZARD AREA. KEEP UNNECESSARY PEOPLE AWAY; ISOLATE HAZARD AREA AND DENY ENTRY.
REPORTABLE QUANTITY (RQ): 5000 POUNDS THE SUPERFUND AMENDMENTS AND REAUTHORIZATION ACT (SARA) SECTION 304 REQUIRES THAT A RELEASE EQUAL TO OR GREATER THAN THE REPORTABLE QUANTITY FOR THIS SUBSTANCE BE IMMEDIATELY REPORTED TO THE LOCAL EMERGENCY PLANNING COMMITTEE AND THE STATE EMERGENCY RESPONSE COMMISSION (40 CFR 355.40). IF THE RELEASE OF THIS SUBSTANCE IS REPORTABLE UNDER CERCLA SECTION 103, THE NATIONAL RESPONSE CENTER MUST BE NOTIFIED IMMEDIATELY AT (800) 424-8802 OR (202) 426-2675 IN THE METROPOLITAN WASHINGTON, D.C. AREA (40 CFR 302.6).

PROTECTIVE EQUIPMENT

VENTILATION: PROVIDE LOCAL EXHAUST OR PROCESS ENCLOSURE VENTILATION TO MEET PUBLISHED EXPOSURE LIMITS.
RESPIRATOR: THE FOLLOWING RESPIRATORS AND MAXIMUM USE CONCENTRATIONS ARE RECOMMENDATIONS BY THE U.S. DEPARTMENT OF HEALTH AND HUMAN SERVICES, NIOSH POCKET GUIDE TO CHEMICAL HAZARDS; NIOSH CRITERIA DOCUMENTS OR BY THE U.S. DEPARTMENT OF LABOR, 29 CFR 1910 SUBPART Z. THE SPECIFIC RESPIRATOR SELECTED MUST BE BASED ON CONTAMINATION LEVELS FOUND IN THE WORK PLACE, MUST NOT EXCEED THE WORKING LIMITS OF THE RESPIRATOR AND BE JOINTLY APPROVED BY THE NATIONAL INSTITUTE FOR OCCUPATIONAL SAFETY AND HEALTH AND THE MINE SAFETY AND HEALTH ADMINISTRATION (NIOSH-MSHA).
FOR FURFURYL ALCOHOL: 250 PPM- CHEMICAL CARTRIDGE RESPIRATOR WITH AN ORGANIC VAPOR CARTRIDGE WITH A FULL FACE-PIECE. GAS MASK WITH AN ORGANIC VAPOR CANISTER (CHIN-STYLE OR FRONT- OR BACK MOUNTED CANISTER). SUPPLIED-AIR RESPIRATOR WITH A FULL FACE-PIECE. SELF-CONTAINED BREATHING APPARATUS WITH A FULL FACE-PIECE.
ESCAPE- GAS MASK WITH AN ORGANIC VAPOR CANISTER (CHIN-STYLE OR FRONT- OR BACK-MOUNTED). SELF-CONTAINED BREATHING APPARATUS.
FOR FIREFIGHTING AND OTHER IMMEDIATELY DANGEROUS TO LIFE OR HEALTH CONDITIONS:
SELF-CONTAINED BREATHING APPARATUS WITH FULL FACEPIECE OPERATED IN PRESSURE-DEMAND OR OTHER POSITIVE PRESSURE MODE.
SUPPLIED-AIR RESPIRATOR WITH FULL FACEPIECE AND OPERATED IN PRESSURE-DEMAND OR OTHER POSITIVE PRESSURE MODE IN COMBINATION WITH AN AUXILIARY SELF-CONTAINED BREATHING APPARATUS OPERATED IN PRESSURE-DEMAND OR OTHER POSITIVE PRESSURE MODE.
CLOTHING: PROTECTIVE CLOTHING NOT REQUIRED. AVOID REPEATED OR PROLONGED CONTACT WITH THIS SUBSTANCE.
GLOVES: EMPLOYEE MUST WEAR APPROPRIATE PROTECTIVE GLOVES TO PREVENT CONTACT WITH THIS SUBSTANCE.
EYE PROTECTION: EMPLOYEE MUST WEAR SPLASH-PROOF OR DUST-RESISTANT SAFETY GOGGLES AND A FACESHIELD TO PREVENT CONTACT WITH THIS SUBSTANCE.
EMERGENCY WASH FACILITIES: WHERE THERE IS ANY POSSIBILITY THAT AN EMPLOYEE'S EYES AND/OR SKIN MAY BE EXPOSED TO THIS SUBSTANCE, THE EMPLOYER SHOULD PROVIDE AN EYE WASH FOUNTAIN AND QUICK DRENCH SHOWER WITHIN THE IMMEDIATE WORK AREA FOR EMERGENCY USE.

AUTHORIZED BY- OCCUPATIONAL HEALTH SERVICES, INC.
CREATION DATE: 10/04/89 ***REVISION DATE:*** 05/15/90

MATERIAL SAFETY DATA SHEET

OCCUPATIONAL HEALTH SERVICES, INC.
AGRICULTURE AND PESTICIDE DIVISION
450 SEVENTH AVENUE, SUITE 2407
NEW YORK, NEW YORK 10123
1-800-445-MSDS OR (212) 967-1100

EMERGENCY CONTACT:
JOHN S. BRANSFORD, JR. (615) 292-1180

SUBSTANCE IDENTIFICATION

CAS-NUMBER 5103-74-2
SUBSTANCE: **BETA-CHLORDANE**
TRADE NAMES/SYNONYMS: 4,7-METHANO-1H-INDENE, 1,2,4,5,6,7,8,8-OCTACHLORO-2,3,3A,4,7,7A- HEXAHYDRO-, (1ALPHA,2BETA,3A ALPHA,4BETA,7BETA,7A ALPHA)-; (1ALPHA,2BETA,3A ALPHA,4BETA,7BETA,7A ALPHA)-1,2,4,5,6,7,8,8-OCTACHLORO-2,3,3A,4,7,7A-HEXAHYDRO-4,7-METHANO-1H-INDENE; 4,7-METHANOINDAN, 1BETA,2ALPHA,4ALPHA,5,6,7ALPHA,8,8-OCTACHLORO-3A BETA,4,7,7A BETA-TETRAHYDRO-; 1BETA,2ALPHA,4ALPHA, 5,6,7 ALPHA,8,8-OCTACHLORO-3A BETA,4,7,7A BETA- TETRAHYDRO-4,7-METHANOINDAN; TRANS-CHLORDAN; BETA-CHLORDAN; TRANS-CHLORDANE; GAMMA-CHLORDANE; CHLORDANE; C10H6CL8; PST10331
CHEMICAL FAMILY: HALOGEN COMPOUND, AROMATIC
MOLECULAR FORMULA: C10-H6-CL8
MOLECULAR WEIGHT: 409.80
CERCLA RATINGS (SCALE 0-3): HEALTH=3 FIRE=0 REACTIVITY=0 PERSISTENCE=3
NFPA RATINGS (SCALE 0-4): HEALTH=U FIRE=0 REACTIVITY=0

COMPONENTS AND CONTAMINANTS

COMPONENT: BETA-CHLORDANE ***PERCENT:*** 100.0
CAS# 5103-74-2
OTHER CONTAMINANTS: NONE
EXPOSURE LIMITS: BETA-CHLORDANE: 0.5 MG/M3 OSHA TWA (SKIN) 0.5 MG/M3 ACGIH TWA (SKIN); 2 MG/M3 ACGIH STEL (NOTICE OF INTENDED CHANGES 1988-89)

PHYSICAL DATA

DESCRIPTION: SOLID. ***BOILING POINT:*** 347 F (175 C) @ 2 MMHG (DEC) (APPROX.)
MELTING POINT: 219-221 F (104-105 C) ***SPECIFIC GRAVITY:*** 1.59-1.67 (APPROX.)
VAPOR PRESSURE: 0.00001 MMHG @ 20 C ***SOLUBILITY IN WATER:*** INSOLUBLE
VAPOR DENSITY: 14 (APPROX.)
SOLVENT SOLUBILITY: SOLUBLE IN ALIPHATIC AND AROMATIC HYDROCARBON SOLVENTS INCLUDING DEODORIZED KEROSENE.

FIRE AND EXPLOSION DATA

FIRE AND EXPLOSION HAZARD: NEGLIGIBLE FIRE HAZARD WHEN EXPOSED TO HEAT OR FLAME.
FIREFIGHTING MEDIA: DRY CHEMICAL, CARBON DIOXIDE, HALON, WATER SPRAY OR STANDARD FOAM (1987 EMERGENCY RESPONSE GUIDEBOOK, DOT P 5800.4).
FOR LARGER FIRES, USE WATER SPRAY, FOG OR STANDARD FOAM (1987 EMERGENCY RESPONSE GUIDEBOOK, DOT P 5800.4).
FIREFIGHTING: MOVE CONTAINERS FROM FIRE AREA IF POSSIBLE (1987 EMERGENCY RESPONSE GUIDEBOOK, DOT P 5800.4, GUIDE PAGE 53).
EXTINGUISH USING AGENT SUITABLE FOR TYPE OF SURROUNDING FIRE. AVOID BREATHING VAPORS AND DUSTS. KEEP UPWIND.

TOXICITY

BETA-CHLORDANE: TOXICITY DATA: 275 MG/KG ORAL-MOUSE LD50. CARCINOGEN STATUS: NONE. ACUTE TOXICITY LEVEL: TOXIC BY INGESTION. TARGET EFFECTS: POISONING MAY AFFECT THE LIVER, KIDNEYS, AND BLOOD.*
* MAY BE BASED ON GENERAL INFORMATION ON CHLORDANE.
CHLORDANE: TOXICITY DATA: 100 MG/M3/4 HOURS INHALATION-CAT LC50; 428 MG/KG SKIN-HUMAN LDLO; 780 MG/KG SKIN-RABBIT LD50; 690 MG/KG SKIN-RAT LD50; 29 MG/KG ORAL-HUMAN LDLO; 3071 UG/KG ORAL-MAN TDLO; 120 UG/KG ORAL-WOMAN LDLO; 200 MG/KG ORAL-RAT LD50; 145 MG/KG ORAL-MOUSE LD50; 100 MG/KG ORAL-RABBIT LD50; 1720 MG/KG ORAL-HAMSTER LD50; 180 MG/KG ORAL-MAMMAL LD50; 50 MG/KG ORAL-DOMESTIC ANIMAL LD50; 100 MG/KG INTRAVENOUS-MOUSE LD50; 10 MG/KG INTRAVENOUS-RABBIT LDLO; 343 MG/KG INTRAPERITONEAL-RAT LD50; 240 MG/KG INTRAPERITONEAL-MOUSE LDLO; 118 MG/KG UNREPORTED-MAN LDLO; MUTAGENIC DATA (RTECS); REPRODUCTIVE EFFECTS DATA (RTECS); TUMORIGENIC DATA (RTECS). CARCINOGEN STATUS: HUMAN INADEQUATE EVIDENCE; ANIMAL LIMITED EVIDENCE (IARC GROUP-3). HEPATOCELLULAR CARCINOMAS WERE PRODUCED IN MICE BY ORAL ADMINISTRATION. ACUTE TOXICITY LEVEL: HIGHLY TOXIC BY INHALATION; TOXIC

BY DERMAL ABSORPTION AND INGESTION. TARGET EFFECTS: CONVULSANT. POISONING MAY ALSO AFFECT THE LIVER, KIDNEYS, AND BLOOD. AT INCREASED RISK FROM EXPOSURE: PERSONS WITH CONVULSIVE DISORDERS. ADDITIONAL DATA: CHLORDANE MAY BE STORED IN ADIPOSE TISSUE; INTENSE ACTIVITY AND STARVATION MAY MOBILIZE THE PESTICIDE RESULTING IN THE REAPPEARANCE OF TOXIC SYMPTOMS. IT CROSSES THE PLACENTA AND MAY BE EXCRETED IN HUMAN MILK. STUDIES OF 2 GROUPS OF WORKERS, ONE INVOLVED IN THE MANUFACTURE OF CHLORDANE, HEPTACHLOR, AND ENDRIN AND THE OTHER OF CHLORDANE AND HEPTACHLOR, REVEALED A STATISTICALLY SIGNIFICANT INCREASE IN DEATHS FROM CEREBROVASCULAR DISEASE IN THE FORMER BUT NOT THE LATTER; THE FORMER STUDY HAD METHODOLOGICAL DEFICIENCIES.

HEALTH EFFECTS AND FIRST AID

INHALATION: CHLORDANE: CONVULSANT/HIGHLY TOXIC. 500 MG/M3 IMMEDIATELY DANGEROUS TO LIFE OR HEALTH. **ACUTE EXPOSURE-** SYMPTOMS OF BLURRED VISION, COUGH, CONFUSION, ATAXIA, HEADACHE, WEAKNESS, DIZZINESS, AND DELIRIUM WERE REPORTED FROM INHALATION EXPOSURE TO CHLORDANE. SYMPTOMS OF CENTRAL NERVOUS SYSTEM STIMULATION MAY ALSO OCCUR AS DETAILED IN ACUTE INGESTION. **CHRONIC EXPOSURE-** HUMAN EXPOSURE TO VAPORS OF 7 PERCENT CHLORDANE FOR 15 MINUTES AT 3-DAY INTERVALS FOR PERIODS OF 15 WEEKS AND REPEATED A YEAR LATER, DID NOT RESULT IN SYMPTOMS OF TOXICITY. IN ADDITION TO THE SYMPTOMS OF ACUTE EXPOSURE, CHRONIC EXPOSURE OF HUMANS TO TECHNICAL CHLORDANE CONTAINING HEPTACHLOR AND OTHER CHEMICALS HAS CAUSED LIGHTHEADEDNESS, NAUSEA, COUGH, CHEST COMPLAINTS, TREMORS, ARTHRALGIAS, FATIGUE, THROMBOCYTOPENIC PURPURA, AND MARKED BRUISING. PANCYTOPENIA, APLASTIC, HEMOLYTIC, AND MEGALOBLASTIC ANEMIAS, LEUKEMIA, AND DEATH HAVE ALSO BEEN REPORTED. EXPOSURE OF MONKEYS TO 100-1,000 UG/M3 FOR 90 DAYS INDUCED A STATISTICALLY SIGNIFICANT INCIDENCE OF LEUKOPENIA AND THROMBOCYTOPENIA, WITH EFFECTS OCCURRING AT THE LOWEST DOSE TESTED.

FIRST AID- REMOVE FROM EXPOSURE AREA TO FRESH AIR IMMEDIATELY. IF BREATHING HAS STOPPED, GIVE ARTIFICIAL RESPIRATION. MAINTAIN AIRWAY AND BLOOD PRESSURE AND ADMINISTER OXYGEN IF AVAILABLE. KEEP AFFECTED PERSON WARM AND AT REST. TREAT SYMPTOMATICALLY AND SUPPORTIVELY. ADMINISTRATION OF OXYGEN SHOULD BE PERFORMED BY QUALIFIED PERSONNEL. GET MEDICAL ATTENTION IMMEDIATELY.

SKIN CONTACT: CHLORDANE: CONVULSANT/TOXIC. **ACUTE EXPOSURE-** MAY BE IRRITATING. SKIN ABSORPTION HAS CAUSED BLURRED VISION, CONFUSION, ATAXIA, HEADACHE, DIZZINESS, WEAKNESS, AND DELIRIUM. IN SEVERE POISONING, CONVULSIONS MAY DEVELOP AND COMA AND DEATH ARE POSSIBLE. IN ONE CASE OF OCCUPATIONAL EXPOSURE, A WOMAN BECAME CONFUSED AND DEVELOPED CONVULSIONS 40 MINUTES AFTER SPILLING A SOLUTION CONTAINING 25% CHLORDANE AND 26% DDT ON HER CLOTHING. SHE DIED SHORTLY THEREAFTER FROM RESPIRATORY FAILURE. **CHRONIC EXPOSURE-** REPEATED CONTACT CAUSED EPISODES OF PARESTHESIA, TWITCHING OF THE RIGHT HAND AND ARM, GRAND MAL SEIZURES, AND UNCONSCIOUSNESS. OTHER EFFECTS MAY OCCUR AS DETAILED IN CHRONIC INHALATION. REPEATED APPLICATION OF 50 MG/KG TO THE SKIN OF RATS FOR 3 OR 4 DAYS CAUSED 100% FATALITIES.

FIRST AID- REMOVE CONTAMINATED CLOTHING AND SHOES IMMEDIATELY. WASH AFFECTED AREA WITH SOAP OR MILD DETERGENT AND LARGE AMOUNTS OF WATER UNTIL NO EVIDENCE OF CHEMICAL REMAINS (APPROXIMATELY 15-20 MINUTES). GET MEDICAL ATTENTION IMMEDIATELY.

EYE CONTACT: CHLORDANE: **ACUTE EXPOSURE-** MAY BE IRRITATING. **CHRONIC EXPOSURE-** NO DATA AVAILABLE.

FIRST AID- WASH EYES IMMEDIATELY WITH LARGE AMOUNTS OF WATER OR NORMAL SALINE, OCCASIONALLY LIFTING UPPER AND LOWER LIDS, UNTIL NO EVIDENCE OF CHEMICAL REMAINS (APPROXIMATELY 15-20 MINUTES). GET MEDICAL ATTENTION IMMEDIATELY.

INGESTION: CHLORDANE: CONVULSANT/LIMITED ANIMAL CARCINOGEN/TOXIC. **ACUTE EXPOSURE-** MAY CAUSE ABDOMINAL PAIN, NAUSEA, VOMITING, AND DIARRHEA. CHLORDANE MAY STIMULATE THE CENTRAL NERVOUS SYSTEM WITH CONVULSIONS SOMETIMES APPEARING AS THE FIRST SYMPTOM OF POISONING. SYMPTOMS OF HEADACHE, BLURRED VISION, HYPEREXCITABILITY, MUSCLE TWITCHING, TREMOR, INCOORDINATION, AND ATAXIA MAY ALSO OCCUR. IN SEVERE CASES OF POISONING, COMA AND DEATH ARE POSSIBLE. EEG PATTERNS SUGGEST THAT DEATH IS DUE TO RESPIRATORY ARREST BETWEEN OR DURING CONVULSIVE EPISODES. CHLORDANE MAY BE EXCRETED SLOWLY FROM THE BODY; THE SERUM HALF-LIFE IN ONE CHILD WAS 88 DAYS. **CHRONIC EXPOSURE-** IN A TWO-YEAR FEEDING STUDY IN RATS, A DIETARY CONCENTRATION OF 150 PPM PRODUCED A NOTED RETARDATION OF GROWTH, LIVER AND KIDNEY DAMAGE, MYOCARDIAL DAMAGE, AND MILD INJURY TO THE LUNGS; MARKED DAMAGE TO THE LUNGS AND INCREASED MORTALITY WERE OBSERVED AT DIETARY CONCENTRATIONS OF 300 PPM. SIMILAR EFFECTS WERE REPORTED IN RABBITS ADMINISTERED 5 MG/KG/DAY. CHLORDANE PRODUCED LIVER NEOPLASMS IN MICE FOLLOWING ORAL ADMINISTRATION; RESULTS FOR RATS WERE INCONCLUSIVE. ORAL ADMINISTRATION OF CHLORDANE ENHANCED THE INCIDENCE OF LIVER TUMORS INDUCED IN MICE BY ORAL ADMINISTRATION OF N-NITROSODIETHYLAMINE. REPRODUCTIVE EFFECTS REPORTED IN ANIMALS INCLUDE DECREASED VIABILTIY OF OFFSPRING IN MICE FED 100 MG/KG/DAY FOR 4 MONTHS; DECREASED FERTILITY IN RATS AND MICE; AND EXCITABILITY AND TREMORS IN OFFSPRING WHEN KEPT WITH TREATED MOTHERS, BUT NOT WITH UNTREATED FEMALES.

FIRST AID- IF THE PERSON IS CONSCIOUS AND NOT CONVULSING, REMOVE BY GIVING SYRUP OF IPECAC (IF VOMITING OCCURS, KEEP THE HEAD BELOW THE HIPS TO PREVENT ASPIRATION). GIVE ACTIVATED CHARCOAL FOLLOWED BY GASTRIC LAVAGE. FOLLOW WITH A SALINE CATHARTIC. DO NOT GIVE FATS OR OILS. INTESTINAL LAVAGE WITH 20% MANNITOL (200 ML) BY STOMACH TUBE IS ALSO USEFUL. GIVE ARTIFICIAL RESPIRATION WITH OXYGEN IF RESPIRATION IS DEPRESSED (DREISBACH, HANDBOOK OF POISONING, 12TH ED.). TREAT SYMPTOMATICALLY AND SUPPORTIVELY. LAVAGE AND ADMINISTRATION OF OXYGEN SHOULD BE PERFORMED BY QUALIFIED MEDICAL PERSONNEL. GET MEDICAL ATTENTION IMMEDIATELY.

ANTIDOTE: NO SPECIFIC ANTIDOTE. TREAT SYMPTOMATICALLY AND SUPPORTIVELY.

REACTIVITY

REACTIVITY: STABLE UNDER NORMAL TEMPERATURES AND PRESSURES.

INCOMPATIBILITIES: BETA-CHLORDANE: ALKALIES (WEAK): DECOMPOSES. OXIDIZERS (STRONG): FIRE AND EXPLOSION HAZARD. PLASTICS, RUBBER, AND COATINGS: MAY BE ATTACKED.

DECOMPOSITION: THERMAL DECOMPOSITION PRODUCTS MAY INCLUDE TOXIC AND CORROSIVE FUMES OF CHLORIDES AND PHOSGENE, AND TOXIC OXIDES OF CARBON.

POLYMERIZATION: HAZARDOUS POLYMERIZATION HAS NOT BEEN REPORTED TO OCCUR UNDER NORMAL TEMPERATURES AND PRESSURES.

STORAGE AND DISPOSAL

OBSERVE ALL FEDERAL, STATE AND LOCAL REGULATIONS WHEN STORING OR DISPOSING OF THIS SUBSTANCE. FOR ASSISTANCE, CONTACT THE DISTRICT DIRECTOR OF THE ENVIRONMENTAL PROTECTION AGENCY.

STORAGE

STORE IN ACCORDANCE WITH 40 CFR 165 RECOMMENDED PROCEDURES FOR THE DISPOSAL AND STORAGE OF PESTICIDES AND PESTICIDE CONTAINERS.
STORE AWAY FROM INCOMPATIBLE SUBSTANCES.

DISPOSAL

DISPOSAL MUST BE IN ACCORDANCE WITH 40 CFR 165 RECOMMENDED PROCEDURES FOR THE DISPOSAL AND STORAGE OF PESTICIDES AND PESTICIDE CONTAINERS.

CONDITIONS TO AVOID

MAY BURN BUT DOES NOT IGNITE READILY.

SPILL AND LEAK PROCEDURES

SOIL SPILL: DIG A HOLDING AREA SUCH AS A PIT, POND OR LAGOON TO CONTAIN SPILL AND DIKE SURFACE FLOW USING BARRIER OF SOIL, SANDBAGS, FOAMED POLYURETHANE OR FOAMED CONCRETE. ABSORB LIQUID MASS WITH FLY ASH OR CEMENT POWDER.
IMMOBILIZE SPILL WITH UNIVERSAL GELLING AGENT.

AIR SPILL: KNOCK DOWN VAPORS WITH WATER SPRAY. KEEP UPWIND. COMBUSTION PRODUCTS INCLUDE CORROSIVE OR TOXIC VAPORS.

WATER SPILL: TRAP SPILLED MATERIAL AT BOTTOM IN DEEP WATER POCKETS, EXCAVATED HOLDING AREAS OR WITHIN SAND BAG BARRIERS. USE ACTIVATED CARBON TO ABSORB SPILLED SUBSTANCE THAT IS DISSOLVED.
USE MECHANICAL DREDGES OR LIFTS TO EXTRACT IMMOBILIZED MASSES OF POLLUTION AND PRECIPITATES.

OCCUPATIONAL SPILL: DO NOT TOUCH SPILLED MATERIAL. STOP LEAK IF YOU CAN DO IT WITHOUT RISK. FOR SMALL SPILLS, TAKE UP WITH SAND OR OTHER ABSORBENT MATERIAL AND PLACE INTO CONTAINERS FOR LATER DISPOSAL. FOR SMALL DRY SPILLS, WITH A CLEAN SHOVEL PLACE MATERIAL INTO CLEAN, DRY CONTAINER AND COVER. MOVE CONTAINERS FROM SPILL AREA. FOR LARGER SPILLS, DIKE FAR AHEAD OF SPILL FOR LATER DISPOSAL. KEEP UNNECESSARY PEOPLE AWAY. ISOLATE HAZARD AREA AND DENY ENTRY.

PROTECTIVE EQUIPMENT

VENTILATION: PROVIDE LOCAL EXHAUST VENTILATION AND/OR GENERAL DILUTION VENTILATION TO MEET PUBLISHED EXPOSURE LIMITS.

RESPIRATOR: THE FOLLOWING RESPIRATORS AND MAXIMUM USE CONCENTRATIONS ARE RECOMMENDATIONS BY THE U.S. DEPARTMENT OF HEALTH AND HUMAN SERVICES, NIOSH POCKET GUIDE TO CHEMICAL HAZARDS; NIOSH CRITERIA DOCUMENTS OR BY THE U.S. DEPARTMENT OF LABOR, 29 CFR 1910 SUBPART Z.

THE SPECIFIC RESPIRATOR SELECTED MUST BE BASED ON CONTAMINATION LEVELS FOUND IN THE WORK PLACE, MUST NOT EXCEED THE WORKING LIMITS OF THE RESPIRATOR AND BE JOINTLY APPROVED BY THE NATIONAL INSTITUTE FOR OCCUPATIONAL SAFETY AND HEALTH AND THE MINE SAFETY AND HEALTH ADMINISTRATION (NIOSH-MSHA).

CHLORDANE:

5 MG/M3- ANY CHEMICAL CARTRIDGE RESPIRATOR WITH ORGANIC VAPOR CARTRIDGE(S) IN COMBINATION WITH A DUST, MIST, AND FUME FILTER. ANY SUPPLIED-AIR RESPIRATOR. ANY SELF-CONTAINED BREATHING APPARATUS.

12.5 MG/M3- ANY SUPPLIED-AIR RESPIRATOR OPERATED IN A CONTINUOUS FLOW MODE. ANY POWERED AIR-PURIFYING RESPIRATOR WITH ORGANIC VAPOR CARTRIDGE(S) IN COMBINATION WITH A DUST, MIST, AND FUME FILTER.

25 MG/M3- ANY CHEMICAL CARTRIDGE RESPIRATOR WITH A FULL FACEPIECE AND ORGANIC VAPOR CARTRIDGE(S) IN COMBINATION WITH A HIGH-EFFICIENCY PARTICULATE FILTER. ANY SUPPLIED-AIR RESPIRATOR WITH A FULL FACEPIECE. ANY SELF-CONTAINED BREATHING APPARATUS WITH A FULL FACEPIECE. ANY POWDERED AIR-PURIFYING RESPIRATOR WITH A TIGHT-FITTING FACEPIECE AND ORGANIC VAPOR CARTRIDGE(S) IN COMBINATION WITH A HIGH-EFFICIENCY PARTICULATE FILTER. ANY AIR-PURIFYING FULL FACEPIECE RESPIRATOR (GAS MASK) WITH A CHIN-STYLE OR FRONT- OR BACK-MOUNTED ORGANIC VAPOR CANISTER HAVING A HIGH-EFFICIENCY PARTICULATE FILTER.

500 MG/M3- ANY SUPPLIED-AIR RESPIRATOR WITH A HALF-MASK AND OPERATED IN A PRESSURE-DEMAND OR OTHER POSITIVE PRESSURE MODE.

ESCAPE- ANY AIR-PURIFYING FULL FACEPIECE RESPIRATOR (GAS MASK) WITH A CHIN-STYLE OR FRONT- OR BACK-MOUNTED ORGANIC VAPOR CANISTER HAVING A HIGH-EFFICIENCY PARTICULATE FILTER. ANY APPROPRIATE ESCAPE-TYPE SELF-CONTAINED BREATHING APPARATUS.

FOR FIREFIGHTING AND OTHER IMMEDIATELY DANGEROUS TO LIFE OR HEALTH CONDITIONS:

SELF-CONTAINED BREATHING APPARATUS WITH FULL FACEPIECE OPERATED IN PRESSURE-DEMAND OR OTHER POSITIVE PRESSURE MODE.

SUPPLIED-AIR RESPIRATOR WITH FULL FACEPIECE AND OPERATED IN PRESSURE-DEMAND OR OTHER POSITIVE PRESSURE MODE IN COMBINATION WITH AN AUXILIARY SELF-CONTAINED BREATHING APPARATUS OPERATED IN PRESSURE-DEMAND OR OTHER POSITIVE PRESSURE MODE.

CLOTHING: EMPLOYEE MUST WEAR APPROPRIATE PROTECTIVE (IMPERVIOUS) CLOTHING AND EQUIPMENT TO PREVENT ANY POSSIBILITY OF SKIN CONTACT WITH THIS SUBSTANCE.

GLOVES: EMPLOYEE MUST WEAR APPROPRIATE PROTECTIVE GLOVES TO PREVENT CONTACT WITH THIS SUBSTANCE.

EYE PROTECTION: EMPLOYEE MUST WEAR SPLASH-PROOF OR DUST-RESISTANT SAFETY GOGGLES AND A FACESHIELD TO PREVENT CONTACT WITH THIS SUBSTANCE.

EMERGENCY WASH FACILITIES: WHERE THERE IS ANY POSSIBILITY THAT AN EMPLOYEE'S EYES AND/OR SKIN MAY BE EXPOSED TO THIS SUBSTANCE, THE EMPLOYER SHOULD PROVIDE AN EYE WASH FOUNTAIN AND QUICK DRENCH SHOWER WITHIN THE IMMEDIATE WORK AREA FOR EMERGENCY USE.

AUTHORIZED BY- OCCUPATIONAL HEALTH SERVICES, INC.
CREATION DATE: 10/04/89 ***REVISION DATE:*** 06/27/90

MATERIAL SAFETY DATA SHEET

OCCUPATIONAL HEALTH SERVICES, INC.
AGRICULTURE AND PESTICIDE DIVISION
450 SEVENTH AVENUE, SUITE 2407
NEW YORK, NEW YORK 10123
1-800-445-MSDS OR (212) 967-1100

EMERGENCY CONTACT:
JOHN S. BRANSFORD, JR. (615) 292-1180

SUBSTANCE IDENTIFICATION

CAS-NUMBER 104-61-0

SUBSTANCE: GAMMA-NONANOLACTONE

TRADE NAMES/SYNONYMS: DIHYDRO-5-PENTYL-2(3H)-FURANONE; ALDEHYDE C18; GAMMA-N-AMYLBUTYROLACTONE; GAMMA-AMYLBUTYROLACTONE; 4-NONANOLIDE; APRICOLON; GAMMA-LACTONE-4-HYDROXY-NONANOIC ACID; 4-HYDROXYNONANOIC ACID LACTONE; GAMMA-NONALACTONE; PRUNOLIDE; COCOS ALDEHYDE; NONAN-1,4-OLIDE; GAMMA-NONANOLIDE; PST10334

CHEMICAL FAMILY: KETONE, ALIPHATIC

MOLECULAR FORMULA: C9-H16-O2

MOLECULAR WEIGHT: 156.25

CERCLA RATINGS (SCALE 0-3): HEALTH=1 FIRE=U REACTIVITY=U PERSISTENCE=1

NFPA RATINGS (SCALE 0-4): HEALTH=1 FIRE=U REACTIVITY=U

COMPONENTS AND CONTAMINANTS

COMPONENT: GAMMA-NONALACTONE ***PERCENT:*** 100
CAS# 104-61-0

OTHER CONTAMINANTS: NONE

EXPOSURE LIMITS: NO OCCUPATIONAL EXPOSURE LIMITS ESTABLISHED BY OSHA, ACGIH, OR NIOSH.

PHYSICAL DATA

DESCRIPTION: CRYSTALS ***MELTING POINT:*** NOT AVAILABLE
SPECIFIC GRAVITY: NOT AVAILABLE ***SOLUBILITY IN WATER:*** NOT AVAILABLE

FIRE AND EXPLOSION DATA

FIRE AND EXPLOSION HAZARD: UNKNOWN FIRE AND EXPLOSION HAZARD.

FIREFIGHTING MEDIA: DRY CHEMICAL, CARBON DIOXIDE, HALON, WATER SPRAY OR STANDARD FOAM (1987 EMERGENCY RESPONSE GUIDEBOOK, DOT P 5800.4). FOR LARGER FIRES, USE WATER SPRAY, FOG OR STANDARD FOAM (1987 EMERGENCY RESPONSE GUIDEBOOK, DOT P 5800.4).

FIREFIGHTING: MOVE CONTAINER FROM FIRE AREA IF POSSIBLE. DO NOT SCATTER SPILLED MATERIAL WITH HIGH PRESSURE WATER STREAMS. DIKE FIRE CONTROL WATER FOR LATER DISPOSAL (1987 EMERGENCY RESPONSE GUIDEBOOK, DOT P 5800.4, GUIDE PAGE 31).

USE AGENTS SUITABLE FOR TYPE OF SURROUNDING FIRE. AVOID BREATHING HAZARDOUS VAPORS, KEEP UPWIND.

TOXICITY

GAMMA-NONANOLACTONE: IRRITATION DATA: 500 MG/24 HOURS SKIN-RABBIT MILD; 100 MG/24 HOURS SKIN-RABBIT SEVERE. TOXICITY DATA: 6600 MG/KG ORAL-RAT LD50; 3440 MG/KG ORAL-GUINEA PIG LD50. MUTAGENIC DATA (RTECS). CARCINOGEN STATUS: NONE. ACUTE TOXICITY LEVEL: SLIGHTLY TOXIC BY INGESTION. TARGET EFFECTS: NO DATA AVAILABLE.

HEALTH EFFECTS AND FIRST AID

INHALATION: GAMMA-NONANOLACTONE: **ACUTE EXPOSURE-** NO DATA AVAILABLE. **CHRONIC EXPOSURE-** NO DATA AVAILABLE.

FIRST AID- REMOVE FROM EXPOSURE AREA TO FRESH AIR IMMEDIATELY. IF BREATHING HAS STOPPED, PERFORM ARTIFICIAL RESPIRATION. KEEP PERSON WARM AND AT REST. TREAT SYMPTOMATICALLY AND SUPPORTIVELY. GET MEDICAL ATTENTION IMMEDIATELY.

SKIN CONTACT: GAMMA-NONANOLACTONE: **ACUTE EXPOSURE-** MAY CAUSE MILD IRRITATION. OTHER GAMMA LACTONES PRODUCE MILD ANESTHETIC EFFECTS ON LABORATORY ANIMALS. **CHRONIC EXPOSURE-** NO DATA AVAILABLE.

FIRST AID- REMOVE CONTAMINATED CLOTHING AND SHOES IMMEDIATELY. WASH AFFECTED AREA WITH SOAP OR MILD DETERGENT AND LARGE AMOUNTS OF WATER UNTIL NO EVIDENCE OF CHEMICAL REMAINS (APPROXIMATELY 15-20 MINUTES). GET MEDICAL ATTENTION IMMEDIATELY.

EYE CONTACT: GAMMA-NONANOLACTONE: **ACUTE EXPOSURE-** NO SPECIFIC DATA AVAILABLE. MAY CAUSE IRRITATION. **CHRONIC EXPOSURE-** NO DATA AVAILABLE.

FIRST AID- WASH EYES IMMEDIATELY WITH LARGE AMOUNTS OF WATER OR NORMAL SALINE, OCCASIONALLY LIFTING UPPER AND LOWER LIDS, UNTIL NO EVIDENCE OF CHEMICAL REMAINS (APPROXIMATELY 15-20 MINUTES). GET MEDICAL ATTENTION IMMEDIATELY.

INGESTION: GAMMA-NONANOLACTONE: **ACUTE EXPOSURE-** THE LETHAL DOSE IN RATS WAS 6600 MG/KG. OTHER GAMMA LACTONES CAUSED MILD SEDATIVE EFFECTS ON HUMANS GIVEN 2.5 GRAMS ORALLY. **CHRONIC EXPOSURE-** NO DATA AVAILABLE.

FIRST AID- TREAT SYMPTOMATICALLY AND SUPPORTIVELY. GET MEDICAL ATTENTION IMMEDIATELY. IF VOMITING OCCURS, KEEP HEAD LOWER THAN HIPS TO PREVENT ASPIRATION.

ANTIDOTE: NO SPECIFIC ANTIDOTE. TREAT SYMPTOMATICALLY AND SUPPORTIVELY.

REACTIVITY

REACTIVITY: NO DATA AVAILABLE.

INCOMPATIBILITIES: NONE KNOWN.

DECOMPOSITION: THERMAL DECOMPOSITION MAY RELEASE TOXIC AND/OR HAZARDOUS GASES.

POLYMERIZATION: NO DATA AVAILABLE.

STORAGE AND DISPOSAL

OBSERVE ALL FEDERAL, STATE AND LOCAL REGULATIONS WHEN STORING OR DISPOSING OF THIS SUBSTANCE. FOR ASSISTANCE, CONTACT THE DISTRICT DIRECTOR OF THE ENVIRONMENTAL PROTECTION AGENCY.

CONDITIONS TO AVOID

MAY BURN BUT DOES NOT IGNITE READILY. AVOID CONTACT WITH STRONG OXIDIZERS, EXCESSIVE HEAT, SPARKS, OR OPEN FLAME.

SPILL AND LEAK PROCEDURES

OCCUPATIONAL SPILL: SWEEP UP AND PLACE IN SUITABLE CLEAN, DRY CONTAINERS FOR RECLAMATION OR LATER DISPOSAL. DO NOT FLUSH SPILLED MATERIAL INTO SEWER. KEEP UNNECESSARY PEOPLE AWAY.

PROTECTIVE EQUIPMENT

VENTILATION: PROVIDE LOCAL EXHAUST OR GENERAL DILUTION VENTILATION. VENTILATION EQUIPMENT MUST BE EXPLOSION-PROOF.

RESPIRATOR: THE FOLLOWING RESPIRATORS ARE RECOMMENDED BASED ON INFORMATION FOUND IN THE PHYSICAL DATA, TOXICITY AND HEALTH EFFECTS SECTIONS. THEY ARE RANKED IN ORDER FROM MINIMUM TO MAXIMUM RESPIRATORY PROTECTION. THE SPECIFIC RESPIRATOR SELECTED MUST BE BASED ON CONTAMINATION LEVELS FOUND IN THE WORK PLACE, MUST NOT EXCEED THE WORKING LIMITS OF THE RESPIRATOR AND BE JOINTLY APPROVED BY THE NATIONAL INSTITUTE FOR OCCUPATIONAL SAFETY AND HEALTH AND THE MINE SAFETY AND HEALTH ADMINISTRATION (NIOSH-MSHA).

DUST AND MIST RESPIRATOR WITH A FULL FACEPIECE.

AIR-PURIFYING FULL FACEPIECE RESPIRATOR WITH A HIGH-EFFICIENCY PARTICULATE FILTER.

POWERED AIR-PURIFYING RESPIRATOR WITH A TIGHT-FITTING FACEPIECE AND HIGH-EFFICIENCY PARTICULATE FILTER.

TYPE 'C' SUPPLIED-AIR RESPIRATOR WITH A FULL FACEPIECE OPERATED IN PRESSURE-DEMAND OR OTHER POSITIVE PRESSURE MODE OR WITH A FULL FACEPIECE, HELMET OR HOOD OPERATED IN CONTINUOUS-FLOW MODE.

SELF-CONTAINED BREATHING APPARATUS WITH A FULL FACEPIECE OPERATED IN PRESSURE-DEMAND OR OTHER POSITIVE PRESSURE MODE.

FOR FIREFIGHTING AND OTHER IMMEDIATELY DANGEROUS TO LIFE OR HEALTH CONDITIONS:

SELF-CONTAINED BREATHING APPARATUS WITH FULL FACEPIECE OPERATED IN PRESSURE-DEMAND OR OTHER POSITIVE PRESSURE MODE.

SUPPLIED-AIR RESPIRATOR WITH FULL FACEPIECE AND OPERATED IN PRESSURE-DEMAND OR OTHER POSITIVE PRESSURE MODE IN COMBINATION WITH AN AUXILIARY SELF-CONTAINED BREATHING APPARATUS OPERATED IN PRESSURE-DEMAND OR OTHER POSITIVE PRESSURE MODE.

CLOTHING: EMPLOYEE MUST WEAR APPROPRIATE PROTECTIVE (IMPERVIOUS) CLOTHING AND EQUIPMENT TO PREVENT REPEATED OR PROLONGED SKIN CONTACT WITH THIS SUBSTANCE.

GLOVES: EMPLOYEE MUST WEAR APPROPRIATE PROTECTIVE GLOVES TO PREVENT CONTACT WITH THIS SUBSTANCE.

EYE PROTECTION: EMPLOYEE MUST WEAR SPLASH-PROOF OR DUST-RESISTANT SAFETY GOGGLES TO PREVENT EYE CONTACT WITH THIS SUBSTANCE.

EMERGENCY EYE WASH: WHERE THERE IS ANY POSSIBILITY THAT AN EMPLOYEE'S EYES MAY BE EXPOSED TO THIS SUBSTANCE, THE EMPLOYER SHOULD PROVIDE AN EYE WASH FOUNTAIN WITHIN THE IMMEDIATE WORK AREA FOR EMERGENCY USE.

AUTHORIZED BY- OCCUPATIONAL HEALTH SERVICES, INC.
CREATION DATE: 10/04/89 ***REVISION DATE:*** 05/31/90

MATERIAL SAFETY DATA SHEET

OCCUPATIONAL HEALTH SERVICES, INC.
AGRICULTURE AND PESTICIDE DIVISION
450 SEVENTH AVENUE, SUITE 2407
NEW YORK, NEW YORK 10123
1-800-445-MSDS OR (212) 967-1100

EMERGENCY CONTACT:
JOHN S. BRANSFORD, JR. (615) 292-1180

SUBSTANCE IDENTIFICATION

SUBSTANCE: **GENCOR CRACK AND CREVICE AEROSOL**

TRADE NAMES/SYNONYMS: ZOECON RF 226 AEROSOL; EPA REG. NO. 2724-312-50809; PST10348

CERCLA RATINGS (SCALE 0-3): HEALTH=3 FIRE=3 REACTIVITY=0 PERSISTENCE=3

NFPA RATINGS (SCALE 0-4): HEALTH=3 FIRE=4 REACTIVITY=0

COMPONENTS AND CONTAMINANTS

COMPONENT: METHYLENE CHLORIDE ***PERCENT:*** >1.0
CAS# 75-09-2

COMPONENT: 1,1,1-TRICHLOROETHANE ***PERCENT:*** >1.0
CAS# 71-55-6

COMPONENT: PROPANE ***PERCENT:*** >1.0
CAS# 74-98-6

COMPONENT: ISOBUTANE ***PERCENT:*** >1.0
CAS# 75-28-5

COMPONENT: HYDROPRENE ***PERCENT:*** 0.6
CAS# 41096-46-2

EXPOSURE LIMITS: DICHLOROMETHANE (METHYLENE CHLORIDE): 500 PPM OSHA TWA; 1000 PPM OSHA CEILING; 2000 PPM/5 MIN IN 2 HOURS OSHA PEAK 50 PPM (174 MG/M3) ACGIH TWA ACGIH A2- SUSPECTED HUMAN CARCINOGEN. LOWEST FEASIBLE LIMIT NIOSH RECOMMENDED EXPOSURE CRITERIA

1000 POUNDS CERCLA SECTION 103 REPORTABLE QUANTITY SUBJECT TO SARA SECTION 313 ANNUAL TOXIC CHEMICAL RELEASE REPORTING SUBJECT TO CALIFORNIA PROPOSITION 65 CANCER AND/OR REPRODUCTIVE TOXICITY WARNING AND RELEASE REQUIREMENTS- (APRIL 1, 1988)

METHYL CHLOROFORM (1,1,1-TRICHLOROETHANE): 350 PPM (1900 MG/M3) OSHA TWA; 450 PPM (2450 MG/M3) OSHA STEL 350 PPM (1900 MG/M3) ACGIH TWA; 450 PPM (2450 MG/M3) ACGIH STEL 350 PPM NIOSH RECOMMENDED 15 MINUTE CEILING

1000 POUNDS CERCLA SECTION 103 REPORTABLE QUANTITY SUBJECT TO SARA SECTION 313 ANNUAL TOXIC CHEMICAL RELEASE REPORTING

PROPANE: 1000 PPM OSHA TWA ISOBUTANE: 800 PPM (1900 MG/M3) ACGIH TWA

PHYSICAL DATA

DESCRIPTION: LIGHT, STRAW COLORED MIXTURE OF LIQUIFIED GASES AND SOLVENTS UNDER PRESSURE WITH AN ODOR OF CHLORINATED SOLVENTS

BOILING POINT: >-44 F (>-42 C)

SPECIFIC GRAVITY: 1.0 ***VOLATILITY:*** 99.4% ***VAPOR PRESSURE:*** 3671 MMHG @ 20 C

EVAPORATION RATE: (BUTYL ACETATE=1) >1 ***SOLUBILITY IN WATER:*** NEGLIGIBLE

FIRE AND EXPLOSION DATA

FIRE AND EXPLOSION HAZARD: DANGEROUS FIRE HAZARD WHEN EXPOSED TO HEAT OR FLAME.

CYLINDER MAY EXPLODE IN HEAT OF FIRE.

GAS-AIR MIXTURES ARE EXPLOSIVE.

FLASH POINT: FLAMMABLE GAS ***UPPER EXPLOSIVE LIMIT:*** 9%

LOWER EXPLOSIVE LIMIT: 2%

FIREFIGHTING MEDIA: DRY CHEMICAL, CARBON DIOXIDE OR HALON (1987 EMERGENCY RESPONSE GUIDEBOOK, DOT P 5800.4).

FOR LARGER FIRES, USE WATER SPRAY OR FOG (1987 EMERGENCY RESPONSE GUIDEBOOK, DOT P 5800.4).

FIREFIGHTING: MOVE CONTAINER FROM FIRE AREA IF POSSIBLE. STAY AWAY FROM STORAGE TANK ENDS. COOL FIRE-EXPOSED CONTAINERS WITH WATER FROM SIDE UNTIL WELL AFTER FIRE IS OUT. FOR MASSIVE FIRE IN STORAGE AREA, USE UNMANNED HOSE HOLDER OR MONITOR NOZZLES, ELSE WITHDRAW FROM AREA AND LET BURN. WITHDRAW IMMEDIATELY IN CASE OF RISING SOUND FROM VENTING SAFETY DEVICE OR ANY DISCOLORATION OF STORAGE TANK DUE TO FIRE. LET STORAGE TANK BURN UNLESS LEAK CAN BE STOPPED; WITH SMALLER TANKS OR CYLINDERS, EXTINGUISH/ISOLATE FROM OTHER FLAMMABLE MATERIALS. (1987 EMERGENCY RESPONSE GUIDEBOOK, DOT P 5800.4, GUIDE PAGE 22).

EXTINGUISH ONLY IF GAS FLOW CAN BE STOPPED. USE FLOODING AMOUNTS OF WATER AS FOG. COOL CYLINDERS WITH FLOODING AMOUNTS OF WATER FROM AS FAR A DISTANCE AS POSSIBLE. AVOID BREATHING VAPORS; KEEP UPWIND. IF FIRE IS UNCONTROLLABLE OR CYLINDERS ARE EXPOSED TO FIRE, EVACUATE FOR A RADIUS OF 1500 FEET. CONSIDER EVACUATION OF DOWNWIND AREA IF MATERIAL IS LEAKING.

TRANSPORTATION DATA

DEPARTMENT OF TRANSPORTATION HAZARD CLASSIFICATION 49 CFR 172.101: FLAMMABLE GAS

DEPARTMENT OF TRANSPORTATION LABELING REQUIREMENTS 49 CFR 172.101 AND SUBPART E: FLAMMABLE GAS

DEPARTMENT OF TRANSPORTATION PACKAGING REQUIREMENTS: 49 CFR 173.302; 49 CFR 173.304 AND 49 CFR 173.305 EXCEPTIONS: 49 CFR 173.306

TOXICITY

GENCOR CRACK AND CREVICE AEROSOL: TOXICITY DATA: >5260 MG/M3 INHALATION-RAT LC50; >5,100 MG/KG SKIN-RABBIT LD50; >5,100 MG/KG ORAL-RAT LD50. CARCINOGEN STATUS: NONE. ACUTE TOXICITY LEVEL: TOXIC BY INHALATION, AND SLIGHTLY TOXIC BY DERMAL ABSORPTION AND INGESTION.

DICHLOROMETHANE (METHYLENE CHLORIDE): IRRITATION DATA: 162 MG EYE-

RABBIT MODERATE; 10 MG EYE-RABBIT MILD; 500 MG/24 HOURS EYE-RABBIT MILD; 810 MG/24 HOURS SKIN-RABBIT SEVERE; 100 MG/24 HOURS SKIN-RABBIT MODERATE. TOXICITY DATA: 500 PPM/1 YEAR-INTERMITTENT INHALATION-HUMAN TCLO; 500 PPM/8 HOURS INHALATION-HUMAN TCLO; 88000 MG/M3/30 MINUTES INHALATION-RAT LC50; 14400 PPM/7 HOURS INHALATION-MOUSE LC50; 10000 PPM/7 HOURS INHALATION-RABBIT LCLO; 5000 PPM/2 HOURS INHALATION-GUINEA PIG LCLO; 14108 PPM/7 HOURS INHALATION-DOG LCLO; 43400 MG/M3/4.5 HOURS INHALATION-CAT LCLO; 357 MG/KG ORAL-HUMAN LDLO; 1600 MG/KG ORAL-RAT LD50; 1900 MG/KG ORAL-RABBIT LDLO; 3 GM/KG ORAL-DOG LDLO; 6460 MG/KG SUBCUTANEOUS-MOUSE LD50; 2700 MG/KG SUBCUTANEOUS-RABBIT LDLO; 2700 MG/KG SUBCUTANEOUS-DOG LDLO; 200 MG/KG INTRAVENOUS-DOG LDLO; 916 MG/KG INTRAPERITONEAL-RAT LD50; 950 MG/KG INTRAPERITONEAL-DOG LDLO; 437 MG/KG INTRAPERITONEAL-MOUSE LD50; 4770 MG/KG UNREPORTED-MOUSE LD50; MUTAGENIC DATA (RTECS); REPRODUCTIVE EFFECTS DATA (RTECS); TUMORIGENIC DATA (RTECS). CARCINOGEN STATUS: ANTICIPATED HUMAN CARCINOGEN (NTP); HUMAN INADEQUATE EVIDENCE, ANIMAL SUFFICIENT EVIDENCE (IARC GROUP-2B). EXPOSURE BY INHALATION INCREASED THE INCIDENCE OF BENIGN AND MALIGNANT LUNG AND LIVER TUMORS IN MICE OF EACH SEX AND THE INCIDENCE OR MULTIPLICITY OF BENIGN MAMMARY TUMORS IN RATS OF EACH SEX; IN MALE RATS, AN INCREASED INCIDENCE OF SARCOMAS LOCATED IN THE NECK WAS ALSO OBSERVED. LOCAL EFFECTS: IRRITANT-INHALATION, SKIN, EYE. ACUTE TOXICITY LEVEL: MODERATELY TOXIC BY INHALATION AND INGESTION. TARGET EFFECTS: CENTRAL NERVOUS SYSTEM DEPRESSANT; CHEMICAL ASPHYXIANT. POISONING MAY AFFECT THE BLOOD, LIVER AND KIDNEYS. AT INCREASED RISK FROM EXPOSURE: PERSONS WITH SKIN, LIVER, KIDNEY, CARDIOVASCULAR DISEASE OR ANEMIA. ADDITIONAL DATA: CONCURRENT EXPOSURE TO OTHER SOURCES OF CARBON MONOXIDE, SMOKING, OR PHYSICAL ACTIVITY MAY INCREASE THE LEVEL OF CARBOXYHEMOGLOBIN IN THE BLOOD RESULTING IN ADDITIVE EFFECTS. ALCOHOLIC BEVERAGES MAY ENHANCE THE TOXIC EFFECTS. STIMULANTS SUCH AS EPINEPHRINE MAY INDUCE CARDIAC ARRHYTHMIAS. ONE STUDY INDICATED THAT CHRONIC EXPOSURE MAY BE ASSOCIATED WITH AN INCREASED RISK OF SPONTANEOUS ABORTION. DICHLOROMETHANE CROSSES THE PLACENTAL BARRIER AND IS EXCRETED IN HUMAN MILK.

METHYL CHLOROFORM (1,1,1-TRICHLOROETHANE): IRRITATION DATA: 450 PPM/8 HOURS EYE-MAN; 5 GM/12 DAYS INTERMITTENT SKIN-RABBIT MILD; 20 MG/24 HOURS SKIN-RABBIT MODERATE; 100 MG EYE-RABBIT MILD; 2 MG/24 HOURS EYE-RABBIT SEVERE. TOXICITY DATA: 27 GM/M3/10 MINUTES INHALATION-MAN LCLO; 350 PPM INHALATION-MAN TCLO; 200 PPM/4 HOURS INHALATION-MAN TCLO; 920 PPM/70 MINUTES INHALATION-HUMAN TCLO; 18000 PPM/4 HOURS INHALATION-RAT LC50; 3911 PPM/2 HOURS INHALATION-MOUSE LC50; 24400 MG/M3 INHALATION-CAT LC50; 15800 MG/KG SKIN-RABBIT LD50 (EPA-600/8-82-003F, 1984); 1 GM/KG SKIN-RABBIT LDLO; 670 MG/KG ORAL-HUMAN TDLO; 10300 MG/KG ORAL-RAT LD50; 11240 MG/KG ORAL-MOUSE LD50; 5660 MG/KG ORAL-RABBIT LD50; 9470 MG/KG ORAL-GUINEA PIG LD50; 750 MG/KG ORAL-DOG LD50; 16 GM/KG SUBCUTANEOUS-MOUSE LD50; 500 MG/KG SUBCUTANEOUS-RABBIT LDLO; 95 MG/KG INTRAVENOUS-DOG LDLO; 3593 MG/KG INTRAPERITONEAL-RAT LD50; 3636 MG/KG INTRAPERITONEAL-MOUSE LD50; 3100 MG/KG INTRAPERITONEAL-DOG LD50; MUTAGENIC DATA (RTECS); REPRODUCTIVE EFFECTS DATA (RTECS). CARCINOGEN STATUS: ANIMAL INADEQUATE EVIDENCE (IARC GROUP-3). LOCAL EFFECTS: IRRITANT- INHALATION, SKIN, EYE. ACUTE TOXICITY LEVEL: SLIGHTLY TOXIC BY INHALATION, DERMAL ABSORPTION AND INGESTION. TARGET EFFECTS: CENTRAL NERVOUS SYSTEM DEPRESSANT. POISONING MAY ALSO AFFECT THE HEART AND POSSIBLY LIVER AND KIDNEYS. AT INCREASED RISK FROM EXPOSURE: PERSONS WITH PRE-EXISTING SKIN DISORDERS, LIVER DISEASE OR CARDIOVASCULAR DISEASE. ADDITIONAL DATA: ALCOHOL MAY POTENTIATE BOTH CARDIAC AND HEPATIC TOXICITY. EPINEPHRINE OR OTHER STIMULANTS MAY INDUCE VENTRICULAR ARRHYTHMIAS.

PROPANE: CARCINOGEN STATUS: NONE. ACUTE TOXICITY LEVEL: NO DATA AVAILABLE. TARGET EFFECTS: CENTRAL NERVOUS SYSTEM DEPRESSANT; SIMPLE ASPHYXIANT. ADDITIONAL DATA: STIMULANTS SUCH AS EPINEPHRINE MAY INDUCE VENTRICULAR FIBRILLATION.

ISOBUTANE: TOXICITY DATA: 1041 GM/M3/2 HOURS INHALATION-MOUSE LCLO; 52 MG/KG/1 HOUR INHALATION-MOUSE LC50 (38MKAJ). CARCINOGEN STATUS: NONE. LOCAL EFFECTS: IRRITANT- MUCOUS MEMBRANES. ACUTE TOXICITY LEVEL: INSUFFICIENT DATA. TARGET EFFECTS: CENTRAL NERVOUS SYSTEM DEPRESSANT; SIMPLE ASPHYXIANT. ADDITIONAL DATA: STIMULANTS SUCH AS EPINEPHRINE MAY INDUCE VENTRICULAR FIBRILLATION.

HEALTH EFFECTS AND FIRST AID

INHALATION: DICHLOROMETHANE (METHYLENE CHLORIDE): IRRITANT/NARCOTIC/CHEMICAL ASPHYXIANT/CARCINOGEN. **ACUTE EXPOSURE-** HUMAN EXPOSURE TO 100 PPM HAS RESULTED IN UPPER RESPIRATORY TRACT IRRITATION; CONCENTRATIONS AS LOW AS 200 PPM HAVE PRODUCED TEMPORARY NEUROBEHAVIOURAL EFFECTS; 500-1000 PPM FOR 1-2 HOURS HAS CAUSED LIGHTHEADEDNESS AND ELEVATED CARBOXYHEMOGLOBIN LEVEL; 2300 PPM FOR 30 MINUTES HAS CAUSED NAUSEA AND NARCOSIS; 5000 PPM HAS CAUSED HEADACHE, FATIGUE, NEURASTHENIC DISORDERS AND DIGESTIVE DISTURBANCES. OTHER SYMPTOMS MAY INCLUDE DIZZINESS, TINGLING, NUMBNESS OF THE EXTREMITIES, A SENSATION OF HEAT, A SENSATION OF FULLNESS IN THE HEAD, DRUNKENNESS, STUPOR, DULLNESS AND MENTAL CONFUSION. MASSIVE EXPOSURE MAY CAUSE PHARYNGEAL EROSION, PULMONARY EDEMA, STAGGERING, HEMOLYSIS WITH GROSS HEMATURIA, RAPID UNCONSCIOUSNESS AND DEATH. RECOVERY IS GENERALLY COMPLETE IF EXPOSURE IS TERMINATED BEFORE ANESTHETIC DEATH. EXPOSURE TO HIGH LEVELS MAY ALSO CAUSE CARDIAC ARRHYTHMIAS. **CHRONIC EXPOSURE-** MORE THAN 100 WORKERS EXPOSED TO LEVELS BELOW 500 PPM HAVE DEVELOPED HEALTH PROBLEMS INCLUDING SIGNIFICANT UPPER RESPIRATORY IRRITATION, EXACERBATION OF CORONARY ARTERY DISEASE, AND A HIGH INCIDENCE OF NEUROTOXICITY; INCREASED COMPLAINTS OF CHEST PAINS WERE REPORTED AT CONCENTRATIONS OF 10 TO 35 PPM. REPEATED HUMAN EXPOSURE TO 500-3600 PPM HAS CAUSED SIGNS OF TOXIC ENCEPHALOPATHY WITH ACOUSTICAL AND OPTICAL DELUSIONS AND HALLUCINATIONS. A CASE OF SERIOUS CEREBRAL DETERIORATION WAS OBSERVED IN AN INDIVIDUAL EXPOSED FOR SEVERAL YEARS TO DICHLOROMETHANE. IN A MORTALITY STUDY OF TWO GROUPS OF WORKERS, ONE EXPOSED TO ACETONE AND THE OTHER TO DICHLOROMETHANE AND ACETONE, A STATISTICALLY SIGNIFICANT DIFFERENCE IN DEATHS FROM DISEASES OF THE CIRCULATORY SYSTEM AND FROM ISCHEMIC HEART DISEASE WERE REPORTED FROM THE DICHLOROMETHANE AND ACETONE GROUP. IN ANOTHER MORTALITY STUDY OF WORKERS EXPOSED TO DICHLOROMETHANE, A SIGNIFICANT INCREASE IN HYPERTENSIVE DISEASE AND A "SUGGESTIVE EXCESS" OF PANCREATIC CANCER WERE REPORTED. LIVER DISEASE HAS BEEN REPORTED IN WORKERS. IN ONE STUDY, AN INCREASE IN SERUM BILIRUBIN WAS OBSERVED IN EXPOSED WORKERS, BUT NO OTHER SIGN OF LIVER INJURY OR HEMOLYSIS WAS REPORTED. ADVERSE LIVER EFFECTS WERE OBSERVED IN SEVERAL ANIMAL SPECIES CHEMICALLY EXPOSED. TESTICULAR ATROPHY WAS REPORTED IN MICE EXPOSED TO 4000 PPM OVER 2 YEARS. REPEATED INHALATION BY RODENTS PRIOR TO AND/OR DURING GESTATION CAUSED FETAL SKELETAL ABNORMALITIES AND BEHAVIORAL EFFECTS IN NEWBORN OFFSPRING. REPEATED INHALATION INCREASED THE INCIDENCE OF BENIGN AND MALIGNANT LUNG AND LIVER TUMORS IN MICE OF EACH SEX AND THE INCIDENCE OR MULTIPLICITY OF BENIGN MAMMARY TUMORS IN RATS OF EACH SEX; IN MALE RATS, AN INCREASED INCIDENCE OF SARCOMAS LOCATED IN THE NECK WAS ALSO OBSERVED.

METHYL CHLOROFORM (1,1,1-TRICHLOROETHANE): IRRITANT/NARCOTIC. 1000 PPM IMMEDIATELY DANGEROUS TO LIFE OR HEALTH. **ACUTE EXPOSURE-** EXPOSURE TO 500 PPM FOR 60 MINUTES SHOULD CAUSE NO EFFECT EXCEPT FOR A DISTINCTIVE ODOR WHILE 900-1000 PPM FOR 20 MINUTES MAY CAUSE MILD RESPIRATORY TRACT IRRITATION AND PROMPT BUT MINIMAL IMPAIRMENT OF EQUILIBRIUM WHICH MAY BE ACCOMPANIED BY HEADACHE, LASSITUDE AND ATAXIA. IMPAIRED PERFORMANCE OF BEHAVIORAL TESTS WAS ALSO REPORTED AT 1000 PPM. HIGHER LEVELS OF 2000-5000 PPM MAY CAUSE INCOORDINATION, ANESTHESIA, LOSS OF CONSCIOUSNESS, COMA AND DEATH. EXCESSIVE CONCENTRATIONS OF 10,000 PPM MAY CAUSE DEATH DUE TO RESPIRATORY OR CARDIAC FAILURE. CARDIAC SENSITIZATION MAY BE A CONTRIBUTING FACTOR. OTHER EFFECTS MAY INCLUDE NAUSEA, VOMITING, DROWSINESS, CONVULSIONS, FALL OF BLOOD PRESSURE LIVER AND KIDNEY DAMAGE, BRADYCARDIA AND BLOOD CLOTTING CHANGES. **CHRONIC EXPOSURE-** NO ADVERSE EFFECTS RELATED TO EXPOSURE WERE REPORTED IN VOLUNTEERS EXPOSED TO 500 PPM FOR 7 HOURS A DAY FOR 5 DAYS, OR IN WORKERS EXPOSED TO 200 PPM FOR SEVERAL MONTHS TO 6 YEARS. EXPOSURE OF ANIMALS FOR 3 MONTHS AT CONCENTRATIONS FROM 1000 TO 10,000 PPM CAUSED SYMPTOMS OF CENTRAL NERVOUS SYSTEM DEPRESSION AND SOME PATHOLOGICAL CHANGES IN THE LIVERS AND LUNGS OF SOME SPECIES. REPRODUCTIVE EFFECTS HAVE BEEN REPORTED IN ANIMALS.

PROPANE: NARCOTIC/SIMPLE ASPHYXIANT. 20,000 PPM IMMEDIATELY DANGEROUS TO LIFE OR HEALTH **ACUTE EXPOSURE-** BRIEF EXPOSURE TO 10,000 PPM CAUSED NO SYMPTOMS IN HUMAN SUBJECTS; 100,000 PPM PRODUCED SLIGHT DIZZINESS IN A FEW MINUTES BUT WAS NOT NOTICEABLY IRRITATING TO THE NOSE OR RESPIRATORY TRACT. HIGH LEVELS MAY PRODUCE DISORIENTATION, EXCITATION, EXCESSIVE SALIVATION, HEADACHE AND VOMITING. IN PRIMATES, 100,000 PPM PRODUCED SOME MYOCARDIAL EFFECTS AND AT 200,000 PPM AGGRAVATION OF THESE PARAMETERS AND RESPIRATORY DEPRESSION. CONCENTATIONS OF 100,000 PPM IN MICE AND 150,000 PPM IN DOGS APPEAR TO PRODUCE NO ARRHYTHMIA BUT WEAK CARDIAC SENSITIZATION. SIMPLE ASPHYXIANTS AT CONCENTRATIONS OF 33% MAY CAUSE RAPID RESPIRATION, DYSPNEA AND REDUCED MENTAL ALERTNESS AND MUSCLE COORDINATION. CONCENTRATIONS OF 75% MAY PRODUCE NAUSEA, VOMITING, PROSTRATION, UNCONSCIOUSNESS, CONVULSIONS, DEEP COMA AND DEATH. **CHRONIC EXPOSURE-** REPEATED CONTACT MAY RESULT IN SYMPTOMS AS DESCRIBED IN ACUTE EXPOSURE.

ISOBUTANE: IRRITANT/NARCOTIC/SIMPLE ASPHYXIANT. 19,000 PPM (LIQUIFIED

PETROLEUM GAS) IMMEDIATELY DANGEROUS TO LIFE OR HEALTH. **ACUTE EXPOSURE-** VAPORS MAY BE IRRITATING TO THE MUCOUS MEMBRANES. HUMANS EXPOSED TO 250-1000 PPM FOR 1 MINUTE TO 8 HOURS DID NOT EXHIBIT ANY ADVERSE EFFECTS. HIGHER CONCENTRATIONS MAY CAUSE CENTRAL NERVOUS SYSTEM DEPRESSION AND ASPHYXIATION. SYMPTOMS MAY INCLUDE DIZZINESS, DIFFICULTY IN BREATHING, LOSS OF CONSCIOUSNESS, MUSCULAR INCOORDINATION, HEADACHE, WEAKNESS, EMOTIONAL INSTABILITY, NAUSEA, VOMITING, PROSTRATION, CONVULSIONS, COMA, AND DEATH. ANIMALS EXPOSED TO NEAR LETHAL LEVELS EXHIBITED CENTRAL NERVOUS SYSTEM DEPRESSION, RAPID AND SHALLOW RESPIRATION, AND APNEA. CARDIAC SENSITIZATION HAS BEEN REPORTED IN ANIMALS. **CHRONIC EXPOSURE-** NO ADVERSE EFFECTS HAVE BEEN REPORTED FROM HUMAN EXPOSURE TO 500 PPM FOR 1-8 HOURS/DAY FOR 10 DAYS.

SIMPLE ASPHYXIANTS: **ACUTE EXPOSURE-** THE SYMPTOMS OF ASPHYXIA DEPEND ON THE RAPIDITY WITH WHICH THE OXYGEN DEFICIENCY DEVELOPS AND HOW LONG IT CONTINUES. IN SUDDEN ACUTE ASPHYXIA, UNCONSCIOUSNESS MAY BE IMMEDIATE. WITH SLOW DEVELOPMENT THERE MAY BE RAPID RESPIRATION AND PULSE, AIR HUNGER, DIZZINESS, REDUCED AWARENESS, TIGHTNESS IN THE HEAD, TINGLING SENSATIONS, INCOORDINATION, FAULTY JUDGEMENT, EMOTIONAL INSTABILITY, AND RAPID FATIGUE. AS THE ASPHYXIA PROGRESSES, NAUSEA, VOMITING, COLLAPSE, UNCONSCIOUSNESS, CONVULSIONS, DEEP COMA AND DEATH ARE POSSIBLE. **CHRONIC EXPOSURE-** NO DATA AVAILABLE.

FIRST AID- REMOVE FROM EXPOSURE AREA TO FRESH AIR IMMEDIATELY. IF BREATHING HAS STOPPED, PERFORM ARTIFICIAL RESPIRATION. KEEP PERSON WARM AND AT REST. TREAT SYMPTOMATICALLY AND SUPPORTIVELY. GET MEDICAL ATTENTION IMMEDIATELY.

SKIN CONTACT: DICHLOROMETHANE (METHYLENE CHLORIDE): IRRITANT. **ACUTE EXPOSURE-** MAY CAUSE EFFECTS RANGING FROM MILD IRRITATION TO SEVERE PAIN, PARESTHESIAS, AND POSSIBLY BURNS, DEPENDING ON THE INTENSITY OF CONTACT. **CHRONIC EXPOSURE-** PROLONGED OR REPEATED CONTACT MAY CAUSE A DRY, SCALY AND FISSURED DERMATITIS DUE TO DEFATTING ACTION OF LIQUID ON SKIN.

METHYL CHLOROFORM (1,1,1-TRICHLOROETHANE): IRRITANT. **ACUTE EXPOSURE-** DIRECT CONTACT MAY CAUSE IRRITATION AND REDNESS. VAPORS ARE POORLY ABSORBED, BUT THE LIQUID, ESPECIALLY IF CONFINED UNDER AN IMPERMEABLE BARRIER MAY BE ABSORBED TO SOME EXTENT. THIS ALONE IS UNLIKELY TO RESULT IN TOXIC EFFECTS, BUT MAY ADD TO THE EFFECTS OF INHALATION EXPOSURE. **CHRONIC EXPOSURE-** REPEATED SKIN CONTACT MAY PRODUCE A DRY, SCALY, FISSURED DERMATITIS DUE TO THE DEFATTING PROPERTIES OF THE LIQUID, AND POSSIBLY BURNS.

PROPANE: **ACUTE EXPOSURE-** NO ADVERSE EFFECTS HAVE BEEN REPORTED FROM THE GAS. DUE TO RAPID EVAPORATION, THE LIQUID MAY CAUSE FROSTBITE WITH REDNESS, TINGLING AND PAIN OR NUMBNESS. IN MORE SEVERE CASES, THE SKIN MAY BECOME HARD AND WHITE AND DEVELOP BLISTERS. **CHRONIC EXPOSURE-** NO ADVERSE EFFECTS REPORTED.

ISOBUTANE: **ACUTE EXPOSURE-** NO ADVERSE EFFECTS HAVE BEEN REPORTED FROM THE GAS. DUE TO RAPID EVAPORATION, THE LIQUID MAY CAUSE FROSTBITE WITH REDNESS, TINGLING AND PAIN OR NUMBNESS. IN MORE SEVERE CASES, THE SKIN MAY BECOME HARD AND WHITE AND DEVELOP BLISTERS. **CHRONIC EXPOSURE-** NO EFFECTS HAVE BEEN REPORTED.

FIRST AID- REMOVE CONTAMINATED CLOTHING AND SHOES IMMEDIATELY. WASH AFFECTED AREA WITH SOAP OR MILD DETERGENT AND LARGE AMOUNTS OF WATER UNTIL NO EVIDENCE OF CHEMICAL REMAINS (APPROXIMATELY 15-20 MINUTES). GET MEDICAL ATTENTION IMMEDIATELY.

EYE CONTACT: DICHLOROMETHANE (METHYLENE CHLORIDE): IRRITANT. **ACUTE EXPOSURE-** VAPOR CONCENTRATIONS ABOVE 2000 PPM MAY CAUSE IRRITATION. DIRECT CONTACT MAY CAUSE PAIN AND EXTREME IRRITATION, BUT IT IS NOT LIKELY TO CAUSE SERIOUS INJURY. 10 MG APPLIED TO RABBIT EYES PRODUCED KERATITIS, IRITIS, INCREASED CORNEAL THICKNESS, AND INFLAMMATION OF THE CONJUNCTIVA AND EYELIDS WITH SOME EFFECTS LASTING UP TO TWO WEEKS. **CHRONIC EXPOSURE-** REPEATED OR PROLONGED EXPOSURE TO IRRITANTS MAY CAUSE CONJUNCTIVITIS.

METHYL CHLOROFORM (1,1,1-TRICHLOROETHANE): IRRITANT. **ACUTE EXPOSURE-** EXPOSURE TO 500 PPM MAY CAUSE IRRITATION AND REDNESS. DIRECT CONTACT WITH THE LIQUID MAY CAUSE TEMPORARY INJURY WITH COMPLETE RECOVERY EXPECTED IN 48 HOURS. DIRECT APPLICATION TO THE EYES OF RABBITS HAS CAUSED CONJUNCTIVAL IRRITATION, BUT NO CORNEAL DAMAGE. **CHRONIC EXPOSURE-** REPEATED OR PROLONGED CONTACT MAY CAUSE CONJUNCTIVITIS.

PROPANE: **ACUTE EXPOSURE-** VAPOR CONCENTRATIONS OF 100,000 PPM WERE NOT NOTICEABLY IRRITATING TO THE EYES. DUE TO RAPID EVAPORATION, THE LIQUID MAY CAUSE FROSTBITE WITH REDNESS, PAIN AND BLURRED VISION. **CHRONIC EXPOSURE-** NO DATA AVAILABLE.

ISOBUTANE: **ACUTE EXPOSURE-** NO ADVERSE EFFECTS HAVE BEEN REPORTED FROM THE GAS. DUE TO RAPID EVAPORATION, THE LIQUID MAY CAUSE FROSTBITE WITH REDNESS, PAIN AND BLURRED VISION. **CHRONIC EXPOSURE-** NO DATA AVAILABLE.

FIRST AID- WASH EYES IMMEDIATELY WITH LARGE AMOUNTS OF WATER OR NORMAL SALINE, OCCASIONALLY LIFTING UPPER AND LOWER LIDS, UNTIL NO EVIDENCE OF CHEMICAL REMAINS (APPROXIMATELY 15-20 MINUTES). GET MEDICAL ATTENTION IMMEDIATELY.

INGESTION: DICHLOROMETHANE (METHYLENE CHLORIDE): NARCOTIC/CHEMICAL ASPHYXIANT. ACUTE EXPOSURE: MAY CAUSE RAPID, THEN SLOWED RESPIRATION, GLOTTAL AND PHARYNGEAL EDEMA, INTRAVASCULAR HEMOLYSIS WITH GROSS HEMATURIA, GASTROINTESTINAL ULCERATION AND HEMORRHAGE, AND CARBOXYHEMOGLOBINEMIA. THESE SYMPTOMS MAY PROGRESS RAPIDLY TO UNCONSCIOUSNESS AND LACK OF RESPONSE TO PAINFUL STIMULI. PHARYNGEAL EROSIONS MAY DISTURB THE SWALLOWING MECHANISM RESULTING IN ASPIRATION PNEUMONIA. IN ADDITION, SYMPTOMS OF CENTRAL NERVOUS SYSTEM DEPRESSION MAY OCCUR FOLLOWED BY CONVULSIONS AND PARESTHESIA OF THE EXTREMITIES. LARGE DOSES MAY CAUSE LIVER AND KIDNEY DAMAGE. THE ESTIMATED LETHAL DOSE FOR AN ADULT IS 25 GRAMS. **CHRONIC EXPOSURE-** REPEATED INGESTION BY RATS AND MICE RESULTED IN HISTOMORPHOLOGICAL CHANGES IN THE LIVER.

METHYL CHLOROFORM (1,1,1-TRICHLOROETHANE): NARCOTIC. **ACUTE EXPOSURE-** MAY CAUSE NAUSEA, VOMITING, DIARRHEA, GASTROINTESTINAL DISTURBANCES AND ABDOMINAL PAIN FOLLOWED BY CENTRAL NERVOUS SYSTEM DEPRESSION WITH HEADACHE, DIZZINESS, WEAKNESS, INCOORDINATION, MENTAL CONFUSION AND UNCONSCIOUSNESS. DEATH MAY OCCUR FROM CHRONIC RESPIRATORY FAILURE. OTHER SYMPTOMS AS DESCRIBED IN ACUTE INHALATION MAY ALSO OCCUR. MYOCARDIAL SENSITIZATION TO EPINEPHRINE AND SUBSEQUENT DEATH DUE TO CARDIAC ARREST MAY OCCUR. ASPIRATION MAY RESULT IN PULMONARY EDEMA OR CHEMICAL PNEUMONITIS. **CHRONIC EXPOSURE-** REPRODUCTIVE EFFECTS HAVE BEEN REPORTED IN ANIMALS.

PROPANE: **ACUTE EXPOSURE-** INGESTION OF A GAS IS UNLIKELY. IF THE LIQUID IS SWALLOWED, FROSTBITE DAMAGE OF THE LIPS, MOUTH AND MUCOUS MEMBRANES MAY OCCUR. **CHRONIC EXPOSURE-** NO DATA AVAILABLE.

ISOBUTANE: **ACUTE EXPOSURE-** INGESTION OF A GAS IS UNLIKELY. IF THE LIQUID IS SWALLOWED, FROSTBITE DAMAGE OF THE LIPS, MOUTH AND MUCOUS MEMBRANES MAY OCCUR. **CHRONIC EXPOSURE-** NO DATA AVAILABLE.

FIRST AID- TREAT SYMPTOMATICALLY AND SUPPORTIVELY. GET MEDICAL ATTENTION IMMEDIATELY. IF VOMITING OCCURS, KEEP HEAD LOWER THAN HIPS TO PREVENT ASPIRATION.

REACTIVITY

REACTIVITY: STABLE UNDER NORMAL TEMPERATURES AND PRESSURES.

INCOMPATIBILITIES: GENCOR CRACK AND CREVICE AEROSOL: ACIDS (STRONG): INCOMPATIBLE. BASES (STRONG): INCOMPATIBLE. METALS (REACTIVE): INCOMPATIBLE. OXIDIZERS (STRONG): FIRE AND EXPLOSION HAZARD.

DICHLOROMETHANE (METHYLENE CHLORIDE): ALKALI METALS: POSSIBLE EXPLOSIVE REACTION. ALUMINUM: VIOLENT, UNCONTROLLABLE REACTION ABOVE 95 C. CAUSTICS (STRONG): VIGOROUS, POSSIBLY VIOLENT REACTION. COPPER: MAY CORRODE AT ELEVATED TEMPERATURES IN THE PRESENCE OF MOISTURE. DINITROGEN PENTOXIDE: POSSIBLE EXPLOSION. DINITROGEN TETROXIDE: FORMS SHOCK-SENSITIVE MIXTURE. IRON: MAY CORRODE AT ELEVATED TEMPERATURES IN THE PRESENCE OF MOISTURE. LITHIUM: FORMS SHOCK-SENSITIVE MIXTURE. MAGNESIUM: POSSIBLE EXPLOSION. NICKEL: MAY CORRODE AT ELEVATED TEMPERATURES IN THE PRESENCE OF MOISTURE. NITRIC ACID: EXOTHERMIC REACTION YIELDING DETONABLE SOLUTION. OXIDIZERS (STRONG): FIRE AND EXPLOSION HAZARD. OXYGEN (LIQUID): EXPLOSIVE REACTION ON IGNITION. PLASTICS, RUBBER, AND COATINGS: MAY BE ATTACKED. POTASSIUM: EXPLOSIVE REACTION. POTASSIUM HYDROXIDE + N-METHYL-N-NITROSO UREA: POSSIBLE EXPLOSION. POTASSIUM TERT-BUTOXIDE: IGNITION REACTION. SODIUM: FORMS SHOCK-SENSITIVE MIXTURE. SODIUM-POTASSIUM ALLOY: FORMS SHOCK-SENSITIVE MIXTURE. STAINLESS STEEL: MAY CORRODE AT ELEVATED TEMPERATURES IN THE PRESENCE OF MOISTURE. TITANIUM: POSSIBLE VIOLENT REACTION. ZINC: POSSIBLE VIOLENT REACTION.

METHYL CHLOROFORM (1,1,1-TRICHLOROETHANE): ACETONE: EXOTHERMIC REACTION. ALKALI (STRONG): POSSIBLE VIOLENT REACTION. ALUMINUM AND ALLOYS: MAY DECOMPOSE VIOLENTLY. BARIUM: FIRE AND EXPLOSION HAZARD. MAGNESIUM: VIOLENT DECOMPOSITION WITH EVOLUTION OF HYDROGEN CHLORIDE. METALS (POWDERED): FIRE AND EXPLOSION HAZARD. NITROGEN TETROXIDE: FORMS EXPLOSIVE MIXTURE. OXIDIZERS (STRONG): POSSIBLE VIOLENT REACTION. OXYGEN (GAS): POSSIBLE EXPLOSION WHEN HEATED @ 100 C. OXYGEN (LIQUID): POSSIBLE VIOLENT EXPLOSION. POTASH: FORMS FLAMMABLE OR EXPLOSIVE PRODUCT. POTASSIUM AND ALLOYS: FORMS SHOCK-SENSITIVE MIXTURE. POTASSIUM HYDROXIDE: FORMATION OF SPONTANEOUSLY FLAMMABLE PRODUCT. RUBBER, PLASTICS, COATINGS: MAY BE ATTACKED. SODIUM AND ALLOYS: FIRE AND EXPLOSION HAZARD. SODIUM HYDROXIDE: FORMS SPONTANEOUSLY FLAMMABLE PRODUCT. SODIUM-POTASSIUM ALLOY: POSSIBLE

EXPLOSION. TIN AND ALLOYS: INCOMPATIBLE. ZINC AND ALLOYS: INCOMPATIBLE. PROPANE: BARIUM PEROXIDE: VIOLENT EXOTHERMIC REACTION. CHLORINE DIOXIDE: SPONTANEOUS EXPLOSION. PLASTICS, RUBBER, COATINGS: ATTACKED BY LIQUID PROPANE. OXIDIZERS (STRONG): FIRE AND EXPLOSION HAZARD. ISOBUTANE: OXIDIZERS: FIRE AND EXPLOSION HAZARD.

DECOMPOSITION: THERMAL DECOMPOSITION PRODUCTS MAY INCLUDE TOXIC AND CORROSIVE FUMES OF CHLORIDES AND PHOSGENE, AND TOXIC OXIDES OF CARBON.

POLYMERIZATION: HAZARDOUS POLYMERIZATION HAS NOT BEEN REPORTED TO OCCUR UNDER NORMAL TEMPERATURES AND PRESSURES.

STORAGE AND DISPOSAL

OBSERVE ALL FEDERAL, STATE AND LOCAL REGULATIONS WHEN STORING OR DISPOSING OF THIS SUBSTANCE. FOR ASSISTANCE, CONTACT THE DISTRICT DIRECTOR OF THE ENVIRONMENTAL PROTECTION AGENCY.

STORAGE

STORE IN ACCORDANCE WITH 29 CFR 1910.106.
DO NOT STORE AT TEMPERATURES ABOVE 120 F.

CONDITIONS TO AVOID

AVOID CONTACT WITH HEAT, SPARKS, FLAMES OR OTHER IGNITION SOURCES. VAPORS MAY BE EXPLOSIVE. DO NOT ALLOW CONTACT WITH SKIN; MATERIAL MAY CAUSE FROSTBITE. CONTENTS ARE UNDER PRESSURE; CONTAINERS MAY RUPTURE VIOLENTLY AND TRAVEL A CONSIDERABLE DISTANCE.
DO NOT PUNCTURE OR INCINERATE AEROSOL CONTAINER.

SPILL AND LEAK PROCEDURES

OCCUPATIONAL SPILL: SHUT OFF IGNITION SOURCES. DO NOT TOUCH SPILLED MATERIAL. STOP LEAK IF YOU CAN DO IT WITHOUT RISK. USE WATER SPRAY TO REDUCE VAPORS. ISOLATE AREA UNTIL GAS HAS DISPERSED. NO SMOKING, FLAMES OR FLARES IN HAZARD AREA! KEEP UNNECESSARY PEOPLE AWAY; ISOLATE HAZARD AREA AND DENY ENTRY. VENTILATE CLOSED SPACES BEFORE ENTERING.

REPORTABLE QUANTITY (RQ): THE SUPERFUND AMENDMENTS AND REAUTHORIZATION ACT (SARA) SECTION 304 REQUIRES THAT A RELEASE EQUAL TO OR GREATER THAN THE REPORTABLE QUANTITY ESTABLISHED FOR THAT SUBSTANCE BE IMMEDIATELY REPORTED TO THE LOCAL EMERGENCY PLANNING COMMITTEE AND THE STATE EMERGENCY RESPONSE COMMISSION (40 CFR 355.40). IF THE RELEASE OF THIS SUBSTANCE IS REPORTABLE UNDER CERCLA SECTION 103, THE NATIONAL RESPONSE CENTER MUST BE NOTIFIED IMMEDIATELY AT (800) 424-8802 OR (202) 426-2675 IN THE METROPOLITAN WASHINGTON, D.C. AREA (40 CFR 302.6).

PROTECTIVE EQUIPMENT

VENTILATION: PROVIDE LOCAL EXHAUST OR PROCESS ENCLOSURE VENTILATION TO MEET THE PUBLISHED EXPOSURE LIMITS. VENTILATION EQUIPMENT MUST BE EXPLOSION-PROOF.

RESPIRATOR: THE FOLLOWING RESPIRATORS ARE RECOMMENDED BASED ON INFORMATION FOUND IN THE PHYSICAL DATA, TOXICITY AND HEALTH EFFECTS SECTIONS. THEY ARE RANKED IN ORDER FROM MINIMUM TO MAXIMUM RESPIRATORY PROTECTION. THE SPECIFIC RESPIRATOR SELECTED MUST BE BASED ON CONTAMINATION LEVELS FOUND IN THE WORK PLACE, MUST NOT EXCEED THE WORKING LIMITS OF THE RESPIRATOR AND BE JOINTLY APPROVED BY THE NATIONAL INSTITUTE FOR OCCUPATIONAL SAFETY AND HEALTH AND THE MINE SAFETY AND HEALTH ADMINISTRATION (NIOSH-MSHA).

TYPE 'C' SUPPLIED-AIR RESPIRATOR WITH A FULL FACEPIECE OPERATED IN PRESSURE-DEMAND OR OTHER POSITIVE PRESSURE MODE OR WITH A FULL FACEPIECE, HELMET OR HOOD OPERATED IN CONTINOUS-FLOW MODE.

SELF-CONTAINED BREATHING APPARATUS WITH A FULL FACEPIECE OPERATED IN PRESSURE-DEMAND OR OTHER POSITIVE PRESSURE MODE.

FOR FIREFIGHTING AND OTHER IMMEDIATELY DANGEROUS TO LIFE OR HEALTH CONDITIONS:

SELF-CONTAINED BREATHING APPARATUS WITH FULL FACEPIECE OPERATED IN PRESSURE-DEMAND OR OTHER POSITIVE PRESSURE MODE.

SUPPLIED-AIR RESPIRATOR WITH FULL FACEPIECE AND OPERATED IN PRESSURE-DEMAND OR OTHER POSITIVE PRESSURE MODE IN COMBINATION WITH AN AUXILIARY SELF-CONTAINED BREATHING APPARATUS OPERATED IN PRESSURE-DEMAND OR OTHER POSITIVE PRESSURE MODE.

CLOTHING: EMPLOYEE MUST WEAR APPROPRIATE PROTECTIVE (IMPERVIOUS) CLOTHING AND EQUIPMENT TO PREVENT REPEATED OR PROLONGED SKIN CONTACT WITH THIS SUBSTANCE.

GLOVES: EMPLOYEE MUST WEAR APPROPRIATE PROTECTIVE GLOVES TO PREVENT CONTACT WITH THIS SUBSTANCE.

EYE PROTECTION: EMPLOYEE MUST WEAR SPLASH-PROOF OR DUST-RESISTANT SAFETY GOGGLES TO PREVENT EYE CONTACT WITH THIS SUBSTANCE.

EMERGENCY EYE WASH: WHERE THERE IS ANY POSSIBILITY THAT AN EMPLOYEE'S EYES MAY BE EXPOSED TO THIS SUBSTANCE, THE EMPLOYER SHOULD PROVIDE AN EYE WASH FOUNTAIN WITHIN THE IMMEDIATE WORK AREA FOR EMERGENCY USE.

AUTHORIZED BY- OCCUPATIONAL HEALTH SERVICES, INC.
CREATION DATE: 10/04/89 ***REVISION DATE:*** 07/12/90

MATERIAL SAFETY DATA SHEET

OCCUPATIONAL HEALTH SERVICES, INC.
AGRICULTURE AND PESTICIDE DIVISION
450 SEVENTH AVENUE, SUITE 2407
NEW YORK, NEW YORK 10123
1-800-445-MSDS OR (212) 967-1100

EMERGENCY CONTACT:
JOHN S. BRANSFORD, JR. (615) 292-1180

SUBSTANCE IDENTIFICATION

CAS-NUMBER 77-06-5

SUBSTANCE: **GIBBERELLIC ACID**

TRADE NAMES/SYNONYMS: 2 BETA,4A-ALPHA,7-TRIHYDROXY-1-METHYL-8 METHYLENE-4B BETA-GIBB-3-ENE-1 ALPHA,10 BETA-DICARBOXYLIC ACID 1,4A-LACTONE; GIBBERELLIN X; 2,4A,7-TRIHYDROXY-1-METHYL-8-METHYLENEGIBB-3-ENE-1,10-CARBOXYLIC ACID 1-4-LACTONE; GIBBERELLIN A3; BERELEX; BRELLIN; FLORALTONE; GIBBERELLIN; GA3; GROCEL; PRO-GIBB; GA; BP-938; PST10405

CHEMICAL FAMILY: CARBOXYLIC ACID, ALICYCLIC

MOLECULAR FORMULA: C19-H22-O6 MOL WT: 346.41

CERCLA RATINGS (SCALE 0-3): HEALTH=1 FIRE=1 REACTIVITY=0 PERSISTENCE=2

NFPA RATINGS (SCALE 0-4): HEALTH=1 FIRE=1 REACTIVITY=0

COMPONENTS AND CONTAMINANTS

COMPONENT: GIBBERELLIC ACID ***PERCENT:*** 100
CAS# 77-06-5

OTHER CONTAMINANTS: NONE

EXPOSURE LIMITS: NO OCCUPATIONAL EXPOSURE LIMITS ESTABLISHED BY OSHA, ACGIH, OR NIOSH.

PHYSICAL DATA

DESCRIPTION: ODORLESS, WHITE POWDER ***MELTING POINT:*** 451-455 F(233-235 C)
PH: ACIDIC IN SOLUTION ***SOLUBILITY IN WATER:*** 0.5%
SOLVENT SOLUBILITY: METHANOL, ETHANOL, ACETONE, ETHYL ACETATE

FIRE AND EXPLOSION DATA

FIRE AND EXPLOSION HAZARD: NEGLIGIBLE FIRE HAZARD WHEN EXPOSED TO HEAT OR FLAME.

FIREFIGHTING MEDIA: DRY CHEMICAL, CARBON DIOXIDE OR HALON (1987 EMERGENCY RESPONSE GUIDEBOOK, DOT P 5800.4).
FOR LARGER FIRES, USE WATER SPRAY, FOG OR STANDARD FOAM (1987 EMERGENCY RESPONSE GUIDEBOOK, DOT P 5800.4).

FIREFIGHTING: NO ACUTE HAZARD. MOVE CONTAINER FROM FIRE AREA IF POSSIBLE. AVOID BREATHING VAPORS OR DUSTS; KEEP UPWIND.

TOXICITY

GIBBERELLIC ACID: TOXICITY DATA: 6300 MG/KG ORAL-RAT LD50; 8500 MG/KG ORAL-MOUSE LD50; MUTAGENIC DATA (RTECS); TUMORIGENIC DATA (RTECS). CARCINOGEN STATUS: NONE. ACUTE TOXICITY LEVEL: SLIGHTLY TOXIC BY INGESTION. TARGET EFFECTS: NO DATA AVAILABLE.

HEALTH EFFECTS AND FIRST AID

INHALATION: GIBBERELLIC ACID: **ACUTE EXPOSURE-** DUST OR MIST MAY IRRITATE RESPIRATORY TRACT. **CHRONIC EXPOSURE-** NO DATA AVAILABLE.

FIRST AID- REMOVE FROM EXPOSURE AREA TO FRESH AIR IMMEDIATELY. IF BREATHING HAS STOPPED, PERFORM ARTIFICIAL RESPIRATION. KEEP PERSON WARM AND AT REST. TREAT SYMPTOMATICALLY AND SUPPORTIVELY. GET MEDICAL ATTENTION IMMEDIATELY.

SKIN CONTACT: GIBBERELLIC ACID: **ACUTE EXPOSURE-** DUST, MIST OR SOLUTION MAY IRRITATE SKIN. **CHRONIC EXPOSURE-** NO DATA AVAILABLE.

FIRST AID- REMOVE CONTAMINATED CLOTHING AND SHOES IMMEDIATELY. WASH AFFECTED AREA WITH SOAP OR MILD DETERGENT AND LARGE AMOUNTS OF WATER UNTIL NO EVIDENCE OF CHEMICAL REMAINS (APPROXIMATELY 15-20 MINUTES). GET MEDICAL ATTENTION IMMEDIATELY.

EYE CONTACT: GIBBERELLIC ACID: **ACUTE EXPOSURE-** DUST, MIST, OR SOLUTION MAY IRRITATE EYES. **CHRONIC EXPOSURE-** NO DATA AVAILABLE.

FIRST AID- WASH EYES IMMEDIATELY WITH LARGE AMOUNTS OF WATER OR NORMAL SALINE, OCCASIONALLY LIFTING UPPER AND LOWER LIDS, UNTIL NO EVIDENCE OF CHEMICAL REMAINS (APPROXIMATELY 15-20 MINUTES). GET MEDICAL ATTENTION IMMEDIATELY.

INGESTION: GIBBERELLIC ACID: **ACUTE EXPOSURE-** NO HUMAN DATA AVAILABLE. IN MICE, AN ORAL DOSE OF 25 MG/KG FAILED TO CAUSE DEATH OR PRODUCE MORE THAN MINOR TOXIC SYMPTOMS. **CHRONIC EXPOSURE-** A CUMULATIVE DOSE OF 142 GM/KG ADMINISTERED ORALLY TO MICE INTERMITTENTLY FOR 78 WEEKS PRODUCED TUMORS OF THE LIVER, LUNGS AND THORAX.

FIRST AID- IN CASE OF INGESTION OF LARGE AMOUNTS, INDUCE VOMITING. GET MEDICAL ATTENTION. (DEICHMANN AND GERARDE, TOXICOLOGY OF DRUGS AND CHEMICALS)

ANTIDOTE: NO SPECIFIC ANTIDOTE. TREAT SYMPTOMATICALLY AND SUPPORTIVELY.

REACTIVITY

REACTIVITY: STABLE UNDER NORMAL TEMPERATURES AND PRESSURES.

INCOMPATIBILITIES: GIBBERELLIC ACID: STRONG OXIDANTS: INCOMPATIBLE. ALKALIS: INCOMPATIBLE. METALLIC OXIDE: INCOMPATIBLE. ACTIVE METALS: INCOMPATIBLE. WATER: MAY BE SLOWLY HYDROLYZED. CHLORINE: MAY RAPIDLY DECOMPOSED WHEN IN SOLUTION WITH WATER. HEAT: MAY RAPIDLY DECOMPOSE WHEN IN SOLUTION WITH WATER. LIME SULFUR: INCOMPATIBLE.

DECOMPOSITION: THERMAL DECOMPOSITION MAY RELEASE ACRID SMOKE AND IRRITATING FUMES.

POLYMERIZATION: HAZARDOUS POLYMERIZATION HAS NOT BEEN REPORTED TO OCCUR UNDER NORMAL TEMPERATURES AND PRESSURES.

CONDITIONS TO AVOID

TEMPERATURES NEAR 234 C CAUSE GIBBERELLIC ACID TO EFFERVESCE.

SPILL AND LEAK PROCEDURES

OCCUPATIONAL SPILL: SWEEP UP AND PLACE IN SUITABLE CLEAN, DRY CONTAINERS FOR RECLAMATION OR LATER DISPOSAL. DO NOT FLUSH SPILLED MATERIAL INTO SEWER. KEEP UNNECESSARY PEOPLE AWAY.

PROTECTIVE EQUIPMENT

VENTILATION: PROVIDE GENERAL DILUTION VENTILATION.

RESPIRATOR: THE FOLLOWING RESPIRATORS ARE RECOMMENDED BASED ON INFORMATION FOUND IN THE PHYSICAL DATA, TOXICITY AND HEALTH EFFECTS SECTIONS. THEY ARE RANKED IN ORDER FROM MINIMUM TO MAXIMUM RESPIRATORY PROTECTION. THE SPECIFIC RESPIRATOR SELECTED MUST BE BASED ON CONTAMINATION LEVELS FOUND IN THE WORK PLACE, MUST NOT EXCEED THE WORKING LIMITS OF THE RESPIRATOR AND BE JOINTLY APPROVED BY THE NATIONAL INSTITUTE FOR OCCUPATIONAL SAFETY AND HEALTH AND THE MINE SAFETY AND HEALTH ADMINISTRATION (NIOSH-MSHA).

DUST AND MIST RESPIRATOR WITH A FULL FACEPIECE.

AIR-PURIFYING FULL FACEPIECE RESPIRATOR WITH A HIGH-EFFICIENCY PARTICULATE FILTER.

POWERED AIR-PURIFYING RESPIRATOR WITH A TIGHT-FITTING FACEPIECE AND HIGH-EFFICIENCY PARTICULATE FILTER.

TYPE 'C' SUPPLIED-AIR RESPIRATOR WITH A FULL FACEPIECE OPERATED IN PRESSURE-DEMAND OR OTHER POSITIVE PRESSURE MODE OR WITH A FULL FACEPIECE, HELMET OR HOOD OPERATED IN CONTINUOUS-FLOW MODE.

SELF-CONTAINED BREATHING APPARATUS WITH A FULL FACEPIECE OPERATED IN PRESSURE-DEMAND OR OTHER POSITIVE PRESSURE MODE.

FOR FIREFIGHTING AND OTHER IMMEDIATELY DANGEROUS TO LIFE OR HEALTH CONDITIONS:

SELF-CONTAINED BREATHING APPARATUS WITH FULL FACEPIECE OPERATED IN PRESSURE-DEMAND OR OTHER POSITIVE PRESSURE MODE.

SUPPLIED-AIR RESPIRATOR WITH FULL FACEPIECE AND OPERATED IN PRESSURE-DEMAND OR OTHER POSITIVE PRESSURE MODE IN COMBINATION WITH AN AUXILIARY SELF-CONTAINED BREATHING APPARATUS OPERATED IN PRESSURE-DEMAND OR OTHER POSITIVE PRESSURE MODE.

CLOTHING: EMPLOYEE MUST WEAR APPROPRIATE PROTECTIVE (IMPERVIOUS) CLOTHING AND EQUIPMENT TO PREVENT REPEATED OR PROLONGED SKIN CONTACT WITH THIS SUBSTANCE.

GLOVES: EMPLOYEE MUST WEAR APPROPRIATE PROTECTIVE GLOVES TO PREVENT CONTACT WITH THIS SUBSTANCE.

EYE PROTECTION: EMPLOYEE MUST WEAR SPLASH-PROOF OR DUST-RESISTANT SAFETY GOGGLES TO PREVENT EYE CONTACT WITH THIS SUBSTANCE.

EMERGENCY EYE WASH: WHERE THERE IS ANY POSSIBILITY THAT AN EMPLOYEE'S EYES MAY BE EXPOSED TO THIS SUBSTANCE, THE EMPLOYER SHOULD PROVIDE AN EYE WASH FOUNTAIN WITHIN THE IMMEDIATE WORK AREA FOR EMERGENCY USE.

AUTHORIZED BY- OCCUPATIONAL HEALTH SERVICES, INC.

CREATION DATE: 10/04/89 ***REVISION DATE:*** 05/31/90

MATERIAL SAFETY DATA SHEET

OCCUPATIONAL HEALTH SERVICES, INC.
AGRICULTURE AND PESTICIDE DIVISION
450 SEVENTH AVENUE, SUITE 2407
NEW YORK, NEW YORK 10123
1-800-445-MSDS OR (212) 967-1100

EMERGENCY CONTACT:
JOHN S. BRANSFORD, JR. (615) 292-1180

SUBSTANCE IDENTIFICATION

CAS-NUMBER 526-95-4

SUBSTANCE: **GLUCONIC ACID**

TRADE NAMES/SYNONYMS: D-GLUCONIC ACID; DEXTRONIC ACID; GLYCONIC ACID; MALTONIC ACID; GLYCOGENIC ACID; PENTAHYDROXYCAPROIC ACID; GLUCONIC ACID, D-; C6H12O7; PST10408

CHEMICAL FAMILY: SUGAR

MOLECULAR FORMULA: C6-H12-O7

MOLECULAR WEIGHT: 196.16

CERCLA RATINGS (SCALE 0-3): HEALTH=U FIRE=0 REACTIVITY=0 PERSISTENCE=0

NFPA RATINGS (SCALE 0-4): HEALTH=U FIRE=0 REACTIVITY=0

COMPONENTS AND CONTAMINANTS

COMPONENT: GLUCONIC ACID ***PERCENT:*** 100

CAS# 526-95-4

OTHER CONTAMINANTS: NONE

EXPOSURE LIMITS: NO OCCUPATIONAL EXPOSURE LIMITS ESTABLISHED BY OSHA, ACGIH, OR NIOSH.

PHYSICAL DATA

DESCRIPTION: LIGHT BROWN CRYSTALS WITH A MILD ACID TASTE.

MELTING POINT: 268 F (131 C) ***SPECIFIC GRAVITY:*** 1.234

SOLUBILITY IN WATER: SOLUBLE

SOLVENT SOLUBILITY: SLIGHTLY SOLUBLE IN ALCOHOL; INSOLUBLE IN ETHER, AND MOST ORGANIC SOLVENTS

FIRE AND EXPLOSION DATA

FIRE AND EXPLOSION HAZARD: NEGLIGIBLE FIRE HAZARD WHEN EXPOSED TO HEAT OR FLAME.

FIREFIGHTING MEDIA: DRY CHEMICAL, CARBON DIOXIDE, HALON, WATER SPRAY OR STANDARD FOAM (1987 EMERGENCY RESPONSE GUIDEBOOK, DOT P 5800.4). FOR LARGER FIRES, USE WATER SPRAY, FOG OR STANDARD FOAM (1987 EMERGENCY RESPONSE GUIDEBOOK, DOT P 5800.4).

FIREFIGHTING: MOVE CONTAINER FROM FIRE AREA IF POSSIBLE. DO NOT SCATTER SPILLED MATERIAL WITH HIGH PRESSURE WATER STREAMS. DIKE FIRE CONTROL WATER FOR LATER DISPOSAL (1987 EMERGENCY RESPONSE GUIDEBOOK, DOT P 5800.4, GUIDE PAGE 31).

USE AGENTS SUITABLE FOR TYPE OF SURROUNDING FIRE. AVOID BREATHING HAZARDOUS VAPORS, KEEP UPWIND.

TOXICITY

GLUCONIC ACID: CARCINOGEN STATUS: NONE. ACUTE TOXICITY DATA: NO DATA AVAILABLE. TARGET EFFECTS: NO DATA AVAILABLE.

HEALTH EFFECTS AND FIRST AID

INHALATION: GLUCONIC ACID: **ACUTE EXPOSURE-** NO DATA AVAILABLE. **CHRONIC EXPOSURE-** NO DATA AVAILABLE.

FIRST AID- REMOVE FROM EXPOSURE AREA TO FRESH AIR IMMEDIATELY. IF BREATHING HAS STOPPED, PERFORM ARTIFICIAL RESPIRATION. KEEP PERSON WARM AND AT REST. TREAT SYMPTOMATICALLY AND SUPPORTIVELY. GET MEDICAL ATTENTION IMMEDIATELY.

SKIN CONTACT: GLUCONIC ACID: **ACUTE EXPOSURE-** NO DATA AVAILABLE. **CHRONIC EXPOSURE-** NO DATA AVAILABLE.

FIRST AID- REMOVE CONTAMINATED CLOTHING AND SHOES IMMEDIATELY. WASH AFFECTED AREA WITH SOAP OR MILD DETERGENT AND LARGE AMOUNTS OF WATER UNTIL NO EVIDENCE OF CHEMICAL REMAINS (APPROXIMATELY 15-20 MINUTES). GET MEDICAL ATTENTION IMMEDIATELY.

EYE CONTACT: GLUCONIC ACID: **ACUTE EXPOSURE-** NO DATA AVAILABLE. **CHRONIC EXPOSURE-** NO DATA AVAILABLE.
FIRST AID- WASH EYES IMMEDIATELY WITH LARGE AMOUNTS OF WATER OR NORMAL SALINE, OCCASIONALLY LIFTING UPPER AND LOWER LIDS, UNTIL NO EVIDENCE OF CHEMICAL REMAINS (APPROXIMATELY 15-20 MINUTES). GET MEDICAL ATTENTION IMMEDIATELY.

INGESTION: GLUCONIC ACID: **ACUTE EXPOSURE-** NO DATA AVAILABLE. **CHRONIC EXPOSURE-** NO DATA AVAILABLE.
FIRST AID- TREAT SYMPTOMATICALLY AND SUPPORTIVELY. GET MEDICAL ATTENTION IMMEDIATELY. IF VOMITING OCCURS, KEEP HEAD LOWER THAN HIPS TO PREVENT ASPIRATION.
ANTIDOTE: NO SPECIFIC ANTIDOTE. TREAT SYMPTOMATICALLY AND SUPPORTIVELY.

REACTIVITY

REACTIVITY: STABLE UNDER NORMAL TEMPERATURES AND PRESSURES.
INCOMPATIBILITIES: GLUCONIC ACID: OXIDIZERS (STRONG): INCOMPATIBLE.
DECOMPOSITION: THERMAL DECOMPOSITION PRODUCTS MAY INCLUDE TOXIC OXIDES OF CARBON.
POLYMERIZATION: HAZARDOUS POLYMERIZATION HAS NOT BEEN REPORTED TO OCCUR UNDER NORMAL TEMPERATURES AND PRESSURES.

STORAGE AND DISPOSAL

OBSERVE ALL FEDERAL, STATE AND LOCAL REGULATIONS WHEN STORING OR DISPOSING OF THIS SUBSTANCE. FOR ASSISTANCE, CONTACT THE DISTRICT DIRECTOR OF THE ENVIRONMENTAL PROTECTION AGENCY.

STORAGE

STORE AWAY FROM INCOMPATIBLE SUBSTANCES.

CONDITIONS TO AVOID

MAY BURN BUT DOES NOT IGNITE READILY. AVOID CONTACT WITH STRONG OXIDIZERS, EXCESSIVE HEAT, SPARKS, OR OPEN FLAME.

SPILL AND LEAK PROCEDURES

OCCUPATIONAL SPILL: SWEEP UP AND PLACE IN SUITABLE CLEAN, DRY CONTAINERS FOR RECLAMATION OR LATER DISPOSAL. DO NOT FLUSH SPILLED MATERIAL INTO SEWER. KEEP UNNECESSARY PEOPLE AWAY.

PROTECTIVE EQUIPMENT

VENTILATION: PROVIDE LOCAL EXHAUST OR PROCESS ENCLOSURE VENTILATION SYSTEM.
RESPIRATOR: THE FOLLOWING RESPIRATORS ARE RECOMMENDED BASED ON INFORMATION FOUND IN THE PHYSICAL DATA, TOXICITY AND HEALTH EFFECTS SECTIONS. THEY ARE RANKED IN ORDER FROM MINIMUM TO MAXIMUM RESPIRATORY PROTECTION. THE SPECIFIC RESPIRATOR SELECTED MUST BE BASED ON CONTAMINATION LEVELS FOUND IN THE WORK PLACE, MUST NOT EXCEED THE WORKING LIMITS OF THE RESPIRATOR AND BE JOINTLY APPROVED BY THE NATIONAL INSTITUTE FOR OCCUPATIONAL SAFETY AND HEALTH AND THE MINE SAFETY AND HEALTH ADMINISTRATION (NIOSH-MSHA).
DUST AND MIST RESPIRATOR WITH A FULL FACEPIECE.
AIR-PURIFYING FULL FACEPIECE RESPIRATOR WITH A HIGH-EFFICIENCY PARTICULATE FILTER.
POWERED AIR-PURIFYING RESPIRATOR WITH A TIGHT-FITTING FACEPIECE AND HIGH-EFFICIENCY PARTICULATE FILTER.
TYPE 'C' SUPPLIED-AIR RESPIRATOR WITH A FULL FACEPIECE OPERATED IN PRESSURE-DEMAND OR OTHER POSITIVE PRESSURE MODE OR WITH A FULL FACEPIECE, HELMET OR HOOD OPERATED IN CONTINUOUS-FLOW MODE.
SELF-CONTAINED BREATHING APPARATUS WITH A FULL FACEPIECE OPERATED IN PRESSURE-DEMAND OR OTHER POSITIVE PRESSURE MODE.
FOR FIREFIGHTING AND OTHER IMMEDIATELY DANGEROUS TO LIFE OR HEALTH CONDITIONS:
SELF-CONTAINED BREATHING APPARATUS WITH FULL FACEPIECE OPERATED IN PRESSURE-DEMAND OR OTHER POSITIVE PRESSURE MODE.
SUPPLIED-AIR RESPIRATOR WITH FULL FACEPIECE AND OPERATED IN PRESSURE-DEMAND OR OTHER POSITIVE PRESSURE MODE IN COMBINATION WITH AN AUXILIARY SELF-CONTAINED BREATHING APPARATUS OPERATED IN PRESSURE-DEMAND OR OTHER POSITIVE PRESSURE MODE.
CLOTHING: EMPLOYEE MUST WEAR APPROPRIATE PROTECTIVE (IMPERVIOUS) CLOTHING AND EQUIPMENT TO PREVENT REPEATED OR PROLONGED SKIN CONTACT WITH THIS SUBSTANCE.
GLOVES: EMPLOYEE MUST WEAR APPROPRIATE PROTECTIVE GLOVES TO PREVENT CONTACT WITH THIS SUBSTANCE.
EYE PROTECTION: EMPLOYEE MUST WEAR SPLASH-PROOF OR DUST-RESISTANT SAFETY GOGGLES TO PREVENT EYE CONTACT WITH THIS SUBSTANCE.
EMERGENCY EYE WASH: WHERE THERE IS ANY POSSIBILITY THAT AN EMPLOYEE'S EYES MAY BE EXPOSED TO THIS SUBSTANCE, THE EMPLOYER SHOULD PROVIDE AN EYE WASH FOUNTAIN WITHIN THE IMMEDIATE WORK AREA FOR EMERGENCY USE.

AUTHORIZED BY- OCCUPATIONAL HEALTH SERVICES, INC.
CREATION DATE: 11/16/89 ***REVISION DATE:*** 05/31/90

MATERIAL SAFETY DATA SHEET

OCCUPATIONAL HEALTH SERVICES, INC.
AGRICULTURE AND PESTICIDE DIVISION
450 SEVENTH AVENUE, SUITE 2407
NEW YORK, NEW YORK 10123
1-800-445-MSDS OR (212) 967-1100

EMERGENCY CONTACT:
JOHN S. BRANSFORD, JR. (615) 292-1180

SUBSTANCE IDENTIFICATION

CAS-NUMBER 111-30-8
***SUBSTANCE:* GLUTARALDEHYDE**
TRADE NAMES/SYNONYMS: CIDEX; 1,5-PENTANEDIONE; 1,5-PENTANEDIAL; GLUTARDIALDEHYDE; GLUTARAL; POTENTIATED ACID GLUTARALDEHYDE; SONACIDE; GLUTARIC DIALDEHYDE; PST10423
CHEMICAL FAMILY: ALDEHYDE, ALIPHATIC
MOLECULAR FORMULA: C5-H8-O2
MOLECULAR WEIGHT: 100.1
CERCLA RATINGS (SCALE 0-3): HEALTH=3 FIRE=0 REACTIVITY=2 PERSISTENCE=0
NFPA RATINGS (SCALE 0-4): HEALTH=3 FIRE=0 REACTIVITY=2

COMPONENTS AND CONTAMINANTS

COMPONENT: GLUTARALDEHYDE ***PERCENT:*** 100
CAS# 111-30-8
OTHER CONTAMINANTS: NONE
EXPOSURE LIMITS: GLUTARALDEHYDE: 0.2 PPM (0.8 MG/M3) OSHA CEILING 0.2 PPM ACGIH CEILING

PHYSICAL DATA

DESCRIPTION: COLORLESS CRYSTALS. ***BOILING POINT:*** 369 F (187 C) DECOMPOSES
SPECIFIC GRAVITY: 0.72 ***VAPOR PRESSURE:*** 17 MMHG @ 20 C
SOLUBILITY IN WATER: SOLUBLE ***VAPOR DENSITY:*** 3.5
SOLVENT SOLUBILITY: ALCOHOL, BENZENE, ACETONE, DMSO, ETHER

FIRE AND EXPLOSION DATA

FIRE AND EXPLOSION HAZARD: NEGLIGIBLE FIRE HAZARD WHEN EXPOSED TO HEAT OR FLAME.
FIREFIGHTING MEDIA: DRY CHEMICAL, CARBON DIOXIDE, HALON, WATER SPRAY OR STANDARD FOAM (1987 EMERGENCY RESPONSE GUIDEBOOK, DOT P 5800.4).
FOR LARGER FIRES, USE WATER SPRAY, FOG OR STANDARD FOAM (1987 EMERGENCY RESPONSE GUIDEBOOK, DOT P 5800.4).
FIREFIGHTING: MOVE CONTAINER FROM FIRE AREA IF POSSIBLE. DO NOT SCATTER SPILLED MATERIAL WITH HIGH PRESSURE WATER STREAMS. DIKE FIRE CONTROL WATER FOR LATER DISPOSAL (1987 EMERGENCY RESPONSE GUIDEBOOK, DOT P 5800.4, GUIDE PAGE 31).
USE AGENTS SUITABLE FOR TYPE OF SURROUNDING FIRE. AVOID BREATHING HAZARDOUS VAPORS, KEEP UPWIND.

TOXICITY

GLUTARALDEHYDE: IRRITATION DATA: 6 MG/3 DAYS INTERMITTENT SKIN-HUMAN SEVERE; 13 MG OPEN SKIN-RABBIT MILD; 2 MG/24 HOURS SKIN-RABBIT SEVERE; 1 MG EYE-RABBIT SEVERE; 250 UG/24 HOURS EYE-RABBIT SEVERE. TOXICITY DATA: 2560 MG/KG SKIN-RABBIT LD50; 134 MG/KG ORAL-RAT LD50; 100 MG/KG ORAL-MOUSE LD50; 50 MG/KG ORAL-GUINEA PIG LD50; 2390 MG/KG SUBCUTANEOUS-RAT LD50; 1430 MG/KG SUBCUTANEOUS-MOUSE LD50; 1530 UG/KG INTRAVENOUS-RAT LD50; 15400 UG/KG INTRAVENOUS-MOUSE LD50; 17900 UG/KG INTRAPERITONEAL-RAT LD50; 13900 UG/KG INTRAPERITONEAL-MOUSE LD50; MUTAGENIC DATA (RTECS); REPRODUCTIVE EFFECTS DATA (RTECS). CARCINOGEN STATUS: NONE. LOCAL EFFECTS: CORROSIVE- EYES; IRRITANT- INHALATION AND SKIN. ACUTE TOXICITY LEVEL: TOXIC BY INGESTION AND SLIGHTLY TOXIC BY DERMAL ABSORPTION. TARGET EFFECTS: SENSITIZER- SKIN. CENTRAL NERVOUS SYSTEM DEPRESSANT.

HEALTH EFFECTS AND FIRST AID

INHALATION: GLUTARALDEHYDE: IRRITANT/NARCOTIC. **ACUTE EXPOSURE-** INHALATION MAY CAUSE NOSE AND UPPER RESPIRATORY TRACT IRRITATION. SEVERE EXPOSURE MAY CAUSE COUGHING, SHORTNESS OF BREATH AND CENTRAL NERVOUS SYSTEM DEPRESSION WITH HEADACHE, DIZZINESS AND DROWSINESS. **CHRONIC EXPOSURE-** PROLONGED OR REPEATED EXPOSURE MAY CAUSE MUCOUS MEMBRANE IRRITATION.

FIRST AID- REMOVE FROM EXPOSURE AREA TO FRESH AIR IMMEDIATELY. IF BREATHING HAS STOPPED, PERFORM ARTIFICIAL RESPIRATION. KEEP PERSON WARM AND AT REST. TREAT SYMPTOMATICALLY AND SUPPORTIVELY. GET MEDICAL ATTENTION IMMEDIATELY.

SKIN CONTACT: GLUTARALDEHYDE: IRRITANT/SENSITIZER/NARCOTIC. **ACUTE EXPOSURE-** CONTACT WITH THE SKIN MAY CAUSE IRRITATION. SENSITIZATION DERMATITIS MAY OCCUR IN PREVIOUSLY EXPOSED PERSONS. SUBSTANCE MAY BE ABSORBED THROUGH INTACT SKIN AND AFFECT THE CENTRAL NERVOUS SYSTEM WITH HEADACHE, DIZZINESS AND DULLNESS. **CHRONIC EXPOSURE-** INTERMITTENT HUMAN EXPOSURE TO A SMALL AMOUNT FOR 3 DAYS PRODUCED SEVERE IRRITATION. REPEATED OR PROLONGED EXPOSURE MAY CAUSE SENSITIZATION DERMATITIS.

FIRST AID- REMOVE CONTAMINATED CLOTHING AND SHOES IMMEDIATELY. WASH AFFECTED AREA WITH SOAP OR MILD DETERGENT AND LARGE AMOUNTS OF WATER UNTIL NO EVIDENCE OF CHEMICAL REMAINS (APPROXIMATELY 15-20 MINUTES). GET MEDICAL ATTENTION IMMEDIATELY.

EYE CONTACT: GLUTARALDEHYDE: CORROSIVE. **ACUTE EXPOSURE-** CONTACT WITH THE EYES MAY CAUSE SEVERE IRRITATION, REDNESS, PAIN, AND POSSIBLY CORNEAL BURNS. HOWEVER, A 40% SOLUTION APPLIED TO RABBIT EYES AND RINSED 2 MINUTES LATER PRODUCED NO INJURY. **CHRONIC EXPOSURE-** PROLONGED OR REPEATED EXPOSURE MAY CAUSE CONJUNCTIVITIS.

FIRST AID- WASH EYES IMMEDIATELY WITH LARGE AMOUNTS OF WATER, OCCASIONALLY LIFTING UPPER AND LOWER LIDS, UNTIL NO EVIDENCE OF CHEMICAL REMAINS (AT LEAST 15-20 MINUTES). CONTINUE IRRIGATING WITH NORMAL SALINE UNTIL THE PH HAS RETURNED TO NORMAL (30-60 MINUTES). COVER WITH STERILE BANDAGES. GET MEDICAL ATTENTION IMMEDIATELY.

INGESTION: GLUTARALDEHYDE: NARCOTIC/TOXIC. **ACUTE EXPOSURE-** INGESTION MAY CAUSE MOUTH AND STOMACH IRRITATION, ABDOMINAL PAIN, NAUSEA AND MAY AFFECT THE CENTRAL NERVOUS SYSTEM. LOW DOSES WERE LETHAL TO RATS AND MICE TESTED. NO SYMPTOMS WERE REPORTED. **CHRONIC EXPOSURE-** MALE AND FEMALE RATS CHRONICALLY FED BEFORE MATING EXHIBITED EFFECTS ON THE REPRODUCTIVE ORGANS. PREGNANT RATS EXHIBITED FETOTOXICITY AND DEVELOPMENTAL ABNORMALITIES OF THE CRANIOFACIAL, MUSCULOSKELETAL, AND CENTRAL NERVOUS SYSTEMS OF THE FETUSES.

FIRST AID- IF THE PERSON IS CONSCIOUS AND NOT CONVULSING, INDUCE EMESIS BY GIVING SYRUP OF IPECAC FOLLOWED BY WATER. (IF VOMITING OCCURS KEEP THE HEAD BELOW THE HIPS TO PREVENT ASPIRATION). REPEAT IN 20 MINUTES IF NOT EFFECTIVE INITIALLY. GIVE ACTIVATED CHARCOAL. IN PATIENTS WITH DEPRESSED RESPIRATION OR IF EMESIS IS NOT PRODUCED, PERFORM GASTRIC LAVAGE CAUTIOUSLY (DREISBACH, HANDBOOK OF POISONING, 12TH ED.). TREAT SYMPTOMATICALLY AND SUPPORTIVELY. GASTRIC LAVAGE SHOULD BE PERFORMED BY QUALIFIED MEDICAL PERSONNEL. GET MEDICAL ATTENTION IMMEDIATELY.

ANTIDOTE: NO SPECIFIC ANTIDOTE. TREAT SYMPTOMATICALLY AND SUPPORTIVELY.

REACTIVITY

REACTIVITY: MAY POLYMERIZE ON EXPOSURE TO AIR OR WATER. IF POLYMERIZATION OCCURS IN A CLOSED CONTAINER, THE INCREASE IN TEMPERATURE AND PRESSURE MAY RUPTURE THE CONTAINER.

INCOMPATIBILITIES: GLUTARALDEHYDE: OXIDIZERS: VIOLENT REACTION. REDUCING AGENTS: INCOMPATIBLE. ACIDS: INCOMPATIBLE. ALKALIES: INCOMPATIBLE.

DECOMPOSITION: THERMAL DECOMPOSITION MAY RELEASE TOXIC AND/OR HAZARDOUS GASES.

POLYMERIZATION: MAY POLYMERIZE ON EXPOSURE TO AIR OR WATER. IF POLYMERIZATION OCCURS IN A CLOSED CONTAINER, THE INCREASE IN TEMPERATURE AND PRESSURE MAY RUPTURE THE CONTAINER.

CONDITIONS TO AVOID

MAY BURN BUT DOES NOT IGNITE READILY. AVOID CONTACT WITH STRONG OXIDIZERS, EXCESSIVE HEAT, SPARKS, OR OPEN FLAME.

SPILL AND LEAK PROCEDURES

OCCUPATIONAL SPILL: STOP LEAK IF YOU CAN DO IT WITHOUT RISK. FOR SMALL SPILLS, TAKE UP WITH SAND OR OTHER ABSORBENT MATERIAL AND PLACE INTO CLEAN, DRY CONTAINERS FOR LATER DISPOSAL. KEEP UNNECESSARY PEOPLE AWAY. ISOLATE HAZARD AREA AND DENY ENTRY.

PROTECTIVE EQUIPMENT

VENTILATION: PROVIDE LOCAL EXHAUST OR PROCESS ENCLOSURE VENTILATION TO MEET PUBLISHED EXPOSURE LIMITS.

RESPIRATOR: THE FOLLOWING RESPIRATORS ARE RECOMMENDED BASED ON INFORMATION FOUND IN THE PHYSICAL DATA, TOXICITY AND HEALTH EFFECTS SECTIONS. THEY ARE RANKED IN ORDER FROM MINIMUM TO MAXIMUM RESPIRATORY PROTECTION. THE SPECIFIC RESPIRATOR SELECTED MUST BE BASED ON CONTAMINATION LEVELS FOUND IN THE WORK PLACE, MUST NOT EXCEED THE WORKING LIMITS OF THE RESPIRATOR AND BE JOINTLY APPROVED BY THE NATIONAL INSTITUTE FOR OCCUPATIONAL SAFETY AND HEALTH AND THE MINE SAFETY AND HEALTH ADMINISTRATION (NIOSH-MSHA).

CHEMICAL CARTRIDGE RESPIRATOR WITH FULL FACEPIECE AND ORGANIC VAPOR CARTRIDGE(S) IN COMBINATION WITH A DUST AND MIST FILTER.

CHEMICAL CARTRIDGE RESPIRATOR WITH FULL FACEPIECE AND ORGANIC VAPOR CARTRIDGE(S) IN COMBINATION WITH A HIGH-EFFICIENCY PARTICULATE FILTER.

GAS MASK WITH ORGANIC VAPOR CANISTER (CHIN-STYLE OR FRONT- OR BACK-MOUNTED CANISTER) WITH A FULL FACEPIECE AND A HIGH-EFFICIENCY PARTICULATE FILTER.

POWERED AIR-PURIFYING RESPIRATOR WITH TIGHT-FITTING FACEPIECE AND ORGANIC VAPOR CARTRIDGE(S) IN COMBINATION WITH A HIGH-EFFICIENCY PARTICULATE FILTER.

TYPE 'C' SUPPLIED-AIR RESPIRATOR WITH A FULL FACEPIECE OPERATED IN PRESSURE-DEMAND OR OTHER POSITIVE PRESSURE MODE OR WITH A FULL FACEPIECE, HELMET OR HOOD OPERATED IN CONTINUOUS-FLOW MODE. SELF-CONTAINED BREATHING APPARATUS WITH A FULL FACEPIECE OPERATED IN PRESSURE-DEMAND OR OTHER POSITIVE PRESSURE MODE.

FOR FIREFIGHTING AND OTHER IMMEDIATELY DANGEROUS TO LIFE OR HEALTH CONDITIONS:

SELF-CONTAINED BREATHING APPARATUS WITH FULL FACEPIECE OPERATED IN PRESSURE-DEMAND OR OTHER POSITIVE PRESSURE MODE.

SUPPLIED-AIR RESPIRATOR WITH FULL FACEPIECE AND OPERATED IN PRESSURE-DEMAND OR OTHER POSITIVE PRESSURE MODE IN COMBINATION WITH AN AUXILIARY SELF-CONTAINED BREATHING APPARATUS OPERATED IN PRESSURE-DEMAND OR OTHER POSITIVE PRESSURE MODE.

CLOTHING: EMPLOYEE MUST WEAR APPROPRIATE PROTECTIVE (IMPERVIOUS) CLOTHING AND EQUIPMENT TO PREVENT REPEATED OR PROLONGED SKIN CONTACT WITH THIS SUBSTANCE.

GLOVES: EMPLOYEE MUST WEAR APPROPRIATE PROTECTIVE GLOVES TO PREVENT CONTACT WITH THIS SUBSTANCE.

EYE PROTECTION: EMPLOYEE MUST WEAR SPLASH-PROOF OR DUST-RESISTANT SAFETY GOGGLES AND A FACESHIELD TO PREVENT CONTACT WITH THIS SUBSTANCE.

EMERGENCY WASH FACILITIES: WHERE THERE IS ANY POSSIBILITY THAT AN EMPLOYEE'S EYES AND/OR SKIN MAY BE EXPOSED TO THIS SUBSTANCE, THE EMPLOYER SHOULD PROVIDE AN EYE WASH FOUNTAIN AND QUICK DRENCH SHOWER WITHIN THE IMMEDIATE WORK AREA FOR EMERGENCY USE.

AUTHORIZED BY- OCCUPATIONAL HEALTH SERVICES, INC.

CREATION DATE: 10/04/89 ***REVISION DATE:*** 05/07/90

MATERIAL SAFETY DATA SHEET

OCCUPATIONAL HEALTH SERVICES, INC.
AGRICULTURE AND PESTICIDE DIVISION
450 SEVENTH AVENUE, SUITE 2407
NEW YORK, NEW YORK 10123
1-800-445-MSDS OR (212) 967-1100

EMERGENCY CONTACT:
JOHN S. BRANSFORD, JR. (615) 292-1180

SUBSTANCE IDENTIFICATION

CAS-NUMBER 56-81-5

SUBSTANCE: **GLYCERIN**

TRADE NAMES/SYNONYMS: GLYCEROL; GLYCERIN ANHYDROUS; GLYCERINE; GLYCERITOL; GLYCYL ALCOHOL; 1,2,3-PROPANETRIOL; PROPANETRIOL; GLYROL; GLYSANIN; TRIHYDROXYPROPANE; 1,2,3-TRIHYDROXYPROPANE; OSMOGLYN; G-31; G-33; C3H8O3; PST10440

CHEMICAL FAMILY: HYDROXYL, ALIPHATIC

MOLECULAR FORMULA: H-O-C-H2-C-H-(O-H)-C-H2-O-H

MOLECULAR WEIGHT: 92.09

CERCLA RATINGS (SCALE 0-3): HEALTH=1 FIRE=1 REACTIVITY=0 PERSISTENCE=0

NFPA RATINGS (SCALE 0-4): HEALTH = 1 FIRE = 1 REACTIVITY = 0

COMPONENTS AND CONTAMINANTS

COMPONENT: GLYCERIN ***PERCENT:*** 99.9
CAS# 56-81-5

EXPOSURE LIMITS: GLYCERIN (MIST): 5 MG/M3 OSHA TWA (RESPIRABLE FRACTION); 10 MG/M3 OSHA TWA (TOTAL MIST) 10 MG/M3 ACGIH TWA

PHYSICAL DATA

DESCRIPTION: ODORLESS, COLORLESS TO PALE YELLOW, HYGROSCOPIC, SYRUPY LIQUID WITH A WARM, SWEET TASTE. ***BOILING POINT:*** 554 F (290 C) DECOMPOSES

MELTING POINT: 68 F (20 C) ***SPECIFIC GRAVITY:*** 1.2613

VAPOR PRESSURE: 0.0025 MMHG @ 50 C ***PH:*** NEUTRAL

SOLUBILITY IN WATER: SOLUBLE ***VAPOR DENSITY:*** 3.1

SOLVENT SOLUBILITY: SOLUBLE IN ALCOHOL, ETHYL ACETATE, ETHYL ETHER; INSOLUBLE IN BENZENE, CHLOROFORM, CARBON TETRACHLORIDE, CARBON DISULFIDE, PETROLEUM ETHER, OILS.

FIRE AND EXPLOSION DATA

FIRE AND EXPLOSION HAZARD: SLIGHT FIRE HAZARD WHEN EXPOSED TO HEAT OR FLAME.

FLASH POINT: 320 F (160 C) (CC) ***LOWER EXPLOSIVE LIMIT:*** 0.9%

AUTOIGNITION TEMP.: 698 F (370 C) ***FLAMMABILITY CLASS(OSHA):*** IIIB

FIREFIGHTING MEDIA: DRY CHEMICAL, CARBON DIOXIDE, HALON, WATER SPRAY OR ALCOHOL FOAM (1987 EMERGENCY RESPONSE GUIDEBOOK, DOT P 5800.4).
FOR LARGER FIRES, USE WATER SPRAY, FOG OR ALCOHOL FOAM (1987 EMERGENCY RESPONSE GUIDEBOOK, DOT P 5800.4).
ALCOHOL FOAM (NFPA 325M, FIRE HAZARD PROPERTIES OF FLAMMABLE LIQUIDS, GASES, AND VOLATILE SOLIDS, 1984).

FIREFIGHTING: MOVE CONTAINER FROM FIRE AREA IF POSSIBLE. DO NOT SCATTER SPILLED MATERIAL WITH HIGH PRESSURE WATER STREAMS. DIKE FIRE CONTROL WATER FOR LATER DISPOSAL (1987 EMERGENCY RESPONSE GUIDEBOOK, DOT P 5800.4, GUIDE PAGE 31).
USE AGENTS SUITABLE FOR TYPE OF SURROUNDING FIRE. AVOID BREATHING HAZARDOUS VAPORS, KEEP UPWIND.
WATER OR FOAM MAY CAUSE FROTHING (NFPA 325M, FIRE HAZARD PROPERTIES OF FLAMMABLE LIQUIDS, GASES, AND VOLATILE SOLIDS, 1984)

TOXICITY

GLYCERIN: IRRITATION DATA: 500 MG/24 HOURS SKIN-RABBIT MILD; 126 MG EYE-RABBIT MILD; 500 MG/24 HOURS EYE-RABBIT MILD. TOXICITY DATA: 1428 MG/KG ORAL-HUMAN TDLO; 12600 MG/KG ORAL-RAT LD50; 4090 MG/KG ORAL-MOUSE LD50; 27 GM/KG ORAL-RABBIT LD50; 7750 MG/KG ORAL-GUINEA PIG 100 MG/KG SUBCUTANEOUS-RAT LD50; 91 MG/KG SUBCUTANEOUS-MOUSE LD50; 5566 MG/KG INTRAVENOUS-RAT LD50; 4250 MG/KG INTRAVENOUS-MOUSE LD50; 53 GM/KG INTRAVENOUS-RABBIT LD50; 4420 MG/KG INTRAPERITONEAL-RAT LD50; 8700 MG/KG INTRAPERITONEAL-MOUSE LD50; MUTAGENIC DATA (RTECS); REPRODUCTIVE EFFECTS DATA (RTECS). CARCINOGEN STATUS: NONE. ACUTE TOXICITY LEVEL: SLIGHTLY TOXIC BY INGESTION. TARGET EFFECTS: POISONING MAY AFFECT THE KIDNEYS AND CENTRAL NERVOUS SYSTEM.

HEALTH EFFECTS AND FIRST AID

INHALATION: GLYCERIN: ACUTE EXPOSURE- DUE TO ITS LOW VAPOR PRESSURE GLYCERIN IS NOT CONSIDERED LIKELY TO BE AN INHALATION HAZARD AT NORMAL ROOM TEMPERATURES. VAPOR OR MIST IN SUFFICIENT CONCENTRATIONS MAY INTERFERE WITH RESPIRATORY FUNCTION. AT ELEVATED TEMPERATURES THE FUME MAY CAUSE IRRITATION AND DEHYDRATION OF THE MUCOUS MEMBRANES. CHRONIC EXPOSURE- NO DATA AVAILABLE.

FIRST AID- REMOVE FROM EXPOSURE AREA TO FRESH AIR IMMEDIATELY. IF BREATHING HAS STOPPED, PERFORM ARTIFICIAL RESPIRATION. KEEP PERSON WARM AND AT REST. TREAT SYMPTOMATICALLY AND SUPPORTIVELY. GET MEDICAL ATTENTION IMMEDIATELY.

SKIN CONTACT: GLYCERIN: ACUTE EXPOSURE- APPLICATION OF CONCENTRATED GLYCERIN MAY CAUSE EFFECTS RANGING FROM MILD IRRITATION TO DEHYDRATION OF THE SKIN WITH SUBSEQUENT IRRITATION AND REDNESS. ALLERGIC REACTIONS ARE RARE, BUT MAY OCCUR IN SENSITIVE INDIVIDUALS. CHRONIC EXPOSURE- REPEATED OR PROLONGED EXPOSURE TO CONCENTRATED SOLUTIONS MAY RESULT IN DERMATITIS.

FIRST AID- REMOVE CONTAMINATED CLOTHING AND SHOES IMMEDIATELY. WASH AFFECTED AREA WITH SOAP OR MILD DETERGENT AND LARGE AMOUNTS OF WATER UNTIL NO EVIDENCE OF CHEMICAL REMAINS (APPROXIMATELY 15-20 MINUTES). GET MEDICAL ATTENTION IMMEDIATELY.

EYE CONTACT: GLYCERIN: ACUTE EXPOSURE- APPLICATION TO HUMAN EYE MAY CAUSE A STRONG STINGING AND BURNING SENSATION, WITH REFLEX TEARING AND DILATION OF THE CONJUNCTIVAL VESSELS, BUT NO INJURY. INSTILLATION INTO THE ANTERIOR CHAMBER RESULTED IN AN INFLAMMATION REACTION AND EDEMA OF THE CORNEA WITH WRINKLING OF THE POSTERIOR SURFACE AND DAMAGE OF ENDOTHELIAL CELLS. CHRONIC EXPOSURE- NO DATA AVAILABLE.

FIRST AID- WASH EYES IMMEDIATELY WITH LARGE AMOUNTS OF WATER OR NORMAL SALINE, OCCASIONALLY LIFTING UPPER AND LOWER LIDS, UNTIL NO EVIDENCE OF CHEMICAL REMAINS (APPROXIMATELY 15-20 MINUTES). GET MEDICAL ATTENTION IMMEDIATELY.

INGESTION: GLYCERIN: ACUTE EXPOSURE- INGESTION OF 100 ML RESULTED IN HEADACHE, NAUSEA AND VOMITING. OTHER SYMPTOMS MAY INCLUDE DIGESTIVE TRACT IRRITATION, INSOMNIA, DIZZINESS, DIARRHEA AND FEVER. LARGE DOSES MAY CAUSE HEMOLYSIS, HEMOGLOBINURIA, HYPERGLYCEMIA, GLYCOSURIA, RENAL FAILURE, CONVULSIONS AND PARALYSIS. GLYCERIN ACTS AS AN OSMOTIC DIURETIC AND AS SUCH MAY LOWER INTRAOCULAR PRESSURE AND CAUSE HYPOVOLEMIA. IN RODENTS IT MAY ALSO CAUSE RESTLESSNESS, MILD CYANOSIS, DROP IN BLOOD PRESSURE, INCREASED RATE AND MAGNITUDE OF RESPIRATION, FOLLOWED BY DEBILITY, DIURESIS, TREMORS, DECREASED RESPIRATION, COLLAPSE, CLONIC CONVULSIONS AND COMA. REPRODUCTIVE EFFECTS WERE REPORTED IN ANIMALS. CHRONIC EXPOSURE- INGESTION OF 30 ML FOR 50 DAYS BY HUMAN VOLUNTEERS RESULTED IN INCREASED THIRST AND A FEELING OF WARMTH.

FIRST AID- REMOVE INGESTED MATERIAL BY GASTRIC LAVAGE OR EMESIS. GIVE ARTIFICIAL RESPIRATION WITH OXYGEN IF RESPIRATION IS DEPRESSED. (DREISBACH HANDBOOK OF POISONING, 11TH ED.). GET MEDICAL ATTENTION IMMEDIATELY. ADMINISTRATION OF GASTRIC LAVAGE SHOULD BE PERFORMED BY QUALIFIED MEDICAL PERSONNEL.

ANTIDOTE: NO SPECIFIC ANTIDOTE. TREAT SYMPTOMATICALLY AND SUPPORTIVELY.

REACTIVITY

REACTIVITY: STABLE UNDER NORMAL TEMPERATURES AND PRESSURES.

INCOMPATIBILITIES: GLYCERIN: ACETIC ANHYDRIDE: VIOLENT REACTION CATALYZED BY PHOSPHORUS OXYCHLORIDE. CALCIUM HYPOCHLORITE: MAY IGNITE SPONTANEOUSLY ON MIXING. CHLORINE (LIQUID): EXPLOSIVE REACTION. CHROMIUM(III) OXIDE: EXPLOSIVE REACTION. CHROMIUM TRIOXIDE: VIOLENT REACTION. HYDROFLUORIC ACID, NITRIC ACID: UNSTABLE MIXTURE. HYDROGEN PEROXIDE: EXPLOSION HAZARD. LEAD OXIDE, PERCHLORIC ACID: EXPLOSION HAZARD. NITRIC ACID, SULFURIC ACID: EXPLOSION HAZARD. OXIDIZERS (STRONG): EXPLOSIVE REACTION. POTASSIUM CHLORATE: EXPLOSIVE REACTION. POTASSIUM PERMANGANATE: EXPLOSIVE REACTION ON CONTACT. POTASSIUM PEROXIDE: FIRE AND EXPLOSION HAZARD. SODIUM HYDRIDE: INTENSE EXOTHERMIC REACTION. SILVER PERCHLORATE: FORMATION OF SHOCK-SENSITIVE SOLVATED SALT. SODIUM PEROXIDE: FIRE AND EXPLOSION HAZARD.

DECOMPOSITION: THERMAL DECOMPOSITION PRODUCTS MAY INCLUDE CORROSIVE ACROLEIN, AND TOXIC AND HAZARDOUS OXIDES OF CARBON.

POLYMERIZATION: HAZARDOUS POLYMERIZATION HAS NOT BEEN REPORTED TO OCCUR UNDER NORMAL TEMPERATURES AND PRESSURES.

STORAGE AND DISPOSAL

OBSERVE ALL FEDERAL, STATE AND LOCAL REGULATIONS WHEN STORING OR DISPOSING OF THIS SUBSTANCE. FOR ASSISTANCE, CONTACT THE DISTRICT DIRECTOR OF THE ENVIRONMENTAL PROTECTION AGENCY.

STORAGE

STORE AWAY FROM INCOMPATIBLE SUBSTANCES.

CONDITIONS TO AVOID

MAY BURN BUT DOES NOT IGNITE READILY. AVOID CONTACT WITH STRONG OXIDIZERS, EXCESSIVE HEAT, SPARKS, OR OPEN FLAME.

SPILL AND LEAK PROCEDURES

OCCUPATIONAL SPILL: STOP LEAK IF YOU CAN DO IT WITHOUT RISK. FOR SMALL SPILLS, TAKE UP WITH SAND OR OTHER ABSORBENT MATERIAL AND PLACE INTO CLEAN, DRY CONTAINERS FOR LATER DISPOSAL. KEEP UNNECESSARY PEOPLE AWAY. ISOLATE HAZARD AREA AND DENY ENTRY.

PROTECTIVE EQUIPMENT

VENTILATION: PROVIDE GENERAL DILUTION VENTILATION TO MEET PUBLISHED EXPOSURE LIMITS.

RESPIRATOR: THE FOLLOWING RESPIRATORS ARE RECOMMENDED BASED ON INFORMATION FOUND IN THE PHYSICAL DATA, TOXICITY AND HEALTH EFFECTS SECTIONS. THEY ARE RANKED IN ORDER FROM MINIMUM TO MAXIMUM RESPIRATORY PROTECTION. THE SPECIFIC RESPIRATOR SELECTED MUST BE BASED ON CONTAMINATION LEVELS FOUND IN THE WORK PLACE, MUST NOT EXCEED THE WORKING LIMITS OF THE RESPIRATOR AND BE JOINTLY APPROVED BY THE NATIONAL INSTITUTE FOR OCCUPATIONAL SAFETY AND HEALTH AND THE MINE

SAFETY AND HEALTH ADMINISTRATION (NIOSH-MSHA).
CHEMICAL CARTRIDGE RESPIRATOR WITH AN ORGANIC VAPOR CARTRIDGE(S) WITH A FULL FACEPIECE.
GAS MASK WITH ORGANIC VAPOR CANISTER (CHIN-STYLE OR FRONT- OR BACK-MOUNTED CANISTER) WITH A FULL FACEPIECE.
TYPE 'C' SUPPLIED-AIR RESPIRATOR WITH A FULL FACEPIECE OPERATED IN PRESSURE-DEMAND OR OTHER POSITIVE PRESSURE MODE OR WITH A FULL FACEPIECE, HELMET OR HOOD OPERATED IN CONTINUOUS-FLOW MODE.
SELF-CONTAINED BREATHING APPARATUS WITH A FULL FACEPIECE OPERATED IN PRESSURE-DEMAND OR OTHER POSITIVE PRESSURE MODE.
FOR FIREFIGHTING AND OTHER IMMEDIATELY DANGEROUS TO LIFE OR HEALTH CONDITIONS:
SELF-CONTAINED BREATHING APPARATUS WITH FULL FACEPIECE OPERATED IN PRESSURE-DEMAND OR OTHER POSITIVE PRESSURE MODE.
SUPPLIED-AIR RESPIRATOR WITH FULL FACEPIECE AND OPERATED IN PRESSURE-DEMAND OR OTHER POSITIVE PRESSURE MODE IN COMBINATION WITH AN AUXILIARY SELF-CONTAINED BREATHING APPARATUS OPERATED IN PRESSURE-DEMAND OR OTHER POSITIVE PRESSURE MODE.

CLOTHING: PROTECTIVE CLOTHING NOT REQUIRED. AVOID REPEATED OR PROLONGED CONTACT WITH THIS SUBSTANCE.

GLOVES: PROTECTIVE GLOVES ARE NOT REQUIRED BUT RECOMMENDED.

EYE PROTECTION: EMPLOYEE MUST WEAR SPLASH-PROOF OR DUST-RESISTANT SAFETY GOGGLES TO PREVENT EYE CONTACT WITH THIS SUBSTANCE.
EMERGENCY EYE WASH: WHERE THERE IS ANY POSSIBILITY THAT AN EMPLOYEE'S EYES MAY BE EXPOSED TO THIS SUBSTANCE, THE EMPLOYER SHOULD PROVIDE AN EYE WASH FOUNTAIN WITHIN THE IMMEDIATE WORK AREA FOR EMERGENCY USE.

AUTHORIZED BY- OCCUPATIONAL HEALTH SERVICES, INC.
CREATION DATE: 11/16/89 ***REVISION DATE:*** 05/14/90

MATERIAL SAFETY DATA SHEET

OCCUPATIONAL HEALTH SERVICES, INC.
AGRICULTURE AND PESTICIDE DIVISION
450 SEVENTH AVENUE, SUITE 2407
NEW YORK, NEW YORK 10123
1-800-445-MSDS OR (212) 967-1100

EMERGENCY CONTACT:
JOHN S. BRANSFORD, JR. (615) 292-1180

SUBSTANCE IDENTIFICATION

CAS-NUMBER 79-14-1

SUBSTANCE: GLYCOLIC ACID

TRADE NAMES/SYNONYMS: HYDROXYETHANOIC ACID; HYDROXYACETIC ACID; 998; A-130; 0-2975; PST10500

CHEMICAL FAMILY: CARBOXYLIC ACID, ALIPHATIC

MOLECULAR FORMULA: C2-H4-O3

MOLECULAR WEIGHT: 76.05

CERCLA RATINGS (SCALE 0-3): HEALTH=2 FIRE=U REACTIVITY=0 PERSISTENCE=0

NFPA RATINGS (SCALE 0-4): HEALTH=2 FIRE=U REACTIVITY=0

COMPONENTS AND CONTAMINANTS

COMPONENT: GLYCOLIC ACID ***PERCENT:*** 100
CAS# 79-14-1

OTHER CONTAMINANTS: NONE

EXPOSURE LIMITS: NO OCCUPATIONAL EXPOSURE LIMITS ESTABLISHED BY OSHA, ACGIH, OR NIOSH.

PHYSICAL DATA

DESCRIPTION: ODORLESS, COLORLESS, HYGROSCOPIC CRYSTALS.

BOILING POINT: DECOMPOSES ***MELTING POINT:*** 176 F (80 C)

SPECIFIC GRAVITY: 1.2 ***PH:*** 1.73 (10% SOLUTION)

SOLUBILITY IN WATER: SOLUBLE

SOLVENT SOLUBILITY: ALCOHOL, ETHER, METHANOL, ACETONE, AND ACETIC ACID

FIRE AND EXPLOSION DATA

FIRE AND EXPLOSION HAZARD: UNKNOWN FIRE AND EXPLOSION HAZARD.

FIREFIGHTING MEDIA: DRY CHEMICAL, CARBON DIOXIDE, WATER SPRAY OR FOAM FOR LARGER FIRES, USE WATER SPRAY, FOG OR ALCOHOL FOAM

FIREFIGHTING: MOVE CONTAINER FROM FIRE AREA IF POSSIBLE. DO NOT SCATTER SPILLED MATERIAL WITH HIGH PRESSURE WATER STREAMS. DIKE FIRE CONTROL WATER FOR LATER DISPOSAL (1987 EMERGENCY RESPONSE GUIDEBOOK, DOT P 5800.4, GUIDE PAGE 31).
USE AGENTS SUITABLE FOR TYPE OF SURROUNDING FIRE. AVOID BREATHING HAZARDOUS VAPORS, KEEP UPWIND.

TRANSPORTATION DATA

DEPARTMENT OF TRANSPORTATION HAZARD CLASSIFICATION 49 CFR 172.101: CORROSIVE MATERIAL
DEPARTMENT OF TRANSPORTATION LABELING REQUIREMENTS 49 CFR 172.101 AND SUBPART E: CORROSIVE
DEPARTMENT OF TRANSPORTATION PACKAGING REQUIREMENTS: 49 CFR 173.245B EXCEPTIONS: 49 CFR 173.244

TOXICITY

GLYCOLIC ACID: IRRITATION DATA: 2 MG EYE-RABBIT SEVERE. TOXICITY DATA: 1950 MG/KG ORAL-RAT LD50; 1920 MG/KG ORAL-GUINEA PIG LD50; 1 GM/KG INTRAVENOUS-CAT LD50. CARCINOGEN STATUS: NONE. LOCAL EFFECTS: CORROSIVE- INHALATION, SKIN, AND EYES. ACUTE TOXICITY LEVEL: MODERATELY TOXIC BY INGESTION. TARGET EFFECTS: NO DATA AVAILABLE.

HEALTH EFFECTS AND FIRST AID

INHALATION: GLYCOLIC ACID: CORROSIVE. **ACUTE EXPOSURE-** INHALATION MAY CAUSE CAUSE IRRITATION, POSSIBLY SEVERE, WITH SORE THROAT, COUGHING, AND SHORTNESS OF BREATH. IF SUFFICIENT QUANTITIES OF A CORROSIVE SUBSTANCE ARE INHALED, PULMONARY EDEMA MAY DEVELOP, OFTEN WITH A LATENCY PERIOD OF 5-72 HOURS. **CHRONIC EXPOSURE-** DEPENDING ON CONCENTRATION AND DURATION OF EXPOSURE, REPEATED OR PROLONGED EXPOSURE MAY BE AS THOSE IN ACUTE EXPOSURE.

FIRST AID- REMOVE FROM EXPOSURE AREA TO FRESH AIR IMMEDIATELY. IF BREATHING HAS STOPPED, GIVE ARTIFICIAL RESPIRATION. MAINTAIN AIRWAY AND BLOOD PRESSURE AND ADMINISTER OXYGEN IF AVAILABLE. KEEP AFFECTED PERSON WARM AND AT REST. TREAT SYMPTOMATICALLY AND SUPPORTIVELY. ADMINISTRATION OF OXYGEN SHOULD BE PERFORMED BY QUALIFIED PERSONNEL. GET MEDICAL ATTENTION IMMEDIATELY.

SKIN CONTACT: GLYCOLIC ACID: CORROSIVE. **ACUTE EXPOSURE-** CONTACT WITH THE SKIN MAY CAUSE IRRITATION, POSSIBLY SEVERE WITH BURNS. THE PRESENCE OF MOISTURE MAY TEND TO INCREASE THE SEVERITY OF IRRITATION. **CHRONIC EXPOSURE-** DEPENDING UPON CONCENTRATION AND DURATION OF EXPOSURE, REPEATED OR PROLONGED EXPOSURE MAY BE AS THOSE IN ACUTE EXPOSURE.

FIRST AID- REMOVE CONTAMINATED CLOTHING AND SHOES IMMEDIATELY. WASH AFFECTED AREA WITH SOAP OR MILD DETERGENT AND LARGE AMOUNTS OF WATER UNTIL NO EVIDENCE OF CHEMICAL REMAINS (AT LEAST 15-20 MINUTES). IN CASE OF CHEMICAL BURNS, COVER AREA WITH STERILE, DRY DRESSING. BANDAGE SECURELY, BUT NOT TOO TIGHTLY. GET MEDICAL ATTENTION IMMEDIATELY.

EYE CONTACT: GLYCOLIC ACID: CORROSIVE. **ACUTE EXPOSURE-** CONTACT WITH THE EYES MAY CAUSE IRRITATION, POSSIBLY SEVERE WITH BURNS. THE PRESENCE OF MOISTURE MAY TEND TO INCREASE THE SEVERITY OF IRRITATION. MODERATELY SEVERE INJURY, GRADED 7 ON A SCALE OF 1-10, OCCURRED WHEN TESTED ON RABBIT EYES. **CHRONIC EXPOSURE-** DEPENDING ON CONCENTRATION AND DURATION OF EXPOSURE, REPEATED OR PROLONGED EXPOSURE MAY CAUSE SYMPTOMS AS THOSE IN ACUTE EXPOSURE.

FIRST AID- WASH EYES IMMEDIATELY WITH LARGE AMOUNTS OF WATER, OCCASIONALLY LIFTING UPPER AND LOWER LIDS, UNTIL NO EVIDENCE OF CHEMICAL REMAINS (AT LEAST 15-20 MINUTES). CONTINUE IRRIGATING WITH NORMAL SALINE UNTIL THE PH HAS RETURNED TO NORMAL (30-60 MINUTES). COVER WITH STERILE BANDAGES. GET MEDICAL ATTENTION IMMEDIATELY.

INGESTION: GLYCOLIC ACID: CORROSIVE. **ACUTE EXPOSURE-** INGESTION MAY CAUSE SEVERE IRRITATION AND POSSIBLE CORROSION OF THE GASTROINTESTINAL TRACT WITH SORE THROAT AND COUGHING. THE REPORTED LETHAL DOSE IN RATS IS 1950 MG/KG. **CHRONIC EXPOSURE-** NO DATA AVAILABLE.

FIRST AID- DO NOT USE GASTRIC LAVAGE OR EMESIS. DILUTE THE ACID IMMEDIATELY BY DRINKING LARGE QUANTITIES OF WATER OR MILK. IF VOMITING PERSISTS, ADMINISTER FLUIDS REPEATEDLY. INGESTED ACID MUST BE DILUTED APPROXIMATELY 100 FOLD TO RENDER IT HARMLESS TO TISSUES. MAINTAIN AIRWAY AND TREAT SHOCK (DREISBACH, HANDBOOK OF POISONING, 12TH ED.). GET MEDICAL ATTENTION IMMEDIATELY. IF VOMITING OCCURS, KEEP HEAD BELOW HIPS TO HELP PREVENT ASPIRATION.

ANTIDOTE: NO SPECIFIC ANTIDOTE. TREAT SYMPTOMATICALLY AND SUPPORTIVELY.

REACTIVITY

REACTIVITY: STABLE UNDER NORMAL TEMPERATURES AND PRESSURES.

INCOMPATIBILITIES: GLYCOLIC ACID: NO DATA AVAILABLE.

DECOMPOSITION: THERMAL DECOMPOSITION MAY RELEASE ACRID SMOKE AND IRRITATING FUMES.

POLYMERIZATION: HAZARDOUS POLYMERIZATION HAS NOT BEEN REPORTED TO OCCUR UNDER NORMAL TEMPERATURES AND PRESSURES.

STORAGE AND DISPOSAL

OBSERVE ALL FEDERAL, STATE AND LOCAL REGULATIONS WHEN STORING OR DISPOSING OF THIS SUBSTANCE. FOR ASSISTANCE, CONTACT THE DISTRICT DIRECTOR OF THE ENVIRONMENTAL PROTECTION AGENCY.

DISPOSAL

DISPOSAL MUST BE IN ACCORDANCE WITH STANDARDS APPLICABLE TO GENERATORS OF HAZARDOUS WASTE, 40 CFR 262. EPA HAZARDOUS WASTE NUMBER D002. 100 POUND CERCLA SECTION 103 REPORTABLE QUANTITY.

CONDITIONS TO AVOID

MAY BURN BUT DOES NOT IGNITE READILY. FLAMMABLE, POISONOUS GASES MAY ACCUMULATE IN TANKS AND HOPPER CARS. MAY IGNITE COMBUSTIBLES (WOOD, PAPER, OIL, ETC.).

SPILL AND LEAK PROCEDURES

OCCUPATIONAL SPILL: DO NOT TOUCH SPILLED MATERIAL. STOP LEAK IF YOU CAN DO IT WITHOUT RISK. FOR SMALL SPILLS, TAKE UP WITH SAND OR OTHER ABSORBENT MATERIAL AND PLACE INTO CONTAINERS FOR LATER DISPOSAL. FOR SMALL DRY SPILLS, WITH CLEAN SHOVEL PLACE MATERIAL INTO CLEAN, DRY CONTAINER AND COVER. MOVE CONTAINERS FROM SPILL AREA. FOR LARGER SPILLS, DIKE FAR AHEAD OF SPILL FOR LATER DISPOSAL. KEEP UNNECESSARY PEOPLE AWAY. ISOLATE HAZARD AREA AND DENY ENTRY.

PROTECTIVE EQUIPMENT

VENTILATION: PROVIDE LOCAL EXHAUST OR GENERAL DILUTION VENTILATION. VENTILATION EQUIPMENT MUST BE EXPLOSION-PROOF.

RESPIRATOR: THE FOLLOWING RESPIRATORS ARE RECOMMENDED BASED ON INFORMATION FOUND IN THE PHYSICAL DATA, TOXICITY AND HEALTH EFFECTS SECTIONS. THEY ARE RANKED IN ORDER FROM MINIMUM TO MAXIMUM RESPIRATORY PROTECTION. THE SPECIFIC RESPIRATOR SELECTED MUST BE BASED ON CONTAMINATION LEVELS FOUND IN THE WORK PLACE, MUST NOT EXCEED THE WORKING LIMITS OF THE RESPIRATOR AND BE JOINTLY APPROVED BY THE NATIONAL INSTITUTE FOR OCCUPATIONAL SAFETY AND HEALTH AND THE MINE SAFETY AND HEALTH ADMINISTRATION (NIOSH-MSHA).

DUST AND MIST RESPIRATOR WITH A FULL FACEPIECE.

AIR-PURIFYING FULL FACEPIECE RESPIRATOR WITH A HIGH-EFFICIENCY PARTICULATE FILTER.

POWERED AIR-PURIFYING RESPIRATOR WITH A TIGHT-FITTING FACEPIECE AND HIGH-EFFICIENCY PARTICULATE FILTER.

TYPE 'C' SUPPLIED-AIR RESPIRATOR WITH A FULL FACEPIECE OPERATED IN PRESSURE-DEMAND OR OTHER POSITIVE PRESSURE MODE OR WITH A FULL FACEPIECE, HELMET OR HOOD OPERATED IN CONTINUOUS-FLOW MODE.

SELF-CONTAINED BREATHING APPARATUS WITH A FULL FACEPIECE OPERATED IN PRESSURE-DEMAND OR OTHER POSITIVE PRESSURE MODE.

FOR FIREFIGHTING AND OTHER IMMEDIATELY DANGEROUS TO LIFE OR HEALTH CONDITIONS:

SELF-CONTAINED BREATHING APPARATUS WITH FULL FACEPIECE OPERATED IN PRESSURE-DEMAND OR OTHER POSITIVE PRESSURE MODE.

SUPPLIED-AIR RESPIRATOR WITH FULL FACEPIECE AND OPERATED IN PRESSURE-DEMAND OR OTHER POSITIVE PRESSURE MODE IN COMBINATION WITH AN AUXILIARY SELF-CONTAINED BREATHING APPARATUS OPERATED IN PRESSURE-DEMAND OR OTHER POSITIVE PRESSURE MODE.

CLOTHING: EMPLOYEE MUST WEAR APPROPRIATE PROTECTIVE (IMPERVIOUS) CLOTHING AND EQUIPMENT TO PREVENT ANY POSSIBILITY OF SKIN CONTACT WITH THIS SUBSTANCE.

GLOVES: EMPLOYEE MUST WEAR APPROPRIATE PROTECTIVE GLOVES TO PREVENT CONTACT WITH THIS SUBSTANCE.

EYE PROTECTION: EMPLOYEE MUST WEAR SPLASH-PROOF OR DUST-RESISTANT SAFETY GOGGLES AND A FACESHIELD TO PREVENT CONTACT WITH THIS SUBSTANCE.

EMERGENCY WASH FACILITIES: WHERE THERE IS ANY POSSIBILITY THAT AN EMPLOYEE'S EYES AND/OR SKIN MAY BE EXPOSED TO THIS SUBSTANCE, THE EMPLOYER SHOULD PROVIDE AN EYE WASH FOUNTAIN AND QUICK DRENCH SHOWER WITHIN THE IMMEDIATE WORK AREA FOR EMERGENCY USE.

AUTHORIZED BY- OCCUPATIONAL HEALTH SERVICES, INC.

CREATION DATE: 11/16/89 ***REVISION DATE:*** 05/25/90

MATERIAL SAFETY DATA SHEET

OCCUPATIONAL HEALTH SERVICES, INC.
AGRICULTURE AND PESTICIDE DIVISION
450 SEVENTH AVENUE, SUITE 2407
NEW YORK, NEW YORK 10123
1-800-445-MSDS OR (212) 967-1100

EMERGENCY CONTACT:
JOHN S. BRANSFORD, JR. (615) 292-1180

SUBSTANCE IDENTIFICATION

CAS-NUMBER 1071-83-6

SUBSTANCE: GLYPHOSATE

TRADE NAMES/SYNONYMS: N-(PHOSPHONOMETHYL)GLYCINE; N-PHOSPHOMETHYLGLYCINE; N-PHOSPHONOMETHYLGLYCINE; PHOSPHONOMETHYLIMINOACETIC ACID; PHOSPHONOMETHYLGLYCINE; GLYCINE, N-(PHOSPHONOMETHYL)-; GLIALKA; MON 0573; C3H8NO5P; PST10515

CHEMICAL FAMILY: ORGANOPHOSPHATE

MOLECULAR FORMULA: C3-H8-N-O5-P

MOLECULAR WEIGHT: 169.07

CERCLA RATINGS (SCALE 0-3): HEALTH=3 FIRE=1 REACTIVITY=0 PERSISTENCE=0

NFPA RATINGS (SCALE 0-4): HEALTH=U FIRE=1 REACTIVITY=0

COMPONENTS AND CONTAMINANTS

COMPONENT: GLYPHOSATE ***PERCENT:*** 100.0
CAS# 1071-83-6

OTHER CONTAMINANTS: NONE

EXPOSURE LIMITS: NO OCCUPATIONAL EXPOSURE LIMITS ESTABLISHED BY OSHA, ACGIH, OR NIOSH.

PHYSICAL DATA

DESCRIPTION: ODORLESS, WHITE SOLID. ***MELTING POINT:*** 446 F (230 C) (DECOMPOSES)

SPECIFIC GRAVITY: 1.74 ***VAPOR PRESSURE:*** NEGLIGIBLE ***PH:*** 2 @ 1% SOLUTION

SOLUBILITY IN WATER: 1.2%

SOLVENT SOLUBILITY: INSOLUBLE IN MOST ORGANIC SOLVENTS.

FIRE AND EXPLOSION DATA

FIRE AND EXPLOSION HAZARD: SLIGHT FIRE HAZARD WHEN EXPOSED TO HEAT OR FLAME.

FIREFIGHTING MEDIA: DRY CHEMICAL, CARBON DIOXIDE, HALON, WATER SPRAY OR STANDARD FOAM (1987 EMERGENCY RESPONSE GUIDEBOOK, DOT P 5800.4). FOR LARGER FIRES, USE WATER SPRAY, FOG OR STANDARD FOAM (1987 EMERGENCY RESPONSE GUIDEBOOK, DOT P 5800.4).

FIREFIGHTING: MOVE CONTAINER FROM FIRE AREA IF POSSIBLE. DO NOT SCATTER SPILLED MATERIAL WITH HIGH PRESSURE WATER STREAMS. DIKE FIRE CONTROL WATER FOR LATER DISPOSAL (1987 EMERGENCY RESPONSE GUIDEBOOK, DOT P 5800.4, GUIDE PAGE 31).

USE AGENTS SUITABLE FOR TYPE OF SURROUNDING FIRE. AVOID BREATHING HAZARDOUS VAPORS, KEEP UPWIND.

TOXICITY

GLYPHOSATE: TOXICITY DATA: 7940 MG/KG SKIN-RABBIT LD50; 4873 MG/KG ORAL-RAT LD50; 1568 MG/KG ORAL-MOUSE LD50; 3800 MG/KG ORAL-RABBIT LD50; 235 MG/KG INTRAPERITONEAL-RAT LD50; 130 MG/KG INTRAPERITONEAL-MOUSE LD50. CARCINOGEN STATUS: NONE. ACUTE TOXICITY LEVEL: MODERATELY TOXIC BY INGESTION; SLIGHTLY TOXIC BY DERMAL ABSORPTION. TARGET EFFECTS: NO DATA AVAILABLE.

HEALTH EFFECTS AND FIRST AID

INHALATION: GLYPHOSATE: ACUTE EXPOSURE- MAY CAUSE IRRITATION OF THE MUCOUS MEMBRANES. CHRONIC EXPOSURE- NO DATA AVAILABLE.

FIRST AID- REMOVE FROM EXPOSURE AREA TO FRESH AIR IMMEDIATELY. IF BREATHING HAS STOPPED, PERFORM ARTIFICIAL RESPIRATION. KEEP PERSON WARM AND AT REST. TREAT SYMPTOMATICALLY AND SUPPORTIVELY. GET MEDICAL ATTENTION IMMEDIATELY.

SKIN CONTACT: GLYPHOSATE: ACUTE EXPOSURE- CONTACT PRODUCED VERY SLIGHT ERYTHEMA IN 2 OF 6 RABBITS TESTED. CHRONIC EXPOSURE- REPEATED APPLICATION TO GUINEA PIG SKIN PRODUCED MODERATE TO SEVERE ERYTHEMA, EDEMA, AND NECROSIS IN SOME OF THE ANIMALS, BUT NO SENSITIZATION REACTION WAS OBSERVED. REPEATED APPLICATION OF 5000 MG/KG TO RABBIT SKIN RESULTED IN A SLIGHT DEGREE OF IRRITATION WITH NO OBSERVABLE HEMATOLOGIC, BIOCHEMICAL OR HISTOPATHOLOGIC EFFECTS.

FIRST AID- REMOVE CONTAMINATED CLOTHING AND SHOES IMMEDIATELY. WASH AFFECTED AREA WITH SOAP OR MILD DETERGENT AND LARGE AMOUNTS OF WATER UNTIL NO EVIDENCE OF CHEMICAL REMAINS (APPROXIMATELY 15-20 MINUTES). GET MEDICAL ATTENTION IMMEDIATELY.

EYE CONTACT: GLYPHOSATE: **ACUTE EXPOSURE-** 1 OF 6 RABBITS DEVELOPED SLIGHT IRRITATION WITH CORNEAL OPACITY AND ULCERATION. NO IRRITATING EFFECTS WERE OBSERVED AFTER SEVEN DAYS. **CHRONIC EXPOSURE-** NO DATA AVAILABLE.
FIRST AID- WASH EYES IMMEDIATELY WITH LARGE AMOUNTS OF WATER OR NORMAL SALINE, OCCASIONALLY LIFTING UPPER AND LOWER LIDS, UNTIL NO EVIDENCE OF CHEMICAL REMAINS (APPROXIMATELY 15-20 MINUTES). GET MEDICAL ATTENTION IMMEDIATELY.

INGESTION: GLYPHOSATE: **ACUTE EXPOSURE-** A LETHAL DOSE IN RATS WAS 470 MG/KG. THE SYMTPOMS WERE NOT REPORTED. **CHRONIC EXPOSURE-** PROLONGED OR REPEATED ADMINISTRATION OF TECHNICAL GLYPHOSATE TO ANIMALS HAS PRODUCED DIARRHEA, NASAL DISCHARGE, INACTIVITY, REDUCED BODY WEIGHT GAIN, STOMACH HEMORRHAGES, THYMIC HYPERPLASIA, MICROSCOPIC CHANGES OF THE LIVER AND KIDNEYS, EFFECTS ON THE UTERUS, AND ADVERSE EFFECTS ON REPRODUCTION.
FIRST AID- REMOVE BY GASTRIC LAVAGE AND CATHARSIS. MAINTAIN BLOOD PRESSURE AND AIRWAY. GIVE OXYGEN IF RESPIRATION IS DEPRESSED. DO NOT PERFORM GASTRIC LAVAGE IF VICTIM IS UNCONSCIOUS. GET MEDICAL ATTENTION IMMEDIATELY (DREISBACH, HANDBOOK OF POISONING, 12TH ED.).
ADMINISTRATION OF LAVAGE OR OXYGEN SHOULD BE PERFORMED BY QUALIFIED MEDICAL PERSONNEL.
ANTIDOTE: NO SPECIFIC ANTIDOTE. TREAT SYMPTOMATICALLY AND SUPPORTIVELY.

REACTIVITY

REACTIVITY: STABLE UNDER NORMAL TEMPERATURES AND PRESSURES.
INCOMPATIBILITIES: GLYPHOSATE: ALKALI (STRONG): POSSIBLE VIOLENT, EXOTHERMIC REACTION. STEEL (UNLINED OR GALVANIZED): REACTS TO FORM HIGHLY FLAMMABLE AND EXPLOSIVE HYDROGEN GAS.
DECOMPOSITION: THERMAL DECOMPOSITION MAY RELEASE TOXIC OXIDES OF NITROGEN, PHOSPHORUS AND CARBON.
POLYMERIZATION: HAZARDOUS POLYMERIZATION HAS NOT BEEN REPORTED TO OCCUR UNDER NORMAL TEMPERATURES AND PRESSURES.

STORAGE AND DISPOSAL

OBSERVE ALL FEDERAL, STATE AND LOCAL REGULATIONS WHEN STORING OR DISPOSING OF THIS SUBSTANCE. FOR ASSISTANCE, CONTACT THE DISTRICT DIRECTOR OF THE ENVIRONMENTAL PROTECTION AGENCY.

****STORAGE****

STORE IN ACCORDANCE WITH 40 CFR 165 RECOMMENDED PROCEDURES FOR THE DISPOSAL AND STORAGE OF PESTICIDES AND PESTICIDE CONTAINERS.
DO NOT USE OR STORE IN GALVANIZED OR UNLINED STEEL SPRAY EQUIPMENT AS IT WILL REACT WITH THE METAL CAUSING A HIGHLY COMBUSTIBLE GAS.

****DISPOSAL****

DISPOSAL MUST BE IN ACCORDANCE WITH 40 CFR 165 RECOMMENDED PROCEDURES FOR THE DISPOSAL AND STORAGE OF PESTICIDES AND PESTICIDE CONTAINERS.

CONDITIONS TO AVOID

MAY BURN BUT DOES NOT IGNITE READILY. AVOID CONTACT WITH STRONG OXIDIZERS, EXCESSIVE HEAT, SPARKS, OR OPEN FLAME.

SPILL AND LEAK PROCEDURES

OCCUPATIONAL SPILL: SWEEP UP AND PLACE IN SUITABLE CLEAN, DRY CONTAINERS FOR RECLAMATION OR LATER DISPOSAL. DO NOT FLUSH SPILLED MATERIAL INTO SEWER. KEEP UNNECESSARY PEOPLE AWAY.

PROTECTIVE EQUIPMENT

VENTILATION: PROVIDE LOCAL EXHAUST OR PROCESS ENCLOSURE VENTILATION SYSTEM.
RESPIRATOR: THE FOLLOWING RESPIRATORS ARE RECOMMENDED BASED ON INFORMATION FOUND IN THE PHYSICAL DATA, TOXICITY AND HEALTH EFFECTS SECTIONS. THEY ARE RANKED IN ORDER FROM MINIMUM TO MAXIMUM RESPIRATORY PROTECTION. THE SPECIFIC RESPIRATOR SELECTED MUST BE BASED ON CONTAMINATION LEVELS FOUND IN THE WORK PLACE, MUST NOT EXCEED THE WORKING LIMITS OF THE RESPIRATOR AND BE JOINTLY APPROVED BY THE NATIONAL INSTITUTE FOR OCCUPATIONAL SAFETY AND HEALTH AND THE MINE SAFETY AND HEALTH ADMINISTRATION (NIOSH-MSHA).
CHEMICAL CARTRIDGE RESPIRATOR WITH AN ORGANIC VAPOR CARTRIDGE(S) IN COMBINATION WITH A DUST AND MIST FILTER.
GAS MASK WITH ORGANIC VAPOR CANISTER (CHIN-STYLE OR FRONT- OR BACK-MOUNTED CANISTER) WITH A DUST AND MIST FILTER.
GAS MASK WITH ORGANIC VAPOR CANISTER (CHIN-STYLE OR FRONT- OR BACK-MOUNTED CANISTER) WITH A PARTICULATE FILTER.
POWERED AIR-PURIFYING RESPIRATOR WITH A HIGH-EFFICIENCY FILTER.
TYPE 'C' SUPPLIED-AIR RESPIRATOR WITH A FULL FACEPIECE OPERATED IN A PRESSURE-DEMAND OR OTHER POSITIVE PRESSURE MODE.
SELF-CONTAINED BREATHING APPARATUS WITH A FULL FACEPIECE OPERATED IN PRESSURE-DEMAND OR OTHER POSITIVE PRESSURE MODE.
FOR FIREFIGHTING AND OTHER IMMEDIATELY DANGEROUS TO LIFE OR HEALTH CONDITIONS:
SELF-CONTAINED BREATHING APPARATUS WITH FULL FACEPIECE OPERATED IN PRESSURE-DEMAND OR OTHER POSITIVE PRESSURE MODE.
SUPPLIED-AIR RESPIRATOR WITH FULL FACEPIECE AND OPERATED IN PRESSURE-DEMAND OR OTHER POSITIVE PRESSURE MODE IN COMBINATION WITH AN AUXILIARY SELF-CONTAINED BREATHING APPARATUS OPERATED IN PRESSURE-DEMAND OR OTHER POSITIVE PRESSURE MODE.
CLOTHING: EMPLOYEE MUST WEAR APPROPRIATE PROTECTIVE (IMPERVIOUS) CLOTHING AND EQUIPMENT TO PREVENT REPEATED OR PROLONGED SKIN CONTACT WITH THIS SUBSTANCE.
GLOVES: EMPLOYEE MUST WEAR APPROPRIATE PROTECTIVE GLOVES TO PREVENT CONTACT WITH THIS SUBSTANCE.
EYE PROTECTION: EMPLOYEE MUST WEAR SPLASH-PROOF OR DUST-RESISTANT SAFETY GOGGLES TO PREVENT EYE CONTACT WITH THIS SUBSTANCE.
EMERGENCY EYE WASH: WHERE THERE IS ANY POSSIBILITY THAT AN EMPLOYEE'S EYES MAY BE EXPOSED TO THIS SUBSTANCE, THE EMPLOYER SHOULD PROVIDE AN EYE WASH FOUNTAIN WITHIN THE IMMEDIATE WORK AREA FOR EMERGENCY USE.

AUTHORIZED BY- OCCUPATIONAL HEALTH SERVICES, INC.
CREATION DATE: 05/04/90 ***REVISION DATE:*** 05/31/90

MATERIAL SAFETY DATA SHEET

OCCUPATIONAL HEALTH SERVICES, INC.
AGRICULTURE AND PESTICIDE DIVISION
450 SEVENTH AVENUE, SUITE 2407
NEW YORK, NEW YORK 10123
1-800-445-MSDS OR (212) 967-1100

EMERGENCY CONTACT:
JOHN S. BRANSFORD, JR. (615) 292-1180

SUBSTANCE IDENTIFICATION

CAS-NUMBER 961-22-8
SUBSTANCE: **GUTHION OXYGEN ANALOG**
TRADE NAMES/SYNONYMS: PHOSPHOROTHIOIC ACID, O,O-DIMETHYL S-((4-OXO-1,2,3-BENZOTRIAZIN-3(4H) -YL) METHYL) ESTER; PHOSPHOROTHIOIC ACID, O,O-DIMETHYL ESTER, S-ESTER WITH 3- (MERCAPTOMETHYL)-1,2,3-BENZOTRIAZIN-4-ONE; AZINPHOSMETHYL OXON; AZINPHOSMETHYL OXYGEN ANALOG; GUTHION OXON; GUTHOXON; GUTOXON; OXOAZINPHOS-METHYL; O,O-DIMETHYL S-(14-OXO-1,2,3-BENZOTRIAZIN-3(4H)-YL)METHYL) PHOSPHOROTHIOATE; O,O-DIMETHYL S-3-(MERCAPTOMETHYL)-1,2,3-BENZOTRIAZIN-4-ONE PHOSPHOROTHIOATE; C10H12N3O4PS; PST10585
CHEMICAL FAMILY: ORGANOPHOSPHATE
MOLECULAR FORMULA: C10-H12-N3-O4-P-S
MOLECULAR WEIGHT: 301.26
CERCLA RATINGS (SCALE 0-3): HEALTH=3 FIRE=1 REACTIVITY=0 PERSISTENCE=0
NFPA RATINGS (SCALE 0-4): HEALTH=3 FIRE=1 REACTIVITY=0

COMPONENTS AND CONTAMINANTS

COMPONENT: GUTHION OXYGEN ANALOG ***PERCENT:*** 100.0
CAS# 961-22-8
OTHER CONTAMINANTS: NONE
EXPOSURE LIMITS: NO OCCUPATIONAL EXPOSURE LIMITS ESTABLISHED BY OSHA, ACGIH, OR NIOSH.

PHYSICAL DATA

DESCRIPTION: WHITE POWDER ***MELTING POINT:*** NOT AVAILABLE
SPECIFIC GRAVITY: NOT AVAILABLE ***SOLUBILITY IN WATER:*** NOT AVAILABLE

FIRE AND EXPLOSION DATA

FIRE AND EXPLOSION HAZARD: SLIGHT FIRE HAZARD WHEN EXPOSED TO HEAT OR

FLAME.

FIREFIGHTING MEDIA: DRY CHEMICAL, CARBON DIOXIDE, HALON, WATER SPRAY OR STANDARD FOAM (1987 EMERGENCY RESPONSE GUIDEBOOK, DOT P 5800.4). FOR LARGER FIRES, USE WATER SPRAY, FOG OR STANDARD FOAM (1987 EMERGENCY RESPONSE GUIDEBOOK, DOT P 5800.4).

FIREFIGHTING: MOVE CONTAINERS FROM FIRE AREA IF POSSIBLE (1987 EMERGENCY RESPONSE GUIDEBOOK, DOT P 5800.4, GUIDE PAGE 53). EXTINGUISH USING AGENT SUITABLE FOR TYPE OF SURROUNDING FIRE. AVOID BREATHING VAPORS AND DUSTS. KEEP UPWIND.

TRANSPORTATION DATA

DEPARTMENT OF TRANSPORTATION HAZARD CLASSIFICATION 49 CFR 172.101: POISON B

DEPARTMENT OF TRANSPORTATION LABELING REQUIREMENTS 49 CFR 172.101 AND SUBPART E: POISON

DEPARTMENT OF TRANSPORTATION PACKAGING REQUIREMENTS: 49 (CFR 173.377 EXCEPTIONS: 49 CFR 173.377

TOXICITY

GUTHION OXYGEN ANALOG: TOXICITY DATA: 13 MG/KG ORAL-RAT LD50 (EPA). CARCINOGEN STATUS: NONE. ACUTE TOXICITY LEVEL: HIGHLY TOXIC BY INGESTION. TARGET EFFECTS: CHOLINESTERASE INHIBITOR. POISONING MAY AFFECT THE NERVOUS SYSTEM.* AT INCREASED RISK FROM EXPOSURE: PERSONS WITH RESPIRATORY AILMENTS, RECENT EXPOSURE TO CHOLINESTERASE INHIBITORS OR IMPAIRED CHOLINESTERASE PRODUCTION, OR LIVER MALFUNCTION.* ADDITIONAL DATA: MAY CROSS THE PLACENTA. HIGH ENVIRONMENTAL TEMPERATURES OR EXPOSURE OF THE CHEMICAL TO VISIBLE OR ULTRAVIOLET LIGHT MAY ENHANCE THE TOXICITY. INTERACTIONS WITH MEDICATIONS MAY OCCUR.*

* MAY BE BASED ON GENERAL INFORMATION ON ORGANOPHOSPHATES.

HEALTH EFFECTS AND FIRST AID

INHALATION: GUTHION OXYGEN ANALOG: SEE INFORMATION ON ORGANOPHOSPHATES.

ORGANOPHOSPHATES: CHOLINESTERASE INHIBITOR. **ACUTE EXPOSURE-** WHEN INHALED, THE FIRST EFFECTS OF CHOLINESTERASE INHIBITORS ARE USUALLY RESPIRATORY AND MAY INCLUDE NASAL HYPEREMIA AND WATERY DISCHARGE, COUGH, CHEST DISCOMFORT, DYSPNEA, AND WHEEZING DUE TO INCREASED BRONCHIAL SECRETIONS AND BRONCHOCONSTRICTION. IF SUFFICIENT AMOUNTS ARE ABSORBED, OTHER SYSTEMIC EFFECTS MAY BEGIN WITHIN A FEW MINUTES OR BE DELAYED FOR UP TO 12 HOURS. SYMPTOMS MAY INCLUDE PALLOR, NAUSEA, VOMITING, DIARRHEA, ABDOMINAL CRAMPS, HEADACHE, DIZZINESS, OCULAR PAIN, BLURRED VISION, MIOSIS OR IN SOME CASES, ESPECIALLY INITIALLY, MYDRIASIS, LACRIMATION, SALIVATION, SWEATING, AND CONFUSION. OTHER REPORTED CENTRAL NERVOUS SYSTEM OR NEUROMUSCULAR EFFECTS MAY INCLUDE ATAXIA, SLURRED SPEECH, AREFLEXIA, WEAKNESS, FATIGUE, FASCICULATIONS, TWITCHING, TREMORS POSSIBLY OF THE TONGUE AND EYELIDS, AND EVENTUALLY PARALYSIS OF THE EXTREMITIES AND POSSIBLY OF THE RESPIRATORY MUSCLES. IN SEVERE CASES THERE MAY ALSO BE INVOLUNTARY DEFECATION AND URINATION, CYANOSIS, PSYCHOSIS, HYPERGLYCEMIA, ACUTE PANCREATITIS, CARDIAC IRREGULARITIES, PULMONARY EDEMA, UNCONSCIOUSNESS, CONVULSIONS, AND COMA. DEATH IS PRIMARILY DUE TO RESPIRATORY FAILURE, ALTHOUGH CARDIOVASCULAR EFFECTS INCLUDING CARDIAC ARREST MAY ALSO BE IMPLICATED. LONG TERM SEQUELAE ARE RARE BUT MAY INCLUDE NEUROPSYCHIATRIC DISORDERS AND MYOPATHY WITH MUSCLE TENDERNESS. SOME ORGANOPHOSPHATES MAY CAUSE A DELAYED NEUROPATHY BEGINNING 1-4 WEEKS AFTER AN ACUTE EXPOSURE WHICH MAY OR MAY NOT HAVE CAUSED ACUTE CHOLINERGIC EFFECTS. NUMBNESS, TINGLING, WEAKNESS AND CRAMPING BEGINNING SYMMETRICALLY IN THE LOWER LIMBS MAY PROGRESS TO ATAXIA AND PARALYSIS. IN SEVERE CASES, UPPER LIMB INVOLVEMENT IS POSSIBLE AND FLACCID PARALYSIS MAY PROGRESS TO SPASTIC PARALYSIS WITH EXAGGERATED REFLEXES. IMPROVEMENT MAY OCCUR OVER MONTHS TO YEARS, BUT SOME RESIDUAL IMPAIRMENT USUALLY REMAINS. **CHRONIC EXPOSURE-** REPEATED OR PROLONGED EXPOSURE MAY RESULT IN THE EFFECTS OF ACUTE EXPOSURE INCLUDING THE DELAYED NEUROPATHY. OTHER EFFECTS REPORTED IN WORKERS REPEATEDLY EXPOSED INCLUDE IMPAIRED MEMORY AND CONCENTRATION, ACUTE PSYCHOSIS, SEVERE DEPRESSIONS, IRRITABILTY, CONFUSION, APATHY, EMOTIONAL LABILITY, SOCIAL WITHDRAWAL, CONFUSION, HEADACHE, SPEECH DIFFICULTIES, DELAYED REACTION TIMES, SPATIAL DISORIENTATION, NIGHTMARES, SLEEPWALKING, AND DROWSINESS OR INSOMNIA. AN INFLUENZA-LIKE CONDITION WITH HEADACHE, NAUSEA, WEAKNESS, ANOREXIA AND MALAISE HAS ALSO BEEN REPORTED.

FIRST AID- REMOVE FROM EXPOSURE AREA TO FRESH AIR IMMEDIATELY. IF BREATHING HAS STOPPED, GIVE ARTIFICIAL RESPIRATION. MAINTAIN AIRWAY AND BLOOD PRESSURE AND ADMINISTER OXYGEN IF AVAILABLE. KEEP AFFECTED PERSON WARM AND AT REST. TREAT SYMPTOMATICALLY AND SUPPORTIVELY. ADMINISTRATION OF OXYGEN SHOULD BE PERFORMED BY QUALIFIED PERSONNEL. GET MEDICAL ATTENTION IMMEDIATELY.

SKIN CONTACT: GUTHION OXYGEN ANALOG: SEE INFORMATION ON ORGANOPHOSPHATES.

ORGANOPHOSPHATES: CHOLINESTERASE INHIBITOR. **ACUTE EXPOSURE-** LOCALIZED SWEATING AND FASCICULATIONS MAY OCCUR AT THE SITE OF CONTACT. IF SUFFICIENT AMOUNTS ARE ABSORBED, OTHER EFFECTS OF CHOLINESTERASE INHIBITION AS DESCRIBED IN ACUTE INHALATION MAY OCCUR. SYMPTOMS MAY BE DELAYED 2-3 HOURS, BUT USUALLY NO MORE THAN 12 HOURS. THE RATE OF ABSORPTION IS INCREASED BY THE PRESENCE OF DERMATITIS OR HIGH AMBIENT TEMPERATURES. DELAYED NEUROPATHY IS ALSO POSSIBLE. **CHRONIC EXPOSURE-** REPEATED OR PROLONGED EXPOSURE MAY CAUSE EFFECTS AS DESCRIBED IN ACUTE EXPOSURE. SOME ORGANOPHOSPHATES MAY CAUSE SENSITIZATION.

FIRST AID- REMOVE CONTAMINATED CLOTHING IMMEDIATELY. WASH CONTAMINATED AREAS WITH SOAP AND WATER FOLLOWED BY ALCOHOL (ARENA, POISONING, 4TH ED.). EMERGENCY PERSONNEL SHOULD WEAR GLOVES AND AVOID CONTAMINATION. TREAT RESPIRATORY DIFFICULTY WITH ARTIFICIAL RESPIRATION. GET MEDICAL ATTENTION IMMEDIATELY.

EYE CONTACT: GUTHION OXYGEN ANALOG: SEE INFORMATION ON ORGANOPHOSPHATES.

ORGANOPHOSPHATES: CHOLINESTERASE INHIBITOR. **ACUTE EXPOSURE-** DIRECT CONTACT MAY CAUSE PAIN, HYPEREMIA, LACRIMATION, TWITCHING OF THE EYELIDS, MIOSIS, AND CILIARY MUSCLE SPASM WITH LOSS OF ACCOMODATION, BLURRED OR DIMMED VISION AND BROWACHE. SOMETIMES MYDRIASIS MAY OCCUR INSTEAD OF MIOSIS. WITH SUFFICIENT EXPOSURE, OTHER SYMPTOMS OF CHOLINESTERASE INHIBITION AS DESCRIBED IN ACUTE INHALATION MAY OCCUR. **CHRONIC EXPOSURE-** REPEATED OR PROLONGED EXPOSURE MAY CAUSE EFFECTS AS DESCRIBED IN ACUTE EXPOSURE. SOME COMPOUNDS HAVE CAUSED TOXIC EFFECTS ON THE CRYSTALLINE LENS, CONJUNCTIVAL THICKENING AND OBSTRUCTION OF THE NASOLACRIMAL CANALS WHEN USED AS MIOTIC EYEDROPS.

FIRST AID- IRRIGATE EYES WITH WATER OR SALINE SOLUTION. IF SYMPTOMS OF POISONING OCCUR, TREAT RESPIRATORY DIFFICULTY WITH ARTIFICIAL RESPIRATION AND OXYGEN. OBSERVE PATIENT FOR AT LEAST 24-36 HOURS (GOSSELIN, CLINICAL TOXICOLOGY OF COMMERCIAL PRODUCTS, 5TH ED.). GET MEDICAL ATTENTION IMMEDIATELY. OXYGEN SHOULD BE ADMINISTERED BY QUALIFIED MEDICAL PERSONNEL.

INGESTION: GUTHION OXYGEN ANALOG: HIGHLY TOXIC. SEE INFORMATION ON ORGANOPHOSPHATES.

ORGANOPHOSPHATES: CHOLINESTERASE INHIBITOR. **ACUTE EXPOSURE-** WHEN INGESTED, THE FIRST EFFECTS MAY BE NAUSEA, VOMITING, ANOREXIA, ABDOMINAL CRAMPS AND DIARRHEA. GASTROINTESTINAL ABSORPTION MAY CAUSE SYMPTOMS OF CHOLINESTERASE INHIBITION AS DESCRIBED IN ACUTE INHALATION. SYMPTOMS MAY BEGIN WITHIN MINUTES OR BE DELAYED FOR HOURS. DELAYED EFFECTS INCLUDING NEUROPATHY MAY ALSO OCCUR. **CHRONIC EXPOSURE-** REPEATED INGESTION MAY CAUSE EFFECTS AS DESCRIBED IN ACUTE EXPOSURE.

FIRST AID- IF PERSON IS ALERT AND RESPIRATION IS NOT DEPRESSED, GIVE SYRUP OF IPECAC FOLLOWED BY WATER (IF VOMITING OCCURS, KEEP HEAD BELOW HIPS TO PREVENT ASPIRATION). IF CONSCIOUSNESS LEVEL DECLINES OR VOMITING HAS NOT OCCURRED IN 15 MINUTES EMPTY STOMACH BY GASTRIC LAVAGE WITH THE AID OF CUFFED ENDOTRACHEAL TUBE USING ISOTONIC SALINE OR 5% SODIUM BICARBONATE FOLLOW WITH ACTIVATED CHARCOAL. ESTABLISH AND MAINTAIN AIRWAY. TREAT RESPIRATORY DIFFICULTY WITH ARTIFICIAL RESPIRATION AND OXYGEN. DO NOT GIVE MORPHINE, AMINOPHYLLINE, PHENOTHIAZINES, RESERPINE, FUROSEMIDE, OR ETHACRYNIC ACID (MORGAN, RECOGNITION AND MANAGEMENT OF PESTICIDE POISONINGS, 3RD ED.). TREAT SYMPTOMATICALLY AND SUPPORTIVELY. ADMINISTRATION OF OXYGEN AND LAVAGE MUST BE PERFORMED BY QUALIFIED MEDICAL PERSONNEL. GET MEDICAL ATTENTION IMMEDIATELY.

ANTIDOTE: THE FOLLOWING ANTIDOTE(S) HAVE BEEN RECOMMENDED. HOWEVER, THE DECISION AS TO WHETHER THE SEVERITY OF POISONING REQUIRES ADMINISTRATION OF ANY ANTIDOTE AND ACTUAL DOSE REQUIRED SHOULD BE MADE BY QUALIFIED MEDICAL PERSONNEL.

FOR CHOLINESTERASE INHIBITORS: ESTABLISH CLEAR AIRWAY AND TISSUE OXYGENATION BY ASPIRATION OF SECRETIONS, AND IF NECESSARY, BY ASSISTED PULMONARY VENTILATION WITH OXYGEN. IMPROVE TISSUE OXYGENATION AS MUCH AS POSSIBLE BEFORE ADMINISTERING ATROPINE TO MINIMIZE THE RISK OF VENTRICULAR FIBRILLATION. ADMINISTER ATROPINE SULFATE INTRAVENOUSLY, OR INTRAMUSCULARLY IF IV INJECTION IS NOT POSSIBLE. IN MODERATELY SEVERE POISONING ADMINISTER ATROPINE SULFATE, 0.4-2.0 MG REPEATED EVERY 15 MINUTES UNTIL ATROPINIZATION IS ACHIEVED (TACHYCARDIA, FLUSHING, DRY MOUTH, MYDRIASIS). MAINTAIN ATROPINIZATION BY REPEATED DOSES FOR 2-12

HOURS, OR LONGER, DEPENDING ON THE SEVERITY OF POISONING. THE APPEARANCE OF RALES IN THE LUNG BASES, MIOSIS, SALIVATION, NAUSEA, BRADYCARDIA, ARE ALL INDICATIONS OF INADEQUATE ATROPINIZATION. SEVERELY POISONED INDIVIDUALS MAY EXHIBIT REMARKABLE TOLERANCE TO ATROPINE; TWO OR MORE TIMES THE DOSAGES SUGGESTED ABOVE MAY BE NEEDED. PERSONS NOT POISONED OR ONLY SLIGHTLY POISONED, HOWEVER, MAY DEVELOP SIGNS OF ATROPINE TOXICITY FROM SUCH LARGE DOSAGES: FEVER, MUSCLE FIBRILLATIONS, AND DELIRIUM ARE THE MAIN SIGNS OF ATROPINE TOXICITY. IF THESE SIGNS APPEAR WHILE THE PATIENT IS FULLY ATROPINIZED, ATROPINE ADMINISTRATION SHOULD BE DISCONTINUED, AT LEAST TEMPORARILY. OBSERVE TREATED PATIENTS CLOSELY AT LEAST 24 HOURS TO INSURE THAT SYMPTOMS (POSSIBLY PULMONARY EDEMA) DO NOT RECUR AS ATROPINIZATION WEARS OFF. IN VERY SEVERE POISONINGS, METABOLIC DISPOSITION OF TOXICANT MAY REQUIRE SEVERAL HOURS OR DAYS DURING WHICH ATROPINIZATION MUST BE MAINTAINED. MARKEDLY LOWER LEVELS OF URINARY METABOLITES INDICATE THAT ATROPINE DOSAGE CAN BE TAPERED OFF. AS DOSAGE IS REDUCED, CHECK THE LUNG BASES FREQUENTLY FOR RALES. IF RALES ARE HEARD OR OTHER SYMPTOMS RETURN, RE-ESTABLISH ATROPINIZATION PROMPTLY (MORGAN, RECOGNITION AND MANAGEMENT OF PESTICIDE POISONINGS, 3RD ED.). ADMINISTRATION OF ANTIDOTE MUST BE PERFORMED BY QUALIFIED MEDICAL PERSONNEL.

IN CASES OF SEVERE POISONING BY ORGANOPHOSPHATE PESTICIDES IN WHICH RESPIRATORY DEPRESSION, MUSCLE WEAKNESS AND TWITCHINGS ARE SEVERE, GIVE PRALIDOXIME (PROTOPAM-AYERST, 2-PAM), 1.0 GRAM INTRAVENOUSLY AT NO MORE THAN 0.5 GRAM PER MINUTE. DOSAGE OF PRALIDOXIME MAY BE REPEATED IN 1-2 HOURS, THEN AT 10-12 HOUR INTERVALS IF NEEDED. IN VERY SEVERE POISONINGS, DOSAGE RATES MAY BE DOUBLED. TREATMENT WITH PRALIDOXIME WILL BE MOST EFFECTIVE IF GIVEN WITHIN THIRTY-SIX HOURS AFTER POISONING (MORGAN, RECOGNITION AND MANAGEMENT OF PESTICIDE POISONINGS, 3RD ED.). ANTIDOTE SHOULD BE ADMINISTERED BY QUALIFIED MEDICAL PERSONNEL.

REACTIVITY

REACTIVITY: STABLE UNDER NORMAL TEMPERATURES AND PRESSURES.

INCOMPATIBILITIES: GUTHION OXYGEN ANALOG: OXIDIZERS (STRONG): FIRE AND EXPLOSION HAZARD.

DECOMPOSITION: THERMAL DECOMPOSITION PRODUCTS MAY INCLUDE TOXIC OXIDES OF NITROGEN, CARBON, PHOSPHORUS, AND SULFUR.

POLYMERIZATION: HAZARDOUS POLYMERIZATION HAS NOT BEEN REPORTED TO OCCUR UNDER NORMAL TEMPERATURES AND PRESSURES.

STORAGE AND DISPOSAL

OBSERVE ALL FEDERAL, STATE AND LOCAL REGULATIONS WHEN STORING OR DISPOSING OF THIS SUBSTANCE. FOR ASSISTANCE, CONTACT THE DISTRICT DIRECTOR OF THE ENVIRONMENTAL PROTECTION AGENCY.

****STORAGE****

STORE AWAY FROM INCOMPATIBLE SUBSTANCES.

CONDITIONS TO AVOID

MAY BURN BUT DOES NOT IGNITE READILY.

SPILL AND LEAK PROCEDURES

OCCUPATIONAL SPILL: DO NOT TOUCH SPILLED MATERIAL. STOP LEAK IF YOU CAN DO IT WITHOUT RISK. FOR SMALL SPILLS, TAKE UP WITH SAND OR OTHER ABSORBENT MATERIAL AND PLACE INTO CONTAINERS FOR LATER DISPOSAL. FOR SMALL DRY SPILLS, WITH A CLEAN SHOVEL PLACE MATERIAL INTO CLEAN, DRY CONTAINER AND COVER. MOVE CONTAINERS FROM SPILL AREA. FOR LARGER SPILLS, DIKE FAR AHEAD OF SPILL FOR LATER DISPOSAL. KEEP UNNECESSARY PEOPLE AWAY. ISOLATE HAZARD AREA AND DENY ENTRY.

PROTECTIVE EQUIPMENT

VENTILATION: PROVIDE LOCAL EXHAUST OR PROCESS ENCLOSURE VENTILATION SYSTEM.

RESPIRATOR: THE FOLLOWING RESPIRATORS ARE RECOMMENDED BASED ON INFORMATION FOUND IN THE PHYSICAL DATA, TOXICITY AND HEALTH EFFECTS SECTIONS. THEY ARE RANKED IN ORDER FROM MINIMUM TO MAXIMUM RESPIRATORY PROTECTION. THE SPECIFIC RESPIRATOR SELECTED MUST BE BASED ON CONTAMINATION LEVELS FOUND IN THE WORK PLACE, MUST NOT EXCEED THE WORKING LIMITS OF THE RESPIRATOR AND BE JOINTLY APPROVED BY THE NATIONAL INSTITUTE FOR OCCUPATIONAL SAFETY AND HEALTH AND THE MINE SAFETY AND HEALTH ADMINISTRATION (NIOSH-MSHA).

CHEMICAL CARTRIDGE RESPIRATOR WITH AN ORGANIC VAPOR CARTRIDGE(S) WITH A FULL FACEPIECE AND ORGANIC VAPOR CARTRIDGE(S) IN COMBINATION WITH A DUST AND MIST FILTER.

POWERED AIR-PURIFYING RESPIRATOR WITH A TIGHT-FITTING FACEPIECE AND ORGANIC VAPOR CARTRIDGE(S) IN COMBINATION WITH A HIGH-EFFICIENCY PARTICULATE FILTER.

TYPE 'C' SUPPLIED-AIR RESPIRATOR WITH A FULL FACEPIECE OPERATED IN A PRESSURE-DEMAND OR OTHER POSITIVE PRESSURE MODE.

SELF-CONTAINED BREATHING APPARATUS WITH A FULL FACEPIECE OPERATED IN PRESSURE-DEMAND OR OTHER POSITIVE PRESSURE MODE.

FOR FIREFIGHTING AND OTHER IMMEDIATELY DANGEROUS TO LIFE OR HEALTH CONDITIONS:

SELF-CONTAINED BREATHING APPARATUS WITH FULL FACEPIECE OPERATED IN PRESSURE-DEMAND OR OTHER POSITIVE PRESSURE MODE.

SUPPLIED-AIR RESPIRATOR WITH FULL FACEPIECE AND OPERATED IN PRESSURE-DEMAND OR OTHER POSITIVE PRESSURE MODE IN COMBINATION WITH AN AUXILIARY SELF-CONTAINED BREATHING APPARATUS OPERATED IN PRESSURE-DEMAND OR OTHER POSITIVE PRESSURE MODE.

CLOTHING: EMPLOYEE MUST WEAR APPROPRIATE PROTECTIVE (IMPERVIOUS) CLOTHING AND EQUIPMENT TO PREVENT ANY POSSIBILITY OF SKIN CONTACT WITH THIS SUBSTANCE.

GLOVES: EMPLOYEE MUST WEAR APPROPRIATE PROTECTIVE GLOVES TO PREVENT CONTACT WITH THIS SUBSTANCE.

EYE PROTECTION: EMPLOYEE MUST WEAR SPLASH-PROOF OR DUST-RESISTANT SAFETY GOGGLES AND A FACESHIELD TO PREVENT CONTACT WITH THIS SUBSTANCE.

EMERGENCY WASH FACILITIES: WHERE THERE IS ANY POSSIBILITY THAT AN EMPLOYEE'S EYES AND/OR SKIN MAY BE EXPOSED TO THIS SUBSTANCE, THE EMPLOYER SHOULD PROVIDE AN EYE WASH FOUNTAIN AND QUICK DRENCH SHOWER WITHIN THE IMMEDIATE WORK AREA FOR EMERGENCY USE.

AUTHORIZED BY- OCCUPATIONAL HEALTH SERVICES, INC.

CREATION DATE: 11/17/89 ***REVISION DATE:*** 05/07/90

MATERIAL SAFETY DATA SHEET

OCCUPATIONAL HEALTH SERVICES, INC.
AGRICULTURE AND PESTICIDE DIVISION
450 SEVENTH AVENUE, SUITE 2407
NEW YORK, NEW YORK 10123
1-800-445-MSDS OR (212) 967-1100

EMERGENCY CONTACT:
JOHN S. BRANSFORD, JR. (615) 292-1180

SUBSTANCE IDENTIFICATION

CAS-NUMBER 76-44-8

SUBSTANCE: **HEPTACHLOR**

TRADE NAMES/SYNONYMS: 4,7-METHANO-1H-INDENE, 1,4,5,6,7,8,8-HEPTACHLORO-3A,4,7,7A-TETRAHYDRO-; 4,7-METHANOINDENE, 1,4,5,6,7,8,8-HEPTACHLORO-3A,4,7,7A-TETRAHYDRO-; 1,4,5,6,7,8,8-HEPTACHLORO-3A,4,7,7A-TETRAHYDRO-4,7-METHANO-1H-INDEND; 1,4,5,6,7,8,8-HEPTACHLORO-3A,4,7,7A-TETRAHYDRO-4,7-METHANOINDENE; AAHEPTA; AGROCERES; HEPTA; VELSICOL 104; DRINOX; RHODIACHLOR; NCI-COO180; OMS 193; ENT 15,152; STCC 4960630; RCRA P059; UN 27617; C10H5CL7; PST10660

CHEMICAL FAMILY: HALOGEN COMPOUND, ALICYCLIC

MOLECULAR FORMULA: C10-H5-CL7

MOLECULAR WEIGHT: 373.35

CERCLA RATINGS (SCALE 0-3): HEALTH=3 FIRE=0 REACTIVITY=0 PERSISTENCE=3

NFPA RATINGS (SCALE 0-4): HEALTH=3 FIRE=0 REACTIVITY=0

COMPONENTS AND CONTAMINANTS

COMPONENT: HEPTACHLOR ***PERCENT:*** 100.0

CAS# 76-44-8

OTHER CONTAMINANTS: HEPTACHLOR EPOXIDE

EXPOSURE LIMITS: HEPTACHLOR: 0.5 MG/M3 OSHA TWA (SKIN) 0.5 MG/M3 ACGIH TWA (SKIN)

1 POUND CERCLA SECTION 103 REPORTABLE QUANTITY SUBJECT TO SARA SECTION 313 ANNUAL TOXIC CHEMICAL RELEASE REPORTING SUBJECT TO CALIFORNIA PROPOSITION 65 CANCER AND/OR REPRODUCTIVE TOXICITY WARNING AND RELEASE REQUIREMENTS- (JULY 1, 1988)

PHYSICAL DATA

DESCRIPTION: WHITE TO LIGHT TAN CRYSTALLINE OR WAXY SOLID WTIH A MILD CAMPHOR OR CEDARLIKE ODOR.

BOILING POINT: 275-293 F (135-145 C) @ 1-1.5 MMHG (DEC)

MELTING POINT: 203-205 F (95-96 C) ***SPECIFIC GRAVITY:*** 1.57-1.59

VAPOR PRESSURE: 0.0003 MMHG @ 25 C ***SOLUBILITY IN WATER:*** 0.056 PPM

ODOR THRESHOLD: 0.02 PPM

SOLVENT SOLUBILITY: SOLUBLE IN XYLENE, ETHER, BENZENE, LIGROIN, CARBON TETRACHLORIDE, CYCLOHEXANONE, ACETONE, KEROSENE, PARAFFINIC AND AROMATIC HYDROCARBONS, MOST ORGANIC SOLVENTS; MODERATELY SOLUBLE IN ETHANOL.

FIRE AND EXPLOSION DATA

FIRE AND EXPLOSION HAZARD: NEGLIGIBLE FIRE HAZARD WHEN EXPOSED TO HEAT OR FLAME.

FIREFIGHTING MEDIA: DRY CHEMICAL, CARBON DIOXIDE, HALON, WATER SPRAY OR STANDARD FOAM (1987 EMERGENCY RESPONSE GUIDEBOOK, DOT P 5800.4). FOR LARGER FIRES, USE WATER SPRAY, FOG OR STANDARD FOAM (1987 EMERGENCY RESPONSE GUIDEBOOK, DOT P 5800.4).

FIREFIGHTING: MOVE CONTAINERS FROM FIRE AREA IF POSSIBLE. FIGHT FIRE FROM MAXIMUM DISTANCE. STAY AWAY FROM STORAGE TANK ENDS. DIKE FIRE CONTROL WATER FOR LATER DISPOSAL. DO NOT SCATTER MATERIAL (1987 EMERGENCY RESPONSE GUIDEBOOK, DOT P 5800.4, GUIDE PAGE 55). EXTINGUISH USING AGENT SUITABLE FOR TYPE OF SURROUNDING FIRE. AVOID BREATHING VAPORS AND DUSTS. KEEP UPWIND.

TRANSPORTATION DATA

DEPARTMENT OF TRANSPORTATION HAZARD CLASSIFICATION 49 CFR 172.101: POISON B

DEPARTMENT OF TRANSPORTATION LABELING REQUIREMENTS 49 CFR 172.101 AND SUBPART E: POISON

DEPARTMENT OF TRANSPORTATION PACKAGING REQUIREMENTS: 49 CFR 173.365 EXCEPTIONS: 49 CFR 173.364

TOXICITY

HEPTACHLOR: TOXICITY DATA: 150 MG/M3/4 HOURS INHALATION-CAT LCLO; 200 MG/M3/4 HOURS INHALATION-MAMMAL LCLO; 119 MG/KG SKIN-RAT LD50; 1 GM/KG SKIN-GUINEA PIG LDLO; 40 MG/KG ORAL-RAT LD50; 116 MG/KG ORAL-GUINEA PIG LD50; 68 MG/KG ORAL-MOUSE LD50; 100 MG/KG ORAL-HAMSTER LD50; 50 MG/KG ORAL-CAT LDLO; 20 MG/KG INTRAVENOUS-MOUSE LDLO; 27 MG/KG INTRAPERITONEAL-RAT LD50; 130 MG/KG INTRAPERITONEAL-MOUSE LD50; 60 MG/KG UNREPORTED-MAMMAL LD50; MUTAGENIC DATA (RTECS); TUMORIGENIC DATA (RTECS). CARCINOGEN STATUS: HUMAN INADEQUATE EVIDENCE, ANIMAL LIMITED EVIDENCE (IARC GROUP-3). ORAL ADMINISTRATION OF HEPTACHLOR CONTAINING ABOUT 20% CHLORDANE PRODUCED LIVER CARCINOMAS IN MICE AND A SUGGESTION OF CARCINOGENIC EFFECTS ON THE THYROID IN FEMALE RATS. ACUTE TOXICITY LEVEL: HIGHLY TOXIC BY DERMAL ABSORPTION AND INGESTION. TARGET EFFECTS: CONVULSANT; HEPATOTOXIN. AT INCREASED RISK FROM EXPOSURE: PERSONS WITH CONVULSIVE DISORDERS AND LIVER DAMAGE. ADDITIONAL DATA: HEPTACHLOR AND ITS METABOLITE, HEPTACHLOR EPOXIDE, ACCUMULATE IN ADIPOSE TISSUE; INTENSE ACTIVITY AND STARVATION MAY MOBILIZE THE PESTICIDE RESULTING IN THE REAPPEARANCE OF TOXIC SYMPTOMS. HEPTACHLOR CROSSES THE PLACENTA AND IS EXCRETED IN HUMAN MILK. STUDIES OF 2 GROUPS OF WORKERS, ONE INVOLVED IN THE MANUFACTURE OF CHLORDANE, HEPTACHLOR, AND ENDRIN AND THE OTHER OF CHLORDANE AND HEPTACHLOR, REVEALED A STATISTICALLY SIGNIFICANT INCREASE IN DEATHS FROM CEREBROVASCULAR DISEASE IN THE FORMER BUT NOT THE LATTER; THE FORMER STUDY HAD METHODOLOGICAL DEFICIENCIES. STIMULANTS SUCH AS EPINEPHRINE MAY INDUCE VENTRICULAR FIBRILLATIONS.

HEALTH EFFECTS AND FIRST AID

INHALATION: HEPTACHLOR: 100 MG/M3 IMMEDIATELY DANGEROUS TO LIFE OR HEALTH. CONVULSANT. **ACUTE EXPOSURE-** MAY BE ABSORBED THROUGH THE LUNGS TO PRODUCE SYMPTOMS CHARACTERISTIC OF CHLORINATED CYCLODIENE PESTICIDES INCLUDING MUSCLE TWITCHING, MYOCLONIC JERKING, AND CONVULSIVE SEIZURES. THE CONVULSIONS MAY OCCUR WITH PERIODS OF UNCONSCIOUSNESS. OTHER SYMPTOMS MAY INCLUDE HEADACHE, NAUSEA, VOMITING, MALAISE, AND DIZZINESS. IN CASES OF GROSS OVEREXPOSURE, CONVULSIONS MAY OCCUR WITHOUT ANY PRIOR SYMPTOMS. ABNORMAL EEG PATTERNS MAY BE OBSERVED AND MAY PERSIST FOR WEEKS OR MONTHS WHILE NO OTHER OBSERVABLE SIGNS OF POISONING MAY EXIST. **CHRONIC EXPOSURE-** IN ADDITION TO THE SYMPTOMS OF ACUTE EXPOSURE, CHRONIC EXPOSURE OF HUMANS TO TECHNICAL CHLORDANE CONTAINING HEPTACHLOR AND OTHER CHEMICALS HAS CAUSED LIGHTHEADEDNESS, NAUSEA, COUGH, CHEST COMPLAINTS, TREMORS, ARTHRALGIAS, FATIGUE, THROMBOCYTOPENIC PURPURA, AND MARKED BRUISING. PANCYTOPENIA, APLASTIC, HEMOLYTIC, AND MEGALOBLASTIC ANEMIAS, LEUKEMIA, AND DEATH HAVE ALSO BEEN REPORTED.

FIRST AID- REMOVE FROM EXPOSURE AREA TO FRESH AIR IMMEDIATELY. IF BREATHING HAS STOPPED, GIVE ARTIFICIAL RESPIRATION. MAINTAIN AIRWAY AND BLOOD PRESSURE AND ADMINISTER OXYGEN IF AVAILABLE. KEEP AFFECTED PERSON WARM AND AT REST. TREAT SYMPTOMATICALLY AND SUPPORTIVELY. ADMINISTRATION OF OXYGEN SHOULD BE PERFORMED BY QUALIFIED PERSONNEL. GET MEDICAL ATTENTION IMMEDIATELY.

SKIN CONTACT: HEPTACHLOR: CONVULSANT/HIGHLY TOXIC. **ACUTE EXPOSURE-** A LETHAL DOSE IN RABBITS FROM DERMAL ABSORPTION OF DRY POWDER WAS 2000 MG/KG; REPORTED SYMPTOMS WERE SEVERE ANOREXIA, HYPEREXCITABILITY, CONVULSIONS, AND DEATH. THE LETHAL DOSE IN RATS FROM DERMAL ABSORPTION OF HEPTACHLOR IN XYLENE WAS 195 MG/KG. CHLORINATED CYCLODIENE PESTICIDES ARE ABSORBED FROM THE SKIN AND MAY PRODUCE CENTRAL NERVOUS SYSTEM EFFECTS WITH SYMPTOMS OF MOTOR HYPEREXCITABILITY THAT MAY INCLUDE MUSCLE TWITCHING, MYOCLONIC JERKING, AND CONVULSIVE SEIZURES. THE CONVULSIONS MAY OCCUR WITH PERIODS OF UNCONSCIOUSNESS. OTHER SYMPTOMS MAY INCLUDE HEADACHE, NAUSEA, VOMITING, MALAISE, AND DIZZINESS. IN CASES OF GROSS OVEREXPOSURE, CONVULSIONS MAY OCCUR WITHOUT ANY PRIOR SYMPTOMS. ABNORMAL EEG PATTERNS MAY BE OBSERVED; THESE CHANGES IN EEG PATTERNS MAY PERSIST FOR WEEKS OR MONTHS WHILE NO OTHER OBSERVABLE SIGNS OF POISONING MAY EXIST. **CHRONIC EXPOSURE-** PROLONGED OR REPEATED EXPOSURE MAY CAUSE EFFECTS AS DETAILED IN CHRONIC INHALATION. WHEN APPLIED TO RABBITS AS A 20% SOLUTION IN DIMETHYL PHTHALATE, THE APPROXIMATE LETHAL DOSE WAS LESS THAN 780 MG/KG BUT WHEN IT WAS APPLIED IN REPEATED SMALLER DOSES, THE APPROXIMATE LD50 WAS LESS THAN 20 MG/KG PER DAY AND THERE WERE NO SURVIVORS AFTER 14 DOSES OF 28 MG/KG.

FIRST AID- REMOVE CONTAMINATED CLOTHING AND SHOES IMMEDIATELY. WASH AFFECTED AREA WITH SOAP OR MILD DETERGENT AND LARGE AMOUNTS OF WATER UNTIL NO EVIDENCE OF CHEMICAL REMAINS (APPROXIMATELY 15-20 MINUTES). GET MEDICAL ATTENTION IMMEDIATELY.

EYE CONTACT: HEPTACHLOR: **ACUTE EXPOSURE-** NO DATA AVAILABLE. **CHRONIC EXPOSURE-** NO DATA AVAILABLE.

FIRST AID- WASH EYES IMMEDIATELY WITH LARGE AMOUNTS OF WATER OR NORMAL SALINE, OCCASIONALLY LIFTING UPPER AND LOWER LIDS, UNTIL NO EVIDENCE OF CHEMICAL REMAINS (APPROXIMATELY 15-20 MINUTES). GET MEDICAL ATTENTION IMMEDIATELY.

INGESTION: HEPTACHLOR: CONVULSANT/HEPATOTOXIN/CARCINOGEN/HIGHLY TOXIC. **ACUTE EXPOSURE-** MAY CAUSE NAUSEA, VOMITING, DIARRHEA, AND GASTROINTESTINAL IRRITATION. IN ANIMAL STUDIES, INGESTION PRODUCED NEUROTOXIC EFFECTS OF HYPOACTIVITY, ATAXIA, TREMORS AND CONVULSIONS, CHANGES IN EEG PATTERNS, AND DEATH. SIMILAR EFFECTS HAVE BEEN OBSERVED IN HUMANS EXPOSED TO CHLORINATED CYCLODIENE PESTICIDES. IN RATS, ACUTE ORAL DOSES PRODUCED LIVER NECROSIS, CELL VACUOLIZATION, LIVER STEATOSIS, AND INCREASED RELATIVE LIVER WEIGHT. OTHER EFFECTS INCLUDED ELEVATED SERUM LEVELS OF ALDOLASE, GLUTAMIC-PYRUVIC TRANSAMINASE, BILIRUBIN, ALKALINE PHOSPHATASE, AND CHOLESTEROL. **CHRONIC EXPOSURE-** LONG-TERM EXPOSURES PRODUCED RENAL TOXICITY, HEMATOLOGIC EFFECTS, AND ADRENOTOXICITY IN ANIMALS. REPEATED ADMINISTRATION TO RATS PRODUCED CHRONIC CONVULSIONS, OPISTHOTONOS, HYPERREFLEXIA, RAPID RESPIRATION, AND CATARACTS. HISTOLOGIC EVIDENCE OF SEVERE LIVER DAMAGE, INCREASED LIVER WEIGHT, INCREASED LEVELS OF SERUM COMPONENTS INDICATIVE OF HEPATIC DAMAGE, AND DECREASED BODY WEIGHTS WERE ALSO OBSERVED IN ANIMAL STUDIES. A DAILY INTAKE OF 1 MG/KG FOR ALMOST A YEAR WAS LETHAL IN DOGS. MALE AND FEMALE MICE THAT RECEIVED HEPTACHLOR IN THE DIET FOR 10 WEEKS WERE UNABLE TO PRODUCE A NEW GENERATION. DECREASED PREGNANCY RATES WERE REPORTED FOLLOWING ORAL ADMINISTRATION OF HEPTACHLOR TO MALE AND FEMALE RATS FOR TWO GENERATIONS. IN MALE AND FEMALE RATS FED HEPTACHLOR, HEPTACHLOR EPOXIDE, OR A MIXTURE OF THE TWO FOR THREE GENERATIONS, THE NUMBER OF RESORBED FETUSES INCREASED AND FERTILITY DECREASED WITH SUCCEEDING GENERATIONS. ORAL ADMINISTRATION OF HEPTACHLOR CONTAINING 20% CHLORDANE PRODUCED LIVER CARCINOMAS IN MICE AND A SUGGESTION OF CARCINOGENIC EFFECTS ON THE THYROID IN FEMALE RATS.

FIRST AID- IF THE PERSON IS CONSCIOUS AND NOT CONVULSING, REMOVE BY GIVING SYRUP OF IPECAC (IF VOMITING OCCURS, KEEP THE HEAD BELOW THE HIPS TO PREVENT ASPIRATION). GIVE ACTIVATED CHARCOAL FOLLOWED BY GASTRIC LAVAGE. FOLLOW WITH A SALINE CATHARTIC. DO NOT GIVE FATS OR OILS. INTESTINAL LAVAGE WITH 20% MANNITOL (200 ML) BY STOMACH TUBE IS ALSO USEFUL. GIVE ARTIFICIAL RESPIRATION WITH OXYGEN IF RESPIRATION IS DEPRESSED (DREISBACH, HANDBOOK OF POISONING, 12TH ED.). TREAT SYMPTOMATICALLY AND SUPPORTIVELY. LAVAGE AND ADMINISTRATION OF OXYGEN SHOULD BE PERFORMED BY QUALIFIED MEDICAL PERSONNEL. GET MEDICAL ATTENTION IMMEDIATELY.

ANTIDOTE: NO SPECIFIC ANTIDOTE. TREAT SYMPTOMATICALLY AND SUPPORTIVELY.

REACTIVITY

REACTIVITY: STABLE UNDER NORMAL TEMPERATURES AND PRESSURES.

INCOMPATIBILITIES: HEPTACHLOR: ALKALI (STRONG): INCOMPATIBLE. IRON AND RUST: CONTACT WITH MELTED HEPTACHLOR MAY PRODUCE TOXIC HYDROGEN CHLORIDE GAS.
DECOMPOSITION: THERMAL DECOMPOSITION MAY RELEASE CORROSIVE FUMES OF HYDROGEN CHLORIDE AND TOXIC OXIDES OF CARBON.
POLYMERIZATION: HAZARDOUS POLYMERIZATION HAS NOT BEEN REPORTED TO OCCUR UNDER NORMAL TEMPERATURES AND PRESSURES.

STORAGE AND DISPOSAL

OBSERVE ALL FEDERAL, STATE AND LOCAL REGULATIONS WHEN STORING OR DISPOSING OF THIS SUBSTANCE. FOR ASSISTANCE, CONTACT THE DISTRICT DIRECTOR OF THE ENVIRONMENTAL PROTECTION AGENCY.

STORAGE

STORE IN ACCORDANCE WITH 40 CFR 165 RECOMMENDED PROCEDURES FOR THE DISPOSAL AND STORAGE OF PESTICIDES AND PESTICIDE CONTAINERS.
STORE AWAY FROM INCOMPATIBLE SUBSTANCES.

DISPOSAL

DISPOSAL MUST BE IN ACCORDANCE WITH 40 CFR 165 RECOMMENDED PROCEDURES FOR THE DISPOSAL AND STORAGE OF PESTICIDES AND PESTICIDE CONTAINERS.
DISPOSAL MUST BE IN ACCORDANCE WITH STANDARDS APPLICABLE TO GENERATORS OF HAZARDOUS WASTE, 40CFR 262. EPA HAZARDOUS WASTE NUMBER P059.
HEPTACHLOR (AND ITS HYDROXIDE) - REGULATORY LEVEL: 0.008 MG/L MATERIALS WHICH CONTAIN THE ABOVE SUBSTANCE AT OR ABOVE THE REGULATORY LEVEL MEET THE EPA CHARACTERISTIC OF TOXICITY, AND MUST BE DISPOSED OF IN ACCORDANCE WITH 40 CFR PART 262. EPA HAZARDOUS WASTE NUMBER D031.

CONDITIONS TO AVOID

MAY BURN BUT DOES NOT IGNITE READILY. AVOID CONTACT WITH STRONG OXIDIZERS, EXCESSIVE HEAT, SPARKS, OR OPEN FLAME.

SPILL AND LEAK PROCEDURES

SOIL SPILL: DIG HOLDING AREA SUCH AS LAGOON, POND OR PIT FOR CONTAINMENT. USE PROTECTIVE COVER SUCH AS A PLASTIC SHEET TO PREVENT MATERIAL FROM DISSOLVING IN FIRE EXTINGUISHING WATER OR RAIN.
WATER SPILL: TRAP SPILLED MATERIAL AT BOTTOM IN DEEP WATER POCKETS, EXCAVATED HOLDING AREAS OR WITHIN SAND BAG BARRIERS.
USE ACTIVATED CARBON TO ABSORB SPILLED SUBSTANCE THAT IS DISSOLVED.
USE SUCTION HOSES TO REMOVE TRAPPED SPILL MATERIAL.
USE MECHANICAL DREDGES OR LIFTS TO EXTRACT IMMOBILIZED MASSES OF POLLUTION AND PRECIPITATES.
THE CALIFORNIA SAFE DRINKING WATER AND TOXIC ENFORCEMENT ACT OF 1986 (PROPOSITION 65) PROHIBITS CONTAMINATING ANY KNOWN SOURCE OF DRINKING WATER WITH SUBSTANCES KNOWN TO CAUSE CANCER AND/OR REPRODUCTIVE TOXICITY.
OCCUPATIONAL SPILL: SWEEP UP AND PLACE IN SUITABLE CLEAN, DRY CONTAINERS FOR RECLAMATION OR LATER DISPOSAL. DO NOT FLUSH SPILLED MATERIAL INTO SEWER. KEEP UNNECESSARY PEOPLE AWAY.
REPORTABLE QUANTITY (RQ): 1 POUND THE SUPERFUND AMENDMENTS AND REAUTHORIZATION ACT (SARA) SECTION 304 REQUIRES THAT A RELEASE EQUAL TO OR GREATER THAN THE REPORTABLE QUANTITY FOR THIS SUBSTANCE BE IMMEDIATELY REPORTED TO THE LOCAL EMERGENCY PLANNING COMMITTEE AND THE STATE EMERGENCY RESPONSE COMMISSION (40 CFR 355.40). IF THE RELEASE OF THIS SUBSTANCE IS REPORTABLE UNDER CERCLA SECTION 103, THE NATIONAL RESPONSE CENTER MUST BE NOTIFIED IMMEDIATELY AT (800) 424-8802 OR (202) 426-2675 IN THE METROPOLITAN WASHINGTON, D.C. AREA (40 CFR 302.6).

PROTECTIVE EQUIPMENT

VENTILATION: PROVIDE LOCAL EXHAUST VENTILATION AND/OR GENERAL DILUTION VENTILATION TO MEET PUBLISHED EXPOSURE LIMITS.
RESPIRATOR: THE FOLLOWING RESPIRATORS AND MAXIMUM USE CONCENTRATIONS ARE RECOMMENDATIONS BY THE U.S. DEPARTMENT OF HEALTH AND HUMAN SERVICES, NIOSH POCKET GUIDE TO CHEMICAL HAZARDS; NIOSH CRITERIA DOCUMENTS OR BY THE U.S. DEPARTMENT OF LABOR, 29 CFR 1910 SUBPART Z. THE SPECIFIC RESPIRATOR SELECTED MUST BE BASED ON CONTAMINATION LEVELS FOUND IN THE WORK PLACE, MUST NOT EXCEED THE WORKING LIMITS OF THE RESPIRATOR AND BE JOINTLY APPROVED BY THE NATIONAL INSTITUTE FOR OCCUPATIONAL SAFETY AND HEALTH AND THE MINE SAFETY AND HEALTH ADMINISTRATION (NIOSH-MSHA).
HEPTACHLOR:
5 MG/M3- ANY SUPPLIED-AIR RESPIRATOR. ANY SELF-CONTAINED BREATHING APPARATUS.
12.5 MG/M3- ANY SUPPLIED-AIR RESPIRATOR OPERATED IN A CONTINUOUS FLOW MODE.
25 MG/M3- ANY SUPPLIED-AIR RESPIRATOR WITH A FULL FACEPIECE. ANY SELF-CONTAINED BREATHING APPARATUS WITH A FULL FACEPIECE. ANY ANY SUPPLIED-AIR RESPIRATOR WITH A TIGHT-FITTING FACEPIECE OPERATED IN A CONTINUOUS FLOW MODE.
100 MG/M3- ANY SUPPLIED-AIR RESPIRATOR WITH A HALF-MASK AND OPERATED IN A PRESSURE-DEMAND OR OTHER POSITIVE PRESSURE MODE.
ESCAPE- ANY AIR-PURIFYING FULL FACEPIECE RESPIRATOR (GAS MASK) WITH A CHIN-STYLE OR FRONT- OR BACK-MOUNTED ORGANIC VAPOR CANISTER HAVING A HIGH-EFFICIENCY PARTICULATE FILTER. ANY APPROPRIATE ESCAPE-TYPE SELF-CONTAINED BREATHING APPARATUS.
FOR FIREFIGHTING AND OTHER IMMEDIATELY DANGEROUS TO LIFE OR HEALTH CONDITIONS:
SELF-CONTAINED BREATHING APPARATUS WITH FULL FACEPIECE OPERATED IN PRESSURE-DEMAND OR OTHER POSITIVE PRESSURE MODE.
SUPPLIED-AIR RESPIRATOR WITH FULL FACEPIECE AND OPERATED IN PRESSURE-DEMAND OR OTHER POSITIVE PRESSURE MODE IN COMBINATION WITH AN AUXILIARY SELF-CONTAINED BREATHING APPARATUS OPERATED IN PRESSURE-DEMAND OR OTHER POSITIVE PRESSURE MODE.
CLOTHING: EMPLOYEE MUST WEAR APPROPRIATE PROTECTIVE (IMPERVIOUS) CLOTHING AND EQUIPMENT TO PREVENT REPEATED OR PROLONGED SKIN CONTACT WITH THIS SUBSTANCE.
GLOVES: EMPLOYEE MUST WEAR APPROPRIATE PROTECTIVE GLOVES TO PREVENT CONTACT WITH THIS SUBSTANCE.
EYE PROTECTION: EMPLOYEE MUST WEAR SPLASH-PROOF OR DUST-RESISTANT SAFETY GOGGLES TO PREVENT EYE CONTACT WITH THIS SUBSTANCE.
EMERGENCY EYE WASH: WHERE THERE IS ANY POSSIBILITY THAT AN EMPLOYEE'S EYES MAY BE EXPOSED TO THIS SUBSTANCE, THE EMPLOYER SHOULD PROVIDE AN EYE WASH FOUNTAIN WITHIN THE IMMEDIATE WORK AREA FOR EMERGENCY USE.

AUTHORIZED BY- OCCUPATIONAL HEALTH SERVICES, INC.
CREATION DATE: 10/04/89 ***REVISION DATE:*** 07/13/90

MATERIAL SAFETY DATA SHEET

OCCUPATIONAL HEALTH SERVICES, INC.
AGRICULTURE AND PESTICIDE DIVISION
450 SEVENTH AVENUE, SUITE 2407
NEW YORK, NEW YORK 10123
1-800-445-MSDS OR (212) 967-1100

EMERGENCY CONTACT:
JOHN S. BRANSFORD, JR. (615) 292-1180

SUBSTANCE IDENTIFICATION

CAS-NUMBER 1024-57-3
SUBSTANCE: HEPTACHLOR EPOXIDE
TRADE NAMES/SYNONYMS: 2,5-METHANO-2H-INDENO(1,2-B)OXIRENE, 2,3,4,5,6,7,7-HEPTACHLORO-1A,1B, 5,5A,6,6A-HEXAHYDRO-, (1A(ALPHA),1B(BETA),2(ALPHA),5(ALPHA),5A(BETA), 6(BETA),6A(ALPHA)-; (1A(ALPHA),1B(BETA),2(ALPHA),5(ALPHA),5A(BETA),6(BETA),6A(ALPHA)-2,3, 4,5,6,7,7-HEPTACHLORO-1A,1B,5,5A,6,6A-HEXAHYDRO-2,5-METHANO-2H-INDENO(1,2-B)OXIRENE; 2,3,4,5,6,7,7-HEPTACHLORO-1A,1B,5,5A,6,6A-HEXAHYDRO-2,5-METHANO-2H- INDENO(1,2-B)OXIRENE; 4,7-METHANOINDAN, 1,4,5,6,7,8,8-HEPTACHLORO-2,3-EPOXY-3A,4,7,7A- TETRAHYDRO-; 1,4,5,6,7,8,8-HEPTACHLORO-2,3-EPOXY-3A,4,7,7A-TETRAHYDRO-4,7- METHANOINDAN; EPOXYHEPTACHLOR; HCE; BETA-HEPTACHLOREPOXIDE; HEPTACHLOR CIS-OXIDE; FNT 25584; VELSICOL 53-CS-17; C10H5CL7O; PST10670
CHEMICAL FAMILY: HALOGEN COMPOUND, ALICYCLIC
MOLECULAR FORMULA: C10-H5-CL7-O
MOLECULAR WEIGHT: 389.32
CERCLA RATINGS (SCALE 0-3): HEALTH=3 FIRE=1 REACTIVITY=0 PERSISTENCE=3
NFPA RATINGS (SCALE 0-4): HEALTH=3 FIRE=1 REACTIVITY=0

COMPONENTS AND CONTAMINANTS

COMPONENT: HEPTACHLOR EPOXIDE ***PERCENT:*** 100.0
CAS# 1024-57-3
OTHER CONTAMINANTS: NONE
EXPOSURE LIMITS: NO OCCUPATIONAL EXPOSURE LIMITS ESTABLISHED BY OSHA, ACGIH, OR NIOSH.
HEPTACHLOR EPOXIDE: 1 POUND CERLCA SECTION 103 REPORTABLE QUANTITY

SUBJECT TO CALIFORNIA PROPOSITION 65 CANCER AND/OR REPRODUCTIVE TOXICITY WARNING AND RELEASE REQUIREMENTS

PHYSICAL DATA

DESCRIPTION: WHITE CRYSTALLINE SOLID. ***MELTING POINT:*** 320-324 F (160-162 C)
SPECIFIC GRAVITY: NOT AVAILABLE ***VAPOR PRESSURE:*** 0.000003 MMHG @ 20 C
SOLUBILITY IN WATER: 0.2 PPM
SOLVENT SOLUBILITY: SOLUBLE IN FAT, MOST ORGANIC SOLVENTS.

FIRE AND EXPLOSION DATA

FIRE AND EXPLOSION HAZARD: SLIGHT FIRE HAZARD WHEN EXPOSED TO HEAT OR FLAME.

FIREFIGHTING MEDIA: DRY CHEMICAL, CARBON DIOXIDE, HALON, WATER SPRAY OR STANDARD FOAM (1987 EMERGENCY RESPONSE GUIDEBOOK, DOT P 5800.4). FOR LARGER FIRES, USE WATER SPRAY, FOG OR STANDARD FOAM (1987 EMERGENCY RESPONSE GUIDEBOOK, DOT P 5800.4).

FIREFIGHTING: MOVE CONTAINERS FROM FIRE AREA IF POSSIBLE (1987 EMERGENCY RESPONSE GUIDEBOOK, DOT P 5800.4, GUIDE PAGE 53). EXTINGUISH ONLY IF FLOW CAN BE STOPPED. EXTINGUISH USING AGENT INDICATED. USE FLOODING AMOUNTS OF WATER AS A FOG. COOL CONTAINERS WITH FLOODING AMOUNTS OF WATER FROM AS FAR A DISTANCE AS POSSIBLE. AVOID BREATHING POISONOUS VAPORS, KEEP UPWIND. CONSIDER EVACUATION OF DOWNWIND AREA IF MATERIAL IS LEAKING.

TRANSPORTATION DATA

DEPARTMENT OF TRANSPORTATION HAZARD CLASSIFICATION 49 CFR 172.101: POISON B
DEPARTMENT OF TRANSPORTATION LABELING REQUIREMENTS 49 CFR 172.101 AND SUBPART E: POISON
DEPARTMENT OF TRANSPORTATION PACKAGING REQUIREMENTS: 49 CFR 173.365
EXCEPTIONS: 49 CFR 173.364

TOXICITY

HEPTACHLOR EPOXIDE: TOXICITY DATA: 15 MG/KG ORAL-RAT LD50; 39 MG/KG ORAL-MOUSE LD50; 144 MG/KG ORAL-RABBIT LD50; 10 MG/KG INTRAVENOUS-MOUSE LDLO; MUTAGENIC DATA (RTECS); TUMORIGENIC DATA (RTECS). CARCINOGEN STATUS: HUMAN INSUFFICIENT EVIDENCE, ANIMAL LIMITED EVIDENCE (IARC GROUP-3). ACUTE TOXICITY LEVEL: HIGHLY TOXIC BY INGESTION. TARGET EFFECTS: CONVULSANT; HEPATOTOXIN. AT INCREASED RISK FROM EXPOSURE: PERSONS WITH CONVULSIVE DISORDERS AND/OR LIVER DAMAGE. ADDITIONAL DATA: THIS CHEMICAL ACCUMULATES IN ADIPOSE TISSUE; INTENSE ACTIVITY AND STARVATION MAY MOBILIZE THE PESTICIDE RESULTING IN THE REAPPEARANCE OF TOXIC SYMPTOMS. IT IS EXCRETED IN HUMAN MILK AND CROSSES THE PLACENTA. STIMULANTS SUCH AS EPINEPHRINE MAY INDUCE VENTRICULAR FIBRILLATION.

HEALTH EFFECTS AND FIRST AID

INHALATION: HEPTACHLOR EPOXIDE: CONVULSANT. **ACUTE EXPOSURE-** CHLORINATED CYCLODIENE PESTICIDES MAY CAUSE MUSCLE TWITCHING, MYOCLONIC JERKING, AND CONVULSIVE SEIZURES. THE CONVULSIONS MAY OCCUR WITH PERIODS OF UNCONSCIOUSNESS. OTHER SYMPTOMS MAY INCLUDE HEADACHE, NAUSEA, VOMITING, MALAISE, AND DIZZINESS. IN CASES OF GROSS OVEREXPOSURE, CONVULSIONS MAY OCCUR WITHOUT ANY PRIOR SYMPTOMS. ABNORMAL EEG PATTERNS MAY BE OBSERVED; THESE CHANGES MAY PERSIST FOR WEEKS OR MONTHS WHILE NO OTHER OBSERVABLE SIGNS OF POISONING MAY EXIST. **CHRONIC EXPOSURE-** A STATISTICALLY SIGNIFICANT INCREASE IN DEATHS FROM CEREBROVASCULAR DISEASE WAS OBSERVED IN A MORTALITY STUDY OF 1,403 WHITE MALES OCCUPATIONALLY EXPOSED TO CHLORDANE, HEPTACHLOR AND ENDRIN DURING MANUFACTURING. INTERMEDIATE AND CHRONIC INHALATION EXPOSURE OF HUMANS TO MIXTURES OF HEPTACHLOR WITH CHLORDANE AND OTHER CHEMICALS HAS BEEN ASSOCIATED WITH PANCYTOPENIA, LEUKEMIA, AND APLASTIC, HEMOLYTIC AND MEGALOBLASTIC ANEMIAS. PROLONGED OR REPEATED EXPOSURE TO CHLORINATED CYCLODIENE PESTICIDES MAY RESULT IN THE ACCUMULATION OF THE PESTICIDE IN THE BLOOD RESULTING IN A PROGRESSION OF THE SYMPTOMS LISTED ABOVE OR IN A SUDDEN ONSET OF SYMPTOMS AFTER AN ACUTE EXPOSURE. IN ADDITION TO SYMPTOMS LISTED ABOVE, HYPERIRRITABILITY, DROWSINESS, AND ANOREXIA MAY OCCUR.

FIRST AID- REMOVE FROM EXPOSURE AREA TO FRESH AIR IMMEDIATELY. IF BREATHING HAS STOPPED, PERFORM ARTIFICIAL RESPIRATION. KEEP PERSON WARM AND AT REST. TREAT SYMPTOMATICALLY AND SUPPORTIVELY. GET MEDICAL ATTENTION IMMEDIATELY.

SKIN CONTACT: HEPTACHLOR EPOXIDE: CONVULSANT. **ACUTE EXPOSURE-** CHLORINATED CYCLODIENE PESTICIDES ARE ABSORBED FROM THE SKIN AND MAY PRODUCE CENTRAL NERVOUS SYSTEM EFFECTS WITH SYMPTOMS OF MOTOR HYPEREXCITABILITY THAT MAY INCLUDE MUSCLE TWITCHING, MYOCLONIC JERKING, AND CONVULSIVE SEIZURES. THE CONVULSIONS MAY OCCUR WITH PERIODS OF UNCONSCIOUSNESS. OTHER SYMPTOMS MAY INCLUDE HEADACHE, NAUSEA, VOMITING, MALAISE, AND DIZZINESS. IN CASES OF GROSS OVEREXPOSURE, CONVULSIONS MAY OCCUR WITHOUT ANY PRIOR SYMPTOMS. ABNORMAL EEG PATTERNS MAY BE OBSERVED; THESE CHANGES IN EEG PATTERNS MAY PERSIST FOR WEEKS OR MONTHS WHILE NO OTHER OBSERVABLE SIGNS OF POISONING MAY EXIST. **CHRONIC EXPOSURE-** PROLONGED OR REPEATED EXPOSURE TO CHLORINATED CYCLODIENE PESTICIDES MAY RESULT IN THE ACCUMULATION OF THE PESTICIDE IN THE BLOOD RESULTING IN A PROGRESSION OF THE SYMPTOMS LISTED ABOVE OR IN A SUDDEN ONSET OF SYMPTOMS AFTER AN ACUTE EXPOSURE. IN ADDITION TO THE SYMPTOMS LISTED ABOVE, HYPERIRRITABILITY, DROWSINESS, AND ANOREXIA MAY OCCUR. **FIRST AID-** REMOVE CONTAMINATED CLOTHING AND SHOES IMMEDIATELY. WASH AFFECTED AREA WITH SOAP OR MILD DETERGENT AND LARGE AMOUNTS OF WATER UNTIL NO EVIDENCE OF CHEMICAL REMAINS (APPROXIMATELY 15-20 MINUTES). GET MEDICAL ATTENTION IMMEDIATELY.

EYE CONTACT: HEPTACHLOR EPOXIDE: **ACUTE EXPOSURE-** NO DATA AVAILABLE. **CHRONIC EXPOSURE-** NO DATA AVAILABLE.

FIRST AID- WASH EYES IMMEDIATELY WITH LARGE AMOUNTS OF WATER OR NORMAL SALINE, OCCASIONALLY LIFTING UPPER AND LOWER LIDS, UNTIL NO EVIDENCE OF CHEMICAL REMAINS (APPROXIMATELY 15-20 MINUTES). GET MEDICAL ATTENTION IMMEDIATELY.

INGESTION: HEPTACHLOR EPOXIDE: CONVULSANT/HEPATOTOXIN/CARCINOGEN/HIGHLY TOXIC. **ACUTE EXPOSURE-** IN ANIMAL STUDIES, INGESTION PRODUCED NEUROTOXIC EFFECTS OF HYPOACTIVITY, ATAXIA, TREMORS, CONVULSIONS, CHANGES IN EEG PATTERN AND DEATH. SIMILAR EFFECTS WERE OBSERVED IN HUMANS EXPOSED TO CHLORINATED CYCLODIENE PESTICIDES. IN RATS, ACUTE ORAL DOSES PRODUCED LIVER NECROSIS CELL VACUOLIZATION, LIVER STEATOSIS, AND INCREASED RELATIVE LIVER WEIGHT. OTHER EFFECTS INCLUDED ELEVATED SERUM LEVELS OF ALDOLASE, GLUTAMIC-PYRUVIC TRANSAMINASE, BILIBUBIN, ALKALINE PHOSPHATASE, AND CHOLESTEROL. **CHRONIC EXPOSURE-** REPEATED OR PROLONGED ADMINISTRATION PRODUCED RENAL TOXICITY, ADRENOTOXICITY, AND HEMATOLOGIC EFFECTS IN ANIMALS. REPEATED ADMINISTRATION TO RATS PRODUCED CHRONIC CONVULSIONS, OPISTHOTONOS, HYPERREFLEXIA, RAPID RESPIRATION, AND CATARACTS. HISTOLOGIC EVIDENCE OF SEVERE LIVER DAMAGE, INCREASED LIVER WEIGHT, INCREASED LEVELS OF SERUM COMPONENTS, AND DECREASED BODY WEIGHTS WERE ALSO OBSERVED. ORAL ADMINISTRATION PRODUCED LIVER CARCINOMAS IN MICE AND HEPATOMAS IN RATS. IN MALE AND FEMALE RATS FED HEPTACHLOR, HEPTACHLOR EPOXIDE, OR A MIXTURE OF THE TWO FOR THREE GENERATIONS, THE NUMBER OF RESORBED FETUSES INCREASED AND FERTILITY DECREASED WITH SUCCEEDING GENERATIONS.

FIRST AID- IF THE PERSON IS CONSCIOUS AND NOT CONVULSING, REMOVE BY GIVING SYRUP OF IPECAC (IF VOMITING OCCURS, KEEP THE HEAD BELOW THE HIPS TO PREVENT ASPIRATION). GIVE ACTIVATED CHARCOAL FOLLOWED BY GASTRIC LAVAGE. FOLLOW WITH A SALINE CATHARTIC. DO NOT GIVE FATS OR OILS. INTESTINAL LAVAGE WITH 20% MANNITOL (200 ML) BY STOMACH TUBE IS ALSO USEFUL. GIVE ARTIFICIAL RESPIRATION WITH OXYGEN IF RESPIRATION IS DEPRESSED (DREISBACH, HANDBOOK OF POISONING, 12TH ED.). TREAT SYMPTOMATICALLY AND SUPPORTIVELY. LAVAGE AND ADMINISTRATION OF OXYGEN SHOULD BE PERFORMED BY QUALIFIED MEDICAL PERSONNEL. GET MEDICAL ATTENTION IMMEDIATELY.

ANTIDOTE: NO SPECIFIC ANTIDOTE. TREAT SYMPTOMATICALLY AND SUPPORTIVELY.

REACTIVITY

REACTIVITY: STABLE UNDER NORMAL TEMPERATURES AND PRESSURES.
INCOMPATIBILITIES: HEPTACHLOR EPOXIDE: OXIDIZERS (STRONG): FIRE AND EXPLOSION HAZARD.
DECOMPOSITION: THERMAL DECOMPOSITION PRODUCTS MAY INCLUDE TOXIC AND CORROSIVE FUMES OF CHLORIDES AND TOXIC OXIDES OF CARBON.
POLYMERIZATION: HAZARDOUS POLYMERIZATION HAS NOT BEEN REPORTED TO OCCUR UNDER NORMAL TEMPERATURES AND PRESSURES.

STORAGE AND DISPOSAL

OBSERVE ALL FEDERAL, STATE AND LOCAL REGULATIONS WHEN STORING OR DISPOSING OF THIS SUBSTANCE. FOR ASSISTANCE, CONTACT THE DISTRICT DIRECTOR OF THE ENVIRONMENTAL PROTECTION AGENCY.

STORAGE

STORE AWAY FROM INCOMPATIBLE SUBSTANCES.

CONDITIONS TO AVOID

MAY BURN BUT DOES NOT IGNITE READILY.

SPILL AND LEAK PROCEDURES

OCCUPATIONAL SPILL: DO NOT TOUCH SPILLED MATERIAL. STOP LEAK IF YOU CAN DO IT WITHOUT RISK. FOR SMALL SPILLS, TAKE UP WITH SAND OR OTHER ABSORBENT MATERIAL AND PLACE INTO CONTAINERS FOR LATER DISPOSAL. FOR SMALL DRY SPILLS, WITH A CLEAN SHOVEL PLACE MATERIAL INTO CLEAN, DRY CONTAINER AND COVER. MOVE CONTAINERS FROM SPILL AREA. FOR LARGER SPILLS, DIKE FAR AHEAD OF SPILL FOR LATER DISPOSAL. KEEP UNNECESSARY PEOPLE AWAY. ISOLATE HAZARD AREA AND DENY ENTRY.
REPORTABLE QUANTITY (RQ): 1 POUND THE SUPERFUND AMENDMENTS AND REAUTHORIZATION ACT (SARA) SECTION 304 REQUIRES THAT A RELEASE EQUAL TO OR GREATER THAN THE REPORTABLE QUANTITY FOR THIS SUBSTANCE BE IMMEDIATELY REPORTED TO THE LOCAL EMERGENCY PLANNING COMMITTEE AND THE STATE EMERGENCY RESPONSE COMMISSION (40 CFR 355.40). IF THE RELEASE OF THIS SUBSTANCE IS REPORTABLE UNDER CERCLA SECTION 103, THE NATIONAL RESPONSE CENTER MUST BE NOTIFIED IMMEDIATELY AT (800) 424-8802 OR (202) 426-2675 IN THE METROPOLITAN WASHINGTON, D.C. AREA (40 CFR 302.6).

PROTECTIVE EQUIPMENT

VENTILATION: PROVIDE LOCAL EXHAUST OR GENERAL DILUTION VENTILATION SYSTEM.

RESPIRATOR: THE FOLLOWING RESPIRATORS AND MAXIMUM USE CONCENTRATIONS ARE RECOMMENDATIONS BY THE U.S. DEPARTMENT OF HEALTH AND HUMAN SERVICES, NIOSH POCKET GUIDE TO CHEMICAL HAZARDS; NIOSH CRITERIA DOCUMENTS OR BY THE U.S. DEPARTMENT OF LABOR, 29 CFR 1910 SUBPART Z. THE SPECIFIC RESPIRATOR SELECTED MUST BE BASED ON CONTAMINATION LEVELS FOUND IN THE WORK PLACE, MUST NOT EXCEED THE WORKING LIMITS OF THE RESPIRATOR AND BE JOINTLY APPROVED BY THE NATIONAL INSTITUTE FOR OCCUPATIONAL SAFETY AND HEALTH AND THE MINE SAFETY AND HEALTH ADMINISTRATION (NIOSH-MSHA).

HEPTACHLOR:

5 MG/M3- ANY SUPPLIED-AIR RESPIRATOR. ANY SELF-CONTAINED BREATHING APPARATUS.

12.5 MG/M3- ANY SUPPLIED-AIR RESPIRATOR OPERATED IN A CONTINUOUS FLOW MODE.

25 MG/M3- ANY SUPPLIED-AIR RESPIRATOR WITH A FULL FACEPIECE. ANY SELF-CONTAINED BREATHING APPARATUS WITH A FULL FACEPIECE. ANY ANY SUPPLIED-AIR RESPIRATOR WITH A TIGHT-FITTING FACEPIECE OPERATED IN A CONTINUOUS FLOW MODE.

100 MG/M3- ANY SUPPLIED-AIR RESPIRATOR WITH A HALF-MASK AND OPERATED IN A PRESSURE-DEMAND OR OTHER POSITIVE PRESSURE MODE.

ESCAPE- ANY AIR-PURIFYING FULL FACEPIECE RESPIRATOR (GAS MASK) WITH A CHIN-STYLE OR FRONT- OR BACK-MOUNTED ORGANIC VAPOR CANISTER HAVING A HIGH-EFFICIENCY PARTICULATE FILTER. ANY APPROPRIATE ESCAPE-TYPE SELF-CONTAINED BREATHING APPARATUS.

FOR FIREFIGHTING AND OTHER IMMEDIATELY DANGEROUS TO LIFE OR HEALTH CONDITIONS:

SELF-CONTAINED BREATHING APPARATUS WITH FULL FACEPIECE OPERATED IN PRESSURE-DEMAND OR OTHER POSITIVE PRESSURE MODE.

SUPPLIED-AIR RESPIRATOR WITH FULL FACEPIECE AND OPERATED IN PRESSURE-DEMAND OR OTHER POSITIVE PRESSURE MODE IN COMBINATION WITH AN AUXILIARY SELF-CONTAINED BREATHING APPARATUS OPERATED IN PRESSURE-DEMAND OR OTHER POSITIVE PRESSURE MODE.

CLOTHING: EMPLOYEE MUST WEAR APPROPRIATE PROTECTIVE (IMPERVIOUS) CLOTHING AND EQUIPMENT TO PREVENT REPEATED OR PROLONGED SKIN CONTACT WITH THIS SUBSTANCE.

GLOVES: EMPLOYEE MUST WEAR APPROPRIATE PROTECTIVE GLOVES TO PREVENT CONTACT WITH THIS SUBSTANCE.

EYE PROTECTION: EMPLOYEE MUST WEAR SPLASH-PROOF OR DUST-RESISTANT SAFETY GOGGLES TO PREVENT EYE CONTACT WITH THIS SUBSTANCE.
EMERGENCY EYE WASH: WHERE THERE IS ANY POSSIBILITY THAT AN EMPLOYEE'S EYES MAY BE EXPOSED TO THIS SUBSTANCE, THE EMPLOYER SHOULD PROVIDE AN EYE WASH FOUNTAIN WITHIN THE IMMEDIATE WORK AREA FOR EMERGENCY USE.

AUTHORIZED BY- OCCUPATIONAL HEALTH SERVICES, INC.
CREATION DATE: 10/04/89 ***REVISION DATE:*** 07/12/90

MATERIAL SAFETY DATA SHEET

OCCUPATIONAL HEALTH SERVICES, INC. EMERGENCY CONTACT:
AGRICULTURE AND PESTICIDE DIVISION JOHN S. BRANSFORD, JR. (615) 292-1180
450 SEVENTH AVENUE, SUITE 2407
NEW YORK, NEW YORK 10123
1-800-445-MSDS OR (212) 967-1100

SUBSTANCE IDENTIFICATION

CAS-NUMBER 23560-59-0

SUBSTANCE: **HEPTENOPHOS**

TRADE NAMES/SYNONYMS: PHOSPHORIC ACID, 7-CHLOROBICYCLO(3.2.0)HEPTA-2,6-DIEN-6-YL DIMETHYL ESTER; 7-CHLOROBICYCLO(3.2.0)HEPTA-2,6-DIEN-6-YL DIMETHYL PHOSPHATE; HOSTAQUICK; RAGADAN; HOE 2982; PST10685

CHEMICAL FAMILY: ORGANOPHOSPHATE

MOLECULAR FORMULA: C9-H12-CL-O4-P

MOLECULAR WEIGHT: 250.63

CERCLA RATINGS (SCALE 0-3): HEALTH=3 FIRE=U REACTIVITY=0 PERSISTENCE=1

NFPA RATINGS (SCALE 0-4): HEALTH=3 FIRE=U REACTIVITY=0

COMPONENTS AND CONTAMINANTS

COMPONENT: HEPTENOPHOS ***PERCENT:*** 100
CAS# 23560-59-0

EXPOSURE LIMITS: NO OCCUPATIONAL EXPOSURE LIMITS ESTABLISHED BY OSHA, ACGIH, OR NIOSH.

PHYSICAL DATA

DESCRIPTION: PALE AMBER LIQUID ***MELTING POINT:*** 147 F (64 C) @ 0.75 MMHG

SPECIFIC GRAVITY: 1.294 ***VAPOR PRESSURE:*** 0.00075 MMHG @ 20 C

SOLUBILITY IN WATER: .22 %

SOLVENT SOLUBILITY: SOLUBLE IN XYLENE, ACETONE, METHYL ALCOHOL AND MOST ORGANIC SOLVENTS

FIRE AND EXPLOSION DATA

FIRE AND EXPLOSION HAZARD: UNKNOWN FIRE AND EXPLOSION HAZARD.

FIREFIGHTING MEDIA: DRY CHEMICAL, CARBON DIOXIDE, HALON, WATER SPRAY OR STANDARD FOAM (1987 EMERGENCY RESPONSE GUIDEBOOK, DOT P 5800.4).
FOR LARGER FIRES, USE WATER SPRAY, FOG OR STANDARD FOAM (1987 EMERGENCY RESPONSE GUIDEBOOK, DOT P 5800.4).

FIREFIGHTING: MOVE CONTAINERS FROM FIRE AREA IF POSSIBLE. FIGHT FIRE FROM MAXIMUM DISTANCE. STAY AWAY FROM STORAGE TANK ENDS. DIKE FIRE CONTROL WATER FOR LATER DISPOSAL. DO NOT SCATTER MATERIAL (1987 EMERGENCY RESPONSE GUIDEBOOK, DOT P 5800.4, GUIDE PAGE 55).

TOXICITY

HEPTENOPHOS: TOXICITY DATA: 2 GM/KG SKIN-RAT LD50; 2 GM/KG SKIN-MOUSE LD50; 96 MG/KG ORAL-RAT LD50; 117 MG/KG UNREPORTED-MAMMAL LD50; 75 MG/KG UNREPORTED-MOUSE LD50. CARCINOGEN STATUS: NONE. ACUTE TOXICITY LEVEL: TOXIC BY INGESTION; MODERATELY TOXIC BY DERMAL ABSORPTION. TARGET EFFECTS: CHOLINESTERASE INHIBITOR. POISONING MAY AFFECT THE NERVOUS SYSTEM.* AT INCREASED RISK FROM EXPOSURE: PERSONS WITH RESPIRATORY AILMENTS, RECENT EXPOSURE TO CHOLINESTERASE INHIBITORS OR IMPAIRED CHOLINESTERASE PRODUCTION, OR LIVER MALFUNCTION.* ADDITIONAL DATA: MAY CROSS THE PLACENTA. HIGH ENVIRONMENTAL TEMPERATURES OR EXPOSURE OF THE CHEMICAL TO VISIBLE OR ULTRAVIOLET LIGHT MAY ENHANCE THE TOXICITY. INTERACTIONS WITH MEDICATIONS MAY OCCUR.*
* MAY BE BASED ON GENERAL INFORMATION ON ORGANOPHOSPHATES.

HEALTH EFFECTS AND FIRST AID

INHALATION: HEPTENOPHOS: SEE INFORMATION ON ORGANOPHOSPHATES.
ORGANOPHOSPHATES: CHOLINESTERASE INHIBITOR. **ACUTE EXPOSURE-** WHEN INHALED, THE FIRST EFFECTS OF CHOLINESTERASE INHIBITORS ARE USUALLY RESPIRATORY AND MAY INCLUDE NASAL HYPEREMIA AND WATERY DISCHARGE, COUGH, CHEST DISCOMFORT, DYSPNEA, AND WHEEZING DUE TO INCREASED BRONCHIAL SECRETIONS AND BRONCHOCONSTRICTION. IF SUFFICIENT AMOUNTS ARE ABSORBED, OTHER SYSTEMIC EFFECTS MAY BEGIN WITHIN A FEW MINUTES OR BE DELAYED FOR UP TO 12 HOURS. SYMPTOMS MAY INCLUDE PALLOR, NAUSEA, VOMITING, DIARRHEA, ABDOMINAL CRAMPS, HEADACHE, DIZZINESS, OCULAR PAIN, BLURRED VISION, MIOSIS OR IN SOME CASES, ESPECIALLY INITIALLY, MYDRIASIS, LACRIMATION, SALIVATION, SWEATING, AND CONFUSION. OTHER REPORTED CENTRAL NERVOUS SYSTEM OR NEUROMUSCULAR EFFECTS MAY INCLUDE ATAXIA, SLURRED SPEECH, AREFLEXIA, WEAKNESS, FATIGUE, FASCICULATIONS, TWITCHING, TREMORS POSSIBLY OF THE TONGUE AND EYELIDS, AND EVENTUALLY PARALYSIS OF THE EXTREMITIES AND POSSIBLY OF THE RESPIRATORY MUSCLES. IN SEVERE CASES THERE MAY ALSO BE INVOLUNTARY DEFECATION AND URINATION, CYANOSIS, PSYCHOSIS, HYPERGLYCEMIA, ACUTE PANCREATITIS, CARDIAC IRREGULARITIES, PULMONARY EDEMA, UNCONSCIOUSNESS, CONVULSIONS, AND COMA. DEATH IS PRIMARILY DUE TO

RESPIRATORY FAILURE, ALTHOUGH CARDIOVASCULAR EFFECTS INCLUDING CARDIAC ARREST MAY ALSO BE IMPLICATED. LONG TERM SEQUELAE ARE RARE BUT MAY INCLUDE NEUROPSYCHIATRIC DISORDERS AND MYOPATHY WITH MUSCLE TENDERNESS. SOME ORGANOPHOSPHATES MAY CAUSE A DELAYED NEUROPATHY BEGINNING 1-4 WEEKS AFTER AN ACUTE EXPOSURE WHICH MAY OR MAY NOT HAVE CAUSED ACUTE CHOLINERGIC EFFECTS. NUMBNESS, TINGLING, WEAKNESS AND CRAMPING BEGINNING SYMMETRICALLY IN THE LOWER LIMBS MAY PROGRESS TO ATAXIA AND PARALYSIS. IN SEVERE CASES, UPPER LIMB INVOLVEMENT IS POSSIBLE AND FLACCID PARALYSIS MAY PROGRESS TO SPASTIC PARALYSIS WITH EXAGGERATED REFLEXES. IMPROVEMENT MAY OCCUR OVER MONTHS TO YEARS, BUT SOME RESIDUAL IMPAIRMENT USUALLY REMAINS. **CHRONIC EXPOSURE-** REPEATED OR PROLONGED EXPOSURE MAY RESULT IN THE EFFECTS OF ACUTE EXPOSURE INCLUDING THE DELAYED NEUROPATHY. OTHER EFFECTS REPORTED IN WORKERS REPEATEDLY EXPOSED INCLUDE IMPAIRED MEMORY AND CONCENTRATION, ACUTE PSYCHOSIS, SEVERE DEPRESSIONS, IRRITABILTY, CONFUSION, APATHY, EMOTIONAL LABILITY, SOCIAL WITHDRAWAL, CONFUSION, HEADACHE, SPEECH DIFFICULTIES, DELAYED REACTION TIMES, SPATIAL DISORIENTATION, NIGHTMARES, SLEEPWALKING, AND DROWSINESS OR INSOMNIA. AN INFLUENZA-LIKE CONDITION WITH HEADACHE, NAUSEA, WEAKNESS, ANOREXIA AND MALAISE HAS ALSO BEEN REPORTED.

FIRST AID- REMOVE FROM EXPOSURE AREA TO FRESH AIR IMMEDIATELY. IF BREATHING HAS STOPPED, GIVE ARTIFICIAL RESPIRATION. MAINTAIN AIRWAY AND BLOOD PRESSURE AND ADMINISTER OXYGEN IF AVAILABLE. KEEP AFFECTED PERSON WARM AND AT REST. TREAT SYMPTOMATICALLY AND SUPPORTIVELY. ADMINISTRATION OF OXYGEN SHOULD BE PERFORMED BY QUALIFIED PERSONNEL. GET MEDICAL ATTENTION IMMEDIATELY.

SKIN CONTACT: HEPTENOPHOS: SEE INFORMATION ON ORGANOPHOSPHATES. ORGANOPHOSPHATES: CHOLINESTERASE INHIBITOR. **ACUTE EXPOSURE-** LOCALIZED SWEATING AND FASCICULATIONS MAY OCCUR AT THE SITE OF CONTACT. IF SUFFICIENT AMOUNTS ARE ABSORBED, OTHER EFFECTS OF CHOLINESTERASE INHIBITION AS DESCRIBED IN ACUTE INHALATION MAY OCCUR. SYMPTOMS MAY BE DELAYED 2-3 HOURS, BUT USUALLY NO MORE THAN 12 HOURS. THE RATE OF ABSORPTION IS INCREASED BY THE PRESENCE OF DERMATITIS OR HIGH AMBIENT TEMPERATURES. DELAYED NEUROPATHY IS ALSO POSSIBLE. **CHRONIC EXPOSURE-** REPEATED OR PROLONGED EXPOSURE MAY CAUSE EFFECTS AS DESCRIBED IN ACUTE EXPOSURE. SOME ORGANOPHOSPHATES MAY CAUSE SENSITIZATION.

FIRST AID- REMOVE CONTAMINATED CLOTHING IMMEDIATELY. WASH CONTAMINATED AREAS WITH SOAP AND WATER FOLLOWED BY ALCOHOL (ARENA, POISONING, 4TH ED.). EMERGENCY PERSONNEL SHOULD WEAR GLOVES AND AVOID CONTAMINATION. TREAT RESPIRATORY DIFFICULTY WITH ARTIFICIAL RESPIRATION. GET MEDICAL ATTENTION IMMEDIATELY.

EYE CONTACT: HEPTENOPHOS: SEE INFORMATION ON ORGANOPHOSPHATES. ORGANOPHOSPHATES: CHOLINESTERASE INHIBITOR. **ACUTE EXPOSURE-** DIRECT CONTACT MAY CAUSE PAIN, HYPEREMIA, LACRIMATION, TWITCHING OF THE EYELIDS, MIOSIS, AND CILIARY MUSCLE SPASM WITH LOSS OF ACCOMODATION, BLURRED OR DIMMED VISION AND BROWACHE. SOMETIMES MYDRIASIS MAY OCCUR INSTEAD OF MIOSIS. WITH SUFFICIENT EXPOSURE, OTHER SYMPTOMS OF CHOLINESTERASE INHIBITION AS DESCRIBED IN ACUTE INHALATION MAY OCCUR. **CHRONIC EXPOSURE-** REPEATED OR PROLONGED EXPOSURE MAY CAUSE EFFECTS AS DESCRIBED IN ACUTE EXPOSURE. SOME COMPOUNDS HAVE CAUSED TOXIC EFFECTS ON THE CRYSTALLINE LENS, CONJUNCTIVAL THICKENING AND OBSTRUCTION OF THE NASOLACRIMAL CANALS WHEN USED AS MIOTIC EYEDROPS.

FIRST AID- IRRIGATE EYES WITH WATER OR SALINE SOLUTION. IF SYMPTOMS OF POISONING OCCUR, TREAT RESPIRATORY DIFFICULTY WITH ARTIFICIAL RESPIRATION AND OXYGEN. OBSERVE PATIENT FOR AT LEAST 24-36 HOURS (GOSSELIN, CLINICAL TOXICOLOGY OF COMMERCIAL PRODUCTS, 5TH ED.). GET MEDICAL ATTENTION IMMEDIATELY. OXYGEN SHOULD BE ADMINISTERED BY QUALIFIED MEDICAL PERSONNEL.

INGESTION: HEPTENOPHOS: TOXIC SEE INFORMATION ON ORGANOPHOSPHATES. ORGANOPHOSPHATES: CHOLINESTERASE INHIBITOR. **ACUTE EXPOSURE-** WHEN INGESTED, THE FIRST EFFECTS MAY BE NAUSEA, VOMITING, ANOREXIA, ABDOMINAL CRAMPS AND DIARRHEA. GASTROINTESTINAL ABSORPTION MAY CAUSE SYMPTOMS OF CHOLINESTERASE INHIBITION AS DESCRIBED IN ACUTE INHALATION. SYMPTOMS MAY BEGIN WITHIN MINUTES OR BE DELAYED FOR HOURS. DELAYED EFFECTS INCLUDING NEUROPATHY MAY ALSO OCCUR. **CHRONIC EXPOSURE-** REPEATED INGESTION MAY CAUSE EFFECTS AS DESCRIBED IN ACUTE EXPOSURE.

FIRST AID- IF PERSON IS ALERT AND RESPIRATION IS NOT DEPRESSED, GIVE SYRUP OF IPECAC FOLLOWED BY WATER (IF VOMITING OCCURS, KEEP HEAD BELOW HIPS TO PREVENT ASPIRATION). IF CONSCIOUSNESS LEVEL DECLINES OR VOMITING HAS NOT OCCURRED IN 15 MINUTES EMPTY STOMACH BY GASTRIC LAVAGE WITH THE AID OF CUFFED ENDOTRACHEAL TUBE USING ISOTONIC SALINE OR 5% SODIUM BICARBONATE FOLLOW WITH ACTIVATED CHARCOAL. ESTABLISH AND MAINTAIN AIRWAY. TREAT RESPIRATORY DIFFICULTY WITH ARTIFICIAL RESPIRATION AND OXYGEN. DO NOT GIVE MORPHINE, AMINOPHYLLINE, PHENOTHIAZINES, RESERPINE, FUROSEMIDE, OR ETHACRYNIC ACID (MORGAN, RECOGNITION AND MANAGEMENT OF PESTICIDE POISONINGS, 3RD ED.). TREAT SYMPTOMATICALLY AND SUPPORTIVELY. ADMINISTRATION OF OXYGEN AND LAVAGE MUST BE PERFORMED BY QUALIFIED MEDICAL PERSONNEL. GET MEDICAL ATTENTION IMMEDIATELY.

ANTIDOTE: THE FOLLOWING ANTIDOTE(S) HAVE BEEN RECOMMENDED. HOWEVER, THE DECISION AS TO WHETHER THE SEVERITY OF POISONING REQUIRES ADMINISTRATION OF ANY ANTIDOTE AND ACTUAL DOSE REQUIRED SHOULD BE MADE BY QUALIFIED MEDICAL PERSONNEL.

FOR CHOLINESTERASE INHIBITORS: ESTABLISH CLEAR AIRWAY AND TISSUE OXYGENATION BY ASPIRATION OF SECRETIONS, AND IF NECESSARY, BY ASSISTED PULMONARY VENTILATION WITH OXYGEN. IMPROVE TISSUE OXYGENATION AS MUCH AS POSSIBLE BEFORE ADMINISTERING ATROPINE TO MINIMIZE THE RISK OF VENTRICULAR FIBRILLATION. ADMINISTER ATROPINE SULFATE INTRAVENOUSLY, OR INTRAMUSCULARLY IF IV INJECTION IS NOT POSSIBLE. IN MODERATELY SEVERE POISONING ADMINISTER ATROPINE SULFATE, 0.4-2.0 MG REPEATED EVERY 15 MINUTES UNTIL ATROPINIZATION IS ACHIEVED (TACHYCARDIA, FLUSHING, DRY MOUTH, MYDRIASIS). MAINTAIN ATROPINIZATION BY REPEATED DOSES FOR 2-12 HOURS, OR LONGER, DEPENDING ON THE SEVERITY OF POISONING. THE APPEARANCE OF RALES IN THE LUNG BASES, MIOSIS, SALIVATION, NAUSEA, BRADYCARDIA, ARE ALL INDICATIONS OF INADEQUATE ATROPINIZATION. SEVERELY POISONED INDIVIDUALS MAY EXHIBIT REMARKABLE TOLERANCE TO ATROPINE; TWO OR MORE TIMES THE DOSAGES SUGGESTED ABOVE MAY BE NEEDED. PERSONS NOT POISONED OR ONLY SLIGHTLY POISONED, HOWEVER, MAY DEVELOP SIGNS OF ATROPINE TOXICITY FROM SUCH LARGE DOSAGES: FEVER, MUSCLE FIBRILLATIONS, AND DELIRIUM ARE THE MAIN SIGNS OF ATROPINE TOXICITY. IF THESE SIGNS APPEAR WHILE THE PATIENT IS FULLY ATROPINIZED, ATROPINE ADMINISTRATION SHOULD BE DISCONTINUED, AT LEAST TEMPORARILY. OBSERVE TREATED PATIENTS CLOSELY AT LEAST 24 HOURS TO INSURE THAT SYMPTOMS (POSSIBLY PULMONARY EDEMA) DO NOT RECUR AS ATROPINIZATION WEARS OFF. IN VERY SEVERE POISONINGS, METABOLIC DISPOSITION OF TOXICANT MAY REQUIRE SEVERAL HOURS OR DAYS DURING WHICH ATROPINIZATION MUST BE MAINTAINED. MARKEDLY LOWER LEVELS OF URINARY METABOLITES INDICATE THAT ATROPINE DOSAGE CAN BE TAPERED OFF. AS DOSAGE IS REDUCED, CHECK THE LUNG BASES FREQUENTLY FOR RALES. IF RALES ARE HEARD OR OTHER SYMPTOMS RETURN, RE-ESTABLISH ATROPINIZATION PROMPTLY (MORGAN, RECOGNITION AND MANAGEMENT OF PESTICIDE POISONINGS, 3RD ED.). ADMINISTRATION OF ANTIDOTE MUST BE PERFORMED BY QUALIFIED MEDICAL PERSONNEL.

IN CASES OF SEVERE POISONING BY ORGANOPHOSPHATE PESTICIDES IN WHICH RESPIRATORY DEPRESSION, MUSCLE WEAKNESS AND TWITCHINGS ARE SEVERE, GIVE PRALIDOXIME (PROTOPAM-AYERST, 2-PAM), 1.0 GRAM INTRAVENOUSLY AT NO MORE THAN 0.5 GRAM PER MINUTE. DOSAGE OF PRALIDOXIME MAY BE REPEATED IN 1-2 HOURS, THEN AT 10-12 HOUR INTERVALS IF NEEDED. IN VERY SEVERE POISONINGS, DOSAGE RATES MAY BE DOUBLED. TREATMENT WITH PRALIDOXIME WILL BE MOST EFFECTIVE IF GIVEN WITHIN THIRTY-SIX HOURS AFTER POISONING (MORGAN, RECOGNITION AND MANAGEMENT OF PESTICIDE POISONINGS, 3RD ED.). ANTIDOTE SHOULD BE ADMINISTERED BY QUALIFIED MEDICAL PERSONNEL.

REACTIVITY

REACTIVITY: STABLE UNDER NORMAL TEMPERATURES AND PRESSURES.
INCOMPATIBILITIES: HEPTENOPHOS: NO DATA AVAILABLE.
DECOMPOSITION: THERMAL DECOMPOSITION MAY RELEASE TOXIC AND/OR HAZARDOUS GASES.
POLYMERIZATION: HAZARDOUS POLYMERIZATION HAS NOT BEEN REPORTED TO OCCUR UNDER NORMAL TEMPERATURES AND PRESSURES.

STORAGE AND DISPOSAL

OBSERVE ALL FEDERAL, STATE AND LOCAL REGULATIONS WHEN STORING OR DISPOSING OF THIS SUBSTANCE. FOR ASSISTANCE, CONTACT THE DISTRICT DIRECTOR OF THE ENVIRONMENTAL PROTECTION AGENCY.

****STORAGE****

STORE IN ACCORDANCE WITH 40 CFR 165 RECOMMENDED PROCEDURES FOR THE DISPOSAL AND STORAGE OF PESTICIDES AND PESTICIDE CONTAINERS.

****DISPOSAL****

DISPOSAL MUST BE IN ACCORDANCE WITH 40 CFR 165 RECOMMENDED PROCEDURES FOR THE DISPOSAL AND STORAGE OF PESTICIDES AND PESTICIDE CONTAINERS.

CONDITIONS TO AVOID

NONE REPORTED.

SPILL AND LEAK PROCEDURES

OCCUPATIONAL SPILL: DO NOT TOUCH SPILLED MATERIAL. STOP LEAK IF YOU CAN DO IT WITHOUT RISK. USE WATER SPRAY TO REDUCE VAPORS. FOR SMALL SPILLS, TAKE UP WITH SAND OR OTHER ABSORBENT MATERIAL AND PLACE INTO CONTAINERS FOR LATER DISPOSAL. FOR SMALL DRY SPILLS, WITH A CLEAN SHOVEL PLACE MATERIAL INTO CLEAN, DRY CONTAINERS AND COVER. MOVE CONTAINERS FROM SPILL AREA. FOR LARGER SPILLS, DIKE FAR AHEAD OF SPILL FOR LATER DISPOSAL. KEEP UNNECESSARY PEOPLE AWAY. ISOLATE HAZARD AREA AND DENY ENTRY. VENTILATE CLOSED SPACES BEFORE ENTERING.

PROTECTIVE EQUIPMENT

VENTILATION: PROVIDE LOCAL EXHAUST OR PROCESS ENCLOSURE VENTILATION SYSTEM.

RESPIRATOR: THE FOLLOWING RESPIRATORS ARE RECOMMENDED BASED ON INFORMATION FOUND IN THE PHYSICAL DATA, TOXICITY AND HEALTH EFFECTS SECTIONS. THEY ARE RANKED IN ORDER FROM MINIMUM TO MAXIMUM RESPIRATORY PROTECTION. THE SPECIFIC RESPIRATOR SELECTED MUST BE BASED ON CONTAMINATION LEVELS FOUND IN THE WORK PLACE, MUST NOT EXCEED THE WORKING LIMITS OF THE RESPIRATOR AND BE JOINTLY APPROVED BY THE NATIONAL INSTITUTE FOR OCCUPATIONAL SAFETY AND HEALTH AND THE MINE SAFETY AND HEALTH ADMINISTRATION (NIOSH-MSHA).

TYPE 'C' SUPPLIED-AIR RESPIRATOR WITH A FULL FACEPIECE OPERATED IN PRESSURE-DEMAND OR OTHER POSITIVE PRESSURE MODE OR WITH A FULL FACEPIECE, HELMET OR HOOD OPERATED IN CONTINOUS-FLOW MODE.

SELF-CONTAINED BREATHING APPARATUS WITH A FULL FACEPIECE OPERATED IN PRESSURE-DEMAND OR OTHER POSITIVE PRESSURE MODE.

FOR FIREFIGHTING AND OTHER IMMEDIATELY DANGEROUS TO LIFE OR HEALTH CONDITIONS:

SELF-CONTAINED BREATHING APPARATUS WITH FULL FACEPIECE OPERATED IN PRESSURE-DEMAND OR OTHER POSITIVE PRESSURE MODE.

SUPPLIED-AIR RESPIRATOR WITH FULL FACEPIECE AND OPERATED IN PRESSURE-DEMAND OR OTHER POSITIVE PRESSURE MODE IN COMBINATION WITH AN AUXILIARY SELF-CONTAINED BREATHING APPARATUS OPERATED IN PRESSURE-DEMAND OR OTHER POSITIVE PRESSURE MODE.

CLOTHING: EMPLOYEE MUST WEAR APPROPRIATE PROTECTIVE (IMPERVIOUS) CLOTHING AND EQUIPMENT TO PREVENT REPEATED OR PROLONGED SKIN CONTACT WITH THIS SUBSTANCE.

GLOVES: EMPLOYEE MUST WEAR APPROPRIATE PROTECTIVE GLOVES TO PREVENT CONTACT WITH THIS SUBSTANCE.

EYE PROTECTION: EMPLOYEE MUST WEAR SPLASH-PROOF OR DUST-RESISTANT SAFETY GOGGLES TO PREVENT EYE CONTACT WITH THIS SUBSTANCE.

EMERGENCY EYE WASH: WHERE THERE IS ANY POSSIBILITY THAT AN EMPLOYEE'S EYES MAY BE EXPOSED TO THIS SUBSTANCE, THE EMPLOYER SHOULD PROVIDE AN EYE WASH FOUNTAIN WITHIN THE IMMEDIATE WORK AREA FOR EMERGENCY USE.

AUTHORIZED BY- OCCUPATIONAL HEALTH SERVICES, INC.

CREATION DATE: 10/04/89 ***REVISION DATE:*** 05/02/90

MATERIAL SAFETY DATA SHEET

OCCUPATIONAL HEALTH SERVICES, INC.
AGRICULTURE AND PESTICIDE DIVISION
450 SEVENTH AVENUE, SUITE 2407
NEW YORK, NEW YORK 10123
1-800-445-MSDS OR (212) 967-1100

EMERGENCY CONTACT:
JOHN S. BRANSFORD, JR. (615) 292-1180

SUBSTANCE IDENTIFICATION

CAS-NUMBER 118-74-1

SUBSTANCE: HEXACHLOROBENZENE

TRADE NAMES/SYNONYMS: AMATIN; ANTICARIE; BUNT-CURE; BUNT-NO-MORE; CO-OP HEXA; NCB; JULIN'S CARBON CHLORIDE; NO BUNT; NO BUNT 40; NO BUNT 80; NO BUNT LIQUID; PENTACHLOROPHENYL CHLORIDE; PERCHLOROBENZENE; PHENYL PERCHLORYL; SANOCIDE; SMUT 60; RCRA U127; UN 2729; PST10730

CHEMICAL FAMILY: HALOGEN COMPOUND, AROMATIC

MOLECULAR FORMULA: C6-CL6

MOLECULAR WEIGHT: 284.76

CERCLA RATINGS (SCALE 0-3): HEALTH=3 FIRE=1 REACTIVITY=0 PERSISTENCE=3

NFPA RATINGS (SCALE 0-4): HEALTH=3 FIRE=1 REACTIVITY=0

COMPONENTS AND CONTAMINANTS

COMPONENT: HEXACHLOROBENZENE ***PERCENT:*** 100
CAS# 118-74-1

OTHER CONTAMINANTS: NONE

EXPOSURE LIMITS: NO OCCUPATIONAL EXPOSURE LIMITS ESTABLISHED BY OSHA, ACGIH, OR NIOSH.

HEXACHLOROBENZENE: 10 POUNDS CERCLA SECTION 103 REPORTABLE QUANTITY SUBJECT TO SARA SECTION 313 ANNUAL TOXIC CHEMICAL RELEASE REPORTING SUBJECT TO CALIFORNIA PROPOSITION 65 CANCER AND/OR REPRODUCTIVE TOXICITY WARNING AND RELEASE REQUIREMENTS- (OCTOBER 1, 1987)

PHYSICAL DATA

DESCRIPTION: WHITE MONOCLINIC PRISMS, MOISTURE SENSITIVE

BOILING POINT: 613 F (323 C) ***MELTING POINT:*** 448 F (231 C)

SPECIFIC GRAVITY: 2.04 ***VAPOR PRESSURE:*** 1 MMHG @ 114 C

SOLUBILITY IN WATER: INSOLUBLE ***VAPOR DENSITY:*** 9.8

SOLVENT SOLUBILITY: BENZENE, HOT ETHER, CHLOROFORM, BOILING ETHANOL; SPARINGLY SOLUBLE IN COLD ETHANOL

FIRE AND EXPLOSION DATA

FIRE AND EXPLOSION HAZARD: SLIGHT FIRE HAZARD WHEN EXPOSED TO HEAT OR FLAME.

FLASH POINT: 468 F (242 C)

FIREFIGHTING MEDIA: DRY CHEMICAL, CARBON DIOXIDE, HALON, WATER SPRAY OR STANDARD FOAM (1987 EMERGENCY RESPONSE GUIDEBOOK, DOT P 5800.4). FOR LARGER FIRES, USE WATER SPRAY, FOG OR STANDARD FOAM (1987 EMERGENCY RESPONSE GUIDEBOOK, DOT P 5800.4).

FIREFIGHTING: MOVE CONTAINERS FROM FIRE AREA IF POSSIBLE (1987 EMERGENCY RESPONSE GUIDEBOOK, DOT P 5800.4, GUIDE PAGE 53).

EXTINGUISH ONLY IF FLOW CAN BE STOPPED. EXTINGUISH USING AGENT INDICATED. USE FLOODING AMOUNTS OF WATER AS A FOG. COOL CONTAINERS WITH FLOODING AMOUNTS OF WATER FROM AS FAR A DISTANCE AS POSSIBLE. AVOID BREATHING POISONOUS VAPORS, KEEP UPWIND. CONSIDER EVACUATION OF DOWNWIND AREA IF MATERIAL IS LEAKING.

TOXICITY

HEXACHLOROBENZENE: TOXICITY DATA: 3600 MG/KG INHALATION-RAT LC50; 1800 MG/M3 INHALATION-RABBIT LC50; 4 GM/M3 INHALATION-MOUSE LC50; 1600 MG/M3 INHALATION-CAT LC50; 10,000 MG/KG ORAL-RAT LD50; 4 MG/KG ORAL-MOUSE LD50; 2600 MG/KG ORAL-RABBIT LD50; 1700 MG/KG ORAL-CAT LD50; 1047 MG/KG ORAL-MAMMAL LD50; 220 MG/KG UNREPORTED-MAN LDLO; MUTAGENIC DATA (RTECS); REPRODUCTIVE EFFECTS DATA (RTECS); TUMORIGENIC DATA (RTECS). CARCINOGEN STATUS: ANTICIPATED HUMAN CARCINOGEN (NTP); HUMAN INADEQUATE EVIDENCE, ANIMAL SUFFICIENT EVIDENCE (IARC GROUP 2B). ORAL ADMINISTRATION PRODUCED LIVER-CELL TUMORS IN MICE, AND LIVER HEMANGIOTHELIOMAS, HEPATOMAS, AND THYROID ADENOMAS IN HAMSTERS. ACUTE TOXICITY LEVEL: TOXIC BY INHALATION AND SLIGHTLY TOXIC BY INGESTION. TARGET EFFECTS: NO DATA AVAILABLE. ADDITIONAL DATA: CUTANEOUS EFFECTS MAY BE AFFRAVATED BY SUNLIGHT AND ALCOHOL.

HEALTH EFFECTS AND FIRST AID

INHALATION: HEXACHLOROBENZENE: TOXIC. ACUTE EXPOSURE- MAY CAUSE COUGHING, DIFFICULTY BREATHING, PULMONARY EDEMA, AND DEATH. CHRONIC EXPOSURE- NO DATA AVAILABLE.

FIRST AID- REMOVE FROM EXPOSURE AREA TO FRESH AIR IMMEDIATELY. IF BREATHING HAS STOPPED, GIVE ARTIFICIAL RESPIRATION. MAINTAIN AIRWAY AND BLOOD PRESSURE AND ADMINISTER OXYGEN IF AVAILABLE. KEEP AFFECTED PERSON WARM AND AT REST. TREAT SYMPTOMATICALLY AND SUPPORTIVELY. ADMINISTRATION OF OXYGEN SHOULD BE PERFORMED BY QUALIFIED PERSONNEL. GET MEDICAL ATTENTION IMMEDIATELY.

SKIN CONTACT: HEXACHLOROBENZENE: ACUTE EXPOSURE- MAY BE IRRITATING TO THE SKIN. CHRONIC EXPOSURE- PROLONGED OR REPEATED EXPOSURE MAY CAUSE EXFOLIATIVE DERMATITIS, AND POSSIBLY, PORPHYRIA.

FIRST AID- REMOVE CONTAMINATED CLOTHING AND SHOES IMMEDIATELY. WASH AFFECTED AREA WITH SOAP OR MILD DETERGENT AND LARGE AMOUNTS OF WATER UNTIL NO EVIDENCE OF CHEMICAL REMAINS (APPROXIMATELY 15-20 MINUTES). GET MEDICAL ATTENTION IMMEDIATELY.

EYE CONTACT: HEXACHLOROBENZENE: ACUTE EXPOSURE- MAY BE IRRITATING. CHRONIC EXPOSURE- NO DATA AVAILABLE.

FIRST AID- WASH EYES IMMEDIATELY WITH LARGE AMOUNTS OF WATER OR NORMAL SALINE, OCCASIONALLY LIFTING UPPER AND LOWER LIDS, UNTIL NO EVIDENCE OF CHEMICAL REMAINS (APPROXIMATELY 15-20 MINUTES). GET MEDICAL ATTENTION IMMEDIATELY.

INGESTION: HEXACHLOROBENZENE: CARCINOGEN. **ACUTE EXPOSURE-** MAY CAUSE NAUSEA, VOMITING, AND ABDOMINAL PAIN. **CHRONIC EXPOSURE-** PROLONGED OR REPEATED INGESTION OF SMALL AMOUNTS MAY CAUSE LETHARGY, WEAKNESS, TREMORS, HYPEREXCITABILITY, HYPERPIGMENTATION, HYPERTRICHOSIS, ALOPECIA, CORNEAL OPACITIES, SKIN ERUPTIONS, DIGITAL DEFORMITIES, EXCESSIVE GROWTH OF HAIR IN UNUSUAL PLACES, AND PORT WINE OR DARKER COLORED URINE. OTHER ORGANS THAT MAY BE AFFECTED INCLUDE LUNGS, HEART, AND LIVER. HEXACHLOROBENZENE MAY CROSS THE PLACENTA, AND MAY BE EXCRETED IN BREAST MILK TO INDUCE TOXIC EFFECTS IN INFANTS. REPEATED ORAL ADMINISTRATION RESULTED IN LIVER-CELL TUMORS IN MICE AND RATS, AND LIVER HEMANGIOTHELIOMAS, HEPATOMAS, AND THYROID ADENOMAS IN HAMSTERS.

FIRST AID- REMOVE BY GASTRIC LAVAGE FOLLOWED BY A SALINE CATHARTIC (DEICHMANN AND GERARDE, TOXICOLOGY OF DRUGS AND CHEMICALS). DO NOT PERFORM GASTRIC LAVAGE ON AN UNCONSCIOUS PERSON. GET MEDICAL ATTENTION IMMEDIATELY. TREATMENT SHOULD BE ADMINISTERED BY QUALIFIED MEDICAL PERSONNEL.

ANTIDOTE: NO SPECIFIC ANTIDOTE. TREAT SYMPTOMATICALLY AND SUPPORTIVELY.

REACTIVITY

REACTIVITY: STABLE UNDER NORMAL TEMPERATURES AND PRESSURES.

INCOMPATIBILITIES: HEXACHLOROBENZENE: DIMETHYLFORMAMIDE: VIOLENT REACTION ABOVE 65 C.

DECOMPOSITION: THERMAL DECOMPOSITION PRODUCTS MAY INCLUDE TOXIC AND CORROSIVE FUMES OF CHLORIDES.

POLYMERIZATION: HAZARDOUS POLYMERIZATION HAS NOT BEEN REPORTED TO OCCUR UNDER NORMAL TEMPERATURES AND PRESSURES.

STORAGE AND DISPOSAL

OBSERVE ALL FEDERAL, STATE AND LOCAL REGULATIONS WHEN STORING OR DISPOSING OF THIS SUBSTANCE. FOR ASSISTANCE, CONTACT THE DISTRICT DIRECTOR OF THE ENVIRONMENTAL PROTECTION AGENCY.

****DISPOSAL****

DISPOSAL MUST BE IN ACCORDANCE WITH STANDARDS APPLICABLE TO GENERATORS OF HAZARDOUS WASTE, 40CFR 262. EPA HAZARDOUS WASTE NUMBER U127.

HEXACHLOROBENZENE - REGULATORY LEVEL: 0.13 MG/L MATERIALS WHICH CONTAIN THE ABOVE SUBSTANCE AT OR ABOVE THE REGULATORY LEVEL MEET THE EPA CHARACTERISTIC OF TOXICITY, AND MUST BE DISPOSED OF IN ACCORDANCE WITH 40 CFR PART 262. EPA HAZARDOUS WASTE NUMBER D032.

CONDITIONS TO AVOID

MAY BURN BUT DOES NOT IGNITE READILY.

SPILL AND LEAK PROCEDURES

WATER SPILL: THE CALIFORNIA SAFE DRINKING WATER AND TOXIC ENFORCEMENT ACT OF 1986 (PROPOSITION 65) PROHIBITS CONTAMINATING ANY KNOWN SOURCE OF DRINKING WATER WITH SUBSTANCES KNOWN TO CAUSE CANCER AND/OR REPRODUCTIVE TOXICITY.

OCCUPATIONAL SPILL: DO NOT TOUCH SPILLED MATERIAL. STOP LEAK IF YOU CAN DO IT WITHOUT RISK. FOR SMALL SPILLS, TAKE UP WITH SAND OR OTHER ABSORBENT MATERIAL AND PLACE INTO CONTAINERS FOR LATER DISPOSAL. FOR SMALL DRY SPILLS, WITH A CLEAN SHOVEL PLACE MATERIAL INTO CLEAN, DRY CONTAINER AND COVER. MOVE CONTAINERS FROM SPILL AREA. FOR LARGER SPILLS, DIKE FAR AHEAD OF SPILL FOR LATER DISPOSAL. KEEP UNNECESSARY PEOPLE AWAY. ISOLATE HAZARD AREA AND DENY ENTRY.

REPORTABLE QUANTITY (RQ): 10 POUNDS THE SUPERFUND AMENDMENTS AND REAUTHORIZATION ACT (SARA) SECTION 304 REQUIRES THAT A RELEASE EQUAL TO OR GREATER THAN THE REPORTABLE QUANTITY FOR THIS SUBSTANCE BE IMMEDIATELY REPORTED TO THE LOCAL EMERGENCY PLANNING COMMITTEE AND THE STATE EMERGENCY RESPONSE COMMISSION (40 CFR 355.40). IF THE RELEASE OF THIS SUBSTANCE IS REPORTABLE UNDER CERCLA SECTION 103, THE NATIONAL RESPONSE CENTER MUST BE NOTIFIED IMMEDIATELY AT (800) 424-8802 OR (202) 426-2675 IN THE METROPOLITAN WASHINGTON, D.C. AREA (40 CFR 302.6).

PROTECTIVE EQUIPMENT

VENTILATION: PROVIDE LOCAL EXHAUST OR PROCESS ENCLOSURE VENTILATION SYSTEM.

RESPIRATOR: THE FOLLOWING RESPIRATORS ARE RECOMMENDED BASED ON INFORMATION FOUND IN THE PHYSICAL DATA, TOXICITY AND HEALTH EFFECTS SECTIONS. THEY ARE RANKED IN ORDER FROM MINIMUM TO MAXIMUM RESPIRATORY PROTECTION. THE SPECIFIC RESPIRATOR SELECTED MUST BE BASED ON CONTAMINATION LEVELS FOUND IN THE WORK PLACE, MUST NOT EXCEED THE WORKING LIMITS OF THE RESPIRATOR AND BE JOINTLY APPROVED BY THE NATIONAL INSTITUTE FOR OCCUPATIONAL SAFETY AND HEALTH AND THE MINE SAFETY AND HEALTH ADMINISTRATION (NIOSH-MSHA).

TYPE 'C' SUPPLIED-AIR RESPIRATOR WITH A FULL FACEPIECE OPERATED IN PRESSURE-DEMAND OR OTHER POSITIVE PRESSURE MODE OR WITH A FULL FACEPIECE, HELMET OR HOOD OPERATED IN CONTINOUS-FLOW MODE.

SELF-CONTAINED BREATHING APPARATUS WITH A FULL FACEPIECE OPERATED IN PRESSURE-DEMAND OR OTHER POSITIVE PRESSURE MODE.

FOR FIREFIGHTING AND OTHER IMMEDIATELY DANGEROUS TO LIFE OR HEALTH CONDITIONS:

SELF-CONTAINED BREATHING APPARATUS WITH FULL FACEPIECE OPERATED IN PRESSURE-DEMAND OR OTHER POSITIVE PRESSURE MODE.

SUPPLIED-AIR RESPIRATOR WITH FULL FACEPIECE AND OPERATED IN PRESSURE-DEMAND OR OTHER POSITIVE PRESSURE MODE IN COMBINATION WITH AN AUXILIARY SELF-CONTAINED BREATHING APPARATUS OPERATED IN PRESSURE-DEMAND OR OTHER POSITIVE PRESSURE MODE.

CLOTHING: EMPLOYEE MUST WEAR APPROPRIATE PROTECTIVE (IMPERVIOUS) CLOTHING AND EQUIPMENT TO PREVENT REPEATED OR PROLONGED SKIN CONTACT WITH THIS SUBSTANCE.

GLOVES: EMPLOYEE MUST WEAR APPROPRIATE PROTECTIVE GLOVES TO PREVENT CONTACT WITH THIS SUBSTANCE.

EYE PROTECTION: EMPLOYEE MUST WEAR SPLASH-PROOF OR DUST-RESISTANT SAFETY GOGGLES TO PREVENT EYE CONTACT WITH THIS SUBSTANCE.

EMERGENCY EYE WASH: WHERE THERE IS ANY POSSIBILITY THAT AN EMPLOYEE'S EYES MAY BE EXPOSED TO THIS SUBSTANCE, THE EMPLOYER SHOULD PROVIDE AN EYE WASH FOUNTAIN WITHIN THE IMMEDIATE WORK AREA FOR EMERGENCY USE.

AUTHORIZED BY- OCCUPATIONAL HEALTH SERVICES, INC.

CREATION DATE: 10/04/89 ***REVISION DATE:*** 07/13/90

MATERIAL SAFETY DATA SHEET

OCCUPATIONAL HEALTH SERVICES, INC.
AGRICULTURE AND PESTICIDE DIVISION
450 SEVENTH AVENUE, SUITE 2407
NEW YORK, NEW YORK 10123
1-800-445-MSDS OR (212) 967-1100

EMERGENCY CONTACT:
JOHN S. BRANSFORD, JR. (615) 292-1180

SUBSTANCE IDENTIFICATION

CAS-NUMBER 70-30-4

SUBSTANCE: **HEXACHLOROPHENE**

TRADE NAMES/SYNONYMS: ACIGENA; ALMEDERM; AT 7; B32; BILEVON; BIS(2-HYDROXY-3,5,6-TRICHLOROPHENYL)METHANE; COTOFILM; DISTODIN; EXOFENE; 2,2'-DIHYDROXY-3,5,6,3',5',6'-HEXACHLORODIPHENYLMETHANE; FOMAC; FOSTRIL; GAMOPHENE; HEXABALM; NABAC; SEPTOPEN; STERAL; SUROFENE; TRICHLOROPHENE; UN 2875; PST10780

CHEMICAL FAMILY: AROMATIC HALOGEN

MOLECULAR FORMULA: C13-H6-CL6-O2

MOLECULAR WEIGHT: 406.89

CERCLA RATINGS (SCALE 0-3): HEALTH=3 FIRE=0 REACTIVITY=0 PERSISTENCE=3

NFPA RATINGS (SCALE 0-4): HEALTH=3 FIRE=0 REACTIVITY=0

COMPONENTS AND CONTAMINANTS

COMPONENT: HEXACHLOROPHENE ***PERCENT:*** 100
CAS# 70-30-4

EXPOSURE LIMITS: HEXACHLOROPHENE: NO OCCUPATIONAL EXPOSURE LIMITS ESTABLISHED BY OSHA, ACGIH, OR NIOSH.
100 POUNDS CERCLA SECTION 103 REPORTABLE QUANTITY

PHYSICAL DATA

DESCRIPTION: ODORLESS, WHITE, FREE-FLOWING POWDER OR CRYSTALS.

MELTING POINT: 327-329 F (164-165 C) ***SPECIFIC GRAVITY:*** NOT AVAILABLE

SOLUBILITY IN WATER: INSOLUBLE

SOLVENT SOLUBILITY: ACETONE, ALCOHOL, ETHER, CHLOROFORM, PROPYLENE GLYCOL, POLYETHYLENE GLYCOLS, OLIVE OIL, COTTONSEED OIL, DILUTED SOLUTIONS OF THE ALKALIES.

FIRE AND EXPLOSION DATA

FIRE AND EXPLOSION HAZARD: NEGLIGIBLE FIRE HAZARD WHEN EXPOSED TO HEAT OR FLAME.

FIREFIGHTING MEDIA: DRY CHEMICAL, CARBON DIOXIDE, HALON, WATER SPRAY OR STANDARD FOAM (1987 EMERGENCY RESPONSE GUIDEBOOK, DOT P 5800.4). FOR LARGER FIRES, USE WATER SPRAY, FOG OR STANDARD FOAM (1987 EMERGENCY RESPONSE GUIDEBOOK, DOT P 5800.4).

FIREFIGHTING: NO ACUTE HAZARD. MOVE CONTAINER FROM FIRE AREA IF POSSIBLE. AVOID BREATHING VAPORS OR DUSTS; KEEP UPWIND.

TOXICITY

HEXACHLOROPHENE: IRRITATION DATA: 3 MG/3 DAYS INTERMITTENT SKIN-HUMAN MILD; 50 UG/24 HOURS SKIN-HUMAN MILD; 30 UG OPEN SKIN-RABBIT MILD; 1250 UG/24 HOURS SKIN-RABBIT MILD; 30 UG OPEN SKIN-GUINEA PIG MILD; 1250 UG/24 HOURS SKIN-GUINEA PIG MILD; 3 MG/24 HOURS EYE-DOG; 1500 MG/24 HOURS EYE-RABBIT. TOXICITY DATA: 340 MG/M3 INHALATION-RAT LC50; 290 MG/M3 INHALATION-MOUSE LC50; 1840 MG/KG SKIN-RAT LD50; 270 MG/KG SKIN-MOUSE LD50; 1100 MG/KG SKIN-GUINEA PIG LD50; 257 MG/KG/7 DAYS INTERMITTENT ORAL-INFANT TDLO; 250 MG/KG ORAL-CHILD LDLO; 600 MG/KG ORAL-WOMAN TDLO; 56 MG/KG ORAL-RAT LD50; 67 MG/KG ORAL-MOUSE LD50; 40 MG/KG ORAL-DOG LDLO; 40,690 UG/KG ORAL-RABBIT LD50; 60 MG/KG ORAL-GUINEA PIG LD50; 30 MG/KG ORAL-MAMMAL LD50; 14700 MG/KG SUBCUTANEOUS-RAT LD50; 7500 UG/KG INTRAVENOUS-RAT LD50; 8500 UG/KG INTRAVENOUS-RABBIT LD50; 5 MG/KG INTRAVENOUS-DOG LDLO; 22 MG/KG INTRAPERITONEAL-RAT LD50; 20 MG/KG INTRAPERITONEAL-MOUSE LD50; 25 MG/KG INTRAPERITONEAL-GUINEA PIG LDLO; 320 MG/KG UNREPORTED-GUINEA PIG LD50; REPRODUCTIVE EFFECTS DATA (RTECS); TUMORIGENIC DATA (RTECS). CARCINOGEN STATUS: ANIMAL INADEQUATE EVIDENCE (IARC GROUP-3). THE AVAILABLE DATA DO NOT ALLOW AN EVALUATION OF THE CARCINOGENICITY OF HEXACHLOROPHENE. LOCAL EFFECTS: IRRITANT- INHALATION, SKIN, AND EYES. ACUTE TOXICITY LEVEL: HIGHLY TOXIC BY INHALATION; TOXIC BY INGESTION AND DERMAL ABSORPTION. TARGET EFFECTS: SENSITIZER- SKIN; NEUROTOXIN.

HEALTH EFFECTS AND FIRST AID

INHALATION: HEXACHLOROPHENE: IRRITANT. **ACUTE EXPOSURE-** INHALATION OF THE DUST MAY CAUSE RESPIRATORY TRACT IRRITATION. **CHRONIC EXPOSURE-** REPEATED OR PROLONGED EXPOSURE MAY CAUSE MUCOUS MEMBRANE IRRITATION.

FIRST AID- REMOVE FROM EXPOSURE AREA TO FRESH AIR IMMEDIATELY. IF BREATHING HAS STOPPED, PERFORM ARTIFICIAL RESPIRATION. KEEP PERSON WARM AND AT REST. TREAT SYMPTOMATICALLY AND SUPPORTIVELY. GET MEDICAL ATTENTION IMMEDIATELY.

SKIN CONTACT: HEXACHOROPHENE: IRRITANT/SENSITIZER/NEUROTOXIN/TOXIC. **ACUTE EXPOSURE-** DUST MAY CAUSE IRRITATION, PHOTOSENSITIVITY AND SENSITIZATION IN PERSONS PREVIOUSLY EXPOSED. MAY BE ABSORBED THROUGH THE SKIN TO CAUSE CONFUSION, DIPLOPIA, LETHARGY, TWITCHING, CONVULSIONS, RESPIRATORY ARREST AND POSSIBLY DEATH. **CHRONIC EXPOSURE-** REPEATED OR PROLONGED EXPOSURE MAY RESULT IN SENSITIZATION DERMATITIS. PROLONGED SKIN ABSORPTION MAY CAUSE DAMAGE TO THE CENTRAL NERVOUS SYSTEM, ESPECIALLY THE WHITE MATTER AND THE SPINAL CORD. MICE EXPOSED TO THE SUBSTANCE FOR 21 WEEKS DEVELOPED SKIN TUMORS. PREGNANT RATS EXPOSED EXHIBITED FETOTOXICITY AND CRANIOFACIAL AND OTHER DEVELOPMENTAL ABNORMALITIES OF THE FETUSES.

FIRST AID- REMOVE CONTAMINATED CLOTHING AND SHOES IMMEDIATELY. WASH AFFECTED AREA WITH SOAP OR MILD DETERGENT AND LARGE AMOUNTS OF WATER UNTIL NO EVIDENCE OF CHEMICAL REMAINS (APPROXIMATELY 15-20 MINUTES). GET MEDICAL ATTENTION IMMEDIATELY.

EYE CONTACT: HEXACHLOROPHENE: IRRITANT. **ACUTE EXPOSURE-** DUST MAY CAUSE IRRITATION. HOWEVER, EXPERIMENTS IN RABBIT AND DOG EYES HAVE SHOWN THAT APPLICATION OF A 3% SOLUTION FOR 2-4 MINUTES DID NOT CAUSE SIGNIFICANT DAMAGE. **CHRONIC EXPOSURE-** REPEATED OR PROLONGED EXPOSURE MAY CAUSE CONJUNCTIVITIS.

FIRST AID- WASH EYES IMMEDIATELY WITH LARGE AMOUNTS OF WATER OR NORMAL SALINE, OCCASIONALLY LIFTING UPPER AND LOWER LIDS, UNTIL NO EVIDENCE OF CHEMICAL REMAINS (APPROXIMATELY 15-20 MINUTES). GET MEDICAL ATTENTION IMMEDIATELY.

INGESTION: HEXACHLOROPHENE: NEUROTOXIN/TOXIC. **ACUTE EXPOSURE-** SYMPTOMS FOLLOWING INGESTION MAY BE NAUSEA, VOMITING, CRAMPS, DIARRHEA, FEVER, ABNORMAL PUPILLARY REFLEXES, TWITCHING, PAPILLEDEMA, NYSTAGMUS, BLINDNESS, WEAKNESS, PARALYSIS INCLUDING FACIAL PARALYSIS, CONVULSIONS, COMA AND POSSIBLY DEATH. OLIGURIA, HYPOTENSION, SHOCK, LETHARGY AND STUPOR MAY OCCUR. A WOMAN EXPOSED EXPERIENCED NAUSEA, VOMITING AND CARDIOMYOPATHY INCLUDING INFARCTION. THE FATAL DOSE IS APPROXIMATELY 2-5 GRAMS. **CHRONIC EXPOSURE-** PERSONS WITH SEVERE CHRONIC EXPOSURE MAY HAVE SYMPTOMS PRIMARILY ASSOCIATED WITH THE CENTRAL NERVOUS SYSTEM. THE EFFECTS INCLUDE DIPLOPIA, IRRITABILITY, WEAKNESS OF THE LOWER EXTREMITIES AND CONVULSIONS. PREGNANT RATS EXPOSED TO THE SUBSTANCE EXHIBITED STILLBIRTHS, CRANIOFACIAL DEVELOPMENTAL ABNORMALITIES OF THE FETUSES, AND ADVERSE EFFECTS ON THE NEWBORNS.

FIRST AID- IF VICTIM IS CONSCIOUS, AND IF CORROSIVE INJURY IS ABSENT, REMOVE POISON BY GASTRIC LAVAGE OR EMESIS. ACTIVATED CHARCOAL IS USEFUL. FOLLOW WITH 240 ML OF MILK. GASTRIC LAVAGE AND EMESIS ARE NOT TO BE USED IN THE PRESENCE OF ESOPHAGEAL INJURY (DREISBACH, HANDBOOK OF POISONING, 12TH ED.). GASTRIC LAVAGE SHOULD BE PERFORMED BY QUALIFIED MEDICAL PERSONNEL. GET MEDICAL ATTENTION IMMEDIATELY.

ANTIDOTE: NO SPECIFIC ANTIDOTE. TREAT SYMPTOMATICALLY AND SUPPORTIVELY.

REACTIVITY

REACTIVITY: STABLE UNDER NORMAL TEMPERATURES AND PRESSURES.

INCOMPATIBILITIES: HEXACHLOROPHENE: NO DATA AVAILABLE.

DECOMPOSITION: THERMAL DECOMPOSITION PRODUCTS MAY INCLUDE TOXIC AND CORROSIVE FUMES OF CHLORIDES.

POLYMERIZATION: HAZARDOUS POLYMERIZATION HAS NOT BEEN REPORTED TO OCCUR UNDER NORMAL TEMPERATURES AND PRESSURES.

CONDITIONS TO AVOID

NONE REPORTED.

SPILL AND LEAK PROCEDURES

OCCUPATIONAL SPILL: NO SPECIAL PRECAUTIONS INDICATED.

REPORTABLE QUANTITY (RQ): 100 POUNDS THE SUPERFUND AMENDMENTS AND REAUTHORIZATION ACT (SARA) SECTION 304 REQUIRES THAT A RELEASE EQUAL TO OR GREATER THAN THE REPORTABLE QUANTITY FOR THIS SUBSTANCE BE IMMEDIATELY REPORTED TO THE LOCAL EMERGENCY PLANNING COMMITTEE AND THE STATE EMERGENCY RESPONSE COMMISSION (40 CFR 355.40). IF THE RELEASE OF THIS SUBSTANCE IS REPORTABLE UNDER CERCLA SECTION 103, THE NATIONAL RESPONSE CENTER MUST BE NOTIFIED IMMEDIATELY AT (800) 424-8802 OR (202) 426-2675 IN THE METROPOLITAN WASHINGTON, D.C. AREA (40 CFR 302.6).

PROTECTIVE EQUIPMENT

VENTILATION: PROVIDE LOCAL EXHAUST OR PROCESS ENCLOSURE VENTILATION SYSTEM.

RESPIRATOR: THE FOLLOWING RESPIRATORS ARE RECOMMENDED BASED ON INFORMATION FOUND IN THE PHYSICAL DATA, TOXICITY AND HEALTH EFFECTS SECTIONS. THEY ARE RANKED IN ORDER FROM MINIMUM TO MAXIMUM RESPIRATORY PROTECTION. THE SPECIFIC RESPIRATOR SELECTED MUST BE BASED ON CONTAMINATION LEVELS FOUND IN THE WORK PLACE, MUST NOT EXCEED THE WORKING LIMITS OF THE RESPIRATOR AND BE JOINTLY APPROVED BY THE NATIONAL INSTITUTE FOR OCCUPATIONAL SAFETY AND HEALTH AND THE MINE SAFETY AND HEALTH ADMINISTRATION (NIOSH-MSHA).

DUST AND MIST RESPIRATOR WITH A FULL FACEPIECE.

AIR-PURIFYING FULL FACEPIECE RESPIRATOR WITH A HIGH-EFFICIENCY PARTICULATE FILTER.

POWERED AIR-PURIFYING RESPIRATOR WITH A TIGHT-FITTING FACEPIECE AND HIGH-EFFICIENCY PARTICULATE FILTER.

TYPE 'C' SUPPLIED-AIR RESPIRATOR WITH A FULL FACEPIECE OPERATED IN PRESSURE-DEMAND OR OTHER POSITIVE PRESSURE MODE OR WITH A FULL FACEPIECE, HELMET OR HOOD OPERATED IN CONTINUOUS-FLOW MODE.

SELF-CONTAINED BREATHING APPARATUS WITH A FULL FACEPIECE OPERATED IN PRESSURE-DEMAND OR OTHER POSITIVE PRESSURE MODE.

FOR FIREFIGHTING AND OTHER IMMEDIATELY DANGEROUS TO LIFE OR HEALTH CONDITIONS:

SELF-CONTAINED BREATHING APPARATUS WITH FULL FACEPIECE OPERATED IN PRESSURE-DEMAND OR OTHER POSITIVE PRESSURE MODE.

SUPPLIED-AIR RESPIRATOR WITH FULL FACEPIECE AND OPERATED IN PRESSURE-DEMAND OR OTHER POSITIVE PRESSURE MODE IN COMBINATION WITH AN AUXILIARY SELF-CONTAINED BREATHING APPARATUS OPERATED IN PRESSURE-DEMAND OR OTHER POSITIVE PRESSURE MODE.

CLOTHING: EMPLOYEE MUST WEAR APPROPRIATE PROTECTIVE (IMPERVIOUS) CLOTHING AND EQUIPMENT TO PREVENT REPEATED OR PROLONGED SKIN CONTACT WITH THIS SUBSTANCE.

GLOVES: EMPLOYEE MUST WEAR APPROPRIATE PROTECTIVE GLOVES TO PREVENT CONTACT WITH THIS SUBSTANCE.

EYE PROTECTION: EMPLOYEE MUST WEAR SPLASH-PROOF OR DUST-RESISTANT SAFETY GOGGLES TO PREVENT EYE CONTACT WITH THIS SUBSTANCE.

EMERGENCY EYE WASH: WHERE THERE IS ANY POSSIBILITY THAT AN EMPLOYEE'S EYES MAY BE EXPOSED TO THIS SUBSTANCE, THE EMPLOYER SHOULD PROVIDE AN EYE WASH FOUNTAIN WITHIN THE IMMEDIATE WORK AREA FOR EMERGENCY USE.

AUTHORIZED BY- OCCUPATIONAL HEALTH SERVICES, INC.
CREATION DATE: 10/04/89 ***REVISION DATE:*** 07/12/90

MATERIAL SAFETY DATA SHEET

OCCUPATIONAL HEALTH SERVICES, INC.
AGRICULTURE AND PESTICIDE DIVISION
450 SEVENTH AVENUE, SUITE 2407
NEW YORK, NEW YORK 10123
1-800-445-MSDS OR (212) 967-1100

EMERGENCY CONTACT:
JOHN S. BRANSFORD, JR. (615) 292-1180

SUBSTANCE IDENTIFICATION

CAS-NUMBER 51235-04-2

SUBSTANCE: **HEXAZINONE**

TRADE NAMES/SYNONYMS: 1,3,5-TRIAZINE-2,4(1H,3H)-DIONE, 3-CYCLOHEXYL-6-(DIMETHYLAMINO) -1-METHYL-; 3-CYCLOHEXYL-6-DIMETHYLAMINO-1-METHYL-1,3,5-TRIAZINE-2,4(1H,3H)-DIONE; 3-CYCLOHEXYL-6-(DIMETHYLAMINO)-1-METHYL-1,3,5-TRIAZINE- 2,4(1H,3H)-DIONE; 3-CYCLOHEXYL-6-(DIMETHYLAMINO)-1-METHYL-S-TRIAZINE-3,4(1H,3H)-DIONE; 3-CYCLOHEXYL-6-DIMETHYLAMINO-1-METHYL-1,3,5-TRIAZINE-2,4-DIONE; DPX 3674; VELPAR; C12H20N4O2; PST10994

CHEMICAL FAMILY: S-TRIAZINE

MOLECULAR FORMULA: C12-H20-N4-O2

MOLECULAR WEIGHT: 252.3

CERCLA RATINGS (SCALE 0-3): HEALTH=2 FIRE=1 REACTIVITY=0 PERSISTENCE=2

NFPA RATINGS (SCALE 0-4): HEALTH=2 FIRE=1 REACTIVITY=0

COMPONENTS AND CONTAMINANTS

COMPONENT: HEXAZINONE ***PERCENT:*** 100.0
CAS# 51235-04-2

OTHER CONTAMINANTS: NONE

EXPOSURE LIMITS: NO OCCUPATIONAL EXPOSURE LIMITS ESTABLISHED BY OSHA, ACGIH, OR NIOSH.

PHYSICAL DATA

DESCRIPTION: ODORLESS, WHITE CRYSTALLINE SOLID

MELTING POINT: 239-243 F (115-117 C) ***SPECIFIC GRAVITY:*** 1.25

VAPOR PRESSURE: NEGLIGIBLE ***SOLUBILITY IN WATER:*** 3.3% @ 25 C

SOLVENT SOLUBILITY: SOLUBLE IN CHLOROFORM, METHANOL, BENZENE, ACETONE, DIMETHYLFORMAMIDE, TOLUENE; SPARINGLY SOLUBLE IN HEXANE

FIRE AND EXPLOSION DATA

FIRE AND EXPLOSION HAZARD: SLIGHT FIRE HAZARD WHEN EXPOSED TO HEAT OR FLAME.

FIREFIGHTING MEDIA: DRY CHEMICAL, CARBON DIOXIDE, HALON, WATER SPRAY OR STANDARD FOAM (1987 EMERGENCY RESPONSE GUIDEBOOK, DOT P 5800.4).
FOR LARGER FIRES, USE WATER SPRAY, FOG OR STANDARD FOAM (1987 EMERGENCY RESPONSE GUIDEBOOK, DOT P 5800.4).

FIREFIGHTING: MOVE CONTAINERS FROM FIRE AREA IF POSSIBLE (1987 EMERGENCY RESPONSE GUIDEBOOK, DOT P 5800.4, GUIDE PAGE 53).
EXTINGUISH USING AGENTS SUITABLE FOR SURROUNDING FIRE. USE FLOODING QUANTITIES OF WATER AS A FOG. KEEP MATERIAL OUT OF SEWERS AND WATER SOURCES. DO NOT TOUCH SPILLED MATERIAL. AVOID BREATHING HAZARDOUS FUMES; KEEP UPWIND.

TOXICITY

HEXAZINONE: IRRITATION DATA: 48 MG EYE-RABBIT MODERATE. TOXICITY DATA: 5278 MG/KG SKIN-RAT LD50; 1690 MG/KG ORAL-RAT LD50; 860 MG/KG ORAL-GUINEA PIG LD50; 530 MG/KG INTRAPERITONEAL-RAT LD50; REPRODUCTIVE EFFECTS DATA (RTECS). CARCINOGEN STATUS: NONE. LOCAL EFFECTS: IRRITANT-EYES. ACUTE TOXICITY DATA: MODERATELY TOXIC BY INGESTION AND SLIGHTLY TOXIC BY DERMAL ABSORPTION. TARGET EFFECTS: NO DATA AVAILABLE.

HEALTH EFFECTS AND FIRST AID

INHALATION: HEXAZINONE: **ACUTE EXPOSURE-** A LETHAL CONCENTRATION IN RATS IS GREATER THAN 7480 MG/M3. SOME TRIAZINES ARE IRRITATING TO THE UPPER RESPIRATORY TRACT. **CHRONIC EXPOSURE-** NO DATA AVAILABLE.

FIRST AID- REMOVE FROM EXPOSURE AREA TO FRESH AIR IMMEDIATELY. IF BREATHING HAS STOPPED, PERFORM ARTIFICIAL RESPIRATION. KEEP PERSON WARM AND AT REST. TREAT SYMPTOMATICALLY AND SUPPORTIVELY. GET MEDICAL ATTENTION IMMEDIATELY.

SKIN CONTACT: HEXAZINONE: **ACUTE EXPOSURE-** THIS MATERIAL WAS SLIGHTLY IRRITATING TO RABBIT SKIN. A LETHAL DOSE IN RABBITS BY DERMAL ABSORPTION WAS GREATER THAN 5278 MG/KG. **CHRONIC EXPOSURE-** NO DATA AVAILABLE.

FIRST AID- REMOVE CONTAMINATED CLOTHING AND SHOES IMMEDIATELY. WASH AFFECTED AREA WITH SOAP OR MILD DETERGENT AND LARGE AMOUNTS OF WATER UNTIL NO EVIDENCE OF CHEMICAL REMAINS (APPROXIMATELY 15-20 MINUTES). GET MEDICAL ATTENTION IMMEDIATELY.

EYE CONTACT: HEXAZINONE: IRRITANT. **ACUTE EXPOSURE-** THIS MATERIAL WAS AN IRRITANT OF RABBIT EYES. **CHRONIC EXPOSURE-** PROLONGED OR REPEATED EXPOSURE TO IRRITANTS MAY CAUSE CONJUNCTIVITIS.

FIRST AID- WASH EYES IMMEDIATELY WITH LARGE AMOUNTS OF WATER OR NORMAL SALINE, OCCASIONALLY LIFTING UPPER AND LOWER LIDS, UNTIL NO EVIDENCE OF CHEMICAL REMAINS (APPROXIMATELY 15-20 MINUTES). GET MEDICAL ATTENTION IMMEDIATELY.

INGESTION: HEXAZINONE: **ACUTE EXPOSURE-** A LETHAL DOSE IN RATS WAS 1690 MG/KG; SYMPTOMS WERE NOT REPORTED. **CHRONIC EXPOSURE-** CHRONIC EFFECTS FROM STUDIES OF ANIMALS REPEATEDLY FED HEXAZINONE WERE MINOR AND CHARACTERIZED BY DECREASED FOOD CONSUMPTION AND BODY WEIGHT GAINS. EFFECTS ON THE NEWBORN OF MALE AND FEMALE RATS REPEATEDLY FED HEXAZINONE BEFORE MATING WERE OBSERVED FROM ONE STUDY.

FIRST AID- REMOVE BY GASTRIC LAVAGE AND CATHARSIS. MAINTAIN BLOOD PRESSURE AND AIRWAY. GIVE OXYGEN IF RESPIRATION IS DEPRESSED. DO NOT PERFORM GASTRIC LAVAGE IF VICTIM IS UNCONSCIOUS. GET MEDICAL ATTENTION IMMEDIATELY (DREISBACH, HANDBOOK OF POISONING, 12TH ED.).
ADMINISTRATION OF LAVAGE OR OXYGEN SHOULD BE PERFORMED BY QUALIFIED MEDICAL PERSONNEL.

ANTIDOTE: NO SPECIFIC ANTIDOTE. TREAT SYMPTOMATICALLY AND SUPPORTIVELY.

REACTIVITY

REACTIVITY: STABLE UNDER NORMAL TEMPERATURES AND PRESSURES.

INCOMPATIBILITIES: HEXAZINONE: NO DATA AVAILABLE.

DECOMPOSITION: THERMAL DECOMPOSITION PRODUCTS MAY INCLUDE TOXIC OXIDES OF CARBON AND NITROGEN.

POLYMERIZATION: HAZARDOUS POLYMERIZATION HAS NOT BEEN REPORTED TO OCCUR UNDER NORMAL TEMPERATURES AND PRESSURES.

STORAGE AND DISPOSAL

OBSERVE ALL FEDERAL, STATE AND LOCAL REGULATIONS WHEN STORING OR DISPOSING OF THIS SUBSTANCE. FOR ASSISTANCE, CONTACT THE DISTRICT DIRECTOR OF THE ENVIRONMENTAL PROTECTION AGENCY.

****STORAGE****

STORE IN ACCORDANCE WITH 40 CFR 165 RECOMMENDED PROCEDURES FOR THE DISPOSAL AND STORAGE OF PESTICIDES AND PESTICIDE CONTAINERS.

****DISPOSAL****

DISPOSAL MUST BE IN ACCORDANCE WITH 40 CFR 165 RECOMMENDED PROCEDURES FOR THE DISPOSAL AND STORAGE OF PESTICIDES AND PESTICIDE CONTAINERS.

CONDITIONS TO AVOID

MAY BURN BUT DOES NOT IGNITE READILY.

SPILL AND LEAK PROCEDURES

OCCUPATIONAL SPILL: DO NOT TOUCH SPILLED MATERIAL. STOP LEAK IF YOU CAN DO IT WITHOUT RISK. FOR SMALL SPILLS, TAKE UP WITH SAND OR OTHER ABSORBENT MATERIAL AND PLACE INTO CONTAINERS FOR LATER DISPOSAL. FOR SMALL DRY SPILLS, WITH A CLEAN SHOVEL PLACE MATERIAL INTO CLEAN, DRY CONTAINER AND COVER. MOVE CONTAINERS FROM SPILL AREA. FOR LARGER SPILLS, DIKE FAR AHEAD OF SPILL FOR LATER DISPOSAL. KEEP UNNECESSARY PEOPLE AWAY. ISOLATE HAZARD AREA AND DENY ENTRY.

PROTECTIVE EQUIPMENT

VENTILATION: PROVIDE LOCAL EXHAUST OR GENERAL DILUTION VENTILATION SYSTEM.

RESPIRATOR: THE FOLLOWING RESPIRATORS ARE RECOMMENDED BASED ON INFORMATION FOUND IN THE PHYSICAL DATA, TOXICITY AND HEALTH EFFECTS SECTIONS. THEY ARE RANKED IN ORDER FROM MINIMUM TO MAXIMUM RESPIRATORY PROTECTION. THE SPECIFIC RESPIRATOR SELECTED MUST BE BASED ON CONTAMINATION LEVELS FOUND IN THE WORK PLACE, MUST NOT EXCEED THE WORKING LIMITS OF THE RESPIRATOR AND BE JOINTLY APPROVED BY THE NATIONAL INSTITUTE FOR OCCUPATIONAL SAFETY AND HEALTH AND THE MINE SAFETY AND HEALTH ADMINISTRATION (NIOSH-MSHA).
CHEMICAL CARTRIDGE RESPIRATOR WITH AN ORGANIC VAPOR CARTRIDGE(S) IN

COMBINATION WITH A DUST AND MIST FILTER.
GAS MASK WITH ORGANIC VAPOR CANISTER (CHIN-STYLE OR FRONT- OR BACK-MOUNTED CANISTER) WITH A DUST AND MIST FILTER.
GAS MASK WITH ORGANIC VAPOR CANISTER (CHIN-STYLE OR FRONT- OR BACK-MOUNTED CANISTER) WITH A PARTICULATE FILTER.
POWERED AIR-PURIFYING RESPIRATOR WITH A HIGH-EFFICIENCY FILTER.
TYPE 'C' SUPPLIED-AIR RESPIRATOR WITH A FULL FACEPIECE OPERATED IN A PRESSURE-DEMAND OR OTHER POSITIVE PRESSURE MODE.
SELF-CONTAINED BREATHING APPARATUS WITH A FULL FACEPIECE OPERATED IN PRESSURE-DEMAND OR OTHER POSITIVE PRESSURE MODE.
FOR FIREFIGHTING AND OTHER IMMEDIATELY DANGEROUS TO LIFE OR HEALTH CONDITIONS:
SELF-CONTAINED BREATHING APPARATUS WITH FULL FACEPIECE OPERATED IN PRESSURE-DEMAND OR OTHER POSITIVE PRESSURE MODE.
SUPPLIED-AIR RESPIRATOR WITH FULL FACEPIECE AND OPERATED IN PRESSURE-DEMAND OR OTHER POSITIVE PRESSURE MODE IN COMBINATION WITH AN AUXILIARY SELF-CONTAINED BREATHING APPARATUS OPERATED IN PRESSURE-DEMAND OR OTHER POSITIVE PRESSURE MODE.

CLOTHING: EMPLOYEE MUST WEAR APPROPRIATE PROTECTIVE (IMPERVIOUS) CLOTHING AND EQUIPMENT TO PREVENT REPEATED OR PROLONGED SKIN CONTACT WITH THIS SUBSTANCE.

GLOVES: EMPLOYEE MUST WEAR APPROPRIATE PROTECTIVE GLOVES TO PREVENT CONTACT WITH THIS SUBSTANCE.

EYE PROTECTION: EMPLOYEE MUST WEAR SPLASH-PROOF OR DUST-RESISTANT SAFETY GOGGLES TO PREVENT EYE CONTACT WITH THIS SUBSTANCE.
EMERGENCY EYE WASH: WHERE THERE IS ANY POSSIBILITY THAT AN EMPLOYEE'S EYES MAY BE EXPOSED TO THIS SUBSTANCE, THE EMPLOYER SHOULD PROVIDE AN EYE WASH FOUNTAIN WITHIN THE IMMEDIATE WORK AREA FOR EMERGENCY USE.

AUTHORIZED BY- OCCUPATIONAL HEALTH SERVICES, INC.
CREATION DATE: 10/04/89 ***REVISION DATE:*** 05/15/90

MATERIAL SAFETY DATA SHEET

OCCUPATIONAL HEALTH SERVICES, INC.
AGRICULTURE AND PESTICIDE DIVISION
450 SEVENTH AVENUE, SUITE 2407
NEW YORK, NEW YORK 10123
1-800-445-MSDS OR (212) 967-1100

EMERGENCY CONTACT:
JOHN S. BRANSFORD, JR. (615) 292-1180

SUBSTANCE IDENTIFICATION

CAS-NUMBER 7647-01-0
SUBSTANCE: **HYDROGEN CHLORIDE, ANHYDROUS**
TRADE NAMES/SYNONYMS: HYDROCHLORIC ACID, ANHYDROUS; HYDROGEN CHLORIDE; SPIRITS OF SALT; MURIATIC ACID; HYDROCHLORIC ACID; HYDROCHLORIC ACID GAS; ANHYDROUS HYDROCHLORIC ACID; HYDROGEN CHLORIDE (HCL); STCC 4904270; UN 1050; CLH; PST11150
CHEMICAL FAMILY: INORGANIC ACID
MOLECULAR FORMULA: H-CL
MOLECULAR WEIGHT: 36.46
CERCLA RATINGS (SCALE 0-3): HEALTH=3 FIRE=0 REACTIVITY=1 PERSISTENCE=0
NFPA RATINGS (SCALE 0-4): HEALTH=3 FIRE=0 REACTIVITY=0

COMPONENTS AND CONTAMINANTS

COMPONENT: HYDROGEN CHLORIDE, ANHYDROUS ***PERCENT:*** 100
CAS# 7647-01-0
OTHER CONTAMINANTS: NONE
EXPOSURE LIMITS: HYDROGEN CHLORIDE (HYDROCHLORIC ACID): 5 PPM OSHA CEILING 5 PPM ACGIH CEILING
500 POUNDS SARA SECTION 302 THRESHOLD PLANNING QUANTITY (GAS) 5000 POUND SARA SECTION 304 REPORTABLE QUANTITY (GAS) 5000 POUNDS CERCLA SECTION 103 REPORTABLE QUANTITY (LIQUID) SUBJECT TO SARA SECTION 313 ANNUAL TOXIC CHEMICAL RELEASE REPORTING

PHYSICAL DATA

DESCRIPTION: COLORLESS GAS OR FUMING LIQUID WITH A SUFFOCATING ODOR.
BOILING POINT: -121 F (-85 C) ***MELTING POINT:*** -175 F (-115 C)
SPECIFIC GRAVITY: 1.187 @ -85 C ***VAPOR PRESSURE:*** 3040 MMHG @ 17.8 C
PH: ACIDIC IN SOLUTION ***SOLUBILITY IN WATER:*** 82.3% @ 0 C
ODOR THRESHOLD: 1-5 PPM ***VAPOR DENSITY:*** 1.268
SOLVENT SOLUBILITY: SOLUBLE IN ALCOHOL, ETHER, BENZENE, METHANOL.

FIRE AND EXPLOSION DATA

FIRE AND EXPLOSION HAZARD: NEGLIGIBLE FIRE HAZARD WHEN EXPOSED TO HEAT OR FLAME.
CYLINDER MAY EXPLODE IN HEAT OF FIRE.
FIREFIGHTING MEDIA: DRY CHEMICAL, CARBON DIOXIDE OR HALON (1987 EMERGENCY RESPONSE GUIDEBOOK, DOT P 5800.4).
FOR LARGER FIRES, USE WATER SPRAY, FOG OR STANDARD FOAM (1987 EMERGENCY RESPONSE GUIDEBOOK, DOT P 5800.4).
FIREFIGHTING: DO NOT GET WATER INSIDE CONTAINER. MOVE CONTAINER FROM FIRE AREA IF POSSIBLE. STAY AWAY FROM STORAGE TANK ENDS. COOL FIRE-EXPOSED CONTAINERS WITH WATER FROM SIDE UNTIL WELL AFTER FIRE IS OUT. ISOLATE AREA UNTIL GAS HAS DISPERSED (1987 EMERGENCY RESPONSE GUIDEBOOK, DOT P 5800.4, GUIDE PAGE 15).
USE AGENT SUITABLE FOR TYPE OF FIRE. COOL CONTAINERS WITH FLOODING QUANTITIES OF WATER, APPLY FROM AS FAR A DISTANCE AS POSSIBLE. AVOID BREATHING CORROSIVE VAPORS, KEEP UPWIND.

TRANSPORTATION DATA

DEPARTMENT OF TRANSPORTATION HAZARD CLASSIFICATION 49 CFR 172.101: NONFLAMMABLE GAS
DEPARTMENT OF TRANSPORTATION LABELING REQUIREMENTS 49 CFR 172.101 AND SUBPART E: NONFLAMMABLE GAS
DEPARTMENT OF TRANSPORTATION PACKAGING REQUIREMENTS: 49 CFR 173.304 EXCEPTIONS: 49 CFR 173.306

TOXICITY

HYDROGEN CHLORIDE (HYDROCHLORIC ACID): IRRITATION DATA: ANHYDROUS: 100 MG RINSED EYE-RABBIT MILD. HYDROCHLORIC ACID: 5 MG/30 SECONDS RINSED EYE-RABBIT MILD. TOXICITY DATA: HYDROGEN CHLORIDE (ANHYDROUS GAS): 4701 PPM/30 MINUTES INHALATION-RAT LC50; 2644 PPM/30 MINUTES INHALATION-MOUSE LC50. MONOHYDRATE: NO DATA AVAILABLE. DIHYDRATE: NO DATA AVAILABLE. TRIHYDRATE: NO DATA AVAILABLE. HEXAHYDRATE: NO DATA AVAILABLE. HYDROGEN CHLORIDE (AEROSOL): 5666 PPM/30 MINUTES INHALATION-RAT LC50; 2142 PPM/30 MINUTES INHALATION-MOUSE LC50. HYDROCHLORIC ACID: 1300 PPM/30 MINUTES INHALATION-HUMAN LCLO; 3000 PPM/5 MINUTES INHALATION-HUMAN LCLO; 81 MG/KG UNREPORTED MAN LDLO; 3124 PPM/1 HOUR INHALATION-RAT LC50; 1108 PPM/1 HOUR INHALATION-MOUSE LC50; 1449 MG/KG INTRAPERITONEAL-MOUSE LD50; 900 MG/KG ORAL-RABBIT LD50; 4416 PPM/30 MINUTES INHALATION-RABBIT LCLO; 4416 PPM/30 MINUTES INHALATION-GUINEA PIG LCLO; 1000 MG/M3/2 HOURS INHALATION-MAMMAL LCLO; MUTAGENIC DATA (RTECS); REPRODUCTIVE EFFECTS DATA (RTECS). CARCINOGEN STATUS: NONE. LOCAL EFFECTS: CORROSIVE- INHALATION, SKIN, EYE AND INGESTION. ACUTE TOXICITY LEVEL: MODERATELY TOXIC BY INHALATION. TARGET EFFECTS: NO DATA AVAILABLE.

HEALTH EFFECTS AND FIRST AID

INHALATION: HYDROGEN CHLORIDE (HYDROCHLORIC ACID): CORROSIVE. 100 PPM IMMEDIATELY DANGEROUS TO LIFE OR HEALTH. **ACUTE EXPOSURE-** INHALATION OF GAS OR FUMES AT LEVELS OF 5-35 PPM MAY CAUSE IRRITATION AND BURNING OF THE THROAT, COUGHING AND CHOKING; 50-100 PPM MAY BE BARELY TOLERABLE FOR 1 HOUR. HIGH LEVELS MAY CAUSE INFLAMMATION AND OCCASIONALLY ULCERATION OF THE NOSE, THROAT OR LARYNX, BRONCHITIS, PNEUMONIA, PALPITATIONS AND HEADACHE. HIGHER CONCENTRATIONS MAY CAUSE NECROSIS OF THE TRACHEAL AND BRONCHIAL EPITHELIUM, NASOSEPTAL PERFORATION, ATELECTASIS, EMPHYSEMA, DAMAGE TO PULMONARY BLOOD VESSELS AND LESIONS OF THE LIVER AND OTHER ORGANS. DEATH MAY BE DUE TO LARYNGEAL SPASM, BRONCHOPNEUMONIA OR PULMONARY EDEMA. 1300-2000 PPM MAY BE DANGEROUS, EVEN ON BRIEF EXPOSURES. REPRODUCTIVE EFFECTS HAVE BEEN REPORTED IN ANIMALS. **CHRONIC EXPOSURE-** REPEATED OR PROLONGED EXPOSURE MAY CAUSE EROSION AND DISCOLORATION OF EXPOSED TEETH, CHRONIC BRONCHITIS AND GASTRITIS.

FIRST AID- REMOVE FROM EXPOSURE AREA TO FRESH AIR IMMEDIATELY. IF BREATHING HAS STOPPED, GIVE ARTIFICIAL RESPIRATION. MAINTAIN AIRWAY AND BLOOD PRESSURE AND ADMINISTER OXYGEN IF AVAILABLE. KEEP AFFECTED PERSON WARM AND AT REST. TREAT SYMPTOMATICALLY AND SUPPORTIVELY. ADMINISTRATION OF OXYGEN SHOULD BE PERFORMED BY QUALIFIED PERSONNEL. GET MEDICAL ATTENTION IMMEDIATELY.

SKIN CONTACT: HYDROGEN CHLORIDE (HYDROCHLORIC ACID): CORROSIVE. **ACUTE EXPOSURE-** CONTACT MAY CAUSE SEVERE IRRITATION, INFLAMMATION, ULCERATION, NECROSIS AND CHEMICAL BURNS. SHOCK SYMPTOMS MAY DEVELOP INCLUDING RAPID PULSE, SWEATING AND COLLAPSE. PHOTOSENSITIZATION REACTIONS MAY OCCUR IN PERSONS PREVIOUSLY

EXPOSED. CONTACT WITH A COMPRESSED GAS MAY CAUSE FROSTBITE. **CHRONIC EXPOSURE-** REPEATED OR PROLONGED CONTACT WITH VAPORS OR DILUTE SOLUTIONS MAY CAUSE DERMATITIS. PHOTOSENSITIZATION MAY OCCUR.

FIRST AID- REMOVE CONTAMINATED CLOTHING AND SHOES IMMEDIATELY. WASH AFFECTED AREA WITH SOAP OR MILD DETERGENT AND LARGE AMOUNTS OF WATER UNTIL NO EVIDENCE OF CHEMICAL REMAINS (AT LEAST 15-20 MINUTES). IN CASE OF CHEMICAL BURNS, COVER AREA WITH STERILE, DRY DRESSING. BANDAGE SECURELY, BUT NOT TOO TIGHTLY. GET MEDICAL ATTENTION IMMEDIATELY.

EYE CONTACT: HYDROGEN CHLORIDE (HYDROCHLORIC ACID): CORROSIVE. **ACUTE EXPOSURE-** CONTACT MAY CAUSE SEVERE IRRITATION, CONJUNCTIVITIS, CORNEAL NECROSIS AND BURNS WITH IMPAIRMENT OR PERMANENT LOSS OF VISION. A DROP OF HYDROCHLORIC ACID SPLASHED IN THE EYE AND IMMEDIATELY WASHED OUT HAS PRODUCED A WHITE COAGULATION OF THE CORNEAL AND CONJUNCTIVAL EPITHELIUM. ANIMALS EXPOSED TO VAPOR CONCENTRATIONS OF 1350 PPM FOR ONE AND A HALF HOURS SHOWED CLOUDING OF THE CORNEA AND 300 PPM FOR 6 HOURS SHOWED SLIGHT EROSION OF THE CORNEAL EPITHELIUM. CONTACT WITH A COMPRESSED GAS MAY CAUSE FROSTBITE. **CHRONIC EXPOSURE-** ANIMALS EXPOSED TO VAPOR AT 100 PPM FOR 6 HOURS DAILY FOR 50 DAYS SHOWED ONLY SLIGHT UNREST AND IRRITATION OF THE EYES, BUT NO OCULAR INJURY. EFFECTS ARE DEPENDENT UPON CONCENTRATION AND DURATION OF EXPOSURE. CONJUNCTIVITIS OR EFFECTS SIMILAR TO THOSE FOR ACUTE EXPOSURE MAY OCCUR.

FIRST AID- WASH EYES IMMEDIATELY WITH LARGE AMOUNTS OF WATER, OCCASIONALLY LIFTING UPPER AND LOWER LIDS, UNTIL NO EVIDENCE OF CHEMICAL REMAINS (AT LEAST 15-20 MINUTES). CONTINUE IRRIGATING WITH NORMAL SALINE UNTIL THE PH HAS RETURNED TO NORMAL (30-60 MINUTES). COVER WITH STERILE BANDAGES. GET MEDICAL ATTENTION IMMEDIATELY.

INGESTION: HYDROGEN CHLORIDE (HYDROCHLORIC ACID): CORROSIVE. **ACUTE EXPOSURE-** INGESTION OF THE ACID MAY CAUSE BURNS OF THE MOUTH, THROAT, ESOPHAGUS AND STOMACH WITH CONSEQUENT PAIN, UNEASINESS, NAUSEA, SALIVATION, VOMITING, DIARRHEA, CHILLS, SHOCK AND INTENSE THIRST. NEPHRITIS, FEVER AND PERFORATION OF THE INTESTINAL TRACT, AND CIRCULATORY COLLAPSE MAY OCCUR. DEATH MAY BE DUE TO ESOPHAGEAL OR GASTRIC NECROSIS. **CHRONIC EXPOSURE-** NO DATA AVAILABLE.

FIRST AID- DO NOT USE GASTRIC LAVAGE OR EMESIS. DILUTE THE ACID IMMEDIATELY BY DRINKING LARGE QUANTITIES OF WATER OR MILK. IF VOMITING PERSISTS, ADMINISTER FLUIDS REPEATEDLY. INGESTED ACID MUST BE DILUTED APPROXIMATELY 100 FOLD TO RENDER IT HARMLESS TO TISSUES. MAINTAIN AIRWAY AND TREAT SHOCK (DREISBACH, HANDBOOK OF POISONING, 12TH ED.). GET MEDICAL ATTENTION IMMEDIATELY. IF VOMITING OCCURS, KEEP HEAD BELOW HIPS TO HELP PREVENT ASPIRATION.

ANTIDOTE: NO SPECIFIC ANTIDOTE. TREAT SYMPTOMATICALLY AND SUPPORTIVELY.

REACTIVITY

REACTIVITY: HYDROGEN CHLORIDE (HYDROCHLORIC ACID): MAY REACT EXOTHERMICALLY WITH WATER.

INCOMPATIBILITIES: HYDROGEN CHLORIDE (HYDROCHLORIC ACID): ACETIC ANHYDRIDE: VIOLENT REACTION. ALCOHOLIC HYDROGEN CYANIDE: EXPLOSIVE REACTION. ALUMINUM: EXPLOSION. ALUMINUM-TITANIUM ALLOYS: IGNITES OR INCANDESCES WHEN HEATED. 2-AMINOETHANOL: VIOLENT REACTION. AMMONIUM HYDROXIDE: VIOLENT REACTION. BASES: VIOLENT REACTION. BRASS: CORRODES. BRONZE: CORRODES. CALCIUM CARBIDE: REACTS WITH INCANDESCENCE. CALCIUM HYPOCHLORITE: IGNITION. CESIUM ACETYLIDE: IGNITES ON CONTACT. CHLORINE + DINITROANILINES: VIGOROUS REACTION WITH RELEASE OF FLAMMABLE HYDROGEN GAS FUMES. CHLOROSULFONIC ACID: VIOLENT REACTION. 1,1-DIFLUOROETHYLENE: EXTREMELY EXOTHERMIC DECOMPOSITION REACTION. DOWICIL 100: DECOMPOSES. ETHYLENE DIAMINE: VIOLENT REACTION. ETHYLENE IMINE: VIOLENT REACTION. FLUORINE: IGNITES ON CONTACT. HEXALITHIUM DISILICIDE: INCANDESCES. IRON: CORRODES WITH EVOLUTION OF FLAMMABLE HYDROGEN GAS. MAGNESIUM BORIDE: PRODUCES A SPONTANEOUSLY FLAMMABLE GAS. MERCURIC SULFATE: VIOLENT REACTION AT 125 C. METAL ACETYLIDES: VIOLENT REACTION. METALS: SEVERE CORROSION WITH EVOLUTION OF FLAMMABLE HYDROGEN GAS. OLEUM: VIOLENT REACTION. OXIDIZERS (STRONG): VIOLENT REACTION. OXYGEN + PLATINUM: IGNITES ON CONTACT. PERCHLORIC ACID: VIOLENT REACTION. PLASTICS, RUBBER, COATINGS: ATTACKS. POTASSIUM PERMANGANATE: EXPLOSION HAZARD. BETA-PROPIOLACTONE: VIOLENT REACTION. PROPYLENE OXIDE: VIOLENT REACTION. RUBIDIUM ACETYLIDE: IGNITES ON CONTACT. SILICA (GEL): INCOMPATIBLE. SODIUM: VIGOROUS OR EXPLOSIVE REACTION. SULFURIC ACID: EXPLOSIVE REACTION WITH RELEASE OF TOXIC HYDROGEN CHLORIDE GAS. TETRASELENIUM TETRANITRIDE: EXPLODES ON CONTACT. VINYL ACETATE: VIOLENT REACTION.

DECOMPOSITION: THERMAL DECOMPOSITION PRODUCTS MAY INCLUDE TOXIC AND CORROSIVE FUMES OF CHLORINE.

POLYMERIZATION: HAZARDOUS POLYMERIZATION HAS NOT BEEN REPORTED TO OCCUR UNDER NORMAL TEMPERATURES AND PRESSURES.

STORAGE AND DISPOSAL

OBSERVE ALL FEDERAL, STATE AND LOCAL REGULATIONS WHEN STORING OR DISPOSING OF THIS SUBSTANCE. FOR ASSISTANCE, CONTACT THE DISTRICT DIRECTOR OF THE ENVIRONMENTAL PROTECTION AGENCY.

****STORAGE****

STORE IN ACCORDANCE WITH 29 CFR 1910.101.

PROTECT AGAINST PHYSICAL DAMAGE. STORE IN COOL, WELL-VENTILATED PLACE, SEPARATED FROM ALL OXIDIZING MATERIALS (NFPA 49, HAZARDOUS CHEMICALS DATA, 1975).

STORE AWAY FROM INCOMPATIBLE SUBSTANCES.

THRESHOLD PLANNING QUANTITY (TPQ): THE SUPERFUND AMENDMENTS AND REAUTHORIZATION ACT (SARA) SECTION 302 REQUIRES THAT EACH FACILITY WHERE ANY EXTREMELY HAZARDOUS SUBSTANCE IS PRESENT IN A QUANTITY EQUAL TO OR GREATER THAN THE TPQ ESTABLISHED FOR THAT SUBSTANCE NOTIFY THE STATE EMERGENCY RESPONSE COMMISSION FOR THE STATE IN WHICH IT IS LOCATED. SECTION 303 OF SARA REQUIRES THESE FACILITIES TO PARTICIPATE IN LOCAL EMERGENCY RESPONSE PLANNING (40 CFR 355.30).

****DISPOSAL****

DISPOSAL MUST BE IN ACCORDANCE WITH STANDARDS APPLICABLE TO GENERATORS OF HAZARDOUS WASTE, 40 CFR 262. EPA HAZARDOUS WASTE NUMBER D002. 100 POUND CERCLA SECTION 103 REPORTABLE QUANTITY.

CONDITIONS TO AVOID

MATERIAL IS EXTREMELY POISONOUS; AVOID INHALATION OF VAPORS OR CONTACT WITH SKIN. CONTENTS MAY BE UNDER PRESSURE; CONTAINERS MAY RUPTURE VIOLENTLY AND TRAVEL A CONSIDERABLE DISTANCE.

SPILL AND LEAK PROCEDURES

SOIL SPILL: DIG HOLDING AREA SUCH AS LAGOON, POND OR PIT FOR CONTAINMENT.
DIKE FLOW OF SPILLED MATERIAL USING SOIL OR SANDBAGS OR FOAMED BARRIERS SUCH AS POLYURETHANE OR CONCRETE.
USE CEMENT POWDER OR FLY ASH TO ABSORB LIQUID MASS.
NEUTRALIZE SPILL WITH SLAKED LIME, SODIUM BICARBONATE OR CRUSHED LIMESTONE.

AIR SPILL: KNOCK DOWN VAPORS WITH WATER SPRAY. KEEP UPWIND.
WATER USED TO KNOCK DOWN VAPORS MAY BECOME CORROSIVE OR TOXIC AND SHOULD BE CONTAINED PROPERLY FOR LATER DISPOSAL.

WATER SPILL: NEUTRALIZE WITH AGRICULTURAL LIME, SLAKED LIME, CRUSHED LIMESTONE, OR SODIUM BICARBONATE.

OCCUPATIONAL SPILL: STOP LEAK IF YOU CAN DO IT WITHOUT RISK. USE WATER SPRAY TO REDUCE VAPORS BUT DO NOT PUT WATER ON LEAK OR SPILL AREA. DO NOT GET WATER INSIDE CONTAINER. ISOLATE AREA UNTIL GAS HAS DISPERSED. FOR SMALL SPILLS, FLUSH AREA WITH FLOODING AMOUNTS OF WATER. FOR LARGER SPILLS, DIKE FAR AHEAD OF SPILL FOR LATER DISPOSAL. KEEP UNNECESSARY PEOPLE AWAY; ISOLATE HAZARD AREA AND DENY ENTRY.
VENTILATE CLOSED SPACES BEFORE ENTERING. EVACUATE AREA ENDANGERED BY GAS.
REPORTABLE QUANTITY (RQ): 5000 POUNDS THE SUPERFUND AMENDMENTS AND REAUTHORIZATION ACT (SARA) SECTION 304 REQUIRES THAT A RELEASE EQUAL TO OR GREATER THAN THE REPORTABLE QUANTITY FOR THIS SUBSTANCE BE IMMEDIATELY REPORTED TO THE LOCAL EMERGENCY PLANNING COMMITTEE AND THE STATE EMERGENCY RESPONSE COMMISSION (40 CFR 355.40). IF THE RELEASE OF THIS SUBSTANCE IS REPORTABLE UNDER CERCLA SECTION 103, THE NATIONAL RESPONSE CENTER MUST BE NOTIFIED IMMEDIATELY AT (800) 424-8802 OR (202) 426-2675 IN THE METROPOLITAN WASHINGTON, D.C. AREA (40 CFR 302.6).

PROTECTIVE EQUIPMENT

VENTILATION: PROVIDE LOCAL EXHAUST OR PROCESS ENCLOSURE VENTILATION TO MEET PUBLISHED EXPOSURE LIMITS.

RESPIRATOR: THE FOLLOWING RESPIRATORS AND MAXIMUM USE CONCENTRATIONS ARE RECOMMENDATIONS BY THE U.S. DEPARTMENT OF HEALTH AND HUMAN SERVICES, NIOSH POCKET GUIDE TO CHEMICAL HAZARDS; NIOSH CRITERIA DOCUMENTS OR BY THE U.S. DEPARTMENT OF LABOR, 29 CFR 1910 SUBPART Z. THE SPECIFIC RESPIRATOR SELECTED MUST BE BASED ON CONTAMINATION LEVELS FOUND IN THE WORK PLACE, MUST NOT EXCEED THE WORKING LIMITS OF THE RESPIRATOR AND BE JOINTLY APPROVED BY THE NATIONAL INSTITUTE FOR OCCUPATIONAL SAFETY AND HEALTH AND THE MINE SAFETY AND HEALTH ADMINISTRATION (NIOSH-MSHA).
HYDROGEN CHLORIDE (HYDROCHLORIC ACID):
50 PPM- ANY SUPPLIED-AIR RESPIRATOR. ANY SELF-CONTAINED BREATHING APPARATUS. ANY CHEMICAL CARTRIDGE RESPIRATOR WITH CARTRIDGE(S) PROVIDING PROTECTION AGAINST HYDROCHLORIC ACID. ANY POWERED AIR-PURIFYING RESPIRATOR WITH CARTRIDGE(S) PROVIDING PROTECTION AGAINST HYDROCHLORIC ACID.

100 PPM- ANY SUPPLIED-AIR RESPIRATOR OPERATED IN A CONTINUOUS FLOW MODE. ANY SUPPLIED-AIR RESPIRATOR WITH A FULL FACEPIECE. ANY SELF-CONTAINED BREATHING APPARATUS WITH A FULL FACEPIECE.
ESCAPE- ANY AIR-PURIFYING FULL FACEPIECE RESPIRATOR (GAS MASK) WITH A CHIN-STYLE OR FRONT- OR BACK-MOUNTED ACID GAS CANISTER. ANY APPROPRIATE ESCAPE-TYPE SELF-CONTAINED BREATHING APPARATUS.
FOR FIREFIGHTING AND OTHER IMMEDIATELY DANGEROUS TO LIFE OR HEALTH CONDITIONS:
SELF-CONTAINED BREATHING APPARATUS WITH FULL FACEPIECE OPERATED IN PRESSURE-DEMAND OR OTHER POSITIVE PRESSURE MODE.
SUPPLIED-AIR RESPIRATOR WITH FULL FACEPIECE AND OPERATED IN PRESSURE-DEMAND OR OTHER POSITIVE PRESSURE MODE IN COMBINATION WITH AN AUXILIARY SELF-CONTAINED BREATHING APPARATUS OPERATED IN PRESSURE-DEMAND OR OTHER POSITIVE PRESSURE MODE.

CLOTHING: EMPLOYEE MUST WEAR APPROPRIATE PROTECTIVE (IMPERVIOUS) CLOTHING AND EQUIPMENT TO PREVENT ANY POSSIBILITY OF SKIN CONTACT WITH THIS SUBSTANCE.

GLOVES: EMPLOYEE MUST WEAR APPROPRIATE PROTECTIVE GLOVES TO PREVENT CONTACT WITH THIS SUBSTANCE.

EYE PROTECTION: EMPLOYEE MUST WEAR SPLASH-PROOF OR DUST-RESISTANT SAFETY GOGGLES AND A FACESHIELD TO PREVENT CONTACT WITH THIS SUBSTANCE.
EMERGENCY WASH FACILITIES: WHERE THERE IS ANY POSSIBILITY THAT AN EMPLOYEE'S EYES AND/OR SKIN MAY BE EXPOSED TO THIS SUBSTANCE, THE EMPLOYER SHOULD PROVIDE AN EYE WASH FOUNTAIN AND QUICK DRENCH SHOWER WITHIN THE IMMEDIATE WORK AREA FOR EMERGENCY USE.

AUTHORIZED BY- OCCUPATIONAL HEALTH SERVICES, INC.
CREATION DATE: 11/17/89 ***REVISION DATE:*** 06/13/90

MATERIAL SAFETY DATA SHEET

OCCUPATIONAL HEALTH SERVICES, INC.
AGRICULTURE AND PESTICIDE DIVISION
450 SEVENTH AVENUE, SUITE 2407
NEW YORK, NEW YORK 10123
1-800-445-MSDS OR (212) 967-1100

EMERGENCY CONTACT:
JOHN S. BRANSFORD, JR. (615) 292-1180

SUBSTANCE IDENTIFICATION

CAS-NUMBER 7722-84-1
SUBSTANCE: **HYDROGEN PEROXIDE**
TRADE NAMES/SYNONYMS: HYDROGEN DIOXIDE; HYDROGEN PEROXIDE (H2O2); ALBONE; ALBONE DS; INHIBINE; PERHYDROL; PEROXAN; T-STUFF; SUPEROXAL; HYDROGEN OXIDE; MICRO ETCH 50 (DELTA ENTERPRISES INC.); STCC 4918335; UN 2015; H2O2; PST11190
CHEMICAL FAMILY: PEROXIDE
MOLECULAR FORMULA: H-O-O-H
MOLECULAR WEIGHT: 34.01
CERCLA RATINGS (SCALE 0-3): HEALTH=3 FIRE=0 REACTIVITY=3 PERSISTENCE=0
NFPA RATINGS (SCALE 0-4): HEALTH=2 FIRE=0 REACTIVITY=3

COMPONENTS AND CONTAMINANTS

COMPONENT: HYDROGEN PEROXIDE ***PERCENT:*** >99.0
CAS# 7722-84-1
OTHER CONTAMINANTS: MAY CONTAIN TRACES OF A STABILIZER.
EXPOSURE LIMITS: HYDROGEN PEROXIDE: 1 PPM (1.4 MG/M3) OSHA TWA 1 PPM (1.5 MG/M3) ACGIH TWA
(CONCENTRATIONS GREATER THAN 52%): 1000 POUNDS SARA SECTION 302 THRESHOLD PLANNING QUANTITY 1 POUND SARA SECTION 304 REPORTABLE QUANTITY

PHYSICAL DATA

DESCRIPTION: COLORLESS LIQUID WITH A BITTER TASTE. ***BOILING POINT:*** 302 F (150 C)
MELTING POINT: 32 F (0 C) ***SPECIFIC GRAVITY:*** 1.4067 @ 25 C
VISCOSITY: 1.245 CPS @ 20 C ***VAPOR PRESSURE:*** 5 MMHG @ 30 C
PH: WEAKLY ACIDIC ***SOLUBILITY IN WATER:*** COMPLETE

FIRE AND EXPLOSION DATA

FIRE AND EXPLOSION HAZARD: NEGLIGIBLE FIRE HAZARD WHEN EXPOSED TO HEAT OR FLAME.
DANGEROUS EXPLOSION HAZARD WHEN EXPOSED TO HEAT OR FLAME.
OXIDIZER: OXIDIZERS DECOMPOSE, ESPECIALLY WHEN HEATED, TO YIELD OXYGEN OR OTHER GASES WHICH WILL INCREASE THE BURNING RATE OF COMBUSTIBLE MATTER. CONTACT WITH EASILY OXIDIZABLE, ORGANIC, OR OTHER COMBUSTIBLE MATERIALS MAY RESULT IN IGNITION, VIOLENT COMBUSTION OR EXPLOSION.

FIREFIGHTING MEDIA: WATER ONLY, NO DRY CHEMICAL, CARBON DIOXIDE OR HALON (1987 EMERGENCY RESPONSE GUIDEBOOK, DOT P 5800.4).
FOR LARGER FIRES, FLOOD AREA WITH WATER FROM A DISTANCE (1987 EMERGENCY RESPONSE GUIDEBOOK, DOT P 5800.4).

FIREFIGHTING: DO NOT MOVE CONTAINERS IF EXPOSURE TO HEAT HAS OCCURRED. COOL CONTAINERS EXPOSED TO FLAMES WITH WATER FROM SIDE UNTIL WELL AFTER FIRE IS OUT. STAY AWAY FROM STORAGE TANK ENDS. FOR MASSIVE FIRE IN CARGO AREA, USE UNMANNED HOSE HOLDER OR MONITOR NOZZLES; ELSE WITHDRAW FROM AREA AND LET FIRE BURN (1987 EMERGENCY RESPONSE GUIDEBOOK, DOT P 5800.4, GUIDE PAGE 47).
USE FLOODING AMOUNTS OF WATER AS FOG. COOL CONTAINERS WITH FLOODING AMOUNTS OF WATER, APPLY FROM AS FAR A DISTANCE AS POSSIBLE. AVOID BREATHING TOXIC VAPORS, KEEP UPWIND. EVACUATE TO A RADIUS OF 2500 FEET FOR UNCONTROLLABLE FIRES.

TRANSPORTATION DATA

DEPARTMENT OF TRANSPORTATION HAZARD CLASSIFICATION 49 CFR 172.101: OXIDIZER
DEPARTMENT OF TRANSPORTATION LABELING REQUIREMENTS 49 CFR 172.101 AND SUBPART E: OXIDIZER AND CORROSIVE
DEPARTMENT OF TRANSPORTATION PACKAGING REQUIREMENTS: 49 CFR 173.266 EXCEPTIONS: NONE

TOXICITY

HYDROGEN PEROXIDE: TOXICITY DATA: 90%: 227 PPM INHALATION-MOUSE LCLO; 500 MG/KG SKIN-RABBIT LDLO; 4060 MG/KG SKIN-RAT LD50; 2 GM/KG SKIN-PIG LDLO; 2 GM/KG ORAL-MOUSE LD50; 15 GM/KG INTRAVENOUS-RABBIT LD50; 2 GM/M3/4 HOURS MULTIPLE-RAT LC50; >2000 PPM/8 HOURS INHALATION-RAT LC50 (VAN WATERS & ROGERS MSDS); MUTAGENIC DATA (RTECS); TUMORIGENIC DATA (RTECS). 75%: 75 MG/KG ORAL-RAT LD50 (VAN WATERS & ROGERS MSDS). 70%: 9200 MG/KG SKIN-RABBIT LD50 (VAN WATERS & ROGERS MSDS). 35%: 2000 MG/M3/4 HOURS INHALATION-RAT LC50 (CIL MSDS). 30%: 1429 MG/KG ORAL-MAN LDLO; MUTAGENIC DATA (RTECS); TUMORIGENIC DATA (RTECS). 8-20%: 1518 MG/KG ORAL-RAT LD50; REPRODUCTIVE EFFECTS DATA (RTECS).
CARCINOGEN STATUS: ANIMAL LIMITED EVIDENCE (IARC GROUP-3). ORAL ADMINISTRATION IN MICE RESULTED IN ADENOMAS AND CARCINOMAS OF THE DUODENUM. OTHER STUDIES INDICATED THAT HYDROGEN PEROXIDE HAS NO TUMOR PROMOTING ACTIVITY. LOCAL EFFECTS: CORROSIVE- INHALATION, SKIN, EYES, INGESTION. ACUTE TOXICITY LEVEL: HIGHLY TOXIC BY INHALATION; TOXIC BY INGESTION; SLIGHTLY TOXIC BY DERMAL ABSORPTION. TARGET EFFECTS: NO DATA AVAILABLE. AT INCREASED RISK FROM EXPOSURE: PERSONS WITH IMPAIRED PULMONARY FUNCTION OR SKIN OR EYE DISORDERS.

HEALTH EFFECTS AND FIRST AID

INHALATION: HYDROGEN PEROXIDE: CORROSIVE/HIGHLY TOXIC. 75 PPM IMMEDIATELY DANGEROUS TO LIFE OR HEALTH. **ACUTE EXPOSURE-** VAPOR OR MIST MAY CAUSE SEVERE IRRITATION OF THE RESPIRATORY TRACT. 10% MAY CAUSE SORE THROAT, COUGHING, AND SHORTNESS OF BREATH; ABOVE 30% BREATHING MAY BECOME LABORED. SEVERE SYSTEMIC POISONING MAY RESULT IN HEADACHE, DIZZINESS, VOMITING, DIARRHEA, TREMORS, IRRITABILITY, INSOMNIA, HYPER-REFLEXIA, NUMBNESS, CONVULSIONS, UNCONSCIOUSNESS, SHOCK, AND DEATH. RESPIRATORY DAMAGE MAY RANGE FROM MILD BRONCHITIS TO PULMONARY EDEMA AND EFFECTS MAY BE DELAYED FOR SEVERAL HOURS.
CHRONIC EXPOSURE- DOGS EXPOSED TO 7 PPM OF 90% SOLUTION FOR 6 HOURS A DAY 5 DAYS A WEEK FOR 6 MONTHS SHOWED NO EFFECTS FOR THE FIRST 23 WEEKS. AFTER WEEK 23 THEY EXHIBITED COUGHING, LACRIMATION, AND BLEACHED HAIR. AUTOPSY SHOWED THICKENING OF THE SKIN WITH NO HAIR FOLLICLE DESTRUCTION, AND IRRITATION OF THE LUNGS. RABBITS EXPOSED TO 22 PPM FOR 3 MONTHS EXHIBITED BLEACHED HAIR AND IRRITATION AROUND THE NOSE.

FIRST AID- REMOVE FROM EXPOSURE AREA TO FRESH AIR IMMEDIATELY. IF BREATHING HAS STOPPED, GIVE ARTIFICIAL RESPIRATION. MAINTAIN AIRWAY AND BLOOD PRESSURE AND ADMINISTER OXYGEN IF AVAILABLE. KEEP AFFECTED PERSON WARM AND AT REST. TREAT SYMPTOMATICALLY AND SUPPORTIVELY. ADMINISTRATION OF OXYGEN SHOULD BE PERFORMED BY QUALIFIED PERSONNEL. GET MEDICAL ATTENTION IMMEDIATELY.

SKIN CONTACT: HYDROGEN PEROXIDE: CORROSIVE. **ACUTE EXPOSURE-** VAPOR OR MIST MAY BE IRRITATING TO THE SKIN. A 6% SOLUTION IS A WEAK IRRITANT. CONTACT WITH LOW CONCENTRATIONS OF THE LIQUID MAY CAUSE TINGLING

AND WHITENING OF THE SKIN. IF NOT REMOVED, ERYTHEMA OR VESICLE FORMATION MAY OCCUR. HIGH CONCENTRATIONS MAY CAUSE SEVERE BURNS WITH ULCERATION. THERE ARE INCONCLUSIVE OR UNVERIFIED REPORTS OF HUMAN SENSITIZATION. **CHRONIC EXPOSURE**- EFFECTS DEPEND ON THE CONCENTRATION AND DURATION OF EXPOSURE. REPEATED OR PROLONGED CONTACT WITH CORROSIVE SUBSTANCES MAY CAUSE DERMATITIS OR EFFECTS SIMILAR TO ACUTE EXPOSURE.

FIRST AID- REMOVE CONTAMINATED CLOTHING AND SHOES IMMEDIATELY. WASH AFFECTED AREA WITH SOAP OR MILD DETERGENT AND LARGE AMOUNTS OF WATER UNTIL NO EVIDENCE OF CHEMICAL REMAINS (AT LEAST 15-20 MINUTES). IN CASE OF CHEMICAL BURNS, COVER AREA WITH STERILE, DRY DRESSING. BANDAGE SECURELY, BUT NOT TOO TIGHTLY. GET MEDICAL ATTENTION IMMEDIATELY.

EYE CONTACT: HYDROGEN PEROXIDE: CORROSIVE. **ACUTE EXPOSURE**- VAPORS MAY CAUSE REDNESS, STINGING, TEARING AND BLURRED VISION. THE LIQUID MAY CAUSE SEVERE CORNEAL OR CONJUNCTIVAL ULCERATION, POSSIBLY RESULTING IN BLINDNESS. EFFECTS MAY BE DELAYED. IN RABBIT EYES, 0.5% CAUSED DISTURBANCES IN THE CORNEAL EPITHELIUM WHICH RETURNED TO NORMAL IN 24 HOURS; 5% CAUSED SEVERE CORNEAL EDEMA, FLARE IN THE AQUEOUS, INTENSE CONGESTION OF THE IRIS AND VASCULARIZATION OF THE CORNEA WITH ONLY PARTIAL IMPROVEMENT AFTER 4-5 MONTHS; 5-30% CAUSED CORNEAL CLOUDING WHICH WAS PERSISTENT AT CONCENTRATIONS >10%. **CHRONIC EXPOSURE**- EFFECTS DEPEND ON THE CONCENTRATION AND DURATION OF EXPOSURE. REPEATED OR PROLONGED EXPOSURE TO CORROSIVE SUBSTANCES MAY CAUSE CONJUNCTIVITIS OR EFFECTS SIMILAR TO ACUTE EXPOSURE. RABBITS EXPOSED TO 7 PPM FOR 10 WEEKS EXHIBITED NO CORNEAL DAMAGE.

FIRST AID- WASH EYES IMMEDIATELY WITH LARGE AMOUNTS OF WATER, OCCASIONALLY LIFTING UPPER AND LOWER LIDS, UNTIL NO EVIDENCE OF CHEMICAL REMAINS (AT LEAST 15-20 MINUTES). CONTINUE IRRIGATING WITH NORMAL SALINE UNTIL THE PH HAS RETURNED TO NORMAL (30-60 MINUTES). COVER WITH STERILE BANDAGES. GET MEDICAL ATTENTION IMMEDIATELY.

INGESTION: HYDROGEN PEROXIDE: CORROSIVE/TOXIC/LIMITED ANIMAL CARCINOGEN. **ACUTE EXPOSURE**- MAY CAUSE SEVERE IRRITATION AND INJURY TO THE MOUTH AND THROAT, DISTENTION OF THE ESOPHAGUS AND STOMACH, AND INTERNAL BLEEDING. 5 HUMANS WHO INGESTED 50 ML OF A 35% SOLUTION EXPERIENCED STOMACH AND CHEST PAINS, RETENTION OF BREATH, FOAMING AT THE MOUTH, AND LOSS OF CONSCIOUSNESS. THEY LATER DEVELOPED MOTOR AND SENSORY DISORDERS, FEVER, MICROHEMORRHAGES, AND MODERATE LEUCOCYTOSIS; 1 DEVELOPED PNEUMONIA. ALL RECOVERED IN 2-3 WEEKS. THE LETHAL DOSE REPORTED IN RATS WAS 75 MG/KG OF A 75% SOLUTION. **CHRONIC EXPOSURE**- GROWTH RETARDATION, INDUCTION OF DENTAL CARIES, AND PATHOLOGICAL CHANGES IN THE PERIODONTIUM WERE OBSERVED IN YOUNG MALE RATS RECEIVING 1.5% HYDROGEN PEROXIDE AS THEIR DRINKING FLUID FOR 8 WEEKS. TREATMENT OF MICE FOR 35 WEEKS WITH 0.15% HYDROGEN PEROXIDE RESULTED IN HYDROPIC DEGENERATION OF HEPATIC AND RENAL TUBULAR EPITHELIAL TISSUES, NECROSIS, INFLAMMATION, IRREGULARITIES OF TISSUE STRUCTURE OF THE STOMACH WALL AND HYPERTROPHY OF THE LYMPHATIC TISSUE OF THE SMALL INTESTINE WALL; CONCENTRATIONS IN EXCESS OF 1% RESULTED IN A PRONOUNCED LOSS OF BODY WEIGHT AND DEATH WITHIN 2 WEEKS. REPEATED ADMINISTRATION TO MICE AND RATS PRODUCED ADENOMAS AND CARCINOMAS OF THE DUODENUM.

FIRST AID- IF THE PERSON IS CONSCIOUS AND NOT CONVULSING, GIVE 2-4 GLASSES OF WATER TO DILUTE THE CHEMICAL. USE GASTRIC TUBE TO RELIEVE THE PRESSURE CAUSED BY EVOLVED OXYGEN (DREISBACH, HANDBOOK OF POISONING, 12TH ED.). TREAT SYMPTOMATICALLY AND SUPPORTIVELY. INTUBATION SHOULD BE PERFORMED BY QUALIFIED MEDICAL PERSONNEL. GET MEDICAL ATTENTION IMMEDIATELY.

ANTIDOTE: NO SPECIFIC ANTIDOTE. TREAT SYMPTOMATICALLY AND SUPPORTIVELY.

REACTIVITY

REACTIVITY: UNSTABLE UNLESS INHIBITED. MAY DECOMPOSE EXPLOSIVELY WHEN EXPOSED TO HEAT; THE DECOMPOSITION BECOMES SELF-SUSTAINING ABOVE 285 F (141 C). EVEN TRACE AMOUNTS OF CONTAMINANTS WILL INCREASE THE POSSIBILITY OF DETONATION.

INCOMPATIBILITIES: HYDROGEN PEROXIDE: ACETALDEHYDE: FORMS EXPLOSIVE COMPOUND. ACETIC ACID: FORMS EXPLOSIVE COMPOUND. ACETONE: EXPLOSION. ALCOHOLS: MAY FORM EXPLOSIVE COMPOUNDS. BENZENESULFONIC ANHYDRIDE: EXPLOSIVE DECOMPOSITION. CARBOXYLIC ACIDS: FORM EXPLOSIVE PEROXYACIDS. CHLOROSULFONIC ACID: MAY FORM EXPLOSIVE COMPOUND. CHLORINE + POTASSIUM HYDROXIDE: REACTS WITH RED LUMINESCENCE. COMBUSTIBLE MATERIALS: MAY ACCELERATE THE BURNING RATE, OR CAUSE IGNITION OR EXPLOSION ON CONTACT. DIETHYL ETHER: EXPLOSIVE MIXTURE. DIMETHYLPHENYLPHOSPHINE: VIOLENT REACTION ON RAPID MIXING. DIPHENYL DISELENIDE: MAY FORM EXPLOSIVE COMPOUND. ETHANOL: EXPLOSION. GADOLINIUM HYDROXIDE: FORMS EXPLOSIVE COMPOUND. HYDROGEN SELENIDE: RAPID INTERACTION. KETENE: FORMS EXPLOSIVE COMPOUND. KETONES + NITRIC ACID: MAY FORM EXPLOSIVE COMPOUNDS. LITHIUM TETRAHYDROALUMINATE: EXPLOSIVE MIXUTURE. METALS (AND ALLOYS): MAY CATALYZE VIOLENT, EXOTHERMIC DECOMPOSITION. METAL OXIDES: VIGOROUS OR VIOLENT REACTION. METAL SALTS: MAY CATALYZE VIOLENT, EXOTHERMIC DECOMPOSITION. NITRIC ACID + THIOUREA: FORMATION OF EXPLOSIVE COMPOUND. NITRIC ACID: UNSTABLE MIXTURE WHEN MORE THAN 50% ACID IS PRESENT. NITROGENOUS BASES: EXPLOSION HAZARD. ORGANIC COMPOUNDS: UNDER CERTAIN CIRCUMSTANCES, MAY IGNITE OR FORM DETONABLE MIXTURES. THE PRESENCE OF A CATALYST MAY INCREASE THE RISK OF A REACTION. OXYGENATED COMPOUNDS + WATER: MAY FORM DETONABLE MIXTURES. PHENYLSELENOKETONES: STRONG, EXOTHERMIC REACTION. PHOSPHOROUS: VIOLENT REACTION IF HEATED. PHOSPHOROUS(V) OXIDE: EXTREMELY VIOLENT REACTION. POTASSIUM: VIOLENT REACTION. POTASSIUM PERMANGANATE: VIOLENT REACTION. REDUCING AGENTS: FIRE AND EXPLOSION HAZARD. SODIUM: VIOLENT REACTION. TETRAHYDROTHIOPENE: MAY FORM EXPLOSIVE COMPOUND. SULFURIC ACID: EXPLOSION HAZARD IF HEATED TO DRYNESS. TIN(II) CHLORIDE: EXOTHERMIC REACTION. WOOD: POSSIBLE IGNITION.

DECOMPOSITION: THERMAL DECOMPOSITION RELEASES FLAMMABLE OXYGEN AND HEAT. REACTION BECOMES SELF-SUSTAINING AT 141 C. DECOMPOSITION IS ACCELERATED BY AGITATION, CONTACT WITH ROUGH SURFACES, ALKALIS, FINELY DIVIDED METALS, AND MANY OTHER SUBSTANCES.

POLYMERIZATION: HAZARDOUS POLYMERIZATION HAS NOT BEEN REPORTED TO OCCUR UNDER NORMAL TEMPERATURES AND PRESSURES.

STORAGE AND DISPOSAL

OBSERVE ALL FEDERAL, STATE AND LOCAL REGULATIONS WHEN STORING OR DISPOSING OF THIS SUBSTANCE. FOR ASSISTANCE, CONTACT THE DISTRICT DIRECTOR OF THE ENVIRONMENTAL PROTECTION AGENCY.

****STORAGE****

CONSULT NFPA PUBLICATION 43A, STORAGE OF LIQUID AND SOLID OXIDIZING MATERIALS, FOR STORAGE REQUIREMENTS.

STORE AWAY FROM INCOMPATIBLE SUBSTANCES.

THRESHOLD PLANNING QUANTITY (TPQ): THE SUPERFUND AMENDMENTS AND REAUTHORIZATION ACT (SARA) SECTION 302 REQUIRES THAT EACH FACILITY WHERE ANY EXTREMELY HAZARDOUS SUBSTANCE IS PRESENT IN A QUANTITY EQUAL TO OR GREATER THAN THE TPQ ESTABLISHED FOR THAT SUBSTANCE NOTIFY THE STATE EMERGENCY RESPONSE COMMISSION FOR THE STATE IN WHICH IT IS LOCATED. SECTION 303 OF SARA REQUIRES THESE FACILITIES TO PARTICIPATE IN LOCAL EMERGENCY RESPONSE PLANNING (40 CFR 355.30).

****DISPOSAL****

DISPOSAL MUST BE IN ACCORDANCE WITH STANDARDS APPLICABLE TO GENERATORS OF HAZARDOUS WASTE, 40 CFR 262. EPA HAZARDOUS WASTE NUMBER D003. 100 POUND CERCLA SECTION 103 REPORTABLE QUANTITY.

CONDITIONS TO AVOID

MAY IGNITE WITH OTHER COMBUSTIBLE MATERIALS (WOOD, PAPER, OIL, ETC.). MIXTURE WITH FUELS MAY EXPLODE. FLAMMABLE, POISONOUS GASES MAY ACCUMULATE IN TANKS AND HOPPER CARS. CONTAINER MAY EXPLODE IN HEAT OF FIRE. MAY EXPLODE FROM FRICTION, HEAT OR CONTAMINATION. RUNOFF TO SEWER MAY CREATE FIRE OR EXPLOSION HAZARD.

SPILL AND LEAK PROCEDURES

OCCUPATIONAL SPILL: KEEP COMBUSTIBLES (WOOD, PAPER, OIL, ETC.) AWAY FROM SPILLED MATERIAL. DO NOT TOUCH SPILLED MATERIAL. STOP LEAK IF YOU CAN DO IT WITHOUT RISK. USE WATER SPRAY TO REDUCE VAPORS. FOR SMALL SPILLS, FLUSH AREA WITH FLOODING AMOUNTS OF WATER. FOR LARGER SPILLS, DIKE SPILL FOR LATER DISPOSAL. KEEP UNNECESSARY PEOPLE AWAY. ISOLATE HAZARD AREA AND DENY ENTRY.

REPORTABLE QUANTITY (RQ): 1 POUND THE SUPERFUND AMENDMENTS AND REAUTHORIZATION ACT (SARA) SECTION 304 REQUIRES THAT A RELEASE EQUAL TO OR GREATER THAN THE REPORTABLE QUANTITY FOR THIS SUBSTANCE BE IMMEDIATELY REPORTED TO THE LOCAL EMERGENCY PLANNING COMMITTEE AND THE STATE EMERGENCY RESPONSE COMMISSION (40 CFR 355.40). IF THE RELEASE OF THIS SUBSTANCE IS REPORTABLE UNDER CERCLA SECTION 103, THE NATIONAL RESPONSE CENTER MUST BE NOTIFIED IMMEDIATELY AT (800) 424-8802 OR (202) 426-2675 IN THE METROPOLITAN WASHINGTON, D.C. AREA (40 CFR 302.6).

PROTECTIVE EQUIPMENT

VENTILATION: PROVIDE LOCAL EXHAUST OR PROCESS ENCLOSURE VENTILATION TO MEET PUBLISHED EXPOSURE LIMITS.

RESPIRATOR: THE FOLLOWING RESPIRATORS AND MAXIMUM USE CONCENTRATIONS ARE RECOMMENDATIONS BY THE U.S. DEPARTMENT OF HEALTH AND HUMAN SERVICES, NIOSH POCKET GUIDE TO CHEMICAL HAZARDS; NIOSH CRITERIA DOCUMENTS OR BY THE U.S. DEPARTMENT OF LABOR, 29 CFR 1910 SUBPART Z.

THE SPECIFIC RESPIRATOR SELECTED MUST BE BASED ON CONTAMINATION LEVELS FOUND IN THE WORK PLACE, MUST NOT EXCEED THE WORKING LIMITS OF THE RESPIRATOR AND BE JOINTLY APPROVED BY THE NATIONAL INSTITUTE FOR OCCUPATIONAL SAFETY AND HEALTH AND THE MINE SAFETY AND HEALTH ADMINISTRATION (NIOSH-MSHA).

HYDROGEN PEROXIDE:

10 PPM- ANY SUPPLIED-AIR RESPIRATOR. ANY SELF-CONTAINED BREATHING APPARATUS.

25 PPM- ANY SUPPLIED-AIR RESPIRATOR OPERATED IN A CONTINUOUS FLOW MODE.

50 PPM- ANY SUPPLIED-AIR RESPIRATOR WITH A FULL FACEPIECE. ANY SELF-CONTAINED BREATHING APPARATUS WITH A FULL FACEPIECE.

75 PPM- ANY SUPPLIED-AIR RESPIRATOR WITH A FULL FACEPIECE OPERATED IN PRESSURE-DEMAND OR OTHER POSITIVE PRESSURE MODE.

ESCAPE- ANY AIR-PURIFYING FULL FACEPIECE RESPIRATOR (GAS MASK) WITH A CHIN-STYLE OR FRONT- OR BACK-MOUNTED CANISTER PROVIDING PROTECTION AGAINST HYDROGEN PEROXIDE. ANY APPROPRIATE ESCAPE-TYPE SELF-CONTAINED BREATHING APPARATUS.

FOR FIREFIGHTING AND OTHER IMMEDIATELY DANGEROUS TO LIFE OR HEALTH CONDITIONS:

SELF-CONTAINED BREATHING APPARATUS WITH FULL FACEPIECE OPERATED IN PRESSURE-DEMAND OR OTHER POSITIVE PRESSURE MODE.

SUPPLIED-AIR RESPIRATOR WITH FULL FACEPIECE AND OPERATED IN PRESSURE-DEMAND OR OTHER POSITIVE PRESSURE MODE IN COMBINATION WITH AN AUXILIARY SELF-CONTAINED BREATHING APPARATUS OPERATED IN PRESSURE-DEMAND OR OTHER POSITIVE PRESSURE MODE.

CLOTHING: EMPLOYEE MUST WEAR APPROPRIATE PROTECTIVE (IMPERVIOUS) CLOTHING AND EQUIPMENT TO PREVENT ANY POSSIBILITY OF SKIN CONTACT WITH THIS SUBSTANCE.

GLOVES: EMPLOYEE MUST WEAR APPROPRIATE PROTECTIVE GLOVES TO PREVENT CONTACT WITH THIS SUBSTANCE.

EYE PROTECTION: EMPLOYEE MUST WEAR SPLASH-PROOF OR DUST-RESISTANT SAFETY GOGGLES AND A FACESHIELD TO PREVENT CONTACT WITH THIS SUBSTANCE.

EMERGENCY WASH FACILITIES: WHERE THERE IS ANY POSSIBILITY THAT AN EMPLOYEE'S EYES AND/OR SKIN MAY BE EXPOSED TO THIS SUBSTANCE, THE EMPLOYER SHOULD PROVIDE AN EYE WASH FOUNTAIN AND QUICK DRENCH SHOWER WITHIN THE IMMEDIATE WORK AREA FOR EMERGENCY USE.

AUTHORIZED BY- OCCUPATIONAL HEALTH SERVICES, INC.

CREATION DATE: 11/17/89 ***REVISION DATE:*** 07/13/90

MATERIAL SAFETY DATA SHEET

OCCUPATIONAL HEALTH SERVICES, INC.
AGRICULTURE AND PESTICIDE DIVISION
450 SEVENTH AVENUE, SUITE 2407
NEW YORK, NEW YORK 10123
1-800-445-MSDS OR (212) 967-1100

EMERGENCY CONTACT:
JOHN S. BRANSFORD, JR. (615) 292-1180

SUBSTANCE IDENTIFICATION

CAS-NUMBER 8001-78-3

SUBSTANCE: CASTOR OIL, HYDROGENATED

TRADE NAMES/SYNONYMS: CASTORWAX; HYDROGENATED CASTOR OIL; PST11225

CHEMICAL FAMILY: FATTY ACID

MOLECULAR FORMULA: VARIES

MOLECULAR WEIGHT: VARIES

CERCLA RATINGS (SCALE 0-3): HEALTH=U FIRE=1 REACTIVITY=0 PERSISTENCE=0

NFPA RATINGS (SCALE 0-4): HEALTH=U FIRE=1 REACTIVITY=0

COMPONENTS AND CONTAMINANTS

COMPONENT: HYDROGENATED CASTOR OIL ***PERCENT:*** 100
CAS# 8001-78-3

EXPOSURE LIMITS: NO OCCUPATIONAL EXPOSURE LIMITS ESTABLISHED BY OSHA, ACGIH, OR NIOSH.

PHYSICAL DATA

DESCRIPTION: OFF-WHITE FLAKES WITH A SLIGHT FATTY ACID ODOR.

MELTING POINT: 189 F (87 C) ***SPECIFIC GRAVITY:*** 0.9

EVAPORATION RATE: (BUTYL ACETATE=1) 0 ***SOLUBILITY IN WATER:*** INSOLUBLE

SOLVENT SOLUBILITY: ALCOHOL, ETHER

FIRE AND EXPLOSION DATA

FIRE AND EXPLOSION HAZARD: SLIGHT FIRE HAZARD WHEN EXPOSED TO HEAT OR FLAME.

FLASH POINT: 585 F (307 C) (OC)

FIREFIGHTING MEDIA: DRY CHEMICAL, CARBON DIOXIDE, HALON, WATER SPRAY OR STANDARD FOAM (1987 EMERGENCY RESPONSE GUIDEBOOK, DOT P 5800.4). FOR LARGER FIRES, USE WATER SPRAY, FOG OR STANDARD FOAM (1987 EMERGENCY RESPONSE GUIDEBOOK, DOT P 5800.4).

FIREFIGHTING: MOVE CONTAINER FROM FIRE AREA IF POSSIBLE. DO NOT SCATTER SPILLED MATERIAL WITH HIGH PRESSURE WATER STREAMS. DIKE FIRE CONTROL WATER FOR LATER DISPOSAL (1987 EMERGENCY RESPONSE GUIDEBOOK, DOT P 5800.4, GUIDE PAGE 31).
USE AGENTS SUITABLE FOR TYPE OF SURROUNDING FIRE. AVOID BREATHING HAZARDOUS VAPORS, KEEP UPWIND.

TOXICITY

HYDROGENATED CASTOR OIL: CARCINOGEN STATUS: NONE. ACUTE TOXICITY LEVEL: NO DATA AVAILABLE. TARGET EFFECTS: NO DATA AVAILABLE.

HEALTH EFFECTS AND FIRST AID

INHALATION: HYDROGENATED CASTOR OIL: **ACUTE EXPOSURE-** HYDROGENATED VEGETABLE OILS ARE GENERALLY NON-TOXIC. WHEN MELTED, THERE ARE NO FUMES OR MIST. HOWEVER IF OVER-HEATED, VAPORS OR ENTRAINED MIST IN SUFFICIENT CONCENTRATION MAY CAUSE RESPIRATORY IRRITATION. **CHRONIC EXPOSURE-** NO DATA AVAILABLE.

FIRST AID- REMOVE FROM EXPOSURE AREA TO FRESH AIR IMMEDIATELY. IF BREATHING HAS STOPPED, PERFORM ARTIFICIAL RESPIRATION. KEEP PERSON WARM AND AT REST. TREAT SYMPTOMATICALLY AND SUPPORTIVELY. GET MEDICAL ATTENTION IMMEDIATELY.

SKIN CONTACT: HYDROGENATED CASTOR OIL: **ACUTE EXPOSURE-** NO DATA AVAILABLE. MAY BE IRRITATING. **CHRONIC EXPOSURE-** NO DATA AVAILABLE.

FIRST AID- REMOVE CONTAMINATED CLOTHING AND SHOES IMMEDIATELY. WASH AFFECTED AREA WITH SOAP OR MILD DETERGENT AND LARGE AMOUNTS OF WATER UNTIL NO EVIDENCE OF CHEMICAL REMAINS (APPROXIMATELY 15-20 MINUTES). GET MEDICAL ATTENTION IMMEDIATELY.

EYE CONTACT: HYDROGENATED CASTOR OIL: **ACUTE EXPOSURE-** NO DATA AVAILABLE. MAY BE IRRITATING. **CHRONIC EXPOSURE-** NO DATA AVAILABLE.

FIRST AID- WASH EYES IMMEDIATELY WITH LARGE AMOUNTS OF WATER OR NORMAL SALINE, OCCASIONALLY LIFTING UPPER AND LOWER LIDS, UNTIL NO EVIDENCE OF CHEMICAL REMAINS (APPROXIMATELY 15-20 MINUTES). GET MEDICAL ATTENTION IMMEDIATELY.

INGESTION: HYDROGENATED CASTOR OIL: **ACUTE EXPOSURE-** NO DATA AVAILABLE. MAY CAUSE GASTROINTESTINAL IRRITATION. **CHRONIC EXPOSURE-** NO DATA AVAILABLE.

FIRST AID- TREAT SYMPTOMATICALLY AND SUPPORTIVELY. GET MEDICAL ATTENTION IMMEDIATELY. IF VOMITING OCCURS, KEEP HEAD LOWER THAN HIPS TO PREVENT ASPIRATION.

ANTIDOTE: NO SPECIFIC ANTIDOTE. TREAT SYMPTOMATICALLY AND SUPPORTIVELY.

REACTIVITY

REACTIVITY: STABLE UNDER NORMAL TEMPERATURES AND PRESSURES.

INCOMPATIBILITIES: HYDROGENATED CASTOR OIL: OXIDIZING MATERIAL: INCOMPATIBLE.

DECOMPOSITION: THERMAL DECOMPOSITION PRODUCTS MAY INCLUDE TOXIC OXIDES OF CARBON.

POLYMERIZATION: HAZARDOUS POLYMERIZATION HAS NOT BEEN REPORTED TO OCCUR UNDER NORMAL TEMPERATURES AND PRESSURES.

CONDITIONS TO AVOID

MAY BURN BUT DOES NOT IGNITE READILY. AVOID CONTACT WITH STRONG OXIDIZERS, EXCESSIVE HEAT, SPARKS, OR OPEN FLAME.

SPILL AND LEAK PROCEDURES

OCCUPATIONAL SPILL: STOP LEAK IF YOU CAN DO IT WITHOUT RISK. FOR SMALL SPILLS, TAKE UP WITH SAND OR OTHER ABSORBENT MATERIAL AND PLACE INTO CLEAN, DRY CONTAINERS FOR LATER DISPOSAL. KEEP UNNECESSARY PEOPLE AWAY. ISOLATE HAZARD AREA AND DENY ENTRY.

PROTECTIVE EQUIPMENT

VENTILATION: PROVIDE LOCAL EXHAUST VENTILATION AND/OR GENERAL DILUTION VENTILATION TO MEET PUBLISHED EXPOSURE LIMITS.

RESPIRATOR: THE FOLLOWING RESPIRATORS ARE RECOMMENDED BASED ON INFORMATION FOUND IN THE PHYSICAL DATA, TOXICITY AND HEALTH EFFECTS SECTIONS. THEY ARE RANKED IN ORDER FROM MINIMUM TO MAXIMUM RESPIRATORY PROTECTION. THE SPECIFIC RESPIRATOR SELECTED MUST BE BASED ON CONTAMINATION LEVELS FOUND IN THE WORK PLACE, MUST NOT EXCEED THE WORKING LIMITS OF THE RESPIRATOR AND BE JOINTLY APPROVED BY THE NATIONAL INSTITUTE FOR OCCUPATIONAL SAFETY AND HEALTH AND THE MINE SAFETY AND HEALTH ADMINISTRATION (NIOSH-MSHA).

DUST AND MIST RESPIRATOR WITH A FULL FACEPIECE.

AIR-PURIFYING FULL FACEPIECE RESPIRATOR WITH A HIGH-EFFICIENCY PARTICULATE FILTER.

POWERED AIR-PURIFYING RESPIRATOR WITH A TIGHT-FITTING FACEPIECE AND HIGH-EFFICIENCY PARTICULATE FILTER.

TYPE 'C' SUPPLIED-AIR RESPIRATOR WITH A FULL FACEPIECE OPERATED IN PRESSURE-DEMAND OR OTHER POSITIVE PRESSURE MODE OR WITH A FULL FACEPIECE, HELMET OR HOOD OPERATED IN CONTINUOUS-FLOW MODE.

SELF-CONTAINED BREATHING APPARATUS WITH A FULL FACEPIECE OPERATED IN PRESSURE-DEMAND OR OTHER POSITIVE PRESSURE MODE.

FOR FIREFIGHTING AND OTHER IMMEDIATELY DANGEROUS TO LIFE OR HEALTH CONDITIONS:

SELF-CONTAINED BREATHING APPARATUS WITH FULL FACEPIECE OPERATED IN PRESSURE-DEMAND OR OTHER POSITIVE PRESSURE MODE.

SUPPLIED-AIR RESPIRATOR WITH FULL FACEPIECE AND OPERATED IN PRESSURE-DEMAND OR OTHER POSITIVE PRESSURE MODE IN COMBINATION WITH AN AUXILIARY SELF-CONTAINED BREATHING APPARATUS OPERATED IN PRESSURE-DEMAND OR OTHER POSITIVE PRESSURE MODE.

CLOTHING: PROTECTIVE CLOTHING NOT REQUIRED. AVOID REPEATED OR PROLONGED CONTACT WITH THIS SUBSTANCE.

GLOVES: EMPLOYEE MUST WEAR APPROPRIATE PROTECTIVE GLOVES TO PREVENT CONTACT WITH THIS SUBSTANCE.

EYE PROTECTION: EMPLOYEE MUST WEAR SPLASH-PROOF OR DUST-RESISTANT SAFETY GOGGLES AND A FACESHIELD TO PREVENT CONTACT WITH THIS SUBSTANCE.

EMERGENCY WASH FACILITIES: WHERE THERE IS ANY POSSIBILITY THAT AN EMPLOYEE'S EYES AND/OR SKIN MAY BE EXPOSED TO THIS SUBSTANCE, THE EMPLOYER SHOULD PROVIDE AN EYE WASH FOUNTAIN AND QUICK DRENCH SHOWER WITHIN THE IMMEDIATE WORK AREA FOR EMERGENCY USE.

AUTHORIZED BY- OCCUPATIONAL HEALTH SERVICES, INC.

CREATION DATE: 02/08/90 ***REVISION DATE:*** 05/25/90

MATERIAL SAFETY DATA SHEET

OCCUPATIONAL HEALTH SERVICES, INC.
AGRICULTURE AND PESTICIDE DIVISION
450 SEVENTH AVENUE, SUITE 2407
NEW YORK, NEW YORK 10123
1-800-445-MSDS OR (212) 967-1100

EMERGENCY CONTACT:
JOHN S. BRANSFORD, JR. (615) 292-1180

SUBSTANCE IDENTIFICATION

CAS-NUMBER 2836-32-0

SUBSTANCE: **HYDROXYACETIC ACID, SODIUM SALT**

TRADE NAMES/SYNONYMS: HYDROXYACETIC ACID, MONOSODIUM SALT; GLYCOLIC ACID, MONOSODIUM SALT; SODIUM GLYCOLATE; SODIUM HYDROXYACETATE; SODIUM ALPHA HYDROXYACETATE; PST11235

CHEMICAL FAMILY: SALT
CARBOXYLIC ACID, ALIPHATIC

MOLECULAR FORMULA: C2-H3-O3.NA

MOLECULAR WEIGHT: 98.04

CERCLA RATINGS (SCALE 0-3): HEALTH=1 FIRE=0 REACTIVITY=0 PERSISTENCE=0

NFPA RATINGS (SCALE 0-4): HEALTH=1 FIRE=0 REACTIVITY=0

COMPONENTS AND CONTAMINANTS

COMPONENT: HYDROXYACETIC ACID SODIUM SALT ***PERCENT:*** 100
CAS# 2836-32-0

EXPOSURE LIMITS: NO OCCUPATIONAL EXPOSURE LIMITS ESTABLISHED BY OSHA, ACGIH, OR NIOSH.

PHYSICAL DATA

DESCRIPTION: SOLID. ***MELTING POINT:*** NOT AVAILABLE

SPECIFIC GRAVITY: NOT AVAILABLE ***SOLUBILITY IN WATER:*** NOT AVAILABLE

FIRE AND EXPLOSION DATA

FIRE AND EXPLOSION HAZARD: NEGLIGIBLE FIRE HAZARD WHEN EXPOSED TO HEAT OR FLAME.

FIREFIGHTING MEDIA: DRY CHEMICAL, CARBON DIOXIDE, HALON, WATER SPRAY OR STANDARD FOAM (1987 EMERGENCY RESPONSE GUIDEBOOK, DOT P 5800.4). FOR LARGER FIRES, USE WATER SPRAY, FOG OR STANDARD FOAM (1987 EMERGENCY RESPONSE GUIDEBOOK, DOT P 5800.4).

FIREFIGHTING: NO ACUTE HAZARD. MOVE CONTAINER FROM FIRE AREA IF POSSIBLE. AVOID BREATHING VAPORS OR DUSTS; KEEP UPWIND.

TOXICITY

HYDROXYACETIC ACID, SODIUM SALT: TOXICITY DATA: 7110 MG/KG ORAL-RAT LD50; 500 MG/KG ORAL-CAT LDLO. CARCINOGEN STATUS: NONE. ACUTE TOXICITY LEVEL: SLIGHTLY TOXIC BY INGESTION. TARGET EFFECTS: NO DATA AVAILABLE.

HEALTH EFFECTS AND FIRST AID

INHALATION: HYDROXYACETIC ACID, SODIUM SALT: **ACUTE EXPOSURE-** NO DATA AVAILABLE. MAY BE IRRITATING TO THE MUCOUS MEMBRANES. **CHRONIC EXPOSURE-** NO DATA AVAILABLE.

FIRST AID- REMOVE FROM EXPOSURE AREA TO FRESH AIR IMMEDIATELY. IF BREATHING HAS STOPPED, PERFORM ARTIFICIAL RESPIRATION. KEEP PERSON WARM AND AT REST. TREAT SYMPTOMATICALLY AND SUPPORTIVELY. GET MEDICAL ATTENTION IMMEDIATELY.

SKIN CONTACT: HYDROXYACETIC ACID, SODIUM SALT: **ACUTE EXPOSURE-** NO DATA AVAILABLE. MAY BE IRRITATING TO THE SKIN AND CAUSE REDNESS AND PAIN. **CHRONIC EXPOSURE-** NO DATA AVAILABLE.

FIRST AID- REMOVE CONTAMINATED CLOTHING AND SHOES IMMEDIATELY. WASH AFFECTED AREA WITH SOAP OR MILD DETERGENT AND LARGE AMOUNTS OF WATER UNTIL NO EVIDENCE OF CHEMICAL REMAINS (APPROXIMATELY 15-20 MINUTES). GET MEDICAL ATTENTION IMMEDIATELY.

EYE CONTACT: HYDROXYACETIC ACID, SODIUM SALT: **ACUTE EXPOSURE-** NO DATA AVAILABLE. MAY BE IRRITATING TO THE EYES. **CHRONIC EXPOSURE-** NO DATA AVAILABLE.

FIRST AID- WASH EYES IMMEDIATELY WITH LARGE AMOUNTS OF WATER OR NORMAL SALINE, OCCASIONALLY LIFTING UPPER AND LOWER LIDS, UNTIL NO EVIDENCE OF CHEMICAL REMAINS (APPROXIMATELY 15-20 MINUTES). GET MEDICAL ATTENTION IMMEDIATELY.

INGESTION: HYDROXYACETIC ACID, SODIUM SALT: **ACUTE EXPOSURE-** ANIMAL STUDIES INDICATE THAT A LARGE DOSE IS NEEDED TO CAUSE POISONING. THERE IS NO DATA AVAILABLE ON SYMPTOMS. **CHRONIC EXPOSURE-** NO DATA AVAILABLE.

FIRST AID- TREAT SYMPTOMATICALLY AND SUPPORTIVELY. GET MEDICAL ATTENTION IMMEDIATELY. IF VOMITING OCCURS, KEEP HEAD LOWER THAN HIPS TO PREVENT ASPIRATION.

ANTIDOTE: NO SPECIFIC ANTIDOTE. TREAT SYMPTOMATICALLY AND SUPPORTIVELY.

REACTIVITY

REACTIVITY: STABLE UNDER NORMAL TEMPERATURES AND PRESSURES.

INCOMPATIBILITIES: HYDROXYACETIC ACID, SODIUM SALT: NO DATA AVAILABLE.

DECOMPOSITION: THERMAL DECOMPOSITION PRODUCTS MAY INCLUDE TOXIC OXIDES OF CARBON.

POLYMERIZATION: NO DATA AVAILABLE.

CONDITIONS TO AVOID

NONE REPORTED.

SPILL AND LEAK PROCEDURES

OCCUPATIONAL SPILL: NO SPECIAL PRECAUTIONS INDICATED.

PROTECTIVE EQUIPMENT

VENTILATION: PROVIDE GENERAL DILUTION VENTILATION.

RESPIRATOR: THE FOLLOWING RESPIRATORS ARE RECOMMENDED BASED ON INFORMATION FOUND IN THE PHYSICAL DATA, TOXICITY AND HEALTH EFFECTS SECTIONS. THEY ARE RANKED IN ORDER FROM MINIMUM TO MAXIMUM RESPIRATORY PROTECTION. THE SPECIFIC RESPIRATOR SELECTED MUST BE BASED ON CONTAMINATION LEVELS FOUND IN THE WORK PLACE, MUST NOT EXCEED THE WORKING LIMITS OF THE RESPIRATOR AND BE JOINTLY APPROVED BY THE NATIONAL INSTITUTE FOR OCCUPATIONAL SAFETY AND HEALTH AND THE MINE SAFETY AND HEALTH ADMINISTRATION (NIOSH-MSHA).

DUST AND MIST RESPIRATOR WITH A FULL FACEPIECE.

AIR-PURIFYING FULL FACEPIECE RESPIRATOR WITH A HIGH-EFFICIENCY PARTICULATE FILTER.
POWERED AIR-PURIFYING RESPIRATOR WITH A TIGHT-FITTING FACEPIECE AND HIGH-EFFICIENCY PARTICULATE FILTER.
TYPE 'C' SUPPLIED-AIR RESPIRATOR WITH A FULL FACEPIECE OPERATED IN PRESSURE-DEMAND OR OTHER POSITIVE PRESSURE MODE OR WITH A FULL FACEPIECE, HELMET OR HOOD OPERATED IN CONTINUOUS-FLOW MODE.
SELF-CONTAINED BREATHING APPARATUS WITH A FULL FACEPIECE OPERATED IN PRESSURE-DEMAND OR OTHER POSITIVE PRESSURE MODE.
FOR FIREFIGHTING AND OTHER IMMEDIATELY DANGEROUS TO LIFE OR HEALTH CONDITIONS:
SELF-CONTAINED BREATHING APPARATUS WITH FULL FACEPIECE OPERATED IN PRESSURE-DEMAND OR OTHER POSITIVE PRESSURE MODE.
SUPPLIED-AIR RESPIRATOR WITH FULL FACEPIECE AND OPERATED IN PRESSURE-DEMAND OR OTHER POSITIVE PRESSURE MODE IN COMBINATION WITH AN AUXILIARY SELF-CONTAINED BREATHING APPARATUS OPERATED IN PRESSURE-DEMAND OR OTHER POSITIVE PRESSURE MODE.

CLOTHING: EMPLOYEE MUST WEAR APPROPRIATE PROTECTIVE (IMPERVIOUS) CLOTHING AND EQUIPMENT TO PREVENT REPEATED OR PROLONGED SKIN CONTACT WITH THIS SUBSTANCE.

GLOVES: EMPLOYEE MUST WEAR APPROPRIATE PROTECTIVE GLOVES TO PREVENT CONTACT WITH THIS SUBSTANCE.

EYE PROTECTION: EMPLOYEE MUST WEAR SPLASH-PROOF OR DUST-RESISTANT SAFETY GOGGLES TO PREVENT EYE CONTACT WITH THIS SUBSTANCE.
EMERGENCY EYE WASH: WHERE THERE IS ANY POSSIBILITY THAT AN EMPLOYEE'S EYES MAY BE EXPOSED TO THIS SUBSTANCE, THE EMPLOYER SHOULD PROVIDE AN EYE WASH FOUNTAIN WITHIN THE IMMEDIATE WORK AREA FOR EMERGENCY USE.

AUTHORIZED BY- OCCUPATIONAL HEALTH SERVICES, INC.
CREATION DATE: 11/16/89 ***REVISION DATE:*** 05/25/90

MATERIAL SAFETY DATA SHEET

OCCUPATIONAL HEALTH SERVICES, INC.
AGRICULTURE AND PESTICIDE DIVISION
450 SEVENTH AVENUE, SUITE 2407
NEW YORK, NEW YORK 10123
1-800-445-MSDS OR (212) 967-1100

EMERGENCY CONTACT:
JOHN S. BRANSFORD, JR. (615) 292-1180

SUBSTANCE IDENTIFICATION

CAS-NUMBER 732-11-6

SUBSTANCE: **PHOSMET**

TRADE NAMES/SYNONYMS: PHOSPHORODITHIOIC ACID, S-((1,3-DIHYDRO-1,3-DIOXO-2H-ISOINDOL-2-YL) METHYL) O,O-DIMETHYL ESTER; PHOSPHORODITHIOIC ACID, O,O-DIMETHYL ESTER, S-ESTER WITH WITH N-(MERCAPTOMETHYL)PHTHALIMIDE; O,O-DIMETHYL S-PHTHALIMIDOMETHYL PHOSPHORODITHIOATE; N-(DIMETHOXYPHOSPHINOTHIOYLTHIOMETHYL)PHTHALIMIDE; N-(MERCAPTOMETHYL)PHTHALIMIDE S-(O,O-DIMETHYL PHOSPHORODITHIOATE; S-((1,3-DIHYDRO-1,3-DIOXO-2H-ISOINDOL-2-7L)METHYL) O,O DIMETHYL PHOSPHORODITHIOATE; DECEMTHION; FTALOPHOS; IMIDAN; IMIDATHION; PHTHALOPHOS; PROLATE; SAFIDON; STAUFFER R 1504; ENT 25,705; PST11307

CHEMICAL FAMILY: THIOPHOSPHATE
PHTHALIMIDE

MOLECULAR FORMULA: C11-H12-N-O4-P-S2

MOLECULAR WEIGHT: 317.33

CERCLA RATINGS (SCALE 0-3): HEALTH=3 FIRE=U REACTIVITY=0 PERSISTENCE=0

NFPA RATINGS (SCALE 0-4): HEALTH=4 FIRE=U REACTIVITY=0

COMPONENTS AND CONTAMINANTS

COMPONENT: PHOSMET ***PERCENT:*** 100.0
CAS# 732-11-6

OTHER CONTAMINANTS: NONE

EXPOSURE LIMITS: NO OCCUPATIONAL EXPOSURE LIMITS ESTABLISHED BY OSHA, ACGIH, OR NIOSH.
PHOSMET: 10/10,000 POUNDS SARA SECTION 302 THRESHOLD PLANNING QUANTITY 1 POUND SARA SECTION 304 REPORTABLE QUANTITY

PHYSICAL DATA

DESCRIPTION: COLORLESS, CRYSTALLINE SOLID WITH A VERY OFFENSIVE ODOR

MELTING POINT: 161 F (72 C) ***SPECIFIC GRAVITY:*** NOT AVAILABLE

VAPOR PRESSURE: 0.001 MMHG @ 25 C ***SOLUBILITY IN WATER:*** 25 PPM @ 20C

SOLVENT SOLUBILITY: ACETONE, DICHLOROMETHANE, MESITYL OXIDE, BUTANONE, XYLENE, AND MOST ORGANIC SOLVENTS EXCEPT ALIPHATIC HYDROCARBONS

FIRE AND EXPLOSION DATA

FIRE AND EXPLOSION HAZARD: UNKNOWN FIRE AND EXPLOSION HAZARD.

FIREFIGHTING MEDIA: DRY CHEMICAL, CARBON DIOXIDE, HALON, WATER SPRAY OR STANDARD FOAM (1987 EMERGENCY RESPONSE GUIDEBOOK, DOT P 5800.4).

FIREFIGHTING: MOVE CONTAINERS FROM FIRE AREA IF POSSIBLE. FIGHT FIRE FROM MAXIMUM DISTANCE. STAY AWAY FROM STORAGE TANK ENDS. DIKE FIRE CONTROL WATER FOR LATER DISPOSAL. DO NOT SCATTER MATERIAL (1987 EMERGENCY RESPONSE GUIDEBOOK, DOT P 5800.4, GUIDE PAGE 55).
EXTINGUISH USING AGENT SUITABLE FOR TYPE OF SURROUNDING FIRE. AVOID BREATHING VAPORS AND DUSTS. KEEP UPWIND.

TRANSPORTATION DATA

DEPARTMENT OF TRANSPORTATION HAZARD CLASSIFICATION 49 CFR 172.101: POISON B
DEPARTMENT OF TRANSPORTATION LABELING REQUIREMENTS 49 CFR 172.101 AND SUBPART E: POISON
DEPARTMENT OF TRANSPORTATION PACKAGING REQUIREMENTS: 49 CFR 173.346 EXCEPTIONS: 49 CFR 173.345

TOXICITY

PHOSMET: TOXICITY DATA: 2 MG/M3/8 HOURS INHALATION-HUMAN TCLO; 54 MG/M3/4 HOURS INHALATION-RAT LC50; 65 MG/M3/4 HOURS INHALATION-CAT LC50; 1326 MG/KG SKIN-RAT LD50; 50 MG/KG ORAL-HUMAN LDLO; 92,500 UG/KG ORAL-RAT LD50; 26 MG/KG ORAL-MOUSE LD50; 200 MG/KG ORAL-GUINEA PIG LD50; 40 MG/KG UNREPORTED-MAMMAL LD50; MUTAGENIC DATA (RTECS); REPRODUCTIVE EFFECTS DATA (RTECS). CARCINOGEN STATUS: NONE. ACUTE TOXICITY LEVEL: HIGHLY TOXIC BY INHALATION; TOXIC BY INGESTION; MODERATELY TOXIC BY DERMAL ABSORPTION. TARGET EFFECTS: CHOLINESTERASE INHIBITOR. POISONING MAY AFFECT THE NERVOUS SYSTEM.* AT INCREASED RISK FROM EXPOSURE: PERSONS WITH RESPIRATORY AILMENTS, RECENT EXPOSURE TO CHOLINESTERASE INHIBITORS OR IMPAIRED CHOLINESTERASE PRODUCTION, OR LIVER MALFUNCTION.* ADDITIONAL DATA: MAY CROSS THE PLACENTA. HIGH ENVIRONMENTAL TEMPERATURES OR EXPOSURE OF THE CHEMICAL TO VISIBLE OR ULTRAVIOLET LIGHT MAY ENHANCE THE TOXICITY. INTERACTIONS WITH MEDICATIONS MAY OCCUR.*
* MAY BE BASED ON GENERAL INFORMATION ON ORGANOPHOSPHATES.

HEALTH EFFECTS AND FIRST AID

INHALATION: PHOSMET: HIGHLY TOXIC. SEE INFORMATION ON ORGANOPHOSPHATES.
ORGANOPHOSPHATES: CHOLINESTERASE INHIBITOR. **ACUTE EXPOSURE-** WHEN INHALED, THE FIRST EFFECTS OF CHOLINESTERASE INHIBITORS ARE USUALLY RESPIRATORY AND MAY INCLUDE NASAL HYPEREMIA AND WATERY DISCHARGE, COUGH, CHEST DISCOMFORT, DYSPNEA, AND WHEEZING DUE TO INCREASED BRONCHIAL SECRETIONS AND BRONCHOCONSTRICTION. IF SUFFICIENT AMOUNTS ARE ABSORBED, OTHER SYSTEMIC EFFECTS MAY BEGIN WITHIN A FEW MINUTES OR BE DELAYED FOR UP TO 12 HOURS. SYMPTOMS MAY INCLUDE PALLOR, NAUSEA, VOMITING, DIARRHEA, ABDOMINAL CRAMPS, HEADACHE, DIZZINESS, OCULAR PAIN, BLURRED VISION, MIOSIS OR IN SOME CASES, ESPECIALLY INITIALLY, MYDRIASIS, LACRIMATION, SALIVATION, SWEATING, AND CONFUSION. OTHER REPORTED CENTRAL NERVOUS SYSTEM OR NEUROMUSCULAR EFFECTS MAY INCLUDE ATAXIA, SLURRED SPEECH, AREFLEXIA, WEAKNESS, FATIGUE, FASCICULATIONS, TWITCHING, TREMORS POSSIBLY OF THE TONGUE AND EYELIDS, AND EVENTUALLY PARALYSIS OF THE EXTREMITIES AND POSSIBLY OF THE RESPIRATORY MUSCLES. IN SEVERE CASES THERE MAY ALSO BE INVOLUNTARY DEFECATION AND URINATION, CYANOSIS, PSYCHOSIS, HYPERGLYCEMIA, ACUTE PANCREATITIS, CARDIAC IRREGULARITIES, PULMONARY EDEMA, UNCONSCIOUSNESS, CONVULSIONS, AND COMA. DEATH IS PRIMARILY DUE TO RESPIRATORY FAILURE, ALTHOUGH CARDIOVASCULAR EFFECTS INCLUDING CARDIAC ARREST MAY ALSO BE IMPLICATED. LONG TERM SEQUELAE ARE RARE BUT MAY INCLUDE NEUROPSYCHIATRIC DISORDERS AND MYOPATHY WITH MUSCLE TENDERNESS. SOME ORGANOPHOSPHATES MAY CAUSE A DELAYED NEUROPATHY BEGINNING 1-4 WEEKS AFTER AN ACUTE EXPOSURE WHICH MAY OR MAY NOT HAVE CAUSED ACUTE CHOLINERGIC EFFECTS. NUMBNESS, TINGLING, WEAKNESS AND CRAMPING BEGINNING SYMMETRICALLY IN THE LOWER LIMBS MAY PROGRESS TO ATAXIA AND PARALYSIS. IN SEVERE CASES, UPPER LIMB INVOLVEMENT IS POSSIBLE AND FLACCID PARALYSIS MAY PROGRESS TO SPASTIC PARALYSIS WITH EXAGGERATED REFLEXES. IMPROVEMENT MAY OCCUR OVER MONTHS TO YEARS, BUT SOME RESIDUAL IMPAIRMENT USUALLY REMAINS.
CHRONIC EXPOSURE- REPEATED OR PROLONGED EXPOSURE MAY RESULT IN THE EFFECTS OF ACUTE EXPOSURE INCLUDING THE DELAYED NEUROPATHY. OTHER

EFFECTS REPORTED IN WORKERS REPEATEDLY EXPOSED INCLUDE IMPAIRED MEMORY AND CONCENTRATION, ACUTE PSYCHOSIS, SEVERE DEPRESSIONS, IRRITABILTY, CONFUSION, APATHY, EMOTIONAL LABILITY, SOCIAL WITHDRAWAL, CONFUSION, HEADACHE, SPEECH DIFFICULTIES, DELAYED REACTION TIMES, SPATIAL DISORIENTATION, NIGHTMARES, SLEEPWALKING, AND DROWSINESS OR INSOMNIA. AN INFLUENZA-LIKE CONDITION WITH HEADACHE, NAUSEA, WEAKNESS, ANOREXIA AND MALAISE HAS ALSO BEEN REPORTED.

FIRST AID- REMOVE FROM EXPOSURE AREA TO FRESH AIR IMMEDIATELY. IF BREATHING HAS STOPPED, PERFORM ARTIFICIAL RESPIRATION. KEEP PERSON WARM AND AT REST. TREAT SYMPTOMATICALLY AND SUPPORTIVELY. GET MEDICAL ATTENTION IMMEDIATELY.

SKIN CONTACT: PHOSMET: SEE INFORMATION ON ORGANOPHOSPHATES. PHOSMET IS MILDLY IRRITATING TO RABBIT SKIN. REPEATED DERMAL APPLICATION OF 10, 30, OR 60 MG/KG 5 DAYS A WEEK FOR 6 WEEKS TO RABBITS RESULTED IN REDUCED PLASMA AND RED BLOOD CELL CHOLINESTERASE ACTIVITY. ORGANOPHOSPHATES: CHOLINESTERASE INHIBITOR. **ACUTE EXPOSURE-** LOCALIZED SWEATING AND FASCICULATIONS MAY OCCUR AT THE SITE OF CONTACT. IF SUFFICIENT AMOUNTS ARE ABSORBED, OTHER EFFECTS OF CHOLINESTERASE INHIBITION AS DESCRIBED IN ACUTE INHALATION MAY OCCUR. SYMPTOMS MAY BE DELAYED 2-3 HOURS, BUT USUALLY NO MORE THAN 12 HOURS. THE RATE OF ABSORPTION IS INCREASED BY THE PRESENCE OF DERMATITIS OR HIGH AMBIENT TEMPERATURES. DELAYED NEUROPATHY IS ALSO POSSIBLE. **CHRONIC EXPOSURE-** REPEATED OR PROLONGED EXPOSURE MAY CAUSE EFFECTS AS DESCRIBED IN ACUTE EXPOSURE. SOME ORGANOPHOSPHATES MAY CAUSE SENSITIZATION.

FIRST AID- REMOVE CONTAMINATED CLOTHING IMMEDIATELY. WASH CONTAMINATED AREAS WITH SOAP AND WATER FOLLOWED BY ALCOHOL (ARENA, POISONING, 4TH ED.). EMERGENCY PERSONNEL SHOULD WEAR GLOVES AND AVOID CONTAMINATION. TREAT RESPIRATORY DIFFICULTY WITH ARTIFICIAL RESPIRATION. GET MEDICAL ATTENTION IMMEDIATELY.

EYE CONTACT: PHOSMET: SEE INFORMATION ON ORGANOPHOSPHATES. CONTACT HAS PRODUCED MILD TO MODERATE IRRITATION IN RABBIT EYES. ORGANOPHOSPHATES: CHOLINESTERASE INHIBITOR. **ACUTE EXPOSURE-** DIRECT CONTACT MAY CAUSE PAIN, HYPEREMIA, LACRIMATION, TWITCHING OF THE EYELIDS, MIOSIS, AND CILIARY MUSCLE SPASM WITH LOSS OF ACCOMODATION, BLURRED OR DIMMED VISION AND BROWACHE. SOMETIMES MYDRIASIS MAY OCCUR INSTEAD OF MIOSIS. WITH SUFFICIENT EXPOSURE, OTHER SYMPTOMS OF CHOLINESTERASE INHIBITION AS DESCRIBED IN ACUTE INHALATION MAY OCCUR. **CHRONIC EXPOSURE-** REPEATED OR PROLONGED EXPOSURE MAY CAUSE EFFECTS AS DESCRIBED IN ACUTE EXPOSURE. SOME COMPOUNDS HAVE CAUSED TOXIC EFFECTS ON THE CRYSTALLINE LENS, CONJUNCTIVAL THICKENING AND OBSTRUCTION OF THE NASOLACRIMAL CANALS WHEN USED AS MIOTIC EYEDROPS.

FIRST AID- IRRIGATE EYES WITH WATER OR SALINE SOLUTION. IF SYMPTOMS OF POISONING OCCUR, TREAT RESPIRATORY DIFFICULTY WITH ARTIFICIAL RESPIRATION AND OXYGEN. OBSERVE PATIENT FOR AT LEAST 24-36 HOURS (GOSSELIN, CLINICAL TOXICOLOGY OF COMMERCIAL PRODUCTS, 5TH ED.). GET MEDICAL ATTENTION IMMEDIATELY. OXYGEN SHOULD BE ADMINISTERED BY QUALIFIED MEDICAL PERSONNEL.

INGESTION: PHOSMET: TOXIC. SEE INFORMATION ON ORGANOPHOSPHATES. REPEATED INGESTION OF 400 PPM PHOSMET IN THE DIET OF RATS RESULTED IN GROWTH SUPPRESSION, INHIBITION OF RED BLOOD COUNT AND PLASMA, AND HEPATIC TOXICITY. PHOSMET FED TO FEMALE RATS ON DAY 13 OF PREGNANCY PRODUCED HYDROCEPHALY IN A LARGE NUMBER OF EMBRYOS. OTHER REPRODUCTIVE EFFECTS HAVE BEEN REPORTED IN ANIMALS. ORGANOPHOSPHATES: CHOLINESTERASE INHIBITOR. **ACUTE EXPOSURE-** WHEN INGESTED, THE FIRST EFFECTS MAY BE NAUSEA, VOMITING, ANOREXIA, ABDOMINAL CRAMPS AND DIARRHEA. GASTROINTESTINAL ABSORPTION MAY CAUSE SYMPTOMS OF CHOLINESTERASE INHIBITION AS DESCRIBED IN ACUTE INHALATION. SYMPTOMS MAY BEGIN WITHIN MINUTES OR BE DELAYED FOR HOURS. DELAYED EFFECTS INCLUDING NEUROPATHY MAY ALSO OCCUR. **CHRONIC EXPOSURE-** REPEATED INGESTION MAY CAUSE EFFECTS AS DESCRIBED IN ACUTE EXPOSURE.

FIRST AID- IF PERSON IS ALERT AND RESPIRATION IS NOT DEPRESSED, GIVE SYRUP OF IPECAC FOLLOWED BY WATER (IF VOMITING OCCURS, KEEP HEAD BELOW HIPS TO PREVENT ASPIRATION). IF CONSCIOUSNESS LEVEL DECLINES OR VOMITING HAS NOT OCCURRED IN 15 MINUTES EMPTY STOMACH BY GASTRIC LAVAGE WITH THE AID OF CUFFED ENDOTRACHEAL TUBE USING ISOTONIC SALINE OR 5% SODIUM BICARBONATE FOLLOW WITH ACTIVATED CHARCOAL. ESTABLISH AND MAINTAIN AIRWAY. TREAT RESPIRATORY DIFFICULTY WITH ARTIFICIAL RESPIRATION AND OXYGEN. DO NOT GIVE MORPHINE, AMINOPHYLLINE, PHENOTHIAZINES, RESERPINE, FUROSEMIDE, OR ETHACRYNIC ACID (MORGAN, RECOGNITION AND MANAGEMENT OF PESTICIDE POISONINGS, 3RD ED.). TREAT SYMPTOMATICALLY AND SUPPORTIVELY. ADMINISTRATION OF OXYGEN AND LAVAGE MUST BE PERFORMED BY QUALIFIED MEDICAL PERSONNEL. GET MEDICAL ATTENTION IMMEDIATELY.

ANTIDOTE: THE FOLLOWING ANTIDOTE HAS BEEN RECOMMENDED. HOWEVER, THE DECISION AS TO WHETHER THE SEVERITY OF POISONING REQUIRES ADMINISTRATION OF ANY ANTIDOTE AND ACTUAL DOSE REQUIRED SHOULD BE MADE BY QUALIFIED MEDICAL PERSONNEL.
FOR CHOLINESTERASE INHIBITORS: ESTABLISH CLEAR AIRWAY AND TISSUE OXYGENATION BY ASPIRATION OF SECRETIONS, AND IF NECESSARY, BY ASSISTED PULMONARY VENTILATION WITH OXYGEN. IMPROVE TISSUE OXYGENATION AS MUCH AS POSSIBLE BEFORE ADMINISTERING ATROPINE TO MINIMIZE THE RISK OF VENTRICULAR FIBRILLATION. ADMINISTER ATROPINE SULFATE INTRAVENOUSLY, OR INTRAMUSCULARLY IF IV INJECTION IS NOT POSSIBLE. IN MODERATELY SEVERE POISONING ADMINISTER ATROPINE SULFATE, 0.4-2.0 MG REPEATED EVERY 15 MINUTES UNTIL ATROPINIZATION IS ACHIEVED (TACHYCARDIA, FLUSHING, DRY MOUTH, MYDRIASIS). MAINTAIN ATROPINIZATION BY REPEATED DOSES FOR 2-12 HOURS, OR LONGER, DEPENDING ON THE SEVERITY OF POISONING. THE APPEARANCE OF RALES IN THE LUNG BASES, MIOSIS, SALIVATION, NAUSEA, BRADYCARDIA, ARE ALL INDICATIONS OF INADEQUATE ATROPINIZATION. SEVERELY POISONED INDIVIDUALS MAY EXHIBIT REMARKABLE TOLERANCE TO ATROPINE; TWO OR MORE TIMES THE DOSAGES SUGGESTED ABOVE MAY BE NEEDED. PERSONS NOT POISONED OR ONLY SLIGHTLY POISONED, HOWEVER, MAY DEVELOP SIGNS OF ATROPINE TOXICITY FROM SUCH LARGE DOSAGES: FEVER, MUSCLE FIBRILLATIONS, AND DELIRIUM ARE THE MAIN SIGNS OF ATROPINE TOXICITY. IF THESE SIGNS APPEAR WHILE THE PATIENT IS FULLY ATROPINIZED, ATROPINE ADMINISTRATION SHOULD BE DISCONTINUED, AT LEAST TEMPORARILY. OBSERVE TREATED PATIENTS CLOSELY AT LEAST 24 HOURS TO INSURE THAT SYMPTOMS (POSSIBLY PULMONARY EDEMA) DO NOT RECUR AS ATROPINIZATION WEARS OFF. IN VERY SEVERE POISONINGS, METABOLIC DISPOSITION OF TOXICANT MAY REQUIRE SEVERAL HOURS OR DAYS DURING WHICH ATROPINIZATION MUST BE MAINTAINED. MARKEDLY LOWER LEVELS OF URINARY METABOLITES INDICATE THAT ATROPINE DOSAGE CAN BE TAPERED OFF. AS DOSAGE IS REDUCED, CHECK THE LUNG BASES FREQUENTLY FOR RALES. IF RALES ARE HEARD OR OTHER SYMPTOMS RETURN, RE-ESTABLISH ATROPINIZATION PROMPTLY (MORGAN, RECOGNITION AND MANAGEMENT OF PESTICIDE POISONINGS, 3RD ED.). ADMINISTRATION OF ANTIDOTE MUST BE PERFORMED BY QUALIFIED MEDICAL PERSONNEL.

REACTIVITY

REACTIVITY: STABLE UNDER NORMAL TEMPERATURES AND PRESSURES.

INCOMPATIBILITIES: PHOSMET: ALKALINE CONDITIONS: IS HYDROLYZED. AQUEOUS SOLUTION: IS HYDROLYZED. OXIDIZING AGENTS: MAY HYDROLYZED.

DECOMPOSITION: THERMAL DECOMPOSITION MAY RELEASE TOXIC AND/OR HAZARDOUS GASES.

POLYMERIZATION: HAZARDOUS POLYMERIZATION HAS NOT BEEN REPORTED TO OCCUR UNDER NORMAL TEMPERATURES AND PRESSURES.

STORAGE AND DISPOSAL

OBSERVE ALL FEDERAL, STATE AND LOCAL REGULATIONS WHEN STORING OR DISPOSING OF THIS SUBSTANCE. FOR ASSISTANCE, CONTACT THE DISTRICT DIRECTOR OF THE ENVIRONMENTAL PROTECTION AGENCY.

STORAGE

STORE IN ACCORDANCE WITH 40 CFR 165 RECOMMENDED PROCEDURES FOR THE DISPOSAL AND STORAGE OF PESTICIDES AND PESTICIDE CONTAINERS.
STORE AWAY FROM INCOMPATIBLE SUBSTANCES.
STORAGE OF FORMULATIONS ABOVE 113 F (45 C) MAY LEAD TO DECOMPOSITION.
THRESHOLD PLANNING QUANTITY (TPQ): THE SUPERFUND AMENDMENTS AND REAUTHORIZATION ACT (SARA) SECTION 302 REQUIRES THAT EACH FACILITY WHERE ANY EXTREMELY HAZARDOUS SUBSTANCE IS PRESENT IN A QUANTITY EQUAL TO OR GREATER THAN THE TPQ ESTABLISHED FOR THAT SUBSTANCE NOTIFY THE STATE EMERGENCY RESPONSE COMMISSION FOR THE STATE IN WHICH IT IS LOCATED. SECTION 303 OF SARA REQUIRES THESE FACILITIES TO PARTICIPATE IN LOCAL EMERGENCY RESPONSE PLANNING (40 CFR 355.30).

DISPOSAL

DISPOSAL MUST BE IN ACCORDANCE WITH 40 CFR 165 RECOMMENDED PROCEDURES FOR THE DISPOSAL AND STORAGE OF PESTICIDES AND PESTICIDE CONTAINERS.

CONDITIONS TO AVOID

NONE REPORTED.

SPILL AND LEAK PROCEDURES

OCCUPATIONAL SPILL: DO NOT TOUCH SPILLED MATERIAL. STOP LEAK IF YOU CAN DO IT WITHOUT RISK. USE WATER SPRAY TO REDUCE VAPORS. FOR SMALL SPILLS, TAKE UP WITH SAND OR OTHER ABSORBENT MATERIAL AND PLACE INTO CONTAINERS FOR LATER DISPOSAL. FOR SMALL DRY SPILLS, WITH A CLEAN SHOVEL PLACE MATERIAL INTO CLEAN, DRY CONTAINERS AND COVER. MOVE

CONTAINERS FROM SPILL AREA. FOR LARGER SPILLS, DIKE FAR AHEAD OF SPILL FOR LATER DISPOSAL. KEEP UNNECESSARY PEOPLE AWAY. ISOLATE HAZARD AREA AND DENY ENTRY. VENTILATE CLOSED SPACES BEFORE ENTERING. REPORTABLE QUANTITY (RQ): 1 POUND THE SUPERFUND AMENDMENTS AND REAUTHORIZATION ACT (SARA) SECTION 304 REQUIRES THAT A RELEASE EQUAL TO OR GREATER THAN THE REPORTABLE QUANTITY FOR THIS SUBSTANCE BE IMMEDIATELY REPORTED TO THE LOCAL EMERGENCY PLANNING COMMITTEE AND THE STATE EMERGENCY RESPONSE COMMISSION (40 CFR 355.40). IF THE RELEASE OF THIS SUBSTANCE IS REPORTABLE UNDER CERCLA SECTION 103, THE NATIONAL RESPONSE CENTER MUST BE NOTIFIED IMMEDIATELY AT (800) 424-8802 OR (202) 426-2675 IN THE METROPOLITAN WASHINGTON, D.C. AREA (40 CFR 302.6).

PROTECTIVE EQUIPMENT

VENTILATION: PROCESS ENCLOSURE RECOMMENDED.

RESPIRATOR: THE FOLLOWING RESPIRATORS ARE RECOMMENDED BASED ON INFORMATION FOUND IN THE PHYSICAL DATA, TOXICITY AND HEALTH EFFECTS SECTIONS. THEY ARE RANKED IN ORDER FROM MINIMUM TO MAXIMUM RESPIRATORY PROTECTION. THE SPECIFIC RESPIRATOR SELECTED MUST BE BASED ON CONTAMINATION LEVELS FOUND IN THE WORK PLACE, MUST NOT EXCEED THE WORKING LIMITS OF THE RESPIRATOR AND BE JOINTLY APPROVED BY THE NATIONAL INSTITUTE FOR OCCUPATIONAL SAFETY AND HEALTH AND THE MINE SAFETY AND HEALTH ADMINISTRATION (NIOSH-MSHA).

TYPE 'C' SUPPLIED-AIR RESPIRATOR WITH A FULL FACEPIECE OPERATED IN PRESSURE-DEMAND OR OTHER POSITIVE PRESSURE MODE OR WITH A FULL FACEPIECE, HELMET OR HOOD OPERATED IN CONTINOUS-FLOW MODE.

SELF-CONTAINED BREATHING APPARATUS WITH A FULL FACEPIECE OPERATED IN PRESSURE-DEMAND OR OTHER POSITIVE PRESSURE MODE.

FOR FIREFIGHTING AND OTHER IMMEDIATELY DANGEROUS TO LIFE OR HEALTH CONDITIONS:

SELF-CONTAINED BREATHING APPARATUS WITH FULL FACEPIECE OPERATED IN PRESSURE-DEMAND OR OTHER POSITIVE PRESSURE MODE.

SUPPLIED-AIR RESPIRATOR WITH FULL FACEPIECE AND OPERATED IN PRESSURE-DEMAND OR OTHER POSITIVE PRESSURE MODE IN COMBINATION WITH AN AUXILIARY SELF-CONTAINED BREATHING APPARATUS OPERATED IN PRESSURE-DEMAND OR OTHER POSITIVE PRESSURE MODE.

CLOTHING: EMPLOYEE MUST WEAR APPROPRIATE PROTECTIVE (IMPERVIOUS) CLOTHING AND EQUIPMENT TO PREVENT ANY POSSIBILITY OF SKIN CONTACT WITH THIS SUBSTANCE.

GLOVES: EMPLOYEE MUST WEAR APPROPRIATE PROTECTIVE GLOVES TO PREVENT CONTACT WITH THIS SUBSTANCE.

EYE PROTECTION: EMPLOYEE MUST WEAR SPLASH-PROOF OR DUST-RESISTANT SAFETY GOGGLES AND A FACESHIELD TO PREVENT CONTACT WITH THIS SUBSTANCE.

EMERGENCY WASH FACILITIES: WHERE THERE IS ANY POSSIBILITY THAT AN EMPLOYEE'S EYES AND/OR SKIN MAY BE EXPOSED TO THIS SUBSTANCE, THE EMPLOYER SHOULD PROVIDE AN EYE WASH FOUNTAIN AND QUICK DRENCH SHOWER WITHIN THE IMMEDIATE WORK AREA FOR EMERGENCY USE.

AUTHORIZED BY- OCCUPATIONAL HEALTH SERVICES, INC.

CREATION DATE: 10/04/89 ***REVISION DATE:*** 05/01/90

MATERIAL SAFETY DATA SHEET

OCCUPATIONAL HEALTH SERVICES, INC.
AGRICULTURE AND PESTICIDE DIVISION
450 SEVENTH AVENUE, SUITE 2407
NEW YORK, NEW YORK 10123
1-800-445-MSDS OR (212) 967-1100

EMERGENCY CONTACT:
JOHN S. BRANSFORD, JR. (615) 292-1180

SUBSTANCE IDENTIFICATION

CAS-NUMBER 81335-77-5

SUBSTANCE: **IMAZETHAPYR**

TRADE NAMES/SYNONYMS: 3-PYRIDINECARBOXYLIC ACID, 2-(4,5-DIHYDRO-4-METHYL-4-(1-METHYLETHYL)-5-OXO-1H-IMIDAZOL-2-YL)-5-ETHYL-; 2-(4,5-DIHYDRO-4-METHYL-4-(1-METHYLETHYL)-5-OXO-1H-IMIDAZOL-2-YL)- 5-ETHYL-3-PYRIDINECARBOXYLIC ACID; (RS)-5-ETHYL-2-(4-ISOPROPYL-4-METHYL-5-OXO-2-IMIDAZOLIN-2-YL)- NICOTINIC ACID; (+/-)-2-(4,5-DIHYDRO-4-METHYL-4-(1-METHYLETHYL)-5-OXO-1H-IMIDAZOL-2-YL)-5-ETHYL-3-PYRIDINECARBOXYLIC ACID; AC 263499; PURSUIT; C15H19N3O3; PST11308

CHEMICAL FAMILY: IMIDAZOLIDINONE PYRIDINE CARBOXYLIC ACID

MOLECULAR FORMULA: C15-H19-N3-O3

MOLECULAR WEIGHT: 289.37

CERCLA RATINGS (SCALE 0-3): HEALTH=U FIRE=1 REACTIVITY=0 PERSISTENCE=2

NFPA RATINGS (SCALE 0-4): HEALTH=U FIRE=1 REACTIVITY=0

COMPONENTS AND CONTAMINANTS

COMPONENT: IMAZETHAPYR ***PERCENT:*** 100.0
CAS# 81335-77-5

OTHER CONTAMINANTS: NONE

EXPOSURE LIMITS: NO OCCUPATIONAL EXPOSURE LIMITS ESTABLISHED BY OSHA, ACGIH, OR NIOSH.

PHYSICAL DATA

DESCRIPTION: COLORLESS TO TAN CRYSTALLINE SOLID WITH A PUNGENT ODOR.

MELTING POINT: 342-347 F (172-175 C) ***SPECIFIC GRAVITY:*** NOT AVAILABLE

VAPOR PRESSURE: NEGLIGIBLE @ 60 C ***PH:*** 2.8 @ 25 C

SOLUBILITY IN WATER: 0.14%

SOLVENT SOLUBILITY: SOLUBLE IN DIMETHYL SULFOXIDE, METHANOL, METHYLENE CHLORIDE; MODERATELY SOLUBLE IN ACETONE AND 2-PROPANOL; SLIGHTLY SOLUBLE IN TOLUENE; VERY SLIGHTLY SOLUBLE IN HEPTANE.

FIRE AND EXPLOSION DATA

FIRE AND EXPLOSION HAZARD: SLIGHT FIRE HAZARD WHEN EXPOSED TO HEAT OR FLAME.

DUST-AIR MIXTURES MAY IGNITE OR EXPLODE.

FIREFIGHTING MEDIA: DRY CHEMICAL, CARBON DIOXIDE, HALON, WATER SPRAY OR STANDARD FOAM (1987 EMERGENCY RESPONSE GUIDEBOOK, DOT P 5800.4). FOR LARGER FIRES, USE WATER SPRAY, FOG OR STANDARD FOAM (1987 EMERGENCY RESPONSE GUIDEBOOK, DOT P 5800.4).

FIREFIGHTING: MOVE CONTAINER FROM FIRE AREA IF POSSIBLE. DO NOT SCATTER SPILLED MATERIAL WITH HIGH PRESSURE WATER STREAMS. DIKE FIRE CONTROL WATER FOR LATER DISPOSAL (1987 EMERGENCY RESPONSE GUIDEBOOK, DOT P 5800.4, GUIDE PAGE 31).

USE AGENTS SUITABLE FOR TYPE OF SURROUNDING FIRE. AVOID BREATHING HAZARDOUS VAPORS, KEEP UPWIND.

TOXICITY

IMAZETHAPYR: TOXICITY DATA: >3.27 MG/L INHALATION-RAT LC50 (PEMNDP); >2000 MG/KG SKIN-RABBIT LD50 (PEMNDP); >5000 MG/KG ORAL-RAT LD50 (PEMNDP); >5000 MG/KG ORAL-MOUSE (PEMNDP). CARCINOGEN STATUS: NONE. ACUTE TOXICITY LEVEL: SLIGHTLY TOXIC BY DERMAL ABSORPTION AND INGESTION. TARGET EFFECTS: NO DATA AVAILABLE.

HEALTH EFFECTS AND FIRST AID

INHALATION: IMAZETHAPYR: **ACUTE EXPOSURE-** THE LC50 REPORTED IN RATS WAS GREATER THAN 3.27 MG/L. **CHRONIC EXPOSURE-** NO DATA AVAILABLE.

FIRST AID- REMOVE FROM EXPOSURE AREA TO FRESH AIR IMMEDIATELY. IF BREATHING HAS STOPPED, PERFORM ARTIFICIAL RESPIRATION. KEEP PERSON WARM AND AT REST. TREAT SYMPTOMATICALLY AND SUPPORTIVELY. GET MEDICAL ATTENTION IMMEDIATELY.

SKIN CONTACT: IMAZETHAPYR: **ACUTE EXPOSURE-** THIS MATERIAL WAS MILDLY IRRITATING TO RABBIT SKIN. **CHRONIC EXPOSURE-** REPEATED APPLICATIONS OF 1000 MG/KG/DAY PRODUCED NO OBSERVABLE EFFECTS IN RABBITS.

FIRST AID- REMOVE CONTAMINATED CLOTHING AND SHOES IMMEDIATELY. WASH AFFECTED AREA WITH SOAP OR MILD DETERGENT AND LARGE AMOUNTS OF WATER UNTIL NO EVIDENCE OF CHEMICAL REMAINS (APPROXIMATELY 15-20 MINUTES). GET MEDICAL ATTENTION IMMEDIATELY.

EYE CONTACT: IMAZETHAPYR: **ACUTE EXPOSURE-** THIS MATERIAL PRODUCED IRRITATION OF RABBIT EYES WITH COMPLETE RECOVERY BY THREE DAYS. **CHRONIC EXPOSURE-** NO DATA AVAILABLE.

FIRST AID- WASH EYES IMMEDIATELY WITH LARGE AMOUNTS OF WATER OR NORMAL SALINE, OCCASIONALLY LIFTING UPPER AND LOWER LIDS, UNTIL NO EVIDENCE OF CHEMICAL REMAINS (APPROXIMATELY 15-20 MINUTES). GET MEDICAL ATTENTION IMMEDIATELY.

INGESTION: IMAZETHAPYR: **ACUTE EXPOSURE-** THE LD50 IN RATS WAS GREATER THAN 5000 MG/KG. **CHRONIC EXPOSURE-** EFFECTS OF DECREASED HEMATOCRIT, VOLUME HEMOGLOBIN AND ERYTHROCYTES WERE OBSERVED IN RABBITS REPEATEDLY RECEIVING 250 MG/KG/DAY; NO SYSTEMIC OBSERVABLE EFFECTS WERE NOTED IN RATS RECEIVING 500 MG/KG/DAY AND MICE RECEIVING 750

MKG/KG/DAY UP TO 2 YEARS. NO TERATOGENIC EFFECTS WERE NOTED IN RABBIT FETUSES AT 1000 MG/KG/DAY.

FIRST AID- TREAT SYMPTOMATICALLY AND SUPPORTIVELY. GET MEDICAL ATTENTION IMMEDIATELY. IF VOMITING OCCURS, KEEP HEAD LOWER THAN HIPS TO PREVENT ASPIRATION.

ANTIDOTE: NO SPECIFIC ANTIDOTE. TREAT SYMPTOMATICALLY AND SUPPORTIVELY.

REACTIVITY

REACTIVITY: STABLE UNDER NORMAL TEMPERATURES AND PRESSURES.

INCOMPATIBILITIES: IMAZETHAPYR: OXIDIZERS (STRONG): FIRE AND EXPLOSION HAZARD.

DECOMPOSITION: THERMAL DECOMPOSITION PRODUCTS MAY INCLUDE TOXIC OXIDES OF CARBON AND NITROGEN.

POLYMERIZATION: HAZARDOUS POLYMERIZATION HAS NOT BEEN REPORTED TO OCCUR UNDER NORMAL TEMPERATURES AND PRESSURES.

STORAGE AND DISPOSAL

OBSERVE ALL FEDERAL, STATE AND LOCAL REGULATIONS WHEN STORING OR DISPOSING OF THIS SUBSTANCE. FOR ASSISTANCE, CONTACT THE DISTRICT DIRECTOR OF THE ENVIRONMENTAL PROTECTION AGENCY.

****STORAGE****

STORE IN ACCORDANCE WITH 40 CFR 165 RECOMMENDED PROCEDURES FOR THE DISPOSAL AND STORAGE OF PESTICIDES AND PESTICIDE CONTAINERS.

STORE AWAY FROM INCOMPATIBLE SUBSTANCES.

****DISPOSAL****

DISPOSAL MUST BE IN ACCORDANCE WITH 40 CFR 165 RECOMMENDED PROCEDURES FOR THE DISPOSAL AND STORAGE OF PESTICIDES AND PESTICIDE CONTAINERS.

CONDITIONS TO AVOID

MAY BURN BUT DOES NOT IGNITE READILY. AVOID CONTACT WITH STRONG OXIDIZERS, EXCESSIVE HEAT, SPARKS, OR OPEN FLAME.

SPILL AND LEAK PROCEDURES

OCCUPATIONAL SPILL: SWEEP UP AND PLACE IN SUITABLE CLEAN, DRY CONTAINERS FOR RECLAMATION OR LATER DISPOSAL. DO NOT FLUSH SPILLED MATERIAL INTO SEWER. KEEP UNNECESSARY PEOPLE AWAY.

PROTECTIVE EQUIPMENT

VENTILATION: PROVIDE GENERAL DILUTION VENTILATION.

RESPIRATOR: THE FOLLOWING RESPIRATORS ARE RECOMMENDED BASED ON INFORMATION FOUND IN THE PHYSICAL DATA, TOXICITY AND HEALTH EFFECTS SECTIONS. THEY ARE RANKED IN ORDER FROM MINIMUM TO MAXIMUM RESPIRATORY PROTECTION. THE SPECIFIC RESPIRATOR SELECTED MUST BE BASED ON CONTAMINATION LEVELS FOUND IN THE WORK PLACE, MUST NOT EXCEED THE WORKING LIMITS OF THE RESPIRATOR AND BE JOINTLY APPROVED BY THE NATIONAL INSTITUTE FOR OCCUPATIONAL SAFETY AND HEALTH AND THE MINE SAFETY AND HEALTH ADMINISTRATION (NIOSH-MSHA).

CHEMICAL CARTRIDGE RESPIRATOR WITH AN ORGANIC VAPOR CARTRIDGE(S) IN COMBINATION WITH A DUST AND MIST FILTER.

GAS MASK WITH ORGANIC VAPOR CANISTER (CHIN-STYLE OR FRONT- OR BACK-MOUNTED CANISTER) WITH A DUST AND MIST FILTER.

GAS MASK WITH ORGANIC VAPOR CANISTER (CHIN-STYLE OR FRONT- OR BACK-MOUNTED CANISTER) WITH A PARTICULATE FILTER.

POWERED AIR-PURIFYING RESPIRATOR WITH A HIGH-EFFICIENCY FILTER.

TYPE 'C' SUPPLIED-AIR RESPIRATOR WITH A FULL FACEPIECE OPERATED IN A PRESSURE-DEMAND OR OTHER POSITIVE PRESSURE MODE. SELF-CONTAINED BREATHING APPARATUS WITH A FULL FACEPIECE OPERATED IN PRESSURE-DEMAND OR OTHER POSITIVE PRESSURE MODE.

FOR FIREFIGHTING AND OTHER IMMEDIATELY DANGEROUS TO LIFE OR HEALTH CONDITIONS:

SELF-CONTAINED BREATHING APPARATUS WITH FULL FACEPIECE OPERATED IN PRESSURE-DEMAND OR OTHER POSITIVE PRESSURE MODE.

SUPPLIED-AIR RESPIRATOR WITH FULL FACEPIECE AND OPERATED IN PRESSURE-DEMAND OR OTHER POSITIVE PRESSURE MODE IN COMBINATION WITH AN AUXILIARY SELF-CONTAINED BREATHING APPARATUS OPERATED IN PRESSURE-DEMAND OR OTHER POSITIVE PRESSURE MODE.

CLOTHING: EMPLOYEE MUST WEAR APPROPRIATE PROTECTIVE (IMPERVIOUS) CLOTHING AND EQUIPMENT TO PREVENT REPEATED OR PROLONGED SKIN CONTACT WITH THIS SUBSTANCE.

GLOVES: EMPLOYEE MUST WEAR APPROPRIATE PROTECTIVE GLOVES TO PREVENT CONTACT WITH THIS SUBSTANCE.

EYE PROTECTION: EMPLOYEE MUST WEAR SPLASH-PROOF OR DUST-RESISTANT SAFETY GOGGLES TO PREVENT EYE CONTACT WITH THIS SUBSTANCE.

EMERGENCY EYE WASH: WHERE THERE IS ANY POSSIBILITY THAT AN EMPLOYEE'S EYES MAY BE EXPOSED TO THIS SUBSTANCE, THE EMPLOYER SHOULD PROVIDE AN EYE WASH FOUNTAIN WITHIN THE IMMEDIATE WORK AREA FOR EMERGENCY USE.

AUTHORIZED BY- OCCUPATIONAL HEALTH SERVICES, INC.

CREATION DATE: 05/18/90 ***REVISION DATE:*** 05/31/90

MATERIAL SAFETY DATA SHEET

OCCUPATIONAL HEALTH SERVICES, INC.
AGRICULTURE AND PESTICIDE DIVISION
450 SEVENTH AVENUE, SUITE 2407
NEW YORK, NEW YORK 10123
1-800-445-MSDS OR (212) 967-1100

EMERGENCY CONTACT:
JOHN S. BRANSFORD, JR. (615) 292-1180

SUBSTANCE IDENTIFICATION

CAS-NUMBER 7553-56-2

SUBSTANCE: **IODINE**

TRADE NAMES/SYNONYMS: IODINE CRYSTALS; IODINE, SUBLIMED; IODINE A.R. CRYSTALS (MALLINCKRODT); IODINE MOLECULE (I2); MOLECULAR IODINE; DIATOMIC IODINE; DIIODINE; I2; PST11400

CHEMICAL FAMILY: HALOGEN

MOLECULAR FORMULA: I2

MOLECULAR WEIGHT: 253.809

CERCLA RATINGS (SCALE 0-3): HEALTH = 1 FIRE = 0 REACTIVITY = 0 PERSISTENCE = 0

NFPA RATINGS (SCALE 0-4): HEALTH = 1 FIRE = 0 REACTIVITY = 0

COMPONENTS AND CONTAMINANTS

COMPONENT: IODINE ***PERCENT:*** 100.0

CAS# 7553-56-2

OTHER CONTAMINANTS: NONE

EXPOSURE LIMITS: IODINE: 0.1 PPM (1 MG/M3) OSHA CEILING 0.1 PPM (1 MG/M3) ACGIH CEILING

PHYSICAL DATA

DESCRIPTION: BLUE-VIOLET TO BLACK CRYSTALS WITH A SHARP, CHARACTERISTIC ODOR.

BOILING POINT: 363 F (184 C) ***MELTING POINT:*** 237 F (114 C)

SPECIFIC GRAVITY: 4.93 ***VAPOR PRESSURE:*** 0.305 MMHG @ 25 C

SOLUBILITY IN WATER: 0.03% @ 20 C ***VAPOR DENSITY:*** 8.8

SOLVENT SOLUBILITY: SOLUBLE IN ALCOHOL, BENZENE, ETHER, CHLOROFORM, GLYCEROL, POTASSIUM IODIDE, CARBON DISULFIDE, IODIDE SOLUTIONS, PYRIDINE, QUINOLINE, AMINES, GLACIAL ACETIC ACID, CARBON TETRACHLORIDE.

FIRE AND EXPLOSION DATA

FIRE AND EXPLOSION HAZARD: NEGLIGIBLE FIRE HAZARD WHEN EXPOSED TO HEAT OR FLAME.

OXIDIZER: OXIDIZERS DECOMPOSE, ESPECIALLY WHEN HEATED, TO YIELD OXYGEN OR OTHER GASES WHICH WILL INCREASE THE BURNING RATE OF COMBUSTIBLE MATTER. CONTACT WITH EASILY OXIDIZABLE, ORGANIC, OR OTHER COMBUSTIBLE MATERIALS MAY RESULT IN IGNITION, VIOLENT COMBUSTION OR EXPLOSION.

FIREFIGHTING MEDIA: WATER ONLY, NO DRY CHEMICAL, CARBON DIOXIDE OR HALON (1987 EMERGENCY RESPONSE GUIDEBOOK, DOT P 5800.4).

FOR LARGER FIRES, FLOOD AREA WITH WATER FROM A DISTANCE (1987 EMERGENCY RESPONSE GUIDEBOOK, DOT P 5800.4).

FIREFIGHTING: MOVE CONTAINERS FROM FIRE AREA IF POSSIBLE. COOL CONTAINERS EXPOSED TO FLAMES WITH WATER FROM SIDE UNTIL WELL AFTER FIRE IS OUT. STAY AWAY FROM STORAGE TANK ENDS. FOR MASSIVE FIRE IN STORAGE AREA, USE UNMANNED HOSE HOLDER OR MONITOR NOZZLES; ELSE WITHDRAW FROM AREA AND LET FIRE BURN (1987 EMERGENCY RESPONSE GUIDEBOOK, DOT P 5800.4 GUIDE PAGE 45).

FLOOD WITH WATER. COOL CONTAINERS WITH FLOODING AMOUNTS OF WATER FROM AS FAR A DISTANCE AS POSSIBLE. AVOID BREATHING CORROSIVE VAPORS OR DUSTS. IF FIRE IS UNCONTROLLABLE, EVACUATE FOR A RADIUS OF 2500 FEET.

TRANSPORTATION DATA

DEPARTMENT OF TRANSPORTATION HAZARD CLASSIFICATION 49 CFR 172.101: OXIDIZER

DEPARTMENT OF TRANSPORTATION LABELING REQUIREMENTS 49 CFR 172.101 AND SUBPART E: OXIDIZER AND CORROSIVE

DEPARTMENT OF TRANSPORTATION PACKAGING REQUIREMENTS: 49 CFR 173.154
EXCEPTIONS: 49 CFR 173.153

TOXICITY

IODINE: TOXICITY DATA: 800 MG/M3/1 HOUR INHALATION-RAT LCLO; 28 MG/KG ORAL-HUMAN LDLO; 26 MG/KG/1 YEAR INTERMITTENT ORAL-WOMAN TDLO; 14 GM/KG ORAL-RAT LD50; 22 GM/KG ORAL-MOUSE LD50; 10 GM/KG ORAL-RABBIT LD50; 800 MG/KG ORAL-DOG LDLO; 175 MG/KG SUBCUTANEOUS-RABBIT LDLO; 40 MG/KG INTRAVENOUS-DOG LDLO; 29 MG/KG UNREPORTED-MAN LDLO; REPRODUCTIVE EFFECTS DATA (RTECS). CARCINOGEN STATUS: NONE. LOCAL EFFECTS: CORROSIVE- INHALATION, SKIN, EYE, INGESTION. ACUTE TOXICITY LEVEL: SLIGHTLY TOXIC BY INGESTION. TARGET EFFECTS: SENSITIZER- DERMAL. POISONING MAY AFFECT THE CIRCULATORY SYSTEM AND KIDNEYS. AT INCREASED RISK FROM EXPOSURE: PERSONS WITH IMPAIRED PULMONARY OR THYROID FUNCTION OR HISTORY OF ASTHMA, ALLERGIES OR KNOWN SENSITIZATION TO IODINE. ADDITIONAL DATA: MAY CROSS REACT WITH IODOFORM, RADIOPAQUE IODINE AND IODIDES IN MEDICATIONS. MAY CROSS THE PLACENTA.*

* MAY BE BASED ON GENERAL INFORMATION ON IODINE COMPOUNDS.

HEALTH EFFECTS AND FIRST AID

INHALATION: IODINE: CORROSIVE. 10 PPM IMMEDIATELY DANGEROUS TO LIFE OR HEALTH. **ACUTE EXPOSURE-** INHALATION MAY CAUSE SEVERE IRRITATION OF THE MUCOUS MEMBRANES, SPARKLING BEFORE THE EYES, SEVERE COUGH, HEADACHE, SOMNOLENCE AND SWELLING OF THE PAROTID GLAND, AND POSSIBLY PULMONARY EDEMA. WORKERS EXPOSED TO IODINE VAPOR EXPERIENCED CATARRHAL RHINITIS, STOMATITIS, AND CHRONIC PHARYNGITIS. LABORATORY TECHNICIANS REPORTED HEADACHES, AND A FEELING OF TIGHTNESS IN THE CHEST FOLLOWING ACCIDENTAL EXPOSURE. **CHRONIC EXPOSURE-** EFFECTS DEPEND ON CONCENTRATION AND DURATION OF EXPOSURE. REPEATED OR PROLONGED CONTACT WITH CORROSIVE SUBSTANCES MAY CAUSE INFLAMMATORY AND ULCERATIVE CHANGES IN THE MOUTH AND POSSIBLY BRONCHIAL AND GASTROINTESTINAL DISTURBANCES.

FIRST AID- REMOVE FROM EXPOSURE AREA TO FRESH AIR IMMEDIATELY. IF BREATHING HAS STOPPED, GIVE ARTIFICIAL RESPIRATION. MAINTAIN AIRWAY AND BLOOD PRESSURE AND ADMINISTER OXYGEN IF AVAILABLE. KEEP AFFECTED PERSON WARM AND AT REST. TREAT SYMPTOMATICALLY AND SUPPORTIVELY. ADMINISTRATION OF OXYGEN SHOULD BE PERFORMED BY QUALIFIED PERSONNEL. GET MEDICAL ATTENTION IMMEDIATELY.

SKIN CONTACT: IODINE: CORROSIVE/SENSITIZER. **ACUTE EXPOSURE-** MAY CAUSE BROWN DISCOLORATION OF THE SKIN WITH MARKED ERYTHEMA, DESQUAMATION AND VESICULATION WITH WEEPING AND CRUSTING. THE LESIONS ARE COMMON AND ARE USUALLY ACNEFORM AND SLOW HEALING. SKIN ABSORPTION MAY OCCUR. DEATH HAS BEEN REPORTED AFTER APPLICATION OF IODINE TINCTURE TO ONE THIRD OF THE BODY SURFACE. ALTHOUGH IODINE IS A RARE SENSITIZER, THE HYPERSENSITIVITY REACTION MAY BE CHARACTERIZED BY DERMATITIS, FEVER, AND A GENERALIZED SKIN ERUPTION AND MAY PROVE FATAL. **CHRONIC EXPOSURE-** REPEATED OR PROLONGED CONTACT MAY CAUSE SENSITIZATION WITH DERMATITIS, LARYNGEAL EDEMA AND SERUM SICKNESS WITH LYMPH NODE ENLARGEMENT AND JOINT PAIN AND SWELLING.

FIRST AID- REMOVE CONTAMINATED CLOTHING AND SHOES IMMEDIATELY. WASH AFFECTED AREA WITH SOAP OR MILD DETERGENT AND LARGE AMOUNTS OF WATER UNTIL NO EVIDENCE OF CHEMICAL REMAINS (AT LEAST 15-20 MINUTES). IN CASE OF CHEMICAL BURNS, COVER AREA WITH STERILE, DRY DRESSING. BANDAGE SECURELY, BUT NOT TOO TIGHTLY. GET MEDICAL ATTENTION IMMEDIATELY.

EYE CONTACT: IODINE: CORROSIVE. **ACUTE EXPOSURE-** IN A HUMAN STUDY, ALL SUBJECTS COMPLAINED OF IRRITATION AFTER TWO MINUTES AT 1.63 PPM. IN ANOTHER STUDY, PATIENTS EXPOSED FOR 3-4 MINUTES TO SATURATED VAPOR EXPERIENCED BROWN STAINING OF THE CORNEAL EPITHELIUM, AND LOSS OF THE LAYER OF TISSUE WITH RECOVERY OCCURRING IN 2-3 DAYS. OCCUPATIONAL EXPOSURE TO IODINE VAPORS HAS BEEN REPORTED TO CAUSE A BURNING SENSATION, LACRIMATION AND BLEPHARITIS. **CHRONIC EXPOSURE-** EFFECTS DEPEND ON CONCENTRATION AND DURATION OF EXPOSURE. CONJUNCTIVITIS OR EFFECTS AS DETAILED IN ACUTE EXPOSURE MAY OCCUR.

FIRST AID- WASH EYES IMMEDIATELY WITH LARGE AMOUNTS OF WATER, OCCASIONALLY LIFTING UPPER AND LOWER LIDS, UNTIL NO EVIDENCE OF CHEMICAL REMAINS (AT LEAST 15-20 MINUTES). CONTINUE IRRIGATING WITH NORMAL SALINE UNTIL THE PH HAS RETURNED TO NORMAL (30-60 MINUTES). COVER WITH STERILE BANDAGES. GET MEDICAL ATTENTION IMMEDIATELY.

INGESTION: IODINE: CORROSIVE. **ACUTE EXPOSURE-** INGESTION MAY CAUSE INFLAMMATION AND CORROSION OF THE GASTROINTESTINAL TRACT WITH BROWN DISCOLORATION OF THE LIPS AND MUCOUS MEMBRANES, A BURNING SENSATION, NAUSEA, SEVERE VOMITING, DIARRHEA, ABDOMINAL PAIN, INTENSE THIRST, METALLIC TASTE, FEVER, DELIRIUM AND STUPOR. RARELY, ULCERATIVE ESOPHAGITIS HAS BEEN REPORTED. LARGE DOSES MAY RESULT IN CONVULSIONS, HEMORRHAGIC NEPHRITIS, ANURIA AND SHOCK. ASPHYXIA FROM EDEMA OF THE EPIGLOTTIS, ASPIRATION, OR PULMONARY EDEMA MAY OCCUR. HYPERSENSITIVITY REACTIONS MAY OCCUR MANIFESTED BY ANGIONEUROTIC EDEMA, FEVER, ARTHRALGIA, LYMPHADENOPATHY, EOSINOPHILIA AND RARELY BY MULTIPLE PETECHIAE OF THE SKIN AND MUCOUS MEMBRANES. DEATH DUE TO CIRCULATORY COLLAPSE AND BRONCHOPNEUMONIA, UREMIA OR DELAYED ESOPHAGEAL AND PYLORIC STENOSIS HAVE BEEN REPORTED. THE MEDIAN LETHAL DOSE REPORTED IN MAN IS 2-4 GRAMS. PATHOLOGIC FINDINGS INCLUDE GLOMERULAR AND TUBULAR NECROSIS. **CHRONIC EXPOSURE-** REPEATED OR PROLONGED INGESTION MAY CAUSE IODISM. THIS SYNDROME IS CHARACTERIZED BY A BURNING SENSATION IN THE MOUTH AND THROAT, BRASSY TASTE, GASTROINTESTINAL IRRITATION AND DIARRHEA, SALIVATION, GINGIVITIS, SNEEZING, RHINITIS, RHINORRHEA, HEADACHE, FEVER, LARYNGITIS, PHARYNGITIS, BRONCHITIS, COUGH, STOMATITIS, PAROTITIS, EDEMA OF THE GLOTTIS, POSSIBLY PULMONARY EDEMA, SLEEPLESSNESS, TREMOR, TACHYCARDIA, NERVOUS SYMPTOMS, ANOREXIA, AND WEIGHT LOSS. VARIOUS SKIN RASHES INCLUDING VESICULAR, VEGETATIVE, MACULOPAPULAR, ACNE-FORM, BULLOUS ERUPTIONS AND POSSIBLY FATAL IODODERMA HAVE BEEN REPORTED. IN HYPERSENSITIVE INDIVIDUALS, IODISM MAY BE PRECIPITATED BY SMALL DOSES. LACRIMATION. EDEMA OF THE EYELIDS, AND CONJUNCTIVAL HYPERMIA MAY OCCUR. REPRODUCTIVE EFFECTS HAVE BEEN REPORTED IN ANIMALS.

FIRST AID- GIVE MILK, ABSORB REMAINING IODINE WITH STARCH SOLUTION MADE BY ADDING 15 GRAMS OF CORNSTARCH OR FLOUR TO 500 ML OF WATER. EMESIS AND LAVAGE ARE NOT INDICATED IN THE PRESENCE OF ESOPHAGEAL INJURY. GIVE MILK EVERY 15 MINUTES TO RELIEVE GASTRIC IRRITATION. (DREISBACH, HANDBOOK OF POISONING, 11TH EDITION).

ANTIDOTE: THE FOLLOWING ANTIDOTE HAS BEEN RECOMMENDED. HOWEVER, THE DECISION AS TO WHETHER THE SEVERITY OF POISONING REQUIRES ADMINISTRATION OF ANY ANTIDOTE AND ACTUAL DOSE REQUIRED SHOULD BE MADE BY QUALIFIED MEDICAL PERSONNEL.
FOR IODINE AND IODINE-RELEASING COMPOUNDS (NOT IODIDE): GIVE SODIUM THIOSULFATE, 100 ML OF 1% SOLUTION ORALLY, TO IMMEDIATELY REDUCE IODINE TO IODIDE (DREISBACH, HANDBOOK OF POISONING, 11TH ED.). ANTIDOTE SHOULD BE ADMINISTERED BY QUALIFIED MEDICAL PERSONNEL.

REACTIVITY

REACTIVITY: STABLE UNDER NORMAL TEMPERATURES AND PRESSURES.

INCOMPATIBILITIES: IODINE: ACETALDEHYDE: VIOLENT REACTION. ACETYLENE: EXPLOSIVE REACTION. ALUMINUM (POWERED): VIOLENT REACTION IN THE PRESENCE OF MOISTURE. AMMONIA OR SOME DERIVATIVES: MAY FORM EXPLOSIVE SALT. BORON: SPONTANEOUS REACTION AT ELEVATED TEMPERATURES. CESIUM OXIDE: INCANDESCENT REACTION AT ELEVATED TEMPERATURES. DIPROPYLMERCURY: VIOLENT REACTION. ETHANOL + PHOSPHOROUS: DANGEROUS REACTION. FORMAMIDE, PYRIDINE + SULFUR TRIOXIDE: PROLONGED STORAGE MAY RESULT IN DANGEROUS BUILDUP OF PRESSURE IN A CLOSED CONTAINER. HALOGENS AND INTERHALOGENS: IGNITE ON CONTACT. LITHIUM SILICIDE: IGNITES ON HEATING. MAGNESIUM: VIOLENT REACTION IN THE PRESENCE OF MOISTURE. MERCURY(II) AMIDE CHLORIDE + ETHANOL: DELAYED EXPLOSION. METAL ACETYLIDES: IGNITION OR INCANDESCENT REACTION AT ELEVATED OR AMBIENT TEMPERATURES. METALS AND ALLOYS: EXOTHERMIC REACTION WITH POSSIBLE IGNITION OR EXPLOSION. OXYGEN DIFLUORIDE: EXPLODES WHEN WARMED. PHOSPHOROUS: IGNITION. POLYACETYLENE: EXPLOSIVE DECOMPOSTION AT 113 C. SILVER AZIDE + ETHER: FORMS HIGHLY EXPLOSIVE IODINE AZIDE. SODIUM: FORMS SHOCK-SENSITIVE MIXTURE. SODIUM HYDRIDE: INCANDESCENT REACTION. SODIUM PHOSPHINATE: VIOLENT EXOTHERMIC REACTION AND IGNITION. TETRAAMINECOPPER(II) SULFATE + ETHANOL: FORMS EXPLOSIVE COMPOUND. TRIOXYGEN DIFLUORIDE: POSSIBLE IGNITION AND EXPLOSION. ZINC: VIOLENT REACTION IN THE PRESENCE OF MOISTURE.

DECOMPOSITION: THERMAL DECOMPOSITION PRODUCTS MAY INCLUDE TOXIC AND HAZARDOUS IODINE VAPORS AND IODIDE FUMES.

POLYMERIZATION: HAZARDOUS POLYMERIZATION HAS NOT BEEN REPORTED TO OCCUR UNDER NORMAL TEMPERATURES AND PRESSURES.

STORAGE AND DISPOSAL

OBSERVE ALL FEDERAL, STATE AND LOCAL REGULATIONS WHEN STORING OR DISPOSING OF THIS SUBSTANCE. FOR ASSISTANCE, CONTACT THE DISTRICT DIRECTOR OF THE ENVIRONMENTAL PROTECTION AGENCY.

STORAGE

CONSULT NFPA PUBLICATION 43A, STORAGE OF LIQUID AND SOLID OXIDIZING MATERIALS, FOR STORAGE REQUIREMENTS.
STORE AWAY FROM INCOMPATIBLE SUBSTANCES.

DISPOSAL

DISPOSAL MUST BE IN ACCORDANCE WITH STANDARDS APPLICABLE TO GENERATORS OF HAZARDOUS WASTE, 40 CFR 262. EPA HAZARDOUS WASTE NUMBER D001. 100 POUND CERCLA SECTION 103 REPORTABLE QUANTITY.

CONDITIONS TO AVOID

MAY IGNITE OTHER COMBUSTIBLE MATERIALS (WOOD, PAPER, OIL, ETC.). REACTION WITH FUELS MAY BE VIOLENT. FLAMMABLE POISONOUS GASES MAY ACCUMULATE IN TANKS AND HOPPER CARS. RUNOFF TO SEWER MAY CREATE FIRE OR EXPLOSION HAZARD.

SPILL AND LEAK PROCEDURES

OCCUPATIONAL SPILL: KEEP COMBUSTIBLES (WOOD, PAPER, OIL, ETC.) AWAY FROM SPILLED MATERIAL. DO NOT TOUCH SPILLED MATERIAL. STOP LEAK IF YOU CAN DO IT WITHOUT RISK. USE WATER SPRAY TO REDUCE VAPORS. DO NOT GET WATER INSIDE CONTAINER. FOR SMALL DRY SPILLS, WITH CLEAN SHOVEL PLACE MATERIAL INTO CLEAN, DRY CONTAINER AND COVER. MOVE CONTAINERS FROM SPILL AREA. FOR SMALL LIQUID SPILLS, FLUSH AREA WITH FLOODING AMOUNTS OF WATER. FOR LARGER SPILLS, DIKE FAR AHEAD OF SPILL FOR LATER DISPOSAL. KEEP UNNECESSARY PEOPLE AWAY. ISOLATE HAZARD AREA AND DENY ENTRY.

PROTECTIVE EQUIPMENT

VENTILATION: PROVIDE LOCAL EXHAUST VENTILATION SYSTEM TO MEET PUBLISHED EXPOSURE LIMITS.

RESPIRATOR: THE FOLLOWING RESPIRATORS AND MAXIMUM USE CONCENTRATIONS ARE RECOMMENDATIONS BY THE U.S. DEPARTMENT OF HEALTH AND HUMAN SERVICES, NIOSH POCKET GUIDE TO CHEMICAL HAZARDS; NIOSH CRITERIA DOCUMENTS OR BY THE U.S. DEPARTMENT OF LABOR, 29 CFR 1910 SUBPART Z. THE SPECIFIC RESPIRATOR SELECTED MUST BE BASED ON CONTAMINATION LEVELS FOUND IN THE WORK PLACE, MUST NOT EXCEED THE WORKING LIMITS OF THE RESPIRATOR AND BE JOINTLY APPROVED BY THE NATIONAL INSTITUTE FOR OCCUPATIONAL SAFETY AND HEALTH AND THE MINE SAFETY AND HEALTH ADMINISTRATION (NIOSH-MSHA).

IODINE:

1 PPM- ANY SUPPLIED-AIR RESPIRATOR. ANY SELF-CONTAINED BREATHING APPARATUS.

2.5 PPM- ANY SUPPLIED-AIR RESPIRATOR OPERATED IN CONTINUOUS-FLOW MODE.

5 PPM- ANY SUPPLIED-AIR RESPIRATOR WITH A FULL FACEPIECE. ANY SELF-CONTAINED BREATHING APPARATUS WITH A FULL FACEPIECE.

10 PPM- ANY SUPPLIED-AIR RESPIRATOR WITH A FULL FACEPIECE AND OPERATED IN PRESSURE-DEMAND OR OTHER POSITIVE PRESSURE MODE.

ESCAPE- ANY AIR-PURIFYING FULL FACEPIECE RESPIRATOR (GAS MASK) WITH A CHIN-STYLE OF FRONT OR BACK-MOUNTED ACID GAS CANISTER HAVING A HIGH-EFFICIENCY PARTICULATE FILTER. ANY APPROPRIATE ESCAPE-TYPE SELF-CONTAINED BREATHING APPARATUS.

FOR FIREFIGHTING AND OTHER IMMEDIATELY DANGEROUS TO LIFE OR HEALTH CONDITIONS:

SELF-CONTAINED BREATHING APPARATUS WITH FULL FACEPIECE OPERATED IN PRESSURE-DEMAND OR OTHER POSITIVE PRESSURE MODE.

SUPPLIED-AIR RESPIRATOR WITH FULL FACEPIECE AND OPERATED IN PRESSURE-DEMAND OR OTHER POSITIVE PRESSURE MODE IN COMBINATION WITH AN AUXILIARY SELF-CONTAINED BREATHING APPARATUS OPERATED IN PRESSURE-DEMAND OR OTHER POSITIVE PRESSURE MODE.

CLOTHING: EMPLOYEE MUST WEAR APPROPRIATE PROTECTIVE (IMPERVIOUS) CLOTHING AND EQUIPMENT TO PREVENT ANY POSSIBILITY OF SKIN CONTACT WITH THIS SUBSTANCE.

GLOVES: EMPLOYEE MUST WEAR APPROPRIATE PROTECTIVE GLOVES TO PREVENT CONTACT WITH THIS SUBSTANCE.

EYE PROTECTION: EMPLOYEE MUST WEAR SPLASH-PROOF OR DUST-RESISTANT SAFETY GOGGLES AND A FACESHIELD TO PREVENT CONTACT WITH THIS SUBSTANCE.

EMERGENCY WASH FACILITIES: WHERE THERE IS ANY POSSIBILITY THAT AN EMPLOYEE'S EYES AND/OR SKIN MAY BE EXPOSED TO THIS SUBSTANCE, THE EMPLOYER SHOULD PROVIDE AN EYE WASH FOUNTAIN AND QUICK DRENCH SHOWER WITHIN THE IMMEDIATE WORK AREA FOR EMERGENCY USE.

AUTHORIZED BY- OCCUPATIONAL HEALTH SERVICES, INC.

CREATION DATE: 10/04/89 ***REVISION DATE:*** 03/28/90

MATERIAL SAFETY DATA SHEET

OCCUPATIONAL HEALTH SERVICES, INC.
AGRICULTURE AND PESTICIDE DIVISION
450 SEVENTH AVENUE, SUITE 2407
NEW YORK, NEW YORK 10123
1-800-445-MSDS OR (212) 967-1100

EMERGENCY CONTACT:
JOHN S. BRANSFORD, JR. (615) 292-1180

SUBSTANCE IDENTIFICATION

CAS-NUMBER 1689-83-4

SUBSTANCE: **IOXYNIL**

TRADE NAMES/SYNONYMS: BENZONITRILE, 4-HYDROXY-3,5-DIIODO-; 4-HYDROXY-3,5-DIIODOBENZONITRILE; 4-HYDROXY-3,5-DIIODOPHENYL CYANIDE; 4-CYANO-2,6-DIIODOPHENOL; BENZONITRILE, 3,5-DIIODO-4-HYDROXY; ACTRIL; ACTRILAWN; ACP 63-303; BENTROL; JOXYNIL; M&B 8873; TREVESPAN; TOXYNIL; C7H3I2NO; PST11468

CHEMICAL FAMILY: NITRILE, AROMATIC HALOGEN

MOLECULAR FORMULA: (I2)-(H-O)-C6-H2-(C-N)

MOLECULAR WEIGHT: 370.92

CERCLA RATINGS (SCALE 0-3): HEALTH=3 FIRE=1 REACTIVITY=0 PERSISTENCE=1

NFPA RATINGS (SCALE 0-4): HEALTH=U FIRE=1 REACTIVITY=0

COMPONENTS AND CONTAMINANTS

COMPONENT: IOXYNIL ***PERCENT:*** 100.0

CAS# 1689-83-4

OTHER CONTAMINANTS: NONE

EXPOSURE LIMITS: NO OCCUPATIONAL EXPOSURE LIMITS ESTABLISHED BY OSHA, ACGIH, OR NIOSH.

PHYSICAL DATA

DESCRIPTION: ODORLESS, COLORLESS TO WHITE CRYSTALLINE SOLID.

MELTING POINT: 392-408 F (200-209 C) (DECOMPOSES)

SPECIFIC GRAVITY: NOT AVAILABLE ***VAPOR PRESSURE:*** NEGLIGIBLE

SOLUBILITY IN WATER: 50 PPM @ 25 C

SOLVENT SOLUBILITY: SOLUBLE IN CYCLOHEXANONE, TETRAHYDROFURAN, METHYL CELLOSOLVE, DIMETHYLFORMAMIDE; MODERATELY SOLUBLE IN ACETONE, ETHANOL, METHANOL, CHLOROFORM, ETHYLENE GLYCOL, PROPYLENE GLYCOL; VERY SLIGHTLY SOLUBLE IN CARBON TETRACHLORIDE. SUBLIMES @ APROXIMATELY 284 F (140 C) @ 0.1 MMHG

FIRE AND EXPLOSION DATA

FIRE AND EXPLOSION HAZARD: SLIGHT FIRE HAZARD WHEN EXPOSED TO HEAT OR FLAME.

DUST-AIR MIXTURES MAY IGNITE OR EXPLODE.

FIREFIGHTING MEDIA: DRY CHEMICAL, CARBON DIOXIDE, HALON, WATER SPRAY OR STANDARD FOAM (1987 EMERGENCY RESPONSE GUIDEBOOK, DOT P 5800.4). FOR LARGER FIRES, USE WATER SPRAY, FOG OR STANDARD FOAM (1987 EMERGENCY RESPONSE GUIDEBOOK, DOT P 5800.4).

FIREFIGHTING: MOVE CONTAINERS FROM FIRE AREA IF POSSIBLE (1987 EMERGENCY RESPONSE GUIDEBOOK, DOT P 5800.4, GUIDE PAGE 53).

EXTINGUISH USING AGENT SUITABLE FOR TYPE OF SURROUNDING FIRE. AVOID BREATHING VAPORS AND DUSTS. KEEP UPWIND.

TOXICITY

IOXYNIL: TOXICITY DATA: >3 MG/L/6 HOURS INHALATION-RAT LC50 (85JFAN); >2000 MG/KG SKIN-RAT LD50 (85JFAN); 210 UG/KG SKIN-RAT LDLO; 28 MG/KG ORAL-HUMAN LDLO; 110 MG/KG ORAL-RAT LD50; 230 MG/KG ORAL-MOUSE LD50; 180 MG/KG ORAL-RABBIT LD50; 76 MG/KG ORAL-GUINEA PIG LD50; 75 MG/KG ORAL-CAT LD50; 56 MG/KG INTRAVENOUS-MOUSE LD50. 230 UG/KG UNREPORTED-MOUSE LD50; 120 MG/KG UNREPORTED-MAMMAL LD50. CARCINOGEN STATUS: NONE. ACUTE TOXICITY LEVEL: TOXIC BY INGESTION. TARGET EFFECTS: NO DATA AVAILABLE. ADDITIONAL DATA: SOME NITRILES RELEASE HIGHLY TOXIC CYANIDE IN THE BODY.

HEALTH EFFECTS AND FIRST AID

INHALATION: IOXYNIL: **ACUTE EXPOSURE-** THE LC50 REPORTED IN RATS WAS GREATER THAN 3 MG/L/6 HOURS. **CHRONIC EXPOSURE-** EFFECTS OF INORDINANT SWEATING AND THIRST, FEVER, HEADACHE, DIZZINESS, VOMITING, ASTHENIA, WEIGHT LOSS, AND MYALGIA OF THE LEGS WERE REPORTED FROM A CASE OF OCCUPATIONAL EXPOSURE TO IOXYNIL AND BROMOXYNIL. THE ONSET OF THESE EFFECTS WERE INSIDIOUS. LABORATORY TESTS REVEALED TRANSITORY ELEVATION OF CREATININE PHOSPHOKINASE, LDH, ALDOLASE, SGOT. REMOVAL OF THE AFFECTED MEN FROM EXPOSURE RESULTED IN PROMPT RECOVERY.

FIRST AID- REMOVE FROM EXPOSURE. IF BREATHING HAS STOPPED OR IS DEPRESSED, GIVE ARTIFICIAL RESPIRATION. MAINTAIN AIRWAY AND ADMINISTER

OXYGEN TO MAINTAIN HIGH BLOOD/OXYGEN TENSION. GET MEDICAL ATTENTION IMMEDIATELY. (DREISBACH, HANDBOOK OF POISONING, 11TH ED.).

SKIN CONTACT: IOXYNIL: **ACUTE EXPOSURE-** THIS MATERIAL WAS SLIGHTLY IRRITATING TO RABBIT SKIN. **CHRONIC EXPOSURE-** EFFECTS OF INORDINANT SWEATING AND THIRST, FEVER, HEADACHE, DIZZINESS, VOMITING, ASTHENIA, WEIGHT LOSS, AND MYALGIA OF THE LEGS WERE REPORTED FROM A CASE OF OCCUPATIONAL EXPOSURE TO IOXYNIL AND BROMOXYNIL. THE ONSET OF THESE EFFECTS WERE INSIDIOUS. LABORATORY TESTS REVEALED TRANSITORY ELEVATION OF CREATININE PHOSPHOKINASE, LDH, ALDOLASE, AND SGOT. REMOVAL OF THE AFFECTED MEN FROM EXPOSURE RESULTED IN PROMPT RECOVERY.

FIRST AID- REMOVE CONTAMINATED CLOTHING AND SHOES AND WASH AFFECTED AREAS WITH SOAP OR MILD DETERGENT AND LARGE AMOUNTS OF WATER, TAKING CARE NOT TO CONTACT THE CHEMICAL. GET MEDICAL ATTENTION IMMEDIATELY. (CAIN, EMERGENCY TREATMENT AND MANAGEMENT, 7TH ED.).

EYE CONTACT: IOXYNIL: **ACUTE EXPOSURE-** THIS MATERIAL WAS SLIGHTLY IRRITATING TO RABBIT EYES. **CHRONIC EXPOSURE-** NO DATA AVAILABLE.

FIRST AID- WASH EYES IMMEDIATELY WITH LARGE AMOUNTS OF WATER OR NORMAL SALINE, OCCASIONALLY LIFTING UPPER AND LOWER LIDS, UNTIL NO EVIDENCE OF CHEMICAL REMAINS (APPROXIMATELY 15-20 MINUTES). GET MEDICAL ATTENTION IMMEDIATELY.

INGESTION: IOXYNIL: TOXIC. **ACUTE EXPOSURE-** HYPEREMIA OF ALL ORGANS AND EDEMA OF THE LUNGS AND BRAIN WERE DETERMINED BY AN AUTOPSY OF A MAN WHO INGESTED APPROXIMATELY 43 MG/KG IOXYNIL IN COMBINATION WITH ALCOHOL. SOME NITRILES MAY CAUSE CYANIDE POISONING WITH DIZZINESS, RAPID RESPIRATION, VOMITING, FLUSHING, HEADACHE, DROWSINESS, DROP IN BLOOD PRESSURE, RAPID PULSE, CYANOSIS, UNCONSCIOUSNESS, CONVULSIONS, AND DEATH. **CHRONIC EXPOSURE-** REPEATED INGESTION OF SMALL AMOUNTS OF IODINE COMPOUNDS MAY CAUSE IODISM CHARACTERIZED BY ERYTHEMA, CONJUNCTIVITIS, STOMATITIS, ACNE, RHINORRHEA, URTICARIA, PAROTITIS, ANOREXIA, WEIGHT LOSS, SLEEPLESSNESS, AND NERVOUS SYMPTOMS.

FIRST AID- IF PATIENT IS ASYMPTOMATIC ADMINISTER SYRUP OF IPECAC AND/OR PERFORM GASTRIC LAVAGE, USING TAP WATER, DILUTE SODIUM BICARBONATE SOLUTION OR PREFERABLY, IF AVAILABLE, DILUTE POTASSIUM PERMANGANATE SOLUTION (1:5000). ACTIVATED CHARCOAL IS INEFFECTIVE. IF BREATHING HAS STOPPED, GIVE ARTIFICIAL RESPIRATION. MAINTAIN AIRWAY. OXYGEN THERAPY MAY BE OF VALUE IN COMBINATION WITH THE ANTIDOTE (GOSSELIN, CLINICAL TOXICOLOGY OF COMMERCIAL PRODUCTS, 5TH ED.). TREATMENT SHOULD BE PERFORMED BY QUALIFIED MEDICAL PERSONNEL. GET MEDICAL ATTENTION IMMEDIATELY.

ANTIDOTE: THE FOLLOWING ANTIDOTE HAS BEEN RECOMMENDED. HOWEVER, THE DECISION AS TO WHETHER THE SEVERITY OF POISONING REQUIRES ADMINISTRATION OF ANY ANTIDOTE AND ACTUAL DOSE REQUIRED SHOULD BE MADE BY QUALIFIED MEDICAL PERSONNEL.

FOR CYANIDE POISONING: IF SYMPTOMS OF CYANIDE POISONING ARE EVIDENT, ADMINISTER IMMEDIATELY BEFORE ANY OTHER FIRST AID MEASURES.

ADMINISTER AMYL NITRITE (AMYL NITRITE PERLES) BY INHALATION FOR 15 TO 30 SECONDS OF EVERY MINUTE, WHILE SODIUM NITRITE SOLUTION IS BEING PREPARED. DISCONTINUE AMYL NITRITE AND IMMEDIATELY INJECT 10 ML OF A 3% SOLUTION OF SODIUM NITRITE INTRAVENOUSLY OVER A PERIOD OF 2 TO 4 MINUTES. IF NECESSARY, INJECT A NON-STERILE SOLUTION. DO NOT REMOVE THE NEEDLE. CAUTION: APPROPRIATE ADJUSTMENTS IN THE DOSE SHOULD BE MADE ON A BODY WEIGHT BASIS. THROUGH THE SAME NEEDLE, INFUSE INTRAVENOUSLY 50 ML OF A 25% AQUEOUS SOLUTION OF SODIUM THIOSULFATE. THE INJECTION SHOULD TAKE ABOUT 10 MINUTES. OTHER CONCENTRATIONS (5 TO 50%) ARE PERMISSIBLE IF THE TOTAL DOSE IS HELD AT APPROXIMATELY 12 GRAMS.

OXYGEN THERAPY MAY BE OF VALUE IN COMBINATION WITH NITRITE AND SODIUM THIOSULFATE THERAPY. IF SYMPTOMS RECUR, THE INJECTIONS OF NITRITE AND THIOSULFATE MAY BE REPEATED AT HALF THE ABOVE DOSES. IN VERY SEVERE POISONINGS IT IS SAFER AND PERHAPS MORE EFFICIENT TO KEEP REPEATING THE THIOSULFATE INJECTIONS INSTEAD OF THE NITRITE (GOSSELIN, SMITH, HODGE, CLINICAL TOXICOLOGY OF COMMERCIAL PRODUCTS, 5TH ED.).

ANTIDOTE SHOULD BE ADMINISTERED BY QUALIFIED MEDICAL PERSONNEL.

REACTIVITY

REACTIVITY: STABLE UNDER NORMAL TEMPERATURES AND PRESSURES.

INCOMPATIBILITIES: IOXYNIL: OXIDIZERS (STRONG): FIRE AND EXPLOSION HAZARD.

DECOMPOSITION: THERMAL DECOMPOSITION PRODUCTS MAY INCLUDE TOXIC AND HAZARDOUS FUMES OF IODINE AND CYANIDE AND OXIDES OF CARBON AND NITROGEN.

POLYMERIZATION: HAZARDOUS POLYMERIZATION HAS NOT BEEN REPORTED TO OCCUR UNDER NORMAL TEMPERATURES AND PRESSURES.

STORAGE AND DISPOSAL

OBSERVE ALL FEDERAL, STATE AND LOCAL REGULATIONS WHEN STORING OR DISPOSING OF THIS SUBSTANCE. FOR ASSISTANCE, CONTACT THE DISTRICT DIRECTOR OF THE ENVIRONMENTAL PROTECTION AGENCY.

****STORAGE****

STORE IN ACCORDANCE WITH 40 CFR 165 RECOMMENDED PROCEDURES FOR THE DISPOSAL AND STORAGE OF PESTICIDES AND PESTICIDE CONTAINERS.

STORE AWAY FROM INCOMPATIBLE SUBSTANCES.

****DISPOSAL****

DISPOSAL MUST BE IN ACCORDANCE WITH 40 CFR 165 RECOMMENDED PROCEDURES FOR THE DISPOSAL AND STORAGE OF PESTICIDES AND PESTICIDE CONTAINERS.

CONDITIONS TO AVOID

MAY BURN BUT DOES NOT IGNITE READILY.

SPILL AND LEAK PROCEDURES

OCCUPATIONAL SPILL: DO NOT TOUCH SPILLED MATERIAL. STOP LEAK IF YOU CAN DO IT WITHOUT RISK. FOR SMALL SPILLS, TAKE UP WITH SAND OR OTHER ABSORBENT MATERIAL AND PLACE INTO CONTAINERS FOR LATER DISPOSAL. FOR SMALL DRY SPILLS, WITH A CLEAN SHOVEL PLACE MATERIAL INTO CLEAN, DRY CONTAINER AND COVER. MOVE CONTAINERS FROM SPILL AREA. FOR LARGER SPILLS, DIKE FAR AHEAD OF SPILL FOR LATER DISPOSAL. KEEP UNNECESSARY PEOPLE AWAY. ISOLATE HAZARD AREA AND DENY ENTRY.

PROTECTIVE EQUIPMENT

VENTILATION: PROVIDE LOCAL EXHAUST OR PROCESS ENCLOSURE VENTILATION SYSTEM.

RESPIRATOR: THE FOLLOWING RESPIRATORS ARE RECOMMENDED BASED ON INFORMATION FOUND IN THE PHYSICAL DATA, TOXICITY AND HEALTH EFFECTS SECTIONS. THEY ARE RANKED IN ORDER FROM MINIMUM TO MAXIMUM RESPIRATORY PROTECTION. THE SPECIFIC RESPIRATOR SELECTED MUST BE BASED ON CONTAMINATION LEVELS FOUND IN THE WORK PLACE, MUST NOT EXCEED THE WORKING LIMITS OF THE RESPIRATOR AND BE JOINTLY APPROVED BY THE NATIONAL INSTITUTE FOR OCCUPATIONAL SAFETY AND HEALTH AND THE MINE SAFETY AND HEALTH ADMINISTRATION (NIOSH-MSHA).

CHEMICAL CARTRIDGE RESPIRATOR WITH AN ORGANIC VAPOR CARTRIDGE(S) IN COMBINATION WITH A DUST AND MIST FILTER.

GAS MASK WITH ORGANIC VAPOR CANISTER (CHIN-STYLE OR FRONT- OR BACK-MOUNTED CANISTER) WITH A DUST AND MIST FILTER.

GAS MASK WITH ORGANIC VAPOR CANISTER (CHIN-STYLE OR FRONT- OR BACK-MOUNTED CANISTER) WITH A PARTICULATE FILTER.

POWERED AIR-PURIFYING RESPIRATOR WITH A HIGH-EFFICIENCY FILTER.

TYPE 'C' SUPPLIED-AIR RESPIRATOR WITH A FULL FACEPIECE OPERATED IN A PRESSURE-DEMAND OR OTHER POSITIVE PRESSURE MODE.

SELF-CONTAINED BREATHING APPARATUS WITH A FULL FACEPIECE OPERATED IN PRESSURE-DEMAND OR OTHER POSITIVE PRESSURE MODE.

FOR FIREFIGHTING AND OTHER IMMEDIATELY DANGEROUS TO LIFE OR HEALTH CONDITIONS:

SELF-CONTAINED BREATHING APPARATUS WITH FULL FACEPIECE OPERATED IN PRESSURE-DEMAND OR OTHER POSITIVE PRESSURE MODE.

SUPPLIED-AIR RESPIRATOR WITH FULL FACEPIECE AND OPERATED IN PRESSURE-DEMAND OR OTHER POSITIVE PRESSURE MODE IN COMBINATION WITH AN AUXILIARY SELF-CONTAINED BREATHING APPARATUS OPERATED IN PRESSURE-DEMAND OR OTHER POSITIVE PRESSURE MODE.

CLOTHING: EMPLOYEE MUST WEAR APPROPRIATE PROTECTIVE (IMPERVIOUS) CLOTHING AND EQUIPMENT TO PREVENT REPEATED OR PROLONGED SKIN CONTACT WITH THIS SUBSTANCE.

GLOVES: EMPLOYEE MUST WEAR APPROPRIATE PROTECTIVE GLOVES TO PREVENT CONTACT WITH THIS SUBSTANCE.

EYE PROTECTION: EMPLOYEE MUST WEAR SPLASH-PROOF OR DUST-RESISTANT SAFETY GOGGLES TO PREVENT EYE CONTACT WITH THIS SUBSTANCE.

EMERGENCY EYE WASH: WHERE THERE IS ANY POSSIBILITY THAT AN EMPLOYEE'S EYES MAY BE EXPOSED TO THIS SUBSTANCE, THE EMPLOYER SHOULD PROVIDE AN EYE WASH FOUNTAIN WITHIN THE IMMEDIATE WORK AREA FOR EMERGENCY USE.

AUTHORIZED BY- OCCUPATIONAL HEALTH SERVICES, INC.

CREATION DATE: 05/23/90 ***REVISION DATE:*** 05/23/90

MATERIAL SAFETY DATA SHEET

OCCUPATIONAL HEALTH SERVICES, INC.
AGRICULTURE AND PESTICIDE DIVISION
450 SEVENTH AVENUE, SUITE 2407
NEW YORK, NEW YORK 10123
1-800-445-MSDS OR (212) 967-1100

EMERGENCY CONTACT:
JOHN S. BRANSFORD, JR. (615) 292-1180

SUBSTANCE IDENTIFICATION

CAS-NUMBER 465-73-6

SUBSTANCE: **ISODRIN**

TRADE NAMES/SYNONYMS: 1,4:5,8-DIMETHANONAPHTHALENE, 1,2,3,4,10,10-HEXACHLORO-1,4,4A,5,8, 8A-HEXAHYDRO-, (1 ALPHA, 4 ALPHA, 4A BETA, 5 BETA, 8 BETA, 8A BETA)-; 1,4:5,8-DIMETHANONAPHTHALENE, 1,2,3,4,10,10-HEXACHLORO-1,4,4A,5,8, 8A-HEXAHYDRO-, ENDO, ENDO; (1R,4S,5R,8S)-1,2,3,4,10,10-HEXACHLORO-1,4,4A,5,8,8A-HEXAHYDRO-1,4: 5,8-DIMETHANONAPHTHALENE; (1 ALPHA, 4 ALPHA 4A BETA, 5 BETA, 8 BETA, 8A BETA)-1,2,3,4,10,10 -HEXACHLORO-1,4,4A,5,8,8A-HEXAHYDRO-1,4:5,8-DIMETHANONAPHTHALENE; ENDO,ENDO-1,2,3,4,10,10-HEXACHLORO-1,4,4A,5,8,8A-HEXAHYDRO-1,4:5,8 DIMETHANONAPHTHALENE; 1,2,3,4,10,10-HEXACHLORO-1,4,4A,5,8,8A-HEXAHYDRO-1,4-ENDO,ENDO-5,8 -DIMETHANONAPHTHALENE; HEXACHLORO-HEXAHYDRO-ENDO,ENDO-DIMETHANONAPHTHALENE; 1,2,3,4,10,10-HEXACHLORO-1,4,4A,5,8,8A-HEXAHYDRO-1,4:5,8 -DIMETHANONAPHTHALENE; COMPOUND 711; SD 3418; ENT 19,244; RCRA P060; C12H8CL6; PST11810

CHEMICAL FAMILY: HALOGEN COMPOUND, ALICYCLIC

MOLECULAR FORMULA: C12-H8-CL6

MOLECULAR WEIGHT: 364.93

CERCLA RATINGS (SCALE 0-3): HEALTH=3 FIRE=0 REACTIVITY=0 PERSISTENCE=3

NFPA RATINGS (SCALE 0-4): HEALTH=4 FIRE=0 REACTIVITY=0

COMPONENTS AND CONTAMINANTS

COMPONENT: ISODRIN ***PERCENT:*** 100
CAS# 465-73-6

OTHER CONTAMINANTS: NONE

EXPOSURE LIMITS: NO OCCUPATIONAL EXPOSURE LIMITS ESTABLISHED BY OSHA, ACGIH, OR NIOSH.
ISODRIN: 100/10,000 POUNDS SARA SECTION 302 THRESHOLD PLANNING QUANTITY 1 POUND SARA SECTION 304 REPORTABLE QUANTITY 1 POUND CERCLA SECTION 103 REPORTABLE QUANTITY

PHYSICAL DATA

DESCRIPTION: CRYSTALS ***BOILING POINT:*** NOT AVAILABLE

MELTING POINT: 462-466 F (239-241 C) ***SPECIFIC GRAVITY:*** NOT AVAILABLE

SOLUBILITY IN WATER: NOT AVAILABLE

FIRE AND EXPLOSION DATA

FIRE AND EXPLOSION HAZARD: NEGLIGIBLE FIRE HAZARD WHEN EXPOSED TO HEAT OR FLAME.

FIREFIGHTING MEDIA: DRY CHEMICAL, CARBON DIOXIDE, HALON, WATER SPRAY OR STANDARD FOAM (1987 EMERGENCY RESPONSE GUIDEBOOK, DOT P 5800.4).
FOR LARGER FIRES, USE WATER SPRAY, FOG OR STANDARD FOAM (1987 EMERGENCY RESPONSE GUIDEBOOK, DOT P 5800.4).

FIREFIGHTING: NO ACUTE HAZARD. MOVE CONTAINER FROM FIRE AREA IF POSSIBLE. AVOID BREATHING VAPORS OR DUSTS; KEEP UPWIND.

TRANSPORTATION DATA

DEPARTMENT OF TRANSPORTATION HAZARD CLASSIFICATION 49 CFR 172.101: POISON B
DEPARTMENT OF TRANSPORTATION LABELING REQUIREMENTS 49 CFR 172.101 AND SUBPART E: POISON
DEPARTMENT OF TRANSPORTATION PACKAGING REQUIREMENTS: 49 CFR 173.376 EXCEPTIONS: 49 CFR 173.364

TOXICITY

ISODRIN: TOXICITY DATA: 23 MG/KG SKIN-RAT LD50; 7 MG/KG ORAL-RAT LD50; 8800 UG/KG ORAL-MOUSE LD50; 6400 UG/KG INTRAPERITONEAL-MOUSE LDLO; 7 MG/KG UNREPORTED-MAMMAL LD50. CARCINOGEN STATUS: NONE. ACUTE TOXICITY LEVEL: HIGHLY TOXIC BY DERMAL ABSORPTION AND INGESTION. TARGET EFFECTS: CONVULSANT. POISONING MAY AFFECT THE LIVER AND KIDNEY. ADDITIONAL DATA: ISODRIN IS A CHLORINATED CYCLODIENE PESTICIDE. THESE PESTICIDES ARE STORED IN THE ADIPOSE TISSUE; SOME ARE STORED FOR WEEKS TO SEVERAL MONTHS BEFORE THEY ARE ELIMINATED FROM THE BODY. INTENSE ACTIVITY AND STARVATION MAY MOBILIZE THE PESTICIDE RESULTING IN THE REAPPEARANCE OF TOXIC SYMPTOMS. THEY MAY BE EXCRETED IN THE MILK OF LACTATING WOMEN. STIMULANTS SUCH AS EPINEPHRINE MAY INDUCE VENTRICULAR FIBRILLATION.

HEALTH EFFECTS AND FIRST AID

INHALATION: ISODRIN: CONVULSANT. **ACUTE EXPOSURE-** ISODRIN IS A CHLORINATED CYCLODIENE PESTICIDE. THESE PESTICIDES ARE ABSORBED FROM THE LUNGS AND MAY PRODUCE CENTRAL NERVOUS SYSTEM EFFECTS WITH SYMPTOMS OF MOTOR HYPEREXCITABILITY THAT MAY INCLUDE MUSCLE TWITCHING, MYOCLONIC JERKING, AND CONVULSIVE SEIZURES. THE CONVULSIONS MAY OCCUR WITH PERIODS OF UNCONSCIOUSNESS. OTHER SYMPTOMS MAY INCLUDE HEADACHE, NAUSEA, VOMITING, MALAISE, AND DIZZINESS. IN CASES OF GROSS OVEREXPOSURE, CONVULSIONS MAY OCCUR WITHOUT ANY PRIOR SYMPTOMS. ABNORMAL EEG PATTERNS MAY BE OBSERVED; THESE CHANGES IN EEG PATTERNS MAY PERSIST FOR WEEKS OR MONTHS WHILE NO OTHER OBSERVABLE SIGNS OF POISONING MAY EXIST. **CHRONIC EXPOSURE-** PROLONGED OR REPEATED EXPOSURE TO CHLORINATED CYCLODIENE PESTICIDES MAY RESULT IN THE ACCUMULATION OF THE PESTICIDE IN THE BLOOD RESULTING IN A PROGRESSION OF THE SYMPTOMS LISTED ABOVE OR IN A SUDDEN ONSET OF SYMPTOMS AFTER AN ACUTE EXPOSURE. IN ADDITION TO SYMPTOMS LISTED ABOVE, HYPERIRRITABILITY, DROWSINESS, AND ANOREXIA MAY OCCUR.

FIRST AID- REMOVE FROM EXPOSURE AREA TO FRESH AIR IMMEDIATELY. IF BREATHING HAS STOPPED, PERFORM ARTIFICIAL RESPIRATION. KEEP PERSON WARM AND AT REST. TREAT SYMPTOMATICALLY AND SUPPORTIVELY. GET MEDICAL ATTENTION IMMEDIATELY.

SKIN CONTACT: ISODRIN: CONVULSANT/HIGHLY TOXIC. **ACUTE EXPOSURE-** A LETHAL DOSE IN RATS BY DERMAL ABSORPTION WAS 23 MG/KG. CHLORINATED CYCLODIENE PESTICIDES ARE ABSORBED FROM THE SKIN AND MAY PRODUCE CENTRAL NERVOUS SYSTEM EFFECTS WITH SYMPTOMS OF MOTOR HYPEREXCITABILITY THAT MAY INCLUDE MUSCLE TWITCHING, MYOCLONIC JERKING, AND CONVULSIVE SEIZURES. THE CONVULSIONS MAY OCCUR WITH PERIODS OF UNCONSCIOUSNESS. OTHER SYMPTOMS MAY INCLUDE HEADACHE, NAUSEA, VOMITING, MALAISE, AND DIZZINESS. IN CASES OF GROSS OVEREXPOSURE, CONVULSIONS MAY OCCUR WITHOUT ANY PRIOR SYMPTOMS. ABNORMAL EEG PATTERNS MAY BE OBSERVED; THESE CHANGES IN EEG PATTERNS MAY PERSIST FOR WEEKS OR MONTHS WHILE NO OTHER OBSERVABLE SIGNS OF POISONING MAY EXIST. **CHRONIC EXPOSURE-** PROLONGED OR REPEATED EXPOSURE TO CHLORINATED CYCLODIENE PESTICIDES MAY RESULT IN THE ACCUMULATION OF THE PESTICIDE IN THE BLOOD RESULTING IN A PROGRESSION OF THE SYMPTOMS LISTED ABOVE OR IN A SUDDEN ONSET OF SYMPTOMS AFTER AN ACUTE EXPOSURE. IN ADDITION TO THE SYMPTOMS LISTED ABOVE HYPERIRRITABILITY, DROWSINESS, AND ANOREXIA MAY OCCUR.

FIRST AID- REMOVE CONTAMINATED CLOTHING AND SHOES IMMEDIATELY. WASH AFFECTED AREA WITH SOAP OR MILD DETERGENT AND LARGE AMOUNTS OF WATER UNTIL NO EVIDENCE OF CHEMICAL REMAINS (APPROXIMATELY 15-20 MINUTES). GET MEDICAL ATTENTION IMMEDIATELY.

EYE CONTACT: ISODRIN: **ACUTE EXPOSURE-** NO DATA AVAILABLE. **CHRONIC EXPOSURE-** NO DATA AVAILABLE.

FIRST AID- WASH EYES IMMEDIATELY WITH LARGE AMOUNTS OF WATER OR NORMAL SALINE, OCCASIONALLY LIFTING UPPER AND LOWER LIDS, UNTIL NO EVIDENCE OF CHEMICAL REMAINS (APPROXIMATELY 15-20 MINUTES). GET MEDICAL ATTENTION IMMEDIATELY.

INGESTION: ISODRIN: CONVULSANT/HIGHLY TOXIC. **ACUTE EXPOSURE-** A LETHAL DOSE IN RATS WAS 7 MG/KG. CHLORINATED CYCLODIENE PESTICIDES MAY PRODUCE CENTRAL NERVOUS SYSTEM EFFECTS WITH SYMPTOMS OF MOTOR HYPEREXCITABILITY THAT MAY INCLUDE MUSCLE TWITCHING, MYOCLONIC JERKING, AND CONVULSIVE SEIZURES. THE CONVULSIONS MAY OCCUR WITH PERIODS OF UNCONSCIOUSNESS. OTHER SYMPTOMS MAY INCLUDE HEADACHE, NAUSEA, VOMITING, MALAISE, AND DIZZINESS. IN CASES OF GROSS OVEREXPOSURE, CONVULSIONS MAY OCCUR WITHOUT ANY PRIOR SYMPTOMS. ABNORMAL EEG PATTERNS MAY BE OBSERVED; THESE CHANGES IN EEG PATTERNS MAY PERSIST FOR WEEKS OR MONTHS WHILE NO OTHER OBSERVABLE SIGNS OF POISONING MAY EXIST. **CHRONIC EXPOSURE-** PROLONGED OR REPEATED EXPOSURE TO CHLORINATED CYCLODIENE PESTICIDES MAY RESULT IN A PROGRESSION OF THE SYMPTOMS LISTED ABOVE OR IN A SUDDEN ONSET OF SYMPTOMS AFTER AN ACUTE EXPOSURE. IN ADDITION TO SYMPTOMS LISTED ABOVE, HYPERIRRITABILITY, DROWSINESS, ANOREXIA, LIVER, AND KIDNEY DAMAGE MAY OCCUR.

FIRST AID- IF THE PERSON IS CONSCIOUS AND NOT CONVULSING, REMOVE BY GIVING SYRUP OF IPECAC (IF VOMITING OCCURS, KEEP THE HEAD BELOW THE HIPS TO PREVENT ASPIRATION). GIVE ACTIVATED CHARCOAL FOLLOWED BY GASTRIC LAVAGE. FOLLOW WITH A SALINE CATHARTIC. DO NOT GIVE FATS OR OILS. INTESTINAL LAVAGE WITH 20% MANNITOL (200 ML) BY STOMACH TUBE IS ALSO USEFUL. GIVE ARTIFICIAL RESPIRATION WITH OXYGEN IF RESPIRATION IS

DEPRESSED (DREISBACH, HANDBOOK OF POISONING, 12TH ED.). TREAT SYMPTOMATICALLY AND SUPPORTIVELY. LAVAGE AND ADMINISTRATION OF OXYGEN SHOULD BE PERFORMED BY QUALIFIED MEDICAL PERSONNEL. GET MEDICAL ATTENTION IMMEDIATELY.

ANTIDOTE: NO SPECIFIC ANTIDOTE. TREAT SYMPTOMATICALLY AND SUPPORTIVELY.

REACTIVITY

REACTIVITY: STABLE UNDER NORMAL TEMPERATURES AND PRESSURES.

INCOMPATIBILITIES: ISODRIN: NO DATA AVAILABLE.

DECOMPOSITION: THERMAL DECOMPOSITION MAY RELEASE TOXIC AND/OR HAZARDOUS GASES.

POLYMERIZATION: HAZARDOUS POLYMERIZATION HAS NOT BEEN REPORTED TO OCCUR UNDER NORMAL TEMPERATURES AND PRESSURES.

STORAGE AND DISPOSAL

OBSERVE ALL FEDERAL, STATE AND LOCAL REGULATIONS WHEN STORING OR DISPOSING OF THIS SUBSTANCE. FOR ASSISTANCE, CONTACT THE DISTRICT DIRECTOR OF THE ENVIRONMENTAL PROTECTION AGENCY.

STORAGE

STORE IN ACCORDANCE WITH 40 CFR 165 RECOMMENDED PROCEDURES FOR THE DISPOSAL AND STORAGE OF PESTICIDES AND PESTICIDE CONTAINERS.

THRESHOLD PLANNING QUANTITY (TPQ): THE SUPERFUND AMENDMENTS AND REAUTHORIZATION ACT (SARA) SECTION 302 REQUIRES THAT EACH FACILITY WHERE ANY EXTREMELY HAZARDOUS SUBSTANCE IS PRESENT IN A QUANTITY EQUAL TO OR GREATER THAN THE TPQ ESTABLISHED FOR THAT SUBSTANCE NOTIFY THE STATE EMERGENCY RESPONSE COMMISSION FOR THE STATE IN WHICH IT IS LOCATED. SECTION 303 OF SARA REQUIRES THESE FACILITIES TO PARTICIPATE IN LOCAL EMERGENCY RESPONSE PLANNING (40 CFR 355.30).

DISPOSAL

DISPOSAL MUST BE IN ACCORDANCE WITH STANDARDS APPLICABLE TO GENERATORS OF HAZARDOUS WASTE, 40CFR 262. EPA HAZARDOUS WASTE NUMBER P060.

CONDITIONS TO AVOID

NONE REPORTED.

SPILL AND LEAK PROCEDURES

OCCUPATIONAL SPILL: NO SPECIAL PRECAUTIONS INDICATED.

REPORTABLE QUANTITY (RQ): 1 POUND THE SUPERFUND AMENDMENTS AND REAUTHORIZATION ACT (SARA) SECTION 304 REQUIRES THAT A RELEASE EQUAL TO OR GREATER THAN THE REPORTABLE QUANTITY FOR THIS SUBSTANCE BE IMMEDIATELY REPORTED TO THE LOCAL EMERGENCY PLANNING COMMITTEE AND THE STATE EMERGENCY RESPONSE COMMISSION (40 CFR 355.40). IF THE RELEASE OF THIS SUBSTANCE IS REPORTABLE UNDER CERCLA SECTION 103, THE NATIONAL RESPONSE CENTER MUST BE NOTIFIED IMMEDIATELY AT (800) 424-8802 OR (202) 426-2675 IN THE METROPOLITAN WASHINGTON, D.C. AREA (40 CFR 302.6).

PROTECTIVE EQUIPMENT

VENTILATION: PROCESS ENCLOSURE RECOMMENDED.

RESPIRATOR: THE FOLLOWING RESPIRATORS ARE RECOMMENDED BASED ON INFORMATION FOUND IN THE PHYSICAL DATA, TOXICITY AND HEALTH EFFECTS SECTIONS. THEY ARE RANKED IN ORDER FROM MINIMUM TO MAXIMUM RESPIRATORY PROTECTION. THE SPECIFIC RESPIRATOR SELECTED MUST BE BASED ON CONTAMINATION LEVELS FOUND IN THE WORK PLACE, MUST NOT EXCEED THE WORKING LIMITS OF THE RESPIRATOR AND BE JOINTLY APPROVED BY THE NATIONAL INSTITUTE FOR OCCUPATIONAL SAFETY AND HEALTH AND THE MINE SAFETY AND HEALTH ADMINISTRATION (NIOSH-MSHA).

TYPE 'C' SUPPLIED-AIR RESPIRATOR WITH A FULL FACEPIECE OPERATED IN PRESSURE-DEMAND OR OTHER POSITIVE PRESSURE MODE OR WITH A FULL FACEPIECE, HELMET OR HOOD OPERATED IN CONTINOUS-FLOW MODE. SELF-CONTAINED BREATHING APPARATUS WITH A FULL FACEPIECE OPERATED IN PRESSURE-DEMAND OR OTHER POSITIVE PRESSURE MODE.

FOR FIREFIGHTING AND OTHER IMMEDIATELY DANGEROUS TO LIFE OR HEALTH CONDITIONS:

SELF-CONTAINED BREATHING APPARATUS WITH FULL FACEPIECE OPERATED IN PRESSURE-DEMAND OR OTHER POSITIVE PRESSURE MODE.

SUPPLIED-AIR RESPIRATOR WITH FULL FACEPIECE AND OPERATED IN PRESSURE-DEMAND OR OTHER POSITIVE PRESSURE MODE IN COMBINATION WITH AN AUXILIARY SELF-CONTAINED BREATHING APPARATUS OPERATED IN PRESSURE-DEMAND OR OTHER POSITIVE PRESSURE MODE.

CLOTHING: EMPLOYEE MUST WEAR APPROPRIATE PROTECTIVE (IMPERVIOUS) CLOTHING AND EQUIPMENT TO PREVENT ANY POSSIBILITY OF SKIN CONTACT WITH THIS SUBSTANCE.

GLOVES: EMPLOYEE MUST WEAR APPROPRIATE PROTECTIVE GLOVES TO PREVENT CONTACT WITH THIS SUBSTANCE.

EYE PROTECTION: EMPLOYEE MUST WEAR SPLASH-PROOF OR DUST-RESISTANT SAFETY GOGGLES AND A FACESHIELD TO PREVENT CONTACT WITH THIS SUBSTANCE.

EMERGENCY WASH FACILITIES: WHERE THERE IS ANY POSSIBILITY THAT AN EMPLOYEE'S EYES AND/OR SKIN MAY BE EXPOSED TO THIS SUBSTANCE, THE EMPLOYER SHOULD PROVIDE AN EYE WASH FOUNTAIN AND QUICK DRENCH SHOWER WITHIN THE IMMEDIATE WORK AREA FOR EMERGENCY USE.

AUTHORIZED BY- OCCUPATIONAL HEALTH SERVICES, INC.
CREATION DATE: 10/04/89 ***REVISION DATE:*** 03/28/90

MATERIAL SAFETY DATA SHEET

OCCUPATIONAL HEALTH SERVICES, INC.
AGRICULTURE AND PESTICIDE DIVISION
450 SEVENTH AVENUE, SUITE 2407
NEW YORK, NEW YORK 10123
1-800-445-MSDS OR (212) 967-1100

EMERGENCY CONTACT:
JOHN S. BRANSFORD, JR. (615) 292-1180

SUBSTANCE IDENTIFICATION

CAS-NUMBER 57052-04-7

SUBSTANCE: ISOMETHIOZIN

TRADE NAMES/SYNONYMS: 1,2,4-TRIAZIN-5(4H)-ONE, 6-(1,1-DIMETHYLETHYL)-4-((2-METHYLPROPYLIDENE)AMINO)-3-(METHYLTHIO)-; 6-(1,1-DIMETHYLETHYL)-4-((2-METHYLPROPYLIDENE)AMINO)-3-(METHYLTHIO) -1,2,4-TRIAZIN-5(4H)-ONE; 6-TERT-BUTYL-4-ISOBUTYLIDENEAMINO-3-METHYLTHIO-1,2,4-TRIAZIN-5(4H) -ONE; ISOMETHIOZINE; TANTIZON; DIC 1577; BAY DIC 1577; C12H20N4OS; PST11844

CHEMICAL FAMILY: TRIAZINE

MOLECULAR FORMULA: C12-H20-N4-O-S

CERCLA RATINGS (SCALE 0-3): HEALTH=1 FIRE=1 REACTIVITY=0 PERSISTENCE=2

NFPA RATINGS (SCALE 0-4): HEALTH=1 FIRE=1 REACTIVITY=0

COMPONENTS AND CONTAMINANTS

COMPONENT: ISOMETHIOZIN ***PERCENT:*** 100.0
CAS# 57052-04-7

OTHER CONTAMINANTS: NONE

EXPOSURE LIMITS: NO OCCUPATIONAL EXPOSURE LIMITS ESTABLISHED BY OSHA, ACGIH, OR NIOSH.

PHYSICAL DATA

DESCRIPTION: COLORLESS CRYSTALLINE SOLID. ***MELTING POINT:*** 318 F (159 C)

SPECIFIC GRAVITY: NOT AVAILABLE ***VAPOR PRESSURE:*** NEGLIGIBLE

SOLUBILITY IN WATER: ALMOST INSOLUBLE

SOLVENT SOLUBILITY: SLIGHTLY SOLUBLE IN CYCLOHEXANONE

FIRE AND EXPLOSION DATA

FIRE AND EXPLOSION HAZARD: SLIGHT FIRE HAZARD WHEN EXPOSED TO HEAT OR FLAME.

FIREFIGHTING MEDIA: DRY CHEMICAL, CARBON DIOXIDE, HALON, WATER SPRAY OR STANDARD FOAM (1987 EMERGENCY RESPONSE GUIDEBOOK, DOT P 5800.4).
FOR LARGER FIRES, USE WATER SPRAY, FOG OR STANDARD FOAM (1987 EMERGENCY RESPONSE GUIDEBOOK, DOT P 5800.4).

FIREFIGHTING: MOVE CONTAINERS FROM FIRE AREA IF POSSIBLE (1987 EMERGENCY RESPONSE GUIDEBOOK, DOT P 5800.4, GUIDE PAGE 53).
EXTINGUISH USING AGENTS SUITABLE FOR SURROUNDING FIRE. USE FLOODING QUANTITIES OF WATER AS A FOG. KEEP MATERIAL OUT OF SEWERS AND WATER SOURCES. DO NOT TOUCH SPILLED MATERIAL. AVOID BREATHING HAZARDOUS FUMES; KEEP UPWIND.

TOXICITY

ISOMETHIOZIN: TOXICITY DATA: >1000 MG/KG SKIN-RAT LD50 (FMCHA2); >10,000 MG/KG ORAL-RAT LD50 (FMCHA2). CARCINOGEN STATUS: NONE. ACUTE TOXICITY LEVEL: TOXIC BY DERMAL ABSORPTION, AND SLIGHTLY TOXIC BY INGESTION. TARGET EFFECTS: NO DATA AVAILABLE.

HEALTH EFFECTS AND FIRST AID

INHALATION: ISOMETHIOZIN: **ACUTE EXPOSURE-** SOME TRIAZINES ARE MILDLY IRRITATING TO THE UPPER RESPIRATORY TRACT. **CHRONIC EXPOSURE-** NO DATA AVAILABLE.

FIRST AID- REMOVE FROM EXPOSURE AREA TO FRESH AIR IMMEDIATELY. IF BREATHING HAS STOPPED, PERFORM ARTIFICIAL RESPIRATION. KEEP PERSON WARM AND AT REST. TREAT SYMPTOMATICALLY AND SUPPORTIVELY. GET MEDICAL ATTENTION IMMEDIATELY.

SKIN CONTACT: ISOMETHIOZIN: **ACUTE EXPOSURE-** A LETHAL DOSE IN RATS BY DERMAL ABSORPTION WAS GREATER THAN 1000 MG/KG. SOME TRIAZINES ARE MILDLY IRRITATING TO THE SKIN. **CHRONIC EXPOSURE-** NO DATA AVAILABLE.

FIRST AID- REMOVE CONTAMINATED CLOTHING AND SHOES IMMEDIATELY. WASH AFFECTED AREA WITH SOAP OR MILD DETERGENT AND LARGE AMOUNTS OF WATER UNTIL NO EVIDENCE OF CHEMICAL REMAINS (APPROXIMATELY 15-20 MINUTES). GET MEDICAL ATTENTION IMMEDIATELY.

EYE CONTACT: ISOMETHIOZIN: **ACUTE EXPOSURE-** SOME TRIAZINES ARE MILDLY IRRITATING TO THE EYES. **CHRONIC EXPOSURE-** NO DATA AVAILABLE.

FIRST AID- WASH EYES IMMEDIATELY WITH LARGE AMOUNTS OF WATER OR NORMAL SALINE, OCCASIONALLY LIFTING UPPER AND LOWER LIDS, UNTIL NO EVIDENCE OF CHEMICAL REMAINS (APPROXIMATELY 15-20 MINUTES). GET MEDICAL ATTENTION IMMEDIATELY.

INGESTION: ISOMETHIOZIN: **ACUTE EXPOSURE-** A LETHAL DOSE IN RATS WAS GREATER THAN 10,000 MG/KG. **CHRONIC EXPOSURE-** IN RATS THE NO-EFFECT LEVEL IN CHRONIC FEEDING STUDIES WAS 100 PPM.

FIRST AID- REMOVE BY GASTRIC LAVAGE AND CATHARSIS. MAINTAIN BLOOD PRESSURE AND AIRWAY. GIVE OXYGEN IF RESPIRATION IS DEPRESSED. DO NOT PERFORM GASTRIC LAVAGE IF VICTIM IS UNCONSCIOUS. GET MEDICAL ATTENTION IMMEDIATELY (DREISBACH, HANDBOOK OF POISONING, 12TH ED.). ADMINISTRATION OF LAVAGE OR OXYGEN SHOULD BE PERFORMED BY QUALIFIED MEDICAL PERSONNEL.

ANTIDOTE: NO SPECIFIC ANTIDOTE. TREAT SYMPTOMATICALLY AND SUPPORTIVELY.

REACTIVITY

REACTIVITY: STABLE UNDER NORMAL TEMPERATURES AND PRESSURES.

INCOMPATIBILITIES: ISOMETHIOZIN: NO DATA AVAILABLE.

DECOMPOSITION: THERMAL DECOMPOSITION PRODUCTS MAY INCLUDE TOXIC OXIDES OF CARBON, NITROGEN, AND SULFUR.

POLYMERIZATION: HAZARDOUS POLYMERIZATION HAS NOT BEEN REPORTED TO OCCUR UNDER NORMAL TEMPERATURES AND PRESSURES.

STORAGE AND DISPOSAL

OBSERVE ALL FEDERAL, STATE AND LOCAL REGULATIONS WHEN STORING OR DISPOSING OF THIS SUBSTANCE. FOR ASSISTANCE, CONTACT THE DISTRICT DIRECTOR OF THE ENVIRONMENTAL PROTECTION AGENCY.

****STORAGE****

STORE IN ACCORDANCE WITH 40 CFR 165 RECOMMENDED PROCEDURES FOR THE DISPOSAL AND STORAGE OF PESTICIDES AND PESTICIDE CONTAINERS.

****DISPOSAL****

DISPOSAL MUST BE IN ACCORDANCE WITH 40 CFR 165 RECOMMENDED PROCEDURES FOR THE DISPOSAL AND STORAGE OF PESTICIDES AND PESTICIDE CONTAINERS.

CONDITIONS TO AVOID

MAY BURN BUT DOES NOT IGNITE READILY.

SPILL AND LEAK PROCEDURES

OCCUPATIONAL SPILL: DO NOT TOUCH SPILLED MATERIAL. STOP LEAK IF YOU CAN DO IT WITHOUT RISK. FOR SMALL SPILLS, TAKE UP WITH SAND OR OTHER ABSORBENT MATERIAL AND PLACE INTO CONTAINERS FOR LATER DISPOSAL. FOR SMALL DRY SPILLS, WITH A CLEAN SHOVEL PLACE MATERIAL INTO CLEAN, DRY CONTAINER AND COVER. MOVE CONTAINERS FROM SPILL AREA. FOR LARGER SPILLS, DIKE FAR AHEAD OF SPILL FOR LATER DISPOSAL. KEEP UNNECESSARY PEOPLE AWAY. ISOLATE HAZARD AREA AND DENY ENTRY.

PROTECTIVE EQUIPMENT

VENTILATION: PROVIDE LOCAL EXHAUST OR GENERAL DILUTION VENTILATION SYSTEM.

RESPIRATOR: THE FOLLOWING RESPIRATORS ARE RECOMMENDED BASED ON INFORMATION FOUND IN THE PHYSICAL DATA, TOXICITY AND HEALTH EFFECTS SECTIONS. THEY ARE RANKED IN ORDER FROM MINIMUM TO MAXIMUM RESPIRATORY PROTECTION. THE SPECIFIC RESPIRATOR SELECTED MUST BE BASED ON CONTAMINATION LEVELS FOUND IN THE WORK PLACE, MUST NOT EXCEED THE WORKING LIMITS OF THE RESPIRATOR AND BE JOINTLY APPROVED BY THE NATIONAL INSTITUTE FOR OCCUPATIONAL SAFETY AND HEALTH AND THE MINE SAFETY AND HEALTH ADMINISTRATION (NIOSH-MSHA).

CHEMICAL CARTRIDGE RESPIRATOR WITH AN ORGANIC VAPOR CARTRIDGE(S) WITH A FULL FACEPIECE AND ORGANIC VAPOR CARTRIDGE(S) IN COMBINATION WITH A DUST AND MIST FILTER.

POWERED AIR-PURIFYING RESPIRATOR WITH A TIGHT-FITTING FACEPIECE AND ORGANIC VAPOR CARTRIDGE(S) IN COMBINATION WITH A HIGH-EFFICIENCY PARTICULATE FILTER.

TYPE 'C' SUPPLIED-AIR RESPIRATOR WITH A FULL FACEPIECE OPERATED IN A PRESSURE-DEMAND OR OTHER POSITIVE PRESSURE MODE.

SELF-CONTAINED BREATHING APPARATUS WITH A FULL FACEPIECE OPERATED IN PRESSURE-DEMAND OR OTHER POSITIVE PRESSURE MODE.

FOR FIREFIGHTING AND OTHER IMMEDIATELY DANGEROUS TO LIFE OR HEALTH CONDITIONS:

SELF-CONTAINED BREATHING APPARATUS WITH FULL FACEPIECE OPERATED IN PRESSURE-DEMAND OR OTHER POSITIVE PRESSURE MODE.

SUPPLIED-AIR RESPIRATOR WITH FULL FACEPIECE AND OPERATED IN PRESSURE-DEMAND OR OTHER POSITIVE PRESSURE MODE IN COMBINATION WITH AN AUXILIARY SELF-CONTAINED BREATHING APPARATUS OPERATED IN PRESSURE-DEMAND OR OTHER POSITIVE PRESSURE MODE.

CLOTHING: EMPLOYEE MUST WEAR APPROPRIATE PROTECTIVE (IMPERVIOUS) CLOTHING AND EQUIPMENT TO PREVENT REPEATED OR PROLONGED SKIN CONTACT WITH THIS SUBSTANCE.

GLOVES: EMPLOYEE MUST WEAR APPROPRIATE PROTECTIVE GLOVES TO PREVENT CONTACT WITH THIS SUBSTANCE.

EYE PROTECTION: EMPLOYEE MUST WEAR SPLASH-PROOF OR DUST-RESISTANT SAFETY GOGGLES TO PREVENT EYE CONTACT WITH THIS SUBSTANCE.

EMERGENCY EYE WASH: WHERE THERE IS ANY POSSIBILITY THAT AN EMPLOYEE'S EYES MAY BE EXPOSED TO THIS SUBSTANCE, THE EMPLOYER SHOULD PROVIDE AN EYE WASH FOUNTAIN WITHIN THE IMMEDIATE WORK AREA FOR EMERGENCY USE.

AUTHORIZED BY- OCCUPATIONAL HEALTH SERVICES, INC.

CREATION DATE: 10/04/89 ***REVISION DATE:*** 05/18/90

MATERIAL SAFETY DATA SHEET

OCCUPATIONAL HEALTH SERVICES, INC.
AGRICULTURE AND PESTICIDE DIVISION
450 SEVENTH AVENUE, SUITE 2407
NEW YORK, NEW YORK 10123
1-800-445-MSDS OR (212) 967-1100

EMERGENCY CONTACT:
JOHN S. BRANSFORD, JR. (615) 292-1180

SUBSTANCE IDENTIFICATION

CAS-NUMBER 25311-71-1

SUBSTANCE: **ISOFENPHOS**

TRADE NAMES/SYNONYMS: 2-((ETHOXY((1-METHYLETHYL)AMINO)PHOSPHINOTHIOYL)OXY)BENZOIC ACID 1-METHYLETHYLESTER; SALICYLIC ACID, ISOPROPYL ESTER, O-ESTER WITH O-ETHYL ISOPROPYLPHOSPHORAMIDOTHIOATE; ISOPROPYL O-(ETHOXY(ISOPROPYLAMINO)PHOSPHINOTHIOYL)SALICYLATE; ISOPROPYL O-(ETHOXY-N-ISOPROPYLAMINO(THIOPHOSPHORYL))SALICYLATE; O-ETHYL O-2-ISOPROPOXYCARBONYLPHENYL ISOPROPYLPHOSPHORAMIDOTHIOATE; 1-METHYLETHYL 2-((ETHOXY((1-METHYLETHYL)AMINO)PHOSPHINOTHIOYL)OXY) BENZOATE; ISOPROPYL SALICYLATE O-ESTER WITH O-ETHYL ISOPROPYLPHOSPHORAMIDO- THIOATE; BENZOIC ACID, 2 -((ETHOXY((1-METHYLETHYL)AMINO)PHOSPHINOTHIOYL)OXY)-, 1-METHYLETHYL ESTER; AMAZE; BAY 92144; ISOPHENPHOS; OFTANOL; SRA 12869; C15H24N04PS; PST11985

CHEMICAL FAMILY: ORGANOPHOSPHATE
CARBOXYLIC ACID, AROMATIC
AMINE, ALIPHATIC

MOLECULAR FORMULA: C15-H24-N-O4-P-S

MOLECULAR WEIGHT: 345.40

CERCLA RATINGS (SCALE 0-3): HEALTH=3 FIRE=0 REACTIVITY=0 PERSISTENCE=1

NFPA RATINGS (SCALE 0-4): HEALTH=4 FIRE=0 REACTIVITY=0

COMPONENTS AND CONTAMINANTS

COMPONENT: ISOFENPHOS ***PERCENT:*** 100
CAS# 25311-71-1

EXPOSURE LIMITS: NO OCCUPATIONAL EXPOSURE LIMITS ESTABLISHED BY OSHA, ACGIH, OR NIOSH.

PHYSICAL DATA

DESCRIPTION: COLORLESS OIL ***BOILING POINT:*** 248 F (120 C) @ 0.01 MMHG
MELTING POINT: <10 F (<-12 C) ***SPECIFIC GRAVITY:*** 1.13
VAPOR PRESSURE: 0.000004 MMHG @ 20 C ***SOLUBILITY IN WATER:*** 20 PPM
SOLVENT SOLUBILITY: SOLUBLE IN ACETONE, KEROSENE, ALCOHOL, ETHER, BENZENE, XYLENE, CYCLOHEXANONE, DICHLOROMETHANE

FIRE AND EXPLOSION DATA

FIRE AND EXPLOSION HAZARD: NEGLIGIBLE FIRE HAZARD WHEN EXPOSED TO HEAT OR FLAME.
FIREFIGHTING MEDIA: DRY CHEMICAL, CARBON DIOXIDE, HALON, WATER SPRAY OR STANDARD FOAM (1987 EMERGENCY RESPONSE GUIDEBOOK, DOT P 5800.4). FOR LARGER FIRES, USE WATER SPRAY, FOG OR STANDARD FOAM (1987 EMERGENCY RESPONSE GUIDEBOOK, DOT P 5800.4).
FIREFIGHTING: MOVE CONTAINERS FROM FIRE AREA IF POSSIBLE. FIGHT FIRE FROM MAXIMUM DISTANCE. STAY AWAY FROM STORAGE TANK ENDS. DIKE FIRE CONTROL WATER FOR LATER DISPOSAL. DO NOT SCATTER MATERIAL (1987 EMERGENCY RESPONSE GUIDEBOOK, DOT P 5800.4, GUIDE PAGE 55). EXTINGUISH USING AGENT SUITABLE FOR TYPE OF SURROUNDING FIRE. AVOID BREATHING VAPORS AND DUSTS. KEEP UPWIND.

TRANSPORTATION DATA

DEPARTMENT OF TRANSPORTATION HAZARD CLASSIFICATION 49 CFR 172.101: POISON B
DEPARTMENT OF TRANSPORTATION LABELING REQUIREMENTS 49 CFR 172.101 AND SUBPART E: POISON
DEPARTMENT OF TRANSPORTATION PACKAGING REQUIREMENTS: 49 CFR 173.346 EXCEPTIONS: 49 CFR 173.345

TOXICITY

ISOFENPHOS: TOXICITY DATA: 144 MG/M3/4 HOURS INHALATION-RAT LC50; 162 MG/KG SKIN-RABBIT LD50; 188 MG/KG SKIN-RAT LD50; 28 MG/KG ORAL-RAT LD50; 91300 UG/KG ORAL-MOUSE LD50. CARCINOGEN STATUS: NONE. LOCAL EFFECTS: IRRITANT- EYE. ACUTE TOXICITY LEVEL: HIGHLY TOXIC BY INHALATION, DERMAL ABSORPTION, AND INGESTION. TARGET EFFECTS: CHOLINESTERASE INHIBITOR. POISONING MAY AFFECT THE NERVOUS SYSTEM.* AT INCREASED RISK FROM EXPOSURE: PERSONS WITH RESPIRATORY AILMENTS, RECENT EXPOSURE TO CHOLINESTERASE INHIBITORS OR IMPAIRED CHOLINESTERASE PRODUCTION, OR LIVER MALFUNCTION.* ADDITIONAL DATA: MAY CROSS THE PLACENTA. HIGH ENVIRONMENTAL TEMPERATURES OR EXPOSURE OF THE CHEMICAL TO VISIBLE OR ULTRAVIOLET LIGHT MAY ENHANCE THE TOXICITY. INTERACTIONS WITH MEDICATIONS MAY OCCUR.*
* MAY BE BASED ON GENERAL INFORMATION ON ORGANOPHOSPHATES.

HEALTH EFFECTS AND FIRST AID

INHALATION: ISOFENPHOS: HIGHLY TOXIC. SEE INFORMATION ON ORGANOPHOSPHATES.
ORGANOPHOSPHATES: CHOLINESTERASE INHIBITOR. **ACUTE EXPOSURE-** WHEN INHALED, THE FIRST EFFECTS OF CHOLINESTERASE INHIBITORS ARE USUALLY RESPIRATORY AND MAY INCLUDE NASAL HYPEREMIA AND WATERY DISCHARGE, COUGH, CHEST DISCOMFORT, DYSPNEA, AND WHEEZING DUE TO INCREASED BRONCHIAL SECRETIONS AND BRONCHOCONSTRICTION. IF SUFFICIENT AMOUNTS ARE ABSORBED, OTHER SYSTEMIC EFFECTS MAY BEGIN WITHIN A FEW MINUTES OR BE DELAYED FOR UP TO 12 HOURS. SYMPTOMS MAY INCLUDE PALLOR, NAUSEA, VOMITING, DIARRHEA, ABDOMINAL CRAMPS, HEADACHE, DIZZINESS, OCULAR PAIN, BLURRED VISION, MIOSIS OR IN SOME CASES, ESPECIALLY INITIALLY, MYDRIASIS, LACRIMATION, SALIVATION, SWEATING, AND CONFUSION. OTHER REPORTED CENTRAL NERVOUS SYSTEM OR NEUROMUSCULAR EFFECTS MAY INCLUDE ATAXIA, SLURRED SPEECH, AREFLEXIA, WEAKNESS, FATIGUE, FASCICULATIONS, TWITCHING, TREMORS POSSIBLY OF THE TONGUE AND EYELIDS, AND EVENTUALLY PARALYSIS OF THE EXTREMITIES AND POSSIBLY OF THE RESPIRATORY MUSCLES. IN SEVERE CASES THERE MAY ALSO BE INVOLUNTARY DEFECATION AND URINATION, CYANOSIS, PSYCHOSIS, HYPERGLYCEMIA, ACUTE PANCREATITIS, CARDIAC IRREGULARITIES, PULMONARY EDEMA, UNCONSCIOUSNESS, CONVULSIONS, AND COMA. DEATH IS PRIMARILY DUE TO RESPIRATORY FAILURE, ALTHOUGH CARDIOVASCULAR EFFECTS INCLUDING CARDIAC ARREST MAY ALSO BE IMPLICATED. LONG TERM SEQUELAE ARE RARE BUT MAY INCLUDE NEUROPSYCHIATRIC DISORDERS AND MYOPATHY WITH MUSCLE TENDERNESS. SOME ORGANOPHOSPHATES MAY CAUSE A DELAYED NEUROPATHY BEGINNING 1-4 WEEKS AFTER AN ACUTE EXPOSURE WHICH MAY OR MAY NOT HAVE CAUSED ACUTE CHOLINERGIC EFFECTS. NUMBNESS, TINGLING, WEAKNESS AND CRAMPING BEGINNING SYMMETRICALLY IN THE LOWER LIMBS MAY PROGRESS TO ATAXIA AND PARALYSIS. IN SEVERE CASES, UPPER LIMB INVOLVEMENT IS POSSIBLE AND FLACCID PARALYSIS MAY PROGRESS TO SPASTIC PARALYSIS WITH EXAGGERATED REFLEXES. IMPROVEMENT MAY OCCUR OVER MONTHS TO YEARS, BUT SOME RESIDUAL IMPAIRMENT USUALLY REMAINS.
CHRONIC EXPOSURE- REPEATED OR PROLONGED EXPOSURE MAY RESULT IN THE EFFECTS OF ACUTE EXPOSURE INCLUDING THE DELAYED NEUROPATHY. OTHER EFFECTS REPORTED IN WORKERS REPEATEDLY EXPOSED INCLUDE IMPAIRED MEMORY AND CONCENTRATION, ACUTE PSYCHOSIS, SEVERE DEPRESSIONS, IRRITABILTY, CONFUSION, APATHY, EMOTIONAL LABILITY, SOCIAL WITHDRAWAL, CONFUSION, HEADACHE, SPEECH DIFFICULTIES, DELAYED REACTION TIMES, SPATIAL DISORIENTATION, NIGHTMARES, SLEEPWALKING, AND DROWSINESS OR INSOMNIA. AN INFLUENZA-LIKE CONDITION WITH HEADACHE, NAUSEA, WEAKNESS, ANOREXIA AND MALAISE HAS ALSO BEEN REPORTED.
FIRST AID- REMOVE FROM EXPOSURE AREA TO FRESH AIR IMMEDIATELY. IF BREATHING HAS STOPPED, GIVE ARTIFICIAL RESPIRATION. MAINTAIN AIRWAY AND BLOOD PRESSURE AND ADMINISTER OXYGEN IF AVAILABLE. KEEP AFFECTED PERSON WARM AND AT REST. TREAT SYMPTOMATICALLY AND SUPPORTIVELY. ADMINISTRATION OF OXYGEN SHOULD BE PERFORMED BY QUALIFIED PERSONNEL. GET MEDICAL ATTENTION IMMEDIATELY.

SKIN CONTACT: ISOFENPHOS: HIGHLY TOXIC. SEE INFORMATION ON ORGANOPHOSPHATES.
ORGANOPHOSPHATES: CHOLINESTERASE INHIBITOR. **ACUTE EXPOSURE-** LOCALIZED SWEATING AND FASCICULATIONS MAY OCCUR AT THE SITE OF CONTACT. IF SUFFICIENT AMOUNTS ARE ABSORBED, OTHER EFFECTS OF CHOLINESTERASE INHIBITION AS DESCRIBED IN ACUTE INHALATION MAY OCCUR. SYMPTOMS MAY BE DELAYED 2-3 HOURS, BUT USUALLY NO MORE THAN 12 HOURS. THE RATE OF ABSORPTION IS INCREASED BY THE PRESENCE OF DERMATITIS OR HIGH AMBIENT TEMPERATURES. DELAYED NEUROPATHY IS ALSO POSSIBLE. **CHRONIC EXPOSURE-** REPEATED OR PROLONGED EXPOSURE MAY CAUSE EFFECTS AS DESCRIBED IN ACUTE EXPOSURE. SOME ORGANOPHOSPHATES MAY CAUSE SENSITIZATION.
FIRST AID- REMOVE CONTAMINATED CLOTHING IMMEDIATELY. WASH CONTAMINATED AREAS WITH SOAP AND WATER FOLLOWED BY ALCOHOL (ARENA, POISONING, 4TH ED.). EMERGENCY PERSONNEL SHOULD WEAR GLOVES AND AVOID CONTAMINATION. TREAT RESPIRATORY DIFFICULTY WITH ARTIFICIAL RESPIRATION. GET MEDICAL ATTENTION IMMEDIATELY.

EYE CONTACT: ISOFENPHOS: IRRITANT. MAY CAUSE IRRITATION. PROLONGED OR REPEATED EXPOSURE MAY CAUSE CONJUNCTIVITIS. SEE INFORMATION ON ORGANOPHOSPHATES.
ORGANOPHOSPHATES: CHOLINESTERASE INHIBITOR. **ACUTE EXPOSURE-** DIRECT CONTACT MAY CAUSE PAIN, HYPEREMIA, LACRIMATION, TWITCHING OF THE EYELIDS, MIOSIS, AND CILIARY MUSCLE SPASM WITH LOSS OF ACCOMODATION, BLURRED OR DIMMED VISION AND BROWACHE. SOMETIMES MYDRIASIS MAY OCCUR INSTEAD OF MIOSIS. WITH SUFFICIENT EXPOSURE, OTHER SYMPTOMS OF CHOLINESTERASE INHIBITION AS DESCRIBED IN ACUTE INHALATION MAY OCCUR. **CHRONIC EXPOSURE-** REPEATED OR PROLONGED EXPOSURE MAY CAUSE EFFECTS AS DESCRIBED IN ACUTE EXPOSURE. SOME COMPOUNDS HAVE CAUSED TOXIC EFFECTS ON THE CRYSTALLINE LENS, CONJUNCTIVAL THICKENING AND OBSTRUCTION OF THE NASOLACRIMAL CANALS WHEN USED AS MIOTIC EYEDROPS.
FIRST AID- IRRIGATE EYES WITH WATER OR SALINE SOLUTION. IF SYMPTOMS OF POISONING OCCUR, TREAT RESPIRATORY DIFFICULTY WITH ARTIFICIAL RESPIRATION AND OXYGEN. OBSERVE PATIENT FOR AT LEAST 24-36 HOURS (GOSSELIN, CLINICAL TOXICOLOGY OF COMMERCIAL PRODUCTS, 5TH ED.). GET MEDICAL ATTENTION IMMEDIATELY. OXYGEN SHOULD BE ADMINISTERED BY QUALIFIED MEDICAL PERSONNEL.

INGESTION: ISOFENPHOS: HIGHLY TOXIC. IN A STUDY OF HENS FOR DELAYED NEUROPATHY, ABOUT A DOZEN HENS DISPLAYED SYMPTOMS OF NEUROLOGICAL DAMAGE. IN A 3-GENERATION STUDY OF RATS, A DIETARY LEVEL OF 10 PPM PRODUCED A DECREASE IN PREGNANCY RATE AND BODY WEIGHT GAIN. SEE INFORMATION ON ORGANOPHOSPHATES.
ORGANOPHOSPHATES: CHOLINESTERASE INHIBITOR. **ACUTE EXPOSURE-** WHEN INGESTED, THE FIRST EFFECTS MAY BE NAUSEA, VOMITING, ANOREXIA, ABDOMINAL CRAMPS AND DIARRHEA. GASTROINTESTINAL ABSORPTION MAY CAUSE SYMPTOMS OF CHOLINESTERASE INHIBITION AS DESCRIBED IN ACUTE INHALATION. SYMPTOMS MAY BEGIN WITHIN MINUTES OR BE DELAYED FOR HOURS. DELAYED EFFECTS INCLUDING NEUROPATHY MAY ALSO OCCUR. **CHRONIC EXPOSURE-** REPEATED INGESTION MAY CAUSE EFFECTS AS DESCRIBED IN ACUTE EXPOSURE.
FIRST AID- IF PERSON IS ALERT AND RESPIRATION IS NOT DEPRESSED, GIVE SYRUP OF IPECAC FOLLOWED BY WATER (IF VOMITING OCCURS, KEEP HEAD BELOW HIPS TO PREVENT ASPIRATION). IF CONSCIOUSNESS LEVEL DECLINES OR VOMITING HAS NOT OCCURRED IN 15 MINUTES EMPTY STOMACH BY GASTRIC LAVAGE WITH THE AID OF CUFFED ENDOTRACHEAL TUBE USING ISOTONIC SALINE OR 5% SODIUM

BICARBONATE FOLLOW WITH ACTIVATED CHARCOAL. ESTABLISH AND MAINTAIN AIRWAY. TREAT RESPIRATORY DIFFICULTY WITH ARTIFICIAL RESPIRATION AND OXYGEN. DO NOT GIVE MORPHINE, AMINOPHYLLINE, PHENOTHIAZINES, RESERPINE, FUROSEMIDE, OR ETHACRYNIC ACID (MORGAN, RECOGNITION AND MANAGEMENT OF PESTICIDE POISONINGS, 3RD ED.). TREAT SYMPTOMATICALLY AND SUPPORTIVELY. ADMINISTRATION OF OXYGEN AND LAVAGE MUST BE PERFORMED BY QUALIFIED MEDICAL PERSONNEL. GET MEDICAL ATTENTION IMMEDIATELY.

ANTIDOTE: THE FOLLOWING ANTIDOTE(S) HAVE BEEN RECOMMENDED. HOWEVER, THE DECISION AS TO WHETHER THE SEVERITY OF POISONING REQUIRES ADMINISTRATION OF ANY ANTIDOTE AND ACTUAL DOSE REQUIRED SHOULD BE MADE BY QUALIFIED MEDICAL PERSONNEL.

FOR CHOLINESTERASE INHIBITORS: ESTABLISH CLEAR AIRWAY AND TISSUE OXYGENATION BY ASPIRATION OF SECRETIONS, AND IF NECESSARY, BY ASSISTED PULMONARY VENTILATION WITH OXYGEN. IMPROVE TISSUE OXYGENATION AS MUCH AS POSSIBLE BEFORE ADMINISTERING ATROPINE TO MINIMIZE THE RISK OF VENTRICULAR FIBRILLATION. ADMINISTER ATROPINE SULFATE INTRAVENOUSLY, OR INTRAMUSCULARLY IF IV INJECTION IS NOT POSSIBLE. IN MODERATELY SEVERE POISONING ADMINISTER ATROPINE SULFATE, 0.4-2.0 MG REPEATED EVERY 15 MINUTES UNTIL ATROPINIZATION IS ACHIEVED (TACHYCARDIA, FLUSHING, DRY MOUTH, MYDRIASIS). MAINTAIN ATROPINIZATION BY REPEATED DOSES FOR 2-12 HOURS, OR LONGER, DEPENDING ON THE SEVERITY OF POISONING. THE APPEARANCE OF RALES IN THE LUNG BASES, MIOSIS, SALIVATION, NAUSEA, BRADYCARDIA, ARE ALL INDICATIONS OF INADEQUATE ATROPINIZATION. SEVERELY POISONED INDIVIDUALS MAY EXHIBIT REMARKABLE TOLERANCE TO ATROPINE; TWO OR MORE TIMES THE DOSAGES SUGGESTED ABOVE MAY BE NEEDED. PERSONS NOT POISONED OR ONLY SLIGHTLY POISONED, HOWEVER, MAY DEVELOP SIGNS OF ATROPINE TOXICITY FROM SUCH LARGE DOSAGES: FEVER, MUSCLE FIBRILLATIONS, AND DELIRIUM ARE THE MAIN SIGNS OF ATROPINE TOXICITY. IF THESE SIGNS APPEAR WHILE THE PATIENT IS FULLY ATROPINIZED, ATROPINE ADMINISTRATION SHOULD BE DISCONTINUED, AT LEAST TEMPORARILY. OBSERVE TREATED PATIENTS CLOSELY AT LEAST 24 HOURS TO INSURE THAT SYMPTOMS (POSSIBLY PULMONARY EDEMA) DO NOT RECUR AS ATROPINIZATION WEARS OFF. IN VERY SEVERE POISONINGS, METABOLIC DISPOSITION OF TOXICANT MAY REQUIRE SEVERAL HOURS OR DAYS DURING WHICH ATROPINIZATION MUST BE MAINTAINED. MARKEDLY LOWER LEVELS OF URINARY METABOLITES INDICATE THAT ATROPINE DOSAGE CAN BE TAPERED OFF. AS DOSAGE IS REDUCED, CHECK THE LUNG BASES FREQUENTLY FOR RALES. IF RALES ARE HEARD OR OTHER SYMPTOMS RETURN, RE-ESTABLISH ATROPINIZATION PROMPTLY (MORGAN, RECOGNITION AND MANAGEMENT OF PESTICIDE POISONINGS, 3RD ED.). ADMINISTRATION OF ANTIDOTE MUST BE PERFORMED BY QUALIFIED MEDICAL PERSONNEL.

IN CASES OF SEVERE POISONING BY ORGANOPHOSPHATE PESTICIDES IN WHICH RESPIRATORY DEPRESSION, MUSCLE WEAKNESS AND TWITCHINGS ARE SEVERE, GIVE PRALIDOXIME (PROTOPAM-AYERST, 2-PAM), 1.0 GRAM INTRAVENOUSLY AT NO MORE THAN 0.5 GRAM PER MINUTE. DOSAGE OF PRALIDOXIME MAY BE REPEATED IN 1-2 HOURS, THEN AT 10-12 HOUR INTERVALS IF NEEDED. IN VERY SEVERE POISONINGS, DOSAGE RATES MAY BE DOUBLED. TREATMENT WITH PRALIDOXIME WILL BE MOST EFFECTIVE IF GIVEN WITHIN THIRTY-SIX HOURS AFTER POISONING (MORGAN, RECOGNITION AND MANAGEMENT OF PESTICIDE POISONINGS, 3RD ED.). ANTIDOTE SHOULD BE ADMINISTERED BY QUALIFIED MEDICAL PERSONNEL.

REACTIVITY

REACTIVITY: STABLE UNDER NORMAL TEMPERATURES AND PRESSURES.

INCOMPATIBILITIES: ISOFENPHOS: ACIDIC CONDITIONS: MAY CAUSE HYDROLYSIS. ALKALINE CONDITIONS: MAY CAUSE HYDROLYSIS.

DECOMPOSITION: THERMAL DECOMPOSITION PRODUCTS MAY INCLUDE TOXIC AND HAZARDOUS FUMES OF SULFUR, NITROGEN AND PHOSPHORUS.

POLYMERIZATION: HAZARDOUS POLYMERIZATION HAS NOT BEEN REPORTED TO OCCUR UNDER NORMAL TEMPERATURES AND PRESSURES.

STORAGE AND DISPOSAL

OBSERVE ALL FEDERAL, STATE AND LOCAL REGULATIONS WHEN STORING OR DISPOSING OF THIS SUBSTANCE. FOR ASSISTANCE, CONTACT THE DISTRICT DIRECTOR OF THE ENVIRONMENTAL PROTECTION AGENCY.

****STORAGE****

STORE IN ACCORDANCE WITH 40 CFR 165 RECOMMENDED PROCEDURES FOR THE DISPOSAL AND STORAGE OF PESTICIDES AND PESTICIDE CONTAINERS.
STORE AWAY FROM INCOMPATIBLE SUBSTANCES.

****DISPOSAL****

DISPOSAL MUST BE IN ACCORDANCE WITH 40 CFR 165 RECOMMENDED PROCEDURES FOR THE DISPOSAL AND STORAGE OF PESTICIDES AND PESTICIDE CONTAINERS.

CONDITIONS TO AVOID

MAY BURN BUT DOES NOT IGNITE READILY. CONTAINERS MAY EXPLODE IN HEAT OF FIRE.

SPILL AND LEAK PROCEDURES

OCCUPATIONAL SPILL: DO NOT TOUCH SPILLED MATERIAL. STOP LEAK IF YOU CAN DO IT WITHOUT RISK. USE WATER SPRAY TO REDUCE VAPORS. FOR SMALL SPILLS, TAKE UP WITH SAND OR OTHER ABSORBENT MATERIAL AND PLACE INTO CONTAINERS FOR LATER DISPOSAL. FOR SMALL DRY SPILLS, WITH A CLEAN SHOVEL PLACE MATERIAL INTO CLEAN, DRY CONTAINERS AND COVER. MOVE CONTAINERS FROM SPILL AREA. FOR LARGER SPILLS, DIKE FAR AHEAD OF SPILL FOR LATER DISPOSAL. KEEP UNNECESSARY PEOPLE AWAY. ISOLATE HAZARD AREA AND DENY ENTRY. VENTILATE CLOSED SPACES BEFORE ENTERING.

PROTECTIVE EQUIPMENT

VENTILATION: PROCESS ENCLOSURE RECOMMENDED.

RESPIRATOR: THE FOLLOWING RESPIRATORS ARE RECOMMENDED BASED ON INFORMATION FOUND IN THE PHYSICAL DATA, TOXICITY AND HEALTH EFFECTS SECTIONS. THEY ARE RANKED IN ORDER FROM MINIMUM TO MAXIMUM RESPIRATORY PROTECTION. THE SPECIFIC RESPIRATOR SELECTED MUST BE BASED ON CONTAMINATION LEVELS FOUND IN THE WORK PLACE, MUST NOT EXCEED THE WORKING LIMITS OF THE RESPIRATOR AND BE JOINTLY APPROVED BY THE NATIONAL INSTITUTE FOR OCCUPATIONAL SAFETY AND HEALTH AND THE MINE SAFETY AND HEALTH ADMINISTRATION (NIOSH-MSHA).

TYPE 'C' SUPPLIED-AIR RESPIRATOR WITH A FULL FACEPIECE OPERATED IN PRESSURE-DEMAND OR OTHER POSITIVE PRESSURE MODE OR WITH A FULL FACEPIECE, HELMET OR HOOD OPERATED IN CONTINOUS-FLOW MODE.

SELF-CONTAINED BREATHING APPARATUS WITH A FULL FACEPIECE OPERATED IN PRESSURE-DEMAND OR OTHER POSITIVE PRESSURE MODE.

FOR FIREFIGHTING AND OTHER IMMEDIATELY DANGEROUS TO LIFE OR HEALTH CONDITIONS:

SELF-CONTAINED BREATHING APPARATUS WITH FULL FACEPIECE OPERATED IN PRESSURE-DEMAND OR OTHER POSITIVE PRESSURE MODE.

SUPPLIED-AIR RESPIRATOR WITH FULL FACEPIECE AND OPERATED IN PRESSURE-DEMAND OR OTHER POSITIVE PRESSURE MODE IN COMBINATION WITH AN AUXILIARY SELF-CONTAINED BREATHING APPARATUS OPERATED IN PRESSURE-DEMAND OR OTHER POSITIVE PRESSURE MODE.

CLOTHING: EMPLOYEE MUST WEAR APPROPRIATE PROTECTIVE (IMPERVIOUS) CLOTHING AND EQUIPMENT TO PREVENT ANY POSSIBILITY OF SKIN CONTACT WITH THIS SUBSTANCE.

GLOVES: EMPLOYEE MUST WEAR APPROPRIATE PROTECTIVE GLOVES TO PREVENT CONTACT WITH THIS SUBSTANCE.

EYE PROTECTION: EMPLOYEE MUST WEAR SPLASH-PROOF OR DUST-RESISTANT SAFETY GOGGLES AND A FACESHIELD TO PREVENT CONTACT WITH THIS SUBSTANCE.

EMERGENCY WASH FACILITIES: WHERE THERE IS ANY POSSIBILITY THAT AN EMPLOYEE'S EYES AND/OR SKIN MAY BE EXPOSED TO THIS SUBSTANCE, THE EMPLOYER SHOULD PROVIDE AN EYE WASH FOUNTAIN AND QUICK DRENCH SHOWER WITHIN THE IMMEDIATE WORK AREA FOR EMERGENCY USE.

AUTHORIZED BY- OCCUPATIONAL HEALTH SERVICES, INC.
CREATION DATE: 10/04/89 ***REVISION DATE:*** 05/02/90

MATERIAL SAFETY DATA SHEET

OCCUPATIONAL HEALTH SERVICES, INC.
AGRICULTURE AND PESTICIDE DIVISION
450 SEVENTH AVENUE, SUITE 2407
NEW YORK, NEW YORK 10123
1-800-445-MSDS OR (212) 967-1100

EMERGENCY CONTACT:
JOHN S. BRANSFORD, JR. (615) 292-1180

SUBSTANCE IDENTIFICATION

CAS-NUMBER 67-63-0

SUBSTANCE: **ISOPROPYL ALCOHOL**

TRADE NAMES/SYNONYMS: ISOPROPANOL; ETHYL CARBINOL; DIMETHYLCARBINOL; 2-PROPANOL; ISOHOL; SEC-PROPYL ALCOHOL; PROPYL ALCOHOL; XEROX FILM REMOVER (UNION CARBIDE); CTL R-53 REDUCER (CHEMICAL TECHNOLOGY LABS., INC.); TEXPADS (THE TEXWIPE COMPANY); CORONA WIRE CLEANER (CANON BUSINESS MACHINES); DISK DRIVE HEAD CLEANING KIT (DIGITAL EQUIPMENT CORPORATION); KENCO #880-T FLUX THINNER (KENCO); LENS CLENS #3 (GENERAL PRODUCTION SERVICES INC.); ISOPROPYL ALCOHOL, ANHYDROUS (EXXON); STCC 4904205; UN 1219; C3H8O; PST12090

CHEMICAL FAMILY: ALCOHOL, ALIPHATIC

MOLECULAR FORMULA: C-H3-C-H-(O-H)-C-H3
MOLECULAR WEIGHT: 60.10
CERCLA RATINGS (SCALE 0-3): HEALTH = 2 FIRE = 3 REACTIVITY = 0 PERSISTENCE = 0
NFPA RATINGS (SCALE 0-4): HEALTH = 1 FIRE = 3 REACTIVITY = 0

COMPONENTS AND CONTAMINANTS

COMPONENT: ISOPROPYL ALCOHOL (ISOPROPANOL) ***PERCENT:*** 100.0
CAS# 67-63-0
OTHER CONTAMINANTS: NONE
EXPOSURE LIMITS: ISOPROPYL ALCOHOL (ISOPROPANOL; 2-PROPANOL): 400 PPM (980 MG/M3) OSHA TWA; 500 PPM (1225 MG/M3) OSHA STEL 400 PPM (980 MG/M3) ACGIH TWA; 500 PPM (1225 MG/M3) ACGIH STEL 400 PPM NIOSH RECOMMENDED 10 HOUR TWA; 800 PPM NIOSH RECOMMENDED 15 MINUTE CEILING
SUBJECT TO SARA SECTION 313 ANNUAL TOXIC CHEMICAL RELEASE REPORTING

PHYSICAL DATA

DESCRIPTION: COLORLESS LIQUID WITH AN ODOR OF ALCOHOL.
BOILING POINT: 180 F (82 C) ***MELTING POINT:*** -129 F (-89 C)
SPECIFIC GRAVITY: 0.7855 ***VISCOSITY:*** 2.1 CPS @ 25 C ***VOLATILITY:*** 100%
VAPOR PRESSURE: 40 MMHG @ 24 C ***EVAPORATION RATE:*** (BUTYL ACETATE = 1) 2.88
SOLUBILITY IN WATER: SOLUBLE ***ODOR THRESHOLD:*** 40-45 PPM
VAPOR DENSITY: 2.1
SOLVENT SOLUBILITY: SOLUBLE IN ALCOHOL, ETHER, CHLOROFORM, ACETONE, BENZENE; INSOLUBLE IN SALT SOLUTIONS.

FIRE AND EXPLOSION DATA

FIRE AND EXPLOSION HAZARD: DANGEROUS FIRE HAZARD WHEN EXPOSED TO HEAT OR FLAME.
VAPORS ARE HEAVIER THAN AIR AND MAY TRAVEL A CONSIDERABLE DISTANCE TO A SOURCE OF IGNITION AND FLASH BACK.
VAPOR-AIR MIXTURES ARE EXPLOSIVE.
FLASH POINT: 53 F (12 C) (CC) ***UPPER EXPLOSIVE LIMIT:*** 12.7% @ 93 C
LOWER EXPLOSIVE LIMIT: 2.0% ***AUTOIGNITION TEMP.:*** 750 F (399 C)
FLAMMABILITY CLASS(OSHA): IB
FIREFIGHTING MEDIA: DRY CHEMICAL, CARBON DIOXIDE, HALON, WATER SPRAY OR ALCOHOL FOAM (1987 EMERGENCY RESPONSE GUIDEBOOK, DOT P 5800.4).
FOR LARGER FIRES, USE WATER SPRAY, FOG OR ALCOHOL FOAM (1987 EMERGENCY RESPONSE GUIDEBOOK, DOT P 5800.4).
ALCOHOL FOAM (NFPA 325M, FIRE HAZARD PROPERTIES OF FLAMMABLE LIQUIDS, GASES, AND VOLATILE SOLIDS, 1984).
FIREFIGHTING: MOVE CONTAINER FROM FIRE AREA IF POSSIBLE. COOL FIRE-EXPOSED CONTAINERS WITH WATER FROM SIDE UNTIL WELL AFTER FIRE IS OUT. STAY AWAY FROM STORAGE TANK ENDS. FOR MASSIVE FIRE IN STORAGE AREA, USE UNMANNED HOSE HOLDER OR MONITOR NOZZLES, ELSE WITHDRAW FROM AREA AND LET FIRE BURN. WITHDRAW IMMEDIATELY IN CASE OF RISING SOUND FROM VENTING SAFETY DEVICE OR ANY DISCOLORATION OF STORAGE TANK DUE TO FIRE (1987 EMERGENCY RESPONSE GUIDEBOOK, DOT P 5800.4, GUIDE PAGE 26).
EXTINGUISH ONLY IF FLOW CAN BE STOPPED; USE WATER IN FLOODING AMOUNTS AS FOG, SOLID STREAMS MAY NOT BE EFFECTIVE. COOL CONTAINERS WITH FLOODING AMOUNTS OF WATER, APPLY FROM AS FAR A DISTANCE AS POSSIBLE. AVOID BREATHING VAPORS, KEEP UPWIND.
WATER MAY BE INEFFECTIVE (NFPA 325M, FIRE HAZARD PROPERTIES OF FLAMMABLE LIQUIDS, GASES, AND VOLATILE SOLIDS, 1984)

TRANSPORTATION DATA

DEPARTMENT OF TRANSPORTATION HAZARD CLASSIFICATION 49 CFR 172.101: FLAMMABLE LIQUID
DEPARTMENT OF TRANSPORTATION LABELING REQUIREMENTS 49 CFR 172.101 AND SUBPART E: FLAMMABLE LIQUID
DEPARTMENT OF TRANSPORTATION PACKAGING REQUIREMENTS: 49 CFR 173.125 EXCEPTIONS: 49 CFR 173.118

TOXICITY

ISOPROPYL ALCOHOL (ISOPROPANOL; 2-PROPANOL): IRRITATION DATA: 500 MG SKIN-RABBIT MILD; 16 MG EYE-RABBIT; 10 MG EYE-RABBIT MODERATE; 100 MG/24 HOURS EYE-RABBIT MODERATE. TOXICITY DATA: 12,800 PPM/3 HOURS INHALATION-MOUSE LCLO; 16,000 PPM/4 HOURS INHALATION-RAT LCLO; 12,800 MG/KG SKIN-RABBIT LD50; 5272 MG/KG ORAL-MAN LDLO; 14,432 MG/KG ORAL-MAN TDLO; 3570 MG/KG ORAL-HUMAN LDLO; 223 MG/KG ORAL-HUMAN TDLO; 5045 MG/KG ORAL-RAT LD50; 3600 MG/KG ORAL-MOUSE LD50; 6410 MG/KG ORAL-RABBIT LD50; 4797 MG/KG ORAL-DOG LD50; 6000 MG/KG SUBCUTANEOUS-MOUSE LDLO; 6 MG/KG SUBCUTANEOUS-MAMMAL LDLO; 1088 MG/KG INTRAVENOUS-RAT LD50; 1509 MG/KG INTRAVENOUS-MOUSE LD50; 1184 MG/KG INTRAVENOUS-RABBIT LD50; 2735 MG/KG INTRAPERITONEAL-RAT LD50; 4477 MG/KG INTRAPERITONEAL-MOUSE LD50; 667 MG/KG INTRAPERITONEAL-RABBIT LD50; 2770 MG/KG UNREPORTED-MAN LDLO; MUTAGENIC DATA (RTECS); REPRODUCTIVE EFFECTS DATA (RTECS). CARCINOGEN STATUS: HUMAN INADEQUATE EVIDENCE, ANIMAL INADEQUATE EVIDENCE (IARC GROUP-3). STRONG ACID MANUFACTURING PROCESS: KNOWN HUMAN CARCINOGEN (NTP); HUMAN SUFFICIENT EVIDENCE (IARC GROUP-1). WORKERS INVOLVED IN THE MANUFACTURE OF ISOPROPYL ALCOHOL BY THE STRONG-ACID PROCESS, INVOLVING THE FORMATION OF ISOPROPYL OILS, SHOWED AN INCREASE IN PARANASAL AND LARYNGEAL CANCERS. LOCAL EFFECTS: IRRITANT- INHALATION, EYE. ACUTE TOXICITY LEVEL: SLIGHTLY TOXIC BY INGESTION, DERMAL ABSORPTION. TARGET EFFECTS: CENTRAL NERVOUS SYSTEM DEPRESSANT. AT INCREASED RISK FROM EXPOSURE: PERSONS WITH PRE-EXISTING SKIN DISORDERS; IMPAIRED LIVER, RENAL AND/OR PULMONARY FUNCTION. ADDITIONAL INFORMATION: POTENTIATES THE EFFECT OF CARBON TETRACHLORIDE AND OTHER HEPATOTOXIC CHLORINATED ALIPHATIC HYDROCARBONS.

HEALTH EFFECTS AND FIRST AID

INHALATION: ISOPROPYL ALCOHOL (ISOPROPANOL; 2-PROPANOL): IRRITANT/NARCOTIC. 12,000 PPM IMMEDIATELY DANGEROUS TO LIFE OR HEALTH. **ACUTE EXPOSURE-** HUMAN SUBJECTS EXPOSED TO 400 PPM FOR 3-5 MINUTES HAD MILD IRRITATION OF THE NOSE AND THROAT. AT 800 PPM THE IRRITATION WAS NOT SEVERE BUT UNCOMFORTABLE. HIGHER CONCENTRATIONS MAY CAUSE EFFECTS AS DETAILED IN ACUTE INGESTION. THE LENGTH OF TIME REQUIRED TO PRODUCE DEEP NARCOSIS IN ANIMALS WAS INVERSELY PROPORTIONAL TO THE CONCENTRATION: THE ONSET OF DEEP NARCOSIS RANGED FROM 460 MINUTES AT 3250 PPM TO 100 MINUTES AT 24,500 PPM. **CHRONIC EXPOSURE-** MICE SUBJECTED TO 10900 PPM ISOPROPYL ALCOHOL IN AIR FOR ABOUT 4 HOURS/DAY UNTIL THEY HAD ACCUMULATED 123 HOURS OF EXPOSURE WERE NARCOTIZED BUT SURVIVED. REVERSIBLE FATTY CHANGES WERE OBSERVED IN THE LIVER. MALE MICE EXPOSED TO EITHER 1000 OR 5000 PPM OF ISOPROPYL ALCOHOL VAPOR FOR 6 HOURS A DAY FOR 9 EXPOSURES EXHIBITED HYALINE DROPLET NEPHROPATHY. REPRODUCTIVE EFFECTS HAVE BEEN REPORTED IN ANIMALS. THERE HAS BEEN AN INCREASED INCIDENCE OF CANCER OF THE PARANASAL SINUSES, AND POSSIBLY OF THE LARYNX, IN THE MANUFACTURE OF ISOPROPYL ALCOHOL BY THE STRONG ACID PROCESS, INVOLVING THE FORMATION OF ISOPROPYL OILS. IT IS NOT CLEAR WHICH SUBSTANCES ARE RESPONSIBLE.
FIRST AID- REMOVE FROM EXPOSURE AREA TO FRESH AIR IMMEDIATELY. IF BREATHING HAS STOPPED, PERFORM ARTIFICIAL RESPIRATION. KEEP PERSON WARM AND AT REST. TREAT SYMPTOMATICALLY AND SUPPORTIVELY. GET MEDICAL ATTENTION IMMEDIATELY.

SKIN CONTACT: ISOPROPYL ALCOHOL (ISOPROPANOL; 2-PROPANOL): NARCOTIC. **ACUTE EXPOSURE-** CONTACT WITH THE SKIN MAY CAUSE SLIGHT IRRITATION. CONTACT DERMATITIS HAS BEEN REPORTED IN A FEW SENSITIVE INDIVIDUALS. SUBSTANCE MAY BE DERMALLY ABSORBED RESULTING IN SYSTEMIC TOXICITY AS DETAILED IN ACUTE INGESTION. TOXIC EFFECTS MAY BECOME MORE MARKED IF ABSORPTION AND INHALATION OCCUR CONCURRENTLY. **CHRONIC EXPOSURE-** REPEATED OR PROLONGED EXPOSURE MAY CAUSE DERMATITIS DUE TO THE DEFATTING ACTION ON THE SKIN. REPEATED AND PROLONGED EXPOSURE TO THE SKIN OF RABBITS CAUSED SLIGHT ERYTHEMA, DRYING, AND SUPERFICIAL DESQUAMATION.
FIRST AID- REMOVE CONTAMINATED CLOTHING AND SHOES IMMEDIATELY. WASH AFFECTED AREA WITH SOAP OR MILD DETERGENT AND LARGE AMOUNTS OF WATER UNTIL NO EVIDENCE OF CHEMICAL REMAINS (APPROXIMATELY 15-20 MINUTES). GET MEDICAL ATTENTION IMMEDIATELY.

EYE CONTACT: ISOPROPYL ALCOHOL (ISOPROPANOL; 2-PROPANOL): IRRITANT. **ACUTE EXPOSURE-** 400-800 PPM MAY CAUSE IRRITATION. IN RABBIT EYES, A DROP CAUSED MILD TRANSITORY INJURY AND A 50% AQUEOUS SOLUTION AFTER 3 MINUTES CAUSED MODERATE IRRITATION. CONTACT WITH A 70% SOLUTION CAUSED CONJUNCTIVITIS, IRITIS, AND CORNEAL OPACITY. **CHRONIC EXPOSURE-** PROLONGED OR REPEATED EXPOSURE TO VAPORS MAY CAUSE CONJUNCTIVITIS.
FIRST AID- WASH EYES IMMEDIATELY WITH LARGE AMOUNTS OF WATER OR NORMAL SALINE, OCCASIONALLY LIFTING UPPER AND LOWER LIDS, UNTIL NO EVIDENCE OF CHEMICAL REMAINS (APPROXIMATELY 15-20 MINUTES). GET MEDICAL ATTENTION IMMEDIATELY.

INGESTION: ISOPROPYL ALCOHOL (ISOPROPANOL; 2-PROPANOL): NARCOTIC. **ACUTE EXPOSURE-** INGESTION MAY CAUSE ABDOMINAL PAIN, HEMATEMESIS, NAUSEA, VOMITING, AND HEMORRHAGE. CENTRAL NERVOUS SYSTEM DEPRESSION MAY OCCUR WITH HEADACHE, DIZZINESS, FLUSHING, INCOORDINATION, STUPOR, CONFUSION, HYPOTENSION, AREFLEXIA, AND REFRACTORY NARCOSIS. OLIGURIA FOLLOWED BY DIURESIS AND COMA MAY ALSO OCCUR. OTHER SYMPTOMS MAY INCLUDE HYPOGLYCEMIA, TENDERNESS AND EDEMA OF MUSCLES, AND ARRHYTHMIAS. VOMITING WITH ASPIRATION MAY CAUSE ASPIRATION PNEUMONIA. DEPRESSED RESPIRATION AND DEATH DUE TO RESPIRATORY

PARALYSIS MAY OCCUR IN A FEW HOURS AFTER EXPOSURE. SEVERE AND PROLONGED SHOCK MAY LEAD TO SERIOUS OR FATAL RENAL DAMAGE AFTER SEVERAL DAYS. PATHOLOGIC FINDINGS HAVE INCLUDED EXTENSIVE HEMORRHAGIC TRACHEOBRONCHITIS, BRONCHOPNEUMONIA AND HEMORRHAGIC PULMONARY EDEMA. **CHRONIC EXPOSURE-** NO ADVERSE EFFECTS RESULTED IN HUMANS FOLLOWING DAILY INGESTION OF 2.6 AND 6.4 MG/KG FOR 6 WEEKS. RATS THAT INGESTED 0.5 TO 10.0% ISOPROPYL ALCOHOL IN DRINKING WATER FOR 27 WEEKS SHOWED DECREASED BODY WEIGHT. PROLONGED ORAL ADMINISTRATION IN RABBITS PRODUCED ANESTHESIA AND DEATH. REPRODUCTIVE EFFECTS HAVE BEEN REPORTED IN ANIMALS.

FIRST AID- IN RESPIRATORY DEPRESSION, GIVE OXYGEN BY ARTIFICIAL RESPIRATION. GIVE ACTIVATED CHARCOAL. GASTRIC LAVAGE WITH PROTECTED AIRWAY IS USEFUL EVEN IF DELAYED. DO NOT ATTEMPT EMESIS IF RESPIRATION IS DEPRESSED. MAINTAIN BLOOD PRESSURE. TREATMENT SHOULD BE ADMINISTERED BY QUALIFIED MEDICAL PERSONNEL. (DREISBACH, HANDBOOK OF POISONING, 12TH ED.) GET MEDICAL ATTENTION.

ANTIDOTE: NO SPECIFIC ANTIDOTE. TREAT SYMPTOMATICALLY AND SUPPORTIVELY.

REACTIVITY

REACTIVITY: ISOPROPYL ALCOHOL (ISOPROPANOL; 2-PROPANOL): STABLE UNDER NORMAL TEMPERATURES AND PRESSURES. MAY SLOWLY PEROXIDISE ON EXPOSURE TO AIR UNDER NORMAL STORAGE CONDITIONS. AN EXPLOSION HAZARD MAY EXIST IF THE SUBSTANCE IS DISTILLED OR ALLOWED TO EVAPORATE TO DRYNESS.

INCOMPATIBILITIES: ISOPROPYL ALCOHOL (ISOPROPANOL; 2-PROPANOL): ALUMINUM: DISSOLUTION IS EXOTHERMIC. BARIUM PERCHLORATE: FORMATION OF EXPLOSIVE COMPOUND. 2-BUTANONE (METHYL ETHYL KETONE): ACCELERATES THE PEROXIDATION OF THE ALCOHOL. CHROMIUM TRIOXIDE (GRANULAR): IGNITION. COATINGS: MAY BE ATTACKED. DIOXYGENYL TETRAFLUOROBORATE: IGNITION AT AMBIENT TEMPERATURES. HYDROGEN + PALLADIUM (PARTICLES): IGNITION ON EXPOSURE TO AIR. HYDROGEN PEROXIDE: FORMATION OF EXPLOSIVE COMPOUND. KETONES: MARKEDLY INCREASES THE POSSIBILITY OF PEROXIDATION. NITROFORM (TRINITROMETHANE): DISSOLVES LIBERATING HEAT AND POSSIBLY EXPLODING. OLEUM: TEMPERATURE AND PRESSURE INCREASE IN CLOSED CONTAINER. OXIDIZERS (STRONG): FIRE AND EXPLOSION HAZARD. OXYGEN (GAS): AUTOXIDATION, ON EXPOSURE TO LIGHT, RESULTS IN FORMATION OF KETONES AND POTENTIALLY EXPLOSIVE HYDROGEN PEROXIDE. PHOSGENE: IN THE PRESENCE OF IRON SALTS, MAY EXPLODE. PLASTICS: MAY BE ATTACKED. POTASSIUM TERT-BUTOXIDE: IGNITION. RUBBER: MAY BE ATTACKED. SODIUM DICHROMATE + SULFURIC ACID: EXOTHERMIC REACTION WITH POSSIBLE INCANDESCENCE. SEE ALSO ALCOHOLS.

ALCOHOLS: ACETALDEHYDE: VIOLENT CONDENSATION REACTION. BARIUM PERCHLORATE: FORMATION OF HIGHLY EXPLOSIVE PERCHLORIC ESTER ON REFLUXING. CHLORINE: FORMATION OF HIGHLY EXPLOSIVE ALKYL HYPOCHLORITES. DIETHYL ALUMINUM BROMIDE: SPONTANEOUS IGNITION. ETHYLENE OXIDE: POSSIBLE EXPLOSION. HEXAMETHYLENE DIISOCYANATE: POSSIBLE EXPLOSION IN ABSENCE OF SOLVENT. HYDROGEN PEROXIDE + SULFURIC ACID: POSSIBLE EXPLOSION. HYPOCHLOROUS ACID: FORMATION OF HIGHLY EXPLOSIVE ALKYL HYPOCHLORITES. ISOCYANATES: POSSIBLE EXPLOSION IN ABSENCE OF SOLVENT. LITHIUM ALUMINUM HYDRIDE: VIGOROUS REACTION. NITROGEN TETROXIDE: POSSIBLE EXPLOSION. PERCHLORIC ACID (HOT): DANGEROUS INTERACTION. PERMONOSULFURIC ACID: POSSIBLE EXPLOSION ON CONTACT WITH PRIMARY OR SECONDARY ALCOHOLS. TRI-ISO-BUTYL ALUMINUM: VIOLENT REACTION.

DECOMPOSITION: THERMAL DECOMPOSITION PRODUCTS MAY INCLUDE TOXIC OXIDES OF CARBON.

POLYMERIZATION: HAZARDOUS POLYMERIZATION HAS NOT BEEN REPORTED TO OCCUR UNDER NORMAL TEMPERATURES AND PRESSURES.

STORAGE AND DISPOSAL

OBSERVE ALL FEDERAL, STATE AND LOCAL REGULATIONS WHEN STORING OR DISPOSING OF THIS SUBSTANCE. FOR ASSISTANCE, CONTACT THE DISTRICT DIRECTOR OF THE ENVIRONMENTAL PROTECTION AGENCY.

****STORAGE****

STORE IN ACCORDANCE WITH 29 CFR 1910.106.

BONDING AND GROUNDING: SUBSTANCES WITH LOW ELECTROCONDUCTIVITY, WHICH MAY BE IGNITED BY ELECTROSTATIC SPARKS, SHOULD BE STORED IN CONTAINERS WHICH MEET THE BONDING AND GROUNDING GUIDELINES SPECIFIED IN NFPA 77-1983, RECOMMENDED PRACTICE ON STATIC ELECTRICITY.

STORE AWAY FROM INCOMPATIBLE SUBSTANCES.

****DISPOSAL****

DISPOSAL MUST BE IN ACCORDANCE WITH STANDARDS APPLICABLE TO GENERATORS OF HAZARDOUS WASTE, 40 CFR 262. EPA HAZARDOUS WASTE NUMBER D001. 100 POUND CERCLA SECTION 103 REPORTABLE QUANTITY.

CONDITIONS TO AVOID

AVOID CONTACT WITH HEAT, SPARKS, FLAMES, OR OTHER SOURCES OF IGNITION. VAPORS MAY BE EXPLOSIVE AND POISONOUS; DO NOT ALLOW UNNECESSARY PERSONNEL IN AREA. DO NOT OVERHEAT CONTAINERS; CONTAINERS MAY VIOLENTLY RUPTURE AND TRAVEL A CONSIDERABLE DISTANCE IN HEAT OF FIRE.

SPILL AND LEAK PROCEDURES

OCCUPATIONAL SPILL: SHUT OFF IGNITION SOURCES. STOP LEAK IF YOU CAN DO IT WITHOUT RISK. USE WATER SPRAY TO REDUCE VAPORS. FOR SMALL SPILLS, TAKE UP WITH SAND OR OTHER ABSORBENT MATERIAL AND PLACE INTO CONTAINERS FOR LATER DISPOSAL. FOR LARGER SPILLS, DIKE FAR AHEAD OF SPILL FOR LATER DISPOSAL. NO SMOKING, FLAMES OR FLARES IN HAZARD AREA. KEEP UNNECESSARY PEOPLE AWAY; ISOLATE HAZARD AREA AND DENY ENTRY.

PROTECTIVE EQUIPMENT

VENTILATION: PROVIDE LOCAL EXHAUST OR GENERAL DILUTION VENTILATION TO MEET PUBLISHED EXPOSURE LIMITS. VENTILATION EQUIPMENT MUST BE EXPLOSION-PROOF.

RESPIRATOR: THE FOLLOWING RESPIRATORS AND MAXIMUM USE CONCENTRATIONS ARE RECOMMENDATIONS BY THE U.S. DEPARTMENT OF HEALTH AND HUMAN SERVICES, NIOSH POCKET GUIDE TO CHEMICAL HAZARDS; NIOSH CRITERIA DOCUMENTS OR BY THE U.S. DEPARTMENT OF LABOR, 29 CFR 1910 SUBPART Z. THE SPECIFIC RESPIRATOR SELECTED MUST BE BASED ON CONTAMINATION LEVELS FOUND IN THE WORK PLACE, MUST NOT EXCEED THE WORKING LIMITS OF THE RESPIRATOR AND BE JOINTLY APPROVED BY THE NATIONAL INSTITUTE FOR OCCUPATIONAL SAFETY AND HEALTH AND THE MINE SAFETY AND HEALTH ADMINISTRATION (NIOSH-MSHA).

ISOPROPYL ALCOHOL:

1000 PPM- ANY POWERED AIR-PURIFYING RESPIRATOR WITH ORGANIC VAPOR CARTRIDGE(S). ANY CHEMICAL CARTRIDGE RESPIRATOR WITH A FULL FACEPIECE AND ORGANIC VAPOR CARTRIDGE(S).

10,000 PPM- ANY SUPPLIED-AIR RESPIRATOR OPERATED IN A CONTINUOUS FLOW MODE.

12,000 PPM- ANY AIR-PURIFYING FULL FACEPIECE RESPIRATOR (GAS MASK) WITH A CHIN-STYLE OR FRONT- OR BACK-MOUNTED ORGANIC VAPOR CANISTER. ANY SELF-CONTAINED BREATHING APPARATUS WITH A FULL FACEPIECE. ANY SUPPLIED-AIR RESPIRATOR WITH A FULL FACEPIECE.

ESCAPE- ANY AIR-PURIFYING FULL FACEPIECE RESPIRATOR (GAS MASK) WITH A CHIN-STYLE OR FRONT- OR BACK-MOUNTED ORGANIC VAPOR CANISTER. ANY APPROPRIATE ESCAPE-TYPE SELF-CONTAINED BREATHING APPARATUS.

FOR FIREFIGHTING AND OTHER IMMEDIATELY DANGEROUS TO LIFE OR HEALTH CONDITIONS:

SELF-CONTAINED BREATHING APPARATUS WITH FULL FACEPIECE OPERATED IN PRESSURE-DEMAND OR OTHER POSITIVE PRESSURE MODE.

SUPPLIED-AIR RESPIRATOR WITH FULL FACEPIECE AND OPERATED IN PRESSURE-DEMAND OR OTHER POSITIVE PRESSURE MODE IN COMBINATION WITH AN AUXILIARY SELF-CONTAINED BREATHING APPARATUS OPERATED IN PRESSURE-DEMAND OR OTHER POSITIVE PRESSURE MODE.

CLOTHING: EMPLOYEE MUST WEAR APPROPRIATE PROTECTIVE (IMPERVIOUS) CLOTHING AND EQUIPMENT TO PREVENT REPEATED OR PROLONGED SKIN CONTACT WITH THIS SUBSTANCE.

GLOVES: EMPLOYEE MUST WEAR APPROPRIATE PROTECTIVE GLOVES TO PREVENT CONTACT WITH THIS SUBSTANCE.

EYE PROTECTION: EMPLOYEE MUST WEAR SPLASH-PROOF OR DUST-RESISTANT SAFETY GOGGLES TO PREVENT EYE CONTACT WITH THIS SUBSTANCE.

EMERGENCY EYE WASH: WHERE THERE IS ANY POSSIBILITY THAT AN EMPLOYEE'S EYES MAY BE EXPOSED TO THIS SUBSTANCE, THE EMPLOYER SHOULD PROVIDE AN EYE WASH FOUNTAIN WITHIN THE IMMEDIATE WORK AREA FOR EMERGENCY USE.

AUTHORIZED BY- OCCUPATIONAL HEALTH SERVICES, INC.

CREATION DATE: 11/15/89 ***REVISION DATE:*** 06/28/90

MATERIAL SAFETY DATA SHEET

OCCUPATIONAL HEALTH SERVICES, INC.
AGRICULTURE AND PESTICIDE DIVISION
450 SEVENTH AVENUE, SUITE 2407
NEW YORK, NEW YORK 10123
1-800-445-MSDS OR (212) 967-1100

EMERGENCY CONTACT:
JOHN S. BRANSFORD, JR. (615) 292-1180

SUBSTANCE IDENTIFICATION

CAS-NUMBER 50512-35-1
SUBSTANCE: **ISOPROTHIOLANE**
TRADE NAMES/SYNONYMS: PROPANEDIOIC ACID, 1,3-DITHIOLAN-2-YLIDENE-, BIS(1-METHYLETHYL) ESTER; FUJI-ONE; DI-ISOPROPYL 1,3-DITHIOLAN-2-YLIDENEMALONATE; IPT; NNF 109; BIS(1-METHYLETHYL) 1,3-DITHIOLAN-2-YLIDENEPROPANEDIOATE; C12H18O4S2; PST12253
CHEMICAL FAMILY: DITHIOLANE
ESTER
MOLECULAR FORMULA: C12-H18-O4-S2
MOLECULAR WEIGHT: 290.42
CERCLA RATINGS (SCALE 0-3): HEALTH=U FIRE=1 REACTIVITY=0 PERSISTENCE=0
NFPA RATINGS (SCALE 0-4): HEALTH=U FIRE=1 REACTIVITY=0

COMPONENTS AND CONTAMINANTS

COMPONENT: ISOPROTHIOLANE ***PERCENT:*** 100.0
CAS# 50512-35-1
OTHER CONTAMINANTS: NONE
EXPOSURE LIMITS: NO OCCUPATIONAL EXPOSURE LIMITS ESTABLISHED BY OSHA, ACGIH, OR NIOSH.

PHYSICAL DATA

DESCRIPTION: COLORLESS TO WHITE CRYSTALLINE POWDER.
BOILING POINT: 333-336 F (167-169 C) @ 0.5 MMHG
MELTING POINT: 122-131 F (50-55 C) ***SPECIFIC GRAVITY:*** NOT AVAILABLE
VAPOR PRESSURE: NEGLIGIBLE ***SOLUBILITY IN WATER:*** 48 PPM
SOLVENT SOLUBILITY: SOLUBLE IN METHANOL, DIMETHYL SULFOXIDE, ACETONE, CHLOROFORM, BENZENE, XYLENE; MODERATELY SOLUBLE IN N-HEXANE.

FIRE AND EXPLOSION DATA

FIRE AND EXPLOSION HAZARD: SLIGHT FIRE HAZARD WHEN EXPOSED TO HEAT OR FLAME.
FIREFIGHTING MEDIA: DRY CHEMICAL, CARBON DIOXIDE, HALON, WATER SPRAY OR STANDARD FOAM (1987 EMERGENCY RESPONSE GUIDEBOOK, DOT P 5800.4).
FOR LARGER FIRES, USE WATER SPRAY, FOG OR STANDARD FOAM (1987 EMERGENCY RESPONSE GUIDEBOOK, DOT P 5800.4).
FIREFIGHTING: MOVE CONTAINER FROM FIRE AREA IF POSSIBLE. DO NOT SCATTER SPILLED MATERIAL WITH HIGH PRESSURE WATER STREAMS. DIKE FIRE CONTROL WATER FOR LATER DISPOSAL (1987 EMERGENCY RESPONSE GUIDEBOOK, DOT P 5800.4, GUIDE PAGE 31).
USE AGENTS SUITABLE FOR TYPE OF SURROUNDING FIRE. AVOID BREATHING HAZARDOUS VAPORS, KEEP UPWIND.

TOXICITY

ISOPROTHIOLANE: TOXICITY DATA: >10,250 MG/KG SKIN-RAT LD50 (FMCHA2); 1190 MG/KG ORAL-RAT LD50; 1340 MG/KG ORAL-MOUSE LD50. CARCINOGEN STATUS: NONE. ACUTE TOXICITY LEVEL: MODERATELY TOXIC BY INGESTION; SLIGHTLY TOXIC BY DERMAL ABSORPTION. TARGET EFFECTS: NO DATA AVAILABLE.

HEALTH EFFECTS AND FIRST AID

INHALATION: ISOPROTHIOLANE: **ACUTE EXPOSURE-** NO DATA AVAILABLE. **CHRONIC EXPOSURE-** NO DATA AVAILABLE.
FIRST AID- REMOVE FROM EXPOSURE AREA TO FRESH AIR IMMEDIATELY. IF BREATHING HAS STOPPED, PERFORM ARTIFICIAL RESPIRATION. KEEP PERSON WARM AND AT REST. TREAT SYMPTOMATICALLY AND SUPPORTIVELY. GET MEDICAL ATTENTION IMMEDIATELY.

SKIN CONTACT: ISOPROTHIOLANE: **ACUTE EXPOSURE-** THE LETHAL DOSE REPORTED IN RATS WAS >10,250 MG/KG. THE SYMPTOMS WERE NOT REPORTED. **CHRONIC EXPOSURE-** NO DATA AVAILABLE.
FIRST AID- REMOVE CONTAMINATED CLOTHING AND SHOES IMMEDIATELY. WASH AFFECTED AREA WITH SOAP OR MILD DETERGENT AND LARGE AMOUNTS OF WATER UNTIL NO EVIDENCE OF CHEMICAL REMAINS (APPROXIMATELY 15-20 MINUTES). GET MEDICAL ATTENTION IMMEDIATELY.

EYE CONTACT: ISOPROTHIOLANE: **ACUTE EXPOSURE-** NO DATA AVAILABLE. **CHRONIC EXPOSURE-** NO DATA AVAILABLE.
FIRST AID- WASH EYES IMMEDIATELY WITH LARGE AMOUNTS OF WATER OR NORMAL SALINE, OCCASIONALLY LIFTING UPPER AND LOWER LIDS, UNTIL NO EVIDENCE OF CHEMICAL REMAINS (APPROXIMATELY 15-20 MINUTES). GET MEDICAL ATTENTION IMMEDIATELY.

INGESTION: ISOPROTHIOLANE: **ACUTE EXPOSURE-** THE LETHAL DOSE REPORTED IN RATS WAS 1190 MG/KG. THE SYMPTOMS WERE NOT REPORTED. **CHRONIC EXPOSURE-** OFFSPRING OF MICE FED 600 MG/KG ISOPROTHIOLANE ON DAYS 6-12 OF GESTATION SHOWED REDUCED FETAL WEIGHT AND OSSIFICATION CENTERS.
FIRST AID- IF THE PERSON IS CONSCIOUS AND NOT CONVULSING, REMOVE BY GASTRIC LAVAGE AND FOLLOW WITH A CATHARTIC (DREISBACH, HANDBOOK OF POISONING, 12TH ED.). TREAT SYMPTOMATICALLY AND SUPPORTIVELY. GASTRIC LAVAGE SHOULD BE PERFORMED BY QUALIFIED MEDICAL PERSONNEL. GET MEDICAL ATTENTION IMMEDIATELY.
ANTIDOTE: NO SPECIFIC ANTIDOTE. TREAT SYMPTOMATICALLY AND SUPPORTIVELY.

REACTIVITY

REACTIVITY: STABLE UNDER NORMAL TEMPERATURES AND PRESSURES.
INCOMPATIBILITIES: ISOPROTHIOLANE: OXIDIZERS (STRONG): FIRE AND EXPLOSION HAZARD.
DECOMPOSITION: THERMAL DECOMPOSITION PRODUCTS MAY INCLUDE TOXIC OXIDES OF SULFUR AND CARBON.
POLYMERIZATION: HAZARDOUS POLYMERIZATION HAS NOT BEEN REPORTED TO OCCUR UNDER NORMAL TEMPERATURES AND PRESSURES.

STORAGE AND DISPOSAL

OBSERVE ALL FEDERAL, STATE AND LOCAL REGULATIONS WHEN STORING OR DISPOSING OF THIS SUBSTANCE. FOR ASSISTANCE, CONTACT THE DISTRICT DIRECTOR OF THE ENVIRONMENTAL PROTECTION AGENCY.

STORAGE

STORE IN ACCORDANCE WITH 40 CFR 165 RECOMMENDED PROCEDURES FOR THE DISPOSAL AND STORAGE OF PESTICIDES AND PESTICIDE CONTAINERS.
STORE AWAY FROM INCOMPATIBLE SUBSTANCES.

DISPOSAL

DISPOSAL MUST BE IN ACCORDANCE WITH 40 CFR 165 RECOMMENDED PROCEDURES FOR THE DISPOSAL AND STORAGE OF PESTICIDES AND PESTICIDE CONTAINERS.

CONDITIONS TO AVOID

MAY BURN BUT DOES NOT IGNITE READILY. AVOID CONTACT WITH STRONG OXIDIZERS, EXCESSIVE HEAT, SPARKS, OR OPEN FLAME.

SPILL AND LEAK PROCEDURES

OCCUPATIONAL SPILL: SWEEP UP AND PLACE IN SUITABLE CLEAN, DRY CONTAINERS FOR RECLAMATION OR LATER DISPOSAL. DO NOT FLUSH SPILLED MATERIAL INTO SEWER. KEEP UNNECESSARY PEOPLE AWAY.

PROTECTIVE EQUIPMENT

VENTILATION: PROVIDE GENERAL DILUTION VENTILATION.
RESPIRATOR: THE FOLLOWING RESPIRATORS ARE RECOMMENDED BASED ON INFORMATION FOUND IN THE PHYSICAL DATA, TOXICITY AND HEALTH EFFECTS SECTIONS. THEY ARE RANKED IN ORDER FROM MINIMUM TO MAXIMUM RESPIRATORY PROTECTION. THE SPECIFIC RESPIRATOR SELECTED MUST BE BASED ON CONTAMINATION LEVELS FOUND IN THE WORK PLACE, MUST NOT EXCEED THE WORKING LIMITS OF THE RESPIRATOR AND BE JOINTLY APPROVED BY THE NATIONAL INSTITUTE FOR OCCUPATIONAL SAFETY AND HEALTH AND THE MINE SAFETY AND HEALTH ADMINISTRATION (NIOSH-MSHA).
CHEMICAL CARTRIDGE RESPIRATOR WITH AN ORGANIC VAPOR CARTRIDGE(S) WITH A FULL FACEPIECE AND ORGANIC VAPOR CARTRIDGE(S) IN COMBINATION WITH A DUST AND MIST FILTER.
POWERED AIR-PURIFYING RESPIRATOR WITH A TIGHT-FITTING FACEPIECE AND ORGANIC VAPOR CARTRIDGE(S) IN COMBINATION WITH A HIGH-EFFICIENCY PARTICULATE FILTER.
TYPE 'C' SUPPLIED-AIR RESPIRATOR WITH A FULL FACEPIECE OPERATED IN A PRESSURE-DEMAND OR OTHER POSITIVE PRESSURE MODE.
SELF-CONTAINED BREATHING APPARATUS WITH A FULL FACEPIECE OPERATED IN PRESSURE-DEMAND OR OTHER POSITIVE PRESSURE MODE.
FOR FIREFIGHTING AND OTHER IMMEDIATELY DANGEROUS TO LIFE OR HEALTH CONDITIONS:
SELF-CONTAINED BREATHING APPARATUS WITH FULL FACEPIECE OPERATED IN PRESSURE-DEMAND OR OTHER POSITIVE PRESSURE MODE.
SUPPLIED-AIR RESPIRATOR WITH FULL FACEPIECE AND OPERATED IN PRESSURE-DEMAND OR OTHER POSITIVE PRESSURE MODE IN COMBINATION WITH AN AUXILIARY SELF-CONTAINED BREATHING APPARATUS OPERATED IN PRESSURE-DEMAND OR OTHER POSITIVE PRESSURE MODE.
CLOTHING: EMPLOYEE MUST WEAR APPROPRIATE PROTECTIVE (IMPERVIOUS) CLOTHING AND EQUIPMENT TO PREVENT REPEATED OR PROLONGED SKIN CONTACT WITH THIS SUBSTANCE.
GLOVES: EMPLOYEE MUST WEAR APPROPRIATE PROTECTIVE GLOVES TO PREVENT CONTACT WITH THIS SUBSTANCE.
EYE PROTECTION: EMPLOYEE MUST WEAR SPLASH-PROOF OR DUST-RESISTANT SAFETY GOGGLES TO PREVENT EYE CONTACT WITH THIS SUBSTANCE.
EMERGENCY EYE WASH: WHERE THERE IS ANY POSSIBILITY THAT AN EMPLOYEE'S

EYES MAY BE EXPOSED TO THIS SUBSTANCE, THE EMPLOYER SHOULD PROVIDE AN EYE WASH FOUNTAIN WITHIN THE IMMEDIATE WORK AREA FOR EMERGENCY USE.

AUTHORIZED BY- OCCUPATIONAL HEALTH SERVICES, INC.
CREATION DATE: 02/02/90 ***REVISION DATE:*** 05/31/90

MATERIAL SAFETY DATA SHEET

OCCUPATIONAL HEALTH SERVICES, INC.
AGRICULTURE AND PESTICIDE DIVISION
450 SEVENTH AVENUE, SUITE 2407
NEW YORK, NEW YORK 10123
1-800-445-MSDS OR (212) 967-1100

EMERGENCY CONTACT:
JOHN S. BRANSFORD, JR. (615) 292-1180

SUBSTANCE IDENTIFICATION

CAS-NUMBER 34123-59-6
SUBSTANCE: **ISOPROTURON**
TRADE NAMES/SYNONYMS: UREA, N,N-DIMETHYL-N'-(4-1-METHYLETHYL)PHENYL)-; UREA, 3-P-CUMENYL-1,1-DIMETHYL-; N,N-DIMETHYL-N'-(4-1-METHYLETHYL)PHENYL)UREA; 3-P-CUMENYL-1,1-DIMETHYLUREA; 3-(4-ISOPROPYLPHENYL)-1,1-DIMETHYLUREA; N-(4-ISOPROPYLPHENYL)-N',N'-DIMETHYLUREA; ARELON; ALON; BELGRAN; CGA 18731; CL 12150; DPX 6774; GRAMINON; HOE 16410; IP 50; IPURON; TOLKAN; C12H18N2O; PST12254
CHEMICAL FAMILY: SUBSTITUTED UREA
MOLECULAR FORMULA: (C-H3)2-C-H-C6-H4-N-H-C-O-N-(C-H3)2
MOLECULAR WEIGHT: 206.32
CERCLA RATINGS (SCALE 0-3): HEALTH=2 FIRE=1 REACTIVITY=0 PERSISTENCE=2
NFPA RATINGS (SCALE 0-4): HEALTH=2 FIRE=1 REACTIVITY=0

COMPONENTS AND CONTAMINANTS

COMPONENT: ISOPROTURON ***PERCENT:*** 100.0
CAS# 34123-59-6
OTHER CONTAMINANTS: NONE
EXPOSURE LIMITS: NO OCCUPATIONAL EXPOSURE LIMITS ESTABLISHED BY OSHA, ACGIH, OR NIOSH.

PHYSICAL DATA

DESCRIPTION: COLORLESS POWDER. ***MELTING POINT:*** 311-313 F (155-156 C)
SPECIFIC GRAVITY: 1.16 ***VAPOR PRESSURE:*** NEGLIGIBLE
SOLUBILITY IN WATER: 55 PPM @ 20 C
SOLVENT SOLUBILITY: SOLUBLE IN DICHLOROMETHANE, METHANOL; SLIGHTLY SOLUBLE IN BENZENE AND HEXANE.
DECOMPOSES ABOVE 446 F (230 C)

FIRE AND EXPLOSION DATA

FIRE AND EXPLOSION HAZARD: SLIGHT FIRE HAZARD WHEN EXPOSED TO HEAT OR FLAME.
FIREFIGHTING MEDIA: DRY CHEMICAL, CARBON DIOXIDE, HALON, WATER SPRAY OR STANDARD FOAM (1987 EMERGENCY RESPONSE GUIDEBOOK, DOT P 5800.4). FOR LARGER FIRES, USE WATER SPRAY, FOG OR STANDARD FOAM (1987 EMERGENCY RESPONSE GUIDEBOOK, DOT P 5800.4).
FIREFIGHTING: MOVE CONTAINERS FROM FIRE AREA IF POSSIBLE. FIGHT FIRE FROM MAXIMUM DISTANCE. STAY AWAY FROM STORAGE TANK ENDS. DIKE FIRE CONTROL WATER FOR LATER DISPOSAL. DO NOT SCATTER MATERIAL (1987 EMERGENCY RESPONSE GUIDEBOOK, DOT P 5800.4, GUIDE PAGE 55). EXTINGUISH USING AGENT SUITABLE FOR TYPE OF SURROUNDING FIRE. USE WATER IN FLOODING QUANTITIES AS FOG. KEEP SPARKS, FLAMES AND OTHER SOURCES OF IGNITION AWAY. KEEP MATERIAL OUT OF WATER SOURCES AND SEWERS. DO NOT TOUCH MATERIAL AND AVOID BREATHING DUSTS AND FUMES FROM BURNING MATERIAL. KEEP UPWIND.

TOXICITY

ISOPROTURON: TOXICITY DATA: 3350 MG/KG ORAL-MOUSE LD50; 1826 MG/KG ORAL-RAT LD50. CARCINOGEN STATUS: NONE. ACUTE TOXICITY LEVEL: MODERATELY TOXIC BY INGESTION. TARGET EFFECTS: NO DATA AVAILABLE.

HEALTH EFFECTS AND FIRST AID

INHALATION: ISOPROTURON: **ACUTE EXPOSURE-** MANY SUBSTITUTED UREA HERBICIDES ARE MODERATELY IRRITATING TO THE MUCOUS MEMBRANES. **CHRONIC EXPOSURE-** NO DATA AVAILABLE.
FIRST AID- REMOVE FROM EXPOSURE AREA TO FRESH AIR IMMEDIATELY. IF BREATHING HAS STOPPED, PERFORM ARTIFICIAL RESPIRATION. KEEP PERSON WARM AND AT REST. TREAT SYMPTOMATICALLY AND SUPPORTIVELY. GET MEDICAL ATTENTION IMMEDIATELY.

SKIN CONTACT: ISOPROTURON: **ACUTE EXPOSURE-** MANY SUBSTITUTED UREA HERBICIDES ARE MODERATELY IRRITATING TO THE SKIN. A LETHAL DOSE IN RATS BY DERMAL ABSORPTION IS GREATER THAN 3170 MG/KG. **CHRONIC EXPOSURE-** NO DATA AVAILABLE.
FIRST AID- REMOVE CONTAMINATED CLOTHING AND SHOES IMMEDIATELY. WASH AFFECTED AREA WITH SOAP OR MILD DETERGENT AND LARGE AMOUNTS OF WATER UNTIL NO EVIDENCE OF CHEMICAL REMAINS (APPROXIMATELY 15-20 MINUTES). GET MEDICAL ATTENTION IMMEDIATELY.

EYE CONTACT: ISOPROTURON: **ACUTE EXPOSURE-** MANY SUBSTITUTED UREA HERBICIDES ARE MODERATELY IRRITATING TO THE EYES. **CHRONIC EXPOSURE-** NO DATA AVAILABLE.
FIRST AID- WASH EYES IMMEDIATELY WITH LARGE AMOUNTS OF WATER OR NORMAL SALINE, OCCASIONALLY LIFTING UPPER AND LOWER LIDS, UNTIL NO EVIDENCE OF CHEMICAL REMAINS (APPROXIMATELY 15-20 MINUTES). GET MEDICAL ATTENTION IMMEDIATELY.

INGESTION: ISOPROTURON: **ACUTE EXPOSURE-** A LETHAL DOSE IN RATS WAS 1826 MG/KG. **CHRONIC EXPOSURE-** NO OBSERVABLE EFFECTS WERE NOTED IN RATS GIVEN 500 PPM FOR 30 DAYS.
FIRST AID- REMOVE BY GASTRIC LAVAGE AND CATHARSIS. MAINTAIN BLOOD PRESSURE AND AIRWAY. GIVE OXYGEN IF RESPIRATION IS DEPRESSED. DO NOT PERFORM GASTRIC LAVAGE IF VICTIM IS UNCONSCIOUS. GET MEDICAL ATTENTION IMMEDIATELY (DREISBACH, HANDBOOK OF POISONING, 12TH ED.). ADMINISTRATION OF LAVAGE OR OXYGEN SHOULD BE PERFORMED BY QUALIFIED MEDICAL PERSONNEL.
ANTIDOTE: NO SPECIFIC ANTIDOTE. TREAT SYMPTOMATICALLY AND SUPPORTIVELY.

REACTIVITY

REACTIVITY: STABLE UNDER NORMAL TEMPERATURES AND PRESSURES.
INCOMPATIBILITIES: ISOPROTURON: OXIDIZERS (STRONG): FIRE AND EXPLOSION HAZARD.
DECOMPOSITION: THERMAL DECOMPOSITION PRODUCTS MAY INCLUDE TOXIC OXIDES OF CARBON AND NITROGEN.
POLYMERIZATION: HAZARDOUS POLYMERIZATION HAS NOT BEEN REPORTED TO OCCUR UNDER NORMAL TEMPERATURES AND PRESSURES.

STORAGE AND DISPOSAL

OBSERVE ALL FEDERAL, STATE AND LOCAL REGULATIONS WHEN STORING OR DISPOSING OF THIS SUBSTANCE. FOR ASSISTANCE, CONTACT THE DISTRICT DIRECTOR OF THE ENVIRONMENTAL PROTECTION AGENCY.

STORAGE

STORE IN ACCORDANCE WITH 40 CFR 165 RECOMMENDED PROCEDURES FOR THE DISPOSAL AND STORAGE OF PESTICIDES AND PESTICIDE CONTAINERS. STORE AWAY FROM INCOMPATIBLE SUBSTANCES.

DISPOSAL

DISPOSAL MUST BE IN ACCORDANCE WITH 40 CFR 165 RECOMMENDED PROCEDURES FOR THE DISPOSAL AND STORAGE OF PESTICIDES AND PESTICIDE CONTAINERS.

CONDITIONS TO AVOID

MAY BURN BUT DOES NOT IGNITE READILY. CONTAINERS MAY EXPLODE IN HEAT OF FIRE.

SPILL AND LEAK PROCEDURES

OCCUPATIONAL SPILL: DO NOT TOUCH SPILLED MATERIAL. STOP LEAK IF YOU CAN DO IT WITHOUT RISK. USE WATER SPRAY TO REDUCE VAPORS. FOR SMALL SPILLS, TAKE UP WITH SAND OR OTHER ABSORBENT MATERIAL AND PLACE INTO CONTAINERS FOR LATER DISPOSAL. FOR SMALL DRY SPILLS, WITH A CLEAN SHOVEL PLACE MATERIAL INTO CLEAN, DRY CONTAINERS AND COVER. MOVE CONTAINERS FROM SPILL AREA. FOR LARGER SPILLS, DIKE FAR AHEAD OF SPILL FOR LATER DISPOSAL. KEEP UNNECESSARY PEOPLE AWAY. ISOLATE HAZARD AREA AND DENY ENTRY. VENTILATE CLOSED SPACES BEFORE ENTERING.

PROTECTIVE EQUIPMENT

VENTILATION: PROVIDE LOCAL EXHAUST OR GENERAL DILUTION VENTILATION SYSTEM.
RESPIRATOR: THE FOLLOWING RESPIRATORS ARE RECOMMENDED BASED ON INFORMATION FOUND IN THE PHYSICAL DATA, TOXICITY AND HEALTH EFFECTS SECTIONS. THEY ARE RANKED IN ORDER FROM MINIMUM TO MAXIMUM

RESPIRATORY PROTECTION. THE SPECIFIC RESPIRATOR SELECTED MUST BE BASED ON CONTAMINATION LEVELS FOUND IN THE WORK PLACE, MUST NOT EXCEED THE WORKING LIMITS OF THE RESPIRATOR AND BE JOINTLY APPROVED BY THE NATIONAL INSTITUTE FOR OCCUPATIONAL SAFETY AND HEALTH AND THE MINE SAFETY AND HEALTH ADMINISTRATION (NIOSH-MSHA).
CHEMICAL CARTRIDGE RESPIRATOR WITH AN ORGANIC VAPOR CARTRIDGE(S) WITH A FULL FACEPIECE AND ORGANIC VAPOR CARTRIDGE(S) IN COMBINATION WITH A DUST AND MIST FILTER.
POWERED AIR-PURIFYING RESPIRATOR WITH A TIGHT-FITTING FACEPIECE AND ORGANIC VAPOR CARTRIDGE(S) IN COMBINATION WITH A HIGH-EFFICIENCY PARTICULATE FILTER.
TYPE 'C' SUPPLIED-AIR RESPIRATOR WITH A FULL FACEPIECE OPERATED IN A PRESSURE-DEMAND OR OTHER POSITIVE PRESSURE MODE.
SELF-CONTAINED BREATHING APPARATUS WITH A FULL FACEPIECE OPERATED IN PRESSURE-DEMAND OR OTHER POSITIVE PRESSURE MODE.
FOR FIREFIGHTING AND OTHER IMMEDIATELY DANGEROUS TO LIFE OR HEALTH CONDITIONS:
SELF-CONTAINED BREATHING APPARATUS WITH FULL FACEPIECE OPERATED IN PRESSURE-DEMAND OR OTHER POSITIVE PRESSURE MODE.
SUPPLIED-AIR RESPIRATOR WITH FULL FACEPIECE AND OPERATED IN PRESSURE-DEMAND OR OTHER POSITIVE PRESSURE MODE IN COMBINATION WITH AN AUXILIARY SELF-CONTAINED BREATHING APPARATUS OPERATED IN PRESSURE-DEMAND OR OTHER POSITIVE PRESSURE MODE.

CLOTHING: EMPLOYEE MUST WEAR APPROPRIATE PROTECTIVE (IMPERVIOUS) CLOTHING AND EQUIPMENT TO PREVENT REPEATED OR PROLONGED SKIN CONTACT WITH THIS SUBSTANCE.

GLOVES: EMPLOYEE MUST WEAR APPROPRIATE PROTECTIVE GLOVES TO PREVENT CONTACT WITH THIS SUBSTANCE.

EYE PROTECTION: EMPLOYEE MUST WEAR SPLASH-PROOF OR DUST-RESISTANT SAFETY GOGGLES TO PREVENT EYE CONTACT WITH THIS SUBSTANCE.
EMERGENCY EYE WASH: WHERE THERE IS ANY POSSIBILITY THAT AN EMPLOYEE'S EYES MAY BE EXPOSED TO THIS SUBSTANCE, THE EMPLOYER SHOULD PROVIDE AN EYE WASH FOUNTAIN WITHIN THE IMMEDIATE WORK AREA FOR EMERGENCY USE.

AUTHORIZED BY- OCCUPATIONAL HEALTH SERVICES, INC.
CREATION DATE: 10/04/89 ***REVISION DATE:*** 05/14/90

MATERIAL SAFETY DATA SHEET

OCCUPATIONAL HEALTH SERVICES, INC.
AGRICULTURE AND PESTICIDE DIVISION
450 SEVENTH AVENUE, SUITE 2407
NEW YORK, NEW YORK 10123
1-800-445-MSDS OR (212) 967-1100

EMERGENCY CONTACT:
JOHN S. BRANSFORD, JR. (615) 292-1180

SUBSTANCE IDENTIFICATION

CAS-NUMBER 36614-38-7

SUBSTANCE: **<u>ISOTHIOATE</u>**

TRADE NAMES/SYNONYMS: O,O-DIMETHYL S-(2-((1-METHYLETHYL)THIO)ETHYL ESTER PHOSPHORODITHIOIC ACID; S-2-ISOPROPYLTHIOETHYL O,O-DIMETHYL PHOSPHORODITHIOATE; O,O-DIMETHYL S-(2((1-METHYLETHYL)THIO)ETHYL)PHOSPHORODITHIOATE; O,O-DIMETHYL S-((2-ISOPROPYLTHIO)ETHYL) PHOSPHORODITHIOATE; PHOSPHORODITHIOIC ACID, O,O-DIMETHYL S-(2-((1-METHYLETHYL)THIO)ETHYL) ESTER; HOSALON; HOSDON; C7H17O2PS3; PST12275

CHEMICAL FAMILY: ORGANOPHOSPHATE

MOLECULAR FORMULA: C7-H17-O2-P-S3

MOLECULAR WEIGHT: 260.39

CERCLA RATINGS (SCALE 0-3): HEALTH=3 FIRE=U REACTIVITY=U PERSISTENCE=0

NFPA RATINGS (SCALE 0-4): HEALTH=3 FIRE=U REACTIVITY=U

COMPONENTS AND CONTAMINANTS

COMPONENT: ISOTHIOATE ***PERCENT:*** 100
CAS# 36614-38-7

EXPOSURE LIMITS: NO OCCUPATIONAL EXPOSURE LIMITS ESTABLISHED BY OSHA, ACGIH, OR NIOSH.

PHYSICAL DATA

DESCRIPTION: COLORLESS, OILY LIQUID WITH A CHARACTERISTIC ODOR

BOILING POINT: 127-133 F (53-56 C) @ 0.01 MMHG ***SPECIFIC GRAVITY:*** 1.19

VAPOR PRESSURE: 0.0022 MMHG @ 20 C ***SOLUBILITY IN WATER:*** 97 PPM @ 25 C

SOLVENT SOLUBILITY: SOLUBLE IN MOST ORGANIC SOLVENTS

FIRE AND EXPLOSION DATA

FIRE AND EXPLOSION HAZARD: UNKNOWN FIRE AND EXPLOSION HAZARD.

FIREFIGHTING MEDIA: DRY CHEMICAL, CARBON DIOXIDE, HALON, WATER SPRAY OR STANDARD FOAM (1987 EMERGENCY RESPONSE GUIDEBOOK, DOT P 5800.4). FOR LARGER FIRES, USE WATER SPRAY, FOG OR STANDARD FOAM (1987 EMERGENCY RESPONSE GUIDEBOOK, DOT P 5800.4).

FIREFIGHTING: MOVE CONTAINERS FROM FIRE AREA IF POSSIBLE. FIGHT FIRE FROM MAXIMUM DISTANCE. STAY AWAY FROM STORAGE TANK ENDS. DIKE FIRE CONTROL WATER FOR LATER DISPOSAL. DO NOT SCATTER MATERIAL (1987 EMERGENCY RESPONSE GUIDEBOOK, DOT P 5800.4, GUIDE PAGE 55).

TOXICITY

ISOTHIOATE: TOXICITY DATA: 240 MG/KG SKIN-MOUSE LD50; 150 MG/KG ORAL-RAT LD50; 50 MG/KG ORAL-MOUSE LD50. CARCINOGEN STATUS: NONE. ACUTE TOXICITY LEVEL: TOXIC BY DERMAL ABSORPTION AND INGESTION. TARGET EFFECTS: CHOLINESTERASE INHIBITOR. POISONING MAY AFFECT THE NERVOUS SYSTEM.* AT INCREASED RISK FROM EXPOSURE: PERSONS WITH RESPIRATORY AILMENTS, RECENT EXPOSURE TO CHOLINESTERASE INHIBITORS OR IMPAIRED CHOLINESTERASE PRODUCTION, OR LIVER MALFUNCTION.* ADDITIONAL DATA: MAY CROSS THE PLACENTA. HIGH ENVIRONMENTAL TEMPERATURES OR EXPOSURE OF THE CHEMICAL TO VISIBLE OR ULTRAVIOLET LIGHT MAY ENHANCE THE TOXICITY. INTERACTIONS WITH MEDICATIONS MAY OCCUR.*
* MAY BE BASED ON GENERAL INFORMATION ON ORGANOPHOSPHATES.

HEALTH EFFECTS AND FIRST AID

INHALATION: ISOTHIOATE: SEE INFORMATION ON ORGANOPHOSPHATES.
ORGANOPHOSPHATES: CHOLINESTERASE INHIBITOR. **<u>ACUTE EXPOSURE-</u>** WHEN INHALED, THE FIRST EFFECTS OF CHOLINESTERASE INHIBITORS ARE USUALLY RESPIRATORY AND MAY INCLUDE NASAL HYPEREMIA AND WATERY DISCHARGE, COUGH, CHEST DISCOMFORT, DYSPNEA, AND WHEEZING DUE TO INCREASED BRONCHIAL SECRETIONS AND BRONCHOCONSTRICTION. IF SUFFICIENT AMOUNTS ARE ABSORBED, OTHER SYSTEMIC EFFECTS MAY BEGIN WITHIN A FEW MINUTES OR BE DELAYED FOR UP TO 12 HOURS. SYMPTOMS MAY INCLUDE PALLOR, NAUSEA, VOMITING, DIARRHEA, ABDOMINAL CRAMPS, HEADACHE, DIZZINESS, OCULAR PAIN, BLURRED VISION, MIOSIS OR IN SOME CASES, ESPECIALLY INITIALLY, MYDRIASIS, LACRIMATION, SALIVATION, SWEATING, AND CONFUSION. OTHER REPORTED CENTRAL NERVOUS SYSTEM OR NEUROMUSCULAR EFFECTS MAY INCLUDE ATAXIA, SLURRED SPEECH, AREFLEXIA, WEAKNESS, FATIGUE, FASCICULATIONS, TWITCHING, TREMORS POSSIBLY OF THE TONGUE AND EYELIDS, AND EVENTUALLY PARALYSIS OF THE EXTREMITIES AND POSSIBLY OF THE RESPIRATORY MUSCLES. IN SEVERE CASES THERE MAY ALSO BE INVOLUNTARY DEFECATION AND URINATION, CYANOSIS, PSYCHOSIS, HYPERGLYCEMIA, ACUTE PANCREATITIS, CARDIAC IRREGULARITIES, PULMONARY EDEMA, UNCONSCIOUSNESS, CONVULSIONS, AND COMA. DEATH IS PRIMARILY DUE TO RESPIRATORY FAILURE, ALTHOUGH CARDIOVASCULAR EFFECTS INCLUDING CARDIAC ARREST MAY ALSO BE IMPLICATED. LONG TERM SEQUELAE ARE RARE BUT MAY INCLUDE NEUROPSYCHIATRIC DISORDERS AND MYOPATHY WITH MUSCLE TENDERNESS. SOME ORGANOPHOSPHATES MAY CAUSE A DELAYED NEUROPATHY BEGINNING 1-4 WEEKS AFTER AN ACUTE EXPOSURE WHICH MAY OR MAY NOT HAVE CAUSED ACUTE CHOLINERGIC EFFECTS. NUMBNESS, TINGLING, WEAKNESS AND CRAMPING BEGINNING SYMMETRICALLY IN THE LOWER LIMBS MAY PROGRESS TO ATAXIA AND PARALYSIS. IN SEVERE CASES, UPPER LIMB INVOLVEMENT IS POSSIBLE AND FLACCID PARALYSIS MAY PROGRESS TO SPASTIC PARALYSIS WITH EXAGGERATED REFLEXES. IMPROVEMENT MAY OCCUR OVER MONTHS TO YEARS, BUT SOME RESIDUAL IMPAIRMENT USUALLY REMAINS.
<u>CHRONIC EXPOSURE-</u> REPEATED OR PROLONGED EXPOSURE MAY RESULT IN THE EFFECTS OF ACUTE EXPOSURE INCLUDING THE DELAYED NEUROPATHY. OTHER EFFECTS REPORTED IN WORKERS REPEATEDLY EXPOSED INCLUDE IMPAIRED MEMORY AND CONCENTRATION, ACUTE PSYCHOSIS, SEVERE DEPRESSIONS, IRRITABILTY, CONFUSION, APATHY, EMOTIONAL LABILITY, SOCIAL WITHDRAWAL, CONFUSION, HEADACHE, SPEECH DIFFICULTIES, DELAYED REACTION TIMES, SPATIAL DISORIENTATION, NIGHTMARES, SLEEPWALKING, AND DROWSINESS OR INSOMNIA. AN INFLUENZA-LIKE CONDITION WITH HEADACHE, NAUSEA, WEAKNESS, ANOREXIA AND MALAISE HAS ALSO BEEN REPORTED.

FIRST AID- REMOVE FROM EXPOSURE AREA TO FRESH AIR IMMEDIATELY. IF BREATHING HAS STOPPED, GIVE ARTIFICIAL RESPIRATION. MAINTAIN AIRWAY AND BLOOD PRESSURE AND ADMINISTER OXYGEN IF AVAILABLE. KEEP AFFECTED PERSON WARM AND AT REST. TREAT SYMPTOMATICALLY AND SUPPORTIVELY. ADMINISTRATION OF OXYGEN SHOULD BE PERFORMED BY QUALIFIED PERSONNEL. GET MEDICAL ATTENTION IMMEDIATELY.

SKIN CONTACT: ISOTHIOATE: TOXIC. SEE INFORMATION ON ORGANOPHOSPHATES. ORGANOPHOSPHATES: CHOLINESTERASE INHIBITOR. **ACUTE EXPOSURE-** LOCALIZED SWEATING AND FASCICULATIONS MAY OCCUR AT THE SITE OF CONTACT. IF SUFFICIENT AMOUNTS ARE ABSORBED, OTHER EFFECTS OF CHOLINESTERASE INHIBITION AS DESCRIBED IN ACUTE INHALATION MAY OCCUR. SYMPTOMS MAY BE DELAYED 2-3 HOURS, BUT USUALLY NO MORE THAN 12 HOURS. THE RATE OF ABSORPTION IS INCREASED BY THE PRESENCE OF DERMATITIS OR HIGH AMBIENT TEMPERATURES. DELAYED NEUROPATHY IS ALSO POSSIBLE. **CHRONIC EXPOSURE-** REPEATED OR PROLONGED EXPOSURE MAY CAUSE EFFECTS AS DESCRIBED IN ACUTE EXPOSURE. SOME ORGANOPHOSPHATES MAY CAUSE SENSITIZATION.

FIRST AID- REMOVE CONTAMINATED CLOTHING IMMEDIATELY. WASH CONTAMINATED AREAS WITH SOAP AND WATER FOLLOWED BY ALCOHOL (ARENA, POISONING, 4TH ED.). EMERGENCY PERSONNEL SHOULD WEAR GLOVES AND AVOID CONTAMINATION. TREAT RESPIRATORY DIFFICULTY WITH ARTIFICIAL RESPIRATION. GET MEDICAL ATTENTION IMMEDIATELY.

EYE CONTACT: ISOTHIOATE: SEE INFORMATION ON ORGANOPHOSPHATES. ORGANOPHOSPHATES: CHOLINESTERASE INHIBITOR. **ACUTE EXPOSURE-** DIRECT CONTACT MAY CAUSE PAIN, HYPEREMIA, LACRIMATION, TWITCHING OF THE EYELIDS, MIOSIS, AND CILIARY MUSCLE SPASM WITH LOSS OF ACCOMODATION, BLURRED OR DIMMED VISION AND BROWACHE. SOMETIMES MYDRIASIS MAY OCCUR INSTEAD OF MIOSIS. WITH SUFFICIENT EXPOSURE, OTHER SYMPTOMS OF CHOLINESTERASE INHIBITION AS DESCRIBED IN ACUTE INHALATION MAY OCCUR. **CHRONIC EXPOSURE-** REPEATED OR PROLONGED EXPOSURE MAY CAUSE EFFECTS AS DESCRIBED IN ACUTE EXPOSURE. SOME COMPOUNDS HAVE CAUSED TOXIC EFFECTS ON THE CRYSTALLINE LENS, CONJUNCTIVAL THICKENING AND OBSTRUCTION OF THE NASOLACRIMAL CANALS WHEN USED AS MIOTIC EYEDROPS.

FIRST AID- IRRIGATE EYES WITH WATER OR SALINE SOLUTION. IF SYMPTOMS OF POISONING OCCUR, TREAT RESPIRATORY DIFFICULTY WITH ARTIFICIAL RESPIRATION AND OXYGEN. OBSERVE PATIENT FOR AT LEAST 24-36 HOURS (GOSSELIN, CLINICAL TOXICOLOGY OF COMMERCIAL PRODUCTS, 5TH ED.). GET MEDICAL ATTENTION IMMEDIATELY. OXYGEN SHOULD BE ADMINISTERED BY QUALIFIED MEDICAL PERSONNEL.

INGESTION: ISOTHIOATE: TOXIC. SEE INFORMATION ON ORGANOPHOSPHATES. ORGANOPHOSPHATES: CHOLINESTERASE INHIBITOR. **ACUTE EXPOSURE-** WHEN INGESTED, THE FIRST EFFECTS MAY BE NAUSEA, VOMITING, ANOREXIA, ABDOMINAL CRAMPS AND DIARRHEA. GASTROINTESTINAL ABSORPTION MAY CAUSE SYMPTOMS OF CHOLINESTERASE INHIBITION AS DESCRIBED IN ACUTE INHALATION. SYMPTOMS MAY BEGIN WITHIN MINUTES OR BE DELAYED FOR HOURS. DELAYED EFFECTS INCLUDING NEUROPATHY MAY ALSO OCCUR. **CHRONIC EXPOSURE-** REPEATED INGESTION MAY CAUSE EFFECTS AS DESCRIBED IN ACUTE EXPOSURE.

FIRST AID- IF PERSON IS ALERT AND RESPIRATION IS NOT DEPRESSED, GIVE SYRUP OF IPECAC FOLLOWED BY WATER (IF VOMITING OCCURS, KEEP HEAD BELOW HIPS TO PREVENT ASPIRATION). IF CONSCIOUSNESS LEVEL DECLINES OR VOMITING HAS NOT OCCURRED IN 15 MINUTES EMPTY STOMACH BY GASTRIC LAVAGE WITH THE AID OF CUFFED ENDOTRACHEAL TUBE USING ISOTONIC SALINE OR 5% SODIUM BICARBONATE FOLLOW WITH ACTIVATED CHARCOAL. ESTABLISH AND MAINTAIN AIRWAY. TREAT RESPIRATORY DIFFICULTY WITH ARTIFICIAL RESPIRATION AND OXYGEN. DO NOT GIVE MORPHINE, AMINOPHYLLINE, PHENOTHIAZINES, RESERPINE, FUROSEMIDE, OR ETHACRYNIC ACID (MORGAN, RECOGNITION AND MANAGEMENT OF PESTICIDE POISONINGS, 3RD ED.). TREAT SYMPTOMATICALLY AND SUPPORTIVELY. ADMINISTRATION OF OXYGEN AND LAVAGE MUST BE PERFORMED BY QUALIFIED MEDICAL PERSONNEL. GET MEDICAL ATTENTION IMMEDIATELY.

ANTIDOTE: THE FOLLOWING ANTIDOTE(S) HAVE BEEN RECOMMENDED. HOWEVER, THE DECISION AS TO WHETHER THE SEVERITY OF POISONING REQUIRES ADMINISTRATION OF ANY ANTIDOTE AND ACTUAL DOSE REQUIRED SHOULD BE MADE BY QUALIFIED MEDICAL PERSONNEL.

FOR CHOLINESTERASE INHIBITORS: ESTABLISH CLEAR AIRWAY AND TISSUE OXYGENATION BY ASPIRATION OF SECRETIONS, AND IF NECESSARY, BY ASSISTED PULMONARY VENTILATION WITH OXYGEN. IMPROVE TISSUE OXYGENATION AS MUCH AS POSSIBLE BEFORE ADMINISTERING ATROPINE TO MINIMIZE THE RISK OF VENTRICULAR FIBRILLATION. ADMINISTER ATROPINE SULFATE INTRAVENOUSLY, OR INTRAMUSCULARLY IF IV INJECTION IS NOT POSSIBLE. IN MODERATELY SEVERE POISONING ADMINISTER ATROPINE SULFATE, 0.4-2.0 MG REPEATED EVERY 15 MINUTES UNTIL ATROPINIZATION IS ACHIEVED (TACHYCARDIA, FLUSHING, DRY MOUTH, MYDRIASIS). MAINTAIN ATROPINIZATION BY REPEATED DOSES FOR 2-12 HOURS, OR LONGER, DEPENDING ON THE SEVERITY OF POISONING. THE APPEARANCE OF RALES IN THE LUNG BASES, MIOSIS, SALIVATION, NAUSEA, BRADYCARDIA, ARE ALL INDICATIONS OF INADEQUATE ATROPINIZATION. SEVERELY POISONED INDIVIDUALS MAY EXHIBIT REMARKABLE TOLERANCE TO ATROPINE; TWO OR MORE TIMES THE DOSAGES SUGGESTED ABOVE MAY BE NEEDED. PERSONS NOT POISONED OR ONLY SLIGHTLY POISONED, HOWEVER, MAY DEVELOP SIGNS OF ATROPINE TOXICITY FROM SUCH LARGE DOSAGES: FEVER, MUSCLE FIBRILLATIONS, AND DELIRIUM ARE THE MAIN SIGNS OF ATROPINE TOXICITY. IF THESE SIGNS APPEAR WHILE THE PATIENT IS FULLY ATROPINIZED, ATROPINE ADMINISTRATION SHOULD BE DISCONTINUED, AT LEAST TEMPORARILY. OBSERVE TREATED PATIENTS CLOSELY AT LEAST 24 HOURS TO INSURE THAT SYMPTOMS (POSSIBLY PULMONARY EDEMA) DO NOT RECUR AS ATROPINIZATION WEARS OFF. IN VERY SEVERE POISONINGS, METABOLIC DISPOSITION OF TOXICANT MAY REQUIRE SEVERAL HOURS OR DAYS DURING WHICH ATROPINIZATION MUST BE MAINTAINED. MARKEDLY LOWER LEVELS OF URINARY METABOLITES INDICATE THAT ATROPINE DOSAGE CAN BE TAPERED OFF. AS DOSAGE IS REDUCED, CHECK THE LUNG BASES FREQUENTLY FOR RALES. IF RALES ARE HEARD OR OTHER SYMPTOMS RETURN, RE-ESTABLISH ATROPINIZATION PROMPTLY (MORGAN, RECOGNITION AND MANAGEMENT OF PESTICIDE POISONINGS, 3RD ED.). ADMINISTRATION OF ANTIDOTE MUST BE PERFORMED BY QUALIFIED MEDICAL PERSONNEL.

IN CASES OF SEVERE POISONING BY ORGANOPHOSPHATE PESTICIDES IN WHICH RESPIRATORY DEPRESSION, MUSCLE WEAKNESS AND TWITCHINGS ARE SEVERE, GIVE PRALIDOXIME (PROTOPAM-AYERST, 2-PAM), 1.0 GRAM INTRAVENOUSLY AT NO MORE THAN 0.5 GRAM PER MINUTE. DOSAGE OF PRALIDOXIME MAY BE REPEATED IN 1-2 HOURS, THEN AT 10-12 HOUR INTERVALS IF NEEDED. IN VERY SEVERE POISONINGS, DOSAGE RATES MAY BE DOUBLED. TREATMENT WITH PRALIDOXIME WILL BE MOST EFFECTIVE IF GIVEN WITHIN THIRTY-SIX HOURS AFTER POISONING (MORGAN, RECOGNITION AND MANAGEMENT OF PESTICIDE POISONINGS, 3RD ED.). ANTIDOTE SHOULD BE ADMINISTERED BY QUALIFIED MEDICAL PERSONNEL.

REACTIVITY

REACTIVITY: NO SPECIFIC DATA AVAILABLE. HOWEVER, A NUMBER OF PHOSPHATE AND THIOPHOSPHATE ESTERS ARE OF LIMITED THERMAL STABILITY AND UNDERGO HIGHLY EXOTHERMIC SELF-ACCELERATING DECOMPOSITION REACTIONS.

INCOMPATIBILITIES: ISOTHIOATE: NO DATA AVAILABLE.

DECOMPOSITION: THERMAL DECOMPOSITION MAY RELEASE TOXIC OXIDES OF PHOSPHORUS AND SULFUR.

POLYMERIZATION: HAZARDOUS POLYMERIZATION HAS NOT BEEN REPORTED TO OCCUR UNDER NORMAL TEMPERATURES AND PRESSURES.

STORAGE AND DISPOSAL

OBSERVE ALL FEDERAL, STATE AND LOCAL REGULATIONS WHEN STORING OR DISPOSING OF THIS SUBSTANCE. FOR ASSISTANCE, CONTACT THE DISTRICT DIRECTOR OF THE ENVIRONMENTAL PROTECTION AGENCY.

STORAGE

STORE IN ACCORDANCE WITH 40 CFR 165 RECOMMENDED PROCEDURES FOR THE DISPOSAL AND STORAGE OF PESTICIDES AND PESTICIDE CONTAINERS.

DISPOSAL

DISPOSAL MUST BE IN ACCORDANCE WITH 40 CFR 165 RECOMMENDED PROCEDURES FOR THE DISPOSAL AND STORAGE OF PESTICIDES AND PESTICIDE CONTAINERS.

CONDITIONS TO AVOID

MAY BURN BUT DOES NOT IGNITE READILY. CONTAINERS MAY EXPLODE IN HEAT OF FIRE.

SPILL AND LEAK PROCEDURES

OCCUPATIONAL SPILL: DO NOT TOUCH SPILLED MATERIAL. STOP LEAK IF YOU CAN DO IT WITHOUT RISK. USE WATER SPRAY TO REDUCE VAPORS. FOR SMALL SPILLS, TAKE UP WITH SAND OR OTHER ABSORBENT MATERIAL AND PLACE INTO CONTAINERS FOR LATER DISPOSAL. FOR SMALL DRY SPILLS, WITH A CLEAN SHOVEL PLACE MATERIAL INTO CLEAN, DRY CONTAINERS AND COVER. MOVE CONTAINERS FROM SPILL AREA. FOR LARGER SPILLS, DIKE FAR AHEAD OF SPILL FOR LATER DISPOSAL. KEEP UNNECESSARY PEOPLE AWAY. ISOLATE HAZARD AREA AND DENY ENTRY. VENTILATE CLOSED SPACES BEFORE ENTERING.

PROTECTIVE EQUIPMENT

VENTILATION: PROVIDE LOCAL EXHAUST OR PROCESS ENCLOSURE VENTILATION SYSTEM.

RESPIRATOR: THE FOLLOWING RESPIRATORS ARE RECOMMENDED BASED ON INFORMATION FOUND IN THE PHYSICAL DATA, TOXICITY AND HEALTH EFFECTS SECTIONS. THEY ARE RANKED IN ORDER FROM MINIMUM TO MAXIMUM RESPIRATORY PROTECTION. THE SPECIFIC RESPIRATOR SELECTED MUST BE BASED ON CONTAMINATION LEVELS FOUND IN THE WORK PLACE, MUST NOT EXCEED THE WORKING LIMITS OF THE RESPIRATOR AND BE JOINTLY APPROVED BY THE NATIONAL INSTITUTE FOR OCCUPATIONAL SAFETY AND HEALTH AND THE MINE SAFETY AND HEALTH ADMINISTRATION (NIOSH-MSHA).

TYPE 'C' SUPPLIED-AIR RESPIRATOR WITH A FULL FACEPIECE OPERATED IN PRESSURE-DEMAND OR OTHER POSITIVE PRESSURE MODE OR WITH A FULL

FACEPIECE, HELMET OR HOOD OPERATED IN CONTINOUS-FLOW MODE.
SELF-CONTAINED BREATHING APPARATUS WITH A FULL FACEPIECE OPERATED IN PRESSURE-DEMAND OR OTHER POSITIVE PRESSURE MODE.
FOR FIREFIGHTING AND OTHER IMMEDIATELY DANGEROUS TO LIFE OR HEALTH CONDITIONS:
SELF-CONTAINED BREATHING APPARATUS WITH FULL FACEPIECE OPERATED IN PRESSURE-DEMAND OR OTHER POSITIVE PRESSURE MODE.
SUPPLIED-AIR RESPIRATOR WITH FULL FACEPIECE AND OPERATED IN PRESSURE-DEMAND OR OTHER POSITIVE PRESSURE MODE IN COMBINATION WITH AN AUXILIARY SELF-CONTAINED BREATHING APPARATUS OPERATED IN PRESSURE-DEMAND OR OTHER POSITIVE PRESSURE MODE.

CLOTHING: EMPLOYEE MUST WEAR APPROPRIATE PROTECTIVE (IMPERVIOUS) CLOTHING AND EQUIPMENT TO PREVENT ANY POSSIBILITY OF SKIN CONTACT WITH THIS SUBSTANCE.

GLOVES: EMPLOYEE MUST WEAR APPROPRIATE PROTECTIVE GLOVES TO PREVENT CONTACT WITH THIS SUBSTANCE.

EYE PROTECTION: EMPLOYEE MUST WEAR SPLASH-PROOF OR DUST-RESISTANT SAFETY GOGGLES AND A FACESHIELD TO PREVENT CONTACT WITH THIS SUBSTANCE.
EMERGENCY WASH FACILITIES: WHERE THERE IS ANY POSSIBILITY THAT AN EMPLOYEE'S EYES AND/OR SKIN MAY BE EXPOSED TO THIS SUBSTANCE, THE EMPLOYER SHOULD PROVIDE AN EYE WASH FOUNTAIN AND QUICK DRENCH SHOWER WITHIN THE IMMEDIATE WORK AREA FOR EMERGENCY USE.

AUTHORIZED BY- OCCUPATIONAL HEALTH SERVICES, INC.
CREATION DATE: 10/04/89 ***REVISION DATE:*** 05/01/90

MATERIAL SAFETY DATA SHEET

OCCUPATIONAL HEALTH SERVICES, INC.
AGRICULTURE AND PESTICIDE DIVISION
450 SEVENTH AVENUE, SUITE 2407
NEW YORK, NEW YORK 10123
1-800-445-MSDS OR (212) 967-1100

EMERGENCY CONTACT:
JOHN S. BRANSFORD, JR. (615) 292-1180

SUBSTANCE IDENTIFICATION

CAS-NUMBER 18854-01-8
SUBSTANCE: **ISOXATHION**
TRADE NAMES/SYNONYMS: O,O-DIETHYL O-(5-PHENYL-3-ISOXAZOLYL)ESTER PHOSPHOROTHIOIC ACID; O,O-DIETHYL O-5-PHENYLISOXAZOL-3-YL PHOSPHOROTHIOATE; O,O-DIETHYL O-(5-PHENYL-3-ISOXAZOLYL)PHOSPHOROTHIOATE; PHOSPHOROTHIOIC ACID, O,O-DIETHYL O-(5-PHENYL-3-ISOXAZOLYL)ESTER; DIETHYL 5-PHENYL-3-ISOXAZOLYL PHOSPHOROTHIONATE; E-48; SI-6711; KARPHOS; C13H16NO4PS; PST12280
CHEMICAL FAMILY: ORGANOPHOSPHATE
MOLECULAR FORMULA: C13-H16-N-O4-P-S
MOLECULAR WEIGHT: 313.33
CERCLA RATINGS (SCALE 0-3): HEALTH=3 FIRE=0 REACTIVITY=U PERSISTENCE=1
NFPA RATINGS (SCALE 0-4): HEALTH=3 FIRE=0 REACTIVITY=U

COMPONENTS AND CONTAMINANTS

COMPONENT: ISOXATHION ***PERCENT:*** 100
CAS# 18854-01-8
EXPOSURE LIMITS: NO OCCUPATIONAL EXPOSURE LIMITS ESTABLISHED BY OSHA, ACGIH, OR NIOSH.

PHYSICAL DATA

DESCRIPTION: SLIGHTLY YELLOW LIQUID ***BOILING POINT:*** 320 F (160 C) @ 0.15 MMHG
VAPOR PRESSURE: 0.0000012 MMHG @ 25C ***SOLUBILITY IN WATER:*** NEARLY INSOLUBLE
SOLVENT SOLUBILITY: SOLUBLE IN MOST ORGANIC SOLVENTS

FIRE AND EXPLOSION DATA

FIRE AND EXPLOSION HAZARD: NEGLIGIBLE FIRE HAZARD WHEN EXPOSED TO HEAT OR FLAME.
FIREFIGHTING MEDIA: DRY CHEMICAL, CARBON DIOXIDE, HALON, WATER SPRAY OR STANDARD FOAM (1987 EMERGENCY RESPONSE GUIDEBOOK, DOT P 5800.4).
FOR LARGER FIRES, USE WATER SPRAY, FOG OR STANDARD FOAM (1987 EMERGENCY RESPONSE GUIDEBOOK, DOT P 5800.4).
FIREFIGHTING: MOVE CONTAINERS FROM FIRE AREA IF POSSIBLE. FIGHT FIRE FROM MAXIMUM DISTANCE. STAY AWAY FROM STORAGE TANK ENDS. DIKE FIRE CONTROL WATER FOR LATER DISPOSAL. DO NOT SCATTER MATERIAL (1987 EMERGENCY RESPONSE GUIDEBOOK, DOT P 5800.4, GUIDE PAGE 55).

TOXICITY

ISOXATHION: TOXICITY DATA: 450 MG/KG SKIN-RAT LD50; 193 MG/KG SKIN-MOUSE LD50; 112 MG/KG ORAL-RAT LD50; 79100 UG/KG ORAL-MOUSE LD50; 720 MG/KG SUBCUTANEOUS-MOUSE LD50; 105 MG/KG INTRAPERITONEAL-MOUSE LD50. CARCINOGEN STATUS: NONE. ACUTE TOXICITY LEVEL: TOXIC BY DERMAL ABSORPTION AND INGESTION. TARGET EFFECTS: CHOLINESTERASE INHIBITOR. POISONING MAY AFFECT THE NERVOUS SYSTEM.* AT INCREASED RISK FROM EXPOSURE: PERSONS WITH RESPIRATORY AILMENTS, RECENT EXPOSURE TO CHOLINESTERASE INHIBITORS OR IMPAIRED CHOLINESTERASE PRODUCTION, OR LIVER MALFUNCTION.* ADDITIONAL DATA: MAY CROSS THE PLACENTA. HIGH ENVIRONMENTAL TEMPERATURES OR EXPOSURE OF THE CHEMICAL TO VISIBLE OR ULTRAVIOLET LIGHT MAY ENHANCE THE TOXICITY. INTERACTIONS WITH MEDICATIONS MAY OCCUR.*
* MAY BE BASED ON GENERAL INFORMATION ON ORGANOPHOSPHATES.

HEALTH EFFECTS AND FIRST AID

INHALATION: ISOXATHION: SEE INFORMATION ON ORGANOPHOSPHATES.
ORGANOPHOSPHATES: CHOLINESTERASE INHIBITOR. **ACUTE EXPOSURE-** WHEN INHALED, THE FIRST EFFECTS OF CHOLINESTERASE INHIBITORS ARE USUALLY RESPIRATORY AND MAY INCLUDE NASAL HYPEREMIA AND WATERY DISCHARGE, COUGH, CHEST DISCOMFORT, DYSPNEA, AND WHEEZING DUE TO INCREASED BRONCHIAL SECRETIONS AND BRONCHOCONSTRICTION. IF SUFFICIENT AMOUNTS ARE ABSORBED, OTHER SYSTEMIC EFFECTS MAY BEGIN WITHIN A FEW MINUTES OR BE DELAYED FOR UP TO 12 HOURS. SYMPTOMS MAY INCLUDE PALLOR, NAUSEA, VOMITING, DIARRHEA, ABDOMINAL CRAMPS, HEADACHE, DIZZINESS, OCULAR PAIN, BLURRED VISION, MIOSIS OR IN SOME CASES, ESPECIALLY INITIALLY, MYDRIASIS, LACRIMATION, SALIVATION, SWEATING, AND CONFUSION. OTHER REPORTED CENTRAL NERVOUS SYSTEM OR NEUROMUSCULAR EFFECTS MAY INCLUDE ATAXIA, SLURRED SPEECH, AREFLEXIA, WEAKNESS, FATIGUE, FASCICULATIONS, TWITCHING, TREMORS POSSIBLY OF THE TONGUE AND EYELIDS, AND EVENTUALLY PARALYSIS OF THE EXTREMITIES AND POSSIBLY OF THE RESPIRATORY MUSCLES. IN SEVERE CASES THERE MAY ALSO BE INVOLUNTARY DEFECATION AND URINATION, CYANOSIS, PSYCHOSIS, HYPERGLYCEMIA, ACUTE PANCREATITIS, CARDIAC IRREGULARITIES, PULMONARY EDEMA, UNCONSCIOUSNESS, CONVULSIONS, AND COMA. DEATH IS PRIMARILY DUE TO RESPIRATORY FAILURE, ALTHOUGH CARDIOVASCULAR EFFECTS INCLUDING CARDIAC ARREST MAY ALSO BE IMPLICATED. LONG TERM SEQUELAE ARE RARE BUT MAY INCLUDE NEUROPSYCHIATRIC DISORDERS AND MYOPATHY WITH MUSCLE TENDERNESS. SOME ORGANOPHOSPHATES MAY CAUSE A DELAYED NEUROPATHY BEGINNING 1-4 WEEKS AFTER AN ACUTE EXPOSURE WHICH MAY OR MAY NOT HAVE CAUSED ACUTE CHOLINERGIC EFFECTS. NUMBNESS, TINGLING, WEAKNESS AND CRAMPING BEGINNING SYMMETRICALLY IN THE LOWER LIMBS MAY PROGRESS TO ATAXIA AND PARALYSIS. IN SEVERE CASES, UPPER LIMB INVOLVEMENT IS POSSIBLE AND FLACCID PARALYSIS MAY PROGRESS TO SPASTIC PARALYSIS WITH EXAGGERATED REFLEXES. IMPROVEMENT MAY OCCUR OVER MONTHS TO YEARS, BUT SOME RESIDUAL IMPAIRMENT USUALLY REMAINS.
CHRONIC EXPOSURE- REPEATED OR PROLONGED EXPOSURE MAY RESULT IN THE EFFECTS OF ACUTE EXPOSURE INCLUDING THE DELAYED NEUROPATHY. OTHER EFFECTS REPORTED IN WORKERS REPEATEDLY EXPOSED INCLUDE IMPAIRED MEMORY AND CONCENTRATION, ACUTE PSYCHOSIS, SEVERE DEPRESSIONS, IRRITABILTY, CONFUSION, APATHY, EMOTIONAL LABILITY, SOCIAL WITHDRAWAL, CONFUSION, HEADACHE, SPEECH DIFFICULTIES, DELAYED REACTION TIMES, SPATIAL DISORIENTATION, NIGHTMARES, SLEEPWALKING, AND DROWSINESS OR INSOMNIA. AN INFLUENZA-LIKE CONDITION WITH HEADACHE, NAUSEA, WEAKNESS, ANOREXIA AND MALAISE HAS ALSO BEEN REPORTED.
FIRST AID- REMOVE FROM EXPOSURE AREA TO FRESH AIR IMMEDIATELY. IF BREATHING HAS STOPPED, GIVE ARTIFICIAL RESPIRATION. MAINTAIN AIRWAY AND BLOOD PRESSURE AND ADMINISTER OXYGEN IF AVAILABLE. KEEP AFFECTED PERSON WARM AND AT REST. TREAT SYMPTOMATICALLY AND SUPPORTIVELY. ADMINISTRATION OF OXYGEN SHOULD BE PERFORMED BY QUALIFIED PERSONNEL. GET MEDICAL ATTENTION IMMEDIATELY.

SKIN CONTACT: ISOXATHION: TOXIC. SEE INFORMATION ON ORGANOPHOSPHATES.
ORGANOPHOSPHATES: CHOLINESTERASE INHIBITOR. **ACUTE EXPOSURE-** LOCALIZED SWEATING AND FASCICULATIONS MAY OCCUR AT THE SITE OF CONTACT. IF SUFFICIENT AMOUNTS ARE ABSORBED, OTHER EFFECTS OF CHOLINESTERASE INHIBITION AS DESCRIBED IN ACUTE INHALATION MAY OCCUR. SYMPTOMS MAY BE DELAYED 2-3 HOURS, BUT USUALLY NO MORE THAN 12 HOURS. THE RATE OF ABSORPTION IS INCREASED BY THE PRESENCE OF DERMATITIS OR HIGH AMBIENT TEMPERATURES. DELAYED NEUROPATHY IS ALSO

POSSIBLE. **CHRONIC EXPOSURE**- REPEATED OR PROLONGED EXPOSURE MAY CAUSE EFFECTS AS DESCRIBED IN ACUTE EXPOSURE. SOME ORGANOPHOSPHATES MAY CAUSE SENSITIZATION.

FIRST AID- REMOVE CONTAMINATED CLOTHING IMMEDIATELY. WASH CONTAMINATED AREAS WITH SOAP AND WATER FOLLOWED BY ALCOHOL (ARENA, POISONING, 4TH ED.). EMERGENCY PERSONNEL SHOULD WEAR GLOVES AND AVOID CONTAMINATION. TREAT RESPIRATORY DIFFICULTY WITH ARTIFICIAL RESPIRATION. GET MEDICAL ATTENTION IMMEDIATELY.

EYE CONTACT: ISOXATHION: SEE INFORMATION ON ORGANOPHOSPHATES. ORGANOPHOSPHATES: CHOLINESTERASE INHIBITOR. **ACUTE EXPOSURE**- DIRECT CONTACT MAY CAUSE PAIN, HYPEREMIA, LACRIMATION, TWITCHING OF THE EYELIDS, MIOSIS, AND CILIARY MUSCLE SPASM WITH LOSS OF ACCOMODATION, BLURRED OR DIMMED VISION AND BROWACHE. SOMETIMES MYDRIASIS MAY OCCUR INSTEAD OF MIOSIS. WITH SUFFICIENT EXPOSURE, OTHER SYMPTOMS OF CHOLINESTERASE INHIBITION AS DESCRIBED IN ACUTE INHALATION MAY OCCUR. **CHRONIC EXPOSURE**- REPEATED OR PROLONGED EXPOSURE MAY CAUSE EFFECTS AS DESCRIBED IN ACUTE EXPOSURE. SOME COMPOUNDS HAVE CAUSED TOXIC EFFECTS ON THE CRYSTALLINE LENS, CONJUNCTIVAL THICKENING AND OBSTRUCTION OF THE NASOLACRIMAL CANALS WHEN USED AS MIOTIC EYEDROPS.

FIRST AID- IRRIGATE EYES WITH WATER OR SALINE SOLUTION. IF SYMPTOMS OF POISONING OCCUR, TREAT RESPIRATORY DIFFICULTY WITH ARTIFICIAL RESPIRATION AND OXYGEN. OBSERVE PATIENT FOR AT LEAST 24-36 HOURS (GOSSELIN, CLINICAL TOXICOLOGY OF COMMERCIAL PRODUCTS, 5TH ED.). GET MEDICAL ATTENTION IMMEDIATELY. OXYGEN SHOULD BE ADMINISTERED BY QUALIFIED MEDICAL PERSONNEL.

INGESTION: ISOXATHION: TOXIC. SEE INFORMATION ON ORGANOPHOSPHATES. ORGANOPHOSPHATES: CHOLINESTERASE INHIBITOR. **ACUTE EXPOSURE**- WHEN INGESTED, THE FIRST EFFECTS MAY BE NAUSEA, VOMITING, ANOREXIA, ABDOMINAL CRAMPS AND DIARRHEA. GASTROINTESTINAL ABSORPTION MAY CAUSE SYMPTOMS OF CHOLINESTERASE INHIBITION AS DESCRIBED IN ACUTE INHALATION. SYMPTOMS MAY BEGIN WITHIN MINUTES OR BE DELAYED FOR HOURS. DELAYED EFFECTS INCLUDING NEUROPATHY MAY ALSO OCCUR. **CHRONIC EXPOSURE**- REPEATED INGESTION MAY CAUSE EFFECTS AS DESCRIBED IN ACUTE EXPOSURE.

FIRST AID- IF PERSON IS ALERT AND RESPIRATION IS NOT DEPRESSED, GIVE SYRUP OF IPECAC FOLLOWED BY WATER (IF VOMITING OCCURS, KEEP HEAD BELOW HIPS TO PREVENT ASPIRATION). IF CONSCIOUSNESS LEVEL DECLINES OR VOMITING HAS NOT OCCURRED IN 15 MINUTES EMPTY STOMACH BY GASTRIC LAVAGE WITH THE AID OF CUFFED ENDOTRACHEAL TUBE USING ISOTONIC SALINE OR 5% SODIUM BICARBONATE FOLLOW WITH ACTIVATED CHARCOAL. ESTABLISH AND MAINTAIN AIRWAY. TREAT RESPIRATORY DIFFICULTY WITH ARTIFICIAL RESPIRATION AND OXYGEN. DO NOT GIVE MORPHINE, AMINOPHYLLINE, PHENOTHIAZINES, RESERPINE, FUROSEMIDE, OR ETHACRYNIC ACID (MORGAN, RECOGNITION AND MANAGEMENT OF PESTICIDE POISONINGS, 3RD ED.). TREAT SYMPTOMATICALLY AND SUPPORTIVELY. ADMINISTRATION OF OXYGEN AND LAVAGE MUST BE PERFORMED BY QUALIFIED MEDICAL PERSONNEL. GET MEDICAL ATTENTION IMMEDIATELY.

ANTIDOTE: THE FOLLOWING ANTIDOTE(S) HAVE BEEN RECOMMENDED. HOWEVER, THE DECISION AS TO WHETHER THE SEVERITY OF POISONING REQUIRES ADMINISTRATION OF ANY ANTIDOTE AND ACTUAL DOSE REQUIRED SHOULD BE MADE BY QUALIFIED MEDICAL PERSONNEL.

FOR CHOLINESTERASE INHIBITORS: ESTABLISH CLEAR AIRWAY AND TISSUE OXYGENATION BY ASPIRATION OF SECRETIONS, AND IF NECESSARY, BY ASSISTED PULMONARY VENTILATION WITH OXYGEN. IMPROVE TISSUE OXYGENATION AS MUCH AS POSSIBLE BEFORE ADMINISTERING ATROPINE TO MINIMIZE THE RISK OF VENTRICULAR FIBRILLATION. ADMINISTER ATROPINE SULFATE INTRAVENOUSLY, OR INTRAMUSCULARLY IF IV INJECTION IS NOT POSSIBLE. IN MODERATELY SEVERE POISONING ADMINISTER ATROPINE SULFATE, 0.4-2.0 MG REPEATED EVERY 15 MINUTES UNTIL ATROPINIZATION IS ACHIEVED (TACHYCARDIA, FLUSHING, DRY MOUTH, MYDRIASIS). MAINTAIN ATROPINIZATION BY REPEATED DOSES FOR 2-12 HOURS, OR LONGER, DEPENDING ON THE SEVERITY OF POISONING. THE APPEARANCE OF RALES IN THE LUNG BASES, MIOSIS, SALIVATION, NAUSEA, BRADYCARDIA, ARE ALL INDICATIONS OF INADEQUATE ATROPINIZATION.

SEVERELY POISONED INDIVIDUALS MAY EXHIBIT REMARKABLE TOLERANCE TO ATROPINE; TWO OR MORE TIMES THE DOSAGES SUGGESTED ABOVE MAY BE NEEDED. PERSONS NOT POISONED OR ONLY SLIGHTLY POISONED, HOWEVER, MAY DEVELOP SIGNS OF ATROPINE TOXICITY FROM SUCH LARGE DOSAGES: FEVER, MUSCLE FIBRILLATIONS, AND DELIRIUM ARE THE MAIN SIGNS OF ATROPINE TOXICITY. IF THESE SIGNS APPEAR WHILE THE PATIENT IS FULLY ATROPINIZED, ATROPINE ADMINISTRATION SHOULD BE DISCONTINUED, AT LEAST TEMPORARILY. OBSERVE TREATED PATIENTS CLOSELY AT LEAST 24 HOURS TO INSURE THAT SYMPTOMS (POSSIBLY PULMONARY EDEMA) DO NOT RECUR AS ATROPINIZATION WEARS OFF. IN VERY SEVERE POISONINGS, METABOLIC DISPOSITION OF TOXICANT MAY REQUIRE SEVERAL HOURS OR DAYS DURING WHICH ATROPINIZATION MUST BE MAINTAINED. MARKEDLY LOWER LEVELS OF URINARY METABOLITES INDICATE THAT ATROPINE DOSAGE CAN BE TAPERED OFF. AS DOSAGE IS REDUCED, CHECK THE LUNG BASES FREQUENTLY FOR RALES. IF RALES ARE HEARD OR OTHER SYMPTOMS RETURN, RE-ESTABLISH ATROPINIZATION PROMPTLY (MORGAN, RECOGNITION AND MANAGEMENT OF PESTICIDE POISONINGS, 3RD ED.). ADMINISTRATION OF ANTIDOTE MUST BE PERFORMED BY QUALIFIED MEDICAL PERSONNEL.

IN CASES OF SEVERE POISONING BY ORGANOPHOSPHATE PESTICIDES IN WHICH RESPIRATORY DEPRESSION, MUSCLE WEAKNESS AND TWITCHINGS ARE SEVERE, GIVE PRALIDOXIME (PROTOPAM-AYERST, 2-PAM), 1.0 GRAM INTRAVENOUSLY AT NO MORE THAN 0.5 GRAM PER MINUTE. DOSAGE OF PRALIDOXIME MAY BE REPEATED IN 1-2 HOURS, THEN AT 10-12 HOUR INTERVALS IF NEEDED. IN VERY SEVERE POISONINGS, DOSAGE RATES MAY BE DOUBLED. TREATMENT WITH PRALIDOXIME WILL BE MOST EFFECTIVE IF GIVEN WITHIN THIRTY-SIX HOURS AFTER POISONING (MORGAN, RECOGNITION AND MANAGEMENT OF PESTICIDE POISONINGS, 3RD ED.). ANTIDOTE SHOULD BE ADMINISTERED BY QUALIFIED MEDICAL PERSONNEL.

REACTIVITY

REACTIVITY: STABLE AT NORMAL TEMPERATURES AND PRESSURES. MAY DECOMPOSE AT HIGH TEMPERATURES.

INCOMPATIBILITIES: ISOXATHION: ALKALI: MAY CAUSE HYDROLYSIS.

DECOMPOSITION: THERMAL DECOMPOSITION PRODUCTS MAY INCLUDE TOXIC AND HAZARDOUS FUMES OF SULFUR, NITROGEN AND PHOSPHORUS.

POLYMERIZATION: HAZARDOUS POLYMERIZATION HAS NOT BEEN REPORTED TO OCCUR UNDER NORMAL TEMPERATURES AND PRESSURES.

STORAGE AND DISPOSAL

OBSERVE ALL FEDERAL, STATE AND LOCAL REGULATIONS WHEN STORING OR DISPOSING OF THIS SUBSTANCE. FOR ASSISTANCE, CONTACT THE DISTRICT DIRECTOR OF THE ENVIRONMENTAL PROTECTION AGENCY.

STORAGE

STORE IN ACCORDANCE WITH 40 CFR 165 RECOMMENDED PROCEDURES FOR THE DISPOSAL AND STORAGE OF PESTICIDES AND PESTICIDE CONTAINERS.

STORE AWAY FROM INCOMPATIBLE SUBSTANCES.

DISPOSAL

DISPOSAL MUST BE IN ACCORDANCE WITH 40 CFR 165 RECOMMENDED PROCEDURES FOR THE DISPOSAL AND STORAGE OF PESTICIDES AND PESTICIDE CONTAINERS.

CONDITIONS TO AVOID

MAY BURN BUT DOES NOT IGNITE READILY. CONTAINERS MAY EXPLODE IN HEAT OF FIRE.

SPILL AND LEAK PROCEDURES

OCCUPATIONAL SPILL: DO NOT TOUCH SPILLED MATERIAL. STOP LEAK IF YOU CAN DO IT WITHOUT RISK. USE WATER SPRAY TO REDUCE VAPORS. FOR SMALL SPILLS, TAKE UP WITH SAND OR OTHER ABSORBENT MATERIAL AND PLACE INTO CONTAINERS FOR LATER DISPOSAL. FOR SMALL DRY SPILLS, WITH A CLEAN SHOVEL PLACE MATERIAL INTO CLEAN, DRY CONTAINERS AND COVER. MOVE CONTAINERS FROM SPILL AREA. FOR LARGER SPILLS, DIKE FAR AHEAD OF SPILL FOR LATER DISPOSAL. KEEP UNNECESSARY PEOPLE AWAY. ISOLATE HAZARD AREA AND DENY ENTRY. VENTILATE CLOSED SPACES BEFORE ENTERING.

PROTECTIVE EQUIPMENT

VENTILATION: PROVIDE LOCAL EXHAUST OR PROCESS ENCLOSURE VENTILATION SYSTEM.

RESPIRATOR: THE FOLLOWING RESPIRATORS ARE RECOMMENDED BASED ON INFORMATION FOUND IN THE PHYSICAL DATA, TOXICITY AND HEALTH EFFECTS SECTIONS. THEY ARE RANKED IN ORDER FROM MINIMUM TO MAXIMUM RESPIRATORY PROTECTION. THE SPECIFIC RESPIRATOR SELECTED MUST BE BASED ON CONTAMINATION LEVELS FOUND IN THE WORK PLACE, MUST NOT EXCEED THE WORKING LIMITS OF THE RESPIRATOR AND BE JOINTLY APPROVED BY THE NATIONAL INSTITUTE FOR OCCUPATIONAL SAFETY AND HEALTH AND THE MINE SAFETY AND HEALTH ADMINISTRATION (NIOSH-MSHA).

TYPE 'C' SUPPLIED-AIR RESPIRATOR WITH A FULL FACEPIECE OPERATED IN PRESSURE-DEMAND OR OTHER POSITIVE PRESSURE MODE OR WITH A FULL FACEPIECE, HELMET OR HOOD OPERATED IN CONTINOUS-FLOW MODE.

SELF-CONTAINED BREATHING APPARATUS WITH A FULL FACEPIECE OPERATED IN PRESSURE-DEMAND OR OTHER POSITIVE PRESSURE MODE.

FOR FIREFIGHTING AND OTHER IMMEDIATELY DANGEROUS TO LIFE OR HEALTH CONDITIONS:

SELF-CONTAINED BREATHING APPARATUS WITH FULL FACEPIECE OPERATED IN PRESSURE-DEMAND OR OTHER POSITIVE PRESSURE MODE.

SUPPLIED-AIR RESPIRATOR WITH FULL FACEPIECE AND OPERATED IN PRESSURE-DEMAND OR OTHER POSITIVE PRESSURE MODE IN COMBINATION WITH AN

AUXILIARY SELF-CONTAINED BREATHING APPARATUS OPERATED IN PRESSURE-DEMAND OR OTHER POSITIVE PRESSURE MODE.

CLOTHING: EMPLOYEE MUST WEAR APPROPRIATE PROTECTIVE (IMPERVIOUS) CLOTHING AND EQUIPMENT TO PREVENT ANY POSSIBILITY OF SKIN CONTACT WITH THIS SUBSTANCE.

GLOVES: EMPLOYEE MUST WEAR APPROPRIATE PROTECTIVE GLOVES TO PREVENT CONTACT WITH THIS SUBSTANCE.

EYE PROTECTION: EMPLOYEE MUST WEAR SPLASH-PROOF OR DUST-RESISTANT SAFETY GOGGLES AND A FACESHIELD TO PREVENT CONTACT WITH THIS SUBSTANCE.

EMERGENCY WASH FACILITIES: WHERE THERE IS ANY POSSIBILITY THAT AN EMPLOYEE'S EYES AND/OR SKIN MAY BE EXPOSED TO THIS SUBSTANCE, THE EMPLOYER SHOULD PROVIDE AN EYE WASH FOUNTAIN AND QUICK DRENCH SHOWER WITHIN THE IMMEDIATE WORK AREA FOR EMERGENCY USE.

AUTHORIZED BY- OCCUPATIONAL HEALTH SERVICES, INC.

CREATION DATE: 10/04/89 ***REVISION DATE:*** 05/01/90

MATERIAL SAFETY DATA SHEET

OCCUPATIONAL HEALTH SERVICES, INC.
AGRICULTURE AND PESTICIDE DIVISION
450 SEVENTH AVENUE, SUITE 2407
NEW YORK, NEW YORK 10123
1-800-445-MSDS OR (212) 967-1100

EMERGENCY CONTACT:
JOHN S. BRANSFORD, JR. (615) 292-1180

SUBSTANCE IDENTIFICATION

CAS-NUMBER 143-50-0

SUBSTANCE: CHLORDECONE

TRADE NAMES/SYNONYMS: DECACHLOROOCTAHYDRO-1,3,4-METHENO-2H-CYCLOBUTA(CD)PENTALEN-2-ONE; 1,1A,3,3A,4,5,5,5A,5B,6-DECACHLOROOCTAHYDRO-1,3,4-METHENO-2H-CYCLOBUTA (CD)PENTALEN-2-ONE; 1,3,4-METHENO-2H-CYCLOBUTA(CD)PENTALEN-2-ONE, 1,1A,3,3A,4,5,5,5A,5B, 6-DECACHLOROOCTAHYDRO-; DECACHLORO-OCTAHYDRO-1,3,4-METHENO-2H-CYCLOBUTA(CD)PENTALEN-2-ONE; CLORDECONE; COMPOUND 1189; DECACHLOROKETONE; GC 1189; KEPONE; NCI-C00191; ENT 16,391; RCRA U142; STCC 4960140; C10CL10O; PST12330

CHEMICAL FAMILY: HALOGEN COMPOUND, ALICYCLIC

MOLECULAR FORMULA: C10-CL10-O

MOLECULAR WEIGHT: 490.68

CERCLA RATINGS (SCALE 0-3): HEALTH=3 FIRE=0 REACTIVITY=0 PERSISTENCE=3

NFPA RATINGS (SCALE 0-4): HEALTH=3 FIRE=0 REACTIVITY=0

COMPONENTS AND CONTAMINANTS

COMPONENT: CHLORDECONE ***PERCENT:*** 100.0
CAS# 143-50-0

OTHER CONTAMINANTS: NONE

EXPOSURE LIMITS: CHLORDECONE: 1 UG/M3 NIOSH RECOMMENDED 10 HOUR TWA
1 POUND CERCLA SECTION 103 REPORTABLE QUANTITY SUBJECT TO CALIFORNIA PROPOSITION 65 CANCER AND/OR REPRODUCTIVE TOXICITY WARNING AND RELEASE REQUIREMENTS- (JANUARY 1, 1988)

PHYSICAL DATA

DESCRIPTION: TAN TO WHITE SOLID. ***MELTING POINT:*** 662 F (350 C) SUBLIMES

SPECIFIC GRAVITY: NOT AVAILABLE ***VAPOR PRESSURE:*** NEGLIGIBLE

SOLUBILITY IN WATER: 0.4% ***VAPOR DENSITY:*** 16.94

SOLVENT SOLUBILITY: SOLUBLE IN ALCOHOLS, KETONES, ACETIC ACID, ETHANOL, ACETONE, STRONGLY ALKALINE AQUEOUS SOLUTIONS, CORN OILS; SLIGHTLY SOLUBLE IN HYDROCARBON SOLVENTS

FIRE AND EXPLOSION DATA

FIRE AND EXPLOSION HAZARD: NEGLIGIBLE FIRE HAZARD WHEN EXPOSED TO HEAT OR FLAME.

FIREFIGHTING MEDIA: DRY CHEMICAL, CARBON DIOXIDE, HALON, WATER SPRAY OR STANDARD FOAM (1987 EMERGENCY RESPONSE GUIDEBOOK, DOT P 5800.4). FOR LARGER FIRES, USE WATER SPRAY, FOG OR STANDARD FOAM (1987 EMERGENCY RESPONSE GUIDEBOOK, DOT P 5800.4).

FIREFIGHTING: MOVE CONTAINERS FROM FIRE AREA IF POSSIBLE. FIGHT FIRE FROM MAXIMUM DISTANCE. STAY AWAY FROM STORAGE TANK ENDS. DIKE FIRE CONTROL WATER FOR LATER DISPOSAL. DO NOT SCATTER MATERIAL (1987 EMERGENCY RESPONSE GUIDEBOOK, DOT P 5800.4, GUIDE PAGE 55).
USE AGENTS SUITABLE FOR TYPE OF FIRE. COOL CONTAINERS WITH FLOODING AMOUNTS OF WATER. AVOID BREATHING VAPORS OR DUSTS, KEEP UPWIND.

TRANSPORTATION DATA

DEPARTMENT OF TRANSPORTATION HAZARD CLASSIFICATION 49 CFR 172.101: ORM-E

DEPARTMENT OF TRANSPORTATION LABELING REQUIREMENTS 49 CFR 172.101 AND SUBPART E: NONE

DEPARTMENT OF TRANSPORTATION PACKAGING REQUIREMENTS: 49 CFR 173.510 EXCEPTIONS: NONE

TOXICITY

CHLORDECONE: TOXICITY DATA: 345 MG/KG SKIN-RABBIT LD50; 95 MG/KG ORAL-RAT LD50; 65 MG/KG ORAL-RABBIT LD50; 250 MG/KG ORAL-DOG LD50; 126 MG/KG UNREPORTED-MAMMAL LD50; MUTAGENIC DATA (RTECS); REPRODUCTIVE EFFECTS DATA (RTECS); TUMORIGENIC DATA (RTECS). CARCINOGEN STATUS: ANTICIPATED HUMAN CARCINOGEN (NTP); ANIMAL SUFFICIENT EVIDENCE (IARC GROUP-2B). CHLORDECONE WAS TESTED IN MICE AND RATS BY ORAL ADMINISTRATION AND PRODUCED HEPATOCELLULAR CARCINOMAS IN MALES AND FEMALES OF BOTH SPECIES. IN THE ABSENCE OF ADEQUATE DATA IN HUMANS, IT IS REASONABLE, FOR PRACTICAL PURPOSES, TO REGARD CHLORDECONE AS IF IT PRESENTED A CARCINOGENIC RISK TO HUMANS. ACUTE TOXICITY LEVEL: TOXIC BY SKIN ABSORPTION, INGESTION. TARGET EFFECTS: NEUROTOXIN. POISONING MAY ALSO AFFECT THE LIVER AND TESTES. ADDITIONAL DATA: MAY BE EXCRETED IN BREAST MILK. STIMULANTS SUCH AS EPINEPHRINE OR EPHEDRINE MAY INDUCE VENTRICULAR FIBRILLATION

HEALTH EFFECTS AND FIRST AID

INHALATION: CHLORDECONE: NEUROTOXIN. **ACUTE EXPOSURE-** EXCESSIVE EXPOSURE TO CHLORDECONE MAY CAUSE EFFECTS AS DESCRIBED IN CHRONIC EXPOSURE. **CHRONIC EXPOSURE-** REPEATED AND PROLONGED EXPOSURE MAY CAUSE DERMATITIS, NERVOUSNESS, TREMORS, CHEST PAINS, MUSCLE WEAKNESS, ATAXIC GAIT, INCOORDINATION, JOINT PAIN, OPSOCLONUS, SLURRED SPEECH, WEIGHT LOSS, TACHYCARDIA, AND SPLEEN AND LIVER ENLARGEMENT. PERSONALITY CHANGES OF IRRITABILITY, MEMORY IMPAIRMENT, AND MILD DEPRESSION MAY OCCUR. EFFECTS ON THE BRAIN MAY INCLUDE HEADACHE, INCREASED INTRACRANIAL PRESSURE, AND PAPILLEDEMA. IMPAIRED TESTICULAR FUNCTION MAY OCCUR AS INDICATED BY OLIGOSPERMIA AND HYPOMOTILE SPERM. DEMYELINATION OF PERIPHERAL NERVES MAY DEVELOP.

FIRST AID- REMOVE FROM EXPOSURE AREA TO FRESH AIR IMMEDIATELY. IF BREATHING HAS STOPPED, PERFORM ARTIFICIAL RESPIRATION. KEEP PERSON WARM AND AT REST. TREAT SYMPTOMATICALLY AND SUPPORTIVELY. GET MEDICAL ATTENTION IMMEDIATELY.

SKIN CONTACT: CHLORDECONE: NEUROTOXIN/TOXIC. **ACUTE EXPOSURE-** A LETHAL DOSE IN RABBITS BY DERMAL ABSORPTION WAS 345 MG/KG. EFFECTS OF DDT-LIKE TREMORS WERE REPORTED. **CHRONIC EXPOSURE-** REPEATED AND PROLONGED EXPOSURE MAY CAUSE DERMATITIS, NERVOUSNESS, TREMORS, CHEST PAINS, MUSCLE WEAKNESS, ATAXIC GAIT, INCOORDINATION, JOINT PAIN, OPSOCLONUS, SLURRED SPEECH, WEIGHT LOSS, TACHYCARDIA, AND SPLEEN AND LIVER ENLARGEMENT. PERSONALITY CHANGES OF IRRITABILITY, MEMORY IMPAIRMENT, AND MILD DEPRESSION MAY OCCUR. EFFECTS ON THE BRAIN MAY INCLUDE HEADACHE, INCREASED INTRACRANIAL PRESSURE, AND PAPILLEDEMA. IMPAIRED TESTICULAR FUNCTION MAY OCCUR AS INDICATED BY OLIGOSPERMIA AND HYPOMOTILE SPERM. DEMYELINATION OF PERIPHERAL NERVES MAY DEVELOP.

FIRST AID- REMOVE CONTAMINATED CLOTHING AND SHOES IMMEDIATELY. WASH AFFECTED AREA WITH SOAP OR MILD DETERGENT AND LARGE AMOUNTS OF WATER UNTIL NO EVIDENCE OF CHEMICAL REMAINS (APPROXIMATELY 15-20 MINUTES). GET MEDICAL ATTENTION IMMEDIATELY.

EYE CONTACT: CHLORDECONE: **ACUTE EXPOSURE-** NO DATA AVAILABLE. **CHRONIC EXPOSURE-** NO DATA AVAILABLE.

FIRST AID- WASH EYES IMMEDIATELY WITH LARGE AMOUNTS OF WATER OR NORMAL SALINE, OCCASIONALLY LIFTING UPPER AND LOWER LIDS, UNTIL NO EVIDENCE OF CHEMICAL REMAINS (APPROXIMATELY 15-20 MINUTES). GET MEDICAL ATTENTION IMMEDIATELY.

INGESTION: CHLORDECONE: NEUROTOXIN/CARCINOGEN/TOXIC. **ACUTE EXPOSURE-** LETHAL DOSES IN ANIMALS PRODUCED TREMORS PRIOR TO DEATH. **CHRONIC EXPOSURE-** REPEATED EXPOSURE MAY CAUSE DERMATITIS, NERVOUSNESS, TREMORS, CHEST PAINS, MUSCLE WEAKNESS, ATAXIC GAIT, INCOORDINATION, JOINT PAIN, OPSOCLONUS, SLURRED SPEECH, WEIGHT LOSS, TACHYCARDIA, AND SPLEEN AND LIVER ENLARGEMENT. PERSONALITY CHANGES OF IRRITABILITY, MEMORY IMPAIRMENT, AND MILD DEPRESSION MAY OCCUR. CRANIAL EFFECTS MAY INCLUDE INCREASED INTRACRANIAL PRESSURE, HEADACHE AND

PAPILLEDEMA. IMPAIRED TESTICULAR FUNCTION MAY OCCUR AS INDICATED BY OLIGOSPERMIA AND HYPOMOTILE SPERM. DEMYELINATION OF PERIPHERAL NERVES MAY DEVELOP. A DECREASE IN THE SIZE AND NUMBERS OF LITTERS WERE OBSERVED IN A STUDY OF FEMALE MICE FED DOSES AS LOW AS 10 MG/KG FOR ONE MONTH PRIOR TO MATING. REDUCED FETAL WEIGHT AND DEGREE OF OSSIFICATION WERE REPORTED FROM A STUDY OF FEMALE RATS FED 6 MG/KG DURING PREGNANCY; HIGHER DOSES RESULTED IN MATERNAL DEATH AND FETAL DEVELOPMENTAL ABNORMALITIES. A LETHAL DOSE IN RATS AFTER 3-MONTHS WAS 3.2 MG/KG/DAY; A LETHAL DOSE IN RATS AFTER 6-MONTHS WAS 1.5 MG/KG. CHLORDECONE PRODUCED HEPATOCELLULAR CARCINOMAS IN MICE AND RATS.

FIRST AID- IF THE PERSON IS CONSCIOUS AND NOT CONVULSING, REMOVE BY GIVING SYRUP OF IPECAC (IF VOMITING OCCURS, KEEP THE HEAD BELOW THE HIPS TO PREVENT ASPIRATION). GIVE ACTIVATED CHARCOAL FOLLOWED BY GASTRIC LAVAGE. FOLLOW WITH A SALINE CATHARTIC. DO NOT GIVE FATS OR OILS. INTESTINAL LAVAGE WITH 20% MANNITOL (200 ML) BY STOMACH TUBE IS ALSO USEFUL. GIVE ARTIFICIAL RESPIRATION WITH OXYGEN IF RESPIRATION IS DEPRESSED (DREISBACH, HANDBOOK OF POISONING, 12TH ED.). TREAT SYMPTOMATICALLY AND SUPPORTIVELY. LAVAGE AND ADMINISTRATION OF OXYGEN SHOULD BE PERFORMED BY QUALIFIED MEDICAL PERSONNEL. GET MEDICAL ATTENTION IMMEDIATELY.

ANTIDOTE: THE FOLLOWING ANTIDOTE HAS BEEN RECOMMENDED. HOWEVER, THE DECISION AS TO WHETHER THE SEVERITY OF POISONING REQUIRES ADMINISTRATION OF ANY ANTIDOTE AND ACTUAL DOSE REQUIRED SHOULD BE MADE BY QUALIFIED MEDICAL PERSONNEL.

CHLORDECONE POISONING: CHOLESTYRAMINE RESIN (QUESTRAN) CAN BE ADMINISTERED TO INCREASE THE ELIMINATION OF CHLORDECONE UP TO 7-FOLD. PERSONNEL INVOLVED IN THERAPY SHOULD WEAR NEOPRENE GLOVES AS PROTECTION AGAINST CONTAMINATION. (DREISBACH, HANDBOOK OF POISONING, 11TH EDITION)

REACTIVITY

REACTIVITY: STABLE UNDER NORMAL TEMPERATURES AND PRESSURES.

INCOMPATIBILITIES: CHLORDECONE: NO DATA AVAILABLE.

DECOMPOSITION: THERMAL DECOMPOSITION PRODUCTS MAY INCLUDE TOXIC AND CORROSIVE FUMES OF CHLORIDES.

POLYMERIZATION: HAZARDOUS POLYMERIZATION HAS NOT BEEN REPORTED TO OCCUR UNDER NORMAL TEMPERATURES AND PRESSURES.

STORAGE AND DISPOSAL

OBSERVE ALL FEDERAL, STATE AND LOCAL REGULATIONS WHEN STORING OR DISPOSING OF THIS SUBSTANCE. FOR ASSISTANCE, CONTACT THE DISTRICT DIRECTOR OF THE ENVIRONMENTAL PROTECTION AGENCY.

****STORAGE****

STORE IN ACCORDANCE WITH 40 CFR 165 RECOMMENDED PROCEDURES FOR THE DISPOSAL AND STORAGE OF PESTICIDES AND PESTICIDE CONTAINERS.

****DISPOSAL****

DISPOSAL MUST BE IN ACCORDANCE WITH STANDARDS APPLICABLE TO GENERATORS OF HAZARDOUS WASTE, 40CFR 262. EPA HAZARDOUS WASTE NUMBER U142.

CONDITIONS TO AVOID

MAY BURN BUT DOES NOT IGNITE READILY. CONTAINERS MAY EXPLODE IN HEAT OF FIRE.

SPILL AND LEAK PROCEDURES

SOIL SPILL: DIG HOLDING AREA SUCH AS LAGOON, POND OR PIT FOR CONTAINMENT. USE PROTECTIVE COVER SUCH AS A PLASTIC SHEET TO PREVENT MATERIAL FROM DISSOLVING IN FIRE EXTINGUISHING WATER OR RAIN.

WATER SPILL: USE ACTIVATED CARBON TO ABSORB SPILLED SUBSTANCE THAT IS DISSOLVED.

USE SUCTION HOSES TO REMOVE TRAPPED SPILL MATERIAL.

USE MECHANICAL DREDGES OR LIFTS TO EXTRACT IMMOBILIZED MASSES OF POLLUTION AND PRECIPITATES.

THE CALIFORNIA SAFE DRINKING WATER AND TOXIC ENFORCEMENT ACT OF 1986 (PROPOSITION 65) PROHIBITS CONTAMINATING ANY KNOWN SOURCE OF DRINKING WATER WITH SUBSTANCES KNOWN TO CAUSE CANCER AND/OR REPRODUCTIVE TOXICITY.

OCCUPATIONAL SPILL: DO NOT TOUCH SPILLED MATERIAL. STOP LEAK IF YOU CAN DO IT WITHOUT RISK. USE WATER SPRAY TO REDUCE VAPORS. FOR SMALL SPILLS, TAKE UP WITH SAND OR OTHER ABSORBENT MATERIAL AND PLACE INTO CONTAINERS FOR LATER DISPOSAL. FOR SMALL DRY SPILLS, WITH A CLEAN SHOVEL PLACE MATERIAL INTO CLEAN, DRY CONTAINERS AND COVER. MOVE CONTAINERS FROM SPILL AREA. FOR LARGER SPILLS, DIKE FAR AHEAD OF SPILL FOR LATER DISPOSAL. KEEP UNNECESSARY PEOPLE AWAY. ISOLATE HAZARD AREA AND DENY ENTRY. VENTILATE CLOSED SPACES BEFORE ENTERING.

REPORTABLE QUANTITY (RQ): 1 POUND THE SUPERFUND AMENDMENTS AND REAUTHORIZATION ACT (SARA) SECTION 304 REQUIRES THAT A RELEASE EQUAL TO OR GREATER THAN THE REPORTABLE QUANTITY FOR THIS SUBSTANCE BE IMMEDIATELY REPORTED TO THE LOCAL EMERGENCY PLANNING COMMITTEE AND THE STATE EMERGENCY RESPONSE COMMISSION (40 CFR 355.40). IF THE RELEASE OF THIS SUBSTANCE IS REPORTABLE UNDER CERCLA SECTION 103, THE NATIONAL RESPONSE CENTER MUST BE NOTIFIED IMMEDIATELY AT (800) 424-8802 OR (202) 426-2675 IN THE METROPOLITAN WASHINGTON, D.C. AREA (40 CFR 302.6).

PROTECTIVE EQUIPMENT

VENTILATION: PROVIDE LOCAL EXHAUST OR PROCESS ENCLOSURE VENTILATION TO MEET PUBLISHED EXPOSURE LIMITS.

RESPIRATOR: THE FOLLOWING RESPIRATORS ARE RECOMMENDED BASED ON INFORMATION FOUND IN THE PHYSICAL DATA, TOXICITY AND HEALTH EFFECTS SECTIONS. THEY ARE RANKED IN ORDER FROM MINIMUM TO MAXIMUM RESPIRATORY PROTECTION. THE SPECIFIC RESPIRATOR SELECTED MUST BE BASED ON CONTAMINATION LEVELS FOUND IN THE WORK PLACE, MUST NOT EXCEED THE WORKING LIMITS OF THE RESPIRATOR AND BE JOINTLY APPROVED BY THE NATIONAL INSTITUTE FOR OCCUPATIONAL SAFETY AND HEALTH AND THE MINE SAFETY AND HEALTH ADMINISTRATION (NIOSH-MSHA).

TYPE 'C' SUPPLIED-AIR RESPIRATOR WITH A FULL FACEPIECE OPERATED IN PRESSURE-DEMAND OR OTHER POSITIVE PRESSURE MODE OR WITH A FULL FACEPIECE, HELMET OR HOOD OPERATED IN CONTINOUS-FLOW MODE.

SELF-CONTAINED BREATHING APPARATUS WITH A FULL FACEPIECE OPERATED IN PRESSURE-DEMAND OR OTHER POSITIVE PRESSURE MODE.

FOR FIREFIGHTING AND OTHER IMMEDIATELY DANGEROUS TO LIFE OR HEALTH CONDITIONS:

SELF-CONTAINED BREATHING APPARATUS WITH FULL FACEPIECE OPERATED IN PRESSURE-DEMAND OR OTHER POSITIVE PRESSURE MODE.

SUPPLIED-AIR RESPIRATOR WITH FULL FACEPIECE AND OPERATED IN PRESSURE-DEMAND OR OTHER POSITIVE PRESSURE MODE IN COMBINATION WITH AN AUXILIARY SELF-CONTAINED BREATHING APPARATUS OPERATED IN PRESSURE-DEMAND OR OTHER POSITIVE PRESSURE MODE.

CLOTHING: EMPLOYEE MUST WEAR APPROPRIATE PROTECTIVE (IMPERVIOUS) CLOTHING AND EQUIPMENT TO PREVENT ANY POSSIBILITY OF SKIN CONTACT WITH THIS SUBSTANCE.

GLOVES: EMPLOYEE MUST WEAR APPROPRIATE PROTECTIVE GLOVES TO PREVENT CONTACT WITH THIS SUBSTANCE.

EYE PROTECTION: EMPLOYEE MUST WEAR SPLASH-PROOF OR DUST-RESISTANT SAFETY GOGGLES WITH OR WITHOUT A FACESHIELD TO PREVENT CONTACT WITH THIS SUBSTANCE.

EMERGENCY EYE WASH: WHERE THERE IS ANY POSSIBILITY THAT AN EMPLOYEE'S EYES MAY BE EXPOSED TO THIS SUBSTANCE, THE EMPLOYER SHOULD PROVIDE AN EYE WASH FOUNTAIN WITHIN THE IMMEDIATE WORK AREA FOR EMERGENCY USE.

AUTHORIZED BY- OCCUPATIONAL HEALTH SERVICES, INC.
CREATION DATE: 10/04/89 ***REVISION DATE:*** 06/27/90

MATERIAL SAFETY DATA SHEET

OCCUPATIONAL HEALTH SERVICES, INC.
AGRICULTURE AND PESTICIDE DIVISION
450 SEVENTH AVENUE, SUITE 2407
NEW YORK, NEW YORK 10123
1-800-445-MSDS OR (212) 967-1100

EMERGENCY CONTACT:
JOHN S. BRANSFORD, JR. (615) 292-1180

SUBSTANCE IDENTIFICATION

CAS-NUMBER 26087-47-8

SUBSTANCE: IBP

TRADE NAMES/SYNONYMS: PHOSPHOROTHIOIC ACID, O,O-BIS(1-METHYLETHYL)S-(PHENYLMETHYL) ESTER; PHOSPHOROTHIOIC ACID, S-BENZYL O,O-DIISOPROPYL ESTER; S-BENZYL O,O-DI-ISOPROPYL PHOSPHOROTHIOATE; O,O-BIS(1-METHYLETHYL) S-PHENYLMETHYL PHOSPHOROTHIOATE; S-BENZYL DIISOPROPYL PHOSPHOROTHIOLATE; KITAZIN L; KITAZIN P; RICID II; RICID P; PST12355

CHEMICAL FAMILY: ORGANOPHOSPHATE

MOLECULAR FORMULA: C13-H21-O3-P-S

MOLECULAR WEIGHT: 288.37

CERCLA RATINGS (SCALE 0-3): HEALTH=3 FIRE=U REACTIVITY=0 PERSISTENCE=1

NFPA RATINGS (SCALE 0-4): HEALTH=3 FIRE=U REACTIVITY=0

COMPONENTS AND CONTAMINANTS

COMPONENT: IBP ***PERCENT:*** 100
CAS# 26087-47-8
EXPOSURE LIMITS: NO OCCUPATIONAL EXPOSURE LIMITS ESTABLISHED BY OSHA, ACGIH, OR NIOSH.

PHYSICAL DATA

DESCRIPTION: COLORLESS LIQUID ***BOILING POINT:*** 259 F (126 C) @ 0.04 MMHG
MELTING POINT: 73-75 F (23-24 C) ***SPECIFIC GRAVITY:*** NOT AVAILABLE
EVAPORATION RATE: NOT AVAILABLE ***SOLUBILITY IN WATER:*** 0.1% @ 18 C
SOLVENT SOLUBILITY: SOLUBLE IN MOST ORGANIC SOLVENTS

FIRE AND EXPLOSION DATA

FIRE AND EXPLOSION HAZARD: UNKNOWN FIRE AND EXPLOSION HAZARD.
FIREFIGHTING MEDIA: DRY CHEMICAL, CARBON DIOXIDE, HALON, WATER SPRAY OR STANDARD FOAM (1987 EMERGENCY RESPONSE GUIDEBOOK, DOT P 5800.4). FOR LARGER FIRES, USE WATER SPRAY, FOG OR STANDARD FOAM (1987 EMERGENCY RESPONSE GUIDEBOOK, DOT P 5800.4).
FIREFIGHTING: MOVE CONTAINERS FROM FIRE AREA IF POSSIBLE. FIGHT FIRE FROM MAXIMUM DISTANCE. STAY AWAY FROM STORAGE TANK ENDS. DIKE FIRE CONTROL WATER FOR LATER DISPOSAL. DO NOT SCATTER MATERIAL (1987 EMERGENCY RESPONSE GUIDEBOOK, DOT P 5800.4, GUIDE PAGE 55). EXTINGUISH USING AGENT SUITABLE FOR TYPE OF SURROUNDING FIRE. AVOID BREATHING VAPORS AND DUSTS. KEEP UPWIND.

TOXICITY

IBP: TOXICITY DATA: 2836 MG/M3 INHALATION-RAT LC50; 3708 MG/KG SKIN-RAT LD50; 4 GM/KG SKIN-MOUSE LD50; 490 MG/KG ORAL-RAT LD50; 488 MG/KG ORAL-MOUSE LD50; 420 MG/KG ORAL-GUINEA PIG LD50; 525 MG/KG SUBCUTANEOUS-RAT LD50; 1590 MG/KG SUBCUTANEOUS-MOUSE LD50; 220 MG/KG INTRAPERITONEAL-RAT LD50; 335 MG/KG INTRAPERITONEAL-MOUSE LD50; 550 MG/KG UNREPORTED-RAT LD50; 435 MG/KG UNREPORTED-MOUSE LD50; 420 MG/KG UNREPORTED-GUINEA PIG LD50. CARCINOGEN STATUS: NONE. ACUTE TOXICITY LEVEL: TOXIC BY INHALATION AND INGESTION; SLIGHTLY TOXIC BY DERMAL ABSORPTION. TARGET EFFECTS: CHOLINESTERASE INHIBITOR. POISONING MAY AFFECT THE NERVOUS SYSTEM.* AT INCREASED RISK FROM EXPOSURE: PERSONS WITH RESPIRATORY AILMENTS, RECENT EXPOSURE TO CHOLINESTERASE INHIBITORS OR IMAPAIRED CHOLINESTERASE PRODUCTION, OR LIVER MALFUNCTION.* ADDITIONAL DATA: MAY CROSS THE PLACENTA. HIGH ENVIRONMENTAL TEMPERATURES OR EXPOSURE OF THE CHEMICAL TO VISIBLE OR ULTRAVIOLET LIGHT MAY ENHANCE THE TOXICITY. INTERACTIONS WITH MEDICATIONS MAY OCCUR.*

* MAY BE BASED ON GENERAL INFORMATION ON ORGANOPHOSPHATES.

HEALTH EFFECTS AND FIRST AID

INHALATION: IBP: TOXIC. SEE INFORMATION ON ORGANOPHOSPHATES.
ORGANOPHOSPHATES: CHOLINESTERASE INHIBITOR. **ACUTE EXPOSURE-** WHEN INHALED, THE FIRST EFFECTS OF CHOLINESTERASE INHIBITORS ARE USUALLY RESPIRATORY AND MAY INCLUDE NASAL HYPEREMIA AND WATERY DISCHARGE, COUGH, CHEST DISCOMFORT, DYSPNEA, AND WHEEZING DUE TO INCREASED BRONCHIAL SECRETIONS AND BRONCHOCONSTRICTION. IF SUFFICIENT AMOUNTS ARE ABSORBED, OTHER SYSTEMIC EFFECTS MAY BEGIN WITHIN A FEW MINUTES OR BE DELAYED FOR UP TO 12 HOURS. SYMPTOMS MAY INCLUDE PALLOR, NAUSEA, VOMITING, DIARRHEA, ABDOMINAL CRAMPS, HEADACHE, DIZZINESS, OCULAR PAIN, BLURRED VISION, MIOSIS OR IN SOME CASES, ESPECIALLY INITIALLY, MYDRIASIS, LACRIMATION, SALIVATION, SWEATING, AND CONFUSION. OTHER REPORTED CENTRAL NERVOUS SYSTEM OR NEUROMUSCULAR EFFECTS MAY INCLUDE ATAXIA, SLURRED SPEECH, AREFLEXIA, WEAKNESS, FATIGUE, FASCICULATIONS, TWITCHING, TREMORS POSSIBLY OF THE TONGUE AND EYELIDS, AND EVENTUALLY PARALYSIS OF THE EXTREMITIES AND POSSIBLY OF THE RESPIRATORY MUSCLES. IN SEVERE CASES THERE MAY ALSO BE INVOLUNTARY DEFECATION AND URINATION, CYANOSIS, PSYCHOSIS, HYPERGLYCEMIA, ACUTE PANCREATITIS, CARDIAC IRREGULARITIES, PULMONARY EDEMA, UNCONSCIOUSNESS, CONVULSIONS, AND COMA. DEATH IS PRIMARILY DUE TO RESPIRATORY FAILURE, ALTHOUGH CARDIOVASCULAR EFFECTS INCLUDING CARDIAC ARREST MAY ALSO BE IMPLICATED. LONG TERM SEQUELAE ARE RARE BUT MAY INCLUDE NEUROPSYCHIATRIC DISORDERS AND MYOPATHY WITH MUSCLE TENDERNESS. SOME ORGANOPHOSPHATES MAY CAUSE A DELAYED NEUROPATHY BEGINNING 1-4 WEEKS AFTER AN ACUTE EXPOSURE WHICH MAY OR MAY NOT HAVE CAUSED ACUTE CHOLINERGIC EFFECTS. NUMBNESS, TINGLING, WEAKNESS AND CRAMPING BEGINNING SYMMETRICALLY IN THE LOWER LIMBS MAY PROGRESS TO ATAXIA AND PARALYSIS. IN SEVERE CASES, UPPER LIMB INVOLVEMENT IS POSSIBLE AND FLACCID PARALYSIS MAY PROGRESS TO SPASTIC PARALYSIS WITH EXAGGERATED REFLEXES. IMPROVEMENT MAY OCCUR OVER MONTHS TO YEARS, BUT SOME RESIDUAL IMPAIRMENT USUALLY REMAINS. **CHRONIC EXPOSURE-** REPEATED OR PROLONGED EXPOSURE MAY RESULT IN THE EFFECTS OF ACUTE EXPOSURE INCLUDING THE DELAYED NEUROPATHY. OTHER EFFECTS REPORTED IN WORKERS REPEATEDLY EXPOSED INCLUDE IMPAIRED MEMORY AND CONCENTRATION, ACUTE PSYCHOSIS, SEVERE DEPRESSIONS, IRRITABILTY, CONFUSION, APATHY, EMOTIONAL LABILITY, SOCIAL WITHDRAWAL, CONFUSION, HEADACHE, SPEECH DIFFICULTIES, DELAYED REACTION TIMES, SPATIAL DISORIENTATION, NIGHTMARES, SLEEPWALKING, AND DROWSINESS OR INSOMNIA. AN INFLUENZA-LIKE CONDITION WITH HEADACHE, NAUSEA, WEAKNESS, ANOREXIA AND MALAISE HAS ALSO BEEN REPORTED.
FIRST AID- REMOVE FROM EXPOSURE AREA TO FRESH AIR IMMEDIATELY. IF BREATHING HAS STOPPED, GIVE ARTIFICIAL RESPIRATION. MAINTAIN AIRWAY AND BLOOD PRESSURE AND ADMINISTER OXYGEN IF AVAILABLE. KEEP AFFECTED PERSON WARM AND AT REST. TREAT SYMPTOMATICALLY AND SUPPORTIVELY. ADMINISTRATION OF OXYGEN SHOULD BE PERFORMED BY QUALIFIED PERSONNEL. GET MEDICAL ATTENTION IMMEDIATELY.

SKIN CONTACT: IBP: SEE INFORMATION ON ORGANOPHOSPHATES.
ORGANOPHOSPHATES: CHOLINESTERASE INHIBITOR. **ACUTE EXPOSURE-** LOCALIZED SWEATING AND FASCICULATIONS MAY OCCUR AT THE SITE OF CONTACT. IF SUFFICIENT AMOUNTS ARE ABSORBED, OTHER EFFECTS OF CHOLINESTERASE INHIBITION AS DESCRIBED IN ACUTE INHALATION MAY OCCUR. SYMPTOMS MAY BE DELAYED 2-3 HOURS, BUT USUALLY NO MORE THAN 12 HOURS. THE RATE OF ABSORPTION IS INCREASED BY THE PRESENCE OF DERMATITIS OR HIGH AMBIENT TEMPERATURES. DELAYED NEUROPATHY IS ALSO POSSIBLE. **CHRONIC EXPOSURE-** REPEATED OR PROLONGED EXPOSURE MAY CAUSE EFFECTS AS DESCRIBED IN ACUTE EXPOSURE. SOME ORGANOPHOSPHATES MAY CAUSE SENSITIZATION.
FIRST AID- REMOVE CONTAMINATED CLOTHING IMMEDIATELY. WASH CONTAMINATED AREAS WITH SOAP AND WATER FOLLOWED BY ALCOHOL (ARENA, POISONING, 4TH ED.). EMERGENCY PERSONNEL SHOULD WEAR GLOVES AND AVOID CONTAMINATION. TREAT RESPIRATORY DIFFICULTY WITH ARTIFICIAL RESPIRATION. GET MEDICAL ATTENTION IMMEDIATELY.

EYE CONTACT: IBP: SEE INFORMATION ON ORGANOPHOSPHATES.
ORGANOPHOSPHATES: CHOLINESTERASE INHIBITOR. **ACUTE EXPOSURE-** DIRECT CONTACT MAY CAUSE PAIN, HYPEREMIA, LACRIMATION, TWITCHING OF THE EYELIDS, MIOSIS, AND CILIARY MUSCLE SPASM WITH LOSS OF ACCOMODATION, BLURRED OR DIMMED VISION AND BROWACHE. SOMETIMES MYDRIASIS MAY OCCUR INSTEAD OF MIOSIS. WITH SUFFICIENT EXPOSURE, OTHER SYMPTOMS OF CHOLINESTERASE INHIBITION AS DESCRIBED IN ACUTE INHALATION MAY OCCUR. **CHRONIC EXPOSURE-** REPEATED OR PROLONGED EXPOSURE MAY CAUSE EFFECTS AS DESCRIBED IN ACUTE EXPOSURE. SOME COMPOUNDS HAVE CAUSED TOXIC EFFECTS ON THE CRYSTALLINE LENS, CONJUNCTIVAL THICKENING AND OBSTRUCTION OF THE NASOLACRIMAL CANALS WHEN USED AS MIOTIC EYEDROPS.
FIRST AID- IRRIGATE EYES WITH WATER OR SALINE SOLUTION. IF SYMPTOMS OF POISONING OCCUR, TREAT RESPIRATORY DIFFICULTY WITH ARTIFICIAL RESPIRATION AND OXYGEN. OBSERVE PATIENT FOR AT LEAST 24-36 HOURS (GOSSELIN, CLINICAL TOXICOLOGY OF COMMERCIAL PRODUCTS, 5TH ED.). GET MEDICAL ATTENTION IMMEDIATELY. OXYGEN SHOULD BE ADMINISTERED BY QUALIFIED MEDICAL PERSONNEL.

INGESTION: IBP: TOXIC. SEE INFORMATION ON ORGANOPHOSPHATES.
ORGANOPHOSPHATES: CHOLINESTERASE INHIBITOR. **ACUTE EXPOSURE-** WHEN INGESTED, THE FIRST EFFECTS MAY BE NAUSEA, VOMITING, ANOREXIA, ABDOMINAL CRAMPS AND DIARRHEA. GASTROINTESTINAL ABSORPTION MAY CAUSE SYMPTOMS OF CHOLINESTERASE INHIBITION AS DESCRIBED IN ACUTE INHALATION. SYMPTOMS MAY BEGIN WITHIN MINUTES OR BE DELAYED FOR HOURS. DELAYED EFFECTS INCLUDING NEUROPATHY MAY ALSO OCCUR. **CHRONIC EXPOSURE-** REPEATED INGESTION MAY CAUSE EFFECTS AS DESCRIBED IN ACUTE EXPOSURE.
FIRST AID- IF PERSON IS ALERT AND RESPIRATION IS NOT DEPRESSED, GIVE SYRUP OF IPECAC FOLLOWED BY WATER (IF VOMITING OCCURS, KEEP HEAD BELOW HIPS TO PREVENT ASPIRATION). IF CONSCIOUSNESS LEVEL DECLINES OR VOMITING HAS NOT OCCURRED IN 15 MINUTES EMPTY STOMACH BY GASTRIC LAVAGE WITH THE AID OF CUFFED ENDOTRACHEAL TUBE USING ISOTONIC SALINE OR 5% SODIUM BICARBONATE FOLLOW WITH ACTIVATED CHARCOAL. ESTABLISH AND MAINTAIN AIRWAY. TREAT RESPIRATORY DIFFICULTY WITH ARTIFICIAL RESPIRATION AND OXYGEN. DO NOT GIVE MORPHINE, AMINOPHYLLINE, PHENOTHIAZINES, RESERPINE, FUROSEMIDE, OR ETHACRYNIC ACID (MORGAN, RECOGNITION AND MANAGEMENT OF PESTICIDE POISONINGS, 3RD ED.). TREAT SYMPTOMATICALLY AND SUPPORTIVELY. ADMINISTRATION OF OXYGEN AND LAVAGE MUST BE PERFORMED BY QUALIFIED MEDICAL PERSONNEL. GET MEDICAL ATTENTION IMMEDIATELY.
ANTIDOTE: THE FOLLOWING ANTIDOTE(S) HAVE BEEN RECOMMENDED. HOWEVER, THE DECISION AS TO WHETHER THE SEVERITY OF POISONING REQUIRES ADMINISTRATION OF ANY ANTIDOTE AND ACTUAL DOSE REQUIRED SHOULD BE MADE BY QUALIFIED MEDICAL PERSONNEL.

FOR CHOLINESTERASE INHIBITORS: ESTABLISH CLEAR AIRWAY AND TISSUE OXYGENATION BY ASPIRATION OF SECRETIONS, AND IF NECESSARY, BY ASSISTED PULMONARY VENTILATION WITH OXYGEN. IMPROVE TISSUE OXYGENATION AS MUCH AS POSSIBLE BEFORE ADMINISTERING ATROPINE TO MINIMIZE THE RISK OF VENTRICULAR FIBRILLATION. ADMINISTER ATROPINE SULFATE INTRAVENOUSLY, OR INTRAMUSCULARLY IF IV INJECTION IS NOT POSSIBLE. IN MODERATELY SEVERE POISONING ADMINISTER ATROPINE SULFATE, 0.4-2.0 MG REPEATED EVERY 15 MINUTES UNTIL ATROPINIZATION IS ACHIEVED (TACHYCARDIA, FLUSHING, DRY MOUTH, MYDRIASIS). MAINTAIN ATROPINIZATION BY REPEATED DOSES FOR 2-12 HOURS, OR LONGER, DEPENDING ON THE SEVERITY OF POISONING. THE APPEARANCE OF RALES IN THE LUNG BASES, MIOSIS, SALIVATION, NAUSEA, BRADYCARDIA, ARE ALL INDICATIONS OF INADEQUATE ATROPINIZATION. SEVERELY POISONED INDIVIDUALS MAY EXHIBIT REMARKABLE TOLERANCE TO ATROPINE; TWO OR MORE TIMES THE DOSAGES SUGGESTED ABOVE MAY BE NEEDED. PERSONS NOT POISONED OR ONLY SLIGHTLY POISONED, HOWEVER, MAY DEVELOP SIGNS OF ATROPINE TOXICITY FROM SUCH LARGE DOSAGES: FEVER, MUSCLE FIBRILLATIONS, AND DELIRIUM ARE THE MAIN SIGNS OF ATROPINE TOXICITY. IF THESE SIGNS APPEAR WHILE THE PATIENT IS FULLY ATROPINIZED, ATROPINE ADMINISTRATION SHOULD BE DISCONTINUED, AT LEAST TEMPORARILY. OBSERVE TREATED PATIENTS CLOSELY AT LEAST 24 HOURS TO INSURE THAT SYMPTOMS (POSSIBLY PULMONARY EDEMA) DO NOT RECUR AS ATROPINIZATION WEARS OFF. IN VERY SEVERE POISONINGS, METABOLIC DISPOSITION OF TOXICANT MAY REQUIRE SEVERAL HOURS OR DAYS DURING WHICH ATROPINIZATION MUST BE MAINTAINED. MARKEDLY LOWER LEVELS OF URINARY METABOLITES INDICATE THAT ATROPINE DOSAGE CAN BE TAPERED OFF. AS DOSAGE IS REDUCED, CHECK THE LUNG BASES FREQUENTLY FOR RALES. IF RALES ARE HEARD OR OTHER SYMPTOMS RETURN, RE-ESTABLISH ATROPINIZATION PROMPTLY (MORGAN, RECOGNITION AND MANAGEMENT OF PESTICIDE POISONINGS, 3RD ED.). ADMINISTRATION OF ANTIDOTE MUST BE PERFORMED BY QUALIFIED MEDICAL PERSONNEL.

IN CASES OF SEVERE POISONING BY ORGANOPHOSPHATE PESTICIDES IN WHICH RESPIRATORY DEPRESSION, MUSCLE WEAKNESS AND TWITCHINGS ARE SEVERE, GIVE PRALIDOXIME (PROTOPAM-AYERST, 2-PAM), 1.0 GRAM INTRAVENOUSLY AT NO MORE THAN 0.5 GRAM PER MINUTE. DOSAGE OF PRALIDOXIME MAY BE REPEATED IN 1-2 HOURS, THEN AT 10-12 HOUR INTERVALS IF NEEDED. IN VERY SEVERE POISONINGS, DOSAGE RATES MAY BE DOUBLED. TREATMENT WITH PRALIDOXIME WILL BE MOST EFFECTIVE IF GIVEN WITHIN THIRTY-SIX HOURS AFTER POISONING (MORGAN, RECOGNITION AND MANAGEMENT OF PESTICIDE POISONINGS, 3RD ED.). ANTIDOTE SHOULD BE ADMINISTERED BY QUALIFIED MEDICAL PERSONNEL.

REACTIVITY

REACTIVITY: STABLE UNDER NORMAL TEMPERATURES AND PRESSURES.

INCOMPATIBILITIES: IBP: NO DATA AVAILABLE.

DECOMPOSITION: THERMAL DECOMPOSITION MAY RELEASE TOXIC OXIDES OF PHOSPHORUS AND SULFUR.

POLYMERIZATION: HAZARDOUS POLYMERIZATION HAS NOT BEEN REPORTED TO OCCUR UNDER NORMAL TEMPERATURES AND PRESSURES.

STORAGE AND DISPOSAL

OBSERVE ALL FEDERAL, STATE AND LOCAL REGULATIONS WHEN STORING OR DISPOSING OF THIS SUBSTANCE. FOR ASSISTANCE, CONTACT THE DISTRICT DIRECTOR OF THE ENVIRONMENTAL PROTECTION AGENCY.

STORAGE

STORE IN ACCORDANCE WITH 40 CFR 165 RECOMMENDED PROCEDURES FOR THE DISPOSAL AND STORAGE OF PESTICIDES AND PESTICIDE CONTAINERS.

DISPOSAL

DISPOSAL MUST BE IN ACCORDANCE WITH 40 CFR 165 RECOMMENDED PROCEDURES FOR THE DISPOSAL AND STORAGE OF PESTICIDES AND PESTICIDE CONTAINERS.

CONDITIONS TO AVOID

NONE REPORTED.

SPILL AND LEAK PROCEDURES

OCCUPATIONAL SPILL: DO NOT TOUCH SPILLED MATERIAL. STOP LEAK IF YOU CAN DO IT WITHOUT RISK. USE WATER SPRAY TO REDUCE VAPORS. FOR SMALL SPILLS, TAKE UP WITH SAND OR OTHER ABSORBENT MATERIAL AND PLACE INTO CONTAINERS FOR LATER DISPOSAL. FOR SMALL DRY SPILLS, WITH A CLEAN SHOVEL PLACE MATERIAL INTO CLEAN, DRY CONTAINERS AND COVER. MOVE CONTAINERS FROM SPILL AREA. FOR LARGER SPILLS, DIKE FAR AHEAD OF SPILL FOR LATER DISPOSAL. KEEP UNNECESSARY PEOPLE AWAY. ISOLATE HAZARD AREA AND DENY ENTRY. VENTILATE CLOSED SPACES BEFORE ENTERING.

PROTECTIVE EQUIPMENT

VENTILATION: PROVIDE LOCAL EXHAUST VENTILATION SYSTEM.

RESPIRATOR: THE FOLLOWING RESPIRATORS ARE RECOMMENDED BASED ON INFORMATION FOUND IN THE PHYSICAL DATA, TOXICITY AND HEALTH EFFECTS SECTIONS. THEY ARE RANKED IN ORDER FROM MINIMUM TO MAXIMUM RESPIRATORY PROTECTION. THE SPECIFIC RESPIRATOR SELECTED MUST BE BASED ON CONTAMINATION LEVELS FOUND IN THE WORK PLACE, MUST NOT EXCEED THE WORKING LIMITS OF THE RESPIRATOR AND BE JOINTLY APPROVED BY THE NATIONAL INSTITUTE FOR OCCUPATIONAL SAFETY AND HEALTH AND THE MINE SAFETY AND HEALTH ADMINISTRATION (NIOSH-MSHA).

TYPE 'C' SUPPLIED-AIR RESPIRATOR WITH A FULL FACEPIECE OPERATED IN PRESSURE-DEMAND OR OTHER POSITIVE PRESSURE MODE OR WITH A FULL FACEPIECE, HELMET OR HOOD OPERATED IN CONTINOUS-FLOW MODE.

SELF-CONTAINED BREATHING APPARATUS WITH A FULL FACEPIECE OPERATED IN PRESSURE-DEMAND OR OTHER POSITIVE PRESSURE MODE.

FOR FIREFIGHTING AND OTHER IMMEDIATELY DANGEROUS TO LIFE OR HEALTH CONDITIONS:

SELF-CONTAINED BREATHING APPARATUS WITH FULL FACEPIECE OPERATED IN PRESSURE-DEMAND OR OTHER POSITIVE PRESSURE MODE. SUPPLIED-AIR RESPIRATOR WITH FULL FACEPIECE AND OPERATED IN PRESSURE-DEMAND OR OTHER POSITIVE PRESSURE MODE IN COMBINATION WITH AN AUXILIARY SELF-CONTAINED BREATHING APPARATUS OPERATED IN PRESSURE-DEMAND OR OTHER POSITIVE PRESSURE MODE.

CLOTHING: EMPLOYEE MUST WEAR APPROPRIATE PROTECTIVE (IMPERVIOUS) CLOTHING AND EQUIPMENT TO PREVENT REPEATED OR PROLONGED SKIN CONTACT WITH THIS SUBSTANCE.

GLOVES: EMPLOYEE MUST WEAR APPROPRIATE PROTECTIVE GLOVES TO PREVENT CONTACT WITH THIS SUBSTANCE.

EYE PROTECTION: EMPLOYEE MUST WEAR SPLASH-PROOF OR DUST-RESISTANT SAFETY GOGGLES TO PREVENT EYE CONTACT WITH THIS SUBSTANCE.

EMERGENCY EYE WASH: WHERE THERE IS ANY POSSIBILITY THAT AN EMPLOYEE'S EYES MAY BE EXPOSED TO THIS SUBSTANCE, THE EMPLOYER SHOULD PROVIDE AN EYE WASH FOUNTAIN WITHIN THE IMMEDIATE WORK AREA FOR EMERGENCY USE.

AUTHORIZED BY- OCCUPATIONAL HEALTH SERVICES, INC.

CREATION DATE: 10/04/89 ***REVISION DATE:*** 05/02/90

MATERIAL SAFETY DATA SHEET

OCCUPATIONAL HEALTH SERVICES, INC.
AGRICULTURE AND PESTICIDE DIVISION
450 SEVENTH AVENUE, SUITE 2407
NEW YORK, NEW YORK 10123
1-800-445-MSDS OR (212) 967-1100

EMERGENCY CONTACT:
JOHN S. BRANSFORD, JR. (615) 292-1180

SUBSTANCE IDENTIFICATION

SUBSTANCE: KNOX OUT 2FM INSECTICIDE

TRADE NAMES/SYNONYMS: EPA REG. NO. 4581-335; PST12357

CHEMICAL FAMILY: MIXTURE, PESTICIDE FORMULATION ORGANOPHOSPHATE

CERCLA RATINGS (SCALE 0-3): HEALTH=3 FIRE=1 REACTIVITY=0 PERSISTENCE=0

NFPA RATINGS (SCALE 0-4): HEALTH=3 FIRE=1 REACTIVITY=0

COMPONENTS AND CONTAMINANTS

COMPONENT: KNOX OUT 2FM INSECTICIDE ***PERCENT:*** 100

CONTAINS:

DIAZINON (23%) CAS# 333-41-5

EXPOSURE LIMITS: DIAZINON: 0.1 MG/M3 OSHA TWA (SKIN) 0.1 MG/M3 ACGIH TWA (SKIN)

1 POUND CERCLA SECTION 103 REPORTABLE QUANTITY

PHYSICAL DATA

DESCRIPTION: BEIGE LIQUID WITH A CHARACTERISTIC ODOR; POLYMERIC MICROCAPSULES DISPERSED AND SUSPENDED IN WATER ***BOILING POINT:*** APPROXIMATELY 212 F (100 C)

MELTING POINT: <32 F (<0 C) ***SPECIFIC GRAVITY:*** 1.036

EVAPORATION RATE: (WATER =1) 1 ***SOLUBILITY IN WATER:*** DISPERSES

FIRE AND EXPLOSION DATA

FIRE AND EXPLOSION HAZARD: SLIGHT FIRE HAZARD WHEN EXPOSED TO HEAT OR FLAME.

FLASH POINT: >205 F (>96 C) (TCC)
FIREFIGHTING MEDIA: DRY CHEMICAL, CARBON DIOXIDE, HALON, WATER SPRAY OR STANDARD FOAM (1987 EMERGENCY RESPONSE GUIDEBOOK, DOT P 5800.4). FOR LARGER FIRES, USE WATER SPRAY, FOG OR STANDARD FOAM (1987 EMERGENCY RESPONSE GUIDEBOOK, DOT P 5800.4).
FIREFIGHTING: MOVE CONTAINER FROM FIRE AREA IF POSSIBLE. DO NOT SCATTER SPILLED MATERIAL WITH HIGH PRESSURE WATER STREAMS. DIKE FIRE CONTROL WATER FOR LATER DISPOSAL (1987 EMERGENCY RESPONSE GUIDEBOOK, DOT P 5800.4, GUIDE PAGE 31).
USE AGENTS SUITABLE FOR TYPE OF SURROUNDING FIRE. AVOID BREATHING HAZARDOUS VAPORS, KEEP UPWIND.

TRANSPORTATION DATA

DEPARTMENT OF TRANSPORTATION HAZARD CLASSIFICATION 49 CFR 172.101: ORM-E
DEPARTMENT OF TRANSPORTATION LABELING REQUIREMENTS 49 CFR 172.101 AND SUBPART E: NONE
DEPARTMENT OF TRANSPORTATION PACKAGING REQUIREMENTS: 49 CFR 173.1300 EXCEPTIONS: NONE

TOXICITY

KNOX OUT (R) 2FM INSECTICIDE: TOXICITY DATA: 22,420 MG/M3/1 HOUR INHALATION-RAT LC50; 10,000 MG/KG SKIN-RABBIT LD50; 21,000 MG/KG ORAL-RAT LD50 (PENNWALT CORP. MSDS). CARCINOGEN STATUS: NONE. ACUTE TOXICITY LEVEL: MODERATELY TOXIC BY INHALATION, SLIGHTLY TOXIC BY DERMAL ABSORPTION, AND RELATIVELY NON-TOXIC BY INGESTION.
DIAZINON: IRRITATION DATA: 100 MG EYE-RABBIT SEVERE; 500 MG OPEN SKIN-RABBIT MODERATE. TOXICITY DATA: 3500 MG/M3/4 HOURS INHALATION-RAT LC50; 1600 MG/M3/4 HOURS INHALATION-MOUSE LC50; 5500 MG/M3/4 HOURS INHALATION-GUINEA PIG LC50; 180 MG/KG SKIN-RABBIT LD50; 180 MG/KG SKIN-RAT LD50; 2750 MG/KG SKIN-MOUSE LD50; 633 MG/KG SKIN-PIG LD50; 214 MG/KG ORAL-HUMAN TDLO; 66 MG/KG ORAL-RAT LD50; 143 MG/KG ORAL-RABBIT LD50; 17 MG/KG ORAL-MOUSE LD50; 250 MG/KG ORAL-GUINEA PIG LD50; 320 MG/KG ORAL-PIG LD50; 58 MG/KG SUBCUTANEOUS-MOUSE LD50; 180 MG/KG INTRAVENOUS-MOUSE LD50; 65 MG/KG INTRAPERITONEAL-RAT LD50; 33 MG/KG INTRAPERITONEAL-MOUSE LD50; 76 MG/KG UNREPORTED-MAMMAL LD50; MUTAGENIC DATA (RTECS); REPRODUCTIVE EFFECTS DATA (RTECS). CARCINOGEN STATUS: NONE. LOCAL EFFECTS: IRRITANT- SKIN, EYE. ACUTE TOXICITY DATA: HIGHLY TOXIC BY DERMAL ABSORPTION; TOXIC BY INHALATION AND INGESTION. TARGET EFFECTS: CHOLINESTERASE INHIBITOR. POISONING MAY AFFECT THE NERVOUS SYSTEM.* AT INCREASED RISK FROM EXPOSURE: PERSONS WITH RESPIRATORY AILMENTS, RECENT EXPOSURE TO CHOLINESTERASE INHIBITORS OR IMPAIRED CHOLINESTERASE PRODUCTION, OR LIVER MALFUNCTION.* ADDITIONAL DATA: MAY CROSS THE PLACENTA. HIGH ENVIRONMENTAL TEMPERATURES OR EXPOSURE OF THE CHEMICAL TO VISIBLE OR ULTRAVIOLET LIGHT MAY ENHANCE THE TOXICITIY. INTERACTIONS WITH MEDICATIONS MAY OCCUR.*
* MAY BE BASED ON GENERAL INFORMATION ON ORGANOPHOSPHATES.

HEALTH EFFECTS AND FIRST AID

INHALATION: DIAZINON: TOXIC. SEE INFORMATION ON ORGANOPHOSPHATES.
ORGANOPHOSPHATES: CHOLINESTERASE INHIBITOR. **ACUTE EXPOSURE-** WHEN INHALED, THE FIRST EFFECTS OF CHOLINESTERASE INHIBITORS ARE USUALLY RESPIRATORY AND MAY INCLUDE NASAL HYPEREMIA AND WATERY DISCHARGE, COUGH, CHEST DISCOMFORT, DYSPNEA, AND WHEEZING DUE TO INCREASED BRONCHIAL SECRETIONS AND BRONCHOCONSTRICTION. IF SUFFICIENT AMOUNTS ARE ABSORBED, OTHER SYSTEMIC EFFECTS MAY BEGIN WITHIN A FEW MINUTES OR BE DELAYED FOR UP TO 12 HOURS. SYMPTOMS MAY INCLUDE PALLOR, NAUSEA, VOMITING, DIARRHEA, ABDOMINAL CRAMPS, HEADACHE, DIZZINESS, OCULAR PAIN, BLURRED VISION, MIOSIS OR IN SOME CASES, ESPECIALLY INITIALLY, MYDRIASIS, LACRIMATION, SALIVATION, SWEATING, AND CONFUSION. OTHER REPORTED CENTRAL NERVOUS SYSTEM OR NEUROMUSCULAR EFFECTS MAY INCLUDE ATAXIA, SLURRED SPEECH, AREFLEXIA, WEAKNESS, FATIGUE, FASCICULATIONS, TWITCHING, TREMORS POSSIBLY OF THE TONGUE AND EYELIDS, AND EVENTUALLY PARALYSIS OF THE EXTREMITIES AND POSSIBLY OF THE RESPIRATORY MUSCLES. IN SEVERE CASES THERE MAY ALSO BE INVOLUNTARY DEFECATION AND URINATION, CYANOSIS, PSYCHOSIS, HYPERGLYCEMIA, ACUTE PANCREATITIS, CARDIAC IRREGULARITIES, PULMONARY EDEMA, UNCONSCIOUSNESS, CONVULSIONS, AND COMA. DEATH IS PRIMARILY DUE TO RESPIRATORY FAILURE, ALTHOUGH CARDIOVASCULAR EFFECTS INCLUDING CARDIAC ARREST MAY ALSO BE IMPLICATED. LONG TERM SEQUELAE ARE RARE BUT MAY INCLUDE NEUROPSYCHIATRIC DISORDERS AND MYOPATHY WITH MUSCLE TENDERNESS. SOME ORGANOPHOSPHATES MAY CAUSE A DELAYED NEUROPATHY BEGINNING 1-4 WEEKS AFTER AN ACUTE EXPOSURE WHICH MAY OR MAY NOT HAVE CAUSED ACUTE CHOLINERGIC EFFECTS. NUMBNESS, TINGLING, WEAKNESS AND CRAMPING BEGINNING SYMMETRICALLY IN THE LOWER LIMBS MAY PROGRESS TO ATAXIA AND PARALYSIS. IN SEVERE CASES, UPPER LIMB INVOLVEMENT IS POSSIBLE AND FLACCID PARALYSIS MAY PROGRESS TO SPASTIC PARALYSIS WITH EXAGGERATED REFLEXES. IMPROVEMENT MAY OCCUR OVER MONTHS TO YEARS, BUT SOME RESIDUAL IMPAIRMENT USUALLY REMAINS.
CHRONIC EXPOSURE- REPEATED OR PROLONGED EXPOSURE MAY RESULT IN THE EFFECTS OF ACUTE EXPOSURE INCLUDING THE DELAYED NEUROPATHY. OTHER EFFECTS REPORTED IN WORKERS REPEATEDLY EXPOSED INCLUDE IMPAIRED MEMORY AND CONCENTRATION, ACUTE PSYCHOSIS, SEVERE DEPRESSIONS, IRRITABILTY, CONFUSION, APATHY, EMOTIONAL LABILITY, SOCIAL WITHDRAWAL, CONFUSION, HEADACHE, SPEECH DIFFICULTIES, DELAYED REACTION TIMES, SPATIAL DISORIENTATION, NIGHTMARES, SLEEPWALKING, AND DROWSINESS OR INSOMNIA. AN INFLUENZA-LIKE CONDITION WITH HEADACHE, NAUSEA, WEAKNESS, ANOREXIA AND MALAISE HAS ALSO BEEN REPORTED.
FIRST AID- REMOVE FROM EXPOSURE AREA TO FRESH AIR IMMEDIATELY. IF BREATHING HAS STOPPED, GIVE ARTIFICIAL RESPIRATION. MAINTAIN AIRWAY AND BLOOD PRESSURE AND ADMINISTER OXYGEN IF AVAILABLE. KEEP AFFECTED PERSON WARM AND AT REST. TREAT SYMPTOMATICALLY AND SUPPORTIVELY. ADMINISTRATION OF OXYGEN SHOULD BE PERFORMED BY QUALIFIED PERSONNEL. GET MEDICAL ATTENTION IMMEDIATELY.

SKIN CONTACT: DIAZINON: IRRITANT/HIGHLY TOXIC. 500 MG APPLIED TO OPEN RABBIT SKIN PRODUCED MODERATE IRRITATION. SEE INFORMATION ON ORGANOPHOSPHATES.
ORGANOPHOSPHATES: CHOLINESTERASE INHIBITOR. **ACUTE EXPOSURE-** LOCALIZED SWEATING AND FASCICULATIONS MAY OCCUR AT THE SITE OF CONTACT. IF SUFFICIENT AMOUNTS ARE ABSORBED, OTHER EFFECTS OF CHOLINESTERASE INHIBITION AS DESCRIBED IN ACUTE INHALATION MAY OCCUR. SYMPTOMS MAY BE DELAYED 2-3 HOURS, BUT USUALLY NO MORE THAN 12 HOURS. THE RATE OF ABSORPTION IS INCREASED BY THE PRESENCE OF DERMATITIS OR HIGH AMBIENT TEMPERATURES. DELAYED NEUROPATHY IS ALSO POSSIBLE. **CHRONIC EXPOSURE-** REPEATED OR PROLONGED EXPOSURE MAY CAUSE EFFECTS AS DESCRIBED IN ACUTE EXPOSURE. SOME ORGANOPHOSPHATES MAY CAUSE SENSITIZATION.
FIRST AID- REMOVE CONTAMINATED CLOTHING IMMEDIATELY. WASH CONTAMINATED AREAS WITH SOAP AND WATER FOLLOWED BY ALCOHOL (ARENA, POISONING, 4TH ED.). EMERGENCY PERSONNEL SHOULD WEAR GLOVES AND AVOID CONTAMINATION. TREAT RESPIRATORY DIFFICULTY WITH ARTIFICIAL RESPIRATION. GET MEDICAL ATTENTION IMMEDIATELY.

EYE CONTACT: DIAZINON: IRRITANT. 100 MG APPLIED TO THE EYES OF RABBITS PRODUCED SEVERE IRRITATION. SEE INFORMATION ON ORGANOPHOSPHATES.
ORGANOPHOSPHATES: CHOLINESTERASE INHIBITOR. **ACUTE EXPOSURE-** DIRECT CONTACT MAY CAUSE PAIN, HYPEREMIA, LACRIMATION, TWITCHING OF THE EYELIDS, MIOSIS, AND CILIARY MUSCLE SPASM WITH LOSS OF ACCOMODATION, BLURRED OR DIMMED VISION AND BROWACHE. SOMETIMES MYDRIASIS MAY OCCUR INSTEAD OF MIOSIS. WITH SUFFICIENT EXPOSURE, OTHER SYMPTOMS OF CHOLINESTERASE INHIBITION AS DESCRIBED IN ACUTE INHALATION MAY OCCUR.
CHRONIC EXPOSURE- REPEATED OR PROLONGED EXPOSURE MAY CAUSE EFFECTS AS DESCRIBED IN ACUTE EXPOSURE. SOME COMPOUNDS HAVE CAUSED TOXIC EFFECTS ON THE CRYSTALLINE LENS, CONJUNCTIVAL THICKENING AND OBSTRUCTION OF THE NASOLACRIMAL CANALS WHEN USED AS MIOTIC EYEDROPS.
FIRST AID- IRRIGATE EYES WITH WATER OR SALINE SOLUTION. IF SYMPTOMS OF POISONING OCCUR, TREAT RESPIRATORY DIFFICULTY WITH ARTIFICIAL RESPIRATION AND OXYGEN. OBSERVE PATIENT FOR AT LEAST 24-36 HOURS (GOSSELIN, CLINICAL TOXICOLOGY OF COMMERCIAL PRODUCTS, 5TH ED.). GET MEDICAL ATTENTION IMMEDIATELY. OXYGEN SHOULD BE ADMINISTERED BY QUALIFIED MEDICAL PERSONNEL.

INGESTION: DIAZINON: TOXIC. A DOSE OF 63.5 MG/KG FED TO PREGNANT RATS PRODUCED ADVERSE EFFECTS ON FERTILITY. CHRONIC ADMINISTRATION TO PREGNANT RATS RESULTED IN FETAL DEVELOPMENTAL ABNORMALITIES. IN PREGNANT MICE, CHRONIC INGESTION PRODUCED ADVERSE EFFECTS ON FERTILITY AND THE NEWBORN AND FETAL DEVELOPMENTAL ABNORMALITIES. SEE INFORMATION ON ORGANOPHOSPHATES.
ORGANOPHOSPHATES: CHOLINESTERASE INHIBITOR. **ACUTE EXPOSURE-** WHEN INGESTED, THE FIRST EFFECTS MAY BE NAUSEA, VOMITING, ANOREXIA, ABDOMINAL CRAMPS AND DIARRHEA. GASTROINTESTINAL ABSORPTION MAY CAUSE SYMPTOMS OF CHOLINESTERASE INHIBITION AS DESCRIBED IN ACUTE INHALATION. SYMPTOMS MAY BEGIN WITHIN MINUTES OR BE DELAYED FOR HOURS. DELAYED EFFECTS INCLUDING NEUROPATHY MAY ALSO OCCUR. **CHRONIC EXPOSURE-** REPEATED INGESTION MAY CAUSE EFFECTS AS DESCRIBED IN ACUTE EXPOSURE.
FIRST AID- IF PERSON IS ALERT AND RESPIRATION IS NOT DEPRESSED, GIVE SYRUP OF IPECAC FOLLOWED BY WATER (IF VOMITING OCCURS, KEEP HEAD BELOW HIPS TO PREVENT ASPIRATION). IF CONSCIOUSNESS LEVEL DECLINES OR VOMITING HAS NOT OCCURRED IN 15 MINUTES EMPTY STOMACH BY GASTRIC LAVAGE WITH THE

AID OF CUFFED ENDOTRACHEAL TUBE USING ISOTONIC SALINE OR 5% SODIUM BICARBONATE FOLLOW WITH ACTIVATED CHARCOAL. ESTABLISH AND MAINTAIN AIRWAY. TREAT RESPIRATORY DIFFICULTY WITH ARTIFICIAL RESPIRATION AND OXYGEN. DO NOT GIVE MORPHINE, AMINOPHYLLINE, PHENOTHIAZINES, RESERPINE, FUROSEMIDE, OR ETHACRYNIC ACID (MORGAN, RECOGNITION AND MANAGEMENT OF PESTICIDE POISONINGS, 3RD ED.). TREAT SYMPTOMATICALLY AND SUPPORTIVELY. ADMINISTRATION OF OXYGEN AND LAVAGE MUST BE PERFORMED BY QUALIFIED MEDICAL PERSONNEL. GET MEDICAL ATTENTION IMMEDIATELY.

ANTIDOTE: THE FOLLOWING ANTIDOTE(S) HAVE BEEN RECOMMENDED. HOWEVER, THE DECISION AS TO WHETHER THE SEVERITY OF POISONING REQUIRES ADMINISTRATION OF ANY ANTIDOTE AND ACTUAL DOSE REQUIRED SHOULD BE MADE BY QUALIFIED MEDICAL PERSONNEL.

FOR CHOLINESTERASE INHIBITORS: ESTABLISH CLEAR AIRWAY AND TISSUE OXYGENATION BY ASPIRATION OF SECRETIONS, AND IF NECESSARY, BY ASSISTED PULMONARY VENTILATION WITH OXYGEN. IMPROVE TISSUE OXYGENATION AS MUCH AS POSSIBLE BEFORE ADMINISTERING ATROPINE TO MINIMIZE THE RISK OF VENTRICULAR FIBRILLATION. ADMINISTER ATROPINE SULFATE INTRAVENOUSLY, OR INTRAMUSCULARLY IF IV INJECTION IS NOT POSSIBLE. IN MODERATELY SEVERE POISONING ADMINISTER ATROPINE SULFATE, 0.4-2.0 MG REPEATED EVERY 15 MINUTES UNTIL ATROPINIZATION IS ACHIEVED (TACHYCARDIA, FLUSHING, DRY MOUTH, MYDRIASIS). MAINTAIN ATROPINIZATION BY REPEATED DOSES FOR 2-12 HOURS, OR LONGER, DEPENDING ON THE SEVERITY OF POISONING. THE APPEARANCE OF RALES IN THE LUNG BASES, MIOSIS, SALIVATION, NAUSEA, BRADYCARDIA, ARE ALL INDICATIONS OF INADEQUATE ATROPINIZATION. SEVERELY POISONED INDIVIDUALS MAY EXHIBIT REMARKABLE TOLERANCE TO ATROPINE; TWO OR MORE TIMES THE DOSAGES SUGGESTED ABOVE MAY BE NEEDED. PERSONS NOT POISONED OR ONLY SLIGHTLY POISONED, HOWEVER, MAY DEVELOP SIGNS OF ATROPINE TOXICITY FROM SUCH LARGE DOSAGES: FEVER, MUSCLE FIBRILLATIONS, AND DELIRIUM ARE THE MAIN SIGNS OF ATROPINE TOXICITY. IF THESE SIGNS APPEAR WHILE THE PATIENT IS FULLY ATROPINIZED, ATROPINE ADMINISTRATION SHOULD BE DISCONTINUED, AT LEAST TEMPORARILY. OBSERVE TREATED PATIENTS CLOSELY AT LEAST 24 HOURS TO INSURE THAT SYMPTOMS (POSSIBLY PULMONARY EDEMA) DO NOT RECUR AS ATROPINIZATION WEARS OFF. IN VERY SEVERE POISONINGS, METABOLIC DISPOSITION OF TOXICANT MAY REQUIRE SEVERAL HOURS OR DAYS DURING WHICH ATROPINIZATION MUST BE MAINTAINED. MARKEDLY LOWER LEVELS OF URINARY METABOLITES INDICATE THAT ATROPINE DOSAGE CAN BE TAPERED OFF. AS DOSAGE IS REDUCED, CHECK THE LUNG BASES FREQUENTLY FOR RALES. IF RALES ARE HEARD OR OTHER SYMPTOMS RETURN, RE-ESTABLISH ATROPINIZATION PROMPTLY (MORGAN, RECOGNITION AND MANAGEMENT OF PESTICIDE POISONINGS, 3RD ED.). ADMINISTRATION OF ANTIDOTE MUST BE PERFORMED BY QUALIFIED MEDICAL PERSONNEL.

IN CASES OF SEVERE POISONING BY ORGANOPHOSPHATE PESTICIDES IN WHICH RESPIRATORY DEPRESSION, MUSCLE WEAKNESS AND TWITCHINGS ARE SEVERE, GIVE PRALIDOXIME (PROTOPAM-AYERST, 2-PAM), 1.0 GRAM INTRAVENOUSLY AT NO MORE THAN 0.5 GRAM PER MINUTE. DOSAGE OF PRALIDOXIME MAY BE REPEATED IN 1-2 HOURS, THEN AT 10-12 HOUR INTERVALS IF NEEDED. IN VERY SEVERE POISONINGS, DOSAGE RATES MAY BE DOUBLED. TREATMENT WITH PRALIDOXIME WILL BE MOST EFFECTIVE IF GIVEN WITHIN THIRTY-SIX HOURS AFTER POISONING (MORGAN, RECOGNITION AND MANAGEMENT OF PESTICIDE POISONINGS, 3RD ED.). ANTIDOTE SHOULD BE ADMINISTERED BY QUALIFIED MEDICAL PERSONNEL.

REACTIVITY

REACTIVITY: STABLE UNDER NORMAL TEMPERATURES AND PRESSURES.

INCOMPATIBILITIES: DIAZINON: WATER: HYDROLYZE SLOWLY. ACIDS: HYDROLYZE SLOWLY. STRONG ALKALIES: HYDROLYZE.

DECOMPOSITION: THERMAL DECOMPOSITION MAY RELEASE TOXIC AND/OR HAZARDOUS GASES.

POLYMERIZATION: HAZARDOUS POLYMERIZATION HAS NOT BEEN REPORTED TO OCCUR UNDER NORMAL TEMPERATURES AND PRESSURES.

STORAGE AND DISPOSAL

OBSERVE ALL FEDERAL, STATE AND LOCAL REGULATIONS WHEN STORING OR DISPOSING OF THIS SUBSTANCE. FOR ASSISTANCE, CONTACT THE DISTRICT DIRECTOR OF THE ENVIRONMENTAL PROTECTION AGENCY.

****STORAGE****

STORE IN ACCORDANCE WITH 40 CFR 165 RECOMMENDED PROCEDURES FOR THE DISPOSAL AND STORAGE OF PESTICIDES AND PESTICIDE CONTAINERS.

STORE AWAY FROM INCOMPATIBLE SUBSTANCES.

****DISPOSAL****

DISPOSAL MUST BE IN ACCORDANCE WITH 40 CFR 165 RECOMMENDED PROCEDURES FOR THE DISPOSAL AND STORAGE OF PESTICIDES AND PESTICIDE CONTAINERS.

CONDITIONS TO AVOID

MAY BURN BUT DOES NOT IGNITE READILY. AVOID CONTACT WITH STRONG OXIDIZERS, EXCESSIVE HEAT, SPARKS, OR OPEN FLAME.

SPILL AND LEAK PROCEDURES

OCCUPATIONAL SPILL: STOP LEAK IF YOU CAN DO IT WITHOUT RISK. FOR SMALL SPILLS, TAKE UP WITH SAND OR OTHER ABSORBENT MATERIAL AND PLACE INTO CLEAN, DRY CONTAINERS FOR LATER DISPOSAL. KEEP UNNECESSARY PEOPLE AWAY. ISOLATE HAZARD AREA AND DENY ENTRY.

REPORTABLE QUANTITY (RQ): THE SUPERFUND AMENDMENTS AND REAUTHORIZATION ACT (SARA) SECTION 304 REQUIRES THAT A RELEASE EQUAL TO OR GREATER THAN THE REPORTABLE QUANTITY ESTABLISHED FOR THAT SUBSTANCE BE IMMEDIATELY REPORTED TO THE LOCAL EMERGENCY PLANNING COMMITTEE AND THE STATE EMERGENCY RESPONSE COMMISSION (40 CFR 355.40). IF THE RELEASE OF THIS SUBSTANCE IS REPORTABLE UNDER CERCLA SECTION 103, THE NATIONAL RESPONSE CENTER MUST BE NOTIFIED IMMEDIATELY AT (800) 424-8802 OR (202) 426-2675 IN THE METROPOLITAN WASHINGTON, D.C. AREA (40 CFR 302.6).

PROTECTIVE EQUIPMENT

VENTILATION: PROVIDE LOCAL EXHAUST VENTILATION AND/OR GENERAL DILUTION VENTILATION TO MEET PUBLISHED EXPOSURE LIMITS.

RESPIRATOR: THE FOLLOWING RESPIRATORS ARE RECOMMENDED BASED ON INFORMATION FOUND IN THE PHYSICAL DATA, TOXICITY AND HEALTH EFFECTS SECTIONS. THEY ARE RANKED IN ORDER FROM MINIMUM TO MAXIMUM RESPIRATORY PROTECTION. THE SPECIFIC RESPIRATOR SELECTED MUST BE BASED ON CONTAMINATION LEVELS FOUND IN THE WORK PLACE, MUST NOT EXCEED THE WORKING LIMITS OF THE RESPIRATOR AND BE JOINTLY APPROVED BY THE NATIONAL INSTITUTE FOR OCCUPATIONAL SAFETY AND HEALTH AND THE MINE SAFETY AND HEALTH ADMINISTRATION (NIOSH-MSHA).

CHEMICAL CARTRIDGE RESPIRATOR WITH FULL FACEPIECE AND PESTICIDE CARTRIDGE.

TYPE 'C' SUPPLIED-AIR RESPIRATOR WITH A FULL FACEPIECE OPERATED IN PRESSURE-DEMAND OR OTHER POSITIVE PRESSURE MODE OR WITH A FULL FACEPIECE, HELMET OR HOOD OPERATED IN CONTINUOUS-FLOW MODE.

SELF-CONTAINED BREATHING APPARATUS OPERATED IN PRESSURE-DEMAND OR OTHER POSITIVE PRESSURE MODE.

FOR FIREFIGHTING AND OTHER IMMEDIATELY DANGEROUS TO LIFE OR HEALTH CONDITIONS:

SELF-CONTAINED BREATHING APPARATUS WITH FULL FACEPIECE OPERATED IN PRESSURE-DEMAND OR OTHER POSITIVE PRESSURE MODE.

SUPPLIED-AIR RESPIRATOR WITH FULL FACEPIECE AND OPERATED IN PRESSURE-DEMAND OR OTHER POSITIVE PRESSURE MODE IN COMBINATION WITH AN AUXILIARY SELF-CONTAINED BREATHING APPARATUS OPERATED IN PRESSURE-DEMAND OR OTHER POSITIVE PRESSURE MODE.

CLOTHING: EMPLOYEE MUST WEAR APPROPRIATE PROTECTIVE (IMPERVIOUS) CLOTHING AND EQUIPMENT TO PREVENT REPEATED OR PROLONGED SKIN CONTACT WITH THIS SUBSTANCE.

GLOVES: EMPLOYEE MUST WEAR APPROPRIATE PROTECTIVE GLOVES TO PREVENT CONTACT WITH THIS SUBSTANCE.

EYE PROTECTION: EMPLOYEE MUST WEAR SPLASH-PROOF OR DUST-RESISTANT SAFETY GOGGLES TO PREVENT EYE CONTACT WITH THIS SUBSTANCE.

EMERGENCY EYE WASH: WHERE THERE IS ANY POSSIBILITY THAT AN EMPLOYEE'S EYES MAY BE EXPOSED TO THIS SUBSTANCE, THE EMPLOYER SHOULD PROVIDE AN EYE WASH FOUNTAIN WITHIN THE IMMEDIATE WORK AREA FOR EMERGENCY USE.

AUTHORIZED BY- OCCUPATIONAL HEALTH SERVICES, INC.

CREATION DATE: 10/04/89 ***REVISION DATE:*** 05/18/90

MATERIAL SAFETY DATA SHEET

OCCUPATIONAL HEALTH SERVICES, INC.
AGRICULTURE AND PESTICIDE DIVISION
450 SEVENTH AVENUE, SUITE 2407
NEW YORK, NEW YORK 10123
1-800-445-MSDS OR (212) 967-1100

EMERGENCY CONTACT:
JOHN S. BRANSFORD, JR. (615) 292-1180

SUBSTANCE IDENTIFICATION

CAS-NUMBER 12407-86-2

SUBSTANCE: LANDRIN

TRADE NAMES/SYNONYMS: PHENOL, 2,3,5(OR 3,4,5)-TRIMETHYL-, METHYLCARBAMATE; 2,3,5(OR 3,4,5)-TRIMETHYLPHENOL METHYLCARBAMATE; CARBAMIC ACID, METHYL-, 2,3,5(OR 3,4,5)-TRIMETHYLPHENYL ESTER; METHYLCARBAMIC 2,3,5(OR 3,4,5)-TRIMETHYLPHENYL ESTER; TRIMETHACARB; C11H15NO2; PST12420
CHEMICAL FAMILY: CARBAMATE
PHENOL
MOLECULAR FORMULA: (C-H3)3-C6-H2-O2-C-N-H-C-H3
MOLECULAR WEIGHT: 193.25
CERCLA RATINGS (SCALE 0-3): HEALTH=3 FIRE=1 REACTIVITY=0 PERSISTENCE=2
NFPA RATINGS (SCALE 0-4): HEALTH=3 FIRE=1 REACTIVITY=0

COMPONENTS AND CONTAMINANTS

COMPONENT: 3,4,5 TRIMETHYLPHENYL METHYL CARBAMATE ***PERCENT:*** 80.0
CAS# 2686-99-9
COMPONENT: 2,3,5 TRIMETHYLPHENYL METHYL CARBAMATE ***PERCENT:*** 20.0
CAS# 2655-15-4
OTHER CONTAMINANTS: NONE
EXPOSURE LIMITS: NO OCCUPATIONAL EXPOSURE LIMITS ESTABLISHED BY OSHA, ACGIH, OR NIOSH.

PHYSICAL DATA

DESCRIPTION: BROWN SOLID. ***MELTING POINT:*** 221-237 F (105-114 C)
SPECIFIC GRAVITY: NOT AVAILABLE ***SOLUBILITY IN WATER:*** NOT AVAILABLE

FIRE AND EXPLOSION DATA

FIRE AND EXPLOSION HAZARD: SLIGHT FIRE HAZARD WHEN EXPOSED TO HEAT OR FLAME.
FIREFIGHTING MEDIA: DRY CHEMICAL, CARBON DIOXIDE, HALON, WATER SPRAY OR STANDARD FOAM (1987 EMERGENCY RESPONSE GUIDEBOOK, DOT P 5800.4). FOR LARGER FIRES, USE WATER SPRAY, FOG OR STANDARD FOAM (1987 EMERGENCY RESPONSE GUIDEBOOK, DOT P 5800.4).
FIREFIGHTING: MOVE CONTAINER FROM FIRE AREA IF POSSIBLE. DO NOT SCATTER SPILLED MATERIAL WITH HIGH PRESSURE WATER STREAMS. DIKE FIRE CONTROL WATER FOR LATER DISPOSAL (1987 EMERGENCY RESPONSE GUIDEBOOK, DOT P 5800.4, GUIDE PAGE 31).
USE AGENTS SUITABLE FOR TYPE OF SURROUNDING FIRE. AVOID BREATHING HAZARDOUS VAPORS, KEEP UPWIND.

TOXICITY

LANDRIN: TOXICITY DATA: 208 MG/KG ORAL-RAT LD50; 1,000 MG/KG SKIN-RAT LD50 (PESTICIDES STUDIED IN MAN). CARCINOGEN STATUS: NONE. ACUTE TOXICITY LEVEL: TOXIC BY DERMAL ABSORPTION AND INGESTION. TARGET EFFECTS: CHOLINESTERASE INHIBITOR. AT INCREASED RISK FROM EXPOSURE: PERSONS WITH ASTHMA, DIABETES, CARDIOVASCULAR DISEASE, MECHANICAL OBSTRUCTION OF THE GASTROINTESTINAL OR UROGENITAL TRACT, AND THOSE IN VAGOTONIC STATES.*
* MAY BE BASED ON GENERAL INFORMATION ON CARBAMATES.

HEALTH EFFECTS AND FIRST AID

INHALATION: LANDRIN: SEE INFORMATION ON CARBAMATES.
CARBAMATES: CHOLINESTERASE INHIBITOR. **ACUTE EXPOSURE-** WHEN INHALED, THE FIRST EFFECTS OF CHOLINESTERASE INHIBITION ARE USUALLY RESPIRATORY AND MAY INCLUDE NASAL HYPEREMIA AND WATERY DISCHARGE, CHEST DISCOMFORT, DYSPNEA, AND WHEEZING DUE TO INCREASED BRONCHIAL SECRETIONS AND BRONCHOCONSTRICTION. OTHER SYSTEMIC EFFECTS MAY BEGIN WITHIN A FEW MINUTES OR SEVERAL HOURS OF EXPOSURE. SYMPTOMS MAY INCLUDE NAUSEA, VOMITING, DIARRHEA, ABDOMINAL CRAMPS, HEADACHE, VERTIGO, OCULAR PAIN, CILIARY MUSCLE SPASM, BLURRING OR DIMNESS OF VISION, MIOSIS, OR IN SOME CASES MYDRIASIS, LACRIMATION, SALIVATION, SWEATING, AND CONFUSION. OTHER REPORTED CENTRAL NERVOUS SYSTEM OR NEUROMUSCULAR EFFECTS INCLUDE ATAXIA, SLURRED SPEECH, AREFLEXIA, WEAKNESS, FATIGUE, TWITCHING, FASCICULATION, TREMOR, AND EVENTUALLY PARALYSIS OF THE EXTREMITIES AND POSSIBLY OF THE RESPIRATORY MUSCLES. IN SEVERE CASES, THERE MAY ALSO BE INVOLUNTARY DEFECATION AND URINATION, BRADYCARDIA, HYPOTENSION, PULMONARY EDEMA, CONVULSIONS, COMA, AND DEATH FROM RESPIRATORY FAILURE OR CARDIAC ARREST. CARBAMATES GENERALLY DO NOT ACCUMULATE IN MAMMALIAN TISSUE AND THE CHOLINESTERASE INHIBITION REVERSES RATHER RAPIDLY. IN NON-FATAL CASES, THE ILLNESS GENERALLY LASTS LESS THAN 24 HOURS. **CHRONIC EXPOSURE-** PROLONGED OR REPEATED EXPOSURE MAY CAUSE EFFECTS AS DESCRIBED IN ACUTE EXPOSURE.
FIRST AID- REMOVE FROM EXPOSURE AREA TO FRESH AIR IMMEDIATELY. IF BREATHING HAS STOPPED, GIVE ARTIFICIAL RESPIRATION. MAINTAIN AIRWAY AND BLOOD PRESSURE AND ADMINISTER OXYGEN IF AVAILABLE. KEEP AFFECTED PERSON WARM AND AT REST. TREAT SYMPTOMATICALLY AND SUPPORTIVELY. ADMINISTRATION OF OXYGEN SHOULD BE PERFORMED BY QUALIFIED PERSONNEL. GET MEDICAL ATTENTION IMMEDIATELY.

SKIN CONTACT: LANDRIN: TOXIC. SEE INFORMATION ON CARBAMATES.
CARBAMATES: CHOLINESTERASE INHIBITOR. **ACUTE EXPOSURE-** SOME COMPOUNDS MAY CAUSE IRRITATION. LOCALIZED SWEATING AND FASCICULATIONS MAY OCCUR AT THE SITE OF CONTACT. IF SUFFICIENT AMOUNTS ARE ABSORBED THROUGH THE SKIN, OTHER EFFECTS OF CHOLINESTERASE INHIBITION MAY OCCUR AS DESCRIBED IN ACUTE INHALATION; SYMPTOMS MAY BE DELAYED FOR 2-3 HOURS, USUALLY NO MORE THAN 8 HOURS. **CHRONIC EXPOSURE-** REPEATED OR PROLONGED EXPOSURE MAY CAUSE EFFECTS AS DESCRIBED IN ACUTE EXPOSURE.
FIRST AID- REMOVE CONTAMINATED CLOTHING IMMEDIATELY. WASH CONTAMINATED AREAS WITH SOAP AND WATER FOLLOWED BY ALCOHOL (ARENA, POISONING, 4TH ED.). EMERGENCY PERSONNEL SHOULD WEAR GLOVES AND AVOID CONTAMINATION. TREAT RESPIRATORY DIFFICULTY WITH ARTIFICIAL RESPIRATION. GET MEDICAL ATTENTION IMMEDIATELY.

EYE CONTACT: LANDRIN: SEE INFORMATION ON CARBAMATES.
CARBAMATES: CHOLINESTERASE INHIBITOR. **ACUTE EXPOSURE-** DIRECT CONTACT MAY CAUSE PAIN, HYPEREMIA, LACRIMATION, TWITCHING OF THE EYELIDS, MIOSIS, AND CILIARY MUSCLE SPASM WITH LOSS OF ACCOMODATION, BLURRED OR DIMMED VISION AND BROWACHE. SOMETIMES MYDRIASIS MAY OCCUR INSTEAD OF MIOSIS. WITH SUFFICIENT EXPOSURE, OTHER SYMPTOMS OF CHOLINESTERASE INHIBITION MAY OCCUR AS DESCRIBED IN ACUTE INHALATION. **CHRONIC EXPOSURE-** PROLONGED EXPOSURE MAY CAUSE EFFECTS AS DESCRIBED IN ACUTE EXPOSURE. SOME COMPOUNDS HAVE CAUSED TOXIC EFFECTS ON THE CRYSTALLINE LENS, CONJUNCTIVAL THICKENING AND OBSTRUCTION OF NASOLACRIMAL CANALS WHEN USED AS MIOTIC EYE DROPS.
FIRST AID- IRRIGATE EYES WITH WATER OR SALINE SOLUTION. IF SYMPTOMS OF POISONING OCCUR, TREAT RESPIRATORY DIFFICULTY WITH ARTIFICIAL RESPIRATION AND OXYGEN. OBSERVE PATIENT FOR AT LEAST 24-36 HOURS (GOSSELIN, CLINICAL TOXICOLOGY OF COMMERCIAL PRODUCTS, 5TH ED.). GET MEDICAL ATTENTION IMMEDIATELY. OXYGEN SHOULD BE ADMINISTERED BY QUALIFIED MEDICAL PERSONNEL.

INGESTION: LANDRIN: TOXIC. SEE INFORMATION ON CARBAMATES.
CARBAMATES: CHOLINESTERASE INHIBITOR. **ACUTE EXPOSURE-** WHEN INGESTED, THE FIRST EFFECTS MAY BE NAUSEA, VOMITING, ANOREXIA, ABDOMINAL CRAMPS, AND DIARRHEA. WITH ABSORPTION FROM THE GASTROINTESTINAL TRACT, THE OTHER EFFECTS OF CHOLINESTERASE INHIBITION AS DESCRIBED IN ACUTE INHALATION MAY OCCUR; SYMPTOMS MAY BEGIN WITHIN MINUTES OR BE DELAYED SEVERAL HOURS. **CHRONIC EXPOSURE-** REPEATED INGESTION MAY CAUSE EFFECTS AS DESCRIBED IN ACUTE EXPOSURE.
FIRST AID- IF PERSON IS ALERT AND RESPIRATION IS NOT DEPRESSED, GIVE SYRUP OF IPECAC FOLLOWED BY WATER (IF VOMITING OCCURS, KEEP HEAD BELOW HIPS TO PREVENT ASPIRATION). IF CONSCIOUSNESS LEVEL DECLINES OR VOMITING HAS NOT OCCURRED IN 15 MINUTES EMPTY STOMACH BY GASTRIC LAVAGE WITH THE AID OF CUFFED ENDOTRACHEAL TUBE USING ISOTONIC SALINE OR 5% SODIUM BICARBONATE FOLLOW WITH ACTIVATED CHARCOAL. ESTABLISH AND MAINTAIN AIRWAY. TREAT RESPIRATORY DIFFICULTY WITH ARTIFICIAL RESPIRATION AND OXYGEN. DO NOT GIVE MORPHINE, AMINOPHYLLINE, PHENOTHIAZINES, RESERPINE, FUROSEMIDE, OR ETHACRYNIC ACID (MORGAN, RECOGNITION AND MANAGEMENT OF PESTICIDE POISONINGS, 3RD ED.). TREAT SYMPTOMATICALLY AND SUPPORTIVELY. ADMINISTRATION OF OXYGEN AND LAVAGE MUST BE PERFORMED BY QUALIFIED MEDICAL PERSONNEL. GET MEDICAL ATTENTION IMMEDIATELY.
ANTIDOTE: THE FOLLOWING ANTIDOTE HAS BEEN RECOMMENDED. HOWEVER, THE DECISION AS TO WHETHER THE SEVERITY OF POISONING REQUIRES ADMINISTRATION OF ANY ANTIDOTE AND ACTUAL DOSE REQUIRED SHOULD BE MADE BY QUALIFIED MEDICAL PERSONNEL.
FOR CHOLINESTERASE INHIBITORS: ESTABLISH CLEAR AIRWAY AND TISSUE OXYGENATION BY ASPIRATION OF SECRETIONS, AND IF NECESSARY, BY ASSISTED PULMONARY VENTILATION WITH OXYGEN. IMPROVE TISSUE OXYGENATION AS MUCH AS POSSIBLE BEFORE ADMINISTERING ATROPINE TO MINIMIZE THE RISK OF VENTRICULAR FIBRILLATION. ADMINISTER ATROPINE SULFATE INTRAVENOUSLY, OR INTRAMUSCULARLY IF IV INJECTION IS NOT POSSIBLE. IN MODERATELY SEVERE POISONING ADMINISTER ATROPINE SULFATE, 0.4-2.0 MG REPEATED EVERY 15 MINUTES UNTIL ATROPINIZATION IS ACHIEVED (TACHYCARDIA, FLUSHING, DRY MOUTH, MYDRIASIS). MAINTAIN ATROPINIZATION BY REPEATED DOSES FOR 2-12 HOURS, OR LONGER, DEPENDING ON THE SEVERITY OF POISONING. THE APPEARANCE OF RALES IN THE LUNG BASES, MIOSIS, SALIVATION, NAUSEA, BRADYCARDIA, ARE ALL INDICATIONS OF INADEQUATE ATROPINIZATION. SEVERELY POISONED INDIVIDUALS MAY EXHIBIT REMARKABLE TOLERANCE TO ATROPINE; TWO OR MORE TIMES THE DOSAGES SUGGESTED ABOVE MAY BE NEEDED. PERSONS NOT POISONED OR ONLY SLIGHTLY POISONED, HOWEVER, MAY

DEVELOP SIGNS OF ATROPINE TOXICITY FROM SUCH LARGE DOSAGES: FEVER, MUSCLE FIBRILLATIONS, AND DELIRIUM ARE THE MAIN SIGNS OF ATROPINE TOXICITY. IF THESE SIGNS APPEAR WHILE THE PATIENT IS FULLY ATROPINIZED, ATROPINE ADMINISTRATION SHOULD BE DISCONTINUED, AT LEAST TEMPORARILY. OBSERVE TREATED PATIENTS CLOSELY AT LEAST 24 HOURS TO INSURE THAT SYMPTOMS (POSSIBLY PULMONARY EDEMA) DO NOT RECUR AS ATROPINIZATION WEARS OFF. IN VERY SEVERE POISONINGS, METABOLIC DISPOSITION OF TOXICANT MAY REQUIRE SEVERAL HOURS OR DAYS DURING WHICH ATROPINIZATION MUST BE MAINTAINED. MARKEDLY LOWER LEVELS OF URINARY METABOLITES INDICATE THAT ATROPINE DOSAGE CAN BE TAPERED OFF. AS DOSAGE IS REDUCED, CHECK THE LUNG BASES FREQUENTLY FOR RALES. IF RALES ARE HEARD OR OTHER SYMPTOMS RETURN, RE-ESTABLISH ATROPINIZATION PROMPTLY (MORGAN, RECOGNITION AND MANAGEMENT OF PESTICIDE POISONINGS, 3RD ED.). ADMINISTRATION OF ANTIDOTE MUST BE PERFORMED BY QUALIFIED MEDICAL PERSONNEL.

REACTIVITY

REACTIVITY: STABLE UNDER NORMAL TEMPERATURES AND PRESSURES.

INCOMPATIBILITIES: LANDRIN: OXIDIZERS (STRONG): FIRE AND EXPLOSION HAZARD.

DECOMPOSITION: THERMAL DECOMPOSITION PRODUCTS MAY INCLUDE TOXIC OXIDES OF CARBON AND NITROGEN.

POLYMERIZATION: HAZARDOUS POLYMERIZATION HAS NOT BEEN REPORTED TO OCCUR UNDER NORMAL TEMPERATURES AND PRESSURES.

STORAGE AND DISPOSAL

OBSERVE ALL FEDERAL, STATE AND LOCAL REGULATIONS WHEN STORING OR DISPOSING OF THIS SUBSTANCE. FOR ASSISTANCE, CONTACT THE DISTRICT DIRECTOR OF THE ENVIRONMENTAL PROTECTION AGENCY.

STORAGE

STORE IN ACCORDANCE WITH 40 CFR 165 RECOMMENDED PROCEDURES FOR THE DISPOSAL AND STORAGE OF PESTICIDES AND PESTICIDE CONTAINERS.

STORE AWAY FROM INCOMPATIBLE SUBSTANCES.

DISPOSAL

DISPOSAL MUST BE IN ACCORDANCE WITH 40 CFR 165 RECOMMENDED PROCEDURES FOR THE DISPOSAL AND STORAGE OF PESTICIDES AND PESTICIDE CONTAINERS.

CONDITIONS TO AVOID

MAY BURN BUT DOES NOT IGNITE READILY. AVOID CONTACT WITH STRONG OXIDIZERS, EXCESSIVE HEAT, SPARKS, OR OPEN FLAME.

SPILL AND LEAK PROCEDURES

OCCUPATIONAL SPILL: SWEEP UP AND PLACE IN SUITABLE CLEAN, DRY CONTAINERS FOR RECLAMATION OR LATER DISPOSAL. DO NOT FLUSH SPILLED MATERIAL INTO SEWER. KEEP UNNECESSARY PEOPLE AWAY.

PROTECTIVE EQUIPMENT

VENTILATION: PROVIDE LOCAL EXHAUST OR GENERAL DILUTION VENTILATION. VENTILATION EQUIPMENT MUST BE EXPLOSION-PROOF.

RESPIRATOR: THE FOLLOWING RESPIRATORS ARE RECOMMENDED BASED ON INFORMATION FOUND IN THE PHYSICAL DATA, TOXICITY AND HEALTH EFFECTS SECTIONS. THEY ARE RANKED IN ORDER FROM MINIMUM TO MAXIMUM RESPIRATORY PROTECTION. THE SPECIFIC RESPIRATOR SELECTED MUST BE BASED ON CONTAMINATION LEVELS FOUND IN THE WORK PLACE, MUST NOT EXCEED THE WORKING LIMITS OF THE RESPIRATOR AND BE JOINTLY APPROVED BY THE NATIONAL INSTITUTE FOR OCCUPATIONAL SAFETY AND HEALTH AND THE MINE SAFETY AND HEALTH ADMINISTRATION (NIOSH-MSHA).

TYPE 'C' SUPPLIED-AIR RESPIRATOR WITH A FULL FACEPIECE OPERATED IN PRESSURE-DEMAND OR OTHER POSITIVE PRESSURE MODE OR WITH A FULL FACEPIECE, HELMET OR HOOD OPERATED IN CONTINOUS-FLOW MODE.

SELF-CONTAINED BREATHING APPARATUS WITH A FULL FACEPIECE OPERATED IN PRESSURE-DEMAND OR OTHER POSITIVE PRESSURE MODE.

FOR FIREFIGHTING AND OTHER IMMEDIATELY DANGEROUS TO LIFE OR HEALTH CONDITIONS:

SELF-CONTAINED BREATHING APPARATUS WITH FULL FACEPIECE OPERATED IN PRESSURE-DEMAND OR OTHER POSITIVE PRESSURE MODE.

SUPPLIED-AIR RESPIRATOR WITH FULL FACEPIECE AND OPERATED IN PRESSURE-DEMAND OR OTHER POSITIVE PRESSURE MODE IN COMBINATION WITH AN AUXILIARY SELF-CONTAINED BREATHING APPARATUS OPERATED IN PRESSURE-DEMAND OR OTHER POSITIVE PRESSURE MODE.

CLOTHING: EMPLOYEE MUST WEAR APPROPRIATE PROTECTIVE (IMPERVIOUS) CLOTHING AND EQUIPMENT TO PREVENT ANY POSSIBILITY OF SKIN CONTACT WITH THIS SUBSTANCE.

GLOVES: EMPLOYEE MUST WEAR APPROPRIATE PROTECTIVE GLOVES TO PREVENT CONTACT WITH THIS SUBSTANCE.

EYE PROTECTION: EMPLOYEE MUST WEAR SPLASH-PROOF OR DUST-RESISTANT SAFETY GOGGLES AND A FACESHIELD TO PREVENT CONTACT WITH THIS SUBSTANCE.

EMERGENCY WASH FACILITIES: WHERE THERE IS ANY POSSIBILITY THAT AN EMPLOYEE'S EYES AND/OR SKIN MAY BE EXPOSED TO THIS SUBSTANCE, THE EMPLOYER SHOULD PROVIDE AN EYE WASH FOUNTAIN AND QUICK DRENCH SHOWER WITHIN THE IMMEDIATE WORK AREA FOR EMERGENCY USE.

AUTHORIZED BY- OCCUPATIONAL HEALTH SERVICES, INC.

CREATION DATE: 10/04/89 ***REVISION DATE:*** 06/12/90

MATERIAL SAFETY DATA SHEET

OCCUPATIONAL HEALTH SERVICES, INC.
AGRICULTURE AND PESTICIDE DIVISION
450 SEVENTH AVENUE, SUITE 2407
NEW YORK, NEW YORK 10123
1-800-445-MSDS OR (212) 967-1100

EMERGENCY CONTACT:
JOHN S. BRANSFORD, JR. (615) 292-1180

SUBSTANCE IDENTIFICATION

CAS-NUMBER 8006-54-0

SUBSTANCE: **LANOLIN**

TRADE NAMES/SYNONYMS: WOOL FAT; OESIPOS; AGNIN; ALAOURIN; AGNILIN; LANUM; LANAIN; LANALIN; LANESIN; LANICHOL; LANIOL; L-7; PST12425

CHEMICAL FAMILY: HYDROCARBON, POLYNUCLEAR ESTER, CARBOXYLIC, ALIPHATIC

CERCLA RATINGS (SCALE 0-3): HEALTH=0 FIRE=1 REACTIVITY=0 PERSISTENCE=1

NFPA RATINGS (SCALE 0-4): HEALTH=0 FIRE=1 REACTIVITY=0

COMPONENTS AND CONTAMINANTS

COMPONENT: LANOLIN ***PERCENT:*** >70

COMPONENT: WATER ***PERCENT:*** <30

OTHER CONTAMINANTS: NONE

EXPOSURE LIMITS: NO OCCUPATIONAL EXPOSURE LIMITS ESTABLISHED BY OSHA, ACGIH, OR NIOSH.

PHYSICAL DATA

DESCRIPTION: YELLOWISH-WHITE UNCTUOUS MASS WITH A SLIGHT ODOR

MELTING POINT: 97 F (36 C) ***SPECIFIC GRAVITY:*** 0.93

SOLUBILITY IN WATER: INSOLUBLE

SOLVENT SOLUBILITY: SOLUBLE IN CHLOROFORM AND ETHER

FIRE AND EXPLOSION DATA

FIRE AND EXPLOSION HAZARD: SLIGHT FIRE HAZARD WHEN EXPOSED TO HEAT OR FLAME.

FLASH POINT: 460 F (238 C) (CC) ***AUTOIGNITION TEMP.:*** 833 F (445 C)

FLAMMABILITY CLASS(OSHA): IIIB

FIREFIGHTING MEDIA: DRY CHEMICAL, CARBON DIOXIDE, HALON, WATER SPRAY OR STANDARD FOAM (1987 EMERGENCY RESPONSE GUIDEBOOK, DOT P 5800.4).
FOR LARGER FIRES, USE WATER SPRAY, FOG OR STANDARD FOAM (1987 EMERGENCY RESPONSE GUIDEBOOK, DOT P 5800.4).

FIREFIGHTING: MOVE CONTAINER FROM FIRE AREA IF POSSIBLE. DO NOT SCATTER SPILLED MATERIAL WITH HIGH PRESSURE WATER STREAMS. DIKE FIRE CONTROL WATER FOR LATER DISPOSAL (1987 EMERGENCY RESPONSE GUIDEBOOK, DOT P 5800.4, GUIDE PAGE 31).
USE AGENTS SUITABLE FOR TYPE OF SURROUNDING FIRE. AVOID BREATHING HAZARDOUS VAPORS, KEEP UPWIND.
WATER OR FOAM MAY CAUSE FROTHING (NFPA 325M, FIRE HAZARD PROPERTIES OF FLAMMABLE LIQUIDS, GASES, AND VOLATILE SOLIDS, 1984)

TOXICITY

LANOLIN: CARCINOGEN STATUS: NONE. ACUTE TOXICITY LEVEL: NO DATA AVAILABLE. TARGET EFFECTS: NO DATA AVAILABLE.

HEALTH EFFECTS AND FIRST AID

INHALATION: LANOLIN: **ACUTE EXPOSURE-** NO DATA AVAILABLE. **CHRONIC EXPOSURE-** NO DATA AVAILABLE.

FIRST AID- REMOVE FROM EXPOSURE AREA TO FRESH AIR IMMEDIATELY. IF BREATHING HAS STOPPED, PERFORM ARTIFICIAL RESPIRATION. KEEP PERSON WARM AND AT REST. TREAT SYMPTOMATICALLY AND SUPPORTIVELY. GET MEDICAL ATTENTION IMMEDIATELY.

SKIN CONTACT: LANOLIN: **ACUTE EXPOSURE-** THE SUBSTANCE DOES NOT CAUSE ANY IMMEDIATELY IRRITATING EFFECTS IN MOST INDIVIDUALS. IT RARELY CAUSES DERMATITIS AND IRRITATION FROM ALLERGENIC REACTIONS. **CHRONIC EXPOSURE-** NONE REPORTED IN HUMANS.

FIRST AID- REMOVE CONTAMINATED CLOTHING AND SHOES IMMEDIATELY. WASH AFFECTED AREA WITH SOAP OR MILD DETERGENT AND LARGE AMOUNTS OF WATER UNTIL NO EVIDENCE OF CHEMICAL REMAINS (APPROXIMATELY 15-20 MINUTES). GET MEDICAL ATTENTION IMMEDIATELY.

EYE CONTACT: LANOLIN: **ACUTE EXPOSURE-** NO DATA AVAILABLE. MAY BE IRRITATING. **CHRONIC EXPOSURE-** NO DATA AVAILABLE.

FIRST AID- WASH EYES IMMEDIATELY WITH LARGE AMOUNTS OF WATER OR NORMAL SALINE, OCCASIONALLY LIFTING UPPER AND LOWER LIDS, UNTIL NO EVIDENCE OF CHEMICAL REMAINS (APPROXIMATELY 15-20 MINUTES). GET MEDICAL ATTENTION IMMEDIATELY.

INGESTION: LANOLIN: **ACUTE EXPOSURE-** SUBSTANCE IS NOT ABSORBED FROM THE ALIMENTARY TRACT. LARGE DOSES MAY CAUSE ABDOMINAL PAIN OR DIARRHEA. **CHRONIC EXPOSURE-** NONE REPORTED IN HUMANS.

FIRST AID- DO NOT INDUCE VOMITING. QUALIFIED MEDICAL PERSONNEL SHOULD REMOVE CHEMICAL BY GASTRIC LAVAGE OR CATHARSIS. ACTIVATED CHARCOAL IS USEFUL. GET MEDICAL ATTENTION IMMEDIATELY.

ANTIDOTE: NO SPECIFIC ANTIDOTE. TREAT SYMPTOMATICALLY AND SUPPORTIVELY.

REACTIVITY

REACTIVITY: STABLE UNDER NORMAL TEMPERATURES AND PRESSURES.

INCOMPATIBILITIES: NONE KNOWN.

DECOMPOSITION: THERMAL DECOMPOSITION PRODUCTS MAY INCLUDE TOXIC OXIDES OF CARBON.

POLYMERIZATION: HAZARDOUS POLYMERIZATION HAS NOT BEEN REPORTED TO OCCUR UNDER NORMAL TEMPERATURES AND PRESSURES.

CONDITIONS TO AVOID

AVOID HEATING TO DECOMPOSITION.

SPILL AND LEAK PROCEDURES

OCCUPATIONAL SPILL: SHUT OFF IGNITION SOURCES. STOP LEAK IF YOU CAN DO IT WITHOUT RISK. USE WATER SPRAY TO REDUCE VAPORS. FOR SMALL SPILLS, TAKE UP WITH SAND OR OTHER ABSORBENT MATERIAL AND PLACE INTO CONTAINERS FOR LATER DISPOSAL. FOR LARGER SPILLS, DIKE FAR AHEAD OF SPILL FOR LATER DISPOSAL. NO SMOKING, FLAMES OR FLARES IN HAZARD AREA. KEEP UNNECESSARY PEOPLE AWAY; ISOLATE HAZARD AREA AND DENY ENTRY.

PROTECTIVE EQUIPMENT

VENTILATION: PROVIDE GENERAL DILUTION VENTILATION.

RESPIRATOR: LOW LEVELS- CHEMICAL CARTRIDGE RESPIRATOR WITH AN ORGANIC VAPOR CARTRIDGE.

FIREFIGHTING- SELF-CONTAINED BREATHING APPARATUS WITH A FULL FACEPIECE OPERATED IN PRESSURE DEMAND OR OTHER POSITIVE PRESSURE MODE.

CLOTHING: PROTECTIVE CLOTHING NOT REQUIRED. AVOID REPEATED OR PROLONGED CONTACT WITH THIS SUBSTANCE.

GLOVES: PROTECTIVE GLOVES ARE NOT REQUIRED BUT RECOMMENDED.

EYE PROTECTION: EYE PROTECTION NOT REQUIRED, BUT ADVISABLE.

AUTHORIZED BY- OCCUPATIONAL HEALTH SERVICES, INC.

CREATION DATE: 11/17/89 ***REVISION DATE:*** 05/18/90

MATERIAL SAFETY DATA SHEET

OCCUPATIONAL HEALTH SERVICES, INC.
AGRICULTURE AND PESTICIDE DIVISION
450 SEVENTH AVENUE, SUITE 2407
NEW YORK, NEW YORK 10123
1-800-445-MSDS OR (212) 967-1100

EMERGENCY CONTACT:
JOHN S. BRANSFORD, JR. (615) 292-1180

SUBSTANCE IDENTIFICATION

SUBSTANCE: **LARIAT FLOWABLE HERBICIDE**

TRADE NAMES/SYNONYMS: EPA REG. NO. 524-329-AA; PST12471

CHEMICAL FAMILY: MIXTURE, PESTICIDE FORMULATION

CERCLA RATINGS (SCALE 0-3): HEALTH = U FIRE = 2 REACTIVITY = 0 PERSISTENCE = 2

NFPA RATINGS (SCALE 0-4): HEALTH = U FIRE = 2 REACTIVITY = 0

COMPONENTS AND CONTAMINANTS

COMPONENT: ALACHLOR ***PERCENT:*** 27.2
CAS# 15972-60-8

COMPONENT: ATRAZINE ***PERCENT:*** 15.5
CAS# 1912-24-9

COMPONENT: RELATED ATRAZINE COMPOUNDS ***PERCENT:*** 0.8

COMPONENT: INERT INGREDIENTS ***PERCENT:*** 56.5
INCLUDING:
CHLOROBENZENE CAS# 108-90-7
ETHYLENE GLYCOL CAS# 107-21-1
EMULSIFIERS

EXPOSURE LIMITS: ALACHLOR: SUBJECT TO CALIFORNIA PROPOSITION 65 CANCER AND/OR REPRODUCTIVE TOXICITY WARNING AND RELEASE REQUIREMENTS-(JANUARY 1, 1989)

ATRAZINE: 5 MG/M3 OSHA TWA 5 MG/M3 ACGIH TWA

CHLOROBENZENE: 75 PPM (350 MG/M3) OSHA TWA 75 PPM (350 MG/M3) ACGIH TWA (NOTICE OF INTENDED CHANGES 1989-1990)

100 POUNDS CERCLA SECTION 103 REPORTABLE QUANTITY SUBJECT TO SARA SECTION 313 ANNUAL TOXIC CHEMICAL RELEASE REPORTING ETHYLENE GLYCOL: 50 PPM (125 MG/M3) OSHA CEILING 50 PPM (125 MG/M3) ACGIH CEILING (VAPOR AND MIST)

SUBJECT TO SARA SECTION 313 ANNUAL TOXIC CHEMICAL RELEASE REPORTING

PHYSICAL DATA

DESCRIPTION: MILKY BLUE EMULSION WITH ODOR SIMILAR TO SHOE POLISH.

BOILING POINT: NOT AVAILABLE ***SPECIFIC GRAVITY:*** 1.1

VAPOR PRESSURE: NOT AVAILABLE ***SOLUBILITY IN WATER:*** SOLUBLE

FIRE AND EXPLOSION DATA

FIRE AND EXPLOSION HAZARD: MODERATE FIRE HAZARD WHEN EXPOSED TO HEAT OR FLAME.

VAPOR-AIR MIXTURES ARE EXPLOSIVE ABOVE FLASH POINT.

FLASH POINT: 102 F (39 C) (CC) ***FLAMMABILITY CLASS(OSHA):*** II

FIREFIGHTING MEDIA: DRY CHEMICAL, CARBON DIOXIDE, HALON, WATER SPRAY OR STANDARD FOAM (1987 EMERGENCY RESPONSE GUIDEBOOK, DOT P 5800.4).

FOR LARGER FIRES, USE WATER SPRAY, FOG OR STANDARD FOAM (1987 EMERGENCY RESPONSE GUIDEBOOK, DOT P 5800.4).

FIREFIGHTING: MOVE CONTAINERS FROM FIRE AREA IF POSSIBLE. COOL CONTAINERS EXPOSED TO FLAMES WITH WATER FROM SIDE UNTIL WELL AFTER FIRE IS OUT. FIGHT FIRE FROM MAXIMUM DISTANCE. STAY AWAY FROM STORAGE TANK ENDS. DIKE FIRE CONTROL WATER FOR LATER DISPOSAL. DO NOT SCATTER MATERIAL. (1987 EMERGENCY RESPONSE GUIDEBOOK, DOT P 5800.4, GUIDE PAGE 57).

EXTINGUISH ONLY IF FLOW CAN BE STOPPED. USE FLOODING AMOUNTS OF WATER AS A FOG; SOLID STREAMS MAY BE INEFFECTIVE. COOL CONTAINERS WITH FLOODING AMOUNTS OF WATER FROM AS FAR A DISTANCE AS POSSIBLE. AVOID BREATHING POISONOUS VAPORS, KEEP UPWIND.

TRANSPORTATION DATA

DEPARTMENT OF TRANSPORTATION HAZARD CLASSIFICATION 49 CFR 172.101: COMBUSTIBLE LIQUID

DEPARTMENT OF TRANSPORTATION LABELING REQUIREMENTS 49 CFR 172.101 AND SUBPART E: NONE

DEPARTMENT OF TRANSPORTATION PACKAGING REQUIREMENTS: NONE EXCEPTIONS: 49 CFR 173.118A

TOXICITY

ALACHLOR: TOXICITY DATA: 3500 MG/KG SKIN-RABBIT LD50; 930 MG/KG ORAL-RAT LD50; 462 MG/KG ORAL-MOUSE LD50; 3000 MG/KG ORAL-MAMMAL LD50; 1200 MG/KG UNREPORTED-MAMMAL LD50; MUTAGENIC DATA (RTECS); TUMORIGENIC DATA (RTECS). CARCINOGEN STATUS: NONE. ACUTE TOXICITY LEVEL: MODERATELY TOXIC BY INGESTION; SLIGHTLY TOXIC BY DERMAL ABSORPTION. TARGET EFFECTS: SENSITIZER- SKIN.

ATRAZINE: IRRITATION DATA: 38 MG OPEN SKIN-RABBIT MILD; 6320 UG EYE-RABBIT SEVERE; 500 MG SKIN-MAMMAL MILD; 100 MG EYE-MAMMAL SEVERE. TOXICITY DATA: 5200 MG/M3/4 HOURS INHALATION-RAT LC50; 7500 MG/KG SKIN-RABBIT LD50; 672 MG/KG ORAL-RAT LD50; 850 MG/KG ORAL-MOUSE LD50; 750 MG/KG ORAL-RABBIT LD50; 1000 MG/KG ORAL-HAMSTER LD50; 235 MG/KG INTRAPERITONEAL-RAT LD50; 626 MG/KG INTRAPERITONEAL-MOUSE LD50; 1400 MG/KG UNREPORTED-MAMMAL LD50; MUTAGENIC DATA (RTECS); REPRODUCTIVE EFFECTS DATA (RTECS); TUMORIGENIC DATA (RTECS). CARCINOGEN STATUS: NONE. LOCAL EFFECTS: IRRITANT- EYE. ACUTE TOXICITY LEVEL: TOXIC BY INHALATION; MODERATELY TOXIC BY INGESTION; SLIGHTLY TOXIC BY DERMAL ABSORPTION. TARGET EFFECTS: NO DATA AVAILABLE.

CHLOROBENZENE: TOXICITY DATA: 15 GM/M3 INHALATION-MOUSE LCLO; 2290

MG/KG ORAL-RAT LD50; 2250 MG/KG ORAL-RABBIT LD50; 2300 MG/KG ORAL-MOUSE LD50; 2250 MG/KG ORAL-GUINEA PIG LD50; 7000 MG/KG SUBCUTANEOUS-RAT LDLO; 7400 MG/KG INTRAPERITONEAL-RAT LDLO; 515 MG/KG INTRAPERITONEAL-MOUSE LD50; 4100 MG/KG INTRAPERITONEAL-GUINEA PIG LDLO; 2300 MG/KG UNREPORTED-MAMMAL LD50; MUTAGENIC DATA (RTECS); REPRODUCTIVE EFFECTS DATA (RTECS). CARCINOGEN STATUS: NONE. LOCAL EFFECTS: IRRITANT- INHALATION, SKIN, EYE. ACUTE TOXICITY LEVEL: MODERATELY TOXIC BY INGESTION. TARGET EFFECTS: CENTRAL NERVOUS SYSTEM DEPRESSANT. POISONING MAY AFFECT THE LIVER AND KIDNEYS. AT INCREASED RISK FROM EXPOSURE: PERSONS WITH PREEXISTING SKIN, LIVER, KIDNEY, OR CHRONIC RESPIRATORY DISEASES. ADDITIONAL DATA: GASTROENTERIC ABSORPTION IS ENHANCED BY THE PRESENCE OF FATS OR OILS. ALCOHOL MAY ENHANCE THE TOXIC EFFECTS.

ETHYLENE GLYCOL: IRRITATION DATA: 555 MG OPEN SKIN-RABBIT MILD; 12 MG/M3/3 DAYS EYE-RAT; 100 MG/1 HOUR EYE-RABBIT MILD; 500 MG/24 HOURS EYE-RABBIT MILD; 12 MG/M3/3 DAYS EYE-RABBIT; 1440 MG/6 HOURS EYE-RABBIT MODERATE. TOXICITY DATA: 10000 MG/M3 INHALATION-HUMAN TCLO; 9530 MG/KG SKIN-RABBIT LD50; 5500 MG/KG ORAL-CHILD TDLO; 786 MG/KG ORAL-HUMAN LDLO; 398 MG/KG ORAL-HUMAN LDLO; 4700 MG/KG ORAL-RAT LD50; 7500 MG/KG ORAL-MOUSE LD50; 6610 MG/KG ORAL-GUINEA PIG LD50; 5500 MG/KG ORAL-DOG LD50; 1650 MG/KG ORAL-CAT LD50; 2800 MG/KG SUBCUTANEOUS-RAT LD50; 2700 MG/KG SUBCUTANEOUS-MOUSE LDLO; 5000 MG/KG SUBCUTANEOUS-GUINEA PIG LDLO; 2000 MG/KG SUBCUTANEOUS-CAT LDLO; 3260 MG/KG INTRAVENOUS-RAT LD50; 3000 MG/KG INTRAVENOUS-MOUSE LD50; 5 GM/KG INTRAVENOUS-RABBIT LDLO; 5010 MG/KG INTRAPERITONEAL-RAT LD50; 5614 MG/KG INTRAPERITONEAL-MOUSE LD50; 1000 MG/KG INTRAPERITONEAL-RABBIT LDLO; 3300 MG/KG INTRAMUSCULAR-RAT LDLO; 5500 MG/KG INTRAMUSCULAR-RABBIT LDLO; 1637 MG/KG UNREPORTED ROUTE-MAN LDLO; MUTAGENIC DATA (RTECS); REPRODUCTIVE EFFECTS DATA (RTECS). CARCINOGEN STATUS: NONE. LOCAL EFFECTS: IRRITANT- INHALATION, SKIN, EYE. ACUTE TOXICITY LEVEL: MODERATELY TOXIC BY INGESTION; SLIGHTLY TOXIC BY DERMAL ABSORPTION. TARGET EFFECTS: CENTRAL NERVOUS SYSTEM DEPRESSANT; NEPHROTOXIN; NEUROTOXIN. POISONING MAY AFFECT THE LUNGS, HEART, BLOOD, BRAIN AND LIVER.

HEALTH EFFECTS AND FIRST AID

INHALATION: ALACHLOR: **ACUTE EXPOSURE-** SLIGHT TO NEGLIGIBLE EFFECTS WERE OBSERVED IN RATS EXPOSED TO 5100 MG/M3/4 HOURS. A CONCENTRATION OF 32600 MG/M3 WAS LETHAL TO RATS. **CHRONIC EXPOSURE-** NO DATA AVAILABLE.

ATRAZINE: TOXIC. **ACUTE EXPOSURE-** EXPOSURE TO LARGE CONCENTRATIONS OF DUST, AEROSOLS OR AQUEOUS EMULSIONS MAY CAUSE IRRITATION OF THE MUCOUS MEMBRANES. A LETHAL CONCENTRATION IN RATS WAS 5200 MG/M3/4 HOURS. **CHRONIC EXPOSURE-** NO DATA AVAILABLE.

CHLOROBENZENE: IRRITANT/NARCOTIC. 2400 PPM IMMEDIATELY DANGEROUS TO LIFE OR HEALTH. **ACUTE EXPOSURE-** INHALATION OF 200 PPM MAY CAUSE MUCOUS MEMBRANE IRRITATION AND COUGHING. AT HIGHER CONCENTRATIONS, CENTRAL NERVOUS SYSTEM DEPRESSION WITH HEADACHE, DIZZINESS, DROWSINESS, SOMNOLENCE, TRANSIENT ANESTHESIA AND INCOHERENCE, CYANOSIS FROM METHEMOGLOBINEMIA, SPASTIC CONTRACTIONS OF THE EXTREMITIES, RAPID RESPIRATION, WEAK AND IRREGULAR PULSE, BURGUNDY-RED URINE, LOSS OF CONSCIOUSNESS, COMA, AND RESPIRATORY AND CIRCULATORY COLLAPSE MAY OCCUR. IN CATS, A CONCENTRATION OF 1200-2900 PPM PRODUCED NARCOSIS WITH RESTLESSNESS, TREMOR AND MUSCULAR SPASMS, BUT NO SERIOUS INJURY OR FATALITY; 3700 PPM WAS LETHAL AFTER SEVERAL HOURS. 8000 PPM PRODUCED SEVERE NARCOSIS AFTER 30 MINUTES AND DEATH WITHIN 2 HOURS AFTER REMOVAL FROM EXPOSURE. PATHOLOGICAL CHANGES MAY INCLUDE HYPERTROPHY AND NECROSIS OF THE LIVER AND BRONCHIAL EPITHELIUM OF THE LUNGS, EDEMA OF THE BRAIN AND SUBMUCOSAL HEMORRHAGE IN THE STOMACH. **CHRONIC EXPOSURE-** WORKERS EXPOSED TO CHLOROBENZENE VAPORS FROM 1-2 YEARS SUFFERED FROM HEADACHE, DIZZINESS, SOMNOLENCE, AND DYSPEPTIC DISORDERS. OTHER SYMPTOMS REPORTED IN SOME OF THE WORKERS WERE ACROPARESTHESIA, SPASTIC CONTRACTIONS OF FINGER MUSCLES, HYPESTHESIA, SPASTIC CONTRACTIONS OF THE GASTROCNEMIUS MUSCLE AND VASOVEGETATIVE INSTABILITY. REPEATED EXPOSURE TO 1000 PPM SEVEN HOURS PER DAY, FIVE DAYS A WEEK FOR 44 DAYS RESULTED IN LUNG, LIVER, AND KIDNEY CHANGES IN ANIMALS. AT 475 PPM THERE WAS ONLY SLIGHT LIVER DAMAGE IN GUINEA PIGS AND NO EFFECTS WERE NOTED AT 200 PPM. REPRODUCTIVE EFFECTS HAVE BEEN REPORTED IN ANIMAL STUDIES.

ETHYLENE GLYCOL: IRRITANT. **ACUTE EXPOSURE-** INHALATION IS UNLIKELY AT ROOM TEMPERATURE, DUE TO THE LOW VAPOR PRESSURE. AEROSOLS AT 140 MG/M3 WERE IRRITATING, AND 200 MG/M3 WERE INTOLERABLE CAUSING A BURNING SENSATION OF THROAT AND COUGHING. EXPOSURE TO HIGH CONCENTRATIONS OF MISTS OR AEROSOLS MAY RESULT IN EFFECTS ON THE HEMATOPOIETIC SYSTEM AND CENTRAL NERVOUS SYSTEM WITH HEADACHE, DIZZINESS AND DROWSINESS. **CHRONIC EXPOSURE-** HUMANS EXPOSED TO AEROSOLS FROM 3-67 MG/M3 CONTINUOUSLY FOR 1 MONTH REPORTED IRRITATION OF THE RESPIRATORY TRACT, OCCASIONALLY SLIGHT HEADACHE AND LOW BACKACHE, BUT NO OTHER SIGNIFICANT ADVERSE EFFECTS. CONTINUED EXPOSURE TO VAPORS FROM A PROCESS UTILIZING A MIXTURE OF ETHYLENE GLYCOL, BORIC ACID AND AMMONIA HEATED ABOVE 100 C RESULTED IN NYSTAGMUS, LYMPHOCYTOSIS AND SUDDEN LOSS OF CONSCIOUSNESS FOR 5-10 MINUTES. NYSTAGMUS OCCURRED 2-3 TIMES WEEKLY UNTIL EXPOSURE CEASED. REPEATED EXPOSURE TO SATURATED ETHYLENE GLYCOL VAPORS PRODUCED SLIGHT NARCOSIS IN RATS. EFFECTS ON THE FETUS HAVE BEEN REPORTED IN RATS AND MICE FOLLOWING EXPOSURE DURING GESTATION. THERE WAS A LIKELIHOOD THAT AT LEAST A PORTION OF THE EFFECTS RESULTED FROM INGESTION SINCE ANIMALS GROOMED CONSTANTLY BEFORE AND AFTER EXPOSURE.

FIRST AID- REMOVE FROM EXPOSURE AREA TO FRESH AIR IMMEDIATELY. IF BREATHING HAS STOPPED, PERFORM ARTIFICIAL RESPIRATION. KEEP PERSON WARM AND AT REST. TREAT SYMPTOMATICALLY AND SUPPORTIVELY. GET MEDICAL ATTENTION IMMEDIATELY.

SKIN CONTACT: ALACHLOR: SENSITIZER. **ACUTE EXPOSURE-** THIS MATERIAL WAS SLIGHTLY IRRITATING TO RABBIT SKIN. ALLERGIC SKIN REACTIONS MAY OCCUR IN PERSONS PREVIOUSLY EXPOSED. **CHRONIC EXPOSURE-** PROLONGED OR REPEATED EXPOSURE TO THIS MATERIAL MAY PRODUCE ALLERGIC SKIN REACTIONS IN SUSCEPTIBLE INDIVIDUALS. REPEATED APPLICATION OF ALACHLOR TO GUINEA PIG SKIN RESULTED IN ERYTHEMA, REDNESS, EDEMA, SWELLING, AND NECROSIS. REPEATED DERMAL APPLICATION OF 4.0 GM/KG PRODUCED SLIGHT TO MODERATE IRRITATION AND INCREASED PITUITARY WEIGHTS IN RABBITS.

ATRAZINE: **ACUTE EXPOSURE-** 38 MG APPLIED TO OPEN RABBIT SKIN WAS MILDLY IRRITATING. A CASE OF ALLERGIC REACTION FROM EXPOSURE TO ATRAZINE WAS REPORTED TO HAVE OCCURRED. ANIMAL STUDIES INDICATE SKIN ABSORPTION MAY OCCUR. **CHRONIC EXPOSURE-** PROLONGED OR REPEATED EXPOSURE MAY CAUSE DERMATITIS.

CHLOROBENZENE: IRRITANT. **ACUTE EXPOSURE-** CONTACT WITH THE LIQUID MAY CAUSE IRRITATION WITH REDNESS AND DEFATTING OF THE SKIN. ACNEFORM ERUPTIONS MAY OCCUR DUE TO CHLOROBENZENE. **CHRONIC EXPOSURE-** PROLONGED CONTACT WITH THE LIQUID MAY CAUSE DERMATITIS DUE TO ITS DEFATTING ACTION, MODERATE ERYTHEMA AND SLIGHT SUPERFICIAL NECROSIS OR BURNS.

ETHYLENE GLYCOL: IRRITANT. **ACUTE EXPOSURE-** LIQUID MAY DEFAT THE SKIN AND CAUSE MINOR IRRITATION. ANIMAL STUDIES INDICATE THAT LETHAL AMOUNTS MAY BE ABSORBED THROUGH INTACT SKIN. ONE CASE HAS BEEN REPORTED OF COMA ACCOMPANIED BY MIOSIS AND SLOWED PULSE 4 HOURS AFTER MASSIVE APPLICATION OF AN ECZEMA REMEDY CONTAINING ETHYLENE GLYCOL. SENSITIZATION REACTIONS MAY OCCUR IN PREVIOUSLY EXPOSED PERSONS. **CHRONIC EXPOSURE-** A SLIGHT MACERATING ACTION ON THE SKIN MAY RESULT FROM VERY SEVERE, PROLONGED EXPOSURE. REPEATED OR PROLONGED CONTACT MAY RESULT IN SENSITIZATION.

FIRST AID- REMOVE CONTAMINATED CLOTHING AND SHOES IMMEDIATELY. WASH AFFECTED AREA WITH SOAP OR MILD DETERGENT AND LARGE AMOUNTS OF WATER UNTIL NO EVIDENCE OF CHEMICAL REMAINS (APPROXIMATELY 15-20 MINUTES). GET MEDICAL ATTENTION IMMEDIATELY.

EYE CONTACT: ALACHLOR: **ACUTE EXPOSURE-** EYE IRRITATION PRODUCED FROM CONTACT WITH TECHNICAL ALACHLOR HAS BEEN REPORTED. HOWEVER, TESTED IN RABBIT EYES, THIS MATERIAL WAS PRACTICALLY NONIRRITATING. **CHRONIC EXPOSURE-** NO DATA AVAILABLE.

ATRAZINE: IRRITANT. **ACUTE EXPOSURE-** 6320 UG APPLIED TO RABBIT EYES WAS SEVERELY IRRITATING. **CHRONIC EXPOSURE-** PROLONGED OR REPEATED EXPOSURE TO IRRITANTS MAY CAUSE CONJUNCTIVITIS.

CHLOROBENZENE: IRRITANT. **ACUTE EXPOSURE-** CONTACT WITH THE LIQUID MAY RESULT IN TRANSIENT CONJUNCTIVAL IRRITATION WITH REDNESS AND PAIN. EYE IRRITATION IN HUMANS HAS BEEN REPORTED FROM EXPOSURE TO VAPORS AT 200 PPM. **CHRONIC EXPOSURE-** REPEATED OR PROLONGED CONTACT WITH IRRITANTS MAY CAUSE CONJUNCTIVITIS.

ETHYLENE GLYCOL: IRRITANT. **ACUTE EXPOSURE-** VAPORS MAY CAUSE REDNESS, AND CONTACT WITH THE LIQUID MAY CAUSE CONJUNCTIVITIS AND IRIDOCYCLITIS, BUT NO PERMANENT DAMAGE. **CHRONIC EXPOSURE-** VAPOR OR SPRAY AT 17 MG/M3/4 WEEKS PRODUCED NO ILL EFFECTS IN HUMANS. RATS EXPOSED CONTINUOUSLY TO 12 MG/M3 FOR SEVERAL DAYS SOMETIMES SHOWED SEVERE EYE IRRITATION, EDEMA OF THE EYELIDS, CORNEAL OPACITY AND APPARENT BLINDNESS, WITHOUT SIGNS OF SYSTEMIC INTOXICATION.

FIRST AID- WASH EYES IMMEDIATELY WITH LARGE AMOUNTS OF WATER OR NORMAL SALINE, OCCASIONALLY LIFTING UPPER AND LOWER LIDS, UNTIL NO EVIDENCE OF CHEMICAL REMAINS (APPROXIMATELY 15-20 MINUTES). GET MEDICAL ATTENTION IMMEDIATELY.

INGESTION: ALACHLOR: **ACUTE EXPOSURE-** A LETHAL DOSE IN RATS WAS 930 MG/KG; SYMPTOMS WERE NOT REPORTED. **CHRONIC EXPOSURE-** EFFECTS OF GASTROINTESTINAL DISTURBANCES, HEMOLYTIC ANEMIA, DECREASED BODY WEIGHTS, INCREASED LIVER WEIGHTS AND INCREASED BROMOSULFOPHTHALEIN RETENTION WERE OBSERVED IN A 1-YEAR STUDY OF DOGS FED 10 MG/KG/DAY. HEPATOTOXICITY WAS CITED IN ANOTHER STUDY OF DOGS. MATERNAL AND FETAL TOXICITY WERE NOTED IN A STUDY OF PREGNANT RATS FED 400 MG/KG/DAY. IN A 3-GENERATION STUDY OF RATS, SOME KIDNEY EFFECTS WERE REPORTED AT A DOSE OF 30 MG/KG/DAY. EFFECTS OF OCULAR LESSIONS, HEPATOTOXICITY, TUMORS OF THE NASAL TURBINATE, STOMACH, LIVER, AND THYROID WERE PRODUCED IN RATS. LUNG BRONCHIOLAR-ALVEOLAR TUMORS IN FEMALES WERE OBSERVED IN MICE FED 260 MG/KG/DAY FOR 79 WEEKS.

ATRAZINE: **ACUTE EXPOSURE-** AFTER CONSUMING A LARGE ORAL DOSE OF ATRAZINE, RATS EXHIBITED MUSCULAR WEAKNESS, HYPOACTIVITY, PTOSIS, DYSPNEA, PROSTRATION, ATAXIA, CONVULSIONS, AND DEATH. **CHRONIC EXPOSURE-** FORTY PERCENT OF RATS THAT RECEIVED ATRAZINE ORALLY FOR 6 MONTHS AT A RATE OF 20 MG/KG/DAY DIED WITH SIGNS OF RESPIRATORY DISTRESS AND PARALYSIS OF THE LIMBS. MORPHOLOGICAL AND BIOCHEMICAL CHANGES IN THE BRAIN, HEART, LIVER, LUNGS, KIDNEY, OVARIES, AND ENDOCRINE ORGANS WERE OBSERVED. MATERNAL TOXICITY WAS OBSERVED IN PREGNANT RATS FED DOSES GREATER THAN 70 MG/KG/DAY AND IN PREGNANT RABBITS FED DOSES GREATER THAN 5 MG/KG/DAY. MINOR FETAL EFFECTS WERE NOTED IN RATS AT THIS LEVEL, AND IN RABBITS FETAL EFFECTS OCCURRED AT DOSES THAT PRODUCED SEVERE MATERNAL TOXICITY, 75 MG/KG/DAY. AN INCREASED INCIDENCE OF FIBROADENOMAS, CARCINOMAS OF THE MAMMARY GLANDS AND ALL MAMMARY TUMORS IN FEMALES WAS REPORTED FROM A 2-YEAR RAT STUDY.

CHLOROBENZENE NARCOTIC. **ACUTE EXPOSURE-** INGESTION MAY CAUSE SALIVATION, ABDOMINAL PAIN, NAUSEA, VOMITING, HEADACHE, LATENT PALLOR, CYANOSIS FROM METHEMOGLOBINEMIA AND COLLAPSE. INGESTION OF THE LIQUID BY A CHILD RESULTED IN PALLOR, CYANOSIS AND COMA FOLLOWED BY COMPLETE RECOVERY. **CHRONIC EXPOSURE-** RATS FED 14.4 MG/KG AND 18.8 MG/KG 5 DAYS PER WEEK FOR 192 DAYS SHOWED NO ADVERSE EFFECTS. AT 144 MG/KG-288 MG/KG PRODUCED INCREASES IN LIVER AND KIDNEY WEIGHTS. A DOSAGE OF 376 MG/KG PER DAY CAUSED SLIGHT CIRRHOSIS AND FOCAL NECROSIS OF THE LIVER AND A SLIGHT DECREASE IN AVERAGE SPLEEN WEIGHTS. EOSINOPHILIA AND INHIBITION OF ERYTHROPOIESIS AND THROMBOCYTOSIS HAVE ALSO BEEN REPORTED IN RATS.

ETHYLENE GLYCOL: NARCOTIC/NEPHROTOXIN/NEUROTOXIN. **ACUTE EXPOSURE-** THE ESTIMATED LETHAL DOSE FOR ADULTS IS 100 MILLILITERS. THERE ARE THREE STAGES OF INTOXICATION FOLLOWING INGESTION OF ETHYLENE GLYCOL: CENTRAL NERVOUS SYSTEM STIMULATION FOLLOWED BY DEPRESSION; CARDIORESPIRATORY FAILURE; AND RENAL FAILURE. AN ACUTE CENTRAL NERVOUS SYSTEM STAGE MAY FOLLOW SHORTLY AFTER INGESTION AND LAST SEVERAL HOURS WITH SYMPTOMS OF NAUSEA, VOMITING, ABDOMINAL PAIN, DEHYDRATION, VISUAL DIFFICULTY, CONFUSION, PERSONALITY CHANGES, HALLUCINATIONS, CONVULSIONS, COMA, MENINGISM, MYOCLONUS, FIXED PUPILS, DECREASED OR LOSS OF VISION, LOSS OF ACCOMMODATION, PAPILLEDEMA, DIPLOPIA, NYSTAGMUS, STRABISMUS, ABNORMAL EYE MOVEMENTS, OPTIC NERVE ATROPHY, CRANIAL NERVE PALSIES, ATAXIA, TREMORS, MYOSITIS, MUSCLE TWITCHING, TETANY, HYPERREFLEXIA, AND AREFLEXIA. LIFE-THREATENING COMPLICATIONS WHICH MAY OCCUR IN THIS PERIOD INCLUDE RESPIRATORY FAILURE, SECONDARY TO CENTRAL NERVOUS SYSTEM DEPRESSION, CARDIOVASCULAR COLLAPSE, PULMONARY EDEMA AND SEVERE METABOLIC ACIDOSIS. WITHOUT TREATMENT, DEATH MAY OCCUR IN 8-24 HOURS. IF DEATH DOES NOT OCCUR EARLY, LUMBAR PAIN, ALBUMINURIA, HEMATURIA AND OLIGURIA PROGRESSING TO ANURIA ARE PROBABLE. ACUTE RENAL FAILURE WITH UREMIA, PERIPHERAL EDEMA, ASCITES, PULMONARY EDEMA, DROWSINESS, CYANOSIS, COMA AND DEATH IN 7-10 DAYS IS POSSIBLE. METABOLISM TO OXALIC ACID RESULTS IN PRECIPITATION OF CALCIUM OXALATE CRYSTALS IN SOFT TISSUES. CAPILLARY DAMAGE MAY RESULT IN EXUDATIVE, CONGESTIVE OR HEMORRHAGIC DAMAGE TO THE BRAIN, PERICARDIUM AND LIVER. MILDER INTOXICATION MAY RESULT IN INEBRIATION FOLLOWED BY AN ASYMPTOMATIC PERIOD OF SEVERAL DAYS BEFORE THE ONSET OF RENAL FAILURE. OLIGURIA MAY BE PERSISTENT, BUT EVENTUAL IMPROVEMENT IN RENAL FUNCTION IS ANTICIPATED IN SURVIVORS. PERMANENT CEREBRAL DAMAGE MAY OCCUR IN SURVIVORS OF PROLONGED COMA OR CONVULSIONS. **CHRONIC EXPOSURE-** REPEATED DAILY INGESTION OF 15-30 ML MAY CAUSE OLIGURIA WITHIN 24-72 HOURS, WHICH MAY PROGRESS RAPIDLY TO ANURIA AND UREMIA. REPEATED ADMINISTRATION TO ANIMALS RESULTED IN SHORTENED LIFE SPAN, CALCIUM OXALATE BLADDER STONES, SEVERE RENAL INJURY, PARTICULARLY OF THE TUBULES, AND CENTRILOBULAR DEGENERATION OF THE LIVER. MATERNAL EFFECTS, EFFECTS ON FERTILITY, FETAL DEVELOPMENTAL ABNORMALITIES AND EFFECTS ON THE EMBRYO AND FETUS HAVE BEEN REPORTED FROM REPEATED ADMINISTRATION TO RATS AND MICE DURING GESTATION; ADMINISTRATION TO LACTATING MICE PRODUCED DELAYED EFFECTS ON THE NEWBORN.

FIRST AID- TREAT SYMPTOMATICALLY AND SUPPORTIVELY. GET MEDICAL ATTENTION IMMEDIATELY. IF VOMITING OCCURS, KEEP HEAD LOWER THAN HIPS TO PREVENT ASPIRATION.

REACTIVITY

REACTIVITY: STABLE UNDER NORMAL TEMPERATURES AND PRESSURES.

INCOMPATIBILITIES: ALACHLOR: ACIDS (STRONG): HYDROLYZES. BASES (STRONG): HYDROLYZES. BLACK IRON: MAY CORRODE. STEEL: MAY CORRODE.

ATRAZINE: ALKALI: MAY BE HYDROLYZED AT HIGHER TEMPERATURES. MINERAL ACIDS: MAY BE HYDROLYZED AT HIGHER TEMPERATURES.

CHLOROBENZENE: DIMETHYL SULFOXIDE: VIOLENT REACTION. OXIDIZERS (STRONG): VIOLENT REACTIONS. PLASTICS, RUBBER AND COATINGS: MAY BE ATTACKED. SILVER PERCHLORATE: REACTS FORMING A SHOCK-SENSITIVE SOLVATED SALT. SODIUM: MAY CAUSE EXPLOSIONS OR THE FORMATION OF AN EXPLOSIVE COMPOUND.

ETHYLENE GLYCOL: AMMONIUM DICHROMATE: IGNITES @ 100 C. CHLOROSULFONIC ACID: TEMPERATURE AND PRESSURE INCREASE IN CLOSED CONTAINER. CHROMIUM TRIOXIDE: IGNITES ON CONTACT. DIMETHYL TEREPHTHALATE + TITANIUM BUTOXIDE: POSSIBLE IGNITION. OLEUM: TEMPERATURE AND PRESSURE INCREASE IN CLOSED CONTAINER. OXIDIZERS (STRONG): FIRE AND EXPLOSION HAZARD. PERCHLORIC ACID: VIOLENT DECOMPOSITION. PHOSPHORUS(V) SULFIDE: EXPLOSIVE REACTION ON HEATING. POTASSIUM DICHROMATE: VIGOROUS EXOTHERMIC REACTION @ 100 C. POTASSIUM PERMANGANATE: IGNITES ON CONTACT. SILVER CHLORATE: IGNITES @ 100 C. SILVERED COPPER WIRE: IGNITES. SODIUM CHLORITE: IGNITES @ 100 C. SODIUM HYDROXIDE: EXPLOSION HAZARD. SODIUM PEROXIDE: IGNITES ON CONTACT. SULFURIC ACID: TEMPERATURE AND PRESSURE INCREASE IN CLOSED CONTAINER. URANYL NITRATE: IGNITES @ 100 C.

DECOMPOSITION: THERMAL DECOMPOSITION PRODUCTS MAY INCLUDE TOXIC AND CORROSIVE FUMES OF CHLORIDES AND TOXIC OXIDES OF CARBON.

POLYMERIZATION: HAZARDOUS POLYMERIZATION HAS NOT BEEN REPORTED TO OCCUR UNDER NORMAL TEMPERATURES AND PRESSURES.

STORAGE AND DISPOSAL

OBSERVE ALL FEDERAL, STATE AND LOCAL REGULATIONS WHEN STORING OR DISPOSING OF THIS SUBSTANCE. FOR ASSISTANCE, CONTACT THE DISTRICT DIRECTOR OF THE ENVIRONMENTAL PROTECTION AGENCY.

****STORAGE****

STORE IN ACCORDANCE WITH 29 CFR 1910.106.

BONDING AND GROUNDING: SUBSTANCES WITH LOW ELECTROCONDUCTIVITY, WHICH MAY BE IGNITED BY ELECTROSTATIC SPARKS, SHOULD BE STORED IN CONTAINERS WHICH MEET THE BONDING AND GROUNDING GUIDELINES SPECIFIED IN NFPA 77-1983, RECOMMENDED PRACTICE ON STATIC ELECTRICITY.

STORE IN ACCORDANCE WITH 40 CFR 165 RECOMMENDED PROCEDURES FOR THE DISPOSAL AND STORAGE OF PESTICIDES AND PESTICIDE CONTAINERS.

STORE ABOVE 40 F (4 C).

STORE AWAY FROM INCOMPATIBLE SUBSTANCES.

STORE ABOVE 40 F (4 C).

****DISPOSAL****

DISPOSAL MUST BE IN ACCORDANCE WITH STANDARDS APPLICABLE TO GENERATORS OF HAZARDOUS WASTE, 40 CFR 262. EPA HAZARDOUS WASTE NUMBER D001. 100 POUND CERCLA SECTION 103 REPORTABLE QUANTITY.

DISPOSAL MUST BE IN ACCORDANCE WITH 40 CFR 165 RECOMMENDED PROCEDURES FOR THE DISPOSAL AND STORAGE OF PESTICIDES AND PESTICIDE CONTAINERS.

CHLOROBENZENE - REGULATORY LEVEL: 100.0 MG/L MATERIALS WHICH CONTAIN THE ABOVE SUBSTANCE AT OR ABOVE THE REGULATORY LEVEL MEET THE EPA CHARACTERISTIC OF TOXICITY, AND MUST BE DISPOSED OF IN ACCORDANCE WITH 40 CFR PART 262. EPA HAZARDOUS WASTE NUMBER D021.

CONDITIONS TO AVOID

MAY BE IGNITED BY HEAT, SPARKS OR FLAMES. CONTAINER MAY EXPLODE IN HEAT OF FIRE. VAPOR EXPLOSION AND POISON HAZARD INDOORS, OUTDOORS OR IN SEWERS.

SPILL AND LEAK PROCEDURES

OCCUPATIONAL SPILL: SHUT OFF IGNITION SOURCES. DO NOT TOUCH SPILLED MATERIAL. STOP LEAK IF YOU CAN DO IT WITHOUT RISK. USE WATER SPRAY TO REDUCE VAPORS. FOR SMALL SPILLS, TAKE UP WITH SAND OR OTHER ABSORBENT MATERIAL AND PLACE INTO CONTAINERS FOR LATER DISPOSAL. FOR SMALL DRY SPILLS, WITH CLEAN SHOVEL PLACE MATERIAL INTO CLEAN, DRY CONTAINERS AND COVER. MOVE CONTAINERS FROM SPILL AREA. FOR LARGER SPILLS, DIKE FAR AHEAD OF SPILL FOR LATER DISPOSAL. NO SMOKING, FLAMES OR FLARES IN HAZARD AREA! KEEP UNNECESSARY PEOPLE AWAY. ISOLATE HAZARD AREA AND DENY ENTRY. VENTILATE CLOSED SPACES BEFORE ENTERING.

PROTECTIVE EQUIPMENT

VENTILATION: PROVIDE LOCAL EXHAUST VENTILATION AND/OR GENERAL DILUTION VENTILATION TO MEET PUBLISHED EXPOSURE LIMITS.

RESPIRATOR: THE FOLLOWING RESPIRATORS ARE RECOMMENDED BASED ON INFORMATION FOUND IN THE PHYSICAL DATA, TOXICITY AND HEALTH EFFECTS SECTIONS. THEY ARE RANKED IN ORDER FROM MINIMUM TO MAXIMUM RESPIRATORY PROTECTION. THE SPECIFIC RESPIRATOR SELECTED MUST BE BASED ON CONTAMINATION LEVELS FOUND IN THE WORK PLACE, MUST NOT EXCEED THE WORKING LIMITS OF THE RESPIRATOR AND BE JOINTLY APPROVED BY THE NATIONAL INSTITUTE FOR OCCUPATIONAL SAFETY AND HEALTH AND THE MINE SAFETY AND HEALTH ADMINISTRATION (NIOSH-MSHA).

CHEMICAL CARTRIDGE RESPIRATOR WITH FULL FACEPIECE AND PESTICIDE CARTRIDGE.

TYPE 'C' SUPPLIED-AIR RESPIRATOR WITH A FULL FACEPIECE OPERATED IN PRESSURE-DEMAND OR OTHER POSITIVE PRESSURE MODE OR WITH A FULL FACEPIECE, HELMET OR HOOD OPERATED IN CONTINUOUS-FLOW MODE.

SELF-CONTAINED BREATHING APPARATUS OPERATED IN PRESSURE-DEMAND OR OTHER POSITIVE PRESSURE MODE.

FOR FIREFIGHTING AND OTHER IMMEDIATELY DANGEROUS TO LIFE OR HEALTH CONDITIONS:

SELF-CONTAINED BREATHING APPARATUS WITH FULL FACEPIECE OPERATED IN PRESSURE-DEMAND OR OTHER POSITIVE PRESSURE MODE.

SUPPLIED-AIR RESPIRATOR WITH FULL FACEPIECE AND OPERATED IN PRESSURE-DEMAND OR OTHER POSITIVE PRESSURE MODE IN COMBINATION WITH AN AUXILIARY SELF-CONTAINED BREATHING APPARATUS OPERATED IN PRESSURE-DEMAND OR OTHER POSITIVE PRESSURE MODE.

CLOTHING: EMPLOYEE MUST WEAR APPROPRIATE PROTECTIVE (IMPERVIOUS) CLOTHING AND EQUIPMENT TO PREVENT REPEATED OR PROLONGED SKIN CONTACT WITH THIS SUBSTANCE.

GLOVES: EMPLOYEE MUST WEAR APPROPRIATE PROTECTIVE GLOVES TO PREVENT CONTACT WITH THIS SUBSTANCE.

EYE PROTECTION: EMPLOYEE MUST WEAR SPLASH-PROOF OR DUST-RESISTANT SAFETY GOGGLES TO PREVENT EYE CONTACT WITH THIS SUBSTANCE.

EMERGENCY EYE WASH: WHERE THERE IS ANY POSSIBILITY THAT AN EMPLOYEE'S EYES MAY BE EXPOSED TO THIS SUBSTANCE, THE EMPLOYER SHOULD PROVIDE AN EYE WASH FOUNTAIN WITHIN THE IMMEDIATE WORK AREA FOR EMERGENCY USE.

AUTHORIZED BY- OCCUPATIONAL HEALTH SERVICES, INC.

CREATION DATE: 10/04/89 ***REVISION DATE:*** 07/13/90

MATERIAL SAFETY DATA SHEET

OCCUPATIONAL HEALTH SERVICES, INC.
AGRICULTURE AND PESTICIDE DIVISION
450 SEVENTH AVENUE, SUITE 2407
NEW YORK, NEW YORK 10123
1-800-445-MSDS OR (212) 967-1100

EMERGENCY CONTACT:
JOHN S. BRANSFORD, JR. (615) 292-1180

SUBSTANCE IDENTIFICATION

SUBSTANCE: LASSO AND ATRAZINE FLOWABLE HERBICIDE

TRADE NAMES/SYNONYMS: EPA REG. NO. 524-329; PST12481

CHEMICAL FAMILY: MIXTURE, PESTICIDE FORMULATION

CERCLA RATINGS (SCALE 0-3): HEALTH=U FIRE=2 REACTIVITY=0 PERSISTENCE=2

NFPA RATINGS (SCALE 0-4): HEALTH=U FIRE=2 REACTIVITY=0

COMPONENTS AND CONTAMINANTS

COMPONENT: ALACHLOR ***PERCENT:*** 27.2
CAS# 15972-60-8

COMPONENT: ATRAZINE ***PERCENT:*** 15.5
CAS# 1912-24-9

COMPONENT: RELATED ATRAZINE COMPOUNDS ***PERCENT:*** 0.8

COMPONENT: INERT INGREDIENTS ***PERCENT:*** 56.5
INCLUDING:
CHLOROBENZENE CAS# 108-90-7
ETHYLENE GLYCOL CAS# 107-21-1
EMULSIFIERS

EXPOSURE LIMITS: ALACHLOR: SUBJECT TO CALIFORNIA PROPOSITION 65 CANCER AND/OR REPRODUCTIVE TOXICITY WARNING AND RELEASE REQUIREMENTS- (JANUARY 1, 1989)

ATRAZINE: 5 MG/M3 OSHA TWA 5 MG/M3 ACGIH TWA

CHLOROBENZENE: 75 PPM (350 MG/M3) OSHA TWA 75 PPM (350 MG/M3) ACGIH TWA (NOTICE OF INTENDED CHANGES 1989-1990)

100 POUNDS CERCLA SECTION 103 REPORTABLE QUANTITY SUBJECT TO SARA SECTION 313 ANNUAL TOXIC CHEMICAL RELEASE REPORTING ETHYLENE GLYCOL: 50 PPM (125 MG/M3) OSHA CEILING 50 PPM (125 MG/M3) ACGIH CEILING (VAPOR AND MIST)

SUBJECT TO SARA SECTION 313 ANNUAL TOXIC CHEMICAL RELEASE REPORTING

PHYSICAL DATA

DESCRIPTION: MILKY BLUE EMULSION WITH ODOR SIMILAR TO SHOE POLISH.

BOILING POINT: NOT AVAILABLE ***SPECIFIC GRAVITY:*** 1.1

VAPOR PRESSURE: NOT AVAILABLE ***SOLUBILITY IN WATER:*** SOLUBLE

FIRE AND EXPLOSION DATA

FIRE AND EXPLOSION HAZARD: MODERATE FIRE HAZARD WHEN EXPOSED TO HEAT OR FLAME.

VAPOR-AIR MIXTURES ARE EXPLOSIVE ABOVE FLASH POINT.

FLASH POINT: 102 F (39 C) (CC) ***FLAMMABILITY CLASS(OSHA):*** II

FIREFIGHTING MEDIA: DRY CHEMICAL, CARBON DIOXIDE, HALON, WATER SPRAY OR STANDARD FOAM (1987 EMERGENCY RESPONSE GUIDEBOOK, DOT P 5800.4).

FOR LARGER FIRES, USE WATER SPRAY, FOG OR STANDARD FOAM (1987 EMERGENCY RESPONSE GUIDEBOOK, DOT P 5800.4).

FIREFIGHTING: MOVE CONTAINERS FROM FIRE AREA IF POSSIBLE. COOL CONTAINERS EXPOSED TO FLAMES WITH WATER FROM SIDE UNTIL WELL AFTER FIRE IS OUT. FIGHT FIRE FROM MAXIMUM DISTANCE. STAY AWAY FROM STORAGE TANK ENDS. DIKE FIRE CONTROL WATER FOR LATER DISPOSAL. DO NOT SCATTER MATERIAL. (1987 EMERGENCY RESPONSE GUIDEBOOK, DOT P 5800.4, GUIDE PAGE 57). EXTINGUISH ONLY IF FLOW CAN BE STOPPED. USE FLOODING AMOUNTS OF WATER AS A FOG; SOLID STREAMS MAY BE INEFFECTIVE. COOL CONTAINERS WITH FLOODING AMOUNTS OF WATER FROM AS FAR A DISTANCE AS POSSIBLE. AVOID BREATHING POISONOUS VAPORS, KEEP UPWIND.

TRANSPORTATION DATA

DEPARTMENT OF TRANSPORTATION HAZARD CLASSIFICATION 49 CFR 172.101: COMBUSTIBLE LIQUID

DEPARTMENT OF TRANSPORTATION LABELING REQUIREMENTS 49 CFR 172.101 AND SUBPART E: NONE

DEPARTMENT OF TRANSPORTATION PACKAGING REQUIREMENTS: NONE EXCEPTIONS: 49 CFR 173.118A

TOXICITY

ALACHLOR: TOXICITY DATA: 3500 MG/KG SKIN-RABBIT LD50; 930 MG/KG ORAL-RAT LD50; 462 MG/KG ORAL-MOUSE LD50; 3000 MG/KG ORAL-MAMMAL LD50; 1200 MG/KG UNREPORTED-MAMMAL LD50; MUTAGENIC DATA (RTECS); TUMORIGENIC DATA (RTECS). CARCINOGEN STATUS: NONE. ACUTE TOXICITY LEVEL: MODERATELY TOXIC BY INGESTION; SLIGHTLY TOXIC BY DERMAL ABSORPTION. TARGET EFFECTS: SENSITIZER- SKIN.

ATRAZINE: IRRITATION DATA: 38 MG OPEN SKIN-RABBIT MILD; 6320 UG EYE-RABBIT SEVERE; 500 MG SKIN-MAMMAL MILD; 100 MG EYE-MAMMAL SEVERE. TOXICITY DATA: 5200 MG/M3/4 HOURS INHALATION-RAT LC50; 7500 MG/KG SKIN-RABBIT LD50; 672 MG/KG ORAL-RAT LD50; 850 MG/KG ORAL-MOUSE LD50; 750 MG/KG ORAL-RABBIT LD50; 1000 MG/KG ORAL-HAMSTER LD50; 235 MG/KG INTRAPERITONEAL-RAT LD50; 626 MG/KG INTRAPERITONEAL-MOUSE LD50; 1400 MG/KG UNREPORTED-MAMMAL LD50; MUTAGENIC DATA (RTECS); REPRODUCTIVE EFFECTS DATA (RTECS); TUMORIGENIC DATA (RTECS). CARCINOGEN STATUS: NONE. LOCAL EFFECTS: IRRITANT- EYE. ACUTE TOXICITY LEVEL: TOXIC BY INHALATION; MODERATELY TOXIC BY INGESTION; SLIGHTLY TOXIC BY DERMAL ABSORPTION. TARGET EFFECTS: NO DATA AVAILABLE.

CHLOROBENZENE: TOXICITY DATA: 15 GM/M3 INHALATION-MOUSE LCLO; 2290 MG/KG ORAL-RAT LD50; 2250 MG/KG ORAL-RABBIT LD50; 2300 MG/KG ORAL-MOUSE LD50; 2250 MG/KG ORAL-GUINEA PIG LD50; 7000 MG/KG SUBCUTANEOUS-RAT LDLO; 7400 MG/KG INTRAPERITONEAL-RAT LDLO; 515 MG/KG INTRAPERITONEAL-MOUSE LD50; 4100 MG/KG INTRAPERITONEAL-GUINEA PIG LDLO; 2300 MG/KG UNREPORTED-MAMMAL LD50; MUTAGENIC DATA (RTECS); REPRODUCTIVE EFFECTS DATA (RTECS). CARCINOGEN STATUS: NONE. LOCAL EFFECTS: IRRITANT- INHALATION, SKIN, EYE. ACUTE TOXICITY LEVEL: MODERATELY TOXIC BY INGESTION. TARGET EFFECTS: CENTRAL NERVOUS SYSTEM DEPRESSANT. POISONING MAY AFFECT THE LIVER AND KIDNEYS. AT INCREASED RISK FROM EXPOSURE: PERSONS WITH PREEXISTING SKIN, LIVER, KIDNEY, OR CHRONIC RESPIRATORY DISEASES. ADDITIONAL DATA: GASTROENTERIC ABSORPTION IS ENHANCED BY THE PRESENCE OF FATS OR OILS. ALCOHOL MAY ENHANCE THE TOXIC EFFECTS.

ETHYLENE GLYCOL: IRRITATION DATA: 555 MG OPEN SKIN-RABBIT MILD; 12 MG/M3/3 DAYS EYE-RAT; 100 MG/1 HOUR EYE-RABBIT MILD; 500 MG/24 HOURS EYE-RABBIT MILD; 12 MG/M3/3 DAYS EYE-RABBIT; 1440 MG/6 HOURS EYE-RABBIT

MODERATE. TOXICITY DATA: 10000 MG/M3 INHALATION-HUMAN TCLO; 9530 MG/KG SKIN-RABBIT LD50; 5500 MG/KG ORAL-CHILD TDLO; 786 MG/KG ORAL-HUMAN LDLO; 398 MG/KG ORAL-HUMAN LDLO; 4700 MG/KG ORAL-RAT LD50; 7500 MG/KG ORAL-MOUSE LD50; 6610 MG/KG ORAL-GUINEA PIG LD50; 5500 MG/KG ORAL-DOG LD50; 1650 MG/KG ORAL-CAT LD50; 2800 MG/KG SUBCUTANEOUS-RAT LD50; 2700 MG/KG SUBCUTANEOUS-MOUSE LDLO; 5000 MG/KG SUBCUTANEOUS-GUINEA PIG LDLO; 2000 MG/KG SUBCUTANEOUS-CAT LDLO; 3260 MG/KG INTRAVENOUS-RAT LD50; 3000 MG/KG INTRAVENOUS-MOUSE LD50; 5 GM/KG INTRAVENOUS-RABBIT LDLO; 5010 MG/KG INTRAPERITONEAL-RAT LD50; 5614 MG/KG INTRAPERITONEAL-MOUSE LD50; 1000 MG/KG INTRAPERITONEAL-RABBIT LDLO; 3300 MG/KG INTRAMUSCULAR-RAT LDLO; 5500 MG/KG INTRAMUSCULAR-RABBIT LDLO; 1637 MG/KG UNREPORTED ROUTE-MAN LDLO; MUTAGENIC DATA (RTECS); REPRODUCTIVE EFFECTS DATA (RTECS). CARCINOGEN STATUS: NONE. LOCAL EFFECTS: IRRITANT- INHALATION, SKIN, EYE. ACUTE TOXICITY LEVEL: MODERATELY TOXIC BY INGESTION; SLIGHTLY TOXIC BY DERMAL ABSORPTION. TARGET EFFECTS: CENTRAL NERVOUS SYSTEM DEPRESSANT; NEPHROTOXIN; NEUROTOXIN. POISONING MAY AFFECT THE LUNGS, HEART, BLOOD, BRAIN AND LIVER.

HEALTH EFFECTS AND FIRST AID

INHALATION: ALACHLOR: **ACUTE EXPOSURE-** SLIGHT TO NEGLIGIBLE EFFECTS WERE OBSERVED IN RATS EXPOSED TO 6100 MG/M3/4 HOURS. A CONCENTRATION OF 32600 MG/M3 WAS LETHAL TO RATS. **CHRONIC EXPOSURE-** NO DATA AVAILABLE.
ATRAZINE: TOXIC. **ACUTE EXPOSURE-** EXPOSURE TO LARGE CONCENTRATIONS OF DUST, AEROSOLS OR AQUEOUS EMULSIONS MAY CAUSE IRRITATION OF THE MUCOUS MEMBRANES. A LETHAL CONCENTRATION IN RATS WAS 5200 MG/M3/4 HOURS. **CHRONIC EXPOSURE-** NO DATA AVAILABLE.
CHLOROBENZENE: IRRITANT/NARCOTIC. 2400 PPM IMMEDIATELY DANGEROUS TO LIFE OR HEALTH. **ACUTE EXPOSURE-** INHALATION OF 200 PPM MAY CAUSE MUCOUS MEMBRANE IRRITATION AND COUGHING. AT HIGHER CONCENTRATIONS, CENTRAL NERVOUS SYSTEM DEPRESSION WITH HEADACHE, DIZZINESS, DROWSINESS, SOMNOLENCE, TRANSIENT ANESTHESIA AND INCOHERENCE, CYANOSIS FROM METHEMOGLOBINEMIA, SPASTIC CONTRACTIONS OF THE EXTREMITIES, RAPID RESPIRATION, WEAK AND IRREGULAR PULSE, BURGUNDY-RED URINE, LOSS OF CONSCIOUSNESS, COMA, AND RESPIRATORY AND CIRCULATORY COLLAPSE MAY OCCUR. IN CATS, A CONCENTRATION OF 1200-2900 PPM PRODUCED NARCOSIS WITH RESTLESSNESS, TREMOR AND MUSCULAR SPASMS, BUT NO SERIOUS INJURY OR FATALITY; 3700 PPM WAS LETHAL AFTER SEVERAL HOURS. 8000 PPM PRODUCED SEVERE NARCOSIS AFTER 30 MINUTES AND DEATH WITHIN 2 HOURS AFTER REMOVAL FROM EXPOSURE. PATHOLOGICAL CHANGES MAY INCLUDE HYPERTROPHY AND NECROSIS OF THE LIVER AND BRONCHIAL EPITHELIUM OF THE LUNGS, EDEMA OF THE BRAIN AND SUBMUCOSAL HEMORRHAGE IN THE STOMACH. **CHRONIC EXPOSURE-** WORKERS EXPOSED TO CHLOROBENZENE VAPORS FROM 1-2 YEARS SUFFERED FROM HEADACHE, DIZZINESS, SOMNOLENCE, AND DYSPEPTIC DISORDERS. OTHER SYMPTOMS REPORTED IN SOME OF THE WORKERS WERE ACROPARESTHESIA, SPASTIC CONTRACTIONS OF FINGER MUSCLES, HYPESTHESIA, SPASTIC CONTRACTIONS OF THE GASTROCNEMIUS MUSCLE AND VASOVEGETATIVE INSTABILITY. REPEATED EXPOSURE TO 1000 PPM SEVEN HOURS PER DAY, FIVE DAYS A WEEK FOR 44 DAYS RESULTED IN LUNG, LIVER, AND KIDNEY CHANGES IN ANIMALS. AT 475 PPM THERE WAS ONLY SLIGHT LIVER DAMAGE IN GUINEA PIGS AND NO EFFECTS WERE NOTED AT 200 PPM. REPRODUCTIVE EFFECTS HAVE BEEN REPORTED IN ANIMAL STUDIES.
ETHYLENE GLYCOL: IRRITANT. **ACUTE EXPOSURE-** INHALATION IS UNLIKELY AT ROOM TEMPERATURE, DUE TO THE LOW VAPOR PRESSURE. AEROSOLS AT 140 MG/M3 WERE IRRITATING, AND 200 MG/M3 WERE INTOLERABLE CAUSING A BURNING SENSATION OF THROAT AND COUGHING. EXPOSURE TO HIGH CONCENTRATIONS OF MISTS OR AEROSOLS MAY RESULT IN EFFECTS ON THE HEMATOPOIETIC SYSTEM AND CENTRAL NERVOUS SYSTEM WITH HEADACHE, DIZZINESS AND DROWSINESS. **CHRONIC EXPOSURE-** HUMANS EXPOSED TO AEROSOLS FROM 3-67 MG/M3 CONTINUOUSLY FOR 1 MONTH REPORTED IRRITATION OF THE RESPIRATORY TRACT, OCCASIONALLY SLIGHT HEADACHE AND LOW BACKACHE, BUT NO OTHER SIGNIFICANT ADVERSE EFFECTS. CONTINUED EXPOSURE TO VAPORS FROM A PROCESS UTILIZING A MIXTURE OF ETHYLENE GLYCOL, BORIC ACID AND AMMONIA HEATED ABOVE 100 C RESULTED IN NYSTAGMUS, LYMPHOCYTOSIS AND SUDDEN LOSS OF CONSCIOUSNESS FOR 5-10 MINUTES. NYSTAGMUS OCCURRED 2-3 TIMES WEEKLY UNTIL EXPOSURE CEASED. REPEATED EXPOSURE TO SATURATED ETHYLENE GLYCOL VAPORS PRODUCED SLIGHT NARCOSIS IN RATS. EFFECTS ON THE FETUS HAVE BEEN REPORTED IN RATS AND MICE FOLLOWING EXPOSURE DURING GESTATION. THERE WAS A LIKELIHOOD THAT AT LEAST A PORTION OF THE EFFECTS RESULTED FROM INGESTION SINCE ANIMALS GROOMED CONSTANTLY BEFORE AND AFTER EXPOSURE.

FIRST AID- REMOVE FROM EXPOSURE AREA TO FRESH AIR IMMEDIATELY. IF BREATHING HAS STOPPED, PERFORM ARTIFICIAL RESPIRATION. KEEP PERSON WARM AND AT REST. TREAT SYMPTOMATICALLY AND SUPPORTIVELY. GET MEDICAL ATTENTION IMMEDIATELY.

SKIN CONTACT: ALACHLOR: SENSITIZER. **ACUTE EXPOSURE-** THIS MATERIAL WAS SLIGHTLY IRRITATING TO RABBIT SKIN. ALLERGIC SKIN REACTIONS MAY OCCUR IN PERSONS PREVIOUSLY EXPOSED. **CHRONIC EXPOSURE-** PROLONGED OR REPEATED EXPOSURE TO THIS MATERIAL MAY PRODUCE ALLERGIC SKIN REACTIONS IN SUSCEPTIBLE INDIVIDUALS. REPEATED APPLICATION OF ALACHLOR TO GUINEA PIG SKIN RESULTED IN ERYTHEMA, REDNESS, EDEMA, SWELLING, AND NECROSIS. REPEATED DERMAL APPLICATION OF 4.0 GM/KG PRODUCED SLIGHT TO MODERATE IRRITATION AND INCREASED PITUITARY WEIGHTS IN RABBITS.
ATRAZINE: **ACUTE EXPOSURE-** 38 MG APPLIED TO OPEN RABBIT SKIN WAS MILDLY IRRITATING. A CASE OF ALLERGIC REACTION FROM EXPOSURE TO ATRAZINE WAS REPORTED TO HAVE OCCURRED. ANIMAL STUDIES INDICATE SKIN ABSORPTION MAY OCCUR. **CHRONIC EXPOSURE-** PROLONGED OR REPEATED EXPOSURE MAY CAUSE DERMATITIS.
CHLOROBENZENE: IRRITANT. **ACUTE EXPOSURE-** CONTACT WITH THE LIQUID MAY CAUSE IRRITATION WITH REDNESS AND DEFATTING OF THE SKIN. ACNEFORM ERUPTIONS MAY OCCUR DUE TO CHLOROBENZENE. **CHRONIC EXPOSURE-** PROLONGED CONTACT WITH THE LIQUID MAY CAUSE DERMATITIS DUE TO ITS DEFATTING ACTION, MODERATE ERYTHEMA AND SLIGHT SUPERFICIAL NECROSIS OR BURNS.
ETHYLENE GLYCOL: IRRITANT. **ACUTE EXPOSURE-** LIQUID MAY DEFAT THE SKIN AND CAUSE MINOR IRRITATION. ANIMAL STUDIES INDICATE THAT LETHAL AMOUNTS MAY BE ABSORBED THROUGH INTACT SKIN. ONE CASE HAS BEEN REPORTED OF COMA ACCOMPANIED BY MIOSIS AND SLOWED PULSE 4 HOURS AFTER MASSIVE APPLICATION OF AN ECZEMA REMEDY CONTAINING ETHYLENE GLYCOL. SENSITIZATION REACTIONS MAY OCCUR IN PREVIOUSLY EXPOSED PERSONS. **CHRONIC EXPOSURE-** A SLIGHT MACERATING ACTION ON THE SKIN MAY RESULT FROM VERY SEVERE, PROLONGED EXPOSURE. REPEATED OR PROLONGED CONTACT MAY RESULT IN SENSITIZATION.

FIRST AID- REMOVE CONTAMINATED CLOTHING AND SHOES IMMEDIATELY. WASH AFFECTED AREA WITH SOAP OR MILD DETERGENT AND LARGE AMOUNTS OF WATER UNTIL NO EVIDENCE OF CHEMICAL REMAINS (APPROXIMATELY 15-20 MINUTES). GET MEDICAL ATTENTION IMMEDIATELY.

EYE CONTACT: ALACHLOR: **ACUTE EXPOSURE-** EYE IRRITATION PRODUCED FROM CONTACT WITH TECHNICAL ALACHLOR HAS BEEN REPORTED. HOWEVER, TESTED IN RABBIT EYES, THIS MATERIAL WAS PRACTICALLY NONIRRITATING. **CHRONIC EXPOSURE-** NO DATA AVAILABLE.
ATRAZINE: IRRITANT. **ACUTE EXPOSURE-** 6320 UG APPLIED TO RABBIT EYES WAS SEVERELY IRRITATING. **CHRONIC EXPOSURE-** PROLONGED OR REPEATED EXPOSURE TO IRRITANTS MAY CAUSE CONJUNCTIVITIS.
CHLOROBENZENE: IRRITANT. **ACUTE EXPOSURE-** CONTACT WITH THE LIQUID MAY RESULT IN TRANSIENT CONJUNCTIVAL IRRITATION WITH REDNESS AND PAIN. EYE IRRITATION IN HUMANS HAS BEEN REPORTED FROM EXPOSURE TO VAPORS AT 200 PPM. **CHRONIC EXPOSURE-** REPEATED OR PROLONGED CONTACT WITH IRRITANTS MAY CAUSE CONJUNCTIVITIS.
ETHYLENE GLYCOL: IRRITANT. **ACUTE EXPOSURE-** VAPORS MAY CAUSE REDNESS, AND CONTACT WITH THE LIQUID MAY CAUSE CONJUNCTIVITIS AND IRIDOCYCLITIS, BUT NO PERMANENT DAMAGE. **CHRONIC EXPOSURE-** VAPOR OR SPRAY AT 17 MG/M3/4 WEEKS PRODUCED NO ILL EFFECTS IN HUMANS. RATS EXPOSED CONTINUOUSLY TO 12 MG/M3 FOR SEVERAL DAYS SOMETIMES SHOWED SEVERE EYE IRRITATION, EDEMA OF THE EYELIDS, CORNEAL OPACITY AND APPARENT BLINDNESS, WITHOUT SIGNS OF SYSTEMIC INTOXICATION.

FIRST AID- WASH EYES IMMEDIATELY WITH LARGE AMOUNTS OF WATER OR NORMAL SALINE, OCCASIONALLY LIFTING UPPER AND LOWER LIDS, UNTIL NO EVIDENCE OF CHEMICAL REMAINS (APPROXIMATELY 15-20 MINUTES). GET MEDICAL ATTENTION IMMEDIATELY.

INGESTION: ALACHLOR: **ACUTE EXPOSURE-** A LETHAL DOSE IN RATS WAS 930 MG/KG; SYMPTOMS WERE NOT REPORTED. **CHRONIC EXPOSURE-** EFFECTS OF GASTROINTESTINAL DISTURBANCES, HEMOLYTIC ANEMIA, DECREASED BODY WEIGHTS, INCREASED LIVER WEIGHTS AND INCREASED BROMOSULFOPHTHALEIN RETENTION WERE OBSERVED IN A 1-YEAR STUDY OF DOGS FED 10 MG/KG/DAY. HEPATOTOXICITY WAS CITED IN ANOTHER STUDY OF DOGS. MATERNAL AND FETAL TOXICITY WERE NOTED IN A STUDY OF PREGNANT RATS FED 400 MG/KG/DAY. IN A 3-GENERATION STUDY OF RATS, SOME KIDNEY EFFECTS WERE REPORTED AT A DOSE OF 30 MG/KG/DAY. EFFECTS OF OCULAR LESSIONS, HEPATOTOXICITY, TUMORS OF THE NASAL TURBINATE, STOMACH, LIVER, AND THYROID WERE PRODUCED IN RATS. LUNG BRONCHIOLAR-ALVEOLAR TUMORS IN FEMALES WERE OBSERVED IN MICE FED 260 MG/KG/DAY FOR 79 WEEKS.
ATRAZINE: **ACUTE EXPOSURE-** AFTER CONSUMING A LARGE ORAL DOSE OF ATRAZINE, RATS EXHIBITED MUSCULAR WEAKNESS, HYPOACTIVITY, PTOSIS, DYSPNEA, PROSTRATION, ATAXIA, CONVULSIONS, AND DEATH. **CHRONIC EXPOSURE-** FORTY PERCENT OF RATS THAT RECEIVED ATRAZINE ORALLY FOR 6 MONTHS AT A RATE OF 20 MG/KG/DAY DIED WITH SIGNS OF RESPIRATORY

DISTRESS AND PARALYSIS OF THE LIMBS. MORPHOLOGICAL AND BIOCHEMICAL CHANGES IN THE BRAIN, HEART, LIVER, LUNGS, KIDNEY, OVARIES, AND ENDOCRINE ORGANS WERE OBSERVED. MATERNAL TOXICITY WAS OBSERVED IN PREGNANT RATS FED DOSES GREATER THAN 70 MG/KG/DAY AND IN PREGNANT RABBITS FED DOSES GREATER THAN 5 MG/KG/DAY. MINOR FETAL EFFECTS WERE NOTED IN RATS AT THIS LEVEL, AND IN RABBITS FETAL EFFECTS OCCURRED AT DOSES THAT PRODUCED SEVERE MATERNAL TOXICITY, 75 MG/KG/DAY. AN INCREASED INCIDENCE OF FIBROADENOMAS, CARCINOMAS OF THE MAMMARY GLANDS AND ALL MAMMARY TUMORS IN FEMALES WAS REPORTED FROM A 2-YEAR RAT STUDY.

CHLOROBENZENE NARCOTIC. **ACUTE EXPOSURE-** INGESTION MAY CAUSE SALIVATION, ABDOMINAL PAIN, NAUSEA, VOMITING, HEADACHE, LATENT PALLOR, CYANOSIS FROM METHEMOGLOBINEMIA AND COLLAPSE. INGESTION OF THE LIQUID BY A CHILD RESULTED IN PALLOR, CYANOSIS AND COMA FOLLOWED BY COMPLETE RECOVERY. **CHRONIC EXPOSURE-** RATS FED 14.4 MG/KG AND 18.8 MG/KG 5 DAYS PER WEEK FOR 192 DAYS SHOWED NO ADVERSE EFFECTS. AT 144 MG/KG-288 MG/KG PRODUCED INCREASES IN LIVER AND KIDNEY WEIGHTS. A DOSAGE OF 376 MG/KG PER DAY CAUSED SLIGHT CIRRHOSIS AND FOCAL NECROSIS OF THE LIVER AND A SLIGHT DECREASE IN AVERAGE SPLEEN WEIGHTS. EOSINOPHILIA AND INHIBITION OF ERYTHROPOIESIS AND THROMBOCYTOSIS HAVE ALSO BEEN REPORTED IN RATS.

ETHYLENE GLYCOL: NARCOTIC/NEPHROTOXIN/NEUROTOXIN. **ACUTE EXPOSURE-** THE ESTIMATED LETHAL DOSE FOR ADULTS IS 100 MILLILITERS. THERE ARE THREE STAGES OF INTOXICATION FOLLOWING INGESTION OF ETHYLENE GLYCOL: CENTRAL NERVOUS SYSTEM STIMULATION FOLLOWED BY DEPRESSION; CARDIORESPIRATORY FAILURE; AND RENAL FAILURE. AN ACUTE CENTRAL NERVOUS SYSTEM STAGE MAY FOLLOW SHORTLY AFTER INGESTION AND LAST SEVERAL HOURS WITH SYMPTOMS OF NAUSEA, VOMITING, ABDOMINAL PAIN, DEHYDRATION, VISUAL DIFFICULTY, CONFUSION, PERSONALITY CHANGES, HALLUCINATIONS, CONVULSIONS, COMA, MENINGISM, MYOCLONUS, FIXED PUPILS, DECREASED OR LOSS OF VISION, LOSS OF ACCOMMODATION, PAPILLEDEMA, DIPLOPIA, NYSTAGMUS, STRABISMUS, ABNORMAL EYE MOVEMENTS, OPTIC NERVE ATROPHY, CRANIAL NERVE PALSIES, ATAXIA, TREMORS, MYOSITIS, MUSCLE TWITCHING, TETANY, HYPERREFLEXIA, AND AREFLEXIA. LIFE-THREATENING COMPLICATIONS WHICH MAY OCCUR IN THIS PERIOD INCLUDE RESPIRATORY FAILURE, SECONDARY TO CENTRAL NERVOUS SYSTEM DEPRESSION, CARDIOVASCULAR COLLAPSE, PULMONARY EDEMA AND SEVERE METABOLIC ACIDOSIS. WITHOUT TREATMENT, DEATH MAY OCCUR IN 8-24 HOURS. IF DEATH DOES NOT OCCUR EARLY, LUMBAR PAIN, ALBUMINURIA, HEMATURIA AND OLIGURIA PROGRESSING TO ANURIA ARE PROBABLE. ACUTE RENAL FAILURE WITH UREMIA, PERIPHERAL EDEMA, ASCITES, PULMONARY EDEMA, DROWSINESS, CYANOSIS, COMA AND DEATH IN 7-10 DAYS IS POSSIBLE. METABOLISM TO OXALIC ACID RESULTS IN PRECIPITATION OF CALCIUM OXALATE CRYSTALS IN SOFT TISSUES. CAPILLARY DAMAGE MAY RESULT IN EXUDATIVE, CONGESTIVE OR HEMORRHAGIC DAMAGE TO THE BRAIN, PERICARDIUM AND LIVER. MILDER INTOXICATION MAY RESULT IN INEBRIATION FOLLOWED BY AN ASYMPTOMATIC PERIOD OF SEVERAL DAYS BEFORE THE ONSET OF RENAL FAILURE. OLIGURIA MAY BE PERSISTENT, BUT EVENTUAL IMPROVEMENT IN RENAL FUNCTION IS ANTICIPATED IN SURVIVORS. PERMANENT CEREBRAL DAMAGE MAY OCCUR IN SURVIVORS OF PROLONGED COMA OR CONVULSIONS. **CHRONIC EXPOSURE-** REPEATED DAILY INGESTION OF 15-30 ML MAY CAUSE OLIGURIA WITHIN 24-72 HOURS, WHICH MAY PROGRESS RAPIDLY TO ANURIA AND UREMIA. REPEATED ADMINISTRATION TO ANIMALS RESULTED IN SHORTENED LIFE SPAN, CALCIUM OXALATE BLADDER STONES, SEVERE RENAL INJURY, PARTICULARLY OF THE TUBULES, AND CENTRILOBULAR DEGENERATION OF THE LIVER. MATERNAL EFFECTS, EFFECTS ON FERTILITY, FETAL DEVELOPMENTAL ABNORMALITIES AND EFFECTS ON THE EMBRYO AND FETUS HAVE BEEN REPORTED FROM REPEATED ADMINISTRATION TO RATS AND MICE DURING GESTATION; ADMINISTRATION TO LACTATING MICE PRODUCED DELAYED EFFECTS ON THE NEWBORN.

FIRST AID- TREAT SYMPTOMATICALLY AND SUPPORTIVELY. GET MEDICAL ATTENTION IMMEDIATELY. IF VOMITING OCCURS, KEEP HEAD LOWER THAN HIPS TO PREVENT ASPIRATION.

REACTIVITY

REACTIVITY: STABLE UNDER NORMAL TEMPERATURES AND PRESSURES.

INCOMPATIBILITIES: ALACHLOR: ACIDS (STRONG): HYDROLYZES. BASES (STRONG): HYDROLYZES. BLACK IRON: MAY CORRODE. STEEL: MAY CORRODE.

ATRAZINE: ALKALI: MAY BE HYDROLYZED AT HIGHER TEMPERATURES. MINERAL ACIDS: MAY BE HYDROLYZED AT HIGHER TEMPERATURES.

CHLOROBENZENE: DIMETHYL SULFOXIDE: VIOLENT REACTION. OXIDIZERS (STRONG): VIOLENT REACTIONS. PLASTICS, RUBBER AND COATINGS: MAY BE ATTACKED. SILVER PERCHLORATE: REACTS FORMING A SHOCK-SENSITIVE SOLVATED SALT. SODIUM: MAY CAUSE EXPLOSIONS OR THE FORMATION OF AN EXPLOSIVE COMPOUND.

ETHYLENE GLYCOL: AMMONIUM DICHROMATE: IGNITES @ 100 C. CHLOROSULFONIC ACID: TEMPERATURE AND PRESSURE INCREASE IN CLOSED CONTAINER. CHROMIUM TRIOXIDE: IGNITES ON CONTACT. DIMETHYL TEREPHTHALATE + TITANIUM BUTOXIDE: POSSIBLE IGNITION. OLEUM: TEMPERATURE AND PRESSURE INCREASE IN CLOSED CONTAINER. OXIDIZERS (STRONG): FIRE AND EXPLOSION HAZARD. PERCHLORIC ACID: VIOLENT DECOMPOSITION. PHOSPHORUS(V) SULFIDE: EXPLOSIVE REACTION ON HEATING. POTASSIUM DICHROMATE: VIGOROUS EXOTHERMIC REACTION @ 100 C. POTASSIUM PERMANGANATE: IGNITES ON CONTACT. SILVER CHLORATE: IGNITES @ 100 C. SILVERED COPPER WIRE: IGNITES. SODIUM CHLORITE: IGNITES @ 100 C. SODIUM HYDROXIDE: EXPLOSION HAZARD. SODIUM PEROXIDE: IGNITES ON CONTACT. SULFURIC ACID: TEMPERATURE AND PRESSURE INCREASE IN CLOSED CONTAINER. URANYL NITRATE: IGNITES @ 100 C.

DECOMPOSITION: THERMAL DECOMPOSITION PRODUCTS MAY INCLUDE TOXIC AND CORROSIVE FUMES OF CHLORIDES AND TOXIC OXIDES OF CARBON.

POLYMERIZATION: HAZARDOUS POLYMERIZATION HAS NOT BEEN REPORTED TO OCCUR UNDER NORMAL TEMPERATURES AND PRESSURES.

STORAGE AND DISPOSAL

OBSERVE ALL FEDERAL, STATE AND LOCAL REGULATIONS WHEN STORING OR DISPOSING OF THIS SUBSTANCE. FOR ASSISTANCE, CONTACT THE DISTRICT DIRECTOR OF THE ENVIRONMENTAL PROTECTION AGENCY.

****STORAGE****

STORE IN ACCORDANCE WITH 29 CFR 1910.106.

BONDING AND GROUNDING: SUBSTANCES WITH LOW ELECTROCONDUCTIVITY, WHICH MAY BE IGNITED BY ELECTROSTATIC SPARKS, SHOULD BE STORED IN CONTAINERS WHICH MEET THE BONDING AND GROUNDING GUIDELINES SPECIFIED IN NFPA 77-1983, RECOMMENDED PRACTICE ON STATIC ELECTRICITY.

STORE IN ACCORDANCE WITH 40 CFR 165 RECOMMENDED PROCEDURES FOR THE DISPOSAL AND STORAGE OF PESTICIDES AND PESTICIDE CONTAINERS.

STORE ABOVE 40 F (4 C).

STORE AWAY FROM INCOMPATIBLE SUBSTANCES.

STORE ABOVE 40 F (4 C).

****DISPOSAL****

DISPOSAL MUST BE IN ACCORDANCE WITH STANDARDS APPLICABLE TO GENERATORS OF HAZARDOUS WASTE, 40 CFR 262. EPA HAZARDOUS WASTE NUMBER D001. 100 POUND CERCLA SECTION 103 REPORTABLE QUANTITY.

DISPOSAL MUST BE IN ACCORDANCE WITH 40 CFR 165 RECOMMENDED PROCEDURES FOR THE DISPOSAL AND STORAGE OF PESTICIDES AND PESTICIDE CONTAINERS.

CHLOROBENZENE - REGULATORY LEVEL: 100.0 MG/L MATERIALS WHICH CONTAIN THE ABOVE SUBSTANCE AT OR ABOVE THE REGULATORY LEVEL MEET THE EPA CHARACTERISTIC OF TOXICITY, AND MUST BE DISPOSED OF IN ACCORDANCE WITH 40 CFR PART 262. EPA HAZARDOUS WASTE NUMBER D021.

CONDITIONS TO AVOID

MAY BE IGNITED BY HEAT, SPARKS OR FLAMES. CONTAINER MAY EXPLODE IN HEAT OF FIRE. VAPOR EXPLOSION AND POISON HAZARD INDOORS, OUTDOORS OR IN SEWERS.

SPILL AND LEAK PROCEDURES

OCCUPATIONAL SPILL: SHUT OFF IGNITION SOURCES. DO NOT TOUCH SPILLED MATERIAL. STOP LEAK IF YOU CAN DO IT WITHOUT RISK. USE WATER SPRAY TO REDUCE VAPORS. FOR SMALL SPILLS, TAKE UP WITH SAND OR OTHER ABSORBENT MATERIAL AND PLACE INTO CONTAINERS FOR LATER DISPOSAL. FOR SMALL DRY SPILLS, WITH CLEAN SHOVEL PLACE MATERIAL INTO CLEAN, DRY CONTAINERS AND COVER. MOVE CONTAINERS FROM SPILL AREA. FOR LARGER SPILLS, DIKE FAR AHEAD OF SPILL FOR LATER DISPOSAL. NO SMOKING, FLAMES OR FLARES IN HAZARD AREA! KEEP UNNECESSARY PEOPLE AWAY. ISOLATE HAZARD AREA AND DENY ENTRY. VENTILATE CLOSED SPACES BEFORE ENTERING.

PROTECTIVE EQUIPMENT

VENTILATION: PROVIDE LOCAL EXHAUST VENTILATION AND/OR GENERAL DILUTION VENTILATION TO MEET PUBLISHED EXPOSURE LIMITS.

RESPIRATOR: THE FOLLOWING RESPIRATORS ARE RECOMMENDED BASED ON INFORMATION FOUND IN THE PHYSICAL DATA, TOXICITY AND HEALTH EFFECTS SECTIONS. THEY ARE RANKED IN ORDER FROM MINIMUM TO MAXIMUM RESPIRATORY PROTECTION. THE SPECIFIC RESPIRATOR SELECTED MUST BE BASED ON CONTAMINATION LEVELS FOUND IN THE WORK PLACE, MUST NOT EXCEED THE WORKING LIMITS OF THE RESPIRATOR AND BE JOINTLY APPROVED BY THE NATIONAL INSTITUTE FOR OCCUPATIONAL SAFETY AND HEALTH AND THE MINE SAFETY AND HEALTH ADMINISTRATION (NIOSH-MSHA).

CHEMICAL CARTRIDGE RESPIRATOR WITH FULL FACEPIECE AND PESTICIDE CARTRIDGE.

TYPE 'C' SUPPLIED-AIR RESPIRATOR WITH A FULL FACEPIECE OPERATED IN PRESSURE-DEMAND OR OTHER POSITIVE PRESSURE MODE OR WITH A FULL FACEPIECE, HELMET OR HOOD OPERATED IN CONTINUOUS-FLOW MODE.

SELF-CONTAINED BREATHING APPARATUS OPERATED IN PRESSURE-DEMAND OR OTHER POSITIVE PRESSURE MODE.
FOR FIREFIGHTING AND OTHER IMMEDIATELY DANGEROUS TO LIFE OR HEALTH CONDITIONS:
SELF-CONTAINED BREATHING APPARATUS WITH FULL FACEPIECE OPERATED IN PRESSURE-DEMAND OR OTHER POSITIVE PRESSURE MODE.
SUPPLIED-AIR RESPIRATOR WITH FULL FACEPIECE AND OPERATED IN PRESSURE-DEMAND OR OTHER POSITIVE PRESSURE MODE IN COMBINATION WITH AN AUXILIARY SELF-CONTAINED BREATHING APPARATUS OPERATED IN PRESSURE-DEMAND OR OTHER POSITIVE PRESSURE MODE.

CLOTHING: EMPLOYEE MUST WEAR APPROPRIATE PROTECTIVE (IMPERVIOUS) CLOTHING AND EQUIPMENT TO PREVENT REPEATED OR PROLONGED SKIN CONTACT WITH THIS SUBSTANCE.

GLOVES: EMPLOYEE MUST WEAR APPROPRIATE PROTECTIVE GLOVES TO PREVENT CONTACT WITH THIS SUBSTANCE.

EYE PROTECTION: EMPLOYEE MUST WEAR SPLASH-PROOF OR DUST-RESISTANT SAFETY GOGGLES TO PREVENT EYE CONTACT WITH THIS SUBSTANCE.
EMERGENCY EYE WASH: WHERE THERE IS ANY POSSIBILITY THAT AN EMPLOYEE'S EYES MAY BE EXPOSED TO THIS SUBSTANCE, THE EMPLOYER SHOULD PROVIDE AN EYE WASH FOUNTAIN WITHIN THE IMMEDIATE WORK AREA FOR EMERGENCY USE.

AUTHORIZED BY- OCCUPATIONAL HEALTH SERVICES, INC.
CREATION DATE: 10/04/89 ***REVISION DATE:*** 07/13/90

MATERIAL SAFETY DATA SHEET

OCCUPATIONAL HEALTH SERVICES, INC.
AGRICULTURE AND PESTICIDE DIVISION
450 SEVENTH AVENUE, SUITE 2407
NEW YORK, NEW YORK 10123
1-800-445-MSDS OR (212) 967-1100

EMERGENCY CONTACT:
JOHN S. BRANSFORD, JR. (615) 292-1180

SUBSTANCE IDENTIFICATION

CAS-NUMBER 112-53-8
SUBSTANCE: LAURYL ALCOHOL
TRADE NAMES/SYNONYMS: 1-DODECANOL; DODECYL ALCOHOL; 1-DODECYL ALCOHOL; 1-HYDROXYDODECANE; LAURIC ALCOHOL; LAURINIC ALCOHOL; DODECANOL; C12H26O; PST12500
CHEMICAL FAMILY: HYDROXYL, ALIPHATIC
MOLECULAR FORMULA: C-H3-(C-H2)10-C-H2-O-H
MOLECULAR WEIGHT: 186.32
CERCLA RATINGS (SCALE 0-3): HEALTH=3 FIRE=1 REACTIVITY=0 PERSISTENCE=0
NFPA RATINGS (SCALE 0-4): HEALTH=0 FIRE=1 REACTIVITY=0

COMPONENTS AND CONTAMINANTS

COMPONENT: LAURYL ALCOHOL ***PERCENT:*** 100
CAS# 112-53-8
OTHER CONTAMINANTS: NONE
EXPOSURE LIMITS: NO OCCUPATIONAL EXPOSURE LIMITS ESTABLISHED BY OSHA, ACGIH, OR NIOSH.

PHYSICAL DATA

DESCRIPTION: COLORLESS LEAFLETS OR THICK LIQUID WITH A FLORAL ODOR.
BOILING POINT: 491-498 F (255-259 C) ***MELTING POINT:*** 79 F (26 C)
SPECIFIC GRAVITY: 0.8309 @ 24 C ***SOLUBILITY IN WATER:*** INSOLUBLE
ODOR THRESHOLD: 7.1 PPB
SOLVENT SOLUBILITY: SOLUBLE IN ETHANOL, ETHER, MOST FIXED OILS, PROPYLENE GLYCOL; INSOLUBLE IN GLYCEROL

FIRE AND EXPLOSION DATA

FIRE AND EXPLOSION HAZARD: SLIGHT FIRE HAZARD WHEN EXPOSED TO HEAT OR FLAME.
FLASH POINT: 260 F (127 C) (CC) ***AUTOIGNITION TEMP.:*** 527 F (275 C)
FLAMMABILITY CLASS(OSHA): IIIB
FIREFIGHTING MEDIA: DRY CHEMICAL, CARBON DIOXIDE, HALON, WATER SPRAY OR ALCOHOL FOAM (1987 EMERGENCY RESPONSE GUIDEBOOK, DOT P 5800.4).
FOR LARGER FIRES, USE WATER SPRAY, FOG OR ALCOHOL FOAM (1987 EMERGENCY RESPONSE GUIDEBOOK, DOT P 5800.4).
FIREFIGHTING: MOVE CONTAINER FROM FIRE AREA IF POSSIBLE. COOL FIRE-EXPOSED CONTAINERS WITH WATER FROM SIDE UNTIL WELL AFTER FIRE IS OUT. STAY AWAY FROM STORAGE TANK ENDS. FOR MASSIVE FIRE IN STORAGE AREA, USE UNMANNED HOSE HOLDER OR MONITOR NOZZLES, ELSE WITHDRAW FROM AREA AND LET FIRE BURN. WITHDRAW IMMEDIATELY IN CASE OF RISING SOUND FROM VENTING SAFETY DEVICE OR ANY DISCOLORATION OF STORAGE TANK DUE TO FIRE (1987 EMERGENCY RESPONSE GUIDEBOOK, DOT P 5800.4, GUIDE PAGE 26).
EXTINGUISH ONLY IF FLOW CAN BE STOPPED. USE FLOODING AMOUNTS OF WATER AS FOG; SOLID STREAMS MAY BE INEFFECTIVE. COOL CONTAINERS WITH FLOODING AMOUNTS OF WATER FROM AS FAR A DISTANCE AS POSSIBLE. AVOID BREATHING VAPORS; KEEP UPWIND.
WATER OR FOAM MAY CAUSE FROTHING (NFPA 325M, FIRE HAZARD PROPERTIES OF FLAMMABLE LIQUIDS, GASES, AND VOLATILE SOLIDS, 1984)

TOXICITY

LAURYL ALCOHOL: IRRITATION DATA: 75 MG/3 DAYS INTERMITTENT SKIN-HUMAN SEVERE. TOXICITY DATA: 12,800 MG/KG ORAL-RAT LD50; 800 MG/KG INTRAPERITONEAL-RAT LD50; TUMORIGENIC DATA (RTECS). CARCINOGEN STATUS: NONE. LOCAL EFFECTS: IRRITANT- INHALATION, SKIN, AND EYES. ACUTE TOXICITY LEVEL: SLIGHTLY TOXIC BY INGESTION. TARGET EFFECTS: NO DATA AVAILABLE.

HEALTH EFFECTS AND FIRST AID

INHALATION: LAURYL ALCOHOL: **ACUTE EXPOSURE-** INHALATION OF VAPORS OF HIGHER ALCOHOLS MAY CAUSE IRRITATION OF MUCOUS MEMBRANES, COUGH, DYSPNEA, AND PULMONARY INJURY. CENTRAL NERVOUS SYSTEM EFFECTS MAY INCLUDE HEADACHE, SLEEPINESS, MUSCLE WEAKNESS, GIDDINESS, CONFUSION, DELIRIUM, AND COMA. **CHRONIC EXPOSURE-** NO DATA AVAILABLE.
FIRST AID- REMOVE FROM EXPOSURE AREA TO FRESH AIR IMMEDIATELY. IF BREATHING HAS STOPPED, PERFORM ARTIFICIAL RESPIRATION. KEEP PERSON WARM AND AT REST. TREAT SYMPTOMATICALLY AND SUPPORTIVELY. GET MEDICAL ATTENTION IMMEDIATELY.

SKIN CONTACT: LAURYL ALCOHOL: IRRITANT. **ACUTE EXPOSURE-** DIRECT CONTACT MAY CAUSE IRRITATION. **CHRONIC EXPOSURE-** APPLICATION OF 75 MG INTERMITTENTLY FOR 3 DAYS RESULTED IN SEVERE IRRITATION IN HUMANS. LAURYL ALCOHOL DEMONSTRATED A WEAK TUMOR-PROMOTING ACTIVITY WHEN APPLIED 3 TIMES WEEKLY FOR 60 WEEKS TO THE SKIN OF MICE PREVIOUSLY TREATED WITH DIMETHYLBENZANTHRACENE.
FIRST AID- REMOVE CONTAMINATED CLOTHING AND SHOES IMMEDIATELY. WASH AFFECTED AREA WITH SOAP OR MILD DETERGENT AND LARGE AMOUNTS OF WATER UNTIL NO EVIDENCE OF CHEMICAL REMAINS (APPROXIMATELY 15-20 MINUTES). GET MEDICAL ATTENTION IMMEDIATELY.

EYE CONTACT: LAURYL ALCOHOL: **ACUTE EXPOSURE-** DIRECT CONTACT WITH LIQUID MAY CAUSE IRRITATION WITH BURNING. **CHRONIC EXPOSURE-** NO DATA AVAILABLE.
FIRST AID- WASH EYES IMMEDIATELY WITH LARGE AMOUNTS OF WATER OR NORMAL SALINE, OCCASIONALLY LIFTING UPPER AND LOWER LIDS, UNTIL NO EVIDENCE OF CHEMICAL REMAINS (APPROXIMATELY 15-20 MINUTES). GET MEDICAL ATTENTION IMMEDIATELY.

INGESTION: LAURYL ALCOHOL: **ACUTE EXPOSURE-** ANIMALS SURVIVING DOSES OF 24 TO 36 ML/KG DEMONSTRATED NO SIGNIFICANT GROSS OR MICROSCOPIC CHANGES. FATTY DEGENERATION OF THE LIVER AND CONFLUENT BRONCHOPNEUMONIA WERE REPORTED IN ONE ANIMAL THAT DIED. ASPIRATION PRODUCED DEATH FROM PULMONARY EDEMA IN RATS. INGESTION OF SOME HIGHER ALCOHOLS MAY CAUSE GASTROINTESTINAL DISTURBANCES WITH NAUSEA, VOMITING, DIARRHEA, ANOREXIA, AND AN ODOR OF ALCOHOL IN EXCRETA. CENTRAL NERVOUS STSTEM EFFECTS MAY INCLUDE HEADACHE, MUSCLE WEAKNESS, GIDDINESS, CONFUSION, DELIRIUM, AND COMA. OCCASIONAL COMPLICATIONS MAY INCLUDE LIVER AND KIDNEY INJURY. DEATH MAY OCCUR DUE TO RESPIRATORY FAILURE OR CARDIAC ARRHYTHMIAS.
CHRONIC EXPOSURE- NO DATA AVAILABLE.
FIRST AID: REMOVE BY GASTRIC LAVAGE WITH COPIOUS AMOUNTS OF WATER. IT MAY BE BENEFICIAL TO INSTILL 60 ML OF MINERAL OIL INTO THE STOMACH (GOSSELIN, SMITH, HODGE, CLINICAL TOXICOLOGY OF COMMERCIAL PRODUCTS, 5TH EDITION). GASTRIC LAVAGE SHOULD BE ADMINISTERED BY QUALIFIED MEDICAL PERSONNEL. GET MEDICAL ATTENTION IMMEDIATELY.
ANTIDOTE: NO SPECIFIC ANTIDOTE. TREAT SYMPTOMATICALLY AND SUPPORTIVELY.

REACTIVITY

REACTIVITY: STABLE UNDER NORMAL TEMPERATURES AND PRESSURES.
INCOMPATIBILITIES: LAURYL ALCOHOL: NO SPECIFIC DATA AVAILABLE. SEE ALSO ALCOHOLS.
ALCOHOLS: ACETALDEHYDE: VIOLENT CONDENSATION REACTION. BARIUM PERCHLORATE: FORMATION OF HIGHLY EXPLOSIVE PERCHLORIC ESTER ON REFLUXING. CHLORINE: FORMATION OF HIGHLY EXPLOSIVE ALKYL

HYPOCHLORITES. DIETHYL ALUMINUM BROMIDE: SPONTANEOUS IGNITION. ETHYLENE OXIDE: POSSIBLE EXPLOSION. HEXAMETHYLENE DIISOCYANATE: POSSIBLE EXPLOSION IN ABSENCE OF SOLVENT. HYDROGEN PEROXIDE + SULFURIC ACID: POSSIBLE EXPLOSION. HYPOCHLOROUS ACID: FORMATION OF HIGHLY EXPLOSIVE ALKYL HYPOCHLORITES. ISOCYANATES: POSSIBLE EXPLOSION IN ABSENCE OF SOLVENT. LITHIUM ALUMINUM HYDRIDE: VIGOROUS REACTION. NITROGEN TETROXIDE: POSSIBLE EXPLOSION. PERCHLORIC ACID (HOT): DANGEROUS INTERACTION. PERMONOSULFURIC ACID: POSSIBLE EXPLOSION ON CONTACT WITH PRIMARY OR SECONDARY ALCOHOLS. TRI-ISO-BUTYL ALUMINUM: VIOLENT REACTION.

DECOMPOSITION: THERMAL DECOMPOSITION MAY RELEASE ACRID SMOKE AND IRRITATING FUMES.

POLYMERIZATION: HAZARDOUS POLYMERIZATION HAS NOT BEEN REPORTED TO OCCUR UNDER NORMAL TEMPERATURES AND PRESSURES.

STORAGE AND DISPOSAL

OBSERVE ALL FEDERAL, STATE AND LOCAL REGULATIONS WHEN STORING OR DISPOSING OF THIS SUBSTANCE. FOR ASSISTANCE, CONTACT THE DISTRICT DIRECTOR OF THE ENVIRONMENTAL PROTECTION AGENCY.

STORAGE

STORE AWAY FROM INCOMPATIBLE SUBSTANCES.

CONDITIONS TO AVOID

AVOID CONTACT WITH HEAT, SPARKS, FLAMES, OR OTHER SOURCES OF IGNITION. VAPORS MAY BE EXPLOSIVE AND POISONOUS; DO NOT ALLOW UNNECESSARY PERSONNEL IN AREA. DO NOT OVERHEAT CONTAINERS; CONTAINERS MAY VIOLENTLY RUPTURE AND TRAVEL A CONSIDERABLE DISTANCE IN HEAT OF FIRE.

SPILL AND LEAK PROCEDURES

OCCUPATIONAL SPILL: SHUT OFF IGNITION SOURCES. STOP LEAK IF YOU CAN DO IT WITHOUT RISK. USE WATER SPRAY TO REDUCE VAPORS. FOR SMALL SPILLS, TAKE UP WITH SAND OR OTHER ABSORBENT MATERIAL AND PLACE INTO CONTAINERS FOR LATER DISPOSAL. FOR LARGER SPILLS, DIKE FAR AHEAD OF SPILL FOR LATER DISPOSAL. NO SMOKING, FLAMES OR FLARES IN HAZARD AREA. KEEP UNNECESSARY PEOPLE AWAY; ISOLATE HAZARD AREA AND DENY ENTRY.

PROTECTIVE EQUIPMENT

VENTILATION: PROVIDE LOCAL EXHAUST OR PROCESS ENCLOSURE VENTILATION SYSTEM.

RESPIRATOR: THE FOLLOWING RESPIRATORS ARE RECOMMENDED BASED ON INFORMATION FOUND IN THE PHYSICAL DATA, TOXICITY AND HEALTH EFFECTS SECTIONS. THEY ARE RANKED IN ORDER FROM MINIMUM TO MAXIMUM RESPIRATORY PROTECTION. THE SPECIFIC RESPIRATOR SELECTED MUST BE BASED ON CONTAMINATION LEVELS FOUND IN THE WORK PLACE, MUST NOT EXCEED THE WORKING LIMITS OF THE RESPIRATOR AND BE JOINTLY APPROVED BY THE NATIONAL INSTITUTE FOR OCCUPATIONAL SAFETY AND HEALTH AND THE MINE SAFETY AND HEALTH ADMINISTRATION (NIOSH-MSHA).

CHEMICAL CARTRIDGE RESPIRATOR WITH AN ORGANIC VAPOR CARTRIDGE(S) WITH A FULL FACEPIECE.

GAS MASK WITH ORGANIC VAPOR CANISTER (CHIN-STYLE OR FRONT- OR BACK-MOUNTED CANISTER) WITH A FULL FACEPIECE.

TYPE 'C' SUPPLIED-AIR RESPIRATOR WITH A FULL FACEPIECE OPERATED IN PRESSURE-DEMAND OR OTHER POSITIVE PRESSURE MODE OR WITH A FULL FACEPIECE, HELMET OR HOOD OPERATED IN CONTINUOUS-FLOW MODE.

SELF-CONTAINED BREATHING APPARATUS WITH A FULL FACEPIECE OPERATED IN PRESSURE-DEMAND OR OTHER POSITIVE PRESSURE MODE.

FOR FIREFIGHTING AND OTHER IMMEDIATELY DANGEROUS TO LIFE OR HEALTH CONDITIONS:

SELF-CONTAINED BREATHING APPARATUS WITH FULL FACEPIECE OPERATED IN PRESSURE-DEMAND OR OTHER POSITIVE PRESSURE MODE.

SUPPLIED-AIR RESPIRATOR WITH FULL FACEPIECE AND OPERATED IN PRESSURE-DEMAND OR OTHER POSITIVE PRESSURE MODE IN COMBINATION WITH AN AUXILIARY SELF-CONTAINED BREATHING APPARATUS OPERATED IN PRESSURE-DEMAND OR OTHER POSITIVE PRESSURE MODE.

CLOTHING: EMPLOYEE MUST WEAR APPROPRIATE PROTECTIVE (IMPERVIOUS) CLOTHING AND EQUIPMENT TO PREVENT REPEATED OR PROLONGED SKIN CONTACT WITH THIS SUBSTANCE.

GLOVES: EMPLOYEE MUST WEAR APPROPRIATE PROTECTIVE GLOVES TO PREVENT CONTACT WITH THIS SUBSTANCE.

EYE PROTECTION: EMPLOYEE MUST WEAR SPLASH-PROOF OR DUST-RESISTANT SAFETY GOGGLES TO PREVENT EYE CONTACT WITH THIS SUBSTANCE.

EMERGENCY EYE WASH: WHERE THERE IS ANY POSSIBILITY THAT AN EMPLOYEE'S EYES MAY BE EXPOSED TO THIS SUBSTANCE, THE EMPLOYER SHOULD PROVIDE AN EYE WASH FOUNTAIN WITHIN THE IMMEDIATE WORK AREA FOR EMERGENCY USE.

AUTHORIZED BY- OCCUPATIONAL HEALTH SERVICES, INC.

CREATION DATE: 11/15/89 ***REVISION DATE:*** 05/11/90

MATERIAL SAFETY DATA SHEET

OCCUPATIONAL HEALTH SERVICES, INC.
AGRICULTURE AND PESTICIDE DIVISION
450 SEVENTH AVENUE, SUITE 2407
NEW YORK, NEW YORK 10123
1-800-445-MSDS OR (212) 967-1100

EMERGENCY CONTACT:
JOHN S. BRANSFORD, JR. (615) 292-1180

SUBSTANCE IDENTIFICATION

CAS-NUMBER 7784-40-9

SUBSTANCE: **LEAD ARSENATE**

TRADE NAMES/SYNONYMS: ARSENIC ACID, LEAD(2+) SALT; ACID LEAD ARSENATE; TALBOT; ACID LEAD ORTHOARSENATE; ARSENATE OF LEAD; LEAD ARSENATE, SOLID; DIBASIC LEAD ARSENITE; ARSENETTE, SCHULTENITE; GYPSINE; DIORTHO LEAD ARSENATE; SOPRABEL; STCC 4923235; UN 1617; PST12540

CHEMICAL FAMILY: INORGANIC SALT

MOLECULAR FORMULA: AS-H-O4-PB

MOLECULAR WEIGHT: 347.12

CERCLA RATINGS (SCALE 0-3): HEALTH=3 FIRE=0 REACTIVITY=0 PERSISTENCE=3

NFPA RATINGS (SCALE 0-4): HEALTH=3 FIRE=0 REACTIVITY=0

COMPONENTS AND CONTAMINANTS

COMPONENT: LEAD ARSENATE ***PERCENT:*** 100
CAS# 7784-40-9

OTHER CONTAMINANTS: NONE

EXPOSURE LIMITS: LEAD ARSENATE: 50 UG(PB)/M3 OSHA 8 HOUR TWA 30 UG(PB)/M3 OSHA 8 HOUR TWA ACTION LEVEL IF AN EMPLOYEE IS EXPOSED TO LEAD FOR MORE THAN 8 HOURS PER DAY THE FOLLOWING FORMULA IS USED: MAXIMUM PERMISSIBLE LIMIT (IN UG/M3) = 400 DIVIDED BY HOURS WORKED IN THE DAY
0.15 MG(PB)/M3 ACGIH TWA (INORGANIC DUSTS AND FUMES) <0.10 MG(PB)/M3 NIOSH RECOMMENDED 10 HOUR TWA 10 UG(AS)/M3 OSHA TWA 2 UG(AS)/M3 NIOSH RECOMMENDED 15 MINUTE CEILING
5000 POUNDS CERCLA SECTION 103 REPORTABLE QUANTITY SUBJECT TO SARA SECTION 313 ANNUAL TOXIC CHEMICAL RELEASE REPORTING SUBJECT TO CALIFORNIA PROPOSITION 65 CANCER AND/OR REPRODUCTIVE TOXICITY WARNING AND RELEASE REQUIREMENTS- (FEBRUARY 27, 1987)

PHYSICAL DATA

DESCRIPTION: WHITE CRYSTALS. ***BOILING POINT:*** DECOMPOSES

MELTING POINT: 1328 F (720 C) ***SPECIFIC GRAVITY:*** 5.8 @ 15 C

SOLUBILITY IN WATER: INSOLUBLE

SOLVENT SOLUBILITY: NITRIC ACID, CAUSTIC ALKALIES, AMMONIA WATER

FIRE AND EXPLOSION DATA

FIRE AND EXPLOSION HAZARD: NEGLIGIBLE FIRE HAZARD WHEN EXPOSED TO HEAT OR FLAME.

FIREFIGHTING MEDIA: DRY CHEMICAL, CARBON DIOXIDE, HALON, WATER SPRAY OR STANDARD FOAM (1987 EMERGENCY RESPONSE GUIDEBOOK, DOT P 5800.4).
FOR LARGER FIRES, USE WATER SPRAY, FOG OR STANDARD FOAM (1987 EMERGENCY RESPONSE GUIDEBOOK, DOT P 5800.4).

FIREFIGHTING: MOVE CONTAINERS FROM FIRE AREA IF POSSIBLE (1987 EMERGENCY RESPONSE GUIDEBOOK, DOT P 5800.4, GUIDE PAGE 53).
USE AGENT SUITABLE FOR TYPE OF FIRE; USE WATER IN FLOODING QUANTITIES AS FOG. AVOID BREATHING POISONOUS VAPORS, KEEP UPWIND.
FIRE FIGHTING PHASES: WATER MAY BE USED TO FIGHT A FIRE IN AN AREA CONTAINING LEAD ARSENATES (NFPA 49B HAZARDOUS CHEMICALS DATA, 1975).

TRANSPORTATION DATA

DEPARTMENT OF TRANSPORTATION HAZARD CLASSIFICATION 49 CFR 172.101: POISON B

DEPARTMENT OF TRANSPORTATION LABELING REQUIREMENTS 49 CFR 172.101 AND SUBPART E: POISON

DEPARTMENT OF TRANSPORTATION PACKAGING REQUIREMENTS: 49 CFR 173.367 EXCEPTIONS: 49 CFR 173.364

TOXICITY

LEAD ARSENATE: TOXICITY DATA: 1050 MG/KG UNREPORTED-MAN LDLO; 100 MG/KG ORAL-RAT LD50; 1526 MG/KG ORAL-MOUSE LD50; 75 MG/KG ORAL-RABBIT LDLO; 128 MG/KG INTRAPERITONEAL-MOUSE LD50. CARCINOGEN STATUS: HUMAN INADEQUATE EVIDENCE, ANIMAL SUFFICIENT EVIDENCE (IARC GROUP-2B FOR INORGANIC LEAD COMPOUNDS). OSHA CARCINOGEN; KNOWN HUMAN CARCINOGEN (NTP); SUFFICIENT HUMAN EVIDENCE, LIMITED ANIMAL EVIDENCE (IARC GROUP-1 FOR ARSENIC COMPOUNDS). AN INCREASED INCIDENCE OF SKIN AND LUNG CANCER HAS BEEN ASSOCIATED WITH INORGANIC ARSENIC COMPOUNDS THROUGH MEDICAL TREATMENT, CONTAMINATED DRINKING WATER OR OCCUPATIONAL EXPOSURE. CANCERS AT OTHER SITES HAVE ALSO BEEN REPORTED, BUT A CLEAR ASSOCIATION HAS NOT BEEN CONFIRMED. LOCAL EFFECTS: IRRITANT- INHALATION, SKIN, AND EYES. ACUTE TOXICITY LEVEL: TOXIC BY INGESTION. TARGET EFFECTS: NEUROTOXIN. POISONING MAY AFFECT THE LIVER, KIDNEY, BONE MARROW, AND CENTRAL NERVOUS AND GASTROINTESTINAL SYSTEMS.

HEALTH EFFECTS AND FIRST AID

INHALATION: LEAD ARSENATE: IRRITANT/NEUROTOXIN/CARCINOGEN. 300 MG/M3 IMMEDIATELY DANGEROUS TO LIFE OR HEALTH. **ACUTE EXPOSURE-** INHALATION OF ARSENIC DUSTS MAY CAUSE ACUTE PULMONARY EDEMA, RESTLESSNESS, DYSPNEA, CYANOSIS, COUGH WITH FOAMY SPUTUM, AND RALES. MAY ALSO CAUSE INFLAMMATION AND ULCERATION OF THE MUCOUS MEMBRANES AND SKIN, NAUSEA, VOMITING, DIARRHEA, LIVER AND KIDNEY DAMAGE, HEMATURIA, INCREASED PIGMENTATION AND KERATINIZATION OF THE SKIN, MUSCULAR PARALYSIS, VISUAL DISTURBANCES, AND EPIDERMOID CARCINOMA. **CHRONIC EXPOSURE-** REPEATED OR PROLONGED EXPOSURE MAY CAUSE DAMAGE TO THE CENTRAL AND PERIPHERAL NERVOUS SYSTEM, LIVER AND KIDNEY DAMAGE, ANEMIA, COLIC, LOSS OF APPETITE AND CONSTIPATION, ANOREXIA, EXCESSIVE TIREDNESS AND WEAKNESS, GINGIVAL LEAD LINE, WRIST DROP, AND NERVOUS IRRITABILITY. INORGANIC ARSENIC COMPOUNDS ARE KNOWN TO CAUSE LUNG CANCER.

FIRST AID- REMOVE FROM EXPOSURE AREA TO FRESH AIR IMMEDIATELY. IF BREATHING HAS STOPPED, PERFORM ARTIFICIAL RESPIRATION. KEEP PERSON WARM AND AT REST. TREAT SYMPTOMATICALLY AND SUPPORTIVELY. GET MEDICAL ATTENTION IMMEDIATELY.

SKIN CONTACT: LEAD ARSENATE: IRRITANT/SENSITIZER/CARCINOGEN. **ACUTE EXPOSURE-** ARSENIC AND COMPOUNDS IRRITATE THE SKIN. SENSITIZATION DERMATITIS MAY OCCUR IN PREVIOUSLY EXPOSED PERSONS, CHARACTERIZED BY ECZEMA WITH SCALING AND HYPERPIGMENTATION OF THE SKIN AND HYPERKERATOSIS OF THE PALMS OF THE HANDS AND THE SOLES OF THE FEET. INORGANIC ARSENIC COMPOUNDS ARE SLIGHTLY ABSORBED THROUGH THE SKIN WHEN ADMINISTERED IN A LIPID VEHICLE. POISONING HAS CAUSED ALOPECIA, BRONZING OF THE SKIN, AND BRITTLE NAILS. **CHRONIC EXPOSURE-** REPEATED EXPOSURE MAY RESULT IN SENSITIZATION DERMATITIS. INORGANIC ARSENIC AND COMPOUNDS ARE SKIN CARCINOGENS.

FIRST AID- REMOVE CONTAMINATED CLOTHING AND SHOES IMMEDIATELY. WASH AFFECTED AREA WITH SOAP OR MILD DETERGENT AND LARGE AMOUNTS OF WATER UNTIL NO EVIDENCE OF CHEMICAL REMAINS (APPROXIMATELY 15-20 MINUTES). GET MEDICAL ATTENTION IMMEDIATELY.

EYE CONTACT: LEAD ARSENATE: IRRITANT. **ACUTE EXPOSURE-** MAY CAUSE IRRITATION AND CONJUNCTIVITIS. POISONING HAS CAUSED EDEMA OF THE EYELIDS, CORNEAL NECROSIS, AND VISUAL DISTURBANCES. **CHRONIC EXPOSURE-** REPEATED OR PROLONGED EYE CONTACT WITH ARSENIC DUST MAY CAUSE CONJUNCTIVITIS. POISONING FROM INHALATION OR INGESTION HAS CAUSED OPTIC NEURITIS.

FIRST AID- WASH EYES IMMEDIATELY WITH LARGE AMOUNTS OF WATER OR NORMAL SALINE, OCCASIONALLY LIFTING UPPER AND LOWER LIDS, UNTIL NO EVIDENCE OF CHEMICAL REMAINS (APPROXIMATELY 15-20 MINUTES). GET MEDICAL ATTENTION IMMEDIATELY.

INGESTION: LEAD ARSENATE: NEUROTOXIN/CARCINOGEN. **ACUTE EXPOSURE-** NON-FATAL DOSES MAY CAUSE RESTLESSNESS, NAUSEA, VOMITING, HEADACHE, DIZZINESS, CHILLS, CRAMPS, IRRITABILITY, AND PARALYSIS. JAUNDICE, OLIGURIA, AND ANURIA MAY OCCUR WITHIN 1-3 DAYS. FATAL DOSES MAY CAUSE GASTROINTESTINAL DISTURBANCES, BURNING PAIN IN THE THROAT, VOMITING, WATERY OR BLOODY DIARRHEA WITH MUCOUS, HYPOTENSION, WEAKNESS, CONVULSIONS, COMA AND DEATH FROM CIRCULATORY FAILURE. THERE IS EVIDENCE THAT ARSENIC COMPOUNDS MAY CROSS THE PLACENTAL BARRIER. RATS SHOWED FERTILITY EFFECTS WITH PRE-IMPLANTATION AND POST-IMPLANTATION MORTALITIES FOLLOWING ORAL ADMINISTRATION. **CHRONIC EXPOSURE-** CHRONIC POISONING MAY AFFECT THE CENTRAL NERVOUS SYSTEM, SKIN, GASTROINTESTINAL TRACT, CARDIOVASCULAR SYSTEM, KIDNEYS AND LIVER. ARSENIC MAY CAUSE CANCER OF THE LUNGS, LIVER, LARYNX, LYMPHATIC SYSTEM, OR VISCERA. IN ONE EPIDEMIOLOGICAL STUDY, SKIN CANCER WAS POSITIVELY CORRELATED WITH HIGH ARSENIC LEVELS IN DRINKING WATER.

FIRST AID- REMOVE BY GASTRIC LAVAGE OR EMESIS. FOLLOW WITH A SALINE CATHARTIC. MAINTAIN BLOOD PRESSURE, AIRWAY, AND GIVE OXYGEN IF RESPIRATION IS DEPRESSED. DO NOT PERFORM GASTRIC LAVAGE OR EMESIS IF VICTIM IS UNCONSCIOUS. GET MEDICAL ATTENTION IMMEDIATELY. (DREISBACH, HANDBOOK OF POISONING, 12TH ED.) ADMINISTRATION OF GASTRIC LAVAGE OR OXYGEN SHOULD BE PERFORMED BY QUALIFIED MEDICAL PERSONNEL.

ANTIDOTE: THE FOLLOWING ANTIDOTE HAS BEEN RECOMMENDED. HOWEVER, THE DECISION AS TO WHETHER THE SEVERITY OF POISONING REQUIRES ADMINISTRATION OF ANY ANTIDOTE AND ACTUAL DOSE REQUIRED SHOULD BE MADE BY QUALIFIED MEDICAL PERSONNEL.

ARSENIC POISONING: GIVE DIMERCAPROL, 3 MG/KG (OR 0.3 ML/KG) EVERY 4 HOURS FOR 2 DAYS AND THEN 2 MG/KG EVERY 2 HOURS FOR A TOTAL OF 10 DAYS. DIMERCAPROL IS AVAILABLE AS A 10% SOLUTION IN OIL FOR INTRAMUSCULAR ADMINISTRATION. NEXT, GIVE PENICILLAMINE, UP TO 100 MG/KG/DAY (MAXIMUM 1 G/DAY) DIVIDED INTO 4 DOSES FOR NO LONGER THAN 1 WEEK. IF A LONGER ADMINISTRATION PERIOD IS WARRANTED, DOSAGE SHOULD NOT EXCEED 40 MG/KG/DAY. GIVE THE DRUG ORALLY HALF AN HOUR BEFORE MEALS. DISCONTINUE ANTIDOTE WHEN URINE ARSENIC LEVEL FALLS BELOW 50 UG/24 HR. (DREISBACH, HANDBOOK OF POISONING, 12TH ED.). ANITDOTE SHOULD BE ADMINISTERED BY QUALIFIED MEDICAL PERSONNEL.

REACTIVITY

REACTIVITY: STABLE UNDER NORMAL TEMPERATURES AND PRESSURES.

INCOMPATIBILITIES: LEAD ARSENATE: NO DATA AVAILABLE.

DECOMPOSITION: THERMAL DECOMPOSITION PRODUCTS MAY INCLUDE TOXIC AND HAZARDOUS FUMES OF LEAD AND ARSENIC.

POLYMERIZATION: HAZARDOUS POLYMERIZATION HAS NOT BEEN REPORTED TO OCCUR UNDER NORMAL TEMPERATURES AND PRESSURES.

STORAGE AND DISPOSAL

OBSERVE ALL FEDERAL, STATE AND LOCAL REGULATIONS WHEN STORING OR DISPOSING OF THIS SUBSTANCE. FOR ASSISTANCE, CONTACT THE DISTRICT DIRECTOR OF THE ENVIRONMENTAL PROTECTION AGENCY.

STORAGE

PROTECT AGAINST PHYSICAL DAMAGE. SEPARATE FROM OTHER STORAGE (NFPA 49, HAZARDOUS CHEMICALS DATA, 1975).

CONDITIONS TO AVOID

MAY BURN BUT DOES NOT IGNITE READILY.

SPILL AND LEAK PROCEDURES

WATER SPILL: THE CALIFORNIA SAFE DRINKING WATER AND TOXIC ENFORCEMENT ACT OF 1986 (PROPOSITION 65) PROHIBITS CONTAMINATING ANY KNOWN SOURCE OF DRINKING WATER WITH SUBSTANCES KNOWN TO CAUSE CANCER AND/OR REPRODUCTIVE TOXICITY.

OCCUPATIONAL SPILL: DO NOT TOUCH SPILLED MATERIAL. STOP LEAK IF YOU CAN DO IT WITHOUT RISK. FOR SMALL SPILLS, TAKE UP WITH SAND OR OTHER ABSORBENT MATERIAL AND PLACE INTO CONTAINERS FOR LATER DISPOSAL. FOR SMALL DRY SPILLS, WITH A CLEAN SHOVEL PLACE MATERIAL INTO CLEAN, DRY CONTAINER AND COVER. MOVE CONTAINERS FROM SPILL AREA. FOR LARGER SPILLS, DIKE FAR AHEAD OF SPILL FOR LATER DISPOSAL. KEEP UNNECESSARY PEOPLE AWAY. ISOLATE HAZARD AREA AND DENY ENTRY.

REPORTABLE QUANTITY (RQ): 5000 POUNDS THE SUPERFUND AMENDMENTS AND REAUTHORIZATION ACT (SARA) SECTION 304 REQUIRES THAT A RELEASE EQUAL TO OR GREATER THAN THE REPORTABLE QUANTITY FOR THIS SUBSTANCE BE IMMEDIATELY REPORTED TO THE LOCAL EMERGENCY PLANNING COMMITTEE AND THE STATE EMERGENCY RESPONSE COMMISSION (40 CFR 355.40). IF THE RELEASE OF THIS SUBSTANCE IS REPORTABLE UNDER CERCLA SECTION 103, THE NATIONAL RESPONSE CENTER MUST BE NOTIFIED IMMEDIATELY AT (800) 424-8802 OR (202) 426-2675 IN THE METROPOLITAN WASHINGTON, D.C. AREA (40 CFR 302.6).

PROTECTIVE EQUIPMENT

VENTILATION: PROVIDE LOCAL EXHAUST OR PROCESS ENCLOSURE VENTILATION TO MEET PUBLISHED EXPOSURE LIMITS.

ARSENIC (INORGANIC): VENTILATION SHOULD MEET THE REQUIREMENTS IN 29 CFR 1910.1018(G).

LEAD (ELEMENTAL, INORGANIC, AND SOAPS): VENTILATION SHOULD MEET THE REQUIREMENTS IN 29 CFR 1910.1025(E).

RESPIRATOR: THE FOLLOWING RESPIRATORS ARE THE MINIMUM LEGAL REQUIREMENTS AS SET FORTH BY THE OCCUPATIONAL SAFETY AND HEALTH ADMINISTRATION FOUND IN 29 CFR 1910, SUBPART Z.

RESPIRATORY PROTECTION FOR INORGANIC ARSENIC PARTICULATE EXCEPT THOSE WITH SIGNIFICANT VAPOR PRESSURE

CONCENTRATION OF INORGANIC ARSENIC (AS) REQUIRED RESPIRATOR OR

CONDITION OF USE
UNKNOWN OR GREATER OR LESS THAN 20,000 UG/M3 (20 MG/M3) OR FIREFIGHTING ANY FULL FACEPIECE, SELF CONTAINED BREATHING APPARATUS, OPERATED IN POSITIVE PRESSURE MODE.
NOT GREATER THAN 20,000 UG/M3 (20 MG/M3) SUPPLIED-AIR RESPIRATOR WITH FULL FACEPIECE, HOOD OR HELMET OR SUIT AND OPERATED IN POSITIVE PRESSURE MODE.
NOT GREATER THAN 10,000 UG/M3 (10 MG/M3) POWERED-AIR PURIFYING RESPIRATORS IN ALL INLET FACE COVERINGS WITH HIGH EFFICIENCY FILTERS; OR HALF-MASK SUPPLIED-AIR RESPIRATOR OPERATED IN POSITIVE PRESSURE MODE.
NOT GREATER THAN 500 UG/M3 FULL FACEPIECE AIR-PURIFYING RESPIRATOR EQUIPPED WITH HIGH EFFICIENCY FILTERS; OR ANY FULL FACEPIECE SUPPLIED-AIR RESPIRATOR; OR ANY FULL FACEPIECE SELF-CONTAINED BREATHING APPARATUS. NOT GREATER THAN 100 UG/M3 HALF-MASK AIR-PURIFYING RESPIRATOR EQUIPPED WITH HIGH EFFICIENCY FILTERS; OR ANY HALF-MASK SUPPLIED-AIR RESPIRATOR.
(HIGH EFFICIENCY FILTER- 99.97% EFFICIENCY AGAINST 0.3 MICROMETER MONODISPERSE DIETHYL-HEXYL PHTHALATE (DOP) PARTICLES)
RESPIRATORY PROTECTION FOR INORGANIC ARSENICALS (SUCH AS ARSENIC TRICHLORIDE OR ARSENIC PHOSPHIDE) WITH SIGNIFICANT VAPOR PRESSURE.
CONCENTRATION OF INORGANIC ARSENIC (AS) REQUIRED RESPIRATOR OR CONDITION OF USE
UNKNOWN OR GREATER OR LESS THAN 20,000 UG/M3 (20 MG/M3) ANY FULL FACEPIECE SELF-CONTAINED BREATHING APPARATUS OPERATED IN POSITIVE PRESSURE MODE.
NOT GREATER THAN 20,000 UG/M3 (20 MG/M3) SUPPLIED-AIR RESPIRATOR WITH A FULL FACEPIECE, HOOD OR HELMET OR SUIT OPERATED IN POSITIVE PRESSURE MODE.
NOT GREATER THAN 10,000 UG/M3 (10 MG/M3) HALF-MASK SUPPLIED AIR RESPIRATOR OPERATED IN POSITIVE PRESSURE MODE.
NOT GREATER THAN 500 UG/M3 FRONT- OR BACK-MOUNTED GAS MASK EQUIPPED WITH HIGH-EFFICIENCY FILTERS AND ACID GAS CANISTER; OR ANY FULL FACEPIECE SUPPLIED AIR RESPIRATOR; OR ANY FULL FACEPIECE SELF-CONTAINED BREATHING APPARATUS.
NOT GREATER THAN 100 UG/M3 HALF-MASK AIR-PURIFYING RESPIRATOR EQUIPPED WITH HIGH EFFICIENCY FILTER AND ACID GAS CARTRIDGE; OR ANY HALF-MASK SUPPLIED-AIR RESPIRATOR.
(HIGH EFFICIENCY FILTER- 99.97% EFFICIENCY AGAINST 0.3 MICROMETER MONODISPERSE DIETHYL-HEXYL PHTHALATE (DOP) PARTICLES) (HALF-MASK RESPIRATORS SHALL NOT BE USED FOR PROTECTION AGAINST ARSENIC TRICHLORIDE, AS IT IS RAPIDLY ABSORBED THROUGH THE SKIN).
THE FOLLOWING RESPIRATORS AND MAXIMUM USE CONCENTRATIONS ARE RECOMMENDATIONS BY THE U.S. DEPARTMENT OF HEALTH AND HUMAN SERVICES, NIOSH POCKET GUIDE TO CHEMICAL HAZARDS; NIOSH CRITERIA DOCUMENTS OR BY THE U.S. DEPARTMENT OF LABOR, 29 CFR 1910 SUBPART Z.
THE SPECIFIC RESPIRATOR SELECTED MUST BE BASED ON CONTAMINATION LEVELS FOUND IN THE WORK PLACE, MUST NOT EXCEED THE WORKING LIMITS OF THE RESPIRATOR AND BE JOINTLY APPROVED BY THE NATIONAL INSTITUTE FOR OCCUPATIONAL SAFETY AND HEALTH AND THE MINE SAFETY AND HEALTH ADMINISTRATION (NIOSH-MSHA).
AT ANY DETECTABLE CONCENTRATION:
SELF-CONTAINED BREATHING APPARATUS WITH FULL FACEPIECE OPERATED IN PRESSURE-DEMAND OR OTHER POSITIVE PRESSURE MODE. SUPPLIED-AIR RESPIRATOR WITH FULL FACEPIECE OPERATED IN PRESSURE-DEMAND OR OTHER POSITIVE PRESSURE MODE IN COMBINATION WITH AN AUXILIARY SELF-CONTAINED BREATHING APPARATUS OPERATED IN PRESSURE-DEMAND OR OTHER POSITIVE PRESSURE MODE.
ESCAPE- AIR-PURIFYING FULL FACEPIECE RESPIRATOR WITH HIGH-EFFICIENCY PARTICULATE FILTER. ESCAPE-TYPE SELF-CONTAINED BREATHING APPARATUS.
FOR FIREFIGHTING AND OTHER IMMEDIATELY DANGEROUS TO LIFE OR HEALTH CONDITIONS:
SELF-CONTAINED BREATHING APPARATUS WITH FULL FACEPIECE OPERATED IN PRESSURE-DEMAND OR OTHER POSITIVE PRESSURE MODE.
SUPPLIED-AIR RESPIRATOR WITH FULL FACEPIECE AND OPERATED IN PRESSURE-DEMAND OR OTHER POSITIVE PRESSURE MODE IN COMBINATION WITH AN AUXILIARY SELF-CONTAINED BREATHING APPARATUS OPERATED IN PRESSURE-DEMAND OR OTHER POSITIVE PRESSURE MODE.

CLOTHING: EMPLOYEE MUST WEAR APPROPRIATE PROTECTIVE (IMPERVIOUS) CLOTHING AND EQUIPMENT TO PREVENT REPEATED OR PROLONGED SKIN CONTACT WITH THIS SUBSTANCE.
ARSENIC (INORGANIC): PROTECTIVE CLOTHING SHOULD MEET THE REQUIREMENTS FOR PROTECTIVE WORK CLOTHING AND EQUIPMENT IN 29 CFR 1910.1018(J).
LEAD (ELEMENTAL, INORGANIC, AND SOAPS): PROTECTIVE CLOTHING SHOULD MEET THE REQUIREMENTS FOR PROTECTIVE WORK CLOTHING AND EQUIPMENT IN 29 CFR 1910.1025(G).

GLOVES: EMPLOYEE MUST WEAR APPROPRIATE PROTECTIVE GLOVES TO PREVENT CONTACT WITH THIS SUBSTANCE.
ARSENIC (INORGANIC): PROTECTIVE GLOVES SHOULD MEET THE REQUIREMENTS FOR PROTECTIVE WORK CLOTHING AND EQUIPMENT IN 29 CFR 1910.1018(J).
LEAD (ELEMENTAL, INORGANIC & SOAPS): PROTECTIVE GLOVES SHOULD MEET THE REQUIREMENTS FOR PROTECTIVE WORK CLOTHING AND EQUIPMENT IN 29 CFR 1910.1025(G).

EYE PROTECTION: EMPLOYEE MUST WEAR SPLASH-PROOF OR DUST-RESISTANT SAFETY GOGGLES WITH OR WITHOUT A FACESHIELD TO PREVENT CONTACT WITH THIS SUBSTANCE.
EMERGENCY EYE WASH: WHERE THERE IS ANY POSSIBILITY THAT AN EMPLOYEE'S EYES MAY BE EXPOSED TO THIS SUBSTANCE, THE EMPLOYER SHOULD PROVIDE AN EYE WASH FOUNTAIN WITHIN THE IMMEDIATE WORK AREA FOR EMERGENCY USE.
ARSENIC (INORGANIC): PROTECTIVE EYE EQUIPMENT SHOULD MEET THE REQUIREMENTS FOR PROTECTIVE WORK CLOTHING AND EQUIPMENT IN 29 CFR 1910.1018(J).
LEAD (ELEMENTAL, INORGANIC, AND SOAPS): PROTECTIVE EYE EQUIPMENT SHOULD MEET THE REQUIREMENTS FOR PROTECTIVE WORK CLOTHING AND EQUIPMENT IN 29 CFR 1910.1025(G).

AUTHORIZED BY- OCCUPATIONAL HEALTH SERVICES, INC.
CREATION DATE: 10/04/89 ***REVISION DATE:*** 07/12/90

MATERIAL SAFETY DATA SHEET

OCCUPATIONAL HEALTH SERVICES, INC.
AGRICULTURE AND PESTICIDE DIVISION
450 SEVENTH AVENUE, SUITE 2407
NEW YORK, NEW YORK 10123
1-800-445-MSDS OR (212) 967-1100

EMERGENCY CONTACT:
JOHN S. BRANSFORD, JR. (615) 292-1180

SUBSTANCE IDENTIFICATION

CAS-NUMBER 25006-32-0
SUBSTANCE: <u>LEPTOPHOS OXYGEN ANALOG</u>
TRADE NAMES/SYNONYMS: PHOSPHONIC ACID, PHENYL-, 4-BROMO-2,5-DICHLOROPHENYL METHYL ESTER; (4-BROMO-2,5-DICHLOROPHENYL)PHENYL METHYL PHOSPHONATE; LEPTOPHOS OA; LEPTOPHOS OXON; O-METHYL O-(4-BROMO-2,5-DICHLOROPHENYL)PHENYL PHOSPHONATE; 4-BROMO-2,5-DICHLOROPHENYL METHYL PHENYLPHOSPHONATE; PHOSVEL OXON; C13H10BRCL2O3P; PST12776
CHEMICAL FAMILY: ORGANOPHOSPHATE
HALOGEN COMPOUND, AROMATIC
MOLECULAR FORMULA: C13-H10-BR-CL2-O3-P
MOLECULAR WEIGHT: 396.01
CERCLA RATINGS (SCALE 0-3): HEALTH=3 FIRE=1 REACTIVITY=0 PERSISTENCE=0
NFPA RATINGS (SCALE 0-4): HEALTH=U FIRE=1 REACTIVITY=0

COMPONENTS AND CONTAMINANTS

COMPONENT: LEPTOPHOS OXYGEN ANALOG ***PERCENT:*** 100.0
CAS# 25006-32-0
OTHER CONTAMINANTS: NONE
EXPOSURE LIMITS: NO OCCUPATIONAL EXPOSURE LIMITS ESTABLISHED BY OSHA, ACGIH, OR NIOSH.

PHYSICAL DATA

DESCRIPTION: WHITE POWDER. ***MELTING POINT:*** NOT AVAILABLE
SPECIFIC GRAVITY: NOT AVAILABLE ***SOLUBILITY IN WATER:*** NOT AVAILABLE

FIRE AND EXPLOSION DATA

FIRE AND EXPLOSION HAZARD: SLIGHT FIRE HAZARD WHEN EXPOSED TO HEAT OR FLAME.
DUST-AIR MIXTURES MAY IGNITE OR EXPLODE.
FIREFIGHTING MEDIA: DRY CHEMICAL, CARBON DIOXIDE, HALON, WATER SPRAY OR STANDARD FOAM (1987 EMERGENCY RESPONSE GUIDEBOOK, DOT P 5800.4).
FOR LARGER FIRES, USE WATER SPRAY, FOG OR STANDARD FOAM (1987 EMERGENCY RESPONSE GUIDEBOOK, DOT P 5800.4).

FIREFIGHTING: MOVE CONTAINERS FROM FIRE AREA IF POSSIBLE (1987 EMERGENCY RESPONSE GUIDEBOOK, DOT P 5800.4, GUIDE PAGE 53).
EXTINGUISH USING AGENT SUITABLE FOR TYPE OF SURROUNDING FIRE. AVOID BREATHING VAPORS AND DUSTS. KEEP UPWIND.

TOXICITY

LEPTOPHOS OXYGEN ANALOG: TOXICITY DATA: 118 MG/KG ORAL-RAT LD50.
CARCINOGEN STATUS: NONE. ACUTE TOXICITY LEVEL: TOXIC BY INGESTION.
TARGET EFFECTS: CHOLINESTERASE INHIBITOR. POISONING MAY AFFECT THE NERVOUS SYSTEM.* AT INCREASED RISK FROM EXPOSURE: PERSONS WITH RESPIRATORY AILMENTS, RECENT EXPOSURE TO CHOLINESTERASE INHIBITORS OR IMAPAIRED CHOLINESTERASE PRODUCTION, OR LIVER MALFUNCTION.*
ADDITIONAL DATA: MAY CROSS THE PLACENTA. HIGH ENVIRONMENTAL TEMPERATURES OR EXPOSURE OF THE CHEMICAL TO VISIBLE OR ULTRAVIOLET LIGHT MAY ENHANCE THE TOXICITY. INTERACTIONS WITH MEDICATIONS MAY OCCURS.*
* MAY BE BASED ON GENERAL INFORMATION ON ORGANOPHOSPHATES.

HEALTH EFFECTS AND FIRST AID

INHALATION: LEPTOPHOS OXYGEN ANALOG: SEE INFORMATION ON ORGANOPHOSPHATES.
ORGANOPHOSPHATES: CHOLINESTERASE INHIBITOR. **ACUTE EXPOSURE-** WHEN INHALED, THE FIRST EFFECTS OF CHOLINESTERASE INHIBITORS ARE USUALLY RESPIRATORY AND MAY INCLUDE NASAL HYPEREMIA AND WATERY DISCHARGE, COUGH, CHEST DISCOMFORT, DYSPNEA, AND WHEEZING DUE TO INCREASED BRONCHIAL SECRETIONS AND BRONCHOCONSTRICTION. IF SUFFICIENT AMOUNTS ARE ABSORBED, OTHER SYSTEMIC EFFECTS MAY BEGIN WITHIN A FEW MINUTES OR BE DELAYED FOR UP TO 12 HOURS. SYMPTOMS MAY INCLUDE PALLOR, NAUSEA, VOMITING, DIARRHEA, ABDOMINAL CRAMPS, HEADACHE, DIZZINESS, OCULAR PAIN, BLURRED VISION, MIOSIS OR IN SOME CASES, ESPECIALLY INITIALLY, MYDRIASIS, LACRIMATION, SALIVATION, SWEATING, AND CONFUSION. OTHER REPORTED CENTRAL NERVOUS SYSTEM OR NEUROMUSCULAR EFFECTS MAY INCLUDE ATAXIA, SLURRED SPEECH, AREFLEXIA, WEAKNESS, FATIGUE, FASCICULATIONS, TWITCHING, TREMORS POSSIBLY OF THE TONGUE AND EYELIDS, AND EVENTUALLY PARALYSIS OF THE EXTREMITIES AND POSSIBLY OF THE RESPIRATORY MUSCLES. IN SEVERE CASES THERE MAY ALSO BE INVOLUNTARY DEFECATION AND URINATION, CYANOSIS, PSYCHOSIS, HYPERGLYCEMIA, ACUTE PANCREATITIS, CARDIAC IRREGULARITIES, PULMONARY EDEMA, UNCONSCIOUSNESS, CONVULSIONS, AND COMA. DEATH IS PRIMARILY DUE TO RESPIRATORY FAILURE, ALTHOUGH CARDIOVASCULAR EFFECTS INCLUDING CARDIAC ARREST MAY ALSO BE IMPLICATED. LONG TERM SEQUELAE ARE RARE BUT MAY INCLUDE NEUROPSYCHIATRIC DISORDERS AND MYOPATHY WITH MUSCLE TENDERNESS. SOME ORGANOPHOSPHATES MAY CAUSE A DELAYED NEUROPATHY BEGINNING 1-4 WEEKS AFTER AN ACUTE EXPOSURE WHICH MAY OR MAY NOT HAVE CAUSED ACUTE CHOLINERGIC EFFECTS. NUMBNESS, TINGLING, WEAKNESS AND CRAMPING BEGINNING SYMMETRICALLY IN THE LOWER LIMBS MAY PROGRESS TO ATAXIA AND PARALYSIS. IN SEVERE CASES, UPPER LIMB INVOLVEMENT IS POSSIBLE AND FLACCID PARALYSIS MAY PROGRESS TO SPASTIC PARALYSIS WITH EXAGGERATED REFLEXES. IMPROVEMENT MAY OCCUR OVER MONTHS TO YEARS, BUT SOME RESIDUAL IMPAIRMENT USUALLY REMAINS. **CHRONIC EXPOSURE-** REPEATED OR PROLONGED EXPOSURE MAY RESULT IN THE EFFECTS OF ACUTE EXPOSURE INCLUDING THE DELAYED NEUROPATHY. OTHER EFFECTS REPORTED IN WORKERS REPEATEDLY EXPOSED INCLUDE IMPAIRED MEMORY AND CONCENTRATION, ACUTE PSYCHOSIS, SEVERE DEPRESSIONS, IRRITABILTY, CONFUSION, APATHY, EMOTIONAL LABILITY, SOCIAL WITHDRAWAL, CONFUSION, HEADACHE, SPEECH DIFFICULTIES, DELAYED REACTION TIMES, SPATIAL DISORIENTATION, NIGHTMARES, SLEEPWALKING, AND DROWSINESS OR INSOMNIA. AN INFLUENZA-LIKE CONDITION WITH HEADACHE, NAUSEA, WEAKNESS, ANOREXIA AND MALAISE HAS ALSO BEEN REPORTED.
FIRST AID- REMOVE FROM EXPOSURE AREA TO FRESH AIR IMMEDIATELY. IF BREATHING HAS STOPPED, PERFORM ARTIFICIAL RESPIRATION. KEEP PERSON WARM AND AT REST. TREAT SYMPTOMATICALLY AND SUPPORTIVELY. GET MEDICAL ATTENTION IMMEDIATELY.

SKIN CONTACT: LEPTOPHOS OXYGEN ANALOG: SEE INFORMATION ON ORGANOPHOSPHATES.
ORGANOPHOSPHATES: CHOLINESTERASE INHIBITOR. **ACUTE EXPOSURE-** LOCALIZED SWEATING AND FASCICULATIONS MAY OCCUR AT THE SITE OF CONTACT. IF SUFFICIENT AMOUNTS ARE ABSORBED, OTHER EFFECTS OF CHOLINESTERASE INHIBITION AS DESCRIBED IN ACUTE INHALATION MAY OCCUR. SYMPTOMS MAY BE DELAYED 2-3 HOURS, BUT USUALLY NO MORE THAN 12 HOURS. THE RATE OF ABSORPTION IS INCREASED BY THE PRESENCE OF DERMATITIS OR HIGH AMBIENT TEMPERATURES. DELAYED NEUROPATHY IS ALSO POSSIBLE. **CHRONIC EXPOSURE-** REPEATED OR PROLONGED EXPOSURE MAY CAUSE EFFECTS AS DESCRIBED IN ACUTE EXPOSURE. SOME ORGANOPHOSPHATES MAY CAUSE SENSITIZATION.
FIRST AID- REMOVE CONTAMINATED CLOTHING IMMEDIATELY. WASH CONTAMINATED AREAS WITH SOAP AND WATER FOLLOWED BY ALCOHOL (ARENA, POISONING, 4TH ED.). EMERGENCY PERSONNEL SHOULD WEAR GLOVES AND AVOID CONTAMINATION. TREAT RESPIRATORY DIFFICULTY WITH ARTIFICIAL RESPIRATION. GET MEDICAL ATTENTION IMMEDIATELY.

EYE CONTACT: LEPTOPHOS OXYGEN ANALOG: SEE INFORMATION ON ORGANOPHOSPHATES.
ORGANOPHOSPHATES: CHOLINESTERASE INHIBITOR. **ACUTE EXPOSURE-** DIRECT CONTACT MAY CAUSE PAIN, HYPEREMIA, LACRIMATION, TWITCHING OF THE EYELIDS, MIOSIS, AND CILIARY MUSCLE SPASM WITH LOSS OF ACCOMODATION, BLURRED OR DIMMED VISION AND BROWACHE. SOMETIMES MYDRIASIS MAY OCCUR INSTEAD OF MIOSIS. WITH SUFFICIENT EXPOSURE, OTHER SYMPTOMS OF CHOLINESTERASE INHIBITION AS DESCRIBED IN ACUTE INHALATION MAY OCCUR. **CHRONIC EXPOSURE-** REPEATED OR PROLONGED EXPOSURE MAY CAUSE EFFECTS AS DESCRIBED IN ACUTE EXPOSURE. SOME COMPOUNDS HAVE CAUSED TOXIC EFFECTS ON THE CRYSTALLINE LENS, CONJUNCTIVAL THICKENING AND OBSTRUCTION OF THE NASOLACRIMAL CANALS WHEN USED AS MIOTIC EYEDROPS.
FIRST AID- IRRIGATE EYES WITH WATER OR SALINE SOLUTION. IF SYMPTOMS OF POISONING OCCUR, TREAT RESPIRATORY DIFFICULTY WITH ARTIFICIAL RESPIRATION AND OXYGEN. OBSERVE PATIENT FOR AT LEAST 24-36 HOURS (GOSSELIN, CLINICAL TOXICOLOGY OF COMMERCIAL PRODUCTS, 5TH ED.). GET MEDICAL ATTENTION IMMEDIATELY. OXYGEN SHOULD BE ADMINISTERED BY QUALIFIED MEDICAL PERSONNEL.

INGESTION: LEPTOPHOS OXYGEN ANALOG: TOXIC. SEE INFORMATION ON ORGANOPHOSPHATES.
ORGANOPHOSPHATES: CHOLINESTERASE INHIBITOR. **ACUTE EXPOSURE-** WHEN INGESTED, THE FIRST EFFECTS MAY BE NAUSEA, VOMITING, ANOREXIA, ABDOMINAL CRAMPS AND DIARRHEA. GASTROINTESTINAL ABSORPTION MAY CAUSE SYMPTOMS OF CHOLINESTERASE INHIBITION AS DESCRIBED IN ACUTE INHALATION. SYMPTOMS MAY BEGIN WITHIN MINUTES OR BE DELAYED FOR HOURS. DELAYED EFFECTS INCLUDING NEUROPATHY MAY ALSO OCCUR. **CHRONIC EXPOSURE-** REPEATED INGESTION MAY CAUSE EFFECTS AS DESCRIBED IN ACUTE EXPOSURE.
FIRST AID- IF PERSON IS ALERT AND RESPIRATION IS NOT DEPRESSED, GIVE SYRUP OF IPECAC FOLLOWED BY WATER (IF VOMITING OCCURS, KEEP HEAD BELOW HIPS TO PREVENT ASPIRATION). IF CONSCIOUSNESS LEVEL DECLINES OR VOMITING HAS NOT OCCURRED IN 15 MINUTES EMPTY STOMACH BY GASTRIC LAVAGE WITH THE AID OF CUFFED ENDOTRACHEAL TUBE USING ISOTONIC SALINE OR 5% SODIUM BICARBONATE FOLLOW WITH ACTIVATED CHARCOAL. ESTABLISH AND MAINTAIN AIRWAY. TREAT RESPIRATORY DIFFICULTY WITH ARTIFICIAL RESPIRATION AND OXYGEN. DO NOT GIVE MORPHINE, AMINOPHYLLINE, PHENOTHIAZINES, RESERPINE, FUROSEMIDE, OR ETHACRYNIC ACID (MORGAN, RECOGNITION AND MANAGEMENT OF PESTICIDE POISONINGS, 3RD ED.). TREAT SYMPTOMATICALLY AND SUPPORTIVELY. ADMINISTRATION OF OXYGEN AND LAVAGE MUST BE PERFORMED BY QUALIFIED MEDICAL PERSONNEL. GET MEDICAL ATTENTION IMMEDIATELY.
ANTIDOTE: THE FOLLOWING ANTIDOTE(S) HAVE BEEN RECOMMENDED. HOWEVER, THE DECISION AS TO WHETHER THE SEVERITY OF POISONING REQUIRES ADMINISTRATION OF ANY ANTIDOTE AND ACTUAL DOSE REQUIRED SHOULD BE MADE BY QUALIFIED MEDICAL PERSONNEL.
FOR CHOLINESTERASE INHIBITORS: ESTABLISH CLEAR AIRWAY AND TISSUE OXYGENATION BY ASPIRATION OF SECRETIONS, AND IF NECESSARY, BY ASSISTED PULMONARY VENTILATION WITH OXYGEN. IMPROVE TISSUE OXYGÊNATION AS MUCH AS POSSIBLE BEFORE ADMINISTERING ATROPINE TO MINIMIZE THE RISK OF VENTRICULAR FIBRILLATION. ADMINISTER ATROPINE SULFATE INTRAVENOUSLY, OR INTRAMUSCULARLY IF IV INJECTION IS NOT POSSIBLE. IN MODERATELY SEVERE POISONING ADMINISTER ATROPINE SULFATE, 0.4-2.0 MG REPEATED EVERY 15 MINUTES UNTIL ATROPINIZATION IS ACHIEVED (TACHYCARDIA, FLUSHING, DRY MOUTH, MYDRIASIS). MAINTAIN ATROPINIZATION BY REPEATED DOSES FOR 2-12 HOURS, OR LONGER, DEPENDING ON THE SEVERITY OF POISONING. THE APPEARANCE OF RALES IN THE LUNG BASES, MIOSIS, SALIVATION, NAUSEA, BRADYCARDIA, ARE ALL INDICATIONS OF INADEQUATE ATROPINIZATION. SEVERELY POISONED INDIVIDUALS MAY EXHIBIT REMARKABLE TOLERANCE TO ATROPINE; TWO OR MORE TIMES THE DOSAGES SUGGESTED ABOVE MAY BE NEEDED. PERSONS NOT POISONED OR ONLY SLIGHTLY POISONED, HOWEVER, MAY DEVELOP SIGNS OF ATROPINE TOXICITY FROM SUCH LARGE DOSAGES: FEVER, MUSCLE FIBRILLATIONS, AND DELIRIUM ARE THE MAIN SIGNS OF ATROPINE TOXICITY. IF THESE SIGNS APPEAR WHILE THE PATIENT IS FULLY ATROPINIZED, ATROPINE ADMINISTRATION SHOULD BE DISCONTINUED, AT LEAST TEMPORARILY. OBSERVE TREATED PATIENTS CLOSELY AT LEAST 24 HOURS TO INSURE THAT SYMPTOMS (POSSIBLY PULMONARY EDEMA) DO NOT RECUR AS ATROPINIZATION WEARS OFF. IN VERY SEVERE POISONINGS, METABOLIC DISPOSITION OF TOXICANT MAY REQUIRE SEVERAL HOURS OR DAYS DURING WHICH ATROPINIZATION MUST BE MAINTAINED. MARKEDLY LOWER LEVELS OF URINARY

METABOLITES INDICATE THAT ATROPINE DOSAGE CAN BE TAPERED OFF. AS DOSAGE IS REDUCED, CHECK THE LUNG BASES FREQUENTLY FOR RALES. IF RALES ARE HEARD OR OTHER SYMPTOMS RETURN, RE-ESTABLISH ATROPINIZATION PROMPTLY (MORGAN, RECOGNITION AND MANAGEMENT OF PESTICIDE POISONINGS, 3RD ED.). ADMINISTRATION OF ANTIDOTE MUST BE PERFORMED BY QUALIFIED MEDICAL PERSONNEL.

IN CASES OF SEVERE POISONING BY ORGANOPHOSPHATE PESTICIDES IN WHICH RESPIRATORY DEPRESSION, MUSCLE WEAKNESS AND TWITCHINGS ARE SEVERE, GIVE PRALIDOXIME (PROTOPAM-AYERST, 2-PAM), 1.0 GRAM INTRAVENOUSLY AT NO MORE THAN 0.5 GRAM PER MINUTE. DOSAGE OF PRALIDOXIME MAY BE REPEATED IN 1-2 HOURS, THEN AT 10-12 HOUR INTERVALS IF NEEDED. IN VERY SEVERE POISONINGS, DOSAGE RATES MAY BE DOUBLED. TREATMENT WITH PRALIDOXIME WILL BE MOST EFFECTIVE IF GIVEN WITHIN THIRTY-SIX HOURS AFTER POISONING (MORGAN, RECOGNITION AND MANAGEMENT OF PESTICIDE POISONINGS, 3RD ED.). ANTIDOTE SHOULD BE ADMINISTERED BY QUALIFIED MEDICAL PERSONNEL.

REACTIVITY

REACTIVITY: STABLE UNDER NORMAL TEMPERATURES AND PRESSURES.

INCOMPATIBILITIES: LEPTOPHOS OXYGEN ANALOG: OXIDIZERS (STRONG): FIRE AND EXPLOSION HAZARD.

DECOMPOSITION: THERMAL DECOMPOSITION MAY RELEASE TOXIC AND/OR HAZARDOUS GASES.

POLYMERIZATION: HAZARDOUS POLYMERIZATION HAS NOT BEEN REPORTED TO OCCUR UNDER NORMAL TEMPERATURES AND PRESSURES.

STORAGE AND DISPOSAL

OBSERVE ALL FEDERAL, STATE AND LOCAL REGULATIONS WHEN STORING OR DISPOSING OF THIS SUBSTANCE. FOR ASSISTANCE, CONTACT THE DISTRICT DIRECTOR OF THE ENVIRONMENTAL PROTECTION AGENCY.

****STORAGE****

STORE AWAY FROM INCOMPATIBLE SUBSTANCES.

CONDITIONS TO AVOID

MAY BURN BUT DOES NOT IGNITE READILY.

SPILL AND LEAK PROCEDURES

OCCUPATIONAL SPILL: DO NOT TOUCH SPILLED MATERIAL. STOP LEAK IF YOU CAN DO IT WITHOUT RISK. FOR SMALL SPILLS, TAKE UP WITH SAND OR OTHER ABSORBENT MATERIAL AND PLACE INTO CONTAINERS FOR LATER DISPOSAL. FOR SMALL DRY SPILLS, WITH A CLEAN SHOVEL PLACE MATERIAL INTO CLEAN, DRY CONTAINER AND COVER. MOVE CONTAINERS FROM SPILL AREA. FOR LARGER SPILLS, DIKE FAR AHEAD OF SPILL FOR LATER DISPOSAL. KEEP UNNECESSARY PEOPLE AWAY. ISOLATE HAZARD AREA AND DENY ENTRY.

PROTECTIVE EQUIPMENT

VENTILATION: PROVIDE LOCAL EXHAUST OR PROCESS ENCLOSURE VENTILATION SYSTEM.

RESPIRATOR: THE FOLLOWING RESPIRATORS ARE RECOMMENDED BASED ON INFORMATION FOUND IN THE PHYSICAL DATA, TOXICITY AND HEALTH EFFECTS SECTIONS. THEY ARE RANKED IN ORDER FROM MINIMUM TO MAXIMUM RESPIRATORY PROTECTION. THE SPECIFIC RESPIRATOR SELECTED MUST BE BASED ON CONTAMINATION LEVELS FOUND IN THE WORK PLACE, MUST NOT EXCEED THE WORKING LIMITS OF THE RESPIRATOR AND BE JOINTLY APPROVED BY THE NATIONAL INSTITUTE FOR OCCUPATIONAL SAFETY AND HEALTH AND THE MINE SAFETY AND HEALTH ADMINISTRATION (NIOSH-MSHA).

TYPE 'C' SUPPLIED-AIR RESPIRATOR WITH A FULL FACEPIECE OPERATED IN PRESSURE-DEMAND OR OTHER POSITIVE PRESSURE MODE OR WITH A FULL FACEPIECE, HELMET OR HOOD OPERATED IN CONTINOUS-FLOW MODE.

SELF-CONTAINED BREATHING APPARATUS WITH A FULL FACEPIECE OPERATED IN PRESSURE-DEMAND OR OTHER POSITIVE PRESSURE MODE.

FOR FIREFIGHTING AND OTHER IMMEDIATELY DANGEROUS TO LIFE OR HEALTH CONDITIONS:

SELF-CONTAINED BREATHING APPARATUS WITH FULL FACEPIECE OPERATED IN PRESSURE-DEMAND OR OTHER POSITIVE PRESSURE MODE.

SUPPLIED-AIR RESPIRATOR WITH FULL FACEPIECE AND OPERATED IN PRESSURE-DEMAND OR OTHER POSITIVE PRESSURE MODE IN COMBINATION WITH AN AUXILIARY SELF-CONTAINED BREATHING APPARATUS OPERATED IN PRESSURE-DEMAND OR OTHER POSITIVE PRESSURE MODE.

CLOTHING: EMPLOYEE MUST WEAR APPROPRIATE PROTECTIVE (IMPERVIOUS) CLOTHING AND EQUIPMENT TO PREVENT ANY POSSIBILITY OF SKIN CONTACT WITH THIS SUBSTANCE.

GLOVES: EMPLOYEE MUST WEAR APPROPRIATE PROTECTIVE GLOVES TO PREVENT CONTACT WITH THIS SUBSTANCE.

EYE PROTECTION: EMPLOYEE MUST WEAR SPLASH-PROOF OR DUST-RESISTANT SAFETY GOGGLES AND A FACESHIELD TO PREVENT CONTACT WITH THIS SUBSTANCE.

EMERGENCY WASH FACILITIES: WHERE THERE IS ANY POSSIBILITY THAT AN EMPLOYEE'S EYES AND/OR SKIN MAY BE EXPOSED TO THIS SUBSTANCE, THE EMPLOYER SHOULD PROVIDE AN EYE WASH FOUNTAIN AND QUICK DRENCH SHOWER WITHIN THE IMMEDIATE WORK AREA FOR EMERGENCY USE.

AUTHORIZED BY- OCCUPATIONAL HEALTH SERVICES, INC.

CREATION DATE: 02/02/90 ***REVISION DATE:*** 04/30/90

MATERIAL SAFETY DATA SHEET

OCCUPATIONAL HEALTH SERVICES, INC.
AGRICULTURE AND PESTICIDE DIVISION
450 SEVENTH AVENUE, SUITE 2407
NEW YORK, NEW YORK 10123
1-800-445-MSDS OR (212) 967-1100

EMERGENCY CONTACT:
JOHN S. BRANSFORD, JR. (615) 292-1180

SUBSTANCE IDENTIFICATION

CAS-NUMBER 21609-90-5

SUBSTANCE: LEPTOPHOS

TRADE NAMES/SYNONYMS: PHENYLPHOSPHONOTHIOIC ACID, O-(4-BROMO-2,5-DICHLOROPHENYL)O-METHYL ESTER; O-4-BROMO-2,5-DICHLOROPHENYL-O-METHYL PHENYLPHOSPHONOTHIOATE; (O-METHYL O-(4-BROMO-2,5-DICHLOROPHENYL) PHENYLPHOSPHONOTHIOATE; O-METHYL O-2,5-DICHLORO-4-BROMOPHENYL PHENYLTHIOPHOSPHONATE; ABAR; FOSVEL; K62-105; MBCP; NK 711; OLEOPHOSVEL; PHOSVEL; VCS 506; VELSICOL 506; PST12780

CHEMICAL FAMILY: PHOSPHONOTHIOATE
AROMATIC
HALOGEN

MOLECULAR FORMULA: C13-H10-BR-CL2-O2-P-S

MOLECULAR WEIGHT: 412.07

CERCLA RATINGS (SCALE 0-3): HEALTH=3 FIRE=U REACTIVITY=0 PERSISTENCE=3

NFPA RATINGS (SCALE 0-4): HEALTH=3 FIRE=U REACTIVITY=0

COMPONENTS AND CONTAMINANTS

COMPONENT: LEPTOPHOS ***PERCENT:*** 100.0
CAS# 21609-90-5

OTHER CONTAMINANTS: NONE

EXPOSURE LIMITS: NO OCCUPATIONAL EXPOSURE LIMITS ESTABLISHED BY OSHA, ACGIH, OR NIOSH.
LEPTOPHOS: 500/10,000 POUNDS SARA SECTION 302 THRESHOLD PLANNING QUANTITY 1 POUND SARA SECTION 304 REPORTABLE QUANTITY

PHYSICAL DATA

DESCRIPTION: WHITE CRYSTALLINE OR COLORLESS AMORPHOUS SOLID

MELTING POINT: 68 F (20 C) ***SPECIFIC GRAVITY:*** 1.53 @ 25 C

SOLUBILITY IN WATER: 0.03 PPM

SOLVENT SOLUBILITY: SOLUBLE IN BENZENE, XYLENE, CYCLOHEXANE, KETONES, AND AROMATIC HYDROCARBONS; SLIGHTLY SOLUBLE IN HEPTANE, ISOPROPANOL

FIRE AND EXPLOSION DATA

FIRE AND EXPLOSION HAZARD: UNKNOWN FIRE AND EXPLOSION HAZARD.

FIREFIGHTING MEDIA: DRY CHEMICAL, CARBON DIOXIDE, HALON, WATER SPRAY OR STANDARD FOAM (1987 EMERGENCY RESPONSE GUIDEBOOK, DOT P 5800.4).
FOR LARGER FIRES, USE WATER SPRAY, FOG OR STANDARD FOAM (1987 EMERGENCY RESPONSE GUIDEBOOK, DOT P 5800.4).

FIREFIGHTING: MOVE CONTAINERS FROM FIRE AREA IF POSSIBLE (1987 EMERGENCY RESPONSE GUIDEBOOK, DOT P 5800.4, GUIDE PAGE 53).
EXTINGUISH ONLY IF FLOW CAN BE STOPPED. EXTINGUISH USING AGENT INDICATED. USE FLOODING AMOUNTS OF WATER AS A FOG. COOL CONTAINERS WITH FLOODING AMOUNTS OF WATER FROM AS FAR A DISTANCE AS POSSIBLE. AVOID BREATHING POISONOUS VAPORS, KEEP UPWIND. CONSIDER EVACUATION OF DOWNWIND AREA IF MATERIAL IS LEAKING.

TRANSPORTATION DATA

DEPARTMENT OF TRANSPORTATION HAZARD CLASSIFICATION 49 CFR 172.101: POISON B

DEPARTMENT OF TRANSPORTATION LABELING REQUIREMENTS 49 CFR 172.101 AND SUBPART E: POISON

DEPARTMENT OF TRANSPORTATION PACKAGING REQUIREMENTS: 49 CFR 173.365

EXCEPTIONS: 49 CFR 173.364

TOXICITY

LEPTOPHOS: TOXICITY DATA: 800 MG/KG SKIN-RABBIT LD50; 44 MG/KG SKIN-RAT LD50; 50 MG/KG SKIN-MAMMAL LD50; 19 MG/KG ORAL-RAT LD50; 65 MG/KG ORAL-MOUSE LD50; 124 MG/KG ORAL-RABBIT LD50; 120 MG/KG SUBCUTANEOUS-MOUSE LD50; 135 MG/KG INTRAPERITONEAL-RAT LD50; MUTAGENIC DATA (RTECS); REPRODUCTIVE EFFECTS DATA (RTECS). CARCINOGEN STATUS: NONE. ACUTE TOXICITY LEVEL: HIGHLY TOXIC BY INGESTION; TOXIC BY DERMAL ABSORPTION. TARGET EFFECTS: CHOLINESTERASE INHIBITOR. NEUROTOXIN. AT INCREASED RISK FROM EXPOSURE: PERSONS WITH RESPIRATORY AILMENTS, RECENT EXPOSURE TO CHOLINESTERASE INHIBITORS OR IMPAIRED CHOLINESTERASE PRODUCTION, OR LIVER MALFUNCTION.* ADDITIONAL DATA: MAY CROSS THE PLACENTA. HIGH ENVIRONMENTAL TEMPERATURES OR EXPOSURE OF THE CHEMICAL TO VISIBLE OR ULTRAVIOLET LIGHT MAY ENHANCE THE TOXICITY. INTERACTIONS WITH MEDICATIONS MAY OCCUR.*

* MAY BE BASED ON GENERAL INFORMATION ON ORGANOPHOSPHATES.

HEALTH EFFECTS AND FIRST AID

INHALATION: LEPTOPHOS: NEUROTOXIN. LEPTOPHOS MAY CAUSE DELAYED NEUROPATHY PRODUCING PARTIAL PARALYSIS, INCOORDINATION, AND ATAXIA. THESE AND OTHER SYMPTOMS MAY APPEAR A WEEK OR MONTHS AFTER EXPOSURE AND MAY BE MISDIAGNOSED AS ENCEPHALITIS OR MULTIPLE SCLEROSIS. SEE INFORMATION ON ORGANOPHOSPHATES.
ORGANOPHOSPHATES: CHOLINESTERASE INHIBITOR. **ACUTE EXPOSURE-** WHEN INHALED, THE FIRST EFFECTS OF CHOLINESTERASE INHIBITORS ARE USUALLY RESPIRATORY AND MAY INCLUDE NASAL HYPEREMIA AND WATERY DISCHARGE, COUGH, CHEST DISCOMFORT, DYSPNEA, AND WHEEZING DUE TO INCREASED BRONCHIAL SECRETIONS AND BRONCHOCONSTRICTION. IF SUFFICIENT AMOUNTS ARE ABSORBED, OTHER SYSTEMIC EFFECTS MAY BEGIN WITHIN A FEW MINUTES OR BE DELAYED FOR UP TO 12 HOURS. SYMPTOMS MAY INCLUDE PALLOR, NAUSEA, VOMITING, DIARRHEA, ABDOMINAL CRAMPS, HEADACHE, DIZZINESS, OCULAR PAIN, BLURRED VISION, MIOSIS OR IN SOME CASES, ESPECIALLY INITIALLY, MYDRIASIS, LACRIMATION, SALIVATION, SWEATING, AND CONFUSION. OTHER REPORTED CENTRAL NERVOUS SYSTEM OR NEUROMUSCULAR EFFECTS MAY INCLUDE ATAXIA, SLURRED SPEECH, AREFLEXIA, WEAKNESS, FATIGUE, FASCICULATIONS, TWITCHING, TREMORS POSSIBLY OF THE TONGUE AND EYELIDS, AND EVENTUALLY PARALYSIS OF THE EXTREMITIES AND POSSIBLY OF THE RESPIRATORY MUSCLES. IN SEVERE CASES THERE MAY ALSO BE INVOLUNTARY DEFECATION AND URINATION, CYANOSIS, PSYCHOSIS, HYPERGLYCEMIA, ACUTE PANCREATITIS, CARDIAC IRREGULARITIES, PULMONARY EDEMA, UNCONSCIOUSNESS, CONVULSIONS, AND COMA. DEATH IS PRIMARILY DUE TO RESPIRATORY FAILURE, ALTHOUGH CARDIOVASCULAR EFFECTS INCLUDING CARDIAC ARREST MAY ALSO BE IMPLICATED. LONG TERM SEQUELAE ARE RARE BUT MAY INCLUDE NEUROPSYCHIATRIC DISORDERS AND MYOPATHY WITH MUSCLE TENDERNESS. SOME ORGANOPHOSPHATES MAY CAUSE A DELAYED NEUROPATHY BEGINNING 1-4 WEEKS AFTER AN ACUTE EXPOSURE WHICH MAY OR MAY NOT HAVE CAUSED ACUTE CHOLINERGIC EFFECTS. NUMBNESS, TINGLING, WEAKNESS AND CRAMPING BEGINNING SYMMETRICALLY IN THE LOWER LIMBS MAY PROGRESS TO ATAXIA AND PARALYSIS. IN SEVERE CASES, UPPER LIMB INVOLVEMENT IS POSSIBLE AND FLACCID PARALYSIS MAY PROGRESS TO SPASTIC PARALYSIS WITH EXAGGERATED REFLEXES. IMPROVEMENT MAY OCCUR OVER MONTHS TO YEARS, BUT SOME RESIDUAL IMPAIRMENT USUALLY REMAINS.
CHRONIC EXPOSURE- REPEATED OR PROLONGED EXPOSURE MAY RESULT IN THE EFFECTS OF ACUTE EXPOSURE INCLUDING THE DELAYED NEUROPATHY. OTHER EFFECTS REPORTED IN WORKERS REPEATEDLY EXPOSED INCLUDE IMPAIRED MEMORY AND CONCENTRATION, ACUTE PSYCHOSIS, SEVERE DEPRESSIONS, IRRITABILTY, CONFUSION, APATHY, EMOTIONAL LABILITY, SOCIAL WITHDRAWAL, CONFUSION, HEADACHE, SPEECH DIFFICULTIES, DELAYED REACTION TIMES, SPATIAL DISORIENTATION, NIGHTMARES, SLEEPWALKING, AND DROWSINESS OR INSOMNIA. AN INFLUENZA-LIKE CONDITION WITH HEADACHE, NAUSEA, WEAKNESS, ANOREXIA AND MALAISE HAS ALSO BEEN REPORTED.

FIRST AID- REMOVE FROM EXPOSURE AREA TO FRESH AIR IMMEDIATELY. IF BREATHING HAS STOPPED, GIVE ARTIFICIAL RESPIRATION. MAINTAIN AIRWAY AND BLOOD PRESSURE AND ADMINISTER OXYGEN IF AVAILABLE. KEEP AFFECTED PERSON WARM AND AT REST. TREAT SYMPTOMATICALLY AND SUPPORTIVELY. ADMINISTRATION OF OXYGEN SHOULD BE PERFORMED BY QUALIFIED PERSONNEL. GET MEDICAL ATTENTION IMMEDIATELY.

SKIN CONTACT: LEPTOPHOS: NEUROTOXIN/TOXIC. POLYNEUROPATHY WAS REPORTED AMONG SOME WORKERS INVOLVED IN THE MANUFACTURING OF LEPTOPHOS AND OTHER NEUROTOXIC CHEMICALS. DUE TO THE INVOLVEMENT OF OTHER CHEMICALS, THE NEUROLOGICAL EFFECTS COULD NOT SOLELY BE ATTRIBUTED TO LEPTOPHOS. SEE INFORMATION ON ORGANOPHOSPHATES.
ORGANOPHOSPHATES: CHOLINESTERASE INHIBITOR. **ACUTE EXPOSURE-** LOCALIZED SWEATING AND FASCICULATIONS MAY OCCUR AT THE SITE OF CONTACT. IF SUFFICIENT AMOUNTS ARE ABSORBED, OTHER EFFECTS OF CHOLINESTERASE INHIBITION AS DESCRIBED IN ACUTE INHALATION MAY OCCUR. SYMPTOMS MAY BE DELAYED 2-3 HOURS, BUT USUALLY NO MORE THAN 12 HOURS. THE RATE OF ABSORPTION IS INCREASED BY THE PRESENCE OF DERMATITIS OR HIGH AMBIENT TEMPERATURES. DELAYED NEUROPATHY IS ALSO POSSIBLE. **CHRONIC EXPOSURE-** REPEATED OR PROLONGED EXPOSURE MAY CAUSE EFFECTS AS DESCRIBED IN ACUTE EXPOSURE. SOME ORGANOPHOSPHATES MAY CAUSE SENSITIZATION.

FIRST AID- REMOVE CONTAMINATED CLOTHING IMMEDIATELY. WASH CONTAMINATED AREAS WITH SOAP AND WATER FOLLOWED BY ALCOHOL (ARENA, POISONING, 4TH ED.). EMERGENCY PERSONNEL SHOULD WEAR GLOVES AND AVOID CONTAMINATION. TREAT RESPIRATORY DIFFICULTY WITH ARTIFICIAL RESPIRATION. GET MEDICAL ATTENTION IMMEDIATELY.

EYE CONTACT: LEPTOPHOS: SEE INFORMATION ON ORGANOPHOSPHATES.
ORGANOPHOSPHATES: CHOLINESTERASE INHIBITOR. **ACUTE EXPOSURE-** DIRECT CONTACT MAY CAUSE PAIN, HYPEREMIA, LACRIMATION, TWITCHING OF THE EYELIDS, MIOSIS, AND CILIARY MUSCLE SPASM WITH LOSS OF ACCOMODATION, BLURRED OR DIMMED VISION AND BROWACHE. SOMETIMES MYDRIASIS MAY OCCUR INSTEAD OF MIOSIS. WITH SUFFICIENT EXPOSURE, OTHER SYMPTOMS OF CHOLINESTERASE INHIBITION AS DESCRIBED IN ACUTE INHALATION MAY OCCUR.
CHRONIC EXPOSURE- REPEATED OR PROLONGED EXPOSURE MAY CAUSE EFFECTS AS DESCRIBED IN ACUTE EXPOSURE. SOME COMPOUNDS HAVE CAUSED TOXIC EFFECTS ON THE CRYSTALLINE LENS, CONJUNCTIVAL THICKENING AND OBSTRUCTION OF THE NASOLACRIMAL CANALS WHEN USED AS MIOTIC EYEDROPS.

FIRST AID- IRRIGATE EYES WITH WATER OR SALINE SOLUTION. IF SYMPTOMS OF POISONING OCCUR, TREAT RESPIRATORY DIFFICULTY WITH ARTIFICIAL RESPIRATION AND OXYGEN. OBSERVE PATIENT FOR AT LEAST 24-36 HOURS (GOSSELIN, CLINICAL TOXICOLOGY OF COMMERCIAL PRODUCTS, 5TH ED.). GET MEDICAL ATTENTION IMMEDIATELY. OXYGEN SHOULD BE ADMINISTERED BY QUALIFIED MEDICAL PERSONNEL.

INGESTION: LEPTOPHOS: NEUROTOXIN/HIGHLY TOXIC. 5 MG/KG/DAY FOR 28 WEEKS WAS NEUROTOXIC TO HENS. CHRONIC ADMINISTRATION BY PREGNANT RATS RESULTED IN FETOTOXICITY. SEE INFORMATION ON ORGANOPHOSPHATES.
ORGANOPHOSPHATES: CHOLINESTERASE INHIBITOR. **ACUTE EXPOSURE-** WHEN INGESTED, THE FIRST EFFECTS MAY BE NAUSEA, VOMITING, ANOREXIA, ABDOMINAL CRAMPS AND DIARRHEA. GASTROINTESTINAL ABSORPTION MAY CAUSE SYMPTOMS OF CHOLINESTERASE INHIBITION AS DESCRIBED IN ACUTE INHALATION. SYMPTOMS MAY BEGIN WITHIN MINUTES OR BE DELAYED FOR HOURS. DELAYED EFFECTS INCLUDING NEUROPATHY MAY ALSO OCCUR. **CHRONIC EXPOSURE-** REPEATED INGESTION MAY CAUSE EFFECTS AS DESCRIBED IN ACUTE EXPOSURE.

FIRST AID- IF PERSON IS ALERT AND RESPIRATION IS NOT DEPRESSED, GIVE SYRUP OF IPECAC FOLLOWED BY WATER (IF VOMITING OCCURS, KEEP HEAD BELOW HIPS TO PREVENT ASPIRATION). IF CONSCIOUSNESS LEVEL DECLINES OR VOMITING HAS NOT OCCURRED IN 15 MINUTES EMPTY STOMACH BY GASTRIC LAVAGE WITH THE AID OF CUFFED ENDOTRACHEAL TUBE USING ISOTONIC SALINE OR 5% SODIUM BICARBONATE FOLLOW WITH ACTIVATED CHARCOAL. ESTABLISH AND MAINTAIN AIRWAY. TREAT RESPIRATORY DIFFICULTY WITH ARTIFICIAL RESPIRATION AND OXYGEN. DO NOT GIVE MORPHINE, AMINOPHYLLINE, PHENOTHIAZINES, RESERPINE, FUROSEMIDE, OR ETHACRYNIC ACID (MORGAN, RECOGNITION AND MANAGEMENT OF PESTICIDE POISONINGS, 3RD ED.). TREAT SYMPTOMATICALLY AND SUPPORTIVELY. ADMINISTRATION OF OXYGEN AND LAVAGE MUST BE PERFORMED BY QUALIFIED MEDICAL PERSONNEL. GET MEDICAL ATTENTION IMMEDIATELY.

ANTIDOTE: THE FOLLOWING ANTIDOTE(S) HAVE BEEN RECOMMENDED. HOWEVER, THE DECISION AS TO WHETHER THE SEVERITY OF POISONING REQUIRES ADMINISTRATION OF ANY ANTIDOTE AND ACTUAL DOSE REQUIRED SHOULD BE MADE BY QUALIFIED MEDICAL PERSONNEL.
FOR CHOLINESTERASE INHIBITORS: ESTABLISH CLEAR AIRWAY AND TISSUE OXYGENATION BY ASPIRATION OF SECRETIONS, AND IF NECESSARY, BY ASSISTED PULMONARY VENTILATION WITH OXYGEN. IMPROVE TISSUE OXYGENATION AS MUCH AS POSSIBLE BEFORE ADMINISTERING ATROPINE TO MINIMIZE THE RISK OF VENTRICULAR FIBRILLATION. ADMINISTER ATROPINE SULFATE INTRAVENOUSLY, OR INTRAMUSCULARLY IF IV INJECTION IS NOT POSSIBLE. IN MODERATELY SEVERE POISONING ADMINISTER ATROPINE SULFATE, 0.4-2.0 MG REPEATED EVERY 15 MINUTES UNTIL ATROPINIZATION IS ACHIEVED (TACHYCARDIA, FLUSHING, DRY MOUTH, MYDRIASIS). MAINTAIN ATROPINIZATION BY REPEATED DOSES FOR 2-12 HOURS, OR LONGER, DEPENDING ON THE SEVERITY OF POISONING. THE APPEARANCE OF RALES IN THE LUNG BASES, MIOSIS, SALIVATION, NAUSEA, BRADYCARDIA, ARE ALL INDICATIONS OF INADEQUATE ATROPINIZATION. SEVERELY POISONED INDIVIDUALS MAY EXHIBIT REMARKABLE TOLERANCE TO ATROPINE; TWO OR MORE TIMES THE DOSAGES SUGGESTED ABOVE MAY BE NEEDED. PERSONS NOT POISONED OR ONLY SLIGHTLY POISONED, HOWEVER, MAY DEVELOP SIGNS OF ATROPINE TOXICITY FROM SUCH LARGE DOSAGES: FEVER,

MUSCLE FIBRILLATIONS, AND DELIRIUM ARE THE MAIN SIGNS OF ATROPINE TOXICITY. IF THESE SIGNS APPEAR WHILE THE PATIENT IS FULLY ATROPINIZED, ATROPINE ADMINISTRATION SHOULD BE DISCONTINUED, AT LEAST TEMPORARILY. OBSERVE TREATED PATIENTS CLOSELY AT LEAST 24 HOURS TO INSURE THAT SYMPTOMS (POSSIBLY PULMONARY EDEMA) DO NOT RECUR AS ATROPINIZATION WEARS OFF. IN VERY SEVERE POISONINGS, METABOLIC DISPOSITION OF TOXICANT MAY REQUIRE SEVERAL HOURS OR DAYS DURING WHICH ATROPINIZATION MUST BE MAINTAINED. MARKEDLY LOWER LEVELS OF URINARY METABOLITES INDICATE THAT ATROPINE DOSAGE CAN BE TAPERED OFF. AS DOSAGE IS REDUCED, CHECK THE LUNG BASES FREQUENTLY FOR RALES. IF RALES ARE HEARD OR OTHER SYMPTOMS RETURN, RE-ESTABLISH ATROPINIZATION PROMPTLY (MORGAN, RECOGNITION AND MANAGEMENT OF PESTICIDE POISONINGS, 3RD ED.). ADMINISTRATION OF ANTIDOTE MUST BE PERFORMED BY QUALIFIED MEDICAL PERSONNEL.

IN CASES OF SEVERE POISONING BY ORGANOPHOSPHATE PESTICIDES IN WHICH RESPIRATORY DEPRESSION, MUSCLE WEAKNESS AND TWITCHINGS ARE SEVERE, GIVE PRALIDOXIME (PROTOPAM-AYERST, 2-PAM), 1.0 GRAM INTRAVENOUSLY AT NO MORE THAN 0.5 GRAM PER MINUTE. DOSAGE OF PRALIDOXIME MAY BE REPEATED IN 1-2 HOURS, THEN AT 10-12 HOUR INTERVALS IF NEEDED. IN VERY SEVERE POISONINGS, DOSAGE RATES MAY BE DOUBLED. TREATMENT WITH PRALIDOXIME WILL BE MOST EFFECTIVE IF GIVEN WITHIN THIRTY-SIX HOURS AFTER POISONING (MORGAN, RECOGNITION AND MANAGEMENT OF PESTICIDE POISONINGS, 3RD ED.). ANTIDOTE SHOULD BE ADMINISTERED BY QUALIFIED MEDICAL PERSONNEL.

REACTIVITY

REACTIVITY: STABLE UNDER NORMAL TEMPERATURES AND PRESSURES.

INCOMPATIBILITIES: LEPTOPHOS: STRONGLY ALKALINE CONDITIONS: MAY CAUSE HYDROLYSIS.

DECOMPOSITION: THERMAL DECOMPOSITION MAY EMIT TOXIC OXIDES OF SULFUR AND PHOSPHORUS, AND TOXIC FUMES OF CHLORINE AND BROMINE.

POLYMERIZATION: HAZARDOUS POLYMERIZATION HAS NOT BEEN REPORTED TO OCCUR UNDER NORMAL TEMPERATURES AND PRESSURES.

STORAGE AND DISPOSAL

OBSERVE ALL FEDERAL, STATE AND LOCAL REGULATIONS WHEN STORING OR DISPOSING OF THIS SUBSTANCE. FOR ASSISTANCE, CONTACT THE DISTRICT DIRECTOR OF THE ENVIRONMENTAL PROTECTION AGENCY.

STORAGE

STORE IN ACCORDANCE WITH 40 CFR 165 RECOMMENDED PROCEDURES FOR THE DISPOSAL AND STORAGE OF PESTICIDES AND PESTICIDE CONTAINERS.

STORE AWAY FROM INCOMPATIBLE SUBSTANCES.

THRESHOLD PLANNING QUANTITY (TPQ): THE SUPERFUND AMENDMENTS AND REAUTHORIZATION ACT (SARA) SECTION 302 REQUIRES THAT EACH FACILITY WHERE ANY EXTREMELY HAZARDOUS SUBSTANCE IS PRESENT IN A QUANTITY EQUAL TO OR GREATER THAN THE TPQ ESTABLISHED FOR THAT SUBSTANCE NOTIFY THE STATE EMERGENCY RESPONSE COMMISSION FOR THE STATE IN WHICH IT IS LOCATED. SECTION 303 OF SARA REQUIRES THESE FACILITIES TO PARTICIPATE IN LOCAL EMERGENCY RESPONSE PLANNING (40 CFR 355.30).

DISPOSAL

DISPOSAL MUST BE IN ACCORDANCE WITH 40 CFR 165 RECOMMENDED PROCEDURES FOR THE DISPOSAL AND STORAGE OF PESTICIDES AND PESTICIDE CONTAINERS.

CONDITIONS TO AVOID

NONE REPORTED.

SPILL AND LEAK PROCEDURES

OCCUPATIONAL SPILL: DO NOT TOUCH SPILLED MATERIAL. STOP LEAK IF YOU CAN DO IT WITHOUT RISK. FOR SMALL SPILLS, TAKE UP WITH SAND OR OTHER ABSORBENT MATERIAL AND PLACE INTO CONTAINERS FOR LATER DISPOSAL. FOR SMALL DRY SPILLS, WITH A CLEAN SHOVEL PLACE MATERIAL INTO CLEAN, DRY CONTAINER AND COVER. MOVE CONTAINERS FROM SPILL AREA. FOR LARGER SPILLS, DIKE FAR AHEAD OF SPILL FOR LATER DISPOSAL. KEEP UNNECESSARY PEOPLE AWAY. ISOLATE HAZARD AREA AND DENY ENTRY.

REPORTABLE QUANTITY (RQ): 1 POUND THE SUPERFUND AMENDMENTS AND REAUTHORIZATION ACT (SARA) SECTION 304 REQUIRES THAT A RELEASE EQUAL TO OR GREATER THAN THE REPORTABLE QUANTITY FOR THIS SUBSTANCE BE IMMEDIATELY REPORTED TO THE LOCAL EMERGENCY PLANNING COMMITTEE AND THE STATE EMERGENCY RESPONSE COMMISSION (40 CFR 355.40). IF THE RELEASE OF THIS SUBSTANCE IS REPORTABLE UNDER CERCLA SECTION 103, THE NATIONAL RESPONSE CENTER MUST BE NOTIFIED IMMEDIATELY AT (800) 424-8802 OR (202) 426-2675 IN THE METROPOLITAN WASHINGTON, D.C. AREA (40 CFR 302.6).

PROTECTIVE EQUIPMENT

VENTILATION: PROCESS ENCLOSURE RECOMMENDED.

RESPIRATOR: THE FOLLOWING RESPIRATORS ARE RECOMMENDED BASED ON INFORMATION FOUND IN THE PHYSICAL DATA, TOXICITY AND HEALTH EFFECTS SECTIONS. THEY ARE RANKED IN ORDER FROM MINIMUM TO MAXIMUM RESPIRATORY PROTECTION. THE SPECIFIC RESPIRATOR SELECTED MUST BE BASED ON CONTAMINATION LEVELS FOUND IN THE WORK PLACE, MUST NOT EXCEED THE WORKING LIMITS OF THE RESPIRATOR AND BE JOINTLY APPROVED BY THE NATIONAL INSTITUTE FOR OCCUPATIONAL SAFETY AND HEALTH AND THE MINE SAFETY AND HEALTH ADMINISTRATION (NIOSH-MSHA).

TYPE 'C' SUPPLIED-AIR RESPIRATOR WITH A FULL FACEPIECE OPERATED IN PRESSURE-DEMAND OR OTHER POSITIVE PRESSURE MODE OR WITH A FULL FACEPIECE, HELMET OR HOOD OPERATED IN CONTINOUS-FLOW MODE.

SELF-CONTAINED BREATHING APPARATUS WITH A FULL FACEPIECE OPERATED IN PRESSURE-DEMAND OR OTHER POSITIVE PRESSURE MODE.

FOR FIREFIGHTING AND OTHER IMMEDIATELY DANGEROUS TO LIFE OR HEALTH CONDITIONS:

SELF-CONTAINED BREATHING APPARATUS WITH FULL FACEPIECE OPERATED IN PRESSURE-DEMAND OR OTHER POSITIVE PRESSURE MODE.

SUPPLIED-AIR RESPIRATOR WITH FULL FACEPIECE AND OPERATED IN PRESSURE-DEMAND OR OTHER POSITIVE PRESSURE MODE IN COMBINATION WITH AN AUXILIARY SELF-CONTAINED BREATHING APPARATUS OPERATED IN PRESSURE-DEMAND OR OTHER POSITIVE PRESSURE MODE.

CLOTHING: EMPLOYEE MUST WEAR APPROPRIATE PROTECTIVE (IMPERVIOUS) CLOTHING AND EQUIPMENT TO PREVENT ANY POSSIBILITY OF SKIN CONTACT WITH THIS SUBSTANCE.

GLOVES: EMPLOYEE MUST WEAR APPROPRIATE PROTECTIVE GLOVES TO PREVENT CONTACT WITH THIS SUBSTANCE.

EYE PROTECTION: EMPLOYEE MUST WEAR SPLASH-PROOF OR DUST-RESISTANT SAFETY GOGGLES AND A FACESHIELD TO PREVENT CONTACT WITH THIS SUBSTANCE.

EMERGENCY WASH FACILITIES: WHERE THERE IS ANY POSSIBILITY THAT AN EMPLOYEE'S EYES AND/OR SKIN MAY BE EXPOSED TO THIS SUBSTANCE, THE EMPLOYER SHOULD PROVIDE AN EYE WASH FOUNTAIN AND QUICK DRENCH SHOWER WITHIN THE IMMEDIATE WORK AREA FOR EMERGENCY USE.

AUTHORIZED BY- OCCUPATIONAL HEALTH SERVICES, INC.

CREATION DATE: 10/04/89 ***REVISION DATE:*** 05/15/90

MATERIAL SAFETY DATA SHEET

OCCUPATIONAL HEALTH SERVICES, INC.
AGRICULTURE AND PESTICIDE DIVISION
450 SEVENTH AVENUE, SUITE 2407
NEW YORK, NEW YORK 10123
1-800-445-MSDS OR (212) 967-1100

EMERGENCY CONTACT:
JOHN S. BRANSFORD, JR. (615) 292-1180

SUBSTANCE IDENTIFICATION

CAS-NUMBER 58-89-9

SUBSTANCE: **LINDANE**

TRADE NAMES/SYNONYMS: CYCLOHEXANE, 1,2,3,4,5,6-HEXACHLORO-, (1ALPHA,2ALPHA,3BETA,4ALPHA, 5ALPHA,6BETA)-; (1ALPHA,2ALPHA,3BETA,4ALPHA,5ALPHA,6BETA)-1,2,3,4,5,6-HEXACHLOROCYCLOHEXANE; 1,2,3,4,5,6-HEXACHLOROCYCLOHEXANE; GAMMA-1,2,3,4,5,6-HEXACHLOROCYCLOHEXANE; BENZENE HEXACHLORIDE; GAMMA-BENZENE HEXACHLORIDE; GAMMA-HEXACHLOROBENZENE; HEXACHLOROCYCLOHEXANE; GAMMA-HEXACHLOROCYCLOHEXANE; GAMMA-BHC; HCH; GAMMA-HCH; NCI-C00204; OMS 17; ENT 7,796; RCRA U129; STCC 4941152; C6H6CL6; PST12810

CHEMICAL FAMILY: HALOGEN COMPOUND, ALICYCLIC

MOLECULAR FORMULA: C6-H6-CL6

MOLECULAR WEIGHT: 290.83

CERCLA RATINGS (SCALE 0-3): HEALTH=3 FIRE=0 REACTIVITY=0 PERSISTENCE=3

NFPA RATINGS (SCALE 0-4): HEALTH=2 FIRE=0 REACTIVITY=0

COMPONENTS AND CONTAMINANTS

COMPONENT: LINDANE ***PERCENT:*** 100.0
CAS# 58-89-9

OTHER CONTAMINANTS: NONE

EXPOSURE LIMITS: LINDANE: 0.5 MG/M3 OSHA TWA (SKIN) 0.5 MG/M3 ACGIH TWA (SKIN)
1000/10,000 POUNDS SARA SECTION 302 THRESHOLD PLANNING QUANTITY 1 POUND SARA SECTION 304 REPORTABLE QUANTITY 1 POUND CERCLA SECTION 103 REPORTABLE QUANTITY SUBJECT TO SARA SECTION 313 ANNUAL TOXIC CHEMICAL RELEASE REPORTING SUBJECT TO CALIFORNIA PROPOSITION 65 CANCER AND/OR REPRODUCTIVE TOXICITY WARNING AND RELEASE REQUIREMENTS- (OCTOBER 1, 1989)

PHYSICAL DATA

DESCRIPTION: ODORLESS, OR WITH SLIGHT MUSTY ODOR, WHITE OR YELLOWISH CRYSTALS, POWDER, OR FLAKES. ***BOILING POINT:*** 613 F (323 C)
MELTING POINT: 233-235 F (112-113 C) ***SPECIFIC GRAVITY:*** 1.89
VAPOR PRESSURE: 0.03 MMHG @ 20 C ***SOLUBILITY IN WATER:*** 10 PPM @ 20 C
SOLVENT SOLUBILITY: SOLUBLE IN ACETONE, BENZENE, CHLOROFORM, CYCLOHEXANONE, ETHER, XYLENE, FATS, OILS; MODERATELY SOLUBLE IN ETHANOL, METHANOL, AND KEROSENE.

FIRE AND EXPLOSION DATA

FIRE AND EXPLOSION HAZARD: NEGLIGIBLE FIRE HAZARD WHEN EXPOSED TO HEAT OR FLAME.
FIREFIGHTING MEDIA: DRY CHEMICAL, CARBON DIOXIDE, HALON, WATER SPRAY OR STANDARD FOAM (1987 EMERGENCY RESPONSE GUIDEBOOK, DOT P 5800.4).
FOR LARGER FIRES, USE WATER SPRAY, FOG OR STANDARD FOAM (1987 EMERGENCY RESPONSE GUIDEBOOK, DOT P 5800.4).
FIREFIGHTING: MOVE CONTAINERS FROM FIRE AREA IF POSSIBLE. FIGHT FIRE FROM MAXIMUM DISTANCE. STAY AWAY FROM STORAGE TANK ENDS. DIKE FIRE CONTROL WATER FOR LATER DISPOSAL. DO NOT SCATTER MATERIAL (1987 EMERGENCY RESPONSE GUIDEBOOK, DOT P 5800.4, GUIDE PAGE 55).
USE AGENTS SUITABLE FOR TYPE OF FIRE. COOL CONTAINERS WITH FLOODING AMOUNTS OF WATER. AVOID BREATHING VAPORS OR DUSTS, KEEP UPWIND.

TRANSPORTATION DATA

DEPARTMENT OF TRANSPORTATION HAZARD CLASSIFICATION 49 CFR 172.101: ORM-A
DEPARTMENT OF TRANSPORTATION LABELING REQUIREMENTS 49 CFR 172.101 AND SUBPART E: NONE
DEPARTMENT OF TRANSPORTATION PACKAGING REQUIREMENTS: 49 CFR 173.510 EXCEPTIONS: 49 CFR 173.505

TOXICITY

LINDANE: TOXICITY DATA: 20 MG/KG/6 WEEKS-INTERMITTENT SKIN-MAN TDLO; 50 MG/KG SKIN-RABBIT LD50; 500 MG/KG SKIN-RAT LD50; 111 MG/KG ORAL-CHILD TDLO; 180 MG/KG ORAL-CHILD TDLO; 76 MG/KG ORAL-RAT LD50; 44 MG/KG ORAL-MOUSE LD50; 60 MG/KG ORAL-RABBIT LD50; 127 MG/KG ORAL-GUINEA PIG LD50; 40 MG/KG ORAL-DOG LD50; 360 MG/KG ORAL-HAMSTER LD50; 25 MG/KG ORAL-CAT LD50; 4500 UG/KG INTRAVENOUS-RABBIT LDLO; 8 MG/KG INTRAVENOUS-DOG LDLO; 35 MG/KG INTRAPERITONEAL-RAT LD50; 125 MG/KG INTRAPERITONEAL-MOUSE LD50; 640 MG/KG INTRAPERITONEAL-HAMSTER LD50; MUTAGENIC DATA (RTECS); REPRODUCTIVE EFFECTS DATA (RTECS); TUMORIGENIC DATA (RTECS).
CARCINOGEN STATUS: ANTICIPATED HUMAN CARCINOGEN (NTP); HUMAN INADEQUATE EVIDENCE, ANIMAL LIMITED EVIDENCE (IARC GROUP-2B). LINDANE PRODUCED BENIGN AND MALIGNANT LIVER TUMORS IN MICE AFTER ORAL ADMINISTRATION. LOCAL EFFECTS: IRRITANT- EYE, SKIN, MUCOUS MEMBRANES.
ACUTE TOXICITY LEVEL: HIGHLY TOXIC BY DERMAL ABSORPTION; TOXIC BY INGESTION. TARGET EFFECTS: CONVULSANT. POISONING MAY AFFECT THE BLOOD, LIVER, AND KIDNEYS. AT INCREASED RISK FROM EXPOSURE: PERSONS WITH KIDNEY, LIVER AND BLOOD DISEASES. ADDITIONAL DATA: LINDANE MAY BE EXCRETED IN THE MILK OF LACTATING WOMEN. STIMULANTS SUCH AS EPINEPHRINE MAY INDUCE VENTRICULAR FIBRILLATION.

HEALTH EFFECTS AND FIRST AID

INHALATION: LINDANE: IRRITANT/CONVULSANT. 1000 MG/M3 IMMEDIATELY DANGEROUS TO LIFE OR HEALTH. **ACUTE EXPOSURE-** THE VAPORS MAY CAUSE IRRITATION OF THE NOSE, THROAT, AND MUCOUS MEMBRANES. LINDANE MAY BE ABSORBED FROM THE LUNGS AND PRODUCE CENTRAL NERVOUS SYSTEM EFFECTS WITH SYMPTOMS OF MOTOR HYPEREXCITABILITY THAT MAY INCLUDE MUSCLE TWITCHING, MYOCLONIC JERKING, AND CONVULSIVE SEIZURES. THE CONVULSIONS MAY OCCUR WITH PERIODS OF UNCONSCIOUSNESS. OTHER SYMPTOMS MAY INCLUDE HEADACHE, NAUSEA, VOMITING, MALAISE, AND DIZZINESS. IN CASES OF GROSS OVEREXPOSURE, CONVULSIONS MAY OCCUR WITHOUT ANY PRIOR SYMPTOMS. ABNORMAL EEG PATTERNS MAY BE OBSERVED; THESE CHANGES IN EEG PATTERNS MAY PERSIST FOR WEEKS OR MONTHS WHILE NO OTHER OBSERVABLE SIGNS OF POISONING MAY EXIST. **CHRONIC EXPOSURE-** PROLONGED OR REPEATED EXPOSURE MAY CAUSE SYMPTOMS AS DESCRIBED IN ACUTE EXPOSURE. SYMPTOMS OF DEPRESSION, HEADACHE, VOMITING, ASTHENIA, EPILEPTIFORM ATTACKS, SLEEPLESSNESS, PROFUSE PERSPIRATION, VARIOUS ABNORMAL REFLEXES AND NEUROLOGICAL SIGNS WERE REPORTED IN ONE CASE OF OCCUPATIONAL EXPOSURE. SEVERAL INCIDENCES OF DIMINUTION OF VISION AND AND BLINDNESS HAVE ALSO BEEN OBSERVED. REPORTS SUGGEST THAT LINDANE IS CAPABLE OF CAUSING BLOOD DYSCRASIAS, PRIMARILY APLASTIC ANEMIA; HOWEVER, THESE REPORTS HAVE NOT BEEN CONFIRMED. CIRRHOSIS AND CHRONIC HEPATITIS WERE OBSERVED IN LIVER BIOPSIES FROM 8 WORKERS HEAVILY EXPOSED TO LINDANE, DDT, OR BOTH FOR 5-13 YEARS.
FIRST AID- REMOVE FROM EXPOSURE AREA TO FRESH AIR IMMEDIATELY. IF BREATHING HAS STOPPED, PERFORM ARTIFICIAL RESPIRATION. KEEP PERSON WARM AND AT REST. TREAT SYMPTOMATICALLY AND SUPPORTIVELY. GET MEDICAL ATTENTION IMMEDIATELY.

SKIN CONTACT: LINDANE: IRRITANT/CONVULSANT/HIGHLY TOXIC. **ACUTE EXPOSURE-** MAY CAUSE IRRITATION. A LETHAL DOSE IN RABBITS BY DERMAL ABSORPTION WAS 50 MG/KG. LINDANE MAY BE ABSORBED THROUGH THE SKIN AND PRODUCE CENTRAL NERVOUS SYSTEM EFFECTS WITH SYMPTOMS OF MOTOR HYPEREXCITABILITY THAT MAY INCLUDE MUSCLE TWITCHING, MYOCLONIC JERKING, AND CONVULSIVE SEIZURES. THE CONVULSIONS MAY OCCUR WITH PERIODS OF UNCONSCIOUSNESS. OTHER SYMPTOMS MAY INCLUDE HEADACHE, NAUSEA, VOMITING, MALAISE, AND DIZZINESS. IN CASES OF GROSS OVEREXPOSURE, CONVULSIONS MAY OCCUR WITHOUT ANY PRIOR SYMPTOMS. ABNORMAL EEG PATTERNS MAY BE OBSERVED, THESE CHANGES IN EEG PATTERNS MAY PERSIST FOR WEEKS OR MONTHS WHILE NO OTHER OBSERVABLE SIGNS OF POISONING MAY EXIST. **CHRONIC EXPOSURE-** PROLONGED OR REPEATED EXPOSURE MAY CAUSE DERMATITIS AND URTICARIA. OTHER SYSTEMIC EFFECTS MAY OCCUR AS DETAILED IN ACUTE EXPOSURE AND CHRONIC INHALATION.
FIRST AID- REMOVE CONTAMINATED CLOTHING AND SHOES IMMEDIATELY. WASH AFFECTED AREA WITH SOAP OR MILD DETERGENT AND LARGE AMOUNTS OF WATER UNTIL NO EVIDENCE OF CHEMICAL REMAINS (APPROXIMATELY 15-20 MINUTES). GET MEDICAL ATTENTION IMMEDIATELY.

EYE CONTACT: LINDANE: IRRITANT. **ACUTE EXPOSURE-** MAY CAUSE IRRITATION. **CHRONIC EXPOSURE-** PROLONGED OR REPEATED EXPOSURE MAY CAUSE CONJUNCTIVITIS.
FIRST AID- WASH EYES IMMEDIATELY WITH LARGE AMOUNTS OF WATER OR NORMAL SALINE, OCCASIONALLY LIFTING UPPER AND LOWER LIDS, UNTIL NO EVIDENCE OF CHEMICAL REMAINS (APPROXIMATELY 15-20 MINUTES). GET MEDICAL ATTENTION IMMEDIATELY.

INGESTION: LINDANE: CONVULSANT/CARCINOGEN/TOXIC. **ACUTE EXPOSURE-** A LETHAL DOSE IN RATS WAS 76 MG/KG. SYMPTOMS OF MALAISE, FAINTNESS, DIZZINESS, NAUSEA, VOMITING, MUSCLE SPASMS, ATAXIA, RESTLESSNESS, TREMOR, CYANOSIS, AND FACIAL PALLOR WERE REPORTED IN CASES OF ACCIDENTAL POISONING. CLONIC AND TONIC CONVULSIONS ALONG WITH UNCONSCIOUSNESS WERE ALSO CHARACTERISTIC SYMPTOMS OF POISONING. POSTICAL COMA OF VARIABLE DURATION LEADING TO RESPIRATORY FAILURE OCCURRED IN FATAL CASES. IN SOME CASES, RETROGRADE AMNESIA WAS REPORTED. **CHRONIC EXPOSURE-** DISTURBANCES OF THE ESTROUS CYCLE, DECREASED FERTILITY, AND LOWERED EMBRYO VIABILITY WITH DELAYED PHYSICAL DEVELOPMENT WAS REPORTED IN A STUDY OF FEMALE RATS FED DAILY DOSES OF 0.5 MG/KG FOR FOUR MONTHS. AN INCREASE INCIDENCE OF STILLBORN PUPS WAS OBSERVED IN LITTERS OF FEMALE BEAGLES FED LINDANE DURING PREGNANCY. REPEATED FEEDING TO RATS OF 800 PPM IN THE DIET RESULTED IN MILD LIVER DAMAGE; KIDNEY DAMAGE OCCURRED AT HIGHER LEVELS. MICE FED 400 PPM IN THE DIET DEVELOPED LIVER TUMORS AND, IN SOME CASES, LUNG METASTASES.
FIRST AID- IF THE PERSON IS CONSCIOUS AND NOT CONVULSING, REMOVE BY GIVING SYRUP OF IPECAC (IF VOMITING OCCURS, KEEP THE HEAD BELOW THE HIPS TO PREVENT ASPIRATION). GIVE ACTIVATED CHARCOAL FOLLOWED BY GASTRIC LAVAGE. FOLLOW WITH A SALINE CATHARTIC. DO NOT GIVE FATS OR OILS. INTESTINAL LAVAGE WITH 20% MANNITOL (200 ML) BY STOMACH TUBE IS ALSO USEFUL. GIVE ARTIFICIAL RESPIRATION WITH OXYGEN IF RESPIRATION IS DEPRESSED (DREISBACH, HANDBOOK OF POISONING, 12TH ED.). TREAT SYMPTOMATICALLY AND SUPPORTIVELY. LAVAGE AND ADMINISTRATION OF OXYGEN SHOULD BE PERFORMED BY QUALIFIED MEDICAL PERSONNEL. GET MEDICAL ATTENTION IMMEDIATELY.

REACTIVITY

REACTIVITY: STABLE UNDER NORMAL TEMPERATURES AND PRESSURES.
INCOMPATIBILITIES: LINDANE: ALKALI: MAY DECOMPOSE. ALUMINUM: MAY DECOMPOSE. N,N-DIMETHYLACETAMIDE: EXOTHERMIC, POSSIBLE VIOLENT REACTION. DIMETHYLFORMAMIDE + IRON: POSSIBLE DANGEROUS REACTION. IRON: MAY DECOMPOSE. ZINC: MAY DECOMPOSE.

DECOMPOSITION: THERMAL DECOMPOSITION PRODUCTS MAY INCLUDE HIGHLY TOXIC FUMES OF PHOSGENE, TOXIC AND CORROSIVE FUMES OF CHLORIDES, AND OXIDES OF CARBON.

POLYMERIZATION: HAZARDOUS POLYMERIZATION HAS NOT BEEN REPORTED TO OCCUR UNDER NORMAL TEMPERATURES AND PRESSURES.

STORAGE AND DISPOSAL

OBSERVE ALL FEDERAL, STATE AND LOCAL REGULATIONS WHEN STORING OR DISPOSING OF THIS SUBSTANCE. FOR ASSISTANCE, CONTACT THE DISTRICT DIRECTOR OF THE ENVIRONMENTAL PROTECTION AGENCY.

STORAGE

STORE IN ACCORDANCE WITH 40 CFR 165 RECOMMENDED PROCEDURES FOR THE DISPOSAL AND STORAGE OF PESTICIDES AND PESTICIDE CONTAINERS.

PROTECT AGAINST PHYSICAL DAMAGE. STORE IN A COOL, DRY, WELL-VENTILATED LOCATION, AWAY FROM ANY AREA WHERE THE FIRE HAZARD MAY BE ACUTE. OUTSIDE OR DETACHED STORAGE IS PREFERRED. SEPARATE FROM OTHER STORAGE. (NFPA 49, HAZARDOUS CHEMICALS DATA, 1975).

STORE AWAY FROM INCOMPATIBLE SUBSTANCES.

THRESHOLD PLANNING QUANTITY (TPQ): THE SUPERFUND AMENDMENTS AND REAUTHORIZATION ACT (SARA) SECTION 302 REQUIRES THAT EACH FACILITY WHERE ANY EXTREMELY HAZARDOUS SUBSTANCE IS PRESENT IN A QUANTITY EQUAL TO OR GREATER THAN THE TPQ ESTABLISHED FOR THAT SUBSTANCE NOTIFY THE STATE EMERGENCY RESPONSE COMMISSION FOR THE STATE IN WHICH IT IS LOCATED. SECTION 303 OF SARA REQUIRES THESE FACILITIES TO PARTICIPATE IN LOCAL EMERGENCY RESPONSE PLANNING (40 CFR 355.30).

DISPOSAL

DISPOSAL MUST BE IN ACCORDANCE WITH STANDARDS APPLICABLE TO GENERATORS OF HAZARDOUS WASTE, 40CFR 262. EPA HAZARDOUS WASTE NUMBER U129.

CONDITIONS TO AVOID

MAY BURN BUT DOES NOT IGNITE READILY. CONTAINERS MAY EXPLODE IN HEAT OF FIRE.

SPILL AND LEAK PROCEDURES

SOIL SPILL: DIG HOLDING AREA SUCH AS LAGOON, POND OR PIT FOR CONTAINMENT. USE PROTECTIVE COVER SUCH AS A PLASTIC SHEET TO PREVENT MATERIAL FROM DISSOLVING IN FIRE EXTINGUISHING WATER OR RAIN.

WATER SPILL: TRAP SPILLED MATERIAL AT BOTTOM IN DEEP WATER POCKETS, EXCAVATED HOLDING AREAS OR WITHIN SAND BAG BARRIERS.

USE SUCTION HOSES TO REMOVE TRAPPED SPILL MATERIAL.

USE MECHANICAL DREDGES OR LIFTS TO EXTRACT IMMOBILIZED MASSES OF POLLUTION AND PRECIPITATES.

USE ACTIVATED CARBON TO ABSORB SPILLED SUBSTANCE THAT IS DISSOLVED.

THE CALIFORNIA SAFE DRINKING WATER AND TOXIC ENFORCEMENT ACT OF 1986 (PROPOSITION 65) PROHIBITS CONTAMINATING ANY KNOWN SOURCE OF DRINKING WATER WITH SUBSTANCES KNOWN TO CAUSE CANCER AND/OR REPRODUCTIVE TOXICITY.

OCCUPATIONAL SPILL: DO NOT TOUCH SPILLED MATERIAL. STOP LEAK IF YOU CAN DO IT WITHOUT RISK. USE WATER SPRAY TO REDUCE VAPORS. FOR SMALL SPILLS, TAKE UP WITH SAND OR OTHER ABSORBENT MATERIAL AND PLACE INTO CONTAINERS FOR LATER DISPOSAL. FOR SMALL DRY SPILLS, WITH A CLEAN SHOVEL PLACE MATERIAL INTO CLEAN, DRY CONTAINERS AND COVER. MOVE CONTAINERS FROM SPILL AREA. FOR LARGER SPILLS, DIKE FAR AHEAD OF SPILL FOR LATER DISPOSAL. KEEP UNNECESSARY PEOPLE AWAY. ISOLATE HAZARD AREA AND DENY ENTRY. VENTILATE CLOSED SPACES BEFORE ENTERING.

REPORTABLE QUANTITY (RQ): 1 POUND THE SUPERFUND AMENDMENTS AND REAUTHORIZATION ACT (SARA) SECTION 304 REQUIRES THAT A RELEASE EQUAL TO OR GREATER THAN THE REPORTABLE QUANTITY FOR THIS SUBSTANCE BE IMMEDIATELY REPORTED TO THE LOCAL EMERGENCY PLANNING COMMITTEE AND THE STATE EMERGENCY RESPONSE COMMISSION (40 CFR 355.40). IF THE RELEASE OF THIS SUBSTANCE IS REPORTABLE UNDER CERCLA SECTION 103, THE NATIONAL RESPONSE CENTER MUST BE NOTIFIED IMMEDIATELY AT (800) 424-8802 OR (202) 426-2675 IN THE METROPOLITAN WASHINGTON, D.C. AREA (40 CFR 302.6).

PROTECTIVE EQUIPMENT

VENTILATION: PROCESS ENCLOSURE RECOMMENDED TO MEET PUBLISHED EXPOSURE LIMITS.

RESPIRATOR: THE FOLLOWING RESPIRATORS AND MAXIMUM USE CONCENTRATIONS ARE RECOMMENDATIONS BY THE U.S. DEPARTMENT OF HEALTH AND HUMAN SERVICES, NIOSH POCKET GUIDE TO CHEMICAL HAZARDS; NIOSH CRITERIA DOCUMENTS OR BY THE U.S. DEPARTMENT OF LABOR, 29 CFR 1910 SUBPART Z. THE SPECIFIC RESPIRATOR SELECTED MUST BE BASED ON CONTAMINATION LEVELS FOUND IN THE WORK PLACE, MUST NOT EXCEED THE WORKING LIMITS OF THE RESPIRATOR AND BE JOINTLY APPROVED BY THE NATIONAL INSTITUTE FOR OCCUPATIONAL SAFETY AND HEALTH AND THE MINE SAFETY AND HEALTH ADMINISTRATION (NIOSH-MSHA).

LINDANE:

5 MG/M3- ANY CHEMICAL CARTRIDGE RESPIRATOR WITH ORGANIC VAPOR CARTRIDGE(S) IN COMBINATION WITH A DUST, MIST, AND FUME FILTER. ANY SUPPLIED-AIR RESPIRATOR. ANY SELF-CONTAINED BREATHING APPARATUS.

12.5 MG/M3- ANY POWERED AIR-PURIFYING RESPIRATOR WITH ORGANIC VAPOR CARTRIDGE(S) IN COMBINATION WITH A DUST, MIST, AND FUME FILTER. ANY SUPPLIED-AIR RESPIRATOR OPERATED IN A CONTINOUS FLOW MODE.

25 MG/M3- ANY CHEMICAL CARTRIDGE RESPIRATOR WITH A FULL FACEPIECE AND ORGANIC VAPOR CARTRIDGE(S) IN COMBINATION WITH A HIGH-EFFICIENCY PARTICULATE FILTER. ANY SELF-CONTAINED BREATHING APPARATUS WITH A FULL FACEPIECE. ANY SUPPLIED-AIR RESPIRATOR WITH A FULL FACEPIECE. ANY AIR-PURIFYING FULL FACEPIECE RESPIRATOR (GAS MASK) WITH A CHIN-STYLE OR FRONT- OR BACK-MOUNTED ORGANIC VAPOR CANISTER HAVING A HIGH-EFFICIENCY PARTICULATE FILTER. ANY POWERED AIR-PURIFYING RESPIRATOR WITH A TIGHT-FITTING FACEPIECE AND ORGANIC VAPOR CARTRIDGE(S) IN COMBINATION WITH A HIGH-EFFICIENCY PARTICULATE FILTER.

500 MG/M3- ANY SUPPLIED-AIR RESPIRATOR WITH A HALF-MASK AND OPERATED IN A PRESSURE-DEMAND OR OTHER POSITIVE PRESSURE MODE.

1000 MG/M3- ANY SUPPLIED-AIR RESPIRATOR WITH A FULL FACEPIECE AND OPERATED IN A PRESSURE-DEMAND OR OTHER POSITIVE PRESSURE MODE.

ESCAPE- ANY AIR-PURIFYING FULL FACEPIECE RESPIRATOR (GAS MASK) WITH A CHIN-STYLE OR FRONT- OR BACK-MOUNTED ORGANIC VAPOR CANISTER HAVING A HIGH-EFFICIENCY PARTICULATE FILTER. ANY APPROPRIATE ESCAPE-TYPE SELF-CONTAINED BREATHING APPARATUS.

FOR FIREFIGHTING AND OTHER IMMEDIATELY DANGEROUS TO LIFE OR HEALTH CONDITIONS:

SELF-CONTAINED BREATHING APPARATUS WITH FULL FACEPIECE OPERATED IN PRESSURE-DEMAND OR OTHER POSITIVE PRESSURE MODE.

SUPPLIED-AIR RESPIRATOR WITH FULL FACEPIECE AND OPERATED IN PRESSURE-DEMAND OR OTHER POSITIVE PRESSURE MODE IN COMBINATION WITH AN AUXILIARY SELF-CONTAINED BREATHING APPARATUS OPERATED IN PRESSURE-DEMAND OR OTHER POSITIVE PRESSURE MODE.

CLOTHING: EMPLOYEE MUST WEAR APPROPRIATE PROTECTIVE (IMPERVIOUS) CLOTHING AND EQUIPMENT TO PREVENT ANY POSSIBILITY OF SKIN CONTACT WITH THIS SUBSTANCE.

GLOVES: EMPLOYEE MUST WEAR APPROPRIATE PROTECTIVE GLOVES TO PREVENT CONTACT WITH THIS SUBSTANCE.

EYE PROTECTION: EMPLOYEE MUST WEAR SPLASH-PROOF OR DUST-RESISTANT SAFETY GOGGLES AND A FACESHIELD TO PREVENT CONTACT WITH THIS SUBSTANCE.

EMERGENCY WASH FACILITIES: WHERE THERE IS ANY POSSIBILITY THAT AN EMPLOYEE'S EYES AND/OR SKIN MAY BE EXPOSED TO THIS SUBSTANCE, THE EMPLOYER SHOULD PROVIDE AN EYE WASH FOUNTAIN AND QUICK DRENCH SHOWER WITHIN THE IMMEDIATE WORK AREA FOR EMERGENCY USE.

AUTHORIZED BY- OCCUPATIONAL HEALTH SERVICES, INC.

CREATION DATE: 10/04/89 ***REVISION DATE:*** 07/12/90

MATERIAL SAFETY DATA SHEET

OCCUPATIONAL HEALTH SERVICES, INC.
AGRICULTURE AND PESTICIDE DIVISION
450 SEVENTH AVENUE, SUITE 2407
NEW YORK, NEW YORK 10123
1-800-445-MSDS OR (212) 967-1100

EMERGENCY CONTACT:
JOHN S. BRANSFORD, JR. (615) 292-1180

SUBSTANCE IDENTIFICATION

CAS-NUMBER 330-55-2

SUBSTANCE: LINURON

TRADE NAMES/SYNONYMS: UREA, N'-(3,4-DICHLOROPHENYL)-N-METHOXY-N-METHYL-; UREA, 3-(3,4-DICHLOROPHENYL)-1-METHOXY-1-METHYL-; N'-(3,4-DICHLOROPHENYL)-N-METHOXY-N-METHYLUREA; 3-(3,4-DICHLOROPHENYL)-1-METHOXY-1-METHYLUREA; AFALON; APHALON; CEPHALON; DU PONT 326; DUPONT HERBICIDE 326; HERBICIDE 326; LINUREX; LOREX; LOROX; METHOXYDIURON; PREMALON; SARCLEX; SINURON; C9H10CL2N2O2; PST12826

CHEMICAL FAMILY: SUBSTITUTED UREA
HALOGEN COMPOUND, AROMATIC

MOLECULAR FORMULA: CL2-C6-H3-N-H-C-O-N-(C-H3)-O-C-H3

MOLECULAR WEIGHT: 249.11

CERCLA RATINGS (SCALE 0-3): HEALTH=2 FIRE=1 REACTIVITY=0 PERSISTENCE=0
NFPA RATINGS (SCALE 0-4): HEALTH=U FIRE=1 REACTIVITY=0

COMPONENTS AND CONTAMINANTS

COMPONENT: LINURON ***PERCENT:*** 100.0
CAS# 330-55-2
OTHER CONTAMINANTS: NONE
EXPOSURE LIMITS: NO OCCUPATIONAL EXPOSURE LIMITS ESTABLISHED BY OSHA, ACGIH, OR NIOSH.

PHYSICAL DATA

DESCRIPTION: COLORLESS OR WHITE CRSTALLINE SOLID.
MELTING POINT: 199-210 F (93-94 C) ***SPECIFIC GRAVITY:*** NOT AVAILABLE
VAPOR PRESSURE: NEGLIGIBLE ***SOLUBILITY IN WATER:*** 0.0081% @ 25 C
SOLVENT SOLUBILITY: SOLUBLE IN ACETONE, ALCOHOL, BENZENE, TOLUENE, XYLENE, AROMATIC HYDROCARBONS; SLIGHTLY SOLUBLE IN ALIPHATIC HYDROCARBONS.

FIRE AND EXPLOSION DATA

FIRE AND EXPLOSION HAZARD: SLIGHT FIRE HAZARD WHEN EXPOSED TO HEAT OR FLAME.
FIREFIGHTING MEDIA: DRY CHEMICAL, CARBON DIOXIDE, HALON, WATER SPRAY OR STANDARD FOAM (1987 EMERGENCY RESPONSE GUIDEBOOK, DOT P 5800.4). FOR LARGER FIRES, USE WATER SPRAY, FOG OR STANDARD FOAM (1987 EMERGENCY RESPONSE GUIDEBOOK, DOT P 5800.4).
FIREFIGHTING: MOVE CONTAINERS FROM FIRE AREA IF POSSIBLE. FIGHT FIRE FROM MAXIMUM DISTANCE. STAY AWAY FROM STORAGE TANK ENDS. DIKE FIRE CONTROL WATER FOR LATER DISPOSAL. DO NOT SCATTER MATERIAL (1987 EMERGENCY RESPONSE GUIDEBOOK, DOT P 5800.4, GUIDE PAGE 55). EXTINGUISH USING AGENT SUITABLE FOR TYPE OF SURROUNDING FIRE. USE WATER IN FLOODING QUANTITIES AS FOG. KEEP SPARKS, FLAMES AND OTHER SOURCES OF IGNITION AWAY. KEEP MATERIAL OUT OF WATER SOURCES AND SEWERS. DO NOT TOUCH MATERIAL AND AVOID BREATHING DUSTS AND FUMES FROM BURNING MATERIAL. KEEP UPWIND.

TOXICITY

LINURON: TOXICITY DATA: 48 MG/M3/4 HOURS INHALATION-RAT LC50; 48 MG/M3/4 HOURS INHALATION-RAT LCLO (85GMAT); >2000 MG/KG SKIN-RABBIT LD50 (85IFAI); 1146 MG/KG ORAL-RAT LD50; 2400 MG/KG ORAL-MOUSE LD50; 500 MG/KG ORAL-DOG LD50; 2250 MG/KG ORAL-RABBIT LD50; MUTAGENIC DATA (RTECS). CARCINOGEN STATUS: NONE. ACUTE TOXICITY LEVEL: HIGHLY TOXIC BY INHALATION; MODERATELY TOXIC BY INGESTION; SLIGHTLY TOXIC BY DERMAL ABSORPTION. TARGET EFFECTS: NO DATA AVAILABLE.

HEALTH EFFECTS AND FIRST AID

INHALATION: LINURON: HIGHLY TOXIC. **ACUTE EXPOSURE-** MAY CAUSE IRRITATION OF THE NOSE, THROAT AND MUCOUS MEMBRANES. THE LOWEST CONCENTRATION TO PRODUCE SYSTEMIC EFFECTS IN RATS WAS 29 MG/M3/4 HOURS; 48 MG/M3/4 HOURS PRODUCED SOME DEATHS. **CHRONIC EXPOSURE-** NO DATA AVAILABLE.
FIRST AID- REMOVE FROM EXPOSURE AREA TO FRESH AIR IMMEDIATELY. IF BREATHING HAS STOPPED, PERFORM ARTIFICIAL RESPIRATION. KEEP PERSON WARM AND AT REST. TREAT SYMPTOMATICALLY AND SUPPORTIVELY. GET MEDICAL ATTENTION IMMEDIATELY.

SKIN CONTACT: LINURON: **ACUTE EXPOSURE-** A 50% SUSPENSION APPLIED TO THE SKIN OF GUINEA PIGS PRODUCED MILD IRRITATION. **CHRONIC EXPOSURE-** NO DATA AVAILABLE.
FIRST AID- REMOVE CONTAMINATED CLOTHING AND SHOES IMMEDIATELY. WASH AFFECTED AREA WITH SOAP OR MILD DETERGENT AND LARGE AMOUNTS OF WATER UNTIL NO EVIDENCE OF CHEMICAL REMAINS (APPROXIMATELY 15-20 MINUTES). GET MEDICAL ATTENTION IMMEDIATELY.

EYE CONTACT: LINURON: **ACUTE EXPOSURE-** MAY CAUSE EYE IRRITATION. **CHRONIC EXPOSURE-** NO DATA AVAILABLE.
FIRST AID- WASH EYES IMMEDIATELY WITH LARGE AMOUNTS OF WATER OR NORMAL SALINE, OCCASIONALLY LIFTING UPPER AND LOWER LIDS, UNTIL NO EVIDENCE OF CHEMICAL REMAINS (APPROXIMATELY 15-20 MINUTES). GET MEDICAL ATTENTION IMMEDIATELY.

INGESTION: LINURON: **ACUTE EXPOSURE-** A LETHAL DOSE IN RATS WAS 1146 MG/KG. **CHRONIC EXPOSURE-** EFFECTS OF HYPOCHROMIC ANEMIA, DECREASED CHOLINESTERASE AND PEROXIDASE ACTIVITIES IN BLOOD, AND ULTRASTRUCTURAL CHANGES IN THE LIVER WERE OBSERVED IN A STUDY OF RATS FED 4 MG/KG/DAY. CHRONIC EFFECTS OF DECREASED RED BLOOD CELL COUNTS, LOWERED HEMOGLOBIN AND HEMATOCRIT, AND EFFECTS ON THE SPLEEN, BONE MARROW, AND ENDOMETRIUM WERE REPORTED IN OTHER ANIMAL STUDIES. PREGNANT RATS FED 625 PPM OF LINURON IN THE DIET EXPERIENCED SIGNIFICANTLY LOWERED MATERNAL BODY WEIGHTS AND AN INCREASED INCIDENCE OF RESORPTIONS. A STATISTICALLY SIGNIFICANT INCREASE IN HEPATOCELLULAR ADENOMAS AND OTHER EFFECTS ON THE LIVER WERE OBSERVED IN A TWO-YEAR STUDY OF MICE. A SIGNIFICANT DOSE-RELATED INCREASE IN BENIGN TESTICULAR ADENOMAS WAS NOTED IN MALE RATS FED 125 AND 625 PPM.
FIRST AID- REMOVE BY GASTRIC LAVAGE AND CATHARSIS. MAINTAIN BLOOD PRESSURE AND AIRWAY. GIVE OXYGEN IF RESPIRATION IS DEPRESSED. DO NOT PERFORM GASTRIC LAVAGE IF VICTIM IS UNCONSCIOUS. GET MEDICAL ATTENTION IMMEDIATELY (DREISBACH, HANDBOOK OF POISONING, 12TH ED.). ADMINISTRATION OF LAVAGE OR OXYGEN SHOULD BE PERFORMED BY QUALIFIED MEDICAL PERSONNEL.
ANTIDOTE: NO SPECIFIC ANTIDOTE. TREAT SYMPTOMATICALLY AND SUPPORTIVELY.

REACTIVITY

REACTIVITY: STABLE UNDER NORMAL TEMPERATURES AND PRESSURES.
INCOMPATIBILITIES: LINURON: ACIDS: HYDROLYZES. ALKALI: HYDROLYZES. OXIDIZERS (STRONG): FIRE AND EXPLOSION HAZARD.
DECOMPOSITION: THERMAL DECOMPOSITION PRODUCTS MAY INCLUDE TOXIC OXIDES OF NITROGEN AND CARBON AND TOXIC AND CORROSIVE FUMES OF CHLORIDES.
POLYMERIZATION: HAZARDOUS POLYMERIZATION HAS NOT BEEN REPORTED TO OCCUR UNDER NORMAL TEMPERATURES AND PRESSURES.

STORAGE AND DISPOSAL

OBSERVE ALL FEDERAL, STATE AND LOCAL REGULATIONS WHEN STORING OR DISPOSING OF THIS SUBSTANCE. FOR ASSISTANCE, CONTACT THE DISTRICT DIRECTOR OF THE ENVIRONMENTAL PROTECTION AGENCY.

STORAGE

STORE IN ACCORDANCE WITH 40 CFR 165 RECOMMENDED PROCEDURES FOR THE DISPOSAL AND STORAGE OF PESTICIDES AND PESTICIDE CONTAINERS.
STORE AWAY FROM INCOMPATIBLE SUBSTANCES.
STORE IN A COOL, DRY PLACE; KEEP CONTAINER TIGHTLY CLOSED WHEN NOT IN USE.

DISPOSAL

DISPOSAL MUST BE IN ACCORDANCE WITH 40 CFR 165 RECOMMENDED PROCEDURES FOR THE DISPOSAL AND STORAGE OF PESTICIDES AND PESTICIDE CONTAINERS.

CONDITIONS TO AVOID

MAY BURN BUT DOES NOT IGNITE READILY. CONTAINERS MAY EXPLODE IN HEAT OF FIRE.

SPILL AND LEAK PROCEDURES

OCCUPATIONAL SPILL: DO NOT TOUCH SPILLED MATERIAL. STOP LEAK IF YOU CAN DO IT WITHOUT RISK. USE WATER SPRAY TO REDUCE VAPORS. FOR SMALL SPILLS, TAKE UP WITH SAND OR OTHER ABSORBENT MATERIAL AND PLACE INTO CONTAINERS FOR LATER DISPOSAL. FOR SMALL DRY SPILLS, WITH A CLEAN SHOVEL PLACE MATERIAL INTO CLEAN, DRY CONTAINERS AND COVER. MOVE CONTAINERS FROM SPILL AREA. FOR LARGER SPILLS, DIKE FAR AHEAD OF SPILL FOR LATER DISPOSAL. KEEP UNNECESSARY PEOPLE AWAY. ISOLATE HAZARD AREA AND DENY ENTRY. VENTILATE CLOSED SPACES BEFORE ENTERING.

PROTECTIVE EQUIPMENT

VENTILATION: PROVIDE LOCAL EXHAUST OR GENERAL DILUTION VENTILATION SYSTEM.
RESPIRATOR: THE FOLLOWING RESPIRATORS ARE RECOMMENDED BASED ON INFORMATION FOUND IN THE PHYSICAL DATA, TOXICITY AND HEALTH EFFECTS SECTIONS. THEY ARE RANKED IN ORDER FROM MINIMUM TO MAXIMUM RESPIRATORY PROTECTION. THE SPECIFIC RESPIRATOR SELECTED MUST BE BASED ON CONTAMINATION LEVELS FOUND IN THE WORK PLACE, MUST NOT EXCEED THE WORKING LIMITS OF THE RESPIRATOR AND BE JOINTLY APPROVED BY THE NATIONAL INSTITUTE FOR OCCUPATIONAL SAFETY AND HEALTH AND THE MINE SAFETY AND HEALTH ADMINISTRATION (NIOSH-MSHA).
CHEMICAL CARTRIDGE RESPIRATOR WITH AN ORGANIC VAPOR CARTRIDGE(S) WITH A FULL FACEPIECE AND ORGANIC VAPOR CARTRIDGE(S) IN COMBINATION WITH A DUST AND MIST FILTER.
POWERED AIR-PURIFYING RESPIRATOR WITH A TIGHT-FITTING FACEPIECE AND ORGANIC VAPOR CARTRIDGE(S) IN COMBINATION WITH A HIGH-EFFICIENCY PARTICULATE FILTER.
TYPE 'C' SUPPLIED-AIR RESPIRATOR WITH A FULL FACEPIECE OPERATED IN A PRESSURE-DEMAND OR OTHER POSITIVE PRESSURE MODE.
SELF-CONTAINED BREATHING APPARATUS WITH A FULL FACEPIECE OPERATED IN PRESSURE-DEMAND OR OTHER POSITIVE PRESSURE MODE.

FOR FIREFIGHTING AND OTHER IMMEDIATELY DANGEROUS TO LIFE OR HEALTH CONDITIONS:
SELF-CONTAINED BREATHING APPARATUS WITH FULL FACEPIECE OPERATED IN PRESSURE-DEMAND OR OTHER POSITIVE PRESSURE MODE.
SUPPLIED-AIR RESPIRATOR WITH FULL FACEPIECE AND OPERATED IN PRESSURE-DEMAND OR OTHER POSITIVE PRESSURE MODE IN COMBINATION WITH AN AUXILIARY SELF-CONTAINED BREATHING APPARATUS OPERATED IN PRESSURE-DEMAND OR OTHER POSITIVE PRESSURE MODE.

CLOTHING: EMPLOYEE MUST WEAR APPROPRIATE PROTECTIVE (IMPERVIOUS) CLOTHING AND EQUIPMENT TO PREVENT REPEATED OR PROLONGED SKIN CONTACT WITH THIS SUBSTANCE.

GLOVES: EMPLOYEE MUST WEAR APPROPRIATE PROTECTIVE GLOVES TO PREVENT CONTACT WITH THIS SUBSTANCE.

EYE PROTECTION: EMPLOYEE MUST WEAR SPLASH-PROOF OR DUST-RESISTANT SAFETY GOGGLES TO PREVENT EYE CONTACT WITH THIS SUBSTANCE.
EMERGENCY EYE WASH: WHERE THERE IS ANY POSSIBILITY THAT AN EMPLOYEE'S EYES MAY BE EXPOSED TO THIS SUBSTANCE, THE EMPLOYER SHOULD PROVIDE AN EYE WASH FOUNTAIN WITHIN THE IMMEDIATE WORK AREA FOR EMERGENCY USE.

AUTHORIZED BY- OCCUPATIONAL HEALTH SERVICES, INC.
CREATION DATE: 10/04/89 ***REVISION DATE:*** 05/10/90

MATERIAL SAFETY DATA SHEET

OCCUPATIONAL HEALTH SERVICES, INC.
AGRICULTURE AND PESTICIDE DIVISION
450 SEVENTH AVENUE, SUITE 2407
NEW YORK, NEW YORK 10123
1-800-445-MSDS OR (212) 967-1100

EMERGENCY CONTACT:
JOHN S. BRANSFORD, JR. (615) 292-1180

SUBSTANCE IDENTIFICATION

CAS-NUMBER 13840-33-0
SUBSTANCE: **LITHIUM HYPOCHLORITE**
TRADE NAMES/SYNONYMS: HYPOCHLOROUS ACID, LITHIUM SALT; LITHIUM HYPOCHLORITE COMPOUND, DRY; STCC 4918727; UN 1471; PST12920
CHEMICAL FAMILY: INORGANIC SALT
MOLECULAR FORMULA: LI-CL-O
MOLECULAR WEIGHT: 58.39
CERCLA RATINGS (SCALE 0-3): HEALTH=U FIRE=0 REACTIVITY=2 PERSISTENCE=0
NFPA RATINGS (SCALE 0-4): HEALTH=U FIRE=0 REACTIVITY=2

COMPONENTS AND CONTAMINANTS

COMPONENT: LITHIUM HYPOCHLORITE ***PERCENT:*** 100
CAS# 13840-33-0
OTHER CONTAMINANTS: NONE
EXPOSURE LIMITS: NO OCCUPATIONAL EXPOSURE LIMITS ESTABLISHED BY OSHA, ACGIH, OR NIOSH.

PHYSICAL DATA

DESCRIPTION: WHITE GRANULAR SOLID OR TABLETS WITH A CHLORINE ODOR.
MELTING POINT: NOT AVAILABLE ***SPECIFIC GRAVITY:*** NOT AVAILABLE
SOLUBILITY IN WATER: DECOMPOSES

FIRE AND EXPLOSION DATA

FIRE AND EXPLOSION HAZARD: NEGLIGIBLE FIRE HAZARD WHEN EXPOSED TO HEAT OR FLAME.
OXIDIZER: OXIDIZERS DECOMPOSE, ESPECIALLY WHEN HEATED, TO YIELD OXYGEN OR OTHER GASES WHICH WILL INCREASE THE BURNING RATE OF COMBUSTIBLE MATTER. CONTACT WITH EASILY OXIDIZABLE, ORGANIC, OR OTHER COMBUSTIBLE MATERIALS MAY RESULT IN IGNITION, VIOLENT COMBUSTION OR EXPLOSION.

FIREFIGHTING MEDIA: DRY CHEMICAL, CARBON DIOXIDE, HALON OR WATER SPRAY (1987 EMERGENCY RESPONSE GUIDEBOOK, DOT P 5800.4).
FOR LARGER FIRES, USE WATER SPRAY OR FOG (1987 EMERGENCY RESPONSE GUIDEBOOK, DOT P 5800.4).

FIREFIGHTING: MOVE CONTAINERS FROM FIRE AREA IF POSSIBLE. COOL CONTAINERS EXPOSED TO FLAME WITH WATER FROM SIDE UNTIL WELL AFTER FIRE IS OUT. KEEP AWAY FROM STORAGE TANK ENDS. FOR MASSIVE FIRE IN STORAGE AREA, USE UNMANNED HOSE HOLDER OR MONITOR NOZZLES (1987 EMERGENCY RESPONSE GUIDEBOOK, DOT 5800.4, GUIDE PAGE 42).
USE FLOODING QUANTITIES OF WATER. COOL CONTAINERS WITH FLOODING AMOUNTS OF WATER, APPLY FROM AS FAR A DISTANCE AS POSSIBLE. AVOID BREATHING TOXIC VAPORS, KEEP UPWIND. EVACUATE TO A RADIUS OF 2500 FEET FOR UNCONTROLLABLE FIRES.

TRANSPORTATION DATA

DEPARTMENT OF TRANSPORTATION HAZARD CLASSIFICATION 49 CFR 172.101: OXIDIZER
DEPARTMENT OF TRANSPORTATION LABELING REQUIREMENTS 49 CFR 172.101 AND SUBPART E: OXIDIZER
DEPARTMENT OF TRANSPORTATION PACKAGING REQUIREMENTS: 49 CFR 173.217 EXCEPTIONS: 49 CFR 173.153

TOXICITY

LITHIUM HYPOCHLORITE: CARCINOGEN STATUS: NONE. LOCAL EFFECTS: IRRITANT-INHALATION. ACUTE TOXICITY LEVEL: NO DATA AVAILABLE. TARGET EFFECTS: POISONING MAY AFFECT THE CENTRAL NERVOUS SYSTEM AND KIDNEYS.*
ADDITIONAL DATA: INCREASED TOXICITY MAY OCCUR IN THE PRESENCE OF LOW SODIUM INTAKE.*
* MAY BE BASED ON GENERAL INFORMATION ON LITHIUM COMPOUNDS.

HEALTH EFFECTS AND FIRST AID

INHALATION: LITHIUM HYPOCHLORITE: IRRITANT. **ACUTE EXPOSURE-** THE CHEMICAL MAY IRRITATE THE RESPIRATORY TRACT. LITHIUM COMPOUNDS MAY CAUSE MUCOUS MEMBRANE IRRITATION, MALAISE, DROWSINESS, ANOREXIA, NAUSEA, VOMITING, DIARRHEA, BLURRED VISION, TINNITUS, WEAKNESS, MUSCLE TREMORS, AND INCREASED TENDON REFLEXES. **CHRONIC EXPOSURE-** NO DATA AVAILABLE.

FIRST AID- REMOVE FROM EXPOSURE AREA TO FRESH AIR IMMEDIATELY. IF BREATHING HAS STOPPED, PERFORM ARTIFICIAL RESPIRATION. KEEP PERSON WARM AND AT REST. TREAT SYMPTOMATICALLY AND SUPPORTIVELY. GET MEDICAL ATTENTION IMMEDIATELY.

SKIN CONTACT: LITHIUM HYPOCHLORITE: **ACUTE EXPOSURE-** MAY BE IRRITATING. **CHRONIC EXPOSURE-** NO DATA AVAILABLE.

FIRST AID- REMOVE CONTAMINATED CLOTHING AND SHOES IMMEDIATELY. WASH AFFECTED AREA WITH SOAP OR MILD DETERGENT AND LARGE AMOUNTS OF WATER UNTIL NO EVIDENCE OF CHEMICAL REMAINS (APPROXIMATELY 15-20 MINUTES). GET MEDICAL ATTENTION IMMEDIATELY.

EYE CONTACT: LITHIUM HYPOCHLORITE: **ACUTE EXPOSURE-** MAY BE IRRITATING. **CHRONIC EXPOSURE-** NO DATA AVAILABLE.

FIRST AID- WASH EYES IMMEDIATELY WITH LARGE AMOUNTS OF WATER OR NORMAL SALINE, OCCASIONALLY LIFTING UPPER AND LOWER LIDS, UNTIL NO EVIDENCE OF CHEMICAL REMAINS (APPROXIMATELY 15-20 MINUTES). GET MEDICAL ATTENTION IMMEDIATELY.

INGESTION: LITHIUM HYPOCHLORITE: **ACUTE EXPOSURE-** LITHIUM SALTS MAY CAUSE DROWSINESS, WEAKNESS, ANOREXIA, NAUSEA, TREMORS, BLURRING OF VISION, TINNITUS, VERTIGO, COMA, AND DEATH. **CHRONIC EXPOSURE-** REPEATED OR PROLONGED EXPOSURE TO LITHIUM SALTS MAY CAUSE DRYNESS OF MOUTH, ANOREXIA, WEAKNESS, DEHYDRATION, THIRST, SALIVATION, NAUSEA, VOMITING, AND DIARRHEA. SYMPTOMS PERTAINING TO THE NERVOUS SYSTEM MAY INCLUDE FINE TREMOR OF HANDS, LIPS, AND JAWS; MUSCULAR WEAKNESS, ATAXIA, GIDDINESS, TINNITUS, DROWSINESS, SLURRED SPEECH, BLURRED VISION, HYPERACTIVE DEEP REFLEXES, MUSCULAR IRRITABILITY, MUSCULAR FASCICULATIONS, NYSTAGMUS, LETHARGY, STUPOR, COMA, AND SEIZURES. EFFECTS ON THE KIDNEY MAY INCLUDE POLYURIA, ELEVATION OF NONPROTEIN NITROGEN, AND OLIGURIA.

FIRST AID- DILUTE THE ALKALI BY GIVING WATER OR MILK IMMEDIATELY AND ALLOW VOMITING TO OCCUR. AVOID GASTRIC LAVAGE OR EMETICS. ESOPHAGOSCOPY IS THE ONLY WAY TO EXCLUDE THE POSSIBLITY OF CORROSION IN THE UPPER GASTROINTESTINAL TRACT; IF CORROSION IS SUSPECTED, ESOPHAGOSCOPY SHOULD USUALLY BE PERFORMED WITHIN 24 HOURS (DREISBACH, HANDBOOK OF POISONING, 12TH ED.). MAINTAIN AIRWAY AND TREAT SHOCK. IF VOMITING OCCURS, KEEP HEAD BELOW HIPS TO HELP PREVENT ASPIRATION. GET MEDICAL ATTENTION IMMEDIATELY.

ANTIDOTE: NO SPECIFIC ANTIDOTE. TREAT SYMPTOMATICALLY AND SUPPORTIVELY.

REACTIVITY

REACTIVITY: REACTS EXOTHERMICALLY WITH WATER EVOLVING CHLORINE GAS. PROLONGED EXPOSURE OF THE MATERIAL TO FIRE OR HEAT MAY RESULT IN ITS VIOLENT DECOMPOSITION AND SUBSEQUENT RUPTURE OF ITS CONTAINER.

INCOMPATIBILITIES: LITHIUM HYPOCHLORITE: ACIDS: VIOLENT REACTION WITH EVOLUTION OF CHLORINE. METALS: MAY BE CORROSIVE IN PRESENCE OF

MOISTURE. ORGANIC MATERIALS: IGNITION HAZARD. UREA: FORMATION OF SPONTANEOUSLY EXPLOSIVE NITROGEN TRICHLORIDE.

DECOMPOSITION: THERMAL DECOMPOSITION PRODUCTS MAY INCLUDE TOXIC AND HAZARDOUS FUMES OF HYDROGEN CHLORIDE AND OXIDES OF LITHIUM.

POLYMERIZATION: HAZARDOUS POLYMERIZATION HAS NOT BEEN REPORTED TO OCCUR UNDER NORMAL TEMPERATURES AND PRESSURES.

STORAGE AND DISPOSAL

OBSERVE ALL FEDERAL, STATE AND LOCAL REGULATIONS WHEN STORING OR DISPOSING OF THIS SUBSTANCE. FOR ASSISTANCE, CONTACT THE DISTRICT DIRECTOR OF THE ENVIRONMENTAL PROTECTION AGENCY.

STORAGE

STORE AWAY FROM INCOMPATIBLE SUBSTANCES.

CONDITIONS TO AVOID

AVOID CONTACT WITH OTHER COMBUSTIBLE MATERIALS (WOOD, PAPER, OIL, ETC.). AVOID CONTACT WITH EYES AND SKIN; MATERIAL MAY BE POISONOUS OR CORROSIVE.

SPILL AND LEAK PROCEDURES

OCCUPATIONAL SPILL: KEEP COMBUSTIBLES (WOOD, PAPER, OIL, ETC.) AWAY FROM SPILLED MATERIAL. DO NOT TOUCH SPILLED MATERIAL. FOR SMALL DRY SPILLS, WITH CLEAN SHOVEL PLACE MATERIAL INTO CLEAN, DRY CONTAINER AND COVER; MOVE CONTAINERS FROM SPILL AREA. FOR LARGER SPILLS, DIKE FAR AHEAD OF SPILL FOR LATER DISPOSAL. KEEP UNNECESSARY PEOPLE AWAY. ISOLATE HAZARD AREA AND DENY ENTRY.

PROTECTIVE EQUIPMENT

VENTILATION: PROVIDE LOCAL EXHAUST OR PROCESS ENCLOSURE VENTILATION TO MEET PUBLISHED EXPOSURE LIMITS.

RESPIRATOR: THE FOLLOWING RESPIRATORS ARE RECOMMENDED BASED ON INFORMATION FOUND IN THE PHYSICAL DATA, TOXICITY AND HEALTH EFFECTS SECTIONS. THEY ARE RANKED IN ORDER FROM MINIMUM TO MAXIMUM RESPIRATORY PROTECTION. THE SPECIFIC RESPIRATOR SELECTED MUST BE BASED ON CONTAMINATION LEVELS FOUND IN THE WORK PLACE, MUST NOT EXCEED THE WORKING LIMITS OF THE RESPIRATOR AND BE JOINTLY APPROVED BY THE NATIONAL INSTITUTE FOR OCCUPATIONAL SAFETY AND HEALTH AND THE MINE SAFETY AND HEALTH ADMINISTRATION (NIOSH-MSHA).

DUST AND MIST RESPIRATOR WITH A FULL FACEPIECE.

AIR-PURIFYING FULL FACEPIECE RESPIRATOR WITH A HIGH-EFFICIENCY PARTICULATE FILTER.

POWERED AIR-PURIFYING RESPIRATOR WITH A TIGHT-FITTING FACEPIECE AND HIGH-EFFICIENCY PARTICULATE FILTER.

TYPE 'C' SUPPLIED-AIR RESPIRATOR WITH A FULL FACEPIECE OPERATED IN PRESSURE-DEMAND OR OTHER POSITIVE PRESSURE MODE OR WITH A FULL FACEPIECE, HELMET OR HOOD OPERATED IN CONTINUOUS-FLOW MODE.

SELF-CONTAINED BREATHING APPARATUS WITH A FULL FACEPIECE OPERATED IN PRESSURE-DEMAND OR OTHER POSITIVE PRESSURE MODE.

FOR FIREFIGHTING AND OTHER IMMEDIATELY DANGEROUS TO LIFE OR HEALTH CONDITIONS:

SELF-CONTAINED BREATHING APPARATUS WITH FULL FACEPIECE OPERATED IN PRESSURE-DEMAND OR OTHER POSITIVE PRESSURE MODE.

SUPPLIED-AIR RESPIRATOR WITH FULL FACEPIECE AND OPERATED IN PRESSURE-DEMAND OR OTHER POSITIVE PRESSURE MODE IN COMBINATION WITH AN AUXILIARY SELF-CONTAINED BREATHING APPARATUS OPERATED IN PRESSURE-DEMAND OR OTHER POSITIVE PRESSURE MODE.

CLOTHING: EMPLOYEE MUST WEAR APPROPRIATE PROTECTIVE (IMPERVIOUS) CLOTHING AND EQUIPMENT TO PREVENT REPEATED OR PROLONGED SKIN CONTACT WITH THIS SUBSTANCE.

GLOVES: EMPLOYEE MUST WEAR APPROPRIATE PROTECTIVE GLOVES TO PREVENT CONTACT WITH THIS SUBSTANCE.

EYE PROTECTION: EMPLOYEE MUST WEAR SPLASH-PROOF OR DUST-RESISTANT SAFETY GOGGLES TO PREVENT EYE CONTACT WITH THIS SUBSTANCE.

EMERGENCY EYE WASH: WHERE THERE IS ANY POSSIBILITY THAT AN EMPLOYEE'S EYES MAY BE EXPOSED TO THIS SUBSTANCE, THE EMPLOYER SHOULD PROVIDE AN EYE WASH FOUNTAIN WITHIN THE IMMEDIATE WORK AREA FOR EMERGENCY USE.

AUTHORIZED BY- OCCUPATIONAL HEALTH SERVICES, INC.

CREATION DATE: 10/04/89 ***REVISION DATE:*** 05/18/90

MATERIAL SAFETY DATA SHEET

OCCUPATIONAL HEALTH SERVICES, INC.
AGRICULTURE AND PESTICIDE DIVISION
450 SEVENTH AVENUE, SUITE 2407
NEW YORK, NEW YORK 10123
1-800-445-MSDS OR (212) 967-1100

EMERGENCY CONTACT:
JOHN S. BRANSFORD, JR. (615) 292-1180

SUBSTANCE IDENTIFICATION

CAS-NUMBER 108-39-4

SUBSTANCE: **M-CRESOL**

TRADE NAMES/SYNONYMS: 3-CRESOL; M-CRESYLIC ACID; 1-HYDROXY-3-METHYLBENZENE; M-HYDROXYTOLUENE; M-METHYLPHENOL; 3-METHYLPHENOL; M-OXYTOLUENE; M-KRESOL; 3-CRESOLE; 1-HYDROXY-3-METHYL BENZENE; M-TOLUOL; 3-HYDROXYTOLUENE; UN 2076; BP-223; U052; PST13080

CHEMICAL FAMILY: HYDROXYL, AROMATIC

MOLECULAR FORMULA: C7-H8-O

MOLECULAR WEIGHT: 108.15

CERCLA RATINGS (SCALE 0-3): HEALTH=3 FIRE=1 REACTIVITY=0 PERSISTENCE=2

NFPA RATINGS (SCALE 0-4): HEALTH=3 FIRE=1 REACTIVITY=0

COMPONENTS AND CONTAMINANTS

COMPONENT: M-CRESOL ***PERCENT:*** >99

CAS# 108-39-4

OTHER CONTAMINANTS: O-CRESOL, P-CRESOL

EXPOSURE LIMITS: CRESOL (ALL ISOMERS): 5 PPM (22 MG/M3) OSHA TWA (SKIN) 5 PPM (22 MG/M3) ACGIH TWA (SKIN) 2.3 PPM (10 MG/M3) NIOSH 10 HOUR RECOMMENDED TWA

1000 POUND CERCLA SECTION 103 REPORTABLE QUANTITY SUBJECT TO SARA SECTION 313 ANNUAL TOXIC CHEMICAL RELEASE REPORTING

PHYSICAL DATA

DESCRIPTION: COLORLESS TO YELLOW LIQUID WITH A PHENOLIC ODOR.

BOILING POINT: 397 F (203 C) ***MELTING POINT:*** 52 F (11 C)

SPECIFIC GRAVITY: 1.0 ***VAPOR PRESSURE:*** 1.0 MMHG @ 52 C

PH: ACIDIC IN SOLUTION ***SOLUBILITY IN WATER:*** SLIGHT ***ODOR THRESHOLD:*** 5 PPM

VAPOR DENSITY: 3.7

SOLVENT SOLUBILITY: ALCOHOL, BENZENE, ETHER, ACETONE, VEGETABLE OILS

FIRE AND EXPLOSION DATA

FIRE AND EXPLOSION HAZARD: SLIGHT FIRE HAZARD WHEN EXPOSED TO HEAT OR FLAME.

MODERATE EXPLOSION HAZARD WHEN EXPOSED TO HEAT OR FLAME.

FLASH POINT: 187 F (86 C) (CC) ***LOWER EXPLOSIVE LIMIT:*** 1.1% @ 302 F

AUTOIGNITION TEMP.: 1038 F (559 C) ***FLAMMABILITY CLASS(OSHA):*** IIIA

FIREFIGHTING MEDIA: DRY CHEMICAL, CARBON DIOXIDE, HALON, WATER SPRAY OR STANDARD FOAM (1987 EMERGENCY RESPONSE GUIDEBOOK, DOT P 5800.4).

FOR LARGER FIRES, USE WATER SPRAY, FOG OR STANDARD FOAM (1987 EMERGENCY RESPONSE GUIDEBOOK, DOT P 5800.4).

FIREFIGHTING: MOVE CONTAINERS FROM FIRE AREA IF POSSIBLE. FIGHT FIRE FROM MAXIMUM DISTANCE. STAY AWAY FROM STORAGE TANK ENDS. DIKE FIRE CONTROL WATER FOR LATER DISPOSAL. DO NOT SCATTER MATERIAL (1987 EMERGENCY RESPONSE GUIDEBOOK, DOT P 5800.4, GUIDE PAGE 55).

USE FLOODING AMOUNTS OF WATER AS A FOG; SOLID STREAMS MAY NOT BE EFFECTIVE. COOL CONTANINERS WITH FLOODING QUANTITIES OF WATER, APPLY FROM AS FAR A DISTANCE AS POSSIBLE. AVOID BREATHING CORROSIVE VAPORS, KEEP UPWIND.

TRANSPORTATION DATA

DEPARTMENT OF TRANSPORTATION HAZARD CLASSIFICATION 49 CFR 172.101: CORROSIVE MATERIAL

DEPARTMENT OF TRANSPORTATION LABELING REQUIREMENTS 49 CFR 172.101 AND SUBPART E: CORROSIVE

DEPARTMENT OF TRANSPORTATION PACKAGING REQUIREMENTS: 49 CFR 173.245 EXCEPTIONS: 49 CFR 173.244

TOXICITY

M-CRESOL: IRRITATION DATA: 517 MG/24 HOURS SKIN-RABBIT SEVERE; 103 MG EYE-RABBIT SEVERE. TOXICITY DATA: 2050 MG/KG SKIN-RABBIT LD50; 1100 MG/KG SKIN-RAT LD50; 242 MG/KG ORAL-RAT LD50; 828 MG/KG ORAL-MOUSE LD50; 1400 MG/KG ORAL-RABBIT LDLO; 900 MG/KG SUBCUTANEOUS-RAT LDLO; 450 MG/KG SUBCUTANEOUS-MOUSE LDLO; 500 MG/KG SUBCUTANEOUS-RABBIT LDLO; 180 MG/KG SUBCUTANEOUS-CAT LDLO; 300 MG/KG SUBCUTANEOUS-GUINEA PIG LDLO; 280 MG/KG INTRAVENOUS-RABBIT LDLO; 150

MG/KG INTRAVENOUS-DOG LDLO; 168 MG/KG INTRAPERITONEAL-MOUSE LD50; 100 MG/KG INTRAPERITONEAL-GUINEA PIG LDLO; 600 MG/KG UNREPORTED-MOUSE LD50; MUTAGENIC DATA (RTECS); REPRODUCTIVE EFFECTS DATA (RTECS); TUMORIGENIC DATA (RTECS). CARCINOGEN STATUS; NONE. LOCAL EFFECTS: CORROSIVE- INHALATION, SKIN, AND EYES. ACUTE TOXICITY LEVEL: TOXIC BY INGESTION AND SLIGHTLY TOXIC BY DERMAL ABSORPTION. TARGET EFFECTS: SENSITIZER- SKIN. CENTRAL NERVOUS SYSTEM DEPRESSANT. POISONING MAY AFFECT THE LIVER AND KIDNEYS AND THE RESPIRATORY AND CARDIOVASCULAR SYSTEMS.

HEALTH EFFECTS AND FIRST AID

INHALATION: M-CRESOL: CORROSIVE/NARCOTIC. 250 PPM IMMEDIATELY DANGEROUS TO LIFE OR HEALTH. **ACUTE EXPOSURE-** HUMANS EXPOSED EXPERIMENTALLY TO 6 MG/M3 OF THE ORTHO ISOMER REPORTED NASAL CONSTRICTION, THROAT IRRITATION, RESPIRATORY MUCOSA DRYNESS AND THE SENSATION OF AN UNSPECIFIED TASTE. HOWEVER, INHALATION IS NOT USUALLY AN ACUTE HAZARD DUE TO THE LOW VAPOR PRESSURE AND THE DISAGREEABLE ODOR WHICH IS DETECTABLE EVEN AT LOW CONCENTRATIONS. EXPOSURE TO AEROSOLS OR TO VAPORS PRODUCED BY HIGH TEMPERATURE PROCESSES MAY CAUSE SEVERE RESPIRATORY TRACT IRRITATION AND SYSTEMIC ABSORPTION. THE SYMPTOMS, POSSIBLY DELAYED 20-30 MINUTES, MAY INCLUDE HEADACHE, DIZZINESS, VOMITING, TINNITUS, DIMNESS OF VISION, RAPID, IRREGULAR RESPIRATION, WEAK PULSE, DYSPNEA, PROFOUND MUSCULAR WEAKNESS, AND OCCASIONALLY, MENTAL CONFUSION. IF SUFFICIENT AMOUNTS ARE ABSORBED, VASCULAR COLLAPSE, SHOCK, HYPOTHERMIA, UNCONSCIOUSNESS, RESPIRATORY FAILURE, AND DEATH ARE POSSIBLE. PATHOLOGIC FINDINGS AS DETAILED IN ACUTE SKIN EXPOSURE MAY BE FOUND. **CHRONIC EXPOSURE-** CHRONIC INHALATION OF VAPORS MAY RESULT IN RESPIRATORY TRACT IRRITATION AND DISTURBANCES OF THE NERVOUS, GASTROINTESTINAL AND VASCULAR SYSTEMS. SYMPTOMS MAY INCLUDE HEADACHE, DIZZINESS, FAINTING, FACIAL MUSCLE SPASMS, TREMORS, MENTAL DISTURBANCES, DIFFICULTY IN SWALLOWING, SALIVATION, NAUSEA, VOMITING, DIARRHEA, ANOREXIA, HYPERTENSION, SLIGHTLY ENLARGED HEART, AND SKIN RASH. LIVER AND KIDNEY DAMAGE ARE POSSIBLE AND, IF SEVERE, MAY RESULT IN DEATH.

FIRST AID- REMOVE FROM EXPOSURE AREA TO FRESH AIR IMMEDIATELY. IF BREATHING HAS STOPPED, GIVE ARTIFICIAL RESPIRATION. MAINTAIN AIRWAY AND BLOOD PRESSURE AND ADMINISTER OXYGEN IF AVAILABLE. KEEP AFFECTED PERSON WARM AND AT REST. TREAT SYMPTOMATICALLY AND SUPPORTIVELY. ADMINISTRATION OF OXYGEN SHOULD BE PERFORMED BY QUALIFIED PERSONNEL. GET MEDICAL ATTENTION IMMEDIATELY.

SKIN CONTACT: M-CRESOL: CORROSIVE/NARCOTIC/SENSITIZER. **ACUTE EXPOSURE-** MAY CAUSE SEVERE IRRITATION. PRICKLING AND INTENSE BURNING MAY OCCUR AFTER A FEW MINUTES FOLLOWED BY LOCAL ANESTHESIA. AFFECTED TISSUES MAY INITIALLY SHOW WHITE DISCOLORATION, WRINKLING, AND SOFTENING, WHICH SUBSEQUENTLY MAY BECOME GANGRENOUS. SENSITIZATION DERMATITIS MAY OCCUR IN PREVIOUSLY EXPOSED PERSONS. IT IS READILY ABSORBED THROUGH THE SKIN TO CAUSE SYSTEMIC EFFECTS WHICH MAY BE DELAYED 20-30 MINUTES. THE SYMPTOMS MAY INCLUDE HEADACHE, DIZZINESS, VOMITING, TINNITUS, DIMNESS OF VISION, IRREGULAR, RAPID RESPIRATION, WEAK PULSE, DYSPNEA, PROFOUND MUSCULAR WEAKNESS, AND OCCASIONALLY, MENTAL CONFUSION. IF SUFFICIENT AMOUNTS ARE ABSORBED, VASCULAR COLLAPSE, SHOCK, HYPOTHERMIA, UNCONSCIOUSNESS, AND DEATH MAY OCCUR. PATHOLOGICAL FINDINGS HAVE INCLUDED PULMONARY HYPEREMIA, EMPHYSEMA, AND EDEMA; BRONCHOPNEUMONIA WITH PETECHIAL HEMORRHAGES IN THE PLEURA; AND NODULAR PNEUMONIA. KIDNEYS HAVE SHOWN PARENCHYMATOUS AND HEMORRHAGIC NEPHRITIS AND TUBULE DAMAGE. THE LIVER HAS SHOWN CONGESTION WITH PALLOR AND NECROSIS OF HEPATIC CELLS. DEGENERATED MYOCARDIUM AND SMALL HEMORRHAGES IN THE EPICARDIUM AND ENDOCARDIUM HAVE BEEN SEEN. CONGESTION IN THE BRAIN AND DAMAGE TO THE PANCREAS AND SPLEEN HAVE ALSO BEEN REPORTED. **CHRONIC EXPOSURE-** REPEATED OR PROLONGED EXPOSURE TO LOW CONCENTRATIONS MAY CAUSE DERMATITIS AND EVEN VERY DILUTE SOLUTIONS MAY CAUSE SENSITIZATION. RARELY, PROLONGED CONTACT MAY RESULT IN A PIGMENTORY DISORDER CALLED OCHRONOSIS, WHICH IS A DARKENING OF THE CONJUNCTIVA, SKIN AND CARTILAGE OF THE NOSE AND EARS. REPEATED ABSORPTION MAY RESULT IN DISTURBANCES OF THE NERVOUS, GASTROINTESTINAL AND VASCULAR SYSTEMS. SYMPTOMS MAY INCLUDE HEADACHE, DIZZINESS, FAINTING, FACIAL MUSCLE SPASMS, TREMORS, MENTAL DISTURBANCES, DIFFICULTY IN SWALLOWING, SALIVATION, NAUSEA, VOMITING, DIARRHEA, ANOREXIA, HYPERTENSION, SLIGHTLY ENLARGED HEART, AND SKIN RASH. LIVER AND KIDNEY DAMAGE ARE POSSIBLE AND, IF SEVERE, MAY RESULT IN DEATH. AS EVALUATED BY RTECS, ADMINISTRATION TO MICE BY SKIN APPLICATION RESULTED IN NEOPLASTIC TUMORS ON SKIN OR APPENDAGES.

FIRST AID- REMOVE CONTAMINATED CLOTHING AND SHOES IMMEDIATELY. WASH AFFECTED AREA WITH SOAP OR MILD DETERGENT AND LARGE AMOUNTS OF WATER UNTIL NO EVIDENCE OF CHEMICAL REMAINS (AT LEAST 15-20 MINUTES). IN CASE OF CHEMICAL BURNS, COVER AREA WITH STERILE, DRY DRESSING. BANDAGE SECURELY, BUT NOT TOO TIGHTLY. GET MEDICAL ATTENTION IMMEDIATELY.

EYE CONTACT: M-CRESOL: CORROSIVE. **ACUTE EXPOSURE-** CRESOL SOLUTIONS SPLASHED IN THE EYE MAY CAUSE PERMANENT CORNEAL OPACIFICATION AND VASCULARIZATION, HYPERMIA, AND SWELLING OF THE CONJUCTIVA. INJURY FROM CRESOLS DEPENDS ON THE CONCENTRATION AND THE DURATION OF CONTACT. **CHRONIC EXPOSURE-** REPEATED OR PROLONGED CONTACT MAY CAUSE EFFECTS SIMILAR TO ACUTE EXPOSURE.

FIRST AID- WASH EYES IMMEDIATELY WITH LARGE AMOUNTS OF WATER, OCCASIONALLY LIFTING UPPER AND LOWER LIDS, UNTIL NO EVIDENCE OF CHEMICAL REMAINS (AT LEAST 15-20 MINUTES). CONTINUE IRRIGATING WITH NORMAL SALINE UNTIL THE PH HAS RETURNED TO NORMAL (30-60 MINUTES). COVER WITH STERILE BANDAGES. GET MEDICAL ATTENTION IMMEDIATELY.

INGESTION: M-CRESOL: CORROSIVE/NARCOTIC/TOXIC. **ACUTE EXPOSURE-** MAY CAUSE SEVERE MUCOSAL IRRITATION, INTENSE BURNING PAIN IN THE MOUTH AND THROAT FOLLOWED BY MARKED ABDOMINAL PAIN AND DISTRESS, NAUSEA, VOMITING, AND DIARRHEA. IT IS READILY ABSORBED BY THE GASTROINTESTINAL TRACT TO CAUSE SYSTEMIC EFFECTS WHICH MAY BE DELAYED 20-30 MINUTES. THE SYMPTOMS MAY INCLUDE HEADACHE, DIZZINESS, TINNITUS, DIMNESS OF VISION, IRREGULAR, RAPID RESPIRATION, WEAK PULSE, DYSPNEA, PROFOUND MUSCULAR WEAKNESS, AND OCCASIONALLY, MENTAL CONFUSION. OTHER POSSIBLE EFFECTS INCLUDE PULMONARY EDEMA, PNEUMONIA, KIDNEY CONGESTION AND FAILURE, PANCREATITIS, AND DAMAGE TO THE LIVER AND SPLEEN. IF SUFFICIENT AMOUNTS ARE ABSORBED, VASCULAR COLLAPSE, SHOCK, HYPOTHERMIA, UNCONSCIOUSNESS, AND DEATH MAY OCCUR. PATHOLOGIC FINDINGS AS DETAILED IN ACUTE SKIN EXPOSURE MAY BE FOUND. **CHRONIC EXPOSURE-** NO SPECIFIC DATA AVAILABLE. MAY CAUSE SYSTEMIC SYMPTOMS AS DETAILED IN CHRONIC INHALATION.

FIRST AID- IN THE ABSENCE OF CORROSIVE INJURY, REMOVE POISON BY IPECAC EMESIS. ACTIVATED CHARCOAL IS ALSO USEFUL. FOLLOW WITH 240 ML OF MILK. GASTRIC LAVAGE AND EMESIS ARE CONTRAINDICATED IN THE PRESENCE OF ESOPHAGEAL INJURY (DREISBACH, HANDBOOK OF POISONING, 12TH EDITION). GET MEDICAL ATTENTION IMMEDIATELY.

ANTIDOTE: NO SPECIFIC ANTIDOTE. TREAT SYMPTOMATICALLY AND SUPPORTIVELY.

REACTIVITY

REACTIVITY: STABLE UNDER NORMAL TEMPERATURES AND PRESSURES.

INCOMPATIBILITIES: M-CRESOL: ACIDS (STRONG): VIOLENT REACTION. CHLOROSULFONIC ACID: INCREASE IN TEMPERATURE AND PRESSURE IN A CLOSED CONTAINER. METALS (ACTIVE): VIOLENT REACTION. NITRIC ACID: INCREASE IN TEMPERATURE AND PRESSURE IN A CLOSED CONTAINER. OLEUM: INCREASE IN TEMPERATURE AND PRESSURE IN A CLOSED CONTAINER. OXIDANTS: VIOLENT REACTION.

DECOMPOSITION: THERMAL DECOMPOSITION MAY RELEASE ACRID SMOKE AND IRRITATING FUMES.

POLYMERIZATION: HAZARDOUS POLYMERIZATION HAS NOT BEEN REPORTED TO OCCUR UNDER NORMAL TEMPERATURES AND PRESSURES.

STORAGE AND DISPOSAL

OBSERVE ALL FEDERAL, STATE AND LOCAL REGULATIONS WHEN STORING OR DISPOSING OF THIS SUBSTANCE. FOR ASSISTANCE, CONTACT THE DISTRICT DIRECTOR OF THE ENVIRONMENTAL PROTECTION AGENCY.

****STORAGE****

PROTECT AGAINST PHYSICAL DAMAGE. STORE IN A COOL, DRY, WELL VENTILATED LOCATION, AWAY FROM ANY AREA WHERE THE FIRE HAZARD MAY BE ACUTE. OUTSIDE OR DETACHED STORAGE IS PREFERRED. SEPARATE FROM OXIDIZING MATERIALS (NFPA 49, HAZARDOUS CHEMICALS DATA, 1975). STORE AWAY FROM INCOMPATIBLE SUBSTANCES.

****DISPOSAL****

DISPOSAL MUST BE IN ACCORDANCE WITH STANDARDS APPLICABLE TO GENERATORS OF HAZARDOUS WASTE, 40CFR 262. EPA HAZARDOUS WASTE NUMBER U052.

M-CRESOL - REGULATORY LEVEL: 200.0 MG/L MATERIALS WHICH CONTAIN THE ABOVE SUBSTANCE AT OR ABOVE THE REGULATORY LEVEL MEET THE EPA CHARACTERISTIC OF TOXICITY, AND MUST BE DISPOSED OF IN ACCORDANCE WITH 40 CFR PART 262. EPA HAZARDOUS WASTE NUMBER D024.

CONDITIONS TO AVOID

MAY BURN BUT DOES NOT IGNITE READILY. CONTAINERS MAY EXPLODE IN HEAT OF FIRE.

SPILL AND LEAK PROCEDURES

SOIL SPILL: DIG HOLDING AREA SUCH AS LAGOON, POND OR PIT FOR CONTAINMENT. DIKE FLOW OF SPILLED MATERIAL USING SOIL OR SANDBAGS OR FOAMED BARRIERS SUCH AS POLYURETHANE OR CONCRETE.

USE CEMENT POWDER OR FLY ASH TO ABSORB LIQUID MASS.

AIR SPILL: KNOCK DOWN VAPORS WITH WATER SPRAY. KEEP UPWIND.

WATER USED TO KNOCK DOWN VAPORS MAY BECOME CORROSIVE OR TOXIC AND SHOULD BE CONTAINED PROPERLY FOR LATER DISPOSAL.

WATER SPILL: USE ACTIVATED CARBON TO ABSORB SPILLED SUBSTANCE THAT IS DISSOLVED.

USE MECHANICAL DREDGES OR LIFTS TO EXTRACT IMMOBILIZED MASSES OF POLLUTION AND PRECIPITATES.

TRAP SPILLED MATERIAL AT BOTTOM IN DEEP WATER POCKETS, EXCAVATED HOLDING AREAS OR WITHIN SAND BAG BARRIERS.

OCCUPATIONAL SPILL: DO NOT TOUCH SPILLED MATERIAL. STOP LEAK IF YOU CAN DO IT WITHOUT RISK. USE WATER SPRAY TO REDUCE VAPORS. FOR SMALL SPILLS, TAKE UP WITH SAND OR OTHER ABSORBENT MATERIAL AND PLACE INTO CONTAINERS FOR LATER DISPOSAL. FOR SMALL DRY SPILLS, WITH A CLEAN SHOVEL PLACE MATERIAL INTO CLEAN, DRY CONTAINERS AND COVER. MOVE CONTAINERS FROM SPILL AREA. FOR LARGER SPILLS, DIKE FAR AHEAD OF SPILL FOR LATER DISPOSAL. KEEP UNNECESSARY PEOPLE AWAY. ISOLATE HAZARD AREA AND DENY ENTRY. VENTILATE CLOSED SPACES BEFORE ENTERING.

REPORTABLE QUANTITY (RQ): 1000 POUNDS THE SUPERFUND AMENDMENTS AND REAUTHORIZATION ACT (SARA) SECTION 304 REQUIRES THAT A RELEASE EQUAL TO OR GREATER THAN THE REPORTABLE QUANTITY FOR THIS SUBSTANCE BE IMMEDIATELY REPORTED TO THE LOCAL EMERGENCY PLANNING COMMITTEE AND THE STATE EMERGENCY RESPONSE COMMISSION (40 CFR 355.40). IF THE RELEASE OF THIS SUBSTANCE IS REPORTABLE UNDER CERCLA SECTION 103, THE NATIONAL RESPONSE CENTER MUST BE NOTIFIED IMMEDIATELY AT (800) 424-8802 OR (202) 426-2675 IN THE METROPOLITAN WASHINGTON, D.C. AREA (40 CFR 302.6).

PROTECTIVE EQUIPMENT

VENTILATION: PROVIDE LOCAL EXHAUST OR PROCESS ENCLOSURE VENTILATION TO MEET PUBLISHED EXPOSURE LIMITS.

RESPIRATOR: THE FOLLOWING RESPIRATORS AND MAXIMUM USE CONCENTRATIONS ARE RECOMMENDATIONS BY THE U.S. DEPARTMENT OF HEALTH AND HUMAN SERVICES, NIOSH POCKET GUIDE TO CHEMICAL HAZARDS; NIOSH CRITERIA DOCUMENTS OR BY THE U.S. DEPARTMENT OF LABOR, 29 CFR 1910 SUBPART Z. THE SPECIFIC RESPIRATOR SELECTED MUST BE BASED ON CONTAMINATION LEVELS FOUND IN THE WORK PLACE, MUST NOT EXCEED THE WORKING LIMITS OF THE RESPIRATOR AND BE JOINTLY APPROVED BY THE NATIONAL INSTITUTE FOR OCCUPATIONAL SAFETY AND HEALTH AND THE MINE SAFETY AND HEALTH ADMINISTRATION (NIOSH-MSHA).

CRESOL (ALL ISOMERS):

23 PPM- ANY CHEMICAL CARTRIDGE RESPIRATOR WITH ORGANIC VAPOR CARTRIDGE(S) IN COMBINATION WITH A DUST AND MIST FILTER. ANY SUPPLIED-AIR RESPIRATOR. ANY SELF-CONTAINED BREATHING APPARATUS.

57.5 PPM- ANY SUPPLIED-AIR RESPIRATOR OPERATED IN CONTINUOUS FLOW MODE. ANY POWERED AIR-PURIFYING RESPIRATOR WITH ORGANIC VAPOR CARTRIDGE(S) IN COMBINATION WITH A DUST AND MIST FILTER.

115 PPM- ANY CHEMICAL CARTRIDGE RESPIRATOR WITH A FULL FACEPIECE AND ORGANIC VAPOR CARTRIDGE(S) IN COMBINATION WITH A HIGH-EFFICIENCY PARTICULATE FILTER. ANY SUPPLIED-AIR RESPIRATOR WITH A FULL FACEPIECE. ANY SELF-CONTAINED BREATHING APPARATUS WITH A FULL FACEPIECE. ANY AIR-PURIFYING FULL FACEPIECE RESPIRATOR (GAS MASK) WITH A CHIN-STYLE OR FRONT- OR BACK-MOUNTED ORGANIC VAPOR CANISTER HAVING A HIGH-EFFICIENCY PARTICULATE FILTER. ANY POWERED AIR-PURIFYING RESPIRATOR WITH A TIGHT-FITTING FACEPIECE AND A HIGH-EFFICIENCY PARTICULATE FILTER. ANY SUPPLIED-AIR RESPIRATOR WITH A TIGHT-FITTING FACEPIECE OPERATED IN A CONTINUOUS FLOW MODE.

250 PPM- ANY SUPPLIED-AIR RESPIRATOR WITH A FULL FACEPIECE AND OPERATED IN A PRESSURE-DEMAND OR OTHER POSITIVE PRESSURE MODE.

ESCAPE- ANY AIR-PURIFYING FULL FACEPIECE RESPIRATOR (GAS MASK) WITH A CHIN-STYLE OR FRONT- OR BACK-MOUNTED ORGANIC VAPOR CANISTER. HAVING A HIGH-EFFICIENCY PARTICULATE FILTER. ANY APPROPRIATE ESCAPE-TYPE SELF-CONTAINED BREATHING APPARATUS.

FOR FIREFIGHTING AND OTHER IMMEDIATELY DANGEROUS TO LIFE OR HEALTH CONDITIONS:

SELF-CONTAINED BREATHING APPARATUS WITH FULL FACEPIECE OPERATED IN PRESSURE-DEMAND OR OTHER POSITIVE PRESSURE MODE.

SUPPLIED-AIR RESPIRATOR WITH FULL FACEPIECE AND OPERATED IN PRESSURE-DEMAND OR OTHER POSITIVE PRESSURE MODE IN COMBINATION WITH AN AUXILIARY SELF-CONTAINED BREATHING APPARATUS OPERATED IN PRESSURE-DEMAND OR OTHER POSITIVE PRESSURE MODE.

CLOTHING: EMPLOYEE MUST WEAR APPROPRIATE PROTECTIVE (IMPERVIOUS) CLOTHING AND EQUIPMENT TO PREVENT ANY POSSIBILITY OF SKIN CONTACT WITH THIS SUBSTANCE.

GLOVES: EMPLOYEE MUST WEAR APPROPRIATE PROTECTIVE GLOVES TO PREVENT CONTACT WITH THIS SUBSTANCE.

EYE PROTECTION: EMPLOYEE MUST WEAR SPLASH-PROOF OR DUST-RESISTANT SAFETY GOGGLES AND A FACESHIELD TO PREVENT CONTACT WITH THIS SUBSTANCE.

EMERGENCY WASH FACILITIES: WHERE THERE IS ANY POSSIBILITY THAT AN EMPLOYEE'S EYES AND/OR SKIN MAY BE EXPOSED TO THIS SUBSTANCE, THE EMPLOYER SHOULD PROVIDE AN EYE WASH FOUNTAIN AND QUICK DRENCH SHOWER WITHIN THE IMMEDIATE WORK AREA FOR EMERGENCY USE.

AUTHORIZED BY- OCCUPATIONAL HEALTH SERVICES, INC.

CREATION DATE: 11/16/89 ***REVISION DATE:*** 07/13/90

MATERIAL SAFETY DATA SHEET

OCCUPATIONAL HEALTH SERVICES, INC.
AGRICULTURE AND PESTICIDE DIVISION
450 SEVENTH AVENUE, SUITE 2407
NEW YORK, NEW YORK 10123
1-800-445-MSDS OR (212) 967-1100

EMERGENCY CONTACT:
JOHN S. BRANSFORD, JR. (615) 292-1180

SUBSTANCE IDENTIFICATION

CAS-NUMBER 7786-30-3

SUBSTANCE: MAGNESIUM CHLORIDE

TRADE NAMES/SYNONYMS: MAGNOGENE; MAGNESIUM DICHLORIDE; AEROTEX ACCELERATOR MX; CHLOROMAGNESITE; MAGNESIUM CHLORIDE (MGCL2); CL2MG; PST13360

CHEMICAL FAMILY: INORGANIC SALT

MOLECULAR FORMULA: MG-CL2

MOLECULAR WEIGHT: 95.21

CERCLA RATINGS (SCALE 0-3): HEALTH=3 FIRE=0 REACTIVITY=1 PERSISTENCE=1

NFPA RATINGS (SCALE 0-4): HEALTH=U FIRE=0 REACTIVITY=1

COMPONENTS AND CONTAMINANTS

COMPONENT: MAGNESIUM CHLORIDE ***PERCENT:*** 100.0
CAS# 7786-30-3

OTHER CONTAMINANTS: NONE

EXPOSURE LIMITS: NO OCCUPATIONAL EXPOSURE LIMITS ESTABLISHED BY OSHA, ACGIH, OR NIOSH.

PHYSICAL DATA

DESCRIPTION: ODORLESS, COLORLESS TO WHITE, LUSTROUS, DELIQUESCENT CRYSTALLINE SOLID. ***BOILING POINT:*** 2574 F (1412 C) ***MELTING POINT:*** 1317 F (714 C)

SPECIFIC GRAVITY: 2.316-2.333 ***SOLUBILITY IN WATER:*** SOLUBLE (REACTS)

SOLVENT SOLUBILITY: SOLUBLE IN ALCOHOL, ETHER.

FIRE AND EXPLOSION DATA

FIRE AND EXPLOSION HAZARD: NEGLIGIBLE FIRE HAZARD WHEN EXPOSED TO HEAT OR FLAME.

FIREFIGHTING MEDIA: EXTINGUISH USING AGENT SUITABLE FOR TYPE OF SURROUNDING FIRE.

FIREFIGHTING: NO ACUTE HAZARD. MOVE CONTAINER FROM FIRE AREA IF POSSIBLE. AVOID BREATHING VAPORS OR DUSTS; KEEP UPWIND.

TOXICITY

MAGNESIUM CHLORIDE: TOXICITY DATA: ANHYDROUS: 2800 MG/KG ORAL-RAT LD50; 900 MG/KG SUBCUTANEOUS-RAT LDLO; 14 MG/KG INTRAVENOUS-MOUSE LD50; 229 MG/KG INTRAVENOUS-DOG LDLO; 225 MG/KG INTRAPERITONEAL-RAT LDLO; 1338 MG/KG INTRAPERITONEAL-MOUSE LD50; 1 GM/KG INTRAMUSCULAR-MAMMAL LD50; MUTAGENIC DATA (RTECS). HEXAHYDRATE: 8100 MG/KG ORAL-RAT LD50; 7600 MG/KG ORAL-MOUSE LD50; 176 MG/KG INTRAVENOUS-RAT LDLO; 250 MG/KG INTRAVENOUS-GUINEA PIG LDLO; 775 MG/KG INTRAPERITONEAL-MOUSE LD50; 250 MG/KG INTRAARTERIAL-GUINEA PIG LDLO; MUTAGENIC DATA (RTECS). CARCINOGEN STATUS: NONE. LOCAL EFFECTS: IRRITANT- MUCOUS MEMBRANES. ACUTE TOXICITY LEVEL: MODERATELY TOXIC BY INGESTION (ANHYDROUS); SLIGHTLY TOXIC BY INGESTION (HEXAHYDRATE). TARGET EFFECTS: POISONING MAY AFFECT THE CENTRAL NERVOUS, CARDIOVASCULAR AND RESPIRATORY SYSTEMS. AT INCREASED RISK FROM EXPOSURE: PERSONS WITH KIDNEY IMPAIRMENT.

HEALTH EFFECTS AND FIRST AID

INHALATION: MAGNESIUM CHLORIDE: IRRITANT. **ACUTE EXPOSURE-** INHALATION OF DUST MAY CAUSE IRRITATION TO THE MUCOUS MEMBRANES WITH SYMPTOMS OF COUGHING AND CHEST DISCOMFORT. **CHRONIC EXPOSURE-** NO DATA AVAILABLE.

FIRST AID- REMOVE FROM EXPOSURE AREA TO FRESH AIR IMMEDIATELY. IF BREATHING HAS STOPPED, PERFORM ARTIFICIAL RESPIRATION. KEEP PERSON WARM AND AT REST. TREAT SYMPTOMATICALLY AND SUPPORTIVELY. GET MEDICAL ATTENTION IMMEDIATELY.

SKIN CONTACT: MAGNESIUM CHLORIDE: **ACUTE EXPOSURE-** MAY CAUSE IRRITATION. **CHRONIC EXPOSURE-** NO DATA AVAILABLE.

FIRST AID- REMOVE CONTAMINATED CLOTHING AND SHOES IMMEDIATELY. WASH AFFECTED AREA WITH SOAP OR MILD DETERGENT AND LARGE AMOUNTS OF WATER UNTIL NO EVIDENCE OF CHEMICAL REMAINS (APPROXIMATELY 15-20 MINUTES). GET MEDICAL ATTENTION IMMEDIATELY.

EYE CONTACT: MAGNESIUM CHLORIDE: **ACUTE EXPOSURE-** DUST MAY CAUSE IRRITATION WITH REDNESS AND PAIN. SOLUTIONS ARE CONSIDERED ESSENTIALLY INNOCUOUS WHEN APPLIED TO THE EYES. A SLURRY OF MAGNESIUM CHLORIDE CRYSTALS APPLIED TO RABBIT EYES CAUSED A SPOTTY CLOUDING OF THE CORNEA AND ANTERIOR LENS CORTEX, BUT CLEARED AFTER A SHORT TIME. **CHRONIC EXPOSURE-** NO DATA AVAILABLE.

FIRST AID- WASH EYES IMMEDIATELY WITH LARGE AMOUNTS OF WATER OR NORMAL SALINE, OCCASIONALLY LIFTING UPPER AND LOWER LIDS, UNTIL NO EVIDENCE OF CHEMICAL REMAINS (APPROXIMATELY 15-20 MINUTES). GET MEDICAL ATTENTION IMMEDIATELY.

INGESTION: MAGNESIUM CHLORIDE: **ACUTE EXPOSURE-** THE LETHAL DOSE IN RATS IS 2800 MG/KG. THE SYMPTOMS WERE NOT REPORTED. THE HYDRATED SALT IS REPORTED TO BE ONLY ONE-THIRD AS TOXIC AS THE UNHYDRATED SALT. MAGNESIUM SALTS ARE POORLY ABSORBED AND RARELY CAUSE TOXIC EFFECTS OTHER THAN POSSIBLE GASTROINTESTINAL IRRITATION WITH PURGING. HOWEVER, ACCUMULATION MAY BE SUFFICIENT TO PRODUCE TOXIC EFFECTS IF RENAL OR INTESTINAL FUNCTION IS IMPAIRED. MASSIVE DOSES MAY CAUSE VOMITING, WATERY DIARRHEA, ELECTROLYTE IMBALANCE, HYPOTENSION, SEDATION, CONFUSION, RESPIRATORY CONGESTION, ABOLITION OF REFLEXES, AND CENTRAL NERVOUS SYSTEM DEPRESSION, WHICH MAY PROGRESS THROUGH COMA TO MEDULLARY PARALYSIS. EFFECTS ON THE CARDIOVASCULAR SYSTEM MAY INCLUDE BRADYCARDIA AND CARDIAC ARREST. FATALITIES ARE RARE BUT HAVE BEEN REPORTED AFTER INGESTION OF DOSES CONTAINING AS LITTLE AS 30 GRAMS MAGNESIUM ION. **CHRONIC EXPOSURE-** LONG-TERM USE OF MAGNESIUM CONTAINING ANTACIDS HAS CAUSED RENAL FAILURE FROM PRECIPITATION OF MAGNESIUM AMMONIUM PHOSPHATE IN THE KIDNEY.

FIRST AID- INDUCE EMESIS OR ADMINISTER LAVAGE. USE SODIUM CATHARTICS WITH CAUTION IN THE PRESENCE OF CARDIAC FAILURE AND RENAL FAILURE. ACTIVATED CHARCOAL IS NOT USEFUL. (BARCELOUX & ELLENHORN, MEDICAL TOXICOLOGY; DIAGNOSIS & TREATMENT OF HUMAN POISONING). TREATMENT SHOULD BE PERFORMED BY MEDICAL PERSONNEL. GET MEDICAL ATTENTION IMMEDIATELY.

ANTIDOTE: THE FOLLOWING ANTIDOTE HAS BEEN RECOMMENDED. HOWEVER, THE DECISION AS TO WHETHER THE SEVERITY OF POISONING REQUIRES ADMINISTRATION OF ANY ANTIDOTE AND ACTUAL DOSE REQUIRED SHOULD BE MADE BY QUALIFIED MEDICAL PERSONNEL.
MAGNESIUM COMPOUND POISONING: WHEN THE SERUM MAGNESIUM LEVEL EXCEEDS 5 MEQ/L AND THE PATIENT EXHIBITS SYMPTOMS, GIVE CALCIUM GLUCONATE, 10 ML OF 10% SOLUTION (INTRAVENOUSLY) OVER SEVERAL MINUTES. THE DOSE MAY BE REPEATED ONCE; THEN THE LEVEL SHOULD BE CHECKED AGAIN. (ELLENHORN AND BARCELOUX, MEDICAL TOXICOLOGY, 1ST ED.). ANTIDOTE SHOULD BE ADMINISTERED BY QUALIFIED MEDICAL PERSONNEL.

REACTIVITY

REACTIVITY: REACTS EXOTHERMICALLY WITH WATER.

INCOMPATIBILITIES: MAGNESIUM CHLORIDE: FURAN-2-PEROXYCARBOXYLIC ACID: EXPLOSION ON CONTACT. OXIDIZERS (STRONG): MAY RELEASE CHLORINE GAS. STEEL: MAY CAUSE RAPID OXIDATION IN THE PRESENCE OF MOISTURE.

DECOMPOSITION: THERMAL DECOMPOSITION PRODUCTS MAY INCLUDE TOXIC AND CORROSIVE FUMES OF CHLORINE.

POLYMERIZATION: HAZARDOUS POLYMERIZATION HAS NOT BEEN REPORTED TO OCCUR UNDER NORMAL TEMPERATURES AND PRESSURES.

STORAGE AND DISPOSAL

OBSERVE ALL FEDERAL, STATE AND LOCAL REGULATIONS WHEN STORING OR DISPOSING OF THIS SUBSTANCE. FOR ASSISTANCE, CONTACT THE DISTRICT DIRECTOR OF THE ENVIRONMENTAL PROTECTION AGENCY.

STORAGE

STORE AWAY FROM INCOMPATIBLE SUBSTANCES.

CONDITIONS TO AVOID

NO REPORTS FOUND.

SPILL AND LEAK PROCEDURES

OCCUPATIONAL SPILL: SWEEP UP AND PLACE IN SUITABLE CLEAN, DRY CONTAINERS FOR RECLAMATION OR LATER DISPOSAL. DO NOT FLUSH SPILLED MATERIAL INTO SEWER. KEEP UNNECESSARY PEOPLE AWAY.

PROTECTIVE EQUIPMENT

VENTILATION: PROVIDE LOCAL EXHAUST OR PROCESS ENCLOSURE VENTILATION SYSTEM.

RESPIRATOR: THE FOLLOWING RESPIRATORS ARE RECOMMENDED BASED ON INFORMATION FOUND IN THE PHYSICAL DATA, TOXICITY AND HEALTH EFFECTS SECTIONS. THEY ARE RANKED IN ORDER FROM MINIMUM TO MAXIMUM RESPIRATORY PROTECTION. THE SPECIFIC RESPIRATOR SELECTED MUST BE BASED ON CONTAMINATION LEVELS FOUND IN THE WORK PLACE, MUST NOT EXCEED THE WORKING LIMITS OF THE RESPIRATOR AND BE JOINTLY APPROVED BY THE NATIONAL INSTITUTE FOR OCCUPATIONAL SAFETY AND HEALTH AND THE MINE SAFETY AND HEALTH ADMINISTRATION (NIOSH-MSHA).
DUST AND MIST RESPIRATOR WITH A FULL FACEPIECE.
AIR-PURIFYING FULL FACEPIECE RESPIRATOR WITH A HIGH-EFFICIENCY PARTICULATE FILTER.
POWERED AIR-PURIFYING RESPIRATOR WITH A TIGHT-FITTING FACEPIECE AND HIGH-EFFICIENCY PARTICULATE FILTER.
TYPE 'C' SUPPLIED-AIR RESPIRATOR WITH A FULL FACEPIECE OPERATED IN PRESSURE-DEMAND OR OTHER POSITIVE PRESSURE MODE OR WITH A FULL FACEPIECE, HELMET OR HOOD OPERATED IN CONTINUOUS-FLOW MODE. SELF-CONTAINED BREATHING APPARATUS WITH A FULL FACEPIECE OPERATED IN PRESSURE-DEMAND OR OTHER POSITIVE PRESSURE MODE.
FOR FIREFIGHTING AND OTHER IMMEDIATELY DANGEROUS TO LIFE OR HEALTH CONDITIONS:
SELF-CONTAINED BREATHING APPARATUS WITH FULL FACEPIECE OPERATED IN PRESSURE-DEMAND OR OTHER POSITIVE PRESSURE MODE.
SUPPLIED-AIR RESPIRATOR WITH FULL FACEPIECE AND OPERATED IN PRESSURE-DEMAND OR OTHER POSITIVE PRESSURE MODE IN COMBINATION WITH AN AUXILIARY SELF-CONTAINED BREATHING APPARATUS OPERATED IN PRESSURE-DEMAND OR OTHER POSITIVE PRESSURE MODE.

CLOTHING: EMPLOYEE MUST WEAR APPROPRIATE PROTECTIVE (IMPERVIOUS) CLOTHING AND EQUIPMENT TO PREVENT REPEATED OR PROLONGED SKIN CONTACT WITH THIS SUBSTANCE.

GLOVES: EMPLOYEE MUST WEAR APPROPRIATE PROTECTIVE GLOVES TO PREVENT CONTACT WITH THIS SUBSTANCE.

EYE PROTECTION: EMPLOYEE MUST WEAR SPLASH-PROOF OR DUST-RESISTANT SAFETY GOGGLES TO PREVENT EYE CONTACT WITH THIS SUBSTANCE.
EMERGENCY EYE WASH: WHERE THERE IS ANY POSSIBILITY THAT AN EMPLOYEE'S EYES MAY BE EXPOSED TO THIS SUBSTANCE, THE EMPLOYER SHOULD PROVIDE AN EYE WASH FOUNTAIN WITHIN THE IMMEDIATE WORK AREA FOR EMERGENCY USE.

AUTHORIZED BY- OCCUPATIONAL HEALTH SERVICES, INC.
CREATION DATE: 11/16/89 ***REVISION DATE:*** 05/31/90

MATERIAL SAFETY DATA SHEET

OCCUPATIONAL HEALTH SERVICES, INC.
AGRICULTURE AND PESTICIDE DIVISION
450 SEVENTH AVENUE, SUITE 2407
NEW YORK, NEW YORK 10123
1-800-445-MSDS OR (212) 967-1100

EMERGENCY CONTACT:
JOHN S. BRANSFORD, JR. (615) 292-1180

SUBSTANCE IDENTIFICATION

CAS-NUMBER 12057-74-8
SUBSTANCE: **MAGNESIUM PHOSPHIDE**
TRADE NAMES/SYNONYMS: TRIMAGNESIUM PHOSPHIDE; UN 2011; PST13480
CHEMICAL FAMILY: INORGANIC SALT
MOLECULAR FORMULA: MG3-P2 MOL WT: 134.88
CERCLA RATINGS (SCALE 0-3): HEALTH=3 FIRE=3 REACTIVITY=2 PERSISTENCE=3

NFPA RATINGS (SCALE 0-4): HEALTH = 3 FIRE = 3 REACTIVITY = 2

COMPONENTS AND CONTAMINANTS

COMPONENT: MAGNESIUM PHOSPHIDE ***PERCENT:*** 100
CAS# 12057-74-8
OTHER CONTAMINANTS: NONE
EXPOSURE LIMITS: MAGNESIUM PHOSPHIDE: NONE ESTABLISHED

PHYSICAL DATA

DESCRIPTION: SOLID ***SPECIFIC GRAVITY:*** 2.1 ***SOLUBILITY IN WATER:*** REACTS
SOLVENT SOLUBILITY: DECOMPOSES IN DILUTE MINERAL ACIDS

FIRE AND EXPLOSION DATA

FIRE AND EXPLOSION HAZARD: DANGEROUS WHEN WET! ON CONTACT WITH WATER OR DAMP AIR, RELEASES SPONTANEOUSLY FLAMMABLE GASES OF PHOSPHINE AND DIPHOSPHINE. IGNITES ON HEATING WITH CHLORINE, BROMINE, OR IODINE VAPORS.
FLASH POINT: FLAMMABLE SOLID
FIREFIGHTING MEDIA: DRY CHEMICAL, SODA ASH, LIME OR SAND (1987 EMERGENCY RESPONSE GUIDEBOOK, DOT P 5800.4).
FOR LARGER FIRE, WITHDRAW FROM AREA AND LET FIRE BURN. ***FIREFIGHTING:*** MOVE CONTAINER FROM FIRE AREA IF POSSIBLE. DO NOT USE WATER OR FOAM! (1987 EMERGENCY RESPONSE GUIDEBOOK, DOT P 5800.4, GUIDE PAGE 41). DANGEROUS WHEN WET.

TRANSPORTATION DATA

DEPARTMENT OF TRANSPORTATION HAZARD CLASSIFICATION 49 CFR 172.101: FLAMMABLE SOLID
DEPARTMENT OF TRANSPORTATION LABELING REQUIREMENTS 49 CFR 172.101 AND SUBPART E: FLAMMABLE SOLID AND DANGEROUS WHEN WET
DEPARTMENT OF TRANSPORTATION PACKAGING REQUIREMENTS: 49 CFR 173.154 EXCEPTIONS: 49 CFR 173.153

TOXICITY

MAGNESIUM PHOSPHIDE: TOXICITY DATA: 580 PPM/1 HR INHALATION-RAT LCLO; 173 PPM/2 HR INHALATION-CAT LCLO; 288 PPM/2 HR INHALATION-GUINEA PIG LCLO. CARCINOGEN STATUS: NONE. ACUTE TOXICITY LEVEL: INSUFFICIENT DATA. TARGET EFFECTS: HEPATOTOXIN. POISONING MAY AFFECT THE CARDIOVASCULAR SYSTEM, KIDNEYS, AND POSSIBLY THE RESPORATORY TRACT.

HEALTH EFFECTS AND FIRST AID

INHALATION: MAGNESIUM PHOSPHIDE: HEPATOTOXIN. **ACUTE EXPOSURE-** PHOSPHIDES MAY CAUSE HEADACHE, DIZZINESS, NAUSEA, VOMITING, FATIGUE, COUGHING, JAUNDICE, PARESTHESIAS, ATAXIA, TREMOR, HYPOTENSION, DYSPNEA, PULMONARY EDEMA, CYANOSIS, SHOCK, CARDIAC ARRHYTHMIAS, CONVULSIONS, AND COMA. IF DEATH IS NOT IMMEDIATE, KIDNEY DAMAGE MAY APPEAR LATER. **CHRONIC EXPOSURE-** PROLONGED PHOSPHIDE INHALATION MAY CAUSE TOOTHACHE, FOLLOWED BY SWELLING OF THE JAW, AND LATER NECROSIS OF THE JAW. OTHER SYMPTOMS MAY INCLUDE WEAKNESS, WEIGHT LOSS, ANOREXIA, ANEMIA, AND SPONTANEOUS BONE FRACTURES.
FIRST AID- REMOVE FROM EXPOSURE AREA TO FRESH AIR IMMEDIATELY. IF BREATHING HAS STOPPED, PERFORM ARTIFICIAL RESPIRATION. KEEP PERSON WARM AND AT REST. TREAT SYMPTOMATICALLY AND SUPPORTIVELY. GET MEDICAL ATTENTION IMMEDIATELY.

SKIN CONTACT: MAGNESIUM PHOSPHIDE: **ACUTE EXPOSURE-** REACTION WITH MOISTURE ON SKIN MAY RESULT IN SERIOUS BURNS. THERE MAY BE IRRITATION AND SMALL SEPTIC BLISTER MAY FORM. **CHRONIC EXPOSURE-** HAS NOT BEEN OBSERVED IN HUMANS.
FIRST AID- REMOVE ALL CONTAMINATED CLOTHING AND SHOES IMMEDIATELY. WIPE ALL MATERIAL OFF SKIN BEFORE WASHING TO PREVENT HYPERTHERMIC REACTION. WASH AFFECTED AREA WITH SOAP OR MILD DETERGENT AND LARGE AMOUNTS OF WATER UNTIL NO EVIDENCE OF CHEMICAL REMAINS. IN CASE OF BURNS, COVER AREA WITH STERILE, DRY DRESSING. BANDAGE SECURELY, BUT NOT TOO TIGHTLY. GET MEDICAL ATTENTION.

EYE CONTACT: MAGNESIUM PHOSPHIDE: **ACUTE EXPOSURE-** DIRECT CONTACT MAY CAUSE SERIOUS CORNEAL BURNS. **CHRONIC EXPOSURE-** HAS NOT BEEN REPORTED IN HUMANS.
FIRST AID- WASH EYES IMMEDIATELY WITH LARGE AMOUNTS OF WATER, OCCASIONALLY LIFTING UPPER AND LOWER LIDS, UNTIL NO EVIDENCE OF CHEMICAL REMAINS (AT LEAST 15-20 MINUTES). CONTINUE IRRIGATING WITH NORMAL SALINE UNTIL THE PH HAS RETURNED TO NORMAL (30-60 MINUTES). COVER WITH STERILE BANDAGES. GET MEDICAL ATTENTION IMMEDIATELY.

INGESTION: MAGNESIUM PHOSPHIDE: HEPATOTOXIN. **ACUTE EXPOSURE-** TOXIC AMOUNTS WILL CAUSE LIVER DAMAGE, WITH TENDER AND ENLARGED LIVER, JAUNDICE, PULMONARY EDEMA, DYSPNEA, CYANOSIS, NAUSEA, VOMITING, DIARRHEA, SHOCK AND CONVULSIONS. **CHRONIC EXPOSURE-** MAY RESULT IN SAME SYMPTOMS AS CHRONIC INHALATION: JAW NECROSIS, ANEMIA, AND BONE FRACTURES.
FIRST AID- REMOVE POISON BY GASTRIC LAVAGE WITH 5-10 LITER OF TAP WATER. TREAT PULMONARY EDEMA, SHOCK AND HEPATIC FAILURE.(DREISBACK, HANDBOOK OF POISONING, 11TH ED.) GET MEDICAL ATTENTION IMMEDIATELY.
ANTIDOTE: NO SPECIFIC ANTIDOTE. TREAT SYMPTOMATICALLY AND SUPPORTIVELY.

REACTIVITY

REACTIVITY: MAGNESIUM PHOSPHIDE: DANGEROUS WHEN WET! REACTS VIOLENTLY WITH WATER, RELEASING TOXIC AND HAZARDOUS GASES.
INCOMPATIBILITIES: MAGNESIUM PHOSPHIDE: WATER: REACTS VIOLENTLY NITRIC ACID: REACTS VIOLENTLY CLORIDE VAPORS: IGNITES WITH HEAT BROMINE VAPORS: IGNITES WITH HEAT IODINE VAPORS: IGNITES WITH HEAT
DECOMPOSITION: MAGNESIUM PHOSPHIDE: DECOMPOSES IN WATER OR MOIST AIR, RELEASING HIGHLY TOXIC AND SPONTANEOUSLY FLAMMABLE PHOSPHINE AND DIPHOSPHINE AND TOXIC OXIDES OF PHOSPHORUS.
POLYMERIZATION: HAZARDOUS POLYMERIZATION HAS NOT BEEN REPORTED TO OCCUR UNDER NORMAL TEMPERATURES AND PRESSURES.

CONDITIONS TO AVOID

MAY IGNITE IN PRESENCE OF MOISTURE AND CONTACT WITH WATER PRODUCES FLAMMABLE GAS. RUNOFF TO SEWER MAY CREATE FIRE OR EXPLOSION HAZARD.

SPILL AND LEAK PROCEDURES

OCCUPATIONAL SPILL: SHUT OFF IGNITION SOUCES. DO NOT TOUCH SPILLED MATERIAL. DO NOT GET WATER ON SPILLED MATERIAL OR INSIDE CONTAINER. FOR SMALL SPILL, WITH CLEAN SHOVEL PLACE MATERIAL INTO CLEAN, DRY CONTAINER AND COVER; MOVE CONTAINERS FROM SPILL AREA. FOR LARGER SPILLS, DIKE SPILL FOR LATER DISPOSAL. COVER POWDER SPILLS WITH PLASTIC SHEET OR TARP TO MINIMIZE SPREADING. CLEAN UP ONLY UNDER SUPERVISION OF AN EXPERT. KEEP UNNECESSARY PEOPLE AWAY. ISOLATE HAZARD AREA AND DENY ENTRY.
USE EXTINGUISHING AGENT SUITABLE FOR TYPE OF SURROUNDING MATERIAL.

PROTECTIVE EQUIPMENT

VENTILATION: PROVIDE LOCAL EXHAUST OR PROCESS ENCLOSURE VENTILATION TO MEET THE PUBLISHED EXPOSURE LIMITS. VENTILATION EQUIPMENT MUST BE EXPLOSION-PROOF.
RESPIRATOR: HIGH LEVELS- SUPPLIED-AIR RESPIRATOR WITH A FULL FACEPIECE, HELMET, OR HOOD. SELF-CONTAINED BREATHING APPARATUS WITH A FULL FACEPIECE.
FIREFIGHTING- SELF-CONTAINED BREATHING APPARATUS WITH A FULL FACEPIECE OPERATED IN PRESSURE-DEMAND OR OTHER POSITIVE PRESSURE MODE.
CLOTHING: EMPLOYEE MUST WEAR APPROPRIATE PROTECTIVE (IMPERVIOUS) CLOTHING AND EQUIPMENT TO PREVENT ANY POSSIBILITY OF SKIN CONTACT WITH THIS SUBSTANCE.
GLOVES: EMPLOYEE MUST WEAR APPROPRIATE PROTECTIVE GLOVES TO PREVENT CONTACT WITH THIS SUBSTANCE.
EYE PROTECTION: EMPLOYEE MUST WEAR SPLASH-PROOF OR DUST-RESISTANT SAFETY GOGGLES AND A FACESHIELD TO PREVENT CONTACT WITH THIS SUBSTANCE.
EMERGENCY WASH FACILITIES: WHERE THERE IS ANY POSSIBILITY THAT AN EMPLOYEE'S EYES AND/OR SKIN MAY BE EXPOSED TO THIS SUBSTANCE, THE EMPLOYER SHOULD PROVIDE AN EYE WASH FOUNTAIN AND QUICK DRENCH SHOWER WITHIN THE IMMEDIATE WORK AREA FOR EMERGENCY USE.

AUTHORIZED BY- OCCUPATIONAL HEALTH SERVICES, INC.
CREATION DATE: 10/04/89 ***REVISION DATE:*** 05/18/90

MATERIAL SAFETY DATA SHEET

OCCUPATIONAL HEALTH SERVICES, INC.
AGRICULTURE AND PESTICIDE DIVISION
450 SEVENTH AVENUE, SUITE 2407
NEW YORK, NEW YORK 10123
1-800-445-MSDS OR (212) 967-1100

EMERGENCY CONTACT:
JOHN S. BRANSFORD, JR. (615) 292-1180

SUBSTANCE IDENTIFICATION

CAS-NUMBER 7487-88-9

SUBSTANCE: **MAGNESIUM SULFATE**

TRADE NAMES/SYNONYMS: MAGNESIUM SULFATE (1:1); MAGNESIUM SULPHATE; SULFURIC ACID MAGNESIUM SALT (1:1); SULFURIC ACID, MAGNESIUM SALT; MGO4S; PST13510

CHEMICAL FAMILY: INORGANIC SALT

MOLECULAR FORMULA: MG-S-O4 ***MOLECULAR WEIGHT:*** 120.36

CERCLA RATINGS (SCALE 0-3): HEALTH=2 FIRE=0 REACTIVITY=0 PERSISTENCE=0

NFPA RATINGS (SCALE 0-4): HEALTH=U FIRE=0 REACTIVITY=0

COMPONENTS AND CONTAMINANTS

COMPONENT: MAGNESIUM SULFATE ***PERCENT:*** 100.0
CAS# 7487-88-9

OTHER CONTAMINANTS: NONE

EXPOSURE LIMITS: NO OCCUPATIONAL EXPOSURE LIMITS ESTABLISHED BY OSHA, ACGIH, OR NIOSH.

PHYSICAL DATA

DESCRIPTION: ODORLESS, COLORLESS TO WHITE, HYGROSCOPIC CRYSTALS WITH A SALINE, BITTER TASTE. ***MELTING POINT:*** 2055 F (1124 C) (DECOMPOSES)

SPECIFIC GRAVITY: 2.66 ***PH:*** NEUTRAL IN SOLUTION

SOLUBILITY IN WATER: 26% @ 0 C

SOLVENT SOLUBILITY: SOLUBLE IN ALCOHOL, GLYCEROL; MODERATELY SOLUBLE IN ETHER; INSOLUBLE IN ACETONE.

FIRE AND EXPLOSION DATA

FIRE AND EXPLOSION HAZARD: NEGLIGIBLE FIRE HAZARD WHEN EXPOSED TO HEAT OR FLAME.

FIREFIGHTING MEDIA: EXTINGUISH USING AGENT SUITABLE FOR TYPE OF SURROUNDING FIRE.

FIREFIGHTING: NO ACUTE HAZARD. MOVE CONTAINER FROM FIRE AREA IF POSSIBLE. AVOID BREATHING VAPORS OR DUSTS; KEEP UPWIND.

TOXICITY

MAGNESIUM SULFATE: ANHYDROUS: 5000 MG/KG ORAL-MOUSE LDLO; 3000 MG/KG ORAL-RABBIT LDLO; 645 MG/KG SUBCUTANEOUS-MOUSE LD50; 1750 MG/KG SUBCUTANEOUS-RABBIT LDLO; 1800 MG/KG SUBCUTANEOUS-GUINEA PIG LDLO; 1500 MG/KG SUBCUTANEOUS-DOG LDLO; 1000 MG/KG SUBCUTANEOUS-CAT LDLO; 80 MG/KG/2 MONTH INTERMITTENT INTRAVENOUS-WOMAN LDLO; 1020 MG/KG INTRAPERITONEAL-MOUSE LD50; 1200 MG/KG INTRAPERITONEAL-DOG LDLO; 20 MG/KG INTRASPINAL-WOMAN TDLO; MUTAGENIC DATA (RTECS); REPRODUCTIVE EFFECTS DATA (RTECS). MONOHYDRATE: NO DATA AVAILABLE. HEPTAHYDRATE: 5344 MG/KG INTRADUODENAL-WOMAN LDLO. CARCINOGEN STATUS: NONE. ACUTE TOXICITY LEVEL: INSUFFICIENT DATA. TARGET EFFECTS: POISONING MAY AFFECT THE CARDIOVASCULAR, RESPIRATORY, AND CENTRAL NERVOUS SYSTEMS. AT INCREASED RISK FROM EXPOSURE: INDIVIDUALS WITH ASTHMA OR KIDNEY IMPAIRMENT.

HEALTH EFFECTS AND FIRST AID

INHALATION: MAGNESIUM SULFATE: **ACUTE EXPOSURE**- DUST MAY BE SLIGHTLY IRRITATING WITH SYMPTOMS OF SORE THROAT AND COUGHING. LEVELS ABOVE 10 UG/M3 OF SUSPENDED SULFATES IN THE AIR MAY CAUSE AN EXCESS RISK OF ASTHMATIC ATTACKS IN SUSCEPTIBLE PERSONS. **CHRONIC EXPOSURE**- REPEATED OR PROLONGED INHALATION OF MAGNESIUM DUST HAS BEEN REPORTED TO CAUSE INCREASED INCIDENCE OF DIGESTIVE DISORDERS.

FIRST AID- REMOVE FROM EXPOSURE AREA TO FRESH AIR IMMEDIATELY. IF BREATHING HAS STOPPED, PERFORM ARTIFICIAL RESPIRATION. KEEP PERSON WARM AND AT REST. TREAT SYMPTOMATICALLY AND SUPPORTIVELY. GET MEDICAL ATTENTION IMMEDIATELY.

SKIN CONTACT: MAGNESIUM SULFATE: **ACUTE EXPOSURE**- MAY CAUSE MINOR IRRITATION, WITH STINGING SENSATION WHEN IN CONTACT WITH SKIN CUTS. **CHRONIC EXPOSURE**- NO DATA AVAILABLE.

FIRST AID- REMOVE CONTAMINATED CLOTHING AND SHOES IMMEDIATELY. WASH AFFECTED AREA WITH SOAP OR MILD DETERGENT AND LARGE AMOUNTS OF WATER UNTIL NO EVIDENCE OF CHEMICAL REMAINS (APPROXIMATELY 15-20 MINUTES). GET MEDICAL ATTENTION IMMEDIATELY.

EYE CONTACT: MAGNESIUM SULFATE: **ACUTE EXPOSURE**- CONTACT WITH THE DUST MAY CAUSE MILD IRRITATION TO THE CONJUNCTIVA WITH REDNESS AND PAIN. IT IS REPORTED TO BE ESSENTIALLY INNOCUOUS WHEN APPLIED IN SOLUTION TO THE EYES. HOWEVER, THERE IS A REPORT OF MODERATE BURNING SENSATION OCCURRING AFTER APPLICATION OF A CONCENTRATED SOLUTION TO HUMAN EYES. **CHRONIC EXPOSURE**- NO DATA AVAILABLE.

FIRST AID- WASH EYES IMMEDIATELY WITH LARGE AMOUNTS OF WATER OR NORMAL SALINE, OCCASIONALLY LIFTING UPPER AND LOWER LIDS, UNTIL NO EVIDENCE OF CHEMICAL REMAINS (APPROXIMATELY 15-20 MINUTES). GET MEDICAL ATTENTION IMMEDIATELY.

INGESTION: MAGNESIUM SULFATE: **ACUTE EXPOSURE**- INGESTION OF LARGE AMOUNTS OF MAGNESIUM SALTS MAY CAUSE DIARRHEA AND ABDOMINAL PAIN. MORE SERIOUS SYMPTOMS OF HYPERMAGNESEMIA, SUCH AS ELECTROLYTE IMBALANCE, CENTRAL NERVOUS SYSTEM DEPRESSION AND NEUROLOGICAL AND CARDIAC IMPAIRMENT, ARE RARE IN THE ABSENCE OF INTESTINAL OR RENAL DISEASE SINCE MAGNESIUM IS POORLY ABSORBED FROM THE GASTROINTESTINAL TRACT AND READILY EXCRETED BY THE KIDNEYS. **CHRONIC EXPOSURE**- A PATIENT WITH NORMAL KIDNEY FUNCTION DEVELOPED SYMPTOMATIC HYPERMAGNESEMIA WITH RESPIRATORY ARREST AND BRADYCARDIA AFTER RECEIVING 90 GRAMS OF MAGNESIUM SULFATE OVER 18 HOURS. MAGNESIUM PREPARATIONS MAY CAUSE PHOSPHORUS DEPLETION SYNDROME. USE OF MAGNESIUM CONTAINING ANTACIDS HAS CAUSED RENAL FAILURE DUE TO PRECIPITATION OF MAGNESIUM AMMONIUM PHOSPHATE IN THE KIDNEY.

FIRST AID- INDUCE EMESIS OR ADMINISTER LAVAGE. USE SODIUM CATHARTICS WITH CAUTION IN THE PRESENCE OF CARDIAC FAILURE AND RENAL FAILURE. ACTIVATED CHARCOAL IS NOT USEFUL. (BARCELOUX & ELLENHORN, MEDICAL TOXICOLOGY; DIAGNOSIS & TREATMENT OF HUMAN POISONING). TREATMENT SHOULD BE PERFORMED BY MEDICAL PERSONNEL. GET MEDICAL ATTENTION IMMEDIATELY.

ANTIDOTE: THE FOLLOWING ANTIDOTE HAS BEEN RECOMMENDED. HOWEVER, THE DECISION AS TO WHETHER THE SEVERITY OF POISONING REQUIRES ADMINISTRATION OF ANY ANTIDOTE AND ACTUAL DOSE REQUIRED SHOULD BE MADE BY QUALIFIED MEDICAL PERSONNEL.

MAGNESIUM COMPOUND POISONING: WHEN THE SERUM MAGNESIUM LEVEL EXCEEDS 5 MEQ/L AND THE PATIENT EXHIBITS SYMPTOMS, GIVE CALCIUM GLUCONATE, 10 ML OF 10% SOLUTION (INTRAVENOUSLY) OVER SEVERAL MINUTES. THE DOSE MAY BE REPEATED ONCE; THEN THE LEVEL SHOULD BE CHECKED AGAIN. (ELLENHORN AND BARCELOUX, MEDICAL TOXICOLOGY, 1ST ED.). ANTIDOTE SHOULD BE ADMINISTERED BY QUALIFIED MEDICAL PERSONNEL.

REACTIVITY

REACTIVITY: STABLE UNDER NORMAL TEMPERATURES AND PRESSURES.

INCOMPATIBILITIES: MAGNESIUM SULFATE: ETHOXYETHYNYL ALCOHOLS + ETHER: MAY INITIATE EXOTHERMIC POLYMERIZATION. MALEIC ANHYDRIDE: INCOMPATIBLE. PHOSPHOROUS: INCOMPATIBLE.

DECOMPOSITION: THERMAL DECOMPOSITION PRODUCTS MAY INCLUDE TOXIC OXIDES OF SULFUR.

POLYMERIZATION: HAZARDOUS POLYMERIZATION HAS NOT BEEN REPORTED TO OCCUR UNDER NORMAL TEMPERATURES AND PRESSURES.

STORAGE AND DISPOSAL

OBSERVE ALL FEDERAL, STATE AND LOCAL REGULATIONS WHEN STORING OR DISPOSING OF THIS SUBSTANCE. FOR ASSISTANCE, CONTACT THE DISTRICT DIRECTOR OF THE ENVIRONMENTAL PROTECTION AGENCY.

STORAGE

STORE IN A TIGHTLY CLOSED CONTAINER.
STORE AWAY FROM INCOMPATIBLE SUBSTANCES.

CONDITIONS TO AVOID

MAY BURN BUT DOES NOT IGNITE READILY. AVOID CONTACT WITH STRONG OXIDIZERS, EXCESSIVE HEAT, SPARKS, OR OPEN FLAME.

SPILL AND LEAK PROCEDURES

OCCUPATIONAL SPILL: SWEEP UP AND PLACE IN SUITABLE CLEAN, DRY CONTAINERS FOR RECLAMATION OR LATER DISPOSAL. DO NOT FLUSH SPILLED MATERIAL INTO SEWER. KEEP UNNECESSARY PEOPLE AWAY.

PROTECTIVE EQUIPMENT

VENTILATION: PROVIDE LOCAL EXHAUST OR GENERAL DILUTION VENTILATION SYSTEM.

RESPIRATOR: THE FOLLOWING RESPIRATORS ARE RECOMMENDED BASED ON INFORMATION FOUND IN THE PHYSICAL DATA, TOXICITY AND HEALTH EFFECTS SECTIONS. THEY ARE RANKED IN ORDER FROM MINIMUM TO MAXIMUM RESPIRATORY PROTECTION. THE SPECIFIC RESPIRATOR SELECTED MUST BE BASED ON CONTAMINATION LEVELS FOUND IN THE WORK PLACE, MUST NOT EXCEED THE WORKING LIMITS OF THE RESPIRATOR AND BE JOINTLY APPROVED BY THE NATIONAL INSTITUTE FOR OCCUPATIONAL SAFETY AND HEALTH AND THE MINE SAFETY AND HEALTH ADMINISTRATION (NIOSH-MSHA).

DUST AND MIST RESPIRATOR WITH A FULL FACEPIECE.

AIR-PURIFYING FULL FACEPIECE RESPIRATOR WITH A HIGH-EFFICIENCY PARTICULATE FILTER.

POWERED AIR-PURIFYING RESPIRATOR WITH A TIGHT-FITTING FACEPIECE AND HIGH-EFFICIENCY PARTICULATE FILTER.
TYPE 'C' SUPPLIED-AIR RESPIRATOR WITH A FULL FACEPIECE OPERATED IN PRESSURE-DEMAND OR OTHER POSITIVE PRESSURE MODE OR WITH A FULL FACEPIECE, HELMET OR HOOD OPERATED IN CONTINUOUS-FLOW MODE.
SELF-CONTAINED BREATHING APPARATUS WITH A FULL FACEPIECE OPERATED IN PRESSURE-DEMAND OR OTHER POSITIVE PRESSURE MODE.
FOR FIREFIGHTING AND OTHER IMMEDIATELY DANGEROUS TO LIFE OR HEALTH CONDITIONS:
SELF-CONTAINED BREATHING APPARATUS WITH FULL FACEPIECE OPERATED IN PRESSURE-DEMAND OR OTHER POSITIVE PRESSURE MODE.
SUPPLIED-AIR RESPIRATOR WITH FULL FACEPIECE AND OPERATED IN PRESSURE-DEMAND OR OTHER POSITIVE PRESSURE MODE IN COMBINATION WITH AN AUXILIARY SELF-CONTAINED BREATHING APPARATUS OPERATED IN PRESSURE-DEMAND OR OTHER POSITIVE PRESSURE MODE.

CLOTHING: EMPLOYEE MUST WEAR APPROPRIATE PROTECTIVE (IMPERVIOUS) CLOTHING AND EQUIPMENT TO PREVENT REPEATED OR PROLONGED SKIN CONTACT WITH THIS SUBSTANCE.

GLOVES: EMPLOYEE MUST WEAR APPROPRIATE PROTECTIVE GLOVES TO PREVENT CONTACT WITH THIS SUBSTANCE.

EYE PROTECTION: EMPLOYEE MUST WEAR SPLASH-PROOF OR DUST-RESISTANT SAFETY GOGGLES TO PREVENT EYE CONTACT WITH THIS SUBSTANCE.
EMERGENCY EYE WASH: WHERE THERE IS ANY POSSIBILITY THAT AN EMPLOYEE'S EYES MAY BE EXPOSED TO THIS SUBSTANCE, THE EMPLOYER SHOULD PROVIDE AN EYE WASH FOUNTAIN WITHIN THE IMMEDIATE WORK AREA FOR EMERGENCY USE.

AUTHORIZED BY- OCCUPATIONAL HEALTH SERVICES, INC.
CREATION DATE: 11/17/89 ***REVISION DATE:*** 05/31/90

MATERIAL SAFETY DATA SHEET

OCCUPATIONAL HEALTH SERVICES, INC.
AGRICULTURE AND PESTICIDE DIVISION
450 SEVENTH AVENUE, SUITE 2407
NEW YORK, NEW YORK 10123
1-800-445-MSDS OR (212) 967-1100

EMERGENCY CONTACT:
JOHN S. BRANSFORD, JR. (615) 292-1180

SUBSTANCE IDENTIFICATION

CAS-NUMBER 569-64-2

SUBSTANCE: **MALACHITE GREEN CHLORIDE**

TRADE NAMES/SYNONYMS: ACRYL BRILLIANT GREEN; ANILINE GREEN; AIZEN MALACHITE GREEN; ASTRA MALACHITE GREEN; BASIC GREEN 4; BENZAL GREEN; CHINA GREEN; C.I. BASIC GEEN 4; DIAMOND GREEN; VICTORIA GREEN; FAST GREEN; TETRAMETHYL DIAPARA-AMINO-TRIPHENYL CARBINOL; A-779; 0-3415; PST13533

CHEMICAL FAMILY: AMINE, ALKYL-ARYL

MOLECULAR FORMULA: C23-H25-N2.CL MOL WT: 364.95

CERCLA RATINGS (SCALE 0-3): HEALTH=3 FIRE=0 REACTIVITY=0 PERSISTENCE=2

NFPA RATINGS (SCALE 0-4): HEALTH=3 FIRE=0 REACTIVITY=0

COMPONENTS AND CONTAMINANTS

COMPONENT: MALACHITE GREEN CHLORIDE ***PERCENT:*** 100%
CAS# 569-64-2

OTHER CONTAMINANTS: NONE.

EXPOSURE LIMITS: MALACHITE GREEN CHLORIDE: NO OCCUPATIONAL EXPOSURE LIMITS ESTABLISHED BY OSHA, ACGIH, OR NIOSH.
SUBJECT TO SARA SECTION 313 ANNUAL TOXIC CHEMICAL RELEASE REPORTING

PHYSICAL DATA

DESCRIPTION: VIOLET TO GREEN CRYSTALS WITH A METALLIC LUSTER.

SOLUBILITY IN WATER: SOLUBLE

SOLVENT SOLUBILITY: ETHYL ALCOHOL, METHYL ALCOHOL, AMYL ALCOHOL

FIRE AND EXPLOSION DATA

FIRE AND EXPLOSION HAZARD: NEGLIGIBLE FIRE HAZARD WHEN EXPOSED TO HEAT OR FLAME.

FIREFIGHTING MEDIA: DRY CHEMICAL, CARBON DIOXIDE, HALON, WATER SPRAY OR STANDARD FOAM (1987 EMERGENCY RESPONSE GUIDEBOOK, DOT P 5800.4).
FOR LARGER FIRES, USE WATER SPRAY, FOG OR STANDARD FOAM (1987 EMERGENCY RESPONSE GUIDEBOOK, DOT P 5800.4).

FIREFIGHTING: NO ACUTE HAZARD. MOVE CONTAINER FROM FIRE AREA IF POSSIBLE. AVOID BREATHING VAPORS OR DUSTS; KEEP UPWIND.

TOXICITY

MALACHITE GREEN CHLORIDE: TOXICITY DATA: 80 MG/KG ORAL-MOUSE LD50; 75 MG/KG ORAL-RABBIT LDLO (85HSAI); 4200 UG/KG INTRAPERITONEAL-MOUSE LD50; MUTAGENIC DATA (RTECS). CARCINOGEN STATUS: NONE. LOCAL EFFECTS: CORROSIVE- EYES; IRRITANT- INHALATION AND SKIN. ACUTE TOXICITY LEVEL: TOXIC BY INGESTION. TARGET EFFECTS: POISONING MAY AFFECT THE KIDNEYS.

HEALTH EFFECTS AND FIRST AID

INHALATION: MALACHITE GREEN CHLORIDE: **ACUTE EXPOSURE**- NO DATA AVAILABLE. CRYSTALS MAY BE IRRITATING. **CHRONIC EXPOSURE**- NO DATA AVAILABLE.

FIRST AID- REMOVE FROM EXPOSURE AREA TO FRESH AIR IMMEDIATELY. IF BREATHING HAS STOPPED, PERFORM ARTIFICIAL RESPIRATION. KEEP PERSON WARM AND AT REST. TREAT SYMPTOMATICALLY AND SUPPORTIVELY. GET MEDICAL ATTENTION IMMEDIATELY.

SKIN CONTACT: MALACHITE GREEN CHLORIDE: **ACUTE EXPOSURE**- NO DATA AVAILABLE. MAY BE IRRITATING AND STAIN THE SKIN. **CHRONIC EXPOSURE**- MAY CAUSE DERMATITIS.

FIRST AID- REMOVE CONTAMINATED CLOTHING AND SHOES IMMEDIATELY. WASH AFFECTED AREA WITH SOAP OR MILD DETERGENT AND LARGE AMOUNTS OF WATER UNTIL NO EVIDENCE OF CHEMICAL REMAINS (APPROXIMATELY 15-20 MINUTES). GET MEDICAL ATTENTION IMMEDIATELY.

EYE CONTACT: MALACHITE GREEN CHLORIDE: CORROSIVE. **ACUTE EXPOSURE**- MAY BE SEVERELY IRRITATING. IT IS REPORTED TO CAUSE CATIONIC INJURY IN RABBITS AND HUMANS. INJURIOUS MEANS THAT IT CAUSED INJURY RANGING IN SEVERITY FROM CONJUNCTIVAL EDEMA, HYPEREMIA, AND PURULENT DISCHARGE TO TOTAL OPACIFICATION AND EVEN NECROSIS AND SLOUGHING OF THE CORNEAL STROMA. **CHRONIC EXPOSURE**- MAY CAUSE CONJUNCTIVITIS.

FIRST AID- WASH EYES IMMEDIATELY WITH LARGE AMOUNTS OF WATER, OCCASIONALLY LIFTING UPPER AND LOWER LIDS, UNTIL NO EVIDENCE OF CHEMICAL REMAINS (AT LEAST 15-20 MINUTES). CONTINUE IRRIGATING WITH NORMAL SALINE UNTIL THE PH HAS RETURNED TO NORMAL (30-60 MINUTES). COVER WITH STERILE BANDAGES. GET MEDICAL ATTENTION IMMEDIATELY.

INGESTION: MALACHITE GREEN CHLORIDE: TOXIC. **ACUTE EXPOSURE**- 80 MG/KG WAS LETHAL TO 50% OF MICE TESTED. MAY CAUSE DIARRHEA, GASTROINTESTINAL IRRITATION, AND ABDOMINAL PAIN. KIDNEY DAMAGE MAY OCCUR. **CHRONIC EXPOSURE**- NO DATA AVAILABLE.

FIRST AID- TREAT SYMPTOMATICALLY AND SUPPORTIVELY. GET MEDICAL ATTENTION IMMEDIATELY. MILK SHOULD BE GIVEN TO DETER THE GASTROINTESTINAL IRRITATION THAT MAY OCCUR. (ARENA, POISONING, 4TH ED.).

REACTIVITY

REACTIVITY: STABLE UNDER NORMAL TEMPERATURES AND PRESSURES.

INCOMPATIBILITIES: NONE KNOWN.

DECOMPOSITION: MALACHITE GREEN CHLORIDE: THERMAL DECOMPOSITION MAY EMIT HIGHLY TOXIC FUMES OF ANALINE AND OXIDES OF NITROGEN.

POLYMERIZATION: HAZARDOUS POLYMERIZATION HAS NOT BEEN REPORTED TO OCCUR UNDER NORMAL TEMPERATURES AND PRESSURES.

CONDITIONS TO AVOID

NONE REPORTED.

SPILL AND LEAK PROCEDURES

OCCUPATIONAL SPILL: NO SPECIAL PRECAUTIONS INDICATED.

PROTECTIVE EQUIPMENT

VENTILATION: PROVIDE LOCAL EXHAUST VENTILATION SYSTEM.

RESPIRATOR: HIGH LEVELS- HIGH-EFFICIENCY PARTICULATE RESPIRATOR WITH A FULL FACEPIECE. SUPPLIED-AIR RESPIRATOR WITH A FULL FACEPIECE, HELMET, OR HOOD. SELF-CONTAINED BREATHING APPARATUS WITH A FULL FACEPIECE.
FIRE FIGHTING- SELF-CONTAINED BREATHING APPARATUS WITH A FULL FACEPIECE, OPERATED IN PRESSURE-DEMAND OR OTHER POSITIVE PRESSURE MODE.

CLOTHING: EMPLOYEE MUST WEAR APPROPRIATE PROTECTIVE (IMPERVIOUS) CLOTHING AND EQUIPMENT TO PREVENT REPEATED OR PROLONGED SKIN CONTACT WITH THIS SUBSTANCE.

GLOVES: EMPLOYEE MUST WEAR APPROPRIATE PROTECTIVE GLOVES TO PREVENT CONTACT WITH THIS SUBSTANCE.

EYE PROTECTION: EMPLOYEE MUST WEAR SPLASH-PROOF OR DUST-RESISTANT SAFETY GOGGLES AND A FACESHIELD TO PREVENT CONTACT WITH THIS

SUBSTANCE.
EMERGENCY WASH FACILITIES: WHERE THERE IS ANY POSSIBILITY THAT AN EMPLOYEE'S EYES AND/OR SKIN MAY BE EXPOSED TO THIS SUBSTANCE, THE EMPLOYER SHOULD PROVIDE AN EYE WASH FOUNTAIN AND QUICK DRENCH SHOWER WITHIN THE IMMEDIATE WORK AREA FOR EMERGENCY USE.

AUTHORIZED BY- OCCUPATIONAL HEALTH SERVICES, INC.
CREATION DATE: 11/15/89 ***REVISION DATE:*** 05/15/90

MATERIAL SAFETY DATA SHEET

OCCUPATIONAL HEALTH SERVICES, INC.
AGRICULTURE AND PESTICIDE DIVISION
450 SEVENTH AVENUE, SUITE 2407
NEW YORK, NEW YORK 10123
1-800-445-MSDS OR (212) 967-1100

EMERGENCY CONTACT:
JOHN S. BRANSFORD, JR. (615) 292-1180

SUBSTANCE IDENTIFICATION

CAS-NUMBER 121-75-5
SUBSTANCE: MALATHION
TRADE NAMES/SYNONYMS: BUTANEDIOIC ACID, ((DIMETHOXYPHOSPHINOTHIOYL)THIO)-, DIETHYL ESTER; SUCCINIC ACID, MERCAPTO-, DIETHYL ESTER, S-ESTER WITH O,O-DIMETHYL PHOSPHORODITHIOATE; ((DIMETHOXYPHOSPHINOTHIOYL)THIO)BUTANEDIOIC ACID DIETHYL ESTER; MERCAPTOSUCCINIC ACID DIETHYL ESTER, S-ESTER WITH O,O-DIMETHYL PHOSPHORODITHIOATE; DIETHYL (DIMETHOXYPHOSPHINOTHIOYLTHIO)SUCCINATE; DIETHYL (DIMETHOXYTHIOPHOSPHORYLTHIO)SUCCINATE; S-1,2-BIS(ETHOXYCARBONYL)ETHYL O,O-DIMETHYL PHOSPHORODITHIOATE; ((DIMETHOXYPHOSPHINOTHIOYL)THIO)BUTANEDIOATE; DIETHYL MERCAPTOSUCCINATE S-ESTER WITH O,O-DIMETHYL PHOSPHORODITHIOATE; O,O-DIMETHYL-S-(1,2-DICARBETHOXYETHYL)PHOSPHORODITHIOATE; O,O-DIMETHYL PHOSPHORODITHIOATE OF DIETHYL MERCAPTOSUCCINATE; S-(1,2-DI(ETHOXYCARBONYL)ETHYL)DIMETHYL PHOSPHOROTHIOLOTHIONATE; CYTHION; KARBOFOS; ENT 17,034; STCC 4941156; C10H19PS2O6; PST13540
CHEMICAL FAMILY: ORGANOPHOSPHATE
MOLECULAR FORMULA: C10-H19-O6-P-S2
MOLECULAR WEIGHT: 330.35
CERCLA RATINGS (SCALE 0-3): HEALTH=3 FIRE=1 REACTIVITY=0 PERSISTENCE=0
NFPA RATINGS (SCALE 0-4): HEALTH=4 FIRE=1 REACTIVITY=0

COMPONENTS AND CONTAMINANTS

COMPONENT: MALATHION ***PERCENT:*** 100.0
CAS# 121-75-5
OTHER CONTAMINANTS: NONE
EXPOSURE LIMITS: MALATHION: 10 MG/M3 OSHA TWA (TOTAL DUST) (SKIN) 10 MG/M3 ACGIH TWA (SKIN) 15 MG/M3 NIOSH RECOMMENDED 10 HOUR TWA 100 POUNDS CERCLA SECTION 103 REPORTABLE QUANTITY

PHYSICAL DATA

DESCRIPTION: YELLOW-BROWN LIQUID WITH A CHARACTERISTIC ODOR.
BOILING POINT: 313-315 F (156-157 C) @ 0.7 MMHG (DEC) ***MELTING POINT:*** 37 F (3 C)
SPECIFIC GRAVITY: 1.2076 ***VISCOSITY:*** 36.78 CPS @ 25 C
VAPOR PRESSURE: NEGLIGIBLE ***SOLUBILITY IN WATER:*** 145 PPM @ 20 C
SOLVENT SOLUBILITY: SOLUBLE IN ALCOHOLS, ESTERS, KETONES, ETHERS, BENZENE, AROMATIC AND ALKYLATED AROMATIC HYDROCARBONS, AND VEGETABLE OILS; LIMITED SOLUBILITY IN PETROLEUM OILS.

FIRE AND EXPLOSION DATA

FIRE AND EXPLOSION HAZARD: SLIGHT FIRE HAZARD WHEN EXPOSED TO HEAT OR FLAME.
FLASH POINT: >325 F (>163 C) (OC) ***FLAMMABILITY CLASS(OSHA):*** IIIB
FIREFIGHTING MEDIA: DRY CHEMICAL, CARBON DIOXIDE, HALON, WATER SPRAY OR STANDARD FOAM (1987 EMERGENCY RESPONSE GUIDEBOOK, DOT P 5800.4). FOR LARGER FIRES, USE WATER SPRAY, FOG OR STANDARD FOAM (1987 EMERGENCY RESPONSE GUIDEBOOK, DOT P 5800.4).
FIREFIGHTING: MOVE CONTAINERS FROM FIRE AREA IF POSSIBLE. FIGHT FIRE FROM MAXIMUM DISTANCE. STAY AWAY FROM STORAGE TANK ENDS. DIKE FIRE CONTROL WATER FOR LATER DISPOSAL. DO NOT SCATTER MATERIAL (1987 EMERGENCY RESPONSE GUIDEBOOK, DOT P 5800.4, GUIDE PAGE 55).
EXTINGUISH ONLY IF FLOW CAN BE STOPPED; USE FLOODING AMOUNTS OF WATER AS FOG, SOLID STREAMS MAY BE INEFFECTIVE. COOL CONTAINERS WITH FLOODING AMOUNTS OF WATER FROM AS FAR A DISTANCE AS POSSIBLE. USE WATER SPRAY TO ABSORB TOXIC VAPORS. AVOID BREATHING TOXIC VAPORS; KEEP UPWIND. CONSIDER EVACUATION OF DOWNWIND AREA IF MATERIAL IS LEAKING.

TRANSPORTATION DATA

DEPARTMENT OF TRANSPORTATION HAZARD CLASSIFICATION 49 CFR 172.101: ORM-A
DEPARTMENT OF TRANSPORTATION LABELING REQUIREMENTS 49 CFR 172.101 AND SUBPART E: NONE
DEPARTMENT OF TRANSPORTATION PACKAGING REQUIREMENTS: 49 CFR 173.510 EXCEPTIONS: 49 CFR 173.505

TOXICITY

MALATHION: TOXICITY DATA: 84,600 UG/M3/4 HOURS INHALATION-RAT LC50; 10 MG/M3/4 HOURS INHALATION-CAT LCLO; 4100 MG/KG SKIN-RABBIT LD50; 2330 MG/KG SKIN-MOUSE LD50; 4444 MG/KG SKIN-RAT LD50; 6700 MG/KG SKIN-GUINEA PIG LD50; 471 MG/KG ORAL-MAN LDLO; 246 MG/KG ORAL-WOMAN LDLO; 290 MG/KG ORAL-RAT LD50; 190 MG/KG ORAL-MOUSE LD50; 250 MG/KG ORAL-RABBIT LD50; 1200 MG/KG ORAL-RABBIT LDLO; 570 MG/KG ORAL-GUINEA PIG LD50; 500 MG/KG ORAL-DOMESTIC ANIMAL LD50; 53 MG/KG ORAL-CATTLE LD50; 1000 MG/KG SUBCUTANEOUS-RAT LD50; 221 MG/KG SUBCUTANEOUS-MOUSE LD50; 184 MG/KG INTRAVENOUS-MOUSE LD50; 50 MG/KG INTRAVENOUS-RAT LD50; 250 MG/KG INTRAPERITONEAL-RAT LD50; 193 MG/KG INTRAPERITONEAL-MOUSE LD50; 1857 MG/KG INTRAPERITONEAL-DOG LD50; 550 MG/KG INTRAPERITONEAL-GUINEA PIG LD50; 2400 MG/KG INTRAPERITONEAL-HAMSTER LD50; 1820 UG/KG INTRAARTERIAL-CAT LDLO; MUTAGENIC DATA (RTECS); REPRODUCTIVE EFFECTS DATA (RTECS). CARCINOGEN STATUS: ANIMAL INADEQUATE EVIDENCE (IARC GROUP-3). ACUTE TOXICITY LEVEL: HIGHLY TOXIC BY INHALATION; TOXIC BY INGESTION; SLIGHTLY TOXIC BY DERMAL ABSORPTION. TARGET EFFECTS: SENSITIZER- DERMAL; CHOLINESTERASE INHIBITOR. AT INCREASED RISK FROM EXPOSURE: PERSONS WITH RESPIRATORY AILMENTS, RECENT EXPOSURE TO CHOLINESTERASE INHIBITORS OR IMPAIRED CHOLINESTERASE PRODUCTION, OR LIVER MALFUNCTION.* ADDITIONAL DATA: EPN, TRICHLORFON AND TRI-O-TOLYL PHOSPHATES MAY POTENTIATE THE TOXICITY OF MALATHION. ANIMAL STUDIES INDICATE THAT MALATHION DOES NOT INDUCE DELAYED NEUROPATHY. MAY CROSS THE PLACENTA. HIGH ENVIRONMENTAL TEMPERATURES OR EXPOSURE OF THE CHEMICAL TO VISIBLE OR ULTRAVIOLET LIGHT MAY ENHANCE THE TOXICITY. INTERACTIONS WITH MEDICATIONS MAY OCCUR.*
* MAY BE BASED ON GENERAL INFORMATION ON ORGANOPHOSPHATES.

HEALTH EFFECTS AND FIRST AID

INHALATION: MALATHION: HIGHLY TOXIC. 5000 MG/M3 IMMEDIATELY DANGEROUS TO LIFE OR HEALTH. SEE INFORMATION ON ORGANOPHOSPHATES.
ORGANOPHOSPHATES: CHOLINESTERASE INHIBITOR. **ACUTE EXPOSURE-** WHEN INHALED, THE FIRST EFFECTS OF CHOLINESTERASE INHIBITORS ARE USUALLY RESPIRATORY AND MAY INCLUDE NASAL HYPEREMIA AND WATERY DISCHARGE, COUGH, CHEST DISCOMFORT, DYSPNEA, AND WHEEZING DUE TO INCREASED BRONCHIAL SECRETIONS AND BRONCHOCONSTRICTION. IF SUFFICIENT AMOUNTS ARE ABSORBED, OTHER SYSTEMIC EFFECTS MAY BEGIN WITHIN A FEW MINUTES OR BE DELAYED FOR UP TO 12 HOURS. SYMPTOMS MAY INCLUDE PALLOR, NAUSEA, VOMITING, DIARRHEA, ABDOMINAL CRAMPS, HEADACHE, DIZZINESS, OCULAR PAIN, BLURRED VISION, MIOSIS OR IN SOME CASES, ESPECIALLY INITIALLY, MYDRIASIS, LACRIMATION, SALIVATION, SWEATING, AND CONFUSION. OTHER REPORTED CENTRAL NERVOUS SYSTEM OR NEUROMUSCULAR EFFECTS MAY INCLUDE ATAXIA, SLURRED SPEECH, AREFLEXIA, WEAKNESS, FATIGUE, FASCICULATIONS, TWITCHING, TREMORS POSSIBLY OF THE TONGUE AND EYELIDS, AND EVENTUALLY PARALYSIS OF THE EXTREMITIES AND POSSIBLY OF THE RESPIRATORY MUSCLES. IN SEVERE CASES THERE MAY ALSO BE INVOLUNTARY DEFECATION AND URINATION, CYANOSIS, PSYCHOSIS, HYPERGLYCEMIA, ACUTE PANCREATITIS, CARDIAC IRREGULARITIES, PULMONARY EDEMA, UNCONSCIOUSNESS, CONVULSIONS, AND COMA. DEATH IS PRIMARILY DUE TO RESPIRATORY FAILURE, ALTHOUGH CARDIOVASCULAR EFFECTS INCLUDING CARDIAC ARREST MAY ALSO BE IMPLICATED. LONG TERM SEQUELAE ARE RARE BUT MAY INCLUDE NEUROPSYCHIATRIC DISORDERS AND MYOPATHY WITH MUSCLE TENDERNESS. **CHRONIC EXPOSURE-** REPEATED OR PROLONGED EXPOSURE MAY RESULT IN THE EFFECTS OF ACUTE EXPOSURE. OTHER EFFECTS REPORTED IN WORKERS REPEATEDLY EXPOSED INCLUDE IMPAIRED MEMORY AND CONCENTRATION, ACUTE PSYCHOSIS, SEVERE DEPRESSIONS, IRRITABILTY, CONFUSION, APATHY, EMOTIONAL LABILITY, SOCIAL WITHDRAWAL, CONFUSION, HEADACHE, SPEECH DIFFICULTIES, DELAYED REACTION TIMES, SPATIAL DISORIENTATION, NIGHTMARES, SLEEPWALKING, AND DROWSINESS OR INSOMNIA.

AN INFLUENZA-LIKE CONDITION WITH HEADACHE, NAUSEA, WEAKNESS, ANOREXIA AND MALAISE HAS ALSO BEEN REPORTED.

FIRST AID- REMOVE FROM EXPOSURE AREA TO FRESH AIR IMMEDIATELY. IF BREATHING HAS STOPPED, GIVE ARTIFICIAL RESPIRATION. MAINTAIN AIRWAY AND BLOOD PRESSURE AND ADMINISTER OXYGEN IF AVAILABLE. KEEP AFFECTED PERSON WARM AND AT REST. TREAT SYMPTOMATICALLY AND SUPPORTIVELY. ADMINISTRATION OF OXYGEN SHOULD BE PERFORMED BY QUALIFIED PERSONNEL. GET MEDICAL ATTENTION IMMEDIATELY.

SKIN CONTACT: MALATHION: SENSITIZER. PROLONGED OR REPEATED EXPOSURE MAY CAUSE SENSITIZATION DERMATITIS. SEE INFORMATION ON ORGANOPHOSPHATES. ORGANOPHOSPHATES: CHOLINESTERASE INHIBITOR. **ACUTE EXPOSURE-** LOCALIZED SWEATING AND FASCICULATIONS MAY OCCUR AT THE SITE OF CONTACT. IF SUFFICIENT AMOUNTS ARE ABSORBED, OTHER EFFECTS OF CHOLINESTERASE INHIBITION AS DESCRIBED IN ACUTE INHALATION MAY OCCUR. SYMPTOMS MAY BE DELAYED 2-3 HOURS, BUT USUALLY NO MORE THAN 12 HOURS. THE RATE OF ABSORPTION IS INCREASED BY THE PRESENCE OF DERMATITIS OR HIGH AMBIENT TEMPERATURES. **CHRONIC EXPOSURE-** REPEATED OR PROLONGED EXPOSURE MAY CAUSE EFFECTS AS DESCRIBED IN ACUTE EXPOSURE. SOME ORGANOPHOSPHATES MAY CAUSE SENSITIZATION.

FIRST AID- REMOVE CONTAMINATED CLOTHING IMMEDIATELY. WASH CONTAMINATED AREAS WITH SOAP AND WATER FOLLOWED BY ALCOHOL (ARENA, POISONING, 4TH ED.). EMERGENCY PERSONNEL SHOULD WEAR GLOVES AND AVOID CONTAMINATION. TREAT RESPIRATORY DIFFICULTY WITH ARTIFICIAL RESPIRATION. GET MEDICAL ATTENTION IMMEDIATELY.

EYE CONTACT: MALATHION: SEE INFORMATION ON ORGANOPHOSPHATES. ORGANOPHOSPHATES: CHOLINESTERASE INHIBITOR. **ACUTE EXPOSURE-** DIRECT CONTACT MAY CAUSE PAIN, HYPEREMIA, LACRIMATION, TWITCHING OF THE EYELIDS, MIOSIS, AND CILIARY MUSCLE SPASM WITH LOSS OF ACCOMODATION, BLURRED OR DIMMED VISION AND BROWACHE. SOMETIMES MYDRIASIS MAY OCCUR INSTEAD OF MIOSIS. WITH SUFFICIENT EXPOSURE, OTHER SYMPTOMS OF CHOLINESTERASE INHIBITION AS DESCRIBED IN ACUTE INHALATION MAY OCCUR. **CHRONIC EXPOSURE-** REPEATED OR PROLONGED EXPOSURE MAY CAUSE EFFECTS AS DESCRIBED IN ACUTE EXPOSURE. SOME COMPOUNDS HAVE CAUSED TOXIC EFFECTS ON THE CRYSTALLINE LENS, CONJUNCTIVAL THICKENING AND OBSTRUCTION OF THE NASOLACRIMAL CANALS WHEN USED AS MIOTIC EYEDROPS.

FIRST AID- IRRIGATE EYES WITH WATER OR SALINE SOLUTION. IF SYMPTOMS OF POISONING OCCUR, TREAT RESPIRATORY DIFFICULTY WITH ARTIFICIAL RESPIRATION AND OXYGEN. OBSERVE PATIENT FOR AT LEAST 24-36 HOURS (GOSSELIN, CLINICAL TOXICOLOGY OF COMMERCIAL PRODUCTS, 5TH ED.). GET MEDICAL ATTENTION IMMEDIATELY. OXYGEN SHOULD BE ADMINISTERED BY QUALIFIED MEDICAL PERSONNEL.

INGESTION: MALATHION: TOXIC. CHROMOSOMAL ABERRATIONS WERE INCREASED IN THE PRIMARY SPERMATOCYTES OF MALE MICE AND BONE-MARROW CELLS OF RATS. EFFECTS OF DECREASED FETAL WEIGHTS, AN INCREASED INCIDENCE IN EXTERNAL HEMORRHAGIC SPOTS, INCREASED SUSCEPTIBILITY TO DISEASE, AND INCREASED MORTALITY, ABSORPTIONS AND ANOMALIES SUCH AS MILD HYDRONEPHROSIS AND HYDROURETER WERE REPORTED IN STUDIES OF RATS. SEE INFORMATION ON ORGANOPHOSPHATES.
ORGANOPHOSPHATES: CHOLINESTERASE INHIBITOR. **ACUTE EXPOSURE-** WHEN INGESTED, THE FIRST EFFECTS MAY BE NAUSEA, VOMITING, ANOREXIA, ABDOMINAL CRAMPS AND DIARRHEA. GASTROINTESTINAL ABSORPTION MAY CAUSE THE SYMPTOMS OF CHOLINESTERASE INHIBITION AS DESCRIBED IN ACUTE INHALATION. SYMPTOMS MAY BEGIN WITHIN MINUTES OR BE DELAYED. **CHRONIC EXPOSURE-** REPEATED INGESTION MAY CAUSE EFFECTS AS DESCRIBED IN ACUTE EXPOSURE.

FIRST AID- IF PERSON IS ALERT AND RESPIRATION IS NOT DEPRESSED, GIVE SYRUP OF IPECAC FOLLOWED BY WATER (IF VOMITING OCCURS, KEEP HEAD BELOW HIPS TO PREVENT ASPIRATION). IF CONSCIOUSNESS LEVEL DECLINES OR VOMITING HAS NOT OCCURRED IN 15 MINUTES EMPTY STOMACH BY GASTRIC LAVAGE WITH THE AID OF CUFFED ENDOTRACHEAL TUBE USING ISOTONIC SALINE OR 5% SODIUM BICARBONATE FOLLOW WITH ACTIVATED CHARCOAL. ESTABLISH AND MAINTAIN AIRWAY. TREAT RESPIRATORY DIFFICULTY WITH ARTIFICIAL RESPIRATION AND OXYGEN. DO NOT GIVE MORPHINE, AMINOPHYLLINE, PHENOTHIAZINES, RESERPINE, FUROSEMIDE, OR ETHACRYNIC ACID (MORGAN, RECOGNITION AND MANAGEMENT OF PESTICIDE POISONINGS, 3RD ED.). TREAT SYMPTOMATICALLY AND SUPPORTIVELY. ADMINISTRATION OF OXYGEN AND LAVAGE MUST BE PERFORMED BY QUALIFIED MEDICAL PERSONNEL. GET MEDICAL ATTENTION IMMEDIATELY.

ANTIDOTE: THE FOLLOWING ANTIDOTE(S) HAVE BEEN RECOMMENDED. HOWEVER, THE DECISION AS TO WHETHER THE SEVERITY OF POISONING REQUIRES ADMINISTRATION OF ANY ANTIDOTE AND ACTUAL DOSE REQUIRED SHOULD BE MADE BY QUALIFIED MEDICAL PERSONNEL.
FOR CHOLINESTERASE INHIBITORS: ESTABLISH CLEAR AIRWAY AND TISSUE OXYGENATION BY ASPIRATION OF SECRETIONS, AND IF NECESSARY, BY ASSISTED PULMONARY VENTILATION WITH OXYGEN. IMPROVE TISSUE OXYGENATION AS MUCH AS POSSIBLE BEFORE ADMINISTERING ATROPINE TO MINIMIZE THE RISK OF VENTRICULAR FIBRILLATION. ADMINISTER ATROPINE SULFATE INTRAVENOUSLY, OR INTRAMUSCULARLY IF IV INJECTION IS NOT POSSIBLE. IN MODERATELY SEVERE POISONING ADMINISTER ATROPINE SULFATE, 0.4-2.0 MG REPEATED EVERY 15 MINUTES UNTIL ATROPINIZATION IS ACHIEVED (TACHYCARDIA, FLUSHING, DRY MOUTH, MYDRIASIS). MAINTAIN ATROPINIZATION BY REPEATED DOSES FOR 2-12 HOURS, OR LONGER, DEPENDING ON THE SEVERITY OF POISONING. THE APPEARANCE OF RALES IN THE LUNG BASES, MIOSIS, SALIVATION, NAUSEA, BRADYCARDIA, ARE ALL INDICATIONS OF INADEQUATE ATROPINIZATION. SEVERELY POISONED INDIVIDUALS MAY EXHIBIT REMARKABLE TOLERANCE TO ATROPINE; TWO OR MORE TIMES THE DOSAGES SUGGESTED ABOVE MAY BE NEEDED. PERSONS NOT POISONED OR ONLY SLIGHTLY POISONED, HOWEVER, MAY DEVELOP SIGNS OF ATROPINE TOXICITY FROM SUCH LARGE DOSAGES: FEVER, MUSCLE FIBRILLATIONS, AND DELIRIUM ARE THE MAIN SIGNS OF ATROPINE TOXICITY. IF THESE SIGNS APPEAR WHILE THE PATIENT IS FULLY ATROPINIZED, ATROPINE ADMINISTRATION SHOULD BE DISCONTINUED, AT LEAST TEMPORARILY. OBSERVE TREATED PATIENTS CLOSELY AT LEAST 24 HOURS TO INSURE THAT SYMPTOMS (POSSIBLY PULMONARY EDEMA) DO NOT RECUR AS ATROPINIZATION WEARS OFF. IN VERY SEVERE POISONINGS, METABOLIC DISPOSITION OF TOXICANT MAY REQUIRE SEVERAL HOURS OR DAYS DURING WHICH ATROPINIZATION MUST BE MAINTAINED. MARKEDLY LOWER LEVELS OF URINARY METABOLITES INDICATE THAT ATROPINE DOSAGE CAN BE TAPERED OFF. AS DOSAGE IS REDUCED, CHECK THE LUNG BASES FREQUENTLY FOR RALES. IF RALES ARE HEARD OR OTHER SYMPTOMS RETURN, RE-ESTABLISH ATROPINIZATION PROMPTLY (MORGAN, RECOGNITION AND MANAGEMENT OF PESTICIDE POISONINGS, 3RD ED.). ADMINISTRATION OF ANTIDOTE MUST BE PERFORMED BY QUALIFIED MEDICAL PERSONNEL.
IN CASES OF SEVERE POISONING BY ORGANOPHOSPHATE PESTICIDES IN WHICH RESPIRATORY DEPRESSION, MUSCLE WEAKNESS AND TWITCHINGS ARE SEVERE, GIVE PRALIDOXIME (PROTOPAM-AYERST, 2-PAM), 1.0 GRAM INTRAVENOUSLY AT NO MORE THAN 0.5 GRAM PER MINUTE. DOSAGE OF PRALIDOXIME MAY BE REPEATED IN 1-2 HOURS, THEN AT 10-12 HOUR INTERVALS IF NEEDED. IN VERY SEVERE POISONINGS, DOSAGE RATES MAY BE DOUBLED. TREATMENT WITH PRALIDOXIME WILL BE MOST EFFECTIVE IF GIVEN WITHIN THIRTY-SIX HOURS AFTER POISONING (MORGAN, RECOGNITION AND MANAGEMENT OF PESTICIDE POISONINGS, 3RD ED.). ANTIDOTE SHOULD BE ADMINISTERED BY QUALIFIED MEDICAL PERSONNEL.

REACTIVITY

REACTIVITY: STABLE UNDER NORMAL TEMPERATURES AND PRESSURES.

INCOMPATIBILITIES: MALATHION: COPPER: MAY CORRODE. IRON: MAY CORRODE. LEAD: MAY CORRODE. OXIDIZERS (STRONG): FIRE AND EXPLOSION HAZARD. PLASTICS, RUBBER AND COATINGS: MAY BE ATTACKED. STEEL: MAY CORRODE. TIN PLATE: MAY CORRODE.

DECOMPOSITION: THERMAL DECOMPOSITION PRODUCTS MAY INCLUDE TOXIC OXIDES OF CARBON, SULFUR, AND PHOSPHORUS.

POLYMERIZATION: HAZARDOUS POLYMERIZATION HAS NOT BEEN REPORTED TO OCCUR UNDER NORMAL TEMPERATURES AND PRESSURES.

STORAGE AND DISPOSAL

OBSERVE ALL FEDERAL, STATE AND LOCAL REGULATIONS WHEN STORING OR DISPOSING OF THIS SUBSTANCE. FOR ASSISTANCE, CONTACT THE DISTRICT DIRECTOR OF THE ENVIRONMENTAL PROTECTION AGENCY.

STORAGE

STORE IN ACCORDANCE WITH 40 CFR 165 RECOMMENDED PROCEDURES FOR THE DISPOSAL AND STORAGE OF PESTICIDES AND PESTICIDE CONTAINERS.
STORE AWAY FROM INCOMPATIBLE SUBSTANCES.

DISPOSAL

DISPOSAL MUST BE IN ACCORDANCE WITH 40 CFR 165 RECOMMENDED PROCEDURES FOR THE DISPOSAL AND STORAGE OF PESTICIDES AND PESTICIDE CONTAINERS.

CONDITIONS TO AVOID

MAY BURN BUT DOES NOT IGNITE READILY. CONTAINERS MAY EXPLODE IN HEAT OF FIRE.

SPILL AND LEAK PROCEDURES

SOIL SPILL: DIG HOLDING AREA SUCH AS LAGOON, POND OR PIT FOR CONTAINMENT. DIKE FLOW OF SPILLED MATERIAL USING SOIL OR SANDBAGS OR FOAMED BARRIERS SUCH AS POLYURETHANE OR CONCRETE.
USE CEMENT POWDER OR FLY ASH TO ABSORB LIQUID MASS.

WATER SPILL: IF DISSOLVED, AT A CONCENTRATION OF 10 PPM OR GREATER, APPLY ACTIVATED CARBON AT TEN TIMES THE AMOUNT THAT HAS BEEN SPILLED.

USE SUCTION HOSES TO REMOVE TRAPPED SPILL MATERIAL.
USE MECHANICAL DREDGES OR LIFTS TO EXTRACT IMMOBILIZED MASSES OF POLLUTION AND PRECIPITATES.

OCCUPATIONAL SPILL: DO NOT TOUCH SPILLED MATERIAL. STOP LEAK IF YOU CAN DO IT WITHOUT RISK. USE WATER SPRAY TO REDUCE VAPORS. FOR SMALL SPILLS, TAKE UP WITH SAND OR OTHER ABSORBENT MATERIAL AND PLACE INTO CONTAINERS FOR LATER DISPOSAL. FOR SMALL DRY SPILLS, WITH A CLEAN SHOVEL PLACE MATERIAL INTO CLEAN, DRY CONTAINERS AND COVER. MOVE CONTAINERS FROM SPILL AREA. FOR LARGER SPILLS, DIKE FAR AHEAD OF SPILL FOR LATER DISPOSAL. KEEP UNNECESSARY PEOPLE AWAY. ISOLATE HAZARD AREA AND DENY ENTRY. VENTILATE CLOSED SPACES BEFORE ENTERING.
REPORTABLE QUANTITY (RQ): 100 POUNDS THE SUPERFUND AMENDMENTS AND REAUTHORIZATION ACT (SARA) SECTION 304 REQUIRES THAT A RELEASE EQUAL TO OR GREATER THAN THE REPORTABLE QUANTITY FOR THIS SUBSTANCE BE IMMEDIATELY REPORTED TO THE LOCAL EMERGENCY PLANNING COMMITTEE AND THE STATE EMERGENCY RESPONSE COMMISSION (40 CFR 355.40). IF THE RELEASE OF THIS SUBSTANCE IS REPORTABLE UNDER CERCLA SECTION 103, THE NATIONAL RESPONSE CENTER MUST BE NOTIFIED IMMEDIATELY AT (800) 424-8802 OR (202) 426-2675 IN THE METROPOLITAN WASHINGTON, D.C. AREA (40 CFR 302.6).

PROTECTIVE EQUIPMENT

VENTILATION: PROVIDE LOCAL EXHAUST VENTILATION AND/OR GENERAL DILUTION VENTILATION TO MEET PUBLISHED EXPOSURE LIMITS.

RESPIRATOR: THE FOLLOWING RESPIRATORS AND MAXIMUM USE CONCENTRATIONS ARE RECOMMENDATIONS BY THE U.S. DEPARTMENT OF HEALTH AND HUMAN SERVICES, NIOSH POCKET GUIDE TO CHEMICAL HAZARDS; NIOSH CRITERIA DOCUMENTS OR BY THE U.S. DEPARTMENT OF LABOR, 29 CFR 1910 SUBPART Z. THE SPECIFIC RESPIRATOR SELECTED MUST BE BASED ON CONTAMINATION LEVELS FOUND IN THE WORK PLACE, MUST NOT EXCEED THE WORKING LIMITS OF THE RESPIRATOR AND BE JOINTLY APPROVED BY THE NATIONAL INSTITUTE FOR OCCUPATIONAL SAFETY AND HEALTH AND THE MINE SAFETY AND HEALTH ADMINISTRATION (NIOSH-MSHA).
MALATHION: 150 MG/M3- ANY SUPPLIED-AIR RESPIRATOR. ANY SELF-CONTAINED BREATHING APPARATUS. ANY CHEMICAL CARTRIDGE RESPIRATOR WITH ORGANIC VAPOR CARTRIDGE(S) IN COMBINATION WITH A DUST, MIST, AND FUME FILTER.
375 MG/M3- ANY SUPPLIED-AIR RESPIRATOR OPERATED IN A CONTINUOUS FLOW MODE. ANY POWERED AIR-PURIFYING RESPIRATOR WITH ORGANIC VAPOR CARTRIDGE(S) IN COMBINATION WITH A DUST, MIST, AND FUME FILTER.
750 MG/M3- ANY SUPPLIED-AIR RESPIRATOR WITH A FULL FACEPIECE. ANY SELF-CONTAINED BREATHING APPARATUS WITH A FULL FACEPIECE. ANY CHEMICAL CARTRIDGE RESPIRATOR WITH A FULL FACEPIECE AND ORGANIC VAPOR CARTRIDGE(S) IN COMBINATION WITH A HIGH-EFFICIENCY PARTICULATE FILTER. ANY AIR-PURIFYING FULL FACEPIECE RESPIRATOR (GAS MASK) WITH A CHIN-STYLE OR FRONT- OR BACK-MOUNTED ORGANIC VAPOR CANISTER HAVING A HIGH-EFFICIENCY PARTICULATE FILTER. ANY POWERED AIR-PURIFYING RESPIRATOR WITH A TIGHT-FITTING FACEPIECE AND ORGANIC VAPOR CARTRIDGE(S) IN COMBINATION WITH A HIGH-EFFICIENCY PARTICULATE FILTER. ANY SUPPLIED-AIR RESPIRATOR WITH A TIGHT-FITTING FACEPIECE OPERATED IN A CONTINUOUS FLOW MODE.
5000 MG/M3- ANY SUPPLIED-AIR RESPIRATOR WITH A FULL FACEPIECE AND OPERATED IN A PRESSURE-DEMAND OR OTHER POSITIVE PRESSURE MODE.
ESCAPE- ANY AIR-PURIFYING FULL FACEPIECE RESPIRATOR (GAS MASK) WITH A CHIN-STYLE OR FRONT- OR BACK-MOUNTED ORGANIC VAPOR CANISTER HAVING A HIGH-EFFICIENCY PARTICULATE FILTER. ANY APPROPRIATE ESCAPE-TYPE SELF-CONTAINED BREATHING APPARATUS.
FOR FIREFIGHTING AND OTHER IMMEDIATELY DANGEROUS TO LIFE OR HEALTH CONDITIONS:
SELF-CONTAINED BREATHING APPARATUS WITH FULL FACEPIECE OPERATED IN PRESSURE-DEMAND OR OTHER POSITIVE PRESSURE MODE.
SUPPLIED-AIR RESPIRATOR WITH FULL FACEPIECE AND OPERATED IN PRESSURE-DEMAND OR OTHER POSITIVE PRESSURE MODE IN COMBINATION WITH AN AUXILIARY SELF-CONTAINED BREATHING APPARATUS OPERATED IN PRESSURE-DEMAND OR OTHER POSITIVE PRESSURE MODE.

CLOTHING: EMPLOYEE MUST WEAR APPROPRIATE PROTECTIVE (IMPERVIOUS) CLOTHING AND EQUIPMENT TO PREVENT REPEATED OR PROLONGED SKIN CONTACT WITH THIS SUBSTANCE.

GLOVES: EMPLOYEE MUST WEAR APPROPRIATE PROTECTIVE GLOVES TO PREVENT CONTACT WITH THIS SUBSTANCE.

EYE PROTECTION: EMPLOYEE MUST WEAR SPLASH-PROOF OR DUST-RESISTANT SAFETY GOGGLES TO PREVENT EYE CONTACT WITH THIS SUBSTANCE.
EMERGENCY EYE WASH: WHERE THERE IS ANY POSSIBILITY THAT AN EMPLOYEE'S EYES MAY BE EXPOSED TO THIS SUBSTANCE, THE EMPLOYER SHOULD PROVIDE AN EYE WASH FOUNTAIN WITHIN THE IMMEDIATE WORK AREA FOR EMERGENCY USE.

AUTHORIZED BY- OCCUPATIONAL HEALTH SERVICES, INC.

CREATION DATE: 10/04/89 ***REVISION DATE:*** 07/12/90

MATERIAL SAFETY DATA SHEET

OCCUPATIONAL HEALTH SERVICES, INC.
AGRICULTURE AND PESTICIDE DIVISION
450 SEVENTH AVENUE, SUITE 2407
NEW YORK, NEW YORK 10123
1-800-445-MSDS OR (212) 967-1100

EMERGENCY CONTACT:
JOHN S. BRANSFORD, JR. (615) 292-1180

SUBSTANCE IDENTIFICATION

CAS-NUMBER 1634-78-2

SUBSTANCE: MALATHION OXYGEN ANALOG

TRADE NAMES/SYNONYMS: BUTANEDIOIC ACID, ((DIMETHOXYPHOSPHINYL)THIO-, DIETHYL ESTER; ((DIMETHOXYPHOSPHINYL)THIO)DIETHYL BUTANEDIOATE; SUCCINIC ACID, MERCAPTO-, DIETHYL ESTER, S-ESTER WITH O,O-DIMETHYL PHOSPHOROTHIOATE; MALAOXON; O,O-DIMETHYL-S-(1,2-DI(ETHOXYCARBONYLETHYL))PHOSPHOROTHIOATE; MALATHION-O-ANALOG; ((DIMETHOXYPHOSPHINYL)THIO)BUTANEDIOIC ACID DIETHYL ESTER; MERCAPTOSUCCINIC ACID DIETHYL ESTER, S-ESTER WITH O,O-DIMETHYL PHOSPHOROTHIOATE; OXYCARBOPHOS; C10H19O7PS; PST13541

CHEMICAL FAMILY: ORGANOPHOSPHATE

MOLECULAR FORMULA: C10-H19-O7-P-S

MOLECULAR WEIGHT: 314.30

CERCLA RATINGS (SCALE 0-3): HEALTH=3 FIRE=1 REACTIVITY=0 PERSISTENCE=0

NFPA RATINGS (SCALE 0-4): HEALTH=U FIRE=1 REACTIVITY=0

COMPONENTS AND CONTAMINANTS

COMPONENT: MALATHION OXYGEN ANALOG ***PERCENT:*** 100.0
CAS# 1634-78-2

OTHER CONTAMINANTS: NONE

EXPOSURE LIMITS: NO OCCUPATIONAL EXPOSURE LIMITS ESTABLISHED BY OSHA, ACGIH, OR NIOSH.

PHYSICAL DATA

DESCRIPTION: CLEAR LIQUID. ***BOILING POINT:*** NOT AVAILABLE

SPECIFIC GRAVITY: NOT AVAILABLE ***VAPOR PRESSURE:*** NOT AVAILABLE

SOLUBILITY IN WATER: NOT AVAILABLE

FIRE AND EXPLOSION DATA

FIRE AND EXPLOSION HAZARD: SLIGHT FIRE HAZARD WHEN EXPOSED TO HEAT OR FLAME.

FLASH POINT: 212 F (100 C) ***FLAMMABILITY CLASS(OSHA):*** IIIB

FIREFIGHTING MEDIA: DRY CHEMICAL, CARBON DIOXIDE, HALON, WATER SPRAY OR STANDARD FOAM (1987 EMERGENCY RESPONSE GUIDEBOOK, DOT P 5800.4). FOR LARGER FIRES, USE WATER SPRAY, FOG OR STANDARD FOAM (1987 EMERGENCY RESPONSE GUIDEBOOK, DOT P 5800.4).

FIREFIGHTING: MOVE CONTAINERS FROM FIRE AREA IF POSSIBLE. FIGHT FIRE FROM MAXIMUM DISTANCE. STAY AWAY FROM STORAGE TANK ENDS. DIKE FIRE CONTROL WATER FOR LATER DISPOSAL. DO NOT SCATTER MATERIAL (1987 EMERGENCY RESPONSE GUIDEBOOK, DOT P 5800.4, GUIDE PAGE 55). EXTINGUISH ONLY IF FLOW CAN BE STOPPED. EXTINGUISH USING AGENT INDICATED. USE FLOODING AMOUNTS OF WATER AS A FOG. COOL CONTAINERS WITH FLOODING AMOUNTS OF WATER FROM AS FAR A DISTANCE AS POSSIBLE. AVOID BREATHING POISONOUS VAPORS, KEEP UPWIND. CONSIDER EVACUATION OF DOWNWIND AREA IF MATERIAL IS LEAKING.

TOXICITY

MALATHION OXYGEN ANALOG: CARCINOGEN STATUS: NONE. TOXICITY DATA: 158 MG/KG ORAL-RAT LD50; 215 MG/KG ORAL-MOUSE LD50; 17500 UG/KG INTRAPERITONEAL-RAT LD50; 75 MG/KG INTRAPERITONEAL-MOUSE LD50; MUTAGENIC DATA (RTECS). ACUTE TOXICITY LEVEL: TOXIC BY INGESTION. TARGET EFFECTS: CHOLINESTERASE INHIBITOR. POISONING MAY AFFECT THE NERVOUS SYSTEM.* AT INCREASED RISK FROM EXPOSURE: PERSONS WITH RESPIRATORY AILMENTS, RECENT EXPOSURE TO CHOLINESTERASE INHIBITORS OR IMPAIRED CHOLINESTERASE PRODUCTION, OR LIVER MALFUNCTION.* ADDITIONAL DATA: MAY CROSS THE PLACENTA. HIGH ENVIRONMENTAL TEMPERATURES OR EXPOSURE OF THE CHEMICAL TO VISIBLE OR ULTRAVIOLET LIGHT MAY ENHANCE THE TOXICITY. INTERACTIONS WITH MEDICATIONS MAY OCCUR.* ANIMAL STUDIES INDICATE MALATHION DOES NOT INDUCE DELAYED NEUROTOXICITY.
* MAY BE BASED ON GENERAL INFORMATION ON ORGANOPHOSPHATES.

HEALTH EFFECTS AND FIRST AID

INHALATION: MALATHION OXYGEN ANALOG: SEE INFORMATION ON ORGANOPHOSPHATES.

ORGANOPHOSPHATES: CHOLINESTERASE INHIBITOR. **ACUTE EXPOSURE-** WHEN INHALED, THE FIRST EFFECTS OF CHOLINESTERASE INHIBITORS ARE USUALLY RESPIRATORY AND MAY INCLUDE NASAL HYPEREMIA AND WATERY DISCHARGE, COUGH, CHEST DISCOMFORT, DYSPNEA, AND WHEEZING DUE TO INCREASED BRONCHIAL SECRETIONS AND BRONCHOCONSTRICTION. IF SUFFICIENT AMOUNTS ARE ABSORBED, OTHER SYSTEMIC EFFECTS MAY BEGIN WITHIN A FEW MINUTES OR BE DELAYED FOR UP TO 12 HOURS. SYMPTOMS MAY INCLUDE PALLOR, NAUSEA, VOMITING, DIARRHEA, ABDOMINAL CRAMPS, HEADACHE, DIZZINESS, OCULAR PAIN, BLURRED VISION, MIOSIS OR IN SOME CASES, ESPECIALLY INITIALLY, MYDRIASIS, LACRIMATION, SALIVATION, SWEATING, AND CONFUSION. OTHER REPORTED CENTRAL NERVOUS SYSTEM OR NEUROMUSCULAR EFFECTS MAY INCLUDE ATAXIA, SLURRED SPEECH, AREFLEXIA, WEAKNESS, FATIGUE, FASCICULATIONS, TWITCHING, TREMORS POSSIBLY OF THE TONGUE AND EYELIDS, AND EVENTUALLY PARALYSIS OF THE EXTREMITIES AND POSSIBLY OF THE RESPIRATORY MUSCLES. IN SEVERE CASES THERE MAY ALSO BE INVOLUNTARY DEFECATION AND URINATION, CYANOSIS, PSYCHOSIS, HYPERGLYCEMIA, ACUTE PANCREATITIS, CARDIAC IRREGULARITIES, PULMONARY EDEMA, UNCONSCIOUSNESS, CONVULSIONS, AND COMA. DEATH IS PRIMARILY DUE TO RESPIRATORY FAILURE, ALTHOUGH CARDIOVASCULAR EFFECTS INCLUDING CARDIAC ARREST MAY ALSO BE IMPLICATED. LONG TERM SEQUELAE ARE RARE BUT MAY INCLUDE NEUROPSYCHIATRIC DISORDERS AND MYOPATHY WITH MUSCLE TENDERNESS. **CHRONIC EXPOSURE-** REPEATED OR PROLONGED EXPOSURE MAY RESULT IN THE EFFECTS OF ACUTE EXPOSURE. OTHER EFFECTS REPORTED IN WORKERS REPEATEDLY EXPOSED INCLUDE IMPAIRED MEMORY AND CONCENTRATION, ACUTE PSYCHOSIS, SEVERE DEPRESSIONS, IRRITABILTY, CONFUSION, APATHY, EMOTIONAL LABILITY, SOCIAL WITHDRAWAL, CONFUSION, HEADACHE, SPEECH DIFFICULTIES, DELAYED REACTION TIMES, SPATIAL DISORIENTATION, NIGHTMARES, SLEEPWALKING, AND DROWSINESS OR INSOMNIA. AN INFLUENZA-LIKE CONDITION WITH HEADACHE, NAUSEA, WEAKNESS, ANOREXIA AND MALAISE HAS ALSO BEEN REPORTED.

FIRST AID- REMOVE FROM EXPOSURE AREA TO FRESH AIR IMMEDIATELY. IF BREATHING HAS STOPPED, GIVE ARTIFICIAL RESPIRATION. MAINTAIN AIRWAY AND BLOOD PRESSURE AND ADMINISTER OXYGEN IF AVAILABLE. KEEP AFFECTED PERSON WARM AND AT REST. TREAT SYMPTOMATICALLY AND SUPPORTIVELY. ADMINISTRATION OF OXYGEN SHOULD BE PERFORMED BY QUALIFIED PERSONNEL. GET MEDICAL ATTENTION IMMEDIATELY.

SKIN CONTACT: MALATHION OXYGEN ANALOG: SEE INFORMATION ON ORGANOPHOSPHATES.

ORGANOPHOSPHATES: CHOLINESTERASE INHIBITOR. **ACUTE EXPOSURE-** LOCALIZED SWEATING AND FASCICULATIONS MAY OCCUR AT THE SITE OF CONTACT. IF SUFFICIENT AMOUNTS ARE ABSORBED, OTHER EFFECTS OF CHOLINESTERASE INHIBITION AS DESCRIBED IN ACUTE INHALATION MAY OCCUR. SYMPTOMS MAY BE DELAYED 2-3 HOURS, BUT USUALLY NO MORE THAN 12 HOURS. THE RATE OF ABSORPTION IS INCREASED BY THE PRESENCE OF DERMATITIS OR HIGH AMBIENT TEMPERATURES. **CHRONIC EXPOSURE-** REPEATED OR PROLONGED EXPOSURE MAY CAUSE EFFECTS AS DESCRIBED IN ACUTE EXPOSURE. SOME ORGANOPHOSPHATES MAY CAUSE SENSITIZATION.

FIRST AID- REMOVE CONTAMINATED CLOTHING IMMEDIATELY. WASH CONTAMINATED AREAS WITH SOAP AND WATER FOLLOWED BY ALCOHOL (ARENA, POISONING, 4TH ED.). EMERGENCY PERSONNEL SHOULD WEAR GLOVES AND AVOID CONTAMINATION. TREAT RESPIRATORY DIFFICULTY WITH ARTIFICIAL RESPIRATION. GET MEDICAL ATTENTION IMMEDIATELY.

EYE CONTACT: MALATHION OXYGEN ANALOG: SEE INFORMATION ON ORGANOPHOSPHATES.

ORGANOPHOSPHATES: CHOLINESTERASE INHIBITOR. **ACUTE EXPOSURE-** DIRECT CONTACT MAY CAUSE PAIN, HYPEREMIA, LACRIMATION, TWITCHING OF THE EYELIDS, MIOSIS, AND CILIARY MUSCLE SPASM WITH LOSS OF ACCOMODATION, BLURRED OR DIMMED VISION AND BROWACHE. SOMETIMES MYDRIASIS MAY OCCUR INSTEAD OF MIOSIS. WITH SUFFICIENT EXPOSURE, OTHER SYMPTOMS OF CHOLINESTERASE INHIBITION AS DESCRIBED IN ACUTE INHALATION MAY OCCUR. **CHRONIC EXPOSURE-** REPEATED OR PROLONGED EXPOSURE MAY CAUSE EFFECTS AS DESCRIBED IN ACUTE EXPOSURE. SOME COMPOUNDS HAVE CAUSED TOXIC EFFECTS ON THE CRYSTALLINE LENS, CONJUNCTIVAL THICKENING AND OBSTRUCTION OF THE NASOLACRIMAL CANALS WHEN USED AS MIOTIC EYEDROPS.

FIRST AID- IRRIGATE EYES WITH WATER OR SALINE SOLUTION. IF SYMPTOMS OF POISONING OCCUR, TREAT RESPIRATORY DIFFICULTY WITH ARTIFICIAL RESPIRATION AND OXYGEN. OBSERVE PATIENT FOR AT LEAST 24-36 HOURS (GOSSELIN, CLINICAL TOXICOLOGY OF COMMERCIAL PRODUCTS, 5TH ED.). GET MEDICAL ATTENTION IMMEDIATELY. OXYGEN SHOULD BE ADMINISTERED BY QUALIFIED MEDICAL PERSONNEL.

INGESTION: MALATHION OXYGEN ANALOG: TOXIC. SEE INFORMATION ON ORGANOPHOSPHATES.

ORGANOPHOSPHATES: CHOLINESTERASE INHIBITOR. **ACUTE EXPOSURE-** WHEN INGESTED, THE FIRST EFFECTS MAY BE NAUSEA, VOMITING, ANOREXIA, ABDOMINAL CRAMPS AND DIARRHEA. GASTROINTESTINAL ABSORPTION MAY CAUSE THE SYMPTOMS OF CHOLINESTERASE INHIBITION AS DESCRIBED IN ACUTE INHALATION. SYMPTOMS MAY BEGIN WITHIN MINUTES OR BE DELAYED. **CHRONIC EXPOSURE-** REPEATED INGESTION MAY CAUSE EFFECTS AS DESCRIBED IN ACUTE EXPOSURE.

FIRST AID- IF PERSON IS ALERT AND RESPIRATION IS NOT DEPRESSED, GIVE SYRUP OF IPECAC FOLLOWED BY WATER (IF VOMITING OCCURS, KEEP HEAD BELOW HIPS TO PREVENT ASPIRATION). IF CONSCIOUSNESS LEVEL DECLINES OR VOMITING HAS NOT OCCURRED IN 15 MINUTES EMPTY STOMACH BY GASTRIC LAVAGE WITH THE AID OF CUFFED ENDOTRACHEAL TUBE USING ISOTONIC SALINE OR 5% SODIUM BICARBONATE FOLLOW WITH ACTIVATED CHARCOAL. ESTABLISH AND MAINTAIN AIRWAY. TREAT RESPIRATORY DIFFICULTY WITH ARTIFICIAL RESPIRATION AND OXYGEN. DO NOT GIVE MORPHINE, AMINOPHYLLINE, PHENOTHIAZINES, RESERPINE, FUROSEMIDE, OR ETHACRYNIC ACID (MORGAN, RECOGNITION AND MANAGEMENT OF PESTICIDE POISONINGS, 3RD ED.). TREAT SYMPTOMATICALLY AND SUPPORTIVELY. ADMINISTRATION OF OXYGEN AND LAVAGE MUST BE PERFORMED BY QUALIFIED MEDICAL PERSONNEL. GET MEDICAL ATTENTION IMMEDIATELY.

ANTIDOTE: THE FOLLOWING ANTIDOTE(S) HAVE BEEN RECOMMENDED. HOWEVER, THE DECISION AS TO WHETHER THE SEVERITY OF POISONING REQUIRES ADMINISTRATION OF ANY ANTIDOTE AND ACTUAL DOSE REQUIRED SHOULD BE MADE BY QUALIFIED MEDICAL PERSONNEL.

FOR CHOLINESTERASE INHIBITORS: ESTABLISH CLEAR AIRWAY AND TISSUE OXYGENATION BY ASPIRATION OF SECRETIONS, AND IF NECESSARY, BY ASSISTED PULMONARY VENTILATION WITH OXYGEN. IMPROVE TISSUE OXYGENATION AS MUCH AS POSSIBLE BEFORE ADMINISTERING ATROPINE TO MINIMIZE THE RISK OF VENTRICULAR FIBRILLATION. ADMINISTER ATROPINE SULFATE INTRAVENOUSLY, OR INTRAMUSCULARLY IF IV INJECTION IS NOT POSSIBLE. IN MODERATELY SEVERE POISONING ADMINISTER ATROPINE SULFATE, 0.4-2.0 MG REPEATED EVERY 15 MINUTES UNTIL ATROPINIZATION IS ACHIEVED (TACHYCARDIA, FLUSHING, DRY MOUTH, MYDRIASIS). MAINTAIN ATROPINIZATION BY REPEATED DOSES FOR 2-12 HOURS, OR LONGER, DEPENDING ON THE SEVERITY OF POISONING. THE APPEARANCE OF RALES IN THE LUNG BASES, MIOSIS, SALIVATION, NAUSEA, BRADYCARDIA, ARE ALL INDICATIONS OF INADEQUATE ATROPINIZATION. SEVERELY POISONED INDIVIDUALS MAY EXHIBIT REMARKABLE TOLERANCE TO ATROPINE; TWO OR MORE TIMES THE DOSAGES SUGGESTED ABOVE MAY BE NEEDED. PERSONS NOT POISONED OR ONLY SLIGHTLY POISONED, HOWEVER, MAY DEVELOP SIGNS OF ATROPINE TOXICITY FROM SUCH LARGE DOSAGES: FEVER, MUSCLE FIBRILLATIONS, AND DELIRIUM ARE THE MAIN SIGNS OF ATROPINE TOXICITY. IF THESE SIGNS APPEAR WHILE THE PATIENT IS FULLY ATROPINIZED, ATROPINE ADMINISTRATION SHOULD BE DISCONTINUED, AT LEAST TEMPORARILY. OBSERVE TREATED PATIENTS CLOSELY AT LEAST 24 HOURS TO INSURE THAT SYMPTOMS (POSSIBLY PULMONARY EDEMA) DO NOT RECUR AS ATROPINIZATION WEARS OFF. IN VERY SEVERE POISONINGS, METABOLIC DISPOSITION OF TOXICANT MAY REQUIRE SEVERAL HOURS OR DAYS DURING WHICH ATROPINIZATION MUST BE MAINTAINED. MARKEDLY LOWER LEVELS OF URINARY METABOLITES INDICATE THAT ATROPINE DOSAGE CAN BE TAPERED OFF. AS DOSAGE IS REDUCED, CHECK THE LUNG BASES FREQUENTLY FOR RALES. IF RALES ARE HEARD OR OTHER SYMPTOMS RETURN, RE-ESTABLISH ATROPINIZATION PROMPTLY (MORGAN, RECOGNITION AND MANAGEMENT OF PESTICIDE POISONINGS, 3RD ED.). ADMINISTRATION OF ANTIDOTE MUST BE PERFORMED BY QUALIFIED MEDICAL PERSONNEL.

IN CASES OF SEVERE POISONING BY ORGANOPHOSPHATE PESTICIDES IN WHICH RESPIRATORY DEPRESSION, MUSCLE WEAKNESS AND TWITCHINGS ARE SEVERE, GIVE PRALIDOXIME (PROTOPAM-AYERST, 2-PAM), 1.0 GRAM INTRAVENOUSLY AT NO MORE THAN 0.5 GRAM PER MINUTE. DOSAGE OF PRALIDOXIME MAY BE REPEATED IN 1-2 HOURS, THEN AT 10-12 HOUR INTERVALS IF NEEDED. IN VERY SEVERE POISONINGS, DOSAGE RATES MAY BE DOUBLED. TREATMENT WITH PRALIDOXIME WILL BE MOST EFFECTIVE IF GIVEN WITHIN THIRTY-SIX HOURS AFTER POISONING (MORGAN, RECOGNITION AND MANAGEMENT OF PESTICIDE POISONINGS, 3RD ED.). ANTIDOTE SHOULD BE ADMINISTERED BY QUALIFIED MEDICAL PERSONNEL.

REACTIVITY

REACTIVITY: STABLE UNDER NORMAL TEMPERATURES AND PRESSURES.

INCOMPATIBILITIES: MALATHION OXYGEN ANALOG: OXIDIZERS (STRONG): FIRE AND EXPLOSION DATA.

DECOMPOSITION: THERMAL DECOMPOSITION PRODUCTS MAY INCLUDE TOXIC OXIDES OF CARBON, SULFUR, AND PHOSPHORUS.

POLYMERIZATION: HAZARDOUS POLYMERIZATION HAS NOT BEEN REPORTED TO OCCUR UNDER NORMAL TEMPERATURES AND PRESSURES.

STORAGE AND DISPOSAL

OBSERVE ALL FEDERAL, STATE AND LOCAL REGULATIONS WHEN STORING OR DISPOSING OF THIS SUBSTANCE. FOR ASSISTANCE, CONTACT THE DISTRICT DIRECTOR OF THE ENVIRONMENTAL PROTECTION AGENCY.

STORAGE

STORE AWAY FROM INCOMPATIBLE SUBSTANCES.

CONDITIONS TO AVOID

MAY BURN BUT DOES NOT IGNITE READILY. CONTAINERS MAY EXPLODE IN HEAT OF FIRE.

SPILL AND LEAK PROCEDURES

OCCUPATIONAL SPILL: DO NOT TOUCH SPILLED MATERIAL. STOP LEAK IF YOU CAN DO IT WITHOUT RISK. USE WATER SPRAY TO REDUCE VAPORS. FOR SMALL SPILLS, TAKE UP WITH SAND OR OTHER ABSORBENT MATERIAL AND PLACE INTO CONTAINERS FOR LATER DISPOSAL. FOR SMALL DRY SPILLS, WITH A CLEAN SHOVEL PLACE MATERIAL INTO CLEAN, DRY CONTAINERS AND COVER. MOVE CONTAINERS FROM SPILL AREA. FOR LARGER SPILLS, DIKE FAR AHEAD OF SPILL FOR LATER DISPOSAL. KEEP UNNECESSARY PEOPLE AWAY. ISOLATE HAZARD AREA AND DENY ENTRY. VENTILATE CLOSED SPACES BEFORE ENTERING.

PROTECTIVE EQUIPMENT

VENTILATION: PROVIDE LOCAL EXHAUST OR PROCESS ENCLOSURE VENTILATION SYSTEM.

RESPIRATOR: THE FOLLOWING RESPIRATORS ARE RECOMMENDED BASED ON INFORMATION FOUND IN THE PHYSICAL DATA, TOXICITY AND HEALTH EFFECTS SECTIONS. THEY ARE RANKED IN ORDER FROM MINIMUM TO MAXIMUM RESPIRATORY PROTECTION. THE SPECIFIC RESPIRATOR SELECTED MUST BE BASED ON CONTAMINATION LEVELS FOUND IN THE WORK PLACE, MUST NOT EXCEED THE WORKING LIMITS OF THE RESPIRATOR AND BE JOINTLY APPROVED BY THE NATIONAL INSTITUTE FOR OCCUPATIONAL SAFETY AND HEALTH AND THE MINE SAFETY AND HEALTH ADMINISTRATION (NIOSH-MSHA).

TYPE 'C' SUPPLIED-AIR RESPIRATOR WITH A FULL FACEPIECE OPERATED IN PRESSURE-DEMAND OR OTHER POSITIVE PRESSURE MODE OR WITH A FULL FACEPIECE, HELMET OR HOOD OPERATED IN CONTINOUS-FLOW MODE.

SELF-CONTAINED BREATHING APPARATUS WITH A FULL FACEPIECE OPERATED IN PRESSURE-DEMAND OR OTHER POSITIVE PRESSURE MODE.

FOR FIREFIGHTING AND OTHER IMMEDIATELY DANGEROUS TO LIFE OR HEALTH CONDITIONS:

SELF-CONTAINED BREATHING APPARATUS WITH FULL FACEPIECE OPERATED IN PRESSURE-DEMAND OR OTHER POSITIVE PRESSURE MODE.

SUPPLIED-AIR RESPIRATOR WITH FULL FACEPIECE AND OPERATED IN PRESSURE-DEMAND OR OTHER POSITIVE PRESSURE MODE IN COMBINATION WITH AN AUXILIARY SELF-CONTAINED BREATHING APPARATUS OPERATED IN PRESSURE-DEMAND OR OTHER POSITIVE PRESSURE MODE.

CLOTHING: EMPLOYEE MUST WEAR APPROPRIATE PROTECTIVE (IMPERVIOUS) CLOTHING AND EQUIPMENT TO PREVENT ANY POSSIBILITY OF SKIN CONTACT WITH THIS SUBSTANCE.

GLOVES: EMPLOYEE MUST WEAR APPROPRIATE PROTECTIVE GLOVES TO PREVENT CONTACT WITH THIS SUBSTANCE.

EYE PROTECTION: EMPLOYEE MUST WEAR SPLASH-PROOF OR DUST-RESISTANT SAFETY GOGGLES AND A FACESHIELD TO PREVENT CONTACT WITH THIS SUBSTANCE.

EMERGENCY WASH FACILITIES: WHERE THERE IS ANY POSSIBILITY THAT AN EMPLOYEE'S EYES AND/OR SKIN MAY BE EXPOSED TO THIS SUBSTANCE, THE EMPLOYER SHOULD PROVIDE AN EYE WASH FOUNTAIN AND QUICK DRENCH SHOWER WITHIN THE IMMEDIATE WORK AREA FOR EMERGENCY USE.

AUTHORIZED BY- OCCUPATIONAL HEALTH SERVICES, INC.

CREATION DATE: 05/03/90 ***REVISION DATE:*** 06/20/90

MATERIAL SAFETY DATA SHEET

OCCUPATIONAL HEALTH SERVICES, INC.
AGRICULTURE AND PESTICIDE DIVISION
450 SEVENTH AVENUE, SUITE 2407
NEW YORK, NEW YORK 10123
1-800-445-MSDS OR (212) 967-1100

EMERGENCY CONTACT:
JOHN S. BRANSFORD, JR. (615) 292-1180

SUBSTANCE IDENTIFICATION

CAS-NUMBER 123-33-1

SUBSTANCE: MALEIC HYDRAZIDE

TRADE NAMES/SYNONYMS: 1,2-DIHYDRO-3,6-PYRIDAZINEDIONE; 6-HYDROXY-3(2H)-PYRIDAZINONE; ANTERGON; ANTRYROST; 3,6-DIHYDROXYPYRIDAZINE; 3,6-DIOXOPYRIDAZINE; MAH; MALEIC ACID CYCLIC HYDRAZIDE; MALEIC ACID HYDRAZIDE; MALEPIN; MALZID; MAZIDE; MH; MH30; REGULOX 36; RCRA U148; PST13570

CHEMICAL FAMILY: PYRIDAZINE

MOLECULAR FORMULA: C4-H4-N2-O2

MOLECULAR WEIGHT: 112.10

CERCLA RATINGS (SCALE 0-3): HEALTH=2 FIRE=0 REACTIVITY=0 PERSISTENCE=2

NFPA RATINGS (SCALE 0-4): HEALTH=2 FIRE=0 REACTIVITY=0

COMPONENTS AND CONTAMINANTS

COMPONENT: MALEIC HYDRAZIDE ***PERCENT:*** 100

CAS# 123-33-1

OTHER CONTAMINANTS: NONE

EXPOSURE LIMITS: MALEIC HYDRAZIDE: NO OCCUPATIONAL EXPOSURE LIMITS ESTABLISHED BY OSHA, ACGIH, OR NIOSH.

5000 POUNDS CERCLA SECTION 103 REPORTABLE QUANTITY

PHYSICAL DATA

DESCRIPTION: COLORLESS CRYSTALS ***BOILING POINT:*** DECOMPOSES

MELTING POINT: 583-586 F (306-308 C) DECOMPOSES ***SPECIFIC GRAVITY:*** 1.6

SOLUBILITY IN WATER: SLIGHT

SOLVENT SOLUBILITY: ETHANOL, AQUEOUS ALKALI AND CERTAIN ORGANIC BASES

FIRE AND EXPLOSION DATA

FIRE AND EXPLOSION HAZARD: NEGLIGIBLE FIRE HAZARD WHEN EXPOSED TO HEAT OR FLAME.

FIREFIGHTING MEDIA: DRY CHEMICAL, CARBON DIOXIDE, HALON, WATER SPRAY OR STANDARD FOAM (1987 EMERGENCY RESPONSE GUIDEBOOK, DOT P 5800.4). FOR LARGER FIRES, USE WATER SPRAY, FOG OR STANDARD FOAM (1987 EMERGENCY RESPONSE GUIDEBOOK, DOT P 5800.4).

FIREFIGHTING: NO ACUTE HAZARD. MOVE CONTAINER FROM FIRE AREA IF POSSIBLE. AVOID BREATHING VAPORS OR DUSTS; KEEP UPWIND.

TOXICITY

MALEIC HYDRAZIDE: TOXICITITY DATA: 3800 MG/KG ORAL-RAT LD50; MUTAGENIC DATA (RTECS); TUMORIGENIC DATA (RTECS). CARCINOGEN STATUS: ANIMAL INADEQUATE EVIDENCE (IARC GROUP-3). LOCAL EFFECTS: IRRITANT- INHALATION, SKIN, EYE. ACUTE TOXICITY LEVEL: MODERATELY TOXIC BY INGESTION. TARGET EFFECTS: NOT DATA AVAILABLE.

HEALTH EFFECTS AND FIRST AID

INHALATION: MALEIC HYDRAZIDE: IRRITANT. **ACUTE EXPOSURE**- MAY CAUSE IRRITATION. **CHRONIC EXPOSURE**- NO DATA AVAILABLE.

FIRST AID- REMOVE FROM EXPOSURE AREA TO FRESH AIR IMMEDIATELY. IF BREATHING HAS STOPPED, PERFORM ARTIFICIAL RESPIRATION. KEEP PERSON WARM AND AT REST. TREAT SYMPTOMATICALLY AND SUPPORTIVELY. GET MEDICAL ATTENTION IMMEDIATELY.

SKIN CONTACT: MALEIC HYDRAZIDE: IRRITANT. **ACUTE EXPOSURE**- MAY CAUSE IRRITATION. **CHRONIC EXPOSURE**- REPEATED OR PROLONGED CONTACT MAY CAUSE DERMATITIS.

FIRST AID- REMOVE CONTAMINATED CLOTHING AND SHOES IMMEDIATELY. WASH AFFECTED AREA WITH SOAP OR MILD DETERGENT AND LARGE AMOUNTS OF WATER UNTIL NO EVIDENCE OF CHEMICAL REMAINS (APPROXIMATELY 15-20 MINUTES). GET MEDICAL ATTENTION IMMEDIATELY.

EYE CONTACT: MALEIC HYDRAZIDE: IRRITANT. **ACUTE EXPOSURE**- MAY CAUSE IRRITATION. **CHRONIC EXPOSURE**- REPEATED OR PROLONGED CONTACT MAY CAUSE CONJUNCTIVITIS.

FIRST AID- WASH EYES IMMEDIATELY WITH LARGE AMOUNTS OF WATER OR NORMAL SALINE, OCCASIONALLY LIFTING UPPER AND LOWER LIDS, UNTIL NO EVIDENCE OF CHEMICAL REMAINS (APPROXIMATELY 15-20 MINUTES). GET MEDICAL ATTENTION IMMEDIATELY.

INGESTION: MALEIC HYDRAZIDE: **ACUTE EXPOSURE**- INGESTION BY LABORATORY ANIMALS HAS RESULTED IN MUSCLE SPASMS, TREMORS AND DEATH. **CHRONIC EXPOSURE**- NO DATA AVAILABLE.

FIRST AID- REMOVE BY GASTRIC LAVAGE AND CATHARSIS. MAINTAIN BLOOD PRESSURE AND AIRWAY. GIVE OXYGEN IF RESPIRATION IS DEPRESSED. DO NOT PERFORM GASTRIC LAVAGE IF VICTIM IS UNCONSCIOUS. GET MEDICAL ATTENTION IMMEDIATELY (DREISBACH, HANDBOOK OF POISONING, 12TH ED.).

ADMINISTRATION OF LAVAGE OR OXYGEN SHOULD BE PERFORMED BY QUALIFIED MEDICAL PERSONNEL.

ANTIDOTE: NO SPECIFIC ANTIDOTE. TREAT SYMPTOMATICALLY AND SUPPORTIVELY.

REACTIVITY

REACTIVITY: STABLE UNDER NORMAL TEMPERATURES AND PRESSURES.

INCOMPATIBILITIES: MALEIC HYDRAZIDE: NO DATA AVAILABLE.

DECOMPOSITION: THERMAL DECOMPOSITION PRODUCTS MAY INCLUDE TOXIC OXIDES OF CARBON AND NITROGEN.

POLYMERIZATION: NO DATA AVAILABLE.

CONDITIONS TO AVOID

NONE REPORTED.

SPILL AND LEAK PROCEDURES

OCCUPATIONAL SPILL: NO SPECIAL PRECAUTIONS INDICATED.

REPORTABLE QUANTITY (RQ): 5000 POUNDS THE SUPERFUND AMENDMENTS AND REAUTHORIZATION ACT (SARA) SECTION 304 REQUIRES THAT A RELEASE EQUAL TO OR GREATER THAN THE REPORTABLE QUANTITY FOR THIS SUBSTANCE BE IMMEDIATELY REPORTED TO THE LOCAL EMERGENCY PLANNING COMMITTEE AND THE STATE EMERGENCY RESPONSE COMMISSION (40 CFR 355.40). IF THE RELEASE OF THIS SUBSTANCE IS REPORTABLE UNDER CERCLA SECTION 103, THE NATIONAL RESPONSE CENTER MUST BE NOTIFIED IMMEDIATELY AT (800) 424-8802 OR (202) 426-2675 IN THE METROPOLITAN WASHINGTON, D.C. AREA (40 CFR 302.6).

PROTECTIVE EQUIPMENT

VENTILATION: PROVIDE LOCAL EXHAUST OR GENERAL DILUTION VENTILATION SYSTEM.

RESPIRATOR: THE FOLLOWING RESPIRATORS ARE RECOMMENDED BASED ON INFORMATION FOUND IN THE PHYSICAL DATA, TOXICITY AND HEALTH EFFECTS SECTIONS. THEY ARE RANKED IN ORDER FROM MINIMUM TO MAXIMUM RESPIRATORY PROTECTION. THE SPECIFIC RESPIRATOR SELECTED MUST BE BASED ON CONTAMINATION LEVELS FOUND IN THE WORK PLACE, MUST NOT EXCEED THE WORKING LIMITS OF THE RESPIRATOR AND BE JOINTLY APPROVED BY THE NATIONAL INSTITUTE FOR OCCUPATIONAL SAFETY AND HEALTH AND THE MINE SAFETY AND HEALTH ADMINISTRATION (NIOSH-MSHA).

DUST AND MIST RESPIRATOR WITH A FULL FACEPIECE.

AIR-PURIFYING FULL FACEPIECE RESPIRATOR WITH A HIGH-EFFICIENCY PARTICULATE FILTER.

POWERED AIR-PURIFYING RESPIRATOR WITH A TIGHT-FITTING FACEPIECE AND HIGH-EFFICIENCY PARTICULATE FILTER.

TYPE 'C' SUPPLIED-AIR RESPIRATOR WITH A FULL FACEPIECE OPERATED IN PRESSURE-DEMAND OR OTHER POSITIVE PRESSURE MODE OR WITH A FULL FACEPIECE, HELMET OR HOOD OPERATED IN CONTINUOUS-FLOW MODE.

SELF-CONTAINED BREATHING APPARATUS WITH A FULL FACEPIECE OPERATED IN PRESSURE-DEMAND OR OTHER POSITIVE PRESSURE MODE.

FOR FIREFIGHTING AND OTHER IMMEDIATELY DANGEROUS TO LIFE OR HEALTH CONDITIONS:

SELF-CONTAINED BREATHING APPARATUS WITH FULL FACEPIECE OPERATED IN PRESSURE-DEMAND OR OTHER POSITIVE PRESSURE MODE.

SUPPLIED-AIR RESPIRATOR WITH FULL FACEPIECE AND OPERATED IN PRESSURE-DEMAND OR OTHER POSITIVE PRESSURE MODE IN COMBINATION WITH AN AUXILIARY SELF-CONTAINED BREATHING APPARATUS OPERATED IN PRESSURE-DEMAND OR OTHER POSITIVE PRESSURE MODE.

CLOTHING: EMPLOYEE MUST WEAR APPROPRIATE PROTECTIVE (IMPERVIOUS) CLOTHING AND EQUIPMENT TO PREVENT REPEATED OR PROLONGED SKIN CONTACT WITH THIS SUBSTANCE.

GLOVES: EMPLOYEE MUST WEAR APPROPRIATE PROTECTIVE GLOVES TO PREVENT CONTACT WITH THIS SUBSTANCE.

EYE PROTECTION: EMPLOYEE MUST WEAR SPLASH-PROOF OR DUST-RESISTANT SAFETY GOGGLES TO PREVENT EYE CONTACT WITH THIS SUBSTANCE.

EMERGENCY EYE WASH: WHERE THERE IS ANY POSSIBILITY THAT AN EMPLOYEE'S EYES MAY BE EXPOSED TO THIS SUBSTANCE, THE EMPLOYER SHOULD PROVIDE AN EYE WASH FOUNTAIN WITHIN THE IMMEDIATE WORK AREA FOR EMERGENCY USE.

AUTHORIZED BY- OCCUPATIONAL HEALTH SERVICES, INC.

CREATION DATE: 10/04/89 ***REVISION DATE:*** 07/12/90

MATERIAL SAFETY DATA SHEET

OCCUPATIONAL HEALTH SERVICES, INC.
AGRICULTURE AND PESTICIDE DIVISION
450 SEVENTH AVENUE, SUITE 2407
NEW YORK, NEW YORK 10123
1-800-445-MSDS OR (212) 967-1100

EMERGENCY CONTACT:
JOHN S. BRANSFORD, JR. (615) 292-1180

SUBSTANCE IDENTIFICATION

CAS-NUMBER 12427-38-2

***SUBSTANCE:* MANEB**

TRADE NAMES/SYNONYMS: MANGANESE, ((1,2-ETHANEDIYLBIS(CARBAMODITHIOATO))(2-))-; MANGANESE, (ETHYLENEBIS(DITHIOCARBAMATO))-; ((1,2-ETHANEDIYLBIS(CARBAMODITHIOATO))(2-))MANGANESE; (ETHYLENEBIS(DITHIOCARBAMATO))MANGANESE; MANGANESE ETHYLENEBIS(DITHIOCARBAMATE); MANGANESE ETHYLENEBISDITHIOCARBAMATE; DITHANE M 22; MANESAN; MANEX; MANZATE; POLYRAM M; RHODIANEBE; TRIMANGOL; ENT 14875; RCRA U114; UN 2968; C4H6NMN2S4; PST13589

CHEMICAL FAMILY: THIOCARBAMATE ORGANOMETALLIC

MOLECULAR FORMULA: C4-H6-N2-S4.MN

MOLECULAR WEIGHT: 266.31

CERCLA RATINGS (SCALE 0-3): HEALTH=3 FIRE=3 REACTIVITY=1 PERSISTENCE=3

NFPA RATINGS (SCALE 0-4): HEALTH=3 FIRE=3 REACTIVITY=1

COMPONENTS AND CONTAMINANTS

COMPONENT: MANEB ***PERCENT:*** 100.0

CAS# 12427-38-2

OTHER CONTAMINANTS: NONE

EXPOSURE LIMITS: MANGANESE COMPOUNDS (AS MN): 5 MG/M3 OSHA CEILING 5 MG/M3 ACGIH TWA

SUBJECT TO SARA 313 ANNUAL TOXIC CHEMICAL RELEASE REPORTING.

MANEB: SUBJECT TO CALIFORNIA PROPOSITION 65 CANCER AND/OR REPRODUCTIVE TOXICITY WARNING AND RELEASE REQUIREMENTS- (JANUARY 1, 1990)

PHYSICAL DATA

DESCRIPTION: ODORLESS, YELLOW CRYSTALLINE SOLID.

MELTING POINT: DECOMPOSES BEFORE MELTING ***SPECIFIC GRAVITY:*** NOT AVAILABLE

VAPOR PRESSURE: NEGLIGIBLE ***SOLUBILITY IN WATER:*** MODERATELY SOLUBLE

SOLVENT SOLUBILITY: SOLUBLE IN CHLOROFORM, PYRIDINE; INSOLUBLE IN MOST ORGANIC SOLVENTS

FIRE AND EXPLOSION DATA

FIRE AND EXPLOSION HAZARD: MAY BE LIABLE TO SPONTANEOUS HEATING AND IGNITION IF CONTACTED WITH MOISTURE.

FIREFIGHTING MEDIA: DRY CHEMICAL, SODA ASH, LIME OR SAND (1987 EMERGENCY RESPONSE GUIDEBOOK, DOT P 5800.4).

FOR LARGER FIRES, FLOOD AREA WITH WATER FROM A DISTANCE (1987 EMERGENCY RESPONSE GUIDEBOOK, DOT P 5800.4).

FIREFIGHTING: DO NOT GET WATER INSIDE CONTAINERS. MOVE CONTAINERS FROM FIRE AREA IF POSSIBLE. COOL CONTAINERS EXPOSED TO FLAMES WITH WATER FROM SIDE UNTIL WELL AFTER FIRE IS OUT. STAY AWAY FROM STORAGE TANK ENDS. FOR MASSIVE FIRE IN STORAGE AREA, USE UNMANNED HOSE HOLDER OR MONITOR NOZZLES; ELSE WITHDRAW FROM AREA AND LET FIRE BURN (1987 EMERGENCY RESPONSE GUIDEBOOK, DOT P 5800.4, GUIDE PAGE 37).

EXTINGUISH USING AGENT FOR TYPE OF FIRE. AVOID BREATHING FUMES FROM BURNING MATERIAL.

TRANSPORTATION DATA

DEPARTMENT OF TRANSPORTATION HAZARD CLASSIFICATION 49 CFR 172.101: ORM-C

DEPARTMENT OF TRANSPORTATION LABELING REQUIREMENTS 49 CFR 172.101 AND SUBPART E: NONE

DEPARTMENT OF TRANSPORTATION PACKAGING REQUIREMENTS: 49 CFR 173.1040 EXCEPTIONS: 49 CFR 173.505

TOXICITY

MANEB: TOXICITY DATA: 3 GM/KG ORAL-RAT LD50; 2600 MG/KG ORAL-MOUSE LD50; 6400 MG/KG ORAL-GUINEA PIG LDLO; 5000 MG/KG UNREPORTED-MAMMAL LD50; 3000 MG/KG UNREPORTED-RAT LD50; MUTAGENIC DATA (RTECS); REPRODUCTIVE EFFECTS DATA (RTECS); TUMORIGENIC DATA (RTECS).

CARCINOGEN STATUS: ANIMAL INADEQUATE EVIDENCE (IARC GROUP-3). A METABOLITE AND DEGRADATION PRODUCT OF MANEB, ETHYLENE THIOUREA, INDUCED BY ORAL ADMINISTRATION HIGHLY SIGNIFICANT INCREASES IN THE

INCIDENCES OF LIVER TUMORS IN TWO STRAINS OF MICE AND THYROID CARCINOMAS AND ADENOMAS IN TWO SEPARATE RAT STUDIES. LOCAL EFFECTS: IRRITANT- SKIN. ACUTE TOXICITY LEVEL: MODERATELY TOXIC BY INGESTION. TARGET EFFECTS: POISONING MAY AFFECT THE THYROID. ADDITIONAL DATA: IN ANIMAL STUDIES, THE METABOLITE, ETHYLENE THIOUREA PRODUCED TETRATOGENIC AND GOITROGENIC EFFECTS.

HEALTH EFFECTS AND FIRST AID

INHALATION: MANEB: **ACUTE EXPOSURE-** INHALATION OF EXCESSIVE AMOUNTS OF DUST OR SPRAY MAY CAUSE IRRITATION OF THE MUCOUS MEMBRANES WITH SCRATCHY THROAT, SNEEZING, COUGH, RHINITIS, PHARYNGITIS AND BRONCHITIS. ONE 62-YEAR-OLD MAN DEVELOPED ACUTE RENAL FAILURE AND ECG ABNORMALITIES AFTER APPLYING THIS COMPOUND TO HIS GARDEN. THE SYMPTOMS WERE RESOLVED PROMPTLY FOLLOWING HEMODIALYSIS. **CHRONIC EXPOSURE-** MALE RATS THAT HAD INHALED MANEB FOR 4 MONTHS AT CONCENTRATIONS OF 2 AND 100 MG/M3 SHOWED CHANGES IN THE ACTIVITY OF LACTATE DEHYDROGENASE ISOENZYMES OF THE TESTIS, SOME BEING INCREASED AND OTHERS DECREASED.

FIRST AID- REMOVE FROM EXPOSURE AREA TO FRESH AIR IMMEDIATELY. IF BREATHING HAS STOPPED, PERFORM ARTIFICIAL RESPIRATION. KEEP PERSON WARM AND AT REST. TREAT SYMPTOMATICALLY AND SUPPORTIVELY. GET MEDICAL ATTENTION IMMEDIATELY.

SKIN CONTACT: MANEB: IRRITANT. **ACUTE EXPOSURE-** EXPOSURE TO A LARGE CONCENTRATION OF DUST OR SPRAY MAY CAUSE IRRITATION. **CHRONIC EXPOSURE-** PROLONGED EXPOSURE TO A LARGE CONCENTRATION MAY CAUSE DERMATITIS.

FIRST AID- REMOVE CONTAMINATED CLOTHING AND SHOES IMMEDIATELY. WASH AFFECTED AREA WITH SOAP OR MILD DETERGENT AND LARGE AMOUNTS OF WATER UNTIL NO EVIDENCE OF CHEMICAL REMAINS (APPROXIMATELY 15-20 MINUTES). GET MEDICAL ATTENTION IMMEDIATELY.

EYE CONTACT: MANEB: **ACUTE EXPOSURE-** MAY CAUSE IRRITATION. **CHRONIC EXPOSURE-** PROLONGED EXPOSURE MAY CAUSE CONJUNCTIVITIS.

FIRST AID- WASH EYES IMMEDIATELY WITH LARGE AMOUNTS OF WATER OR NORMAL SALINE, OCCASIONALLY LIFTING UPPER AND LOWER LIDS, UNTIL NO EVIDENCE OF CHEMICAL REMAINS (APPROXIMATELY 15-20 MINUTES). GET MEDICAL ATTENTION IMMEDIATELY.

INGESTION: MANEB: **ACUTE EXPOSURE-** SINGLE TOXIC DOSES OF MANEB IN RATS INDUCED HYPOTONIA, BRADYCARDIA, DECREASED RESPIRATORY FREQUENCY, FUNCTIONAL ABNORMALITIES OF LIVER AND THYROID, INFILTRATIONS IN THE LUNGS, BRONCHITIS AND TRACHEITIS. SINGLE ACUTE DOSES OF 770 MG/KG GIVEN ON DAY 11 OF PREGNANCY PRODUCED ADVERSE EFFECTS ON FERTILITY AND THE FETUS, AND FETAL DEVELOPMENTAL ABNORMALITIES. **CHRONIC EXPOSURE-** RATS THAT RECEIVED 1,500 MG/KG/DAY FOR 10 DAYS SHOWED WEIGHT LOSS, WEAKNESS OF THE HIND LEGS, AND INCREASED MORTALITY. RATS GIVEN 0.25% MANEB IN THE DIET FOR 2 YEARS DEVELOPED THYROID HYPERPLASIA AND NODULAR GOITER. OTHER EFFECTS OBSERVED IN STUDIES OF LABORATORY ANIMALS INCLUDED DEPRESSION OF REFLEXES, PARALYSIS, IMPAIRED KIDNEY FUNCTION, AND ADENOMAS OF THE LUNGS. FETAL DEVELOPMENTAL ABNORMALITIES WERE REPORTED FROM A CHRONIC INGESTION STUDY OF PREGNANT MICE. A METABOLITE AND DEGRADATION PRODUCT OF MANEB, ETHYLENE THIOUREA, INDUCED HIGHLY SIGNIFICANT INCREASES IN THE INCIDENCE OF LIVER TUMORS IN TWO STRAINS OF MICE, AND OF THYROID CARCINOMAS AND ADENOMAS IN TWO SEPARATE RAT STUDIES.

FIRST AID- GIVE SYRUP OF IPECAC, FOLLOWED BY 1-2 GLASSES OF WATER, TO INDUCE VOMITING (ADULTS: 30 ML). FOLLOWING EMESIS, ADMINISTER 30-50 GRAMS ACTIVATED CHARCOAL. FOLLOW CHARCOAL WITH SODIUM OR MAGNESIUM SULFATE, 250 MG/KG, TO REMOVE TOXICANT FROM THE GUT BY CATHARSIS (EPA, RECOGNITION AND MANAGEMENT OF PESTICIDE POISONINGS, 3RD ED.). FIRST AID SHOULD BE ADMINISTERED UNDER THE DIRECTION OF QUALIFIED MEDICAL PERSONNEL. GET MEDICAL ATTENTION.

ANTIDOTE: NO SPECIFIC ANTIDOTE. TREAT SYMPTOMATICALLY AND SUPPORTIVELY.

REACTIVITY

REACTIVITY: THE MATERIAL IS SOLUBLE IN WATER, BUT CONTACT WITH SMALL AMOUNTS OF MOISTURE (SUCH AS HIGH HUMIDITY) MAY RESULT IN DECOMPOSITION AND SUBSEQUENT IGNITION.

INCOMPATIBILITIES: MANEB: ACIDS: DECOMPOSE ON CONTACT. ALKALIS: MAY DECOMPOSE.

DECOMPOSITION: THERMAL DECOMPOSITION MAY RELEASE TOXIC OXIDES OF NITROGEN AND SULFUR.

POLYMERIZATION: HAZARDOUS POLYMERIZATION HAS NOT BEEN REPORTED TO OCCUR UNDER NORMAL TEMPERATURES AND PRESSURES.

STORAGE AND DISPOSAL

OBSERVE ALL FEDERAL, STATE AND LOCAL REGULATIONS WHEN STORING OR DISPOSING OF THIS SUBSTANCE. FOR ASSISTANCE, CONTACT THE DISTRICT DIRECTOR OF THE ENVIRONMENTAL PROTECTION AGENCY.

****STORAGE****

STORE IN ACCORDANCE WITH 40 CFR 165 RECOMMENDED PROCEDURES FOR THE DISPOSAL AND STORAGE OF PESTICIDES AND PESTICIDE CONTAINERS.
STORE AWAY FROM INCOMPATIBLE SUBSTANCES.
MAY SPONTANEOUSLY DECOMPOSE VIGOROUSLY WHEN STORED IN BULK.
STORE IN TIGHTLY CLOSED CONTAINERS; PREVENT EXPOSURE TO MOISTURE.

****DISPOSAL****

DISPOSAL MUST BE IN ACCORDANCE WITH STANDARDS APPLICABLE TO GENERATORS OF HAZARDOUS WASTE, 40CFR 262. EPA HAZARDOUS WASTE NUMBER U114.

CONDITIONS TO AVOID

AVOID EXPOSURE TO MOISTURE AND OVERHEATING WHICH MAY CAUSE DECOMPOSITION OF THE PRODUCT WITH THE RISK OF SPONTANEOUS COMBUSTION.

SPILL AND LEAK PROCEDURES

WATER SPILL: THE CALIFORNIA SAFE DRINKING WATER AND TOXIC ENFORCEMENT ACT OF 1986 (PROPOSITION 65) PROHIBITS CONTAMINATING ANY KNOWN SOURCE OF DRINKING WATER WITH SUBSTANCES KNOWN TO CAUSE CANCER AND/OR REPRODUCTIVE TOXICITY.

OCCUPATIONAL SPILL: SWEEP UP AND PLACE IN SUITABLE CLEAN, DRY CONTAINERS FOR RECLAMATION OR LATER DISPOSAL. DO NOT FLUSH SPILLED MATERIAL INTO SEWER. KEEP UNNECESSARY PEOPLE AWAY.

PROTECTIVE EQUIPMENT

VENTILATION: PROVIDE LOCAL EXHAUST OR GENERAL DILUTION VENTILATION SYSTEM.

RESPIRATOR: THE FOLLOWING RESPIRATORS AND MAXIMUM USE CONCENTRATIONS ARE RECOMMENDATIONS BY THE U.S. DEPARTMENT OF HEALTH AND HUMAN SERVICES, NIOSH POCKET GUIDE TO CHEMICAL HAZARDS; NIOSH CRITERIA DOCUMENTS OR BY THE U.S. DEPARTMENT OF LABOR, 29 CFR 1910 SUBPART Z. THE SPECIFIC RESPIRATOR SELECTED MUST BE BASED ON CONTAMINATION LEVELS FOUND IN THE WORK PLACE, MUST NOT EXCEED THE WORKING LIMITS OF THE RESPIRATOR AND BE JOINTLY APPROVED BY THE NATIONAL INSTITUTE FOR OCCUPATIONAL SAFETY AND HEALTH AND THE MINE SAFETY AND HEALTH ADMINISTRATION (NIOSH-MSHA).

MANGANESE AND COMPOUNDS (AS MN):

50 MG/M3- ANY DUST AND MIST RESPIRATOR (IF NOT PRESENT AS A FUME). ANY SUPPLIED-AIR RESPIRATOR. ANY SELF-CONTAINED BREATHING APPARATUS.

125 MG/M3- ANY POWERED AIR-PURIFYING RESPIRATOR WITH A DUST AND MIST FILTER (IF NOT PRESENT AS A FUME). ANY SUPPLIED-AIR RESPIRATOR OPERATED IN A CONTINUOUS FLOW MODE.

250 MG/M3- ANY AIR-PURIFYING FULL FACEPIECE RESPIRATOR WITH A HIGH-EFFICIENCY PARTICULATE FILTER. ANY POWERED AIR-PURIFYING RESPIRATOR WITH A TIGHT-FITTING FACEPIECE AND A HIGH-EFFICIENCY PARTICULATE FILTER. ANY SELF-CONTAINED BREATHING APPARATUS WITH A FULL FACEPIECE. ANY SUPPLIED-AIR RESPIRATOR WITH A FULL FACEPIECE. ANY SUPPLIED-AIR RESPIRATOR WITH A TIGHT-FITTING FACEPIECE OPERATED IN A CONTINUOUS FLOW MODE.

5000 MG/M3- ANY SUPPLIED-AIR RESPIRATOR WITH A HALF-MASK AND OPERATED IN A PRESSURE-DEMAND OR OTHER POSITIVE PRESSURE MODE.

7500 MG/M3- ANY SUPPLIED-AIR RESPIRATOR WITH A FULL FACEPIECE AND OPERATED IN A PRESSURE-DEMAND OR OTHER POSITIVE PRESSURE MODE.

ESCAPE- ANY AIR-PURIFYING FULL FACEPIECE RESPIRATOR WITH A HIGH-EFFICIENCY PARTICULATE FILTER. ANY APPROPRIATE ESCAPE-TYPE SELF-CONTAINED BREATHING APPARATUS.

FOR FIREFIGHTING AND OTHER IMMEDIATELY DANGEROUS TO LIFE OR HEALTH CONDITIONS:

SELF-CONTAINED BREATHING APPARATUS WITH FULL FACEPIECE OPERATED IN PRESSURE-DEMAND OR OTHER POSITIVE PRESSURE MODE.

SUPPLIED-AIR RESPIRATOR WITH FULL FACEPIECE AND OPERATED IN PRESSURE-DEMAND OR OTHER POSITIVE PRESSURE MODE IN COMBINATION WITH AN AUXILIARY SELF-CONTAINED BREATHING APPARATUS OPERATED IN PRESSURE-DEMAND OR OTHER POSITIVE PRESSURE MODE.

CLOTHING: EMPLOYEE MUST WEAR APPROPRIATE PROTECTIVE (IMPERVIOUS) CLOTHING AND EQUIPMENT TO PREVENT REPEATED OR PROLONGED SKIN CONTACT WITH THIS SUBSTANCE.

GLOVES: EMPLOYEE MUST WEAR APPROPRIATE PROTECTIVE GLOVES TO PREVENT CONTACT WITH THIS SUBSTANCE.

EYE PROTECTION: EMPLOYEE MUST WEAR SPLASH-PROOF OR DUST-RESISTANT SAFETY GOGGLES TO PREVENT EYE CONTACT WITH THIS SUBSTANCE.

EMERGENCY EYE WASH: WHERE THERE IS ANY POSSIBILITY THAT AN EMPLOYEE'S EYES MAY BE EXPOSED TO THIS SUBSTANCE, THE EMPLOYER SHOULD PROVIDE AN EYE WASH FOUNTAIN WITHIN THE IMMEDIATE WORK AREA FOR EMERGENCY USE.

AUTHORIZED BY- OCCUPATIONAL HEALTH SERVICES, INC.
CREATION DATE: 10/04/89 ***REVISION DATE:*** 07/12/90

MATERIAL SAFETY DATA SHEET

OCCUPATIONAL HEALTH SERVICES, INC.
AGRICULTURE AND PESTICIDE DIVISION
450 SEVENTH AVENUE, SUITE 2407
NEW YORK, NEW YORK 10123
1-800-445-MSDS OR (212) 967-1100

EMERGENCY CONTACT:
JOHN S. BRANSFORD, JR. (615) 292-1180

SUBSTANCE IDENTIFICATION

CAS-NUMBER 2595-54-2

SUBSTANCE: MECARBAM

TRADE NAMES/SYNONYMS: 7-OXA-5-THIA-2-AZA-6-PHOSPHANONANOIC ACID, 6-ETHOXY-2-METHYL-3-, OXO-, ETHYL ESTER, 6-SULFIDE; CARBAMIC ACID, (MERCAPTOACETYL)METHYL-, ETHYL ESTER, S-ESTER WITH O,O-DIETHYL PHOSPHORODITHIOATE; ETHYL (DIETHOXYPHOSPHINOTHIOYLTHIO)ACETYL(METHYL)CARBAMATE; ETHYL N-(DIETHOXYTHIOPHOSPHORYLTHIO)ACETYL-N-METHYLCARBAMATE; S-(N-ETHOXYCARBONYL-N-METHYLCARBAMOYLMETHYL) O,O-DIETHYL PHOSPHORODITHIOATE; ETHYL 6-ETHOXY-2-METHYL-3-OXO-7-OXA-5-THIA-2-AZA-6-PHOSPHANONANOATE 6-SULFIDE; ETHYL (((DIETHOXYPHOSPHINOTHIOYL)THIO)ACETYL)METHYLCARBAMATE; ETHYL (MERCAPTOACETYL)METHYLCARBAMATE S-ESTER WITH O,O-DIETHYL PHOSPHORODITHIOATE; S-(N-ETHOXYCARBONYL-N-METHYLCARBAMOYLMETHYL)-DIETHYL PHOSPHORODITHIOATE; O,O-DIETHYL S-(N-ETHOXYCARBONYL-N-METHYLCARBAMOYLMETHYL) PHOSPHORODITHIOATE; MURFOTOX; PESTAN; PST13675

CHEMICAL FAMILY: ORGANOPHOSPHATE

MOLECULAR FORMULA: C10-H20-N-O5-P-S2

MOLECULAR WEIGHT: 329.40

CERCLA RATINGS (SCALE 0-3): HEALTH=3 FIRE=0 REACTIVITY=U PERSISTENCE=0

NFPA RATINGS (SCALE 0-4): HEALTH=3 FIRE=0 REACTIVITY=U

COMPONENTS AND CONTAMINANTS

COMPONENT: MECARBAM ***PERCENT:*** 100.0
CAS# 2595-54-2

EXPOSURE LIMITS: NO OCCUPATIONAL EXPOSURE LIMITS ESTABLISHED BY OSHA, ACGIH, OR NIOSH.

PHYSICAL DATA

DESCRIPTION: COLORLESS, OILY LIQUID WHEN PURE; TECHNICAL GRADE IS PALE YELLOW TO BROWN ***BOILING POINT:*** 291 F (144 C) @ 0.02 MMHG

MELTING POINT: 48 F (9 C) ***SPECIFIC GRAVITY:*** 1.223

EVAPORATION RATE: NOT AVAILABLE ***SOLUBILITY IN WATER:*** 0.1%

SOLVENT SOLUBILITY: SOLUBLE IN ALCOHOLS, KETONES, ESTERS, AROMATIC HYDROCARBONS, CHLORINATED HYDROCARBONS, MOST ORGANIC SOLVENTS; PRACTICALLY INSOLUBLE IN ALIPHATIC HYDROCARBONS

FIRE AND EXPLOSION DATA

FIRE AND EXPLOSION HAZARD: NEGLIGIBLE FIRE HAZARD WHEN EXPOSED TO HEAT OR FLAME.

FIREFIGHTING MEDIA: DRY CHEMICAL, CARBON DIOXIDE, HALON, WATER SPRAY OR STANDARD FOAM (1987 EMERGENCY RESPONSE GUIDEBOOK, DOT P 5800.4). FOR LARGER FIRES, USE WATER SPRAY, FOG OR STANDARD FOAM (1987 EMERGENCY RESPONSE GUIDEBOOK, DOT P 5800.4).

FIREFIGHTING: MOVE CONTAINERS FROM FIRE AREA IF POSSIBLE. FIGHT FIRE FROM MAXIMUM DISTANCE. STAY AWAY FROM STORAGE TANK ENDS. DIKE FIRE CONTROL WATER FOR LATER DISPOSAL. DO NOT SCATTER MATERIAL (1987 EMERGENCY RESPONSE GUIDEBOOK, DOT P 5800.4, GUIDE PAGE 55). EXTINGUISH ONLY IF FLOW CAN BE STOPPED; USE FLOODING AMOUNTS OF WATER AS FOG, SOLID STREAMS MAY BE INEFFECTIVE. COOL CONTAINERS WITH FLOODING AMOUNTS OF WATER FROM AS FAR A DISTANCE AS POSSIBLE. USE WATER SPRAY TO ABSORB TOXIC VAPORS. AVOID BREATHING TOXIC VAPORS; KEEP UPWIND. CONSIDER EVACUATION OF DOWNWIND AREA IF MATERIAL IS LEAKING.

TRANSPORTATION DATA

DEPARTMENT OF TRANSPORTATION HAZARD CLASSIFICATION 49 CFR 172.101: POISON B

DEPARTMENT OF TRANSPORTATION LABELING REQUIREMENTS 49 CFR 172.101 AND SUBPART E: POISON

TOXICITY

MECARBAM: TOXICITY DATA: 380 MG/KG SKIN-RAT LD50; 31 MG/KG ORAL-RAT LD50; 106 MG/KG ORAL-MOUSE LD50; 65 MG/KG ORAL-GUINEA PIG LD50; 60 MG/KG ORAL-RABBIT LD50; 50 MG/KG SUBCUTANEOUS-GUINEA PIG LDLO; 36 MG/KG UNREPORTED-RAT LD50. CARCINOGEN STATUS: NONE. ACUTE TOXICITY LEVEL: HIGHLY TOXIC BY INGESTION AND TOXIC BY DERMAL ABSORPTION. TARGET EFFECTS: CHOLINESTERASE INHIBITOR. POISONING MAY AFFECT THE NERVOUS SYSTEM.* AT INCREASED RISK FROM EXPOSURE: PERSONS WITH RESPIRATORY AILMENTS, RECENT EXPOSURE TO CHOLINESTERASE INHIBITORS OR IMPAIRED CHOLINESTERASE PRODUCTION, OR LIVER MALFUNCTION.* ADDITIONAL DATA: MAY CROSS THE PLACENTA. HIGH ENVIRONMENTAL TEMPERATURES OR EXPOSURE OF THE CHEMICAL TO VISIBLE OR ULTRAVIOLET LIGHT MAY ENHANCE THE TOXICITY. INTERACTIONS WITH MEDICATIONS MAY OCCUR.*

* MAY BE BASED ON GENERAL INFORMATION ON ORGANOPHOSPHATES.

HEALTH EFFECTS AND FIRST AID

INHALATION: MECARBAM: SEE INFORMATION ON ORGANOPHOSPHATES.
ORGANOPHOSPHATES: CHOLINESTERASE INHIBITOR. **ACUTE EXPOSURE-** WHEN INHALED, THE FIRST EFFECTS OF CHOLINESTERASE INHIBITORS ARE USUALLY RESPIRATORY AND MAY INCLUDE NASAL HYPEREMIA AND WATERY DISCHARGE, COUGH, CHEST DISCOMFORT, DYSPNEA, AND WHEEZING DUE TO INCREASED BRONCHIAL SECRETIONS AND BRONCHOCONSTRICTION. IF SUFFICIENT AMOUNTS ARE ABSORBED, OTHER SYSTEMIC EFFECTS MAY BEGIN WITHIN A FEW MINUTES OR BE DELAYED FOR UP TO 12 HOURS. SYMPTOMS MAY INCLUDE PALLOR, NAUSEA, VOMITING, DIARRHEA, ABDOMINAL CRAMPS, HEADACHE, DIZZINESS, OCULAR PAIN, BLURRED VISION, MIOSIS OR IN SOME CASES, ESPECIALLY INITIALLY, MYDRIASIS, LACRIMATION, SALIVATION, SWEATING, AND CONFUSION. OTHER REPORTED CENTRAL NERVOUS SYSTEM OR NEUROMUSCULAR EFFECTS MAY INCLUDE ATAXIA, SLURRED SPEECH, AREFLEXIA, WEAKNESS, FATIGUE, FASCICULATIONS, TWITCHING, TREMORS POSSIBLY OF THE TONGUE AND EYELIDS, AND EVENTUALLY PARALYSIS OF THE EXTREMITIES AND POSSIBLY OF THE RESPIRATORY MUSCLES. IN SEVERE CASES THERE MAY ALSO BE INVOLUNTARY DEFECATION AND URINATION, CYANOSIS, PSYCHOSIS, HYPERGLYCEMIA, ACUTE PANCREATITIS, CARDIAC IRREGULARITIES, PULMONARY EDEMA, UNCONSCIOUSNESS, CONVULSIONS, AND COMA. DEATH IS PRIMARILY DUE TO RESPIRATORY FAILURE, ALTHOUGH CARDIOVASCULAR EFFECTS INCLUDING CARDIAC ARREST MAY ALSO BE IMPLICATED. LONG TERM SEQUELAE ARE RARE BUT MAY INCLUDE NEUROPSYCHIATRIC DISORDERS AND MYOPATHY WITH MUSCLE TENDERNESS. SOME ORGANOPHOSPHATES MAY CAUSE A DELAYED NEUROPATHY BEGINNING 1-4 WEEKS AFTER AN ACUTE EXPOSURE WHICH MAY OR MAY NOT HAVE CAUSED ACUTE CHOLINERGIC EFFECTS. NUMBNESS, TINGLING, WEAKNESS AND CRAMPING BEGINNING SYMMETRICALLY IN THE LOWER LIMBS MAY PROGRESS TO ATAXIA AND PARALYSIS. IN SEVERE CASES, UPPER LIMB INVOLVEMENT IS POSSIBLE AND FLACCID PARALYSIS MAY PROGRESS TO SPASTIC PARALYSIS WITH EXAGGERATED REFLEXES. IMPROVEMENT MAY OCCUR OVER MONTHS TO YEARS, BUT SOME RESIDUAL IMPAIRMENT USUALLY REMAINS.
CHRONIC EXPOSURE- REPEATED OR PROLONGED EXPOSURE MAY RESULT IN THE EFFECTS OF ACUTE EXPOSURE INCLUDING THE DELAYED NEUROPATHY. OTHER EFFECTS REPORTED IN WORKERS REPEATEDLY EXPOSED INCLUDE IMPAIRED MEMORY AND CONCENTRATION, ACUTE PSYCHOSIS, SEVERE DEPRESSIONS, IRRITABILTY, CONFUSION, APATHY, EMOTIONAL LABILITY, SOCIAL WITHDRAWAL, CONFUSION, HEADACHE, SPEECH DIFFICULTIES, DELAYED REACTION TIMES, SPATIAL DISORIENTATION, NIGHTMARES, SLEEPWALKING, AND DROWSINESS OR INSOMNIA. AN INFLUENZA-LIKE CONDITION WITH HEADACHE, NAUSEA, WEAKNESS, ANOREXIA AND MALAISE HAS ALSO BEEN REPORTED.

FIRST AID- REMOVE FROM EXPOSURE AREA TO FRESH AIR IMMEDIATELY. IF BREATHING HAS STOPPED, GIVE ARTIFICIAL RESPIRATION. MAINTAIN AIRWAY AND BLOOD PRESSURE AND ADMINISTER OXYGEN IF AVAILABLE. KEEP AFFECTED PERSON WARM AND AT REST. TREAT SYMPTOMATICALLY AND SUPPORTIVELY. ADMINISTRATION OF OXYGEN SHOULD BE PERFORMED BY QUALIFIED PERSONNEL. GET MEDICAL ATTENTION IMMEDIATELY.

SKIN CONTACT: MECARBAM: TOXIC. SEE INFORMATION ON ORGANOPHOSPHATES.
ORGANOPHOSPHATES: CHOLINESTERASE INHIBITOR. **ACUTE EXPOSURE-** LOCALIZED SWEATING AND FASCICULATIONS MAY OCCUR AT THE SITE OF CONTACT. IF SUFFICIENT AMOUNTS ARE ABSORBED, OTHER EFFECTS OF

CHOLINESTERASE INHIBITION AS DESCRIBED IN ACUTE INHALATION MAY OCCUR. SYMPTOMS MAY BE DELAYED 2-3 HOURS, BUT USUALLY NO MORE THAN 12 HOURS. THE RATE OF ABSORPTION IS INCREASED BY THE PRESENCE OF DERMATITIS OR HIGH AMBIENT TEMPERATURES. DELAYED NEUROPATHY IS ALSO POSSIBLE. **CHRONIC EXPOSURE-** REPEATED OR PROLONGED EXPOSURE MAY CAUSE EFFECTS AS DESCRIBED IN ACUTE EXPOSURE. SOME ORGANOPHOSPHATES MAY CAUSE SENSITIZATION.

FIRST AID- REMOVE CONTAMINATED CLOTHING IMMEDIATELY. WASH CONTAMINATED AREAS WITH SOAP AND WATER FOLLOWED BY ALCOHOL (ARENA, POISONING, 4TH ED.). EMERGENCY PERSONNEL SHOULD WEAR GLOVES AND AVOID CONTAMINATION. TREAT RESPIRATORY DIFFICULTY WITH ARTIFICIAL RESPIRATION. GET MEDICAL ATTENTION IMMEDIATELY.

EYE CONTACT: MECARBAM. SEE INFORMATION ON ORGANOPHOSPHATES.
ORGANOPHOSPHATES: CHOLINESTERASE INHIBITOR. **ACUTE EXPOSURE-** DIRECT CONTACT MAY CAUSE PAIN, HYPEREMIA, LACRIMATION, TWITCHING OF THE EYELIDS, MIOSIS, AND CILIARY MUSCLE SPASM WITH LOSS OF ACCOMODATION, BLURRED OR DIMMED VISION AND BROWACHE. SOMETIMES MYDRIASIS MAY OCCUR INSTEAD OF MIOSIS. WITH SUFFICIENT EXPOSURE, OTHER SYMPTOMS OF CHOLINESTERASE INHIBITION AS DESCRIBED IN ACUTE INHALATION MAY OCCUR. **CHRONIC EXPOSURE-** REPEATED OR PROLONGED EXPOSURE MAY CAUSE EFFECTS AS DESCRIBED IN ACUTE EXPOSURE. SOME COMPOUNDS HAVE CAUSED TOXIC EFFECTS ON THE CRYSTALLINE LENS, CONJUNCTIVAL THICKENING AND OBSTRUCTION OF THE NASOLACRIMAL CANALS WHEN USED AS MIOTIC EYEDROPS.

FIRST AID- IRRIGATE EYES WITH WATER OR SALINE SOLUTION. IF SYMPTOMS OF POISONING OCCUR, TREAT RESPIRATORY DIFFICULTY WITH ARTIFICIAL RESPIRATION AND OXYGEN. OBSERVE PATIENT FOR AT LEAST 24-36 HOURS (GOSSELIN, CLINICAL TOXICOLOGY OF COMMERCIAL PRODUCTS, 5TH ED.). GET MEDICAL ATTENTION IMMEDIATELY. OXYGEN SHOULD BE ADMINISTERED BY QUALIFIED MEDICAL PERSONNEL.

INGESTION: MECARBAM: HIGHLY TOXIC. IN A SIX MONTH FEEDING STUDY OF RATS, A DAILY DOSE OF 4.56 MG/KG PRODUCED A SLIGHT DEPRESSION OF THE GROWTH RATE. SEE INFORMATION ON ORGANOPHOSPHATES.
ORGANOPHOSPHATES: CHOLINESTERASE INHIBITOR. **ACUTE EXPOSURE-** WHEN INGESTED, THE FIRST EFFECTS MAY BE NAUSEA, VOMITING, ANOREXIA, ABDOMINAL CRAMPS AND DIARRHEA. GASTROINTESTINAL ABSORPTION MAY CAUSE SYMPTOMS OF CHOLINESTERASE INHIBITION AS DESCRIBED IN ACUTE INHALATION. SYMPTOMS MAY BEGIN WITHIN MINUTES OR BE DELAYED FOR HOURS. DELAYED EFFECTS INCLUDING NEUROPATHY MAY ALSO OCCUR. **CHRONIC EXPOSURE-** REPEATED INGESTION MAY CAUSE EFFECTS AS DESCRIBED IN ACUTE EXPOSURE.

FIRST AID- IF PERSON IS ALERT AND RESPIRATION IS NOT DEPRESSED, GIVE SYRUP OF IPECAC FOLLOWED BY WATER (IF VOMITING OCCURS, KEEP HEAD BELOW HIPS TO PREVENT ASPIRATION). IF CONSCIOUSNESS LEVEL DECLINES OR VOMITING HAS NOT OCCURRED IN 15 MINUTES EMPTY STOMACH BY GASTRIC LAVAGE WITH THE AID OF CUFFED ENDOTRACHEAL TUBE USING ISOTONIC SALINE OR 5% SODIUM BICARBONATE FOLLOW WITH ACTIVATED CHARCOAL. ESTABLISH AND MAINTAIN AIRWAY. TREAT RESPIRATORY DIFFICULTY WITH ARTIFICIAL RESPIRATION AND OXYGEN. DO NOT GIVE MORPHINE, AMINOPHYLLINE, PHENOTHIAZINES, RESERPINE, FUROSEMIDE, OR ETHACRYNIC ACID (MORGAN, RECOGNITION AND MANAGEMENT OF PESTICIDE POISONINGS, 3RD ED.). TREAT SYMPTOMATICALLY AND SUPPORTIVELY. ADMINISTRATION OF OXYGEN AND LAVAGE MUST BE PERFORMED BY QUALIFIED MEDICAL PERSONNEL. GET MEDICAL ATTENTION IMMEDIATELY.

ANTIDOTE: THE FOLLOWING ANTIDOTE(S) HAVE BEEN RECOMMENDED. HOWEVER, THE DECISION AS TO WHETHER THE SEVERITY OF POISONING REQUIRES ADMINISTRATION OF ANY ANTIDOTE AND ACTUAL DOSE REQUIRED SHOULD BE MADE BY QUALIFIED MEDICAL PERSONNEL.
FOR CHOLINESTERASE INHIBITORS: ESTABLISH CLEAR AIRWAY AND TISSUE OXYGENATION BY ASPIRATION OF SECRETIONS, AND IF NECESSARY, BY ASSISTED PULMONARY VENTILATION WITH OXYGEN. IMPROVE TISSUE OXYGENATION AS MUCH AS POSSIBLE BEFORE ADMINISTERING ATROPINE TO MINIMIZE THE RISK OF VENTRICULAR FIBRILLATION. ADMINISTER ATROPINE SULFATE INTRAVENOUSLY, OR INTRAMUSCULARLY IF IV INJECTION IS NOT POSSIBLE. IN MODERATELY SEVERE POISONING ADMINISTER ATROPINE SULFATE, 0.4-2.0 MG REPEATED EVERY 15 MINUTES UNTIL ATROPINIZATION IS ACHIEVED (TACHYCARDIA, FLUSHING, DRY MOUTH, MYDRIASIS). MAINTAIN ATROPINIZATION BY REPEATED DOSES FOR 2-12 HOURS, OR LONGER, DEPENDING ON THE SEVERITY OF POISONING.
THE APPEARANCE OF RALES IN THE LUNG BASES, MIOSIS, SALIVATION, NAUSEA, BRADYCARDIA, ARE ALL INDICATIONS OF INADEQUATE ATROPINIZATION.
SEVERELY POISONED INDIVIDUALS MAY EXHIBIT REMARKABLE TOLERANCE TO ATROPINE; TWO OR MORE TIMES THE DOSAGES SUGGESTED ABOVE MAY BE NEEDED. PERSONS NOT POISONED OR ONLY SLIGHTLY POISONED, HOWEVER, MAY DEVELOP SIGNS OF ATROPINE TOXICITY FROM SUCH LARGE DOSAGES: FEVER, MUSCLE FIBRILLATIONS, AND DELIRIUM ARE THE MAIN SIGNS OF ATROPINE TOXICITY. IF THESE SIGNS APPEAR WHILE THE PATIENT IS FULLY ATROPINIZED, ATROPINE ADMINISTRATION SHOULD BE DISCONTINUED, AT LEAST TEMPORARILY. OBSERVE TREATED PATIENTS CLOSELY AT LEAST 24 HOURS TO INSURE THAT SYMPTOMS (POSSIBLY PULMONARY EDEMA) DO NOT RECUR AS ATROPINIZATION WEARS OFF. IN VERY SEVERE POISONINGS, METABOLIC DISPOSITION OF TOXICANT MAY REQUIRE SEVERAL HOURS OR DAYS DURING WHICH ATROPINIZATION MUST BE MAINTAINED. MARKEDLY LOWER LEVELS OF URINARY METABOLITES INDICATE THAT ATROPINE DOSAGE CAN BE TAPERED OFF. AS DOSAGE IS REDUCED, CHECK THE LUNG BASES FREQUENTLY FOR RALES. IF RALES ARE HEARD OR OTHER SYMPTOMS RETURN, RE-ESTABLISH ATROPINIZATION PROMPTLY (MORGAN, RECOGNITION AND MANAGEMENT OF PESTICIDE POISONINGS, 3RD ED.). ADMINISTRATION OF ANTIDOTE MUST BE PERFORMED BY QUALIFIED MEDICAL PERSONNEL.
IN CASES OF SEVERE POISONING BY ORGANOPHOSPHATE PESTICIDES IN WHICH RESPIRATORY DEPRESSION, MUSCLE WEAKNESS AND TWITCHINGS ARE SEVERE, GIVE PRALIDOXIME (PROTOPAM-AYERST, 2-PAM), 1.0 GRAM INTRAVENOUSLY AT NO MORE THAN 0.5 GRAM PER MINUTE. DOSAGE OF PRALIDOXIME MAY BE REPEATED IN 1-2 HOURS, THEN AT 10-12 HOUR INTERVALS IF NEEDED. IN VERY SEVERE POISONINGS, DOSAGE RATES MAY BE DOUBLED. TREATMENT WITH PRALIDOXIME WILL BE MOST EFFECTIVE IF GIVEN WITHIN THIRTY-SIX HOURS AFTER POISONING (MORGAN, RECOGNITION AND MANAGEMENT OF PESTICIDE POISONINGS, 3RD ED.). ANTIDOTE SHOULD BE ADMINISTERED BY QUALIFIED MEDICAL PERSONNEL.

REACTIVITY

REACTIVITY: NO SPECIFIC DATA AVAILABLE. HOWEVER, A NUMBER OF PHOSPHATE AND THIOPHOSPHATE ESTERS ARE OF LIMITED THERMAL STABILITY AND UNDERGO HIGHLY EXOTHERMIC SELF-ACCELERATING DECOMPOSITION REACTIONS.

INCOMPATIBILITIES: MECARBAM: ACIDIC CONDITIONS (PH BELOW 3): MAY CAUSE HYDROLYSIS. ALKALINE CONDITIONS (HIGHLY): INCOMPATIBLE. METALS: MAY BE ATTACKED.

DECOMPOSITION: THERMAL DECOMPOSITION PRODUCTS MAY INCLUDE TOXIC AND HAZARDOUS FUMES OF SULFUR, NITROGEN AND PHOSPHORUS.

POLYMERIZATION: HAZARDOUS POLYMERIZATION HAS NOT BEEN REPORTED TO OCCUR UNDER NORMAL TEMPERATURES AND PRESSURES.

STORAGE AND DISPOSAL

OBSERVE ALL FEDERAL, STATE AND LOCAL REGULATIONS WHEN STORING OR DISPOSING OF THIS SUBSTANCE. FOR ASSISTANCE, CONTACT THE DISTRICT DIRECTOR OF THE ENVIRONMENTAL PROTECTION AGENCY.

STORAGE

STORE IN ACCORDANCE WITH 40 CFR 165 RECOMMENDED PROCEDURES FOR THE DISPOSAL AND STORAGE OF PESTICIDES AND PESTICIDE CONTAINERS.
STORE AWAY FROM INCOMPATIBLE SUBSTANCES.

DISPOSAL

DISPOSAL MUST BE IN ACCORDANCE WITH 40 CFR 165 RECOMMENDED PROCEDURES FOR THE DISPOSAL AND STORAGE OF PESTICIDES AND PESTICIDE CONTAINERS.

CONDITIONS TO AVOID

NONE REPORTED.

SPILL AND LEAK PROCEDURES

OCCUPATIONAL SPILL: DO NOT TOUCH SPILLED MATERIAL. STOP LEAK IF YOU CAN DO IT WITHOUT RISK. USE WATER SPRAY TO REDUCE VAPORS. FOR SMALL SPILLS, TAKE UP WITH SAND OR OTHER ABSORBENT MATERIAL AND PLACE INTO CONTAINERS FOR LATER DISPOSAL. FOR SMALL DRY SPILLS, WITH A CLEAN SHOVEL PLACE MATERIAL INTO CLEAN, DRY CONTAINERS AND COVER. MOVE CONTAINERS FROM SPILL AREA. FOR LARGER SPILLS, DIKE FAR AHEAD OF SPILL FOR LATER DISPOSAL. KEEP UNNECESSARY PEOPLE AWAY. ISOLATE HAZARD AREA AND DENY ENTRY. VENTILATE CLOSED SPACES BEFORE ENTERING.

PROTECTIVE EQUIPMENT

VENTILATION: PROVIDE LOCAL EXHAUST OR PROCESS ENCLOSURE VENTILATION SYSTEM.

RESPIRATOR: THE FOLLOWING RESPIRATORS ARE RECOMMENDED BASED ON INFORMATION FOUND IN THE PHYSICAL DATA, TOXICITY AND HEALTH EFFECTS SECTIONS. THEY ARE RANKED IN ORDER FROM MINIMUM TO MAXIMUM RESPIRATORY PROTECTION. THE SPECIFIC RESPIRATOR SELECTED MUST BE BASED ON CONTAMINATION LEVELS FOUND IN THE WORK PLACE, MUST NOT EXCEED THE WORKING LIMITS OF THE RESPIRATOR AND BE JOINTLY APPROVED BY THE NATIONAL INSTITUTE FOR OCCUPATIONAL SAFETY AND HEALTH AND THE MINE SAFETY AND HEALTH ADMINISTRATION (NIOSH-MSHA).
TYPE 'C' SUPPLIED-AIR RESPIRATOR WITH A FULL FACEPIECE OPERATED IN PRESSURE-DEMAND OR OTHER POSITIVE PRESSURE MODE OR WITH A FULL

FACEPIECE, HELMET OR HOOD OPERATED IN CONTINOUS-FLOW MODE.
SELF-CONTAINED BREATHING APPARATUS WITH A FULL FACEPIECE OPERATED IN PRESSURE-DEMAND OR OTHER POSITIVE PRESSURE MODE.
FOR FIREFIGHTING AND OTHER IMMEDIATELY DANGEROUS TO LIFE OR HEALTH CONDITIONS:
SELF-CONTAINED BREATHING APPARATUS WITH FULL FACEPIECE OPERATED IN PRESSURE-DEMAND OR OTHER POSITIVE PRESSURE MODE.
SUPPLIED-AIR RESPIRATOR WITH FULL FACEPIECE AND OPERATED IN PRESSURE-DEMAND OR OTHER POSITIVE PRESSURE MODE IN COMBINATION WITH AN AUXILIARY SELF-CONTAINED BREATHING APPARATUS OPERATED IN PRESSURE-DEMAND OR OTHER POSITIVE PRESSURE MODE.

CLOTHING: EMPLOYEE MUST WEAR APPROPRIATE PROTECTIVE (IMPERVIOUS) CLOTHING AND EQUIPMENT TO PREVENT ANY POSSIBILITY OF SKIN CONTACT WITH THIS SUBSTANCE.

GLOVES: EMPLOYEE MUST WEAR APPROPRIATE PROTECTIVE GLOVES TO PREVENT CONTACT WITH THIS SUBSTANCE.

EYE PROTECTION: EMPLOYEE MUST WEAR SPLASH-PROOF OR DUST-RESISTANT SAFETY GOGGLES AND A FACESHIELD TO PREVENT CONTACT WITH THIS SUBSTANCE.
EMERGENCY WASH FACILITIES: WHERE THERE IS ANY POSSIBILITY THAT AN EMPLOYEE'S EYES AND/OR SKIN MAY BE EXPOSED TO THIS SUBSTANCE, THE EMPLOYER SHOULD PROVIDE AN EYE WASH FOUNTAIN AND QUICK DRENCH SHOWER WITHIN THE IMMEDIATE WORK AREA FOR EMERGENCY USE.

AUTHORIZED BY- OCCUPATIONAL HEALTH SERVICES, INC.
CREATION DATE: 10/04/89 ***REVISION DATE:*** 05/11/90

MATERIAL SAFETY DATA SHEET

OCCUPATIONAL HEALTH SERVICES, INC.
AGRICULTURE AND PESTICIDE DIVISION
450 SEVENTH AVENUE, SUITE 2407
NEW YORK, NEW YORK 10123
1-800-445-MSDS OR (212) 967-1100

EMERGENCY CONTACT:
JOHN S. BRANSFORD, JR. (615) 292-1180

SUBSTANCE IDENTIFICATION

CAS-NUMBER 950-10-7

SUBSTANCE: **MEPHOSFOLAN**

TRADE NAMES/SYNONYMS: PHOSPHORAMIDIC ACID, (4-METHYL-1,3-DITHIOLAN-2-YLIDENE)-, DIETHYL ESTER; IMIDOCARBONIC ACID, PHOSPHONODITHIO-,CYCLIC PROPYLENE P,P-DIETHYL ESTER; (4-METHYL-1,3-DITHIOLAN-2-YLIDENE)PHOSPHORAMIDIC ACID DIETHYL ESTER; PHOSPHONODITHIOIMIDOCARBONIC ACID CYCLIC PROPYLENE P,P-DIETHYL ESTER; DIETHYL 4-METHYL-1,3-DITHIOLAN-2-YLIDENEPHOSPHORAMIDATE; 2-(DIETHOXYPHOSPHINYLIMINO)-4-METHYL-1,3-DITHIOLANE; DIETHYL (4-METHYL-1,3-DITHIOLAN-2-YLIDENE)PHOSPHORAMIDATE; CYCLIC PROPYLENE P,P-DIETHYL PHOSPHONODITHIOIMIDOCARBONATE; DIETHYL N-(4-METHHYL-1,3-DITHIOLAN-2-YLIDENE)-PHOSPHORAMIDATE; AC 47470; CL 47470; CYTROLANE; EI 47470; ENT 25991; PST13735

CHEMICAL FAMILY: ORGANOPHOSPHATE HETEROCYCLIC SULFUR

MOLECULAR FORMULA: C8-H16-N-O3-P-S2

MOLECULAR WEIGHT: 269.31

CERCLA RATINGS (SCALE 0-3): HEALTH=3 FIRE=0 REACTIVITY=0 PERSISTENCE=0

NFPA RATINGS (SCALE 0-4): HEALTH=4 FIRE=0 REACTIVITY=0

COMPONENTS AND CONTAMINANTS

COMPONENT: MEPHOSFOLAN ***PERCENT:*** 100
CAS# 950-10-7

EXPOSURE LIMITS: MEPHOSFOLAN: NO OCCUPATION EXPOSURE LIMITS ESTABLISHED BY OSHA, ACGIH OR NIOSH.
500 POUNDS SARA SECTION 302 THRESHOLD PLANNING QUANTITY 1 POUND SARA SECTION 304 REPORTABLE QUANTITY

PHYSICAL DATA

DESCRIPTION: YELLOW TO AMBER LIQUID ***BOILING POINT:*** 248 F (120 C) @ 0.001 MMHG

SPECIFIC GRAVITY: 1.539 ***SOLUBILITY IN WATER:*** 57 MG/L

SOLVENT SOLUBILITY: SOLUBLE IN ACETONE, ETHANOL, BENZENE, 1,2-DICHLOROETHANE

FIRE AND EXPLOSION DATA

FIRE AND EXPLOSION HAZARD: NEGLIGIBLE FIRE HAZARD WHEN EXPOSED TO HEAT OR FLAME.

FIREFIGHTING MEDIA: DRY CHEMICAL, CARBON DIOXIDE, HALON, WATER SPRAY OR STANDARD FOAM (1987 EMERGENCY RESPONSE GUIDEBOOK, DOT P 5800.4). FOR LARGER FIRES, USE WATER SPRAY, FOG OR STANDARD FOAM (1987 EMERGENCY RESPONSE GUIDEBOOK, DOT P 5800.4).

FIREFIGHTING: MOVE CONTAINERS FROM FIRE AREA IF POSSIBLE. FIGHT FIRE FROM MAXIMUM DISTANCE. STAY AWAY FROM STORAGE TANK ENDS. DIKE FIRE CONTROL WATER FOR LATER DISPOSAL. DO NOT SCATTER MATERIAL (1987 EMERGENCY RESPONSE GUIDEBOOK, DOT P 5800.4, GUIDE PAGE 55).
EXTINGUISH ONLY IF FLOW CAN BE STOPPED; USE FLOODING AMOUNTS OF WATER AS FOG, SOLID STREAMS MAY BE INEFFECTIVE. COOL CONTAINERS WITH FLOODING AMOUNTS OF WATER FROM AS FAR A DISTANCE AS POSSIBLE. USE WATER SPRAY TO ABSORB TOXIC VAPORS. AVOID BREATHING TOXIC VAPORS; KEEP UPWIND. CONSIDER EVACUATION OF DOWNWIND AREA IF MATERIAL IS LEAKING.

TRANSPORTATION DATA

DEPARTMENT OF TRANSPORTATION HAZARD CLASSIFICATION 49 CFR 172.101: POISON B
DEPARTMENT OF TRANSPORTATION LABELING REQUIREMENTS 49 CFR 172.101 AND SUBPART E: POISON
DEPARTMENT OF TRANSPORTATION PACKAGING REQUIREMENTS: 49 CFR 173.346 EXCEPTIONS: 49 CFR 173.345

TOXICITY

MEPHOSFOLAN: TOXICITY DATA: 28,700 UG/KG SKIN-RABBIT LD50; 9 MG/KG ORAL-RAT LD50; 11 MG/KG ORAL-MOUSE LD50. CARCINOGEN STATUS: NONE. ACUTE TOXICITY LEVEL: HIGHLY TOXIC BY INGESTION AND DERMAL ABSORPTION. TARGET EFFECTS: CHOLINESTERASE INHIBITOR. POISONING MAY AFFECT THE NERVOUS SYSTEM.* AT INCREASED RISK FROM EXPOSURE: PERSONS WITH RESPIRATORY AILMENTS, RECENT EXPOSURE TO CHOLINESTERASE INHIBITORS OR IMPAIRED CHOLINESTERASE PRODUCTION, OR LIVER MALFUNCTION.* ADDITIONAL DATA: MAY CROSS THE PLACENTA. HIGH ENVIRONMENTAL TEMPERATURES OR EXPOSURE OF THE CHEMICAL TO VISIBLE OR ULTRAVIOLET LIGHT MAY ENHANCE THE TOXICITY. INTERACTIONS WITH MEDICATIONS MAY OCCUR.*
* MAY BE BASED ON GENERAL INFORMATION ON ORGANOPHOSPHATES.

HEALTH EFFECTS AND FIRST AID

INHALATION: MEPHOSFOLAN: SEE INFORMATION ON ORGANOPHOSPHATES.
ORGANOPHOSPHATES: CHOLINESTERASE INHIBITOR. **ACUTE EXPOSURE-** WHEN INHALED, THE FIRST EFFECTS OF CHOLINESTERASE INHIBITORS ARE USUALLY RESPIRATORY AND MAY INCLUDE NASAL HYPEREMIA AND WATERY DISCHARGE, COUGH, CHEST DISCOMFORT, DYSPNEA, AND WHEEZING DUE TO INCREASED BRONCHIAL SECRETIONS AND BRONCHOCONSTRICTION. IF SUFFICIENT AMOUNTS ARE ABSORBED, OTHER SYSTEMIC EFFECTS MAY BEGIN WITHIN A FEW MINUTES OR BE DELAYED FOR UP TO 12 HOURS. SYMPTOMS MAY INCLUDE PALLOR, NAUSEA, VOMITING, DIARRHEA, ABDOMINAL CRAMPS, HEADACHE, DIZZINESS, OCULAR PAIN, BLURRED VISION, MIOSIS OR IN SOME CASES, ESPECIALLY INITIALLY, MYDRIASIS, LACRIMATION, SALIVATION, SWEATING, AND CONFUSION. OTHER REPORTED CENTRAL NERVOUS SYSTEM OR NEUROMUSCULAR EFFECTS MAY INCLUDE ATAXIA, SLURRED SPEECH, AREFLEXIA, WEAKNESS, FATIGUE, FASCICULATIONS, TWITCHING, TREMORS POSSIBLY OF THE TONGUE AND EYELIDS, AND EVENTUALLY PARALYSIS OF THE EXTREMITIES AND POSSIBLY OF THE RESPIRATORY MUSCLES. IN SEVERE CASES THERE MAY ALSO BE INVOLUNTARY DEFECATION AND URINATION, CYANOSIS, PSYCHOSIS, HYPERGLYCEMIA, ACUTE PANCREATITIS, CARDIAC IRREGULARITIES, PULMONARY EDEMA, UNCONSCIOUSNESS, CONVULSIONS, AND COMA. DEATH IS PRIMARILY DUE TO RESPIRATORY FAILURE, ALTHOUGH CARDIOVASCULAR EFFECTS INCLUDING CARDIAC ARREST MAY ALSO BE IMPLICATED. LONG TERM SEQUELAE ARE RARE BUT MAY INCLUDE NEUROPSYCHIATRIC DISORDERS AND MYOPATHY WITH MUSCLE TENDERNESS. SOME ORGANOPHOSPHATES MAY CAUSE A DELAYED NEUROPATHY BEGINNING 1-4 WEEKS AFTER AN ACUTE EXPOSURE WHICH MAY OR MAY NOT HAVE CAUSED ACUTE CHOLINERGIC EFFECTS. NUMBNESS, TINGLING, WEAKNESS AND CRAMPING BEGINNING SYMMETRICALLY IN THE LOWER LIMBS MAY PROGRESS TO ATAXIA AND PARALYSIS. IN SEVERE CASES, UPPER LIMB INVOLVEMENT IS POSSIBLE AND FLACCID PARALYSIS MAY PROGRESS TO SPASTIC PARALYSIS WITH EXAGGERATED REFLEXES. IMPROVEMENT MAY OCCUR OVER MONTHS TO YEARS, BUT SOME RESIDUAL IMPAIRMENT USUALLY REMAINS.
CHRONIC EXPOSURE- REPEATED OR PROLONGED EXPOSURE MAY RESULT IN THE EFFECTS OF ACUTE EXPOSURE INCLUDING THE DELAYED NEUROPATHY. OTHER EFFECTS REPORTED IN WORKERS REPEATEDLY EXPOSED INCLUDE IMPAIRED MEMORY AND CONCENTRATION, ACUTE PSYCHOSIS, SEVERE DEPRESSIONS, IRRITABILTY, CONFUSION, APATHY, EMOTIONAL LABILITY, SOCIAL WITHDRAWAL,

CONFUSION, HEADACHE, SPEECH DIFFICULTIES, DELAYED REACTION TIMES, SPATIAL DISORIENTATION, NIGHTMARES, SLEEPWALKING, AND DROWSINESS OR INSOMNIA. AN INFLUENZA-LIKE CONDITION WITH HEADACHE, NAUSEA, WEAKNESS, ANOREXIA AND MALAISE HAS ALSO BEEN REPORTED.

FIRST AID- REMOVE FROM EXPOSURE AREA TO FRESH AIR IMMEDIATELY. IF BREATHING HAS STOPPED, GIVE ARTIFICIAL RESPIRATION. MAINTAIN AIRWAY AND BLOOD PRESSURE AND ADMINISTER OXYGEN IF AVAILABLE. KEEP AFFECTED PERSON WARM AND AT REST. TREAT SYMPTOMATICALLY AND SUPPORTIVELY. ADMINISTRATION OF OXYGEN SHOULD BE PERFORMED BY QUALIFIED PERSONNEL. GET MEDICAL ATTENTION IMMEDIATELY.

SKIN CONTACT: MEPHOSFOLAN: HIGHLY TOXIC. SEE INFORMATION ON ORGANOPHOSPHATES.
ORGANOPHOSPHATES: CHOLINESTERASE INHIBITOR. **ACUTE EXPOSURE**- LOCALIZED SWEATING AND FASCICULATIONS MAY OCCUR AT THE SITE OF CONTACT. IF SUFFICIENT AMOUNTS ARE ABSORBED, OTHER EFFECTS OF CHOLINESTERASE INHIBITION AS DESCRIBED IN ACUTE INHALATION MAY OCCUR. SYMPTOMS MAY BE DELAYED 2-3 HOURS, BUT USUALLY NO MORE THAN 12 HOURS. THE RATE OF ABSORPTION IS INCREASED BY THE PRESENCE OF DERMATITIS OR HIGH AMBIENT TEMPERATURES. DELAYED NEUROPATHY IS ALSO POSSIBLE. **CHRONIC EXPOSURE**- REPEATED OR PROLONGED EXPOSURE MAY CAUSE EFFECTS AS DESCRIBED IN ACUTE EXPOSURE. SOME ORGANOPHOSPHATES MAY CAUSE SENSITIZATION.

FIRST AID- REMOVE CONTAMINATED CLOTHING IMMEDIATELY. WASH CONTAMINATED AREAS WITH SOAP AND WATER FOLLOWED BY ALCOHOL (ARENA, POISONING, 4TH ED.). EMERGENCY PERSONNEL SHOULD WEAR GLOVES AND AVOID CONTAMINATION. TREAT RESPIRATORY DIFFICULTY WITH ARTIFICIAL RESPIRATION. GET MEDICAL ATTENTION IMMEDIATELY.

EYE CONTACT: MEPHOSFOLAN: SEE INFORMATION ON ORGANOPHOSPHATES.
ORGANOPHOSPHATES: CHOLINESTERASE INHIBITOR. **ACUTE EXPOSURE**- DIRECT CONTACT MAY CAUSE PAIN, HYPEREMIA, LACRIMATION, TWITCHING OF THE EYELIDS, MIOSIS, AND CILIARY MUSCLE SPASM WITH LOSS OF ACCOMODATION, BLURRED OR DIMMED VISION AND BROWACHE. SOMETIMES MYDRIASIS MAY OCCUR INSTEAD OF MIOSIS. WITH SUFFICIENT EXPOSURE, OTHER SYMPTOMS OF CHOLINESTERASE INHIBITION AS DESCRIBED IN ACUTE INHALATION MAY OCCUR. **CHRONIC EXPOSURE**- REPEATED OR PROLONGED EXPOSURE MAY CAUSE EFFECTS AS DESCRIBED IN ACUTE EXPOSURE. SOME COMPOUNDS HAVE CAUSED TOXIC EFFECTS ON THE CRYSTALLINE LENS, CONJUNCTIVAL THICKENING AND OBSTRUCTION OF THE NASOLACRIMAL CANALS WHEN USED AS MIOTIC EYEDROPS.

FIRST AID- IRRIGATE EYES WITH WATER OR SALINE SOLUTION. IF SYMPTOMS OF POISONING OCCUR, TREAT RESPIRATORY DIFFICULTY WITH ARTIFICIAL RESPIRATION AND OXYGEN. OBSERVE PATIENT FOR AT LEAST 24-36 HOURS (GOSSELIN, CLINICAL TOXICOLOGY OF COMMERCIAL PRODUCTS, 5TH ED.). GET MEDICAL ATTENTION IMMEDIATELY. OXYGEN SHOULD BE ADMINISTERED BY QUALIFIED MEDICAL PERSONNEL.

INGESTION: MEPHOSFOLAN: HIGHLY TOXIC. SEE INFORMATION ON ORGANOPHOSPHATES.
ORGANOPHOSPHATES: CHOLINESTERASE INHIBITOR. **ACUTE EXPOSURE**- WHEN INGESTED, THE FIRST EFFECTS MAY BE NAUSEA, VOMITING, ANOREXIA, ABDOMINAL CRAMPS AND DIARRHEA. GASTROINTESTINAL ABSORPTION MAY CAUSE SYMPTOMS OF CHOLINESTERASE INHIBITION AS DESCRIBED IN ACUTE INHALATION. SYMPTOMS MAY BEGIN WITHIN MINUTES OR BE DELAYED FOR HOURS. DELAYED EFFECTS INCLUDING NEUROPATHY MAY ALSO OCCUR. **CHRONIC EXPOSURE**- REPEATED INGESTION MAY CAUSE EFFECTS AS DESCRIBED IN ACUTE EXPOSURE.

FIRST AID- IF PERSON IS ALERT AND RESPIRATION IS NOT DEPRESSED, GIVE SYRUP OF IPECAC FOLLOWED BY WATER (IF VOMITING OCCURS, KEEP HEAD BELOW HIPS TO PREVENT ASPIRATION). IF CONSCIOUSNESS LEVEL DECLINES OR VOMITING HAS NOT OCCURRED IN 15 MINUTES EMPTY STOMACH BY GASTRIC LAVAGE WITH THE AID OF CUFFED ENDOTRACHEAL TUBE USING ISOTONIC SALINE OR 5% SODIUM BICARBONATE FOLLOW WITH ACTIVATED CHARCOAL. ESTABLISH AND MAINTAIN AIRWAY. TREAT RESPIRATORY DIFFICULTY WITH ARTIFICIAL RESPIRATION AND OXYGEN. DO NOT GIVE MORPHINE, AMINOPHYLLINE, PHENOTHIAZINES, RESERPINE, FUROSEMIDE, OR ETHACRYNIC ACID (MORGAN, RECOGNITION AND MANAGEMENT OF PESTICIDE POISONINGS, 3RD ED.). TREAT SYMPTOMATICALLY AND SUPPORTIVELY. ADMINISTRATION OF OXYGEN AND LAVAGE MUST BE PERFORMED BY QUALIFIED MEDICAL PERSONNEL. GET MEDICAL ATTENTION IMMEDIATELY.

ANTIDOTE: THE FOLLOWING ANTIDOTE(S) HAVE BEEN RECOMMENDED. HOWEVER, THE DECISION AS TO WHETHER THE SEVERITY OF POISONING REQUIRES ADMINISTRATION OF ANY ANTIDOTE AND ACTUAL DOSE REQUIRED SHOULD BE MADE BY QUALIFIED MEDICAL PERSONNEL.
FOR CHOLINESTERASE INHIBITORS: ESTABLISH CLEAR AIRWAY AND TISSUE OXYGENATION BY ASPIRATION OF SECRETIONS, AND IF NECESSARY, BY ASSISTED PULMONARY VENTILATION WITH OXYGEN. IMPROVE TISSUE OXYGENATION AS MUCH AS POSSIBLE BEFORE ADMINISTERING ATROPINE TO MINIMIZE THE RISK OF VENTRICULAR FIBRILLATION. ADMINISTER ATROPINE SULFATE INTRAVENOUSLY, OR INTRAMUSCULARLY IF IV INJECTION IS NOT POSSIBLE. IN MODERATELY SEVERE POISONING ADMINISTER ATROPINE SULFATE, 0.4-2.0 MG REPEATED EVERY 15 MINUTES UNTIL ATROPINIZATION IS ACHIEVED (TACHYCARDIA, FLUSHING, DRY MOUTH, MYDRIASIS). MAINTAIN ATROPINIZATION BY REPEATED DOSES FOR 2-12 HOURS, OR LONGER, DEPENDING ON THE SEVERITY OF POISONING. THE APPEARANCE OF RALES IN THE LUNG BASES, MIOSIS, SALIVATION, NAUSEA, BRADYCARDIA, ARE ALL INDICATIONS OF INADEQUATE ATROPINIZATION. SEVERELY POISONED INDIVIDUALS MAY EXHIBIT REMARKABLE TOLERANCE TO ATROPINE; TWO OR MORE TIMES THE DOSAGES SUGGESTED ABOVE MAY BE NEEDED. PERSONS NOT POISONED OR ONLY SLIGHTLY POISONED, HOWEVER, MAY DEVELOP SIGNS OF ATROPINE TOXICITY FROM SUCH LARGE DOSAGES: FEVER, MUSCLE FIBRILLATIONS, AND DELIRIUM ARE THE MAIN SIGNS OF ATROPINE TOXICITY. IF THESE SIGNS APPEAR WHILE THE PATIENT IS FULLY ATROPINIZED, ATROPINE ADMINISTRATION SHOULD BE DISCONTINUED, AT LEAST TEMPORARILY. OBSERVE TREATED PATIENTS CLOSELY AT LEAST 24 HOURS TO INSURE THAT SYMPTOMS (POSSIBLY PULMONARY EDEMA) DO NOT RECUR AS ATROPINIZATION WEARS OFF. IN VERY SEVERE POISONINGS, METABOLIC DISPOSITION OF TOXICANT MAY REQUIRE SEVERAL HOURS OR DAYS DURING WHICH ATROPINIZATION MUST BE MAINTAINED. MARKEDLY LOWER LEVELS OF URINARY METABOLITES INDICATE THAT ATROPINE DOSAGE CAN BE TAPERED OFF. AS DOSAGE IS REDUCED, CHECK THE LUNG BASES FREQUENTLY FOR RALES. IF RALES ARE HEARD OR OTHER SYMPTOMS RETURN, RE-ESTABLISH ATROPINIZATION PROMPTLY (MORGAN, RECOGNITION AND MANAGEMENT OF PESTICIDE POISONINGS, 3RD ED.). ADMINISTRATION OF ANTIDOTE MUST BE PERFORMED BY QUALIFIED MEDICAL PERSONNEL.
IN CASES OF SEVERE POISONING BY ORGANOPHOSPHATE PESTICIDES IN WHICH RESPIRATORY DEPRESSION, MUSCLE WEAKNESS AND TWITCHINGS ARE SEVERE, GIVE PRALIDOXIME (PROTOPAM-AYERST, 2-PAM), 1.0 GRAM INTRAVENOUSLY AT NO MORE THAN 0.5 GRAM PER MINUTE. DOSAGE OF PRALIDOXIME MAY BE REPEATED IN 1-2 HOURS, THEN AT 10-12 HOUR INTERVALS IF NEEDED. IN VERY SEVERE POISONINGS, DOSAGE RATES MAY BE DOUBLED. TREATMENT WITH PRALIDOXIME WILL BE MOST EFFECTIVE IF GIVEN WITHIN THIRTY-SIX HOURS AFTER POISONING (MORGAN, RECOGNITION AND MANAGEMENT OF PESTICIDE POISONINGS, 3RD ED.). ANTIDOTE SHOULD BE ADMINISTERED BY QUALIFIED MEDICAL PERSONNEL.

REACTIVITY

REACTIVITY: STABLE UNDER NORMAL TEMPERATURES AND PRESSURES.

INCOMPATIBILITIES: MEPHOSFOLAN: ACIDS: MAY HYDROLYZED ON CONTACT.
ALKALI: MAY HYDROLYZED ON CONTACT.

DECOMPOSITION: THERMAL DECOMPOSITION PRODUCTS MAY INCLUDE TOXIC AND HAZARDOUS FUMES OF SULFUR, NITROGEN AND PHOSPHORUS.

POLYMERIZATION: HAZARDOUS POLYMERIZATION HAS NOT BEEN REPORTED TO OCCUR UNDER NORMAL TEMPERATURES AND PRESSURES.

STORAGE AND DISPOSAL

OBSERVE ALL FEDERAL, STATE AND LOCAL REGULATIONS WHEN STORING OR DISPOSING OF THIS SUBSTANCE. FOR ASSISTANCE, CONTACT THE DISTRICT DIRECTOR OF THE ENVIRONMENTAL PROTECTION AGENCY.

STORAGE

STORE IN ACCORDANCE WITH 40 CFR 165 RECOMMENDED PROCEDURES FOR THE DISPOSAL AND STORAGE OF PESTICIDES AND PESTICIDE CONTAINERS.
STORE AWAY FROM INCOMPATIBLE SUBSTANCES.
THRESHOLD PLANNING QUANTITY (TPQ): THE SUPERFUND AMENDMENTS AND REAUTHORIZATION ACT (SARA) SECTION 302 REQUIRES THAT EACH FACILITY WHERE ANY EXTREMELY HAZARDOUS SUBSTANCE IS PRESENT IN A QUANTITY EQUAL TO OR GREATER THAN THE TPQ ESTABLISHED FOR THAT SUBSTANCE NOTIFY THE STATE EMERGENCY RESPONSE COMMISSION FOR THE STATE IN WHICH IT IS LOCATED. SECTION 303 OF SARA REQUIRES THESE FACILITIES TO PARTICIPATE IN LOCAL EMERGENCY RESPONSE PLANNING (40 CFR 355.30).

DISPOSAL

DISPOSAL MUST BE IN ACCORDANCE WITH 40 CFR 165 RECOMMENDED PROCEDURES FOR THE DISPOSAL AND STORAGE OF PESTICIDES AND PESTICIDE CONTAINERS.

CONDITIONS TO AVOID

NONE REPORTED.

SPILL AND LEAK PROCEDURES

OCCUPATIONAL SPILL: DO NOT TOUCH SPILLED MATERIAL. STOP LEAK IF YOU CAN DO IT WITHOUT RISK. USE WATER SPRAY TO REDUCE VAPORS. FOR SMALL SPILLS, TAKE UP WITH SAND OR OTHER ABSORBENT MATERIAL AND PLACE INTO CONTAINERS FOR LATER DISPOSAL. FOR SMALL DRY SPILLS, WITH A CLEAN

SHOVEL PLACE MATERIAL INTO CLEAN, DRY CONTAINERS AND COVER. MOVE CONTAINERS FROM SPILL AREA. FOR LARGER SPILLS, DIKE FAR AHEAD OF SPILL FOR LATER DISPOSAL. KEEP UNNECESSARY PEOPLE AWAY. ISOLATE HAZARD AREA AND DENY ENTRY. VENTILATE CLOSED SPACES BEFORE ENTERING.
REPORTABLE QUANTITY (RQ): 1 POUND THE SUPERFUND AMENDMENTS AND REAUTHORIZATION ACT (SARA) SECTION 304 REQUIRES THAT A RELEASE EQUAL TO OR GREATER THAN THE REPORTABLE QUANTITY FOR THIS SUBSTANCE BE IMMEDIATELY REPORTED TO THE LOCAL EMERGENCY PLANNING COMMITTEE AND THE STATE EMERGENCY RESPONSE COMMISSION (40 CFR 355.40). IF THE RELEASE OF THIS SUBSTANCE IS REPORTABLE UNDER CERCLA SECTION 103, THE NATIONAL RESPONSE CENTER MUST BE NOTIFIED IMMEDIATELY AT (800) 424-8802 OR (202) 426-2675 IN THE METROPOLITAN WASHINGTON, D.C. AREA (40 CFR 302.6).

PROTECTIVE EQUIPMENT

VENTILATION: PROCESS ENCLOSURE RECOMMENDED.

RESPIRATOR: THE FOLLOWING RESPIRATORS ARE RECOMMENDED BASED ON INFORMATION FOUND IN THE PHYSICAL DATA, TOXICITY AND HEALTH EFFECTS SECTIONS. THEY ARE RANKED IN ORDER FROM MINIMUM TO MAXIMUM RESPIRATORY PROTECTION. THE SPECIFIC RESPIRATOR SELECTED MUST BE BASED ON CONTAMINATION LEVELS FOUND IN THE WORK PLACE, MUST NOT EXCEED THE WORKING LIMITS OF THE RESPIRATOR AND BE JOINTLY APPROVED BY THE NATIONAL INSTITUTE FOR OCCUPATIONAL SAFETY AND HEALTH AND THE MINE SAFETY AND HEALTH ADMINISTRATION (NIOSH-MSHA).
TYPE 'C' SUPPLIED-AIR RESPIRATOR WITH A FULL FACEPIECE OPERATED IN PRESSURE-DEMAND OR OTHER POSITIVE PRESSURE MODE OR WITH A FULL FACEPIECE, HELMET OR HOOD OPERATED IN CONTINOUS-FLOW MODE.
SELF-CONTAINED BREATHING APPARATUS WITH A FULL FACEPIECE OPERATED IN PRESSURE-DEMAND OR OTHER POSITIVE PRESSURE MODE.
FOR FIREFIGHTING AND OTHER IMMEDIATELY DANGEROUS TO LIFE OR HEALTH CONDITIONS:
SELF-CONTAINED BREATHING APPARATUS WITH FULL FACEPIECE OPERATED IN PRESSURE-DEMAND OR OTHER POSITIVE PRESSURE MODE.
SUPPLIED-AIR RESPIRATOR WITH FULL FACEPIECE AND OPERATED IN PRESSURE-DEMAND OR OTHER POSITIVE PRESSURE MODE IN COMBINATION WITH AN AUXILIARY SELF-CONTAINED BREATHING APPARATUS OPERATED IN PRESSURE-DEMAND OR OTHER POSITIVE PRESSURE MODE.

CLOTHING: EMPLOYEE MUST WEAR APPROPRIATE PROTECTIVE (IMPERVIOUS) CLOTHING AND EQUIPMENT TO PREVENT ANY POSSIBILITY OF SKIN CONTACT WITH THIS SUBSTANCE.

GLOVES: EMPLOYEE MUST WEAR APPROPRIATE PROTECTIVE GLOVES TO PREVENT CONTACT WITH THIS SUBSTANCE.

EYE PROTECTION: EMPLOYEE MUST WEAR SPLASH-PROOF OR DUST-RESISTANT SAFETY GOGGLES AND A FACESHIELD TO PREVENT CONTACT WITH THIS SUBSTANCE.
EMERGENCY WASH FACILITIES: WHERE THERE IS ANY POSSIBILITY THAT AN EMPLOYEE'S EYES AND/OR SKIN MAY BE EXPOSED TO THIS SUBSTANCE, THE EMPLOYER SHOULD PROVIDE AN EYE WASH FOUNTAIN AND QUICK DRENCH SHOWER WITHIN THE IMMEDIATE WORK AREA FOR EMERGENCY USE.

AUTHORIZED BY- OCCUPATIONAL HEALTH SERVICES, INC.
CREATION DATE: 10/04/89 ***REVISION DATE:*** 04/26/90

MATERIAL SAFETY DATA SHEET

OCCUPATIONAL HEALTH SERVICES, INC.
AGRICULTURE AND PESTICIDE DIVISION
450 SEVENTH AVENUE, SUITE 2407
NEW YORK, NEW YORK 10123
1-800-445-MSDS OR (212) 967-1100

EMERGENCY CONTACT:
JOHN S. BRANSFORD, JR. (615) 292-1180

SUBSTANCE IDENTIFICATION

CAS-NUMBER 149-30-4

SUBSTANCE: **MERCAPTOBENZOTHIAZOLE**

TRADE NAMES/SYNONYMS: 2(3H)-BENZOTHIAZOLETHIONE; MBT; CAPTAX; THIOTAX A; 2-BENZOTHIAZOLETHIOLE; ROTAX; 2-BENZOTHIAZOLETHIOL; ACCELERATOR M; BENZOTHIAZOLE-2-THIONE; EKAGOM G; KAPTAX; MEBETIZOLE; MERTAX; PNEUMAX MBT; 2-BENZOTHIAZOLETHIONE; 2-BENZOTHIAZOLINETHIONE; 2-MERCAPTOBENZOTHIAZOLE; THIOTAX ACCELERATOR; C7H5NS2; PST13738

CHEMICAL FAMILY: THIOL (MERCAPTAN)

MOLECULAR FORMULA: C7-H5-N-S2

MOLECULAR WEIGHT: 167.24

CERCLA RATINGS (SCALE 0-3): HEALTH=3 FIRE=1 REACTIVITY=0 PERSISTENCE=2

NFPA RATINGS (SCALE 0-4): HEALTH=U FIRE=1 REACTIVITY=0

COMPONENTS AND CONTAMINANTS

COMPONENT: MERCAPTOBENZOTHIAZOLE ***PERCENT:*** 100
CAS# 149-30-4

OTHER CONTAMINANTS: NONE

EXPOSURE LIMITS: MERCAPTOBENZOTHIAZOL: NO OCCUPATIONAL EXPOSURE LIMITS ESTABLISHED BY OSHA, ACGIH, OR NIOSH. MONSANTO RECOMMENDS APPLICATION OF EXPOSURE LIMITS ESTABLISHED FOR NUISANCE DUSTS.
NUISANCE PARTICULATES (NUISANCE DUST): 5 MG/M3 OSHA TWA (RESPIRABLE DUST); 15 MG/M3 OSHA TWA (TOTAL DUST) 10 MG/M3 ACGIH TWA (TOTAL DUST) (NO ASBESTOS AND < 1% CRYSTALLINE SILICA)

PHYSICAL DATA

DESCRIPTION: PALE, YELLOW, MONOCLINIC NEEDLES OR LEAFLETS WITH A DISAGREEABLE ODOR.

BOILING POINT: 500 F (260 C) (DECOMPOSES)

MELTING POINT: 356-360 F (180-182C)

SPECIFIC GRAVITY: 1.42 ***VAPOR PRESSURE:*** 0.000019 @ 25 C

SOLUBILITY IN WATER: 0.032% @ 25 C ***ODOR THRESHOLD:*** 1.76 PPM

SOLVENT SOLUBILITY: SOLUBLE IN ALKALIES, ALKALI CARBONATE SOLUTIONS, AND ACETONE; MODERATELY SOLUBLE IN GLACIAL ACETIC ACID; SLIGHTLY SOLUBLE IN ETHER, ALCOHOL, BENZENE, CARBON TETRACHLORIDE AND NAPHTHA; INSOLUBLE IN GASOLINE.

FIRE AND EXPLOSION DATA

FIRE AND EXPLOSION HAZARD: SLIGHT FIRE HAZARD WHEN EXPOSED TO HEAT OR FLAME.
DUST-AIR MIXTURES MAY IGNITE OR EXPLODE.

FLASH POINT: 485 F (252 C) (COC) ***LOWER EXPLOSIVE LIMIT:*** 0.2 OZ/FT3

FIREFIGHTING MEDIA: DRY CHEMICAL, CARBON DIOXIDE, HALON, WATER SPRAY OR STANDARD FOAM (1987 EMERGENCY RESPONSE GUIDEBOOK, DOT P 5800.4).
FOR LARGER FIRES, USE WATER SPRAY, FOG OR STANDARD FOAM (1987 EMERGENCY RESPONSE GUIDEBOOK, DOT P 5800.4).

FIREFIGHTING: MOVE CONTAINER FROM FIRE AREA IF POSSIBLE. DO NOT SCATTER SPILLED MATERIAL WITH HIGH PRESSURE WATER STREAMS. DIKE FIRE CONTROL WATER FOR LATER DISPOSAL (1987 EMERGENCY RESPONSE GUIDEBOOK, DOT P 5800.4, GUIDE PAGE 31).
USE AGENTS SUITABLE FOR TYPE OF SURROUNDING FIRE. AVOID BREATHING HAZARDOUS VAPORS, KEEP UPWIND.

TOXICITY

MERCAPTOBENZOTHIAZOLE: TOXICITY DATA: 100 MG/KG ORAL-RAT LD50; 1851 MG/KG ORAL-MOUSE LD50; >7940 MG/KG SKIN-RABBIT LD50 (MONSANTO MSDS); 300 MG/KG INTRAPERITONEAL-RAT LD50; 100 MG/KG INTRAPERITONEAL-MOUSE LD50; MUTAGENIC DATA (RTECS); REPRODUCTIVE EFFECTS DATA (RTECS); TUMORIGENIC DATA (RTECS). CARCINOGEN STATUS: NONE. IN A 2-YEAR GAVAGE STUDY, THERE WAS SOME EVIDENCE OF CARCINOGENIC ACTIVITY IN MALE AND FEMALE RATS, AND EQUIVOCAL EVIDENCE IN FEMALE MICE (NTP TR 332). ACUTE TOXICITY LEVEL: TOXIC BY INGESTION; SLIGHTLY TOXIC BY DERMAL ABSORPTION. TARGET EFFECTS: POISONING MAY AFFECT THE LIVER, KIDNEYS, AND CENTRAL NERVOUS SYSTEM.

HEALTH EFFECTS AND FIRST AID

INHALATION: MERCAPTOBENZOTHIAZOLE: **ACUTE EXPOSURE-** NO DATA AVAILABLE.
CHRONIC EXPOSURE- NO SPECIFIC DATA AVAILABLE. PROLONGED OR REPEATED EXPOSURE MAY RESULT IN NEUROLOGIC EFFECTS.

FIRST AID- REMOVE FROM EXPOSURE AREA TO FRESH AIR IMMEDIATELY. IF BREATHING HAS STOPPED, PERFORM ARTIFICIAL RESPIRATION. KEEP PERSON WARM AND AT REST. TREAT SYMPTOMATICALLY AND SUPPORTIVELY. GET MEDICAL ATTENTION IMMEDIATELY.

SKIN CONTACT: MERCAPTOBENZOTHIAZOLE: SENSITIZER. **ACUTE EXPOSURE-** NOT EXPECTED TO CAUSE IRRITATION BASED ON HUMAN AND ANIMAL TESTING. SENSITIZATION DERMATITIS MAY OCCUR IN PREVIOUSLY EXPOSED PERSONS. ANIMAL STUDIES INDICATED SYSTEMIC TOXICITY IS UNLIKELY FROM SKIN ABSORPTION. **CHRONIC EXPOSURE-** IN SOME INDIVIDUALS PROLONGED OR REPEATED CONTACT MAY RESULT IN SENSITIZATION WITH ERYTHEMATOUS, VESICULAR DERMATITIS.

FIRST AID- REMOVE CONTAMINATED CLOTHING AND SHOES IMMEDIATELY. WASH AFFECTED AREA WITH SOAP OR MILD DETERGENT AND LARGE AMOUNTS OF WATER UNTIL NO EVIDENCE OF CHEMICAL REMAINS (APPROXIMATELY 15-20 MINUTES). GET MEDICAL ATTENTION IMMEDIATELY.

EYE CONTACT: MERCAPTOBENZOTHIAZOLE: **ACUTE EXPOSURE-** DIRECT CONTACT MAY CAUSE IRRITATION. IN TESTS ON RABBITS IT RATED 3.2 ON A SCALE OF 110. **CHRONIC EXPOSURE-** NO DATA AVAILABLE.
FIRST AID- WASH EYES IMMEDIATELY WITH LARGE AMOUNTS OF WATER OR NORMAL SALINE, OCCASIONALLY LIFTING UPPER AND LOWER LIDS, UNTIL NO EVIDENCE OF CHEMICAL REMAINS (APPROXIMATELY 15-20 MINUTES). GET MEDICAL ATTENTION IMMEDIATELY.

INGESTION: MERCAPTOBENZOTHIAZOLE: TOXIC. **ACUTE EXPOSURE-** FATAL DOSES CAUSED INCREASED SALIVATION, PERIPHERAL VASODILATION, TONIC AND CLONIC CONVULSIONS, AND DEATH WITHIN 24 HOURS IN ANIMALS. **CHRONIC EXPOSURE-** PROLONGED FEEDING STUDIES IN ANIMALS RESULTED IN LIVER DAMAGE, HEPATOMEGALY, DECREASED WEIGHT GAIN, LETHARGY, LACRIMATION, SALIVATION, AND CLONIC SEIZURES. IN A 2-YEAR GAVAGE STUDY, SOME EVIDENCE OF CARCINOGENIC ACTIVITY WAS NOTED IN MALE AND FEMALE RATS AS INDICATED BY INCREASED INCIDENCES OF MONONUCLEAR CELL LEUKEMIA, PANCREATIC ACINAR CELL ADENOMAS, ADRENAL GLAND PHEOCHROMOCYTOMAS, PREPUTIAL GLAND ADENOMAS AND PITUITARY GLAND ADENOMAS. EQUIVOCAL EVIDENCE OF CARCINOGENIC ACTIVITY WAS NOTED IN FEMALE MICE INDICATED BY INCREASED INCIDENCES OF HEPATOCELLULAR ADENOMAS OR CARCINOMAS.
FIRST AID- TREAT SYMPTOMATICALLY AND SUPPORTIVELY. GET MEDICAL ATTENTION IMMEDIATELY. IF VOMITING OCCURS, KEEP HEAD LOWER THAN HIPS TO PREVENT ASPIRATION.
ANTIDOTE: NO SPECIFIC ANTIDOTE. TREAT SYMPTOMATICALLY AND SUPPORTIVELY.

REACTIVITY

REACTIVITY: STABLE UNDER NORMAL TEMPERATURES AND PRESSURES.
INCOMPATIBILITIES: MERCAPTOBENZOTHIAZOLE: ACIDS: DECOMPOSES AND LIBERATES TOXIC FUMES OF HYDROGEN SULFIDE. OXIDIZERS (STRONG): FIRE AND EXPLOSION HAZARD. SEE ALSO MERCAPTANS.
MERCAPTANS: CALCIUM HYPOCHLORITE: VIOLENT REACTION.
DECOMPOSITION: THERMAL DECOMPOSITION PRODUCTS MAY INCLUDE TOXIC OXIDES OF CARBON, NITROGEN, AND SULFUR.
POLYMERIZATION: HAZARDOUS POLYMERIZATION HAS NOT BEEN REPORTED TO OCCUR UNDER NORMAL TEMPERATURES AND PRESSURES.

STORAGE AND DISPOSAL

OBSERVE ALL FEDERAL, STATE AND LOCAL REGULATIONS WHEN STORING OR DISPOSING OF THIS SUBSTANCE. FOR ASSISTANCE, CONTACT THE DISTRICT DIRECTOR OF THE ENVIRONMENTAL PROTECTION AGENCY.

STORAGE

STORE AWAY FROM INCOMPATIBLE SUBSTANCES.

CONDITIONS TO AVOID

MAY BURN BUT DOES NOT IGNITE READILY. AVOID CONTACT WITH STRONG OXIDIZERS, EXCESSIVE HEAT, SPARKS, OR OPEN FLAME.
AVOID DISPERSION OF DUST IN AIR. FINELY DIVIDED PARTICLES, DUST, OR FUMES MAY BE FLAMMABLE OR EXPLOSIVE. KEEP AWAY FROM SPARKS OR IGNITION SOURCES.

SPILL AND LEAK PROCEDURES

OCCUPATIONAL SPILL: FOR LARGE SPILLS, SWEEP UP WITH A MINIMUM OF DUSTING AND PLACE INTO SUITABLE CLEAN, DRY CONTAINERS FOR RECLAMATION OR LATER DISPOSAL.
RESIDUE SHOULD BE CLEANED UP USING A HIGH-EFFICIENCY PARTICULATE FILTER VACUUM.

PROTECTIVE EQUIPMENT

VENTILATION: PROVIDE LOCAL EXHAUST VENTILATION AND/OR GENERAL DILUTION VENTILATION TO MEET PUBLISHED EXPOSURE LIMITS.
RESPIRATOR: THE FOLLOWING RESPIRATORS ARE RECOMMENDED BASED ON INFORMATION FOUND IN THE PHYSICAL DATA, TOXICITY AND HEALTH EFFECTS SECTIONS. THEY ARE RANKED IN ORDER FROM MINIMUM TO MAXIMUM RESPIRATORY PROTECTION. THE SPECIFIC RESPIRATOR SELECTED MUST BE BASED ON CONTAMINATION LEVELS FOUND IN THE WORK PLACE, MUST NOT EXCEED THE WORKING LIMITS OF THE RESPIRATOR AND BE JOINTLY APPROVED BY THE NATIONAL INSTITUTE FOR OCCUPATIONAL SAFETY AND HEALTH AND THE MINE SAFETY AND HEALTH ADMINISTRATION (NIOSH-MSHA).
DUST AND MIST RESPIRATOR WITH A FULL FACEPIECE.
AIR-PURIFYING FULL FACEPIECE RESPIRATOR WITH A HIGH-EFFICIENCY PARTICULATE FILTER.
POWERED AIR-PURIFYING RESPIRATOR WITH A TIGHT-FITTING FACEPIECE AND HIGH-EFFICIENCY PARTICULATE FILTER.
TYPE 'C' SUPPLIED-AIR RESPIRATOR WITH A FULL FACEPIECE OPERATED IN PRESSURE-DEMAND OR OTHER POSITIVE PRESSURE MODE OR WITH A FULL FACEPIECE, HELMET OR HOOD OPERATED IN CONTINUOUS-FLOW MODE.
SELF-CONTAINED BREATHING APPARATUS WITH A FULL FACEPIECE OPERATED IN PRESSURE-DEMAND OR OTHER POSITIVE PRESSURE MODE.
FOR FIREFIGHTING AND OTHER IMMEDIATELY DANGEROUS TO LIFE OR HEALTH CONDITIONS:
SELF-CONTAINED BREATHING APPARATUS WITH FULL FACEPIECE OPERATED IN PRESSURE-DEMAND OR OTHER POSITIVE PRESSURE MODE.
SUPPLIED-AIR RESPIRATOR WITH FULL FACEPIECE AND OPERATED IN PRESSURE-DEMAND OR OTHER POSITIVE PRESSURE MODE IN COMBINATION WITH AN AUXILIARY SELF-CONTAINED BREATHING APPARATUS OPERATED IN PRESSURE-DEMAND OR OTHER POSITIVE PRESSURE MODE.
CLOTHING: EMPLOYEE MUST WEAR APPROPRIATE PROTECTIVE (IMPERVIOUS) CLOTHING AND EQUIPMENT TO PREVENT ANY POSSIBILITY OF SKIN CONTACT WITH THIS SUBSTANCE.
GLOVES: EMPLOYEE MUST WEAR APPROPRIATE PROTECTIVE GLOVES TO PREVENT CONTACT WITH THIS SUBSTANCE.
EYE PROTECTION: EMPLOYEE MUST WEAR SPLASH-PROOF OR DUST-RESISTANT SAFETY GOGGLES AND A FACESHIELD TO PREVENT CONTACT WITH THIS SUBSTANCE.
EMERGENCY WASH FACILITIES: WHERE THERE IS ANY POSSIBILITY THAT AN EMPLOYEE'S EYES AND/OR SKIN MAY BE EXPOSED TO THIS SUBSTANCE, THE EMPLOYER SHOULD PROVIDE AN EYE WASH FOUNTAIN AND QUICK DRENCH SHOWER WITHIN THE IMMEDIATE WORK AREA FOR EMERGENCY USE.

AUTHORIZED BY- OCCUPATIONAL HEALTH SERVICES, INC.
CREATION DATE: 10/04/89 ***REVISION DATE:*** 05/25/90

MATERIAL SAFETY DATA SHEET

OCCUPATIONAL HEALTH SERVICES, INC.
AGRICULTURE AND PESTICIDE DIVISION
450 SEVENTH AVENUE, SUITE 2407
NEW YORK, NEW YORK 10123
1-800-445-MSDS OR (212) 967-1100

EMERGENCY CONTACT:
JOHN S. BRANSFORD, JR. (615) 292-1180

SUBSTANCE IDENTIFICATION

CAS-NUMBER 7487-94-7
SUBSTANCE: MERCURIC CHLORIDE
TRADE NAMES/SYNONYMS: MERCURY BICHLORIDE; MERCURY PERCHLORIDE; CORROSIVE MERCURY CHLORIDE; CORROSIVE SUBLIMATE; FUNGCHEX; MERCURY(II) CHLORIDE; BICHLORIDE OF MERCURY; MERCURIC BICHLORIDE; MERCURIC CHLORIDE, SOLID; PERCHLORIDE OF MERCURY; STCC 4923245; UN 1624; PST13800
CHEMICAL FAMILY: INORGANIC SALT
MOLECULAR FORMULA: HG-CL2
MOLECULAR WEIGHT: 271.5
CERCLA RATINGS (SCALE 0-3): HEALTH=3 FIRE=0 REACTIVITY=0 PERSISTENCE=3
NFPA RATINGS (SCALE 0-4): HEALTH=3 FIRE=0 REACTIVITY=0

COMPONENTS AND CONTAMINANTS

COMPONENT: MERCURIC CHLORIDE ***PERCENT:*** 100
CAS# 7487-94-7
OTHER CONTAMINANTS: NONE
EXPOSURE LIMITS: MERCURY, ALL FORMS EXCEPT ALKYL (AS HG): 0.05 MG/M3 OSHA TWA (VAPOR); 0.1 MG/M3 OSHA CEILING (SKIN) 0.05 MG/M3 ACGIH TWA (VAPOR); 0.10 MG/M3 ACGIH TWA (ARYL & INORGANIC)-(SKIN) 0.05 MG/M3 NIOSH RECOMMENDED 10 HOUR TWA
SUBJECT TO SARA SECTION 313 ANNUAL TOXIC CHEMICAL RELEASE REPORTING
SUBJECT TO CALIFORNIA PROPOSITION 65 CANCER AND/OR REPRODUCTIVE TOXICITY WARNING AND RELEASE REQUIREMENTS- (JULY 1, 1990)
MERCURIC CHLORIDE: 500/10,000 POUNDS SARA SECTION 302 THRESHOLD PLANNING QUANTITY 1 POUND SARA SECTION 304 REPORTABLE QUANTITY
SUBJECT TO SARA SECTION 313 ANNUAL TOXIC CHEMICAL RELEASE REPORTING

PHYSICAL DATA

DESCRIPTION: ODORLESS, WHITE CRYSTALS OR POWDER. ***BOILING POINT:*** 576 F (302 C)
MELTING POINT: 529 F (276 C) ***SPECIFIC GRAVITY:*** 5.0 ***PH:*** 4.7
SOLUBILITY IN WATER: 6.9%
SOLVENT SOLUBILITY: ALCOHOL, ACETONE, ETHER, GLYCEROL, PYRIDINE

FIRE AND EXPLOSION DATA

FIRE AND EXPLOSION HAZARD: NEGLIGIBLE FIRE HAZARD WHEN EXPOSED TO HEAT OR FLAME.
FLASH POINT: NONFLAMMABLE
FIREFIGHTING MEDIA: DRY CHEMICAL, CARBON DIOXIDE, HALON, WATER SPRAY OR STANDARD FOAM (1987 EMERGENCY RESPONSE GUIDEBOOK, DOT P 5800.4). FOR LARGER FIRES, USE WATER SPRAY, FOG OR STANDARD FOAM (1987 EMERGENCY RESPONSE GUIDEBOOK, DOT P 5800.4).
FIREFIGHTING: MOVE CONTAINERS FROM FIRE AREA IF POSSIBLE (1987 EMERGENCY RESPONSE GUIDEBOOK, DOT P 5800.4, GUIDE PAGE 53). USE AGENTS SUITABLE FOR TYPE OF FIRE. USE WATER IN FLOODING AMOUNTS AS FOG. AVOID BREATHING POISONOUS DUSTS AND FUMES FROM BURNING MATERIAL.

TRANSPORTATION DATA

DEPARTMENT OF TRANSPORTATION HAZARD CLASSIFICATION 49 CFR 172.101: POISON B
DEPARTMENT OF TRANSPORTATION LABELING REQUIREMENTS 49 CFR 172.101 AND SUBPART E: POISON
DEPARTMENT OF TRANSPORTATION PACKAGING REQUIREMENTS: 49 CFR 173.372 EXCEPTIONS: 49 CFR 173.364

TOXICITY

MERCURIC CHLORIDE: IRRITATION DATA: 500 MG/24 HOURS SKIN-RABBIT SEVERE; 50 UG/24 HOURS EYE-RABBIT SEVERE. TOXICITY DATA: 300 MG/M3/10 MINUTES INHALATION-MOUSE LCLO; 41 MG/KG SKIN-RAT LD50; 345 MG/KG SKIN-GUINEA PIG LDLO; 50 MG/KG ORAL-WOMAN TDLO; 29 MG/KG ORAL-HUMAN LDLO; 29 MG/KG ORAL-MAN TDLO; 1 MG/KG ORAL-RAT LD50; 6 MG/KG ORAL-MOUSE LD50; 10 MG/KG ORAL-DOG LDLO; 20 MG/KG ORAL-RABBIT LDLO; 14 MG/KG SUBCUTANEOUS-RAT LD50; 4500 UG/KG SUBCUTANEOUS-MOUSE LD50; 10 MG/KG SUBACUTANEOUS-RABBIT LDLO; 1272 UG/KG INTRAVENOUS-RAT LD50; 4992 UG/KG INTRAVENOUS-MOUSE LD50; 2710 UG/KG INTRAVENOUS-DOG LDLO; 2 MG/KG INTRAVENOUS-RABBIT LDLO; 3210 UG/KG INTRAPERITONEAL-RAT LD50; 6 MG/KG INTRAPERITONEAL-MOUSE LD50; 345 MG/KG INTRAPERITONEAL-GUINEA PIG LDLO; 7300 UG/KG INTRAMUSCULAR-RABBIT LD50; 7253 UG/KG UNREPORTED-MAN LDLO; MUTAGENIC DATA (RTECS); REPRODUCTIVE EFFECTS DATA (RTECS). CARCINOGEN STATUS: NONE. LOCAL EFFECTS: IRRITANT- INHALATION, SKIN AND EYES. ACUTE TOXICITY LEVEL: HIGHLY TOXIC BY DERMAL ABSORPTION AND INGESTION. TARGET EFFECTS: SENSITIZER- PULMONARY AND SKIN. NEUROTOXIN; NEPHROTOXIN. POISONING MAY AFFECT THE RESPIRATORY SYSTEM AND LIVER.

HEALTH EFFECTS AND FIRST AID

INHALATION: MERCURIC CHLORIDE: IRRITANT/NEUROTOXIN/NEPHROTOXIN. 28 MG(HG)/M3 IMMEDIATELY DANGEROUS TO LIFE OR HEALTH. **ACUTE EXPOSURE-** HIGH DUST CONCENTRATIONS MAY CAUSE SORE THROAT, COUGHING, DYSPNEA, LABORED BREATHING, AND DELAYED PULMONARY EDEMA. INHALATION OF A HIGH CONCENTRATION OF MERCURY VAPOR CAN CAUSE ALMOST IMMEDIATE DYSPNEA, COUGH, FEVER, NAUSEA, VOMITING DIARRHEA, INFLAMMATION OF THE MOUTH, SALIVATION, AND METALLIC TASTE. THE SYMPTOMS MAY RESOLVE OR MAY PROGRESS TO NECROTIZING BRONCHIOLITIS, PNEUMONITIS, PULMONARY EDEMA, AND PNEUMOTHORAX. ACIDOSIS AND RENAL DAMAGE WITH RENAL FAILURE MAY OCCUR. **CHRONIC EXPOSURE-** INHALATION OF MERCURY VAPOR AND DUSTS OVER A LONG PERIOD MAY CAUSE MERCURIALISM. FINDINGS ARE EXTREMELY VARIABLE AND MAY INCLUDE TREMORS, SALIVATION, INFLAMMATION OF THE MOUTH, LOSSENING OF THE TEETH, A BLUE LINE ON THE GUMS, PAIN, AND NUMBNESS IN THE EXTREMETIES, NEPHRITIS, DIARRHEA, ANXIETY, HEADACHE, WEIGHT LOSS, ANOREXIA, MENTAL DEPRESSION, INSOMNIA, IRRITABILITY, INSTABILITY, AND HALLUCINATIONS.
FIRST AID- REMOVE FROM EXPOSURE AREA TO FRESH AIR IMMEDIATELY. IF BREATHING HAS STOPPED, GIVE ARTIFICIAL RESPIRATION. MAINTAIN AIRWAY AND BLOOD PRESSURE AND ADMINISTER OXYGEN IF AVAILABLE. KEEP AFFECTED PERSON WARM AND AT REST. TREAT SYMPTOMATICALLY AND SUPPORTIVELY. ADMINISTRATION OF OXYGEN SHOULD BE PERFORMED BY QUALIFIED PERSONNEL. GET MEDICAL ATTENTION IMMEDIATELY.

SKIN CONTACT: MERCURIC CHLORIDE: IRRITANT/SENSITIZER/NEUROTOXIN/NEPHROTOXIN/HIGHLY TOXIC. **ACUTE EXPOSURE-** MAY CAUSE REDNESS AND IRRITATION. SENSITIZATION DERMATITIS MAY OCCUR IN PREVIOUSLY EXPOSED WORKERS. SUBSTANCE MAY BE ABSORBED THROUGH INTACT SKIN CAUSING ANURIA. **CHRONIC EXPOSURE-** MAY CAUSE IRRITATION AND SENSITIZATION DERMATITIS. MAY RESULT IN PSYCHIC DISTURBANCES, PERIPHERAL NEUROPATHY, AND KIDNEY DAMAGE AS IN CHRONIC INHALATION.
FIRST AID- REMOVE CONTAMINATED CLOTHING AND SHOES IMMEDIATELY. WASH AFFECTED AREA WITH SOAP OR MILD DETERGENT AND LARGE AMOUNTS OF WATER UNTIL NO EVIDENCE OF CHEMICAL REMAINS (APPROXIMATELY 15-20 MINUTES). GET MEDICAL ATTENTION IMMEDIATELY.

EYE CONTACT: MERCURIC CHLODRIDE: CORROSIVE. **ACUTE EXPOSURE-** DIRECT CONTACT WITH HIGHLY CONCENTRATED SOLUTIONS HAS CAUSED SEVERE BURNS IN HUMANS EYES. IN VERY RARE INSTANCES VISION HAS RECOVERED, DESPITE SEVERE DAMAGE AND NECROSIS IN THE CONJUNCTIVA. ON RABBIT EYES, SOLUTIONS HAVE CAUSED SEVERE CORNEAL INJURY. TREATMENT WITH SODIUM EDETATE DIRECTLY AFTER CONTACT HAS NOT PREVENTED SEVERE CORNEAL OPACIFICATION AND NECROSIS. **CHRONIC EXPOSURE-** NOT REPORTED IN HUMANS.
FIRST AID- WASH EYES IMMEDIATELY WITH LARGE AMOUNTS OF WATER, OCCASIONALLY LIFTING UPPER AND LOWER LIDS, UNTIL NO EVIDENCE OF CHEMICAL REMAINS (AT LEAST 15-20 MINUTES). CONTINUE IRRIGATING WITH NORMAL SALINE UNTIL THE PH HAS RETURNED TO NORMAL (30-60 MINUTES). COVER WITH STERILE BANDAGES. GET MEDICAL ATTENTION IMMEDIATELY.

INGESTION: MERCURIC CHLORIDE: NEUROTOXIC/NEPHROTOXIC/HIGHLY TOXIC. **ACUTE EXPOSURE-** WHEN INGESTED, NECROSIS BEGINS IMMEDIATELY IN THE MOUTH, THROAT, ESOPHAGUS, AND STOMACH. WITHIN A FEW MINUTES, VIOLENT PAIN, PROFUSE VOMITING, AND SEVERE PURGING MAY OCCUR. THE PATIENT MAY DIE WITHIN A FEW MINUTES FROM FLUID/ELECTROLYTE LOSSES AND PERIPHERAL VASCULAR COLLAPSE, BUT DEATH (FROM UREMIA) IS USUALLY DELAYED 5 TO 12 DAYS. IF THE VICTIM SURVIVES THIS PHASE, THE PRIMARY GASTROINTESTINAL DISTURBANCES USUALLY SUBSIDE. A SECOND PHASE COMMONLY DEVELOPS WITHIN 1 TO 3 DAYS AFTER EXPOSURE, AND IS CHARACTERIZED BY INFLAMMATION OF THE MOUTH, MEMBRANOUS COLITIS, AND TUBULAR NEPHROSIS. THE SALIVARY GLANDS, KIDNEYS, AND GASTROINTESTINAL MUCOSA MAY SLOWLY EXCRETE LARGE AMOUNTS OF MERCURY. DEATH MAY OCCUR IN THIS PHASE FROM RENAL FAILURE. A MEAN LETHAL DOSE FOR ADULTS IS BETWEEN 1 AND 4 GRAMS. **CHRONIC EXPOSURE-** THE PRINCIPAL MANIFESTATIONS OF CHRONIC POISONING ARE METALLIC TASTE, EXCESSIVE SALIVATION, GINGIVITIS, PYORRHEA WITH LOOSENING OF THE TEETH, DIGESTIVE DISORDERS, ABDOMINAL DISTRESS, AND SKIN ERUPTIONS PROGRESSING TO DERMATITIS. THE SENSORY AND MOTOR NERVES MAY BE AFFECTED WITH NUMBNESS AND WEAKNESS. LIVER AND KIDNEY DAMAGE MAY OCCUR PROGRESSING TO ACUTE RENAL FAILURE WITH ANURIA. SUBTLE OR DRAMATIC BEHAVIOR AND PERSONALITY CHANGES (ERITHISM) HAVE BEEN ASSOCIATED WITH CHRONIC MERCURIAL POISONING.
FIRST AID- REMOVE BY GASTRIC LAVAGE OR EMESIS. MAINTAIN BLOOD PRESSURE AND AIRWAY. GIVE OXYGEN IF RESPIRATION IS DEPRESSED. DO NOT PERFORM GASTRIC LAVAGE OR EMESIS IF VICTIM IS UNCONSCIOUS. GET MEDICAL ATTENTION IMMEDIATELY (DREISBACH, HANDBOOK OF POISONING, 11TH ED.). ADMINISTRATION OF GASTRIC LAVAGE OR OXYGEN SHOULD BE PERFORMED BY QUALIFIED MEDICAL PERSONNEL.
ANTIDOTE: THE FOLLOWING ANTIDOTE HAS BEEN RECOMMENDED. HOWEVER, THE DECISION AS TO WHETHER THE SEVERITY OF POISONING REQUIRES ADMINISTRATION OF ANY ANTIDOTE AND ACTUAL DOSE REQUIRED SHOULD BE MADE BY QUALIFIED MEDICAL PERSONNEL.
MERCURY POISONING: GIVE DIMERCAPROL, 3 MG/KG (OR 0.3 ML/10 KG) EVERY 4 HOURS FOR THE FIRST 2 DAYS AND THEN 2 MG/KG EVERY 12 HOURS FOR A TOTAL OF 10 DAYS IF NECESSARY. DIMERCAPROL IS AVAILABLE AS A 10% SOLUTION IN OIL FOR INTRAMUSCULAR ADMINISTRATION. HEMODIALYSIS WILL SPEED THE REMOVAL OF THE MERCURY-DIMERCAPROL COMPLEX. PENICILLAMINE IS ALSO EFFECTIVE. GIVE UP TO 100 MG/KG/DAY (MAXIMUM 1 GR/DAY) DIVIDED INTO 4 DOSES FOR NO LONGER THAN 1 WEEK. IF A LONGER ADMINISTRATION PERIOD IS WARRANTED, DOSAGE SHOULD NOT EXCEED 40 MG/KG/DAY. GIVE THE DRUG ORALLY HALF AN HOUR BEFORE MEALS. A CHELATING AGENT SHOULD BE BE CONTINUED UNTIL THE URINE-MERCURY LEVEL FALLS BELOW 50 UG/24 HOURS (DREISBACH, HANDBOOK OF POISONING, 12TH ED.). ANTIDOTE SHOULD BE ADMINISTERED BY QUALIFIED MEDICAL PERSONNEL.

REACTIVITY

REACTIVITY: STABLE UNDER NORMAL TEMPERATURES AND PRESSURES.
INCOMPATIBILITIES: MERCURIC CHLORIDE: POTASSIUM: STRONG EXPLOSION ON IMPACT. SODIUM: STRONG EXPLOSION ON IMPACT.
DECOMPOSITION: THERMAL DECOMPOSITION MAY RELEASE CORROSIVE HYDROGEN CHLORIDE.
POLYMERIZATION: HAZARDOUS POLYMERIZATION HAS NOT BEEN REPORTED TO OCCUR UNDER NORMAL TEMPERATURES AND PRESSURES.

STORAGE AND DISPOSAL

OBSERVE ALL FEDERAL, STATE AND LOCAL REGULATIONS WHEN STORING OR DISPOSING OF THIS SUBSTANCE. FOR ASSISTANCE, CONTACT THE DISTRICT DIRECTOR OF THE ENVIRONMENTAL PROTECTION AGENCY.

STORAGE

THRESHOLD PLANNING QUANTITY (TPQ): THE SUPERFUND AMENDMENTS AND REAUTHORIZATION ACT (SARA) SECTION 302 REQUIRES THAT EACH FACILITY WHERE ANY EXTREMELY HAZARDOUS SUBSTANCE IS PRESENT IN A QUANTITY EQUAL TO OR GREATER THAN THE TPQ ESTABLISHED FOR THAT SUBSTANCE NOTIFY THE STATE EMERGENCY RESPONSE COMMISSION FOR THE STATE IN WHICH IT IS LOCATED. SECTION 303 OF SARA REQUIRES THESE FACILITIES TO PARTICIPATE IN LOCAL EMERGENCY RESPONSE PLANNING (40 CFR 355.30).

DISPOSAL

MERCURY - REGULATORY LEVEL: 0.2 MG/L MATERIALS WHICH CONTAIN THE ABOVE SUBSTANCE AT OR ABOVE THE REGULATORY LEVEL MEET THE EPA CHARACTERISTIC OF TOXICITY, AND MUST BE DISPOSED OF IN ACCORDANCE WITH 40 CFR PART 262. EPA HAZARDOUS WASTE NUMBER D009.

CONDITIONS TO AVOID

MAY BURN BUT DOES NOT IGNITE READILY.

SPILL AND LEAK PROCEDURES

WATER SPILL: THE CALIFORNIA SAFE DRINKING WATER AND TOXIC ENFORCEMENT ACT OF 1986 (PROPOSITION 65) PROHIBITS CONTAMINATING ANY KNOWN SOURCE OF DRINKING WATER WITH SUBSTANCES KNOWN TO CAUSE CANCER AND/OR REPRODUCTIVE TOXICITY.

OCCUPATIONAL SPILL: DO NOT TOUCH SPILLED MATERIAL. STOP LEAK IF YOU CAN DO IT WITHOUT RISK. FOR SMALL SPILLS, TAKE UP WITH SAND OR OTHER ABSORBENT MATERIAL AND PLACE INTO CONTAINERS FOR LATER DISPOSAL. FOR SMALL DRY SPILLS, WITH A CLEAN SHOVEL PLACE MATERIAL INTO CLEAN, DRY CONTAINER AND COVER. MOVE CONTAINERS FROM SPILL AREA. FOR LARGER SPILLS, DIKE FAR AHEAD OF SPILL FOR LATER DISPOSAL. KEEP UNNECESSARY PEOPLE AWAY. ISOLATE HAZARD AREA AND DENY ENTRY.

REPORTABLE QUANTITY (RQ): 1 POUND THE SUPERFUND AMENDMENTS AND REAUTHORIZATION ACT (SARA) SECTION 304 REQUIRES THAT A RELEASE EQUAL TO OR GREATER THAN THE REPORTABLE QUANTITY FOR THIS SUBSTANCE BE IMMEDIATELY REPORTED TO THE LOCAL EMERGENCY PLANNING COMMITTEE AND THE STATE EMERGENCY RESPONSE COMMISSION (40 CFR 355.40). IF THE RELEASE OF THIS SUBSTANCE IS REPORTABLE UNDER CERCLA SECTION 103, THE NATIONAL RESPONSE CENTER MUST BE NOTIFIED IMMEDIATELY AT (800) 424-8802 OR (202) 426-2675 IN THE METROPOLITAN WASHINGTON, D.C. AREA (40 CFR 302.6).

PROTECTIVE EQUIPMENT

VENTILATION: PROVIDE LOCAL EXHAUST VENTILATION SYSTEM TO MEET PUBLISHED EXPOSURE LIMITS.

RESPIRATOR: THE FOLLOWING RESPIRATORS AND MAXIMUM USE CONCENTRATIONS ARE RECOMMENDATIONS BY THE U.S. DEPARTMENT OF HEALTH AND HUMAN SERVICES, NIOSH POCKET GUIDE TO CHEMICAL HAZARDS; NIOSH CRITERIA DOCUMENTS OR BY THE U.S. DEPARTMENT OF LABOR, 29 CFR 1910 SUBPART Z. THE SPECIFIC RESPIRATOR SELECTED MUST BE BASED ON CONTAMINATION LEVELS FOUND IN THE WORK PLACE, MUST NOT EXCEED THE WORKING LIMITS OF THE RESPIRATOR AND BE JOINTLY APPROVED BY THE NATIONAL INSTITUTE FOR OCCUPATIONAL SAFETY AND HEALTH AND THE MINE SAFETY AND HEALTH ADMINISTRATION (NIOSH-MSHA).

MERCURY, ALL FORMS EXCEPT ALKYL (AS HG):

0.5 MG/M3- ANY AIR-PURIFYING RESPIRATOR WITH A HIGH-EFFICIENCY PARTICULATE FILTER. ANY SUPPLIED-AIR RESPIRATOR. ANY SELF-CONTAINED BREATHING APPARATUS.

1.25 MG/M3- ANY SUPPLIED-AIR RESPIRATOR OPERATED IN A CONTINUOUS FLOW MODE. ANY POWERED AIR-PURIFYING RESPIRATOR WITH A HIGH-EFFICIENCY PARTICULATE FILTER.

2.5 MG/M3- ANY SUPPLIED-AIR RESPIRATOR WITH A FULL FACEPIECE. ANY SELF-CONTAINED BREATHING APPARATUS WITH A FULL FACEPIECE. ANY AIR-PURIFYING FULL FACEPIECE RESPIRATOR WITH A HIGH-EFFICIENCY PARTICULATE FILTER. ANY POWERED AIR-PURIFYING RESPIRATOR WITH A TIGHT-FITTING FACEPIECE AND A HIGH-EFFICIENCY PARTICULATE FILTER. ANY SUPPLIED-AIR RESPIRATOR WITH A TIGHT-FITTING FACEPIECE OPERATED IN A CONTINUOUS FLOW MODE.

28 MG/M3- ANY SUPPLIED-AIR RESPIRATOR WITH A HALF-MASK AND OPERATED IN A PRESSURE-DEMAND OR OTHER POSITIVE PRESSURE MODE.

ESCAPE- ANY AIR-PURIFYING FULL FACEPIECE RESPIRATOR WITH A HIGH-EFFICIENCY PARTICULATE FILTER. ANY APPROPRIATE ESCAPE-TYPE SELF-CONTAINED BREATHING APPARATUS.

FOR FIREFIGHTING AND OTHER IMMEDIATELY DANGEROUS TO LIFE OR HEALTH CONDITIONS:

SELF-CONTAINED BREATHING APPARATUS WITH FULL FACEPIECE OPERATED IN PRESSURE-DEMAND OR OTHER POSITIVE PRESSURE MODE.

SUPPLIED-AIR RESPIRATOR WITH FULL FACEPIECE AND OPERATED IN PRESSURE-DEMAND OR OTHER POSITIVE PRESSURE MODE IN COMBINATION WITH AN AUXILIARY SELF-CONTAINED BREATHING APPARATUS OPERATED IN PRESSURE-DEMAND OR OTHER POSITIVE PRESSURE MODE.

CLOTHING: EMPLOYEE MUST WEAR APPROPRIATE PROTECTIVE (IMPERVIOUS) CLOTHING AND EQUIPMENT TO PREVENT REPEATED OR PROLONGED SKIN CONTACT WITH THIS SUBSTANCE.

GLOVES: EMPLOYEE MUST WEAR APPROPRIATE PROTECTIVE GLOVES TO PREVENT CONTACT WITH THIS SUBSTANCE.

EYE PROTECTION: EMPLOYEE MUST WEAR SPLASH-PROOF OR DUST-RESISTANT SAFETY GOGGLES AND A FACESHIELD TO PREVENT CONTACT WITH THIS SUBSTANCE.

EMERGENCY WASH FACILITIES: WHERE THERE IS ANY POSSIBILITY THAT AN EMPLOYEE'S EYES AND/OR SKIN MAY BE EXPOSED TO THIS SUBSTANCE, THE EMPLOYER SHOULD PROVIDE AN EYE WASH FOUNTAIN AND QUICK DRENCH SHOWER WITHIN THE IMMEDIATE WORK AREA FOR EMERGENCY USE.

AUTHORIZED BY- OCCUPATIONAL HEALTH SERVICES, INC.
CREATION DATE: 10/04/89 ***REVISION DATE:*** 07/13/90

MATERIAL SAFETY DATA SHEET

OCCUPATIONAL HEALTH SERVICES, INC.
AGRICULTURE AND PESTICIDE DIVISION
450 SEVENTH AVENUE, SUITE 2407
NEW YORK, NEW YORK 10123
1-800-445-MSDS OR (212) 967-1100

EMERGENCY CONTACT:
JOHN S. BRANSFORD, JR. (615) 292-1180

SUBSTANCE IDENTIFICATION

CAS-NUMBER 108-62-3

SUBSTANCE: METALDEHYDE

TRADE NAMES/SYNONYMS: 2,4,6,8-TETRAMETHYL-1,3,5,7-TETROXOCANE; ANTIMILACE; ACETALDEHYDE, TETRAMER; ARIOTOX; CORRY'S SLUG DEATH; HALIZAN; CEKUMETA; META; METACETALDEHYDE; METASON; NAMEKIL; SLUG-TOX; UN 1332; PST14090

CHEMICAL FAMILY: ALDEHYDE, HETEROCYCLIC

MOLECULAR FORMULA: C8-H16-O4

MOLECULAR WEIGHT: 176.24

CERCLA RATINGS (SCALE 0-3): HEALTH=2 FIRE=3 REACTIVITY=1 PERSISTENCE=0

NFPA RATINGS (SCALE 0-4): HEALTH=1 FIRE=3 REACTIVITY=1

COMPONENTS AND CONTAMINANTS

COMPONENT: METALDEHYDE ***PERCENT:*** 100.00
CAS# 108-62-3

EXPOSURE LIMITS: NO OCCUPATIONAL EXPOSURE LIMITS ESTABLISHED BY OSHA, ACGIH, OR NIOSH.

PHYSICAL DATA

DESCRIPTION: WHITE CRYSTALLINE POWDER WITH AN ALDEHYDE ODOR

BOILING POINT: 234-239 F(112-115 C) ***MELTING POINT:*** 475 F (246 C)

SPECIFIC GRAVITY: 1.27 ***SOLUBILITY IN WATER:*** INSOLUBLE

SOLVENT SOLUBILITY: BENZENE, CHLOROFORM

FIRE AND EXPLOSION DATA

FIRE AND EXPLOSION HAZARD: DANGEROUS FIRE HAZARD WHEN EXPOSED TO HEAT OR FLAME.

DUST-AIR MIXTURES MAY IGNITE OR EXPLODE.

FLASH POINT: 97 F 36 C (CC)

FIREFIGHTING MEDIA: DRY CHEMICAL, SAND, WATER SPRAY OR FOAM (1987 EMERGENCY RESPONSE GUIDEBOOK, DOT P 5800.4).

FOR LARGER FIRES, USE WATER SPRAY, FOG OR STANDARD FOAM (1987 EMERGENCY RESPONSE GUIDEBOOK, DOT P 5800.4).

FIREFIGHTING: MOVE CONTAINER FROM FIRE AREA IF POSSIBLE. COOL CONTAINERS EXPOSED TO FLAME WITH WATER FROM SIDE UNTIL WELL AFTER FIRE IS OUT. STAY AWAY FROM STORAGE TANK ENDS. FOR MASSIVE FIRE IN CARGO AREA, USE UNMANNED HOSE HOLDER OR MONITOR NOZZLES; ELSE WITHDRAW AND LET FIRE BURN (1987 EMERGENCY RESPONSE GUIDEBOOK, DOT P 5800.4, GUIDE PAGE 32).

EXTINGUISH USING AGENT FOR TYPE OF FIRE. AVOID BREATHING FUMES FROM BURNING MATERIAL.

TRANSPORTATION DATA

DEPARTMENT OF TRANSPORTATION HAZARD CLASSIFICATION 49 CFR 172.101: FLAMMABLE SOLID
DEPARTMENT OF TRANSPORTATION LABELING REQUIREMENTS 49 CFR 172.101 AND SUBPART E: FLAMMABLE SOLID
DEPARTMENT OF TRANSPORTATION PACKAGING REQUIREMENTS: 49 CFR 173.154 EXCEPTIONS: 49 CFR 173.153

TOXICITY

METALDEHYDE: TOXICITY DATA: 203 MG/M3/4 HOURS INHALATION-RAT LC50; 348 MG/M3/2 HOURS INHALATION-MOUSE LC50; 2275 MG/KG SKIN-RAT LD50; 100 MG/KG ORAL-CHILD LDLO; 227 MG/KG ORAL-RAT LD50; 200 MG/KG ORAL-MOUSE LD50; 290 MG/KG ORAL-RABBIT LD50; 175 MG/KG ORAL-GUINEA PIG LD50; 207 MG/KG ORAL-CAT LD50; 600 MG/KG ORAL-DOG LD50; 600 MG/KG UNREPORTED-MAMMAL LD50; MUTAGENIC DATA (RTECS); REPRODUCTIVE EFFECTS DATA (RTECS). CARCINOGEN STATUS: NONE. LOCAL EFFECTS: IRRITANT- INHALATION, SKIN, AND EYES. ACUTE TOXICITY LEVEL: HIGHLY TOXIC BY INHALATION, TOXIC BY INGESTION, AND SLIGHTLY TOXIC BY DERMAL ABSORPTION. TARGET EFFECTS: CONVULSANT. POISONING MAY AFFECT THE LIVER AND KIDNEYS.

HEALTH EFFECTS AND FIRST AID

INHALATION: METALDEHYDE: IRRITANT. **ACUTE EXPOSURE-** EXPOSURE TO VAPORS OF THIS MATERIAL MAY CAUSE SEVERE IRRITATION OF THE MUCOUS MEMBRANES. **CHRONIC EXPOSURE-** NO DATA AVAILABLE.
FIRST AID- REMOVE FROM EXPOSURE AREA TO FRESH AIR IMMEDIATELY. IF BREATHING HAS STOPPED, PERFORM ARTIFICIAL RESPIRATION. KEEP PERSON WARM AND AT REST. TREAT SYMPTOMATICALLY AND SUPPORTIVELY. GET MEDICAL ATTENTION IMMEDIATELY.

SKIN CONTACT: METALDEHYDE: IRRITANT. **ACUTE EXPOSURE-** DIRECT CONTACT MAY RESULT IN IRRITATION. **CHRONIC EXPOSURE-** REPEATED OR PROLONGED EXPOSURE MAY RESULT IN DERMATITIS.
FIRST AID- REMOVE CONTAMINATED CLOTHING AND SHOES IMMEDIATELY. WASH AFFECTED AREA WITH SOAP OR MILD DETERGENT AND LARGE AMOUNTS OF WATER UNTIL NO EVIDENCE OF CHEMICAL REMAINS (APPROXIMATELY 15-20 MINUTES). GET MEDICAL ATTENTION IMMEDIATELY.

EYE CONTACT: METALDEHYDE: IRRITANT. **ACUTE EXPOSURE-** DIRECT CONTACT MAY CAUSE REDNESS AND IRRITATION. **CHRONIC EXPOSURE-** PROLONGED OR REPEATED EXPOSURE MAY CAUSE CONJUNCTIVITIS.
FIRST AID- WASH EYES IMMEDIATELY WITH LARGE AMOUNTS OF WATER OR NORMAL SALINE, OCCASIONALLY LIFTING UPPER AND LOWER LIDS, UNTIL NO EVIDENCE OF CHEMICAL REMAINS (APPROXIMATELY 15-20 MINUTES). GET MEDICAL ATTENTION IMMEDIATELY.

INGESTION: METALDEHYDE: CONVULSANT/TOXIC. **ACUTE EXPOSURE-** THIS MATERIAL IS DECOMPOSED SLOWLY TO ACETALDEHYDE IN THE BODY. INGESTION OF LESS THAN 50 MG/KG MAY CAUSE NAUSEA, RETCHING, SEVERE VOMITING, ABDOMINAL PAIN, TEMPERATURE ELEVATION, MUSCULAR RIGIDITY, AND HYPERVENTILATION. INGESTION OF MORE THAN 100 MG/KG CAUSES HYPERREFLEXIA, CONVULSIONS, AND COMA. DEATH FROM RESPIRATORY FAILURE CAN OCCUR UP TO 48 HOURS AFTER INGESTION. LIVER AND KIDNEY INJURY ALSO OCCURS. THE ONSET OF SYMPTOMS MAY BE DELAYED FOR 1 TO 3 HOURS. MENTAL DEFICITS FROM POISONING MAY PERSIST FOR A YEAR OR MORE. **CHRONIC EXPOSURE-** A THREE-GENERATION STUDY ON THE EFFECT OF CHRONIC INGESTION OF THIS MATERIAL IN RATS, RESULTED IN ADVERSE EFFECTS ON MALE AND FEMALE REPRODUCTION AND THE SURVIVAL RATE OF THE OFFSPRING.
FIRST AID- REMOVE POISON BY GASTRIC LAVAGE OR EMESIS. GASTRIC LAVAGE WITH 2-5% SODIUM BICARBONATE SOLUTION WILL REDUCE CONVERSION TO ACETALDEHYDE. ACTIVATED CHARCOAL IS USEFUL. FOLLOW WITH SALINE CATHARSIS. GASTRIC LAVAGE AND CATHARSIS ARE EFFECTIVE UP TO 12-24 HOURS AFTER POISONING. MAINTAIN AIRWAY AND RESPIRATION. GIVE OXYGEN IF RESPIRATION IS DEPRESSED. DO NOT PERFORM GASTRIC LAVAGE OR EMESIS IF VICTIM IS UNCONSCIOUS. GET MEDICAL ATTENTION IMMEDIATELY. (DREISBACH, HANDBOOK OF POISONING, 11TH EDITION) ADMINISTRATION OF GASTRIC LAVAGE OR OXYGEN SHOULD BE PERFORMED BY QUALIFIED MEDICAL PERSONNEL.
ANTIDOTE: NO SPECIFIC ANTIDOTE. TREAT SYMPTOMATICALLY AND SUPPORTIVELY.

REACTIVITY

REACTIVITY: METALDEHYDE: MAY DECOMPOSE UPON HEATING. ***INCOMPATIBILITIES:*** METALDEHYDE: STRONG OXIDANTS: MAY REACT. ACIDS: MAY SLOWLY DECOMPOSE INTO ACETALDEHYDE.
DECOMPOSITION: METALDEHYDE: THERMAL DECOMPOSITION MAY RELEASE TOXIC OXIDES OF CARBON.
POLYMERIZATION: HAZARDOUS POLYMERIZATION HAS NOT BEEN REPORTED TO OCCUR UNDER NORMAL TEMPERATURES AND PRESSURES.

CONDITIONS TO AVOID

AVOID CONTACT WITH HEAT, SPARKS, FLAMES OR OTHER SOURCES OF IGNITION. MATERIAL IS EXTREMELY FLAMMABLE AND MAY BURN RAPIDLY WITH FLARE-BURNING EFFECT.

SPILL AND LEAK PROCEDURES

OCCUPATIONAL SPILL: SHUT OFF IGNITION SOURCES. DO NOT TOUCH SPILLED MATERIAL. FOR SMALL SPILLS, WITH CLEAN SHOVEL, PLACE MATERIAL INTO CLEAN, DRY CONTAINER AND COVER; MOVE CONTAINERS FROM SPILL AREA. FOR LARGER SPILLS, WET DOWN WITH WATER AND DIKE FOR LATER DISPOSAL. NO SMOKING, FLAMES OR FLARES IN HAZARD AREA! KEEP UNNECESSARY PEOPLE AWAY. ISOLATE HAZARD AREA AND DENY ENTRY.

PROTECTIVE EQUIPMENT

VENTILATION: PROVIDE LOCAL EXHAUST OR GENERAL DILUTION VENTILATION. VENTILATION EQUIPMENT MUST BE EXPLOSION-PROOF.
RESPIRATOR: THE FOLLOWING RESPIRATORS ARE RECOMMENDED BASED ON INFORMATION FOUND IN THE PHYSICAL DATA, TOXICITY AND HEALTH EFFECTS SECTIONS. THEY ARE RANKED IN ORDER FROM MINIMUM TO MAXIMUM RESPIRATORY PROTECTION. THE SPECIFIC RESPIRATOR SELECTED MUST BE BASED ON CONTAMINATION LEVELS FOUND IN THE WORK PLACE, MUST NOT EXCEED THE WORKING LIMITS OF THE RESPIRATOR AND BE JOINTLY APPROVED BY THE NATIONAL INSTITUTE FOR OCCUPATIONAL SAFETY AND HEALTH AND THE MINE SAFETY AND HEALTH ADMINISTRATION (NIOSH-MSHA).
DUST AND MIST RESPIRATOR WITH A FULL FACEPIECE.
AIR-PURIFYING FULL FACEPIECE RESPIRATOR WITH A HIGH-EFFICIENCY PARTICULATE FILTER.
POWERED AIR-PURIFYING RESPIRATOR WITH A TIGHT-FITTING FACEPIECE AND HIGH-EFFICIENCY PARTICULATE FILTER.
TYPE 'C' SUPPLIED-AIR RESPIRATOR WITH A FULL FACEPIECE OPERATED IN PRESSURE-DEMAND OR OTHER POSITIVE PRESSURE MODE OR WITH A FULL FACEPIECE, HELMET OR HOOD OPERATED IN CONTINUOUS-FLOW MODE.
SELF-CONTAINED BREATHING APPARATUS WITH A FULL FACEPIECE OPERATED IN PRESSURE-DEMAND OR OTHER POSITIVE PRESSURE MODE.
FOR FIREFIGHTING AND OTHER IMMEDIATELY DANGEROUS TO LIFE OR HEALTH CONDITIONS:
SELF-CONTAINED BREATHING APPARATUS WITH FULL FACEPIECE OPERATED IN PRESSURE-DEMAND OR OTHER POSITIVE PRESSURE MODE.
SUPPLIED-AIR RESPIRATOR WITH FULL FACEPIECE AND OPERATED IN PRESSURE-DEMAND OR OTHER POSITIVE PRESSURE MODE IN COMBINATION WITH AN AUXILIARY SELF-CONTAINED BREATHING APPARATUS OPERATED IN PRESSURE-DEMAND OR OTHER POSITIVE PRESSURE MODE.
CLOTHING: EMPLOYEE MUST WEAR APPROPRIATE PROTECTIVE (IMPERVIOUS) CLOTHING AND EQUIPMENT TO PREVENT REPEATED OR PROLONGED SKIN CONTACT WITH THIS SUBSTANCE.
GLOVES: EMPLOYEE MUST WEAR APPROPRIATE PROTECTIVE GLOVES TO PREVENT CONTACT WITH THIS SUBSTANCE.
EYE PROTECTION: EMPLOYEE MUST WEAR SPLASH-PROOF OR DUST-RESISTANT SAFETY GOGGLES AND A FACESHIELD TO PREVENT CONTACT WITH THIS SUBSTANCE.
EMERGENCY WASH FACILITIES: WHERE THERE IS ANY POSSIBILITY THAT AN EMPLOYEE'S EYES AND/OR SKIN MAY BE EXPOSED TO THIS SUBSTANCE, THE EMPLOYER SHOULD PROVIDE AN EYE WASH FOUNTAIN AND QUICK DRENCH SHOWER WITHIN THE IMMEDIATE WORK AREA FOR EMERGENCY USE.

AUTHORIZED BY- OCCUPATIONAL HEALTH SERVICES, INC.
CREATION DATE: 10/04/89 ***REVISION DATE:*** 05/29/90

MATERIAL SAFETY DATA SHEET

OCCUPATIONAL HEALTH SERVICES, INC.
AGRICULTURE AND PESTICIDE DIVISION
450 SEVENTH AVENUE, SUITE 2407
NEW YORK, NEW YORK 10123
1-800-445-MSDS OR (212) 967-1100

EMERGENCY CONTACT:
JOHN S. BRANSFORD, JR. (615) 292-1180

SUBSTANCE IDENTIFICATION

CAS-NUMBER 41394-05-2
SUBSTANCE: **METAMITRON**

TRADE NAMES/SYNONYMS: 4-AMINO-3-METHYL-6-PHENYL-1,2,4-TRIAZINE-5(4H)-ONE; 1,2,4-TRIAZINE-5-(4H)-ONE, 4-AMINO-3-METHYL-6-PHENYL-; 4-AMINO-4,5-DIHYDRO-3-METHYL-6-PHENYL-1,2,4-TRIAZIN-5-ONE; 4-AMINO-3-METHYL-6-PHENYL-1,2,4-TRIAZIN-5(4H)-ONE; GOLTIX; DRW-1139; BAY-DRW 1139; C10H10N4O; PST14095
CHEMICAL FAMILY: TRIAZINE
KETONE
MOLECULAR FORMULA: C10-H10-N4-O
MOLECULAR WEIGHT: 202.22
CERCLA RATINGS (SCALE 0-3): HEALTH = 2 FIRE = 1 REACTIVITY = 0 PERSISTENCE = 2
NFPA RATINGS (SCALE 0-4): HEALTH = 2 FIRE = 1 REACTIVITY = 0

COMPONENTS AND CONTAMINANTS

COMPONENT: METAMITRON ***PERCENT:*** 100
CAS# 41394-05-2
OTHER CONTAMINANTS: NONE
EXPOSURE LIMITS: NO OCCUPATIONAL EXPOSURE LIMITS ESTABLISHED BY OSHA, ACGIH, OR NIOSH.

PHYSICAL DATA

DESCRIPTION: CRYSTALLINE SOLID ***MELTING POINT:*** 329-333 F (165-167 C)
SPECIFIC GRAVITY: NOT AVAILABLE. ***VAPOR PRESSURE:*** 0.000075 MMHG @ 20 C
SOLUBILITY IN WATER: 0.18%
SOLVENT SOLUBILITY: SOLUBLE IN ACETONE, METHANOL, CHLOROFORM, CYCLOHEXANONE

FIRE AND EXPLOSION DATA

FIRE AND EXPLOSION HAZARD: SLIGHT FIRE HAZARD WHEN EXPOSED TO HEAT OR FLAME.
FIREFIGHTING MEDIA: DRY CHEMICAL, CARBON DIOXIDE, HALON, WATER SPRAY OR STANDARD FOAM (1987 EMERGENCY RESPONSE GUIDEBOOK, DOT P 5800.4).
FOR LARGER FIRES, USE WATER SPRAY, FOG OR STANDARD FOAM (1987 EMERGENCY RESPONSE GUIDEBOOK, DOT P 5800.4).
FIREFIGHTING: MOVE CONTAINERS FROM FIRE AREA IF POSSIBLE (1987 EMERGENCY RESPONSE GUIDEBOOK, DOT P 5800.4, GUIDE PAGE 53).
EXTINGUISH USING AGENTS SUITABLE FOR SURROUNDING FIRE. USE FLOODING QUANTITIES OF WATER AS A FOG. KEEP MATERIAL OUT OF SEWERS AND WATER SOURCES. DO NOT TOUCH SPILLED MATERIAL. AVOID BREATHING HAZARDOUS FUMES; KEEP UPWIND.

TOXICITY

METAMITRON: TOXICITY DATA: >0.33 MG/L INHALATION-RAT LC50 (85JFAN); >1000 MG/KG SKIN-RAT LD50 (FMCHA2); 1447 MG/KG ORAL-RAT LD50; 1450 MG/KG ORAL-MOUSE LD50; MUTAGENIC DATA (RTECS). CARCINOGEN STATUS: NONE. ACUTE TOXICITY LEVEL: MODERATELY TOXIC BY INGESTION. TARGET EFFECTS: NO DATA AVAILABLE.

HEALTH EFFECTS AND FIRST AID

INHALATION: METAMITRON: **ACUTE EXPOSURE**- THE LETHAL DOSE REPORTED IN RATS WAS GREATER THAN 0.33 MG/L. **CHRONIC EXPOSURE**- NO DATA AVAILABLE.
FIRST AID- REMOVE FROM EXPOSURE AREA TO FRESH AIR IMMEDIATELY. IF BREATHING HAS STOPPED, PERFORM ARTIFICIAL RESPIRATION. KEEP PERSON WARM AND AT REST. TREAT SYMPTOMATICALLY AND SUPPORTIVELY. GET MEDICAL ATTENTION IMMEDIATELY.

SKIN CONTACT: METAMITRON: **ACUTE EXPOSURE**- A LETHAL DOSE IN RATS BY DERMAL ABSORPTION IS GREATER THAN 1000 MG/KG. **CHRONIC EXPOSURE**- NO DATA AVAILABLE.
FIRST AID- REMOVE CONTAMINATED CLOTHING AND SHOES IMMEDIATELY. WASH AFFECTED AREA WITH SOAP OR MILD DETERGENT AND LARGE AMOUNTS OF WATER UNTIL NO EVIDENCE OF CHEMICAL REMAINS (APPROXIMATELY 15-20 MINUTES). GET MEDICAL ATTENTION IMMEDIATELY.

EYE CONTACT: METAMITRON: **ACUTE EXPOSURE**- NO DATA AVAILABLE. **CHRONIC EXPOSURE**- NO DATA AVAILABLE.
FIRST AID- WASH EYES IMMEDIATELY WITH LARGE AMOUNTS OF WATER OR NORMAL SALINE, OCCASIONALLY LIFTING UPPER AND LOWER LIDS, UNTIL NO EVIDENCE OF CHEMICAL REMAINS (APPROXIMATELY 15-20 MINUTES). GET MEDICAL ATTENTION IMMEDIATELY.

INGESTION: METAMITRON: **ACUTE EXPOSURE**- A LETHAL DOSE IN RATS WAS 1447 MG/KG; NO SYMPTOMS WERE REPORTED. **CHRONIC EXPOSURE**- NO ADVERSE EFFECTS WERE OBSERVED IN DOGS FED 500 PPM FOR 3 MONTHS.
FIRST AID- REMOVE BY GASTRIC LAVAGE AND CATHARSIS. MAINTAIN BLOOD PRESSURE AND AIRWAY. GIVE OXYGEN IF RESPIRATION IS DEPRESSED. DO NOT PERFORM GASTRIC LAVAGE IF VICTIM IS UNCONSCIOUS. GET MEDICAL ATTENTION IMMEDIATELY (DREISBACH, HANDBOOK OF POISONING, 12TH ED.).
ADMINISTRATION OF LAVAGE OR OXYGEN SHOULD BE PERFORMED BY QUALIFIED MEDICAL PERSONNEL.
ANTIDOTE: NO SPECIFIC ANTIDOTE. TREAT SYMPTOMATICALLY AND SUPPORTIVELY.

REACTIVITY

REACTIVITY: STABLE UNDER NORMAL TEMPERATURES AND PRESSURES.
INCOMPATIBILITIES: METAMITRON: ALKALINE SOLUTIONS: DECOMPOSES. OXIDIZERS (STRONG): FIRE AND EXPLOSION HAZARD.
DECOMPOSITION: THERMAL DECOMPOSITION PRODUCTS MAY INCLUDE TOXIC OXIDES OF CARBON AND NITROGEN.
POLYMERIZATION: HAZARDOUS POLYMERIZATION HAS NOT BEEN REPORTED TO OCCUR UNDER NORMAL TEMPERATURES AND PRESSURES.

STORAGE AND DISPOSAL

OBSERVE ALL FEDERAL, STATE AND LOCAL REGULATIONS WHEN STORING OR DISPOSING OF THIS SUBSTANCE. FOR ASSISTANCE, CONTACT THE DISTRICT DIRECTOR OF THE ENVIRONMENTAL PROTECTION AGENCY.

STORAGE

STORE IN ACCORDANCE WITH 40 CFR 165 RECOMMENDED PROCEDURES FOR THE DISPOSAL AND STORAGE OF PESTICIDES AND PESTICIDE CONTAINERS.
STORE AWAY FROM INCOMPATIBLE SUBSTANCES.

DISPOSAL

DISPOSAL MUST BE IN ACCORDANCE WITH 40 CFR 165 RECOMMENDED PROCEDURES FOR THE DISPOSAL AND STORAGE OF PESTICIDES AND PESTICIDE CONTAINERS.

CONDITIONS TO AVOID

MAY BURN BUT DOES NOT IGNITE READILY.

SPILL AND LEAK PROCEDURES

OCCUPATIONAL SPILL: DO NOT TOUCH SPILLED MATERIAL. STOP LEAK IF YOU CAN DO IT WITHOUT RISK. FOR SMALL SPILLS, TAKE UP WITH SAND OR OTHER ABSORBENT MATERIAL AND PLACE INTO CONTAINERS FOR LATER DISPOSAL. FOR SMALL DRY SPILLS, WITH A CLEAN SHOVEL PLACE MATERIAL INTO CLEAN, DRY CONTAINER AND COVER. MOVE CONTAINERS FROM SPILL AREA. FOR LARGER SPILLS, DIKE FAR AHEAD OF SPILL FOR LATER DISPOSAL. KEEP UNNECESSARY PEOPLE AWAY. ISOLATE HAZARD AREA AND DENY ENTRY.

PROTECTIVE EQUIPMENT

VENTILATION: PROVIDE LOCAL EXHAUST OR GENERAL DILUTION VENTILATION SYSTEM.
RESPIRATOR: THE FOLLOWING RESPIRATORS ARE RECOMMENDED BASED ON INFORMATION FOUND IN THE PHYSICAL DATA, TOXICITY AND HEALTH EFFECTS SECTIONS. THEY ARE RANKED IN ORDER FROM MINIMUM TO MAXIMUM RESPIRATORY PROTECTION. THE SPECIFIC RESPIRATOR SELECTED MUST BE BASED ON CONTAMINATION LEVELS FOUND IN THE WORK PLACE, MUST NOT EXCEED THE WORKING LIMITS OF THE RESPIRATOR AND BE JOINTLY APPROVED BY THE NATIONAL INSTITUTE FOR OCCUPATIONAL SAFETY AND HEALTH AND THE MINE SAFETY AND HEALTH ADMINISTRATION (NIOSH-MSHA).
CHEMICAL CARTRIDGE RESPIRATOR WITH AN ORGANIC VAPOR CARTRIDGE(S) WITH A FULL FACEPIECE AND ORGANIC VAPOR CARTRIDGE(S) IN COMBINATION WITH A DUST AND MIST FILTER.
POWERED AIR-PURIFYING RESPIRATOR WITH A TIGHT-FITTING FACEPIECE AND ORGANIC VAPOR CARTRIDGE(S) IN COMBINATION WITH A HIGH-EFFICIENCY PARTICULATE FILTER.
TYPE 'C' SUPPLIED-AIR RESPIRATOR WITH A FULL FACEPIECE OPERATED IN A PRESSURE-DEMAND OR OTHER POSITIVE PRESSURE MODE.
SELF-CONTAINED BREATHING APPARATUS WITH A FULL FACEPIECE OPERATED IN PRESSURE-DEMAND OR OTHER POSITIVE PRESSURE MODE.
FOR FIREFIGHTING AND OTHER IMMEDIATELY DANGEROUS TO LIFE OR HEALTH CONDITIONS:
SELF-CONTAINED BREATHING APPARATUS WITH FULL FACEPIECE OPERATED IN PRESSURE-DEMAND OR OTHER POSITIVE PRESSURE MODE.
SUPPLIED-AIR RESPIRATOR WITH FULL FACEPIECE AND OPERATED IN PRESSURE-DEMAND OR OTHER POSITIVE PRESSURE MODE IN COMBINATION WITH AN AUXILIARY SELF-CONTAINED BREATHING APPARATUS OPERATED IN PRESSURE-DEMAND OR OTHER POSITIVE PRESSURE MODE.
CLOTHING: EMPLOYEE MUST WEAR APPROPRIATE PROTECTIVE (IMPERVIOUS) CLOTHING AND EQUIPMENT TO PREVENT REPEATED OR PROLONGED SKIN CONTACT WITH THIS SUBSTANCE.
GLOVES: EMPLOYEE MUST WEAR APPROPRIATE PROTECTIVE GLOVES TO PREVENT CONTACT WITH THIS SUBSTANCE.
EYE PROTECTION: EMPLOYEE MUST WEAR SPLASH-PROOF OR DUST-RESISTANT SAFETY GOGGLES TO PREVENT EYE CONTACT WITH THIS SUBSTANCE.
EMERGENCY EYE WASH: WHERE THERE IS ANY POSSIBILITY THAT AN EMPLOYEE'S

EYES MAY BE EXPOSED TO THIS SUBSTANCE, THE EMPLOYER SHOULD PROVIDE AN EYE WASH FOUNTAIN WITHIN THE IMMEDIATE WORK AREA FOR EMERGENCY USE.

AUTHORIZED BY- OCCUPATIONAL HEALTH SERVICES, INC.
CREATION DATE: 10/04/89 ***REVISION DATE:*** 05/07/90

MATERIAL SAFETY DATA SHEET

OCCUPATIONAL HEALTH SERVICES, INC.
AGRICULTURE AND PESTICIDE DIVISION
450 SEVENTH AVENUE, SUITE 2407
NEW YORK, NEW YORK 10123
1-800-445-MSDS OR (212) 967-1100

EMERGENCY CONTACT:
JOHN S. BRANSFORD, JR. (615) 292-1180

SUBSTANCE IDENTIFICATION

CAS-NUMBER 2674-91-1
SUBSTANCE: METASYSTOX-S
TRADE NAMES/SYNONYMS: PHOSPHOROTHIOIC ACID, S-(2-(ETHYLSULFINYL)-1-METHYLETHYL) O,O-DIMETHYL ESTER; S-2-ETHYLSULPHINYL-1-METHYLETHYL O,O-DIMETHYL PHOSPHOROTHIOATE; S-2-ETHYLSULFINYL-1-METHYLETHYL O,O-DIMETHYL PHOSPHOROTHIOATE; S-(2-(ETHYLSULFINYL)-1-METHYLETHYL) O,O-DIMETHYL PHOSPHOROTHIOATE; DIMETHYL S-(2-ETHYLSULFINYLISOPROPYL) PHOSPHOROTHIOLATE; BAY 23655; ESP; ESTOX; OXYDEPROFOS; S 410; THIOMETAN; ENT 25,674; PST14105
CHEMICAL FAMILY: ORGANOPHOSPHATE
MOLECULAR FORMULA: C7-H17-O4-P-S2
MOLECULAR WEIGHT: 261.33
CERCLA RATINGS (SCALE 0-3): HEALTH=3 FIRE=U REACTIVITY=0 PERSISTENCE=0
NFPA RATINGS (SCALE 0-4): HEALTH=3 FIRE=U REACTIVITY=0

COMPONENTS AND CONTAMINANTS

COMPONENT: METASYSTOX S ***PERCENT:*** 100
CAS# 2674-91-1
EXPOSURE LIMITS: NO OCCUPATIONAL EXPOSURE LIMITS ESTABLISHED BY OSHA, ACGIH, OR NIOSH.

PHYSICAL DATA

DESCRIPTION: PRATICALLY ODORLESS, YELLOWISH OILY LIQUID
BOILING POINT: 239 F (115 C) @ 0.02 MMHG ***SPECIFIC GRAVITY:*** 1.257
VAPOR PRESSURE: 0.0000035 MMHG ***EVAPORATION RATE:*** NOT AVAILABLE
SOLUBILITY IN WATER: SOLUBLE
SOLVENT SOLUBILITY: SOLUBLE IN MOST ORGANIC SOLVENTS EXCEPT ALIPHATIC HYDROCARBONS

FIRE AND EXPLOSION DATA

FIRE AND EXPLOSION HAZARD: UNKNOWN FIRE AND EXPLOSION HAZARD.
FIREFIGHTING MEDIA: DRY CHEMICAL, CARBON DIOXIDE, HALON, WATER SPRAY OR STANDARD FOAM (1987 EMERGENCY RESPONSE GUIDEBOOK, DOT P 5800.4). FOR LARGER FIRES, USE WATER SPRAY, FOG OR STANDARD FOAM (1987 EMERGENCY RESPONSE GUIDEBOOK, DOT P 5800.4).
FIREFIGHTING: MOVE CONTAINERS FROM FIRE AREA IF POSSIBLE. FIGHT FIRE FROM MAXIMUM DISTANCE. STAY AWAY FROM STORAGE TANK ENDS. DIKE FIRE CONTROL WATER FOR LATER DISPOSAL. DO NOT SCATTER MATERIAL (1987 EMERGENCY RESPONSE GUIDEBOOK, DOT P 5800.4, GUIDE PAGE 55). EXTINGUISH USING AGENT SUITABLE FOR TYPE OF SURROUNDING FIRE. AVOID BREATHING VAPORS AND DUSTS. KEEP UPWIND.

TOXICITY

METASYSTOX-S: TOXICITY DATA: 1000 MG/KG SKIN-RAT LD50; 103 MG/KG ORAL-RAT LD50; 58700 UG/KG ORAL-MOUSE LD50; 225 MG/KG ORAL-GUINEA PIG LD50; 50 MG/KG INTRAPERITONEAL-RAT LD50; 30 MG/KG INTRAPERITONEAL-MOUSE LD50; 100 MG/KG INTRAPERITONEAL-GUINEA PIG LD50; 105 MG/KG UNREPORTED-RAT LD50; MUTAGENIC DATA (RTECS). CARCINOGEN STATUS: NONE. ACUTE TOXICITY LEVEL: TOXIC BY DERMAL ABSORPTION AND INGESTION. TARGET EFFECTS: CHOLINESTERASE INHIBITOR. POISONING MAY AFFECT THE NERVOUS SYSTEM.* AT INCREASED RISK FROM EXPOSURE: PERSONS WITH RESPIRATORY AILMENTS, RECENT EXPOSURE TO CHOLINESTERASE INHIBITORS OR IMPAIRED CHOLINESTERASE PRODUCTION, OR LIVER MALFUNCTION.* ADDITIONAL DATA: MAY CROSS THE PLACENTA. HIGH ENVIRONMENTAL TEMPERATURES OR EXPOSURE OF THE CHEMICAL TO VISIBLE OR ULTRAVIOLET LIGHT MAY ENHANCE THE TOXICITY. INTERACTIONS WITH MEDICATIONS MAY OCCUR.*
* MAY BE BASED ON GENERAL INFORMATION ON ORGANOPHOSPHATES.

HEALTH EFFECTS AND FIRST AID

INHALATION: METASYSTOX-S: SEE INFORMATION ON ORGANOPHOSPHATES.
ORGANOPHOSPHATES: CHOLINESTERASE INHIBITOR. **ACUTE EXPOSURE-** WHEN INHALED, THE FIRST EFFECTS OF CHOLINESTERASE INHIBITORS ARE USUALLY RESPIRATORY AND MAY INCLUDE NASAL HYPEREMIA AND WATERY DISCHARGE, COUGH, CHEST DISCOMFORT, DYSPNEA, AND WHEEZING DUE TO INCREASED BRONCHIAL SECRETIONS AND BRONCHOCONSTRICTION. IF SUFFICIENT AMOUNTS ARE ABSORBED, OTHER SYSTEMIC EFFECTS MAY BEGIN WITHIN A FEW MINUTES OR BE DELAYED FOR UP TO 12 HOURS. SYMPTOMS MAY INCLUDE PALLOR, NAUSEA, VOMITING, DIARRHEA, ABDOMINAL CRAMPS, HEADACHE, DIZZINESS, OCULAR PAIN, BLURRED VISION, MIOSIS OR IN SOME CASES, ESPECIALLY INITIALLY, MYDRIASIS, LACRIMATION, SALIVATION, SWEATING, AND CONFUSION. OTHER REPORTED CENTRAL NERVOUS SYSTEM OR NEUROMUSCULAR EFFECTS MAY INCLUDE ATAXIA, SLURRED SPEECH, AREFLEXIA, WEAKNESS, FATIGUE, FASCICULATIONS, TWITCHING, TREMORS POSSIBLY OF THE TONGUE AND EYELIDS, AND EVENTUALLY PARALYSIS OF THE EXTREMITIES AND POSSIBLY OF THE RESPIRATORY MUSCLES. IN SEVERE CASES THERE MAY ALSO BE INVOLUNTARY DEFECATION AND URINATION, CYANOSIS, PSYCHOSIS, HYPERGLYCEMIA, ACUTE PANCREATITIS, CARDIAC IRREGULARITIES, PULMONARY EDEMA, UNCONSCIOUSNESS, CONVULSIONS, AND COMA. DEATH IS PRIMARILY DUE TO RESPIRATORY FAILURE, ALTHOUGH CARDIOVASCULAR EFFECTS INCLUDING CARDIAC ARREST MAY ALSO BE IMPLICATED. LONG TERM SEQUELAE ARE RARE BUT MAY INCLUDE NEUROPSYCHIATRIC DISORDERS AND MYOPATHY WITH MUSCLE TENDERNESS. SOME ORGANOPHOSPHATES MAY CAUSE A DELAYED NEUROPATHY BEGINNING 1-4 WEEKS AFTER AN ACUTE EXPOSURE WHICH MAY OR MAY NOT HAVE CAUSED ACUTE CHOLINERGIC EFFECTS. NUMBNESS, TINGLING, WEAKNESS AND CRAMPING BEGINNING SYMMETRICALLY IN THE LOWER LIMBS MAY PROGRESS TO ATAXIA AND PARALYSIS. IN SEVERE CASES, UPPER LIMB INVOLVEMENT IS POSSIBLE AND FLACCID PARALYSIS MAY PROGRESS TO SPASTIC PARALYSIS WITH EXAGGERATED REFLEXES. IMPROVEMENT MAY OCCUR OVER MONTHS TO YEARS, BUT SOME RESIDUAL IMPAIRMENT USUALLY REMAINS.
CHRONIC EXPOSURE- REPEATED OR PROLONGED EXPOSURE MAY RESULT IN THE EFFECTS OF ACUTE EXPOSURE INCLUDING THE DELAYED NEUROPATHY. OTHER EFFECTS REPORTED IN WORKERS REPEATEDLY EXPOSED INCLUDE IMPAIRED MEMORY AND CONCENTRATION, ACUTE PSYCHOSIS, SEVERE DEPRESSIONS, IRRITABILTY, CONFUSION, APATHY, EMOTIONAL LABILITY, SOCIAL WITHDRAWAL, CONFUSION, HEADACHE, SPEECH DIFFICULTIES, DELAYED REACTION TIMES, SPATIAL DISORIENTATION, NIGHTMARES, SLEEPWALKING, AND DROWSINESS OR INSOMNIA. AN INFLUENZA-LIKE CONDITION WITH HEADACHE, NAUSEA, WEAKNESS, ANOREXIA AND MALAISE HAS ALSO BEEN REPORTED.
FIRST AID- REMOVE FROM EXPOSURE AREA TO FRESH AIR IMMEDIATELY. IF BREATHING HAS STOPPED, GIVE ARTIFICIAL RESPIRATION. MAINTAIN AIRWAY AND BLOOD PRESSURE AND ADMINISTER OXYGEN IF AVAILABLE. KEEP AFFECTED PERSON WARM AND AT REST. TREAT SYMPTOMATICALLY AND SUPPORTIVELY. ADMINISTRATION OF OXYGEN SHOULD BE PERFORMED BY QUALIFIED PERSONNEL. GET MEDICAL ATTENTION IMMEDIATELY.

SKIN CONTACT: METASYSTOX-S TOXIC. SEE INFORMATION ON ORGANOPHOSPHATES.
ORGANOPHOSPHATES: CHOLINESTERASE INHIBITOR. **ACUTE EXPOSURE-** LOCALIZED SWEATING AND FASCICULATIONS MAY OCCUR AT THE SITE OF CONTACT. IF SUFFICIENT AMOUNTS ARE ABSORBED, OTHER EFFECTS OF CHOLINESTERASE INHIBITION AS DESCRIBED IN ACUTE INHALATION MAY OCCUR. SYMPTOMS MAY BE DELAYED 2-3 HOURS, BUT USUALLY NO MORE THAN 12 HOURS. THE RATE OF ABSORPTION IS INCREASED BY THE PRESENCE OF DERMATITIS OR HIGH AMBIENT TEMPERATURES. DELAYED NEUROPATHY IS ALSO POSSIBLE. **CHRONIC EXPOSURE-** REPEATED OR PROLONGED EXPOSURE MAY CAUSE EFFECTS AS DESCRIBED IN ACUTE EXPOSURE. SOME ORGANOPHOSPHATES MAY CAUSE SENSITIZATION.
FIRST AID- REMOVE CONTAMINATED CLOTHING IMMEDIATELY. WASH CONTAMINATED AREAS WITH SOAP AND WATER FOLLOWED BY ALCOHOL (ARENA, POISONING, 4TH ED.). EMERGENCY PERSONNEL SHOULD WEAR GLOVES AND AVOID CONTAMINATION. TREAT RESPIRATORY DIFFICULTY WITH ARTIFICIAL RESPIRATION. GET MEDICAL ATTENTION IMMEDIATELY.

EYE CONTACT: METASYSTOX-S: SEE INFORMATION ON ORGANOPHOSPHATES.
ORGANOPHOSPHATES: CHOLINESTERASE INHIBITOR. **ACUTE EXPOSURE-** DIRECT CONTACT MAY CAUSE PAIN, HYPEREMIA, LACRIMATION, TWITCHING OF THE EYELIDS, MIOSIS, AND CILIARY MUSCLE SPASM WITH LOSS OF ACCOMODATION, BLURRED OR DIMMED VISION AND BROWACHE. SOMETIMES MYDRIASIS MAY OCCUR INSTEAD OF MIOSIS. WITH SUFFICIENT EXPOSURE, OTHER SYMPTOMS OF CHOLINESTERASE INHIBITION AS DESCRIBED IN ACUTE INHALATION MAY OCCUR.

CHRONIC EXPOSURE- REPEATED OR PROLONGED EXPOSURE MAY CAUSE EFFECTS AS DESCRIBED IN ACUTE EXPOSURE. SOME COMPOUNDS HAVE CAUSED TOXIC EFFECTS ON THE CRYSTALLINE LENS, CONJUNCTIVAL THICKENING AND OBSTRUCTION OF THE NASOLACRIMAL CANALS WHEN USED AS MIOTIC EYEDROPS.

FIRST AID- IRRIGATE EYES WITH WATER OR SALINE SOLUTION. IF SYMPTOMS OF POISONING OCCUR, TREAT RESPIRATORY DIFFICULTY WITH ARTIFICIAL RESPIRATION AND OXYGEN. OBSERVE PATIENT FOR AT LEAST 24-36 HOURS (GOSSELIN, CLINICAL TOXICOLOGY OF COMMERCIAL PRODUCTS, 5TH ED.). GET MEDICAL ATTENTION IMMEDIATELY. OXYGEN SHOULD BE ADMINISTERED BY QUALIFIED MEDICAL PERSONNEL.

INGESTION: METASYSTOX-S: TOXIC. SEE INFORMATION ON ORGANOPHOSPHATES. ORGANOPHOSPHATES: CHOLINESTERASE INHIBITOR. **ACUTE EXPOSURE-** WHEN INGESTED, THE FIRST EFFECTS MAY BE NAUSEA, VOMITING, ANOREXIA, ABDOMINAL CRAMPS AND DIARRHEA. GASTROINTESTINAL ABSORPTION MAY CAUSE SYMPTOMS OF CHOLINESTERASE INHIBITION AS DESCRIBED IN ACUTE INHALATION. SYMPTOMS MAY BEGIN WITHIN MINUTES OR BE DELAYED FOR HOURS. DELAYED EFFECTS INCLUDING NEUROPATHY MAY ALSO OCCUR. **CHRONIC EXPOSURE-** REPEATED INGESTION MAY CAUSE EFFECTS AS DESCRIBED IN ACUTE EXPOSURE.

FIRST AID- IF PERSON IS ALERT AND RESPIRATION IS NOT DEPRESSED, GIVE SYRUP OF IPECAC FOLLOWED BY WATER (IF VOMITING OCCURS, KEEP HEAD BELOW HIPS TO PREVENT ASPIRATION). IF CONSCIOUSNESS LEVEL DECLINES OR VOMITING HAS NOT OCCURRED IN 15 MINUTES EMPTY STOMACH BY GASTRIC LAVAGE WITH THE AID OF CUFFED ENDOTRACHEAL TUBE USING ISOTONIC SALINE OR 5% SODIUM BICARBONATE FOLLOW WITH ACTIVATED CHARCOAL. ESTABLISH AND MAINTAIN AIRWAY. TREAT RESPIRATORY DIFFICULTY WITH ARTIFICIAL RESPIRATION AND OXYGEN. DO NOT GIVE MORPHINE, AMINOPHYLLINE, PHENOTHIAZINES, RESERPINE, FUROSEMIDE, OR ETHACRYNIC ACID (MORGAN, RECOGNITION AND MANAGEMENT OF PESTICIDE POISONINGS, 3RD ED.). TREAT SYMPTOMATICALLY AND SUPPORTIVELY. ADMINISTRATION OF OXYGEN AND LAVAGE MUST BE PERFORMED BY QUALIFIED MEDICAL PERSONNEL. GET MEDICAL ATTENTION IMMEDIATELY.

ANTIDOTE: THE FOLLOWING ANTIDOTE(S) HAVE BEEN RECOMMENDED. HOWEVER, THE DECISION AS TO WHETHER THE SEVERITY OF POISONING REQUIRES ADMINISTRATION OF ANY ANTIDOTE AND ACTUAL DOSE REQUIRED SHOULD BE MADE BY QUALIFIED MEDICAL PERSONNEL.

FOR CHOLINESTERASE INHIBITORS: ESTABLISH CLEAR AIRWAY AND TISSUE OXYGENATION BY ASPIRATION OF SECRETIONS, AND IF NECESSARY, BY ASSISTED PULMONARY VENTILATION WITH OXYGEN. IMPROVE TISSUE OXYGENATION AS MUCH AS POSSIBLE BEFORE ADMINISTERING ATROPINE TO MINIMIZE THE RISK OF VENTRICULAR FIBRILLATION. ADMINISTER ATROPINE SULFATE INTRAVENOUSLY, OR INTRAMUSCULARLY IF IV INJECTION IS NOT POSSIBLE. IN MODERATELY SEVERE POISONING ADMINISTER ATROPINE SULFATE, 0.4-2.0 MG REPEATED EVERY 15 MINUTES UNTIL ATROPINIZATION IS ACHIEVED (TACHYCARDIA, FLUSHING, DRY MOUTH, MYDRIASIS). MAINTAIN ATROPINIZATION BY REPEATED DOSES FOR 2-12 HOURS, OR LONGER, DEPENDING ON THE SEVERITY OF POISONING. THE APPEARANCE OF RALES IN THE LUNG BASES, MIOSIS, SALIVATION, NAUSEA, BRADYCARDIA, ARE ALL INDICATIONS OF INADEQUATE ATROPINIZATION. SEVERELY POISONED INDIVIDUALS MAY EXHIBIT REMARKABLE TOLERANCE TO ATROPINE; TWO OR MORE TIMES THE DOSAGES SUGGESTED ABOVE MAY BE NEEDED. PERSONS NOT POISONED OR ONLY SLIGHTLY POISONED, HOWEVER, MAY DEVELOP SIGNS OF ATROPINE TOXICITY FROM SUCH LARGE DOSAGES: FEVER, MUSCLE FIBRILLATIONS, AND DELIRIUM ARE THE MAIN SIGNS OF ATROPINE TOXICITY. IF THESE SIGNS APPEAR WHILE THE PATIENT IS FULLY ATROPINIZED, ATROPINE ADMINISTRATION SHOULD BE DISCONTINUED, AT LEAST TEMPORARILY. OBSERVE TREATED PATIENTS CLOSELY AT LEAST 24 HOURS TO INSURE THAT SYMPTOMS (POSSIBLY PULMONARY EDEMA) DO NOT RECUR AS ATROPINIZATION WEARS OFF. IN VERY SEVERE POISONINGS, METABOLIC DISPOSITION OF TOXICANT MAY REQUIRE SEVERAL HOURS OR DAYS DURING WHICH ATROPINIZATION MUST BE MAINTAINED. MARKEDLY LOWER LEVELS OF URINARY METABOLITES INDICATE THAT ATROPINE DOSAGE CAN BE TAPERED OFF. AS DOSAGE IS REDUCED, CHECK THE LUNG BASES FREQUENTLY FOR RALES. IF RALES ARE HEARD OR OTHER SYMPTOMS RETURN, RE-ESTABLISH ATROPINIZATION PROMPTLY (MORGAN, RECOGNITION AND MANAGEMENT OF PESTICIDE POISONINGS, 3RD ED.). ADMINISTRATION OF ANTIDOTE MUST BE PERFORMED BY QUALIFIED MEDICAL PERSONNEL.

IN CASES OF SEVERE POISONING BY ORGANOPHOSPHATE PESTICIDES IN WHICH RESPIRATORY DEPRESSION, MUSCLE WEAKNESS AND TWITCHINGS ARE SEVERE, GIVE PRALIDOXIME (PROTOPAM-AYERST, 2-PAM), 1.0 GRAM INTRAVENOUSLY AT NO MORE THAN 0.5 GRAM PER MINUTE. DOSAGE OF PRALIDOXIME MAY BE REPEATED IN 1-2 HOURS, THEN AT 10-12 HOUR INTERVALS IF NEEDED. IN VERY SEVERE POISONINGS, DOSAGE RATES MAY BE DOUBLED. TREATMENT WITH PRALIDOXIME WILL BE MOST EFFECTIVE IF GIVEN WITHIN THIRTY-SIX HOURS AFTER POISONING (MORGAN, RECOGNITION AND MANAGEMENT OF PESTICIDE POISONINGS, 3RD ED.). ANTIDOTE SHOULD BE ADMINISTERED BY QUALIFIED MEDICAL PERSONNEL.

REACTIVITY

REACTIVITY: STABLE UNDER NORMAL TEMPERATURES AND PRESSURES.

INCOMPATIBILITIES: METASYSTOX-S: OXIDIZERS (STRONG): FIRE AND EXPLOSION HAZARD.

DECOMPOSITION: THERMAL DECOMPOSITION MAY RELEASE TOXIC AND/OR HAZARDOUS GASES.

POLYMERIZATION: HAZARDOUS POLYMERIZATION HAS NOT BEEN REPORTED TO OCCUR UNDER NORMAL TEMPERATURES AND PRESSURES.

STORAGE AND DISPOSAL

OBSERVE ALL FEDERAL, STATE AND LOCAL REGULATIONS WHEN STORING OR DISPOSING OF THIS SUBSTANCE. FOR ASSISTANCE, CONTACT THE DISTRICT DIRECTOR OF THE ENVIRONMENTAL PROTECTION AGENCY.

STORAGE

STORE IN ACCORDANCE WITH 40 CFR 165 RECOMMENDED PROCEDURES FOR THE DISPOSAL AND STORAGE OF PESTICIDES AND PESTICIDE CONTAINERS.

DISPOSAL

DISPOSAL MUST BE IN ACCORDANCE WITH 40 CFR 165 RECOMMENDED PROCEDURES FOR THE DISPOSAL AND STORAGE OF PESTICIDES AND PESTICIDE CONTAINERS.

CONDITIONS TO AVOID

NONE REPORTED.

SPILL AND LEAK PROCEDURES

OCCUPATIONAL SPILL: DO NOT TOUCH SPILLED MATERIAL. STOP LEAK IF YOU CAN DO IT WITHOUT RISK. USE WATER SPRAY TO REDUCE VAPORS. FOR SMALL SPILLS, TAKE UP WITH SAND OR OTHER ABSORBENT MATERIAL AND PLACE INTO CONTAINERS FOR LATER DISPOSAL. FOR SMALL DRY SPILLS, WITH A CLEAN SHOVEL PLACE MATERIAL INTO CLEAN, DRY CONTAINERS AND COVER. MOVE CONTAINERS FROM SPILL AREA. FOR LARGER SPILLS, DIKE FAR AHEAD OF SPILL FOR LATER DISPOSAL. KEEP UNNECESSARY PEOPLE AWAY. ISOLATE HAZARD AREA AND DENY ENTRY. VENTILATE CLOSED SPACES BEFORE ENTERING.

PROTECTIVE EQUIPMENT

VENTILATION: PROVIDE LOCAL EXHAUST OR PROCESS ENCLOSURE VENTILATION SYSTEM.

RESPIRATOR: THE FOLLOWING RESPIRATORS ARE RECOMMENDED BASED ON INFORMATION FOUND IN THE PHYSICAL DATA, TOXICITY AND HEALTH EFFECTS SECTIONS. THEY ARE RANKED IN ORDER FROM MINIMUM TO MAXIMUM RESPIRATORY PROTECTION. THE SPECIFIC RESPIRATOR SELECTED MUST BE BASED ON CONTAMINATION LEVELS FOUND IN THE WORK PLACE, MUST NOT EXCEED THE WORKING LIMITS OF THE RESPIRATOR AND BE JOINTLY APPROVED BY THE NATIONAL INSTITUTE FOR OCCUPATIONAL SAFETY AND HEALTH AND THE MINE SAFETY AND HEALTH ADMINISTRATION (NIOSH-MSHA).

TYPE 'C' SUPPLIED-AIR RESPIRATOR WITH A FULL FACEPIECE OPERATED IN PRESSURE-DEMAND OR OTHER POSITIVE PRESSURE MODE OR WITH A FULL FACEPIECE, HELMET OR HOOD OPERATED IN CONTINOUS-FLOW MODE.

SELF-CONTAINED BREATHING APPARATUS WITH A FULL FACEPIECE OPERATED IN PRESSURE-DEMAND OR OTHER POSITIVE PRESSURE MODE.

FOR FIREFIGHTING AND OTHER IMMEDIATELY DANGEROUS TO LIFE OR HEALTH CONDITIONS:

SELF-CONTAINED BREATHING APPARATUS WITH FULL FACEPIECE OPERATED IN PRESSURE-DEMAND OR OTHER POSITIVE PRESSURE MODE.

SUPPLIED-AIR RESPIRATOR WITH FULL FACEPIECE AND OPERATED IN PRESSURE-DEMAND OR OTHER POSITIVE PRESSURE MODE IN COMBINATION WITH AN AUXILIARY SELF-CONTAINED BREATHING APPARATUS OPERATED IN PRESSURE-DEMAND OR OTHER POSITIVE PRESSURE MODE.

CLOTHING: EMPLOYEE MUST WEAR APPROPRIATE PROTECTIVE (IMPERVIOUS) CLOTHING AND EQUIPMENT TO PREVENT ANY POSSIBILITY OF SKIN CONTACT WITH THIS SUBSTANCE.

GLOVES: EMPLOYEE MUST WEAR APPROPRIATE PROTECTIVE GLOVES TO PREVENT CONTACT WITH THIS SUBSTANCE.

EYE PROTECTION: EMPLOYEE MUST WEAR SPLASH-PROOF OR DUST-RESISTANT SAFETY GOGGLES AND A FACESHIELD TO PREVENT CONTACT WITH THIS SUBSTANCE.

EMERGENCY WASH FACILITIES: WHERE THERE IS ANY POSSIBILITY THAT AN EMPLOYEE'S EYES AND/OR SKIN MAY BE EXPOSED TO THIS SUBSTANCE, THE EMPLOYER SHOULD PROVIDE AN EYE WASH FOUNTAIN AND QUICK DRENCH SHOWER WITHIN THE IMMEDIATE WORK AREA FOR EMERGENCY USE.

AUTHORIZED BY- OCCUPATIONAL HEALTH SERVICES, INC.

CREATION DATE: 10/04/89 ***REVISION DATE:*** 08/05/90

MATERIAL SAFETY DATA SHEET

OCCUPATIONAL HEALTH SERVICES, INC.
AGRICULTURE AND PESTICIDE DIVISION
450 SEVENTH AVENUE, SUITE 2407
NEW YORK, NEW YORK 10123
1-800-445-MSDS OR (212) 967-1100

EMERGENCY CONTACT:
JOHN S. BRANSFORD, JR. (615) 292-1180

SUBSTANCE IDENTIFICATION

CAS-NUMBER 67129-08-2
SUBSTANCE: **METAZACHLOR**
TRADE NAMES/SYNONYMS: ACETAMIDE, 2-CHLORO-N-(2,6-DIMETHYLPHENYL)-N-(1H-PYRAZOL-1-YLMETHYL)-; 2-CHLORO-N-(2,6-DIMETHYLPHENYL)-N-(1H-PYRAZOL-1-YLMETHYL)ACETAMIDE; 2-CHLORO-N-(PYRAZOL-1-YLMETHYL)ACET-2',6'-XYLIDIDE; BUTISAN S; METAZACHLORE; C14H16CLN3O; PST14106
CHEMICAL FAMILY: PYRAZOLE AMIDE
MOLECULAR FORMULA: C14-H16-CL-N3-O
MOLECULAR WEIGHT: 277.75
CERCLA RATINGS (SCALE 0-3): HEALTH=U FIRE=1 REACTIVITY=0 PERSISTENCE=3
NFPA RATINGS (SCALE 0-4): HEALTH=U FIRE=1 REACTIVITY=0

COMPONENTS AND CONTAMINANTS

COMPONENT: METAZACHLOR ***PERCENT:*** 100.0
CAS# 67129-08-2
OTHER CONTAMINANTS: NONE
EXPOSURE LIMITS: NO OCCUPATIONAL EXPOSURE LIMITS ESTABLISHED BY OSHA, ACGIH, OR NIOSH.

PHYSICAL DATA

DESCRIPTION: YELLOWISH CRYSTALS OR BEIGE SOLID.
MELTING POINT: 185 F (85C)
SPECIFIC GRAVITY: NOT AVAILABLE ***VAPOR PRESSURE:*** NEGLIGIBLE
SOLUBILITY IN WATER: 17 PPM
SOLVENT SOLUBILITY: SOLUBLE IN ACETONE, CHLOROFORM, ETHYL ACETATE AND ETHANOL.

FIRE AND EXPLOSION DATA

FIRE AND EXPLOSION HAZARD: SLIGHT FIRE HAZARD WHEN EXPOSED TO HEAT OR FLAME.
FIREFIGHTING MEDIA: DRY CHEMICAL, CARBON DIOXIDE, HALON, WATER SPRAY OR STANDARD FOAM (1987 EMERGENCY RESPONSE GUIDEBOOK, DOT P 5800.4).
FOR LARGER FIRES, USE WATER SPRAY, FOG OR STANDARD FOAM (1987 EMERGENCY RESPONSE GUIDEBOOK, DOT P 5800.4).
FIREFIGHTING: MOVE CONTAINER FROM FIRE AREA IF POSSIBLE. DO NOT SCATTER SPILLED MATERIAL WITH HIGH PRESSURE WATER STREAMS. DIKE FIRE CONTROL WATER FOR LATER DISPOSAL (1987 EMERGENCY RESPONSE GUIDEBOOK, DOT P 5800.4, GUIDE PAGE 31).
USE AGENTS SUITABLE FOR TYPE OF SURROUNDING FIRE. AVOID BREATHING HAZARDOUS VAPORS, KEEP UPWIND.

TOXICITY

METAZACHLOR: TOXICITY DATA: >6810 MG/KG SKIN-RAT LD50 (85JFAN); 1 GM/KG ORAL-RAT LD50. CARCINOGEN STATUS: NONE. ACUTE TOXICITY LEVEL: MODERATELY TOXIC BY INGESTION; SLIGHTLY TOXIC BY DERMAL ABSORPTION. TARGET EFFECTS: NO DATA AVAILABLE.

HEALTH EFFECTS AND FIRST AID

INHALATION: METAZACHLOR: **ACUTE EXPOSURE-** NO IRRITATION OF MUCOUS MEMBRANES WAS OBSERVED IN RABBITS. **CHRONIC EXPOSURE-** NO DATA AVAILABLE.
FIRST AID- REMOVE FROM EXPOSURE AREA TO FRESH AIR IMMEDIATELY. IF BREATHING HAS STOPPED, PERFORM ARTIFICIAL RESPIRATION. KEEP PERSON WARM AND AT REST. TREAT SYMPTOMATICALLY AND SUPPORTIVELY. GET MEDICAL ATTENTION IMMEDIATELY.

SKIN CONTACT: METAZACHLOR: **ACUTE EXPOSURE-** THE LD50 IN RATS WAS GREATER THAN 6810 MG/KG. **CHRONIC EXPOSURE-** NO DATA AVAILABLE.
FIRST AID- REMOVE CONTAMINATED CLOTHING AND SHOES IMMEDIATELY. WASH AFFECTED AREA WITH SOAP OR MILD DETERGENT AND LARGE AMOUNTS OF WATER UNTIL NO EVIDENCE OF CHEMICAL REMAINS (APPROXIMATELY 15-20 MINUTES). GET MEDICAL ATTENTION IMMEDIATELY.

EYE CONTACT: METAZACHLOR: **ACUTE EXPOSURE-** NO IRRITATION OF THE MUCOUS MEMBRANES WAS OBSERVED IN RABBITS. **CHRONIC EXPOSURE-** NO DATA AVAILABLE.
FIRST AID- WASH EYES IMMEDIATELY WITH LARGE AMOUNTS OF WATER OR NORMAL SALINE, OCCASIONALLY LIFTING UPPER AND LOWER LIDS, UNTIL NO EVIDENCE OF CHEMICAL REMAINS (APPROXIMATELY 15-20 MINUTES). GET MEDICAL ATTENTION IMMEDIATELY.

INGESTION: METAZACHLOR: **ACUTE EXPOSURE-** A LETHAL DOSE REPORTED IN RATS WAS 2150 MG/KG; SYMPTOMS WERE NOT REPORTED. **CHRONIC EXPOSURE-** NO DATA AVAILABLE.
FIRST AID- IF THE PERSON IS CONSCIOUS AND NOT CONVULSING, REMOVE BY GASTRIC LAVAGE AND FOLLOW WITH A CATHARTIC (DREISBACH, HANDBOOK OF POISONING, 12TH ED.). TREAT SYMPTOMATICALLY AND SUPPORTIVELY. GASTRIC LAVAGE SHOULD BE PERFORMED BY QUALIFIED MEDICAL PERSONNEL. GET MEDICAL ATTENTION IMMEDIATELY.
ANTIDOTE: NO SPECIFIC ANTIDOTE. TREAT SYMPTOMATICALLY AND SUPPORTIVELY.

REACTIVITY

REACTIVITY: STABLE UNDER NORMAL TEMPERATURES AND PRESSURES.
INCOMPATIBILITIES: METAZACHLOR: OXIDIZERS (STRONG): FIRE AND EXPLOSION HAZARD.
DECOMPOSITION: THERMAL DECOMPOSITION PRODUCTS MAY INCLUDE TOXIC OXIDES OF NITROGEN AND CARBON AND TOXIC AND CORROSIVE FUMES OF CHLORIDES.
POLYMERIZATION: HAZARDOUS POLYMERIZATION HAS NOT BEEN REPORTED TO OCCUR UNDER NORMAL TEMPERATURES AND PRESSURES.

STORAGE AND DISPOSAL

OBSERVE ALL FEDERAL, STATE AND LOCAL REGULATIONS WHEN STORING OR DISPOSING OF THIS SUBSTANCE. FOR ASSISTANCE, CONTACT THE DISTRICT DIRECTOR OF THE ENVIRONMENTAL PROTECTION AGENCY.

STORAGE

STORE IN ACCORDANCE WITH 40 CFR 165 RECOMMENDED PROCEDURES FOR THE DISPOSAL AND STORAGE OF PESTICIDES AND PESTICIDE CONTAINERS.
STORE AWAY FROM INCOMPATIBLE SUBSTANCES.

DISPOSAL

DISPOSAL MUST BE IN ACCORDANCE WITH 40 CFR 165 RECOMMENDED PROCEDURES FOR THE DISPOSAL AND STORAGE OF PESTICIDES AND PESTICIDE CONTAINERS.

CONDITIONS TO AVOID

MAY BURN BUT DOES NOT IGNITE READILY. AVOID CONTACT WITH STRONG OXIDIZERS, EXCESSIVE HEAT, SPARKS, OR OPEN FLAME.

SPILL AND LEAK PROCEDURES

OCCUPATIONAL SPILL: SWEEP UP AND PLACE IN SUITABLE CLEAN, DRY CONTAINERS FOR RECLAMATION OR LATER DISPOSAL. DO NOT FLUSH SPILLED MATERIAL INTO SEWER. KEEP UNNECESSARY PEOPLE AWAY.

PROTECTIVE EQUIPMENT

VENTILATION: PROVIDE LOCAL EXHAUST OR GENERAL DILUTION VENTILATION SYSTEM.
RESPIRATOR: THE FOLLOWING RESPIRATORS ARE RECOMMENDED BASED ON INFORMATION FOUND IN THE PHYSICAL DATA, TOXICITY AND HEALTH EFFECTS SECTIONS. THEY ARE RANKED IN ORDER FROM MINIMUM TO MAXIMUM RESPIRATORY PROTECTION. THE SPECIFIC RESPIRATOR SELECTED MUST BE BASED ON CONTAMINATION LEVELS FOUND IN THE WORK PLACE, MUST NOT EXCEED THE WORKING LIMITS OF THE RESPIRATOR AND BE JOINTLY APPROVED BY THE NATIONAL INSTITUTE FOR OCCUPATIONAL SAFETY AND HEALTH AND THE MINE SAFETY AND HEALTH ADMINISTRATION (NIOSH-MSHA).
CHEMICAL CARTRIDGE RESPIRATOR WITH AN ORGANIC VAPOR CARTRIDGE(S) IN COMBINATION WITH A DUST AND MIST FILTER.
GAS MASK WITH ORGANIC VAPOR CANISTER (CHIN-STYLE OR FRONT- OR BACK-MOUNTED CANISTER) WITH A DUST AND MIST FILTER.
GAS MASK WITH ORGANIC VAPOR CANISTER (CHIN-STYLE OR FRONT- OR BACK-MOUNTED CANISTER) WITH A PARTICULATE FILTER.
POWERED AIR-PURIFYING RESPIRATOR WITH A HIGH-EFFICIENCY FILTER.
TYPE 'C' SUPPLIED-AIR RESPIRATOR WITH A FULL FACEPIECE OPERATED IN A PRESSURE-DEMAND OR OTHER POSITIVE PRESSURE MODE.
SELF-CONTAINED BREATHING APPARATUS WITH A FULL FACEPIECE OPERATED IN PRESSURE-DEMAND OR OTHER POSITIVE PRESSURE MODE.
FOR FIREFIGHTING AND OTHER IMMEDIATELY DANGEROUS TO LIFE OR HEALTH CONDITIONS:
SELF-CONTAINED BREATHING APPARATUS WITH FULL FACEPIECE OPERATED IN

PRESSURE-DEMAND OR OTHER POSITIVE PRESSURE MODE.
SUPPLIED-AIR RESPIRATOR WITH FULL FACEPIECE AND OPERATED IN PRESSURE-DEMAND OR OTHER POSITIVE PRESSURE MODE IN COMBINATION WITH AN AUXILIARY SELF-CONTAINED BREATHING APPARATUS OPERATED IN PRESSURE-DEMAND OR OTHER POSITIVE PRESSURE MODE.

CLOTHING: EMPLOYEE MUST WEAR APPROPRIATE PROTECTIVE (IMPERVIOUS) CLOTHING AND EQUIPMENT TO PREVENT REPEATED OR PROLONGED SKIN CONTACT WITH THIS SUBSTANCE.

GLOVES: EMPLOYEE MUST WEAR APPROPRIATE PROTECTIVE GLOVES TO PREVENT CONTACT WITH THIS SUBSTANCE.

EYE PROTECTION: EMPLOYEE MUST WEAR SPLASH-PROOF OR DUST-RESISTANT SAFETY GOGGLES TO PREVENT EYE CONTACT WITH THIS SUBSTANCE.
EMERGENCY EYE WASH: WHERE THERE IS ANY POSSIBILITY THAT AN EMPLOYEE'S EYES MAY BE EXPOSED TO THIS SUBSTANCE, THE EMPLOYER SHOULD PROVIDE AN EYE WASH FOUNTAIN WITHIN THE IMMEDIATE WORK AREA FOR EMERGENCY USE.

AUTHORIZED BY- OCCUPATIONAL HEALTH SERVICES, INC.
CREATION DATE: 12/20/89 ***REVISION DATE:*** 05/31/90

MATERIAL SAFETY DATA SHEET

OCCUPATIONAL HEALTH SERVICES, INC.
AGRICULTURE AND PESTICIDE DIVISION
450 SEVENTH AVENUE, SUITE 2407
NEW YORK, NEW YORK 10123
1-800-445-MSDS OR (212) 967-1100

EMERGENCY CONTACT:
JOHN S. BRANSFORD, JR. (615) 292-1180

SUBSTANCE IDENTIFICATION

CAS-NUMBER 18691-97-9

SUBSTANCE: METHABENZTHIAZURON

TRADE NAMES/SYNONYMS: UREA, N-2-BENZOTHIAZOLYL-N,N'-DIMETHYL-; UREA, 1-(2-BENZOTHIAZOLYL)-1,3-DIMETHYL-; N-2-BENZOTHIAZOLYL-N,N'-DIMETHYLUREA; 1-(2-BENZOTHIAZOLYL)-1,3-DIMETHYLUREA; 1-BENZOTHIAZOL-2-YL-1,3-DIMETHYLUREA; 1,3-DIMETHYL-3-(2-BENZOTHIAZOLYL)UREA; BAYER 74283; METABENZTHIAZURON; METHBENZTHIAZURON; TRIBUNIL; C10H11N3OS; PST14108

CHEMICAL FAMILY: SUBSTITUTED UREA

MOLECULAR FORMULA: C10-H11-N3-O-S

MOLECULAR WEIGHT: 221.30

CERCLA RATINGS (SCALE 0-3): HEALTH=2 FIRE=1 REACTIVITY=0 PERSISTENCE=2

NFPA RATINGS (SCALE 0-4): HEALTH=2 FIRE=1 REACTIVITY=0

COMPONENTS AND CONTAMINANTS

COMPONENT: METHABENZTHIAZURON ***PERCENT:*** 100
CAS# 18691-97-9

OTHER CONTAMINANTS: NONE

EXPOSURE LIMITS: NO OCCUPATIONAL EXPOSURE LIMITS ESTABLISHED BY OSHA, ACGIH, OR NIOSH.

PHYSICAL DATA

DESCRIPTION: COLORLESS CRYSTALLINE SOLID. ***MELTING POINT:*** 246-248 F (119-120 C)

SPECIFIC GRAVITY: NOT AVAILABLE ***VAPOR PRESSURE:*** NEGLIGIBLE

SOLUBILITY IN WATER: 0.0059% @ 20 C

SOLVENT SOLUBILITY: SOLUBLE IN ACETONE, DIMETHYLFORMAMIDE AND METHANOL.

FIRE AND EXPLOSION DATA

FIRE AND EXPLOSION HAZARD: SLIGHT FIRE HAZARD WHEN EXPOSED TO HEAT OR FLAME.

FIREFIGHTING MEDIA: DRY CHEMICAL, CARBON DIOXIDE, HALON, WATER SPRAY OR STANDARD FOAM (1987 EMERGENCY RESPONSE GUIDEBOOK, DOT P 5800.4). FOR LARGER FIRES, USE WATER SPRAY, FOG OR STANDARD FOAM (1987 EMERGENCY RESPONSE GUIDEBOOK, DOT P 5800.4).

FIREFIGHTING: MOVE CONTAINERS FROM FIRE AREA IF POSSIBLE. FIGHT FIRE FROM MAXIMUM DISTANCE. STAY AWAY FROM STORAGE TANK ENDS. DIKE FIRE CONTROL WATER FOR LATER DISPOSAL. DO NOT SCATTER MATERIAL (1987 EMERGENCY RESPONSE GUIDEBOOK, DOT P 5800.4, GUIDE PAGE 55).
EXTINGUISH USING AGENT SUITABLE FOR TYPE OF SURROUNDING FIRE. USE WATER IN FLOODING QUANTITIES AS FOG. KEEP SPARKS, FLAMES AND OTHER SOURCES OF IGNITION AWAY. KEEP MATERIAL OUT OF WATER SOURCES AND SEWERS. DO NOT TOUCH MATERIAL AND AVOID BREATHING DUSTS AND FUMES FROM BURNING MATERIAL. KEEP UPWIND.

TOXICITY

METHABENZTHIAZURON: TOXICITY DATA: 1000 MG/KG ORAL-RAT LD50 (85ARE); 2500 MG/KG UNREPORTED-MAMMAL LD50. CARCINOGEN STATUS: NONE. ACUTE TOXICITY LEVEL: MODERATELY TOXIC BY INGESTION. TARGET EFFECTS: NO DATA AVAILABLE.

HEALTH EFFECTS AND FIRST AID

INHALATION: METHABENZTHIAZURON: **ACUTE EXPOSURE-** MANY SUBSTITUTED UREA HERBICIDES ARE MODERATELY IRRITATING TO THE MUCOUS MEMBRANES.
CHRONIC EXPOSURE- NO DATA AVAILABLE.

FIRST AID- REMOVE FROM EXPOSURE AREA TO FRESH AIR IMMEDIATELY. IF BREATHING HAS STOPPED, PERFORM ARTIFICIAL RESPIRATION. KEEP PERSON WARM AND AT REST. TREAT SYMPTOMATICALLY AND SUPPORTIVELY. GET MEDICAL ATTENTION IMMEDIATELY.

SKIN CONTACT: METHABENZTHIAZURON: **ACUTE EXPOSURE-** MANY SUBSTITUTED UREA HERBICIDES ARE MODERATELY IRRITATING TO THE SKIN. A LETHAL DOSE IN RATS BY DERMAL ABSORPTION IS GREATER THAN 500 MG/KG. **CHRONIC EXPOSURE-** NO DATA AVAILABLE.

FIRST AID- REMOVE CONTAMINATED CLOTHING AND SHOES IMMEDIATELY. WASH AFFECTED AREA WITH SOAP OR MILD DETERGENT AND LARGE AMOUNTS OF WATER UNTIL NO EVIDENCE OF CHEMICAL REMAINS (APPROXIMATELY 15-20 MINUTES). GET MEDICAL ATTENTION IMMEDIATELY.

EYE CONTACT: METHABENZTHIAZURON: **ACUTE EXPOSURE-** MANY SUBSTITUTED UREA HERBICIDES ARE MODERATELY IRRITATING TO THE EYES. **CHRONIC EXPOSURE-** NO DATA AVAILABLE.

FIRST AID- WASH EYES IMMEDIATELY WITH LARGE AMOUNTS OF WATER OR NORMAL SALINE, OCCASIONALLY LIFTING UPPER AND LOWER LIDS, UNTIL NO EVIDENCE OF CHEMICAL REMAINS (APPROXIMATELY 15-20 MINUTES). GET MEDICAL ATTENTION IMMEDIATELY.

INGESTION: METHABENZTHIAZURON: **ACUTE EXPOSURE-** A LETHAL DOSE IN RATS WAS 1000 MG/KG. **CHRONIC EXPOSURE-** NO OBSERVABLE EFFECTS WERE NOTED IN A 2-YEAR STUDY OF RATS RECEIVING 150 MG/KG DIET.

FIRST AID- TREAT SYMPTOMATICALLY AND SUPPORTIVELY. GET MEDICAL ATTENTION IMMEDIATELY. IF VOMITING OCCURS, KEEP HEAD LOWER THAN HIPS TO PREVENT ASPIRATION.

ANTIDOTE: NO SPECIFIC ANTIDOTE. TREAT SYMPTOMATICALLY AND SUPPORTIVELY.

REACTIVITY

REACTIVITY: STABLE UNDER NORMAL TEMPERATURES AND PRESSURES.

INCOMPATIBILITIES: METHABENZTHIAZURON: OXIDIZERS (STRONG): FIRE AND EXPLOSION HAZARD.

DECOMPOSITION: THERMAL DECOMPOSITION PRODUCTS MAY INCLUDE TOXIC OXIDES OF CARBON, NITROGEN, AND SULFUR.

POLYMERIZATION: HAZARDOUS POLYMERIZATION HAS NOT BEEN REPORTED TO OCCUR UNDER NORMAL TEMPERATURES AND PRESSURES.

STORAGE AND DISPOSAL

OBSERVE ALL FEDERAL, STATE AND LOCAL REGULATIONS WHEN STORING OR DISPOSING OF THIS SUBSTANCE. FOR ASSISTANCE, CONTACT THE DISTRICT DIRECTOR OF THE ENVIRONMENTAL PROTECTION AGENCY.

****STORAGE****

STORE IN ACCORDANCE WITH 40 CFR 165 RECOMMENDED PROCEDURES FOR THE DISPOSAL AND STORAGE OF PESTICIDES AND PESTICIDE CONTAINERS.
STORE AWAY FROM INCOMPATIBLE SUBSTANCES.

****DISPOSAL****

DISPOSAL MUST BE IN ACCORDANCE WITH 40 CFR 165 RECOMMENDED PROCEDURES FOR THE DISPOSAL AND STORAGE OF PESTICIDES AND PESTICIDE CONTAINERS.

CONDITIONS TO AVOID

MAY BURN BUT DOES NOT IGNITE READILY. CONTAINERS MAY EXPLODE IN HEAT OF FIRE.

SPILL AND LEAK PROCEDURES

OCCUPATIONAL SPILL: DO NOT TOUCH SPILLED MATERIAL. STOP LEAK IF YOU CAN DO IT WITHOUT RISK. USE WATER SPRAY TO REDUCE VAPORS. FOR SMALL SPILLS, TAKE UP WITH SAND OR OTHER ABSORBENT MATERIAL AND PLACE INTO CONTAINERS FOR LATER DISPOSAL. FOR SMALL DRY SPILLS, WITH A CLEAN SHOVEL PLACE MATERIAL INTO CLEAN, DRY CONTAINERS AND COVER. MOVE

CONTAINERS FROM SPILL AREA. FOR LARGER SPILLS, DIKE FAR AHEAD OF SPILL FOR LATER DISPOSAL. KEEP UNNECESSARY PEOPLE AWAY. ISOLATE HAZARD AREA AND DENY ENTRY. VENTILATE CLOSED SPACES BEFORE ENTERING.

PROTECTIVE EQUIPMENT

VENTILATION: PROVIDE LOCAL EXHAUST OR GENERAL DILUTION VENTILATION SYSTEM.

RESPIRATOR: THE FOLLOWING RESPIRATORS ARE RECOMMENDED BASED ON INFORMATION FOUND IN THE PHYSICAL DATA, TOXICITY AND HEALTH EFFECTS SECTIONS. THEY ARE RANKED IN ORDER FROM MINIMUM TO MAXIMUM RESPIRATORY PROTECTION. THE SPECIFIC RESPIRATOR SELECTED MUST BE BASED ON CONTAMINATION LEVELS FOUND IN THE WORK PLACE, MUST NOT EXCEED THE WORKING LIMITS OF THE RESPIRATOR AND BE JOINTLY APPROVED BY THE NATIONAL INSTITUTE FOR OCCUPATIONAL SAFETY AND HEALTH AND THE MINE SAFETY AND HEALTH ADMINISTRATION (NIOSH-MSHA).

CHEMICAL CARTRIDGE RESPIRATOR WITH AN ORGANIC VAPOR CARTRIDGE(S) WITH A FULL FACEPIECE AND ORGANIC VAPOR CARTRIDGE(S) IN COMBINATION WITH A DUST AND MIST FILTER.

POWERED AIR-PURIFYING RESPIRATOR WITH A TIGHT-FITTING FACEPIECE AND ORGANIC VAPOR CARTRIDGE(S) IN COMBINATION WITH A HIGH-EFFICIENCY PARTICULATE FILTER.

TYPE 'C' SUPPLIED-AIR RESPIRATOR WITH A FULL FACEPIECE OPERATED IN A PRESSURE-DEMAND OR OTHER POSITIVE PRESSURE MODE.

SELF-CONTAINED BREATHING APPARATUS WITH A FULL FACEPIECE OPERATED IN PRESSURE-DEMAND OR OTHER POSITIVE PRESSURE MODE.

FOR FIREFIGHTING AND OTHER IMMEDIATELY DANGEROUS TO LIFE OR HEALTH CONDITIONS:

SELF-CONTAINED BREATHING APPARATUS WITH FULL FACEPIECE OPERATED IN PRESSURE-DEMAND OR OTHER POSITIVE PRESSURE MODE.

SUPPLIED-AIR RESPIRATOR WITH FULL FACEPIECE AND OPERATED IN PRESSURE-DEMAND OR OTHER POSITIVE PRESSURE MODE IN COMBINATION WITH AN AUXILIARY SELF-CONTAINED BREATHING APPARATUS OPERATED IN PRESSURE-DEMAND OR OTHER POSITIVE PRESSURE MODE.

CLOTHING: EMPLOYEE MUST WEAR APPROPRIATE PROTECTIVE (IMPERVIOUS) CLOTHING AND EQUIPMENT TO PREVENT REPEATED OR PROLONGED SKIN CONTACT WITH THIS SUBSTANCE.

GLOVES: EMPLOYEE MUST WEAR APPROPRIATE PROTECTIVE GLOVES TO PREVENT CONTACT WITH THIS SUBSTANCE.

EYE PROTECTION: EMPLOYEE MUST WEAR SPLASH-PROOF OR DUST-RESISTANT SAFETY GOGGLES TO PREVENT EYE CONTACT WITH THIS SUBSTANCE.

EMERGENCY EYE WASH: WHERE THERE IS ANY POSSIBILITY THAT AN EMPLOYEE'S EYES MAY BE EXPOSED TO THIS SUBSTANCE, THE EMPLOYER SHOULD PROVIDE AN EYE WASH FOUNTAIN WITHIN THE IMMEDIATE WORK AREA FOR EMERGENCY USE.

AUTHORIZED BY- OCCUPATIONAL HEALTH SERVICES, INC.

CREATION DATE: 10/04/89 ***REVISION DATE:*** 05/11/90

MATERIAL SAFETY DATA SHEET

OCCUPATIONAL HEALTH SERVICES, INC.
AGRICULTURE AND PESTICIDE DIVISION
450 SEVENTH AVENUE, SUITE 2407
NEW YORK, NEW YORK 10123
1-800-445-MSDS OR (212) 967-1100

EMERGENCY CONTACT:
JOHN S. BRANSFORD, JR. (615) 292-1180

SUBSTANCE IDENTIFICATION

CAS-NUMBER 950-37-8

SUBSTANCE: **METHIDATHION**

TRADE NAMES/SYNONYMS: PHOSPHORODITHIOIC ACID, S-((5-METHOXY-2-OXO-1,3,4-THIADIAZOL-3(2H)-YL) METHYL) O,O-DIMETHYL ESTER; PHOSPHORODITHIOIC ACID, O,O-DIMETHYL ESTER, S-ESTER WITH 4-(MERCAPTOMETHYL)-2-METHOXY-DELTA 2-1,2,4-THIADIAZOLIN-5-ONE; S-2,3-DIHYDRO-5-METHOXY-2-OXO-1,3,4-THIADIAZOL-3-YLMETHYL O,O DIMETHYL PHOSPHORODITHIOATE; 3-DIMETHOXYPHOSPHINOTHIOYLTHIOMETHYL-5-METHOXY-1,3,4-THIADIAZOL -2(3H)ONE; S-((5-METHOXY-2-OXO-1,3,4-THIADIAZOL-3(2H)-YL)METHYL) O,O-DIMETHYL PHOSPHORODITHIOATE; O,O-DIMETHYL PHOSPHORODITHIOATE S-ESTER WITH 4-(MERCAPTOMETHYL) -2-METHOXY-DELTA 2-1,3,4-THIADIAZOLIN-5-ONE; O,O-DIMETHYL S-(2,3-DIHYDRO-5-METHOXY-2-OXO-1,3,4-THIADIAZOL -3-YLMETHYL)PHOSPHORODITHIOATE; O,O-DIMETHYL -S-((2-METHOXY-1,3,4-THIADIAZOLE-5-(4H)-ONE-4-YL)METHYL) DITHIOPHOSPHATE; SUPRACIDE; ULTRACID; ENT 27193; PST14175

CHEMICAL FAMILY: ORGANOPHOSPHATE

MOLECULAR FORMULA: C6-H11-N2-O4-P-S3

MOLECULAR WEIGHT: 302.34

CERCLA RATINGS (SCALE 0-3): HEALTH=3 FIRE=0 REACTIVITY=0 PERSISTENCE=0

NFPA RATINGS (SCALE 0-4): HEALTH=4 FIRE=0 REACTIVITY=0

COMPONENTS AND CONTAMINANTS

COMPONENT: METHIDATHION ***PERCENT:*** 100

CAS# 950-37-8

EXPOSURE LIMITS: METHIDATHION: NO OCCUPATIONAL EXPOSURE LIMITS ESTABLISHED BY OSHA, ACGIH, OR NIOSH.

500/10,000 POUNDS SARA SECTION 302 THRESHOLD PLANNING QUANTITY 1 POUND SARA SECTION 304 REPORTABLE QUANTITY

PHYSICAL DATA

DESCRIPTION: COLORLESS CRYSTALS ***MELTING POINT:*** 102 F (39 C)

SPECIFIC GRAVITY: NOT AVAILABLE ***VAPOR PRESSURE:*** 0.000001

SOLUBILITY IN WATER: 240 PPM

SOLVENT SOLUBILITY: SOLUBLE IN ACETONE, BENZENE, METHANOL, ETHANOL, XYLENE, AND MOST ORGANIC SOLVENTS

FIRE AND EXPLOSION DATA

FIRE AND EXPLOSION HAZARD: NEGLIGIBLE FIRE HAZARD WHEN EXPOSED TO HEAT OR FLAME.

FIREFIGHTING MEDIA: DRY CHEMICAL, CARBON DIOXIDE, HALON, WATER SPRAY OR STANDARD FOAM (1987 EMERGENCY RESPONSE GUIDEBOOK, DOT P 5800.4).

FOR LARGER FIRES, USE WATER SPRAY, FOG OR STANDARD FOAM (1987 EMERGENCY RESPONSE GUIDEBOOK, DOT P 5800.4).

FIREFIGHTING: MOVE CONTAINERS FROM FIRE AREA IF POSSIBLE. FIGHT FIRE FROM MAXIMUM DISTANCE. STAY AWAY FROM STORAGE TANK ENDS. DIKE FIRE CONTROL WATER FOR LATER DISPOSAL. DO NOT SCATTER MATERIAL (1987 EMERGENCY RESPONSE GUIDEBOOK, DOT P 5800.4, GUIDE PAGE 55).

EXTINGUISH ONLY IF FLOW CAN BE STOPPED; USE FLOODING AMOUNTS OF WATER AS FOG, SOLID STREAMS MAY BE INEFFECTIVE. COOL CONTAINERS WITH FLOODING AMOUNTS OF WATER FROM AS FAR A DISTANCE AS POSSIBLE. USE WATER SPRAY TO ABSORB TOXIC VAPORS. AVOID BREATHING TOXIC VAPORS; KEEP UPWIND. CONSIDER EVACUATION OF DOWNWIND AREA IF MATERIAL IS LEAKING.

TRANSPORTATION DATA

DEPARTMENT OF TRANSPORTATION HAZARD CLASSIFICATION 49 CFR 172.101: POISON B

DEPARTMENT OF TRANSPORTATION LABELING REQUIREMENTS 49 CFR 172.101 AND SUBPART E: POISON

DEPARTMENT OF TRANSPORTATION PACKAGING REQUIREMENTS: 49 CFR 173.365 EXCEPTIONS: 49 CFR 173.364

TOXICITY

METHIDATHION: IRRITATION DATA: 24,400 UG EYE-RABBIT SEVERE. TOXICITY DATA: 50 MG/M3/4 HOURS INHALATION-RAT LC50; 196 MG/KG SKIN-RABBIT LD50; 25 MG/KG SKIN-RAT LD50; 20 MG/KG ORAL-RAT LD50; 25 MG/KG ORAL-MOUSE LD50; 63 MG/KG ORAL-RABBIT LD50; 25 MG/KG ORAL-GUINEA PIG LD50; 30 MG/KG ORAL-HAMSTER LD50; 25 MG/KG UNREPORTED-MAMMAL LD50; MUTAGENIC DATA (RTECS). CARCINOGEN STATUS: NONE. ACUTE TOXICITY LEVEL: HIGHLY TOXIC BY INHALATION, INGESTION, AND DERMAL ABSORPTION. TARGET EFFECTS: CHOLINESTERASE INHIBITOR. POISONING MAY AFFECT THE NERVOUS SYSTEM.* AT INCREASED RISK FROM EXPOSURE: PERSONS WITH RESPIRATORY AILMENTS, RECENT EXPOSURE TO CHOLINESTERASE INHIBITORS OR IMPAIRED CHOLINESTERASE PRODUCTION, OR LIVER MALFUNCTION.* ADDITIONAL DATA: MAY CROSS THE PLACENTA. HIGH ENVIRONMENTAL TEMPERATURES OR EXPOSURE OF THE CHEMICAL TO VISIBLE OR ULTRAVIOLET LIGHT MAY ENHANCE THE TOXICITY. INTERACTIONS WITH MEDICATIONS MAY OCCUR.*

* MAY BE BASED ON GENERAL INFORMATION ON ORGANOPHOSPHATES.

HEALTH EFFECTS AND FIRST AID

INHALATION: METHIDATHION: HIGHLY TOXIC. SEE INFORMATION ON ORGANOPHOSPHATES.

ORGANOPHOSPHATES: CHOLINESTERASE INHIBITOR. **ACUTE EXPOSURE**- WHEN INHALED, THE FIRST EFFECTS OF CHOLINESTERASE INHIBITORS ARE USUALLY RESPIRATORY AND MAY INCLUDE NASAL HYPEREMIA AND WATERY DISCHARGE, COUGH, CHEST DISCOMFORT, DYSPNEA, AND WHEEZING DUE TO INCREASED BRONCHIAL SECRETIONS AND BRONCHOCONSTRICTION. IF SUFFICIENT AMOUNTS ARE ABSORBED, OTHER SYSTEMIC EFFECTS MAY BEGIN WITHIN A FEW MINUTES OR BE DELAYED FOR UP TO 12 HOURS. SYMPTOMS MAY INCLUDE PALLOR,

NAUSEA, VOMITING, DIARRHEA, ABDOMINAL CRAMPS, HEADACHE, DIZZINESS, OCULAR PAIN, BLURRED VISION, MIOSIS OR IN SOME CASES, ESPECIALLY INITIALLY, MYDRIASIS, LACRIMATION, SALIVATION, SWEATING, AND CONFUSION. OTHER REPORTED CENTRAL NERVOUS SYSTEM OR NEUROMUSCULAR EFFECTS MAY INCLUDE ATAXIA, SLURRED SPEECH, AREFLEXIA, WEAKNESS, FATIGUE, FASCICULATIONS, TWITCHING, TREMORS POSSIBLY OF THE TONGUE AND EYELIDS, AND EVENTUALLY PARALYSIS OF THE EXTREMITIES AND POSSIBLY OF THE RESPIRATORY MUSCLES. IN SEVERE CASES THERE MAY ALSO BE INVOLUNTARY DEFECATION AND URINATION, CYANOSIS, PSYCHOSIS, HYPERGLYCEMIA, ACUTE PANCREATITIS, CARDIAC IRREGULARITIES, PULMONARY EDEMA, UNCONSCIOUSNESS, CONVULSIONS, AND COMA. DEATH IS PRIMARILY DUE TO RESPIRATORY FAILURE, ALTHOUGH CARDIOVASCULAR EFFECTS INCLUDING CARDIAC ARREST MAY ALSO BE IMPLICATED. LONG TERM SEQUELAE ARE RARE BUT MAY INCLUDE NEUROPSYCHIATRIC DISORDERS AND MYOPATHY WITH MUSCLE TENDERNESS. SOME ORGANOPHOSPHATES MAY CAUSE A DELAYED NEUROPATHY BEGINNING 1-4 WEEKS AFTER AN ACUTE EXPOSURE WHICH MAY OR MAY NOT HAVE CAUSED ACUTE CHOLINERGIC EFFECTS. NUMBNESS, TINGLING, WEAKNESS AND CRAMPING BEGINNING SYMMETRICALLY IN THE LOWER LIMBS MAY PROGRESS TO ATAXIA AND PARALYSIS. IN SEVERE CASES, UPPER LIMB INVOLVEMENT IS POSSIBLE AND FLACCID PARALYSIS MAY PROGRESS TO SPASTIC PARALYSIS WITH EXAGGERATED REFLEXES. IMPROVEMENT MAY OCCUR OVER MONTHS TO YEARS, BUT SOME RESIDUAL IMPAIRMENT USUALLY REMAINS. **CHRONIC EXPOSURE**- REPEATED OR PROLONGED EXPOSURE MAY RESULT IN THE EFFECTS OF ACUTE EXPOSURE INCLUDING THE DELAYED NEUROPATHY. OTHER EFFECTS REPORTED IN WORKERS REPEATEDLY EXPOSED INCLUDE IMPAIRED MEMORY AND CONCENTRATION, ACUTE PSYCHOSIS, SEVERE DEPRESSIONS, IRRITABILTY, CONFUSION, APATHY, EMOTIONAL LABILITY, SOCIAL WITHDRAWAL, CONFUSION, HEADACHE, SPEECH DIFFICULTIES, DELAYED REACTION TIMES, SPATIAL DISORIENTATION, NIGHTMARES, SLEEPWALKING, AND DROWSINESS OR INSOMNIA. AN INFLUENZA-LIKE CONDITION WITH HEADACHE, NAUSEA, WEAKNESS, ANOREXIA AND MALAISE HAS ALSO BEEN REPORTED.

FIRST AID- REMOVE FROM EXPOSURE AREA TO FRESH AIR IMMEDIATELY. IF BREATHING HAS STOPPED, GIVE ARTIFICIAL RESPIRATION. MAINTAIN AIRWAY AND BLOOD PRESSURE AND ADMINISTER OXYGEN IF AVAILABLE. KEEP AFFECTED PERSON WARM AND AT REST. TREAT SYMPTOMATICALLY AND SUPPORTIVELY. ADMINISTRATION OF OXYGEN SHOULD BE PERFORMED BY QUALIFIED PERSONNEL. GET MEDICAL ATTENTION IMMEDIATELY.

SKIN CONTACT: METHIDATHION: HIGHLY TOXIC. THIS MATERIAL APPLIED TO THE SKIN OF RABBITS WAS SLIGHTLY IRRITATING. SEE INFORMATION ON ORGANOPHOSPHATES.
ORGANOPHOSPHATES: CHOLINESTERASE INHIBITOR. **ACUTE EXPOSURE**- LOCALIZED SWEATING AND FASCICULATIONS MAY OCCUR AT THE SITE OF CONTACT. IF SUFFICIENT AMOUNTS ARE ABSORBED, OTHER EFFECTS OF CHOLINESTERASE INHIBITION AS DESCRIBED IN ACUTE INHALATION MAY OCCUR. SYMPTOMS MAY BE DELAYED 2-3 HOURS, BUT USUALLY NO MORE THAN 12 HOURS. THE RATE OF ABSORPTION IS INCREASED BY THE PRESENCE OF DERMATITIS OR HIGH AMBIENT TEMPERATURES. DELAYED NEUROPATHY IS ALSO POSSIBLE. **CHRONIC EXPOSURE**- REPEATED OR PROLONGED EXPOSURE MAY CAUSE EFFECTS AS DESCRIBED IN ACUTE EXPOSURE. SOME ORGANOPHOSPHATES MAY CAUSE SENSITIZATION.

FIRST AID- REMOVE CONTAMINATED CLOTHING IMMEDIATELY. WASH CONTAMINATED AREAS WITH SOAP AND WATER FOLLOWED BY ALCOHOL (ARENA, POISONING, 4TH ED.). EMERGENCY PERSONNEL SHOULD WEAR GLOVES AND AVOID CONTAMINATION. TREAT RESPIRATORY DIFFICULTY WITH ARTIFICIAL RESPIRATION. GET MEDICAL ATTENTION IMMEDIATELY.

EYE CONTACT: METHIDATHION: THIS MATERIAL APPLIED TO THE EYES OF RABBITS WAS NOT IRRITATING, HOWEVER A EMULSIFIABLE CONCENTRATE FORMULATION WAS SEVERELY IRRITATING. SEE INFORMATION ON ORGANOPHOSPHATES.
ORGANOPHOSPHATES: CHOLINESTERASE INHIBITOR. **ACUTE EXPOSURE**- DIRECT CONTACT MAY CAUSE PAIN, HYPEREMIA, LACRIMATION, TWITCHING OF THE EYELIDS, MIOSIS, AND CILIARY MUSCLE SPASM WITH LOSS OF ACCOMODATION, BLURRED OR DIMMED VISION AND BROWACHE. SOMETIMES MYDRIASIS MAY OCCUR INSTEAD OF MIOSIS. WITH SUFFICIENT EXPOSURE, OTHER SYMPTOMS OF CHOLINESTERASE INHIBITION AS DESCRIBED IN ACUTE INHALATION MAY OCCUR. **CHRONIC EXPOSURE**- REPEATED OR PROLONGED EXPOSURE MAY CAUSE EFFECTS AS DESCRIBED IN ACUTE EXPOSURE. SOME COMPOUNDS HAVE CAUSED TOXIC EFFECTS ON THE CRYSTALLINE LENS, CONJUNCTIVAL THICKENING AND OBSTRUCTION OF THE NASOLACRIMAL CANALS WHEN USED AS MIOTIC EYEDROPS.

FIRST AID- IRRIGATE EYES WITH WATER OR SALINE SOLUTION. IF SYMPTOMS OF POISONING OCCUR, TREAT RESPIRATORY DIFFICULTY WITH ARTIFICIAL RESPIRATION AND OXYGEN. OBSERVE PATIENT FOR AT LEAST 24-36 HOURS (GOSSELIN, CLINICAL TOXICOLOGY OF COMMERCIAL PRODUCTS, 5TH ED.). GET MEDICAL ATTENTION IMMEDIATELY. OXYGEN SHOULD BE ADMINISTERED BY QUALIFIED MEDICAL PERSONNEL.

INGESTION: METHIDATHION: HIGHLY TOXIC. SEE INFORMATION ON ORGANOPHOSPHATES.
ORGANOPHOSPHATES: CHOLINESTERASE INHIBITOR. **ACUTE EXPOSURE**- WHEN INGESTED, THE FIRST EFFECTS MAY BE NAUSEA, VOMITING, ANOREXIA, ABDOMINAL CRAMPS AND DIARRHEA. GASTROINTESTINAL ABSORPTION MAY CAUSE SYMPTOMS OF CHOLINESTERASE INHIBITION AS DESCRIBED IN ACUTE INHALATION. SYMPTOMS MAY BEGIN WITHIN MINUTES OR BE DELAYED FOR HOURS. DELAYED EFFECTS INCLUDING NEUROPATHY MAY ALSO OCCUR. **CHRONIC EXPOSURE**- REPEATED INGESTION MAY CAUSE EFFECTS AS DESCRIBED IN ACUTE EXPOSURE.

FIRST AID- IF PERSON IS ALERT AND RESPIRATION IS NOT DEPRESSED, GIVE SYRUP OF IPECAC FOLLOWED BY WATER (IF VOMITING OCCURS, KEEP HEAD BELOW HIPS TO PREVENT ASPIRATION). IF CONSCIOUSNESS LEVEL DECLINES OR VOMITING HAS NOT OCCURRED IN 15 MINUTES EMPTY STOMACH BY GASTRIC LAVAGE WITH THE AID OF CUFFED ENDOTRACHEAL TUBE USING ISOTONIC SALINE OR 5% SODIUM BICARBONATE FOLLOW WITH ACTIVATED CHARCOAL. ESTABLISH AND MAINTAIN AIRWAY. TREAT RESPIRATORY DIFFICULTY WITH ARTIFICIAL RESPIRATION AND OXYGEN. DO NOT GIVE MORPHINE, AMINOPHYLLINE, PHENOTHIAZINES, RESERPINE, FUROSEMIDE, OR ETHACRYNIC ACID (MORGAN, RECOGNITION AND MANAGEMENT OF PESTICIDE POISONINGS, 3RD ED.). TREAT SYMPTOMATICALLY AND SUPPORTIVELY. ADMINISTRATION OF OXYGEN AND LAVAGE MUST BE PERFORMED BY QUALIFIED MEDICAL PERSONNEL. GET MEDICAL ATTENTION IMMEDIATELY.

ANTIDOTE: THE FOLLOWING ANTIDOTE(S) HAVE BEEN RECOMMENDED. HOWEVER, THE DECISION AS TO WHETHER THE SEVERITY OF POISONING REQUIRES ADMINISTRATION OF ANY ANTIDOTE AND ACTUAL DOSE REQUIRED SHOULD BE MADE BY QUALIFIED MEDICAL PERSONNEL.
FOR CHOLINESTERASE INHIBITORS: ESTABLISH CLEAR AIRWAY AND TISSUE OXYGENATION BY ASPIRATION OF SECRETIONS, AND IF NECESSARY, BY ASSISTED PULMONARY VENTILATION WITH OXYGEN. IMPROVE TISSUE OXYGENATION AS MUCH AS POSSIBLE BEFORE ADMINISTERING ATROPINE TO MINIMIZE THE RISK OF VENTRICULAR FIBRILLATION. ADMINISTER ATROPINE SULFATE INTRAVENOUSLY, OR INTRAMUSCULARLY IF IV INJECTION IS NOT POSSIBLE. IN MODERATELY SEVERE POISONING ADMINISTER ATROPINE SULFATE, 0.4-2.0 MG REPEATED EVERY 15 MINUTES UNTIL ATROPINIZATION IS ACHIEVED (TACHYCARDIA, FLUSHING, DRY MOUTH, MYDRIASIS). MAINTAIN ATROPINIZATION BY REPEATED DOSES FOR 2-12 HOURS, OR LONGER, DEPENDING ON THE SEVERITY OF POISONING. THE APPEARANCE OF RALES IN THE LUNG BASES, MIOSIS, SALIVATION, NAUSEA, BRADYCARDIA, ARE ALL INDICATIONS OF INADEQUATE ATROPINIZATION. SEVERELY POISONED INDIVIDUALS MAY EXHIBIT REMARKABLE TOLERANCE TO ATROPINE; TWO OR MORE TIMES THE DOSAGES SUGGESTED ABOVE MAY BE NEEDED. PERSONS NOT POISONED OR ONLY SLIGHTLY POISONED, HOWEVER, MAY DEVELOP SIGNS OF ATROPINE TOXICITY FROM SUCH LARGE DOSAGES: FEVER, MUSCLE FIBRILLATIONS, AND DELIRIUM ARE THE MAIN SIGNS OF ATROPINE TOXICITY. IF THESE SIGNS APPEAR WHILE THE PATIENT IS FULLY ATROPINIZED, ATROPINE ADMINISTRATION SHOULD BE DISCONTINUED, AT LEAST TEMPORARILY. OBSERVE TREATED PATIENTS CLOSELY AT LEAST 24 HOURS TO INSURE THAT SYMPTOMS (POSSIBLY PULMONARY EDEMA) DO NOT RECUR AS ATROPINIZATION WEARS OFF. IN VERY SEVERE POISONINGS, METABOLIC DISPOSITION OF TOXICANT MAY REQUIRE SEVERAL HOURS OR DAYS DURING WHICH ATROPINIZATION MUST BE MAINTAINED. MARKEDLY LOWER LEVELS OF URINARY METABOLITES INDICATE THAT ATROPINE DOSAGE CAN BE TAPERED OFF. AS DOSAGE IS REDUCED, CHECK THE LUNG BASES FREQUENTLY FOR RALES. IF RALES ARE HEARD OR OTHER SYMPTOMS RETURN, RE-ESTABLISH ATROPINIZATION PROMPTLY (MORGAN, RECOGNITION AND MANAGEMENT OF PESTICIDE POISONINGS, 3RD ED.). ADMINISTRATION OF ANTIDOTE MUST BE PERFORMED BY QUALIFIED MEDICAL PERSONNEL.
IN CASES OF SEVERE POISONING BY ORGANOPHOSPHATE PESTICIDES IN WHICH RESPIRATORY DEPRESSION, MUSCLE WEAKNESS AND TWITCHINGS ARE SEVERE, GIVE PRALIDOXIME (PROTOPAM-AYERST, 2-PAM), 1.0 GRAM INTRAVENOUSLY AT NO MORE THAN 0.5 GRAM PER MINUTE. DOSAGE OF PRALIDOXIME MAY BE REPEATED IN 1-2 HOURS, THEN AT 10-12 HOUR INTERVALS IF NEEDED. IN VERY SEVERE POISONINGS, DOSAGE RATES MAY BE DOUBLED. TREATMENT WITH PRALIDOXIME WILL BE MOST EFFECTIVE IF GIVEN WITHIN THIRTY-SIX HOURS AFTER POISONING (MORGAN, RECOGNITION AND MANAGEMENT OF PESTICIDE POISONINGS, 3RD ED.). ANTIDOTE SHOULD BE ADMINISTERED BY QUALIFIED MEDICAL PERSONNEL.

REACTIVITY

REACTIVITY: STABLE UNDER NORMAL TEMPERATURES AND PRESSURES.

INCOMPATIBILITIES: METHIDATHION: ALKALINE CONDITION: MAY CAUSE HYDROLYSIS.

DECOMPOSITION: THERMAL DECOMPOSITION MAY RELEASE TOXIC AND/OR HAZARDOUS GASES.

POLYMERIZATION: HAZARDOUS POLYMERIZATION HAS NOT BEEN REPORTED TO OCCUR UNDER NORMAL TEMPERATURES AND PRESSURES.

STORAGE AND DISPOSAL

OBSERVE ALL FEDERAL, STATE AND LOCAL REGULATIONS WHEN STORING OR DISPOSING OF THIS SUBSTANCE. FOR ASSISTANCE, CONTACT THE DISTRICT DIRECTOR OF THE ENVIRONMENTAL PROTECTION AGENCY.

STORAGE

STORE IN ACCORDANCE WITH 40 CFR 165 RECOMMENDED PROCEDURES FOR THE DISPOSAL AND STORAGE OF PESTICIDES AND PESTICIDE CONTAINERS.
STORE AWAY FROM INCOMPATIBLE SUBSTANCES.
THRESHOLD PLANNING QUANTITY (TPQ): THE SUPERFUND AMENDMENTS AND REAUTHORIZATION ACT (SARA) SECTION 302 REQUIRES THAT EACH FACILITY WHERE ANY EXTREMELY HAZARDOUS SUBSTANCE IS PRESENT IN A QUANTITY EQUAL TO OR GREATER THAN THE TPQ ESTABLISHED FOR THAT SUBSTANCE NOTIFY THE STATE EMERGENCY RESPONSE COMMISSION FOR THE STATE IN WHICH IT IS LOCATED. SECTION 303 OF SARA REQUIRES THESE FACILITIES TO PARTICIPATE IN LOCAL EMERGENCY RESPONSE PLANNING (40 CFR 355.30).

DISPOSAL

DISPOSAL MUST BE IN ACCORDANCE WITH 40 CFR 165 RECOMMENDED PROCEDURES FOR THE DISPOSAL AND STORAGE OF PESTICIDES AND PESTICIDE CONTAINERS.

CONDITIONS TO AVOID

NONE REPORTED.

SPILL AND LEAK PROCEDURES

OCCUPATIONAL SPILL: DO NOT TOUCH SPILLED MATERIAL. STOP LEAK IF YOU CAN DO IT WITHOUT RISK. USE WATER SPRAY TO REDUCE VAPORS. FOR SMALL SPILLS, TAKE UP WITH SAND OR OTHER ABSORBENT MATERIAL AND PLACE INTO CONTAINERS FOR LATER DISPOSAL. FOR SMALL DRY SPILLS, WITH A CLEAN SHOVEL PLACE MATERIAL INTO CLEAN, DRY CONTAINERS AND COVER. MOVE CONTAINERS FROM SPILL AREA. FOR LARGER SPILLS, DIKE FAR AHEAD OF SPILL FOR LATER DISPOSAL. KEEP UNNECESSARY PEOPLE AWAY. ISOLATE HAZARD AREA AND DENY ENTRY. VENTILATE CLOSED SPACES BEFORE ENTERING.
REPORTABLE QUANTITY (RQ): 1 POUND THE SUPERFUND AMENDMENTS AND REAUTHORIZATION ACT (SARA) SECTION 304 REQUIRES THAT A RELEASE EQUAL TO OR GREATER THAN THE REPORTABLE QUANTITY FOR THIS SUBSTANCE BE IMMEDIATELY REPORTED TO THE LOCAL EMERGENCY PLANNING COMMITTEE AND THE STATE EMERGENCY RESPONSE COMMISSION (40 CFR 355.40). IF THE RELEASE OF THIS SUBSTANCE IS REPORTABLE UNDER CERCLA SECTION 103, THE NATIONAL RESPONSE CENTER MUST BE NOTIFIED IMMEDIATELY AT (800) 424-8802 OR (202) 426-2675 IN THE METROPOLITAN WASHINGTON, D.C. AREA (40 CFR 302.6).

PROTECTIVE EQUIPMENT

VENTILATION: PROCESS ENCLOSURE RECOMMENDED.

RESPIRATOR: THE FOLLOWING RESPIRATORS ARE RECOMMENDED BASED ON INFORMATION FOUND IN THE PHYSICAL DATA, TOXICITY AND HEALTH EFFECTS SECTIONS. THEY ARE RANKED IN ORDER FROM MINIMUM TO MAXIMUM RESPIRATORY PROTECTION. THE SPECIFIC RESPIRATOR SELECTED MUST BE BASED ON CONTAMINATION LEVELS FOUND IN THE WORK PLACE, MUST NOT EXCEED THE WORKING LIMITS OF THE RESPIRATOR AND BE JOINTLY APPROVED BY THE NATIONAL INSTITUTE FOR OCCUPATIONAL SAFETY AND HEALTH AND THE MINE SAFETY AND HEALTH ADMINISTRATION (NIOSH-MSHA).
TYPE 'C' SUPPLIED-AIR RESPIRATOR WITH A FULL FACEPIECE OPERATED IN PRESSURE-DEMAND OR OTHER POSITIVE PRESSURE MODE OR WITH A FULL FACEPIECE, HELMET OR HOOD OPERATED IN CONTINOUS-FLOW MODE.
SELF-CONTAINED BREATHING APPARATUS WITH A FULL FACEPIECE OPERATED IN PRESSURE-DEMAND OR OTHER POSITIVE PRESSURE MODE.
FOR FIREFIGHTING AND OTHER IMMEDIATELY DANGEROUS TO LIFE OR HEALTH CONDITIONS:
SELF-CONTAINED BREATHING APPARATUS WITH FULL FACEPIECE OPERATED IN PRESSURE-DEMAND OR OTHER POSITIVE PRESSURE MODE. SUPPLIED-AIR RESPIRATOR WITH FULL FACEPIECE AND OPERATED IN PRESSURE-DEMAND OR OTHER POSITIVE PRESSURE MODE IN COMBINATION WITH AN AUXILIARY SELF-CONTAINED BREATHING APPARATUS OPERATED IN PRESSURE-DEMAND OR OTHER POSITIVE PRESSURE MODE.

CLOTHING: EMPLOYEE MUST WEAR APPROPRIATE PROTECTIVE (IMPERVIOUS) CLOTHING AND EQUIPMENT TO PREVENT ANY POSSIBILITY OF SKIN CONTACT WITH THIS SUBSTANCE.

GLOVES: EMPLOYEE MUST WEAR APPROPRIATE PROTECTIVE GLOVES TO PREVENT CONTACT WITH THIS SUBSTANCE.

EYE PROTECTION: EMPLOYEE MUST WEAR SPLASH-PROOF OR DUST-RESISTANT SAFETY GOGGLES AND A FACESHIELD TO PREVENT CONTACT WITH THIS SUBSTANCE.
EMERGENCY WASH FACILITIES: WHERE THERE IS ANY POSSIBILITY THAT AN EMPLOYEE'S EYES AND/OR SKIN MAY BE EXPOSED TO THIS SUBSTANCE, THE EMPLOYER SHOULD PROVIDE AN EYE WASH FOUNTAIN AND QUICK DRENCH SHOWER WITHIN THE IMMEDIATE WORK AREA FOR EMERGENCY USE.

AUTHORIZED BY- OCCUPATIONAL HEALTH SERVICES, INC.
CREATION DATE: 10/04/89 ***REVISION DATE:*** 05/01/90

MATERIAL SAFETY DATA SHEET

OCCUPATIONAL HEALTH SERVICES, INC.
AGRICULTURE AND PESTICIDE DIVISION
450 SEVENTH AVENUE, SUITE 2407
NEW YORK, NEW YORK 10123
1-800-445-MSDS OR (212) 967-1100

EMERGENCY CONTACT:
JOHN S. BRANSFORD, JR. (615) 292-1180

SUBSTANCE IDENTIFICATION

CAS-NUMBER 2032-65-7

SUBSTANCE: METHIOCARB

TRADE NAMES/SYNONYMS: PHENOL, 3,5-DIMETHYL-4-(METHYLTHIO)-, METHYLCARBAMATE; CARBAMIC ACID, METHYL-, 4-(METHYLTHIO)-3,5-XYLYL ESTER; 3,5-DIMETHYL-4-(METHYLTHIO)PHENOL METHYLCARBAMATE; METHYLCARBAMIC ACID 4-(METHYLTHIO)-3,5-XYLYL ESTER; 4-METHYLTHIO-3,5-XYLYL METHYLCARBAMATE; 3,5-DIMETHYL-4-(METHYLTHIO)PHENYL METHYLCARBAMATE; 4-(METHYLTHIO)-3,5-XYLYL METHYLCARBAMATE; 4-METHYLTHIO-3,5-DIMETHYLPHENYL N-METHYLCARBAMATE; 3,5-DIMETHYL-4-METHYLTHIOPHENYL METHYLCARBAMATE; MERCAPTODIMETHUR; METMERCAPTURON; MESUROL; DRAZA; ENT 25 726; C11H15NO2S; PST14190

CHEMICAL FAMILY: CARBAMATE

MOLECULAR FORMULA: C11-H15-N-O2-S

MOLECULAR WEIGHT: 225.33

CERCLA RATINGS (SCALE 0-3): HEALTH=3 FIRE=1 REACTIVITY=0 PERSISTENCE=2

NFPA RATINGS (SCALE 0-4): HEALTH=3 FIRE=1 REACTIVITY=0

COMPONENTS AND CONTAMINANTS

COMPONENT: METHIOCARB ***PERCENT:*** 100.00
CAS# 2032-65-7

EXPOSURE LIMITS: NO OCCUPATIONAL EXPOSURE LIMITS ESTABLISHED BY OSHA, ACGIH, OR NIOSH.
METHIOCARB: 500/10,000 POUNDS SARA SECTION 302 THRESHOLD PLANNING QUANTITY 10 POUNDS SARA SECTION 304 REPORTABLE QUANTITY 10 POUNDS CERCLA SECTION 103 REPORTABLE QUANTITY

PHYSICAL DATA

DESCRIPTION: WHITE CRYSTALLINE POWDER WITH A MILD ODOR

MELTING POINT: 250 F (121 C) ***SPECIFIC GRAVITY:*** NOT AVAILABLE

SOLUBILITY IN WATER: 10 PPM @ 20 C

SOLVENT SOLUBILITY: SOLUBLE IN ACETONE, ALCOHOL, DICHLOROMETHANE, PROPAN-2-OL, ORGANIC SOLVENTS

FIRE AND EXPLOSION DATA

FIRE AND EXPLOSION HAZARD: SLIGHT FIRE HAZARD WHEN EXPOSED TO HEAT OR FLAME.

FIREFIGHTING MEDIA: DRY CHEMICAL, CARBON DIOXIDE, HALON, WATER SPRAY OR STANDARD FOAM (1987 EMERGENCY RESPONSE GUIDEBOOK, DOT P 5800.4).
FOR LARGER FIRES, USE WATER SPRAY, FOG OR STANDARD FOAM (1987 EMERGENCY RESPONSE GUIDEBOOK, DOT P 5800.4).

FIREFIGHTING: MOVE CONTAINERS FROM FIRE AREA IF POSSIBLE (1987 EMERGENCY RESPONSE GUIDEBOOK, DOT P 5800.4, GUIDE PAGE 53).
EXTINGUISH USING AGENTS SUITABLE FOR TYPE OF SURROUNDING FIRE. USE FLOODING AMOUNTS OF WATER AS FOG. AVOID BREATHING TOXIC DUST AND FUMES FROM BURNING MATERIAL; KEEP UPWIND.

TRANSPORTATION DATA

DEPARTMENT OF TRANSPORTATION HAZARD CLASSIFICATION 49 CFR 172.101: POISON B
DEPARTMENT OF TRANSPORTATION LABELING REQUIREMENTS 49 CFR 172.101 AND SUBPART E: POISON
DEPARTMENT OF TRANSPORTATION PACKAGING REQUIREMENTS: 49 CFR 173.365 EXCEPTIONS: 49 CFR 173.364

TOXICITY

METHIOCARB: TOXICITY DATA: 350 MG/KG SKIN-RAT LD50; 10 MG/KG ORAL-RAT LD50; 25,200 UG/KG ORAL-MOUSE LD50; 40 MG/KG ORAL-GUINEA PIG LD50; 940 MG/KG SUBCUTANEOUS-MOUSE LD50; 16 MG/KG INTRAPERITONEAL-MOUSE LD50; 100 MG/KG UNREPORTED-RAT LD50. CARCINOGEN STATUS: NONE. ACUTE TOXICITY LEVEL: HIGHLY TOXIC BY INGESTION; TOXIC BY DERMAL ABSORPTION. TARGET EFFECTS: CHOLINESTERASE INHIBITOR. AT INCREASED RISK FROM EXPOSURE: PERSONS WITH ASTHMA, DIABETES, CARDIOVASCULAR DISEASE, MECHANICAL OBSTRUCTION OF THE GASTROINTESTINAL OR UROGENITAL TRACT, AND THOSE IN VAGOTONIC STATES.*

* MAY BE BASED ON GENERAL INFORMATION ON CARBAMATES.

HEALTH EFFECTS AND FIRST AID

INHALATION: METHIOCARB: SEE INFORMATION ON CARBAMATES.

CARBAMATES: CHOLINESTERASE INHIBITOR. **ACUTE EXPOSURE-** WHEN INHALED, THE FIRST EFFECTS OF CHOLINESTERASE INHIBITION ARE USUALLY RESPIRATORY AND MAY INCLUDE NASAL HYPEREMIA AND WATERY DISCHARGE, CHEST DISCOMFORT, DYSPNEA, AND WHEEZING DUE TO INCREASED BRONCHIAL SECRETIONS AND BRONCHOCONSTRICTION. OTHER SYSTEMIC EFFECTS MAY BEGIN WITHIN A FEW MINUTES OR SEVERAL HOURS OF EXPOSURE. SYMPTOMS MAY INCLUDE NAUSEA, VOMITING, DIARRHEA, ABDOMINAL CRAMPS, HEADACHE, VERTIGO, OCULAR PAIN, CILIARY MUSCLE SPASM, BLURRING OR DIMNESS OF VISION, MIOSIS, OR IN SOME CASES MYDRIASIS, LACRIMATION, SALIVATION, SWEATING, AND CONFUSION. OTHER REPORTED CENTRAL NERVOUS SYSTEM OR NEUROMUSCULAR EFFECTS INCLUDE ATAXIA, SLURRED SPEECH, AREFLEXIA, WEAKNESS, FATIGUE, TWITCHING, FASCICULATION, TREMOR, AND EVENTUALLY PARALYSIS OF THE EXTREMITIES AND POSSIBLY OF THE RESPIRATORY MUSCLES. IN SEVERE CASES, THERE MAY ALSO BE INVOLUNTARY DEFECATION AND URINATION, BRADYCARDIA, HYPOTENSION, PULMONARY EDEMA, CONVULSIONS, COMA, AND DEATH FROM RESPIRATORY FAILURE OR CARDIAC ARREST. CARBAMATES GENERALLY DO NOT ACCUMULATE IN MAMMALIAN TISSUE AND THE CHOLINESTERASE INHIBITION REVERSES RATHER RAPIDLY. IN NON-FATAL CASES, THE ILLNESS GENERALLY LASTS LESS THAN 24 HOURS. **CHRONIC EXPOSURE-** PROLONGED OR REPEATED EXPOSURE MAY CAUSE EFFECTS AS DESCRIBED IN ACUTE EXPOSURE.

FIRST AID- REMOVE FROM EXPOSURE AREA TO FRESH AIR IMMEDIATELY. IF BREATHING HAS STOPPED, GIVE ARTIFICIAL RESPIRATION. MAINTAIN AIRWAY AND BLOOD PRESSURE AND ADMINISTER OXYGEN IF AVAILABLE. KEEP AFFECTED PERSON WARM AND AT REST. TREAT SYMPTOMATICALLY AND SUPPORTIVELY. ADMINISTRATION OF OXYGEN SHOULD BE PERFORMED BY QUALIFIED PERSONNEL. GET MEDICAL ATTENTION IMMEDIATELY.

SKIN CONTACT: METHIOCARB: TOXIC. SEE INFORMATION ON CARBAMATES.

CARBAMATES: CHOLINESTERASE INHIBITOR. **ACUTE EXPOSURE-** SOME COMPOUNDS MAY CAUSE IRRITATION. LOCALIZED SWEATING AND FASCICULATIONS MAY OCCUR AT THE SITE OF CONTACT. IF SUFFICIENT AMOUNTS ARE ABSORBED THROUGH THE SKIN, OTHER EFFECTS OF CHOLINESTERASE INHIBITION MAY OCCUR AS DESCRIBED IN ACUTE INHALATION; SYMPTOMS MAY BE DELAYED FOR 2-3 HOURS, USUALLY NO MORE THAN 8 HOURS. **CHRONIC EXPOSURE-** REPEATED OR PROLONGED EXPOSURE MAY CAUSE EFFECTS AS DESCRIBED IN ACUTE EXPOSURE.

FIRST AID- REMOVE CONTAMINATED CLOTHING IMMEDIATELY. WASH CONTAMINATED AREAS WITH SOAP AND WATER FOLLOWED BY ALCOHOL (ARENA, POISONING, 4TH ED.). EMERGENCY PERSONNEL SHOULD WEAR GLOVES AND AVOID CONTAMINATION. TREAT RESPIRATORY DIFFICULTY WITH ARTIFICIAL RESPIRATION. GET MEDICAL ATTENTION IMMEDIATELY.

EYE CONTACT: METHIOCARB: SEE INFORMATION ON CARBAMATES.

CARBAMATES: CHOLINESTERASE INHIBITOR. **ACUTE EXPOSURE-** DIRECT CONTACT MAY CAUSE PAIN, HYPEREMIA, LACRIMATION, TWITCHING OF THE EYELIDS, MIOSIS, AND CILIARY MUSCLE SPASM WITH LOSS OF ACCOMODATION, BLURRED OR DIMMED VISION AND BROWACHE. SOMETIMES MYDRIASIS MAY OCCUR INSTEAD OF MIOSIS. WITH SUFFICIENT EXPOSURE, OTHER SYMPTOMS OF CHOLINESTERASE INHIBITION MAY OCCUR AS DESCRIBED IN ACUTE INHALATION. **CHRONIC EXPOSURE-** PROLONGED EXPOSURE MAY CAUSE EFFECTS AS DESCRIBED IN ACUTE EXPOSURE. SOME COMPOUNDS HAVE CAUSED TOXIC EFFECTS ON THE CRYSTALLINE LENS, CONJUNCTIVAL THICKENING AND OBSTRUCTION OF NASOLACRIMAL CANALS WHEN USED AS MIOTIC EYE DROPS.

FIRST AID- IRRIGATE EYES WITH WATER OR SALINE SOLUTION. IF SYMPTOMS OF POISONING OCCUR, TREAT RESPIRATORY DIFFICULTY WITH ARTIFICIAL RESPIRATION AND OXYGEN. OBSERVE PATIENT FOR AT LEAST 24-36 HOURS (GOSSELIN, CLINICAL TOXICOLOGY OF COMMERCIAL PRODUCTS, 5TH ED.). GET MEDICAL ATTENTION IMMEDIATELY. OXYGEN SHOULD BE ADMINISTERED BY QUALIFIED MEDICAL PERSONNEL.

INGESTION: METHIOCARB: HIGHLY TOXIC. NO MYELIN DEGENERATION WAS OBSERVED IN A DELAYED NEUROTOXICITY STUDY OF HENS. SEE INFORMATION ON CARBAMATES.

CARBAMATES: CHOLINESTERASE INHIBITOR. **ACUTE EXPOSURE-** WHEN INGESTED, THE FIRST EFFECTS MAY BE NAUSEA, VOMITING, ANOREXIA, ABDOMINAL CRAMPS, AND DIARRHEA. WITH ABSORPTION FROM THE GASTROINTESTINAL TRACT, THE OTHER EFFECTS OF CHOLINESTERASE INHIBITION AS DESCRIBED IN ACUTE INHALATION MAY OCCUR; SYMPTOMS MAY BEGIN WITHIN MINUTES OR BE DELAYED SEVERAL HOURS. **CHRONIC EXPOSURE-** REPEATED INGESTION MAY CAUSE EFFECTS AS DESCRIBED IN ACUTE EXPOSURE.

FIRST AID- IF PERSON IS ALERT AND RESPIRATION IS NOT DEPRESSED, GIVE SYRUP OF IPECAC FOLLOWED BY WATER (IF VOMITING OCCURS, KEEP HEAD BELOW HIPS TO PREVENT ASPIRATION). IF CONSCIOUSNESS LEVEL DECLINES OR VOMITING HAS NOT OCCURRED IN 15 MINUTES EMPTY STOMACH BY GASTRIC LAVAGE WITH THE AID OF CUFFED ENDOTRACHEAL TUBE USING ISOTONIC SALINE OR 5% SODIUM BICARBONATE FOLLOW WITH ACTIVATED CHARCOAL. ESTABLISH AND MAINTAIN AIRWAY. TREAT RESPIRATORY DIFFICULTY WITH ARTIFICIAL RESPIRATION AND OXYGEN. DO NOT GIVE MORPHINE, AMINOPHYLLINE, PHENOTHIAZINES, RESERPINE, FUROSEMIDE, OR ETHACRYNIC ACID (MORGAN, RECOGNITION AND MANAGEMENT OF PESTICIDE POISONINGS, 3RD ED.). TREAT SYMPTOMATICALLY AND SUPPORTIVELY. ADMINISTRATION OF OXYGEN AND LAVAGE MUST BE PERFORMED BY QUALIFIED MEDICAL PERSONNEL. GET MEDICAL ATTENTION IMMEDIATELY.

ANTIDOTE: THE FOLLOWING ANTIDOTE HAS BEEN RECOMMENDED. HOWEVER, THE DECISION AS TO WHETHER THE SEVERITY OF POISONING REQUIRES ADMINISTRATION OF ANY ANTIDOTE AND ACTUAL DOSE REQUIRED SHOULD BE MADE BY QUALIFIED MEDICAL PERSONNEL.

FOR CHOLINESTERASE INHIBITORS: ESTABLISH CLEAR AIRWAY AND TISSUE OXYGENATION BY ASPIRATION OF SECRETIONS, AND IF NECESSARY, BY ASSISTED PULMONARY VENTILATION WITH OXYGEN. IMPROVE TISSUE OXYGENATION AS MUCH AS POSSIBLE BEFORE ADMINISTERING ATROPINE TO MINIMIZE THE RISK OF VENTRICULAR FIBRILLATION. ADMINISTER ATROPINE SULFATE INTRAVENOUSLY, OR INTRAMUSCULARLY IF IV INJECTION IS NOT POSSIBLE. IN MODERATELY SEVERE POISONING ADMINISTER ATROPINE SULFATE, 0.4-2.0 MG REPEATED EVERY 15 MINUTES UNTIL ATROPINIZATION IS ACHIEVED (TACHYCARDIA, FLUSHING, DRY MOUTH, MYDRIASIS). MAINTAIN ATROPINIZATION BY REPEATED DOSES FOR 2-12 HOURS, OR LONGER, DEPENDING ON THE SEVERITY OF POISONING. THE APPEARANCE OF RALES IN THE LUNG BASES, MIOSIS, SALIVATION, NAUSEA, BRADYCARDIA, ARE ALL INDICATIONS OF INADEQUATE ATROPINIZATION. SEVERELY POISONED INDIVIDUALS MAY EXHIBIT REMARKABLE TOLERANCE TO ATROPINE; TWO OR MORE TIMES THE DOSAGES SUGGESTED ABOVE MAY BE NEEDED. PERSONS NOT POISONED OR ONLY SLIGHTLY POISONED, HOWEVER, MAY DEVELOP SIGNS OF ATROPINE TOXICITY FROM SUCH LARGE DOSAGES: FEVER, MUSCLE FIBRILLATIONS, AND DELIRIUM ARE THE MAIN SIGNS OF ATROPINE TOXICITY. IF THESE SIGNS APPEAR WHILE THE PATIENT IS FULLY ATROPINIZED, ATROPINE ADMINISTRATION SHOULD BE DISCONTINUED, AT LEAST TEMPORARILY. OBSERVE TREATED PATIENTS CLOSELY AT LEAST 24 HOURS TO INSURE THAT SYMPTOMS (POSSIBLY PULMONARY EDEMA) DO NOT RECUR AS ATROPINIZATION WEARS OFF. IN VERY SEVERE POISONINGS, METABOLIC DISPOSITION OF TOXICANT MAY REQUIRE SEVERAL HOURS OR DAYS DURING WHICH ATROPINIZATION MUST BE MAINTAINED. MARKEDLY LOWER LEVELS OF URINARY METABOLITES INDICATE THAT ATROPINE DOSAGE CAN BE TAPERED OFF. AS DOSAGE IS REDUCED, CHECK THE LUNG BASES FREQUENTLY FOR RALES. IF RALES ARE HEARD OR OTHER SYMPTOMS RETURN, RE-ESTABLISH ATROPINIZATION PROMPTLY (MORGAN, RECOGNITION AND MANAGEMENT OF PESTICIDE POISONINGS, 3RD ED.). ADMINISTRATION OF ANTIDOTE MUST BE PERFORMED BY QUALIFIED MEDICAL PERSONNEL.

REACTIVITY

REACTIVITY: STABLE UNDER NORMAL TEMPERATURES AND PRESSURES.

INCOMPATIBILITIES: METHIOCARB: ALKALINE MATERIAL: MAY HYDROLYZE.

DECOMPOSITION: THERMAL DECOMPOSITION MAY RELEASE TOXIC OXIDES OF NITROGEN AND SULFUR.

POLYMERIZATION: HAZARDOUS POLYMERIZATION HAS NOT BEEN REPORTED TO OCCUR UNDER NORMAL TEMPERATURES AND PRESSURES.

STORAGE AND DISPOSAL

OBSERVE ALL FEDERAL, STATE AND LOCAL REGULATIONS WHEN STORING OR DISPOSING OF THIS SUBSTANCE. FOR ASSISTANCE, CONTACT THE DISTRICT DIRECTOR OF THE ENVIRONMENTAL PROTECTION AGENCY.

STORAGE

STORE IN ACCORDANCE WITH 40 CFR 165 RECOMMENDED PROCEDURES FOR THE DISPOSAL AND STORAGE OF PESTICIDES AND PESTICIDE CONTAINERS.

STORE AWAY FROM INCOMPATIBLE SUBSTANCES. THRESHOLD PLANNING QUANTITY (TPQ): THE SUPERFUND AMENDMENTS AND REAUTHORIZATION ACT (SARA) SECTION 302 REQUIRES THAT EACH FACILITY WHERE ANY EXTREMELY HAZARDOUS SUBSTANCE IS PRESENT IN A QUANTITY EQUAL TO OR GREATER THAN THE TPQ ESTABLISHED FOR THAT SUBSTANCE NOTIFY THE STATE

EMERGENCY RESPONSE COMMISSION FOR THE STATE IN WHICH IT IS LOCATED. SECTION 303 OF SARA REQUIRES THESE FACILITIES TO PARTICIPATE IN LOCAL EMERGENCY RESPONSE PLANNING (40 CFR 355.30).

DISPOSAL

DISPOSAL MUST BE IN ACCORDANCE WITH 40 CFR 165 RECOMMENDED PROCEDURES FOR THE DISPOSAL AND STORAGE OF PESTICIDES AND PESTICIDE CONTAINERS.

CONDITIONS TO AVOID

NONE REPORTED.

SPILL AND LEAK PROCEDURES

OCCUPATIONAL SPILL: DO NOT TOUCH SPILLED MATERIAL. STOP LEAK IF YOU CAN DO IT WITHOUT RISK. FOR SMALL SPILLS, TAKE UP WITH SAND OR OTHER ABSORBENT MATERIAL AND PLACE INTO CONTAINERS FOR LATER DISPOSAL. FOR SMALL DRY SPILLS, WITH A CLEAN SHOVEL PLACE MATERIAL INTO CLEAN, DRY CONTAINER AND COVER. MOVE CONTAINERS FROM SPILL AREA. FOR LARGER SPILLS, DIKE FAR AHEAD OF SPILL FOR LATER DISPOSAL. KEEP UNNECESSARY PEOPLE AWAY. ISOLATE HAZARD AREA AND DENY ENTRY.

REPORTABLE QUANTITY (RQ): 10 POUNDS THE SUPERFUND AMENDMENTS AND REAUTHORIZATION ACT (SARA) SECTION 304 REQUIRES THAT A RELEASE EQUAL TO OR GREATER THAN THE REPORTABLE QUANTITY FOR THIS SUBSTANCE BE IMMEDIATELY REPORTED TO THE LOCAL EMERGENCY PLANNING COMMITTEE AND THE STATE EMERGENCY RESPONSE COMMISSION (40 CFR 355.40). IF THE RELEASE OF THIS SUBSTANCE IS REPORTABLE UNDER CERCLA SECTION 103, THE NATIONAL RESPONSE CENTER MUST BE NOTIFIED IMMEDIATELY AT (800) 424-8802 OR (202) 426-2675 IN THE METROPOLITAN WASHINGTON, D.C. AREA (40 CFR 302.6).

PROTECTIVE EQUIPMENT

VENTILATION: PROVIDE LOCAL EXHAUST OR PROCESS ENCLOSURE VENTILATION SYSTEM.

RESPIRATOR: THE FOLLOWING RESPIRATORS ARE RECOMMENDED BASED ON INFORMATION FOUND IN THE PHYSICAL DATA, TOXICITY AND HEALTH EFFECTS SECTIONS. THEY ARE RANKED IN ORDER FROM MINIMUM TO MAXIMUM RESPIRATORY PROTECTION. THE SPECIFIC RESPIRATOR SELECTED MUST BE BASED ON CONTAMINATION LEVELS FOUND IN THE WORK PLACE, MUST NOT EXCEED THE WORKING LIMITS OF THE RESPIRATOR AND BE JOINTLY APPROVED BY THE NATIONAL INSTITUTE FOR OCCUPATIONAL SAFETY AND HEALTH AND THE MINE SAFETY AND HEALTH ADMINISTRATION (NIOSH-MSHA).

TYPE 'C' SUPPLIED-AIR RESPIRATOR WITH A FULL FACEPIECE OPERATED IN PRESSURE-DEMAND OR OTHER POSITIVE PRESSURE MODE OR WITH A FULL FACEPIECE, HELMET OR HOOD OPERATED IN CONTINOUS-FLOW MODE.

SELF-CONTAINED BREATHING APPARATUS WITH A FULL FACEPIECE OPERATED IN PRESSURE-DEMAND OR OTHER POSITIVE PRESSURE MODE.

FOR FIREFIGHTING AND OTHER IMMEDIATELY DANGEROUS TO LIFE OR HEALTH CONDITIONS:

SELF-CONTAINED BREATHING APPARATUS WITH FULL FACEPIECE OPERATED IN PRESSURE-DEMAND OR OTHER POSITIVE PRESSURE MODE.

SUPPLIED-AIR RESPIRATOR WITH FULL FACEPIECE AND OPERATED IN PRESSURE-DEMAND OR OTHER POSITIVE PRESSURE MODE IN COMBINATION WITH AN AUXILIARY SELF-CONTAINED BREATHING APPARATUS OPERATED IN PRESSURE-DEMAND OR OTHER POSITIVE PRESSURE MODE.

CLOTHING: EMPLOYEE MUST WEAR APPROPRIATE PROTECTIVE (IMPERVIOUS) CLOTHING AND EQUIPMENT TO PREVENT ANY POSSIBILITY OF SKIN CONTACT WITH THIS SUBSTANCE.

GLOVES: EMPLOYEE MUST WEAR APPROPRIATE PROTECTIVE GLOVES TO PREVENT CONTACT WITH THIS SUBSTANCE.

EYE PROTECTION: EMPLOYEE MUST WEAR SPLASH-PROOF OR DUST-RESISTANT SAFETY GOGGLES AND A FACESHIELD TO PREVENT CONTACT WITH THIS SUBSTANCE.

EMERGENCY WASH FACILITIES: WHERE THERE IS ANY POSSIBILITY THAT AN EMPLOYEE'S EYES AND/OR SKIN MAY BE EXPOSED TO THIS SUBSTANCE, THE EMPLOYER SHOULD PROVIDE AN EYE WASH FOUNTAIN AND QUICK DRENCH SHOWER WITHIN THE IMMEDIATE WORK AREA FOR EMERGENCY USE.

AUTHORIZED BY- OCCUPATIONAL HEALTH SERVICES, INC.

CREATION DATE: 10/04/89 ***REVISION DATE:*** 06/12/90

MATERIAL SAFETY DATA SHEET

OCCUPATIONAL HEALTH SERVICES, INC.
AGRICULTURE AND PESTICIDE DIVISION
450 SEVENTH AVENUE, SUITE 2407
NEW YORK, NEW YORK 10123
1-800-445-MSDS OR (212) 967-1100

EMERGENCY CONTACT:
JOHN S. BRANSFORD, JR. (615) 292-1180

SUBSTANCE IDENTIFICATION

CAS-NUMBER 2635-10-1

SUBSTANCE: METHIOCARB SULFOXIDE

TRADE NAMES/SYNONYMS: PHENOL, 3,5-DIMETHYL-4-(METHYLSULFINYL)-, METHYLCARBAMATE; 3,5-DIMETHYL-4-(METHYLSULFINYL)PHENOL METHYLCARBAMATE; CARBAMIC ACID, METHYL-, 4-(METHYLSULFINYL)-3,5-XYLYL ESTER; 4-(METHYLSULFINYL)-3,5-XYLYL ESTER METHYLCARBAMIC ACID; MESUROL SULFOXIDE; 4-(METHYLSULFINYL)-3,5-XYLYL METHYLCARBAMATE; C11H15NO3S; PST14191

CHEMICAL FAMILY: CARBAMATE
SULFOXIDE
AROMATIC

MOLECULAR FORMULA: C-H3-S-O-C6-H2-(C-H3)2-O-C-O-N-H-C-H3

MOLECULAR WEIGHT: 241.31

CERCLA RATINGS (SCALE 0-3): HEALTH=3 FIRE=1 REACTIVITY=0 PERSISTENCE=1

NFPA RATINGS (SCALE 0-4): HEALTH=4 FIRE=1 REACTIVITY=0

COMPONENTS AND CONTAMINANTS

COMPONENT: METHIOCARB SULFOXIDE ***PERCENT:*** 100.0
CAS# 2635-10-1

OTHER CONTAMINANTS: NONE

EXPOSURE LIMITS: NO OCCUPATIONAL EXPOSURE LIMITS ESTABLISHED BY OSHA, ACGIH, OR NIOSH.

PHYSICAL DATA

DESCRIPTION: WHITE ROCKY POWDER.

MELTING POINT: 248-279 F (120-137 C) (DECOMPOSES)

SPECIFIC GRAVITY: NOT AVAILABLE ***SOLUBILITY IN WATER:*** NOT AVAILABLE

FIRE AND EXPLOSION DATA

FIRE AND EXPLOSION HAZARD: SLIGHT FIRE HAZARD WHEN EXPOSED TO HEAT OR FLAME.

DUST-AIR MIXTURES MAY IGNITE OR EXPLODE.

FIREFIGHTING MEDIA: DRY CHEMICAL, CARBON DIOXIDE, HALON, WATER SPRAY OR STANDARD FOAM (1987 EMERGENCY RESPONSE GUIDEBOOK, DOT P 5800.4).

FOR LARGER FIRES, USE WATER SPRAY, FOG OR STANDARD FOAM (1987 EMERGENCY RESPONSE GUIDEBOOK, DOT P 5800.4).

FIREFIGHTING: MOVE CONTAINERS FROM FIRE AREA IF POSSIBLE (1987 EMERGENCY RESPONSE GUIDEBOOK, DOT P 5800.4, GUIDE PAGE 53).

EXTINGUISH USING AGENT SUITABLE FOR TYPE OF SURROUNDING FIRE. AVOID BREATHING VAPORS AND DUSTS. KEEP UPWIND.

TRANSPORTATION DATA

DEPARTMENT OF TRANSPORTATION HAZARD CLASSIFICATION 49 CFR 172.101: POISON B

DEPARTMENT OF TRANSPORTATION LABELING REQUIREMENTS 49 CFR 172.101 AND SUBPART E: POISON

DEPARTMENT OF TRANSPORTATION PACKAGING REQUIREMENTS: 49 CFR 173.365 EXCEPTIONS: 49 CFR 173.364

TOXICITY

METHIOCARB SULFOXIDE: TOXICITY DATA: 42 MG/KG ORAL-RAT LD50. CARCINOGEN STATUS: NONE. ACUTE TOXICITY LEVEL: HIGHLY TOXIC BY INGESTION. TARGET EFFECTS: CHOLINESTERASE INHIBITOR. AT INCREASED RISK FROM EXPOSURE: PERSONS WITH ASTHMA, DIABETES, CARDIOVASCULAR DISEASE, MECHANICAL OBSTRUCTION OF THE GASTROINTESTINAL OR UROGENITAL TRACT, AND THOSE IN VAGOTONIC STATES.*

* MAY BE BASED ON GENERAL INFORMATION ON CARBAMATES.

HEALTH EFFECTS AND FIRST AID

INHALATION: METHIOCARB SULFOXIDE: SEE INFORMATION ON CARBAMATES.

CARBAMATES: CHOLINESTERASE INHIBITOR. ACUTE EXPOSURE- WHEN INHALED, THE FIRST EFFECTS OF CHOLINESTERASE INHIBITION ARE USUALLY RESPIRATORY AND MAY INCLUDE NASAL HYPEREMIA AND WATERY DISCHARGE, CHEST DISCOMFORT, DYSPNEA, AND WHEEZING DUE TO INCREASED BRONCHIAL SECRETIONS AND BRONCHOCONSTRICTION. OTHER SYSTEMIC EFFECTS MAY BEGIN WITHIN A FEW MINUTES OR SEVERAL HOURS OF EXPOSURE. SYMPTOMS MAY INCLUDE NAUSEA, VOMITING, DIARRHEA, ABDOMINAL CRAMPS, HEADACHE, VERTIGO, OCULAR PAIN, CILIARY MUSCLE SPASM, BLURRING OR DIMNESS OF VISION, MIOSIS, OR IN SOME CASES MYDRIASIS, LACRIMATION, SALIVATION,

SWEATING, AND CONFUSION. OTHER REPORTED CENTRAL NERVOUS SYSTEM OR NEUROMUSCULAR EFFECTS INCLUDE ATAXIA, SLURRED SPEECH, AREFLEXIA, WEAKNESS, FATIGUE, TWITCHING, FASCICULATION, TREMOR, AND EVENTUALLY PARALYSIS OF THE EXTREMITIES AND POSSIBLY OF THE RESPIRATORY MUSCLES. IN SEVERE CASES, THERE MAY ALSO BE INVOLUNTARY DEFECATION AND URINATION, BRADYCARDIA, HYPOTENSION, PULMONARY EDEMA, CONVULSIONS, COMA, AND DEATH FROM RESPIRATORY FAILURE OR CARDIAC ARREST. CARBAMATES GENERALLY DO NOT ACCUMULATE IN MAMMALIAN TISSUE AND THE CHOLINESTERASE INHIBITION REVERSES RATHER RAPIDLY. IN NON-FATAL CASES, THE ILLNESS GENERALLY LASTS LESS THAN 24 HOURS. **CHRONIC EXPOSURE**- PROLONGED OR REPEATED EXPOSURE MAY CAUSE EFFECTS AS DESCRIBED IN ACUTE EXPOSURE.

FIRST AID- REMOVE FROM EXPOSURE AREA TO FRESH AIR IMMEDIATELY. IF BREATHING HAS STOPPED, GIVE ARTIFICIAL RESPIRATION. MAINTAIN AIRWAY AND BLOOD PRESSURE AND ADMINISTER OXYGEN IF AVAILABLE. KEEP AFFECTED PERSON WARM AND AT REST. TREAT SYMPTOMATICALLY AND SUPPORTIVELY. ADMINISTRATION OF OXYGEN SHOULD BE PERFORMED BY QUALIFIED PERSONNEL. GET MEDICAL ATTENTION IMMEDIATELY.

SKIN CONTACT: METHIOCARB SULFOXIDE: SEE INFORMATION ON CARBAMATES. CARBAMATES: CHOLINESTERASE INHIBITOR. **ACUTE EXPOSURE**- SOME COMPOUNDS MAY CAUSE IRRITATION. LOCALIZED SWEATING AND FASCICULATIONS MAY OCCUR AT THE SITE OF CONTACT. IF SUFFICIENT AMOUNTS ARE ABSORBED THROUGH THE SKIN, OTHER EFFECTS OF CHOLINESTERASE INHIBITION MAY OCCUR AS DESCRIBED IN ACUTE INHALATION; SYMPTOMS MAY BE DELAYED FOR 2-3 HOURS, USUALLY NO MORE THAN 8 HOURS. **CHRONIC EXPOSURE**- REPEATED OR PROLONGED EXPOSURE MAY CAUSE EFFECTS AS DESCRIBED IN ACUTE EXPOSURE.

FIRST AID- REMOVE CONTAMINATED CLOTHING IMMEDIATELY. WASH CONTAMINATED AREAS WITH SOAP AND WATER FOLLOWED BY ALCOHOL (ARENA, POISONING, 4TH ED.). EMERGENCY PERSONNEL SHOULD WEAR GLOVES AND AVOID CONTAMINATION. TREAT RESPIRATORY DIFFICULTY WITH ARTIFICIAL RESPIRATION. GET MEDICAL ATTENTION IMMEDIATELY.

EYE CONTACT: METHIOCARB SULFOXIDE: SEE INFORMATION ON CARBAMATES. CARBAMATES: CHOLINESTERASE INHIBITOR. **ACUTE EXPOSURE**- DIRECT CONTACT MAY CAUSE PAIN, HYPEREMIA, LACRIMATION, TWITCHING OF THE EYELIDS, MIOSIS, AND CILIARY MUSCLE SPASM WITH LOSS OF ACCOMODATION, BLURRED OR DIMMED VISION AND BROWACHE. SOMETIMES MYDRIASIS MAY OCCUR INSTEAD OF MIOSIS. WITH SUFFICIENT EXPOSURE, OTHER SYMPTOMS OF CHOLINESTERASE INHIBITION MAY OCCUR AS DESCRIBED IN ACUTE INHALATION. **CHRONIC EXPOSURE**- PROLONGED EXPOSURE MAY CAUSE EFFECTS AS DESCRIBED IN ACUTE EXPOSURE. SOME COMPOUNDS HAVE CAUSED TOXIC EFFECTS ON THE CRYSTALLINE LENS, CONJUNCTIVAL THICKENING AND OBSTRUCTION OF NASOLACRIMAL CANALS WHEN USED AS MIOTIC EYE DROPS.

FIRST AID- IRRIGATE EYES WITH WATER OR SALINE SOLUTION. IF SYMPTOMS OF POISONING OCCUR, TREAT RESPIRATORY DIFFICULTY WITH ARTIFICIAL RESPIRATION AND OXYGEN. OBSERVE PATIENT FOR AT LEAST 24-36 HOURS (GOSSELIN, CLINICAL TOXICOLOGY OF COMMERCIAL PRODUCTS, 5TH ED.). GET MEDICAL ATTENTION IMMEDIATELY. OXYGEN SHOULD BE ADMINISTERED BY QUALIFIED MEDICAL PERSONNEL.

INGESTION: METHIOCARB SULFOXIDE: HIGHLY TOXIC. SEE INFORMATION ON CARBAMATES. THE LETHAL DOSE REPORTED IN RATS WAS 42 M/KG. CARBAMATES: CHOLINESTERASE INHIBITOR. **ACUTE EXPOSURE**- WHEN INGESTED, THE FIRST EFFECTS MAY BE NAUSEA, VOMITING, ANOREXIA, ABDOMINAL CRAMPS, AND DIARRHEA. WITH ABSORPTION FROM THE GASTROINTESTINAL TRACT, THE OTHER EFFECTS OF CHOLINESTERASE INHIBITION AS DESCRIBED IN ACUTE INHALATION MAY OCCUR; SYMPTOMS MAY BEGIN WITHIN MINUTES OR BE DELAYED SEVERAL HOURS. **CHRONIC EXPOSURE**- REPEATED INGESTION MAY CAUSE EFFECTS AS DESCRIBED IN ACUTE EXPOSURE.

FIRST AID- IF PERSON IS ALERT AND RESPIRATION IS NOT DEPRESSED, GIVE SYRUP OF IPECAC FOLLOWED BY WATER (IF VOMITING OCCURS, KEEP HEAD BELOW HIPS TO PREVENT ASPIRATION). IF CONSCIOUSNESS LEVEL DECLINES OR VOMITING HAS NOT OCCURRED IN 15 MINUTES EMPTY STOMACH BY GASTRIC LAVAGE WITH THE AID OF CUFFED ENDOTRACHEAL TUBE USING ISOTONIC SALINE OR 5% SODIUM BICARBONATE FOLLOW WITH ACTIVATED CHARCOAL. ESTABLISH AND MAINTAIN AIRWAY. TREAT RESPIRATORY DIFFICULTY WITH ARTIFICIAL RESPIRATION AND OXYGEN. DO NOT GIVE MORPHINE, AMINOPHYLLINE, PHENOTHIAZINES, RESERPINE, FUROSEMIDE, OR ETHACRYNIC ACID (MORGAN, RECOGNITION AND MANAGEMENT OF PESTICIDE POISONINGS, 3RD ED.). TREAT SYMPTOMATICALLY AND SUPPORTIVELY. ADMINISTRATION OF OXYGEN AND LAVAGE MUST BE PERFORMED BY QUALIFIED MEDICAL PERSONNEL. GET MEDICAL ATTENTION IMMEDIATELY.

ANTIDOTE: THE FOLLOWING ANTIDOTE HAS BEEN RECOMMENDED. HOWEVER, THE DECISION AS TO WHETHER THE SEVERITY OF POISONING REQUIRES ADMINISTRATION OF ANY ANTIDOTE AND ACTUAL DOSE REQUIRED SHOULD BE MADE BY QUALIFIED MEDICAL PERSONNEL.
FOR CHOLINESTERASE INHIBITORS: ESTABLISH CLEAR AIRWAY AND TISSUE OXYGENATION BY ASPIRATION OF SECRETIONS, AND IF NECESSARY, BY ASSISTED PULMONARY VENTILATION WITH OXYGEN. IMPROVE TISSUE OXYGENATION AS MUCH AS POSSIBLE BEFORE ADMINISTERING ATROPINE TO MINIMIZE THE RISK OF VENTRICULAR FIBRILLATION. ADMINISTER ATROPINE SULFATE INTRAVENOUSLY, OR INTRAMUSCULARLY IF IV INJECTION IS NOT POSSIBLE. IN MODERATELY SEVERE POISONING ADMINISTER ATROPINE SULFATE, 0.4-2.0 MG REPEATED EVERY 15 MINUTES UNTIL ATROPINIZATION IS ACHIEVED (TACHYCARDIA, FLUSHING, DRY MOUTH, MYDRIASIS). MAINTAIN ATROPINIZATION BY REPEATED DOSES FOR 2-12 HOURS, OR LONGER, DEPENDING ON THE SEVERITY OF POISONING. THE APPEARANCE OF RALES IN THE LUNG BASES, MIOSIS, SALIVATION, NAUSEA, BRADYCARDIA, ARE ALL INDICATIONS OF INADEQUATE ATROPINIZATION. SEVERELY POISONED INDIVIDUALS MAY EXHIBIT REMARKABLE TOLERANCE TO ATROPINE; TWO OR MORE TIMES THE DOSAGES SUGGESTED ABOVE MAY BE NEEDED. PERSONS NOT POISONED OR ONLY SLIGHTLY POISONED, HOWEVER, MAY DEVELOP SIGNS OF ATROPINE TOXICITY FROM SUCH LARGE DOSAGES: FEVER, MUSCLE FIBRILLATIONS, AND DELIRIUM ARE THE MAIN SIGNS OF ATROPINE TOXICITY. IF THESE SIGNS APPEAR WHILE THE PATIENT IS FULLY ATROPINIZED, ATROPINE ADMINISTRATION SHOULD BE DISCONTINUED, AT LEAST TEMPORARILY. OBSERVE TREATED PATIENTS CLOSELY AT LEAST 24 HOURS TO INSURE THAT SYMPTOMS (POSSIBLY PULMONARY EDEMA) DO NOT RECUR AS ATROPINIZATION WEARS OFF. IN VERY SEVERE POISONINGS, METABOLIC DISPOSITION OF TOXICANT MAY REQUIRE SEVERAL HOURS OR DAYS DURING WHICH ATROPINIZATION MUST BE MAINTAINED. MARKEDLY LOWER LEVELS OF URINARY METABOLITES INDICATE THAT ATROPINE DOSAGE CAN BE TAPERED OFF. AS DOSAGE IS REDUCED, CHECK THE LUNG BASES FREQUENTLY FOR RALES. IF RALES ARE HEARD OR OTHER SYMPTOMS RETURN, RE-ESTABLISH ATROPINIZATION PROMPTLY (MORGAN, RECOGNITION AND MANAGEMENT OF PESTICIDE POISONINGS, 3RD ED.). ADMINISTRATION OF ANTIDOTE MUST BE PERFORMED BY QUALIFIED MEDICAL PERSONNEL.

REACTIVITY

REACTIVITY: STABLE UNDER NORMAL TEMPERATURES AND PRESSURES.

INCOMPATIBILITIES: METHIOCARB SULFOXIDE: OXIDIZERS (STRONG): FIRE AND EXPLOSION HAZARD.

DECOMPOSITION: THERMAL DECOMPOSITION PRODUCTS MAY INCLUDE TOXIC OXIDES OF CARBON, NITROGEN, AND SULFUR.

POLYMERIZATION: HAZARDOUS POLYMERIZATION HAS NOT BEEN REPORTED TO OCCUR UNDER NORMAL TEMPERATURES AND PRESSURES.

STORAGE AND DISPOSAL

OBSERVE ALL FEDERAL, STATE AND LOCAL REGULATIONS WHEN STORING OR DISPOSING OF THIS SUBSTANCE. FOR ASSISTANCE, CONTACT THE DISTRICT DIRECTOR OF THE ENVIRONMENTAL PROTECTION AGENCY.

STORAGE

STORE IN ACCORDANCE WITH 40 CFR 165 RECOMMENDED PROCEDURES FOR THE DISPOSAL AND STORAGE OF PESTICIDES AND PESTICIDE CONTAINERS.
STORE AWAY FROM INCOMPATIBLE SUBSTANCES.

DISPOSAL

DISPOSAL MUST BE IN ACCORDANCE WITH 40 CFR 165 RECOMMENDED PROCEDURES FOR THE DISPOSAL AND STORAGE OF PESTICIDES AND PESTICIDE CONTAINERS.

CONDITIONS TO AVOID

MAY BURN BUT DOES NOT IGNITE READILY.

SPILL AND LEAK PROCEDURES

OCCUPATIONAL SPILL: DO NOT TOUCH SPILLED MATERIAL. STOP LEAK IF YOU CAN DO IT WITHOUT RISK. FOR SMALL SPILLS, TAKE UP WITH SAND OR OTHER ABSORBENT MATERIAL AND PLACE INTO CONTAINERS FOR LATER DISPOSAL. FOR SMALL DRY SPILLS, WITH A CLEAN SHOVEL PLACE MATERIAL INTO CLEAN, DRY CONTAINER AND COVER. MOVE CONTAINERS FROM SPILL AREA. FOR LARGER SPILLS, DIKE FAR AHEAD OF SPILL FOR LATER DISPOSAL. KEEP UNNECESSARY PEOPLE AWAY. ISOLATE HAZARD AREA AND DENY ENTRY.

PROTECTIVE EQUIPMENT

VENTILATION: PROCESS ENCLOSURE RECOMMENDED.

RESPIRATOR: THE FOLLOWING RESPIRATORS ARE RECOMMENDED BASED ON INFORMATION FOUND IN THE PHYSICAL DATA, TOXICITY AND HEALTH EFFECTS SECTIONS. THEY ARE RANKED IN ORDER FROM MINIMUM TO MAXIMUM RESPIRATORY PROTECTION. THE SPECIFIC RESPIRATOR SELECTED MUST BE BASED ON CONTAMINATION LEVELS FOUND IN THE WORK PLACE, MUST NOT EXCEED THE WORKING LIMITS OF THE RESPIRATOR AND BE JOINTLY APPROVED BY THE NATIONAL INSTITUTE FOR OCCUPATIONAL SAFETY AND HEALTH AND THE MINE SAFETY AND HEALTH ADMINISTRATION (NIOSH-MSHA).

TYPE 'C' SUPPLIED-AIR RESPIRATOR WITH A FULL FACEPIECE OPERATED IN PRESSURE-DEMAND OR OTHER POSITIVE PRESSURE MODE OR WITH A FULL FACEPIECE, HELMET OR HOOD OPERATED IN CONTINOUS-FLOW MODE.
SELF-CONTAINED BREATHING APPARATUS WITH A FULL FACEPIECE OPERATED IN PRESSURE-DEMAND OR OTHER POSITIVE PRESSURE MODE.
FOR FIREFIGHTING AND OTHER IMMEDIATELY DANGEROUS TO LIFE OR HEALTH CONDITIONS:
SELF-CONTAINED BREATHING APPARATUS WITH FULL FACEPIECE OPERATED IN PRESSURE-DEMAND OR OTHER POSITIVE PRESSURE MODE.
SUPPLIED-AIR RESPIRATOR WITH FULL FACEPIECE AND OPERATED IN PRESSURE-DEMAND OR OTHER POSITIVE PRESSURE MODE IN COMBINATION WITH AN AUXILIARY SELF-CONTAINED BREATHING APPARATUS OPERATED IN PRESSURE-DEMAND OR OTHER POSITIVE PRESSURE MODE.

CLOTHING: EMPLOYEE MUST WEAR APPROPRIATE PROTECTIVE (IMPERVIOUS) CLOTHING AND EQUIPMENT TO PREVENT ANY POSSIBILITY OF SKIN CONTACT WITH THIS SUBSTANCE.

GLOVES: EMPLOYEE MUST WEAR APPROPRIATE PROTECTIVE GLOVES TO PREVENT CONTACT WITH THIS SUBSTANCE.

EYE PROTECTION: EMPLOYEE MUST WEAR SPLASH-PROOF OR DUST-RESISTANT SAFETY GOGGLES AND A FACESHIELD TO PREVENT CONTACT WITH THIS SUBSTANCE.
EMERGENCY WASH FACILITIES: WHERE THERE IS ANY POSSIBILITY THAT AN EMPLOYEE'S EYES AND/OR SKIN MAY BE EXPOSED TO THIS SUBSTANCE, THE EMPLOYER SHOULD PROVIDE AN EYE WASH FOUNTAIN AND QUICK DRENCH SHOWER WITHIN THE IMMEDIATE WORK AREA FOR EMERGENCY USE.

AUTHORIZED BY- OCCUPATIONAL HEALTH SERVICES, INC.
CREATION DATE: 06/20/90 ***REVISION DATE:*** 06/20/90

MATERIAL SAFETY DATA SHEET

OCCUPATIONAL HEALTH SERVICES, INC.
AGRICULTURE AND PESTICIDE DIVISION
450 SEVENTH AVENUE, SUITE 2407
NEW YORK, NEW YORK 10123
1-800-445-MSDS OR (212) 967-1100

EMERGENCY CONTACT:
JOHN S. BRANSFORD, JR. (615) 292-1180

SUBSTANCE IDENTIFICATION

CAS-NUMBER 16752-77-5

SUBSTANCE: **METHOMYL**

TRADE NAMES/SYNONYMS: ETHANIMIDOTHIOIC ACID, N-(((METHYLAMINO)CARBONYL)OXY)-, METHYL ESTER; N-(((METHYLAMINO)CARBONYL)OXY)ETHANIMIDOTHIOIC ACID METHYL ESTER; N-((METHYLCARBAMOYL)OXYTHIOACETIMIDIC ACID METHYL ESTER; S-METHYL N-((METHYLCARBAMOYL)OXY)THIOACETIMIDATE; METHYL O-(METHYLCARBAMOYL)THIOLACETOHYDROXAMATE; METHYL N-(((METHYLAMINO)CARBONYL)OXY)ETHANIMIDOTHIOATE; METHYL N-((METHYLCARBOMOYL)OXY)THIOACETIMIDATE; LANNATE; NUDRIN; ENT 27,341; RCRA P066; C5H10N2O2S; PST14200

CHEMICAL FAMILY: CARBAMATE

MOLECULAR FORMULA: C5-H10-N2-O2-S

MOLECULAR WEIGHT: 162.23

CERCLA RATINGS (SCALE 0-3): HEALTH=3 FIRE=0 REACTIVITY=0 PERSISTENCE=0

NFPA RATINGS (SCALE 0-4): HEALTH=4 FIRE=0 REACTIVITY=0

COMPONENTS AND CONTAMINANTS

COMPONENT: METHOMYL ***PERCENT:*** 100
CAS# 16752-77-5

OTHER CONTAMINANTS: NONE

EXPOSURE LIMITS: METHOMYL: 2.5 MG/M3 OSHA TWA 2.5 MG/M3 ACGIH TWA 500/10,000 POUNDS SARA SECTION 302 THRESHOLD QUANTITY 100 POUNDS SARA SECTION 304 REPORTABLE QUANTITY 100 POUNDS CERCLA SECTION 103 REPORTABLE QUANTITY

PHYSICAL DATA

DESCRIPTION: WHITE CRYSTALLINE SOLID WITH A SLIGHTLY SULFUROUS ODOR

MELTING POINT: 172 F (78 C) ***SPECIFIC GRAVITY:*** 1.2946 @ 24 C

VAPOR PRESSURE: 0.00005 MMHG @ 25 C ***SOLUBILITY IN WATER:*** 5.8% @ 25 C

SOLVENT SOLUBILITY: SOLUBLE IN METHANOL, ACETONE, ETHANOL, ISOPROPANOL, AND MOST ORGANIC SOLVENTS; SLIGHTLY SOLUBLE IN TOLUENE

FIRE AND EXPLOSION DATA

FIRE AND EXPLOSION HAZARD: NEGLIGIBLE FIRE HAZARD WHEN EXPOSED TO HEAT OR FLAME.

FIREFIGHTING MEDIA: DRY CHEMICAL, CARBON DIOXIDE, HALON, WATER SPRAY OR STANDARD FOAM (1987 EMERGENCY RESPONSE GUIDEBOOK, DOT P 5800.4). FOR LARGER FIRES, USE WATER SPRAY, FOG OR STANDARD FOAM (1987 EMERGENCY RESPONSE GUIDEBOOK, DOT P 5800.4).

FIREFIGHTING: MOVE CONTAINERS FROM FIRE AREA IF POSSIBLE. FIGHT FIRE FROM MAXIMUM DISTANCE. STAY AWAY FROM STORAGE TANK ENDS. DIKE FIRE CONTROL WATER FOR LATER DISPOSAL. DO NOT SCATTER MATERIAL (1987 EMERGENCY RESPONSE GUIDEBOOK, DOT P 5800.4, GUIDE PAGE 55). EXTINGUISH ONLY IF FLOW CAN BE STOPPED; USE FLOODING AMOUNTS OF WATER AS FOG, SOLID STREAMS MAY BE INEFFECTIVE. COOL CONTAINERS WITH FLOODING AMOUNTS OF WATER FROM AS FAR A DISTANCE AS POSSIBLE. USE WATER SPRAY TO ABSORB TOXIC VAPORS. AVOID BREATHING TOXIC VAPORS; KEEP UPWIND. CONSIDER EVACUATION OF DOWNWIND AREA IF MATERIAL IS LEAKING.

TRANSPORTATION DATA

DEPARTMENT OF TRANSPORTATION HAZARD CLASSIFICATION 49 CFR 172.101: POISON B
DEPARTMENT OF TRANSPORTATION LABELING REQUIREMENTS 49 CFR 172.101 AND SUBPART E: POISON
DEPARTMENT OF TRANSPORTATION PACKAGING REQUIREMENTS: 49 CFR 173.365 EXCEPTIONS: 49 CFR 173.364

TOXICITY

METHOMYL: TOXICITY DATA: 77 PPM INHALATION-RAT LC50; 5880 MG/KG SKIN-RABBIT LD50; 17 MG/KG ORAL-RAT LD50; 10 MG/KG ORAL-MOUSE LD50; 30 MG/KG ORAL-DOG LDLO; 15 MG/KG ORAL-GUINEA PIG LDLO; 40 MG/KG ORAL-MONKEY LDLO; 9 MG/KG SUBCUTANEOUS-RAT LD50; MUTAGENIC DATA (RTECS). CARCINOGEN STATUS: NONE. ACUTE TOXICITY: HIGHLY TOXIC BY INHALATION AND INGESTION; SLIGHTLY TOXIC BY DERMAL ABSORPTION. TARGET EFFECTS: CHOLINESTERASE INHIBITOR. AT INCREASED RISK FROM EXPOSURE: PERSONS WITH ASTHMA, DIABETES, CARDIOVASCULAR DISEASE, MECHANICAL OBSTRUCTION OF THE GASTROINTESTINAL OR UROGENITAL TRACT, AND THOSE IN VAGOTONIC STATES.* * MAY BE BASED ON GENERAL INFORMATION ON CARBAMATES.

HEALTH EFFECTS AND FIRST AID

INHALATION: METHOMYL: HIGHLY TOXIC. THIS MATERIAL MAY CAUSE MILD IRRITATION OF THE MUCOUS MEMBRANES. SEE INFORMATION ON CARBAMATES.
CARBAMATES: CHOLINESTERASE INHIBITOR. **ACUTE EXPOSURE-** WHEN INHALED, THE FIRST EFFECTS OF CHOLINESTERASE INHIBITION ARE USUALLY RESPIRATORY AND MAY INCLUDE NASAL HYPEREMIA AND WATERY DISCHARGE, CHEST DISCOMFORT, DYSPNEA, AND WHEEZING DUE TO INCREASED BRONCHIAL SECRETIONS AND BRONCHOCONSTRICTION. OTHER SYSTEMIC EFFECTS MAY BEGIN WITHIN A FEW MINUTES OR SEVERAL HOURS OF EXPOSURE. SYMPTOMS MAY INCLUDE NAUSEA, VOMITING, DIARRHEA, ABDOMINAL CRAMPS, HEADACHE, VERTIGO, OCULAR PAIN, CILIARY MUSCLE SPASM, BLURRING OR DIMNESS OF VISION, MIOSIS, OR IN SOME CASES MYDRIASIS, LACRIMATION, SALIVATION, SWEATING, AND CONFUSION. OTHER REPORTED CENTRAL NERVOUS SYSTEM OR NEUROMUSCULAR EFFECTS INCLUDE ATAXIA, SLURRED SPEECH, AREFLEXIA, WEAKNESS, FATIGUE, TWITCHING, FASCICULATION, TREMOR, AND EVENTUALLY PARALYSIS OF THE EXTREMITIES AND POSSIBLY OF THE RESPIRATORY MUSCLES. IN SEVERE CASES, THERE MAY ALSO BE INVOLUNTARY DEFECATION AND URINATION, BRADYCARDIA, HYPOTENSION, PULMONARY EDEMA, CONVULSIONS, COMA, AND DEATH FROM RESPIRATORY FAILURE OR CARDIAC ARREST. CARBAMATES GENERALLY DO NOT ACCUMULATE IN MAMMALIAN TISSUE AND THE CHOLINESTERASE INHIBITION REVERSES RATHER RAPIDLY. IN NON-FATAL CASES, THE ILLNESS GENERALLY LASTS LESS THAN 24 HOURS. **CHRONIC EXPOSURE-** PROLONGED OR REPEATED EXPOSURE MAY CAUSE EFFECTS AS DESCRIBED IN ACUTE EXPOSURE.

FIRST AID- REMOVE FROM EXPOSURE AREA TO FRESH AIR IMMEDIATELY. IF BREATHING HAS STOPPED, GIVE ARTIFICIAL RESPIRATION. MAINTAIN AIRWAY AND BLOOD PRESSURE AND ADMINISTER OXYGEN IF AVAILABLE. KEEP AFFECTED PERSON WARM AND AT REST. TREAT SYMPTOMATICALLY AND SUPPORTIVELY. ADMINISTRATION OF OXYGEN SHOULD BE PERFORMED BY QUALIFIED PERSONNEL. GET MEDICAL ATTENTION IMMEDIATELY.

SKIN CONTACT: METHOMYL: THIS MATERIAL WAS MILDLY IRRITATING TO THE SKIN OF GUINEA PIGS. SEE INFORMATION ON CARBAMATES.
CARBAMATES: CHOLINESTERASE INHIBITOR. **ACUTE EXPOSURE-** SOME COMPOUNDS MAY CAUSE IRRITATION. LOCALIZED SWEATING AND FASCICULATIONS MAY OCCUR AT THE SITE OF CONTACT. IF SUFFICIENT

AMOUNTS ARE ABSORBED THROUGH THE SKIN, OTHER EFFECTS OF CHOLINESTERASE INHIBITION MAY OCCUR AS DESCRIBED IN ACUTE INHALATION; SYMPTOMS MAY BE DELAYED FOR 2-3 HOURS, USUALLY NO MORE THAN 8 HOURS. **CHRONIC EXPOSURE-** REPEATED OR PROLONGED EXPOSURE MAY CAUSE EFFECTS AS DESCRIBED IN ACUTE EXPOSURE.

FIRST AID- REMOVE CONTAMINATED CLOTHING IMMEDIATELY. WASH CONTAMINATED AREAS WITH SOAP AND WATER FOLLOWED BY ALCOHOL (ARENA, POISONING, 4TH ED.). EMERGENCY PERSONNEL SHOULD WEAR GLOVES AND AVOID CONTAMINATION. TREAT RESPIRATORY DIFFICULTY WITH ARTIFICIAL RESPIRATION. GET MEDICAL ATTENTION IMMEDIATELY.

EYE CONTACT: METHOMYL: AN APPLICATION OF THE DRY MATERIAL OR A 10% SOLUTION PRODUCED MILD CONJUCTIVITIS BUT NO CORNEAL INJURY IN THE EYES OF RABBITS. SEE INFORMATION ON CARBAMATES.

CARBAMATES: CHOLINESTERASE INHIBITOR. **ACUTE EXPOSURE-** DIRECT CONTACT MAY CAUSE PAIN, HYPEREMIA, LACRIMATION, TWITCHING OF THE EYELIDS, MIOSIS, AND CILIARY MUSCLE SPASM WITH LOSS OF ACCOMODATION, BLURRED OR DIMMED VISION AND BROWACHE. SOMETIMES MYDRIASIS MAY OCCUR INSTEAD OF MIOSIS. WITH SUFFICIENT EXPOSURE, OTHER SYMPTOMS OF CHOLINESTERASE INHIBITION MAY OCCUR AS DESCRIBED IN ACUTE INHALATION. **CHRONIC EXPOSURE-** PROLONGED EXPOSURE MAY CAUSE EFFECTS AS DESCRIBED IN ACUTE EXPOSURE. SOME COMPOUNDS HAVE CAUSED TOXIC EFFECTS ON THE CRYSTALLINE LENS, CONJUNCTIVAL THICKENING AND OBSTRUCTION OF NASOLACRIMAL CANALS WHEN USED AS MIOTIC EYE DROPS.

FIRST AID- IRRIGATE EYES WITH WATER OR SALINE SOLUTION. IF SYMPTOMS OF POISONING OCCUR, TREAT RESPIRATORY DIFFICULTY WITH ARTIFICIAL RESPIRATION AND OXYGEN. OBSERVE PATIENT FOR AT LEAST 24-36 HOURS (GOSSELIN, CLINICAL TOXICOLOGY OF COMMERCIAL PRODUCTS, 5TH ED.). GET MEDICAL ATTENTION IMMEDIATELY. OXYGEN SHOULD BE ADMINISTERED BY QUALIFIED MEDICAL PERSONNEL.

INGESTION: METHOMYL: HIGHLY TOXIC. GROWTH SUPPRESSION WAS OBSERVED IN A 2-YEAR STUDY OF RATS FED AT A LEVEL OF 400 PPM. SEE INFORMATION ON CARBAMATES.

CARBAMATES: CHOLINESTERASE INHIBITOR. **ACUTE EXPOSURE-** WHEN INGESTED, THE FIRST EFFECTS MAY BE NAUSEA, VOMITING, ANOREXIA, ABDOMINAL CRAMPS, AND DIARRHEA. WITH ABSORPTION FROM THE GASTROINTESTINAL TRACT, THE OTHER EFFECTS OF CHOLINESTERASE INHIBITION AS DESCRIBED IN ACUTE INHALATION MAY OCCUR; SYMPTOMS MAY BEGIN WITHIN MINUTES OR BE DELAYED SEVERAL HOURS. **CHRONIC EXPOSURE-** REPEATED INGESTION MAY CAUSE EFFECTS AS DESCRIBED IN ACUTE EXPOSURE.

FIRST AID- IF PERSON IS ALERT AND RESPIRATION IS NOT DEPRESSED, GIVE SYRUP OF IPECAC FOLLOWED BY WATER (IF VOMITING OCCURS, KEEP HEAD BELOW HIPS TO PREVENT ASPIRATION). IF CONSCIOUSNESS LEVEL DECLINES OR VOMITING HAS NOT OCCURRED IN 15 MINUTES EMPTY STOMACH BY GASTRIC LAVAGE WITH THE AID OF CUFFED ENDOTRACHEAL TUBE USING ISOTONIC SALINE OR 5% SODIUM BICARBONATE FOLLOW WITH ACTIVATED CHARCOAL. ESTABLISH AND MAINTAIN AIRWAY. TREAT RESPIRATORY DIFFICULTY WITH ARTIFICIAL RESPIRATION AND OXYGEN. DO NOT GIVE MORPHINE, AMINOPHYLLINE, PHENOTHIAZINES, RESERPINE, FUROSEMIDE, OR ETHACRYNIC ACID (MORGAN, RECOGNITION AND MANAGEMENT OF PESTICIDE POISONINGS, 3RD ED.). TREAT SYMPTOMATICALLY AND SUPPORTIVELY. ADMINISTRATION OF OXYGEN AND LAVAGE MUST BE PERFORMED BY QUALIFIED MEDICAL PERSONNEL. GET MEDICAL ATTENTION IMMEDIATELY.

ANTIDOTE: THE FOLLOWING ANTIDOTE HAS BEEN RECOMMENDED. HOWEVER, THE DECISION AS TO WHETHER THE SEVERITY OF POISONING REQUIRES ADMINISTRATION OF ANY ANTIDOTE AND ACTUAL DOSE REQUIRED SHOULD BE MADE BY QUALIFIED MEDICAL PERSONNEL.

FOR CHOLINESTERASE INHIBITORS: ESTABLISH CLEAR AIRWAY AND TISSUE OXYGENATION BY ASPIRATION OF SECRETIONS, AND IF NECESSARY, BY ASSISTED PULMONARY VENTILATION WITH OXYGEN. IMPROVE TISSUE OXYGENATION AS MUCH AS POSSIBLE BEFORE ADMINISTERING ATROPINE TO MINIMIZE THE RISK OF VENTRICULAR FIBRILLATION. ADMINISTER ATROPINE SULFATE INTRAVENOUSLY OR INTRAMUSCULARLY IF IV INJECTION IS NOT POSSIBLE. IN MODERATELY SEVERE POISONING ADMINISTER ATROPINE SULFATE, 0.4-2.0 MG REPEATED EVERY 15 MINUTES UNTIL ATROPINIZATION IS ACHIEVED (TACHYCARDIA, FLUSHING, DRY MOUTH, MYDRIASIS). MAINTAIN ATROPINIZATION BY REPEATED DOSES FOR 2-12 HOURS, OR LONGER, DEPENDING ON THE SEVERITY OF POISONING. THE APPEARANCE OF RALES IN THE LUNG BASES, MIOSIS, SALIVATION, NAUSEA, BRADYCARDIA, ARE ALL INDICATIONS OF INADEQUATE ATROPINIZATION. SEVERELY POISONED INDIVIDUALS MAY EXHIBIT REMARKABLE TOLERANCE TO ATROPINE; TWO OR MORE TIMES THE DOSAGES SUGGESTED ABOVE MAY BE NEEDED. PERSONS NOT POISONED OR ONLY SLIGHTLY POISONED, HOWEVER, MAY DEVELOP SIGNS OF ATROPINE TOXICITY FROM SUCH LARGE DOSAGES: FEVER, MUSCLE FIBRILLATIONS, AND DELIRIUM ARE THE MAIN SIGNS OF ATROPINE TOXICITY. IF THESE SIGNS APPEAR WHILE THE PATIENT IS FULLY ATROPINIZED, ATROPINE ADMINISTRATION SHOULD BE DISCONTINUED, AT LEAST TEMPORARILY. OBSERVE TREATED PATIENTS CLOSELY AT LEAST 24 HOURS TO INSURE THAT SYMPTOMS (POSSIBLY PULMONARY EDEMA) DO NOT RECUR AS ATROPINIZATION WEARS OFF. IN VERY SEVERE POISONINGS, METABOLIC DISPOSITION OF TOXICANT MAY REQUIRE SEVERAL HOURS OR DAYS DURING WHICH ATROPINIZATION MUST BE MAINTAINED. MARKEDLY LOWER LEVELS OF URINARY METABOLITES INDICATE THAT ATROPINE DOSAGE CAN BE TAPERED OFF. AS DOSAGE IS REDUCED, CHECK THE LUNG BASES FREQUENTLY FOR RALES. IF RALES ARE HEARD OR OTHER SYMPTOMS RETURN, RE-ESTABLISH ATROPINIZATION PROMPTLY (MORGAN, RECOGNITION AND MANAGEMENT OF PESTICIDE POISONINGS, 3RD ED.). ADMINISTRATION OF ANTIDOTE MUST BE PERFORMED BY QUALIFIED MEDICAL PERSONNEL.

REACTIVITY

REACTIVITY: STABLE UNDER NORMAL TEMPERATURES AND PRESSURES.

INCOMPATIBILITIES: METHOMYL: STRONG OXIDIZERS: MAY REACT TO PRODUCE FIRE AND EXPLOSION HAZARD.

DECOMPOSITION: THERMAL DECOMPOSITION PRODUCTS INCLUDE TOXIC OXIDES OF NITROGEN AND SULFUR.

POLYMERIZATION: HAZARDOUS POLYMERIZATION HAS NOT BEEN REPORTED TO OCCUR UNDER NORMAL TEMPERATURES AND PRESSURES.

STORAGE AND DISPOSAL

OBSERVE ALL FEDERAL, STATE AND LOCAL REGULATIONS WHEN STORING OR DISPOSING OF THIS SUBSTANCE. FOR ASSISTANCE, CONTACT THE DISTRICT DIRECTOR OF THE ENVIRONMENTAL PROTECTION AGENCY.

****STORAGE****

STORE IN ACCORDANCE WITH 40 CFR 165 RECOMMENDED PROCEDURES FOR THE DISPOSAL AND STORAGE OF PESTICIDES AND PESTICIDE CONTAINERS.

STORE AWAY FROM INCOMPATIBLE SUBSTANCES.

THRESHOLD PLANNING QUANTITY (TPQ): THE SUPERFUND AMENDMENTS AND REAUTHORIZATION ACT (SARA) SECTION 302 REQUIRES THAT EACH FACILITY WHERE ANY EXTREMELY HAZARDOUS SUBSTANCE IS PRESENT IN A QUANTITY EQUAL TO OR GREATER THAN THE TPQ ESTABLISHED FOR THAT SUBSTANCE NOTIFY THE STATE EMERGENCY RESPONSE COMMISSION FOR THE STATE IN WHICH IT IS LOCATED. SECTION 303 OF SARA REQUIRES THESE FACILITIES TO PARTICIPATE IN LOCAL EMERGENCY RESPONSE PLANNING (40 CFR 355.30).

****DISPOSAL****

DISPOSAL MUST BE IN ACCORDANCE WITH STANDARDS APPLICABLE TO GENERATORS OF HAZARDOUS WASTE, 40CFR 262. EPA HAZARDOUS WASTE NUMBER P066.

CONDITIONS TO AVOID

AVOID BREATHING DUST. AVOID SKIN CONTACT WITH DUST OR SOLUTIONS.

SPILL AND LEAK PROCEDURES

OCCUPATIONAL SPILL: DO NOT TOUCH SPILLED MATERIAL. STOP LEAK IF YOU CAN DO IT WITHOUT RISK. USE WATER SPRAY TO REDUCE VAPORS. FOR SMALL SPILLS, TAKE UP WITH SAND OR OTHER ABSORBENT MATERIAL AND PLACE INTO CONTAINERS FOR LATER DISPOSAL. FOR SMALL DRY SPILLS, WITH A CLEAN SHOVEL PLACE MATERIAL INTO CLEAN, DRY CONTAINERS AND COVER. MOVE CONTAINERS FROM SPILL AREA. FOR LARGER SPILLS, DIKE FAR AHEAD OF SPILL FOR LATER DISPOSAL. KEEP UNNECESSARY PEOPLE AWAY. ISOLATE HAZARD AREA AND DENY ENTRY. VENTILATE CLOSED SPACES BEFORE ENTERING.

REPORTABLE QUANTITY (RQ): 100 POUNDS THE SUPERFUND AMENDMENTS AND REAUTHORIZATION ACT (SARA) SECTION 304 REQUIRES THAT A RELEASE EQUAL TO OR GREATER THAN THE REPORTABLE QUANTITY FOR THIS SUBSTANCE BE IMMEDIATELY REPORTED TO THE LOCAL EMERGENCY PLANNING COMMITTEE AND THE STATE EMERGENCY RESPONSE COMMISSION (40 CFR 355.40). IF THE RELEASE OF THIS SUBSTANCE IS REPORTABLE UNDER CERCLA SECTION 103, THE NATIONAL RESPONSE CENTER MUST BE NOTIFIED IMMEDIATELY AT (800) 424-8802 OR (202) 426-2675 IN THE METROPOLITAN WASHINGTON, D.C. AREA (40 CFR 302.6).

PROTECTIVE EQUIPMENT

VENTILATION: PROCESS ENCLOSURE RECOMMENDED TO MEET PUBLISHED EXPOSURE LIMITS.

RESPIRATOR: THE FOLLOWING RESPIRATORS ARE RECOMMENDED BASED ON INFORMATION FOUND IN THE PHYSICAL DATA, TOXICITY AND HEALTH EFFECTS SECTIONS. THEY ARE RANKED IN ORDER FROM MINIMUM TO MAXIMUM RESPIRATORY PROTECTION. THE SPECIFIC RESPIRATOR SELECTED MUST BE BASED ON CONTAMINATION LEVELS FOUND IN THE WORK PLACE, MUST NOT EXCEED THE WORKING LIMITS OF THE RESPIRATOR AND BE JOINTLY APPROVED BY THE NATIONAL INSTITUTE FOR OCCUPATIONAL SAFETY AND HEALTH AND THE MINE SAFETY AND HEALTH ADMINISTRATION (NIOSH-MSHA).

TYPE 'C' SUPPLIED-AIR RESPIRATOR WITH A FULL FACEPIECE OPERATED IN PRESSURE-DEMAND OR OTHER POSITIVE PRESSURE MODE OR WITH A FULL

FACEPIECE, HELMET OR HOOD OPERATED IN CONTINOUS-FLOW MODE.
SELF-CONTAINED BREATHING APPARATUS WITH A FULL FACEPIECE OPERATED IN PRESSURE-DEMAND OR OTHER POSITIVE PRESSURE MODE.
FOR FIREFIGHTING AND OTHER IMMEDIATELY DANGEROUS TO LIFE OR HEALTH CONDITIONS:
SELF-CONTAINED BREATHING APPARATUS WITH FULL FACEPIECE OPERATED IN PRESSURE-DEMAND OR OTHER POSITIVE PRESSURE MODE.
SUPPLIED-AIR RESPIRATOR WITH FULL FACEPIECE AND OPERATED IN PRESSURE-DEMAND OR OTHER POSITIVE PRESSURE MODE IN COMBINATION WITH AN AUXILIARY SELF-CONTAINED BREATHING APPARATUS OPERATED IN PRESSURE-DEMAND OR OTHER POSITIVE PRESSURE MODE.

CLOTHING: EMPLOYEE MUST WEAR APPROPRIATE PROTECTIVE (IMPERVIOUS) CLOTHING AND EQUIPMENT TO PREVENT ANY POSSIBILITY OF SKIN CONTACT WITH THIS SUBSTANCE.

GLOVES: EMPLOYEE MUST WEAR APPROPRIATE PROTECTIVE GLOVES TO PREVENT CONTACT WITH THIS SUBSTANCE.

EYE PROTECTION: EMPLOYEE MUST WEAR SPLASH-PROOF OR DUST-RESISTANT SAFETY GOGGLES WITH OR WITHOUT A FACESHIELD TO PREVENT CONTACT WITH THIS SUBSTANCE.
EMERGENCY EYE WASH: WHERE THERE IS ANY POSSIBILITY THAT AN EMPLOYEE'S EYES MAY BE EXPOSED TO THIS SUBSTANCE, THE EMPLOYER SHOULD PROVIDE AN EYE WASH FOUNTAIN WITHIN THE IMMEDIATE WORK AREA FOR EMERGENCY USE.

AUTHORIZED BY- OCCUPATIONAL HEALTH SERVICES, INC.
CREATION DATE: 10/04/89 ***REVISION DATE:*** 06/12/90

MATERIAL SAFETY DATA SHEET

OCCUPATIONAL HEALTH SERVICES, INC.
AGRICULTURE AND PESTICIDE DIVISION
450 SEVENTH AVENUE, SUITE 2407
NEW YORK, NEW YORK 10123
1-800-445-MSDS OR (212) 967-1100

EMERGENCY CONTACT:
JOHN S. BRANSFORD, JR. (615) 292-1180

SUBSTANCE IDENTIFICATION

CAS-NUMBER 841-06-5
SUBSTANCE: METHOPROTRYNE
TRADE NAMES/SYNONYMS: 1,3,5-TRIAZINE-2,4-DIAMINE, N-(3-METHOXYPROPYL)-N'-(1-METHYLETHYL) -6-(METHYLTHIO)-; S-TRIAZINE, 2-(ISOPROPYLAMINO)-4-((3-METHOXYPROPYL)AMINO)-6 -(METHYLTHIO)-; N-(3-METHOXYPROPYL)-N'-(1-METHYLETHYL)-6-(METHYLTHIO)-1,3,5-TRIAZINE -2,4-DIAMINE; 2-(ISOPROPYLAMINO)-4-((3-METHOXYPROPYL)AMINO)-6-(METHYLTHIO) -S-TRIAZINE; 2-ISOPROPYLAMINO-4-(3-METHOXYPROPYLAMINO)-6-METHYLTHIO-1,3,5-TRIAZINE; G-36393; GESARAN; METHOPROPTRYNE; METHOPROTRYN; METHOTRYNE; C11H21N5OS; PST14204
CHEMICAL FAMILY: S-TRIAZINE
MOLECULAR FORMULA: C11-H21-N5-O-S
MOLECULAR WEIGHT: 271.43
CERCLA RATINGS (SCALE 0-3): HEALTH=2 FIRE=1 REACTIVITY=0 PERSISTENCE=2
NFPA RATINGS (SCALE 0-4): HEALTH=2 FIRE=1 REACTIVITY=0

COMPONENTS AND CONTAMINANTS

COMPONENT: METHOPROTRYNE ***PERCENT:*** 100.0
CAS# 841-06-5
OTHER CONTAMINANTS: NONE
EXPOSURE LIMITS: NO OCCUPATIONAL EXPOSURE LIMITS ESTABLISHED BY OSHA, ACGIH, OR NIOSH.

PHYSICAL DATA

DESCRIPTION: COLORLESS POWDER. ***MELTING POINT:*** 154-158 F (68-70 C)
SPECIFIC GRAVITY: 1.186 ***VISCOSITY:*** NEGLIGIBLE
SOLUBILITY IN WATER: 320 PPM @ 20 C
SOLVENT SOLUBILITY: SOLUBLE IN ACETONE, DICHLOROMETHANE, METHANOL, TOLUENE, OCTAN-1-OL, AND MOST ORGANIC SOLVENTS; SLIGHTLY SOLUBLE IN HEXANE

FIRE AND EXPLOSION DATA

FIRE AND EXPLOSION HAZARD: SLIGHT FIRE HAZARD WHEN EXPOSED TO HEAT OR FLAME.

FIREFIGHTING MEDIA: DRY CHEMICAL, CARBON DIOXIDE, HALON, WATER SPRAY OR STANDARD FOAM (1987 EMERGENCY RESPONSE GUIDEBOOK, DOT P 5800.4).
FOR LARGER FIRES, USE WATER SPRAY, FOG OR STANDARD FOAM (1987 EMERGENCY RESPONSE GUIDEBOOK, DOT P 5800.4).

FIREFIGHTING: MOVE CONTAINERS FROM FIRE AREA IF POSSIBLE (1987 EMERGENCY RESPONSE GUIDEBOOK, DOT P 5800.4, GUIDE PAGE 53).
EXTINGUISH USING AGENTS SUITABLE FOR SURROUNDING FIRE. USE FLOODING QUANTITIES OF WATER AS A FOG. KEEP MATERIAL OUT OF SEWERS AND WATER SOURCES. DO NOT TOUCH SPILLED MATERIAL. AVOID BREATHING HAZARDOUS FUMES; KEEP UPWIND.

TOXICITY

METHOPROTRYNE: TOXICITY DATA: 5000 MG/KG ORAL-RAT LD50; 2400 MG/KG ORAL-MOUSE LD50. CARCINOGEN STATUS: NONE. ACUTE TOXICITY LEVEL: MODERATELY TOXIC BY INGESTION. TARGET EFFECTS: NO DATA AVAILABLE.

HEALTH EFFECTS AND FIRST AID

INHALATION: METHOPROTRYNE: ACUTE EXPOSURE- SOME TRIAZINES ARE MILDLY IRRITATING TO THE UPPER RESPIRATORY TRACT. CHRONIC EXPOSURE- NO DATA AVAILABLE.
FIRST AID- REMOVE FROM EXPOSURE AREA TO FRESH AIR IMMEDIATELY. IF BREATHING HAS STOPPED, PERFORM ARTIFICIAL RESPIRATION. KEEP PERSON WARM AND AT REST. TREAT SYMPTOMATICALLY AND SUPPORTIVELY. GET MEDICAL ATTENTION IMMEDIATELY.

SKIN CONTACT: METHOPROTRYNE: ACUTE EXPOSURE- A LETHAL DOSE IN RATS BY DERMAL ABSORPTION WAS GREATER THAN 150 MG/KG. SOME TRIAZINES ARE MILDLY IRRITATING TO THE SKIN. CHRONIC EXPOSURE- NO DATA AVAILABLE.
FIRST AID- REMOVE CONTAMINATED CLOTHING AND SHOES IMMEDIATELY. WASH AFFECTED AREA WITH SOAP OR MILD DETERGENT AND LARGE AMOUNTS OF WATER UNTIL NO EVIDENCE OF CHEMICAL REMAINS (APPROXIMATELY 15-20 MINUTES). GET MEDICAL ATTENTION IMMEDIATELY.

EYE CONTACT: METHOPROTRYNE: ACUTE EXPOSURE- SOME TRIAZINES ARE MILDLY IRRITATING TO THE EYES. CHRONIC EXPOSURE- NO DATA AVAILABLE.
FIRST AID- WASH EYES IMMEDIATELY WITH LARGE AMOUNTS OF WATER OR NORMAL SALINE, OCCASIONALLY LIFTING UPPER AND LOWER LIDS, UNTIL NO EVIDENCE OF CHEMICAL REMAINS (APPROXIMATELY 15-20 MINUTES). GET MEDICAL ATTENTION IMMEDIATELY.

INGESTION: METHOPROTRYNE: ACUTE EXPOSURE- A LETHAL DOSE IN RATS WAS 5000 MG/KG; SYMPTOMS WERE NOT REPORTED. CHRONIC EXPOSURE- NO ADVERSE EFFECTS WERE NOTED IN A 90-DAY STUDY OF RATS FED 250 MG/KG/DAY AND DOGS FED 375 MG/KG/DAY.
FIRST AID- REMOVE BY GASTRIC LAVAGE AND CATHARSIS. MAINTAIN BLOOD PRESSURE AND AIRWAY. GIVE OXYGEN IF RESPIRATION IS DEPRESSED. DO NOT PERFORM GASTRIC LAVAGE IF VICTIM IS UNCONSCIOUS. GET MEDICAL ATTENTION IMMEDIATELY (DREISBACH, HANDBOOK OF POISONING, 12TH ED.).
ADMINISTRATION OF LAVAGE OR OXYGEN SHOULD BE PERFORMED BY QUALIFIED MEDICAL PERSONNEL.
ANTIDOTE: NO SPECIFIC ANTIDOTE. TREAT SYMPTOMATICALLY AND SUPPORTIVELY.

REACTIVITY

REACTIVITY: STABLE UNDER NORMAL TEMPERATURES AND PRESSURES.
INCOMPATIBILITIES: METHOPROTRYNE: NO DATA AVAILABLE.
DECOMPOSITION: THERMAL DECOMPOSITION PRODUCTS MAY INCLUDE TOXIC OXIDES OF CARBON, NITROGEN, AND SULFUR.
POLYMERIZATION: HAZARDOUS POLYMERIZATION HAS NOT BEEN REPORTED TO OCCUR UNDER NORMAL TEMPERATURES AND PRESSURES.

STORAGE AND DISPOSAL

OBSERVE ALL FEDERAL, STATE AND LOCAL REGULATIONS WHEN STORING OR DISPOSING OF THIS SUBSTANCE. FOR ASSISTANCE, CONTACT THE DISTRICT DIRECTOR OF THE ENVIRONMENTAL PROTECTION AGENCY.

STORAGE

STORE IN ACCORDANCE WITH 40 CFR 165 RECOMMENDED PROCEDURES FOR THE DISPOSAL AND STORAGE OF PESTICIDES AND PESTICIDE CONTAINERS.

DISPOSAL

DISPOSAL MUST BE IN ACCORDANCE WITH 40 CFR 165 RECOMMENDED PROCEDURES FOR THE DISPOSAL AND STORAGE OF PESTICIDES AND PESTICIDE CONTAINERS.

CONDITIONS TO AVOID

MAY BURN BUT DOES NOT IGNITE READILY.

SPILL AND LEAK PROCEDURES

OCCUPATIONAL SPILL: DO NOT TOUCH SPILLED MATERIAL. STOP LEAK IF YOU CAN DO IT WITHOUT RISK. FOR SMALL SPILLS, TAKE UP WITH SAND OR OTHER ABSORBENT MATERIAL AND PLACE INTO CONTAINERS FOR LATER DISPOSAL. FOR SMALL DRY SPILLS, WITH A CLEAN SHOVEL PLACE MATERIAL INTO CLEAN, DRY CONTAINER AND COVER. MOVE CONTAINERS FROM SPILL AREA. FOR LARGER SPILLS, DIKE FAR AHEAD OF SPILL FOR LATER DISPOSAL. KEEP UNNECESSARY PEOPLE AWAY. ISOLATE HAZARD AREA AND DENY ENTRY.

PROTECTIVE EQUIPMENT

VENTILATION: PROVIDE LOCAL EXHAUST OR GENERAL DILUTION VENTILATION SYSTEM.

RESPIRATOR: THE FOLLOWING RESPIRATORS ARE RECOMMENDED BASED ON INFORMATION FOUND IN THE PHYSICAL DATA, TOXICITY AND HEALTH EFFECTS SECTIONS. THEY ARE RANKED IN ORDER FROM MINIMUM TO MAXIMUM RESPIRATORY PROTECTION. THE SPECIFIC RESPIRATOR SELECTED MUST BE BASED ON CONTAMINATION LEVELS FOUND IN THE WORK PLACE, MUST NOT EXCEED THE WORKING LIMITS OF THE RESPIRATOR AND BE JOINTLY APPROVED BY THE NATIONAL INSTITUTE FOR OCCUPATIONAL SAFETY AND HEALTH AND THE MINE SAFETY AND HEALTH ADMINISTRATION (NIOSH-MSHA).

CHEMICAL CARTRIDGE RESPIRATOR WITH AN ORGANIC VAPOR CARTRIDGE(S) WITH A FULL FACEPIECE AND ORGANIC VAPOR CARTRIDGE(S) IN COMBINATION WITH A DUST AND MIST FILTER.

POWERED AIR-PURIFYING RESPIRATOR WITH A TIGHT-FITTING FACEPIECE AND ORGANIC VAPOR CARTRIDGE(S) IN COMBINATION WITH A HIGH-EFFICIENCY PARTICULATE FILTER.

TYPE 'C' SUPPLIED-AIR RESPIRATOR WITH A FULL FACEPIECE OPERATED IN A PRESSURE-DEMAND OR OTHER POSITIVE PRESSURE MODE.

SELF-CONTAINED BREATHING APPARATUS WITH A FULL FACEPIECE OPERATED IN PRESSURE-DEMAND OR OTHER POSITIVE PRESSURE MODE.

FOR FIREFIGHTING AND OTHER IMMEDIATELY DANGEROUS TO LIFE OR HEALTH CONDITIONS:

SELF-CONTAINED BREATHING APPARATUS WITH FULL FACEPIECE OPERATED IN PRESSURE-DEMAND OR OTHER POSITIVE PRESSURE MODE.

SUPPLIED-AIR RESPIRATOR WITH FULL FACEPIECE AND OPERATED IN PRESSURE-DEMAND OR OTHER POSITIVE PRESSURE MODE IN COMBINATION WITH AN AUXILIARY SELF-CONTAINED BREATHING APPARATUS OPERATED IN PRESSURE-DEMAND OR OTHER POSITIVE PRESSURE MODE.

CLOTHING: EMPLOYEE MUST WEAR APPROPRIATE PROTECTIVE (IMPERVIOUS) CLOTHING AND EQUIPMENT TO PREVENT REPEATED OR PROLONGED SKIN CONTACT WITH THIS SUBSTANCE.

GLOVES: EMPLOYEE MUST WEAR APPROPRIATE PROTECTIVE GLOVES TO PREVENT CONTACT WITH THIS SUBSTANCE.

EYE PROTECTION: EMPLOYEE MUST WEAR SPLASH-PROOF OR DUST-RESISTANT SAFETY GOGGLES TO PREVENT EYE CONTACT WITH THIS SUBSTANCE.

EMERGENCY EYE WASH: WHERE THERE IS ANY POSSIBILITY THAT AN EMPLOYEE'S EYES MAY BE EXPOSED TO THIS SUBSTANCE, THE EMPLOYER SHOULD PROVIDE AN EYE WASH FOUNTAIN WITHIN THE IMMEDIATE WORK AREA FOR EMERGENCY USE.

AUTHORIZED BY- OCCUPATIONAL HEALTH SERVICES, INC.

CREATION DATE: 10/04/89 ***REVISION DATE:*** 05/16/90

MATERIAL SAFETY DATA SHEET

OCCUPATIONAL HEALTH SERVICES, INC.
AGRICULTURE AND PESTICIDE DIVISION
450 SEVENTH AVENUE, SUITE 2407
NEW YORK, NEW YORK 10123
1-800-445-MSDS OR (212) 967-1100

EMERGENCY CONTACT:
JOHN S. BRANSFORD, JR. (615) 292-1180

SUBSTANCE IDENTIFICATION

CAS-NUMBER 59-05-2

SUBSTANCE: METHOTREXATE

TRADE NAMES/SYNONYMS: AMETHOPTERIN; METHYLAMINOPTERIN; L-GLUTAMIC ACID, N-(4-(((2,4-DIAMINO-6-PTERIDINYL)METHYL)- METHYLAMINO)BENZOYL)-; N-(4-(((2,4-DIAMINO-6-PTERIDINYL)METHYL)METHYLAMINO)BENZOYL)- L-GLUTAMIC ACID; GLUTAMIC ACID, N-(P-(((2,4-DIAMINO-6-PTERIDINYL)METHYL) METHYLAMINO)BENZOYL)-, L-(+)-; L-(+)-N-(P-(((2,4-DIAMINO-6-PTERIDINYL)METHYL)METHYLAMINO)BENZOYL)- GLUTAMIC ACID; AMETHOPTERINE; L-METHOTREXATE; MEXATE; C20H22N8O5; PST14210

CHEMICAL FAMILY: CARBOXYLIC ACID, ALICYCLIC

MOLECULAR FORMULA: C20-H22-N8-O5

MOLECULAR WEIGHT: 454.46

CERCLA RATINGS (SCALE 0-3): HEALTH=3 FIRE=1 REACTIVITY=0 PERSISTENCE=1

NFPA RATINGS (SCALE 0-4): HEALTH=U FIRE=1 REACTIVITY=0

COMPONENTS AND CONTAMINANTS

COMPONENT: METHOTREXATE ***PERCENT:*** 100.0

CAS# 59-05-2

OTHER CONTAMINANTS: NONE

EXPOSURE LIMITS: NO OCCUPATIONAL EXPOSURE LIMITS ESTABLISHED BY OSHA, ACGIH, OR NIOSH.

METHOTREXATE: AMERICAN CYANAMID RECOMMENDED PERMISSIBLE EXPOSURE LIMITS:

FOR FEMALES OF CHILD BEARING POTENTIAL: 0.01 MG/M3-SINGLE EXPOSURE NOT REPEATED WITHOUT MINIMUM INTERRUPTION OF ONE WEEK 0.001 MG/M3-EXPOSURE FOR 5 CONSECUTIVE DAYS 0.0002 MG/M3-EXPOSURE FOR 5 CONSECUTIVE DAYS; REPEATED AT 7 TO 9 DAY INTERVALS 0.00002 MG/M3-DAILY EXPOSURE FOR 5 DAYS OR MORE, INTERRUPTED BY NOT MORE THAN 2 DAYS (E.G., CONTINUOUS REPETITION OF 5 DAY/WEEK SHIFTS)

FOR ALL OTHER ADULTS: 0.1 MG/M3-SINGLE EXPOSURE NOT REPEATED WITHOUT MINIMUM INTERRUPTION OF ONE WEEK 0.02 MG/M3-EXPOSURE FOR 5 CONSECUTIVE DAYS 0.01 MG/M3-EXPOSURE FOR 5 CONSECUTIVE DAYS, REPEATED AT 7 TO 9 DAY INTERVALS 0.001 MG/M3-DAILY EXPOSURE FOR 5 DAYS OR MORE, INTERRUPTED BY NOT MORE THAN 2 DAYS (E.G., CONTINUOUS REPETITION OF 5 DAY/WEEK SHIFTS)

SUBJECT TO CALIFORNIA PROPOSITION 65 CANCER AND/OR REPRODUCTIVE TOXICITY WARNING AND RELEASE REQUIREMENTS- (JANUARY 1, 1989)

PHYSICAL DATA

DESCRIPTION: ODORLESS, ORANGE-YELLOW TO ORANGE-BROWN CRYSTALLINE POWDER.

MELTING POINT: 365-399 F (185-204 C) (DECOMPOSES) (H2O)

SPECIFIC GRAVITY: NOT AVAILABLE ***SOLUBILITY IN WATER:*** INSOLUBLE

SOLVENT SOLUBILITY: SOLUBLE IN DILUTE SOLUTIONS OF HYDROCHLORIC ACID, ALKALI, CARBONATES; INSOLUBLE IN CHLOROFORM, ALCOHOL, ETHER.

FIRE AND EXPLOSION DATA

FIRE AND EXPLOSION HAZARD: SLIGHT FIRE HAZARD WHEN EXPOSED TO HEAT OR FLAME.

FIREFIGHTING MEDIA: DRY CHEMICAL, CARBON DIOXIDE, HALON, WATER SPRAY OR STANDARD FOAM (1987 EMERGENCY RESPONSE GUIDEBOOK, DOT P 5800.4).

FOR LARGER FIRES, USE WATER SPRAY, FOG OR STANDARD FOAM (1987 EMERGENCY RESPONSE GUIDEBOOK, DOT P 5800.4).

FIREFIGHTING: MOVE CONTAINERS FROM FIRE AREA IF POSSIBLE (1987 EMERGENCY RESPONSE GUIDEBOOK, DOT P 5800.4, GUIDE PAGE 53).

EXTINGUISH USING AGENT SUITABLE FOR TYPE OF SURROUNDING FIRE. AVOID BREATHING VAPORS AND DUSTS. KEEP UPWIND.

TOXICITY

METHOTREXATE: IRRITATION DATA: 150 MG/KG NON-STANDARD EXPOSURE EYE-HUMAN. TOXICITY DATA: ANHYDROUS: 43 MG/KG/5 YEARS ORAL-HUMAN TDLO; 2 MG/KG/12 DAYS ORAL-CHILD TDLO; 643 UG/KG/6 WEEKS INTERMITTENT ORAL-MAN TDLO; 2 MG/KG/17 WEEKS INTERMITTENT ORAL-WOMAN TDLO; 135 MG/KG ORAL-RAT LD50; 146 MG/KG ORAL-MOUSE LD50; 200 MG/KG/5 YEARS INTRAMUSCULAR-HUMAN TDLO; 35 MG/KG/28 WEEKS INTRAMUSCULAR-HUMAN TDLO; 6 MG/KG INTRAPERITONEAL-RAT LD50; 36 MG/KG/15 DAYS INTRASPINAL-WOMAN LDLO; 4,650 UG/KG/4 WEEKS INTERMITTENT INTRAVENOUS-HUMAN TDLO; 740 MG/KG INTRAVENOUS-MAN TDLO; 100 MG/KG/4 HOURS INTRAVENOUS-CHILD TDLO; 14 MG/KG INTRAVENOUS-RAT LD50; 2600 UG/KG PARENTERAL-WOMAN TDLO; 250 MG/KG SUBCUTANEOUS-MOUSE LD50; 410 UG/KG UNREPORTED-MAN TDLO; 150 MG/KG UNREPORTED-WOMAN TDLO; MUTAGENIC DATA (RTECS); REPRODUCTIVE EFFECTS DATA (RTECS); TUMORIGENIC DATA (RTECS). MONOHYDRATE: NO DATA AVAILABLE. TETRAHYDRATE: NO DATA AVAILABLE. CARCINOGEN STATUS: HUMAN INADEQUATE EVIDENCE, ANIMAL INADEQUATE EVIDENCE (IARC GROUP-3). LOCAL EFFECTS: IRRITANT- SKIN, EYE. ACUTE TOXICITY LEVEL: TOXIC BY INGESTION. TARGET EFFECTS: NEPHROTOXIN; HEPATOTOXIN; BONE MARROW DEPRESSANT; TERATOGEN. POISONING MAY ALSO AFFECT THE GASTROINTESTINAL OR CENTRAL NERVOUS SYSTEMS, THE BLOOD, AND THE LUNGS. AT INCREASED RISK FROM EXPOSURE: FAMILIAL HISTORY OF PORPHYRIA OR HEPATIC DYSFUNCTION; RENAL DYSFUNCTION; BONE MARROW DEPRESSION; BLOOD DYSCRASIAS; GASTROINTESTINAL DISORDERS; EXCESSIVE ULTRAVIOLET RADIATION EXPOSURE. ADDITIONAL DATA: THE USE OF ALCOHOLIC BEVERAGES MAY ENHANCE THE TOXIC EFFECTS. INTERACTIONS WITH MEDICATIONS HAVE BEEN REPORTED.

HEALTH EFFECTS AND FIRST AID

INHALATION: METHOTREXATE: **ACUTE EXPOSURE-** IF SUFFICIENT AMOUNTS ARE INHALED, SYSTEMIC POISONING MAY OCCUR AS DETAILED IN ACUTE INGESTION. **CHRONIC EXPOSURE-** IF SUFFICIENT AMOUNTS ARE INHALED, SYSTEMIC POISONING MAY OCCUR AS DETAILED IN CHRONIC INGESTION.

FIRST AID- REMOVE FROM EXPOSURE AREA TO FRESH AIR IMMEDIATELY. IF BREATHING HAS STOPPED, PERFORM ARTIFICIAL RESPIRATION. KEEP PERSON WARM AND AT REST. TREAT SYMPTOMATICALLY AND SUPPORTIVELY. GET MEDICAL ATTENTION IMMEDIATELY.

SKIN CONTACT: METHOTREXATE: IRRITANT. **ACUTE EXPOSURE-** CONTACT MAY CAUSE IRRITATION. SENSITIZATION DERMATITIS MAY OCCUR IN PREVIOUSLY EXPOSED INDIVIDUALS. **CHRONIC EXPOSURE-** REPEATED AND PROLONGED CONTACT WITH IRRITANTS MAY CAUSE DERMATITIS. SOME PERCUTANEOUS ABSORPTION MAY OCCUR AND RESULT IN TOXICITY. REPEATED CONTACT MAY LEAD TO SENSITIZATION DERMATITIS. THERAPEUTIC USE HAS BEEN REPORTED TO CAUSE ERYTHEMATOUS RASHES, PRURITUS, URTICARIA, DERMATITIS, ECCHYMOSIS, TELANGIECTASIA, ACNE AND FURUNCULOSIS, FOLLICULITIS, ALOPECIA, PHOTOSENSITIVITY, AND HYPER- OR DEPIGMENTATION. CASES OF MALIGNANT SKIN CANCER HAVE BEEN REPORTED IN PERSONS TREATED WITH METHOTREXATE FOR PSORIASIS.

FIRST AID- REMOVE CONTAMINATED CLOTHING AND SHOES IMMEDIATELY. WASH AFFECTED AREA WITH SOAP OR MILD DETERGENT AND LARGE AMOUNTS OF WATER UNTIL NO EVIDENCE OF CHEMICAL REMAINS (APPROXIMATELY 15-20 MINUTES). GET MEDICAL ATTENTION IMMEDIATELY.

EYE CONTACT: METHOTREXATE: IRRITANT. **ACUTE EXPOSURE-** CONTACT MAY CAUSE IRRITATION. **CHRONIC EXPOSURE-** REPEATED OR PROLONGED EXPOSURE MAY CAUSE CONJUNCTIVITIS.

FIRST AID- WASH EYES IMMEDIATELY WITH LARGE AMOUNTS OF WATER OR NORMAL SALINE, OCCASIONALLY LIFTING UPPER AND LOWER LIDS, UNTIL NO EVIDENCE OF CHEMICAL REMAINS (APPROXIMATELY 15-20 MINUTES). GET MEDICAL ATTENTION IMMEDIATELY.

INGESTION: METHOTREXATE: NEPHROTOXIN/HEPATOTOXIN/BONE MARROW DEPRESSANT/TERATOGEN/TOXIC. **ACUTE EXPOSURE-** A DOSE OF 135 MG/KG WAS LETHAL IN RATS. ANIMALS GIVEN A MINIMAL LETHAL DOSE SURVIVE FOR AT LEAST 48 HOURS AND USUALLY DIE WITHIN 3 TO 5 DAYS. EFFECTS MAY INCLUDE RARE GASTROINTESTINAL TOXICITY WITH ANOREXIA, PROGRESSIVE WEIGHT LOSS AND BLOODY DIARRHEA, LEUKOPENIA, DEPRESSION AND COMA. LESIONS OF THE INTESTINAL TRACT AND BONE MARROW, DESQUAMATION OF EPITHELIAL CELLS, SEVERE HEMORRHAGIC DESQUAMATING ENTERITIS OF THE INTESTINE AND DEGENERATION OF BONE MARROW MAY ALSO OCCUR. **CHRONIC EXPOSURE-** THERAPEUTIC USE MAY MOST FREQUENTLY CAUSE NAUSEA, VOMITING, ABDOMINAL DISTRESS, ANOREXIA, UNDUE FATIGUE, DIZZINESS, FEVER, CHILLS, ALOPECIA, LEUKOPENIA AND DECREASED RESISTANCE TO INFECTION. ULCERATIVE STOMATITIS, GINGIVITIS, GLOSSITIS, PHARYNGITIS, ESOPHAGITIS, ALTERED TASTE AND SMELL, HEMORRHAGIC ENTERITIS, HEMATEMESIS, BLOODY DIARRHEA, HEADACHE, DROWSINESS, BLURRED VISION, APHASIA, PARESTHESIA, PARESIS, CONVULSIONS AND COMA MAY OCCUR. DERMAL EFFECTS CONSISTING OF ERYTHEMATOUS RASHES, PRURITUS, URTICARIA, DERMATITIS, ECCHYMOSIS, TELANGIECTASIA, ACNE AND FURUNCULOSIS, FOLLICULITIS, ALOPECIA, PHOTOSENSITIVITY, AND HYPER- OR DEPIGMENTATION HAVE BEEN REPORTED. PULMONARY EFFECTS MAY INCLUDE DYSPNEA, NON-PRODUCTIVE COUGH, HYPOXEMIA, CHRONIC INTERSTITIAL OBSTRUCTIVE PULMONARY DISEASE AND INTERSTITIAL PNEUMONITIS. HISTOLOGICALLY, PATCHY INTRA-ALVEOLAR AND INTERSTITIAL INFILTRATES INCLUDING EOSINOPHILS HAVE BEEN REPORTED. GENITOURINARY SYSTEM EFFECTS MAY INCLUDE CYSTITIS, AZOTEMIA, HYPERURICEMIA, HEMATURIA, TUBULAR PRECIPITATES, RENAL TUBULAR NECROSIS, RENAL FAILURE, DEFECTIVE OOGENESIS OR SPERMATOGENESIS, TRANSIENT OLIGOSPERMIA, MENSTRUAL DYSFUNCTION, AND INFERTILITY. HEPATOTOXICITY IS GREATER IN PATIENTS RECEIVING FREQUENT SMALL DOSES THAN THOSE RECEIVING LARGE INTERMITTENT DOSES AND MAY CONSIST OF LIVER ATROPHY, FATTY METAMORPHOSIS, NECROSIS, CIRRHOSIS, PORPHYRIA, STEATOSIS, INTRAHEPATIC CHOLESTASIS, PORTAL INFLAMMATORY REACTIONS, PERIPORTAL FIBROSIS, REVERSIBLE ENZYME ELEVATIONS AND EXACERBATION OF PREEXISTING CIRRHOTIC LIVER DAMAGE WITH POTENTIAL HEPATIC COMA. HEMATOLOGIC EFFECTS MAY INCLUDE MEGALOBLASTIC ANEMIA AND BONE MARROW DEPRESSION WITH PANCYTOPENIA, APLASIA AND RARELY LEUKEMIA. SKELETAL EFFECTS MANIFESTED BY BONE PAIN, FRACTURES, ASEPTIC NECROSIS OF THE HEAD OF THE FEMUR AND OSTEOPOROSIS MAY OCCUR. OTHER REPORTED EFFECTS MAY INCLUDE METABOLIC CHANGES, PRECIPITATING DIABETES, ABNORMAL TISSUE CELL CHANGES, VASCULITIS, FOLIC ACID DEFICIENCY, DECREASED DEEP TENDON REFLEXES AND SUDDEN DEATH. DEATHS HAVE BEEN REPORTED DUE TO PULMONARY EFFECTS, SEPTICEMIA, INTESTINAL PERFORATION OR HEMORRHAGE. TWO PSORIATIC PATIENTS DIED FOLLOWING ORAL TREATMENT WITH METHOTREXATE; ONE RECEIVED 5 MG/DAY FOR 5 DAYS; THE OTHER FOR 7 DAYS. CORTICOSTEROID THERAPY MAY HAVE BEEN A COMPLICATING FACTOR. MATERNAL USE HAS PRODUCED ABORTION, FETAL DEATH OR CONGENITAL ABNORMALITIES. HUMAN MATERNAL INGESTION OF 2.5 MG DAILY FOR 5 DAYS BETWEEN THE 8TH AND 10TH WEEK PRODUCED DEFECTS IN A CHILD INCLUDING ABSENCE OF THE FRONTAL BONES, PREMATURE CRANIOSYNOSTOSIS OF THE CORONAL AND LAMBDOID SUTURES, FLAT NASAL BRIDGE, HYPERTELORISM, LIMB REDUCTION DEFECTS, RIB DEFECTS AND THE ABSENCE OF DIGITS. A SIMILAR REPORT EXISTS FROM 5 MG DAILY FOR THE FIRST 2 MONTHS OF PREGNANCY. METHOTREXATE GIVEN ORALLY TO CATS ON DAYS 11-20 OF PREGNANCY PRODUCED VISCERAL ABNORMALITIES INCLUDING UMBILICAL HERNIA, CLEFT PALATES, HYDROCEPHALUS, SPINA BIFIDA AND MALFORMED LIMBS. IN MICE, NO TERATOGENIC DEFECTS WERE FOUND AT 10 MG/KG BUT AT 25 AND 50 MG/KG EXENCEPHALY, OMPHALOCELE, ECTRODACTYLY AND CLEFT PALATE WERE FOUND. A NUMBER OF CASES HAVE BEEN REPORTED OF MALIGNANCIES DEVELOPING IN PATIENTS TREATED WITH METHOTREXATE, OFTEN IN COMBINATION WITH OTHER AGENTS, FOR PSORIASIS OR PREVIOUS CANCER. NO EXCESS OF CANCER WAS FOUND IN TWO EPIDEMIOLOGICAL STUDIES OF PATIENTS WHO RECEIVED METHOTREXATE FOR PSORIASIS OR AS TREATMENT FOR CHORIOCARCINOMA.

FIRST AID- IF EXTENSIVE VOMITING HAS NOT OCCURRED, THE SUBSTANCE SHOULD BE REMOVED BY EMESIS OR GASTRIC LAVAGE PROVIDED THAT THE PATIENT IS CONSCIOUS AND CONVULSIONS ARE NOT PRESENT. KEEP HEAD BELOW HIPS DURING VOMITING TO PREVENT ASPIRATION. DO NOT ATTEMPT TO MAKE AN UNCONSCIOUS PERSON VOMIT. TREAT SYMPTOMATICALLY AND SUPPORTIVELY. GET MEDICAL ATTENTION IMMEDIATELY (DREISBACH, HANDBOOK OF POISONING, 12TH ED.). TREATMENT SHOULD BE PERFORMED BY QUALIFIED MEDICAL PERSONNEL.

ANTIDOTE: THE FOLLOWING ANTIDOTE HAS BEEN RECOMMENDED. HOWEVER, THE DECISION AS TO WHETHER THE SEVERITY OF POISONING REQUIRES ADMINISTRATION OF ANY ANTIDOTE AND ACTUAL DOSE REQUIRED SHOULD BE MADE BY QUALIFIED MEDICAL PERSONNEL.

METHOTREXATE POISONING: WHERE LARGE DOSES OR OVERDOSES HAVE BEEN GIVEN, CALCIUM LEUCOVORIN MAY BE ADMINISTERED BY INTRAVENOUS INFUSION IN DOSES UP TO 75 MG WITHIN TWELVE HOURS, FOLLOWED BY 12 MG INTRAMUSCULARLY EVERY SIX HOURS FOR FOUR DOSES. WHERE AVERAGE DOSES OF METHOTREXATE APPEAR TO HAVE HAD AN ADVERSE EFFECT, 2 TO 4 ML (6-12 MG) OF CALCIUM LEUCOVORIN MAY BE GIVEN INTRAMUSCULARLY EVERY SIX HOURS FOR FOUR DOSES. IN GENERAL, WHERE OVERDOSAGE IS SUSPECTED, THE DOSE OF LEUCOVORIN SHOULD BE EQUAL TO OR HIGHER THAN THE OFFENDING DOSE OF METHOTREXATE AND SHOULD BEST BE ADMINISTERED WITHIN THE FIRST HOUR. USE OF CALCIUM LEUCOVORIN AFTER AN HOUR DELAY IS MUCH LESS EFFECTIVE. (ARENA, POISONING, 4TH EDITION). TREATMENT SHOULD BE ADMINISTERED BY QUALIFIED MEDICAL PERSONNEL ONLY.

REACTIVITY

REACTIVITY: STABLE UNDER NORMAL TEMPERATURES AND PRESSURES.

INCOMPATIBILITIES: METHOTREXATE: OXIDIZERS (STRONG): FIRE AND EXPLOSION HAZARD.

DECOMPOSITION: THERMAL DECOMPOSITION PRODUCTS MAY INCLUDE TOXIC OXIDES OF CARBON AND NITROGEN.

POLYMERIZATION: HAZARDOUS POLYMERIZATION HAS NOT BEEN REPORTED TO OCCUR UNDER NORMAL TEMPERATURES AND PRESSURES.

STORAGE AND DISPOSAL

OBSERVE ALL FEDERAL, STATE AND LOCAL REGULATIONS WHEN STORING OR DISPOSING OF THIS SUBSTANCE. FOR ASSISTANCE, CONTACT THE DISTRICT DIRECTOR OF THE ENVIRONMENTAL PROTECTION AGENCY.

****STORAGE****

STORE AWAY FROM INCOMPATIBLE SUBSTANCES.

KEEP CONTAINER TIGHTLY CLOSED. PROTECT FROM EXPOSURE TO AIR OR LIGHT.

CONDITIONS TO AVOID

MAY BURN BUT DOES NOT IGNITE READILY.

SPILL AND LEAK PROCEDURES

WATER SPILL: THE CALIFORNIA SAFE DRINKING WATER AND TOXIC ENFORCEMENT ACT OF 1986 (PROPOSITION 65) PROHIBITS CONTAMINATING ANY KNOWN SOURCE OF DRINKING WATER WITH SUBSTANCES KNOWN TO CAUSE CANCER AND/OR REPRODUCTIVE TOXICITY.

OCCUPATIONAL SPILL: DO NOT TOUCH SPILLED MATERIAL. STOP LEAK IF YOU CAN DO IT WITHOUT RISK. FOR SMALL SPILLS, TAKE UP WITH SAND OR OTHER ABSORBENT MATERIAL AND PLACE INTO CONTAINERS FOR LATER DISPOSAL. FOR SMALL DRY SPILLS, WITH A CLEAN SHOVEL PLACE MATERIAL INTO CLEAN, DRY CONTAINER AND COVER. MOVE CONTAINERS FROM SPILL AREA. FOR LARGER

SPILLS, DIKE FAR AHEAD OF SPILL FOR LATER DISPOSAL. KEEP UNNECESSARY PEOPLE AWAY. ISOLATE HAZARD AREA AND DENY ENTRY.

PROTECTIVE EQUIPMENT

VENTILATION: PROVIDE LOCAL EXHAUST OR PROCESS ENCLOSURE VENTILATION SYSTEM.

RESPIRATOR: THE FOLLOWING RESPIRATORS ARE RECOMMENDED BASED ON INFORMATION FOUND IN THE PHYSICAL DATA, TOXICITY AND HEALTH EFFECTS SECTIONS. THEY ARE RANKED IN ORDER FROM MINIMUM TO MAXIMUM RESPIRATORY PROTECTION. THE SPECIFIC RESPIRATOR SELECTED MUST BE BASED ON CONTAMINATION LEVELS FOUND IN THE WORK PLACE, MUST NOT EXCEED THE WORKING LIMITS OF THE RESPIRATOR AND BE JOINTLY APPROVED BY THE NATIONAL INSTITUTE FOR OCCUPATIONAL SAFETY AND HEALTH AND THE MINE SAFETY AND HEALTH ADMINISTRATION (NIOSH-MSHA).

DUST AND MIST RESPIRATOR WITH A FULL FACEPIECE.

AIR-PURIFYING FULL FACEPIECE RESPIRATOR WITH A HIGH-EFFICIENCY PARTICULATE FILTER.

POWERED AIR-PURIFYING RESPIRATOR WITH A TIGHT-FITTING FACEPIECE AND HIGH-EFFICIENCY PARTICULATE FILTER. TYPE 'C' SUPPLIED-AIR RESPIRATOR WITH A FULL FACEPIECE OPERATED IN PRESSURE-DEMAND OR OTHER POSITIVE PRESSURE MODE OR WITH A FULL FACEPIECE, HELMET OR HOOD OPERATED IN CONTINUOUS-FLOW MODE.

SELF-CONTAINED BREATHING APPARATUS WITH A FULL FACEPIECE OPERATED IN PRESSURE-DEMAND OR OTHER POSITIVE PRESSURE MODE.

FOR FIREFIGHTING AND OTHER IMMEDIATELY DANGEROUS TO LIFE OR HEALTH CONDITIONS:

SELF-CONTAINED BREATHING APPARATUS WITH FULL FACEPIECE OPERATED IN PRESSURE-DEMAND OR OTHER POSITIVE PRESSURE MODE.

SUPPLIED-AIR RESPIRATOR WITH FULL FACEPIECE AND OPERATED IN PRESSURE-DEMAND OR OTHER POSITIVE PRESSURE MODE IN COMBINATION WITH AN AUXILIARY SELF-CONTAINED BREATHING APPARATUS OPERATED IN PRESSURE-DEMAND OR OTHER POSITIVE PRESSURE MODE.

CLOTHING: EMPLOYEE MUST WEAR APPROPRIATE PROTECTIVE (IMPERVIOUS) CLOTHING AND EQUIPMENT TO PREVENT REPEATED OR PROLONGED SKIN CONTACT WITH THIS SUBSTANCE.

GLOVES: EMPLOYEE MUST WEAR APPROPRIATE PROTECTIVE GLOVES TO PREVENT CONTACT WITH THIS SUBSTANCE.

EYE PROTECTION: EMPLOYEE MUST WEAR SPLASH-PROOF OR DUST-RESISTANT SAFETY GOGGLES TO PREVENT EYE CONTACT WITH THIS SUBSTANCE.

EMERGENCY EYE WASH: WHERE THERE IS ANY POSSIBILITY THAT AN EMPLOYEE'S EYES MAY BE EXPOSED TO THIS SUBSTANCE, THE EMPLOYER SHOULD PROVIDE AN EYE WASH FOUNTAIN WITHIN THE IMMEDIATE WORK AREA FOR EMERGENCY USE.

AUTHORIZED BY- OCCUPATIONAL HEALTH SERVICES, INC.

CREATION DATE: 10/04/89 ***REVISION DATE:*** 07/12/90

MATERIAL SAFETY DATA SHEET

OCCUPATIONAL HEALTH SERVICES, INC.
AGRICULTURE AND PESTICIDE DIVISION
450 SEVENTH AVENUE, SUITE 2407
NEW YORK, NEW YORK 10123
1-800-445-MSDS OR (212) 967-1100

EMERGENCY CONTACT:
JOHN S. BRANSFORD, JR. (615) 292-1180

SUBSTANCE IDENTIFICATION

CAS-NUMBER 15475-56-6

SUBSTANCE: <u>METHOTREXATE SODIUM</u>

TRADE NAMES/SYNONYMS: AMETHOPTERIN SODIUM; METHYLAMINOPTERIN SODIUM; L-GLUTAMIC ACID, N-(4-(((2,4-DIAMINO-6-PTERIDINYL)METHYL)METHYLAMINO) BENZOYL)-, SODIUM SALT; N-(4-(((2,4-DIAMINO-6-PTERIDINYL)METHYLAMINO)BENZOYL-L-GLUTAMIC ACID, SODIUM SALT; GLUTAMIC ACID, N-(P-(((2,4-DIAMINO-6-PTERIDINYL)METHYL)METHYLAMINO) BENZOYL), L-(+)-, SODIUM SALT; L-(+)-N-(P-(((2,4-DIAMINO-6-PTERIDINYL)METHYL)METHYLAMINO)BENZOYL)- GLUTAMIC ACID, SODIUM SALT; AMETHOPTERINE SODIUM; L-METHOTREXATE SODIUM; MEXATE SODIUM; METHOTREXATE; C20H22N8O5; PST14211

CHEMICAL FAMILY: CARBOXYLIC ACID, ALICYCLIC

MOLECULAR FORMULA: C20-H22-N8-O5.X(NA)

CERCLA RATINGS (SCALE 0-3): HEALTH=U FIRE=1 REACTIVITY=0 PERSISTENCE=1

NFPA RATINGS (SCALE 0-4): HEALTH=U FIRE=1 REACTIVITY=0

COMPONENTS AND CONTAMINANTS

COMPONENT: METHOTREXATE SODIUM ***PERCENT:*** 100.0
CAS# 15475-56-6

OTHER CONTAMINANTS: NONE

EXPOSURE LIMITS: METHOTREXATE SODIUM: SUBJECT TO CALIFORNIA PROPOSITION 65 CANCER AND/OR REPRODUCTIVE TOXICITY WARNING AND RELEASE REQUIREMENTS- (APRIL 1, 1990)

PHYSICAL DATA

DESCRIPTION: ODORLESS, YELLOW-ORANGE POWDER. ***MELTING POINT:*** NOT AVAILABLE

SPECIFIC GRAVITY: NOT AVAILABLE ***SOLUBILITY IN WATER:*** SOLUBLE

SOLVENT SOLUBILITY: SOLUBLE IN DILUTE HYDROCHLORIC ACID, ALKALI SOLUTIONS; SLIGHTLY SOLUBLE IN CARBONATES; INSOLUBLE IN CHLOROFORM, ALCOHOL, ETHER.

FIRE AND EXPLOSION DATA

FIRE AND EXPLOSION HAZARD: SLIGHT FIRE HAZARD WHEN EXPOSED TO HEAT OR FLAME.

FIREFIGHTING MEDIA: DRY CHEMICAL, CARBON DIOXIDE, HALON, WATER SPRAY OR STANDARD FOAM (1987 EMERGENCY RESPONSE GUIDEBOOK, DOT P 5800.4). FOR LARGER FIRES, USE WATER SPRAY, FOG OR STANDARD FOAM (1987 EMERGENCY RESPONSE GUIDEBOOK, DOT P 5800.4).

FIREFIGHTING: MOVE CONTAINERS FROM FIRE AREA IF POSSIBLE (1987 EMERGENCY RESPONSE GUIDEBOOK, DOT P 5800.4, GUIDE PAGE 53).
EXTINGUISH USING AGENT SUITABLE FOR TYPE OF SURROUNDING FIRE. AVOID BREATHING VAPORS AND DUSTS. KEEP UPWIND.

TOXICITY

METHOTREXATE SODIUM: TOXICITY DATA: 27 MG/KG INTRAPERITONEAL-MOUSE LD50; 380 MG/KG UNREPORTED-MOUSE LD50; MUTAGENIC DATA (RTECS); REPRODUCTIVE EFFECTS DATA (RTECS). CARCINOGEN STATUS: NONE. ACUTE TOXICITY LEVEL: INSUFFICIENT DATA. TARGET EFFECTS: NO DATA AVAILABLE.

HEALTH EFFECTS AND FIRST AID

INHALATION: METHOTREXATE SODIUM: <u>**ACUTE EXPOSURE-**</u> IF SUFFICIENT QUANTITIES ARE INHALED, SYSTEMIC TOXICITY MAY RESULT AS DETAILED IN ACUTE INGESTION. <u>**CHRONIC EXPOSURE-**</u> IF SUFFICIENT QUANTITIES ARE INHALED, SYSTEMIC TOXICITY MAY RESULT AS DETAILED IN CHRONIC INGESTION.

FIRST AID- REMOVE FROM EXPOSURE AREA TO FRESH AIR IMMEDIATELY. IF BREATHING HAS STOPPED, PERFORM ARTIFICIAL RESPIRATION. KEEP PERSON WARM AND AT REST. TREAT SYMPTOMATICALLY AND SUPPORTIVELY. GET MEDICAL ATTENTION IMMEDIATELY.

SKIN CONTACT: METHOTREXATE SODIUM: <u>**ACUTE EXPOSURE-**</u> IF SUFFICIENT QUANTITIES ARE ABSORBED, SYSTEMIC TOXICITY MAY RESULT. <u>**CHRONIC EXPOSURE-**</u> THERAPEUTIC USE HAS BEEN REPORTED TO CAUSE ERYTHEMATOUS RASHES, PRURITUS, URTICARIA, DERMATITIS, ECCHYMOSIS, TELANGIECTASIA, ACNE AND FURUNCULOSIS, FOLLICULITIS, ALOPECIA, PHOTOSENSITIVITY, AND HYPER- OR DEPIGMENTATION. CASES OF MALIGNANT SKIN CANCER HAVE BEEN REPORTED IN PERSONS TREATED WITH METHOTREXATE FOR PSORIASIS. **FIRST AID-** REMOVE CONTAMINATED CLOTHING AND SHOES IMMEDIATELY. WASH AFFECTED AREA WITH SOAP OR MILD DETERGENT AND LARGE AMOUNTS OF WATER UNTIL NO EVIDENCE OF CHEMICAL REMAINS (APPROXIMATELY 15-20 MINUTES). GET MEDICAL ATTENTION IMMEDIATELY.

EYE CONTACT: METHOTREXATE SODIUM: <u>**ACUTE EXPOSURE-**</u> NO DATA AVAILABLE. <u>**CHRONIC EXPOSURE-**</u> NO DATA AVAILABLE.

FIRST AID- WASH EYES IMMEDIATELY WITH LARGE AMOUNTS OF WATER OR NORMAL SALINE, OCCASIONALLY LIFTING UPPER AND LOWER LIDS, UNTIL NO EVIDENCE OF CHEMICAL REMAINS (APPROXIMATELY 15-20 MINUTES). GET MEDICAL ATTENTION IMMEDIATELY.

INGESTION: METHOTREXATE SODIUM: <u>**ACUTE EXPOSURE-**</u> ANIMALS GIVEN A MINIMAL LETHAL DOSE OF METHOTREXATE SURVIVE FOR AT LEAST 48 HOURS AND USUALLY DIE WITHIN 3 TO 5 DAYS. EFFECTS MAY INCLUDE RARE GASTROINTESTINAL TOXICITY WITH ANOREXIA, PROGRESSIVE WEIGHT LOSS AND BLOODY DIARRHEA, LEUKOPENIA, DEPRESSION AND COMA. LESIONS OF THE INTESTINAL TRACT AND BONE MARROW, DESQUAMATION OF EPITHELIAL CELLS, SEVERE HEMORRHAGIC DESQUAMATING ENTERITIS OF THE INTESTINE AND DEGENERATION OF BONE MARROW MAY ALSO OCCUR. <u>**CHRONIC EXPOSURE-**</u> THERAPEUTIC USE OF METHOTREXATE MAY MOST FREQUENTLY CAUSE NAUSEA, VOMITING, ABDOMINAL DISTRESS, ANOREXIA, UNDUE FATIGUE, DIZZINESS, FEVER, CHILLS, ALOPECIA, LEUKOPENIA AND DECREASED RESISTANCE TO

INFECTION. ULCERATIVE STOMATITIS, GINGIVITIS, GLOSSITIS, PHARYNGITIS, ESOPHAGITIS, ALTERED TASTE AND SMELL, HEMORRHAGIC ENTERITIS, HEMATEMESIS, BLOODY DIARRHEA, HEADACHE, DROWSINESS, BLURRED VISION, APHASIA, PARESTHESIA, PARESIS, CONVULSIONS AND COMA MAY OCCUR. DERMAL EFFECTS CONSISTING OF ERYTHEMATOUS RASHES, PRURITUS, URTICARIA, DERMATITIS, ECCHYMOSIS, TELANGIECTASIA, ACNE AND FURUNCULOSIS, FOLLICULITIS, ALOPECIA, PHOTOSENSITIVITY, AND HYPER- OR DEPIGMENTATION HAVE BEEN REPORTED. PULMONARY EFFECTS MAY INCLUDE DYSPNEA, NON-PRODUCTIVE COUGH, HYPOXEMIA, CHRONIC INTERSTITIAL OBSTRUCTIVE PULMONARY DISEASE AND INTERSTITIAL PNEUMONITIS. HISTOLOGICALLY, PATCHY INTRA-ALVEOLAR AND INTERSTITIAL INFILTRATES INCLUDING EOSINOPHILS HAVE BEEN REPORTED. GENITOURINARY SYSTEM EFFECTS MAY INCLUDE CYSTITIS, AZOTEMIA, HYPERURICEMIA, HEMATURIA, TUBULAR PRECIPITATES, RENAL TUBULAR NECROSIS, RENAL FAILURE, DEFECTIVE OOGENESIS OR SPERMATOGENESIS, TRANSIENT OLIGOSPERMIA, MENSTRUAL DYSFUNCTION, AND INFERTILITY. HEPATOTOXICITY IS GREATER IN PATIENTS RECEIVING FREQUENT SMALL DOSES THAN THOSE RECEIVING LARGE INTERMITTENT DOSES AND MAY CONSIST OF LIVER ATROPHY, FATTY METAMORPHOSIS, NECROSIS, CIRRHOSIS, PORPHYRIA, STEATOSIS, INTRAHEPATIC CHOLESTASIS, PORTAL INFLAMMATORY REACTIONS, PERIPORTAL FIBROSIS, REVERSIBLE ENZYME ELEVATIONS AND EXACERBATION OF PREEXISTING CIRRHOTIC LIVER DAMAGE WITH POTENTIAL HEPATIC COMA. HEMATOLOGIC EFFECTS MAY INCLUDE MEGALOBLASTIC ANEMIA AND BONE MARROW DEPRESSION WITH PANCYTOPENIA, APLASIA AND RARELY LEUKEMIA. SKELETAL EFFECTS MANIFESTED BY BONE PAIN, FRACTURES, ASEPTIC NECROSIS OF THE HEAD OF THE FEMUR AND OSTEOPOROSIS MAY OCCUR. OTHER REPORTED EFFECTS MAY INCLUDE METABOLIC CHANGES, PRECIPITATING DIABETES, ABNORMAL TISSUE CELL CHANGES, VASCULITIS, FOLIC ACID DEFICIENCY, DECREASED DEEP TENDON REFLEXES AND SUDDEN DEATH. DEATHS HAVE BEEN REPORTED DUE TO PULMONARY EFFECTS, SEPTICEMIA, INTESTINAL PERFORATION OR HEMORRHAGE. TWO PSORIATIC PATIENTS DIED FOLLOWING ORAL TREATMENT WITH METHOTREXATE; ONE RECEIVED 5 MG/DAY FOR 5 DAYS; THE OTHER FOR 7 DAYS. CORTICOSTEROID THERAPY MAY HAVE BEEN A COMPLICATING FACTOR. MATERNAL USE HAS PRODUCED ABORTION, FETAL DEATH OR CONGENITAL ABNORMALITIES. HUMAN MATERNAL INGESTION OF 2.5 MG DAILY FOR 5 DAYS BETWEEN THE 8TH AND 10TH WEEK PRODUCED DEFECTS IN A CHILD INCLUDING ABSENCE OF THE FRONTAL BONES, PREMATURE CRANIOSYNOSTOSIS OF THE CORONAL AND LAMBDOID SUTURES, FLAT NASAL BRIDGE, HYPERTELORISM, LIMB REDUCTION DEFECTS, RIB DEFECTS AND THE ABSENCE OF DIGITS. A SIMILAR REPORT EXISTS FROM 5 MG DAILY FOR THE FIRST 2 MONTHS OF PREGNANCY. METHOTREXATE GIVEN ORALLY TO CATS ON DAYS 11-20 OF PREGNANCY PRODUCED VISCERAL ABNORMALITIES INCLUDING UMBILICAL HERNIA, CLEFT PALATES, HYDROCEPHALUS, SPINA BIFIDA AND MALFORMED LIMBS. IN MICE, NO TERATOGENIC DEFECTS WERE FOUND AT 10 MG/KG BUT AT 25 AND 50 MG/KG EXENCEPHALY, OMPHALOCELE, ECTRODACTYLY AND CLEFT PALATE WERE FOUND.

FIRST AID- IF EXTENSIVE VOMITING HAS NOT OCCURRED, THE SUBSTANCE SHOULD BE REMOVED BY EMESIS OR GASTRIC LAVAGE PROVIDED THAT THE PATIENT IS CONSCIOUS AND CONVULSIONS ARE NOT PRESENT. KEEP HEAD BELOW HIPS DURING VOMITING TO PREVENT ASPIRATION. DO NOT ATTEMPT TO MAKE AN UNCONSCIOUS PERSON VOMIT. TREAT SYMPTOMATICALLY AND SUPPORTIVELY. GET MEDICAL ATTENTION IMMEDIATELY (DREISBACH, HANDBOOK OF POISONING, 12TH ED.). TREATMENT SHOULD BE PERFORMED BY QUALIFIED MEDICAL PERSONNEL.

ANTIDOTE: THE FOLLOWING ANTIDOTE HAS BEEN RECOMMENDED. HOWEVER, THE DECISION AS TO WHETHER THE SEVERITY OF POISONING REQUIRES ADMINISTRATION OF ANY ANTIDOTE AND ACTUAL DOSE REQUIRED SHOULD BE MADE BY QUALIFIED MEDICAL PERSONNEL.

METHOTREXATE POISONING: WHERE LARGE DOSES OR OVERDOSES HAVE BEEN GIVEN, CALCIUM LEUCOVORIN MAY BE ADMINISTERED BY INTRAVENOUS INFUSION IN DOSES UP TO 75 MG WITHIN TWELVE HOURS, FOLLOWED BY 12 MG INTRAMUSCULARLY EVERY SIX HOURS FOR FOUR DOSES. WHERE AVERAGE DOSES OF METHOTREXATE APPEAR TO HAVE HAD AN ADVERSE EFFECT, 2 TO 4 ML (6-12 MG) OF CALCIUM LEUCOVORIN MAY BE GIVEN INTRAMUSCULARLY EVERY SIX HOURS FOR FOUR DOSES. IN GENERAL, WHERE OVERDOSAGE IS SUSPECTED, THE DOSE OF LEUCOVORIN SHOULD BE EQUAL TO OR HIGHER THAN THE OFFENDING DOSE OF METHOTREXATE AND SHOULD BEST BE ADMINISTERED WITHIN THE FIRST HOUR. USE OF CALCIUM LEUCOVORIN AFTER AN HOUR DELAY IS MUCH LESS EFFECTIVE. (ARENA, POISONING, 4TH EDITION). TREATMENT SHOULD BE ADMINISTERED BY QUALIFIED MEDICAL PERSONNEL ONLY.

REACTIVITY

REACTIVITY: STABLE UNDER NORMAL TEMPERATURES AND PRESSURES.

INCOMPATIBILITIES: METHOTREXATE: OXIDIZERS (STRONG): FIRE AND EXPLOSION HAZARD.

DECOMPOSITION: THERMAL DECOMPOSITION PRODUCTS MAY INCLUDE TOXIC OXIDES OF CARBON AND NITROGEN.

POLYMERIZATION: HAZARDOUS POLYMERIZATION HAS NOT BEEN REPORTED TO OCCUR UNDER NORMAL TEMPERATURES AND PRESSURES.

STORAGE AND DISPOSAL

OBSERVE ALL FEDERAL, STATE AND LOCAL REGULATIONS WHEN STORING OR DISPOSING OF THIS SUBSTANCE. FOR ASSISTANCE, CONTACT THE DISTRICT DIRECTOR OF THE ENVIRONMENTAL PROTECTION AGENCY.

****STORAGE****

STORE AWAY FROM INCOMPATIBLE SUBSTANCES.

KEEP CONTAINER TIGHTLY CLOSED. PROTECT FROM EXPOSURE TO AIR OR LIGHT.

CONDITIONS TO AVOID

MAY BURN BUT DOES NOT IGNITE READILY.

SPILL AND LEAK PROCEDURES

WATER SPILL: THE CALIFORNIA SAFE DRINKING WATER AND TOXIC ENFORCEMENT ACT OF 1986 (PROPOSITION 65) PROHIBITS CONTAMINATING ANY KNOWN SOURCE OF DRINKING WATER WITH SUBSTANCES KNOWN TO CAUSE CANCER AND/OR REPRODUCTIVE TOXICITY.

OCCUPATIONAL SPILL: DO NOT TOUCH SPILLED MATERIAL. STOP LEAK IF YOU CAN DO IT WITHOUT RISK. FOR SMALL SPILLS, TAKE UP WITH SAND OR OTHER ABSORBENT MATERIAL AND PLACE INTO CONTAINERS FOR LATER DISPOSAL. FOR SMALL DRY SPILLS, WITH A CLEAN SHOVEL PLACE MATERIAL INTO CLEAN, DRY CONTAINER AND COVER. MOVE CONTAINERS FROM SPILL AREA. FOR LARGER SPILLS, DIKE FAR AHEAD OF SPILL FOR LATER DISPOSAL. KEEP UNNECESSARY PEOPLE AWAY. ISOLATE HAZARD AREA AND DENY ENTRY.

PROTECTIVE EQUIPMENT

VENTILATION: PROVIDE LOCAL EXHAUST OR PROCESS ENCLOSURE VENTILATION SYSTEM.

RESPIRATOR: THE FOLLOWING RESPIRATORS ARE RECOMMENDED BASED ON INFORMATION FOUND IN THE PHYSICAL DATA, TOXICITY AND HEALTH EFFECTS SECTIONS. THEY ARE RANKED IN ORDER FROM MINIMUM TO MAXIMUM RESPIRATORY PROTECTION. THE SPECIFIC RESPIRATOR SELECTED MUST BE BASED ON CONTAMINATION LEVELS FOUND IN THE WORK PLACE, MUST NOT EXCEED THE WORKING LIMITS OF THE RESPIRATOR AND BE JOINTLY APPROVED BY THE NATIONAL INSTITUTE FOR OCCUPATIONAL SAFETY AND HEALTH AND THE MINE SAFETY AND HEALTH ADMINISTRATION (NIOSH-MSHA).

DUST AND MIST RESPIRATOR WITH A FULL FACEPIECE.

AIR-PURIFYING FULL FACEPIECE RESPIRATOR WITH A HIGH-EFFICIENCY PARTICULATE FILTER.

POWERED AIR-PURIFYING RESPIRATOR WITH A TIGHT-FITTING FACEPIECE AND HIGH-EFFICIENCY PARTICULATE FILTER.

TYPE 'C' SUPPLIED-AIR RESPIRATOR WITH A FULL FACEPIECE OPERATED IN PRESSURE-DEMAND OR OTHER POSITIVE PRESSURE MODE OR WITH A FULL FACEPIECE, HELMET OR HOOD OPERATED IN CONTINUOUS-FLOW MODE.

SELF-CONTAINED BREATHING APPARATUS WITH A FULL FACEPIECE OPERATED IN PRESSURE-DEMAND OR OTHER POSITIVE PRESSURE MODE.

FOR FIREFIGHTING AND OTHER IMMEDIATELY DANGEROUS TO LIFE OR HEALTH CONDITIONS:

SELF-CONTAINED BREATHING APPARATUS WITH FULL FACEPIECE OPERATED IN PRESSURE-DEMAND OR OTHER POSITIVE PRESSURE MODE.

SUPPLIED-AIR RESPIRATOR WITH FULL FACEPIECE AND OPERATED IN PRESSURE-DEMAND OR OTHER POSITIVE PRESSURE MODE IN COMBINATION WITH AN AUXILIARY SELF-CONTAINED BREATHING APPARATUS OPERATED IN PRESSURE-DEMAND OR OTHER POSITIVE PRESSURE MODE.

CLOTHING: EMPLOYEE MUST WEAR APPROPRIATE PROTECTIVE (IMPERVIOUS) CLOTHING AND EQUIPMENT TO PREVENT REPEATED OR PROLONGED SKIN CONTACT WITH THIS SUBSTANCE.

GLOVES: EMPLOYEE MUST WEAR APPROPRIATE PROTECTIVE GLOVES TO PREVENT CONTACT WITH THIS SUBSTANCE.

EYE PROTECTION: EMPLOYEE MUST WEAR SPLASH-PROOF OR DUST-RESISTANT SAFETY GOGGLES TO PREVENT EYE CONTACT WITH THIS SUBSTANCE.

EMERGENCY EYE WASH: WHERE THERE IS ANY POSSIBILITY THAT AN EMPLOYEE'S EYES MAY BE EXPOSED TO THIS SUBSTANCE, THE EMPLOYER SHOULD PROVIDE AN EYE WASH FOUNTAIN WITHIN THE IMMEDIATE WORK AREA FOR EMERGENCY USE.

AUTHORIZED BY- OCCUPATIONAL HEALTH SERVICES, INC.

CREATION DATE: 10/04/89 ***REVISION DATE:*** 07/10/90

MATERIAL SAFETY DATA SHEET

OCCUPATIONAL HEALTH SERVICES, INC.
AGRICULTURE AND PESTICIDE DIVISION
450 SEVENTH AVENUE, SUITE 2407
NEW YORK, NEW YORK 10123
1-800-445-MSDS OR (212) 967-1100

EMERGENCY CONTACT:
JOHN S. BRANSFORD, JR. (615) 292-1180

SUBSTANCE IDENTIFICATION

CAS-NUMBER 72-43-5

SUBSTANCE: **METHOXYCHLOR**

TRADE NAMES/SYNONYMS: BENZENE, 1,1'-(2,2,2-TRICHLOROETHYLIDENE)BIS(4-METHOXY-; ETHANE, 1,1,1-TRICHLORO-2,2-BIS(P-METHOXYPHENYL)-; 1,1'-(2,2,2-TRICHLOROETHYLIDENE)BIS(4-METHOXYBENZENE); 1,1,1-TRICHLORO-2,2-BIS(P-METHOXYPHENYL)ETHANE; 1,1,1-TRICHLORO-2,2-DI(4-METHOXYPHENYL)ETHANE; 2,2-BIS(P-METHOXYPHENYL)1,1,1-TRICHLOROETHANE; 2,2-DI-P-ANISYL-1,1,1-TRICHLOROETHANE; DIMETHOXY-DDT; P,P'-DMDT; DMDT; P,P'-METHOXYCHLOR; MARLATE; METHOXY-DDT; OMS 466; ENT 1716; STCC 4960647; RCRA U247; C16H15CL3O2; PST14220

CHEMICAL FAMILY: HALOGEN COMPOUND, AROMATIC

MOLECULAR FORMULA: C-H3-O-C6-H4-C-H(C-CL3)-C6-H4-O-C-H3

MOLECULAR WEIGHT: 347.65

CERCLA RATINGS (SCALE 0-3): HEALTH=3 FIRE=1 REACTIVITY=0 PERSISTENCE=3

NFPA RATINGS (SCALE 0-4): HEALTH=3 FIRE=1 REACTIVITY=0

COMPONENTS AND CONTAMINANTS

COMPONENT: METHOXYCHLOR ***PERCENT:*** 100
CAS# 72-43-5

OTHER CONTAMINANTS: NONE

EXPOSURE LIMITS: METHOXYCHLOR: 10 MG/M3 OSHA TWA (TOTAL DUST) 10 MG/M3 ACGIH TWA
1 POUND CERCLA SECTION 103 REPORTABLE QUANTITY SUBJECT TO SARA SECTION 313 ANNUAL TOXIC CHEMICAL RELEASE REPORTING

PHYSICAL DATA

DESCRIPTION: COLORLESS TO WHITE DIMORPHIC CRYSTALS WITH A SLIGHTLY FRUITY ODOR.

BOILING POINT: DECOMPOSES ***MELTING POINT:*** 192 F (89 C)

SPECIFIC GRAVITY: 1.41 @ 25 C ***SOLUBILITY IN WATER:*** 0.1 PPM

VAPOR DENSITY: 12

SOLVENT SOLUBILITY: SOLUBLE IN BENZENE, ETHER, DIMETHYL SULFOXIDE, ETHANOL, ACETONE, XYLENE, AROMATIC SOLVENTS, CHLORINATED SOLVENTS, PARAFFINIC SOLVENTS, PETROLEUM OILS

FIRE AND EXPLOSION DATA

FIRE AND EXPLOSION HAZARD: SLIGHT FIRE HAZARD WHEN EXPOSED TO HEAT OR FLAME.

FIREFIGHTING MEDIA: DRY CHEMICAL, CARBON DIOXIDE, HALON, WATER SPRAY OR STANDARD FOAM (1987 EMERGENCY RESPONSE GUIDEBOOK, DOT P 5800.4). FOR LARGER FIRES, USE WATER SPRAY, FOG OR STANDARD FOAM (1987 EMERGENCY RESPONSE GUIDEBOOK, DOT P 5800.4).

FIREFIGHTING: MOVE CONTAINERS FROM FIRE AREA IF POSSIBLE. FIGHT FIRE FROM MAXIMUM DISTANCE. STAY AWAY FROM STORAGE TANK ENDS. DIKE FIRE CONTROL WATER FOR LATER DISPOSAL. DO NOT SCATTER MATERIAL (1987 EMERGENCY RESPONSE GUIDEBOOK, DOT P 5800.4, GUIDE PAGE 55).
USE AGENTS SUITABLE FOR TYPE OF FIRE. COOL CONTAINERS WITH FLOODING AMOUNTS OF WATER. AVOID BREATHING VAPORS OR DUSTS, KEEP UPWIND.

TOXICITY

METHOXYCHLOR: TOXICITY DATA: 2414 MG/KG SKIN-HUMAN TDLO; 6430 MG/KG ORAL-HUMAN LDLO; 5000 MG/KG ORAL-RAT LD50; 1 GM/KG ORAL-MOUSE LD50; 500 MG/KG INTRAPERITONEAL-HAMSTER LD50; MUTAGENIC DATA (RTECS); REPRODUCTIVE EFFECTS DATA (RTECS); TUMORIGENIC DATA (RTECS). CARCINOGEN STATUS: ANIMAL INADEQUATE EVIDENCE (IARC GROUP 3). ACUTE TOXICITY LEVEL: MODERATELY TOXIC BY INGESTION. TARGET EFFECTS: CONVULSANT. POISONING MAY AFFECT THE KIDNEYS AND LIVER. AT INCREASED RISK FROM EXPOSURE: PERSONS WITH LIVER OR KIDNEY DISEASE AND CONVULSIVE AND OTHER NEUROLOGIC DISORDERS. ADDITIONAL DATA: MAY BE EXCRETED IN BREAST MILK. STIMULANTS SUCH AS EPINEPHRINE MAY INDUCE VENTRICULAR FIBRILLATION.

HEALTH EFFECTS AND FIRST AID

INHALATION: METHOXYCHLOR: 7500 MG/M3 IMMEDIATELY DANGEROUS TO LIFE OR HEALTH. **ACUTE EXPOSURE-** METHOXYCHLOR IS AN ORGANOCHLORINE PESTICIDE. THESE PESTICIDES HAVE DIRECT ACTION ON THE CENTRAL NERVOUS SYSTEM PRODUCING SYMPTOMS OF APPREHENSION, EXCITABILITY, DIZZINESS, HEADACHE, DISORIENTATION, WEAKNESS, PARESTHESIAS, MUSCLE TWITCHING, TREMORS, AND CONVULSIONS. SYMPTOMS USUALLY APPEAR WITHIN SEVERAL HOURS OF OVEREXPOSURE. **CHRONIC EXPOSURE-** PROLONGED OR REPEATED EXPOSURE TO ORGANOCHLORINE PESTICIDES ARE AS DESCRIBED IN ACUTE EXPOSURE.

FIRST AID- REMOVE FROM EXPOSURE AREA TO FRESH AIR IMMEDIATELY. IF BREATHING HAS STOPPED, PERFORM ARTIFICIAL RESPIRATION. KEEP PERSON WARM AND AT REST. TREAT SYMPTOMATICALLY AND SUPPORTIVELY. GET MEDICAL ATTENTION IMMEDIATELY.

SKIN CONTACT: METHOXYCHLOR: **ACUTE EXPOSURE-** IN ONE INDIVIDUAL, DERMAL EXPOSURE TO 2414 MG/KG PRODUCED ADVERSE EFFECTS INCLUDING SOMNOLENCE. ORGANOCHLORINE PESTICIDES ARE ABSORBED THROUGH THE SKIN AND PRODUCE SYMPTOMS OF APPREHENSION, EXCITABILITY, DIZZINESS, HEADACHE, DISORIENTATION, WEAKNESS, PARESTHESIAS, MUSCLE TWITCHING, TREMORS, AND CONVULSIONS. SYMPTOMS USUALLY APPEAR WITHIN SEVERAL HOURS OF OVEREXPOSURE. **CHRONIC EXPOSURE-** REPEATED APPLICATION OF METHOXYCHLOR TO THE SKIN OF MALE RABBITS PRODUCED ATROPHY OF THE TESTES. OTHER ADVERSE EFFECTS INCLUDED SEVERE ANOREXIA, DEPRESSION, AND EMACIATION; ONE RABBIT DEVELOPED SEVERE CHRONIC INTERSTITIAL FIBROSIS OF THE KIDNEY WITH CHANGES IN THE SKIN AND BONE MARROW ALSO OBSERVED. IN ANOTHER STUDY OF RABBITS, EFFECTS OF PARALYSIS OF THE FORELIMBS, SOME FATTY DEGENERATION OF THE LIVER, AND LESIONS OF THE CENTRAL NERVOUS SYSTEM WERE OBSERVED AFTER REPEATED APPLICATION TO THE SKIN.

FIRST AID- REMOVE CONTAMINATED CLOTHING AND SHOES IMMEDIATELY. WASH AFFECTED AREA WITH SOAP OR MILD DETERGENT AND LARGE AMOUNTS OF WATER UNTIL NO EVIDENCE OF CHEMICAL REMAINS (APPROXIMATELY 15-20 MINUTES). GET MEDICAL ATTENTION IMMEDIATELY.

EYE CONTACT: METHOXYCHLOR: **ACUTE EXPOSURE-** NO DATA AVAILABLE. MAY BE IRRITATING. **CHRONIC EXPOSURE-** NO DATA AVAILABLE.

FIRST AID- WASH EYES IMMEDIATELY WITH LARGE AMOUNTS OF WATER OR NORMAL SALINE, OCCASIONALLY LIFTING UPPER AND LOWER LIDS, UNTIL NO EVIDENCE OF CHEMICAL REMAINS (APPROXIMATELY 15-20 MINUTES). GET MEDICAL ATTENTION IMMEDIATELY.

INGESTION: METHOXYCHLOR: **ACUTE EXPOSURE-** A REPORTED HUMAN LETHAL DOSE WAS 6430 MG/KG. INGESTION OF ORGANOCHLORINE PESTICIDES MAY CAUSE GASTROINTESTINAL EFFECTS OF NAUSEA, VOMITING, DIARRHEA, AND STOMACH PAINS. OTHER SYMPTOMS OF APPREHENSION, EXCITABILITY, DIZZINESS, HEADACHE, DISORIENTATION, WEAKNESS, PARESTHESIAS, MUSCLE TWITCHING, TREMOR, AND CONVULSIONS MAY OCCUR. DEATH MAY BE DUE TO RESPIRATORY FAILURE OR VENTRICULAR FIBRILLATION. EFFECTS MAY OCCUR WITHIN SEVERAL HOURS AFTER EXPOSURE. METHOXYCHLOR IS EXCRETED RAPIDLY BY HUMANS, USUALLY WITHIN 3-4 DAYS OF INGESTION. **CHRONIC EXPOSURE-** DOGS FED A DAILY DIET CONTAINING 4 GM/KG OF METHOXYCHLOR DEVELOPED FASCICULATIONS, TREMOR, HYPERESTHESIA, TONIC SEIZURES, AND TETANIC CONVULSIONS AFTER 5 TO 8 WEEKS; MOST DOGS DIED WITHIN 3 WEEKS AFTER ONSET OF EFFECTS. RABBITS GIVEN 200 MG/KG ORALLY PER DAY DIED AFTER 4 TO 5 DOSES; AUTOPSY FINDINGS INCLUDED MILD LIVER DAMAGE AND NEPHROSIS. ADMINISTRATION OF 1000 MG/KG DIET METHOXYCHLOR TO PREGNANT RATS CAUSED EARLY VAGINAL OPENINGS IN THEIR OFFSPRING; AND BOTH MALE AND FEMALE OFFSPRING HAD REDUCED FERTILITY WHEN THEY ATTAINED MATURITY. FETOTOXICITY, AN INCREASE IN THE INCIDENCE OF WAVY RIBS, AND REDUCED MATERNAL BODY WEIGHT GAIN WAS OBSERVED IN A STUDY OF PREGNANT RATS FED REPEATED DOSES OF METHOXYCHLOR. SUBSEQUENTLY TO THE REVIEW OF METHOXYCHLOR BY IARC, SEVERAL STUDIES RELEASED DATA INDICATING THAT METHOXYCHLOR INDUCED TESTICULAR CARCINOMAS IN MALE BALB/C MICE AND LIVER CARCINOMAS IN MICE AND RATS. A SIGNIFICANTLY INCREASED OF CARCINOMAS OF THE OVARY WAS ALSO REPORTED IN FEMALE RATS.

FIRST AID- IF THE PERSON IS CONSCIOUS AND NOT CONVULSING, REMOVE BY GIVING SYRUP OF IPECAC (IF VOMITING OCCURS, KEEP THE HEAD BELOW THE HIPS TO PREVENT ASPIRATION). GIVE ACTIVATED CHARCOAL FOLLOWED BY GASTRIC LAVAGE. FOLLOW WITH A SALINE CATHARTIC. DO NOT GIVE FATS OR OILS. INTESTINAL LAVAGE WITH 20% MANNITOL (200 ML) BY STOMACH TUBE IS ALSO USEFUL. GIVE ARTIFICIAL RESPIRATION WITH OXYGEN IF RESPIRATION IS DEPRESSED (DREISBACH, HANDBOOK OF POISONING, 12TH ED.). TREAT SYMPTOMATICALLY AND SUPPORTIVELY. LAVAGE AND ADMINISTRATION OF OXYGEN SHOULD BE PERFORMED BY QUALIFIED MEDICAL PERSONNEL. GET MEDICAL ATTENTION IMMEDIATELY.

ANTIDOTE: NO SPECIFIC ANTIDOTE. TREAT SYMPTOMATICALLY AND SUPPORTIVELY.

REACTIVITY

REACTIVITY: STABLE UNDER NORMAL TEMPERATURES AND PRESSURES.
INCOMPATIBILITIES: METHOXYCHLOR: ALKALINE MATERIALS: MAY REACT. METAL CATALYSTS (HEAVY): MAY CAUSE DEHYDROCHLORINATION. OXIDIZERS (STRONG): MAY CAUSE FIRES AND EXPLOSIONS. PLASTICS, RUBBER, AND COATINGS: SOME FORMS MAY BE ATTACKED.
DECOMPOSITION: THERMAL DECOMPOSITION PRODUCTS MAY INCLUDE TOXIC AND CORROSIVE FUMES OF CHLORIDES AND TOXIC OXIDES OF CARBON.
POLYMERIZATION: HAZARDOUS POLYMERIZATION HAS NOT BEEN REPORTED TO OCCUR UNDER NORMAL TEMPERATURES AND PRESSURES.

STORAGE AND DISPOSAL

OBSERVE ALL FEDERAL, STATE AND LOCAL REGULATIONS WHEN STORING OR DISPOSING OF THIS SUBSTANCE. FOR ASSISTANCE, CONTACT THE DISTRICT DIRECTOR OF THE ENVIRONMENTAL PROTECTION AGENCY.

STORAGE

STORE IN ACCORDANCE WITH 40 CFR 165 RECOMMENDED PROCEDURES FOR THE DISPOSAL AND STORAGE OF PESTICIDES AND PESTICIDE CONTAINERS.
STORE AWAY FROM INCOMPATIBLE SUBSTANCES.

DISPOSAL

DISPOSAL MUST BE IN ACCORDANCE WITH 40 CFR 165 RECOMMENDED PROCEDURES FOR THE DISPOSAL AND STORAGE OF PESTICIDES AND PESTICIDE CONTAINERS.
DISPOSAL MUST BE IN ACCORDANCE WITH STANDARDS APPLICABLE TO GENERATORS OF HAZARDOUS WASTE, 40CFR 262. EPA HAZARDOUS WASTE NUMBER U247.
METHOXYCHLOR - REGULATORY LEVEL: 10.0 MG/L MATERIALS WHICH CONTAIN THE ABOVE SUBSTANCE AT OR ABOVE THE REGULATORY LEVEL MEET THE EPA CHARACTERISTIC OF TOXICITY, AND MUST BE DISPOSED OF IN ACCORDANCE WITH 40 CFR PART 262. EPA HAZARDOUS WASTE NUMBER D014.

CONDITIONS TO AVOID

MAY BURN BUT DOES NOT IGNITE READILY. CONTAINERS MAY EXPLODE IN HEAT OF FIRE.

SPILL AND LEAK PROCEDURES

SOIL SPILL: DIG A HOLDING AREA SUCH AS PIT, POND OR LAGOON TO CONTAIN SPILLED MATERIAL. USE PROTECTIVE COVER SUCH AS A PLASTIC SHEET TO PREVENT DISSOLVING IN FIREFIGHTING WATER OR RAIN.
WATER SPILL: USE NATURAL DEEP WATER POCKETS, EXCAVATED LAGOONS, OR SAND BAG BARRIERS TO TRAP MATERIAL AT BOTTOM. USE ACTIVATED CARBON AT 10 TIMES THE SPILLED AMOUNT IF IT IS DISSOLVED AT 10 PPM OR GREATER CONCENTRATION. REMOVE TRAPPED MATERIAL WITH SUCTION HOSES. USE MECHANICAL DREDGES OR LIFTS TO REMOVE IMMOBILIZED MASSES OF POLLUTION AND PRECIPITATES.
OCCUPATIONAL SPILL: DO NOT TOUCH SPILLED MATERIAL. STOP LEAK IF YOU CAN DO IT WITHOUT RISK. USE WATER SPRAY TO REDUCE VAPORS. FOR SMALL SPILLS, TAKE UP WITH SAND OR OTHER ABSORBENT MATERIAL AND PLACE INTO CONTAINERS FOR LATER DISPOSAL. FOR SMALL DRY SPILLS, WITH A CLEAN SHOVEL PLACE MATERIAL INTO CLEAN, DRY CONTAINERS AND COVER. MOVE CONTAINERS FROM SPILL AREA. FOR LARGER SPILLS, DIKE FAR AHEAD OF SPILL FOR LATER DISPOSAL. KEEP UNNECESSARY PEOPLE AWAY. ISOLATE HAZARD AREA AND DENY ENTRY. VENTILATE CLOSED SPACES BEFORE ENTERING.
REPORTABLE QUANTITY (RQ): 1 POUND THE SUPERFUND AMENDMENTS AND REAUTHORIZATION ACT (SARA) SECTION 304 REQUIRES THAT A RELEASE EQUAL TO OR GREATER THAN THE REPORTABLE QUANTITY FOR THIS SUBSTANCE BE IMMEDIATELY REPORTED TO THE LOCAL EMERGENCY PLANNING COMMITTEE AND THE STATE EMERGENCY RESPONSE COMMISSION (40 CFR 355.40). IF THE RELEASE OF THIS SUBSTANCE IS REPORTABLE UNDER CERCLA SECTION 103, THE NATIONAL RESPONSE CENTER MUST BE NOTIFIED IMMEDIATELY AT (800) 424-8802 OR (202) 426-2675 IN THE METROPOLITAN WASHINGTON, D.C. AREA (40 CFR 302.6).

PROTECTIVE EQUIPMENT

VENTILATION: PROVIDE LOCAL EXHAUST VENTILATION AND/OR GENERAL DILUTION VENTILATION TO MEET PUBLISHED EXPOSURE LIMITS.
RESPIRATOR: THE FOLLOWING RESPIRATORS AND MAXIMUM USE CONCENTRATIONS ARE RECOMMENDATIONS BY THE U.S. DEPARTMENT OF HEALTH AND HUMAN SERVICES, NIOSH POCKET GUIDE TO CHEMICAL HAZARDS; NIOSH CRITERIA DOCUMENTS OR BY THE U.S. DEPARTMENT OF LABOR, 29 CFR 1910 SUBPART Z. THE SPECIFIC RESPIRATOR SELECTED MUST BE BASED ON CONTAMINATION LEVELS FOUND IN THE WORK PLACE, MUST NOT EXCEED THE WORKING LIMITS OF THE RESPIRATOR AND BE JOINTLY APPROVED BY THE NATIONAL INSTITUTE FOR OCCUPATIONAL SAFETY AND HEALTH AND THE MINE SAFETY AND HEALTH ADMINISTRATION (NIOSH-MSHA).
100 MG/M3- ANY CHEMICAL CARTRIDGE RESPIRATOR WITH ORGANIC VAPOR CARTRIDGE(S) IN COMBINATION WITH A DUST, MIST, AND FUME FILTER. ANY SUPPLIED-AIR RESPIRATOR. ANY SELF-CONTAINED BREATHING APPARATUS.
250 MG/M3- ANY SUPPLIED-AIR RESPIRATOR OPERATED IN A CONTINUOUS FLOW MODE. ANY POWERED AIR-PURIFYING RESPIRATOR WITH ORGANIC VAPOR CARTRIDGE(S) IN COMBINATION WITH A DUST, MIST, AND FUME FILTER.
500 MG/M3- ANY CHEMICAL CARTRIDGE RESPIRATOR WITH A FULL FACEPIECE AND ORGANIC VAPOR CARTRIDGE(S) IN COMBINATION WITH A HIGH-EFFICIENCY PARTICULATE FILTER. ANY SUPPLIED-AIR RESPIRATOR WITH A FULL FACEPIECE. ANY POWERED AIR-PURIFYING RESPIRATOR WITH A TIGHT-FITTING FACEPIECE AND ORGANIC VAPOR CARTRIDGE(S) IN COMBINATION WITH A HIGH-EFFICIENCY PARTICULATE FILTER. ANY SELF-CONTAINED BREATHING APPARATUS WITH A FULL FACEPIECE. ANY AIR-PURIFYING FULL FACEPIECE RESPIRATOR WITH A CHIN-STYLE OR FRONT- OR BACK-MOUNTED ORGANIC VAPOR CANISTER HAVING A HIGH-EFFICIENCY PARTICULATE FILTER. ANY SUPPLIED-AIR RESPIRATOR WITH A TIGHT-FITTING FACEPIECE OPERATED IN A CONTINUOUS FLOW MODE.
7500 MG/M3- ANY SUPPLIED-AIR RESPIRATOR WITH A HALF-MASK AND OPERATED IN A PRESSURE-DEMAND OR OTHER POSITIVE PRESSURE MODE.
ESCAPE- ANY AIR-PURIFYING FULL FACEPIECE RESPIRATOR (GAS MASK) WITH A CHIN-STYLE OR FRONT- OR BACK-MOUNTED ORGANIC VAPOR CANISTER HAVING A HIGH-EFFICIENCY PARTICULATE FILTER. ANY APPROPRIATE ESCAPE-TYPE SELF-CONTAINED BREATHING APPARATUS.
FOR FIREFIGHTING AND OTHER IMMEDIATELY DANGEROUS TO LIFE OR HEALTH CONDITIONS:
SELF-CONTAINED BREATHING APPARATUS WITH FULL FACEPIECE OPERATED IN PRESSURE-DEMAND OR OTHER POSITIVE PRESSURE MODE.
SUPPLIED-AIR RESPIRATOR WITH FULL FACEPIECE AND OPERATED IN PRESSURE-DEMAND OR OTHER POSITIVE PRESSURE MODE IN COMBINATION WITH AN AUXILIARY SELF-CONTAINED BREATHING APPARATUS OPERATED IN PRESSURE-DEMAND OR OTHER POSITIVE PRESSURE MODE.
CLOTHING: EMPLOYEE MUST WEAR APPROPRIATE PROTECTIVE (IMPERVIOUS) CLOTHING AND EQUIPMENT TO PREVENT REPEATED OR PROLONGED SKIN CONTACT WITH THIS SUBSTANCE.
GLOVES: EMPLOYEE MUST WEAR APPROPRIATE PROTECTIVE GLOVES TO PREVENT CONTACT WITH THIS SUBSTANCE.
EYE PROTECTION: EMPLOYEE MUST WEAR SPLASH-PROOF OR DUST-RESISTANT SAFETY GOGGLES TO PREVENT EYE CONTACT WITH THIS SUBSTANCE.
EMERGENCY EYE WASH: WHERE THERE IS ANY POSSIBILITY THAT AN EMPLOYEE'S EYES MAY BE EXPOSED TO THIS SUBSTANCE, THE EMPLOYER SHOULD PROVIDE AN EYE WASH FOUNTAIN WITHIN THE IMMEDIATE WORK AREA FOR EMERGENCY USE.

AUTHORIZED BY- OCCUPATIONAL HEALTH SERVICES, INC.
CREATION DATE: 10/04/89 ***REVISION DATE:*** 07/13/90

MATERIAL SAFETY DATA SHEET

OCCUPATIONAL HEALTH SERVICES, INC.
AGRICULTURE AND PESTICIDE DIVISION
450 SEVENTH AVENUE, SUITE 2407
NEW YORK, NEW YORK 10123
1-800-445-MSDS OR (212) 967-1100

EMERGENCY CONTACT:
JOHN S. BRANSFORD, JR. (615) 292-1180

SUBSTANCE IDENTIFICATION

CAS-NUMBER 67-56-1
SUBSTANCE: **METHYL ALCOHOL**
TRADE NAMES/SYNONYMS: METHANOL; WOOD ALCOHOL; METHYL HYDROXIDE; CARBINOL; MONOHYDROXYMETHANE; WOOD SPIRIT; WOOD NAPHTHA; METHYLOL; COLONIAL SPIRIT; COLUMBIAN SPIRIT; PYROXYLIC SPIRIT; BOOSTER FUEL (HENES PRODUCT CORP.); METHANOL (ELECTROKLEIN) (ROK); METHANOL, SPECTRO QUALITY (MCB MANF. CHEMIST); COULOMATIC (R) CONDITIONER SOLUTION; STANDARD WATER IN METHANOL; STCC 4904230; RCRA U154; UN 1230; CH4O; PST14280
CHEMICAL FAMILY: HYDROXYL, ALIPHATIC
MOLECULAR FORMULA: C-H3-O-H
MOLECULAR WEIGHT: 32.04
CERCLA RATINGS (SCALE 0-3): HEALTH=3 FIRE=3 REACTIVITY=0 PERSISTENCE=0
NFPA RATINGS (SCALE 0-4): HEALTH=1 FIRE=3 REACTIVITY=0

COMPONENTS AND CONTAMINANTS

COMPONENT: METHYL ALCOHOL (METHANOL) ***PERCENT:*** 100
CAS# 67-56-1

OTHER CONTAMINANTS: NONE
EXPOSURE LIMITS: METHYL ALCOHOL (METHANOL): 200 PPM (260 MG/M3) OSHA TWA (SKIN); 250 PPM (325 MG/M3) OSHA STEL 200 PPM (260 MG/M3) ACGIH TWA (SKIN); 250 PPM (310 MG/M3) ACGIH STEL 200 PPM NIOSH RECOMMENDED 10 HOUR TWA; 800 PPM NIOSH RECOMMENDED 15 MINUTE CEILING
5000 POUNDS CERCLA SECTION 103 REPORTABLE QUANTITY SUBJECT TO SARA SECTION 313 ANNUAL TOXIC CHEMICAL RELEASE REPORTING

PHYSICAL DATA

DESCRIPTION: CLEAR, COLORLESS LIQUID WITH A CHARACTERISTIC ALCOHOLIC ODOR.
BOILING POINT: 149 F (65 C) ***MELTING POINT:*** -137 F (-94 C)
SPECIFIC GRAVITY: 0.7914 ***VISCOSITY:*** 0.59 CPS @ 20 C
VAPOR PRESSURE: 97.25 MMHG @ 20 C
EVAPORATION RATE: (BUTYL ACETATE = 1)4.6
SOLUBILITY IN WATER: VERY SOLUBLE ***ODOR THRESHOLD:*** 100 PPM
VAPOR DENSITY: 1.11
SOLVENT SOLUBILITY: ETHER, BENZENE, ALCOHOL, ACETONE, CHLOROFORM, ETHANOL.

FIRE AND EXPLOSION DATA

FIRE AND EXPLOSION HAZARD: DANGEROUS FIRE HAZARD WHEN EXPOSED TO HEAT, FLAME, OR OXIDIZERS.
VAPORS ARE HEAVIER THAN AIR AND MAY TRAVEL A CONSIDERABLE DISTANCE TO A SOURCE OF IGNITION AND FLASH BACK.
VAPOR-AIR MIXTURES ARE EXPLOSIVE.
FLASH POINT: 52 F (11 C) (CC) ***UPPER EXPLOSIVE LIMIT:*** 36.0%
LOWER EXPLOSIVE LIMIT: 6.0% ***AUTOIGNITION TEMP.:*** 725 F (385 C)
FLAMMABILITY CLASS(OSHA): IB
FIREFIGHTING MEDIA: DRY CHEMICAL, CARBON DIOXIDE, HALON, WATER SPRAY OR ALCOHOL FOAM (1987 EMERGENCY RESPONSE GUIDEBOOK, DOT P 5800.4).
FOR LARGER FIRES, USE WATER SPRAY, FOG OR ALCOHOL FOAM (1987 EMERGENCY RESPONSE GUIDEBOOK, DOT P 5800.4).
FIREFIGHTING: MOVE CONTAINER FROM FIRE AREA IF POSSIBLE. DIKE FIRE CONTROL WATER FOR LATER DISPOSAL; DO NOT SCATTER THE MATERIAL. COOL FIRE-EXPOSED CONTAINERS WITH WATER FROM SIDE UNTIL WELL AFTER FIRE IS OUT. STAY AWAY FROM STORAGE TANK ENDS. WITHDRAW IMMEDIATELY IN CASE OF RISING SOUND FROM VENTING SAFETY DEVICE OR ANY DISCOLORATION OF STORAGE TANK DUE TO FIRE (1987 EMERGENCY RESPONSE GUIDEBOOK, DOT P 5800.4, GUIDE PAGE 28).
EXTINGUISH ONLY IF FLOW CAN BE STOPPED; USE WATER IN FLOODING AMOUNTS AS FOG, SOLID STREAMS MAY NOT BE EFFECTIVE. COOL CONTAINERS WITH FLOODING QUANTITIES OF WATER, APPLY FROM AS FAR A DISTANCE AS POSSIBLE. AVOID BREATHING TOXIC VAPORS, KEEP UPWIND.

TRANSPORTATION DATA

DEPARTMENT OF TRANSPORTATION HAZARD CLASSIFICATION 49 CFR 172.101: FLAMMABLE LIQUID
DEPARTMENT OF TRANSPORTATION LABELING REQUIREMENTS 49 CFR 172.101 AND SUBPART E: FLAMMABLE LIQUID
DEPARTMENT OF TRANSPORTATION PACKAGING REQUIREMENTS: 49 CFR 173.119 EXCEPTIONS: 49 CFR 173.118

TOXICITY

METHYL ALCOHOL (METHANOL): IRRITATION DATA: 20 MG/24 HOURS SKIN-RABBIT MODERATE; 40 MG EYE-RABBIT MODERATE; 100 MG/24 HOURS EYE-RABBIT MODERATE. TOXICITY DATA: 86,000 MG/M3 INHALATION-HUMAN TCLO; 300 PPM INHALATION-HUMAN TCLO; 64,000 PPM/4 HOURS INHALATION-RAT LC50; 1000 PPM INHALATION-MONKEY LCLO; 50 GM/M3/2 HOURS INHALATION-MOUSE LCLO; 44,000 MG/M3/6 HOURS INHALATION-CAT LCLO; 15,800 MG/KG SKIN-RABBIT LD50; 393 MG/KG SKIN-MONKEY LDLO; 428 MG/KG ORAL-HUMAN LDLO; 143 MG/KG ORAL-HUMAN LDLO; 6422 MG/KG ORAL-MAN LDLO; 3429 MG/KG ORAL-MAN TDLO; 4 GM/KG ORAL-WOMAN TDLO; 7 GM/KG ORAL-MONKEY LD50; 5628 MG/KG ORAL-RAT LD50; 7300 MG/KG ORAL-MOUSE LD50; 14,200 MG/KG ORAL-RABBIT LD50; 7500 MG/KG ORAL-DOG LDLO; 9800 MG/KG SUBCUTANEOUS-MOUSE LD50; 2131 MG/KG INTRAVENOUS-RAT LD50; 4710 MG/KG INTRAVENOUS-MOUSE LD50; 8907 MG/KG INTRAVENOUS-RABBIT LD50; 7529 MG/KG INTRAPERITONEAL-RAT LD50; 10,765 MG/KG INTRAPERITONEAL-MOUSE LD50; 1826 MG/KG INTRAPERITONEAL-RABBIT LD50; 868 MG/KG UNREPORTED-MAN LDLO; MUTAGENIC DATA (RTECS); REPRODUCTIVE EFFECTS DATA (RTECS). CARCINOGEN STATUS: NONE. LOCAL EFFECTS: IRRITANT- SKIN, EYE. ACUTE TOXICITY LEVEL: SLIGHTLY TOXIC BY INHALATION, DERMAL ABSORPTION, INGESTION. TARGET EFFECTS: NEUROTOXIN; CENTRAL NERVOUS SYSTEM DEPRESSANT. AT INCREASED RISK FROM EXPOSURE: PERSONS WITH KIDNEY, EYE OR SKIN DISORDERS.

HEALTH EFFECTS AND FIRST AID

INHALATION: METHYL ALCOHOL (METHANOL): NARCOTIC/NEUROTOXIN. 25,000 PPM IMMEDIATELY DANGEROUS TO LIFE OR HEALTH. **ACUTE EXPOSURE-** MAY CAUSE IRRITATION OF THE MUCOUS MEMBRANES, COUGHING, OPPRESSION IN THE CHEST, TRACHEITIS, BRONCHITIS, TINNITUS, UNSTEADY GAIT, TWITCHING, COLIC, CONSTIPATION, NYSTAGMUS, AND BLEPHAROSPASM. SYMPTOMS FROM OCCUPATIONAL EXPOSURE INCLUDE PARESTHESIAS, NUMBNESS AND SHOOTING PAINS IN THE HANDS AND FOREARMS. METABOLIC ACIDOSIS, AND EFFECTS ON THE EYES AND CENTRAL NERVOUS SYSTEM MAY OCCUR AS DETAILED IN ACUTE INGESTION. **CHRONIC EXPOSURE-** REPEATED OR PROLONGED EXPOSURE MAY CAUSE EFFECTS AS IN ACUTE INGESTION. REPEATED EXPOSURE TO 200-375 PPM CAUSED RECURRENT HEADACHES IN WORKERS. EXPOSURE FOR 4 YEARS TO 1200-8000 PPM RESULTED IN MARKED DIMINUTION OF VISION AND ENLARGEMENT OF THE LIVER IN A WORKMAN. REPRODUCTIVE EFFECTS HAVE BEEN REPORTED IN ANIMALS.
FIRST AID- REMOVE FROM EXPOSURE AREA TO FRESH AIR IMMEDIATELY. IF BREATHING HAS STOPPED, PERFORM ARTIFICIAL RESPIRATION. KEEP PERSON WARM AND AT REST. TREAT SYMPTOMATICALLY AND SUPPORTIVELY. GET MEDICAL ATTENTION IMMEDIATELY.

SKIN CONTACT: METHYL ALCOHOL (METHANOL): IRRITANT/NARCOTIC/NEUROTOXIN. **ACUTE EXPOSURE-** CONTACT WITH LIQUID MAY CAUSE IRRITATION. SKIN ABSORPTION MAY OCCUR AND CAUSE METABOLIC ACIDOSIS AND EFFECTS ON THE EYES AND CENTRAL NERVOUS SYSTEM AS DETAILED IN ACUTE INGESTION. **CHRONIC EXPOSURE-** REPEATED OR PROLONGED CONTACT WITH THE LIQUID MAY CAUSE DEFATTING OF THE SKIN RESULTING IN ERYTHEMA, SCALING, AND ECZEMATOID DERMATITIS. CHRONIC ABSORPTION MAY RESULT METABOLIC ACIDOSIS AND EFFECTS AS DETAILED IN ACUTE INGESTION.
FIRST AID- REMOVE CONTAMINATED CLOTHING AND SHOES IMMEDIATELY. WASH AFFECTED AREA WITH SOAP OR MILD DETERGENT AND LARGE AMOUNTS OF WATER UNTIL NO EVIDENCE OF CHEMICAL REMAINS (APPROXIMATELY 15-20 MINUTES). GET MEDICAL ATTENTION IMMEDIATELY.

EYE CONTACT: METHYL ALCOHOL (METHANOL): IRRITANT. **ACUTE EXPOSURE-** VAPORS MAY CAUSE IRRITATION. HIGH CONCENTRATIONS HAVE BEEN REPORTED TO CAUSE VIOLENT INFLAMMATION OF THE CONJUNCTIVA AND EPITHELIAL DEFECTS ON THE CORNEA. MILD IRRITATION MAY OCCUR WITH DILUTE SOLUTIONS; THE UNDILUTED LIQUID HAS PRODUCED MODERATE CORNEAL OPACITY AND CONJUNCTIVAL REDNESS IN RABBITS. APPLICATION OF A DROP OF METHANOL IN RABBIT EYES CAUSED A MILD REVERSIBLE REACTION, GRADED 3 ON A SCALE OF 1-10 AFTER 24 HOURS. **CHRONIC EXPOSURE-** REPEATED OR PROLONGED CONTACT MAY CAUSE CONJUNCTIVITIS.
FIRST AID- WASH EYES IMMEDIATELY WITH LARGE AMOUNTS OF WATER OR NORMAL SALINE, OCCASIONALLY LIFTING UPPER AND LOWER LIDS, UNTIL NO EVIDENCE OF CHEMICAL REMAINS (APPROXIMATELY 15-20 MINUTES). GET MEDICAL ATTENTION IMMEDIATELY.

INGESTION: METHYL ALCOHOL (METHANOL): NARCOTIC/NEUROTOXIN. **ACUTE EXPOSURE-** MAY CAUSE MILD AND TRANSIENT INEBRIATION AND SUBSEQUENT DROWSINESS FOLLOWED BY AN ASYMPTOMATIC PERIOD LASTING 8-48 HOURS. FOLLOWING THE DELAY, COUGHING, DYSPNEA, HEADACHE, DULLNESS, WEAKNESS, VERTIGO OR DIZZINESS, NAUSEA, VOMITING, OCCASIONAL DIARRHEA, ANOREXIA, VIOLENT PAIN IN THE BACK, ABDOMEN, AND EXTREMITIES, RESTLESSNESS, APATHY OR DELIUIUM, AND RARELY, EXCITEMENT AND MANIA MAY OCCUR. RAPID, SHALLOW RESPIRATION DUE TO METABOLIC ACIDOSIS, COLD AND CLAMMY SKIN, HYPOTENSION, CYANOSIS, OPISTHOTONOS, CONVULSIONS, MILD TACHYCARDIA, CARDIAC DEPRESSION, PERIPHERAL NEURITIS, CEREBRAL AND PULMONARY EDEMA, UNCONSCIOUSNESS, AND COMA ARE POSSIBLE. EFFECTS ON THE EYE MAY INCLUDE OPTIC NEURITIS, BLURRED OR DIMMED VISION, DILATED, UNRESPONSIVE PUPILS, PTOSIS, EYE PAIN, CONCENTRIC CONSTRICTION OF VISUAL FIELDS, DIPLOPIA, CHANGE IN COLOR PERCEPTION, PHOTOPHOBIA, AND OPTIC NERVE ATROPHY. PARTIAL BLINDNESS OR POSSIBLY DELAYED TRANSIENT OR PERMANENT BLINDNESS MAY OCCUR. BILATERAL SENSORINEURAL DEAFNESS HAS BEEN REPORTED IN A SINGLE CASE. LIVER, KIDNEY, HEART, STOMACH, INTESTINAL AND PANCREATIC DAMAGE MAY ALSO OCCUR. DEATH MAY BE DUE TO RESPIRATORY FAILURE OR RARELY FROM CIRCULATORY COLLAPSE. AS LITTLE AS 15 ML HAS CAUSED BLINDNESS; THE USUAL FATAL DOSE IS 60-240 ML. PROLONGED ASTHENIA AND IRREVERSIBLE EFFECTS ON THE NERVOUS SYSTEM INCLUDING DIFFICULTY IN SPEECH, MOTOR DYSFUNCTION WITH RIGIDITY, SPASTICITY, AND HYPOKINESIS HAVE BEEN REPORTED. **CHRONIC EXPOSURE-** REPEATED INGESTION MAY CAUSE VISUAL IMPAIRMENT AND BLINDNESS AND OTHER SYSTEMIC EFFECTS AS DETAILED IN ACUTE INGESTION. REPRODUCTIVE EFFECTS HAVE BEEN REPORTED IN ANIMALS.
FIRST AID- IF INGESTION OF METHANOL IS DISCOVERED WITHIN 2 HOURS, GIVE SYRUP OF IPECAC. LAVAGE THOROUGHLY WITH 2-4 L OF TAP WATER WITH SODIUM BICARBONATE (20 G/L) ADDED. GET MEDICAL ATTENTION IMMEDIATELY.

LAVAGE SHOULD BE PERFORMED BY QUALIFIED MEDICAL PERSONNEL (DREISBACH, HANDBOOK OF POISONING, 12TH ED.).

ANTIDOTE: THE FOLLOWING ANTIDOTE(S) HAVE BEEN RECOMMENDED. HOWEVER, THE DECISION AS TO WHETHER THE SEVERITY OF POISONING REQUIRES ADMINISTRATION OF ANY ANTIDOTE AND ACTUAL DOSE REQUIRED SHOULD BE MADE BY QUALIFIED MEDICAL PERSONNEL.

METHANOL POISONING: GIVE ETHANOL, 50% (100 PROOF), 1.5 ML/KG ORALLY INITIALLY, DILUTED TO NOT MORE THAN 5% SOLUTION, FOLLOWED BY 0.5-1.0 ML/KG EVERY 2 HOURS ORALLY OR INTRAVENOUSLY FOR 4 DAYS IN ORDER TO REDUCE METABOLISM OF METHANOL AND TO ALLOW TIME FOR ITS EXCRETION. BLOOD ETHANOL LEVEL SHOULD BE IN THE RANGE OF 1-1.5 MG/ML (DREISBACH, HANDBOOK OF POISONING, 12TH ED.). ANTIDOTE SHOULD BE ADMINISTERED BY QUALIFIED MEDICAL PERSONNEL.

ORAL OR INTRAVENOUS ADMINISTRATION OF 4-METHYLPYRAZOLE INHIBITS ALCOHOL DEHYDROGENASE AND HAS BEEN USED EFFECTIVELY AS AN ANTIDOTE FOR METHANOL OR ETHYLENE GLYCOL POISONING (ELLENHORN AND BARCELOUX, MEDICAL TOXICOLOGY).

REACTIVITY

REACTIVITY: STABLE UNDER NORMAL TEMPERATURES AND PRESSURES.

INCOMPATIBILITIES: METHYL ALCOHOL (METHANOL): ACETYL BROMIDE: VIOLENT REACTION WITH FORMATION OF HYDROGEN BROMIDE. ALKYLALUMINUM SOLUTIONS: VIOLENT REACTION. ALUMINUM: EXPLOSION HAZARD. BARIUM PERCHLORATE: DISTILLATION YIELDS HIGHLY EXPLOSIVE ALKYL PERCHLORATE. BERYLLIUM HYDRIDE: VIOLENT REACTION, EVEN AT -196 C. BROMINE: VIGOROUSLY EXOTHERMIC REACTION. CALCIUM CARBIDE: VIOLENT REACTION. CHLORINE: POSSIBLE IGNITION AND EXPLOSION HAZARD. CHLOROFORM AND SODIUM HYDROXIDE: EXPLOSIVE REACTION. CHROMIUM TRIOXIDE (CHROMIC ANHYDRIDE): POSSIBLE IGNITION. CYANURIC CHLORIDE: VIOLENT REACTION. DICHLOROMETHANE: POSSIBLE IGNITION AND EXPLOSION. DIETHYL ZINC: POSSIBLE IGNITION AND EXPLOSION. HYDROGEN PEROXIDE + WATER: EXPLOSION HAZARD. IODINE + ETHANOL + MERCURIC OXIDE: EXPLOSION HAZARD. LEAD: CORRODES. LEAD PERCHLORATE: EXPLOSION HAZARD. MAGNESIUM: VIOLENT REACTION. MAGNESIUM (POWDERED): MIXTURES ARE CAPABLE OF DETONATION. NICKEL: POSSIBLE IGNITION IN THE PRESENCE OF NICKEL CATALYST. NITRIC ACID (CONCENTRATED): MIXTURES OF GREATER THAN 25% ACID MAY DECOMPOSE VIOLENTLY. OXIDIZERS (STRONG): FIRE AND EXPLOSION HAZARD. PERCHLORIC ACID: EXPLOSION HAZARD. PHOSPHOROUS TRIOXIDE: POSSIBLE VIOLENT REACTION AND IGNITION. POTASSIUM: POSSIBLE DANGEROUS REACTION. POTASSIUM HYDROXIDE + CHLOROFORM: EXOTHERMIC REACTION. POTASSIUM TERT-BUTOXIDE: FIRE AND EXPLOSION HAZARD. SODIUM + CHLOROFORM: POSSIBLE EXPLOSION. SODIUM HYPOCHLORITE: EXPLOSION HAZARD. SODIUM METHOXIDE + CHLOROFORM: POSSIBLE EXPLOSION. SULFURIC ACID: FIRE AND EXPLOSION HAZARD. ZINC: EXPLOSION HAZARD.

DECOMPOSITION: THERMAL DECOMPOSITION PRODUCTS MAY INCLUDE TOXIC OXIDES OF CARBON.

POLYMERIZATION: HAZARDOUS POLYMERIZATION HAS NOT BEEN REPORTED TO OCCUR UNDER NORMAL TEMPERATURES AND PRESSURES.

STORAGE AND DISPOSAL

OBSERVE ALL FEDERAL, STATE AND LOCAL REGULATIONS WHEN STORING OR DISPOSING OF THIS SUBSTANCE. FOR ASSISTANCE, CONTACT THE DISTRICT DIRECTOR OF THE ENVIRONMENTAL PROTECTION AGENCY.

STORAGE

STORE IN ACCORDANCE WITH 29 CFR 1910.106.
STORE AWAY FROM INCOMPATIBLE SUBSTANCES.

DISPOSAL

DISPOSAL MUST BE IN ACCORDANCE WITH STANDARDS APPLICABLE TO GENERATORS OF HAZARDOUS WASTE, 40 CFR 262. EPA HAZARDOUS WASTE NUMBER U154.

CONDITIONS TO AVOID

AVOID CONTACT WITH HEAT, SPARKS, FLAMES OR OTHER IGNITION SOURCES. VAPORS MAY BE EXPLOSIVE. MATERIAL IS POISONOUS; AVOID INHALATION OF VAPORS OR CONTACT WITH SKIN. DO NOT ALLOW MATERIAL TO CONTAMINATE WATER SOURCES.

SPILL AND LEAK PROCEDURES

SOIL SPILL: DIG HOLDING AREA SUCH AS LAGOON, POND OR PIT FOR CONTAINMENT. DIKE FLOW OF SPILLED MATERIAL USING SOIL OR SANDBAGS OR FOAMED BARRIERS SUCH AS POLYURETHANE OR CONCRETE.

AIR SPILL: APPLY WATER SPRAY TO KNOCK DOWN VAPORS.

WATER SPILL: ALLOW SPILLED MATERIAL TO AERATE.

LIMIT SPILL MOTION AND DISPERSION WITH NATURAL BARRIERS OR OIL SPILL CONTROL BOOMS. USE SUCTION HOSES TO REMOVE TRAPPED SPILL MATERIAL.

OCCUPATIONAL SPILL: SHUT OFF IGNITION SOURCES. DO NOT TOUCH SPILLED MATERIAL. STOP LEAK IF YOU CAN DO IT WITHOUT RISK. USE WATER SPRAY TO REDUCE VAPORS. FOR SMALL SPILLS, TAKE UP WITH SAND OR OTHER ABSORBENT MATERIAL AND PLACE INTO CONTAINERS FOR LATER DISPOSAL. FOR LARGER SPILLS, DIKE FAR AHEAD OF SPILL FOR LATER DISPOSAL. NO SMOKING, FLAMES OR FLARES IN HAZARD AREA! KEEP UNNECESSARY PEOPLE AWAY; ISOLATE HAZARD AREA AND DENY ENTRY.

REPORTABLE QUANTITY (RQ): 5000 POUNDS THE SUPERFUND AMENDMENTS AND REAUTHORIZATION ACT (SARA) SECTION 304 REQUIRES THAT A RELEASE EQUAL TO OR GREATER THAN THE REPORTABLE QUANTITY FOR THIS SUBSTANCE BE IMMEDIATELY REPORTED TO THE LOCAL EMERGENCY PLANNING COMMITTEE AND THE STATE EMERGENCY RESPONSE COMMISSION (40 CFR 355.40). IF THE RELEASE OF THIS SUBSTANCE IS REPORTABLE UNDER CERCLA SECTION 103, THE NATIONAL RESPONSE CENTER MUST BE NOTIFIED IMMEDIATELY AT (800) 424-8802 OR (202) 426-2675 IN THE METROPOLITAN WASHINGTON, D.C. AREA (40 CFR 302.6).

PROTECTIVE EQUIPMENT

VENTILATION: PROVIDE LOCAL EXHAUST OR PROCESS ENCLOSURE VENTILATION TO MEET THE PUBLISHED EXPOSURE LIMITS. VENTILATION EQUIPMENT MUST BE EXPLOSION-PROOF.

RESPIRATOR: THE FOLLOWING RESPIRATORS AND MAXIMUM USE CONCENTRATIONS ARE RECOMMENDATIONS BY THE U.S. DEPARTMENT OF HEALTH AND HUMAN SERVICES, NIOSH POCKET GUIDE TO CHEMICAL HAZARDS; NIOSH CRITERIA DOCUMENTS OR BY THE U.S. DEPARTMENT OF LABOR, 29 CFR 1910 SUBPART Z. THE SPECIFIC RESPIRATOR SELECTED MUST BE BASED ON CONTAMINATION LEVELS FOUND IN THE WORK PLACE, MUST NOT EXCEED THE WORKING LIMITS OF THE RESPIRATOR AND BE JOINTLY APPROVED BY THE NATIONAL INSTITUTE FOR OCCUPATIONAL SAFETY AND HEALTH AND THE MINE SAFETY AND HEALTH ADMINISTRATION (NIOSH-MSHA).

METHYL ALCOHOL (METHANOL):

2000 PPM- ANY SUPPLIED-AIR RESPIRATOR. ANY SELF-CONTAINED BREATHING APPARATUS.

5000 PPM- ANY SUPPLIED-AIR RESPIRATOR OPERATED IN A CONTINUOUS FLOW MODE.

10,000 PPM- ANY SELF-CONTAINED BREATHING APPARATUS WITH A FULL FACEPIECE. ANY SUPPLIED-AIR RESPIRATOR WITH A FULL FACEPIECE. ANY SUPPLIED-AIR RESPIRATOR WITH A TIGHT-FITTING FACEPIECE OPERATED IN A CONTINUOUS FLOW MODE.

25,000 PPM- ANY SUPPLIED-AIR RESPIRATOR WITH A FULL FACEPIECE AND OPERATED IN A PRESSURE-DEMAND OR OTHER POSITIVE PRESSURE MODE.

ESCAPE- ANY APPROPRIATE ESCAPE-TYPE SELF-CONTAINED BREATHING APPARATUS.

FOR FIREFIGHTING AND OTHER IMMEDIATELY DANGEROUS TO LIFE OR HEALTH CONDITIONS:

SELF-CONTAINED BREATHING APPARATUS WITH FULL FACEPIECE OPERATED IN PRESSURE-DEMAND OR OTHER POSITIVE PRESSURE MODE.

SUPPLIED-AIR RESPIRATOR WITH FULL FACEPIECE AND OPERATED IN PRESSURE-DEMAND OR OTHER POSITIVE PRESSURE MODE IN COMBINATION WITH AN AUXILIARY SELF-CONTAINED BREATHING APPARATUS OPERATED IN PRESSURE-DEMAND OR OTHER POSITIVE PRESSURE MODE.

CLOTHING: EMPLOYEE MUST WEAR APPROPRIATE PROTECTIVE (IMPERVIOUS) CLOTHING AND EQUIPMENT TO PREVENT REPEATED OR PROLONGED SKIN CONTACT WITH THIS SUBSTANCE.

GLOVES: EMPLOYEE MUST WEAR APPROPRIATE PROTECTIVE GLOVES TO PREVENT CONTACT WITH THIS SUBSTANCE.

EYE PROTECTION: EMPLOYEE MUST WEAR SPLASH-PROOF OR DUST-RESISTANT SAFETY GOGGLES TO PREVENT EYE CONTACT WITH THIS SUBSTANCE.

EMERGENCY EYE WASH: WHERE THERE IS ANY POSSIBILITY THAT AN EMPLOYEE'S EYES MAY BE EXPOSED TO THIS SUBSTANCE, THE EMPLOYER SHOULD PROVIDE AN EYE WASH FOUNTAIN WITHIN THE IMMEDIATE WORK AREA FOR EMERGENCY USE.

AUTHORIZED BY- OCCUPATIONAL HEALTH SERVICES, INC.

CREATION DATE: 11/15/89 ***REVISION DATE:*** 05/15/90

MATERIAL SAFETY DATA SHEET

OCCUPATIONAL HEALTH SERVICES, INC.
AGRICULTURE AND PESTICIDE DIVISION

EMERGENCY CONTACT:
JOHN S. BRANSFORD, JR. (615) 292-1180

450 SEVENTH AVENUE, SUITE 2407
NEW YORK, NEW YORK 10123
1-800-445-MSDS OR (212) 967-1100

SUBSTANCE IDENTIFICATION

CAS-NUMBER 74-83-9

SUBSTANCE: **METHYL BROMIDE**

TRADE NAMES/SYNONYMS: BROMOMETHANE; MBX; METHYL BROMIDE, LIQUID; METHOGAS; ROTOX; BROMOGAS; CELFUME; DOW FUME; DOWFUME MC-2; METAFUME; EMBAFUME; ISCOBROME; PESTMASTER; PROFUME; TERR-O-GAS 100; ZYTOX; HALON 1001; MONOBROMOMETHANE; RCRA U029; UN 1062; PST14300

CHEMICAL FAMILY: HALOGEN COMPOUND, ALIPHATIC

MOLECULAR FORMULA: C-H3-BR

MOLECULAR WEIGHT: 95

CERCLA RATINGS (SCALE 0-3): HEALTH=3 FIRE=1 REACTIVITY=0 PERSISTENCE=1

NFPA RATINGS (SCALE 0-4): HEALTH=3 FIRE=1 REACTIVITY=0

COMPONENTS AND CONTAMINANTS

COMPONENT: METHYL BROMIDE ***PERCENT:*** 100
CAS# 74-83-9

OTHER CONTAMINANTS: NONE

EXPOSURE LIMITS: METHYL BROMIDE: 5 PPM (20 MG/M3) OSHA TWA (SKIN) 5 PPM (20 MG/M3) ACGIH TWA (SKIN) LOWEST FEASIBLE LIMIT NIOSH RECOMMENDED EXPOSURE CRITERIA

1000 POUNDS SARA SECTION 302 THRESHOLD PLANNING QUANTITY 1000 POUNDS SARA SECTION 304 REPORTABLE QUANTITY 1000 POUNDS CERCLA SECTION 103 REPORTABLE QUANTITY SUBJECT TO SARA SECTION 313 ANNUAL TOXIC CHEMICAL RELEASE REPORTING

PHYSICAL DATA

DESCRIPTION: COLORLESS, TRANSPARENT, GAS OR VOLATILE LIQUID WITH A BURNING TASTE, AND CHLOROFORM-LIKE ODOR. ***BOILING POINT:*** 38 F (4 C)

MELTING POINT: -135 F (-93 C) ***SPECIFIC GRAVITY:*** 1.7 @ 0 C

VAPOR PRESSURE: 1250 MMHG @ 20 C ***SOLUBILITY IN WATER:*** 1.75% @ 20 C

VAPOR DENSITY: 3.3

SOLVENT SOLUBILITY: ALCOHOL, CHLOROFORM, ETHER, BENZENE, CARBON DISULFIDE, CARBON TETRACHLORIDE

FIRE AND EXPLOSION DATA

FIRE AND EXPLOSION HAZARD: SLIGHT FIRE HAZARD WHEN EXPOSED TO HEAT OR FLAME.

UPPER EXPLOSIVE LIMIT: 16% ***LOWER EXPLOSIVE LIMIT:*** 10%

AUTOIGNITION TEMP.: 1000 F (538 C)

FIREFIGHTING MEDIA: DRY CHEMICAL, CARBON DIOXIDE, HALON, WATER SPRAY OR STANDARD FOAM (1987 EMERGENCY RESPONSE GUIDEBOOK, DOT P 5800.4).
FOR LARGER FIRES, USE WATER SPRAY, FOG OR STANDARD FOAM (1987 EMERGENCY RESPONSE GUIDEBOOK, DOT P 5800.4).

FIREFIGHTING: MOVE CONTAINERS FROM FIRE AREA IF POSSIBLE. FIGHT FIRE FROM MAXIMUM DISTANCE. STAY AWAY FROM STORAGE TANK ENDS. DIKE FIRE CONTROL WATER FOR LATER DISPOSAL. DO NOT SCATTER MATERIAL (1987 EMERGENCY RESPONSE GUIDEBOOK, DOT P 5800.4, GUIDE PAGE 55).
USE AGENTS SUITABLE FOR TYPE OF FIRE. USE WATER IN FLOODING AMOUNTS AS FOG. COOL CONTAINERS WITH FLOODING AMOUNTS OF WATER, APPLY FROM AS FAR A DISTANCE AS POSSIBLE. AVOID BREATHING POISONOUS VAPORS, KEEP UPWIND. CONSIDER EVACUATION OF DOWNWIND AREA IF MATERIAL IS LEAKING.
FIRE FIGHTING PHASES: USE WATER SPRAY, FOAM, CARBON DIOXIDE, OR DRY CHEMICAL. DO NOT WALK INTO SPILLS OF LIQUID OR ENTER HIGH CONCENTRATIONS OF VAPORS (NFPA 49, HAZARDOUS CHEMICALS DATA, 1975).

TRANSPORTATION DATA

DEPARTMENT OF TRANSPORTATION HAZARD CLASSIFICATION 49 CFR 172.101: POISON B
DEPARTMENT OF TRANSPORTATION LABELING REQUIREMENTS 49 CFR 172.101 AND SUBPART E: POISON
DEPARTMENT OF TRANSPORTATION PACKAGING REQUIREMENTS: 49 CFR 173.353 EXCEPTIONS: NONE

TOXICITY

METHYL BROMIDE: TOXICITY DATA: 1 GM/M3/2 HOURS INHALATION-CHILD LCLO; 35 PPM INHALATION-HUMAN TCLO; 60,000 PPM/2 HOURS INHALATION-MAN LCLO; 302 PPM/8 HOURS INHALATION-RAT LC50; 1540 MG/M3/2 HOURS INHALATION-MOUSE LCLO; 28,900 MG/M3/30 MINUTES INHALATION-RABBIT LC50; 300 PPM/9 HOURS INHALATION-GUINEA PIG LCLO; 35 GM/M3/40 MINUTES INTERMITTENT SKIN-HUMAN TDLO; 214 MG/KG ORAL-RAT LD50; 135 MG/KG SUBCUTANEOUS-RAT LD50; MUTAGENIC DATA (RTECS); TUMORIGENIC DATA (RTECS). CARCINOGEN STATUS: ANIMAL LIMITED EVIDENCE (IARC GROUP-3). IN ONE 90 DAY STUDY BY ORAL ADMINISTRATION IN RATS, METHYL BROMIDE WAS REPORTED TO PRODUCE SQUAMOUS-CELL CARCINOMAS OF THE FORESTOMACH. LOCAL EFFECTS: IRRITANT- SKIN, EYE. ACUTE TOXICITY LEVEL: TOXIC BY INHALATION AND INGESTION. TARGET EFFECTS: CENTRAL NERVOUS SYSTEM DEPRESSANT. POISONING MAY AFFECT THE BRAIN, KIDNEYS, AND LIVER. ADDITIONAL INFORMATION: STIMULANTS SUCH AS EPINEPHINE MAY INDUCE VENTRICULAR FIBRILLATION.*

* BASED ON GENERAL INFORMATION ON HALOGENATED ALKANES.

HEALTH EFFECTS AND FIRST AID

INHALATION: METHYL BROMIDE: NARCOTIC/TOXIC. **ACUTE EXPOSURE-** SYMPTOMS MAY BE DELAYED FROM 1-12 HOURS AFTER EXPOSURE TO HIGH CONCENTRATIONS; LOWER CONCENTRATIONS RESULT IN LESS SEVERE SYMPTOMS WITH A LATENT PERIOD OF 12 TO 24 HOURS. REPORTED EFFECTS INCLUDE HEADACHE, VISUAL DISTURBANCES, NAUSEA, VOMITING, ANOREXIA, ABDOMINAL PAIN, WEAKNESS, MALAISE, VERTIGO, PARESTHESIAS AND PARALYSIS OF THE EXTREMITIES, OLIGURIA OR ANURIA, DROWSINESS, CONFUSION, HYPERACTIVITY, HYPOTENSION, MANIA, HALLUCINATIONS, TREMORS OR TWITCHING, ATAXIA, AND CONVULSIONS. HIGH CONCENTRATIONS MAY CAUSE RAPID NARCOSIS AND DEATH FROM RESPIRATORY FAILURE. LESSER CONCENTRATIONS MAY CAUSE PULMONARY IRRITATION, COUGHING, CHEST PAIN, SHORTNESS OF BREATH, CONGESTION, EDEMA, AND DEVELOPMENT OF BRONCHITIS OR PNEUMONITIS. JAUNDICE AND CYANOSIS MAY ALSO RESULT. UNCONSCIOUSNESS, COMA, AND DEATH DUE TO RESPIRATORY OR CIRCULATORY COLLAPSE MAY OCCUR. TUBULAR DAMAGE IN THE KIDNEYS HAS BEEN OBSERVED IN FATAL CASES. SURVIVING INDIVIDUALS MAY HAVE PERSISTENT CENTRAL AND PERIPHERAL NERVOUS SYSTEM EFFECTS INCLUDING VERTIGO, DEPRESSION, HALLUCINATIONS, ANMESIA, ANXIETY, INABILITY TO CONCENTRATE, SENSORY DISTURBANCES, WEAKNESS, AND IRRITABILITY. **CHRONIC EXPOSURE-** REPEATED EXPOSURE MAY RESULT IN ADVERSE CENTRAL NERVOUS SYSTEM EFFECTS INCLUDING LETHARGY, MUSCULAR PAINS, VISUAL, SPEECH, AND SENSORY DISTURBANCES, MENTAL CONFUSION, BLURRED VISION, PAPILLEDEMA, HALLUCINATIONS, SOMNOLENCE, FAINTING ATTACKS, BRONCHOSPASMS, AND CENTRAL NERVOUS SYSTEM EDEMA. PERIPHERAL NEUROPATHY MAY BE INDICATED BY PARALYSIS OF THE EXTREMITIES, MYOCLONUS, POLYNEURITIS, AND CONVULSIONS. LIVER, KIDNEY AND PERMANENT BRAIN DAMAGE MAY OCCUR.

FIRST AID- REMOVE FROM EXPOSURE AREA TO FRESH AIR IMMEDIATELY. IF BREATHING HAS STOPPED, PERFORM ARTIFICIAL RESPIRATION. KEEP PERSON WARM AND AT REST. TREAT SYMPTOMATICALLY AND SUPPORTIVELY. GET MEDICAL ATTENTION IMMEDIATELY.

SKIN CONTACT: METHYL BROMIDE: IRRITANT. **ACUTE EXPOSURE-** CONTACT WITH THE LIQUID MAY CAUSE IRRITATION, ERYTHEMA, EDEMA, SCALING, AND ITCHING DERMATITIS. THE LIQUID MAY BE ABSORBED THROUGH INTACT SKIN. **CHRONIC EXPOSURE-** REPEATED OR PROLONGED EXPOSURE MAY LEAD TO VESICULATION AND POSSIBLE DEEP BURNS.

FIRST AID- REMOVE CONTAMINATED CLOTHING AND SHOES IMMEDIATELY. WASH AFFECTED AREA WITH SOAP OR MILD DETERGENT AND LARGE AMOUNTS OF WATER UNTIL NO EVIDENCE OF CHEMICAL REMAINS (APPROXIMATELY 15-20 MINUTES). GET MEDICAL ATTENTION IMMEDIATELY.

EYE CONTACT: METHYL BROMIDE: **ACUTE EXPOSURE-** VAPORS AND LIQUID MAY CAUSE TRANSIENT IRRITATION AND CONJUNCTIVITIS. RABBITS EXPOSED TO CONCENTRATED VAPORS FOR 1 MINUTE 30 SECONDS RESULTED IN LOSS OF EYE SURFACE LUSTER, LOSS OF CORNEAL EPITHELIUM, EDEMA OF THE CONJUNCTIVAE AND LIDS, AND TRANSIENT CORNEAL OPACITY. **CHRONIC EXPOSURE-** REPEATED OR PROLONGED EXPOSURE MAY CAUSE CONJUNCTIVITIS.

FIRST AID- WASH EYES IMMEDIATELY WITH LARGE AMOUNTS OF WATER OR NORMAL SALINE, OCCASIONALLY LIFTING UPPER AND LOWER LIDS, UNTIL NO EVIDENCE OF CHEMICAL REMAINS (APPROXIMATELY 15-20 MINUTES). GET MEDICAL ATTENTION IMMEDIATELY.

INGESTION: METHYL BROMIDE: TOXIC/LIMITED ANIMAL CARCINOGEN. **ACUTE EXPOSURE-** INGESTION OF LIQUID MAY RESULT IN SYSTEMIC TOXICITY AS DETAILED IN ACUTE INHALATION. THE LETHAL DOSE REPORTED IN RATS WAS 214 MG/KG. THE SYMPTOMS WERE NOT REPORTED. **CHRONIC EXPOSURE-** DEGENERATION OF PERIPHERAL NERVES AND THE DORSAL COLUMNS OF THE SPINAL CORD HAS BEEN REPORTED IN RATS FED DIETS WITH METHYL BROMIDE. REPEATED ADMINISTRATION TO RATS BY ORAL GAVAGE INDUCED TUMORS OF THE FORESTOMACH.

FIRST AID- TREAT SYMPTOMATICALLY AND SUPPORTIVELY. GET MEDICAL ATTENTION IMMEDIATELY. IF VOMITING OCCURS, KEEP HEAD LOWER THAN HIPS TO PREVENT ASPIRATION.
ANTIDOTE: NO SPECIFIC ANTIDOTE. TREAT SYMPTOMATICALLY AND SUPPORTIVELY.

REACTIVITY

REACTIVITY: STABLE UNDER NORMAL TEMPERATURES AND PRESSURES.
INCOMPATIBILITIES: METHYL BROMIDE: ALUMINUM: SEVERE EXPLOSION HAZARD. MAGNESIUM: SEVERE EXPLOSION HAZARD. ZINC: SEVERE EXPLOSION HAZARD. DIMETHYL SULFOXIDE: DELAYED EXPLOSION HAZARD. STRONG OXIDIZERS: VIGOROUS REACTION. ETHYLENE OXIDE: VIGOROUS REACTION.
DECOMPOSITION: THERMAL DECOMPOSITION MAY RELEASE CORROSIVE FUMES OF BROMIDE.
POLYMERIZATION: HAZARDOUS POLYMERIZATION HAS NOT BEEN REPORTED TO OCCUR UNDER NORMAL TEMPERATURES AND PRESSURES.

STORAGE AND DISPOSAL

OBSERVE ALL FEDERAL, STATE AND LOCAL REGULATIONS WHEN STORING OR DISPOSING OF THIS SUBSTANCE. FOR ASSISTANCE, CONTACT THE DISTRICT DIRECTOR OF THE ENVIRONMENTAL PROTECTION AGENCY.

STORAGE

THRESHOLD PLANNING QUANTITY (TPQ): THE SUPERFUND AMENDMENTS AND REAUTHORIZATION ACT (SARA) SECTION 302 REQUIRES THAT EACH FACILITY WHERE ANY EXTREMELY HAZARDOUS SUBSTANCE IS PRESENT IN A QUANTITY EQUAL TO OR GREATER THAN THE TPQ ESTABLISHED FOR THAT SUBSTANCE NOTIFY THE STATE EMERGENCY RESPONSE COMMISSION FOR THE STATE IN WHICH IT IS LOCATED. SECTION 303 OF SARA REQUIRES THESE FACILITIES TO PARTICIPATE IN LOCAL EMERGENCY RESPONSE PLANNING (40 CFR 355.30).
PROTECT AGAINST PHYSICAL DAMAGE. STORE ONE-POUND CONTAINERS IN DRY LOCATION TO PREVENT RUSTING. OUTSIDE OR DETACHED STORAGE IS PREFERRED FOR CYLINDERS. STORE IN WELL-VENTILATED LOCATION OUT OF THE DIRECT RAYS OF THE SUN AND PROTECTED FROM SNOW AND ICE (NFPA 49, HAZARDOUS CHEMICALS DATA, 1975).
STORE AWAY FROM INCOMPATIBLE SUBSTANCES.

DISPOSAL

DISPOSAL MUST BE IN ACCORDANCE WITH STANDARDS APPLICABLE TO GENERATORS OF HAZARDOUS WASTE, 40CFR 262. EPA HAZARDOUS WASTE NUMBER U029.

CONDITIONS TO AVOID

MAY BURN BUT DOES NOT IGNITE READILY. CONTAINERS MAY EXPLODE IN HEAT OF FIRE.
METHYL BROMIDE: IT WILL BURN IN AIR IN THE PRESENCE OF A HIGH ENERGY SOURCE OF IGNITION AND WHEN WITHIN A NARROW FLAMMABILITY RANGE.

SPILL AND LEAK PROCEDURES

OCCUPATIONAL SPILL: DO NOT TOUCH SPILLED MATERIAL. STOP LEAK IF YOU CAN DO IT WITHOUT RISK. USE WATER SPRAY TO REDUCE VAPORS. FOR SMALL SPILLS, TAKE UP WITH SAND OR OTHER ABSORBENT MATERIAL AND PLACE INTO CONTAINERS FOR LATER DISPOSAL. FOR SMALL DRY SPILLS, WITH A CLEAN SHOVEL PLACE MATERIAL INTO CLEAN, DRY CONTAINERS AND COVER. MOVE CONTAINERS FROM SPILL AREA. FOR LARGER SPILLS, DIKE FAR AHEAD OF SPILL FOR LATER DISPOSAL. KEEP UNNECESSARY PEOPLE AWAY. ISOLATE HAZARD AREA AND DENY ENTRY. VENTILATE CLOSED SPACES BEFORE ENTERING.
REPORTABLE QUANTITY (RQ): 1000 POUNDS THE SUPERFUND AMENDMENTS AND REAUTHORIZATION ACT (SARA) SECTION 304 REQUIRES THAT A RELEASE EQUAL TO OR GREATER THAN THE REPORTABLE QUANTITY FOR THIS SUBSTANCE BE IMMEDIATELY REPORTED TO THE LOCAL EMERGENCY PLANNING COMMITTEE AND THE STATE EMERGENCY RESPONSE COMMISSION (40 CFR 355.40). IF THE RELEASE OF THIS SUBSTANCE IS REPORTABLE UNDER CERCLA SECTION 103, THE NATIONAL RESPONSE CENTER MUST BE NOTIFIED IMMEDIATELY AT (800) 424-8802 OR (202) 426-2675 IN THE METROPOLITAN WASHINGTON, D.C. AREA (40 CFR 302.6).

PROTECTIVE EQUIPMENT

VENTILATION: PROVIDE LOCAL EXHAUST OR PROCESS ENCLOSURE VENTILATION TO MEET PUBLISHED EXPOSURE LIMITS.
RESPIRATOR: THE FOLLOWING RESPIRATORS AND MAXIMUM USE CONCENTRATIONS ARE RECOMMENDATIONS BY THE U.S. DEPARTMENT OF HEALTH AND HUMAN SERVICES, NIOSH POCKET GUIDE TO CHEMICAL HAZARDS; NIOSH CRITERIA DOCUMENTS OR BY THE U.S. DEPARTMENT OF LABOR, 29 CFR 1910 SUBPART Z. THE SPECIFIC RESPIRATOR SELECTED MUST BE BASED ON CONTAMINATION LEVELS FOUND IN THE WORK PLACE, MUST NOT EXCEED THE WORKING LIMITS OF THE RESPIRATOR AND BE JOINTLY APPROVED BY THE NATIONAL INSTITUTE FOR OCCUPATIONAL SAFETY AND HEALTH AND THE MINE SAFETY AND HEALTH ADMINISTRATION (NIOSH-MSHA).
AT ANY DETECTABLE CONCENTRATION:
SELF-CONTAINED BREATHING APPARATUS WITH FULL FACEPIECE OPERATED IN PRESSURE-DEMAND OR OTHER POSITIVE PRESSURE MODE. SUPPLIED-AIR RESPIRATOR WITH FULL FACEPIECE OPERATED IN PRESSURE-DEMAND OR OTHER POSITIVE PRESSURE MODE IN COMBINATION WITH AN AUXILIARY SELF-CONTAINED BREATHING APPARATUS OPERATED IN PRESSURE-DEMAND OR OTHER POSITIVE PRESSURE MODE.
ESCAPE- AIR-PURIFYING FULL FACEPIECE RESPIRATOR (GAS MASK) WITH A CHIN-STYLE OR FRONT- OR BACK-MOUNTED ORGANIC VAPOR CANISTER. ESCAPE-TYPE SELF-CONTAINED BREATHING APPARATUS.
FOR FIREFIGHTING AND OTHER IMMEDIATELY DANGEROUS TO LIFE OR HEALTH CONDITIONS:
SELF-CONTAINED BREATHING APPARATUS WITH FULL FACEPIECE OPERATED IN PRESSURE-DEMAND OR OTHER POSITIVE PRESSURE MODE.
SUPPLIED-AIR RESPIRATOR WITH FULL FACEPIECE AND OPERATED IN PRESSURE-DEMAND OR OTHER POSITIVE PRESSURE MODE IN COMBINATION WITH AN AUXILIARY SELF-CONTAINED BREATHING APPARATUS OPERATED IN PRESSURE-DEMAND OR OTHER POSITIVE PRESSURE MODE.
CLOTHING: EMPLOYEE MUST WEAR APPROPRIATE PROTECTIVE (IMPERVIOUS) CLOTHING AND EQUIPMENT TO PREVENT ANY POSSIBILITY OF SKIN CONTACT WITH THIS SUBSTANCE.
GLOVES: EMPLOYEE MUST WEAR APPROPRIATE PROTECTIVE GLOVES TO PREVENT CONTACT WITH THIS SUBSTANCE.
EYE PROTECTION: EMPLOYEE MUST WEAR SPLASH-PROOF OR DUST-RESISTANT SAFETY GOGGLES AND A FACESHIELD TO PREVENT CONTACT WITH THIS SUBSTANCE.
EMERGENCY WASH FACILITIES: WHERE THERE IS ANY POSSIBILITY THAT AN EMPLOYEE'S EYES AND/OR SKIN MAY BE EXPOSED TO THIS SUBSTANCE, THE EMPLOYER SHOULD PROVIDE AN EYE WASH FOUNTAIN AND QUICK DRENCH SHOWER WITHIN THE IMMEDIATE WORK AREA FOR EMERGENCY USE.

AUTHORIZED BY- OCCUPATIONAL HEALTH SERVICES, INC.
CREATION DATE: 10/04/89 ***REVISION DATE:*** 07/13/90

MATERIAL SAFETY DATA SHEET

OCCUPATIONAL HEALTH SERVICES, INC.
AGRICULTURE AND PESTICIDE DIVISION
450 SEVENTH AVENUE, SUITE 2407
NEW YORK, NEW YORK 10123
1-800-445-MSDS OR (212) 967-1100

EMERGENCY CONTACT:
JOHN S. BRANSFORD, JR. (615) 292-1180

SUBSTANCE IDENTIFICATION

CAS-NUMBER 109-86-4
SUBSTANCE: **ETHYLENE GLYCOL MONOMETHYL ETHER**
TRADE NAMES/SYNONYMS: ETHANOL, 2-METHOXY; DOWANOL EM; EKTASOLVE EM; ETHYLENE GLYCOL METHYL ETHER; GLYCOL METHYL ETHER; METHOXYETHANOL; BETA-METHOXYETHANOL; 2-METHOXYETHANOL; 2-METHOXYETHYL ALCOHOL; METHOXYETHYLENE GLYCOL; METHOXYHYDROXYETHANE; METHYL CELLOSOLVE; METHYL GLYCOL; METHYL OXITOL; MONOMETHYLGLYCOL; POLY-SOLV EM; STCC 4913162; UN 1188; E-182; O-3487; C3H8O2; PST14340
CHEMICAL FAMILY: GLYCOL ETHER
MOLECULAR FORMULA: H-O-C-H2-C-H2-O-C-H3
MOLECULAR WEIGHT: 76.10
CERCLA RATINGS (SCALE 0-3): HEALTH=2 FIRE=2 REACTIVITY=0 PERSISTENCE=0
NFPA RATINGS (SCALE 0-4): HEALTH=2 FIRE=2 REACTIVITY=0

COMPONENTS AND CONTAMINANTS

COMPONENT: ETHYLENE GLYCOL MONOMETHYL ETHER ***PERCENT:*** 100
CAS# 109-86-4
OTHER CONTAMINANTS: NONE
EXPOSURE LIMITS: ETHYLENE GLYCOL MONOMETHYL ETHER (METHYL CELLOSOLVE): 25 PPM (80 MG/M3) OSHA TWA (SKIN) 5 PPM (16 MG/M3) ACGIH TWA (SKIN) LOWEST FEASIBLE LIMIT NIOSH RECOMMENDED EXPOSURE CRITERIA
SUBJECT TO SARA SECTION 313 ANNUAL TOXIC CHEMICAL RELEASE REPORTING
SUBJECT TO CALIFORNIA PROPOSITION 65 CANCER AND/OR REPRODUCTIVE TOXICITY WARNING AND RELEASE REQUIREMENTS- (JANUARY 1, 1989)

PHYSICAL DATA

DESCRIPTION: COLORLESS LIQUID WITH A MILD AGREEABLE ODOR.
BOILING POINT: 255 F (124 C) ***MELTING POINT:*** -121 F (-85 C)

SPECIFIC GRAVITY: 0.9647 ***VISCOSITY:*** 0.85 CPS @ 16 C
VAPOR PRESSURE: 9.7 MMHG @ 20 C ***SOLUBILITY IN WATER:*** SOLUBLE
ODOR THRESHOLD: 60 PPM ***VAPOR DENSITY:*** 2.6
SOLVENT SOLUBILITY: SOLUBLE IN ALCOHOL, ETHER, ACETONE, BENZENE, GLYCEROL, DIMETHYLFORMAMIDE.

FIRE AND EXPLOSION DATA

FIRE AND EXPLOSION HAZARD: MODERATE FIRE HAZARD WHEN EXPOSED TO HEAT OR FLAME.
VAPOR-AIR MIXTURES ARE EXPLOSIVE ABOVE FLASH POINT.
VAPORS ARE HEAVIER THAN AIR AND MAY TRAVEL A CONSIDERABLE DISTANCE TO A SOURCE OF IGNITION AND FLASH BACK.
FLASH POINT: 102 F (39 C) (CC) ***UPPER EXPLOSIVE LIMIT:*** 14%
LOWER EXPLOSIVE LIMIT: 1.8% ***AUTOIGNITION TEMP.:*** 545 F (285 C)
FLAMMABILITY CLASS(OSHA): II
FIREFIGHTING MEDIA: DRY CHEMICAL, CARBON DIOXIDE, HALON, WATER SPRAY OR ALCOHOL FOAM (1987 EMERGENCY RESPONSE GUIDEBOOK, DOT P 5800.4).
FOR LARGER FIRES, USE WATER SPRAY, FOG OR ALCOHOL FOAM (1987 EMERGENCY RESPONSE GUIDEBOOK, DOT P 5800.4).
ALCOHOL FOAM (NFPA 325M, FIRE HAZARD PROPERTIES OF FLAMMABLE LIQUIDS, GASES, AND VOLATILE SOLIDS, 1984).
FIREFIGHTING: MOVE CONTAINER FROM FIRE AREA IF POSSIBLE. COOL FIRE-EXPOSED CONTAINERS WITH WATER FROM SIDE UNTIL WELL AFTER FIRE IS OUT. STAY AWAY FROM STORAGE TANK ENDS. FOR MASSIVE FIRE IN STORAGE AREA, USE UNMANNED HOSE HOLDER OR MONITOR NOZZLES, ELSE WITHDRAW FROM AREA AND LET FIRE BURN. WITHDRAW IMMEDIATELY IN CASE OF RISING SOUND FROM VENTING SAFETY DEVICE OR ANY DISCOLORATION OF STORAGE TANK DUE TO FIRE (1987 EMERGENCY RESPONSE GUIDEBOOK, DOT P 5800.4, GUIDE PAGE 26). EXTINGUISH ONLY IF FLOW CAN BE STOPPED; USE FLOODING AMOUNTS OF WATER AS FOG, SOLID STREAMS MAY NOT BE EFFECTIVE, APPLY FROM AS FAR A DISTANCE AS POSSIBLE. COOL CONTAINERS WITH FLOODING QUANTITIES OF WATER. AVOID BREATHING TOXIC VAPORS, KEEP UPWIND.

TRANSPORTATION DATA

DEPARTMENT OF TRANSPORTATION HAZARD CLASSIFICATION 49 CFR 172.101: COMBUSTIBLE LIQUID
DEPARTMENT OF TRANSPORTATION LABELING REQUIREMENTS 49 CFR 172.101 AND SUBPART E: NONE
DEPARTMENT OF TRANSPORTATION PACKAGING REQUIREMENTS: NONE
EXCEPTIONS: 49 CFR 173.118A

TOXICITY

ETHYLENE GLYCOL MONOMETHYL ETHER (METHYL CELLOSOLVE): IRRITATION DATA: 483 MG/24 HOURS SKIN-RABBIT MILD; 97 MG EYE-RABBIT; 500 MG/24 HOURS EYE-RABBIT MILD; 10 UG EYE-GUINEA PIG MILD. TOXICITY DATA: 25 PPM INHALATION-HUMAN TCLO; 1500 PPM/7 HOURS INHALATION-RAT LC50; 1480 PPM/7 HOURS INHALATION-MOUSE LC50; 1280 MG/KG SKIN-RABBIT LD50; 3380 MG/KG ORAL-HUMAN LDLO; 2460 MG/KG ORAL-RAT LD50; 2560 MG/KG ORAL-MOUSE LD50; 890 MG/KG ORAL-RABBIT LD50; 950 MG/KG ORAL-GUINEA PIG LD50; 2147 MG/KG INTRAPERITONEAL-MOUSE LD50; 2500 MG/KG INTRAPERITONEAL-RAT LD50; 2140 MG/KG INTRAVENOUS-RAT LD50; MUTAGENIC DATA (RTECS); REPRODUCTIVE EFFECTS DATA (RTECS). CARCINOGEN STATUS: NONE. ACUTE TOXICITY LEVEL: TOXIC BY INHALATION; MODERATELY TOXIC BY DERMAL ABSORPTION AND INGESTION. TARGET EFFECTS: CENTRAL NERVOUS SYSTEM DEPRESSANT; NEPHROTOXIN. POISONING MAY ALSO AFFECT THE HEMATOPOIETIC AND NERVOUS SYSTEMS AND THE LIVER. ADDITIONAL DATA: NIOSH RECOMMENDS THAT ETHYLENE GLYCOL MONOMETHYL ETHER IN THE WORKPLACE BE REGARDED AS HAVING THE POTENTIAL TO CAUSE ADVERSE REPRODUCTIVE EFFECTS IN WORKERS, INCLUDING TERATOGENESIS IN THE OFFSPRING OF EXPOSED PREGNANT FEMALES.

HEALTH EFFECTS AND FIRST AID

INHALATION: ETHYLENE GLYCOL MONOMETHYL ETHER (METHYL CELLOSOLVE): NARCOTIC/NEPHROTOXIN/TOXIC. **ACUTE EXPOSURE-** VAPORS MAY CAUSE IRRITATION OF THE UPPER RESPIRATORY TRACT AND EFFECT THE CENTRAL NERVOUS SYSTEM. SYMPTOMS MAY INCLUDE DROWSINESS, WEAKNESS AND SHAKING. IN ANIMAL STUDIES, DEATH RESULTED FROM LUNG AND KIDNEY INJURY. **CHRONIC EXPOSURE-** REPEATED OR PROLONGED EXPOSURE MAY CAUSE EFFECTS ON THE CENTRAL NERVOUS SYSTEM AND TOXIC ENCEPHALOPATHY. SYMPTOMS MAY INCLUDE HEADACHE, DIZZINESS, DROWSINESS, FATIGUE, LETHARGY, WEAKNESS, ATAXIA, TREMORS, HYPERREFLEXIA, GASTROINTESTINAL UPSET, ANOREXIA, WEIGHT LOSS, PERSONALITY CHANGES, DISORIENTATION, AND MENTAL RETARDATION. UNEQUAL PUPILS, DISTURBANCES IN VISION, HEARING AND SPEECH, ANKLE CLONUS AND BED WETTING HAVE BEEN REPORTED. BONE MARROW DEPRESSION, LEUKOCYTE IMMATURITY, DECREASED ERYTHROID ELEMENTS, THROMBOCYTOPENIA, AND MACROCYTIC ANEMIA MAY OCCUR. SIGNS AND SYMPTOMS USUALLY DISAPPEAR SEVERAL WEEKS TO MONTHS AFTER EXPOSURE CEASES. EXPOSURE OF RABBITS TO 800-1600 PPM FOR 4-10 DAYS HAS CAUSED KIDNEY DAMAGE WITH HEMATURIA, ALBUMINURIA, CALCIFIED CASTS IN THE URINE AND SEVERE GLOMERULITIS. REPRODUCTIVE EFFECTS HAVE BEEN REPORTED IN ANIMALS INCLUDING TESTICULAR ATROPHY, TEMPORARY STERILITY IN MALES, ABNORMAL SPERM MORPHOLOGY, FETOTOXICITY AND MALFORMATIONS, ESPECIALLY SKELETAL AND CARDIOVASCULAR.
FIRST AID- REMOVE FROM EXPOSURE AREA TO FRESH AIR IMMEDIATELY. IF BREATHING HAS STOPPED, PERFORM ARTIFICIAL RESPIRATION. KEEP PERSON WARM AND AT REST. TREAT SYMPTOMATICALLY AND SUPPORTIVELY. GET MEDICAL ATTENTION IMMEDIATELY.

SKIN CONTACT: ETHYLENE GLYCOL MONOMETHYL ETHER (METHYL CELLOSOLVE): NARCOTIC/NEPHROTOXIN. **ACUTE EXPOSURE-** NO APPRECIABLE IRRITATION HAS BEEN REPORTED FROM ANIMAL STUDIES. THE SUBSTANCE MAY BE READILY ABSORBED WITH SIGNS OF INTOXICATION AS DESCRIBED IN ACUTE INHALATION. **CHRONIC EXPOSURE-** REPEATED OR PROLONGED CONTACT MAY CAUSE DRYING AND DEFATTING. ENCEPHALOPATHY, CONFUSION, DISORIENTATION, LETHARGY, ANOREXIA, TREMORS, AGITATION, WEIGHT LOSS, BLURRED VISION, HEADACHE, FEVER, BED WETTING, MARKED ANEMIA AND DAMAGE TO THE BONE MARROW HAVE BEEN REPORTED IN 2 CASES WHERE SKIN CONTACT WAS CONSIDERED THE MAIN ROUTE OF ABSORPTION. OTHER SYSTEMIC EFFECTS AS DESCRIBED FOR CHRONIC INHALATION MAY ALSO OCCUR. EFFECTS ON THE MALE REPRODUCTIVE SYSTEM OF GUINEA PIGS HAVE BEEN REPORTED FROM REPEATED SKIN APPLICATION.
FIRST AID- REMOVE CONTAMINATED CLOTHING AND SHOES IMMEDIATELY. WASH AFFECTED AREA WITH SOAP OR MILD DETERGENT AND LARGE AMOUNTS OF WATER UNTIL NO EVIDENCE OF CHEMICAL REMAINS (APPROXIMATELY 15-20 MINUTES). GET MEDICAL ATTENTION IMMEDIATELY.

EYE CONTACT: ETHYLENE GLYCOL MONOMETHYL ETHER (METHYL CELLOSOLVE): **ACUTE EXPOSURE-** HIGH VAPOR CONCENTRATIONS OR DIRECT CONTACT MAY CAUSE IRRITATION. APPLICATION TO RABBIT EYES CAUSED SLIGHT IRRITATION GRADED 3 ON A SCALE OF 1-10 IN ONE STUDY AND IMMEDIATE PAIN, CONJUNCTIVAL IRRITATION AND SLIGHT, TRANSITORY CLOUDINESS OF THE CORNEA WHICH CLEARED WITHIN 24 HOURS IN ANOTHER STUDY. **CHRONIC EXPOSURE-** REPEATED OR PROLONGED EXPOSURE MAY CAUSE CONJUNCTIVITIS.
FIRST AID- WASH EYES IMMEDIATELY WITH LARGE AMOUNTS OF WATER OR NORMAL SALINE, OCCASIONALLY LIFTING UPPER AND LOWER LIDS, UNTIL NO EVIDENCE OF CHEMICAL REMAINS (APPROXIMATELY 15-20 MINUTES). GET MEDICAL ATTENTION IMMEDIATELY.

INGESTION: ETHYLENE GLYCOL MONOMETHYL ETHER (METHYL CELLOSOLVE): NARCOTIC/NEPHROTOXIN. **ACUTE EXPOSURE-** IN HUMANS, A NON-FATAL DOSE HAS CAUSED MUSCULAR WEAKNESS, NAUSEA, VOMITING, CONFUSION, METABOLIC ACIDOSIS, OXALURIA, AND PARTIAL KIDNEY FAILURE FOLLOWED BY RECOVERY. A DOSE OF ABOUT 3 GM/KG CAUSED COMA AND DEATH WITHIN 5 HOURS; AUTOPSY REVEALED MARKED DEGENERATION OF KIDNEY TUBULES, ACUTE HEMORRHAGIC GASTRITIS, FATTY DEGENERATION OF THE LIVER, EARLY NECROSIS OF THE PANCREAS, AND BRAIN EDEMA. EFFECTS ON THE REPRODUCTIVE SYSTEM OF MALE RATS HAVE BEEN REPORTED FROM A SINGLE EXPOSURE. **CHRONIC EXPOSURE-** 7 DAILY DOSES OF 0.1 ML/KG IN RABBITS PRODUCED HEMATURIA. LARGER DOSES ALSO CAUSED TREMORS, EXHAUSTION, AND ALBUMINURIA. DEATH WAS DELAYED AND DUE TO SEVERE KIDNEY DAMAGE AND FAILURE. REPRODUCTIVE EFFECTS, INCLUDING TESTICULAR ATROPHY, HAVE BEEN REPORTED IN ANIMALS.
FIRST AID- REMOVE BY GASTRIC LAVAGE OR EMESIS. MAINTAIN BLOOD PRESSURE AND AIRWAY. GIVE OXYGEN IF RESPIRATION IS DEPRESSED. DO NOT PERFORM GASTRIC LAVAGE OR EMESIS IF VICTIM IS UNCONSCIOUS. GET MEDICAL ATTENTION IMMEDIATELY (DREISBACH, HANDBOOK OF POISONING, 11TH ED.). ADMINISTRATION OF GASTRIC LAVAGE OR OXYGEN SHOULD BE PERFORMED BY QUALIFIED MEDICAL PERSONNEL.
ANTIDOTE: NO SPECIFIC ANTIDOTE. TREAT SYMPTOMATICALLY AND SUPPORTIVELY.

REACTIVITY

REACTIVITY: STABLE UNDER NORMAL TEMPERATURES AND PRESSURES. MAY FORM EXPLOSIVE PEROXIDES ON PROLONGED EXPOSURE TO AIR.
INCOMPATIBILITIES: ETHYLENE GLYCOL MONOMETHYL ETHER (METHYL CELLOSOLVE): CAUSTICS: INCOMPATIBLE. OXIDIZERS (STRONG): FIRE AND EXPLOSION HAZARD. PLASTICS, RUBBER AND COATINGS: ATTACKS.
DECOMPOSITION: THERMAL DECOMPOSITION PRODUCTS MAY INCLUDE TOXIC OXIDES OF CARBON.
POLYMERIZATION: HAZARDOUS POLYMERIZATION HAS NOT BEEN REPORTED TO OCCUR UNDER NORMAL TEMPERATURES AND PRESSURES.

STORAGE AND DISPOSAL

OBSERVE ALL FEDERAL, STATE AND LOCAL REGULATIONS WHEN STORING OR DISPOSING OF THIS SUBSTANCE. FOR ASSISTANCE, CONTACT THE DISTRICT DIRECTOR OF THE ENVIRONMENTAL PROTECTION AGENCY.

STORAGE

STORE IN ACCORDANCE WITH 29 CFR 1910.106.
BONDING AND GROUNDING: SUBSTANCES WITH LOW ELECTROCONDUCTIVITY, WHICH MAY BE IGNITED BY ELECTROSTATIC SPARKS, SHOULD BE STORED IN CONTAINERS WHICH MEET THE BONDING AND GROUNDING GUIDELINES SPECIFIED IN NFPA 77-1983, RECOMMENDED PRACTICE ON STATIC ELECTRICITY.
ON PROLONGED STORAGE IN CONTACT WITH OXYGEN OR AIR, ETHERS MAY FORM DANGEROUSLY EXPLOSIVE PEROXIDES. STORE IN A TIGHTLY CLOSED CONTAINERS, PROTECTED FROM HEAT AND LIGHT. CHECK FOR PEROXIDE CONTENT OFTEN; NEVER DISTILL TO DRYNESS.
STORE AWAY FROM INCOMPATIBLE SUBSTANCES.

DISPOSAL

DISPOSAL MUST BE IN ACCORDANCE WITH STANDARDS APPLICABLE TO GENERATORS OF HAZARDOUS WASTE, 40 CFR 262. EPA HAZARDOUS WASTE NUMBER D001. 100 POUND CERCLA SECTION 103 REPORTABLE QUANTITY.

CONDITIONS TO AVOID

AVOID CONTACT WITH HEAT, SPARKS, FLAMES, OR OTHER SOURCES OF IGNITION. VAPORS MAY BE EXPLOSIVE AND POISONOUS; DO NOT ALLOW UNNECESSARY PERSONNEL IN AREA. DO NOT OVERHEAT CONTAINERS; CONTAINERS MAY VIOLENTLY RUPTURE AND TRAVEL A CONSIDERABLE DISTANCE IN HEAT OF FIRE.

SPILL AND LEAK PROCEDURES

WATER SPILL: THE CALIFORNIA SAFE DRINKING WATER AND TOXIC ENFORCEMENT ACT OF 1986 (PROPOSITION 65) PROHIBITS CONTAMINATING ANY KNOWN SOURCE OF DRINKING WATER WITH SUBSTANCES KNOWN TO CAUSE CANCER AND/OR REPRODUCTIVE TOXICITY.

OCCUPATIONAL SPILL: SHUT OFF IGNITION SOURCES. STOP LEAK IF YOU CAN DO IT WITHOUT RISK. USE WATER SPRAY TO REDUCE VAPORS. FOR SMALL SPILLS, TAKE UP WITH SAND OR OTHER ABSORBENT MATERIAL AND PLACE INTO CONTAINERS FOR LATER DISPOSAL. FOR LARGER SPILLS, DIKE FAR AHEAD OF SPILL FOR LATER DISPOSAL. NO SMOKING, FLAMES OR FLARES IN HAZARD AREA. KEEP UNNECESSARY PEOPLE AWAY; ISOLATE HAZARD AREA AND DENY ENTRY.

PROTECTIVE EQUIPMENT

VENTILATION: PROVIDE LOCAL EXHAUST VENTILATION SYSTEM TO MEET PUBLISHED EXPOSURE LIMITS.

RESPIRATOR: THE FOLLOWING RESPIRATORS AND MAXIMUM USE CONCENTRATIONS ARE RECOMMENDATIONS BY THE U.S. DEPARTMENT OF HEALTH AND HUMAN SERVICES, NIOSH POCKET GUIDE TO CHEMICAL HAZARDS; NIOSH CRITERIA DOCUMENTS OR BY THE U.S. DEPARTMENT OF LABOR, 29 CFR 1910 SUBPART Z.
THE SPECIFIC RESPIRATOR SELECTED MUST BE BASED ON CONTAMINATION LEVELS FOUND IN THE WORK PLACE, MUST NOT EXCEED THE WORKING LIMITS OF THE RESPIRATOR AND BE JOINTLY APPROVED BY THE NATIONAL INSTITUTE FOR OCCUPATIONAL SAFETY AND HEALTH AND THE MINE SAFETY AND HEALTH ADMINISTRATION (NIOSH-MSHA).
ETHYLENE GLYCOL MONOMETHYL ETHER (METHYL CELLOSOLVE): AT ANY DETECTABLE CONCENTRATION: ANY SELF-CONTAINED BREATHING APPARATUS WITH FULL FACEPIECE AND OPERATED IN A PRESSURE-DEMAND OR OTHER POSITIVE PRESSURE MODE. ANY SUPPLIED-AIR RESPIRATOR WITH A FULL FACEPIECE AND OPERATED IN PRESSURE-DEMAND OR OTHER POSITIVE PRESSURE MODE IN COMBINATION WITH AN AUXILIARY SELF-CONTAINED BREATHING APPARATUS OPERATED IN PRESSURE-DEMAND OR OTHER POSITIVE PRESSURE MODE.
ESCAPE- ANY AIR-PURIFYING FULL FACEPIECE RESPIRATOR (GAS MASK) WITH A CHIN-STYLE OR FRONT OR BACK-MOUNTED ORGANIC VAPOR CANISTER. ANY APPROPRIATE ESCAPE-TYPE SELF-CONTAINED BREATHING APPARATUS.
FOR FIREFIGHTING AND OTHER IMMEDIATELY DANGEROUS TO LIFE OR HEALTH CONDITIONS:
SELF-CONTAINED BREATHING APPARATUS WITH FULL FACEPIECE OPERATED IN PRESSURE-DEMAND OR OTHER POSITIVE PRESSURE MODE.
SUPPLIED-AIR RESPIRATOR WITH FULL FACEPIECE AND OPERATED IN PRESSURE-DEMAND OR OTHER POSITIVE PRESSURE MODE IN COMBINATION WITH AN AUXILIARY SELF-CONTAINED BREATHING APPARATUS OPERATED IN PRESSURE-DEMAND OR OTHER POSITIVE PRESSURE MODE.

CLOTHING: EMPLOYEE MUST WEAR APPROPRIATE PROTECTIVE (IMPERVIOUS) CLOTHING AND EQUIPMENT TO PREVENT REPEATED OR PROLONGED SKIN CONTACT WITH THIS SUBSTANCE.

GLOVES: EMPLOYEE MUST WEAR APPROPRIATE PROTECTIVE GLOVES TO PREVENT CONTACT WITH THIS SUBSTANCE.

EYE PROTECTION: EMPLOYEE MUST WEAR SPLASH-PROOF OR DUST-RESISTANT SAFETY GOGGLES TO PREVENT EYE CONTACT WITH THIS SUBSTANCE.

EMERGENCY EYE WASH: WHERE THERE IS ANY POSSIBILITY THAT AN EMPLOYEE'S EYES MAY BE EXPOSED TO THIS SUBSTANCE, THE EMPLOYER SHOULD PROVIDE AN EYE WASH FOUNTAIN WITHIN THE IMMEDIATE WORK AREA FOR EMERGENCY USE.

AUTHORIZED BY- OCCUPATIONAL HEALTH SERVICES, INC.
CREATION DATE: 10/04/89 ***REVISION DATE:*** 05/07/90

MATERIAL SAFETY DATA SHEET

OCCUPATIONAL HEALTH SERVICES, INC.
AGRICULTURE AND PESTICIDE DIVISION
450 SEVENTH AVENUE, SUITE 2407
NEW YORK, NEW YORK 10123
1-800-445-MSDS OR (212) 967-1100

EMERGENCY CONTACT:
JOHN S. BRANSFORD, JR. (615) 292-1180

SUBSTANCE IDENTIFICATION

CAS-NUMBER 71-55-6

SUBSTANCE: METHYL CHLOROFORM

TRADE NAMES/SYNONYMS: 1,1,1-TRICHLOROETHANE; ALPHA-TRICHLOROETHANE; AEROTHENE TT; METHYLTRICHLOROMETHANE; METHYLCHLOROFORM; TRICHLOROMETHYLMETHANE; TRICHLOROETHANE; ETHANE, 1,1,1-TRICHLOROETHANE; CHLORTEN; 1,1,1-TRICHLORETHANE; TRICHLOROETHANE 111 DEGREASE COLD/VAPOR (ASHLAND); ST-1000A CLEANER (STRESSCOAT); BLACO-THANE (BARON-BLAKESLEE); PERM ETHANE DG (DETREX CHEMICALS); SAFETY SOLVENT (LOCTITE CORPORATION); ACTIVATOR 711, 702, 703 (LOCTITE CORPORATION); STCC 4941176; RCRA U226; UN 2831; C2H3CL3; PST14370

CHEMICAL FAMILY: HALOGEN COMPOUND, ALIPHATIC

MOLECULAR FORMULA: C-H3-C-CL3

MOLECULAR WEIGHT: 133.40

CERCLA RATINGS (SCALE 0-3): HEALTH=2 FIRE=1 REACTIVITY=0 PERSISTENCE=3

NFPA RATINGS (SCALE 0-4): HEALTH=2 FIRE=1 REACTIVITY=0

COMPONENTS AND CONTAMINANTS

COMPONENT: METHYL CHLOROFORM ***PERCENT:*** 100.0
CAS# 71-55-6

OTHER CONTAMINANTS: NONE

EXPOSURE LIMITS: METHYL CHLOROFORM (1,1,1-TRICHLOROETHANE): 350 PPM (1900 MG/M3) OSHA TWA; 450 PPM (2450 MG/M3) OSHA STEL 350 PPM (1900 MG/M3) ACGIH TWA; 450 PPM (2450 MG/M3) ACGIH STEL 350 PPM NIOSH RECOMMENDED 15 MINUTE CEILING
1000 POUNDS CERCLA SECTION 103 REPORTABLE QUANTITY SUBJECT TO SARA SECTION 313 ANNUAL TOXIC CHEMICAL RELEASE REPORTING

PHYSICAL DATA

DESCRIPTION: CLEAR, COLORLESS LIQUID WITH A MILD CHLOROFORM-LIKE ODOR.

BOILING POINT: 165 F (74 C) ***MELTING POINT:*** -26 F (-32 C)

SPECIFIC GRAVITY: 1.3390 ***VISCOSITY:*** 0.858 CPS @ 20 C

VAPOR PRESSURE: 100 MMHG @ 20 C

EVAPORATION RATE: (BUTYL ACETATE=1)5.0

SOLUBILITY IN WATER: 0.078% @ 25 C ***ODOR THRESHOLD:*** 44-100 PPM

VAPOR DENSITY: 4.55

SOLVENT SOLUBILITY: SOLUBLE IN ACETONE, BENZENE, CHLOROFORM, METHANOL, ETHANOL, CARBON DISULFIDE, ETHER, CARBON TETRACHLORIDE, N-HEPTANE.

FIRE AND EXPLOSION DATA

FIRE AND EXPLOSION HAZARD: SLIGHT FIRE HAZARD WHEN EXPOSED TO HEAT OR FLAME.

UPPER EXPLOSIVE LIMIT: 12.5% ***LOWER EXPLOSIVE LIMIT:*** 7.5%

AUTOIGNITION TEMP.: 998 F (537 C)

FIREFIGHTING MEDIA: DRY CHEMICAL, CARBON DIOXIDE OR HALON (1987 EMERGENCY RESPONSE GUIDEBOOK, DOT P 5800.4).
FOR LARGER FIRES, USE WATER SPRAY, FOG OR STANDARD FOAM (1987 EMERGENCY RESPONSE GUIDEBOOK, DOT P 5800.4).

FIREFIGHTING: STAY AWAY FROM STORAGE TANK ENDS. COOL CONTAINERS EXPOSED TO FLAMES WITH WATER FROM SIDE UNTIL WELL AFTER FIRE IS OUT (1987 EMERGENCY RESPONSE GUIDEBOOK, DOT P 5800.4, GUIDE PAGE 74).
EXTINGUISH USING AGENTS FOR SURROUNDING FIRE. COOL FIRE-EXPOSED CONTAINERS WITH FLOODING AMOUNTS OF WATER APPLIED FROM AS FAR A

DISTANCE AS POSSIBLE. DO NOT ALLOW RUN-OFF WATER INTO SEWERS AND WATER SOURCES. AVOID BREATHING VAPORS.

TRANSPORTATION DATA

DEPARTMENT OF TRANSPORTATION HAZARD CLASSIFICATION 49 CFR 172.101: ORM-A

DEPARTMENT OF TRANSPORTATION LABELING REQUIREMENTS 49 CFR 172.101 AND SUBPART E: NONE

DEPARTMENT OF TRANSPORTATION PACKAGING REQUIREMENTS: 49 CFR 173.605 EXCEPTIONS: 49 CFR 173.505

TOXICITY

METHYL CHLOROFORM (1,1,1-TRICHLOROETHANE): IRRITATION DATA: 450 PPM/8 HOURS EYE-MAN; 5 GM/12 DAYS INTERMITTENT SKIN-RABBIT MILD; 20 MG/24 HOURS SKIN-RABBIT MODERATE; 100 MG EYE-RABBIT MILD; 2 MG/24 HOURS EYE-RABBIT SEVERE. TOXICITY DATA: 27 GM/M3/10 MINUTES INHALATION-MAN LCLO; 350 PPM INHALATION-MAN TCLO; 200 PPM/4 HOURS INHALATION-MAN TCLO; 920 PPM/70 MINUTES INHALATION-HUMAN TCLO; 18000 PPM/4 HOURS INHALATION-RAT LC50; 3911 PPM/2 HOURS INHALATION-MOUSE LC50; 24400 MG/M3 INHALATION-CAT LC50; 15800 MG/KG SKIN-RABBIT LD50 (EPA-600/8-82-003F, 1984); 1 GM/KG SKIN-RABBIT LDLO; 670 MG/KG ORAL-HUMAN TDLO; 10300 MG/KG ORAL-RAT LD50; 11240 MG/KG ORAL-MOUSE LD50; 5660 MG/KG ORAL-RABBIT LD50; 9470 MG/KG ORAL-GUINEA PIG LD50; 750 MG/KG ORAL-DOG LD50; 16 GM/KG SUBCUTANEOUS-MOUSE LD50; 500 MG/KG SUBCUTANEOUS-RABBIT LDLO; 95 MG/KG INTRAVENOUS-DOG LDLO; 3593 MG/KG INTRAPERITONEAL-RAT LD50; 3636 MG/KG INTRAPERITONEAL-MOUSE LD50; 3100 MG/KG INTRAPERITONEAL-DOG LD50; MUTAGENIC DATA (RTECS); REPRODUCTIVE EFFECTS DATA (RTECS). CARCINOGEN STATUS: ANIMAL INADEQUATE EVIDENCE (IARC GROUP-3). LOCAL EFFECTS: IRRITANT- INHALATION, SKIN, EYE. ACUTE TOXICITY LEVEL: SLIGHTLY TOXIC BY INHALATION, DERMAL ABSORPTION AND INGESTION. TARGET EFFECTS: CENTRAL NERVOUS SYSTEM DEPRESSANT. POISONING MAY ALSO AFFECT THE HEART AND POSSIBLY LIVER AND KIDNEYS. AT INCREASED RISK FROM EXPOSURE: PERSONS WITH PRE-EXISTING SKIN DISORDERS, LIVER DISEASE OR CARDIOVASCULAR DISEASE. ADDITIONAL DATA: ALCOHOL MAY POTENTIATE BOTH CARDIAC AND HEPATIC TOXICITY. EPINEPHRINE OR OTHER STIMULANTS MAY INDUCE VENTRICULAR ARRHYTHMIAS.

HEALTH EFFECTS AND FIRST AID

INHALATION: METHYL CHLOROFORM (1,1,1-TRICHLOROETHANE): IRRITANT/NARCOTIC. 1000 PPM IMMEDIATELY DANGEROUS TO LIFE OR HEALTH. **ACUTE EXPOSURE-** EXPOSURE TO 500 PPM FOR 60 MINUTES SHOULD CAUSE NO EFFECT EXCEPT FOR A DISTINCTIVE ODOR WHILE 900-1000 PPM FOR 20 MINUTES MAY CAUSE MILD RESPIRATORY TRACT IRRITATION AND PROMPT BUT MINIMAL IMPAIRMENT OF EQUILIBRIUM WHICH MAY BE ACCOMPANIED BY HEADACHE, LASSITUDE AND ATAXIA. IMPAIRED PERFORMANCE OF BEHAVIORAL TESTS WAS ALSO REPORTED AT 1000 PPM. HIGHER LEVELS OF 2000-5000 PPM MAY CAUSE INCOORDINATION, ANESTHESIA, LOSS OF CONSCIOUSNESS, COMA AND DEATH. EXCESSIVE CONCENTRATIONS OF 10,000 PPM MAY CAUSE DEATH DUE TO RESPIRATORY OR CARDIAC FAILURE. CARDIAC SENSITIZATION MAY BE A CONTRIBUTING FACTOR. OTHER EFFECTS MAY INCLUDE NAUSEA, VOMITING, DROWSINESS, CONVULSIONS, FALL OF BLOOD PRESSURE LIVER AND KIDNEY DAMAGE, BRADYCARDIA AND BLOOD CLOTTING CHANGES. **CHRONIC EXPOSURE-** NO ADVERSE EFFECTS RELATED TO EXPOSURE WERE REPORTED IN VOLUNTEERS EXPOSED TO 500 PPM FOR 7 HOURS A DAY FOR 5 DAYS, OR IN WORKERS EXPOSED TO 200 PPM FOR SEVERAL MONTHS TO 6 YEARS. EXPOSURE OF ANIMALS FOR 3 MONTHS AT CONCENTRATIONS FROM 1000 TO 10,000 PPM CAUSED SYMPTOMS OF CENTRAL NERVOUS SYSTEM DEPRESSION AND SOME PATHOLOGICAL CHANGES IN THE LIVERS AND LUNGS OF SOME SPECIES. REPRODUCTIVE EFFECTS HAVE BEEN REPORTED IN ANIMALS.

FIRST AID- REMOVE FROM EXPOSURE AREA TO FRESH AIR IMMEDIATELY. IF BREATHING HAS STOPPED, GIVE ARTIFICIAL RESPIRATION. MAINTAIN AIRWAY AND BLOOD PRESSURE AND ADMINISTER OXYGEN IF AVAILABLE. KEEP AFFECTED PERSON WARM AND AT REST. TREAT SYMPTOMATICALLY AND SUPPORTIVELY. ADMINISTRATION OF OXYGEN SHOULD BE PERFORMED BY QUALIFIED PERSONNEL. GET MEDICAL ATTENTION IMMEDIATELY.

SKIN CONTACT: METHYL CHLOROFORM (1,1,1-TRICHLOROETHANE): IRRITANT. **ACUTE EXPOSURE-** DIRECT CONTACT MAY CAUSE IRRITATION AND REDNESS. VAPORS ARE POORLY ABSORBED, BUT THE LIQUID, ESPECIALLY IF CONFINED UNDER AN IMPERMEABLE BARRIER MAY BE ABSORBED TO SOME EXTENT. THIS ALONE IS UNLIKELY TO RESULT IN TOXIC EFFECTS, BUT MAY ADD TO THE EFFECTS OF INHALATION EXPOSURE. **CHRONIC EXPOSURE-** REPEATED SKIN CONTACT MAY PRODUCE A DRY, SCALY, FISSURED DERMATITIS DUE TO THE DEFATTING PROPERTIES OF THE LIQUID, AND POSSIBLY BURNS.

FIRST AID- REMOVE CONTAMINATED CLOTHING AND SHOES IMMEDIATELY. WASH AFFECTED AREA WITH SOAP OR MILD DETERGENT AND LARGE AMOUNTS OF WATER UNTIL NO EVIDENCE OF CHEMICAL REMAINS (APPROXIMATELY 15-20 MINUTES). GET MEDICAL ATTENTION IMMEDIATELY.

EYE CONTACT: METHYL CHLOROFORM (1,1,1-TRICHLOROETHANE): IRRITANT. **ACUTE EXPOSURE-** EXPOSURE TO 500 PPM MAY CAUSE IRRITATION AND REDNESS. DIRECT CONTACT WITH THE LIQUID MAY CAUSE TEMPORARY INJURY WITH COMPLETE RECOVERY EXPECTED IN 48 HOURS. DIRECT APPLICATION TO THE EYES OF RABBITS HAS CAUSED CONJUNCTIVAL IRRITATION, BUT NO CORNEAL DAMAGE. **CHRONIC EXPOSURE-** REPEATED OR PROLONGED CONTACT MAY CAUSE CONJUNCTIVITIS.

FIRST AID- WASH EYES IMMEDIATELY WITH LARGE AMOUNTS OF WATER OR NORMAL SALINE, OCCASIONALLY LIFTING UPPER AND LOWER LIDS, UNTIL NO EVIDENCE OF CHEMICAL REMAINS (APPROXIMATELY 15-20 MINUTES). GET MEDICAL ATTENTION IMMEDIATELY.

INGESTION: METHYL CHLOROFORM (1,1,1-TRICHLOROETHANE): NARCOTIC. **ACUTE EXPOSURE-** MAY CAUSE NAUSEA, VOMITING, DIARRHEA, GASTROINTESTINAL DISTURBANCES AND ABDOMINAL PAIN FOLLOWED BY CENTRAL NERVOUS SYSTEM DEPRESSION WITH HEADACHE, DIZZINESS, WEAKNESS, INCOORDINATION, MENTAL CONFUSION AND UNCONSCIOUSNESS. DEATH MAY OCCUR FROM CHRONIC RESPIRATORY FAILURE. OTHER SYMPTOMS AS DESCRIBED IN ACUTE INHALATION MAY ALSO OCCUR. MYOCARDIAL SENSITIZATION TO EPINEPHRINE AND SUBSEQUENT DEATH DUE TO CARDIAC ARREST MAY OCCUR. ASPIRATION MAY RESULT IN PULMONARY EDEMA OR CHEMICAL PNEUMONITIS. **CHRONIC EXPOSURE-** REPRODUCTIVE EFFECTS HAVE BEEN REPORTED IN ANIMALS.

FIRST AID- TREAT SYMPTOMATICALLY AND SUPPORTIVELY. GET MEDICAL ATTENTION AND ADVICE ON WHETHER TO USE GASTRIC LAVAGE. EXTREME CARE MUST BE TAKEN TO PREVENT ASPIRATION. A CUFFED ENDOTRACHEAL TUBE USED BY QUALIFIED MEDICAL PERSONNEL MIGHT BE ADVISABLE. KEEP HEAD LOWER THAN HIPS TO PREVENT ASPIRATION SHOULD VOMITING OCCUR.

ANTIDOTE: NO SPECIFIC ANTIDOTE. TREAT SYMPTOMATICALLY AND SUPPORTIVELY.

REACTIVITY

REACTIVITY: SLOWLY DECOMPOSES OVER TIME YIELDING HYDROGEN CHLORIDE. AN INHIBITOR MAY BE ADDED TO SCAVENGE THE ACID THAT IS FORMED AND PREVENT CORROSION TO METALS. WATER MAY REACT WITH THE INHIBITOR AND ALLOW THE NATURAL DECOMPOSITION TO OCCUR.

INCOMPATIBILITIES: METHYL CHLOROFORM (1,1,1-TRICHLOROETHANE): ACETONE: EXOTHERMIC REACTION. ALKALI (STRONG): POSSIBLE VIOLENT REACTION. ALUMINUM AND ALLOYS: MAY DECOMPOSE VIOLENTLY. BARIUM: FIRE AND EXPLOSION HAZARD. MAGNESIUM: VIOLENT DECOMPOSITION WITH EVOLUTION OF HYDROGEN CHLORIDE. METALS (POWDERED): FIRE AND EXPLOSION HAZARD. NITROGEN TETROXIDE: FORMS EXPLOSIVE MIXTURE. OXIDIZERS (STRONG): POSSIBLE VIOLENT REACTION. OXYGEN (GAS): POSSIBLE EXPLOSION WHEN HEATED @ 100 C. OXYGEN (LIQUID): POSSIBLE VIOLENT EXPLOSION. POTASH: FORMS FLAMMABLE OR EXPLOSIVE PRODUCT. POTASSIUM AND ALLOYS: FORMS SHOCK-SENSITIVE MIXTURE. POTASSIUM HYDROXIDE: FORMATION OF SPONTANEOUSLY FLAMMABLE PRODUCT. RUBBER, PLASTICS, COATINGS: MAY BE ATTACKED. SODIUM AND ALLOYS: FIRE AND EXPLOSION HAZARD. SODIUM HYDROXIDE: FORMS SPONTANEOUSLY FLAMMABLE PRODUCT. SODIUM-POTASSIUM ALLOY: POSSIBLE EXPLOSION. TIN AND ALLOYS: INCOMPATIBLE. ZINC AND ALLOYS: INCOMPATIBLE.

DECOMPOSITION: THERMAL DECOMPOSITION PRODUCTS MAY INCLUDE TOXIC AND CORROSIVE FUMES OF CHLORIDES, TOXIC FUMES OF PHOSGENE AND CHLOROACETYLENES, AND OXIDES OF CARBON.

POLYMERIZATION: HAZARDOUS POLYMERIZATION HAS NOT BEEN REPORTED TO OCCUR UNDER NORMAL TEMPERATURES AND PRESSURES.

STORAGE AND DISPOSAL

OBSERVE ALL FEDERAL, STATE AND LOCAL REGULATIONS WHEN STORING OR DISPOSING OF THIS SUBSTANCE. FOR ASSISTANCE, CONTACT THE DISTRICT DIRECTOR OF THE ENVIRONMENTAL PROTECTION AGENCY.

STORAGE

STORE IN A COOL, DRY, WELL-VENTILATED LOCATION, AWAY FROM ANY AREA WHERE THE FIRE HAZARD MAY BE ACUTE (NFPA 49, HAZARDOUS CHEMICALS DATA, 1975).

STORE AWAY FROM INCOMPATIBLE SUBSTANCES.

DISPOSAL

DISPOSAL MUST BE IN ACCORDANCE WITH STANDARDS APPLICABLE TO GENERATORS OF HAZARDOUS WASTE, 40CFR 262. EPA HAZARDOUS WASTE NUMBER U226.

CONDITIONS TO AVOID

MAY BURN BUT DOES NOT IGNITE READILY. CONTAINER MAY EXPLODE IN HEAT OF FIRE.

SPILL AND LEAK PROCEDURES

SOIL SPILL: DIG A HOLDING AREA SUCH AS A PIT, POND OR LAGOON TO CONTAIN SPILL AND DIKE SURFACE FLOW USING BARRIER OF SOIL, SANDBAGS, FOAMED POLYURETHANE OR FOAMED CONCRETE. ABSORB LIQUID MASS WITH FLY ASH OR CEMENT POWDER.

WATER SPILL: LIMIT SPILL MOTION AND DISPERSION WITH NATURAL BARRIERS OR OIL SPILL CONTROL BOOMS.
TRAP SPILLED MATERIAL AT BOTTOM IN DEEP WATER POCKETS, EXCAVATED HOLDING AREAS OR WITHIN SAND BAG BARRIERS.
USE SUCTION HOSES TO REMOVE TRAPPED SPILL MATERIAL.
THE CALIFORNIA SAFE DRINKING WATER AND TOXIC ENFORCEMENT ACT OF 1986 (PROPOSITION 65) PROHIBITS CONTAMINATING ANY KNOWN SOURCE OF DRINKING WATER WITH SUBSTANCES KNOWN TO CAUSE CANCER AND/OR REPRODUCTIVE TOXICITY.

OCCUPATIONAL SPILL: SHUT OFF IGNITION SOURCES. STOP LEAK IF YOU CAN DO IT WITHOUT RISK. FOR SMALL LIQUID SPILLS, TAKE UP WITH SAND, EARTH OR OTHER ABSORBENT MATERIAL. FOR LARGER SPILLS, DIKE FAR AHEAD OF SPILL FOR LATER DISPOSAL. NO SMOKING, FLAMES OR FLARES IN HAZARD AREA! KEEP UNNECESSARY PEOPLE AWAY.
REPORTABLE QUANTITY (RQ): 1000 POUNDS THE SUPERFUND AMENDMENTS AND REAUTHORIZATION ACT (SARA) SECTION 304 REQUIRES THAT A RELEASE EQUAL TO OR GREATER THAN THE REPORTABLE QUANTITY FOR THIS SUBSTANCE BE IMMEDIATELY REPORTED TO THE LOCAL EMERGENCY PLANNING COMMITTEE AND THE STATE EMERGENCY RESPONSE COMMISSION (40 CFR 355.40). IF THE RELEASE OF THIS SUBSTANCE IS REPORTABLE UNDER CERCLA SECTION 103, THE NATIONAL RESPONSE CENTER MUST BE NOTIFIED IMMEDIATELY AT (800) 424-8802 OR (202) 426-2675 IN THE METROPOLITAN WASHINGTON, D.C. AREA (40 CFR 302.6).

PROTECTIVE EQUIPMENT

VENTILATION: PROVIDE LOCAL EXHAUST OR PROCESS ENCLOSURE VENTILATION TO MEET PUBLISHED EXPOSURE LIMITS.

RESPIRATOR: THE FOLLOWING RESPIRATORS AND MAXIMUM USE CONCENTRATIONS ARE RECOMMENDATIONS BY THE U.S. DEPARTMENT OF HEALTH AND HUMAN SERVICES, NIOSH POCKET GUIDE TO CHEMICAL HAZARDS; NIOSH CRITERIA DOCUMENTS OR BY THE U.S. DEPARTMENT OF LABOR, 29 CFR 1910 SUBPART Z. THE SPECIFIC RESPIRATOR SELECTED MUST BE BASED ON CONTAMINATION LEVELS FOUND IN THE WORK PLACE, MUST NOT EXCEED THE WORKING LIMITS OF THE RESPIRATOR AND BE JOINTLY APPROVED BY THE NATIONAL INSTITUTE FOR OCCUPATIONAL SAFETY AND HEALTH AND THE MINE SAFETY AND HEALTH ADMINISTRATION (NIOSH-MSHA).
METHYL CHLOROFORM (1,1,1-TRICHLOROETHANE):
1000 PPM- ANY SUPPLIED-AIR RESPIRATOR WITH FULL FACEPIECE. ANY SELF-CONTAINED BREATHING APPARATUS WITH FULL FACEPIECE.
ESCAPE- ANY AIR-PURIFYING FULL FACEPIECE RESPIRATOR (GAS MASK) WITH A CHIN-STYLE OR FRONT OR BACK-MOUNTED ORGANIC VAPOR CANISTER. ANY APPROPRIATE ESCAPE-TYPE SELF-CONTAINED BREATHING APPARATUS.
FOR FIREFIGHTING AND OTHER IMMEDIATELY DANGEROUS TO LIFE OR HEALTH CONDITIONS:
SELF-CONTAINED BREATHING APPARATUS WITH FULL FACEPIECE OPERATED IN PRESSURE-DEMAND OR OTHER POSITIVE PRESSURE MODE.
SUPPLIED-AIR RESPIRATOR WITH FULL FACEPIECE AND OPERATED IN PRESSURE-DEMAND OR OTHER POSITIVE PRESSURE MODE IN COMBINATION WITH AN AUXILIARY SELF-CONTAINED BREATHING APPARATUS OPERATED IN PRESSURE-DEMAND OR OTHER POSITIVE PRESSURE MODE.

CLOTHING: EMPLOYEE MUST WEAR APPROPRIATE PROTECTIVE (IMPERVIOUS) CLOTHING AND EQUIPMENT TO PREVENT ANY POSSIBILITY OF SKIN CONTACT WITH THIS SUBSTANCE.

GLOVES: EMPLOYEE MUST WEAR APPROPRIATE PROTECTIVE GLOVES TO PREVENT CONTACT WITH THIS SUBSTANCE.

EYE PROTECTION: EMPLOYEE MUST WEAR SPLASH-PROOF OR DUST-RESISTANT SAFETY GOGGLES AND A FACESHIELD TO PREVENT CONTACT WITH THIS SUBSTANCE.
EMERGENCY WASH FACILITIES: WHERE THERE IS ANY POSSIBILITY THAT AN EMPLOYEE'S EYES AND/OR SKIN MAY BE EXPOSED TO THIS SUBSTANCE, THE EMPLOYER SHOULD PROVIDE AN EYE WASH FOUNTAIN AND QUICK DRENCH SHOWER WITHIN THE IMMEDIATE WORK AREA FOR EMERGENCY USE.

AUTHORIZED BY- OCCUPATIONAL HEALTH SERVICES, INC.
CREATION DATE: 10/04/89 ***REVISION DATE:*** 07/12/90

MATERIAL SAFETY DATA SHEET

OCCUPATIONAL HEALTH SERVICES, INC.
AGRICULTURE AND PESTICIDE DIVISION
450 SEVENTH AVENUE, SUITE 2407
NEW YORK, NEW YORK 10123
1-800-445-MSDS OR (212) 967-1100

EMERGENCY CONTACT:
JOHN S. BRANSFORD, JR. (615) 292-1180

SUBSTANCE IDENTIFICATION

CAS-NUMBER 8022-00-2

SUBSTANCE: **METHYL DEMETON**

TRADE NAMES/SYNONYMS: PHOSPHOROTHIOIC ACID, O-(2-(ETHYLTHIO)ETHYL) O,O-DIMETHYL ESTER, MIXTURE WITH S-(2-(ETHYLTHIO)ETHYL) O,O-DIMETHYL PHOSPHOROTHIOATE; PHOSPHOROTHIOIC ACID, O-(2-(ETHYLTHIO)ETHYL) O,O-DIMETHYL ESTER, MIXTURE WITH S-(2-(ETHYLTHIO)ETHYL) O,O-DIMETHYL ESTER; O,O-DIMETHYL 2-ETHYLTHIOETHYL PHOSPHOROTHIOATE; O,O-DIMETHYL 2-ETHYLMERCAPTOETHYL THIOPHOSPHATE; BAYER 21/116; DEMETON METHYL; METASYSTOX; METASYSTOX FORTE; METHYLMERCAPTOPHOS; METHYL SYSTOX; PST14438

CHEMICAL FAMILY: ORGANOPHOSPHATE

MOLECULAR FORMULA: C6-H15-O3-P-S2

MOLECULAR WEIGHT: 230.30

CERCLA RATINGS (SCALE 0-3): HEALTH=3 FIRE=0 REACTIVITY=0 PERSISTENCE=0

NFPA RATINGS (SCALE 0-4): HEALTH=4 FIRE=0 REACTIVITY=0

COMPONENTS AND CONTAMINANTS

COMPONENT: O,O-DIMETHYL-O-2-(ETHYLTHIO)ETHYL PHOSPHOROTHIOATE ***PERCENT:*** 70

COMPONENT: O,O-DIMETHYL-S-2-(ETHYLTHIO)ETHYL PHOSPHOROTHIOATE ***PERCENT:*** 30

EXPOSURE LIMITS: METHYL DEMETON: 0.5 MG/M3 OSHA TWA (SKIN) 0.5 MG/M3 ACGIH TWA (SKIN)

PHYSICAL DATA

DESCRIPTION: LIGHT YELLOW, OILY LIQUID ***BOILING POINT:*** 165 F (74 C) @ 0.15 MMHG

SPECIFIC GRAVITY: 1.20 ***EVAPORATION RATE:*** NOT AVAILABLE

SOLUBILITY IN WATER: SLIGHTLY SOLUBLE

SOLVENT SOLUBILITY: SOLUBLE IN MOST ORGANIC SOLVENTS

FIRE AND EXPLOSION DATA

FIRE AND EXPLOSION HAZARD: NEGLIGIBLE FIRE HAZARD WHEN EXPOSED TO HEAT OR FLAME.

FIREFIGHTING MEDIA: DRY CHEMICAL, CARBON DIOXIDE, HALON, WATER SPRAY OR STANDARD FOAM (1987 EMERGENCY RESPONSE GUIDEBOOK, DOT P 5800.4). FOR LARGER FIRES, USE WATER SPRAY, FOG OR STANDARD FOAM (1987 EMERGENCY RESPONSE GUIDEBOOK, DOT P 5800.4).

FIREFIGHTING: MOVE CONTAINERS FROM FIRE AREA IF POSSIBLE. FIGHT FIRE FROM MAXIMUM DISTANCE. STAY AWAY FROM STORAGE TANK ENDS. DIKE FIRE CONTROL WATER FOR LATER DISPOSAL. DO NOT SCATTER MATERIAL (1987 EMERGENCY RESPONSE GUIDEBOOK, DOT P 5800.4, GUIDE PAGE 55). EXTINGUISH ONLY IF FLOW CAN BE STOPPED; USE FLOODING AMOUNTS OF WATER AS FOG, SOLID STREAMS MAY BE INEFFECTIVE. COOL CONTAINERS WITH FLOODING AMOUNTS OF WATER FROM AS FAR A DISTANCE AS POSSIBLE. USE WATER SPRAY TO ABSORB TOXIC VAPORS. AVOID BREATHING TOXIC VAPORS; KEEP UPWIND. CONSIDER EVACUATION OF DOWNWIND AREA IF MATERIAL IS LEAKING.

TRANSPORTATION DATA

DEPARTMENT OF TRANSPORTATION HAZARD CLASSIFICATION 49 CFR 172.101: POISON B
DEPARTMENT OF TRANSPORTATION LABELING REQUIREMENTS 49 CFR 172.101 AND SUBPART E: POISON
DEPARTMENT OF TRANSPORTATION PACKAGING REQUIREMENTS: 49 CFR 173.346 EXCEPTIONS: 49 CFR 173.345

TOXICITY

METHYL DEMETON: TOXICITY DATA: 20 MG/M3/4 HOURS INHALATION-CAT LCLO; 100 MG/KG SKIN-RABBIT LDLO; 300 MG/KG SKIN-RAT LD50; 65 MG/KG ORAL-RAT LD50; 26 MG/KG ORAL-MOUSE LD50; 30 MG/KG ORAL-CAT LDLO; 150 MG/KG ORAL-RABBIT LDLO; 80 MG/KG UNREPORTED-MAMMAL LD50. CARCINOGEN STATUS: NONE. ACUTE TOXICITY LEVEL: TOXIC BY DERMAL ABSORPTION AND INGESTION. TARGET EFFECTS: CHOLINESTERASE INHIBITOR. POISONING MAY AFFECT THE NERVOUS SYSTEM.* AT INCREASED RISK FROM EXPOSURE: PERSONS WITH RESPIRATORY AILMENTS, RECENT EXPOSURE TO CHOLINESTERASE INHIBITORS OR IMPAIRED CHOLINESTERASE PRODUCTION, OR LIVER

MALFUNCTION.* ADDITIONAL DATA: MAY CROSS THE PLACENTA. HIGH ENVIRONMENTAL TEMPERATURES ORP EXPOSURE OF THE CHEMICAL TO VISIBLE OR ULTRAVIOLET LIGHT MAY ENHANCE THE TOXICITY. INTERACTIONS WITH MEDICATIONS MAY OCCUR.* * MAY BE BASED ON GENERAL INFORMATION ON ORGANOPHOSPHATES.

HEALTH EFFECTS AND FIRST AID

INHALATION: METHYL DEMETON: SEE INFORMATION ON ORGANOPHOSPHATES. ORGANOPHOSPHATES: CHOLINESTERASE INHIBITOR. **ACUTE EXPOSURE-** WHEN INHALED, THE FIRST EFFECTS OF CHOLINESTERASE INHIBITORS ARE USUALLY RESPIRATORY AND MAY INCLUDE NASAL HYPEREMIA AND WATERY DISCHARGE, COUGH, CHEST DISCOMFORT, DYSPNEA, AND WHEEZING DUE TO INCREASED BRONCHIAL SECRETIONS AND BRONCHOCONSTRICTION. IF SUFFICIENT AMOUNTS ARE ABSORBED, OTHER SYSTEMIC EFFECTS MAY BEGIN WITHIN A FEW MINUTES OR BE DELAYED FOR UP TO 12 HOURS. SYMPTOMS MAY INCLUDE PALLOR, NAUSEA, VOMITING, DIARRHEA, ABDOMINAL CRAMPS, HEADACHE, DIZZINESS, OCULAR PAIN, BLURRED VISION, MIOSIS OR IN SOME CASES, ESPECIALLY INITIALLY, MYDRIASIS, LACRIMATION, SALIVATION, SWEATING, AND CONFUSION. OTHER REPORTED CENTRAL NERVOUS SYSTEM OR NEUROMUSCULAR EFFECTS MAY INCLUDE ATAXIA, SLURRED SPEECH, AREFLEXIA, WEAKNESS, FATIGUE, FASCICULATIONS, TWITCHING, TREMORS POSSIBLY OF THE TONGUE AND EYELIDS, AND EVENTUALLY PARALYSIS OF THE EXTREMITIES AND POSSIBLY OF THE RESPIRATORY MUSCLES. IN SEVERE CASES THERE MAY ALSO BE INVOLUNTARY DEFECATION AND URINATION, CYANOSIS, PSYCHOSIS, HYPERGLYCEMIA, ACUTE PANCREATITIS, CARDIAC IRREGULARITIES, PULMONARY EDEMA, UNCONSCIOUSNESS, CONVULSIONS, AND COMA. DEATH IS PRIMARILY DUE TO RESPIRATORY FAILURE, ALTHOUGH CARDIOVASCULAR EFFECTS INCLUDING CARDIAC ARREST MAY ALSO BE IMPLICATED. LONG TERM SEQUELAE ARE RARE BUT MAY INCLUDE NEUROPSYCHIATRIC DISORDERS AND MYOPATHY WITH MUSCLE TENDERNESS. SOME ORGANOPHOSPHATES MAY CAUSE A DELAYED NEUROPATHY BEGINNING 1-4 WEEKS AFTER AN ACUTE EXPOSURE WHICH MAY OR MAY NOT HAVE CAUSED ACUTE CHOLINERGIC EFFECTS. NUMBNESS, TINGLING, WEAKNESS AND CRAMPING BEGINNING SYMMETRICALLY IN THE LOWER LIMBS MAY PROGRESS TO ATAXIA AND PARALYSIS. IN SEVERE CASES, UPPER LIMB INVOLVEMENT IS POSSIBLE AND FLACCID PARALYSIS MAY PROGRESS TO SPASTIC PARALYSIS WITH EXAGGERATED REFLEXES. IMPROVEMENT MAY OCCUR OVER MONTHS TO YEARS, BUT SOME RESIDUAL IMPAIRMENT USUALLY REMAINS. **CHRONIC EXPOSURE-** REPEATED OR PROLONGED EXPOSURE MAY RESULT IN THE EFFECTS OF ACUTE EXPOSURE INCLUDING THE DELAYED NEUROPATHY. OTHER EFFECTS REPORTED IN WORKERS REPEATEDLY EXPOSED INCLUDE IMPAIRED MEMORY AND CONCENTRATION, ACUTE PSYCHOSIS, SEVERE DEPRESSIONS, IRRITABILTY, CONFUSION, APATHY, EMOTIONAL LABILITY, SOCIAL WITHDRAWAL, CONFUSION, HEADACHE, SPEECH DIFFICULTIES, DELAYED REACTION TIMES, SPATIAL DISORIENTATION, NIGHTMARES, SLEEPWALKING, AND DROWSINESS OR INSOMNIA. AN INFLUENZA-LIKE CONDITION WITH HEADACHE, NAUSEA, WEAKNESS, ANOREXIA AND MALAISE HAS ALSO BEEN REPORTED.

FIRST AID- REMOVE FROM EXPOSURE AREA TO FRESH AIR IMMEDIATELY. IF BREATHING HAS STOPPED, GIVE ARTIFICIAL RESPIRATION. MAINTAIN AIRWAY AND BLOOD PRESSURE AND ADMINISTER OXYGEN IF AVAILABLE. KEEP AFFECTED PERSON WARM AND AT REST. TREAT SYMPTOMATICALLY AND SUPPORTIVELY. ADMINISTRATION OF OXYGEN SHOULD BE PERFORMED BY QUALIFIED PERSONNEL. GET MEDICAL ATTENTION IMMEDIATELY.

SKIN CONTACT: METHYL DEMETON: TOXIC. SEE INFORMATION ON ORGANOPHOSPHATES.
ORGANOPHOSPHATES: CHOLINESTERASE INHIBITOR. **ACUTE EXPOSURE-** LOCALIZED SWEATING AND FASCICULATIONS MAY OCCUR AT THE SITE OF CONTACT. IF SUFFICIENT AMOUNTS ARE ABSORBED, OTHER EFFECTS OF CHOLINESTERASE INHIBITION AS DESCRIBED IN ACUTE INHALATION MAY OCCUR. SYMPTOMS MAY BE DELAYED 2-3 HOURS, BUT USUALLY NO MORE THAN 12 HOURS. THE RATE OF ABSORPTION IS INCREASED BY THE PRESENCE OF DERMATITIS OR HIGH AMBIENT TEMPERATURES. DELAYED NEUROPATHY IS ALSO POSSIBLE. **CHRONIC EXPOSURE-** REPEATED OR PROLONGED EXPOSURE MAY CAUSE EFFECTS AS DESCRIBED IN ACUTE EXPOSURE. SOME ORGANOPHOSPHATES MAY CAUSE SENSITIZATION.

FIRST AID- REMOVE CONTAMINATED CLOTHING IMMEDIATELY. WASH CONTAMINATED AREAS WITH SOAP AND WATER FOLLOWED BY ALCOHOL (ARENA, POISONING, 4TH ED.). EMERGENCY PERSONNEL SHOULD WEAR GLOVES AND AVOID CONTAMINATION. TREAT RESPIRATORY DIFFICULTY WITH ARTIFICIAL RESPIRATION. GET MEDICAL ATTENTION IMMEDIATELY.

EYE CONTACT: METHYL DEMETON:
SEE INFORMATION ON ORGANOPHOSPHATES.
ORGANOPHOSPHATES: CHOLINESTERASE INHIBITOR. **ACUTE EXPOSURE-** DIRECT CONTACT MAY CAUSE PAIN, HYPEREMIA, LACRIMATION, TWITCHING OF THE EYELIDS, MIOSIS, AND CILIARY MUSCLE SPASM WITH LOSS OF ACCOMODATION, BLURRED OR DIMMED VISION AND BROWACHE. SOMETIMES MYDRIASIS MAY OCCUR INSTEAD OF MIOSIS. WITH SUFFICIENT EXPOSURE, OTHER SYMPTOMS OF CHOLINESTERASE INHIBITION AS DESCRIBED IN ACUTE INHALATION MAY OCCUR. **CHRONIC EXPOSURE-** REPEATED OR PROLONGED EXPOSURE MAY CAUSE EFFECTS AS DESCRIBED IN ACUTE EXPOSURE. SOME COMPOUNDS HAVE CAUSED TOXIC EFFECTS ON THE CRYSTALLINE LENS, CONJUNCTIVAL THICKENING AND OBSTRUCTION OF THE NASOLACRIMAL CANALS WHEN USED AS MIOTIC EYEDROPS.

FIRST AID- IRRIGATE EYES WITH WATER OR SALINE SOLUTION. IF SYMPTOMS OF POISONING OCCUR, TREAT RESPIRATORY DIFFICULTY WITH ARTIFICIAL RESPIRATION AND OXYGEN. OBSERVE PATIENT FOR AT LEAST 24-36 HOURS (GOSSELIN, CLINICAL TOXICOLOGY OF COMMERCIAL PRODUCTS, 5TH ED.). GET MEDICAL ATTENTION IMMEDIATELY. OXYGEN SHOULD BE ADMINISTERED BY QUALIFIED MEDICAL PERSONNEL.

INGESTION: METHYL DEMETON: TOXIC. SEE INFORMATION ON ORGANOPHOSPHATES. ORGANOPHOSPHATES: CHOLINESTERASE INHIBITOR. **ACUTE EXPOSURE-** WHEN INGESTED, THE FIRST EFFECTS MAY BE NAUSEA, VOMITING, ANOREXIA, ABDOMINAL CRAMPS AND DIARRHEA. GASTROINTESTINAL ABSORPTION MAY CAUSE SYMPTOMS OF CHOLINESTERASE INHIBITION AS DESCRIBED IN ACUTE INHALATION. SYMPTOMS MAY BEGIN WITHIN MINUTES OR BE DELAYED FOR HOURS. DELAYED EFFECTS INCLUDING NEUROPATHY MAY ALSO OCCUR. **CHRONIC EXPOSURE-** REPEATED INGESTION MAY CAUSE EFFECTS AS DESCRIBED IN ACUTE EXPOSURE.

FIRST AID- IF PERSON IS ALERT AND RESPIRATION IS NOT DEPRESSED, GIVE SYRUP OF IPECAC FOLLOWED BY WATER (IF VOMITING OCCURS, KEEP HEAD BELOW HIPS TO PREVENT ASPIRATION). IF CONSCIOUSNESS LEVEL DECLINES OR VOMITING HAS NOT OCCURRED IN 15 MINUTES EMPTY STOMACH BY GASTRIC LAVAGE WITH THE AID OF CUFFED ENDOTRACHEAL TUBE USING ISOTONIC SALINE OR 5% SODIUM BICARBONATE FOLLOW WITH ACTIVATED CHARCOAL. ESTABLISH AND MAINTAIN AIRWAY. TREAT RESPIRATORY DIFFICULTY WITH ARTIFICIAL RESPIRATION AND OXYGEN. DO NOT GIVE MORPHINE, AMINOPHYLLINE, PHENOTHIAZINES, RESERPINE, FUROSEMIDE, OR ETHACRYNIC ACID (MORGAN, RECOGNITION AND MANAGEMENT OF PESTICIDE POISONINGS, 3RD ED.). TREAT SYMPTOMATICALLY AND SUPPORTIVELY. ADMINISTRATION OF OXYGEN AND LAVAGE MUST BE PERFORMED BY QUALIFIED MEDICAL PERSONNEL. GET MEDICAL ATTENTION IMMEDIATELY.

ANTIDOTE: THE FOLLOWING ANTIDOTE(S) HAVE BEEN RECOMMENDED. HOWEVER, THE DECISION AS TO WHETHER THE SEVERITY OF POISONING REQUIRES ADMINISTRATION OF ANY ANTIDOTE AND ACTUAL DOSE REQUIRED SHOULD BE MADE BY QUALIFIED MEDICAL PERSONNEL.
FOR CHOLINESTERASE INHIBITORS: ESTABLISH CLEAR AIRWAY AND TISSUE OXYGENATION BY ASPIRATION OF SECRETIONS, AND IF NECESSARY, BY ASSISTED PULMONARY VENTILATION WITH OXYGEN. IMPROVE TISSUE OXYGENATION AS MUCH AS POSSIBLE BEFORE ADMINISTERING ATROPINE TO MINIMIZE THE RISK OF VENTRICULAR FIBRILLATION. ADMINISTER ATROPINE SULFATE INTRAVENOUSLY, OR INTRAMUSCULARLY IF IV INJECTION IS NOT POSSIBLE. IN MODERATELY SEVERE POISONING ADMINISTER ATROPINE SULFATE, 0.4-2.0 MG REPEATED EVERY 15 MINUTES UNTIL ATROPINIZATION IS ACHIEVED (TACHYCARDIA, FLUSHING, DRY MOUTH, MYDRIASIS). MAINTAIN ATROPINIZATION BY REPEATED DOSES FOR 2-12 HOURS, OR LONGER, DEPENDING ON THE SEVERITY OF POISONING. THE APPEARANCE OF RALES IN THE LUNG BASES, MIOSIS, SALIVATION, NAUSEA, BRADYCARDIA, ARE ALL INDICATIONS OF INADEQUATE ATROPINIZATION. SEVERELY POISONED INDIVIDUALS MAY EXHIBIT REMARKABLE TOLERANCE TO ATROPINE; TWO OR MORE TIMES THE DOSAGES SUGGESTED ABOVE MAY BE NEEDED. PERSONS NOT POISONED OR ONLY SLIGHTLY POISONED, HOWEVER, MAY DEVELOP SIGNS OF ATROPINE TOXICITY FROM SUCH LARGE DOSAGES: FEVER, MUSCLE FIBRILLATIONS, AND DELIRIUM ARE THE MAIN SIGNS OF ATROPINE TOXICITY. IF THESE SIGNS APPEAR WHILE THE PATIENT IS FULLY ATROPINIZED, ATROPINE ADMINISTRATION SHOULD BE DISCONTINUED, AT LEAST TEMPORARILY. OBSERVE TREATED PATIENTS CLOSELY AT LEAST 24 HOURS TO INSURE THAT SYMPTOMS (POSSIBLY PULMONARY EDEMA) DO NOT RECUR AS ATROPINIZATION WEARS OFF. IN VERY SEVERE POISONINGS, METABOLIC DISPOSITION OF TOXICANT MAY REQUIRE SEVERAL HOURS OR DAYS DURING WHICH ATROPINIZATION MUST BE MAINTAINED. MARKEDLY LOWER LEVELS OF URINARY METABOLITES INDICATE THAT ATROPINE DOSAGE CAN BE TAPERED OFF. AS DOSAGE IS REDUCED, CHECK THE LUNG BASES FREQUENTLY FOR RALES. IF RALES ARE HEARD OR OTHER SYMPTOMS RETURN, RE-ESTABLISH ATROPINIZATION PROMPTLY (MORGAN, RECOGNITION AND MANAGEMENT OF PESTICIDE POISONINGS, 3RD ED.). ADMINISTRATION OF ANTIDOTE MUST BE PERFORMED BY QUALIFIED MEDICAL PERSONNEL.
IN CASES OF SEVERE POISONING BY ORGANOPHOSPHATE PESTICIDES IN WHICH RESPIRATORY DEPRESSION, MUSCLE WEAKNESS AND TWITCHINGS ARE SEVERE, GIVE PRALIDOXIME (PROTOPAM-AYERST, 2-PAM), 1.0 GRAM INTRAVENOUSLY AT NO MORE THAN 0.5 GRAM PER MINUTE. DOSAGE OF PRALIDOXIME MAY BE REPEATED IN 1-2 HOURS, THEN AT 10-12 HOUR INTERVALS IF NEEDED. IN VERY SEVERE POISONINGS, DOSAGE RATES MAY BE DOUBLED. TREATMENT WITH

PRALIDOXIME WILL BE MOST EFFECTIVE IF GIVEN WITHIN THIRTY-SIX HOURS AFTER POISONING (MORGAN, RECOGNITION AND MANAGEMENT OF PESTICIDE POISONINGS, 3RD ED.). ANTIDOTE SHOULD BE ADMINISTERED BY QUALIFIED MEDICAL PERSONNEL.

REACTIVITY

REACTIVITY: STABLE UNDER NORMAL TEMPERATURES AND PRESSURES.

INCOMPATIBILITIES: METHYL DEMETON: ALKALI: HYDROLYZE. STRONG OXIDIZERS: INCOMPATIBLE.

DECOMPOSITION: THERMAL DECOMPOSITION MAY RELEASE TOXIC OXIDES OF PHOSPHORUS AND SULFUR.

POLYMERIZATION: HAZARDOUS POLYMERIZATION HAS NOT BEEN REPORTED TO OCCUR UNDER NORMAL TEMPERATURES AND PRESSURES.

STORAGE AND DISPOSAL

OBSERVE ALL FEDERAL, STATE AND LOCAL REGULATIONS WHEN STORING OR DISPOSING OF THIS SUBSTANCE. FOR ASSISTANCE, CONTACT THE DISTRICT DIRECTOR OF THE ENVIRONMENTAL PROTECTION AGENCY.

STORAGE

STORE IN ACCORDANCE WITH 40 CFR 165 RECOMMENDED PROCEDURES FOR THE DISPOSAL AND STORAGE OF PESTICIDES AND PESTICIDE CONTAINERS.
STORE AWAY FROM INCOMPATIBLE SUBSTANCES.

DISPOSAL

DISPOSAL MUST BE IN ACCORDANCE WITH 40 CFR 165 RECOMMENDED PROCEDURES FOR THE DISPOSAL AND STORAGE OF PESTICIDES AND PESTICIDE CONTAINERS.

CONDITIONS TO AVOID

NONE REPORTED.

SPILL AND LEAK PROCEDURES

OCCUPATIONAL SPILL: DO NOT TOUCH SPILLED MATERIAL. STOP LEAK IF YOU CAN DO IT WITHOUT RISK. USE WATER SPRAY TO REDUCE VAPORS. FOR SMALL SPILLS, TAKE UP WITH SAND OR OTHER ABSORBENT MATERIAL AND PLACE INTO CONTAINERS FOR LATER DISPOSAL. FOR SMALL DRY SPILLS, WITH A CLEAN SHOVEL PLACE MATERIAL INTO CLEAN, DRY CONTAINERS AND COVER. MOVE CONTAINERS FROM SPILL AREA. FOR LARGER SPILLS, DIKE FAR AHEAD OF SPILL FOR LATER DISPOSAL. KEEP UNNECESSARY PEOPLE AWAY. ISOLATE HAZARD AREA AND DENY ENTRY. VENTILATE CLOSED SPACES BEFORE ENTERING.

PROTECTIVE EQUIPMENT

VENTILATION: PROCESS ENCLOSURE RECOMMENDED TO MEET PUBLISHED EXPOSURE LIMITS.

RESPIRATOR: THE FOLLOWING RESPIRATORS ARE RECOMMENDED BASED ON INFORMATION FOUND IN THE PHYSICAL DATA, TOXICITY AND HEALTH EFFECTS SECTIONS. THEY ARE RANKED IN ORDER FROM MINIMUM TO MAXIMUM RESPIRATORY PROTECTION. THE SPECIFIC RESPIRATOR SELECTED MUST BE BASED ON CONTAMINATION LEVELS FOUND IN THE WORK PLACE, MUST NOT EXCEED THE WORKING LIMITS OF THE RESPIRATOR AND BE JOINTLY APPROVED BY THE NATIONAL INSTITUTE FOR OCCUPATIONAL SAFETY AND HEALTH AND THE MINE SAFETY AND HEALTH ADMINISTRATION (NIOSH-MSHA).
TYPE 'C' SUPPLIED-AIR RESPIRATOR WITH A FULL FACEPIECE OPERATED IN PRESSURE-DEMAND OR OTHER POSITIVE PRESSURE MODE OR WITH A FULL FACEPIECE, HELMET OR HOOD OPERATED IN CONTINOUS-FLOW MODE.
SELF-CONTAINED BREATHING APPARATUS WITH A FULL FACEPIECE OPERATED IN PRESSURE-DEMAND OR OTHER POSITIVE PRESSURE MODE.
FOR FIREFIGHTING AND OTHER IMMEDIATELY DANGEROUS TO LIFE OR HEALTH CONDITIONS:
SELF-CONTAINED BREATHING APPARATUS WITH FULL FACEPIECE OPERATED IN PRESSURE-DEMAND OR OTHER POSITIVE PRESSURE MODE.
SUPPLIED-AIR RESPIRATOR WITH FULL FACEPIECE AND OPERATED IN PRESSURE-DEMAND OR OTHER POSITIVE PRESSURE MODE IN COMBINATION WITH AN AUXILIARY SELF-CONTAINED BREATHING APPARATUS OPERATED IN PRESSURE-DEMAND OR OTHER POSITIVE PRESSURE MODE.

CLOTHING: EMPLOYEE MUST WEAR APPROPRIATE PROTECTIVE (IMPERVIOUS) CLOTHING AND EQUIPMENT TO PREVENT ANY POSSIBILITY OF SKIN CONTACT WITH THIS SUBSTANCE.

GLOVES: EMPLOYEE MUST WEAR APPROPRIATE PROTECTIVE GLOVES TO PREVENT CONTACT WITH THIS SUBSTANCE.

EYE PROTECTION: EMPLOYEE MUST WEAR SPLASH-PROOF OR DUST-RESISTANT SAFETY GOGGLES AND A FACESHIELD TO PREVENT CONTACT WITH THIS SUBSTANCE.
EMERGENCY WASH FACILITIES: WHERE THERE IS ANY POSSIBILITY THAT AN EMPLOYEE'S EYES AND/OR SKIN MAY BE EXPOSED TO THIS SUBSTANCE, THE EMPLOYER SHOULD PROVIDE AN EYE WASH FOUNTAIN AND QUICK DRENCH SHOWER WITHIN THE IMMEDIATE WORK AREA FOR EMERGENCY USE.

AUTHORIZED BY- OCCUPATIONAL HEALTH SERVICES, INC.
CREATION DATE: 10/04/89 ***REVISION DATE:*** 05/04/90

MATERIAL SAFETY DATA SHEET

OCCUPATIONAL HEALTH SERVICES, INC.
AGRICULTURE AND PESTICIDE DIVISION
450 SEVENTH AVENUE, SUITE 2407
NEW YORK, NEW YORK 10123
1-800-445-MSDS OR (212) 967-1100

EMERGENCY CONTACT:
JOHN S. BRANSFORD, JR. (615) 292-1180

SUBSTANCE IDENTIFICATION

CAS-NUMBER 78-93-3

SUBSTANCE: METHYL ETHYL KETONE

TRADE NAMES/SYNONYMS: BUTANONE; 2-BUTANONE; ETHYL METHYL KETONE; METHYL ACETONE; 3-BUTANONE; MEK; SCOTCH-GRIP (R) BRAND SOLVENT #3 (3M); STOP, SHIELD, PEEL REDUCER (PYRAMID PLASTICS, INC.); STABOND C-THINNER (STABOND CORP.); OATEY CLEANER (OATEY COMPANY); RCRA U159; STCC 4904243; UN 1193; C4H8O; PST14460

CHEMICAL FAMILY: KETONE, ALIPHATIC

MOLECULAR FORMULA: C-H3-C-H2-C-O-C-H3

MOLECULAR WEIGHT: 72.12

CERCLA RATINGS (SCALE 0-3): HEALTH=3 FIRE=3 REACTIVITY=0 PERSISTENCE=0

NFPA RATINGS (SCALE 0-4): HEALTH=1 FIRE=3 REACTIVITY=0

COMPONENTS AND CONTAMINANTS

COMPONENT: METHYL ETHYL KETONE ***PERCENT:*** 100
CAS# 78-93-3

OTHER CONTAMINANTS: NONE

EXPOSURE LIMITS: METHYL ETHYL KETONE: 200 PPM (590 MG/M3) OSHA TWA; 300 PPM (885 MG/M3) OSHA STEL 200 PPM (590 MG/M3) ACGIH TWA; 300 PPM (885 MG/M3) ACGIH STEL 200 PPM (590 MG/M3) NIOSH RECOMMENDED 10 HOUR TWA 5000 POUNDS CERCLA SECTION 103 REPORTABLE QUANTITY SUBJECT TO SARA SECTION 313 ANNUAL TOXIC CHEMICAL RELEASE REPORTING

PHYSICAL DATA

DESCRIPTION: COLORLESS LIQUID WITH AN ACETONE-LIKE ODOR.

BOILING POINT: 176 F (80 C) ***MELTING POINT:*** -123 F (-86 C)

SPECIFIC GRAVITY: 0.8054 ***VISCOSITY:*** 0.40 CPS @ 25 C

VAPOR PRESSURE: 100 MMHG @ 25 C ***EVAPORATION RATE:*** (ETHER=1) 2.7

SOLUBILITY IN WATER: 27.5% ***ODOR THRESHOLD:*** 10 PPM ***VAPOR DENSITY:*** 2.5

SOLVENT SOLUBILITY: ALCOHOL, ETHER, BENZENE, ACETONE, OILS

FIRE AND EXPLOSION DATA

FIRE AND EXPLOSION HAZARD: DANGEROUS FIRE HAZARD WHEN EXPOSED TO HEAT OR FLAME.
VAPORS ARE HEAVIER THAN AIR AND MAY TRAVEL A CONSIDERABLE DISTANCE TO A SOURCE OF IGNITION AND FLASH BACK.
VAPOR-AIR MIXTURES ARE EXPLOSIVE ABOVE FLASH POINT.

FLASH POINT: 16 F (-9 C) (CC) ***UPPER EXPLOSIVE LIMIT:*** 11.4% @ 200 F

LOWER EXPLOSIVE LIMIT: 1.4% @ 200 F ***AUTOIGNITION TEMP.:*** 759 F (404 C)

FLAMMABILITY CLASS(OSHA): IB

FIREFIGHTING MEDIA: DRY CHEMICAL, CARBON DIOXIDE, HALON, WATER SPRAY OR ALCOHOL FOAM (1987 EMERGENCY RESPONSE GUIDEBOOK, DOT P 5800.4).
FOR LARGER FIRES, USE WATER SPRAY, FOG OR ALCOHOL FOAM (1987 EMERGENCY RESPONSE GUIDEBOOK, DOT P 5800.4).
ALCOHOL FOAM (NFPA 325M, FIRE HAZARD PROPERTIES OF FLAMMABLE LIQUIDS, GASES, AND VOLATILE SOLIDS, 1984).

FIREFIGHTING: MOVE CONTAINER FROM FIRE AREA IF POSSIBLE. COOL FIRE-EXPOSED CONTAINERS WITH WATER FROM SIDE UNTIL WELL AFTER FIRE IS OUT. STAY AWAY FROM STORAGE TANK ENDS. FOR MASSIVE FIRE IN STORAGE AREA, USE UNMANNED HOSE HOLDER OR MONITOR NOZZLES, ELSE WITHDRAW FROM AREA AND LET FIRE BURN. WITHDRAW IMMEDIATELY IN CASE OF RISING SOUND FROM VENTING SAFETY DEVICE OR ANY DISCOLORATION OF STORAGE TANK DUE TO FIRE (1987 EMERGENCY RESPONSE GUIDEBOOK, DOT P 5800.4, GUIDE PAGE 26). EXTINGUISH ONLY IF FLOW CAN BE STOPPED; USE WATER IN FLOODING AMOUNTS AS FOG, SOLID STREAMS MAY NOT BE EFFECTIVE. COOL CONTAINERS WITH FLOODING QUANTITIES OF WATER. APPLY FROM AS FAR A DISTANCE AS POSSIBLE. AVOID BREATHING VAPORS, KEEP UPWIND.

WATER MAY BE INEFFECTIVE (NFPA 325M, FIRE HAZARD PROPERTIES OF FLAMMABLE LIQUIDS, GASES, AND VOLATILE SOLIDS, 1984)

TRANSPORTATION DATA

DEPARTMENT OF TRANSPORTATION HAZARD CLASSIFICATION 49 CFR 172.101: FLAMMABLE LIQUID
DEPARTMENT OF TRANSPORTATION LABELING REQUIREMENTS 49 CFR 172.101 AND SUBPART E: FLAMMABLE LIQUID DEPARTMENT OF TRANSPORTATION PACKAGING REQUIREMENTS: 49 CFR 173.119 EXCEPTIONS: 49 CFR 173.118

TOXICITY

METHYL ETHYL KETONE: IRRITATION DATA: 500 MG/24 HOURS SKIN-RABBIT MODERATE; 402 MG/24 HOURS SKIN-RABBIT MILD; 13,780 UG/24 HOURS OPEN SKIN-RABBIT MILD; 350 PPM EYE-HUMAN; 80 MG EYE-RABBIT. TOXICITY DATA: 100 PPM/5 MINUTES INHALATION-HUMAN TCLO; 23,500 MG/M3/8 HOURS INHALATION-RAT LC50; 40 GM/M3/2 HOURS INHALATION-MOUSE LC50; 38 GM/M3 INHALATION-MAMMAL LC50; 6480 MG/KG SKIN-RABBIT LD50; 2737 MG/KG ORAL-RAT LD50; 4050 MG/KG ORAL-MOUSE LD50; 607 MG/KG INTRAPERITONEAL-RAT LD50; 616 MG/KG INTRAPERITONEAL-MOUSE LD50; 2000 MG/KG INTRAPERITONEAL-GUINEA PIG LDLO; MUTAGENIC DATA (RTECS); REPRODUCTIVE EFFECTS DATA (RTECS). CARCINOGEN STATUS: NONE. LOCAL EFFECTS: IRRITANT-INHALATION, SKIN AND EYES. ACUTE TOXICITY LEVEL: MODERATELY TOXIC BY INHALATION AND INGESTION; SLIGHTLY TOXIC BY DERMAL ABSORPTION. TARGET EFFECTS: CENTRAL NERVOUS SYSTEM DEPRESSANT. AT INCREASED RISK FROM EXPOSURE: PERSONS WITH A HISTORY OF CHRONIC SKIN OR RESPIRATORY DISEASE. ADDITIONAL DATA: METHYL ETHYL KETONE MAY ENHANCE THE NEUROTOXIC EFFECTS OF N-HEXANE OR METHYL N-BUTYL KETONE, AND PREDISPOSE THE LIVER TO INJURY FROM HEPATOTOXINS. INTERACTIONS WITH ALCOHOL MAY OCCUR. ONE STUDY SHOWS AN INCREASED RISK OF LEUKEMIA FOR CHILDREN WHOSE FATHERS HAD OCCUPATIONAL EXPOSURE TO METHYL ETHYL KETONE AFTER THE BIRTH OF THE CHILD.

HEALTH EFFECTS AND FIRST AID

INHALATION: METHYL ETHYL KETONE: IRRITANT/NARCOTIC. 3000 PPM IMMEDIATELY DANGEROUS TO LIFE OR HEALTH. **ACUTE EXPOSURE-** INHALATION OF VAPOR CONCENTRATIONS OF 100-200 PPM CAUSED MILD NOSE AND THROAT IRRITATION; 300-500 PPM WAS OBJECTIONABLE AND CAUSED THROAT IRRITATION, HEADACHE, AND NAUSEA; 3,300 PPM WAS MODERATELY IRRITATING; AND MOMENTARY EXPOSURE TO 33,000 AND 100,000 PPM PRODUCED INTOLERABLE IRRITATION OF THE NOSE AND THROAT. WORKERS EXPOSED TO 90-270 PPM/4 HOURS SHOWED SHORTENED TIME ESTIMATIONS IN MEN AND INCREASED THE VARIATION IN TIME ESTIMATION TESTS IN WOMEN. EXTREMELY HIGH CONCENTRATIONS MAY CAUSE COUGHING AND SHORTNESS OF BREATH, AND CENTRAL NERVOUS SYSTEM DEPRESSION WITH HEADACHE, LIGHTHEADEDNESS, NAUSEA, VOMITING, DIZZINESS, INCOORDINATION, AND NARCOSIS. GUINEA PIGS EXPOSED TO 10,000 PPM DEVELOPED IRRITATION RAPIDLY, AND NARCOSIS DEVELOPED AFTER 5 HOURS; 33,000 PPM/200 MINUTES PRODUCED NARCOSIS AND DEATH; AND 100,000 PPM/55 MINUTES PRODUCED NARCOSIS AFTER 10 MINUTES. ODOR AND IRRITATION ARE GENERALLY SUFFICENT TO PREVENT OVEREXPOSURE. METHYL ETHYL KETONE MAY ENHANCE THE NEUROTOXIC EFFECTS OF N-HEXANE AND METHYL N-BUTYL KETONE. **CHRONIC EXPOSURE-** WORKERS EXPOSED VIA INHALATION AND SKIN CONTACT TO 300-600 PPM COMPLAINED OF NUMBNESS IN THE ARMS AND FINGERS; ONE WORKER COMPLAINED OF NUMBNESS IN THE LEGS AND A TENDENCY FOR THEM TO GIVE WAY. SEVERAL CASES OF PERIPHERAL NEUROPATHY, INCLUDING OPTIC NEURITIS DUE TO METABOLITES, HAVE BEEN REPORTED IN WORKERS. PERIPHERAL NEUROPATHY HAS NOT BEEN INDUCED IN ANIMALS BY METHYL ETHYL KETONE ALONE. HOWEVER, IT HAS BEEN DEMONSTRATED IN HUMANS AND ANIMALS THAT METHYL ETHYL KETONE POTENTIATES THE NEUROTOXIC EFFECTS OF N-HEXANE AND METHYL N-BUTYL KETONE. EXPOSURE RELATED EFFECTS ON THE LIVER AND BRAIN HAVE BEEN REPORTED IN RATS AT EXPOSURES UP TO 5000 PPM. OFFSPRING OF PREGNANT RATS EXPOSED TO 1,000 OR 3,000 PPM EXHIBITED ACAUDIA, IMPERFORATE ANUS, BRACHYGNATHIA, AND FETAL DEVELOPMENTAL RETARDATION. THE SAME INVESTIGATORS REPEATED THE STUDY AND 3,000 PPM PRODUCED SLIGHT MATERNAL TOXICITY AND SLIGHT FETOTOXICITY, BUT NO EMBRYO TOXICITY OR TERATOGENICITY WERE SEEN.

FIRST AID- REMOVE FROM EXPOSURE AREA TO FRESH AIR IMMEDIATELY. IF BREATHING HAS STOPPED, PERFORM ARTIFICIAL RESPIRATION. KEEP PERSON WARM AND AT REST. TREAT SYMPTOMATICALLY AND SUPPORTIVELY. GET MEDICAL ATTENTION IMMEDIATELY.

SKIN CONTACT: METHYL ETHYL KETONE: IRRITANT. **ACUTE EXPOSURE-** CONTACT WITH LIQUID OR CONCENTRATED VAPORS MAY CAUSE DERMATITIS. DIRECT CONTACT WITH THE LIQUID MAY CAUSE EXTREME THICKENING OF THE FINGERNAILS, WITH PERMANENT DESTRUCTION OF THE NAIL BEDS. APPLICATION OF A LETHAL DOSE TO RABBIT SKIN PRODUCED ERYTHEMA, EDEMA, AND NECROSIS. LIVER AND INTESTINAL CONGESTION WERE ALSO REPORTED. **CHRONIC EXPOSURE-** REPEATED OR PROLONGED EXPOSURE MAY CAUSE DEFATTING OF THE SKIN PRODUCING A DRY, SCALY, FISSURED DERMATITIS. WORKERS EXPOSED VIA SKIN CONTACT AND INHALATION TO 300-600 PPM COMPLAINED OF NUMBNESS IN THE ARMS AND FINGERS; ONE WORKER COMPLAINED OF NUMBNESS IN THE LEGS AND A TENDENCY FOR THEM TO GIVE WAY. REPEATED CONTACT WITH METHYL ETHYL KETONE AND TETRAHYDROFURAN PRODUCED BILATERAL PARESTHESIA AND LOSS OF MUSCLE STRENGTH IN A WORKER. SYMPTOMS PERSISTED FOR 2 MONTHS FOLLOWING CESSATION OF EXPOSURE.

FIRST AID- REMOVE CONTAMINATED CLOTHING AND SHOES IMMEDIATELY. WASH AFFECTED AREA WITH SOAP OR MILD DETERGENT AND LARGE AMOUNTS OF WATER UNTIL NO EVIDENCE OF CHEMICAL REMAINS (APPROXIMATELY 15-20 MINUTES). GET MEDICAL ATTENTION IMMEDIATELY.

EYE CONTACT: METHYL ETHYL KETONE: IRRITANT. **ACUTE EXPOSURE-** EXPOSURE TO VAPOR CONCENTRATIONS OF 200 PPM CAUSED IRRITATION AND A BURNING SENSATION OF THE EYELIDS; 3,300 PPM PRODUCED MODERATE IRRITATION; AND 10,000 PPM WAS INTOLERABLE TO HUMANS. DIRECT CONTACT OF THE LIQUID WITH THE EYES CAUSED PAINFUL IRRITATION AND TEMPORARY CORNEAL INJURY IN RABBITS, GRADED 5 ON A SCALE OF 1-10. IN GUINEA PIGS, 10% VAPOR FOR 30 MINUTES CAUSED TEMPORARY CORNEAL OPACITY WHICH CLEARED WITHIN 8 DAYS. **CHRONIC EXPOSURE-** REPEATED OR PROLONGED EXPOSURE MAY CAUSE CONJUNCTIVITIS. A CASE OF OPTIC NEURITIS WAS REPORTED AS A RESULT OF SYSTEMIC POISONING FOLLOWING REPEATED INHALATION EXPOSURE.

FIRST AID- WASH EYES IMMEDIATELY WITH LARGE AMOUNTS OF WATER OR NORMAL SALINE, OCCASIONALLY LIFTING UPPER AND LOWER LIDS, UNTIL NO EVIDENCE OF CHEMICAL REMAINS (APPROXIMATELY 15-20 MINUTES). GET MEDICAL ATTENTION IMMEDIATELY.

INGESTION: METHYL ETHYL KETONE: NARCOTIC. **ACUTE EXPOSURE-** INGESTION MAY CAUSE IRRITATION OF THE GASTROINTESTINAL TRACT WITH ABDOMINAL SPASMS, NAUSEA, VOMITING, AND POSSIBLY CENTRAL NERVOUS SYSTEM DEPRESSION, INCLUDING NARCOSIS. ADMINISTRATION OF A LETHAL DOSE TO RATS PRODUCED CONGESTED AND HEMORRHAGIC LUNGS, AND CONGESTION OF THE LIVER, ALIMENTARY TRACT, AND PERITONEAL WALL. ANIMAL STUDIES SHOW THAT METHYL ETHYL KETONE STIMULATES THE HEPATIC DRUG-METABOLIZING SYSTEM AND POTENTIATES THE HEPATOTOXIC AND NEPHROTOXIC EFFECTS OF CHLOROFORM AND THE HEPATOTOXIC EFFECTS OF CARBON TETRACHLORIDE. **CHRONIC EXPOSURE-** NO DATA AVAILABLE.

FIRST AID- IF THE PERSON IS CONSCIOUS AND NOT CONVULSING, INDUCE EMESIS BY GIVING SYRUP OF IPECAC FOLLOWED BY WATER. (IF VOMITING OCCURS KEEP THE HEAD BELOW THE HIPS TO PREVENT ASPIRATION). REPEAT IN 20 MINUTES IF NOT EFFECTIVE INITIALLY. GIVE ACTIVATED CHARCOAL. IN PATIENTS WITH DEPRESSED RESPIRATION OR IF EMESIS IS NOT PRODUCED, PERFORM GASTRIC LAVAGE CAUTIOUSLY (DREISBACH, HANDBOOK OF POISONING, 12TH ED.). TREAT SYMPTOMATICALLY AND SUPPORTIVELY. GASTRIC LAVAGE SHOULD BE PERFORMED BY QUALIFIED MEDICAL PERSONNEL. GET MEDICAL ATTENTION IMMEDIATELY.

ANTIDOTE: NO SPECIFIC ANTIDOTE. TREAT SYMPTOMATICALLY AND SUPPORTIVELY.

REACTIVITY

REACTIVITY: STABLE UNDER NORMAL TEMPERATURES AND PRESSURES.

INCOMPATIBILITIES: METHYL ETHYL KETONE: CHLOROFORM: VIGOROUS, EXOTHERMIC REACTION IN THE PRESENCE OF A BASE. CHLOROSULFONIC ACID: MIXING IN CLOSED CONTAINER MAY RESULT IN INCREASED TEMPERATURE AND PRESSURE. HYDROGEN PEROXIDE, NITRIC ACID: PRODUCES SHOCK AND HEAT SENSITIVE OILY PEROXIDE. ISOPROPANOL: ACCELERATES PEROXIDATION OF THE ALCOHOL PRODUCING AN EXPLOSIVE PRODUCT. OLEUM: MIXING IN CLOSED CONTAINER MAY RESULT IN INCREASED TEMPERATURE AND PRESSURE. OXIDIZERS (STRONG): POSSIBLE FIRE AND EXPLOSION HAZARD. PLASTICS: MAY BE ATTACKED. POTASSIUM TERT-BUTOXIDE: IGNITION REACTION. RESINS: MAY BE ATTACKED. RUBBER: MAY BE ATTACKED.

DECOMPOSITION: THERMAL DECOMPOSITION PRODUCTS MAY INCLUDE TOXIC OXIDES OF CARBON.

POLYMERIZATION: HAZARDOUS POLYMERIZATION HAS NOT BEEN REPORTED TO OCCUR UNDER NORMAL TEMPERATURES AND PRESSURES.

STORAGE AND DISPOSAL

OBSERVE ALL FEDERAL, STATE AND LOCAL REGULATIONS WHEN STORING OR DISPOSING OF THIS SUBSTANCE. FOR ASSISTANCE, CONTACT THE DISTRICT DIRECTOR OF THE ENVIRONMENTAL PROTECTION AGENCY.

****STORAGE****

STORE IN ACCORDANCE WITH 29 CFR 1910.106.
BONDING AND GROUNDING: SUBSTANCES WITH LOW ELECTROCONDUCTIVITY, WHICH MAY BE IGNITED BY ELECTROSTATIC SPARKS, SHOULD BE STORED IN

CONTAINERS WHICH MEET THE BONDING AND GROUNDING GUIDELINES SPECIFIED IN NFPA 77-1983, RECOMMENDED PRACTICE ON STATIC ELECTRICITY.
STORE AWAY FROM INCOMPATIBLE SUBSTANCES.

****DISPOSAL****

DISPOSAL MUST BE IN ACCORDANCE WITH STANDARDS APPLICABLE TO GENERATORS OF HAZARDOUS WASTE, 40CFR 262. EPA HAZARDOUS WASTE NUMBER U159.
METHYL ETHYL KETONE - REGULATORY LEVEL: 200.0 MG/L MATERIALS WHICH CONTAIN THE ABOVE SUBSTANCE AT OR ABOVE THE REGULATORY LEVEL MEET THE EPA CHARACTERISTIC OF TOXICITY, AND MUST BE DISPOSED OF IN ACCORDANCE WITH 40 CFR PART 262. EPA HAZARDOUS WASTE NUMBER D035.

CONDITIONS TO AVOID

AVOID CONTACT WITH HEAT, SPARKS, FLAMES, OR OTHER SOURCES OF IGNITION. VAPORS MAY BE EXPLOSIVE AND POISONOUS; DO NOT ALLOW UNNECESSARY PERSONNEL IN AREA. DO NOT OVERHEAT CONTAINERS; CONTAINERS MAY VIOLENTLY RUPTURE AND TRAVEL A CONSIDERABLE DISTANCE IN HEAT OF FIRE.

SPILL AND LEAK PROCEDURES

SOIL SPILL: DIG HOLDING AREA SUCH AS LAGOON, POND OR PIT FOR CONTAINMENT. ABSORB BULK LIQUID WITH FLY ASH, CEMENT POWDER, SAWDUST, OR COMMERCIAL SORBENTS.

AIR SPILL: APPLY WATER SPRAY TO KNOCK DOWN VAPORS.

WATER SPILL: LIMIT SPILL MOTION AND DISPERSION WITH NATURAL BARRIERS OR OIL SPILL CONTROL BOOMS.
USE SUCTION HOSES TO REMOVE TRAPPED SPILL MATERIAL.

OCCUPATIONAL SPILL: SHUT OFF IGNITION SOURCES. STOP LEAK IF YOU CAN DO IT WITHOUT RISK. USE WATER SPRAY TO REDUCE VAPORS. FOR SMALL SPILLS, TAKE UP WITH SAND OR OTHER ABSORBENT MATERIAL AND PLACE INTO CONTAINERS FOR LATER DISPOSAL. FOR LARGER SPILLS, DIKE FAR AHEAD OF SPILL FOR LATER DISPOSAL. NO SMOKING, FLAMES OR FLARES IN HAZARD AREA. KEEP UNNECESSARY PEOPLE AWAY; ISOLATE HAZARD AREA AND DENY ENTRY.
REPORTABLE QUANTITY (RQ): 5000 POUNDS THE SUPERFUND AMENDMENTS AND REAUTHORIZATION ACT (SARA) SECTION 304 REQUIRES THAT A RELEASE EQUAL TO OR GREATER THAN THE REPORTABLE QUANTITY FOR THIS SUBSTANCE BE IMMEDIATELY REPORTED TO THE LOCAL EMERGENCY PLANNING COMMITTEE AND THE STATE EMERGENCY RESPONSE COMMISSION (40 CFR 355.40). IF THE RELEASE OF THIS SUBSTANCE IS REPORTABLE UNDER CERCLA SECTION 103, THE NATIONAL RESPONSE CENTER MUST BE NOTIFIED IMMEDIATELY AT (800) 424-8802 OR (202) 426-2675 IN THE METROPOLITAN WASHINGTON, D.C. AREA (40 CFR 302.6).

PROTECTIVE EQUIPMENT

VENTILATION: PROVIDE LOCAL EXHAUST OR GENERAL DILUTION VENTILATION TO MEET PUBLISHED EXPOSURE LIMITS. VENTILATION EQUIPMENT MUST BE EXPLOSION-PROOF.

RESPIRATOR: THE FOLLOWING RESPIRATORS AND MAXIMUM USE CONCENTRATIONS ARE RECOMMENDATIONS BY THE U.S. DEPARTMENT OF HEALTH AND HUMAN SERVICES, NIOSH POCKET GUIDE TO CHEMICAL HAZARDS; NIOSH CRITERIA DOCUMENTS OR BY THE U.S. DEPARTMENT OF LABOR, 29 CFR 1910 SUBPART Z.
THE SPECIFIC RESPIRATOR SELECTED MUST BE BASED ON CONTAMINATION LEVELS FOUND IN THE WORK PLACE, MUST NOT EXCEED THE WORKING LIMITS OF THE RESPIRATOR AND BE JOINTLY APPROVED BY THE NATIONAL INSTITUTE FOR OCCUPATIONAL SAFETY AND HEALTH AND THE MINE SAFETY AND HEALTH ADMINISTRATION (NIOSH-MSHA).
METHYL ETHYL KETONE: 1000 PPM- ANY POWERED AIR-PURIFYING RESPIRATOR WITH ORGANIC VAPOR CARTRIDGE. ANY CHEMICAL CARTRIDGE RESPIRATOR WITH FULL FACEPIECE AND ORGANIC VAPOR CARTRIDGE.
3000 PPM- ANY AIR-PURIFYING FULL FACEPIECE RESPIRATOR (GAS MASK) WITH CHIN-STYLE OR FRONT- OR BACK-MOUNTED ORGANIC VAPOR CARTRIDGE. ANY SUPPLIED-AIR RESPIRATOR OPERATED IN CONTINUOUS FLOW MODE. ANY SELF-CONTAINED BREATHING APPARATUS WITH A FULL FACEPIECE. ANY SUPPLIED-AIR RESPIRATOR WITH FULL FACEPIECE.
ESCAPE- ANY AIR-PURIFYING FULL FACEPIECE RESPIRATOR (GAS MASK) WITH CHIN-STYLE OR FRONT- OR BACK-MOUNTED ORGANIC VAPOR CANISTER. ANY APPROPRIATE ESCAPE-TYPE SELF-CONTAINED BREATHING APPARATUS.
FOR FIREFIGHTING AND OTHER IMMEDIATELY DANGEROUS TO LIFE OR HEALTH CONDITIONS:
SELF-CONTAINED BREATHING APPARATUS WITH FULL FACEPIECE OPERATED IN PRESSURE-DEMAND OR OTHER POSITIVE PRESSURE MODE.
SUPPLIED-AIR RESPIRATOR WITH FULL FACEPIECE AND OPERATED IN PRESSURE-DEMAND OR OTHER POSITIVE PRESSURE MODE IN COMBINATION WITH AN AUXILIARY SELF-CONTAINED BREATHING APPARATUS OPERATED IN PRESSURE-DEMAND OR OTHER POSITIVE PRESSURE MODE.

CLOTHING: EMPLOYEE MUST WEAR APPROPRIATE PROTECTIVE (IMPERVIOUS) CLOTHING AND EQUIPMENT TO PREVENT REPEATED OR PROLONGED SKIN CONTACT WITH THIS SUBSTANCE.

GLOVES: EMPLOYEE MUST WEAR APPROPRIATE PROTECTIVE GLOVES TO PREVENT CONTACT WITH THIS SUBSTANCE.

EYE PROTECTION: EMPLOYEE MUST WEAR SPLASH-PROOF OR DUST-RESISTANT SAFETY GOGGLES TO PREVENT EYE CONTACT WITH THIS SUBSTANCE.
EMERGENCY EYE WASH: WHERE THERE IS ANY POSSIBILITY THAT AN EMPLOYEE'S EYES MAY BE EXPOSED TO THIS SUBSTANCE, THE EMPLOYER SHOULD PROVIDE AN EYE WASH FOUNTAIN WITHIN THE IMMEDIATE WORK AREA FOR EMERGENCY USE.

AUTHORIZED BY- OCCUPATIONAL HEALTH SERVICES, INC.
CREATION DATE: 10/04/89 ***REVISION DATE:*** 07/13/90

MATERIAL SAFETY DATA SHEET

OCCUPATIONAL HEALTH SERVICES, INC.
AGRICULTURE AND PESTICIDE DIVISION
450 SEVENTH AVENUE, SUITE 2407
NEW YORK, NEW YORK 10123
1-800-445-MSDS OR (212) 967-1100

EMERGENCY CONTACT:
JOHN S. BRANSFORD, JR. (615) 292-1180

SUBSTANCE IDENTIFICATION

CAS-NUMBER 108-10-1

SUBSTANCE: **METHYL ISOBUTYL KETONE**

TRADE NAMES/SYNONYMS: 2-PENTANONE, 4-METHYL-; HEXONE; ISOBUTYL METHYL KETONE; ISOPROPYL ACETONE; 2-METHYLPROPYL METHYL KETONE; 4-METHYL-2-PENTANONE; MIBK; MIK; UN 1245; RCRA U161; STCC 4909245; C6H12O; PST14550

CHEMICAL FAMILY: KETONE, ALIPHATIC

MOLECULAR FORMULA: (C-H3)2-C-H-C-H2-C-(O)-C-H3

MOLECULAR WEIGHT: 100.16

CERCLA RATINGS (SCALE 0-3): HEALTH=2 FIRE=3 REACTIVITY=0 PERSISTENCE=0

NFPA RATINGS (SCALE 0-4): HEALTH=2 FIRE=3 REACTIVITY=0

COMPONENTS AND CONTAMINANTS

COMPONENT: METHYL ISOBUTYL KETONE ***PERCENT:*** 100.0
CAS# 108-10-1

OTHER CONTAMINANTS: NONE

EXPOSURE LIMITS: METHYL ISOBUTYL KETONE: 50 PPM (205 MG/M3) OSHA TWA; 75 PPM (308 MG/M3) OSHA STEL 50 PPM (205 MG/M3) ACGIH TWA; 75 PPM (308 MG/M3) ACGIH STEL 50 PPM (205 MG/M3) NIOSH RECOMMENDED 10 HOUR TWA 5000 POUNDS CERCLA SECTION 103 REPORTABLE QUANTITY SUBJECT TO SARA SECTION 313 ANNUAL TOXIC CHEMICAL RELEASE REPORTING

PHYSICAL DATA

DESCRIPTION: COLORLESS LIQUID WITH A FAINT, PLEASANT KETONIC AND CAMPHOR ODOR.

BOILING POINT: 242 F (117 C) ***MELTING POINT:*** -119 F (-85 C)

SPECIFIC GRAVITY: 0.7978 ***VOLATILITY:*** 100%

VAPOR PRESSURE: 16 MMHG @ 20C

EVAPORATION RATE: (BUTYL ACETATE=1) 1.6 ***SOLUBILITY IN WATER:*** 2%

ODOR THRESHOLD: 0.3-0.5 PPM ***VAPOR DENSITY:*** 3.5

SOLVENT SOLUBILITY: SOLUBLE IN ALCOHOL, ETHER, BENZENE, ACETONE AND CHLOROFORM.

FIRE AND EXPLOSION DATA

FIRE AND EXPLOSION HAZARD: DANGEROUS FIRE HAZARD WHEN EXPOSED TO HEAT OR FLAME.
VAPORS ARE HEAVIER THAN AIR AND MAY TRAVEL A CONSIDERABLE DISTANCE TO A SOURCE OF IGNITION AND FLASH BACK.
VAPOR-AIR MIXTURES ARE EXPLOSIVE.

FLASH POINT: 64 F (18 C) (CC) ***UPPER EXPLOSIVE LIMIT:*** 7.5%

LOWER EXPLOSIVE LIMIT: 1.4% ***AUTOIGNITION TEMP.:*** 840 F (448 C)

FLAMMABILITY CLASS(OSHA): IB

FIREFIGHTING MEDIA: DRY CHEMICAL, CARBON DIOXIDE, HALON, WATER SPRAY OR ALCOHOL FOAM (1987 EMERGENCY RESPONSE GUIDEBOOK, DOT P 5800.4).
FOR LARGER FIRES, USE WATER SPRAY, FOG OR ALCOHOL FOAM (1987 EMERGENCY RESPONSE GUIDEBOOK, DOT P 5800.4).
ALCOHOL FOAM (NFPA 325M, FIRE HAZARD PROPERTIES OF FLAMMABLE LIQUIDS, GASES, AND VOLATILE SOLIDS, 1984).

FIREFIGHTING: MOVE CONTAINER FROM FIRE AREA IF POSSIBLE. COOL FIRE-EXPOSED CONTAINERS WITH WATER FROM SIDE UNTIL WELL AFTER FIRE IS OUT. STAY AWAY FROM STORAGE TANK ENDS. FOR MASSIVE FIRE IN STORAGE AREA, USE UNMANNED HOSE HOLDER OR MONITOR NOZZLES, ELSE WITHDRAW FROM AREA AND LET FIRE BURN. WITHDRAW IMMEDIATELY IN CASE OF RISING SOUND FROM VENTING SAFETY DEVICE OR ANY DISCOLORATION OF STORAGE TANK DUE TO FIRE (1987 EMERGENCY RESPONSE GUIDEBOOK, DOT P 5800.4, GUIDE PAGE 26). EXTINGUISH ONLY IF FLOW CAN BE STOPPED; USE FLOODING AMOUNTS OF WATER AS A FOG, SOLID STREAMS MAY BE INEFFECTIVE. COOL CONTAINERS WITH FLOODING AMOUNTS OF WATER, APPLY FROM AS FAR A DISTANCE AS POSSIBLE. AVOID BREATHING VAPORS, KEEP UPWIND.
WATER MAY BE INEFFECTIVE (NFPA 325M, FIRE HAZARD PROPERTIES OF FLAMMABLE LIQUIDS, GASES, AND VOLATILE SOLIDS, 1984)

TRANSPORTATION DATA

DEPARTMENT OF TRANSPORTATION HAZARD CLASSIFICATION 49 CFR 172.101: FLAMMABLE LIQUID
DEPARTMENT OF TRANSPORTATION LABELING REQUIREMENTS 49 CFR 172.101 AND SUBPART E: FLAMMABLE LIQUID
DEPARTMENT OF TRANSPORTATION PACKAGING REQUIREMENTS: 49 CFR 173.119 EXCEPTIONS: 49 CFR 173.118

TOXICITY

METHYL ISOBUTYL KETONE: IRRITATION DATA: 500 MG/24 HOURS SKIN-RABBIT MILD; 200 PPM/15 MINUTES EYE-HUMAN; 40 MG EYE-RABBIT SEVERE; 500 MG/24 HOURS EYE-RABBIT MILD. TOXICITY DATA: 23,300 MG/M3 INHALATION-MOUSE LC50; 2080 MG/KG ORAL-RAT LD50; 2671 MG/KG ORAL-MOUSE LD50; 1600 MG/KG ORAL-GUINEA PIG LD50; 400 MG/KG INTRAPERITONEAL-RAT LD50; 268 MG/KG INTRAPERITONEAL-MOUSE LD50; 800 MG/KG INTRAPERITONEAL-GUINEA PIG LD50; 1396 MG/KG UNREPORTED-MAMMAL LD50; REPRODUCTIVE EFFECTS DATA (RTECS). CARCINOGEN STATUS: NONE. LOCAL EFFECTS: IRRITANT- INHALATION, SKIN, EYE. ACUTE TOXICITY LEVEL: MODERATELY TOXIC BY INHALATION, INGESTION. TARGET EFFECTS: CENTRAL NERVOUS SYSTEM DEPRESSANT. POISONING MAY AFFECT THE LIVER AND KIDNEYS. ADDITIONAL DATA: USE OF ALCOHOLIC BEVERAGES MAY ENHANCE THE TOXIC EFFECTS.

HEALTH EFFECTS AND FIRST AID

INHALATION: METHYL ISOBUTYL KETONE: IRRITANT/NARCOTIC. 3000 PPM IMMEDIATELY DANGEROUS TO LIFE OR HEALTH. **ACUTE EXPOSURE-** VAPOR CONCENTRATIONS OF 100 PPM MAY CAUSE HEADACHE AND NAUSEA. EXPOSURE TO 200 PPM IS IRRITATING TO THE EYES AND RESPIRATORY TRACT. EXPOSURE TO CONCENTRATIONS FROM 100 TO 500 PPM MAY ALSO PRODUCE GASTROINTESTINAL EFFECTS SUCH AS NAUSEA, VOMITING, LOSS OF APPETITE AND DIARRHEA. HIGH CONCENTRATIONS MAY CAUSE CENTRAL NERVOUS SYSTEM DEPRESSION WITH LIGHTHEADEDNESS, DIZZINESS, DULLNESS, INCOORDINATION, ATAXIA, UNCONSCIOUSNESS AND COMA. EXPOSURE OF RATS TO 4000 PPM FOR 4 HOURS CAUSED DEATH, WHILE 2000 PPM FOR 4 HOURS WAS NOT LETHAL.
CHRONIC EXPOSURE- WORKERS EXPOSED TO 80-500 PPM FOR 30 MINUTES PER DAY COMPLAINED OF THROAT IRRITATION, WEAKNESS, LOSS OF APPETITE, HEADACHE, NAUSEA, AND VOMITING. FEW WORKERS EXPERIENCED INSOMNIA, SOMNOLENCE, HEARTBURN, INTESTINAL PAIN AND SLIGHT LIVER ENLARGEMENT. RATS EXPOSED TO 100 PPM FOR 90 DAYS RESULTED IN HEAVIER LIVERS AND KIDNEYS WITH REVERSIBLE NEPHROSIS OF THE KIDNEYS. EXPOSURE OF RATS TO 20-30 PPM FOR 4 HOURS PER DAY FOR 4 AND 1/2 MONTHS CAUSED DISTURBANCES IN CONDITIONED REFLEXES, INTERFERENCE WITH DETOXIFYING FUNCTION OF THE LIVER AND ELEVATED EOSINOPHIL COUNT. MINIMAL DISTAL AXONAL CHANGES RESULTED FROM EXPOSURE TO 1500 PPM FOR 5 MONTHS. REPRODUCTIVE EFFECTS HAVE BEEN REPORTED IN ANIMALS.
FIRST AID- REMOVE FROM EXPOSURE AREA TO FRESH AIR IMMEDIATELY. IF BREATHING HAS STOPPED, PERFORM ARTIFICIAL RESPIRATION. KEEP PERSON WARM AND AT REST. TREAT SYMPTOMATICALLY AND SUPPORTIVELY. GET MEDICAL ATTENTION IMMEDIATELY.

SKIN CONTACT: METHYL ISOBUTYL KETONE: IRRITANT. **ACUTE EXPOSURE-** VAPOR MAY CAUSE IRRITATION WITH REDNESS. 500 MG APPLIED TO RABBIT SKIN PRODUCED MODERATE IRRITATION WITH TRANSIENT ERYTHEMA. **CHRONIC EXPOSURE-** REPEATED OR PROLONGED SKIN CONTACT MAY CAUSE DEFATTING OF THE SKIN WITH PRIMARY IRRITATION AND DESQUAMATION. APPLICATION OF 10 ML FOR 7 DAYS TO RABBIT SKIN CAUSED DRYING AND FLAKING.
FIRST AID- REMOVE CONTAMINATED CLOTHING AND SHOES IMMEDIATELY. WASH AFFECTED AREA WITH SOAP OR MILD DETERGENT AND LARGE AMOUNTS OF WATER UNTIL NO EVIDENCE OF CHEMICAL REMAINS (APPROXIMATELY 15-20 MINUTES). GET MEDICAL ATTENTION IMMEDIATELY.

EYE CONTACT: METHYL ISOBUTYL KETONE: IRRITANT. **ACUTE EXPOSURE-** VAPOR CONCENTRATIONS OF 200 PPM ARE IRRITATING TO THE EYES. DIRECT CONTACT WITH LIQUID MAY CAUSE PAIN AND IRRITATION. EXPOSURE OF >1000 PPM TO GUINEA PIGS CAUSED SEVERE IRRITATION WITH LACRIMATION. **CHRONIC EXPOSURE-** REPEATED OR PROLONGED CONTACT WITH IRRITANTS MAY CAUSE CONJUNCTIVITIS.
FIRST AID- WASH EYES IMMEDIATELY WITH LARGE AMOUNTS OF WATER OR NORMAL SALINE, OCCASIONALLY LIFTING UPPER AND LOWER LIDS, UNTIL NO EVIDENCE OF CHEMICAL REMAINS (APPROXIMATELY 15-20 MINUTES). GET MEDICAL ATTENTION IMMEDIATELY.

INGESTION: METHYL ISOBUTYL KETONE: NARCOTIC. **ACUTE EXPOSURE-** MAY CAUSE COUGHING, GASTROENTERITIS, AND CENTRAL NERVOUS SYSTEM DEPRESSION WITH HEADACHE, DIZZINESS, DULLNESS AND VOMITING. **CHRONIC EXPOSURE-** NO DATA AVAILABLE.
FIRST AID: IF PERSON IS CONSCIOUS, GIVE LARGE AMOUNTS OF WATER IMMEDIATELY. REMOVE BY EMESIS OR GASTRIC LAVAGE. DO NOT MAKE AN UNCONSCIOUS PERSON VOMIT OR DRINK ANYTHING. GIVE ACTIVATED CHARCOAL. GIVE OXYGEN IF RESPIRATION IS DEPRESSED. MAINTAIN AIRWAY AND BLOOD PRESSURE. GET MEDICAL ATTENTION. (DREISBACH, HANDBOOK OF POISONING, 11TH ED.) LAVAGE OR OXYGEN MUST BE ADMINISTERED BY QUALIFIED MEDICAL PERSONNEL.
ANTIDOTE: NO SPECIFIC ANTIDOTE. TREAT SYMPTOMATICALLY AND SUPPORTIVELY.

REACTIVITY

REACTIVITY: STABLE UNDER NORMAL TEMPERATURES AND PRESSURES.
INCOMPATIBILITIES: METHYL ISOBUTYL KETONE: ALDEHYDES: INCOMPATIBLE. OXIDIZERS (STRONG): FIRE AND EXPLOSION HAZARD. PLASTICS, RUBBER AND RESINS: MAY BE ATTACKED. POTASSIUM-TERT-BUTOXIDE: IGNITES ON CONTACT. REDUCING MATERIALS: VIGOROUS REACTION.
DECOMPOSITION: THERMAL DECOMPOSITION PRODUCTS MAY INCLUDE TOXIC OXIDES OF CARBON.
POLYMERIZATION: HAZARDOUS POLYMERIZATION HAS NOT BEEN REPORTED TO OCCUR UNDER NORMAL TEMPERATURES AND PRESSURES.

STORAGE AND DISPOSAL

OBSERVE ALL FEDERAL, STATE AND LOCAL REGULATIONS WHEN STORING OR DISPOSING OF THIS SUBSTANCE. FOR ASSISTANCE, CONTACT THE DISTRICT DIRECTOR OF THE ENVIRONMENTAL PROTECTION AGENCY.

****STORAGE****

STORE IN ACCORDANCE WITH 29 CFR 1910.106.
BONDING AND GROUNDING: SUBSTANCES WITH LOW ELECTROCONDUCTIVITY, WHICH MAY BE IGNITED BY ELECTROSTATIC SPARKS, SHOULD BE STORED IN CONTAINERS WHICH MEET THE BONDING AND GROUNDING GUIDELINES SPECIFIED IN NFPA 77-1983, RECOMMENDED PRACTICE ON STATIC ELECTRICITY.
STORAGE: PROTECT AGAINST PHYSICAL DAMAGE. OUTSIDE OR DETACHED STORAGE IS PREFERABLE. INSIDE STORAGE SHOULD BE IN A STANDARD FLAMMABLE LIQUIDS STORAGE ROOM OR CABINET. SEPARATE FROM OXIDIZING MATERIALS (NFPA 49, HAZARDOUS CHEMICALS DATA, 1975).
STORE AWAY FROM INCOMPATIBLE SUBSTANCES.

****DISPOSAL****

DISPOSAL MUST BE IN ACCORDANCE WITH STANDARDS APPLICABLE TO GENERATORS OF HAZARDOUS WASTE, 40CFR 262. EPA HAZARDOUS WASTE NUMBER U161.

CONDITIONS TO AVOID

AVOID CONTACT WITH HEAT, SPARKS, FLAMES, OR OTHER SOURCES OF IGNITION. VAPORS MAY BE EXPLOSIVE AND POISONOUS; DO NOT ALLOW UNNECESSARY PERSONNEL IN AREA. DO NOT OVERHEAT CONTAINERS; CONTAINERS MAY VIOLENTLY RUPTURE AND TRAVEL A CONSIDERABLE DISTANCE IN HEAT OF FIRE.

SPILL AND LEAK PROCEDURES

OCCUPATIONAL SPILL: SHUT OFF IGNITION SOURCES. STOP LEAK IF YOU CAN DO IT WITHOUT RISK. USE WATER SPRAY TO REDUCE VAPORS. FOR SMALL SPILLS, TAKE UP WITH SAND OR OTHER ABSORBENT MATERIAL AND PLACE INTO CONTAINERS FOR LATER DISPOSAL. FOR LARGER SPILLS, DIKE FAR AHEAD OF SPILL FOR LATER DISPOSAL. NO SMOKING, FLAMES OR FLARES IN HAZARD AREA. KEEP UNNECESSARY PEOPLE AWAY; ISOLATE HAZARD AREA AND DENY ENTRY.
REPORTABLE QUANTITY (RQ): 5000 POUNDS THE SUPERFUND AMENDMENTS AND REAUTHORIZATION ACT (SARA) SECTION 304 REQUIRES THAT A RELEASE EQUAL TO OR GREATER THAN THE REPORTABLE QUANTITY FOR THIS SUBSTANCE BE IMMEDIATELY REPORTED TO THE LOCAL EMERGENCY PLANNING COMMITTEE AND THE STATE EMERGENCY RESPONSE COMMISSION (40 CFR 355.40). IF THE RELEASE OF THIS SUBSTANCE IS REPORTABLE UNDER CERCLA SECTION 103, THE NATIONAL RESPONSE CENTER MUST BE NOTIFIED IMMEDIATELY AT (800) 424-8802 OR (202) 426-2675 IN THE METROPOLITAN WASHINGTON, D.C. AREA (40 CFR 302.6).

MATERIAL SAFETY DATA SHEET

OCCUPATIONAL HEALTH SERVICES, INC.
AGRICULTURE AND PESTICIDE DIVISION
450 SEVENTH AVENUE, SUITE 2407
NEW YORK, NEW YORK 10123
1-800-445-MSDS OR (212) 967-1100

EMERGENCY CONTACT:
JOHN S. BRANSFORD, JR. (615) 292-1180

SUBSTANCE IDENTIFICATION

CAS-NUMBER 112-12-9

SUBSTANCE: **METHYL NONYL KETONE**

TRADE NAMES/SYNONYMS: 2-UNDECANONE; 2-HENDECANONE; METHYL N-NONYL KETONE; NONYL METHYL KETONE; MGK DOG AND CAT REPELLENT; C11H22O; PST14675

CHEMICAL FAMILY: KETONE, ALIPHATIC

MOLECULAR FORMULA: C-H3-(C-H2)8-C-O-C-H3

MOLECULAR WEIGHT: 170.30

CERCLA RATINGS (SCALE 0-3): HEALTH=2 FIRE=2 REACTIVITY=0 PERSISTENCE=1

NFPA RATINGS (SCALE 0-4): HEALTH=0 FIRE=2 REACTIVITY=0

COMPONENTS AND CONTAMINANTS

COMPONENT: METHYL NONYL KETONE ***PERCENT:*** 100
CAS# 112-12-9

OTHER CONTAMINANTS: NONE.

EXPOSURE LIMITS: NO OCCUPATIONAL EXPOSURE LIMITS ESTABLISHED BY OSHA, ACGIH, OR NIOSH.

PHYSICAL DATA

DESCRIPTION: COLORLESS OILY LIQUID WITH A STRONG ODOR.

BOILING POINT: 448-450 F (231-232 C) ***MELTING POINT:*** 59 F (15 C)

SPECIFIC GRAVITY: 0.8250 ***SOLUBILITY IN WATER:*** INSOLUBLE.

SOLVENT SOLUBILITY: SOLUBLE IN ALCOHOL, ETHER, ACETONE, BENZENE, CHLOROFORM, PETROLEUM HYDROCARBONS, AROMATICS

FIRE AND EXPLOSION DATA

FIRE AND EXPLOSION HAZARD: MODERATE FIRE HAZARD WHEN EXPOSED TO HEAT OR FLAME.

FLASH POINT: 192 F (89 C) (CC) ***FLAMMABILITY CLASS(OSHA):*** IIIA

FIREFIGHTING MEDIA: DRY CHEMICAL, CARBON DIOXIDE, HALON, WATER SPRAY OR ALCOHOL FOAM (1987 EMERGENCY RESPONSE GUIDEBOOK, DOT P 5800.4). FOR LARGER FIRES, USE WATER SPRAY, FOG OR ALCOHOL FOAM (1987 EMERGENCY RESPONSE GUIDEBOOK, DOT P 5800.4).

FIREFIGHTING: MOVE CONTAINER FROM FIRE AREA IF POSSIBLE. COOL FIRE-EXPOSED CONTAINERS WITH WATER FROM SIDE UNTIL WELL AFTER FIRE IS OUT. STAY AWAY FROM STORAGE TANK ENDS. FOR MASSIVE FIRE IN STORAGE AREA, USE UNMANNED HOSE HOLDER OR MONITOR NOZZLES, ELSE WITHDRAW FROM AREA AND LET FIRE BURN. WITHDRAW IMMEDIATELY IN CASE OF RISING SOUND FROM VENTING SAFETY DEVICE OR ANY DISCOLORATION OF STORAGE TANK DUE TO FIRE (1987 EMERGENCY RESPONSE GUIDEBOOK, DOT P 5800.4, GUIDE PAGE 26). EXTINGUISH ONLY IF FLOW CAN BE STOPPED; USE FLOODING AMOUNTS OF WATER AS A FOG, SOLID STREAMS MAY BE INEFFECTIVE. COOL CONTAINERS WITH FLOODING AMOUNTS OF WATER, APPLY FROM AS FAR A DISTANCE AS POSSIBLE. AVOID BREATHING VAPORS, KEEP UPWIND.

TOXICITY

METHYL NONYL KETONE: TOXICITY DATA: 5 GM/KG ORAL-RAT LD50; 3880 MG/KG ORAL-MOUSE LD50. CARCINOGEN STATUS: NONE. ACUTE TOXICITY LEVEL: MODERATELY TOXIC BY INGESTION. TARGET EFFECTS: POISONING MAY AFFECT THE NERVOUS SYSTEM.

HEALTH EFFECTS AND FIRST AID

INHALATION: METHYL NONYL KETONE: **ACUTE EXPOSURE-** EXPOSURE TO THE VAPORS OF KETONES MAY CAUSE IRRITATION OF THE NOSE, THROAT, AND MUCOUS MEMBRANES. AT HIGH CONCENTRATIONS, VAPORS OF KETONES PRODUCE CENTRAL NERVOUS SYSTEM DEPRESSION WITH SYMPTOMS OF HEADACHE, NAUSEA, VERTIGO, INCOORDINATION, NARCOSIS, AND CARDIORESPIRATORY FAILURE. EXCESSIVE EXPOSURE TO SOME KETONES HAS ALSO CAUSED POLYNEUROPATHY WITH SYMPTOMS OF BILATERALLY SYMMETRICAL PARESTHESIA AND MUSCLE WEAKNESS, PRIMARILY IN THE LEGS AND ARMS. **CHRONIC EXPOSURE-** NO DATA AVAILABLE.

FIRST AID- REMOVE FROM EXPOSURE AREA TO FRESH AIR IMMEDIATELY. IF BREATHING HAS STOPPED, PERFORM ARTIFICIAL RESPIRATION. KEEP PERSON WARM AND AT REST. TREAT SYMPTOMATICALLY AND SUPPORTIVELY. GET MEDICAL ATTENTION IMMEDIATELY.

SKIN CONTACT: METHYL NONYL KETONE: **ACUTE EXPOSURE-** THE KETONES ARE IRRITATING TO THE SKIN AND MAY BE ABSORBED THROUGH THE SKIN. **CHRONIC EXPOSURE-** PROLONGED OR REPEATED EXPOSURE TO KETONES MAY PRODUCE DEFATTING, DEHYDRATION, AND DERMATITIS.

FIRST AID- REMOVE CONTAMINATED CLOTHING AND SHOES IMMEDIATELY. WASH AFFECTED AREA WITH SOAP OR MILD DETERGENT AND LARGE AMOUNTS OF WATER UNTIL NO EVIDENCE OF CHEMICAL REMAINS (APPROXIMATELY 15-20 MINUTES). GET MEDICAL ATTENTION IMMEDIATELY.

EYE CONTACT: METHYL NONYL KETONE: **ACUTE EXPOSURE-** THE VAPORS OF KETONES ARE IRRITATING TO THE EYES. **CHRONIC EXPOSURE-** NO DATA AVAILABLE.

FIRST AID- WASH EYES IMMEDIATELY WITH LARGE AMOUNTS OF WATER OR NORMAL SALINE, OCCASIONALLY LIFTING UPPER AND LOWER LIDS, UNTIL NO EVIDENCE OF CHEMICAL REMAINS (APPROXIMATELY 15-20 MINUTES). GET MEDICAL ATTENTION IMMEDIATELY.

PROTECTIVE EQUIPMENT

VENTILATION: PROVIDE LOCAL EXHAUST OR GENERAL DILUTION VENTILATION TO MEET PUBLISHED EXPOSURE LIMITS. VENTILATION EQUIPMENT MUST BE EXPLOSION-PROOF.

RESPIRATOR: THE FOLLOWING RESPIRATORS AND MAXIMUM USE CONCENTRATIONS ARE RECOMMENDATIONS BY THE U.S. DEPARTMENT OF HEALTH AND HUMAN SERVICES, NIOSH POCKET GUIDE TO CHEMICAL HAZARDS; NIOSH CRITERIA DOCUMENTS OR BY THE U.S. DEPARTMENT OF LABOR, 29 CFR 1910 SUBPART Z. THE SPECIFIC RESPIRATOR SELECTED MUST BE BASED ON CONTAMINATION LEVELS FOUND IN THE WORK PLACE, MUST NOT EXCEED THE WORKING LIMITS OF THE RESPIRATOR AND BE JOINTLY APPROVED BY THE NATIONAL INSTITUTE FOR OCCUPATIONAL SAFETY AND HEALTH AND THE MINE SAFETY AND HEALTH ADMINISTRATION (NIOSH-MSHA).

METHYL ISOBUTYL KETONE (HEXONE):

500 PPM- ANY CHEMICAL CARTRIDGE RESPIRATOR WITH ORGANIC VAPOR CARTRIDGE. ANY SUPPLIED-AIR RESPIRATOR. ANY SELF-CONTAINED BREATHING APPARATUS.

1000 PPM- ANY POWERED AIR-PURFYING RESPIRATOR WITH ORGANIC VAPOR CARTRIDGE(S). ANY CHEMICAL CARTRIDGE RESPIRATOR WITH A FULL FACEPIECE AND ORGANIC VAPOR CARTRIDGE(S).

1250 PPM- ANY SUPPLIED-AIR RESPIRATOR OPERATED IN A CONTINUOUS FLOW MODE.

2500 PPM- ANY AIR-PURIFYING FULL FACEPIECE RESPIRATOR (GAS MASK) WITH A CHIN-STYLE OR FRONT OR BACK-MOUNTED ORGANIC VAPOR CANISTER. ANY SELF-CONTAINED BREATHING APPARATUS WITH FULL FACEPIECE. ANY SUPPLIED-AIR RESPIRATOR WITH FULL FACEPIECE. ANY SUPPLIED-AIR RESPIRATOR WITH TIGHT-FITTING FACEPIECE OPERATED IN CONTINUOUS FLOW MODE.

3000 PPM- ANY SUPPLIED-AIR RESPIRATOR WITH A HALF-MASK AND OPERATED IN PRESSURE-DEMAND OR OTHER POSITIVE PRESSURE MODE.

ESCAPE- ANY AIR-PURIFYING FULL FACEPIECE RESPIRATOR (GAS MASK) WITH A CHIN-STYLE OR FRONT OR BACK-MOUNTED ORGANIC VAPOR CANISTER. ANY APPROPRIATE ESCAPE-TYPE SELF-CONTAINED BREATHING APPARATUS.

FOR FIREFIGHTING AND OTHER IMMEDIATELY DANGEROUS TO LIFE OR HEALTH CONDITIONS:

SELF-CONTAINED BREATHING APPARATUS WITH FULL FACEPIECE OPERATED IN PRESSURE-DEMAND OR OTHER POSITIVE PRESSURE MODE.

SUPPLIED-AIR RESPIRATOR WITH FULL FACEPIECE AND OPERATED IN PRESSURE-DEMAND OR OTHER POSITIVE PRESSURE MODE IN COMBINATION WITH AN AUXILIARY SELF-CONTAINED BREATHING APPARATUS OPERATED IN PRESSURE-DEMAND OR OTHER POSITIVE PRESSURE MODE.

CLOTHING: EMPLOYEE MUST WEAR APPROPRIATE PROTECTIVE (IMPERVIOUS) CLOTHING AND EQUIPMENT TO PREVENT REPEATED OR PROLONGED SKIN CONTACT WITH THIS SUBSTANCE. ***GLOVES:*** EMPLOYEE MUST WEAR APPROPRIATE PROTECTIVE GLOVES TO PREVENT CONTACT WITH THIS SUBSTANCE.

EYE PROTECTION: EMPLOYEE MUST WEAR SPLASH-PROOF OR DUST-RESISTANT SAFETY GOGGLES TO PREVENT EYE CONTACT WITH THIS SUBSTANCE. EMERGENCY EYE WASH: WHERE THERE IS ANY POSSIBILITY THAT AN EMPLOYEE'S EYES MAY BE EXPOSED TO THIS SUBSTANCE, THE EMPLOYER SHOULD PROVIDE AN EYE WASH FOUNTAIN WITHIN THE IMMEDIATE WORK AREA FOR EMERGENCY USE.

AUTHORIZED BY- OCCUPATIONAL HEALTH SERVICES, INC.
CREATION DATE: 11/17/89 ***REVISION DATE:*** 06/07/90

INGESTION: METHYL NONYL KETONE. **ACUTE EXPOSURE**- A LETHAL DOSE IN RATS WAS 5000 MG/KG. **CHRONIC EXPOSURE**- NO DATA AVAILABLE.

FIRST AID- TREAT SYMPTOMATICALLY AND SUPPORTIVELY. GET MEDICAL ATTENTION IMMEDIATELY. IF VOMITING OCCURS, KEEP HEAD LOWER THAN HIPS TO PREVENT ASPIRATION.

ANTIDOTE: NO SPECIFIC ANTIDOTE. TREAT SYMPTOMATICALLY AND SUPPORTIVELY.

REACTIVITY

REACTIVITY: STABLE UNDER NORMAL TEMPERATURES AND PRESSURES.

INCOMPATIBILITIES: METHYL NONYL KETONE: OXIDIZERS (STRONG): FIRE AND EXPLOSION HAZARD. SEE ALSO KETONES.

KETONES: ACETALDEHYDE: VIOLENT CONDENSATION REACTION. NITRIC ACID + HYDROGEN PEROXIDE: FORMATION OF EXPLOSIVE PRODUCT. PERCHLORIC ACID: VIOLENT DECOMPOSITION.

DECOMPOSITION: THERMAL DECOMPOSITION PRODUCTS MAY INCLUDE TOXIC OXIDES OF CARBON.

POLYMERIZATION: HAZARDOUS POLYMERIZATION HAS NOT BEEN REPORTED TO OCCUR UNDER NORMAL TEMPERATURES AND PRESSURES.

STORAGE AND DISPOSAL

OBSERVE ALL FEDERAL, STATE AND LOCAL REGULATIONS WHEN STORING OR DISPOSING OF THIS SUBSTANCE. FOR ASSISTANCE, CONTACT THE DISTRICT DIRECTOR OF THE ENVIRONMENTAL PROTECTION AGENCY.

STORAGE

STORE IN ACCORDANCE WITH 29 CFR 1910.106. STORE AWAY FROM INCOMPATIBLE SUBSTANCES.

DISPOSAL

DISPOSAL MUST BE IN ACCORDANCE WITH STANDARDS APPLICABLE TO GENERATORS OF HAZARDOUS WASTE, 40 CFR 262. EPA HAZARDOUS WASTE NUMBER D001. 100 POUND CERCLA SECTION 103 REPORTABLE QUANTITY.

CONDITIONS TO AVOID

AVOID CONTACT WITH HEAT, SPARKS, FLAMES, OR OTHER SOURCES OF IGNITION. VAPORS MAY BE EXPLOSIVE AND POISONOUS; DO NOT ALLOW UNNECESSARY PERSONNEL IN AREA. DO NOT OVERHEAT CONTAINERS; CONTAINERS MAY VIOLENTLY RUPTURE AND TRAVEL A CONSIDERABLE DISTANCE IN HEAT OF FIRE.

SPILL AND LEAK PROCEDURES

OCCUPATIONAL SPILL: SHUT OFF IGNITION SOURCES. STOP LEAK IF YOU CAN DO IT WITHOUT RISK. USE WATER SPRAY TO REDUCE VAPORS. FOR SMALL SPILLS, TAKE UP WITH SAND OR OTHER ABSORBENT MATERIAL AND PLACE INTO CONTAINERS FOR LATER DISPOSAL. FOR LARGER SPILLS, DIKE FAR AHEAD OF SPILL FOR LATER DISPOSAL. NO SMOKING, FLAMES OR FLARES IN HAZARD AREA. KEEP UNNECESSARY PEOPLE AWAY; ISOLATE HAZARD AREA AND DENY ENTRY.

PROTECTIVE EQUIPMENT

VENTILATION: PROVIDE LOCAL EXHAUST VENTILATION SYSTEM.

RESPIRATOR: THE FOLLOWING RESPIRATORS ARE RECOMMENDED BASED ON INFORMATION FOUND IN THE PHYSICAL DATA, TOXICITY AND HEALTH EFFECTS SECTIONS. THEY ARE RANKED IN ORDER FROM MINIMUM TO MAXIMUM RESPIRATORY PROTECTION. THE SPECIFIC RESPIRATOR SELECTED MUST BE BASED ON CONTAMINATION LEVELS FOUND IN THE WORK PLACE, MUST NOT EXCEED THE WORKING LIMITS OF THE RESPIRATOR AND BE JOINTLY APPROVED BY THE NATIONAL INSTITUTE FOR OCCUPATIONAL SAFETY AND HEALTH AND THE MINE SAFETY AND HEALTH ADMINISTRATION (NIOSH-MSHA).

CHEMICAL CARTRIDGE RESPIRATOR WITH AN ORGANIC VAPOR CARTRIDGE(S) WITH A FULL FACEPIECE.

GAS MASK WITH ORGANIC VAPOR CANISTER (CHIN-STYLE OR FRONT- OR BACK-MOUNTED CANISTER) WITH A FULL FACEPIECE.

TYPE 'C' SUPPLIED-AIR RESPIRATOR WITH A FULL FACEPIECE OPERATED IN PRESSURE-DEMAND OR OTHER POSITIVE PRESSURE MODE OR WITH A FULL FACEPIECE, HELMET OR HOOD OPERATED IN CONTINUOUS-FLOW MODE.

SELF-CONTAINED BREATHING APPARATUS WITH A FULL FACEPIECE OPERATED IN PRESSURE-DEMAND OR OTHER POSITIVE PRESSURE MODE.

FOR FIREFIGHTING AND OTHER IMMEDIATELY DANGEROUS TO LIFE OR HEALTH CONDITIONS:

SELF-CONTAINED BREATHING APPARATUS WITH FULL FACEPIECE OPERATED IN PRESSURE-DEMAND OR OTHER POSITIVE PRESSURE MODE.

SUPPLIED-AIR RESPIRATOR WITH FULL FACEPIECE AND OPERATED IN PRESSURE-DEMAND OR OTHER POSITIVE PRESSURE MODE IN COMBINATION WITH AN AUXILIARY SELF-CONTAINED BREATHING APPARATUS OPERATED IN PRESSURE-DEMAND OR OTHER POSITIVE PRESSURE MODE.

CLOTHING: EMPLOYEE MUST WEAR APPROPRIATE PROTECTIVE (IMPERVIOUS) CLOTHING AND EQUIPMENT TO PREVENT REPEATED OR PROLONGED SKIN CONTACT WITH THIS SUBSTANCE.

GLOVES: EMPLOYEE MUST WEAR APPROPRIATE PROTECTIVE GLOVES TO PREVENT CONTACT WITH THIS SUBSTANCE.

EYE PROTECTION: EMPLOYEE MUST WEAR SPLASH-PROOF OR DUST-RESISTANT SAFETY GOGGLES TO PREVENT EYE CONTACT WITH THIS SUBSTANCE. EMERGENCY EYE WASH: WHERE THERE IS ANY POSSIBILITY THAT AN EMPLOYEE'S EYES MAY BE EXPOSED TO THIS SUBSTANCE, THE EMPLOYER SHOULD PROVIDE AN EYE WASH FOUNTAIN WITHIN THE IMMEDIATE WORK AREA FOR EMERGENCY USE.

AUTHORIZED BY- OCCUPATIONAL HEALTH SERVICES, INC.
CREATION DATE: 10/04/89 ***REVISION DATE:*** 05/16/90

MATERIAL SAFETY DATA SHEET

OCCUPATIONAL HEALTH SERVICES, INC.
AGRICULTURE AND PESTICIDE DIVISION
450 SEVENTH AVENUE, SUITE 2407
NEW YORK, NEW YORK 10123
1-800-445-MSDS OR (212) 967-1100

EMERGENCY CONTACT:
JOHN S. BRANSFORD, JR. (615) 292-1180

SUBSTANCE IDENTIFICATION

CAS-NUMBER 99-76-3

SUBSTANCE: **METHYL PARABEN**

TRADE NAMES/SYNONYMS: METHYL P-HYDROXYBENZOATE; P-HYDROXYBENZOIC ACID, METHYL ESTER; 4-HYDROXYBENZOIC ACID, METHYL ESTER; NIPAGIN M; TEGOSEPT M; METHYL CHEMOSEPT; METHYL PARASEPT; PARASEPT; ABIOL; ASEPTOFORM; METHYLBEN; MASEPTOL; METHYL P-OXYBENZOATE; PARIDOL; PRESERVAL M; SEPTOS; SOLBROL M; METHYL PARAHYDROXYBENZOATE; C8H8O3; PST14677

CHEMICAL FAMILY: ESTER, CARBOXYLIC, AROMATIC

MOLECULAR FORMULA: H-O-C6-H4-C-O2-C-H3

MOLECULAR WEIGHT: 152.14

CERCLA RATINGS (SCALE 0-3): HEALTH=2 FIRE=1 REACTIVITY=0 PERSISTENCE=0

NFPA RATINGS (SCALE 0-4): HEALTH=U FIRE=1 REACTIVITY=0

COMPONENTS AND CONTAMINANTS

COMPONENT: METHYL PARABEN ***PERCENT:*** 100.0
CAS# 99-76-3

EXPOSURE LIMITS: NO OCCUPATIONAL EXPOSURE LIMITS ESTABLISHED BY OSHA, ACGIH, OR NIOSH.

PHYSICAL DATA

DESCRIPTION: ODORLESS, COLORLESS CRYSTALS OR WHITE CRYSTALLINE POWDER WITH A SLIGHT BURNING TASTE. ***BOILING POINT:*** 518-536 F (270-280 C) (DECOMPOSES)

MELTING POINT: 268 F (131 C) ***SPECIFIC GRAVITY:*** 0.6-0.7

SOLUBILITY IN WATER: 0.25% @ 20 C

SOLVENT SOLUBILITY: SOLUBLE IN ALCOHOL, ACETONE, ETHER; SLIGHTLY SOLUBLE IN BENZENE, CARBON TETRACHLORIDE, WARM OIL OR GLYCEROL

FIRE AND EXPLOSION DATA

FIRE AND EXPLOSION HAZARD: SLIGHT FIRE HAZARD WHEN EXPOSED TO HEAT OR FLAME.

FIREFIGHTING MEDIA: DRY CHEMICAL, CARBON DIOXIDE, HALON, WATER SPRAY OR STANDARD FOAM (1987 EMERGENCY RESPONSE GUIDEBOOK, DOT P 5800.4). FOR LARGER FIRES, USE WATER SPRAY, FOG OR ALCOHOL FOAM (1987 EMERGENCY RESPONSE GUIDEBOOK, DOT P 5800.4).

FIREFIGHTING: MOVE CONTAINER FROM FIRE AREA IF POSSIBLE. DO NOT SCATTER SPILLED MATERIAL WITH HIGH PRESSURE WATER STREAMS. DIKE FIRE CONTROL WATER FOR LATER DISPOSAL (1987 EMERGENCY RESPONSE GUIDEBOOK, DOT P 5800.4, GUIDE PAGE 31).

USE AGENTS SUITABLE FOR TYPE OF SURROUNDING FIRE. AVOID BREATHING HAZARDOUS VAPORS, KEEP UPWIND.

TOXICITY

METHYL PARABEN (METHYL P-HYDROXYBENZOATE): TOXICITY DATA: 6 GM/KG ORAL-RABBIT LD50; 3000 MG/KG ORAL-DOG LD50; 3 GM/KG ORAL-GUINEA PIG LD50; 1200 MG/KG SUBCUTANEOUS-MOUSE LD50; 960 MG/KG INTRAPERITONEAL-MOUSE LD50; MUTAGENIC DATA (RTECS). CARCINOGEN STATUS: NONE. LOCAL EFFECTS: IRRITANT- EYE. ACUTE TOXICITY LEVEL: MODERATELY TOXIC BY

INGESTION. TARGET EFFECTS: SENSITIZER- DERMAL. ADDITIONAL DATA: CROSS-SENSITIVITY WITH OTHER PARABENS IS POSSIBLE.

HEALTH EFFECTS AND FIRST AID

INHALATION: METHYL PARABEN (METHYL P-HYDROXYBENZOATE): **ACUTE EXPOSURE-** DUST MAY IRRITATE THE NOSE AND THROAT AND CAUSE COUGHING AND CHEST DISCOMFORT. **CHRONIC EXPOSURE-** NO DATA AVAILABLE.

FIRST AID- REMOVE FROM EXPOSURE AREA TO FRESH AIR IMMEDIATELY. IF BREATHING HAS STOPPED, PERFORM ARTIFICIAL RESPIRATION. KEEP PERSON WARM AND AT REST. TREAT SYMPTOMATICALLY AND SUPPORTIVELY. GET MEDICAL ATTENTION IMMEDIATELY.

SKIN CONTACT: METHYL PARABEN (METHYL P-HYDROXYBENZOATE): SENSITIZER. **ACUTE EXPOSURE-** MAY CAUSE ALLERGIC CONTACT URTICARIA OR DERMATITIS IN PREVIOUSLY EXPOSED PERSONS, ESPECIALLY WHEN APPLIED TO A SITE OF PREVIOUS, HEALED DERMATITIS. **CHRONIC EXPOSURE-** REPEATED CONTACT, ESPECIALLY WITH DAMAGED SKIN, MAY LEAD TO SENSITIZATION DERMATITIS, WHICH MAY BE SEVERE.

FIRST AID- REMOVE CONTAMINATED CLOTHING AND SHOES IMMEDIATELY. WASH AFFECTED AREA WITH SOAP OR MILD DETERGENT AND LARGE AMOUNTS OF WATER UNTIL NO EVIDENCE OF CHEMICAL REMAINS (APPROXIMATELY 15-20 MINUTES). GET MEDICAL ATTENTION IMMEDIATELY.

EYE CONTACT: METHYL PARABEN (METHYL P-HYDROXYBENZOATE): IRRITANT. **ACUTE EXPOSURE-** SATURATED AQUEOUS SOLUTIONS MAY CAUSE MODERATE IRRITATION. EYEDROPS CONTAINING 0.04% METHYL PARABEN AND 0.02% PROPYL PARABEN IN 0.9% SODIUM CHLORIDE SOLUTION REPORTEDLY CAUSED SMARTING OF THE EYES IN 75% OF THE PEOPLE TESTED; NO PERSISTENT EFFECTS WERE NOTED. **CHRONIC EXPOSURE-** REPEATED OR PROLONGED EXPOSURE TO IRRITANTS MAY CAUSE CONJUNCTIVITIS. ALLERGIC CONTACT DERMATITIS WITH REDNESS AND SWELLING OF THE EYELIDS HAS OCCASIONALLY OCCURRED FROM APPLICATION OF PRODUCTS CONTAINING PARABENS TO THE AREA AROUND THE EYES.

FIRST AID- WASH EYES IMMEDIATELY WITH LARGE AMOUNTS OF WATER OR NORMAL SALINE, OCCASIONALLY LIFTING UPPER AND LOWER LIDS, UNTIL NO EVIDENCE OF CHEMICAL REMAINS (APPROXIMATELY 15-20 MINUTES). GET MEDICAL ATTENTION IMMEDIATELY.

INGESTION: METHYL PARABEN (METHYL P-HYDROXYBENZOATE): **ACUTE EXPOSURE-** 0.03% AQUEOUS SOLUTIONS MAY CAUSE NUMB AND FELT-LIKE SENSATIONS IN THE MOUTH AND IRRITATION OF THE INTESTINAL MUCOSA. **CHRONIC EXPOSURE-** RATS FED UP TO 4 GM/KG FOR 96 WEEKS SHOWED NO SIGNIFICANT ORGAN CHANGES.

FIRST AID- TREAT SYMPTOMATICALLY AND SUPPORTIVELY. GET MEDICAL ATTENTION IMMEDIATELY. IF VOMITING OCCURS, KEEP HEAD LOWER THAN HIPS TO PREVENT ASPIRATION.

ANTIDOTE: NO SPECIFIC ANTIDOTE. TREAT SYMPTOMATICALLY AND SUPPORTIVELY.

REACTIVITY

REACTIVITY: STABLE UNDER NORMAL TEMPERATURES AND PRESSURES.

INCOMPATIBILITIES: METHYL PARABEN (METHYL P-HYDROXYBENZOATE): OXIDIZERS (STRONG): FIRE AND EXPLOSION HAZARD.

DECOMPOSITION: THERMAL DECOMPOSITION PRODUCTS MAY INCLUDE TOXIC OXIDES OF CARBON.

POLYMERIZATION: HAZARDOUS POLYMERIZATION HAS NOT BEEN REPORTED TO OCCUR UNDER NORMAL TEMPERATURES AND PRESSURES.

STORAGE AND DISPOSAL

OBSERVE ALL FEDERAL, STATE AND LOCAL REGULATIONS WHEN STORING OR DISPOSING OF THIS SUBSTANCE. FOR ASSISTANCE, CONTACT THE DISTRICT DIRECTOR OF THE ENVIRONMENTAL PROTECTION AGENCY.

STORAGE

STORE AWAY FROM INCOMPATIBLE SUBSTANCES.

KEEP IN A TIGHTLY CLOSED CONTAINER. STORE IN A COOL, DRY, VENTILATED AREA.

CONDITIONS TO AVOID

MAY BURN BUT DOES NOT IGNITE READILY. AVOID CONTACT WITH STRONG OXIDIZERS, EXCESSIVE HEAT, SPARKS, OR OPEN FLAME.

SPILL AND LEAK PROCEDURES

OCCUPATIONAL SPILL: SWEEP UP AND PLACE IN SUITABLE CLEAN, DRY CONTAINERS FOR RECLAMATION OR LATER DISPOSAL. DO NOT FLUSH SPILLED MATERIAL INTO SEWER. KEEP UNNECESSARY PEOPLE AWAY.

PROTECTIVE EQUIPMENT

VENTILATION: PROVIDE LOCAL EXHAUST OR GENERAL DILUTION VENTILATION SYSTEM.

RESPIRATOR: THE FOLLOWING RESPIRATORS ARE RECOMMENDED BASED ON INFORMATION FOUND IN THE PHYSICAL DATA, TOXICITY AND HEALTH EFFECTS SECTIONS. THEY ARE RANKED IN ORDER FROM MINIMUM TO MAXIMUM RESPIRATORY PROTECTION. THE SPECIFIC RESPIRATOR SELECTED MUST BE BASED ON CONTAMINATION LEVELS FOUND IN THE WORK PLACE, MUST NOT EXCEED THE WORKING LIMITS OF THE RESPIRATOR AND BE JOINTLY APPROVED BY THE NATIONAL INSTITUTE FOR OCCUPATIONAL SAFETY AND HEALTH AND THE MINE SAFETY AND HEALTH ADMINISTRATION (NIOSH-MSHA).

DUST AND MIST RESPIRATOR.

AIR-PURIFYING RESPIRATOR WITH A HIGH-EFFICIENCY PARTICULATE FILTER.

POWERED AIR-PURIFYING RESPIRATOR WITH A DUST AND MIST FILTER.

POWERED AIR-PURIFYING RESPIRATOR WITH A HIGH-EFFICIENCY PARTICULATE FILTER.

TYPE 'C' SUPPLIED-AIR RESPIRATOR OPERATED IN THE PRESSURE-DEMAND OR OTHER POSITIVE PRESSURE OR CONTINUOUS-FLOW MODE.

SELF-CONTAINED BREATHING APPARATUS.

FOR FIREFIGHTING AND OTHER IMMEDIATELY DANGEROUS TO LIFE OR HEALTH CONDITIONS:

SELF-CONTAINED BREATHING APPARATUS WITH FULL FACEPIECE OPERATED IN PRESSURE-DEMAND OR OTHER POSITIVE PRESSURE MODE.

SUPPLIED-AIR RESPIRATOR WITH FULL FACEPIECE AND OPERATED IN PRESSURE-DEMAND OR OTHER POSITIVE PRESSURE MODE IN COMBINATION WITH AN AUXILIARY SELF-CONTAINED BREATHING APPARATUS OPERATED IN PRESSURE-DEMAND OR OTHER POSITIVE PRESSURE MODE.

CLOTHING: EMPLOYEE MUST WEAR APPROPRIATE PROTECTIVE (IMPERVIOUS) CLOTHING AND EQUIPMENT TO PREVENT REPEATED OR PROLONGED SKIN CONTACT WITH THIS SUBSTANCE.

GLOVES: EMPLOYEE MUST WEAR APPROPRIATE PROTECTIVE GLOVES TO PREVENT CONTACT WITH THIS SUBSTANCE.

EYE PROTECTION: EMPLOYEE MUST WEAR SPLASH-PROOF OR DUST-RESISTANT SAFETY GOGGLES TO PREVENT EYE CONTACT WITH THIS SUBSTANCE.

EMERGENCY EYE WASH: WHERE THERE IS ANY POSSIBILITY THAT AN EMPLOYEE'S EYES MAY BE EXPOSED TO THIS SUBSTANCE, THE EMPLOYER SHOULD PROVIDE AN EYE WASH FOUNTAIN WITHIN THE IMMEDIATE WORK AREA FOR EMERGENCY USE.

AUTHORIZED BY- OCCUPATIONAL HEALTH SERVICES, INC.

CREATION DATE: 11/17/89 ***REVISION DATE:*** 05/31/90

MATERIAL SAFETY DATA SHEET

OCCUPATIONAL HEALTH SERVICES, INC.
AGRICULTURE AND PESTICIDE DIVISION
450 SEVENTH AVENUE, SUITE 2407
NEW YORK, NEW YORK 10123
1-800-445-MSDS OR (212) 967-1100

EMERGENCY CONTACT:
JOHN S. BRANSFORD, JR. (615) 292-1180

SUBSTANCE IDENTIFICATION

CAS-NUMBER 950-35-6

SUBSTANCE: **METHYL PARAOXON**

TRADE NAMES/SYNONYMS: DIMETHYL P-NITROPHENYL PHOSPHATE; DIMETHYL 4-NITROPHENYL PHOSPHATE; DIMETHYL PARAOXON; PARAOXON METHYL; PHOSPHORIC ACID, DIMETHYL 4-NITROPHENYL ESTER; PHOSPHORIC ACID, DIMETHYL P-NITROPHENYL ESTER; METHYLPARAOXON; METHYL PARATHION OXYGEN ANALOG; C8H10NO6P; PST14678

CHEMICAL FAMILY: ORGANOPHOSPHATE

MOLECULAR FORMULA: (C-H3-O)2-P-(O)-O-C6-H4-N-O2

MOLECULAR WEIGHT: 247.16

CERCLA RATINGS (SCALE 0-3): HEALTH=3 FIRE=U REACTIVITY=0 PERSISTENCE=0

NFPA RATINGS (SCALE 0-4): HEALTH=3 FIRE=U REACTIVITY=0

COMPONENTS AND CONTAMINANTS

COMPONENT: METHYL PARAOXON ***PERCENT:*** 100.0

CAS# 950-35-6

OTHER CONTAMINANTS: NONE

EXPOSURE LIMITS: NO OCCUPATIONAL EXPOSURE LIMITS ESTABLISHED BY OSHA, ACGIH, OR NIOSH.

PHYSICAL DATA

DESCRIPTION: CLEAR, DARK AMBER LIQUID. ***BOILING POINT:*** 295-300 F (146-151 C)
SPECIFIC GRAVITY: NOT AVAILABLE ***VAPOR PRESSURE:*** NOT AVAILABLE
SOLUBILITY IN WATER: NOT AVAILABLE

FIRE AND EXPLOSION DATA

FIRE AND EXPLOSION HAZARD: UNKNOWN FIRE AND EXPLOSION HAZARD.

FIREFIGHTING MEDIA: DRY CHEMICAL, CARBON DIOXIDE, HALON, WATER SPRAY OR STANDARD FOAM (1987 EMERGENCY RESPONSE GUIDEBOOK, DOT P 5800.4). FOR LARGER FIRES, USE WATER SPRAY, FOG OR STANDARD FOAM (1987 EMERGENCY RESPONSE GUIDEBOOK, DOT P 5800.4).

FIREFIGHTING: MOVE CONTAINER FROM FIRE AREA IF POSSIBLE. DIKE FIRE CONTROL WATER FOR LATER DISPOSAL; DO NOT SCATTER THE MATERIAL. COOL FIRE-EXPOSED CONTAINERS WITH WATER FROM SIDE UNTIL WELL AFTER FIRE IS OUT. STAY AWAY FROM STORAGE TANK ENDS. WITHDRAW IMMEDIATELY IN CASE OF RISING SOUND FROM VENTING SAFETY DEVICE OR ANY DISCOLORATION OF STORAGE TANK DUE TO FIRE (1987 EMERGENCY RESPONSE GUIDEBOOK, DOT P 5800.4, GUIDE PAGE 28).
EXTINGUISH ONLY IF FLOW CAN BE STOPPED. USE FLOODING AMOUNTS OF WATER AS A FOG; SOLID STREAMS MAY BE INEFFECTIVE. COOL CONTAINERS WITH FLOODING AMOUNTS OF WATER FROM AS FAR A DISTANCE AS POSSIBLE. AVOID BREATHING POISONOUS VAPORS, KEEP UPWIND.

TRANSPORTATION DATA

DEPARTMENT OF TRANSPORTATION HAZARD CLASSIFICATION 49 CFR 172.101: POISON B
DEPARTMENT OF TRANSPORTATION LABELING REQUIREMENTS 49 CFR 172.101 AND SUBPART E: POISON
DEPARTMENT OF TRANSPORTATION PACKAGING REQUIREMENTS: 49 CFR 173.359 EXCEPTIONS: 49 CFR 173.359

TOXICITY

METHYL PARAOXON: TOXICITY DATA: 3270 UG/KG ORAL-RAT LD50; 2100 UG/KG ORAL-MOUSE LD50; 83 MG/KG ORAL-GUINEA PIG LD50; 500 UG/KG SUBCUTANEOUS-RAT LDLO; 1400 UG/KG SUBCUTANEOUS-MOUSE LDLO; 457 UG/KG INTRAVENOUS-RAT LD50; 550 UG/KG INTRAVENOUS-MOUSE LD50; 2200 UG/KG INTRAVENOUS-GUINEA PIG LD50; 500 UG/KG INTRAPERITONEAL-MOUSE LD50; 1690 UG/KG INTRAMUSCULAR-RAT LD50; 5 UG/KG INTRACEREBRAL-MOUSE LD50; 21 MG/KG UNREPORTED-MOUSE LD50. CARCINOGEN STATUS: NONE. ACUTE TOXICITY LEVEL: HIGHLY TOXIC BY INGESTION. TARGET EFFECTS: CHOLINESTERASE INHIBITOR. POISONING MAY AFFECT THE NERVOUS SYSTEM.* AT INCREASED RISK FROM EXPOSURE: PERSONS WITH RESPIRATORY AILMENTS, RECENT EXPOSURE TO CHOLINESTERASE INHIBITORS OR IMPAIRED CHOLINESTERASE PRODUCTION, OR LIVER MALFUNCTION.* ADDITIONAL DATA: MAY CROSS THE PLACENTA. HIGH ENVIRONMENTAL TEMPERATURES OR EXPOSURE OF THE CHEMICAL TO VISIBLE OR ULTRAVIOLET LIGHT MAY ENHANCE THE TOXICITY. INTERACTIONS WITH MEDICATIONS MAY OCCUR.*
* MAY BE BASED ON GENERAL INFORMATION ON ORGANOPHOSPHATES.

HEALTH EFFECTS AND FIRST AID

INHALATION: METHYL PARAOXON: SEE INFORMATION ON ORGANOPHOSPHATES. ORGANOPHOSPHATES: CHOLINESTERASE INHIBITOR. **ACUTE EXPOSURE-** WHEN INHALED, THE FIRST EFFECTS OF CHOLINESTERASE INHIBITORS ARE USUALLY RESPIRATORY AND MAY INCLUDE NASAL HYPEREMIA AND WATERY DISCHARGE, COUGH, CHEST DISCOMFORT, DYSPNEA, AND WHEEZING DUE TO INCREASED BRONCHIAL SECRETIONS AND BRONCHOCONSTRICTION. IF SUFFICIENT AMOUNTS ARE ABSORBED, OTHER SYSTEMIC EFFECTS MAY BEGIN WITHIN A FEW MINUTES OR BE DELAYED FOR UP TO 12 HOURS. SYMPTOMS MAY INCLUDE PALLOR, NAUSEA, VOMITING, DIARRHEA, ABDOMINAL CRAMPS, HEADACHE, DIZZINESS, OCULAR PAIN, BLURRED VISION, MIOSIS OR IN SOME CASES, ESPECIALLY INITIALLY, MYDRIASIS, LACRIMATION, SALIVATION, SWEATING, AND CONFUSION. OTHER REPORTED CENTRAL NERVOUS SYSTEM OR NEUROMUSCULAR EFFECTS MAY INCLUDE ATAXIA, SLURRED SPEECH, AREFLEXIA, WEAKNESS, FATIGUE, FASCICULATIONS, TWITCHING, TREMORS POSSIBLY OF THE TONGUE AND EYELIDS, AND EVENTUALLY PARALYSIS OF THE EXTREMITIES AND POSSIBLY OF THE RESPIRATORY MUSCLES. IN SEVERE CASES THERE MAY ALSO BE INVOLUNTARY DEFECATION AND URINATION, CYANOSIS, PSYCHOSIS, HYPERGLYCEMIA, ACUTE PANCREATITIS, CARDIAC IRREGULARITIES, PULMONARY EDEMA, UNCONSCIOUSNESS, CONVULSIONS, AND COMA. DEATH IS PRIMARILY DUE TO RESPIRATORY FAILURE, ALTHOUGH CARDIOVASCULAR EFFECTS INCLUDING CARDIAC ARREST MAY ALSO BE IMPLICATED. LONG TERM SEQUELAE ARE RARE BUT MAY INCLUDE NEUROPSYCHIATRIC DISORDERS AND MYOPATHY WITH MUSCLE TENDERNESS. SOME ORGANOPHOSPHATES MAY CAUSE A DELAYED NEUROPATHY BEGINNING 1-4 WEEKS AFTER AN ACUTE EXPOSURE WHICH MAY OR MAY NOT HAVE CAUSED ACUTE CHOLINERGIC EFFECTS. NUMBNESS, TINGLING, WEAKNESS AND CRAMPING BEGINNING SYMMETRICALLY IN THE LOWER LIMBS MAY PROGRESS TO ATAXIA AND PARALYSIS. IN SEVERE CASES, UPPER LIMB INVOLVEMENT IS POSSIBLE AND FLACCID PARALYSIS MAY PROGRESS TO SPASTIC PARALYSIS WITH EXAGGERATED REFLEXES. IMPROVEMENT MAY OCCUR OVER MONTHS TO YEARS, BUT SOME RESIDUAL IMPAIRMENT USUALLY REMAINS. **CHRONIC EXPOSURE-** REPEATED OR PROLONGED EXPOSURE MAY RESULT IN THE EFFECTS OF ACUTE EXPOSURE INCLUDING THE DELAYED NEUROPATHY. OTHER EFFECTS REPORTED IN WORKERS REPEATEDLY EXPOSED INCLUDE IMPAIRED MEMORY AND CONCENTRATION, ACUTE PSYCHOSIS, SEVERE DEPRESSIONS, IRRITABILTY, CONFUSION, APATHY, EMOTIONAL LABILITY, SOCIAL WITHDRAWAL, CONFUSION, HEADACHE, SPEECH DIFFICULTIES, DELAYED REACTION TIMES, SPATIAL DISORIENTATION, NIGHTMARES, SLEEPWALKING, AND DROWSINESS OR INSOMNIA. AN INFLUENZA-LIKE CONDITION WITH HEADACHE, NAUSEA, WEAKNESS, ANOREXIA AND MALAISE HAS ALSO BEEN REPORTED.

FIRST AID- REMOVE FROM EXPOSURE AREA TO FRESH AIR IMMEDIATELY. IF BREATHING HAS STOPPED, GIVE ARTIFICIAL RESPIRATION. MAINTAIN AIRWAY AND BLOOD PRESSURE AND ADMINISTER OXYGEN IF AVAILABLE. KEEP AFFECTED PERSON WARM AND AT REST. TREAT SYMPTOMATICALLY AND SUPPORTIVELY. ADMINISTRATION OF OXYGEN SHOULD BE PERFORMED BY QUALIFIED PERSONNEL. GET MEDICAL ATTENTION IMMEDIATELY.

SKIN CONTACT: METHYL PARAOXON: SEE INFORMATION ON ORGANOPHOSPHATES. ORGANOPHOSPHATES: CHOLINESTERASE INHIBITOR. **ACUTE EXPOSURE-** LOCALIZED SWEATING AND FASCICULATIONS MAY OCCUR AT THE SITE OF CONTACT. IF SUFFICIENT AMOUNTS ARE ABSORBED, OTHER EFFECTS OF CHOLINESTERASE INHIBITION AS DESCRIBED IN ACUTE INHALATION MAY OCCUR. SYMPTOMS MAY BE DELAYED 2-3 HOURS, BUT USUALLY NO MORE THAN 12 HOURS. THE RATE OF ABSORPTION IS INCREASED BY THE PRESENCE OF DERMATITIS OR HIGH AMBIENT TEMPERATURES. DELAYED NEUROPATHY IS ALSO POSSIBLE. **CHRONIC EXPOSURE-** REPEATED OR PROLONGED EXPOSURE MAY CAUSE EFFECTS AS DESCRIBED IN ACUTE EXPOSURE. SOME ORGANOPHOSPHATES MAY CAUSE SENSITIZATION.

FIRST AID- REMOVE CONTAMINATED CLOTHING IMMEDIATELY. WASH CONTAMINATED AREAS WITH SOAP AND WATER FOLLOWED BY ALCOHOL (ARENA, POISONING, 4TH ED.). EMERGENCY PERSONNEL SHOULD WEAR GLOVES AND AVOID CONTAMINATION. TREAT RESPIRATORY DIFFICULTY WITH ARTIFICIAL RESPIRATION. GET MEDICAL ATTENTION IMMEDIATELY.

EYE CONTACT: METHYL PARAOXON: SEE INFORMATION ON ORGANOPHOSPHATES. ORGANOPHOSPHATES: CHOLINESTERASE INHIBITOR. **ACUTE EXPOSURE-** DIRECT CONTACT MAY CAUSE PAIN, HYPEREMIA, LACRIMATION, TWITCHING OF THE EYELIDS, MIOSIS, AND CILIARY MUSCLE SPASM WITH LOSS OF ACCOMODATION, BLURRED OR DIMMED VISION AND BROWACHE. SOMETIMES MYDRIASIS MAY OCCUR INSTEAD OF MIOSIS. WITH SUFFICIENT EXPOSURE, OTHER SYMPTOMS OF CHOLINESTERASE INHIBITION AS DESCRIBED IN ACUTE INHALATION MAY OCCUR. **CHRONIC EXPOSURE-** REPEATED OR PROLONGED EXPOSURE MAY CAUSE EFFECTS AS DESCRIBED IN ACUTE EXPOSURE. SOME COMPOUNDS HAVE CAUSED TOXIC EFFECTS ON THE CRYSTALLINE LENS, CONJUNCTIVAL THICKENING AND OBSTRUCTION OF THE NASOLACRIMAL CANALS WHEN USED AS MIOTIC EYEDROPS.

FIRST AID- IRRIGATE EYES WITH WATER OR SALINE SOLUTION. IF SYMPTOMS OF POISONING OCCUR, TREAT RESPIRATORY DIFFICULTY WITH ARTIFICIAL RESPIRATION AND OXYGEN. OBSERVE PATIENT FOR AT LEAST 24-36 HOURS (GOSSELIN, CLINICAL TOXICOLOGY OF COMMERCIAL PRODUCTS, 5TH ED.). GET MEDICAL ATTENTION IMMEDIATELY. OXYGEN SHOULD BE ADMINISTERED BY QUALIFIED MEDICAL PERSONNEL.

INGESTION: METHYL PARAOXON: HIGHLY TOXIC. THE LETHAL DOSE REPORTED IN RATS WAS 3 MG/KG. SEE INFORMATION ON ORGANOPHOSPHATES. ORGANOPHOSPHATES: CHOLINESTERASE INHIBITOR. **ACUTE EXPOSURE-** WHEN INGESTED, THE FIRST EFFECTS MAY BE NAUSEA, VOMITING, ANOREXIA, ABDOMINAL CRAMPS AND DIARRHEA. GASTROINTESTINAL ABSORPTION MAY CAUSE SYMPTOMS OF CHOLINESTERASE INHIBITION AS DESCRIBED IN ACUTE INHALATION. SYMPTOMS MAY BEGIN WITHIN MINUTES OR BE DELAYED FOR HOURS. DELAYED EFFECTS INCLUDING NEUROPATHY MAY ALSO OCCUR. **CHRONIC EXPOSURE-** REPEATED INGESTION MAY CAUSE EFFECTS AS DESCRIBED IN ACUTE EXPOSURE.

FIRST AID- IF PERSON IS ALERT AND RESPIRATION IS NOT DEPRESSED, GIVE SYRUP OF IPECAC FOLLOWED BY WATER (IF VOMITING OCCURS, KEEP HEAD BELOW HIPS TO PREVENT ASPIRATION). IF CONSCIOUSNESS LEVEL DECLINES OR VOMITING HAS NOT OCCURRED IN 15 MINUTES EMPTY STOMACH BY GASTRIC LAVAGE WITH THE AID OF CUFFED ENDOTRACHEAL TUBE USING ISOTONIC SALINE OR 5% SODIUM BICARBONATE FOLLOW WITH ACTIVATED CHARCOAL. ESTABLISH AND MAINTAIN AIRWAY. TREAT RESPIRATORY DIFFICULTY WITH ARTIFICIAL RESPIRATION AND OXYGEN. DO NOT GIVE MORPHINE, AMINOPHYLLINE, PHENOTHIAZINES, RESERPINE, FUROSEMIDE, OR ETHACRYNIC ACID (MORGAN, RECOGNITION AND MANAGEMENT OF PESTICIDE POISONINGS, 3RD ED.). TREAT SYMPTOMATICALLY AND

SUPPORTIVELY. ADMINISTRATION OF OXYGEN AND LAVAGE MUST BE PERFORMED BY QUALIFIED MEDICAL PERSONNEL. GET MEDICAL ATTENTION IMMEDIATELY.

ANTIDOTE: THE FOLLOWING ANTIDOTE(S) HAVE BEEN RECOMMENDED. HOWEVER, THE DECISION AS TO WHETHER THE SEVERITY OF POISONING REQUIRES ADMINISTRATION OF ANY ANTIDOTE AND ACTUAL DOSE REQUIRED SHOULD BE MADE BY QUALIFIED MEDICAL PERSONNEL.

FOR CHOLINESTERASE INHIBITORS: ESTABLISH CLEAR AIRWAY AND TISSUE OXYGENATION BY ASPIRATION OF SECRETIONS, AND IF NECESSARY, BY ASSISTED PULMONARY VENTILATION WITH OXYGEN. IMPROVE TISSUE OXYGENATION AS MUCH AS POSSIBLE BEFORE ADMINISTERING ATROPINE TO MINIMIZE THE RISK OF VENTRICULAR FIBRILLATION. ADMINISTER ATROPINE SULFATE INTRAVENOUSLY, OR INTRAMUSCULARLY IF IV INJECTION IS NOT POSSIBLE. IN MODERATELY SEVERE POISONING ADMINISTER ATROPINE SULFATE, 0.4-2.0 MG REPEATED EVERY 15 MINUTES UNTIL ATROPINIZATION IS ACHIEVED (TACHYCARDIA, FLUSHING, DRY MOUTH, MYDRIASIS). MAINTAIN ATROPINIZATION BY REPEATED DOSES FOR 2-12 HOURS, OR LONGER, DEPENDING ON THE SEVERITY OF POISONING. THE APPEARANCE OF RALES IN THE LUNG BASES, MIOSIS, SALIVATION, NAUSEA, BRADYCARDIA, ARE ALL INDICATIONS OF INADEQUATE ATROPINIZATION. SEVERELY POISONED INDIVIDUALS MAY EXHIBIT REMARKABLE TOLERANCE TO ATROPINE; TWO OR MORE TIMES THE DOSAGES SUGGESTED ABOVE MAY BE NEEDED. PERSONS NOT POISONED OR ONLY SLIGHTLY POISONED, HOWEVER, MAY DEVELOP SIGNS OF ATROPINE TOXICITY FROM SUCH LARGE DOSAGES: FEVER, MUSCLE FIBRILLATIONS, AND DELIRIUM ARE THE MAIN SIGNS OF ATROPINE TOXICITY. IF THESE SIGNS APPEAR WHILE THE PATIENT IS FULLY ATROPINIZED, ATROPINE ADMINISTRATION SHOULD BE DISCONTINUED, AT LEAST TEMPORARILY. OBSERVE TREATED PATIENTS CLOSELY AT LEAST 24 HOURS TO INSURE THAT SYMPTOMS (POSSIBLY PULMONARY EDEMA) DO NOT RECUR AS ATROPINIZATION WEARS OFF. IN VERY SEVERE POISONINGS, METABOLIC DISPOSITION OF TOXICANT MAY REQUIRE SEVERAL HOURS OR DAYS DURING WHICH ATROPINIZATION MUST BE MAINTAINED. MARKEDLY LOWER LEVELS OF URINARY METABOLITES INDICATE THAT ATROPINE DOSAGE CAN BE TAPERED OFF. AS DOSAGE IS REDUCED, CHECK THE LUNG BASES FREQUENTLY FOR RALES. IF RALES ARE HEARD OR OTHER SYMPTOMS RETURN, RE-ESTABLISH ATROPINIZATION PROMPTLY (MORGAN, RECOGNITION AND MANAGEMENT OF PESTICIDE POISONINGS, 3RD ED.). ADMINISTRATION OF ANTIDOTE MUST BE PERFORMED BY QUALIFIED MEDICAL PERSONNEL.

IN CASES OF SEVERE POISONING BY ORGANOPHOSPHATE PESTICIDES IN WHICH RESPIRATORY DEPRESSION, MUSCLE WEAKNESS AND TWITCHINGS ARE SEVERE, GIVE PRALIDOXIME (PROTOPAM-AYERST, 2-PAM), 1.0 GRAM INTRAVENOUSLY AT NO MORE THAN 0.5 GRAM PER MINUTE. DOSAGE OF PRALIDOXIME MAY BE REPEATED IN 1-2 HOURS, THEN AT 10-12 HOUR INTERVALS IF NEEDED. IN VERY SEVERE POISONINGS, DOSAGE RATES MAY BE DOUBLED. TREATMENT WITH PRALIDOXIME WILL BE MOST EFFECTIVE IF GIVEN WITHIN THIRTY-SIX HOURS AFTER POISONING (MORGAN, RECOGNITION AND MANAGEMENT OF PESTICIDE POISONINGS, 3RD ED.). ANTIDOTE SHOULD BE ADMINISTERED BY QUALIFIED MEDICAL PERSONNEL.

REACTIVITY

REACTIVITY: STABLE UNDER NORMAL TEMPERATURES AND PRESSURES.

INCOMPATIBILITIES: METHYL PARAOXON: OXIDIZERS (STRONG): FIRE AND EXPLOSION HAZARD.

DECOMPOSITION: THERMAL DECOMPOSITION MAY RELEASE TOXIC OXIDES OF NITROGEN, PHOSPHORUS AND CARBON.

POLYMERIZATION: HAZARDOUS POLYMERIZATION HAS NOT BEEN REPORTED TO OCCUR UNDER NORMAL TEMPERATURES AND PRESSURES.

STORAGE AND DISPOSAL

OBSERVE ALL FEDERAL, STATE AND LOCAL REGULATIONS WHEN STORING OR DISPOSING OF THIS SUBSTANCE. FOR ASSISTANCE, CONTACT THE DISTRICT DIRECTOR OF THE ENVIRONMENTAL PROTECTION AGENCY.

STORAGE

STORE AWAY FROM INCOMPATIBLE SUBSTANCES.

CONDITIONS TO AVOID

AVOID CONTACT WITH HEAT, SPARKS, FLAMES OR OTHER IGNITION SOURCES. VAPORS MAY BE EXPLOSIVE. MATERIAL IS POISONOUS; AVOID INHALATION OF VAPORS OR CONTACT WITH SKIN. DO NOT ALLOW MATERIAL TO CONTAMINATE WATER SOURCES.

SPILL AND LEAK PROCEDURES

OCCUPATIONAL SPILL: SHUT OFF IGNITION SOURCES. DO NOT TOUCH SPILLED MATERIAL. STOP LEAK IF YOU CAN DO IT WITHOUT RISK. USE WATER SPRAY TO REDUCE VAPORS. FOR SMALL SPILLS, TAKE UP WITH SAND OR OTHER ABSORBENT MATERIAL AND PLACE INTO CONTAINERS FOR LATER DISPOSAL. FOR LARGER SPILLS, DIKE FAR AHEAD OF SPILL FOR LATER DISPOSAL. NO SMOKING, FLAMES OR FLARES IN HAZARD AREA! KEEP UNNECESSARY PEOPLE AWAY; ISOLATE HAZARD AREA AND DENY ENTRY.

PROTECTIVE EQUIPMENT

VENTILATION: PROVIDE LOCAL EXHAUST OR PROCESS ENCLOSURE VENTILATION. VENTILATION EQUIPMENT MUST BE EXPLOSION-PROOF.

RESPIRATOR: THE FOLLOWING RESPIRATORS ARE RECOMMENDED BASED ON INFORMATION FOUND IN THE PHYSICAL DATA, TOXICITY AND HEALTH EFFECTS SECTIONS. THEY ARE RANKED IN ORDER FROM MINIMUM TO MAXIMUM RESPIRATORY PROTECTION. THE SPECIFIC RESPIRATOR SELECTED MUST BE BASED ON CONTAMINATION LEVELS FOUND IN THE WORK PLACE, MUST NOT EXCEED THE WORKING LIMITS OF THE RESPIRATOR AND BE JOINTLY APPROVED BY THE NATIONAL INSTITUTE FOR OCCUPATIONAL SAFETY AND HEALTH AND THE MINE SAFETY AND HEALTH ADMINISTRATION (NIOSH-MSHA).

CHEMICAL CARTRIDGE RESPIRATOR WITH FULL FACEPIECE AND PESTICIDE CARTRIDGE.

TYPE 'C' SUPPLIED-AIR RESPIRATOR WITH A FULL FACEPIECE OPERATED IN PRESSURE-DEMAND OR OTHER POSITIVE PRESSURE MODE OR WITH A FULL FACEPIECE, HELMET OR HOOD OPERATED IN CONTINUOUS-FLOW MODE.

SELF-CONTAINED BREATHING APPARATUS OPERATED IN PRESSURE-DEMAND OR OTHER POSITIVE PRESSURE MODE.

FOR FIREFIGHTING AND OTHER IMMEDIATELY DANGEROUS TO LIFE OR HEALTH CONDITIONS:

SELF-CONTAINED BREATHING APPARATUS WITH FULL FACEPIECE OPERATED IN PRESSURE-DEMAND OR OTHER POSITIVE PRESSURE MODE.

SUPPLIED-AIR RESPIRATOR WITH FULL FACEPIECE AND OPERATED IN PRESSURE-DEMAND OR OTHER POSITIVE PRESSURE MODE IN COMBINATION WITH AN AUXILIARY SELF-CONTAINED BREATHING APPARATUS OPERATED IN PRESSURE-DEMAND OR OTHER POSITIVE PRESSURE MODE.

CLOTHING: EMPLOYEE MUST WEAR APPROPRIATE PROTECTIVE (IMPERVIOUS) CLOTHING AND EQUIPMENT TO PREVENT ANY POSSIBILITY OF SKIN CONTACT WITH THIS SUBSTANCE.

GLOVES: EMPLOYEE MUST WEAR APPROPRIATE PROTECTIVE GLOVES TO PREVENT CONTACT WITH THIS SUBSTANCE.

EYE PROTECTION: EMPLOYEE MUST WEAR SPLASH-PROOF OR DUST-RESISTANT SAFETY GOGGLES AND A FACESHIELD TO PREVENT CONTACT WITH THIS SUBSTANCE.

EMERGENCY WASH FACILITIES: WHERE THERE IS ANY POSSIBILITY THAT AN EMPLOYEE'S EYES AND/OR SKIN MAY BE EXPOSED TO THIS SUBSTANCE, THE EMPLOYER SHOULD PROVIDE AN EYE WASH FOUNTAIN AND QUICK DRENCH SHOWER WITHIN THE IMMEDIATE WORK AREA FOR EMERGENCY USE.

AUTHORIZED BY- OCCUPATIONAL HEALTH SERVICES, INC.

CREATION DATE: 11/17/89 ***REVISION DATE:*** 05/01/90

MATERIAL SAFETY DATA SHEET

OCCUPATIONAL HEALTH SERVICES, INC.
AGRICULTURE AND PESTICIDE DIVISION
450 SEVENTH AVENUE, SUITE 2407
NEW YORK, NEW YORK 10123
1-800-445-MSDS OR (212) 967-1100

EMERGENCY CONTACT:
JOHN S. BRANSFORD, JR. (615) 292-1180

SUBSTANCE IDENTIFICATION

CAS-NUMBER 298-00-0

SUBSTANCE: **METHYL PARATHION**

TRADE NAMES/SYNONYMS: PHOSPHOROTHIOIC ACID, O,O-DIMETHYL O-(4-NITROPHENYL)ESTER; PHOSPHOROTHIOIC ACID, O,O-DIMETHYL O-(P-NITROPHENYL)ESTER; O,O-DIMETHYL O-(P-NITROPHENYL) PHOSPHOROTHIOATE; O,O-DIMETHYL O-P-NITROPHENYL PHOSPHOROTHIOATE; O,O-DIMETHYL O-P-NITROPHENYL THIOPHOSPHATE; O,O-DIMETHYL O-4-NITROPHENYL PHOSPHOROTHIOATE; O,O-DIMETHYL O-(4-NITROPHENYL) PHOSPHOROTHIOATE; DIMETHYL PARATHION; PARATHION-METHYL; PARATHION-METHYL HOMOLOG; METACIDE; METAPHOS; METHYLTHIOPHOS; RCRA P071; NCI-C02971; ENT 17,292; STCC 4921443; PST14680

CHEMICAL FAMILY: ORGANOPHOSPHATE

MOLECULAR FORMULA: C8-H10-N-O5-P-S

MOLECULAR WEIGHT: 263.22

CERCLA RATINGS (SCALE 0-3): HEALTH=3 FIRE=1 REACTIVITY=2 PERSISTENCE=2

NFPA RATINGS (SCALE 0-4): HEALTH=4 FIRE=1 REACTIVITY=2

COMPONENTS AND CONTAMINANTS

COMPONENT: METHYL PARATHION ***PERCENT:*** 100.00
CAS# 298-00-0

EXPOSURE LIMITS: METHYL PARATHION: 0.2 MG/M3 OSHA TWA (SKIN) 0.2 MG/M3 ACGIH TWA (SKIN) 0.2 MG/M3 NIOSH RECOMMENDED 10 HOUR TWA 100/10,000 POUNDS SARA SECTION 302 THRESHOLD PLANNING QUANTITY 100 POUNDS SARA SECTION 304 REPORTABLE QUANTITY 100 POUNDS CERCLA SECTION 103 REPORTABLE QUANTITY

PHYSICAL DATA

DESCRIPTION: WHITE CRYSTALLINE POWDER ***BOILING POINT:*** 228 F (109 C) @ 0.05 MMHG

MELTING POINT: 97 F (36 C) ***SPECIFIC GRAVITY:*** 1.358

VAPOR PRESSURE: 0.000097 MMHG @ 20 C ***SOLUBILITY IN WATER:*** 55-60 PPM @ 25 C

SOLVENT SOLUBILITY: SOLUBLE IN DICHLOROMETHANE, PROPAN-2-OL, AND MOST ORGANIC SOLVENTS; SLIGHTLY SOLUBLE IN ALIPHATIC HYDROCARBONS, LIGHT PETROLEUM, AND MINERAL OILS

FIRE AND EXPLOSION DATA

FIRE AND EXPLOSION HAZARD: SLIGHT FIRE HAZARD WHEN EXPOSED TO HEAT OR FLAME.

FIREFIGHTING MEDIA: DRY CHEMICAL, CARBON DIOXIDE, HALON, WATER SPRAY OR STANDARD FOAM (1987 EMERGENCY RESPONSE GUIDEBOOK, DOT P 5800.4). FOR LARGER FIRES, USE WATER SPRAY, FOG OR STANDARD FOAM (1987 EMERGENCY RESPONSE GUIDEBOOK, DOT P 5800.4).

FIREFIGHTING: MOVE CONTAINERS FROM FIRE AREA IF POSSIBLE. FIGHT FIRE FROM MAXIMUM DISTANCE. STAY AWAY FROM STORAGE TANK ENDS. DIKE FIRE CONTROL WATER FOR LATER DISPOSAL. DO NOT SCATTER MATERIAL (1987 EMERGENCY RESPONSE GUIDEBOOK, DOT P 5800.4, GUIDE PAGE 55).
EXTINGUISH ONLY IF FLOW CAN BE STOPPED; USE FLOODING AMOUNTS OF WATER AS FOG, SOLID STREAMS MAY BE INEFFECTIVE. COOL CONTAINERS WITH FLOODING AMOUNTS OF WATER FROM AS FAR A DISTANCE AS POSSIBLE. USE WATER SPRAY TO ABSORB TOXIC VAPORS. AVOID BREATHING TOXIC VAPORS; KEEP UPWIND. CONSIDER EVACUATION OF DOWNWIND AREA IF MATERIAL IS LEAKING.
FIRE FIGHTING PHASES: DANGEROUS EXPOSURE TO PERSONS FIGHTING FIRES. IN ADVANCED OR MASSIVE FIRES, FIRE FIGHTING SHOULD BE DONE FROM A SAFE DISTANCE OR FROM A PROTECTED LOCATION. USE WATER SPRAY, DRY CHEMICAL, FOAM, OR CARBON D OXIDE. USE WATER TO KEEP FIRE-EXPOSED CONTAINERS COOL. IF A LEAK OR SPILL HAS NOT IGNITED, USE WATER SPRAY TO DISPERSE THE VAPORS. IF IT IS NECESSARY TO STOP A LEAK, USE WATER SPRAY TO PROTECT MEN ATTEMPTING TO DO SO. WATER SPRAY MAY BE USED TO FLUSH SPILLS AWAT FROM EXPOSURES (NFPA 49, HAZARDOUS CHEMICALS DATA, 1975).

TRANSPORTATION DATA

DEPARTMENT OF TRANSPORTATION HAZARD CLASSIFICATION 49 CFR 172.101: POISON B

DEPARTMENT OF TRANSPORTATION LABELING REQUIREMENTS 49 CFR 172.101 AND SUBPART E: POISON

DEPARTMENT OF TRANSPORTATION PACKAGING REQUIREMENTS: 49 CFR 173.358 EXCEPTIONS: NONE

TOXICITY

METHYL PARATHION: TOXICITY DATA: 34 MG/M3/4 HOURS INHALATION-RAT LC50; 120 MG/M3/4 HOURS INHALATION-MOUSE LC50; 300 MG/KG SKIN-RABBIT LD50; 63 MG/KG SKIN-RAT LD50; 1200 MG/KG SKIN-MOUSE LD50; 6010 UG/KG ORAL-RAT LD50; 18 MG/KG ORAL-MOUSE LD50; 420 MG/KG ORAL-RABBIT LD50; 1270 MG/KG ORAL-GUINEA PIG LD50; 90 MG/KG ORAL-DOG LD50; 57 MG/KG ORAL-MAMMAL LD50; 6 MG/KG SUBCUTANEOUS-RAT LD50; 18 MG/KG SUBCUTANEOUS-MOUSE LD50; 9 MG/KG INTRAVENOUS-RAT LD50; 9800 UG/KG INTRAVENOUS-MOUSE LD50; 50 MG/KG INTRAVENOUS-GUINEA PIG LD50; 2800 UG/KG INTRAPERITONEAL-RAT LD50; 5400 UG/KG INTRAPERITONEAL-MOUSE LD50; 47 MG/KG INTRACEREBRAL-MOUSE LD50; 10 MG/KG UNREPORTED-RAT LD50; 23 MG/KG UNREPORTED-MOUSE LD50; 25 MG/KG UNREPORTED-MAMMAL LD50; MUTAGENIC DATA (RTECS); REPRODUCTIVE EFFECTS DATA (RTECS). CARCINOGEN STATUS: NONE. (IARC GROUP 3). ACUTE TOXICITY LEVEL: HIGHLY TOXIC BY INHALATION AND INGESTION, AND TOXIC BY DERMAL ABSORPTION. TARGET EFFECTS: CHOLINESTERASE INHIBITOR. POISONING MAY AFFECT THE NERVOUS SYSTEM.* AT INCREASED RISK FROM EXPOSURE: PERSONS WITH RESPIRATORY AILMENTS, RECENT EXPOSURE TO CHOLINESTERASE INHIBITORS OR IMPAIRED CHOLINESTERASE PRODUCTION, OR LIVER MALFUNCTION.* ADDITIONAL DATA: MAY CROSS THE PLACENTA. HIGH ENVIRONMENTAL TEMPERATURES OR EXPOSURE OF THE CHEMICAL TO VISIBLE OR ULTRAVIOLET LIGHT MAY ENHANCE THE TOXICITY. INTERACTIONS WITH MEDICATIONS MAY OCCUR.*

* MAY BE BASED ON GENERAL INFORMATION ON ORGANOPHOSPHATES.

HEALTH EFFECTS AND FIRST AID

INHALATION: METHYL PARATHION: HIGHLY TOXIC. SEE INFORMATION ON ORGANOPHOSPHATES.
ORGANOPHOSPHATES: CHOLINESTERASE INHIBITOR. **ACUTE EXPOSURE-** WHEN INHALED, THE FIRST EFFECTS OF CHOLINESTERASE INHIBITORS ARE USUALLY RESPIRATORY AND MAY INCLUDE NASAL HYPEREMIA AND WATERY DISCHARGE, COUGH, CHEST DISCOMFORT, DYSPNEA, AND WHEEZING DUE TO INCREASED BRONCHIAL SECRETIONS AND BRONCHOCONSTRICTION. IF SUFFICIENT AMOUNTS ARE ABSORBED, OTHER SYSTEMIC EFFECTS MAY BEGIN WITHIN A FEW MINUTES OR BE DELAYED FOR UP TO 12 HOURS. SYMPTOMS MAY INCLUDE PALLOR, NAUSEA, VOMITING, DIARRHEA, ABDOMINAL CRAMPS, HEADACHE, DIZZINESS, OCULAR PAIN, BLURRED VISION, MIOSIS OR IN SOME CASES, ESPECIALLY INITIALLY, MYDRIASIS, LACRIMATION, SALIVATION, SWEATING, AND CONFUSION. OTHER REPORTED CENTRAL NERVOUS SYSTEM OR NEUROMUSCULAR EFFECTS MAY INCLUDE ATAXIA, SLURRED SPEECH, AREFLEXIA, WEAKNESS, FATIGUE, FASCICULATIONS, TWITCHING, TREMORS POSSIBLY OF THE TONGUE AND EYELIDS, AND EVENTUALLY PARALYSIS OF THE EXTREMITIES AND POSSIBLY OF THE RESPIRATORY MUSCLES. IN SEVERE CASES THERE MAY ALSO BE INVOLUNTARY DEFECATION AND URINATION, CYANOSIS, PSYCHOSIS, HYPERGLYCEMIA, ACUTE PANCREATITIS, CARDIAC IRREGULARITIES, PULMONARY EDEMA, UNCONSCIOUSNESS, CONVULSIONS, AND COMA. DEATH IS PRIMARILY DUE TO RESPIRATORY FAILURE, ALTHOUGH CARDIOVASCULAR EFFECTS INCLUDING CARDIAC ARREST MAY ALSO BE IMPLICATED. LONG TERM SEQUELAE ARE RARE BUT MAY INCLUDE NEUROPSYCHIATRIC DISORDERS AND MYOPATHY WITH MUSCLE TENDERNESS. SOME ORGANOPHOSPHATES MAY CAUSE A DELAYED NEUROPATHY BEGINNING 1-4 WEEKS AFTER AN ACUTE EXPOSURE WHICH MAY OR MAY NOT HAVE CAUSED ACUTE CHOLINERGIC EFFECTS. NUMBNESS, TINGLING, WEAKNESS AND CRAMPING BEGINNING SYMMETRICALLY IN THE LOWER LIMBS MAY PROGRESS TO ATAXIA AND PARALYSIS. IN SEVERE CASES, UPPER LIMB INVOLVEMENT IS POSSIBLE AND FLACCID PARALYSIS MAY PROGRESS TO SPASTIC PARALYSIS WITH EXAGGERATED REFLEXES. IMPROVEMENT MAY OCCUR OVER MONTHS TO YEARS, BUT SOME RESIDUAL IMPAIRMENT USUALLY REMAINS.
CHRONIC EXPOSURE- REPEATED OR PROLONGED EXPOSURE MAY RESULT IN THE EFFECTS OF ACUTE EXPOSURE INCLUDING THE DELAYED NEUROPATHY. OTHER EFFECTS REPORTED IN WORKERS REPEATEDLY EXPOSED INCLUDE IMPAIRED MEMORY AND CONCENTRATION, ACUTE PSYCHOSIS, SEVERE DEPRESSIONS, IRRITABILTY, CONFUSION, APATHY, EMOTIONAL LABILITY, SOCIAL WITHDRAWAL, CONFUSION, HEADACHE, SPEECH DIFFICULTIES, DELAYED REACTION TIMES, SPATIAL DISORIENTATION, NIGHTMARES, SLEEPWALKING, AND DROWSINESS OR INSOMNIA. AN INFLUENZA-LIKE CONDITION WITH HEADACHE, NAUSEA, WEAKNESS, ANOREXIA AND MALAISE HAS ALSO BEEN REPORTED.

FIRST AID- REMOVE FROM EXPOSURE AREA TO FRESH AIR IMMEDIATELY. IF BREATHING HAS STOPPED, GIVE ARTIFICIAL RESPIRATION. MAINTAIN AIRWAY AND BLOOD PRESSURE AND ADMINISTER OXYGEN IF AVAILABLE. KEEP AFFECTED PERSON WARM AND AT REST. TREAT SYMPTOMATICALLY AND SUPPORTIVELY. ADMINISTRATION OF OXYGEN SHOULD BE PERFORMED BY QUALIFIED PERSONNEL. GET MEDICAL ATTENTION IMMEDIATELY.

SKIN CONTACT: METHYL PARATHION: TOXIC. SEE INFORMATION ON ORGANOPHOSPHATES.
ORGANOPHOSPHATES: CHOLINESTERASE INHIBITOR. **ACUTE EXPOSURE-** LOCALIZED SWEATING AND FASCICULATIONS MAY OCCUR AT THE SITE OF CONTACT. IF SUFFICIENT-AMOUNTS ARE ABSORBED, OTHER EFFECTS OF CHOLINESTERASE INHIBITION AS DESCRIBED IN ACUTE INHALATION MAY OCCUR. SYMPTOMS MAY BE DELAYED 2-3 HOURS, BUT USUALLY NO MORE THAN 12 HOURS. THE RATE OF ABSORPTION IS INCREASED BY THE PRESENCE OF DERMATITIS OR HIGH AMBIENT TEMPERATURES. DELAYED NEUROPATHY IS ALSO POSSIBLE. **CHRONIC EXPOSURE-** REPEATED OR PROLONGED EXPOSURE MAY CAUSE EFFECTS AS DESCRIBED IN ACUTE EXPOSURE. SOME ORGANOPHOSPHATES MAY CAUSE SENSITIZATION.

FIRST AID- REMOVE CONTAMINATED CLOTHING IMMEDIATELY. WASH CONTAMINATED AREAS WITH SOAP AND WATER FOLLOWED BY ALCOHOL (ARENA, POISONING, 4TH ED.). EMERGENCY PERSONNEL SHOULD WEAR GLOVES AND AVOID CONTAMINATION. TREAT RESPIRATORY DIFFICULTY WITH ARTIFICIAL RESPIRATION. GET MEDICAL ATTENTION IMMEDIATELY.

EYE CONTACT: METHYL PARATHION: SEE INFORMATION ON ORGANOPHOSPHATES.
ORGANOPHOSPHATES: CHOLINESTERASE INHIBITOR. **ACUTE EXPOSURE-** DIRECT CONTACT MAY CAUSE PAIN, HYPEREMIA, LACRIMATION, TWITCHING OF THE EYELIDS, MIOSIS, AND CILIARY MUSCLE SPASM WITH LOSS OF ACCOMODATION, BLURRED OR DIMMED VISION AND BROWACHE. SOMETIMES MYDRIASIS MAY OCCUR INSTEAD OF MIOSIS. WITH SUFFICIENT EXPOSURE, OTHER SYMPTOMS OF CHOLINESTERASE INHIBITION AS DESCRIBED IN ACUTE INHALATION MAY OCCUR. **CHRONIC EXPOSURE-** REPEATED OR PROLONGED EXPOSURE MAY CAUSE EFFECTS AS DESCRIBED IN ACUTE EXPOSURE. SOME COMPOUNDS HAVE CAUSED TOXIC

EFFECTS ON THE CRYSTALLINE LENS, CONJUNCTIVAL THICKENING AND OBSTRUCTION OF THE NASOLACRIMAL CANALS WHEN USED AS MIOTIC EYEDROPS.

FIRST AID- IRRIGATE EYES WITH WATER OR SALINE SOLUTION. IF SYMPTOMS OF POISONING OCCUR, TREAT RESPIRATORY DIFFICULTY WITH ARTIFICIAL RESPIRATION AND OXYGEN. OBSERVE PATIENT FOR AT LEAST 24-36 HOURS (GOSSELIN, CLINICAL TOXICOLOGY OF COMMERCIAL PRODUCTS, 5TH ED.). GET MEDICAL ATTENTION IMMEDIATELY. OXYGEN SHOULD BE ADMINISTERED BY QUALIFIED MEDICAL PERSONNEL.

INGESTION: METHYL PARATHION: HIGHLY TOXIC. CHRONIC ADMINISTRATION TO PREGNANT RATS RESULTED IN ADVERSE EFFECTS ON THE NEWBORN, FETUS, AND FERTILITY. SEE INFORMATION ON ORGANOPHOSPHATES.
ORGANOPHOSPHATES: CHOLINESTERASE INHIBITOR. **ACUTE EXPOSURE**- WHEN INGESTED, THE FIRST EFFECTS MAY BE NAUSEA, VOMITING, ANOREXIA, ABDOMINAL CRAMPS AND DIARRHEA. GASTROINTESTINAL ABSORPTION MAY CAUSE SYMPTOMS OF CHOLINESTERASE INHIBITION AS DESCRIBED IN ACUTE INHALATION. SYMPTOMS MAY BEGIN WITHIN MINUTES OR BE DELAYED FOR HOURS. DELAYED EFFECTS INCLUDING NEUROPATHY MAY ALSO OCCUR. **CHRONIC EXPOSURE**- REPEATED INGESTION MAY CAUSE EFFECTS AS DESCRIBED IN ACUTE EXPOSURE.

FIRST AID- IF PERSON IS ALERT AND RESPIRATION IS NOT DEPRESSED, GIVE SYRUP OF IPECAC FOLLOWED BY WATER (IF VOMITING OCCURS, KEEP HEAD BELOW HIPS TO PREVENT ASPIRATION). IF CONSCIOUSNESS LEVEL DECLINES OR VOMITING HAS NOT OCCURRED IN 15 MINUTES EMPTY STOMACH BY GASTRIC LAVAGE WITH THE AID OF CUFFED ENDOTRACHEAL TUBE USING ISOTONIC SALINE OR 5% SODIUM BICARBONATE FOLLOW WITH ACTIVATED CHARCOAL. ESTABLISH AND MAINTAIN AIRWAY. TREAT RESPIRATORY DIFFICULTY WITH ARTIFICIAL RESPIRATION AND OXYGEN. DO NOT GIVE MORPHINE, AMINOPHYLLINE, PHENOTHIAZINES, RESERPINE, FUROSEMIDE, OR ETHACRYNIC ACID (MORGAN, RECOGNITION AND MANAGEMENT OF PESTICIDE POISONINGS, 3RD ED.). TREAT SYMPTOMATICALLY AND SUPPORTIVELY. ADMINISTRATION OF OXYGEN AND LAVAGE MUST BE PERFORMED BY QUALIFIED MEDICAL PERSONNEL. GET MEDICAL ATTENTION IMMEDIATELY.

ANTIDOTE: THE FOLLOWING ANTIDOTE(S) HAVE BEEN RECOMMENDED. HOWEVER, THE DECISION AS TO WHETHER THE SEVERITY OF POISONING REQUIRES ADMINISTRATION OF ANY ANTIDOTE AND ACTUAL DOSE REQUIRED SHOULD BE MADE BY QUALIFIED MEDICAL PERSONNEL.
FOR CHOLINESTERASE INHIBITORS: ESTABLISH CLEAR AIRWAY AND TISSUE OXYGENATION BY ASPIRATION OF SECRETIONS, AND IF NECESSARY, BY ASSISTED PULMONARY VENTILATION WITH OXYGEN. IMPROVE TISSUE OXYGENATION AS MUCH AS POSSIBLE BEFORE ADMINISTERING ATROPINE TO MINIMIZE THE RISK OF VENTRICULAR FIBRILLATION. ADMINISTER ATROPINE SULFATE INTRAVENOUSLY, OR INTRAMUSCULARLY IF IV INJECTION IS NOT POSSIBLE. IN MODERATELY SEVERE POISONING ADMINISTER ATROPINE SULFATE, 0.4-2.0 MG REPEATED EVERY 15 MINUTES UNTIL ATROPINIZATION IS ACHIEVED (TACHYCARDIA, FLUSHING, DRY MOUTH, MYDRIASIS). MAINTAIN ATROPINIZATION BY REPEATED DOSES FOR 2-12 HOURS, OR LONGER, DEPENDING ON THE SEVERITY OF POISONING. THE APPEARANCE OF RALES IN THE LUNG BASES, MIOSIS, SALIVATION, NAUSEA, BRADYCARDIA, ARE ALL INDICATIONS OF INADEQUATE ATROPINIZATION. SEVERELY POISONED INDIVIDUALS MAY EXHIBIT REMARKABLE TOLERANCE TO ATROPINE; TWO OR MORE TIMES THE DOSAGES SUGGESTED ABOVE MAY BE NEEDED. PERSONS NOT POISONED OR ONLY SLIGHTLY POISONED, HOWEVER, MAY DEVELOP SIGNS OF ATROPINE TOXICITY FROM SUCH LARGE DOSAGES: FEVER, MUSCLE FIBRILLATIONS, AND DELIRIUM ARE THE MAIN SIGNS OF ATROPINE TOXICITY. IF THESE SIGNS APPEAR WHILE THE PATIENT IS FULLY ATROPINIZED, ATROPINE ADMINISTRATION SHOULD BE DISCONTINUED, AT LEAST TEMPORARILY. OBSERVE TREATED PATIENTS CLOSELY AT LEAST 24 HOURS TO INSURE THAT SYMPTOMS (POSSIBLY PULMONARY EDEMA) DO NOT RECUR AS ATROPINIZATION WEARS OFF. IN VERY SEVERE POISONINGS, METABOLIC DISPOSITION OF TOXICANT MAY REQUIRE SEVERAL HOURS OR DAYS DURING WHICH ATROPINIZATION MUST BE MAINTAINED. MARKEDLY LOWER LEVELS OF URINARY METABOLITES INDICATE THAT ATROPINE DOSAGE CAN BE TAPERED OFF. AS DOSAGE IS REDUCED, CHECK THE LUNG BASES FREQUENTLY FOR RALES. IF RALES ARE HEARD OR OTHER SYMPTOMS RETURN, RE-ESTABLISH ATROPINIZATION PROMPTLY (MORGAN, RECOGNITION AND MANAGEMENT OF PESTICIDE POISONINGS, 3RD ED.). ADMINISTRATION OF ANTIDOTE MUST BE PERFORMED BY QUALIFIED MEDICAL PERSONNEL.
IN CASES OF SEVERE POISONING BY ORGANOPHOSPHATE PESTICIDES IN WHICH RESPIRATORY DEPRESSION, MUSCLE WEAKNESS AND TWITCHINGS ARE SEVERE, GIVE PRALIDOXIME (PROTOPAM-AYERST, 2-PAM), 1.0 GRAM INTRAVENOUSLY AT NO MORE THAN 0.5 GRAM PER MINUTE. DOSAGE OF PRALIDOXIME MAY BE REPEATED IN 1-2 HOURS, THEN AT 10-12 HOUR INTERVALS IF NEEDED. IN VERY SEVERE POISONINGS, DOSAGE RATES MAY BE DOUBLED. TREATMENT WITH PRALIDOXIME WILL BE MOST EFFECTIVE IF GIVEN WITHIN THIRTY-SIX HOURS AFTER POISONING (MORGAN, RECOGNITION AND MANAGEMENT OF PESTICIDE POISONINGS, 3RD ED.). ANTIDOTE SHOULD BE ADMINISTERED BY QUALIFIED MEDICAL PERSONNEL.

REACTIVITY

REACTIVITY: DECOMPOSES ABOVE 122 F (50 C) WITH POSSIBLE EXPLOSIVE FORCE.

INCOMPATIBILITIES: METHYL PARATHION: STRONG OXIDIZERS: MAY REACT.
ALKALINE MATERIALS: HYDROLYZED.

DECOMPOSITION: THERMAL DECOMPOSITION MAY RELEASE TOXIC OXIDES OF NITROGEN, PHOSPHORUS, SULFUR AND CARBON.

POLYMERIZATION: HAZARDOUS POLYMERIZATION HAS NOT BEEN REPORTED TO OCCUR UNDER NORMAL TEMPERATURES AND PRESSURES.

STORAGE AND DISPOSAL

OBSERVE ALL FEDERAL, STATE AND LOCAL REGULATIONS WHEN STORING OR DISPOSING OF THIS SUBSTANCE. FOR ASSISTANCE, CONTACT THE DISTRICT DIRECTOR OF THE ENVIRONMENTAL PROTECTION AGENCY.

****STORAGE****

STORE IN ACCORDANCE WITH 40 CFR 165 RECOMMENDED PROCEDURES FOR THE DISPOSAL AND STORAGE OF PESTICIDES AND PESTICIDE CONTAINERS.
STORE AWAY FROM INCOMPATIBLE SUBSTANCES.
PROTECT AGAINST PHYSICAL DAMAGE. DO NOT STORE AT HIGH AMBIENT TEMPERATURES (AT 120 F SOME DECOMPOSITION OCCURS WITH RESULTING PRESSURE INCREASE). STORE IN AREAS WHERE ANY SPILLAGE FROM CONTAINERS WILL NOT ENDANGER WORKERS OR CONTAMINATE OTHER STORAGE. SEPARATE FROM OXIDIZING MATERIALS AND AVOID STORAGE NEAR COMBUSTIBLES (NFPA 49, HAZARDOUS CHEMICALS DATA, 1975).
STORE AT TEMPERATURES ABOVE 65 F (18 C) TO AVOID CRYSTALLIZATION.
THRESHOLD PLANNING QUANTITY (TPQ): THE SUPERFUND AMENDMENTS AND REAUTHORIZATION ACT (SARA) SECTION 302 REQUIRES THAT EACH FACILITY WHERE ANY EXTREMELY HAZARDOUS SUBSTANCE IS PRESENT IN A QUANTITY EQUAL TO OR GREATER THAN THE TPQ ESTABLISHED FOR THAT SUBSTANCE NOTIFY THE STATE EMERGENCY RESPONSE COMMISSION FOR THE STATE IN WHICH IT IS LOCATED. SECTION 303 OF SARA REQUIRES THESE FACILITIES TO PARTICIPATE IN LOCAL EMERGENCY RESPONSE PLANNING (40 CFR 355.30).

****DISPOSAL****

DISPOSAL MUST BE IN ACCORDANCE WITH 40 CFR 165 RECOMMENDED PROCEDURES FOR THE DISPOSAL AND STORAGE OF PESTICIDES AND PESTICIDE CONTAINERS.

CONDITIONS TO AVOID

MAY BURN BUT DOES NOT IGNITE READILY. CONTAINERS MAY EXPLODE IN HEAT OF FIRE.
DO NOT HEAT PRODUCT ABOVE 131 F (55 C).

SPILL AND LEAK PROCEDURES

SOIL SPILL: DIG HOLDING AREA SUCH AS LAGOON, POND OR PIT FOR CONTAINMENT. USE PROTECTIVE COVER SUCH AS A PLASTIC SHEET TO PREVENT MATERIAL FROM DISSOLVING IN FIRE EXTINGUISHING WATER OR RAIN.

WATER SPILL: TRAP SPILLED MATERIAL AT BOTTOM IN DEEP WATER POCKETS, EXCAVATED HOLDING AREAS OR WITHIN SAND BAG BARRIERS.
IF DISSOLVED, APPLY ACTIVATED CARBON AT TEN TIMES THE SPILLED AMOUNT IN REGIONS OF 10 PPM OR GREATER CONCENTRATION.
USE SUCTION HOSES TO REMOVE TRAPPED SPILL MATERIAL.
USE MECHANICAL DREDGES OR LIFTS TO EXTRACT IMMOBILIZED MASSES OF POLLUTION AND PRECIPITATES.

OCCUPATIONAL SPILL: DO NOT TOUCH SPILLED MATERIAL. STOP LEAK IF YOU CAN DO IT WITHOUT RISK. USE WATER SPRAY TO REDUCE VAPORS. FOR SMALL SPILLS, TAKE UP WITH SAND OR OTHER ABSORBENT MATERIAL AND PLACE INTO CONTAINERS FOR LATER DISPOSAL. FOR SMALL DRY SPILLS, WITH A CLEAN SHOVEL PLACE MATERIAL INTO CLEAN, DRY CONTAINERS AND COVER. MOVE CONTAINERS FROM SPILL AREA. FOR LARGER SPILLS, DIKE FAR AHEAD OF SPILL FOR LATER DISPOSAL. KEEP UNNECESSARY PEOPLE AWAY. ISOLATE HAZARD AREA AND DENY ENTRY. VENTILATE CLOSED SPACES BEFORE ENTERING.
REPORTABLE QUANTITY (RQ): 100 POUNDS THE SUPERFUND AMENDMENTS AND REAUTHORIZATION ACT (SARA) SECTION 304 REQUIRES THAT A RELEASE EQUAL TO OR GREATER THAN THE REPORTABLE QUANTITY FOR THIS SUBSTANCE BE IMMEDIATELY REPORTED TO THE LOCAL EMERGENCY PLANNING COMMITTEE AND THE STATE EMERGENCY RESPONSE COMMISSION (40 CFR 355.40). IF THE RELEASE OF THIS SUBSTANCE IS REPORTABLE UNDER CERCLA SECTION 103, THE NATIONAL RESPONSE CENTER MUST BE NOTIFIED IMMEDIATELY AT (800) 424-8802 OR (202) 426-2675 IN THE METROPOLITAN WASHINGTON, D.C. AREA (40 CFR 302.6).

PROTECTIVE EQUIPMENT

VENTILATION: PROCESS ENCLOSURE RECOMMENDED TO MEET PUBLISHED EXPOSURE LIMITS.

RESPIRATOR: THE FOLLOWING RESPIRATORS AND MAXIMUM USE CONCENTRATIONS ARE RECOMMENDATIONS BY THE U.S. DEPARTMENT OF HEALTH AND HUMAN

SERVICES, NIOSH POCKET GUIDE TO CHEMICAL HAZARDS; NIOSH CRITERIA DOCUMENTS OR BY THE U.S. DEPARTMENT OF LABOR, 29 CFR 1910 SUBPART Z. THE SPECIFIC RESPIRATOR SELECTED MUST BE BASED ON CONTAMINATION LEVELS FOUND IN THE WORK PLACE, MUST NOT EXCEED THE WORKING LIMITS OF THE RESPIRATOR AND BE JOINTLY APPROVED BY THE NATIONAL INSTITUTE FOR OCCUPATIONAL SAFETY AND HEALTH AND THE MINE SAFETY AND HEALTH ADMINISTRATION (NIOSH-MSHA).

2 MG/M3 OR LESS- HALF-MASK PESTICIDE RESPIRATOR. TYPE C SUPPLIED-AIR RESPIRATOR, DEMAND TYPE (NEGATIVE PRESSURE), WITH HALF-MASK FACEPIECE.

10 MG/M3 OR LESS- FULLFACE GAS MASK (CHIN STYLE OR CHEST- OR BACK-MOUNTED TYPE). TYPE C SUPPLIED-AIR RESPIRATOR, DEMAND TYPE (NEGATIVE PRESSURE), WITH FULL FACEPIECE.

200 MG/M3 OR LESS- TYPE C SUPPLIED-AIR RESPIRATOR, CONTINUOUS-FLOW TYPE, WITH FULL FACEPIECE OR SUIT. PRESSUARE-DEMAND TYPE RESPIRATOR WITH FULL FACEPIECE AND IMPERVIOUS PLASTIC SHROUD.

EMERGENCY- SELF-CONTAINED BREATHING APPARATUS, POSITIVE PRESSURE TYPE, WITH FULL FACEPIECE. COMBINATION SUPPLIED-AIR RESPIRATOR, PRESSURE-DEMAND TYPE, WITH AUXILIARY SELF-CONTAINED AIR SUPPLY.

FOR FIREFIGHTING AND OTHER IMMEDIATELY DANGEROUS TO LIFE OR HEALTH CONDITIONS:

SELF-CONTAINED BREATHING APPARATUS WITH FULL FACEPIECE OPERATED IN PRESSURE-DEMAND OR OTHER POSITIVE PRESSURE MODE.

SUPPLIED-AIR RESPIRATOR WITH FULL FACEPIECE AND OPERATED IN PRESSURE-DEMAND OR OTHER POSITIVE PRESSURE MODE IN COMBINATION WITH AN AUXILIARY SELF-CONTAINED BREATHING APPARATUS OPERATED IN PRESSURE-DEMAND OR OTHER POSITIVE PRESSURE MODE.

CLOTHING: EMPLOYEE MUST WEAR APPROPRIATE PROTECTIVE (IMPERVIOUS) CLOTHING AND EQUIPMENT TO PREVENT ANY POSSIBILITY OF SKIN CONTACT WITH THIS SUBSTANCE.

GLOVES: EMPLOYEE MUST WEAR APPROPRIATE PROTECTIVE GLOVES TO PREVENT CONTACT WITH THIS SUBSTANCE.

EYE PROTECTION: EMPLOYEE MUST WEAR SPLASH-PROOF OR DUST-RESISTANT SAFETY GOGGLES AND A FACESHIELD TO PREVENT CONTACT WITH THIS SUBSTANCE.

EMERGENCY WASH FACILITIES: WHERE THERE IS ANY POSSIBILITY THAT AN EMPLOYEE'S EYES AND/OR SKIN MAY BE EXPOSED TO THIS SUBSTANCE, THE EMPLOYER SHOULD PROVIDE AN EYE WASH FOUNTAIN AND QUICK DRENCH SHOWER WITHIN THE IMMEDIATE WORK AREA FOR EMERGENCY USE.

AUTHORIZED BY- OCCUPATIONAL HEALTH SERVICES, INC.

CREATION DATE: 10/04/89 ***REVISION DATE:*** 07/12/90

MATERIAL SAFETY DATA SHEET

OCCUPATIONAL HEALTH SERVICES, INC.
AGRICULTURE AND PESTICIDE DIVISION
450 SEVENTH AVENUE, SUITE 2407
NEW YORK, NEW YORK 10123
1-800-445-MSDS OR (212) 967-1100

EMERGENCY CONTACT:
JOHN S. BRANSFORD, JR. (615) 292-1180

SUBSTANCE IDENTIFICATION

SUBSTANCE: METHYL PARATHION 80%

TRADE NAMES/SYNONYMS: STCC 4921442; PST14681

CERCLA RATINGS (SCALE 0-3): HEALTH=3 FIRE=3 REACTIVITY=2 PERSISTENCE=1

NFPA RATINGS (SCALE 0-4): HEALTH=4 FIRE=3 REACTIVITY=2

COMPONENTS AND CONTAMINANTS

COMPONENT: METHYL PARATHION ***PERCENT:*** 80.00
CAS# 298-00-0

COMPONENT: XYLENE ***PERCENT:*** 20.00
CAS# 1330-20-7

EXPOSURE LIMITS: METHYL PARATHION: 0.2 MG/M3 OSHA TWA (SKIN) 0.2 MG/M3 ACGIH TWA (SKIN) 0.2 MG/M3 NIOSH RECOMMENDED 10 HOUR TWA 100/10,000 POUNDS SARA SECTION 302 THRESHOLD PLANNING QUANTITY 100 POUNDS SARA SECTION 304 REPORTABLE QUANTITY 100 POUNDS CERCLA SECTION 103 REPORTABLE QUANTITY

XYLENE: 100 PPM (435 MG/M3) OSHA TWA; 150 PPM (655 MG/M3) OSHA STEL 100 PPM (435 MG/M3) ACGIH TWA; 150 PPM (655 MG/M3) ACGIH STEL 100 PPM (435 MG/M3) NIOSH RECOMMENDED 10 HOUR TWA; 200 PPM (870 MG/M3) NIOSH RECOMMENDED 10 MINUTE CEILING

1000 POUNDS CERCLA SECTION 103 REPORTABLE QUANTITY SUBJECT TO SARA SECTION 313 ANNUAL TOXIC CHEMICAL RELEASE REPORTING

PHYSICAL DATA

DESCRIPTION: LIGHT YELLOW LIQUID WITH A DIHYDROGEN SULFIDE OR SULFUROUS ODOR

BOILING POINT: 293 F (145 C) ***SPECIFIC GRAVITY:*** 1.24

VAPOR PRESSURE: <20 MMHG @ 30 C ***EVAPORATION RATE:*** NOT AVAILABLE

SOLUBILITY IN WATER: INSOLUBLE

SOLVENT SOLUBILITY: SOLUBLE IN MOST ORGANIC SOLVENTS

FIRE AND EXPLOSION DATA

FIRE AND EXPLOSION HAZARD: DANGEROUS FIRE HAZARD WHEN EXPOSED TO HEAT OR FLAME.

VAPOR-AIR MIXTURES ARE EXPLOSIVE ABOVE FLASH POINT.

FLASH POINT: 115 F (46 C) (OC) ***FLAMMABILITY CLASS(OSHA):*** II

FIREFIGHTING MEDIA: DRY CHEMICAL, CARBON DIOXIDE, HALON, WATER SPRAY OR STANDARD FOAM (1987 EMERGENCY RESPONSE GUIDEBOOK, DOT P 5800.4). FOR LARGER FIRES, USE WATER SPRAY, FOG OR STANDARD FOAM (1987 EMERGENCY RESPONSE GUIDEBOOK, DOT P 5800.4).

FIREFIGHTING: MOVE CONTAINERS FROM FIRE AREA IF POSSIBLE. FIGHT FIRE FROM MAXIMUM DISTANCE. STAY AWAY FROM STORAGE TANK ENDS. DIKE FIRE CONTROL WATER FOR LATER DISPOSAL. DO NOT SCATTER MATERIAL (1987 EMERGENCY RESPONSE GUIDEBOOK, DOT P 5800.4, GUIDE PAGE 55). EXTINGUISH ONLY IF FLOW CAN BE STOPPED; USE FLOODING AMOUNTS OF WATER AS FOG, SOLID STREAMS MAY BE INEFFECTIVE. COOL CONTAINERS WITH FLOODING AMOUNTS OF WATER FROM AS FAR A DISTANCE AS POSSIBLE. USE WATER SPRAY TO ABSORB TOXIC VAPORS. AVOID BREATHING TOXIC VAPORS; KEEP UPWIND. CONSIDER EVACUATION OF DOWNWIND AREA IF MATERIAL IS LEAKING.

TRANSPORTATION DATA

DEPARTMENT OF TRANSPORTATION HAZARD CLASSIFICATION 49 CFR 172.101: POISON B

DEPARTMENT OF TRANSPORTATION LABELING REQUIREMENTS 49 CFR 172.101 AND SUBPART E: POISON

DEPARTMENT OF TRANSPORTATION PACKAGING REQUIREMENTS: 49 CFR 173.359 EXCEPTIONS: NONE

TOXICITY

METHYL PARATHION: TOXICITY DATA: 34 MG/M3/4 HOURS INHALATION-RAT LC50; 120 MG/M3/4 HOURS INHALATION-MOUSE LC50; 300 MG/KG SKIN-RABBIT LD50; 63 MG/KG SKIN-RAT LD50; 1200 MG/KG SKIN-MOUSE LD50; 6010 UG/KG ORAL-RAT LD50; 18 MG/KG ORAL-MOUSE LD50; 420 MG/KG ORAL-RABBIT LD50; 1270 MG/KG ORAL-GUINEA PIG LD50; 90 MG/KG ORAL-DOG LD50; 57 MG/KG ORAL-MAMMAL LD50; 6 MG/KG SUBCUTANEOUS-RAT LD50; 18 MG/KG SUBCUTANEOUS-MOUSE LD50; 9 MG/KG INTRAVENOUS-RAT LD50; 9800 UG/KG INTRAVENOUS-MOUSE LD50; 50 MG/KG INTRAVENOUS-GUINEA PIG LD50; 2800 UG/KG INTRAPERITONEAL-RAT LD50; 5400 UG/KG INTRAPERITONEAL-MOUSE LD50; 47 MG/KG INTRACEREBRAL-MOUSE LD50; 10 MG/KG UNREPORTED-RAT LD50; 23 MG/KG UNREPORTED-MOUSE LD50; 25 MG/KG UNREPORTED-MAMMAL LD50; MUTAGENIC DATA (RTECS); REPRODUCTIVE EFFECTS DATA (RTECS). CARCINOGEN STATUS: NONE. (IARC GROUP 3). ACUTE TOXICITY LEVEL: HIGHLY TOXIC BY INHALATION AND INGESTION, AND TOXIC BY DERMAL ABSORPTION. TARGET EFFECTS: CHOLINESTERASE INHIBITOR. POISONING MAY AFFECT THE NERVOUS SYSTEM.* AT INCREASED RISK FROM EXPOSURE: PERSONS WITH RESPIRATORY AILMENTS, RECENT EXPOSURE TO CHOLINESTERASE INHIBITORS OR IMPAIRED CHOLINESTERASE PRODUCTION, OR LIVER MALFUNCTION.* ADDITIONAL DATA: MAY CROSS THE PLACENTA. HIGH ENVIRONMENTAL TEMPERATURES OR EXPOSURE OF THE CHEMICAL TO VISIBLE OR ULTRAVIOLET LIGHT MAY ENHANCE THE TOXICITY. INTERACTIONS WITH MEDICATIONS MAY OCCUR.*

* MAY BE BASED ON GENERAL INFORMATION ON ORGANOPHOSPHATES.

XYLENE: IRRITATION DATA: 200 PPM EYE-HUMAN; 87 MG EYE-RABBIT MILD; 5 MG/24 HOURS EYE-RABBIT SEVERE; 100% SKIN-RABBIT MODERATE; 500 MG/24 HOURS SKIN-RABBIT MODERATE. TOXICITY DATA: 10000 PPM/6 HOURS INHALATION-MAN LCLO; 200 PPM INHALATION-HUMAN TCLO; 5000 PPM/4 HOURS INHALATION-RAT LC50; 450 PPM INHALATION-GUINEA PIG LCLO; 50 MG/KG ORAL-HUMAN LDLO; 4300 MG/KG ORAL-RAT LD50; 1700 MG/KG SUBCUTANEOUS-RAT LD50; 129 MG/KG INTRAVENOUS-RABBIT LDLO; 2 GM/KG INTRAPERITONEAL-MAMMAL LDLO; 2459 MG/KG INTRAPERITONEAL-RAT LD50; 1548 MG/KG INTRAPERITONEAL-MOUSE LD50; 2000 MG/KG INTRAPERITONEAL-GUINEA PIG LDLO; REPRODUCTIVE EFFECTS DATA (RTECS). CARCINOGEN STATUS: NONE. LOCAL EFFECTS: IRRITANT- INHALATION, SKIN, EYE. ACUTE TOXICITY LEVEL: MODERATELY TOXIC BY INHALATION, INGESTION. TARGET EFFECTS: CENTRAL NERVOUS SYSTEM DEPRESSANT. POISONING MAY ALSO AFFECT THE NERVOUS SYSTEM, LIVER AND KIDNEYS. AT INCREASED RISK FROM EXPOSURE: PREGNANT

WOMEN. ADDITIONAL INFORMATION: CONSUMPTION OF ALCOHOLIC BEVERAGES MAY ENHANCE THE TOXIC EFFECTS. STIMULANTS SUCH AS EPINEPHRINE OR EPHEDRINE MAY INDUCE VENTRICULAR FIBRILLATION.

HEALTH EFFECTS AND FIRST AID

INHALATION: METHYL PARATHION: HIGHLY TOXIC. SEE INFORMATION ON ORGANOPHOSPHATES.

ORGANOPHOSPHATES: CHOLINESTERASE INHIBITOR. **ACUTE EXPOSURE-** WHEN INHALED, THE FIRST EFFECTS OF CHOLINESTERASE INHIBITORS ARE USUALLY RESPIRATORY AND MAY INCLUDE NASAL HYPEREMIA AND WATERY DISCHARGE, COUGH, CHEST DISCOMFORT, DYSPNEA, AND WHEEZING DUE TO INCREASED BRONCHIAL SECRETIONS AND BRONCHOCONSTRICTION. IF SUFFICIENT AMOUNTS ARE ABSORBED, OTHER SYSTEMIC EFFECTS MAY BEGIN WITHIN A FEW MINUTES OR BE DELAYED FOR UP TO 12 HOURS. SYMPTOMS MAY INCLUDE PALLOR, NAUSEA, VOMITING, DIARRHEA, ABDOMINAL CRAMPS, HEADACHE, DIZZINESS, OCULAR PAIN, BLURRED VISION, MIOSIS OR IN SOME CASES, ESPECIALLY INITIALLY, MYDRIASIS, LACRIMATION, SALIVATION, SWEATING, AND CONFUSION. OTHER REPORTED CENTRAL NERVOUS SYSTEM OR NEUROMUSCULAR EFFECTS MAY INCLUDE ATAXIA, SLURRED SPEECH, AREFLEXIA, WEAKNESS, FATIGUE, FASCICULATIONS, TWITCHING, TREMORS POSSIBLY OF THE TONGUE AND EYELIDS, AND EVENTUALLY PARALYSIS OF THE EXTREMITIES AND POSSIBLY OF THE RESPIRATORY MUSCLES. IN SEVERE CASES THERE MAY ALSO BE INVOLUNTARY DEFECATION AND URINATION, CYANOSIS, PSYCHOSIS, HYPERGLYCEMIA, ACUTE PANCREATITIS, CARDIAC IRREGULARITIES, PULMONARY EDEMA, UNCONSCIOUSNESS, CONVULSIONS, AND COMA. DEATH IS PRIMARILY DUE TO RESPIRATORY FAILURE, ALTHOUGH CARDIOVASCULAR EFFECTS INCLUDING CARDIAC ARREST MAY ALSO BE IMPLICATED. LONG TERM SEQUELAE ARE RARE BUT MAY INCLUDE NEUROPSYCHIATRIC DISORDERS AND MYOPATHY WITH MUSCLE TENDERNESS. SOME ORGANOPHOSPHATES MAY CAUSE A DELAYED NEUROPATHY BEGINNING 1-4 WEEKS AFTER AN ACUTE EXPOSURE WHICH MAY OR MAY NOT HAVE CAUSED ACUTE CHOLINERGIC EFFECTS. NUMBNESS, TINGLING, WEAKNESS AND CRAMPING BEGINNING SYMMETRICALLY IN THE LOWER LIMBS MAY PROGRESS TO ATAXIA AND PARALYSIS. IN SEVERE CASES, UPPER LIMB INVOLVEMENT IS POSSIBLE AND FLACCID PARALYSIS MAY PROGRESS TO SPASTIC PARALYSIS WITH EXAGGERATED REFLEXES. IMPROVEMENT MAY OCCUR OVER MONTHS TO YEARS, BUT SOME RESIDUAL IMPAIRMENT USUALLY REMAINS. **CHRONIC EXPOSURE-** REPEATED OR PROLONGED EXPOSURE MAY RESULT IN THE EFFECTS OF ACUTE EXPOSURE INCLUDING THE DELAYED NEUROPATHY. OTHER EFFECTS REPORTED IN WORKERS REPEATEDLY EXPOSED INCLUDE IMPAIRED MEMORY AND CONCENTRATION, ACUTE PSYCHOSIS, SEVERE DEPRESSIONS, IRRITABILTY, CONFUSION, APATHY, EMOTIONAL LABILITY, SOCIAL WITHDRAWAL, CONFUSION, HEADACHE, SPEECH DIFFICULTIES, DELAYED REACTION TIMES, SPATIAL DISORIENTATION, NIGHTMARES, SLEEPWALKING, AND DROWSINESS OR INSOMNIA. AN INFLUENZA-LIKE CONDITION WITH HEADACHE, NAUSEA, WEAKNESS, ANOREXIA AND MALAISE HAS ALSO BEEN REPORTED.

XYLENE: IRRITANT/NARCOTIC. 1000 PPM IMMEDIATELY DANGEROUS TO LIFE OR HEALTH. **ACUTE EXPOSURE-** IRRITATION OF THE UPPER RESPIRATORY TRACT MAY OCCUR AT 200 PPM. EXPOSURE TO HIGHER CONCENTRATIONS MAY CAUSE MORE SEVERE IRRITATION AND INITIAL CENTRAL NERVOUS SYSTEM EXCITATION FOLLOWED BY DEPRESSION. SIGNS AND SYMPTOMS MAY INCLUDE RESPIRATORY DIFFICULTY AND SUBSTERNAL PAIN, TRANSIENT EUPHORIA AND EMOTIONAL LABILITY, HEADACHE, NAUSEA, VOMITING, ANOREXIA, ABDOMINAL PAIN, DIZZINESS, DROWSINESS, ATAXIA, AND STAGGERING. THERE MAY BE SALIVATION, SLURRED SPEECH, BLURRED VISION, NYSTAGMUS, TINNITUS, TREMORS, CONFUSION, AND FLUSHING OF THE FACE AND A FEELING OF INCREASED BODY HEAT. IN SEVERE EXPOSURES, THERE MAY BE STUPOR, ANESTHESIA, UNCONSCIOUSNESS, AND COMA WHICH MAY BE PUNCTUATED BY EPISODES OF NEUROIRRITABILITY, BUT RARELY FRANK CONVULSIONS, EXCEPT IN TERMINAL ASPHYXIA. LIVER AND KIDNEY DAMAGE MAY OCCUR, BUT ARE USUALLY MILD AND TRANSIENT. A GROUP OF SUBJECTS WHO INHALED 12.3 UMOL/L OF XYLENE WHILE EXERCISING BECAME SIGNIFICANTLY IMPAIRED ON 3 NEUROPSYCHOLOGICAL TESTS. EXPOSURE OF 3 PAINTERS TO APPROXIMATELY 10,000 PPM FOR 18.5 HOURS RESULTED IN 1 DEATH FROM PULMONARY EDEMA AND PETECHIAL BRAIN HEMORRHAGE. BOTH SURVIVORS WERE UNCONSCIOUS FOR 19-24 HOURS AND EXPERIENCED RETROGRADE AMNESIA, HYPOTHERMIA, AND LUNG CONGESTION. RENAL AND HEPATIC IMPAIRMENT ALSO DEVELOPED. COMPLETE RECOVERY TOOK 15 DAYS. HIGH CONCENTRATIONS MAY CAUSE DEATH FROM SUDDEN VENTRICULAR FIBRILLATION, BUT MORE FREQUENTLY DEATH OCCURS FROM RESPIRATORY ARREST. **CHRONIC EXPOSURE-** REPEATED OR PROLONGED INHALATION OF VAPORS ABOVE 200 PPM MAY CAUSE NAUSEA, VOMITING, ABDOMINAL PAIN, AND ANOREXIA. OTHER COMMON COMPLAINTS INCLUDE HEADACHE, FATIGUE, LASSITUDE, IRRITABILITY, BREATHING DIFFICULTIES, AND FLATULENCE. EFFECTS ON THE NERVOUS SYSTEM MAY RESULT IN EXCITATION, FOLLOWED BY DEPRESSION, PARESTHESIAS, TREMORS, APPREHENSION, IMPAIRED MEMORY, INSOMNIA, VERTIGO, AND TINNITUS. EFFECTS ON REACTION TIME, MANUAL COORDINATION, BODY BALANCE AND EEG OCCURRED WITH REPEATED EXPOSURE TO 90 PPM OF M-XYLENE. SWEETISH TASTE IN THE MOUTH, DRY NOSE AND THROAT, STRONG THIRST, MUCOSAL HEMORRHAGE, AND ANEMIA HAVE BEEN REPORTED. EFFECTS ON THE LIVER, KIDNEY, CARDIOVASCULAR SYSTEM, AND THE BONE MARROW HAVE ALSO BEEN REPORTED, ALTHOUGH THE LATTER HAS BEEN QUESTIONED. EXPOSURE OF RABBITS TO 1150 PPM FOR 40-55 DAYS RESULTED IN A REVERSIBLE DECREASE IN THE RED AND WHITE CELL COUNTS AND AN INCREASE IN THE PLATELETS. ONE CASE OF AN APPARENT EPILEPTIFORM SEIZURE FOLLOWING A RELATIVELY BRIEF EXPOSURE HAS OCCURRED. WOMEN MAY DEVELOP MENSTRUAL DISORDERS, SUCH AS MENORRHAGIA OR METRORRHAGIA, INFERTILITY, AND PATHOLOGICAL PREGNANCY CONDITIONS INCLUDING TOXICOSIS, DANGER OF MISCARRIAGE, AND HEMORRHAGING DURING DELIVERY. REPEATED EXPOSURE OF PREGNANT MICE, RATS AND RABBITS TO THE INDIVIDUAL OR THE MIXED ISOMERS HAS RESULTED IN MATERNAL EFFECTS AND EFFECTS ON FERTILITY, ON THE EMBRYO OR FETUS, AND SPECIFIC DEVELOPMENTAL ABNORMALITIES. INCLUDED AMONG THESE EFFECTS ARE FETAL DEATH, FETOTOXICITY, PRE- AND POST-IMPLANTATION MORTALITY, ABORTION, CRANIOFACIAL AND MUSCULOSKELETAL ABNORMALITIES, AND EXTRA EMBRYONIC STRUCTURES.

FIRST AID- REMOVE FROM EXPOSURE AREA TO FRESH AIR IMMEDIATELY. IF BREATHING HAS STOPPED, GIVE ARTIFICIAL RESPIRATION. MAINTAIN AIRWAY AND BLOOD PRESSURE AND ADMINISTER OXYGEN IF AVAILABLE. KEEP AFFECTED PERSON WARM AND AT REST. TREAT SYMPTOMATICALLY AND SUPPORTIVELY. ADMINISTRATION OF OXYGEN SHOULD BE PERFORMED BY QUALIFIED PERSONNEL. GET MEDICAL ATTENTION IMMEDIATELY.

SKIN CONTACT: METHYL PARATHION: TOXIC. SEE INFORMATION ON ORGANOPHOSPHATES.

ORGANOPHOSPHATES: CHOLINESTERASE INHIBITOR. **ACUTE EXPOSURE-** LOCALIZED SWEATING AND FASCICULATIONS MAY OCCUR AT THE SITE OF CONTACT. IF SUFFICIENT AMOUNTS ARE ABSORBED, OTHER EFFECTS OF CHOLINESTERASE INHIBITION AS DESCRIBED IN ACUTE INHALATION MAY OCCUR. SYMPTOMS MAY BE DELAYED 2-3 HOURS, BUT USUALLY NO MORE THAN 12 HOURS. THE RATE OF ABSORPTION IS INCREASED BY THE PRESENCE OF DERMATITIS OR HIGH AMBIENT TEMPERATURES. DELAYED NEUROPATHY IS ALSO POSSIBLE. **CHRONIC EXPOSURE-** REPEATED OR PROLONGED EXPOSURE MAY CAUSE EFFECTS AS DESCRIBED IN ACUTE EXPOSURE. SOME ORGANOPHOSPHATES MAY CAUSE SENSITIZATION.

XYLENE: IRRITANT. **ACUTE EXPOSURE-** LIQUID XYLENE IS A DEFATTING AGENT AND MAY CAUSE A BURNING SENSATION, DRYING, VASODILATION, ERYTHEMA, AND POSSIBLY BLISTERING. THE LIQUID IS READILY ABSORBED THROUGH INTACT OR BROKEN SKIN AT A RATE OF APPROXIMATELY 4-10 MG/CM2/HOUR, BUT SYSTEMIC EFFECTS HAVE NOT BEEN REPORTED. **CHRONIC EXPOSURE-** REPEATED OR PROLONGED CONTACT MAY CAUSE DEFATTING OF THE SKIN WITH DRYING, ERYTHEMA, CRACKING, THICKENING AND BLISTERING. REPEATED APPLICATION OF 95% XYLENE TO RABBIT SKIN CAUSED MODERATE TO MARKED IRRITATION WITH ERYTHEMA AND MODERATE NECROSIS. ONE CASE OF ALLERGIC CONTACT URTICARIA HAS BEEN REPORTED.

FIRST AID- REMOVE CONTAMINATED CLOTHING IMMEDIATELY. WASH CONTAMINATED AREAS WITH SOAP AND WATER FOLLOWED BY ALCOHOL (ARENA, POISONING, 4TH ED.). EMERGENCY PERSONNEL SHOULD WEAR GLOVES AND AVOID CONTAMINATION. TREAT RESPIRATORY DIFFICULTY WITH ARTIFICIAL RESPIRATION. GET MEDICAL ATTENTION IMMEDIATELY.

EYE CONTACT: METHYL PARATHION: SEE INFORMATION ON ORGANOPHOSPHATES.

ORGANOPHOSPHATES: CHOLINESTERASE INHIBITOR. **ACUTE EXPOSURE-** DIRECT CONTACT MAY CAUSE PAIN, HYPEREMIA, LACRIMATION, TWITCHING OF THE EYELIDS, MIOSIS, AND CILIARY MUSCLE SPASM WITH LOSS OF ACCOMODATION, BLURRED OR DIMMED VISION AND BROWACHE. SOMETIMES MYDRIASIS MAY OCCUR INSTEAD OF MIOSIS. WITH SUFFICIENT EXPOSURE, OTHER SYMPTOMS OF CHOLINESTERASE INHIBITION AS DESCRIBED IN ACUTE INHALATION MAY OCCUR. **CHRONIC EXPOSURE-** REPEATED OR PROLONGED EXPOSURE MAY CAUSE EFFECTS AS DESCRIBED IN ACUTE EXPOSURE. SOME COMPOUNDS HAVE CAUSED TOXIC EFFECTS ON THE CRYSTALLINE LENS, CONJUNCTIVAL THICKENING AND OBSTRUCTION OF THE NASOLACRIMAL CANALS WHEN USED AS MIOTIC EYEDROPS.

XYLENE: IRRITANT. **ACUTE EXPOSURE-** 200 PPM HAS CAUSED CONJUNCTIVAL IRRITATION IN HUMANS; AT HIGHER CONCENTRATIONS, IRRITATION MAY BE SEVERE. VAPOR EXPOSURE HAS ALSO CAUSED TEARING AND PHOTOPHOBIA. AN ACCIDENTAL SPLASH IN THE HUMAN EYE CAUSED TRANSIENT SUPERFICIAL DAMAGE WITH RAPID RECOVERY, ALTHOUGH REVERSIBLE CORNEAL BURNS HAVE ALSO BEEN REPORTED. **CHRONIC EXPOSURE-** REPEATED OR PROLONGED EXPOSURE TO HIGH VAPOR CONCENTRATIONS MAY CAUSE A BURNING SENSATION, CONJUNCTIVITIS AND BLURRED VISION; REVERSIBLE VACUOLAR, EPITHELIAL KERATOPATHY HAS BEEN REPORTED IN SOME WORKERS.

FIRST AID- IRRIGATE EYES WITH WATER OR SALINE SOLUTION. IF SYMPTOMS OF POISONING OCCUR, TREAT RESPIRATORY DIFFICULTY WITH ARTIFICIAL

RESPIRATION AND OXYGEN. OBSERVE PATIENT FOR AT LEAST 24-36 HOURS (GOSSELIN, CLINICAL TOXICOLOGY OF COMMERCIAL PRODUCTS, 5TH ED.). GET MEDICAL ATTENTION IMMEDIATELY. OXYGEN SHOULD BE ADMINISTERED BY QUALIFIED MEDICAL PERSONNEL.

INGESTION: METHYL PARATHION: HIGHLY TOXIC. CHRONIC ADMINISTRATION TO PREGNANT RATS RESULTED IN ADVERSE EFFECTS ON THE NEWBORN, FETUS, AND FERTILITY. SEE INFORMATION ON ORGANOPHOSPHATES.
ORGANOPHOSPHATES: CHOLINESTERASE INHIBITOR. **ACUTE EXPOSURE-** WHEN INGESTED, THE FIRST EFFECTS MAY BE NAUSEA, VOMITING, ANOREXIA, ABDOMINAL CRAMPS AND DIARRHEA. GASTROINTESTINAL ABSORPTION MAY CAUSE SYMPTOMS OF CHOLINESTERASE INHIBITION AS DESCRIBED IN ACUTE INHALATION. SYMPTOMS MAY BEGIN WITHIN MINUTES OR BE DELAYED FOR HOURS. DELAYED EFFECTS INCLUDING NEUROPATHY MAY ALSO OCCUR. **CHRONIC EXPOSURE-** REPEATED INGESTION MAY CAUSE EFFECTS AS DESCRIBED IN ACUTE EXPOSURE.
XYLENE: NARCOTIC. **ACUTE EXPOSURE-** MAY CAUSE A BURNING SENSATION IN THE MOUTH AND STOMACH, SALIVATION, SEVERE GASTROINTESTINAL DISTRESS WITH NAUSEA AND VOMITING, POSSIBLY HEMATEMESIS, AND TOXIC EFFECTS INCLUDING SIGNS OF CENTRAL NERVOUS SYSTEM DEPRESSION AND OTHER SYMPTOMS AS IN ACUTE INHALATION, INCLUDING VENTRICULAR FIBRILLATION AND LIVER AND KIDNEY INJURY. INGESTION OF SMALL QUANTITIES OF 90% XYLENE PLUS TOLUENE PRODUCED URINARY DEXTROSE AND UROBILINOGEN EXCRETION WITH TOXIC HEPATITIS, WHICH WAS REVERSIBLE IN 20 DAYS. A DOSE OF 15-30 MILLILITERS (ABOUT 1/2-1 OUNCE) IS THE EXPECTED HUMAN LETHAL DOSE. WITH ASPIRATION OF EVEN A FEW MILLILITERS INTO THE LUNGS, SEVERE COUGHING, DISTRESS, CHEMICAL PNEUMONITIS, RAPIDLY DEVELOPING PULMONARY EDEMA, AND HEMORRHAGE MAY OCCUR. **CHRONIC EXPOSURE-** NO DATA AVAILABLE ON THE ORTHO-ISOMER. REPEATED INGESTION OF THE MIXED, META-, OR PARA-ISOMERS BY PREGNANT MICE RESULTED IN EFFECTS ON FERTILITY, ON THE EMBRYO OR FETUS, OR SPECIFIC DEVELOPMENTAL ABNORMALITIES. INCLUDED AMONG THESE EFFECTS WERE FETOTOXICITY, LITTER SIZE, CRANIOFACIAL AND MUSCULOSKELETAL SYSTEM ABNORMALITIES, AND POST-IMPLANTATION MORTALITY.

FIRST AID- IF PERSON IS ALERT AND RESPIRATION IS NOT DEPRESSED, GIVE SYRUP OF IPECAC FOLLOWED BY WATER (IF VOMITING OCCURS, KEEP HEAD BELOW HIPS TO PREVENT ASPIRATION). IF CONSCIOUSNESS LEVEL DECLINES OR VOMITING HAS NOT OCCURRED IN 15 MINUTES EMPTY STOMACH BY GASTRIC LAVAGE WITH THE AID OF CUFFED ENDOTRACHEAL TUBE USING ISOTONIC SALINE OR 5% SODIUM BICARBONATE FOLLOW WITH ACTIVATED CHARCOAL. ESTABLISH AND MAINTAIN AIRWAY. TREAT RESPIRATORY DIFFICULTY WITH ARTIFICIAL RESPIRATION AND OXYGEN. DO NOT GIVE MORPHINE, AMINOPHYLLINE, PHENOTHIAZINES, RESERPINE, FUROSEMIDE, OR ETHACRYNIC ACID (MORGAN, RECOGNITION AND MANAGEMENT OF PESTICIDE POISONINGS, 3RD ED.). TREAT SYMPTOMATICALLY AND SUPPORTIVELY. ADMINISTRATION OF OXYGEN AND LAVAGE MUST BE PERFORMED BY QUALIFIED MEDICAL PERSONNEL. GET MEDICAL ATTENTION IMMEDIATELY.

ANTIDOTE: BECAUSE IT IS DIFFICULT TO DETERMINE HOW CHEMICALS WILL INTERACT ONCE COMBINED IN A MIXTURE, AN ANTIDOTE IS NOT NORMALLY LISTED. HOWEVER DUE TO THE SEVERE POISONING POTENTIAL OF METHYL PARATHION, THE ANTIDOTE IS MENTIONED MERELY AS A POSSIBLE AID TO A QUALIFIED MEDICAL PERSON TO DETERMINE IF THE SYMPTOMS DISPLAYED BY THE POISONED VICTIM MERIT THE USE OF THE ANTIDOTE.
FOR CHOLINESTERASE INHIBITORS: ESTABLISH CLEAR AIRWAY AND TISSUE OXYGENATION BY ASPIRATION OF SECRETIONS, AND IF NECESSARY, BY ASSISTED PULMONARY VENTILATION WITH OXYGEN. IMPROVE TISSUE OXYGENATION AS MUCH AS POSSIBLE BEFORE ADMINISTERING ATROPINE TO MINIMIZE THE RISK OF VENTRICULAR FIBRILLATION. ADMINISTER ATROPINE SULFATE INTRAVENOUSLY, OR INTRAMUSCULARLY IF IV INJECTION IS NOT POSSIBLE. IN MODERATELY SEVERE POISONING ADMINISTER ATROPINE SULFATE, 0.4-2.0 MG REPEATED EVERY 15 MINUTES UNTIL ATROPINIZATION IS ACHIEVED (TACHYCARDIA, FLUSHING, DRY MOUTH, MYDRIASIS). MAINTAIN ATROPINIZATION BY REPEATED DOSES FOR 2-12 HOURS, OR LONGER, DEPENDING ON THE SEVERITY OF POISONING. THE APPEARANCE OF RALES IN THE LUNG BASES, MIOSIS, SALIVATION, NAUSEA, BRADYCARDIA, ARE ALL INDICATIONS OF INADEQUATE ATROPINIZATION. SEVERELY POISONED INDIVIDUALS MAY EXHIBIT REMARKABLE TOLERANCE TO ATROPINE; TWO OR MORE TIMES THE DOSAGES SUGGESTED ABOVE MAY BE NEEDED. PERSONS NOT POISONED OR ONLY SLIGHTLY POISONED, HOWEVER, MAY DEVELOP SIGNS OF ATROPINE TOXICITY FROM SUCH LARGE DOSAGES: FEVER, MUSCLE FIBRILLATIONS, AND DELIRIUM ARE THE MAIN SIGNS OF ATROPINE TOXICITY. IF THESE SIGNS APPEAR WHILE THE PATIENT IS FULLY ATROPINIZED, ATROPINE ADMINISTRATION SHOULD BE DISCONTINUED, AT LEAST TEMPORARILY. OBSERVE TREATED PATIENTS CLOSELY AT LEAST 24 HOURS TO INSURE THAT SYMPTOMS (POSSIBLY PULMONARY EDEMA) DO NOT RECUR AS ATROPINIZATION WEARS OFF. IN VERY SEVERE POISONINGS, METABOLIC DISPOSITION OF TOXICANT MAY REQUIRE SEVERAL HOURS OR DAYS DURING WHICH ATROPINIZATION MUST BE MAINTAINED. MARKEDLY LOWER LEVELS OF URINARY METABOLITES INDICATE THAT ATROPINE DOSAGE CAN BE TAPERED OFF. AS DOSAGE IS REDUCED, CHECK THE LUNG BASES FREQUENTLY FOR RALES. IF RALES ARE HEARD OR OTHER SYMPTOMS RETURN, RE-ESTABLISH ATROPINIZATION PROMPTLY (MORGAN, RECOGNITION AND MANAGEMENT OF PESTICIDE POISONINGS, 3RD ED.). ADMINISTRATION OF ANTIDOTE MUST BE PERFORMED BY QUALIFIED MEDICAL PERSONNEL.
IN CASES OF SEVERE POISONING BY ORGANOPHOSPHATE PESTICIDES IN WHICH RESPIRATORY DEPRESSION, MUSCLE WEAKNESS AND TWITCHINGS ARE SEVERE, GIVE PRALIDOXIME (PROTOPAM-AYERST, 2-PAM), 1.0 GRAM INTRAVENOUSLY AT NO MORE THAN 0.5 GRAM PER MINUTE. DOSAGE OF PRALIDOXIME MAY BE REPEATED IN 1-2 HOURS, THEN AT 10-12 HOUR INTERVALS IF NEEDED. IN VERY SEVERE POISONINGS, DOSAGE RATES MAY BE DOUBLED. TREATMENT WITH PRALIDOXIME WILL BE MOST EFFECTIVE IF GIVEN WITHIN THIRTY-SIX HOURS AFTER POISONING (MORGAN, RECOGNITION AND MANAGEMENT OF PESTICIDE POISONINGS, 3RD ED.). ANTIDOTE SHOULD BE ADMINISTERED BY QUALIFIED MEDICAL PERSONNEL.

REACTIVITY

REACTIVITY: DECOMPOSES ABOVE 122 F (50 C) WITH POSSIBLE EXPLOSIVE FORCE.

INCOMPATIBILITIES: METHYL PARATHION: STRONG OXIDIZERS: MAY REACT.
ALKALINE MATERIALS: HYDROLYZED.
XYLENE: NITRIC ACID: EXOTHERMIC REACTION. OXIDIZERS (STRONG): FIRE AND EXPLOSION HAZARD. PLASTICS, RUBBER, COATINGS: MAY BE ATTACKED.
SULFURIC ACID: EXOTHERMIC REACTION.

DECOMPOSITION: THERMAL DECOMPOSITION MAY RELEASE TOXIC AND/OR HAZARDOUS GASES.

POLYMERIZATION: HAZARDOUS POLYMERIZATION HAS NOT BEEN REPORTED TO OCCUR UNDER NORMAL TEMPERATURES AND PRESSURES.

STORAGE AND DISPOSAL

OBSERVE ALL FEDERAL, STATE AND LOCAL REGULATIONS WHEN STORING OR DISPOSING OF THIS SUBSTANCE. FOR ASSISTANCE, CONTACT THE DISTRICT DIRECTOR OF THE ENVIRONMENTAL PROTECTION AGENCY.

STORAGE

STORE IN ACCORDANCE WITH 40 CFR 165 RECOMMENDED PROCEDURES FOR THE DISPOSAL AND STORAGE OF PESTICIDES AND PESTICIDE CONTAINERS.
STORE AWAY FROM INCOMPATIBLE SUBSTANCES.
PROTECT AGAINST PHYSICAL DAMAGE. DO NOT STORE AT HIGH AMBIENT TEMPERATURES (AT 120 F SOME DECOMPOSITION OCCURS WITH RESULTING PRESSURE INCREASE). STORE IN AREAS WHERE ANY SPILLAGE FROM CONTAINERS WILL NOT ENDANGER WORKERS OR CONTAMINATE OTHER STORAGE. SEPARATE FROM OXIDIZING MATERIALS AND AVOID STORAGE NEAR COMBUSTIBLES (NFPA 49, HAZARDOUS CHEMICALS DATA, 1975).

DISPOSAL

DISPOSAL MUST BE IN ACCORDANCE WITH 40 CFR 165 RECOMMENDED PROCEDURES FOR THE DISPOSAL AND STORAGE OF PESTICIDES AND PESTICIDE CONTAINERS.

CONDITIONS TO AVOID

MAY BE IGNITED BY HEAT, SPARKS OR FLAMES. CONTAINER MAY EXPLODE IN HEAT OF FIRE. VAPOR EXPLOSION AND POISON HAZARD INDOORS, OUTDOORS OR IN SEWERS.

SPILL AND LEAK PROCEDURES

SOIL SPILL: DIG HOLDING AREA SUCH AS LAGOON, POND OR PIT FOR CONTAINMENT.
DIKE FLOW OF SPILLED MATERIAL USING SOIL OR SANDBAGS OR FOAMED BARRIERS SUCH AS POLYURETHANE OR CONCRETE.
USE CEMENT POWDER OR FLY ASH TO ABSORB LIQUID MASS.

AIR SPILL: KNOCK DOWN VAPORS WITH WATER SPRAY. KEEP UPWIND.

WATER SPILL: LIMIT SPILL MOTION AND DISPERSION WITH NATURAL BARRIERS OR OIL SPILL CONTROL BOOMS.
APPLY DETERGENTS, SOAPS, ALCOHOLS OR ANOTHER SURFACE ACTIVE AGENT.
APPLY UNIVERSAL GELLING AGENT TO IMMOBILIZE TRAPPED SPILL AND INCREASE EFFICIENCY OF REMOVAL.
IF DISSOLVED, APPLY ACTIVATED CARBON AT TEN TIMES THE SPILLED AMOUNT IN REGIONS OF 10 PPM OR GREATER CONCENTRATION.
USE SUCTION HOSES TO REMOVE TRAPPED SPILL MATERIAL.
USE MECHANICAL DREDGES OR LIFTS TO EXTRACT IMMOBILIZED MASSES OF POLLUTION AND PRECIPITATES.

OCCUPATIONAL SPILL: SHUT OFF IGNITION SOURCES. DO NOT TOUCH SPILLED MATERIAL. STOP LEAK IF YOU CAN DO IT WITHOUT RISK. USE WATER SPRAY TO REDUCE VAPORS. FOR SMALL SPILLS, TAKE UP WITH SAND OR OTHER ABSORBENT MATERIAL AND PLACE INTO CONTAINERS FOR LATER DISPOSAL. FOR SMALL DRY SPILLS, WITH CLEAN SHOVEL PLACE MATERIAL INTO CLEAN, DRY CONTAINERS AND COVER. MOVE CONTAINERS FROM SPILL AREA. FOR LARGER SPILLS, DIKE FAR AHEAD OF SPILL FOR LATER DISPOSAL. NO SMOKING, FLAMES OR FLARES IN

HAZARD AREA! KEEP UNNECESSARY PEOPLE AWAY. ISOLATE HAZARD AREA AND DENY ENTRY. VENTILATE CLOSED SPACES BEFORE ENTERING.

PROTECTIVE EQUIPMENT

VENTILATION: PROCESS ENCLOSURE RECOMMENDED TO MEET PUBLISHED EXPOSURE LIMITS.

RESPIRATOR: THE FOLLOWING RESPIRATORS AND MAXIMUM USE CONCENTRATIONS ARE RECOMMENDATIONS BY THE U.S. DEPARTMENT OF HEALTH AND HUMAN SERVICES, NIOSH POCKET GUIDE TO CHEMICAL HAZARDS; NIOSH CRITERIA DOCUMENTS OR BY THE U.S. DEPARTMENT OF LABOR, 29 CFR 1910 SUBPART Z. THE SPECIFIC RESPIRATOR SELECTED MUST BE BASED ON CONTAMINATION LEVELS FOUND IN THE WORK PLACE, MUST NOT EXCEED THE WORKING LIMITS OF THE RESPIRATOR AND BE JOINTLY APPROVED BY THE NATIONAL INSTITUTE FOR OCCUPATIONAL SAFETY AND HEALTH AND THE MINE SAFETY AND HEALTH ADMINISTRATION (NIOSH-MSHA).

2 MG/M3 OR LESS- HALF-MASK PESTICIDE RESPIRATOR. TYPE C SUPPLIED-AIR RESPIRATOR, DEMAND TYPE (NEGATIVE PRESSURE), WITH HALF-MASK FACEPIECE.

10 MG/M3 OR LESS- FULLFACE GAS MASK (CHIN STYLE OR CHEST- OR BACK-MOUNTED TYPE). TYPE C SUPPLIED-AIR RESPIRATOR, DEMAND TYPE (NEGATIVE PRESSURE), WITH FULL FACEPIECE.

200 MG/M3 OR LESS- TYPE C SUPPLIED-AIR RESPIRATOR, CONTINUOUS-FLOW TYPE, WITH FULL FACEPIECE OR SUIT. PRESSUARE-DEMAND TYPE RESPIRATOR WITH FULL FACEPIECE AND IMPERVIOUS PLASTIC SHROUD.

EMERGENCY- SELF-CONTAINED BREATHING APPARATUS, POSITIVE PRESSURE TYPE, WITH FULL FACEPIECE. COMBINATION SUPPLIED-AIR RESPIRATOR, PRESSURE-DEMAND TYPE, WITH AUXILIARY SELF-CONTAINED AIR SUPPLY.

FOR FIREFIGHTING AND OTHER IMMEDIATELY DANGEROUS TO LIFE OR HEALTH CONDITIONS:

SELF-CONTAINED BREATHING APPARATUS WITH FULL FACEPIECE OPERATED IN PRESSURE-DEMAND OR OTHER POSITIVE PRESSURE MODE.

SUPPLIED-AIR RESPIRATOR WITH FULL FACEPIECE AND OPERATED IN PRESSURE-DEMAND OR OTHER POSITIVE PRESSURE MODE IN COMBINATION WITH AN AUXILIARY SELF-CONTAINED BREATHING APPARATUS OPERATED IN PRESSURE-DEMAND OR OTHER POSITIVE PRESSURE MODE.

CLOTHING: EMPLOYEE MUST WEAR APPROPRIATE PROTECTIVE (IMPERVIOUS) CLOTHING AND EQUIPMENT TO PREVENT ANY POSSIBILITY OF SKIN CONTACT WITH THIS SUBSTANCE.

GLOVES: EMPLOYEE MUST WEAR APPROPRIATE PROTECTIVE GLOVES TO PREVENT CONTACT WITH THIS SUBSTANCE.

EYE PROTECTION: EMPLOYEE MUST WEAR SPLASH-PROOF OR DUST-RESISTANT SAFETY GOGGLES AND A FACESHIELD TO PREVENT CONTACT WITH THIS SUBSTANCE.

EMERGENCY WASH FACILITIES: WHERE THERE IS ANY POSSIBILITY THAT AN EMPLOYEE'S EYES AND/OR SKIN MAY BE EXPOSED TO THIS SUBSTANCE, THE EMPLOYER SHOULD PROVIDE AN EYE WASH FOUNTAIN AND QUICK DRENCH SHOWER WITHIN THE IMMEDIATE WORK AREA FOR EMERGENCY USE.

AUTHORIZED BY- OCCUPATIONAL HEALTH SERVICES, INC.
CREATION DATE: 10/04/89 ***REVISION DATE:*** 07/12/90

MATERIAL SAFETY DATA SHEET

OCCUPATIONAL HEALTH SERVICES, INC.
AGRICULTURE AND PESTICIDE DIVISION
450 SEVENTH AVENUE, SUITE 2407
NEW YORK, NEW YORK 10123
1-800-445-MSDS OR (212) 967-1100

EMERGENCY CONTACT:
JOHN S. BRANSFORD, JR. (615) 292-1180

SUBSTANCE IDENTIFICATION

CAS-NUMBER 119-36-8

SUBSTANCE: METHYL SALICYLATE

TRADE NAMES/SYNONYMS: SALICYLIC ACID, METHYL ESTER; BENZOIC ACID, 2-HYDROXY-, METHYL ESTER; O-HYDROXYBENZOIC ACID METHYL ESTER; 2-HYDROXYBENZOIC ACID METHYL ESTER; 2-(METHOXYCARBONYL)PHENOL; METHYL O-HYDROXYBENZOATE; METHYL 2-HYDROXYBENZOATE; ANALGIT; ANTHRAPOLE ND; EXAGIEN; FLUCARMIT; PST14720

CHEMICAL FAMILY: ESTER, CARBOXYLIC, ALIPHATIC

MOLECULAR FORMULA: C8-H8-O3

MOLECULAR WEIGHT: 152.16

CERCLA RATINGS (SCALE 0-3): HEALTH=2 FIRE=1 REACTIVITY=0 PERSISTENCE=0

NFPA RATINGS (SCALE 0-4): HEALTH=1 FIRE=1 REACTIVITY=0

COMPONENTS AND CONTAMINANTS

COMPONENT: METHYL SALICYLATE ***PERCENT:*** 100
CAS# 119-36-8

OTHER CONTAMINANTS: NONE

EXPOSURE LIMITS: NO OCCUPATIONAL EXPOSURE LIMITS ESTABLISHED BY OSHA, ACGIH, OR NIOSH.

PHYSICAL DATA

DESCRIPTION: COLORLESS, YELLOWISH, OR REDDISH OILY LIQUID WITH THE ODOR AND TASTE OF WINTERGREEN ***BOILING POINT:*** 433 F (223 C)

MELTING POINT: 18 F (-8 C) ***SPECIFIC GRAVITY:*** 1.184

VAPOR PRESSURE: 1 MMHG @ 54 C ***SOLUBILITY IN WATER:*** SLIGHTLY SOLUBLE

VAPOR DENSITY: 5.24

SOLVENT SOLUBILITY: SOLUBLE IN ALCOHOL, CHLOROFORM, ETHER, GLACIAL ACETIC ACID

FIRE AND EXPLOSION DATA

FIRE AND EXPLOSION HAZARD: SLIGHT FIRE HAZARD WHEN EXPOSED TO HEAT OR FLAME.

FLASH POINT: 205 F (96 C) (CC) ***AUTOIGNITION TEMP.:*** 850 F (454 C)

FLAMMABILITY CLASS(OSHA): IIIB

FIREFIGHTING MEDIA: DRY CHEMICAL, CARBON DIOXIDE, WATER SPRAY OR FOAM FOR LARGER FIRES, USE WATER SPRAY, FOG OR ALCOHOL FOAM

FIREFIGHTING: MOVE CONTAINER FROM FIRE AREA IF POSSIBLE. DO NOT SCATTER SPILLED MATERIAL WITH MORE WATER THAN NEEDED FOR FIRE CONTROL. DIKE FIRE CONTROL WATER FOR LATER DISPOSAL

USE AGENTS SUITABLE FOR TYPE OF SURROUNDING FIRE. AVOID BREATHING HAZARDOUS VAPORS, KEEP UPWIND.

TOXICITY

METHYL SALICYLATE: IRRITATION DATA: 500 MG/24 HOURS SKIN-RABBIT MODERATE; 500 MG/24 HOURS EYE-RABBIT MILD; 100% SKIN-GUINEA PIG SEVERE; 100% EYE-GUINEA PIG SEVERE. TOXICITY DATA: 506 MG/KG ORAL-HUMAN LDLO; 355 MG/KG ORAL-WOMAN LDLO; 101 MG/KG ORAL-MAN LDLO; 228 MG/KG ORAL-CHILD LDLO; 700 MG/KG ORAL-CHILD LDLO; 1480 MG/KG ORAL-INFANT LDLO; 887 MG/KG ORAL-RAT LD50; 2100 MG/KG ORAL-DOG LD50; 1110 MG/KG ORAL-MOUSE LD50; 1300 MG/KG ORAL-RABBIT LD50; 1060 MG/KG ORAL-GUINEA PIG LD50; 4250 MG/KG SUBCUTANEOUS-RABBIT LDLO; 1500 MG/KG SUBCUTANEOUS-GUINEA PIG LDLO; 2250 MG/KG SUBCUTANEOUS-DOG LDLO; 522 MG/KG UNREPORTED-MAN LDLO; REPRODUCTIVE EFFECTS DATA (RTECS). CARCINOGEN STATUS: NONE. LOCAL EFFECTS: IRRITANT- INHALATION, SKIN, AND EYES. ACUTE TOXICITY LEVEL: MODERATELY TOXIC BY INGESTION. TARGET EFFECTS: POISONING MAY AFFECT THE CENTRAL NERVOUS SYSTEM AND KIDNEYS. ADDITIONAL DATA: SALICYLATES MAY CROSS THE PLACENTA AND BE EXCRETED IN BREAST MILK. INTERACTIONS WITH MEDICATIONS HAVE BEEN REPORTED.

HEALTH EFFECTS AND FIRST AID

INHALATION: METHYL SALICYLATE: IRRITANT. **ACUTE EXPOSURE-** MAY CAUSE IRRITATION. **CHRONIC EXPOSURE-** PROLONGED OR REPEATED EXPOSURE MAY CAUSE IRRITATION.

FIRST AID- REMOVE FROM EXPOSURE AREA TO FRESH AIR IMMEDIATELY. IF BREATHING HAS STOPPED, PERFORM ARTIFICIAL RESPIRATION. KEEP PERSON WARM AND AT REST. TREAT SYMPTOMATICALLY AND SUPPORTIVELY. GET MEDICAL ATTENTION IMMEDIATELY.

SKIN CONTACT: METHYL SALICYLATE: IRRITANT/SENSITIZER. **ACUTE EXPOSURE-** MAY CAUSE IRRITATION. THIS MATERIAL MAY PRODUCE SENSITIZATION IN PREDISPOSED INDIVIDUALS. SYSTEMIC EFFECTS AS DESCRIBED IN ACUTE INGESTION MAY OCCUR FROM PERCUTANEOUS ABSORPTION. 5250 MG/KG, APPLIED TO THE SKIN OF FEMALE HAMSTERS ON DAY 7 OF PREGNANCY, PRODUCED FETAL DEVELOPMENTAL ABNORMALITIES. **CHRONIC EXPOSURE-** REPEATED OR PROLONGED EXPOSURE MAY CAUSE SENSITIZATION DERMATITIS. CHRONIC POISONING FROM SKIN ABSORPTION MAY CAUSE TINNITUS, GASTRIC OR RETINAL BLEEDING, GASTRIC ULCER, WEIGHT LOSS, MENTAL DETERIORATION, AND SKIN ERUPTIONS. LIVER DAMAGE MAY OCCUR.

FIRST AID- REMOVE CONTAMINATED CLOTHING AND SHOES IMMEDIATELY. WASH AFFECTED AREA WITH SOAP OR MILD DETERGENT AND LARGE AMOUNTS OF WATER UNTIL NO EVIDENCE OF CHEMICAL REMAINS (APPROXIMATELY 15-20 MINUTES). GET MEDICAL ATTENTION IMMEDIATELY.

EYE CONTACT: METHYL SALICYLATE: IRRITANT. **ACUTE EXPOSURE-** MAY CAUSE IRRITATION. **CHRONIC EXPOSURE-** REPEATED OR PROLONGED EXPOSURE MAY CAUSE CONJUCTIVITIS.

FIRST AID- WASH EYES IMMEDIATELY WITH LARGE AMOUNTS OF WATER OR NORMAL SALINE, OCCASIONALLY LIFTING UPPER AND LOWER LIDS, UNTIL NO EVIDENCE OF CHEMICAL REMAINS (APPROXIMATELY 15-20 MINUTES). GET MEDICAL ATTENTION IMMEDIATELY.

INGESTION: METHYL SALICYLATE: ACUTE EXPOSURE- MAY CAUSE BURNING PAIN IN THE THROAT AND STOMACH AND PROMPT VOMITING. AN ASYMPTOMATIC INTERVAL OF SEVERAL HOURS MAY OCCUR FOLLOWED BY DEEP AND RAPID BREATHING, APATHY, LASSITUDE, ANOREXIA, NAUSEA, DIARRHEA, HEADACHE, DIZZINESS, TINNITUS, DIFFICULTY IN HEARING, AND DIMNESS OF VISION. OTHER SYMPTOMS OF IRRITABILITY, RESTLESSNESS, HYPERVENTILATION, HYPERTHERMIA, HYPER-OR HYPOGLYCEMIA, CONFUSION, DISORIENTATION, DELIRIUM, MANIA, AND GENERALIZED CONVULSIONS MAY ALSO OCCUR. SOME OF THESE EFFECTS ARE DUE TO OR AGGRAVATED BY A SEVERE DISTURBANCE IN ACID-BASE BALANCE. IN SEVERE POISONING, THE SYMPTOMS MAY PROGRESS TO PULMONARY EDEMA, HEMORRHAGE, OLIGURIA, ACUTE RENAL FAILURE, COMA, AND DEATH DUE TO RESPIRATORY FAILURE AND/OR CARDIOVASCULAR COLLAPSE. THE AVERAGE LETHAL DOSE IS 10 ML IN CHILDREN AND 30 ML IN ADULTS. 1750 MG/KG, FED TO FEMALE HAMSTERS ON DAY 7 OF PREGNANCY, PRODUCED FETAL DEVELOPMENTAL ABNORMALITIES. CHRONIC EXPOSURE- CHRONIC POISONING MAY CAUSE TINNITUS, GASTRIC OR RETINAL BLEEDING, GASTRIC ULCER, WEIGHT LOSS, MENTAL DETERIORATION, AND SKIN ERUPTIONS. LIVER DAMAGE MAY OCCUR. ADVERSE EFFECTS ON THE NEWBORN WERE OBSERVED IN A MULTIGENERATION STUDY OF RATS.

FIRST AID- INDUCE EMESIS WITH SYRUP OF IPECAC UNLESS RESPIRATION IS DEPRESSED, IF SO USE AIRWAY-PROTECTED GASTRIC LAVAGE. GIVE ACTIVATED CHARCOAL. LAVAGE AND CATHARSIS ARE HELPFUL UP TO 12 HOURS AFTER INGESTION. DO NOT USE APOMORPHINE OR OTHER CENTRAL NERVOUS SYSTEM DEPRESSANTS SUCH AS BARBITURATES. MAINTAIN AIRWAY AND BLOOD PRESSURE. GIVE ARTIFICIAL RESPIRATIONWITH OXYGEN IF BREATHING IS STOPPED OR RESPIRATION IS DEPRESSED. (DREISBACH, HANDBOOK OF POISONING, 12TH ED.) GET MEDICAL ATTENTION IMMEDIATELY. ADMINISTRATION OF LAVAGE AND OXYGEN SHOULD BE PERFORMED BY QUALIFIED MEDICAL PERSONNEL. ***ANTIDOTE:*** NO SPECIFIC ANTIDOTE. TREAT SYMPTOMATICALLY AND SUPPORTIVELY.

REACTIVITY

REACTIVITY: STABLE UNDER NORMAL TEMPERATURES AND PRESSURES.

INCOMPATIBILITIES: METHYL SALICYLATE: OXIDIZING MATERIALS: REACT.

DECOMPOSITION: THERMAL DECOMPOSITION MAY RELEASE ACRID SMOKE AND IRRITATING FUMES.

POLYMERIZATION: HAZARDOUS POLYMERIZATION HAS NOT BEEN REPORTED TO OCCUR UNDER NORMAL TEMPERATURES AND PRESSURES.

STORAGE AND DISPOSAL

OBSERVE ALL FEDERAL, STATE AND LOCAL REGULATIONS WHEN STORING OR DISPOSING OF THIS SUBSTANCE. FOR ASSISTANCE, CONTACT THE DISTRICT DIRECTOR OF THE ENVIRONMENTAL PROTECTION AGENCY.

STORAGE

STORE AWAY FROM INCOMPATIBLE SUBSTANCES.

CONDITIONS TO AVOID

NONE REPORTED.

SPILL AND LEAK PROCEDURES

OCCUPATIONAL SPILL: STOP LEAK IF YOU CAN DO IT WITHOUT RISK. FOR SMALL SPILLS, TAKE UP WITH SAND OR OTHER ABSORBENT MATERIAL AND PLACE INTO CLEAN, DRY CONTAINERS FOR LATER DISPOSAL. KEEP UNNECESSARY PEOPLE AWAY. ISOLATE HAZARD AREA AND DENY ENTRY.

PROTECTIVE EQUIPMENT

VENTILATION: PROVIDE LOCAL EXHAUST OR GENERAL DILUTION VENTILATION SYSTEM.

RESPIRATOR: THE FOLLOWING RESPIRATORS ARE RECOMMENDED BASED ON INFORMATION FOUND IN THE PHYSICAL DATA, TOXICITY AND HEALTH EFFECTS SECTIONS. THEY ARE RANKED IN ORDER FROM MINIMUM TO MAXIMUM RESPIRATORY PROTECTION. THE SPECIFIC RESPIRATOR SELECTED MUST BE BASED ON CONTAMINATION LEVELS FOUND IN THE WORK PLACE, MUST NOT EXCEED THE WORKING LIMITS OF THE RESPIRATOR AND BE JOINTLY APPROVED BY THE NATIONAL INSTITUTE FOR OCCUPATIONAL SAFETY AND HEALTH AND THE MINE SAFETY AND HEALTH ADMINISTRATION (NIOSH-MSHA).

CHEMICAL CARTRIDGE RESPIRATOR WITH AN ORGANIC VAPOR CARTRIDGE(S) WITH A FULL FACEPIECE.

GAS MASK WITH ORGANIC VAPOR CANISTER (CHIN-STYLE OR FRONT- OR BACK-MOUNTED CANISTER) WITH A FULL FACEPIECE.

TYPE 'C' SUPPLIED-AIR RESPIRATOR WITH A FULL FACEPIECE OPERATED IN PRESSURE-DEMAND OR OTHER POSITIVE PRESSURE MODE OR WITH A FULL FACEPIECE, HELMET OR HOOD OPERATED IN CONTINUOUS-FLOW MODE.

SELF-CONTAINED BREATHING APPARATUS WITH A FULL FACEPIECE OPERATED IN PRESSURE-DEMAND OR OTHER POSITIVE PRESSURE MODE.

FOR FIREFIGHTING AND OTHER IMMEDIATELY DANGEROUS TO LIFE OR HEALTH CONDITIONS:

SELF-CONTAINED BREATHING APPARATUS WITH FULL FACEPIECE OPERATED IN PRESSURE-DEMAND OR OTHER POSITIVE PRESSURE MODE.

SUPPLIED-AIR RESPIRATOR WITH FULL FACEPIECE AND OPERATED IN PRESSURE-DEMAND OR OTHER POSITIVE PRESSURE MODE IN COMBINATION WITH AN AUXILIARY SELF-CONTAINED BREATHING APPARATUS OPERATED IN PRESSURE-DEMAND OR OTHER POSITIVE PRESSURE MODE.

CLOTHING: EMPLOYEE MUST WEAR APPROPRIATE PROTECTIVE (IMPERVIOUS) CLOTHING AND EQUIPMENT TO PREVENT REPEATED OR PROLONGED SKIN CONTACT WITH THIS SUBSTANCE.

GLOVES: EMPLOYEE MUST WEAR APPROPRIATE PROTECTIVE GLOVES TO PREVENT CONTACT WITH THIS SUBSTANCE.

EYE PROTECTION: EMPLOYEE MUST WEAR SPLASH-PROOF OR DUST-RESISTANT SAFETY GOGGLES TO PREVENT EYE CONTACT WITH THIS SUBSTANCE.

EMERGENCY EYE WASH: WHERE THERE IS ANY POSSIBILITY THAT AN EMPLOYEE'S EYES MAY BE EXPOSED TO THIS SUBSTANCE, THE EMPLOYER SHOULD PROVIDE AN EYE WASH FOUNTAIN WITHIN THE IMMEDIATE WORK AREA FOR EMERGENCY USE.

AUTHORIZED BY- OCCUPATIONAL HEALTH SERVICES, INC.

CREATION DATE: 11/17/89 ***REVISION DATE:*** 05/07/90

MATERIAL SAFETY DATA SHEET

OCCUPATIONAL HEALTH SERVICES, INC.
AGRICULTURE AND PESTICIDE DIVISION
450 SEVENTH AVENUE, SUITE 2407
NEW YORK, NEW YORK 10123
1-800-445-MSDS OR (212) 967-1100

EMERGENCY CONTACT:
JOHN S. BRANSFORD, JR. (615) 292-1180

SUBSTANCE IDENTIFICATION

CAS-NUMBER 75-09-2

SUBSTANCE: DICHLOROMETHANE

TRADE NAMES/SYNONYMS: METHANE, DICHLORO-; METHYLENE CHLORIDE; METHYLENE DICHLORIDE; AEROTHENE MM; NARKOTIL; SOLAESTHIN; SOLMETHINE; TC 523 EPOXY DISSOLVER (TECHFORM); LACCO METHYLENE CHLORIDE (PPG INDUSTRIES INC.); AEROTHENE (R) MM SOLVENT (DOW CHEMICAL); EQUIPMENT FLUSHING SOLVENT (LOCTITE CORPORATION); LS-303 (POLYTECH); RCRA U080; STCC 4941132; UN 1593; CH2CL2; PST14930

CHEMICAL FAMILY: HALOGEN COMPOUND, ALIPHATIC

MOLECULAR FORMULA: C-H2-CL2

MOLECULAR WEIGHT: 84.93

CERCLA RATINGS (SCALE 0-3): HEALTH=3 FIRE=1 REACTIVITY=0 PERSISTENCE=1

NFPA RATINGS (SCALE 0-4): HEALTH=2 FIRE=1 REACTIVITY=0

COMPONENTS AND CONTAMINANTS

COMPONENT: DICHLOROMETHANE ***PERCENT:*** 100.0
CAS# 75-09-2

OTHER CONTAMINANTS: NONE

EXPOSURE LIMITS: DICHLOROMETHANE (METHYLENE CHLORIDE): 500 PPM OSHA TWA; 1000 PPM OSHA CEILING; 2000 PPM/5 MIN IN 2 HOURS OSHA PEAK 50 PPM (174 MG/M3) ACGIH TWA ACGIH A2- SUSPECTED HUMAN CARCINOGEN. LOWEST FEASIBLE LIMIT NIOSH RECOMMENDED EXPOSURE CRITERIA

1000 POUNDS CERCLA SECTION 103 REPORTABLE QUANTITY SUBJECT TO SARA SECTION 313 ANNUAL TOXIC CHEMICAL RELEASE REPORTING SUBJECT TO CALIFORNIA PROPOSITION 65 CANCER AND/OR REPRODUCTIVE TOXICITY WARNING AND RELEASE REQUIREMENTS- (APRIL 1, 1988)

PHYSICAL DATA

DESCRIPTION: CLEAR, COLORLESS LIQUID WITH A MILD, CHLOROFORM-LIKE ODOR.

BOILING POINT: 104 F (40 C) ***MELTING POINT:*** -139 F (-95 C)

SPECIFIC GRAVITY: 1.3266 ***VISCOSITY:*** 0.441 CPS @ 20 C ***VOLATILITY:*** 100%

VAPOR PRESSURE: 400 MMHG @ 24 C ***EVAPORATION RATE:*** (BUTYL ACETATE=1) 27.5

SOLUBILITY IN WATER: 1.32% @ 20 C ***ODOR THRESHOLD:*** 25-50 PPM

VAPOR DENSITY: 2.9

SOLVENT SOLUBILITY: SOLUBLE IN ALCOHOL, ETHER, DIMETHYLFORMAMIDE, PHENOLS, ALDEHYDES, KETONES, GLACIAL ACETIC ACID, TRIETHYL PHOSPHATE, ACETOACETIC ACID, CYCLOHEXYLAMINE, CHLORINATED SOLVENTS.

FIRE AND EXPLOSION DATA

FIRE AND EXPLOSION HAZARD: SLIGHT FIRE HAZARD WHEN EXPOSED TO HEAT OR FLAME.

UPPER EXPLOSIVE LIMIT: 23% ***LOWER EXPLOSIVE LIMIT:*** 13%

AUTOIGNITION TEMP.: 1033 F (556 C) ***FLAMMABILITY CLASS(OSHA):*** IIIB

FIREFIGHTING MEDIA: DRY CHEMICAL, CARBON DIOXIDE OR HALON (1987 EMERGENCY RESPONSE GUIDEBOOK, DOT P 5800.4).

FOR LARGER FIRES, USE WATER SPRAY, FOG OR STANDARD FOAM (1987 EMERGENCY RESPONSE GUIDEBOOK, DOT P 5800.4).

FIREFIGHTING: STAY AWAY FROM STORAGE TANK ENDS. COOL CONTAINERS EXPOSED TO FLAMES WITH WATER FROM SIDE UNTIL WELL AFTER FIRE IS OUT (1987 EMERGENCY RESPONSE GUIDEBOOK, DOT P 5800.4, GUIDE PAGE 74). EXTINGUISH USING AGENTS SUITABLE FOR SURROUNDING FIRE. USE FLOODING QUANTITIES OF WATER TO COOL AFFECTED CONTAINERS, APPLYING FROM AS FAR A DISTANCE AS POSSIBLE. AVOID BREATHING HAZARDOUS VAPORS, KEEP UNWIND.

TRANSPORTATION DATA

DEPARTMENT OF TRANSPORTATION HAZARD CLASSIFICATION 49 CFR 172.101: ORM-A

DEPARTMENT OF TRANSPORTATION LABELING REQUIREMENTS 49 CFR 172.101 AND SUBPART E: NONE

DEPARTMENT OF TRANSPORTATION PACKAGING REQUIREMENTS: 49 CFR 173.605 EXCEPTIONS: 49 CFR 173.505

TOXICITY

DICHLOROMETHANE (METHYLENE CHLORIDE): IRRITATION DATA: 162 MG EYE-RABBIT MODERATE; 10 MG EYE-RABBIT MILD; 500 MG/24 HOURS EYE-RABBIT MILD; 810 MG/24 HOURS SKIN-RABBIT SEVERE; 100 MG/24 HOURS SKIN-RABBIT MODERATE. TOXICITY DATA: 500 PPM/1 YEAR-INTERMITTENT INHALATION-HUMAN TCLO; 500 PPM/8 HOURS INHALATION-HUMAN TCLO; 88000 MG/M3/30 MINUTES INHALATION-RAT LC50; 14400 PPM/7 HOURS INHALATION-MOUSE LC50; 10000 PPM/7 HOURS INHALATION-RABBIT LCLO; 5000 PPM/2 HOURS INHALATION-GUINEA PIG LCLO; 14108 PPM/7 HOURS INHALATION-DOG LCLO; 43400 MG/M3/4.5 HOURS INHALATION-CAT LCLO; 357 MG/KG ORAL-HUMAN LDLO; 1600 MG/KG ORAL-RAT LD50; 1900 MG/KG ORAL-RABBIT LDLO; 3 GM/KG ORAL-DOG LDLO; 6460 MG/KG SUBCUTANEOUS-MOUSE LD50; 2700 MG/KG SUBCUTANEOUS-RABBIT LDLO; 2700 MG/KG SUBCUTANEOUS-DOG LDLO; 200 MG/KG INTRAVENOUS-DOG LDLO; 916 MG/KG INTRAPERITONEAL-RAT LD50; 950 MG/KG INTRAPERITONEAL-DOG LDLO; 437 MG/KG INTRAPERITONEAL-MOUSE LD50; 4770 MG/KG UNREPORTED-MOUSE LD50; MUTAGENIC DATA (RTECS); REPRODUCTIVE EFFECTS DATA (RTECS); TUMORIGENIC DATA (RTECS). CARCINOGEN STATUS: ANTICIPATED HUMAN CARCINOGEN (NTP); HUMAN INADEQUATE EVIDENCE, ANIMAL SUFFICIENT EVIDENCE (IARC GROUP-2B). EXPOSURE BY INHALATION INCREASED THE INCIDENCE OF BENIGN AND MALIGNANT LUNG AND LIVER TUMORS IN MICE OF EACH SEX AND THE INCIDENCE OR MULTIPLICITY OF BENIGN MAMMARY TUMORS IN RATS OF EACH SEX; IN MALE RATS, AN INCREASED INCIDENCE OF SARCOMAS LOCATED IN THE NECK WAS ALSO OBSERVED. LOCAL EFFECTS: IRRITANT-INHALATION, SKIN, EYE. ACUTE TOXICITY LEVEL: MODERATELY TOXIC BY INHALATION AND INGESTION. TARGET EFFECTS: CENTRAL NERVOUS SYSTEM DEPRESSANT; CHEMICAL ASPHYXIANT. POISONING MAY AFFECT THE BLOOD, LIVER AND KIDNEYS. AT INCREASED RISK FROM EXPOSURE: PERSONS WITH SKIN, LIVER, KIDNEY, CARDIOVASCULAR DISEASE OR ANEMIA. ADDITIONAL DATA: CONCURRENT EXPOSURE TO OTHER SOURCES OF CARBON MONOXIDE, SMOKING, OR PHYSICAL ACTIVITY MAY INCREASE THE LEVEL OF CARBOXYHEMOGLOBIN IN THE BLOOD RESULTING IN ADDITIVE EFFECTS. ALCOHOLIC BEVERAGES MAY ENHANCE THE TOXIC EFFECTS. STIMULANTS SUCH AS EPINEPHRINE MAY INDUCE CARDIAC ARRHYTHMIAS. ONE STUDY INDICATED THAT CHRONIC EXPOSURE MAY BE ASSOCIATED WITH AN INCREASED RISK OF SPONTANEOUS ABORTION. DICHLOROMETHANE CROSSES THE PLACENTAL BARRIER AND IS EXCRETED IN HUMAN MILK.

HEALTH EFFECTS AND FIRST AID

INHALATION: DICHLOROMETHANE (METHYLENE CHLORIDE): IRRITANT/NARCOTIC/CHEMICAL ASPHYXIANT/CARCINOGEN. **ACUTE EXPOSURE-** HUMAN EXPOSURE TO 100 PPM HAS RESULTED IN UPPER RESPIRATORY TRACT IRRITATION; CONCENTRATIONS AS LOW AS 200 PPM HAVE PRODUCED TEMPORARY NEUROBEHAVIOURAL EFFECTS; 500-1000 PPM FOR 1-2 HOURS HAS CAUSED LIGHTHEADEDNESS AND ELEVATED CARBOXYHEMOGLOBIN LEVEL; 2300 PPM FOR 30 MINUTES HAS CAUSED NAUSEA AND NARCOSIS; 5000 PPM HAS CAUSED HEADACHE, FATIGUE, NEURASTHENIC DISORDERS AND DIGESTIVE DISTURBANCES. OTHER SYMPTOMS MAY INCLUDE DIZZINESS, TINGLING, NUMBNESS OF THE EXTREMITIES, A SENSATION OF HEAT, A SENSATION OF FULLNESS IN THE HEAD, DRUNKENNESS, STUPOR, DULLNESS AND MENTAL CONFUSION. MASSIVE EXPOSURE MAY CAUSE PHARYNGEAL EROSION, PULMONARY EDEMA, STAGGERING, HEMOLYSIS WITH GROSS HEMATURIA, RAPID UNCONSCIOUSNESS AND DEATH. RECOVERY IS GENERALLY COMPLETE IF EXPOSURE IS TERMINATED BEFORE ANESTHETIC DEATH. EXPOSURE TO HIGH LEVELS MAY ALSO CAUSE CARDIAC ARRHYTHMIAS. **CHRONIC EXPOSURE-** MORE THAN 100 WORKERS EXPOSED TO LEVELS BELOW 500 PPM HAVE DEVELOPED HEALTH PROBLEMS INCLUDING SIGNIFICANT UPPER RESPIRATORY IRRITATION, EXACERBATION OF CORONARY ARTERY DISEASE, AND A HIGH INCIDENCE OF NEUROTOXICITY; INCREASED COMPLAINTS OF CHEST PAINS WERE REPORTED AT CONCENTRATIONS OF 10 TO 35 PPM. REPEATED HUMAN EXPOSURE TO 500-3600 PPM HAS CAUSED SIGNS OF TOXIC ENCEPHALOPATHY WITH ACOUSTICAL AND OPTICAL DELUSIONS AND HALLUCINATIONS. A CASE OF SERIOUS CEREBRAL DETERIORATION WAS OBSERVED IN AN INDIVIDUAL EXPOSED FOR SEVERAL YEARS TO DICHLOROMETHANE. IN A MORTALITY STUDY OF TWO GROUPS OF WORKERS, ONE EXPOSED TO ACETONE AND THE OTHER TO DICHLOROMETHANE AND ACETONE, A STATISTICALLY SIGNIFICANT DIFFERENCE IN DEATHS FROM DISEASES OF THE CIRCULATORY SYSTEM AND FROM ISCHEMIC HEART DISEASE WERE REPORTED FROM THE DICHLOROMETHANE AND ACETONE GROUP. IN ANOTHER MORTALITY STUDY OF WORKERS EXPOSED TO DICHLOROMETHANE, A SIGNIFICANT INCREASE IN HYPERTENSIVE DISEASE AND A "SUGGESTIVE EXCESS" OF PANCREATIC CANCER WERE REPORTED. LIVER DISEASE HAS BEEN REPORTED IN WORKERS. IN ONE STUDY, AN INCREASE IN SERUM BILIRUBIN WAS OBSERVED IN EXPOSED WORKERS, BUT NO OTHER SIGN OF LIVER INJURY OR HEMOLYSIS WAS REPORTED. ADVERSE LIVER EFFECTS WERE OBSERVED IN SEVERAL ANIMAL SPECIES CHEMICALLY EXPOSED. TESTICULAR ATROPHY WAS REPORTED IN MICE EXPOSED TO 4000 PPM OVER 2 YEARS. REPEATED INHALATION BY RODENTS PRIOR TO AND/OR DURING GESTATION CAUSED FETAL SKELETAL ABNORMALITIES AND BEHAVIORAL EFFECTS IN NEWBORN OFFSPRING. REPEATED INHALATION INCREASED THE INCIDENCE OF BENIGN AND MALIGNANT LUNG AND LIVER TUMORS IN MICE OF EACH SEX AND THE INCIDENCE OR MULTIPLICITY OF BENIGN MAMMARY TUMORS IN RATS OF EACH SEX; IN MALE RATS, AN INCREASED INCIDENCE OF SARCOMAS LOCATED IN THE NECK WAS ALSO OBSERVED.

FIRST AID- REMOVE FROM EXPOSURE AREA TO FRESH AIR IMMEDIATELY. IF BREATHING HAS STOPPED, GIVE ARTIFICIAL RESPIRATION. MAINTAIN AIRWAY AND BLOOD PRESSURE AND ADMINISTER OXYGEN IF AVAILABLE. KEEP AFFECTED PERSON WARM AND AT REST. TREAT SYMPTOMATICALLY AND SUPPORTIVELY. ADMINISTRATION OF OXYGEN SHOULD BE PERFORMED BY QUALIFIED PERSONNEL. GET MEDICAL ATTENTION IMMEDIATELY.

SKIN CONTACT: DICHLOROMETHANE (METHYLENE CHLORIDE): IRRITANT. **ACUTE EXPOSURE-** MAY CAUSE EFFECTS RANGING FROM MILD IRRITATION TO SEVERE PAIN, PARESTHESIAS, AND POSSIBLY BURNS, DEPENDING ON THE INTENSITY OF CONTACT. **CHRONIC EXPOSURE-** PROLONGED OR REPEATED CONTACT MAY CAUSE A DRY, SCALY AND FISSURED DERMATITIS DUE TO DEFATTING ACTION OF LIQUID ON SKIN.

FIRST AID- REMOVE CONTAMINATED CLOTHING AND SHOES IMMEDIATELY. WASH AFFECTED AREA WITH SOAP OR MILD DETERGENT AND LARGE AMOUNTS OF WATER UNTIL NO EVIDENCE OF CHEMICAL REMAINS (APPROXIMATELY 15-20 MINUTES). GET MEDICAL ATTENTION IMMEDIATELY.

EYE CONTACT: DICHLOROMETHANE (METHYLENE CHLORIDE): IRRITANT. **ACUTE EXPOSURE-** VAPOR CONCENTRATIONS ABOVE 2000 PPM MAY CAUSE IRRITATION. DIRECT CONTACT MAY CAUSE PAIN AND EXTREME IRRITATION, BUT IT IS NOT LIKELY TO CAUSE SERIOUS INJURY. 10 MG APPLIED TO RABBIT EYES PRODUCED KERATITIS, IRITIS, INCREASED CORNEAL THICKNESS, AND INFLAMMATION OF THE CONJUNCTIVA AND EYELIDS WITH SOME EFFECTS LASTING UP TO TWO WEEKS. **CHRONIC EXPOSURE-** REPEATED OR PROLONGED EXPOSURE TO IRRITANTS MAY CAUSE CONJUNCTIVITIS.

FIRST AID- WASH EYES IMMEDIATELY WITH LARGE AMOUNTS OF WATER OR NORMAL SALINE, OCCASIONALLY LIFTING UPPER AND LOWER LIDS, UNTIL NO EVIDENCE OF CHEMICAL REMAINS (APPROXIMATELY 15-20 MINUTES). GET MEDICAL ATTENTION IMMEDIATELY.

INGESTION: DICHLOROMETHANE (METHYLENE CHLORIDE): NARCOTIC/CHEMICAL ASPHYXIANT. ACUTE EXPOSURE: MAY CAUSE RAPID, THEN SLOWED RESPIRATION, GLOTTAL AND PHARYNGEAL EDEMA, INTRAVASCULAR HEMOLYSIS WITH GROSS HEMATURIA, GASTROINTESTINAL ULCERATION AND HEMORRHAGE, AND CARBOXYHEMOGLOBINEMIA. THESE SYMPTOMS MAY PROGRESS RAPIDLY TO UNCONSCIOUSNESS AND LACK OF RESPONSE TO PAINFUL STIMULI. PHARYNGEAL EROSIONS MAY DISTURB THE SWALLOWING MECHANISM RESULTING IN ASPIRATION PNEUMONIA. IN ADDITION, SYMPTOMS OF CENTRAL NERVOUS SYSTEM DEPRESSION MAY OCCUR FOLLOWED BY CONVULSIONS AND PARESTHESIA OF THE EXTREMITIES. LARGE DOSES MAY CAUSE LIVER AND KIDNEY

DAMAGE. THE ESTIMATED LETHAL DOSE FOR AN ADULT IS 25 GRAMS. CHRONIC EXPOSURE- REPEATED INGESTION BY RATS AND MICE RESULTED IN HISTOMORPHOLOGICAL CHANGES IN THE LIVER.

FIRST AID- REMOVE BY GASTRIC LAVAGE OR EMESIS. MAINTAIN BLOOD PRESSURE AND AIRWAY. GIVE OXYGEN IF RESPIRATION IS DEPRESSED. DO NOT PERFORM GASTRIC LAVAGE OR EMESIS IF VICTIM IS UNCONSCIOUS. GET MEDICAL ATTENTION IMMEDIATELY (DREISBACH, HANDBOOK OF POISONING, 11TH ED.). ADMINISTRATION OF GASTRIC LAVAGE OR OXYGEN SHOULD BE PERFORMED BY QUALIFIED MEDICAL PERSONNEL.

ANTIDOTE: NO SPECIFIC ANTIDOTE. TREAT SYMPTOMATICALLY AND SUPPORTIVELY.

REACTIVITY

REACTIVITY: STABLE UNDER NORMAL TEMPERATURES AND PRESSURES.

INCOMPATIBILITIES: DICHLOROMETHANE (METHYLENE CHLORIDE): ALKALI METALS: POSSIBLE EXPLOSIVE REACTION. ALUMINUM: VIOLENT, UNCONTROLLABLE REACTION ABOVE 95 C. CAUSTICS (STRONG): VIGOROUS, POSSIBLY VIOLENT REACTION. COPPER: MAY CORRODE AT ELEVATED TEMPERATURES IN THE PRESENCE OF MOISTURE. DINITROGEN PENTOXIDE: POSSIBLE EXPLOSION. DINITROGEN TETROXIDE: FORMS SHOCK-SENSITIVE MIXTURE. IRON: MAY CORRODE AT ELEVATED TEMPERATURES IN THE PRESENCE OF MOISTURE. LITHIUM: FORMS SHOCK-SENSITIVE MIXTURE. MAGNESIUM: POSSIBLE EXPLOSION. NICKEL: MAY CORRODE AT ELEVATED TEMPERATURES IN THE PRESENCE OF MOISTURE. NITRIC ACID: EXOTHERMIC REACTION YIELDING DETONABLE SOLUTION. OXIDIZERS (STRONG): FIRE AND EXPLOSION HAZARD. OXYGEN (LIQUID): EXPLOSIVE REACTION ON IGNITION. PLASTICS, RUBBER, AND COATINGS: MAY BE ATTACKED. POTASSIUM: EXPLOSIVE REACTION. POTASSIUM HYDROXIDE + N-METHYL-N-NITROSO UREA: POSSIBLE EXPLOSION. POTASSIUM TERT-BUTOXIDE: IGNITION REACTION. SODIUM: FORMS SHOCK-SENSITIVE MIXTURE. SODIUM-POTASSIUM ALLOY: FORMS SHOCK-SENSITIVE MIXTURE. STAINLESS STEEL: MAY CORRODE AT ELEVATED TEMPERATURES IN THE PRESENCE OF MOISTURE. TITANIUM: POSSIBLE VIOLENT REACTION. ZINC: POSSIBLE VIOLENT REACTION. ***DECOMPOSITION:*** THERMAL DECOMPOSITION PRODUCTS MAY INCLUDE TOXIC AND HAZARDOUS PHOSGENE GAS, TOXIC AND CORROSIVE FUMES OF CHLORIDES, AND OXIDES OF CARBON.

POLYMERIZATION: HAZARDOUS POLYMERIZATION HAS NOT BEEN REPORTED TO OCCUR UNDER NORMAL TEMPERATURES AND PRESSURES.

STORAGE AND DISPOSAL

OBSERVE ALL FEDERAL, STATE AND LOCAL REGULATIONS WHEN STORING OR DISPOSING OF THIS SUBSTANCE. FOR ASSISTANCE, CONTACT THE DISTRICT DIRECTOR OF THE ENVIRONMENTAL PROTECTION AGENCY.

****STORAGE****

PROTECT AGAINST PHYSICAL DAMAGE. STORE IN COOL, DRY, WELL VENTILATED LOCATION, AWAY FROM ANY AREA WHERE THE FIRE HAZARD MAY BE ACUTE (NFPA 49, HAZARDOUS CHEMICALS DATA, 1975).

STORE AWAY FROM INCOMPATIBLE SUBSTANCES.

****DISPOSAL****

DISPOSAL MUST BE IN ACCORDANCE WITH STANDARDS APPLICABLE TO GENERATORS OF HAZARDOUS WASTE, 40CFR 262. EPA HAZARDOUS WASTE NUMBER U080.

CONDITIONS TO AVOID

MAY BURN BUT DOES NOT IGNITE READILY. CONTAINER MAY EXPLODE IN HEAT OF FIRE.

SPILL AND LEAK PROCEDURES

SOIL SPILL: DIG HOLDING AREA SUCH AS LAGOON, POND OR PIT FOR CONTAINMENT. DIKE FLOW OF SPILLED MATERIAL USING SOIL OR SANDBAGS OR FOAMED BARRIERS SUCH AS POLYURETHANE OR CONCRETE.

USE CEMENT POWDER OR FLY ASH TO ABSORB LIQUID MASS.

AIR SPILL: APPLY WATER SPRAY TO KNOCK DOWN VAPORS.

WATER SPILL: TRAP SPILLED MATERIAL AT BOTTOM IN DEEP WATER POCKETS, EXCAVATED HOLDING AREAS OR WITHIN SAND BAG BARRIERS.

USE SUCTION HOSES TO REMOVE TRAPPED SPILL MATERIAL.

THE CALIFORNIA SAFE DRINKING WATER AND TOXIC ENFORCEMENT ACT OF 1986 (PROPOSITION 65) PROHIBITS CONTAMINATING ANY KNOWN SOURCE OF DRINKING WATER WITH SUBSTANCES KNOWN TO CAUSE CANCER AND/OR REPRODUCTIVE TOXICITY.

OCCUPATIONAL SPILL: SHUT OFF IGNITION SOURCES. STOP LEAK IF YOU CAN DO IT WITHOUT RISK. FOR SMALL LIQUID SPILLS, TAKE UP WITH SAND, EARTH OR OTHER ABSORBENT MATERIAL. FOR LARGER SPILLS, DIKE FAR AHEAD OF SPILL FOR LATER DISPOSAL. NO SMOKING, FLAMES OR FLARES IN HAZARD AREA! KEEP UNNECESSARY PEOPLE AWAY.

REPORTABLE QUANTITY (RQ): 1000 POUNDS THE SUPERFUND AMENDMENTS AND REAUTHORIZATION ACT (SARA) SECTION 304 REQUIRES THAT A RELEASE EQUAL TO OR GREATER THAN THE REPORTABLE QUANTITY FOR THIS SUBSTANCE BE IMMEDIATELY REPORTED TO THE LOCAL EMERGENCY PLANNING COMMITTEE AND THE STATE EMERGENCY RESPONSE COMMISSION (40 CFR 355.40). IF THE RELEASE OF THIS SUBSTANCE IS REPORTABLE UNDER CERCLA SECTION 103, THE NATIONAL RESPONSE CENTER MUST BE NOTIFIED IMMEDIATELY AT (800) 424-8802 OR (202) 426-2675 IN THE METROPOLITAN WASHINGTON, D.C. AREA (40 CFR 302.6).

PROTECTIVE EQUIPMENT

VENTILATION: PROVIDE LOCAL EXHAUST VENTILATION AND/OR GENERAL DILUTION VENTILATION TO MEET PUBLISHED EXPOSURE LIMITS.

RESPIRATOR: THE FOLLOWING RESPIRATORS AND MAXIMUM USE CONCENTRATIONS ARE RECOMMENDATIONS BY THE U.S. DEPARTMENT OF HEALTH AND HUMAN SERVICES, NIOSH POCKET GUIDE TO CHEMICAL HAZARDS; NIOSH CRITERIA DOCUMENTS OR BY THE U.S. DEPARTMENT OF LABOR, 29 CFR 1910 SUBPART Z. THE SPECIFIC RESPIRATOR SELECTED MUST BE BASED ON CONTAMINATION LEVELS FOUND IN THE WORK PLACE, MUST NOT EXCEED THE WORKING LIMITS OF THE RESPIRATOR AND BE JOINTLY APPROVED BY THE NATIONAL INSTITUTE FOR OCCUPATIONAL SAFETY AND HEALTH AND THE MINE SAFETY AND HEALTH ADMINISTRATION (NIOSH-MSHA).

FOR DICHLOROMETHANE (METHYLENE CHLORIDE): AT ANY DETECTABLE CONCENTRATION:

ANY SELF-CONTAINED BREATHING APPARATUS WITH FULL FACEPIECE OPERATED IN PRESSURE-DEMAND OR OTHER POSITIVE PRESSURE MODE. ANY SUPPLIED-AIR RESPIRATOR WITH FULL FACEPIECE OPERATED IN PRESSURE-DEMAND OR OTHER POSITIVE PRESSURE MODE IN COMBINATION WITH AN AXILIARY SELF-CONTAINED BREATHING APPARATUS OPERATED IN PRESSURE-DEMAND OR OTHER POSITIVE PRESSURE MODE.

ESCAPE- ANY AIR-PURIFYING FULL FACEPIECE RESPIRATOR (GAS MASK) WITH ORGANIC VAPOR CANISTER. ANY APPROPRIATE ESCAPE-TYPE SELF-CONTAINED BREATHING APPARATUS.

FOR FIREFIGHTING AND OTHER IMMEDIATELY DANGEROUS TO LIFE OR HEALTH CONDITIONS:

SELF-CONTAINED BREATHING APPARATUS WITH FULL FACEPIECE OPERATED IN PRESSURE-DEMAND OR OTHER POSITIVE PRESSURE MODE.

SUPPLIED-AIR RESPIRATOR WITH FULL FACEPIECE AND OPERATED IN PRESSURE-DEMAND OR OTHER POSITIVE PRESSURE MODE IN COMBINATION WITH AN AUXILIARY SELF-CONTAINED BREATHING APPARATUS OPERATED IN PRESSURE-DEMAND OR OTHER POSITIVE PRESSURE MODE.

CLOTHING: EMPLOYEE MUST WEAR APPROPRIATE PROTECTIVE (IMPERVIOUS) CLOTHING AND EQUIPMENT TO PREVENT REPEATED OR PROLONGED SKIN CONTACT WITH THIS SUBSTANCE.

GLOVES: EMPLOYEE MUST WEAR APPROPRIATE PROTECTIVE GLOVES TO PREVENT CONTACT WITH THIS SUBSTANCE.

EYE PROTECTION: EMPLOYEE MUST WEAR SPLASH-PROOF OR DUST-RESISTANT SAFETY GOGGLES AND A FACESHIELD TO PREVENT CONTACT WITH THIS SUBSTANCE.

EMERGENCY WASH FACILITIES: WHERE THERE IS ANY POSSIBILITY THAT AN EMPLOYEE'S EYES AND/OR SKIN MAY BE EXPOSED TO THIS SUBSTANCE, THE EMPLOYER SHOULD PROVIDE AN EYE WASH FOUNTAIN AND QUICK DRENCH SHOWER WITHIN THE IMMEDIATE WORK AREA FOR EMERGENCY USE.

AUTHORIZED BY- OCCUPATIONAL HEALTH SERVICES, INC.

CREATION DATE: 10/04/89 ***REVISION DATE:*** 07/12/90

MATERIAL SAFETY DATA SHEET

OCCUPATIONAL HEALTH SERVICES, INC.	EMERGENCY CONTACT:
AGRICULTURE AND PESTICIDE DIVISION	JOHN S. BRANSFORD, JR. (615) 292-1180
450 SEVENTH AVENUE, SUITE 2407	
NEW YORK, NEW YORK 10123	
1-800-445-MSDS OR (212) 967-1100	

SUBSTANCE IDENTIFICATION

CAS-NUMBER 556-61-6

SUBSTANCE: METHYLISOTHIOCYANATE

TRADE NAMES/SYNONYMS: METHANE, ISOTHIOCYANATO-; ISOTHIOCYANIC ACID, METHYL ESTER; ISOTHIOCYANATOMETHANE; METHYL ISOTHIOCYANATE; METHYL MUSTARD OIL; METHYL MUSTARD; METHYL THIOISOCYANATE; TRAPEX; UN 2477; C2H3NS; PST14950

CHEMICAL FAMILY: ISOCYANATE THIO

MOLECULAR FORMULA: C-H3-N-C-S

MOLECULAR WEIGHT: 73.11
CERCLA RATINGS (SCALE 0-3): HEALTH = 3 FIRE = 3 REACTIVITY = 1 PERSISTENCE = 1
NFPA RATINGS (SCALE 0-4): HEALTH = 4 FIRE = 3 REACTIVITY = 1

COMPONENTS AND CONTAMINANTS

COMPONENT: METHYLISOTHIOCYANATE ***PERCENT:*** 100.0
CAS# 556-61-6
OTHER CONTAMINANTS: NONE
EXPOSURE LIMITS: NO OCCUPATIONAL EXPOSURE LIMITS ESTABLISHED BY OSHA, ACGIH, OR NIOSH.
METHYL ISOTHIOCYANATE: 500 POUNDS SARA SECTION 302 THRESHOLD PLANNING QUANTITY 1 POUND SARA SECTION 304 REPORTABLE QUANTITY

PHYSICAL DATA

DESCRIPTION: COLORLESS CRYSTALS OR LIQUID WITH AN UNPLEASANT, HORSERADISH-LIKE ODOR. ***BOILING POINT:*** 246 F (119 C) @ 758 MMHG
MELTING POINT: 86-97 F (30-36 C) ***SPECIFIC GRAVITY:*** 1.0691 @ 37 C
VOLATILITY: 100% ***VAPOR PRESSURE:*** 20.25 MMHG @ 20 C
EVAPORATION RATE: (ETHER = 1) < 1 ***SOLUBILITY IN WATER:*** REACTS
VAPOR DENSITY: > 1
SOLVENT SOLUBILITY: SOLUBLE IN ETHANOL, METHANOL, CYCLOHEXANONE, ETHER, BENZENE, METHYLENE CHLORIDE, LIGHT PETROLEUM.

FIRE AND EXPLOSION DATA

FIRE AND EXPLOSION HAZARD: DANGEROUS FIRE HAZARD WHEN EXPOSED TO HEAT OR FLAME.
VAPORS ARE HEAVIER THAN AIR AND MAY TRAVEL A CONSIDERABLE DISTANCE TO A SOURCE OF IGNITION AND FLASH BACK.
VAPOR-AIR MIXTURES ARE EXPLOSIVE ABOVE FLASH POINT.
FLASH POINT: 90 F (32 C) (CC) ***FLAMMABILITY CLASS(OSHA):*** IC
FIREFIGHTING MEDIA: DRY CHEMICAL, CARBON DIOXIDE, HALON, WATER SPRAY OR STANDARD FOAM (1987 EMERGENCY RESPONSE GUIDEBOOK, DOT P 5800.4).
FOR LARGER FIRES, USE WATER SPRAY, FOG OR STANDARD FOAM (1987 EMERGENCY RESPONSE GUIDEBOOK, DOT P 5800.4).
FIREFIGHTING: MOVE CONTAINER FROM FIRE AREA IF POSSIBLE. DIKE FIRE CONTROL WATER FOR LATER DISPOSAL; DO NOT SCATTER THE MATERIAL. COOL FIRE-EXPOSED CONTAINERS WITH WATER FROM SIDE UNTIL WELL AFTER FIRE IS OUT. STAY AWAY FROM STORAGE TANK ENDS. WITHDRAW IMMEDIATELY IN CASE OF RISING SOUND FROM VENTING SAFETY DEVICE OR ANY DISCOLORATION OF STORAGE TANK DUE TO FIRE (1987 EMERGENCY RESPONSE GUIDEBOOK, DOT P 5800.4, GUIDE PAGE 28).
EXTINGUISH ONLY IF FLOW CAN BE STOPPED. USE FLOODING AMOUNTS OF WATER AS A FOG; SOLID STREAMS MAY BE INEFFECTIVE. COOL CONTAINERS WITH FLOODING AMOUNTS OF WATER FROM AS FAR A DISTANCE AS POSSIBLE. AVOID BREATHING POISONOUS VAPORS, KEEP UPWIND.

TRANSPORTATION DATA

DEPARTMENT OF TRANSPORTATION HAZARD CLASSIFICATION 49 CFR 172.101: FLAMMABLE LIQUID
DEPARTMENT OF TRANSPORTATION LABELING REQUIREMENTS 49 CFR 172.101 AND SUBPART E: FLAMMABLE LIQUID AND POISON
DEPARTMENT OF TRANSPORTATION PACKAGING REQUIREMENTS: 49 CFR 173.119 EXCEPTIONS: NONE

TOXICITY

METHYLISOTHIOCYANATE: TOXICITY DATA: 33 MG/KG SKIN-RABBIT LD50; 2780 MG/KG SKIN-RAT LD50; 1820 MG/KG SKIN-MOUSE LD50; 1 GM/KG ORAL-WOMAN LDLO; 97 MG/KG ORAL-RAT LD50; 97 MG/KG ORAL-MOUSE LD50; 50 MG/KG SUBCUTANEOUS-MOUSE LD50. CARCINOGEN STATUS: NONE. LOCAL EFFECTS: CORROSIVE- SKIN, EYE, INGESTION. ACUTE TOXICITY LEVEL: HIGHLY TOXIC BY DERMAL ABSORPTION; TOXIC BY INGESTION. TARGET EFFECTS: POISONING MAY AFFECT THE KIDNEYS AND LIVER.

HEALTH EFFECTS AND FIRST AID

INHALATION: METHYLISOTHIOCYANATE: **ACUTE EXPOSURE-** MAY CAUSE IRRITATION OF THE MUCOUS MEMBRANES. IF SUFFICIENT AMOUNTS ARE ABSORBED MAY CAUSE CONVULSIONS, CHANGE IN MOTOR ACTIVITY, COMA, AND DEATH.
CHRONIC EXPOSURE- NO DATA AVAILABLE.
FIRST AID- REMOVE FROM EXPOSURE AREA TO FRESH AIR IMMEDIATELY. IF BREATHING HAS STOPPED, GIVE ARTIFICIAL RESPIRATION. MAINTAIN AIRWAY AND BLOOD PRESSURE AND ADMINISTER OXYGEN IF AVAILABLE. KEEP AFFECTED PERSON WARM AND AT REST. TREAT SYMPTOMATICALLY AND SUPPORTIVELY. ADMINISTRATION OF OXYGEN SHOULD BE PERFORMED BY QUALIFIED PERSONNEL. GET MEDICAL ATTENTION IMMEDIATELY.

SKIN CONTACT: METHYLISOTHIOCYANATE: CORROSIVE/HIGHLY TOXIC. **ACUTE EXPOSURE-** MAY CAUSE SEVERE IRRITATION AND BLISTERING. MAY BE ABSORBED AND MAY CAUSE CONVULSIONS, CHANGE IN MOTOR ACTIVITY, COMA AND DEATH. **CHRONIC EXPOSURE-** REPEATED OR PROLONGED EXPOSURE MAY CAUSE DERMATITIS. ABSORPTION MAY CAUSE LIVER OR KIDNEY DAMAGE.
FIRST AID- REMOVE CONTAMINATED CLOTHING AND SHOES IMMEDIATELY. WASH AFFECTED AREA WITH SOAP OR MILD DETERGENT AND LARGE AMOUNTS OF WATER UNTIL NO EVIDENCE OF CHEMICAL REMAINS (AT LEAST 15-20 MINUTES). IN CASE OF CHEMICAL BURNS, COVER AREA WITH STERILE, DRY DRESSING. BANDAGE SECURELY, BUT NOT TOO TIGHTLY. GET MEDICAL ATTENTION IMMEDIATELY.

EYE CONTACT: METHYLISOTHIOCYANATE: CORROSIVE/LACRIMATOR. **ACUTE EXPOSURE-** DIRECT CONTACT MAY CAUSE SEVERE IRRITATION, PAIN, LACRIMATION, AND BURNS, POSSIBLY SEVERE. THE DEGREE OF INJURY DEPENDS ON THE CONCENTRATION AND DURATION OF CONTACT. THE FULL EXTENT OF INJURY MAY NOT BE IMMEDIATELY APPARENT. **CHRONIC EXPOSURE-** EFFECTS DEPEND ON THE CONCENTRATION AND DURATION OF EXPOSURE. REPEATED OR PROLONGED CONTACT MAY RESULT IN CONJUNCTIVITIS OR EFFECTS AS IN ACUTE EXPOSURE.
FIRST AID- WASH EYES IMMEDIATELY WITH LARGE AMOUNTS OF WATER, OCCASIONALLY LIFTING UPPER AND LOWER LIDS, UNTIL NO EVIDENCE OF CHEMICAL REMAINS (AT LEAST 15-20 MINUTES). CONTINUE IRRIGATING WITH NORMAL SALINE UNTIL THE PH HAS RETURNED TO NORMAL (30-60 MINUTES). COVER WITH STERILE BANDAGES. GET MEDICAL ATTENTION IMMEDIATELY.

INGESTION: METHYLISOTHIOCYANATE: CORROSIVE/TOXIC. **ACUTE EXPOSURE-** INTENTIONAL POISONING FROM THE INGESTION OF 50 G DISSOLVED IN WATER RESULTED IN SUBSTERNAL AND EPIGASTRIC BURNING PAIN FOLLOWED BY REPEATED VOMITING AND A FEW MINUTES LATER TONIC AND CLONIC SEIZURES. LOSS OF CONSCIOUSNESS, DEEP COMA, AND DEATH OCCURRED ABOUT 8 HOURS LATER. EXTENSIVE MUCOSAL NECROSIS OF THE ESOPHAGUS, STOMACH AND DUODENUM AND A BLACKENING OF THE MUCOSA RESEMBLING DAMAGE BY A CORROSIVE WAS SEEN. **CHRONIC EXPOSURE-** MAY CAUSE LIVER AND KIDNEY DAMAGE.
FIRST AID- IF THE PERSON IS CONSCIOUS AND NOT CONVULSING, INDUCE EMESIS BY GIVING SYRUP OF IPECAC FOLLOWED BY WATER. (IF VOMITING OCCURS KEEP THE HEAD BELOW THE HIPS TO PREVENT ASPIRATION). REPEAT IN 20 MINUTES IF NOT EFFECTIVE INITIALLY. GIVE ACTIVATED CHARCOAL. IN PATIENTS WITH DEPRESSED RESPIRATION OR IF EMESIS IS NOT PRODUCED, PERFORM GASTRIC LAVAGE CAUTIOUSLY (DREISBACH, HANDBOOK OF POISONING, 12TH ED.). TREAT SYMPTOMATICALLY AND SUPPORTIVELY. GASTRIC LAVAGE SHOULD BE PERFORMED BY QUALIFIED MEDICAL PERSONNEL. GET MEDICAL ATTENTION IMMEDIATELY.
ANTIDOTE: NO SPECIFIC ANTIDOTE. TREAT SYMPTOMATICALLY AND SUPPORTIVELY.

REACTIVITY

REACTIVITY: MAY BE HYDROLYZED ON CONTACT WITH WATER.
INCOMPATIBILITIES: METHYLISOTHIOCYANATE: ALCOHOLS: INCOMPATIBLE. ALKALI: INCOMPATIBLE. AMINES: INCOMPATIBLE. HALOGENS: INCOMPATIBLE. HYDRAZINE: INCOMPATIBLE. OXIDIZERS (STRONG): FIRE AND EXPLOSION HAZARD.
DECOMPOSITION: THERMAL DECOMPOSITION PRODUCTS MAY INCLUDE HIGHLY TOXIC FUMES OF HYDROGEN CYANIDE, HYDROGEN SULFIDE AND TOXIC OXIDES OF NITROGEN, SULFUR, AND CARBON.
POLYMERIZATION: HAZARDOUS POLYMERIZATION HAS NOT BEEN REPORTED TO OCCUR UNDER NORMAL TEMPERATURES AND PRESSURES.

STORAGE AND DISPOSAL

OBSERVE ALL FEDERAL, STATE AND LOCAL REGULATIONS WHEN STORING OR DISPOSING OF THIS SUBSTANCE. FOR ASSISTANCE, CONTACT THE DISTRICT DIRECTOR OF THE ENVIRONMENTAL PROTECTION AGENCY.

STORAGE

STORE IN ACCORDANCE WITH 29 CFR 1910.106.
BONDING AND GROUNDING: SUBSTANCES WITH LOW ELECTROCONDUCTIVITY, WHICH MAY BE IGNITED BY ELECTROSTATIC SPARKS, SHOULD BE STORED IN CONTAINERS WHICH MEET THE BONDING AND GROUNDING GUIDELINES SPECIFIED IN NFPA 77-1983, RECOMMENDED PRACTICE ON STATIC ELECTRICITY.
STORE AWAY FROM INCOMPATIBLE SUBSTANCES.
THRESHOLD PLANNING QUANTITY (TPQ): THE SUPERFUND AMENDMENTS AND REAUTHORIZATION ACT (SARA) SECTION 302 REQUIRES THAT EACH FACILITY WHERE ANY EXTREMELY HAZARDOUS SUBSTANCE IS PRESENT IN A QUANTITY EQUAL TO OR GREATER THAN THE TPQ ESTABLISHED FOR THAT SUBSTANCE NOTIFY THE STATE EMERGENCY RESPONSE COMMISSION FOR THE STATE IN WHICH IT IS LOCATED. SECTION 303 OF SARA REQUIRES THESE FACILITIES TO PARTICIPATE IN LOCAL EMERGENCY RESPONSE PLANNING (40 CFR 355.30).

****DISPOSAL****

DISPOSAL MUST BE IN ACCORDANCE WITH STANDARDS APPLICABLE TO GENERATORS OF HAZARDOUS WASTE, 40 CFR 262. EPA HAZARDOUS WASTE NUMBER D001. 100 POUND CERCLA SECTION 103 REPORTABLE QUANTITY.

CONDITIONS TO AVOID

AVOID CONTACT WITH HEAT, SPARKS, FLAMES OR OTHER IGNITION SOURCES. VAPORS MAY BE EXPLOSIVE. MATERIAL IS POISONOUS; AVOID INHALATION OF VAPORS OR CONTACT WITH SKIN. DO NOT ALLOW MATERIAL TO CONTAMINATE WATER SOURCES.

SPILL AND LEAK PROCEDURES

OCCUPATIONAL SPILL: SHUT OFF IGNITION SOURCES. DO NOT TOUCH SPILLED MATERIAL. STOP LEAK IF YOU CAN DO IT WITHOUT RISK. USE WATER SPRAY TO REDUCE VAPORS. FOR SMALL SPILLS, TAKE UP WITH SAND OR OTHER ABSORBENT MATERIAL AND PLACE INTO CONTAINERS FOR LATER DISPOSAL. FOR LARGER SPILLS, DIKE FAR AHEAD OF SPILL FOR LATER DISPOSAL. NO SMOKING, FLAMES OR FLARES IN HAZARD AREA! KEEP UNNECESSARY PEOPLE AWAY; ISOLATE HAZARD AREA AND DENY ENTRY.

REPORTABLE QUANTITY (RQ): 1 POUND THE SUPERFUND AMENDMENTS AND REAUTHORIZATION ACT (SARA) SECTION 304 REQUIRES THAT A RELEASE EQUAL TO OR GREATER THAN THE REPORTABLE QUANTITY FOR THIS SUBSTANCE BE IMMEDIATELY REPORTED TO THE LOCAL EMERGENCY PLANNING COMMITTEE AND THE STATE EMERGENCY RESPONSE COMMISSION (40 CFR 355.40). IF THE RELEASE OF THIS SUBSTANCE IS REPORTABLE UNDER CERCLA SECTION 103, THE NATIONAL RESPONSE CENTER MUST BE NOTIFIED IMMEDIATELY AT (800) 424-8802 OR (202) 426-2675 IN THE METROPOLITAN WASHINGTON, D.C. AREA (40 CFR 302.6).

PROTECTIVE EQUIPMENT

VENTILATION: PROCESS ENCLOSURE RECOMMENDED. VENTILATION EQUIPMENT MUST BE EXPLOSION-PROOF.

RESPIRATOR: THE FOLLOWING RESPIRATORS ARE RECOMMENDED BASED ON INFORMATION FOUND IN THE PHYSICAL DATA, TOXICITY AND HEALTH EFFECTS SECTIONS. THEY ARE RANKED IN ORDER FROM MINIMUM TO MAXIMUM RESPIRATORY PROTECTION. THE SPECIFIC RESPIRATOR SELECTED MUST BE BASED ON CONTAMINATION LEVELS FOUND IN THE WORK PLACE, MUST NOT EXCEED THE WORKING LIMITS OF THE RESPIRATOR AND BE JOINTLY APPROVED BY THE NATIONAL INSTITUTE FOR OCCUPATIONAL SAFETY AND HEALTH AND THE MINE SAFETY AND HEALTH ADMINISTRATION (NIOSH-MSHA).

TYPE 'C' SUPPLIED-AIR RESPIRATOR WITH A FULL FACEPIECE OPERATED IN PRESSURE-DEMAND OR OTHER POSITIVE PRESSURE MODE OR WITH A FULL FACEPIECE, HELMET OR HOOD OPERATED IN CONTINOUS-FLOW MODE.

SELF-CONTAINED BREATHING APPARATUS WITH A FULL FACEPIECE OPERATED IN PRESSURE-DEMAND OR OTHER POSITIVE PRESSURE MODE.

FOR FIREFIGHTING AND OTHER IMMEDIATELY DANGEROUS TO LIFE OR HEALTH CONDITIONS:

SELF-CONTAINED BREATHING APPARATUS WITH FULL FACEPIECE OPERATED IN PRESSURE-DEMAND OR OTHER POSITIVE PRESSURE MODE.

SUPPLIED-AIR RESPIRATOR WITH FULL FACEPIECE AND OPERATED IN PRESSURE-DEMAND OR OTHER POSITIVE PRESSURE MODE IN COMBINATION WITH AN AUXILIARY SELF-CONTAINED BREATHING APPARATUS OPERATED IN PRESSURE-DEMAND OR OTHER POSITIVE PRESSURE MODE.

CLOTHING: EMPLOYEE MUST WEAR APPROPRIATE PROTECTIVE (IMPERVIOUS) CLOTHING AND EQUIPMENT TO PREVENT ANY POSSIBILITY OF SKIN CONTACT WITH THIS SUBSTANCE.

GLOVES: EMPLOYEE MUST WEAR APPROPRIATE PROTECTIVE GLOVES TO PREVENT CONTACT WITH THIS SUBSTANCE.

EYE PROTECTION: EMPLOYEE MUST WEAR SPLASH-PROOF OR DUST-RESISTANT SAFETY GOGGLES AND A FACESHIELD TO PREVENT CONTACT WITH THIS SUBSTANCE.

EMERGENCY WASH FACILITIES: WHERE THERE IS ANY POSSIBILITY THAT AN EMPLOYEE'S EYES AND/OR SKIN MAY BE EXPOSED TO THIS SUBSTANCE, THE EMPLOYER SHOULD PROVIDE AN EYE WASH FOUNTAIN AND QUICK DRENCH SHOWER WITHIN THE IMMEDIATE WORK AREA FOR EMERGENCY USE.

AUTHORIZED BY- OCCUPATIONAL HEALTH SERVICES, INC.

CREATION DATE: 10/04/89 ***REVISION DATE:*** 05/14/90

MATERIAL SAFETY DATA SHEET

OCCUPATIONAL HEALTH SERVICES, INC. EMERGENCY CONTACT:
AGRICULTURE AND PESTICIDE DIVISION JOHN S. BRANSFORD, JR. (615) 292-1180
450 SEVENTH AVENUE, SUITE 2407
NEW YORK, NEW YORK 10123
1-800-445-MSDS OR (212) 967-1100

SUBSTANCE IDENTIFICATION

CAS-NUMBER 51218-45-2

SUBSTANCE: **METOLACHLOR**

TRADE NAMES/SYNONYMS: ACETAMIDE, 2-CHLORO-N-(2-ETHYL-6-METHYLPHENYL)-N-(2-METHOXY-1- METHYLETHYL)-; 2-CHLORO-N-(2-ETHYL-6-METHYLPHENYL)-N-(2-METHOXY-1-METHYLETHYL) ACETAMIDE; 2-CHLORO-6'-ETHYL-N-(2-METHOXY-1-METHYLETHYL)ACETO-O-TOLUIDIDE; ALPHA-CHLORO-2'-ETHYL-6'-METHYL-N-(1-METHYL-2-METHOXYETHYL)ACETANILIDE; CGA-24705; CODAL; DUAL; METOLACHLORE; METELILACHLOR; C15H22CLNO2; PST15003

CHEMICAL FAMILY: HALOGENATED ACETAMIDE

MOLECULAR FORMULA: C15-H22-CL-N-O2

MOLECULAR WEIGHT: 283.81

CERCLA RATINGS (SCALE 0-3): HEALTH=2 FIRE=U REACTIVITY=0 PERSISTENCE=2

NFPA RATINGS (SCALE 0-4): HEALTH=U FIRE=U REACTIVITY=0

COMPONENTS AND CONTAMINANTS

COMPONENT: METOLACHLOR ***PERCENT:*** 100.0
CAS# 51218-45-2

OTHER CONTAMINANTS: NONE

EXPOSURE LIMITS: NO OCCUPATIONAL EXPOSURE LIMITS ESTABLISHED BY OSHA, ACGIH, OR NIOSH.

PHYSICAL DATA

DESCRIPTION: ODORLESS, CLEAR, WHITE TO TAN LIQUID.

BOILING POINT: 212 F (100 C) @ 0.001 MMHG ***SPECIFIC GRAVITY:*** 1.085

VAPOR PRESSURE: 0.000013 MMHG @ 20 C ***SOLUBILITY IN WATER:*** 0.053% @ 20 C

SOLVENT SOLUBILITY: SOLUBLE IN ACETONE, BENZENE, DICHLOROMETHANE, HEXANE, METHANOL, OCTANOL, AND MOST OTHER ORGANIC SOLVENTS; INSOLUBLE IN ETHYLENE GLYCOL AND PROPYLENE GLYCOL.

FIRE AND EXPLOSION DATA

FIRE AND EXPLOSION HAZARD: UNKNOWN FIRE AND EXPLOSION HAZARD.

FLASH POINT: NOT AVAILABLE

FIREFIGHTING MEDIA: DRY CHEMICAL, CARBON DIOXIDE, HALON, WATER SPRAY OR STANDARD FOAM (1987 EMERGENCY RESPONSE GUIDEBOOK, DOT P 5800.4). FOR LARGER FIRES, USE WATER SPRAY, FOG OR STANDARD FOAM (1987 EMERGENCY RESPONSE GUIDEBOOK, DOT P 5800.4).

FIREFIGHTING: MOVE CONTAINER FROM FIRE AREA IF POSSIBLE. COOL FIRE-EXPOSED CONTAINERS WITH WATER FROM SIDE UNTIL WELL AFTER FIRE IS OUT. STAY AWAY FROM STORAGE TANK ENDS. FOR MASSIVE FIRE IN STORAGE AREA, USE UNMANNED HOSE HOLDER OR MONITOR NOZZLES, ELSE WITHDRAW FROM AREA AND LET FIRE BURN. WITHDRAW IMMEDIATELY IN CASE OF RISING SOUND FROM VENTING SAFETY DEVICE OR ANY DISCOLORATION OF STORAGE TANK DUE TO FIRE (1987 EMERGENCY RESPONSE GUIDEBOOK, DOT P 5800.4, GUIDE PAGE 27). EXTINGUISH ONLY IF FLOW CAN BE STOPPED; USE FLOODING AMOUNTS OF WATER AS A FOG, SOLID STREAMS MAY BE INEFFECTIVE. COOL CONTAINERS WITH FLOODING AMOUNTS OF WATER, APPLY FROM AS FAR A DISTANCE AS POSSIBLE. AVOID BREATHING VAPORS, KEEP UPWIND.

TOXICITY

METOLACHLOR: IRRITATION DATA: 334 MG SKIN-RABBIT MILD. TOXICITY DATA: 3170 MG/KG SKIN-RAT LD50; 2534 MG/KG ORAL-RAT LD50; MUTAGENIC DATA (RTECS). CARCINOGEN STATUS: NONE. ACUTE TOXICITY LEVEL: MODERATELY TOXIC BY INGESTION; SLIGHTLY TOXIC BY DERMAL ABSORPTION. TARGET EFFECTS: SENSITIZER-SKIN.

HEALTH EFFECTS AND FIRST AID

INHALATION: METOLACHLOR: **ACUTE EXPOSURE-** NO DEATHS WERE OBSERVED IN RATS EXPOSED TO A CONCENTRATION OF 1752 MG/M3/4 HOURS. **CHRONIC EXPOSURE-** NO DATA AVAILABLE.

FIRST AID- REMOVE FROM EXPOSURE AREA TO FRESH AIR IMMEDIATELY. IF BREATHING HAS STOPPED, PERFORM ARTIFICIAL RESPIRATION. KEEP PERSON WARM AND AT REST. TREAT SYMPTOMATICALLY AND SUPPORTIVELY. GET MEDICAL ATTENTION IMMEDIATELY.

SKIN CONTACT: METOLACHLOR: SENSITIZER. **ACUTE EXPOSURE-** 334 MG APPLIED TO RABBIT SKIN WAS MILDLY IRRITATING. HOWEVER, EMULSIFIABLE CONCENTRATE FORMULATIONS APPLIED TO RABBIT SKIN PRODUCED MODERATE ERYTHMA, EDEMA, AND SECOND DEGREE BURNS AT 72 HOURS. THIS MATERIAL PRODUCED

SENSITIZATION WHEN APPLIED TO GUINEA PIG SKIN. **CHRONIC EXPOSURE-** PROLONGED OR REPEATED EXPOSURE MAY CAUSE SENSITIZATION. REPEATED APPLICATION OF 1080 MG/KG/DAY OF METOLACHLOR IN A FORMULATION RESULTED IN DECREASED WEIGHT GAIN IN ANIMALS.

FIRST AID- REMOVE CONTAMINATED CLOTHING AND SHOES IMMEDIATELY. WASH AFFECTED AREA WITH SOAP OR MILD DETERGENT AND LARGE AMOUNTS OF WATER UNTIL NO EVIDENCE OF CHEMICAL REMAINS (APPROXIMATELY 15-20 MINUTES). GET MEDICAL ATTENTION IMMEDIATELY.

EYE CONTACT: METOLACHLOR: **ACUTE EXPOSURE-** THIS MATERIAL WAS NOT IRRITATING TO RABBIT EYES. HOWEVER, A EMULSIFIABLE CONCENTRATE FORMULATION PRODUCED SEVERE IRRITATION IN UNRINSED RABBIT EYES. **CHRONIC EXPOSURE-** NO DATA AVAILABLE.

FIRST AID- WASH EYES IMMEDIATELY WITH LARGE AMOUNTS OF WATER OR NORMAL SALINE, OCCASIONALLY LIFTING UPPER AND LOWER LIDS, UNTIL NO EVIDENCE OF CHEMICAL REMAINS (APPROXIMATELY 15-20 MINUTES). GET MEDICAL ATTENTION IMMEDIATELY.

INGESTION: METOLACHLOR: **ACUTE EXPOSURE-** THIS MATERIAL PRODUCED EMESIS IN DOGS. **CHRONIC EXPOSURE-** ADMINISTRATION OF 1000 PPM IN THE DIET FOR 6 MONTHS PRODUCED DECREASED WEIGHT GAIN IN DOGS.

FIRST AID- REMOVE BY GASTRIC LAVAGE AND CATHARSIS. MAINTAIN BLOOD PRESSURE AND AIRWAY. GIVE OXYGEN IF RESPIRATION IS DEPRESSED. DO NOT PERFORM GASTRIC LAVAGE IF VICTIM IS UNCONSCIOUS. GET MEDICAL ATTENTION IMMEDIATELY (DREISBACH, HANDBOOK OF POISONING, 12TH ED.).
ADMINISTRATION OF LAVAGE OR OXYGEN SHOULD BE PERFORMED BY QUALIFIED MEDICAL PERSONNEL.

ANTIDOTE: NO SPECIFIC ANTIDOTE. TREAT SYMPTOMATICALLY AND SUPPORTIVELY.

REACTIVITY

REACTIVITY: STABLE UNDER NORMAL TEMPERATURES AND PRESSURES.

INCOMPATIBILITIES: METOLACHLOR: OXIDIZERS (STRONG): FIRE AND EXPLOSION HAZARD.

DECOMPOSITION: THERMAL DECOMPOSITION PRODUCTS MAY INCLUDE TOXIC OXIDES OF NITROGEN AND CARBON AND TOXIC AND CORROSIVE FUMES OF CHLORIDES.

POLYMERIZATION: HAZARDOUS POLYMERIZATION HAS NOT BEEN REPORTED TO OCCUR UNDER NORMAL TEMPERATURES AND PRESSURES.

STORAGE AND DISPOSAL

OBSERVE ALL FEDERAL, STATE AND LOCAL REGULATIONS WHEN STORING OR DISPOSING OF THIS SUBSTANCE. FOR ASSISTANCE, CONTACT THE DISTRICT DIRECTOR OF THE ENVIRONMENTAL PROTECTION AGENCY.

****STORAGE****

STORE IN ACCORDANCE WITH 40 CFR 165 RECOMMENDED PROCEDURES FOR THE DISPOSAL AND STORAGE OF PESTICIDES AND PESTICIDE CONTAINERS.
STORE AWAY FROM INCOMPATIBLE SUBSTANCES.
STORE IN A COOL, DRY PLACE; KEEP CONTAINER TIGHTLY CLOSED WHEN NOT IN USE.

****DISPOSAL****

DISPOSAL MUST BE IN ACCORDANCE WITH 40 CFR 165 RECOMMENDED PROCEDURES FOR THE DISPOSAL AND STORAGE OF PESTICIDES AND PESTICIDE CONTAINERS.

CONDITIONS TO AVOID

AVOID CONTACT WITH HEAT, SPARKS, FLAMES, OR OTHER SOURCES OF IGNITION. VAPORS MAY BE EXPLOSIVE. AVOID OVERHEATING OF CONTAINERS; CONTAINERS MAY VIOLENTLY RUPTURE IN HEAT OF FIRE. AVOID CONTAMINATION OF WATER SOURCES.

SPILL AND LEAK PROCEDURES

OCCUPATIONAL SPILL: SHUT OFF IGNITION SOURCES. STOP LEAK IF YOU CAN DO IT WITHOUT RISK. USE WATER SPRAY TO REDUCE VAPORS. FOR SMALL SPILLS, TAKE UP WITH SAND OR OTHER ABSORBENT MATERIAL AND PLACE INTO CONTAINERS FOR LATER DISPOSAL. FOR LARGER SPILLS, DIKE FAR AHEAD OF SPILL FOR LATER DISPOSAL. NO SMOKING, FLAMES OR FLARES IN HAZARD AREA. KEEP UNNECESSARY PEOPLE AWAY; ISOLATE HAZARD AREA AND RESTRICT ENTRY.

PROTECTIVE EQUIPMENT

VENTILATION: PROVIDE LOCAL EXHAUST OR GENERAL DILUTION VENTILATION SYSTEM.

RESPIRATOR: THE FOLLOWING RESPIRATORS ARE RECOMMENDED BASED ON INFORMATION FOUND IN THE PHYSICAL DATA, TOXICITY AND HEALTH EFFECTS SECTIONS. THEY ARE RANKED IN ORDER FROM MINIMUM TO MAXIMUM RESPIRATORY PROTECTION. THE SPECIFIC RESPIRATOR SELECTED MUST BE BASED ON CONTAMINATION LEVELS FOUND IN THE WORK PLACE, MUST NOT EXCEED THE WORKING LIMITS OF THE RESPIRATOR AND BE JOINTLY APPROVED BY THE NATIONAL INSTITUTE FOR OCCUPATIONAL SAFETY AND HEALTH AND THE MINE SAFETY AND HEALTH ADMINISTRATION (NIOSH-MSHA).
CHEMICAL CARTRIDGE RESPIRATOR WITH FULL FACEPIECE AND PESTICIDE CARTRIDGE. TYPE 'C' SUPPLIED-AIR RESPIRATOR WITH A FULL FACEPIECE OPERATED IN PRESSURE-DEMAND OR OTHER POSITIVE PRESSURE MODE OR WITH A FULL FACEPIECE, HELMET OR HOOD OPERATED IN CONTINUOUS-FLOW MODE.
SELF-CONTAINED BREATHING APPARATUS OPERATED IN PRESSURE-DEMAND OR OTHER POSITIVE PRESSURE MODE.
FOR FIREFIGHTING AND OTHER IMMEDIATELY DANGEROUS TO LIFE OR HEALTH CONDITIONS:
SELF-CONTAINED BREATHING APPARATUS WITH FULL FACEPIECE OPERATED IN PRESSURE-DEMAND OR OTHER POSITIVE PRESSURE MODE.
SUPPLIED-AIR RESPIRATOR WITH FULL FACEPIECE AND OPERATED IN PRESSURE-DEMAND OR OTHER POSITIVE PRESSURE MODE IN COMBINATION WITH AN AUXILIARY SELF-CONTAINED BREATHING APPARATUS OPERATED IN PRESSURE-DEMAND OR OTHER POSITIVE PRESSURE MODE.

CLOTHING: EMPLOYEE MUST WEAR APPROPRIATE PROTECTIVE (IMPERVIOUS) CLOTHING AND EQUIPMENT TO PREVENT REPEATED OR PROLONGED SKIN CONTACT WITH THIS SUBSTANCE.

GLOVES: EMPLOYEE MUST WEAR APPROPRIATE PROTECTIVE GLOVES TO PREVENT CONTACT WITH THIS SUBSTANCE.

EYE PROTECTION: EMPLOYEE MUST WEAR SPLASH-PROOF OR DUST-RESISTANT SAFETY GOGGLES TO PREVENT EYE CONTACT WITH THIS SUBSTANCE.
EMERGENCY EYE WASH: WHERE THERE IS ANY POSSIBILITY THAT AN EMPLOYEE'S EYES MAY BE EXPOSED TO THIS SUBSTANCE, THE EMPLOYER SHOULD PROVIDE AN EYE WASH FOUNTAIN WITHIN THE IMMEDIATE WORK AREA FOR EMERGENCY USE.

AUTHORIZED BY- OCCUPATIONAL HEALTH SERVICES, INC.
CREATION DATE: 10/04/89 ***REVISION DATE:*** 05/14/90

MATERIAL SAFETY DATA SHEET

OCCUPATIONAL HEALTH SERVICES, INC.
AGRICULTURE AND PESTICIDE DIVISION
450 SEVENTH AVENUE, SUITE 2407
NEW YORK, NEW YORK 10123
1-800-445-MSDS OR (212) 967-1100

EMERGENCY CONTACT:
JOHN S. BRANSFORD, JR. (615) 292-1180

SUBSTANCE IDENTIFICATION

CAS-NUMBER 21087-64-9

SUBSTANCE: **METRIBUZIN**

TRADE NAMES/SYNONYMS: 1,2,4-TRIAZIN-5(4H)-ONE, 4-AMINO-6-(1,1-DIMETHYLETHYL)-3-(METHYLTHIO)-; AS-TRIAZIN-5(4H)-ONE, 4-AMINO-6-TERT-BUTYL-3-(METHYLTHIO)-; 4-AMINO-6-(1,1-DIMETHYLETHYL)-3-(METHYLTHIO)-1,2,4-TRIAZIN-5(4H)-ONE; 4-AMINO-6-TERT-BUTYL-3-(METHYLTHIO)-AS-TRIAZIN-5(4H)-ONE; 4-AMINO-6-TERT-BUTYL-3-METHYLTHIO-1,2,4-TRIAZIN-5(4H)-ONE; 4-AMINO-6-TERT-BUTYL-4,5-DIHYDRO-3-METHYLTHIO-1,2,4-TRIAZIN-5-ONE; BAY 94337; BAY 6159H; LEXONEEX; SENCOR; SENCORAL; SENCOREX; C8H14N4OS; PST15006

CHEMICAL FAMILY: TRIAZINE

MOLECULAR FORMULA: C8-H14-N4-O-S

MOLECULAR WEIGHT: 214.28

CERCLA RATINGS (SCALE 0-3): HEALTH=3 FIRE=0 REACTIVITY=0 PERSISTENCE=1

NFPA RATINGS (SCALE 0-4): HEALTH=U FIRE=0 REACTIVITY=0

COMPONENTS AND CONTAMINANTS

COMPONENT: METRIBUZIN ***PERCENT:*** 100.00
CAS# 21087-64-9

EXPOSURE LIMITS: METRIBUZIN: 5 MG/M3 OSHA TWA 5 MG/M3 ACGIH TWA

PHYSICAL DATA

DESCRIPTION: WHITE CRYSTALINE SOLID ***MELTING POINT:*** 261 F (127 C)

SPECIFIC GRAVITY: 1.28 ***VAPOR PRESSURE:*** NEGLIGIBLE

SOLUBILITY IN WATER: 1200 PPM

SOLVENT SOLUBILITY: SOLUBLE IN METHANOL, ETHANOL, GLYCOL ETHER ACETATE, ACETONE, BENZENE, CHLOROFORM, CYCLOHEXANONE, TOLUENE; SLIGHTLY SOLUBLE IN HEXANE; INSOLUBLE IN AROMATIC AND ALIPHATIC SOLVENTS.

FIRE AND EXPLOSION DATA

FIRE AND EXPLOSION HAZARD: NEGLIGIBLE FIRE HAZARD WHEN EXPOSED TO HEAT OR FLAME.

FIREFIGHTING MEDIA: DRY CHEMICAL, CARBON DIOXIDE, HALON, WATER SPRAY OR STANDARD FOAM (1987 EMERGENCY RESPONSE GUIDEBOOK, DOT P 5800.4). FOR LARGER FIRES, USE WATER SPRAY, FOG OR STANDARD FOAM (1987 EMERGENCY RESPONSE GUIDEBOOK, DOT P 5800.4).

FIREFIGHTING: MOVE CONTAINER FROM FIRE AREA IF POSSIBLE. DO NOT SCATTER SPILLED MATERIAL WITH HIGH PRESSURE WATER STREAMS. DIKE FIRE CONTROL WATER FOR LATER DISPOSAL (1987 EMERGENCY RESPONSE GUIDEBOOK, DOT P 5800.4, GUIDE PAGE 31).
USE AGENTS SUITABLE FOR TYPE OF SURROUNDING FIRE. AVOID BREATHING HAZARDOUS VAPORS, KEEP UPWIND.

TOXICITY

METRIBUZIN: TOXICITY DATA: 2 GM/KG SKIN-RAT LD50; 1100 MG/KG ORAL-RAT LD50; 698 MG/KG ORAL-MOUSE LD50; 250 MG/KG ORAL-GUINEA PIG LD50; 210 MG/KG INTRAPERITONEAL-MOUSE LD50. CARCINOGEN STATUS: NONE. ACUTE TOXICITY LEVEL: MODERATELY TOXIC BY DERMAL ABSORPTION AND INGESTION. TARGET EFFECTS: NO DATA AVAILABLE.

HEALTH EFFECTS AND FIRST AID

INHALATION: METRIBUZIN: **ACUTE EXPOSURE-** SOME TRIAZINES ARE MILDLY IRRITATING TO THE UPPER RESPIRATORY TRACT. A CONCENTRATION OF 865 MG/M3/4 HOURS WAS LETHAL TO HALF OF THE RATS TESTED. **CHRONIC EXPOSURE-** NO OBSERVABLE EFFECTS WAS NOTED IN RATS EXPOSED TO AN AEROSOL CONCENTRATION OF 31 MG/M3/6 HOURS, FIVE DAYS A WEEK, FOR 3 WEEKS.

FIRST AID- REMOVE FROM EXPOSURE AREA TO FRESH AIR IMMEDIATELY. IF BREATHING HAS STOPPED, PERFORM ARTIFICIAL RESPIRATION. KEEP PERSON WARM AND AT REST. TREAT SYMPTOMATICALLY AND SUPPORTIVELY. GET MEDICAL ATTENTION IMMEDIATELY.

SKIN CONTACT: METRIBUZIN: **ACUTE EXPOSURE-** ANIMAL STUDIES, ALONG WITH STUDIES ON HUMAN VOLUNTEERS, HAVE SHOWN THAT THIS SUBSTANCE IS NOT IRRITATING TO THE SKIN. NO SENSITIZATION REACTIONS HAVE BEEN DOCUMENTED. **CHRONIC EXPOSURE-** NO OBSERVABLE EFFECTS WERE NOTED IN RATS RECEIVING A DAILY DERMAL APPLICATION OF 1000 MG/KG OF A 70% WETTABLE POWDER FOR 3 WEEKS.

FIRST AID- REMOVE CONTAMINATED CLOTHING AND SHOES IMMEDIATELY. WASH AFFECTED AREA WITH SOAP OR MILD DETERGENT AND LARGE AMOUNTS OF WATER UNTIL NO EVIDENCE OF CHEMICAL REMAINS (APPROXIMATELY 15-20 MINUTES). GET MEDICAL ATTENTION IMMEDIATELY.

EYE CONTACT: METRIBUZIN: **ACUTE EXPOSURE-** STUDIES INDICATE METRIBUZIN IS NOT IRRITATING TO RABBIT EYES. **CHRONIC EXPOSURE-** NO DATA AVAILABLE.

FIRST AID- WASH EYES IMMEDIATELY WITH LARGE AMOUNTS OF WATER OR NORMAL SALINE, OCCASIONALLY LIFTING UPPER AND LOWER LIDS, UNTIL NO EVIDENCE OF CHEMICAL REMAINS (APPROXIMATELY 15-20 MINUTES). GET MEDICAL ATTENTION IMMEDIATELY.

INGESTION: METRIBUZIN: **ACUTE EXPOSURE-** A LETHAL DOSE IN RATS PRODUCED SEDATION, LABORED BREATHING, AND DEATH WITHIN 24 HOURS; SURVIVORS RECOVERED SLOWLY WITHOUT PERMANENT EFFECTS. **CHRONIC EXPOSURE-** WEIGHT REDUCTION, HEMATOLOGICAL CHANGES, INCREASED MORTALITY, AND LIVER AND KIDNEY DAMAGE WERE OBSERVED IN DOGS FED AT A DIETARY LEVEL OF 1500 PPM FOR TWO YEARS. FATIGUE, APATHY, BODY WEIGHT LOSS, AND CHANGES IN THE METABOLISM OF CARBOHYDRATES, PROTEINS, AND GLYCOPROTEINS OF THE LIVER WERE NOTED IN GUINEA PIGS RECEIVING 250 MG/KG, 6 TIMES A WEEK FOR 30 TO 90 DAYS.

FIRST AID- REMOVE BY GASTRIC LAVAGE AND CATHARSIS. MAINTAIN BLOOD PRESSURE AND AIRWAY. GIVE OXYGEN IF RESPIRATION IS DEPRESSED. DO NOT PERFORM GASTRIC LAVAGE IF VICTIM IS UNCONSCIOUS. GET MEDICAL ATTENTION IMMEDIATELY (DREISBACH, HANDBOOK OF POISONING, 12TH ED.). ADMINISTRATION OF LAVAGE OR OXYGEN SHOULD BE PERFORMED BY QUALIFIED MEDICAL PERSONNEL.

ANTIDOTE: NO SPECIFIC ANTIDOTE. TREAT SYMPTOMATICALLY AND SUPPORTIVELY.

REACTIVITY

REACTIVITY: STABLE UNDER NORMAL TEMPERATURES AND PRESSURES.

INCOMPATIBILITIES: METRIBUZIN: NO DATA AVAILABLE.

DECOMPOSITION: THERMAL DECOMPOSITION MAY RELEASE TOXIC OXIDES OF CARBON, NITROGEN AND SULFUR.

POLYMERIZATION: HAZARDOUS POLYMERIZATION HAS NOT BEEN REPORTED TO OCCUR UNDER NORMAL TEMPERATURES AND PRESSURES.

STORAGE AND DISPOSAL

OBSERVE ALL FEDERAL, STATE AND LOCAL REGULATIONS WHEN STORING OR DISPOSING OF THIS SUBSTANCE. FOR ASSISTANCE, CONTACT THE DISTRICT DIRECTOR OF THE ENVIRONMENTAL PROTECTION AGENCY.

****STORAGE****

STORE IN ACCORDANCE WITH 40 CFR 165 RECOMMENDED PROCEDURES FOR THE DISPOSAL AND STORAGE OF PESTICIDES AND PESTICIDE CONTAINERS.

****DISPOSAL****

DISPOSAL MUST BE IN ACCORDANCE WITH 40 CFR 165 RECOMMENDED PROCEDURES FOR THE DISPOSAL AND STORAGE OF PESTICIDES AND PESTICIDE CONTAINERS.

CONDITIONS TO AVOID

MAY BURN BUT DOES NOT IGNITE READILY. AVOID CONTACT WITH STRONG OXIDIZERS, EXCESSIVE HEAT, SPARKS, OR OPEN FLAME.

SPILL AND LEAK PROCEDURES

OCCUPATIONAL SPILL: SWEEP UP AND PLACE IN SUITABLE CLEAN, DRY CONTAINERS FOR RECLAMATION OR LATER DISPOSAL. DO NOT FLUSH SPILLED MATERIAL INTO SEWER. KEEP UNNECESSARY PEOPLE AWAY.

PROTECTIVE EQUIPMENT

VENTILATION: PROVIDE LOCAL EXHAUST VENTILATION AND/OR GENERAL DILUTION VENTILATION TO MEET PUBLISHED EXPOSURE LIMITS.

RESPIRATOR: THE FOLLOWING RESPIRATORS ARE RECOMMENDED BASED ON INFORMATION FOUND IN THE PHYSICAL DATA, TOXICITY AND HEALTH EFFECTS SECTIONS. THEY ARE RANKED IN ORDER FROM MINIMUM TO MAXIMUM RESPIRATORY PROTECTION. THE SPECIFIC RESPIRATOR SELECTED MUST BE BASED ON CONTAMINATION LEVELS FOUND IN THE WORK PLACE, MUST NOT EXCEED THE WORKING LIMITS OF THE RESPIRATOR AND BE JOINTLY APPROVED BY THE NATIONAL INSTITUTE FOR OCCUPATIONAL SAFETY AND HEALTH AND THE MINE SAFETY AND HEALTH ADMINISTRATION (NIOSH-MSHA).
CHEMICAL CARTRIDGE RESPIRATOR WITH AN ORGANIC VAPOR CARTRIDGE(S) IN COMBINATION WITH A DUST AND MIST FILTER.
GAS MASK WITH ORGANIC VAPOR CANISTER (CHIN-STYLE OR FRONT- OR BACK-MOUNTED CANISTER) WITH A DUST AND MIST FILTER.
GAS MASK WITH ORGANIC VAPOR CANISTER (CHIN-STYLE OR FRONT- OR BACK-MOUNTED CANISTER) WITH A PARTICULATE FILTER. POWERED AIR-PURIFYING RESPIRATOR WITH A HIGH-EFFICIENCY FILTER.
TYPE 'C' SUPPLIED-AIR RESPIRATOR WITH A FULL FACEPIECE OPERATED IN A PRESSURE-DEMAND OR OTHER POSITIVE PRESSURE MODE.
SELF-CONTAINED BREATHING APPARATUS WITH A FULL FACEPIECE OPERATED IN PRESSURE-DEMAND OR OTHER POSITIVE PRESSURE MODE.
FOR FIREFIGHTING AND OTHER IMMEDIATELY DANGEROUS TO LIFE OR HEALTH CONDITIONS:
SELF-CONTAINED BREATHING APPARATUS WITH FULL FACEPIECE OPERATED IN PRESSURE-DEMAND OR OTHER POSITIVE PRESSURE MODE.
SUPPLIED-AIR RESPIRATOR WITH FULL FACEPIECE AND OPERATED IN PRESSURE-DEMAND OR OTHER POSITIVE PRESSURE MODE IN COMBINATION WITH AN AUXILIARY SELF-CONTAINED BREATHING APPARATUS OPERATED IN PRESSURE-DEMAND OR OTHER POSITIVE PRESSURE MODE.

CLOTHING: EMPLOYEE MUST WEAR APPROPRIATE PROTECTIVE (IMPERVIOUS) CLOTHING AND EQUIPMENT TO PREVENT REPEATED OR PROLONGED SKIN CONTACT WITH THIS SUBSTANCE.

GLOVES: EMPLOYEE MUST WEAR APPROPRIATE PROTECTIVE GLOVES TO PREVENT CONTACT WITH THIS SUBSTANCE.

EYE PROTECTION: EMPLOYEE MUST WEAR SPLASH-PROOF OR DUST-RESISTANT SAFETY GOGGLES TO PREVENT EYE CONTACT WITH THIS SUBSTANCE.
EMERGENCY EYE WASH: WHERE THERE IS ANY POSSIBILITY THAT AN EMPLOYEE'S EYES MAY BE EXPOSED TO THIS SUBSTANCE, THE EMPLOYER SHOULD PROVIDE AN EYE WASH FOUNTAIN WITHIN THE IMMEDIATE WORK AREA FOR EMERGENCY USE.

AUTHORIZED BY- OCCUPATIONAL HEALTH SERVICES, INC.
CREATION DATE: 10/04/89 ***REVISION DATE:*** 05/31/90

MATERIAL SAFETY DATA SHEET

OCCUPATIONAL HEALTH SERVICES, INC.
AGRICULTURE AND PESTICIDE DIVISION
450 SEVENTH AVENUE, SUITE 2407
NEW YORK, NEW YORK 10123
1-800-445-MSDS OR (212) 967-1100

EMERGENCY CONTACT:
JOHN S. BRANSFORD, JR. (615) 292-1180

SUBSTANCE IDENTIFICATION

CAS-NUMBER 3060-89-7

SUBSTANCE: **METOBROMURON**

TRADE NAMES/SYNONYMS: UREA, N'-(4-BROMOPHENYL)-N-METHOXY-N-METHYL-; UREA, 3-(P-BROMOPHENYL)-1-METHOXY-1-METHYL-; N'-(4-BROMOPHENYL)-N-METHOXY-N-METHYLUREA; 3-(P-BROMOPHENYL)-1-METHOXY-1-METHYLUREA; 3-(4-BROMOPHENYL)-1-METHOXY-1-METHYLUREA; C 3126; METBROMURON; PATORAN; C9H11BRN2O2; PST15008

CHEMICAL FAMILY: SUBSTITUTED UREA
HALOGEN COMPOUND, AROMATIC

MOLECULAR FORMULA: C9-H11-BR-N2-O2

MOLECULAR WEIGHT: 259.13

CERCLA RATINGS (SCALE 0-3): HEALTH=2 FIRE=1 REACTIVITY=0 PERSISTENCE=3

NFPA RATINGS (SCALE 0-4): HEALTH=2 FIRE=1 REACTIVITY=0

COMPONENTS AND CONTAMINANTS

COMPONENT: METOBROMURON ***PERCENT:*** 100
CAS# 3060-89-7

OTHER CONTAMINANTS: NONE

EXPOSURE LIMITS: NO OCCUPATIONAL EXPOSURE LIMITS ESTABLISHED BY OSHA, ACGIH, OR NIOSH.

PHYSICAL DATA

DESCRIPTION: COLORLESS CRYSTALLINE SOLID.

MELTING POINT: 203-205 F (95-96C)

SPECIFIC GRAVITY: 1.60 ***VAPOR PRESSURE:*** NEGLIGIBLE

SOLUBILITY IN WATER: 0.032% @ 20 C

SOLVENT SOLUBILITY: SOLUBLE IN METHANOL, ETHANOL, ACETONE, CHLOROFORM, DICHLOROMETHANE, 1-OCTANOL, TOLUENE; SLIGHTLY SOLUBLE IN HEXANE.

FIRE AND EXPLOSION DATA

FIRE AND EXPLOSION HAZARD: SLIGHT FIRE HAZARD WHEN EXPOSED TO HEAT OR FLAME.

FIREFIGHTING MEDIA: DRY CHEMICAL, CARBON DIOXIDE, HALON, WATER SPRAY OR STANDARD FOAM (1987 EMERGENCY RESPONSE GUIDEBOOK, DOT P 5800.4).
FOR LARGER FIRES, USE WATER SPRAY, FOG OR STANDARD FOAM (1987 EMERGENCY RESPONSE GUIDEBOOK, DOT P 5800.4).

FIREFIGHTING: MOVE CONTAINERS FROM FIRE AREA IF POSSIBLE. FIGHT FIRE FROM MAXIMUM DISTANCE. STAY AWAY FROM STORAGE TANK ENDS. DIKE FIRE CONTROL WATER FOR LATER DISPOSAL. DO NOT SCATTER MATERIAL (1987 EMERGENCY RESPONSE GUIDEBOOK, DOT P 5800.4, GUIDE PAGE 55).
EXTINGUISH USING AGENT SUITABLE FOR TYPE OF SURROUNDING FIRE. USE WATER IN FLOODING QUANTITIES AS FOG. KEEP SPARKS, FLAMES AND OTHER SOURCES OF IGNITION AWAY. KEEP MATERIAL OUT OF WATER SOURCES AND SEWERS. DO NOT TOUCH MATERIAL AND AVOID BREATHING DUSTS AND FUMES FROM BURNING MATERIAL. KEEP UPWIND.

TOXICITY

METOBROMURON: IRRITATION DATA: 50 MG EYE-RABBIT MILD. TOXICITY DATA: 2000 MG/KG ORAL-RAT LD50; 2098 MG/KG ORAL-MOUSE LD50; 430 MG/KG INTRAPERITONEAL-RAT LD50; 847 MG/KG INTRAPERITONEAL-MOUSE LD50. CARCINOGEN STATUS: NONE. ACUTE TOXICITY LEVEL: MODERATELY TOXIC BY INGESTION. TARGET EFFECTS: NO DATA AVAILABLE.

HEALTH EFFECTS AND FIRST AID

INHALATION: METOBROMURON: **ACUTE EXPOSURE-** A LETHAL CONCENTRATION IN RATS WAS GREATER THAN 1100 MG/M3/4 HOURS. MANY SUBSTITUTED UREA HERBICIDES ARE MODERATELY IRRITATING TO THE MUCOUS MEMBRANES. **CHRONIC EXPOSURE-** NO DATA AVAILABLE.

FIRST AID- REMOVE FROM EXPOSURE AREA TO FRESH AIR IMMEDIATELY. IF BREATHING HAS STOPPED, PERFORM ARTIFICIAL RESPIRATION. KEEP PERSON WARM AND AT REST. TREAT SYMPTOMATICALLY AND SUPPORTIVELY. GET MEDICAL ATTENTION IMMEDIATELY.

SKIN CONTACT: METOBROMURON: **ACUTE EXPOSURE-** THIS MATERIAL WAS SLIGHTLY IRRITATING TO RABBIT SKIN. A LETHAL DOSE IN RATS BY DERMAL ABSORPTION IS GREATER THAN 3000 MG/KG. **CHRONIC EXPOSURE-** NO DATA AVAILABLE.

FIRST AID- REMOVE CONTAMINATED CLOTHING AND SHOES IMMEDIATELY. WASH AFFECTED AREA WITH SOAP OR MILD DETERGENT AND LARGE AMOUNTS OF WATER UNTIL NO EVIDENCE OF CHEMICAL REMAINS (APPROXIMATELY 15-20 MINUTES). GET MEDICAL ATTENTION IMMEDIATELY.

EYE CONTACT: METOBROMURON: **ACUTE EXPOSURE-** THIS MATERIAL WAS SLIGHTLY IRRITATING TO RABBIT EYES. **CHRONIC EXPOSURE-** NO DATA AVAILABLE.

FIRST AID- WASH EYES IMMEDIATELY WITH LARGE AMOUNTS OF WATER OR NORMAL SALINE, OCCASIONALLY LIFTING UPPER AND LOWER LIDS, UNTIL NO EVIDENCE OF CHEMICAL REMAINS (APPROXIMATELY 15-20 MINUTES). GET MEDICAL ATTENTION IMMEDIATELY.

INGESTION: METOBROMURON: **ACUTE EXPOSURE-** A LETHAL DOSE IN RATS WAS 2000 MG/KG. **CHRONIC EXPOSURE-** NO OBSERVABLE EFFECTS WERE REPORTED FROM A 2-YEAR STUDY OF RATS FED 17 MG/KG/DAY OR DOGS FED 3 MG/KG/DAY.

FIRST AID- REMOVE BY GASTRIC LAVAGE AND CATHARSIS. MAINTAIN BLOOD PRESSURE AND AIRWAY. GIVE OXYGEN IF RESPIRATION IS DEPRESSED. DO NOT PERFORM GASTRIC LAVAGE IF VICTIM IS UNCONSCIOUS. GET MEDICAL ATTENTION IMMEDIATELY (DREISBACH, HANDBOOK OF POISONING, 12TH ED.).
ADMINISTRATION OF LAVAGE OR OXYGEN SHOULD BE PERFORMED BY QUALIFIED MEDICAL PERSONNEL.

ANTIDOTE: NO SPECIFIC ANTIDOTE. TREAT SYMPTOMATICALLY AND SUPPORTIVELY.

REACTIVITY

REACTIVITY: STABLE UNDER NORMAL TEMPERATURES AND PRESSURES.

INCOMPATIBILITIES: METOBROMURON: OXIDIZERS (STRONG): FIRE AND EXPLOSION HAZARD.

DECOMPOSITION: THERMAL DECOMPOSITION PRODUCTS MAY INCLUDE TOXIC AND CORROSIVE FUMES OF BROMIDES, AND TOXIC OXIDES OF CARBON AND NITROGEN.

POLYMERIZATION: HAZARDOUS POLYMERIZATION HAS NOT BEEN REPORTED TO OCCUR UNDER NORMAL TEMPERATURES AND PRESSURES.

STORAGE AND DISPOSAL

OBSERVE ALL FEDERAL, STATE AND LOCAL REGULATIONS WHEN STORING OR DISPOSING OF THIS SUBSTANCE. FOR ASSISTANCE, CONTACT THE DISTRICT DIRECTOR OF THE ENVIRONMENTAL PROTECTION AGENCY.

STORAGE

STORE IN ACCORDANCE WITH 40 CFR 165 RECOMMENDED PROCEDURES FOR THE DISPOSAL AND STORAGE OF PESTICIDES AND PESTICIDE CONTAINERS.
STORE AWAY FROM INCOMPATIBLE SUBSTANCES.

DISPOSAL

DISPOSAL MUST BE IN ACCORDANCE WITH 40 CFR 165 RECOMMENDED PROCEDURES FOR THE DISPOSAL AND STORAGE OF PESTICIDES AND PESTICIDE CONTAINERS.

CONDITIONS TO AVOID

MAY BURN BUT DOES NOT IGNITE READILY. CONTAINERS MAY EXPLODE IN HEAT OF FIRE.

SPILL AND LEAK PROCEDURES

OCCUPATIONAL SPILL: DO NOT TOUCH SPILLED MATERIAL. STOP LEAK IF YOU CAN DO IT WITHOUT RISK. USE WATER SPRAY TO REDUCE VAPORS. FOR SMALL SPILLS, TAKE UP WITH SAND OR OTHER ABSORBENT MATERIAL AND PLACE INTO CONTAINERS FOR LATER DISPOSAL. FOR SMALL DRY SPILLS, WITH A CLEAN SHOVEL PLACE MATERIAL INTO CLEAN, DRY CONTAINERS AND COVER. MOVE CONTAINERS FROM SPILL AREA. FOR LARGER SPILLS, DIKE FAR AHEAD OF SPILL FOR LATER DISPOSAL. KEEP UNNECESSARY PEOPLE AWAY. ISOLATE HAZARD AREA AND DENY ENTRY. VENTILATE CLOSED SPACES BEFORE ENTERING.

PROTECTIVE EQUIPMENT

VENTILATION: PROVIDE LOCAL EXHAUST OR GENERAL DILUTION VENTILATION SYSTEM.

RESPIRATOR: THE FOLLOWING RESPIRATORS ARE RECOMMENDED BASED ON INFORMATION FOUND IN THE PHYSICAL DATA, TOXICITY AND HEALTH EFFECTS SECTIONS. THEY ARE RANKED IN ORDER FROM MINIMUM TO MAXIMUM RESPIRATORY PROTECTION. THE SPECIFIC RESPIRATOR SELECTED MUST BE BASED ON CONTAMINATION LEVELS FOUND IN THE WORK PLACE, MUST NOT EXCEED THE WORKING LIMITS OF THE RESPIRATOR AND BE JOINTLY APPROVED BY THE NATIONAL INSTITUTE FOR OCCUPATIONAL SAFETY AND HEALTH AND THE MINE SAFETY AND HEALTH ADMINISTRATION (NIOSH-MSHA).
CHEMICAL CARTRIDGE RESPIRATOR WITH AN ORGANIC VAPOR CARTRIDGE(S) WITH A FULL FACEPIECE AND ORGANIC VAPOR CARTRIDGE(S) IN COMBINATION WITH A DUST AND MIST FILTER.
POWERED AIR-PURIFYING RESPIRATOR WITH A TIGHT-FITTING FACEPIECE AND

ORGANIC VAPOR CARTRIDGE(S) IN COMBINATION WITH A HIGH-EFFICIENCY PARTICULATE FILTER.
TYPE 'C' SUPPLIED-AIR RESPIRATOR WITH A FULL FACEPIECE OPERATED IN A PRESSURE-DEMAND OR OTHER POSITIVE PRESSURE MODE.
SELF-CONTAINED BREATHING APPARATUS WITH A FULL FACEPIECE OPERATED IN PRESSURE-DEMAND OR OTHER POSITIVE PRESSURE MODE.
FOR FIREFIGHTING AND OTHER IMMEDIATELY DANGEROUS TO LIFE OR HEALTH CONDITIONS: SELF-CONTAINED BREATHING APPARATUS WITH FULL FACEPIECE OPERATED IN PRESSURE-DEMAND OR OTHER POSITIVE PRESSURE MODE.
SUPPLIED-AIR RESPIRATOR WITH FULL FACEPIECE AND OPERATED IN PRESSURE-DEMAND OR OTHER POSITIVE PRESSURE MODE IN COMBINATION WITH AN AUXILIARY SELF-CONTAINED BREATHING APPARATUS OPERATED IN PRESSURE-DEMAND OR OTHER POSITIVE PRESSURE MODE.

CLOTHING: EMPLOYEE MUST WEAR APPROPRIATE PROTECTIVE (IMPERVIOUS) CLOTHING AND EQUIPMENT TO PREVENT REPEATED OR PROLONGED SKIN CONTACT WITH THIS SUBSTANCE.

GLOVES: EMPLOYEE MUST WEAR APPROPRIATE PROTECTIVE GLOVES TO PREVENT CONTACT WITH THIS SUBSTANCE.

EYE PROTECTION: EMPLOYEE MUST WEAR SPLASH-PROOF OR DUST-RESISTANT SAFETY GOGGLES TO PREVENT EYE CONTACT WITH THIS SUBSTANCE.
EMERGENCY EYE WASH: WHERE THERE IS ANY POSSIBILITY THAT AN EMPLOYEE'S EYES MAY BE EXPOSED TO THIS SUBSTANCE, THE EMPLOYER SHOULD PROVIDE AN EYE WASH FOUNTAIN WITHIN THE IMMEDIATE WORK AREA FOR EMERGENCY USE.

AUTHORIZED BY- OCCUPATIONAL HEALTH SERVICES, INC.
CREATION DATE: 10/04/89 ***REVISION DATE:*** 05/11/90

MATERIAL SAFETY DATA SHEET

OCCUPATIONAL HEALTH SERVICES, INC.
AGRICULTURE AND PESTICIDE DIVISION
450 SEVENTH AVENUE, SUITE 2407
NEW YORK, NEW YORK 10123
1-800-445-MSDS OR (212) 967-1100

EMERGENCY CONTACT:
JOHN S. BRANSFORD, JR. (615) 292-1180

SUBSTANCE IDENTIFICATION

CAS-NUMBER 19937-59-8

SUBSTANCE: METOXURON

TRADE NAMES/SYNONYMS: UREA, N'-(3-CHLORO-4-METHOXYPHENYL)-N,N-DIMETHYL-; UREA, 3-(3-CHLORO-4-METHOXYPHENYL)-1,1-DIMETHYL-; 3-(3-CHLORO-4-METHOXYPHENYL)-1,1-DIMETHYLUREA; N'-(3-CHLORO-4-METHOXYPHENYL)-N,N-DIMETHYLUREA; DOSANEX; DEFTOR; DOSAFLO; METOXURAN; PURIVEL; SAN 6602; SAN 7102; C10H13CLN2O2; PST15009

CHEMICAL FAMILY: SUBSTITUTED UREA
HALOGEN COMPOUND, AROMATIC

MOLECULAR FORMULA: C10-H13-CL-N2-O2

MOLECULAR WEIGHT: 228.70

CERCLA RATINGS (SCALE 0-3): HEALTH=2 FIRE=1 REACTIVITY=0 PERSISTENCE=3

NFPA RATINGS (SCALE 0-4): HEALTH=2 FIRE=1 REACTIVITY=0

COMPONENTS AND CONTAMINANTS

COMPONENT: METOXURON ***PERCENT:*** 100.0
CAS# 19937-59-8

OTHER CONTAMINANTS: NONE

EXPOSURE LIMITS: NO OCCUPATIONAL EXPOSURE LIMITS ESTABLISHED BY OSHA, ACGIH, OR NIOSH.

PHYSICAL DATA

DESCRIPTION: COLORLESS CRYSTALLINE SOLID. ***MELTING POINT:*** 259-261 F (126-127 C)

SPECIFIC GRAVITY: NOT AVAILABLE ***VAPOR PRESSURE:*** NEGLIGIBLE

SOLUBILITY IN WATER: 0.0678% @ 24 C

SOLVENT SOLUBILITY: SOLUBLE IN ACETONE, CYCLOHEXANONE, HOT ETHANOL; MODERATELY SOLUBLE IN ETHER, TOLUENE, COLD ETHANOL; VERY SLIGHTLY SOLUBLE IN PETROLEUM SPIRITS.

FIRE AND EXPLOSION DATA

FIRE AND EXPLOSION HAZARD: SLIGHT FIRE HAZARD WHEN EXPOSED TO HEAT OR FLAME.

FIREFIGHTING MEDIA: DRY CHEMICAL, CARBON DIOXIDE, HALON, WATER SPRAY OR STANDARD FOAM (1987 EMERGENCY RESPONSE GUIDEBOOK, DOT P 5800.4).
FOR LARGER FIRES, USE WATER SPRAY, FOG OR STANDARD FOAM (1987 EMERGENCY RESPONSE GUIDEBOOK, DOT P 5800.4).

FIREFIGHTING: MOVE CONTAINERS FROM FIRE AREA IF POSSIBLE. FIGHT FIRE FROM MAXIMUM DISTANCE. STAY AWAY FROM STORAGE TANK ENDS. DIKE FIRE CONTROL WATER FOR LATER DISPOSAL. DO NOT SCATTER MATERIAL (1987 EMERGENCY RESPONSE GUIDEBOOK, DOT P 5800.4, GUIDE PAGE 55).
EXTINGUISH USING AGENT SUITABLE FOR TYPE OF SURROUNDING FIRE. USE WATER IN FLOODING QUANTITIES AS FOG. KEEP SPARKS, FLAMES AND OTHER SOURCES OF IGNITION AWAY. KEEP MATERIAL OUT OF WATER SOURCES AND SEWERS. DO NOT TOUCH MATERIAL AND AVOID BREATHING DUSTS AND FUMES FROM BURNING MATERIAL. KEEP UPWIND.

TOXICITY

METOXURON: TOXICITY DATA: 1600 MG/KG ORAL-RAT LD50; 2542 MG/KG ORAL-MOUSE LD50; 2300 MG/KG ORAL-RABBIT LD50; MUTAGENIC DATA (RTECS).
CARCINOGEN STATUS: NONE. ACUTE TOXICITY LEVEL: MODERATELY TOXIC BY INGESTION. TARGET EFFECTS: NO DATA AVAILABLE.

HEALTH EFFECTS AND FIRST AID

INHALATION: METOXURON: **ACUTE EXPOSURE-** MANY SUBSTITUTED UREA HERBICIDES ARE MODERATELY IRRITATING TO THE MUCOUS MEMBRANES.
CHRONIC EXPOSURE- NO DATA AVAILABLE.

FIRST AID- REMOVE FROM EXPOSURE AREA TO FRESH AIR IMMEDIATELY. IF BREATHING HAS STOPPED, PERFORM ARTIFICIAL RESPIRATION. KEEP PERSON WARM AND AT REST. TREAT SYMPTOMATICALLY AND SUPPORTIVELY. GET MEDICAL ATTENTION IMMEDIATELY.

SKIN CONTACT: METOXURON: **ACUTE EXPOSURE-** THIS MATERIAL DID NOT PRODUCED EITHER DERMAL IRRITATION OR ALLERGIC SKIN REACTION. A LETHAL DOSE IN RATS BY DERMAL ABSORPTION IS GREATER THAN 2000 MG/KG. **CHRONIC EXPOSURE-** NO DATA AVAILABLE.

FIRST AID- REMOVE CONTAMINATED CLOTHING AND SHOES IMMEDIATELY. WASH AFFECTED AREA WITH SOAP OR MILD DETERGENT AND LARGE AMOUNTS OF WATER UNTIL NO EVIDENCE OF CHEMICAL REMAINS (APPROXIMATELY 15-20 MINUTES). GET MEDICAL ATTENTION IMMEDIATELY.

EYE CONTACT: METOXURON: **ACUTE EXPOSURE-** MANY SUBSTITUTED UREA HERBICIDES ARE MODERATELY IRRITATING TO THE EYES. **CHRONIC EXPOSURE-** NO DATA AVAILABLE.

FIRST AID- WASH EYES IMMEDIATELY WITH LARGE AMOUNTS OF WATER OR NORMAL SALINE, OCCASIONALLY LIFTING UPPER AND LOWER LIDS, UNTIL NO EVIDENCE OF CHEMICAL REMAINS (APPROXIMATELY 15-20 MINUTES). GET MEDICAL ATTENTION IMMEDIATELY.

INGESTION: METOXURON: **ACUTE EXPOSURE-** A LETHAL DOSE IN RATS WAS 1600 MG/KG. **CHRONIC EXPOSURE-** NO OBSERVABLE EFFECTS WERE REPORTED FROM A 90-DAY STUDY OF RATS FED 1250 PPM OF DOGS FED 2500 PPM.

FIRST AID- REMOVE BY GASTRIC LAVAGE AND CATHARSIS. MAINTAIN BLOOD PRESSURE AND AIRWAY. GIVE OXYGEN IF RESPIRATION IS DEPRESSED. DO NOT PERFORM GASTRIC LAVAGE IF VICTIM IS UNCONSCIOUS. GET MEDICAL ATTENTION IMMEDIATELY (DREISBACH, HANDBOOK OF POISONING, 12TH ED.).
ADMINISTRATION OF LAVAGE OR OXYGEN SHOULD BE PERFORMED BY QUALIFIED MEDICAL PERSONNEL.

ANTIDOTE: NO SPECIFIC ANTIDOTE. TREAT SYMPTOMATICALLY AND SUPPORTIVELY.

REACTIVITY

REACTIVITY: STABLE UNDER NORMAL TEMPERATURES AND PRESSURES.

INCOMPATIBILITIES: METOXURON: ACIDS (STRONG): MAY HYDROLYZE AT ELEVATED TEMPERATURES. ALKALIES (STRONG): MAY HYDROLYZE AT ELEVATED TEMPERATURES. OXIDIZERS (STRONG): FIRE AND EXPLOSION HAZARD.

DECOMPOSITION: THERMAL DECOMPOSITION PRODUCTS MAY INCLUDE TOXIC OXIDES OF NITROGEN AND CARBON AND TOXIC AND CORROSIVE FUMES OF CHLORIDES.

POLYMERIZATION: HAZARDOUS POLYMERIZATION HAS NOT BEEN REPORTED TO OCCUR UNDER NORMAL TEMPERATURES AND PRESSURES.

STORAGE AND DISPOSAL

OBSERVE ALL FEDERAL, STATE AND LOCAL REGULATIONS WHEN STORING OR DISPOSING OF THIS SUBSTANCE. FOR ASSISTANCE, CONTACT THE DISTRICT DIRECTOR OF THE ENVIRONMENTAL PROTECTION AGENCY.

****STORAGE****

STORE IN ACCORDANCE WITH 40 CFR 165 RECOMMENDED PROCEDURES FOR THE DISPOSAL AND STORAGE OF PESTICIDES AND PESTICIDE CONTAINERS.
STORE AWAY FROM INCOMPATIBLE SUBSTANCES.

DISPOSAL

DISPOSAL MUST BE IN ACCORDANCE WITH 40 CFR 165 RECOMMENDED PROCEDURES FOR THE DISPOSAL AND STORAGE OF PESTICIDES AND PESTICIDE CONTAINERS.

CONDITIONS TO AVOID

MAY BURN BUT DOES NOT IGNITE READILY. CONTAINERS MAY EXPLODE IN HEAT OF FIRE.

SPILL AND LEAK PROCEDURES

OCCUPATIONAL SPILL: DO NOT TOUCH SPILLED MATERIAL. STOP LEAK IF YOU CAN DO IT WITHOUT RISK. USE WATER SPRAY TO REDUCE VAPORS. FOR SMALL SPILLS, TAKE UP WITH SAND OR OTHER ABSORBENT MATERIAL AND PLACE INTO CONTAINERS FOR LATER DISPOSAL. FOR SMALL DRY SPILLS, WITH A CLEAN SHOVEL PLACE MATERIAL INTO CLEAN, DRY CONTAINERS AND COVER. MOVE CONTAINERS FROM SPILL AREA. FOR LARGER SPILLS, DIKE FAR AHEAD OF SPILL FOR LATER DISPOSAL. KEEP UNNECESSARY PEOPLE AWAY. ISOLATE HAZARD AREA AND DENY ENTRY. VENTILATE CLOSED SPACES BEFORE ENTERING.

PROTECTIVE EQUIPMENT

VENTILATION: PROVIDE LOCAL EXHAUST OR GENERAL DILUTION VENTILATION SYSTEM.

RESPIRATOR: THE FOLLOWING RESPIRATORS ARE RECOMMENDED BASED ON INFORMATION FOUND IN THE PHYSICAL DATA, TOXICITY AND HEALTH EFFECTS SECTIONS. THEY ARE RANKED IN ORDER FROM MINIMUM TO MAXIMUM RESPIRATORY PROTECTION. THE SPECIFIC RESPIRATOR SELECTED MUST BE BASED ON CONTAMINATION LEVELS FOUND IN THE WORK PLACE, MUST NOT EXCEED THE WORKING LIMITS OF THE RESPIRATOR AND BE JOINTLY APPROVED BY THE NATIONAL INSTITUTE FOR OCCUPATIONAL SAFETY AND HEALTH AND THE MINE SAFETY AND HEALTH ADMINISTRATION (NIOSH-MSHA).

CHEMICAL CARTRIDGE RESPIRATOR WITH AN ORGANIC VAPOR CARTRIDGE(S) WITH A FULL FACEPIECE AND ORGANIC VAPOR CARTRIDGE(S) IN COMBINATION WITH A DUST AND MIST FILTER.

POWERED AIR-PURIFYING RESPIRATOR WITH A TIGHT-FITTING FACEPIECE AND ORGANIC VAPOR CARTRIDGE(S) IN COMBINATION WITH A HIGH-EFFICIENCY PARTICULATE FILTER.

TYPE 'C' SUPPLIED-AIR RESPIRATOR WITH A FULL FACEPIECE OPERATED IN A PRESSURE-DEMAND OR OTHER POSITIVE PRESSURE MODE.

SELF-CONTAINED BREATHING APPARATUS WITH A FULL FACEPIECE OPERATED IN PRESSURE-DEMAND OR OTHER POSITIVE PRESSURE MODE. FOR FIREFIGHTING AND OTHER IMMEDIATELY DANGEROUS TO LIFE OR HEALTH CONDITIONS:

SELF-CONTAINED BREATHING APPARATUS WITH FULL FACEPIECE OPERATED IN PRESSURE-DEMAND OR OTHER POSITIVE PRESSURE MODE.

SUPPLIED-AIR RESPIRATOR WITH FULL FACEPIECE AND OPERATED IN PRESSURE-DEMAND OR OTHER POSITIVE PRESSURE MODE IN COMBINATION WITH AN AUXILIARY SELF-CONTAINED BREATHING APPARATUS OPERATED IN PRESSURE-DEMAND OR OTHER POSITIVE PRESSURE MODE.

CLOTHING: EMPLOYEE MUST WEAR APPROPRIATE PROTECTIVE (IMPERVIOUS) CLOTHING AND EQUIPMENT TO PREVENT REPEATED OR PROLONGED SKIN CONTACT WITH THIS SUBSTANCE.

GLOVES: EMPLOYEE MUST WEAR APPROPRIATE PROTECTIVE GLOVES TO PREVENT CONTACT WITH THIS SUBSTANCE.

EYE PROTECTION: EMPLOYEE MUST WEAR SPLASH-PROOF OR DUST-RESISTANT SAFETY GOGGLES TO PREVENT EYE CONTACT WITH THIS SUBSTANCE.

EMERGENCY EYE WASH: WHERE THERE IS ANY POSSIBILITY THAT AN EMPLOYEE'S EYES MAY BE EXPOSED TO THIS SUBSTANCE, THE EMPLOYER SHOULD PROVIDE AN EYE WASH FOUNTAIN WITHIN THE IMMEDIATE WORK AREA FOR EMERGENCY USE.

AUTHORIZED BY- OCCUPATIONAL HEALTH SERVICES, INC.

CREATION DATE: 10/04/89 ***REVISION DATE:*** 05/14/90

MATERIAL SAFETY DATA SHEET

OCCUPATIONAL HEALTH SERVICES, INC.
AGRICULTURE AND PESTICIDE DIVISION
450 SEVENTH AVENUE, SUITE 2407
NEW YORK, NEW YORK 10123
1-800-445-MSDS OR (212) 967-1100

EMERGENCY CONTACT:
JOHN S. BRANSFORD, JR. (615) 282-1150

SUBSTANCE IDENTIFICATION

CAS-NUMBER 315-18-4

SUBSTANCE: **MEXACARBATE**

TRADE NAMES/SYNONYMS: PHENOL, 4-(DIMETHYLAMINO)-3,5-DIMETHYL-, METHYLCARBAMATE (ESTER); CARBAMIC ACID, METHYL-, 4-(DIMETHYLAMINO)-3,5-XYLYL ESTER; 4-(DIMETHYLAMINO)-3,5-DIMETHYLPHENOL METHYLCARBAMATE (ESTER); METHYLCARBAMIC ACID 4-(DIMETHYLAMINO)-3,5-XYLYL ESTER; DOWCO 139; ZECTANE; ZECTRAN; ZEXTRAN; OMS 47; NCI-C0054; ENT 25,766; STCC 4921542; C12H18N2O2; PST15010

CHEMICAL FAMILY: CARBAMATE

MOLECULAR FORMULA: C12-H18-N2-O2

MOLECULAR WEIGHT: 222.29

CERCLA RATINGS (SCALE 0-3): HEALTH=3 FIRE=1 REACTIVITY=0 PERSISTENCE=2

NFPA RATINGS (SCALE 0-4): HEALTH=4 FIRE=1 REACTIVITY=0

COMPONENTS AND CONTAMINANTS

COMPONENT: MEXACARBATE ***PERCENT:*** 100.0
CAS# 315-18-4

OTHER CONTAMINANTS: NONE

EXPOSURE LIMITS: NO OCCUPATIONAL EXPOSURE LIMITS ESTABLISHED BY OSHA, ACGIH, OR NIOSH.

MEXACARBATE: 500/10,000 POUNDS SARA SECTION 302 THRESHOLD PLANNING QUANTITY 1000 POUNDS SARA SECTION 304 REPORTABLE QUANTITY 1000 POUNDS CERCLA SECTION 103 REPORTABLE QUANTITY

PHYSICAL DATA

DESCRIPTION: ODORLESS, WHITE CRYSTALLINE SOLID.

MELTING POINT: 185 F (85C)

SPECIFIC GRAVITY: >1.0 ***VAPOR PRESSURE:*** <0.1 MMHG @ 139 C

SOLUBILITY IN WATER: 0.01% @ 25 C

SOLVENT SOLUBILITY: SOLUBLE IN ACETONE, ACETONITRILE, METHYLENE CHLORIDE, ETHANOL, BENZENE, XYLENE, ISOPROPYL ALCOHOL; MODERATELY SOLUBLE IN PETROLEUM SOLVENTS AND N-HEXANE.

DECOMPOSES ABOVE 282 F (139 C)

FIRE AND EXPLOSION DATA

FIRE AND EXPLOSION HAZARD: SLIGHT FIRE HAZARD WHEN EXPOSED TO HEAT OR FLAME.

FIREFIGHTING MEDIA: DRY CHEMICAL, CARBON DIOXIDE, HALON, WATER SPRAY OR STANDARD FOAM (1987 EMERGENCY RESPONSE GUIDEBOOK, DOT P 5800.4).

FOR LARGER FIRES, USE WATER SPRAY, FOG OR STANDARD FOAM (1987 EMERGENCY RESPONSE GUIDEBOOK, DOT P 5800.4).

FIREFIGHTING: MOVE CONTAINERS FROM FIRE AREA IF POSSIBLE. FIGHT FIRE FROM MAXIMUM DISTANCE. STAY AWAY FROM STORAGE TANK ENDS. DIKE FIRE CONTROL WATER FOR LATER DISPOSAL. DO NOT SCATTER MATERIAL (1987 EMERGENCY RESPONSE GUIDEBOOK, DOT P 5800.4, GUIDE PAGE 55).

EXTINGUISH ONLY IF FLOW CAN BE STOPPED. EXTINGUISH USING AGENT INDICATED. USE FLOODING AMOUNTS OF WATER AS A FOG. COOL CONTAINERS WITH FLOODING AMOUNTS OF WATER FROM AS FAR A DISTANCE AS POSSIBLE. AVOID BREATHING POISONOUS VAPORS, KEEP UPWIND. CONSIDER EVACUATION OF DOWNWIND AREA IF MATERIAL IS LEAKING.

TRANSPORTATION DATA

DEPARTMENT OF TRANSPORTATION HAZARD CLASSIFICATION 49 CFR 172.101: POISON B

DEPARTMENT OF TRANSPORTATION LABELING REQUIREMENTS 49 CFR 172.101 AND SUBPART E: POISON

DEPARTMENT OF TRANSPORTATION PACKAGING REQUIREMENTS: 49 CFR 173.346 EXCEPTIONS: 49 CFR 173.345

TOXICITY

MEXACARBATE: TOXICITY DATA: 107 MG/KG SKIN-MOUSE LD50; 14 MG/KG ORAL-RAT LD50; 12 MG/KG ORAL-MOUSE LD50; 37 MG/KG ORAL-RABBIT LD50; 15 MG/KG ORAL-GUINEA PIG LD50; 22 MG/KG ORAL-DOG LD50; 20 MG/KG ORAL-MAMMAL LD50; 15 MG/KG ORAL-DOMESTIC ANIMAL LD50; 7800 UG/KG INTRAPERITONEAL-MOUSE LD50; REPRODUCTIVE EFFECTS DATA (RTECS); TUMORIGENIC DATA (RTECS). CARCINOGEN STATUS: ANIMAL INADEQUATE EVIDENCE (IARC GROUP-3). ACUTE TOXICITY LEVEL: HIGHLY TOXIC BY DERMAL ABSORPTION AND INGESTION. TARGET EFFECTS: CHOLINESTERASE INHIBITOR. AT INCREASED RISK FROM EXPOSURE: PERSONS WITH ASTHMA, DIABETES, CARDIOVASCULAR DISEASE, MECHANICAL OBSTRUCTION OF THE GASTROINTESTINAL OR UROGENITAL TRACT, AND THOSE IN VAGOTONIC STATES.*

* MAY BE BASED ON GENERAL INFORMATION ON CARBAMATES.

HEALTH EFFECTS AND FIRST AID

INHALATION: MEXACARBATE: SEE INFORMATION ON CARBAMATES.

CARBAMATES: CHOLINESTERASE INHIBITOR. **ACUTE EXPOSURE-** WHEN INHALED, THE FIRST EFFECTS OF CHOLINESTERASE INHIBITION ARE USUALLY RESPIRATORY AND MAY INCLUDE NASAL HYPEREMIA AND WATERY DISCHARGE, CHEST DISCOMFORT, DYSPNEA, AND WHEEZING DUE TO INCREASED BRONCHIAL SECRETIONS AND BRONCHOCONSTRICTION. OTHER SYSTEMIC EFFECTS MAY BEGIN WITHIN A FEW MINUTES OR SEVERAL HOURS OF EXPOSURE. SYMPTOMS MAY INCLUDE NAUSEA, VOMITING, DIARRHEA, ABDOMINAL CRAMPS, HEADACHE, VERTIGO, OCULAR PAIN, CILIARY MUSCLE SPASM, BLURRING OR DIMNESS OF VISION, MIOSIS, OR IN SOME CASES MYDRIASIS, LACRIMATION, SALIVATION, SWEATING, AND CONFUSION. OTHER REPORTED CENTRAL NERVOUS SYSTEM OR NEUROMUSCULAR EFFECTS INCLUDE ATAXIA, SLURRED SPEECH, AREFLEXIA, WEAKNESS, FATIGUE, TWITCHING, FASCICULATION, TREMOR, AND EVENTUALLY PARALYSIS OF THE EXTREMITIES AND POSSIBLY OF THE RESPIRATORY MUSCLES. IN SEVERE CASES, THERE MAY ALSO BE INVOLUNTARY DEFECATION AND URINATION, BRADYCARDIA, HYPOTENSION, PULMONARY EDEMA, CONVULSIONS, COMA, AND DEATH FROM RESPIRATORY FAILURE OR CARDIAC ARREST. CARBAMATES GENERALLY DO NOT ACCUMULATE IN MAMMALIAN TISSUE AND THE CHOLINESTERASE INHIBITION REVERSES RATHER RAPIDLY. IN NON-FATAL CASES, THE ILLNESS GENERALLY LASTS LESS THAN 24 HOURS. **CHRONIC EXPOSURE-** PROLONGED OR REPEATED EXPOSURE MAY CAUSE EFFECTS AS DESCRIBED IN ACUTE EXPOSURE.

FIRST AID- REMOVE FROM EXPOSURE AREA TO FRESH AIR IMMEDIATELY. IF BREATHING HAS STOPPED, GIVE ARTIFICIAL RESPIRATION. MAINTAIN AIRWAY AND BLOOD PRESSURE AND ADMINISTER OXYGEN IF AVAILABLE. KEEP AFFECTED PERSON WARM AND AT REST. TREAT SYMPTOMATICALLY AND SUPPORTIVELY. ADMINISTRATION OF OXYGEN SHOULD BE PERFORMED BY QUALIFIED PERSONNEL. GET MEDICAL ATTENTION IMMEDIATELY.

SKIN CONTACT: MEXACARBATE: HIGHLY TOXIC. SEE INFORMATION ON CARBAMATES.

CARBAMATES: CHOLINESTERASE INHIBITOR. **ACUTE EXPOSURE-** SOME COMPOUNDS MAY CAUSE IRRITATION. LOCALIZED SWEATING AND FASCICULATIONS MAY OCCUR AT THE SITE OF CONTACT. IF SUFFICIENT AMOUNTS ARE ABSORBED THROUGH THE SKIN, OTHER EFFECTS OF CHOLINESTERASE INHIBITION MAY OCCUR AS DESCRIBED IN ACUTE INHALATION; SYMPTOMS MAY BE DELAYED FOR 2-3 HOURS, USUALLY NO MORE THAN 8 HOURS. **CHRONIC EXPOSURE-** REPEATED OR PROLONGED EXPOSURE MAY CAUSE EFFECTS AS DESCRIBED IN ACUTE EXPOSURE.

FIRST AID- REMOVE CONTAMINATED CLOTHING IMMEDIATELY. WASH CONTAMINATED AREAS WITH SOAP AND WATER FOLLOWED BY ALCOHOL (ARENA, POISONING, 4TH ED.). EMERGENCY PERSONNEL SHOULD WEAR GLOVES AND AVOID CONTAMINATION. TREAT RESPIRATORY DIFFICULTY WITH ARTIFICIAL RESPIRATION. GET MEDICAL ATTENTION IMMEDIATELY.

EYE CONTACT: MEXACARBATE: SEE INFORMATION ON CARBAMATES.

CARBAMATES: CHOLINESTERASE INHIBITOR. **ACUTE EXPOSURE-** DIRECT CONTACT MAY CAUSE PAIN, HYPEREMIA, LACRIMATION, TWITCHING OF THE EYELIDS, MIOSIS, AND CILIARY MUSCLE SPASM WITH LOSS OF ACCOMODATION, BLURRED OR DIMMED VISION AND BROWACHE. SOMETIMES MYDRIASIS MAY OCCUR INSTEAD OF MIOSIS. WITH SUFFICIENT EXPOSURE, OTHER SYMPTOMS OF CHOLINESTERASE INHIBITION MAY OCCUR AS DESCRIBED IN ACUTE INHALATION. **CHRONIC EXPOSURE-** PROLONGED EXPOSURE MAY CAUSE EFFECTS AS DESCRIBED IN ACUTE EXPOSURE. SOME COMPOUNDS HAVE CAUSED TOXIC EFFECTS ON THE CRYSTALLINE LENS, CONJUNCTIVAL THICKENING AND OBSTRUCTION OF NASOLACRIMAL CANALS WHEN USED AS MIOTIC EYE DROPS.

FIRST AID- IRRIGATE EYES WITH WATER OR SALINE SOLUTION. IF SYMPTOMS OF POISONING OCCUR, TREAT RESPIRATORY DIFFICULTY WITH ARTIFICIAL RESPIRATION AND OXYGEN. OBSERVE PATIENT FOR AT LEAST 24-36 HOURS (GOSSELIN, CLINICAL TOXICOLOGY OF COMMERCIAL PRODUCTS, 5TH ED.). GET MEDICAL ATTENTION IMMEDIATELY. OXYGEN SHOULD BE ADMINISTERED BY QUALIFIED MEDICAL PERSONNEL.

INGESTION: MEXACARBATE: HIGHLY TOXIC. SEE INFORMATION ON CARBAMATES.

CARBAMATES: CHOLINESTERASE INHIBITOR. **ACUTE EXPOSURE-** WHEN INGESTED, THE FIRST EFFECTS MAY BE NAUSEA, VOMITING, ANOREXIA, ABDOMINAL CRAMPS, AND DIARRHEA. WITH ABSORPTION FROM THE GASTROINTESTINAL TRACT, THE OTHER EFFECTS OF CHOLINESTERASE INHIBITION AS DESCRIBED IN ACUTE INHALATION MAY OCCUR; SYMPTOMS MAY BEGIN WITHIN MINUTES OR BE DELAYED SEVERAL HOURS. **CHRONIC EXPOSURE-** REPEATED INGESTION MAY CAUSE EFFECTS AS DESCRIBED IN ACUTE EXPOSURE.

FIRST AID- IF PERSON IS ALERT AND RESPIRATION IS NOT DEPRESSED, GIVE SYRUP OF IPECAC FOLLOWED BY WATER (IF VOMITING OCCURS, KEEP HEAD BELOW HIPS TO PREVENT ASPIRATION). IF CONSCIOUSNESS LEVEL DECLINES OR VOMITING HAS NOT OCCURRED IN 15 MINUTES EMPTY STOMACH BY GASTRIC LAVAGE WITH THE AID OF CUFFED ENDOTRACHEAL TUBE USING ISOTONIC SALINE OR 5% SODIUM BICARBONATE FOLLOW WITH ACTIVATED CHARCOAL. ESTABLISH AND MAINTAIN AIRWAY. TREAT RESPIRATORY DIFFICULTY WITH ARTIFICIAL RESPIRATION AND OXYGEN. DO NOT GIVE MORPHINE, AMINOPHYLLINE, PHENOTHIAZINES, RESERPINE, FUROSEMIDE, OR ETHACRYNIC ACID (MORGAN, RECOGNITION AND MANAGEMENT OF PESTICIDE POISONINGS, 3RD ED.). TREAT SYMPTOMATICALLY AND SUPPORTIVELY. ADMINISTRATION OF OXYGEN AND LAVAGE MUST BE PERFORMED BY QUALIFIED MEDICAL PERSONNEL. GET MEDICAL ATTENTION IMMEDIATELY.

ANTIDOTE: THE FOLLOWING ANTIDOTE HAS BEEN RECOMMENDED. HOWEVER, THE DECISION AS TO WHETHER THE SEVERITY OF POISONING REQUIRES ADMINISTRATION OF ANY ANTIDOTE AND ACTUAL DOSE REQUIRED SHOULD BE MADE BY QUALIFIED MEDICAL PERSONNEL.

FOR CHOLINESTERASE INHIBITORS: ESTABLISH CLEAR AIRWAY AND TISSUE OXYGENATION BY ASPIRATION OF SECRETIONS, AND IF NECESSARY, BY ASSISTED PULMONARY VENTILATION WITH OXYGEN. IMPROVE TISSUE OXYGENATION AS MUCH AS POSSIBLE BEFORE ADMINISTERING ATROPINE TO MINIMIZE THE RISK OF VENTRICULAR FIBRILLATION. ADMINISTER ATROPINE SULFATE INTRAVENOUSLY, OR INTRAMUSCULARLY IF IV INJECTION IS NOT POSSIBLE. IN MODERATELY SEVERE POISONING ADMINISTER ATROPINE SULFATE, 0.4-2.0 MG REPEATED EVERY 15 MINUTES UNTIL ATROPINIZATION IS ACHIEVED (TACHYCARDIA, FLUSHING, DRY MOUTH, MYDRIASIS). MAINTAIN ATROPINIZATION BY REPEATED DOSES FOR 2-12 HOURS, OR LONGER, DEPENDING ON THE SEVERITY OF POISONING. THE APPEARANCE OF RALES IN THE LUNG BASES, MIOSIS, SALIVATION, NAUSEA, BRADYCARDIA, ARE ALL INDICATIONS OF INADEQUATE ATROPINIZATION. SEVERELY POISONED INDIVIDUALS MAY EXHIBIT REMARKABLE TOLERANCE TO ATROPINE; TWO OR MORE TIMES THE DOSAGES SUGGESTED ABOVE MAY BE NEEDED. PERSONS NOT POISONED OR ONLY SLIGHTLY POISONED, HOWEVER, MAY DEVELOP SIGNS OF ATROPINE TOXICITY FROM SUCH LARGE DOSAGES: FEVER, MUSCLE FIBRILLATIONS, AND DELIRIUM ARE THE MAIN SIGNS OF ATROPINE TOXICITY. IF THESE SIGNS APPEAR WHILE THE PATIENT IS FULLY ATROPINIZED, ATROPINE ADMINISTRATION SHOULD BE DISCONTINUED, AT LEAST TEMPORARILY. OBSERVE TREATED PATIENTS CLOSELY AT LEAST 24 HOURS TO INSURE THAT SYMPTOMS (POSSIBLY PULMONARY EDEMA) DO NOT RECUR AS ATROPINIZATION WEARS OFF. IN VERY SEVERE POISONINGS, METABOLIC DISPOSITION OF TOXICANT MAY REQUIRE SEVERAL HOURS OR DAYS DURING WHICH ATROPINIZATION MUST BE MAINTAINED. MARKEDLY LOWER LEVELS OF URINARY METABOLITES INDICATE THAT ATROPINE DOSAGE CAN BE TAPERED OFF. AS DOSAGE IS REDUCED, CHECK THE LUNG BASES FREQUENTLY FOR RALES. IF RALES ARE HEARD OR OTHER SYMPTOMS RETURN, RE-ESTABLISH ATROPINIZATION PROMPTLY (MORGAN, RECOGNITION AND MANAGEMENT OF PESTICIDE POISONINGS, 3RD ED.). ADMINISTRATION OF ANTIDOTE MUST BE PERFORMED BY QUALIFIED MEDICAL PERSONNEL.

REACTIVITY

REACTIVITY: STABLE UNDER NORMAL TEMPERATURES AND PRESSURES.

INCOMPATIBILITIES: MEXACARBATE: OXIDIZERS (STRONG): FIRE AND EXPLOSION HAZARD.

DECOMPOSITION: THERMAL DECOMPOSITION PRODUCTS MAY INCLUDE TOXIC OXIDES OF CARBON AND NITROGEN.

POLYMERIZATION: HAZARDOUS POLYMERIZATION HAS NOT BEEN REPORTED TO OCCUR UNDER NORMAL TEMPERATURES AND PRESSURES.

STORAGE AND DISPOSAL

OBSERVE ALL FEDERAL, STATE AND LOCAL REGULATIONS WHEN STORING OR DISPOSING OF THIS SUBSTANCE. FOR ASSISTANCE, CONTACT THE DISTRICT DIRECTOR OF THE ENVIRONMENTAL PROTECTION AGENCY.

STORAGE

STORE IN ACCORDANCE WITH 40 CFR 165 RECOMMENDED PROCEDURES FOR THE DISPOSAL AND STORAGE OF PESTICIDES AND PESTICIDE CONTAINERS.

STORE AWAY FROM INCOMPATIBLE SUBSTANCES.

THRESHOLD PLANNING QUANTITY (TPQ): THE SUPERFUND AMENDMENTS AND REAUTHORIZATION ACT (SARA) SECTION 302 REQUIRES THAT EACH FACILITY WHERE ANY EXTREMELY HAZARDOUS SUBSTANCE IS PRESENT IN A QUANTITY EQUAL TO OR GREATER THAN THE TPQ ESTABLISHED FOR THAT SUBSTANCE NOTIFY THE STATE EMERGENCY RESPONSE COMMISSION FOR THE STATE IN WHICH IT IS LOCATED. SECTION 303 OF SARA REQUIRES THESE FACILITIES TO PARTICIPATE IN LOCAL EMERGENCY RESPONSE PLANNING (40 CFR 355.30).

KEEP IN A TIGHTLY CLOSED CONTAINER. STORE IN A COOL, DRY, VENTILATED AREA.

DISPOSAL

DISPOSAL MUST BE IN ACCORDANCE WITH 40 CFR 165 RECOMMENDED PROCEDURES FOR THE DISPOSAL AND STORAGE OF PESTICIDES AND PESTICIDE CONTAINERS.

CONDITIONS TO AVOID

MAY BURN BUT DOES NOT IGNITE READILY. CONTAINERS MAY EXPLODE IN HEAT OF FIRE.

SPILL AND LEAK PROCEDURES

SOIL SPILL: DIG A PIT, POND, LAGOON OR HOLDING AREA TO CONTAIN LIQUID OR SOLID MATERIAL. COVER SOLIDS WITH A PLASTIC SHEET TO PREVENT DISSOLVING IN RAIN OR FIREFIGHTING WATER.

WATER SPILL: USE NATURAL DEEP WATER POCKETS, EXCAVATED LAGOONS, OR SAND BAG BARRIERS TO TRAP MATERIAL AT BOTTOM. IF DISSOLVED, APPLY ACTIVATED CARBON AT 10 TIMES SPILLED AMOUNT AT 10 PPM OR GREATER CONCENTRATION. USE MECHANICAL DREDGES OR LIFTS TO REMOVE IMMOBILIZED MASSES OF POLLUTION AND PRECIPITATES.

OCCUPATIONAL SPILL: DO NOT TOUCH SPILLED MATERIAL. STOP LEAK IF YOU CAN DO IT WITHOUT RISK. USE WATER SPRAY TO REDUCE VAPORS. FOR SMALL SPILLS, TAKE UP WITH SAND OR OTHER ABSORBENT MATERIAL AND PLACE INTO CONTAINERS FOR LATER DISPOSAL. FOR SMALL DRY SPILLS, WITH A CLEAN SHOVEL PLACE MATERIAL INTO CLEAN, DRY CONTAINERS AND COVER. MOVE CONTAINERS FROM SPILL AREA. FOR LARGER SPILLS, DIKE FAR AHEAD OF SPILL FOR LATER DISPOSAL. KEEP UNNECESSARY PEOPLE AWAY. ISOLATE HAZARD AREA AND DENY ENTRY. VENTILATE CLOSED SPACES BEFORE ENTERING. REPORTABLE QUANTITY (RQ): 1000 POUNDS THE SUPERFUND AMENDMENTS AND REAUTHORIZATION ACT (SARA) SECTION 304 REQUIRES THAT A RELEASE EQUAL TO OR GREATER THAN THE REPORTABLE QUANTITY FOR THIS SUBSTANCE BE IMMEDIATELY REPORTED TO THE LOCAL EMERGENCY PLANNING COMMITTEE AND THE STATE EMERGENCY RESPONSE COMMISSION (40 CFR 355.40). IF THE RELEASE OF THIS SUBSTANCE IS REPORTABLE UNDER CERCLA SECTION 103, THE NATIONAL RESPONSE CENTER MUST BE NOTIFIED IMMEDIATELY AT (800) 424-8802 OR (202) 426-2675 IN THE METROPOLITAN WASHINGTON, D.C. AREA (40 CFR 302.6).

PROTECTIVE EQUIPMENT

VENTILATION: PROVIDE LOCAL EXHAUST VENTILATION AND/OR GENERAL DILUTION VENTILATION TO MEET PUBLISHED EXPOSURE LIMITS.

RESPIRATOR: THE FOLLOWING RESPIRATORS ARE RECOMMENDED BASED ON INFORMATION FOUND IN THE PHYSICAL DATA, TOXICITY AND HEALTH EFFECTS SECTIONS. THEY ARE RANKED IN ORDER FROM MINIMUM TO MAXIMUM RESPIRATORY PROTECTION. THE SPECIFIC RESPIRATOR SELECTED MUST BE BASED ON CONTAMINATION LEVELS FOUND IN THE WORK PLACE, MUST NOT EXCEED THE WORKING LIMITS OF THE RESPIRATOR AND BE JOINTLY APPROVED BY THE NATIONAL INSTITUTE FOR OCCUPATIONAL SAFETY AND HEALTH AND THE MINE SAFETY AND HEALTH ADMINISTRATION (NIOSH-MSHA).

TYPE 'C' SUPPLIED-AIR RESPIRATOR WITH A FULL FACEPIECE OPERATED IN PRESSURE-DEMAND OR OTHER POSITIVE PRESSURE MODE OR WITH A FULL FACEPIECE, HELMET OR HOOD OPERATED IN CONTINOUS-FLOW MODE.

SELF-CONTAINED BREATHING APPARATUS WITH A FULL FACEPIECE OPERATED IN PRESSURE-DEMAND OR OTHER POSITIVE PRESSURE MODE.

FOR FIREFIGHTING AND OTHER IMMEDIATELY DANGEROUS TO LIFE OR HEALTH CONDITIONS:

SELF-CONTAINED BREATHING APPARATUS WITH FULL FACEPIECE OPERATED IN PRESSURE-DEMAND OR OTHER POSITIVE PRESSURE MODE.

SUPPLIED-AIR RESPIRATOR WITH FULL FACEPIECE AND OPERATED IN PRESSURE-DEMAND OR OTHER POSITIVE PRESSURE MODE IN COMBINATION WITH AN AUXILIARY SELF-CONTAINED BREATHING APPARATUS OPERATED IN PRESSURE-DEMAND OR OTHER POSITIVE PRESSURE MODE.

CLOTHING: EMPLOYEE MUST WEAR APPROPRIATE PROTECTIVE (IMPERVIOUS) CLOTHING AND EQUIPMENT TO PREVENT REPEATED OR PROLONGED SKIN CONTACT WITH THIS SUBSTANCE.

GLOVES: EMPLOYEE MUST WEAR APPROPRIATE PROTECTIVE GLOVES TO PREVENT CONTACT WITH THIS SUBSTANCE.

EYE PROTECTION: EMPLOYEE MUST WEAR SPLASH-PROOF OR DUST-RESISTANT SAFETY GOGGLES TO PREVENT EYE CONTACT WITH THIS SUBSTANCE.

EMERGENCY EYE WASH: WHERE THERE IS ANY POSSIBILITY THAT AN EMPLOYEE'S EYES MAY BE EXPOSED TO THIS SUBSTANCE, THE EMPLOYER SHOULD PROVIDE AN EYE WASH FOUNTAIN WITHIN THE IMMEDIATE WORK AREA FOR EMERGENCY USE.

AUTHORIZED BY- OCCUPATIONAL HEALTH SERVICES, INC.

CREATION DATE: 10/04/89 ***REVISION DATE:*** 07/12/90

MATERIAL SAFETY DATA SHEET

OCCUPATIONAL HEALTH SERVICES, INC.
AGRICULTURE AND PESTICIDE DIVISION
450 SEVENTH AVENUE, SUITE 2407
NEW YORK, NEW YORK 10123
1-800-445-MSDS OR (212) 967-1100

EMERGENCY CONTACT:
JOHN S. BRANSFORD, JR. (615) 292-1180

SUBSTANCE IDENTIFICATION

CAS-NUMBER 371-86-8

SUBSTANCE: MIPAFOX

TRADE NAMES/SYNONYMS: PHOSPHORODIAMIDIC FLUORIDE, N,N'-BIS(1-METHYLETHYL)-; PHOSPHORODIAMIDIC FLUORIDE N,N'-DIISOPROPYL; N,N'-DI-ISOPROPYLPHOSPHORODIAMIDIC FLUORIDE; N,N'-BIS(1-METHYLETHYL)PHOSPHORODIAMIDIC FLUORIDE; N,N'-DIISOPROPYLPHOSPHORODIAMIDIC FLUORIDE; BIS(ISOPROPYLAMINO)FLUOROPHOSPHINE OXIDE; BIS(MONOISOPROPYLAMINO)FLUOROPHOSPHINE OXIDE; ISOPESTOX; PESTON XV; PESTON 15; STCC 4941158; PST15030

CHEMICAL FAMILY: ORGANOPHOSPHATE

MOLECULAR FORMULA: C6-H16-F-N2-O-P

MOLECULAR WEIGHT: 182.21

CERCLA RATINGS (SCALE 0-3): HEALTH=3 FIRE=0 REACTIVITY=0 PERSISTENCE=0

NFPA RATINGS (SCALE 0-4): HEALTH=3 FIRE=0 REACTIVITY=0

COMPONENTS AND CONTAMINANTS

COMPONENT: MIPAFOX ***PERCENT:*** 100

CAS# 371-86-8

EXPOSURE LIMITS: INORGANIC FLUORIDES (AS F): 2.5 MG/M3 OSHA TWA 2.5 MG/M3 ACGIH TWA 2.5 MG/M3 NIOSH RECOMMENDED 10 HOUR TWA

PHYSICAL DATA

DESCRIPTION: WHITE CRYSTALLINE SUBSTANCE ***BOILING POINT:*** 257 F (125 C) @ 2 MMHG

MELTING POINT: 142-144 F (61-62 C) ***SPECIFIC GRAVITY:*** 1.2

VAPOR PRESSURE: 0.0025 MMHG @ 25 C ***SOLUBILITY IN WATER:*** 8%

SOLVENT SOLUBILITY: SOLUBLE IN POLAR ORGANIC SOLVENTS; SLIGHTLY SOLUBLE IN PETROLEUM OILS

FIRE AND EXPLOSION DATA

FIRE AND EXPLOSION HAZARD: NEGLIGIBLE FIRE HAZARD WHEN EXPOSED TO HEAT OR FLAME.

FIREFIGHTING MEDIA: DRY CHEMICAL, CARBON DIOXIDE, HALON, WATER SPRAY OR STANDARD FOAM (1987 EMERGENCY RESPONSE GUIDEBOOK, DOT P 5800.4). FOR LARGER FIRES, USE WATER SPRAY, FOG OR STANDARD FOAM (1987 EMERGENCY RESPONSE GUIDEBOOK, DOT P 5800.4).

FIREFIGHTING: MOVE CONTAINERS FROM FIRE AREA IF POSSIBLE. FIGHT FIRE FROM MAXIMUM DISTANCE. STAY AWAY FROM STORAGE TANK ENDS. DIKE FIRE CONTROL WATER FOR LATER DISPOSAL. DO NOT SCATTER MATERIAL (1987 EMERGENCY RESPONSE GUIDEBOOK, DOT P 5800.4, GUIDE PAGE 55). EXTINGUISH ONLY IF FLOW CAN BE STOPPED; USE FLOODING AMOUNTS OF WATER AS FOG, SOLID STREAMS MAY BE INEFFECTIVE. COOL CONTAINERS WITH FLOODING AMOUNTS OF WATER FROM AS FAR A DISTANCE AS POSSIBLE. USE WATER SPRAY TO ABSORB TOXIC VAPORS. AVOID BREATHING TOXIC VAPORS; KEEP UPWIND. CONSIDER EVACUATION OF DOWNWIND AREA IF MATERIAL IS LEAKING.

TRANSPORTATION DATA

DEPARTMENT OF TRANSPORTATION HAZARD CLASSIFICATION 49 CFR 172.101: ORM-A

DEPARTMENT OF TRANSPORTATION LABELING REQUIREMENTS 49 CFR 172.101 AND SUBPART E: NONE

DEPARTMENT OF TRANSPORTATION PACKAGING REQUIREMENTS: 49 CFR 173.510 EXCEPTIONS: 49 CFR 173.505

TOXICITY

MIPAFOX: TOXICITY DATA: 80 MG/KG ORAL-GUINEA PIG LD50; 100 MG/KG ORAL-RABBIT LD50; 14 MG/KG INTRAPERITONEAL-MOUSE LD50; 90 MG/KG INTRAPERITONEAL-RAT LD50; 75 MG/KG SUBCUTANEOUS-RAT LD50; 50 MG/KG UNREPORTED-RAT LD50; CARCINOGEN STATUS: NONE. ACUTE TOXICITY LEVEL: TOXIC BY INGESTION. TARGET EFFECTS: CHOLINESTERASE INHIBITOR. NEUROTOXIN. AT INCREASED RISK FROM EXPOSURE: PERSONS WITH RESPIRATORY AILMENTS, RECENT EXPOSURE TO CHOLINESTERASE INHIBITORS OR IMPAIRED CHOLINESTERASE PRODUCTION, OR LIVER MALFUNCTION.* ADDITIONAL DATA: MAY CROSS THE PLACENTA. HIGH ENVIRONMENTAL TEMPERATURES OR EXPOSURE OF THE CHEMICAL TO VISIBLE OR ULTRAVIOLET LIGHT MAY ENHANCE

THE TOXICITY. INTERACTIONS WITH MEDICATIONS MAY OCCUR.*
* MAY BE BASED ON GENERAL INFORMATION ON ORGANOPHOSPHATES.

HEALTH EFFECTS AND FIRST AID

INHALATION: MIPAFOX: NEUROTOXIN. EXPOSURE TO SUBLETHAL DOSES MAY CAUSE DELAYED NEUROTOXICITY WITH THE ONSET OF SYMPTOMS DELAYED FOR AS MUCH AS 30 DAYS. SEE INFORMATION ON ORGANOPHOSPHATES. ORGANOPHOSPHATES: CHOLINESTERASE INHIBITOR. **ACUTE EXPOSURE-** WHEN INHALED, THE FIRST EFFECTS OF CHOLINESTERASE INHIBITORS ARE USUALLY RESPIRATORY AND MAY INCLUDE NASAL HYPEREMIA AND WATERY DISCHARGE, COUGH, CHEST DISCOMFORT, DYSPNEA, AND WHEEZING DUE TO INCREASED BRONCHIAL SECRETIONS AND BRONCHOCONSTRICTION. IF SUFFICIENT AMOUNTS ARE ABSORBED, OTHER SYSTEMIC EFFECTS MAY BEGIN WITHIN A FEW MINUTES OR BE DELAYED FOR UP TO 12 HOURS. SYMPTOMS MAY INCLUDE PALLOR, NAUSEA, VOMITING, DIARRHEA, ABDOMINAL CRAMPS, HEADACHE, DIZZINESS, OCULAR PAIN, BLURRED VISION, MIOSIS OR IN SOME CASES, ESPECIALLY INITIALLY, MYDRIASIS, LACRIMATION, SALIVATION, SWEATING, AND CONFUSION. OTHER REPORTED CENTRAL NERVOUS SYSTEM OR NEUROMUSCULAR EFFECTS MAY INCLUDE ATAXIA, SLURRED SPEECH, AREFLEXIA, WEAKNESS, FATIGUE, FASCICULATIONS, TWITCHING, TREMORS POSSIBLY OF THE TONGUE AND EYELIDS, AND EVENTUALLY PARALYSIS OF THE EXTREMITIES AND POSSIBLY OF THE RESPIRATORY MUSCLES. IN SEVERE CASES THERE MAY ALSO BE INVOLUNTARY DEFECATION AND URINATION, CYANOSIS, PSYCHOSIS, HYPERGLYCEMIA, ACUTE PANCREATITIS, CARDIAC IRREGULARITIES, PULMONARY EDEMA, UNCONSCIOUSNESS, CONVULSIONS, AND COMA. DEATH IS PRIMARILY DUE TO RESPIRATORY FAILURE, ALTHOUGH CARDIOVASCULAR EFFECTS INCLUDING CARDIAC ARREST MAY ALSO BE IMPLICATED. LONG TERM SEQUELAE ARE RARE BUT MAY INCLUDE NEUROPSYCHIATRIC DISORDERS AND MYOPATHY WITH MUSCLE TENDERNESS. SOME ORGANOPHOSPHATES MAY CAUSE A DELAYED NEUROPATHY BEGINNING 1-4 WEEKS AFTER AN ACUTE EXPOSURE WHICH MAY OR MAY NOT HAVE CAUSED ACUTE CHOLINERGIC EFFECTS. NUMBNESS, TINGLING, WEAKNESS AND CRAMPING BEGINNING SYMMETRICALLY IN THE LOWER LIMBS MAY PROGRESS TO ATAXIA AND PARALYSIS. IN SEVERE CASES, UPPER LIMB INVOLVEMENT IS POSSIBLE AND FLACCID PARALYSIS MAY PROGRESS TO SPASTIC PARALYSIS WITH EXAGGERATED REFLEXES. IMPROVEMENT MAY OCCUR OVER MONTHS TO YEARS, BUT SOME RESIDUAL IMPAIRMENT USUALLY REMAINS. **CHRONIC EXPOSURE-** REPEATED OR PROLONGED EXPOSURE MAY RESULT IN THE EFFECTS OF ACUTE EXPOSURE INCLUDING THE DELAYED NEUROPATHY. OTHER EFFECTS REPORTED IN WORKERS REPEATEDLY EXPOSED INCLUDE IMPAIRED MEMORY AND CONCENTRATION, ACUTE PSYCHOSIS, SEVERE DEPRESSIONS, IRRITABILTY, CONFUSION, APATHY, EMOTIONAL LABILITY, SOCIAL WITHDRAWAL, CONFUSION, HEADACHE, SPEECH DIFFICULTIES, DELAYED REACTION TIMES, SPATIAL DISORIENTATION, NIGHTMARES, SLEEPWALKING, AND DROWSINESS OR INSOMNIA. AN INFLUENZA-LIKE CONDITION WITH HEADACHE, NAUSEA, WEAKNESS, ANOREXIA AND MALAISE HAS ALSO BEEN REPORTED.

FIRST AID- REMOVE FROM EXPOSURE AREA TO FRESH AIR IMMEDIATELY. IF BREATHING HAS STOPPED, GIVE ARTIFICIAL RESPIRATION. MAINTAIN AIRWAY AND BLOOD PRESSURE AND ADMINISTER OXYGEN IF AVAILABLE. KEEP AFFECTED PERSON WARM AND AT REST. TREAT SYMPTOMATICALLY AND SUPPORTIVELY. ADMINISTRATION OF OXYGEN SHOULD BE PERFORMED BY QUALIFIED PERSONNEL. GET MEDICAL ATTENTION IMMEDIATELY.

SKIN CONTACT: MIPAFOX: NEUROTOXIN. EXPOSURE TO SUBLETHAL DOSES MAY CAUSE DELAYED NEUROTOXICITY. SEE INFORMATION ON ORGANOPHOSPHATES. ORGANOPHOSPHATES: CHOLINESTERASE INHIBITOR. **ACUTE EXPOSURE-** LOCALIZED SWEATING AND FASCICULATIONS MAY OCCUR AT THE SITE OF CONTACT. IF SUFFICIENT AMOUNTS ARE ABSORBED, OTHER EFFECTS OF CHOLINESTERASE INHIBITION AS DESCRIBED IN ACUTE INHALATION MAY OCCUR. SYMPTOMS MAY BE DELAYED 2-3 HOURS, BUT USUALLY NO MORE THAN 12 HOURS. THE RATE OF ABSORPTION IS INCREASED BY THE PRESENCE OF DERMATITIS OR HIGH AMBIENT TEMPERATURES. DELAYED NEUROPATHY IS ALSO POSSIBLE. **CHRONIC EXPOSURE-** REPEATED OR PROLONGED EXPOSURE MAY CAUSE EFFECTS AS DESCRIBED IN ACUTE EXPOSURE. SOME ORGANOPHOSPHATES MAY CAUSE SENSITIZATION.

FIRST AID- REMOVE CONTAMINATED CLOTHING IMMEDIATELY. WASH CONTAMINATED AREAS WITH SOAP AND WATER FOLLOWED BY ALCOHOL (ARENA, POISONING, 4TH ED.). EMERGENCY PERSONNEL SHOULD WEAR GLOVES AND AVOID CONTAMINATION. TREAT RESPIRATORY DIFFICULTY WITH ARTIFICIAL RESPIRATION. GET MEDICAL ATTENTION IMMEDIATELY.

EYE CONTACT: MIPAFOX: SEE INFORMATION ON ORGANOPHOSPHATES. ORGANOPHOSPHATES: CHOLINESTERASE INHIBITOR. **ACUTE EXPOSURE-** DIRECT CONTACT MAY CAUSE PAIN, HYPEREMIA, LACRIMATION, TWITCHING OF THE EYELIDS, MIOSIS, AND CILIARY MUSCLE SPASM WITH LOSS OF ACCOMODATION, BLURRED OR DIMMED VISION AND BROWACHE. SOMETIMES MYDRIASIS MAY OCCUR INSTEAD OF MIOSIS. WITH SUFFICIENT EXPOSURE, OTHER SYMPTOMS OF CHOLINESTERASE INHIBITION AS DESCRIBED IN ACUTE INHALATION MAY OCCUR. **CHRONIC EXPOSURE-** REPEATED OR PROLONGED EXPOSURE MAY CAUSE EFFECTS AS DESCRIBED IN ACUTE EXPOSURE. SOME COMPOUNDS HAVE CAUSED TOXIC EFFECTS ON THE CRYSTALLINE LENS, CONJUNCTIVAL THICKENING AND OBSTRUCTION OF THE NASOLACRIMAL CANALS WHEN USED AS MIOTIC EYEDROPS.

FIRST AID- IRRIGATE EYES WITH WATER OR SALINE SOLUTION. IF SYMPTOMS OF POISONING OCCUR, TREAT RESPIRATORY DIFFICULTY WITH ARTIFICIAL RESPIRATION AND OXYGEN. OBSERVE PATIENT FOR AT LEAST 24-36 HOURS (GOSSELIN, CLINICAL TOXICOLOGY OF COMMERCIAL PRODUCTS, 5TH ED.). GET MEDICAL ATTENTION IMMEDIATELY. OXYGEN SHOULD BE ADMINISTERED BY QUALIFIED MEDICAL PERSONNEL.

INGESTION: MIPAFOX: TOXIC. SEE INFORMATION ON ORGANOPHOSPHATES. ORGANOPHOSPHATES: CHOLINESTERASE INHIBITOR. **ACUTE EXPOSURE-** WHEN INGESTED, THE FIRST EFFECTS MAY BE NAUSEA, VOMITING, ANOREXIA, ABDOMINAL CRAMPS AND DIARRHEA. GASTROINTESTINAL ABSORPTION MAY CAUSE SYMPTOMS OF CHOLINESTERASE INHIBITION AS DESCRIBED IN ACUTE INHALATION. SYMPTOMS MAY BEGIN WITHIN MINUTES OR BE DELAYED FOR HOURS. DELAYED EFFECTS INCLUDING NEUROPATHY MAY ALSO OCCUR. **CHRONIC EXPOSURE-** REPEATED INGESTION MAY CAUSE EFFECTS AS DESCRIBED IN ACUTE EXPOSURE.

FIRST AID- IF PERSON IS ALERT AND RESPIRATION IS NOT DEPRESSED, GIVE SYRUP OF IPECAC FOLLOWED BY WATER (IF VOMITING OCCURS, KEEP HEAD BELOW HIPS TO PREVENT ASPIRATION). IF CONSCIOUSNESS LEVEL DECLINES OR VOMITING HAS NOT OCCURRED IN 15 MINUTES EMPTY STOMACH BY GASTRIC LAVAGE WITH THE AID OF CUFFED ENDOTRACHEAL TUBE USING ISOTONIC SALINE OR 5% SODIUM BICARBONATE FOLLOW WITH ACTIVATED CHARCOAL. ESTABLISH AND MAINTAIN AIRWAY. TREAT RESPIRATORY DIFFICULTY WITH ARTIFICIAL RESPIRATION AND OXYGEN. DO NOT GIVE MORPHINE, AMINOPHYLLINE, PHENOTHIAZINES, RESERPINE, FUROSEMIDE, OR ETHACRYNIC ACID (MORGAN, RECOGNITION AND MANAGEMENT OF PESTICIDE POISONINGS, 3RD ED.). TREAT SYMPTOMATICALLY AND SUPPORTIVELY. ADMINISTRATION OF OXYGEN AND LAVAGE MUST BE PERFORMED BY QUALIFIED MEDICAL PERSONNEL. GET MEDICAL ATTENTION IMMEDIATELY.

ANTIDOTE: THE FOLLOWING ANTIDOTE(S) HAVE BEEN RECOMMENDED. HOWEVER, THE DECISION AS TO WHETHER THE SEVERITY OF POISONING REQUIRES ADMINISTRATION OF ANY ANTIDOTE AND ACTUAL DOSE REQUIRED SHOULD BE MADE BY QUALIFIED MEDICAL PERSONNEL.

FOR CHOLINESTERASE INHIBITORS: ESTABLISH CLEAR AIRWAY AND TISSUE OXYGENATION BY ASPIRATION OF SECRETIONS, AND IF NECESSARY, BY ASSISTED PULMONARY VENTILATION WITH OXYGEN. IMPROVE TISSUE OXYGENATION AS MUCH AS POSSIBLE BEFORE ADMINISTERING ATROPINE TO MINIMIZE THE RISK OF VENTRICULAR FIBRILLATION. ADMINISTER ATROPINE SULFATE INTRAVENOUSLY, OR INTRAMUSCULARLY IF IV INJECTION IS NOT POSSIBLE. IN MODERATELY SEVERE POISONING ADMINISTER ATROPINE SULFATE, 0.4-2.0 MG REPEATED EVERY 15 MINUTES UNTIL ATROPINIZATION IS ACHIEVED (TACHYCARDIA, FLUSHING, DRY MOUTH, MYDRIASIS). MAINTAIN ATROPINIZATION BY REPEATED DOSES FOR 2-12 HOURS, OR LONGER, DEPENDING ON THE SEVERITY OF POISONING. THE APPEARANCE OF RALES IN THE LUNG BASES, MIOSIS, SALIVATION, NAUSEA, BRADYCARDIA, ARE ALL INDICATIONS OF INADEQUATE ATROPINIZATION. SEVERELY POISONED INDIVIDUALS MAY EXHIBIT REMARKABLE TOLERANCE TO ATROPINE; TWO OR MORE TIMES THE DOSAGES SUGGESTED ABOVE MAY BE NEEDED. PERSONS NOT POISONED OR ONLY SLIGHTLY POISONED, HOWEVER, MAY DEVELOP SIGNS OF ATROPINE TOXICITY FROM SUCH LARGE DOSAGES: FEVER, MUSCLE FIBRILLATIONS, AND DELIRIUM ARE THE MAIN SIGNS OF ATROPINE TOXICITY. IF THESE SIGNS APPEAR WHILE THE PATIENT IS FULLY ATROPINIZED, ATROPINE ADMINISTRATION SHOULD BE DISCONTINUED, AT LEAST TEMPORARILY. OBSERVE TREATED PATIENTS CLOSELY AT LEAST 24 HOURS TO INSURE THAT SYMPTOMS (POSSIBLY PULMONARY EDEMA) DO NOT RECUR AS ATROPINIZATION WEARS OFF. IN VERY SEVERE POISONINGS, METABOLIC DISPOSITION OF TOXICANT MAY REQUIRE SEVERAL HOURS OR DAYS DURING WHICH ATROPINIZATION MUST BE MAINTAINED. MARKEDLY LOWER LEVELS OF URINARY METABOLITES INDICATE THAT ATROPINE DOSAGE CAN BE TAPERED OFF. AS DOSAGE IS REDUCED, CHECK THE LUNG BASES FREQUENTLY FOR RALES. IF RALES ARE HEARD OR OTHER SYMPTOMS RETURN, RE-ESTABLISH ATROPINIZATION PROMPTLY (MORGAN, RECOGNITION AND MANAGEMENT OF PESTICIDE POISONINGS, 3RD ED.). ADMINISTRATION OF ANTIDOTE MUST BE PERFORMED BY QUALIFIED MEDICAL PERSONNEL.

IN CASES OF SEVERE POISONING BY ORGANOPHOSPHATE PESTICIDES IN WHICH RESPIRATORY DEPRESSION, MUSCLE WEAKNESS AND TWITCHINGS ARE SEVERE, GIVE PRALIDOXIME (PROTOPAM-AYERST, 2-PAM), 1.0 GRAM INTRAVENOUSLY AT NO MORE THAN 0.5 GRAM PER MINUTE. DOSAGE OF PRALIDOXIME MAY BE REPEATED IN 1-2 HOURS, THEN AT 10-12 HOUR INTERVALS IF NEEDED. IN VERY SEVERE POISONINGS, DOSAGE RATES MAY BE DOUBLED. TREATMENT WITH PRALIDOXIME WILL BE MOST EFFECTIVE IF GIVEN WITHIN THIRTY-SIX HOURS AFTER POISONING (MORGAN, RECOGNITION AND MANAGEMENT OF PESTICIDE

POISONINGS, 3RD ED.). ANTIDOTE SHOULD BE ADMINISTERED BY QUALIFIED MEDICAL PERSONNEL.

REACTIVITY

REACTIVITY: STABLE UNDER NORMAL TEMPERATURES AND PRESSURES.
INCOMPATIBILITIES: MIPAFOX: NO DATA AVAILABLE.
DECOMPOSITION: THERMAL DECOMPOSITION MAY RELEASE TOXIC AND/OR HAZARDOUS GASES.
POLYMERIZATION: HAZARDOUS POLYMERIZATION HAS NOT BEEN REPORTED TO OCCUR UNDER NORMAL TEMPERATURES AND PRESSURES.

STORAGE AND DISPOSAL

OBSERVE ALL FEDERAL, STATE AND LOCAL REGULATIONS WHEN STORING OR DISPOSING OF THIS SUBSTANCE. FOR ASSISTANCE, CONTACT THE DISTRICT DIRECTOR OF THE ENVIRONMENTAL PROTECTION AGENCY.

****STORAGE****

STORE IN ACCORDANCE WITH 40 CFR 165 RECOMMENDED PROCEDURES FOR THE DISPOSAL AND STORAGE OF PESTICIDES AND PESTICIDE CONTAINERS.

****DISPOSAL****

DISPOSAL MUST BE IN ACCORDANCE WITH 40 CFR 165 RECOMMENDED PROCEDURES FOR THE DISPOSAL AND STORAGE OF PESTICIDES AND PESTICIDE CONTAINERS.

CONDITIONS TO AVOID

NONE REPORTED.

SPILL AND LEAK PROCEDURES

SOIL SPILL: DIG HOLDING AREA SUCH AS LAGOON, POND OR PIT FOR CONTAINMENT. USE PROTECTIVE COVER SUCH AS A PLASTIC SHEET TO PREVENT MATERIAL FROM DISSOLVING IN FIRE EXTINGUISHING WATER OR RAIN.
WATER SPILL: LIMIT SPILL MOTION AND DISPERSION WITH NATURAL BARRIERS OR OIL SPILL CONTROL BOOMS.
IF DISSOLVED, APPLY ACTIVATED CARBON AT TEN TIMES THE SPILLED AMOUNT IN REGIONS OF 10 PPM OR GREATER CONCENTRATION.
USE MECHANICAL DREDGES OR LIFTS TO EXTRACT IMMOBILIZED MASSES OF POLLUTION AND PRECIPITATES.
OCCUPATIONAL SPILL: DO NOT TOUCH SPILLED MATERIAL. STOP LEAK IF YOU CAN DO IT WITHOUT RISK. USE WATER SPRAY TO REDUCE VAPORS. FOR SMALL SPILLS, TAKE UP WITH SAND OR OTHER ABSORBENT MATERIAL AND PLACE INTO CONTAINERS FOR LATER DISPOSAL. FOR SMALL DRY SPILLS, WITH A CLEAN SHOVEL PLACE MATERIAL INTO CLEAN, DRY CONTAINERS AND COVER. MOVE CONTAINERS FROM SPILL AREA. FOR LARGER SPILLS, DIKE FAR AHEAD OF SPILL FOR LATER DISPOSAL. KEEP UNNECESSARY PEOPLE AWAY. ISOLATE HAZARD AREA AND DENY ENTRY. VENTILATE CLOSED SPACES BEFORE ENTERING.

PROTECTIVE EQUIPMENT

VENTILATION: PROVIDE LOCAL EXHAUST OR PROCESS ENCLOSURE VENTILATION TO MEET PUBLISHED EXPOSURE LIMITS.
RESPIRATOR: THE FOLLOWING RESPIRATORS AND MAXIMUM USE CONCENTRATIONS ARE RECOMMENDATIONS BY THE U.S. DEPARTMENT OF HEALTH AND HUMAN SERVICES, NIOSH POCKET GUIDE TO CHEMICAL HAZARDS; NIOSH CRITERIA DOCUMENTS OR BY THE U.S. DEPARTMENT OF LABOR, 29 CFR 1910 SUBPART Z. THE SPECIFIC RESPIRATOR SELECTED MUST BE BASED ON CONTAMINATION LEVELS FOUND IN THE WORK PLACE, MUST NOT EXCEED THE WORKING LIMITS OF THE RESPIRATOR AND BE JOINTLY APPROVED BY THE NATIONAL INSTITUTE FOR OCCUPATIONAL SAFETY AND HEALTH AND THE MINE SAFETY AND HEALTH ADMINISTRATION (NIOSH-MSHA).
FLUORIDES (AS F):
12.5 MG/M3- ANY DUST AND MIST RESPIRATOR EXCEPT SINGLE-USE RESPIRATORS.
25 MG/M3- ANY DUST AND MIST RESPIRATOR EXCEPT SINGLE-USE AND QUARTER-MASK RESPIRATORS. ANY SUPPLIED AIR RESPIRATOR. ANY SELF-CONTAINED BREATHING APPARATUS.
62.5 MG/M3- ANY POWERED AIR-PURIFYING RESPIRATOR WITH A DUST AND MIST FILTER. (MAY NEED ACID GAS SORBENT) ANY SUPPLIED-AIR RESPIRATOR OPERATED IN A CONTINUOUS FLOW MODE.
125 MG/M3- ANY SELF-CONTAINED BREATHING APPARATUS WITH A FULL FACEPIECE. ANY AIR-PURIFYING FULL FACEPIECE RESPIRATOR WITH A HIGH-EFFICIENCY PARTICULATE FILTER. (MAY NEED ACID GAS SORBENT) ANY SUPPLIED-AIR RESPIRATOR WITH A FULL FACEPIECE.
500 MG/M3- ANY SUPPLIED-AIR RESPIRATOR WITH A FULL FACEPIECE AND OPERATED IN A PRESSURE-DEMAND OR OTHER POSITIVE PRESSURE MODE.
ESCAPE- ANY AIR-PURIFYING FULL FACEPIECE RESPIRATOR (GAS MASK) WITH A CHIN-STYLE OR FRONT- OR BACK-MOUNTED ACID GAS CANISTER HAVING A HIGH-EFFICIENCY PARTICULATE FILTER. ANY APPROPRIATE ESCAPE-TYPE SELF-CONTAINED BREATHING APPARATUS.
FOR FIREFIGHTING AND OTHER IMMEDIATELY DANGEROUS TO LIFE OR HEALTH CONDITIONS:
SELF-CONTAINED BREATHING APPARATUS WITH FULL FACEPIECE OPERATED IN PRESSURE-DEMAND OR OTHER POSITIVE PRESSURE MODE.
SUPPLIED-AIR RESPIRATOR WITH FULL FACEPIECE AND OPERATED IN PRESSURE-DEMAND OR OTHER POSITIVE PRESSURE MODE IN COMBINATION WITH AN AUXILIARY SELF-CONTAINED BREATHING APPARATUS OPERATED IN PRESSURE-DEMAND OR OTHER POSITIVE PRESSURE MODE.
CLOTHING: EMPLOYEE MUST WEAR APPROPRIATE PROTECTIVE (IMPERVIOUS) CLOTHING AND EQUIPMENT TO PREVENT ANY POSSIBILITY OF SKIN CONTACT WITH THIS SUBSTANCE.
GLOVES: EMPLOYEE MUST WEAR APPROPRIATE PROTECTIVE GLOVES TO PREVENT CONTACT WITH THIS SUBSTANCE.
EYE PROTECTION: EMPLOYEE MUST WEAR SPLASH-PROOF OR DUST-RESISTANT SAFETY GOGGLES AND A FACESHIELD TO PREVENT CONTACT WITH THIS SUBSTANCE.
EMERGENCY WASH FACILITIES: WHERE THERE IS ANY POSSIBILITY THAT AN EMPLOYEE'S EYES AND/OR SKIN MAY BE EXPOSED TO THIS SUBSTANCE, THE EMPLOYER SHOULD PROVIDE AN EYE WASH FOUNTAIN AND QUICK DRENCH SHOWER WITHIN THE IMMEDIATE WORK AREA FOR EMERGENCY USE.

AUTHORIZED BY- OCCUPATIONAL HEALTH SERVICES, INC.
CREATION DATE: 10/04/89 ***REVISION DATE:*** 05/15/90

MATERIAL SAFETY DATA SHEET

OCCUPATIONAL HEALTH SERVICES, INC.
AGRICULTURE AND PESTICIDE DIVISION
450 SEVENTH AVENUE, SUITE 2407
NEW YORK, NEW YORK 10123
1-800-445-MSDS OR (212) 967-1100

EMERGENCY CONTACT:
JOHN S. BRANSFORD, JR. (615) 292-1180

SUBSTANCE IDENTIFICATION

CAS-NUMBER 42509-80-8
SUBSTANCE: ISAZOPHOS
TRADE NAMES/SYNONYMS: PHOSPHOROTHIOIC ACID, O-(5-CHLORO-1-(1-METHYLETHYL)-1H-1,2,4-TRIAZOL -3-YL) O,O-DIETHYL ESTER; O-5-CHLORO-1-ISOPROPYL-1H-1,2,4-TRIAZOL-3-YL O,O-DIETHYL PHOSPHOROTHIOATE; O-(5-CHLORO-1-(1-METHYLETHYL)-1H-1,2,4-TRIAZOL-3-YL) O,O-DIETHYL PHOSPHOROTHIOATE; CGA-12223; ISAZOFOS; MIRAL; C9H17CLN3O3PS; PST15035
CHEMICAL FAMILY: ORGANOPHOSPHATE
MOLECULAR FORMULA: C10-H18-CL-N2-O3-P-S
MOLECULAR WEIGHT: 312.78
CERCLA RATINGS (SCALE 0-3): HEALTH=3 FIRE=0 REACTIVITY=0 PERSISTENCE=0
NFPA RATINGS (SCALE 0-4): HEALTH=4 FIRE=0 REACTIVITY=0

COMPONENTS AND CONTAMINANTS

COMPONENT: ISAZOPHOS ***PERCENT:*** 100
CAS# 42509-80-8
EXPOSURE LIMITS: NO OCCUPATIONAL EXPOSURE LIMITS ESTABLISHED BY OSHA, ACGIH, OR NIOSH.

PHYSICAL DATA

DESCRIPTION: YELLOWISH LIQUID ***BOILING POINT:*** 212 F (100 C) @ 0.001 MMHG
EVAPORATION RATE: NOT AVAILABLE ***SOLUBILITY IN WATER:*** 150 PPM
SOLVENT SOLUBILITY: SOLUBLE IN BENZENE, CHLOROFORM, HEXANE, METHANOL, AND ORGANIC SOLVENTS

FIRE AND EXPLOSION DATA

FIRE AND EXPLOSION HAZARD: NEGLIGIBLE FIRE HAZARD WHEN EXPOSED TO HEAT OR FLAME.
FIREFIGHTING MEDIA: DRY CHEMICAL, CARBON DIOXIDE, HALON, WATER SPRAY OR STANDARD FOAM (1987 EMERGENCY RESPONSE GUIDEBOOK, DOT P 5800.4).
FOR LARGER FIRES, USE WATER SPRAY, FOG OR STANDARD FOAM (1987 EMERGENCY RESPONSE GUIDEBOOK, DOT P 5800.4).
FIREFIGHTING: MOVE CONTAINERS FROM FIRE AREA IF POSSIBLE. FIGHT FIRE FROM MAXIMUM DISTANCE. STAY AWAY FROM STORAGE TANK ENDS. DIKE FIRE CONTROL WATER FOR LATER DISPOSAL. DO NOT SCATTER MATERIAL (1987 EMERGENCY RESPONSE GUIDEBOOK, DOT P 5800.4, GUIDE PAGE 55).
EXTINGUISH ONLY IF FLOW CAN BE STOPPED; USE FLOODING AMOUNTS OF

WATER AS FOG, SOLID STREAMS MAY BE INEFFECTIVE. COOL CONTAINERS WITH FLOODING AMOUNTS OF WATER FROM AS FAR A DISTANCE AS POSSIBLE. USE WATER SPRAY TO ABSORB TOXIC VAPORS. AVOID BREATHING TOXIC VAPORS; KEEP UPWIND. CONSIDER EVACUATION OF DOWNWIND AREA IF MATERIAL IS LEAKING.

TRANSPORTATION DATA

DEPARTMENT OF TRANSPORTATION HAZARD CLASSIFICATION 49 CFR 172.101: POISON B
DEPARTMENT OF TRANSPORTATION LABELING REQUIREMENTS 49 CFR 172.101 AND SUBPART E: POISON
DEPARTMENT OF TRANSPORTATION PACKAGING REQUIREMENTS: 49 CFR 173.346 EXCEPTIONS: 49 CFR 173.345

TOXICITY

ISAZOPHOS: TOXICITY DATA: 236 MG/M3/4 HOURS INHALATION-RAT LC50; 755 MG/KG SKIN-RABBIT LD50; 118 MG/KG SKIN-RAT LD50; 40 MG/KG ORAL-RAT LD50; 34 MG/KG ORAL-MOUSE LD50; 184 MG/KG ORAL-RABBIT LD50; 66 MG/KG ORAL-HAMSTER LD50. CARCINOGEN STATUS: NONE. ACUTE TOXICITY LEVEL: HIGHLY TOXIC BY INHALATION AND INGESTION; TOXIC BY DERMAL ABSORPTION. TARGET EFFECTS: CHOLINESTERASE INHIBITOR. POISONING MAY AFFECT THE NERVOUS SYSTEM.* AT INCREASED RISK FROM EXPOSURE: PERSONS WITH RESPIRATORY AILMENTS, RECENT EXPOSURE TO CHOLINESTERASE INHIBITORS OR IMPAIRED CHOLINESTERASE PRODUCTION, OR LIVER MALFUNCTION.* ADDITIONAL DATA: MAY CROSS THE PLACENTA. HIGH ENVIRONMENTAL TEMPERATURES OR EXPOSURE OF THE CHEMICAL TO VISIBLE OR ULTRAVIOLET LIGHT MAY ENHANCE THE TOXICITY. INTERACTIONS WITH MEDICATIONS MAY OCCUR.*
* MAY BE BASED ON GENERAL INFORMATION ON ORGANOPHOSPHATES.

HEALTH EFFECTS AND FIRST AID

INHALATION: ISAZOPHOS: HIGHLY TOXIC. SEE INFORMATION ON ORGANOPHOSPHATES.
ORGANOPHOSPHATES: CHOLINESTERASE INHIBITOR. **ACUTE EXPOSURE**- WHEN INHALED, THE FIRST EFFECTS OF CHOLINESTERASE INHIBITORS ARE USUALLY RESPIRATORY AND MAY INCLUDE NASAL HYPEREMIA AND WATERY DISCHARGE, COUGH, CHEST DISCOMFORT, DYSPNEA, AND WHEEZING DUE TO INCREASED BRONCHIAL SECRETIONS AND BRONCHOCONSTRICTION. IF SUFFICIENT AMOUNTS ARE ABSORBED, OTHER SYSTEMIC EFFECTS MAY BEGIN WITHIN A FEW MINUTES OR BE DELAYED FOR UP TO 12 HOURS. SYMPTOMS MAY INCLUDE PALLOR, NAUSEA, VOMITING, DIARRHEA, ABDOMINAL CRAMPS, HEADACHE, DIZZINESS, OCULAR PAIN, BLURRED VISION, MIOSIS OR IN SOME CASES, ESPECIALLY INITIALLY, MYDRIASIS, LACRIMATION, SALIVATION, SWEATING, AND CONFUSION. OTHER REPORTED CENTRAL NERVOUS SYSTEM OR NEUROMUSCULAR EFFECTS MAY INCLUDE ATAXIA, SLURRED SPEECH, AREFLEXIA, WEAKNESS, FATIGUE, FASCICULATIONS, TWITCHING, TREMORS POSSIBLY OF THE TONGUE AND EYELIDS, AND EVENTUALLY PARALYSIS OF THE EXTREMITIES AND POSSIBLY OF THE RESPIRATORY MUSCLES. IN SEVERE CASES THERE MAY ALSO BE INVOLUNTARY DEFECATION AND URINATION, CYANOSIS, PSYCHOSIS, HYPERGLYCEMIA, ACUTE PANCREATITIS, CARDIAC IRREGULARITIES, PULMONARY EDEMA, UNCONSCIOUSNESS, CONVULSIONS, AND COMA. DEATH IS PRIMARILY DUE TO RESPIRATORY FAILURE, ALTHOUGH CARDIOVASCULAR EFFECTS INCLUDING CARDIAC ARREST MAY ALSO BE IMPLICATED. LONG TERM SEQUELAE ARE RARE BUT MAY INCLUDE NEUROPSYCHIATRIC DISORDERS AND MYOPATHY WITH MUSCLE TENDERNESS. SOME ORGANOPHOSPHATES MAY CAUSE A DELAYED NEUROPATHY BEGINNING 1-4 WEEKS AFTER AN ACUTE EXPOSURE WHICH MAY OR MAY NOT HAVE CAUSED ACUTE CHOLINERGIC EFFECTS. NUMBNESS, TINGLING, WEAKNESS AND CRAMPING BEGINNING SYMMETRICALLY IN THE LOWER LIMBS MAY PROGRESS TO ATAXIA AND PARALYSIS. IN SEVERE CASES, UPPER LIMB INVOLVEMENT IS POSSIBLE AND FLACCID PARALYSIS MAY PROGRESS TO SPASTIC PARALYSIS WITH EXAGGERATED REFLEXES. IMPROVEMENT MAY OCCUR OVER MONTHS TO YEARS, BUT SOME RESIDUAL IMPAIRMENT USUALLY REMAINS. **CHRONIC EXPOSURE**- REPEATED OR PROLONGED EXPOSURE MAY RESULT IN THE EFFECTS OF ACUTE EXPOSURE INCLUDING THE DELAYED NEUROPATHY. OTHER EFFECTS REPORTED IN WORKERS REPEATEDLY EXPOSED INCLUDE IMPAIRED MEMORY AND CONCENTRATION, ACUTE PSYCHOSIS, SEVERE DEPRESSIONS, IRRITABILTY, CONFUSION, APATHY, EMOTIONAL LABILITY, SOCIAL WITHDRAWAL, CONFUSION, HEADACHE, SPEECH DIFFICULTIES, DELAYED REACTION TIMES, SPATIAL DISORIENTATION, NIGHTMARES, SLEEPWALKING, AND DROWSINESS OR INSOMNIA. AN INFLUENZA-LIKE CONDITION WITH HEADACHE, NAUSEA, WEAKNESS, ANOREXIA AND MALAISE HAS ALSO BEEN REPORTED.
FIRST AID- REMOVE FROM EXPOSURE AREA TO FRESH AIR IMMEDIATELY. IF BREATHING HAS STOPPED, GIVE ARTIFICIAL RESPIRATION. MAINTAIN AIRWAY AND BLOOD PRESSURE AND ADMINISTER OXYGEN IF AVAILABLE. KEEP AFFECTED PERSON WARM AND AT REST. TREAT SYMPTOMATICALLY AND SUPPORTIVELY. ADMINISTRATION OF OXYGEN SHOULD BE PERFORMED BY QUALIFIED PERSONNEL. GET MEDICAL ATTENTION IMMEDIATELY.

SKIN CONTACT: ISAZOPHOS: TOXIC. THIS MATERIAL WAS MILDLY IRRITATING TO SKIN OF RABBITS. SEE INFORMATION ON ORGANOPHOSPHATES.
ORGANOPHOSPHATES: CHOLINESTERASE INHIBITOR. **ACUTE EXPOSURE**- LOCALIZED SWEATING AND FASCICULATIONS MAY OCCUR AT THE SITE OF CONTACT. IF SUFFICIENT AMOUNTS ARE ABSORBED, OTHER EFFECTS OF CHOLINESTERASE INHIBITION AS DESCRIBED IN ACUTE INHALATION MAY OCCUR. SYMPTOMS MAY BE DELAYED 2-3 HOURS, BUT USUALLY NO MORE THAN 12 HOURS. THE RATE OF ABSORPTION IS INCREASED BY THE PRESENCE OF DERMATITIS OR HIGH AMBIENT TEMPERATURES. DELAYED NEUROPATHY IS ALSO POSSIBLE. **CHRONIC EXPOSURE**- REPEATED OR PROLONGED EXPOSURE MAY CAUSE EFFECTS AS DESCRIBED IN ACUTE EXPOSURE. SOME ORGANOPHOSPHATES MAY CAUSE SENSITIZATION.
FIRST AID- REMOVE CONTAMINATED CLOTHING IMMEDIATELY. WASH CONTAMINATED AREAS WITH SOAP AND WATER FOLLOWED BY ALCOHOL (ARENA, POISONING, 4TH ED.). EMERGENCY PERSONNEL SHOULD WEAR GLOVES AND AVOID CONTAMINATION. TREAT RESPIRATORY DIFFICULTY WITH ARTIFICIAL RESPIRATION. GET MEDICAL ATTENTION IMMEDIATELY.

EYE CONTACT: ISAZOPHOS: THIS MATERIAL WAS MILDLY IRRITATING TO THE EYES OF RABBITS. SEE INFORMATION ON ORGANOPHOSPHATES.
ORGANOPHOSPHATES: CHOLINESTERASE INHIBITOR. **ACUTE EXPOSURE**- DIRECT CONTACT MAY CAUSE PAIN, HYPEREMIA, LACRIMATION, TWITCHING OF THE EYELIDS, MIOSIS, AND CILIARY MUSCLE SPASM WITH LOSS OF ACCOMODATION, BLURRED OR DIMMED VISION AND BROWACHE. SOMETIMES MYDRIASIS MAY OCCUR INSTEAD OF MIOSIS. WITH SUFFICIENT EXPOSURE, OTHER SYMPTOMS OF CHOLINESTERASE INHIBITION AS DESCRIBED IN ACUTE INHALATION MAY OCCUR. **CHRONIC EXPOSURE**- REPEATED OR PROLONGED EXPOSURE MAY CAUSE EFFECTS AS DESCRIBED IN ACUTE EXPOSURE. SOME COMPOUNDS HAVE CAUSED TOXIC EFFECTS ON THE CRYSTALLINE LENS, CONJUNCTIVAL THICKENING AND OBSTRUCTION OF THE NASOLACRIMAL CANALS WHEN USED AS MIOTIC EYEDROPS.
FIRST AID- IRRIGATE EYES WITH WATER OR SALINE SOLUTION. IF SYMPTOMS OF POISONING OCCUR, TREAT RESPIRATORY DIFFICULTY WITH ARTIFICIAL RESPIRATION AND OXYGEN. OBSERVE PATIENT FOR AT LEAST 24-36 HOURS (GOSSELIN, CLINICAL TOXICOLOGY OF COMMERCIAL PRODUCTS, 5TH ED.). GET MEDICAL ATTENTION IMMEDIATELY. OXYGEN SHOULD BE ADMINISTERED BY QUALIFIED MEDICAL PERSONNEL.

INGESTION: ISAZOPHOS: HIGHLY TOXIC. DELAYED NEUROTOXICITY WAS NOT OBSERVED IN A STUDY OF FEMALE CHICKENS FED APPROXIMATELY 25.4 MG/KG. FETOTOXICITY (RUNTS) WAS OBSERVED IN A STUDY OF PREGNANT RATS FED 9 MG/KG/DAY. SEE INFORMATION ON ORGANOPHOSPHATES.
ORGANOPHOSPHATES: CHOLINESTERASE INHIBITOR. **ACUTE EXPOSURE**- WHEN INGESTED, THE FIRST EFFECTS MAY BE NAUSEA, VOMITING, ANOREXIA, ABDOMINAL CRAMPS AND DIARRHEA. GASTROINTESTINAL ABSORPTION MAY CAUSE SYMPTOMS OF CHOLINESTERASE INHIBITION AS DESCRIBED IN ACUTE INHALATION. SYMPTOMS MAY BEGIN WITHIN MINUTES OR BE DELAYED FOR HOURS. DELAYED EFFECTS INCLUDING NEUROPATHY MAY ALSO OCCUR. **CHRONIC EXPOSURE**- REPEATED INGESTION MAY CAUSE EFFECTS AS DESCRIBED IN ACUTE EXPOSURE.
FIRST AID- IF PERSON IS ALERT AND RESPIRATION IS NOT DEPRESSED, GIVE SYRUP OF IPECAC FOLLOWED BY WATER (IF VOMITING OCCURS, KEEP HEAD BELOW HIPS TO PREVENT ASPIRATION). IF CONSCIOUSNESS LEVEL DECLINES OR VOMITING HAS NOT OCCURRED IN 15 MINUTES EMPTY STOMACH BY GASTRIC LAVAGE WITH THE AID OF CUFFED ENDOTRACHEAL TUBE USING ISOTONIC SALINE OR 5% SODIUM BICARBONATE FOLLOW WITH ACTIVATED CHARCOAL. ESTABLISH AND MAINTAIN AIRWAY. TREAT RESPIRATORY DIFFICULTY WITH ARTIFICIAL RESPIRATION AND OXYGEN. DO NOT GIVE MORPHINE, AMINOPHYLLINE, PHENOTHIAZINES, RESERPINE, FUROSEMIDE, OR ETHACRYNIC ACID (MORGAN, RECOGNITION AND MANAGEMENT OF PESTICIDE POISONINGS, 3RD ED.). TREAT SYMPTOMATICALLY AND SUPPORTIVELY. ADMINISTRATION OF OXYGEN AND LAVAGE MUST BE PERFORMED BY QUALIFIED MEDICAL PERSONNEL. GET MEDICAL ATTENTION IMMEDIATELY.
ANTIDOTE: THE FOLLOWING ANTIDOTE(S) HAVE BEEN RECOMMENDED. HOWEVER, THE DECISION AS TO WHETHER THE SEVERITY OF POISONING REQUIRES ADMINISTRATION OF ANY ANTIDOTE AND ACTUAL DOSE REQUIRED SHOULD BE MADE BY QUALIFIED MEDICAL PERSONNEL.
FOR CHOLINESTERASE INHIBITORS: ESTABLISH CLEAR AIRWAY AND TISSUE OXYGENATION BY ASPIRATION OF SECRETIONS, AND IF NECESSARY, BY ASSISTED PULMONARY VENTILATION WITH OXYGEN. IMPROVE TISSUE OXYGENATION AS MUCH AS POSSIBLE BEFORE ADMINISTERING ATROPINE TO MINIMIZE THE RISK OF VENTRICULAR FIBRILLATION. ADMINISTER ATROPINE SULFATE INTRAVENOUSLY, OR INTRAMUSCULARLY IF IV INJECTION IS NOT POSSIBLE. IN MODERATELY SEVERE POISONING ADMINISTER ATROPINE SULFATE, 0.4-2.0 MG REPEATED EVERY 15 MINUTES UNTIL ATROPINIZATION IS ACHIEVED (TACHYCARDIA, FLUSHING, DRY MOUTH, MYDRIASIS). MAINTAIN ATROPINIZATION BY REPEATED DOSES FOR 2-12

HOURS, OR LONGER, DEPENDING ON THE SEVERITY OF POISONING. THE APPEARANCE OF RALES IN THE LUNG BASES, MIOSIS, SALIVATION, NAUSEA, BRADYCARDIA, ARE ALL INDICATIONS OF INADEQUATE ATROPINIZATION. SEVERELY POISONED INDIVIDUALS MAY EXHIBIT REMARKABLE TOLERANCE TO ATROPINE; TWO OR MORE TIMES THE DOSAGES SUGGESTED ABOVE MAY BE NEEDED. PERSONS NOT POISONED OR ONLY SLIGHTLY POISONED, HOWEVER, MAY DEVELOP SIGNS OF ATROPINE TOXICITY FROM SUCH LARGE DOSAGES: FEVER, MUSCLE FIBRILLATIONS, AND DELIRIUM ARE THE MAIN SIGNS OF ATROPINE TOXICITY. IF THESE SIGNS APPEAR WHILE THE PATIENT IS FULLY ATROPINIZED, ATROPINE ADMINISTRATION SHOULD BE DISCONTINUED, AT LEAST TEMPORARILY. OBSERVE TREATED PATIENTS CLOSELY AT LEAST 24 HOURS TO INSURE THAT SYMPTOMS (POSSIBLY PULMONARY EDEMA) DO NOT RECUR AS ATROPINIZATION WEARS OFF. IN VERY SEVERE POISONINGS, METABOLIC DISPOSITION OF TOXICANT MAY REQUIRE SEVERAL HOURS OR DAYS DURING WHICH ATROPINIZATION MUST BE MAINTAINED. MARKEDLY LOWER LEVELS OF URINARY METABOLITES INDICATE THAT ATROPINE DOSAGE CAN BE TAPERED OFF. AS DOSAGE IS REDUCED, CHECK THE LUNG BASES FREQUENTLY FOR RALES. IF RALES ARE HEARD OR OTHER SYMPTOMS RETURN, RE-ESTABLISH ATROPINIZATION PROMPTLY (MORGAN, RECOGNITION AND MANAGEMENT OF PESTICIDE POISONINGS, 3RD ED.). ADMINISTRATION OF ANTIDOTE MUST BE PERFORMED BY QUALIFIED MEDICAL PERSONNEL.

IN CASES OF SEVERE POISONING BY ORGANOPHOSPHATE PESTICIDES IN WHICH RESPIRATORY DEPRESSION, MUSCLE WEAKNESS AND TWITCHINGS ARE SEVERE, GIVE PRALIDOXIME (PROTOPAM-AYERST, 2-PAM), 1.0 GRAM INTRAVENOUSLY AT NO MORE THAN 0.5 GRAM PER MINUTE. DOSAGE OF PRALIDOXIME MAY BE REPEATED IN 1-2 HOURS, THEN AT 10-12 HOUR INTERVALS IF NEEDED. IN VERY SEVERE POISONINGS, DOSAGE RATES MAY BE DOUBLED. TREATMENT WITH PRALIDOXIME WILL BE MOST EFFECTIVE IF GIVEN WITHIN THIRTY-SIX HOURS AFTER POISONING (MORGAN, RECOGNITION AND MANAGEMENT OF PESTICIDE POISONINGS, 3RD ED.). ANTIDOTE SHOULD BE ADMINISTERED BY QUALIFIED MEDICAL PERSONNEL.

REACTIVITY

REACTIVITY: STABLE UNDER NORMAL TEMPERATURES AND PRESSURES.
INCOMPATIBILITIES: ISAZOPHOS: NO DATA AVAILABLE.
DECOMPOSITION: THERMAL DECOMPOSITION MAY RELEASE TOXIC AND/OR HAZARDOUS GASES.
POLYMERIZATION: HAZARDOUS POLYMERIZATION HAS NOT BEEN REPORTED TO OCCUR UNDER NORMAL TEMPERATURES AND PRESSURES.

STORAGE AND DISPOSAL

OBSERVE ALL FEDERAL, STATE AND LOCAL REGULATIONS WHEN STORING OR DISPOSING OF THIS SUBSTANCE. FOR ASSISTANCE, CONTACT THE DISTRICT DIRECTOR OF THE ENVIRONMENTAL PROTECTION AGENCY.

STORAGE

STORE IN ACCORDANCE WITH 40 CFR 165 RECOMMENDED PROCEDURES FOR THE DISPOSAL AND STORAGE OF PESTICIDES AND PESTICIDE CONTAINERS.

DISPOSAL

DISPOSAL MUST BE IN ACCORDANCE WITH 40 CFR 165 RECOMMENDED PROCEDURES FOR THE DISPOSAL AND STORAGE OF PESTICIDES AND PESTICIDE CONTAINERS.

CONDITIONS TO AVOID

NONE REPORTED.

SPILL AND LEAK PROCEDURES

OCCUPATIONAL SPILL: DO NOT TOUCH SPILLED MATERIAL. STOP LEAK IF YOU CAN DO IT WITHOUT RISK. USE WATER SPRAY TO REDUCE VAPORS. FOR SMALL SPILLS, TAKE UP WITH SAND OR OTHER ABSORBENT MATERIAL AND PLACE INTO CONTAINERS FOR LATER DISPOSAL. FOR SMALL DRY SPILLS, WITH A CLEAN SHOVEL PLACE MATERIAL INTO CLEAN, DRY CONTAINERS AND COVER. MOVE CONTAINERS FROM SPILL AREA. FOR LARGER SPILLS, DIKE FAR AHEAD OF SPILL FOR LATER DISPOSAL. KEEP UNNECESSARY PEOPLE AWAY. ISOLATE HAZARD AREA AND DENY ENTRY. VENTILATE CLOSED SPACES BEFORE ENTERING.

PROTECTIVE EQUIPMENT

VENTILATION: PROVIDE LOCAL EXHAUST OR PROCESS ENCLOSURE VENTILATION SYSTEM.
RESPIRATOR: THE FOLLOWING RESPIRATORS ARE RECOMMENDED BASED ON INFORMATION FOUND IN THE PHYSICAL DATA, TOXICITY AND HEALTH EFFECTS SECTIONS. THEY ARE RANKED IN ORDER FROM MINIMUM TO MAXIMUM RESPIRATORY PROTECTION. THE SPECIFIC RESPIRATOR SELECTED MUST BE BASED ON CONTAMINATION LEVELS FOUND IN THE WORK PLACE, MUST NOT EXCEED THE WORKING LIMITS OF THE RESPIRATOR AND BE JOINTLY APPROVED BY THE NATIONAL INSTITUTE FOR OCCUPATIONAL SAFETY AND HEALTH AND THE MINE SAFETY AND HEALTH ADMINISTRATION (NIOSH-MSHA).

TYPE 'C' SUPPLIED-AIR RESPIRATOR WITH A FULL FACEPIECE OPERATED IN PRESSURE-DEMAND OR OTHER POSITIVE PRESSURE MODE OR WITH A FULL FACEPIECE, HELMET OR HOOD OPERATED IN CONTINOUS-FLOW MODE.
SELF-CONTAINED BREATHING APPARATUS WITH A FULL FACEPIECE OPERATED IN PRESSURE-DEMAND OR OTHER POSITIVE PRESSURE MODE.
FOR FIREFIGHTING AND OTHER IMMEDIATELY DANGEROUS TO LIFE OR HEALTH CONDITIONS:
SELF-CONTAINED BREATHING APPARATUS WITH FULL FACEPIECE OPERATED IN PRESSURE-DEMAND OR OTHER POSITIVE PRESSURE MODE.
SUPPLIED-AIR RESPIRATOR WITH FULL FACEPIECE AND OPERATED IN PRESSURE-DEMAND OR OTHER POSITIVE PRESSURE MODE IN COMBINATION WITH AN AUXILIARY SELF-CONTAINED BREATHING APPARATUS OPERATED IN PRESSURE-DEMAND OR OTHER POSITIVE PRESSURE MODE.
CLOTHING: EMPLOYEE MUST WEAR APPROPRIATE PROTECTIVE (IMPERVIOUS) CLOTHING AND EQUIPMENT TO PREVENT ANY POSSIBILITY OF SKIN CONTACT WITH THIS SUBSTANCE.
GLOVES: EMPLOYEE MUST WEAR APPROPRIATE PROTECTIVE GLOVES TO PREVENT CONTACT WITH THIS SUBSTANCE.
EYE PROTECTION: EMPLOYEE MUST WEAR SPLASH-PROOF OR DUST-RESISTANT SAFETY GOGGLES AND A FACESHIELD TO PREVENT CONTACT WITH THIS SUBSTANCE.
EMERGENCY WASH FACILITIES: WHERE THERE IS ANY POSSIBILITY THAT AN EMPLOYEE'S EYES AND/OR SKIN MAY BE EXPOSED TO THIS SUBSTANCE, THE EMPLOYER SHOULD PROVIDE AN EYE WASH FOUNTAIN AND QUICK DRENCH SHOWER WITHIN THE IMMEDIATE WORK AREA FOR EMERGENCY USE.

AUTHORIZED BY- OCCUPATIONAL HEALTH SERVICES, INC.
CREATION DATE: 10/04/89 ***REVISION DATE:*** 05/01/90

MATERIAL SAFETY DATA SHEET

OCCUPATIONAL HEALTH SERVICES, INC.
AGRICULTURE AND PESTICIDE DIVISION
450 SEVENTH AVENUE, SUITE 2407
NEW YORK, NEW YORK 10123
1-800-445-MSDS OR (212) 967-1100

EMERGENCY CONTACT:
JOHN S. BRANSFORD, JR. (615) 292-1180

SUBSTANCE IDENTIFICATION

CAS-NUMBER 13194-48-4
SUBSTANCE: <u>ETHOPROP</u>
TRADE NAMES/SYNONYMS: PHOSPHORODITHIOIC ACID, O-ETHYL S,S DIPROPYL ESTER; ETHYL PROPYL PHOSPHORODITHIOATE; O-ETHYL S,S-DIPROPYL PHOSPHORODITHIOATE; S,S-DIPROPYL ETHYL PHOSPHORODITHIOLATE; ETHOPROPHOS; MOCAP; PROFOS; PROPHOS; ROVOKIL; VC 9-104; ENT 27318; PST15080
CHEMICAL FAMILY: ORGANOPHOSPHATE
MOLECULAR FORMULA: C8-H19-O2-P-S2
MOLECULAR WEIGHT: 242.36
CERCLA RATINGS (SCALE 0-3): HEALTH=3 FIRE=U REACTIVITY=0 PERSISTENCE=0
NFPA RATINGS (SCALE 0-4): HEALTH=4 FIRE=U REACTIVITY=0

COMPONENTS AND CONTAMINANTS

COMPONENT: ETHOPROP ***PERCENT:*** 100
CAS# 13194-48-4
EXPOSURE LIMITS: ETHOPROP: NO OCCUPATIONAL EXPOSURE LIMITS ESTABLISHED BY OSHA, ACGIH, OR NIOSH.
1000 POUNDS SARA SECTION 302 THRESHOLD PLANNING QUANTITY 1 POUND SARA SECTION 304 REPORTABLE QUANTITY

PHYSICAL DATA

DESCRIPTION: CLEAR PALE YELLOW LIQUID
BOILING POINT: 187-196 F (86-91 C) @ 0.2 MMHG ***MELTING POINT:*** 68 F (20 C)
SPECIFIC GRAVITY: 1.094 ***VAPOR PRESSURE:*** 0.00035 MMHG @ 26 C
SOLUBILITY IN WATER: 750 PPM
SOLVENT SOLUBILITY: SOLUBLE IN ACETONE, CYCLOHEXANE, 1,2-DICHLOROETHANE, DIETHYL ETHER, ETHANOL, ETHYL ACETATE, PETROLEUM SPIRIT, XYLENE, AND MOST ORGANIC SOLVENTS

FIRE AND EXPLOSION DATA

FIRE AND EXPLOSION HAZARD: UNKNOWN FIRE AND EXPLOSION HAZARD.

FIREFIGHTING MEDIA: DRY CHEMICAL, CARBON DIOXIDE, HALON, WATER SPRAY OR STANDARD FOAM (1987 EMERGENCY RESPONSE GUIDEBOOK, DOT P 5800.4). FOR LARGER FIRES, USE WATER SPRAY, FOG OR STANDARD FOAM (1987 EMERGENCY RESPONSE GUIDEBOOK, DOT P 5800.4).

FIREFIGHTING: MOVE CONTAINERS FROM FIRE AREA IF POSSIBLE. FIGHT FIRE FROM MAXIMUM DISTANCE. STAY AWAY FROM STORAGE TANK ENDS. DIKE FIRE CONTROL WATER FOR LATER DISPOSAL. DO NOT SCATTER MATERIAL (1987 EMERGENCY RESPONSE GUIDEBOOK, DOT P 5800.4, GUIDE PAGE 55). EXTINGUISH ONLY IF FLOW CAN BE STOPPED; USE FLOODING AMOUNTS OF WATER AS FOG, SOLID STREAMS MAY BE INEFFECTIVE. COOL CONTAINERS WITH FLOODING AMOUNTS OF WATER FROM AS FAR A DISTANCE AS POSSIBLE. USE WATER SPRAY TO ABSORB TOXIC VAPORS. AVOID BREATHING TOXIC VAPORS; KEEP UPWIND. CONSIDER EVACUATION OF DOWNWIND AREA IF MATERIAL IS LEAKING.

TRANSPORTATION DATA

DEPARTMENT OF TRANSPORTATION HAZARD CLASSIFICATION 49 CFR 172.101: POISON B

DEPARTMENT OF TRANSPORTATION LABELING REQUIREMENTS 49 CFR 172.101 AND SUBPART E: POISON

TOXICITY

ETHOPROP: TOXICITY DATA: 2400 UG/KG SKIN-RABBIT LD50; 60 MG/KG SKIN-RAT LD50; 34 MG/KG ORAL-RAT LD50; 55 MG/KG ORAL-RABBIT LD50. CARCINOGEN STATUS: NONE. ACUTE TOXICITY LEVEL: HIGHLY TOXIC BY INGESTION AND DERMAL ABSORPTION. TARGET EFFECTS: CHOLINESTERASE INHIBITOR. POISONING MAY AFFECT THE NERVOUS SYSTEM.* AT INCREASED RISK FROM EXPOSURE: PERSONS WITH RESPIRATORY AILMENTS, RECENT EXPOSURE TO CHOLINESTERASE INHIBITORS OR IMPAIRED CHOLINESTERASE PRODUCTION, OR LIVER MALFUNCTION.* ADDITIONAL DATA: MAY CROSS THE PLACENTA. HIGH ENVIRONMENTAL TEMPERATURES OR EXPOSURE OF THE CHEMICAL TO VISIBLE OR ULTRAVIOLET LIGHT MAY ENHANCE THE TOXICITY. INTERACTIONS WITH MEDICATIONS MAY OCCUR.*

* MAY BE BASED ON GENERAL INFORMATION ON ORGANOPHOSPHATES.

HEALTH EFFECTS AND FIRST AID

INHALATION: ETHOPROP: NO CHOLINESTERASE INHIBITION WAS OBSERVED IN HUMANS WHO WERE EXPOSED TO CONCENTRATIONS OF 0.003 MG/M3 (DURATION UNSTATED). SEE INFORMATION ON ORGANOPHOSPHATES.

ORGANOPHOSPHATES: CHOLINESTERASE INHIBITOR. **ACUTE EXPOSURE-** WHEN INHALED, THE FIRST EFFECTS OF CHOLINESTERASE INHIBITORS ARE USUALLY RESPIRATORY AND MAY INCLUDE NASAL HYPEREMIA AND WATERY DISCHARGE, COUGH, CHEST DISCOMFORT, DYSPNEA, AND WHEEZING DUE TO INCREASED BRONCHIAL SECRETIONS AND BRONCHOCONSTRICTION. IF SUFFICIENT AMOUNTS ARE ABSORBED, OTHER SYSTEMIC EFFECTS MAY BEGIN WITHIN A FEW MINUTES OR BE DELAYED FOR UP TO 12 HOURS. SYMPTOMS MAY INCLUDE PALLOR, NAUSEA, VOMITING, DIARRHEA, ABDOMINAL CRAMPS, HEADACHE, DIZZINESS, OCULAR PAIN, BLURRED VISION, MIOSIS OR IN SOME CASES, ESPECIALLY INITIALLY, MYDRIASIS, LACRIMATION, SALIVATION, SWEATING, AND CONFUSION. OTHER REPORTED CENTRAL NERVOUS SYSTEM OR NEUROMUSCULAR EFFECTS MAY INCLUDE ATAXIA, SLURRED SPEECH, AREFLEXIA, WEAKNESS, FATIGUE, FASCICULATIONS, TWITCHING, TREMORS POSSIBLY OF THE TONGUE AND EYELIDS, AND EVENTUALLY PARALYSIS OF THE EXTREMITIES AND POSSIBLY OF THE RESPIRATORY MUSCLES. IN SEVERE CASES THERE MAY ALSO BE INVOLUNTARY DEFECATION AND URINATION, CYANOSIS, PSYCHOSIS, HYPERGLYCEMIA, ACUTE PANCREATITIS, CARDIAC IRREGULARITIES, PULMONARY EDEMA, UNCONSCIOUSNESS, CONVULSIONS, AND COMA. DEATH IS PRIMARILY DUE TO RESPIRATORY FAILURE, ALTHOUGH CARDIOVASCULAR EFFECTS INCLUDING CARDIAC ARREST MAY ALSO BE IMPLICATED. LONG TERM SEQUELAE ARE RARE BUT MAY INCLUDE NEUROPSYCHIATRIC DISORDERS AND MYOPATHY WITH MUSCLE TENDERNESS. SOME ORGANOPHOSPHATES MAY CAUSE A DELAYED NEUROPATHY BEGINNING 1-4 WEEKS AFTER AN ACUTE EXPOSURE WHICH MAY OR MAY NOT HAVE CAUSED ACUTE CHOLINERGIC EFFECTS. NUMBNESS, TINGLING, WEAKNESS AND CRAMPING BEGINNING SYMMETRICALLY IN THE LOWER LIMBS MAY PROGRESS TO ATAXIA AND PARALYSIS. IN SEVERE CASES, UPPER LIMB INVOLVEMENT IS POSSIBLE AND FLACCID PARALYSIS MAY PROGRESS TO SPASTIC PARALYSIS WITH EXAGGERATED REFLEXES. IMPROVEMENT MAY OCCUR OVER MONTHS TO YEARS, BUT SOME RESIDUAL IMPAIRMENT USUALLY REMAINS. **CHRONIC EXPOSURE-** REPEATED OR PROLONGED EXPOSURE MAY RESULT IN THE EFFECTS OF ACUTE EXPOSURE INCLUDING THE DELAYED NEUROPATHY. OTHER EFFECTS REPORTED IN WORKERS REPEATEDLY EXPOSED INCLUDE IMPAIRED MEMORY AND CONCENTRATION, ACUTE PSYCHOSIS, SEVERE DEPRESSIONS, IRRITABILTY, CONFUSION, APATHY, EMOTIONAL LABILITY, SOCIAL WITHDRAWAL, CONFUSION, HEADACHE, SPEECH DIFFICULTIES, DELAYED REACTION TIMES, SPATIAL DISORIENTATION, NIGHTMARES, SLEEPWALKING, AND DROWSINESS OR INSOMNIA. AN INFLUENZA-LIKE CONDITION WITH HEADACHE, NAUSEA, WEAKNESS, ANOREXIA AND MALAISE HAS ALSO BEEN REPORTED.

FIRST AID- REMOVE FROM EXPOSURE AREA TO FRESH AIR IMMEDIATELY. IF BREATHING HAS STOPPED, GIVE ARTIFICIAL RESPIRATION. MAINTAIN AIRWAY AND BLOOD PRESSURE AND ADMINISTER OXYGEN IF AVAILABLE. KEEP AFFECTED PERSON WARM AND AT REST. TREAT SYMPTOMATICALLY AND SUPPORTIVELY. ADMINISTRATION OF OXYGEN SHOULD BE PERFORMED BY QUALIFIED PERSONNEL. GET MEDICAL ATTENTION IMMEDIATELY.

SKIN CONTACT: ETHOPROP: HIGHLY TOXIC. SEE INFORMATION ON ORGANOPHOSPHATES.

ORGANOPHOSPHATES: CHOLINESTERASE INHIBITOR. **ACUTE EXPOSURE-** LOCALIZED SWEATING AND FASCICULATIONS MAY OCCUR AT THE SITE OF CONTACT. IF SUFFICIENT AMOUNTS ARE ABSORBED, OTHER EFFECTS OF CHOLINESTERASE INHIBITION AS DESCRIBED IN ACUTE INHALATION MAY OCCUR. SYMPTOMS MAY BE DELAYED 2-3 HOURS, BUT USUALLY NO MORE THAN 12 HOURS. THE RATE OF ABSORPTION IS INCREASED BY THE PRESENCE OF DERMATITIS OR HIGH AMBIENT TEMPERATURES. DELAYED NEUROPATHY IS ALSO POSSIBLE. **CHRONIC EXPOSURE-** REPEATED OR PROLONGED EXPOSURE MAY CAUSE EFFECTS AS DESCRIBED IN ACUTE EXPOSURE. SOME ORGANOPHOSPHATES MAY CAUSE SENSITIZATION.

FIRST AID- REMOVE CONTAMINATED CLOTHING IMMEDIATELY. WASH CONTAMINATED AREAS WITH SOAP AND WATER FOLLOWED BY ALCOHOL (ARENA, POISONING, 4TH ED.). EMERGENCY PERSONNEL SHOULD WEAR GLOVES AND AVOID CONTAMINATION. TREAT RESPIRATORY DIFFICULTY WITH ARTIFICIAL RESPIRATION. GET MEDICAL ATTENTION IMMEDIATELY.

EYE CONTACT: ETHOPROP: SEE INFORMATION ON ORGANOPHOSPHATES.

ORGANOPHOSPHATES: CHOLINESTERASE INHIBITOR. **ACUTE EXPOSURE-** DIRECT CONTACT MAY CAUSE PAIN, HYPEREMIA, LACRIMATION, TWITCHING OF THE EYELIDS, MIOSIS, AND CILIARY MUSCLE SPASM WITH LOSS OF ACCOMODATION, BLURRED OR DIMMED VISION AND BROWACHE. SOMETIMES MYDRIASIS MAY OCCUR INSTEAD OF MIOSIS. WITH SUFFICIENT EXPOSURE, OTHER SYMPTOMS OF CHOLINESTERASE INHIBITION AS DESCRIBED IN ACUTE INHALATION MAY OCCUR. **CHRONIC EXPOSURE-** REPEATED OR PROLONGED EXPOSURE MAY CAUSE EFFECTS AS DESCRIBED IN ACUTE EXPOSURE. SOME COMPOUNDS HAVE CAUSED TOXIC EFFECTS ON THE CRYSTALLINE LENS, CONJUNCTIVAL THICKENING AND OBSTRUCTION OF THE NASOLACRIMAL CANALS WHEN USED AS MIOTIC EYEDROPS.

FIRST AID- IRRIGATE EYES WITH WATER OR SALINE SOLUTION. IF SYMPTOMS OF POISONING OCCUR, TREAT RESPIRATORY DIFFICULTY WITH ARTIFICIAL RESPIRATION AND OXYGEN. OBSERVE PATIENT FOR AT LEAST 24-36 HOURS (GOSSELIN, CLINICAL TOXICOLOGY OF COMMERCIAL PRODUCTS, 5TH ED.). GET MEDICAL ATTENTION IMMEDIATELY. OXYGEN SHOULD BE ADMINISTERED BY QUALIFIED MEDICAL PERSONNEL.

INGESTION: ETHOPROP: HIGHLY TOXIC. NO DEMYELINATION WAS OBSERVED IN HENS FROM A SINGLE DOSE OF 6.14 MG/KG. SEE INFORMATION ON ORGANOPHOSPHATES.

ORGANOPHOSPHATES: CHOLINESTERASE INHIBITOR. **ACUTE EXPOSURE-** WHEN INGESTED, THE FIRST EFFECTS MAY BE NAUSEA, VOMITING, ANOREXIA, ABDOMINAL CRAMPS AND DIARRHEA. GASTROINTESTINAL ABSORPTION MAY CAUSE SYMPTOMS OF CHOLINESTERASE INHIBITION AS DESCRIBED IN ACUTE INHALATION. SYMPTOMS MAY BEGIN WITHIN MINUTES OR BE DELAYED FOR HOURS. DELAYED EFFECTS INCLUDING NEUROPATHY MAY ALSO OCCUR. **CHRONIC EXPOSURE-** REPEATED INGESTION MAY CAUSE EFFECTS AS DESCRIBED IN ACUTE EXPOSURE. **FIRST AID-** IF PERSON IS ALERT AND RESPIRATION IS NOT DEPRESSED, GIVE SYRUP OF IPECAC FOLLOWED BY WATER (IF VOMITING OCCURS, KEEP HEAD BELOW HIPS TO PREVENT ASPIRATION). IF CONSCIOUSNESS LEVEL DECLINES OR VOMITING HAS NOT OCCURRED IN 15 MINUTES EMPTY STOMACH BY GASTRIC LAVAGE WITH THE AID OF CUFFED ENDOTRACHEAL TUBE USING ISOTONIC SALINE OR 5% SODIUM BICARBONATE FOLLOW WITH ACTIVATED CHARCOAL. ESTABLISH AND MAINTAIN AIRWAY. TREAT RESPIRATORY DIFFICULTY WITH ARTIFICIAL RESPIRATION AND OXYGEN. DO NOT GIVE MORPHINE, AMINOPHYLLINE, PHENOTHIAZINES, RESERPINE, FUROSEMIDE, OR ETHACRYNIC ACID (MORGAN, RECOGNITION AND MANAGEMENT OF PESTICIDE POISONINGS, 3RD ED.). TREAT SYMPTOMATICALLY AND SUPPORTIVELY. ADMINISTRATION OF OXYGEN AND LAVAGE MUST BE PERFORMED BY QUALIFIED MEDICAL PERSONNEL. GET MEDICAL ATTENTION IMMEDIATELY.

ANTIDOTE: THE FOLLOWING ANTIDOTE(S) HAVE BEEN RECOMMENDED. HOWEVER, THE DECISION AS TO WHETHER THE SEVERITY OF POISONING REQUIRES ADMINISTRATION OF ANY ANTIDOTE AND ACTUAL DOSE REQUIRED SHOULD BE MADE BY QUALIFIED MEDICAL PERSONNEL.

FOR CHOLINESTERASE INHIBITORS: ESTABLISH CLEAR AIRWAY AND TISSUE OXYGENATION BY ASPIRATION OF SECRETIONS, AND IF NECESSARY, BY ASSISTED PULMONARY VENTILATION WITH OXYGEN. IMPROVE TISSUE OXYGENATION AS MUCH AS POSSIBLE BEFORE ADMINISTERING ATROPINE TO MINIMIZE THE RISK OF

VENTRICULAR FIBRILLATION. ADMINISTER ATROPINE SULFATE INTRAVENOUSLY, OR INTRAMUSCULARLY IF IV INJECTION IS NOT POSSIBLE. IN MODERATELY SEVERE POISONING ADMINISTER ATROPINE SULFATE, 0.4-2.0 MG REPEATED EVERY 15 MINUTES UNTIL ATROPINIZATION IS ACHIEVED (TACHYCARDIA, FLUSHING, DRY MOUTH, MYDRIASIS). MAINTAIN ATROPINIZATION BY REPEATED DOSES FOR 2-12 HOURS, OR LONGER, DEPENDING ON THE SEVERITY OF POISONING. THE APPEARANCE OF RALES IN THE LUNG BASES, MIOSIS, SALIVATION, NAUSEA, BRADYCARDIA, ARE ALL INDICATIONS OF INADEQUATE ATROPINIZATION.
SEVERELY POISONED INDIVIDUALS MAY EXHIBIT REMARKABLE TOLERANCE TO ATROPINE; TWO OR MORE TIMES THE DOSAGES SUGGESTED ABOVE MAY BE NEEDED. PERSONS NOT POISONED OR ONLY SLIGHTLY POISONED, HOWEVER, MAY DEVELOP SIGNS OF ATROPINE TOXICITY FROM SUCH LARGE DOSAGES: FEVER, MUSCLE FIBRILLATIONS, AND DELIRIUM ARE THE MAIN SIGNS OF ATROPINE TOXICITY. IF THESE SIGNS APPEAR WHILE THE PATIENT IS FULLY ATROPINIZED, ATROPINE ADMINISTRATION SHOULD BE DISCONTINUED, AT LEAST TEMPORARILY. OBSERVE TREATED PATIENTS CLOSELY AT LEAST 24 HOURS TO INSURE THAT SYMPTOMS (POSSIBLY PULMONARY EDEMA) DO NOT RECUR AS ATROPINIZATION WEARS OFF. IN VERY SEVERE POISONINGS, METABOLIC DISPOSITION OF TOXICANT MAY REQUIRE SEVERAL HOURS OR DAYS DURING WHICH ATROPINIZATION MUST BE MAINTAINED. MARKEDLY LOWER LEVELS OF URINARY METABOLITES INDICATE THAT ATROPINE DOSAGE CAN BE TAPERED OFF. AS DOSAGE IS REDUCED, CHECK THE LUNG BASES FREQUENTLY FOR RALES. IF RALES ARE HEARD OR OTHER SYMPTOMS RETURN, RE-ESTABLISH ATROPINIZATION PROMPTLY (MORGAN, RECOGNITION AND MANAGEMENT OF PESTICIDE POISONINGS, 3RD ED.). ADMINISTRATION OF ANTIDOTE MUST BE PERFORMED BY QUALIFIED MEDICAL PERSONNEL.
IN CASES OF SEVERE POISONING BY ORGANOPHOSPHATE PESTICIDES IN WHICH RESPIRATORY DEPRESSION, MUSCLE WEAKNESS AND TWITCHINGS ARE SEVERE, GIVE PRALIDOXIME (PROTOPAM-AYERST, 2-PAM), 1.0 GRAM INTRAVENOUSLY AT NO MORE THAN 0.5 GRAM PER MINUTE. DOSAGE OF PRALIDOXIME MAY BE REPEATED IN 1-2 HOURS, THEN AT 10-12 HOUR INTERVALS IF NEEDED. IN VERY SEVERE POISONINGS, DOSAGE RATES MAY BE DOUBLED. TREATMENT WITH PRALIDOXIME WILL BE MOST EFFECTIVE IF GIVEN WITHIN THIRTY-SIX HOURS AFTER POISONING (MORGAN, RECOGNITION AND MANAGEMENT OF PESTICIDE POISONINGS, 3RD ED.). ANTIDOTE SHOULD BE ADMINISTERED BY QUALIFIED MEDICAL PERSONNEL.

REACTIVITY

REACTIVITY: STABLE UNDER NORMAL TEMPERATURES AND PRESSURES.
INCOMPATIBILITIES: ETHOPROP: ALKALINE CONDITIONS: MAY CAUSE HYDROLYSIS.
DECOMPOSITION: THERMAL DECOMPOSITION PRODUCTS MAY INCLUDE TOXIC AND HAZARDOUS FUMES OF SULFUR, NITROGEN AND PHOSPHORUS.
POLYMERIZATION: HAZARDOUS POLYMERIZATION HAS NOT BEEN REPORTED TO OCCUR UNDER NORMAL TEMPERATURES AND PRESSURES.

STORAGE AND DISPOSAL

OBSERVE ALL FEDERAL, STATE AND LOCAL REGULATIONS WHEN STORING OR DISPOSING OF THIS SUBSTANCE. FOR ASSISTANCE, CONTACT THE DISTRICT DIRECTOR OF THE ENVIRONMENTAL PROTECTION AGENCY.

STORAGE

STORE IN ACCORDANCE WITH 40 CFR 165 RECOMMENDED PROCEDURES FOR THE DISPOSAL AND STORAGE OF PESTICIDES AND PESTICIDE CONTAINERS.
STORE AWAY FROM INCOMPATIBLE SUBSTANCES.
THRESHOLD PLANNING QUANTITY (TPQ): THE SUPERFUND AMENDMENTS AND REAUTHORIZATION ACT (SARA) SECTION 302 REQUIRES THAT EACH FACILITY WHERE ANY EXTREMELY HAZARDOUS SUBSTANCE IS PRESENT IN A QUANTITY EQUAL TO OR GREATER THAN THE TPQ ESTABLISHED FOR THAT SUBSTANCE NOTIFY THE STATE EMERGENCY RESPONSE COMMISSION FOR THE STATE IN WHICH IT IS LOCATED. SECTION 303 OF SARA REQUIRES THESE FACILITIES TO PARTICIPATE IN LOCAL EMERGENCY RESPONSE PLANNING (40 CFR 355.30).

DISPOSAL

DISPOSAL MUST BE IN ACCORDANCE WITH 40 CFR 165 RECOMMENDED PROCEDURES FOR THE DISPOSAL AND STORAGE OF PESTICIDES AND PESTICIDE CONTAINERS.

CONDITIONS TO AVOID

NONE REPORTED.

SPILL AND LEAK PROCEDURES

OCCUPATIONAL SPILL: DO NOT TOUCH SPILLED MATERIAL. STOP LEAK IF YOU CAN DO IT WITHOUT RISK. USE WATER SPRAY TO REDUCE VAPORS. FOR SMALL SPILLS, TAKE UP WITH SAND OR OTHER ABSORBENT MATERIAL AND PLACE INTO CONTAINERS FOR LATER DISPOSAL. FOR SMALL DRY SPILLS, WITH A CLEAN SHOVEL PLACE MATERIAL INTO CLEAN, DRY CONTAINERS AND COVER. MOVE CONTAINERS FROM SPILL AREA. FOR LARGER SPILLS, DIKE FAR AHEAD OF SPILL FOR LATER DISPOSAL. KEEP UNNECESSARY PEOPLE AWAY. ISOLATE HAZARD AREA AND DENY ENTRY. VENTILATE CLOSED SPACES BEFORE ENTERING.
REPORTABLE QUANTITY (RQ): 1 POUND THE SUPERFUND AMENDMENTS AND REAUTHORIZATION ACT (SARA) SECTION 304 REQUIRES THAT A RELEASE EQUAL TO OR GREATER THAN THE REPORTABLE QUANTITY FOR THIS SUBSTANCE BE IMMEDIATELY REPORTED TO THE LOCAL EMERGENCY PLANNING COMMITTEE AND THE STATE EMERGENCY RESPONSE COMMISSION (40 CFR 355.40). IF THE RELEASE OF THIS SUBSTANCE IS REPORTABLE UNDER CERCLA SECTION 103, THE NATIONAL RESPONSE CENTER MUST BE NOTIFIED IMMEDIATELY AT (800) 424-8802 OR (202) 426-2675 IN THE METROPOLITAN WASHINGTON, D.C. AREA (40 CFR 302.6).

PROTECTIVE EQUIPMENT

VENTILATION: PROCESS ENCLOSURE RECOMMENDED.
RESPIRATOR: THE FOLLOWING RESPIRATORS ARE RECOMMENDED BASED ON INFORMATION FOUND IN THE PHYSICAL DATA, TOXICITY AND HEALTH EFFECTS SECTIONS. THEY ARE RANKED IN ORDER FROM MINIMUM TO MAXIMUM RESPIRATORY PROTECTION. THE SPECIFIC RESPIRATOR SELECTED MUST BE BASED ON CONTAMINATION LEVELS FOUND IN THE WORK PLACE, MUST NOT EXCEED THE WORKING LIMITS OF THE RESPIRATOR AND BE JOINTLY APPROVED BY THE NATIONAL INSTITUTE FOR OCCUPATIONAL SAFETY AND HEALTH AND THE MINE SAFETY AND HEALTH ADMINISTRATION (NIOSH-MSHA).
TYPE 'C' SUPPLIED-AIR RESPIRATOR WITH A FULL FACEPIECE OPERATED IN PRESSURE-DEMAND OR OTHER POSITIVE PRESSURE MODE OR WITH A FULL FACEPIECE, HELMET OR HOOD OPERATED IN CONTINOUS-FLOW MODE.
SELF-CONTAINED BREATHING APPARATUS WITH A FULL FACEPIECE OPERATED IN PRESSURE-DEMAND OR OTHER POSITIVE PRESSURE MODE.
FOR FIREFIGHTING AND OTHER IMMEDIATELY DANGEROUS TO LIFE OR HEALTH CONDITIONS:
SELF-CONTAINED BREATHING APPARATUS WITH FULL FACEPIECE OPERATED IN PRESSURE-DEMAND OR OTHER POSITIVE PRESSURE MODE.
SUPPLIED-AIR RESPIRATOR WITH FULL FACEPIECE AND OPERATED IN PRESSURE-DEMAND OR OTHER POSITIVE PRESSURE MODE IN COMBINATION WITH AN AUXILIARY SELF-CONTAINED BREATHING APPARATUS OPERATED IN PRESSURE-DEMAND OR OTHER POSITIVE PRESSURE MODE.
CLOTHING: EMPLOYEE MUST WEAR APPROPRIATE PROTECTIVE (IMPERVIOUS) CLOTHING AND EQUIPMENT TO PREVENT ANY POSSIBILITY OF SKIN CONTACT WITH THIS SUBSTANCE.
GLOVES: EMPLOYEE MUST WEAR APPROPRIATE PROTECTIVE GLOVES TO PREVENT CONTACT WITH THIS SUBSTANCE.
EYE PROTECTION: EMPLOYEE MUST WEAR SPLASH-PROOF OR DUST-RESISTANT SAFETY GOGGLES AND A FACESHIELD TO PREVENT CONTACT WITH THIS SUBSTANCE.
EMERGENCY WASH FACILITIES: WHERE THERE IS ANY POSSIBILITY THAT AN EMPLOYEE'S EYES AND/OR SKIN MAY BE EXPOSED TO THIS SUBSTANCE, THE EMPLOYER SHOULD PROVIDE AN EYE WASH FOUNTAIN AND QUICK DRENCH SHOWER WITHIN THE IMMEDIATE WORK AREA FOR EMERGENCY USE.

AUTHORIZED BY- OCCUPATIONAL HEALTH SERVICES, INC.
CREATION DATE: 10/04/89 ***REVISION DATE:*** 04/27/90

MATERIAL SAFETY DATA SHEET

OCCUPATIONAL HEALTH SERVICES, INC.
AGRICULTURE AND PESTICIDE DIVISION
450 SEVENTH AVENUE, SUITE 2407
NEW YORK, NEW YORK 10123
1-800-445-MSDS OR (212) 967-1100

EMERGENCY CONTACT:
JOHN S. BRANSFORD, JR. (615) 292-1180

SUBSTANCE IDENTIFICATION

CAS-NUMBER 10265-92-6
SUBSTANCE: METHAMIDOPHOS
TRADE NAMES/SYNONYMS: PHOSPHORAMIDOTHIOIC ACID, O,S-DIMETHYL ESTER; METHYL PHOSPHORAMIDOTHIOATE; O,S-DIMETHYL PHOSPHORAMIDOTHIOATE; O,S-DIMETHYL THIOPHOSPHORAMIDE; METAMIDOPHOS; MONITOR; TAMARON; ENT 27,396; PST15160
CHEMICAL FAMILY: ORGANOPHOSPHATE
MOLECULAR FORMULA: C2-H8-N-O2-P-S
MOLECULAR WEIGHT: 141.14
CERCLA RATINGS (SCALE 0-3): HEALTH=3 FIRE=0 REACTIVITY=0 PERSISTENCE=0
NFPA RATINGS (SCALE 0-4): HEALTH=4 FIRE=0 REACTIVITY=0

COMPONENTS AND CONTAMINANTS

COMPONENT: METHAMIDOPHOS ***PERCENT:*** 100
CAS# 10265-92-6

EXPOSURE LIMITS: METHAMIDOPHOS: NO OCCUPATIONAL EXPOSURE LIMITS ESTABLISHED BY OSHA, ACGIH, OR NIOSH.
100/10,000 POUNDS SARA SECTION 302 THRESHOLD PLANNING QUANTITY 1 POUND SARA SECTION 304 REPORTABLE QUANTITY

PHYSICAL DATA

DESCRIPTION: COLORLESS, CRYSTALLINE SOLID ***MELTING POINT:*** 113 F (45 C)
SPECIFIC GRAVITY: 1.31 ***VAPOR PRESSURE:*** 0.0003 MMHG @ 30 C
SOLUBILITY IN WATER: SOLUBLE
SOLVENT SOLUBILITY: SOLULBLE IN ALCOHOLS, KETONES, BENZENE, XYLENE, CHLOROFORM, DICHLOROMETHANE, ALIPHATIC CHLORINATED AND ALIPHATIC HYDROCARBONS; SLIGHTLY SOLUBLE IN ETHER; PRACTICALLY INSOLUBLE IN PETROLEUM ETHER

FIRE AND EXPLOSION DATA

FIRE AND EXPLOSION HAZARD: NEGLIGIBLE FIRE HAZARD WHEN EXPOSED TO HEAT OR FLAME.

FIREFIGHTING MEDIA: DRY CHEMICAL, CARBON DIOXIDE, HALON, WATER SPRAY OR STANDARD FOAM (1987 EMERGENCY RESPONSE GUIDEBOOK, DOT P 5800.4).
FOR LARGER FIRES, USE WATER SPRAY, FOG OR STANDARD FOAM (1987 EMERGENCY RESPONSE GUIDEBOOK, DOT P 5800.4).

FIREFIGHTING: MOVE CONTAINERS FROM FIRE AREA IF POSSIBLE. FIGHT FIRE FROM MAXIMUM DISTANCE. STAY AWAY FROM STORAGE TANK ENDS. DIKE FIRE CONTROL WATER FOR LATER DISPOSAL. DO NOT SCATTER MATERIAL (1987 EMERGENCY RESPONSE GUIDEBOOK, DOT P 5800.4, GUIDE PAGE 55).
EXTINGUISH ONLY IF FLOW CAN BE STOPPED; USE FLOODING AMOUNTS OF WATER AS FOG, SOLID STREAMS MAY BE INEFFECTIVE. COOL CONTAINERS WITH FLOODING AMOUNTS OF WATER FROM AS FAR A DISTANCE AS POSSIBLE. USE WATER SPRAY TO ABSORB TOXIC VAPORS. AVOID BREATHING TOXIC VAPORS; KEEP UPWIND. CONSIDER EVACUATION OF DOWNWIND AREA IF MATERIAL IS LEAKING.

TRANSPORTATION DATA

DEPARTMENT OF TRANSPORTATION HAZARD CLASSIFICATION 49 CFR 172.101: POISON B
DEPARTMENT OF TRANSPORTATION LABELING REQUIREMENTS 49 CFR 172.101 AND SUBPART E: POISON
DEPARTMENT OF TRANSPORTATION PACKAGING REQUIREMENTS: 49 CFR 173.365 EXCEPTIONS: 49 CFR 173.364

TOXICITY

METHAMIDOPHOS: TOXICITY DATA: 9 MG/KG INHALATION-RAT LD50; 19 MG/KG INHALATION-MOUSE LD50; 118 MG/KG SKIN-RABBIT LD50; 50 MG/KG SKIN-RAT LD50; 360 MG/KG ORAL-WOMAN TDLO; 257 MG/KG ORAL-MAN TDLO; 7500 UG/KG ORAL-RAT LD50; 14 MG/KG ORAL-MOUSE LD50; 10 MG/KG ORAL-RABBIT LD50; 30 MG/KG ORAL-GUINEA PIG LD50; 10 MG/KG SUBCUTANEOUS-GUINEA PIG LDLO; 5300 UG/KG INTRAPERITONEAL-MOUSE LD50; 15 MG/KG INTRAPERITONEAL-RAT LD50; 10 MG/KG INTRAVENOUS-RAT LD50; 27 MG/KG UNREPORTED-MOUSE LD50; MUTAGENIC DATA (RTECS); REPRODUCTIVE EFFECTS DATA (RTECS). CARCINOGEN STATUS: NONE. ACUTE TOXICITY LEVEL: HIGHLY TOXIC BY INHALATION, DERMAL ABSORPTION, AND INGESTION. TARGET EFFECTS: CHOLINESTERASE INHIBITOR. POISONING MAY AFFECT THE NERVOUS SYSTEM.* AT INCREASED RISK FROM EXPOSURE: PERSONS WITH RESPIRATORY AILMENTS, RECENT EXPOSURE TO CHOLINESTERASE INHIBITORS OR IMPAIRED CHOLINESTERASE PRODUCTION, OR LIVER MALFUNCTION.* ADDITIONAL DATA: MAY CROSS THE PLACENTA. HIGH ENVIRONMENTAL TEMPERATURES OR EXPOSURE OF THE CHEMICAL TO VISIBLE OR ULTRAVIOLET LIGHT MAY ENHANCE THE TOXICITY. INTERACTIONS WITH MEDICATIONS MAY OCCUR.*
* MAY BE BASED ON GENERAL INFORMATION ON ORGANOPHOSPHATES.

HEALTH EFFECTS AND FIRST AID

INHALATION: METHAMIDOPHOS: HIGHLY TOXIC. SEE INFORMATION ON ORGANOPHOSPHATES.
ORGANOPHOSPHATES: CHOLINESTERASE INHIBITOR. **ACUTE EXPOSURE-** WHEN INHALED, THE FIRST EFFECTS OF CHOLINESTERASE INHIBITORS ARE USUALLY RESPIRATORY AND MAY INCLUDE NASAL HYPEREMIA AND WATERY DISCHARGE, COUGH, CHEST DISCOMFORT, DYSPNEA, AND WHEEZING DUE TO INCREASED BRONCHIAL SECRETIONS AND BRONCHOCONSTRICTION. IF SUFFICIENT AMOUNTS ARE ABSORBED, OTHER SYSTEMIC EFFECTS MAY BEGIN WITHIN A FEW MINUTES OR BE DELAYED FOR UP TO 12 HOURS. SYMPTOMS MAY INCLUDE PALLOR, NAUSEA, VOMITING, DIARRHEA, ABDOMINAL CRAMPS, HEADACHE, DIZZINESS, OCULAR PAIN, BLURRED VISION, MIOSIS OR IN SOME CASES, ESPECIALLY INITIALLY, MYDRIASIS, LACRIMATION, SALIVATION, SWEATING, AND CONFUSION. OTHER REPORTED CENTRAL NERVOUS SYSTEM OR NEUROMUSCULAR EFFECTS MAY INCLUDE ATAXIA, SLURRED SPEECH, AREFLEXIA, WEAKNESS, FATIGUE, FASCICULATIONS, TWITCHING, TREMORS POSSIBLY OF THE TONGUE AND EYELIDS, AND EVENTUALLY PARALYSIS OF THE EXTREMITIES AND POSSIBLY OF THE RESPIRATORY MUSCLES. IN SEVERE CASES THERE MAY ALSO BE INVOLUNTARY DEFECATION AND URINATION, CYANOSIS, PSYCHOSIS, HYPERGLYCEMIA, ACUTE PANCREATITIS, CARDIAC IRREGULARITIES, PULMONARY EDEMA, UNCONSCIOUSNESS, CONVULSIONS, AND COMA. DEATH IS PRIMARILY DUE TO RESPIRATORY FAILURE, ALTHOUGH CARDIOVASCULAR EFFECTS INCLUDING CARDIAC ARREST MAY ALSO BE IMPLICATED. LONG TERM SEQUELAE ARE RARE BUT MAY INCLUDE NEUROPSYCHIATRIC DISORDERS AND MYOPATHY WITH MUSCLE TENDERNESS. SOME ORGANOPHOSPHATES MAY CAUSE A DELAYED NEUROPATHY BEGINNING 1-4 WEEKS AFTER AN ACUTE EXPOSURE WHICH MAY OR MAY NOT HAVE CAUSED ACUTE CHOLINERGIC EFFECTS. NUMBNESS, TINGLING, WEAKNESS AND CRAMPING BEGINNING SYMMETRICALLY IN THE LOWER LIMBS MAY PROGRESS TO ATAXIA AND PARALYSIS. IN SEVERE CASES, UPPER LIMB INVOLVEMENT IS POSSIBLE AND FLACCID PARALYSIS MAY PROGRESS TO SPASTIC PARALYSIS WITH EXAGGERATED REFLEXES. IMPROVEMENT MAY OCCUR OVER MONTHS TO YEARS, BUT SOME RESIDUAL IMPAIRMENT USUALLY REMAINS.
CHRONIC EXPOSURE- REPEATED OR PROLONGED EXPOSURE MAY RESULT IN THE EFFECTS OF ACUTE EXPOSURE INCLUDING THE DELAYED NEUROPATHY. OTHER EFFECTS REPORTED IN WORKERS REPEATEDLY EXPOSED INCLUDE IMPAIRED MEMORY AND CONCENTRATION, ACUTE PSYCHOSIS, SEVERE DEPRESSIONS, IRRITABILTY, CONFUSION, APATHY, EMOTIONAL LABILITY, SOCIAL WITHDRAWAL, CONFUSION, HEADACHE, SPEECH DIFFICULTIES, DELAYED REACTION TIMES, SPATIAL DISORIENTATION, NIGHTMARES, SLEEPWALKING, AND DROWSINESS OR INSOMNIA. AN INFLUENZA-LIKE CONDITION WITH HEADACHE, NAUSEA, WEAKNESS, ANOREXIA AND MALAISE HAS ALSO BEEN REPORTED.

FIRST AID- REMOVE FROM EXPOSURE AREA TO FRESH AIR IMMEDIATELY. IF BREATHING HAS STOPPED, GIVE ARTIFICIAL RESPIRATION. MAINTAIN AIRWAY AND BLOOD PRESSURE AND ADMINISTER OXYGEN IF AVAILABLE. KEEP AFFECTED PERSON WARM AND AT REST. TREAT SYMPTOMATICALLY AND SUPPORTIVELY. ADMINISTRATION OF OXYGEN SHOULD BE PERFORMED BY QUALIFIED PERSONNEL. GET MEDICAL ATTENTION IMMEDIATELY.

SKIN CONTACT: METHAMIDOPHOS: HIGHLY TOXIC. SEE INFORMATION ON ORGANOPHOSPHATES.
ORGANOPHOSPHATES: CHOLINESTERASE INHIBITOR. **ACUTE EXPOSURE-** LOCALIZED SWEATING AND FASCICULATIONS MAY OCCUR AT THE SITE OF CONTACT. IF SUFFICIENT AMOUNTS ARE ABSORBED, OTHER EFFECTS OF CHOLINESTERASE INHIBITION AS DESCRIBED IN ACUTE INHALATION MAY OCCUR. SYMPTOMS MAY BE DELAYED 2-3 HOURS, BUT USUALLY NO MORE THAN 12 HOURS. THE RATE OF ABSORPTION IS INCREASED BY THE PRESENCE OF DERMATITIS OR HIGH AMBIENT TEMPERATURES. DELAYED NEUROPATHY IS ALSO POSSIBLE. **CHRONIC EXPOSURE-** REPEATED OR PROLONGED EXPOSURE MAY CAUSE EFFECTS AS DESCRIBED IN ACUTE EXPOSURE. SOME ORGANOPHOSPHATES MAY CAUSE SENSITIZATION.

FIRST AID- REMOVE CONTAMINATED CLOTHING IMMEDIATELY. WASH CONTAMINATED AREAS WITH SOAP AND WATER FOLLOWED BY ALCOHOL (ARENA, POISONING, 4TH ED.). EMERGENCY PERSONNEL SHOULD WEAR GLOVES AND AVOID CONTAMINATION. TREAT RESPIRATORY DIFFICULTY WITH ARTIFICIAL RESPIRATION. GET MEDICAL ATTENTION IMMEDIATELY.

EYE CONTACT: METHAMIDOPHOS: SEE INFORMATION ON ORGANOPHOSPHATES.
ORGANOPHOSPHATES: CHOLINESTERASE INHIBITOR. **ACUTE EXPOSURE-** DIRECT CONTACT MAY CAUSE PAIN, HYPEREMIA, LACRIMATION, TWITCHING OF THE EYELIDS, MIOSIS, AND CILIARY MUSCLE SPASM WITH LOSS OF ACCOMODATION, BLURRED OR DIMMED VISION AND BROWACHE. SOMETIMES MYDRIASIS MAY OCCUR INSTEAD OF MIOSIS. WITH SUFFICIENT EXPOSURE, OTHER SYMPTOMS OF CHOLINESTERASE INHIBITION AS DESCRIBED IN ACUTE INHALATION MAY OCCUR.
CHRONIC EXPOSURE- REPEATED OR PROLONGED EXPOSURE MAY CAUSE EFFECTS AS DESCRIBED IN ACUTE EXPOSURE. SOME COMPOUNDS HAVE CAUSED TOXIC EFFECTS ON THE CRYSTALLINE LENS, CONJUNCTIVAL THICKENING AND OBSTRUCTION OF THE NASOLACRIMAL CANALS WHEN USED AS MIOTIC EYEDROPS.

FIRST AID- IRRIGATE EYES WITH WATER OR SALINE SOLUTION. IF SYMPTOMS OF POISONING OCCUR, TREAT RESPIRATORY DIFFICULTY WITH ARTIFICIAL RESPIRATION AND OXYGEN. OBSERVE PATIENT FOR AT LEAST 24-36 HOURS (GOSSELIN, CLINICAL TOXICOLOGY OF COMMERCIAL PRODUCTS, 5TH ED.). GET MEDICAL ATTENTION IMMEDIATELY. OXYGEN SHOULD BE ADMINISTERED BY QUALIFIED MEDICAL PERSONNEL.

INGESTION: METHAMIDOPHOS: HIGHLY TOXIC. SEE INFORMATION ON ORGANOPHOSPHATES.
ORGANOPHOSPHATES: CHOLINESTERASE INHIBITOR. **ACUTE EXPOSURE-** WHEN INGESTED, THE FIRST EFFECTS MAY BE NAUSEA, VOMITING, ANOREXIA,

ABDOMINAL CRAMPS AND DIARRHEA. GASTROINTESTINAL ABSORPTION MAY CAUSE SYMPTOMS OF CHOLINESTERASE INHIBITION AS DESCRIBED IN ACUTE INHALATION. SYMPTOMS MAY BEGIN WITHIN MINUTES OR BE DELAYED FOR HOURS. DELAYED EFFECTS INCLUDING NEUROPATHY MAY ALSO OCCUR. **CHRONIC EXPOSURE-** REPEATED INGESTION MAY CAUSE EFFECTS AS DESCRIBED IN ACUTE EXPOSURE.

FIRST AID- IF PERSON IS ALERT AND RESPIRATION IS NOT DEPRESSED, GIVE SYRUP OF IPECAC FOLLOWED BY WATER (IF VOMITING OCCURS, KEEP HEAD BELOW HIPS TO PREVENT ASPIRATION). IF CONSCIOUSNESS LEVEL DECLINES OR VOMITING HAS NOT OCCURRED IN 15 MINUTES EMPTY STOMACH BY GASTRIC LAVAGE WITH THE AID OF CUFFED ENDOTRACHEAL TUBE USING ISOTONIC SALINE OR 5% SODIUM BICARBONATE FOLLOW WITH ACTIVATED CHARCOAL. ESTABLISH AND MAINTAIN AIRWAY. TREAT RESPIRATORY DIFFICULTY WITH ARTIFICIAL RESPIRATION AND OXYGEN. DO NOT GIVE MORPHINE, AMINOPHYLLINE, PHENOTHIAZINES, RESERPINE, FUROSEMIDE, OR ETHACRYNIC ACID (MORGAN, RECOGNITION AND MANAGEMENT OF PESTICIDE POISONINGS, 3RD ED.). TREAT SYMPTOMATICALLY AND SUPPORTIVELY. ADMINISTRATION OF OXYGEN AND LAVAGE MUST BE PERFORMED BY QUALIFIED MEDICAL PERSONNEL. GET MEDICAL ATTENTION IMMEDIATELY.

ANTIDOTE: THE FOLLOWING ANTIDOTE(S) HAVE BEEN RECOMMENDED. HOWEVER, THE DECISION AS TO WHETHER THE SEVERITY OF POISONING REQUIRES ADMINISTRATION OF ANY ANTIDOTE AND ACTUAL DOSE REQUIRED SHOULD BE MADE BY QUALIFIED MEDICAL PERSONNEL.

FOR CHOLINESTERASE INHIBITORS: ESTABLISH CLEAR AIRWAY AND TISSUE OXYGENATION BY ASPIRATION OF SECRETIONS, AND IF NECESSARY, BY ASSISTED PULMONARY VENTILATION WITH OXYGEN. IMPROVE TISSUE OXYGENATION AS MUCH AS POSSIBLE BEFORE ADMINISTERING ATROPINE TO MINIMIZE THE RISK OF VENTRICULAR FIBRILLATION. ADMINISTER ATROPINE SULFATE INTRAVENOUSLY, OR INTRAMUSCULARLY IF IV INJECTION IS NOT POSSIBLE. IN MODERATELY SEVERE POISONING ADMINISTER ATROPINE SULFATE, 0.4-2.0 MG REPEATED EVERY 15 MINUTES UNTIL ATROPINIZATION IS ACHIEVED (TACHYCARDIA, FLUSHING, DRY MOUTH, MYDRIASIS). MAINTAIN ATROPINIZATION BY REPEATED DOSES FOR 2-12 HOURS, OR LONGER, DEPENDING ON THE SEVERITY OF POISONING. THE APPEARANCE OF RALES IN THE LUNG BASES, MIOSIS, SALIVATION, NAUSEA, BRADYCARDIA, ARE ALL INDICATIONS OF INADEQUATE ATROPINIZATION. SEVERELY POISONED INDIVIDUALS MAY EXHIBIT REMARKABLE TOLERANCE TO ATROPINE; TWO OR MORE TIMES THE DOSAGES SUGGESTED ABOVE MAY BE NEEDED. PERSONS NOT POISONED OR ONLY SLIGHTLY POISONED, HOWEVER, MAY DEVELOP SIGNS OF ATROPINE TOXICITY FROM SUCH LARGE DOSAGES: FEVER, MUSCLE FIBRILLATIONS, AND DELIRIUM ARE THE MAIN SIGNS OF ATROPINE TOXICITY. IF THESE SIGNS APPEAR WHILE THE PATIENT IS FULLY ATROPINIZED, ATROPINE ADMINISTRATION SHOULD BE DISCONTINUED, AT LEAST TEMPORARILY. OBSERVE TREATED PATIENTS CLOSELY AT LEAST 24 HOURS TO INSURE THAT SYMPTOMS (POSSIBLY PULMONARY EDEMA) DO NOT RECUR AS ATROPINIZATION WEARS OFF. IN VERY SEVERE POISONINGS, METABOLIC DISPOSITION OF TOXICANT MAY REQUIRE SEVERAL HOURS OR DAYS DURING WHICH ATROPINIZATION MUST BE MAINTAINED. MARKEDLY LOWER LEVELS OF URINARY METABOLITES INDICATE THAT ATROPINE DOSAGE CAN BE TAPERED OFF. AS DOSAGE IS REDUCED, CHECK THE LUNG BASES FREQUENTLY FOR RALES. IF RALES ARE HEARD OR OTHER SYMPTOMS RETURN, RE-ESTABLISH ATROPINIZATION PROMPTLY (MORGAN, RECOGNITION AND MANAGEMENT OF PESTICIDE POISONINGS, 3RD ED.). ADMINISTRATION OF ANTIDOTE MUST BE PERFORMED BY QUALIFIED MEDICAL PERSONNEL.

IN CASES OF SEVERE POISONING BY ORGANOPHOSPHATE PESTICIDES IN WHICH RESPIRATORY DEPRESSION, MUSCLE WEAKNESS AND TWITCHINGS ARE SEVERE, GIVE PRALIDOXIME (PROTOPAM-AYERST, 2-PAM), 1.0 GRAM INTRAVENOUSLY AT NO MORE THAN 0.5 GRAM PER MINUTE. DOSAGE OF PRALIDOXIME MAY BE REPEATED IN 1-2 HOURS, THEN AT 10-12 HOUR INTERVALS IF NEEDED. IN VERY SEVERE POISONINGS, DOSAGE RATES MAY BE DOUBLED. TREATMENT WITH PRALIDOXIME WILL BE MOST EFFECTIVE IF GIVEN WITHIN THIRTY-SIX HOURS AFTER POISONING (MORGAN, RECOGNITION AND MANAGEMENT OF PESTICIDE POISONINGS, 3RD ED.). ANTIDOTE SHOULD BE ADMINISTERED BY QUALIFIED MEDICAL PERSONNEL.

REACTIVITY

REACTIVITY: STABLE UNDER NORMAL TEMPERATURES AND PRESSURES.

INCOMPATIBILITIES: METHAMIDOPHOS: ACIDS: MAY HYDROLYZE. ALKALIS: MAY HYDROLYZE. COPPER-CONTAINING ALLOYS: MAY BE CORROSIVE. MILD STEEL: MAY BE CORROSIVE.

DECOMPOSITION: THERMAL DECOMPOSITION MAY RELEASE TOXIC AND/OR HAZARDOUS GASES.

POLYMERIZATION: HAZARDOUS POLYMERIZATION HAS NOT BEEN REPORTED TO OCCUR UNDER NORMAL TEMPERATURES AND PRESSURES.

STORAGE AND DISPOSAL

OBSERVE ALL FEDERAL, STATE AND LOCAL REGULATIONS WHEN STORING OR DISPOSING OF THIS SUBSTANCE. FOR ASSISTANCE, CONTACT THE DISTRICT DIRECTOR OF THE ENVIRONMENTAL PROTECTION AGENCY.

****STORAGE****

STORE IN ACCORDANCE WITH 40 CFR 165 RECOMMENDED PROCEDURES FOR THE DISPOSAL AND STORAGE OF PESTICIDES AND PESTICIDE CONTAINERS.

STORE AWAY FROM INCOMPATIBLE SUBSTANCES.

THRESHOLD PLANNING QUANTITY (TPQ): THE SUPERFUND AMENDMENTS AND REAUTHORIZATION ACT (SARA) SECTION 302 REQUIRES THAT EACH FACILITY WHERE ANY EXTREMELY HAZARDOUS SUBSTANCE IS PRESENT IN A QUANTITY EQUAL TO OR GREATER THAN THE TPQ ESTABLISHED FOR THAT SUBSTANCE NOTIFY THE STATE EMERGENCY RESPONSE COMMISSION FOR THE STATE IN WHICH IT IS LOCATED. SECTION 303 OF SARA REQUIRES THESE FACILITIES TO PARTICIPATE IN LOCAL EMERGENCY RESPONSE PLANNING (40 CFR 355.30).

****DISPOSAL****

DISPOSAL MUST BE IN ACCORDANCE WITH 40 CFR 165 RECOMMENDED PROCEDURES FOR THE DISPOSAL AND STORAGE OF PESTICIDES AND PESTICIDE CONTAINERS.

CONDITIONS TO AVOID

NONE REPORTED.

SPILL AND LEAK PROCEDURES

OCCUPATIONAL SPILL: DO NOT TOUCH SPILLED MATERIAL. STOP LEAK IF YOU CAN DO IT WITHOUT RISK. USE WATER SPRAY TO REDUCE VAPORS. FOR SMALL SPILLS, TAKE UP WITH SAND OR OTHER ABSORBENT MATERIAL AND PLACE INTO CONTAINERS FOR LATER DISPOSAL. FOR SMALL DRY SPILLS, WITH A CLEAN SHOVEL PLACE MATERIAL INTO CLEAN, DRY CONTAINERS AND COVER. MOVE CONTAINERS FROM SPILL AREA. FOR LARGER SPILLS, DIKE FAR AHEAD OF SPILL FOR LATER DISPOSAL. KEEP UNNECESSARY PEOPLE AWAY. ISOLATE HAZARD AREA AND DENY ENTRY. VENTILATE CLOSED SPACES BEFORE ENTERING.

REPORTABLE QUANTITY (RQ): 1 POUND THE SUPERFUND AMENDMENTS AND REAUTHORIZATION ACT (SARA) SECTION 304 REQUIRES THAT A RELEASE EQUAL TO OR GREATER THAN THE REPORTABLE QUANTITY FOR THIS SUBSTANCE BE IMMEDIATELY REPORTED TO THE LOCAL EMERGENCY PLANNING COMMITTEE AND THE STATE EMERGENCY RESPONSE COMMISSION (40 CFR 355.40). IF THE RELEASE OF THIS SUBSTANCE IS REPORTABLE UNDER CERCLA SECTION 103, THE NATIONAL RESPONSE CENTER MUST BE NOTIFIED IMMEDIATELY AT (800) 424-8802 OR (202) 426-2675 IN THE METROPOLITAN WASHINGTON, D.C. AREA (40 CFR 302.6).

PROTECTIVE EQUIPMENT

VENTILATION: PROCESS ENCLOSURE RECOMMENDED.

RESPIRATOR: THE FOLLOWING RESPIRATORS ARE RECOMMENDED BASED ON INFORMATION FOUND IN THE PHYSICAL DATA, TOXICITY AND HEALTH EFFECTS SECTIONS. THEY ARE RANKED IN ORDER FROM MINIMUM TO MAXIMUM RESPIRATORY PROTECTION. THE SPECIFIC RESPIRATOR SELECTED MUST BE BASED ON CONTAMINATION LEVELS FOUND IN THE WORK PLACE, MUST NOT EXCEED THE WORKING LIMITS OF THE RESPIRATOR AND BE JOINTLY APPROVED BY THE NATIONAL INSTITUTE FOR OCCUPATIONAL SAFETY AND HEALTH AND THE MINE SAFETY AND HEALTH ADMINISTRATION (NIOSH-MSHA).

TYPE 'C' SUPPLIED-AIR RESPIRATOR WITH A FULL FACEPIECE OPERATED IN PRESSURE-DEMAND OR OTHER POSITIVE PRESSURE MODE OR WITH A FULL FACEPIECE, HELMET OR HOOD OPERATED IN CONTINOUS-FLOW MODE.

SELF-CONTAINED BREATHING APPARATUS WITH A FULL FACEPIECE OPERATED IN PRESSURE-DEMAND OR OTHER POSITIVE PRESSURE MODE.

FOR FIREFIGHTING AND OTHER IMMEDIATELY DANGEROUS TO LIFE OR HEALTH CONDITIONS:

SELF-CONTAINED BREATHING APPARATUS WITH FULL FACEPIECE OPERATED IN PRESSURE-DEMAND OR OTHER POSITIVE PRESSURE MODE.

SUPPLIED-AIR RESPIRATOR WITH FULL FACEPIECE AND OPERATED IN PRESSURE-DEMAND OR OTHER POSITIVE PRESSURE MODE IN COMBINATION WITH AN AUXILIARY SELF-CONTAINED BREATHING APPARATUS OPERATED IN PRESSURE-DEMAND OR OTHER POSITIVE PRESSURE MODE.

CLOTHING: EMPLOYEE MUST WEAR APPROPRIATE PROTECTIVE (IMPERVIOUS) CLOTHING AND EQUIPMENT TO PREVENT ANY POSSIBILITY OF SKIN CONTACT WITH THIS SUBSTANCE.

GLOVES: EMPLOYEE MUST WEAR APPROPRIATE PROTECTIVE GLOVES TO PREVENT CONTACT WITH THIS SUBSTANCE.

EYE PROTECTION: EMPLOYEE MUST WEAR SPLASH-PROOF OR DUST-RESISTANT SAFETY GOGGLES AND A FACESHIELD TO PREVENT CONTACT WITH THIS SUBSTANCE.

EMERGENCY WASH FACILITIES: WHERE THERE IS ANY POSSIBILITY THAT AN EMPLOYEE'S EYES AND/OR SKIN MAY BE EXPOSED TO THIS SUBSTANCE, THE EMPLOYER SHOULD PROVIDE AN EYE WASH FOUNTAIN AND QUICK DRENCH SHOWER WITHIN THE IMMEDIATE WORK AREA FOR EMERGENCY USE.

AUTHORIZED BY- OCCUPATIONAL HEALTH SERVICES, INC.
CREATION DATE: 10/04/89 ***REVISION DATE:*** 05/03/90

MATERIAL SAFETY DATA SHEET

OCCUPATIONAL HEALTH SERVICES, INC.
AGRICULTURE AND PESTICIDE DIVISION
450 SEVENTH AVENUE, SUITE 2407
NEW YORK, NEW YORK 10123
1-800-445-MSDS OR (212) 967-1100

EMERGENCY CONTACT:
JOHN S. BRANSFORD, JR. (615) 292-1180

SUBSTANCE IDENTIFICATION

CAS-NUMBER 6923-22-4

SUBSTANCE: MONOCROTOPHOS

TRADE NAMES/SYNONYMS: PHOSPHORIC ACID, DIMETHYL 1-METHYL-3-(METHYLAMINO)-3-OXO-1-PROPENYL ESTER, (E); PHOSPHORIC ACID, DIMETHYL ESTER, ESTER WITH 3-HYDROXY-N-METHYL CROTONAMIDE, (E)-; DIMETHYL (E)-1-METHYL-2-(METHYLCARBAMOYL)VINYL PHOSPHATE; 3-DIMETHOXYPHOSPHINOYLOXY-N-METHYLISOCROTONAMIDE; 3-(DIMETHOXYPHOSPHINYLOXY)-N-METHYLISOCROTONAMIDE; (E)-DIMETHYL 1-METHYL-3-(METHYLAMINO)-3-OXO-1-PROPENYL PHOSPHATE; DIMETHYL PHOSPHATE ESTER WITH (E)-3-HYDROXY-N-METHYLCROTONAMIDE; 3-(DIMETHOXYPHOSPHINYLOXY)-N-METHYL-CIS-CROTONAMIDE; DIMETHYL 2-METHYLCARBAMOYL-1-METHYLVINYL PHOSPHATE; DIMETHYL PHOSPHATE OF 3-HYDROXY-N-METHYL-CIS-CROTONAMIDE; AZODRIN; SD 9129; NUVACRON; ENT 27129; PST15165

CHEMICAL FAMILY: ORGANOPHOSPHATE

MOLECULAR FORMULA: C7-H14-N-O5-P

MOLECULAR WEIGHT: 223.19

CERCLA RATINGS (SCALE 0-3): HEALTH=3 FIRE=1 REACTIVITY=0 PERSISTENCE=0

NFPA RATINGS (SCALE 0-4): HEALTH=4 FIRE=1 REACTIVITY=0

COMPONENTS AND CONTAMINANTS

COMPONENT: MONOCROTOPHOS ***PERCENT:*** 100
CAS# 6923-22-4

EXPOSURE LIMITS: MONOCROTOPHOS: 0.25 MG/M3 OSHA TWA 0.25 MG/M3 ACGIH TWA (SKIN)
10/10,000 POUNDS SARA SECTION 302 THRESHOLD PLANNING QUANTITY 1 POUND SARA SECTION 304 REPORTABLE QUANTITY

PHYSICAL DATA

DESCRIPTION: COLORLESS, HYGROSCOPIC CRYSTALS

BOILING POINT: 257 F (125 C) @ 0.0005 MMHG ***MELTING POINT:*** 129 F (54 C)

VAPOR PRESSURE: 0.00007 MMHG @ 20 C ***SOLUBILITY IN WATER:*** SOLUBLE

SOLVENT SOLUBILITY: SOLUBLE IN ACETONE, ALCOHOL, DICHLOROMETHANE, METHANOL, OCTAN-1-OL, TOLUENE, POLAR ORGANIC SOLVENTS; SLIGHTLY SOLUBLE IN ALKANES, MINERAL OILS, KEROSENE AND DIESEL FUEL

FIRE AND EXPLOSION DATA

FIRE AND EXPLOSION HAZARD: SLIGHT FIRE HAZARD WHEN EXPOSED TO HEAT OR FLAME.

FLASH POINT: >200 F (>93 C) (CC) ***FLAMMABILITY CLASS(OSHA):*** IIIB

FIREFIGHTING MEDIA: DRY CHEMICAL, CARBON DIOXIDE, HALON, WATER SPRAY OR STANDARD FOAM (1987 EMERGENCY RESPONSE GUIDEBOOK, DOT P 5800.4). FOR LARGER FIRES, USE WATER SPRAY, FOG OR STANDARD FOAM (1987 EMERGENCY RESPONSE GUIDEBOOK, DOT P 5800.4).

FIREFIGHTING: MOVE CONTAINERS FROM FIRE AREA IF POSSIBLE. FIGHT FIRE FROM MAXIMUM DISTANCE. STAY AWAY FROM STORAGE TANK ENDS. DIKE FIRE CONTROL WATER FOR LATER DISPOSAL. DO NOT SCATTER MATERIAL (1987 EMERGENCY RESPONSE GUIDEBOOK, DOT P 5800.4, GUIDE PAGE 55). EXTINGUISH ONLY IF FLOW CAN BE STOPPED; USE FLOODING AMOUNTS OF WATER AS FOG, SOLID STREAMS MAY BE INEFFECTIVE. COOL CONTAINERS WITH FLOODING AMOUNTS OF WATER FROM AS FAR A DISTANCE AS POSSIBLE. USE WATER SPRAY TO ABSORB TOXIC VAPORS. AVOID BREATHING TOXIC VAPORS; KEEP UPWIND. CONSIDER EVACUATION OF DOWNWIND AREA IF MATERIAL IS LEAKING.

TRANSPORTATION DATA

DEPARTMENT OF TRANSPORTATION HAZARD CLASSIFICATION 49 CFR 172.101: POISON B

DEPARTMENT OF TRANSPORTATION LABELING REQUIREMENTS 49 CFR 172.101 AND SUBPART E: POISON

DEPARTMENT OF TRANSPORTATION PACKAGING REQUIREMENTS: 49 CFR 173.365 EXCEPTIONS: 49 CFR 173.364

TOXICITY

MONOCROTOPHOS: TOXICITY DATA: 63 MG/M3/4 HOURS INHALATION-RAT LC50; 354 MG/KG SKIN-RABBIT LD50; 112 SKIN-RAT LD50; 8 MG/KG ORAL-RAT LD50; 15 MG/KG ORAL-MOUSE LD50; 8710 UG/KG SUBCUTANEOUS-MOUSE LD50; 6964 UG/KG SUBCUTANEOUS-RAT LD50; 9200 UG/KG INTRAVENOUS-RAT LD50; 9200 UG/KG INTRAVENOUS-MOUSE LD50; 20 MG/KG INTRAPERITONEAL-RAT LDLO; 3800 UG/KG INTRAPERITONEAL-MOUSE LD50; MUTAGENIC DATA (RTECS). CARCINOGEN STATUS: NONE. ACUTE TOXICITY LEVEL: HIGHLY TOXIC BY INHALATION AND INGESTION AND TOXIC BY DERMAL ABSORPTION. TARGET EFFECTS: CHOLINESTERASE INHIBITOR. POISONING MAY AFFECT THE NERVOUS SYSTEM.* AT INCREASED RISK FROM EXPOSURE: PERSONS WITH RESPIRATORY AILMENTS, RECENT EXPOSURE TO CHOLINESTERASE INHIBITORS OR IMPAIRED CHOLINESTERASE PRODUCTION, OR LIVER MALFUNCTION.* ADDITIONAL DATA: MAY CROSS THE PLACENTA. HIGH ENVIRONMENTAL TEMPERATURES OR EXPOSURE OF THE CHEMICAL TO VISIBLE OR ULTRAVIOLET LIGHT MAY ENHANCE THE TOXICITY. INTERACTIONS WITH MEDICATIONS MAY OCCUR.*
* MAY BE BASED ON GENERAL INFORMATION ON ORGANOPHOSPHATES.

HEALTH EFFECTS AND FIRST AID

INHALATION: MONOCROTOPHOS: HIGHLY TOXIC. SEE INFORMATION ON ORGANOPHOSPHATES.
ORGANOPHOSPHATES: CHOLINESTERASE INHIBITOR. **ACUTE EXPOSURE-** WHEN INHALED, THE FIRST EFFECTS OF CHOLINESTERASE INHIBITORS ARE USUALLY RESPIRATORY AND MAY INCLUDE NASAL HYPEREMIA AND WATERY DISCHARGE, COUGH, CHEST DISCOMFORT, DYSPNEA, AND WHEEZING DUE TO INCREASED BRONCHIAL SECRETIONS AND BRONCHOCONSTRICTION. IF SUFFICIENT AMOUNTS ARE ABSORBED, OTHER SYSTEMIC EFFECTS MAY BEGIN WITHIN A FEW MINUTES OR BE DELAYED FOR UP TO 12 HOURS. SYMPTOMS MAY INCLUDE PALLOR, NAUSEA, VOMITING, DIARRHEA, ABDOMINAL CRAMPS, HEADACHE, DIZZINESS, OCULAR PAIN, BLURRED VISION, MIOSIS OR IN SOME CASES, ESPECIALLY INITIALLY, MYDRIASIS, LACRIMATION, SALIVATION, SWEATING, AND CONFUSION. OTHER REPORTED CENTRAL NERVOUS SYSTEM OR NEUROMUSCULAR EFFECTS MAY INCLUDE ATAXIA, SLURRED SPEECH, AREFLEXIA, WEAKNESS, FATIGUE, FASCICULATIONS, TWITCHING, TREMORS POSSIBLY OF THE TONGUE AND EYELIDS, AND EVENTUALLY PARALYSIS OF THE EXTREMITIES AND POSSIBLY OF THE RESPIRATORY MUSCLES. IN SEVERE CASES THERE MAY ALSO BE INVOLUNTARY DEFECATION AND URINATION, CYANOSIS, PSYCHOSIS, HYPERGLYCEMIA, ACUTE PANCREATITIS, CARDIAC IRREGULARITIES, PULMONARY EDEMA, UNCONSCIOUSNESS, CONVULSIONS, AND COMA. DEATH IS PRIMARILY DUE TO RESPIRATORY FAILURE, ALTHOUGH CARDIOVASCULAR EFFECTS INCLUDING CARDIAC ARREST MAY ALSO BE IMPLICATED. LONG TERM SEQUELAE ARE RARE BUT MAY INCLUDE NEUROPSYCHIATRIC DISORDERS AND MYOPATHY WITH MUSCLE TENDERNESS. SOME ORGANOPHOSPHATES MAY CAUSE A DELAYED NEUROPATHY BEGINNING 1-4 WEEKS AFTER AN ACUTE EXPOSURE WHICH MAY OR MAY NOT HAVE CAUSED ACUTE CHOLINERGIC EFFECTS. NUMBNESS, TINGLING, WEAKNESS AND CRAMPING BEGINNING SYMMETRICALLY IN THE LOWER LIMBS MAY PROGRESS TO ATAXIA AND PARALYSIS. IN SEVERE CASES, UPPER LIMB INVOLVEMENT IS POSSIBLE AND FLACCID PARALYSIS MAY PROGRESS TO SPASTIC PARALYSIS WITH EXAGGERATED REFLEXES. IMPROVEMENT MAY OCCUR OVER MONTHS TO YEARS, BUT SOME RESIDUAL IMPAIRMENT USUALLY REMAINS. **CHRONIC EXPOSURE-** REPEATED OR PROLONGED EXPOSURE MAY RESULT IN THE EFFECTS OF ACUTE EXPOSURE INCLUDING THE DELAYED NEUROPATHY. OTHER EFFECTS REPORTED IN WORKERS REPEATEDLY EXPOSED INCLUDE IMPAIRED MEMORY AND CONCENTRATION, ACUTE PSYCHOSIS, SEVERE DEPRESSIONS, IRRITABILTY, CONFUSION, APATHY, EMOTIONAL LABILITY, SOCIAL WITHDRAWAL, CONFUSION, HEADACHE, SPEECH DIFFICULTIES, DELAYED REACTION TIMES, SPATIAL DISORIENTATION, NIGHTMARES, SLEEPWALKING, AND DROWSINESS OR INSOMNIA. AN INFLUENZA-LIKE CONDITION WITH HEADACHE, NAUSEA, WEAKNESS, ANOREXIA AND MALAISE HAS ALSO BEEN REPORTED. **FIRST AID-** REMOVE FROM EXPOSURE AREA TO FRESH AIR IMMEDIATELY. IF BREATHING HAS STOPPED, GIVE ARTIFICIAL RESPIRATION. MAINTAIN AIRWAY AND BLOOD PRESSURE AND ADMINISTER OXYGEN IF AVAILABLE. KEEP AFFECTED PERSON WARM AND AT REST. TREAT SYMPTOMATICALLY AND SUPPORTIVELY. ADMINISTRATION OF OXYGEN SHOULD BE PERFORMED BY QUALIFIED PERSONNEL. GET MEDICAL ATTENTION IMMEDIATELY.

SKIN CONTACT: MONOCROTOPHOS: TOXIC. SEE INFORMATION ON ORGANOPHOSPHATES.
ORGANOPHOSPHATES: CHOLINESTERASE INHIBITOR. **ACUTE EXPOSURE-** LOCALIZED SWEATING AND FASCICULATIONS MAY OCCUR AT THE SITE OF CONTACT. IF SUFFICIENT AMOUNTS ARE ABSORBED, OTHER EFFECTS OF CHOLINESTERASE INHIBITION AS DESCRIBED IN ACUTE INHALATION MAY OCCUR. SYMPTOMS MAY BE DELAYED 2-3 HOURS, BUT USUALLY NO MORE THAN 12 HOURS. THE RATE OF ABSORPTION IS INCREASED BY THE PRESENCE OF DERMATITIS OR HIGH AMBIENT TEMPERATURES. DELAYED NEUROPATHY IS ALSO

POSSIBLE. **CHRONIC EXPOSURE-** REPEATED OR PROLONGED EXPOSURE MAY CAUSE EFFECTS AS DESCRIBED IN ACUTE EXPOSURE. SOME ORGANOPHOSPHATES MAY CAUSE SENSITIZATION.

FIRST AID- REMOVE CONTAMINATED CLOTHING IMMEDIATELY. WASH CONTAMINATED AREAS WITH SOAP AND WATER FOLLOWED BY ALCOHOL (ARENA, POISONING, 4TH ED.). EMERGENCY PERSONNEL SHOULD WEAR GLOVES AND AVOID CONTAMINATION. TREAT RESPIRATORY DIFFICULTY WITH ARTIFICIAL RESPIRATION. GET MEDICAL ATTENTION IMMEDIATELY.

EYE CONTACT: MONOCROTOPHOS: SEE INFORMATION ON ORGANOPHOSPHATES. ORGANOPHOSPHATES: CHOLINESTERASE INHIBITOR. **ACUTE EXPOSURE-** DIRECT CONTACT MAY CAUSE PAIN, HYPEREMIA, LACRIMATION, TWITCHING OF THE EYELIDS, MIOSIS, AND CILIARY MUSCLE SPASM WITH LOSS OF ACCOMODATION, BLURRED OR DIMMED VISION AND BROWACHE. SOMETIMES MYDRIASIS MAY OCCUR INSTEAD OF MIOSIS. WITH SUFFICIENT EXPOSURE, OTHER SYMPTOMS OF CHOLINESTERASE INHIBITION AS DESCRIBED IN ACUTE INHALATION MAY OCCUR. **CHRONIC EXPOSURE-** REPEATED OR PROLONGED EXPOSURE MAY CAUSE EFFECTS AS DESCRIBED IN ACUTE EXPOSURE. SOME COMPOUNDS HAVE CAUSED TOXIC EFFECTS ON THE CRYSTALLINE LENS, CONJUNCTIVAL THICKENING AND OBSTRUCTION OF THE NASOLACRIMAL CANALS WHEN USED AS MIOTIC EYEDROPS.

FIRST AID- IRRIGATE EYES WITH WATER OR SALINE SOLUTION. IF SYMPTOMS OF POISONING OCCUR, TREAT RESPIRATORY DIFFICULTY WITH ARTIFICIAL RESPIRATION AND OXYGEN. OBSERVE PATIENT FOR AT LEAST 24-36 HOURS (GOSSELIN, CLINICAL TOXICOLOGY OF COMMERCIAL PRODUCTS, 5TH ED.). GET MEDICAL ATTENTION IMMEDIATELY. OXYGEN SHOULD BE ADMINISTERED BY QUALIFIED MEDICAL PERSONNEL.

INGESTION: MONOCROTOPHOS: HIGHLY TOXIC. SEE INFORMATION ON ORGANOPHOSPHATES. ORGANOPHOSPHATES: CHOLINESTERASE INHIBITOR. **ACUTE EXPOSURE-** WHEN INGESTED, THE FIRST EFFECTS MAY BE NAUSEA, VOMITING, ANOREXIA, ABDOMINAL CRAMPS AND DIARRHEA. GASTROINTESTINAL ABSORPTION MAY CAUSE SYMPTOMS OF CHOLINESTERASE INHIBITION AS DESCRIBED IN ACUTE INHALATION. SYMPTOMS MAY BEGIN WITHIN MINUTES OR BE DELAYED FOR HOURS. DELAYED EFFECTS INCLUDING NEUROPATHY MAY ALSO OCCUR. **CHRONIC EXPOSURE-** REPEATED INGESTION MAY CAUSE EFFECTS AS DESCRIBED IN ACUTE EXPOSURE.

FIRST AID- IF PERSON IS ALERT AND RESPIRATION IS NOT DEPRESSED, GIVE SYRUP OF IPECAC FOLLOWED BY WATER (IF VOMITING OCCURS, KEEP HEAD BELOW HIPS TO PREVENT ASPIRATION). IF CONSCIOUSNESS LEVEL DECLINES OR VOMITING HAS NOT OCCURRED IN 15 MINUTES EMPTY STOMACH BY GASTRIC LAVAGE WITH THE AID OF CUFFED ENDOTRACHEAL TUBE USING ISOTONIC SALINE OR 5% SODIUM BICARBONATE FOLLOW WITH ACTIVATED CHARCOAL. ESTABLISH AND MAINTAIN AIRWAY. TREAT RESPIRATORY DIFFICULTY WITH ARTIFICIAL RESPIRATION AND OXYGEN. DO NOT GIVE MORPHINE, AMINOPHYLLINE, PHENOTHIAZINES, RESERPINE, FUROSEMIDE, OR ETHACRYNIC ACID (MORGAN, RECOGNITION AND MANAGEMENT OF PESTICIDE POISONINGS, 3RD ED.). TREAT SYMPTOMATICALLY AND SUPPORTIVELY. ADMINISTRATION OF OXYGEN AND LAVAGE MUST BE PERFORMED BY QUALIFIED MEDICAL PERSONNEL. GET MEDICAL ATTENTION IMMEDIATELY.

ANTIDOTE: THE FOLLOWING ANTIDOTE(S) HAVE BEEN RECOMMENDED. HOWEVER, THE DECISION AS TO WHETHER THE SEVERITY OF POISONING REQUIRES ADMINISTRATION OF ANY ANTIDOTE AND ACTUAL DOSE REQUIRED SHOULD BE MADE BY QUALIFIED MEDICAL PERSONNEL.

FOR CHOLINESTERASE INHIBITORS: ESTABLISH CLEAR AIRWAY AND TISSUE OXYGENATION BY ASPIRATION OF SECRETIONS, AND IF NECESSARY, BY ASSISTED PULMONARY VENTILATION WITH OXYGEN. IMPROVE TISSUE OXYGENATION AS MUCH AS POSSIBLE BEFORE ADMINISTERING ATROPINE TO MINIMIZE THE RISK OF VENTRICULAR FIBRILLATION. ADMINISTER ATROPINE SULFATE INTRAVENOUSLY, OR INTRAMUSCULARLY IF IV INJECTION IS NOT POSSIBLE. IN MODERATELY SEVERE POISONING ADMINISTER ATROPINE SULFATE, 0.4-2.0 MG REPEATED EVERY 15 MINUTES UNTIL ATROPINIZATION IS ACHIEVED (TACHYCARDIA, FLUSHING, DRY MOUTH, MYDRIASIS). MAINTAIN ATROPINIZATION BY REPEATED DOSES FOR 2-12 HOURS, OR LONGER, DEPENDING ON THE SEVERITY OF POISONING.

THE APPEARANCE OF RALES IN THE LUNG BASES, MIOSIS, SALIVATION, NAUSEA, BRADYCARDIA, ARE ALL INDICATIONS OF INADEQUATE ATROPINIZATION.

SEVERELY POISONED INDIVIDUALS MAY EXHIBIT REMARKABLE TOLERANCE TO ATROPINE; TWO OR MORE TIMES THE DOSAGES SUGGESTED ABOVE MAY BE NEEDED. PERSONS NOT POISONED OR ONLY SLIGHTLY POISONED, HOWEVER, MAY DEVELOP SIGNS OF ATROPINE TOXICITY FROM SUCH LARGE DOSAGES: FEVER, MUSCLE FIBRILLATIONS, AND DELIRIUM ARE THE MAIN SIGNS OF ATROPINE TOXICITY. IF THESE SIGNS APPEAR WHILE THE PATIENT IS FULLY ATROPINIZED, ATROPINE ADMINISTRATION SHOULD BE DISCONTINUED, AT LEAST TEMPORARILY. OBSERVE TREATED PATIENTS CLOSELY AT LEAST 24 HOURS TO INSURE THAT SYMPTOMS (POSSIBLY PULMONARY EDEMA) DO NOT RECUR AS ATROPINIZATION WEARS OFF. IN VERY SEVERE POISONINGS, METABOLIC DISPOSITION OF TOXICANT MAY REQUIRE SEVERAL HOURS OR DAYS DURING WHICH ATROPINIZATION MUST BE MAINTAINED. MARKEDLY LOWER LEVELS OF URINARY METABOLITES INDICATE THAT ATROPINE DOSAGE CAN BE TAPERED OFF. AS DOSAGE IS REDUCED, CHECK THE LUNG BASES FREQUENTLY FOR RALES. IF RALES ARE HEARD OR OTHER SYMPTOMS RETURN, RE-ESTABLISH ATROPINIZATION PROMPTLY (MORGAN, RECOGNITION AND MANAGEMENT OF PESTICIDE POISONINGS, 3RD ED.). ADMINISTRATION OF ANTIDOTE MUST BE PERFORMED BY QUALIFIED MEDICAL PERSONNEL.

IN CASES OF SEVERE POISONING BY ORGANOPHOSPHATE PESTICIDES IN WHICH RESPIRATORY DEPRESSION, MUSCLE WEAKNESS AND TWITCHINGS ARE SEVERE, GIVE PRALIDOXIME (PROTOPAM-AYERST, 2-PAM), 1.0 GRAM INTRAVENOUSLY AT NO MORE THAN 0.5 GRAM PER MINUTE. DOSAGE OF PRALIDOXIME MAY BE REPEATED IN 1-2 HOURS, THEN AT 10-12 HOUR INTERVALS IF NEEDED. IN VERY SEVERE POISONINGS, DOSAGE RATES MAY BE DOUBLED. TREATMENT WITH PRALIDOXIME WILL BE MOST EFFECTIVE IF GIVEN WITHIN THIRTY-SIX HOURS AFTER POISONING (MORGAN, RECOGNITION AND MANAGEMENT OF PESTICIDE POISONINGS, 3RD ED.). ANTIDOTE SHOULD BE ADMINISTERED BY QUALIFIED MEDICAL PERSONNEL.

REACTIVITY

REACTIVITY: STABLE UNDER NORMAL TEMPERATURES AND PRESSURES.

INCOMPATIBILITIES: MONOCROTOPHOS: ADSORBENTS: DECOMPOSE READILY. ALKALINE COMPOUNDS: MAY CAUSE HYDROLYSIS. BLACK IRON: MAY BE CORRODED. BRASS: MAY BE CORRODED. DRUM STEEL: MAY BE CORRODED. STAINLESS STEEL: MAY BE CORRODED.

DECOMPOSITION: THERMAL DECOMPOSITION MAY EMIT TOXIC OXIDES OF NITROGEN AND PHOSPHORUS.

POLYMERIZATION: HAZARDOUS POLYMERIZATION HAS NOT BEEN REPORTED TO OCCUR UNDER NORMAL TEMPERATURES AND PRESSURES.

STORAGE AND DISPOSAL

OBSERVE ALL FEDERAL, STATE AND LOCAL REGULATIONS WHEN STORING OR DISPOSING OF THIS SUBSTANCE. FOR ASSISTANCE, CONTACT THE DISTRICT DIRECTOR OF THE ENVIRONMENTAL PROTECTION AGENCY.

STORAGE

STORE IN ACCORDANCE WITH 40 CFR 165 RECOMMENDED PROCEDURES FOR THE DISPOSAL AND STORAGE OF PESTICIDES AND PESTICIDE CONTAINERS.

STORE AWAY FROM INCOMPATIBLE SUBSTANCES.

DO NOT STORE AT TEMPERATURES BELOW 40 F (4 C) OR ABOVE 80 F (26 C) FOR PROLONGED PERIODS.

THRESHOLD PLANNING QUANTITY (TPQ): THE SUPERFUND AMENDMENTS AND REAUTHORIZATION ACT (SARA) SECTION 302 REQUIRES THAT EACH FACILITY WHERE ANY EXTREMELY HAZARDOUS SUBSTANCE IS PRESENT IN A QUANTITY EQUAL TO OR GREATER THAN THE TPQ ESTABLISHED FOR THAT SUBSTANCE NOTIFY THE STATE EMERGENCY RESPONSE COMMISSION FOR THE STATE IN WHICH IT IS LOCATED. SECTION 303 OF SARA REQUIRES THESE FACILITIES TO PARTICIPATE IN LOCAL EMERGENCY RESPONSE PLANNING (40 CFR 355.30).

DISPOSAL

DISPOSAL MUST BE IN ACCORDANCE WITH 40 CFR 165 RECOMMENDED PROCEDURES FOR THE DISPOSAL AND STORAGE OF PESTICIDES AND PESTICIDE CONTAINERS.

CONDITIONS TO AVOID

NONE REPORTED.

SPILL AND LEAK PROCEDURES

OCCUPATIONAL SPILL: DO NOT TOUCH SPILLED MATERIAL. STOP LEAK IF YOU CAN DO IT WITHOUT RISK. USE WATER SPRAY TO REDUCE VAPORS. FOR SMALL SPILLS, TAKE UP WITH SAND OR OTHER ABSORBENT MATERIAL AND PLACE INTO CONTAINERS FOR LATER DISPOSAL. FOR SMALL DRY SPILLS, WITH A CLEAN SHOVEL PLACE MATERIAL INTO CLEAN, DRY CONTAINERS AND COVER. MOVE CONTAINERS FROM SPILL AREA. FOR LARGER SPILLS, DIKE FAR AHEAD OF SPILL FOR LATER DISPOSAL. KEEP UNNECESSARY PEOPLE AWAY. ISOLATE HAZARD AREA AND DENY ENTRY. VENTILATE CLOSED SPACES BEFORE ENTERING.

REPORTABLE QUANTITY (RQ): 1 POUND THE SUPERFUND AMENDMENTS AND REAUTHORIZATION ACT (SARA) SECTION 304 REQUIRES THAT A RELEASE EQUAL TO OR GREATER THAN THE REPORTABLE QUANTITY FOR THIS SUBSTANCE BE IMMEDIATELY REPORTED TO THE LOCAL EMERGENCY PLANNING COMMITTEE AND THE STATE EMERGENCY RESPONSE COMMISSION (40 CFR 355.40). IF THE RELEASE OF THIS SUBSTANCE IS REPORTABLE UNDER CERCLA SECTION 103, THE NATIONAL RESPONSE CENTER MUST BE NOTIFIED IMMEDIATELY AT (800) 424-8802 OR (202) 426-2675 IN THE METROPOLITAN WASHINGTON, D.C. AREA (40 CFR 302.6).

PROTECTIVE EQUIPMENT

VENTILATION: PROCESS ENCLOSURE RECOMMENDED TO MEET PUBLISHED EXPOSURE LIMITS.

RESPIRATOR: THE FOLLOWING RESPIRATORS ARE RECOMMENDED BASED ON INFORMATION FOUND IN THE PHYSICAL DATA, TOXICITY AND HEALTH EFFECTS SECTIONS. THEY ARE RANKED IN ORDER FROM MINIMUM TO MAXIMUM RESPIRATORY PROTECTION. THE SPECIFIC RESPIRATOR SELECTED MUST BE BASED ON CONTAMINATION LEVELS FOUND IN THE WORK PLACE, MUST NOT EXCEED THE WORKING LIMITS OF THE RESPIRATOR AND BE JOINTLY APPROVED BY THE NATIONAL INSTITUTE FOR OCCUPATIONAL SAFETY AND HEALTH AND THE MINE SAFETY AND HEALTH ADMINISTRATION (NIOSH-MSHA).
TYPE 'C' SUPPLIED-AIR RESPIRATOR WITH A FULL FACEPIECE OPERATED IN PRESSURE-DEMAND OR OTHER POSITIVE PRESSURE MODE OR WITH A FULL FACEPIECE, HELMET OR HOOD OPERATED IN CONTINOUS-FLOW MODE.
SELF-CONTAINED BREATHING APPARATUS WITH A FULL FACEPIECE OPERATED IN PRESSURE-DEMAND OR OTHER POSITIVE PRESSURE MODE.
FOR FIREFIGHTING AND OTHER IMMEDIATELY DANGEROUS TO LIFE OR HEALTH CONDITIONS:
SELF-CONTAINED BREATHING APPARATUS WITH FULL FACEPIECE OPERATED IN PRESSURE-DEMAND OR OTHER POSITIVE PRESSURE MODE. SUPPLIED-AIR RESPIRATOR WITH FULL FACEPIECE AND OPERATED IN PRESSURE-DEMAND OR OTHER POSITIVE PRESSURE MODE IN COMBINATION WITH AN AUXILIARY SELF-CONTAINED BREATHING APPARATUS OPERATED IN PRESSURE-DEMAND OR OTHER POSITIVE PRESSURE MODE.

CLOTHING: EMPLOYEE MUST WEAR APPROPRIATE PROTECTIVE (IMPERVIOUS) CLOTHING AND EQUIPMENT TO PREVENT ANY POSSIBILITY OF SKIN CONTACT WITH THIS SUBSTANCE.

GLOVES: EMPLOYEE MUST WEAR APPROPRIATE PROTECTIVE GLOVES TO PREVENT CONTACT WITH THIS SUBSTANCE.

EYE PROTECTION: EMPLOYEE MUST WEAR SPLASH-PROOF OR DUST-RESISTANT SAFETY GOGGLES AND A FACESHIELD TO PREVENT CONTACT WITH THIS SUBSTANCE.
EMERGENCY WASH FACILITIES: WHERE THERE IS ANY POSSIBILITY THAT AN EMPLOYEE'S EYES AND/OR SKIN MAY BE EXPOSED TO THIS SUBSTANCE, THE EMPLOYER SHOULD PROVIDE AN EYE WASH FOUNTAIN AND QUICK DRENCH SHOWER WITHIN THE IMMEDIATE WORK AREA FOR EMERGENCY USE.

AUTHORIZED BY- OCCUPATIONAL HEALTH SERVICES, INC.
CREATION DATE: 10/04/89 ***REVISION DATE:*** 05/03/90

MATERIAL SAFETY DATA SHEET

OCCUPATIONAL HEALTH SERVICES, INC.
AGRICULTURE AND PESTICIDE DIVISION
450 SEVENTH AVENUE, SUITE 2407
NEW YORK, NEW YORK 10123
1-800-445-MSDS OR (212) 967-1100

EMERGENCY CONTACT:
JOHN S. BRANSFORD, JR. (615) 292-1180

SUBSTANCE IDENTIFICATION

CAS-NUMBER 1746-81-2

SUBSTANCE: MONOLINURON

TRADE NAMES/SYNONYMS: UREA, N'-(4-CHLOROPHENYL)-N-METHOXY-N-METHYL-; UREA, 3-(P-CHLOROPHENYL)-1-METHOXY-1-METHYL-; N'-(4-CHLOROPHENYL)-N-METHOXY-N-METHYLUREA; 3-(P-CHLOROPHENYL)-1-METHOXY-1-METHYLUREA; 3-(4-CHLOROPHENYL)-1-METHOXY-1-METHYLUREA; AFESIN; ARRESIN; ARESIN; AREZIN; AREZINE; HOE 2747; MONOROTOX; C9H11CLN2O2; PST15174

CHEMICAL FAMILY: SUBSTITUTED UREA
HALOGEN COMPOUND, AROMATIC

MOLECULAR FORMULA: CL-C6-H4-N-H-C-O-N-(C-H3)-O-C-H3

MOLECULAR WEIGHT: 214.67

CERCLA RATINGS (SCALE 0-3): HEALTH=3 FIRE=1 REACTIVITY=0 PERSISTENCE=0

NFPA RATINGS (SCALE 0-4): HEALTH=3 FIRE=1 REACTIVITY=0

COMPONENTS AND CONTAMINANTS

COMPONENT: MONOLINURON ***PERCENT:*** 100.0
CAS# 1746-81-2

OTHER CONTAMINANTS: NONE

EXPOSURE LIMITS: NO OCCUPATIONAL EXPOSURE LIMITS ESTABLISHED BY OSHA, ACGIH, OR NIOSH.

PHYSICAL DATA

DESCRIPTION: COLORLESS, CRYSTALLINE SOLID.

MELTING POINT: 178-181 F (80-83C)

SPECIFIC GRAVITY: NOT AVAILABLE ***VAPOR PRESSURE:*** 0.048 MMHG @ 65 C

SOLUBILITY IN WATER: 0.0735% @ 25 C

SOLVENT SOLUBILITY: SOLUBLE IN ACETONE, DIOXANE, ETHANOL AND XYLENE. DECOMPOSES ABOVE 428 F (220 C)

FIRE AND EXPLOSION DATA

FIRE AND EXPLOSION HAZARD: SLIGHT FIRE HAZARD WHEN EXPOSED TO HEAT OR FLAME.

FIREFIGHTING MEDIA: DRY CHEMICAL, CARBON DIOXIDE, HALON, WATER SPRAY OR STANDARD FOAM (1987 EMERGENCY RESPONSE GUIDEBOOK, DOT P 5800.4). FOR LARGER FIRES, USE WATER SPRAY, FOG OR STANDARD FOAM (1987 EMERGENCY RESPONSE GUIDEBOOK, DOT P 5800.4).

FIREFIGHTING: MOVE CONTAINERS FROM FIRE AREA IF POSSIBLE. FIGHT FIRE FROM MAXIMUM DISTANCE. STAY AWAY FROM STORAGE TANK ENDS. DIKE FIRE CONTROL WATER FOR LATER DISPOSAL. DO NOT SCATTER MATERIAL (1987 EMERGENCY RESPONSE GUIDEBOOK, DOT P 5800.4, GUIDE PAGE 55). EXTINGUISH USING AGENT SUITABLE FOR TYPE OF SURROUNDING FIRE. USE WATER IN FLOODING QUANTITIES AS FOG. KEEP SPARKS, FLAMES AND OTHER SOURCES OF IGNITION AWAY. KEEP MATERIAL OUT OF WATER SOURCES AND SEWERS. DO NOT TOUCH MATERIAL AND AVOID BREATHING DUSTS AND FUMES FROM BURNING MATERIAL. KEEP UPWIND.

TOXICITY

MONOLINURON: TOXICITY DATA: 1800 MG/KG ORAL-RAT LD50; 500 MG/KG ORAL-DOG LD50; REPRODUCTIVE EFFECTS DATA (RTECS). CARCINOGEN STATUS: NONE. ACUTE TOXICITY LEVEL: MODERATELY TOXIC BY INGESTION. TARGET EFFECTS: NO DATA AVAILABLE.

HEALTH EFFECTS AND FIRST AID

INHALATION: MONOLINURON: **ACUTE EXPOSURE**- MANY SUBSTITUTED UREA HERBICIDES ARE MODERATELY IRRITATING TO THE MUCOUS MEMBRANES. **CHRONIC EXPOSURE**- NO DATA AVAILABLE.

FIRST AID- REMOVE FROM EXPOSURE AREA TO FRESH AIR IMMEDIATELY. IF BREATHING HAS STOPPED, PERFORM ARTIFICIAL RESPIRATION. KEEP PERSON WARM AND AT REST. TREAT SYMPTOMATICALLY AND SUPPORTIVELY. GET MEDICAL ATTENTION IMMEDIATELY.

SKIN CONTACT: MONOLINURON: **ACUTE EXPOSURE**- MANY SUBSTITUTED UREA HERBICIDES ARE MODERATELY IRRITATING TO THE SKIN. **CHRONIC EXPOSURE**- NO DATA AVAILABLE.

FIRST AID- REMOVE CONTAMINATED CLOTHING AND SHOES IMMEDIATELY. WASH AFFECTED AREA WITH SOAP OR MILD DETERGENT AND LARGE AMOUNTS OF WATER UNTIL NO EVIDENCE OF CHEMICAL REMAINS (APPROXIMATELY 15-20 MINUTES). GET MEDICAL ATTENTION IMMEDIATELY.

EYE CONTACT: MONOLINURON: **ACUTE EXPOSURE**- MANY SUBSTITUTED UREA HERBICIDES ARE MODERATELY IRRITATING TO THE EYES. **CHRONIC EXPOSURE**- NO DATA AVAILABLE.

FIRST AID- WASH EYES IMMEDIATELY WITH LARGE AMOUNTS OF WATER OR NORMAL SALINE, OCCASIONALLY LIFTING UPPER AND LOWER LIDS, UNTIL NO EVIDENCE OF CHEMICAL REMAINS (APPROXIMATELY 15-20 MINUTES). GET MEDICAL ATTENTION IMMEDIATELY.

INGESTION: MONOLINURON: **ACUTE EXPOSURE**- A LETHAL DOSE IN RATS WAS 1800 MG/KG; SYMPTOMS WERE NOT REPORTED. **CHRONIC EXPOSURE**- AN INCREASE RATE OF POSTIMPLANTATIVE LOSSES AND MORTALITY OF THE OFFSPRING WAS OBSERVED IN A STUDY OF PREGNANT MICE REPEATEDLY FED MONOLINURON; OTHER REPORTED FETAL EFFECTS INCLUDED AN INCREASE IN THE INCIDENCE OF CLEFT PALATES, HYPOPLASIA OF THE UPPER JAW, AND WAVY AND FUSED RIBS.

FIRST AID- REMOVE BY GASTRIC LAVAGE AND CATHARSIS. MAINTAIN BLOOD PRESSURE AND AIRWAY. GIVE OXYGEN IF RESPIRATION IS DEPRESSED. DO NOT PERFORM GASTRIC LAVAGE IF VICTIM IS UNCONSCIOUS. GET MEDICAL ATTENTION IMMEDIATELY (DREISBACH, HANDBOOK OF POISONING, 12TH ED.). ADMINISTRATION OF LAVAGE OR OXYGEN SHOULD BE PERFORMED BY QUALIFIED MEDICAL PERSONNEL.

ANTIDOTE: NO SPECIFIC ANTIDOTE. TREAT SYMPTOMATICALLY AND SUPPORTIVELY.

REACTIVITY

REACTIVITY: STABLE UNDER NORMAL TEMPERATURES AND PRESSURES.

INCOMPATIBILITIES: MONOLINURON: ACIDS: SLOWLY DECOMPOSES. ALKALIES: SLOWLY DECOMPOSES. OXIDIZERS (STRONG): FIRE AND EXPLOSION HAZARD.

DECOMPOSITION: THERMAL DECOMPOSITION PRODUCTS MAY INCLUDE TOXIC OXIDES OF NITROGEN AND CARBON AND TOXIC AND CORROSIVE FUMES OF CHLORIDES.

POLYMERIZATION: HAZARDOUS POLYMERIZATION HAS NOT BEEN REPORTED TO OCCUR UNDER NORMAL TEMPERATURES AND PRESSURES.

STORAGE AND DISPOSAL

OBSERVE ALL FEDERAL, STATE AND LOCAL REGULATIONS WHEN STORING OR DISPOSING OF THIS SUBSTANCE. FOR ASSISTANCE, CONTACT THE DISTRICT DIRECTOR OF THE ENVIRONMENTAL PROTECTION AGENCY.

STORAGE

STORE IN ACCORDANCE WITH 40 CFR 165 RECOMMENDED PROCEDURES FOR THE DISPOSAL AND STORAGE OF PESTICIDES AND PESTICIDE CONTAINERS. STORE AWAY FROM INCOMPATIBLE SUBSTANCES.

DISPOSAL

DISPOSAL MUST BE IN ACCORDANCE WITH 40 CFR 165 RECOMMENDED PROCEDURES FOR THE DISPOSAL AND STORAGE OF PESTICIDES AND PESTICIDE CONTAINERS.

CONDITIONS TO AVOID

MAY BURN BUT DOES NOT IGNITE READILY. CONTAINERS MAY EXPLODE IN HEAT OF FIRE.

SPILL AND LEAK PROCEDURES

OCCUPATIONAL SPILL: DO NOT TOUCH SPILLED MATERIAL. STOP LEAK IF YOU CAN DO IT WITHOUT RISK. USE WATER SPRAY TO REDUCE VAPORS. FOR SMALL SPILLS, TAKE UP WITH SAND OR OTHER ABSORBENT MATERIAL AND PLACE INTO CONTAINERS FOR LATER DISPOSAL. FOR SMALL DRY SPILLS, WITH A CLEAN SHOVEL PLACE MATERIAL INTO CLEAN, DRY CONTAINERS AND COVER. MOVE CONTAINERS FROM SPILL AREA. FOR LARGER SPILLS, DIKE FAR AHEAD OF SPILL FOR LATER DISPOSAL. KEEP UNNECESSARY PEOPLE AWAY. ISOLATE HAZARD AREA AND DENY ENTRY. VENTILATE CLOSED SPACES BEFORE ENTERING.

PROTECTIVE EQUIPMENT

VENTILATION: PROVIDE LOCAL EXHAUST OR GENERAL DILUTION VENTILATION SYSTEM.

RESPIRATOR: THE FOLLOWING RESPIRATORS ARE RECOMMENDED BASED ON INFORMATION FOUND IN THE PHYSICAL DATA, TOXICITY AND HEALTH EFFECTS SECTIONS. THEY ARE RANKED IN ORDER FROM MINIMUM TO MAXIMUM RESPIRATORY PROTECTION. THE SPECIFIC RESPIRATOR SELECTED MUST BE BASED ON CONTAMINATION LEVELS FOUND IN THE WORK PLACE, MUST NOT EXCEED THE WORKING LIMITS OF THE RESPIRATOR AND BE JOINTLY APPROVED BY THE NATIONAL INSTITUTE FOR OCCUPATIONAL SAFETY AND HEALTH AND THE MINE SAFETY AND HEALTH ADMINISTRATION (NIOSH-MSHA).

CHEMICAL CARTRIDGE RESPIRATOR WITH AN ORGANIC VAPOR CARTRIDGE(S) WITH A FULL FACEPIECE AND ORGANIC VAPOR CARTRIDGE(S) IN COMBINATION WITH A DUST AND MIST FILTER.

POWERED AIR-PURIFYING RESPIRATOR WITH A TIGHT-FITTING FACEPIECE AND ORGANIC VAPOR CARTRIDGE(S) IN COMBINATION WITH A HIGH-EFFICIENCY PARTICULATE FILTER.

TYPE 'C' SUPPLIED-AIR RESPIRATOR WITH A FULL FACEPIECE OPERATED IN A PRESSURE-DEMAND OR OTHER POSITIVE PRESSURE MODE. SELF-CONTAINED BREATHING APPARATUS WITH A FULL FACEPIECE OPERATED IN PRESSURE-DEMAND OR OTHER POSITIVE PRESSURE MODE.

FOR FIREFIGHTING AND OTHER IMMEDIATELY DANGEROUS TO LIFE OR HEALTH CONDITIONS:

SELF-CONTAINED BREATHING APPARATUS WITH FULL FACEPIECE OPERATED IN PRESSURE-DEMAND OR OTHER POSITIVE PRESSURE MODE.

SUPPLIED-AIR RESPIRATOR WITH FULL FACEPIECE AND OPERATED IN PRESSURE-DEMAND OR OTHER POSITIVE PRESSURE MODE IN COMBINATION WITH AN AUXILIARY SELF-CONTAINED BREATHING APPARATUS OPERATED IN PRESSURE-DEMAND OR OTHER POSITIVE PRESSURE MODE.

CLOTHING: EMPLOYEE MUST WEAR APPROPRIATE PROTECTIVE (IMPERVIOUS) CLOTHING AND EQUIPMENT TO PREVENT REPEATED OR PROLONGED SKIN CONTACT WITH THIS SUBSTANCE.

GLOVES: EMPLOYEE MUST WEAR APPROPRIATE PROTECTIVE GLOVES TO PREVENT CONTACT WITH THIS SUBSTANCE.

EYE PROTECTION: EMPLOYEE MUST WEAR SPLASH-PROOF OR DUST-RESISTANT SAFETY GOGGLES TO PREVENT EYE CONTACT WITH THIS SUBSTANCE.

EMERGENCY EYE WASH: WHERE THERE IS ANY POSSIBILITY THAT AN EMPLOYEE'S EYES MAY BE EXPOSED TO THIS SUBSTANCE, THE EMPLOYER SHOULD PROVIDE AN EYE WASH FOUNTAIN WITHIN THE IMMEDIATE WORK AREA FOR EMERGENCY USE.

AUTHORIZED BY- OCCUPATIONAL HEALTH SERVICES, INC.

CREATION DATE: 10/04/89 ***REVISION DATE:*** 05/09/90

MATERIAL SAFETY DATA SHEET

OCCUPATIONAL HEALTH SERVICES, INC.
AGRICULTURE AND PESTICIDE DIVISION
450 SEVENTH AVENUE, SUITE 2407
NEW YORK, NEW YORK 10123
1-800-445-MSDS OR (212) 967-1100

EMERGENCY CONTACT:
JOHN S. BRANSFORD, JR. (615) 292-1180

SUBSTANCE IDENTIFICATION

CAS-NUMBER 2163-80-6

SUBSTANCE: MONOSODIUM METHANE ARSONATE

TRADE NAMES/SYNONYMS: METHYL ARSONIC ACID, MONOSODIUM SALT; METHANEARSONIC ACID, MONOSODIUM SALT; MONOSODIUM ACID METHANE ARSONATE; MONOSODIUM METHANEARSONATE; MSMA; UN 1557; NA 9188; PST15180

CHEMICAL FAMILY: ORGANOMETALLIC

MOLECULAR FORMULA: C-H4-AS-O3 . NA

MOLECULAR WEIGHT: 161.96

CERCLA RATINGS (SCALE 0-3): HEALTH=3 FIRE=U REACTIVITY=0 PERSISTENCE=3

NFPA RATINGS (SCALE 0-4): HEALTH=3 FIRE=U REACTIVITY=0

COMPONENTS AND CONTAMINANTS

COMPONENT: MONOSODIUM METHANE ARSONATE ***PERCENT:*** 100.0
CAS# 2163-80-6

OTHER CONTAMINANTS: NONE.

EXPOSURE LIMITS: ARSENIC, ORGANIC AND SOLUBLE COMPOUNDS (AS AS): 0.5 MG/M3 OSHA TWA 0.2 MG/M3 ACGIH TWA

SUBJECT TO SARA SECTION 313 ANNUAL TOXIC CHEMICAL RELEASE REPORTING

PHYSICAL DATA

DESCRIPTION: WHITE CRYSTALLINE POWDER. ***MELTING POINT:*** 239 F (115 C) DECOMPOSES

SPECIFIC GRAVITY: 1.4-1.6 (SOLUTION) ***SOLUBILITY IN WATER:*** SOLUBLE

SOLVENT SOLUBILITY: SOLUBLE IN METHANOL AND ALCOHOL; INSOLUBLE IN ETHER AND ORGANIC SOLVENTS.

FIRE AND EXPLOSION DATA

FIRE AND EXPLOSION HAZARD: UNKNOWN FIRE AND EXPLOSION HAZARD.

FIREFIGHTING MEDIA: DRY CHEMICAL, CARBON DIOXIDE, HALON, WATER SPRAY OR STANDARD FOAM (1987 EMERGENCY RESPONSE GUIDEBOOK, DOT P 5800.4). FOR LARGER FIRES, USE WATER SPRAY, FOG OR STANDARD FOAM (1987 EMERGENCY RESPONSE GUIDEBOOK, DOT P 5800.4).

FIREFIGHTING: MOVE CONTAINERS FROM FIRE AREA IF POSSIBLE (1987 EMERGENCY RESPONSE GUIDEBOOK, DOT P 5800.4, GUIDE PAGE 53).

USE AGENTS INDICATED. DO NOT USE WATER ON MATERIAL. FOR LARGE FIRES USE WATER IN FLOODING AMOUNTS AS FOG AND SPRAY. USE WATER TO ABSORB VAPORS. AVOID BREATHING POISONOUS VAPORS, KEEP UPWIND.

TOXICITY

MONOSODIUM METHANE ARSONATE: IRRITATION DATA: 54 MG OPEN SKIN-RABBIT MILD; 34 MG EYE-RABBIT MILD. TOXICITY DATA: 20 GM/M3 INHALATION-RAT LC50; 2500 MG/KG SKIN-RABBIT LD50; 700 MG/KG ORAL-RAT LD50; 102 MG/KG ORAL-RABBIT LD50; 230 MG/KG ORAL-CATTLE LD50; 50 MG/KG UNREPORTED-MAMMAL LD50. CARCINOGEN STATUS: NONE. NO ADEQUATE DATA ON ORGANIC ARSENICALS WERE AVAILABLE FOR EVALUATION (IARC). LOCAL EFFECTS: IRRITANT- SKIN AND EYE. ACUTE TOXICITY LEVEL: TOXIC BY INHALATION; MODERATELY TOXIC BY INGESTION; SLIGHTLY TOXIC BY DERMAL ABSORPTION. TARGET EFFECTS: POISONING MAY AFFECT THE LIVER, KIDNEYS, AND GASTROINTESTINAL AND PERIPHERAL NERVOUS SYSTEMS.

HEALTH EFFECTS AND FIRST AID

INHALATION: MONOSODIUM METHANE ARSONATE: ACUTE EXPOSURE- NO SPECIFIC DATA AVAILABLE. INHALATION OF ARSENICAL DUSTS MAY CAUSE ACUTE PULMONARY EDEMA, RESTLESSNESS, DYSPNEA, CYANOSIS, COUGH WITH FOAMY SPUTUM, AND RALES. CHRONIC EXPOSURE- CHRONIC POISONING DUE TO INHALATION OF ARSENICAL DUSTS MAY LEAD TO POLYNEURITIS, ANESTHESIAS, BURNING PAINS IN THE HANDS AND FEET, BRONZING OF THE SKIN, DERMATITIS, CIRRHOSIS OF THE LIVER, CRAMPS, ANEMIA, WEIGHT LOSS, SALIVATION, AND HEART FAILURE. THERE IS INADEQUATE EVIDENCE FOR THE CARCINOGENICITY OF ARSENIC COMPOUNDS IN ANIMALS.

FIRST AID- REMOVE FROM EXPOSURE AREA TO FRESH AIR IMMEDIATELY. IF BREATHING HAS STOPPED, GIVE ARTIFICIAL RESPIRATION. MAINTAIN AIRWAY AND BLOOD PRESSURE AND ADMINISTER OXYGEN IF AVAILABLE. KEEP AFFECTED PERSON WARM AND AT REST. TREAT SYMPTOMATICALLY AND SUPPORTIVELY.

ADMINISTRATION OF OXYGEN SHOULD BE PERFORMED BY QUALIFIED PERSONNEL. GET MEDICAL ATTENTION IMMEDIATELY.

SKIN CONTACT: MONOSODIUM METHANE ARSONATE: **ACUTE EXPOSURE-** APPLICATION OF 54 MG MONOSODIUM METHANE ARSONATE TO THE SKIN OF RABBITS RESULTED IN MILD IRRITATION. SKIN CONTACT WITH AIRBORNE ARSENICAL DUSTS MAY RESULT IN A DERMATITIS WHICH STARTS WITH ERYTHEMA, SWELLING, ITCHING AND BURNING. IF THE DERMATITIS BECOMES SEVERE THE SKIN MAY ALSO BE MARKED BY PAPULAR OR VESICULAR ERUPTIONS. **CHRONIC EXPOSURE-** A FEATURE OF CHRONIC SKIN EXPOSURE TO ARSENIC COMPOUNDS, AS WELL AS OF SYSTEMIC POISONING DUE TO INHALATION OR INGESTION, IS THE DEVELOPMENT OF HYPERKERITOSIS AND HYPERPIGMENTATION OF THE SKIN, ESPECIALLY OF THE HANDS AND FEET. PERSONS CHRONICALLY EXPOSED MAY ALSO EXHIBIT EXCESSIVE SWEATING AND MEE'S LINES IN THE FINGERNAILS.

FIRST AID- REMOVE CONTAMINATED CLOTHING AND SHOES IMMEDIATELY. WASH AFFECTED AREA WITH SOAP OR MILD DETERGENT AND LARGE AMOUNTS OF WATER UNTIL NO EVIDENCE OF CHEMICAL REMAINS (APPROXIMATELY 15-20 MINUTES). GET MEDICAL ATTENTION IMMEDIATELY.

EYE CONTACT: MONOSODIUM METHANE ARSONATE: **ACUTE EXPOSURE-** WHEN 34 MG MONOSODIUM METHANE ARSONATE WAS APPLIED TO THE EYES OF RABBITS, MILD IRRITATION ENSUED. DERMATITIS OF THE FACE AND EYELIDS IS SOMETIMES ACCOMPANIED BY CONJUNCTIVITIS WITH REDNESS, SWELLING AND PAIN. **CHRONIC EXPOSURE-** NO DATA AVAILABLE.

FIRST AID- WASH EYES IMMEDIATELY WITH LARGE AMOUNTS OF WATER OR NORMAL SALINE, OCCASIONALLY LIFTING UPPER AND LOWER LIDS, UNTIL NO EVIDENCE OF CHEMICAL REMAINS (APPROXIMATELY 15-20 MINUTES). GET MEDICAL ATTENTION IMMEDIATELY.

INGESTION: MONOSODIUM METHANE ARSONATE: **ACUTE EXPOSURE-** HALF OF THE RATS INGESTING A MODERATE AMOUNT OF MONOSODIUM METHANE ARSONATE DIED. INGESTION OF ARSENIC CONTAINING COMPOUNDS MAY RESULT IN SUDDEN AND EXPLOSIVE GASTROENTERITIS, WHICH MAY BE DELAYED A HALF-HOUR OR MORE. PERSONS MAY ALSO EXPERIENCE A METALLIC TASTE, A CONSTRICTION OF THE THROAT, HOARSE VOICE, NAUSEA, PERSISTENT VOMITING, BLOODY DIARRHEA, SEVERE CRAMPS, GARLIC ODOR OF THE BREATH, SALIVATION, THIRST, PALLOR, MOIST SKIN, TREMORS, AND CONVULSIONS. MASSIVE DOSES MAY KILL WITHIN A FEW HOURS, WITH DEATH RESULTING FROM SHOCK AND PERIPHERAL VASCULAR FAILURE. **CHRONIC EXPOSURE-** NO SPECIFIC DATA AVAILABLE. CHRONIC INGESTION OF ARSENIC CONTAINING COMPOUNDS MAY RESULT IN A INSIDIOUS GENERAL WEAKNESS, ANOREXIA, NAUSEA, VOMITING, NOSEBLEED, BLEEDING GUMS, MEE'S LINES IN THE FINGERNAILS, INCREASED SKIN PIGMENTATION, CIRRHOSIS OF THE LIVER, AND ANEMIA. PERSONS EXPOSED CHRONICALLY TO ARSENIC COMPOUNDS MAY ALSO BE AT INCREASED RISK TO SKIN AND LUNG CANCER, AND LEUKEMIA.

FIRST AID- REMOVE BY GASTRIC LAVAGE OR EMESIS. FOLLOW WITH A SALINE CATHARTIC. MAINTAIN BLOOD PRESSURE, AIRWAY, AND GIVE OXYGEN IF RESPIRATION IS DEPRESSED. DO NOT PERFORM GASTRIC LAVAGE OR EMESIS IF VICTIM IS UNCONSCIOUS. GET MEDICAL ATTENTION IMMEDIATELY. (DREISBACH, HANDBOOK OF POISONING, 12TH ED.) ADMINISTRATION OF GASTRIC LAVAGE OR OXYGEN SHOULD BE PERFORMED BY QUALIFIED MEDICAL PERSONNEL.

ANTIDOTE: THE FOLLOWING ANTIDOTE HAS BEEN RECOMMENDED. HOWEVER, THE DECISION AS TO WHETHER THE SEVERITY OF POISONING REQUIRES ADMINISTRATION OF ANY ANTIDOTE AND ACTUAL DOSE REQUIRED SHOULD BE MADE BY QUALIFIED MEDICAL PERSONNEL.

ARSENIC POISONING: GIVE DIMERCAPROL, 3 MG/KG (OR 0.3 ML/KG) EVERY 4 HOURS FOR 2 DAYS AND THEN 2 MG/KG EVERY 2 HOURS FOR A TOTAL OF 10 DAYS. DIMERCAPROL IS AVAILABLE AS A 10% SOLUTION IN OIL FOR INTRAMUSCULAR ADMINISTRATION. NEXT, GIVE PENICILLAMINE, UP TO 100 MG/KG/DAY (MAXIMUM 1 G/DAY) DIVIDED INTO 4 DOSES FOR NO LONGER THAN 1 WEEK. IF A LONGER ADMINISTRATION PERIOD IS WARRANTED, DOSAGE SHOULD NOT EXCEED 40 MG/KG/DAY. GIVE THE DRUG ORALLY HALF AN HOUR BEFORE MEALS. DISCONTINUE ANTIDOTE WHEN URINE ARSENIC LEVEL FALLS BELOW 50 UG/24 HR. (DREISBACH, HANDBOOK OF POISONING, 12TH ED.). ANITDOTE SHOULD BE ADMINISTERED BY QUALIFIED MEDICAL PERSONNEL.

REACTIVITY

REACTIVITY: STABLE UNDER NORMAL TEMPERATURES AND PRESSURES.

INCOMPATIBILITIES: MONOSODIUM METHANE ARSONATE: REDUCING AGENTS: MAY REACT. STRONG OXIDIZERS: MAY REACT.

DECOMPOSITION: THERMAL DECOMPOSITION MAY RELEASE TOXIC FUMES OF ARSENIC OXIDES, AND OXIDES OF SODIUM.

POLYMERIZATION: HAZARDOUS POLYMERIZATION HAS NOT BEEN REPORTED TO OCCUR UNDER NORMAL TEMPERATURES AND PRESSURES.

STORAGE AND DISPOSAL

OBSERVE ALL FEDERAL, STATE AND LOCAL REGULATIONS WHEN STORING OR DISPOSING OF THIS SUBSTANCE. FOR ASSISTANCE, CONTACT THE DISTRICT DIRECTOR OF THE ENVIRONMENTAL PROTECTION AGENCY.

****DISPOSAL****

ARSENIC - REGULATORY LEVEL: 5.0 MG/L MATERIALS WHICH CONTAIN THE ABOVE SUBSTANCE AT OR ABOVE THE REGULATORY LEVEL MEET THE EPA CHARACTERISTIC OF TOXICITY, AND MUST BE DISPOSED OF IN ACCORDANCE WITH 40 CFR PART 262. EPA HAZARDOUS WASTE NUMBER D004.

CONDITIONS TO AVOID

MAY BURN BUT DOES NOT IGNITE READILY.

SPILL AND LEAK PROCEDURES

OCCUPATIONAL SPILL: DO NOT TOUCH SPILLED MATERIAL. STOP LEAK IF YOU CAN DO IT WITHOUT RISK. FOR SMALL SPILLS, TAKE UP WITH SAND OR OTHER ABSORBENT MATERIAL AND PLACE INTO CONTAINERS FOR LATER DISPOSAL. FOR SMALL DRY SPILLS, WITH A CLEAN SHOVEL PLACE MATERIAL INTO CLEAN, DRY CONTAINER AND COVER. MOVE CONTAINERS FROM SPILL AREA. FOR LARGER SPILLS, DIKE FAR AHEAD OF SPILL FOR LATER DISPOSAL. KEEP UNNECESSARY PEOPLE AWAY. ISOLATE HAZARD AREA AND DENY ENTRY.

PROTECTIVE EQUIPMENT

VENTILATION: PROVIDE LOCAL EXHAUST OR PROCESS ENCLOSURE VENTILATION TO MEET PUBLISHED EXPOSURE LIMITS.

RESPIRATOR: THE FOLLOWING RESPIRATORS ARE THE MINIMUM LEGAL REQUIREMENTS AS SET FORTH BY THE OCCUPATIONAL SAFETY AND HEALTH ADMINISTRATION FOUND IN 29 CFR 1910, SUBPART Z.

RESPIRATORY PROTECTION FOR INORGANIC ARSENIC PARTICULATE EXCEPT THOSE WITH SIGNIFICANT VAPOR PRESSURE

CONCENTRATION OF INORGANIC ARSENIC (AS) REQUIRED RESPIRATOR OR CONDITION OF USE

UNKNOWN OR GREATER OR LESS THAN 20,000 ANY FULL FACEPIECE, SELF UG/M3 (20 MG/M3) OR FIREFIGHTING CONTAINED BREATHING APPARATUS, OPERATED IN POSITIVE PRESSURE MODE.

NOT GREATER THAN 20,000 UG/M3 SUPPLIED-AIR RESPIRATOR WITH FULL (20 MG/M3) FACEPIECE, HOOD OR HELMET OR SUIT AND OPERATED IN POSITIVE PRESSURE MODE.

NOT GREATER THAN 10,000 UG/M3 POWERED-AIR PURIFYING RESPIRATORS (10 MG/M3) IN ALL INLET FACE COVERINGS WITH HIGH EFFICIENCY FILTERS; OR HALF-MASK SUPPLIED-AIR RESPIRATOR OPERATED IN POSITIVE PRESSURE MODE.

NOT GREATER THAN 500 UG/M3 FULL FACEPIECE AIR-PURIFYING RESPIRATOR EQUIPPED WITH HIGH EFFICIENCY FILTERS; OR ANY FULL FACEPIECE SUPPLIED-AIR RESPIRATOR; OR ANY FULL FACEPIECE SELF-CONTAINED BREATHING APPARATUS. NOT GREATER THAN 100 UG/M3 HALF-MASK AIR-PURIFYING RESPIRATOR EQUIPPED WITH HIGH EFFICIENCY FILTERS; OR ANY HALF-MASK SUPPLIED-AIR RESPIRATOR.

(HIGH EFFICIENCY FILTER- 99.97% EFFICIENCY AGAINST 0.3 MICROMETER MONODISPERSE DIETHYL-HEXYL PHTHALATE (DOP) PARTICLES)

RESPIRATORY PROTECTION FOR INORGANIC ARSENICALS (SUCH AS ARSENIC TRICHLORIDE OR ARSENIC PHOSPHIDE) WITH SIGNIFICANT VAPOR PRESSURE.

CONCENTRATION OF INORGANIC ARSENIC (AS) REQUIRED RESPIRATOR OR CONDITION OF USE

UNKNOWN OR GREATER OR LESS THAN 20,000 ANY FULL FACEPIECE SELF-CONTAINED UG/M3 (20 MG/M3) BREATHING APPARATUS OPERATED IN POSITIVE PRESSURE MODE.

NOT GREATER THAN 20,000 UG/M3 SUPPLIED-AIR RESPIRATOR WITH A (20 MG/M3) FULL FACEPIECE, HOOD OR HELMET OR SUIT OPERATED IN POSITIVE PRESSURE MODE.

NOT GREATER THAN 10,000 UG/M3 HALF-MASK SUPPLIED AIR RESPIRATOR (10 MG/M3) OPERATED IN POSITIVE PRESSURE MODE.

NOT GREATER THAN 500 UG/M3 FRONT- OR BACK-MOUNTED GAS MASK EQUIPPED WITH HIGH-EFFICIENCY FILTERS AND ACID GAS CANISTER; OR ANY FULL FACEPIECE SUPPLIED AIR RESPIRATOR; OR ANY FULL FACEPIECE SELF-CONTAINED BREATHING APPARATUS.

NOT GREATER THAN 100 UG/M3 HALF-MASK AIR-PURIFYING RESPIRATOR EQUIPPED WITH HIGH EFFICIENCY FILTER AND ACID GAS CARTRIDGE; OR ANY HALF-MASK SUPPLIED-AIR RESPIRATOR.

(HIGH EFFICIENCY FILTER- 99.97% EFFICIENCY AGAINST 0.3 MICROMETER MONODISPERSE DIETHYL-HEXYL PHTHALATE (DOP) PARTICLES) (HALF-MASK RESPIRATORS SHALL NOT BE USED FOR PROTECTION AGAINST ARSENIC TRICHLORIDE, AS IT IS RAPIDLY ABSORBED THROUGH THE SKIN).

FOR FIREFIGHTING AND OTHER IMMEDIATELY DANGEROUS TO LIFE OR HEALTH CONDITIONS:

SELF-CONTAINED BREATHING APPARATUS WITH FULL FACEPIECE OPERATED IN PRESSURE-DEMAND OR OTHER POSITIVE PRESSURE MODE.
SUPPLIED-AIR RESPIRATOR WITH FULL FACEPIECE AND OPERATED IN PRESSURE-DEMAND OR OTHER POSITIVE PRESSURE MODE IN COMBINATION WITH AN AUXILIARY SELF-CONTAINED BREATHING APPARATUS OPERATED IN PRESSURE-DEMAND OR OTHER POSITIVE PRESSURE MODE.

CLOTHING: EMPLOYEE MUST WEAR APPROPRIATE PROTECTIVE (IMPERVIOUS) CLOTHING AND EQUIPMENT TO PREVENT REPEATED OR PROLONGED SKIN CONTACT WITH THIS SUBSTANCE.

GLOVES: EMPLOYEE MUST WEAR APPROPRIATE PROTECTIVE GLOVES TO PREVENT CONTACT WITH THIS SUBSTANCE.

EYE PROTECTION: EMPLOYEE MUST WEAR SPLASH-PROOF OR DUST-RESISTANT SAFETY GOGGLES TO PREVENT EYE CONTACT WITH THIS SUBSTANCE.
EMERGENCY EYE WASH: WHERE THERE IS ANY POSSIBILITY THAT AN EMPLOYEE'S EYES MAY BE EXPOSED TO THIS SUBSTANCE, THE EMPLOYER SHOULD PROVIDE AN EYE WASH FOUNTAIN WITHIN THE IMMEDIATE WORK AREA FOR EMERGENCY USE.

AUTHORIZED BY- OCCUPATIONAL HEALTH SERVICES, INC.
CREATION DATE: 10/04/89 ***REVISION DATE:*** 07/13/90

MATERIAL SAFETY DATA SHEET

OCCUPATIONAL HEALTH SERVICES, INC.
AGRICULTURE AND PESTICIDE DIVISION
450 SEVENTH AVENUE, SUITE 2407
NEW YORK, NEW YORK 10123
1-800-445-MSDS OR (212) 967-1100

EMERGENCY CONTACT:
JOHN S. BRANSFORD, JR. (615) 292-1180

SUBSTANCE IDENTIFICATION

CAS-NUMBER 7558-80-7

SUBSTANCE: **SODIUM PHOSPHATE, MONOBASIC**

TRADE NAMES/SYNONYMS: MONOSODIUM PHOSPHATE; SODIUM DIHYDROGEN PHOSPHATE; MONOSODIUM DIHYDROGEN PHOSPHATE; SODIUM BIPHOSPHATE; ACID SODIUM PHOSPHATE; MONOSODIUM ORTHOPHOSPHATE; MSP; PHOSPHORIC ACID, MONOSODIUM SALT; DIHYDROGEN SODIUM PHOSPHATE; MONOBASIC SODIUM PHOSPHATE; MONOSODIUM HYDROGEN PHOSPHATE; SODIUM DIPHOSPHATE ANHYDROUS; SODIUM DIHYDROGEN, MONOPHOSPHATE; SODIUM DIHYDROGEN ORTHOPHOSPHATE; SODIUM PHOSPHATE (NA(H2PO4)); SODIUM PRIMARY PHOSPHATE; SODIUM PHOSPHATE; NAH2PO4; PST15190

CHEMICAL FAMILY: INORGANIC SALT

MOLECULAR FORMULA: NA-H2-P-O4

MOLECULAR WEIGHT: 119.98

CERCLA RATINGS (SCALE 0-3): HEALTH=3 FIRE=1 REACTIVITY=0 PERSISTENCE=0

NFPA RATINGS (SCALE 0-4): HEALTH=U FIRE=1 REACTIVITY=0

COMPONENTS AND CONTAMINANTS

COMPONENT: SODIUM PHOSPHATE, MONOBASIC ***PERCENT:*** 100
CAS# 7558-80-7

OTHER CONTAMINANTS: NONE

EXPOSURE LIMITS: NO OCCUPATIONAL EXPOSURE LIMITS ESTABLISHED BY OSHA, ACGIH, OR NIOSH.

PHYSICAL DATA

DESCRIPTION: WHITE, CRYSTALLINE POWDER. ***MELTING POINT:*** NOT AVAILABLE

SPECIFIC GRAVITY: APPROX 2.0 ***VAPOR PRESSURE:*** NEGLIGIBLE

SOLUBILITY IN WATER: VERY SOLUBLE

SOLVENT SOLUBILITY: VERY SLIGHTLY SOLUBLE IN ETHER, CHLOROFORM, TOLUENE; INSOLUBLE IN ALCOHOL.

DECOMPOSES ABOVE 225 C.

FIRE AND EXPLOSION DATA

FIRE AND EXPLOSION HAZARD: SLIGHT FIRE HAZARD WHEN EXPOSED TO HEAT OR FLAME.

FIREFIGHTING MEDIA: DRY CHEMICAL, CARBON DIOXIDE, HALON, WATER SPRAY OR STANDARD FOAM (1987 EMERGENCY RESPONSE GUIDEBOOK, DOT P 5800.4).
FOR LARGER FIRES, USE WATER SPRAY, FOG OR STANDARD FOAM (1987 EMERGENCY RESPONSE GUIDEBOOK, DOT P 5800.4).

FIREFIGHTING: MOVE CONTAINER FROM FIRE AREA IF POSSIBLE. DO NOT SCATTER SPILLED MATERIAL WITH HIGH PRESSURE WATER STREAMS. DIKE FIRE CONTROL WATER FOR LATER DISPOSAL (1987 EMERGENCY RESPONSE GUIDEBOOK, DOT P 5800.4, GUIDE PAGE 31).
USE AGENTS SUITABLE FOR TYPE OF SURROUNDING FIRE. AVOID BREATHING HAZARDOUS VAPORS, KEEP UPWIND.

TOXICITY

SODIUM PHOSPHATE, MONOBASIC: IRRITATION DATA: 50 MG EYE-HUMAN MILD; 150 MG EYE-RABBIT MILD. TOXICITY DATA: 8290 MG/KG ORAL-RAT LD50; 250 MG/KG INTRAMUSCULAR-RAT LD50. CARCINOGEN STATUS: NONE. ACUTE TOXICITY LEVEL: SLIGHTLY TOXIC BY INGESTION. TARGET EFFECTS: POISONING MAY AFFECT THE CALCIUM METABOLISM.

HEALTH EFFECTS AND FIRST AID

INHALATION: SODIUM PHOSPHATE, MONOBASIC: **ACUTE EXPOSURE-** INHALATION OF DUST MAY CAUSE IRRITATION. **CHRONIC EXPOSURE-** NO DATA AVAILABLE.

FIRST AID- REMOVE FROM EXPOSURE AREA TO FRESH AIR IMMEDIATELY. IF BREATHING HAS STOPPED, PERFORM ARTIFICIAL RESPIRATION. KEEP PERSON WARM AND AT REST. TREAT SYMPTOMATICALLY AND SUPPORTIVELY. GET MEDICAL ATTENTION IMMEDIATELY.

SKIN CONTACT: SODIUM PHOSPHATE, MONOBASIC: **ACUTE EXPOSURE-** MAY CAUSE IRRITATION. **CHRONIC EXPOSURE-** REPEATED AND PROLONGED CONTACT MAY CAUSE DERMATITIS.

FIRST AID- REMOVE CONTAMINATED CLOTHING AND SHOES IMMEDIATELY. WASH AFFECTED AREA WITH SOAP OR MILD DETERGENT AND LARGE AMOUNTS OF WATER UNTIL NO EVIDENCE OF CHEMICAL REMAINS (APPROXIMATELY 15-20 MINUTES). GET MEDICAL ATTENTION IMMEDIATELY.

EYE CONTACT: SODIUM PHOSPHATE, MONOBASIC: **ACUTE EXPOSURE-** MAY CAUSE TRANSIENT IRRITATION. TESTED ON RABBIT EYES BY CONTINUOUS EXPOSURE FOR THREE HOURS AT 0.1 M SOLUTION AT PH 7.0 TO 7.5 MADE UP TO 0.46 OSMOLAR WITH SODIUM CHLORIDE OR SUCROSE, CAUSED NO DISTURBANCE OF THE CORNEA. **CHRONIC EXPOSURE-** NO DATA AVAILABLE.

FIRST AID- WASH EYES IMMEDIATELY WITH LARGE AMOUNTS OF WATER OR NORMAL SALINE, OCCASIONALLY LIFTING UPPER AND LOWER LIDS, UNTIL NO EVIDENCE OF CHEMICAL REMAINS (APPROXIMATELY 15-20 MINUTES). GET MEDICAL ATTENTION IMMEDIATELY.

INGESTION: SODIUM PHOSPHATE, MONOBASIC: **ACUTE EXPOSURE-** INGESTION MAY RESULT IN ABDOMINAL PAIN, NAUSEA, VOMITING, DIARRHEA, CRAMPS, PAIN AND BURNING IN THE MOUTH. DOSES OF 250 GM/KG GIVEN ORALLY TO GUINEA PIGS, RATS AND RABBITS PRODUCED DIARRHEA. GENERALLY, PHOSPHATES ARE SLOWLY AND INCOMPLETELY ABSORBED, THEREFORE SYSTEMIC REACTIONS ARE UNLIKELY WHEN THESE SALTS ARE GIVEN ORALLY. SODIUM PHOSPHATES ARE CAPABLE OF SERIOUSLY REDUCING THE IONIC SERUM CALCIUM. **CHRONIC EXPOSURE-** SODIUM PHOSPHATE, MONOBASIC IS USED AS A FOOD ADDITIVE. NO ADVERSE EFFECTS HAVE BEEN REPORTED.

FIRST AID- TREAT SYMPTOMATICALLY AND SUPPORTIVELY. GET MEDICAL ATTENTION IMMEDIATELY. IF VOMITING OCCURS, KEEP HEAD LOWER THAN HIPS TO PREVENT ASPIRATION.

ANTIDOTE: THE FOLLOWING ANTIDOTE HAS BEEN RECOMMENDED. HOWEVER, THE DECISION AS TO WHETHER THE SEVERITY OF POISONING REQUIRES ADMINISTRATION OF ANY ANTIDOTE AND ACTUAL DOSE REQUIRED SHOULD BE MADE BY QUALIFIED MEDICAL PERSONNEL.
PHOSPHATES: FOR HYPOCALCEMIA, AFTER PHOSPHATE INGESTION, GIVE CALCIUM GLUCONATE, 5 ML OF 10% SOLUTION SLOWLY INTRAVENOUSLY, TO RESTORE IONIC CALCIUM TO NORMAL LEVEL (DREISBACH, HANDBOOK OF POISONING, 12TH ED.). ANTIDOTE SHOULD BE ADMINISTERED BY QUALIFIED MEDICAL PERSONNEL.

REACTIVITY

REACTIVITY: STABLE UNDER NORMAL TEMPERATURES AND PRESSURES.

INCOMPATIBILITIES: SODIUM PHOSPHATE, MONOBASIC: BRASS: MAY BE CORROSIVE IN THE PRESENCE OF MOISTURE. METALS: SOLUTIONS MAY BE CORROSIVE. STEEL: MAY BE CORROSIVE IN THE PRESENCE OF MOISTURE.

DECOMPOSITION: THERMAL DECOMPOSITION PRODUCTS MAY INCLUDE TOXIC AND HAZARDOUS SODIUM OXIDE AND OXIDES OF PHOSPHORUS.

POLYMERIZATION: HAZARDOUS POLYMERIZATION HAS NOT BEEN REPORTED TO OCCUR UNDER NORMAL TEMPERATURES AND PRESSURES.

STORAGE AND DISPOSAL

OBSERVE ALL FEDERAL, STATE AND LOCAL REGULATIONS WHEN STORING OR DISPOSING OF THIS SUBSTANCE. FOR ASSISTANCE, CONTACT THE DISTRICT DIRECTOR OF THE ENVIRONMENTAL PROTECTION AGENCY.

****STORAGE****

STORE AWAY FROM INCOMPATIBLE SUBSTANCES.

CONDITIONS TO AVOID

MAY BURN BUT DOES NOT IGNITE READILY. AVOID CONTACT WITH STRONG OXIDIZERS, EXCESSIVE HEAT, SPARKS, OR OPEN FLAME.

SPILL AND LEAK PROCEDURES

OCCUPATIONAL SPILL: STOP LEAK IF YOU CAN DO IT WITHOUT RISK. FOR SMALL SPILLS, TAKE UP WITH SAND OR OTHER ABSORBENT MATERIAL AND PLACE INTO CLEAN, DRY CONTAINERS FOR LATER DISPOSAL. KEEP UNNECESSARY PEOPLE AWAY. ISOLATE HAZARD AREA AND DENY ENTRY.

PROTECTIVE EQUIPMENT

VENTILATION: PROVIDE LOCAL EXHAUST OR PROCESS ENCLOSURE VENTILATION SYSTEM.

RESPIRATOR: THE FOLLOWING RESPIRATORS ARE RECOMMENDED BASED ON INFORMATION FOUND IN THE PHYSICAL DATA, TOXICITY AND HEALTH EFFECTS SECTIONS. THEY ARE RANKED IN ORDER FROM MINIMUM TO MAXIMUM RESPIRATORY PROTECTION. THE SPECIFIC RESPIRATOR SELECTED MUST BE BASED ON CONTAMINATION LEVELS FOUND IN THE WORK PLACE, MUST NOT EXCEED THE WORKING LIMITS OF THE RESPIRATOR AND BE JOINTLY APPROVED BY THE NATIONAL INSTITUTE FOR OCCUPATIONAL SAFETY AND HEALTH AND THE MINE SAFETY AND HEALTH ADMINISTRATION (NIOSH-MSHA).

DUST AND MIST RESPIRATOR WITH A FULL FACEPIECE.

AIR-PURIFYING FULL FACEPIECE RESPIRATOR WITH A HIGH-EFFICIENCY PARTICULATE FILTER.

POWERED AIR-PURIFYING RESPIRATOR WITH A TIGHT-FITTING FACEPIECE AND HIGH-EFFICIENCY PARTICULATE FILTER.

TYPE 'C' SUPPLIED-AIR RESPIRATOR WITH A FULL FACEPIECE OPERATED IN PRESSURE-DEMAND OR OTHER POSITIVE PRESSURE MODE OR WITH A FULL FACEPIECE, HELMET OR HOOD OPERATED IN CONTINUOUS-FLOW MODE.

SELF-CONTAINED BREATHING APPARATUS WITH A FULL FACEPIECE OPERATED IN PRESSURE-DEMAND OR OTHER POSITIVE PRESSURE MODE.

FOR FIREFIGHTING AND OTHER IMMEDIATELY DANGEROUS TO LIFE OR HEALTH CONDITIONS: SELF-CONTAINED BREATHING APPARATUS WITH FULL FACEPIECE OPERATED IN PRESSURE-DEMAND OR OTHER POSITIVE PRESSURE MODE.

SUPPLIED-AIR RESPIRATOR WITH FULL FACEPIECE AND OPERATED IN PRESSURE-DEMAND OR OTHER POSITIVE PRESSURE MODE IN COMBINATION WITH AN AUXILIARY SELF-CONTAINED BREATHING APPARATUS OPERATED IN PRESSURE-DEMAND OR OTHER POSITIVE PRESSURE MODE.

CLOTHING: EMPLOYEE MUST WEAR APPROPRIATE PROTECTIVE (IMPERVIOUS) CLOTHING AND EQUIPMENT TO PREVENT REPEATED OR PROLONGED SKIN CONTACT WITH THIS SUBSTANCE.

GLOVES: EMPLOYEE MUST WEAR APPROPRIATE PROTECTIVE GLOVES TO PREVENT CONTACT WITH THIS SUBSTANCE.

EYE PROTECTION: EMPLOYEE MUST WEAR SPLASH-PROOF OR DUST-RESISTANT SAFETY GOGGLES TO PREVENT EYE CONTACT WITH THIS SUBSTANCE.

EMERGENCY EYE WASH: WHERE THERE IS ANY POSSIBILITY THAT AN EMPLOYEE'S EYES MAY BE EXPOSED TO THIS SUBSTANCE, THE EMPLOYER SHOULD PROVIDE AN EYE WASH FOUNTAIN WITHIN THE IMMEDIATE WORK AREA FOR EMERGENCY USE.

AUTHORIZED BY- OCCUPATIONAL HEALTH SERVICES, INC.

CREATION DATE: 11/16/89 ***REVISION DATE:*** 11/16/89

MATERIAL SAFETY DATA SHEET

OCCUPATIONAL HEALTH SERVICES, INC.
AGRICULTURE AND PESTICIDE DIVISION
450 SEVENTH AVENUE, SUITE 2407
NEW YORK, NEW YORK 10123
1-800-445-MSDS OR (212) 967-1100

EMERGENCY CONTACT:
JOHN S. BRANSFORD, JR. (615) 292-1180

SUBSTANCE IDENTIFICATION

CAS-NUMBER 150-68-5

SUBSTANCE: **MONURON**

TRADE NAMES/SYNONYMS: UREA, N'-(4-CHLOROPHENYL)-N,N-DIMETHYL-; UREA, 3-(P-CHLOROPHENYL)-1,1-DIMETHYL-; N'-(4-CHLOROPHENYL)-N,N-DIMETHYLUREA; 3-(P-CHLOROPHENYL)-1,1-DIMETHYLUREA; 3-(4-CHLOROPHENYL)-1,1-DIMETHYLUREA; 1,1-DIMETHYL-3-(P-CHLOROPHENYL)UREA; CHLORFENIDIM; CMU; MONUREX; TELVAR; C9H11CLN2O; PST15196

CHEMICAL FAMILY: SUBSTITUTED UREA HALOGEN COMPOUND, AROMATIC

MOLECULAR FORMULA: CL-C6-H4-N-H-C-O-N-(C-H3)2

MOLECULAR WEIGHT: 198.65

CERCLA RATINGS (SCALE 0-3): HEALTH=3 FIRE=1 REACTIVITY=0 PERSISTENCE=2

NFPA RATINGS (SCALE 0-4): HEALTH=U FIRE=1 REACTIVITY=0

COMPONENTS AND CONTAMINANTS

COMPONENT: MONURON ***PERCENT:*** 100
CAS# 150-68-5

OTHER CONTAMINANTS: NONE

EXPOSURE LIMITS: NO OCCUPATIONAL EXPOSURE LIMITS ESTABLISHED BY OSHA, ACGIH, OR NIOSH.

PHYSICAL DATA

DESCRIPTION: WHITE CRYSTALLINE SOLID WITH A SLIGHT ODOR.

BOILING POINT: 365-342 F (185-200 C) (DECOMPOSES)

MELTING POINT: 338-340 F (170-171 C) ***SPECIFIC GRAVITY:*** 1.27

VAPOR PRESSURE: NEGLIGIBLE ***PH:*** 6.26 (SAT. SOLN.)

SOLUBILITY IN WATER: 0.023%

SOLVENT SOLUBILITY: MODERATELY SOLUBLE IN METHANOL, ETHANOL AND ACETONE; SLIGHTLY SOLUBLE IN NO. 3 DIESEL OIL, PETROLEUM OILS AND POLAR ORGANIC SOLVENTS.

FIRE AND EXPLOSION DATA

FIRE AND EXPLOSION HAZARD: SLIGHT FIRE HAZARD WHEN EXPOSED TO HEAT OR FLAME.

FIREFIGHTING MEDIA: DRY CHEMICAL, CARBON DIOXIDE, HALON, WATER SPRAY OR STANDARD FOAM (1987 EMERGENCY RESPONSE GUIDEBOOK, DOT P 5800.4). FOR LARGER FIRES, USE WATER SPRAY, FOG OR STANDARD FOAM (1987 EMERGENCY RESPONSE GUIDEBOOK, DOT P 5800.4).

FIREFIGHTING: MOVE CONTAINERS FROM FIRE AREA IF POSSIBLE. FIGHT FIRE FROM MAXIMUM DISTANCE. STAY AWAY FROM STORAGE TANK ENDS. DIKE FIRE CONTROL WATER FOR LATER DISPOSAL. DO NOT SCATTER MATERIAL (1987 EMERGENCY RESPONSE GUIDEBOOK, DOT P 5800.4, GUIDE PAGE 55). EXTINGUISH USING AGENT SUITABLE FOR TYPE OF SURROUNDING FIRE. USE WATER IN FLOODING QUANTITIES AS FOG. KEEP SPARKS, FLAMES AND OTHER SOURCES OF IGNITION AWAY. KEEP MATERIAL OUT OF WATER SOURCES AND SEWERS. DO NOT TOUCH MATERIAL AND AVOID BREATHING DUSTS AND FUMES FROM BURNING MATERIAL. KEEP UPWIND.

TOXICITY

MONURON: TOXICITY DATA: 1053 MG/KG ORAL-RAT LD50; 670 MG/KG ORAL-GUINEA PIG LDLO; 1000 MG/KG INTRAPERITONEAL-MOUSE LD50; 3600 MG/KG UNREPORTED-RAT LD50; 3500 MG/KG UNREPORTED-MAMMAL LD50; MUTAGENIC DATA (RTECS); REPRODUCTIVE EFFECTS DATA (RTECS); TUMORIGENIC DATA (RTECS). CARCINOGEN STATUS: ANIMAL LIMITED EVIDENCE (IARC GROUP-3). ORAL ADMINISTRATION INDUCED AN INCREASED INCIDENCE OF LUNG TUMORS IN MALES OF ONE OF TWO STRAINS OF MICE. IN ANOTHER STUDY, AN INCREASED INCIDENCE OF HEPATOMAS WAS OBSERVED IN MICE FED MONURON; BUT SURVIVAL RATES OF THE CONTROLS WERE NOT REPORTED. IN ONE STUDY BY ORAL ADMINISTRATION IN MALE RATS, TUMORS WERE OBSERVED AT VARIOUS SITES; NONE WERE OBSERVED IN CONCURRENT CONTROLS. TWO YEAR FEED STUDIES HAVE SHOWN CLEAR EVIDENCE OF CARCINOGENICITY FOR MALE RATS IN THAT MONURON CAUSED INCREASED INCIDENCES OF TUBULAR CELL ADENOCARCINOMAS OF THE KIDNEY AND NEOPLASTIC NODULES OR CARCINOMAS (COMBINED) OF THE LIVER (NTP TR 266). ACUTE TOXICITY LEVEL: MODERATELY TOXIC BY INGESTION. TARGET EFFECTS: POISONING MAY AFFECT THE LIVER, KIDNEYS, AND BLOOD.

HEALTH EFFECTS AND FIRST AID

INHALATION: MONURON: **ACUTE EXPOSURE-** MANY UREA DERIVATIVE HERBICIDES ARE MODERATELY IRRITATING TO THE MUCOUS MEMBRANES. **CHRONIC EXPOSURE-** NO DATA AVAILABLE.

FIRST AID- REMOVE FROM EXPOSURE AREA TO FRESH AIR IMMEDIATELY. IF BREATHING HAS STOPPED, PERFORM ARTIFICIAL RESPIRATION. KEEP PERSON WARM AND AT REST. TREAT SYMPTOMATICALLY AND SUPPORTIVELY. GET MEDICAL ATTENTION IMMEDIATELY.

SKIN CONTACT: MONURON: **ACUTE EXPOSURE-** MAY CAUSE MILD IRRITATION. **CHRONIC EXPOSURE-** NO DATA AVAILABLE.

FIRST AID- REMOVE CONTAMINATED CLOTHING AND SHOES IMMEDIATELY. WASH AFFECTED AREA WITH SOAP OR MILD DETERGENT AND LARGE AMOUNTS OF WATER UNTIL NO EVIDENCE OF CHEMICAL REMAINS (APPROXIMATELY 15-20 MINUTES). GET MEDICAL ATTENTION IMMEDIATELY.

EYE CONTACT: MONURON: **ACUTE EXPOSURE-** MANY UREA DERIVATIVE HERBICIDES ARE MODERATELY IRRITATING TO THE EYES. **CHRONIC EXPOSURE-** NO DATA AVAILABLE.

FIRST AID- WASH EYES IMMEDIATELY WITH LARGE AMOUNTS OF WATER OR NORMAL SALINE, OCCASIONALLY LIFTING UPPER AND LOWER LIDS, UNTIL NO EVIDENCE OF CHEMICAL REMAINS (APPROXIMATELY 15-20 MINUTES). GET MEDICAL ATTENTION IMMEDIATELY.

INGESTION: MONURON: LIMITED ANIMAL CARCINOGEN. **ACUTE EXPOSURE-** ADMINISTRATION TO RATS PRODUCED ATAXIA, DROWSINESS, HYPOREFLEXIA, PALLOR AND TACHYPNEA, PROGRESSING TO DACRYORRHEA, ACIDURIA, DIARRHEA, EPISTAXIS, HYPERREFLEXIA AND IRRITABILITY. ADIPSIA, DYSPNEA, HYPOTHERMIA AND ANURIA PRECEDED DEATH FROM CARDIAC OR RESPIRATORY FAILURE. LABORATORY ANALYSIS OF SURVIVING RATS REVEALED DIURESIS, ALKALINURIA, HEMATURIA, GLYCOSURIA, AND PROTEINURIA. PATHOLOGIC FINDINGS INCLUDED GASTROENTERITIS, FATTY NECROSIS OF THE LIVER, RENAL AND SPLENIC PALLOR, AND DEGENERATIVE CHANGES IN KIDNEYS, MUSCLE, SALIVARY GLANDS AND TESTES. **CHRONIC EXPOSURE-** REPEATED DOSES IN RATS PRODUCED ANEMIA, LIVER DAMAGE, METHEMOGLOBINEMIA, AND RENAL TUBULAR CELL CYTOMEGALY. REPRODUCTIVE EFFECTS HAVE BEEN REPORTED IN ANIMALS. IN A STUDY OF TWO STRAINS OF MICE, MONURON INDUCED AN INCREASED INCIDENCE OF LUNG TUMORS IN ONE STRAIN OF MALES. IN ANOTHER MOUSE STUDY, AN INCREASED INCIDENCE OF HEPATOMAS WAS OBSERVED; BUT SURVIVAL RATES OF THE CONTROLS WERE NOT REPORTED. IN ONE STUDY, TUMORS WERE OBSERVED AT VARIOUS SITES; NONE WERE OBSERVED IN CONCURRENT CONTROLS. ADDITIONALLY, INCREASED INCIDENCES OF TUBULAR CELL ADENOCARCINOMAS OF THE KIDNEY AND NEOPLASTIC NODULES OR CARCINOMAS (COMBINED) OF THE LIVER HAVE BEEN REPORTED IN RATS.

FIRST AID- REMOVE BY GASTRIC LAVAGE AND CATHARSIS. MAINTAIN BLOOD PRESSURE AND AIRWAY. GIVE OXYGEN IF RESPIRATION IS DEPRESSED. DO NOT PERFORM GASTRIC LAVAGE IF VICTIM IS UNCONSCIOUS. GET MEDICAL ATTENTION IMMEDIATELY (DREISBACH, HANDBOOK OF POISONING, 12TH ED.). ADMINISTRATION OF LAVAGE OR OXYGEN SHOULD BE PERFORMED BY QUALIFIED MEDICAL PERSONNEL.

ANTIDOTE: NO SPECIFIC ANTIDOTE. TREAT SYMPTOMATICALLY AND SUPPORTIVELY.

REACTIVITY

REACTIVITY: STABLE UNDER NORMAL TEMPERATURES AND PRESSURES.

INCOMPATIBILITIES: MONURON: OXIDIZERS (STRONG): FIRE AND EXPLOSION HAZARD.

DECOMPOSITION: THERMAL DECOMPOSITION PRODUCTS MAY INCLUDE TOXIC AND CORROSIVE FUMES OF CHLORIDES AND TOXIC OXIDES OF NITROGEN.

POLYMERIZATION: HAZARDOUS POLYMERIZATION HAS NOT BEEN REPORTED TO OCCUR UNDER NORMAL TEMPERATURES AND PRESSURES.

STORAGE AND DISPOSAL

OBSERVE ALL FEDERAL, STATE AND LOCAL REGULATIONS WHEN STORING OR DISPOSING OF THIS SUBSTANCE. FOR ASSISTANCE, CONTACT THE DISTRICT DIRECTOR OF THE ENVIRONMENTAL PROTECTION AGENCY.

****STORAGE****

STORE IN ACCORDANCE WITH 40 CFR 165 RECOMMENDED PROCEDURES FOR THE DISPOSAL AND STORAGE OF PESTICIDES AND PESTICIDE CONTAINERS.
STORE AWAY FROM INCOMPATIBLE SUBSTANCES.
KEEP COOL AND DRY.

****DISPOSAL****

DISPOSAL MUST BE IN ACCORDANCE WITH 40 CFR 165 RECOMMENDED PROCEDURES FOR THE DISPOSAL AND STORAGE OF PESTICIDES AND PESTICIDE CONTAINERS.

CONDITIONS TO AVOID

MAY BURN BUT DOES NOT IGNITE READILY. CONTAINERS MAY EXPLODE IN HEAT OF FIRE.

SPILL AND LEAK PROCEDURES

OCCUPATIONAL SPILL: SWEEP UP AND PLACE IN SUITABLE CLEAN, DRY CONTAINERS FOR RECLAMATION OR LATER DISPOSAL. DO NOT FLUSH SPILLED MATERIAL INTO SEWER. KEEP UNNECESSARY PEOPLE AWAY.

PROTECTIVE EQUIPMENT

VENTILATION: PROVIDE LOCAL EXHAUST OR GENERAL DILUTION VENTILATION SYSTEM.

RESPIRATOR: THE FOLLOWING RESPIRATORS ARE RECOMMENDED BASED ON INFORMATION FOUND IN THE PHYSICAL DATA, TOXICITY AND HEALTH EFFECTS SECTIONS. THEY ARE RANKED IN ORDER FROM MINIMUM TO MAXIMUM RESPIRATORY PROTECTION. THE SPECIFIC RESPIRATOR SELECTED MUST BE BASED ON CONTAMINATION LEVELS FOUND IN THE WORK PLACE, MUST NOT EXCEED THE WORKING LIMITS OF THE RESPIRATOR AND BE JOINTLY APPROVED BY THE NATIONAL INSTITUTE FOR OCCUPATIONAL SAFETY AND HEALTH AND THE MINE SAFETY AND HEALTH ADMINISTRATION (NIOSH-MSHA).
TYPE 'C' SUPPLIED-AIR RESPIRATOR WITH A FULL FACEPIECE OPERATED IN PRESSURE-DEMAND OR OTHER POSITIVE PRESSURE MODE OR WITH A FULL FACEPIECE, HELMET OR HOOD OPERATED IN CONTINOUS-FLOW MODE.
SELF-CONTAINED BREATHING APPARATUS WITH A FULL FACEPIECE OPERATED IN PRESSURE-DEMAND OR OTHER POSITIVE PRESSURE MODE.
FOR FIREFIGHTING AND OTHER IMMEDIATELY DANGEROUS TO LIFE OR HEALTH CONDITIONS:
SELF-CONTAINED BREATHING APPARATUS WITH FULL FACEPIECE OPERATED IN PRESSURE-DEMAND OR OTHER POSITIVE PRESSURE MODE.
SUPPLIED-AIR RESPIRATOR WITH FULL FACEPIECE AND OPERATED IN PRESSURE-DEMAND OR OTHER POSITIVE PRESSURE MODE IN COMBINATION WITH AN AUXILIARY SELF-CONTAINED BREATHING APPARATUS OPERATED IN PRESSURE-DEMAND OR OTHER POSITIVE PRESSURE MODE.

CLOTHING: EMPLOYEE MUST WEAR APPROPRIATE PROTECTIVE (IMPERVIOUS) CLOTHING AND EQUIPMENT TO PREVENT REPEATED OR PROLONGED SKIN CONTACT WITH THIS SUBSTANCE.

GLOVES: EMPLOYEE MUST WEAR APPROPRIATE PROTECTIVE GLOVES TO PREVENT CONTACT WITH THIS SUBSTANCE.

EYE PROTECTION: EMPLOYEE MUST WEAR SPLASH-PROOF OR DUST-RESISTANT SAFETY GOGGLES TO PREVENT EYE CONTACT WITH THIS SUBSTANCE.
EMERGENCY EYE WASH: WHERE THERE IS ANY POSSIBILITY THAT AN EMPLOYEE'S EYES MAY BE EXPOSED TO THIS SUBSTANCE, THE EMPLOYER SHOULD PROVIDE AN EYE WASH FOUNTAIN WITHIN THE IMMEDIATE WORK AREA FOR EMERGENCY USE.

AUTHORIZED BY- OCCUPATIONAL HEALTH SERVICES, INC.
CREATION DATE: 10/04/89 ***REVISION DATE:*** 07/13/90

MATERIAL SAFETY DATA SHEET

OCCUPATIONAL HEALTH SERVICES, INC.
AGRICULTURE AND PESTICIDE DIVISION
450 SEVENTH AVENUE, SUITE 2407
NEW YORK, NEW YORK 10123
1-800-445-MSDS OR (212) 967-1100

EMERGENCY CONTACT:
JOHN S. BRANSFORD, JR. (615) 292-1180

SUBSTANCE IDENTIFICATION

CAS-NUMBER 140-41-0

***SUBSTANCE:* MONURON TCA**

TRADE NAMES/SYNONYMS: ACETIC ACID, TRICHLORO-, COMPOUND WITH N'-(4-CHLOROPHENYL)-N,N- DIMETHYLUREA (1:1); ACETIC ACID, TRICHLORO-, COMPOUND WITH 3-(P-CHLOROPHENYL)-1,1- DIMETHYLUREA (1:1); TRICHLOROACETIC ACID COMPOUND WITH N'-(4-CHLOROPHENYL)-N,N-DIMETHYLUREA; TRICHLOROACETIC ACID COMPOUND WITH 3-(P-CHLOROPHENYL)-1,1-DIMETHYLUREA; 3-(4-CHLOROPHENYL)-1,1-DIMETHYLURONIUM TRICHLOROACETATE; 3-(P-CHLOROPHENYL)-1,1-DIMETHYLUREA TRICHLOROACETATE; ACEITC ACID, TRICHLORO-, COMPOUND WITH 3-(P-CHLOROPHENYL)-1,1- DIMETHYLUREA(1:1); TRICHLOROACETIC ACID COMPOUND WITH N'-(4-CHLOROPHENYL)-N,N- DIMETHYL UREA(1:1); TRICHLOROACETIC ACID COMPOUND WITH 3-(P-CHLOROPHENYL)-1,1- DIMETHYL UREA(1:1); N'-(4-CHLOROPHENYL)-1,1-DIMETHYLUREA TRICHLOROACETATE; GC 2996; UROX; MONURON TRICHLOROACETATE; C11H12CL4N2O3; PST15197

CHEMICAL FAMILY: SUBSTITUTED UREA
HALOGEN COMPOUND, AROMATIC

MOLECULAR FORMULA: CL-C6-H4-N-H-C-O-N-(C-H3)2.CL3-C-C-O2-H

MOLECULAR WEIGHT: 362.05

CERCLA RATINGS (SCALE 0-3): HEALTH=2 FIRE=1 REACTIVITY=0 PERSISTENCE=1

NFPA RATINGS (SCALE 0-4): HEALTH=2 FIRE=1 REACTIVITY=0

COMPONENTS AND CONTAMINANTS

COMPONENT: MONURON TCA ***PERCENT:*** 100
CAS# 140-41-0

OTHER CONTAMINANTS: NONE

EXPOSURE LIMITS: NO OCCUPATIONAL EXPOSURE LIMITS ESTABLISHED BY OSHA, ACGIH, OR NIOSH.

PHYSICAL DATA

DESCRIPTION: CRYSTALLINE SOLID. ***MELTING POINT:*** 172-178 F (78-81 C)

SPECIFIC GRAVITY: NOT AVAILABLE ***SOLUBILITY IN WATER:*** 0.0918%
SOLVENT SOLUBILITY: SOLUBLE IN DICHLOROETHANE, ACETONE, XYLENE, METHANOL, ETHANOL AND AROMATIC SOLVENTS.
DECOMPOSES ABOVE 194 F (90 C)

FIRE AND EXPLOSION DATA

FIRE AND EXPLOSION HAZARD: SLIGHT FIRE HAZARD WHEN EXPOSED TO HEAT OR FLAME.

FIREFIGHTING MEDIA: DRY CHEMICAL, CARBON DIOXIDE, HALON, WATER SPRAY OR STANDARD FOAM (1987 EMERGENCY RESPONSE GUIDEBOOK, DOT P 5800.4).
FOR LARGER FIRES, USE WATER SPRAY, FOG OR STANDARD FOAM (1987 EMERGENCY RESPONSE GUIDEBOOK, DOT P 5800.4).

FIREFIGHTING: MOVE CONTAINERS FROM FIRE AREA IF POSSIBLE. FIGHT FIRE FROM MAXIMUM DISTANCE. STAY AWAY FROM STORAGE TANK ENDS. DIKE FIRE CONTROL WATER FOR LATER DISPOSAL. DO NOT SCATTER MATERIAL (1987 EMERGENCY RESPONSE GUIDEBOOK, DOT P 5800.4, GUIDE PAGE 55).
EXTINGUISH USING AGENT SUITABLE FOR TYPE OF SURROUNDING FIRE. USE WATER IN FLOODING QUANTITIES AS FOG. KEEP SPARKS, FLAMES AND OTHER SOURCES OF IGNITION AWAY. KEEP MATERIAL OUT OF WATER SOURCES AND SEWERS. DO NOT TOUCH MATERIAL AND AVOID BREATHING DUSTS AND FUMES FROM BURNING MATERIAL. KEEP UPWIND.

TOXICITY

MONURON TCA: TOXICITY DATA: 1000 MG/KG SKIN-RABBIT LD50 (FMCHA2); 2300 MG/KG ORAL-RAT LD50. CARCINOGEN STATUS: NONE. LOCAL EFFECTS: IRRITANT-INHALATION, SKIN, AND EYES. ACUTE TOXICITY LEVEL: TOXIC BY DERMAL ABSORPTION AND MODERATELY TOXIC BY INGESTION. TARGET EFFECTS: NO DATA AVAILABLE.

HEALTH EFFECTS AND FIRST AID

INHALATION: MONURON TCA: **ACUTE EXPOSURE-** MAY CAUSE IRRITATION OF THE MUCOUS MEMBRANES. **CHRONIC EXPOSURE-** NO DATA AVAILABLE.

FIRST AID- REMOVE FROM EXPOSURE AREA TO FRESH AIR IMMEDIATELY. IF BREATHING HAS STOPPED, PERFORM ARTIFICIAL RESPIRATION. KEEP PERSON WARM AND AT REST. TREAT SYMPTOMATICALLY AND SUPPORTIVELY. GET MEDICAL ATTENTION IMMEDIATELY.

SKIN CONTACT: MONURON TCA: TOXIC. **ACUTE EXPOSURE-** MAY CAUSE IRRITATION. A LETHAL DOSE IN RABBITS BY DERMAL ABSORPTION WAS 1000 MG/KG. **CHRONIC EXPOSURE-** NO DATA AVAILABLE.

FIRST AID- REMOVE CONTAMINATED CLOTHING AND SHOES IMMEDIATELY. WASH AFFECTED AREA WITH SOAP OR MILD DETERGENT AND LARGE AMOUNTS OF WATER UNTIL NO EVIDENCE OF CHEMICAL REMAINS (APPROXIMATELY 15-20 MINUTES). GET MEDICAL ATTENTION IMMEDIATELY.

EYE CONTACT: MONURON TCA: **ACUTE EXPOSURE-** MAY CAUSE IRRITATION. **CHRONIC EXPOSURE-** NO DATA AVAILABLE.

FIRST AID- WASH EYES IMMEDIATELY WITH LARGE AMOUNTS OF WATER OR NORMAL SALINE, OCCASIONALLY LIFTING UPPER AND LOWER LIDS, UNTIL NO EVIDENCE OF CHEMICAL REMAINS (APPROXIMATELY 15-20 MINUTES). GET MEDICAL ATTENTION IMMEDIATELY.

INGESTION: MONURON TCA: **ACUTE EXPOSURE-** HIGH ACUTE ORAL DOSES HAVE PRODUCED SYMPTOMS OF ANEMIA, METHEMOGLOBINEMIA AND PATHOLOGICAL CHANGES IN THE SPLEEN, BONE MARROW, LIVER AND KIDNEYS OF LABORATORY ANIMALS. **CHRONIC EXPOSURE-** IN ADDITION TO THE EFFECTS PRODUCED FROM ACUTE DOSES, EFFECTS ON THE LUNG AND TESTES WERE DEMONSTRATED IN LONGER TERM STUDIES OF LABORATORY ANIMALS AT HIGH DIETARY LEVELS. AN INCREASED INCIDENCE OF HEPATOMAS, LUNG TUMORS, AND OTHER TUMORS AT VARIOUS SITES WERE OBSERVED IN ORAL ADMINISTRATION STUDIES OF MONURON FED TO RODENTS.

FIRST AID- REMOVE BY GASTRIC LAVAGE AND CATHARSIS. MAINTAIN BLOOD PRESSURE AND AIRWAY. GIVE OXYGEN IF RESPIRATION IS DEPRESSED. DO NOT PERFORM GASTRIC LAVAGE IF VICTIM IS UNCONSCIOUS. GET MEDICAL ATTENTION IMMEDIATELY (DREISBACH, HANDBOOK OF POISONING, 12TH ED.). ADMINISTRATION OF LAVAGE OR OXYGEN SHOULD BE PERFORMED BY QUALIFIED MEDICAL PERSONNEL.

REACTIVITY

REACTIVITY: STABLE UNDER NORMAL TEMPERATURES AND PRESSURES.

INCOMPATIBILITIES: MONURON TCA: ALKALINE MATERIALS: INCOMPATIBLE. OXIDIZERS (STRONG): FIRE AND EXPLOSION HAZARD.

DECOMPOSITION: THERMAL DECOMPOSITION PRODUCTS MAY INCLUDE TOXIC OXIDES OF NITROGEN AND CARBON AND TOXIC AND CORROSIVE FUMES OF CHLORIDES.

POLYMERIZATION: HAZARDOUS POLYMERIZATION HAS NOT BEEN REPORTED TO OCCUR UNDER NORMAL TEMPERATURES AND PRESSURES.

STORAGE AND DISPOSAL

OBSERVE ALL FEDERAL, STATE AND LOCAL REGULATIONS WHEN STORING OR DISPOSING OF THIS SUBSTANCE. FOR ASSISTANCE, CONTACT THE DISTRICT DIRECTOR OF THE ENVIRONMENTAL PROTECTION AGENCY.

****STORAGE****

STORE IN ACCORDANCE WITH 40 CFR 165 RECOMMENDED PROCEDURES FOR THE DISPOSAL AND STORAGE OF PESTICIDES AND PESTICIDE CONTAINERS.
AVOID STORAGE AT TEMPERATURES BELOW FREEZING OR ABOVE 100 F (212 C).
STORE AWAY FROM INCOMPATIBLE SUBSTANCES.

****DISPOSAL****

DISPOSAL MUST BE IN ACCORDANCE WITH 40 CFR 165 RECOMMENDED PROCEDURES FOR THE DISPOSAL AND STORAGE OF PESTICIDES AND PESTICIDE CONTAINERS.

CONDITIONS TO AVOID

MAY BURN BUT DOES NOT IGNITE READILY. CONTAINERS MAY EXPLODE IN HEAT OF FIRE.

SPILL AND LEAK PROCEDURES

OCCUPATIONAL SPILL: DO NOT TOUCH SPILLED MATERIAL. STOP LEAK IF YOU CAN DO IT WITHOUT RISK. USE WATER SPRAY TO REDUCE VAPORS. FOR SMALL SPILLS, TAKE UP WITH SAND OR OTHER ABSORBENT MATERIAL AND PLACE INTO CONTAINERS FOR LATER DISPOSAL. FOR SMALL DRY SPILLS, WITH A CLEAN SHOVEL PLACE MATERIAL INTO CLEAN, DRY CONTAINERS AND COVER. MOVE CONTAINERS FROM SPILL AREA. FOR LARGER SPILLS, DIKE FAR AHEAD OF SPILL FOR LATER DISPOSAL. KEEP UNNECESSARY PEOPLE AWAY. ISOLATE HAZARD AREA AND DENY ENTRY. VENTILATE CLOSED SPACES BEFORE ENTERING.

PROTECTIVE EQUIPMENT

VENTILATION: PROVIDE LOCAL EXHAUST OR PROCESS ENCLOSURE VENTILATION SYSTEM.

RESPIRATOR: THE FOLLOWING RESPIRATORS ARE RECOMMENDED BASED ON INFORMATION FOUND IN THE PHYSICAL DATA, TOXICITY AND HEALTH EFFECTS SECTIONS. THEY ARE RANKED IN ORDER FROM MINIMUM TO MAXIMUM RESPIRATORY PROTECTION. THE SPECIFIC RESPIRATOR SELECTED MUST BE BASED ON CONTAMINATION LEVELS FOUND IN THE WORK PLACE, MUST NOT EXCEED THE WORKING LIMITS OF THE RESPIRATOR AND BE JOINTLY APPROVED BY THE NATIONAL INSTITUTE FOR OCCUPATIONAL SAFETY AND HEALTH AND THE MINE SAFETY AND HEALTH ADMINISTRATION (NIOSH-MSHA).
TYPE 'C' SUPPLIED-AIR RESPIRATOR WITH A FULL FACEPIECE OPERATED IN PRESSURE-DEMAND OR OTHER POSITIVE PRESSURE MODE OR WITH A FULL FACEPIECE, HELMET OR HOOD OPERATED IN CONTINOUS-FLOW MODE.
SELF-CONTAINED BREATHING APPARATUS WITH A FULL FACEPIECE OPERATED IN PRESSURE-DEMAND OR OTHER POSITIVE PRESSURE MODE.
FOR FIREFIGHTING AND OTHER IMMEDIATELY DANGEROUS TO LIFE OR HEALTH CONDITIONS:
SELF-CONTAINED BREATHING APPARATUS WITH FULL FACEPIECE OPERATED IN PRESSURE-DEMAND OR OTHER POSITIVE PRESSURE MODE.
SUPPLIED-AIR RESPIRATOR WITH FULL FACEPIECE AND OPERATED IN PRESSURE-DEMAND OR OTHER POSITIVE PRESSURE MODE IN COMBINATION WITH AN AUXILIARY SELF-CONTAINED BREATHING APPARATUS OPERATED IN PRESSURE-DEMAND OR OTHER POSITIVE PRESSURE MODE.

CLOTHING: EMPLOYEE MUST WEAR APPROPRIATE PROTECTIVE (IMPERVIOUS) CLOTHING AND EQUIPMENT TO PREVENT ANY POSSIBILITY OF SKIN CONTACT WITH THIS SUBSTANCE.

GLOVES: EMPLOYEE MUST WEAR APPROPRIATE PROTECTIVE GLOVES TO PREVENT CONTACT WITH THIS SUBSTANCE.

EYE PROTECTION: EMPLOYEE MUST WEAR SPLASH-PROOF OR DUST-RESISTANT SAFETY GOGGLES WITH OR WITHOUT A FACESHIELD TO PREVENT CONTACT WITH THIS SUBSTANCE.
EMERGENCY EYE WASH: WHERE THERE IS ANY POSSIBILITY THAT AN EMPLOYEE'S EYES MAY BE EXPOSED TO THIS SUBSTANCE, THE EMPLOYER SHOULD PROVIDE AN EYE WASH FOUNTAIN WITHIN THE IMMEDIATE WORK AREA FOR EMERGENCY USE.

AUTHORIZED BY- OCCUPATIONAL HEALTH SERVICES, INC.
CREATION DATE: 10/04/89 ***REVISION DATE:*** 05/09/90

MATERIAL SAFETY DATA SHEET

OCCUPATIONAL HEALTH SERVICES, INC.
AGRICULTURE AND PESTICIDE DIVISION
450 SEVENTH AVENUE, SUITE 2407
NEW YORK, NEW YORK 10123
1-800-445-MSDS OR (212) 967-1100

EMERGENCY CONTACT:
JOHN S. BRANSFORD, JR. (615) 292-1180

SUBSTANCE IDENTIFICATION

CAS-NUMBER 628-63-7

SUBSTANCE: N-AMYL ACETATE

TRADE NAMES/SYNONYMS: ACETIC ACID, AMYL ESTER; ACETIC ACID, N-AMYL ESTER; N-PENTYL ACETATE; PENTYL ACETATE; AMYL ACETATE; AMYL ACETATE ETHER; ACETIC ACID, PENTYL ESTER; AMYL ACETIC ESTER; AMYL ACETIC ETHER; BIRNENOEL; 1-PENTANOL ACETATE; 1-PENTYL ACETATE; PRIMARY AMYL ACETATE; BANANA OIL; CLEAR LACQUER 1830 (RAFFI AND SWANSON, INC.); STCC 4909111; UN 1104; A-718; PST15270

CHEMICAL FAMILY: ESTER, CARBOXYLIC, ALIPHATIC

MOLECULAR FORMULA: C7-H14-O2

MOLECULAR WEIGHT: 130.21

CERCLA RATINGS (SCALE 0-3): HEALTH=1 FIRE=3 REACTIVITY=0 PERSISTENCE=0

NFPA RATINGS (SCALE 0-4): HEALTH=1 FIRE=3 REACTIVITY=0

COMPONENTS AND CONTAMINANTS

COMPONENT: N-AMYL ACETATE ***PERCENT:*** 100
CAS# 628-63-7

OTHER CONTAMINANTS: NONE

EXPOSURE LIMITS: N-AMYL ACETATE: 100 PPM OSHA TWA 100 PPM (530 MG/M3) ACGIH TWA

PHYSICAL DATA

DESCRIPTION: COLORLESS TO YELLOW LIQUID WITH A MILD, PLEASANT, CHARACTERISTIC, BANANA OR PEAR-LIKE ODOR. ***BOILING POINT:*** 300 F (149 C)

MELTING POINT: -95 F (-71 C) ***SPECIFIC GRAVITY:*** 0.8756

VAPOR PRESSURE: 4 MMHG @ 20 C ***EVAPORATION RATE:*** (BU ACETATE=1) 0.42

SOLUBILITY IN WATER: VERY SLIGHTLY ***ODOR THRESHOLD:*** 0.08 PPM

VAPOR DENSITY: 4.5

SOLVENT SOLUBILITY: SOLUBLE WITH ALCOHOL, ETHER

FIRE AND EXPLOSION DATA

FIRE AND EXPLOSION HAZARD: DANGEROUS FIRE HAZARD WHEN EXPOSED TO HEAT OR FLAME.
VAPOR-AIR MIXTURES ARE EXPLOSIVE ABOVE FLASH POINT.
VAPORS ARE HEAVIER THAN AIR AND MAY TRAVEL A CONSIDERABLE DISTANCE TO A SOURCE OF IGNITION AND FLASH BACK.

FLASH POINT: 60 F (16 C) ***UPPER EXPLOSIVE LIMIT:*** 7.5%

LOWER EXPLOSIVE LIMIT: 1.1% ***AUTOIGNITION TEMP.:*** 714 F (379 C)

FLAMMABILITY CLASS(OSHA): IC

FIREFIGHTING MEDIA: DRY CHEMICAL, CARBON DIOXIDE, HALON, WATER SPRAY OR ALCOHOL FOAM (1987 EMERGENCY RESPONSE GUIDEBOOK, DOT P 5800.4).
FOR LARGER FIRES, USE WATER SPRAY, FOG OR ALCOHOL FOAM (1987 EMERGENCY RESPONSE GUIDEBOOK, DOT P 5800.4).
ALCOHOL FOAM (NFPA 325M, FIRE HAZARD PROPERTIES OF FLAMMABLE LIQUIDS, GASES, AND VOLATILE SOLIDS, 1984).

FIREFIGHTING: MOVE CONTAINER FROM FIRE AREA IF POSSIBLE. COOL FIRE-EXPOSED CONTAINERS WITH WATER FROM SIDE UNTIL WELL AFTER FIRE IS OUT. STAY AWAY FROM STORAGE TANK ENDS. FOR MASSIVE FIRE IN STORAGE AREA, USE UNMANNED HOSE HOLDER OR MONITOR NOZZLES, ELSE WITHDRAW FROM AREA AND LET FIRE BURN. WITHDRAW IMMEDIATELY IN CASE OF RISING SOUND FROM VENTING SAFETY DEVICE OR ANY DISCOLORATION OF STORAGE TANK DUE TO FIRE (1987 EMERGENCY RESPONSE GUIDEBOOK, DOT P 5800.4, GUIDE PAGE 26). EXTINGUISH ONLY IF FLOW CAN BE STOPPED; USE WATER IN FLOODING AMOUNTS AS FOG, SOLID STREAMS MAY NOT BE EFFECTIVE. COOL CONTAINERS WITH FLOODING QUATITIES OF WATER, APPLY FROM AS FAR A DISTANCE AS POSSIBLE. AVOID BREATHING TOXIC VAPORS, KEEP UPWIND.
WATER MAY BE INEFFECTIVE (NFPA 325M, FIRE HAZARD PROPERTIES OF FLAMMABLE LIQUIDS, GASES, AND VOLATILE SOLIDS, 1984)

TRANSPORTATION DATA

DEPARTMENT OF TRANSPORTATION HAZARD CLASSIFICATION 49 CFR 172.101: FLAMMABLE LIQUID
DEPARTMENT OF TRANSPORTATION LABELING REQUIREMENTS 49 CFR 172.101 AND SUBPART E: FLAMMABLE LIQUID
DEPARTMENT OF TRANSPORTATION PACKAGING REQUIREMENTS: 49 CFR 173.119 EXCEPTIONS: 49 CFR 173.118

TOXICITY

N-AMYL ACETATE: IRRITATION DATA: 300 PPM EYE-HUMAN. TOXICITY DATA: 5000 MG/M3/30 MINUTES INHALATION-HUMAN TCLO; 200 PPM INHALATION-HUMAN TCLO; 5200 PPM INHALATION-RAT LCLO; 6500 MG/KG ORAL-RAT LD50; 7400 MG/KG ORAL-RABBIT LD50; 1500 MG/KG INTRAPERITONEAL-GUINEA PIG LDLO. CARCINOGEN STATUS: NONE. LOCAL EFFECTS: IRRITANT- INHALATION, SKIN, AND EYES. ACUTE TOXICITY LEVEL: SLIGHTLY TOXIC BY INGESTION. TARGET EFFECTS: CENTRAL NERVOUS SYSTEM DEPRESSANT. AT INCREASED RISK FROM EXPOSURE: PERSONS WITH A HISTORY OF CHRONIC RESPIRATORY DISEASE OR SKIN DISEASE.

HEALTH EFFECTS AND FIRST AID

INHALATION: N-AMYL ACETATE: IRRITANT/NARCOTIC. 4000 PPM IMMEDIATELY DANGEROUS TO LIFE OR HEALTH. **ACUTE EXPOSURE-** EXPOSURE TO 900 PPM FOR 30 MINUTES PRODUCED IRRITATION OF THE EYES, NOSE, AND THROAT, WITH COUGH AND SLIGHT FATIGUE. AN INDIVIDUAL EXPOSED TO 5000 MG/M3 FOR 30 MINUTES EXPERIENCED SOMNOLENCE AND ADVERSE EFFECTS ON THE LUNGS, THORAX AND RESPIRATION. A CONCENTRATION OF 5000 PPM PRODUCED NARCOSIS IN GUINEA PIGS WITH INJURY TO THE LUNGS, LIVER, AND KIDNEYS. IT IS EXPECTED THAT SEVERE EXPOSURE WILL ALSO PRODUCE SYMPTOMS OF NARCOSIS IN HUMANS. **CHRONIC EXPOSURE-** PROLONGED EXPOSURE TO HIGH CONCENTRATIONS MAY CAUSE HEADACHE, WEAKNESS, DIZZINESS AND OTHER SYMPTOMS OF NARCOSIS.

FIRST AID- REMOVE FROM EXPOSURE AREA TO FRESH AIR IMMEDIATELY. IF BREATHING HAS STOPPED, PERFORM ARTIFICIAL RESPIRATION. KEEP PERSON WARM AND AT REST. TREAT SYMPTOMATICALLY AND SUPPORTIVELY. GET MEDICAL ATTENTION IMMEDIATELY.

SKIN CONTACT: N-AMYL ACETATE: IRRITANT. **ACUTE EXPOSURE-** MAY CAUSE IRRITATION. **CHRONIC EXPOSURE-** THIS MATERIAL IS A DEFATTING AGENT AND PROLONGED EXPOSURE MAY CAUSE DERMATITIS.

FIRST AID- REMOVE CONTAMINATED CLOTHING AND SHOES IMMEDIATELY. WASH AFFECTED AREA WITH SOAP OR MILD DETERGENT AND LARGE AMOUNTS OF WATER UNTIL NO EVIDENCE OF CHEMICAL REMAINS (APPROXIMATELY 15-20 MINUTES). GET MEDICAL ATTENTION IMMEDIATELY.

EYE CONTACT: N-AMYL ACETATE: IRRITANT. **ACUTE EXPOSURE-** EXPOSURE TO VAPOR CONCENTRATIONS MAY CAUSE IRRITATION. VAPOR CONCENTRATIONS OF 300 PPM ARE NOTICEABLY IRRITATING TO HUMAN EYES. AT HIGHER CONCENTRATIONS IT CAUSES A BURNING SENSATION IN THE EYES AND HYPEREMIA OF THE CONJUNCTIVA, BUT NO CORNEAL DAMAGE HAS BEEN OBSERVED. **CHRONIC EXPOSURE-** CHRONIC EXPOSURE OF 30 WORKERS TO 20 TO 80 MG/LITER PRODUCED HYPEREMIA OF THE BULBAR CONJUNCTIVA, BUT NO CORNEAL DAMAGE WAS OBSERVED.

FIRST AID- WASH EYES IMMEDIATELY WITH LARGE AMOUNTS OF WATER OR NORMAL SALINE, OCCASIONALLY LIFTING UPPER AND LOWER LIDS, UNTIL NO EVIDENCE OF CHEMICAL REMAINS (APPROXIMATELY 15-20 MINUTES). GET MEDICAL ATTENTION IMMEDIATELY.

INGESTION: N-AMYL ACETATE: **ACUTE EXPOSURE-** THIS MATERIAL MAY CAUSE NAUSEA, VOMITING AND OTHER SYMPTOMS OF GASTROINTESTINAL DISTURBANCES. EXPOSURE CAUSED DEPRESSION, ROUGH FUR, AND COMA IN RATS. IT HAS A LOW ORAL TOXICITY IN RATS WITH A LETHAL DOSE OF 6500 MG/KG. DEATH OCCURRED WITHIN 4 HOURS TO 2 DAYS FOLLOWING INGESTION. **CHRONIC EXPOSURE-** NO HUMAN DATA AVAILABLE.

FIRST AID- REMOVE BY GASTRIC LAVAGE OR EMESIS. MAINTAIN BLOOD PRESSURE AND AIRWAY. GIVE OXYGEN IF RESPIRATION IS DEPRESSED. DO NOT PERFORM GASTRIC LAVAGE OR EMESIS IF VICTIM IS UNCONSCIOUS. GET MEDICAL ATTENTION IMMEDIATELY (DREISBACH, HANDBOOK OF POISONING, 11TH ED.). ADMINISTRATION OF GASTRIC LAVAGE OR OXYGEN SHOULD BE PERFORMED BY QUALIFIED MEDICAL PERSONNEL.

ANTIDOTE: NO SPECIFIC ANTIDOTE. TREAT SYMPTOMATICALLY AND SUPPORTIVELY.

REACTIVITY

REACTIVITY: STABLE UNDER NORMAL TEMPERATURES AND PRESSURES.

INCOMPATIBILITIES: N-AMYL ACETATE: STRONG ACIDS: INCOMPATIBLE. NITRATES: INCOMPATIBLE. STRONG OXIDIZERS: INCOMPATIBLE. STRONG ALKALIES: INCOMPATIBLE.

DECOMPOSITION: THERMAL DECOMPOSITION MAY RELEASE ACRID SMOKE AND IRRITATING FUMES.

POLYMERIZATION: HAZARDOUS POLYMERIZATION HAS NOT BEEN REPORTED TO OCCUR UNDER NORMAL TEMPERATURES AND PRESSURES.

STORAGE AND DISPOSAL

OBSERVE ALL FEDERAL, STATE AND LOCAL REGULATIONS WHEN STORING OR DISPOSING OF THIS SUBSTANCE. FOR ASSISTANCE, CONTACT THE DISTRICT DIRECTOR OF THE ENVIRONMENTAL PROTECTION AGENCY.

STORAGE

STORE IN ACCORDANCE WITH 29 CFR 1910.106.

BONDING AND GROUNDING: SUBSTANCES WITH LOW ELECTROCONDUCTIVITY, WHICH MAY BE IGNITED BY ELECTROSTATIC SPARKS, SHOULD BE STORED IN CONTAINERS WHICH MEET THE BONDING AND GROUNDING GUIDELINES SPECIFIED IN NFPA 77-1983, RECOMMENDED PRACTICE ON STATIC ELECTRICITY.

STORE AWAY FROM INCOMPATIBLE SUBSTANCES.

DISPOSAL

DISPOSAL MUST BE IN ACCORDANCE WITH STANDARDS APPLICABLE TO GENERATORS OF HAZARDOUS WASTE, 40 CFR 262. EPA HAZARDOUS WASTE NUMBER D001. 100 POUND CERCLA SECTION 103 REPORTABLE QUANTITY.

CONDITIONS TO AVOID

AVOID CONTACT WITH HEAT, SPARKS, FLAMES, OR OTHER SOURCES OF IGNITION. VAPORS MAY BE EXPLOSIVE AND POISONOUS; DO NOT ALLOW UNNECESSARY PERSONNEL IN AREA. DO NOT OVERHEAT CONTAINERS; CONTAINERS MAY VIOLENTLY RUPTURE AND TRAVEL A CONSIDERABLE DISTANCE IN HEAT OF FIRE.

SPILL AND LEAK PROCEDURES

SOIL SPILL: DIG A HOLDING AREA SUCH AS PIT, POND OR LAGOON TO CONTAIN SPILL AND DIKE SURFACE FLOW WITH BARRIER OF SOIL, SANDBAGS, FOAMED POLYURETHANE OR FOAMED CONCRETE.

ABSORB BULK LIQUID WITH FLY ASH, CEMENT POWDER, SAWDUST, OR COMMERCIAL SORBENTS.

REDUCE VAPOR AND FIRE HAZARD WITH APPROPRIATE FOAM.

AIR SPILL: KNOCK DOWN VAPORS WITH WATER SPRAY. KEEP UPWIND.

WATER SPILL: LIMIT SPILL MOTION AND DISPERSION WITH NATURAL BARRIERS OR OIL SPILL CONTROL BOOMS.

APPLY DETERGENTS, SOAPS, ALCOHOLS OR ANOTHER SURFACE ACTIVE AGENT.

APPLY UNIVERSAL GELLING AGENT TO IMMOBILIZE TRAPPED SPILL AND INCREASE EFFICIENCY OF REMOVAL.

USE ACTIVATED CARBON TO ABSORB SPILLED SUBSTANCE THAT IS DISSOLVED.

USE SUCTION HOSES TO REMOVE TRAPPED SPILL MATERIAL.

USE MECHANICAL DREDGES OR LIFTS TO EXTRACT IMMOBILIZED MASSES OF POLLUTION AND PRECIPITATES.

OCCUPATIONAL SPILL: SHUT OFF IGNITION SOURCES. STOP LEAK IF YOU CAN DO IT WITHOUT RISK. USE WATER SPRAY TO REDUCE VAPORS. FOR SMALL SPILLS, TAKE UP WITH SAND OR OTHER ABSORBENT MATERIAL AND PLACE INTO CONTAINERS FOR LATER DISPOSAL. FOR LARGER SPILLS, DIKE FAR AHEAD OF SPILL FOR LATER DISPOSAL. NO SMOKING, FLAMES OR FLARES IN HAZARD AREA. KEEP UNNECESSARY PEOPLE AWAY; ISOLATE HAZARD AREA AND DENY ENTRY.

PROTECTIVE EQUIPMENT

VENTILATION: PROVIDE GENERAL DILUTION VENTILATION TO MEET PUBLISHED EXPOSURE LIMITS.

RESPIRATOR: THE FOLLOWING RESPIRATORS AND MAXIMUM USE CONCENTRATIONS ARE RECOMMENDATIONS BY THE U.S. DEPARTMENT OF HEALTH AND HUMAN SERVICES, NIOSH POCKET GUIDE TO CHEMICAL HAZARDS; NIOSH CRITERIA DOCUMENTS OR BY THE U.S. DEPARTMENT OF LABOR, 29 CFR 1910 SUBPART Z.

THE SPECIFIC RESPIRATOR SELECTED MUST BE BASED ON CONTAMINATION LEVELS FOUND IN THE WORK PLACE, MUST NOT EXCEED THE WORKING LIMITS OF THE RESPIRATOR AND BE JOINTLY APPROVED BY THE NATIONAL INSTITUTE FOR OCCUPATIONAL SAFETY AND HEALTH AND THE MINE SAFETY AND HEALTH ADMINISTRATION (NIOSH-MSHA).

FOR AMYL ACETATE: 1000 PPM- ANY POWERED AIR-PURIFYING RESPIRATOR WITH ORGANIC VAPOR CARTRIDGE(S). CHEMICAL CARTRIDGE RESPIRATOR WITH ORGANIC VAPOR CARTRIDGE OR CANISTER. ANY SUPPLIED-AIR RESPIRATOR. ANY SELF-CONTAINED BREATHING APPARATUS.

2500 PPM- ANY SUPPLIED-AIR RESPIRATOR OPERATED IN A CONTINUOUS FLOW MODE.

4000 PPM- ANY AIR-PURIFYING FULL FACEPIECE RESPIRATOR (GAS MASK) WITH A CHIN-STYLE OR FRONT- OR BACK-MOUNTED ORGANIC VAPOR CANISTER. ANY SUPPLIED-AIR RESPIRATOR WITH A FULL FACEPIECE. ANY SELF-CONTAINED BREATHING APPARATUS WITH A FULL FACEPIECE.

ESCAPE- ANY AIR-PURIFYING FULL FACEPIECE RESPIRATOR (GAS MASK) WITH A CHIN-STYLE OR FRONT- OR BACK-MOUNTED ORGANIC VAPOR CANISTER. ANY APPROPRIATE ESCAPE-TYPE SELF-CONTAINED BREATHING APPARATUS.

FOR FIREFIGHTING AND OTHER IMMEDIATELY DANGEROUS TO LIFE OR HEALTH CONDITIONS:

SELF-CONTAINED BREATHING APPARATUS WITH FULL FACEPIECE OPERATED IN PRESSURE-DEMAND OR OTHER POSITIVE PRESSURE MODE.

SUPPLIED-AIR RESPIRATOR WITH FULL FACEPIECE AND OPERATED IN PRESSURE-DEMAND OR OTHER POSITIVE PRESSURE MODE IN COMBINATION WITH AN AUXILIARY SELF-CONTAINED BREATHING APPARATUS OPERATED IN PRESSURE-DEMAND OR OTHER POSITIVE PRESSURE MODE.

CLOTHING: EMPLOYEE MUST WEAR APPROPRIATE PROTECTIVE (IMPERVIOUS) CLOTHING AND EQUIPMENT TO PREVENT REPEATED OR PROLONGED SKIN CONTACT WITH THIS SUBSTANCE.

GLOVES: EMPLOYEE MUST WEAR APPROPRIATE PROTECTIVE GLOVES TO PREVENT CONTACT WITH THIS SUBSTANCE.

EYE PROTECTION: EMPLOYEE MUST WEAR SPLASH-PROOF OR DUST-RESISTANT SAFETY GOGGLES AND A FACESHIELD TO PREVENT CONTACT WITH THIS SUBSTANCE.

EMERGENCY WASH FACILITIES: WHERE THERE IS ANY POSSIBILITY THAT AN EMPLOYEE'S EYES AND/OR SKIN MAY BE EXPOSED TO THIS SUBSTANCE, THE EMPLOYER SHOULD PROVIDE AN EYE WASH FOUNTAIN AND QUICK DRENCH SHOWER WITHIN THE IMMEDIATE WORK AREA FOR EMERGENCY USE.

AUTHORIZED BY- OCCUPATIONAL HEALTH SERVICES, INC.
CREATION DATE: 11/15/89 ***REVISION DATE:*** 05/18/90

MATERIAL SAFETY DATA SHEET

OCCUPATIONAL HEALTH SERVICES, INC.
AGRICULTURE AND PESTICIDE DIVISION
450 SEVENTH AVENUE, SUITE 2407
NEW YORK, NEW YORK 10123
1-800-445-MSDS OR (212) 967-1100

EMERGENCY CONTACT:
JOHN S. BRANSFORD, JR. (615) 292-1180

SUBSTANCE IDENTIFICATION

CAS-NUMBER 111-27-3

SUBSTANCE: N-HEXANOL

TRADE NAMES/SYNONYMS: HEXYL ALCOHOL; 1-HEXANOL; AMYLCARBINOL; CAPROYL ALCOHOL; HEXANOL; N-HEXYL ALCOHOL; 1-HEXYL ALCOHOL; 1-HYDROXYHEXANE; PENTYLCARBINOL; ALCOHOL C-6; HEXAN-1-OL; N-HEXAN-1-OL; STCC 4913126; UN 2282; PST15630

CHEMICAL FAMILY: HYDROXYL, ALIPHATIC

MOLECULAR FORMULA: C6-H14-O

MOLECULAR WEIGHT: 102.20

CERCLA RATINGS (SCALE 0-3): HEALTH=2 FIRE=2 REACTIVITY=0 PERSISTENCE=0

NFPA RATINGS (SCALE 0-4): HEALTH=1 FIRE=2 REACTIVITY=0

COMPONENTS AND CONTAMINANTS

COMPONENT: N-HEXANOL ***PERCENT:*** 100.0
CAS# 111-27-3

OTHER CONTAMINANTS: NONE

EXPOSURE LIMITS: NO OCCUPATIONAL EXPOSURE LIMITS ESTABLISHED BY OSHA, ACGIH, OR NIOSH.

PHYSICAL DATA

DESCRIPTION: CLEAR, COLORLESS, MOBILE LIQUID WITH A MILD, SWEET, CHARACTERISTIC ODOR. ***BOILING POINT:*** 311 F (155 C)

MELTING POINT: -62 F (-52 C) ***SPECIFIC GRAVITY:*** 0.8136

VISCOSITY: 0.453 CENTIPOISE @ 24 C ***VAPOR PRESSURE:*** 1 MMHG @ 24.4 C

EVAPORATION RATE: NOT AVAILABLE ***SOLUBILITY IN WATER:*** SLIGHTLY SOLUBLE

ODOR THRESHOLD: 5.2 PPM ***VAPOR DENSITY:*** 3.52

SOLVENT SOLUBILITY: SOLUBLE IN ETHANOL, ETHER, BENZENE, ACETONE, CHLOROFORM

FIRE AND EXPLOSION DATA

FIRE AND EXPLOSION HAZARD: MODERATE FIRE HAZARD WHEN EXPOSED TO HEAT OR FLAME.

VAPORS ARE HEAVIER THAN AIR AND MAY TRAVEL A CONSIDERABLE DISTANCE TO A SOURCE OF IGNITION AND FLASH BACK.

VAPOR-AIR MIXTURES ARE EXPLOSIVE ABOVE FLASH POINT.

FLASH POINT: 145 F (63 C) (CC) ***UPPER EXPLOSIVE LIMIT:*** 7.7%

LOWER EXPLOSIVE LIMIT: 2.1% ***AUTOIGNITION TEMP.:*** 559 F (292 C)

FLAMMABILITY CLASS(OSHA): IIIA

FIREFIGHTING MEDIA: DRY CHEMICAL, CARBON DIOXIDE, HALON, WATER SPRAY OR ALCOHOL FOAM (1987 EMERGENCY RESPONSE GUIDEBOOK, DOT P 5800.4).

FOR LARGER FIRES, USE WATER SPRAY, FOG OR ALCOHOL FOAM (1987 EMERGENCY RESPONSE GUIDEBOOK, DOT P 5800.4).

ALCOHOL FOAM (NFPA 325M, FIRE HAZARD PROPERTIES OF FLAMMABLE LIQUIDS, GASES, AND VOLATILE SOLIDS, 1984).

FIREFIGHTING: MOVE CONTAINER FROM FIRE AREA IF POSSIBLE. COOL FIRE-EXPOSED CONTAINERS WITH WATER FROM SIDE UNTIL WELL AFTER FIRE IS OUT. STAY AWAY FROM STORAGE TANK ENDS. FOR MASSIVE FIRE IN STORAGE AREA, USE UNMANNED HOSE HOLDER OR MONITOR NOZZLES, ELSE WITHDRAW FROM AREA AND LET FIRE BURN. WITHDRAW IMMEDIATELY IN CASE OF RISING SOUND FROM VENTING SAFETY DEVICE OR ANY DISCOLORATION OF STORAGE TANK DUE TO FIRE (1987 EMERGENCY RESPONSE GUIDEBOOK, DOT P 5800.4, GUIDE PAGE 26). EXTINGUISH ONLY IF FLOW CAN BE STOPPED. USE FLOODING AMOUNTS OF WATER AS FOG; SOLID STREAMS MAY BE INEFFECTIVE. COOL CONTAINERS WITH FLOODING AMOUNTS OF WATER FROM AS FAR A DISTANCE AS POSSIBLE. AVOID BREATHING VAPORS; KEEP UPWIND.

TRANSPORTATION DATA

DEPARTMENT OF TRANSPORTATION HAZARD CLASSIFICATION 49 CFR 172.101: COMBUSTIBLE LIQUID

DEPARTMENT OF TRANSPORTATION LABELING REQUIREMENTS 49 CFR 172.101 AND SUBPART E: NONE

DEPARTMENT OF TRANSPORTATION PACKAGING REQUIREMENTS: NONE EXCEPTIONS: 49 CFR 173.118A

TOXICITY

N-HEXANOL (HEXYL ALCOHOL): IRRITATION DATA: 410 MG OPEN SKIN-RABBIT MILD; 10 MG/24 HOURS OPEN SKIN-RABBIT MILD; 250 UG OPEN EYE-RABBIT SEVERE. TOXICITY DATA: 3100 MG/KG SKIN-RABBIT LD50; 720 MG/KG ORAL-RAT LD50; 1950 MG/KG ORAL-MOUSE LD50; 103 MG/KGINTRAVENOUS-MOUSE LD50; 2442 MG/KG UNREPORTED-MAMMAL LD50. CARCINOGEN STATUS: NONE. LOCAL EFFECTS: CORROSIVE- EYES; IRRITANT- INHALATION AND SKIN. ACUTE TOXICITY LEVEL: TOXIC BY INGESTION AND SLIGHTLY TOXIC BY DERMAL ABSORPTION. TARGET EFFECTS: CENTRAL NERVOUS SYSTEM DEPRESSANT. ADDITIONAL DATA: THE USE OF ALCOHOLIC BEVERAGES MAY ENHANCE THE TOXIC EFFECT.

HEALTH EFFECTS AND FIRST AID

INHALATION: N-HEXANOL (HEXYL ALCOHOL): IRRITANT/NARCOTIC. **ACUTE EXPOSURE-** MAY BE IRRITATING TO THE MUCOUS MEMBRANES. DUE TO THE LOW VAPOR PRESSURE OF THIS SUBSTANCE INHALATION IS UNLIKELY. HOWEVER, INHALATION OF HIGH CONCENTRATIONS MAY CAUSE CENTRAL NERVOUS SYSTEM DEPRESSION WITH HEADACHE, DIZZINESS, DROWSINESS AND VERTIGO. **CHRONIC EXPOSURE-** NO DATA AVAILABLE.

FIRST AID- REMOVE FROM EXPOSURE AREA TO FRESH AIR IMMEDIATELY. IF BREATHING HAS STOPPED, PERFORM ARTIFICIAL RESPIRATION. KEEP PERSON WARM AND AT REST. TREAT SYMPTOMATICALLY AND SUPPORTIVELY. GET MEDICAL ATTENTION IMMEDIATELY.

SKIN CONTACT: N-HEXANOL (HEXYL ALCOHOL): IRRITANT/NARCOTIC. **ACUTE EXPOSURE-** MAY CAUSE IRRITATION WITH REDNESS AND PAIN. MAY BE ABSORBED THROUGH THE SKIN TO CAUSE SYSTEMIC TOXICITY. **CHRONIC EXPOSURE-** REPEATED OR PROLONGED SKIN CONTACT MAY CAUSE DERMATITIS DUE TO DEFATTING.

FIRST AID- REMOVE CONTAMINATED CLOTHING AND SHOES IMMEDIATELY. WASH AFFECTED AREA WITH SOAP OR MILD DETERGENT AND LARGE AMOUNTS OF WATER UNTIL NO EVIDENCE OF CHEMICAL REMAINS (APPROXIMATELY 15-20 MINUTES). GET MEDICAL ATTENTION IMMEDIATELY.

EYE CONTACT: N-HEXANOL (HEXYL ALCOHOL): CORROSIVE. **ACUTE EXPOSURE-** MAY CAUSE SEVERE IRRITATION AND EYE BURNS. **CHRONIC EXPOSURE-** EFFECTS DEPEND ON CONCENTATION AND DURATION OF EXPOSURE. REPEATED OR PROLONGED CONTACT WITH CORROSIVE SUBSTANCES MAY RESULT IN CONJUNCTIVITIS OR EFFECTS AN IN ACUTE EXPOSURE.

FIRST AID- WASH EYES IMMEDIATELY WITH LARGE AMOUNTS OF WATER, OCCASIONALLY LIFTING UPPER AND LOWER LIDS, UNTIL NO EVIDENCE OF CHEMICAL REMAINS (AT LEAST 15-20 MINUTES). CONTINUE IRRIGATING WITH NORMAL SALINE UNTIL THE PH HAS RETURNED TO NORMAL (30-60 MINUTES). COVER WITH STERILE BANDAGES. GET MEDICAL ATTENTION IMMEDIATELY.

INGESTION: N-HEXANOL (HEXYL ALCOHOL): NARCOTIC. **ACUTE EXPOSURE-** THE LETHAL DOSE IN RATS IS 720 MG/KG. THE SYMPTOMS OF POISONING WERE NOT REPORTED. INGESTION OF ALCOHOLS IN GENERAL CAUSE CENTRAL NERVOUS SYSTEM DEPRESSION WITH HEADACHE, DIZZINESS, DROWSINESS, AND VERTIGO. ASPIRATION INTO THE LUNGS MAY OCCUR CAUSING RESPIRATORY ARREST AND DEATH. **CHRONIC EXPOSURE-** NO DATA AVAILABLE.

FIRST AID- TREAT SYMPTOMATICALLY AND SUPPORTIVELY. GET MEDICAL ATTENTION IMMEDIATELY. IF VOMITING OCCURS, KEEP HEAD LOWER THAN HIPS TO PREVENT ASPIRATION.

ANTIDOTE: NO SPECIFIC ANTIDOTE. TREAT SYMPTOMATICALLY AND SUPPORTIVELY.

REACTIVITY

REACTIVITY: STABLE UNDER NORMAL TEMPERATURES AND PRESSURES.

INCOMPATIBILITIES: N-HEXANOL (HEXYL ALCOHOL): OXIDIZING AGENTS: INCOMPATIBLE.

DECOMPOSITION: THERMAL DECOMPOSITION MAY RELEASE TOXIC AND/OR HAZARDOUS GASES.

POLYMERIZATION: HAZARDOUS POLYMERIZATION HAS NOT BEEN REPORTED TO OCCUR UNDER NORMAL TEMPERATURES AND PRESSURES.

STORAGE AND DISPOSAL

OBSERVE ALL FEDERAL, STATE AND LOCAL REGULATIONS WHEN STORING OR DISPOSING OF THIS SUBSTANCE. FOR ASSISTANCE, CONTACT THE DISTRICT DIRECTOR OF THE ENVIRONMENTAL PROTECTION AGENCY.

****STORAGE****

STORE IN ACCORDANCE WITH 29 CFR 1910.106.

BONDING AND GROUNDING: SUBSTANCES WITH LOW ELECTROCONDUCTIVITY, WHICH MAY BE IGNITED BY ELECTROSTATIC SPARKS, SHOULD BE STORED IN CONTAINERS WHICH MEET THE BONDING AND GROUNDING GUIDELINES SPECIFIED IN NFPA 77-1983, RECOMMENDED PRACTICE ON STATIC ELECTRICITY.

STORE AWAY FROM INCOMPATIBLE SUBSTANCES.

****DISPOSAL****

DISPOSAL MUST BE IN ACCORDANCE WITH STANDARDS APPLICABLE TO GENERATORS OF HAZARDOUS WASTE, 40 CFR 262. EPA HAZARDOUS WASTE NUMBER D001. 100 POUND CERCLA SECTION 103 REPORTABLE QUANTITY.

CONDITIONS TO AVOID

AVOID CONTACT WITH HEAT, SPARKS, FLAMES, OR OTHER SOURCES OF IGNITION. VAPORS MAY BE EXPLOSIVE AND POISONOUS; DO NOT ALLOW UNNECESSARY PERSONNEL IN AREA. DO NOT OVERHEAT CONTAINERS; CONTAINERS MAY VIOLENTLY RUPTURE AND TRAVEL A CONSIDERABLE DISTANCE IN HEAT OF FIRE.

SPILL AND LEAK PROCEDURES

OCCUPATIONAL SPILL: SHUT OFF IGNITION SOURCES. STOP LEAK IF YOU CAN DO IT WITHOUT RISK. USE WATER SPRAY TO REDUCE VAPORS. FOR SMALL SPILLS, TAKE UP WITH SAND OR OTHER ABSORBENT MATERIAL AND PLACE INTO CONTAINERS FOR LATER DISPOSAL. FOR LARGER SPILLS, DIKE FAR AHEAD OF SPILL FOR LATER DISPOSAL. NO SMOKING, FLAMES OR FLARES IN HAZARD AREA. KEEP UNNECESSARY PEOPLE AWAY; ISOLATE HAZARD AREA AND DENY ENTRY.

PROTECTIVE EQUIPMENT

VENTILATION: PROVIDE LOCAL EXHAUST VENTILATION SYSTEM.

RESPIRATOR: THE FOLLOWING RESPIRATORS ARE RECOMMENDED BASED ON INFORMATION FOUND IN THE PHYSICAL DATA, TOXICITY AND HEALTH EFFECTS SECTIONS. THEY ARE RANKED IN ORDER FROM MINIMUM TO MAXIMUM RESPIRATORY PROTECTION. THE SPECIFIC RESPIRATOR SELECTED MUST BE BASED ON CONTAMINATION LEVELS FOUND IN THE WORK PLACE, MUST NOT EXCEED THE WORKING LIMITS OF THE RESPIRATOR AND BE JOINTLY APPROVED BY THE NATIONAL INSTITUTE FOR OCCUPATIONAL SAFETY AND HEALTH AND THE MINE SAFETY AND HEALTH ADMINISTRATION (NIOSH-MSHA).

CHEMICAL CARTRIDGE RESPIRATOR WITH AN ORGANIC VAPOR CARTRIDGE(S) WITH A FULL FACEPIECE.

GAS MASK WITH ORGANIC VAPOR CANISTER (CHIN-STYLE OR FRONT- OR BACK-MOUNTED CANISTER) WITH A FULL FACEPIECE.

TYPE 'C' SUPPLIED-AIR RESPIRATOR WITH A FULL FACEPIECE OPERATED IN PRESSURE-DEMAND OR OTHER POSITIVE PRESSURE MODE OR WITH A FULL FACEPIECE, HELMET OR HOOD OPERATED IN CONTINUOUS-FLOW MODE.

SELF-CONTAINED BREATHING APPARATUS WITH A FULL FACEPIECE OPERATED IN PRESSURE-DEMAND OR OTHER POSITIVE PRESSURE MODE.

FOR FIREFIGHTING AND OTHER IMMEDIATELY DANGEROUS TO LIFE OR HEALTH CONDITIONS:

SELF-CONTAINED BREATHING APPARATUS WITH FULL FACEPIECE OPERATED IN PRESSURE-DEMAND OR OTHER POSITIVE PRESSURE MODE.

SUPPLIED-AIR RESPIRATOR WITH FULL FACEPIECE AND OPERATED IN PRESSURE-DEMAND OR OTHER POSITIVE PRESSURE MODE IN COMBINATION WITH AN AUXILIARY SELF-CONTAINED BREATHING APPARATUS OPERATED IN PRESSURE-DEMAND OR OTHER POSITIVE PRESSURE MODE.

CLOTHING: EMPLOYEE MUST WEAR APPROPRIATE PROTECTIVE (IMPERVIOUS) CLOTHING AND EQUIPMENT TO PREVENT REPEATED OR PROLONGED SKIN CONTACT WITH THIS SUBSTANCE.

GLOVES: EMPLOYEE MUST WEAR APPROPRIATE PROTECTIVE GLOVES TO PREVENT CONTACT WITH THIS SUBSTANCE.

EYE PROTECTION: EMPLOYEE MUST WEAR SPLASH-PROOF OR DUST-RESISTANT SAFETY GOGGLES TO PREVENT EYE CONTACT WITH THIS SUBSTANCE.

EMERGENCY EYE WASH: WHERE THERE IS ANY POSSIBILITY THAT AN EMPLOYEE'S

EYES MAY BE EXPOSED TO THIS SUBSTANCE, THE EMPLOYER SHOULD PROVIDE AN EYE WASH FOUNTAIN WITHIN THE IMMEDIATE WORK AREA FOR EMERGENCY USE.

AUTHORIZED BY- OCCUPATIONAL HEALTH SERVICES, INC.
CREATION DATE: 11/15/89 ***REVISION DATE:*** 05/07/90

MATERIAL SAFETY DATA SHEET

OCCUPATIONAL HEALTH SERVICES, INC.
AGRICULTURE AND PESTICIDE DIVISION
450 SEVENTH AVENUE, SUITE 2407
NEW YORK, NEW YORK 10123
1-800-445-MSDS OR (212) 967-1100

EMERGENCY CONTACT:
JOHN S. BRANSFORD, JR. (615) 292-1180

SUBSTANCE IDENTIFICATION

CAS-NUMBER 113-48-4
SUBSTANCE: **N-OCTYL BICYCLOHEPTENE DICARBOXIMIDE**
TRADE NAMES/SYNONYMS: 2-(2-ETHYLHEXYL)-3A,4,7,7A-TETRAHYDRO-4,7-METHANO-1H-ISOINDOLE-1,3(2H) -DIONE; N-(2-ETHYLHEXYL)-5-NORBORNENE-2,3-DICARBOXIMIDE; CARBOXIMIDE; DICARBOXIMIDE; MGK 264; OCTACIDE; SINEPYRIN 222; SYNERGIST 264; VAN DYKE 264; PST15955
CHEMICAL FAMILY: IMIDE, CARBOXYLIC
MOLECULAR FORMULA: C17-H25-N-O2
MOLECULAR WEIGHT: 275.43
CERCLA RATINGS (SCALE 0-3): HEALTH=3 FIRE=1 REACTIVITY=0 PERSISTENCE=2
NFPA RATINGS (SCALE 0-4): HEALTH=3 FIRE=1 REACTIVITY=0

COMPONENTS AND CONTAMINANTS

COMPONENT: N-OCTYL BICYCLOHEPTENE DICARBOXIMIDE ***PERCENT:*** 100
CAS# 113-48-4
EXPOSURE LIMITS: NO OCCUPATIONAL EXPOSURE LIMITS ESTABLISHED BY OSHA, ACGIH, OR NIOSH.

PHYSICAL DATA

DESCRIPTION: COLORLESS TO LIGHT YELLOW LIQUID WITH A SLIGHTLY SWEET MILD AROMATIC ODOR. ***BOILING POINT:*** 316 F (158 C)
MELTING POINT: < -4 F (-20C)
SPECIFIC GRAVITY: 1.050 ***VAPOR PRESSURE:*** NOT AVAILABLE
EVAPORATION RATE: NOT AVAILABLE ***SOLUBILITY IN WATER:*** INSOLUBLE
SOLVENT SOLUBILITY: MOST ORGANIC SOLVENTS AND OILS

FIRE AND EXPLOSION DATA

FIRE AND EXPLOSION HAZARD: SLIGHT FIRE HAZARD WHEN EXPOSED TO HEAT OR FLAME.
FLASH POINT: > 350 F (> 177 C) (OC)
FIREFIGHTING MEDIA: DRY CHEMICAL, CARBON DIOXIDE, HALON, WATER SPRAY OR STANDARD FOAM (1987 EMERGENCY RESPONSE GUIDEBOOK, DOT P 5800.4).
FOR LARGER FIRES, USE WATER SPRAY, FOG OR STANDARD FOAM (1987 EMERGENCY RESPONSE GUIDEBOOK, DOT P 5800.4).
FIREFIGHTING: MOVE CONTAINER FROM FIRE AREA IF POSSIBLE. DO NOT SCATTER SPILLED MATERIAL WITH HIGH PRESSURE WATER STREAMS. DIKE FIRE CONTROL WATER FOR LATER DISPOSAL (1987 EMERGENCY RESPONSE GUIDEBOOK, DOT P 5800.4, GUIDE PAGE 31).
USE AGENTS SUITABLE FOR TYPE OF SURROUNDING FIRE. AVOID BREATHING HAZARDOUS VAPORS, KEEP UPWIND.

TOXICITY

N-OCTYL BICYCLOHEPTENE DICARBOXIMIDE (MGK 264): TOXICITY DATA: 470 MG/KG SKIN-RABBIT LD50; 470 MG/KG SKIN-RAT LD50; 2800 MG/KG ORAL-RAT LD50; 1 GM/KG ORAL-MOUSE LD50; REPRODUCTIVE EFFECTS DATA (RTECS). CARCINOGEN STATUS: NONE. ACUTE TOXICITY LEVEL: TOXIC BY DERMAL ABSORPTION; MODERATELY TOXIC BY INGESTION. TARGET EFFECTS: POISONING MAY AFFECT THE CENTRAL NERVOUS SYSTEM.

HEALTH EFFECTS AND FIRST AID

INHALATION: N-OCTYL BICYCLOHEPTENE CARBOXIMIDE (MGK 264): **ACUTE EXPOSURE-** NO DATA AVAILABLE. **CHRONIC EXPOSURE-** A HEMATOTOXICITY STUDY WAS DONE IN INTACT, TOTALLY AND SUBTOTALLY SPLENECTOMIZED DOGS BY FOGGING THEM FOR 5 MINUTE PERIODS ON 4 CONSECUTIVE DAYS WITH 1.5% N-OCTYL BICYCLOHEPTENE CARBOXIMIDE. NO HEMATALOGIC CHANGES WERE NOTED IN SUBSEQUENT BLOOD OR BONE MARROW SAMPLES.
FIRST AID- REMOVE FROM EXPOSURE AREA TO FRESH AIR IMMEDIATELY. IF BREATHING HAS STOPPED, PERFORM ARTIFICIAL RESPIRATION. KEEP PERSON WARM AND AT REST. TREAT SYMPTOMATICALLY AND SUPPORTIVELY. GET MEDICAL ATTENTION IMMEDIATELY.

SKIN CONTACT: N-OCTYL BICYCLOHEPTENE CARBOXIMIDE (MGK 264): TOXIC. **ACUTE EXPOSURE-** NOT EXPECTED TO CAUSE IRRITATION. IN RABBITS THE LETHAL DOSE WAS 470 MG/KG. SYSTEMIC EFFECTS INCLUDE CENTRAL NERVOUS EXCITATION FOLLOWED BY DEPRESSION. **CHRONIC EXPOSURE-** NO DATA AVAILABLE.
FIRST AID- REMOVE CONTAMINATED CLOTHING AND SHOES IMMEDIATELY. WASH AFFECTED AREA WITH SOAP OR MILD DETERGENT AND LARGE AMOUNTS OF WATER UNTIL NO EVIDENCE OF CHEMICAL REMAINS (APPROXIMATELY 15-20 MINUTES). GET MEDICAL ATTENTION IMMEDIATELY.

EYE CONTACT: N-OCTYL BICYCLOHEPTENE DICARBOXIMIDE (MGK 264): **ACUTE EXPOSURE-** NO DATA AVAILABLE. **CHRONIC EXPOSURE-** NO DATA AVAILABLE.
FIRST AID- WASH EYES IMMEDIATELY WITH LARGE AMOUNTS OF WATER OR NORMAL SALINE, OCCASIONALLY LIFTING UPPER AND LOWER LIDS, UNTIL NO EVIDENCE OF CHEMICAL REMAINS (APPROXIMATELY 15-20 MINUTES). GET MEDICAL ATTENTION IMMEDIATELY.

INGESTION: N-OCTYL BICYCLOHEPTENE DICARBOXIMIDE (MGK 264): **ACUTE EXPOSURE-** MAY CAUSE HEADACHE AND DIARRHEA. LARGE DOSES MAY CAUSE CENTRAL NERVOUS SYSTEM STIMULATION FOLLOWED BY DEPRESSION. **CHRONIC EXPOSURE-** A 2 YEAR FEEDING STUDY ON RATS AND SWINE PRODUCED NO TOXIC EFFECTS AT LEVELS OF 1000 MG/KG AND 300 MG/KG RESPECTIVELY. EFFECTS ON FEMALE FERTILITY, LITTER SIZE AND GROWTH RATIO HAVE BEEN REPORTED IN MULTIGENERATIONAL STUDIES WITH RATS.
FIRST AID- TREAT SYMPTOMATICALLY AND SUPPORTIVELY. GET MEDICAL ATTENTION IMMEDIATELY. IF VOMITING OCCURS, KEEP HEAD LOWER THAN HIPS TO PREVENT ASPIRATION.
ANTIDOTE: NO SPECIFIC ANTIDOTE. TREAT SYMPTOMATICALLY AND SUPPORTIVELY.

REACTIVITY

REACTIVITY: STABLE UNDER NORMAL TEMPERATURES AND PRESSURES.
INCOMPATIBILITIES: N-OCYTL BICYCLOHEPTENE DICARBOXIMIDE (MGK 264): ACIDS (STRONG): POSSIBLE REACTION. ALKALIS (STRONG): POSSIBLE REACTION.
DECOMPOSITION: THERMAL DECOMPOSITION PRODUCTS MAY INCLUDE TOXIC OXIDES OF NITROGEN.
POLYMERIZATION: HAZARDOUS POLYMERIZATION HAS NOT BEEN REPORTED TO OCCUR UNDER NORMAL TEMPERATURES AND PRESSURES.

STORAGE AND DISPOSAL

OBSERVE ALL FEDERAL, STATE AND LOCAL REGULATIONS WHEN STORING OR DISPOSING OF THIS SUBSTANCE. FOR ASSISTANCE, CONTACT THE DISTRICT DIRECTOR OF THE ENVIRONMENTAL PROTECTION AGENCY.

STORAGE

STORE AWAY FROM INCOMPATIBLE SUBSTANCES.

CONDITIONS TO AVOID

MAY BURN BUT DOES NOT IGNITE READILY. AVOID CONTACT WITH STRONG OXIDIZERS, EXCESSIVE HEAT, SPARKS, OR OPEN FLAME.

SPILL AND LEAK PROCEDURES

OCCUPATIONAL SPILL: STOP LEAK IF YOU CAN DO IT WITHOUT RISK. FOR SMALL SPILLS, TAKE UP WITH SAND OR OTHER ABSORBENT MATERIAL AND PLACE INTO CLEAN, DRY CONTAINERS FOR LATER DISPOSAL. KEEP UNNECESSARY PEOPLE AWAY. ISOLATE HAZARD AREA AND DENY ENTRY.

PROTECTIVE EQUIPMENT

VENTILATION: PROVIDE LOCAL EXHAUST OR PROCESS ENCLOSURE VENTILATION SYSTEM.
RESPIRATOR: THE FOLLOWING RESPIRATORS ARE RECOMMENDED BASED ON INFORMATION FOUND IN THE PHYSICAL DATA, TOXICITY AND HEALTH EFFECTS SECTIONS. THEY ARE RANKED IN ORDER FROM MINIMUM TO MAXIMUM RESPIRATORY PROTECTION. THE SPECIFIC RESPIRATOR SELECTED MUST BE BASED ON CONTAMINATION LEVELS FOUND IN THE WORK PLACE, MUST NOT EXCEED THE WORKING LIMITS OF THE RESPIRATOR AND BE JOINTLY APPROVED BY THE NATIONAL INSTITUTE FOR OCCUPATIONAL SAFETY AND HEALTH AND THE MINE SAFETY AND HEALTH ADMINISTRATION (NIOSH-MSHA).
CHEMICAL CARTRIDGE RESPIRATOR WITH PESTICIDE CARTRIDGE.
GAS MASK WITH A PESTICIDE CANISTER (CHIN-STYLE OR FRONT- OR BACK-MOUNTED CANISTER).

TYPE 'C' SUPPLIED-AIR RESPIRATOR OPERATED IN THE PRESSURE-DEMAND OR OTHER POSITIVE PRESSURE OR CONTINUOUS-FLOW MODE.
SELF-CONTAINED BREATHING APPARATUS.
FOR FIREFIGHTING AND OTHER IMMEDIATELY DANGEROUS TO LIFE OR HEALTH CONDITIONS:
SELF-CONTAINED BREATHING APPARATUS WITH FULL FACEPIECE OPERATED IN PRESSURE-DEMAND OR OTHER POSITIVE PRESSURE MODE.
SUPPLIED-AIR RESPIRATOR WITH FULL FACEPIECE AND OPERATED IN PRESSURE-DEMAND OR OTHER POSITIVE PRESSURE MODE IN COMBINATION WITH AN AUXILIARY SELF-CONTAINED BREATHING APPARATUS OPERATED IN PRESSURE-DEMAND OR OTHER POSITIVE PRESSURE MODE.

CLOTHING: EMPLOYEE MUST WEAR APPROPRIATE PROTECTIVE (IMPERVIOUS) CLOTHING AND EQUIPMENT TO PREVENT ANY POSSIBILITY OF SKIN CONTACT WITH THIS SUBSTANCE.

GLOVES: EMPLOYEE MUST WEAR APPROPRIATE PROTECTIVE GLOVES TO PREVENT CONTACT WITH THIS SUBSTANCE.

EYE PROTECTION: EMPLOYEE MUST WEAR SPLASH-PROOF OR DUST-RESISTANT SAFETY GOGGLES AND A FACESHIELD TO PREVENT CONTACT WITH THIS SUBSTANCE.
EMERGENCY WASH FACILITIES: WHERE THERE IS ANY POSSIBILITY THAT AN EMPLOYEE'S EYES AND/OR SKIN MAY BE EXPOSED TO THIS SUBSTANCE, THE EMPLOYER SHOULD PROVIDE AN EYE WASH FOUNTAIN AND QUICK DRENCH SHOWER WITHIN THE IMMEDIATE WORK AREA FOR EMERGENCY USE.

AUTHORIZED BY- OCCUPATIONAL HEALTH SERVICES, INC.
CREATION DATE: 10/04/89 ***REVISION DATE:*** 10/31/89

MATERIAL SAFETY DATA SHEET

OCCUPATIONAL HEALTH SERVICES, INC.
AGRICULTURE AND PESTICIDE DIVISION
450 SEVENTH AVENUE, SUITE 2407
NEW YORK, NEW YORK 10123
1-800-445-MSDS OR (212) 967-1100

EMERGENCY CONTACT:
JOHN S. BRANSFORD, JR. (615) 292-1180

SUBSTANCE IDENTIFICATION

CAS-NUMBER 142-59-6

SUBSTANCE: NABAM

TRADE NAMES/SYNONYMS: CARBAMODITHIOIC ACID, 1,2-ETHANEDIYLBIS-, DISODIUM SALT; CARBAMIC ACID, ETHYLENEBIS(DITHIO-, DISODIUM SALT; 1,2-ETHANEDIYLBISCARBAMODITHIOIC ACID DISODIUM SALT; ETHYLENEBIS(DITHIOCARBAMIC ACID) DISODIUM SALT; DISODIUM ETHYLENEBIS(DITHIOCARBAMATE); DISODIUM 1,2-ETHANEDIYLBIS(CARBAMODITHIOATE); DISODIUM ETHYLENE BISDITHIOCARBAMATE; DISODIUM ETHYLENE-1,2-BISDITHIOCARBAMATE; CHEM BAM; DITHANE A 40 (FORMULATION); DSE; PARAZATE; C4H6N2NA2S4; PST16080

CHEMICAL FAMILY: THIOCARBAMATE

MOLECULAR FORMULA: NA-S-C-(S)-N-H-(C-H2)2-N-H-C-(S)-S-NA

MOLECULAR WEIGHT: 256.35

CERCLA RATINGS (SCALE 0-3): HEALTH=3 FIRE=1 REACTIVITY=1 PERSISTENCE=1

NFPA RATINGS (SCALE 0-4): HEALTH=U FIRE=1 REACTIVITY=1

COMPONENTS AND CONTAMINANTS

COMPONENT: NABAM ***PERCENT:*** 100.0
CAS# 142-59-6

OTHER CONTAMINANTS: NONE

EXPOSURE LIMITS: NO OCCUPATIONAL EXPOSURE LIMITS ESTABLISHED BY OSHA, ACGIH, OR NIOSH.

PHYSICAL DATA

DESCRIPTION: COLORLESS CRYSTALS WITH A SLIGHT SULFIDE ODOR; MAY DARKEN ON STORAGE.

MELTING POINT: DECOMPOSES ***SPECIFIC GRAVITY:*** 1.14 @ 20 C

SOLUBILITY IN WATER: 20% @ 20 C

SOLVENT SOLUBILITY: SOLUBLE IN ALCOHOL.

FIRE AND EXPLOSION DATA

FIRE AND EXPLOSION HAZARD: NEGLIGIBLE FIRE HAZARD WHEN EXPOSED TO HEAT OR FLAME.

FIREFIGHTING MEDIA: DRY CHEMICAL, CARBON DIOXIDE, HALON, WATER SPRAY OR STANDARD FOAM (1987 EMERGENCY RESPONSE GUIDEBOOK, DOT P 5800.4).
FOR LARGER FIRES, USE WATER SPRAY, FOG OR STANDARD FOAM (1987 EMERGENCY RESPONSE GUIDEBOOK, DOT P 5800.4).

FIREFIGHTING: MOVE CONTAINERS FROM FIRE AREA IF POSSIBLE (1987 EMERGENCY RESPONSE GUIDEBOOK, DOT P 5800.4, GUIDE PAGE 53).
EXTINGUISH USING AGENT SUITABLE FOR TYPE OF SURROUNDING FIRE. AVOID BREATHING VAPORS AND DUSTS. KEEP UPWIND.

TOXICITY

NABAM: TOXICITY DATA: 395 MG/KG ORAL-RAT LD50; 580 MG/KG ORAL-MOUSE LD50; 580 MG/KG SUBCUTANEOUS-MOUSE LD50; 500 MG/KG INTRAPERITONEAL-RAT LD50; MUTAGENIC DATA (RTECS); REPRODUCTIVE EFFECTS DATA (RTECS). CARCINOGEN STATUS: NONE. ORAL ADMINISTRATION OF ETHYLENE THIOUREA, A METABOLITE AND DEGRADATION PRODUCT OF NABAM, INDUCED HIGHLY SIGNIFICANT INCREASES IN THE INCIDENCES OF LIVER TUMORS IN TWO STRAINS OF MICE, AND OF THYROID CARCINOMAS AND ADENOMAS IN TWO SEPARATE RAT STUDIES. LOCAL EFFECTS: IRRITANT- INHALATION, SKIN, EYE. ACUTE TOXICITY LEVEL: TOXIC BY INGESTION. TARGET EFFECTS: SENSITIZER- DERMAL. POISONING MAY ALSO AFFECT THE THYROID. ADDITIONAL DATA: ALCOHOL MAY ENHANCE THE TOXIC EFFECTS. OILS AND FATS MAY INCREASE ABSORPTION AND TOXICITY.

HEALTH EFFECTS AND FIRST AID

INHALATION: NABAM: IRRITANT. **ACUTE EXPOSURE-** INHALATION OF DUSTS OR SPRAYS MAY CAUSE MUCOUS MEMBRANE IRRITATION, SNEEZING, COUGHING, PHARYNGITIS, RHINITIS, AND BRONCHITIS. HIGH CONCENTRATIONS MAY CAUSE NARCOSIS. **CHRONIC EXPOSURE-** NO DATA AVAILABLE.

FIRST AID- REMOVE FROM EXPOSURE AREA TO FRESH AIR IMMEDIATELY. IF BREATHING HAS STOPPED, PERFORM ARTIFICIAL RESPIRATION. KEEP PERSON WARM AND AT REST. TREAT SYMPTOMATICALLY AND SUPPORTIVELY. GET MEDICAL ATTENTION IMMEDIATELY.

SKIN CONTACT: NABAM: IRRITANT/SENSITIZER. **ACUTE EXPOSURE-** CONTACT WITH DUST OR SOLUTIONS MAY CAUSE IRRITATION, MILD TO SEVERE ERYTHEMA, EDEMA AND VESICULATION. SENSITIZATION DERMATITIS MAY OCCUR IN PREVIOUSLY EXPOSED INDIVIDUALS. **CHRONIC EXPOSURE-** PROLONGED OR REPEATED EXPOSURE MAY CAUSE CONTACT OR SENSITIZATION DERMATITIS.

FIRST AID- REMOVE CONTAMINATED CLOTHING AND SHOES IMMEDIATELY. WASH AFFECTED AREA WITH SOAP OR MILD DETERGENT AND LARGE AMOUNTS OF WATER UNTIL NO EVIDENCE OF CHEMICAL REMAINS (APPROXIMATELY 15-20 MINUTES). GET MEDICAL ATTENTION IMMEDIATELY.

EYE CONTACT: NABAM: IRRITANT. **ACUTE EXPOSURE-** CONTACT WITH DUST OR SPRAY MAY CAUSE IRRITATION. **CHRONIC EXPOSURE-** PROLONGED OR REPEATED CONTACT WITH IRRITANTS MAY CAUSE CONJUNCTIVITIS.

FIRST AID- WASH EYES IMMEDIATELY WITH LARGE AMOUNTS OF WATER OR NORMAL SALINE, OCCASIONALLY LIFTING UPPER AND LOWER LIDS, UNTIL NO EVIDENCE OF CHEMICAL REMAINS (APPROXIMATELY 15-20 MINUTES). GET MEDICAL ATTENTION IMMEDIATELY.

INGESTION: NABAM: TOXIC. **ACUTE EXPOSURE-** TOXIC DOSES IN ANIMALS HAVE CAUSED CENTRAL NERVOUS SYSTEM STIMULATION FOLLOWED BY DEPRESSION, BLOODY DIARRHEA, GENERAL WEAKNESS, PROSTRATION, AND DEATH FROM RESPIRATORY ARREST. AT NECROPSY, SEVERE IRRITATION OF THE GASTROINTESTINAL TRACT AND RENAL NECROSIS WERE REPORTED. **CHRONIC EXPOSURE-** RATS FED 1000-2500 MG/KG FOR 10 DAYS EXHIBITED GOITROGENIC EFFECTS; 8.4-30.5 MG/KG/DAY FOR 28 DAYS DECREASED T4 AND INCREASED T3 SECRETION; 275 PPM FOR 14 DAYS CAUSED INCREASED LIVER WEIGHTS AND ENZYME CHANGES. NEONATAL DEATHS HAVE BEEN REPORTED IN OFFSPRING OF PREGNANT MICE FED NABAM. ORAL ADMINISTRATION OF ETHYLENE THIOUREA, A METABOLITE AND DEGRADATION PRODUCT OF NABAM, INDUCED HIGHLY SIGNIFICANT INCREASES IN THE INCIDENCE OF LIVER TUMORS IN TWO STRAINS OF MICE, AND OF THYROID CARCINOMAS AND ADENOMAS IN TWO SEPARATE RAT STUDIES.

FIRST AID- GIVE SYRUP OF IPECAC, FOLLOWED BY 1-2 GLASSES OF WATER, TO INDUCE VOMITING (ADULTS: 30 ML). FOLLOWING EMESIS, ADMINISTER 30-50 GRAMS ACTIVATED CHARCOAL. FOLLOW CHARCOAL WITH SODIUM OR MAGNESIUM SULFATE, 250 MG/KG, TO REMOVE TOXICANT FROM THE GUT BY CATHARSIS (EPA, RECOGNITION AND MANAGEMENT OF PESTICIDE POISONINGS, 3RD ED.). FIRST AID SHOULD BE ADMINISTERED UNDER THE DIRECTION OF QUALIFIED MEDICAL PERSONNEL. GET MEDICAL ATTENTION.

ANTIDOTE: NO SPECIFIC ANTIDOTE. TREAT SYMPTOMATICALLY AND SUPPORTIVELY.

REACTIVITY

REACTIVITY: NABAM: DECOMPOSES ON HEATING OR MIXING WIITH BOILING WATER

RELEASING TOXIC AND FLAMMABLE VAPORS. DECOMPOSED BY AIR OR LIGHT.

INCOMPATIBILITIES: NABAM: METALLIC IONS: MAY BE POLYMERIZED. OXIDIZERS (STRONG): FIRE AND EXPLOSION HAZARD.

DECOMPOSITION: THERMAL DECOMPOSITION PRODUCTS MAY INCLUDE TOXIC OXIDES OF NITROGEN AND SULFUR, AND TOXIC AND FLAMMABLE HYDROGEN SULFIDE.

POLYMERIZATION: HAZARDOUS POLYMERIZATION HAS NOT BEEN REPORTED TO OCCUR UNDER NORMAL TEMPERATURES AND PRESSURES.

STORAGE AND DISPOSAL

OBSERVE ALL FEDERAL, STATE AND LOCAL REGULATIONS WHEN STORING OR DISPOSING OF THIS SUBSTANCE. FOR ASSISTANCE, CONTACT THE DISTRICT DIRECTOR OF THE ENVIRONMENTAL PROTECTION AGENCY.

STORAGE

STORE IN ACCORDANCE WITH 40 CFR 165 RECOMMENDED PROCEDURES FOR THE DISPOSAL AND STORAGE OF PESTICIDES AND PESTICIDE CONTAINERS.
STORE AWAY FROM INCOMPATIBLE SUBSTANCES.

DISPOSAL

DISPOSAL MUST BE IN ACCORDANCE WITH 40 CFR 165 RECOMMENDED PROCEDURES FOR THE DISPOSAL AND STORAGE OF PESTICIDES AND PESTICIDE CONTAINERS.
DISPOSAL MUST BE IN ACCORDANCE WITH STANDARDS APPLICABLE TO GENERATORS OF HAZARDOUS WASTE, 40CFR 262. EPA HAZARDOUS WASTE NUMBER U114.

CONDITIONS TO AVOID

MAY BURN BUT DOES NOT IGNITE READILY.

SPILL AND LEAK PROCEDURES

OCCUPATIONAL SPILL: DO NOT TOUCH SPILLED MATERIAL. STOP LEAK IF YOU CAN DO IT WITHOUT RISK. FOR SMALL SPILLS, TAKE UP WITH SAND OR OTHER ABSORBENT MATERIAL AND PLACE INTO CONTAINERS FOR LATER DISPOSAL. FOR SMALL DRY SPILLS, WITH A CLEAN SHOVEL PLACE MATERIAL INTO CLEAN, DRY CONTAINER AND COVER. MOVE CONTAINERS FROM SPILL AREA. FOR LARGER SPILLS, DIKE FAR AHEAD OF SPILL FOR LATER DISPOSAL. KEEP UNNECESSARY PEOPLE AWAY. ISOLATE HAZARD AREA AND DENY ENTRY.

PROTECTIVE EQUIPMENT

VENTILATION: PROVIDE LOCAL EXHAUST OR PROCESS ENCLOSURE VENTILATION SYSTEM.

RESPIRATOR: THE FOLLOWING RESPIRATORS ARE RECOMMENDED BASED ON INFORMATION FOUND IN THE PHYSICAL DATA, TOXICITY AND HEALTH EFFECTS SECTIONS. THEY ARE RANKED IN ORDER FROM MINIMUM TO MAXIMUM RESPIRATORY PROTECTION. THE SPECIFIC RESPIRATOR SELECTED MUST BE BASED ON CONTAMINATION LEVELS FOUND IN THE WORK PLACE, MUST NOT EXCEED THE WORKING LIMITS OF THE RESPIRATOR AND BE JOINTLY APPROVED BY THE NATIONAL INSTITUTE FOR OCCUPATIONAL SAFETY AND HEALTH AND THE MINE SAFETY AND HEALTH ADMINISTRATION (NIOSH-MSHA).
TYPE 'C' SUPPLIED-AIR RESPIRATOR WITH A FULL FACEPIECE OPERATED IN PRESSURE-DEMAND OR OTHER POSITIVE PRESSURE MODE OR WITH A FULL FACEPIECE, HELMET OR HOOD OPERATED IN CONTINOUS-FLOW MODE.
SELF-CONTAINED BREATHING APPARATUS WITH A FULL FACEPIECE OPERATED IN PRESSURE-DEMAND OR OTHER POSITIVE PRESSURE MODE.
FOR FIREFIGHTING AND OTHER IMMEDIATELY DANGEROUS TO LIFE OR HEALTH CONDITIONS:
SELF-CONTAINED BREATHING APPARATUS WITH FULL FACEPIECE OPERATED IN PRESSURE-DEMAND OR OTHER POSITIVE PRESSURE MODE.
SUPPLIED-AIR RESPIRATOR WITH FULL FACEPIECE AND OPERATED IN PRESSURE-DEMAND OR OTHER POSITIVE PRESSURE MODE IN COMBINATION WITH AN AUXILIARY SELF-CONTAINED BREATHING APPARATUS OPERATED IN PRESSURE-DEMAND OR OTHER POSITIVE PRESSURE MODE.

CLOTHING: EMPLOYEE MUST WEAR APPROPRIATE PROTECTIVE (IMPERVIOUS) CLOTHING AND EQUIPMENT TO PREVENT ANY POSSIBILITY OF SKIN CONTACT WITH THIS SUBSTANCE.

GLOVES: EMPLOYEE MUST WEAR APPROPRIATE PROTECTIVE GLOVES TO PREVENT CONTACT WITH THIS SUBSTANCE.

EYE PROTECTION: EMPLOYEE MUST WEAR SPLASH-PROOF OR DUST-RESISTANT SAFETY GOGGLES WITH OR WITHOUT A FACESHIELD TO PREVENT CONTACT WITH THIS SUBSTANCE.
EMERGENCY EYE WASH: WHERE THERE IS ANY POSSIBILITY THAT AN EMPLOYEE'S EYES MAY BE EXPOSED TO THIS SUBSTANCE, THE EMPLOYER SHOULD PROVIDE AN EYE WASH FOUNTAIN WITHIN THE IMMEDIATE WORK AREA FOR EMERGENCY USE.

AUTHORIZED BY- OCCUPATIONAL HEALTH SERVICES, INC.
CREATION DATE: 03/30/90 ***REVISION DATE:*** 03/30/90

MATERIAL SAFETY DATA SHEET

OCCUPATIONAL HEALTH SERVICES, INC.
AGRICULTURE AND PESTICIDE DIVISION
450 SEVENTH AVENUE, SUITE 2407
NEW YORK, NEW YORK 10123
1-800-445-MSDS OR (212) 967-1100

EMERGENCY CONTACT:
JOHN S. BRANSFORD, JR. (615) 292-1180

SUBSTANCE IDENTIFICATION

CAS-NUMBER 91-20-3

SUBSTANCE: **NAPHTHALENE**

TRADE NAMES/SYNONYMS: NAPHTHALIN; TAR CAMPHOR; WHITE TAR; NAPHTHENE; MOTH BALLS; MOTH FLAKES; NAPHTHALINE; NAPHTHALEN; ALBOCARBON; CAMPHOR TAR; U165; STCC 4940361; UN 1334; N-7; N-134; N-136; PST16120

CHEMICAL FAMILY: HYDROCARBON, POLYNUCLEAR

MOLECULAR FORMULA: C10-H8 MOL WT: 128

CERCLA RATINGS (SCALE 0-3): HEALTH=2 FIRE=2 REACTIVITY=0 PERSISTENCE=3

NFPA RATINGS (SCALE 0-4): HEALTH=2 FIRE=2 REACTIVITY=0

COMPONENTS AND CONTAMINANTS

COMPONENT: NAPHTHALENE ***PERCENT:*** 100
CAS# 91-20-3

OTHER CONTAMINANTS: NONE

EXPOSURE LIMITS: NAPHTHALENE: 10 PPM (50 MG/M3) OSHA TWA; 15 PPM (75 MG/M3) OSHA STEL 10 PPM (50 MG/M3) ACGIH TWA; 15 PPM (75 MG/M3) ACGIH STEL
100 POUNDS CERCLA SECTION 103 REPORTABLE QUANTITY SUBJECT TO SARA SECTION 313 ANNUAL TOXIC CHEMCIALS RELEASE REPORTING

PHYSICAL DATA

DESCRIPTION: WHITE CRYSTALLINE, VOLATILE FLAKES; ODOR OF MOTH BALLS.

BOILING POINT: 424 F (218 C) ***MELTING POINT:*** 176 F (80 C)

SPECIFIC GRAVITY: 1.1 ***VAPOR PRESSURE:*** 0.05 MMHG @ 20 C

EVAPORATION RATE: (BU ACETATE=1) <<1.0 ***SOLUBILITY IN WATER:*** INSOLUBLE

VAPOR DENSITY: 4.4

SOLVENT SOLUBILITY: ALCOHOL, BENZENE, CCL4, FIXED & VOLATILE OILS.

FIRE AND EXPLOSION DATA

FIRE AND EXPLOSION HAZARD: MODERATE FIRE HAZARD WHEN EXPOSED TO HEAT OR FLAME, AND A MODERATE EXPLOSION HAZARD IN THE FORM OF DUST AT 176 F. REACTIONS WITH INCOMPATIBLE SUBSTANCES MAY CAUSE FIRES AND EXPLOSIONS.
VAPOR-AIR MIXTURES ARE EXPLOSIVE ABOVE FLASH POINT.

FLASH POINT: 174 F (79 C) (CC) ***UPPER EXPLOSIVE LIMIT:*** 5.9%

LOWER EXPLOSIVE LIMIT: 0.9% ***AUTOIGNITION TEMP.:*** 979 F (526 C)

FIREFIGHTING MEDIA: DRY CHEMICAL, SAND, WATER SPRAY OR FOAM (1987 EMERGENCY RESPONSE GUIDEBOOK, DOT P 5800.4).
FOR LARGER FIRES, USE WATER SPRAY, FOG OR STANDARD FOAM (1987 EMERGENCY RESPONSE GUIDEBOOK, DOT P 5800.4).

FIREFIGHTING: MOVE CONTAINER FROM FIRE AREA IF POSSIBLE. COOL CONTAINERS EXPOSED TO FLAME WITH WATER FROM SIDE UNTIL WELL AFTER FIRE IS OUT. STAY AWAY FROM STORAGE TANK ENDS. FOR MASSIVE FIRE IN CARGO AREA, USE UNMANNED HOSE HOLDER OR MONITOR NOZZLES; ELSE WITHDRAW AND LET FIRE BURN (1987 EMERGENCY RESPONSE GUIDEBOOK, DOT P 5800.4, GUIDE PAGE 32).
EXTINGUISH ONLY IF FLOW CAN BE STOPPED; USE WATER IN FLOODING QUANTITIES AS FOG, SOLID STREAMS MAY NOT BE EFFECTIVE. COOL CONTAINERS WITH FLOODING AMOUNTS OF WATER, APPLY FROM AS FAR A DISTANCE AS POSSIBLE. AVOID BREATHING VAPORS OR DUSTS.
WATER MAY BE INEFFECTIVE (NFPA 325M, FIRE HAZARD PROPERTIES OF FLAMMABLE LIQUIDS, GASES, AND VOLATILE SOLIDS, 1984)

TRANSPORTATION DATA

DEPARTMENT OF TRANSPORTATION HAZARD CLASSIFICATION 49 CFR 172.101: ORM-A
DEPARTMENT OF TRANSPORTATION LABELING REQUIREMENTS 49 CFR 172.101 AND SUBPART E: NONE

DEPARTMENT OF TRANSPORTATION PACKAGING REQUIREMENTS: 49 CFR 173.655
EXCEPTIONS: 49 CFR 173.505

TOXICITY

NAPHTHALENE: IRRITATION DATA: 495 MG OPEN SKIN-RABBIT MILD; 100 MG EYE-RABBIT MILD. TOXICITY DATA: 100 MG/KG ORAL-CHILD LDLO; 490 MG/KG ORAL-RAT LD50; 533 MG/KG ORAL-MOUSE LD50; 3 GM/KG ORAL-RABBIT LDLO; 1200 MG/KG ORAL-GUINEA PIG LD50; 400 MG/KG ORAL-DOG LDLO; 1000 MG/KG ORAL-CAT LDLO; 969 MG/KG SUBCUTANEOUS-MOUSE LD50; 100 MG/KG INTRAVENOUS-MOUSE LD50; 150 MG/KG INTRAPERITONEAL-MOUSE LD50; 29 MG/KG UNREPORTED-HUMAN LDLO; 74 MG/KG UNREPORTED-MAN LDLO; REPRODUCTIVE EFFECTS DATA (RTECS); TUMORIGENIC DATA (RTECS). CARCINOGEN STATUS: NONE. LOCAL EFFECTS: IRRITANT- INHALATION, SKIN, EYE. ACUTE TOXICITY LEVEL: TOXIC BY INGESTION. TARGET EFFECTS: SENSITIZER- DERMAL. HEMOLYTIC AGENT. AT INCREASED RISK FORM EXPOSURE: PERSONS WITH A DEFICIENCY OF GLUCOSE-6-PHOSPHATE DEHYDROGENASE MAY BE MORE SUSCEPTIBLE TO THE HEMOLYTIC EFFECTS. ADDITIONAL DATA: MAY CROSS THE PLACENTAL BARRIER.

HEALTH EFFECTS AND FIRST AID

INHALATION: NAPHTHALENE: IRRITANT/HEMOLYTIC AGENT. 500 PPM IMMEDIATELY DANGEROUS TO LIFE OR HEALTH. **ACUTE EXPOSURE-** VAPORS MAY CAUSE RESPIRATORY TRACT IRRITATION, HEADACHE, NAUSEA, VOMITING, ABDOMINAL CRAMPS, DIARRHEA, PERSPIRATION, CONFUSION, AND EXCITEMENT. OPTIC NEURITIS HAS BEEN REPORTED. ACUTE INTRAVASCULAR HEMOLYSIS IS MOSTLY LIKELY TO OCCUR IN SUSCEPTIBLE INDIVIDUALS INCLUDING THOSE WITH GLUCOSE-6-PHOSPHATE DEHYDROGENASE DEFICIENCY. EFFECTS MAY BE DELAYED 2-7 DAYS AND INCLUDE ACUTE HEMOLYTIC ANEMIA WITH NUCLEATED AND FRAGMENTED ERYTHROCYTES, ANISOCYTOSIS, POIKILOCYTOSIS, HEINZ BODIES, LEUKOCYTOSIS, HEMOGLOBINEMIA, HEMOGLOBINURIA, PALLOR, JAUNDICE, FEVER, AND LETHARGY. MILD METHEMOGLOBINEMIA MAY OCCUR. A POTENTIALLY FATAL HYPERKALEMIA MAY DEVELOP. BLADDER IRRITATION WITH URGENCY, DYSURIA AND DARK URINE MAY OCCUR. COMA, WITH OR WITHOUT CONVULSIONS, AND LIVER INJURY ARE POSSIBLE. RENAL TUBULAR BLOCKADE AND ACUTE RENAL FAILURE, POSSIBLY FATAL, MAY FOLLOW A HEMOLYTIC CRISIS. **CHRONIC EXPOSURE-** REPEATED OR PROLONGED EXPOSURE TO VAPORS MAY CAUSE MALAISE, HEADACHE, AND VOMITING. CATARACTS AND CORNEAL ULCERATIONS HAVE BEEN INDUCED IN ANIMALS AND OCCASIONALLY REPORTED IN HUMANS.

FIRST AID- REMOVE FROM EXPOSURE AREA TO FRESH AIR IMMEDIATELY. IF BREATHING HAS STOPPED, PERFORM ARTIFICIAL RESPIRATION. KEEP PERSON WARM AND AT REST. TREAT SYMPTOMATICALLY AND SUPPORTIVELY. GET MEDICAL ATTENTION IMMEDIATELY.

SKIN CONTACT: NAPHTHALENE: IRRITANT/SENSITIZER/HEMOLYTIC AGENT. **ACUTE EXPOSURE-** CONTACT MAY CAUSE IRRITATION, AND IN THE CASE OF A SENSITIZED PERSON, SEVERE DERMATITIS. HEMOLYTIC ANEMIA AND OTHER SYSTEMIC EFFECTS HAVE BEEN REPORTED DUE TO SKIN ABSORPTION ONLY IN INFANTS. THE ABSORPTION MAY HAVE BEEN ENHANCED BY THE USE OF BABY OILS AND THE TOXICITY MAY HAVE BEEN CONTRIBUTED TO BY CONCOMMITENT VAPOR INHALATION. **CHRONIC EXPOSURE-** REPEATED OR PROLONGED SKIN CONTACT MAY PRODUCE A DERMATITIS CHARACTERIZED BY ITCHING, REDNESS, SCALING, WEEPING, AND CRUSTING OF THE SKIN. REPEATED CONTACT MAY LEAD TO SENSITIZATION DERMATITIS. CHRONIC ABSORPTION MAY RESULT IN CATARACTS AND OCULAR IRRITATION.

FIRST AID- REMOVE CONTAMINATED CLOTHING AND SHOES IMMEDIATELY. WASH AFFECTED AREA WITH SOAP OR MILD DETERGENT AND LARGE AMOUNTS OF WATER UNTIL NO EVIDENCE OF CHEMICAL REMAINS (APPROXIMATELY 15-20 MINUTES). GET MEDICAL ATTENTION IMMEDIATELY.

EYE CONTACT: NAPHTHALENE: IRRITANT. **ACUTE EXPOSURE-** VAPOR MAY CAUSE IRRITATION AT 15 PPM. DIRECT CONTACT MAY CAUSE CONJUNCTIVITIS, INJURY TO THE CORNEA, CHORIORETINITIS, SCOTOMA, AND DIMINISHED VISUAL ACUITY. WHEN PURE CRYSTALLINE NAPHTHALENE WAS APPLIED TO RABBIT EYES AND ALLOWED TO REMAIN FOR AN UNSPECIFIED PERIOD, LOCAL EPITHELIAL INJURY AND SLIGHT TURBIDITY OF THE UNDERLYING STROMA WERE OBSERVED BUT CLEARED AND HEALED COMPLETELY IN 2 WEEKS. **CHRONIC EXPOSURE-** REPEATED OR PROLONGED EXPOSURE MAY CAUSE CONJUNCTIVITIS.

FIRST AID- WASH EYES IMMEDIATELY WITH LARGE AMOUNTS OF WATER OR NORMAL SALINE, OCCASIONALLY LIFTING UPPER AND LOWER LIDS, UNTIL NO EVIDENCE OF CHEMICAL REMAINS (APPROXIMATELY 15-20 MINUTES). GET MEDICAL ATTENTION IMMEDIATELY.

INGESTION: NAPHTHALENE: HEMOLYTIC AGENT/TOXIC. **ACUTE EXPOSURE-** INGESTION MAY CAUSE ABDOMINAL CRAMPS, NAUSEA, VOMITING, DIARRHEA, HEADACHE, PROFUSE PERSPIRATION, LISTLESSNESS, AND CONFUSION. SIGNS AND SYMPTOMS OF INTRAVASCULAR HEMOLYSIS, BLADDER IRRITATION, COMA, CONVULSIONS, LIVER INJURY AND ACUTE RENAL FAILURE AS DESCRIBED IN ACUTE INHALATION MAY OCCUR. INDIVIDUALS WITH GLUCOSE-6-DEHYDROGENASE DEFICIENCY ARE MORE SUSCEPTIBLE TO THE HEMOLYTIC EFFECTS. AMONG SENSITIVE INDIVIDUALS MINUTE DOSES HAVE INDUCED DANGEROUS REACTIONS. THE MEAN LETHAL DOSE IN NONSENSITIVE INDIVIDUALS IS BETWEEN 5 AND 15 GRAMS. **CHRONIC EXPOSURE-** 50 CASES OF SEVERE CHRONIC EFFECTS FROM REPEATED INGESTION OF A NAPHTHALENE-ISOPROPYL ALCOHOL "COCKTAIL" HAVE BEEN REPORTED WITH SYMPTOMS RESEMBLING THOSE OF ETHANOL INTOXICATION INCLUDING TREMORS, RESTLESSNESS, EXTREME APPREHENSION, AND HALLUCINATIONS; EFFECTS SUBSIDED IN A FEW DAYS. IN EXPERIMENTAL ANIMALS CHRONIC INGESTION HAS LED TO OCULAR EFFECTS. 1 GM/KG/DAY IN RABBITS HAS CAUSED LENTICULAR CHANGES INITIALLY OBSERVED AS A SWELLING IN THE PERIPHERAL PORTION OF THE LENS. VACUOLES FORM BETWEEN THE EPITHELIUM CELLS WITHIN SIX HOURS AFTER THE FIRST DOSE, SPREAD TOWARD THE NUCLEUS, AND WITHIN 2 WEEKS THE WHOLE LENS IS AFFECTED WITH A MATURE CATARACT. THE STAGES OF NAPHTHALENE-INDUCED CATARACT ARE SIMILAR TO THOSE THAT OCCUR IN THE DEVELOPMENT OF HUMAN SENILE CATARACT. REPRODUCTIVE EFFECTS HAVE BEEN REPORTED IN ANIMALS.

FIRST AID- REMOVE BY GASTRIC LAVAGE OR EMESIS. MAINTAIN BLOOD PRESSURE AND AIRWAY. GIVE OXYGEN IF RESPIRATION IS DEPRESSED. DO NOT PERFORM GASTRIC LAVAGE OR EMESIS IF VICTIM IS UNCONSCIOUS. GET MEDICAL ATTENTION IMMEDIATELY (DREISBACH, HANDBOOK OF POISONING, 11TH ED.). ADMINISTRATION OF GASTRIC LAVAGE OR OXYGEN SHOULD BE PERFORMED BY QUALIFIED MEDICAL PERSONNEL.

ANTIDOTE: NO SPECIFIC ANTIDOTE. TREAT SYMPTOMATICALLY AND SUPPORTIVELY.

REACTIVITY

REACTIVITY: STABLE UNDER NORMAL TEMPERATURES AND PRESSURES.

INCOMPATIBILITIES: NAPHTHALENE: CHROMIC ANHYDRIDE: VIOLENT REACTION. ALUMINUM TRICHLORIDE + BENZOYL CHLORIDE MIXTURE: VIOLENT REACTION. STRONG OXIDIZERS: VIOLENT REACTION. DINITROGEN PENTAOXIDE: POSSIBLE EXPLOSION. PLASTICS: MELTED FORM WILL ATTACK. RUBBER: MELTED FORM WILL ATTACK. COATINGS: MELTED FORM WILL ATTACK.

DECOMPOSITION: THERMAL DECOMPOSITION PRODUCTS MAY INCLUDE TOXIC OXIDES OF CARBON.

POLYMERIZATION: HAZARDOUS POLYMERIZATION HAS NOT BEEN REPORTED TO OCCUR UNDER NORMAL TEMPERATURES AND PRESSURES.

STORAGE AND DISPOSAL

OBSERVE ALL FEDERAL, STATE AND LOCAL REGULATIONS WHEN STORING OR DISPOSING OF THIS SUBSTANCE. FOR ASSISTANCE, CONTACT THE DISTRICT DIRECTOR OF THE ENVIRONMENTAL PROTECTION AGENCY.

****STORAGE****

STORAGE: PROTECT AGAINST PHYSICAL DAMAGE. STORE IN A COOL PLACE, AWAY FROM SOURCES OF HEAT AND IGNITION. SEPARATE FROM OXIDIZING MATERIALS (NFPA 49, HAZARDOUS CHEMICALS DATA, 1975).

****DISPOSAL****

DISPOSAL MUST BE IN ACCORDANCE WITH STANDARDS APPLICABLE TO GENERATORS OF HAZARDOUS WASTE, 40CFR 262. EPA HAZARDOUS WASTE NUMBER I165.

SPILL AND LEAK PROCEDURES

OCCUPATIONAL SPILL: SHUT OFF IGNITION SOURCES. DO NOT TOUCH SPILLED MATERIAL. FOR SMALL SPILLS, WITH CLEAN SHOVEL, PLACE MATERIAL INTO CLEAN, DRY CONTAINER AND COVER; MOVE CONTAINERS FROM SPILL AREA. FOR LARGER SPILLS, WET DOWN WITH WATER AND DIKE FOR LATER DISPOSAL. NO SMOKING, FLAMES OR FLARES IN HAZARD AREA! KEEP UNNECESSARY PEOPLE AWAY. ISOLATE HAZARD AREA AND DENY ENTRY.

REPORTABLE QUANTITY (RQ): 100 POUNDS THE SUPERFUND AMENDMENTS AND REAUTHORIZATION ACT (SARA) SECTION 304 REQUIRES THAT A RELEASE EQUAL TO OR GREATER THAN THE REPORTABLE QUANTITY FOR THIS SUBSTANCE BE IMMEDIATELY REPORTED TO THE LOCAL EMERGENCY PLANNING COMMITTEE AND THE STATE EMERGENCY RESPONSE COMMISSION (40 CFR 355.40). IF THE RELEASE OF THIS SUBSTANCE IS REPORTABLE UNDER CERCLA SECTION 103, THE NATIONAL RESPONSE CENTER MUST BE NOTIFIED IMMEDIATELY AT (800) 424-8802 OR (202) 426-2675 IN THE METROPOLITAN WASHINGTON, D.C. AREA (40 CFR 302.6).

PROTECTIVE EQUIPMENT

VENTILATION: PROVIDE LOCAL EXHAUST VENTILATION SYSTEM TO MEET PUBLISHED EXPOSURE LIMITS.

RESPIRATOR: THE FOLLOWING RESPIRATORS AND MAXIMUM USE CONCENTRATIONS ARE RECOMMENDATIONS BY THE U.S. DEPARTMENT OF HEALTH AND HUMAN SERVICES, NIOSH POCKET GUIDE TO CHEMICAL HAZARDS; NIOSH CRITERIA DOCUMENTS OR BY THE U.S. DEPARTMENT OF LABOR, 29 CFR 1910 SUBPART Z. THE SPECIFIC RESPIRATOR SELECTED MUST BE BASED ON CONTAMINATION LEVELS FOUND IN THE WORK PLACE, MUST NOT EXCEED THE WORKING LIMITS OF

THE RESPIRATOR AND BE JOINTLY APPROVED BY THE NATIONAL INSTITUTE FOR OCCUPATIONAL SAFETY AND HEALTH AND THE MINE SAFETY AND HEALTH ADMINISTRATION (NIOSH-MSHA).

500 PPM- CHEMICAL CARTRIDGE RESPIRATOR WITH AN ORGANIC VAPOR CARTRIDGE AND A DUST FILTER. GAS MASK WITH A CHIN-STYLE, FRONT-, OR BACK-MOUNTED ORGANIC VAPOR CANISTER AND A DUST FILTER. SUPPLIED-AIR RESPIRATOR WITH A FULL FACEPIECE, HELMET, OR HOOD. SELF-CONTAINED BREATHING APPARATUS WITH A FULL FACEPIECE.

ESCAPE- GAS MASK WITH A CHIN-STYLE, FRONT-, OR BACK-MOUNTED ORGANIC VAPOR CANISTER AND A HIGH-EFFICIENCY PARTICULATE FILTER. ANY ESCAPE SELF-CONTAINED BREATHING APPARATUS.

FOR FIREFIGHTING AND OTHER IMMEDIATELY DANGEROUS TO LIFE OR HEALTH CONDITIONS:

SELF-CONTAINED BREATHING APPARATUS WITH FULL FACEPIECE OPERATED IN PRESSURE-DEMAND OR OTHER POSITIVE PRESSURE MODE.

SUPPLIED-AIR RESPIRATOR WITH FULL FACEPIECE AND OPERATED IN PRESSURE-DEMAND OR OTHER POSITIVE PRESSURE MODE IN COMBINATION WITH AN AUXILIARY SELF-CONTAINED BREATHING APPARATUS OPERATED IN PRESSURE-DEMAND OR OTHER POSITIVE PRESSURE MODE.

CLOTHING: PROTECTIVE CLOTHING NOT REQUIRED. AVOID REPEATED OR PROLONGED CONTACT WITH THIS SUBSTANCE.

GLOVES: EMPLOYEE MUST WEAR APPROPRIATE PROTECTIVE GLOVES TO PREVENT CONTACT WITH THIS SUBSTANCE.

EYE PROTECTION: EMPLOYEE MUST WEAR SPLASH-PROOF OR DUST-RESISTANT SAFETY GOGGLES AND A FACESHIELD TO PREVENT CONTACT WITH THIS SUBSTANCE.

EMERGENCY WASH FACILITIES: WHERE THERE IS ANY POSSIBILITY THAT AN EMPLOYEE'S EYES AND/OR SKIN MAY BE EXPOSED TO THIS SUBSTANCE, THE EMPLOYER SHOULD PROVIDE AN EYE WASH FOUNTAIN AND QUICK DRENCH SHOWER WITHIN THE IMMEDIATE WORK AREA FOR EMERGENCY USE.

AUTHORIZED BY- OCCUPATIONAL HEALTH SERVICES, INC.

CREATION DATE: 10/04/89 ***REVISION DATE:*** 03/28/90

MATERIAL SAFETY DATA SHEET

OCCUPATIONAL HEALTH SERVICES, INC.
AGRICULTURE AND PESTICIDE DIVISION
450 SEVENTH AVENUE, SUITE 2407
NEW YORK, NEW YORK 10123
1-800-445-MSDS OR (212) 967-1100

EMERGENCY CONTACT:
JOHN S. BRANSFORD, JR. (615) 292-1180

SUBSTANCE IDENTIFICATION

CAS-NUMBER 21548-32-3

SUBSTANCE: FOSTHIETAN

TRADE NAMES/SYNONYMS: PHOSPHORAMIDIC ACID, 1,3-DITHIETAN-2-YLIDENE-, DIETHYL ESTER; 1,3-DITHIETAN-2-YLIDENE- DIETHYL PHOSPHORAMIDATE; IMIDOCARBONIC ACID, PHOSPHONODITHIO-, CYCLIC METHYLENE P,P-DIETHYL ESTER; CYCLIC METHYLENE P,P-DIETHYL, PHOSPHONODITHIOIMIDOCARBONATE; AC 64475; ACCONEM; 2-(DIETHOXYPHOSPHINYLIMINO)-1,3-DIETHIETANE; GEOFOS; NEM-A-TAK; CYCLIC METHYLENE(DIETHOXYPHOSPHINYL) DITHIOIMIDOCARBONATE; CL 64475; PHOSPHONODITHIOIMIDOCARBONIC ACID CYCLIC METHYLENE P,P-DIETHYL ESTER; C6H12NO3PS2; PST16141

CHEMICAL FAMILY: ORGANOPHOSPHATE
AMINE
THIO

MOLECULAR FORMULA: (C-H3-C-H2-O)2-P-(O)-N-C-S2-C-H2

MOLECULAR WEIGHT: 241.26

CERCLA RATINGS (SCALE 0-3): HEALTH=3 FIRE=U REACTIVITY=0 PERSISTENCE=0

NFPA RATINGS (SCALE 0-4): HEALTH=4 FIRE=U REACTIVITY=0

COMPONENTS AND CONTAMINANTS

COMPONENT: FOSTHIETAN ***PERCENT:*** 100.0
CAS# 21548-32-3

OTHER CONTAMINANTS: NONE

EXPOSURE LIMITS: NO OCCUPATIONAL EXPOSURE LIMITS ESTABLISHED BY OSHA, ACGIH, OR NIOSH.
FOSTHIETAN: 500 POUNDS SARA SECTION 302 THRESHOLD PLANNING QUANTITY
1 POUND SARA SECTION 304 REPORTABLE QUANTITY

PHYSICAL DATA

DESCRIPTION: PALE YELLOW OIL WITH A MERCAPTAN-LIKE ODOR.

BOILING POINT: NOT AVAILABLE ***SPECIFIC GRAVITY:*** 1.3 @ 25 C

VAPOR PRESSURE: NEGLIGIBLE ***SOLUBILITY IN WATER:*** 5% @ 25 C

SOLVENT SOLUBILITY: SOLUBLE IN ACETONE, CHLOROFORM, METHANOL, TOLUENE

FIRE AND EXPLOSION DATA

FIRE AND EXPLOSION HAZARD: UNKNOWN FIRE AND EXPLOSION HAZARD.

FLASH POINT: NOT AVAILABLE

FIREFIGHTING MEDIA: DRY CHEMICAL, CARBON DIOXIDE, HALON, WATER SPRAY OR STANDARD FOAM (1987 EMERGENCY RESPONSE GUIDEBOOK, DOT P 5800.4). FOR LARGER FIRES, USE WATER SPRAY, FOG OR STANDARD FOAM (1987 EMERGENCY RESPONSE GUIDEBOOK, DOT P 5800.4).

FIREFIGHTING: MOVE CONTAINERS FROM FIRE AREA IF POSSIBLE. COOL CONTAINERS EXPOSED TO FLAMES WITH WATER FROM SIDE UNTIL WELL AFTER FIRE IS OUT. FIGHT FIRE FROM MAXIMUM DISTANCE. STAY AWAY FROM STORAGE TANK ENDS. DIKE FIRE CONTROL WATER FOR LATER DISPOSAL. DO NOT SCATTER MATERIAL. (1987 EMERGENCY RESPONSE GUIDEBOOK, DOT P 5800.4, GUIDE PAGE 57). EXTINGUISH ONLY IF FLOW CAN BE STOPPED. USE FLOODING AMOUNTS OF WATER AS A FOG; SOLID STREAMS MAY BE INEFFECTIVE. COOL CONTAINERS WITH FLOODING AMOUNTS OF WATER FROM AS FAR A DISTANCE AS POSSIBLE. AVOID BREATHING POISONOUS VAPORS, KEEP UPWIND.

TRANSPORTATION DATA

DEPARTMENT OF TRANSPORTATION HAZARD CLASSIFICATION 49 CFR 172.101: POISON B

DEPARTMENT OF TRANSPORTATION LABELING REQUIREMENTS 49 CFR 172.101 AND SUBPART E: POISON

DEPARTMENT OF TRANSPORTATION PACKAGING REQUIREMENTS: 49 CFR 173.346 EXCEPTIONS: 49 CFR 173.345

TOXICITY

FOSTHIETAN: TOXICITY DATA: 4700 UG/KG ORAL-RAT LD50; 18 MG/KG ORAL-MOUSE LD50. CARCINOGEN STATUS: NONE. ACUTE TOXICITY LEVEL: HIGHLY TOXIC BY INGESTION. TARGET EFFECTS: CHOLINESTERASE INHIBITOR. POISONING MAY AFFECT THE NERVOUS SYSTEM.* AT INCREASED RISK FROM EXPOSURE: PERSONS WITH RESPIRATORY AILMENTS, RECENT EXPOSURE TO CHOLINESTERASE INHIBITORS OR IMPAIRED CHOLINESTERASE PRODUCTION, OR LIVER MALFUNCTION.* ADDITIONAL DATA: MAY CROSS THE PLACENTA. HIGH ENVIRONMENTAL TEMPERATURES OR EXPOSURE OF THE CHEMICAL TO VISIBLE OR ULTRAVIOLET LIGHT MAY ENHANCE THE TOXICITY. INTERACTIONS WITH MEDICATIONS MAY OCCUR.*

* MAY BE BASED ON GENERAL INFORMATION ON ORGANOPHOSPHATES.

HEALTH EFFECTS AND FIRST AID

INHALATION: FOSTHIETAN: SEE INFORMATION ON ORGANOPHOSPHATES.
ORGANOPHOSPHATES: CHOLINESTERASE INHIBITOR. ACUTE EXPOSURE- WHEN INHALED, THE FIRST EFFECTS OF CHOLINESTERASE INHIBITORS ARE USUALLY RESPIRATORY AND MAY INCLUDE NASAL HYPEREMIA AND WATERY DISCHARGE, COUGH, CHEST DISCOMFORT, DYSPNEA, AND WHEEZING DUE TO INCREASED BRONCHIAL SECRETIONS AND BRONCHOCONSTRICTION. IF SUFFICIENT AMOUNTS ARE ABSORBED, OTHER SYSTEMIC EFFECTS MAY BEGIN WITHIN A FEW MINUTES OR BE DELAYED FOR UP TO 12 HOURS. SYMPTOMS MAY INCLUDE PALLOR, NAUSEA, VOMITING, DIARRHEA, ABDOMINAL CRAMPS, HEADACHE, DIZZINESS, OCULAR PAIN, BLURRED VISION, MIOSIS OR IN SOME CASES, ESPECIALLY INITIALLY, MYDRIASIS, LACRIMATION, SALIVATION, SWEATING, AND CONFUSION. OTHER REPORTED CENTRAL NERVOUS SYSTEM OR NEUROMUSCULAR EFFECTS MAY INCLUDE ATAXIA, SLURRED SPEECH, AREFLEXIA, WEAKNESS, FATIGUE, FASCICULATIONS, TWITCHING, TREMORS POSSIBLY OF THE TONGUE AND EYELIDS, AND EVENTUALLY PARALYSIS OF THE EXTREMITIES AND POSSIBLY OF THE RESPIRATORY MUSCLES. IN SEVERE CASES THERE MAY ALSO BE INVOLUNTARY DEFECATION AND URINATION, CYANOSIS, PSYCHOSIS, HYPERGLYCEMIA, ACUTE PANCREATITIS, CARDIAC IRREGULARITIES, PULMONARY EDEMA, UNCONSCIOUSNESS, CONVULSIONS, AND COMA. DEATH IS PRIMARILY DUE TO RESPIRATORY FAILURE, ALTHOUGH CARDIOVASCULAR EFFECTS INCLUDING CARDIAC ARREST MAY ALSO BE IMPLICATED. LONG TERM SEQUELAE ARE RARE BUT MAY INCLUDE NEUROPSYCHIATRIC DISORDERS AND MYOPATHY WITH MUSCLE TENDERNESS. SOME ORGANOPHOSPHATES MAY CAUSE A DELAYED NEUROPATHY BEGINNING 1-4 WEEKS AFTER AN ACUTE EXPOSURE WHICH MAY OR MAY NOT HAVE CAUSED ACUTE CHOLINERGIC EFFECTS. NUMBNESS, TINGLING, WEAKNESS AND CRAMPING BEGINNING SYMMETRICALLY IN THE LOWER LIMBS MAY PROGRESS TO ATAXIA AND PARALYSIS. IN SEVERE CASES, UPPER LIMB INVOLVEMENT IS POSSIBLE AND FLACCID PARALYSIS MAY PROGRESS TO SPASTIC PARALYSIS WITH EXAGGERATED REFLEXES. IMPROVEMENT MAY OCCUR OVER MONTHS TO YEARS, BUT SOME RESIDUAL IMPAIRMENT USUALLY REMAINS.

CHRONIC EXPOSURE- REPEATED OR PROLONGED EXPOSURE MAY RESULT IN THE EFFECTS OF ACUTE EXPOSURE INCLUDING THE DELAYED NEUROPATHY. OTHER EFFECTS REPORTED IN WORKERS REPEATEDLY EXPOSED INCLUDE IMPAIRED MEMORY AND CONCENTRATION, ACUTE PSYCHOSIS, SEVERE DEPRESSIONS, IRRITABILTY, CONFUSION, APATHY, EMOTIONAL LABILITY, SOCIAL WITHDRAWAL, CONFUSION, HEADACHE, SPEECH DIFFICULTIES, DELAYED REACTION TIMES, SPATIAL DISORIENTATION, NIGHTMARES, SLEEPWALKING, AND DROWSINESS OR INSOMNIA. AN INFLUENZA-LIKE CONDITION WITH HEADACHE, NAUSEA, WEAKNESS, ANOREXIA AND MALAISE HAS ALSO BEEN REPORTED.

FIRST AID- REMOVE FROM EXPOSURE AREA TO FRESH AIR IMMEDIATELY. IF BREATHING HAS STOPPED, GIVE ARTIFICIAL RESPIRATION. MAINTAIN AIRWAY AND BLOOD PRESSURE AND ADMINISTER OXYGEN IF AVAILABLE. KEEP AFFECTED PERSON WARM AND AT REST. TREAT SYMPTOMATICALLY AND SUPPORTIVELY. ADMINISTRATION OF OXYGEN SHOULD BE PERFORMED BY QUALIFIED PERSONNEL. GET MEDICAL ATTENTION IMMEDIATELY.

SKIN CONTACT: FOSTHIETAN: MAY CAUSE IRRITATION. SEE INFORMATION ON ORGANOPHOSPHATES.

ORGANOPHOSPHATES: CHOLINESTERASE INHIBITOR. **ACUTE EXPOSURE-** LOCALIZED SWEATING AND FASCICULATIONS MAY OCCUR AT THE SITE OF CONTACT. IF SUFFICIENT AMOUNTS ARE ABSORBED, OTHER EFFECTS OF CHOLINESTERASE INHIBITION AS DESCRIBED IN ACUTE INHALATION MAY OCCUR. SYMPTOMS MAY BE DELAYED 2-3 HOURS, BUT USUALLY NO MORE THAN 12 HOURS. THE RATE OF ABSORPTION IS INCREASED BY THE PRESENCE OF DERMATITIS OR HIGH AMBIENT TEMPERATURES. DELAYED NEUROPATHY IS ALSO POSSIBLE. **CHRONIC EXPOSURE-** REPEATED OR PROLONGED EXPOSURE MAY CAUSE EFFECTS AS DESCRIBED IN ACUTE EXPOSURE. SOME ORGANOPHOSPHATES MAY CAUSE SENSITIZATION.

FIRST AID- REMOVE CONTAMINATED CLOTHING IMMEDIATELY. WASH CONTAMINATED AREAS WITH SOAP AND WATER FOLLOWED BY ALCOHOL (ARENA, POISONING, 4TH ED.). EMERGENCY PERSONNEL SHOULD WEAR GLOVES AND AVOID CONTAMINATION. TREAT RESPIRATORY DIFFICULTY WITH ARTIFICIAL RESPIRATION. GET MEDICAL ATTENTION IMMEDIATELY.

EYE CONTACT: FOSTHIETAN: MAY CAUSE IRRITATION. SEE INFORMATION ON ORGANOPHOSPHATES.

ORGANOPHOSPHATES: CHOLINESTERASE INHIBITOR. **ACUTE EXPOSURE-** DIRECT CONTACT MAY CAUSE PAIN, HYPEREMIA, LACRIMATION, TWITCHING OF THE EYELIDS, MIOSIS, AND CILIARY MUSCLE SPASM WITH LOSS OF ACCOMODATION, BLURRED OR DIMMED VISION AND BROWACHE. SOMETIMES MYDRIASIS MAY OCCUR INSTEAD OF MIOSIS. WITH SUFFICIENT EXPOSURE, OTHER SYMPTOMS OF CHOLINESTERASE INHIBITION AS DESCRIBED IN ACUTE INHALATION MAY OCCUR. **CHRONIC EXPOSURE-** REPEATED OR PROLONGED EXPOSURE MAY CAUSE EFFECTS AS DESCRIBED IN ACUTE EXPOSURE. SOME COMPOUNDS HAVE CAUSED TOXIC EFFECTS ON THE CRYSTALLINE LENS, CONJUNCTIVAL THICKENING AND OBSTRUCTION OF THE NASOLACRIMAL CANALS WHEN USED AS MIOTIC EYEDROPS.

FIRST AID- IRRIGATE EYES WITH WATER OR SALINE SOLUTION. IF SYMPTOMS OF POISONING OCCUR, TREAT RESPIRATORY DIFFICULTY WITH ARTIFICIAL RESPIRATION AND OXYGEN. OBSERVE PATIENT FOR AT LEAST 24-36 HOURS (GOSSELIN, CLINICAL TOXICOLOGY OF COMMERCIAL PRODUCTS, 5TH ED.). GET MEDICAL ATTENTION IMMEDIATELY. OXYGEN SHOULD BE ADMINISTERED BY QUALIFIED MEDICAL PERSONNEL.

INGESTION: FOSTHIETAN: HIGHLY TOXIC. SEE INFORMATION ON ORGANOPHOSPHATES.

ORGANOPHOSPHATES: CHOLINESTERASE INHIBITOR. **ACUTE EXPOSURE-** WHEN INGESTED, THE FIRST EFFECTS MAY BE NAUSEA, VOMITING, ANOREXIA, ABDOMINAL CRAMPS AND DIARRHEA. GASTROINTESTINAL ABSORPTION MAY CAUSE SYMPTOMS OF CHOLINESTERASE INHIBITION AS DESCRIBED IN ACUTE INHALATION. SYMPTOMS MAY BEGIN WITHIN MINUTES OR BE DELAYED FOR HOURS. DELAYED EFFECTS INCLUDING NEUROPATHY MAY ALSO OCCUR. **CHRONIC EXPOSURE-** REPEATED INGESTION MAY CAUSE EFFECTS AS DESCRIBED IN ACUTE EXPOSURE.

FIRST AID- IF PERSON IS ALERT AND RESPIRATION IS NOT DEPRESSED, GIVE SYRUP OF IPECAC FOLLOWED BY WATER (IF VOMITING OCCURS, KEEP HEAD BELOW HIPS TO PREVENT ASPIRATION). IF CONSCIOUSNESS LEVEL DECLINES OR VOMITING HAS NOT OCCURRED IN 15 MINUTES EMPTY STOMACH BY GASTRIC LAVAGE WITH THE AID OF CUFFED ENDOTRACHEAL TUBE USING ISOTONIC SALINE OR 5% SODIUM BICARBONATE FOLLOW WITH ACTIVATED CHARCOAL. ESTABLISH AND MAINTAIN AIRWAY. TREAT RESPIRATORY DIFFICULTY WITH ARTIFICIAL RESPIRATION AND OXYGEN. DO NOT GIVE MORPHINE, AMINOPHYLLINE, PHENOTHIAZINES, RESERPINE, FUROSEMIDE, OR ETHACRYNIC ACID (MORGAN, RECOGNITION AND MANAGEMENT OF PESTICIDE POISONINGS, 3RD ED.). TREAT SYMPTOMATICALLY AND SUPPORTIVELY. ADMINISTRATION OF OXYGEN AND LAVAGE MUST BE PERFORMED BY QUALIFIED MEDICAL PERSONNEL. GET MEDICAL ATTENTION IMMEDIATELY.

ANTIDOTE: THE FOLLOWING ANTIDOTE(S) HAVE BEEN RECOMMENDED. HOWEVER, THE DECISION AS TO WHETHER THE SEVERITY OF POISONING REQUIRES ADMINISTRATION OF ANY ANTIDOTE AND ACTUAL DOSE REQUIRED SHOULD BE MADE BY QUALIFIED MEDICAL PERSONNEL.

FOR CHOLINESTERASE INHIBITORS: ESTABLISH CLEAR AIRWAY AND TISSUE OXYGENATION BY ASPIRATION OF SECRETIONS, AND IF NECESSARY, BY ASSISTED PULMONARY VENTILATION WITH OXYGEN. IMPROVE TISSUE OXYGENATION AS MUCH AS POSSIBLE BEFORE ADMINISTERING ATROPINE TO MINIMIZE THE RISK OF VENTRICULAR FIBRILLATION. ADMINISTER ATROPINE SULFATE INTRAVENOUSLY, OR INTRAMUSCULARLY IF IV INJECTION IS NOT POSSIBLE. IN MODERATELY SEVERE POISONING ADMINISTER ATROPINE SULFATE, 0.4-2.0 MG REPEATED EVERY 15 MINUTES UNTIL ATROPINIZATION IS ACHIEVED (TACHYCARDIA, FLUSHING, DRY MOUTH, MYDRIASIS). MAINTAIN ATROPINIZATION BY REPEATED DOSES FOR 2-12 HOURS, OR LONGER, DEPENDING ON THE SEVERITY OF POISONING. THE APPEARANCE OF RALES IN THE LUNG BASES, MIOSIS, SALIVATION, NAUSEA, BRADYCARDIA, ARE ALL INDICATIONS OF INADEQUATE ATROPINIZATION. SEVERELY POISONED INDIVIDUALS MAY EXHIBIT REMARKABLE TOLERANCE TO ATROPINE; TWO OR MORE TIMES THE DOSAGES SUGGESTED ABOVE MAY BE NEEDED. PERSONS NOT POISONED OR ONLY SLIGHTLY POISONED, HOWEVER, MAY DEVELOP SIGNS OF ATROPINE TOXICITY FROM SUCH LARGE DOSAGES: FEVER, MUSCLE FIBRILLATIONS, AND DELIRIUM ARE THE MAIN SIGNS OF ATROPINE TOXICITY. IF THESE SIGNS APPEAR WHILE THE PATIENT IS FULLY ATROPINIZED, ATROPINE ADMINISTRATION SHOULD BE DISCONTINUED, AT LEAST TEMPORARILY. OBSERVE TREATED PATIENTS CLOSELY AT LEAST 24 HOURS TO INSURE THAT SYMPTOMS (POSSIBLY PULMONARY EDEMA) DO NOT RECUR AS ATROPINIZATION WEARS OFF. IN VERY SEVERE POISONINGS, METABOLIC DISPOSITION OF TOXICANT MAY REQUIRE SEVERAL HOURS OR DAYS DURING WHICH ATROPINIZATION MUST BE MAINTAINED. MARKEDLY LOWER LEVELS OF URINARY METABOLITES INDICATE THAT ATROPINE DOSAGE CAN BE TAPERED OFF. AS DOSAGE IS REDUCED, CHECK THE LUNG BASES FREQUENTLY FOR RALES. IF RALES ARE HEARD OR OTHER SYMPTOMS RETURN, RE-ESTABLISH ATROPINIZATION PROMPTLY (MORGAN, RECOGNITION AND MANAGEMENT OF PESTICIDE POISONINGS, 3RD ED.). ADMINISTRATION OF ANTIDOTE MUST BE PERFORMED BY QUALIFIED MEDICAL PERSONNEL.

IN CASES OF SEVERE POISONING BY ORGANOPHOSPHATE PESTICIDES IN WHICH RESPIRATORY DEPRESSION, MUSCLE WEAKNESS AND TWITCHINGS ARE SEVERE, GIVE PRALIDOXIME (PROTOPAM-AYERST, 2-PAM), 1.0 GRAM INTRAVENOUSLY AT NO MORE THAN 0.5 GRAM PER MINUTE. DOSAGE OF PRALIDOXIME MAY BE REPEATED IN 1-2 HOURS, THEN AT 10-12 HOUR INTERVALS IF NEEDED. IN VERY SEVERE POISONINGS, DOSAGE RATES MAY BE DOUBLED. TREATMENT WITH PRALIDOXIME WILL BE MOST EFFECTIVE IF GIVEN WITHIN THIRTY-SIX HOURS AFTER POISONING (MORGAN, RECOGNITION AND MANAGEMENT OF PESTICIDE POISONINGS, 3RD ED.). ANTIDOTE SHOULD BE ADMINISTERED BY QUALIFIED MEDICAL PERSONNEL.

REACTIVITY

REACTIVITY: STABLE UNDER NORMAL TEMPERATURES AND PRESSURES.

INCOMPATIBILITIES: FOSTHIETAN: OXIDIZERS (STRONG): FIRE AND EXPLOSION HAZARD.

DECOMPOSITION: THERMAL DECOMPOSITION PRODUCTS MAY INCLUDE TOXIC OXIDES OF NITROGEN, CARBON, PHOSPHORUS, AND SULFUR.

POLYMERIZATION: HAZARDOUS POLYMERIZATION HAS NOT BEEN REPORTED TO OCCUR UNDER NORMAL TEMPERATURES AND PRESSURES.

STORAGE AND DISPOSAL

OBSERVE ALL FEDERAL, STATE AND LOCAL REGULATIONS WHEN STORING OR DISPOSING OF THIS SUBSTANCE. FOR ASSISTANCE, CONTACT THE DISTRICT DIRECTOR OF THE ENVIRONMENTAL PROTECTION AGENCY.

STORAGE

STORE IN ACCORDANCE WITH 40 CFR 165 RECOMMENDED PROCEDURES FOR THE DISPOSAL AND STORAGE OF PESTICIDES AND PESTICIDE CONTAINERS.

STORE AWAY FROM INCOMPATIBLE SUBSTANCES.

THRESHOLD PLANNING QUANTITY (TPQ): THE SUPERFUND AMENDMENTS AND REAUTHORIZATION ACT (SARA) SECTION 302 REQUIRES THAT EACH FACILITY WHERE ANY EXTREMELY HAZARDOUS SUBSTANCE IS PRESENT IN A QUANTITY EQUAL TO OR GREATER THAN THE TPQ ESTABLISHED FOR THAT SUBSTANCE NOTIFY THE STATE EMERGENCY RESPONSE COMMISSION FOR THE STATE IN WHICH IT IS LOCATED. SECTION 303 OF SARA REQUIRES THESE FACILITIES TO PARTICIPATE IN LOCAL EMERGENCY RESPONSE PLANNING (40 CFR 355.30).

DISPOSAL

DISPOSAL MUST BE IN ACCORDANCE WITH 40 CFR 165 RECOMMENDED PROCEDURES FOR THE DISPOSAL AND STORAGE OF PESTICIDES AND PESTICIDE CONTAINERS.

CONDITIONS TO AVOID

MAY BE IGNITED BY HEAT, SPARKS OR FLAMES. CONTAINER MAY EXPLODE IN HEAT OF FIRE. VAPOR EXPLOSION AND POISON HAZARD INDOORS, OUTDOORS OR IN SEWERS.

SPILL AND LEAK PROCEDURES

OCCUPATIONAL SPILL: SHUT OFF IGNITION SOURCES. DO NOT TOUCH SPILLED MATERIAL. STOP LEAK IF YOU CAN DO IT WITHOUT RISK. USE WATER SPRAY TO REDUCE VAPORS. FOR SMALL SPILLS, TAKE UP WITH SAND OR OTHER ABSORBENT MATERIAL AND PLACE INTO CONTAINERS FOR LATER DISPOSAL. FOR SMALL DRY SPILLS, WITH CLEAN SHOVEL PLACE MATERIAL INTO CLEAN, DRY CONTAINERS AND COVER. MOVE CONTAINERS FROM SPILL AREA. FOR LARGER SPILLS, DIKE FAR AHEAD OF SPILL FOR LATER DISPOSAL. NO SMOKING, FLAMES OR FLARES IN HAZARD AREA! KEEP UNNECESSARY PEOPLE AWAY. ISOLATE HAZARD AREA AND DENY ENTRY. VENTILATE CLOSED SPACES BEFORE ENTERING.

REPORTABLE QUANTITY (RQ): 1 POUND THE SUPERFUND AMENDMENTS AND REAUTHORIZATION ACT (SARA) SECTION 304 REQUIRES THAT A RELEASE EQUAL TO OR GREATER THAN THE REPORTABLE QUANTITY FOR THIS SUBSTANCE BE IMMEDIATELY REPORTED TO THE LOCAL EMERGENCY PLANNING COMMITTEE AND THE STATE EMERGENCY RESPONSE COMMISSION (40 CFR 355.40). IF THE RELEASE OF THIS SUBSTANCE IS REPORTABLE UNDER CERCLA SECTION 103, THE NATIONAL RESPONSE CENTER MUST BE NOTIFIED IMMEDIATELY AT (800) 424-8802 OR (202) 426-2675 IN THE METROPOLITAN WASHINGTON, D.C. AREA (40 CFR 302.6).

PROTECTIVE EQUIPMENT

VENTILATION: PROCESS ENCLOSURE RECOMMENDED.

RESPIRATOR: THE FOLLOWING RESPIRATORS ARE RECOMMENDED BASED ON INFORMATION FOUND IN THE PHYSICAL DATA, TOXICITY AND HEALTH EFFECTS SECTIONS. THEY ARE RANKED IN ORDER FROM MINIMUM TO MAXIMUM RESPIRATORY PROTECTION. THE SPECIFIC RESPIRATOR SELECTED MUST BE BASED ON CONTAMINATION LEVELS FOUND IN THE WORK PLACE, MUST NOT EXCEED THE WORKING LIMITS OF THE RESPIRATOR AND BE JOINTLY APPROVED BY THE NATIONAL INSTITUTE FOR OCCUPATIONAL SAFETY AND HEALTH AND THE MINE SAFETY AND HEALTH ADMINISTRATION (NIOSH-MSHA).

TYPE 'C' SUPPLIED-AIR RESPIRATOR WITH A FULL FACEPIECE OPERATED IN PRESSURE-DEMAND OR OTHER POSITIVE PRESSURE MODE OR WITH A FULL FACEPIECE, HELMET OR HOOD OPERATED IN CONTINOUS-FLOW MODE.

SELF-CONTAINED BREATHING APPARATUS WITH A FULL FACEPIECE OPERATED IN PRESSURE-DEMAND OR OTHER POSITIVE PRESSURE MODE.

FOR FIREFIGHTING AND OTHER IMMEDIATELY DANGEROUS TO LIFE OR HEALTH CONDITIONS:

SELF-CONTAINED BREATHING APPARATUS WITH FULL FACEPIECE OPERATED IN PRESSURE-DEMAND OR OTHER POSITIVE PRESSURE MODE.

SUPPLIED-AIR RESPIRATOR WITH FULL FACEPIECE AND OPERATED IN PRESSURE-DEMAND OR OTHER POSITIVE PRESSURE MODE IN COMBINATION WITH AN AUXILIARY SELF-CONTAINED BREATHING APPARATUS OPERATED IN PRESSURE-DEMAND OR OTHER POSITIVE PRESSURE MODE.

CLOTHING: EMPLOYEE MUST WEAR APPROPRIATE PROTECTIVE (IMPERVIOUS) CLOTHING AND EQUIPMENT TO PREVENT ANY POSSIBILITY OF SKIN CONTACT WITH THIS SUBSTANCE.

GLOVES: EMPLOYEE MUST WEAR APPROPRIATE PROTECTIVE GLOVES TO PREVENT CONTACT WITH THIS SUBSTANCE.

EYE PROTECTION: EMPLOYEE MUST WEAR SPLASH-PROOF OR DUST-RESISTANT SAFETY GOGGLES AND A FACESHIELD TO PREVENT CONTACT WITH THIS SUBSTANCE.

EMERGENCY WASH FACILITIES: WHERE THERE IS ANY POSSIBILITY THAT AN EMPLOYEE'S EYES AND/OR SKIN MAY BE EXPOSED TO THIS SUBSTANCE, THE EMPLOYER SHOULD PROVIDE AN EYE WASH FOUNTAIN AND QUICK DRENCH SHOWER WITHIN THE IMMEDIATE WORK AREA FOR EMERGENCY USE.

AUTHORIZED BY- OCCUPATIONAL HEALTH SERVICES, INC.
CREATION DATE: 10/04/89 ***REVISION DATE:*** 06/19/90

MATERIAL SAFETY DATA SHEET

OCCUPATIONAL HEALTH SERVICES, INC.
AGRICULTURE AND PESTICIDE DIVISION
450 SEVENTH AVENUE, SUITE 2407
NEW YORK, NEW YORK 10123
1-800-445-MSDS OR (212) 967-1100

EMERGENCY CONTACT:
JOHN S. BRANSFORD, JR. (615) 292-1180

SUBSTANCE IDENTIFICATION

CAS-NUMBER 555-37-3

SUBSTANCE: **NEBURON**

TRADE NAMES/SYNONYMS: UREA, N-BUTYL-N'-(3,4-DICHLOROPHENYL)-N-METHYL-; UREA, 1-BUTYL-3-(3,4-DICHLOROPHENYL)-1-METHYL-; N-BUTYL-N'-(3,4-DICHLOROPHENYL)-N-METHYLUREA; 1-BUTYL-3-(3,4-DICHLOROPHENYL)-1-METHYLUREA; 3-(3,4-DICHLOROPHENYL)-1-METHYL-1-N-BUTYLUREA; 1-N-BUTYL-3-(3,4-DICHLOROPHENYL)-1-METHYLUREA; KLOBEN; NEBUREX; NEBUREA; C12H16CL2N2O; PST16143

CHEMICAL FAMILY: SUBSTITUTED UREA
HALOGEN COMPOUND, AROMATIC

MOLECULAR FORMULA: C12-H16-CL2-N2-O

MOLECULAR WEIGHT: 275.18

CERCLA RATINGS (SCALE 0-3): HEALTH=1 FIRE=1 REACTIVITY=0 PERSISTENCE=3

NFPA RATINGS (SCALE 0-4): HEALTH=1 FIRE=1 REACTIVITY=0

COMPONENTS AND CONTAMINANTS

COMPONENT: NEBURON ***PERCENT:*** 100
CAS# 555-37-3

OTHER CONTAMINANTS: NONE

EXPOSURE LIMITS: NO OCCUPATIONAL EXPOSURE LIMITS ESTABLISHED BY OSHA, ACGIH, OR NIOSH.

PHYSICAL DATA

DESCRIPTION: WHITE CRYSTALLINE SOLID. ***MELTING POINT:*** 216-217 F (102-103 C)

SPECIFIC GRAVITY: NOT AVAILABLE ***VAPOR PRESSURE:*** NEGLIGIBLE

SOLUBILITY IN WATER: 0.0048% @ 24 C

SOLVENT SOLUBILITY: VERY SLIGHTLY SOLUBLE IN HYDROCARBON SOLVENTS.

FIRE AND EXPLOSION DATA

FIRE AND EXPLOSION HAZARD: SLIGHT FIRE HAZARD WHEN EXPOSED TO HEAT OR FLAME.
DUST-AIR MIXTURES MAY IGNITE OR EXPLODE.

FIREFIGHTING MEDIA: DRY CHEMICAL, CARBON DIOXIDE, HALON, WATER SPRAY OR STANDARD FOAM (1987 EMERGENCY RESPONSE GUIDEBOOK, DOT P 5800.4).
FOR LARGER FIRES, USE WATER SPRAY, FOG OR STANDARD FOAM (1987 EMERGENCY RESPONSE GUIDEBOOK, DOT P 5800.4).

FIREFIGHTING: MOVE CONTAINERS FROM FIRE AREA IF POSSIBLE. FIGHT FIRE FROM MAXIMUM DISTANCE. STAY AWAY FROM STORAGE TANK ENDS. DIKE FIRE CONTROL WATER FOR LATER DISPOSAL. DO NOT SCATTER MATERIAL (1987 EMERGENCY RESPONSE GUIDEBOOK, DOT P 5800.4, GUIDE PAGE 55).
EXTINGUISH USING AGENT SUITABLE FOR TYPE OF SURROUNDING FIRE. USE WATER IN FLOODING QUANTITIES AS FOG. KEEP SPARKS, FLAMES AND OTHER SOURCES OF IGNITION AWAY. KEEP MATERIAL OUT OF WATER SOURCES AND SEWERS. DO NOT TOUCH MATERIAL AND AVOID BREATHING DUSTS AND FUMES FROM BURNING MATERIAL. KEEP UPWIND.

TOXICITY

NEBURON: TOXICITY DATA: 1100 MG/KG ORAL-RAT LD50; 180 MG/KG INTRAVENOUS-MOUSE LD50. CARCINOGEN STATUS: NONE. ACUTE TOXICITY LEVEL: MODERATELY TOXIC BY INGESTION. TARGET EFFECTS: NO DATA AVAILABLE.

HEALTH EFFECTS AND FIRST AID

INHALATION: NEBURON: **ACUTE EXPOSURE-** MANY UREA DERIVATIVE HERBICIDES ARE MODERATELY IRRITATING TO THE MUCOUS MEMBRANES. **CHRONIC EXPOSURE-** NO DATA AVAILABLE.

FIRST AID- REMOVE FROM EXPOSURE AREA TO FRESH AIR IMMEDIATELY. IF BREATHING HAS STOPPED, PERFORM ARTIFICIAL RESPIRATION. KEEP PERSON WARM AND AT REST. TREAT SYMPTOMATICALLY AND SUPPORTIVELY. GET MEDICAL ATTENTION IMMEDIATELY.

SKIN CONTACT: NEBURON: **ACUTE EXPOSURE-** THIS MATERIAL WAS MILDLY IRRITATING TO THE SHAVED BACKS OF GUINEA-PIGS; NO SENSITIZATION WAS OBSERVED. **CHRONIC EXPOSURE-** NO DATA AVAILABLE.

FIRST AID- REMOVE CONTAMINATED CLOTHING AND SHOES IMMEDIATELY. WASH AFFECTED AREA WITH SOAP OR MILD DETERGENT AND LARGE AMOUNTS OF WATER UNTIL NO EVIDENCE OF CHEMICAL REMAINS (APPROXIMATELY 15-20 MINUTES). GET MEDICAL ATTENTION IMMEDIATELY.

EYE CONTACT: NEBURON: **ACUTE EXPOSURE-** MANY UREA DERIVATIVE HERBICIDES ARE MODERATELY IRRITATING TO THE EYES. **CHRONIC EXPOSURE-** NO DATA AVAILABLE.

FIRST AID- WASH EYES IMMEDIATELY WITH LARGE AMOUNTS OF WATER OR NORMAL SALINE, OCCASIONALLY LIFTING UPPER AND LOWER LIDS, UNTIL NO EVIDENCE OF

CHEMICAL REMAINS (APPROXIMATELY 15-20 MINUTES). GET MEDICAL ATTENTION IMMEDIATELY.

INGESTION: NEBURON: **ACUTE EXPOSURE-** A LETHAL DOSE IN RATS WAS 1100 MG/KG; SYMPTOMS WERE NOT REPORTED. **CHRONIC EXPOSURE-** NO DATA AVAILABLE.

FIRST AID- REMOVE BY GASTRIC LAVAGE AND CATHARSIS. MAINTAIN BLOOD PRESSURE AND AIRWAY. GIVE OXYGEN IF RESPIRATION IS DEPRESSED. DO NOT PERFORM GASTRIC LAVAGE IF VICTIM IS UNCONSCIOUS. GET MEDICAL ATTENTION IMMEDIATELY (DREISBACH, HANDBOOK OF POISONING, 12TH ED.). ADMINISTRATION OF LAVAGE OR OXYGEN SHOULD BE PERFORMED BY QUALIFIED MEDICAL PERSONNEL.

ANTIDOTE: NO SPECIFIC ANTIDOTE. TREAT SYMPTOMATICALLY AND SUPPORTIVELY.

REACTIVITY

REACTIVITY: STABLE UNDER NORMAL TEMPERATURES AND PRESSURES.

INCOMPATIBILITIES: NEBURON: ACIDS: HYDROLYSIS MAY OCCUR. ALKALI: HYDROLYSIS MAY OCCUR. OXIDIZERS (STRONG): FIRE AND EXPLOSION HAZARD.

DECOMPOSITION: THERMAL DECOMPOSITION PRODUCTS MAY INCLUDE TOXIC OXIDES OF NITROGEN AND CARBON AND TOXIC AND CORROSIVE FUMES OF CHLORIDES.

POLYMERIZATION: HAZARDOUS POLYMERIZATION HAS NOT BEEN REPORTED TO OCCUR UNDER NORMAL TEMPERATURES AND PRESSURES.

STORAGE AND DISPOSAL

OBSERVE ALL FEDERAL, STATE AND LOCAL REGULATIONS WHEN STORING OR DISPOSING OF THIS SUBSTANCE. FOR ASSISTANCE, CONTACT THE DISTRICT DIRECTOR OF THE ENVIRONMENTAL PROTECTION AGENCY.

****STORAGE****

STORE IN ACCORDANCE WITH 40 CFR 165 RECOMMENDED PROCEDURES FOR THE DISPOSAL AND STORAGE OF PESTICIDES AND PESTICIDE CONTAINERS.
STORE AWAY FROM INCOMPATIBLE SUBSTANCES.
KEEP COOL AND DRY.

****DISPOSAL****

DISPOSAL MUST BE IN ACCORDANCE WITH 40 CFR 165 RECOMMENDED PROCEDURES FOR THE DISPOSAL AND STORAGE OF PESTICIDES AND PESTICIDE CONTAINERS.

CONDITIONS TO AVOID

MAY BURN BUT DOES NOT IGNITE READILY. CONTAINERS MAY EXPLODE IN HEAT OF FIRE.

SPILL AND LEAK PROCEDURES

OCCUPATIONAL SPILL: DO NOT TOUCH SPILLED MATERIAL. STOP LEAK IF YOU CAN DO IT WITHOUT RISK. USE WATER SPRAY TO REDUCE VAPORS. FOR SMALL SPILLS, TAKE UP WITH SAND OR OTHER ABSORBENT MATERIAL AND PLACE INTO CONTAINERS FOR LATER DISPOSAL. FOR SMALL DRY SPILLS, WITH A CLEAN SHOVEL PLACE MATERIAL INTO CLEAN, DRY CONTAINERS AND COVER. MOVE CONTAINERS FROM SPILL AREA. FOR LARGER SPILLS, DIKE FAR AHEAD OF SPILL FOR LATER DISPOSAL. KEEP UNNECESSARY PEOPLE AWAY. ISOLATE HAZARD AREA AND DENY ENTRY. VENTILATE CLOSED SPACES BEFORE ENTERING.

PROTECTIVE EQUIPMENT

VENTILATION: PROVIDE GENERAL DILUTION VENTILATION.

RESPIRATOR: THE FOLLOWING RESPIRATORS ARE RECOMMENDED BASED ON INFORMATION FOUND IN THE PHYSICAL DATA, TOXICITY AND HEALTH EFFECTS SECTIONS. THEY ARE RANKED IN ORDER FROM MINIMUM TO MAXIMUM RESPIRATORY PROTECTION. THE SPECIFIC RESPIRATOR SELECTED MUST BE BASED ON CONTAMINATION LEVELS FOUND IN THE WORK PLACE, MUST NOT EXCEED THE WORKING LIMITS OF THE RESPIRATOR AND BE JOINTLY APPROVED BY THE NATIONAL INSTITUTE FOR OCCUPATIONAL SAFETY AND HEALTH AND THE MINE SAFETY AND HEALTH ADMINISTRATION (NIOSH-MSHA).
CHEMICAL CARTRIDGE RESPIRATOR WITH AN ORGANIC VAPOR CARTRIDGE(S) WITH A FULL FACEPIECE AND ORGANIC VAPOR CARTRIDGE(S) IN COMBINATION WITH A DUST AND MIST FILTER.
POWERED AIR-PURIFYING RESPIRATOR WITH A TIGHT-FITTING FACEPIECE AND ORGANIC VAPOR CARTRIDGE(S) IN COMBINATION WITH A HIGH-EFFICIENCY PARTICULATE FILTER.
TYPE 'C' SUPPLIED-AIR RESPIRATOR WITH A FULL FACEPIECE OPERATED IN A PRESSURE-DEMAND OR OTHER POSITIVE PRESSURE MODE.
SELF-CONTAINED BREATHING APPARATUS WITH A FULL FACEPIECE OPERATED IN PRESSURE-DEMAND OR OTHER POSITIVE PRESSURE MODE.
FOR FIREFIGHTING AND OTHER IMMEDIATELY DANGEROUS TO LIFE OR HEALTH CONDITIONS:
SELF-CONTAINED BREATHING APPARATUS WITH FULL FACEPIECE OPERATED IN PRESSURE-DEMAND OR OTHER POSITIVE PRESSURE MODE.
SUPPLIED-AIR RESPIRATOR WITH FULL FACEPIECE AND OPERATED IN PRESSURE-DEMAND OR OTHER POSITIVE PRESSURE MODE IN COMBINATION WITH AN AUXILIARY SELF-CONTAINED BREATHING APPARATUS OPERATED IN PRESSURE-DEMAND OR OTHER POSITIVE PRESSURE MODE.

CLOTHING: EMPLOYEE MUST WEAR APPROPRIATE PROTECTIVE (IMPERVIOUS) CLOTHING AND EQUIPMENT TO PREVENT REPEATED OR PROLONGED SKIN CONTACT WITH THIS SUBSTANCE.

GLOVES: EMPLOYEE MUST WEAR APPROPRIATE PROTECTIVE GLOVES TO PREVENT CONTACT WITH THIS SUBSTANCE.

EYE PROTECTION: EMPLOYEE MUST WEAR SPLASH-PROOF OR DUST-RESISTANT SAFETY GOGGLES TO PREVENT EYE CONTACT WITH THIS SUBSTANCE.
EMERGENCY EYE WASH: WHERE THERE IS ANY POSSIBILITY THAT AN EMPLOYEE'S EYES MAY BE EXPOSED TO THIS SUBSTANCE, THE EMPLOYER SHOULD PROVIDE AN EYE WASH FOUNTAIN WITHIN THE IMMEDIATE WORK AREA FOR EMERGENCY USE.

AUTHORIZED BY- OCCUPATIONAL HEALTH SERVICES, INC.
CREATION DATE: 10/04/89 ***REVISION DATE:*** 05/14/90

MATERIAL SAFETY DATA SHEET

OCCUPATIONAL HEALTH SERVICES, INC.
AGRICULTURE AND PESTICIDE DIVISION
450 SEVENTH AVENUE, SUITE 2407
NEW YORK, NEW YORK 10123
1-800-445-MSDS OR (212) 967-1100

EMERGENCY CONTACT:
JOHN S. BRANSFORD, JR. (615) 292-1180

SUBSTANCE IDENTIFICATION

CAS-NUMBER 31972-44-8

SUBSTANCE: **FENAMIPHOS SULFONE**

TRADE NAMES/SYNONYMS: PHOSPHORAMIDIC ACID, (1-METHYLETHYL)-, ETHYL 3-METHYL-4- (METHYLSULFONYL)PHENYL ESTER; PHOSPHORAMIDIC ACID, ISOPROPYL-, ETHYL-4-(METHYLSULFONYL)-M-TOLYL ESTER; (1-METHYLETHYL)PHOSPHORAMIDIC ACID ETHYL 3-METHYL-4-(METHYLSULFONYL) PHENYL ESTER; ISOPROPYLPHOSPHORAMIDIC ACID ETHYL-4-(METHYLSULFONYL)-M-TOLYL ESTER; ETHYL 4-(METHYLSULFONYL)-M-TOLYL ISOPROPYL PHOSPHORAMIDATE; NEMACUR SULFONE (FORMULATION); BAY 68138 SULFONE; C13H22NO5PS; PST16144

CHEMICAL FAMILY: ORGANOPHOSPHATE

MOLECULAR FORMULA: C13-H22-N-O5-P-S

MOLECULAR WEIGHT: 335.36

CERCLA RATINGS (SCALE 0-3): HEALTH=3 FIRE=1 REACTIVITY=0 PERSISTENCE=1

NFPA RATINGS (SCALE 0-4): HEALTH=3 FIRE=1 REACTIVITY=0

COMPONENTS AND CONTAMINANTS

COMPONENT: FENAMIPHOS SULFONE ***PERCENT:*** 100.0
CAS# 31972-44-8

OTHER CONTAMINANTS: NONE

EXPOSURE LIMITS: NO OCCUPATIONAL EXPOSURE LIMITS ESTABLISHED BY OSHA, ACGIH, OR NIOSH.

PHYSICAL DATA

DESCRIPTION: HYGROSCOPIC, WHITE POWDER. ***MELTING POINT:*** 190 F (88 C)

SPECIFIC GRAVITY: NOT AVAILABLE ***SOLUBILITY IN WATER:*** NOT AVAILABLE

FIRE AND EXPLOSION DATA

FIRE AND EXPLOSION HAZARD: SLIGHT FIRE HAZARD WHEN EXPOSED TO HEAT OR FLAME.

FIREFIGHTING MEDIA: DRY CHEMICAL, CARBON DIOXIDE, HALON, WATER SPRAY OR STANDARD FOAM (1987 EMERGENCY RESPONSE GUIDEBOOK, DOT P 5800.4).
FOR LARGER FIRES, USE WATER SPRAY, FOG OR STANDARD FOAM (1987 EMERGENCY RESPONSE GUIDEBOOK, DOT P 5800.4).

FIREFIGHTING: MOVE CONTAINERS FROM FIRE AREA IF POSSIBLE (1987 EMERGENCY RESPONSE GUIDEBOOK, DOT P 5800.4, GUIDE PAGE 53).
EXTINGUISH USING AGENT SUITABLE FOR TYPE OF SURROUNDING FIRE. AVOID BREATHING VAPORS AND DUSTS. KEEP UPWIND.

TRANSPORTATION DATA

DEPARTMENT OF TRANSPORTATION HAZARD CLASSIFICATION 49 CFR 172.101: POISON B

DEPARTMENT OF TRANSPORTATION LABELING REQUIREMENTS 49 CFR 172.101 AND SUBPART E: POISON
DEPARTMENT OF TRANSPORTATION PACKAGING REQUIREMENTS: 49 (CFR 173.377 EXCEPTIONS: 49 CFR 173.377

TOXICITY

FENAMIPHOS SULFONE: TOXICITY DATA: 2.1-3.5 MG/KG ORAL-RAT LD50 (EPA). CARCINOGEN STATUS: NONE. ACUTE TOXICITY LEVEL: HIGHLY TOXIC BY INGESTION. TARGET EFFECTS: CHOLINESTERASE INHIBITOR. POISONING MAY AFFECT THE NERVOUS SYSTEM.* AT INCREASED RISK FROM EXPOSURE: PERSONS WITH RESPIRATORY AILMENTS, RECENT EXPOSURE TO CHOLINESTERASE INHIBITORS OR IMPAIRED CHOLINESTERASE PRODUCTION, OR LIVER MALFUNCTION.* ADDITIONAL DATA: MAY CROSS THE PLACENTA. HIGH ENVIRONMENTAL TEMPERATURES OR EXPOSURE OF THE CHEMICAL TO VISIBLE OR ULTRAVIOLET LIGHT MAY ENHANCE THE TOXICITY. INTERACTIONS WITH MEDICATIONS MAY OCCUR.*

* MAY BE BASED ON GENERAL INFORMATION ON ORGANOPHOSPHATES.

HEALTH EFFECTS AND FIRST AID

INHALATION: FENAMIPHOS SULFONE: SEE INFORMATION ON ORGANOPHOSPHATES.
ORGANOPHOSPHATES: CHOLINESTERASE INHIBITOR. **ACUTE EXPOSURE-** WHEN INHALED, THE FIRST EFFECTS OF CHOLINESTERASE INHIBITORS ARE USUALLY RESPIRATORY AND MAY INCLUDE NASAL HYPEREMIA AND WATERY DISCHARGE, COUGH, CHEST DISCOMFORT, DYSPNEA, AND WHEEZING DUE TO INCREASED BRONCHIAL SECRETIONS AND BRONCHOCONSTRICTION. IF SUFFICIENT AMOUNTS ARE ABSORBED, OTHER SYSTEMIC EFFECTS MAY BEGIN WITHIN A FEW MINUTES OR BE DELAYED FOR UP TO 12 HOURS. SYMPTOMS MAY INCLUDE PALLOR, NAUSEA, VOMITING, DIARRHEA, ABDOMINAL CRAMPS, HEADACHE, DIZZINESS, OCULAR PAIN, BLURRED VISION, MIOSIS OR IN SOME CASES, ESPECIALLY INITIALLY, MYDRIASIS, LACRIMATION, SALIVATION, SWEATING, AND CONFUSION. OTHER REPORTED CENTRAL NERVOUS SYSTEM OR NEUROMUSCULAR EFFECTS MAY INCLUDE ATAXIA, SLURRED SPEECH, AREFLEXIA, WEAKNESS, FATIGUE, FASCICULATIONS, TWITCHING, TREMORS POSSIBLY OF THE TONGUE AND EYELIDS, AND EVENTUALLY PARALYSIS OF THE EXTREMITIES AND POSSIBLY OF THE RESPIRATORY MUSCLES. IN SEVERE CASES THERE MAY ALSO BE INVOLUNTARY DEFECATION AND URINATION, CYANOSIS, PSYCHOSIS, HYPERGLYCEMIA, ACUTE PANCREATITIS, CARDIAC IRREGULARITIES, PULMONARY EDEMA, UNCONSCIOUSNESS, CONVULSIONS, AND COMA. DEATH IS PRIMARILY DUE TO RESPIRATORY FAILURE, ALTHOUGH CARDIOVASCULAR EFFECTS INCLUDING CARDIAC ARREST MAY ALSO BE IMPLICATED. LONG TERM SEQUELAE ARE RARE BUT MAY INCLUDE NEUROPSYCHIATRIC DISORDERS AND MYOPATHY WITH MUSCLE TENDERNESS. SOME ORGANOPHOSPHATES MAY CAUSE A DELAYED NEUROPATHY BEGINNING 1-4 WEEKS AFTER AN ACUTE EXPOSURE WHICH MAY OR MAY NOT HAVE CAUSED ACUTE CHOLINERGIC EFFECTS. NUMBNESS, TINGLING, WEAKNESS AND CRAMPING BEGINNING SYMMETRICALLY IN THE LOWER LIMBS MAY PROGRESS TO ATAXIA AND PARALYSIS. IN SEVERE CASES, UPPER LIMB INVOLVEMENT IS POSSIBLE AND FLACCID PARALYSIS MAY PROGRESS TO SPASTIC PARALYSIS WITH EXAGGERATED REFLEXES. IMPROVEMENT MAY OCCUR OVER MONTHS TO YEARS, BUT SOME RESIDUAL IMPAIRMENT USUALLY REMAINS. **CHRONIC EXPOSURE-** REPEATED OR PROLONGED EXPOSURE MAY RESULT IN THE EFFECTS OF ACUTE EXPOSURE INCLUDING THE DELAYED NEUROPATHY. OTHER EFFECTS REPORTED IN WORKERS REPEATEDLY EXPOSED INCLUDE IMPAIRED MEMORY AND CONCENTRATION, ACUTE PSYCHOSIS, SEVERE DEPRESSIONS, IRRITABILTY, CONFUSION, APATHY, EMOTIONAL LABILITY, SOCIAL WITHDRAWAL, CONFUSION, HEADACHE, SPEECH DIFFICULTIES, DELAYED REACTION TIMES, SPATIAL DISORIENTATION, NIGHTMARES, SLEEPWALKING, AND DROWSINESS OR INSOMNIA. AN INFLUENZA-LIKE CONDITION WITH HEADACHE, NAUSEA, WEAKNESS, ANOREXIA AND MALAISE HAS ALSO BEEN REPORTED.

FIRST AID- REMOVE FROM EXPOSURE AREA TO FRESH AIR IMMEDIATELY. IF BREATHING HAS STOPPED, GIVE ARTIFICIAL RESPIRATION. MAINTAIN AIRWAY AND BLOOD PRESSURE AND ADMINISTER OXYGEN IF AVAILABLE. KEEP AFFECTED PERSON WARM AND AT REST. TREAT SYMPTOMATICALLY AND SUPPORTIVELY. ADMINISTRATION OF OXYGEN SHOULD BE PERFORMED BY QUALIFIED PERSONNEL. GET MEDICAL ATTENTION IMMEDIATELY.

SKIN CONTACT: FENAMIPHOS SULFONE: SEE INFORMATION ON ORGANOPHOSPHATES.
ORGANOPHOSPHATES: CHOLINESTERASE INHIBITOR. **ACUTE EXPOSURE-** LOCALIZED SWEATING AND FASCICULATIONS MAY OCCUR AT THE SITE OF CONTACT. IF SUFFICIENT AMOUNTS ARE ABSORBED, OTHER EFFECTS OF CHOLINESTERASE INHIBITION AS DESCRIBED IN ACUTE INHALATION MAY OCCUR. SYMPTOMS MAY BE DELAYED 2-3 HOURS, BUT USUALLY NO MORE THAN 12 HOURS. THE RATE OF ABSORPTION IS INCREASED BY THE PRESENCE OF DERMATITIS OR HIGH AMBIENT TEMPERATURES. DELAYED NEUROPATHY IS ALSO POSSIBLE. **CHRONIC EXPOSURE-** REPEATED OR PROLONGED EXPOSURE MAY CAUSE EFFECTS AS DESCRIBED IN ACUTE EXPOSURE. SOME ORGANOPHOSPHATES MAY CAUSE SENSITIZATION. **FIRST AID-** REMOVE CONTAMINATED CLOTHING IMMEDIATELY. WASH CONTAMINATED AREAS WITH SOAP AND WATER FOLLOWED BY ALCOHOL (ARENA, POISONING, 4TH ED.). EMERGENCY PERSONNEL SHOULD WEAR GLOVES AND AVOID CONTAMINATION. TREAT RESPIRATORY DIFFICULTY WITH ARTIFICIAL RESPIRATION. GET MEDICAL ATTENTION IMMEDIATELY.

EYE CONTACT: FENAMIPHOS SULFONE: SEE INFORMATION ON ORGANOPHOSPHATES.
ORGANOPHOSPHATES: CHOLINESTERASE INHIBITOR. **ACUTE EXPOSURE-** DIRECT CONTACT MAY CAUSE PAIN, HYPEREMIA, LACRIMATION, TWITCHING OF THE EYELIDS, MIOSIS, AND CILIARY MUSCLE SPASM WITH LOSS OF ACCOMODATION, BLURRED OR DIMMED VISION AND BROWACHE. SOMETIMES MYDRIASIS MAY OCCUR INSTEAD OF MIOSIS. WITH SUFFICIENT EXPOSURE, OTHER SYMPTOMS OF CHOLINESTERASE INHIBITION AS DESCRIBED IN ACUTE INHALATION MAY OCCUR. **CHRONIC EXPOSURE-** REPEATED OR PROLONGED EXPOSURE MAY CAUSE EFFECTS AS DESCRIBED IN ACUTE EXPOSURE. SOME COMPOUNDS HAVE CAUSED TOXIC EFFECTS ON THE CRYSTALLINE LENS, CONJUNCTIVAL THICKENING AND OBSTRUCTION OF THE NASOLACRIMAL CANALS WHEN USED AS MIOTIC EYEDROPS.

FIRST AID- IRRIGATE EYES WITH WATER OR SALINE SOLUTION. IF SYMPTOMS OF POISONING OCCUR, TREAT RESPIRATORY DIFFICULTY WITH ARTIFICIAL RESPIRATION AND OXYGEN. OBSERVE PATIENT FOR AT LEAST 24-36 HOURS (GOSSELIN, CLINICAL TOXICOLOGY OF COMMERCIAL PRODUCTS, 5TH ED.). GET MEDICAL ATTENTION IMMEDIATELY. OXYGEN SHOULD BE ADMINISTERED BY QUALIFIED MEDICAL PERSONNEL.

INGESTION: FENAMIPHOS SULFONE: HIGHLY TOXIC. SEE INFORMATION ON ORGANOPHOSPHATES.
ORGANOPHOSPHATES: CHOLINESTERASE INHIBITOR. **ACUTE EXPOSURE-** WHEN INGESTED, THE FIRST EFFECTS MAY BE NAUSEA, VOMITING, ANOREXIA, ABDOMINAL CRAMPS AND DIARRHEA. GASTROINTESTINAL ABSORPTION MAY CAUSE SYMPTOMS OF CHOLINESTERASE INHIBITION AS DESCRIBED IN ACUTE INHALATION. SYMPTOMS MAY BEGIN WITHIN MINUTES OR BE DELAYED FOR HOURS. DELAYED EFFECTS INCLUDING NEUROPATHY MAY ALSO OCCUR. **CHRONIC EXPOSURE-** REPEATED INGESTION MAY CAUSE EFFECTS AS DESCRIBED IN ACUTE EXPOSURE.

FIRST AID- IF PERSON IS ALERT AND RESPIRATION IS NOT DEPRESSED, GIVE SYRUP OF IPECAC FOLLOWED BY WATER (IF VOMITING OCCURS, KEEP HEAD BELOW HIPS TO PREVENT ASPIRATION). IF CONSCIOUSNESS LEVEL DECLINES OR VOMITING HAS NOT OCCURRED IN 15 MINUTES EMPTY STOMACH BY GASTRIC LAVAGE WITH THE AID OF CUFFED ENDOTRACHEAL TUBE USING ISOTONIC SALINE OR 5% SODIUM BICARBONATE FOLLOW WITH ACTIVATED CHARCOAL. ESTABLISH AND MAINTAIN AIRWAY. TREAT RESPIRATORY DIFFICULTY WITH ARTIFICIAL RESPIRATION AND OXYGEN. DO NOT GIVE MORPHINE, AMINOPHYLLINE, PHENOTHIAZINES, RESERPINE, FUROSEMIDE, OR ETHACRYNIC ACID (MORGAN, RECOGNITION AND MANAGEMENT OF PESTICIDE POISONINGS, 3RD ED.). TREAT SYMPTOMATICALLY AND SUPPORTIVELY. ADMINISTRATION OF OXYGEN AND LAVAGE MUST BE PERFORMED BY QUALIFIED MEDICAL PERSONNEL. GET MEDICAL ATTENTION IMMEDIATELY.

ANTIDOTE: THE FOLLOWING ANTIDOTE(S) HAVE BEEN RECOMMENDED. HOWEVER, THE DECISION AS TO WHETHER THE SEVERITY OF POISONING REQUIRES ADMINISTRATION OF ANY ANTIDOTE AND ACTUAL DOSE REQUIRED SHOULD BE MADE BY QUALIFIED MEDICAL PERSONNEL.
FOR CHOLINESTERASE INHIBITORS: ESTABLISH CLEAR AIRWAY AND TISSUE OXYGENATION BY ASPIRATION OF SECRETIONS, AND IF NECESSARY, BY ASSISTED PULMONARY VENTILATION WITH OXYGEN. IMPROVE TISSUE OXYGENATION AS MUCH AS POSSIBLE BEFORE ADMINISTERING ATROPINE TO MINIMIZE THE RISK OF VENTRICULAR FIBRILLATION. ADMINISTER ATROPINE SULFATE INTRAVENOUSLY, OR INTRAMUSCULARLY IF IV INJECTION IS NOT POSSIBLE. IN MODERATELY SEVERE POISONING ADMINISTER ATROPINE SULFATE, 0.4-2.0 MG REPEATED EVERY 15 MINUTES UNTIL ATROPINIZATION IS ACHIEVED (TACHYCARDIA, FLUSHING, DRY MOUTH, MYDRIASIS). MAINTAIN ATROPINIZATION BY REPEATED DOSES FOR 2-12 HOURS, OR LONGER, DEPENDING ON THE SEVERITY OF POISONING. THE APPEARANCE OF RALES IN THE LUNG BASES, MIOSIS, SALIVATION, NAUSEA, BRADYCARDIA, ARE ALL INDICATIONS OF INADEQUATE ATROPINIZATION. SEVERELY POISONED INDIVIDUALS MAY EXHIBIT REMARKABLE TOLERANCE TO ATROPINE; TWO OR MORE TIMES THE DOSAGES SUGGESTED ABOVE MAY BE NEEDED. PERSONS NOT POISONED OR ONLY SLIGHTLY POISONED, HOWEVER, MAY DEVELOP SIGNS OF ATROPINE TOXICITY FROM SUCH LARGE DOSAGES: FEVER, MUSCLE FIBRILLATIONS, AND DELIRIUM ARE THE MAIN SIGNS OF ATROPINE TOXICITY. IF THESE SIGNS APPEAR WHILE THE PATIENT IS FULLY ATROPINIZED, ATROPINE ADMINISTRATION SHOULD BE DISCONTINUED, AT LEAST TEMPORARILY. OBSERVE TREATED PATIENTS CLOSELY AT LEAST 24 HOURS TO INSURE THAT SYMPTOMS (POSSIBLY PULMONARY EDEMA) DO NOT RECUR AS ATROPINIZATION WEARS OFF. IN VERY SEVERE POISONINGS, METABOLIC DISPOSITION OF TOXICANT MAY REQUIRE SEVERAL HOURS OR DAYS DURING WHICH ATROPINIZATION MUST BE MAINTAINED. MARKEDLY LOWER LEVELS OF URINARY METABOLITES INDICATE THAT ATROPINE DOSAGE CAN BE TAPERED OFF. AS

DOSAGE IS REDUCED, CHECK THE LUNG BASES FREQUENTLY FOR RALES. IF RALES ARE HEARD OR OTHER SYMPTOMS RETURN, RE-ESTABLISH ATROPINIZATION PROMPTLY (MORGAN, RECOGNITION AND MANAGEMENT OF PESTICIDE POISONINGS, 3RD ED.). ADMINISTRATION OF ANTIDOTE MUST BE PERFORMED BY QUALIFIED MEDICAL PERSONNEL.

IN CASES OF SEVERE POISONING BY ORGANOPHOSPHATE PESTICIDES IN WHICH RESPIRATORY DEPRESSION, MUSCLE WEAKNESS AND TWITCHINGS ARE SEVERE, GIVE PRALIDOXIME (PROTOPAM-AYERST, 2-PAM), 1.0 GRAM INTRAVENOUSLY AT NO MORE THAN 0.5 GRAM PER MINUTE. DOSAGE OF PRALIDOXIME MAY BE REPEATED IN 1-2 HOURS, THEN AT 10-12 HOUR INTERVALS IF NEEDED. IN VERY SEVERE POISONINGS, DOSAGE RATES MAY BE DOUBLED. TREATMENT WITH PRALIDOXIME WILL BE MOST EFFECTIVE IF GIVEN WITHIN THIRTY-SIX HOURS AFTER POISONING (MORGAN, RECOGNITION AND MANAGEMENT OF PESTICIDE POISONINGS, 3RD ED.). ANTIDOTE SHOULD BE ADMINISTERED BY QUALIFIED MEDICAL PERSONNEL.

REACTIVITY

REACTIVITY: STABLE UNDER NORMAL TEMPERATURES AND PRESSURES.

INCOMPATIBILITIES: FENAMIPHOS SULFONE: OXIDIZERS (STRONG): FIRE AND EXPLOSION HAZARD.

DECOMPOSITION: THERMAL DECOMPOSITION PRODUCTS MAY INCLUDE TOXIC OXIDES OF NITROGEN, CARBON, PHOSPHORUS, AND SULFUR.

POLYMERIZATION: HAZARDOUS POLYMERIZATION HAS NOT BEEN REPORTED TO OCCUR UNDER NORMAL TEMPERATURES AND PRESSURES.

STORAGE AND DISPOSAL

OBSERVE ALL FEDERAL, STATE AND LOCAL REGULATIONS WHEN STORING OR DISPOSING OF THIS SUBSTANCE. FOR ASSISTANCE, CONTACT THE DISTRICT DIRECTOR OF THE ENVIRONMENTAL PROTECTION AGENCY.

STORAGE

STORE AWAY FROM INCOMPATIBLE SUBSTANCES.

STORE IN TIGHTLY CLOSED CONTAINERS; PREVENT EXPOSURE TO MOISTURE.

STORE IN ACCORDANCE WITH 40 CFR 165 RECOMMENDED PROCEDURES FOR THE DISPOSAL AND STORAGE OF PESTICIDES AND PESTICIDE CONTAINERS.

DISPOSAL

DISPOSAL MUST BE IN ACCORDANCE WITH 40 CFR 165 RECOMMENDED PROCEDURES FOR THE DISPOSAL AND STORAGE OF PESTICIDES AND PESTICIDE CONTAINERS.

CONDITIONS TO AVOID

MAY BURN BUT DOES NOT IGNITE READILY.

SPILL AND LEAK PROCEDURES

OCCUPATIONAL SPILL: DO NOT TOUCH SPILLED MATERIAL. STOP LEAK IF YOU CAN DO IT WITHOUT RISK. FOR SMALL SPILLS, TAKE UP WITH SAND OR OTHER ABSORBENT MATERIAL AND PLACE INTO CONTAINERS FOR LATER DISPOSAL. FOR SMALL DRY SPILLS, WITH A CLEAN SHOVEL PLACE MATERIAL INTO CLEAN, DRY CONTAINER AND COVER. MOVE CONTAINERS FROM SPILL AREA. FOR LARGER SPILLS, DIKE FAR AHEAD OF SPILL FOR LATER DISPOSAL. KEEP UNNECESSARY PEOPLE AWAY. ISOLATE HAZARD AREA AND DENY ENTRY.

PROTECTIVE EQUIPMENT

VENTILATION: PROVIDE LOCAL EXHAUST OR PROCESS ENCLOSURE VENTILATION SYSTEM.

RESPIRATOR: THE FOLLOWING RESPIRATORS ARE RECOMMENDED BASED ON INFORMATION FOUND IN THE PHYSICAL DATA, TOXICITY AND HEALTH EFFECTS SECTIONS. THEY ARE RANKED IN ORDER FROM MINIMUM TO MAXIMUM RESPIRATORY PROTECTION. THE SPECIFIC RESPIRATOR SELECTED MUST BE BASED ON CONTAMINATION LEVELS FOUND IN THE WORK PLACE, MUST NOT EXCEED THE WORKING LIMITS OF THE RESPIRATOR AND BE JOINTLY APPROVED BY THE NATIONAL INSTITUTE FOR OCCUPATIONAL SAFETY AND HEALTH AND THE MINE SAFETY AND HEALTH ADMINISTRATION (NIOSH-MSHA).

TYPE 'C' SUPPLIED-AIR RESPIRATOR WITH A FULL FACEPIECE OPERATED IN PRESSURE-DEMAND OR OTHER POSITIVE PRESSURE MODE OR WITH A FULL FACEPIECE, HELMET OR HOOD OPERATED IN CONTINOUS-FLOW MODE.

SELF-CONTAINED BREATHING APPARATUS WITH A FULL FACEPIECE OPERATED IN PRESSURE-DEMAND OR OTHER POSITIVE PRESSURE MODE.

FOR FIREFIGHTING AND OTHER IMMEDIATELY DANGEROUS TO LIFE OR HEALTH CONDITIONS:

SELF-CONTAINED BREATHING APPARATUS WITH FULL FACEPIECE OPERATED IN PRESSURE-DEMAND OR OTHER POSITIVE PRESSURE MODE.

SUPPLIED-AIR RESPIRATOR WITH FULL FACEPIECE AND OPERATED IN PRESSURE-DEMAND OR OTHER POSITIVE PRESSURE MODE IN COMBINATION WITH AN AUXILIARY SELF-CONTAINED BREATHING APPARATUS OPERATED IN PRESSURE-DEMAND OR OTHER POSITIVE PRESSURE MODE.

CLOTHING: EMPLOYEE MUST WEAR APPROPRIATE PROTECTIVE (IMPERVIOUS) CLOTHING AND EQUIPMENT TO PREVENT ANY POSSIBILITY OF SKIN CONTACT WITH THIS SUBSTANCE.

GLOVES: EMPLOYEE MUST WEAR APPROPRIATE PROTECTIVE GLOVES TO PREVENT CONTACT WITH THIS SUBSTANCE.

EYE PROTECTION: EMPLOYEE MUST WEAR SPLASH-PROOF OR DUST-RESISTANT SAFETY GOGGLES TO PREVENT EYE CONTACT WITH THIS SUBSTANCE.

EMERGENCY EYE WASH: WHERE THERE IS ANY POSSIBILITY THAT AN EMPLOYEE'S EYES MAY BE EXPOSED TO THIS SUBSTANCE, THE EMPLOYER SHOULD PROVIDE AN EYE WASH FOUNTAIN WITHIN THE IMMEDIATE WORK AREA FOR EMERGENCY USE.

AUTHORIZED BY- OCCUPATIONAL HEALTH SERVICES, INC.

CREATION DATE: 10/04/89 ***REVISION DATE:*** 05/01/90

MATERIAL SAFETY DATA SHEET

OCCUPATIONAL HEALTH SERVICES, INC.
AGRICULTURE AND PESTICIDE DIVISION
450 SEVENTH AVENUE, SUITE 2407
NEW YORK, NEW YORK 10123
1-800-445-MSDS OR (212) 967-1100

EMERGENCY CONTACT:
JOHN S. BRANSFORD, JR. (615) 292-1180

SUBSTANCE IDENTIFICATION

CAS-NUMBER 22224-92-6

SUBSTANCE: FENAMIPHOS

TRADE NAMES/SYNONYMS: PHOSPHORAMIDIC ACID, (1-METHYLETHYL)-, ETHYL 3-METHYL-4-(METHYLTHIO) PHENYL ESTER; PHOSPHORAMIDIC ACID, ISOPROPYL-, ETHYL 4-(METHYLTHIO)-M-TOLYL ESTER; (1-METHYLETHYL)PHOSPHORAMIDIC ACID ETHYL 3-METHYL-4-(METHYLTHIO) PHENYL ESTER; ISOPROPYLPHOSPHORAMIDIC ACID ETHYL 4-(METHYLTHIO)-M-TOLYL ESTER; BAY 68138; NEMACUR; PHENAMIPHOS; C13H22NO3PS; PST16145

CHEMICAL FAMILY: ORGANOPHOSPHATE

MOLECULAR FORMULA: C13-H22-N-O3-P-S

MOLECULAR WEIGHT: 303.39

CERCLA RATINGS (SCALE 0-3): HEALTH=3 FIRE=1 REACTIVITY=0 PERSISTENCE=1

NFPA RATINGS (SCALE 0-4): HEALTH=4 FIRE=1 REACTIVITY=0

COMPONENTS AND CONTAMINANTS

COMPONENT: FENAMIPHOS ***PERCENT:*** 100.0

CAS# 22224-92-6

OTHER CONTAMINANTS: NONE

EXPOSURE LIMITS: FENAMIPHOS: 0.1 MG/M3 OSHA TWA (SKIN) 0.1 MG/M3 ACGIH TWA (SKIN)

10/10,000 POUNDS SARA SECTION 302 THRESHOLD PLANNING QUANTITY 1 POUND SARA SECTION 304 REPORTABLE QUANTITY

PHYSICAL DATA

DESCRIPTION: WHITE CRYSTALLINE SOLID. ***MELTING POINT:*** 120 F (49 C)

SPECIFIC GRAVITY: 1.14 ***VAPOR PRESSURE:*** NEGLIGIBLE

SOLUBILITY IN WATER: 700 PPM @ 20 C

SOLVENT SOLUBILITY: SOLUBLE IN DICHLOROMETHANE, ISOPROPANOL AND MOST ORGANIC SOLVENTS; INSOLUBLE IN ALIPHATIC HYDROCARBONS.

FIRE AND EXPLOSION DATA

FIRE AND EXPLOSION HAZARD: SLIGHT FIRE HAZARD WHEN EXPOSED TO HEAT OR FLAME.

FIREFIGHTING MEDIA: DRY CHEMICAL, CARBON DIOXIDE, HALON, WATER SPRAY OR STANDARD FOAM (1987 EMERGENCY RESPONSE GUIDEBOOK, DOT P 5800.4).

FOR LARGER FIRES, USE WATER SPRAY, FOG OR STANDARD FOAM (1987 EMERGENCY RESPONSE GUIDEBOOK, DOT P 5800.4).

FIREFIGHTING: MOVE CONTAINERS FROM FIRE AREA IF POSSIBLE (1987 EMERGENCY RESPONSE GUIDEBOOK, DOT P 5800.4, GUIDE PAGE 53).

EXTINGUISH USING AGENT SUITABLE FOR TYPE OF SURROUNDING FIRE. AVOID BREATHING VAPORS AND DUSTS. KEEP UPWIND.

TRANSPORTATION DATA

DEPARTMENT OF TRANSPORTATION HAZARD CLASSIFICATION 49 CFR 172.101: POISON B

DEPARTMENT OF TRANSPORTATION LABELING REQUIREMENTS 49 CFR 172.101 AND SUBPART E: POISON

DEPARTMENT OF TRANSPORTATION PACKAGING REQUIREMENTS: 49 (CFR 173.377 EXCEPTIONS: 49 CFR 173.377

TOXICITY

FENAMIPHOS: TOXICITY DATA: 91 MG/M3/4 HOURS INHALATION-RAT LC50; 178 MG/KG SKIN-RABBIT LD50; 80 MG/KG SKIN-RAT LD50; 8 MG/KG ORAL-RAT LD50; 22700 UG/KG ORAL-MOUSE LD50; 10 MG/KG ORAL-CAT LD50; 10 MG/KG ORAL-DOG LD50; 10 MG/KG ORAL-RABBIT LD50; 75 MG/KG ORAL-GUINEA PIG LD50. CARCINOGEN STATUS: NONE. ACUTE TOXICITY LEVEL: HIGHLY TOXIC BY INHALATION, DERMAL ABSORPTION, AND INGESTION. TARGET EFFECTS: CHOLINESTERASE INHIBITOR. POISONING MAY AFFECT THE NERVOUS SYSTEM.* AT INCREASED RISK FROM EXPOSURE: PERSONS WITH RESPIRATORY AILMENTS, RECENT EXPOSURE TO CHOLINESTERASE INHIBITORS OR IMPAIRED CHOLINESTERASE PRODUCTION, OR LIVER MALFUNCTION.* ADDITIONAL DATA: MAY CROSS THE PLACENTA. HIGH ENVIRONMENTAL TEMPERATURES OR EXPOSURE OF THE CHEMICAL TO VISIBLE OR ULTRAVIOLET LIGHT MAY ENHANCE THE TOXICITY. INTERACTIONS WITH MEDICATIONS MAY OCCUR.*

* MAY BE BASED ON GENERAL INFORMATION ON ORGANOPHOSPHATES.

HEALTH EFFECTS AND FIRST AID

INHALATION: FENAMIPHOS: HIGHLY TOXIC. SEE INFORMATION ON ORGANOPHOSPHATES.

ORGANOPHOSPHATES: CHOLINESTERASE INHIBITOR. **ACUTE EXPOSURE-** WHEN INHALED, THE FIRST EFFECTS OF CHOLINESTERASE INHIBITORS ARE USUALLY RESPIRATORY AND MAY INCLUDE NASAL HYPEREMIA AND WATERY DISCHARGE, COUGH, CHEST DISCOMFORT, DYSPNEA, AND WHEEZING DUE TO INCREASED BRONCHIAL SECRETIONS AND BRONCHOCONSTRICTION. IF SUFFICIENT AMOUNTS ARE ABSORBED, OTHER SYSTEMIC EFFECTS MAY BEGIN WITHIN A FEW MINUTES OR BE DELAYED FOR UP TO 12 HOURS. SYMPTOMS MAY INCLUDE PALLOR, NAUSEA, VOMITING, DIARRHEA, ABDOMINAL CRAMPS, HEADACHE, DIZZINESS, OCULAR PAIN, BLURRED VISION, MIOSIS OR IN SOME CASES, ESPECIALLY INITIALLY, MYDRIASIS, LACRIMATION, SALIVATION, SWEATING, AND CONFUSION. OTHER REPORTED CENTRAL NERVOUS SYSTEM OR NEUROMUSCULAR EFFECTS MAY INCLUDE ATAXIA, SLURRED SPEECH, AREFLEXIA, WEAKNESS, FATIGUE, FASCICULATIONS, TWITCHING, TREMORS POSSIBLY OF THE TONGUE AND EYELIDS, AND EVENTUALLY PARALYSIS OF THE EXTREMITIES AND POSSIBLY OF THE RESPIRATORY MUSCLES. IN SEVERE CASES THERE MAY ALSO BE INVOLUNTARY DEFECATION AND URINATION, CYANOSIS, PSYCHOSIS, HYPERGLYCEMIA, ACUTE PANCREATITIS, CARDIAC IRREGULARITIES, PULMONARY EDEMA, UNCONSCIOUSNESS, CONVULSIONS, AND COMA. DEATH IS PRIMARILY DUE TO RESPIRATORY FAILURE, ALTHOUGH CARDIOVASCULAR EFFECTS INCLUDING CARDIAC ARREST MAY ALSO BE IMPLICATED. LONG TERM SEQUELAE ARE RARE BUT MAY INCLUDE NEUROPSYCHIATRIC DISORDERS AND MYOPATHY WITH MUSCLE TENDERNESS. SOME ORGANOPHOSPHATES MAY CAUSE A DELAYED NEUROPATHY BEGINNING 1-4 WEEKS AFTER AN ACUTE EXPOSURE WHICH MAY OR MAY NOT HAVE CAUSED ACUTE CHOLINERGIC EFFECTS. NUMBNESS, TINGLING, WEAKNESS AND CRAMPING BEGINNING SYMMETRICALLY IN THE LOWER LIMBS MAY PROGRESS TO ATAXIA AND PARALYSIS. IN SEVERE CASES, UPPER LIMB INVOLVEMENT IS POSSIBLE AND FLACCID PARALYSIS MAY PROGRESS TO SPASTIC PARALYSIS WITH EXAGGERATED REFLEXES. IMPROVEMENT MAY OCCUR OVER MONTHS TO YEARS, BUT SOME RESIDUAL IMPAIRMENT USUALLY REMAINS. **CHRONIC EXPOSURE-** REPEATED OR PROLONGED EXPOSURE MAY RESULT IN THE EFFECTS OF ACUTE EXPOSURE INCLUDING THE DELAYED NEUROPATHY. OTHER EFFECTS REPORTED IN WORKERS REPEATEDLY EXPOSED INCLUDE IMPAIRED MEMORY AND CONCENTRATION, ACUTE PSYCHOSIS, SEVERE DEPRESSIONS, IRRITABILTY, CONFUSION, APATHY, EMOTIONAL LABILITY, SOCIAL WITHDRAWAL, CONFUSION, HEADACHE, SPEECH DIFFICULTIES, DELAYED REACTION TIMES, SPATIAL DISORIENTATION, NIGHTMARES, SLEEPWALKING, AND DROWSINESS OR INSOMNIA. AN INFLUENZA-LIKE CONDITION WITH HEADACHE, NAUSEA, WEAKNESS, ANOREXIA AND MALAISE HAS ALSO BEEN REPORTED.

FIRST AID- REMOVE FROM EXPOSURE AREA TO FRESH AIR IMMEDIATELY. IF BREATHING HAS STOPPED, GIVE ARTIFICIAL RESPIRATION. MAINTAIN AIRWAY AND BLOOD PRESSURE AND ADMINISTER OXYGEN IF AVAILABLE. KEEP AFFECTED PERSON WARM AND AT REST. TREAT SYMPTOMATICALLY AND SUPPORTIVELY. ADMINISTRATION OF OXYGEN SHOULD BE PERFORMED BY QUALIFIED PERSONNEL. GET MEDICAL ATTENTION IMMEDIATELY.

SKIN CONTACT: FENAMIPHOS: HIGHLY TOXIC. SEE INFORMATION ON ORGANOPHOSPHATES.

ORGANOPHOSPHATES: CHOLINESTERASE INHIBITOR. **ACUTE EXPOSURE-** LOCALIZED SWEATING AND FASCICULATIONS MAY OCCUR AT THE SITE OF CONTACT. IF SUFFICIENT AMOUNTS ARE ABSORBED, OTHER EFFECTS OF CHOLINESTERASE INHIBITION AS DESCRIBED IN ACUTE INHALATION MAY OCCUR. SYMPTOMS MAY BE DELAYED 2-3 HOURS, BUT USUALLY NO MORE THAN 12 HOURS. THE RATE OF ABSORPTION IS INCREASED BY THE PRESENCE OF DERMATITIS OR HIGH AMBIENT TEMPERATURES. DELAYED NEUROPATHY IS ALSO POSSIBLE. **CHRONIC EXPOSURE-** REPEATED OR PROLONGED EXPOSURE MAY CAUSE EFFECTS AS DESCRIBED IN ACUTE EXPOSURE. SOME ORGANOPHOSPHATES MAY CAUSE SENSITIZATION.

FIRST AID- REMOVE CONTAMINATED CLOTHING IMMEDIATELY. WASH CONTAMINATED AREAS WITH SOAP AND WATER FOLLOWED BY ALCOHOL (ARENA, POISONING, 4TH ED.). EMERGENCY PERSONNEL SHOULD WEAR GLOVES AND AVOID CONTAMINATION. TREAT RESPIRATORY DIFFICULTY WITH ARTIFICIAL RESPIRATION. GET MEDICAL ATTENTION IMMEDIATELY.

EYE CONTACT: FENAMIPHOS: SEE INFORMATION ON ORGANOPHOSPHATES.

ORGANOPHOSPHATES: CHOLINESTERASE INHIBITOR. **ACUTE EXPOSURE-** DIRECT CONTACT MAY CAUSE PAIN, HYPEREMIA, LACRIMATION, TWITCHING OF THE EYELIDS, MIOSIS, AND CILIARY MUSCLE SPASM WITH LOSS OF ACCOMODATION, BLURRED OR DIMMED VISION AND BROWACHE. SOMETIMES MYDRIASIS MAY OCCUR INSTEAD OF MIOSIS. WITH SUFFICIENT EXPOSURE, OTHER SYMPTOMS OF CHOLINESTERASE INHIBITION AS DESCRIBED IN ACUTE INHALATION MAY OCCUR. **CHRONIC EXPOSURE-** REPEATED OR PROLONGED EXPOSURE MAY CAUSE EFFECTS AS DESCRIBED IN ACUTE EXPOSURE. SOME COMPOUNDS HAVE CAUSED TOXIC EFFECTS ON THE CRYSTALLINE LENS, CONJUNCTIVAL THICKENING AND OBSTRUCTION OF THE NASOLACRIMAL CANALS WHEN USED AS MIOTIC EYEDROPS.

FIRST AID- IRRIGATE EYES WITH WATER OR SALINE SOLUTION. IF SYMPTOMS OF POISONING OCCUR, TREAT RESPIRATORY DIFFICULTY WITH ARTIFICIAL RESPIRATION AND OXYGEN. OBSERVE PATIENT FOR AT LEAST 24-36 HOURS (GOSSELIN, CLINICAL TOXICOLOGY OF COMMERCIAL PRODUCTS, 5TH ED.). GET MEDICAL ATTENTION IMMEDIATELY. OXYGEN SHOULD BE ADMINISTERED BY QUALIFIED MEDICAL PERSONNEL.

INGESTION: FENAMIPHOS: HIGHLY TOXIC. SEE INFORMATION ON ORGANOPHOSPHATES. ADMINISTRATION TO RABBITS DURING GESTATION PRODUCED A SIGNIFICANT INCREASE IN THE INCIDENCE OF CHAIN-FUSED STERNEBRAE IN OFFSPRING.

ORGANOPHOSPHATES: CHOLINESTERASE INHIBITOR. **ACUTE EXPOSURE-** WHEN INGESTED, THE FIRST EFFECTS MAY BE NAUSEA, VOMITING, ANOREXIA, ABDOMINAL CRAMPS AND DIARRHEA. GASTROINTESTINAL ABSORPTION MAY CAUSE SYMPTOMS OF CHOLINESTERASE INHIBITION AS DESCRIBED IN ACUTE INHALATION. SYMPTOMS MAY BEGIN WITHIN MINUTES OR BE DELAYED FOR HOURS. DELAYED EFFECTS INCLUDING NEUROPATHY MAY ALSO OCCUR. **CHRONIC EXPOSURE-** REPEATED INGESTION MAY CAUSE EFFECTS AS DESCRIBED IN ACUTE EXPOSURE.

FIRST AID- IF PERSON IS ALERT AND RESPIRATION IS NOT DEPRESSED, GIVE SYRUP OF IPECAC FOLLOWED BY WATER (IF VOMITING OCCURS, KEEP HEAD BELOW HIPS TO PREVENT ASPIRATION). IF CONSCIOUSNESS LEVEL DECLINES OR VOMITING HAS NOT OCCURRED IN 15 MINUTES EMPTY STOMACH BY GASTRIC LAVAGE WITH THE AID OF CUFFED ENDOTRACHEAL TUBE USING ISOTONIC SALINE OR 5% SODIUM BICARBONATE FOLLOW WITH ACTIVATED CHARCOAL. ESTABLISH AND MAINTAIN AIRWAY. TREAT RESPIRATORY DIFFICULTY WITH ARTIFICIAL RESPIRATION AND OXYGEN. DO NOT GIVE MORPHINE, AMINOPHYLLINE, PHENOTHIAZINES, RESERPINE, FUROSEMIDE, OR ETHACRYNIC ACID (MORGAN, RECOGNITION AND MANAGEMENT OF PESTICIDE POISONINGS, 3RD ED.). TREAT SYMPTOMATICALLY AND SUPPORTIVELY. ADMINISTRATION OF OXYGEN AND LAVAGE MUST BE PERFORMED BY QUALIFIED MEDICAL PERSONNEL. GET MEDICAL ATTENTION IMMEDIATELY.

ANTIDOTE: THE FOLLOWING ANTIDOTE(S) HAVE BEEN RECOMMENDED. HOWEVER, THE DECISION AS TO WHETHER THE SEVERITY OF POISONING REQUIRES ADMINISTRATION OF ANY ANTIDOTE AND ACTUAL DOSE REQUIRED SHOULD BE MADE BY QUALIFIED MEDICAL PERSONNEL.

FOR CHOLINESTERASE INHIBITORS: ESTABLISH CLEAR AIRWAY AND TISSUE OXYGENATION BY ASPIRATION OF SECRETIONS, AND IF NECESSARY, BY ASSISTED PULMONARY VENTILATION WITH OXYGEN. IMPROVE TISSUE OXYGENATION AS MUCH AS POSSIBLE BEFORE ADMINISTERING ATROPINE TO MINIMIZE THE RISK OF VENTRICULAR FIBRILLATION. ADMINISTER ATROPINE SULFATE INTRAVENOUSLY, OR INTRAMUSCULARLY IF IV INJECTION IS NOT POSSIBLE. IN MODERATELY SEVERE POISONING ADMINISTER ATROPINE SULFATE, 0.4-2.0 MG REPEATED EVERY 15 MINUTES UNTIL ATROPINIZATION IS ACHIEVED (TACHYCARDIA, FLUSHING, DRY MOUTH, MYDRIASIS). MAINTAIN ATROPINIZATION BY REPEATED DOSES FOR 2-12 HOURS, OR LONGER, DEPENDING ON THE SEVERITY OF POISONING. THE APPEARANCE OF RALES IN THE LUNG BASES, MIOSIS, SALIVATION, NAUSEA, BRADYCARDIA, ARE ALL INDICATIONS OF INADEQUATE ATROPINIZATION. SEVERELY POISONED INDIVIDUALS MAY EXHIBIT REMARKABLE TOLERANCE TO ATROPINE; TWO OR MORE TIMES THE DOSAGES SUGGESTED ABOVE MAY BE NEEDED. PERSONS NOT POISONED OR ONLY SLIGHTLY POISONED, HOWEVER, MAY DEVELOP SIGNS OF ATROPINE TOXICITY FROM SUCH LARGE DOSAGES: FEVER, MUSCLE FIBRILLATIONS, AND DELIRIUM ARE THE MAIN SIGNS OF ATROPINE TOXICITY. IF THESE SIGNS APPEAR WHILE THE PATIENT IS FULLY ATROPINIZED, ATROPINE ADMINISTRATION SHOULD BE DISCONTINUED, AT LEAST TEMPORARILY. OBSERVE TREATED PATIENTS CLOSELY AT LEAST 24 HOURS TO INSURE THAT

SYMPTOMS (POSSIBLY PULMONARY EDEMA) DO NOT RECUR AS ATROPINIZATION WEARS OFF. IN VERY SEVERE POISONINGS, METABOLIC DISPOSITION OF TOXICANT MAY REQUIRE SEVERAL HOURS OR DAYS DURING WHICH ATROPINIZATION MUST BE MAINTAINED. MARKEDLY LOWER LEVELS OF URINARY METABOLITES INDICATE THAT ATROPINE DOSAGE CAN BE TAPERED OFF. AS DOSAGE IS REDUCED, CHECK THE LUNG BASES FREQUENTLY FOR RALES. IF RALES ARE HEARD OR OTHER SYMPTOMS RETURN, RE-ESTABLISH ATROPINIZATION PROMPTLY (MORGAN, RECOGNITION AND MANAGEMENT OF PESTICIDE POISONINGS, 3RD ED.). ADMINISTRATION OF ANTIDOTE MUST BE PERFORMED BY QUALIFIED MEDICAL PERSONNEL.
IN CASES OF SEVERE POISONING BY ORGANOPHOSPHATE PESTICIDES IN WHICH RESPIRATORY DEPRESSION, MUSCLE WEAKNESS AND TWITCHINGS ARE SEVERE, GIVE PRALIDOXIME (PROTOPAM-AYERST, 2-PAM), 1.0 GRAM INTRAVENOUSLY AT NO MORE THAN 0.5 GRAM PER MINUTE. DOSAGE OF PRALIDOXIME MAY BE REPEATED IN 1-2 HOURS, THEN AT 10-12 HOUR INTERVALS IF NEEDED. IN VERY SEVERE POISONINGS, DOSAGE RATES MAY BE DOUBLED. TREATMENT WITH PRALIDOXIME WILL BE MOST EFFECTIVE IF GIVEN WITHIN THIRTY-SIX HOURS AFTER POISONING (MORGAN, RECOGNITION AND MANAGEMENT OF PESTICIDE POISONINGS, 3RD ED.). ANTIDOTE SHOULD BE ADMINISTERED BY QUALIFIED MEDICAL PERSONNEL.

REACTIVITY

REACTIVITY: STABLE UNDER NORMAL TEMPERATURES AND PRESSURES.
INCOMPATIBILITIES: FENAMIPHOS: OXIDIZERS (STRONG): FIRE AND EXPLOSION HAZARD.
DECOMPOSITION: THERMAL DECOMPOSITION PRODUCTS MAY INCLUDE TOXIC OXIDES OF NITROGEN, CARBON, PHOSPHORUS, AND SULFUR.
POLYMERIZATION: HAZARDOUS POLYMERIZATION HAS NOT BEEN REPORTED TO OCCUR UNDER NORMAL TEMPERATURES AND PRESSURES.

STORAGE AND DISPOSAL

OBSERVE ALL FEDERAL, STATE AND LOCAL REGULATIONS WHEN STORING OR DISPOSING OF THIS SUBSTANCE. FOR ASSISTANCE, CONTACT THE DISTRICT DIRECTOR OF THE ENVIRONMENTAL PROTECTION AGENCY.

STORAGE

STORE IN ACCORDANCE WITH 40 CFR 165 RECOMMENDED PROCEDURES FOR THE DISPOSAL AND STORAGE OF PESTICIDES AND PESTICIDE CONTAINERS.
STORE AWAY FROM INCOMPATIBLE SUBSTANCES.
THRESHOLD PLANNING QUANTITY (TPQ): THE SUPERFUND AMENDMENTS AND REAUTHORIZATION ACT (SARA) SECTION 302 REQUIRES THAT EACH FACILITY WHERE ANY EXTREMELY HAZARDOUS SUBSTANCE IS PRESENT IN A QUANTITY EQUAL TO OR GREATER THAN THE TPQ ESTABLISHED FOR THAT SUBSTANCE NOTIFY THE STATE EMERGENCY RESPONSE COMMISSION FOR THE STATE IN WHICH IT IS LOCATED. SECTION 303 OF SARA REQUIRES THESE FACILITIES TO PARTICIPATE IN LOCAL EMERGENCY RESPONSE PLANNING (40 CFR 355.30).

DISPOSAL

DISPOSAL MUST BE IN ACCORDANCE WITH 40 CFR 165 RECOMMENDED PROCEDURES FOR THE DISPOSAL AND STORAGE OF PESTICIDES AND PESTICIDE CONTAINERS.

CONDITIONS TO AVOID

MAY BURN BUT DOES NOT IGNITE READILY.

SPILL AND LEAK PROCEDURES

OCCUPATIONAL SPILL: DO NOT TOUCH SPILLED MATERIAL. STOP LEAK IF YOU CAN DO IT WITHOUT RISK. USE WATER SPRAY TO REDUCE VAPORS. FOR SMALL SPILLS, TAKE UP WITH SAND OR OTHER ABSORBENT MATERIAL AND PLACE INTO CONTAINERS FOR LATER DISPOSAL. FOR SMALL DRY SPILLS, WITH A CLEAN SHOVEL PLACE MATERIAL INTO CLEAN, DRY CONTAINERS AND COVER. MOVE CONTAINERS FROM SPILL AREA. FOR LARGER SPILLS, DIKE FAR AHEAD OF SPILL FOR LATER DISPOSAL. KEEP UNNECESSARY PEOPLE AWAY. ISOLATE HAZARD AREA AND DENY ENTRY. VENTILATE CLOSED SPACES BEFORE ENTERING.
REPORTABLE QUANTITY (RQ): 1 POUND THE SUPERFUND AMENDMENTS AND REAUTHORIZATION ACT (SARA) SECTION 304 REQUIRES THAT A RELEASE EQUAL TO OR GREATER THAN THE REPORTABLE QUANTITY FOR THIS SUBSTANCE BE IMMEDIATELY REPORTED TO THE LOCAL EMERGENCY PLANNING COMMITTEE AND THE STATE EMERGENCY RESPONSE COMMISSION (40 CFR 355.40). IF THE RELEASE OF THIS SUBSTANCE IS REPORTABLE UNDER CERCLA SECTION 103, THE NATIONAL RESPONSE CENTER MUST BE NOTIFIED IMMEDIATELY AT (800) 424-8802 OR (202) 426-2675 IN THE METROPOLITAN WASHINGTON, D.C. AREA (40 CFR 302.6).

PROTECTIVE EQUIPMENT

VENTILATION: PROVIDE LOCAL EXHAUST OR PROCESS ENCLOSURE VENTILATION TO MEET PUBLISHED EXPOSURE LIMITS.
RESPIRATOR: THE FOLLOWING RESPIRATORS ARE RECOMMENDED BASED ON INFORMATION FOUND IN THE PHYSICAL DATA, TOXICITY AND HEALTH EFFECTS SECTIONS. THEY ARE RANKED IN ORDER FROM MINIMUM TO MAXIMUM RESPIRATORY PROTECTION. THE SPECIFIC RESPIRATOR SELECTED MUST BE BASED ON CONTAMINATION LEVELS FOUND IN THE WORK PLACE, MUST NOT EXCEED THE WORKING LIMITS OF THE RESPIRATOR AND BE JOINTLY APPROVED BY THE NATIONAL INSTITUTE FOR OCCUPATIONAL SAFETY AND HEALTH AND THE MINE SAFETY AND HEALTH ADMINISTRATION (NIOSH-MSHA).
TYPE 'C' SUPPLIED-AIR RESPIRATOR WITH A FULL FACEPIECE OPERATED IN PRESSURE-DEMAND OR OTHER POSITIVE PRESSURE MODE OR WITH A FULL FACEPIECE, HELMET OR HOOD OPERATED IN CONTINOUS-FLOW MODE.
SELF-CONTAINED BREATHING APPARATUS WITH A FULL FACEPIECE OPERATED IN PRESSURE-DEMAND OR OTHER POSITIVE PRESSURE MODE.
FOR FIREFIGHTING AND OTHER IMMEDIATELY DANGEROUS TO LIFE OR HEALTH CONDITIONS:
SELF-CONTAINED BREATHING APPARATUS WITH FULL FACEPIECE OPERATED IN PRESSURE-DEMAND OR OTHER POSITIVE PRESSURE MODE.
SUPPLIED-AIR RESPIRATOR WITH FULL FACEPIECE AND OPERATED IN PRESSURE-DEMAND OR OTHER POSITIVE PRESSURE MODE IN COMBINATION WITH AN AUXILIARY SELF-CONTAINED BREATHING APPARATUS OPERATED IN PRESSURE-DEMAND OR OTHER POSITIVE PRESSURE MODE.
CLOTHING: EMPLOYEE MUST WEAR APPROPRIATE PROTECTIVE (IMPERVIOUS) CLOTHING AND EQUIPMENT TO PREVENT ANY POSSIBILITY OF SKIN CONTACT WITH THIS SUBSTANCE.
GLOVES: EMPLOYEE MUST WEAR APPROPRIATE PROTECTIVE GLOVES TO PREVENT CONTACT WITH THIS SUBSTANCE.
EYE PROTECTION: EMPLOYEE MUST WEAR SPLASH-PROOF OR DUST-RESISTANT SAFETY GOGGLES AND A FACESHIELD TO PREVENT CONTACT WITH THIS SUBSTANCE.
EMERGENCY WASH FACILITIES: WHERE THERE IS ANY POSSIBILITY THAT AN EMPLOYEE'S EYES AND/OR SKIN MAY BE EXPOSED TO THIS SUBSTANCE, THE EMPLOYER SHOULD PROVIDE AN EYE WASH FOUNTAIN AND QUICK DRENCH SHOWER WITHIN THE IMMEDIATE WORK AREA FOR EMERGENCY USE.

AUTHORIZED BY- OCCUPATIONAL HEALTH SERVICES, INC.
CREATION DATE: 10/04/89 ***REVISION DATE:*** 04/30/90

MATERIAL SAFETY DATA SHEET

OCCUPATIONAL HEALTH SERVICES, INC.
AGRICULTURE AND PESTICIDE DIVISION
450 SEVENTH AVENUE, SUITE 2407
NEW YORK, NEW YORK 10123
1-800-445-MSDS OR (212) 967-1100

EMERGENCY CONTACT:
JOHN S. BRANSFORD, JR. (615) 292-1180

SUBSTANCE IDENTIFICATION

CAS-NUMBER 31972-43-7
SUBSTANCE: FENAMIPHOS SULFOXIDE
TRADE NAMES/SYNONYMS: PHOSPHORAMIDIC ACID, (1-METHYLETHYL)-, ETHYL 3-METHYL-4- (METHYLSULFINYL)PHENYL ESTER; (1-METHYLETHYL)PHOSPHORAMIDIC ACID ETHYL 3-METHYL4-(METHYLSULFINYL) PHENYL ESTER; PHOSPHORAMIDIC ACID, ISOPROPYL-, ETHYL 4-(ETHYLSULFINYL)-M-TOLYL ESTER; ISOPROPYLPHOSPHORAMIDIC ACID ETHYL 4-(ETHYLSULFINYL)-M-TOLYL ESTER; ETHYL 4-(ETHYLSULFINYL)-M-TOLYL ISOPROPYLPHOS PHORAMIDATE; NEMACUR SULFOXIDE; C13H22NO4PS; PST16146
CHEMICAL FAMILY: ORGANOPHOSPHATE
MOLECULAR FORMULA: C13-H22-N-O4-P-S
MOLECULAR WEIGHT: 319.36
CERCLA RATINGS (SCALE 0-3): HEALTH=3 FIRE=1 REACTIVITY=0 PERSISTENCE=1
NFPA RATINGS (SCALE 0-4): HEALTH=3 FIRE=1 REACTIVITY=0

COMPONENTS AND CONTAMINANTS

COMPONENT: FENAMIPHOS SULFOXIDE ***PERCENT:*** 100.0
CAS# 31972-43-7
OTHER CONTAMINANTS: NONE
EXPOSURE LIMITS: NO OCCUPATIONAL EXPOSURE LIMITS ESTABLISHED BY OSHA, ACGIH, OR NIOSH.

PHYSICAL DATA

DESCRIPTION: WHITE POWDER. ***MELTING POINT:*** 153-194 F (67-90 C)
SPECIFIC GRAVITY: NOT AVAILABLE ***SOLUBILITY IN WATER:*** NOT AVAILABLE

FIRE AND EXPLOSION DATA

FIRE AND EXPLOSION HAZARD: SLIGHT FIRE HAZARD WHEN EXPOSED TO HEAT OR FLAME.

FIREFIGHTING MEDIA: DRY CHEMICAL, CARBON DIOXIDE, HALON, WATER SPRAY OR STANDARD FOAM (1987 EMERGENCY RESPONSE GUIDEBOOK, DOT P 5800.4). FOR LARGER FIRES, USE WATER SPRAY, FOG OR STANDARD FOAM (1987 EMERGENCY RESPONSE GUIDEBOOK, DOT P 5800.4).

FIREFIGHTING: MOVE CONTAINERS FROM FIRE AREA IF POSSIBLE (1987 EMERGENCY RESPONSE GUIDEBOOK, DOT P 5800.4, GUIDE PAGE 53).
EXTINGUISH USING AGENT SUITABLE FOR TYPE OF SURROUNDING FIRE. AVOID BREATHING VAPORS AND DUSTS. KEEP UPWIND.

TRANSPORTATION DATA

DEPARTMENT OF TRANSPORTATION HAZARD CLASSIFICATION 49 CFR 172.101: POISON B
DEPARTMENT OF TRANSPORTATION LABELING REQUIREMENTS 49 CFR 172.101 AND SUBPART E: POISON
DEPARTMENT OF TRANSPORTATION PACKAGING REQUIREMENTS: 49 (CFR 173.377 EXCEPTIONS: 49 CFR 173.377

TOXICITY

FENAMIPHOS SULFOXIDE: TOXICITY DATA: 2.1-3.5 MG/KG ORAL-RAT LD50 (EPA). CARCINOGEN STATUS: NONE. ACUTE TOXICITY LEVEL: HIGHLY TOXIC BY INGESTION. TARGET EFFECTS: CHOLINESTERASE INHIBITOR. POISONING MAY AFFECT THE NERVOUS SYSTEM.* AT INCREASED RISK FROM EXPOSURE: PERSONS WITH RESPIRATORY AILMENTS, RECENT EXPOSURE TO CHOLINESTERASE INHIBITORS OR IMPAIRED CHOLINESTERASE PRODUCTION, OR LIVER MALFUNCTION.* ADDITIONAL DATA: MAY CROSS THE PLACENTA. HIGH ENVIRONMENTAL TEMPERATURES OR EXPOSURE OF THE CHEMICAL TO VISIBLE OR ULTRAVIOLET LIGHT MAY ENHANCE THE TOXICITY. INTERACTIONS WITH MEDICATIONS MAY OCCUR.*

* MAY BE BASED ON GENERAL INFORMATION ON ORGANOPHOSPHATES.

HEALTH EFFECTS AND FIRST AID

INHALATION: FENAMIPHOS SULFOXIDE: SEE INFORMATION ON ORGANOPHOSPHATES.
ORGANOPHOSPHATES: CHOLINESTERASE INHIBITOR. **ACUTE EXPOSURE-** WHEN INHALED, THE FIRST EFFECTS OF CHOLINESTERASE INHIBITORS ARE USUALLY RESPIRATORY AND MAY INCLUDE NASAL HYPEREMIA AND WATERY DISCHARGE, COUGH, CHEST DISCOMFORT, DYSPNEA, AND WHEEZING DUE TO INCREASED BRONCHIAL SECRETIONS AND BRONCHOCONSTRICTION. IF SUFFICIENT AMOUNTS ARE ABSORBED, OTHER SYSTEMIC EFFECTS MAY BEGIN WITHIN A FEW MINUTES OR BE DELAYED FOR UP TO 12 HOURS. SYMPTOMS MAY INCLUDE PALLOR, NAUSEA, VOMITING, DIARRHEA, ABDOMINAL CRAMPS, HEADACHE, DIZZINESS, OCULAR PAIN, BLURRED VISION, MIOSIS OR IN SOME CASES, ESPECIALLY INITIALLY, MYDRIASIS, LACRIMATION, SALIVATION, SWEATING, AND CONFUSION. OTHER REPORTED CENTRAL NERVOUS SYSTEM OR NEUROMUSCULAR EFFECTS MAY INCLUDE ATAXIA, SLURRED SPEECH, AREFLEXIA, WEAKNESS, FATIGUE, FASCICULATIONS, TWITCHING, TREMORS POSSIBLY OF THE TONGUE AND EYELIDS, AND EVENTUALLY PARALYSIS OF THE EXTREMITIES AND POSSIBLY OF THE RESPIRATORY MUSCLES. IN SEVERE CASES THERE MAY ALSO BE INVOLUNTARY DEFECATION AND URINATION, CYANOSIS, PSYCHOSIS, HYPERGLYCEMIA, ACUTE PANCREATITIS, CARDIAC IRREGULARITIES, PULMONARY EDEMA, UNCONSCIOUSNESS, CONVULSIONS, AND COMA. DEATH IS PRIMARILY DUE TO RESPIRATORY FAILURE, ALTHOUGH CARDIOVASCULAR EFFECTS INCLUDING CARDIAC ARREST MAY ALSO BE IMPLICATED. LONG TERM SEQUELAE ARE RARE BUT MAY INCLUDE NEUROPSYCHIATRIC DISORDERS AND MYOPATHY WITH MUSCLE TENDERNESS. SOME ORGANOPHOSPHATES MAY CAUSE A DELAYED NEUROPATHY BEGINNING 1-4 WEEKS AFTER AN ACUTE EXPOSURE WHICH MAY OR MAY NOT HAVE CAUSED ACUTE CHOLINERGIC EFFECTS. NUMBNESS, TINGLING, WEAKNESS AND CRAMPING BEGINNING SYMMETRICALLY IN THE LOWER LIMBS MAY PROGRESS TO ATAXIA AND PARALYSIS. IN SEVERE CASES, UPPER LIMB INVOLVEMENT IS POSSIBLE AND FLACCID PARALYSIS MAY PROGRESS TO SPASTIC PARALYSIS WITH EXAGGERATED REFLEXES. IMPROVEMENT MAY OCCUR OVER MONTHS TO YEARS, BUT SOME RESIDUAL IMPAIRMENT USUALLY REMAINS. **CHRONIC EXPOSURE-** REPEATED OR PROLONGED EXPOSURE MAY RESULT IN THE EFFECTS OF ACUTE EXPOSURE INCLUDING THE DELAYED NEUROPATHY. OTHER EFFECTS REPORTED IN WORKERS REPEATEDLY EXPOSED INCLUDE IMPAIRED MEMORY AND CONCENTRATION, ACUTE PSYCHOSIS, SEVERE DEPRESSIONS, IRRITABILTY, CONFUSION, APATHY, EMOTIONAL LABILITY, SOCIAL WITHDRAWAL, CONFUSION, HEADACHE, SPEECH DIFFICULTIES, DELAYED REACTION TIMES, SPATIAL DISORIENTATION, NIGHTMARES, SLEEPWALKING, AND DROWSINESS OR INSOMNIA. AN INFLUENZA-LIKE CONDITION WITH HEADACHE, NAUSEA, WEAKNESS, ANOREXIA AND MALAISE HAS ALSO BEEN REPORTED.

FIRST AID- REMOVE FROM EXPOSURE AREA TO FRESH AIR IMMEDIATELY. IF BREATHING HAS STOPPED, GIVE ARTIFICIAL RESPIRATION. MAINTAIN AIRWAY AND BLOOD PRESSURE AND ADMINISTER OXYGEN IF AVAILABLE. KEEP AFFECTED PERSON WARM AND AT REST. TREAT SYMPTOMATICALLY AND SUPPORTIVELY. ADMINISTRATION OF OXYGEN SHOULD BE PERFORMED BY QUALIFIED PERSONNEL. GET MEDICAL ATTENTION IMMEDIATELY.

SKIN CONTACT: FENAMIPHOS SULFOXIDE: SEE INFORMATION ON ORGANOPHOSPHATES.
ORGANOPHOSPHATES: CHOLINESTERASE INHIBITOR. **ACUTE EXPOSURE-** LOCALIZED SWEATING AND FASCICULATIONS MAY OCCUR AT THE SITE OF CONTACT. IF SUFFICIENT AMOUNTS ARE ABSORBED, OTHER EFFECTS OF CHOLINESTERASE INHIBITION AS DESCRIBED IN ACUTE INHALATION MAY OCCUR. SYMPTOMS MAY BE DELAYED 2-3 HOURS, BUT USUALLY NO MORE THAN 12 HOURS. THE RATE OF ABSORPTION IS INCREASED BY THE PRESENCE OF DERMATITIS OR HIGH AMBIENT TEMPERATURES. DELAYED NEUROPATHY IS ALSO POSSIBLE. **CHRONIC EXPOSURE-** REPEATED OR PROLONGED EXPOSURE MAY CAUSE EFFECTS AS DESCRIBED IN ACUTE EXPOSURE. SOME ORGANOPHOSPHATES MAY CAUSE SENSITIZATION.

FIRST AID- REMOVE CONTAMINATED CLOTHING IMMEDIATELY. WASH CONTAMINATED AREAS WITH SOAP AND WATER FOLLOWED BY ALCOHOL (ARENA, POISONING, 4TH ED.). EMERGENCY PERSONNEL SHOULD WEAR GLOVES AND AVOID CONTAMINATION. TREAT RESPIRATORY DIFFICULTY WITH ARTIFICIAL RESPIRATION. GET MEDICAL ATTENTION IMMEDIATELY.

EYE CONTACT: FENAMIPHOS SULFOXIDE: SEE INFORMATION ON ORGANOPHOSPHATES.
ORGANOPHOSPHATES: CHOLINESTERASE INHIBITOR. **ACUTE EXPOSURE-** DIRECT CONTACT MAY CAUSE PAIN, HYPEREMIA, LACRIMATION, TWITCHING OF THE EYELIDS, MIOSIS, AND CILIARY MUSCLE SPASM WITH LOSS OF ACCOMODATION, BLURRED OR DIMMED VISION AND BROWACHE. SOMETIMES MYDRIASIS MAY OCCUR INSTEAD OF MIOSIS. WITH SUFFICIENT EXPOSURE, OTHER SYMPTOMS OF CHOLINESTERASE INHIBITION AS DESCRIBED IN ACUTE INHALATION MAY OCCUR. **CHRONIC EXPOSURE-** REPEATED OR PROLONGED EXPOSURE MAY CAUSE EFFECTS AS DESCRIBED IN ACUTE EXPOSURE. SOME COMPOUNDS HAVE CAUSED TOXIC EFFECTS ON THE CRYSTALLINE LENS, CONJUNCTIVAL THICKENING AND OBSTRUCTION OF THE NASOLACRIMAL CANALS WHEN USED AS MIOTIC EYEDROPS.

FIRST AID- IRRIGATE EYES WITH WATER OR SALINE SOLUTION. IF SYMPTOMS OF POISONING OCCUR, TREAT RESPIRATORY DIFFICULTY WITH ARTIFICIAL RESPIRATION AND OXYGEN. OBSERVE PATIENT FOR AT LEAST 24-36 HOURS (GOSSELIN, CLINICAL TOXICOLOGY OF COMMERCIAL PRODUCTS, 5TH ED.). GET MEDICAL ATTENTION IMMEDIATELY. OXYGEN SHOULD BE ADMINISTERED BY QUALIFIED MEDICAL PERSONNEL.

INGESTION: FENAMIPHOS SULFOXIDE: HIGHLY TOXIC. SEE INFORMATION ON ORGANOPHOSPHATES.
ORGANOPHOSPHATES: CHOLINESTERASE INHIBITOR. **ACUTE EXPOSURE-** WHEN INGESTED, THE FIRST EFFECTS MAY BE NAUSEA, VOMITING, ANOREXIA, ABDOMINAL CRAMPS AND DIARRHEA. GASTROINTESTINAL ABSORPTION MAY CAUSE SYMPTOMS OF CHOLINESTERASE INHIBITION AS DESCRIBED IN ACUTE INHALATION. SYMPTOMS MAY BEGIN WITHIN MINUTES OR BE DELAYED FOR HOURS. DELAYED EFFECTS INCLUDING NEUROPATHY MAY ALSO OCCUR. **CHRONIC EXPOSURE-** REPEATED INGESTION MAY CAUSE EFFECTS AS DESCRIBED IN ACUTE EXPOSURE.

FIRST AID- IF PERSON IS ALERT AND RESPIRATION IS NOT DEPRESSED, GIVE SYRUP OF IPECAC FOLLOWED BY WATER (IF VOMITING OCCURS, KEEP HEAD BELOW HIPS TO PREVENT ASPIRATION). IF CONSCIOUSNESS LEVEL DECLINES OR VOMITING HAS NOT OCCURRED IN 15 MINUTES EMPTY STOMACH BY GASTRIC LAVAGE WITH THE AID OF CUFFED ENDOTRACHEAL TUBE USING ISOTONIC SALINE OR 5% SODIUM BICARBONATE FOLLOW WITH ACTIVATED CHARCOAL. ESTABLISH AND MAINTAIN AIRWAY. TREAT RESPIRATORY DIFFICULTY WITH ARTIFICIAL RESPIRATION AND OXYGEN. DO NOT GIVE MORPHINE, AMINOPHYLLINE, PHENOTHIAZINES, RESERPINE, FUROSEMIDE, OR ETHACRYNIC ACID (MORGAN, RECOGNITION AND MANAGEMENT OF PESTICIDE POISONINGS, 3RD ED.). TREAT SYMPTOMATICALLY AND SUPPORTIVELY. ADMINISTRATION OF OXYGEN AND LAVAGE MUST BE PERFORMED BY QUALIFIED MEDICAL PERSONNEL. GET MEDICAL ATTENTION IMMEDIATELY.

ANTIDOTE: THE FOLLOWING ANTIDOTE(S) HAVE BEEN RECOMMENDED. HOWEVER, THE DECISION AS TO WHETHER THE SEVERITY OF POISONING REQUIRES ADMINISTRATION OF ANY ANTIDOTE AND ACTUAL DOSE REQUIRED SHOULD BE MADE BY QUALIFIED MEDICAL PERSONNEL.
FOR CHOLINESTERASE INHIBITORS: ESTABLISH CLEAR AIRWAY AND TISSUE OXYGENATION BY ASPIRATION OF SECRETIONS, AND IF NECESSARY, BY ASSISTED PULMONARY VENTILATION WITH OXYGEN. IMPROVE TISSUE OXYGENATION AS MUCH AS POSSIBLE BEFORE ADMINISTERING ATROPINE TO MINIMIZE THE RISK OF VENTRICULAR FIBRILLATION. ADMINISTER ATROPINE SULFATE INTRAVENOUSLY, OR INTRAMUSCULARLY IF IV INJECTION IS NOT POSSIBLE. IN MODERATELY SEVERE POISONING ADMINISTER ATROPINE SULFATE, 0.4-2.0 MG REPEATED EVERY 15 MINUTES UNTIL ATROPINIZATION IS ACHIEVED (TACHYCARDIA, FLUSHING, DRY

MOUTH, MYDRIASIS). MAINTAIN ATROPINIZATION BY REPEATED DOSES FOR 2-12 HOURS, OR LONGER, DEPENDING ON THE SEVERITY OF POISONING. THE APPEARANCE OF RALES IN THE LUNG BASES, MIOSIS, SALIVATION, NAUSEA, BRADYCARDIA, ARE ALL INDICATIONS OF INADEQUATE ATROPINIZATION. SEVERELY POISONED INDIVIDUALS MAY EXHIBIT REMARKABLE TOLERANCE TO ATROPINE; TWO OR MORE TIMES THE DOSAGES SUGGESTED ABOVE MAY BE NEEDED. PERSONS NOT POISONED OR ONLY SLIGHTLY POISONED, HOWEVER, MAY DEVELOP SIGNS OF ATROPINE TOXICITY FROM SUCH LARGE DOSAGES: FEVER, MUSCLE FIBRILLATIONS, AND DELIRIUM ARE THE MAIN SIGNS OF ATROPINE TOXICITY. IF THESE SIGNS APPEAR WHILE THE PATIENT IS FULLY ATROPINIZED, ATROPINE ADMINISTRATION SHOULD BE DISCONTINUED, AT LEAST TEMPORARILY. OBSERVE TREATED PATIENTS CLOSELY AT LEAST 24 HOURS TO INSURE THAT SYMPTOMS (POSSIBLY PULMONARY EDEMA) DO NOT RECUR AS ATROPINIZATION WEARS OFF. IN VERY SEVERE POISONINGS, METABOLIC DISPOSITION OF TOXICANT MAY REQUIRE SEVERAL HOURS OR DAYS DURING WHICH ATROPINIZATION MUST BE MAINTAINED. MARKEDLY LOWER LEVELS OF URINARY METABOLITES INDICATE THAT ATROPINE DOSAGE CAN BE TAPERED OFF. AS DOSAGE IS REDUCED, CHECK THE LUNG BASES FREQUENTLY FOR RALES. IF RALES ARE HEARD OR OTHER SYMPTOMS RETURN, RE-ESTABLISH ATROPINIZATION PROMPTLY (MORGAN, RECOGNITION AND MANAGEMENT OF PESTICIDE POISONINGS, 3RD ED.). ADMINISTRATION OF ANTIDOTE MUST BE PERFORMED BY QUALIFIED MEDICAL PERSONNEL.

IN CASES OF SEVERE POISONING BY ORGANOPHOSPHATE PESTICIDES IN WHICH RESPIRATORY DEPRESSION, MUSCLE WEAKNESS AND TWITCHINGS ARE SEVERE, GIVE PRALIDOXIME (PROTOPAM-AYERST, 2-PAM), 1.0 GRAM INTRAVENOUSLY AT NO MORE THAN 0.5 GRAM PER MINUTE. DOSAGE OF PRALIDOXIME MAY BE REPEATED IN 1-2 HOURS, THEN AT 10-12 HOUR INTERVALS IF NEEDED. IN VERY SEVERE POISONINGS, DOSAGE RATES MAY BE DOUBLED. TREATMENT WITH PRALIDOXIME WILL BE MOST EFFECTIVE IF GIVEN WITHIN THIRTY-SIX HOURS AFTER POISONING (MORGAN, RECOGNITION AND MANAGEMENT OF PESTICIDE POISONINGS, 3RD ED.). ANTIDOTE SHOULD BE ADMINISTERED BY QUALIFIED MEDICAL PERSONNEL.

REACTIVITY

REACTIVITY: STABLE UNDER NORMAL TEMPERATURES AND PRESSURES.

INCOMPATIBILITIES: FENAMIPHOS SULFOXIDE: OXIDIZERS (STRONG): FIRE AND EXPLOSION HAZARD.

DECOMPOSITION: THERMAL DECOMPOSITION PRODUCTS MAY INCLUDE TOXIC OXIDES OF NITROGEN, CARBON, PHOSPHORUS, AND SULFUR.

POLYMERIZATION: HAZARDOUS POLYMERIZATION HAS NOT BEEN REPORTED TO OCCUR UNDER NORMAL TEMPERATURES AND PRESSURES.

STORAGE AND DISPOSAL

OBSERVE ALL FEDERAL, STATE AND LOCAL REGULATIONS WHEN STORING OR DISPOSING OF THIS SUBSTANCE. FOR ASSISTANCE, CONTACT THE DISTRICT DIRECTOR OF THE ENVIRONMENTAL PROTECTION AGENCY.

STORAGE

STORE AWAY FROM INCOMPATIBLE SUBSTANCES.

CONDITIONS TO AVOID

MAY BURN BUT DOES NOT IGNITE READILY.

SPILL AND LEAK PROCEDURES

OCCUPATIONAL SPILL: DO NOT TOUCH SPILLED MATERIAL. STOP LEAK IF YOU CAN DO IT WITHOUT RISK. FOR SMALL SPILLS, TAKE UP WITH SAND OR OTHER ABSORBENT MATERIAL AND PLACE INTO CONTAINERS FOR LATER DISPOSAL. FOR SMALL DRY SPILLS, WITH A CLEAN SHOVEL PLACE MATERIAL INTO CLEAN, DRY CONTAINER AND COVER. MOVE CONTAINERS FROM SPILL AREA. FOR LARGER SPILLS, DIKE FAR AHEAD OF SPILL FOR LATER DISPOSAL. KEEP UNNECESSARY PEOPLE AWAY. ISOLATE HAZARD AREA AND DENY ENTRY.

PROTECTIVE EQUIPMENT

VENTILATION: PROVIDE LOCAL EXHAUST OR PROCESS ENCLOSURE VENTILATION SYSTEM.

RESPIRATOR: THE FOLLOWING RESPIRATORS ARE RECOMMENDED BASED ON INFORMATION FOUND IN THE PHYSICAL DATA, TOXICITY AND HEALTH EFFECTS SECTIONS. THEY ARE RANKED IN ORDER FROM MINIMUM TO MAXIMUM RESPIRATORY PROTECTION. THE SPECIFIC RESPIRATOR SELECTED MUST BE BASED ON CONTAMINATION LEVELS FOUND IN THE WORK PLACE, MUST NOT EXCEED THE WORKING LIMITS OF THE RESPIRATOR AND BE JOINTLY APPROVED BY THE NATIONAL INSTITUTE FOR OCCUPATIONAL SAFETY AND HEALTH AND THE MINE SAFETY AND HEALTH ADMINISTRATION (NIOSH-MSHA).

TYPE 'C' SUPPLIED-AIR RESPIRATOR WITH A FULL FACEPIECE OPERATED IN PRESSURE-DEMAND OR OTHER POSITIVE PRESSURE MODE OR WITH A FULL FACEPIECE, HELMET OR HOOD OPERATED IN CONTINOUS-FLOW MODE.

SELF-CONTAINED BREATHING APPARATUS WITH A FULL FACEPIECE OPERATED IN PRESSURE-DEMAND OR OTHER POSITIVE PRESSURE MODE.

FOR FIREFIGHTING AND OTHER IMMEDIATELY DANGEROUS TO LIFE OR HEALTH CONDITIONS:

SELF-CONTAINED BREATHING APPARATUS WITH FULL FACEPIECE OPERATED IN PRESSURE-DEMAND OR OTHER POSITIVE PRESSURE MODE.

SUPPLIED-AIR RESPIRATOR WITH FULL FACEPIECE AND OPERATED IN PRESSURE-DEMAND OR OTHER POSITIVE PRESSURE MODE IN COMBINATION WITH AN AUXILIARY SELF-CONTAINED BREATHING APPARATUS OPERATED IN PRESSURE-DEMAND OR OTHER POSITIVE PRESSURE MODE.

CLOTHING: EMPLOYEE MUST WEAR APPROPRIATE PROTECTIVE (IMPERVIOUS) CLOTHING AND EQUIPMENT TO PREVENT ANY POSSIBILITY OF SKIN CONTACT WITH THIS SUBSTANCE.

GLOVES: EMPLOYEE MUST WEAR APPROPRIATE PROTECTIVE GLOVES TO PREVENT CONTACT WITH THIS SUBSTANCE.

EYE PROTECTION: EMPLOYEE MUST WEAR SPLASH-PROOF OR DUST-RESISTANT SAFETY GOGGLES TO PREVENT EYE CONTACT WITH THIS SUBSTANCE.

EMERGENCY EYE WASH: WHERE THERE IS ANY POSSIBILITY THAT AN EMPLOYEE'S EYES MAY BE EXPOSED TO THIS SUBSTANCE, THE EMPLOYER SHOULD PROVIDE AN EYE WASH FOUNTAIN WITHIN THE IMMEDIATE WORK AREA FOR EMERGENCY USE.

AUTHORIZED BY- OCCUPATIONAL HEALTH SERVICES, INC.

CREATION DATE: 10/04/89 ***REVISION DATE:*** 05/01/90

MATERIAL SAFETY DATA SHEET

OCCUPATIONAL HEALTH SERVICES, INC.
AGRICULTURE AND PESTICIDE DIVISION
450 SEVENTH AVENUE, SUITE 2407
NEW YORK, NEW YORK 10123
1-800-445-MSDS OR (212) 967-1100

EMERGENCY CONTACT:
JOHN S. BRANSFORD, JR. (615) 292-1180

SUBSTANCE IDENTIFICATION

CAS-NUMBER 10101-97-0

SUBSTANCE: NICKEL SULFATE, HEXAHYDRATE

TRADE NAMES/SYNONYMS: NICKEL(II) SULFATE, HEXAHYDRATE (1:1:6); BLUE SALT; SULFURIC ACID, NICKEL(2+) SALT(1:1), HEXAHYDRATE; SULFURIC ACID, NICKEL(2+) SALT, HEXAHYDRATE; M & T NICKEL SULFATE (M & T CHEM.); NICKEL MONOSULFATE HEXAHYDRATE; NICKEL(2+) SULFATE HEXAHYDRATE; NICKEL SULFATE (NISO4) HEXAHYDRATE; NICKEL(II) SULFATE HEXAHYDRATE; STCC 4966368; H14NIO10SI; PST16410

CHEMICAL FAMILY: INORGANIC SALT

MOLECULAR FORMULA: NI-O4-S.6(H2-O)

MOLECULAR WEIGHT: 262.84

CERCLA RATINGS (SCALE 0-3): HEALTH=3 FIRE=0 REACTIVITY=0 PERSISTENCE=3

NFPA RATINGS (SCALE 0-4): HEALTH=3 FIRE=0 REACTIVITY=0

COMPONENTS AND CONTAMINANTS

COMPONENT: NICKEL SULFATE, HEXAHYDRATE ***PERCENT:*** 100.0
CAS# 10101-97-0

OTHER CONTAMINANTS: NONE

EXPOSURE LIMITS: NICKEL, SOLUBLE COMPOUNDS (AS NI): 0.1 MG/M3 OSHA TWA 0.1 MG/M3 ACGIH TWA (NOTICE OF INTENDED CHANGES 1989-1990) 15 UG/M3 NIOSH RECOMMENDED 10 HOUR TWA

SUBJECT TO SARA SECTION 313 ANNUAL TOXIC CHEMICAL RELEASE REPORTING

SUBJECT TO CALIFORNIA PROPOSITION 65 CANCER AND/OR REPRODUCTIVE TOXICITY WARNING AND RELEASE REQUIREMENTS- (OCTOBER 1, 1989) (NICKEL AND CERTAIN NICKEL COMPOUNDS)

PHYSICAL DATA

DESCRIPTION: ODORLESS, BLUE OR EMERALD GREEN, EFFLORESCENT CRYSTALS WITH A SWEET ASTRINGENT TASTE. ***BOILING POINT:*** 217 F (103 C) (-6H2O)ES

MELTING POINT: 128 F (53 C) ***SPECIFIC GRAVITY:*** 2.07

VAPOR PRESSURE: 0 @ 20 C ***PH:*** ACID IN SOLUTION

SOLUBILITY IN WATER: 40% @ 20 C

SOLVENT SOLUBILITY: VERY SOLUBLE IN ETHANOL, METHANOL, AMMONIUM HYDROXIDE.

DECOMPOSES ABOVE 1472 F(800C)

HANDBOOK OF POISONING, 11TH ED.) OR DILUTED VINEGAR AND/OR COLD RUNNING WATER (GOSSELIN, CLINICAL TOXICOLOGY OF COMMERCIAL PRODUCTS). GIVE ARTIFICIAL RESPIRATION, USING OXYGEN IF POSSIBLE. TREAT CONVULSIONS.

EYE CONTACT: NICOTINE: IRRITANT. **ACUTE EXPOSURE-** MAY CAUSE IRRITATION. DIRECT CONTACT IN A ONE PERSON'S EYE PRODUCED SEVERE PAIN, MUCH CONJUNCTIVAL REACTION AND CORNEAL INFILTRATION. THE EYE HEALED WITH PARTIAL OPACIFICATION OF THE CORNEA. NICOTINE INJECTED INTO THE ANTERIOR CHAMBER OF RABBITS HAS CAUSED INFLAMMATION OF THE ANTERIOR SEGMENT OF THE EYE AND MIOSIS. **CHRONIC EXPOSURE-** NEAR-LETHAL DOSES WERE ADMINISTERED TO RABBITS DAILY FOR EIGHTY DAYS, AND RESULTED IN MYDRIASIS AND POOR RESPONSE OF THE PUPILS TO LIGHT, ATTRIBUTABLE TO DEGENERATION INDUCED IN THE RETINAL GANGLION CELLS, HOWEVER THE ERG WAS UNAFFECTED.

FIRST AID- WASH EYES IMMEDIATELY WITH LARGE AMOUNTS OF WATER OR NORMAL SALINE, OCCASIONALLY LIFTING UPPER AND LOWER LIDS, UNTIL NO EVIDENCE OF CHEMICAL REMAINS (APPROXIMATELY 15-20 MINUTES). GET MEDICAL ATTENTION IMMEDIATELY.

INGESTION: NICOTINE: HIGHLY TOXIC. **ACUTE EXPOSURE-** INGESTION MAY CAUSE ABSORPTION OF THIS MATERIAL INTO THE BODY AND PRODUCE SYSTEMIC INTOXICATION. SYMPTOMS OF SYSTEMIC POISONING FROM SMALL DOSES INCLUDE NAUSEA, VOMITING, DIARRHEA, HEADACHE, DIZZINESS, AND NEUROLOGIC STIMULATION, RESULTING IN TACHYCARDIA, HYPERTENSION, HYPERPNEA, TACHYPNEA, SWEATING, AND SALIVATION. WITH SEVERE INTOXICATION, THERE MAY BE A BURNING OF THE MOUTH, THROAT AND STOMACH AS WELL AS CONVULSIONS, MYOCARDIAL ARRHYTHMIAS AND COMA. DEATH MAY OCCUR WITHIN 5 MINUTES TO 4 HOURS. **CHRONIC EXPOSURE-** ONE BABY EXPERIENCED DEVELOPMENTAL ABNORMALITY OF THE CARDIOVASCULAR SYSTEM WHEN ITS MOTHER INGESTED 40 UG/KG OF THIS MATERIAL DURING THE 24TH WEEK OF PREGNANCY. CHRONIC ADMINISTRATION TO MICE DURING PREGNANCY RESULTED IN FETOTOXICITY. THE OFFSPRING OF RATS EXHIBITED ADVERSE BEHAVIORAL, BIOCHEMICAL AND METABOLIC EFFECTS WHEN THEIR MOTHERS WERE FED A TOTAL DOSE OF 59400 UG/KG FOR 22 DAYS WHILE PREGNANT. IN ANOTHER STUDY, CHRONIC ADMINISTRATION OF A TOTAL DOSE OF 594 MG/KG TO MALE AND FEMALE RATS 4 WEEKS PRIOR TO MATING AND 3 WEEKS DURING LACTATION RESULTED IN ADVERSE EFFECTS ON THE GROWTH STATISTICS OF THE OFFSPRING.

FIRST AID- GIVE ACTIVATED CHARCOAL TO ADSORB NICOTINE NOT ALREADY EXPELLED BY VOMITING. REMOVE BY THOROUGH GASTRIC LAVAGE WITH TAP WATER CONTAINING ACTIVATED CHARCOAL (DREISBACH, HANDBOOK OF POISONING, 11TH ED.) OR 0.05% SOLUTION OF TANNIC ACID OR 1:1500 SOLUTION OF POTASSIUM PERMANGANATE (GOSSELIN, CLINICAL TOXICOLOGY OF COMMERCIAL PRODUCTS). POSITIVE PRESSURE VENTILATION OF THE LUNGS WITH OXYGEN MAY BE NECESSARY WHEN RESPIRATION IS ARRESTED (RECOGNITION AND MANAGEMENT OF PESTICIDE POISONINGS, 3RD EDITION). GASTRIC LAVAGE AND OXYGEN SHOULD BE ADMINISTERED BY QUALIFIED MEDICAL PERSONNEL.

ANTIDOTE: THE FOLLOWING ANTIDOTE HAS BEEN RECOMMENDED. HOWEVER, THE DECISION AS TO WHETHER THE SEVERITY OF POISONING REQUIRES ADMINISTRATION OF ANY ANTIDOTE AND ACTUAL DOSE REQUIRED SHOULD BE MADE BY QUALIFIED MEDICAL PERSONNEL.

NICOTINE: (TO CONTROL THE SYMPTOMS OF PARASYMPATHETIC OVERSTIMULATION.) GIVE ATROPINE IN MAXIMUM DOSES (2 MG INTRAMUSCULARLY, AND REPEAT EVERY 3-8 MINUTES UNTIL SIGNS OF ATROPINIZATION APPEAR (FLUSHED FACE, DRY MOUTH, WIDELY DILATED PUPILS, FAST PULSE). REPEAT 2 MG OF ATROPINE FREQUENTLY TO MAINTAIN MARKED SIGNS OF ATROPINIZATION. AS MUCH AS 12 MG OF ATROPINE HAS BEEN GIVEN SAFELY IN THE FIRST 2 HOURS. INTERRUPTION OF ATROPINE THERAPY MAY BE RAPIDLY FOLLOWED BY FATAL PULMONARY EDEMA OR RESPIRATORY FAILURE. GIVE PHENTOLAMINE, 1-5 MG INTRAMUSCULARLY OR INTRAVENOUSLY, TO CONTROL SIGNS OF SYMPATHETIC HYPERACTIVITY, SUCH AS HYPERTENSION (DREISBACH, HANDBOOK OF POISONING, 11TH ED.). ANTIDOTE SHOULD BE ADMINISTERED BY QUALIFIED MEDICAL PERSONNEL.

REACTIVITY

REACTIVITY: NORMALLY STABLE BUT MAY BECOME UNSTABLE AT ELEVATED TEMPERATURES AND PRESSURE.
REACTS VIOLENTLY WITH STRONG OXIDANTS AND ACIDS, GIVING OFF TOXIC AND/OR IRRITATING FUMES.

INCOMPATIBILITIES: STRONG OXIDIZERS: VIOLENT REACTION.

DECOMPOSITION: THERMAL DECOMPOSITION PRODUCTS MAY INCLUDE TOXIC OXIDES OF CARBON AND NITROGEN.

POLYMERIZATION: HAZARDOUS POLYMERIZATION HAS NOT BEEN REPORTED TO OCCUR UNDER NORMAL TEMPERATURES AND PRESSURES.

STORAGE AND DISPOSAL

OBSERVE ALL FEDERAL, STATE AND LOCAL REGULATIONS WHEN STORING OR DISPOSING OF THIS SUBSTANCE. FOR ASSISTANCE, CONTACT THE DISTRICT DIRECTOR OF THE ENVIRONMENTAL PROTECTION AGENCY.

STORAGE

THRESHOLD PLANNING QUANTITY (TPQ): THE SUPERFUND AMENDMENTS AND REAUTHORIZATION ACT (SARA) SECTION 302 REQUIRES THAT EACH FACILITY WHERE ANY EXTREMELY HAZARDOUS SUBSTANCE IS PRESENT IN A QUANTITY EQUAL TO OR GREATER THAN THE TPQ ESTABLISHED FOR THAT SUBSTANCE NOTIFY THE STATE EMERGENCY RESPONSE COMMISSION FOR THE STATE IN WHICH IT IS LOCATED. SECTION 303 OF SARA REQUIRES THESE FACILITIES TO PARTICIPATE IN LOCAL EMERGENCY RESPONSE PLANNING (40 CFR 355.30).

CONDITIONS TO AVOID

MAY BURN BUT DOES NOT IGNITE READILY. CONTAINERS MAY EXPLODE IN HEAT OF FIRE.

SPILL AND LEAK PROCEDURES

SOIL SPILL: USE CEMENT POWDER OR FLY ASH TO ABSORB LIQUID MASS. DIKE FLOW OF SPILLED MATERIAL USING SOIL OR SANDBAGS OR FOAMED BARRIERS SUCH AS POLYURETHANE OR CONCRETE.

AIR SPILL: WATER USED TO KNOCK DOWN VAPORS MAY BECOME CORROSIVE OR TOXIC AND SHOULD BE CONTAINED PROPERLY FOR LATER DISPOSAL.

WATER SPILL: THE CALIFORNIA SAFE DRINKING WATER AND TOXIC ENFORCEMENT ACT OF 1986 (PROPOSITION 65) PROHIBITS CONTAMINATING ANY KNOWN SOURCE OF DRINKING WATER WITH SUBSTANCES KNOWN TO CAUSE CANCER AND/OR REPRODUCTIVE TOXICITY.

OCCUPATIONAL SPILL: DO NOT TOUCH SPILLED MATERIAL. STOP LEAK IF YOU CAN DO IT WITHOUT RISK. USE WATER SPRAY TO REDUCE VAPORS. FOR SMALL SPILLS, TAKE UP WITH SAND OR OTHER ABSORBENT MATERIAL AND PLACE INTO CONTAINERS FOR LATER DISPOSAL. FOR SMALL DRY SPILLS, WITH A CLEAN SHOVEL PLACE MATERIAL INTO CLEAN, DRY CONTAINERS AND COVER. MOVE CONTAINERS FROM SPILL AREA. FOR LARGER SPILLS, DIKE FAR AHEAD OF SPILL FOR LATER DISPOSAL. KEEP UNNECESSARY PEOPLE AWAY. ISOLATE HAZARD AREA AND DENY ENTRY. VENTILATE CLOSED SPACES BEFORE ENTERING.
REPORTABLE QUANTITY (RQ): 100 POUNDS THE SUPERFUND AMENDMENTS AND REAUTHORIZATION ACT (SARA) SECTION 304 REQUIRES THAT A RELEASE EQUAL TO OR GREATER THAN THE REPORTABLE QUANTITY FOR THIS SUBSTANCE BE IMMEDIATELY REPORTED TO THE LOCAL EMERGENCY PLANNING COMMITTEE AND THE STATE EMERGENCY RESPONSE COMMISSION (40 CFR 355.40). IF THE RELEASE OF THIS SUBSTANCE IS REPORTABLE UNDER CERCLA SECTION 103, THE NATIONAL RESPONSE CENTER MUST BE NOTIFIED IMMEDIATELY AT (800) 424-8802 OR (202) 426-2675 IN THE METROPOLITAN WASHINGTON, D.C. AREA (40 CFR 302.6).

PROTECTIVE EQUIPMENT

VENTILATION: PROVIDE LOCAL EXHAUST OR PROCESS ENCLOSURE VENTILATION TO MEET PUBLISHED EXPOSURE LIMITS.

RESPIRATOR: THE FOLLOWING RESPIRATORS AND MAXIMUM USE CONCENTRATIONS ARE RECOMMENDATIONS BY THE U.S. DEPARTMENT OF HEALTH AND HUMAN SERVICES, NIOSH POCKET GUIDE TO CHEMICAL HAZARDS; NIOSH CRITERIA DOCUMENTS OR BY THE U.S. DEPARTMENT OF LABOR, 29 CFR 1910 SUBPART Z. THE SPECIFIC RESPIRATOR SELECTED MUST BE BASED ON CONTAMINATION LEVELS FOUND IN THE WORK PLACE, MUST NOT EXCEED THE WORKING LIMITS OF THE RESPIRATOR AND BE JOINTLY APPROVED BY THE NATIONAL INSTITUTE FOR OCCUPATIONAL SAFETY AND HEALTH AND THE MINE SAFETY AND HEALTH ADMINISTRATION (NIOSH-MSHA).

NICOTINE:

5 MG/M3- ANY SUPPLIED-AIR RESPIRATOR. ANY SELF-CONTAINED BREATHING APPARATUS.

12.5 MG/M3- ANY SUPPLIED-AIR RESPIRATOR OPERATED IN A CONTINUOUS FLOW MODE.

25 MG/M3- ANY SELF-CONTAINED BREATHING APPARATUS WITH FULL FACEPIECE. ANY SUPPLIED-AIR RESPIRATOR WITH FULL FACEPIECE. ANY SUPPLIED-AIR RESPIRATOR WITH TIGHT-FITTING FACEPIECE OPERATED IN A CONTINUOUS FLOW MODE.

35 MG/M3- ANY SUPPLIED-AIR RESPIRATOR WITH A HALF-MASK AND OPERATED IN A PRESSURE-DEMAND OR OTHER POSITIVE-PRESSURE MODE.

ESCAPE- ANY AIR-PURIFYING FULL FACEPIECE RESPIRATOR (GAS MASK) WITH CHIN-STYLE OR FRONT- OR BACK-MOUNTED ORGANIC VAPOR CANISTER. ANY APPROPRIATE ESCAPE-TYPE SELF-CONTAINED BREATHING APPARATUS.

FOR FIREFIGHTING AND OTHER IMMEDIATELY DANGEROUS TO LIFE OR HEALTH CONDITIONS:

SELF-CONTAINED BREATHING APPARATUS WITH FULL FACEPIECE OPERATED IN PRESSURE-DEMAND OR OTHER POSITIVE PRESSURE MODE.

SUPPLIED-AIR RESPIRATOR WITH FULL FACEPIECE AND OPERATED IN PRESSURE-DEMAND OR OTHER POSITIVE PRESSURE MODE IN COMBINATION WITH AN

AUXILIARY SELF-CONTAINED BREATHING APPARATUS OPERATED IN PRESSURE-DEMAND OR OTHER POSITIVE PRESSURE MODE.

CLOTHING: EMPLOYEE MUST WEAR APPROPRIATE PROTECTIVE (IMPERVIOUS) CLOTHING AND EQUIPMENT TO PREVENT ANY POSSIBILITY OF SKIN CONTACT WITH THIS SUBSTANCE.

GLOVES: EMPLOYEE MUST WEAR APPROPRIATE PROTECTIVE GLOVES TO PREVENT CONTACT WITH THIS SUBSTANCE.

EYE PROTECTION: EMPLOYEE MUST WEAR SPLASH-PROOF OR DUST-RESISTANT SAFETY GOGGLES AND A FACESHIELD TO PREVENT CONTACT WITH THIS SUBSTANCE.

EMERGENCY WASH FACILITIES: WHERE THERE IS ANY POSSIBILITY THAT AN EMPLOYEE'S EYES AND/OR SKIN MAY BE EXPOSED TO THIS SUBSTANCE, THE EMPLOYER SHOULD PROVIDE AN EYE WASH FOUNTAIN AND QUICK DRENCH SHOWER WITHIN THE IMMEDIATE WORK AREA FOR EMERGENCY USE.

AUTHORIZED BY- OCCUPATIONAL HEALTH SERVICES, INC.

CREATION DATE: 10/04/89 ***REVISION DATE:*** 07/10/90

MATERIAL SAFETY DATA SHEET

OCCUPATIONAL HEALTH SERVICES, INC.
AGRICULTURE AND PESTICIDE DIVISION
450 SEVENTH AVENUE, SUITE 2407
NEW YORK, NEW YORK 10123
1-800-445-MSDS OR (212) 967-1100

EMERGENCY CONTACT:
JOHN S. BRANSFORD, JR. (615) 292-1180

SUBSTANCE IDENTIFICATION

CAS-NUMBER 29790-52-1

SUBSTANCE: **NICOTINE SALICYLATE**

TRADE NAMES/SYNONYMS: NICOTINE MONOSALICYLATE; EUDERMOL; 1-METHYL-2-(3-PYRIDYL)PYRROLIDINE SALICYLATE; PST16450

CHEMICAL FAMILY: PYRIDINE

MOLECULAR FORMULA: C10-H14-N2.C7-H6-O3

MOLECULAR WEIGHT: 300.39

CERCLA RATINGS (SCALE 0-3): HEALTH=3 FIRE=0 REACTIVITY=0 PERSISTENCE=2

NFPA RATINGS (SCALE 0-4): HEALTH=3 FIRE=0 REACTIVITY=0

COMPONENTS AND CONTAMINANTS

COMPONENT: NICOTINE SALICYLATE ***PERCENT:*** 100
CAS# 29790-52-1

OTHER CONTAMINANTS: NONE

EXPOSURE LIMITS: NO OCCUPATIONAL EXPOSURE LIMITS ESTABLISHED BY OSHA, ACGIH, OR NIOSH.

PHYSICAL DATA

DESCRIPTION: WHITE HEXAGONAL PLATES ***MELTING POINT:*** 244 F (118 C)

SOLUBILITY IN WATER: SOLUBLE

SOLVENT SOLUBILITY: ALCOHOL, ETHER

FIRE AND EXPLOSION DATA

FIRE AND EXPLOSION HAZARD: NEGLIGIBLE FIRE HAZARD WHEN EXPOSED TO HEAT OR FLAME.

FLASH POINT: COMBUSTIBLE

FIREFIGHTING MEDIA: DRY CHEMICAL, CARBON DIOXIDE, HALON, WATER SPRAY OR STANDARD FOAM (1987 EMERGENCY RESPONSE GUIDEBOOK, DOT P 5800.4). FOR LARGER FIRES, USE WATER SPRAY, FOG OR STANDARD FOAM (1987 EMERGENCY RESPONSE GUIDEBOOK, DOT P 5800.4).

FIREFIGHTING: MOVE CONTAINERS FROM FIRE AREA IF POSSIBLE (1987 EMERGENCY RESPONSE GUIDEBOOK, DOT P 5800.4, GUIDE PAGE 53).
USE AGENTS SUITABLE FOR TYPE OF FIRE. USE WATER IN FLOODING AMOUNTS AS FOG. AVOID BREATHING POISONOUS VAPORS, KEEP UPWIND.

TRANSPORTATION DATA

DEPARTMENT OF TRANSPORTATION HAZARD CLASSIFICATION 49 CFR 172.101: POISON B

DEPARTMENT OF TRANSPORTATION LABELING REQUIREMENTS 49 CFR 172.101 AND SUBPART E: POISON

DEPARTMENT OF TRANSPORTATION PACKAGING REQUIREMENTS: 49 CFR 173.365 EXCEPTIONS: 49 CFR 173.364

TOXICITY

NICOTINE SALICYLATE: CARCINOGEN STATUS: NONE. ACUTE TOXICITY LEVEL: NO DATA AVAILABLE. TARGET EFFECTS: POISONING MAY AFFECT THE CENTRAL NERVOUS, NEUROMUSCULAR, CARDIOVASCULAR, AND RESPIRATORY SYSTEMS.

HEALTH EFFECTS AND FIRST AID

INHALATION: NICOTINE SALICYLATE: IRRITANT/NEUROTOXIN. **ACUTE EXPOSURE**- MAY CAUSE RESPIRATORY IRRITATION AND SYSTEMIC EFFECTS SIMILAR TO INGESTION: TRANSIENT STIMULATION AND SUBSEQUENT DEPRESSION OR PARALYSIS OF CENTRAL NERVOUS SYSTEM, ALL PERIPHERAL AUTONOMIC GANGLIA AND MOTOR END-PLATES IN SKELETAL MUSCLES. GASTROINTESTINAL SYMPTOMS MAY BE LESS SEVERE THAN BY INGESTION EXPOSURE. **CHRONIC EXPOSURE**- REPEATED EXPOSURE MAY RESULT IN INCREASED TOLERANCE OR HABITUALIZATION TO NICOTINE. PROLONGED EXPOSURE MAY CAUSE RESPIRATORY IRRITATION, AND CARDIOVASCULAR AND CENTRAL NERVOUS SYSTEM DAMAGE.

FIRST AID- REMOVE FROM EXPOSURE AREA TO FRESH AIR IMMEDIATELY. IF BREATHING HAS STOPPED, GIVE ARTIFICIAL RESPIRATION. MAINTAIN AIRWAY AND BLOOD PRESSURE AND ADMINISTER OXYGEN IF AVAILABLE. KEEP AFFECTED PERSON WARM AND AT REST. TREAT SYMPTOMATICALLY AND SUPPORTIVELY. ADMINISTRATION OF OXYGEN SHOULD BE PERFORMED BY QUALIFIED PERSONNEL. GET MEDICAL ATTENTION IMMEDIATELY.

SKIN CONTACT: NICOTINE SALICYLATE: IRRITANT/NEUROTOXIN. **ACUTE EXPOSURE**- MAY CAUSE LOCAL IRRITATION AND SYSTEMIC EFFECTS SIMILAR TO INHALATION EXPOSURE. NICOTINE SALTS ARE LESS READILY ABSORBED THROUGH INTACT SKIN THAN IS NICOTINE.

CHRONIC EXPOSURE- MAY CAUSE DERMATITIS AND EFFECTS SIMILAR TO CHRONIC INGESTION.

FIRST AID- REMOVE CONTAMINATED CLOTHING AND SHOES IMMEDIATELY. WASH AFFECTED AREA WITH SOAP OR MILD DETERGENT AND LARGE AMOUNTS OF WATER UNTIL NO EVIDENCE OF CHEMICAL REMAINS (APPROXIMATELY 15-20 MINUTES). GET MEDICAL ATTENTION IMMEDIATELY.

EYE CONTACT: NICOTINE SALICYLATE: IRRITANT. **ACUTE EXPOSURE**- PARTICULATES IN THE EYE MAY CAUSE IRRITATION, LACRIMATION, AND CONJUNCTIVITIS. **CHRONIC EXPOSURE**- CONJUNCTIVITIS MAY OCCUR.

FIRST AID- WASH EYES IMMEDIATELY WITH LARGE AMOUNTS OF WATER OR NORMAL SALINE, OCCASIONALLY LIFTING UPPER AND LOWER LIDS, UNTIL NO EVIDENCE OF CHEMICAL REMAINS (APPROXIMATELY 15-20 MINUTES). GET MEDICAL ATTENTION IMMEDIATELY.

INGESTION: NICOTINE SALICYLATE: NEUROTOXIN. **ACUTE EXPOSURE**- INGESTION MAY CAUSE A BURNING PAIN IN THE MOUTH AND THROAT, WITH SALIVATION, NAUSEA, ABDOMINAL PAIN, VOMITING, AND DIARRHEA, FOLLOWED BY AGITATION, HEADACHE, SWEATING, DIZZINESS, AUDITORY AND VISUAL DISTURBANCES, CONFUSION, WEAKNESS, INCOORDINATION, AND POSSIBLY COLLAPSE. RESPIRATION INITIALLY IS DEEP AND RAPID, WITH HYPERTENSION, SLOW PULSE, AND CARDIAC FIBRILLATION. CENTRAL NERVOUS SYSTEM EXCITATION, TREMORS AND POSSIBLE CONVULSIONS ARE FOLLOWED BY CENTRAL NERVOUS SYSTEM DEPRESSION, WITH MYDRIASIS, HYPOTENSION, AND RAPID OR IRREGULAR PULSE. FAINTNESS, PROSTRATION, CYANOSIS, AND DYSPNEA MAY PROGRESS TO COLLAPSE AND DEATH FROM RESPIRATORY PARALYSIS WITHIN A FEW MINUTES TO 4 HOURS OF INGESTION. NICOTINE IS ELIMINATED FROM THE BODY WITHIN 16 HOURS; IF VICTIM'S RESPIRATION CAN BE MAINTAINED OVER THIS PERIOD, SURVIVAL WITH FULL RECOVERY GENERALLY FOLLOWS.

CHRONIC EXPOSURE- REPEATED EXPOSURE CAN RESULT IN INCREASED TOLERANCE FOR NICOTINE AND POSSIBLE HABITUALIZATION. PROLONGED EXPOSURE MAY CAUSE CARDIOVASCULAR AND CENTRAL NERVOUS SYSTEM DAMAGE.

FIRST AID- GIVE ACTIVATED CHARCOAL TO ADSORB NICOTINE NOT ALREADY EXPELLED BY VOMITING. REMOVE BY THOROUGH GASTRIC LAVAGE WITH TAP WATER CONTAINING ACTIVATED CHARCOAL (DREISBACH, HANDBOOK OF POISONING, 11TH ED.) OR 0.05% SOLUTION OF TANNIC ACID OR 1:1500 SOLUTION OF POTASSIUM PERMANGANATE (GOSSELIN, CLINICAL TOXICOLOGY OF COMMERCIAL PRODUCTS). POSITIVE PRESSURE VENTILATION OF THE LUNGS WITH OXYGEN MAY BE NECESSARY WHEN RESPIRATION IS ARRESTED (RECOGNITION AND MANAGEMENT OF PESTICIDE POISONINGS, 3RD EDITION). GASTRIC LAVAGE AND OXYGEN SHOULD BE ADMINISTERED BY QUALIFIED MEDICAL PERSONNEL.

ANTIDOTE: THE FOLLOWING ANTIDOTE HAS BEEN RECOMMENDED. HOWEVER, THE DECISION AS TO WHETHER THE SEVERITY OF POISONING REQUIRES ADMINISTRATION OF ANY ANTIDOTE AND ACTUAL DOSE REQUIRED SHOULD BE MADE BY QUALIFIED MEDICAL PERSONNEL.

NICOTINE: (TO CONTROL THE SYMPTOMS OF PARASYMPATHETIC OVERSTIMULATION.) GIVE ATROPINE IN MAXIMUM DOSES (2 MG INTRAMUSCULARLY, AND REPEAT EVERY 3-8 MINUTES UNTIL SIGNS OF ATROPINIZATION APPEAR (FLUSHED FACE, DRY MOUTH, WIDELY DILATED PUPILS, FAST PULSE). REPEAT 2 MG OF ATROPINE FREQUENTLY TO MAINTAIN MARKED

SIGNS OF ATROPINIZATION. AS MUCH AS 12 MG OF ATROPINE HAS BEEN GIVEN SAFELY IN THE FIRST 2 HOURS. INTERRUPTION OF ATROPINE THERAPY MAY BE RAPIDLY FOLLOWED BY FATAL PULMONARY EDEMA OR RESPIRATORY FAILURE. GIVE PHENTOLAMINE, 1-5 MG INTRAMUSCULARLY OR INTRAVENOUSLY, TO CONTROL SIGNS OF SYMPATHETIC HYPERACTIVITY, SUCH AS HYPERTENSION (DREISBACH, HANDBOOK OF POISONING, 11TH ED.). ANTIDOTE SHOULD BE ADMINISTERED BY QUALIFIED MEDICAL PERSONNEL.

REACTIVITY

REACTIVITY: STABLE UNDER NORMAL TEMPERATURES AND PRESSURES.
INCOMPATIBILITIES: NICOTINE SALICYLATE: STRONG OXIDIZERS: VIOLENT REACTION.
DECOMPOSITION: THERMAL DECOMPOSITION PRODUCTS MAY INCLUDE TOXIC OXIDES OF CARBON AND NITROGEN.
POLYMERIZATION: HAZARDOUS POLYMERIZATION HAS NOT BEEN REPORTED TO OCCUR UNDER NORMAL TEMPERATURES AND PRESSURES.

CONDITIONS TO AVOID

MAY BURN BUT DOES NOT IGNITE READILY.

SPILL AND LEAK PROCEDURES

OCCUPATIONAL SPILL: DO NOT TOUCH SPILLED MATERIAL. STOP LEAK IF YOU CAN DO IT WITHOUT RISK. FOR SMALL SPILLS, TAKE UP WITH SAND OR OTHER ABSORBENT MATERIAL AND PLACE INTO CONTAINERS FOR LATER DISPOSAL. FOR SMALL DRY SPILLS, WITH A CLEAN SHOVEL PLACE MATERIAL INTO CLEAN, DRY CONTAINER AND COVER. MOVE CONTAINERS FROM SPILL AREA. FOR LARGER SPILLS, DIKE FAR AHEAD OF SPILL FOR LATER DISPOSAL. KEEP UNNECESSARY PEOPLE AWAY. ISOLATE HAZARD AREA AND DENY ENTRY.

PROTECTIVE EQUIPMENT

VENTILATION: PROVIDE LOCAL EXHAUST OR PROCESS ENCLOSURE VENTILATION SYSTEM.
RESPIRATOR: THE FOLLOWING RESPIRATORS ARE RECOMMENDED BASED ON INFORMATION FOUND IN THE PHYSICAL DATA, TOXICITY AND HEALTH EFFECTS SECTIONS. THEY ARE RANKED IN ORDER FROM MINIMUM TO MAXIMUM RESPIRATORY PROTECTION. THE SPECIFIC RESPIRATOR SELECTED MUST BE BASED ON CONTAMINATION LEVELS FOUND IN THE WORK PLACE, MUST NOT EXCEED THE WORKING LIMITS OF THE RESPIRATOR AND BE JOINTLY APPROVED BY THE NATIONAL INSTITUTE FOR OCCUPATIONAL SAFETY AND HEALTH AND THE MINE SAFETY AND HEALTH ADMINISTRATION (NIOSH-MSHA).
TYPE 'C' SUPPLIED-AIR RESPIRATOR WITH A FULL FACEPIECE OPERATED IN PRESSURE-DEMAND OR OTHER POSITIVE PRESSURE MODE OR WITH A FULL FACEPIECE, HELMET OR HOOD OPERATED IN CONTINOUS-FLOW MODE.
SELF-CONTAINED BREATHING APPARATUS WITH A FULL FACEPIECE OPERATED IN PRESSURE-DEMAND OR OTHER POSITIVE PRESSURE MODE.
CLOTHING: EMPLOYEE MUST WEAR APPROPRIATE PROTECTIVE (IMPERVIOUS) CLOTHING AND EQUIPMENT TO PREVENT ANY POSSIBILITY OF SKIN CONTACT WITH THIS SUBSTANCE.
GLOVES: EMPLOYEE MUST WEAR APPROPRIATE PROTECTIVE GLOVES TO PREVENT CONTACT WITH THIS SUBSTANCE.
EYE PROTECTION: EMPLOYEE MUST WEAR SPLASH-PROOF OR DUST-RESISTANT SAFETY GOGGLES AND A FACESHIELD TO PREVENT CONTACT WITH THIS SUBSTANCE.
EMERGENCY WASH FACILITIES: WHERE THERE IS ANY POSSIBILITY THAT AN EMPLOYEE'S EYES AND/OR SKIN MAY BE EXPOSED TO THIS SUBSTANCE, THE EMPLOYER SHOULD PROVIDE AN EYE WASH FOUNTAIN AND QUICK DRENCH SHOWER WITHIN THE IMMEDIATE WORK AREA FOR EMERGENCY USE.

AUTHORIZED BY- OCCUPATIONAL HEALTH SERVICES, INC.
CREATION DATE: 10/04/89 ***REVISION DATE:*** 05/11/90

MATERIAL SAFETY DATA SHEET

OCCUPATIONAL HEALTH SERVICES, INC.
AGRICULTURE AND PESTICIDE DIVISION
450 SEVENTH AVENUE, SUITE 2407
NEW YORK, NEW YORK 10123
1-800-445-MSDS OR (212) 967-1100

EMERGENCY CONTACT:
JOHN S. BRANSFORD, JR. (615) 292-1180

SUBSTANCE IDENTIFICATION

CAS-NUMBER 65-30-5
SUBSTANCE: NICOTINE SULFATE, LIQUID
TRADE NAMES/SYNONYMS: BLACK LEAF 40; NICOTINE SULFATE SOLUTION; NICOTINE SULFATE; PST16459
CHEMICAL FAMILY: PYRIDINE
MOLECULAR FORMULA: C20-H28-N4.H2-S-O4
MOLECULAR WEIGHT: 418.56
CERCLA RATINGS (SCALE 0-3): HEALTH=3 FIRE=0 REACTIVITY=0 PERSISTENCE=2
NFPA RATINGS (SCALE 0-4): HEALTH=3 FIRE=0 REACTIVITY=0

COMPONENTS AND CONTAMINANTS

COMPONENT: NICOTINE SULFATE ***PERCENT:*** 40
COMPONENT: WATER ***PERCENT:*** 60
OTHER CONTAMINANTS: NONE
EXPOSURE LIMITS: NICOTINE SULFATE: NO OCCUPATIONAL EXPOSURE LIMITS ESTABLISHED BY OSHA, ACGIH, OR NIOSH.
100/10,000 POUNDS SARA SECTION 302 THRESHOLD PLANNING QUANTITY 1 POUND SARA SECTION 304 REPORTABLE QUANTITY

PHYSICAL DATA

DESCRIPTION: LIGHT BROWN SOLUTION WITH TOBACCO ODOR
SOLUBILITY IN WATER: SOLUBLE
SOLVENT SOLUBILITY: ALCOHOL, ETHER

FIRE AND EXPLOSION DATA

FIRE AND EXPLOSION HAZARD: NEGLIGIBLE FIRE HAZARD WHEN EXPOSED TO HEAT OR FLAME.
FIREFIGHTING MEDIA: DRY CHEMICAL, CARBON DIOXIDE, HALON, WATER SPRAY OR STANDARD FOAM (1987 EMERGENCY RESPONSE GUIDEBOOK, DOT P 5800.4).
FOR LARGER FIRES, USE WATER SPRAY, FOG OR STANDARD FOAM (1987 EMERGENCY RESPONSE GUIDEBOOK, DOT P 5800.4).
FIREFIGHTING: MOVE CONTAINERS FROM FIRE AREA IF POSSIBLE. FIGHT FIRE FROM MAXIMUM DISTANCE. STAY AWAY FROM STORAGE TANK ENDS. DIKE FIRE CONTROL WATER FOR LATER DISPOSAL. DO NOT SCATTER MATERIAL (1987 EMERGENCY RESPONSE GUIDEBOOK, DOT P 5800.4, GUIDE PAGE 55).
USE AGENTS SUITABLE FOR TYPE OF FIRE. USE WATER IN FLOODING AMOUNTS AS FOG. AVOID BREATHING POISONOUS VAPORS, KEEP UPWIND.

TRANSPORTATION DATA

DEPARTMENT OF TRANSPORTATION HAZARD CLASSIFICATION 49 CFR 172.101: POISON B
DEPARTMENT OF TRANSPORTATION LABELING REQUIREMENTS 49 CFR 172.101 AND SUBPART E: POISON
DEPARTMENT OF TRANSPORTATION PACKAGING REQUIREMENTS: 49 CFR 173.346 EXCEPTIONS: 49 CFR 173.345

TOXICITY

NICOTINE SULFATE, LIQUID: TOXICITY DATA: 22 MG/M3 INHALATION-RAT LC50; 50 MG/KG SKIN-RABBIT LD50; 285 MG/KG SKIN-RAT LD50; 50 MG/KG ORAL-RAT LD50; 8550 UG/KG ORAL-MOUSE LD50; 29 MG/KG INTRAPERITONEAL-RAT LD90; 10200 UG/KG INTRAPERITONEAL-MOUSE LD50; 20 MG/KG INTRAPERITONEAL-CAT LD50. CARCINOGEN STATUS: NONE. LOCAL EFFECTS: IRRITANT- INHALATION, SKIN, AND EYES. ACUTE TOXICITY LEVEL: HIGHLY TOXIC BY INHALATION, DERMAL ABSORPTION, AND INGESTION. TARGET EFFECTS: NEUROTOXIN. POISONING MAY AFFECT THE CENTRAL NERVOUS SYSTEM, NEUROMUSCULAR, CARDIOVASCULAR AND RESPIRATORY SYSTEMS.

HEALTH EFFECTS AND FIRST AID

INHALATION: NICOTINE SULFATE, LIQUID: IRRITANT/NEUROTOXIN. **ACUTE EXPOSURE-** MAY CAUSE RESPIRATORY IRRITATION AND MAY CAUSE SYSTEMIC EFFECTS INCLUDING TRANSIENT STIMULATION AND SUBSEQUENT DEPRESSION OF THE CENTRAL AND PERIPHERAL NERVOUS SYSTEMS. **CHRONIC EXPOSURE-** REPEATED EXPOSURE MAY RESULT IN INCREASED TOLERANCE OR HABITUALIZATION TO NICOTINE. PROLONGED EXPOSURE MAY CAUSE RESPIRATORY IRRITATION, AND CARDIOVASCULAR AND CENTRAL NERVOUS SYSTEM DAMAGE.
FIRST AID- REMOVE FROM EXPOSURE AREA TO FRESH AIR IMMEDIATELY. IF BREATHING HAS STOPPED, GIVE ARTIFICIAL RESPIRATION. MAINTAIN AIRWAY AND BLOOD PRESSURE AND ADMINISTER OXYGEN IF AVAILABLE. KEEP AFFECTED PERSON WARM AND AT REST. TREAT SYMPTOMATICALLY AND SUPPORTIVELY. ADMINISTRATION OF OXYGEN SHOULD BE PERFORMED BY QUALIFIED PERSONNEL. GET MEDICAL ATTENTION IMMEDIATELY.

SKIN CONTACT: NICOTINE SULFATE, LIQUID: IRRITANT/NEUROTOXIN/HIGHLY TOXIC. **ACUTE EXPOSURE-** MAY CAUSE LOCAL IRRITATION AND SYSTEMIC EFFECTS INCLUDING TRANSIENT STIMULATION AND SUBSEQUENT DEPRESSION OF THE CENTRAL AND PERIPHERAL NERVOUS SYSTEMS. **CHRONIC EXPOSURE-** MAY CAUSE DERMATITIS.

FIRST AID- REMOVE CONTAMINATED CLOTHING AND SHOES IMMEDIATELY. WASH AFFECTED AREA WITH SOAP OR MILD DETERGENT AND LARGE AMOUNTS OF WATER UNTIL NO EVIDENCE OF CHEMICAL REMAINS (APPROXIMATELY 15-20 MINUTES). GET MEDICAL ATTENTION IMMEDIATELY.

EYE CONTACT: NICOTINE SULFATE, LIQUID: IRRITANT. **ACUTE EXPOSURE**- MAY CAUSE IRRITATION, LACRIMATION, AND CONJUNCTIVITIS. **CHRONIC EXPOSURE**- PROLONGED OR REPEATED EXPOSURE MAY CAUSE CONJUNCTIVITIS.

FIRST AID- WASH EYES IMMEDIATELY WITH LARGE AMOUNTS OF WATER OR NORMAL SALINE, OCCASIONALLY LIFTING UPPER AND LOWER LIDS, UNTIL NO EVIDENCE OF CHEMICAL REMAINS (APPROXIMATELY 15-20 MINUTES). GET MEDICAL ATTENTION IMMEDIATELY.

INGESTION: NICOTINE SULFATE, LIQUID: NEUROTOXIN/TOXIC. **ACUTE EXPOSURE**- INGESTION MAY CAUSE A BURNING PAIN IN THE MOUTH AND THROAT, SALIVATION, NAUSEA, ABDOMINAL PAIN, VOMITING, AND DIARRHEA, FOLLOWED BY AGITATION, HEADACHE, SWEATING, DIZZINESS, AUDITORY AND VISUAL DISTURBANCES, CONFUSION, WEAKNESS, INCOORDINATION, AND POSSIBLY COLLAPSE. RESPIRATION INITIALLY IS DEEP AND RAPID, WITH HYPERTENSION, SLOW PULSE, AND CARDIAC FIBRILLATION. CENTRAL NERVOUS SYSTEM EXCITATION, TREMORS AND CONVULSIONS MAY BE FOLLOWED BY CENTRAL NERVOUS SYSTEM DEPRESSION, WITH MYDRIASIS, HYPOTENSION, AND RAPID OR IRREGULAR PULSE. FAINTNESS, CYANOSIS, PROSTRATION, AND DYSPNEA MAY PROGRESS TO COLLAPSE AND DEATH FROM RESPIRATORY PARALYSIS WITHIN A FEW MINUTES TO 4 HOURS OF INGESTION. **CHRONIC EXPOSURE**- REPEATED EXPOSURE CAN RESULT IN INCREASED TOLERANCE FOR NICOTINE AND POSSIBLE HABITUALIZATION. PROLONGED EXPOSURE MAY CAUSE CARDIOVASCULAR AND CENTRAL NERVOUS SYSTEM DAMAGE.

FIRST AID- GIVE ACTIVATED CHARCOAL TO ADSORB NICOTINE NOT ALREADY EXPELLED BY VOMITING. REMOVE BY THOROUGH GASTRIC LAVAGE WITH TAP WATER CONTAINING ACTIVATED CHARCOAL (DREISBACH, HANDBOOK OF POISONING, 11TH ED.) OR 0.05% SOLUTION OF TANNIC ACID OR 1:1500 SOLUTION OF POTASSIUM PERMANGANATE (GOSSELIN, CLINICAL TOXICOLOGY OF COMMERCIAL PRODUCTS). POSITIVE PRESSURE VENTILATION OF THE LUNGS WITH OXYGEN MAY BE NECESSARY WHEN RESPIRATION IS ARRESTED (RECOGNITION AND MANAGEMENT OF PESTICIDE POISONINGS, 3RD EDITION). GASTRIC LAVAGE AND OXYGEN SHOULD BE ADMINISTERED BY QUALIFIED MEDICAL PERSONNEL.

ANTIDOTE: THE FOLLOWING ANTIDOTE HAS BEEN RECOMMENDED. HOWEVER, THE DECISION AS TO WHETHER THE SEVERITY OF POISONING REQUIRES ADMINISTRATION OF ANY ANTIDOTE AND ACTUAL DOSE REQUIRED SHOULD BE MADE BY QUALIFIED MEDICAL PERSONNEL.

NICOTINE: (TO CONTROL THE SYMPTOMS OF PARASYMPATHETIC OVERSTIMULATION.) GIVE ATROPINE IN MAXIMUM DOSES (2 MG INTRAMUSCULARLY, AND REPEAT EVERY 3-8 MINUTES UNTIL SIGNS OF ATROPINIZATION APPEAR (FLUSHED FACE, DRY MOUTH, WIDELY DILATED PUPILS, FAST PULSE). REPEAT 2 MG OF ATROPINE FREQUENTLY TO MAINTAIN MARKED SIGNS OF ATROPINIZATION. AS MUCH AS 12 MG OF ATROPINE HAS BEEN GIVEN SAFELY IN THE FIRST 2 HOURS. INTERRUPTION OF ATROPINE THERAPY MAY BE RAPIDLY FOLLOWED BY FATAL PULMONARY EDEMA OR RESPIRATORY FAILURE.

GIVE PHENTOLAMINE, 1-5 MG INTRAMUSCULARLY OR INTRAVENOUSLY, TO CONTROL SIGNS OF SYMPATHETIC HYPERACTIVITY, SUCH AS HYPERTENSION (DREISBACH, HANDBOOK OF POISONING, 11TH ED.). ANTIDOTE SHOULD BE ADMINISTERED BY QUALIFIED MEDICAL PERSONNEL.

REACTIVITY

REACTIVITY: STABLE UNDER NORMAL TEMPERATURES AND PRESSURES.

INCOMPATIBILITIES: NICOTINE SULFATE, LIQUID: STRONG OXIDIZERS: VIOLENT REACTION.

DECOMPOSITION: THERMAL DECOMPOSITION PRODUCTS MAY INCLUDE TOXIC OXIDES OF CARBON, NITROGEN, AND SULFUR.

POLYMERIZATION: HAZARDOUS POLYMERIZATION HAS NOT BEEN REPORTED TO OCCUR UNDER NORMAL TEMPERATURES AND PRESSURES.

STORAGE AND DISPOSAL

OBSERVE ALL FEDERAL, STATE AND LOCAL REGULATIONS WHEN STORING OR DISPOSING OF THIS SUBSTANCE. FOR ASSISTANCE, CONTACT THE DISTRICT DIRECTOR OF THE ENVIRONMENTAL PROTECTION AGENCY.

****STORAGE****

STORE AWAY FROM INCOMPATIBLE SUBSTANCES.

THRESHOLD PLANNING QUANTITY (TPQ): THE SUPERFUND AMENDMENTS AND REAUTHORIZATION ACT (SARA) SECTION 302 REQUIRES THAT EACH FACILITY WHERE ANY EXTREMELY HAZARDOUS SUBSTANCE IS PRESENT IN A QUANTITY EQUAL TO OR GREATER THAN THE TPQ ESTABLISHED FOR THAT SUBSTANCE NOTIFY THE STATE EMERGENCY RESPONSE COMMISSION FOR THE STATE IN WHICH IT IS LOCATED. SECTION 303 OF SARA REQUIRES THESE FACILITIES TO PARTICIPATE IN LOCAL EMERGENCY RESPONSE PLANNING (40 CFR 355.30).

CONDITIONS TO AVOID

MAY BURN BUT DOES NOT IGNITE READILY. CONTAINERS MAY EXPLODE IN HEAT OF FIRE.

SPILL AND LEAK PROCEDURES

OCCUPATIONAL SPILL: DO NOT TOUCH SPILLED MATERIAL. STOP LEAK IF YOU CAN DO IT WITHOUT RISK. USE WATER SPRAY TO REDUCE VAPORS. FOR SMALL SPILLS, TAKE UP WITH SAND OR OTHER ABSORBENT MATERIAL AND PLACE INTO CONTAINERS FOR LATER DISPOSAL. FOR SMALL DRY SPILLS, WITH A CLEAN SHOVEL PLACE MATERIAL INTO CLEAN, DRY CONTAINERS AND COVER. MOVE CONTAINERS FROM SPILL AREA. FOR LARGER SPILLS, DIKE FAR AHEAD OF SPILL FOR LATER DISPOSAL. KEEP UNNECESSARY PEOPLE AWAY. ISOLATE HAZARD AREA AND DENY ENTRY. VENTILATE CLOSED SPACES BEFORE ENTERING.

REPORTABLE QUANTITY (RQ): 1 POUND THE SUPERFUND AMENDMENTS AND REAUTHORIZATION ACT (SARA) SECTION 304 REQUIRES THAT A RELEASE EQUAL TO OR GREATER THAN THE REPORTABLE QUANTITY FOR THIS SUBSTANCE BE IMMEDIATELY REPORTED TO THE LOCAL EMERGENCY PLANNING COMMITTEE AND THE STATE EMERGENCY RESPONSE COMMISSION (40 CFR 355.40). IF THE RELEASE OF THIS SUBSTANCE IS REPORTABLE UNDER CERCLA SECTION 103, THE NATIONAL RESPONSE CENTER MUST BE NOTIFIED IMMEDIATELY AT (800) 424-8802 OR (202) 426-2675 IN THE METROPOLITAN WASHINGTON, D.C. AREA (40 CFR 302.6).

PROTECTIVE EQUIPMENT

VENTILATION: PROVIDE LOCAL EXHAUST OR PROCESS ENCLOSURE VENTILATION SYSTEM.

RESPIRATOR: THE FOLLOWING RESPIRATORS ARE RECOMMENDED BASED ON INFORMATION FOUND IN THE PHYSICAL DATA, TOXICITY AND HEALTH EFFECTS SECTIONS. THEY ARE RANKED IN ORDER FROM MINIMUM TO MAXIMUM RESPIRATORY PROTECTION. THE SPECIFIC RESPIRATOR SELECTED MUST BE BASED ON CONTAMINATION LEVELS FOUND IN THE WORK PLACE, MUST NOT EXCEED THE WORKING LIMITS OF THE RESPIRATOR AND BE JOINTLY APPROVED BY THE NATIONAL INSTITUTE FOR OCCUPATIONAL SAFETY AND HEALTH AND THE MINE SAFETY AND HEALTH ADMINISTRATION (NIOSH-MSHA).

TYPE 'C' SUPPLIED-AIR RESPIRATOR WITH A FULL FACEPIECE OPERATED IN PRESSURE-DEMAND OR OTHER POSITIVE PRESSURE MODE OR WITH A FULL FACEPIECE, HELMET OR HOOD OPERATED IN CONTINOUS-FLOW MODE.

SELF-CONTAINED BREATHING APPARATUS WITH A FULL FACEPIECE OPERATED IN PRESSURE-DEMAND OR OTHER POSITIVE PRESSURE MODE.

FOR FIREFIGHTING AND OTHER IMMEDIATELY DANGEROUS TO LIFE OR HEALTH CONDITIONS:

SELF-CONTAINED BREATHING APPARATUS WITH FULL FACEPIECE OPERATED IN PRESSURE-DEMAND OR OTHER POSITIVE PRESSURE MODE.

SUPPLIED-AIR RESPIRATOR WITH FULL FACEPIECE AND OPERATED IN PRESSURE-DEMAND OR OTHER POSITIVE PRESSURE MODE IN COMBINATION WITH AN AUXILIARY SELF-CONTAINED BREATHING APPARATUS OPERATED IN PRESSURE-DEMAND OR OTHER POSITIVE PRESSURE MODE. ***CLOTHING:*** EMPLOYEE MUST WEAR APPROPRIATE PROTECTIVE (IMPERVIOUS) CLOTHING AND EQUIPMENT TO PREVENT ANY POSSIBILITY OF SKIN CONTACT WITH THIS SUBSTANCE.

GLOVES: EMPLOYEE MUST WEAR APPROPRIATE PROTECTIVE GLOVES TO PREVENT CONTACT WITH THIS SUBSTANCE.

EYE PROTECTION: EMPLOYEE MUST WEAR SPLASH-PROOF OR DUST-RESISTANT SAFETY GOGGLES AND A FACESHIELD TO PREVENT CONTACT WITH THIS SUBSTANCE.

EMERGENCY WASH FACILITIES: WHERE THERE IS ANY POSSIBILITY THAT AN EMPLOYEE'S EYES AND/OR SKIN MAY BE EXPOSED TO THIS SUBSTANCE, THE EMPLOYER SHOULD PROVIDE AN EYE WASH FOUNTAIN AND QUICK DRENCH SHOWER WITHIN THE IMMEDIATE WORK AREA FOR EMERGENCY USE.

AUTHORIZED BY- OCCUPATIONAL HEALTH SERVICES, INC.

CREATION DATE: 10/04/89 ***REVISION DATE:*** 05/18/90

MATERIAL SAFETY DATA SHEET

OCCUPATIONAL HEALTH SERVICES, INC.	EMERGENCY CONTACT:
AGRICULTURE AND PESTICIDE DIVISION	JOHN S. BRANSFORD, JR. (615) 292-1180
450 SEVENTH AVENUE, SUITE 2407	
NEW YORK, NEW YORK 10123	
1-800-445-MSDS OR (212) 967-1100	

SUBSTANCE IDENTIFICATION

CAS-NUMBER 65-30-5
SUBSTANCE: **NICOTINE SULFATE, SOLID**
TRADE NAMES/SYNONYMS: NEUTRAL NICOTINE SULFATE; NICOTINE SULFATE (2:1); 1-METHYL(3-PYRIDYL)-PYRROLIDINE SULFATE; 1-METHYL-2-PYRROLIDINYL PYRIDINE SULFATE; 1-1-METHYL-2-(3-PYRIDYL)-PYRROLIDINE SULFATE; STCC 4921452; UN 1658; PST16460
CHEMICAL FAMILY: PYRIDINE
MOLECULAR FORMULA: (C10-H14-N2)2.H2-S-O4
MOLECULAR WEIGHT: 418.56
CERCLA RATINGS (SCALE 0-3): HEALTH=3 FIRE=0 REACTIVITY=0 PERSISTENCE=2
NFPA RATINGS (SCALE 0-4): HEALTH=3 FIRE=0 REACTIVITY=0

COMPONENTS AND CONTAMINANTS

COMPONENT: NICOTINE SULFATE, SOLID ***PERCENT:*** 100
CAS# 65-30-5
OTHER CONTAMINANTS: NONE
EXPOSURE LIMITS: NICOTINE SULFATE: NO OCCUPATIONAL EXPOSURE LIMITS ESTABLISHED BY OSHA, ACGIH, OR NIOSH.
100/10,000 POUNDS SARA SECTION 302 THRESHOLD PLANNING QUANTITY 1 POUND SARA SECTION 304 REPORTABLE QUANTITY

PHYSICAL DATA

DESCRIPTION: ODORLESS, WHITE TO LIGHT BROWN CRYSTALLINE SOLID WHICH DARKENS ON EXPOSURE TO LIGHT ***MELTING POINT:*** DECOMPOSES
SOLUBILITY IN WATER: SOLUBLE
SOLVENT SOLUBILITY: ALCOHOL, ETHER

FIRE AND EXPLOSION DATA

FIRE AND EXPLOSION HAZARD: NEGLIGIBLE FIRE HAZARD WHEN EXPOSED TO HEAT OR FLAME.
FIREFIGHTING MEDIA: DRY CHEMICAL, CARBON DIOXIDE, HALON, WATER SPRAY OR STANDARD FOAM (1987 EMERGENCY RESPONSE GUIDEBOOK, DOT P 5800.4).
FOR LARGER FIRES, USE WATER SPRAY, FOG OR STANDARD FOAM (1987 EMERGENCY RESPONSE GUIDEBOOK, DOT P 5800.4).
FIREFIGHTING: MOVE CONTAINERS FROM FIRE AREA IF POSSIBLE. FIGHT FIRE FROM MAXIMUM DISTANCE. STAY AWAY FROM STORAGE TANK ENDS. DIKE FIRE CONTROL WATER FOR LATER DISPOSAL. DO NOT SCATTER MATERIAL (1987 EMERGENCY RESPONSE GUIDEBOOK, DOT P 5800.4, GUIDE PAGE 55).
USE AGENTS SUITABLE FOR TYPE OF FIRE. USE WATER IN FLOODING AMOUNTS AS FOG. AVOID BREATHING POISONOUS VAPORS, KEEP UPWIND.

TRANSPORTATION DATA

DEPARTMENT OF TRANSPORTATION HAZARD CLASSIFICATION 49 CFR 172.101: POISON B
DEPARTMENT OF TRANSPORTATION LABELING REQUIREMENTS 49 CFR 172.101 AND SUBPART E: POISON
DEPARTMENT OF TRANSPORTATION PACKAGING REQUIREMENTS: 49 CFR 173.365 EXCEPTIONS: 49 CFR 173.364

TOXICITY

NICOTINE SULFATE, SOLID: TOXICITY DATA: 22 MG/M3 INHALATION-RAT LC50; 50 MG/KG SKIN-RABBIT LD50; 285 MG/KG SKIN-RAT LD50; 50 MG/KG ORAL-RAT LD50; 8550 UG/KG ORAL-MOUSE LD50; 29 MG/KG INTRAPERITONEAL-RAT LD90; 10200 UG/KG INTRAPERITONEAL-MOUSE LD50; 20 MG/KG INTRAPERITONEAL-CAT LD50. CARCINOGEN STATUS: NONE. LOCAL EFFECTS: IRRITANT- INHALATION, SKIN, AND EYE. ACUTE TOXICITY LEVEL: HIGHLY TOXIC BY INHALATION, DERMAL ABSORPTION AND INGESTION. TARGET EFFECTS: NEUROTOXIN. POISONING MAY AFFECT THE CENTRAL NERVOUS SYSTEM, NEUROMUSCULAR, CARDIOVASCULAR AND RESPIRATORY SYSTEMS.

HEALTH EFFECTS AND FIRST AID

INHALATION: NICOTINE SULFATE, SOLID: IRRITANT/NEUROTOXIN. **ACUTE EXPOSURE-** MAY CAUSE RESPIRATORY IRRITATION AND MAY CAUSE SYSTEMIC EFFECTS INCLUDING TRANSIENT STIMULATION AND SUBSEQUENT DEPRESSION OF THE CENTRAL AND PERIPHERAL NERVOUS SYSTEMS. **CHRONIC EXPOSURE-** REPEATED EXPOSURE MAY RESULT IN INCREASED TOLERANCE OR HABITUALIZATION TO NICOTINE. PROLONGED EXPOSURE MAY CAUSE RESPIRATORY IRRITATION, AND CARDIOVASCULAR AND CENTRAL NERVOUS SYSTEM DAMAGE.
FIRST AID- REMOVE FROM EXPOSURE AREA TO FRESH AIR IMMEDIATELY. IF BREATHING HAS STOPPED, GIVE ARTIFICIAL RESPIRATION. MAINTAIN AIRWAY AND BLOOD PRESSURE AND ADMINISTER OXYGEN IF AVAILABLE. KEEP AFFECTED PERSON WARM AND AT REST. TREAT SYMPTOMATICALLY AND SUPPORTIVELY. ADMINISTRATION OF OXYGEN SHOULD BE PERFORMED BY QUALIFIED PERSONNEL. GET MEDICAL ATTENTION IMMEDIATELY.

SKIN CONTACT: NICOTINE SULFATE, SOLID: IRRITANT/NEUROTOXIN/HIGHLY TOXIC. **ACUTE EXPOSURE-** MAY CAUSE LOCAL IRRITATION AND SYSTEMIC EFFECTS INCLUDING TRANSIENT STIMULATION AND SUBSEQUENT DEPRESSION OF THE CENTRAL AND PERIPHERAL NERVOUS SYSTEMS. **CHRONIC EXPOSURE-** MAY CAUSE DERMATITIS.
FIRST AID- REMOVE CONTAMINATED CLOTHING AND SHOES IMMEDIATELY. WASH AFFECTED AREA WITH SOAP OR MILD DETERGENT AND LARGE AMOUNTS OF WATER UNTIL NO EVIDENCE OF CHEMICAL REMAINS (APPROXIMATELY 15-20 MINUTES). GET MEDICAL ATTENTION IMMEDIATELY.

EYE CONTACT: NICOTINE SULFATE, SOLID: IRRITANT. **ACUTE EXPOSURE-** MAY CAUSE IRRITATION, LACRIMATION, AND CONJUNCTIVITIS. **CHRONIC EXPOSURE-** PROLONGED OR REPEATED EXPOSURE MAY CAUSE CONJUNCTIVITIS.
FIRST AID- WASH EYES IMMEDIATELY WITH LARGE AMOUNTS OF WATER OR NORMAL SALINE, OCCASIONALLY LIFTING UPPER AND LOWER LIDS, UNTIL NO EVIDENCE OF CHEMICAL REMAINS (APPROXIMATELY 15-20 MINUTES). GET MEDICAL ATTENTION IMMEDIATELY.

INGESTION: NICOTINE SULFATE, SOLID: NEUROTOXIN/TOXIC. **ACUTE EXPOSURE-** INGESTION MAY CAUSE A BURNING PAIN IN THE MOUTH AND THROAT, SALIVATION, NAUSEA, ABDOMINAL PAIN, VOMITING, AND DIARRHEA, FOLLOWED BY AGITATION, HEADACHE, SWEATING, DIZZINESS, AUDITORY AND VISUAL DISTURBANCES, CONFUSION, WEAKNESS, INCOORDINATION, AND POSSIBLY COLLAPSE. RESPIRATION INITIALLY IS DEEP AND RAPID, WITH HYPERTENSION, SLOW PULSE, AND CARDIAC FIBRILLATION. CENTRAL NERVOUS SYSTEM EXCITATION, TREMORS AND CONVULSIONS MAY BE FOLLOWED BY CENTRAL NERVOUS SYSTEM DEPRESSION, WITH MYDRIASIS, HYPOTENSION, AND RAPID OR IRREGULAR PULSE. FAINTNESS, CYANOSIS, PROSTRATION, AND DYSPNEA MAY PROGRESS TO COLLAPSE AND DEATH FROM RESPIRATORY PARALYSIS WITHIN A FEW MINUTES TO 4 HOURS OF INGESTION. **CHRONIC EXPOSURE-** REPEATED EXPOSURE CAN RESULT IN INCREASED TOLERANCE FOR NICOTINE AND POSSIBLE HABITUALIZATION. PROLONGED EXPOSURE MAY CAUSE CARDIOVASCULAR AND CENTRAL NERVOUS SYSTEM DAMAGE.
FIRST AID- GIVE ACTIVATED CHARCOAL TO ADSORB NICOTINE NOT ALREADY EXPELLED BY VOMITING. REMOVE BY THOROUGH GASTRIC LAVAGE WITH TAP WATER CONTAINING ACTIVATED CHARCOAL (DREISBACH, HANDBOOK OF POISONING, 11TH ED.) OR 0.05% SOLUTION OF TANNIC ACID OR 1:1500 SOLUTION OF POTASSIUM PERMANGANATE (GOSSELIN, CLINICAL TOXICOLOGY OF COMMERCIAL PRODUCTS). POSITIVE PRESSURE VENTILATION OF THE LUNGS WITH OXYGEN MAY BE NECESSARY WHEN RESPIRATION IS ARRESTED (RECOGNITION AND MANAGEMENT OF PESTICIDE POISONINGS, 3RD EDITION). GASTRIC LAVAGE AND OXYGEN SHOULD BE ADMINISTERED BY QUALIFIED MEDICAL PERSONNEL.
ANTIDOTE: THE FOLLOWING ANTIDOTE HAS BEEN RECOMMENDED. HOWEVER, THE DECISION AS TO WHETHER THE SEVERITY OF POISONING REQUIRES ADMINISTRATION OF ANY ANTIDOTE AND ACTUAL DOSE REQUIRED SHOULD BE MADE BY QUALIFIED MEDICAL PERSONNEL.
NICOTINE: (TO CONTROL THE SYMPTOMS OF PARASYMPATHETIC OVERSTIMULATION.) GIVE ATROPINE IN MAXIMUM DOSES (2 MG INTRAMUSCULARLY, AND REPEAT EVERY 3-8 MINUTES UNTIL SIGNS OF ATROPINIZATION APPEAR (FLUSHED FACE, DRY MOUTH, WIDELY DILATED PUPILS, FAST PULSE). REPEAT 2 MG OF ATROPINE FREQUENTLY TO MAINTAIN MARKED SIGNS OF ATROPINIZATION. AS MUCH AS 12 MG OF ATROPINE HAS BEEN GIVEN SAFELY IN THE FIRST 2 HOURS. INTERRUPTION OF ATROPINE THERAPY MAY BE RAPIDLY FOLLOWED BY FATAL PULMONARY EDEMA OR RESPIRATORY FAILURE. GIVE PHENTOLAMINE, 1-5 MG INTRAMUSCULARLY OR INTRAVENOUSLY, TO CONTROL SIGNS OF SYMPATHETIC HYPERACTIVITY, SUCH AS HYPERTENSION (DREISBACH, HANDBOOK OF POISONING, 11TH ED.). ANTIDOTE SHOULD BE ADMINISTERED BY QUALIFIED MEDICAL PERSONNEL.

REACTIVITY

REACTIVITY: STABLE UNDER NORMAL TEMPERATURES AND PRESSURES.
INCOMPATIBILITIES: NICOTINE SULFATE, SOLID: STRONG OXIDIZERS: VIOLENT REACTION.
DECOMPOSITION: THERMAL DECOMPOSITION PRODUCTS MAY INCLUDE TOXIC OXIDES OF CARBON, NITROGEN, AND SULFUR.
POLYMERIZATION: HAZARDOUS POLYMERIZATION HAS NOT BEEN REPORTED TO OCCUR UNDER NORMAL TEMPERATURES AND PRESSURES.

STORAGE AND DISPOSAL

OBSERVE ALL FEDERAL, STATE AND LOCAL REGULATIONS WHEN STORING OR DISPOSING OF THIS SUBSTANCE. FOR ASSISTANCE, CONTACT THE DISTRICT DIRECTOR OF THE ENVIRONMENTAL PROTECTION AGENCY.

****STORAGE****

THRESHOLD PLANNING QUANTITY (TPQ): THE SUPERFUND AMENDMENTS AND REAUTHORIZATION ACT (SARA) SECTION 302 REQUIRES THAT EACH FACILITY

WHERE ANY EXTREMELY HAZARDOUS SUBSTANCE IS PRESENT IN A QUANTITY EQUAL TO OR GREATER THAN THE TPQ ESTABLISHED FOR THAT SUBSTANCE NOTIFY THE STATE EMERGENCY RESPONSE COMMISSION FOR THE STATE IN WHICH IT IS LOCATED. SECTION 303 OF SARA REQUIRES THESE FACILITIES TO PARTICIPATE IN LOCAL EMERGENCY RESPONSE PLANNING (40 CFR 355.30). STORE AWAY FROM INCOMPATIBLE SUBSTANCES.

CONDITIONS TO AVOID

MAY BURN BUT DOES NOT IGNITE READILY. CONTAINERS MAY EXPLODE IN HEAT OF FIRE.

SPILL AND LEAK PROCEDURES

OCCUPATIONAL SPILL: DO NOT TOUCH SPILLED MATERIAL. STOP LEAK IF YOU CAN DO IT WITHOUT RISK. USE WATER SPRAY TO REDUCE VAPORS. FOR SMALL SPILLS, TAKE UP WITH SAND OR OTHER ABSORBENT MATERIAL AND PLACE INTO CONTAINERS FOR LATER DISPOSAL. FOR SMALL DRY SPILLS, WITH A CLEAN SHOVEL PLACE MATERIAL INTO CLEAN, DRY CONTAINERS AND COVER. MOVE CONTAINERS FROM SPILL AREA. FOR LARGER SPILLS, DIKE FAR AHEAD OF SPILL FOR LATER DISPOSAL. KEEP UNNECESSARY PEOPLE AWAY. ISOLATE HAZARD AREA AND DENY ENTRY. VENTILATE CLOSED SPACES BEFORE ENTERING.
REPORTABLE QUANTITY (RQ): 1 POUND THE SUPERFUND AMENDMENTS AND REAUTHORIZATION ACT (SARA) SECTION 304 REQUIRES THAT A RELEASE EQUAL TO OR GREATER THAN THE REPORTABLE QUANTITY FOR THIS SUBSTANCE BE IMMEDIATELY REPORTED TO THE LOCAL EMERGENCY PLANNING COMMITTEE AND THE STATE EMERGENCY RESPONSE COMMISSION (40 CFR 355.40). IF THE RELEASE OF THIS SUBSTANCE IS REPORTABLE UNDER CERCLA SECTION 103, THE NATIONAL RESPONSE CENTER MUST BE NOTIFIED IMMEDIATELY AT (800) 424-8802 OR (202) 426-2675 IN THE METROPOLITAN WASHINGTON, D.C. AREA (40 CFR 302.6).

PROTECTIVE EQUIPMENT

VENTILATION: PROVIDE LOCAL EXHAUST OR PROCESS ENCLOSURE VENTILATION SYSTEM.

RESPIRATOR: THE FOLLOWING RESPIRATORS ARE RECOMMENDED BASED ON INFORMATION FOUND IN THE PHYSICAL DATA, TOXICITY AND HEALTH EFFECTS SECTIONS. THEY ARE RANKED IN ORDER FROM MINIMUM TO MAXIMUM RESPIRATORY PROTECTION. THE SPECIFIC RESPIRATOR SELECTED MUST BE BASED ON CONTAMINATION LEVELS FOUND IN THE WORK PLACE, MUST NOT EXCEED THE WORKING LIMITS OF THE RESPIRATOR AND BE JOINTLY APPROVED BY THE NATIONAL INSTITUTE FOR OCCUPATIONAL SAFETY AND HEALTH AND THE MINE SAFETY AND HEALTH ADMINISTRATION (NIOSH-MSHA).
TYPE 'C' SUPPLIED-AIR RESPIRATOR WITH A FULL FACEPIECE OPERATED IN PRESSURE-DEMAND OR OTHER POSITIVE PRESSURE MODE OR WITH A FULL FACEPIECE, HELMET OR HOOD OPERATED IN CONTINOUS-FLOW MODE.
SELF-CONTAINED BREATHING APPARATUS WITH A FULL FACEPIECE OPERATED IN PRESSURE-DEMAND OR OTHER POSITIVE PRESSURE MODE.
FOR FIREFIGHTING AND OTHER IMMEDIATELY DANGEROUS TO LIFE OR HEALTH CONDITIONS:
SELF-CONTAINED BREATHING APPARATUS WITH FULL FACEPIECE OPERATED IN PRESSURE-DEMAND OR OTHER POSITIVE PRESSURE MODE. SUPPLIED-AIR RESPIRATOR WITH FULL FACEPIECE AND OPERATED IN PRESSURE-DEMAND OR OTHER POSITIVE PRESSURE MODE IN COMBINATION WITH AN AUXILIARY SELF-CONTAINED BREATHING APPARATUS OPERATED IN PRESSURE-DEMAND OR OTHER POSITIVE PRESSURE MODE.

CLOTHING: EMPLOYEE MUST WEAR APPROPRIATE PROTECTIVE (IMPERVIOUS) CLOTHING AND EQUIPMENT TO PREVENT ANY POSSIBILITY OF SKIN CONTACT WITH THIS SUBSTANCE.

GLOVES: EMPLOYEE MUST WEAR APPROPRIATE PROTECTIVE GLOVES TO PREVENT CONTACT WITH THIS SUBSTANCE.

EYE PROTECTION: EMPLOYEE MUST WEAR SPLASH-PROOF OR DUST-RESISTANT SAFETY GOGGLES AND A FACESHIELD TO PREVENT CONTACT WITH THIS SUBSTANCE.
EMERGENCY WASH FACILITIES: WHERE THERE IS ANY POSSIBILITY THAT AN EMPLOYEE'S EYES AND/OR SKIN MAY BE EXPOSED TO THIS SUBSTANCE, THE EMPLOYER SHOULD PROVIDE AN EYE WASH FOUNTAIN AND QUICK DRENCH SHOWER WITHIN THE IMMEDIATE WORK AREA FOR EMERGENCY USE.

AUTHORIZED BY- OCCUPATIONAL HEALTH SERVICES, INC.
CREATION DATE: 10/04/89 ***REVISION DATE:*** 05/17/90

MATERIAL SAFETY DATA SHEET

OCCUPATIONAL HEALTH SERVICES, INC.
AGRICULTURE AND PESTICIDE DIVISION
450 SEVENTH AVENUE, SUITE 2407
NEW YORK, NEW YORK 10123
1-800-445-MSDS OR (212) 967-1100

EMERGENCY CONTACT:
JOHN S. BRANSFORD, JR. (615) 292-1180

SUBSTANCE IDENTIFICATION

CAS-NUMBER 65-31-6

SUBSTANCE: NICOTINE TARTRATE

TRADE NAMES/SYNONYMS: NICOTINE ACID TARTRATE; NICOTINE BITARTRATE; NICOTINE HYDROGEN TARTRATE; NICOTINE TARTRATE (1:2); -(-)NICOTINE HYDROGEN TARTRATE; PST16470

CHEMICAL FAMILY: PYRIDINE
CARBOXYLIC ACID, ALIPHATIC

MOLECULAR FORMULA: C10-H14-N2.2C4-H6-O6 MOL WT: 462.46

CERCLA RATINGS (SCALE 0-3): HEALTH=3 FIRE=0 REACTIVITY=0 PERSISTENCE=2

NFPA RATINGS (SCALE 0-4): HEALTH=3 FIRE=0 REACTIVITY=0

COMPONENTS AND CONTAMINANTS

COMPONENT: NICOTINE TARTRATE ***PERCENT:*** 100
CAS# 65-31-6

OTHER CONTAMINANTS: NONE

EXPOSURE LIMITS: NO OCCUPATIONAL EXPOSURE LIMITS ESTABLISHED BY OSHA, ACGIH, OR NIOSH.

PHYSICAL DATA

DESCRIPTION: REDDISH-WHITE CRYSTALS ***MELTING POINT:*** 194 F (90 C)

SOLUBILITY IN WATER: SOLUBLE

SOLVENT SOLUBILITY: ALCOHOL, ETHER

FIRE AND EXPLOSION DATA

FIRE AND EXPLOSION HAZARD: NEGLIGIBLE FIRE HAZARD WHEN EXPOSED TO HEAT OR FLAME.

FIREFIGHTING MEDIA: DRY CHEMICAL, CARBON DIOXIDE, HALON, WATER SPRAY OR STANDARD FOAM (1987 EMERGENCY RESPONSE GUIDEBOOK, DOT P 5800.4). FOR LARGER FIRES, USE WATER SPRAY, FOG OR STANDARD FOAM (1987 EMERGENCY RESPONSE GUIDEBOOK, DOT P 5800.4).

FIREFIGHTING: MOVE CONTAINERS FROM FIRE AREA IF POSSIBLE (1987 EMERGENCY RESPONSE GUIDEBOOK, DOT P 5800.4, GUIDE PAGE 53).
USE AGENTS SUITABLE FOR TYPE OF FIRE. USE WATER IN FLOODING AMOUNTS AS FOG. AVOID BREATHING POISONOUS VAPORS, KEEP UPWIND.

TRANSPORTATION DATA

DEPARTMENT OF TRANSPORTATION HAZARD CLASSIFICATION 49 CFR 172.101: POISON B
DEPARTMENT OF TRANSPORTATION LABELING REQUIREMENTS 49 CFR 172.101 AND SUBPART E: POISON
DEPARTMENT OF TRANSPORTATION PACKAGING REQUIREMENTS: 49 CFR 173.365 EXCEPTIONS: 49 CFR 173.364

TOXICITY

NICOTINE TARTRATE: TOXICITY DATA: 65 MG/KG ORAL-RAT LD50; 65 MG/KG ORAL-MOUSE LD50; 53 MG/KG SUBCUTANEOUS-MOUSE LD50; 600 MG/KG INTRAVENOUS-RAT LD50; 300 UG/KG INTRAVENOUS-MOUSE LD50; 83 MG/KG INTRAPERITONEAL-RAT LD50; 9100 UG/KG INTRAPERITONEAL-MOUSE LD50; 125 MG/KG INTRAPERITONEAL-HAMSTER LD50; 33500 UG/KG PARENTERAL-RAT LD50; 30 MG/KG UNREPORTED-RAT LD50; REPRODUCTIVE EFFECTS DATA (RTECS).
CARCINOGEN STATUS: NONE. ACUTE TOXICITY LEVEL: TOXIC BY INGESTION.
TARGET EFFECTS: POISONING MAY AFFECT THE CENTRAL AND PERIPHERAL NERVOUS SYSTEMS.

HEALTH EFFECTS AND FIRST AID

INHALATION: NICOTINE TARTRATE: **ACUTE EXPOSURE-** NICOTINE COMPOUNDS MAY CAUSE RESPIRATORY IRRITATION AND MAY CAUSE SYSTEMIC EFFECTS INCLUDING TRANSIENT STIMULATION AND SUBSEQUENT DEPRESSION OF THE CENTRAL AND PERIPHERAL NERVOUS SYSTEMS. **CHRONIC EXPOSURE-** REPEATED EXPOSURE TO NICOTINE MAY RESULT IN TOLERANCE OR HABITUALIZATION TO NICOTINE. PROLONGED EXPOSURE MAY CAUSE RESPIRATORY IRRITATION, AND CARDIOVASCULAR AND CENTRAL NERVOUS SYSTEM DAMAGE.

FIRST AID- REMOVE FROM EXPOSURE AREA TO FRESH AIR IMMEDIATELY. IF BREATHING HAS STOPPED, GIVE ARTIFICIAL RESPIRATION. MAINTAIN AIRWAY AND BLOOD PRESSURE AND ADMINISTER OXYGEN IF AVAILABLE. KEEP AFFECTED PERSON WARM AND AT REST. TREAT SYMPTOMATICALLY AND SUPPORTIVELY. ADMINISTRATION OF OXYGEN SHOULD BE PERFORMED BY QUALIFIED PERSONNEL. GET MEDICAL ATTENTION IMMEDIATELY.

SKIN CONTACT: NICOTINE TARTRATE: **ACUTE EXPOSURE-** NICOTINE COMPOUNDS MAY CAUSE LOCAL IRRITATION AND SYSTEMIC EFFECTS INCLUDING TRANSIENT STIMULATION AND SUBSEQUENT DEPRESSION OF THE CENTRAL AND PERIPHERAL NERVOUS SYSTEMS. **CHRONIC EXPOSURE-** MAY CAUSE DERMATITIS.

FIRST AID- REMOVE CONTAMINATED CLOTHING AND SHOES IMMEDIATELY. WASH AFFECTED AREA WITH SOAP OR MILD DETERGENT AND LARGE AMOUNTS OF WATER UNTIL NO EVIDENCE OF CHEMICAL REMAINS (APPROXIMATELY 15-20 MINUTES). GET MEDICAL ATTENTION IMMEDIATELY.

EYE CONTACT: NICOTINE TARTRATE: **ACUTE EXPOSURE-** NICOTINE COMPOUNDS MAY CAUSE REDNESS AND IRRITATION. **CHRONIC EXPOSURE-** PROLONGED OR REPEATED EXPOSURE TO NICOTINE COMPOUNDS MAY CAUSE CONJUNCTIVITIS.

FIRST AID- WASH EYES IMMEDIATELY WITH LARGE AMOUNTS OF WATER OR NORMAL SALINE, OCCASIONALLY LIFTING UPPER AND LOWER LIDS, UNTIL NO EVIDENCE OF CHEMICAL REMAINS (APPROXIMATELY 15-20 MINUTES). GET MEDICAL ATTENTION IMMEDIATELY.

INGESTION: NICOTINE TARTRATE: TOXIC. **ACUTE EXPOSURE-** INGESTION OF NICOTINE COMPOUNDS MAY CAUSE BURNING PAIN IN THE MOUTH AND THROAT, SALIVATION, NAUSEA, ABDOMINAL PAIN, VOMITING, AND DIARRHEA, FOLLOWED BY AGITATION, HEADACHE, SWEATING, DIZZINESS, AUDITORY AND VISUAL DISTURBANCES, CONFUSION, WEAKNESS, INCOORDINATION, AND POSSIBLY COLLAPSE. RESPIRATION MAY BE DEEP AND RAPID, WITH HYPERTENSION, SLOW PULSE, CARDIAC FIBRILLATION, CENTRAL NERVOUS SYSTEM EXCITATION, TREMORS AND CONVULSIONS, CENTRAL NERVOUS SYSTEM DEPRESSION, WITH MYDRIASIS, HYPOTENSION, AND RAPID OR IRREGULAR PULSE. FAINTNESS, CYANOSIS, PROSTRATION, AND DYSPNEA MAY PROGRESS TO COLLAPSE AND DEATH FROM RESPIRATORY PARALYSIS WITHIN A FEW MINUTES TO 4 HOURS OF INGESTION. **CHRONIC EXPOSURE-** REPEATED EXPOSURE CAN RESULT IN INCREASED TOLERANCE FOR NICOTINE AND POSSIBLE HABITUALIZATION. PROLONGED EXPOSURE MAY CAUSE CARDIOVASCULAR AND CENTRAL NERVOUS SYSTEM DAMAGE.

FIRST AID- GIVE ACTIVATED CHARCOAL TO ADSORB NICOTINE NOT ALREADY EXPELLED BY VOMITING. REMOVE BY THOROUGH GASTRIC LAVAGE WITH TAP WATER CONTAINING ACTIVATED CHARCOAL (DREISBACH, HANDBOOK OF POISONING, 11TH ED.) OR 0.05% SOLUTION OF TANNIC ACID OR 1:1500 SOLUTION OF POTASSIUM PERMANGANATE (GOSSELIN, CLINICAL TOXICOLOGY OF COMMERCIAL PRODUCTS). POSITIVE PRESSURE VENTILATION OF THE LUNGS WITH OXYGEN MAY BE NECESSARY WHEN RESPIRATION IS ARRESTED (RECOGNITION AND MANAGEMENT OF PESTICIDE POISONINGS, 3RD EDITION). GASTRIC LAVAGE AND OXYGEN SHOULD BE ADMINISTERED BY QUALIFIED MEDICAL PERSONNEL.

ANTIDOTE: THE FOLLOWING ANTIDOTE HAS BEEN RECOMMENDED. HOWEVER, THE DECISION AS TO WHETHER THE SEVERITY OF POISONING REQUIRES ADMINISTRATION OF ANY ANTIDOTE AND ACTUAL DOSE REQUIRED SHOULD BE MADE BY QUALIFIED MEDICAL PERSONNEL.

NICOTINE: (TO CONTROL THE SYMPTOMS OF PARASYMPATHETIC OVERSTIMULATION.) GIVE ATROPINE IN MAXIMUM DOSES (2 MG INTRAMUSCULARLY, AND REPEAT EVERY 3-8 MINUTES UNTIL SIGNS OF ATROPINIZATION APPEAR (FLUSHED FACE, DRY MOUTH, WIDELY DILATED PUPILS, FAST PULSE). REPEAT 2 MG OF ATROPINE FREQUENTLY TO MAINTAIN MARKED SIGNS OF ATROPINIZATION. AS MUCH AS 12 MG OF ATROPINE HAS BEEN GIVEN SAFELY IN THE FIRST 2 HOURS. INTERRUPTION OF ATROPINE THERAPY MAY BE RAPIDLY FOLLOWED BY FATAL PULMONARY EDEMA OR RESPIRATORY FAILURE.

GIVE PHENTOLAMINE, 1-5 MG INTRAMUSCULARLY OR INTRAVENOUSLY, TO CONTROL SIGNS OF SYMPATHETIC HYPERACTIVITY, SUCH AS HYPERTENSION (DREISBACH, HANDBOOK OF POISONING, 11TH ED.). ANTIDOTE SHOULD BE ADMINISTERED BY QUALIFIED MEDICAL PERSONNEL.

REACTIVITY

REACTIVITY: STABLE UNDER NORMAL TEMPERATURES AND PRESSURES.

INCOMPATIBILITIES: NICOTINE TARTRATE: STRONG OXIDIZERS: VIOLENT REACTION.

DECOMPOSITION: THERMAL DECOMPOSITION PRODUCTS MAY INCLUDE TOXIC OXIDES OF CARBON AND NITROGEN.

POLYMERIZATION: HAZARDOUS POLYMERIZATION HAS NOT BEEN REPORTED TO OCCUR UNDER NORMAL TEMPERATURES AND PRESSURES.

CONDITIONS TO AVOID

MAY BURN BUT DOES NOT IGNITE READILY.

SPILL AND LEAK PROCEDURES

OCCUPATIONAL SPILL: DO NOT TOUCH SPILLED MATERIAL. STOP LEAK IF YOU CAN DO IT WITHOUT RISK. FOR SMALL SPILLS, TAKE UP WITH SAND OR OTHER ABSORBENT MATERIAL AND PLACE INTO CONTAINERS FOR LATER DISPOSAL. FOR SMALL DRY SPILLS, WITH A CLEAN SHOVEL PLACE MATERIAL INTO CLEAN, DRY CONTAINER AND COVER. MOVE CONTAINERS FROM SPILL AREA. FOR LARGER SPILLS, DIKE FAR AHEAD OF SPILL FOR LATER DISPOSAL. KEEP UNNECESSARY PEOPLE AWAY. ISOLATE HAZARD AREA AND DENY ENTRY.

PROTECTIVE EQUIPMENT

VENTILATION: PROVIDE LOCAL EXHAUST OR PROCESS ENCLOSURE VENTILATION SYSTEM.

RESPIRATOR: THE FOLLOWING RESPIRATORS ARE RECOMMENDED BASED ON INFORMATION FOUND IN THE PHYSICAL DATA, TOXICITY AND HEALTH EFFECTS SECTIONS. THEY ARE RANKED IN ORDER FROM MINIMUM TO MAXIMUM RESPIRATORY PROTECTION. THE SPECIFIC RESPIRATOR SELECTED MUST BE BASED ON CONTAMINATION LEVELS FOUND IN THE WORK PLACE, MUST NOT EXCEED THE WORKING LIMITS OF THE RESPIRATOR AND BE JOINTLY APPROVED BY THE NATIONAL INSTITUTE FOR OCCUPATIONAL SAFETY AND HEALTH AND THE MINE SAFETY AND HEALTH ADMINISTRATION (NIOSH-MSHA).

TYPE 'C' SUPPLIED-AIR RESPIRATOR WITH A FULL FACEPIECE OPERATED IN PRESSURE-DEMAND OR OTHER POSITIVE PRESSURE MODE OR WITH A FULL FACEPIECE, HELMET OR HOOD OPERATED IN CONTINOUS-FLOW MODE.

SELF-CONTAINED BREATHING APPARATUS WITH A FULL FACEPIECE OPERATED IN PRESSURE-DEMAND OR OTHER POSITIVE PRESSURE MODE.

FOR FIREFIGHTING AND OTHER IMMEDIATELY DANGEROUS TO LIFE OR HEALTH CONDITIONS:

SELF-CONTAINED BREATHING APPARATUS WITH FULL FACEPIECE OPERATED IN PRESSURE-DEMAND OR OTHER POSITIVE PRESSURE MODE.

SUPPLIED-AIR RESPIRATOR WITH FULL FACEPIECE AND OPERATED IN PRESSURE-DEMAND OR OTHER POSITIVE PRESSURE MODE IN COMBINATION WITH AN AUXILIARY SELF-CONTAINED BREATHING APPARATUS OPERATED IN PRESSURE-DEMAND OR OTHER POSITIVE PRESSURE MODE.

CLOTHING: EMPLOYEE MUST WEAR APPROPRIATE PROTECTIVE (IMPERVIOUS) CLOTHING AND EQUIPMENT TO PREVENT ANY POSSIBILITY OF SKIN CONTACT WITH THIS SUBSTANCE.

GLOVES: EMPLOYEE MUST WEAR APPROPRIATE PROTECTIVE GLOVES TO PREVENT CONTACT WITH THIS SUBSTANCE.

EYE PROTECTION: EMPLOYEE MUST WEAR SPLASH-PROOF OR DUST-RESISTANT SAFETY GOGGLES AND A FACESHIELD TO PREVENT CONTACT WITH THIS SUBSTANCE.

EMERGENCY WASH FACILITIES: WHERE THERE IS ANY POSSIBILITY THAT AN EMPLOYEE'S EYES AND/OR SKIN MAY BE EXPOSED TO THIS SUBSTANCE, THE EMPLOYER SHOULD PROVIDE AN EYE WASH FOUNTAIN AND QUICK DRENCH SHOWER WITHIN THE IMMEDIATE WORK AREA FOR EMERGENCY USE.

AUTHORIZED BY- OCCUPATIONAL HEALTH SERVICES, INC.

CREATION DATE: 10/04/89 ***REVISION DATE:*** 05/17/90

MATERIAL SAFETY DATA SHEET

OCCUPATIONAL HEALTH SERVICES, INC.
AGRICULTURE AND PESTICIDE DIVISION
450 SEVENTH AVENUE, SUITE 2407
NEW YORK, NEW YORK 10123
1-800-445-MSDS OR (212) 967-1100

EMERGENCY CONTACT:
JOHN S. BRANSFORD, JR. (615) 292-1180

SUBSTANCE IDENTIFICATION

CAS-NUMBER 4726-14-1

SUBSTANCE: **NITRALIN**

TRADE NAMES/SYNONYMS: BENZENAMINE, 4-(METHYLSULFONYL)-2,6-DINITRO-N,N-DIPROPYL-; ANILINE, 4-(METHYLSULFONYL)-2,6-DINITRO-N,N-DIPROPYL-; 4-(METHYLSULFONYL)-2,6-DINITRO-N,N-DIPROPYLBENZENAMINE; 4-(METHYLSULFONYL)-2,6-DINITRO-N,N-DIPROPYLANILINE; 4-METHYLSULPHONYL-2,6-DINITRO-N,N-DIPROPYLANILINE; 4-METHYLSULFONYL-2,6-DINITRO-N,N-DIPROPYLANILINE; NITRALINE; PLANAVIN; SD 11831; C13H19N3O6S; PST16525

CHEMICAL FAMILY: ANILINE DERIVATIVE

MOLECULAR FORMULA: C13-H19-N3-O6-S

MOLECULAR WEIGHT: 345.37

CERCLA RATINGS (SCALE 0-3): HEALTH=U FIRE=1 REACTIVITY=0 PERSISTENCE=2

NFPA RATINGS (SCALE 0-4): HEALTH=U FIRE=1 REACTIVITY=0

COMPONENTS AND CONTAMINANTS

COMPONENT: NITRALIN ***PERCENT:*** 100.0

CAS# 4726-14-1

OTHER CONTAMINANTS: NONE

EXPOSURE LIMITS: NO OCCUPATIONAL EXPOSURE LIMITS ESTABLISHED BY OSHA, ACGIH, OR NIOSH.

PHYSICAL DATA

DESCRIPTION: LIGHT YELLOW TO ORANGE CRYSTALS WITH MILD CHEMICAL ODOR.
MELTING POINT: 302-304 F (150-151 C) ***SPECIFIC GRAVITY:*** 1.39
VAPOR PRESSURE: NEGLIGIBLE ***SOLUBILITY IN WATER:*** 0.6 PPM @ 22 C
SOLVENT SOLUBILITY: SOLUBLE IN ACETONE, DIMETHYL SULFOXIDE, 2-NITROPROPANE, AND POLAR ORGANIC SOLVENTS; SPARINGLY SOLUBLE IN HYDROCARBONS, AROMATIC SOLVENTS AND ALCOHOLS.

FIRE AND EXPLOSION DATA

FIRE AND EXPLOSION HAZARD: SLIGHT FIRE HAZARD WHEN EXPOSED TO HEAT OR FLAME.
FIREFIGHTING MEDIA: DRY CHEMICAL, CARBON DIOXIDE, HALON, WATER SPRAY OR STANDARD FOAM (1987 EMERGENCY RESPONSE GUIDEBOOK, DOT P 5800.4). FOR LARGER FIRES, USE WATER SPRAY, FOG OR STANDARD FOAM (1987 EMERGENCY RESPONSE GUIDEBOOK, DOT P 5800.4).
FIREFIGHTING: MOVE CONTAINER FROM FIRE AREA IF POSSIBLE. DO NOT SCATTER SPILLED MATERIAL WITH HIGH PRESSURE WATER STREAMS. DIKE FIRE CONTROL WATER FOR LATER DISPOSAL (1987 EMERGENCY RESPONSE GUIDEBOOK, DOT P 5800.4, GUIDE PAGE 31).
USE AGENTS SUITABLE FOR TYPE OF SURROUNDING FIRE. AVOID BREATHING HAZARDOUS VAPORS, KEEP UPWIND.

TOXICITY

NITRALIN: TOXICITY DATA: >2000 MG/KG SKIN-RABBIT LD50 (85JFAN); >6000 MG/KG ORAL-RAT LD50 (85JFAN); >2000 MG/KG ORAL-MICE LD50 (85JFAN). CARCINOGEN STATUS: NONE. ACUTE TOXICITY: SLIGHTLY TOXIC BY DERMAL ABSORPTION AND INGESTION. TARGET EFFECTS: NO DATA AVAILABLE.

HEALTH EFFECTS AND FIRST AID

INHALATION: NITRALIN: **ACUTE EXPOSURE-** SOME SUBSTITUTED DINITROANILINE HERBICIDES ARE IRRITATING TO THE MUCOUS MEMBRANES. **CHRONIC EXPOSURE-** NO DATA AVAILABLE.
FIRST AID- REMOVE FROM EXPOSURE AREA TO FRESH AIR IMMEDIATELY. IF BREATHING HAS STOPPED, PERFORM ARTIFICIAL RESPIRATION. KEEP PERSON WARM AND AT REST. TREAT SYMPTOMATICALLY AND SUPPORTIVELY. GET MEDICAL ATTENTION IMMEDIATELY.

SKIN CONTACT: NITRALIN: **ACUTE EXPOSURE-** SOME SUBSTITUTED DINITROANILINE HERBICIDES ARE IRRITATING TO THE SKIN. **CHRONIC EXPOSURE-** NO DATA AVAILABLE.
FIRST AID- REMOVE CONTAMINATED CLOTHING AND SHOES IMMEDIATELY. WASH AFFECTED AREA WITH SOAP OR MILD DETERGENT AND LARGE AMOUNTS OF WATER UNTIL NO EVIDENCE OF CHEMICAL REMAINS (APPROXIMATELY 15-20 MINUTES). GET MEDICAL ATTENTION IMMEDIATELY.

EYE CONTACT: NITRALIN: **ACUTE EXPOSURE-** SOME SUBSTITUTED DINITROANILINE HERBICIDES ARE IRRITATING TO THE EYES. **CHRONIC EXPOSURE-** NO DATA AVAILABLE.
FIRST AID- WASH EYES IMMEDIATELY WITH LARGE AMOUNTS OF WATER OR NORMAL SALINE, OCCASIONALLY LIFTING UPPER AND LOWER LIDS, UNTIL NO EVIDENCE OF CHEMICAL REMAINS (APPROXIMATELY 15-20 MINUTES). GET MEDICAL ATTENTION IMMEDIATELY.

INGESTION: NITRALIN: **ACUTE EXPOSURE-** THE LD50 FOR RATS WAS >6000 MG/KG. **CHRONIC EXPOSURE-** INCREASED LIVER WEIGHTS WERE NOTED IN A 12-WEEK STUDY OF RATS RECEIVING 3000 PPM.
FIRST AID- IF THE PERSON IS CONSCIOUS AND NOT CONVULSING, REMOVE BY GASTRIC LAVAGE AND FOLLOW WITH A CATHARTIC (DREISBACH, HANDBOOK OF POISONING, 12TH ED.). TREAT SYMPTOMATICALLY AND SUPPORTIVELY. GASTRIC LAVAGE SHOULD BE PERFORMED BY QUALIFIED MEDICAL PERSONNEL. GET MEDICAL ATTENTION IMMEDIATELY.
ANTIDOTE: NO SPECIFIC ANTIDOTE. TREAT SYMPTOMATICALLY AND SUPPORTIVELY.

REACTIVITY

REACTIVITY: STABLE UNDER NORMAL TEMPERATURES AND PRESSURES.
INCOMPATIBILITIES: NITRALIN: OXIDIZERS (STRONG): FIRE AND EXPLOSION HAZARD.
DECOMPOSITION: THERMAL DECOMPOSITION PRODUCTS MAY INCLUDE TOXIC OXIDES OF CARBON, NITROGEN, AND SULFUR.
POLYMERIZATION: HAZARDOUS POLYMERIZATION HAS NOT BEEN REPORTED TO OCCUR UNDER NORMAL TEMPERATURES AND PRESSURES.

STORAGE AND DISPOSAL

OBSERVE ALL FEDERAL, STATE AND LOCAL REGULATIONS WHEN STORING OR DISPOSING OF THIS SUBSTANCE. FOR ASSISTANCE, CONTACT THE DISTRICT DIRECTOR OF THE ENVIRONMENTAL PROTECTION AGENCY.

STORAGE

STORE IN ACCORDANCE WITH 40 CFR 165 RECOMMENDED PROCEDURES FOR THE DISPOSAL AND STORAGE OF PESTICIDES AND PESTICIDE CONTAINERS.
STORE AWAY FROM INCOMPATIBLE SUBSTANCES.

DISPOSAL

DISPOSAL MUST BE IN ACCORDANCE WITH 40 CFR 165 RECOMMENDED PROCEDURES FOR THE DISPOSAL AND STORAGE OF PESTICIDES AND PESTICIDE CONTAINERS.

CONDITIONS TO AVOID

MAY BURN BUT DOES NOT IGNITE READILY. AVOID CONTACT WITH STRONG OXIDIZERS, EXCESSIVE HEAT, SPARKS, OR OPEN FLAME.

SPILL AND LEAK PROCEDURES

OCCUPATIONAL SPILL: SWEEP UP AND PLACE IN SUITABLE CLEAN, DRY CONTAINERS FOR RECLAMATION OR LATER DISPOSAL. DO NOT FLUSH SPILLED MATERIAL INTO SEWER. KEEP UNNECESSARY PEOPLE AWAY.

PROTECTIVE EQUIPMENT

VENTILATION: PROVIDE LOCAL EXHAUST OR GENERAL DILUTION VENTILATION SYSTEM.
RESPIRATOR: THE FOLLOWING RESPIRATORS ARE RECOMMENDED BASED ON INFORMATION FOUND IN THE PHYSICAL DATA, TOXICITY AND HEALTH EFFECTS SECTIONS. THEY ARE RANKED IN ORDER FROM MINIMUM TO MAXIMUM RESPIRATORY PROTECTION. THE SPECIFIC RESPIRATOR SELECTED MUST BE BASED ON CONTAMINATION LEVELS FOUND IN THE WORK PLACE, MUST NOT EXCEED THE WORKING LIMITS OF THE RESPIRATOR AND BE JOINTLY APPROVED BY THE NATIONAL INSTITUTE FOR OCCUPATIONAL SAFETY AND HEALTH AND THE MINE SAFETY AND HEALTH ADMINISTRATION (NIOSH-MSHA).
CHEMICAL CARTRIDGE RESPIRATOR WITH AN ORGANIC VAPOR CARTRIDGE(S) WITH A FULL FACEPIECE AND ORGANIC VAPOR CARTRIDGE(S) IN COMBINATION WITH A DUST AND MIST FILTER.
POWERED AIR-PURIFYING RESPIRATOR WITH A TIGHT-FITTING FACEPIECE AND ORGANIC VAPOR CARTRIDGE(S) IN COMBINATION WITH A HIGH-EFFICIENCY PARTICULATE FILTER.
TYPE 'C' SUPPLIED-AIR RESPIRATOR WITH A FULL FACEPIECE OPERATED IN A PRESSURE-DEMAND OR OTHER POSITIVE PRESSURE MODE.
SELF-CONTAINED BREATHING APPARATUS WITH A FULL FACEPIECE OPERATED IN PRESSURE-DEMAND OR OTHER POSITIVE PRESSURE MODE.
FOR FIREFIGHTING AND OTHER IMMEDIATELY DANGEROUS TO LIFE OR HEALTH CONDITIONS:
SELF-CONTAINED BREATHING APPARATUS WITH FULL FACEPIECE OPERATED IN PRESSURE-DEMAND OR OTHER POSITIVE PRESSURE MODE.
SUPPLIED-AIR RESPIRATOR WITH FULL FACEPIECE AND OPERATED IN PRESSURE-DEMAND OR OTHER POSITIVE PRESSURE MODE IN COMBINATION WITH AN AUXILIARY SELF-CONTAINED BREATHING APPARATUS OPERATED IN PRESSURE-DEMAND OR OTHER POSITIVE PRESSURE MODE. ***CLOTHING:*** EMPLOYEE MUST WEAR APPROPRIATE PROTECTIVE (IMPERVIOUS) CLOTHING AND EQUIPMENT TO PREVENT REPEATED OR PROLONGED SKIN CONTACT WITH THIS SUBSTANCE.
GLOVES: EMPLOYEE MUST WEAR APPROPRIATE PROTECTIVE GLOVES TO PREVENT CONTACT WITH THIS SUBSTANCE.
EYE PROTECTION: EMPLOYEE MUST WEAR SPLASH-PROOF OR DUST-RESISTANT SAFETY GOGGLES TO PREVENT EYE CONTACT WITH THIS SUBSTANCE.
EMERGENCY EYE WASH: WHERE THERE IS ANY POSSIBILITY THAT AN EMPLOYEE'S EYES MAY BE EXPOSED TO THIS SUBSTANCE, THE EMPLOYER SHOULD PROVIDE AN EYE WASH FOUNTAIN WITHIN THE IMMEDIATE WORK AREA FOR EMERGENCY USE.

AUTHORIZED BY- OCCUPATIONAL HEALTH SERVICES, INC.
CREATION DATE: 10/04/89 ***REVISION DATE:*** 05/31/90

MATERIAL SAFETY DATA SHEET

OCCUPATIONAL HEALTH SERVICES, INC.
AGRICULTURE AND PESTICIDE DIVISION
450 SEVENTH AVENUE, SUITE 2407
NEW YORK, NEW YORK 10123
1-800-445-MSDS OR (212) 967-1100

EMERGENCY CONTACT:
JOHN S. BRANSFORD, JR. (615) 292-1180

SUBSTANCE IDENTIFICATION

CAS-NUMBER 1929-82-4

SUBSTANCE: **NITRAPYRIN**

TRADE NAMES/SYNONYMS: PYRIDINE, 2-CHLORO-6-(TRICHLOROMETHYL); 2-CHLORO-6-(TRICHLOROMETHYL)PYRIDINE; 2-CHLORO-6-TRICLOROMETHYLPYRIDINE; NITRAPYRINE; N-SERVE; DOWCO-163; C6H3CL4N; PST16530

CHEMICAL FAMILY: PYRIDINE
HALOGEN

MOLECULAR FORMULA: (CL3-C)-C5-N-H3-(CL)

MOLECULAR WEIGHT: 230.90

CERCLA RATINGS (SCALE 0-3): HEALTH=3 FIRE=1 REACTIVITY=0 PERSISTENCE=1

NFPA RATINGS (SCALE 0-4): HEALTH=3 FIRE=1 REACTIVITY=0

COMPONENTS AND CONTAMINANTS

COMPONENT: NITRAPYRIN ***PERCENT:*** 100
CAS# 1929-82-4

OTHER CONTAMINANTS: NONE

EXPOSURE LIMITS: NITRAPYRIN: 5 MG/M3 OSHA TWA (RESPIRABLE DUST); 15 MG/M3 OSHA TWA (TOTAL DUST) 10 MG/M3 ACGIH TWA; 20 MG/M3 ACGIH STEL

PHYSICAL DATA

DESCRIPTION: COLORLESS TO WHITE CRYSTALLINE SOLID WITH A MILDLY SWEET ODOR.

BOILING POINT: 279 F (137 C) @ 11 MMHG ***MELTING POINT:*** 144-145 F (62-63 C)

SPECIFIC GRAVITY: NOT AVAILABLE ***VAPOR PRESSURE:*** 0.0028 MMHG @ 23 C

SOLUBILITY IN WATER: 40 PPM

SOLVENT SOLUBILITY: SOLUBLE IN ANHYDROUS AMMONIA, ETHANOL, ACETONE, DICHLOROMETHANE, AND XYLENE.

FIRE AND EXPLOSION DATA

FIRE AND EXPLOSION HAZARD: SLIGHT FIRE HAZARD WHEN EXPOSED TO HEAT OR FLAME.

FLASH POINT: >200 F (>93 C) (CC)

FIREFIGHTING MEDIA: DRY CHEMICAL, CARBON DIOXIDE, HALON, WATER SPRAY OR STANDARD FOAM (1987 EMERGENCY RESPONSE GUIDEBOOK, DOT P 5800.4).
FOR LARGER FIRES, USE WATER SPRAY, FOG OR STANDARD FOAM (1987 EMERGENCY RESPONSE GUIDEBOOK, DOT P 5800.4).

FIREFIGHTING: MOVE CONTAINERS FROM FIRE AREA IF POSSIBLE (1987 EMERGENCY RESPONSE GUIDEBOOK, DOT P 5800.4, GUIDE PAGE 53).
EXTINGUISH USING AGENT SUITABLE FOR TYPE OF SURROUNDING FIRE. AVOID BREATHING VAPORS AND DUSTS. KEEP UPWIND.

TOXICITY

NITRAPYRIN: TOXICITY DATA: 850 MG/KG SKIN-RABBIT LD50; 940 MG/KG ORAL-RAT LD50; 710 MG/KG ORAL-MOUSE LD50; 3675 MG/KG UNREPORTED-RAT LD50; 3113 MG/KG UNREPORTED-MOUSE LD50; MUTAGENIC DATA (RTECS). CARCINOGEN STATUS: NONE. LOCAL EFFECTS: IRRITANT- SKIN, EYE. ACUTE TOXICITY LEVEL: TOXIC BY DERMAL ABSORPTION; MODERATELY TOXIC BY INGESTION. TARGET EFFECTS: NO DATA AVAILABLE.

HEALTH EFFECTS AND FIRST AID

INHALATION: NITRAPYRIN: **ACUTE EXPOSURE-** DUST MAY CAUSE IRRITATION TO UPPER RESPIRATORY TRACT. **CHRONIC EXPOSURE-** NO DATA AVAILABLE.

FIRST AID- REMOVE FROM EXPOSURE AREA TO FRESH AIR IMMEDIATELY. IF BREATHING HAS STOPPED, PERFORM ARTIFICIAL RESPIRATION. KEEP PERSON WARM AND AT REST. TREAT SYMPTOMATICALLY AND SUPPORTIVELY. GET MEDICAL ATTENTION IMMEDIATELY.

SKIN CONTACT: NITRAPYRIN: IRRITANT/TOXIC. **ACUTE EXPOSURE-** MAY CAUSE IRRITATION. A LETHAL DOSE REPORTED IN RABBITS WAS 850 MG/KG; SYMPTOMS WERE NOT REPORTED. **CHRONIC EXPOSURE-** PROLONGED OR REPEATED EXPOSURE MAY CAUSE SOME SKIN IRRITATION, EVEN A BURN. MAY RARELY CAUSE AN ALLERGIC SKIN RESPONSE.

FIRST AID- REMOVE CONTAMINATED CLOTHING AND SHOES IMMEDIATELY. WASH AFFECTED AREA WITH SOAP OR MILD DETERGENT AND LARGE AMOUNTS OF WATER UNTIL NO EVIDENCE OF CHEMICAL REMAINS (APPROXIMATELY 15-20 MINUTES). GET MEDICAL ATTENTION IMMEDIATELY.

EYE CONTACT: NITRAPYRIN: IRRITANT. **ACUTE EXPOSURE-** MAY CAUSE SLIGHT TRANSIENT IRRITATION WITH CORNEAL INJURY. **CHRONIC EXPOSURE-** PROLONGED OR REPEATED EXPOSURE TO IRRITANTS MAY CAUSE CONJUNCTIVITIS.

FIRST AID- WASH EYES IMMEDIATELY WITH LARGE AMOUNTS OF WATER OR NORMAL SALINE, OCCASIONALLY LIFTING UPPER AND LOWER LIDS, UNTIL NO EVIDENCE OF CHEMICAL REMAINS (APPROXIMATELY 15-20 MINUTES). GET MEDICAL ATTENTION IMMEDIATELY.

INGESTION: NITRAPYRIN: **ACUTE EXPOSURE-** THE LETHAL DOSE REPORTED IN RATS WAS 940 MG/KG; SYMPTOMS WERE NOT REPORTED. **CHRONIC EXPOSURE-** SLIGHT MATERNAL TOXICITY INCLUDING LIVER AND KIDNEY EFFECTS WAS OBSERVED IN RATS AND RABBITS AT DOSES OF 50 MG/KG/DAY TO 30 MG/KG/DAY. SLIGHT FETOTOXIC EFFECTS WITH A STATISTICAL INCREASE IN THE INCIDENCE OF CROOKED HYOID BONES WERE REPORTED IN RABBITS.

FIRST AID- IF THE PERSON IS CONSCIOUS AND NOT CONVULSING, REMOVE BY GASTRIC LAVAGE AND FOLLOW WITH A CATHARTIC (DREISBACH, HANDBOOK OF POISONING, 12TH ED.). TREAT SYMPTOMATICALLY AND SUPPORTIVELY. GASTRIC LAVAGE SHOULD BE PERFORMED BY QUALIFIED MEDICAL PERSONNEL. GET MEDICAL ATTENTION IMMEDIATELY.

ANTIDOTE: NO SPECIFIC ANTIDOTE. TREAT SYMPTOMATICALLY AND SUPPORTIVELY.

REACTIVITY

REACTIVITY: STABLE UNDER NORMAL TEMPERATURES AND PRESSURES.

INCOMPATIBILITIES: NITRAPYRIN: ALUMINUM AND ITS ALLOYS: MAY CORRODE. MAGNESIUM AND ITS ALLOYS: MAY CORRODE. OXIDIZERS (STRONG): FIRE AND EXPLOSION HAZARD.

DECOMPOSITION: THERMAL DECOMPOSITION PRODUCTS MAY INCLUDE TOXIC OXIDES OF NITROGEN AND CARBON AND TOXIC AND CORROSIVE FUMES OF CHLORIDES.

POLYMERIZATION: HAZARDOUS POLYMERIZATION HAS NOT BEEN REPORTED TO OCCUR UNDER NORMAL TEMPERATURES AND PRESSURES.

STORAGE AND DISPOSAL

OBSERVE ALL FEDERAL, STATE AND LOCAL REGULATIONS WHEN STORING OR DISPOSING OF THIS SUBSTANCE. FOR ASSISTANCE, CONTACT THE DISTRICT DIRECTOR OF THE ENVIRONMENTAL PROTECTION AGENCY.

STORAGE

STORE IN ACCORDANCE WITH 40 CFR 165 RECOMMENDED PROCEDURES FOR THE DISPOSAL AND STORAGE OF PESTICIDES AND PESTICIDE CONTAINERS.
STORE AWAY FROM INCOMPATIBLE SUBSTANCES.

DISPOSAL

DISPOSAL MUST BE IN ACCORDANCE WITH 40 CFR 165 RECOMMENDED PROCEDURES FOR THE DISPOSAL AND STORAGE OF PESTICIDES AND PESTICIDE CONTAINERS.

CONDITIONS TO AVOID

MAY BURN BUT DOES NOT IGNITE READILY.

SPILL AND LEAK PROCEDURES

OCCUPATIONAL SPILL: DO NOT TOUCH SPILLED MATERIAL. STOP LEAK IF YOU CAN DO IT WITHOUT RISK. FOR SMALL SPILLS, TAKE UP WITH SAND OR OTHER ABSORBENT MATERIAL AND PLACE INTO CONTAINERS FOR LATER DISPOSAL. FOR SMALL DRY SPILLS, WITH A CLEAN SHOVEL PLACE MATERIAL INTO CLEAN, DRY CONTAINER AND COVER. MOVE CONTAINERS FROM SPILL AREA. FOR LARGER SPILLS, DIKE FAR AHEAD OF SPILL FOR LATER DISPOSAL. KEEP UNNECESSARY PEOPLE AWAY. ISOLATE HAZARD AREA AND DENY ENTRY.

PROTECTIVE EQUIPMENT

VENTILATION: PROVIDE LOCAL EXHAUST OR PROCESS ENCLOSURE VENTILATION TO MEET PUBLISHED EXPOSURE LIMITS.

RESPIRATOR: THE FOLLOWING RESPIRATORS ARE RECOMMENDED BASED ON INFORMATION FOUND IN THE PHYSICAL DATA, TOXICITY AND HEALTH EFFECTS SECTIONS. THEY ARE RANKED IN ORDER FROM MINIMUM TO MAXIMUM RESPIRATORY PROTECTION. THE SPECIFIC RESPIRATOR SELECTED MUST BE BASED ON CONTAMINATION LEVELS FOUND IN THE WORK PLACE, MUST NOT EXCEED THE WORKING LIMITS OF THE RESPIRATOR AND BE JOINTLY APPROVED BY THE NATIONAL INSTITUTE FOR OCCUPATIONAL SAFETY AND HEALTH AND THE MINE SAFETY AND HEALTH ADMINISTRATION (NIOSH-MSHA).
TYPE 'C' SUPPLIED-AIR RESPIRATOR WITH A FULL FACEPIECE OPERATED IN PRESSURE-DEMAND OR OTHER POSITIVE PRESSURE MODE OR WITH A FULL FACEPIECE, HELMET OR HOOD OPERATED IN CONTINOUS-FLOW MODE.
SELF-CONTAINED BREATHING APPARATUS WITH A FULL FACEPIECE OPERATED IN PRESSURE-DEMAND OR OTHER POSITIVE PRESSURE MODE.
FOR FIREFIGHTING AND OTHER IMMEDIATELY DANGEROUS TO LIFE OR HEALTH CONDITIONS:
SELF-CONTAINED BREATHING APPARATUS WITH FULL FACEPIECE OPERATED IN PRESSURE-DEMAND OR OTHER POSITIVE PRESSURE MODE. SUPPLIED-AIR RESPIRATOR WITH FULL FACEPIECE AND OPERATED IN PRESSURE-DEMAND OR OTHER POSITIVE PRESSURE MODE IN COMBINATION WITH AN AUXILIARY SELF-CONTAINED BREATHING APPARATUS OPERATED IN PRESSURE-DEMAND OR OTHER POSITIVE PRESSURE MODE.

CLOTHING: EMPLOYEE MUST WEAR APPROPRIATE PROTECTIVE (IMPERVIOUS) CLOTHING AND EQUIPMENT TO PREVENT ANY POSSIBILITY OF SKIN CONTACT WITH THIS SUBSTANCE.
GLOVES: EMPLOYEE MUST WEAR APPROPRIATE PROTECTIVE GLOVES TO PREVENT CONTACT WITH THIS SUBSTANCE.
EYE PROTECTION: EMPLOYEE MUST WEAR SPLASH-PROOF OR DUST-RESISTANT SAFETY GOGGLES AND A FACESHIELD TO PREVENT CONTACT WITH THIS SUBSTANCE.
EMERGENCY WASH FACILITIES: WHERE THERE IS ANY POSSIBILITY THAT AN EMPLOYEE'S EYES AND/OR SKIN MAY BE EXPOSED TO THIS SUBSTANCE, THE EMPLOYER SHOULD PROVIDE AN EYE WASH FOUNTAIN AND QUICK DRENCH SHOWER WITHIN THE IMMEDIATE WORK AREA FOR EMERGENCY USE.

AUTHORIZED BY- OCCUPATIONAL HEALTH SERVICES, INC.
CREATION DATE: 10/04/89 ***REVISION DATE:*** 04/02/90

MATERIAL SAFETY DATA SHEET

OCCUPATIONAL HEALTH SERVICES, INC.
AGRICULTURE AND PESTICIDE DIVISION
450 SEVENTH AVENUE, SUITE 2407
NEW YORK, NEW YORK 10123
1-800-445-MSDS OR (212) 967-1100

EMERGENCY CONTACT:
JOHN S. BRANSFORD, JR. (615) 292-1180

SUBSTANCE IDENTIFICATION

CAS-NUMBER 9016-45-9
SUBSTANCE: ETHOXYLATED NONYLPHENOL
TRADE NAMES/SYNONYMS: NONOXYNOL; POLYOXYETHYLENE ETHER NONYLPHENOL; NONYL PHENYL POLYETHYLENE GLYCOL; NONYL PHENYL POLYETHYLENE GLYCOL ETHER; NONYLPHENOL POLYETHYLENE OXIDE; NONYPHENOXY POLYETHOXY ETHANOL; NONYLPHENOL ETHOXYLATE; OXYETHYLATED NONYLPHENOL; OXYETHYLENE NONYLPHENYL ETHER; POLYETHOXYLATED NONYLPHENOL; POLYOXYETHYLATED NONYLPHENOL; NONYLPHENOXYPOLY(ETHYLENE OXY) ETHANOL; PST16835
CHEMICAL FAMILY: ALKYL ARYL POLYETHER ALCOHOL
NONIONIC SURFACTANT
MOLECULAR FORMULA: (C2-H4-O)X.C15-H24-O
CERCLA RATINGS (SCALE 0-3): HEALTH=2 FIRE=1 REACTIVITY=0 PERSISTENCE=1
NFPA RATINGS (SCALE 0-4): HEALTH=2 FIRE=1 REACTIVITY=0

COMPONENTS AND CONTAMINANTS

COMPONENT: ETHOXYLATED NONYLPHENOL ***PERCENT:*** 100
CAS# 9016-45-9
OTHER CONTAMINANTS: NONE
EXPOSURE LIMITS: NO OCCUPATIONAL EXPOSURE LIMITS ESTABLISHED BY OSHA, ACGIH, OR NIOSH.

PHYSICAL DATA

DESCRIPTION: SLIGHTLY VISCOUS LIQUID TO WAX. ***BOILING POINT:*** NOT AVAILABLE
MELTING POINT: NOT AVAILABLE ***SPECIFIC GRAVITY:*** NOT AVAILABLE
SOLUBILITY IN WATER: SOLUBLE

FIRE AND EXPLOSION DATA

FIRE AND EXPLOSION HAZARD: SLIGHT FIRE HAZARD WHEN EXPOSED TO HEAT OR FLAME.
FLASH POINT: 460 F (238 C) (OC)
FIREFIGHTING MEDIA: DRY CHEMICAL, CARBON DIOXIDE, HALON, WATER SPRAY OR STANDARD FOAM (1987 EMERGENCY RESPONSE GUIDEBOOK, DOT P 5800.4).
FOR LARGER FIRES, USE WATER SPRAY, FOG OR STANDARD FOAM (1987 EMERGENCY RESPONSE GUIDEBOOK, DOT P 5800.4).
FIREFIGHTING: MOVE CONTAINER FROM FIRE AREA IF POSSIBLE. DO NOT SCATTER SPILLED MATERIAL WITH HIGH PRESSURE WATER STREAMS. DIKE FIRE CONTROL WATER FOR LATER DISPOSAL (1987 EMERGENCY RESPONSE GUIDEBOOK, DOT P 5800.4, GUIDE PAGE 31).
USE AGENTS SUITABLE FOR TYPE OF SURROUNDING FIRE. AVOID BREATHING HAZARDOUS VAPORS, KEEP UPWIND.

TOXICITY

ETHOXYLATED NONYL PHENOL: IRRITATION DATA: 500 MG OPEN SKIN-RABBIT MILD; 5 MG EYE-RABBIT SEVERE. TOXICITY DATA: 2000 MG/KG SKIN-RABBIT LD50; 1310 MG/KG ORAL-RAT LD50. CARCINOGEN STATUS: NONE. LOCAL EFFECTS: IRRITANT- EYE. ACUTE TOXICITY LEVEL: MODERATELY TOXIC BY DERMAL ABSORPTION AND INGESTION. TARGET EFFECTS: NO DATA AVAILABLE.

HEALTH EFFECTS AND FIRST AID

INHALATION: ETHOXYLATED NONYL PHENOL: **ACUTE EXPOSURE-** NO DATA AVAILABLE. SINCE MOST ALKYL ARYL POLYETHER ALCOHOLS HAVE LOW VAPOR PRESSURES, NO SIGNIFICANT HEALTH HAZARD FROM INHALATION IS LIKELY TO OCCUR AT NORMAL ROOM TEMPERATURES. INHALATION OF DUST, GENERATED MIST, OR VAPORS PRODUCED FROM ELEVATED TEMPERATURES MAY CAUSE IRRITATION OF THE MUCOUS MEMBRANES. **CHRONIC EXPOSURE-** NO DATA AVAILABLE.
FIRST AID- REMOVE FROM EXPOSURE AREA TO FRESH AIR IMMEDIATELY. IF BREATHING HAS STOPPED, PERFORM ARTIFICIAL RESPIRATION. KEEP PERSON WARM AND AT REST. TREAT SYMPTOMATICALLY AND SUPPORTIVELY. GET MEDICAL ATTENTION IMMEDIATELY.

SKIN CONTACT: ETHOXYLATED NONYL PHENOL: **ACUTE EXPOSURE-** MAY CAUSE IRRITATION. THIS MATERIAL APPLIED TO THE SKIN OF RABBITS PRODUCED MILD IRRITATION AND A MODERATE DOSE WAS LETHAL BY SKIN ABSORPTION. **CHRONIC EXPOSURE-** PROLONGED OR REPEATED EXPOSURE TO CONCENTRATED ETHOXYLATED ALKYLPHENOLS DRY AND DEFAT THE SKIN CAUSING IRRITATION AND DERMATITIS.
FIRST AID- REMOVE CONTAMINATED CLOTHING AND SHOES IMMEDIATELY. WASH AFFECTED AREA WITH SOAP OR MILD DETERGENT AND LARGE AMOUNTS OF WATER UNTIL NO EVIDENCE OF CHEMICAL REMAINS (APPROXIMATELY 15-20 MINUTES). GET MEDICAL ATTENTION IMMEDIATELY.

EYE CONTACT: ETHOXYLATED NONYL PHENOL: IRRITANT. **ACUTE EXPOSURE-** MAY CAUSE SEVERE IRRITATION; 5 MG APPLIED TO THE EYES OF RABBITS PRODUCED SEVERE IRRITATION. ALKYL ARYL POLYETHER ALCOHOLS, IN CONCENTRATED FORM, CAUSED MODERATE TO SEVERE CORNEAL DAMAGE IN THE EYES OF RABBITS. SOME NONIONIC SURFACTANTS HAVE A LOCAL ANESTHETIC EFFECT ON THE CORNEA, THIS EFFECT MAY ELIMINATE THE WARNING DISCOMFORT AND ALLOW DAMAGE TO OCCUR TO THE EYE. **CHRONIC EXPOSURE-** PROLONGED OR REPEATED CONTACT MAY CAUSE SYMPTOMS AS DISCRIBED IN ACUTE EXPOSURE.
FIRST AID- WASH EYES IMMEDIATELY WITH LARGE AMOUNTS OF WATER OR NORMAL SALINE, OCCASIONALLY LIFTING UPPER AND LOWER LIDS, UNTIL NO EVIDENCE OF CHEMICAL REMAINS (APPROXIMATELY 15-20 MINUTES). GET MEDICAL ATTENTION IMMEDIATELY.

INGESTION: ETHOXYLATED NONYL PHENOL: **ACUTE EXPOSURE-** IN ANIMAL STUDIES, ETHOXYLATED ALKYLPHENOLS PRODUCED DIARRHEA, BLOATING AND OTHER SYMPTOMS OF GASTROINTESTINAL IRRITATION WITH LITTLE INTESTINAL ABSORPTION OR DECOMPOSITION. A MODERATE DOSE WAS LETHAL IN RATS. **CHRONIC EXPOSURE-** NO DATA AVAILABLE.
FIRST AID- TREAT SYMPTOMATICALLY AND SUPPORTIVELY. GET MEDICAL ATTENTION IMMEDIATELY. IF VOMITING OCCURS, KEEP HEAD LOWER THAN HIPS TO PREVENT ASPIRATION.
ANTIDOTE: NO SPECIFIC ANTIDOTE. TREAT SYMPTOMATICALLY AND SUPPORTIVELY.

REACTIVITY

REACTIVITY: STABLE UNDER NORMAL TEMPERATURES AND PRESSURES.
INCOMPATIBILITIES: ETHOXYLATED NONYL PHENOL: OXIDIZERS: MAY REACT VIOLENTLY OR VIGOROUSLY.
DECOMPOSITION: THERMAL DECOMPOSITION MAY RELEASE ACRID SMOKE AND IRRITATING FUMES.
POLYMERIZATION: HAZARDOUS POLYMERIZATION HAS NOT BEEN REPORTED TO OCCUR UNDER NORMAL TEMPERATURES AND PRESSURES.

CONDITIONS TO AVOID

MAY BURN BUT DOES NOT IGNITE READILY. AVOID CONTACT WITH STRONG OXIDIZERS, EXCESSIVE HEAT, SPARKS, OR OPEN FLAME.
TRACES OF ETHYLENE OXIDE MAY BE PRESENT IN ETHOXYLATES. THESE TRACES MAY ACCUMULATE IN THE HEADSPACE AREAS OF STORAGE AND TRANSPORT VESSELS.

SPILL AND LEAK PROCEDURES

OCCUPATIONAL SPILL: STOP LEAK IF YOU CAN DO IT WITHOUT RISK. FOR SMALL SPILLS, TAKE UP WITH SAND OR OTHER ABSORBENT MATERIAL AND PLACE INTO CLEAN, DRY CONTAINERS FOR LATER DISPOSAL. KEEP UNNECESSARY PEOPLE AWAY. ISOLATE HAZARD AREA AND DENY ENTRY.

PROTECTIVE EQUIPMENT

VENTILATION: PROVIDE LOCAL EXHAUST OR GENERAL DILUTION VENTILATION SYSTEM.

RESPIRATOR: THE FOLLOWING RESPIRATORS ARE RECOMMENDED BASED ON INFORMATION FOUND IN THE PHYSICAL DATA, TOXICITY AND HEALTH EFFECTS SECTIONS. THEY ARE RANKED IN ORDER FROM MINIMUM TO MAXIMUM RESPIRATORY PROTECTION. THE SPECIFIC RESPIRATOR SELECTED MUST BE BASED ON CONTAMINATION LEVELS FOUND IN THE WORK PLACE, MUST NOT EXCEED THE WORKING LIMITS OF THE RESPIRATOR AND BE JOINTLY APPROVED BY THE NATIONAL INSTITUTE FOR OCCUPATIONAL SAFETY AND HEALTH AND THE MINE SAFETY AND HEALTH ADMINISTRATION (NIOSH-MSHA).

CHEMICAL CARTRIDGE RESPIRATOR WITH AN ORGANIC VAPOR CARTRIDGE(S) WITH A FULL FACEPIECE.

GAS MASK WITH ORGANIC VAPOR CANISTER (CHIN-STYLE OR FRONT- OR BACK-MOUNTED CANISTER) WITH A FULL FACEPIECE.

TYPE 'C' SUPPLIED-AIR RESPIRATOR WITH A FULL FACEPIECE OPERATED IN PRESSURE-DEMAND OR OTHER POSITIVE PRESSURE MODE OR WITH A FULL FACEPIECE, HELMET OR HOOD OPERATED IN CONTINUOUS-FLOW MODE.

SELF-CONTAINED BREATHING APPARATUS WITH A FULL FACEPIECE OPERATED IN PRESSURE-DEMAND OR OTHER POSITIVE PRESSURE MODE.

FOR FIREFIGHTING AND OTHER IMMEDIATELY DANGEROUS TO LIFE OR HEALTH CONDITIONS:

SELF-CONTAINED BREATHING APPARATUS WITH FULL FACEPIECE OPERATED IN PRESSURE-DEMAND OR OTHER POSITIVE PRESSURE MODE.

SUPPLIED-AIR RESPIRATOR WITH FULL FACEPIECE AND OPERATED IN PRESSURE-DEMAND OR OTHER POSITIVE PRESSURE MODE IN COMBINATION WITH AN AUXILIARY SELF-CONTAINED BREATHING APPARATUS OPERATED IN PRESSURE-DEMAND OR OTHER POSITIVE PRESSURE MODE.

CLOTHING: EMPLOYEE MUST WEAR APPROPRIATE PROTECTIVE (IMPERVIOUS) CLOTHING AND EQUIPMENT TO PREVENT REPEATED OR PROLONGED SKIN CONTACT WITH THIS SUBSTANCE.

GLOVES: EMPLOYEE MUST WEAR APPROPRIATE PROTECTIVE GLOVES TO PREVENT CONTACT WITH THIS SUBSTANCE.

EYE PROTECTION: EMPLOYEE MUST WEAR SPLASH-PROOF OR DUST-RESISTANT SAFETY GOGGLES TO PREVENT CONTACT WITH THIS SUBSTANCE.

EMERGENCY WASH FACILITIES: WHERE THERE IS ANY POSSIBILITY THAT AN EMPLOYEE'S EYES AND/OR SKIN MAY BE EXPOSED TO THIS SUBSTANCE, THE EMPLOYER SHOULD PROVIDE AN EYE WASH FOUNTAIN AND QUICK DRENCH SHOWER WITHIN THE IMMEDIATE WORK AREA FOR EMERGENCY USE.

AUTHORIZED BY- OCCUPATIONAL HEALTH SERVICES, INC.

CREATION DATE: 10/04/89 ***REVISION DATE:*** 05/17/90

MATERIAL SAFETY DATA SHEET

OCCUPATIONAL HEALTH SERVICES, INC.
AGRICULTURE AND PESTICIDE DIVISION
450 SEVENTH AVENUE, SUITE 2407
NEW YORK, NEW YORK 10123
1-800-445-MSDS OR (212) 967-1100

EMERGENCY CONTACT:
JOHN S. BRANSFORD, JR. (615) 292-1180

SUBSTANCE IDENTIFICATION

CAS-NUMBER 95-50-1

SUBSTANCE: **O-DICHLOROBENZENE, LIQUID**

TRADE NAMES/SYNONYMS: BENZENE, 1,2-DICHLORO-; 1,2-DICHLOROBENZENE; BENZENE, O-DICHLORO-; O-DICHLOROBENZENE; CHLOROBEN; DOWTHERM E; STCC 4941127; UN 1591; C6H2CL2; PST16970

CHEMICAL FAMILY: HALOGEN COMPOUND, AROMATIC

MOLECULAR FORMULA: C6-H4-CL2

MOLECULAR WEIGHT: 147.00

CERCLA RATINGS (SCALE 0-3): HEALTH=2 FIRE=2 REACTIVITY=0 PERSISTENCE=3

NFPA RATINGS (SCALE 0-4): HEALTH=2 FIRE=2 REACTIVITY=0

COMPONENTS AND CONTAMINANTS

COMPONENT: O-DICHLOROBENZENE ***PERCENT:*** 100.0
CAS# 95-50-1

OTHER CONTAMINANTS: NONE

EXPOSURE LIMITS: O-DICHLOROBENZENE, LIQUID: 50 PPM (300 MG/M3) OSHA CEILING 50 PPM (300 MG/M3) ACGIH CEILING

100 POUNDS CERCLA SECTION 103 REPORTABLE QUANTITY SUBJECT TO SARA SECTION 313 ANNUAL TOXIC CHEMICAL RELEASE REPORTING

PHYSICAL DATA

DESCRIPTION: COLORLESS TO PALE YELLOW LIQUID WITH A PLEASANT AROMATIC ODOR.

BOILING POINT: 358 F (181 C) ***MELTING POINT:*** 1 F (-17 C)

SPECIFIC GRAVITY: 1.3048 @ 20 C ***VAPOR PRESSURE:*** 1.2 MMHG @ 20 C

EVAPORATION RATE: (BUTYL ACETATE=1) <1.0 ***SOLUBILITY IN WATER:*** 0.015% @ 20 C

ODOR THRESHOLD: 50 PPM ***VAPOR DENSITY:*** 5.1

SOLVENT SOLUBILITY: SOLUBLE IN ALCOHOL, ETHER, OILS, FATS, BENZENE, CARBON TETRACHLORIDE, LIGROIN.

FIRE AND EXPLOSION DATA

FIRE AND EXPLOSION HAZARD: MODERATE FIRE HAZARD WHEN EXPOSED TO HEAT OR FLAME.

VAPORS ARE HEAVIER THAN AIR AND MAY TRAVEL A CONSIDERABLE DISTANCE TO A SOURCE OF IGNITION AND FLASH BACK.

VAPOR-AIR MIXTURES ARE EXPLOSIVE ABOVE FLASH POINT.

FLASH POINT: 151 F (66 C) (CC) ***UPPER EXPLOSIVE LIMIT:*** 9.2%

LOWER EXPLOSIVE LIMIT: 2.2% ***AUTOIGNITION TEMP.:*** 1198 F (648 C)

FLAMMABILITY CLASS(OSHA): IIIA

FIREFIGHTING MEDIA: DRY CHEMICAL, CARBON DIOXIDE, HALON, WATER SPRAY OR STANDARD FOAM (1987 EMERGENCY RESPONSE GUIDEBOOK, DOT P 5800.4).

FOR LARGER FIRES, USE WATER SPRAY, FOG OR STANDARD FOAM (1987 EMERGENCY RESPONSE GUIDEBOOK, DOT P 5800.4).

FIREFIGHTING: MOVE CONTAINER FROM FIRE AREA IF POSSIBLE. COOL FIRE-EXPOSED CONTAINERS WITH WATER FROM SIDE UNTIL WELL AFTER FIRE IS OUT. STAY AWAY FROM STORAGE TANK ENDS. FOR MASSIVE FIRE IN STORAGE AREA, USE UNMANNED HOSE HOLDER OR MONITOR NOZZLES, ELSE WITHDRAW FROM AREA AND LET FIRE BURN. WITHDRAW IMMEDIATELY IN CASE OF RISING SOUND FROM VENTING SAFETY DEVICE OR ANY DISCOLORATION OF STORAGE TANK DUE TO FIRE (1987 EMERGENCY RESPONSE GUIDEBOOK, DOT P 5800.4, GUIDE PAGE 27).

EXTINGUISH ONLY IF FLOW CAN BE STOPPED; USE FLOODING AMOUNTS OF WATER AS A FOG, SOLID STREAMS MAY BE INEFFECTIVE. COOL CONTAINERS WITH FLOODING AMOUNTS OF WATER, APPLY FROM AS FAR A DISTANCE AS POSSIBLE. AVOID BREATHING VAPORS, KEEP UPWIND.

WATER MAY BE USED TO BLANKET FIRE (NFPA 325M FIRE HAZARD PROPERTIES OF FLAMMABLE LIQUIDS, GASES, AND VOLATILE SOLIDS, 1984)

TRANSPORTATION DATA

DEPARTMENT OF TRANSPORTATION HAZARD CLASSIFICATION 49 CFR 172.101: ORM-A

DEPARTMENT OF TRANSPORTATION LABELING REQUIREMENTS 49 CFR 172.101 AND SUBPART E: NONE

DEPARTMENT OF TRANSPORTATION PACKAGING REQUIREMENTS: 49 CFR 173.510 EXCEPTIONS: 49 CFR 173.505

TOXICITY

O-DICHLOROBENZENE: IRRITATION DATA: 100 MG/30 SECONDS RINSED EYE-RABBIT MILD. TOXICITY DATA: 800 PPM/24 HOURS INHALATION-GUINEA PIG LCLO; 821 PPM/7 HOURS INHALATION-RAT LCLO; >10,000 MG/KG SKIN-RABBIT LD50; 500 MG/KG ORAL-RAT LD50; 4386 MG/KG ORAL-MOUSE LD50; 500 MG/KG ORAL-RABBIT LD50; 2 GM/KG ORAL-GUINEA PIG LDLO; 400 MG/KG INTRAVENOUS-MOUSE LDLO; 250 MG/KG INTRAVENOUS-RABBIT LDLO; 1228 MG/KG INTRAPERITONEAL-MOUSE LD50; 840 MG/KG INTRAPERITONEAL-RAT LD50; MUTAGENIC DATA (RTECS); REPRODUCTIVE EFFECTS DATA (RTECS). CARCINOGEN STATUS: HUMAN INADEQUATE EVIDENCE, ANIMAL INADEQUATE EVIDENCE (IARC GROUP-3). LOCAL EFFECTS: IRRITANT- INHALATION, SKIN, EYE. ACUTE TOXICITY LEVEL: TOXIC BY INGESTION; SLIGHTLY TOXIC BY DERMAL ABSORPTION. TARGET EFFECTS: CENTRAL NERVOUS SYSTEM DEPRESSANT; POISONING MAY ALSO AFFECT THE BLOOD, KIDNEYS AND LIVER. AT INCREASED RISK FROM EXPOSURE: PERSONS WITH PREEXISTING HEPATIC, RENAL, LUNG, CENTRAL NERVOUS SYSTEM, BLOOD OR METABOLIC DISORDERS.

HEALTH EFFECTS AND FIRST AID

INHALATION: O-DICHLOROBENZENE: IRRITANT/NARCOTIC. 1700 PPM IMMEDIATELY DANGEROUS TO LIFE AND HEALTH. **ACUTE EXPOSURE-** VAPORS MAY CAUSE IRRITATION OF THE NOSE, THROAT, AND UPPER RESPIRATORY TRACT. LONG EXPOSURE TO HIGH CONCENTRATIONS MAY CAUSE ABDOMINAL TENDERNESS, JAUNDICE, AND CENTRAL NERVOUS SYSTEM DEPRESSION. OTHER EFFECTS MAY INCLUDE DIZZINESS, SEVERE HEADACHE, PERIORBITAL SWELLING, FATIGUE, NAUSEA, UNCONSCIOUSNESS, AND DEATH. RATS EXPOSED TO 539 PPM FOR 3 HOURS SHOWED PATHOLOGICAL FINDINGS INCLUDING CENTROLOBULAR NECROSIS OF THE LIVER AND CLOUDY SWELLING OF THE TUBULAR EPITHELIUM OF THE KIDNEYS. LARGE DOSES IN RATS PRODUCED DEPRESSED CONDITIONED REFLEX ACTIVITY, DECREASED ERYTHROPOIESIS, NEUTROPENIA, AND A RISE IN

URINARY STEROIDS. **CHRONIC EXPOSURE-** ACCIDENTAL EXPOSURE, 8 HOURS/DAY FOR 4 DAYS, PRODUCED IRRITATION OF THE NOSE AND THROAT, DIZZINESS, SEVERE HEADACHE, FATIGUE, AND NAUSEA. A FEW ISOLATED REPORTS HAVE SUGGESTED AN ASSOCIATION BETWEEN O-DICHLOROBENZENE AND AN INCREASED INCIDENCE OF BLOOD DYSCRASIAS AND LEUKEMIA IN HUMANS. EXPOSURE TO DICHLOROBENZENE IN HUMANS IS REPORTED TO CAUSE LIVER NECROSIS AND HEMOLYTIC ANEMIA. CHROMOSOME STUDIES SHOWED SIGNIFICANT ALTERATIONS IN THE LEUKOCYTES OF EXPOSED WORKERS, HOWEVER THEY APPEARED REVERSIBLE SIX MONTHS LATER. REPEATED OR PROLONGED EXPOSURE IN ANIMALS CAUSED LUNG, LIVER AND KIDNEY DAMAGE; DECREASED BODY WEIGHT GAIN; DECREASED CHOLINESTERASE ACTIVITY; AND CENTRAL NERVOUS SYSTEM DEPRESSION. REPRODUCTIVE EFFECTS HAVE BEEN REPORTED IN ANIMALS.

FIRST AID- REMOVE FROM EXPOSURE AREA TO FRESH AIR IMMEDIATELY. IF BREATHING HAS STOPPED, PERFORM ARTIFICIAL RESPIRATION. KEEP PERSON WARM AND AT REST. TREAT SYMPTOMATICALLY AND SUPPORTIVELY. GET MEDICAL ATTENTION IMMEDIATELY.

SKIN CONTACT: O-DICHLOROBENZENE: IRRITANT. **ACUTE EXPOSURE-** MAY CAUSE IRRITATION LEADING TO BLISTERING, SENSITIZATION DERMATITIS, AND PIGMENTATION. LIQUID CHLORINATED BENZENES MAY CAUSE BURNS. THERE IS NO EVIDENCE OF SIGNIFICANT ABSORPTION THROUGH THE SKIN, HOWEVER, DERMAL EXPOSURE COULD CONTRIBUTE TO THE OVERALL TOXICITY OF THE CHEMICAL. IF SUFFICIENT AMOUNTS ARE ABSORBED, EFFECTS MAY OCCUR AS DETAILED IN ACUTE INHALATION. **CHRONIC EXPOSURE-** REPEATED OR PROLONGED EXPOSURE TO IRRITANTS MAY CAUSE DERMATITIS. REPEATED DERMAL APPLICATION IN RATS PRODUCED DEATH. A FEW ISOLATED REPORTS HAVE SUGGESTED AN ASSOCIATION BETWEEN O-DICHLOROBENZENE AND AN INCREASED INCIDENCE OF BLOOD DYSCRASIAS AND LEUKEMIA IN HUMANS.

FIRST AID- REMOVE CONTAMINATED CLOTHING AND SHOES IMMEDIATELY. WASH AFFECTED AREA WITH SOAP OR MILD DETERGENT AND LARGE AMOUNTS OF WATER UNTIL NO EVIDENCE OF CHEMICAL REMAINS (APPROXIMATELY 15-20 MINUTES). GET MEDICAL ATTENTION IMMEDIATELY.

EYE CONTACT: O-DICHLOROBENZENE: IRRITANT. **ACUTE EXPOSURE-** MAY CAUSE IRRITATION TO THE CORNEA AND CONJUNCTIVA, LENS OPACITIES, BURNING, AND TISSUE DAMAGE. **CHRONIC EXPOSURE-** REPEATED OR PROLONGED EXPOSURE TO IRRITANTS MAY CAUSE CONJUNCTIVITIS.

FIRST AID- WASH EYES IMMEDIATELY WITH LARGE AMOUNTS OF WATER OR NORMAL SALINE, OCCASIONALLY LIFTING UPPER AND LOWER LIDS, UNTIL NO EVIDENCE OF CHEMICAL REMAINS (APPROXIMATELY 15-20 MINUTES). GET MEDICAL ATTENTION IMMEDIATELY.

INGESTION: O-DICHLOROBENZENE: TOXIC. **ACUTE EXPOSURE-** THE LETHAL DOSE IN RATS WAS 500 MG/KG. THE SYMPTOMS WERE NOT REPORTED. **CHRONIC EXPOSURE-** THE MAXIMUM REPORTED TOLERATED DOSE FOR RATS FED BY GAVAGE 5 DAYS/WEEK FOR 28 DAYS WAS 19-190 MG/KG PER DAY. 455 MG/KG FOR 15 DAYS RESULTED IN PORPHYRIA WITH HEPATIC NECROSIS AND FATTY CHANGES. PROLONGED FEEDING IN ANIMALS RESULTED IN AN INCREASE IN LIVER AND KIDNEY WEIGHTS, SLIGHT HISTOPATHOLOGICAL CHANGES IN THE LIVER, AND MULTIFOCAL MINERALIZATION OF THE MYOCARDIAL FIBERS OF THE HEART AND SKELETAL MUSCLES.

FIRST AID- IF THE PERSON IS CONSCIOUS AND NOT CONVULSING, INDUCE EMESIS BY GIVING SYRUP OF IPECAC (KEEPING THE HEAD BELOW THE HIPS TO PREVENT ASPIRATION), FOLLOWED BY WATER. REPEAT IN 20 MINUTES IF NOT EFFECTIVE INITIALLY. IN PATIENTS WITH DEPRESSED RESPIRATION OR IF EMESIS IS NOT PRODUCED, PERFORM GASTRIC LAVAGE CAUTIOUSLY (DREISBACH, HANDBOOK OF POISONING, 12TH ED.). TREAT SYMPTOMATICALLY AND SUPPORTIVELY. GASTRIC LAVAGE SHOULD BE PERFORMED BY QUALIFIED MEDICAL PERSONNEL. GET MEDICAL ATTENTION IMMEDIATELY.

ANTIDOTE: NO SPECIFIC ANTIDOTE. TREAT SYMPTOMATICALLY AND SUPPORTIVELY.

REACTIVITY

REACTIVITY: STABLE UNDER NORMAL TEMPERATURES AND PRESSURES.

INCOMPATIBILITIES: O-DICHLORBENZENE, LIQUID: ALUMINUM (HOT) OR ALUMINUM ALLOYS: TEMPERATURE AND PRESSURE INCREASE IN A CLOSED CONTAINER. ETHYLENE DICHLORIDE AND PROPYLENE DICHLORIDE: TEMPERATURE AND PRESSURE INCREASE IN A CLOSED CONTAINER. OXIDIZERS (STRONG): FIRE AND EXPLOSION HAZARD. PLASTICS, RUBBER, AND COATINGS: MAY BE ATTACKED.

DECOMPOSITION: THERMAL DECOMPOSITION PRODUCTS MAY INCLUDE TOXIC AND/OR CORROSIVE VAPORS OF HYDROGEN CHLORIDE, CHLORINE, AND CARBON MONOXIDE.

POLYMERIZATION: HAZARDOUS POLYMERIZATION HAS NOT BEEN REPORTED TO OCCUR UNDER NORMAL TEMPERATURES AND PRESSURES.

STORAGE AND DISPOSAL

OBSERVE ALL FEDERAL, STATE AND LOCAL REGULATIONS WHEN STORING OR DISPOSING OF THIS SUBSTANCE. FOR ASSISTANCE, CONTACT THE DISTRICT DIRECTOR OF THE ENVIRONMENTAL PROTECTION AGENCY.

****STORAGE****

STORE IN ACCORDANCE WITH 29 CFR 1910.106.

DISPOSAL MUST BE IN ACCORDANCE WITH STANDARDS APPLICABLE TO GENERATORS OF HAZARDOUS WASTE, 40CFR 262. EPA HAZARDOUS WASTE NUMBER U070.

STORE AWAY FROM INCOMPATIBLE SUBSTANCES.

CONDITIONS TO AVOID

AVOID CONTACT WITH HEAT, SPARKS, FLAMES, OR OTHER SOURCES OF IGNITION. VAPORS MAY BE EXPLOSIVE. AVOID OVERHEATING OF CONTAINERS; CONTAINERS MAY VIOLENTLY RUPTURE IN HEAT OF FIRE. AVOID CONTAMINATION OF WATER SOURCES.

SPILL AND LEAK PROCEDURES

SOIL SPILL: DIG HOLDING AREA SUCH AS LAGOON, POND OR PIT FOR CONTAINMENT. DIKE FLOW OF SPILLED MATERIAL USING SOIL OR SANDBAGS OR FOAMED BARRIERS SUCH AS POLYURETHANE OR CONCRETE.

USE CEMENT POWDER OR FLY ASH TO ABSORB LIQUID MASS.

IMMOBILIZE SPILL WITH UNIVERSAL GELLING AGENT.

WATER SPILL: USE ACTIVATED CARBON TO ABSORB SPILLED SUBSTANCE THAT IS DISSOLVED.

USE MECHANICAL DREDGES OR LIFTS TO EXTRACT IMMOBILIZED MASSES OF POLLUTION AND PRECIPITATES.

TRAP SPILLED MATERIAL AT BOTTOM IN DEEP WATER POCKETS, EXCAVATED HOLDING AREAS OR WITHIN SAND BAG BARRIERS.

USE SUCTION HOSES TO REMOVE TRAPPED SPILL MATERIAL.

OCCUPATIONAL SPILL: SHUT OFF IGNITION SOURCES. STOP LEAK IF YOU CAN DO IT WITHOUT RISK. USE WATER SPRAY TO REDUCE VAPORS. FOR SMALL SPILLS, TAKE UP WITH SAND OR OTHER ABSORBENT MATERIAL AND PLACE INTO CONTAINERS FOR LATER DISPOSAL. FOR LARGER SPILLS, DIKE FAR AHEAD OF SPILL FOR LATER DISPOSAL. NO SMOKING, FLAMES OR FLARES IN HAZARD AREA. KEEP UNNECESSARY PEOPLE AWAY; ISOLATE HAZARD AREA AND RESTRICT ENTRY.

REPORTABLE QUANTITY (RQ): 100 POUNDS THE SUPERFUND AMENDMENTS AND REAUTHORIZATION ACT (SARA) SECTION 304 REQUIRES THAT A RELEASE EQUAL TO OR GREATER THAN THE REPORTABLE QUANTITY FOR THIS SUBSTANCE BE IMMEDIATELY REPORTED TO THE LOCAL EMERGENCY PLANNING COMMITTEE AND THE STATE EMERGENCY RESPONSE COMMISSION (40 CFR 355.40). IF THE RELEASE OF THIS SUBSTANCE IS REPORTABLE UNDER CERCLA SECTION 103, THE NATIONAL RESPONSE CENTER MUST BE NOTIFIED IMMEDIATELY AT (800) 424-8802 OR (202) 426-2675 IN THE METROPOLITAN WASHINGTON, D.C. AREA (40 CFR 302.6).

PROTECTIVE EQUIPMENT

VENTILATION: PROVIDE LOCAL EXHAUST OR PROCESS ENCLOSURE VENTILATION TO MEET PUBLISHED EXPOSURE LIMITS.

RESPIRATOR: THE FOLLOWING RESPIRATORS AND MAXIMUM USE CONCENTRATIONS ARE RECOMMENDATIONS BY THE U.S. DEPARTMENT OF HEALTH AND HUMAN SERVICES, NIOSH POCKET GUIDE TO CHEMICAL HAZARDS; NIOSH CRITERIA DOCUMENTS OR BY THE U.S. DEPARTMENT OF LABOR, 29 CFR 1910 SUBPART Z. THE SPECIFIC RESPIRATOR SELECTED MUST BE BASED ON CONTAMINATION LEVELS FOUND IN THE WORK PLACE, MUST NOT EXCEED THE WORKING LIMITS OF THE RESPIRATOR AND BE JOINTLY APPROVED BY THE NATIONAL INSTITUTE FOR OCCUPATIONAL SAFETY AND HEALTH AND THE MINE SAFETY AND HEALTH ADMINISTRATION (NIOSH-MSHA).

O-DICHLOROBENZENE:

1000 PPM- ANY POWERED AIR-PURIFYING RESPIRATOR WITH ORGANIC VAPOR CARTRIDGE(S). ANY CHEMICAL CARTRIDGE RESPIRATOR WITH A FULL FACEPIECE AND ORGANIC VAPOR CARTRIDGE(S).

1250 PPM- ANY SUPPLIED AIR RESPIRATOR OPERATED IN A CONTINUOUS FLOW MODE.

1700 PPM- ANY AIR-PURIFYING FULL FACEPIECE RESPIRATOR (GAS MASK) WITH A CHIN-STYLE OR FRONT- OR BACK-MOUNTED ORGANIC VAPOR CANISTER. ANY SELF-CONTAINED BREATHING APPARATUS WITH A FULL FACEPIECE. ANY SUPPLIED-AIR RESPIRATOR WITH A FULL FACEPIECE.

ESCAPE- ANY AIR-PURIFYING FULL FACEPIECE RESPIRATOR (GAS MASK) WITH A CHIN-STYLE OR FRONT- OR BACK-MOUNTED ORGANIC VAPOR CANISTER. ANY APPROPRIATE ESCAPE-TYPE SELF-CONTAINED BREATHING APPARATUS. FOR FIREFIGHTING AND OTHER IMMEDIATELY DANGEROUS TO LIFE OR HEALTH CONDITIONS:

SELF-CONTAINED BREATHING APPARATUS WITH FULL FACEPIECE OPERATED IN PRESSURE-DEMAND OR OTHER POSITIVE PRESSURE MODE.

SUPPLIED-AIR RESPIRATOR WITH FULL FACEPIECE AND OPERATED IN PRESSURE-DEMAND OR OTHER POSITIVE PRESSURE MODE IN COMBINATION WITH AN AUXILIARY SELF-CONTAINED BREATHING APPARATUS OPERATED IN PRESSURE-

DEMAND OR OTHER POSITIVE PRESSURE MODE.

CLOTHING: EMPLOYEE MUST WEAR APPROPRIATE PROTECTIVE (IMPERVIOUS) CLOTHING AND EQUIPMENT TO PREVENT REPEATED OR PROLONGED SKIN CONTACT WITH THIS SUBSTANCE.

GLOVES: EMPLOYEE MUST WEAR APPROPRIATE PROTECTIVE GLOVES TO PREVENT CONTACT WITH THIS SUBSTANCE.

EYE PROTECTION: EMPLOYEE MUST WEAR SPLASH-PROOF OR DUST-RESISTANT SAFETY GOGGLES TO PREVENT EYE CONTACT WITH THIS SUBSTANCE.
EMERGENCY EYE WASH: WHERE THERE IS ANY POSSIBILITY THAT AN EMPLOYEE'S EYES MAY BE EXPOSED TO THIS SUBSTANCE, THE EMPLOYER SHOULD PROVIDE AN EYE WASH FOUNTAIN WITHIN THE IMMEDIATE WORK AREA FOR EMERGENCY USE.

AUTHORIZED BY- OCCUPATIONAL HEALTH SERVICES, INC.
CREATION DATE: 10/04/89 ***REVISION DATE:*** 07/12/90

MATERIAL SAFETY DATA SHEET

OCCUPATIONAL HEALTH SERVICES, INC.
AGRICULTURE AND PESTICIDE DIVISION
450 SEVENTH AVENUE, SUITE 2407
NEW YORK, NEW YORK 10123
1-800-445-MSDS OR (212) 967-1100

EMERGENCY CONTACT:
JOHN S. BRANSFORD, JR. (615) 292-1180

SUBSTANCE IDENTIFICATION

CAS-NUMBER 111-87-5

SUBSTANCE: N-OCTYL ALCOHOL

TRADE NAMES/SYNONYMS: 1-OCTANOL; OCTYL ALCOHOL; CAPRYLIC ALCOHOL; 1-HYDROXYOCTANE; HEPTYL CARBINOL; OCTANOL; N-OCTANOL; PRIMARY OCTYL ALCOHOL; STCC 4913158; C8H18O; PST17270

CHEMICAL FAMILY: ALCOHOL, ALIPHATIC

MOLECULAR FORMULA: C-H3-(C-H2)6-C-H2-O-H

MOLECULAR WEIGHT: 130.23

CERCLA RATINGS (SCALE 0-3): HEALTH=2 FIRE=2 REACTIVITY=0 PERSISTENCE=0

NFPA RATINGS (SCALE 0-4): HEALTH=1 FIRE=2 REACTIVITY=0

COMPONENTS AND CONTAMINANTS

COMPONENT: N-OCTYL ALCOHOL ***PERCENT:*** 100.0
CAS# 111-87-5

OTHER CONTAMINANTS: NONE

EXPOSURE LIMITS: NO OCCUPATIONAL EXPOSURE LIMITS ESTABLISHED BY OSHA, ACGIH, OR NIOSH.

PHYSICAL DATA

DESCRIPTION: CLEAR COLORLESS LIQUID WITH A PENETRATING, AROMATIC ODOR.

BOILING POINT: 381 F (194 C) ***MELTING POINT:*** 1 F (-17 C)

SPECIFIC GRAVITY: 0.8270 ***VISCOSITY:*** 8.4 CPS @ 20 C

VAPOR PRESSURE: 0.2 MMHG @ 20 C ***SOLUBILITY IN WATER:*** 0.06% @ 25 C

VAPOR DENSITY: 4.5

SOLVENT SOLUBILITY: SOLUBLE IN ALCOHOL, ETHER, CHLOROFORM, MINERAL OIL, PETROLEUM ETHER, PROPYLENE GLYCOL; INSOLUBLE IN GLYCEROL.

FIRE AND EXPLOSION DATA

FIRE AND EXPLOSION HAZARD: MODERATE FIRE HAZARD WHEN EXPOSED TO HEAT OR FLAME.
VAPORS ARE HEAVIER THAN AIR AND MAY TRAVEL A CONSIDERABLE DISTANCE TO A SOURCE OF IGNITION AND FLASH BACK.

FLASH POINT: 178 F (81 C) (CC) ***FLAMMABILITY CLASS(OSHA):*** IIIA

FIREFIGHTING MEDIA: DRY CHEMICAL, CARBON DIOXIDE, HALON, WATER SPRAY OR ALCOHOL FOAM (1987 EMERGENCY RESPONSE GUIDEBOOK, DOT P 5800.4).
FOR LARGER FIRES, USE WATER SPRAY, FOG OR ALCOHOL FOAM (1987 EMERGENCY RESPONSE GUIDEBOOK, DOT P 5800.4).

FIREFIGHTING: MOVE CONTAINER FROM FIRE AREA IF POSSIBLE. COOL FIRE-EXPOSED CONTAINERS WITH WATER FROM SIDE UNTIL WELL AFTER FIRE IS OUT. STAY AWAY FROM STORAGE TANK ENDS. FOR MASSIVE FIRE IN STORAGE AREA, USE UNMANNED HOSE HOLDER OR MONITOR NOZZLES, ELSE WITHDRAW FROM AREA AND LET FIRE BURN. WITHDRAW IMMEDIATELY IN CASE OF RISING SOUND FROM VENTING SAFETY DEVICE OR ANY DISCOLORATION OF STORAGE TANK DUE TO FIRE (1987 EMERGENCY RESPONSE GUIDEBOOK, DOT P 5800.4, GUIDE PAGE 26). EXTINGUISH ONLY IF FLOW CAN BE STOPPED. USE FLOODING AMOUNTS OF WATER AS FOG; SOLID STREAMS MAY BE INEFFECTIVE. COOL CONTAINERS WITH FLOODING AMOUNTS OF WATER FROM AS FAR A DISTANCE AS POSSIBLE. AVOID BREATHING VAPORS; KEEP UPWIND.

TRANSPORTATION DATA

DEPARTMENT OF TRANSPORTATION HAZARD CLASSIFICATION 49 CFR 172.101: COMBUSTIBLE LIQUID
DEPARTMENT OF TRANSPORTATION LABELING REQUIREMENTS 49 CFR 172.101 AND SUBPART E: NONE
DEPARTMENT OF TRANSPORTATION PACKAGING REQUIREMENTS: NONE
EXCEPTIONS: 49 CFR 173.118A

TOXICITY

N-OCTYL ALCOHOL (1-OCTANOL): IRRITATION DATA: 500 MG/24 HOURS SKIN-RABBIT MILD. TOXICITY DATA: 5600 MG/M3/4 HOURS INHALATION-RAT LCLO; 1790 MG/KG ORAL-MOUSE LD50; 69 MG/KG INTRAVENOUS-MOUSE LD50; 1240 MG/KG PARENTERAL-FROG LDLO; 4 GM/KG UNREPORTED-MAMMAL LD50; MUTAGENIC DATA (RTECS). CARCINOGEN STATUS: NONE. ACUTE TOXICITY LEVEL: MODERATELY TOXIC BY INGESTION. TARGET EFFECTS: CENTRAL NERVOUS SYSTEM DEPRESSANT.

HEALTH EFFECTS AND FIRST AID

INHALATION: N-OCTYL ALCOHOL (1-OCTANOL): **ACUTE EXPOSURE-** MAY BE IRRITATING IN HIGH CONCENTRATIONS. THREE OF 10 RATS EXPOSED TO 5600 MG/M3 FOR 4 HOURS, DIED WITHIN 2 DAYS FOLLOWING THE EXPOSURE; SEVERAL TREATMENT-RELATED LESIONS WERE PRESENT IN THE LUNGS. IF SUFFICIENT AMOUNTS OF HIGHER ALIPHATIC ALCOHOLS ARE INHALED SYSTEMIC TOXICITY MAY OCCUR AS DETAILED IN ACUTE INGESTION. **CHRONIC EXPOSURE-** NO DATA AVAILABLE.

FIRST AID- REMOVE FROM EXPOSURE AREA TO FRESH AIR IMMEDIATELY. IF BREATHING HAS STOPPED, PERFORM ARTIFICIAL RESPIRATION. KEEP PERSON WARM AND AT REST. TREAT SYMPTOMATICALLY AND SUPPORTIVELY. GET MEDICAL ATTENTION IMMEDIATELY.

SKIN CONTACT: N-OCTYL ALCOHOL (1-OCTANOL): **ACUTE EXPOSURE-** MAY CAUSE IRRITATION AND MAY BE ABSORBED THROUGH THE SKIN. APPLICATION OF 500 MG FOR 24 HOURS TO RABBIT SKIN CAUSED MILD IRRITATION. **CHRONIC EXPOSURE-** REPEATED AND PROLONGED EXPOSURE MAY CAUSE DRY SKIN AND DERMATITIS DUE TO DEFATTING ACTION.

FIRST AID- REMOVE CONTAMINATED CLOTHING AND SHOES IMMEDIATELY. WASH AFFECTED AREA WITH SOAP OR MILD DETERGENT AND LARGE AMOUNTS OF WATER UNTIL NO EVIDENCE OF CHEMICAL REMAINS (APPROXIMATELY 15-20 MINUTES). GET MEDICAL ATTENTION IMMEDIATELY.

EYE CONTACT: N-OCTYL ALCOHOL (1-OCTANOL): **ACUTE EXPOSURE-** DIRECT CONTACT MAY CAUSE IRRITATION. **CHRONIC EXPOSURE-** NO DATA AVAILABLE.

FIRST AID- WASH EYES IMMEDIATELY WITH LARGE AMOUNTS OF WATER OR NORMAL SALINE, OCCASIONALLY LIFTING UPPER AND LOWER LIDS, UNTIL NO EVIDENCE OF CHEMICAL REMAINS (APPROXIMATELY 15-20 MINUTES). GET MEDICAL ATTENTION IMMEDIATELY.

INGESTION: N-OCTYL ALCOHOL (1-OCTANOL): NARCOTIC. **ACUTE EXPOSURE-** HIGHER ALIPHATIC ALCOHOLS MAY CAUSE GASTROINTESTINAL EFFECTS INCLUDING NAUSEA, VOMITING AND DIARRHEA, AND CENTRAL NERVOUS SYSTEM DEPRESSION WITH SYMPTOMS OF HEADACHE, MUSCLE WEAKNESS, GIDDINESS, ATAXIA, CONFUSION, DELIRIUM, COMA AND DEATH DUE TO RESPIRATORY FAILURE. OTHER SYMPTOMS OF INTOXICATION MAY INCLUDE DISTURBANCES OF CARDIAC RHYTHM AND CARDIAC FAILURE, GASTROINTESTINAL HEMORRHAGE, PULMONARY EDEMA, AND LIVER AND KIDNEY DAMAGE. ASPIRATION MAY ALSO BE POSSIBLE. **CHRONIC EXPOSURE-** NO DATA AVAILABLE.

FIRST AID- REMOVE INGESTED MATERIAL BY GASTRIC LAVAGE OR EMESIS. GIVE ARTIFICIAL RESPIRATION WITH OXYGEN IF RESPIRATION IS DEPRESSED. (DREISBACH HANDBOOK OF POISONING, 11TH ED.). GET MEDICAL ATTENTION IMMEDIATELY. ADMINISTRATION OF GASTRIC LAVAGE SHOULD BE PERFORMED BY QUALIFIED MEDICAL PERSONNEL.

ANTIDOTE: NO SPECIFIC ANTIDOTE. TREAT SYMPTOMATICALLY AND SUPPORTIVELY.

REACTIVITY

REACTIVITY: STABLE UNDER NORMAL TEMPERATURES AND PRESSURES.

INCOMPATIBILITIES: N-OCTYL ALCOHOL (1-OCTANOL): ACID CHLORIDES: INCOMPATIBLE. ACIDS: INCOMPATIBLE. OXIDIZERS (STRONG): FIRE AND EXPLOSION HAZARD. SEE ALSO ALCOHOLS.
ALCOHOLS: ACETALDEHYDE: VIOLENT CONDENSATION REACTION. BARIUM PERCHLORATE: FORMATION OF HIGHLY EXPLOSIVE PERCHLORIC ESTER ON REFLUXING. CHLORINE: FORMATION OF HIGHLY EXPLOSIVE ALKYL HYPOCHLORITES. DIETHYL ALUMINUM BROMIDE: SPONTANEOUS IGNITION.

ETHYLENE OXIDE: POSSIBLE EXPLOSION. HEXAMETHYLENE DIISOCYANATE: POSSIBLE EXPLOSION IN ABSENCE OF SOLVENT. HYDROGEN PEROXIDE + SULFURIC ACID: POSSIBLE EXPLOSION. HYPOCHLOROUS ACID: FORMATION OF HIGHLY EXPLOSIVE ALKYL HYPOCHLORITES. ISOCYANATES: POSSIBLE EXPLOSION IN ABSENCE OF SOLVENT. LITHIUM ALUMINUM HYDRIDE: VIGOROUS REACTION. NITROGEN TETROXIDE: POSSIBLE EXPLOSION. PERCHLORIC ACID (HOT): DANGEROUS INTERACTION. PERMONOSULFURIC ACID: POSSIBLE EXPLOSION ON CONTACT WITH PRIMARY OR SECONDARY ALCOHOLS. TRI-ISO-BUTYL ALUMINUM: VIOLENT REACTION.

DECOMPOSITION: THERMAL DECOMPOSITION PRODUCTS MAY INCLUDE TOXIC OXIDES OF CARBON.

POLYMERIZATION: HAZARDOUS POLYMERIZATION HAS NOT BEEN REPORTED TO OCCUR UNDER NORMAL TEMPERATURES AND PRESSURES.

STORAGE AND DISPOSAL

OBSERVE ALL FEDERAL, STATE AND LOCAL REGULATIONS WHEN STORING OR DISPOSING OF THIS SUBSTANCE. FOR ASSISTANCE, CONTACT THE DISTRICT DIRECTOR OF THE ENVIRONMENTAL PROTECTION AGENCY.

STORAGE

STORE IN ACCORDANCE WITH 29 CFR 1910.106.
STORE AWAY FROM INCOMPATIBLE SUBSTANCES.

CONDITIONS TO AVOID

AVOID CONTACT WITH HEAT, SPARKS, FLAMES, OR OTHER SOURCES OF IGNITION. VAPORS MAY BE EXPLOSIVE AND POISONOUS; DO NOT ALLOW UNNECESSARY PERSONNEL IN AREA. DO NOT OVERHEAT CONTAINERS; CONTAINERS MAY VIOLENTLY RUPTURE AND TRAVEL A CONSIDERABLE DISTANCE IN HEAT OF FIRE.

SPILL AND LEAK PROCEDURES

OCCUPATIONAL SPILL: SHUT OFF IGNITION SOURCES. STOP LEAK IF YOU CAN DO IT WITHOUT RISK. USE WATER SPRAY TO REDUCE VAPORS. FOR SMALL SPILLS, TAKE UP WITH SAND OR OTHER ABSORBENT MATERIAL AND PLACE INTO CONTAINERS FOR LATER DISPOSAL. FOR LARGER SPILLS, DIKE FAR AHEAD OF SPILL FOR LATER DISPOSAL. NO SMOKING, FLAMES OR FLARES IN HAZARD AREA. KEEP UNNECESSARY PEOPLE AWAY; ISOLATE HAZARD AREA AND DENY ENTRY.

PROTECTIVE EQUIPMENT

VENTILATION: PROVIDE LOCAL EXHAUST VENTILATION SYSTEM.

RESPIRATOR: THE FOLLOWING RESPIRATORS ARE RECOMMENDED BASED ON INFORMATION FOUND IN THE PHYSICAL DATA, TOXICITY AND HEALTH EFFECTS SECTIONS. THEY ARE RANKED IN ORDER FROM MINIMUM TO MAXIMUM RESPIRATORY PROTECTION. THE SPECIFIC RESPIRATOR SELECTED MUST BE BASED ON CONTAMINATION LEVELS FOUND IN THE WORK PLACE, MUST NOT EXCEED THE WORKING LIMITS OF THE RESPIRATOR AND BE JOINTLY APPROVED BY THE NATIONAL INSTITUTE FOR OCCUPATIONAL SAFETY AND HEALTH AND THE MINE SAFETY AND HEALTH ADMINISTRATION (NIOSH-MSHA).

TYPE 'C' SUPPLIED-AIR RESPIRATOR WITH A FULL FACEPIECE OPERATED IN PRESSURE-DEMAND OR OTHER POSITIVE PRESSURE MODE OR WITH A FULL FACEPIECE, HELMET OR HOOD OPERATED IN CONTINOUS-FLOW MODE.

SELF-CONTAINED BREATHING APPARATUS WITH A FULL FACEPIECE OPERATED IN PRESSURE-DEMAND OR OTHER POSITIVE PRESSURE MODE.

FOR FIREFIGHTING AND OTHER IMMEDIATELY DANGEROUS TO LIFE OR HEALTH CONDITIONS:

SELF-CONTAINED BREATHING APPARATUS WITH FULL FACEPIECE OPERATED IN PRESSURE-DEMAND OR OTHER POSITIVE PRESSURE MODE.

SUPPLIED-AIR RESPIRATOR WITH FULL FACEPIECE AND OPERATED IN PRESSURE-DEMAND OR OTHER POSITIVE PRESSURE MODE IN COMBINATION WITH AN AUXILIARY SELF-CONTAINED BREATHING APPARATUS OPERATED IN PRESSURE-DEMAND OR OTHER POSITIVE PRESSURE MODE.

CLOTHING: EMPLOYEE MUST WEAR APPROPRIATE PROTECTIVE (IMPERVIOUS) CLOTHING AND EQUIPMENT TO PREVENT REPEATED OR PROLONGED SKIN CONTACT WITH THIS SUBSTANCE.

GLOVES: EMPLOYEE MUST WEAR APPROPRIATE PROTECTIVE GLOVES TO PREVENT CONTACT WITH THIS SUBSTANCE.

EYE PROTECTION: EMPLOYEE MUST WEAR SPLASH-PROOF OR DUST-RESISTANT SAFETY GOGGLES TO PREVENT EYE CONTACT WITH THIS SUBSTANCE.

EMERGENCY EYE WASH: WHERE THERE IS ANY POSSIBILITY THAT AN EMPLOYEE'S EYES MAY BE EXPOSED TO THIS SUBSTANCE, THE EMPLOYER SHOULD PROVIDE AN EYE WASH FOUNTAIN WITHIN THE IMMEDIATE WORK AREA FOR EMERGENCY USE.

AUTHORIZED BY- OCCUPATIONAL HEALTH SERVICES, INC.

CREATION DATE: 11/15/89 ***REVISION DATE:*** 05/07/90

MATERIAL SAFETY DATA SHEET

OCCUPATIONAL HEALTH SERVICES, INC.
AGRICULTURE AND PESTICIDE DIVISION
450 SEVENTH AVENUE, SUITE 2407
NEW YORK, NEW YORK 10123
1-800-445-MSDS OR (212) 967-1100

EMERGENCY CONTACT:
JOHN S. BRANSFORD, JR. (615) 292-1180

SUBSTANCE IDENTIFICATION

CAS-NUMBER 112-80-1

SUBSTANCE: **OLEIC ACID**

TRADE NAMES/SYNONYMS: 9-OCTADECANOIC ACID (Z)-; RED OIL; EMERSOL 210; ENERSOL 213; WHITE OLEIC ACID; GLYCON RO; CIS-OCTADEC-9-ENOIC ACID; CIS-9-OCTADECENOIC; GROCO 2; (Z)-9-OCTADECANOIC ACID; CIS-OLEIC ACID; C18H34O2; PST17305

CHEMICAL FAMILY: CARBOXYLIC ACID, ALIPHATIC

MOLECULAR FORMULA: C18-H34-O2

MOLECULAR WEIGHT: 282.52

CERCLA RATINGS (SCALE 0-3): HEALTH = 3 FIRE = 1 REACTIVITY = 0 PERSISTENCE = 0

NFPA RATINGS (SCALE 0-4): HEALTH = 0 FIRE = 1 REACTIVITY = 0

COMPONENTS AND CONTAMINANTS

COMPONENT: OLEIC ACID ***PERCENT:*** 100
CAS# 112-80-1

OTHER CONTAMINANTS: NONE

EXPOSURE LIMITS: NUISANCE PARTICULATES (NUISANCE DUST): 5 MG/M3 OSHA TWA (RESPIRABLE DUST); 15 MG/M3 OSHA TWA (TOTAL DUST) 10 MG/M3 ACGIH TWA (TOTAL DUST) (NO ASBESTOS AND < 1% CRYSTALLINE SILICA)

PHYSICAL DATA

DESCRIPTION: COLORLESS LIQUID WHEN PURE; INDUSTRIAL GRADES ARE PALE RED TO PALE BROWN, OILY LIQUIDS WHICH DARKEN ON EXPOSURE TO AIR; LARD-LIKE OR RANCID ODOR.

BOILING POINT: 547 F (286 C) @ 100 MMHG ***MELTING POINT:*** 61 F (16 C)

SPECIFIC GRAVITY: 0.8935 ***VAPOR PRESSURE:*** 1 MM @ 176.5 C

SOLUBILITY IN WATER: INSOLUBLE

SOLVENT SOLUBILITY: SOLUBLE IN ETHANOL, BENZENE, ETHER, CHLOROFORM, METHANOL, CARBON TETRACHLORIDE, ACETONE, FIXED AND VOLATILE OILS, MOST ORGANIC SOLVENTS

FIRE AND EXPLOSION DATA

FIRE AND EXPLOSION HAZARD: SLIGHT FIRE HAZARD WHEN EXPOSED TO HEAT OR FLAME.

FLASH POINT: 372 F (189 C) (CC) ***AUTOIGNITION TEMP.:*** 685 F (363 C)

FLAMMABILITY CLASS(OSHA): IIIB

FIREFIGHTING MEDIA: DRY CHEMICAL, CARBON DIOXIDE, HALON, WATER SPRAY OR STANDARD FOAM (1987 EMERGENCY RESPONSE GUIDEBOOK, DOT P 5800.4).
FOR LARGER FIRES, USE WATER SPRAY, FOG OR STANDARD FOAM (1987 EMERGENCY RESPONSE GUIDEBOOK, DOT P 5800.4).

FIREFIGHTING: MOVE CONTAINER FROM FIRE AREA IF POSSIBLE. DO NOT SCATTER SPILLED MATERIAL WITH HIGH PRESSURE WATER STREAMS. DIKE FIRE CONTROL WATER FOR LATER DISPOSAL (1987 EMERGENCY RESPONSE GUIDEBOOK, DOT P 5800.4, GUIDE PAGE 31).
USE AGENTS SUITABLE FOR TYPE OF SURROUNDING FIRE. AVOID BREATHING HAZARDOUS VAPORS, KEEP UPWIND.
WATER OR FOAM MAY CAUSE FROTHING (NFPA 325M, FIRE HAZARD PROPERTIES OF FLAMMABLE LIQUIDS, GASES, AND VOLATILE SOLIDS, 1984)

TOXICITY

OLEIC ACID: IRRITATION DATA: 15 MG/3 DAYS INTERMITTENT SKIN-HUMAN MODERATE; 500 MG OPEN SKIN-RABBIT MILD; 100 MG EYE-RABBIT MILD. TOXICITY DATA: 74 GM/KG ORAL-RAT LD50; 2400 UG/KG INTRAVENOUS-RAT LD50; 230 MG/KG INTRAVENOUS-MOUSE LD50; MUTAGENIC DATA (RTECS); TUMORIGENIC DATA (RTECS). CARCINOGEN STATUS: NONE. ACUTE TOXICITY LEVEL: RELATIVELY NONTOXIC BY INGESTION. TARGET EFFECTS: NO DATA AVAILABLE.

HEALTH EFFECTS AND FIRST AID

INHALATION: OLEIC ACID: **ACUTE EXPOSURE-** SUFFICIENT CONCENTRATIONS OF VAPOR OR MIST MAY INTERFERE WITH RESPIRATORY FUNCTIONS. **CHRONIC EXPOSURE-** NO DATA AVAILABLE.

FIRST AID- REMOVE FROM EXPOSURE AREA TO FRESH AIR IMMEDIATELY. IF BREATHING HAS STOPPED, PERFORM ARTIFICIAL RESPIRATION. KEEP PERSON

WARM AND AT REST. TREAT SYMPTOMATICALLY AND SUPPORTIVELY. GET MEDICAL ATTENTION IMMEDIATELY.

SKIN CONTACT: OLEIC ACID: **ACUTE EXPOSURE-** MAY CAUSE MILD IRRITATION. **CHRONIC EXPOSURE-** INTERMITTENT CONTACT WITH HUMAN SKIN FOR 3 DAYS CAUSED MODERATE IRRITATION.
FIRST AID- REMOVE CONTAMINATED CLOTHING AND SHOES IMMEDIATELY. WASH AFFECTED AREA WITH SOAP OR MILD DETERGENT AND LARGE AMOUNTS OF WATER UNTIL NO EVIDENCE OF CHEMICAL REMAINS (APPROXIMATELY 15-20 MINUTES). GET MEDICAL ATTENTION IMMEDIATELY.

EYE CONTACT: OLEIC ACID: **ACUTE EXPOSURE-** MAY CAUSE MILD IRRITATION. **CHRONIC EXPOSURE-** NO DATA AVAILABLE.
FIRST AID- WASH EYES IMMEDIATELY WITH LARGE AMOUNTS OF WATER OR NORMAL SALINE, OCCASIONALLY LIFTING UPPER AND LOWER LIDS, UNTIL NO EVIDENCE OF CHEMICAL REMAINS (APPROXIMATELY 15-20 MINUTES). GET MEDICAL ATTENTION IMMEDIATELY.

INGESTION: OLEIC ACID: **ACUTE EXPOSURE-** THE LETHAL DOSE IN RATS WAS 74 GM/KG. SYMPTOMS WERE NOT REPORTED. INGESTION OF LARGE AMOUNTS MAY RESULT IN GASTROINTESTINAL DISTURBANCES WITH IRRITATION TO THE MOUTH AND STOMACH. **CHRONIC EXPOSURE-** OLEIC ACID DERIVED FROM TALL OIL FATTY ACIDS IS ON THE FDA LIST OF FOOD ADDITIVES PERMITTED FOR DIRECT ADDITION TO FOOD FOR HUMAN CONSUMPTION.
FIRST AID- TREAT SYMPTOMATICALLY AND SUPPORTIVELY. GET MEDICAL ATTENTION IMMEDIATELY. IF VOMITING OCCURS, KEEP HEAD LOWER THAN HIPS TO PREVENT ASPIRATION.
ANTIDOTE: NO SPECIFIC ANTIDOTE. TREAT SYMPTOMATICALLY AND SUPPORTIVELY.

REACTIVITY

REACTIVITY: STABLE UNDER NORMAL TEMPERATURES AND PRESSURES.
INCOMPATIBILITIES: OLEIC ACID: ALUMINUM POWDER: POSSIBLE FORMATION OF AN EXPLOSIVE PRODUCT. PERCHLORIC ACID: FORMATION OF AN EXPLOSIVE PRODUCT BY HEATING. PERCHLORATES: FORMATION OF AN EXPLOSIVE PRODUCT BY HEATING. OXIDIZERS (STRONG): REACTION.
DECOMPOSITION: THERMAL DECOMPOSITION MAY RELEASE ACRID SMOKE AND IRRITATING FUMES.
POLYMERIZATION: HAZARDOUS POLYMERIZATION HAS NOT BEEN REPORTED TO OCCUR UNDER NORMAL TEMPERATURES AND PRESSURES.

STORAGE AND DISPOSAL

OBSERVE ALL FEDERAL, STATE AND LOCAL REGULATIONS WHEN STORING OR DISPOSING OF THIS SUBSTANCE. FOR ASSISTANCE, CONTACT THE DISTRICT DIRECTOR OF THE ENVIRONMENTAL PROTECTION AGENCY.

STORAGE

STORE AWAY FROM INCOMPATIBLE SUBSTANCES.

CONDITIONS TO AVOID

MAY BURN BUT DOES NOT IGNITE READILY. AVOID CONTACT WITH STRONG OXIDIZERS, EXCESSIVE HEAT, SPARKS, OR OPEN FLAME.

SPILL AND LEAK PROCEDURES

OCCUPATIONAL SPILL: STOP LEAK IF YOU CAN DO IT WITHOUT RISK. FOR SMALL SPILLS, TAKE UP WITH SAND OR OTHER ABSORBENT MATERIAL AND PLACE INTO CLEAN, DRY CONTAINERS FOR LATER DISPOSAL. KEEP UNNECESSARY PEOPLE AWAY. ISOLATE HAZARD AREA AND DENY ENTRY.

PROTECTIVE EQUIPMENT

VENTILATION: PROVIDE LOCAL EXHAUST OR PROCESS ENCLOSURE VENTILATION TO MEET PUBLISHED EXPOSURE LIMITS.
RESPIRATOR: THE FOLLOWING RESPIRATORS ARE RECOMMENDED BASED ON INFORMATION FOUND IN THE PHYSICAL DATA, TOXICITY AND HEALTH EFFECTS SECTIONS. THEY ARE RANKED IN ORDER FROM MINIMUM TO MAXIMUM RESPIRATORY PROTECTION. THE SPECIFIC RESPIRATOR SELECTED MUST BE BASED ON CONTAMINATION LEVELS FOUND IN THE WORK PLACE, MUST NOT EXCEED THE WORKING LIMITS OF THE RESPIRATOR AND BE JOINTLY APPROVED BY THE NATIONAL INSTITUTE FOR OCCUPATIONAL SAFETY AND HEALTH AND THE MINE SAFETY AND HEALTH ADMINISTRATION (NIOSH-MSHA).
CHEMICAL CARTRIDGE RESPIRATOR WITH AN ORGANIC VAPOR CARTRIDGE(S)
GAS MASK WITH ORGANIC VAPOR CANISTER (CHIN-STYLE OR FRONT- OR BACK-MOUNTED CANISTER).
TYPE 'C' SUPPLIED-AIR RESPIRATOR OPERATED IN THE PRESSURE-DEMAND OR OTHER POSITIVE PRESSURE OR CONTINUOUS-FLOW MODE.
SELF-CONTAINED BREATHING APPARATUS.
FOR FIREFIGHTING AND OTHER IMMEDIATELY DANGEROUS TO LIFE OR HEALTH CONDITIONS:
SELF-CONTAINED BREATHING APPARATUS WITH FULL FACEPIECE OPERATED IN PRESSURE-DEMAND OR OTHER POSITIVE PRESSURE MODE.
SUPPLIED-AIR RESPIRATOR WITH FULL FACEPIECE AND OPERATED IN PRESSURE-DEMAND OR OTHER POSITIVE PRESSURE MODE IN COMBINATION WITH AN AUXILIARY SELF-CONTAINED BREATHING APPARATUS OPERATED IN PRESSURE-DEMAND OR OTHER POSITIVE PRESSURE MODE.
CLOTHING: EMPLOYEE MUST WEAR APPROPRIATE PROTECTIVE (IMPERVIOUS) CLOTHING AND EQUIPMENT TO PREVENT REPEATED OR PROLONGED SKIN CONTACT WITH THIS SUBSTANCE.
GLOVES: EMPLOYEE MUST WEAR APPROPRIATE PROTECTIVE GLOVES TO PREVENT CONTACT WITH THIS SUBSTANCE.
EYE PROTECTION: EMPLOYEE MUST WEAR SPLASH-PROOF OR DUST-RESISTANT SAFETY GOGGLES TO PREVENT EYE CONTACT WITH THIS SUBSTANCE.
EMERGENCY EYE WASH: WHERE THERE IS ANY POSSIBILITY THAT AN EMPLOYEE'S EYES MAY BE EXPOSED TO THIS SUBSTANCE, THE EMPLOYER SHOULD PROVIDE AN EYE WASH FOUNTAIN WITHIN THE IMMEDIATE WORK AREA FOR EMERGENCY USE.

AUTHORIZED BY- OCCUPATIONAL HEALTH SERVICES, INC.
CREATION DATE: 02/08/90 ***REVISION DATE:*** 05/07/90

MATERIAL SAFETY DATA SHEET

OCCUPATIONAL HEALTH SERVICES, INC.
AGRICULTURE AND PESTICIDE DIVISION
450 SEVENTH AVENUE, SUITE 2407
NEW YORK, NEW YORK 10123
1-800-445-MSDS OR (212) 967-1100

EMERGENCY CONTACT:
JOHN S. BRANSFORD, JR. (615) 292-1180

SUBSTANCE IDENTIFICATION

CAS-NUMBER 64742-52-5
SUBSTANCE: **ORTHO SPRAY STOCK "L"**
TRADE NAMES/SYNONYMS: LUBRICATING BASE OIL; PST17323
CHEMICAL FAMILY: PETROLEUM HYDROCARBON
CERCLA RATINGS (SCALE 0-3): HEALTH=U FIRE=1 REACTIVITY=0 PERSISTENCE=0
NFPA RATINGS (SCALE 0-4): HEALTH=U FIRE=1 REACTIVITY=0

COMPONENTS AND CONTAMINANTS

COMPONENT: HEAVY NAPHTHENIC DISTILLATE ***PERCENT:*** 100.0
CAS# 64742-52-5
OTHER CONTAMINANTS: NONE
EXPOSURE LIMITS: MINERAL OIL MIST: 5 MG/M3 OSHA TWA 5 MG/M3 ACGIH TWA; 10 MG/M3 ACGIH STEL

PHYSICAL DATA

DESCRIPTION: STRAW COLORED OILY LIQUID ***BOILING POINT:*** NOT AVAILABLE
SPECIFIC GRAVITY: 0.89 @ 20 C ***VISCOSITY:*** 41 CST @ 40 C
VAPOR PRESSURE: NOT AVAILABLE ***EVAPORATION RATE:*** NOT AVAILABLE
SOLUBILITY IN WATER: INSOLUBLE ***VAPOR DENSITY:*** NOT AVAILABLE
SOLVENT SOLUBILITY: PETROLEUM HYDROCARBON SOLVENTS

FIRE AND EXPLOSION DATA

FIRE AND EXPLOSION HAZARD: SLIGHT FIRE HAZARD WHEN EXPOSED TO HEAT OR FLAME.
FLASH POINT: 305 F (152 C) (CC) ***FLAMMABILITY CLASS(OSHA):*** IIIB
FIREFIGHTING MEDIA: CARBON DIOXIDE, DRY CHEMICAL POWDER OR FOAM EXTINGUISHER. DO NOT USE WATER EXCEPT AS A FOG.
FIREFIGHTING: MOVE CONTAINER FROM FIRE AREA IF POSSIBLE. DO NOT SCATTER SPILLED MATERIAL WITH HIGH PRESSURE WATER STREAMS. DIKE FIRE CONTROL WATER FOR LATER DISPOSAL (1987 EMERGENCY RESPONSE GUIDEBOOK, DOT P 5800.4, GUIDE PAGE 31).
USE AGENTS SUITABLE FOR TYPE OF SURROUNDING FIRE. AVOID BREATHING HAZARDOUS VAPORS, KEEP UPWIND.

TOXICITY

HEAVY NAPHTHENIC DISTILLATE (ORTHO SPRAY STOCK "L"): CARCINOGEN STATUS: HUMAN INADEQUATE EVIDENCE, ANIMAL INADEQUATE EVIDENCE (IARC GROUP-3). THERE IS INADEQUATE EVIDENCE ON SEVERELY HYDROTREATED OILS TO PERMIT AN EVALUATION OF THEIR CARCINOGENICITY. HEAVY NAPHTHENIC DISTILLATE TOXICITY HAS NOT BEEN QUANTIFIED. THE MAJOR SITES AFFECTED

BY PETROLEUM DERIVED OILS ARE THE SKIN AND LUNGS. PREEXISTING SKIN OR RESPIRATORY DISORDERS MAY BE AGGRAVATED BY EXPOSURE.

HEALTH EFFECTS AND FIRST AID

INHALATION: HEAVY NAPHTHENIC DISTILLATE (ORTHO SPRAY STOCK "L"): IRRITANT. **ACUTE EXPOSURE-** INHALATION HAZARD IS LOW UNLESS HEATED OR MISTED WHICH MAY RESULT IN PULMONARY IRRITATION. **CHRONIC EXPOSURE-** PROLONGED OR REPEATED INHALATION OF OIL MISTS MAY CAUSE LIPID PNEUMONIA, INFLAMMATION WITH OR WITHOUT PNEUMONIA, FIBROSIS AND PARAFFINOMA.

FIRST AID- REMOVE FROM EXPOSURE AREA TO FRESH AIR IMMEDIATELY. IF BREATHING HAS STOPPED, PERFORM ARTIFICIAL RESPIRATION. KEEP PERSON WARM AND AT REST. TREAT SYMPTOMATICALLY AND SUPPORTIVELY. GET MEDICAL ATTENTION IMMEDIATELY.

SKIN CONTACT: HEAVY NAPHTHENIC DISTILLATE (ORTHO SPRAY STOCK "L"): IRRITANT. **ACUTE EXPOSURE-** NO DATA AVAILABLE ON THIS OIL. **CHRONIC EXPOSURE-** REPEATED OR PROLONGED CONTACT WITH PETROLEUM DERIVED OILS MAY CAUSE VARIOUS SKIN DISORDERS SUCH AS ECZEMATOUS OR CONTACT DERMATITIS, FOLLICULITIS, OIL ACNE, LIPID GRANULOMA, MELANOSIS, AND RARELY, PRECANCEROUS WARTS ON THE FOREARMS, BACKS OF HANDS OR SCROTUM. REPEATED EXPOSURE OF A CUMULATIVE DOSE OF 398-402 GM/KG APPLIED TO THE SKIN OF MICE INTERMITTENTLY FOR 22-78 WEEKS PRODUCED TUMORS AT THE SITE OF APPLICATION.

FIRST AID- REMOVE EXCESS OIL WITH A CLEAN, DRY CLOTH. WASH THOROUGHLY WITH A MILD DETERGENT AND SOFT BRUSH. AVOID THE USE OF SOLVENTS, PARAFFIN AND STRONG DETERGENTS. GET MEDICAL ATTENTION IF SKIN IRRITATION OCCURS.

EYE CONTACT: HEAVY NAPHTHENIC DISTILLATE (ORHGO SPRAY STOCK "L"): **ACUTE EXPOSURE-** NO SPECIFIC DATA AVAILABLE. GENERALLY OILS OF THIS TYPE CAUSE NO MORE THAN MINIMAL IRRITATION. **CHRONIC EXPOSURE-** NO DATA AVAILABLE.

FIRST AID- WASH EYES IMMEDIATELY WITH LARGE AMOUNTS OF WATER OR NORMAL SALINE, OCCASIONALLY LIFTING UPPER AND LOWER LIDS, UNTIL NO EVIDENCE OF CHEMICAL REMAINS (APPROXIMATELY 15-20 MINUTES). GET MEDICAL ATTENTION IMMEDIATELY.

INGESTION: HEAVY NAPHTHENIC DISTILLATE (ORTHO SPRAY STOCK "L"): **ACUTE EXPOSURE-** NO DATA AVAILABLE, ALTHOUGH MINERAL OILS ARE GENERALLY OF A LOW ORDER OF TOXICITY. INGESTION MAY CAUSE GASTROINTESTINAL DISTURBANCES SUCH AS DIARRHEA. ASPIRATION MAY OCCUR FROM INGESTION OR VOMITING THIS PRODUCT AND MAY LEAD TO CHEMICAL PNEUMONITIS. **CHRONIC EXPOSURE-** NO DATA AVAILABLE.

FIRST AID- DO NOT INDUCE VOMITING. GIVE MILK OR WATER. IF VOMITING OCCURS, KEEP HEAD LOWER THAN HIPS TO PREVENT ASPIRATION. TREAT SYMPTOMATICALLY AND SUPPORTIVELY. GET MEDICAL ATTENTION IMMEDIATELY.

ANTIDOTE: NO SPECIFIC ANTIDOTE. TREAT SYMPTOMATICALLY AND SUPPORTIVELY.

REACTIVITY

REACTIVITY: STABLE UNDER NORMAL TEMPERATURES AND PRESSURES.

INCOMPATIBILITIES: OXIDIZERS (STRONG): FIRE AND EXPLOSION HAZARD.

DECOMPOSITION: THERMAL DECOMPOSITION PRODUCTS MAY INCLUDE TOXIC OXIDES OF CARBON.

POLYMERIZATION: HAZARDOUS POLYMERIZATION HAS NOT BEEN REPORTED TO OCCUR UNDER NORMAL TEMPERATURES AND PRESSURES.

CONDITIONS TO AVOID

MAY BURN BUT DOES NOT IGNITE READILY. AVOID CONTACT WITH STRONG OXIDIZERS, EXCESSIVE HEAT, SPARKS, OR OPEN FLAME.

SPILL AND LEAK PROCEDURES

OCCUPATIONAL SPILL: STOP LEAK IF YOU CAN DO IT WITHOUT RISK. FOR SMALL SPILLS, TAKE UP WITH SAND OR OTHER ABSORBENT MATERIAL AND PLACE INTO CLEAN, DRY CONTAINERS FOR LATER DISPOSAL. KEEP UNNECESSARY PEOPLE AWAY. ISOLATE HAZARD AREA AND DENY ENTRY.

PROTECTIVE EQUIPMENT

VENTILATION: PROVIDE LOCAL EXHAUST VENTILATION AND/OR GENERAL DILUTION VENTILATION TO MEET PUBLISHED EXPOSURE LIMITS.

RESPIRATOR: THE FOLLOWING RESPIRATORS AND MAXIMUM USE CONCENTRATIONS ARE RECOMMENDATIONS BY THE U.S. DEPARTMENT OF HEALTH AND HUMAN SERVICES, NIOSH POCKET GUIDE TO CHEMICAL HAZARDS; NIOSH CRITERIA DOCUMENTS OR BY THE U.S. DEPARTMENT OF LABOR, 29 CFR 1910 SUBPART Z. THE SPECIFIC RESPIRATOR SELECTED MUST BE BASED ON CONTAMINATION LEVELS FOUND IN THE WORK PLACE, MUST NOT EXCEED THE WORKING LIMITS OF THE RESPIRATOR AND BE JOINTLY APPROVED BY THE NATIONAL INSTITUTE FOR OCCUPATIONAL SAFETY AND HEALTH AND THE MINE SAFETY AND HEALTH ADMINISTRATION (NIOSH-MSHA).

MINERAL OIL MIST:

50 MG/M3- ANY SUPPLIED-AIR RESPIRATOR. ANY SELF-CONTAINED BREATHING APPARATUS. ANY AIR-PURIFYING RESPIRATOR WITH A HIGH-EFFICIENCY PARTICULATE FILTER.

125 MG/M3- ANY SUPPLIED-AIR RESPIRATOR OPERATED IN A CONTINUOUS FLOW MODE. ANY POWERED AIR-PURIFYING RESPIRATOR WITH A HIGH-EFFICIENCY PARTICULATE FILTER.

250 MG/M3- ANY AIR-PURIFYING FULL FACEPIECE RESPIRATOR WITH A HIGH-EFFICIENCY PARTICULATE FILTER. ANY POWERED AIR-PURIFYING RESPIRATOR WITH A TIGHT-FITTING FACEPIECE AND A HIGH-EFFICIENCY PARTICULATE FILTER. ANY SUPPLIED-AIR RESPIRATOR WITH A TIGHT-FITTING FACEPIECE OPERATED IN A CONTINUOUS FLOW MODE. ANY SELF-CONTAINED BREATHING APPARATUS WITH A FULL FACEPIECE. ANY SUPPLIED-AIR RESPIRATOR WITH A FULL FACEPIECE.

2500 MG/M3- ANY SUPPLIED-AIR RESPIRATOR WITH A HALF-MASK AND OPERATED IN A PRESSURE-DEMAND OR OTHER POSITIVE PRESSURE MODE.

ESCAPE- ANY AIR-PURIFYING FULL FACEPIECE RESPIRATOR WITH A HIGH-EFFICIENCY PARTICULATE FILTER. ANY APPROPRIATE ESCAPE-TYPE SELF-CONTAINED BREATHING APPARATUS.

FOR FIREFIGHTING AND OTHER IMMEDIATELY DANGEROUS TO LIFE OR HEALTH CONDITIONS:

SELF-CONTAINED BREATHING APPARATUS WITH FULL FACEPIECE OPERATED IN PRESSURE-DEMAND OR OTHER POSITIVE PRESSURE MODE.

SUPPLIED-AIR RESPIRATOR WITH FULL FACEPIECE AND OPERATED IN PRESSURE-DEMAND OR OTHER POSITIVE PRESSURE MODE IN COMBINATION WITH AN AUXILIARY SELF-CONTAINED BREATHING APPARATUS OPERATED IN PRESSURE-DEMAND OR OTHER POSITIVE PRESSURE MODE.

CLOTHING: WEAR OIL IMPERVIOUS CLOTHING. AVOID PROLONGED OR REPEATED CONTACT WITH SUBSTANCE. AVOID WEARING OIL SOAKED CLOTHING.

GLOVES: EMPLOYEE MUST WEAR APPROPRIATE PROTECTIVE GLOVES TO PREVENT CONTACT WITH THIS SUBSTANCE.

EYE PROTECTION: EMPLOYEE MUST WEAR SPLASH-PROOF OR DUST-RESISTANT SAFETY GOGGLES TO PREVENT EYE CONTACT WITH THIS SUBSTANCE. EMERGENCY EYE WASH: WHERE THERE IS ANY POSSIBILITY THAT AN EMPLOYEE'S EYES MAY BE EXPOSED TO THIS SUBSTANCE, THE EMPLOYER SHOULD PROVIDE AN EYE WASH FOUNTAIN WITHIN THE IMMEDIATE WORK AREA FOR EMERGENCY USE.

AUTHORIZED BY- OCCUPATIONAL HEALTH SERVICES, INC.
CREATION DATE: 10/04/89 ***REVISION DATE:*** 07/12/90

MATERIAL SAFETY DATA SHEET

OCCUPATIONAL HEALTH SERVICES, INC.
AGRICULTURE AND PESTICIDE DIVISION
450 SEVENTH AVENUE, SUITE 2407
NEW YORK, NEW YORK 10123
1-800-445-MSDS OR (212) 967-1100

EMERGENCY CONTACT:
JOHN S. BRANSFORD, JR. (615) 292-1180

SUBSTANCE IDENTIFICATION

CAS-NUMBER 19044-88-3

***SUBSTANCE:* ORYZALIN**

TRADE NAMES/SYNONYMS: BENZENESULFONAMIDE, 4-(DIPROPYLAMINO)-3,5-DINITRO-; SULFANILAMIDE, 3,5-DINITRO-N4,N4-DIPROPYL-; 3,5-DINITRO-N4,N4-DIPROPYLSULPHANILAMIDE; 3,5-DINITRO-N4,N4-DIPROPYLSULFANILAMIDE; 4-(DIPROPYLAMINO)-3,5-DINITROBENZENESULFONAMIDE; DIRIMAL; EL 119; RYZELAN; SURFLAN; C12H18N4O6S; PST17324

CHEMICAL FAMILY: SULFONAMIDE
HYDROCARBON, AROMATIC
NITRO

MOLECULAR FORMULA: C12-H18-N4-O6-S

MOLECULAR WEIGHT: 346.40

CERCLA RATINGS (SCALE 0-3): HEALTH=1 FIRE=1 REACTIVITY=0 PERSISTENCE=1

NFPA RATINGS (SCALE 0-4): HEALTH=U FIRE=1 REACTIVITY=0

COMPONENTS AND CONTAMINANTS

COMPONENT: ORYZALIN ***PERCENT:*** 100
CAS# 19044-88-3

OTHER CONTAMINANTS: MAY CONTAIN N-NITROSODIPROPYLAMINE

EXPOSURE LIMITS: NO OCCUPATIONAL EXPOSURE LIMITS ESTABLISHED BY OSHA, ACGIH, OR NIOSH.

PHYSICAL DATA

DESCRIPTION: YELLOW TO ORANGE CRYSTALLINE SOLID, DECOMPOSED BY UV LIGHT.

MELTING POINT: 286-288 F (141-142 C) ***SPECIFIC GRAVITY:*** NOT AVAILABLE

VAPOR PRESSURE: NEGLIGIBLE ***PH:*** 6.3 @ 50% SUSP *

SOLUBILITY IN WATER: 2.5 PPM @ 25 C

SOLVENT SOLUBILITY: SOLUBLE IN ACETONE, ALCOHOL, METHANOL, ACETONITRILE, METHYL CELLOSOLVE, DICHLOROMETHANE, AND ORGANIC SOLVENTS; SLIGHTLY SOLUBLE IN BENZENE AND XYLENE; VERY SLIGHTLY SOLUBLE IN HEXANE.

* - BASED ON TECHNICAL PRODUCT

FIRE AND EXPLOSION DATA

FIRE AND EXPLOSION HAZARD: SLIGHT FIRE HAZARD WHEN EXPOSED TO HEAT OR FLAME.
DUST-AIR MIXTURES MAY IGNITE OR EXPLODE.

AUTOIGNITION TEMP.: 392 F (200 C) (LAYER); 714 F (379 C) (CLOUD) *

FIREFIGHTING MEDIA: DRY CHEMICAL, CARBON DIOXIDE, HALON, WATER SPRAY OR STANDARD FOAM (1987 EMERGENCY RESPONSE GUIDEBOOK, DOT P 5800.4).
FOR LARGER FIRES, USE WATER SPRAY, FOG OR STANDARD FOAM (1987 EMERGENCY RESPONSE GUIDEBOOK, DOT P 5800.4).

FIREFIGHTING: MOVE CONTAINER FROM FIRE AREA IF POSSIBLE. DO NOT SCATTER SPILLED MATERIAL WITH HIGH PRESSURE WATER STREAMS. DIKE FIRE CONTROL WATER FOR LATER DISPOSAL (1987 EMERGENCY RESPONSE GUIDEBOOK, DOT P 5800.4, GUIDE PAGE 31).
USE AGENTS SUITABLE FOR TYPE OF SURROUNDING FIRE. AVOID BREATHING HAZARDOUS VAPORS, KEEP UPWIND.

TOXICITY

ORYZALIN: TOXICITY DATA: >2000 MG/KG SKIN-RABBIT LD50 (85JFAN); 10,000 MG/KG ORAL-RAT LD50; 1 GM/KG ORAL-CAT LD50; MUTAGENIC DATA (RTECS). CARCINOGEN STATUS: NONE. ACUTE TOXICITY LEVEL: SLIGHTLY TOXIC BY DERMAL ABSORPTION AND INGESTION. TARGET EFFECTS: POISONING MAY AFFECT THE THYROID.

HEALTH EFFECTS AND FIRST AID

INHALATION: ORYZALIN: **ACUTE EXPOSURE-** NO ADVERSE EFFECTS WERE OBSERVED IN RATS EXPOSED TO A SOLID PARTICULATE AEROSOL OF 0.88 MG/LITER FOR ONE HOUR. **CHRONIC EXPOSURE-** REPORTS OF MISCARRIAGES AND BIRTH DEFECTS AMONG WORKERS INVOLVED IN THE PRODUCTION OF ORYZALIN WERE INVESTIGATED BY THE NEW YORK INSTITUTE OF BIRTH DEFECTS. THE INSTITUTE CONCLUDED THAT THESE DEFECTS WERE "MULTIPLE COINCIDENCES" AND COULD NOT BE LINKED TO WORKER EXPOSURE.

FIRST AID- REMOVE FROM EXPOSURE AREA TO FRESH AIR IMMEDIATELY. IF BREATHING HAS STOPPED, PERFORM ARTIFICIAL RESPIRATION. KEEP PERSON WARM AND AT REST. TREAT SYMPTOMATICALLY AND SUPPORTIVELY. GET MEDICAL ATTENTION IMMEDIATELY.

SKIN CONTACT: ORYZALIN: **ACUTE EXPOSURE-** THIS MATERIAL APPLIED TO SHAVED AND ABRADED SKINS OF RABBITS AT A DOSE OF 2000 MG/KG PRODUCED SLIGHT IRRITATION; NO SIGNS OF SYSTEMIC POISONING WERE OBSERVED. **CHRONIC EXPOSURE-** NO SENSITIZATION WAS REPORTED FOR THE TECHNICAL MATERIAL, HOWEVER, THE AQUEOUS SUSPENSION MAY CAUSE SKIN SENSITIZATION REACTIONS IN CERTAIN INDIVIDUALS.

FIRST AID- REMOVE CONTAMINATED CLOTHING AND SHOES IMMEDIATELY. WASH AFFECTED AREA WITH SOAP OR MILD DETERGENT AND LARGE AMOUNTS OF WATER UNTIL NO EVIDENCE OF CHEMICAL REMAINS (APPROXIMATELY 15-20 MINUTES). GET MEDICAL ATTENTION IMMEDIATELY.

EYE CONTACT: ORYZALIN: **ACUTE EXPOSURE-** THIS MATERIAL APPLIED TO THE EYES OF RABBITS PRODUCED SLIGHT IRRITATION WHICH CLEARED IN SEVEN DAYS. **CHRONIC EXPOSURE-** NO DATA AVAILABLE.

FIRST AID- WASH EYES IMMEDIATELY WITH LARGE AMOUNTS OF WATER OR NORMAL SALINE, OCCASIONALLY LIFTING UPPER AND LOWER LIDS, UNTIL NO EVIDENCE OF CHEMICAL REMAINS (APPROXIMATELY 15-20 MINUTES). GET MEDICAL ATTENTION IMMEDIATELY.

INGESTION: ORYZALIN: **ACUTE EXPOSURE-** A LETHAL DOSE IN RATS WAS 10,000 MG/KG OF THE TECHNICAL GRADE OF ORYZALIN. **CHRONIC EXPOSURE-** THYROID TUMORS, POSSIBLY SECONDARY TO THE ANTITHYROID ACTION OF THE COMPOUND, AND BENIGN SKIN AND MAMMARY TUMORS WERE OBSERVED IN A STUDY OF RATS FED A DIETARY LEVEL OF 900 PPM FOR TWO YEARS; OTHER EFFECTS OF BLOOD CHANGES, INCREASED LIVER AND KIDNEY WEIGHTS, INHIBITION OF GROWTH, AND DECREASED SURVIVAL WERE ALSO REPORTED. DECREASED URTERINE AND OVARIAN WEIGHTS WERE REPORTED FROM A CHRONIC FEEDING STUDY OF MICE AT DIETARY LEVELS OF 1350 PPM; NO EFFECTS WERE OBSERVED IN MICE AT DIETARY LEVELS OF 500 PPM (71.4 MG/KG/DAY). NO REPRODUCTIVE EFFECTS WERE REPORTED FROM A 3-GENERATION STUDY OF RATS RECEIVING 250, 750 AND 2250 PPM IN THE DIET. REPEATED INGESTION OF LARGE DOSES IN DOGS RESULTED IN ADVERSE EFFECTS ON THE HEMATOPOIETIC SYSTEM.

FIRST AID- IF THE PERSON IS CONSCIOUS AND NOT CONVULSING, REMOVE BY GASTRIC LAVAGE AND FOLLOW WITH A CATHARTIC (DREISBACH, HANDBOOK OF POISONING, 12TH ED.). TREAT SYMPTOMATICALLY AND SUPPORTIVELY. GASTRIC LAVAGE SHOULD BE PERFORMED BY QUALIFIED MEDICAL PERSONNEL. GET MEDICAL ATTENTION IMMEDIATELY.

ANTIDOTE: NO SPECIFIC ANTIDOTE. TREAT SYMPTOMATICALLY AND SUPPORTIVELY.

REACTIVITY

REACTIVITY: STABLE UNDER NORMAL TEMPERATURES AND PRESSURES.

INCOMPATIBILITIES: ORYZALIN: OXIDIZERS (STRONG): FIRE AND EXPLOSION HAZARD.

DECOMPOSITION: THERMAL DECOMPOSITION MAY RELEASE TOXIC OXIDES OF NITROGEN AND SULFUR.

POLYMERIZATION: HAZARDOUS POLYMERIZATION HAS NOT BEEN REPORTED TO OCCUR UNDER NORMAL TEMPERATURES AND PRESSURES.

STORAGE AND DISPOSAL

OBSERVE ALL FEDERAL, STATE AND LOCAL REGULATIONS WHEN STORING OR DISPOSING OF THIS SUBSTANCE. FOR ASSISTANCE, CONTACT THE DISTRICT DIRECTOR OF THE ENVIRONMENTAL PROTECTION AGENCY.

STORAGE

STORE IN ACCORDANCE WITH 40 CFR 165 RECOMMENDED PROCEDURES FOR THE DISPOSAL AND STORAGE OF PESTICIDES AND PESTICIDE CONTAINERS.
STORE AWAY FROM INCOMPATIBLE SUBSTANCES.

DISPOSAL

DISPOSAL MUST BE IN ACCORDANCE WITH 40 CFR 165 RECOMMENDED PROCEDURES FOR THE DISPOSAL AND STORAGE OF PESTICIDES AND PESTICIDE CONTAINERS.

CONDITIONS TO AVOID

MAY BURN BUT DOES NOT IGNITE READILY. AVOID CONTACT WITH STRONG OXIDIZERS, EXCESSIVE HEAT, SPARKS, OR OPEN FLAME.

SPILL AND LEAK PROCEDURES

OCCUPATIONAL SPILL: SWEEP UP AND PLACE IN SUITABLE CLEAN, DRY CONTAINERS FOR RECLAMATION OR LATER DISPOSAL. DO NOT FLUSH SPILLED MATERIAL INTO SEWER. KEEP UNNECESSARY PEOPLE AWAY.

PROTECTIVE EQUIPMENT

VENTILATION: PROVIDE GENERAL DILUTION VENTILATION.

RESPIRATOR: THE FOLLOWING RESPIRATORS ARE RECOMMENDED BASED ON INFORMATION FOUND IN THE PHYSICAL DATA, TOXICITY AND HEALTH EFFECTS SECTIONS. THEY ARE RANKED IN ORDER FROM MINIMUM TO MAXIMUM RESPIRATORY PROTECTION. THE SPECIFIC RESPIRATOR SELECTED MUST BE BASED ON CONTAMINATION LEVELS FOUND IN THE WORK PLACE, MUST NOT EXCEED THE WORKING LIMITS OF THE RESPIRATOR AND BE JOINTLY APPROVED BY THE NATIONAL INSTITUTE FOR OCCUPATIONAL SAFETY AND HEALTH AND THE MINE SAFETY AND HEALTH ADMINISTRATION (NIOSH-MSHA).

CHEMICAL CARTRIDGE RESPIRATOR WITH AN ORGANIC VAPOR CARTRIDGE(S) WITH A FULL FACEPIECE AND ORGANIC VAPOR CARTRIDGE(S) IN COMBINATION WITH A DUST AND MIST FILTER.

POWERED AIR-PURIFYING RESPIRATOR WITH A TIGHT-FITTING FACEPIECE AND ORGANIC VAPOR CARTRIDGE(S) IN COMBINATION WITH A HIGH-EFFICIENCY PARTICULATE FILTER.

TYPE 'C' SUPPLIED-AIR RESPIRATOR WITH A FULL FACEPIECE OPERATED IN A PRESSURE-DEMAND OR OTHER POSITIVE PRESSURE MODE.

SELF-CONTAINED BREATHING APPARATUS WITH A FULL FACEPIECE OPERATED IN PRESSURE-DEMAND OR OTHER POSITIVE PRESSURE MODE.

FOR FIREFIGHTING AND OTHER IMMEDIATELY DANGEROUS TO LIFE OR HEALTH CONDITIONS:

SELF-CONTAINED BREATHING APPARATUS WITH FULL FACEPIECE OPERATED IN PRESSURE-DEMAND OR OTHER POSITIVE PRESSURE MODE.

SUPPLIED-AIR RESPIRATOR WITH FULL FACEPIECE AND OPERATED IN PRESSURE-DEMAND OR OTHER POSITIVE PRESSURE MODE IN COMBINATION WITH AN AUXILIARY SELF-CONTAINED BREATHING APPARATUS OPERATED IN PRESSURE-DEMAND OR OTHER POSITIVE PRESSURE MODE.

CLOTHING: EMPLOYEE MUST WEAR APPROPRIATE PROTECTIVE (IMPERVIOUS) CLOTHING AND EQUIPMENT TO PREVENT REPEATED OR PROLONGED SKIN CONTACT WITH THIS SUBSTANCE.
GLOVES: EMPLOYEE MUST WEAR APPROPRIATE PROTECTIVE GLOVES TO PREVENT CONTACT WITH THIS SUBSTANCE.
EYE PROTECTION: EMPLOYEE MUST WEAR SPLASH-PROOF OR DUST-RESISTANT SAFETY GOGGLES TO PREVENT EYE CONTACT WITH THIS SUBSTANCE.
EMERGENCY EYE WASH: WHERE THERE IS ANY POSSIBILITY THAT AN EMPLOYEE'S EYES MAY BE EXPOSED TO THIS SUBSTANCE, THE EMPLOYER SHOULD PROVIDE AN EYE WASH FOUNTAIN WITHIN THE IMMEDIATE WORK AREA FOR EMERGENCY USE.

AUTHORIZED BY- OCCUPATIONAL HEALTH SERVICES, INC.
CREATION DATE: 10/04/89 ***REVISION DATE:*** 05/31/90

MATERIAL SAFETY DATA SHEET

OCCUPATIONAL HEALTH SERVICES, INC.
AGRICULTURE AND PESTICIDE DIVISION
450 SEVENTH AVENUE, SUITE 2407
NEW YORK, NEW YORK 10123
1-800-445-MSDS OR (212) 967-1100

EMERGENCY CONTACT:
JOHN S. BRANSFORD, JR. (615) 292-1180

SUBSTANCE IDENTIFICATION

CAS-NUMBER 1113-02-6
SUBSTANCE: OMETHOATE
TRADE NAMES/SYNONYMS: PHOSPHOROTHIOIC ACID, O,O-DIMETHYL S-(2-(METHYLAMINO)-2-OXOETHYL)ESTER; PHOSPHOROTHIOIC ACID, O,O-DIMETHYL ESTER, S-ESTER WITH 2-MERCAPTO -N-METHYLACETAMIDE; O,O-DIMETHYL S-METHYLCARBAMOYLMETHYL PHOSPHOROTHIOATE; 2-DIMETHOXYPHOSPHINOYLTHIO-N-METHYLACETAMIDE; O,O-DIMETHYL S-(2-(METHYLAMINO)-2-OXOETHYL) PHOSPHOROTHIOATE; O,O-DIMETHYL PHOSPHOROTHIOATE S-ESTER WITH 2-MERCAPTO -N-METHYLACETAMIDE; DIMETHYL S-(N-METHYLCARBAMOYLMETHYL)PHOSPHOROTHIOLATE; BAY 45432; DIMETHOATE O-ANALOG; DIMETHOATE OXON; DIMETHOATE OXYGEN ANALOG; DIMETHOATE PO ISOLOGUE; DIMETHOXON; FOLIMAT; PO-DIMETHOATE; ENT 25,776; PST17328
CHEMICAL FAMILY: ORGANOPHOSPHATE
MOLECULAR FORMULA: C5-H12-N-O4-P-S
MOLECULAR WEIGHT: 213.21
CERCLA RATINGS (SCALE 0-3): HEALTH=3 FIRE=0 REACTIVITY=0 PERSISTENCE=0
NFPA RATINGS (SCALE 0-4): HEALTH=3 FIRE=0 REACTIVITY=0

COMPONENTS AND CONTAMINANTS

COMPONENT: OMETHOATE ***PERCENT:*** 100.0
CAS# 1113-02-6
EXPOSURE LIMITS: NO OCCUPATIONAL EXPOSURE LIMITS ESTABLISHED BY OSHA, ACGIH, OR NIOSH.

PHYSICAL DATA

DESCRIPTION: COLORLESS TO SLIGHTLY YELLOWISH OILY LIQUID
BOILING POINT: NOT AVAILABLE ***SPECIFIC GRAVITY:*** 1.3943
SOLUBILITY IN WATER: SOLUBLE
SOLVENT SOLUBILITY: SOLUBLE IN ACETONE, ETHANOL AND MANY HYDROCARBONS; SLIGHTLY SOLUBLE IN DIETHYL ETHER; ALMOST INSOLUBLE IN LIGHT PETROLEUM DECOMPOSES AT 275 F (135 C)

FIRE AND EXPLOSION DATA

FIRE AND EXPLOSION HAZARD: NEGLIGIBLE FIRE HAZARD WHEN EXPOSED TO HEAT OR FLAME.
FIREFIGHTING MEDIA: DRY CHEMICAL, CARBON DIOXIDE, HALON, WATER SPRAY OR STANDARD FOAM (1987 EMERGENCY RESPONSE GUIDEBOOK, DOT P 5800.4). FOR LARGER FIRES, USE WATER SPRAY, FOG OR STANDARD FOAM (1987 EMERGENCY RESPONSE GUIDEBOOK, DOT P 5800.4).
FIREFIGHTING: MOVE CONTAINERS FROM FIRE AREA IF POSSIBLE. FIGHT FIRE FROM MAXIMUM DISTANCE. STAY AWAY FROM STORAGE TANK ENDS. DIKE FIRE CONTROL WATER FOR LATER DISPOSAL. DO NOT SCATTER MATERIAL (1987 EMERGENCY RESPONSE GUIDEBOOK, DOT P 5800.4, GUIDE PAGE 55). EXTINGUISH ONLY IF FLOW CAN BE STOPPED; USE FLOODING AMOUNTS OF WATER AS FOG, SOLID STREAMS MAY BE INEFFECTIVE. COOL CONTAINERS WITH FLOODING AMOUNTS OF WATER FROM AS FAR A DISTANCE AS POSSIBLE. USE WATER SPRAY TO ABSORB TOXIC VAPORS. AVOID BREATHING TOXIC VAPORS; KEEP UPWIND. CONSIDER EVACUATION OF DOWNWIND AREA IF MATERIAL IS LEAKING.

TRANSPORTATION DATA

DEPARTMENT OF TRANSPORTATION HAZARD CLASSIFICATION 49 CFR 172.101: POISON B
DEPARTMENT OF TRANSPORTATION LABELING REQUIREMENTS 49 CFR 172.101 AND SUBPART E: POISON

TOXICITY

OMETHOATE: TOXICITY DATA: 700 MG/KG SKIN-RAT LD50; 30 MG/KG ORAL-RAT LD50; 24 MG/KG ORAL-MOUSE LD50; 50 MG/KG ORAL-RABBIT LD50; 100 MG/KG ORAL-GUINEA PIG LD50; 50 MG/KG ORAL-CAT LD50; 13 MG/KG INTRAPERITONEAL-MOUSE LD50; 55 MG/KG UNREPORTED-RAT LD50; MUTAGENIC DATA (RTECS). CARCINOGEN STATUS: NONE. ACUTE TOXICITY LEVEL: HIGHLY TOXIC BY INGESTION; TOXIC BY DERMAL ABSORPTION. TARGET EFFECTS: CHOLINESTERASE INHIBITOR. POISONING MAY AFFECT THE NERVOUS SYSTEM.* AT INCREASED RISK FROM EXPOSURE: PERSONS WITH RESPIRATORY AILMENTS, RECENT EXPOSURE TO CHOLINESTERASE INHIBITORS OR IMPAIRED CHOLINESTERASE PRODUCTION, OR LIVER MALFUNCTION.* ADDITIONAL DATA: MAY CROSS THE PLACENTA. HIGH ENVIRONMENTAL TEMPERATURES OR EXPOSURE OF THE CHEMICAL TO VISIBLE OR ULTRAVIOLET LIGHT MAY ENHANCE THE TOXICITY. INTERACTIONS WITH MEDICATIONS MAY OCCUR.*
* MAY BE BASED ON GENERAL INFORMATION ON ORGANOPHOSPHATES.

HEALTH EFFECTS AND FIRST AID

INHALATION: OMETHOATE: SEE INFORMATION ON ORGANOPHOSPHATES.
ORGANOPHOSPHATES: CHOLINESTERASE INHIBITOR. **ACUTE EXPOSURE-** WHEN INHALED, THE FIRST EFFECTS OF CHOLINESTERASE INHIBITORS ARE USUALLY RESPIRATORY AND MAY INCLUDE NASAL HYPEREMIA AND WATERY DISCHARGE, COUGH, CHEST DISCOMFORT, DYSPNEA, AND WHEEZING DUE TO INCREASED BRONCHIAL SECRETIONS AND BRONCHOCONSTRICTION. IF SUFFICIENT AMOUNTS ARE ABSORBED, OTHER SYSTEMIC EFFECTS MAY BEGIN WITHIN A FEW MINUTES OR BE DELAYED FOR UP TO 12 HOURS. SYMPTOMS MAY INCLUDE PALLOR, NAUSEA, VOMITING, DIARRHEA, ABDOMINAL CRAMPS, HEADACHE, DIZZINESS, OCULAR PAIN, BLURRED VISION, MIOSIS OR IN SOME CASES, ESPECIALLY INITIALLY, MYDRIASIS, LACRIMATION, SALIVATION, SWEATING, AND CONFUSION. OTHER REPORTED CENTRAL NERVOUS SYSTEM OR NEUROMUSCULAR EFFECTS MAY INCLUDE ATAXIA, SLURRED SPEECH, AREFLEXIA, WEAKNESS, FATIGUE, FASCICULATIONS, TWITCHING, TREMORS POSSIBLY OF THE TONGUE AND EYELIDS, AND EVENTUALLY PARALYSIS OF THE EXTREMITIES AND POSSIBLY OF THE RESPIRATORY MUSCLES. IN SEVERE CASES THERE MAY ALSO BE INVOLUNTARY DEFECATION AND URINATION, CYANOSIS, PSYCHOSIS, HYPERGLYCEMIA, ACUTE PANCREATITIS, CARDIAC IRREGULARITIES, PULMONARY EDEMA, UNCONSCIOUSNESS, CONVULSIONS, AND COMA. DEATH IS PRIMARILY DUE TO RESPIRATORY FAILURE, ALTHOUGH CARDIOVASCULAR EFFECTS INCLUDING CARDIAC ARREST MAY ALSO BE IMPLICATED. LONG TERM SEQUELAE ARE RARE BUT MAY INCLUDE NEUROPSYCHIATRIC DISORDERS AND MYOPATHY WITH MUSCLE TENDERNESS. SOME ORGANOPHOSPHATES MAY CAUSE A DELAYED NEUROPATHY BEGINNING 1-4 WEEKS AFTER AN ACUTE EXPOSURE WHICH MAY OR MAY NOT HAVE CAUSED ACUTE CHOLINERGIC EFFECTS. NUMBNESS, TINGLING, WEAKNESS AND CRAMPING BEGINNING SYMMETRICALLY IN THE LOWER LIMBS MAY PROGRESS TO ATAXIA AND PARALYSIS. IN SEVERE CASES, UPPER LIMB INVOLVEMENT IS POSSIBLE AND FLACCID PARALYSIS MAY PROGRESS TO SPASTIC PARALYSIS WITH EXAGGERATED REFLEXES. IMPROVEMENT MAY OCCUR OVER MONTHS TO YEARS, BUT SOME RESIDUAL IMPAIRMENT USUALLY REMAINS.
CHRONIC EXPOSURE- REPEATED OR PROLONGED EXPOSURE MAY RESULT IN THE EFFECTS OF ACUTE EXPOSURE INCLUDING THE DELAYED NEUROPATHY. OTHER EFFECTS REPORTED IN WORKERS REPEATEDLY EXPOSED INCLUDE IMPAIRED MEMORY AND CONCENTRATION, ACUTE PSYCHOSIS, SEVERE DEPRESSIONS, IRRITABILTY, CONFUSION, APATHY, EMOTIONAL LABILITY, SOCIAL WITHDRAWAL, CONFUSION, HEADACHE, SPEECH DIFFICULTIES, DELAYED REACTION TIMES, SPATIAL DISORIENTATION, NIGHTMARES, SLEEPWALKING, AND DROWSINESS OR INSOMNIA. AN INFLUENZA-LIKE CONDITION WITH HEADACHE, NAUSEA, WEAKNESS, ANOREXIA AND MALAISE HAS ALSO BEEN REPORTED.
FIRST AID- REMOVE FROM EXPOSURE AREA TO FRESH AIR IMMEDIATELY. IF BREATHING HAS STOPPED, GIVE ARTIFICIAL RESPIRATION. MAINTAIN AIRWAY AND BLOOD PRESSURE AND ADMINISTER OXYGEN IF AVAILABLE. KEEP AFFECTED PERSON WARM AND AT REST. TREAT SYMPTOMATICALLY AND SUPPORTIVELY. ADMINISTRATION OF OXYGEN SHOULD BE PERFORMED BY QUALIFIED PERSONNEL. GET MEDICAL ATTENTION IMMEDIATELY.

SKIN CONTACT: OMETHOATE: TOXIC. MAY CAUSE IRRITATION. SEE INFORMATION ON ORGANOPHOSPHATES.

ORGANOPHOSPHATES: CHOLINESTERASE INHIBITOR. **ACUTE EXPOSURE-** LOCALIZED SWEATING AND FASCICULATIONS MAY OCCUR AT THE SITE OF CONTACT. IF SUFFICIENT AMOUNTS ARE ABSORBED, OTHER EFFECTS OF CHOLINESTERASE INHIBITION AS DESCRIBED IN ACUTE INHALATION MAY OCCUR. SYMPTOMS MAY BE DELAYED 2-3 HOURS, BUT USUALLY NO MORE THAN 12 HOURS. THE RATE OF ABSORPTION IS INCREASED BY THE PRESENCE OF DERMATITIS OR HIGH AMBIENT TEMPERATURES. DELAYED NEUROPATHY IS ALSO POSSIBLE. **CHRONIC EXPOSURE-** REPEATED OR PROLONGED EXPOSURE MAY CAUSE EFFECTS AS DESCRIBED IN ACUTE EXPOSURE. SOME ORGANOPHOSPHATES MAY CAUSE SENSITIZATION.

FIRST AID- REMOVE CONTAMINATED CLOTHING IMMEDIATELY. WASH CONTAMINATED AREAS WITH SOAP AND WATER FOLLOWED BY ALCOHOL (ARENA, POISONING, 4TH ED.). EMERGENCY PERSONNEL SHOULD WEAR GLOVES AND AVOID CONTAMINATION. TREAT RESPIRATORY DIFFICULTY WITH ARTIFICIAL RESPIRATION. GET MEDICAL ATTENTION IMMEDIATELY.

EYE CONTACT: OMETHOATE: SEE INFORMATION ON ORGANOPHOSPHATES.
ORGANOPHOSPHATES: CHOLINESTERASE INHIBITOR. **ACUTE EXPOSURE-** DIRECT CONTACT MAY CAUSE PAIN, HYPEREMIA, LACRIMATION, TWITCHING OF THE EYELIDS, MIOSIS, AND CILIARY MUSCLE SPASM WITH LOSS OF ACCOMODATION, BLURRED OR DIMMED VISION AND BROWACHE. SOMETIMES MYDRIASIS MAY OCCUR INSTEAD OF MIOSIS. WITH SUFFICIENT EXPOSURE, OTHER SYMPTOMS OF CHOLINESTERASE INHIBITION AS DESCRIBED IN ACUTE INHALATION MAY OCCUR. **CHRONIC EXPOSURE-** REPEATED OR PROLONGED EXPOSURE MAY CAUSE EFFECTS AS DESCRIBED IN ACUTE EXPOSURE. SOME COMPOUNDS HAVE CAUSED TOXIC EFFECTS ON THE CRYSTALLINE LENS, CONJUNCTIVAL THICKENING AND OBSTRUCTION OF THE NASOLACRIMAL CANALS WHEN USED AS MIOTIC EYEDROPS.

FIRST AID- IRRIGATE EYES WITH WATER OR SALINE SOLUTION. IF SYMPTOMS OF POISONING OCCUR, TREAT RESPIRATORY DIFFICULTY WITH ARTIFICIAL RESPIRATION AND OXYGEN. OBSERVE PATIENT FOR AT LEAST 24-36 HOURS (GOSSELIN, CLINICAL TOXICOLOGY OF COMMERCIAL PRODUCTS, 5TH ED.). GET MEDICAL ATTENTION IMMEDIATELY. OXYGEN SHOULD BE ADMINISTERED BY QUALIFIED MEDICAL PERSONNEL.

INGESTION: OMETHOATE: HIGHLY TOXIC. SEE INFORMATION ON ORGANOPHOSPHATES.
ORGANOPHOSPHATES: CHOLINESTERASE INHIBITOR. **ACUTE EXPOSURE-** WHEN INGESTED, THE FIRST EFFECTS MAY BE NAUSEA, VOMITING, ANOREXIA, ABDOMINAL CRAMPS AND DIARRHEA. GASTROINTESTINAL ABSORPTION MAY CAUSE SYMPTOMS OF CHOLINESTERASE INHIBITION AS DESCRIBED IN ACUTE INHALATION. SYMPTOMS MAY BEGIN WITHIN MINUTES OR BE DELAYED FOR HOURS. DELAYED EFFECTS INCLUDING NEUROPATHY MAY ALSO OCCUR. **CHRONIC EXPOSURE-** REPEATED INGESTION MAY CAUSE EFFECTS AS DESCRIBED IN ACUTE EXPOSURE.

FIRST AID- IF PERSON IS ALERT AND RESPIRATION IS NOT DEPRESSED, GIVE SYRUP OF IPECAC FOLLOWED BY WATER (IF VOMITING OCCURS, KEEP HEAD BELOW HIPS TO PREVENT ASPIRATION). IF CONSCIOUSNESS LEVEL DECLINES OR VOMITING HAS NOT OCCURRED IN 15 MINUTES EMPTY STOMACH BY GASTRIC LAVAGE WITH THE AID OF CUFFED ENDOTRACHEAL TUBE USING ISOTONIC SALINE OR 5% SODIUM BICARBONATE FOLLOW WITH ACTIVATED CHARCOAL. ESTABLISH AND MAINTAIN AIRWAY. TREAT RESPIRATORY DIFFICULTY WITH ARTIFICIAL RESPIRATION AND OXYGEN. DO NOT GIVE MORPHINE, AMINOPHYLLINE, PHENOTHIAZINES, RESERPINE, FUROSEMIDE, OR ETHACRYNIC ACID (MORGAN, RECOGNITION AND MANAGEMENT OF PESTICIDE POISONINGS, 3RD ED.). TREAT SYMPTOMATICALLY AND SUPPORTIVELY. ADMINISTRATION OF OXYGEN AND LAVAGE MUST BE PERFORMED BY QUALIFIED MEDICAL PERSONNEL. GET MEDICAL ATTENTION IMMEDIATELY.

ANTIDOTE: THE FOLLOWING ANTIDOTE(S) HAVE BEEN RECOMMENDED. HOWEVER, THE DECISION AS TO WHETHER THE SEVERITY OF POISONING REQUIRES ADMINISTRATION OF ANY ANTIDOTE AND ACTUAL DOSE REQUIRED SHOULD BE MADE BY QUALIFIED MEDICAL PERSONNEL.
FOR CHOLINESTERASE INHIBITORS: ESTABLISH CLEAR AIRWAY AND TISSUE OXYGENATION BY ASPIRATION OF SECRETIONS, AND IF NECESSARY, BY ASSISTED PULMONARY VENTILATION WITH OXYGEN. IMPROVE TISSUE OXYGENATION AS MUCH AS POSSIBLE BEFORE ADMINISTERING ATROPINE TO MINIMIZE THE RISK OF VENTRICULAR FIBRILLATION. ADMINISTER ATROPINE SULFATE INTRAVENOUSLY, OR INTRAMUSCULARLY IF IV INJECTION IS NOT POSSIBLE. IN MODERATELY SEVERE POISONING ADMINISTER ATROPINE SULFATE, 0.4-2.0 MG REPEATED EVERY 15 MINUTES UNTIL ATROPINIZATION IS ACHIEVED (TACHYCARDIA, FLUSHING, DRY MOUTH, MYDRIASIS). MAINTAIN ATROPINIZATION BY REPEATED DOSES FOR 2-12 HOURS, OR LONGER, DEPENDING ON THE SEVERITY OF POISONING. THE APPEARANCE OF RALES IN THE LUNG BASES, MIOSIS, SALIVATION, NAUSEA, BRADYCARDIA, ARE ALL INDICATIONS OF INADEQUATE ATROPINIZATION. SEVERELY POISONED INDIVIDUALS MAY EXHIBIT REMARKABLE TOLERANCE TO ATROPINE; TWO OR MORE TIMES THE DOSAGES SUGGESTED ABOVE MAY BE NEEDED. PERSONS NOT POISONED OR ONLY SLIGHTLY POISONED, HOWEVER, MAY DEVELOP SIGNS OF ATROPINE TOXICITY FROM SUCH LARGE DOSAGES: FEVER, MUSCLE FIBRILLATIONS, AND DELIRIUM ARE THE MAIN SIGNS OF ATROPINE TOXICITY. IF THESE SIGNS APPEAR WHILE THE PATIENT IS FULLY ATROPINIZED, ATROPINE ADMINISTRATION SHOULD BE DISCONTINUED, AT LEAST TEMPORARILY. OBSERVE TREATED PATIENTS CLOSELY AT LEAST 24 HOURS TO INSURE THAT SYMPTOMS (POSSIBLY PULMONARY EDEMA) DO NOT RECUR AS ATROPINIZATION WEARS OFF. IN VERY SEVERE POISONINGS, METABOLIC DISPOSITION OF TOXICANT MAY REQUIRE SEVERAL HOURS OR DAYS DURING WHICH ATROPINIZATION MUST BE MAINTAINED. MARKEDLY LOWER LEVELS OF URINARY METABOLITES INDICATE THAT ATROPINE DOSAGE CAN BE TAPERED OFF. AS DOSAGE IS REDUCED, CHECK THE LUNG BASES FREQUENTLY FOR RALES. IF RALES ARE HEARD OR OTHER SYMPTOMS RETURN, RE-ESTABLISH ATROPINIZATION PROMPTLY (MORGAN, RECOGNITION AND MANAGEMENT OF PESTICIDE POISONINGS, 3RD ED.). ADMINISTRATION OF ANTIDOTE MUST BE PERFORMED BY QUALIFIED MEDICAL PERSONNEL.
IN CASES OF SEVERE POISONING BY ORGANOPHOSPHATE PESTICIDES IN WHICH RESPIRATORY DEPRESSION, MUSCLE WEAKNESS AND TWITCHINGS ARE SEVERE, GIVE PRALIDOXIME (PROTOPAM-AYERST, 2-PAM), 1.0 GRAM INTRAVENOUSLY AT NO MORE THAN 0.5 GRAM PER MINUTE. DOSAGE OF PRALIDOXIME MAY BE REPEATED IN 1-2 HOURS, THEN AT 10-12 HOUR INTERVALS IF NEEDED. IN VERY SEVERE POISONINGS, DOSAGE RATES MAY BE DOUBLED. TREATMENT WITH PRALIDOXIME WILL BE MOST EFFECTIVE IF GIVEN WITHIN THIRTY-SIX HOURS AFTER POISONING (MORGAN, RECOGNITION AND MANAGEMENT OF PESTICIDE POISONINGS, 3RD ED.). ANTIDOTE SHOULD BE ADMINISTERED BY QUALIFIED MEDICAL PERSONNEL.

REACTIVITY

REACTIVITY: STABLE UNDER NORMAL TEMPERATURES AND PRESSURES.

INCOMPATIBILITIES: OMETHOATE: NO DATA AVAILABLE.

DECOMPOSITION: THERMAL DECOMPOSITION MAY RELEASE TOXIC AND/OR HAZARDOUS GASES.

POLYMERIZATION: HAZARDOUS POLYMERIZATION HAS NOT BEEN REPORTED TO OCCUR UNDER NORMAL TEMPERATURES AND PRESSURES.

STORAGE AND DISPOSAL

OBSERVE ALL FEDERAL, STATE AND LOCAL REGULATIONS WHEN STORING OR DISPOSING OF THIS SUBSTANCE. FOR ASSISTANCE, CONTACT THE DISTRICT DIRECTOR OF THE ENVIRONMENTAL PROTECTION AGENCY.

STORAGE

STORE IN ACCORDANCE WITH 40 CFR 165 RECOMMENDED PROCEDURES FOR THE DISPOSAL AND STORAGE OF PESTICIDES AND PESTICIDE CONTAINERS.

DISPOSAL

DISPOSAL MUST BE IN ACCORDANCE WITH 40 CFR 165 RECOMMENDED PROCEDURES FOR THE DISPOSAL AND STORAGE OF PESTICIDES AND PESTICIDE CONTAINERS.

CONDITIONS TO AVOID

NONE REPORTED.

SPILL AND LEAK PROCEDURES

OCCUPATIONAL SPILL: DO NOT TOUCH SPILLED MATERIAL. STOP LEAK IF YOU CAN DO IT WITHOUT RISK. USE WATER SPRAY TO REDUCE VAPORS. FOR SMALL SPILLS, TAKE UP WITH SAND OR OTHER ABSORBENT MATERIAL AND PLACE INTO CONTAINERS FOR LATER DISPOSAL. FOR SMALL DRY SPILLS, WITH A CLEAN SHOVEL PLACE MATERIAL INTO CLEAN, DRY CONTAINERS AND COVER. MOVE CONTAINERS FROM SPILL AREA. FOR LARGER SPILLS, DIKE FAR AHEAD OF SPILL FOR LATER DISPOSAL. KEEP UNNECESSARY PEOPLE AWAY. ISOLATE HAZARD AREA AND DENY ENTRY. VENTILATE CLOSED SPACES BEFORE ENTERING.

PROTECTIVE EQUIPMENT

VENTILATION: PROVIDE LOCAL EXHAUST OR PROCESS ENCLOSURE VENTILATION SYSTEM.

RESPIRATOR: THE FOLLOWING RESPIRATORS ARE RECOMMENDED BASED ON INFORMATION FOUND IN THE PHYSICAL DATA, TOXICITY AND HEALTH EFFECTS SECTIONS. THEY ARE RANKED IN ORDER FROM MINIMUM TO MAXIMUM RESPIRATORY PROTECTION. THE SPECIFIC RESPIRATOR SELECTED MUST BE BASED ON CONTAMINATION LEVELS FOUND IN THE WORK PLACE, MUST NOT EXCEED THE WORKING LIMITS OF THE RESPIRATOR AND BE JOINTLY APPROVED BY THE NATIONAL INSTITUTE FOR OCCUPATIONAL SAFETY AND HEALTH AND THE MINE SAFETY AND HEALTH ADMINISTRATION (NIOSH-MSHA).
TYPE 'C' SUPPLIED-AIR RESPIRATOR WITH A FULL FACEPIECE OPERATED IN PRESSURE-DEMAND OR OTHER POSITIVE PRESSURE MODE OR WITH A FULL FACEPIECE, HELMET OR HOOD OPERATED IN CONTINOUS-FLOW MODE.
SELF-CONTAINED BREATHING APPARATUS WITH A FULL FACEPIECE OPERATED IN PRESSURE-DEMAND OR OTHER POSITIVE PRESSURE MODE.
FOR FIREFIGHTING AND OTHER IMMEDIATELY DANGEROUS TO LIFE OR HEALTH

CONDITIONS:
SELF-CONTAINED BREATHING APPARATUS WITH FULL FACEPIECE OPERATED IN PRESSURE-DEMAND OR OTHER POSITIVE PRESSURE MODE.
SUPPLIED-AIR RESPIRATOR WITH FULL FACEPIECE AND OPERATED IN PRESSURE-DEMAND OR OTHER POSITIVE PRESSURE MODE IN COMBINATION WITH AN AUXILIARY SELF-CONTAINED BREATHING APPARATUS OPERATED IN PRESSURE-DEMAND OR OTHER POSITIVE PRESSURE MODE.

CLOTHING: EMPLOYEE MUST WEAR APPROPRIATE PROTECTIVE (IMPERVIOUS) CLOTHING AND EQUIPMENT TO PREVENT ANY POSSIBILITY OF SKIN CONTACT WITH THIS SUBSTANCE.

GLOVES: EMPLOYEE MUST WEAR APPROPRIATE PROTECTIVE GLOVES TO PREVENT CONTACT WITH THIS SUBSTANCE.

EYE PROTECTION: EMPLOYEE MUST WEAR SPLASH-PROOF OR DUST-RESISTANT SAFETY GOGGLES AND A FACESHIELD TO PREVENT CONTACT WITH THIS SUBSTANCE.
EMERGENCY WASH FACILITIES: WHERE THERE IS ANY POSSIBILITY THAT AN EMPLOYEE'S EYES AND/OR SKIN MAY BE EXPOSED TO THIS SUBSTANCE, THE EMPLOYER SHOULD PROVIDE AN EYE WASH FOUNTAIN AND QUICK DRENCH SHOWER WITHIN THE IMMEDIATE WORK AREA FOR EMERGENCY USE.

AUTHORIZED BY- OCCUPATIONAL HEALTH SERVICES, INC.
CREATION DATE: 10/04/89 ***REVISION DATE:*** 04/25/90

MATERIAL SAFETY DATA SHEET

OCCUPATIONAL HEALTH SERVICES, INC.
AGRICULTURE AND PESTICIDE DIVISION
450 SEVENTH AVENUE, SUITE 2407
NEW YORK, NEW YORK 10123
1-800-445-MSDS OR (212) 967-1100

EMERGENCY CONTACT:
JOHN S. BRANSFORD, JR. (615) 292-1180

SUBSTANCE IDENTIFICATION

CAS-NUMBER 144-62-7

SUBSTANCE: **OXALIC ACID**

TRADE NAMES/SYNONYMS: ETHANEDIOIC ACID; AKTISAL; AQUISAL; DICARBOXYLIC ACID; PHOSPHOTEX 760 GRAIN REFINER (MACDERMID INCORPORATED); C2H2O4; PST17360

CHEMICAL FAMILY: CARBOXYLIC ACID, ALIPHATIC

MOLECULAR FORMULA: H-O2-C-C-O2-H

MOLECULAR WEIGHT: 90.04

CERCLA RATINGS (SCALE 0-3): HEALTH=3 FIRE=1 REACTIVITY=0 PERSISTENCE=0

NFPA RATINGS (SCALE 0-4): HEALTH=1 FIRE=1 REACTIVITY=0

COMPONENTS AND CONTAMINANTS

COMPONENT: OXALIC ACID ***PERCENT:*** 100.0
CAS# 144-62-7

OTHER CONTAMINANTS: NONE

EXPOSURE LIMITS: OXALIC ACID: 1 MG/M3 OSHA TWA; 2 MG/M3 OSHA STEL 1 MG/M3 ACGIH TWA; 2 MG/M3 ACGIH STEL

PHYSICAL DATA

DESCRIPTION: ODORLESS, COLORLESS TO WHITE, MONOCLINIC OR RHOMBIC HYGROSCOPIC CRYSTALS. ***MELTING POINT:*** 374 F (190 C) (SUBLIMES)

SPECIFIC GRAVITY: 1.900 @ 17 C ***VAPOR PRESSURE:*** <0.001 MMHG @ 20 C

PH: 1.3 @ 0.1 M SOLN. ***SOLUBILITY IN WATER:*** 10%

SOLVENT SOLUBILITY: SOLUBLE IN ALCOHOL, GLYCEROL; SLIGHTLY SOLUBLE IN ETHER; INSOLUBLE IN BENZENE, CHLOROFORM, PETROLEUM ETHER.

FIRE AND EXPLOSION DATA

FIRE AND EXPLOSION HAZARD: SLIGHT FIRE HAZARD WHEN EXPOSED TO HEAT OR FLAME.

FIREFIGHTING MEDIA: DRY CHEMICAL, CARBON DIOXIDE, HALON, WATER SPRAY OR STANDARD FOAM (1987 EMERGENCY RESPONSE GUIDEBOOK, DOT P 5800.4).
FOR LARGER FIRES, USE WATER SPRAY, FOG OR STANDARD FOAM (1987 EMERGENCY RESPONSE GUIDEBOOK, DOT P 5800.4).

FIREFIGHTING: MOVE CONTAINERS FROM FIRE AREA IF POSSIBLE. COOL CONTAINERS EXPOSED TO FLAMES WITH WATER FROM SIDE UNTIL WELL AFTER FIRE IS OUT. STAY AWAY FROM STORAGE TANK ENDS (1987 EMERGENCY RESPONSE GUIDEBOOK, DOT P 5800.4, GUIDE PAGE 60).
EXTINGUISH USING AGENT INDICATED; DO NOT USE WATER DIRECTLY ON MATERIAL. IF LARGE AMOUNTS OF COMBUSTIBLE MATERIALS ARE INVOLVED, USE WATER SPRAY OR FOG IN FLOODING AMOUNTS. AVOID BREATHING CORROSIVE DUSTS AND FUMES FROM BURNING MATERIAL, KEEP UPWIND.

TRANSPORTATION DATA

DEPARTMENT OF TRANSPORTATION HAZARD CLASSIFICATION 49 CFR 172.101: CORROSIVE MATERIAL
DEPARTMENT OF TRANSPORTATION LABELING REQUIREMENTS 49 CFR 172.101 AND SUBPART E: CORROSIVE
DEPARTMENT OF TRANSPORTATION PACKAGING REQUIREMENTS: 49 CFR 173.245B EXCEPTIONS: 49 CFR 173.244

TOXICITY

OXALIC ACID: IRRITATION DATA: ANHYDROUS: 500 MG/24 HOURS SKIN-RABBIT MILD; 250 UG/24 HOURS EYE-RABBIT SEVERE; 100 MG/4 SECONDS RINSED EYE-RABBIT SEVERE. DIHYDRATE: NO DATA AVAILABLE. TOXICITY DATA: ANHYDROUS: 375 MG/KG ORAL-RAT LD50; 1000 MG/KG ORAL-DOG LDLO; 112 MG/KG SUBCUTANEOUS-CAT LDLO; 1400 MG/KG UNREPORTED-RAT LD50; REPRODUCTIVE EFFECTS DATA (RTECS). DIHYDRATE: NO DATA AVAILABLE. CARCINOGEN STATUS: NONE. LOCAL EFFECTS: CORROSIVE- INHALATION, SKIN, EYES, INGESTION. ACUTE TOXICITY LEVEL: TOXIC BY INGESTION. TARGET EFFECTS: NEPHROTOXIN. POISONING MAY ALSO AFFECT THE BRAIN AND CARDIOVASCULAR AND CENTRAL NERVOUS SYSTEMS. AT INCREASED RISK FROM EXPOSURE: PERSONS WITH CHRONIC RESPIRATORY, KIDNEY, EYE, OR SKIN DISEASE OR CONVULSIVE DISORDERS.

HEALTH EFFECTS AND FIRST AID

INHALATION: OXALIC ACID: CORROSIVE/NEPHROTOXIN. 500 MG/M3 IMMEDIATELY DANGEROUS TO LIFE OR HEALTH. **ACUTE EXPOSURE-** INHALATION OF DUST OR VAPORS MAY CAUSE IRRITATION AND ULCERATION OF THE MUCOUS MEMBRANES OF THE UPPER RESPIRATORY TRACT, SEVERE HEADACHES, CHRONIC COUGH, NOSEBLEEDS, SHORTNESS OF BREATH, REPEATED VOMITING, BACKACHE, WEIGHT LOSS, MUSCULAR IRRITABILITY, NERVOUSNESS, ANEMIA, ALBUMINURIA, AND PROSTRATION. IF SUFFICIENT AMOUNTS ARE ABSORBED, RENAL IMPAIRMENT MAY OCCUR AS DESCRIBED IN ACUTE INGESTION. **CHRONIC EXPOSURE-** REPEATED INHALATION OF HOT OXALIC ACID FUMES RESULTED IN WEIGHT LOSS, CHRONIC INFLAMMATION OF THE UPPER RESPIRATORY TRACT AND RENAL IMPAIRMENT.

FIRST AID- REMOVE FROM EXPOSURE AREA TO FRESH AIR IMMEDIATELY. IF BREATHING HAS STOPPED, GIVE ARTIFICIAL RESPIRATION. MAINTAIN AIRWAY AND BLOOD PRESSURE AND ADMINISTER OXYGEN IF AVAILABLE. KEEP AFFECTED PERSON WARM AND AT REST. TREAT SYMPTOMATICALLY AND SUPPORTIVELY. ADMINISTRATION OF OXYGEN SHOULD BE PERFORMED BY QUALIFIED PERSONNEL. GET MEDICAL ATTENTION IMMEDIATELY.

SKIN CONTACT: OXALIC ACID: CORROSIVE. **ACUTE EXPOSURE-** CONTACT WITH CRYSTALS OR SOLUTIONS MAY CAUSE SEVERE IRRITATION WITH TINGLING, PAIN, REDNESS AND BURNS. IF SUFFICIENT AMOUNTS ARE ABSORBED, SYMPTOMS MAY OCCUR AS IN ACUTE INGESTION. **CHRONIC EXPOSURE-** PROLONGED OR REPEATED EXPOSURE MAY CAUSE DERMATITIS, PARESTHESIA, CYANOSIS OF THE FINGERS, DISCOLORATION AND BRITTLENESS OF FINGERNAILS, AND GANGRENOUS LESIONS CHARACTERIZED BY CRACKING, FISSURING, AND SLOW-HEALING ULCERS.

FIRST AID- REMOVE CONTAMINATED CLOTHING AND SHOES IMMEDIATELY. WASH AFFECTED AREA WITH SOAP OR MILD DETERGENT AND LARGE AMOUNTS OF WATER UNTIL NO EVIDENCE OF CHEMICAL REMAINS (AT LEAST 15-20 MINUTES). IN CASE OF CHEMICAL BURNS, COVER AREA WITH STERILE, DRY DRESSING. BANDAGE SECURELY, BUT NOT TOO TIGHTLY. GET MEDICAL ATTENTION IMMEDIATELY.

EYE CONTACT: OXALIC ACID: CORROSIVE. **ACUTE EXPOSURE-** DIRECT CONTACT MAY CAUSE SEVERE IRRITATION WITH REDNESS, PAIN, BURNS, BLURRED VISION AND REVERSIBLE CORNEAL DAMAGE. PROLONGED CONTACT WITH THE SOLUTION MAY CAUSE IRREVERSIBLE EYE DAMAGE. **CHRONIC EXPOSURE-** EFFECTS DEPEND ON CONCENTRATION AND DURATION OF EXPOSURE. CONTACT WITH CORROSIVE SUBSTANCES MAY RESULT IN CONJUNCTIVITIS OR EFFECTS SIMILAR TO ACUTE EXPOSURE.

FIRST AID- WASH EYES IMMEDIATELY WITH LARGE AMOUNTS OF WATER, OCCASIONALLY LIFTING UPPER AND LOWER LIDS, UNTIL NO EVIDENCE OF CHEMICAL REMAINS (AT LEAST 15-20 MINUTES). CONTINUE IRRIGATING WITH NORMAL SALINE UNTIL THE PH HAS RETURNED TO NORMAL (30-60 MINUTES). COVER WITH STERILE BANDAGES. GET MEDICAL ATTENTION IMMEDIATELY.

INGESTION: OXALIC ACID: CORROSIVE/NEPHROTOXIN/TOXIC. **ACUTE EXPOSURE-** CONCENTRATED DOSES MAY CAUSE SEVERE IRRITATION OF THE MUCOUS MEMBRANES OF THE DIGESTIVE TRACT, AN IMMEDIATE SOUR OR BITTER TASTE, A BURNING SENSATION, EPIGASTRIC PAIN, DIFFICULTY SWALLOWING, VOMITING OF BLOOD, NAUSEA, DIARRHEA, BLOODY STOOLS, DEHYDRATION, AND DEATH FROM

GASTROINTESTINAL INJURY AND SECONDARY SHOCK. IF DEATH DOES NOT OCCUR FROM LOCAL EFFECTS, SYSTEMIC EFFECTS MAY INCLUDE SHOCK, HYPOTENSION AND HYPOCALCEMIA WITH RESPIRATORY, NEUROLOGICAL, CARDIOVASCULAR, AND MUSCULAR EFFECTS, COLLAPSE, CONVULSIONS, AND COMA. PYLORIC OBSTRUCTION IS THE MOST COMMON LONG TERM SEQUELA. KIDNEY DAMAGE, INDICATED BY OLIGURIA, ANURIA, UREMIA, ALBUMINURIA AND HEMATURIA, MAY BE DUE TO MECHANICAL INJURY FROM THE OXALATE DEPOSITS, OR FROM TUBULAR NECROSIS AS A RESULT OF VASCULAR EFFECTS FROM HYPOCALCEMIA. PATHOLOGICALLY, THE KIDNEYS SHOW CLOUDY SWELLING, SCLEROSIS OF TUBULES AND HYALINE DEGENERATION.
GASTROINTESTINAL SYMPTOMS MAY BE ABSENT WITH DILUTE SOLUTIONS. THE FIRST SIGNS OF POISONING MAY BE MUSCLE TWITCHING, CRAMPS OR CENTRAL NERVOUS SYSTEM DEPRESSION. OTHER SYMPTOMS MAY INCLUDE WEAK AND IRREGULAR PULSE,SALIVATION, NASAL DISCHARGE, PROGRESSIVE WEAKNESS, ANOREXIA, AND CEREBRAL EDEMA. DEATH MAY ALSO BE CAUSED BY RENAL OBSTRUCTION OR CARDIAC FAILURE. **CHRONIC EXPOSURE**- PROLONGED OR REPEATED EXPOSURE MAY RESULT IN DEPOSITS OF CALCIUM OXALATE IN THE KIDNEY TUBULES AND THE BRAIN, WITH EFFECTS ON THE CARDIAC AND NERVOUS TISSUES. CHRONIC ANIMAL FEEDING STUDIES INDICATE A RESTRICTED GROWTH RATE, REDUCED ORGAN WEIGHT, INCREASED ORGAN/BODY WEIGHT RATIO, AND DISRUPTION OF THE ESTROUS CYCLE IN FEMALE RATS.

FIRST AID- PRECIPITATE OXALATE BY GIVING CALCIUM IN ANY FORM ORALLY, SUCH AS MILK, LIME WATER, CHALK, CALCIUM GLUCONATE, CALCIUM CHLORIDE, OR CALCIUM LACTATE. DO NOT USE GASTRIC LAVAGE OR EMESIS IF TISSUE CORROSION HAS OCCURRED. DISSOLVE 10 G (2 TEASPOONS) OF CALCIUM LACTATE IN LAVAGE OR EMESIS FLUIDS. (DREISBACH, HANDBOOK OF POISONING, 11TH EDITION) GASTRIC LAVAGE SHOULD BE PERFORMED BY A QUALIFIED MEDICAL PERSONNEL.

ANTIDOTE: THE FOLLOWING ANTIDOTE HAS BEEN RECOMMENDED. HOWEVER, THE DECISION AS TO WHETHER THE SEVERITY OF POISONING REQUIRES ADMINISTRATION OF ANY ANTIDOTE AND ACTUAL DOSE REQUIRED SHOULD BE MADE BY QUALIFIED MEDICAL PERSONNEL.
OXALATES (OXALIC ACID): GIVE 10% CALCIUM GLUCONATE, 10 ML SLOWLY INTRAVENOUSLY, AND REPEAT IF SYMPTOMS PERSIST (DREISBACH, HANDBOOK OF POISONING, 11TH ED.). ANTIDOTE SHOULD BE ADMINISTERED BY QUALIFIED MEDICAL PERSONNEL.

REACTIVITY

REACTIVITY: STABLE UNDER NORMAL TEMPERATURES AND PRESSURES.

INCOMPATIBILITIES: OXALIC ACID: ALKALIES: VIOLENT REACTION. FURFURYL ALCOHOL: POSSIBLE VIOLENT REACTION. OXIDIZERS (STRONG): FIRE AND EXPLOSION HAZARD. SILVER AND SILVER COMPOUNDS: FORMS EXPLOSIVE SILVER OXALATES. SODIUM CHLORITE: POSSIBLE EXPLOSION HAZARD. SODIUM HYPOCHLORITE: POSSIBLE EXPLOSION HAZARD.

DECOMPOSITION: THERMAL DECOMPOSITION MAY RELEASE HIGHLY TOXIC CARBON MONOXIDE AND IRRITATING AND TOXIC FUMES OF FORMIC ACID.

POLYMERIZATION: HAZARDOUS POLYMERIZATION HAS NOT BEEN REPORTED TO OCCUR UNDER NORMAL TEMPERATURES AND PRESSURES.

STORAGE AND DISPOSAL

OBSERVE ALL FEDERAL, STATE AND LOCAL REGULATIONS WHEN STORING OR DISPOSING OF THIS SUBSTANCE. FOR ASSISTANCE, CONTACT THE DISTRICT DIRECTOR OF THE ENVIRONMENTAL PROTECTION AGENCY.

STORAGE

PROTECT AGAINST PHYSICAL DAMAGE. STORE IN A COOL, DRY, WELL-VENTILATED LOCATION, AWAY FROM ANY AREA WHERE THE FIRE HAZARD MAY BE ACUTE. OUTSIDE STORAGE IS PREFERRED. SEPARATE FROM OXIDIZING MATERIALS (NFPA 49, HAZARDOUS CHEMICALS DATA, 1975).
STORE AWAY FROM INCOMPATIBLE SUBSTANCES.

CONDITIONS TO AVOID

MAY BURN BUT DOES NOT IGNITE READILY. FLAMMABLE, POISONOUS GASES MAY ACCUMULATE IN TANKS AND HOPPER CARS. MAY IGNITE COMBUSTIBLES (WOOD, PAPER, OIL, ETC.).

SPILL AND LEAK PROCEDURES

OCCUPATIONAL SPILL: DO NOT TOUCH SPILLED MATERIAL. STOP LEAK IF YOU CAN DO IT WITHOUT RISK. FOR SMALL SPILLS, TAKE UP WITH SAND OR OTHER ABSORBENT MATERIAL AND PLACE INTO CONTAINERS FOR LATER DISPOSAL. FOR SMALL DRY SPILLS, WITH CLEAN SHOVEL PLACE MATERIAL INTO CLEAN, DRY CONTAINER AND COVER. MOVE CONTAINERS FROM SPILL AREA. FOR LARGER SPILLS, DIKE FAR AHEAD OF SPILL FOR LATER DISPOSAL. KEEP UNNECESSARY PEOPLE AWAY. ISOLATE HAZARD AREA AND DENY ENTRY.

PROTECTIVE EQUIPMENT

VENTILATION: PROVIDE LOCAL EXHAUST OR PROCESS ENCLOSURE VENTILATION TO MEET PUBLISHED EXPOSURE LIMITS.

RESPIRATOR: THE FOLLOWING RESPIRATORS AND MAXIMUM USE CONCENTRATIONS ARE RECOMMENDATIONS BY THE U.S. DEPARTMENT OF HEALTH AND HUMAN SERVICES, NIOSH POCKET GUIDE TO CHEMICAL HAZARDS; NIOSH CRITERIA DOCUMENTS OR BY THE U.S. DEPARTMENT OF LABOR, 29 CFR 1910 SUBPART Z. THE SPECIFIC RESPIRATOR SELECTED MUST BE BASED ON CONTAMINATION LEVELS FOUND IN THE WORK PLACE, MUST NOT EXCEED THE WORKING LIMITS OF THE RESPIRATOR AND BE JOINTLY APPROVED BY THE NATIONAL INSTITUTE FOR OCCUPATIONAL SAFETY AND HEALTH AND THE MINE SAFETY AND HEALTH ADMINISTRATION (NIOSH-MSHA).
OXALIC ACID: 25 MG/M3- ANY POWERED AIR-PURIFYING RESPIRATOR WITH A DUST AND MIST FILTER. ANY SUPPLIED-AIR RESPIRATOR OPERATED IN A CONTINUOUS FLOW MODE.
50 MG/M3- ANY AIR-PURIFYING FULL FACEPIECE RESPIRATOR WITH A HIGH-EFFICIENCY PARTICULATE FILTER. ANY SELF-CONTAINED BREATHING APPARATUS WITH A FULL FACEPIECE. ANY SUPPLIED-AIR RESPIRATOR WITH A FULL FACEPIECE.
500 MG/M3- ANY SUPPLIED-AIR RESPIRATOR WITH A FULL FACEPIECE AND OPERATED IN PRESSURE-DEMAND OR OTHER POSITIVE PRESSURE MODE.
ESCAPE- ANY AIR-PURIFYING FULL FACEPIECE RESPIRATOR WITH A HIGH-EFFICIENCY PARTICULATE FILTER. ANY APPROPRIATE ESCAPE-TYPE SELF-CONTAINED BREATHING APPARATUS.
FOR FIREFIGHTING AND OTHER IMMEDIATELY DANGEROUS TO LIFE OR HEALTH CONDITIONS:
SELF-CONTAINED BREATHING APPARATUS WITH FULL FACEPIECE OPERATED IN PRESSURE-DEMAND OR OTHER POSITIVE PRESSURE MODE.
SUPPLIED-AIR RESPIRATOR WITH FULL FACEPIECE AND OPERATED IN PRESSURE-DEMAND OR OTHER POSITIVE PRESSURE MODE IN COMBINATION WITH AN AUXILIARY SELF-CONTAINED BREATHING APPARATUS OPERATED IN PRESSURE-DEMAND OR OTHER POSITIVE PRESSURE MODE.

CLOTHING: EMPLOYEE MUST WEAR APPROPRIATE PROTECTIVE (IMPERVIOUS) CLOTHING AND EQUIPMENT TO PREVENT ANY POSSIBILITY OF SKIN CONTACT WITH THIS SUBSTANCE.

GLOVES: EMPLOYEE MUST WEAR APPROPRIATE PROTECTIVE GLOVES TO PREVENT CONTACT WITH THIS SUBSTANCE.

EYE PROTECTION: EMPLOYEE MUST WEAR SPLASH-PROOF OR DUST-RESISTANT SAFETY GOGGLES AND A FACESHIELD TO PREVENT CONTACT WITH THIS SUBSTANCE.
EMERGENCY WASH FACILITIES: WHERE THERE IS ANY POSSIBILITY THAT AN EMPLOYEE'S EYES AND/OR SKIN MAY BE EXPOSED TO THIS SUBSTANCE, THE EMPLOYER SHOULD PROVIDE AN EYE WASH FOUNTAIN AND QUICK DRENCH SHOWER WITHIN THE IMMEDIATE WORK AREA FOR EMERGENCY USE.

AUTHORIZED BY- OCCUPATIONAL HEALTH SERVICES, INC.
CREATION DATE: 11/17/89 ***REVISION DATE:*** 05/07/90

MATERIAL SAFETY DATA SHEET

OCCUPATIONAL HEALTH SERVICES, INC.
AGRICULTURE AND PESTICIDE DIVISION
450 SEVENTH AVENUE, SUITE 2407
NEW YORK, NEW YORK 10123
1-800-445-MSDS OR (212) 967-1100

EMERGENCY CONTACT:
JOHN S. BRANSFORD, JR. (615) 292-1180

SUBSTANCE IDENTIFICATION

CAS-NUMBER 23135-22-0

SUBSTANCE: **OXAMYL**

TRADE NAMES/SYNONYMS: 2-(DIMETHYLAMINO)-N-(((METHYLAMINO)CARBONYL)OXYL)-2 -OXOETHANIMIDOTHIOIC ACID METHYL ESTER; N',N'-DIMETHYL-N-((METHYLCARBAMOYL)OXY)-1-THIOOXAMIMIDIC ACID METHYL ESTER; METHYL 2-(DIMETHYLAMINO)N-(((METHYLAMINO)CARBONYL)OXYL)-2 -OXOETHANIMIDOTHIOATE; METHYL N',N'-DIMETHYL-N-((METHYLCARBAMOYL)OXY)-1-THIOOXAMIMIDATE; THIOXAMYL; VYDATE; C7H13N3O2S; PST17370

CHEMICAL FAMILY: CARBOXYLIC ACID
AMINE

MOLECULAR FORMULA: C7-H13-N3-O3-S

MOLECULAR WEIGHT: 219.29

CERCLA RATINGS (SCALE 0-3): HEALTH=3 FIRE=1 REACTIVITY=0 PERSISTENCE=1

NFPA RATINGS (SCALE 0-4): HEALTH=4 FIRE=1 REACTIVITY=0

COMPONENTS AND CONTAMINANTS

COMPONENT: OXAMYL ***PERCENT:*** 100.0
CAS# 23135-22-0

OTHER CONTAMINANTS: NONE

EXPOSURE LIMITS: NO OCCUPATIONAL EXPOSURE LIMITS ESTABLISHED BY OSHA, ACGIH, OR NIOSH.
OXAMYL: 100/10,000 POUNDS SARA SECTION 302 THRESHOLD PLANNING QUANTITY 1 POUND SARA SECTION 304 REPORTABLE QUANTITY

PHYSICAL DATA

DESCRIPTION: WHITE CRYSTALLINE SOLID WITH A SLIGHT SULFUROUS ODOR.

MELTING POINT: 212-216 F (100-102 C) ***SPECIFIC GRAVITY:*** NOT AVAILABLE

VAPOR PRESSURE: 0.00023 MMHG @ 25 C ***SOLUBILITY IN WATER:*** 25%

SOLVENT SOLUBILITY: SOLUBLE IN METHANOL, ACETONE, ETHANOL, ISOPROPANOL; SLIGHTLY SOLUBLE IN TOLUENE.

FIRE AND EXPLOSION DATA

FIRE AND EXPLOSION HAZARD: SLIGHT FIRE HAZARD WHEN EXPOSED TO HEAT OR FLAME.

FIREFIGHTING MEDIA: DRY CHEMICAL, CARBON DIOXIDE, HALON, WATER SPRAY OR STANDARD FOAM (1987 EMERGENCY RESPONSE GUIDEBOOK, DOT P 5800.4).
FOR LARGER FIRES, USE WATER SPRAY, FOG OR STANDARD FOAM (1987 EMERGENCY RESPONSE GUIDEBOOK, DOT P 5800.4).

FIREFIGHTING: MOVE CONTAINERS FROM FIRE AREA IF POSSIBLE (1987 EMERGENCY RESPONSE GUIDEBOOK, DOT P 5800.4, GUIDE PAGE 53).
EXTINGUISH USING AGENT SUITABLE FOR TYPE OF SURROUNDING FIRE. AVOID BREATHING VAPORS AND DUSTS. KEEP UPWIND.

TRANSPORTATION DATA

DEPARTMENT OF TRANSPORTATION HAZARD CLASSIFICATION 49 CFR 172.101: POISON B
DEPARTMENT OF TRANSPORTATION LABELING REQUIREMENTS 49 CFR 172.101 AND SUBPART E: POISON
DEPARTMENT OF TRANSPORTATION PACKAGING REQUIREMENTS: 49 CFR 173.365 EXCEPTIONS: 49 CFR 173.364

TOXICITY

OXAMYL: TOXICITY DATA: 170 MG/M3/1 HOUR INHALATION-RAT LC50; 740 MG/KG SKIN-RABBIT LD50; 300 MG/KG SKIN-RAT LDLO; 2500 UG/KG ORAL-RAT LD50; 2300 UG/KG ORAL-MOUSE LD50; 7 MG/KG ORAL-GUINEA PIG LD50; 30 MG/KG ORAL-DOG LDLO; 4 MG/KG INTRAPERITONEAL-RAT LD50; 2300 UG/KG INTRAPERITONEAL-MOUSE LDLO; 5100 UG/KG INTRAPERITONEAL-GUINEA PIG LDLO; REPRODUCTIVE EFFECTS DATA (RTECS). CARCINOGEN STATUS: NONE. ACUTE TOXICITY LEVEL: HIGHLY TOXIC BY INHALATION, INGESTION; TOXIC BY DERMAL ABSORPTION. TARGET EFFECTS: CHOLINESTERASE INHIBITOR. AT INCREASED RISK FROM EXPOSURE: PERSONS WITH ASTHMA, DIABETES, CARDIOVASCULAR DISEASE, MECHANICAL OBSTRUCTION OF THE GASTROINTESTINAL OR UROGENITAL TRACT, AND THOSE IN VAGOTONIC STATES.*
* MAY BE BASED ON GENERAL INFORMATION ON CARBAMATES.

HEALTH EFFECTS AND FIRST AID

INHALATION: OXAMYL: HIGHLY TOXIC. SEE INFORMATION ON CARBAMATES.
CARBAMATES: CHOLINESTERASE INHIBITOR. **ACUTE EXPOSURE-** WHEN INHALED, THE FIRST EFFECTS OF CHOLINESTERASE INHIBITION ARE USUALLY RESPIRATORY AND MAY INCLUDE NASAL HYPEREMIA AND WATERY DISCHARGE, CHEST DISCOMFORT, DYSPNEA, AND WHEEZING DUE TO INCREASED BRONCHIAL SECRETIONS AND BRONCHOCONSTRICTION. OTHER SYSTEMIC EFFECTS MAY BEGIN WITHIN A FEW MINUTES OR SEVERAL HOURS OF EXPOSURE. SYMPTOMS MAY INCLUDE NAUSEA, VOMITING, DIARRHEA, ABDOMINAL CRAMPS, HEADACHE, VERTIGO, OCULAR PAIN, CILIARY MUSCLE SPASM, BLURRING OR DIMNESS OF VISION, MIOSIS, OR IN SOME CASES MYDRIASIS, LACRIMATION, SALIVATION, SWEATING, AND CONFUSION. OTHER REPORTED CENTRAL NERVOUS SYSTEM OR NEUROMUSCULAR EFFECTS INCLUDE ATAXIA, SLURRED SPEECH, AREFLEXIA, WEAKNESS, FATIGUE, TWITCHING, FASCICULATION, TREMOR, AND EVENTUALLY PARALYSIS OF THE EXTREMITIES AND POSSIBLY OF THE RESPIRATORY MUSCLES. IN SEVERE CASES, THERE MAY ALSO BE INVOLUNTARY DEFECATION AND URINATION, BRADYCARDIA, HYPOTENSION, PULMONARY EDEMA, CONVULSIONS, COMA, AND DEATH FROM RESPIRATORY FAILURE OR CARDIAC ARREST. CARBAMATES GENERALLY DO NOT ACCUMULATE IN MAMMALIAN TISSUE AND THE CHOLINESTERASE INHIBITION REVERSES RATHER RAPIDLY. IN NON-FATAL CASES, THE ILLNESS GENERALLY LASTS LESS THAN 24 HOURS. **CHRONIC EXPOSURE-** PROLONGED OR REPEATED EXPOSURE MAY CAUSE EFFECTS AS DESCRIBED IN ACUTE EXPOSURE.

FIRST AID- REMOVE FROM EXPOSURE AREA TO FRESH AIR IMMEDIATELY. IF BREATHING HAS STOPPED, GIVE ARTIFICIAL RESPIRATION. MAINTAIN AIRWAY AND BLOOD PRESSURE AND ADMINISTER OXYGEN IF AVAILABLE. KEEP AFFECTED PERSON WARM AND AT REST. TREAT SYMPTOMATICALLY AND SUPPORTIVELY. ADMINISTRATION OF OXYGEN SHOULD BE PERFORMED BY QUALIFIED PERSONNEL. GET MEDICAL ATTENTION IMMEDIATELY.

SKIN CONTACT: OXAMYL: TOXIC. SEE INFORMATION ON CARBAMATES.
CARBAMATES: CHOLINESTERASE INHIBITOR. **ACUTE EXPOSURE-** SOME COMPOUNDS MAY CAUSE IRRITATION. LOCALIZED SWEATING AND FASCICULATIONS MAY OCCUR AT THE SITE OF CONTACT. IF SUFFICIENT AMOUNTS ARE ABSORBED THROUGH THE SKIN, OTHER EFFECTS OF CHOLINESTERASE INHIBITION MAY OCCUR AS DESCRIBED IN ACUTE INHALATION; SYMPTOMS MAY BE DELAYED FOR 2-3 HOURS, USUALLY NO MORE THAN 8 HOURS. **CHRONIC EXPOSURE-** REPEATED OR PROLONGED EXPOSURE MAY CAUSE EFFECTS AS DESCRIBED IN ACUTE EXPOSURE.

FIRST AID- REMOVE CONTAMINATED CLOTHING IMMEDIATELY. WASH CONTAMINATED AREAS WITH SOAP AND WATER FOLLOWED BY ALCOHOL (ARENA, POISONING, 4TH ED.). EMERGENCY PERSONNEL SHOULD WEAR GLOVES AND AVOID CONTAMINATION. TREAT RESPIRATORY DIFFICULTY WITH ARTIFICIAL RESPIRATION. GET MEDICAL ATTENTION IMMEDIATELY.

EYE CONTACT: OXAMYL: SEE INFORMATION ON CARBAMATES.
CARBAMATES: CHOLINESTERASE INHIBITOR. **ACUTE EXPOSURE-** DIRECT CONTACT MAY CAUSE PAIN, HYPEREMIA, LACRIMATION, TWITCHING OF THE EYELIDS, MIOSIS, AND CILIARY MUSCLE SPASM WITH LOSS OF ACCOMODATION, BLURRED OR DIMMED VISION AND BROWACHE. SOMETIMES MYDRIASIS MAY OCCUR INSTEAD OF MIOSIS. WITH SUFFICIENT EXPOSURE, OTHER SYMPTOMS OF CHOLINESTERASE INHIBITION MAY OCCUR AS DESCRIBED IN ACUTE INHALATION. **CHRONIC EXPOSURE-** PROLONGED EXPOSURE MAY CAUSE EFFECTS AS DESCRIBED IN ACUTE EXPOSURE. SOME COMPOUNDS HAVE CAUSED TOXIC EFFECTS ON THE CRYSTALLINE LENS, CONJUNCTIVAL THICKENING AND OBSTRUCTION OF NASOLACRIMAL CANALS WHEN USED AS MIOTIC EYE DROPS.

FIRST AID- IRRIGATE EYES WITH WATER OR SALINE SOLUTION. IF SYMPTOMS OF POISONING OCCUR, TREAT RESPIRATORY DIFFICULTY WITH ARTIFICIAL RESPIRATION AND OXYGEN. OBSERVE PATIENT FOR AT LEAST 24-36 HOURS (GOSSELIN, CLINICAL TOXICOLOGY OF COMMERCIAL PRODUCTS, 5TH ED.). GET MEDICAL ATTENTION IMMEDIATELY. OXYGEN SHOULD BE ADMINISTERED BY QUALIFIED MEDICAL PERSONNEL.

INGESTION: OXAMYL: HIGHLY TOXIC. SEE INFORMATION ON CARBAMATES.
CARBAMATES: CHOLINESTERASE INHIBITOR. **ACUTE EXPOSURE-** WHEN INGESTED, THE FIRST EFFECTS MAY BE NAUSEA, VOMITING, ANOREXIA, ABDOMINAL CRAMPS, AND DIARRHEA. WITH ABSORPTION FROM THE GASTROINTESTINAL TRACT, THE OTHER EFFECTS OF CHOLINESTERASE INHIBITION AS DESCRIBED IN ACUTE INHALATION MAY OCCUR; SYMPTOMS MAY BEGIN WITHIN MINUTES OR BE DELAYED SEVERAL HOURS. **CHRONIC EXPOSURE-** REPEATED INGESTION MAY CAUSE EFFECTS AS DESCRIBED IN ACUTE EXPOSURE.

FIRST AID- IF PERSON IS ALERT AND RESPIRATION IS NOT DEPRESSED, GIVE SYRUP OF IPECAC FOLLOWED BY WATER (IF VOMITING OCCURS, KEEP HEAD BELOW HIPS TO PREVENT ASPIRATION). IF CONSCIOUSNESS LEVEL DECLINES OR VOMITING HAS NOT OCCURRED IN 15 MINUTES EMPTY STOMACH BY GASTRIC LAVAGE WITH THE AID OF CUFFED ENDOTRACHEAL TUBE USING ISOTONIC SALINE OR 5% SODIUM BICARBONATE FOLLOW WITH ACTIVATED CHARCOAL. ESTABLISH AND MAINTAIN AIRWAY. TREAT RESPIRATORY DIFFICULTY WITH ARTIFICIAL RESPIRATION AND OXYGEN. DO NOT GIVE MORPHINE, AMINOPHYLLINE, PHENOTHIAZINES, RESERPINE, FUROSEMIDE, OR ETHACRYNIC ACID (MORGAN, RECOGNITION AND MANAGEMENT OF PESTICIDE POISONINGS, 3RD ED.). TREAT SYMPTOMATICALLY AND SUPPORTIVELY. ADMINISTRATION OF OXYGEN AND LAVAGE MUST BE PERFORMED BY QUALIFIED MEDICAL PERSONNEL. GET MEDICAL ATTENTION IMMEDIATELY.

ANTIDOTE: THE FOLLOWING ANTIDOTE HAS BEEN RECOMMENDED. HOWEVER, THE DECISION AS TO WHETHER THE SEVERITY OF POISONING REQUIRES ADMINISTRATION OF ANY ANTIDOTE AND ACTUAL DOSE REQUIRED SHOULD BE MADE BY QUALIFIED MEDICAL PERSONNEL.
FOR CHOLINESTERASE INHIBITORS: ESTABLISH CLEAR AIRWAY AND TISSUE OXYGENATION BY ASPIRATION OF SECRETIONS, AND IF NECESSARY, BY ASSISTED PULMONARY VENTILATION WITH OXYGEN. IMPROVE TISSUE OXYGENATION AS MUCH AS POSSIBLE BEFORE ADMINISTERING ATROPINE TO MINIMIZE THE RISK OF VENTRICULAR FIBRILLATION. ADMINISTER ATROPINE SULFATE INTRAVENOUSLY, OR INTRAMUSCULARLY IF IV INJECTION IS NOT POSSIBLE. IN MODERATELY SEVERE POISONING ADMINISTER ATROPINE SULFATE, 0.4-2.0 MG REPEATED EVERY 15 MINUTES UNTIL ATROPINIZATION IS ACHIEVED (TACHYCARDIA, FLUSHING, DRY MOUTH, MYDRIASIS). MAINTAIN ATROPINIZATION BY REPEATED DOSES FOR 2-12 HOURS, OR LONGER, DEPENDING ON THE SEVERITY OF POISONING. THE APPEARANCE OF RALES IN THE LUNG BASES, MIOSIS, SALIVATION, NAUSEA, BRADYCARDIA, ARE ALL INDICATIONS OF INADEQUATE ATROPINIZATION.
SEVERELY POISONED INDIVIDUALS MAY EXHIBIT REMARKABLE TOLERANCE TO ATROPINE; TWO OR MORE TIMES THE DOSAGES SUGGESTED ABOVE MAY BE

NEEDED. PERSONS NOT POISONED OR ONLY SLIGHTLY POISONED, HOWEVER, MAY DEVELOP SIGNS OF ATROPINE TOXICITY FROM SUCH LARGE DOSAGES: FEVER, MUSCLE FIBRILLATIONS, AND DELIRIUM ARE THE MAIN SIGNS OF ATROPINE TOXICITY. IF THESE SIGNS APPEAR WHILE THE PATIENT IS FULLY ATROPINIZED, ATROPINE ADMINISTRATION SHOULD BE DISCONTINUED, AT LEAST TEMPORARILY. OBSERVE TREATED PATIENTS CLOSELY AT LEAST 24 HOURS TO INSURE THAT SYMPTOMS (POSSIBLY PULMONARY EDEMA) DO NOT RECUR AS ATROPINIZATION WEARS OFF. IN VERY SEVERE POISONINGS, METABOLIC DISPOSITION OF TOXICANT MAY REQUIRE SEVERAL HOURS OR DAYS DURING WHICH ATROPINIZATION MUST BE MAINTAINED. MARKEDLY LOWER LEVELS OF URINARY METABOLITES INDICATE THAT ATROPINE DOSAGE CAN BE TAPERED OFF. AS DOSAGE IS REDUCED, CHECK THE LUNG BASES FREQUENTLY FOR RALES. IF RALES ARE HEARD OR OTHER SYMPTOMS RETURN, RE-ESTABLISH ATROPINIZATION PROMPTLY (MORGAN, RECOGNITION AND MANAGEMENT OF PESTICIDE POISONINGS, 3RD ED.). ADMINISTRATION OF ANTIDOTE MUST BE PERFORMED BY QUALIFIED MEDICAL PERSONNEL.

REACTIVITY

REACTIVITY: STABLE UNDER NORMAL TEMPERATURES AND PRESSURES.

INCOMPATIBILITIES: OXAMYL: OXIDIZERS (STRONG): MAY CAUSE FIRE AND EXPLOSION HAZARD.

DECOMPOSITION: THERMAL DECOMPOSITION MAY RELEASE TOXIC OXIDES OF NITROGEN AND SULFUR.

POLYMERIZATION: HAZARDOUS POLYMERIZATION HAS NOT BEEN REPORTED TO OCCUR UNDER NORMAL TEMPERATURES AND PRESSURES.

STORAGE AND DISPOSAL

OBSERVE ALL FEDERAL, STATE AND LOCAL REGULATIONS WHEN STORING OR DISPOSING OF THIS SUBSTANCE. FOR ASSISTANCE, CONTACT THE DISTRICT DIRECTOR OF THE ENVIRONMENTAL PROTECTION AGENCY.

STORAGE

STORE IN ACCORDANCE WITH 40 CFR 165 RECOMMENDED PROCEDURES FOR THE DISPOSAL AND STORAGE OF PESTICIDES AND PESTICIDE CONTAINERS.

STORE AWAY FROM INCOMPATIBLE SUBSTANCES.

THRESHOLD PLANNING QUANTITY (TPQ): THE SUPERFUND AMENDMENTS AND REAUTHORIZATION ACT (SARA) SECTION 302 REQUIRES THAT EACH FACILITY WHERE ANY EXTREMELY HAZARDOUS SUBSTANCE IS PRESENT IN A QUANTITY EQUAL TO OR GREATER THAN THE TPQ ESTABLISHED FOR THAT SUBSTANCE NOTIFY THE STATE EMERGENCY RESPONSE COMMISSION FOR THE STATE IN WHICH IT IS LOCATED. SECTION 303 OF SARA REQUIRES THESE FACILITIES TO PARTICIPATE IN LOCAL EMERGENCY RESPONSE PLANNING (40 CFR 355.30).

DISPOSAL

DISPOSAL MUST BE IN ACCORDANCE WITH 40 CFR 165 RECOMMENDED PROCEDURES FOR THE DISPOSAL AND STORAGE OF PESTICIDES AND PESTICIDE CONTAINERS.

CONDITIONS TO AVOID

MAY BURN BUT DOES NOT IGNITE READILY.

SPILL AND LEAK PROCEDURES

OCCUPATIONAL SPILL: DO NOT TOUCH SPILLED MATERIAL. STOP LEAK IF YOU CAN DO IT WITHOUT RISK. FOR SMALL SPILLS, TAKE UP WITH SAND OR OTHER ABSORBENT MATERIAL AND PLACE INTO CONTAINERS FOR LATER DISPOSAL. FOR SMALL DRY SPILLS, WITH A CLEAN SHOVEL PLACE MATERIAL INTO CLEAN, DRY CONTAINER AND COVER. MOVE CONTAINERS FROM SPILL AREA. FOR LARGER SPILLS, DIKE FAR AHEAD OF SPILL FOR LATER DISPOSAL. KEEP UNNECESSARY PEOPLE AWAY. ISOLATE HAZARD AREA AND DENY ENTRY.

REPORTABLE QUANTITY (RQ): 1 POUND THE SUPERFUND AMENDMENTS AND REAUTHORIZATION ACT (SARA) SECTION 304 REQUIRES THAT A RELEASE EQUAL TO OR GREATER THAN THE REPORTABLE QUANTITY FOR THIS SUBSTANCE BE IMMEDIATELY REPORTED TO THE LOCAL EMERGENCY PLANNING COMMITTEE AND THE STATE EMERGENCY RESPONSE COMMISSION (40 CFR 355.40). IF THE RELEASE OF THIS SUBSTANCE IS REPORTABLE UNDER CERCLA SECTION 103, THE NATIONAL RESPONSE CENTER MUST BE NOTIFIED IMMEDIATELY AT (800) 424-8802 OR (202) 426-2675 IN THE METROPOLITAN WASHINGTON, D.C. AREA (40 CFR 302.6).

PROTECTIVE EQUIPMENT

VENTILATION: PROCESS ENCLOSURE RECOMMENDED. VENTILATION EQUIPMENT MUST BE EXPLOSION-PROOF.

RESPIRATOR: THE FOLLOWING RESPIRATORS ARE RECOMMENDED BASED ON INFORMATION FOUND IN THE PHYSICAL DATA, TOXICITY AND HEALTH EFFECTS SECTIONS. THEY ARE RANKED IN ORDER FROM MINIMUM TO MAXIMUM RESPIRATORY PROTECTION. THE SPECIFIC RESPIRATOR SELECTED MUST BE BASED ON CONTAMINATION LEVELS FOUND IN THE WORK PLACE, MUST NOT EXCEED THE WORKING LIMITS OF THE RESPIRATOR AND BE JOINTLY APPROVED BY THE NATIONAL INSTITUTE FOR OCCUPATIONAL SAFETY AND HEALTH AND THE MINE SAFETY AND HEALTH ADMINISTRATION (NIOSH-MSHA).

TYPE 'C' SUPPLIED-AIR RESPIRATOR WITH A FULL FACEPIECE OPERATED IN PRESSURE-DEMAND OR OTHER POSITIVE PRESSURE MODE OR WITH A FULL FACEPIECE, HELMET OR HOOD OPERATED IN CONTINOUS-FLOW MODE.

SELF-CONTAINED BREATHING APPARATUS WITH A FULL FACEPIECE OPERATED IN PRESSURE-DEMAND OR OTHER POSITIVE PRESSURE MODE.

FOR FIREFIGHTING AND OTHER IMMEDIATELY DANGEROUS TO LIFE OR HEALTH CONDITIONS:

SELF-CONTAINED BREATHING APPARATUS WITH FULL FACEPIECE OPERATED IN PRESSURE-DEMAND OR OTHER POSITIVE PRESSURE MODE.

SUPPLIED-AIR RESPIRATOR WITH FULL FACEPIECE AND OPERATED IN PRESSURE-DEMAND OR OTHER POSITIVE PRESSURE MODE IN COMBINATION WITH AN AUXILIARY SELF-CONTAINED BREATHING APPARATUS OPERATED IN PRESSURE-DEMAND OR OTHER POSITIVE PRESSURE MODE.

CLOTHING: EMPLOYEE MUST WEAR APPROPRIATE PROTECTIVE (IMPERVIOUS) CLOTHING AND EQUIPMENT TO PREVENT ANY POSSIBILITY OF SKIN CONTACT WITH THIS SUBSTANCE.

GLOVES: EMPLOYEE MUST WEAR APPROPRIATE PROTECTIVE GLOVES TO PREVENT CONTACT WITH THIS SUBSTANCE.

EYE PROTECTION: EMPLOYEE MUST WEAR SPLASH-PROOF OR DUST-RESISTANT SAFETY GOGGLES AND A FACESHIELD TO PREVENT CONTACT WITH THIS SUBSTANCE.

EMERGENCY WASH FACILITIES: WHERE THERE IS ANY POSSIBILITY THAT AN EMPLOYEE'S EYES AND/OR SKIN MAY BE EXPOSED TO THIS SUBSTANCE, THE EMPLOYER SHOULD PROVIDE AN EYE WASH FOUNTAIN AND QUICK DRENCH SHOWER WITHIN THE IMMEDIATE WORK AREA FOR EMERGENCY USE.

AUTHORIZED BY- OCCUPATIONAL HEALTH SERVICES, INC.

CREATION DATE: 10/04/89 ***REVISION DATE:*** 06/12/90

MATERIAL SAFETY DATA SHEET

OCCUPATIONAL HEALTH SERVICES, INC.
AGRICULTURE AND PESTICIDE DIVISION
450 SEVENTH AVENUE, SUITE 2407
NEW YORK, NEW YORK 10123
1-800-445-MSDS OR (212) 967-1100

EMERGENCY CONTACT:
JOHN S. BRANSFORD, JR. (615) 292-1180

SUBSTANCE IDENTIFICATION

CAS-NUMBER 27304-13-8

SUBSTANCE: OXYCHLORDANE

TRADE NAMES/SYNONYMS: 2,5-METHANO-2H-INDENO(1,2-B)OXIRENE, 2,3,4,5,6,6A,7,7-OCTACHLORO-1A, 1B,5,5A,6,6A-HEXAHYDRO-, (1A ALPHA,1B BETA,2ALPHA,5ALPHA,5A BETA, 6BETA,6A ALPHA)-; (1A ALPHA,1B BETA,2ALPHA,5ALPHA,5A BETA,6BETA,6A ALPHA)-2,3,4,5,6, 6A,7,7-OCTACHLORO-1A,1B,5,5A,6,6A-HEXAHYDRO-2,5-METHANO-2H-INDENO (1,2-B)OXIRENE; 4,7-METHANOINDAN, 1,2,4,5,6,7,8,8-OCTACHLORO-2,3-EPOXY-3A,4,7,7A- TETRAHYDRO-, EXO,ENDO-; EXO,ENDO-1,2,4,5,6,7,8,8-OCTACHLORO-2,3-EPOXY-3A,4,7,7,7A-TETRAHYDRO- 4,7-METHANOINDAN; OCTACHLOR EPOXIDE; OXYCHLORDAN; C10H4CL8O; PST17372

CHEMICAL FAMILY: HALOGEN COMPOUND, AROMATIC

MOLECULAR FORMULA: C10-H4-CL8-O

MOLECULAR WEIGHT: 423.74

CERCLA RATINGS (SCALE 0-3): HEALTH=3 FIRE=0 REACTIVITY=0 PERSISTENCE=3

NFPA RATINGS (SCALE 0-4): HEALTH=3 FIRE=0 REACTIVITY=0

COMPONENTS AND CONTAMINANTS

COMPONENT: OXYCHLORDANE ***PERCENT:*** 100.0
CAS# 27304-13-8

OTHER CONTAMINANTS: NONE

EXPOSURE LIMITS: NO OCCUPATIONAL EXPOSURE LIMITS ESTABLISHED BY OSHA, ACGIH, OR NIOSH.

PHYSICAL DATA

DESCRIPTION: SOLID. ***MELTING POINT:*** NOT AVAILABLE

SPECIFIC GRAVITY: NOT AVAILABLE ***SOLUBILITY IN WATER:*** NOT AVAILABLE

FIRE AND EXPLOSION DATA

FIRE AND EXPLOSION HAZARD: NEGLIGIBLE FIRE HAZARD WHEN EXPOSED TO HEAT OR FLAME.

FIREFIGHTING MEDIA: DRY CHEMICAL, CARBON DIOXIDE, HALON, WATER SPRAY OR STANDARD FOAM (1987 EMERGENCY RESPONSE GUIDEBOOK, DOT P 5800.4). FOR LARGER FIRES, USE WATER SPRAY, FOG OR STANDARD FOAM (1987 EMERGENCY RESPONSE GUIDEBOOK, DOT P 5800.4).

FIREFIGHTING: MOVE CONTAINERS FROM FIRE AREA IF POSSIBLE (1987 EMERGENCY RESPONSE GUIDEBOOK, DOT P 5800.4, GUIDE PAGE 53). EXTINGUISH USING AGENT SUITABLE FOR TYPE OF SURROUNDING FIRE. AVOID BREATHING VAPORS AND DUSTS. KEEP UPWIND.

TRANSPORTATION DATA

DEPARTMENT OF TRANSPORTATION HAZARD CLASSIFICATION 49 CFR 172.101: POISON B

DEPARTMENT OF TRANSPORTATION LABELING REQUIREMENTS 49 CFR 172.101 AND SUBPART E: POISON

DEPARTMENT OF TRANSPORTATION PACKAGING REQUIREMENTS: 49 CFR 173.365 EXCEPTIONS: 49 CFR 173.364

TOXICITY

OXYCHLORDANE: TOXICITY DATA: 20 MG/KG ORAL-RAT LD50 (VELSICOL); 457 MG/KG ORAL-RAT LD50; 40 MG/KG ORAL-MOUSE LD50. CARCINOGEN STATUS: NONE. ACUTE TOXICITY LEVEL: HIGHLY TOXIC BY INGESTION. TARGET EFFECTS: POISONING MAY AFFECT THE LIVER, KIDNEYS, BLOOD, AND CARDIOVASCULAR SYSTEM.* AT INCREASED RISK FROM EXPOSURE: PERSONS WITH CONVULSIVE DISORDERS.* ADDITIONAL DATA: MAY BE STORED IN ADIPOSE TISSUE; MAY CROSS THE PLACENTA AND BE EXCRETED IN HUMAN MILK. STIMULANTS SUCH AS EPINEPHRINE MAY INDUCE VENTRICULAR FIBRILLATIONS.*

* MAY BE BASED ON GENERAL INFORMATION ON CHLORINATED CYCLODIENE DERIVATIVES.

HEALTH EFFECTS AND FIRST AID

INHALATION: OXYCHLORDANE: **ACUTE EXPOSURE-** CHLORINATED CYCLODIENE DERIVATIVES MAY PRODUCE HEADACHE, NAUSEA, VOMITING, MALAISE, DIZZINESS, APPREHENSION, PARESTHESIA, HYPERIRRITABILITY, ATAXIA, MUSCLE TWITCHING, MYOCLONIC JERKING, AND CONVULSIVE SEIZURES. IN SEVERE CASES, CONVULSIONS MAY OCCUR WITHOUT ANY ANY PRIOR SYMPTOMS. THE CONVULSIONS MAY BE CONTINUOUS WITH ELEVATED BODY TEMPERATURE, UNCONSCIOUSNESS, LABORED BREATHING WITH VIGOROUS, RAPID HEART BEAT, AND DEATH FROM RESPIRATORY DEPRESSION. **CHRONIC EXPOSURE-** CHRONIC INTOXICATION FROM CHLORINATED CYCLODIENE DERIVATIVES MAY BE CHARACTERIZED BY NERVOUS SYSTEM, LIVER, AND KIDNEY DAMAGE, CARDIOVASCULAR DISTURBANCES, AND BLOOD AND CAPILLARY DISTURBANCES. IN ADDITION TO THE SYMPTOMS DETAILED IN ACUTE EXPOSURE, ANOREXIA, BLURRED VISION, AND DROWSINESS MAY ALSO OCCUR.

FIRST AID- REMOVE FROM EXPOSURE AREA TO FRESH AIR IMMEDIATELY. IF BREATHING HAS STOPPED, PERFORM ARTIFICIAL RESPIRATION. KEEP PERSON WARM AND AT REST. TREAT SYMPTOMATICALLY AND SUPPORTIVELY. GET MEDICAL ATTENTION IMMEDIATELY.

SKIN CONTACT: OXYCHLORDANE: **ACUTE EXPOSURE-** CHLORINATED CYCLODIENE DERIVATIVES MAY PRODUCE HEADACHE, NAUSEA, VOMITING, MALAISE, DIZZINESS, APPREHENSION, PARESTHESIA, HYPERIRRITABILITY, ATAXIA, MUSCLE TWITCHING, MYOCLONIC JERKING, AND CONVULSIVE SEIZURES. IN SEVERE CASES, CONVULSIONS MAY OCCUR WITHOUT ANY PRIOR SYMPTOMS. THE CONVULSIONS MAY BE CONTINUOUS WITH ELEVATED BODY TEMPERATURES, UNCONSCIOUSNESS, LABORED BREATHING WITH VIGOROUS, RAPID HEART BEAT, AND DEATH FROM RESPIRATORY DEPRESSION. **CHRONIC EXPOSURE-** CHRONIC INTOXICATION FROM CHLORINATED CYCLODIENE DERIVATIVES MAY BE CHARACTERIZED BY NERVOUS SYSTEM, LIVER, AND KIDNEY DAMAGE, CARDIOVASCULAR DISTURBANCES, AND BLOOD AND CAPILLARY DISTURBANCES. IN ADDITION TO THE SYMPTOMS DETAILED IN ACUTE EXPOSURE, SKIN IRRITATION, ANOREXIA, BLURRED VISION, AND DROWSINESS MAY ALSO OCCUR.

FIRST AID- REMOVE CONTAMINATED CLOTHING AND SHOES IMMEDIATELY. WASH AFFECTED AREA WITH SOAP OR MILD DETERGENT AND LARGE AMOUNTS OF WATER UNTIL NO EVIDENCE OF CHEMICAL REMAINS (APPROXIMATELY 15-20 MINUTES). GET MEDICAL ATTENTION IMMEDIATELY.

EYE CONTACT: OXYCHLORDANE: **ACUTE EXPOSURE-** NO DATA AVAILABLE. **CHRONIC EXPOSURE-** NO DATA AVAILABLE.

FIRST AID- WASH EYES IMMEDIATELY WITH LARGE AMOUNTS OF WATER OR NORMAL SALINE, OCCASIONALLY LIFTING UPPER AND LOWER LIDS, UNTIL NO EVIDENCE OF CHEMICAL REMAINS (APPROXIMATELY 15-20 MINUTES). GET MEDICAL ATTENTION IMMEDIATELY.

INGESTION: OXYCHLORDANE: HIGHLY TOXIC. **ACUTE EXPOSURE-** CHLORINATED CYCLODIENE DERIVATIVES MAY PRODUCE HEADACHE, NAUSEA, VOMITING, MALAISE, DIZZINESS, APPREHENSION, PARESTHESIA, HYPERIRRITABILITY, ATAXIA, MUSCLE TWITCHING, MYOCLONIC JERKING, AND CONVULSIVE SEIZURES. IN SEVERE CASES, CONVULSIONS MAY OCCUR WITHOUT ANY PRIOR SYMPTOMS. THE CONVULSIONS MAY BE CONTINUOUS WITH ELEVATED BODY TEMPERATURE, UNCONSCIOUSNESS, LABORED BREATHING WITH VIGOROUS, RAPID HEART BEAT, AND DEATH FROM RESPIRATORY DEPRESSION. **CHRONIC EXPOSURE-** ADMINISTRATION OF 5 PPM/90 DAYS TO RATS PRODUCED MILD HEPATOCYTOMEGLIA; 25 AND 50 PPM PRODUCED SOME DEATHS. PATHOLOGIC FINDINGS INCLUDED DECREASED BODY WEIGHT GAIN AND HEPATOCYTOMEGLIA. CHRONIC INTOXICATION FROM CHLORINATED CYCLODIENE DERIVATIVES MAY BE CHARACTERIZED BY NERVOUS SYSTEM, LIVER, AND KIDNEY DAMAGE, CARDIOVASCULAR DISTURBANCES, AND BLOOD AND CAPILLARY DISTURBANCES. IN ADDITION TO THE SYMPTOMS DETAILED IN ACUTE EXPOSURE, ANOREXIA, BLURRED VISION, AND DROWSINESS MAY ALSO OCCUR.

FIRST AID- IF THE PERSON IS CONSCIOUS AND NOT CONVULSING, REMOVE BY GIVING SYRUP OF IPECAC (IF VOMITING OCCURS, KEEP THE HEAD BELOW THE HIPS TO PREVENT ASPIRATION). GIVE ACTIVATED CHARCOAL FOLLOWED BY GASTRIC LAVAGE. FOLLOW WITH A SALINE CATHARTIC. DO NOT GIVE FATS OR OILS. INTESTINAL LAVAGE WITH 20% MANNITOL (200 ML) BY STOMACH TUBE IS ALSO USEFUL. GIVE ARTIFICIAL RESPIRATION WITH OXYGEN IF RESPIRATION IS DEPRESSED (DREISBACH, HANDBOOK OF POISONING, 12TH ED.). TREAT SYMPTOMATICALLY AND SUPPORTIVELY. LAVAGE AND ADMINISTRATION OF OXYGEN SHOULD BE PERFORMED BY QUALIFIED MEDICAL PERSONNEL. GET MEDICAL ATTENTION IMMEDIATELY.

ANTIDOTE: NO SPECIFIC ANTIDOTE. TREAT SYMPTOMATICALLY AND SUPPORTIVELY.

REACTIVITY

REACTIVITY: STABLE UNDER NORMAL TEMPERATURES AND PRESSURES.

INCOMPATIBILITIES: OXYCHLORDANE: OXIDIZERS (STRONG): FIRE AND EXPLOSION HAZARD.

DECOMPOSITION: THERMAL DECOMPOSITION PRODUCTS MAY INCLUDE HIGHLY TOXIC FUMES OF PHOSGENE, TOXIC AND CORROSIVE FUMES OF CHLORIDES, AND OXIDES OF CARBON.

POLYMERIZATION: HAZARDOUS POLYMERIZATION HAS NOT BEEN REPORTED TO OCCUR UNDER NORMAL TEMPERATURES AND PRESSURES.

STORAGE AND DISPOSAL

OBSERVE ALL FEDERAL, STATE AND LOCAL REGULATIONS WHEN STORING OR DISPOSING OF THIS SUBSTANCE. FOR ASSISTANCE, CONTACT THE DISTRICT DIRECTOR OF THE ENVIRONMENTAL PROTECTION AGENCY.

****STORAGE****

STORE IN ACCORDANCE WITH 40 CFR 165 RECOMMENDED PROCEDURES FOR THE DISPOSAL AND STORAGE OF PESTICIDES AND PESTICIDE CONTAINERS.

****DISPOSAL****

DISPOSAL MUST BE IN ACCORDANCE WITH 40 CFR 165 RECOMMENDED PROCEDURES FOR THE DISPOSAL AND STORAGE OF PESTICIDES AND PESTICIDE CONTAINERS.

CONDITIONS TO AVOID

MAY BURN BUT DOES NOT IGNITE READILY.

SPILL AND LEAK PROCEDURES

OCCUPATIONAL SPILL: DO NOT TOUCH SPILLED MATERIAL. STOP LEAK IF YOU CAN DO IT WITHOUT RISK. FOR SMALL SPILLS, TAKE UP WITH SAND OR OTHER ABSORBENT MATERIAL AND PLACE INTO CONTAINERS FOR LATER DISPOSAL. FOR SMALL DRY SPILLS, WITH A CLEAN SHOVEL PLACE MATERIAL INTO CLEAN, DRY CONTAINER AND COVER. MOVE CONTAINERS FROM SPILL AREA. FOR LARGER SPILLS, DIKE FAR AHEAD OF SPILL FOR LATER DISPOSAL. KEEP UNNECESSARY PEOPLE AWAY. ISOLATE HAZARD AREA AND DENY ENTRY.

PROTECTIVE EQUIPMENT

VENTILATION: PROVIDE LOCAL EXHAUST OR PROCESS ENCLOSURE VENTILATION SYSTEM.

RESPIRATOR: THE FOLLOWING RESPIRATORS ARE RECOMMENDED BASED ON INFORMATION FOUND IN THE PHYSICAL DATA, TOXICITY AND HEALTH EFFECTS SECTIONS. THEY ARE RANKED IN ORDER FROM MINIMUM TO MAXIMUM RESPIRATORY PROTECTION. THE SPECIFIC RESPIRATOR SELECTED MUST BE BASED ON CONTAMINATION LEVELS FOUND IN THE WORK PLACE, MUST NOT EXCEED THE WORKING LIMITS OF THE RESPIRATOR AND BE JOINTLY APPROVED BY THE NATIONAL INSTITUTE FOR OCCUPATIONAL SAFETY AND HEALTH AND THE MINE SAFETY AND HEALTH ADMINISTRATION (NIOSH-MSHA).

TYPE 'C' SUPPLIED-AIR RESPIRATOR WITH A FULL FACEPIECE OPERATED IN PRESSURE-DEMAND OR OTHER POSITIVE PRESSURE MODE OR WITH A FULL FACEPIECE, HELMET OR HOOD OPERATED IN CONTINOUS-FLOW MODE.

SELF-CONTAINED BREATHING APPARATUS WITH A FULL FACEPIECE OPERATED IN PRESSURE-DEMAND OR OTHER POSITIVE PRESSURE MODE.
FOR FIREFIGHTING AND OTHER IMMEDIATELY DANGEROUS TO LIFE OR HEALTH CONDITIONS:
SELF-CONTAINED BREATHING APPARATUS WITH FULL FACEPIECE OPERATED IN PRESSURE-DEMAND OR OTHER POSITIVE PRESSURE MODE.
SUPPLIED-AIR RESPIRATOR WITH FULL FACEPIECE AND OPERATED IN PRESSURE-DEMAND OR OTHER POSITIVE PRESSURE MODE IN COMBINATION WITH AN AUXILIARY SELF-CONTAINED BREATHING APPARATUS OPERATED IN PRESSURE-DEMAND OR OTHER POSITIVE PRESSURE MODE.

CLOTHING: EMPLOYEE MUST WEAR APPROPRIATE PROTECTIVE (IMPERVIOUS) CLOTHING AND EQUIPMENT TO PREVENT ANY POSSIBILITY OF SKIN CONTACT WITH THIS SUBSTANCE.

GLOVES: EMPLOYEE MUST WEAR APPROPRIATE PROTECTIVE GLOVES TO PREVENT CONTACT WITH THIS SUBSTANCE.

EYE PROTECTION: EMPLOYEE MUST WEAR SPLASH-PROOF OR DUST-RESISTANT SAFETY GOGGLES AND A FACESHIELD TO PREVENT CONTACT WITH THIS SUBSTANCE.
EMERGENCY WASH FACILITIES: WHERE THERE IS ANY POSSIBILITY THAT AN EMPLOYEE'S EYES AND/OR SKIN MAY BE EXPOSED TO THIS SUBSTANCE, THE EMPLOYER SHOULD PROVIDE AN EYE WASH FOUNTAIN AND QUICK DRENCH SHOWER WITHIN THE IMMEDIATE WORK AREA FOR EMERGENCY USE.

AUTHORIZED BY- OCCUPATIONAL HEALTH SERVICES, INC.
CREATION DATE: 10/04/89 ***REVISION DATE:*** 03/28/90

MATERIAL SAFETY DATA SHEET

OCCUPATIONAL HEALTH SERVICES, INC.
AGRICULTURE AND PESTICIDE DIVISION
450 SEVENTH AVENUE, SUITE 2407
NEW YORK, NEW YORK 10123
1-800-445-MSDS OR (212) 967-1100

EMERGENCY CONTACT:
JOHN S. BRANSFORD, JR. (615) 292-1180

SUBSTANCE IDENTIFICATION

CAS-NUMBER 5259-88-1

SUBSTANCE: OXYCARBOXIN

TRADE NAMES/SYNONYMS: 1,4-OXATHIIN-3-CARBOXAMIDE, 5,6-DIHYDRO-2-METHYL-N-PHENYL-4,4-DIOXIDE; 1,4-OXATHIIN-3-CARBOXANILIDE, 5,6-DIHYDRO-2-METHYL-, 4,4-DIOXIDE; 5,6-DIHYDRO-2-METHYL-1,4-OXATHI-INE-3-CARBOXANILIDE 4,4-DIOXIDE; 5,6-DIHYDRO-2-METHYL-1,4-OXATHI-IN-3-CARBOXANILIDE 4,4-DIOXIDE; 2,3-DIHYDRO-6-METHYL-5-PHENYLCARBAMOYL-1,4-OXATHI-IN 4,4-DIOXIDE; 5,6-DIHYDRO-2-METHYL-N-PHENYL-1,4-OXATHIIN-3-CARBOXAMIDE 4,4-DIOXIDE; 5,6-DIHYDRO-2-METHYL-1,4-OXATHIIN-3-CARBOXANILIDE 4,4-DIOXIDE; CARBOXIN SULFONE; DCMOD; F 461; OXICARBOXIN; OXYCARBOXINE; PLANTVAX; VITAVAX SULFONE; C12H13NO4S; PST17373

CHEMICAL FAMILY: OXATHION

MOLECULAR FORMULA: C12-H13-N-O4-S

MOLECULAR WEIGHT: 267.32

CERCLA RATINGS (SCALE 0-3): HEALTH=2 FIRE=1 REACTIVITY=0 PERSISTENCE=1

NFPA RATINGS (SCALE 0-4): HEALTH=2 FIRE=1 REACTIVITY=0

COMPONENTS AND CONTAMINANTS

COMPONENT: OXYCARBOXIN ***PERCENT:*** 100
CAS# 5259-88-1

EXPOSURE LIMITS: NO OCCUPATIONAL EXPOSURE LIMITS ESTABLISHED BY OSHA, ACGIH, OR NIOSH.

PHYSICAL DATA

DESCRIPTION: ESSENTIALLY ODORLESS, OFF-WHITE CRYSTALS

MELTING POINT: 262-266 F (128-130 C) ***SPECIFIC GRAVITY:*** 1.35

VAPOR PRESSURE: <1.0 MMHG ***PH:*** 8.49 (1% SOLUTION)

SOLUBILITY IN WATER: 0.14%

SOLVENT SOLUBILITY: SOLUBLE IN ACETONE, DIMETHYL SULPHOXIDE, ETHANOL, METHANOL

FIRE AND EXPLOSION DATA

FIRE AND EXPLOSION HAZARD: SLIGHT FIRE HAZARD WHEN EXPOSED TO HEAT OR FLAME.

FLASH POINT: 426 F (219 C) (OC) ***LOWER EXPLOSIVE LIMIT:*** .052 OZ./FT3

AUTOIGNITION TEMP.: 824 F (440 C)

FIREFIGHTING MEDIA: DRY CHEMICAL, CARBON DIOXIDE, WATER SPRAY OR FOAM FOR LARGER FIRES, USE WATER SPRAY, FOG OR ALCOHOL FOAM

FIREFIGHTING: MOVE CONTAINER FROM FIRE AREA IF POSSIBLE. DO NOT SCATTER SPILLED MATERIAL WITH MORE WATER THAN NEEDED FOR FIRE CONTROL. DIKE FIRE CONTROL WATER FOR LATER DISPOSAL
USE AGENTS SUITABLE FOR TYPE OF SURROUNDING FIRE. AVOID BREATHING HAZARDOUS VAPORS, KEEP UPWIND.

TOXICITY

OXYCARBOXIN: TOXICITY DATA: 2000 MG/KG ORAL-RAT LD50. CARCINOGEN STATUS: NONE. ACUTE TOXICITY DATA: MODERATELY TOXIC BY INGESTION. TARGET EFFECTS: NO DATA AVAILABLE.

HEALTH EFFECTS AND FIRST AID

INHALATION: OXYCARBOXIN: **ACUTE EXPOSURE-** NO DATA AVAILABLE. **CHRONIC EXPOSURE-** NO DATA AVAILABLE.

FIRST AID- REMOVE FROM EXPOSURE AREA TO FRESH AIR IMMEDIATELY. IF BREATHING HAS STOPPED, PERFORM ARTIFICIAL RESPIRATION. KEEP PERSON WARM AND AT REST. TREAT SYMPTOMATICALLY AND SUPPORTIVELY. GET MEDICAL ATTENTION IMMEDIATELY.

SKIN CONTACT: OXYCARBOXIN: **ACUTE EXPOSURE-** A LETHAL DOSE IN RABBITS IS GREATER THAN 16,000 MG/KG. **CHRONIC EXPOSURE-** NO DATA AVAILABLE.

FIRST AID- REMOVE CONTAMINATED CLOTHING AND SHOES IMMEDIATELY. WASH AFFECTED AREA WITH SOAP OR MILD DETERGENT AND LARGE AMOUNTS OF WATER UNTIL NO EVIDENCE OF CHEMICAL REMAINS (APPROXIMATELY 15-20 MINUTES). GET MEDICAL ATTENTION IMMEDIATELY.

EYE CONTACT: OXYCARBOXIN: **ACUTE EXPOSURE-** MAY CAUSE EYE IRRITATION. **CHRONIC EXPOSURE-** NO DATA AVAILABLE.

FIRST AID- WASH EYES IMMEDIATELY WITH LARGE AMOUNTS OF WATER OR NORMAL SALINE, OCCASIONALLY LIFTING UPPER AND LOWER LIDS, UNTIL NO EVIDENCE OF CHEMICAL REMAINS (APPROXIMATELY 15-20 MINUTES). GET MEDICAL ATTENTION IMMEDIATELY.

INGESTION: OXYCARBOXIN: **ACUTE EXPOSURE-** A LETHAL DOSE IN RATS WAS 2000 MG/KG. OXYCARBOXIN INHIBITS OXIDATIVE METABOLISM AND SUCCINIC DEHYDROGENASE IN MITOCHONDRIA OF LIVER AND BONE. **CHRONIC EXPOSURE-** NO ADVERSE EFFECTS WERE REPORTED IN RATS AND DOGS FROM A 2 YEAR FEEDING STUDY AT LEVELS UP TO 3000 MG/KG.

FIRST AID- REMOVE BY GASTRIC LAVAGE AND CATHARSIS. MAINTAIN BLOOD PRESSURE AND AIRWAY. GIVE OXYGEN IF RESPIRATION IS DEPRESSED. DO NOT PERFORM GASTRIC LAVAGE IF VICTIM IS UNCONSCIOUS. GET MEDICAL ATTENTION IMMEDIATELY (DREISBACH, HANDBOOK OF POISONING, 12TH ED.). ADMINISTRATION OF LAVAGE OR OXYGEN SHOULD BE PERFORMED BY QUALIFIED MEDICAL PERSONNEL.

ANTIDOTE: NO SPECIFIC ANTIDOTE. TREAT SYMPTOMATICALLY AND SUPPORTIVELY.

REACTIVITY

REACTIVITY: STABLE UNDER NORMAL TEMPERATURES AND PRESSURES.

INCOMPATIBILITIES: OXYCARBOXIN: STRONG ACIDS: HYDROLYZES. STRONG ALKALIS: HYDROLYZES.

DECOMPOSITION: THERMAL DECOMPOSITION MAY RELEASE TOXIC OXIDES OF SULFUR.

POLYMERIZATION: HAZARDOUS POLYMERIZATION HAS NOT BEEN REPORTED TO OCCUR UNDER NORMAL TEMPERATURES AND PRESSURES.

STORAGE AND DISPOSAL

OBSERVE ALL FEDERAL, STATE AND LOCAL REGULATIONS WHEN STORING OR DISPOSING OF THIS SUBSTANCE. FOR ASSISTANCE, CONTACT THE DISTRICT DIRECTOR OF THE ENVIRONMENTAL PROTECTION AGENCY.

****STORAGE****

STORE IN ACCORDANCE WITH 40 CFR 165 RECOMMENDED PROCEDURES FOR THE DISPOSAL AND STORAGE OF PESTICIDES AND PESTICIDE CONTAINERS.
STORE AWAY FROM INCOMPATIBLE SUBSTANCES.

****DISPOSAL****

DISPOSAL MUST BE IN ACCORDANCE WITH 40 CFR 165 RECOMMENDED PROCEDURES FOR THE DISPOSAL AND STORAGE OF PESTICIDES AND PESTICIDE CONTAINERS.

CONDITIONS TO AVOID

NONE REPORTED.

SPILL AND LEAK PROCEDURES

OCCUPATIONAL SPILL: NO SPECIAL PRECAUTIONS INDICATED.

PROTECTIVE EQUIPMENT

VENTILATION: PROVIDE LOCAL EXHAUST OR GENERAL DILUTION VENTILATION SYSTEM.

RESPIRATOR: THE FOLLOWING RESPIRATORS ARE RECOMMENDED BASED ON INFORMATION FOUND IN THE PHYSICAL DATA, TOXICITY AND HEALTH EFFECTS SECTIONS. THEY ARE RANKED IN ORDER FROM MINIMUM TO MAXIMUM RESPIRATORY PROTECTION. THE SPECIFIC RESPIRATOR SELECTED MUST BE BASED ON CONTAMINATION LEVELS FOUND IN THE WORK PLACE, MUST NOT EXCEED THE WORKING LIMITS OF THE RESPIRATOR AND BE JOINTLY APPROVED BY THE NATIONAL INSTITUTE FOR OCCUPATIONAL SAFETY AND HEALTH AND THE MINE SAFETY AND HEALTH ADMINISTRATION (NIOSH-MSHA).

CHEMICAL CARTRIDGE RESPIRATOR WITH AN ORGANIC VAPOR CARTRIDGE(S) WITH A FULL FACEPIECE AND ORGANIC VAPOR CARTRIDGE(S) IN COMBINATION WITH A DUST AND MIST FILTER.

POWERED AIR-PURIFYING RESPIRATOR WITH A TIGHT-FITTING FACEPIECE AND ORGANIC VAPOR CARTRIDGE(S) IN COMBINATION WITH A HIGH-EFFICIENCY PARTICULATE FILTER.

TYPE 'C' SUPPLIED-AIR RESPIRATOR WITH A FULL FACEPIECE OPERATED IN A PRESSURE-DEMAND OR OTHER POSITIVE PRESSURE MODE.

SELF-CONTAINED BREATHING APPARATUS WITH A FULL FACEPIECE OPERATED IN PRESSURE-DEMAND OR OTHER POSITIVE PRESSURE MODE.

FOR FIREFIGHTING AND OTHER IMMEDIATELY DANGEROUS TO LIFE OR HEALTH CONDITIONS:

SELF-CONTAINED BREATHING APPARATUS WITH FULL FACEPIECE OPERATED IN PRESSURE-DEMAND OR OTHER POSITIVE PRESSURE MODE.

SUPPLIED-AIR RESPIRATOR WITH FULL FACEPIECE AND OPERATED IN PRESSURE-DEMAND OR OTHER POSITIVE PRESSURE MODE IN COMBINATION WITH AN AUXILIARY SELF-CONTAINED BREATHING APPARATUS OPERATED IN PRESSURE-DEMAND OR OTHER POSITIVE PRESSURE MODE.

CLOTHING: EMPLOYEE MUST WEAR APPROPRIATE PROTECTIVE (IMPERVIOUS) CLOTHING AND EQUIPMENT TO PREVENT REPEATED OR PROLONGED SKIN CONTACT WITH THIS SUBSTANCE. ***GLOVES:*** EMPLOYEE MUST WEAR APPROPRIATE PROTECTIVE GLOVES TO PREVENT CONTACT WITH THIS SUBSTANCE.

EYE PROTECTION: EMPLOYEE MUST WEAR SPLASH-PROOF OR DUST-RESISTANT SAFETY GOGGLES TO PREVENT EYE CONTACT WITH THIS SUBSTANCE.

EMERGENCY EYE WASH: WHERE THERE IS ANY POSSIBILITY THAT AN EMPLOYEE'S EYES MAY BE EXPOSED TO THIS SUBSTANCE, THE EMPLOYER SHOULD PROVIDE AN EYE WASH FOUNTAIN WITHIN THE IMMEDIATE WORK AREA FOR EMERGENCY USE.

AUTHORIZED BY- OCCUPATIONAL HEALTH SERVICES, INC.

CREATION DATE: 10/04/89 ***REVISION DATE:*** 05/14/90

MATERIAL SAFETY DATA SHEET

OCCUPATIONAL HEALTH SERVICES, INC.
AGRICULTURE AND PESTICIDE DIVISION
450 SEVENTH AVENUE, SUITE 2407
NEW YORK, NEW YORK 10123
1-800-445-MSDS OR (212) 967-1100

EMERGENCY CONTACT:
JOHN S. BRANSFORD, JR. (615) 292-1180

SUBSTANCE IDENTIFICATION

CAS-NUMBER 301-12-2

SUBSTANCE: OXYDEMETON-METHYL

TRADE NAMES/SYNONYMS: PHOSPHOROTHIOIC ACID, S-(2-(ETHYLSULFINYL)ETHYL) O,O-DIMETHYL ESTER; S-2-ETHYLSULPHINYLETHYL O,O-DIMETHYL PHOSPHOROTHIOATE; S-2-ETHYLSULFINYLETHYL O,O-DIMETHYL PHOSPHOROTHIOATE; S-(2-(ETHYLSULFINYL)ETHYL) O,O-DIMETHYL PHOSPHOROTHIOATE; DIMETHYL S-(2-ETHYLSULFINYLETHYL)PHOSPHOROTHIOLATE; O,O-DIMETHYL-S-2-(ETHYLSULFINYL)ETHYL PHOSPHOROTHIOATE; BAY 210974; DEMETON-S METHYL SULFOXIDE; METAISOSYSTOX SULFOXIDE; METASYSTOX R; METHYL OXYDEMETON S; R 2170; ODM; ENT 24964; PST17375

CHEMICAL FAMILY: ORGANOPHOSPHATE

MOLECULAR FORMULA: C6-H15-O4-P-S2

MOLECULAR WEIGHT: 230.30

CERCLA RATINGS (SCALE 0-3): HEALTH=3 FIRE=U REACTIVITY=0 PERSISTENCE=0

NFPA RATINGS (SCALE 0-4): HEALTH=4 FIRE=U REACTIVITY=0

COMPONENTS AND CONTAMINANTS

COMPONENT: OXYDEMETON-METHYL ***PERCENT:*** 100
CAS# 301-12-2

EXPOSURE LIMITS: NO OCCUPATIONAL EXPOSURE LIMITS ESTABLISHED BY OSHA, ACGIH, OR NIOSH.

PHYSICAL DATA

DESCRIPTION: CLEAR AMBER-COLORED LIQUID

BOILING POINT: 223 F (106 C) @ 0.01 MMHG ***MELTING POINT:*** 14 F (-10 C)

SPECIFIC GRAVITY: 1.289 ***VAPOR PRESSURE:*** 3.8 MPA @ 20 C

EVAPORATION RATE: NOT AVAILABLE ***SOLUBILITY IN WATER:*** SOLUBLE

SOLVENT SOLUBILITY: SOLUBLE IN MOST ORGANIC SOLVENTS EXCEPT LIGHT PETROLEUM ETHER

FIRE AND EXPLOSION DATA

FIRE AND EXPLOSION HAZARD: UNKNOWN FIRE AND EXPLOSION HAZARD.

FIREFIGHTING MEDIA: DRY CHEMICAL, CARBON DIOXIDE, HALON, WATER SPRAY OR STANDARD FOAM (1987 EMERGENCY RESPONSE GUIDEBOOK, DOT P 5800.4).

FOR LARGER FIRES, USE WATER SPRAY, FOG OR STANDARD FOAM (1987 EMERGENCY RESPONSE GUIDEBOOK, DOT P 5800.4).

FIREFIGHTING: MOVE CONTAINERS FROM FIRE AREA IF POSSIBLE. FIGHT FIRE FROM MAXIMUM DISTANCE. STAY AWAY FROM STORAGE TANK ENDS. DIKE FIRE CONTROL WATER FOR LATER DISPOSAL. DO NOT SCATTER MATERIAL (1987 EMERGENCY RESPONSE GUIDEBOOK, DOT P 5800.4, GUIDE PAGE 55).

EXTINGUISH ONLY IF FLOW CAN BE STOPPED; USE FLOODING AMOUNTS OF WATER AS FOG, SOLID STREAMS MAY BE INEFFECTIVE. COOL CONTAINERS WITH FLOODING AMOUNTS OF WATER FROM AS FAR A DISTANCE AS POSSIBLE. USE WATER SPRAY TO ABSORB TOXIC VAPORS. AVOID BREATHING TOXIC VAPORS; KEEP UPWIND. CONSIDER EVACUATION OF DOWNWIND AREA IF MATERIAL IS LEAKING.

TRANSPORTATION DATA

DEPARTMENT OF TRANSPORTATION HAZARD CLASSIFICATION 49 CFR 172.101: POISON B

DEPARTMENT OF TRANSPORTATION LABELING REQUIREMENTS 49 CFR 172.101 AND SUBPART E: POISON

DEPARTMENT OF TRANSPORTATION PACKAGING REQUIREMENTS: 49 CFR 173.346 EXCEPTIONS: 49 CFR 173.345

TOXICITY

OXYDEMETON-METHYL: TOXICITY DATA: 1500 MG/M3/1 HOUR INHALATION-RAT LC50; 100 MG/KG SKIN-RAT LD50; 30 MG/KG ORAL-RAT LD50; 10 MG/KG ORAL-MOUSE LD50; 120 MG/KG ORAL-GUINEA PIG LD50; 47 MG/KG INTRAVENOUS-RAT LD50; 20 MG/KG INTRAPERITONEAL-RAT LD50; 8 MG/KG INTRAPERITONEAL-MOUSE LD50; 30 MG/KG INTRAPERITONEAL-GUINEA PIG LD50; 65 MG/KG UNREPORTED-RAT LD50; MUTAGENIC DATA (RTECS); REPRODUCTIVE EFFECTS DATA (52FR37248). CARCINOGEN STATUS: NONE. ACUTE TOXICITY LEVEL: HIGHLY TOXIC BY INHALATION, DERMAL ABSORPTION, AND INGESTION. TARGET EFFECTS: CHOLINESTERASE INHIBITOR. AT INCREASED RISK FROM EXPOSURE: PERSONS WITH RESPIRATORY AILMENTS, RECENT EXPOSURE TO CHOLINESTERASE INHIBITORS OR IMPAIRED CHOLINESTERASE PRODUCTION, OR LIVER MALFUNCTION.* ADDITIONAL DATA: MAY CROSS THE PLACENTA. HIGH ENVIRONMENTAL TEMPERATURES OR EXPOSURE OF THE CHEMICAL TO VISIBLE OR ULTRAVIOLET LIGHT MAY ENHANCE THE TOXICITY. INTERACTIONS WITH MEDICATIONS MAY OCCUR.*

* MAY BE BASED ON GENERAL INFORMATION ON ORGANOPHOSPHATES.

HEALTH EFFECTS AND FIRST AID

INHALATION: OXYDEMETON-METHYL: HIGHLY TOXIC. SEE INFORMATION ON ORGANOPHOSPHATES.

ORGANOPHOSPHATES: CHOLINESTERASE INHIBITOR. ACUTE EXPOSURE- WHEN INHALED, THE FIRST EFFECTS OF CHOLINESTERASE INHIBITORS ARE USUALLY RESPIRATORY AND MAY INCLUDE NASAL HYPEREMIA AND WATERY DISCHARGE, COUGH, CHEST DISCOMFORT, DYSPNEA, AND WHEEZING DUE TO INCREASED BRONCHIAL SECRETIONS AND BRONCHOCONSTRICTION. IF SUFFICIENT AMOUNTS ARE ABSORBED, OTHER SYSTEMIC EFFECTS MAY BEGIN WITHIN A FEW MINUTES OR BE DELAYED FOR UP TO 12 HOURS. SYMPTOMS MAY INCLUDE PALLOR, NAUSEA, VOMITING, DIARRHEA, ABDOMINAL CRAMPS, HEADACHE, DIZZINESS, OCULAR PAIN, BLURRED VISION, MIOSIS OR IN SOME CASES, ESPECIALLY INITIALLY, MYDRIASIS, LACRIMATION, SALIVATION, SWEATING, AND CONFUSION. OTHER REPORTED CENTRAL NERVOUS SYSTEM OR NEUROMUSCULAR EFFECTS MAY INCLUDE ATAXIA, SLURRED SPEECH, AREFLEXIA, WEAKNESS, FATIGUE, FASCICULATIONS, TWITCHING, TREMORS POSSIBLY OF THE TONGUE AND EYELIDS, AND EVENTUALLY PARALYSIS OF THE EXTREMITIES AND POSSIBLY OF THE RESPIRATORY MUSCLES. IN SEVERE CASES THERE MAY ALSO BE INVOLUNTARY DEFECATION AND URINATION, CYANOSIS, PSYCHOSIS, HYPERGLYCEMIA, ACUTE PANCREATITIS, CARDIAC IRREGULARITIES, PULMONARY EDEMA,

UNCONSCIOUSNESS, CONVULSIONS, AND COMA. DEATH IS PRIMARILY DUE TO RESPIRATORY FAILURE, ALTHOUGH CARDIOVASCULAR EFFECTS INCLUDING CARDIAC ARREST MAY ALSO BE IMPLICATED. LONG TERM SEQUELAE ARE RARE BUT MAY INCLUDE NEUROPSYCHIATRIC DISORDERS AND MYOPATHY WITH MUSCLE TENDERNESS. **CHRONIC EXPOSURE-** REPEATED OR PROLONGED EXPOSURE MAY RESULT IN THE EFFECTS OF ACUTE EXPOSURE. OTHER EFFECTS REPORTED IN WORKERS REPEATEDLY EXPOSED INCLUDE IMPAIRED MEMORY AND CONCENTRATION, ACUTE PSYCHOSIS, SEVERE DEPRESSIONS, IRRITABILTY, CONFUSION, APATHY, EMOTIONAL LABILITY, SOCIAL WITHDRAWAL, CONFUSION, HEADACHE, SPEECH DIFFICULTIES, DELAYED REACTION TIMES, SPATIAL DISORIENTATION, NIGHTMARES, SLEEPWALKING, AND DROWSINESS OR INSOMNIA. AN INFLUENZA-LIKE CONDITION WITH HEADACHE, NAUSEA, WEAKNESS, ANOREXIA AND MALAISE HAS ALSO BEEN REPORTED.

FIRST AID- REMOVE FROM EXPOSURE AREA TO FRESH AIR IMMEDIATELY. IF BREATHING HAS STOPPED, GIVE ARTIFICIAL RESPIRATION. MAINTAIN AIRWAY AND BLOOD PRESSURE AND ADMINISTER OXYGEN IF AVAILABLE. KEEP AFFECTED PERSON WARM AND AT REST. TREAT SYMPTOMATICALLY AND SUPPORTIVELY. ADMINISTRATION OF OXYGEN SHOULD BE PERFORMED BY QUALIFIED PERSONNEL. GET MEDICAL ATTENTION IMMEDIATELY.

SKIN CONTACT: OXYDEMETON-METHYL: HIGHLY TOXIC. SEE INFORMATION ON ORGANOPHOSPHATES.

ORGANOPHOSPHATES: CHOLINESTERASE INHIBITOR. **ACUTE EXPOSURE-** LOCALIZED SWEATING AND FASCICULATIONS MAY OCCUR AT THE SITE OF CONTACT. IF SUFFICIENT AMOUNTS ARE ABSORBED, OTHER EFFECTS OF CHOLINESTERASE INHIBITION AS DESCRIBED IN ACUTE INHALATION MAY OCCUR. SYMPTOMS MAY BE DELAYED 2-3 HOURS, BUT USUALLY NO MORE THAN 12 HOURS. THE RATE OF ABSORPTION IS INCREASED BY THE PRESENCE OF DERMATITIS OR HIGH AMBIENT TEMPERATURES. **CHRONIC EXPOSURE-** REPEATED OR PROLONGED EXPOSURE MAY CAUSE EFFECTS AS DESCRIBED IN ACUTE EXPOSURE. SOME ORGANOPHOSPHATES MAY CAUSE SENSITIZATION.

FIRST AID- REMOVE CONTAMINATED CLOTHING IMMEDIATELY. WASH CONTAMINATED AREAS WITH SOAP AND WATER FOLLOWED BY ALCOHOL (ARENA, POISONING, 4TH ED.). EMERGENCY PERSONNEL SHOULD WEAR GLOVES AND AVOID CONTAMINATION. TREAT RESPIRATORY DIFFICULTY WITH ARTIFICIAL RESPIRATION. GET MEDICAL ATTENTION IMMEDIATELY.

EYE CONTACT: OXYDEMETON-METHYL: SEE INFORMATION ON ORGANOPHOSPHATES.

ORGANOPHOSPHATES: CHOLINESTERASE INHIBITOR. **ACUTE EXPOSURE-** DIRECT CONTACT MAY CAUSE PAIN, HYPEREMIA, LACRIMATION, TWITCHING OF THE EYELIDS, MIOSIS, AND CILIARY MUSCLE SPASM WITH LOSS OF ACCOMODATION, BLURRED OR DIMMED VISION AND BROWACHE. SOMETIMES MYDRIASIS MAY OCCUR INSTEAD OF MIOSIS. WITH SUFFICIENT EXPOSURE, OTHER SYMPTOMS OF CHOLINESTERASE INHIBITION AS DESCRIBED IN ACUTE INHALATION MAY OCCUR. **CHRONIC EXPOSURE-** REPEATED OR PROLONGED EXPOSURE MAY CAUSE EFFECTS AS DESCRIBED IN ACUTE EXPOSURE. SOME COMPOUNDS HAVE CAUSED TOXIC EFFECTS ON THE CRYSTALLINE LENS, CONJUNCTIVAL THICKENING AND OBSTRUCTION OF THE NASOLACRIMAL CANALS WHEN USED AS MIOTIC EYEDROPS.

FIRST AID- IRRIGATE EYES WITH WATER OR SALINE SOLUTION. IF SYMPTOMS OF POISONING OCCUR, TREAT RESPIRATORY DIFFICULTY WITH ARTIFICIAL RESPIRATION AND OXYGEN. OBSERVE PATIENT FOR AT LEAST 24-36 HOURS (GOSSELIN, CLINICAL TOXICOLOGY OF COMMERCIAL PRODUCTS, 5TH ED.). GET MEDICAL ATTENTION IMMEDIATELY. OXYGEN SHOULD BE ADMINISTERED BY QUALIFIED MEDICAL PERSONNEL.

INGESTION: OXYDEMETON-METHYL: HIGHLY TOXIC. OXYDEMETON-METHYL DID NOT INDUCED DELAYED NEUROTOXIC SIGNS OF POISONING IN HENS. IN CHRONIC INGESTION STUDIES WITH OXYDEMETON-METHYL INCORPORATED INTO THE DIET OF RATS, THE OBSERVED EFFECTS INCLUDED DECREASES IN THE FERTILITY INDEX, TESTICULAR WEIGHT, LITTER SIZE, PUP WEIGHT, AND PUP SURVIVABILITY. HISTOPATHOLOGIC CHANGES IN THE EPIDIDYMIS, AND ALTERATIONS IN SPERM MORPHOLOGY AND MOTILITY WERE ALSO NOTED. SEE INFORMATION ON ORGANOPHOSPHATES.

ORGANOPHOSPHATES: CHOLINESTERASE INHIBITOR. **ACUTE EXPOSURE-** WHEN INGESTED, THE FIRST EFFECTS MAY BE NAUSEA, VOMITING, ANOREXIA, ABDOMINAL CRAMPS AND DIARRHEA. GASTROINTESTINAL ABSORPTION MAY CAUSE THE SYMPTOMS OF CHOLINESTERASE INHIBITION AS DESCRIBED IN ACUTE INHALATION. SYMPTOMS MAY BEGIN WITHIN MINUTES OR BE DELAYED. **CHRONIC EXPOSURE-** REPEATED INGESTION MAY CAUSE EFFECTS AS DESCRIBED IN ACUTE EXPOSURE.

FIRST AID- IF PERSON IS ALERT ANDRESPIRATION IS NOT DEPRESSED, GIVE SYRUP OF IPECAC FOLLOWED BY WATER(IF VOMITING OCCURS, KEEP HEAD BELOW HIPS TO PREVENT ASPIRATION).IF CONSCIOUSNESS LEVEL DECLINES OR VOMITING HAS NOT OCCURRED IN 15MINUTES EMPTY STOMACH BY GASTRIC LAVAGE WITH THE AID OF CUFFEDENDOTRACHEAL TUBE USING ISOTONIC SALINE OR 5% SODIUM BICARBONATEFOLLOW WITH ACTIVATED CHARCOAL. ESTABLISH AND MAINTAIN AIRWAY.TREAT RESPIRATORY DIFFICULTY WITH ARTIFICIAL RESPIRATION AND OXYGEN.DO NOT GIVE MORPHINE, AMINOPHYLLINE, PHENOTHIAZINES,RESERPINE, FUROSEMIDE, OR ETHACRYNIC ACID (MORGAN,RECOGNITION AND MANAGEMENT OF PESTICIDE POISONINGS, 3RD ED.).TREAT SYMPTOMATICALLY AND SUPPORTIVELY. ADMINISTRATION OFOXYGEN AND LAVAGE MUST BE PERFORMED BY QUALIFIED MEDICAL PERSONNEL. GET MEDICAL ATTENTION IMMEDIATELY.

ANTIDOTE: THE FOLLOWING ANTIDOTE(S) HAVE BEEN RECOMMENDED. HOWEVER, THE DECISION AS TO WHETHER THE SEVERITY OF POISONING REQUIRES ADMINISTRATION OF ANY ANTIDOTE AND ACTUAL DOSE REQUIRED SHOULD BE MADE BY QUALIFIED MEDICAL PERSONNEL.

FOR CHOLINESTERASE INHIBITORS: ESTABLISH CLEAR AIRWAY AND TISSUE OXYGENATION BY ASPIRATION OF SECRETIONS, AND IF NECESSARY, BY ASSISTED PULMONARY VENTILATION WITH OXYGEN. IMPROVE TISSUE OXYGENATION AS MUCH AS POSSIBLE BEFORE ADMINISTERING ATROPINE TO MINIMIZE THE RISK OF VENTRICULAR FIBRILLATION. ADMINISTER ATROPINE SULFATE INTRAVENOUSLY, OR INTRAMUSCULARLY IF IV INJECTION IS NOT POSSIBLE. IN MODERATELY SEVERE POISONING ADMINISTER ATROPINE SULFATE, 0.4-2.0 MG REPEATED EVERY 15 MINUTES UNTIL ATROPINIZATION IS ACHIEVED (TACHYCARDIA, FLUSHING, DRY MOUTH, MYDRIASIS). MAINTAIN ATROPINIZATION BY REPEATED DOSES FOR 2-12 HOURS, OR LONGER, DEPENDING ON THE SEVERITY OF POISONING. THE APPEARANCE OF RALES IN THE LUNG BASES, MIOSIS, SALIVATION, NAUSEA, BRADYCARDIA, ARE ALL INDICATIONS OF INADEQUATE ATROPINIZATION. SEVERELY POISONED INDIVIDUALS MAY EXHIBIT REMARKABLE TOLERANCE TO ATROPINE; TWO OR MORE TIMES THE DOSAGES SUGGESTED ABOVE MAY BE NEEDED. PERSONS NOT POISONED OR ONLY SLIGHTLY POISONED, HOWEVER, MAY DEVELOP SIGNS OF ATROPINE TOXICITY FROM SUCH LARGE DOSAGES: FEVER, MUSCLE FIBRILLATIONS, AND DELIRIUM ARE THE MAIN SIGNS OF ATROPINE TOXICITY. IF THESE SIGNS APPEAR WHILE THE PATIENT IS FULLY ATROPINIZED, ATROPINE ADMINISTRATION SHOULD BE DISCONTINUED, AT LEAST TEMPORARILY. OBSERVE TREATED PATIENTS CLOSELY AT LEAST 24 HOURS TO INSURE THAT SYMPTOMS (POSSIBLY PULMONARY EDEMA) DO NOT RECUR AS ATROPINIZATION WEARS OFF. IN VERY SEVERE POISONINGS, METABOLIC DISPOSITION OF TOXICANT MAY REQUIRE SEVERAL HOURS OR DAYS DURING WHICH ATROPINIZATION MUST BE MAINTAINED. MARKEDLY LOWER LEVELS OF URINARY METABOLITES INDICATE THAT ATROPINE DOSAGE CAN BE TAPERED OFF. AS DOSAGE IS REDUCED, CHECK THE LUNG BASES FREQUENTLY FOR RALES. IF RALES ARE HEARD OR OTHER SYMPTOMS RETURN, RE-ESTABLISH ATROPINIZATION PROMPTLY (MORGAN, RECOGNITION AND MANAGEMENT OF PESTICIDE POISONINGS, 3RD ED.). ADMINISTRATION OF ANTIDOTE MUST BE PERFORMED BY QUALIFIED MEDICAL PERSONNEL.

IN CASES OF SEVERE POISONING BY ORGANOPHOSPHATE PESTICIDES IN WHICH RESPIRATORY DEPRESSION, MUSCLE WEAKNESS AND TWITCHINGS ARE SEVERE, GIVE PRALIDOXIME (PROTOPAM-AYERST, 2-PAM), 1.0 GRAM INTRAVENOUSLY AT NO MORE THAN 0.5 GRAM PER MINUTE. DOSAGE OF PRALIDOXIME MAY BE REPEATED IN 1-2 HOURS, THEN AT 10-12 HOUR INTERVALS IF NEEDED. IN VERY SEVERE POISONINGS, DOSAGE RATES MAY BE DOUBLED. TREATMENT WITH PRALIDOXIME WILL BE MOST EFFECTIVE IF GIVEN WITHIN THIRTY-SIX HOURS AFTER POISONING (MORGAN, RECOGNITION AND MANAGEMENT OF PESTICIDE POISONINGS, 3RD ED.). ANTIDOTE SHOULD BE ADMINISTERED BY QUALIFIED MEDICAL PERSONNEL.

REACTIVITY

REACTIVITY: STABLE UNDER NORMAL TEMPERATURES AND PRESSURES.

INCOMPATIBILITIES: OXYDEMETON-METHYL: ALKALINE MEDIA: MAY HYDROLYZED.

DECOMPOSITION: THERMAL DECOMPOSITION MAY RELEASE TOXIC AND/OR HAZARDOUS GASES.

POLYMERIZATION: HAZARDOUS POLYMERIZATION HAS NOT BEEN REPORTED TO OCCUR UNDER NORMAL TEMPERATURES AND PRESSURES.

STORAGE AND DISPOSAL

OBSERVE ALL FEDERAL, STATE AND LOCAL REGULATIONS WHEN STORING OR DISPOSING OF THIS SUBSTANCE. FOR ASSISTANCE, CONTACT THE DISTRICT DIRECTOR OF THE ENVIRONMENTAL PROTECTION AGENCY.

****STORAGE****

STORE IN ACCORDANCE WITH 40 CFR 165 RECOMMENDED PROCEDURES FOR THE DISPOSAL AND STORAGE OF PESTICIDES AND PESTICIDE CONTAINERS. STORE AWAY FROM INCOMPATIBLE SUBSTANCES.

****DISPOSAL****

DISPOSAL MUST BE IN ACCORDANCE WITH 40 CFR 165 RECOMMENDED PROCEDURES FOR THE DISPOSAL AND STORAGE OF PESTICIDES AND PESTICIDE CONTAINERS.

CONDITIONS TO AVOID

NONE REPORTED.

SPILL AND LEAK PROCEDURES

OCCUPATIONAL SPILL: DO NOT TOUCH SPILLED MATERIAL. STOP LEAK IF YOU CAN DO IT WITHOUT RISK. USE WATER SPRAY TO REDUCE VAPORS. FOR SMALL SPILLS, TAKE UP WITH SAND OR OTHER ABSORBENT MATERIAL AND PLACE INTO CONTAINERS FOR LATER DISPOSAL. FOR SMALL DRY SPILLS, WITH A CLEAN SHOVEL PLACE MATERIAL INTO CLEAN, DRY CONTAINERS AND COVER. MOVE CONTAINERS FROM SPILL AREA. FOR LARGER SPILLS, DIKE FAR AHEAD OF SPILL FOR LATER DISPOSAL. KEEP UNNECESSARY PEOPLE AWAY. ISOLATE HAZARD AREA AND DENY ENTRY. VENTILATE CLOSED SPACES BEFORE ENTERING.

PROTECTIVE EQUIPMENT

VENTILATION: PROCESS ENCLOSURE RECOMMENDED.

RESPIRATOR: THE FOLLOWING RESPIRATORS ARE RECOMMENDED BASED ON INFORMATION FOUND IN THE PHYSICAL DATA, TOXICITY AND HEALTH EFFECTS SECTIONS. THEY ARE RANKED IN ORDER FROM MINIMUM TO MAXIMUM RESPIRATORY PROTECTION. THE SPECIFIC RESPIRATOR SELECTED MUST BE BASED ON CONTAMINATION LEVELS FOUND IN THE WORK PLACE, MUST NOT EXCEED THE WORKING LIMITS OF THE RESPIRATOR AND BE JOINTLY APPROVED BY THE NATIONAL INSTITUTE FOR OCCUPATIONAL SAFETY AND HEALTH AND THE MINE SAFETY AND HEALTH ADMINISTRATION (NIOSH-MSHA).

TYPE 'C' SUPPLIED-AIR RESPIRATOR WITH A FULL FACEPIECE OPERATED IN PRESSURE-DEMAND OR OTHER POSITIVE PRESSURE MODE OR WITH A FULL FACEPIECE, HELMET OR HOOD OPERATED IN CONTINOUS-FLOW MODE.

SELF-CONTAINED BREATHING APPARATUS WITH A FULL FACEPIECE OPERATED IN PRESSURE-DEMAND OR OTHER POSITIVE PRESSURE MODE.

FOR FIREFIGHTING AND OTHER IMMEDIATELY DANGEROUS TO LIFE OR HEALTH CONDITIONS:

SELF-CONTAINED BREATHING APPARATUS WITH FULL FACEPIECE OPERATED IN PRESSURE-DEMAND OR OTHER POSITIVE PRESSURE MODE.

SUPPLIED-AIR RESPIRATOR WITH FULL FACEPIECE AND OPERATED IN PRESSURE-DEMAND OR OTHER POSITIVE PRESSURE MODE IN COMBINATION WITH AN AUXILIARY SELF-CONTAINED BREATHING APPARATUS OPERATED IN PRESSURE-DEMAND OR OTHER POSITIVE PRESSURE MODE.

CLOTHING: EMPLOYEE MUST WEAR APPROPRIATE PROTECTIVE (IMPERVIOUS) CLOTHING AND EQUIPMENT TO PREVENT ANY POSSIBILITY OF SKIN CONTACT WITH THIS SUBSTANCE.

GLOVES: EMPLOYEE MUST WEAR APPROPRIATE PROTECTIVE GLOVES TO PREVENT CONTACT WITH THIS SUBSTANCE.

EYE PROTECTION: EMPLOYEE MUST WEAR SPLASH-PROOF OR DUST-RESISTANT SAFETY GOGGLES AND A FACESHIELD TO PREVENT CONTACT WITH THIS SUBSTANCE.

EMERGENCY WASH FACILITIES: WHERE THERE IS ANY POSSIBILITY THAT AN EMPLOYEE'S EYES AND/OR SKIN MAY BE EXPOSED TO THIS SUBSTANCE, THE EMPLOYER SHOULD PROVIDE AN EYE WASH FOUNTAIN AND QUICK DRENCH SHOWER WITHIN THE IMMEDIATE WORK AREA FOR EMERGENCY USE.

AUTHORIZED BY- OCCUPATIONAL HEALTH SERVICES, INC.
CREATION DATE: 10/04/89 ***REVISION DATE:*** 06/20/90

MATERIAL SAFETY DATA SHEET

OCCUPATIONAL HEALTH SERVICES, INC.
AGRICULTURE AND PESTICIDE DIVISION
450 SEVENTH AVENUE, SUITE 2407
NEW YORK, NEW YORK 10123
1-800-445-MSDS OR (212) 967-1100

EMERGENCY CONTACT:
JOHN S. BRANSFORD, JR. (615) 292-1180

SUBSTANCE IDENTIFICATION

CAS-NUMBER 2497-07-6

SUBSTANCE: **OXYDISULFOTON**

TRADE NAMES/SYNONYMS: PHOSPHORODITHIOIC ACID, O,O-DIETHYL S-(2-(ETHYLSULFINYL)ETHYL) ESTER; O,O-DIETHYL S-2-ETHYLSULPHINYLETHYL PHOSPHORODITHIOATE; O,O-DIETHYL S-2-ETHYLSULFINYLETHYL PHOSPHORODITHIOATE; O,O-DIETHYL S-(2-(ETHYLSULFINYL)ETHYL) PHOSPHORODITHIOATE; DIETHYL S-(2-ETHYLSULFINYLETHYL)PHOSPHOROTHIOLOTHIONATE; DISULFOTON SULFOXIDE; DISYSTON SULFOXIDE; ETHYLTHIOMETON SULFOXIDE; PST17385

CHEMICAL FAMILY: ORGANOPHOSPHATE

MOLECULAR FORMULA: C8-H19-O3-P-S3

MOLECULAR WEIGHT: 290.42

CERCLA RATINGS (SCALE 0-3): HEALTH=3 FIRE=0 REACTIVITY=0 PERSISTENCE=0

NFPA RATINGS (SCALE 0-4): HEALTH=4 FIRE=0 REACTIVITY=0

COMPONENTS AND CONTAMINANTS

COMPONENT: OXYDISULFOTON ***PERCENT:*** 100
CAS# 2497-07-6

EXPOSURE LIMITS: OXYDISULFOTON: 500 POUNDS SARA SECTION 302 THRESHOLD PLANNING QUANTITY 1 POUND SARA SECTION 304 REPORTABLE QUANTITY

PHYSICAL DATA

DESCRIPTION: LIGHT BROWN UNDISTILLABLE LIQUID ***BOILING POINT:*** NOT AVAILABLE

SPECIFIC GRAVITY: 1.209 ***SOLUBILITY IN WATER:*** 10 PPM

SOLVENT SOLUBILITY: SOLUBLE IN MOST ORGANIC SOLVENTS EXCEPT LIGROIN

FIRE AND EXPLOSION DATA

FIRE AND EXPLOSION HAZARD: NEGLIGIBLE FIRE HAZARD WHEN EXPOSED TO HEAT OR FLAME.

FIREFIGHTING MEDIA: DRY CHEMICAL, CARBON DIOXIDE, HALON, WATER SPRAY OR STANDARD FOAM (1987 EMERGENCY RESPONSE GUIDEBOOK, DOT P 5800.4). FOR LARGER FIRES, USE WATER SPRAY, FOG OR STANDARD FOAM (1987 EMERGENCY RESPONSE GUIDEBOOK, DOT P 5800.4).

FIREFIGHTING: MOVE CONTAINERS FROM FIRE AREA IF POSSIBLE. FIGHT FIRE FROM MAXIMUM DISTANCE. STAY AWAY FROM STORAGE TANK ENDS. DIKE FIRE CONTROL WATER FOR LATER DISPOSAL. DO NOT SCATTER MATERIAL (1987 EMERGENCY RESPONSE GUIDEBOOK, DOT P 5800.4, GUIDE PAGE 55). EXTINGUISH ONLY IF FLOW CAN BE STOPPED; USE FLOODING AMOUNTS OF WATER AS FOG, SOLID STREAMS MAY BE INEFFECTIVE. COOL CONTAINERS WITH FLOODING AMOUNTS OF WATER FROM AS FAR A DISTANCE AS POSSIBLE. USE WATER SPRAY TO ABSORB TOXIC VAPORS. AVOID BREATHING TOXIC VAPORS; KEEP UPWIND. CONSIDER EVACUATION OF DOWNWIND AREA IF MATERIAL IS LEAKING.

TRANSPORTATION DATA

DEPARTMENT OF TRANSPORTATION HAZARD CLASSIFICATION 49 CFR 172.101: POISON B

DEPARTMENT OF TRANSPORTATION LABELING REQUIREMENTS 49 CFR 172.101 AND SUBPART E: POISON

TOXICITY

OXYDISULFOTON: TOXICITY DATA: 92 MG/KG SKIN-RAT LD50; 263 MG/KG SKIN-MOUSE LD50; 3500 UG/KG ORAL-RAT LD50; 12 MG/KG ORAL-MOUSE LD50. CARCINOGEN STATUS: NONE. ACUTE TOXICITY LEVEL: HIGHLY TOXIC BY INGESTION AND DERMAL ABSORPTION. TARGET EFFECTS: CHOLINESTERASE INHIBITOR. POISONING MAY AFFECT THE NERVOUS SYSTEM.* AT INCREASED RISK FROM EXPOSURE: PERSONS WITH RESPIRATORY AILMENTS, RECENT EXPOSURE TO CHOLINESTERASE INHIBITORS OR IMPAIRED CHOLINESTERASE PRODUCTION, OR LIVER MALFUNCTION.* ADDITIONAL DATA: MAY CROSS THE PLACENTA. HIGH ENVIRONMENTAL TEMPERATURES OR EXPOSURE OF THE CHEMICAL TO VISIBLE OR ULTRAVIOLET LIGHT MAY ENHANCE THE TOXICITY. INTERACTIONS WITH MEDICATIONS MAY OCCUR.*

* MAY BE BASED ON GENERAL INFORMATION ON ORGANOPHOSPHATES.

HEALTH EFFECTS AND FIRST AID

INHALATION: OXYDISULFOTON: SEE INFORMATION ON ORGANOPHOSPHATES.
ORGANOPHOSPHATES: CHOLINESTERASE INHIBITOR. **ACUTE EXPOSURE-** WHEN INHALED, THE FIRST EFFECTS OF CHOLINESTERASE INHIBITORS ARE USUALLY RESPIRATORY AND MAY INCLUDE NASAL HYPEREMIA AND WATERY DISCHARGE, COUGH, CHEST DISCOMFORT, DYSPNEA, AND WHEEZING DUE TO INCREASED BRONCHIAL SECRETIONS AND BRONCHOCONSTRICTION. IF SUFFICIENT AMOUNTS ARE ABSORBED, OTHER SYSTEMIC EFFECTS MAY BEGIN WITHIN A FEW MINUTES OR BE DELAYED FOR UP TO 12 HOURS. SYMPTOMS MAY INCLUDE PALLOR, NAUSEA, VOMITING, DIARRHEA, ABDOMINAL CRAMPS, HEADACHE, DIZZINESS, OCULAR PAIN, BLURRED VISION, MIOSIS OR IN SOME CASES, ESPECIALLY INITIALLY, MYDRIASIS, LACRIMATION, SALIVATION, SWEATING, AND CONFUSION. OTHER REPORTED CENTRAL NERVOUS SYSTEM OR NEUROMUSCULAR EFFECTS MAY INCLUDE ATAXIA, SLURRED SPEECH, AREFLEXIA, WEAKNESS, FATIGUE, FASCICULATIONS, TWITCHING, TREMORS POSSIBLY OF THE TONGUE AND EYELIDS, AND EVENTUALLY PARALYSIS OF THE EXTREMITIES AND POSSIBLY OF THE RESPIRATORY MUSCLES. IN SEVERE CASES THERE MAY ALSO BE INVOLUNTARY DEFECATION AND URINATION, CYANOSIS, PSYCHOSIS, HYPERGLYCEMIA, ACUTE PANCREATITIS, CARDIAC IRREGULARITIES, PULMONARY EDEMA, UNCONSCIOUSNESS, CONVULSIONS, AND COMA. DEATH IS PRIMARILY DUE TO RESPIRATORY FAILURE, ALTHOUGH CARDIOVASCULAR EFFECTS INCLUDING CARDIAC ARREST MAY ALSO BE IMPLICATED. LONG TERM SEQUELAE ARE RARE

BUT MAY INCLUDE NEUROPSYCHIATRIC DISORDERS AND MYOPATHY WITH MUSCLE TENDERNESS. SOME ORGANOPHOSPHATES MAY CAUSE A DELAYED NEUROPATHY BEGINNING 1-4 WEEKS AFTER AN ACUTE EXPOSURE WHICH MAY OR MAY NOT HAVE CAUSED ACUTE CHOLINERGIC EFFECTS. NUMBNESS, TINGLING, WEAKNESS AND CRAMPING BEGINNING SYMMETRICALLY IN THE LOWER LIMBS MAY PROGRESS TO ATAXIA AND PARALYSIS. IN SEVERE CASES, UPPER LIMB INVOLVEMENT IS POSSIBLE AND FLACCID PARALYSIS MAY PROGRESS TO SPASTIC PARALYSIS WITH EXAGGERATED REFLEXES. IMPROVEMENT MAY OCCUR OVER MONTHS TO YEARS, BUT SOME RESIDUAL IMPAIRMENT USUALLY REMAINS. **CHRONIC EXPOSURE-** REPEATED OR PROLONGED EXPOSURE MAY RESULT IN THE EFFECTS OF ACUTE EXPOSURE INCLUDING THE DELAYED NEUROPATHY. OTHER EFFECTS REPORTED IN WORKERS REPEATEDLY EXPOSED INCLUDE IMPAIRED MEMORY AND CONCENTRATION, ACUTE PSYCHOSIS, SEVERE DEPRESSIONS, IRRITABILTY, CONFUSION, APATHY, EMOTIONAL LABILITY, SOCIAL WITHDRAWAL, CONFUSION, HEADACHE, SPEECH DIFFICULTIES, DELAYED REACTION TIMES, SPATIAL DISORIENTATION, NIGHTMARES, SLEEPWALKING, AND DROWSINESS OR INSOMNIA. AN INFLUENZA-LIKE CONDITION WITH HEADACHE, NAUSEA, WEAKNESS, ANOREXIA AND MALAISE HAS ALSO BEEN REPORTED.

FIRST AID- REMOVE FROM EXPOSURE AREA TO FRESH AIR IMMEDIATELY. IF BREATHING HAS STOPPED, GIVE ARTIFICIAL RESPIRATION. MAINTAIN AIRWAY AND BLOOD PRESSURE AND ADMINISTER OXYGEN IF AVAILABLE. KEEP AFFECTED PERSON WARM AND AT REST. TREAT SYMPTOMATICALLY AND SUPPORTIVELY. ADMINISTRATION OF OXYGEN SHOULD BE PERFORMED BY QUALIFIED PERSONNEL. GET MEDICAL ATTENTION IMMEDIATELY.

SKIN CONTACT: OXYDISULFOTON: HIGHLY TOXIC. SEE INFORMATION ON ORGANOPHOSPHATES.
ORGANOPHOSPHATES: CHOLINESTERASE INHIBITOR. **ACUTE EXPOSURE-** LOCALIZED SWEATING AND FASCICULATIONS MAY OCCUR AT THE SITE OF CONTACT. IF SUFFICIENT AMOUNTS ARE ABSORBED, OTHER EFFECTS OF CHOLINESTERASE INHIBITION AS DESCRIBED IN ACUTE INHALATION MAY OCCUR. SYMPTOMS MAY BE DELAYED 2-3 HOURS, BUT USUALLY NO MORE THAN 12 HOURS. THE RATE OF ABSORPTION IS INCREASED BY THE PRESENCE OF DERMATITIS OR HIGH AMBIENT TEMPERATURES. DELAYED NEUROPATHY IS ALSO POSSIBLE. **CHRONIC EXPOSURE-** REPEATED OR PROLONGED EXPOSURE MAY CAUSE EFFECTS AS DESCRIBED IN ACUTE EXPOSURE. SOME ORGANOPHOSPHATES MAY CAUSE SENSITIZATION.

FIRST AID- REMOVE CONTAMINATED CLOTHING IMMEDIATELY. WASH CONTAMINATED AREAS WITH SOAP AND WATER FOLLOWED BY ALCOHOL (ARENA, POISONING, 4TH ED.). EMERGENCY PERSONNEL SHOULD WEAR GLOVES AND AVOID CONTAMINATION. TREAT RESPIRATORY DIFFICULTY WITH ARTIFICIAL RESPIRATION. GET MEDICAL ATTENTION IMMEDIATELY.

EYE CONTACT: OXYDISULFOTON: SEE INFORMATION ON ORGANOPHOSPHATES.
ORGANOPHOSPHATES: CHOLINESTERASE INHIBITOR. **ACUTE EXPOSURE-** DIRECT CONTACT MAY CAUSE PAIN, HYPEREMIA, LACRIMATION, TWITCHING OF THE EYELIDS, MIOSIS, AND CILIARY MUSCLE SPASM WITH LOSS OF ACCOMODATION, BLURRED OR DIMMED VISION AND BROWACHE. SOMETIMES MYDRIASIS MAY OCCUR INSTEAD OF MIOSIS. WITH SUFFICIENT EXPOSURE, OTHER SYMPTOMS OF CHOLINESTERASE INHIBITION AS DESCRIBED IN ACUTE INHALATION MAY OCCUR. **CHRONIC EXPOSURE-** REPEATED OR PROLONGED EXPOSURE MAY CAUSE EFFECTS AS DESCRIBED IN ACUTE EXPOSURE. SOME COMPOUNDS HAVE CAUSED TOXIC EFFECTS ON THE CRYSTALLINE LENS, CONJUNCTIVAL THICKENING AND OBSTRUCTION OF THE NASOLACRIMAL CANALS WHEN USED AS MIOTIC EYEDROPS.

FIRST AID- IRRIGATE EYES WITH WATER OR SALINE SOLUTION. IF SYMPTOMS OF POISONING OCCUR, TREAT RESPIRATORY DIFFICULTY WITH ARTIFICIAL RESPIRATION AND OXYGEN. OBSERVE PATIENT FOR AT LEAST 24-36 HOURS (GOSSELIN, CLINICAL TOXICOLOGY OF COMMERCIAL PRODUCTS, 5TH ED.). GET MEDICAL ATTENTION IMMEDIATELY. OXYGEN SHOULD BE ADMINISTERED BY QUALIFIED MEDICAL PERSONNEL.

INGESTION: OXYDISULFOTON: HIGHLY TOXIC. SEE INFORMATION ON ORGANOPHOSPHATES.
ORGANOPHOSPHATES: CHOLINESTERASE INHIBITOR. **ACUTE EXPOSURE-** WHEN INGESTED, THE FIRST EFFECTS MAY BE NAUSEA, VOMITING, ANOREXIA, ABDOMINAL CRAMPS AND DIARRHEA. GASTROINTESTINAL ABSORPTION MAY CAUSE SYMPTOMS OF CHOLINESTERASE INHIBITION AS DESCRIBED IN ACUTE INHALATION. SYMPTOMS MAY BEGIN WITHIN MINUTES OR BE DELAYED FOR HOURS. DELAYED EFFECTS INCLUDING NEUROPATHY MAY ALSO OCCUR. **CHRONIC EXPOSURE-** REPEATED INGESTION MAY CAUSE EFFECTS AS DESCRIBED IN ACUTE EXPOSURE.

FIRST AID- IF PERSON IS ALERT AND RESPIRATION IS NOT DEPRESSED, GIVE SYRUP OF IPECAC FOLLOWED BY WATER (IF VOMITING OCCURS, KEEP HEAD BELOW HIPS TO PREVENT ASPIRATION). IF CONSCIOUSNESS LEVEL DECLINES OR VOMITING HAS NOT OCCURRED IN 15 MINUTES EMPTY STOMACH BY GASTRIC LAVAGE WITH THE AID OF CUFFED ENDOTRACHEAL TUBE USING ISOTONIC SALINE OR 5% SODIUM BICARBONATE FOLLOW WITH ACTIVATED CHARCOAL. ESTABLISH AND MAINTAIN AIRWAY. TREAT RESPIRATORY DIFFICULTY WITH ARTIFICIAL RESPIRATION AND OXYGEN. DO NOT GIVE MORPHINE, AMINOPHYLLINE, PHENOTHIAZINES, RESERPINE, FUROSEMIDE, OR ETHACRYNIC ACID (MORGAN, RECOGNITION AND MANAGEMENT OF PESTICIDE POISONINGS, 3RD ED.). TREAT SYMPTOMATICALLY AND SUPPORTIVELY. ADMINISTRATION OF OXYGEN AND LAVAGE MUST BE PERFORMED BY QUALIFIED MEDICAL PERSONNEL. GET MEDICAL ATTENTION IMMEDIATELY.

ANTIDOTE: THE FOLLOWING ANTIDOTE(S) HAVE BEEN RECOMMENDED. HOWEVER, THE DECISION AS TO WHETHER THE SEVERITY OF POISONING REQUIRES ADMINISTRATION OF ANY ANTIDOTE AND ACTUAL DOSE REQUIRED SHOULD BE MADE BY QUALIFIED MEDICAL PERSONNEL.
FOR CHOLINESTERASE INHIBITORS: ESTABLISH CLEAR AIRWAY AND TISSUE OXYGENATION BY ASPIRATION OF SECRETIONS, AND IF NECESSARY, BY ASSISTED PULMONARY VENTILATION WITH OXYGEN. IMPROVE TISSUE OXYGENATION AS MUCH AS POSSIBLE BEFORE ADMINISTERING ATROPINE TO MINIMIZE THE RISK OF VENTRICULAR FIBRILLATION. ADMINISTER ATROPINE SULFATE INTRAVENOUSLY, OR INTRAMUSCULARLY IF IV INJECTION IS NOT POSSIBLE. IN MODERATELY SEVERE POISONING ADMINISTER ATROPINE SULFATE, 0.4-2.0 MG REPEATED EVERY 15 MINUTES UNTIL ATROPINIZATION IS ACHIEVED (TACHYCARDIA, FLUSHING, DRY MOUTH, MYDRIASIS). MAINTAIN ATROPINIZATION BY REPEATED DOSES FOR 2-12 HOURS, OR LONGER, DEPENDING ON THE SEVERITY OF POISONING. THE APPEARANCE OF RALES IN THE LUNG BASES, MIOSIS, SALIVATION, NAUSEA, BRADYCARDIA, ARE ALL INDICATIONS OF INADEQUATE ATROPINIZATION. SEVERELY POISONED INDIVIDUALS MAY EXHIBIT REMARKABLE TOLERANCE TO ATROPINE; TWO OR MORE TIMES THE DOSAGES SUGGESTED ABOVE MAY BE NEEDED. PERSONS NOT POISONED OR ONLY SLIGHTLY POISONED, HOWEVER, MAY DEVELOP SIGNS OF ATROPINE TOXICITY FROM SUCH LARGE DOSAGES: FEVER, MUSCLE FIBRILLATIONS, AND DELIRIUM ARE THE MAIN SIGNS OF ATROPINE TOXICITY. IF THESE SIGNS APPEAR WHILE THE PATIENT IS FULLY ATROPINIZED, ATROPINE ADMINISTRATION SHOULD BE DISCONTINUED, AT LEAST TEMPORARILY. OBSERVE TREATED PATIENTS CLOSELY AT LEAST 24 HOURS TO INSURE THAT SYMPTOMS (POSSIBLY PULMONARY EDEMA) DO NOT RECUR AS ATROPINIZATION WEARS OFF. IN VERY SEVERE POISONINGS, METABOLIC DISPOSITION OF TOXICANT MAY REQUIRE SEVERAL HOURS OR DAYS DURING WHICH ATROPINIZATION MUST BE MAINTAINED. MARKEDLY LOWER LEVELS OF URINARY METABOLITES INDICATE THAT ATROPINE DOSAGE CAN BE TAPERED OFF. AS DOSAGE IS REDUCED, CHECK THE LUNG BASES FREQUENTLY FOR RALES. IF RALES ARE HEARD OR OTHER SYMPTOMS RETURN, RE-ESTABLISH ATROPINIZATION PROMPTLY (MORGAN, RECOGNITION AND MANAGEMENT OF PESTICIDE POISONINGS, 3RD ED.). ADMINISTRATION OF ANTIDOTE MUST BE PERFORMED BY QUALIFIED MEDICAL PERSONNEL.
IN CASES OF SEVERE POISONING BY ORGANOPHOSPHATE PESTICIDES IN WHICH RESPIRATORY DEPRESSION, MUSCLE WEAKNESS AND TWITCHINGS ARE SEVERE, GIVE PRALIDOXIME (PROTOPAM-AYERST, 2-PAM), 1.0 GRAM INTRAVENOUSLY AT NO MORE THAN 0.5 GRAM PER MINUTE. DOSAGE OF PRALIDOXIME MAY BE REPEATED IN 1-2 HOURS, THEN AT 10-12 HOUR INTERVALS IF NEEDED. IN VERY SEVERE POISONINGS, DOSAGE RATES MAY BE DOUBLED. TREATMENT WITH PRALIDOXIME WILL BE MOST EFFECTIVE IF GIVEN WITHIN THIRTY-SIX HOURS AFTER POISONING (MORGAN, RECOGNITION AND MANAGEMENT OF PESTICIDE POISONINGS, 3RD ED.). ANTIDOTE SHOULD BE ADMINISTERED BY QUALIFIED MEDICAL PERSONNEL.

REACTIVITY

REACTIVITY: STABLE UNDER NORMAL TEMPERATURES AND PRESSURES.

INCOMPATIBILITIES: OXYDISULFOTON: OXIDIZERS (STRONG): FIRE AND EXPLOSION HAZARD.

DECOMPOSITION: THERMAL DECOMPOSITION MAY RELEASE TOXIC OXIDES OF PHOSPHORUS AND SULFUR.

POLYMERIZATION: HAZARDOUS POLYMERIZATION HAS NOT BEEN REPORTED TO OCCUR UNDER NORMAL TEMPERATURES AND PRESSURES.

STORAGE AND DISPOSAL

OBSERVE ALL FEDERAL, STATE AND LOCAL REGULATIONS WHEN STORING OR DISPOSING OF THIS SUBSTANCE. FOR ASSISTANCE, CONTACT THE DISTRICT DIRECTOR OF THE ENVIRONMENTAL PROTECTION AGENCY.

****STORAGE****

STORE IN ACCORDANCE WITH 40 CFR 165 RECOMMENDED PROCEDURES FOR THE DISPOSAL AND STORAGE OF PESTICIDES AND PESTICIDE CONTAINERS.
THRESHOLD PLANNING QUANTITY (TPQ): THE SUPERFUND AMENDMENTS AND REAUTHORIZATION ACT (SARA) SECTION 302 REQUIRES THAT EACH FACILITY WHERE ANY EXTREMELY HAZARDOUS SUBSTANCE IS PRESENT IN A QUANTITY EQUAL TO OR GREATER THAN THE TPQ ESTABLISHED FOR THAT SUBSTANCE NOTIFY THE STATE EMERGENCY RESPONSE COMMISSION FOR THE STATE IN WHICH IT IS LOCATED. SECTION 303 OF SARA REQUIRES THESE FACILITIES TO PARTICIPATE IN LOCAL EMERGENCY RESPONSE PLANNING (40 CFR 355.30).

****DISPOSAL****

DISPOSAL MUST BE IN ACCORDANCE WITH 40 CFR 165 RECOMMENDED PROCEDURES FOR THE DISPOSAL AND STORAGE OF PESTICIDES AND PESTICIDE CONTAINERS.

CONDITIONS TO AVOID

NONE REPORTED.

SPILL AND LEAK PROCEDURES

OCCUPATIONAL SPILL: DO NOT TOUCH SPILLED MATERIAL. STOP LEAK IF YOU CAN DO IT WITHOUT RISK. USE WATER SPRAY TO REDUCE VAPORS. FOR SMALL SPILLS, TAKE UP WITH SAND OR OTHER ABSORBENT MATERIAL AND PLACE INTO CONTAINERS FOR LATER DISPOSAL. FOR SMALL DRY SPILLS, WITH A CLEAN SHOVEL PLACE MATERIAL INTO CLEAN, DRY CONTAINERS AND COVER. MOVE CONTAINERS FROM SPILL AREA. FOR LARGER SPILLS, DIKE FAR AHEAD OF SPILL FOR LATER DISPOSAL. KEEP UNNECESSARY PEOPLE AWAY. ISOLATE HAZARD AREA AND DENY ENTRY. VENTILATE CLOSED SPACES BEFORE ENTERING.

REPORTABLE QUANTITY (RQ): 1 POUND THE SUPERFUND AMENDMENTS AND REAUTHORIZATION ACT (SARA) SECTION 304 REQUIRES THAT A RELEASE EQUAL TO OR GREATER THAN THE REPORTABLE QUANTITY FOR THIS SUBSTANCE BE IMMEDIATELY REPORTED TO THE LOCAL EMERGENCY PLANNING COMMITTEE AND THE STATE EMERGENCY RESPONSE COMMISSION (40 CFR 355.40). IF THE RELEASE OF THIS SUBSTANCE IS REPORTABLE UNDER CERCLA SECTION 103, THE NATIONAL RESPONSE CENTER MUST BE NOTIFIED IMMEDIATELY AT (800) 424-8802 OR (202) 426-2675 IN THE METROPOLITAN WASHINGTON, D.C. AREA (40 CFR 302.6).

PROTECTIVE EQUIPMENT

VENTILATION: PROCESS ENCLOSURE RECOMMENDED.

RESPIRATOR: THE FOLLOWING RESPIRATORS ARE RECOMMENDED BASED ON INFORMATION FOUND IN THE PHYSICAL DATA, TOXICITY AND HEALTH EFFECTS SECTIONS. THEY ARE RANKED IN ORDER FROM MINIMUM TO MAXIMUM RESPIRATORY PROTECTION. THE SPECIFIC RESPIRATOR SELECTED MUST BE BASED ON CONTAMINATION LEVELS FOUND IN THE WORK PLACE, MUST NOT EXCEED THE WORKING LIMITS OF THE RESPIRATOR AND BE JOINTLY APPROVED BY THE NATIONAL INSTITUTE FOR OCCUPATIONAL SAFETY AND HEALTH AND THE MINE SAFETY AND HEALTH ADMINISTRATION (NIOSH-MSHA).

TYPE 'C' SUPPLIED-AIR RESPIRATOR WITH A FULL FACEPIECE OPERATED IN PRESSURE-DEMAND OR OTHER POSITIVE PRESSURE MODE OR WITH A FULL FACEPIECE, HELMET OR HOOD OPERATED IN CONTINOUS-FLOW MODE.

SELF-CONTAINED BREATHING APPARATUS WITH A FULL FACEPIECE OPERATED IN PRESSURE-DEMAND OR OTHER POSITIVE PRESSURE MODE.

FOR FIREFIGHTING AND OTHER IMMEDIATELY DANGEROUS TO LIFE OR HEALTH CONDITIONS:

SELF-CONTAINED BREATHING APPARATUS WITH FULL FACEPIECE OPERATED IN PRESSURE-DEMAND OR OTHER POSITIVE PRESSURE MODE.

SUPPLIED-AIR RESPIRATOR WITH FULL FACEPIECE AND OPERATED IN PRESSURE-DEMAND OR OTHER POSITIVE PRESSURE MODE IN COMBINATION WITH AN AUXILIARY SELF-CONTAINED BREATHING APPARATUS OPERATED IN PRESSURE-DEMAND OR OTHER POSITIVE PRESSURE MODE.

CLOTHING: EMPLOYEE MUST WEAR APPROPRIATE PROTECTIVE (IMPERVIOUS) CLOTHING AND EQUIPMENT TO PREVENT ANY POSSIBILITY OF SKIN CONTACT WITH THIS SUBSTANCE.

GLOVES: EMPLOYEE MUST WEAR APPROPRIATE PROTECTIVE GLOVES TO PREVENT CONTACT WITH THIS SUBSTANCE.

EYE PROTECTION: EMPLOYEE MUST WEAR SPLASH-PROOF OR DUST-RESISTANT SAFETY GOGGLES AND A FACESHIELD TO PREVENT CONTACT WITH THIS SUBSTANCE.

EMERGENCY WASH FACILITIES: WHERE THERE IS ANY POSSIBILITY THAT AN EMPLOYEE'S EYES AND/OR SKIN MAY BE EXPOSED TO THIS SUBSTANCE, THE EMPLOYER SHOULD PROVIDE AN EYE WASH FOUNTAIN AND QUICK DRENCH SHOWER WITHIN THE IMMEDIATE WORK AREA FOR EMERGENCY USE.

AUTHORIZED BY- OCCUPATIONAL HEALTH SERVICES, INC.

CREATION DATE: 10/04/89 ***REVISION DATE:*** 04/25/90

MATERIAL SAFETY DATA SHEET

OCCUPATIONAL HEALTH SERVICES, INC.
AGRICULTURE AND PESTICIDE DIVISION
450 SEVENTH AVENUE, SUITE 2407
NEW YORK, NEW YORK 10123

EMERGENCY CONTACT:
JOHN S. BRANSFORD, JR. (615) 292-1180
1-800-445-MSDS OR (212) 967-1100

SUBSTANCE IDENTIFICATION

CAS-NUMBER 79-57-2

SUBSTANCE: **<u>OXYTETRACYCLINE</u>**

TRADE NAMES/SYNONYMS: 2-NAPHTHACENECARBOXAMIDE, 4-(DIMETHYLAMINO)-1,4,4A,5,5A,6,11,12A- OCTAHYDRO-3,5,6,10,12,12A-HEXAHYDROXY-6-METHYL-1,11-DIOXO-, (4S-(4 ALPHA,4A ALPHA,5 ALPHA,5A ALPHA,6 ALPHA,12A ALPHA))-; 2-NAPHTHACENECARBOXAMIDE, 4-(DIMETHYLAMINO)-1,4,4S,5,5A,6,11,12A- OCTAHYDRO-3,5,6,10,12,12A-HEXAHYDROXY-6-METHYL-1,11-DIOXO-; ADAMYCIN; BIOSTAT; DABICYCLINE; FANTERRIN; GEOMYCIN; LENOCYCLINE; LIQUAMYCIN; MACOCYN; OTC; OXYTERRACIN; OXYTETRACYCLINE AMPHOTERIE; PROTEROXYNA; RIOMITSIN; TERAVIT; TERRAMYCIN; PST17414

CHEMICAL FAMILY: ANTIBIOTIC

MOLECULAR FORMULA: C22-H24-N2-O9

MOLECULAR WEIGHT: 496.94

CERCLA RATINGS (SCALE 0-3): HEALTH = 1 FIRE = 0 REACTIVITY = 0 PERSISTENCE = 2

NFPA RATINGS (SCALE 0-4): HEALTH = 1 FIRE = 0 REACTIVITY = 0

COMPONENTS AND CONTAMINANTS

COMPONENT: OXYTETRACYCLINE ***PERCENT:*** 100
CAS# 79-57-2

OTHER CONTAMINANTS: NONE

EXPOSURE LIMITS: NO OCCUPATIONAL EXPOSURE LIMITS ESTABLISHED BY OSHA, ACGIH, OR NIOSH.

PHYSICAL DATA

DESCRIPTION: PALE YELLOW TO TAN, ODORLESS, CRYSTALLINE POWDER WITH A BITTER TASTE; CONTACT WITH MOIST AIR CAUSES DARKENING.

MELTING POINT: 354-360 F (179-182) DECOMPOSES ***SPECIFIC GRAVITY:*** NOT AVAILABLE

PH: 6.5 (SATURATED SOLN) ***SOLUBILITY IN WATER:*** SOLUBLE

SOLVENT SOLUBILITY: SOLUBLE IN ETHANOL AND METHANOL; INSOLUBLE IN ETHER AND CHLOROFORM

FIRE AND EXPLOSION DATA

FIRE AND EXPLOSION HAZARD: NEGLIGIBLE FIRE HAZARD WHEN EXPOSED TO HEAT OR FLAME.

FIREFIGHTING MEDIA: DRY CHEMICAL, CARBON DIOXIDE, HALON, WATER SPRAY OR STANDARD FOAM (1987 EMERGENCY RESPONSE GUIDEBOOK, DOT P 5800.4).
FOR LARGER FIRES, USE WATER SPRAY, FOG OR STANDARD FOAM (1987 EMERGENCY RESPONSE GUIDEBOOK, DOT P 5800.4).

FIREFIGHTING: MOVE CONTAINER FROM FIRE AREA IF POSSIBLE. DO NOT SCATTER SPILLED MATERIAL WITH HIGH PRESSURE WATER STREAMS. DIKE FIRE CONTROL WATER FOR LATER DISPOSAL (1987 EMERGENCY RESPONSE GUIDEBOOK, DOT P 5800.4, GUIDE PAGE 31).
USE AGENTS SUITABLE FOR TYPE OF SURROUNDING FIRE. AVOID BREATHING HAZARDOUS VAPORS, KEEP UPWIND.

TOXICITY

OXYTETRACYCLINE: TOXICITY DATA: 114 MG/KG/4 DAYS ORAL-MAN TDLO; 4800 MG/KG ORAL-RAT LD50; 2240 MG/KG ORAL-MOUSE LD50; 2250 MG/KG INTRAPERITONEAL-GUINEA PIG LDLO; 5706 MG/KG INTRAPERITONEAL-MOUSE LD50; 220 MG/KG INTRAVENOUS-DOG LDLO; 140 MG/KG INTRAVENOUS-MOUSE LD50; 260 MG/KG INTRAVENOUS-RAT LD50; 136 MG/KG PARENTERAL-INFANT TDLO; 700 MG/KG SUBCUTANEOUS-MOUSE LD50; MUTAGENIC DATA (RTECS); REPRODUCTIVE EFFECTS DATA (RTECS). CARCINOGEN STATUS: NONE. ACUTE TOXICITY LEVEL: MODERATELY TOXIC BY INGESTION. TARGET EFFECTS: NO DATA AVAILABLE. AT INCREASED RISK FROM EXPOSURE: PERSONS WITH RENAL OR HEPATIC DYSFUNCTION. ADDITIONAL DATA: INTERACTIONS WITH MEDICATIONS HAVE BEEN REPORTED.

HEALTH EFFECTS AND FIRST AID

INHALATION: OXYTETRACYCLINE: **<u>ACUTE EXPOSURE-</u>** NO DATA AVAILABLE. DUSTS MAY IRRITATE MUCOUS MEMBRANES. **<u>CHRONIC EXPOSURE-</u>** NO DATA AVAILABLE.

FIRST AID- REMOVE FROM EXPOSURE AREA TO FRESH AIR IMMEDIATELY. IF BREATHING HAS STOPPED, PERFORM ARTIFICIAL RESPIRATION. KEEP PERSON WARM AND AT REST. TREAT SYMPTOMATICALLY AND SUPPORTIVELY. GET MEDICAL ATTENTION IMMEDIATELY.

SKIN CONTACT: OXYTETRACYCLINE: **<u>ACUTE EXPOSURE-</u>** CONTACT MAY CAUSE SKIN IRRITATION IN SOME INDIVIDUALS. THERE IS A POSSIBILITY OF SENSITIZATION REACTIONS IN INDIVIDUALS WHO HAVE EXHIBITED HYPERSENSITIVITY TO TETRACYCLINES. **<u>CHRONIC EXPOSURE-</u>** REPEATED ORAL EXPOSURES TO

OXYTETRACYCLINE HAS PRODUCED DERMATITIS, PHOTO-ONYCHOLYSIS AND PORPHYRIA-LIKE CUTANEOUS CHANGES.

FIRST AID- REMOVE CONTAMINATED CLOTHING AND SHOES IMMEDIATELY. WASH AFFECTED AREA WITH SOAP OR MILD DETERGENT AND LARGE AMOUNTS OF WATER UNTIL NO EVIDENCE OF CHEMICAL REMAINS (APPROXIMATELY 15-20 MINUTES). GET MEDICAL ATTENTION IMMEDIATELY.

EYE CONTACT: OXYTETRACYCLINE: **ACUTE EXPOSURE**- NO DATA AVAILABLE. HOWEVER 1% TETRACYCLINE IN AN OINTMENT CAUSED NO DETECTABLE INJURY TO RABBIT'S EYES. **CHRONIC EXPOSURE**- NO DATA AVAILABLE.

FIRST AID- WASH EYES IMMEDIATELY WITH LARGE AMOUNTS OF WATER OR NORMAL SALINE, OCCASIONALLY LIFTING UPPER AND LOWER LIDS, UNTIL NO EVIDENCE OF CHEMICAL REMAINS (APPROXIMATELY 15-20 MINUTES). GET MEDICAL ATTENTION IMMEDIATELY.

INGESTION: OXYTETRACYCLINE: **ACUTE EXPOSURE**- A DOSE OF 4800 MG/KG WAS LETHAL IN RATS. TETRACYCLINES MAY CAUSE NAUSEA, GASTROINTESTINAL IRRITATION, VOMITING, ABDOMINAL PAIN, ESOPHAGEAL ULCERS, EPIGASTRIC PAIN AND BURNING, DIARRHEA, DYSPHAGIA, ENTEROCOLITIS, ANOREXIA, UREMIA, PANCYTOPENIA, ACIDOSIS, HYPERKALEMIA, AND CARDIAC ARRHYTHMIAS. LARGE ORAL DOSES MAY CAUSE HYPERSENSITIVITY, PHOTOTOXIC, NEPHROTOXIC, AND HEPATOTOXIC REACTIONS IN HUMANS PREVIOUSLY EXPOSED TO TETRACYCLINES. **CHRONIC EXPOSURE**- REPEATED OR PROLONGED USE OF OXYTETRACYCLINES IS ASSOCIATED WITH 3 KINDS OF RENAL DISEASE: ACUTE NON-OLIGURIC RENAL FAILURE IN PERSONS WITH PANCREATITIS OR FATTY LIVER; UREMIA, IN PERSONS WITH PREVIOUSLY IMPAIRED RENAL FUNCTION; AND A FALCONI'-LIKE SYNDROME, USUALLY ASSOCIATED WITH OUTDATED OR DEGRADED TETRACYCLINES. TETRACYCLINES TEND TO BE DEPOSITED IN THE BONES AND THE TEETH AT SITES OF ACTIVE CALCIFICATION. PROLONGED USE HAS CAUSED DISCOLORATION OF THE TEETH AND A 40% DEPRESSION OF BONE GROWTH IN NEONATES, INFANTS AND CHILDREN. SENSITIZATION REACTIONS MAY OCCUR, CHARACTERIZED BY BURNING OF THE EYES, JAUNDICE, FATTY LIVER, CHEILOSIS, GLOSSITIS, PRURITUS, CONJUNCTIVITIS, DERMATITIS, EOSINOPHILIA, LEUKOCYTOSIS, THROMBOCYTOPENIC PURPURA, AND PHOTOSENSITIVITY MANIFESTED BY EXAGGERATED SUNBURN. CROSS-SENSITIZATION IS COMMON AMONG THE VARIOUS TETRACYCLINES. IN PERSONS WITH IMPAIRED RENAL FUNCTION, HIGH SERUM LEVELS OF TETRACYCLINE MAY LEAD TO AZOTEMIA, HYPERPHOSPHATEMIA, ACIDOSIS, AND IN INFANTS TENSE BULGING OF THE FONTANELS. TETRACYCLINES MAY CAUSE BENIGN INTRACRANIAL HYPERTENSION WITH PAPILLEDEMA AND RETINAL HEMORRHAGES; THIS MAY OCCUR MORE FREQUENTLY IN CHILDREN THAN ADULTS. PREGNANT WOMEN APPEAR TO BE MORE SUSCEPTIBLE TO SEVERE HEPATIC DAMAGE. TETRACYCLINES MAY INTERFERE WITH VITAMIN K SYNTHESIS AND BLOOD COAGULATION. REPEATED USE OF ANTIBIOTICS MAY LEAD TO THE DEVELOPMENT OF VAGINAL, ORAL, PHARYNGEAL, INTESTINAL AND SYSTEMIC SUPRAINFECTIONS DUE TO OVERGROWTH OF ORGANISMS NOT AFFECTED BY THE ANTIBIOTIC. IN SOME CASES, THESE ORGANISMS PRODUCE TOXINS THAT CAUSE SEVERE VOMITING, DIARRHEA AND CIRCULATORY COLLAPSE. EFFECTS ON FERTILITY AND EFFECTS ON THE FETUS OR EMBRYO HAVE BEEN REPORTED FROM INGESTION ON DAY 6-15 OF PREGNANCY IN RATS. EFFECTS ON THE REPRODUCTIVE SYSTEM OF FEMALES HAVE BEEN REPORTED FROM INGESTION ON DAY 6-15 OF PREGNANCY IN MICE.

FIRST AID- IN PRESENCE OF SYMPTOMS, REMOVE BY IPECAC EMESIS UNLESS PATIENT IS UNCONSCIOUS OR CONVULSING. 4-8 OUNCES OF CLEAR FLUID MAY BE GIVEN AFTER IPECAC. REPEAT IN 20-30 MINUTES IF VOMITING DOES NOT OCCUR. IN COMATOSE OR CONVULSING PATIENTS, USE GASTRIC LAVAGE WITH ENDOTRACHEAL INTUBATION. ACTIVATED CHARCOAL AND CATHARTICS MAY BE ADMINISTERED 1-1.5 HOURS AFTER EMESIS IS INDUCED OR THEY MAY BE PUT INTO THE LAVAGE TUBE AFTER THE STOMACH WASHOUT. (ELLENHORN AND BARCELOUX, MEDICAL TOXICOLOGY). MAINTAIN AIRWAY, RESPIRATION AND BLOOD PRESSURE. TREAT SYMPTOMATICALLY AND SUPPORTIVELY. GET MEDICAL ATTENTION IMMEDIATELY.

ANTIDOTE: NO SPECIFIC ANTIDOTE. TREAT SYMPTOMATICALLY AND SUPPORTIVELY.

REACTIVITY

REACTIVITY: STABLE UNDER NORMAL TEMPERATURES AND PRESSURES. STRONG SUNLIGHT IN MOIST AIR CAUSES DARKENING. TEMPERATURES EXCEEDING 90 C IN MOIST AIR CAUSES DARKENING. CONCENTRATED AQUEOUS SOLUTIONS AT NEUTRAL PH HYDROLYZE ON STANDING AND DEPOSIT CRYSTALS OF OXYTETRACYCLINE.

INCOMPATIBILITIES: OXYTETRACYCLINE: SOLUTIONS HAVING PH BELOW 2: DIMINISHED POTENCY. ALKALI HYDROXIDE SOLUTIONS: RAPIDLY DESTROYED.

DECOMPOSITION: WHEN HEATED TO DECOMPOSITION IT MAY RELEASE CORROSIVE HYDROGEN CHLORIDE FUMES AND TOXIC OXIDES OF NITROGEN.

POLYMERIZATION: HAZARDOUS POLYMERIZATION HAS NOT BEEN REPORTED TO OCCUR UNDER NORMAL TEMPERATURES AND PRESSURES.

STORAGE AND DISPOSAL

OBSERVE ALL FEDERAL, STATE AND LOCAL REGULATIONS WHEN STORING OR DISPOSING OF THIS SUBSTANCE. FOR ASSISTANCE, CONTACT THE DISTRICT DIRECTOR OF THE ENVIRONMENTAL PROTECTION AGENCY.

STORAGE

STORE AWAY FROM INCOMPATIBLE SUBSTANCES.

CONDITIONS TO AVOID

MAY BURN BUT DOES NOT IGNITE READILY. AVOID CONTACT WITH STRONG OXIDIZERS, EXCESSIVE HEAT, SPARKS, OR OPEN FLAME.

SPILL AND LEAK PROCEDURES

OCCUPATIONAL SPILL: SWEEP UP AND PLACE IN SUITABLE CLEAN, DRY CONTAINERS FOR RECLAMATION OR LATER DISPOSAL. DO NOT FLUSH SPILLED MATERIAL INTO SEWER. KEEP UNNECESSARY PEOPLE AWAY.

PROTECTIVE EQUIPMENT

VENTILATION: PROVIDE LOCAL EXHAUST OR GENERAL DILUTION VENTILATION SYSTEM.

RESPIRATOR: THE FOLLOWING RESPIRATORS ARE RECOMMENDED BASED ON INFORMATION FOUND IN THE PHYSICAL DATA, TOXICITY AND HEALTH EFFECTS SECTIONS. THEY ARE RANKED IN ORDER FROM MINIMUM TO MAXIMUM RESPIRATORY PROTECTION. THE SPECIFIC RESPIRATOR SELECTED MUST BE BASED ON CONTAMINATION LEVELS FOUND IN THE WORK PLACE, MUST NOT EXCEED THE WORKING LIMITS OF THE RESPIRATOR AND BE JOINTLY APPROVED BY THE NATIONAL INSTITUTE FOR OCCUPATIONAL SAFETY AND HEALTH AND THE MINE SAFETY AND HEALTH ADMINISTRATION (NIOSH-MSHA).

DUST AND MIST RESPIRATOR WITH A FULL FACEPIECE.

AIR-PURIFYING FULL FACEPIECE RESPIRATOR WITH A HIGH-EFFICIENCY PARTICULATE FILTER.

POWERED AIR-PURIFYING RESPIRATOR WITH A TIGHT-FITTING FACEPIECE AND HIGH-EFFICIENCY PARTICULATE FILTER.

TYPE 'C' SUPPLIED-AIR RESPIRATOR WITH A FULL FACEPIECE OPERATED IN PRESSURE-DEMAND OR OTHER POSITIVE PRESSURE MODE OR WITH A FULL FACEPIECE, HELMET OR HOOD OPERATED IN CONTINUOUS-FLOW MODE.

SELF-CONTAINED BREATHING APPARATUS WITH A FULL FACEPIECE OPERATED IN PRESSURE-DEMAND OR OTHER POSITIVE PRESSURE MODE.

FOR FIREFIGHTING AND OTHER IMMEDIATELY DANGEROUS TO LIFE OR HEALTH CONDITIONS:

SELF-CONTAINED BREATHING APPARATUS WITH FULL FACEPIECE OPERATED IN PRESSURE-DEMAND OR OTHER POSITIVE PRESSURE MODE.

SUPPLIED-AIR RESPIRATOR WITH FULL FACEPIECE AND OPERATED IN PRESSURE-DEMAND OR OTHER POSITIVE PRESSURE MODE IN COMBINATION WITH AN AUXILIARY SELF-CONTAINED BREATHING APPARATUS OPERATED IN PRESSURE-DEMAND OR OTHER POSITIVE PRESSURE MODE.

CLOTHING: EMPLOYEE MUST WEAR APPROPRIATE PROTECTIVE (IMPERVIOUS) CLOTHING AND EQUIPMENT TO PREVENT REPEATED OR PROLONGED SKIN CONTACT WITH THIS SUBSTANCE.

GLOVES: EMPLOYEE MUST WEAR APPROPRIATE PROTECTIVE GLOVES TO PREVENT CONTACT WITH THIS SUBSTANCE.

EYE PROTECTION: EMPLOYEE MUST WEAR SPLASH-PROOF OR DUST-RESISTANT SAFETY GOGGLES TO PREVENT EYE CONTACT WITH THIS SUBSTANCE. EMERGENCY EYE WASH: WHERE THERE IS ANY POSSIBILITY THAT AN EMPLOYEE'S EYES MAY BE EXPOSED TO THIS SUBSTANCE, THE EMPLOYER SHOULD PROVIDE AN EYE WASH FOUNTAIN WITHIN THE IMMEDIATE WORK AREA FOR EMERGENCY USE.

AUTHORIZED BY- OCCUPATIONAL HEALTH SERVICES, INC.

CREATION DATE: 10/04/89 ***REVISION DATE:*** 05/31/90

MATERIAL SAFETY DATA SHEET

OCCUPATIONAL HEALTH SERVICES, INC.
AGRICULTURE AND PESTICIDE DIVISION
450 SEVENTH AVENUE, SUITE 2407
NEW YORK, NEW YORK 10123
1-800-445-MSDS OR (212) 967-1100

EMERGENCY CONTACT:
JOHN S. BRANSFORD, JR. (615) 292-1180

SUBSTANCE IDENTIFICATION

CAS-NUMBER 98-54-4

SUBSTANCE: **P-TERT-BUTYLPHENOL**

TRADE NAMES/SYNONYMS: PHENOL, 4-(1,1-DIMETHYLETHYL)-; 4-(1,1-DIMETHYLETHYL)PHENOL; PHENOL, P-TERT-BUTYL-; 4-T-BUTYLPHENOL; C10H14O; PST17440
CHEMICAL FAMILY: PHENOL
MOLECULAR FORMULA: H-O-C6-H4-C-(C-H3)3
MOLECULAR WEIGHT: 150.22
CERCLA RATINGS (SCALE 0-3): HEALTH=2 FIRE=1 REACTIVITY=0 PERSISTENCE=2
NFPA RATINGS (SCALE 0-4): HEALTH=2 FIRE=1 REACTIVITY=0

COMPONENTS AND CONTAMINANTS

COMPONENT: P-TERT-BUTYLPHENOL ***PERCENT:*** 100.0
CAS# 98-54-4
OTHER CONTAMINANTS: NONE
EXPOSURE LIMITS: NO OCCUPATIONAL EXPOSURE LIMITS ESTABLISHED BY OSHA, ACGIH, OR NIOSH.

PHYSICAL DATA

DESCRIPTION: WHITE OR NEARLY WHITE CRYSTALS OR FLAKES WITH A PHENOLIC ODOR.
BOILING POINT: 464 F (240 C) ***MELTING POINT:*** 214 F (101 C)
SPECIFIC GRAVITY: 0.908 @ 80 C ***VOLATILITY:*** NIL
VAPOR PRESSURE: 1.0 MMHG @ 70 C ***SOLUBILITY IN WATER:*** 0.07% @ 20 C
VAPOR DENSITY: 5.1
SOLVENT SOLUBILITY: SOLUBLE IN ALCOHOL AND ETHER.

FIRE AND EXPLOSION DATA

FIRE AND EXPLOSION HAZARD: SLIGHT FIRE HAZARD WHEN EXPOSED TO HEAT OR FLAME. DUST-AIR MIXTURES MAY IGNITE OR EXPLODE.
FLASH POINT: 235 F (113 C) (OC) ***FLAMMABILITY CLASS(OSHA):*** IIIB
FIREFIGHTING MEDIA: DRY CHEMICAL, CARBON DIOXIDE, HALON, WATER SPRAY OR STANDARD FOAM (1987 EMERGENCY RESPONSE GUIDEBOOK, DOT P 5800.4). FOR LARGER FIRES, USE WATER SPRAY, FOG OR STANDARD FOAM (1987 EMERGENCY RESPONSE GUIDEBOOK, DOT P 5800.4).
FIREFIGHTING: MOVE CONTAINERS FROM FIRE AREA IF POSSIBLE (1987 EMERGENCY RESPONSE GUIDEBOOK, DOT P 5800.4, GUIDE PAGE 53).
EXTINGUISH USING AGENT SUITABLE FOR TYPE OF SURROUNDING FIRE. AVOID BREATHING VAPORS AND DUSTS. KEEP UPWIND.

TOXICITY

P-TERT-BUTYL PHENOL: IRRITATION DATA: 500 MG/4 HOURS SKIN-RABBIT MILD; 500 MG/24 HOURS SKIN-RABBIT MILD; 10 MG EYES-RABBIT SEVERE; 50 UG/24 HOURS EYES-RABBIT SEVERE. TOXICITY DATA: 5600 MG/M3/4 HOURS INHALATION-RAT LCLO; 2288 MG/KG SKIN-RABBIT LD50; 1580 MG/KG SKIN-MAMMAL LD50; 2951 MG/KG ORAL-RAT LD50; 1500 MG/KG ORAL-MAMMAL LD50; 78 MG/KG INTRAPERITONEAL-MOUSE LD50; TUMORIGENIC DATA (RTECS). CARCINOGEN STATUS: NONE. LOCAL EFFECTS: CORROSIVE- INHALATION, SKIN, AND EYES. ACUTE TOXICITY LEVEL: MODERATELY TOXIC BY INGESTION; SLIGHTLY TOXIC BY DERMAL ABSORPTION. TARGET EFFECTS: SENSITIZER- SKIN.

HEALTH EFFECTS AND FIRST AID

INHALATION: P-TERT-BUTYL PHENOL: IRRITANT. **ACUTE EXPOSURE-** INHALATION OF DUST OR VAPORS MAY BE IRRITATING TO THE MUCOUS MEMBRANES OF THE RESPIRATORY TRACT AND MAY CAUSE SHORTNESS OF BREATH AND NOCTURNAL WHEEZING. **CHRONIC EXPOSURE-** INADVERTENT INHALATION MAY PLAY A ROLE IN THE PRODUCTION OF DEPIGMENTATION OF A WIDESPREAD NATURE. REPEATED AND PROLONGED EXPOSURE MAY PRODUCE HEPATOSPLENOMEGALY AND DIFFUSE THYROID ENLARGEMENT IN WORKERS.
FIRST AID- REMOVE FROM EXPOSURE AREA TO FRESH AIR IMMEDIATELY. IF BREATHING HAS STOPPED, PERFORM ARTIFICIAL RESPIRATION. KEEP PERSON WARM AND AT REST. TREAT SYMPTOMATICALLY AND SUPPORTIVELY. GET MEDICAL ATTENTION IMMEDIATELY.

SKIN CONTACT: P-TERT-BUTYL PHENOL: IRRITANT/SENSITIZER. **ACUTE EXPOSURE-** IRRITATING TO THE SKIN AND MAY CAUSE CONTACT DERMATITIS AND POSSIBLE BURNS. SENSITIZATION DERMATITIS MAY OCCUR IN PREVIOUSLY EXPOSED INDIVIDUALS. DEPIGMENTATION MAY OCCUR. **CHRONIC EXPOSURE-** REPEATED AND PROLONGED EXPOSURE TO IRRITANTS MAY CAUSE DERMATITIS AND POSSIBLE SENSITIZATION. MAY CAUSE DEPIGMENTATION WHICH MAY OCCUR WITHOUT PRECEDING DERMATITIS OR BURNS. DEPIGMENTATION MAY BECOME WIDESPREAD AND MAY OCCUR ON AREAS OTHER THAN THOSE IN DIRECT CONTACT WITH CHEMICAL.
FIRST AID- REMOVE CONTAMINATED CLOTHING AND SHOES IMMEDIATELY. WASH AFFECTED AREA WITH SOAP OR MILD DETERGENT AND LARGE AMOUNTS OF WATER UNTIL NO EVIDENCE OF CHEMICAL REMAINS (APPROXIMATELY 15-20 MINUTES). GET MEDICAL ATTENTION IMMEDIATELY.

EYE CONTACT: P-TERT-BUTYL PHENOL: CORROSIVE. **ACUTE EXPOSURE-** DIRECT CONTACT MAY CAUSE CORNEAL BURNS. 454 MG CAUSED SEVERE IRRITATION OF RABBIT EYES. **CHRONIC EXPOSURE-** EFFECTS DEPEND ON CONCENTRATION AND DURATION OF EXPOSURE. REPEATED OR PROLONGED CONTACT WITH CORROSIVE SUBSTANCES MAY RESULT IN CONJUNCTIVITIS OR EFFECTS AS IN ACUTE EXPOSURE.
FIRST AID- WASH EYES IMMEDIATELY WITH LARGE AMOUNTS OF WATER, OCCASIONALLY LIFTING UPPER AND LOWER LIDS, UNTIL NO EVIDENCE OF CHEMICAL REMAINS (AT LEAST 15-20 MINUTES). CONTINUE IRRIGATING WITH NORMAL SALINE UNTIL THE PH HAS RETURNED TO NORMAL (30-60 MINUTES). COVER WITH STERILE BANDAGES. GET MEDICAL ATTENTION IMMEDIATELY.

INGESTION: P-TERT-BUTYL PHENOL: **ACUTE EXPOSURE-** MAY CAUSE IRRITATION TO THE GASTROINTESTINAL TRACT, POSSIBLY SEVERE. **CHRONIC EXPOSURE-** REPEATED INGESTION OF SMALL QUANTITIES MAY PLAY A ROLE IN THE PRODUCTION OF DEPIGMENTATION OF A WIDESPREAD NATURE. AS EVALUATED BY RTECS, ADMINISTRATION TO HAMSTERS BY INGESTION RESULTED IN A STATISTICALLY SIGNIFICANT INCREASE IN THE INCIDENCE OF GASTROINTESTINAL NEOPLASTIC TUMORS.
FIRST AID- TREAT SYMPTOMATICALLY AND SUPPORTIVELY. GET MEDICAL ATTENTION IMMEDIATELY. IF VOMITING OCCURS, KEEP HEAD LOWER THAN HIPS TO PREVENT ASPIRATION.
ANTIDOTE: NO SPECIFIC ANTIDOTE. TREAT SYMPTOMATICALLY AND SUPPORTIVELY.

REACTIVITY

REACTIVITY: STABLE UNDER NORMAL TEMPERATURES AND PRESSURES.
INCOMPATIBILITIES: P-TERT-BUTYL PHENOL: OXIDIZERS (STRONG): FIRE AND EXPLOSION HAZARD.
DECOMPOSITION: THERMAL DECOMPOSITION PRODUCTS MAY INCLUDE TOXIC OXIDES OF CARBON.
POLYMERIZATION: HAZARDOUS POLYMERIZATION HAS NOT BEEN REPORTED TO OCCUR UNDER NORMAL TEMPERATURES AND PRESSURES.

STORAGE AND DISPOSAL

OBSERVE ALL FEDERAL, STATE AND LOCAL REGULATIONS WHEN STORING OR DISPOSING OF THIS SUBSTANCE. FOR ASSISTANCE, CONTACT THE DISTRICT DIRECTOR OF THE ENVIRONMENTAL PROTECTION AGENCY.

STORAGE

STORE AWAY FROM INCOMPATIBLE SUBSTANCES.

CONDITIONS TO AVOID

MAY BURN BUT DOES NOT IGNITE READILY.

SPILL AND LEAK PROCEDURES

OCCUPATIONAL SPILL: DO NOT TOUCH SPILLED MATERIAL. STOP LEAK IF YOU CAN DO IT WITHOUT RISK. FOR SMALL SPILLS, TAKE UP WITH SAND OR OTHER ABSORBENT MATERIAL AND PLACE INTO CONTAINERS FOR LATER DISPOSAL. FOR SMALL DRY SPILLS, WITH A CLEAN SHOVEL PLACE MATERIAL INTO CLEAN, DRY CONTAINER AND COVER. MOVE CONTAINERS FROM SPILL AREA. FOR LARGER SPILLS, DIKE FAR AHEAD OF SPILL FOR LATER DISPOSAL. KEEP UNNECESSARY PEOPLE AWAY. ISOLATE HAZARD AREA AND DENY ENTRY.

PROTECTIVE EQUIPMENT

VENTILATION: PROVIDE LOCAL EXHAUST OR GENERAL DILUTION VENTILATION SYSTEM.
RESPIRATOR: THE FOLLOWING RESPIRATORS ARE RECOMMENDED BASED ON INFORMATION FOUND IN THE PHYSICAL DATA, TOXICITY AND HEALTH EFFECTS SECTIONS. THEY ARE RANKED IN ORDER FROM MINIMUM TO MAXIMUM RESPIRATORY PROTECTION. THE SPECIFIC RESPIRATOR SELECTED MUST BE BASED ON CONTAMINATION LEVELS FOUND IN THE WORK PLACE, MUST NOT EXCEED THE WORKING LIMITS OF THE RESPIRATOR AND BE JOINTLY APPROVED BY THE NATIONAL INSTITUTE FOR OCCUPATIONAL SAFETY AND HEALTH AND THE MINE SAFETY AND HEALTH ADMINISTRATION (NIOSH-MSHA).
CHEMICAL CARTRIDGE RESPIRATOR WITH FULL FACEPIECE AND ORGANIC VAPOR CARTRIDGE(S) IN COMBINATION WITH A DUST AND MIST FILTER.
CHEMICAL CARTRIDGE RESPIRATOR WITH FULL FACEPIECE AND ORGANIC VAPOR CARTRIDGE(S) IN COMBINATION WITH A HIGH-EFFICIENCY PARTICULATE FILTER.
GAS MASK WITH ORGANIC VAPOR CANISTER (CHIN-STYLE OR FRONT- OR BACK-MOUNTED CANISTER) WITH A FULL FACEPIECE AND A HIGH-EFFICIENCY PARTICULATE FILTER.
POWERED AIR-PURIFYING RESPIRATOR WITH TIGHT-FITTING FACEPIECE AND ORGANIC VAPOR CARTRIDGE(S) IN COMBINATION WITH A HIGH-EFFICIENCY PARTICULATE FILTER.
TYPE 'C' SUPPLIED-AIR RESPIRATOR WITH A FULL FACEPIECE OPERATED IN PRESSURE-DEMAND OR OTHER POSITIVE PRESSURE MODE OR WITH A FULL

FACEPIECE, HELMET OR HOOD OPERATED IN CONTINUOUS-FLOW MODE.
SELF-CONTAINED BREATHING APPARATUS WITH A FULL FACEPIECE OPERATED IN PRESSURE-DEMAND OR OTHER POSITIVE PRESSURE MODE.
FOR FIREFIGHTING AND OTHER IMMEDIATELY DANGEROUS TO LIFE OR HEALTH CONDITIONS:
SELF-CONTAINED BREATHING APPARATUS WITH FULL FACEPIECE OPERATED IN PRESSURE-DEMAND OR OTHER POSITIVE PRESSURE MODE.
SUPPLIED-AIR RESPIRATOR WITH FULL FACEPIECE AND OPERATED IN PRESSURE-DEMAND OR OTHER POSITIVE PRESSURE MODE IN COMBINATION WITH AN AUXILIARY SELF-CONTAINED BREATHING APPARATUS OPERATED IN PRESSURE-DEMAND OR OTHER POSITIVE PRESSURE MODE.

CLOTHING: EMPLOYEE MUST WEAR APPROPRIATE PROTECTIVE (IMPERVIOUS) CLOTHING AND EQUIPMENT TO PREVENT REPEATED OR PROLONGED SKIN CONTACT WITH THIS SUBSTANCE.

GLOVES: EMPLOYEE MUST WEAR APPROPRIATE PROTECTIVE GLOVES TO PREVENT CONTACT WITH THIS SUBSTANCE.

EYE PROTECTION: EMPLOYEE MUST WEAR SPLASH-PROOF OR DUST-RESISTANT SAFETY GOGGLES AND A FACESHIELD TO PREVENT CONTACT WITH THIS SUBSTANCE.
EMERGENCY WASH FACILITIES: WHERE THERE IS ANY POSSIBILITY THAT AN EMPLOYEE'S EYES AND/OR SKIN MAY BE EXPOSED TO THIS SUBSTANCE, THE EMPLOYER SHOULD PROVIDE AN EYE WASH FOUNTAIN AND QUICK DRENCH SHOWER WITHIN THE IMMEDIATE WORK AREA FOR EMERGENCY USE.

AUTHORIZED BY- OCCUPATIONAL HEALTH SERVICES, INC.
CREATION DATE: 10/04/89 ***REVISION DATE:*** 05/18/90

MATERIAL SAFETY DATA SHEET

OCCUPATIONAL HEALTH SERVICES, INC.
AGRICULTURE AND PESTICIDE DIVISION
450 SEVENTH AVENUE, SUITE 2407
NEW YORK, NEW YORK 10123
1-800-445-MSDS OR (212) 967-1100

EMERGENCY CONTACT:
JOHN S. BRANSFORD, JR. (615) 292-1180

SUBSTANCE IDENTIFICATION

CAS-NUMBER 106-46-7

SUBSTANCE: P-DICHLOROBENZENE

TRADE NAMES/SYNONYMS: BENZENE, 1,4-DICHLORO-; 1,4-DICHLOROBENZENE; P-CHLOROPHENYL CHLORIDE; EVOLA; PARADI; PARADICHLORBENZENE; PARADOW; PARAMOTH; SANTOCHLOR; BENZENE, P-DICHLORO-; DICHLOROBENZENE, PARA, SOLID; STCC 4941128; UN 1592; C6H4CL2; PST17640

CHEMICAL FAMILY: HALOGEN COMPOUND, AROMATIC

MOLECULAR FORMULA: C6-H4-CL2

MOLECULAR WEIGHT: 147.00

CERCLA RATINGS (SCALE 0-3): HEALTH=2 FIRE=2 REACTIVITY=0 PERSISTENCE=3

NFPA RATINGS (SCALE 0-4): HEALTH=2 FIRE=2 REACTIVITY=0

COMPONENTS AND CONTAMINANTS

COMPONENT: P-DICHLOROBENZENE ***PERCENT:*** 100.0
CAS# 106-46-7

EXPOSURE LIMITS: P-DICHLOROBENZENE: 75 PPM (450 MG/M3) OSHA TWA; 110 PPM (675 MG/M3) OSHA STEL 75 PPM (450 MG/M3) ACGIH TWA; 110 PPM (675 MG/M3) ACGIH STEL
100 POUNDS CERCLA SECTION 103 REPORTABLE QUANTITY SUBJECT TO SARA SECTION 313 ANNUAL TOXIC CHEMICAL RELEASE REPORTING SUBJECT TO CALIFORNIA PROPOSITION 65 CANCER AND/OR REPRODUCTIVE TOXICITY WARNING AND RELEASE REQUIREMENTS- (JANUARY 1, 1989)

PHYSICAL DATA

DESCRIPTION: COLORLESS OR WHITE CRYSTALS WITH AN ODOR LIKE MOTHBALLS.

BOILING POINT: 345 F (174 C) ***MELTING POINT:*** 127 F (53 C)

SPECIFIC GRAVITY: 1.2475 ***VAPOR PRESSURE:*** 0.6 MMHG @ 20 C

SOLUBILITY IN WATER: 0.008% @ 25 C ***ODOR THRESHOLD:*** 15-30 PPM

VAPOR DENSITY: 5.1

SOLVENT SOLUBILITY: SOLUBLE IN ETHANOL, CARBON DISULFIDE, ACETONE, CHLOROFORM, ETHER.

FIRE AND EXPLOSION DATA

FIRE AND EXPLOSION HAZARD: MODERATE FIRE HAZARD WHEN EXPOSED TO HEAT OR FLAME.
VAPORS ARE HEAVIER THAN AIR AND MAY TRAVEL A CONSIDERABLE DISTANCE TO A SOURCE OF IGNITION AND FLASH BACK.

FLASH POINT: 150 F (66 C) (CC) ***LOWER EXPLOSIVE LIMIT:*** 2.5%

FLAMMABILITY CLASS(OSHA): IIIA

FIREFIGHTING MEDIA: DRY CHEMICAL, CARBON DIOXIDE, HALON, WATER SPRAY OR STANDARD FOAM (1987 EMERGENCY RESPONSE GUIDEBOOK, DOT P 5800.4).
FOR LARGER FIRES, USE WATER SPRAY, FOG OR STANDARD FOAM (1987 EMERGENCY RESPONSE GUIDEBOOK, DOT P 5800.4).

FIREFIGHTING: MOVE CONTAINER FROM FIRE AREA IF POSSIBLE. COOL FIRE-EXPOSED CONTAINERS WITH WATER FROM SIDE UNTIL WELL AFTER FIRE IS OUT. STAY AWAY FROM STORAGE TANK ENDS. FOR MASSIVE FIRE IN STORAGE AREA, USE UNMANNED HOSE HOLDER OR MONITOR NOZZLES, ELSE WITHDRAW FROM AREA AND LET FIRE BURN. WITHDRAW IMMEDIATELY IN CASE OF RISING SOUND FROM VENTING SAFETY DEVICE OR ANY DISCOLORATION OF STORAGE TANK DUE TO FIRE (1987 EMERGENCY RESPONSE GUIDEBOOK, DOT P 5800.4, GUIDE PAGE 27).
EXTINGUISH ONLY IF FLOW CAN BE STOPPED; USE FLOODING AMOUNTS OF WATER AS A FOG, SOLID STREAMS MAY BE INEFFECTIVE. COOL CONTAINERS WITH FLOODING AMOUNTS OF WATER, APPLY FROM AS FAR A DISTANCE AS POSSIBLE. AVOID BREATHING VAPORS, KEEP UPWIND.
WATER MAY BE USED TO BLANKET FIRE (NFPA 325M FIRE HAZARD PROPERTIES OF FLAMMABLE LIQUIDS, GASES, AND VOLATILE SOLIDS, 1984)

TRANSPORTATION DATA

DEPARTMENT OF TRANSPORTATION HAZARD CLASSIFICATION 49 CFR 172.101: ORM-A
DEPARTMENT OF TRANSPORTATION LABELING REQUIREMENTS 49 CFR 172.101 AND SUBPART E: NONE
DEPARTMENT OF TRANSPORTATION PACKAGING REQUIREMENTS: 49 CFR 173.510 EXCEPTIONS: 49 CFR 173.505

TOXICITY

P-DICHLOROBENZENE: IRRITATION DATA: 80 PPM EYE-HUMAN. TOXICITY DATA: 300 MG/KG ORAL-HUMAN TDLO; 857 MG/KG ORAL-HUMAN LDLO; 500 MG/KG ORAL-RAT LD50; 2950 MG/KG ORAL-MOUSE LD50; 2830 MG/KG ORAL-RABBIT LD50; 2800 MG/KG ORAL-GUINEA PIG LDLO; >5010 MG/KG SKIN-RABBIT LD50 (MONSANTO MSDS); 5145 MG/KG SUBCUTANEOUS-MOUSE LD50; 2562 MG/KG INTRAPERITONEAL-RAT LD50; 2 GM/KG INTRAPERITONEAL-MOUSE LD50; 357 MG/KG UNREPORTED-HUMAN LDLO; 221 MG/KG UNREPORTED MAN-LDLO; MUTAGENIC DATA (RTECS); REPRODUCTIVE EFFECTS DATA (RTECS); TUMORIGENIC DATA (RTECS). CARCINOGEN STATUS: ANTICIPATED HUMAN CARCINOGEN (NTP); HUMAN INADEQUATE EVIDENCE, ANIMAL SUFFICIENT EVIDENCE (IARC GROUP-2B). GAVAGE ADMINISTRATION INDUCED INCREASED INCIDENCES OF HEPATOCELLULAR CARCINOMAS AND ADENOMAS, AND PHEOCHROMOCYTOMAS OF THE ADRENAL GLAND IN MICE; INCREASED INCIDENCES OF RENAL TUBULAR CELL ADENOCARCINOMAS AND MONONUCLEAR CELL LEUKEMIA WERE INDUCED IN MALE RATS. LOCAL EFFECTS: IRRITANT- INHALATION, EYE. ACUTE TOXICITY LEVEL: TOXIC BY INGESTION. TARGET EFFECTS: HEPATOTOXIN. POISONING MAY ALSO AFFECT THE CENTRAL NERVOUS SYSTEM, KIDNEYS, AND LUNGS. AT INCREASED RISK FROM EXPOSURE: PERSONS WITH PREEXISTING HEPATIC, RENAL, LUNG, CENTRAL NERVOUS SYSTEM, BLOOD AND METABOLIC DISORDERS. ADDITIONAL DATA: WORKERS DEVELOP SOME ACCLIMATION TO THE COMPOUND AND BECOME ABLE TO TOLERATE LEVELS AS HIGH AS 725 PPM.

HEALTH EFFECTS AND FIRST AID

INHALATION: P-DICHLOROBENZENE: IRRITANT/HEPATOTOXIN. 1000 PPM IMMEDIATELY DANGEROUS TO LIFE OR HEALTH. **ACUTE EXPOSURE-** IN HUMANS, EXPOSURES FROM 50-160 PPM CAUSE EYE, SKIN, AND MUCOUS MEMBRANE IRRITATION, SEVERE HEADACHE, DYSPNEA, ASTHENIA, NUMBNESS, BURNING SENSATION IN THE LEGS, COUGHING, RESTLESSNESS, FAINTNESS, TREMORS, LOSS OF APPETITE, NAUSEA, VOMITING, WEIGHT LOSS, VERTIGO, PERIORBITAL SWELLING, PROFUSE RHINITIS, CENTRAL NERVOUS SYSTEM STIMULATION FOLLOWED BY DEPRESSION, SWELLING OF THE HANDS, FEET, AND ANKLES, ACUTE GLOMERULAR NEPHRITIS, AND LIVER DAMAGE WITH YELLOW JAUNDICE AND POSSIBLY DEATH. IF DEATH DOES NOT OCCUR CIRRHOSIS MAY BE PRODUCED. SYMPTOMS SUBSIDED WITHIN 24 HOURS AFTER CESSATION OF EXPOSURE.
CHRONIC EXPOSURE- IN ADDITION TO THE EFFECTS REPORTED IN ACUTE INHALATION, REPEATED OR PROLONGED EXPOSURE MAY CAUSE HEMOLYTIC ANEMIA AND BLOOD DYSCRASIAS, INCLUDING LEUKEMIA, GRANULOMASTOSIS, HYPOGRANULOCYTOSIS, METHEMOGLOBINEMIA, LUNG, KIDNEY, AND LIVER DAMAGE, HEPATIC NECROSIS WITH JAUNDICE, OLIGURIA, CIRRHOSIS, AND DEATH. NYSTAGMUS, RAPID AND LABORED RESPIRATION, UNKEMPT APPEARANCE, AND REPRODUCTIVE EFFECTS HAVE BEEN REPORTED IN VARIOUS ANIMAL STUDIES.

FIRST AID- REMOVE FROM EXPOSURE AREA TO FRESH AIR IMMEDIATELY. IF BREATHING HAS STOPPED, PERFORM ARTIFICIAL RESPIRATION. KEEP PERSON

WARM AND AT REST. TREAT SYMPTOMATICALLY AND SUPPORTIVELY. GET MEDICAL ATTENTION IMMEDIATELY.

SKIN CONTACT: P-DICHLOROBENZENE: **ACUTE EXPOSURE-** CONTACT WITH THE SOLID CAUSES SLIGHT IRRITATION, ALTHOUGH PROLONGED CONTACT MAY CAUSE A BURNING SENSATION. ONE CASE OF ALLERGIC PURPURA HAS BEEN REPORTED. THERE IS NO EVIDENCE OF SIGNIFICANT ABSORPTION THROUGH THE SKIN, HOWEVER DERMAL EXPOSURE COULD CONTRIBUTE TO THE OVERALL TOXICITY OF THE CHEMICAL. IF SUFFICIENT AMOUNTS ARE ABSORBED, EFFECTS MAY OCCUR AS DETAILED IN ACUTE INHALATION. **CHRONIC EXPOSURE-** REPEATED OR PROLONGED CONTACT WITH WARM FUMES OR STRONG SOLUTIONS MAY CAUSE IRRITATION.

FIRST AID- REMOVE CONTAMINATED CLOTHING AND SHOES IMMEDIATELY. WASH AFFECTED AREA WITH SOAP OR MILD DETERGENT AND LARGE AMOUNTS OF WATER UNTIL NO EVIDENCE OF CHEMICAL REMAINS (APPROXIMATELY 15-20 MINUTES). GET MEDICAL ATTENTION IMMEDIATELY.

EYE CONTACT: P-DICHLOROBENZENE: IRRITANT. **ACUTE EXPOSURE-** SOLID PARTICLES MAY CAUSE REDNESS AND PAIN, BUT NO SERIOUS INJURY. VAPORS AT 50-80 PPM ARE PAINFUL TO MOST PEOPLE AND DISCOMFORT IS SEVERE AT 160 PPM. **CHRONIC EXPOSURE-** REPEATED OR PROLONGED CONTACT MAY CAUSE CONJUNCTIVITIS. RABBITS REPEATEDLY EXPOSED DEVELOPED TRANSIENT EDEMA OF THE CORNEA AND VARIOUS OTHER EDEMAS, HOWEVER THE EYES RETURNED TO NORMAL WITHIN 17 DAYS AFTER EXPOSURE WAS DISCONTINUED.

FIRST AID- WASH EYES IMMEDIATELY WITH LARGE AMOUNTS OF WATER OR NORMAL SALINE, OCCASIONALLY LIFTING UPPER AND LOWER LIDS, UNTIL NO EVIDENCE OF CHEMICAL REMAINS (APPROXIMATELY 15-20 MINUTES). GET MEDICAL ATTENTION IMMEDIATELY.

INGESTION: P-DICHLOROBENZENE: CARCINOGEN/TOXIC. **ACUTE EXPOSURE-** MAY CAUSE ABDOMINAL PAIN, VOMITING, DIARRHEA, COUGHING RESTLESSNESS, FAINTNESS, AND TREMBLING. IF SUFFICIENT AMOUNTS ARE INGESTED EFFECTS MAY OCCUR AS DETAILED IN ACUTE INHALATION. **CHRONIC EXPOSURE-** IN ANIMALS, CHRONIC FEEDING RESULTED IN WEIGHT LOSS, TREMORS, PORPHYRIA, WEAKNESS, SLIGHT EFFECTS ON THE KIDNEYS, CIRRHOSIS AND FOCAL NECROSIS IN THE LIVER, AND NONNEOPLASTIC LESIONS OF THE THYROID GLAND AND ADRENAL GLAND. DEATH OF SOME RABBITS OCCURRED AT A LEVEL OF 1000 MG/KG WHEN 92 DOSES WERE GIVEN OVER A 219 DAY PERIOD. A 2 YEAR GAVAGE STUDY SHOWED AN INCREASE IN THE INCIDENCE OF HEPATOCELLULAR CARCINOMAS AND ADENOMAS, AND PHEOCHROMOCYTOMAS OF THE ADRENAL GLAND IN MALE MICE. INCREASED INCIDENCES OF RENAL TUBULAR CELL ADENOCARCINOMAS AND MONONUCLEAR CELL LEUKEMIA WERE REPORTED IN RATS. REPRODUCTIVE EFFECTS HAVE BEEN REPORTED IN ANIMALS.

FIRST AID- REMOVE BY GASTRIC LAVAGE OR EMESIS. MAINTAIN BLOOD PRESSURE AND AIRWAY. DO NOT PERFORM GASTRIC LAVAGE OR EMESIS IF VICTIM IS UNCONSCIOUS. DO NOT GIVE STIMULANTS WHICH MAY INDUCE VENTRICULAR FIBRILLATION. GET MEDICAL ATTENTION IMMEDIATELY. (DREISBACH, HANDBOOK OF POISONING, 11TH EDITION) ADMINISTRATION OF GASTRIC LAVAGE SHOULD BE PERFORMED BY QUALIFIED MEDICAL PERSONNEL.

ANTIDOTE: NO SPECIFIC ANTIDOTE. TREAT SYMPTOMATICALLY AND SUPPORTIVELY.

REACTIVITY

REACTIVITY: STABLE UNDER NORMAL TEMPERATURES AND PRESSURES.

INCOMPATIBILITIES: P-DICHLOROBENZENE: ALKALI METALS: VIOLENT REACTION. METAL POWDERS: VIOLENT REACTION. OXIDIZERS(STRONG): FIRE AND EXPLOSION HAZARD. PLASTICS, RUBBER, AND COATINGS: MAY BE ATTACKED.

DECOMPOSITION: THERMAL DECOMPOSITION PRODUCTS MAY INCLUDE TOXIC AND CORROSIVE FUMES OF CHLORIDES AND TOXIC OXIDES OF CARBON.

POLYMERIZATION: HAZARDOUS POLYMERIZATION HAS NOT BEEN REPORTED TO OCCUR UNDER NORMAL TEMPERATURES AND PRESSURES.

STORAGE AND DISPOSAL

OBSERVE ALL FEDERAL, STATE AND LOCAL REGULATIONS WHEN STORING OR DISPOSING OF THIS SUBSTANCE. FOR ASSISTANCE, CONTACT THE DISTRICT DIRECTOR OF THE ENVIRONMENTAL PROTECTION AGENCY.

****STORAGE****

STORE AWAY FROM INCOMPATIBLE SUBSTANCES.

****DISPOSAL****

1,4-DICHLOROBENZENE - REGULATORY LEVEL: 7.5 MG/L MATERIALS WHICH CONTAIN THE ABOVE SUBSTANCE AT OR ABOVE THE REGULATORY LEVEL MEET THE EPA CHARACTERISTIC OF TOXICITY, AND MUST BE DISPOSED OF IN ACCORDANCE WITH 40 CFR PART 262. EPA HAZARDOUS WASTE NUMBER D027.

CONDITIONS TO AVOID

AVOID CONTACT WITH HEAT, SPARKS, FLAMES, OR OTHER SOURCES OF IGNITION. VAPORS MAY BE EXPLOSIVE. AVOID OVERHEATING OF CONTAINERS; CONTAINERS MAY VIOLENTLY RUPTURE IN HEAT OF FIRE. AVOID CONTAMINATION OF WATER SOURCES.

SPILL AND LEAK PROCEDURES

SOIL SPILL: DIG A PIT, POND, LAGOON OR HOLDING AREA TO CONTAIN LIQUID OR SOLID MATERIAL. COVER SOLIDS WITH A PLASTIC SHEET TO PREVENT DISSOLVING IN RAIN OR FIREFIGHTING WATER.

WATER SPILL: USE NATURAL DEEP WATER POCKETS, EXCAVATED LAGOONS, OR SAND BAG BARRIERS TO TRAP MATERIAL AT BOTTOM. USE ACTIVATED CARBON AT 10 TIMES THE SPILLED AMOUNT IF IT IS DISSOLVED AT 10 PPM OR GREATER CONCENTRATION. REMOVE TRAPPED MATERIAL WITH SUCTION HOSES. USE MECHANICAL DREDGES OR LIFTS TO REMOVE IMMOBILIZED MASSES OF POLLUTION AND PRECIPITATES.

THE CALIFORNIA SAFE DRINKING WATER AND TOXIC ENFORCEMENT ACT OF 1986 (PROPOSITION 65) PROHIBITS CONTAMINATING ANY KNOWN SOURCE OF DRINKING WATER WITH SUBSTANCES KNOWN TO CAUSE CANCER AND/OR REPRODUCTIVE TOXICITY.

OCCUPATIONAL SPILL: SHUT OFF IGNITION SOURCES. STOP LEAK IF YOU CAN DO IT WITHOUT RISK. USE WATER SPRAY TO REDUCE VAPORS. FOR SMALL SPILLS, TAKE UP WITH SAND OR OTHER ABSORBENT MATERIAL AND PLACE INTO CONTAINERS FOR LATER DISPOSAL. FOR LARGER SPILLS, DIKE FAR AHEAD OF SPILL FOR LATER DISPOSAL. NO SMOKING, FLAMES OR FLARES IN HAZARD AREA. KEEP UNNECESSARY PEOPLE AWAY; ISOLATE HAZARD AREA AND RESTRICT ENTRY.

REPORTABLE QUANTITY (RQ): 100 POUNDS THE SUPERFUND AMENDMENTS AND REAUTHORIZATION ACT (SARA) SECTION 304 REQUIRES THAT A RELEASE EQUAL TO OR GREATER THAN THE REPORTABLE QUANTITY FOR THIS SUBSTANCE BE IMMEDIATELY REPORTED TO THE LOCAL EMERGENCY PLANNING COMMITTEE AND THE STATE EMERGENCY RESPONSE COMMISSION (40 CFR 355.40). IF THE RELEASE OF THIS SUBSTANCE IS REPORTABLE UNDER CERCLA SECTION 103, THE NATIONAL RESPONSE CENTER MUST BE NOTIFIED IMMEDIATELY AT (800) 424-8802 OR (202) 426-2675 IN THE METROPOLITAN WASHINGTON, D.C. AREA (40 CFR 302.6).

PROTECTIVE EQUIPMENT

VENTILATION: PROVIDE LOCAL EXHAUST VENTILATION AND/OR GENERAL DILUTION VENTILATION TO MEET PUBLISHED EXPOSURE LIMITS.

RESPIRATOR: THE FOLLOWING RESPIRATORS AND MAXIMUM USE CONCENTRATIONS ARE RECOMMENDATIONS BY THE U.S. DEPARTMENT OF HEALTH AND HUMAN SERVICES, NIOSH POCKET GUIDE TO CHEMICAL HAZARDS; NIOSH CRITERIA DOCUMENTS OR BY THE U.S. DEPARTMENT OF LABOR, 29 CFR 1910 SUBPART Z. THE SPECIFIC RESPIRATOR SELECTED MUST BE BASED ON CONTAMINATION LEVELS FOUND IN THE WORK PLACE, MUST NOT EXCEED THE WORKING LIMITS OF THE RESPIRATOR AND BE JOINTLY APPROVED BY THE NATIONAL INSTITUTE FOR OCCUPATIONAL SAFETY AND HEALTH AND THE MINE SAFETY AND HEALTH ADMINISTRATION (NIOSH-MSHA).

P-DICHLOROBENZENE: 1000 PPM- ANY SUPPLIED-AIR RESPIRATOR OPERATED IN A CONTINUOUS FLOW MODE. ANY POWERED AIR-PURIFYING RESPIRATOR WITH ORGANIC VAPOR CARTRIDGES. ANY CHEMICAL CARTRIDGE RESPIRATOR WITH A FULL FACEPIECE AND ORGANIC VAPOR CARTRIDGES. ANY SUPPLIED-AIR RESPIRATOR WITH A FULL FACEPIECE. ANY SELF-CONTAINED BREATHING APPARATUS WITH A FULL FACEPIECE.

ESCAPE- ANY AIR-PURIFYING FULL FACEPIECE RESPIRATOR (GAS MASK) WITH A CHIN-STYLE OR FRONT OR BACK-MOUNTED ORGANIC VAPOR CANISTER. ANY APPROPRIATE ESCAPE-TYPE SELF-CONTAINED BREATHING APPARATUS.

FOR FIREFIGHTING AND OTHER IMMEDIATELY DANGEROUS TO LIFE OR HEALTH CONDITIONS:

SELF-CONTAINED BREATHING APPARATUS WITH FULL FACEPIECE OPERATED IN PRESSURE-DEMAND OR OTHER POSITIVE PRESSURE MODE.

SUPPLIED-AIR RESPIRATOR WITH FULL FACEPIECE AND OPERATED IN PRESSURE-DEMAND OR OTHER POSITIVE PRESSURE MODE IN COMBINATION WITH AN AUXILIARY SELF-CONTAINED BREATHING APPARATUS OPERATED IN PRESSURE-DEMAND OR OTHER POSITIVE PRESSURE MODE.

CLOTHING: EMPLOYEE MUST WEAR APPROPRIATE PROTECTIVE (IMPERVIOUS) CLOTHING AND EQUIPMENT TO PREVENT REPEATED OR PROLONGED SKIN CONTACT WITH THIS SUBSTANCE.

GLOVES: EMPLOYEE MUST WEAR APPROPRIATE PROTECTIVE GLOVES TO PREVENT CONTACT WITH THIS SUBSTANCE.

EYE PROTECTION: EMPLOYEE MUST WEAR SPLASH-PROOF OR DUST-RESISTANT SAFETY GOGGLES TO PREVENT EYE CONTACT WITH THIS SUBSTANCE.

EMERGENCY EYE WASH: WHERE THERE IS ANY POSSIBILITY THAT AN EMPLOYEE'S EYES MAY BE EXPOSED TO THIS SUBSTANCE, THE EMPLOYER SHOULD PROVIDE AN EYE WASH FOUNTAIN WITHIN THE IMMEDIATE WORK AREA FOR EMERGENCY USE.

AUTHORIZED BY- OCCUPATIONAL HEALTH SERVICES, INC.

CREATION DATE: 10/04/89 ***REVISION DATE:*** 07/13/90

MATERIAL SAFETY DATA SHEET

OCCUPATIONAL HEALTH SERVICES, INC.
AGRICULTURE AND PESTICIDE DIVISION
450 SEVENTH AVENUE, SUITE 2407
NEW YORK, NEW YORK 10123
1-800-445-MSDS OR (212) 967-1100

EMERGENCY CONTACT:
JOHN S. BRANSFORD, JR. (615) 292-1180

SUBSTANCE IDENTIFICATION

CAS-NUMBER 100-02-7

SUBSTANCE: **P-NITROPHENOL**

TRADE NAMES/SYNONYMS: 4-NITROPHENOL; 4-HYDROXYNITROBENZENE; PARA-NITROPHENOL; P-HYDROXYNITROBENZENE; NIPHEN; STCC 4963394; UN 1663; N-105; 192-P; BP-612; RCRA U170; PST17800

CHEMICAL FAMILY: NITRO PHENOL

MOLECULAR FORMULA: C6-H5-N-O3

MOLECULAR WEIGHT: 139.12

CERCLA RATINGS (SCALE 0-3): HEALTH=3 FIRE=1 REACTIVITY=0 PERSISTENCE=2

NFPA RATINGS (SCALE 0-4): HEALTH=3 FIRE=1 REACTIVITY=0

COMPONENTS AND CONTAMINANTS

COMPONENT: P-NITROPHENOL ***PERCENT:*** 100
CAS# 100-02-7

OTHER CONTAMINANTS: NONE

EXPOSURE LIMITS: P-NITROPHENOL: NO OCCUPATIONAL EXPOSURE LIMITS ESTABLISHED BY OSHA, ACGIH, OR NIOSH.
100 POUNDS CERCLA SECTION 103 REPORTABLE QUANTITY SUBJECT TO SARA SECTION 313 ANNUAL TOXIC CHEMICAL RELEASE REPORTING

PHYSICAL DATA

DESCRIPTION: COLORLESS TO SLIGHTLY YELLOW TO BROWN MONOCLINIC PRISMATIC CRYSTALS WITH A SLIGHT CHARACTERISTIC SWEET ODOR AND A SWEET THEN BURNING TASTE.

BOILING POINT: 534 F (279 C) DECOMPOSES

MELTING POINT: 237-241 F (114-116C)

SPECIFIC GRAVITY: 1.479 ***VAPOR PRESSURE:*** 1.3 @ 49.3 C

SOLUBILITY IN WATER: 1.6% ***ODOR THRESHOLD:*** 58.3 MG/L ***VAPOR DENSITY:*** 4.8

SOLVENT SOLUBILITY: SOLUBLE IN ALCOHOL, ETHER, ACETONE, PYRIDINE, CARBON DISULFIDE, BENZENE, CHLOROFORM, SOLUTIONS OF FIXED ALKALI HYDROXIDES AND CARBONATES

FIRE AND EXPLOSION DATA

FIRE AND EXPLOSION HAZARD: SLIGHT FIRE HAZARD WHEN EXPOSED TO HEAT OR FLAME.

FLASH POINT: 433 F (223 C)

FIREFIGHTING MEDIA: DRY CHEMICAL, CARBON DIOXIDE, HALON, WATER SPRAY OR STANDARD FOAM (1987 EMERGENCY RESPONSE GUIDEBOOK, DOT P 5800.4).
FOR LARGER FIRES, USE WATER SPRAY, FOG OR STANDARD FOAM (1987 EMERGENCY RESPONSE GUIDEBOOK, DOT P 5800.4).

FIREFIGHTING: MOVE CONTAINERS FROM FIRE AREA IF POSSIBLE. FIGHT FIRE FROM MAXIMUM DISTANCE. STAY AWAY FROM STORAGE TANK ENDS. DIKE FIRE CONTROL WATER FOR LATER DISPOSAL. DO NOT SCATTER MATERIAL (1987 EMERGENCY RESPONSE GUIDEBOOK, DOT P 5800.4, GUIDE PAGE 55).
EXTINGUISH ONLY IF FLOW CAN BE STOPPED; USE WATER IN FLOODING AMOUNTS AS FOG COOL CONTAINERS WITH FLOODING QUANTITIES OF WATER, APPLY FROM AS FAR A DISTANCE AS POSSIBLE. SOLID STREAMS MAY NOT BE EFFECTIVE. AVOID BREATHING TOXIC VAPORS.

TRANSPORTATION DATA

DEPARTMENT OF TRANSPORTATION HAZARD CLASSIFICATION 49 CFR 172.101: ORM-E
DEPARTMENT OF TRANSPORTATION LABELING REQUIREMENTS 49 CFR 172.101 AND SUBPART E: NONE
DEPARTMENT OF TRANSPORTATION PACKAGING REQUIREMENTS: 49 CFR 173.510 EXCEPTIONS: NONE

TOXICITY

P-NITROPHENOL: TOXICITY DATA: 920 MG/KG SKIN-MAMMAL LD50; 250 MG/KG ORAL-RAT LD50; 380 MG/KG ORAL-MOUSE LD50; 247 MG/KG ORAL-MAMMAL LD50; 200 MG/KG SUBCUTANEOUS-RAT LDLO; 200 MG/KG SUBCUTANEOUS-GUINEA PIG LDLO; 10 MG/KG INTRAVENOUS-DOG LDLO; 75 MG/KG INTRAPERITONEAL-MOUSE LD50; 90 MG/KG INTRACEREBRAL-MOUSE LD50; 150 MG/KG UNREPORTED-CAT LD50; MUTAGENIC DATA (RTECS). CARCINOGEN STATUS: NONE. LOCAL EFFECTS: IRRITANT- INHALATION, SKIN. CORROSIVE-EYE. ACUTE TOXICITY LEVEL: TOXIC BY DERMAL ABSORPTION AND INGESTION. TARGET EFFECTS: METHEMOGLOBIN FORMER. POISONING MAY AFFECT THE LIVER, KIDNEYS, BLOOD, AND INCREASE CELL METABOLISM. AT INCREASED RISK FROM EXPOSURE: PERSONS WITH CARDIOVASCULAR, RENAL OR PULMONARY DISEASE OR ANEMIA.

HEALTH EFFECTS AND FIRST AID

INHALATION: P-NITROPHENOL: IRRITANT/METHEMOGLOBIN FORMER. **ACUTE EXPOSURE**- INHALATION OF DUST MAY CAUSE MUCOUS MEMBRANE IRRITATION AND SYSTEMIC POISONING. ANIMAL STUDIES INDICATE THAT CENTRAL AND PERIPHERAL VAGUS STIMULATION, CENTRAL NERVOUS SYSTEM DEPRESSION, METHEMOGLOBINEMIA, DYSPNEA AND HYPERTHERMIA MAY OCCUR. AT LOW CONCENTRATIONS OF METHEMOGLOBIN, OBSERVABLE CYANOSIS WITH A BLUE COLOR OF THE LIPS, EARLOBES AND FINGERNAILS MAY OCCUR. SYMPTOMS MAY BE ABSENT, ALTHOUGH EUPHORIA, FLUSHED FACIES AND HEADACHE ARE COMMON. MODERATE CONCENTRATIONS MAY CAUSE MARKED HEADACHE, ATAXIA, SHALLOW RESPIRATION, DROWSINESS, NAUSEA, VOMITING, CONFUSION, LETHARGY AND STUPOR. AT HIGH CONCENTRATIONS, TACHYCARDIA, CONVULSIONS AND COMA MAY OCCUR. **CHRONIC EXPOSURE**- ANIMAL STUDIES INDICATE THAT LIVER AND KIDNEY DAMAGE MAY OCCUR. REPEATED OR PROLONGED EXPOSURE TO AROMATIC NITRO COMPOUNDS MAY RESULT IN ANEMIA.

FIRST AID- REMOVE FROM EXPOSURE AREA TO FRESH AIR IMMEDIATELY. IF BREATHING HAS STOPPED, GIVE ARTIFICIAL RESPIRATION. MAINTAIN AIRWAY AND BLOOD PRESSURE AND ADMINISTER OXYGEN IF AVAILABLE. KEEP AFFECTED PERSON WARM AND AT REST. TREAT SYMPTOMATICALLY AND SUPPORTIVELY. ADMINISTRATION OF OXYGEN SHOULD BE PERFORMED BY QUALIFIED PERSONNEL. GET MEDICAL ATTENTION IMMEDIATELY.

SKIN CONTACT: P-NITROPHENOL: IRRITANT/METHEMOGLOBIN FORMER/TOXIC. **ACUTE EXPOSURE**- CONTACT MAY CAUSE REDNESS AND IRRITATION, POSSIBLY SEVERE. SYSTEMIC POISONING MAY OCCUR DUE TO SKIN ABSORPTION. ANIMAL STUDIES INDICATE THAT CENTRAL AND PERIPHERAL VAGUS STIMULATION, CENTRAL NERVOUS SYSTEM DEPRESSION, METHEMOGLOBINEMIA, DYSPNEA AND HYPERTHERMIA MAY OCCUR. AT LOW CONCENTRATIONS OF METHEMOGLOBIN, OBSERVABLE CYANOSIS WITH A BLUE COLOR OF THE LIPS, EARLOBES AND FINGERNAILS MAY OCCUR. SYMPTOMS MAY BE ABSENT, ALTHOUGH EUPHORIA, FLUSHED FACIES AND HEADACHE ARE COMMON. MODERATE CONCENTRATIONS MAY CAUSE MARKED CYANOSIS, WEAKNESS, DIZZINESS, LIGHTHEADEDNESS, INCREASINGLY SEVERE HEADACHE, ATAXIA, SHALLOW RESPIRATION, DROWSINESS, NAUSEA, VOMITING, CONFUSION, LETHARGY AND STUPOR. AT HIGH CONCENTRATIONS, TACHYCARDIA, CONVULSIONS AND COMA MAY OCCUR. **CHRONIC EXPOSURE**- EFFECTS ARE DEPENDENT UPON CONCENTRATION AND DURATION OF EXPOSURE. DERMATITIS OR EFFECTS SIMILAR TO THOSE FOR ACUTE EXPOSURE MAY OCCUR. ANIMAL STUDIES INDICATE THAT LIVER AND KIDNEY DAMAGE MAY OCCUR. REPEATED OR PROLONGED EXPOSURE TO AROMATIC NITRO COMPOUNDS MAY RESULT IN ANEMIA.

FIRST AID- REMOVE CONTAMINATED CLOTHING AND SHOES IMMEDIATELY. WASH AFFECTED AREA WITH SOAP OR MILD DETERGENT AND LARGE AMOUNTS OF WATER UNTIL NO EVIDENCE OF CHEMICAL REMAINS (APPROXIMATELY 15-20 MINUTES). GET MEDICAL ATTENTION IMMEDIATELY.

EYE CONTACT: P-NITROPHENOL: CORROSIVE. **ACUTE EXPOSURE**- DIRECT CONTACT MAY CAUSE IRRITATION WITH REDNESS, AND PAIN. THE META ISOMER HAS CAUSED SEVERE IRRITATION IN TESTS ON RABBIT EYES. **CHRONIC EXPOSURE**- EFFECTS ARE DEPENDENT UPON CONCENTRATION AND DURATION OF EXPOSURE. CONJUNCTIVIVIS OR EFFECTS SIMILAR TO THOSE FOR ACUTE EXPOSURE MAY OCCUR.

FIRST AID- WASH EYES IMMEDIATELY WITH LARGE AMOUNTS OF WATER OR NORMAL SALINE, OCCASIONALLY LIFTING UPPER AND LOWER LIDS, UNTIL NO EVIDENCE OF CHEMICAL REMAINS (APPROXIMATELY 15-20 MINUTES). GET MEDICAL ATTENTION IMMEDIATELY.

INGESTION: P-NITROPHENOL: METHEMOGLOBIN FORMER/TOXIC. **ACUTE EXPOSURE**- INGESTION MAY CAUSE SYSTEMIC POISONING. ANIMAL STUDIES INDICATE THAT CENTRAL AND PERIPHERAL VAGUS STIMULATION, CENTRAL NERVOUS SYSTEM DEPRESSION, METHEMOGLOBINEMIA, DYSPNEA AND HYPERTHERMIA MAY OCCUR. AT LOW CONCENTRATIONS OF METHEMOGLOBIN, OBSERVABLE CYANOSIS WITH A BLUE COLOR OF THE LIPS, EARLOBES AND FINGERNAILS MAY OCCUR. SYMPTOMS MAY BE ABSENT, ALTHOUGH EUPHORIA, FLUSHED FACIES AND HEADACHE ARE COMMON. MODERATE CONCENTRATIONS MAY CAUSE MARKED CYANOSIS, WEAKNESS, DIZZINESS, LIGHTHEADEDNESS, INCREASINGLY SEVERE HEADACHE,

ATAXIA, SHALLOW RESPIRATION, DROWSINESS, NAUSEA, VOMITING, CONFUSION, LETHARGY AND STUPOR. AT HIGH CONCENTRATIONS, TACHYCARDIA, CONVULSIONS AND COMA MAY OCCUR. THE PROBALBE HUMAN LETHAL DOSE IS BETWEEN 1 TEASPOON AND 1 OUNCE. **CHRONIC EXPOSURE-** ANIMAL STUDIES INDICATE THAT LIVER AND KIDNEY DAMAGE MAY OCCUR. CHRONIC ADMINISTRATION TO MAMMALS CAUSED ALTERATIONS OF NEUROHUMORAL REGULATION AND PATHOLOGICAL CHANGES INCLUDING COLITIS, ENTERITIS, HEPATITIS, GASTRITIS, HYPERPLASIA OF THE SPLEEN, AND NEURITIS.

FIRST AID- IF THE PERSON IS CONSCIOUS AND NOT CONVULSING, INDUCE EMESIS BY GIVING SYRUP OF IPECAC FOLLOWED BY WATER. (IF VOMITING OCCURS KEEP THE HEAD BELOW THE HIPS TO PREVENT ASPIRATION). REPEAT IN 20 MINUTES IF NOT EFFECTIVE INITIALLY. GIVE ACTIVATED CHARCOAL. IN PATIENTS WITH DEPRESSED RESPIRATION OR IF EMESIS IS NOT PRODUCED, PERFORM GASTRIC LAVAGE CAUTIOUSLY (DREISBACH, HANDBOOK OF POISONING, 12TH ED.). TREAT SYMPTOMATICALLY AND SUPPORTIVELY. GASTRIC LAVAGE SHOULD BE PERFORMED BY QUALIFIED MEDICAL PERSONNEL. GET MEDICAL ATTENTION IMMEDIATELY.

ANTIDOTE: THE FOLLOWING ANTIDOTE HAS BEEN RECOMMENDED. HOWEVER, THE DECISION AS TO WHETHER THE SEVERITY OF POISONING REQUIRES ADMINISTRATION OF ANY ANTIDOTE AND ACTUAL DOSE REQUIRED SHOULD BE MADE BY QUALIFIED MEDICAL PERSONNEL.

METHEMOGLOBINEMIA: (WHEN METHEMOGLOBIN CONCENTRATION IS OVER 25-40% OR IN PRESENCE OF SYMPTOMS.) GIVE METHYLENE BLUE, 1% SOLUTION, 0.1 ML/KG INTRAVENOUSLY OVER A 10-MINUTE PERIOD. CYANOSIS MAY DISAPPEAR WITHIN MINUTES OR PERSIST LONGER DEPENDING ON DEGREE OF METHEMOGLOBINEMIA. INTRAVENOUS ADMINISTRATION OF THERAPEUTIC DOSES OF METHYLENE BLUE MAY CAUSE A RISE IN BLOOD PRESSURE, NAUSEA, AND DIZZINESS. LARGER DOSES (>500 MG) CAUSE VOMITING, DIARRHEA, CHEST PAIN, MENTAL CONFUSION, CYANOSIS, AND SWEATING. HEMOLYTIC ANEMIA HAS ALSO OCCURRED SEVERAL DAYS AFTER ADMINISTRATION. THESE EFFECTS ARE TEMPORARY, AND FATALITIES HAVE NOT BEEN REPORTED. IF METHYLENE BLUE IS NOT AVAILABLE, GIVE ASCORBIC ACID, 1 GRAM SLOWLY INTRAVENOUSLY. WITHOUT TREATMENT, METHEMOGLOBINEMIA LEVELS OF 20-30% REVERT TO NORMAL WITHIN 3 DAYS (DREISBACH, HANDBOOK OF POISONING, 12TH ED.). ANTIDOTE SHOULD BE ADMINISTERED BY QUALIFIED MEDICAL PERSONNEL.

REACTIVITY

REACTIVITY: STABLE UNDER NORMAL TEMPERATURES AND PRESSURES. CAN DECOMPOSE VIOLENTLY AND EXPLOSIVELY WHEN HEATED TO 279 C AND BURN IN THE ABSENCE OF AIR.

INCOMPATIBILITIES: P-NITROPHENOL: COMBUSTIBLE MATERIALS: VIOLENT REACTION. DIETHYL PHOSPHITE: RUNAWAY REACTION AND EXPLOSION. REDUCING MATERIALS: VIOLENT REACTION.

DECOMPOSITION: THERMAL DECOMPOSITION PRODUCTS MAY INCLUDE TOXIC OXIDES OF NITROGEN.

POLYMERIZATION: HAZARDOUS POLYMERIZATION HAS NOT BEEN REPORTED TO OCCUR UNDER NORMAL TEMPERATURES AND PRESSURES.

STORAGE AND DISPOSAL

OBSERVE ALL FEDERAL, STATE AND LOCAL REGULATIONS WHEN STORING OR DISPOSING OF THIS SUBSTANCE. FOR ASSISTANCE, CONTACT THE DISTRICT DIRECTOR OF THE ENVIRONMENTAL PROTECTION AGENCY.

STORAGE

STORAGE: PROTECT FROM PHYSICAL DAMAGE. SEPARATE FROM COMBUSTIBLE, ORGANIC OR OTHER READILY OXIDIZABLE MATERIALS (NFPA 49, HAZARDOUS CHEMICALS DATA, 1975).

DISPOSAL

DISPOSAL MUST BE IN ACCORDANCE WITH STANDARDS APPLICABLE TO GENERATORS OF HAZARDOUS WASTE, 40CFR 262. EPA HAZARDOUS WASTE NUMBER U0170.

CONDITIONS TO AVOID

MAY BURN BUT DOES NOT IGNITE READILY. CONTAINERS MAY EXPLODE IN HEAT OF FIRE.

SPILL AND LEAK PROCEDURES

SOIL SPILL: DIG A HOLDING AREA SUCH AS PIT, POND OR LAGOON TO CONTAIN SPILLED MATERIAL. USE PROTECTIVE COVER SUCH AS A PLASTIC SHEET TO PREVENT DISSOLVING IN FIREFIGHTING WATER OR RAIN.

NEUTRALIZE SPILL WITH SLAKED LIME, SODIUM BICARBONATE OR CRUSHED LIMESTONE.

WATER SPILL: NEUTRALIZE WITH AGRICULTURAL LIME, SLAKED LIME, CRUSHED LIMESTONE, OR SODIUM BICARBONATE.

IF DISSOLVED, AT A CONCENTRATION OF 10 PPM OR GREATER, APPLY ACTIVATED CARBON AT TEN TIMES THE AMOUNT THAT HAS BEEN SPILLED.

USE MECHANICAL DREDGES OR LIFTS TO EXTRACT IMMOBILIZED MASSES OF POLLUTION AND PRECIPITATES.

OCCUPATIONAL SPILL: DO NOT TOUCH SPILLED MATERIAL. STOP LEAK IF YOU CAN DO IT WITHOUT RISK. USE WATER SPRAY TO REDUCE VAPORS. FOR SMALL SPILLS, TAKE UP WITH SAND OR OTHER ABSORBENT MATERIAL AND PLACE INTO CONTAINERS FOR LATER DISPOSAL. FOR SMALL DRY SPILLS, WITH A CLEAN SHOVEL PLACE MATERIAL INTO CLEAN, DRY CONTAINERS AND COVER. MOVE CONTAINERS FROM SPILL AREA. FOR LARGER SPILLS, DIKE FAR AHEAD OF SPILL FOR LATER DISPOSAL. KEEP UNNECESSARY PEOPLE AWAY. ISOLATE HAZARD AREA AND DENY ENTRY. VENTILATE CLOSED SPACES BEFORE ENTERING.

REPORTABLE QUANTITY (RQ): 100 POUNDS THE SUPERFUND AMENDMENTS AND REAUTHORIZATION ACT (SARA) SECTION 304 REQUIRES THAT A RELEASE EQUAL TO OR GREATER THAN THE REPORTABLE QUANTITY FOR THIS SUBSTANCE BE IMMEDIATELY REPORTED TO THE LOCAL EMERGENCY PLANNING COMMITTEE AND THE STATE EMERGENCY RESPONSE COMMISSION (40 CFR 355.40). IF THE RELEASE OF THIS SUBSTANCE IS REPORTABLE UNDER CERCLA SECTION 103, THE NATIONAL RESPONSE CENTER MUST BE NOTIFIED IMMEDIATELY AT (800) 424-8802 OR (202) 426-2675 IN THE METROPOLITAN WASHINGTON, D.C. AREA (40 CFR 302.6).

PROTECTIVE EQUIPMENT

VENTILATION: PROVIDE LOCAL EXHAUST OR PROCESS ENCLOSURE VENTILATION SYSTEM.

RESPIRATOR: THE FOLLOWING RESPIRATORS ARE RECOMMENDED BASED ON INFORMATION FOUND IN THE PHYSICAL DATA, TOXICITY AND HEALTH EFFECTS SECTIONS. THEY ARE RANKED IN ORDER FROM MINIMUM TO MAXIMUM RESPIRATORY PROTECTION. THE SPECIFIC RESPIRATOR SELECTED MUST BE BASED ON CONTAMINATION LEVELS FOUND IN THE WORK PLACE, MUST NOT EXCEED THE WORKING LIMITS OF THE RESPIRATOR AND BE JOINTLY APPROVED BY THE NATIONAL INSTITUTE FOR OCCUPATIONAL SAFETY AND HEALTH AND THE MINE SAFETY AND HEALTH ADMINISTRATION (NIOSH-MSHA).

TYPE 'C' SUPPLIED-AIR RESPIRATOR WITH A FULL FACEPIECE OPERATED IN PRESSURE-DEMAND OR OTHER POSITIVE PRESSURE MODE OR WITH A FULL FACEPIECE, HELMET OR HOOD OPERATED IN CONTINOUS-FLOW MODE.

SELF-CONTAINED BREATHING APPARATUS WITH A FULL FACEPIECE OPERATED IN PRESSURE-DEMAND OR OTHER POSITIVE PRESSURE MODE.

FOR FIREFIGHTING AND OTHER IMMEDIATELY DANGEROUS TO LIFE OR HEALTH CONDITIONS:

SELF-CONTAINED BREATHING APPARATUS WITH FULL FACEPIECE OPERATED IN PRESSURE-DEMAND OR OTHER POSITIVE PRESSURE MODE. SUPPLIED-AIR RESPIRATOR WITH FULL FACEPIECE AND OPERATED IN PRESSURE-DEMAND OR OTHER POSITIVE PRESSURE MODE IN COMBINATION WITH AN AUXILIARY SELF-CONTAINED BREATHING APPARATUS OPERATED IN PRESSURE-DEMAND OR OTHER POSITIVE PRESSURE MODE.

CLOTHING: EMPLOYEE MUST WEAR APPROPRIATE PROTECTIVE (IMPERVIOUS) CLOTHING AND EQUIPMENT TO PREVENT ANY POSSIBILITY OF SKIN CONTACT WITH THIS SUBSTANCE.

GLOVES: EMPLOYEE MUST WEAR APPROPRIATE PROTECTIVE GLOVES TO PREVENT CONTACT WITH THIS SUBSTANCE.

EYE PROTECTION: EMPLOYEE MUST WEAR SPLASH-PROOF OR DUST-RESISTANT SAFETY GOGGLES AND A FACESHIELD TO PREVENT CONTACT WITH THIS SUBSTANCE.

EMERGENCY WASH FACILITIES: WHERE THERE IS ANY POSSIBILITY THAT AN EMPLOYEE'S EYES AND/OR SKIN MAY BE EXPOSED TO THIS SUBSTANCE, THE EMPLOYER SHOULD PROVIDE AN EYE WASH FOUNTAIN AND QUICK DRENCH SHOWER WITHIN THE IMMEDIATE WORK AREA FOR EMERGENCY USE.

AUTHORIZED BY- OCCUPATIONAL HEALTH SERVICES, INC.

CREATION DATE: 10/04/89 ***REVISION DATE:*** 05/14/90

MATERIAL SAFETY DATA SHEET

OCCUPATIONAL HEALTH SERVICES, INC.
AGRICULTURE AND PESTICIDE DIVISION
450 SEVENTH AVENUE, SUITE 2407
NEW YORK, NEW YORK 10123
1-800-445-MSDS OR (212) 967-1100

EMERGENCY CONTACT:
JOHN S. BRANSFORD, JR. (615) 292-1180

SUBSTANCE IDENTIFICATION

CAS-NUMBER 30525-89-4

SUBSTANCE: **PARAFORMALDEHYDE**

TRADE NAMES/SYNONYMS: ALDACIDE; FLO-MOR; PARAFORM; STCC 4941143; UN 2213; 0-4042; POLYOXYMETHYLENE; FORMAGENE; POLYMERIZED FORMALDEHYDE; FORMALDEHYDE POLYMER; POLYFORMALDEHYDE; PST18000

CHEMICAL FAMILY: ALDEHYDE, ALIPHATIC POLYMER

MOLECULAR FORMULA: (C-H2-O)X

MOLECULAR WEIGHT: (30.03)X

CERCLA RATINGS (SCALE 0-3): HEALTH=2 FIRE=1 REACTIVITY=0 PERSISTENCE=0

NFPA RATINGS (SCALE 0-4): HEALTH=2 FIRE=1 REACTIVITY=0

COMPONENTS AND CONTAMINANTS

COMPONENT: PARAFORMALDEHYDE ***PERCENT:*** 100
CAS# 30525-89-4

OTHER CONTAMINANTS: NONE

EXPOSURE LIMITS: PARAFORMALDEHYDE: NO OCCUPATIONAL EXPOSURE LIMITS ESTABLISHED BY OSHA, ACGIH, OR NIOSH.
1000 POUNDS CERCLA SECTION 103 REPORTABLE QUANTITY

PHYSICAL DATA

DESCRIPTION: WHITE FLAKES OR FINE POWDER WITH A STRONG, PUNGENT ODOR OF FORMALDEHYDE. ***BOILING POINT:*** DECOMPOSES

MELTING POINT: 248-356 F (120-180 C) SUBLIMES ***SPECIFIC GRAVITY:*** 1.46

VOLATILITY: <10% ***VAPOR PRESSURE:*** 1.45 MMHG @ 25 C ***PH:*** NEUTRAL

SOLUBILITY IN WATER: COMPLETE ***VAPOR DENSITY:*** 1.03

SOLVENT SOLUBILITY: SOLUBLE IN STRONG ALKALI SOLUTIONS; INSOLUBLE IN ALCOHOL, ETHER, MOST ORGANIC SOLVENTS

FIRE AND EXPLOSION DATA

FIRE AND EXPLOSION HAZARD: SLIGHT FIRE HAZARD WHEN EXPOSED TO HEAT OR FLAME.
PARAFORMALDEHYDE IS A VOLATILE SOLID THAT GIVES OFF FLAMMABLE VAPORS OF FORMALDEHYDE WHEN HEATED OR HYDRATED IN ACID OR ALKALI SOLUTIONS.
VAPOR OR DUST MAY FORM EXPLOSIVE MIXTURES IN AIR.

FLASH POINT: 158 F (70 C) (TCC) ***UPPER EXPLOSIVE LIMIT:*** 73%

LOWER EXPLOSIVE LIMIT: 7.0% ***AUTOIGNITION TEMP.:*** 572 F (300 C)

FIREFIGHTING MEDIA: DRY CHEMICAL, SAND, WATER SPRAY OR FOAM (1987 EMERGENCY RESPONSE GUIDEBOOK, DOT P 5800.4).
FOR LARGER FIRES, USE WATER SPRAY, FOG OR STANDARD FOAM (1987 EMERGENCY RESPONSE GUIDEBOOK, DOT P 5800.4).
ALCOHOL FOAM (NFPA 325M, FIRE HAZARD PROPERTIES OF FLAMMABLE LIQUIDS, GASES, AND VOLATILE SOLIDS, 1984).

FIREFIGHTING: MOVE CONTAINER FROM FIRE AREA IF POSSIBLE. COOL CONTAINERS EXPOSED TO FLAME WITH WATER FROM SIDE UNTIL WELL AFTER FIRE IS OUT. STAY AWAY FROM STORAGE TANK ENDS. FOR MASSIVE FIRE IN CARGO AREA, USE UNMANNED HOSE HOLDER OR MONITOR NOZZLES; ELSE WITHDRAW AND LET FIRE BURN (1987 EMERGENCY RESPONSE GUIDEBOOK, DOT P 5800.4, GUIDE PAGE 32).
EXTINGUISH ONLY IF FLOW CAN BE STOPPED; USE WATER IN FLOODING AMOUNTS AS FOG. COOL CONTAINERS WITH FLOODING AMOUNTS OF WATER, APPLY FROM AS FAR A DISTANCE AS POSSIBLE. AVOID BREATHING TOXIC VAPORS, KEEP UPWIND.

TRANSPORTATION DATA

DEPARTMENT OF TRANSPORTATION HAZARD CLASSIFICATION 49 CFR 172.101: ORM-A
DEPARTMENT OF TRANSPORTATION LABELING REQUIREMENTS 49 CFR 172.101 AND SUBPART E: NONE
DEPARTMENT OF TRANSPORTATION PACKAGING REQUIREMENTS: 49 CFR 173.510 EXCEPTIONS: 49 CFR 173.505

TOXICITY

PARAFORMALDEHYDE: IRRITATION DATA: 500 MG/24 HOURS SKIN-RABBIT SEVERE; 100 MG EYE-RABBIT SEVERE. TOXICITY DATA: 10,000 MG/KG SKIN-RABBIT LDLO; 800 MG/KG ORAL-RAT LD50; MUTAGENIC DATA (RTECS). CARCINOGEN STATUS: NONE. LOCAL EFFECTS: CORROSIVE- INHALATION AND EYES; IRRITANT- SKIN. ACUTE TOXICITY LEVEL: MODERATELY TOXIC BY INGESTION. TARGET EFFECTS: POISONING MAY AFFECT THE LIVER AND KIDNEYS. AT INCREASED RISK FROM EXPOSURE: WORKERS WITH PRE-EXISTING RESPIRATORY OR SKIN DISEASE.

HEALTH EFFECTS AND FIRST AID

INHALATION: PARAFORMALDEHYDE: CORROSIVE. **ACUTE EXPOSURE-** MAY CAUSE SEVERE IRRITATION, RHINITIS, ANOSMIA, PHARYNGITIS, LARYNGOSPASM, TRACHEITIS, BRONCHITIS, PULMONARY EDEMA, COUGH, DYSPNEA, COLLAPSE AND GASTROENTERITIS. EXPOSURE TO 50-100 PPM PRODUCES A FEELING OF RESTRICTED CHEST, HEADACHE, PALPITATIONS AND IN EXTREME CASES, DEATH DUE TO EDEMA OR SPASM OF THE GLOTTIS. **CHRONIC EXPOSURE-** REPEATED AND PROLONGED CONTACT MAY CAUSE MUCOUS MEMBRANE IRRITATION, ASTHMA AND KIDNEY INJURY.

FIRST AID- REMOVE FROM EXPOSURE AREA TO FRESH AIR IMMEDIATELY. IF BREATHING HAS STOPPED, GIVE ARTIFICIAL RESPIRATION. MAINTAIN AIRWAY AND BLOOD PRESSURE AND ADMINISTER OXYGEN IF AVAILABLE. KEEP AFFECTED PERSON WARM AND AT REST. TREAT SYMPTOMATICALLY AND SUPPORTIVELY. ADMINISTRATION OF OXYGEN SHOULD BE PERFORMED BY QUALIFIED PERSONNEL. GET MEDICAL ATTENTION IMMEDIATELY.

SKIN CONTACT: PARAFORMALDEHYDE: IRRITANT. **ACUTE EXPOSURE-** MAY CAUSE SEVERE IRRITATION WITH REDNESS, PAIN, BROWNISH DISCOLORATION OF THE SKIN AND URTICARIA. SENSITIZATION MAY ALSO OCCUR. ANIMAL STUDIES INDICATE SKIN ABSORPTION MAY OCCUR AND RESULT IN SYSTEMIC EFFECTS. **CHRONIC EXPOSURE-** REPEATED AND PROLONGED CONTACT MAY CAUSE SENSITIZATION DERMATITIS.

FIRST AID- REMOVE CONTAMINATED CLOTHING AND SHOES IMMEDIATELY. WASH AFFECTED AREA WITH SOAP OR MILD DETERGENT AND LARGE AMOUNTS OF WATER UNTIL NO EVIDENCE OF CHEMICAL REMAINS (APPROXIMATELY 15-20 MINUTES). GET MEDICAL ATTENTION IMMEDIATELY.

EYE CONTACT: PARAFORMALDEHYDE: CORROSIVE. **ACUTE EXPOSURE-** MAY CAUSE SEVERE IRRITATION, REDNESS, PAIN, LACRIMATION, CORNEAL BURNS AND BLURRED VISION. **CHRONIC EXPOSURE-** DEPENDING ON THE CONCENTRATION AND DURATION OF EXPOSURE, EFFECTS SIMILAR TO ACUTE EXPOSURE MAY OCCUR.

FIRST AID- WASH EYES IMMEDIATELY WITH LARGE AMOUNTS OF WATER, OCCASIONALLY LIFTING UPPER AND LOWER LIDS, UNTIL NO EVIDENCE OF CHEMICAL REMAINS (AT LEAST 15-20 MINUTES). CONTINUE IRRIGATING WITH NORMAL SALINE UNTIL THE PH HAS RETURNED TO NORMAL (30-60 MINUTES). COVER WITH STERILE BANDAGES. GET MEDICAL ATTENTION IMMEDIATELY.

INGESTION: PARAFORMALDEHYDE: CORROSIVE. **ACUTE EXPOSURE-** MAY CAUSE SEVERE IRRITATION WITH BURNING IN THE MOUTH AND ESOPHAGUS, NAUSEA AND VOMITING, ABDOMINAL PAIN, DIARRHEA, VERTIGO, UNCONSCIOUSNESS, JAUNDICE, ALBUMINURIA, HEMATURIA, ANURIA, AND ACIDOSIS. INGESTION OF VERY LARGE QUANTITIES MAY CAUSE CONVULSIONS AND DEATH. **CHRONIC EXPOSURE-** REPEATED AND PROLONGED CONTACT MAY CAUSE LIVER AND KIDNEY DAMAGE.

FIRST AID- ADMINISTER BY MOUTH ONE OR MORE OF THE FOLLOWING: WATER, MILK, 0.2% AMMONIA WATER (2 TO 3 TEASPOONS OF HOUSEHOLD AMMONIA DILUTED WITH 1 PINT OF WATER), AMMONIUM ACETATE (3 TEASPOONFULS IN WATER), EGG WHITES, ACTIVATED CHARCOAL. AMMONIUM SALTS ARE PROBABLY EFFECTIVE BECAUSE THEY TRANSFORM FORMALDEHYDE INTO METHENAMINE (GOSSELIN, SMITH, HODGE, CLINICAL TOXICOLOGY OF COMMERICAL PRODUCTS, 5TH ED.) TREATMENT SHOULD BE ADMINISTERED BY QUALIFIED MEDICAL PERSONNEL. GET MEDICAL ATTENTION IMMEDIATELY.

ANTIDOTE: NO SPECIFIC ANTIDOTE. TREAT SYMPTOMATICALLY AND SUPPORTIVELY.

REACTIVITY

REACTIVITY: STABLE UNDER NORMAL TEMPERATURES AND PRESSURES, HOWEVER, MAY DEPOLYMERIZE WITH THE RELEASE OF FORMALDEHYDE GAS WHEN HEATED.

INCOMPATIBILITIES: PARAFORMALDEHYDE: ACIDS: MAY CAUSE DEPOLYMERIZATION WITH RELEASE OF FORMALDEHYDE. ALKALIES (STRONG): MAY CAUSE DEPOLYMERIZATION WITH RELEASE OF FORMALDEHYDE. ANHYDRIDES: INCOMPATIBLE. ISOCYANATES: INCOMPATIBLE. KETONES: INCOMPATIBLE. OXIDES: INCOMPATIBLE. OXIDIZERS (STRONG): FIRE AND EXPLOSION HAZARD. OXYGEN (LIQUID): MAY EXPLODE. PEROXIDES: INCOMPATIBLE.

DECOMPOSITION: THERMAL DECOMPOSITION MAY YIELD TOXIC AND HAZARDOUS FORMALDEHYDE GAS, FORMIC ACID OR TOXIC OXIDES OF CARBON.

POLYMERIZATION: HAZARDOUS POLYMERIZATION HAS NOT BEEN REPORTED TO OCCUR UNDER NORMAL TEMPERATURES AND PRESSURES.

STORAGE AND DISPOSAL

OBSERVE ALL FEDERAL, STATE AND LOCAL REGULATIONS WHEN STORING OR DISPOSING OF THIS SUBSTANCE. FOR ASSISTANCE, CONTACT THE DISTRICT DIRECTOR OF THE ENVIRONMENTAL PROTECTION AGENCY.

STORAGE

STORAGE: PROTECT AGAINST PHYSICAL DAMAGE. STORE IN COOL, DRY, WELL VENTILATED PLACE AWAY FROM SOURCES OF HEAT AND IGNITION. SEPARATE FROM COMBUSTIBLES, AND ACIDIC, ALKALINE, AND OXIDIZING MATERIALS (NFPA 49, HAZARDOUS CHEMICALS DATA, 1975).
STORE IN ACCORDANCE WITH 29 CFR 1910.106.
BONDING AND GROUNDING: SUBSTANCES WITH LOW ELECTROCONDUCTIVITY,

WHICH MAY BE IGNITED BY ELECTROSTATIC SPARKS, SHOULD BE STORED IN CONTAINERS WHICH MEET THE BONDING AND GROUNDING GUIDELINES SPECIFIED IN NFPA 77-1983, RECOMMENDED PRACTICE ON STATIC ELECTRICITY.
STORE AWAY FROM INCOMPATIBLE SUBSTANCES.

DISPOSAL

DISPOSAL MUST BE IN ACCORDANCE WITH STANDARDS APPLICABLE TO GENERATORS OF HAZARDOUS WASTE, 40 CFR 262. EPA HAZARDOUS WASTE NUMBER D001. 100 POUND CERCLA SECTION 103 REPORTABLE QUANTITY.

CONDITIONS TO AVOID

AVOID CONTACT WITH HEAT, SPARKS, FLAMES OR OTHER SOURCES OF IGNITION. MATERIAL IS EXTREMELY FLAMMABLE AND MAY BURN RAPIDLY WITH FLARE-BURNING EFFECT.

SPILL AND LEAK PROCEDURES

SOIL SPILL: DIG HOLDING AREA SUCH AS LAGOON, POND OR PIT FOR CONTAINMENT. USE PROTECTIVE COVER SUCH AS A PLASTIC SHEET TO PREVENT MATERIAL FROM DISSOLVING IN FIRE EXTINGUISHING WATER OR RAIN.

WATER SPILL: TRAP SPILLED MATERIAL AT BOTTOM IN DEEP WATER POCKETS, EXCAVATED HOLDING AREAS OR WITHIN SAND BAG BARRIERS.
USE SUCTION HOSES TO REMOVE TRAPPED SPILL MATERIAL.
USE MECHANICAL DREDGES OR LIFTS TO EXTRACT IMMOBILIZED MASSES OF POLLUTION AND PRECIPITATES.

OCCUPATIONAL SPILL: SHUT OFF IGNITION SOURCES. DO NOT TOUCH SPILLED MATERIAL. FOR SMALL SPILLS, WITH CLEAN SHOVEL, PLACE MATERIAL INTO CLEAN, DRY CONTAINER AND COVER; MOVE CONTAINERS FROM SPILL AREA. FOR LARGER SPILLS, WET DOWN WITH WATER AND DIKE FOR LATER DISPOSAL. NO SMOKING, FLAMES OR FLARES IN HAZARD AREA! KEEP UNNECESSARY PEOPLE AWAY. ISOLATE HAZARD AREA AND DENY ENTRY.
REPORTABLE QUANTITY (RQ): 1000 POUNDS THE SUPERFUND AMENDMENTS AND REAUTHORIZATION ACT (SARA) SECTION 304 REQUIRES THAT A RELEASE EQUAL TO OR GREATER THAN THE REPORTABLE QUANTITY FOR THIS SUBSTANCE BE IMMEDIATELY REPORTED TO THE LOCAL EMERGENCY PLANNING COMMITTEE AND THE STATE EMERGENCY RESPONSE COMMISSION (40 CFR 355.40). IF THE RELEASE OF THIS SUBSTANCE IS REPORTABLE UNDER CERCLA SECTION 103, THE NATIONAL RESPONSE CENTER MUST BE NOTIFIED IMMEDIATELY AT (800) 424-8802 OR (202) 426-2675 IN THE METROPOLITAN WASHINGTON, D.C. AREA (40 CFR 302.6).

PROTECTIVE EQUIPMENT

VENTILATION: PROVIDE LOCAL EXHAUST OR GENERAL DILUTION VENTILATION SYSTEM.

RESPIRATOR: THE FOLLOWING RESPIRATORS ARE RECOMMENDED BASED ON INFORMATION FOUND IN THE PHYSICAL DATA, TOXICITY AND HEALTH EFFECTS SECTIONS. THEY ARE RANKED IN ORDER FROM MINIMUM TO MAXIMUM RESPIRATORY PROTECTION. THE SPECIFIC RESPIRATOR SELECTED MUST BE BASED ON CONTAMINATION LEVELS FOUND IN THE WORK PLACE, MUST NOT EXCEED THE WORKING LIMITS OF THE RESPIRATOR AND BE JOINTLY APPROVED BY THE NATIONAL INSTITUTE FOR OCCUPATIONAL SAFETY AND HEALTH AND THE MINE SAFETY AND HEALTH ADMINISTRATION (NIOSH-MSHA).
CHEMICAL CARTRIDGE RESPIRATOR WITH FULL FACEPIECE AND ORGANIC VAPOR CARTRIDGE(S) IN COMBINATION WITH A DUST AND MIST FILTER.
CHEMICAL CARTRIDGE RESPIRATOR WITH FULL FACEPIECE AND ORGANIC VAPOR CARTRIDGE(S) IN COMBINATION WITH A HIGH-EFFICIENCY PARTICULATE FILTER.
GAS MASK WITH ORGANIC VAPOR CANISTER (CHIN-STYLE OR FRONT- OR BACK-MOUNTED CANISTER) WITH A FULL FACEPIECE AND A HIGH-EFFICIENCY PARTICULATE FILTER.
POWERED AIR-PURIFYING RESPIRATOR WITH TIGHT-FITTING FACEPIECE AND ORGANIC VAPOR CARTRIDGE(S) IN COMBINATION WITH A HIGH-EFFICIENCY PARTICULATE FILTER.
TYPE 'C' SUPPLIED-AIR RESPIRATOR WITH A FULL FACEPIECE OPERATED IN PRESSURE-DEMAND OR OTHER POSITIVE PRESSURE MODE OR WITH A FULL FACEPIECE, HELMET OR HOOD OPERATED IN CONTINUOUS-FLOW MODE.
SELF-CONTAINED BREATHING APPARATUS WITH A FULL FACEPIECE OPERATED IN PRESSURE-DEMAND OR OTHER POSITIVE PRESSURE MODE.
FOR FIREFIGHTING AND OTHER IMMEDIATELY DANGEROUS TO LIFE OR HEALTH CONDITIONS:
SELF-CONTAINED BREATHING APPARATUS WITH FULL FACEPIECE OPERATED IN PRESSURE-DEMAND OR OTHER POSITIVE PRESSURE MODE.
SUPPLIED-AIR RESPIRATOR WITH FULL FACEPIECE AND OPERATED IN PRESSURE-DEMAND OR OTHER POSITIVE PRESSURE MODE IN COMBINATION WITH AN AUXILIARY SELF-CONTAINED BREATHING APPARATUS OPERATED IN PRESSURE-DEMAND OR OTHER POSITIVE PRESSURE MODE.

CLOTHING: EMPLOYEE MUST WEAR APPROPRIATE PROTECTIVE (IMPERVIOUS) CLOTHING AND EQUIPMENT TO PREVENT ANY POSSIBILITY OF SKIN CONTACT WITH THIS SUBSTANCE.

GLOVES: EMPLOYEE MUST WEAR APPROPRIATE PROTECTIVE GLOVES TO PREVENT CONTACT WITH THIS SUBSTANCE.

EYE PROTECTION: EMPLOYEE MUST WEAR SPLASH-PROOF OR DUST-RESISTANT SAFETY GOGGLES AND A FACESHIELD TO PREVENT CONTACT WITH THIS SUBSTANCE.
EMERGENCY WASH FACILITIES: WHERE THERE IS ANY POSSIBILITY THAT AN EMPLOYEE'S EYES AND/OR SKIN MAY BE EXPOSED TO THIS SUBSTANCE, THE EMPLOYER SHOULD PROVIDE AN EYE WASH FOUNTAIN AND QUICK DRENCH SHOWER WITHIN THE IMMEDIATE WORK AREA FOR EMERGENCY USE.

AUTHORIZED BY- OCCUPATIONAL HEALTH SERVICES, INC.
CREATION DATE: 05/22/90 ***REVISION DATE:*** 05/22/90

MATERIAL SAFETY DATA SHEET

OCCUPATIONAL HEALTH SERVICES, INC.
AGRICULTURE AND PESTICIDE DIVISION
450 SEVENTH AVENUE, SUITE 2407
NEW YORK, NEW YORK 10123
1-800-445-MSDS OR (212) 967-1100

EMERGENCY CONTACT:
JOHN S. BRANSFORD, JR. (615) 292-1180

SUBSTANCE IDENTIFICATION

CAS-NUMBER 1910-42-5

SUBSTANCE: PARAQUAT DICHLORIDE

TRADE NAMES/SYNONYMS: 4,4'-BIPYRIDINIUM, 1,1'-DIMETHYL-, DICHLORIDE; 1,1'-DIMETHYL-4,4'-BIPYRIDINIUM DICHLORIDE; DIMETHYL VIOLGEN CHLORIDE; METHYL VIOLOGEN; METHYLVIOLOGEN CHLORIDE; METHYL VIOLOGEN DICHLORIDE; GRAMIXEL; GRAMOXONE; GRAMOXONE DICHLORIDE; PARAQUAT; C12H14N2.2CL; PST18020

CHEMICAL FAMILY: BIPYRIDYL COMPOUND
SALT

MOLECULAR FORMULA: C12-H14-N2-CL2

MOLECULAR WEIGHT: 257.18

CERCLA RATINGS (SCALE 0-3): HEALTH=3 FIRE=0 REACTIVITY=0 PERSISTENCE=2

NFPA RATINGS (SCALE 0-4): HEALTH=4 FIRE=0 REACTIVITY=0

COMPONENTS AND CONTAMINANTS

COMPONENT: PARAQUAT DICHLORIDE ***PERCENT:*** 100.0
CAS# 1910-42-5

OTHER CONTAMINANTS: NONE

EXPOSURE LIMITS: PARAQUAT: 0.1 MG/M3 OSHA TWA (SKIN) (RESPIRIBLE PARTICLES) 0.1 MG/M3 ACGIH TWA (RESPIRABLE PARTICLES, <5 UM) 0.5 MG/M3 ACGIH TWA (NON-RESPIRABLE PARTICLES, >5 UM)
PARAQUAT DICHLORIDE: 10/10,000 POUNDS SARA SECTION 302 THRESHOLD PLANNING QUANTITY 1 POUND SARA SECTION 304 REPORTABLE QUANTITY

PHYSICAL DATA

DESCRIPTION: HYGROSCOPIC, WHITE CRYSTALLINE SOLID.
MELTING POINT: >572 F (>300 C) DECOMPOSES ***SPECIFIC GRAVITY:*** 1.24-1.26
VAPOR PRESSURE: 0.0000001 MMHG ***SOLUBILITY IN WATER:*** VERY SOLUBLE
SOLVENT SOLUBILITY: SLIGHTLY SOLUBLE IN LOWER ALCOHOLS; INSOLUBLE IN ACETONE, ETHANOL, ORGANIC SOLVENTS

FIRE AND EXPLOSION DATA

FIRE AND EXPLOSION HAZARD: NEGLIGIBLE FIRE HAZARD WHEN EXPOSED TO HEAT OR FLAME.

FIREFIGHTING MEDIA: DRY CHEMICAL, CARBON DIOXIDE, HALON, WATER SPRAY OR STANDARD FOAM (1987 EMERGENCY RESPONSE GUIDEBOOK, DOT P 5800.4).
FOR LARGER FIRES, USE WATER SPRAY, FOG OR STANDARD FOAM (1987 EMERGENCY RESPONSE GUIDEBOOK, DOT P 5800.4).

FIREFIGHTING: MOVE CONTAINER FROM FIRE AREA IF POSSIBLE. DO NOT SCATTER SPILLED MATERIAL WITH HIGH PRESSURE WATER STREAMS. DIKE FIRE CONTROL WATER FOR LATER DISPOSAL (1987 EMERGENCY RESPONSE GUIDEBOOK, DOT P 5800.4, GUIDE PAGE 31).
USE AGENTS SUITABLE FOR TYPE OF SURROUNDING FIRE. AVOID BREATHING HAZARDOUS VAPORS, KEEP UPWIND.

TOXICITY

PARAQUAT DICHLORIDE: IRRITATION DATA: 25 MG EYE-RABBIT MILD; 12500 UG EYE-RABBIT SEVERE. TOXICITY DATA: 1 MG/M3/6 HOURS INHALATION-RAT LC50 (BJIMAG 25,304,68); 325 MG/KG SKIN-RABBIT LD50; 80 MG/KG SKIN-RAT LD50;

48.4 MG OCULAR-RABBIT LDLO (BECTA6 9,163,73); 32 MG/KG ORAL-MAN TDLO; 43 MG/MG ORAL-MAN LDLO; 111 MG/KG ORAL-WOMAN LDLO; 3000 MG/KG ORAL-WOMAN LDLO; 214 MG/KG ORAL-HUMAN LDLO; 57 MG/KG ORAL-RAT LD50; 120 MG/KG ORAL-MOUSE LD50; 25 MG/KG ORAL-DOG LD50; 50 MG/KG ORAL-MONKEY LD50; 35 MG/KG ORAL-CAT LD50; 22 MG/KG ORAL-GUINEA PIG LD50; 30 MG/KG ORAL-PIG LD50; 30 MG/KG ORAL-DOMESTIC ANIMAL LD50; 24 MG/KG SUBCUTANEOUS-RAT LD50; 21 MG/KG INTRAVENOUS-RAT LD50; 180 MG/KG INTRAVENOUS-MOUSE LD50; 1 MG/KG INTRAVENOUS-DOMESTIC ANIMAL LD50; 34500 UG/KG INTRAVENOUS-DOG LDLO; 26 MG/KG INTRAPERITONEAL-RAT LD50; 20 MG/KG INTRAPERITONEAL-MOUSE LD50; 18 MG/KG INTRAPERITONEAL-RABBIT LD50; 3 MG/KG INTRAPERITONEAL-GUINEA PIG LD50; MUTAGENIC DATA (RTECS); REPRODUCTIVE EFFECTS DATA (RTECS). CARCINOGEN STATUS: NONE. LOCAL EFFECTS: CORROSIVE- EYE, INGESTION; IRRITANT- SKIN, INHALATION. ACUTE TOXICITY LEVEL: HIGHLY TOXIC BY INHALATION; TOXIC BY DERMAL ABSORPTION AND INGESTION. TARGET EFFECTS: POISONING MAY AFFECT THE LUNGS, LIVER, AND KIDNEYS. ADDITIONAL DATA: THE ADMINISTRATION OF OXYGEN MAY AGGRAVATE THE PARAQUAT-INDUCED LUNG DAMAGE.

HEALTH EFFECTS AND FIRST AID

INHALATION: PARAQUAT DICHLORIDE: IRRITANT/HIGHLY TOXIC. 1.5 MG/M3 IMMEDIATELY DANGEROUS TO LIFE OR HEALTH. **ACUTE EXPOSURE-** EXPOSURE TO THE SPRAY MIST OF PARAQUAT AND ITS SALTS HAS PRODUCED IN WORKERS, IRRITATION AND INFLAMMATION OF THE MOUTH AND UPPER RESPIRATORY TRACT, COUGH, NOSEBLEEDS, CHEST PAIN, ASTHMATIC ATTACKS, FRONTAL HEADACHE, VOMITING, AND PAIN AND SWELLING OF THE JOINTS. INHALATION OF A SUFFICIENT QUANTITY MAY CAUSE SYSTEMIC POISONING WITH SYMPTOMS OF HEPATIC, RENAL AND RESPIRATORY INSUFFICIENCY AS DESCRIBED IN ACUTE INGESTION. AN AEROSOL OF PARAQUAT ADMINISTERED IN THE RESPIRABLE SIZE RANGE OF 3 UM TO 5 UM AT A CONCENTRATION OF 1 MG/M3 FOR 6 HOURS WAS LETHAL IN RATS. PARTICLES SMALLER OR GREATER THAN THE 3 UM TO 5 UM SIZE RANGE ARE NOT AS EFFECTIVE AT REACHING THE LOWER RESPIRATORY PASSAGES AND THEREBY DO NOT PRODUCE AS SEVERE A POISONING. **CHRONIC EXPOSURE-** PROLONGED OR REPEATED EXPOSURE MAY CAUSE SYMPTOMS AS DESCRIBED IN ACUTE EXPOSURE. PULMONARY, LIVER AND KIDNEY DAMAGE, AND LEUKOPENIA WERE OBSERVED IN RATS EXPOSED TO 1.1 MG/M3/DAY FOR 5 MONTHS. EXPOSURE TO 100 MG/M3 OF NONRESPIRABLE SIZE PARTICLES OF PARAQUAT FOR 6 HOURS/DAY, 5 DAYS A WEEK FOR 3 WEEKS WAS TOLERATED BY RATS, DOGS AND GUINEA PIGS WITH SOME REPORTS OF NOSEBLEEDS.

FIRST AID- REMOVE FROM EXPOSURE AREA TO FRESH AIR IMMEDIATELY. IF BREATHING HAS STOPPED, PERFORM ARTIFICIAL RESPIRATION. KEEP PERSON WARM AND AT REST. TREAT SYMPTOMATICALLY AND SUPPORTIVELY. GET MEDICAL ATTENTION IMMEDIATELY. OXYGEN THERAPY MAY ENHANCE THE TOXICITY. QUALIFIED MEDICAL PERSONNEL SHOULD CONSIDER THE NEED VERSUS THE INCREASED RISK OF OXYGEN ADMINISTRATION.

SKIN CONTACT: PARAQUAT DICHLORIDE: IRRITANT/TOXIC. **ACUTE EXPOSURE-** PARAQUAT AND ITS SALTS MAY CAUSE SEVERE IRRITATION AND DERMATITIS WITH ERYTHEMA, EDEMA AND EXUDATION. THEY ALSO CAN DELAY HEALING OF CUTS AND WOUNDS. THEY MAY BE ABSORBED THROUGH THE SKIN AND PRODUCE SYSTEMIC POISONING WITH SYMPTOMS OF RENAL, HEPATIC AND RESPIRATORY INSUFFICIENCY AS DESCRIBED IN ACUTE INGESTION. SEVERAL CASES OF LETHAL POISONING FROM DERMAL ABSORPTION OF PARAQUAT AND ITS SALTS ARE DOCUMENTED. A LETHAL DOSE IN RABBITS BY DERMAL ABSORPTION WAS 325 MG/KG. **CHRONIC EXPOSURE-** PROLONGED OR REPEATED EXPOSURE MAY CAUSE EFFECTS AS DESCRIBED IN ACUTE EXPOSURE. PROLONGED OR REPEATED EXPOSURE MAY ALSO PRODUCE FISSURING OF THE SKIN OF THE HANDS, AND CRACKING, DISCOLORATION, AND SOMETIMES LOSS OF THE FINGERNAILS. REGENERATION OF THE NAILS WILL OCCUR AFTER CESSATION OF EXPOSURE TO PARAQUAT AND ITS SALTS. PREMALIGNANT SKIN LESIONS OF HYPERPIGMENTED MACULES AND HYPERKERATOSIS WERE OBSERVED AMONG WORKERS INVOLVED IN THE MANUFACTURE OF PARAQUAT. ANALYSIS OF THE DATA SUGGESTED THAT EXPOSURE TO BIPYRIDINE PRECURSORS ALONG WITH SUNLIGHT, RATHER THAN PARAQUAT, WAS RESPONSIBLE.

FIRST AID- REMOVE CONTAMINATED CLOTHING AND SHOES IMMEDIATELY. WASH AFFECTED AREA WITH SOAP OR MILD DETERGENT AND LARGE AMOUNTS OF WATER UNTIL NO EVIDENCE OF CHEMICAL REMAINS (APPROXIMATELY 15-20 MINUTES). GET MEDICAL ATTENTION IMMEDIATELY.

EYE CONTACT: PARAQUAT DICHLORIDE: CORROSIVE. **ACUTE EXPOSURE-** PARAQUAT AND ITS SALTS MAY PRODUCE SEVERE, PROGRESSIVE INFLAMMATION OF THE EYES WHICH MAY PEAK 12 TO 24 HOURS AFTER EXPOSURE. LOSS OF CONJUNCTIVAL EPITHELIUM AND SUPERFICIAL LAYERS OF THE CORNEA MAY OCCUR AND SEVERE CASES MAY RESULT IN PROTRACTED OPACIFICATION OF THE CORNEA. THE ADDITION OF SURFACTANTS TO PARAQUAT SALTS MAY INCREASE THE IRRITATING EFFECTS. 48.4 MG OF PARAQUAT APPLIED TO THE EYES OF RABBITS WAS LETHAL. **CHRONIC EXPOSURE-** PROLONGED OR REPEATED EXPOSURE MAY CAUSE EFFECTS AS DESCRIBED IN ACUTE EXPOSURE.

FIRST AID- WASH EYES IMMEDIATELY WITH LARGE AMOUNTS OF WATER, OCCASIONALLY LIFTING UPPER AND LOWER LIDS, UNTIL NO EVIDENCE OF CHEMICAL REMAINS (AT LEAST 15-20 MINUTES). CONTINUE IRRIGATING WITH NORMAL SALINE UNTIL THE PH HAS RETURNED TO NORMAL (30-60 MINUTES). COVER WITH STERILE BANDAGES. GET MEDICAL ATTENTION IMMEDIATELY.

INGESTION: PARAQUAT DICHLORIDE: CORROSIVE/HIGHLY TOXIC. **ACUTE EXPOSURE-** INGESTION MAY CAUSE INITIAL SYMPTOMS OF BURNING DISCOMFORT OR PAIN IN THE MOUTH, PHARYNX, ESOPHAGUS AND ABDOMEN, HEADACHE, NAUSEA, DIARRHEA WITH BLOODY STOOLS, AND REPEATED VOMITING WITH HEMATEMESIS. SEVERE POISONING MAY RESULT IN PULMONARY OR CEREBRAL HEMORRHAGE OR IN RENAL, HEPATIC OR CARDIAC FAILURE WHICH IS FATAL WITHIN SEVERAL DAYS OF POISONING. AFTER INGESTION OF SMALLER AMOUNTS OR DILUTE SOLUTIONS, INITIAL SYMPTOMS MAY BE FOLLOWED WITHIN 24 HOURS BY SORE THROAT, EXCORIATED LIPS, ULCERS OF THE TONGUE, BUCCAL MUCOSA AND PHARYNX. WITHIN 2 TO 6 DAYS, RENAL FAILURE, INDICATED BY PROTEINURIA AND OLIGURIA, MAY OCCUR WITH POSSIBLE HEPATIC INSUFFICIENCY WITH EFFECTS OF ANOREXIA AND JAUNDICE AND EARLY PULMONARY INVOLVEMENT WITH DYSPNEA, RALES, AND EDEMA. NECROSIS OF THE ADRENAL CORTEX WITH EFFECTS OF FEVER, ABDOMINAL PAIN, LETHARGY, SOMNOLENCE, HYPOVOLEMIC VASCULAR SHOCK AND CYANOSIS FROM HYPOXIA OR METHEMOGLOBINEMIA ARE ALSO POSSIBLE. SURVIVAL AT THIS POINT MAY OCCUR WITH COMPLETE RECOVERY OR WITH A LATENT PERIOD OF 2 WEEKS IN WHICH THERE IS AN APPEARANCE OF RECOVERY WITH IMPROVED KIDNEY FUNCTION. IF THE EFFECTS OF POISONING PROGRESS A RAPID DEVELOPMENT OF PULMONARY FIBROSIS WILL OCCUR WITH THE GRADUAL DETERIORATION OF PULMONARY FUNCTION. THE PULMONARY FUNCTION MAY DETERIORATE TO THE POINT OF CYANOSIS. DEATH MAY RESULT FROM RESPIRATORY FAILURE. SURVIVORS HAVE EXPERIENCED COMPLETE RECOVERY, HOWEVER, PULMONARY FUNCTION TESTS MAY BE ABNORMAL FOR MONTHS. IN FIVE CASES OF POISONING, FATAL APLASTIC ANEMIA WAS REPORTED. A DOSE AS LITTLE AS 14 MG/KG CAN BE FATAL IN HUMANS. **CHRONIC EXPOSURE-** A SIGNIFICANT INCREASE IN EYE LESIONS WAS OBSERVED IN RATS FED 75 AND 150 PPM FOR 110 WEEKS. MORTALITY IN MALE RATS AT 75 PPM EXCEEDED 50%. A SIGNIFICANT INCREASE IN POSTNATAL MORTALITY OF THE OFFSPRING WAS OBSERVED IN A STUDY OF PREGNANT MICE FED PARAQUAT. A SLIGHT INCREASE IN THE INCIDENCE OF RENAL HYDROPIC DEGENERATION OF THE OFFSPRING WAS NOTED IN A THREE GENERATION STUDY OF RATS.

FIRST AID- INTUBATE THE STOMACH, ASPIRATE CONTENTS, THEN LAVAGE WITH AT LEAST TWO LITERS OF A SLURRY OF ADSORBENT IN NORMAL SALINE. THEN, SLOWLY INSTILL SEVERAL HUNDRED ADDITIONAL ML OF ADSORBENT SLURRY, ALLOWING THE STOMACH AND INTESTINE TO ACCOMMODATE THIS VOLUME WITHOUT OVERDISTENSION AND VOMITING. THE IDEAL ADSORBENT IS BENTONITE. IF NOT IMMEDIATELY AVAILABLE, USE ACTIVATED CHARCOAL. AS SOON AS BENTONITE HAS BEEN OBTAINED, ADMINISTER IT AS RAPIDLY AS THE PATIENT WILL TOLERATE IT. IF PATIENT CANNOT SWALLOW BENTONITE, ADMINISTER IT BY STOMACH TUBE AT THE HIGHEST CONCENTRATION THAT WILL FLOW THROUGH THE TUBE. INITIATE SALINE CATHARSIS. GIVE SODIUM SULFATE AND REPEAT IN TWO HOURS IF NO BOWEL MOVEMENT HAS OCCURRED. MAGNESIUM SALTS ARE PROBABLY CONTRAINDICATED, BECAUSE OF THE RISK OF MAGNESIUM RETENTION IN THE PRESENCE OF IMPAIRED RENAL FUNCTION. CONTINUE ADMINISTERING BENTONITE SUSPENSION AND SODIUM SULFATE UNTIL THE GUT HAS BEEN THOROUGHLY FLUSHED. HEMODIALYSIS AND/OR HEMOPERFUSION OVER SPECIALLY COATED CHARCOAL IS AN EFFECTIVE PROCEDURE FOR REMOVING POISONING FROM THE BLOOD. OXYGEN THERAPY MAY ENHANCE THE TOXICITY. (MORGAN, RECOGNITION AND MANAGEMENT OF PESTICIDE POISONINGS, THIRD EDITION). TREATMENT SHOULD BE PERFORMED BY QUALIFIED MEDICAL PERSONNEL. GET MEDICAL ATTENTION IMMEDIATELY.

ANTIDOTE: NO SPECIFIC ANTIDOTE. TREAT SYMPTOMATICALLY AND SUPPORTIVELY.

REACTIVITY

REACTIVITY: STABLE UNDER NORMAL TEMPERATURES AND PRESSURES. MAY DECOMPOSE ON EXPOSURE TO SUNLIGHT OR ULTRAVIOLET LIGHT.

INCOMPATIBILITIES: PARAQUAT DICHLORIDE: ALKALINE SOLUTIONS: HYDROLYZE. ANIONIC SURFACTANTS: INACTIVATE. CLAYS (INERT): INACTIVATE. METALS: CORROSIVE. OXIDIZERS (STRONG): FIRE AND EXPLOSION HAZARD.

DECOMPOSITION: THERMAL DECOMPOSITION PRODUCTS MAY INCLUDE TOXIC OXIDES OF NITROGEN AND CARBON AND TOXIC AND CORROSIVE FUMES OF CHLORIDES.

POLYMERIZATION: HAZARDOUS POLYMERIZATION HAS NOT BEEN REPORTED TO OCCUR UNDER NORMAL TEMPERATURES AND PRESSURES.

STORAGE AND DISPOSAL

OBSERVE ALL FEDERAL, STATE AND LOCAL REGULATIONS WHEN STORING OR DISPOSING OF THIS SUBSTANCE. FOR ASSISTANCE, CONTACT THE DISTRICT DIRECTOR OF THE ENVIRONMENTAL PROTECTION AGENCY.

STORAGE

STORE IN ACCORDANCE WITH 40 CFR 165 RECOMMENDED PROCEDURES FOR THE DISPOSAL AND STORAGE OF PESTICIDES AND PESTICIDE CONTAINERS.
STORE AWAY FROM INCOMPATIBLE SUBSTANCES.
THRESHOLD PLANNING QUANTITY (TPQ): THE SUPERFUND AMENDMENTS AND REAUTHORIZATION ACT (SARA) SECTION 302 REQUIRES THAT EACH FACILITY WHERE ANY EXTREMELY HAZARDOUS SUBSTANCE IS PRESENT IN A QUANTITY EQUAL TO OR GREATER THAN THE TPQ ESTABLISHED FOR THAT SUBSTANCE NOTIFY THE STATE EMERGENCY RESPONSE COMMISSION FOR THE STATE IN WHICH IT IS LOCATED. SECTION 303 OF SARA REQUIRES THESE FACILITIES TO PARTICIPATE IN LOCAL EMERGENCY RESPONSE PLANNING (40 CFR 355.30).

DISPOSAL

DISPOSAL MUST BE IN ACCORDANCE WITH 40 CFR 165 RECOMMENDED PROCEDURES FOR THE DISPOSAL AND STORAGE OF PESTICIDES AND PESTICIDE CONTAINERS.

CONDITIONS TO AVOID

MAY BURN BUT DOES NOT IGNITE READILY. AVOID CONTACT WITH STRONG OXIDIZERS, EXCESSIVE HEAT, SPARKS, OR OPEN FLAME.

SPILL AND LEAK PROCEDURES

OCCUPATIONAL SPILL: SWEEP UP AND PLACE IN SUITABLE CLEAN, DRY CONTAINERS FOR RECLAMATION OR LATER DISPOSAL. DO NOT FLUSH SPILLED MATERIAL INTO SEWER. KEEP UNNECESSARY PEOPLE AWAY.
REPORTABLE QUANTITY (RQ): 1 POUND THE SUPERFUND AMENDMENTS AND REAUTHORIZATION ACT (SARA) SECTION 304 REQUIRES THAT A RELEASE EQUAL TO OR GREATER THAN THE REPORTABLE QUANTITY FOR THIS SUBSTANCE BE IMMEDIATELY REPORTED TO THE LOCAL EMERGENCY PLANNING COMMITTEE AND THE STATE EMERGENCY RESPONSE COMMISSION (40 CFR 355.40). IF THE RELEASE OF THIS SUBSTANCE IS REPORTABLE UNDER CERCLA SECTION 103, THE NATIONAL RESPONSE CENTER MUST BE NOTIFIED IMMEDIATELY AT (800) 424-8802 OR (202) 426-2675 IN THE METROPOLITAN WASHINGTON, D.C. AREA (40 CFR 302.6).

PROTECTIVE EQUIPMENT

VENTILATION: PROCESS ENCLOSURE RECOMMENDED TO MEET PUBLISHED EXPOSURE LIMITS.

RESPIRATOR: THE FOLLOWING RESPIRATORS AND MAXIMUM USE CONCENTRATIONS ARE RECOMMENDATIONS BY THE U.S. DEPARTMENT OF HEALTH AND HUMAN SERVICES, NIOSH POCKET GUIDE TO CHEMICAL HAZARDS; NIOSH CRITERIA DOCUMENTS OR BY THE U.S. DEPARTMENT OF LABOR, 29 CFR 1910 SUBPART Z.
THE SPECIFIC RESPIRATOR SELECTED MUST BE BASED ON CONTAMINATION LEVELS FOUND IN THE WORK PLACE, MUST NOT EXCEED THE WORKING LIMITS OF THE RESPIRATOR AND BE JOINTLY APPROVED BY THE NATIONAL INSTITUTE FOR OCCUPATIONAL SAFETY AND HEALTH AND THE MINE SAFETY AND HEALTH ADMINISTRATION (NIOSH-MSHA).
PARAQUAT COMPOUNDS: 1 MG/M3- ANY CHEMICAL CARTRIDGE RESPIRATOR WITH ORGANIC VAPOR CARTRIDGE(S) IN COMBINATION WITH A DUST, MIST, AND FUME FILTER. ANY SUPPLIED-AIR RESPIRATOR. ANY SELF-CONTAINED BREATHING APPARATUS.
1.5 MG/M3- ANY CHEMICAL CARTRIDGE RESPIRATOR WITH A FULL FACEPIECE AND ORGANIC VAPOR CARTRIDGE(S) IN COMBINATION WITH A DUST, MIST, AND FUME FILTER. ANY SUPPLIED-AIR RESPIRATOR OPERATED IN A CONTINUOUS FLOW MODE. ANY SELF-CONTAINED BREATHING APPARATUS WITH A FULL FACEPIECE. ANY SUPPLIED-AIR RESPIRATOR WITH A FULL FACEPIECE. ANY POWERED AIR-PURIFYING RESPIRATOR WITH ORGANIC VAPOR CARTRIDGE(S) IN COMBINATION WITH A DUST, MIST, AND FUME FILTER.
ESCAPE- ANY AIR-PURIFYING FULL FACEPIECE RESPIRATOR (GAS MASK) WITH A CHIN-STYLE OR FRONT- OR BACK-MOUNTED ORGANIC VAPOR CANISTER HAVING A HIGH-EFFICIENCY PARTICULATE FILTER. ANY APPROPRIATE ESCAPE-TYPE SELF-CONTAINED BREATHING APPARATUS.
FOR FIREFIGHTING AND OTHER IMMEDIATELY DANGEROUS TO LIFE OR HEALTH CONDITIONS:
SELF-CONTAINED BREATHING APPARATUS WITH FULL FACEPIECE OPERATED IN PRESSURE-DEMAND OR OTHER POSITIVE PRESSURE MODE.
SUPPLIED-AIR RESPIRATOR WITH FULL FACEPIECE AND OPERATED IN PRESSURE-DEMAND OR OTHER POSITIVE PRESSURE MODE IN COMBINATION WITH AN AUXILIARY SELF-CONTAINED BREATHING APPARATUS OPERATED IN PRESSURE-DEMAND OR OTHER POSITIVE PRESSURE MODE.

CLOTHING: EMPLOYEE MUST WEAR APPROPRIATE PROTECTIVE (IMPERVIOUS) CLOTHING AND EQUIPMENT TO PREVENT ANY POSSIBILITY OF SKIN CONTACT WITH THIS SUBSTANCE.

GLOVES: EMPLOYEE MUST WEAR APPROPRIATE PROTECTIVE GLOVES TO PREVENT CONTACT WITH THIS SUBSTANCE.

EYE PROTECTION: EMPLOYEE MUST WEAR SPLASH-PROOF OR DUST-RESISTANT SAFETY GOGGLES AND A FACESHIELD TO PREVENT CONTACT WITH THIS SUBSTANCE.

EMERGENCY WASH FACILITIES: WHERE THERE IS ANY POSSIBILITY THAT AN EMPLOYEE'S EYES AND/OR SKIN MAY BE EXPOSED TO THIS SUBSTANCE, THE EMPLOYER SHOULD PROVIDE AN EYE WASH FOUNTAIN AND QUICK DRENCH SHOWER WITHIN THE IMMEDIATE WORK AREA FOR EMERGENCY USE.

AUTHORIZED BY- OCCUPATIONAL HEALTH SERVICES, INC.
CREATION DATE: 10/04/89 ***REVISION DATE:*** 05/31/90

MATERIAL SAFETY DATA SHEET

OCCUPATIONAL HEALTH SERVICES, INC.
AGRICULTURE AND PESTICIDE DIVISION
450 SEVENTH AVENUE, SUITE 2407
NEW YORK, NEW YORK 10123
1-800-445-MSDS OR (212) 967-1100

EMERGENCY CONTACT:
JOHN S. BRANSFORD, JR. (615) 292-1180

SUBSTANCE IDENTIFICATION

CAS-NUMBER 56-38-2
SUBSTANCE: PARATHION

TRADE NAMES/SYNONYMS: PHOSPHOROTHIOIC ACID, O,O-DIETHYL O-(4-NITROPHENYL)ESTER; PHOSPHOROTHIOIC ACID, O,O-DIETHYL O-(P-NITROPHENYL)ESTER; O,O-DIETHYL O-(P-NITROPHENYL)PHOSPHOROTHIOATE; DIETHYL-P-NITROPHENYL MONOTHIOPHOSPHATE; O,O-DIETHYL O-4-NITROPHENYL PHOSPHOROTHIOATE; O,O-DIETHYL O-(4-NITROPHENYL) PHOSPHOROTHIOATE; DIETHYL P-NITROPHENYL PHOSPHOROTHIONATE; O,O-DIETHYL O-(P-NITROPHENYL) THIONOPHOSPHATE; DIETHYL PARATHION; ETHYL PARATHION; PARATHION-ETHYL; ALKRON; ALLERON; FOLIDOL; PARAPHOS; THIOPHOS; ENT 15,108; STCC 4921469; RCRA P089; C10H14NO5PS; PST18040

CHEMICAL FAMILY: ORGANOPHOSPHATE

MOLECULAR FORMULA: C10-H14-N-O5-P-S

MOLECULAR WEIGHT: 291.28

CERCLA RATINGS (SCALE 0-3): HEALTH=3 FIRE=1 REACTIVITY=2 PERSISTENCE=2

NFPA RATINGS (SCALE 0-4): HEALTH=4 FIRE=1 REACTIVITY=2

COMPONENTS AND CONTAMINANTS

COMPONENT: PARATHION ***PERCENT:*** 100.0
CAS# 56-38-2

OTHER CONTAMINANTS: NONE

EXPOSURE LIMITS: PARATHION: 0.1 MG/M3 OSHA TWA (SKIN) 0.1 MG/M3 ACGIH TWA (SKIN) 0.05 MG/M3 NIOSH RECOMMENDED 10 HOUR TWA
100 POUNDS SARA SECTION 302 THRESHOLD PLANNING QUANTITY 1 POUND SARA SECTION 304 REPORTABLE QUANTITY 10 POUNDS CERCLA SECTION 103 REPORTABLE QUANTITY SUBJECT TO SARA SECTION 313 ANNUAL TOXIC CHEMICAL RELEASE REPORTING

PHYSICAL DATA

DESCRIPTION: PALE YELLOW LIQUID WITH FAINT ODOR OF GARLIC.

BOILING POINT: 707 F (375 C) ***MELTING POINT:*** 43 F (6 C)

SPECIFIC GRAVITY: 1.2704 ***VISCOSITY:*** 15.30 CPS @ 25 C

VAPOR PRESSURE: 0.00004 MMHG @ 20 C ***SOLUBILITY IN WATER:*** 24 PPM

ODOR THRESHOLD: 0.04 PPM

SOLVENT SOLUBILITY: SOLUBLE IN ALCOHOL, ETHERS, ESTERS, KETONES, ACIDS, CHLORINATED HYDROCARBONS, AROMATIC HYDROCARBONS, ANIMAL OR VEGETABLE OIL; INSOLUBLE IN PETROLEUM ETHER, KEROSENE, OR SPRAY OIL

FIRE AND EXPLOSION DATA

FIRE AND EXPLOSION HAZARD: SLIGHT FIRE HAZARD WHEN EXPOSED TO HEAT OR FLAME.

FLASH POINT: >200 F >93 C ***FLAMMABILITY CLASS(OSHA):*** IIIB

FIREFIGHTING MEDIA: DRY CHEMICAL, CARBON DIOXIDE, HALON, WATER SPRAY OR STANDARD FOAM (1987 EMERGENCY RESPONSE GUIDEBOOK, DOT P 5800.4).
FOR LARGER FIRES, USE WATER SPRAY, FOG OR STANDARD FOAM (1987 EMERGENCY RESPONSE GUIDEBOOK, DOT P 5800.4).

FIREFIGHTING: MOVE CONTAINER FROM FIRE AREA IF POSSIBLE. DIKE FIRE CONTROL WATER FOR LATER DISPOSAL; DO NOT SCATTER THE MATERIAL. COOL FIRE-EXPOSED CONTAINERS WITH WATER FROM SIDE UNTIL WELL AFTER FIRE IS OUT. STAY AWAY FROM STORAGE TANK ENDS. WITHDRAW IMMEDIATELY IN CASE OF RISING SOUND FROM VENTING SAFETY DEVICE OR ANY DISCOLORATION OF STORAGE TANK DUE TO FIRE (1987 EMERGENCY RESPONSE GUIDEBOOK, DOT P 5800.4, GUIDE PAGE 28).

EXTINGUISH ONLY IF FLOW CAN BE STOPPED. USE FLOODING AMOUNTS OF WATER AS A FOG; SOLID STREAMS MAY BE INEFFECTIVE. COOL CONTAINERS WITH FLOODING AMOUNTS OF WATER FROM AS FAR A DISTANCE AS POSSIBLE. AVOID BREATHING POISONOUS VAPORS, KEEP UPWIND.

TRANSPORTATION DATA

DEPARTMENT OF TRANSPORTATION HAZARD CLASSIFICATION 49 CFR 172.101: POISON B

DEPARTMENT OF TRANSPORTATION LABELING REQUIREMENTS 49 CFR 172.101 AND SUBPART E: POISON

DEPARTMENT OF TRANSPORTATION PACKAGING REQUIREMENTS: 49 CFR 173.358 EXCEPTIONS: NONE

TOXICITY

PARATHION: TOXICITY DATA: 84 MG/M3/4 HOURS INHALATION-RAT LC50;15 MG/M3 INHALATION-MOUSE LCLO; 14 MG/M3/2 HOURS INHALATION-GUINEA PIG LCLO; 50 MG/M3/2 HOURS INHALATION-RABBIT LCLO; 7143 UG/KG SKIN-HUMAN LDLO; 15 MG/KG SKIN-RABBIT LD50; 6800 UG/KG SKIN-RAT LD50; 19 MG/KG SKIN-MOUSE LD50; 45 MG/KG SKIN-GUINEA PIG LD50; 171 UG/KG ORAL-HUMAN LDLO; 3 MG/KG ORAL-HUMAN LD50; 429 UG/KG/4 DAYS INTERMITTENT ORAL-MAN TDLO; 5670 UG/KG ORAL-WOMAN TDLO; 2 MG/KG ORAL-RAT LD50; 5 MG/KG ORAL-MOUSE LD50; 10 MG/KG ORAL-RABBIT LD50; 8 MG/KG ORAL-GUINEA PIG LD50; 3 MG/KG ORAL-DOG LD50; 930 UG/KG ORAL-CAT LD50; 49 MG/KG ORAL-MAMMAL LD50; 5 MG/KG ORAL-HORSE LD50; 100 MG/KG ORAL-DOMESTIC ANIMAL LDLO; 714 UG/KG INTRATRACHEAL-HUMAN LDLO; 10 MG/KG SUBCUTANEOUS-MOUSE LD50; 3800 UG/KG INTRAVENOUS-RAT LD50; 13 MG/KG INTRAVENOUS-MOUSE LD50; 12 MG/KG INTRAVENOUS-DOG LD50; 3 MG/KG INTRAVENOUS-CAT LD50; 2 MG/KG INTRAPERITONEAL-RAT LD50; 3 MG/KG INTRAPERITONEAL-MOUSE LD50; 12 MG/KG INTRAPERITONEAL-GUINEA PIG LD50; 12 MG/KG INTRAPERITONEAL-DOG LD50; 3 MG/KG INTRAPERITONEAL-CAT LD50; 6 MG/KG INTRAMUSCULAR-RAT LD50; 7200 UG/KG INTRAMUSCULAR-MOUSE LD50; 20 MG/KG INTRAMUSCULAR-DOMESTIC ANIMAL LDLO; 1471 UG/KG UNREPORTED-MAN LDLO; MUTAGENIC DATA (RTECS); REPRODUCTIVE EFFECTS DATA (RTECS); TUMORIGENIC DATA DATA (RTECS). CARCINOGEN STATUS: ANIMAL INADEQUATE EVIDENCE (IARC GROUP-3). ACUTE TOXICITY LEVEL: HIGHLY TOXIC BY INHALATION, DERMAL ABSORPTION, AND INGESTION. TARGET EFFECTS: CHOLINESTERASE INHIBITOR. POISONING MAY AFFECT THE NERVOUS SYSTEM.* AT INCREASED RISK FROM EXPOSURE: PERSONS WITH CARDIOVASCULAR, HEPATIC, OR RENAL DISEASES, GLAUCOMA, OR CENTRAL NERVOUS SYSTEMS ABNORMALITIES. ADDITIONAL DATA: MAY CROSS THE PLACENTA. HIGH ENVIRONMENTAL TEMPERATURES OR EXPOSURE OF THE CHEMICAL TO VISIBLE OR ULTRAVIOLET LIGHT MAY ENHANCE THE TOXICITY. INTERACTIONS WITH MEDICATIONS MAY OCCUR.*

* MAY BE BASED ON GENERAL INFORMATION ON ORGANOPHOSPHATES.

HEALTH EFFECTS AND FIRST AID

INHALATION: PARATHION: HIGHLY TOXIC. 20 MG/M3 IMMEDIATELY DANGEROUS TO LIFE OR HEALTH. SEE INFORMATION ON ORGANOPHOSPHATES.
ORGANOPHOSPHATES: CHOLINESTERASE INHIBITOR. **ACUTE EXPOSURE-** WHEN INHALED, THE FIRST EFFECTS OF CHOLINESTERASE INHIBITORS ARE USUALLY RESPIRATORY AND MAY INCLUDE NASAL HYPEREMIA AND WATERY DISCHARGE, COUGH, CHEST DISCOMFORT, DYSPNEA, AND WHEEZING DUE TO INCREASED BRONCHIAL SECRETIONS AND BRONCHOCONSTRICTION. IF SUFFICIENT AMOUNTS ARE ABSORBED, OTHER SYSTEMIC EFFECTS MAY BEGIN WITHIN A FEW MINUTES OR BE DELAYED FOR UP TO 12 HOURS. SYMPTOMS MAY INCLUDE PALLOR, NAUSEA, VOMITING, DIARRHEA, ABDOMINAL CRAMPS, HEADACHE, DIZZINESS, OCULAR PAIN, BLURRED VISION, MIOSIS OR IN SOME CASES, ESPECIALLY INITIALLY, MYDRIASIS, LACRIMATION, SALIVATION, SWEATING, AND CONFUSION. OTHER REPORTED CENTRAL NERVOUS SYSTEM OR NEUROMUSCULAR EFFECTS MAY INCLUDE ATAXIA, SLURRED SPEECH, AREFLEXIA, WEAKNESS, FATIGUE, FASCICULATIONS, TWITCHING, TREMORS POSSIBLY OF THE TONGUE AND EYELIDS, AND EVENTUALLY PARALYSIS OF THE EXTREMITIES AND POSSIBLY OF THE RESPIRATORY MUSCLES. IN SEVERE CASES THERE MAY ALSO BE INVOLUNTARY DEFECATION AND URINATION, CYANOSIS, PSYCHOSIS, HYPERGLYCEMIA, ACUTE PANCREATITIS, CARDIAC IRREGULARITIES, PULMONARY EDEMA, UNCONSCIOUSNESS, CONVULSIONS, AND COMA. DEATH IS PRIMARILY DUE TO RESPIRATORY FAILURE, ALTHOUGH CARDIOVASCULAR EFFECTS INCLUDING CARDIAC ARREST MAY ALSO BE IMPLICATED. LONG TERM SEQUELAE ARE RARE BUT MAY INCLUDE NEUROPSYCHIATRIC DISORDERS AND MYOPATHY WITH MUSCLE TENDERNESS. SOME ORGANOPHOSPHATES MAY CAUSE A DELAYED NEUROPATHY BEGINNING 1-4 WEEKS AFTER AN ACUTE EXPOSURE WHICH MAY OR MAY NOT HAVE CAUSED ACUTE CHOLINERGIC EFFECTS. NUMBNESS, TINGLING, WEAKNESS AND CRAMPING BEGINNING SYMMETRICALLY IN THE LOWER LIMBS MAY PROGRESS TO ATAXIA AND PARALYSIS. IN SEVERE CASES, UPPER LIMB INVOLVEMENT IS POSSIBLE AND FLACCID PARALYSIS MAY PROGRESS TO SPASTIC PARALYSIS WITH EXAGGERATED REFLEXES. IMPROVEMENT MAY OCCUR OVER MONTHS TO YEARS, BUT SOME RESIDUAL IMPAIRMENT USUALLY REMAINS. **CHRONIC EXPOSURE-** REPEATED OR PROLONGED EXPOSURE MAY RESULT IN THE EFFECTS OF ACUTE EXPOSURE INCLUDING THE DELAYED NEUROPATHY. OTHER EFFECTS REPORTED IN WORKERS REPEATEDLY EXPOSED INCLUDE IMPAIRED MEMORY AND CONCENTRATION, ACUTE PSYCHOSIS, SEVERE DEPRESSIONS, IRRITABILTY, CONFUSION, APATHY, EMOTIONAL LABILITY, SOCIAL WITHDRAWAL, CONFUSION, HEADACHE, SPEECH DIFFICULTIES, DELAYED REACTION TIMES, SPATIAL DISORIENTATION, NIGHTMARES, SLEEPWALKING, AND DROWSINESS OR INSOMNIA. AN INFLUENZA-LIKE CONDITION WITH HEADACHE, NAUSEA, WEAKNESS, ANOREXIA AND MALAISE HAS ALSO BEEN REPORTED.

FIRST AID- REMOVE FROM EXPOSURE AREA TO FRESH AIR IMMEDIATELY. IF BREATHING HAS STOPPED, GIVE ARTIFICIAL RESPIRATION. MAINTAIN AIRWAY AND BLOOD PRESSURE AND ADMINISTER OXYGEN IF AVAILABLE. KEEP AFFECTED PERSON WARM AND AT REST. TREAT SYMPTOMATICALLY AND SUPPORTIVELY. ADMINISTRATION OF OXYGEN SHOULD BE PERFORMED BY QUALIFIED PERSONNEL. GET MEDICAL ATTENTION IMMEDIATELY.

SKIN CONTACT: PARATHION: HIGHLY TOXIC. SEE INFORMATION ON ORGANOPHOSPHATES.
ORGANOPHOSPHATES: CHOLINESTERASE INHIBITOR. **ACUTE EXPOSURE-** LOCALIZED SWEATING AND FASCICULATIONS MAY OCCUR AT THE SITE OF CONTACT. IF SUFFICIENT AMOUNTS ARE ABSORBED, OTHER EFFECTS OF CHOLINESTERASE INHIBITION AS DESCRIBED IN ACUTE INHALATION MAY OCCUR. SYMPTOMS MAY BE DELAYED 2-3 HOURS, BUT USUALLY NO MORE THAN 12 HOURS. THE RATE OF ABSORPTION IS INCREASED BY THE PRESENCE OF DERMATITIS OR HIGH AMBIENT TEMPERATURES. DELAYED NEUROPATHY IS ALSO POSSIBLE. **CHRONIC EXPOSURE-** REPEATED OR PROLONGED EXPOSURE MAY CAUSE EFFECTS AS DESCRIBED IN ACUTE EXPOSURE. SOME ORGANOPHOSPHATES MAY CAUSE SENSITIZATION.

FIRST AID- REMOVE CONTAMINATED CLOTHING IMMEDIATELY. WASH CONTAMINATED AREAS WITH SOAP AND WATER FOLLOWED BY ALCOHOL (ARENA, POISONING, 4TH ED.). EMERGENCY PERSONNEL SHOULD WEAR GLOVES AND AVOID CONTAMINATION. TREAT RESPIRATORY DIFFICULTY WITH ARTIFICIAL RESPIRATION. GET MEDICAL ATTENTION IMMEDIATELY.

EYE CONTACT: PARATHION: SEE INFORMATION ON ORGANOPHOSPHATES.
ORGANOPHOSPHATES: CHOLINESTERASE INHIBITOR. **ACUTE EXPOSURE-** DIRECT CONTACT MAY CAUSE PAIN, HYPEREMIA, LACRIMATION, TWITCHING OF THE EYELIDS, MIOSIS, AND CILIARY MUSCLE SPASM WITH LOSS OF ACCOMODATION, BLURRED OR DIMMED VISION AND BROWACHE. SOMETIMES MYDRIASIS MAY OCCUR INSTEAD OF MIOSIS. WITH SUFFICIENT EXPOSURE, OTHER SYMPTOMS OF CHOLINESTERASE INHIBITION AS DESCRIBED IN ACUTE INHALATION MAY OCCUR. **CHRONIC EXPOSURE-** REPEATED OR PROLONGED EXPOSURE MAY CAUSE EFFECTS AS DESCRIBED IN ACUTE EXPOSURE. SOME COMPOUNDS HAVE CAUSED TOXIC EFFECTS ON THE CRYSTALLINE LENS, CONJUNCTIVAL THICKENING AND OBSTRUCTION OF THE NASOLACRIMAL CANALS WHEN USED AS MIOTIC EYEDROPS.

FIRST AID- IRRIGATE EYES WITH WATER OR SALINE SOLUTION. IF SYMPTOMS OF POISONING OCCUR, TREAT RESPIRATORY DIFFICULTY WITH ARTIFICIAL RESPIRATION AND OXYGEN. OBSERVE PATIENT FOR AT LEAST 24-36 HOURS (GOSSELIN, CLINICAL TOXICOLOGY OF COMMERCIAL PRODUCTS, 5TH ED.). GET MEDICAL ATTENTION IMMEDIATELY. OXYGEN SHOULD BE ADMINISTERED BY QUALIFIED MEDICAL PERSONNEL.

INGESTION: PARATHION: HIGHLY TOXIC. THE MINIMUM LETHAL DOSE FOR HUMANS HAS BEEN ESTIMATED TO RANGE FROM LESS THAN 10 MG UP TO 120 MG. CHRONIC ADMINISTRATION TO PREGNANT RATS RESULTED IN A REDUCTION IN PSEUDOCHOLINESTERASE AND PLASMA RENIN ACTIVITIES AND ALTERED ELECTROCARDIOGRAPHIC PATTERNS IN THE 24-DAY-OLD PROGENY. REPEATED FEEDINGS IN FEMALE RATS PRIOR TO MATING RESULTED IN ADVERSE EFFECTS ON THE REPRODUCTIVE SYSTEM. SEE INFORMATION ON ORGANOPHOSPHATES.
ORGANOPHOSPHATES: CHOLINESTERASE INHIBITOR. **ACUTE EXPOSURE-** WHEN INGESTED, THE FIRST EFFECTS MAY BE NAUSEA, VOMITING, ANOREXIA, ABDOMINAL CRAMPS AND DIARRHEA. GASTROINTESTINAL ABSORPTION MAY CAUSE SYMPTOMS OF CHOLINESTERASE INHIBITION AS DESCRIBED IN ACUTE INHALATION. SYMPTOMS MAY BEGIN WITHIN MINUTES OR BE DELAYED FOR HOURS. DELAYED EFFECTS INCLUDING NEUROPATHY MAY ALSO OCCUR. **CHRONIC EXPOSURE-** REPEATED INGESTION MAY CAUSE EFFECTS AS DESCRIBED IN ACUTE EXPOSURE.

FIRST AID- IF PERSON IS ALERT AND RESPIRATION IS NOT DEPRESSED, GIVE SYRUP OF IPECAC FOLLOWED BY WATER (IF VOMITING OCCURS, KEEP HEAD BELOW HIPS TO PREVENT ASPIRATION). IF CONSCIOUSNESS LEVEL DECLINES OR VOMITING HAS NOT OCCURRED IN 15 MINUTES EMPTY STOMACH BY GASTRIC LAVAGE WITH THE AID OF CUFFED ENDOTRACHEAL TUBE USING ISOTONIC SALINE OR 5% SODIUM BICARBONATE FOLLOW WITH ACTIVATED CHARCOAL. ESTABLISH AND MAINTAIN AIRWAY. TREAT RESPIRATORY DIFFICULTY WITH ARTIFICIAL RESPIRATION AND

OXYGEN. DO NOT GIVE MORPHINE, AMINOPHYLLINE, PHENOTHIAZINES, RESERPINE, FUROSEMIDE, OR ETHACRYNIC ACID (MORGAN, RECOGNITION AND MANAGEMENT OF PESTICIDE POISONINGS, 3RD ED.). TREAT SYMPTOMATICALLY AND SUPPORTIVELY. ADMINISTRATION OF OXYGEN AND LAVAGE MUST BE PERFORMED BY QUALIFIED MEDICAL PERSONNEL. GET MEDICAL ATTENTION IMMEDIATELY.

ANTIDOTE: THE FOLLOWING ANTIDOTE(S) HAVE BEEN RECOMMENDED. HOWEVER, THE DECISION AS TO WHETHER THE SEVERITY OF POISONING REQUIRES ADMINISTRATION OF ANY ANTIDOTE AND ACTUAL DOSE REQUIRED SHOULD BE MADE BY QUALIFIED MEDICAL PERSONNEL.

FOR CHOLINESTERASE INHIBITORS: ESTABLISH CLEAR AIRWAY AND TISSUE OXYGENATION BY ASPIRATION OF SECRETIONS, AND IF NECESSARY, BY ASSISTED PULMONARY VENTILATION WITH OXYGEN. IMPROVE TISSUE OXYGENATION AS MUCH AS POSSIBLE BEFORE ADMINISTERING ATROPINE TO MINIMIZE THE RISK OF VENTRICULAR FIBRILLATION. ADMINISTER ATROPINE SULFATE INTRAVENOUSLY, OR INTRAMUSCULARLY IF IV INJECTION IS NOT POSSIBLE. IN MODERATELY SEVERE POISONING ADMINISTER ATROPINE SULFATE, 0.4-2.0 MG REPEATED EVERY 15 MINUTES UNTIL ATROPINIZATION IS ACHIEVED (TACHYCARDIA, FLUSHING, DRY MOUTH, MYDRIASIS). MAINTAIN ATROPINIZATION BY REPEATED DOSES FOR 2-12 HOURS, OR LONGER, DEPENDING ON THE SEVERITY OF POISONING. THE APPEARANCE OF RALES IN THE LUNG BASES, MIOSIS, SALIVATION, NAUSEA, BRADYCARDIA, ARE ALL INDICATIONS OF INADEQUATE ATROPINIZATION.

SEVERELY POISONED INDIVIDUALS MAY EXHIBIT REMARKABLE TOLERANCE TO ATROPINE; TWO OR MORE TIMES THE DOSAGES SUGGESTED ABOVE MAY BE NEEDED. PERSONS NOT POISONED OR ONLY SLIGHTLY POISONED, HOWEVER, MAY DEVELOP SIGNS OF ATROPINE TOXICITY FROM SUCH LARGE DOSAGES: FEVER, MUSCLE FIBRILLATIONS, AND DELIRIUM ARE THE MAIN SIGNS OF ATROPINE TOXICITY. IF THESE SIGNS APPEAR WHILE THE PATIENT IS FULLY ATROPINIZED, ATROPINE ADMINISTRATION SHOULD BE DISCONTINUED, AT LEAST TEMPORARILY. OBSERVE TREATED PATIENTS CLOSELY AT LEAST 24 HOURS TO INSURE THAT SYMPTOMS (POSSIBLY PULMONARY EDEMA) DO NOT RECUR AS ATROPINIZATION WEARS OFF. IN VERY SEVERE POISONINGS, METABOLIC DISPOSITION OF TOXICANT MAY REQUIRE SEVERAL HOURS OR DAYS DURING WHICH ATROPINIZATION MUST BE MAINTAINED. MARKEDLY LOWER LEVELS OF URINARY METABOLITES INDICATE THAT ATROPINE DOSAGE CAN BE TAPERED OFF. AS DOSAGE IS REDUCED, CHECK THE LUNG BASES FREQUENTLY FOR RALES. IF RALES ARE HEARD OR OTHER SYMPTOMS RETURN, RE-ESTABLISH ATROPINIZATION PROMPTLY (MORGAN, RECOGNITION AND MANAGEMENT OF PESTICIDE POISONINGS, 3RD ED.). ADMINISTRATION OF ANTIDOTE MUST BE PERFORMED BY QUALIFIED MEDICAL PERSONNEL.

IN CASES OF SEVERE POISONING BY ORGANOPHOSPHATE PESTICIDES IN WHICH RESPIRATORY DEPRESSION, MUSCLE WEAKNESS AND TWITCHINGS ARE SEVERE, GIVE PRALIDOXIME (PROTOPAM-AYERST, 2-PAM), 1.0 GRAM INTRAVENOUSLY AT NO MORE THAN 0.5 GRAM PER MINUTE. DOSAGE OF PRALIDOXIME MAY BE REPEATED IN 1-2 HOURS, THEN AT 10-12 HOUR INTERVALS IF NEEDED. IN VERY SEVERE POISONINGS, DOSAGE RATES MAY BE DOUBLED. TREATMENT WITH PRALIDOXIME WILL BE MOST EFFECTIVE IF GIVEN WITHIN THIRTY-SIX HOURS AFTER POISONING (MORGAN, RECOGNITION AND MANAGEMENT OF PESTICIDE POISONINGS, 3RD ED.). ANTIDOTE SHOULD BE ADMINISTERED BY QUALIFIED MEDICAL PERSONNEL.

REACTIVITY

REACTIVITY: DECOMPOSES AT ELEVATED TEMPERATURES AND MAY DEVELOP SUFFICIENT PRESSURE TO CAUSE THE CONTAINER TO RUPTURE VIOLENTLY.

INCOMPATIBILITIES: PARATHION: OXIDIZERS (STRONG): FIRE AND EXPLOSION HAZARD. PLASTICS, RUBBER AND COATINGS: MAY BE ATTACKED.

DECOMPOSITION: THERMAL DECOMPOSITION MAY RELEASE TOXIC OXIDES OF NITROGEN, PHOSPHORUS, SULFUR AND CARBON.

POLYMERIZATION: HAZARDOUS POLYMERIZATION HAS NOT BEEN REPORTED TO OCCUR UNDER NORMAL TEMPERATURES AND PRESSURES.

STORAGE AND DISPOSAL

OBSERVE ALL FEDERAL, STATE AND LOCAL REGULATIONS WHEN STORING OR DISPOSING OF THIS SUBSTANCE. FOR ASSISTANCE, CONTACT THE DISTRICT DIRECTOR OF THE ENVIRONMENTAL PROTECTION AGENCY.

****STORAGE****

STORE IN ACCORDANCE WITH 40 CFR 165 RECOMMENDED PROCEDURES FOR THE DISPOSAL AND STORAGE OF PESTICIDES AND PESTICIDE CONTAINERS.

PROTECT AGAINST PHYSICAL DAMAGE. STORE IN AREAS WHERE ANY SPILLAGE FROM CONTAINERS WILL NOT ENDANGER WORKERS OR CONTAMINATE OTHER MATERIALS (NFPA 49, HAZARDOUS CHEMICALS DATA, 1975).

THRESHOLD PLANNING QUANTITY (TPQ): THE SUPERFUND AMENDMENTS AND REAUTHORIZATION ACT (SARA) SECTION 302 REQUIRES THAT EACH FACILITY WHERE ANY EXTREMELY HAZARDOUS SUBSTANCE IS PRESENT IN A QUANTITY EQUAL TO OR GREATER THAN THE TPQ ESTABLISHED FOR THAT SUBSTANCE NOTIFY THE STATE EMERGENCY RESPONSE COMMISSION FOR THE STATE IN WHICH IT IS LOCATED. SECTION 303 OF SARA REQUIRES THESE FACILITIES TO PARTICIPATE IN LOCAL EMERGENCY RESPONSE PLANNING (40 CFR 355.30).

STORE AWAY FROM INCOMPATIBLE SUBSTANCES.

****DISPOSAL****

DISPOSAL MUST BE IN ACCORDANCE WITH 40 CFR 165 RECOMMENDED PROCEDURES FOR THE DISPOSAL AND STORAGE OF PESTICIDES AND PESTICIDE CONTAINERS.

DISPOSAL MUST BE IN ACCORDANCE WITH STANDARDS APPLICABLE TO GENERATORS OF HAZARDOUS WASTE, 40CFR 262. EPA HAZARDOUS WASTE NUMBER P089.

CONDITIONS TO AVOID

AVOID CONTACT WITH HEAT, SPARKS, FLAMES OR OTHER IGNITION SOURCES. VAPORS MAY BE EXPLOSIVE. MATERIAL IS POISONOUS; AVOID INHALATION OF VAPORS OR CONTACT WITH SKIN. DO NOT ALLOW MATERIAL TO CONTAMINATE WATER SOURCES.

SPILL AND LEAK PROCEDURES

SOIL SPILL: DIG HOLDING AREA SUCH AS LAGOON, POND OR PIT FOR CONTAINMENT. DIKE FLOW OF SPILLED MATERIAL USING SOIL OR SANDBAGS OR FOAMED BARRIERS SUCH AS POLYURETHANE OR CONCRETE.

USE CEMENT POWDER OR FLY ASH TO ABSORB LIQUID MASS.

AIR SPILL: APPLY WATER SPRAY TO KNOCK DOWN VAPORS.

WATER SPILL: TRAP SPILLED MATERIAL AT BOTTOM IN DEEP WATER POCKETS, EXCAVATED HOLDING AREAS OR WITHIN SAND BAG BARRIERS.

USE ACTIVATED CARBON TO ABSORB SPILLED SUBSTANCE THAT IS DISSOLVED.

USE SUCTION HOSES TO REMOVE TRAPPED SPILL MATERIAL.

USE MECHANICAL DREDGES OR LIFTS TO EXTRACT IMMOBILIZED MASSES OF POLLUTION AND PRECIPITATES.

OCCUPATIONAL SPILL: SHUT OFF IGNITION SOURCES. DO NOT TOUCH SPILLED MATERIAL. STOP LEAK IF YOU CAN DO IT WITHOUT RISK. USE WATER SPRAY TO REDUCE VAPORS. FOR SMALL SPILLS, TAKE UP WITH SAND OR OTHER ABSORBENT MATERIAL AND PLACE INTO CONTAINERS FOR LATER DISPOSAL. FOR LARGER SPILLS, DIKE FAR AHEAD OF SPILL FOR LATER DISPOSAL. NO SMOKING, FLAMES OR FLARES IN HAZARD AREA! KEEP UNNECESSARY PEOPLE AWAY; ISOLATE HAZARD AREA AND DENY ENTRY.

REPORTABLE QUANTITY (RQ): THE SUPERFUND AMENDMENTS AND REAUTHORIZATION ACT (SARA) SECTION 304 REQUIRES THAT A RELEASE EQUAL TO OR GREATER THAN THE REPORTABLE QUANTITY ESTABLISHED FOR THAT SUBSTANCE BE IMMEDIATELY REPORTED TO THE LOCAL EMERGENCY PLANNING COMMITTEE AND THE STATE EMERGENCY RESPONSE COMMISSION (40 CFR 355.40). IF THE RELEASE OF THIS SUBSTANCE IS REPORTABLE UNDER CERCLA SECTION 103, THE NATIONAL RESPONSE CENTER MUST BE NOTIFIED IMMEDIATELY AT (800) 424-8802 OR (202) 426-2675 IN THE METROPOLITAN WASHINGTON, D.C. AREA (40 CFR 302.6).

PROTECTIVE EQUIPMENT

VENTILATION: PROCESS ENCLOSURE RECOMMENDED TO MEET PUBLISHED EXPOSURE LIMITS.

RESPIRATOR: THE FOLLOWING RESPIRATORS AND MAXIMUM USE CONCENTRATIONS ARE RECOMMENDATIONS BY THE U.S. DEPARTMENT OF HEALTH AND HUMAN SERVICES, NIOSH POCKET GUIDE TO CHEMICAL HAZARDS; NIOSH CRITERIA DOCUMENTS OR BY THE U.S. DEPARTMENT OF LABOR, 29 CFR 1910 SUBPART Z. THE SPECIFIC RESPIRATOR SELECTED MUST BE BASED ON CONTAMINATION LEVELS FOUND IN THE WORK PLACE, MUST NOT EXCEED THE WORKING LIMITS OF THE RESPIRATOR AND BE JOINTLY APPROVED BY THE NATIONAL INSTITUTE FOR OCCUPATIONAL SAFETY AND HEALTH AND THE MINE SAFETY AND HEALTH ADMINISTRATION (NIOSH-MSHA).

PARATHION:

0.5 MG/M3- ANY CHEMICAL CARTRIDGE RESPIRATOR WITH ORGANIC VAPOR CARTRIDGE(S) IN COMBINATION WITH A DUST, MIST, AND FUME FILTER. ANY SUPPLIED-AIR RESPIRATOR. ANY SELF-CONTAINED BREATHING APPARATUS.

1.25 MG/M3- ANY SUPPLIED-AIR RESPIRATOR OPERATED IN A CONTINUOUS FLOW MODE. ANY POWERED AIR-PURIFYING RESPIRATOR WITH ORGANIC VAPOR CARTRIDGE(S) IN COMBINATION WITH A DUST, MIST, AND FUME FILTER.

2.5 MG/M3- ANY CHEMICAL CARTRIDGE RESPIRATOR WITH A FULL FACEPIECE AND ORGANIC VAPOR CARTRIDGE(S) IN COMBINATION WITH A HIGH-EFFICIENCY PARTICULATE FILTER. ANY SUPPLIED-AIR RESPIRATOR WITH A FULL FACEPIECE. ANY SELF-CONTAINED BREATHING APPARATUS WITH A FULL FACEPIECE. ANY POWERED AIR-PURIFYING RESPIRATOR WITH A TIGHT-FITTING FACEPIECE AND ORGANIC VAPOR CARTRIDGE(S) IN COMBINATION WITH A HIGH-EFFICIENCY PARTICULATE FILTER. ANY SUPPLIED-AIR RESPIRATOR WITH A TIGHT-FITTING FACEPIECE OPERATED IN A CONTINUOUS FLOW MODE.

20 MG/M3- ANY SUPPLIED-AIR RESPIRATOR WITH A HALF-MASK AND OPERATED IN A PRESSURE-DEMAND OR OTHER POSITIVE PRESSURE MODE.

ESCAPE- ANY AIR-PURIFYING FULL FACEPIECE RESPIRATOR (GAS MASK) WITH A CHIN-STYLE OR FRONT- OR BACK-MOUNTED ORGANIC VAPOR CANISTER HAVING A

HIGH-EFFICIENCY PARTICULATE FILTER. ANY APPROPRIATE ESCAPE-TYPE SELF-CONTAINED BREATHING APPARATUS.
FOR FIREFIGHTING AND OTHER IMMEDIATELY DANGEROUS TO LIFE OR HEALTH CONDITIONS:
SELF-CONTAINED BREATHING APPARATUS WITH FULL FACEPIECE OPERATED IN PRESSURE-DEMAND OR OTHER POSITIVE PRESSURE MODE.
SUPPLIED-AIR RESPIRATOR WITH FULL FACEPIECE AND OPERATED IN PRESSURE-DEMAND OR OTHER POSITIVE PRESSURE MODE IN COMBINATION WITH AN AUXILIARY SELF-CONTAINED BREATHING APPARATUS OPERATED IN PRESSURE-DEMAND OR OTHER POSITIVE PRESSURE MODE.

CLOTHING: EMPLOYEE MUST WEAR APPROPRIATE PROTECTIVE (IMPERVIOUS) CLOTHING AND EQUIPMENT TO PREVENT ANY POSSIBILITY OF SKIN CONTACT WITH THIS SUBSTANCE.

GLOVES: EMPLOYEE MUST WEAR APPROPRIATE PROTECTIVE GLOVES TO PREVENT CONTACT WITH THIS SUBSTANCE.

EYE PROTECTION: EMPLOYEE MUST WEAR SPLASH-PROOF OR DUST-RESISTANT SAFETY GOGGLES AND A FACESHIELD TO PREVENT CONTACT WITH THIS SUBSTANCE.
EMERGENCY WASH FACILITIES: WHERE THERE IS ANY POSSIBILITY THAT AN EMPLOYEE'S EYES AND/OR SKIN MAY BE EXPOSED TO THIS SUBSTANCE, THE EMPLOYER SHOULD PROVIDE AN EYE WASH FOUNTAIN AND QUICK DRENCH SHOWER WITHIN THE IMMEDIATE WORK AREA FOR EMERGENCY USE.

AUTHORIZED BY- OCCUPATIONAL HEALTH SERVICES, INC.
CREATION DATE: 10/04/89 ***REVISION DATE:*** 07/12/90

MATERIAL SAFETY DATA SHEET

OCCUPATIONAL HEALTH SERVICES, INC.
AGRICULTURE AND PESTICIDE DIVISION
450 SEVENTH AVENUE, SUITE 2407
NEW YORK, NEW YORK 10123
1-800-445-MSDS OR (212) 967-1100

EMERGENCY CONTACT:
JOHN S. BRANSFORD, JR. (615) 292-1180

SUBSTANCE IDENTIFICATION

CAS-NUMBER 82-68-8
SUBSTANCE: **PENTACHLORONITROBENZENE**
TRADE NAMES/SYNONYMS: AVICOL; BARTILEX; BOTRILEX; BRASSICOL; EARTHCIDE; FARTOX; FOLOSAN; FOMAC 2; FUNGICLOR; GC 3944-3-4; KOBU; KOBUTOL; KP 2; OLPISAN; PCNB; QUINTOZENE; PENTAGEN; PKHNB; QUINTOCENE; RCRA U185; PST18140
CHEMICAL FAMILY: HALOGEN COMPOUND, AROMATIC NITRO
MOLECULAR FORMULA: C6-CL5-N-O2
MOLECULAR WEIGHT: 295.32
CERCLA RATINGS (SCALE 0-3): HEALTH=3 FIRE=1 REACTIVITY=0 PERSISTENCE=3
NFPA RATINGS (SCALE 0-4): HEALTH=3 FIRE=1 REACTIVITY=0

COMPONENTS AND CONTAMINANTS

COMPONENT: PENTACHLORONITROBENZENE ***PERCENT:*** 89.0-99.0
CAS# 82-68-8
COMPONENT: HEXACHLOROBENZENE ***PERCENT:*** 1-11%
CAS# 118-74-1
OTHER CONTAMINANTS: 2,3,4,5-TETRACHLORONITROBENZENE, PENTACHLOROBENZENE
EXPOSURE LIMITS: PENTACHLORONITROBENZENE: 0.5 MG/M3 ACGIH TWA (PROPOSED ADDITION 1989-1990)
100 POUNDS CERCLA SECTION 103 REPORTABLE QUANTITY SUBJECT TO SARA SECTION 313 ANNUAL TOXIC CHEMICAL RELEASE REPORTING

PHYSICAL DATA

DESCRIPTION: CREAM COLORED CRYSTALS WITH A MUSTY ODOR.
BOILING POINT: 622 F (328 C) DECOMPOSES ***MELTING POINT:*** 295 F (146 C)
SPECIFIC GRAVITY: 1.718 @ 25 C ***VAPOR PRESSURE:*** 0.013 MMHG @ 25 C
SOLUBILITY IN WATER: PRACTICALLY INSOL
SOLVENT SOLUBILITY: ALCOHOL, CHLOROFORM, BENZENE, CARBON DISULFIDE, ETHANOL

FIRE AND EXPLOSION DATA

FIRE AND EXPLOSION HAZARD: NEGLIGIBLE FIRE HAZARD WHEN EXPOSED TO HEAT OR FLAME.
FIREFIGHTING MEDIA: DRY CHEMICAL, CARBON DIOXIDE, HALON, WATER SPRAY OR STANDARD FOAM (1987 EMERGENCY RESPONSE GUIDEBOOK, DOT P 5800.4).
FOR LARGER FIRES, USE WATER SPRAY, FOG OR STANDARD FOAM (1987 EMERGENCY RESPONSE GUIDEBOOK, DOT P 5800.4).
FIREFIGHTING: MOVE CONTAINER FROM FIRE AREA IF POSSIBLE. DO NOT SCATTER SPILLED MATERIAL WITH HIGH PRESSURE WATER STREAMS. DIKE FIRE CONTROL WATER FOR LATER DISPOSAL (1987 EMERGENCY RESPONSE GUIDEBOOK, DOT P 5800.4, GUIDE PAGE 31).
USE AGENTS SUITABLE FOR TYPE OF SURROUNDING FIRE. AVOID BREATHING HAZARDOUS VAPORS, KEEP UPWIND.

TOXICITY

PENTACHLORONITROBENZENE: TOXICITY DATA: 1400 MG/M3 INHALATION-RAT LC50; 2 GM/M3 INHALATION-MOUSE LC50; 4 GM/KG SKIN-RAT LD50; 1100 MG/KG ORAL-RAT LD50; 1400 MG/KG ORAL-MOUSE LD50; 800 MG/KG ORAL-RABBIT LD50; 4500 MG/KG INTRAPERITONEAL-MOUSE LD50; MUTAGENIC DATA (RTECS); REPRODUCTIVE EFFECTS DATA (RTECS); TUMORIGENIC DATA (RTECS).
CARCINOGEN STATUS: ANIMAL LIMITED EVIDENCE (IARC GROUP-3). PRELIMINARY STUDY BY THE ORAL ROUTE IN TWO STRAINS OF MICE PRODUCED AN INCREASED INCIDENCE OF HEPATOMAS IN MALES OF ONE STRAIN. ACUTE TOXICITY LEVEL: HIGHLY TOXIC BY INHALATION; MODERATELY TOXIC BY INGESTION; SLIGHTLY TOXIC BY DERMAL ABSORPTION. TARGET EFFECTS: SENSITIZER- SKIN.
HEXACHLOROBENZENE: TOXICITY DATA: 3600 MG/KG INHALATION-RAT LC50; 1800 MG/M3 INHALATION-RABBIT LC50; 4 GM/M3 INHALATION-MOUSE LC50; 1600 MG/M3 INHALATION-CAT LC50; 10,000 MG/KG ORAL-RAT LD50; 4 MG/KG ORAL-MOUSE LD50; 2600 MG/KG ORAL-RABBIT LD50; 1700 MG/KG ORAL-CAT LD50; 1047 MG/KG ORAL-MAMMAL LD50; 220 MG/KG UNREPORTED-MAN LDLO; MUTAGENIC DATA (RTECS); REPRODUCTIVE EFFECTS DATA (RTECS); TUMORIGENIC DATA (RTECS). CARCINOGEN STATUS: ANTICIPATED HUMAN CARCINOGEN (NTP); HUMAN INADEQUATE EVIDENCE, ANIMAL SUFFICIENT EVIDENCE (IARC GROUP 2B). ORAL ADMINISTRATION PRODUCED LIVER-CELL TUMORS IN MICE, AND LIVER HEMANGIOTHELIOMAS, HEPATOMAS, AND THYROID ADENOMAS IN HAMSTERS. ACUTE TOXICITY LEVEL: TOXIC BY INHALATION AND SLIGHTLY TOXIC BY INGESTION. TARGET EFFECTS: NO DATA AVAILABLE. ADDITIONAL DATA: CUTANEOUS EFFECTS MAY BE AFFRAVATED BY SUNLIGHT AND ALCOHOL.

HEALTH EFFECTS AND FIRST AID

INHALATION: PENTACHLORONITROBENZENE: HIGHLY TOXIC. **ACUTE EXPOSURE-** ANIMAL STUDIES INDICATE THAT INHALATION OF LOW LEVELS MAY BE LETHAL. HUMAN EXPOSURE TO SOME AROMATIC NITRO COMPOUNDS HAS RESULTED IN CYANOSIS AND CENTRAL NERVOUS SYSTEM DEPRESSION. **CHRONIC EXPOSURE-** NO DATA AVAILABLE. PROLONGED OR REPEATED EXPOSURE TO SOME AROMATIC NITRO COMPOUNDS MAY CAUSE ANEMIA, CYANOSIS, FATIGUE, INSOMNIA, WEIGHT LOSS, AND KIDNEY DAMAGE.
HEXACHLOROBENZENE: TOXIC. **ACUTE EXPOSURE-** MAY CAUSE COUGHING, DIFFICULTY BREATHING, PULMONARY EDEMA, AND DEATH. **CHRONIC EXPOSURE-** NO DATA AVAILABLE.
FIRST AID- REMOVE FROM EXPOSURE AREA TO FRESH AIR IMMEDIATELY. IF BREATHING HAS STOPPED, PERFORM ARTIFICIAL RESPIRATION. KEEP PERSON WARM AND AT REST. TREAT SYMPTOMATICALLY AND SUPPORTIVELY. GET MEDICAL ATTENTION IMMEDIATELY.

SKIN CONTACT: PENTACHLORONITROBENZENE: SENSITIZER. **ACUTE EXPOSURE-** MAY CAUSE SENSITIZATION DERMATITIS WITH ITCHING, ERYTHEMA, EDEMA, AND SMALL VESICLE FORMATION IN PREVIOUSLY EXPOSED PERSONS. THE REACTION MAY BE DELAYED SEVERAL HOURS TO DAYS. **CHRONIC EXPOSURE-** PROLONGED OR REPEATED EXPOSURE MAY CAUSE SENSITIZATION.
HEXACHLOROBENZENE: **ACUTE EXPOSURE-** MAY BE IRRITATING TO THE SKIN. **CHRONIC EXPOSURE-** PROLONGED OR REPEATED EXPOSURE MAY CAUSE EXFOLIATIVE DERMATITIS, AND POSSIBLY, PORPHYRIA.
FIRST AID- REMOVE CONTAMINATED CLOTHING AND SHOES IMMEDIATELY. WASH AFFECTED AREA WITH SOAP OR MILD DETERGENT AND LARGE AMOUNTS OF WATER UNTIL NO EVIDENCE OF CHEMICAL REMAINS (APPROXIMATELY 15-20 MINUTES). GET MEDICAL ATTENTION IMMEDIATELY.

EYE CONTACT: PENTACHLORONITROBENZENE: **ACUTE EXPOSURE-** CONTACT WITH SOLUTIONS MAY CAUSE CONJUNCTIVITIS AND CORNEAL INJURY. **CHRONIC EXPOSURE-** PROLONGED OR REPEATED EXPOSURE MAY CAUSE CONJUNCTIVITIS.
HEXACHLOROBENZENE: **ACUTE EXPOSURE-** MAY BE IRRITATING. **CHRONIC EXPOSURE-** NO DATA AVAILABLE.
FIRST AID- WASH EYES IMMEDIATELY WITH LARGE AMOUNTS OF WATER OR NORMAL SALINE, OCCASIONALLY LIFTING UPPER AND LOWER LIDS, UNTIL NO EVIDENCE OF CHEMICAL REMAINS (APPROXIMATELY 15-20 MINUTES). GET MEDICAL ATTENTION IMMEDIATELY.

INGESTION: PENTACHLORONITROBENZENE: LIMITED ANIMAL CARCINOGEN. ACUTE EXPOSURE- INGESTION OF LARGE DOSES HAS CAUSED VOMITING IN DOGS, AND SOME FORMATION OF METHEMOGLOBIN IN CATS. CHRONIC EXPOSURE- ANIMAL STUDIES INDICATE REPEATED INGESTION MAY CAUSE ADVERSE EFFECTS ON THE LIVER AND BONE MARROW. REPRODUCTIVE EFFECTS HAVE BEEN REPORTED FOLLOWING ORAL ADMINISTRATION TO PREGNANT RATS. ORAL ADMINISTRATION TO MICE RESULTED IN AN INCREASED INCIDENCE OF HEPATOMAS, SKIN ABSCESSES, FIBROMAS, AND FIBROSARCOMAS.
HEXACHLOROBENZENE: CARCINOGEN. ACUTE EXPOSURE- MAY CAUSE NAUSEA, VOMITING, AND ABDOMINAL PAIN. CHRONIC EXPOSURE- PROLONGED OR REPEATED INGESTION OF SMALL AMOUNTS MAY CAUSE LETHARGY, WEAKNESS, TREMORS, HYPEREXCITABILITY, HYPERPIGMENTATION, HYPERTRICHOSIS, ALOPECIA, CORNEAL OPACITIES, SKIN ERUPTIONS, DIGITAL DEFORMITIES, EXCESSIVE GROWTH OF HAIR IN UNUSUAL PLACES, AND PORT WINE OR DARKER COLORED URINE. OTHER ORGANS THAT MAY BE AFFECTED INCLUDE LUNGS, HEART, AND LIVER. HEXACHLOROBENZENE MAY CROSS THE PLACENTA, AND MAY BE EXCRETED IN BREAST MILK TO INDUCE TOXIC EFFECTS IN INFANTS. REPEATED ORAL ADMINISTRATION RESULTED IN LIVER-CELL TUMORS IN MICE AND RATS, AND LIVER HEMANGIOTHELIOMAS, HEPATOMAS, AND THYROID ADENOMAS IN HAMSTERS.

FIRST AID- IF THE PERSON IS CONSCIOUS AND NOT CONVULSING, INDUCE EMESIS BY GIVING SYRUP OF IPECAC FOLLOWED BY WATER. (IF VOMITING OCCURS KEEP THE HEAD BELOW THE HIPS TO PREVENT ASPIRATION). REPEAT IN 20 MINUTES IF NOT EFFECTIVE INITIALLY. GIVE ACTIVATED CHARCOAL. IN PATIENTS WITH DEPRESSED RESPIRATION OR IF EMESIS IS NOT PRODUCED, PERFORM GASTRIC LAVAGE CAUTIOUSLY (DREISBACH, HANDBOOK OF POISONING, 12TH ED.). TREAT SYMPTOMATICALLY AND SUPPORTIVELY. GASTRIC LAVAGE SHOULD BE PERFORMED BY QUALIFIED MEDICAL PERSONNEL. GET MEDICAL ATTENTION IMMEDIATELY.

ANTIDOTE: THE FOLLOWING ANTIDOTE HAS BEEN RECOMMENDED. HOWEVER, THE DECISION AS TO WHETHER THE SEVERITY OF POISONING REQUIRES ADMINISTRATION OF ANY ANTIDOTE AND ACTUAL DOSE REQUIRED SHOULD BE MADE BY QUALIFIED MEDICAL PERSONNEL.
METHEMOGLOBINEMIA: (WHEN METHEMOGLOBIN CONCENTRATION IS OVER 25-40% OR IN PRESENCE OF SYMPTOMS.) GIVE METHYLENE BLUE, 1% SOLUTION, 0.1 ML/KG INTRAVENOUSLY OVER A 10-MINUTE PERIOD. CYANOSIS MAY DISAPPEAR WITHIN MINUTES OR PERSIST LONGER DEPENDING ON DEGREE OF METHEMOGLOBINEMIA. INTRAVENOUS ADMINISTRATION OF THERAPEUTIC DOSES OF METHYLENE BLUE MAY CAUSE A RISE IN BLOOD PRESSURE, NAUSEA, AND DIZZINESS. LARGER DOSES (>500 MG) CAUSE VOMITING, DIARRHEA, CHEST PAIN, MENTAL CONFUSION, CYANOSIS, AND SWEATING. HEMOLYTIC ANEMIA HAS ALSO OCCURRED SEVERAL DAYS AFTER ADMINISTRATION. THESE EFFECTS ARE TEMPORARY, AND FATALITIES HAVE NOT BEEN REPORTED. IF METHYLENE BLUE IS NOT AVAILABLE, GIVE ASCORBIC ACID, 1 GRAM SLOWLY INTRAVENOUSLY. WITHOUT TREATMENT, METHEMOGLOBINEMIA LEVELS OF 20-30% REVERT TO NORMAL WITHIN 3 DAYS (DREISBACH, HANDBOOK OF POISONING, 12TH ED.). ANTIDOTE SHOULD BE ADMINISTERED BY QUALIFIED MEDICAL PERSONNEL.

REACTIVITY

REACTIVITY: STABLE UNDER NORMAL TEMPERATURES AND PRESSURES.

INCOMPATIBILITIES: PENTACHLORONITROBENZENE: NO DATA AVAILABLE.
HEXACHLOROBENZENE: DIMETHYLFORMAMIDE: VIOLENT REACTION ABOVE 65 C.

DECOMPOSITION: THERMAL DECOMPOSITION PRODUCTS MAY INCLUDE TOXIC AND HAZARDOUS OXIDES OF NITROGEN AND CARBON, AND HYDROGEN CHLORIDE.

POLYMERIZATION: HAZARDOUS POLYMERIZATION HAS NOT BEEN REPORTED TO OCCUR UNDER NORMAL TEMPERATURES AND PRESSURES.

STORAGE AND DISPOSAL

OBSERVE ALL FEDERAL, STATE AND LOCAL REGULATIONS WHEN STORING OR DISPOSING OF THIS SUBSTANCE. FOR ASSISTANCE, CONTACT THE DISTRICT DIRECTOR OF THE ENVIRONMENTAL PROTECTION AGENCY.

DISPOSAL

DISPOSAL MUST BE IN ACCORDANCE WITH STANDARDS APPLICABLE TO GENERATORS OF HAZARDOUS WASTE, 40CFR 262. EPA HAZARDOUS WASTE NUMBER U186.

CONDITIONS TO AVOID

MAY BURN BUT DOES NOT IGNITE READILY. AVOID CONTACT WITH STRONG OXIDIZERS, EXCESSIVE HEAT, SPARKS, OR OPEN FLAME.

SPILL AND LEAK PROCEDURES

OCCUPATIONAL SPILL: SWEEP UP AND PLACE IN SUITABLE CLEAN, DRY CONTAINERS FOR RECLAMATION OR LATER DISPOSAL. DO NOT FLUSH SPILLED MATERIAL INTO SEWER. KEEP UNNECESSARY PEOPLE AWAY.
REPORTABLE QUANTITY (RQ): 100 POUNDS THE SUPERFUND AMENDMENTS AND REAUTHORIZATION ACT (SARA) SECTION 304 REQUIRES THAT A RELEASE EQUAL TO OR GREATER THAN THE REPORTABLE QUANTITY FOR THIS SUBSTANCE BE IMMEDIATELY REPORTED TO THE LOCAL EMERGENCY PLANNING COMMITTEE AND THE STATE EMERGENCY RESPONSE COMMISSION (40 CFR 355.40). IF THE RELEASE OF THIS SUBSTANCE IS REPORTABLE UNDER CERCLA SECTION 103, THE NATIONAL RESPONSE CENTER MUST BE NOTIFIED IMMEDIATELY AT (800) 424-8802 OR (202) 426-2675 IN THE METROPOLITAN WASHINGTON, D.C. AREA (40 CFR 302.6).

PROTECTIVE EQUIPMENT

VENTILATION: PROCESS ENCLOSURE RECOMMENDED.

RESPIRATOR: THE FOLLOWING RESPIRATORS ARE RECOMMENDED BASED ON INFORMATION FOUND IN THE PHYSICAL DATA, TOXICITY AND HEALTH EFFECTS SECTIONS. THEY ARE RANKED IN ORDER FROM MINIMUM TO MAXIMUM RESPIRATORY PROTECTION. THE SPECIFIC RESPIRATOR SELECTED MUST BE BASED ON CONTAMINATION LEVELS FOUND IN THE WORK PLACE, MUST NOT EXCEED THE WORKING LIMITS OF THE RESPIRATOR AND BE JOINTLY APPROVED BY THE NATIONAL INSTITUTE FOR OCCUPATIONAL SAFETY AND HEALTH AND THE MINE SAFETY AND HEALTH ADMINISTRATION (NIOSH-MSHA).
TYPE 'C' SUPPLIED-AIR RESPIRATOR WITH A FULL FACEPIECE OPERATED IN PRESSURE-DEMAND OR OTHER POSITIVE PRESSURE MODE OR WITH A FULL FACEPIECE, HELMET OR HOOD OPERATED IN CONTINOUS-FLOW MODE.
SELF-CONTAINED BREATHING APPARATUS WITH A FULL FACEPIECE OPERATED IN PRESSURE-DEMAND OR OTHER POSITIVE PRESSURE MODE.
FOR FIREFIGHTING AND OTHER IMMEDIATELY DANGEROUS TO LIFE OR HEALTH CONDITIONS:
SELF-CONTAINED BREATHING APPARATUS WITH FULL FACEPIECE OPERATED IN PRESSURE-DEMAND OR OTHER POSITIVE PRESSURE MODE.
SUPPLIED-AIR RESPIRATOR WITH FULL FACEPIECE AND OPERATED IN PRESSURE-DEMAND OR OTHER POSITIVE PRESSURE MODE IN COMBINATION WITH AN AUXILIARY SELF-CONTAINED BREATHING APPARATUS OPERATED IN PRESSURE-DEMAND OR OTHER POSITIVE PRESSURE MODE.

CLOTHING: EMPLOYEE MUST WEAR APPROPRIATE PROTECTIVE (IMPERVIOUS) CLOTHING AND EQUIPMENT TO PREVENT REPEATED OR PROLONGED SKIN CONTACT WITH THIS SUBSTANCE.

GLOVES: EMPLOYEE MUST WEAR APPROPRIATE PROTECTIVE GLOVES TO PREVENT CONTACT WITH THIS SUBSTANCE.

EYE PROTECTION: EMPLOYEE MUST WEAR SPLASH-PROOF OR DUST-RESISTANT SAFETY GOGGLES TO PREVENT EYE CONTACT WITH THIS SUBSTANCE.
EMERGENCY EYE WASH: WHERE THERE IS ANY POSSIBILITY THAT AN EMPLOYEE'S EYES MAY BE EXPOSED TO THIS SUBSTANCE, THE EMPLOYER SHOULD PROVIDE AN EYE WASH FOUNTAIN WITHIN THE IMMEDIATE WORK AREA FOR EMERGENCY USE.

AUTHORIZED BY- OCCUPATIONAL HEALTH SERVICES, INC.
CREATION DATE: 10/04/89 ***REVISION DATE:*** 07/13/90

MATERIAL SAFETY DATA SHEET

OCCUPATIONAL HEALTH SERVICES, INC.
AGRICULTURE AND PESTICIDE DIVISION
450 SEVENTH AVENUE, SUITE 2407
NEW YORK, NEW YORK 10123
1-800-445-MSDS OR (212) 967-1100

EMERGENCY CONTACT:
JOHN S. BRANSFORD, JR. (615) 292-1180

SUBSTANCE IDENTIFICATION

CAS-NUMBER 87-86-5

SUBSTANCE: PENTACHLOROPHENOL

TRADE NAMES/SYNONYMS: PHENOL, PENTACHLORO-; DOWICIDE 7; FUNGIFEN; 1-HYDROXYPENTACHLOROBENZENE; LAUXTOL; LIROPREM; PCP; PENCHLOROL; PERMASAN; SANTOPHEN 20; STCC 4961380; RCRA U242; NA 2020; C6HCL5O; PST18150

CHEMICAL FAMILY: HALOGEN COMPOUND, AROMATIC

MOLECULAR FORMULA: CL5-C6-O-H

MOLECULAR WEIGHT: 266.34

CERCLA RATINGS (SCALE 0-3): HEALTH=3 FIRE=0 REACTIVITY=0 PERSISTENCE=3

NFPA RATINGS (SCALE 0-4): HEALTH=3 FIRE=0 REACTIVITY=0

COMPONENTS AND CONTAMINANTS

COMPONENT: PENTACHLOROPHENOL ***PERCENT:*** 100.0
CAS# 87-86-5

OTHER CONTAMINANTS: TECHNICAL GRADE MATERIAL MAY CONTAIN TRACES OF CHLORINATED DIBENZODIOXINS

EXPOSURE LIMITS: PENTACHLOROPHENOL: 0.5 MG/M3 OSHA TWA (SKIN) 0.5 MG/M3 ACGIH TWA (SKIN)

10 POUNDS CERCLA SECTION 103 REPORTABLE QUANTITY SUBJECT TO SARA SECTION 313 ANNUAL TOXIC CHEMICAL RELEASE REPORTING SUBJECT TO CALIFORNIA PROPOSITION 65 CANCER AND/OR REPRODUCTIVE TOXICITY WARNING AND RELEASE REQUIREMENTS- (JANUARY 1, 1990)

PHYSICAL DATA

DESCRIPTION: WHITE POWDER OR CRYSTALS OR DARK-COLORED FLAKES WITH A VERY PUNGENT ODOR WHEN HOT. ***BOILING POINT:*** 588-590 F (309-310 C) @ 754 MMHG (DEC)

MELTING POINT: 374-376 F (190-191 C) ***SPECIFIC GRAVITY:*** 1.978 @ 22 C

VAPOR PRESSURE: 0.00017 MMHG @ 20 C ***SOLUBILITY IN WATER:*** 14 PPM @ 20 C

VAPOR DENSITY: 9.2

SOLVENT SOLUBILITY: SOLUBLE IN ALCOHOL, ETHER, BENZENE, CARBITOL, XYLENE, CELLOSOLVE, DIETHYLENE GLYCOL, PARAFINIC PETROLEUM OILS, DILUTE ALKALI; MODERATELY SOLUBLE IN ETHYLENE GLYCOL, CARBON TETRACHLORIDE. TECHNICAL GRADE MATERIAL MAY MELT ABOVE 338 F (170 C)

FIRE AND EXPLOSION DATA

FIRE AND EXPLOSION HAZARD: NEGLIGIBLE FIRE HAZARD WHEN EXPOSED TO HEAT OR FLAME.

FIREFIGHTING MEDIA: DRY CHEMICAL, CARBON DIOXIDE, HALON, WATER SPRAY OR STANDARD FOAM (1987 EMERGENCY RESPONSE GUIDEBOOK, DOT P 5800.4). FOR LARGER FIRES, USE WATER SPRAY, FOG OR STANDARD FOAM (1987 EMERGENCY RESPONSE GUIDEBOOK, DOT P 5800.4).

FIREFIGHTING: MOVE CONTAINERS FROM FIRE AREA IF POSSIBLE (1987 EMERGENCY RESPONSE GUIDEBOOK, DOT P 5800.4, GUIDE PAGE 53).

USE AGENTS SUITABLE FOR TYPE OF FIRE. AVOID BREATHING HAZARDOUS VAPORS, KEEP UPWIND.

TRANSPORTATION DATA

DEPARTMENT OF TRANSPORTATION HAZARD CLASSIFICATION 49 CFR 172.101: POISON B

DEPARTMENT OF TRANSPORTATION LABELING REQUIREMENTS 49 CFR 172.101 AND SUBPART E: POISON

DEPARTMENT OF TRANSPORTATION PACKAGING REQUIREMENTS: 49 CFR 173.365 EXCEPTIONS: 49 CFR 173.364

TOXICITY

PENTACHLOROPHENOL: IRRITATION DATA: 10 MG/24 HOURS OPEN SKIN-RABBIT MILD. TOXICITY DATA: 355 MG/M3 INHALATION-RAT LC50; 225 MG/M3 INHALATION-MOUSE LC50; 40 MG/KG SKIN-RABBIT LDLO; 96 MG/KG SKIN-RAT LD50; 401 MG/KG ORAL-MAN LDLO; 27 MG/KG ORAL-RAT LD50; 117 MG/KG ORAL-MOUSE LD50; 70 MG/KG ORAL-RABBIT LDLO; 168 MG/KG ORAL-HAMSTER LD50; 100 MG/KG SUBCUTANEOUS-RAT LD50; 70 MG/KG SUBCUTANEOUS-RABBIT LDLO; 135 MG/KG SUBCUTANEOUS-DOG LDLO; 56 MG/KG INTRAPERITONEAL-RAT LD50; 58 MG/KG INTRAPERITONEAL-MOUSE LD50; 135 MG/KG INTRAPERITONEAL-RABBIT LDLO; 100 MG/KG UNREPORTED-GUINEA PIG LD50; 70 MG/KG UNREPORTED-DOG LD50; MUTAGENIC DATA (RTECS); REPRODUCTIVE EFFECTS DATA (RTECS); TUMORIGENIC DATA (RTECS). CARCINOGEN STATUS: HUMAN LIMITED EVIDENCE (IARC GROUP-2B FOR CHLOROPHENOLS); ANIMAL INADEQUATE EVIDENCE (IARC). STUDIES REVEALED A SIGNIFICANT INCREASE IN SOFT-TISSUE SARCOMA AND LUNG, NASAL AND NASOPHARYNGEAL CANCER IN WORKERS EXPOSED TO CHLOROPHENOLS. THERE WAS CLEAR EVIDENCE OF CARCINOGENIC ACTIVITY IN MICE FED A TECHNICAL-GRADE AND A TECHNICAL-GRADE FORMULATION AS SHOWN BY INCREASED INCIDENCES OF ADRENAL MEDULLARY AND HEPATOCELLULAR NEOPLASMS AND HEMANGIOSARCOMAS (NTP TR-349). LOCAL EFFECTS: IRRITANT- INHALATION, SKIN, EYE. ACUTE TOXICITY LEVEL: HIGHLY TOXIC BY INHALATION, DERMAL ABSORPTION AND INGESTION. TARGET EFFECTS: POISONING MAY INCREASE THE METABOLIC RATE AND AFFECT THE CARDIOVASCULAR AND NERVOUS SYSTEMS, LIVER, AND KIDNEYS. AT INCREASED RISK FROM EXPOSURE: PERSONS WITH RENAL OR HEPATIC DISEASES. ADDITIONAL DATA: HOT ENVIRONMENTS MAY ENHANCE ABSORPTION AND THE TOXIC EFFECTS.

HEALTH EFFECTS AND FIRST AID

INHALATION: PENTACHLOROPHENOL: IRRITANT/HIGHLY TOXIC. 150 MG/M3 IMMEDIATELY DANGEROUS TO LIFE OR HEALTH. **ACUTE EXPOSURE-** MAY CAUSE IRRITATION OF THE UPPER RESPIRATORY TRACT WITH CONCENTRATIONS GREATER THAN 1 MG/M3 PRODUCING PAIN IN THE NOSE AND THROAT, VIOLENT SNEEZING, AND COUGH. SYMPTOMS OF SYSTEMIC POISONING MAY INCLUDE HEADACHE, FEVER, INTENSE THIRST, EXCESSIVE PERSPIRATION, GENERALIZED WEAKNESS, DIZZINESS, TACHYCARDIA, TACHYPNEA, DYSPNEA, CHEST PAIN, PAIN IN THE EXTREMITIES, ANOREXIA, WEIGHT LOSS, METABOLIC ACIDOSIS, AND GASTROINTESTINAL UPSET WITH NAUSEA, VOMITING, AND ABDOMINAL PAIN. IN SEVERE POISONINGS, THESE EFFECTS MAY PROGRESS TO MUSCLE SPASM, DEHYDRATION, HYPERPYREXIA, ANESTHESIA, LEUKOCYTOSIS, HYPERGLYCEMIA, EDEMA AND HEMORRHAGE IN THE LUNGS, CEREBRAL EDEMA, STUPOR, CONVULSIONS, AND COMA. LIVER AND KIDNEY DAMAGE MAY OCCUR. DEATH MAY BE DUE TO VASCULAR COLLAPSE AND HEART FAILURE AND MAY OCCUR WITHIN HOURS OF THE ONSET OF SYMPTOMS FOLLOWED RAPIDLY BY RIGOR MORTIS. IMPAIRMENT OF AUTONOMIC FUNCTION AND CIRCULATION AND VISUAL DAMAGE WERE OBSERVED IN SOME SERIOUS CASES OF POISONING. **CHRONIC EXPOSURE-** REPEATED EXPOSURE TO LOW-LEVELS MAY CAUSE IRRITATION OF THE NOSE, THROAT, AND LUNGS LEADING TO BRONCHITIS AND SINUSITIS. IN ADDITION TO THE SYSTEMIC EFFECTS LISTED ABOVE, REPEATED OR PROLONGED EXPOSURE HAS BEEN ASSOCIATED WITH THE DEVELOPMENT OF ACUTE PANCREATITIS, LEUKOPENIA, IMMUNOLOGICAL CHANGES, APLASTIC ANEMIA, INTRAVASCULAR HEMOLYSIS, AND POLYNEURITIS.

FIRST AID- REMOVE FROM EXPOSURE AREA TO FRESH AIR IMMEDIATELY. IF BREATHING HAS STOPPED, PERFORM ARTIFICIAL RESPIRATION. ADMINISTER OXYGEN. TREAT SYMPTOMATICALLY AND SUPPORTIVELY. GET MEDICAL ATTENTION IMMEDIATELY.

SKIN CONTACT: PENTACHLOROPHENOL: IRRITANT/HIGHLY TOXIC. **ACUTE EXPOSURE-** BRIEF, SINGLE EXPOSURE TO SOLUTIONS CONTAINING APPROXIMATELY 10% PENTACHLOROPHENOL MAY CAUSE IRRITATION. SOLIDS AND CONCENTRATED SOLUTIONS MAY POSSIBLY PRODUCE SKIN BURNS. THIS MATERIAL MAY BE ABSORBED THROUGH THE SKIN IN FATAL AMOUNTS AND PRODUCE SYSTEMIC EFFECTS AS DESCRIBED IN ACUTE INHALATION. **CHRONIC EXPOSURE-** PROLONGED OR REPEATED EXPOSURE MAY CAUSE DERMATITIS AND A RARE ALLERGIC SKIN RESPONSE; SOLUTIONS CONTAINING AS LITTLE AS 1% MAY CAUSE IRRITATION. REPEATED ABSORPTION MAY RESULT IN SYSTEMIC EFFECTS AS DESCRIBED IN INHALATION. CHLORACNE AND DISORDERS OF THE NERVOUS SYSTEM, LIVER, AND PORPHYRIA MAY OCCUR DUE TO THE PRESENCE OF CHLORINATED DIBENZODIOXINS.

FIRST AID- REMOVE CONTAMINATED CLOTHING AND SHOES IMMEDIATELY. THEN REMOVE SKIN AND HAIR CONTAMINATION BY SCRUBBING WITH SOAP AND WATER. IF BODY TEMPERATURE IS ELEVATED, REDUCE TO 37 C BY SPONGE BATH, IMMERSION IN COOL WATER OR BY APPLYING COOLING BLANKET. IF BODY TEMPERATURE IS ABOVE 40 C, ICE WATER IS NECESSARY (DREISBACH, HANDBOOK OF POISONING, 12TH EDITION; MORGAN, EPA RECOGNITION AND MANAGEMENT OF PESTICIDE POISONINGS, 3RD EDITION). GET MEDICAL ATTENTION IMMEDIATELY.

EYE CONTACT: PENTACHLOROPHENOL: IRRITANT. **ACUTE EXPOSURE-** EXPOSURE TO FINE DUST AND SPRAYS MAY CAUSE PAINFUL IRRITATION, LACRIMATION, CORNEAL NUMBNESS, SLIGHT MYDRIASIS, AND INFLAMMATION THAT MAY PROGRESS TO PERMANENT CORNEAL INJURY. **CHRONIC EXPOSURE-** REPEATED OR PROLONGED EXPOSURE MAY CAUSE CONJUNCTIVITIS.

FIRST AID- WASH EYES IMMEDIATELY WITH LARGE AMOUNTS OF WATER OR NORMAL SALINE, OCCASIONALLY LIFTING UPPER AND LOWER LIDS, UNTIL NO EVIDENCE OF CHEMICAL REMAINS (APPROXIMATELY 15-20 MINUTES). GET MEDICAL ATTENTION IMMEDIATELY.

INGESTION: PENTACHLOROPHENOL: HIGHLY TOXIC. **ACUTE EXPOSURE-** MAY CAUSE SEVERE IRRITATION OF THE GASTROINTESTINAL TRACT AND SYSTEMIC EFFECTS AS DESCRIBED IN INHALATION. SEVERE TOXIC EFFECTS MAY OCCUR IN HUMANS WITH INGESTION OF 2 GRAMS. **CHRONIC EXPOSURE-** MAY CAUSE EFFECTS AS DESCRIBED IN INHALATION. ENLARGEMENT OF THE LIVER, CHANGES IN VARIOUS ENZYME ACTIVITIES, AND OTHER HEPATIC EFFECTS WERE OBSERVED IN RATS RECEIVING PENTACHLOROPHENOL FOR PERIODS OF THREE TO EIGHT MONTHS. FETOTOXIC EFFECTS, FETAL DEATHS AND RESORPTIONS HAVE BEEN REPORTED IN RODENTS. INCREASED INCIDENCES OF ADRENAL MEDULLARY AND HEPATOCELLULAR NEOPLASMS AND HEMANGIOSARCOMAS WERE OBSERVED IN A 2-YEAR STUDY OF MICE.

FIRST AID- IF VICTIM IS ALERT AND RESPIRATION IS NOT DEPRESSED, INDUCE EMESIS WITH SYRUP OF IPECAC. IF VICTIM IS NOT FULLY ALERT, EMPTY THE STOMACH IMMEDIATELY BY INTUBATION, ASPIRATION, AND LAVAGE, USING ISOTONIC SALINE OR 5% SODIUM BICARBONATE. FOLLOW EMESIS OR LAVAGE WITH ACTIVATED CHARCOAL. GIVE SODIUM SULFATE AS A CATHARTIC. REDUCE ELEVATED BODY TEMPERATURE TO 37 C BY SPONGE BATHS, IMMERSION IN COOL WATER OR BY APPLYING COOLING BLANKET. (MORGAN, EPA RECOGNITION AND MANAGEMENT OF PESTICIDE POISONINGS, THIRD EDITION). GET MEDICAL ATTENTION.

ANTIDOTE: NO SPECIFIC ANTIDOTE. TREAT SYMPTOMATICALLY AND SUPPORTIVELY.

REACTIVITY

REACTIVITY: STABLE UNDER NORMAL TEMPERATURES AND PRESSURES.

INCOMPATIBILITIES: PENTACHLOROPHENOL: OXIDIZERS (STRONG): FIRE AND EXPLOSION HAZARD.

DECOMPOSITION: THERMAL DECOMPOSITION PRODUCTS MAY INCLUDE TOXIC AND CORROSIVE CHLORIDE FUMES, TOXIC AND HAZARDOUS CHLORINATED PHENOLS AND OXIDES OF CARBON.

POLYMERIZATION: HAZARDOUS POLYMERIZATION HAS NOT BEEN REPORTED TO OCCUR UNDER NORMAL TEMPERATURES AND PRESSURES.

STORAGE AND DISPOSAL

OBSERVE ALL FEDERAL, STATE AND LOCAL REGULATIONS WHEN STORING OR DISPOSING OF THIS SUBSTANCE. FOR ASSISTANCE, CONTACT THE DISTRICT DIRECTOR OF THE ENVIRONMENTAL PROTECTION AGENCY.

****STORAGE****

PROTECT AGAINST PHYSICAL DAMAGE. STORE IN A COOL, DRY, WELL VENTILATED LOCATION, AWAY FROM ANY AREA WHERE THE FIRE HAZARD MAY BE ACUTE. OUTSIDE OR DETACHED STORAGE IS PREFERRED (NFPA 49, HAZARDOUS CHEMICALS DATA, 1975).

STORE AT 4 C, PROTECT FROM LIGHT AND KEEP DRY.

STORE AWAY FROM INCOMPATIBLE SUBSTANCES.

****DISPOSAL****

PENTACHLOROPHENOL - REGULATORY LEVEL: 100.0 MG/L MATERIALS WHICH CONTAIN THE ABOVE SUBSTANCE AT OR ABOVE THE REGULATORY LEVEL MEET THE EPA CHARACTERISTIC OF TOXICITY, AND MUST BE DISPOSED OF IN ACCORDANCE WITH 40 CFR PART 262. EPA HAZARDOUS WASTE NUMBER D037.

CONDITIONS TO AVOID

MAY BURN BUT DOES NOT IGNITE READILY.

SPILL AND LEAK PROCEDURES

SOIL SPILL: DIG A PIT, POND, LAGOON OR HOLDING AREA TO CONTAIN LIQUID OR SOLID MATERIAL. COVER SOLIDS WITH A PLASTIC SHEET TO PREVENT DISSOLVING IN RAIN OR FIREFIGHTING WATER.

WATER SPILL: USE NATURAL DEEP WATER POCKETS, EXCAVATED LAGOONS, OR SAND BAG BARRIERS TO TRAP MATERIAL AT BOTTOM. USE ACTIVATED CARBON AT 10 TIMES THE SPILLED AMOUNT IF IT IS DISSOLVED AT 10 PPM OR GREATER CONCENTRATION. REMOVE TRAPPED MATERIAL WITH SUCTION HOSES. USE MECHANICAL DREDGES OR LIFTS TO REMOVE IMMOBILIZED MASSES OF POLLUTION AND PRECIPITATES. THE CALIFORNIA SAFE DRINKING WATER AND TOXIC ENFORCEMENT ACT OF 1986 (PROPOSITION 65) PROHIBITS CONTAMINATING ANY KNOWN SOURCE OF DRINKING WATER WITH SUBSTANCES KNOWN TO CAUSE CANCER AND/OR REPRODUCTIVE TOXICITY.

OCCUPATIONAL SPILL: DO NOT TOUCH SPILLED MATERIAL. STOP LEAK IF YOU CAN DO IT WITHOUT RISK. FOR SMALL SPILLS, TAKE UP WITH SAND OR OTHER ABSORBENT MATERIAL AND PLACE INTO CONTAINERS FOR LATER DISPOSAL. FOR SMALL DRY SPILLS, WITH A CLEAN SHOVEL PLACE MATERIAL INTO CLEAN, DRY CONTAINER AND COVER. MOVE CONTAINERS FROM SPILL AREA. FOR LARGER SPILLS, DIKE FAR AHEAD OF SPILL FOR LATER DISPOSAL. KEEP UNNECESSARY PEOPLE AWAY. ISOLATE HAZARD AREA AND DENY ENTRY.

REPORTABLE QUANTITY (RQ): 10 POUNDS THE SUPERFUND AMENDMENTS AND REAUTHORIZATION ACT (SARA) SECTION 304 REQUIRES THAT A RELEASE EQUAL TO OR GREATER THAN THE REPORTABLE QUANTITY FOR THIS SUBSTANCE BE IMMEDIATELY REPORTED TO THE LOCAL EMERGENCY PLANNING COMMITTEE AND THE STATE EMERGENCY RESPONSE COMMISSION (40 CFR 355.40). IF THE RELEASE OF THIS SUBSTANCE IS REPORTABLE UNDER CERCLA SECTION 103, THE NATIONAL RESPONSE CENTER MUST BE NOTIFIED IMMEDIATELY AT (800) 424-8802 OR (202) 426-2675 IN THE METROPOLITAN WASHINGTON, D.C. AREA (40 CFR 302.6).

PROTECTIVE EQUIPMENT

VENTILATION: PROCESS ENCLOSURE RECOMMENDED TO MEET PUBLISHED EXPOSURE LIMITS.

RESPIRATOR: THE FOLLOWING RESPIRATORS AND MAXIMUM USE CONCENTRATIONS ARE RECOMMENDATIONS BY THE U.S. DEPARTMENT OF HEALTH AND HUMAN SERVICES, NIOSH POCKET GUIDE TO CHEMICAL HAZARDS; NIOSH CRITERIA DOCUMENTS OR BY THE U.S. DEPARTMENT OF LABOR, 29 CFR 1910 SUBPART Z. THE SPECIFIC RESPIRATOR SELECTED MUST BE BASED ON CONTAMINATION LEVELS FOUND IN THE WORK PLACE, MUST NOT EXCEED THE WORKING LIMITS OF THE RESPIRATOR AND BE JOINTLY APPROVED BY THE NATIONAL INSTITUTE FOR OCCUPATIONAL SAFETY AND HEALTH AND THE MINE SAFETY AND HEALTH ADMINISTRATION (NIOSH-MSHA).

PENTACHLOROPHENOL:

5.0 MG/M3- CHEMICAL CARTRIDGE RESPIRATOR WITH ORGANIC VAPOR CARTRIDGE(S) IN COMBINATION WITH A DUST, MIST, AND FUME FILTER. SUPPLIED-AIR RESPIRATOR. SELF-CONTAINED BREATHING APPARATUS.

12.5 MG/M3- SUPPLIED-AIR RESPIRATOR OPERATED IN CONTINUOUS FLOW MODE. POWERED AIR-PURIFYING RESPIRATOR WITH ORGANIC VAPOR CARTRIDGE(S) IN COMBINATION WITH A DUST, MIST, AND FUME FILTER.

25.0 MG/M3- CHEMICAL CARTRIDGE RESPIRATOR WITH FULL FACEPIECE AND ORGANIC VAPOR CARTRIDGE(S) IN COMBINATION WITH A HIGH-EFFICIENCY PARTICULATE FILTER. SUPPLIED-AIR RESPIRATOR WITH FULL FACEPIECE. SELF-CONTAINED BREATHING APPARATUS WITH FULL FACEPIECE.

150 MG/M3- SUPPLIED-AIR RESPIRATOR WITH A FULL FACEPIECE AND OPERATED IN PRESSURE DEMAND OR OTHER POSITIVE PRESSURE MODE.

ESCAPE- AIR-PURIFYING FULL FACEPIECE RESPIRATOR (GAS MASK) WITH A CHIN-STYLE OR FRONT- OR BACK-MOUNTED ORGANIC VAPOR CANISTER HAVING A HIGH-EFFICIENCY PARTICULATE FILTER. ESCAPE-TYPE SELF-CONTAINED BREATHING APPARATUS.

FOR FIREFIGHTING AND OTHER IMMEDIATELY DANGEROUS TO LIFE OR HEALTH CONDITIONS:

SELF-CONTAINED BREATHING APPARATUS WITH FULL FACEPIECE OPERATED IN PRESSURE-DEMAND OR OTHER POSITIVE PRESSURE MODE.

SUPPLIED-AIR RESPIRATOR WITH FULL FACEPIECE AND OPERATED IN PRESSURE-DEMAND OR OTHER POSITIVE PRESSURE MODE IN COMBINATION WITH AN AUXILIARY SELF-CONTAINED BREATHING APPARATUS OPERATED IN PRESSURE-DEMAND OR OTHER POSITIVE PRESSURE MODE.

CLOTHING: EMPLOYEE MUST WEAR APPROPRIATE PROTECTIVE (IMPERVIOUS) CLOTHING AND EQUIPMENT TO PREVENT ANY POSSIBILITY OF SKIN CONTACT WITH THIS SUBSTANCE.

GLOVES: EMPLOYEE MUST WEAR APPROPRIATE PROTECTIVE GLOVES TO PREVENT CONTACT WITH THIS SUBSTANCE.

EYE PROTECTION: EMPLOYEE MUST WEAR SPLASH-PROOF OR DUST-RESISTANT SAFETY GOGGLES AND A FACESHIELD TO PREVENT CONTACT WITH THIS SUBSTANCE.

EMERGENCY WASH FACILITIES: WHERE THERE IS ANY POSSIBILITY THAT AN EMPLOYEE'S EYES AND/OR SKIN MAY BE EXPOSED TO THIS SUBSTANCE, THE EMPLOYER SHOULD PROVIDE AN EYE WASH FOUNTAIN AND QUICK DRENCH SHOWER WITHIN THE IMMEDIATE WORK AREA FOR EMERGENCY USE.

AUTHORIZED BY- OCCUPATIONAL HEALTH SERVICES, INC.

CREATION DATE: 10/04/89 ***REVISION DATE:*** 07/13/90

MATERIAL SAFETY DATA SHEET

OCCUPATIONAL HEALTH SERVICES, INC.
AGRICULTURE AND PESTICIDE DIVISION
450 SEVENTH AVENUE, SUITE 2407
NEW YORK, NEW YORK 10123
1-800-445-MSDS OR (212) 967-1100

EMERGENCY CONTACT:
JOHN S. BRANSFORD, JR. (615) 292-1180

SUBSTANCE IDENTIFICATION

CAS-NUMBER 79-21-0

SUBSTANCE: **PEROXYACETIC ACID**

TRADE NAMES/SYNONYMS: PAA; PERACETIC ACID; ACETYL HYDROPEROXIDE; OSBON AC; PERACTIC ACID SOLUTION; ETHANEPEROXOIC ACID; PEROXOACETIC ACID; ACETIC PEROXIDE; STCC 4919570; UN 2131; NA 2131; PST18310

CHEMICAL FAMILY: CARBOXYLIC ACID, ALIPHATIC PEROXIDE

MOLECULAR FORMULA: C2-H4-O3

MOLECULAR WEIGHT: 76.06

CERCLA RATINGS (SCALE 0-3): HEALTH=3 FIRE=2 REACTIVITY=3 PERSISTENCE=0

NFPA RATINGS (SCALE 0-4): HEALTH=3 FIRE=2 REACTIVITY=4

COMPONENTS AND CONTAMINANTS

COMPONENT: PEROXYACETIC ACID ***PERCENT:*** <43

COMPONENT: ACETIC ACID ***PERCENT:*** >40

COMPONENT: WATER ***PERCENT:*** >13

COMPONENT: HYDROGEN PEROXIDE ***PERCENT:*** <6

COMPONENT: SULFURIC ACID ***PERCENT:*** <1

OTHER CONTAMINANTS: STABILIZER

EXPOSURE LIMITS: PEROXYACETIC ACID: NO OCCUPATIONAL EXPOSURE LIMITS ESTABLISHED BY OSHA, ACGIH, OR NIOSH.

500 POUNDS SARA SECTION 302 THRESHOLD PLANNING QUANTITY 1 POUND SARA SECTION 304 REPORTABLE QUANTITY SUBJECT TO SARA SECTION 313 ANNUAL TOXIC CHEMICAL RELEASE REPORTING

PHYSICAL DATA

DESCRIPTION: COLORLESS LIQUID WITH A STRONG, PUNGENT, IRRITATING ODOR.

BOILING POINT: 221 F (105 C) ***MELTING POINT:*** -22 F (-30 C)
SPECIFIC GRAVITY: 1.15 ***PH:*** ACIDIC ***SOLUBILITY IN WATER:*** VERY SOLUBLE
VAPOR DENSITY: 2.6
SOLVENT SOLUBILITY: SOLUBLE IN ETHANOL, ETHER, SULFURIC ACID

FIRE AND EXPLOSION DATA

FIRE AND EXPLOSION HAZARD: MODERATE FIRE HAZARD WHEN EXPOSED TO HEAT OR FLAME.
MAY EXPLODE VIOLENTLY WHEN HEATED ABOVE BOILING POINT.
VAPORS ARE HEAVIER THAN AIR AND MAY TRAVEL A CONSIDERABLE DISTANCE TO A SOURCE OF IGNITION AND FLASH BACK.
VAPOR-AIR MIXTURES ARE EXPLOSIVE ABOVE FLASH POINT.
FLASH POINT: 105 F (41 C) (OC) ***AUTOIGNITION TEMP.:*** 392 F (200 C)
FLAMMABILITY CLASS(OSHA): II
FIREFIGHTING MEDIA: DRY CHEMICAL, CARBON DIOXIDE, HALON, WATER SPRAY OR STANDARD FOAM (1987 EMERGENCY RESPONSE GUIDEBOOK, DOT P 5800.4).
FOR LARGER FIRES, FLOOD AREA WITH WATER FROM A DISTANCE (1987 EMERGENCY RESPONSE GUIDEBOOK, DOT P 5800.4).
FIREFIGHTING: FOR MASSIVE FIRE IN STORAGE AREA, USE UNMANNED HOSE HOLDER OR MONITOR NOZZLES. IF FIRE CAN BE CONTROLLED, COOL CONTAINERS FROM UNMANNED HOSE HOLDER OR MONITOR NOZZLES UNTIL WELL AFTER FIRE IS OUT; ELSE WITHDRAW FROM AREA AND LET FIRE BURN (1987 EMERGENCY RESPONSE GUIDEBOOK, DOT P 5800.4, GUIDE PAGE 51).
USE FLOODING AMOUNTS OF WATER AS FOG, SOLID STREAMS MAY NOT BE EFFECTIVE. COOL CONTAINERS WITH FLOODING AMOUNTS OF WATER, APPLY FROM AS FAR A DISTANCE AS POSSIBLE. AVOID BREATHING CORROSIVE VAPORS, KEEP UPWIND. MATERIAL IS DANGEROUSLY EXPLOSIVE. EVACUATE TO A RADIUS OF 2500 FEET FOR UNCONTROLLABLE FIRES, KEEP UPWIND.

TRANSPORTATION DATA

DEPARTMENT OF TRANSPORTATION HAZARD CLASSIFICATION 49 CFR 172.101: ORGANIC PEROXIDE
DEPARTMENT OF TRANSPORTATION LABELING REQUIREMENTS 49 CFR 172.101 AND SUBPART E: ORGANIC PEROXIDE
DEPARTMENT OF TRANSPORTATION PACKAGING REQUIREMENTS: 49 CFR 173.223 EXCEPTIONS: 49 CFR 173.223

TOXICITY

PEROXYACETIC ACID: IRRITATION DATA: 500 MG OPEN SKIN-RABBIT SEVERE; 1 MG EYE-RABBIT SEVERE. TOXICITY DATA: 450 MG/M3 INHALATION-RAT LC50; 1410 MG/KG SKIN-RABBIT LD50; 1540 MG/KG ORAL-RAT LD50; 210 MG/KG ORAL-MOUSE LD50; 10 MG/KG ORAL-GUINEA PIG LD50; 17860 UG/KG INTRAVENOUS-MOUSE LD50; TUMORIGENIC DATA (RTECS). CARCINOGEN STATUS: NONE. LOCAL EFFECTS: CORROSIVE- INHALATION, SKIN, AND EYES. ACUTE TOXICITY LEVEL: HIGHLY TOXIC BY INHALATION; MODERATELY TOXIC BY DERMAL ABSORPTION AND INGESTION. TARGET EFFECTS: POISONING MAY AFFECT THE CENTRAL NERVOUS SYSTEM.

HEALTH EFFECTS AND FIRST AID

INHALATION: PEROXYACETIC ACID: CORROSIVE. **ACUTE EXPOSURE-** INHALATION OF ACIDIC SUBSTANCES MAY CAUSE SYMPTOMS OF SEVERE RESPIRATORY TRACT IRRITATION POSSIBLY INCLUDING COUGHING, CHOKING, PAIN IN THE NOSE, MOUTH AND THROAT AND BURNS OF THE MUCOUS MEMBRANES. IF SUFFICIENT QUANTITIES ARE INHALED, PULMONARY EDEMA MAY DEVELOP, OFTEN WITH A LATENT PERIOD OF 5-72 HOURS. THE SYMPTOMS MAY INCLUDE TIGHTNESS IN THE CHEST, DYSPNEA, FROTHY SPUTUM, CYANOSIS, AND DIZZINESS. PHYSICAL FINDINGS MAY INCLUDE WEAK, RAPID PULSE, HYPOTENSION, MOIST RALES, AND HEMOCONCENTRATION. RECOVERY MAY BE PROLONGED AND RELAPSES ARE POSSIBLE. IN SEVERE EXPOSURES, DEATH DUE TO ANOXIA MAY OCCUR WITHIN A FEW HOURS AFTER ONSET OF PULMONARY EDEMA SYMPTOMS OR FOLLOWING A RELAPSE. THE VAPORS OF SOME ORGANIC PEROXIDES MAY CAUSE HEADACHES AND INTOXICATION SIMILAR TO ALCOHOL. **CHRONIC EXPOSURE-** DEPENDING ON THE CONCENTRATION AND DURATION OF EXPOSURE, REPEATED OR PROLONGED EXPOSURE TO ACIDIC SUBSTANCES MAY CAUSE EROSION OF THE TEETH AND INFLAMMATORY AND ULCERATIVE CHANGES IN THE MOUTH. BRONCHIAL AND GASTROINTESTINAL DISTURBANCES ARE ALSO POSSIBLE.
FIRST AID- REMOVE FROM EXPOSURE AREA TO FRESH AIR IMMEDIATELY. IF BREATHING HAS STOPPED, GIVE ARTIFICIAL RESPIRATION. MAINTAIN AIRWAY AND BLOOD PRESSURE AND ADMINISTER OXYGEN IF AVAILABLE. KEEP AFFECTED PERSON WARM AND AT REST. TREAT SYMPTOMATICALLY AND SUPPORTIVELY. ADMINISTRATION OF OXYGEN SHOULD BE PERFORMED BY QUALIFIED PERSONNEL. GET MEDICAL ATTENTION IMMEDIATELY.

SKIN CONTACT: PEROXYACETIC ACID: CORROSIVE. **ACUTE EXPOSURE-** MAY CAUSE REDNESS, PAIN, AND BURNS. **CHRONIC EXPOSURE-** EFFECTS DEPEND ON CONCENTRATION AND DURATION OF EXPOSURE. REPEATED OR PROLONGED CONTACT WITH CORROSIVE SUBSTANCES MAY RESULT IN DERMATITIS OR EFFECTS SIMILAR TO ACUTE EXPOSURE.
FIRST AID- REMOVE CONTAMINATED CLOTHING AND SHOES IMMEDIATELY. WASH AFFECTED AREA WITH SOAP OR MILD DETERGENT AND LARGE AMOUNTS OF WATER UNTIL NO EVIDENCE OF CHEMICAL REMAINS (AT LEAST 15-20 MINUTES). IN CASE OF CHEMICAL BURNS, COVER AREA WITH STERILE, DRY DRESSING. BANDAGE SECURELY, BUT NOT TOO TIGHTLY. GET MEDICAL ATTENTION IMMEDIATELY.

EYE CONTACT: PEROXYACETIC ACID: CORROSIVE. **ACUTE EXPOSURE-** MAY CAUSE SEVERE IRRITATION WITH REDNESS, PAIN, BLURRED VISION, AND BURNS. **CHRONIC EXPOSURE-** EFFECTS DEPEND ON CONCENTRATION AND DURATION OF EXPOSURE. REPEATED OR PROLONGED CONTACT WITH CORROSIVE SUBSTANCES MAY RESULT IN CONJUNCTIVITIS OR EFFECTS AS IN ACUTE EXPOSURE.
FIRST AID- WASH EYES IMMEDIATELY WITH LARGE AMOUNTS OF WATER, OCCASIONALLY LIFTING UPPER AND LOWER LIDS, UNTIL NO EVIDENCE OF CHEMICAL REMAINS (AT LEAST 15-20 MINUTES). CONTINUE IRRIGATING WITH NORMAL SALINE UNTIL THE PH HAS RETURNED TO NORMAL (30-60 MINUTES). COVER WITH STERILE BANDAGES. GET MEDICAL ATTENTION IMMEDIATELY.

INGESTION: PEROXYACETIC ACID: CORROSIVE. **ACUTE EXPOSURE-** MAY CAUSE BURNS OF THE MOUTH AND STOMACH. ABDOMINAL PAIN, NAUSEA, AND DIARRHEA MAY OCCUR. CORROSIVE SUBSTANCES MAY CAUSE DISCOLORATION OF THE TISSUES; SWALLOWING AND SPEECH MAY BE DIFFICULT AT FIRST AND THEN ALMOST IMPOSSIBLE. EDEMA OF THE EPIGLOTTIS AND SHOCK MAY OCCUR. INGESTION OF ORGANIC PEROXIDES MAY CAUSE DECREASED PULSE AND TEMPERATURE, DYSPNEA, AND STUPOR. **CHRONIC EXPOSURE-** DEPENDING ON THE CONCENTRATION, REPEATED INGESTION OF CORROSIVE SUBSTANCES MAY RESULT IN EFFECTS AS WITH ACUTE INGESTION.
FIRST AID- DO NOT USE GASTRIC LAVAGE OR EMESIS. DILUTE THE ACID IMMEDIATELY BY DRINKING LARGE QUANTITIES OF WATER OR MILK. IF VOMITING PERSISTS, ADMINISTER FLUIDS REPEATEDLY. INGESTED ACID MUST BE DILUTED APPROXIMATELY 100 FOLD TO RENDER IT HARMLESS TO TISSUES. MAINTAIN AIRWAY AND TREAT SHOCK (DREISBACH, HANDBOOK OF POISONING, 12TH ED.). GET MEDICAL ATTENTION IMMEDIATELY. IF VOMITING OCCURS, KEEP HEAD BELOW HIPS TO HELP PREVENT ASPIRATION.
ANTIDOTE: NO SPECIFIC ANTIDOTE. TREAT SYMPTOMATICALLY AND SUPPORTIVELY.

REACTIVITY

REACTIVITY: SHOCK AND HEAT SENSITIVE. EXPLODES WHEN HEATED TO 230 F (110 C).
INCOMPATIBILITIES: PEROXYACETIC ACID: ACETIC ANHYDRIDE: FORMS SHOCK SENSITIVE ACETYL PEROXIDE. 5-P-CHLOROPHENYL-2,2-DIMETHYL -3-HEXANONE: POSSIBLE EXPLOSION. ETHER SOLVENTS: VIOLENT REACTION. FLAMMABLE MATERIALS: FIRE AND EXPLOSION HAZARD. METAL CHLORIDES: VIOLENT EXOTHERMIC REACTION. 3-METHYL-3-BUTEN-1-YL TETRAHYDROPYRANYL ETHER: POSSIBLE FORMATION OF A HEAT AND SHOCK SENSITIVE COMPOUND. 1-OCTENE: POSSIBLE FORMATION OF HEAT AND SHOCK SENSITIVE COMPOUND. OLEFINS: VIOLENT, EXOTHERMIC REACTION. ORGANIC MATERIALS: IGNITION OR POSSIBLE EXPLOSION. OXIDIZABLE MATERIALS: FIRE AND EXPLOSION HAZARD.
DECOMPOSITION: THERMAL DECOMPOSITION MAY RELEASE ACRID SMOKE AND IRRITATING FUMES.
POLYMERIZATION: HAZARDOUS POLYMERIZATION HAS NOT BEEN REPORTED TO OCCUR UNDER NORMAL TEMPERATURES AND PRESSURES.

STORAGE AND DISPOSAL

****STORAGE****

STORE AWAY FROM INCOMPATIBLE SUBSTANCES.
SHOULD BE STORED IN COOL, VENTILATED, UNHEATED, WELL-DETACHED NONCOMBUSTIBLE BUILDING WITH NONCOMBUSTIBLE FLOORS. ISOLATE FROM OTHER STORED MATERIAL, PARTICULARLY ACCELERATORS, READILY OXIDIZABLE, ORGANIC, OR FLAMMABLE MATERIALS. PROHIBIT POSSIBLE SOURCES OF IGNITION, INCLUDING ELECTRICAL INSTALLATION*. LARGE-QUANTITY STORAGE SHOULD BE PROTECTED BY AUTOMATICDELUGE SPRINKLER SYSTEMS. PROTECT CONTAINERS AGAINST PHYSICAL DAMAGE (NFPA 49, HAZARDOUS CHEMICALS DATA, 1975). * SEE FLAMMABLE AND COMBUSTIBLE LIQUIDS CODE (NFPA NO. 30), NATIONAL ELECTRICAL CODE (NFPA NO. 70), FIRE-HAZARD PROPERTIES OF FLAMMABLE LIQUIDS, GASES, AND VOLATILE SOLIDS (NFPA NO. 325M), AND FIRE AND EXPLOSION HAZARDS OF ORGANIC PEROXIDES (AMERICAN INSURANCE ASSOCIATION (NBFU) RESEARCH REPORT NO. 11).
THRESHOLD PLANNING QUANTITY (TPQ): THE SUPERFUND AMENDMENTS AND REAUTHORIZATION ACT (SARA) SECTION 302 REQUIRES THAT EACH FACILITY WHERE ANY EXTREMELY HAZARDOUS SUBSTANCE IS PRESENT IN A QUANTITY EQUAL TO OR GREATER THAN THE TPQ ESTABLISHED FOR THAT SUBSTANCE NOTIFY THE STATE EMERGENCY RESPONSE COMMISSION FOR THE STATE IN

WHICH IT IS LOCATED. SECTION 303 OF SARA REQUIRES THESE FACILITIES TO PARTICIPATE IN LOCAL EMERGENCY RESPONSE PLANNING (40 CFR 355.30).

CONDITIONS TO AVOID

MAY BE IGNITED BY HEAT, SPARKS OR FLAMES. MAY EXPLODE FROM HEAT OR CONTAMINATION. CONTAINER MAY EXPLODE IN HEAT OF FIRE. RUNOFF TO SEWER MAY CREATE FIRE OR EXPLOSION HAZARD.

SPILL AND LEAK PROCEDURES

OCCUPATIONAL SPILL: SHUT OFF IGNITION SOURCES. DO NOT TOUCH SPILLED MATERIAL. STOP LEAK IF YOU CAN DO IT WITHOUT RISK. FOR SMALL SPILLS, TAKE UP WITH INERT, DAMP MATERIAL. MOVE CONTAINERS FROM SPILL AREA. FOR LARGER SPILLS, WET DOWN WITH WATER AND DIKE FOR LATER DISPOSAL. NO SMOKING, FLAMES OR FLARES IN HAZARD AREA! KEEP UNNECESSARY PEOPLE AWAY. ISOLATE HAZARD AREA AND DENY ENTRY.

REPORTABLE QUANTITY (RQ): 1 POUND THE SUPERFUND AMENDMENTS AND REAUTHORIZATION ACT (SARA) SECTION 304 REQUIRES THAT A RELEASE EQUAL TO OR GREATER THAN THE REPORTABLE QUANTITY FOR THIS SUBSTANCE BE IMMEDIATELY REPORTED TO THE LOCAL EMERGENCY PLANNING COMMITTEE AND THE STATE EMERGENCY RESPONSE COMMISSION (40 CFR 355.40). IF THE RELEASE OF THIS SUBSTANCE IS REPORTABLE UNDER CERCLA SECTION 103, THE NATIONAL RESPONSE CENTER MUST BE NOTIFIED IMMEDIATELY AT (800) 424-8802 OR (202) 426-2675 IN THE METROPOLITAN WASHINGTON, D.C. AREA (40 CFR 302.6).

PROTECTIVE EQUIPMENT

VENTILATION: PROVIDE LOCAL EXHAUST OR PROCESS ENCLOSURE VENTILATION SYSTEM.

RESPIRATOR: THE FOLLOWING RESPIRATORS ARE RECOMMENDED BASED ON INFORMATION FOUND IN THE PHYSICAL DATA, TOXICITY AND HEALTH EFFECTS SECTIONS. THEY ARE RANKED IN ORDER FROM MINIMUM TO MAXIMUM RESPIRATORY PROTECTION. THE SPECIFIC RESPIRATOR SELECTED MUST BE BASED ON CONTAMINATION LEVELS FOUND IN THE WORK PLACE, MUST NOT EXCEED THE WORKING LIMITS OF THE RESPIRATOR AND BE JOINTLY APPROVED BY THE NATIONAL INSTITUTE FOR OCCUPATIONAL SAFETY AND HEALTH AND THE MINE SAFETY AND HEALTH ADMINISTRATION (NIOSH-MSHA).

CHEMICAL CARTRIDGE RESPIRATOR WITH AN ORGANIC VAPOR CARTRIDGE(S) WITH AN ACID GAS CARTRIDGE(S) AND A FULL FACEPIECE.

GAS MASK WITH ORGANIC VAPOR CANISTER (CHIN-STYLE OR FRONT- OR BACK-MOUNTED CANISTER), WITH A FULL FACEPIECE, PROVIDING PROTECTION AGAINST ACID GASES.

TYPE 'C' SUPPLIED-AIR RESPIRATOR WITH A FULL FACEPIECE OPERATED IN PRESSURE-DEMAND OR OTHER POSITIVE PRESSURE MODE OR WITH A FULL FACEPIECE, HELMET OR HOOD OPERATED IN CONTINUOUS-FLOW MODE.

SELF-CONTAINED BREATHING APPARATUS WITH A FULL FACEPIECE OPERATED IN PRESSURE-DEMAND OR OTHER POSITIVE PRESSURE MODE.

FOR FIREFIGHTING AND OTHER IMMEDIATELY DANGEROUS TO LIFE OR HEALTH CONDITIONS:

SELF-CONTAINED BREATHING APPARATUS WITH FULL FACEPIECE OPERATED IN PRESSURE-DEMAND OR OTHER POSITIVE PRESSURE MODE.

SUPPLIED-AIR RESPIRATOR WITH FULL FACEPIECE AND OPERATED IN PRESSURE-DEMAND OR OTHER POSITIVE PRESSURE MODE IN COMBINATION WITH AN AUXILIARY SELF-CONTAINED BREATHING APPARATUS OPERATED IN PRESSURE-DEMAND OR OTHER POSITIVE PRESSURE MODE.

CLOTHING: EMPLOYEE MUST WEAR APPROPRIATE PROTECTIVE (IMPERVIOUS) CLOTHING AND EQUIPMENT TO PREVENT ANY POSSIBILITY OF SKIN CONTACT WITH THIS SUBSTANCE.

GLOVES: EMPLOYEE MUST WEAR APPROPRIATE PROTECTIVE GLOVES TO PREVENT CONTACT WITH THIS SUBSTANCE.

EYE PROTECTION: EMPLOYEE MUST WEAR SPLASH-PROOF OR DUST-RESISTANT SAFETY GOGGLES AND A FACESHIELD TO PREVENT CONTACT WITH THIS SUBSTANCE.

EMERGENCY WASH FACILITIES: WHERE THERE IS ANY POSSIBILITY THAT AN EMPLOYEE'S EYES AND/OR SKIN MAY BE EXPOSED TO THIS SUBSTANCE, THE EMPLOYER SHOULD PROVIDE AN EYE WASH FOUNTAIN AND QUICK DRENCH SHOWER WITHIN THE IMMEDIATE WORK AREA FOR EMERGENCY USE.

AUTHORIZED BY- OCCUPATIONAL HEALTH SERVICES, INC.
CREATION DATE: 11/17/89 ***REVISION DATE:*** 05/18/90

MATERIAL SAFETY DATA SHEET

OCCUPATIONAL HEALTH SERVICES, INC.
AGRICULTURE AND PESTICIDE DIVISION
450 SEVENTH AVENUE, SUITE 2407
NEW YORK, NEW YORK 10123
1-800-445-MSDS OR (212) 967-1100

EMERGENCY CONTACT:
JOHN S. BRANSFORD, JR. (615) 292-1180

SUBSTANCE IDENTIFICATION

CAS-NUMBER 68608-26-4
SUBSTANCE: **PETRONATE L**
TRADE NAMES/SYNONYMS: SODIUM PETROLEUM SULFONIC ACIDS; PST18339
CHEMICAL FAMILY: PETROLEUM HYDROCARBON
CERCLA RATINGS (SCALE 0-3): HEALTH=1 FIRE=1 REACTIVITY=0 PERSISTENCE=1
NFPA RATINGS (SCALE 0-4): HEALTH=1 FIRE=1 REACTIVITY=0

COMPONENTS AND CONTAMINANTS

COMPONENT: SODIUM SULFONIC ACIDS ***PERCENT:*** APPROX. 62
COMPONENT: MINERAL OIL (SEVERELY SOLVENT REFINED) ***PERCENT:*** APPROX. 33
COMPONENT: WATER ***PERCENT:*** APPROX. 5
OTHER CONTAMINANTS: NONE
EXPOSURE LIMITS: MINERAL OIL MIST: 5 MG/M3 OSHA TWA 5 MG/M3 ACGIH TWA; 10 MG/M3 ACGIH STEL

PHYSICAL DATA

DESCRIPTION: CLEAR, VISCOUS, BROWN LIQUID WITH A MILD PETROLEUM ODOR
BOILING POINT: 212 F (100 C) (WATER) ***SPECIFIC GRAVITY:*** <1 @ 70 C
VOLATILITY: NIL ***VAPOR PRESSURE:*** <0.5 MMHG @ 20 C ***EVAPORATION RATE:*** NIL
PH: 10-11 ***SOLUBILITY IN WATER:*** DISPERSIBLE

FIRE AND EXPLOSION DATA

FIRE AND EXPLOSION HAZARD: SLIGHT FIRE HAZARD WHEN EXPOSED TO HEAT OR FLAME.
FLASH POINT: >300 F (>150 C) (CC) ***FLAMMABILITY CLASS(OSHA):*** IIIB
FIREFIGHTING MEDIA: DRY CHEMICAL, CARBON DIOXIDE, HALON, WATER SPRAY OR STANDARD FOAM (1987 EMERGENCY RESPONSE GUIDEBOOK, DOT P 5800.4). FOR LARGER FIRES, USE WATER SPRAY OR FOG (FLOODING AMOUNTS) (1987 EMERGENCY RESPONSE GUIDEBOOK, DOT P 5800.4).
FIREFIGHTING: MOVE CONTAINERS FROM FIRE AREA IF POSSIBLE (1987 EMERGENCY RESPONSE GUIDEBOOK, DOT P 5800.4, GUIDE PAGE 61).
USE AGENTS SUITABLE FOR TYPE OF SURROUNDING FIRE. AVOID BREATHING HAZARDOUS VAPORS, KEEP UPWIND.

TOXICITY

PETRONATE L: TOXICITY DATA: 6.0 GM/KG ORAL-RAT LD50 (WITCO MSDS). CARCINOGEN STATUS: NONE. LOCAL EFFECTS: IRRITANT- INHALATION AND EYES. ACUTE TOXICITY LEVEL: SLIGHTLY TOXIC BY INGESTION. TARGET EFFECTS: NO DATA AVAILABLE.

HEALTH EFFECTS AND FIRST AID

INHALATION: PETRONATE L: IRRITANT. **ACUTE EXPOSURE-** INHALATION HAZARD IS LOW UNLESS HEATED OR MISTED WHICH MAY RESULT IN IRRITATION. **CHRONIC EXPOSURE-** NO DATA AVAILABLE ON THIS COMPOUND. REPEATED INHALATION OF OIL MISTS MAY CAUSE LIPID PNEUMONIA, INFLAMMATION WITH OR WITHOUT PNEUMONIA, FIBROSIS AND PARAFFINOMA.
FIRST AID- REMOVE FROM EXPOSURE AREA TO FRESH AIR IMMEDIATELY. IF BREATHING HAS STOPPED, PERFORM ARTIFICIAL RESPIRATION. KEEP PERSON WARM AND AT REST. TREAT SYMPTOMATICALLY AND SUPPORTIVELY. GET MEDICAL ATTENTION IMMEDIATELY.

SKIN CONTACT: PETRONATE L: **ACUTE EXPOSURE-** NO DATA AVAILABLE ON THIS COMPOUND. **CHRONIC EXPOSURE-** NO DATA AVAILABLE. SIMILAR COMPOUNDS SUCH AS SODIUM ALKYL ARYL SULFONATES HAVE CAUSED IRRITATION ON REPEATED OR PROLONGED CONTACT. CHRONIC EXPOSURE TO MINERAL OILS MAY CAUSE VARIOUS SKIN DISORDERS SUCH AS ECZEMATOUS OR CONTACT DERMATITIS, FOLLICULITIS, OIL ACNE, LIPID GRANULOMA, MELANOSIS, AND RARELY, PRECANCEROUS WARTS ON THE FOREARMS, BACKS OF HANDS OR SCROTUM.
FIRST AID- REMOVE CONTAMINATED CLOTHING AND SHOES IMMEDIATELY. WASH AFFECTED AREA WITH SOAP OR MILD DETERGENT AND LARGE AMOUNTS OF WATER UNTIL NO EVIDENCE OF CHEMICAL REMAINS (APPROXIMATELY 15-20 MINUTES). GET MEDICAL ATTENTION IMMEDIATELY.

EYE CONTACT: PETRONATE L: IRRITANT. **ACUTE EXPOSURE-** DIRECT CONTACT MAY CAUSE IRRITATION. **CHRONIC EXPOSURE-** REPEATED OR PROLONGED CONTACT MAY CAUSE CONJUNCTIVITIS.

FIRST AID- WASH EYES IMMEDIATELY WITH LARGE AMOUNTS OF WATER OR NORMAL SALINE, OCCASIONALLY LIFTING UPPER AND LOWER LIDS, UNTIL NO EVIDENCE OF CHEMICAL REMAINS (APPROXIMATELY 15-20 MINUTES). GET MEDICAL ATTENTION IMMEDIATELY.

INGESTION: PETRONATE L: ACUTE EXPOSURE- A DOSE OF 6 GM/KG WAS LETHAL TO 50% OF A TEST GROUP OF RATS. THE MINERAL OIL CONTENT MAY CAUSE GASTROINTESTINAL DISTURBANCES SUCH AS DIARRHEA. CHRONIC EXPOSURE- NO DATA AVAILABLE.
FIRST AID- TREAT SYMPTOMATICALLY AND SUPPORTIVELY. GET MEDICAL ATTENTION IMMEDIATELY. IF VOMITING OCCURS, KEEP HEAD LOWER THAN HIPS TO PREVENT ASPIRATION.
ANTIDOTE: NO SPECIFIC ANTIDOTE. TREAT SYMPTOMATICALLY AND SUPPORTIVELY.

REACTIVITY

REACTIVITY: STABLE UNDER NORMAL TEMPERATURES AND PRESSURES.
INCOMPATIBILITIES: PETRONATE L: OXIDIZERS: INCOMPATIBLE.
DECOMPOSITION: THERMAL DECOMPOSITION PRODUCTS MAY INCLUDE TOXIC OXIDES OF CARBON, NITROGEN, AND SULFUR.
POLYMERIZATION: HAZARDOUS POLYMERIZATION HAS NOT BEEN REPORTED TO OCCUR UNDER NORMAL TEMPERATURES AND PRESSURES.

CONDITIONS TO AVOID

MAY BURN BUT DOES NOT IGNITE READILY. AVOID CONTACT WITH STRONG OXIDIZERS, EXCESSIVE HEAT, SPARKS, OR OPEN FLAME.

SPILL AND LEAK PROCEDURES

OCCUPATIONAL SPILL: STOP LEAK IF YOU CAN DO IT WITHOUT RISK. FOR SMALL SPILLS, TAKE UP WITH SAND OR OTHER ABSORBENT MATERIAL AND PLACE INTO CLEAN, DRY CONTAINERS FOR LATER DISPOSAL. KEEP UNNECESSARY PEOPLE AWAY. ISOLATE HAZARD AREA AND DENY ENTRY.

PROTECTIVE EQUIPMENT

VENTILATION: PROVIDE GENERAL DILUTION VENTILATION TO MEET PUBLISHED EXPOSURE LIMITS.
RESPIRATOR: THE FOLLOWING RESPIRATORS ARE RECOMMENDED BASED ON INFORMATION FOUND IN THE PHYSICAL DATA, TOXICITY AND HEALTH EFFECTS SECTIONS. THEY ARE RANKED IN ORDER FROM MINIMUM TO MAXIMUM RESPIRATORY PROTECTION. THE SPECIFIC RESPIRATOR SELECTED MUST BE BASED ON CONTAMINATION LEVELS FOUND IN THE WORK PLACE, MUST NOT EXCEED THE WORKING LIMITS OF THE RESPIRATOR AND BE JOINTLY APPROVED BY THE NATIONAL INSTITUTE FOR OCCUPATIONAL SAFETY AND HEALTH AND THE MINE SAFETY AND HEALTH ADMINISTRATION (NIOSH-MSHA).
CHEMICAL CARTRIDGE RESPIRATOR WITH AN ORGANIC VAPOR CARTRIDGE(S) WITH A FULL FACEPIECE.
GAS MASK WITH ORGANIC VAPOR CANISTER (CHIN-STYLE OR FRONT- OR BACK-MOUNTED CANISTER) WITH A FULL FACEPIECE.
TYPE 'C' SUPPLIED-AIR RESPIRATOR WITH A FULL FACEPIECE OPERATED IN PRESSURE-DEMAND OR OTHER POSITIVE PRESSURE MODE OR WITH A FULL FACEPIECE, HELMET OR HOOD OPERATED IN CONTINUOUS-FLOW MODE.
SELF-CONTAINED BREATHING APPARATUS WITH A FULL FACEPIECE OPERATED IN PRESSURE-DEMAND OR OTHER POSITIVE PRESSURE MODE.
FOR FIREFIGHTING AND OTHER IMMEDIATELY DANGEROUS TO LIFE OR HEALTH CONDITIONS:
SELF-CONTAINED BREATHING APPARATUS WITH FULL FACEPIECE OPERATED IN PRESSURE-DEMAND OR OTHER POSITIVE PRESSURE MODE.
SUPPLIED-AIR RESPIRATOR WITH FULL FACEPIECE AND OPERATED IN PRESSURE-DEMAND OR OTHER POSITIVE PRESSURE MODE IN COMBINATION WITH AN AUXILIARY SELF-CONTAINED BREATHING APPARATUS OPERATED IN PRESSURE-DEMAND OR OTHER POSITIVE PRESSURE MODE.
CLOTHING: EMPLOYEE MUST WEAR APPROPRIATE PROTECTIVE (IMPERVIOUS) CLOTHING AND EQUIPMENT TO PREVENT REPEATED OR PROLONGED SKIN CONTACT WITH THIS SUBSTANCE.
GLOVES: EMPLOYEE MUST WEAR APPROPRIATE PROTECTIVE GLOVES TO PREVENT CONTACT WITH THIS SUBSTANCE.
EYE PROTECTION: EMPLOYEE MUST WEAR SPLASH-PROOF OR DUST-RESISTANT SAFETY GOGGLES TO PREVENT EYE CONTACT WITH THIS SUBSTANCE.
EMERGENCY EYE WASH: WHERE THERE IS ANY POSSIBILITY THAT AN EMPLOYEE'S EYES MAY BE EXPOSED TO THIS SUBSTANCE, THE EMPLOYER SHOULD PROVIDE AN EYE WASH FOUNTAIN WITHIN THE IMMEDIATE WORK AREA FOR EMERGENCY USE.

AUTHORIZED BY- OCCUPATIONAL HEALTH SERVICES, INC.
CREATION DATE: 11/17/89 ***REVISION DATE:*** 05/18/90

MATERIAL SAFETY DATA SHEET

OCCUPATIONAL HEALTH SERVICES, INC.
AGRICULTURE AND PESTICIDE DIVISION
450 SEVENTH AVENUE, SUITE 2407
NEW YORK, NEW YORK 10123
1-800-445-MSDS OR (212) 967-1100

EMERGENCY CONTACT:
JOHN S. BRANSFORD, JR. (615) 292-1180

SUBSTANCE IDENTIFICATION

CAS-NUMBER 62-44-2
SUBSTANCE: PHENACETIN
TRADE NAMES/SYNONYMS: ACETOPHENETIDIN; EMPIRIN COMPOUND; ASA COMPOUND; SINUTAB; TERRACYDIN; BROMO SELTZER; P-ACETOPHENETIDIDE; P-ETHOXY ACETANILIDE; 1- ACETAMIDO-4-ETHOXYBENZENE; 4-ETHOXYACETANILIDE; N-PARA-ETHOXYACETANILIDE; N-(4-ETHOXYPHENYL) ACETAMIDE; N-ACETYL-P-PHENETIDINE; ACETYLPHENETIDIN; ACETAMIDE, N-(4-ETHOXYPHENYL)-; RCRA U187; C10H13NO2; PST18340
CHEMICAL FAMILY: AMIDE, AROMATIC
MOLECULAR FORMULA: C10-H13-N-O2
MOLECULAR WEIGHT: 179.24
CERCLA RATINGS (SCALE 0-3): HEALTH = 2 FIRE = 0 REACTIVITY = 0 PERSISTENCE = 1
NFPA RATINGS (SCALE 0-4): HEALTH = 2 FIRE = 0 REACTIVITY = 0

COMPONENTS AND CONTAMINANTS

COMPONENT: PHENACETIN ***PERCENT:*** 100
CAS# 62-44-2
OTHER CONTAMINANTS: NONE
EXPOSURE LIMITS: NO OCCUPATIONAL EXPOSURE LIMITS ESTABLISHED BY OSHA, ACGIH, OR NIOSH.
PHENACETIN: 100 POUNDS CERCLA SECTION 103 REPORTABLE QUANTITY.
SUBJECT TO CALIFORNIA PROPOSITION 65 CANCER AND/OR REPRODUCTIVE TOXICITY WARNING AND RELEASE REQUIREMENTS- (OCTOBER 1, 1989)

PHYSICAL DATA

DESCRIPTION: ODORLESS, SLIGHTLY BITTER, COLORLESS CRYSTALS OR POWDER.
BOILING POINT: DECOMPOSES ***MELTING POINT:*** 273 F (134 C)
SOLUBILITY IN WATER: SLIGHTLY SOLUBLE
SOLVENT SOLUBILITY: ALCOHOL, ETHER, CHLOROFORM, PYRIMIDINE

FIRE AND EXPLOSION DATA

FIRE AND EXPLOSION HAZARD: NEGLIGIBLE FIRE HAZARD WHEN EXPOSED TO HEAT OR FLAME.
FIREFIGHTING MEDIA: DRY CHEMICAL, CARBON DIOXIDE, HALON, WATER SPRAY OR STANDARD FOAM (1987 EMERGENCY RESPONSE GUIDEBOOK, DOT P 5800.4).
FOR LARGER FIRES, USE WATER SPRAY, FOG OR STANDARD FOAM (1987 EMERGENCY RESPONSE GUIDEBOOK, DOT P 5800.4).
FIREFIGHTING: MOVE CONTAINER FROM FIRE AREA IF POSSIBLE. DO NOT SCATTER SPILLED MATERIAL WITH HIGH PRESSURE WATER STREAMS. DIKE FIRE CONTROL WATER FOR LATER DISPOSAL (1987 EMERGENCY RESPONSE GUIDEBOOK, DOT P 5800.4, GUIDE PAGE 31).
USE AGENTS SUITABLE FOR TYPE OF SURROUNDING FIRE. AVOID BREATHING HAZARDOUS VAPORS, KEEP UPWIND.

TOXICITY

PHENACETIN: TOXICITY DATA: 3600 MG/KG ORAL-RAT LD50; 866 MG/KG ORAL-MOUSE LD50; 2500 MG/KG ORAL-RABBIT LD50; 1690 MG/KG ORAL-HAMSTER LD50; 1870 MG/KG ORAL-GUINEA PIG LD50; 1625 MG/KG SUBCUTANEOUS-MOUSE LD50; 1 GM/KG SUBCUTANEOUS-RABBIT LD50; 260 MG/KG INTRAVENOUS-DOG LDLO; 630 MG/KG INTRAPERITONEAL-RAT LD50; 540 MG/KG INTRAPERITONEAL-MOUSE LD50; 74 MG/KG UNREPORTED-MAN LDLO; MUTAGENIC DATA (RTECS); REPRODUCTIVE EFFECTS DATA (RTECS); TUMORIGENIC DATA (RTECS).
CARCINOGEN STATUS: HUMAN LIMITED EVIDENCE, ANIMAL SUFFICIENT EVIDENCE (IARC GROUP-2A); ANTICIPATED HUMAN CARCINOGEN (NTP). AVAILABLE DATA INDICATE THAT HEAVY USE OF ANALGESIC MIXTURES CONTAINING PHENACETIN IS ASSOCIATED WITH PAPILLARY NECROSIS OF THE KIDNEY AND SUGGEST A RELATIONSHIP BETWEEN SUCH USE AND THE DEVELOPMENT OF TRANSITIONAL-CELL CARCINOMA OF THE RENAL PELVIS. ACUTE TOXICITY LEVEL: MODERATELY TOXIC BY INGESTION. TARGET EFFECTS: METHEMOGLOBIN FORMER. POISONING MAY ALSO AFFECT THE LIVER, KIDNEYS, HEART AND CENTRAL NERVOUS SYSTEM.

HEALTH EFFECTS AND FIRST AID

INHALATION: **ACUTE EXPOSURE-** NO DATA AVAILABLE. MAY CAUSE IRRITATION. **CHRONIC EXPOSURE-** NO DATA AVAILABLE.

FIRST AID- REMOVE FROM EXPOSURE AREA TO FRESH AIR IMMEDIATELY. IF BREATHING HAS STOPPED, PERFORM ARTIFICIAL RESPIRATION. KEEP PERSON WARM AND AT REST. TREAT SYMPTOMATICALLY AND SUPPORTIVELY. GET MEDICAL ATTENTION IMMEDIATELY.

SKIN CONTACT: **ACUTE EXPOSURE-** NO DATA AVAILABLE. MAY CAUSE IRRITATION. **CHRONIC EXPOSURE-** NO DATA AVAILABLE.

FIRST AID- REMOVE CONTAMINATED CLOTHING AND SHOES IMMEDIATELY. WASH AFFECTED AREA WITH SOAP OR MILD DETERGENT AND LARGE AMOUNTS OF WATER UNTIL NO EVIDENCE OF CHEMICAL REMAINS (APPROXIMATELY 15-20 MINUTES). GET MEDICAL ATTENTION IMMEDIATELY.

EYE CONTACT: **ACUTE EXPOSURE-** NO IRRITATION DATA AVAILABLE. SYSTEMIC EFFECTS INCLUDE LACRIMATION IN MICE FEEDING STUDIES. **CHRONIC EXPOSURE-** NO DATA AVAILABLE.

FIRST AID- WASH EYES IMMEDIATELY WITH LARGE AMOUNTS OF WATER OR NORMAL SALINE, OCCASIONALLY LIFTING UPPER AND LOWER LIDS, UNTIL NO EVIDENCE OF CHEMICAL REMAINS (APPROXIMATELY 15-20 MINUTES). GET MEDICAL ATTENTION IMMEDIATELY.

INGESTION: METHEMOGLOBIN FORMER. **ACUTE EXPOSURE-** MAY CAUSE RELAXATION, DROWSINESS, EUPHORIA, STIMULATION AND INCREASED EFFICIENCY. A LARGE DOSE MAY CAUSE CYANOSIS, DIZZINESS, EXCITEMENT, HEMOLYSIS, DEPRESSED RESPIRATION, AND TOXIC PSYCHOSIS. METHEMOGLOBINEMIA, HEMOLYTIC ANEMIA, ARRHYTHMIAS, AND CARDIAC ARREST MAY OCCUR. IN ACUTE POISONING, SURVIVAL FOR FOUR DAYS INDICATES THAT RECOVERY WILL USUALLY OCCUR. LACRIMATION, CONVULSIONS AND EFFECTS ON SEIZURE THRESHOLD, AND CHANGES IN THE STRUCTURE OR FUNCTION OF THE SALIVARY GLANDS OCCURRED IN MICE FEEDING STUDIES. **CHRONIC EXPOSURE-** MAY CAUSE WEIGHT LOSS, SHORTNESS OF BREATH, ABDOMINAL PAINS, HEADACHE, CYANOSIS DUE TO METHEMOGLOBINEMIA, HEMOLYTIC ANEMIA, WEAKNESS, DIZZINESS, IRRITABILITY, LOW BLOOD PRESSURE, SLEEPLESSNESS, AND SKIN ERUPTIONS CHARACTERIZED BY ERYTHEMA AND PAPULAR OR ULCERATIVE ACNE. REPORTS OF MASSIVE INGESTION OVER PERIODS OF MONTHS OR EVEN YEARS INDICATE THE POSSIBLE OCCURRENCE OF PHENACETIN DEPENDENCE. HOWEVER, SKIN RASH AND OTHER ALLERGIC REACTIONS MAY OCCUR. IT MAY BE ACCOMPANIED BY DRUG FEVER AND MUCOSAL LESIONS. PATIENTS WHO ARE SENSITIVE TO SALICYLATE MAY EXHIBIT SENSITIVITY. IN CHRONIC POISONING, RECOVERY IS GENERALLY THE RULE. HOWEVER, 3-10 GRAMS DAILY FOR MONTHS TO YEARS, HAS CAUSED SEVERE RENAL INJURY CHARACTERIZED BY CHRONIC INTERSTITIAL NEPHRITIS WITH PAPILLARY NECROSIS AND SEVERE TUBULAR DEGENERATION, WHICH IS SOMETIMES IRREVERSIBLE AND FATAL. CARCINOMA OF THE RENAL PELVIS AND BLADDER IS REPORTED TO BE INCREASED AFTER PROLONGED USE. KIDNEY TUMORS OCCURRED IN A MAN USING 57 GM/KG FOR 47 YEARS INTERMITTENTLY, BY A WOMAN USING 80 GM/KG FOR 63 YEARS INTERMITTENTLY, AND BY A HUMAN USING 73 GM/KG FOR ONE YEAR CONTINUOUSLY. TUMORS OF THE NOSE, EAR, LIVER, AND BLADDER HAVE BEEN REPORTED IN RAT FEEDING STUDIES. TUMORS OF THE BLADDER, KIDNEYS, AND SKIN HAVE BEEN REPORTED IN MICE FEEDING STUDIES.

FIRST AID- REMOVE INGESTED DRUG BY EMESIS WITH SYRUP OF IPECAC UNLESS RESPIRATION IS DEPRESSED. DO NOT USE APOMORPHINE. ACTIVATED CHARCOAL INTERFERES WITH THE USE OF N-ACETYLCYSTEINE. GIVE A SALINE CATHARTIC. IF RESPIRATION IS DEPRESSED, USE AIRWAY-PROTECTED GASTRIC LAVAGE. EFFORTS TO REMOVE THE DRUG ARE USELESS AFTER FOUR HOURS. GET MEDICAL ATTENTION IMMEDIATELY. TREATMENT SHOULD BE ADMINISTERED BY QUALIFIED MEDICAL PERSONNEL. (DREISBACH, HANDBOOK OF POISONING 11TH ED.).

ANTIDOTE: THE FOLLOWING ANTIDOTE HAS BEEN RECOMMENDED. HOWEVER, THE DECISION AS TO WHETHER THE SEVERITY OF POISONING REQUIRES ADMINISTRATION OF ANY ANTIDOTE AND ACTUAL DOSE REQUIRED SHOULD BE MADE BY QUALIFIED MEDICAL PERSONNEL.

ACETAMINOPHEN OR PHENACETIN POISONING: IF THE 4-HOUR PLASMA ACETAMINOPHEN LEVEL EXCEEDS 150 UG/ML, THE ADMINISTRATION OF N-ACETYLCYSTEINE (AVAILABLE AS MUCOMYST) IS SUGGESTED. N-ACETYLCYSTEINE IS GIVEN ORALLY, 140 MG OF 20% SOLUTION PER KILOGRAM AS A LOADING DOSE, FOLLOWED BY 70 MG/KG EVERY 4 HOURS FOR 3 DAYS (DREISBACH, HANDBOOK OF POISONING, 11TH ED.). ANTIDOTE SHOULD BE ADMINISTERED BY QUALIFIED MEDICAL PERSONNEL.

REACTIVITY

REACTIVITY: STABLE UNDER NORMAL TEMPERATURES AND PRESSURES.

INCOMPATIBILITIES: NONE KNOWN.

DECOMPOSITION: THERMAL DECOMPOSITION PRODUCTS MAY INCLUDE TOXIC OXIDES OF CARBON AND NITROGEN.

POLYMERIZATION: HAZARDOUS POLYMERIZATION HAS NOT BEEN REPORTED TO OCCUR UNDER NORMAL TEMPERATURES AND PRESSURES.

CONDITIONS TO AVOID

MAY BURN BUT DOES NOT IGNITE READILY. AVOID CONTACT WITH STRONG OXIDIZERS, EXCESSIVE HEAT, SPARKS, OR OPEN FLAME.

SPILL AND LEAK PROCEDURES

OCCUPATIONAL SPILL: SWEEP UP AND PLACE IN SUITABLE CLEAN, DRY CONTAINERS FOR RECLAMATION OR LATER DISPOSAL. DO NOT FLUSH SPILLED MATERIAL INTO SEWER. KEEP UNNECESSARY PEOPLE AWAY.

REPORTABLE QUANTITY (RQ): 100 POUNDS THE SUPERFUND AMENDMENTS AND REAUTHORIZATION ACT (SARA) SECTION 304 REQUIRES THAT A RELEASE EQUAL TO OR GREATER THAN THE REPORTABLE QUANTITY FOR THIS SUBSTANCE BE IMMEDIATELY REPORTED TO THE LOCAL EMERGENCY PLANNING COMMITTEE AND THE STATE EMERGENCY RESPONSE COMMISSION (40 CFR 355.40). IF THE RELEASE OF THIS SUBSTANCE IS REPORTABLE UNDER CERCLA SECTION 103, THE NATIONAL RESPONSE CENTER MUST BE NOTIFIED IMMEDIATELY AT (800) 424-8802 OR (202) 426-2675 IN THE METROPOLITAN WASHINGTON, D.C. AREA (40 CFR 302.6).

PROTECTIVE EQUIPMENT

VENTILATION: PROVIDE LOCAL EXHAUST OR GENERAL DILUTION VENTILATION SYSTEM.

RESPIRATOR: HIGH LEVELS- HIGH-EFFICIENCY PARTICULATE RESPIRATOR. SUPPLIED-AIR RESPIRATOR. SELF-CONTAINED BREATHING APPARATUS.

FIRE FIGHTING- SELF-CONTAINED BREATHING APPARATUS WITH A FULL FACEPIECE, OPERATED IN PRESSURE-DEMAND OR OTHER POSITIVE PRESSURE MODE.

CLOTHING: PROTECTIVE CLOTHING NOT REQUIRED. AVOID REPEATED OR PROLONGED CONTACT WITH THIS SUBSTANCE.

GLOVES: PROTECTIVE GLOVES ARE NOT REQUIRED BUT RECOMMENDED.

EYE PROTECTION: EMPLOYEE MUST WEAR SPLASH-PROOF OR DUST-RESISTANT SAFETY GOGGLES TO PREVENT EYE CONTACT WITH THIS SUBSTANCE.

EMERGENCY EYE WASH: WHERE THERE IS ANY POSSIBILITY THAT AN EMPLOYEE'S EYES MAY BE EXPOSED TO THIS SUBSTANCE, THE EMPLOYER SHOULD PROVIDE AN EYE WASH FOUNTAIN WITHIN THE IMMEDIATE WORK AREA FOR EMERGENCY USE.

AUTHORIZED BY- OCCUPATIONAL HEALTH SERVICES, INC.
CREATION DATE: 10/04/89 ***REVISION DATE:*** 07/12/90

MATERIAL SAFETY DATA SHEET

OCCUPATIONAL HEALTH SERVICES, INC.
AGRICULTURE AND PESTICIDE DIVISION
450 SEVENTH AVENUE, SUITE 2407
NEW YORK, NEW YORK 10123
1-800-445-MSDS OR (212) 967-1100

EMERGENCY CONTACT:
JOHN S. BRANSFORD, JR. (615) 292-1180

SUBSTANCE IDENTIFICATION

CAS-NUMBER 2275-14-1

SUBSTANCE: **PHENCAPTON**

TRADE NAMES/SYNONYMS: PHOSPHORODITHIOIC ACID, S-((2,4-DICHLOROPHENYL)THIO)METHYL) O,O-DIETHYL ESTER; S-2,5,-DICHLOROPHENYLTHIOMETHYL O,O-DIETHYL PHOSPHORODITHIOATE; S-(((2,5-DICHLOROPHENYL)THIO)METHYL) O,O-DIETHYL PHOSPHORODITHIOATE; S-(2,5-DICHLOROPHENYLTHIOMETHYL)DIETHYL PHOSPHOROTHIOLOTHIONATE; O,O-DIETHYL S-(2,5-DICHLOROPHENYLTHIOMETHYL) PHOSPHORODITHIOATE; CMP; G 28029; GEIGY 28029; GEIGY G 28029; PHENKAPTON; PHENKAPTONE; PHENUDIN; PHENUDINE; ENT 25585; STCC 4941163; PST18373

CHEMICAL FAMILY: ORGANOPHOSPHATE

MOLECULAR FORMULA: C11-H13-CL2-O2-P-S3

MOLECULAR WEIGHT: 375.29

CERCLA RATINGS (SCALE 0-3): HEALTH=3 FIRE=U REACTIVITY=U PERSISTENCE=3

NFPA RATINGS (SCALE 0-4): HEALTH=3 FIRE=U REACTIVITY=U

COMPONENTS AND CONTAMINANTS

COMPONENT: PHENCAPTAN ***PERCENT:*** 100
CAS# 2275-14-1

OTHER CONTAMINANTS: NONE

EXPOSURE LIMITS: NO OCCUPATIONAL EXPOSURE LIMITS ESTABLISHED BY OSHA, ACGIH, OR NIOSH.

PHYSICAL DATA

DESCRIPTION: YELLOWISH LIQUID WITH A SLIGHT ODOR
BOILING POINT: 248 F (120 C) @ 0.001 MMHG
MELTING POINT: APPROXIMATELY 61 F (16 C) ***SPECIFIC GRAVITY:*** 1.3507 @ 21 C
EVAPORATION RATE: NOT AVAILABLE ***SOLUBILITY IN WATER:*** INSOLUBLE
SOLVENT SOLUBILITY: SLIGHTLY SOLUBLE IN METHANOL, GLYCOL, GLYCEROL AND OTHER POLAR SOLVENTS; HIGHLY SOLUBLE IN NONPOLAR SOLVENTS

FIRE AND EXPLOSION DATA

FIRE AND EXPLOSION HAZARD: UNKNOWN FIRE AND EXPLOSION HAZARD.
FIREFIGHTING MEDIA: DRY CHEMICAL, CARBON DIOXIDE, HALON, WATER SPRAY OR STANDARD FOAM (1987 EMERGENCY RESPONSE GUIDEBOOK, DOT P 5800.4). FOR LARGER FIRES, USE WATER SPRAY, FOG OR STANDARD FOAM (1987 EMERGENCY RESPONSE GUIDEBOOK, DOT P 5800.4).
FIREFIGHTING: MOVE CONTAINERS FROM FIRE AREA IF POSSIBLE. FIGHT FIRE FROM MAXIMUM DISTANCE. STAY AWAY FROM STORAGE TANK ENDS. DIKE FIRE CONTROL WATER FOR LATER DISPOSAL. DO NOT SCATTER MATERIAL (1987 EMERGENCY RESPONSE GUIDEBOOK, DOT P 5800.4, GUIDE PAGE 55). EXTINGUISH ONLY IF FLOW CAN BE STOPPED; USE FLOODING AMOUNTS OF WATER AS FOG, SOLID STREAMS MAY BE INEFFECTIVE. COOL CONTAINERS WITH FLOODING AMOUNTS OF WATER FROM AS FAR A DISTANCE AS POSSIBLE. USE WATER SPRAY TO ABSORB TOXIC VAPORS. AVOID BREATHING TOXIC VAPORS; KEEP UPWIND. CONSIDER EVACUATION OF DOWNWIND AREA IF MATERIAL IS LEAKING.

TRANSPORTATION DATA

DEPARTMENT OF TRANSPORTATION HAZARD CLASSIFICATION 49 CFR 172.101: ORM-A
DEPARTMENT OF TRANSPORTATION LABELING REQUIREMENTS 49 CFR 172.101 AND SUBPART E: NONE
DEPARTMENT OF TRANSPORTATION PACKAGING REQUIREMENTS: 49 CFR 173.510 EXCEPTIONS: 49 CFR 173.505

TOXICITY

PHENCAPTON: TOXICITY DATA: 652 MG/KG SKIN-RAT LD50; 44 MG/KG ORAL-RAT LD50; 220 MG/KG ORAL-MOUSE LD50; 200 MG/KG UNREPORTED-MAMMAL LD50. CARCINOGEN STATUS: NONE. ACUTE TOXICITY LEVEL: HIGHLY TOXIC BY INGESTION; TOXIC BY DERMAL ABSORPTION. TARGET EFFECTS: CHOLINESTERASE INHIBITOR. POISONING MAY AFFECT THE NERVOUS SYSTEM.* AT INCREASED RISK FROM EXPOSURE: PERSONS WITH RESPIRATORY AILMENTS, RECENT EXPOSURE TO CHOLINESTERASE INHIBITORS OR IMPAIRED CHOLINESTERASE PRODUCTION, OR LIVER MALFUNCTION.* ADDITIONAL DATA: MAY CROSS THE PLACENTA. HIGH ENVIRONMENTAL TEMPERATURES OR EXPOSURE OF THE CHEMICAL TO VISIBLE OR ULTRAVIOLET LIGHT MAY ENHANCE THE TOXICITY. INTERACTIONS WITH MEDICATIONS MAY OCCUR.*

* MAY BE BASED ON GENERAL INFORMATION ON ORGANOPHOSPHATES.

HEALTH EFFECTS AND FIRST AID

INHALATION: PHENCAPTON: SEE INFORMATION ON ORGANOPHOSPHATES.
ORGANOPHOSPHATES: CHOLINESTERASE INHIBITOR. **ACUTE EXPOSURE-** WHEN INHALED, THE FIRST EFFECTS OF CHOLINESTERASE INHIBITORS ARE USUALLY RESPIRATORY AND MAY INCLUDE NASAL HYPEREMIA AND WATERY DISCHARGE, COUGH, CHEST DISCOMFORT, DYSPNEA, AND WHEEZING DUE TO INCREASED BRONCHIAL SECRETIONS AND BRONCHOCONSTRICTION. IF SUFFICIENT AMOUNTS ARE ABSORBED, OTHER SYSTEMIC EFFECTS MAY BEGIN WITHIN A FEW MINUTES OR BE DELAYED FOR UP TO 12 HOURS. SYMPTOMS MAY INCLUDE PALLOR, NAUSEA, VOMITING, DIARRHEA, ABDOMINAL CRAMPS, HEADACHE, DIZZINESS, OCULAR PAIN, BLURRED VISION, MIOSIS OR IN SOME CASES, ESPECIALLY INITIALLY, MYDRIASIS, LACRIMATION, SALIVATION, SWEATING, AND CONFUSION. OTHER REPORTED CENTRAL NERVOUS SYSTEM OR NEUROMUSCULAR EFFECTS MAY INCLUDE ATAXIA, SLURRED SPEECH, AREFLEXIA, WEAKNESS, FATIGUE, FASCICULATIONS, TWITCHING, TREMORS POSSIBLY OF THE TONGUE AND EYELIDS, AND EVENTUALLY PARALYSIS OF THE EXTREMITIES AND POSSIBLY OF THE RESPIRATORY MUSCLES. IN SEVERE CASES THERE MAY ALSO BE INVOLUNTARY DEFECATION AND URINATION, CYANOSIS, PSYCHOSIS, HYPERGLYCEMIA, ACUTE PANCREATITIS, CARDIAC IRREGULARITIES, PULMONARY EDEMA, UNCONSCIOUSNESS, CONVULSIONS, AND COMA. DEATH IS PRIMARILY DUE TO RESPIRATORY FAILURE, ALTHOUGH CARDIOVASCULAR EFFECTS INCLUDING CARDIAC ARREST MAY ALSO BE IMPLICATED. LONG TERM SEQUELAE ARE RARE BUT MAY INCLUDE NEUROPSYCHIATRIC DISORDERS AND MYOPATHY WITH MUSCLE TENDERNESS. SOME ORGANOPHOSPHATES MAY CAUSE A DELAYED NEUROPATHY BEGINNING 1-4 WEEKS AFTER AN ACUTE EXPOSURE WHICH MAY OR MAY NOT HAVE CAUSED ACUTE CHOLINERGIC EFFECTS. NUMBNESS, TINGLING, WEAKNESS AND CRAMPING BEGINNING SYMMETRICALLY IN THE LOWER LIMBS MAY PROGRESS TO ATAXIA AND PARALYSIS. IN SEVERE CASES, UPPER LIMB INVOLVEMENT IS POSSIBLE AND FLACCID PARALYSIS MAY PROGRESS TO SPASTIC PARALYSIS WITH EXAGGERATED REFLEXES. IMPROVEMENT MAY OCCUR OVER MONTHS TO YEARS, BUT SOME RESIDUAL IMPAIRMENT USUALLY REMAINS. **CHRONIC EXPOSURE-** REPEATED OR PROLONGED EXPOSURE MAY RESULT IN THE EFFECTS OF ACUTE EXPOSURE INCLUDING THE DELAYED NEUROPATHY. OTHER EFFECTS REPORTED IN WORKERS REPEATEDLY EXPOSED INCLUDE IMPAIRED MEMORY AND CONCENTRATION, ACUTE PSYCHOSIS, SEVERE DEPRESSIONS, IRRITABILTY, CONFUSION, APATHY, EMOTIONAL LABILITY, SOCIAL WITHDRAWAL, CONFUSION, HEADACHE, SPEECH DIFFICULTIES, DELAYED REACTION TIMES, SPATIAL DISORIENTATION, NIGHTMARES, SLEEPWALKING, AND DROWSINESS OR INSOMNIA. AN INFLUENZA-LIKE CONDITION WITH HEADACHE, NAUSEA, WEAKNESS, ANOREXIA AND MALAISE HAS ALSO BEEN REPORTED.
FIRST AID- REMOVE FROM EXPOSURE AREA TO FRESH AIR IMMEDIATELY. IF BREATHING HAS STOPPED, GIVE ARTIFICIAL RESPIRATION. MAINTAIN AIRWAY AND BLOOD PRESSURE AND ADMINISTER OXYGEN IF AVAILABLE. KEEP AFFECTED PERSON WARM AND AT REST. TREAT SYMPTOMATICALLY AND SUPPORTIVELY. ADMINISTRATION OF OXYGEN SHOULD BE PERFORMED BY QUALIFIED PERSONNEL. GET MEDICAL ATTENTION IMMEDIATELY.

SKIN CONTACT: PHENCAPTON: TOXIC. SEE INFORMATION ON ORGANOPHOSPHATES.
ORGANOPHOSPHATES: CHOLINESTERASE INHIBITOR. **ACUTE EXPOSURE-** LOCALIZED SWEATING AND FASCICULATIONS MAY OCCUR AT THE SITE OF CONTACT. IF SUFFICIENT AMOUNTS ARE ABSORBED, OTHER EFFECTS OF CHOLINESTERASE INHIBITION AS DESCRIBED IN ACUTE INHALATION MAY OCCUR. SYMPTOMS MAY BE DELAYED 2-3 HOURS, BUT USUALLY NO MORE THAN 12 HOURS. THE RATE OF ABSORPTION IS INCREASED BY THE PRESENCE OF DERMATITIS OR HIGH AMBIENT TEMPERATURES. DELAYED NEUROPATHY IS ALSO POSSIBLE. **CHRONIC EXPOSURE-** REPEATED OR PROLONGED EXPOSURE MAY CAUSE EFFECTS AS DESCRIBED IN ACUTE EXPOSURE. SOME ORGANOPHOSPHATES MAY CAUSE SENSITIZATION.
FIRST AID- REMOVE CONTAMINATED CLOTHING IMMEDIATELY. WASH CONTAMINATED AREAS WITH SOAP AND WATER FOLLOWED BY ALCOHOL (ARENA, POISONING, 4TH ED.). EMERGENCY PERSONNEL SHOULD WEAR GLOVES AND AVOID CONTAMINATION. TREAT RESPIRATORY DIFFICULTY WITH ARTIFICIAL RESPIRATION. GET MEDICAL ATTENTION IMMEDIATELY.

EYE CONTACT: PHENCAPTON: SEE INFORMATION ON ORGANOPHOSPHATES.
ORGANOPHOSPHATES: CHOLINESTERASE INHIBITOR. **ACUTE EXPOSURE-** DIRECT CONTACT MAY CAUSE PAIN, HYPEREMIA, LACRIMATION, TWITCHING OF THE EYELIDS, MIOSIS, AND CILIARY MUSCLE SPASM WITH LOSS OF ACCOMODATION, BLURRED OR DIMMED VISION AND BROWACHE. SOMETIMES MYDRIASIS MAY OCCUR INSTEAD OF MIOSIS. WITH SUFFICIENT EXPOSURE, OTHER SYMPTOMS OF CHOLINESTERASE INHIBITION AS DESCRIBED IN ACUTE INHALATION MAY OCCUR. **CHRONIC EXPOSURE-** REPEATED OR PROLONGED EXPOSURE MAY CAUSE EFFECTS AS DESCRIBED IN ACUTE EXPOSURE. SOME COMPOUNDS HAVE CAUSED TOXIC EFFECTS ON THE CRYSTALLINE LENS, CONJUNCTIVAL THICKENING AND OBSTRUCTION OF THE NASOLACRIMAL CANALS WHEN USED AS MIOTIC EYEDROPS.
FIRST AID- IRRIGATE EYES WITH WATER OR SALINE SOLUTION. IF SYMPTOMS OF POISONING OCCUR, TREAT RESPIRATORY DIFFICULTY WITH ARTIFICIAL RESPIRATION AND OXYGEN. OBSERVE PATIENT FOR AT LEAST 24-36 HOURS (GOSSELIN, CLINICAL TOXICOLOGY OF COMMERCIAL PRODUCTS, 5TH ED.). GET MEDICAL ATTENTION IMMEDIATELY. OXYGEN SHOULD BE ADMINISTERED BY QUALIFIED MEDICAL PERSONNEL.

INGESTION: PHENCAPTON: HIGHLY TOXIC. SEE INFORMATION ON ORGANOPHOSPHATES.
ORGANOPHOSPHATES: CHOLINESTERASE INHIBITOR. **ACUTE EXPOSURE-** WHEN INGESTED, THE FIRST EFFECTS MAY BE NAUSEA, VOMITING, ANOREXIA, ABDOMINAL CRAMPS AND DIARRHEA. GASTROINTESTINAL ABSORPTION MAY CAUSE SYMPTOMS OF CHOLINESTERASE INHIBITION AS DESCRIBED IN ACUTE INHALATION. SYMPTOMS MAY BEGIN WITHIN MINUTES OR BE DELAYED FOR HOURS. DELAYED EFFECTS INCLUDING NEUROPATHY MAY ALSO OCCUR. **CHRONIC EXPOSURE-** REPEATED INGESTION MAY CAUSE EFFECTS AS DESCRIBED IN ACUTE EXPOSURE.
FIRST AID- IF PERSON IS ALERT AND RESPIRATION IS NOT DEPRESSED, GIVE SYRUP OF IPECAC FOLLOWED BY WATER (IF VOMITING OCCURS, KEEP HEAD BELOW HIPS TO PREVENT ASPIRATION). IF CONSCIOUSNESS LEVEL DECLINES OR VOMITING HAS NOT OCCURRED IN 15 MINUTES EMPTY STOMACH BY GASTRIC LAVAGE WITH THE AID OF CUFFED ENDOTRACHEAL TUBE USING ISOTONIC SALINE OR 5% SODIUM BICARBONATE FOLLOW WITH ACTIVATED CHARCOAL. ESTABLISH AND MAINTAIN AIRWAY. TREAT RESPIRATORY DIFFICULTY WITH ARTIFICIAL RESPIRATION AND OXYGEN. DO NOT GIVE MORPHINE, AMINOPHYLLINE, PHENOTHIAZINES, RESERPINE, FUROSEMIDE, OR ETHACRYNIC ACID (MORGAN, RECOGNITION AND MANAGEMENT

OF PESTICIDE POISONINGS, 3RD ED.). TREAT SYMPTOMATICALLY AND SUPPORTIVELY. ADMINISTRATION OF OXYGEN AND LAVAGE MUST BE PERFORMED BY QUALIFIED MEDICAL PERSONNEL. GET MEDICAL ATTENTION IMMEDIATELY.

ANTIDOTE: THE FOLLOWING ANTIDOTE(S) HAVE BEEN RECOMMENDED. HOWEVER, THE DECISION AS TO WHETHER THE SEVERITY OF POISONING REQUIRES ADMINISTRATION OF ANY ANTIDOTE AND ACTUAL DOSE REQUIRED SHOULD BE MADE BY QUALIFIED MEDICAL PERSONNEL.

FOR CHOLINESTERASE INHIBITORS: ESTABLISH CLEAR AIRWAY AND TISSUE OXYGENATION BY ASPIRATION OF SECRETIONS, AND IF NECESSARY, BY ASSISTED PULMONARY VENTILATION WITH OXYGEN. IMPROVE TISSUE OXYGENATION AS MUCH AS POSSIBLE BEFORE ADMINISTERING ATROPINE TO MINIMIZE THE RISK OF VENTRICULAR FIBRILLATION. ADMINISTER ATROPINE SULFATE INTRAVENOUSLY, OR INTRAMUSCULARLY IF IV INJECTION IS NOT POSSIBLE. IN MODERATELY SEVERE POISONING ADMINISTER ATROPINE SULFATE, 0.4-2.0 MG REPEATED EVERY 15 MINUTES UNTIL ATROPINIZATION IS ACHIEVED (TACHYCARDIA, FLUSHING, DRY MOUTH, MYDRIASIS). MAINTAIN ATROPINIZATION BY REPEATED DOSES FOR 2-12 HOURS, OR LONGER, DEPENDING ON THE SEVERITY OF POISONING. THE APPEARANCE OF RALES IN THE LUNG BASES, MIOSIS, SALIVATION, NAUSEA, BRADYCARDIA, ARE ALL INDICATIONS OF INADEQUATE ATROPINIZATION. SEVERELY POISONED INDIVIDUALS MAY EXHIBIT REMARKABLE TOLERANCE TO ATROPINE; TWO OR MORE TIMES THE DOSAGES SUGGESTED ABOVE MAY BE NEEDED. PERSONS NOT POISONED OR ONLY SLIGHTLY POISONED, HOWEVER, MAY DEVELOP SIGNS OF ATROPINE TOXICITY FROM SUCH LARGE DOSAGES: FEVER, MUSCLE FIBRILLATIONS, AND DELIRIUM ARE THE MAIN SIGNS OF ATROPINE TOXICITY. IF THESE SIGNS APPEAR WHILE THE PATIENT IS FULLY ATROPINIZED, ATROPINE ADMINISTRATION SHOULD BE DISCONTINUED, AT LEAST TEMPORARILY. OBSERVE TREATED PATIENTS CLOSELY AT LEAST 24 HOURS TO INSURE THAT SYMPTOMS (POSSIBLY PULMONARY EDEMA) DO NOT RECUR AS ATROPINIZATION WEARS OFF. IN VERY SEVERE POISONINGS, METABOLIC DISPOSITION OF TOXICANT MAY REQUIRE SEVERAL HOURS OR DAYS DURING WHICH ATROPINIZATION MUST BE MAINTAINED. MARKEDLY LOWER LEVELS OF URINARY METABOLITES INDICATE THAT ATROPINE DOSAGE CAN BE TAPERED OFF. AS DOSAGE IS REDUCED, CHECK THE LUNG BASES FREQUENTLY FOR RALES. IF RALES ARE HEARD OR OTHER SYMPTOMS RETURN, RE-ESTABLISH ATROPINIZATION PROMPTLY (MORGAN, RECOGNITION AND MANAGEMENT OF PESTICIDE POISONINGS, 3RD ED.). ADMINISTRATION OF ANTIDOTE MUST BE PERFORMED BY QUALIFIED MEDICAL PERSONNEL.

IN CASES OF SEVERE POISONING BY ORGANOPHOSPHATE PESTICIDES IN WHICH RESPIRATORY DEPRESSION, MUSCLE WEAKNESS AND TWITCHINGS ARE SEVERE, GIVE PRALIDOXIME (PROTOPAM-AYERST, 2-PAM), 1.0 GRAM INTRAVENOUSLY AT NO MORE THAN 0.5 GRAM PER MINUTE. DOSAGE OF PRALIDOXIME MAY BE REPEATED IN 1-2 HOURS, THEN AT 10-12 HOUR INTERVALS IF NEEDED. IN VERY SEVERE POISONINGS, DOSAGE RATES MAY BE DOUBLED. TREATMENT WITH PRALIDOXIME WILL BE MOST EFFECTIVE IF GIVEN WITHIN THIRTY-SIX HOURS AFTER POISONING (MORGAN, RECOGNITION AND MANAGEMENT OF PESTICIDE POISONINGS, 3RD ED.). ANTIDOTE SHOULD BE ADMINISTERED BY QUALIFIED MEDICAL PERSONNEL.

REACTIVITY

REACTIVITY: NO SPECIFIC DATA AVAILABLE. HOWEVER, A NUMBER OF PHOSPHATE AND THIOPHOSPHATE ESTERS ARE OF LIMITED THERMAL STABILITY AND UNDERGO HIGHLY EXOTHERMIC SELF-ACCELERATING DECOMPOSITION REACTIONS.

INCOMPATIBILITIES: PHENCAPTON: NO DATA AVAILABLE.

DECOMPOSITION: THERMAL DECOMPOSITION PRODUCTS MAY INCLUDE TOXIC AND HAZARDOUS FUMES OF CHLORINE AND OXIDES OF OXIDES OF SULFUR AND PHOSPHORUS.

POLYMERIZATION: HAZARDOUS POLYMERIZATION HAS NOT BEEN REPORTED TO OCCUR UNDER NORMAL TEMPERATURES AND PRESSURES.

STORAGE AND DISPOSAL

OBSERVE ALL FEDERAL, STATE AND LOCAL REGULATIONS WHEN STORING OR DISPOSING OF THIS SUBSTANCE. FOR ASSISTANCE, CONTACT THE DISTRICT DIRECTOR OF THE ENVIRONMENTAL PROTECTION AGENCY.

STORAGE

STORE IN ACCORDANCE WITH 40 CFR 165 RECOMMENDED PROCEDURES FOR THE DISPOSAL AND STORAGE OF PESTICIDES AND PESTICIDE CONTAINERS.

DISPOSAL

DISPOSAL MUST BE IN ACCORDANCE WITH 40 CFR 165 RECOMMENDED PROCEDURES FOR THE DISPOSAL AND STORAGE OF PESTICIDES AND PESTICIDE CONTAINERS.

CONDITIONS TO AVOID

NONE REPORTED.

SPILL AND LEAK PROCEDURES

OCCUPATIONAL SPILL: DO NOT TOUCH SPILLED MATERIAL. STOP LEAK IF YOU CAN DO IT WITHOUT RISK. USE WATER SPRAY TO REDUCE VAPORS. FOR SMALL SPILLS, TAKE UP WITH SAND OR OTHER ABSORBENT MATERIAL AND PLACE INTO CONTAINERS FOR LATER DISPOSAL. FOR SMALL DRY SPILLS, WITH A CLEAN SHOVEL PLACE MATERIAL INTO CLEAN, DRY CONTAINERS AND COVER. MOVE CONTAINERS FROM SPILL AREA. FOR LARGER SPILLS, DIKE FAR AHEAD OF SPILL FOR LATER DISPOSAL. KEEP UNNECESSARY PEOPLE AWAY. ISOLATE HAZARD AREA AND DENY ENTRY. VENTILATE CLOSED SPACES BEFORE ENTERING.

PROTECTIVE EQUIPMENT

VENTILATION: PROVIDE LOCAL EXHAUST OR PROCESS ENCLOSURE VENTILATION SYSTEM.

RESPIRATOR: THE FOLLOWING RESPIRATORS ARE RECOMMENDED BASED ON INFORMATION FOUND IN THE PHYSICAL DATA, TOXICITY AND HEALTH EFFECTS SECTIONS. THEY ARE RANKED IN ORDER FROM MINIMUM TO MAXIMUM RESPIRATORY PROTECTION. THE SPECIFIC RESPIRATOR SELECTED MUST BE BASED ON CONTAMINATION LEVELS FOUND IN THE WORK PLACE, MUST NOT EXCEED THE WORKING LIMITS OF THE RESPIRATOR AND BE JOINTLY APPROVED BY THE NATIONAL INSTITUTE FOR OCCUPATIONAL SAFETY AND HEALTH AND THE MINE SAFETY AND HEALTH ADMINISTRATION (NIOSH-MSHA).

TYPE 'C' SUPPLIED-AIR RESPIRATOR WITH A FULL FACEPIECE OPERATED IN PRESSURE-DEMAND OR OTHER POSITIVE PRESSURE MODE OR WITH A FULL FACEPIECE, HELMET OR HOOD OPERATED IN CONTINOUS-FLOW MODE.

SELF-CONTAINED BREATHING APPARATUS WITH A FULL FACEPIECE OPERATED IN PRESSURE-DEMAND OR OTHER POSITIVE PRESSURE MODE.

FOR FIREFIGHTING AND OTHER IMMEDIATELY DANGEROUS TO LIFE OR HEALTH CONDITIONS:

SELF-CONTAINED BREATHING APPARATUS WITH FULL FACEPIECE OPERATED IN PRESSURE-DEMAND OR OTHER POSITIVE PRESSURE MODE.

SUPPLIED-AIR RESPIRATOR WITH FULL FACEPIECE AND OPERATED IN PRESSURE-DEMAND OR OTHER POSITIVE PRESSURE MODE IN COMBINATION WITH AN AUXILIARY SELF-CONTAINED BREATHING APPARATUS OPERATED IN PRESSURE-DEMAND OR OTHER POSITIVE PRESSURE MODE.

CLOTHING: EMPLOYEE MUST WEAR APPROPRIATE PROTECTIVE (IMPERVIOUS) CLOTHING AND EQUIPMENT TO PREVENT ANY POSSIBILITY OF SKIN CONTACT WITH THIS SUBSTANCE.

GLOVES: EMPLOYEE MUST WEAR APPROPRIATE PROTECTIVE GLOVES TO PREVENT CONTACT WITH THIS SUBSTANCE.

EYE PROTECTION: EMPLOYEE MUST WEAR SPLASH-PROOF OR DUST-RESISTANT SAFETY GOGGLES AND A FACESHIELD TO PREVENT CONTACT WITH THIS SUBSTANCE.

EMERGENCY WASH FACILITIES: WHERE THERE IS ANY POSSIBILITY THAT AN EMPLOYEE'S EYES AND/OR SKIN MAY BE EXPOSED TO THIS SUBSTANCE, THE EMPLOYER SHOULD PROVIDE AN EYE WASH FOUNTAIN AND QUICK DRENCH SHOWER WITHIN THE IMMEDIATE WORK AREA FOR EMERGENCY USE.

AUTHORIZED BY- OCCUPATIONAL HEALTH SERVICES, INC.
CREATION DATE: 10/04/89 ***REVISION DATE:*** 04/25/90

MATERIAL SAFETY DATA SHEET

OCCUPATIONAL HEALTH SERVICES, INC.
AGRICULTURE AND PESTICIDE DIVISION
450 SEVENTH AVENUE, SUITE 2407
NEW YORK, NEW YORK 10123
1-800-445-MSDS OR (212) 967-1100

EMERGENCY CONTACT:
JOHN S. BRANSFORD, JR. (615) 292-1180

SUBSTANCE IDENTIFICATION

CAS-NUMBER 108-95-2

SUBSTANCE: PHENOL

TRADE NAMES/SYNONYMS: BENZENOL; CARBOLIC ACID; HYDROXYBENZENE; MONOHYDROXYBENZENE; MONOPHENOL; OXYBENZENE; PHENIC ACID; PHENYL ALCOHOL; PHENYL HYDRATE; PHENYL HYDROXIDE; PHENYLIC ACID; PHENYLIC ALCOHOL; RCRA U188; STCC 4921220; UN 1671; C6H6O; PST18380

CHEMICAL FAMILY: HYDROXYL, AROMATIC

MOLECULAR FORMULA: C6-H5-O-H

MOLECULAR WEIGHT: 94.11

CERCLA RATINGS (SCALE 0-3): HEALTH=3 FIRE=2 REACTIVITY=0 PERSISTENCE=1

NFPA RATINGS (SCALE 0-4): HEALTH=3 FIRE=2 REACTIVITY=0

COMPONENTS AND CONTAMINANTS

COMPONENT: PHENOL ***PERCENT:*** 100.0
CAS# 108-95-2

OTHER CONTAMINANTS: NONE

EXPOSURE LIMITS: PHENOL: 5 PPM (19 MG/M3) OSHA TWA (SKIN) 5 PPM (19 MG/M3) ACGIH TWA (SKIN) 20 MG/M3 (5.2 PPM) NIOSH RECOMMENDED 10 HOUR TWA; 60 MG/M3 (15.6 PPM) NIOSH RECOMMENDED 15 MINUTE CEILING
500/10,000 POUNDS SARA SECTION 302 THRESHOLD PLANNING QUANTITY 1000 POUNDS SARA SECTION 304 REPORTABLE QUANTITY 1000 POUNDS CERCLA SECTION 103 REPORTABLE QUANTITY SUBJECT TO SARA SECTION 313 ANNUAL TOXIC CHEMICAL RELEASE REPORTING

PHYSICAL DATA

DESCRIPTION: COLORLESS, WHITE, OR PINK, CRYSTALLINE SOLID WITH A SWEET, TARRY ODOR.

BOILING POINT: 360 F (182 C) ***MELTING POINT:*** 109 F (43 C)

SPECIFIC GRAVITY: 1.0576 ***VISCOSITY:*** 1.51 CPS @ 80 C

VAPOR PRESSURE: 0.35 MMHG @ 25 C

EVAPORATION RATE: (BUTYL ACETATE=1)<0.01

PH: 6 (AQUEOUS SOLUTION) ***SOLUBILITY IN WATER:*** 6.7%

ODOR THRESHOLD: 3PPM

VAPOR DENSITY: 3.2

SOLVENT SOLUBILITY: SOLUBLE IN ALCOHOL, BENZENE, CHLOROFORM, ETHER, CARBON DISULFIDE, GLYCEROL, ACETONE, PETROLATUM, VOLATILE AND FIXED OILS, AQUEOUS ALKALI HYDROXIDES, DIMETHYL FORMAMIDE; ALMOST INSOLUBLE IN PETROLEUM ETHER.

FIRE AND EXPLOSION DATA

FIRE AND EXPLOSION HAZARD: MODERATE FIRE HAZARD WHEN EXPOSED TO HEAT OR FLAME.
VAPOR-AIR MIXTURES ARE EXPLOSIVE ABOVE FLASH POINT.
VAPORS ARE HEAVIER THAN AIR AND MAY TRAVEL A CONSIDERABLE DISTANCE TO A SOURCE OF IGNITION AND FLASH BACK.

FLASH POINT: 175 F (79 C) (CC) ***UPPER EXPLOSIVE LIMIT:*** 8.6%

LOWER EXPLOSIVE LIMIT: 1.8% ***AUTOIGNITION TEMP.:*** 1319 F (715 C)

FIREFIGHTING MEDIA: DRY CHEMICAL, CARBON DIOXIDE, HALON, WATER SPRAY OR ALCOHOL FOAM (1987 EMERGENCY RESPONSE GUIDEBOOK, DOT P 5800.4).
FOR LARGER FIRES, USE WATER SPRAY, FOG OR ALCOHOL FOAM (1987 EMERGENCY RESPONSE GUIDEBOOK, DOT P 5800.4).
ALCOHOL FOAM (NFPA 325M, FIRE HAZARD PROPERTIES OF FLAMMABLE LIQUIDS, GASES, AND VOLATILE SOLIDS, 1984).

FIREFIGHTING: MOVE CONTAINERS FROM FIRE AREA IF POSSIBLE. FIGHT FIRE FROM MAXIMUM DISTANCE. STAY AWAY FROM STORAGE TANK ENDS. DIKE FIRE CONTROL WATER FOR LATER DISPOSAL. DO NOT SCATTER MATERIAL (1987 EMERGENCY RESPONSE GUIDEBOOK, DOT P 5800.4, GUIDE PAGE 55).
EXTINGUISH USING AGENTS INDICATED. USE FLOODING QUANTITIES OF WATER AS A FOG, SOLID STREAMS MAY BE INEFFECTIVE. COOL FIRE-EXPOSED CONTAINERS WITH FLOODING AMOUNTS OF WATER. APPLY WATER FROM AS FAR A DISTANCE AS POSSIBLE. DIKE WATER TO PREVENT ENTRY INTO SEWERS AND WATERWAYS. AVOID BREATHING FUMES; KEEP UPWIND.

TRANSPORTATION DATA

DEPARTMENT OF TRANSPORTATION HAZARD CLASSIFICATION 49 CFR 172.101: POISON B
DEPARTMENT OF TRANSPORTATION LABELING REQUIREMENTS 49 CFR 172.101 AND SUBPART E: POISON
DEPARTMENT OF TRANSPORTATION PACKAGING REQUIREMENTS: 49 CFR 173.369 EXCEPTIONS: 49 CFR 173.364

TOXICITY

PHENOL: IRRITATION DATA: 500 MG/24 HOURS SKIN-RABBIT SEVERE; 535 MG OPEN SKIN-RABBIT SEVERE; 100 MG SKIN-RABBIT MILD; 5 MG EYE-RABBIT SEVERE; 5 MG/30 SECONDS RINSED EYE-RABBIT MILD. TOXICITY DATA: 316 MG/M3 INHALATION-RAT LC50; 177 MG/M3 INHALATION-MOUSE LC50; 74 MG/M3 INHALATION-MAMMAL LC50; 850 MG/KG SKIN-RABBIT LD50; 669 MG/KG SKIN-RAT LD50; 14 GM/KG ORAL-HUMAN LDLO; 140 MG/KG ORAL-HUMAN LDLO; 10 MG/KG ORAL-INFANT LDLO; 317 MG/KG ORAL-RAT LD50; 270 MG/KG ORAL-MOUSE LD50; 420 MG/KG ORAL-RABBIT LDLO; 80 MG/KG ORAL-CAT LDLO; 500 MG/KG ORAL-DOG LDLO; 80 MG/KG SUBCUTANEOUS-CAT LDLO; 450 MG/KG SUBCUTANEOUS-GUINEA PIG LDLO; 344 MG/KG SUBCUTANEOUS-MOUSE LD50; 460 MG/KG SUBCUTANEOUS-RAT LD50; 620 MG/KG SUBCUTANEOUS-RABBIT LDLO; 112 MG/KG INTRAVENOUS-MOUSE LD50; 180 MG/KG INTRAVENOUS-RABBIT LDLO; 300 MG/KG INTRAPERITONEAL-GUINEA PIG LDLO; 180 MG/KG INTRAPERITONEAL-MOUSE LD50; 127 MG/KG INTRAPERITONEAL-RAT LD50; MUTAGENIC DATA (RTECS); REPRODUCTIVE EFFECTS DATA (RTECS); TUMORIGENIC DATA (RTECS). CARCINOGEN STATUS: NONE. LOCAL EFFECTS: CORROSIVE- EYE, SKIN, AND MUCOUS MEMBRANE. ACUTE TOXICITY LEVEL: HIGHLY TOXIC BY INHALATION; TOXIC BY DERMAL ABSORPTION AND INGESTION. TARGET EFFECTS: NEUROTOXIN; CENTRAL NERVOUS SYSTEM DEPRESSANT. POISONING MAY ALSO AFFECT THE LIVER AND KIDNEYS. AT INCREASED RISK FROM EXPOSURE: PERSONS WITH CONVULSIVE DISORDERS AND ABNORMALITIES OF THE SKIN, RESPIRATORY TRACT, LIVER AND KIDNEYS.

HEALTH EFFECTS AND FIRST AID

INHALATION: PHENOL: CORROSIVE/NEUROTOXIN/NARCOTIC/HIGHLY TOXIC. 250 PPM IMMEDIATELY DANGEROUS TO LIFE OR HEALTH. **ACUTE EXPOSURE-** INHALATION MAY CAUSE SEVERE IRRITATION OF THE MUCOUS MEMBRANES, PROFUSE SWEATING, HEADACHE, INTENSE THIRST, NAUSEA AND VOMITING, ABDOMINAL PAIN, DIARRHEA, SALIVATION, CYANOSIS, TINNITUS, TWITCHING, TREMORS, AND CONVULSIONS. THE CENTRAL NERVOUS SYSTEM MAY INITIALLY BE STIMULATED FOLLOWED BY SEVERE, PROFOUND DEPRESSION PROGRESSING TO COMA. THE HEART RATE MAY INCREASE THEN BECOME SLOW AND IRREGULAR. THE BLOOD PRESSURE MAY INCREASE SLIGHTLY AND THEN FALL MARKEDLY WITH DYSPNEA AND FALL IN BODY TEMPERATURE. STERTOROUS BREATHING, MUCOUS RALES, AND FROTHING AT THE MOUTH AND NOSE MAY INDICATE THE PRESENCE OF PULMONARY EDEMA, WHICH MAY BE FOLLOWED BY PNEUMONIA. METHEMOGLOBINEMIA AND HEMOLYSIS HAVE BEEN REPORTED OCCASIONALLY. DEATH MAY OCCUR FROM RESPIRATORY, CIRCULATORY OR CARDIAC FAILURE. IF DEATH IS NOT IMMEDIATE, JAUNDICE AND OLIGURIA OR ANURIA MAY OCCUR. **CHRONIC EXPOSURE-** SYMPTOMS OF CHRONIC PHENOL POISONING MAY INCLUDE VOMITING, DIFFICULTY SWALLOWING, PTYALISM, DIARRHEA, ANOREXIA, HEADACHE, VERTIGO, MUSCLE WEAKNESS AND PAIN, MENTAL DISTURBANCES, DARK OR SMOKEY URINE AND POSSIBLY SKIN ERUPTIONS. EXTENSIVE DAMAGE TO THE LIVER AND KIDNEYS MAY BE FATAL. HIND LIMB PARALYSIS HAS BEEN REPORTED IN ANIMALS. PATHOLOGIC FINDINGS IN ANIMALS REPEATEDLY EXPOSED TO PHENOL VAPORS INCLUDE EXTENSIVE NECROSIS OF THE MYOCARDIUM, ACUTE LOBULAR PNEUMONIA, VASCULAR DAMAGE, AND LIVER AND KIDNEY DAMAGE.

FIRST AID- REMOVE FROM EXPOSURE AREA TO FRESH AIR IMMEDIATELY. IF BREATHING HAS STOPPED, GIVE ARTIFICIAL RESPIRATION. MAINTAIN AIRWAY AND BLOOD PRESSURE AND ADMINISTER OXYGEN IF AVAILABLE. KEEP AFFECTED PERSON WARM AND AT REST. TREAT SYMPTOMATICALLY AND SUPPORTIVELY. ADMINISTRATION OF OXYGEN SHOULD BE PERFORMED BY QUALIFIED PERSONNEL. GET MEDICAL ATTENTION IMMEDIATELY.

SKIN CONTACT: PHENOL: CORROSIVE/NEUROTOXIN/NARCOTIC/TOXIC. **ACUTE EXPOSURE-** CONTACT WITH 0.5% SOLUTIONS MAY CAUSE LOCAL ANESTHESIA, 1% SOLUTIONS SOMETIMES CAUSE SKIN NECROSIS, AND 10% SOLUTIONS MAY CAUSE BURNS. PHENOL BURNS MAY BE SEVERE, BUT PAINLESS DUE TO DAMAGE TO NERVE ENDINGS. THE SKIN MAY TURN WHITE, AND LATER YELLOWISH-BROWN AND MAY BE DEEPLY ERODED AND SCARRED. GANGRENE MAY OCCUR AT THE SITE OF CONTACT. VAPORS AND LIQUID MAY BE READILY ABSORBED THROUGH THE SKIN TO CAUSE SYSTEMIC EFFECTS AS DETAILED IN ACUTE INHALATION EXPOSURE. THERE HAVE BEEN SEVERAL REPORTS OF CARDIAC ARRHYTHMIAS ASSOCIATED WITH APPLICATION OF SOLUTIONS OF PHENOL, HEXACHLOROPHENE, AND CROTON OIL TO THE SKIN. PROFOUND COMA AND DEATH HAVE BEEN REPORTED TO OCCUR WITHIN 10 MINUTES FOLLOWING SKIN CONTACT PATHOLOGIC FINDINGS INCLUDED CONGESTION OF THE LUNGS, LIVER, SPLEEN, AND KIDNEYS. **CHRONIC EXPOSURE-** PROLONGED EXPOSURE MAY CAUSE A BLUE OR BROWNISH DISCOLORATION OF THE TENDONS OVER THE KNUCKLES OF THE HANDS, DERMATITIS, VITILIGO, AND RARELY, SKIN SENSITIZATION. SYMPTOMS OF CHRONIC PHENOL POISONING MAY OCCUR AS DETAILED AS IN CHRONIC INHALATION EXPOSURE. ANIMAL STUDIES INDICATE PHENOL MAY HAVE TUMOR PROMOTING AND/OR PRODUCING CAPABILITIES.

FIRST AID- REMOVE CONTAMINATED CLOTHING AND SHOES IMMEDIATELY. WASH AFFECTED AREA WITH SOAP OR MILD DETERGENT AND LARGE AMOUNTS OF WATER UNTIL NO EVIDENCE OF CHEMICAL REMAINS (AT LEAST 15-20 MINUTES). IN CASE OF CHEMICAL BURNS, COVER AREA WITH STERILE, DRY DRESSING. BANDAGE SECURELY, BUT NOT TOO TIGHTLY. GET MEDICAL ATTENTION IMMEDIATELY.

EYE CONTACT: PHENOL: CORROSIVE. **ACUTE EXPOSURE-** VAPORS HAVE CAUSED MARKED IRRITATION FROM BRIEF, INTERMITTENT INDUSTRIAL EXPOSURE TO 48 PPM. CONCENTRATED LIQUID OR SOLID MAY CAUSE SEVERE IRRITATION WITH REDNESS, PAIN, AND BLURRED VISION. CONCENTRATED PHENOL IN HUMAN EYES HAS CAUSED CHEMOTIC CONJUNCTIVA, HYPESTHETIC, WHITE CORNEA, EDEMATOUS EYELIDS, AND SEVERE IRITIS. IN SOME CASES, THE EYELIDS HAVE BEEN SO SEVERELY DAMAGED THAT THEY REQUIRED PLASTIC SURGERY. THE FINAL VISUAL RESULTS HAVE VARIED FROM COMPLETE RECOVERY, TO PARTIAL RECOVERY, TO BLINDNESS AND LOSS OF THE EYE. CRYSTALLINE OR CONCENTRATED AQUEOUS PHENOL ON RABBITS EYES CAUSES ALMOST INSTANTANEOUS WHITE OPACIFICATION OF THE CORNEAL EPITHELIUM. EIGHT

HOURS LATER, THE CORNEA WAS ANESTHETIC, THE SURFACE ULCERATED, AND THE STROMA OPAQUE. FIVE WEEKS LATER, ENTROPION, SCARRING OF THE CONJUNCTIVA AND OPACITY OF THE CORNEA OCCURRED. **CHRONIC EXPOSURE**- REPEATED OR PROLONGED EXPOSURE TO PHENOL VAPORS MAY CAUSE CONJUNCTIVITIS AND HAS CAUSED GRAY DISCOLORATION OF THE SCLERA WITH BROWN SPOTS NEAR THE INSERTION OF THE RECTUS MUSCLE TENDON. **FIRST AID**- WASH EYES IMMEDIATELY WITH LARGE AMOUNTS OF WATER, OCCASIONALLY LIFTING UPPER AND LOWER LIDS, UNTIL NO EVIDENCE OF CHEMICAL REMAINS (AT LEAST 15-20 MINUTES). CONTINUE IRRIGATING WITH NORMAL SALINE UNTIL THE PH HAS RETURNED TO NORMAL (30-60 MINUTES). COVER WITH STERILE BANDAGES. GET MEDICAL ATTENTION IMMEDIATELY.

INGESTION: PHENOL: CORROSIVE/NEUROTOXIN/NARCOTIC/TOXIC. **ACUTE EXPOSURE**- INGESTION MAY CAUSE IMMEDIATE INTENSE BURNING OF THE MOUTH AND THROAT, WHITE OR BROWNISH STAINS AND AREAS OF NECROSIS ON THE LIPS AND IN THE MOUTH AND ESOPHAGUS, MARKED ABDOMINAL PAIN, PALE FACE, AND CONTRACTED OR DILATED PUPILS. SYSTEMIC EFFECTS MAY OCCUR AS DETAILED IN ACUTE INHALATION EXPOSURE. THE APPROXIMATE LETHAL DOSE IN MAN IS 140 MG/KG. **CHRONIC EXPOSURE**- PERSONS INGESTING PHENOL CONTAMINATED WELL WATER EXPERIENCED DIARRHEA, DARK URINE, AND SORES AND BURNING IN THE MOUTH. OTHER SYMPTOMS OF CHRONIC PHENOL POISONING MAY OCCUR AS DETAILED IN CHRONIC INHALATION EXPOSURE. ADMINISTRATION OF PHENOL IN DRINKING WATER TO RATS FOR THREE GENERATIONS PRODUCED STUNTED GROWTH AT 7000 PPM OVER 2 GENERATIONS; OFFSPRING OF RATS GIVEN 10,000 PPM DIED; AT 12,000 PPM ANIMALS DID NOT REPRODUCE.

FIRST AID- IF VICTIM IS CONSCIOUS, AND IF CORROSIVE INJURY IS ABSENT, REMOVE POISON BY GASTRIC LAVAGE OR EMESIS. ACTIVATED CHARCOAL IS USEFUL. FOLLOW WITH 240 ML OF MILK. GASTRIC LAVAGE AND EMESIS ARE NOT TO BE USED IN THE PRESENCE OF ESOPHAGEAL INJURY (DREISBACH, HANDBOOK OF POISONING, 12TH ED.). GASTRIC LAVAGE SHOULD BE PERFORMED BY QUALIFIED MEDICAL PERSONNEL. GET MEDICAL ATTENTION IMMEDIATELY.

ANTIDOTE: NO SPECIFIC ANTIDOTE. TREAT SYMPTOMATICALLY AND SUPPORTIVELY.

REACTIVITY

REACTIVITY: STABLE UNDER NORMAL TEMPERATURES AND PRESSURES.

INCOMPATIBILITIES: PHENOL: ACETALDEHYDE: VIOLENT REACTION. ALUMINUM AND ALLOYS: MAY CORRODE. ALUMINUM CHLORIDE + NITROBENZENE: VIOLENT EXPLOSION. 1,3-BUTADIENE, BORON TRIFLUORIDE, AND DIETHYLETHERATE: POSSIBLE EXPLOSION. CALCIUM HYPOCHLORITE: EXOTHERMIC REACTION WITH POSSIBLE IGNITION. FORMALDEHYDE: POSSIBLE EXOTHERMIC REACTION. LEAD AND ALLOYS: MAY CORRODE. MAGNESIUM AND ALLOYS: MAY CORRODE. METALS AND ALLOYS: MAY CORRODE. OXIDIZERS (STRONG): FIRE AND EXPLOSION HAZARD. PEROXODISULFURIC ACID: POSSIBLE EXPLOSION. PEROXOMONOSULFURIC ACID: EXPLOSION. PLASTICS, RUBBER, COATINGS: MAY CORRODE. SODIUM NITRATE + TRIFLUOROACETIC ACID: VIOLENT EXOTHERMIC REACTION. SODIUM NITRITE: MAY EXPLODE. ZINC AND ALLOYS: MAY CORRODE.

DECOMPOSITION: THERMAL DECOMPOSITION PRODUCTS MAY INCLUDE TOXIC OXIDES OF CARBON.

POLYMERIZATION: HAZARDOUS POLYMERIZATION HAS NOT BEEN REPORTED TO OCCUR UNDER NORMAL TEMPERATURES AND PRESSURES.

STORAGE AND DISPOSAL

OBSERVE ALL FEDERAL, STATE AND LOCAL REGULATIONS WHEN STORING OR DISPOSING OF THIS SUBSTANCE. FOR ASSISTANCE, CONTACT THE DISTRICT DIRECTOR OF THE ENVIRONMENTAL PROTECTION AGENCY.

****STORAGE****

PROTECT AGAINST PHYSICAL DAMAGE. STORE IN A COOL, DRY, WELL-VENTILATED LOCATION, AWAY FROM ANY AREAS WHERE THE FIRE HAZARD MAY BE ACUTE. OUTSIDE OR DETACHED STORAGE IS PREFERRED. SEPARATE FROM OTHER STORAGE. SPILLS MUST BE DISPOSED OF IMMEDIATELY BY PROPERLY PROTECTED PERSONNEL; NO OTHERS SHOULD REMAIN IN AREA. FLUSH WITH FLOODING QUANTITIES OF WATER, THEN USE CAUSTIC SODA SOLUTION FOR NEUTRALIZATION (NFPA 49, HAZARDOUS CHEMICALS DATA, 1975).

STORE AWAY FROM INCOMPATIBLE SUBSTANCES.

THRESHOLD PLANNING QUANTITY (TPQ): THE SUPERFUND AMENDMENTS AND REAUTHORIZATION ACT (SARA) SECTION 302 REQUIRES THAT EACH FACILITY WHERE ANY EXTREMELY HAZARDOUS SUBSTANCE IS PRESENT IN A QUANTITY EQUAL TO OR GREATER THAN THE TPQ ESTABLISHED FOR THAT SUBSTANCE NOTIFY THE STATE EMERGENCY RESPONSE COMMISSION FOR THE STATE IN WHICH IT IS LOCATED. SECTION 303 OF SARA REQUIRES THESE FACILITIES TO PARTICIPATE IN LOCAL EMERGENCY RESPONSE PLANNING (40 CFR 355.30).

****DISPOSAL****

DISPOSAL MUST BE IN ACCORDANCE WITH STANDARDS APPLICABLE TO GENERATORS OF HAZARDOUS WASTE, 40CFR 262. EPA HAZARDOUS WASTE NUMBER U118.

CONDITIONS TO AVOID

MAY BURN BUT DOES NOT IGNITE READILY. CONTAINERS MAY EXPLODE IN HEAT OF FIRE.

SPILL AND LEAK PROCEDURES

SOIL SPILL: DIG A HOLDING AREA SUCH AS PIT, POND OR LAGOON TO CONTAIN SPILLED MATERIAL. USE PROTECTIVE COVER SUCH AS A PLASTIC SHEET TO PREVENT DISSOLVING IN FIREFIGHTING WATER OR RAIN.
NEUTRALIZE SPILL WITH SLAKED LIME, SODIUM BICARBONATE OR CRUSHED LIMESTONE.

AIR SPILL: APPLY WATER SPRAY TO KNOCK DOWN AND REDUCE VAPORS. KNOCK-DOWN WATER IS CORROSIVE AND TOXIC AND SHOULD BE DIKED FOR CONTAINMENT AND LATER DISPOSAL.

WATER SPILL: IF DISSOLVED, AT A CONCENTRATION OF 10 PPM OR GREATER, APPLY ACTIVATED CARBON AT TEN TIMES THE AMOUNT THAT HAS BEEN SPILLED.
USE MECHANICAL DREDGES OR LIFTS TO EXTRACT IMMOBILIZED MASSES OF POLLUTION AND PRECIPITATES.

OCCUPATIONAL SPILL: DO NOT TOUCH SPILLED MATERIAL. STOP LEAK IF YOU CAN DO IT WITHOUT RISK. USE WATER SPRAY TO REDUCE VAPORS. FOR SMALL SPILLS, TAKE UP WITH SAND OR OTHER ABSORBENT MATERIAL AND PLACE INTO CONTAINERS FOR LATER DISPOSAL. FOR SMALL DRY SPILLS, WITH A CLEAN SHOVEL PLACE MATERIAL INTO CLEAN, DRY CONTAINERS AND COVER. MOVE CONTAINERS FROM SPILL AREA. FOR LARGER SPILLS, DIKE FAR AHEAD OF SPILL FOR LATER DISPOSAL. KEEP UNNECESSARY PEOPLE AWAY. ISOLATE HAZARD AREA AND DENY ENTRY. VENTILATE CLOSED SPACES BEFORE ENTERING.
REPORTABLE QUANTITY (RQ): 1000 POUNDS THE SUPERFUND AMENDMENTS AND REAUTHORIZATION ACT (SARA) SECTION 304 REQUIRES THAT A RELEASE EQUAL TO OR GREATER THAN THE REPORTABLE QUANTITY FOR THIS SUBSTANCE BE IMMEDIATELY REPORTED TO THE LOCAL EMERGENCY PLANNING COMMITTEE AND THE STATE EMERGENCY RESPONSE COMMISSION (40 CFR 355.40). IF THE RELEASE OF THIS SUBSTANCE IS REPORTABLE UNDER CERCLA SECTION 103, THE NATIONAL RESPONSE CENTER MUST BE NOTIFIED IMMEDIATELY AT (800) 424-8802 OR (202) 426-2675 IN THE METROPOLITAN WASHINGTON, D.C. AREA (40 CFR 302.6).

PROTECTIVE EQUIPMENT

VENTILATION: PROCESS ENCLOSURE RECOMMENDED TO MEET PUBLISHED EXPOSURE LIMITS.

RESPIRATOR: THE FOLLOWING RESPIRATORS AND MAXIMUM USE CONCENTRATIONS ARE RECOMMENDATIONS BY THE U.S. DEPARTMENT OF HEALTH AND HUMAN SERVICES, NIOSH POCKET GUIDE TO CHEMICAL HAZARDS; NIOSH CRITERIA DOCUMENTS OR BY THE U.S. DEPARTMENT OF LABOR, 29 CFR 1910 SUBPART Z. THE SPECIFIC RESPIRATOR SELECTED MUST BE BASED ON CONTAMINATION LEVELS FOUND IN THE WORK PLACE, MUST NOT EXCEED THE WORKING LIMITS OF THE RESPIRATOR AND BE JOINTLY APPROVED BY THE NATIONAL INSTITUTE FOR OCCUPATIONAL SAFETY AND HEALTH AND THE MINE SAFETY AND HEALTH ADMINISTRATION (NIOSH-MSHA).

PHENOL:

50 PPM- ANY CHEMICAL CARTRIDGE RESPIRATOR WITH ORGANIC VAPOR CARTRIDGE(S) IN COMBINATION WITH A DUST AND MIST FILTER. ANY SUPPLIED-AIR RESPIRATOR. ANY SELF-CONTAINED BREATHING APPARATUS.

125 PPM- ANY SUPPLIED-AIR RESPIRATOR OPERATED IN A CONTINUOUS FLOW MODE ANY POWERED AIR-PURIFYING RESPIRATOR WITH ORGANIC VAPOR CARTRIDGE(S) IN COMBINATION WITH A DUST AND MIST FILTER.

250 PPM- ANY SELF-CONTAINED BREATHING APPARATUS WITH A FULL FACEPIECE. ANY SUPPLIED-AIR RESPIRATOR WITH A FULL FACEPIECE. ANY CHEMICAL CARTRIDGE RESPIRATOR WITH A FULL FACEPIECE AND ORGANIC VAPOR CARTRIDGE(S) IN COMBINATION WITH A HIGH-EFFICIENCY PARTICULATE FILTER. ANY AIR-PURIFYING FULL FACEPIECE RESPIRATOR (GAS MASK) WITH A CHIN-STYLE OR FRONT- OR BACK-MOUNTED ORGANIC VAPOR CANISTER HAVING A HIGH-EFFICIENCY PARTICULATE FILTER. ANY POWERED AIR-PURIFYING RESPIRATOR WITH A TIGHT-FITTING FACEPIECE AND ORGANIC VAPOR CARTRIDGE(S) IN COMBINATION WITH A HIGH-EFFICIENCY PARTICULATE FILTER.

ESCAPE- ANY AIR-PURIFYING FULL FACEPIECE RESPIRATOR (GAS MASK) WITH A CHIN-STYLE OR FRONT- OR BACK-MOUNTED ORGANIC VAPOR CANISTER HAVING A HIGH-EFFICIENCY PARTICULATE FILTER. ANY APPROPRIATE ESCAPE-TYPE SELF-CONTAINED BREATHING APPARAUTS.

FOR FIREFIGHTING AND OTHER IMMEDIATELY DANGEROUS TO LIFE OR HEALTH CONDITIONS:

SELF-CONTAINED BREATHING APPARATUS WITH FULL FACEPIECE OPERATED IN PRESSURE-DEMAND OR OTHER POSITIVE PRESSURE MODE.

SUPPLIED-AIR RESPIRATOR WITH FULL FACEPIECE AND OPERATED IN PRESSURE-DEMAND OR OTHER POSITIVE PRESSURE MODE IN COMBINATION WITH AN AUXILIARY SELF-CONTAINED BREATHING APPARATUS OPERATED IN PRESSURE-DEMAND OR OTHER POSITIVE PRESSURE MODE.

CLOTHING: EMPLOYEE MUST WEAR APPROPRIATE PROTECTIVE (IMPERVIOUS) CLOTHING AND EQUIPMENT TO PREVENT ANY POSSIBILITY OF SKIN CONTACT WITH THIS SUBSTANCE.

GLOVES: EMPLOYEE MUST WEAR APPROPRIATE PROTECTIVE GLOVES TO PREVENT CONTACT WITH THIS SUBSTANCE.

EYE PROTECTION: EMPLOYEE MUST WEAR SPLASH-PROOF OR DUST-RESISTANT SAFETY GOGGLES AND A FACESHIELD TO PREVENT CONTACT WITH THIS SUBSTANCE.

EMERGENCY WASH FACILITIES: WHERE THERE IS ANY POSSIBILITY THAT AN EMPLOYEE'S EYES AND/OR SKIN MAY BE EXPOSED TO THIS SUBSTANCE, THE EMPLOYER SHOULD PROVIDE AN EYE WASH FOUNTAIN AND QUICK DRENCH SHOWER WITHIN THE IMMEDIATE WORK AREA FOR EMERGENCY USE.

AUTHORIZED BY- OCCUPATIONAL HEALTH SERVICES, INC.
CREATION DATE: 11/17/89 ***REVISION DATE:*** 05/11/90

MATERIAL SAFETY DATA SHEET

OCCUPATIONAL HEALTH SERVICES, INC.
AGRICULTURE AND PESTICIDE DIVISION
450 SEVENTH AVENUE, SUITE 2407
NEW YORK, NEW YORK 10123
1-800-445-MSDS OR (212) 967-1100

EMERGENCY CONTACT:
JOHN S. BRANSFORD, JR. (615) 292-1180

SUBSTANCE IDENTIFICATION

CAS-NUMBER 92-84-2

SUBSTANCE: PHENOTHIAZINE

TRADE NAMES/SYNONYMS: AFI-TIAZIN; AGRAZINE; ANTIVERM; COUTAVERM; ENT 38; DIBENZOPARATHIAZINE; DIBENZO-1,4-THIAZINE; THIODIPHENYLAMINE; BIVERM; FEENO; DIBENZOTHIAZINE; FENOVERM; FENTIAZIN; HELMETINA; LETHELMIN; NEMAZENE; ORIMON; PADOPHENE; PENTHAZINE; VERMITIN; PST18400

CHEMICAL FAMILY: AMINE, AROMATIC

MOLECULAR FORMULA: C12-H9-N-S

MOLECULAR WEIGHT: 199.27

CERCLA RATINGS (SCALE 0-3): HEALTH=2 FIRE=0 REACTIVITY=0 PERSISTENCE=3

NFPA RATINGS (SCALE 0-4): HEALTH=2 FIRE=0 REACTIVITY=0

COMPONENTS AND CONTAMINANTS

COMPONENT: PHENOTHIAZINE ***PERCENT:*** 100
CAS# 92-84-2

OTHER CONTAMINANTS: NONE

EXPOSURE LIMITS: PHENOTHIAZINE: 5 MG/M3 OSHA TWA (SKIN) 5 MG/M3 ACGIH TWA (SKIN)

PHYSICAL DATA

DESCRIPTION: TASTELESS, GRAYISH-GREEN TO GREENISH YELLOW POWDER, GRANULES OR FLAKES WITH A SLIGHT ODOR.

BOILING POINT: 700 F (371 C) DECOMPOSES ***MELTING POINT:*** 367 F (186 C)

SPECIFIC GRAVITY: NOT AVAILABLE ***VAPOR PRESSURE:*** 40 MMHG @ 290 C

SOLUBILITY IN WATER: INSOLUBLE

SOLVENT SOLUBILITY: ACETONE, BENZENE, ETHER, ALCOHOLS, HOT ACETIC ACID

FIRE AND EXPLOSION DATA

FIRE AND EXPLOSION HAZARD: NEGLIGIBLE FIRE HAZARD WHEN EXPOSED TO HEAT OR FLAME.

FIREFIGHTING MEDIA: DRY CHEMICAL, CARBON DIOXIDE, HALON, WATER SPRAY OR STANDARD FOAM (1987 EMERGENCY RESPONSE GUIDEBOOK, DOT P 5800.4). FOR LARGER FIRES, USE WATER SPRAY, FOG OR STANDARD FOAM (1987 EMERGENCY RESPONSE GUIDEBOOK, DOT P 5800.4).

FIREFIGHTING: MOVE CONTAINER FROM FIRE AREA IF POSSIBLE. DO NOT SCATTER SPILLED MATERIAL WITH HIGH PRESSURE WATER STREAMS. DIKE FIRE CONTROL WATER FOR LATER DISPOSAL (1987 EMERGENCY RESPONSE GUIDEBOOK, DOT P 5800.4, GUIDE PAGE 31).
USE AGENTS SUITABLE FOR TYPE OF SURROUNDING FIRE. AVOID BREATHING HAZARDOUS VAPORS, KEEP UPWIND.

TOXICITY

PHENOTHIAZINE: TOXICITY DATA: 425 MG/KG/5 DAYS ORAL-CHILD LDLO; 4 GM/KG ORAL-RABBIT LD50; 5000 MG/KG ORAL-MOUSE LD50; 500 MG/KG ORAL-CATTLE LD50; 178 MG/KG INTRAVENOUS-MOUSE LD50; REPRODUCTIVE EFFECTS DATA (RTECS). CARCINOGEN STATUS: NONE. LOCAL AFFECTS: CORROSIVE- INHALATION, SKIN, EYE, AND INGESTION. ACUTE TOXICITY LEVEL: MODERATELY TOXIC BY INGESTION. TARGET EFFECTS: SENSITIZER-DERMAL; CENTRAL NERVOUS SYSTEM DEPRESSANT. POISONING MAY ALSO AFFECT THE KIDNEYS, LIVER, BLOOD AND MUSCLES. AT INCREASED RISK FROM EXPOSURE: PERSONS WITH DISEASES OF THE BLOOD, SKIN, LIVER AND KIDNEYS.

HEALTH EFFECTS AND FIRST AID

INHALATION: PHENOTHIAZINE: CORROSIVE. **ACUTE EXPOSURE-** MAY CAUSE IRRITATION, WITH SORE THROAT, COUGHING, AND DYSPNEA. **CHRONIC EXPOSURE-** NO DATA AVAILABLE.

FIRST AID- REMOVE FROM EXPOSURE AREA TO FRESH AIR IMMEDIATELY. IF BREATHING HAS STOPPED, GIVE ARTIFICIAL RESPIRATION. MAINTAIN AIRWAY AND BLOOD PRESSURE AND ADMINISTER OXYGEN IF AVAILABLE. KEEP AFFECTED PERSON WARM AND AT REST. TREAT SYMPTOMATICALLY AND SUPPORTIVELY. ADMINISTRATION OF OXYGEN SHOULD BE PERFORMED BY QUALIFIED PERSONNEL. GET MEDICAL ATTENTION IMMEDIATELY.

SKIN CONTACT: PHENOTHIAZINE: CORROSIVE/SENSITIZER. **ACUTE EXPOSURE-** MAY CAUSE IRRITATION WITH REDNESS, PAIN AND SOMETIMES BURNS, ERYTHEMA AND ITCHING. IT IS A PHOTOSENSITIZING COMPOUND AND CAN CAUSE SKIN ERUPTIONS PROVOKED BY SUNLIGHT. IT IS ABSORBED THROUGH THE SKIN AND MAY CAUSE NAUSEA, VOMITING, DIARRHEA, AND HEADACHE. **CHRONIC EXPOSURE-** REPEATED AND PROLONGED CONTACT MAY CAUSE SENSITIZATION DERMATITIS. IT IS ABSORBED THROUGH THE SKIN AND REPEATED ABSORPTION MAY RESULT IN HYPOTHERMIA OR HYPERTHERMIA, HEMOLYTIC ANEMIA, JAUNDICE, HYPERGLYCENIA, UNSTEADINESS AND STUMBLING. IT MAY ALSO PRODUCE AN ENLARGED SPLEEN AND LIVER.

FIRST AID- REMOVE CONTAMINATED CLOTHING AND SHOES IMMEDIATELY. WASH AFFECTED AREA WITH SOAP OR MILD DETERGENT AND LARGE AMOUNTS OF WATER UNTIL NO EVIDENCE OF CHEMICAL REMAINS (AT LEAST 15-20 MINUTES). IN CASE OF CHEMICAL BURNS, COVER AREA WITH STERILE, DRY DRESSING. BANDAGE SECURELY, BUT NOT TOO TIGHTLY. GET MEDICAL ATTENTION IMMEDIATELY.

EYE CONTACT: PHENOTHIAZINE: CORROSIVE. **ACUTE EXPOSURE-** MAY CAUSE SEVERE IRRITATION OF THE EYES AND PHOTOSENSITIZED KERATITIS WITH CORNEAL EDEMA, WHICH ONLY DEVELOPS IN SUNLIGHT. **CHRONIC EXPOSURE-** REPEATED AND PROLONGED CONTACT MAY CAUSE CONJUNCTIVITIS, BLURRING OF VISION, NIGHT BLINDNESS OR DECREASE VISION IN SUBDUED LIGHT, PHOTOPHOBIA, DILATED OR SLUGGISH PUPILS, OCCASIONALLY MIOTIC PUPILS, IRIDOPLEGIA OR CYCLOPLEGIA, DRYNESS OF THE EYES, DISCOLORATION OF THE CONJUNCTIVA, SCLERA AND THE SKIN SURROUNDING THE EYES, PIGMENT MIGRATION IN THE RETINA, PARESIS OF EXTRAOCULAR MUSCLES, OCULOGYRIC CRISES, ELECTROOCULOGRAM DISTURBANCES AND LENTICULAR OR CORNEAL OPACITIES.

FIRST AID- WASH EYES IMMEDIATELY WITH LARGE AMOUNTS OF WATER, OCCASIONALLY LIFTING UPPER AND LOWER LIDS, UNTIL NO EVIDENCE OF CHEMICAL REMAINS (AT LEAST 15-20 MINUTES). CONTINUE IRRIGATING WITH NORMAL SALINE UNTIL THE PH HAS RETURNED TO NORMAL (30-60 MINUTES). COVER WITH STERILE BANDAGES. GET MEDICAL ATTENTION IMMEDIATELY.

INGESTION: PHENOTHIAZINE: NARCOTIC. **ACUTE EXPOSURE-** MAY CAUSE IRRITATION OF THE GASTROINTESTINAL TRACT, NAUSEA, VOMITING, DIARRHEA, ABDOMINAL SPASMS AND CENTRAL NERVOUS SYSTEM DEPRESSION WITH HEADACHE, WEAKNESS AND DIZZINESS. THE MOST COMMON EFFECT FROM OVERDOSAGE IS DEEP SLEEP OR COMA. **CHRONIC EXPOSURE-** REPEATED EXPOSURE TO LARGE DOSES MAY RESULT IN INITIAL SEDATION AND MAY BE FOLLOWED BY RESTLESSNESS AND OCCASIONALLY BY TONIC AND CLONIC CONVULSIONS. OTHER MANIFESTATIONS ARE HYPOTHERMIA OR HYPERTHERMIA, HEMOLYTIC ANEMIA, JAUNDICE, HYPERGLYCEMIA, ACETONEMIA, REVERSIBLE (RARELY PERMANENT) CENTRAL NERVOUS SYSTEM EFFECTS OF SPASTICITY, PATHOLOGICAL REFLEXES, CATALEPTOID STATES, OCULOGYRIC CRISES, PARKINSONIAN SYMPTOMS, AND A VARIETY OF DYSTONIC DISORDERS (ALKINESIA, DYSKINESIA, AKATHISIA, PARKINSONISM). RESTLESS LEGS, UNSTEADINESS, STUMBLING, PROPULSION AND SHUFFLING GAIT OFTEN OCCUR. THE NECK-FACE SYNDROME, A DYSTONIA INVOLVING THE MUSCULATURE OF THE FACE AND NECK IS A PARTICULARLY FREQUENT OCCURRENCE. IT MAY ALSO PRODUCE AN ENLARGED SPLEEN AND LIVER.

FIRST AID- EMESIS OR GASTRIC LAVAGE ARE INDICATED, FOLLOWED BY ADMINISTRATION OF ACTIVATED CHARCOAL AND A SALINE CATHARTIC. DRUGS THAT CAN POTENTIATE THE DEPRESSANT EFFECT ON PHENOTHIZINE, SUCH AS BARBITURATES, SEDATIVES, ALCOHOL, NARCOTICS, AND ANESTHETICS ARE BEST AVOIDED. (CASARETT AND DOULL'S, TOXICOLOGY, 2ND EDITION). GASTRIC LAVAGE SHOULD NOT BE PERFORMED ON AN UNCONSCIOUS PERSON AND SHOULD ONLY BE PERFORMED BY QUALIFIED MEDICAL PERSONNEL. GET MEDICAL ATTENTION IMMEDIATELY.

ANTIDOTE: NO SPECIFIC ANTIDOTE. TREAT SYMPTOMATICALLY AND SUPPORTIVELY.

REACTIVITY

REACTIVITY: STABLE UNDER NORMAL TEMPERATURES AND PRESSURES.
INCOMPATIBILITIES: NONE KNOWN.
DECOMPOSITION: THERMAL DECOMPOSITION PRODUCTS MAY INCLUDE TOXIC OXIDES OF CARBON, NITROGEN, AND SULFUR.
POLYMERIZATION: HAZARDOUS POLYMERIZATION HAS NOT BEEN REPORTED TO OCCUR UNDER NORMAL TEMPERATURES AND PRESSURES.

CONDITIONS TO AVOID

MAY BURN BUT DOES NOT IGNITE READILY. AVOID CONTACT WITH STRONG OXIDIZERS, EXCESSIVE HEAT, SPARKS, OR OPEN FLAME.

SPILL AND LEAK PROCEDURES

OCCUPATIONAL SPILL: SWEEP UP AND PLACE IN SUITABLE CLEAN, DRY CONTAINERS FOR RECLAMATION OR LATER DISPOSAL. DO NOT FLUSH SPILLED MATERIAL INTO SEWER. KEEP UNNECESSARY PEOPLE AWAY.

PROTECTIVE EQUIPMENT

VENTILATION: PROVIDE LOCAL EXHAUST OR GENERAL DILUTION VENTILATION SYSTEM.
RESPIRATOR: THE FOLLOWING RESPIRATORS ARE RECOMMENDED BASED ON INFORMATION FOUND IN THE PHYSICAL DATA, TOXICITY AND HEALTH EFFECTS SECTIONS. THEY ARE RANKED IN ORDER FROM MINIMUM TO MAXIMUM RESPIRATORY PROTECTION. THE SPECIFIC RESPIRATOR SELECTED MUST BE BASED ON CONTAMINATION LEVELS FOUND IN THE WORK PLACE, MUST NOT EXCEED THE WORKING LIMITS OF THE RESPIRATOR AND BE JOINTLY APPROVED BY THE NATIONAL INSTITUTE FOR OCCUPATIONAL SAFETY AND HEALTH AND THE MINE SAFETY AND HEALTH ADMINISTRATION (NIOSH-MSHA).
CHEMICAL CARTRIDGE RESPIRATOR WITH FULL FACEPIECE.
TYPE 'C' SUPPLIED-AIR RESPIRATOR WITH A FULL FACEPIECE OPERATED IN PRESSURE-DEMAND OR OTHER POSITIVE PRESSURE MODE OR WITH A FULL FACEPIECE, HELMET OR HOOD OPERATED IN CONTINUOUS-FLOW MODE.
SELF-CONTAINED BREATHING APPARATUS WITH A FULL FACEPIECE OPERATED IN PRESSURE-DEMAND OR OTHER POSITIVE PRESSURE MODE.
FOR FIREFIGHTING AND OTHER IMMEDIATELY DANGEROUS TO LIFE OR HEALTH CONDITIONS:
SELF-CONTAINED BREATHING APPARATUS WITH FULL FACEPIECE OPERATED IN PRESSURE-DEMAND OR OTHER POSITIVE PRESSURE MODE.
SUPPLIED-AIR RESPIRATOR WITH FULL FACEPIECE AND OPERATED IN PRESSURE-DEMAND OR OTHER POSITIVE PRESSURE MODE IN COMBINATION WITH AN AUXILIARY SELF-CONTAINED BREATHING APPARATUS OPERATED IN PRESSURE-DEMAND OR OTHER POSITIVE PRESSURE MODE.
CLOTHING: EMPLOYEE MUST WEAR APPROPRIATE PROTECTIVE (IMPERVIOUS) CLOTHING AND EQUIPMENT TO PREVENT ANY POSSIBILITY OF SKIN CONTACT WITH THIS SUBSTANCE.
GLOVES: EMPLOYEE MUST WEAR APPROPRIATE PROTECTIVE GLOVES TO PREVENT CONTACT WITH THIS SUBSTANCE.
EYE PROTECTION: EMPLOYEE MUST WEAR SPLASH-PROOF OR DUST-RESISTANT SAFETY GOGGLES AND A FACESHIELD TO PREVENT CONTACT WITH THIS SUBSTANCE.
EMERGENCY WASH FACILITIES: WHERE THERE IS ANY POSSIBILITY THAT AN EMPLOYEE'S EYES AND/OR SKIN MAY BE EXPOSED TO THIS SUBSTANCE, THE EMPLOYER SHOULD PROVIDE AN EYE WASH FOUNTAIN AND QUICK DRENCH SHOWER WITHIN THE IMMEDIATE WORK AREA FOR EMERGENCY USE.

AUTHORIZED BY- OCCUPATIONAL HEALTH SERVICES, INC.
CREATION DATE: 10/04/89 ***REVISION DATE:*** 05/31/90

MATERIAL SAFETY DATA SHEET

OCCUPATIONAL HEALTH SERVICES, INC.
AGRICULTURE AND PESTICIDE DIVISION
450 SEVENTH AVENUE, SUITE 2407
NEW YORK, NEW YORK 10123
1-800-445-MSDS OR (212) 967-1100

EMERGENCY CONTACT:
JOHN S. BRANSFORD, JR. (615) 292-1180

SUBSTANCE IDENTIFICATION

CAS-NUMBER 90-43-7
SUBSTANCE: **ORTHO-PHENYLPHENOL**

TRADE NAMES/SYNONYMS: 2-BIPHENYLOL; (1,1'-BIPHENYL)-2-OL; O-BIPHENYLOL; O-DIPHENYLOL; DOWICIDE 1 ANTIMICROBIAL; O-HYDROXYBIPHENYL; 2-HYDROXYBIPHENYL; O-HYDROXYDIPHENYL; 2-PHENYLPHENOL; 2-HYDROXYDIPHENYL; O-PHENYLPHENOL; O-PHENYL PHENOL; REMOL TRF; O-XENOL; ANTHRAPOLE 73; TORSITE; INVALON OP; NECTRYL; TETROSIN OE-N; C12H10O; PST18470
CHEMICAL FAMILY: PHENOL
MOLECULAR FORMULA: C12-H10-O
MOLECULAR WEIGHT: 170.22
CERCLA RATINGS (SCALE 0-3): HEALTH=2 FIRE=1 REACTIVITY=0 PERSISTENCE=1
NFPA RATINGS (SCALE 0-4): HEALTH=1 FIRE=1 REACTIVITY=0

COMPONENTS AND CONTAMINANTS

COMPONENT: ORTHO-PHENYLPHENOL ***PERCENT:*** 100
CAS# 90-43-7
OTHER CONTAMINANTS: NONE
EXPOSURE LIMITS: ORTHO-PHENYLPHENOL: NO OCCUPATIONAL EXPOSURE LIMITS ESTABLISHED BY OSHA, ACGIH, OR NIOSH.
SUBJECT TO SARA SECTION 313 ANNUAL TOXIC CHEMICAL RELEASE REPORTING

PHYSICAL DATA

DESCRIPTION: NEARLY WHITE TO PALE PINK OR LIGHT BUFF FLAKY CRYSTALS OR NEEDLES WITH A MILD CHARACTERISTIC ODOR. ***BOILING POINT:*** 547 F (286 C)
MELTING POINT: 135-137 F (57-58 C) ***SPECIFIC GRAVITY:*** 1.213
VAPOR PRESSURE: 1 MMHG @ 100.0 C ***SOLUBILITY IN WATER:*** <1 MG/ML @ 18 C
SOLVENT SOLUBILITY: ALCOHOL, ALKALI HYDROXIDES, BENZENE, PETROLEUM ETHER, ETHER, PYRIMIDENE, ETHANOL, ETHYLENE GLYCOL, ACETONE, ISOPROPANOL, GLYCOL ETHERS, POLYGLYCOLS, DIMETHYLSULFOXIDE

FIRE AND EXPLOSION DATA

FIRE AND EXPLOSION HAZARD: SLIGHT FIRE HAZARD WHEN EXPOSED TO HEAT OR FLAME.
FLASH POINT: 255 F (124 C) ***AUTOIGNITION TEMP.:*** 986 F (530 C)
FIREFIGHTING MEDIA: DRY CHEMICAL, CARBON DIOXIDE, HALON, WATER SPRAY OR STANDARD FOAM (1987 EMERGENCY RESPONSE GUIDEBOOK, DOT P 5800.4).
FOR LARGER FIRES, USE WATER SPRAY, FOG OR STANDARD FOAM (1987 EMERGENCY RESPONSE GUIDEBOOK, DOT P 5800.4).
ALCOHOL FOAM (NFPA 325M, FIRE HAZARD PROPERTIES OF FLAMMABLE LIQUIDS, GASES, AND VOLATILE SOLIDS, 1984).
FIREFIGHTING: MOVE CONTAINER FROM FIRE AREA IF POSSIBLE. DO NOT SCATTER SPILLED MATERIAL WITH HIGH PRESSURE WATER STREAMS. DIKE FIRE CONTROL WATER FOR LATER DISPOSAL (1987 EMERGENCY RESPONSE GUIDEBOOK, DOT P 5800.4, GUIDE PAGE 31).
USE AGENTS SUITABLE FOR TYPE OF SURROUNDING FIRE. AVOID BREATHING HAZARDOUS VAPORS, KEEP UPWIND.
WATER OR FOAM MAY CAUSE FROTHING (NFPA 325M, FIRE HAZARD PROPERTIES OF FLAMMABLE LIQUIDS, GASES, AND VOLATILE SOLIDS, 1984)

TOXICITY

ORTHO-PHENYLPHENOL: IRRITATION DATA: 250 MG SKIN-RABBIT; 20 MG/24 HOURS SKIN-RABBIT MODERATE; 50 UG/24 HOURS EYE-RABBIT SEVERE. TOXICITY DATA: 2000 MG/KG ORAL-RAT LD50; 1050 MG/KG ORAL-MOUSE LD50; 500 MG/KG ORAL-CAT LD50; 50 MG/KG INTRAPERITONEAL-MOUSE LD50; MUTAGENIC DATA (RTECS); REPRODUCTIVE EFFECTS DATA (RTECS); TUMORIGENIC DATA (RTECS). CARCINOGEN STATUS: ANIMAL INADEQUATE EVIDENCE (IARC GROUP-3). LOCAL EFFECTS: CORROSIVE- EYE; IRRITANT- INHALATION, SKIN. ACUTE TOXICITY LEVEL: MODERATELY TOXIC BY INGESTION. TARGET EFFECTS: NO DATA AVAILABLE.

HEALTH EFFECTS AND FIRST AID

INHALATION: ORTHO-PHENYLPHENOL: IRRITANT. **ACUTE EXPOSURE-** INHALATION OF DUST MAY CAUSE IRRITATION. **CHRONIC EXPOSURE-** NO DATA AVAILABLE.
FIRST AID- REMOVE FROM EXPOSURE AREA TO FRESH AIR IMMEDIATELY. IF BREATHING HAS STOPPED, PERFORM ARTIFICIAL RESPIRATION. KEEP PERSON WARM AND AT REST. TREAT SYMPTOMATICALLY AND SUPPORTIVELY. GET MEDICAL ATTENTION IMMEDIATELY.

SKIN CONTACT: ORTHO-PHENYLPHENOL: IRRITANT. **ACUTE EXPOSURE-** CONTACT MAY CAUSE IRRITATION. A 5% SOLUTION CAUSED NEITHER PRIMARY IRRITATION NOR SENSITIZATION ON HUMAN SKIN. DERMAL DAMAGE HAS OCCURRED WHEN ORTHO-PHENYLPHENOL WAS PAINTED ON ANIMAL SKIN. SYSTEMIC POISONING MAY OCCUR DUE TO SLIGHT SKIN ABSORPTION. **CHRONIC EXPOSURE-** IN A 4 WEEK DERMAL APPLICATION STUDY WITH MICE, AN ULCERATIVE LESION WAS SEEN AT THE CHEMICAL APPLICATION SITE, BUT WAS NOT CONSIDERED SEVERE. IN A 2 YEAR STUDY, ORTHO-PHENYLPHENOL CAUSED NON-NEOPLASTIC LESIONS WHICH

INCLUDED ULCERATION, INFLAMMATION; HYPERKERATOSIS AND ACANTHOSIS AT THE SITE OF APPLICATION.

FIRST AID- REMOVE CONTAMINATED CLOTHING AND SHOES IMMEDIATELY. WASH AFFECTED AREA WITH SOAP OR MILD DETERGENT AND LARGE AMOUNTS OF WATER UNTIL NO EVIDENCE OF CHEMICAL REMAINS (APPROXIMATELY 15-20 MINUTES). GET MEDICAL ATTENTION IMMEDIATELY.

EYE CONTACT: ORTHO-PHENYLPHENOL: CORROSIVE. **ACUTE EXPOSURE-** ANIMAL STUDIES INDICATE THAT CONTACT MAY CAUSE SEVERE IRRITATION AND CORNEAL NECROSIS. **CHRONIC EXPOSURE-** EFFECTS ARE DEPENDENT UPON CONCENTRATION AND DURATION OF EXPOSURE. CONJUNCTIVITIS OF EFFECTS SIMILAR TO THOSE FOR ACUTE EXPOSURE MAY OCCUR.

FIRST AID- WASH EYES IMMEDIATELY WITH LARGE AMOUNTS OF WATER, OCCASIONALLY LIFTING UPPER AND LOWER LIDS, UNTIL NO EVIDENCE OF CHEMICAL REMAINS (AT LEAST 15-20 MINUTES). CONTINUE IRRIGATING WITH NORMAL SALINE UNTIL THE PH HAS RETURNED TO NORMAL (30-60 MINUTES). COVER WITH STERILE BANDAGES. GET MEDICAL ATTENTION IMMEDIATELY.

INGESTION: ORTHO-PHENYLPHENOL: **ACUTE EXPOSURE-** ANIMAL STUDIES INDICATE THAT ACUTE INTOXICATION MAY INCLUDE RESPIRATORY FAILURE AND HEMORRHAGES IN THE LUNG, LIVER, GASTROINTESTINAL LUMEN AND MYOCARDIUM. DEATH IS DUE TO CENTRAL NERVOUS SYSTEM DEPRESSION. **CHRONIC EXPOSURE-** RATS RECEIVING 2% IN THEIR DIET FOR 2 YEARS SHOWED SIGNIFICANT GROWTH RETARDATION AND INCREASED TESTICULAR WEIGHT IN MALES AND MARKED TUBULAR DILATION AND ACUTE AND CHRONIC INFLAMMATION OF THE KIDNEYS. THOSE FED 2% IN THEIR DIET FOR 90 DAYS SHOWED FOCAL TUBULAR NECROSIS OF THE KIDNEYS. RATS FED A TOTAL DOSE OF 478 GM/KG FOR 91 WEEKS DEVELOPED LIVER AND URINARY TRACT TUMORS. HISTOLOGICALLY, THE LESIONS OF THE URINARY BLADDER WERE CLASSIFIED AS HYPERPLASIA, PAPILLOMA AND TRANSITIONAL CELL CARCINOMA.

FIRST AID- IF THE PATIENT IS ALERT AND ABLE TO SWALLOW, GIVE A SLURRY OF ACTIVATED CHARCOAL IN WATER. DO NOT GIVE EMETICS. CAREFUL GASTRIC LAVAGE WITH WATER IS RECOMMENDED IF THERE ARE NO DEEP BURNS IN THE MOUTH OR PHARYNX. OLDER RECOMMENDATIONS TO LAVAGE WITH OLIVE OR OTHER VEGETABLE OILS DO NOT APPEAR TO BE SUBSTANTIATED. IN ANY CASE AVOID MINERAL OIL AND ALCOHOL. (GOSSELIN, CLINICAL TOXICOLOGY OF COMMERCIAL PRODUCTS, 5TH ED.). LAVAGE MUST BE PERFORMED BY QUALIFIED MEDICAL PERSONNEL.

ANTIDOTE: NO SPECIFIC ANTIDOTE. TREAT SYMPTOMATICALLY AND SUPPORTIVELY.

REACTIVITY

REACTIVITY: STABLE UNDER NORMAL TEMPERATURES AND PRESSURES.

INCOMPATIBILITIES: ORTHO-PHENYLPHENOL: STRONG OXIDIZERS: POSSIBLE REACTION. SODIUM HYDROXIDE (AQUEOUS): REACTS TO FORM SODIUM ORTHO-PHENYLPHENATE WHICH IS TOXIC AND CORROSIVE.

DECOMPOSITION: THERMAL DECOMPOSITION MAY RELEASE ACRID SMOKE AND IRRITATING FUMES.

POLYMERIZATION: HAZARDOUS POLYMERIZATION HAS NOT BEEN REPORTED TO OCCUR UNDER NORMAL TEMPERATURES AND PRESSURES.

STORAGE AND DISPOSAL

OBSERVE ALL FEDERAL, STATE AND LOCAL REGULATIONS WHEN STORING OR DISPOSING OF THIS SUBSTANCE. FOR ASSISTANCE, CONTACT THE DISTRICT DIRECTOR OF THE ENVIRONMENTAL PROTECTION AGENCY.

****STORAGE****

STORE IN ACCORDANCE WITH 40 CFR 165 RECOMMENDED PROCEDURES FOR THE DISPOSAL AND STORAGE OF PESTICIDES AND PESTICIDE CONTAINERS.
STORE AWAY FROM INCOMPATIBLE SUBSTANCES.

****DISPOSAL****

DISPOSAL MUST BE IN ACCORDANCE WITH 40 CFR 165 RECOMMENDED PROCEDURES FOR THE DISPOSAL AND STORAGE OF PESTICIDES AND PESTICIDE CONTAINERS.

CONDITIONS TO AVOID

MAY BURN BUT DOES NOT IGNITE READILY. AVOID CONTACT WITH STRONG OXIDIZERS, EXCESSIVE HEAT, SPARKS, OR OPEN FLAME.

SPILL AND LEAK PROCEDURES

OCCUPATIONAL SPILL: SWEEP UP AND PLACE IN SUITABLE CLEAN, DRY CONTAINERS FOR RECLAMATION OR LATER DISPOSAL. DO NOT FLUSH SPILLED MATERIAL INTO SEWER. KEEP UNNECESSARY PEOPLE AWAY.

PROTECTIVE EQUIPMENT

VENTILATION: PROVIDE GENERAL DILUTION VENTILATION.

RESPIRATOR: THE FOLLOWING RESPIRATORS ARE RECOMMENDED BASED ON INFORMATION FOUND IN THE PHYSICAL DATA, TOXICITY AND HEALTH EFFECTS SECTIONS. THEY ARE RANKED IN ORDER FROM MINIMUM TO MAXIMUM RESPIRATORY PROTECTION. THE SPECIFIC RESPIRATOR SELECTED MUST BE BASED ON CONTAMINATION LEVELS FOUND IN THE WORK PLACE, MUST NOT EXCEED THE WORKING LIMITS OF THE RESPIRATOR AND BE JOINTLY APPROVED BY THE NATIONAL INSTITUTE FOR OCCUPATIONAL SAFETY AND HEALTH AND THE MINE SAFETY AND HEALTH ADMINISTRATION (NIOSH-MSHA).

CHEMICAL CARTRIDGE RESPIRATOR WITH AN ORGANIC VAPOR CARTRIDGE(S) WITH A FULL FACEPIECE AND ORGANIC VAPOR CARTRIDGE(S) IN COMBINATION WITH A DUST AND MIST FILTER.

POWERED AIR-PURIFYING RESPIRATOR WITH A TIGHT-FITTING FACEPIECE AND ORGANIC VAPOR CARTRIDGE(S) IN COMBINATION WITH A HIGH-EFFICIENCY PARTICULATE FILTER.

TYPE 'C' SUPPLIED-AIR RESPIRATOR WITH A FULL FACEPIECE OPERATED IN A PRESSURE-DEMAND OR OTHER POSITIVE PRESSURE MODE.

SELF-CONTAINED BREATHING APPARATUS WITH A FULL FACEPIECE OPERATED IN PRESSURE-DEMAND OR OTHER POSITIVE PRESSURE MODE.

FOR FIREFIGHTING AND OTHER IMMEDIATELY DANGEROUS TO LIFE OR HEALTH CONDITIONS:

SELF-CONTAINED BREATHING APPARATUS WITH FULL FACEPIECE OPERATED IN PRESSURE-DEMAND OR OTHER POSITIVE PRESSURE MODE.

SUPPLIED-AIR RESPIRATOR WITH FULL FACEPIECE AND OPERATED IN PRESSURE-DEMAND OR OTHER POSITIVE PRESSURE MODE IN COMBINATION WITH AN AUXILIARY SELF-CONTAINED BREATHING APPARATUS OPERATED IN PRESSURE-DEMAND OR OTHER POSITIVE PRESSURE MODE.

CLOTHING: EMPLOYEE MUST WEAR APPROPRIATE PROTECTIVE (IMPERVIOUS) CLOTHING AND EQUIPMENT TO PREVENT REPEATED OR PROLONGED SKIN CONTACT WITH THIS SUBSTANCE.

GLOVES: EMPLOYEE MUST WEAR APPROPRIATE PROTECTIVE GLOVES TO PREVENT CONTACT WITH THIS SUBSTANCE.

EYE PROTECTION: EMPLOYEE MUST WEAR SPLASH-PROOF OR DUST-RESISTANT SAFETY GOGGLES AND A FACESHIELD TO PREVENT CONTACT WITH THIS SUBSTANCE.

EMERGENCY WASH FACILITIES: WHERE THERE IS ANY POSSIBILITY THAT AN EMPLOYEE'S EYES AND/OR SKIN MAY BE EXPOSED TO THIS SUBSTANCE, THE EMPLOYER SHOULD PROVIDE AN EYE WASH FOUNTAIN AND QUICK DRENCH SHOWER WITHIN THE IMMEDIATE WORK AREA FOR EMERGENCY USE.

AUTHORIZED BY- OCCUPATIONAL HEALTH SERVICES, INC.
CREATION DATE: 10/04/89 ***REVISION DATE:*** 07/12/90

MATERIAL SAFETY DATA SHEET

OCCUPATIONAL HEALTH SERVICES, INC.
AGRICULTURE AND PESTICIDE DIVISION
450 SEVENTH AVENUE, SUITE 2407
NEW YORK, NEW YORK 10123
1-800-445-MSDS OR (212) 967-1100

EMERGENCY CONTACT:
JOHN S. BRANSFORD, JR. (615) 292-1180

SUBSTANCE IDENTIFICATION

CAS-NUMBER 62-38-4

SUBSTANCE: **PHENYLMERCURIC ACETATE**

TRADE NAMES/SYNONYMS: (ACETATO) PHENYLMERCURY; PHENYLMERCURY ACETATE; MERCURIPHENYL ACETATE; PHENOMERCURIC ACETATE; PHENYL MERCURIC ACETATE; PMA; PM ACETATE; FUNGITOX OR; PHENMAD; ACETIC ACID, PHENYL MERCURY DERIV.; GALLOTOX; RCRA P092; UN 1674; ACETOXYPHENYLMERCURY; MERSOLITE; SPOR-KIL; PST18560

CHEMICAL FAMILY: ORGANOMETALLIC

MOLECULAR FORMULA: C8-H8-HG-O2

MOLECULAR WEIGHT: 336.75

CERCLA RATINGS (SCALE 0-3): HEALTH=3 FIRE=1 REACTIVITY=0 PERSISTENCE=3

NFPA RATINGS (SCALE 0-4): HEALTH=3 FIRE=1 REACTIVITY=0

COMPONENTS AND CONTAMINANTS

COMPONENT: PHENYLMERCURIC ACETATE ***PERCENT:*** 100
CAS# 62-38-4

OTHER CONTAMINANTS: NONE

EXPOSURE LIMITS: MERCURY, ALL FORMS EXCEPT ALKYL (AS HG): 0.05 MG/M3 OSHA TWA (VAPOR); 0.1 MG/M3 OSHA CEILING (SKIN) 0.05 MG/M3 ACGIH TWA (VAPOR); 0.10 MG/M3 ACGIH TWA (ARYL & INORGANIC)-(SKIN) 0.05 MG/M3 NIOSH RECOMMENDED 10 HOUR TWA

SUBJECT TO SARA SECTION 313 ANNUAL TOXIC CHEMICAL RELEASE REPORTING SUBJECT TO CALIFORNIA PROPOSITION 65 CANCER AND/OR REPRODUCTIVE TOXICITY WARNING AND RELEASE REQUIREMENTS- (JULY 1, 1990) PHENYLMERCURIC ACETATE: 500/10,000 POUNDS SARA SECTION 302 THRESHOLD PLANNING QUANTITY 100 POUNDS SARA SECTION 304 REPORTABLE QUANTITY 100 POUNDS CERCLA SECTION 103 REPORTABLE QUANTITY

PHYSICAL DATA

DESCRIPTION: ODORLESS, WHITE TO CREAMY-WHITE CRYSTALLINE POWDER OR SMALL PRISMS OR LEAFLETS. ***MELTING POINT:*** 300 F (149 C)

SPECIFIC GRAVITY: NOT AVAILABLE ***SOLUBILITY IN WATER:*** SLIGHTLY SOLUBLE

SOLVENT SOLUBILITY: SOLUBLE IN ALCOHOL, BENZENE, GLACIAL ACETIC ACID, ACETONE

FIRE AND EXPLOSION DATA

FIRE AND EXPLOSION HAZARD: NEGLIGIBLE FIRE HAZARD WHEN EXPOSED TO HEAT OR FLAME.

FIREFIGHTING MEDIA: DRY CHEMICAL, CARBON DIOXIDE, HALON, WATER SPRAY OR STANDARD FOAM (1987 EMERGENCY RESPONSE GUIDEBOOK, DOT P 5800.4). FOR LARGER FIRES, USE WATER SPRAY, FOG OR STANDARD FOAM (1987 EMERGENCY RESPONSE GUIDEBOOK, DOT P 5800.4).

FIREFIGHTING: MOVE CONTAINERS FROM FIRE AREA IF POSSIBLE. FIGHT FIRE FROM MAXIMUM DISTANCE. STAY AWAY FROM STORAGE TANK ENDS. DIKE FIRE CONTROL WATER FOR LATER DISPOSAL. DO NOT SCATTER MATERIAL (1987 EMERGENCY RESPONSE GUIDEBOOK, DOT P 5800.4, GUIDE PAGE 55). EXTINGUISH USING AGENT SUITABLE FOR TYPE OF SURROUNDING FIRE. AVOID BREATHING VAPORS AND DUSTS. KEEP UPWIND.

TRANSPORTATION DATA

DEPARTMENT OF TRANSPORTATION HAZARD CLASSIFICATION 49 CFR 172.101: POISON B

DEPARTMENT OF TRANSPORTATION LABELING REQUIREMENTS 49 CFR 172.101 AND SUBPART E: POISON

DEPARTMENT OF TRANSPORTATION PACKAGING REQUIREMENTS: 49 CFR 173.365 EXCEPTIONS: 49 CFR 173.364

TOXICITY

PHENYLMERCURIC ACETATE: IRRITATION DATA: 100 UG/24 HOURS SKIN-HUMAN SEVERE; 50 UG/24 HOURS EYE-RABBIT SEVERE. TOXICITY DATA: 22 MG/KG ORAL-RAT LD50; 13250 UG/KG ORAL-MOUSE LD50; 12 MG/KG SUBCUTANEOUS-MOUSE LD50; 20 MG/KG INTRAVENOUS-RAT LDLO; 18 MG/KG INTRAVENOUS-MOUSE LD50; 5 MG/KG INTRAVENOUS-DOG LDLO; 13 MG/KG INTRAPERITONEAL-MOUSE LD50; 10 MG/KG INTRAPERITONEAL-MAMMAL LD50; 17 MG/KG UNREPORTED-MAMMAL LD50; MUTAGENIC DATA (RTECS); REPRODUCTIVE EFFECTS DATA (RTECS). CARCINOGEN STATUS: NONE. LOCAL EFFECTS: IRRITANT- SKIN, EYE. ACUTE TOXICITY LEVEL: HIGHLY TOXIC BY INGESTION. TARGET EFFECTS: POISONING MAY AFFECT THE CENTRAL NERVOUS SYSTEM AND KIDNEYS.

HEALTH EFFECTS AND FIRST AID

INHALATION: PHENYLMERCURIC ACETATE: **ACUTE EXPOSURE-** NO SPECIFIC DATA AVAILABLE. ARYL (PHENYL) MERCURIALS MAY CAUSE IRRITATION OF THE MUCOUS MEMBRANES. THESE COMPOUNDS ARE CONCENTRATED IN THE CENTRAL NERVOUS SYSTEM, INCLUDING BRAIN, AND MAY CAUSE ALMOST IMMEDIATE DYSPNEA, COUGH, FEVER, NAUSEA, VOMITING, DIARRHEA, HEADACHE, SALIVATION, CHEST AND ABDOMINAL PAIN, METALLIC TASTE, MYALGIA, ATAXIA, SPASTICITY, RIGIDITY, TREMORS, EMOTIONAL INSTABILITY, MENTAL CONFUSION, AND MEMORY DEFECTS. THESE SYMPTOMS MAY RESOLVE OR PROGRESS TO NECROTIZING BRONCHIOLITIS, PNEUMONITIS, PULMONARY EDEMA, AND PNEUMOTHORAX. **CHRONIC EXPOSURE-** NO SPECIFIC DATA AVAILABLE. REPEATED OR PROLONGED EXPOSURE TO ARYL (PHENYL) MERCURIALS MAY CAUSE MERCURIALISM. SYMPTOMS MAY INCLUDE FINE TREMORS OF THE HANDS, FACE, ARMS, AND LEGS, ERETHISM INCLUDING ABNORMAL SHYNESS, DEPRESSION OR DESPONDENCY, IRRITABILITY OR EXCITABILITY, HEADACHE, FATIGUE, AND INSOMNIA, SCANNING SPEECH WITH MODERATE SLURRING AND DIFFICULTY IN PRONUNCIATION, UNSTEADY GAIT PROGRESSING TO SEVERE ATAXIA OF THE ARMS AND LEGS, SENSORY DISTURBANCES INCLUDING TUNNEL VISION, BLINDNESS, AND DEAFNESS, SALIVATION, STOMATITIS, LOOSENING OF THE TEETH, GINGIVITIS, BLUE LINE ON THE GUMS, PAIN AND NUMBNESS IN THE EXTREMITIES, DIARRHEA, ANXIETY, HEADACHE, WEIGHT LOSS, AND ANOREXIA. POISONING MAY RESULT IN KIDNEY DAMAGE INCLUDING NEPHRITIS. MERCURY CROSSES THE PLACENTA AND IS EXCRETED IN BREAST MILK.

FIRST AID- REMOVE FROM EXPOSURE AREA TO FRESH AIR IMMEDIATELY. IF BREATHING HAS STOPPED, GIVE ARTIFICIAL RESPIRATION. MAINTAIN AIRWAY AND BLOOD PRESSURE AND ADMINISTER OXYGEN IF AVAILABLE. KEEP AFFECTED PERSON WARM AND AT REST. TREAT SYMPTOMATICALLY AND SUPPORTIVELY. ADMINISTRATION OF OXYGEN SHOULD BE PERFORMED BY QUALIFIED PERSONNEL. GET MEDICAL ATTENTION IMMEDIATELY.

SKIN CONTACT: PHENYLMERCURIC ACETATE: IRRITANT. **ACUTE EXPOSURE-** DIRECT CONTACT MAY RESULT IN SEVERE IRRITATION AND MAY BE ABSORBED THROUGH THE SKIN WITH DELAYED SYSTEMIC EFFECTS. ARYL (PHENYL) MERCURIALS MAY CAUSE PRIMARY SKIN IRRITATION WITH ERYTHEMA, INTENSE ITCHING, EDEMA, AND SENSITIZATION. CONTACT WITH CONCENTRATED SOLUTIONS MAY RESULT IN CHEMICAL BURNS AND BLISTERING. **CHRONIC EXPOSURE-** NO SPECIFIC DATA AVAILABLE. REPEATED OR PROLONGED EXPOSURE TO ARYL (PHENYL) MERCURIALS MAY CAUSE SENSITIZATION, URTICARIA PROGRESSING TO WEEPING DERMATITIS, AND MERCURIALISM, WITH SYMPTOMS SIMILAR TO THOSE IN CHRONIC INHALATION.

FIRST AID- REMOVE CONTAMINATED CLOTHING AND SHOES IMMEDIATELY. WASH AFFECTED AREA WITH SOAP OR MILD DETERGENT AND LARGE AMOUNTS OF WATER UNTIL NO EVIDENCE OF CHEMICAL REMAINS (AT LEAST 15-20 MINUTES). IN CASE OF CHEMICAL BURNS, COVER AREA WITH STERILE, DRY DRESSING. BANDAGE SECURELY, BUT NOT TOO TIGHTLY. GET MEDICAL ATTENTION IMMEDIATELY.

EYE CONTACT: PHENYLMERCURIC ACETATE: IRRITANT. **ACUTE EXPOSURE-** NO SPECIFIC DATA AVAILABLE. ARYL (PHENYL) MERCURIALS MAY CAUSE IRRITATION. **CHRONIC EXPOSURE-** REPEATED OR PROLONGED CONTACT WITH LOW CONCENTRATIONS (0.002%) OF PHENYLMERCURIC ACETATE MAY RESULT IN MERCURIALENTIS WITH CONSTRICTION OF VISUAL FIELD, SCOTOMATA, AND MICROSCOPIC DISCOLORATION AND CHANGES IN TRANSPARENCY OF THE FRONT OF THE LENS AND CONJUNCTIVITIS. CONCENTRATED SOLUTIONS MAY RESULT IN INJURY TO THE CORNEA.

FIRST AID- WASH EYES IMMEDIATELY WITH LARGE AMOUNTS OF WATER, OCCASIONALLY LIFTING UPPER AND LOWER LIDS, UNTIL NO EVIDENCE OF CHEMICAL REMAINS (AT LEAST 15-20 MINUTES). CONTINUE IRRIGATING WITH NORMAL SALINE UNTIL THE PH HAS RETURNED TO NORMAL (30-60 MINUTES). COVER WITH STERILE BANDAGES. GET MEDICAL ATTENTION IMMEDIATELY.

INGESTION: PHENYLMERCURIC ACETATE: HIGHLY TOXIC. **ACUTE EXPOSURE-** INGESTION OF 22 MG/KG OF PHENYLMERCURIC ACETATE WAS LETHAL TO RATS. ARYL (PHENYL) MERCURIALS ARE CONCENTRATED IN THE CENTRAL NERVOUS SYSTEM AND MAY CAUSE GINGIVITIS, ATHETOSIS, STOMATITIS, CHOREA, GASTROINTESTINAL DISTURBANCES, METALLIC TASTE, CONSTRICTION OF VISUAL FIELD, AUDITORY AND SPEECH DISTURBANCES, TREMORS, ATAXIA, EMOTIONAL INSTABILITY, MENTAL CONFUSION, AND MEMORY DEFECTS. DAMAGE IS USUALLY IRREVERSIBLE. INGESTION OF LARGE AMOUNTS MAY CAUSE RENAL AND LIVER DAMAGE. **CHRONIC EXPOSURE-** NO SPECIFIC DATA AVAILABLE. REPEATED OR PROLONGED INGESTION OF ARYL (PHENYL) MERCURIALS MAY RESULT IN ABSORPTION OF SUFFICIENT AMOUNTS TO PRODUCE EFFECTS AS IN CHRONIC INHALATION EXPOSURE.

FIRST AID- REMOVE INGESTED POISON BY GASTRIC LAVAGE WITH TAP WATER OR BY EMESIS AND CATHARSIS. MAINTAIN BLOOD PRESSURE, AIRWAY, AND GIVE OXYGEN IF RESPIRATION IS DEPRESSED. GET MEDICAL ATTENTION IMMEDIATELY. (DREISBACH, HANDBOOK OF POISONING, 11TH EDITION) ADMINISTRATION OF GASTRIC LAVAGE OR OXYGEN SHOLD BE PERFORMED BY QUALIFIED MEDICAL PERSONNEL.

ANTIDOTE: THE FOLLOWING ANTIDOTE HAS BEEN RECOMMENDED. HOWEVER, THE DECISION AS TO WHETHER THE SEVERITY OF POISONING REQUIRES ADMINISTRATION OF ANY ANTIDOTE AND ACTUAL DOSE REQUIRED SHOULD BE MADE BY QUALIFIED MEDICAL PERSONNEL.

POISONING FROM ORGANIC MERCURY COMPOUNDS: GIVE N-ACETYL-D,L-PENICILLAMINE (OR IF NOT AVAILABLE D-PENICILLAMINE) BY MOUTH, 250 MG, 4 TIMES DAILY FOR 5-10 DAYS. DIMERCAPROL IS LESS EFFECTIVE AND MAY BE CONTRAINDICATED (GOSSELIN, CLINICAL TOXICOLOGY OF COMMERCIAL PRODUCTS, 5TH EDITION). ANTIDOTE SHOULD BE ADMINISTERED BY QUALIFIED MEDICAL PERSONNEL.

REACTIVITY

REACTIVITY: STABLE UNDER NORMAL TEMPERATURES AND PRESSURES.

INCOMPATIBILITIES: MERCURY: ACETYLENIC COMPOUNDS: INCOMPATIBLE. AMMONIA: INCOMPATIBLE. BORON DIIODOPHOSPHIDE: INCOMPATIBLE. ETHYLENE OXIDE: INCOMPATIBLE. METALS: INCOMPATIBLE. METHYL AZIDE: INCOMPATIBLE. METHYLSILANE OXYGEN: INCOMPATIBLE. OXIDANTS: INCOMPATIBLE. TETRACARBONYL NICKEL OXYGEN: INCOMPATIBLE.

DECOMPOSITION: THERMAL DECOMPOSITION PRODUCTS MAY INCLUDE TOXIC AND HAZARDOUS FUMES OF MERCURY AND OXIDES OF CARBON.

POLYMERIZATION: HAZARDOUS POLYMERIZATION HAS NOT BEEN REPORTED TO OCCUR UNDER NORMAL TEMPERATURES AND PRESSURES.

STORAGE AND DISPOSAL

OBSERVE ALL FEDERAL, STATE AND LOCAL REGULATIONS WHEN STORING OR DISPOSING OF THIS SUBSTANCE. FOR ASSISTANCE, CONTACT THE DISTRICT DIRECTOR OF THE ENVIRONMENTAL PROTECTION AGENCY.

STORAGE

THRESHOLD PLANNING QUANTITY (TPQ): THE SUPERFUND AMENDMENTS AND REAUTHORIZATION ACT (SARA) SECTION 302 REQUIRES THAT EACH FACILITY WHERE ANY EXTREMELY HAZARDOUS SUBSTANCE IS PRESENT IN A QUANTITY EQUAL TO OR GREATER THAN THE TPQ ESTABLISHED FOR THAT SUBSTANCE NOTIFY THE STATE EMERGENCY RESPONSE COMMISSION FOR THE STATE IN WHICH IT IS LOCATED. SECTION 303 OF SARA REQUIRES THESE FACILITIES TO PARTICIPATE IN LOCAL EMERGENCY RESPONSE PLANNING (40 CFR 355.30). PROTECT AGAINST PHYSICAL DAMAGE AND STORE IN DRY LOCATION. SEPARATE FROM OXIDIZING MATERIALS. OUTSIDE OR DETACHED STORAGE IS PREFERABLE. STORE SOLUTIONS IN FLAMMABLE LIQUIDS STORAGE ROOM OR CABINET (NFPA 49, HAZARDOUS CHEMICALS DATA, 1975).

DISPOSAL

MERCURY - REGULATORY LEVEL: 0.2 MG/L MATERIALS WHICH CONTAIN THE ABOVE SUBSTANCE AT OR ABOVE THE REGULATORY LEVEL MEET THE EPA CHARACTERISTIC OF TOXICITY, AND MUST BE DISPOSED OF IN ACCORDANCE WITH 40 CFR PART 262. EPA HAZARDOUS WASTE NUMBER D009.

CONDITIONS TO AVOID

MAY BURN BUT DOES NOT IGNITE READILY. CONTAINERS MAY EXPLODE IN HEAT OF FIRE.

SPILL AND LEAK PROCEDURES

WATER SPILL: THE CALIFORNIA SAFE DRINKING WATER AND TOXIC ENFORCEMENT ACT OF 1986 (PROPOSITION 65) PROHIBITS CONTAMINATING ANY KNOWN SOURCE OF DRINKING WATER WITH SUBSTANCES KNOWN TO CAUSE CANCER AND/OR REPRODUCTIVE TOXICITY.

OCCUPATIONAL SPILL: DO NOT TOUCH SPILLED MATERIAL. STOP LEAK IF YOU CAN DO IT WITHOUT RISK. USE WATER SPRAY TO REDUCE VAPORS. FOR SMALL SPILLS, TAKE UP WITH SAND OR OTHER ABSORBENT MATERIAL AND PLACE INTO CONTAINERS FOR LATER DISPOSAL. FOR SMALL DRY SPILLS, WITH A CLEAN SHOVEL PLACE MATERIAL INTO CLEAN, DRY CONTAINERS AND COVER. MOVE CONTAINERS FROM SPILL AREA. FOR LARGER SPILLS, DIKE FAR AHEAD OF SPILL FOR LATER DISPOSAL. KEEP UNNECESSARY PEOPLE AWAY. ISOLATE HAZARD AREA AND DENY ENTRY. VENTILATE CLOSED SPACES BEFORE ENTERING. REPORTABLE QUANTITY (RQ): 100 POUNDS THE SUPERFUND AMENDMENTS AND REAUTHORIZATION ACT (SARA) SECTION 304 REQUIRES THAT A RELEASE EQUAL TO OR GREATER THAN THE REPORTABLE QUANTITY FOR THIS SUBSTANCE BE IMMEDIATELY REPORTED TO THE LOCAL EMERGENCY PLANNING COMMITTEE AND THE STATE EMERGENCY RESPONSE COMMISSION (40 CFR 355.40). IF THE RELEASE OF THIS SUBSTANCE IS REPORTABLE UNDER CERCLA SECTION 103, THE NATIONAL RESPONSE CENTER MUST BE NOTIFIED IMMEDIATELY AT (800) 424-8802 OR (202) 426-2675 IN THE METROPOLITAN WASHINGTON, D.C. AREA (40 CFR 302.6).

PROTECTIVE EQUIPMENT

VENTILATION: PROVIDE LOCAL EXHAUST OR PROCESS ENCLOSURE VENTILATION TO MEET PUBLISHED EXPOSURE LIMITS.

RESPIRATOR: THE FOLLOWING RESPIRATORS AND MAXIMUM USE CONCENTRATIONS ARE RECOMMENDATIONS BY THE U.S. DEPARTMENT OF HEALTH AND HUMAN SERVICES, NIOSH POCKET GUIDE TO CHEMICAL HAZARDS; NIOSH CRITERIA DOCUMENTS OR BY THE U.S. DEPARTMENT OF LABOR, 29 CFR 1910 SUBPART Z. THE SPECIFIC RESPIRATOR SELECTED MUST BE BASED ON CONTAMINATION LEVELS FOUND IN THE WORK PLACE, MUST NOT EXCEED THE WORKING LIMITS OF THE RESPIRATOR AND BE JOINTLY APPROVED BY THE NATIONAL INSTITUTE FOR OCCUPATIONAL SAFETY AND HEALTH AND THE MINE SAFETY AND HEALTH ADMINISTRATION (NIOSH-MSHA).

MERCURY, ALL FORMS EXCEPT ALKYL (AS HG):

0.5 MG/M3- ANY AIR-PURIFYING RESPIRATOR WITH A HIGH-EFFICIENCY PARTICULATE FILTER. ANY SUPPLIED-AIR RESPIRATOR. ANY SELF-CONTAINED BREATHING APPARATUS.

1.25 MG/M3- ANY SUPPLIED-AIR RESPIRATOR OPERATED IN A CONTINUOUS FLOW MODE. ANY POWERED AIR-PURIFYING RESPIRATOR WITH A HIGH-EFFICIENCY PARTICULATE FILTER.

2.5 MG/M3- ANY SUPPLIED-AIR RESPIRATOR WITH A FULL FACEPIECE. ANY SELF-CONTAINED BREATHING APPARATUS WITH A FULL FACEPIECE. ANY AIR-PURIFYING FULL FACEPIECE RESPIRATOR WITH A HIGH-EFFICIENCY PARTICULATE FILTER. ANY POWERED AIR-PURIFYING RESPIRATOR WITH A TIGHT-FITTING FACEPIECE AND A HIGH-EFFICIENCY PARTICULATE FILTER. ANY SUPPLIED-AIR RESPIRATOR WITH A TIGHT-FITTING FACEPIECE OPERATED IN A CONTINUOUS FLOW MODE.

28 MG/M3- ANY SUPPLIED-AIR RESPIRATOR WITH A HALF-MASK AND OPERATED IN A PRESSURE-DEMAND OR OTHER POSITIVE PRESSURE MODE.

ESCAPE- ANY AIR-PURIFYING FULL FACEPIECE RESPIRATOR WITH A HIGH-EFFICIENCY PARTICULATE FILTER. ANY APPROPRIATE ESCAPE-TYPE SELF-CONTAINED BREATHING APPARATUS.

FOR FIREFIGHTING AND OTHER IMMEDIATELY DANGEROUS TO LIFE OR HEALTH CONDITIONS:

SELF-CONTAINED BREATHING APPARATUS WITH FULL FACEPIECE OPERATED IN PRESSURE-DEMAND OR OTHER POSITIVE PRESSURE MODE.

SUPPLIED-AIR RESPIRATOR WITH FULL FACEPIECE AND OPERATED IN PRESSURE-DEMAND OR OTHER POSITIVE PRESSURE MODE IN COMBINATION WITH AN AUXILIARY SELF-CONTAINED BREATHING APPARATUS OPERATED IN PRESSURE-DEMAND OR OTHER POSITIVE PRESSURE MODE.

CLOTHING: EMPLOYEE MUST WEAR APPROPRIATE PROTECTIVE (IMPERVIOUS) CLOTHING AND EQUIPMENT TO PREVENT ANY POSSIBILITY OF SKIN CONTACT WITH THIS SUBSTANCE.

GLOVES: EMPLOYEE MUST WEAR APPROPRIATE PROTECTIVE GLOVES TO PREVENT CONTACT WITH THIS SUBSTANCE.

EYE PROTECTION: EMPLOYEE MUST WEAR SPLASH-PROOF OR DUST-RESISTANT SAFETY GOGGLES AND A FACESHIELD TO PREVENT CONTACT WITH THIS SUBSTANCE.

EMERGENCY WASH FACILITIES: WHERE THERE IS ANY POSSIBILITY THAT AN EMPLOYEE'S EYES AND/OR SKIN MAY BE EXPOSED TO THIS SUBSTANCE, THE EMPLOYER SHOULD PROVIDE AN EYE WASH FOUNTAIN AND QUICK DRENCH SHOWER WITHIN THE IMMEDIATE WORK AREA FOR EMERGENCY USE.

AUTHORIZED BY- OCCUPATIONAL HEALTH SERVICES, INC.

CREATION DATE: 10/04/89 ***REVISION DATE:*** 07/13/90

MATERIAL SAFETY DATA SHEET

OCCUPATIONAL HEALTH SERVICES, INC.
AGRICULTURE AND PESTICIDE DIVISION
450 SEVENTH AVENUE, SUITE 2407
NEW YORK, NEW YORK 10123
1-800-445-MSDS OR (212) 967-1100

EMERGENCY CONTACT:
JOHN S. BRANSFORD, JR. (615) 292-1180

SUBSTANCE IDENTIFICATION

CAS-NUMBER 100-56-1

SUBSTANCE: PHENYLMERCURIC CHLORIDE

TRADE NAMES/SYNONYMS: CHLOROPHENYL MERCURY; MERCURIPHENYL CHLORIDE; CHLOROPHENYLMERCURY; PHENYL MERCURIC CHLORIDE; PHENYL CHLOROMERCURY; PHENYLMERCURY CHLORIDE; PMC; (CHLOROMERCURI) BENZENE; MERFAZIN; MERSOLITE 2; STOPSPOT; PST18570

CHEMICAL FAMILY: ORGANOMETALLIC

MOLECULAR FORMULA: C6-H5-CL-HG

MOLECULAR WEIGHT: 313.15

CERCLA RATINGS (SCALE 0-3): HEALTH=3 FIRE=0 REACTIVITY=0 PERSISTENCE=3

NFPA RATINGS (SCALE 0-4): HEALTH=4 FIRE=0 REACTIVITY=0

COMPONENTS AND CONTAMINANTS

COMPONENT: PHENYLMERCURIC CHLORIDE ***PERCENT:*** 100

CAS# 100-56-1

OTHER CONTAMINANTS: NONE

EXPOSURE LIMITS: MERCURY, ALL FORMS EXCEPT ALKYL (AS HG): 0.05 MG/M3 OSHA TWA (VAPOR); 0.1 MG/M3 OSHA CEILING (SKIN) 0.05 MG/M3 ACGIH TWA (VAPOR); 0.10 MG/M3 ACGIH TWA (ARYL & INORGANIC)-(SKIN) 0.05 MG/M3 NIOSH RECOMMENDED 10 HOUR TWA

SUBJECT TO SARA SECTION 313 ANNUAL TOXIC CHEMICAL RELEASE REPORTING

SUBJECT TO CALIFORNIA PROPOSITION 65 CANCER AND/OR REPRODUCTIVE TOXICITY WARNING AND RELEASE REQUIREMENTS- (JULY 1, 1990)

PHYSICAL DATA

DESCRIPTION: WHITE SATINY LEAFLETS OR CRYSTALS ***BOILING POINT:*** SUBLIMES

MELTING POINT: 482 F (250 C) ***SOLUBILITY IN WATER:*** VERY SLIGHTLY SOL.

SOLVENT SOLUBILITY: SOLUBLE IN BENZENE, ETHER, PYRIDINE, SLIGHTLY SOLUBLE IN HOT ALCOHOL

FIRE AND EXPLOSION DATA

FIRE AND EXPLOSION HAZARD: NEGLIGIBLE FIRE HAZARD WHEN EXPOSED TO HEAT OR FLAME.

FIREFIGHTING MEDIA: DRY CHEMICAL, CARBON DIOXIDE, HALON, WATER SPRAY OR STANDARD FOAM (1987 EMERGENCY RESPONSE GUIDEBOOK, DOT P 5800.4).

FOR LARGER FIRES, USE WATER SPRAY, FOG OR STANDARD FOAM (1987 EMERGENCY RESPONSE GUIDEBOOK, DOT P 5800.4).

FIREFIGHTING: MOVE CONTAINER FROM FIRE AREA IF POSSIBLE. DO NOT SCATTER SPILLED MATERIAL WITH HIGH PRESSURE WATER STREAMS. DIKE FIRE CONTROL WATER FOR LATER DISPOSAL (1987 EMERGENCY RESPONSE GUIDEBOOK, DOT P 5800.4, GUIDE PAGE 31). USE AGENTS SUITABLE FOR TYPE OF SURROUNDING FIRE. AVOID BREATHING HAZARDOUS VAPORS, KEEP UPWIND.

TOXICITY

PHENYLMERCURIC CHLORIDE: TOXICITY DATA: 60 MG/KG ORAL-RAT LD50; 47 MG/KG SUBCUTANEOUS-RAT LD50; 50 MG/KG INTRAPERITONEAL-RAT LDLO; 50 MG/KG UNREPORTED-RAT LD50; MUTAGENIC DATA (RTECS). CARCINOGEN STATUS: NONE. LOCAL EFFECTS: IRRITANT- INHALATION, SKIN, EYE. ACUTE TOXICITY LEVEL: TOXIC BY INGESTION. TARGET EFFECTS: SENSITIZER- DERMAL; CENTRAL NERVOUS SYSTEM DEPRESSANT. POISONING MAY ALSO AFFECT THE KIDNEYS.

HEALTH EFFECTS AND FIRST AID

INHALATION: PHENYLMERCURIC CHLORIDE: IRRITANT/NARCOTIC. **ACUTE EXPOSURE-** EXPOSURE TO DUST OR VAPORS MAY CAUSE IRRITATION AND BURNING SENSATION OF THE MUCOUS MEMBRANES. ALMOST IMMEDIATE DYSPNEA, COUGH, FEVER, NAUSEA, VOMITING, DIARRHEA, SALIVATION, CHEST AND ABDOMINAL PAINS, MOTOR WEAKNESS, GINGIVITIS, DYSARTHRIA, ABNORMAL REFLEXES, SALIVATION AND METALLIC TASTE CAN OCCUR. THESE SYMPTOMS MAY RESOLVE OR PROGRESS TO NECROTIZING BRONCHIOLITIS, PNEUMONITIS, PULMONARY EDEMA AND PNEUMOTHORAX. DEATH MAY OCCUR. **CHRONIC EXPOSURE-** AFTER REPEATED OR PROLONGED EXPOSURE, THERE MAY BE SIGNS OF CENTRAL NERVOUS SYSTEM DISTURBANCES CALLED MERCURIALISM. IT INCLUDES EXCITABILITY AND IRRITABILITY, LOSS OF CONCENTRATION ABILITY, DEPRESSION, INDECISIVENESS, HEADACHE, FATIGUE, MEMORY LOSS, FINE TREMORS OF THE HANDS, HEAD, LIPS, TONGUE OR JAW. PARESTHESIAS, AFFECTIONS OF TASTE OR SMELL, NEURALGIA AND DERMOGRAPHIS MAY OCCUR. THE HIGH CONCENTRATION ATTAINED DURING RENAL EXCRETION MAY LEAD TO SPECIFIC DAMAGE TO RENAL GLOMERULI AND TUBULES. CHRONIC NASAL CATARRH AND EPISTAXIS IS COMMON. PATHOLOGICAL FINDINGS ARE ACUTE TUBULAR AND GLOMERULAR DEGENERATION OR HEMORRHAGIC GLOMERULAR NEPHRITIS.

IRST AID- REMOVE FROM EXPOSURE AREA TO FRESH AIR IMMEDIATELY. IF BREATHING HAS STOPPED, GIVE ARTIFICIAL RESPIRATION. MAINTAIN AIRWAY AND BLOOD PRESSURE AND ADMINISTER OXYGEN IF AVAILABLE. KEEP AFFECTED PERSON WARM AND AT REST. TREAT SYMPTOMATICALLY AND SUPPORTIVELY. ADMINISTRATION OF OXYGEN SHOULD BE PERFORMED BY QUALIFIED PERSONNEL. GET MEDICAL ATTENTION IMMEDIATELY.

SKIN CONTACT: PHENYLMERCURIC CHLORIDE: IRRITANT/SENSITIZER. **ACUTE EXPOSURE-** MAY CAUSE IRRITATION, REDNESS, DERMATITIS AND SKIN RASHES. SYSTEMIC POISONING MAY OCCUR DUE TO ABSORPTION THROUGH INTACT SKIN AND RESULT IN KIDNEY DAMAGE. SOME OF THE EFFECTS OF MERCURY POISONING ARE DUE TO A SENSITIZATION REACTION IN PERSONS WHO HAVE A GENETIC PREDISPOSITION. **CHRONIC EXPOSURE-** MAY CAUSE SENSITIZATION DERMATITIS. MERCURIALISM MAY OCCUR AFTER REPEATED OR PROLONGED EXPOSURE. FINDINGS ARE VARIABLE AND INCLUDE TREMORS, SALIVATION, STOMATITIS, LOSSENING OF THE TEETH, BLUE LINE ON THE GUMS, PAIN AND NUMBNESS IN THE EXTREMITIES, NEPHRITIS, DIARRHEA, ANXIETY, HEADACHE, WEIGHT LOSS, ANOREXIA, MENTAL DEPRESSION, INSOMNIA, INSTABILITY, IRRITABILITY, HALLUCINATIONS AND EVIDENCES OF MENTAL DETERIORATION.

FIRST AID- REMOVE CONTAMINATED CLOTHING AND SHOES IMMEDIATELY. WASH AFFECTED AREA WITH SOAP OR MILD DETERGENT AND LARGE AMOUNTS OF WATER UNTIL NO EVIDENCE OF CHEMICAL REMAINS (APPROXIMATELY 15-20 MINUTES). GET MEDICAL ATTENTION IMMEDIATELY.

EYE CONTACT: PHENYLMERCURIC CHLORIDE: IRRITANT. **ACUTE EXPOSURE-** CONCENTRATED SOLUTIONS MAY BE INJURIOUS TO THE CORNEA. A SEVERE REACTION IS INDUCED BY 0.1 M OF PHENYLMERCURIC CHLORIDE. **CHRONIC EXPOSURE-** THE EFFECTS OF MERCURY ARE CUMMULATIVE AND AFTER REPEATED OR PROLONGED EXPOSURE, THERE MAY BE CHANGES IN THE TRANSPARENCY OF THE FRONT OF THE LENS CALLED MERCURIALENTIS.

FIRST AID- WASH EYES IMMEDIATELY WITH LARGE AMOUNTS OF WATER OR NORMAL SALINE, OCCASIONALLY LIFTING UPPER AND LOWER LIDS, UNTIL NO EVIDENCE OF CHEMICAL REMAINS (APPROXIMATELY 15-20 MINUTES). GET MEDICAL ATTENTION IMMEDIATELY.

INGESTION: PHENYLMERCURIC CHLORIDE: SENSITIZER/TOXIC. **ACUTE EXPOSURE-** MAY CAUSE INFLAMMATION, CONGESTION AND COAGULATION OF THE MUCOSA OF THE GASTROINTESTINAL TRACT. SYMPTOMS INCLUDE FATIGUE, HEADACHE, IRRITABILITY, DELIRIUM, TREMORS, NUMBNESS OF THE MOUTH, TONGUE AND LIMBS, PROTEINURIA, BLURRED VISION, LOSS OF COORDINATION, WEIGHT LOSS AND LOSS OF MEMORY. SYMPTOMS MAY PROGRESS AND PRODUCE SEVERE BRAIN DAMAGE WITH DEAFNESS, INABILITY TO WALK OF TALK, MENTAL RETARDATION, PARALYSIS OF LIMBS AND POSSIBLE COMA. CHILDREN BORN DURING AN EXPOSURE MAY EXHIBIT DELAYED SIMILAR SYMPTOMS AND BIRTH DEFECTS. DEATH MAY OCCUR DUE TO RENAL DAMAGE. **CHRONIC EXPOSURE-** MAY CAUSE DELAYED HYPERSENSITIVE REACTIONS. THE EFFECTS OF MERCURY ARE CUMULATIVE SO SMALL AMOUNTS INGESTED OVER A PERIOD OF TIME MAY PRODUCE DELAYED SYMPTOMS.

FIRST AID- REMOVE BY GASTRIC LAVAGE OR EMESIS. MAINTAIN BLOOD PRESSURE AND AIRWAY. GIVE OXYGEN IF RESPIRATION IS DEPRESSED. DO NOT PERFORM GASTRIC LAVAGE OR EMESIS IF VICTIM IS UNCONSCIOUS. GET MEDICAL ATTENTION IMMEDIATELY (DREISBACH, HANDBOOK OF POISONING, 11TH ED.). ADMINISTRATION OF GASTRIC LAVAGE OR OXYGEN SHOULD BE PERFORMED BY QUALIFIED MEDICAL PERSONNEL.

ANTIDOTE: THE FOLLOWING ANTIDOTE HAS BEEN RECOMMENDED. HOWEVER, THE DECISION AS TO WHETHER THE SEVERITY OF POISONING REQUIRES ADMINISTRATION OF ANY ANTIDOTE AND ACTUAL DOSE REQUIRED SHOULD BE MADE BY QUALIFIED MEDICAL PERSONNEL.

MERCURY POISONING: GIVE DIMERCAPROL, 3 MG/KG (OR 0.3 ML/10 KG) EVERY 4 HOURS FOR THE FIRST 2 DAYS AND THEN 2 MG/KG EVERY 12 HOURS FOR A TOTAL OF 10 DAYS IF NECESSARY. DIMERCAPROL IS AVAILABLE AS A 10% SOLUTION IN OIL FOR INTRAMUSCULAR ADMINISTRATION. HEMODIALYSIS WILL SPEED THE REMOVAL OF THE MERCURY-DIMERCAPROL COMPLEX. PENICILLAMINE IS ALSO EFFECTIVE. GIVE UP TO 100 MG/KG/DAY (MAXIMUM 1 GR/DAY) DIVIDED INTO 4 DOSES FOR NO LONGER THAN 1 WEEK. IF A LONGER ADMINISTRATION PERIOD IS WARRANTED, DOSAGE SHOULD NOT EXCEED 40 MG/KG/DAY. GIVE THE DRUG ORALLY HALF AN HOUR BEFORE MEALS. A CHELATING AGENT SHOULD BE BE CONTINUED UNTIL THE URINE-MERCURY LEVEL FALLS BELOW 50 UG/24 HOURS (DREISBACH, HANDBOOK OF POISONING, 12TH ED.). ANTIDOTE SHOULD BE ADMINISTERED BY QUALIFIED MEDICAL PERSONNEL.

REACTIVITY

REACTIVITY: STABLE UNDER NORMAL TEMPERATURES AND PRESSURES.

INCOMPATIBILITIES: MERCURY: ACETYLENIC COMPOUNDS: INCOMPATIBLE. AMMONIA: INCOMPATIBLE. BORON DIIODOPHOSPHIDE: INCOMPATIBLE. ETHYLENE OXIDE: INCOMPATIBLE. METALS: INCOMPATIBLE. METHYL AZIDE: INCOMPATIBLE. METHYLSILANE OXYGEN: INCOMPATIBLE. OXIDANTS: INCOMPATIBLE. TETRACARBONYL NICKEL OXYGEN: INCOMPATIBLE.

DECOMPOSITION: THERMAL DECOMPOSITION MAY PRODUCE TOXIC FUMES OF MERCURY.
THERMAL DECOMPOSITION PRODUCTS MAY INCLUDE TOXIC AND CORROSIVE FUMES OF CHLORINE.

POLYMERIZATION: HAZARDOUS POLYMERIZATION HAS NOT BEEN REPORTED TO OCCUR UNDER NORMAL TEMPERATURES AND PRESSURES.

STORAGE AND DISPOSAL

OBSERVE ALL FEDERAL, STATE AND LOCAL REGULATIONS WHEN STORING OR DISPOSING OF THIS SUBSTANCE. FOR ASSISTANCE, CONTACT THE DISTRICT DIRECTOR OF THE ENVIRONMENTAL PROTECTION AGENCY.

DISPOSAL

MERCURY - REGULATORY LEVEL: 0.2 MG/L MATERIALS WHICH CONTAIN THE ABOVE SUBSTANCE AT OR ABOVE THE REGULATORY LEVEL MEET THE EPA CHARACTERISTIC OF TOXICITY, AND MUST BE DISPOSED OF IN ACCORDANCE WITH 40 CFR PART 262. EPA HAZARDOUS WASTE NUMBER D009.

CONDITIONS TO AVOID

MAY BURN BUT DOES NOT IGNITE READILY. AVOID CONTACT WITH STRONG OXIDIZERS, EXCESSIVE HEAT, SPARKS, OR OPEN FLAME.

SPILL AND LEAK PROCEDURES

WATER SPILL: THE CALIFORNIA SAFE DRINKING WATER AND TOXIC ENFORCEMENT ACT OF 1986 (PROPOSITION 65) PROHIBITS CONTAMINATING ANY KNOWN SOURCE OF DRINKING WATER WITH SUBSTANCES KNOWN TO CAUSE CANCER AND/OR REPRODUCTIVE TOXICITY.

OCCUPATIONAL SPILL: SWEEP UP AND PLACE IN SUITABLE CLEAN, DRY CONTAINERS FOR RECLAMATION OR LATER DISPOSAL. DO NOT FLUSH SPILLED MATERIAL INTO SEWER. KEEP UNNECESSARY PEOPLE AWAY.

PROTECTIVE EQUIPMENT

VENTILATION: PROVIDE LOCAL EXHAUST OR PROCESS ENCLOSURE VENTILATION TO MEET PUBLISHED EXPOSURE LIMITS.

RESPIRATOR: THE FOLLOWING RESPIRATORS AND MAXIMUM USE CONCENTRATIONS ARE RECOMMENDATIONS BY THE U.S. DEPARTMENT OF HEALTH AND HUMAN SERVICES, NIOSH POCKET GUIDE TO CHEMICAL HAZARDS; NIOSH CRITERIA DOCUMENTS OR BY THE U.S. DEPARTMENT OF LABOR, 29 CFR 1910 SUBPART Z. THE SPECIFIC RESPIRATOR SELECTED MUST BE BASED ON CONTAMINATION

LEVELS FOUND IN THE WORK PLACE, MUST NOT EXCEED THE WORKING LIMITS OF THE RESPIRATOR AND BE JOINTLY APPROVED BY THE NATIONAL INSTITUTE FOR OCCUPATIONAL SAFETY AND HEALTH AND THE MINE SAFETY AND HEALTH ADMINISTRATION (NIOSH-MSHA).

MERCURY, ALL FORMS EXCEPT ALKYL (AS HG):

0.5 MG/M3- ANY AIR-PURIFYING RESPIRATOR WITH A HIGH-EFFICIENCY PARTICULATE FILTER. ANY SUPPLIED-AIR RESPIRATOR. ANY SELF-CONTAINED BREATHING APPARATUS.

1.25 MG/M3- ANY SUPPLIED-AIR RESPIRATOR OPERATED IN A CONTINUOUS FLOW MODE. ANY POWERED AIR-PURIFYING RESPIRATOR WITH A HIGH-EFFICIENCY PARTICULATE FILTER.

2.5 MG/M3- ANY SUPPLIED-AIR RESPIRATOR WITH A FULL FACEPIECE. ANY SELF-CONTAINED BREATHING APPARATUS WITH A FULL FACEPIECE. ANY AIR-PURIFYING FULL FACEPIECE RESPIRATOR WITH A HIGH-EFFICIENCY PARTICULATE FILTER. ANY POWERED AIR-PURIFYING RESPIRATOR WITH A TIGHT-FITTING FACEPIECE AND A HIGH-EFFICIENCY PARTICULATE FILTER. ANY SUPPLIED-AIR RESPIRATOR WITH A TIGHT-FITTING FACEPIECE OPERATED IN A CONTINUOUS FLOW MODE.

28 MG/M3- ANY SUPPLIED-AIR RESPIRATOR WITH A HALF-MASK AND OPERATED IN A PRESSURE-DEMAND OR OTHER POSITIVE PRESSURE MODE.

ESCAPE- ANY AIR-PURIFYING FULL FACEPIECE RESPIRATOR WITH A HIGH-EFFICIENCY PARTICULATE FILTER. ANY APPROPRIATE ESCAPE-TYPE SELF-CONTAINED BREATHING APPARATUS.

FOR FIREFIGHTING AND OTHER IMMEDIATELY DANGEROUS TO LIFE OR HEALTH CONDITIONS:

SELF-CONTAINED BREATHING APPARATUS WITH FULL FACEPIECE OPERATED IN PRESSURE-DEMAND OR OTHER POSITIVE PRESSURE MODE.

SUPPLIED-AIR RESPIRATOR WITH FULL FACEPIECE AND OPERATED IN PRESSURE-DEMAND OR OTHER POSITIVE PRESSURE MODE IN COMBINATION WITH AN AUXILIARY SELF-CONTAINED BREATHING APPARATUS OPERATED IN PRESSURE-DEMAND OR OTHER POSITIVE PRESSURE MODE.

CLOTHING: EMPLOYEE MUST WEAR APPROPRIATE PROTECTIVE (IMPERVIOUS) CLOTHING AND EQUIPMENT TO PREVENT REPEATED OR PROLONGED SKIN CONTACT WITH THIS SUBSTANCE.

GLOVES: EMPLOYEE MUST WEAR APPROPRIATE PROTECTIVE GLOVES TO PREVENT CONTACT WITH THIS SUBSTANCE.

EYE PROTECTION: EMPLOYEE MUST WEAR SPLASH-PROOF OR DUST-RESISTANT SAFETY GOGGLES TO PREVENT EYE CONTACT WITH THIS SUBSTANCE.

EMERGENCY EYE WASH: WHERE THERE IS ANY POSSIBILITY THAT AN EMPLOYEE'S EYES MAY BE EXPOSED TO THIS SUBSTANCE, THE EMPLOYER SHOULD PROVIDE AN EYE WASH FOUNTAIN WITHIN THE IMMEDIATE WORK AREA FOR EMERGENCY USE.

AUTHORIZED BY- OCCUPATIONAL HEALTH SERVICES, INC.

CREATION DATE: 10/04/89 ***REVISION DATE:*** 07/13/90

MATERIAL SAFETY DATA SHEET

OCCUPATIONAL HEALTH SERVICES, INC.
AGRICULTURE AND PESTICIDE DIVISION
450 SEVENTH AVENUE, SUITE 2407
NEW YORK, NEW YORK 10123
1-800-445-MSDS OR (212) 967-1100

EMERGENCY CONTACT:
JOHN S. BRANSFORD, JR. (615) 292-1180

SUBSTANCE IDENTIFICATION

CAS-NUMBER 100-57-2

SUBSTANCE: **PHENYLMERCURIC HYDROXIDE**

TRADE NAMES/SYNONYMS: PHENYLMERCURY HYDROXIDE; HYDROXYPHENYL MERCURY; HYDROXYPHENYLMERCURY; MERSOLITE 1; PHENYL HYDROXYMERCURY; UN 1894; PST18580

CHEMICAL FAMILY: ORGANOMETALLIC

MOLECULAR FORMULA: C6-H6-HG-O

MOLECULAR WEIGHT: 294.71

CERCLA RATINGS (SCALE 0-3): HEALTH=3 FIRE=0 REACTIVITY=0 PERSISTENCE=3

NFPA RATINGS (SCALE 0-4): HEALTH=4 FIRE=0 REACTIVITY=0

COMPONENTS AND CONTAMINANTS

COMPONENT: PHENYLMERCURIC HYDROXIDE ***PERCENT:*** 100
CAS# 100-57-2

OTHER CONTAMINANTS: NONE

EXPOSURE LIMITS: MERCURY, ALL FORMS EXCEPT ALKYL (AS HG): 0.05 MG/M3 OSHA TWA (VAPOR); 0.1 MG/M3 OSHA CEILING (SKIN) 0.05 MG/M3 ACGIH TWA (VAPOR); 0.10 MG/M3 ACGIH TWA (ARYL & INORGANIC)-(SKIN) 0.05 MG/M3 NIOSH RECOMMENDED 10 HOUR TWA

SUBJECT TO SARA SECTION 313 ANNUAL TOXIC CHEMICAL RELEASE REPORTING

SUBJECT TO CALIFORNIA PROPOSITION 65 CANCER AND/OR REPRODUCTIVE TOXICITY WARNING AND RELEASE REQUIREMENTS- (JULY 1, 1990)

PHYSICAL DATA

DESCRIPTION: FINE WHITE TO CREAM CRYSTALS

MELTING POINT: 386.6 F (197 C) DECOMPOSES ***SPECIFIC GRAVITY:*** NOT AVAILABLE

SOLUBILITY IN WATER: SLIGHTLY SOLUBLE

SOLVENT SOLUBILITY: SOLUBLE IN ACETIC ACID AND ALCOHOL

FIRE AND EXPLOSION DATA

FIRE AND EXPLOSION HAZARD: NEGLIGIBLE FIRE HAZARD WHEN EXPOSED TO HEAT OR FLAME.

FIREFIGHTING MEDIA: DRY CHEMICAL, CARBON DIOXIDE, HALON, WATER SPRAY OR STANDARD FOAM (1987 EMERGENCY RESPONSE GUIDEBOOK, DOT P 5800.4). FOR LARGER FIRES, USE WATER SPRAY, FOG OR STANDARD FOAM (1987 EMERGENCY RESPONSE GUIDEBOOK, DOT P 5800.4).

FIREFIGHTING: MOVE CONTAINERS FROM FIRE AREA IF POSSIBLE (1987 EMERGENCY RESPONSE GUIDEBOOK, DOT P 5800.4, GUIDE PAGE 53).
EXTINGUISH ONLY IF FLOW CAN BE STOPPED. EXTINGUISH USING AGENT INDICATED. USE FLOODING AMOUNTS OF WATER AS A FOG. COOL CONTAINERS WITH FLOODING AMOUNTS OF WATER FROM AS FAR A DISTANCE AS POSSIBLE. AVOID BREATHING POISONOUS VAPORS, KEEP UPWIND. CONSIDER EVACUATION OF DOWNWIND AREA IF MATERIAL IS LEAKING.

TRANSPORTATION DATA

DEPARTMENT OF TRANSPORTATION HAZARD CLASSIFICATION 49 CFR 172.101: POISON B

DEPARTMENT OF TRANSPORTATION LABELING REQUIREMENTS 49 CFR 172.101 AND SUBPART E: POISON

DEPARTMENT OF TRANSPORTATION PACKAGING REQUIREMENTS: 49 CFR 173.365 EXCEPTIONS: 49 CFR 173.364

TOXICITY

PHENYLMERCURIC HYDROXIDE: TOXICITY DATA: 18 MG/KG INTRAVENOUS-MOUSE LD50; MUTAGENIC DATA (RTECS). CARCINOGEN STATUS: NONE. LOCAL EFFECTS: IRRITANT- INHALATION, SKIN, AND EYES. ACUTE TOXICITY LEVEL: INSUFFICIENT DATA. TARGET EFFECTS: POISONING MAY AFFECT THE KIDNEYS AND CENTRAL NERVOUS SYSTEM.

HEALTH EFFECTS AND FIRST AID

INHALATION: PHENYLMERCURIC HYDROXIDE: NARCOTIC. **ACUTE EXPOSURE-** EXPOSURE TO DUST OR VAPORS MAY CAUSE IRRITATION AND BURNING SENSATION OF THE MUCOUS MEMBRANES. ALMOST IMMEDIATE DYSPNEA, COUGH, FEVER, NAUSEA, VOMITING, DIARRHEA, , SALIVATION, CHEST AND ABDOMINAL PAINS, MOTOR WEAKNESS, GINGIVITIS, DYSARTHRIA, ABNORMAL REFLEXES, SALIVATION AND METALLIC TASTE CAN OCCUR. THESE SYMPTOMS MAY RESOLVE OR PROGRESS TO NECROTIZING BRONCHIOLITIS, PNEUMONITIS, PULMONARY EDEMA AND PNEUMOTHORAX. DEATH MAY OCCUR. **CHRONIC EXPOSURE-** AFTER REPEATED OR PROLONGED EXPOSURE, THERE MAY BE SIGNS OF CENTRAL NERVOUS SYSTEM DISTURBANCES CALLED MERCURIALISM. IT INCLUDES EXCITABILITY AND IRRITABILITY, LOSS OF CONCENTRATION ABILITY, DEPRESSION, INDECISIVENESS, HEADACHE, FATIGUE, MEMORY LOSS, FINE TREMORS OF THE HANDS, HEAD, LIPS, TONGUE OR JAW. PARESTHESIAS, AFFECTIONS OF TASTE OR SMELL, NEURALGIA AND DERMOGRAPHIS MAY OCCUR. THE HIGH CONCENTRATION ATTAINED DURING RENAL EXCRETION MAY LEAD TO SPECIFIC DAMAGE TO RENAL GLOMERULI AND TUBULES. CHRONIC NASAL CATARRH AND EPISTAXIS IS COMMON. PATHOLOGICAL FINDINGS ARE ACUTE TUBULAR AND GLOMERULAR DEGENERATION OR HEMORRHAGIC GLOMERULAR NEPHRITIS.

FIRST AID- REMOVE FROM EXPOSURE AREA TO FRESH AIR IMMEDIATELY. IF BREATHING HAS STOPPED, GIVE ARTIFICIAL RESPIRATION. MAINTAIN AIRWAY AND BLOOD PRESSURE AND ADMINISTER OXYGEN IF AVAILABLE. KEEP AFFECTED PERSON WARM AND AT REST. TREAT SYMPTOMATICALLY AND SUPPORTIVELY. ADMINISTRATION OF OXYGEN SHOULD BE PERFORMED BY QUALIFIED PERSONNEL. GET MEDICAL ATTENTION IMMEDIATELY.

SKIN CONTACT: PHENYLMERCURIC HYDROXIDE: IRRITANT/SENSITIZER. **ACUTE EXPOSURE-** MAY CAUSE IRRITATION, REDNESS, DERMATITIS AND SKIN RASHES. SYSTEMIC POISONING MAY OCCUR DUE TO ABSORPTION THROUGH INTACT SKIN AND RESULT IN KIDNEY DAMAGE. **CHRONIC EXPOSURE-** MAY CAUSE SENSITIZATION DERMATITIS. MERCURIALISM MAY OCCUR AFTER REPEATED OR PROLONGED EXPOSURE. FINDINGS ARE VARIABLE AND INCLUDE TREMORS, SALIVATION, STOMATITIS, LOSSENING OF THE TEETH, BLUE LINE ON THE GUMS,

PAIN AND NUMBNESS IN THE EXTREMITIES, NEPHRITIS, DIARRHEA, ANXIETY, HEADACHE, WEIGHT LOSS, ANOREXIA, MENTAL DEPRESSION, INSOMNIA, INSTABILITY, IRRITABILITY, HALLUCINATIONS AND EVIDENCES OF MENTAL DETERIORATION.

FIRST AID- REMOVE CONTAMINATED CLOTHING AND SHOES IMMEDIATELY. WASH AFFECTED AREA WITH SOAP OR MILD DETERGENT AND LARGE AMOUNTS OF WATER UNTIL NO EVIDENCE OF CHEMICAL REMAINS (APPROXIMATELY 15-20 MINUTES). GET MEDICAL ATTENTION IMMEDIATELY.

EYE CONTACT: PHENYLMERCURIC HYDROXIDE: IRRITANT. **ACUTE EXPOSURE**- MAY CAUSE IRRITATION AND CORNEAL INJURY IN CONCENTRATED SOLUTIONS. A SEVERE REACTION IS INDUCED BY 0.1 M OF PHENYLMERCURIC HYDROXIDE. THE INJURIOUS ACTIONS MAY BE ASSOCIATED WITH A HIGH REACTIVITY TOWARD SULFHYDRIL GROUPS OF TISSUE. **CHRONIC EXPOSURE**- THE EFFECTS OF MERCURY ARE CUMMULATIVE AND AFTER REPEATED OR PROLONGED EXPOSURE, THERE MAY BE CHANGES IN THE TRANSPARENCY OF THE FRONT OF THE LENS CALLED MERCURIALENTIS.

FIRST AID- WASH EYES IMMEDIATELY WITH LARGE AMOUNTS OF WATER OR NORMAL SALINE, OCCASIONALLY LIFTING UPPER AND LOWER LIDS, UNTIL NO EVIDENCE OF CHEMICAL REMAINS (APPROXIMATELY 15-20 MINUTES). GET MEDICAL ATTENTION IMMEDIATELY.

INGESTION: PHENYLMERCURIC HYDROXIDE: SENSITIZER. **ACUTE EXPOSURE**- MAY CAUSE CORROSION, INFLAMMATION, CONGESTION AND COAGULATION OF THE MUCOSA OF THE GASTROINTESTINAL TRACT. SYMPTOMS INCLUDE FATIGUE, HEADACHE, IRRITABILITY, DELIRIUM, TREMORS, NUMBNESS OF THE MOUTH, TONGUE AND LIMBS, PROTEINURIA, BLURRED VISION, LOSS OF COORDINATION, WEIGHT LOSS AND LOSS OF MEMORY. SYMPTOMS MAY PROGRESS AND PRODUCE SEVERE BRAIN DAMAGE WITH DEAFNESS, INABILITY TO WALK OR TALK, MENTAL RETARDATION, PARALYSIS OF LIMBS AND POSSIBLE COMA. CHILDREN BORN DURING AN EXPOSURE MAY EXHIBIT DELAYED SIMILAR SYMPTOMS AND BIRTH DEFECTS. DEATH MAY OCCUR DUE TO RENAL DAMAGE. PHENYLMERCURIC HYDROXIDE IS USED AS A DENATURANT FOR ALCOHOL SO THERE IS A POSSIBILITY OF INGESTION OF LARGE QUANTITIES. **CHRONIC EXPOSURE**- MAY CAUSE DELAYED HYPERSENSITIVE REACTIONS. THE EFFECTS OF MERCURY ARE CUMULATIVE SO SMALL AMOUNTS INGESTED OVER A PERIOD OF TIME MAY PRODUCE DELAYED SYMPTOMS.

FIRST AID- REMOVE BY GASTRIC LAVAGE OR EMESIS. MAINTAIN BLOOD PRESSURE AND AIRWAY. GIVE OXYGEN IF RESPIRATION IS DEPRESSED. DO NOT PERFORM GASTRIC LAVAGE OR EMESIS IF VICTIM IS UNCONSCIOUS. GET MEDICAL ATTENTION IMMEDIATELY (DREISBACH, HANDBOOK OF POISONING, 11TH ED.). ADMINISTRATION OF GASTRIC LAVAGE OR OXYGEN SHOULD BE PERFORMED BY QUALIFIED MEDICAL PERSONNEL.

ANTIDOTE: THE FOLLOWING ANTIDOTE HAS BEEN RECOMMENDED. HOWEVER, THE DECISION AS TO WHETHER THE SEVERITY OF POISONING REQUIRES ADMINISTRATION OF ANY ANTIDOTE AND ACTUAL DOSE REQUIRED SHOULD BE MADE BY QUALIFIED MEDICAL PERSONNEL.

MERCURY POISONING: GIVE DIMERCAPROL, 3 MG/KG (OR 0.3 ML/10 KG) EVERY 4 HOURS FOR THE FIRST 2 DAYS AND THEN 2 MG/KG EVERY 12 HOURS FOR A TOTAL OF 10 DAYS IF NECESSARY. DIMERCAPROL IS AVAILABLE AS A 10% SOLUTION IN OIL FOR INTRAMUSCULAR ADMINISTRATION. HEMODIALYSIS WILL SPEED THE REMOVAL OF THE MERCURY-DIMERCAPROL COMPLEX. PENICILLAMINE IS ALSO EFFECTIVE. GIVE UP TO 100 MG/KG/DAY (MAXIMUM 1 GR/DAY) DIVIDED INTO 4 DOSES FOR NO LONGER THAN 1 WEEK. IF A LONGER ADMINISTRATION PERIOD IS WARRANTED, DOSAGE SHOULD NOT EXCEED 40 MG/KG/DAY. GIVE THE DRUG ORALLY HALF AN HOUR BEFORE MEALS. A CHELATING AGENT SHOULD BE BE CONTINUED UNTIL THE URINE-MERCURY LEVEL FALLS BELOW 50 UG/24 HOURS (DREISBACH, HANDBOOK OF POISONING, 12TH ED.). ANTIDOTE SHOULD BE ADMINISTERED BY QUALIFIED MEDICAL PERSONNEL.

REACTIVITY

REACTIVITY: STABLE UNDER NORMAL TEMPERATURES AND PRESSURES.

INCOMPATIBILITIES: MERCURY: ACETYLENIC COMPOUNDS: INCOMPATIBLE. AMMONIA: INCOMPATIBLE. BORON DIIODOPHOSPHIDE: INCOMPATIBLE. ETHYLENE OXIDE: INCOMPATIBLE. METALS: INCOMPATIBLE. METHYL AZIDE: INCOMPATIBLE. METHYLSILANE OXYGEN: INCOMPATIBLE. OXIDANTS: INCOMPATIBLE. TETRACARBONYL NICKEL OXYGEN: INCOMPATIBLE.

DECOMPOSITION: THERMAL DECOMPOSITION MAY PRODUCE TOXIC FUMES OF MERCURY.

POLYMERIZATION: HAZARDOUS POLYMERIZATION HAS NOT BEEN REPORTED TO OCCUR UNDER NORMAL TEMPERATURES AND PRESSURES.

STORAGE AND DISPOSAL

OBSERVE ALL FEDERAL, STATE AND LOCAL REGULATIONS WHEN STORING OR DISPOSING OF THIS SUBSTANCE. FOR ASSISTANCE, CONTACT THE DISTRICT DIRECTOR OF THE ENVIRONMENTAL PROTECTION AGENCY.

****DISPOSAL****

MERCURY - REGULATORY LEVEL: 0.2 MG/L MATERIALS WHICH CONTAIN THE ABOVE SUBSTANCE AT OR ABOVE THE REGULATORY LEVEL MEET THE EPA CHARACTERISTIC OF TOXICITY, AND MUST BE DISPOSED OF IN ACCORDANCE WITH 40 CFR PART 262. EPA HAZARDOUS WASTE NUMBER D009.

CONDITIONS TO AVOID

MAY BURN BUT DOES NOT IGNITE READILY.

SPILL AND LEAK PROCEDURES

WATER SPILL: THE CALIFORNIA SAFE DRINKING WATER AND TOXIC ENFORCEMENT ACT OF 1986 (PROPOSITION 65) PROHIBITS CONTAMINATING ANY KNOWN SOURCE OF DRINKING WATER WITH SUBSTANCES KNOWN TO CAUSE CANCER AND/OR REPRODUCTIVE TOXICITY.

OCCUPATIONAL SPILL: DO NOT TOUCH SPILLED MATERIAL. STOP LEAK IF YOU CAN DO IT WITHOUT RISK. FOR SMALL SPILLS, TAKE UP WITH SAND OR OTHER ABSORBENT MATERIAL AND PLACE INTO CONTAINERS FOR LATER DISPOSAL. FOR SMALL DRY SPILLS, WITH A CLEAN SHOVEL PLACE MATERIAL INTO CLEAN, DRY CONTAINER AND COVER. MOVE CONTAINERS FROM SPILL AREA. FOR LARGER SPILLS, DIKE FAR AHEAD OF SPILL FOR LATER DISPOSAL. KEEP UNNECESSARY PEOPLE AWAY. ISOLATE HAZARD AREA AND DENY ENTRY.

PROTECTIVE EQUIPMENT

VENTILATION: PROVIDE LOCAL EXHAUST OR PROCESS ENCLOSURE VENTILATION TO MEET PUBLISHED EXPOSURE LIMITS.

RESPIRATOR: THE FOLLOWING RESPIRATORS AND MAXIMUM USE CONCENTRATIONS ARE RECOMMENDATIONS BY THE U.S. DEPARTMENT OF HEALTH AND HUMAN SERVICES, NIOSH POCKET GUIDE TO CHEMICAL HAZARDS; NIOSH CRITERIA DOCUMENTS OR BY THE U.S. DEPARTMENT OF LABOR, 29 CFR 1910 SUBPART Z. THE SPECIFIC RESPIRATOR SELECTED MUST BE BASED ON CONTAMINATION LEVELS FOUND IN THE WORK PLACE, MUST NOT EXCEED THE WORKING LIMITS OF THE RESPIRATOR AND BE JOINTLY APPROVED BY THE NATIONAL INSTITUTE FOR OCCUPATIONAL SAFETY AND HEALTH AND THE MINE SAFETY AND HEALTH ADMINISTRATION (NIOSH-MSHA).

MERCURY, ALL FORMS EXCEPT ALKYL (AS HG):

0.5 MG/M3- ANY AIR-PURIFYING RESPIRATOR WITH A HIGH-EFFICIENCY PARTICULATE FILTER. ANY SUPPLIED-AIR RESPIRATOR. ANY SELF-CONTAINED BREATHING APPARATUS.

1.25 MG/M3- ANY SUPPLIED-AIR RESPIRATOR OPERATED IN A CONTINUOUS FLOW MODE. ANY POWERED AIR-PURIFYING RESPIRATOR WITH A HIGH-EFFICIENCY PARTICULATE FILTER.

2.5 MG/M3- ANY SUPPLIED-AIR RESPIRATOR WITH A FULL FACEPIECE. ANY SELF-CONTAINED BREATHING APPARATUS WITH A FULL FACEPIECE. ANY AIR-PURIFYING FULL FACEPIECE RESPIRATOR WITH A HIGH-EFFICIENCY PARTICULATE FILTER. ANY POWERED AIR-PURIFYING RESPIRATOR WITH A TIGHT-FITTING FACEPIECE AND A HIGH-EFFICIENCY PARTICULATE FILTER. ANY SUPPLIED-AIR RESPIRATOR WITH A TIGHT-FITTING FACEPIECE OPERATED IN A CONTINUOUS FLOW MODE.

28 MG/M3- ANY SUPPLIED-AIR RESPIRATOR WITH A HALF-MASK AND OPERATED IN A PRESSURE-DEMAND OR OTHER POSITIVE PRESSURE MODE.

ESCAPE- ANY AIR-PURIFYING FULL FACEPIECE RESPIRATOR WITH A HIGH-EFFICIENCY PARTICULATE FILTER. ANY APPROPRIATE ESCAPE-TYPE SELF-CONTAINED BREATHING APPARATUS.

FOR FIREFIGHTING AND OTHER IMMEDIATELY DANGEROUS TO LIFE OR HEALTH CONDITIONS:

SELF-CONTAINED BREATHING APPARATUS WITH FULL FACEPIECE OPERATED IN PRESSURE-DEMAND OR OTHER POSITIVE PRESSURE MODE.

SUPPLIED-AIR RESPIRATOR WITH FULL FACEPIECE AND OPERATED IN PRESSURE-DEMAND OR OTHER POSITIVE PRESSURE MODE IN COMBINATION WITH AN AUXILIARY SELF-CONTAINED BREATHING APPARATUS OPERATED IN PRESSURE-DEMAND OR OTHER POSITIVE PRESSURE MODE.

CLOTHING: EMPLOYEE MUST WEAR APPROPRIATE PROTECTIVE (IMPERVIOUS) CLOTHING AND EQUIPMENT TO PREVENT REPEATED OR PROLONGED SKIN CONTACT WITH THIS SUBSTANCE.

GLOVES: EMPLOYEE MUST WEAR APPROPRIATE PROTECTIVE GLOVES TO PREVENT CONTACT WITH THIS SUBSTANCE.

EYE PROTECTION: EMPLOYEE MUST WEAR SPLASH-PROOF OR DUST-RESISTANT SAFETY GOGGLES TO PREVENT EYE CONTACT WITH THIS SUBSTANCE.

EMERGENCY EYE WASH: WHERE THERE IS ANY POSSIBILITY THAT AN EMPLOYEE'S EYES MAY BE EXPOSED TO THIS SUBSTANCE, THE EMPLOYER SHOULD PROVIDE AN EYE WASH FOUNTAIN WITHIN THE IMMEDIATE WORK AREA FOR EMERGENCY USE.

AUTHORIZED BY- OCCUPATIONAL HEALTH SERVICES, INC.

CREATION DATE: 10/04/89 ***REVISION DATE:*** 07/13/90

MATERIAL SAFETY DATA SHEET

OCCUPATIONAL HEALTH SERVICES, INC.
AGRICULTURE AND PESTICIDE DIVISION
450 SEVENTH AVENUE, SUITE 2407
NEW YORK, NEW YORK 10123
1-800-445-MSDS OR (212) 967-1100

EMERGENCY CONTACT:
JOHN S. BRANSFORD, JR. (615) 292-1180

SUBSTANCE IDENTIFICATION

CAS-NUMBER 298-02-2

SUBSTANCE: **PHORATE**

TRADE NAMES/SYNONYMS: PHOSPHORODITHIOIC ACID, O,O-DIETHYL S-((ETHYLTHIO)METHYL) ESTER; O,O-DIETHYL S-ETHYLTHIOMETHYL PHOSPHORODITHIOATE; O,O-DIETHYL S-((ETHYLTHIO)METHYL) PHOSPHORODITHIOATE; DIETHYL S-(ETHYLTHIOMETHYL) PHOSPHOROTHIOLOTHIONATE; O,O-DIETHYL S-(ETHYLTHIO)METHYL PHOSPHORODITHIOATE; O,O-DIETHYL S-ETHYLMERCAPTOMETHYL DITHIOPHOSPHATE; AMERICAN CYANAMID 3,911; EXPERIMENTAL INSECTICIDE 3911; GRANUTOX (FORMULATION); THIMET (FORMULATION); TIMET (FORMULATION); ENT 24,042; RCRA P094; C7H17O2PS3; PST18640

CHEMICAL FAMILY: ORGANOPHOSPHATE

MOLECULAR FORMULA: (C2-H5-O)2-P(S)-S-C-H2-S-C2-H5

MOLECULAR WEIGHT: 260.39

CERCLA RATINGS (SCALE 0-3): HEALTH=3 FIRE=1 REACTIVITY=0 PERSISTENCE=2

NFPA RATINGS (SCALE 0-4): HEALTH=4 FIRE=1 REACTIVITY=0

COMPONENTS AND CONTAMINANTS

COMPONENT: PHORATE ***PERCENT:*** 100.0
CAS# 298-02-2

OTHER CONTAMINANTS: NONE

EXPOSURE LIMITS: PHORATE: 0.05 MG/M3 OSHA TWA (SKIN); 0.2 MG/M3 OSHA STEL
0.05 MG/M3 ACGIH TWA (SKIN); 0.2 MG/M3 ACGIH STEL
10 POUNDS SARA SECTION 302 THRESHOLD PLANNING QUANTITY 10 POUNDS SARA SECTION 304 REPORTABLE QUANTITY 10 POUNDS CERCLA SECTION 103 REPORTABLE QUANTITY

PHYSICAL DATA

DESCRIPTION: CLEAR MOBILE LIQUID.

BOILING POINT: 244-248 F (118-120 C) @ 0.8 MMHG

MELTING POINT: <5 F (<-15C)

SPECIFIC GRAVITY: 1.156 ***VAPOR PRESSURE:*** 0.00084 MMHG @ 20 C

SOLUBILITY IN WATER: 50 PPM

SOLVENT SOLUBILITY: SOLUBLE IN CARBON TETRACHLORIDE, DIOXANE, XYLENE, ALCOHOLS, ESTERS, ETHERS, VEGETABLE OILS, METHYL CELLOSOLVE, DIBUTYL PHTHALATE.

FIRE AND EXPLOSION DATA

FIRE AND EXPLOSION HAZARD: SLIGHT FIRE HAZARD WHEN EXPOSED TO HEAT OR FLAME.

FIREFIGHTING MEDIA: DRY CHEMICAL, CARBON DIOXIDE, HALON, WATER SPRAY OR STANDARD FOAM (1987 EMERGENCY RESPONSE GUIDEBOOK, DOT P 5800.4).
FOR LARGER FIRES, USE WATER SPRAY, FOG OR STANDARD FOAM (1987 EMERGENCY RESPONSE GUIDEBOOK, DOT P 5800.4).

FIREFIGHTING: MOVE CONTAINERS FROM FIRE AREA IF POSSIBLE (1987 EMERGENCY RESPONSE GUIDEBOOK, DOT P 5800.4, GUIDE PAGE 53).
EXTINGUISH USING AGENT SUITABLE FOR TYPE OF SURROUNDING FIRE. AVOID BREATHING VAPORS AND DUSTS. KEEP UPWIND.

TRANSPORTATION DATA

DEPARTMENT OF TRANSPORTATION HAZARD CLASSIFICATION 49 CFR 172.101: POISON B
DEPARTMENT OF TRANSPORTATION LABELING REQUIREMENTS 49 CFR 172.101 AND SUBPART E: POISON
DEPARTMENT OF TRANSPORTATION PACKAGING REQUIREMENTS: 49 CFR 173.359 EXCEPTIONS: 49 CFR 173.359

TOXICITY

PHORATE: TOXICITY DATA: 11 MG/M3/1 HOUR INHALATION-RAT LC50; 99 MG/KG SKIN-RABBIT LD50; 2500 UG/KG SKIN-RAT LD50; 20 MG/KG SKIN-GUINEA PIG LD50; 1 MG/KG ORAL-RAT LD50; 6590 UG/KG ORAL-MOUSE LD50; 1200 UG/KG INTRAVENOUS-RAT LD50; 1866 UG/KG INTRAPERITONEAL- GERBIL LD50; MUTAGENIC DATA (RTECS); REPRODUCTIVE EFFECTS DATA (RTECS). CARCINOGEN STATUS: NONE. ACUTE TOXICITY LEVEL: HIGHLY TOXIC BY INHALATION, DERMAL ABSORPTION, INGESTION. TARGET EFFECTS: CHOLINESTERASE INHIBITOR. POISONING MAY AFFECT THE NERVOUS SYSTEM.* AT INCREASED RISK FROM EXPOSURE: PERSONS WITH RESPIRATORY AILMENTS, RECENT EXPOSURE TO CHOLINESTERASE INHIBITORS OR IMPAIRED CHOLINESTERASE PRODUCTION, OR LIVER MALFUNCTION.* ADDITIONAL DATA: MAY CROSS THE PLACENTA. HIGH ENVIRONMENTAL TEMPERATURES OR EXPOSURE OF THE CHEMICAL TO VISIBLE OR ULTRAVIOLET LIGHT MAY ENHANCE THE TOXICITY. INTERACTIONS WITH MEDICATIONS MAY OCCUR.*
* MAY BE BASED ON GENERAL INFORMATION ON ORGANOPHOSPHATES.

HEALTH EFFECTS AND FIRST AID

INHALATION: PHORATE: HIGHLY TOXIC. SEE INFORMATION ON ORGANOPHOSPHATES.
ORGANOPHOSPHATES: CHOLINESTERASE INHIBITOR. **ACUTE EXPOSURE-** WHEN INHALED, THE FIRST EFFECTS OF CHOLINESTERASE INHIBITORS ARE USUALLY RESPIRATORY AND MAY INCLUDE NASAL HYPEREMIA AND WATERY DISCHARGE, COUGH, CHEST DISCOMFORT, DYSPNEA, AND WHEEZING DUE TO INCREASED BRONCHIAL SECRETIONS AND BRONCHOCONSTRICTION. IF SUFFICIENT AMOUNTS ARE ABSORBED, OTHER SYSTEMIC EFFECTS MAY BEGIN WITHIN A FEW MINUTES OR BE DELAYED FOR UP TO 12 HOURS. SYMPTOMS MAY INCLUDE PALLOR, NAUSEA, VOMITING, DIARRHEA, ABDOMINAL CRAMPS, HEADACHE, DIZZINESS, OCULAR PAIN, BLURRED VISION, MIOSIS OR IN SOME CASES, ESPECIALLY INITIALLY, MYDRIASIS, LACRIMATION, SALIVATION, SWEATING, AND CONFUSION. OTHER REPORTED CENTRAL NERVOUS SYSTEM OR NEUROMUSCULAR EFFECTS MAY INCLUDE ATAXIA, SLURRED SPEECH, AREFLEXIA, WEAKNESS, FATIGUE, FASCICULATIONS, TWITCHING, TREMORS POSSIBLY OF THE TONGUE AND EYELIDS, AND EVENTUALLY PARALYSIS OF THE EXTREMITIES AND POSSIBLY OF THE RESPIRATORY MUSCLES. IN SEVERE CASES THERE MAY ALSO BE INVOLUNTARY DEFECATION AND URINATION, CYANOSIS, PSYCHOSIS, HYPERGLYCEMIA, ACUTE PANCREATITIS, CARDIAC IRREGULARITIES, PULMONARY EDEMA, UNCONSCIOUSNESS, CONVULSIONS, AND COMA. DEATH IS PRIMARILY DUE TO RESPIRATORY FAILURE, ALTHOUGH CARDIOVASCULAR EFFECTS INCLUDING CARDIAC ARREST MAY ALSO BE IMPLICATED. LONG TERM SEQUELAE ARE RARE BUT MAY INCLUDE NEUROPSYCHIATRIC DISORDERS AND MYOPATHY WITH MUSCLE TENDERNESS. SOME ORGANOPHOSPHATES MAY CAUSE A DELAYED NEUROPATHY BEGINNING 1-4 WEEKS AFTER AN ACUTE EXPOSURE WHICH MAY OR MAY NOT HAVE CAUSED ACUTE CHOLINERGIC EFFECTS. NUMBNESS, TINGLING, WEAKNESS AND CRAMPING BEGINNING SYMMETRICALLY IN THE LOWER LIMBS MAY PROGRESS TO ATAXIA AND PARALYSIS. IN SEVERE CASES, UPPER LIMB INVOLVEMENT IS POSSIBLE AND FLACCID PARALYSIS MAY PROGRESS TO SPASTIC PARALYSIS WITH EXAGGERATED REFLEXES. IMPROVEMENT MAY OCCUR OVER MONTHS TO YEARS, BUT SOME RESIDUAL IMPAIRMENT USUALLY REMAINS.
CHRONIC EXPOSURE- REPEATED OR PROLONGED EXPOSURE MAY RESULT IN THE EFFECTS OF ACUTE EXPOSURE INCLUDING THE DELAYED NEUROPATHY. OTHER EFFECTS REPORTED IN WORKERS REPEATEDLY EXPOSED INCLUDE IMPAIRED MEMORY AND CONCENTRATION, ACUTE PSYCHOSIS, SEVERE DEPRESSIONS, IRRITABILTY, CONFUSION, APATHY, EMOTIONAL LABILITY, SOCIAL WITHDRAWAL, CONFUSION, HEADACHE, SPEECH DIFFICULTIES, DELAYED REACTION TIMES, SPATIAL DISORIENTATION, NIGHTMARES, SLEEPWALKING, AND DROWSINESS OR INSOMNIA. AN INFLUENZA-LIKE CONDITION WITH HEADACHE, NAUSEA, WEAKNESS, ANOREXIA AND MALAISE HAS ALSO BEEN REPORTED.

FIRST AID- REMOVE FROM EXPOSURE AREA TO FRESH AIR IMMEDIATELY. IF BREATHING HAS STOPPED, GIVE ARTIFICIAL RESPIRATION. MAINTAIN AIRWAY AND BLOOD PRESSURE AND ADMINISTER OXYGEN IF AVAILABLE. KEEP AFFECTED PERSON WARM AND AT REST. TREAT SYMPTOMATICALLY AND SUPPORTIVELY. ADMINISTRATION OF OXYGEN SHOULD BE PERFORMED BY QUALIFIED PERSONNEL. GET MEDICAL ATTENTION IMMEDIATELY.

SKIN CONTACT: PHORATE: HIGHLY TOXIC. SEE INFORMATION ON ORGANOPHOSPHATES. ABSORPTION THROUGH THE SKIN IS SO RAPID THAT DEATH HAS OCCURRED IN ANIMALS WITHIN AN 1-2 HOURS OF CONTACT.
ORGANOPHOSPHATES: CHOLINESTERASE INHIBITOR. **ACUTE EXPOSURE-** LOCALIZED SWEATING AND FASCICULATIONS MAY OCCUR AT THE SITE OF CONTACT. IF SUFFICIENT AMOUNTS ARE ABSORBED, OTHER EFFECTS OF CHOLINESTERASE INHIBITION AS DESCRIBED IN ACUTE INHALATION MAY OCCUR. SYMPTOMS MAY BE DELAYED 2-3 HOURS, BUT USUALLY NO MORE THAN 12 HOURS. THE RATE OF ABSORPTION IS INCREASED BY THE PRESENCE OF DERMATITIS OR HIGH AMBIENT TEMPERATURES. DELAYED NEUROPATHY IS ALSO POSSIBLE. **CHRONIC EXPOSURE-** REPEATED OR PROLONGED EXPOSURE MAY CAUSE EFFECTS AS DESCRIBED IN ACUTE EXPOSURE. SOME ORGANOPHOSPHATES MAY CAUSE SENSITIZATION.

FIRST AID- REMOVE CONTAMINATED CLOTHING IMMEDIATELY. WASH CONTAMINATED AREAS WITH SOAP AND WATER FOLLOWED BY ALCOHOL (ARENA, POISONING, 4TH ED.). EMERGENCY PERSONNEL SHOULD WEAR GLOVES AND

AVOID CONTAMINATION. TREAT RESPIRATORY DIFFICULTY WITH ARTIFICIAL RESPIRATION. GET MEDICAL ATTENTION IMMEDIATELY.

EYE CONTACT: PHORATE: SEE INFORMATION ON ORGANOPHOSPHATES. ORGANOPHOSPHATES: CHOLINESTERASE INHIBITOR. **ACUTE EXPOSURE-** DIRECT CONTACT MAY CAUSE PAIN, HYPEREMIA, LACRIMATION, TWITCHING OF THE EYELIDS, MIOSIS, AND CILIARY MUSCLE SPASM WITH LOSS OF ACCOMODATION, BLURRED OR DIMMED VISION AND BROWACHE. SOMETIMES MYDRIASIS MAY OCCUR INSTEAD OF MIOSIS. WITH SUFFICIENT EXPOSURE, OTHER SYMPTOMS OF CHOLINESTERASE INHIBITION AS DESCRIBED IN ACUTE INHALATION MAY OCCUR. **CHRONIC EXPOSURE-** REPEATED OR PROLONGED EXPOSURE MAY CAUSE EFFECTS AS DESCRIBED IN ACUTE EXPOSURE. SOME COMPOUNDS HAVE CAUSED TOXIC EFFECTS ON THE CRYSTALLINE LENS, CONJUNCTIVAL THICKENING AND OBSTRUCTION OF THE NASOLACRIMAL CANALS WHEN USED AS MIOTIC EYEDROPS.

FIRST AID- IRRIGATE EYES WITH WATER OR SALINE SOLUTION. IF SYMPTOMS OF POISONING OCCUR, TREAT RESPIRATORY DIFFICULTY WITH ARTIFICIAL RESPIRATION AND OXYGEN. OBSERVE PATIENT FOR AT LEAST 24-36 HOURS (GOSSELIN, CLINICAL TOXICOLOGY OF COMMERCIAL PRODUCTS, 5TH ED.). GET MEDICAL ATTENTION IMMEDIATELY. OXYGEN SHOULD BE ADMINISTERED BY QUALIFIED MEDICAL PERSONNEL.

INGESTION: PHORATE: HIGHLY TOXIC. SEE INFORMATION ON ORGANOPHOSPHATES. ORGANOPHOSPHATES: CHOLINESTERASE INHIBITOR. **ACUTE EXPOSURE-** WHEN INGESTED, THE FIRST EFFECTS MAY BE NAUSEA, VOMITING, ANOREXIA, ABDOMINAL CRAMPS AND DIARRHEA. GASTROINTESTINAL ABSORPTION MAY CAUSE SYMPTOMS OF CHOLINESTERASE INHIBITION AS DESCRIBED IN ACUTE INHALATION. SYMPTOMS MAY BEGIN WITHIN MINUTES OR BE DELAYED FOR HOURS. DELAYED EFFECTS INCLUDING NEUROPATHY MAY ALSO OCCUR. **CHRONIC EXPOSURE-** REPEATED INGESTION MAY CAUSE EFFECTS AS DESCRIBED IN ACUTE EXPOSURE.

FIRST AID- IF PERSON IS ALERT AND RESPIRATION IS NOT DEPRESSED, GIVE SYRUP OF IPECAC FOLLOWED BY WATER (IF VOMITING OCCURS, KEEP HEAD BELOW HIPS TO PREVENT ASPIRATION). IF CONSCIOUSNESS LEVEL DECLINES OR VOMITING HAS NOT OCCURRED IN 15 MINUTES EMPTY STOMACH BY GASTRIC LAVAGE WITH THE AID OF CUFFED ENDOTRACHEAL TUBE USING ISOTONIC SALINE OR 5% SODIUM BICARBONATE FOLLOW WITH ACTIVATED CHARCOAL. ESTABLISH AND MAINTAIN AIRWAY. TREAT RESPIRATORY DIFFICULTY WITH ARTIFICIAL RESPIRATION AND OXYGEN. DO NOT GIVE MORPHINE, AMINOPHYLLINE, PHENOTHIAZINES, RESERPINE, FUROSEMIDE, OR ETHACRYNIC ACID (MORGAN, RECOGNITION AND MANAGEMENT OF PESTICIDE POISONINGS, 3RD ED.). TREAT SYMPTOMATICALLY AND SUPPORTIVELY. ADMINISTRATION OF OXYGEN AND LAVAGE MUST BE PERFORMED BY QUALIFIED MEDICAL PERSONNEL. GET MEDICAL ATTENTION IMMEDIATELY.

ANTIDOTE: THE FOLLOWING ANTIDOTE(S) HAVE BEEN RECOMMENDED. HOWEVER, THE DECISION AS TO WHETHER THE SEVERITY OF POISONING REQUIRES ADMINISTRATION OF ANY ANTIDOTE AND ACTUAL DOSE REQUIRED SHOULD BE MADE BY QUALIFIED MEDICAL PERSONNEL.
FOR CHOLINESTERASE INHIBITORS: ESTABLISH CLEAR AIRWAY AND TISSUE OXYGENATION BY ASPIRATION OF SECRETIONS, AND IF NECESSARY, BY ASSISTED PULMONARY VENTILATION WITH OXYGEN. IMPROVE TISSUE OXYGENATION AS MUCH AS POSSIBLE BEFORE ADMINISTERING ATROPINE TO MINIMIZE THE RISK OF VENTRICULAR FIBRILLATION. ADMINISTER ATROPINE SULFATE INTRAVENOUSLY, OR INTRAMUSCULARLY IF IV INJECTION IS NOT POSSIBLE. IN MODERATELY SEVERE POISONING ADMINISTER ATROPINE SULFATE, 0.4-2.0 MG REPEATED EVERY 15 MINUTES UNTIL ATROPINIZATION IS ACHIEVED (TACHYCARDIA, FLUSHING, DRY MOUTH, MYDRIASIS). MAINTAIN ATROPINIZATION BY REPEATED DOSES FOR 2-12 HOURS, OR LONGER, DEPENDING ON THE SEVERITY OF POISONING. THE APPEARANCE OF RALES IN THE LUNG BASES, MIOSIS, SALIVATION, NAUSEA, BRADYCARDIA, ARE ALL INDICATIONS OF INADEQUATE ATROPINIZATION. SEVERELY POISONED INDIVIDUALS MAY EXHIBIT REMARKABLE TOLERANCE TO ATROPINE; TWO OR MORE TIMES THE DOSAGES SUGGESTED ABOVE MAY BE NEEDED. PERSONS NOT POISONED OR ONLY SLIGHTLY POISONED, HOWEVER, MAY DEVELOP SIGNS OF ATROPINE TOXICITY FROM SUCH LARGE DOSAGES: FEVER, MUSCLE FIBRILLATIONS, AND DELIRIUM ARE THE MAIN SIGNS OF ATROPINE TOXICITY. IF THESE SIGNS APPEAR WHILE THE PATIENT IS FULLY ATROPINIZED, ATROPINE ADMINISTRATION SHOULD BE DISCONTINUED, AT LEAST TEMPORARILY. OBSERVE TREATED PATIENTS CLOSELY AT LEAST 24 HOURS TO INSURE THAT SYMPTOMS (POSSIBLY PULMONARY EDEMA) DO NOT RECUR AS ATROPINIZATION WEARS OFF. IN VERY SEVERE POISONINGS, METABOLIC DISPOSITION OF TOXICANT MAY REQUIRE SEVERAL HOURS OR DAYS DURING WHICH ATROPINIZATION MUST BE MAINTAINED. MARKEDLY LOWER LEVELS OF URINARY METABOLITES INDICATE THAT ATROPINE DOSAGE CAN BE TAPERED OFF. AS DOSAGE IS REDUCED, CHECK THE LUNG BASES FREQUENTLY FOR RALES. IF RALES ARE HEARD OR OTHER SYMPTOMS RETURN, RE-ESTABLISH ATROPINIZATION PROMPTLY (MORGAN, RECOGNITION AND MANAGEMENT OF PESTICIDE POISONINGS, 3RD ED.). ADMINISTRATION OF ANTIDOTE MUST BE PERFORMED BY QUALIFIED MEDICAL PERSONNEL.
IN CASES OF SEVERE POISONING BY ORGANOPHOSPHATE PESTICIDES IN WHICH RESPIRATORY DEPRESSION, MUSCLE WEAKNESS AND TWITCHINGS ARE SEVERE, GIVE PRALIDOXIME (PROTOPAM-AYERST, 2-PAM), 1.0 GRAM INTRAVENOUSLY AT NO MORE THAN 0.5 GRAM PER MINUTE. DOSAGE OF PRALIDOXIME MAY BE REPEATED IN 1-2 HOURS, THEN AT 10-12 HOUR INTERVALS IF NEEDED. IN VERY SEVERE POISONINGS, DOSAGE RATES MAY BE DOUBLED. TREATMENT WITH PRALIDOXIME WILL BE MOST EFFECTIVE IF GIVEN WITHIN THIRTY-SIX HOURS AFTER POISONING (MORGAN, RECOGNITION AND MANAGEMENT OF PESTICIDE POISONINGS, 3RD ED.). ANTIDOTE SHOULD BE ADMINISTERED BY QUALIFIED MEDICAL PERSONNEL.

REACTIVITY

REACTIVITY: STABLE UNDER NORMAL TEMPERATURES AND PRESSURES.

INCOMPATIBILITIES: PHORATE: OXIDIZERS (STRONG): FIRE AND EXPLOSION HAZARD.

DECOMPOSITION: THERMAL DECOMPOSITION PRODUCTS MAY INCLUDE TOXIC OXIDES OF CARBON, SULFUR, AND PHOSPHORUS.

POLYMERIZATION: HAZARDOUS POLYMERIZATION HAS NOT BEEN REPORTED TO OCCUR UNDER NORMAL TEMPERATURES AND PRESSURES.

STORAGE AND DISPOSAL

OBSERVE ALL FEDERAL, STATE AND LOCAL REGULATIONS WHEN STORING OR DISPOSING OF THIS SUBSTANCE. FOR ASSISTANCE, CONTACT THE DISTRICT DIRECTOR OF THE ENVIRONMENTAL PROTECTION AGENCY.

****STORAGE****

STORE IN ACCORDANCE WITH 40 CFR 165 RECOMMENDED PROCEDURES FOR THE DISPOSAL AND STORAGE OF PESTICIDES AND PESTICIDE CONTAINERS.
STORE AWAY FROM INCOMPATIBLE SUBSTANCES.
THRESHOLD PLANNING QUANTITY (TPQ): THE SUPERFUND AMENDMENTS AND REAUTHORIZATION ACT (SARA) SECTION 302 REQUIRES THAT EACH FACILITY WHERE ANY EXTREMELY HAZARDOUS SUBSTANCE IS PRESENT IN A QUANTITY EQUAL TO OR GREATER THAN THE TPQ ESTABLISHED FOR THAT SUBSTANCE NOTIFY THE STATE EMERGENCY RESPONSE COMMISSION FOR THE STATE IN WHICH IT IS LOCATED. SECTION 303 OF SARA REQUIRES THESE FACILITIES TO PARTICIPATE IN LOCAL EMERGENCY RESPONSE PLANNING (40 CFR 355.30).

****DISPOSAL****

DISPOSAL MUST BE IN ACCORDANCE WITH 40 CFR 165 RECOMMENDED PROCEDURES FOR THE DISPOSAL AND STORAGE OF PESTICIDES AND PESTICIDE CONTAINERS.
DISPOSAL MUST BE IN ACCORDANCE WITH STANDARDS APPLICABLE TO GENERATORS OF HAZARDOUS WASTE, 40CFR 262. EPA HAZARDOUS WASTE NUMBER P094.

CONDITIONS TO AVOID

MAY BURN BUT DOES NOT IGNITE READILY.

SPILL AND LEAK PROCEDURES

OCCUPATIONAL SPILL: DO NOT TOUCH SPILLED MATERIAL. STOP LEAK IF YOU CAN DO IT WITHOUT RISK. FOR SMALL SPILLS, TAKE UP WITH SAND OR OTHER ABSORBENT MATERIAL AND PLACE INTO CONTAINERS FOR LATER DISPOSAL. FOR SMALL DRY SPILLS, WITH A CLEAN SHOVEL PLACE MATERIAL INTO CLEAN, DRY CONTAINER AND COVER. MOVE CONTAINERS FROM SPILL AREA. FOR LARGER SPILLS, DIKE FAR AHEAD OF SPILL FOR LATER DISPOSAL. KEEP UNNECESSARY PEOPLE AWAY. ISOLATE HAZARD AREA AND DENY ENTRY.
REPORTABLE QUANTITY (RQ): 10 POUNDS THE SUPERFUND AMENDMENTS AND REAUTHORIZATION ACT (SARA) SECTION 304 REQUIRES THAT A RELEASE EQUAL TO OR GREATER THAN THE REPORTABLE QUANTITY FOR THIS SUBSTANCE BE IMMEDIATELY REPORTED TO THE LOCAL EMERGENCY PLANNING COMMITTEE AND THE STATE EMERGENCY RESPONSE COMMISSION (40 CFR 355.40). IF THE RELEASE OF THIS SUBSTANCE IS REPORTABLE UNDER CERCLA SECTION 103, THE NATIONAL RESPONSE CENTER MUST BE NOTIFIED IMMEDIATELY AT (800) 424-8802 OR (202) 426-2675 IN THE METROPOLITAN WASHINGTON, D.C. AREA (40 CFR 302.6).

PROTECTIVE EQUIPMENT

VENTILATION: PROVIDE LOCAL EXHAUST OR PROCESS ENCLOSURE VENTILATION TO MEET PUBLISHED EXPOSURE LIMITS.

RESPIRATOR: THE FOLLOWING RESPIRATORS ARE RECOMMENDED BASED ON INFORMATION FOUND IN THE PHYSICAL DATA, TOXICITY AND HEALTH EFFECTS SECTIONS. THEY ARE RANKED IN ORDER FROM MINIMUM TO MAXIMUM RESPIRATORY PROTECTION. THE SPECIFIC RESPIRATOR SELECTED MUST BE BASED ON CONTAMINATION LEVELS FOUND IN THE WORK PLACE, MUST NOT EXCEED THE WORKING LIMITS OF THE RESPIRATOR AND BE JOINTLY APPROVED BY THE NATIONAL INSTITUTE FOR OCCUPATIONAL SAFETY AND HEALTH AND THE MINE SAFETY AND HEALTH ADMINISTRATION (NIOSH-MSHA).
TYPE 'C' SUPPLIED-AIR RESPIRATOR WITH A FULL FACEPIECE OPERATED IN PRESSURE-DEMAND OR OTHER POSITIVE PRESSURE MODE OR WITH A FULL

FACEPIECE, HELMET OR HOOD OPERATED IN CONTINOUS-FLOW MODE.
SELF-CONTAINED BREATHING APPARATUS WITH A FULL FACEPIECE OPERATED IN PRESSURE-DEMAND OR OTHER POSITIVE PRESSURE MODE.
FOR FIREFIGHTING AND OTHER IMMEDIATELY DANGEROUS TO LIFE OR HEALTH CONDITIONS:
SELF-CONTAINED BREATHING APPARATUS WITH FULL FACEPIECE OPERATED IN PRESSURE-DEMAND OR OTHER POSITIVE PRESSURE MODE.
SUPPLIED-AIR RESPIRATOR WITH FULL FACEPIECE AND OPERATED IN PRESSURE-DEMAND OR OTHER POSITIVE PRESSURE MODE IN COMBINATION WITH AN AUXILIARY SELF-CONTAINED BREATHING APPARATUS OPERATED IN PRESSURE-DEMAND OR OTHER POSITIVE PRESSURE MODE.

CLOTHING: EMPLOYEE MUST WEAR APPROPRIATE PROTECTIVE (IMPERVIOUS) CLOTHING AND EQUIPMENT TO PREVENT ANY POSSIBILITY OF SKIN CONTACT WITH THIS SUBSTANCE.

GLOVES: EMPLOYEE MUST WEAR APPROPRIATE PROTECTIVE GLOVES TO PREVENT CONTACT WITH THIS SUBSTANCE.

EYE PROTECTION: EMPLOYEE MUST WEAR SPLASH-PROOF OR DUST-RESISTANT SAFETY GOGGLES WITH OR WITHOUT A FACESHIELD TO PREVENT CONTACT WITH THIS SUBSTANCE.
EMERGENCY EYE WASH: WHERE THERE IS ANY POSSIBILITY THAT AN EMPLOYEE'S EYES MAY BE EXPOSED TO THIS SUBSTANCE, THE EMPLOYER SHOULD PROVIDE AN EYE WASH FOUNTAIN WITHIN THE IMMEDIATE WORK AREA FOR EMERGENCY USE.

AUTHORIZED BY- OCCUPATIONAL HEALTH SERVICES, INC.
CREATION DATE: 10/04/89 ***REVISION DATE:*** 04/25/90

MATERIAL SAFETY DATA SHEET

OCCUPATIONAL HEALTH SERVICES, INC.
AGRICULTURE AND PESTICIDE DIVISION
450 SEVENTH AVENUE, SUITE 2407
NEW YORK, NEW YORK 10123
1-800-445-MSDS OR (212) 967-1100

EMERGENCY CONTACT:
JOHN S. BRANSFORD, JR. (615) 292-1180

SUBSTANCE IDENTIFICATION

CAS-NUMBER 2600-69-3

SUBSTANCE: PHORATOXON

TRADE NAMES/SYNONYMS: PHOSPHOROTHIOIC ACID, O,O-DIETHYL S-((ETHYLTHIO)METHYL)ESTER; PHORATE OXON; PHORATE OXYGEN ANALOG; PHORATE THIOLATE ANALOG; THIMET OXON; THIMET OXYGEN ANALOG; C7H17O3PS2; PST18641

CHEMICAL FAMILY: ORGANOPHOSPHATE

MOLECULAR FORMULA: (C2-H5-O)2-P-(O)-S-C-H2-S-C2-H5

MOLECULAR WEIGHT: 244.33

CERCLA RATINGS (SCALE 0-3): HEALTH=3 FIRE=U REACTIVITY=0 PERSISTENCE=1

NFPA RATINGS (SCALE 0-4): HEALTH=3 FIRE=U REACTIVITY=0

COMPONENTS AND CONTAMINANTS

COMPONENT: PHORATOXON ***PERCENT:*** 100.0
CAS# 2600-69-3

OTHER CONTAMINANTS: NONE

EXPOSURE LIMITS: NO OCCUPATIONAL EXPOSURE LIMITS ESTABLISHED BY OSHA, ACGIH, OR NIOSH.

PHYSICAL DATA

DESCRIPTION: CLEAR LIQUID. ***BOILING POINT:*** NOT AVAILABLE

SPECIFIC GRAVITY: NOT AVAILABLE ***SOLUBILITY IN WATER:*** NOT AVAILABLE

FIRE AND EXPLOSION DATA

FIRE AND EXPLOSION HAZARD: UNKNOWN FIRE AND EXPLOSION HAZARD.

FLASH POINT: NOT AVAILABLE

FIREFIGHTING MEDIA: DRY CHEMICAL, CARBON DIOXIDE, HALON, WATER SPRAY OR STANDARD FOAM (1987 EMERGENCY RESPONSE GUIDEBOOK, DOT P 5800.4).
FOR LARGER FIRES, USE WATER SPRAY, FOG OR STANDARD FOAM (1987 EMERGENCY RESPONSE GUIDEBOOK, DOT P 5800.4).

FIREFIGHTING: MOVE CONTAINER FROM FIRE AREA IF POSSIBLE. DIKE FIRE CONTROL WATER FOR LATER DISPOSAL; DO NOT SCATTER THE MATERIAL. COOL FIRE-EXPOSED CONTAINERS WITH WATER FROM SIDE UNTIL WELL AFTER FIRE IS OUT. STAY AWAY FROM STORAGE TANK ENDS. WITHDRAW IMMEDIATELY IN CASE OF RISING SOUND FROM VENTING SAFETY DEVICE OR ANY DISCOLORATION OF STORAGE TANK DUE TO FIRE (1987 EMERGENCY RESPONSE GUIDEBOOK, DOT P 5800.4, GUIDE PAGE 28).
EXTINGUISH ONLY IF FLOW CAN BE STOPPED. USE FLOODING AMOUNTS OF WATER AS A FOG; SOLID STREAMS MAY BE INEFFECTIVE. COOL CONTAINERS WITH FLOODING AMOUNTS OF WATER FROM AS FAR A DISTANCE AS POSSIBLE. AVOID BREATHING POISONOUS VAPORS, KEEP UPWIND.

TRANSPORTATION DATA

DEPARTMENT OF TRANSPORTATION HAZARD CLASSIFICATION 49 CFR 172.101: POISON B
DEPARTMENT OF TRANSPORTATION LABELING REQUIREMENTS 49 CFR 172.101 AND SUBPART E: POISON
DEPARTMENT OF TRANSPORTATION PACKAGING REQUIREMENTS: 49 CFR 173.359 EXCEPTIONS: 49 CFR 173.359

TOXICITY

PHORATOXON: TOXICITY DATA: 250 UG/KG ORAL-RAT LD50. CARCINOGEN STATUS: NONE. ACUTE TOXICITY LEVEL: HIGHLY TOXIC BY INGESTION. TARGET EFFECTS: CHOLINESTERASE INHIBITOR. POISONING MAY AFFECT THE NERVOUS SYSTEM.* AT INCREASED RISK FROM EXPOSURE: PERSONS WITH RESPIRATORY AILMENTS, RECENT EXPOSURE TO CHOLINESTERASE INHIBITORS OR IMPAIRED CHOLINESTERASE PRODUCTION, OR LIVER MALFUNCTION.* ADDITIONAL DATA: MAY CROSS THE PLACENTA. HIGH ENVIRONMENTAL TEMPERATURES OR EXPOSURE OF THE CHEMICAL TO VISIBLE OR ULTRAVIOLET LIGHT MAY ENHANCE THE TOXICITY. INTERACTIONS WITH MEDICATIONS MAY OCCUR.*
* MAY BE BASED ON GENERAL INFORMATION ON ORGANOPHOSPHATES.

HEALTH EFFECTS AND FIRST AID

INHALATION: PHORATOXON: SEE INFORMATION ON ORGANOPHOSPHATES.
ORGANOPHOSPHATES: CHOLINESTERASE INHIBITOR. **ACUTE EXPOSURE**- WHEN INHALED, THE FIRST EFFECTS OF CHOLINESTERASE INHIBITORS ARE USUALLY RESPIRATORY AND MAY INCLUDE NASAL HYPEREMIA AND WATERY DISCHARGE, COUGH, CHEST DISCOMFORT, DYSPNEA, AND WHEEZING DUE TO INCREASED BRONCHIAL SECRETIONS AND BRONCHOCONSTRICTION. IF SUFFICIENT AMOUNTS ARE ABSORBED, OTHER SYSTEMIC EFFECTS MAY BEGIN WITHIN A FEW MINUTES OR BE DELAYED FOR UP TO 12 HOURS. SYMPTOMS MAY INCLUDE PALLOR, NAUSEA, VOMITING, DIARRHEA, ABDOMINAL CRAMPS, HEADACHE, DIZZINESS, OCULAR PAIN, BLURRED VISION, MIOSIS OR IN SOME CASES, ESPECIALLY INITIALLY, MYDRIASIS, LACRIMATION, SALIVATION, SWEATING, AND CONFUSION. OTHER REPORTED CENTRAL NERVOUS SYSTEM OR NEUROMUSCULAR EFFECTS MAY INCLUDE ATAXIA, SLURRED SPEECH, AREFLEXIA, WEAKNESS, FATIGUE, FASCICULATIONS, TWITCHING, TREMORS POSSIBLY OF THE TONGUE AND EYELIDS, AND EVENTUALLY PARALYSIS OF THE EXTREMITIES AND POSSIBLY OF THE RESPIRATORY MUSCLES. IN SEVERE CASES THERE MAY ALSO BE INVOLUNTARY DEFECATION AND URINATION, CYANOSIS, PSYCHOSIS, HYPERGLYCEMIA, ACUTE PANCREATITIS, CARDIAC IRREGULARITIES, PULMONARY EDEMA, UNCONSCIOUSNESS, CONVULSIONS, AND COMA. DEATH IS PRIMARILY DUE TO RESPIRATORY FAILURE, ALTHOUGH CARDIOVASCULAR EFFECTS INCLUDING CARDIAC ARREST MAY ALSO BE IMPLICATED. LONG TERM SEQUELAE ARE RARE BUT MAY INCLUDE NEUROPSYCHIATRIC DISORDERS AND MYOPATHY WITH MUSCLE TENDERNESS. SOME ORGANOPHOSPHATES MAY CAUSE A DELAYED NEUROPATHY BEGINNING 1-4 WEEKS AFTER AN ACUTE EXPOSURE WHICH MAY OR MAY NOT HAVE CAUSED ACUTE CHOLINERGIC EFFECTS. NUMBNESS, TINGLING, WEAKNESS AND CRAMPING BEGINNING SYMMETRICALLY IN THE LOWER LIMBS MAY PROGRESS TO ATAXIA AND PARALYSIS. IN SEVERE CASES, UPPER LIMB INVOLVEMENT IS POSSIBLE AND FLACCID PARALYSIS MAY PROGRESS TO SPASTIC PARALYSIS WITH EXAGGERATED REFLEXES. IMPROVEMENT MAY OCCUR OVER MONTHS TO YEARS, BUT SOME RESIDUAL IMPAIRMENT USUALLY REMAINS.
CHRONIC EXPOSURE- REPEATED OR PROLONGED EXPOSURE MAY RESULT IN THE EFFECTS OF ACUTE EXPOSURE INCLUDING THE DELAYED NEUROPATHY. OTHER EFFECTS REPORTED IN WORKERS REPEATEDLY EXPOSED INCLUDE IMPAIRED MEMORY AND CONCENTRATION, ACUTE PSYCHOSIS, SEVERE DEPRESSIONS, IRRITABILTY, CONFUSION, APATHY, EMOTIONAL LABILITY, SOCIAL WITHDRAWAL, CONFUSION, HEADACHE, SPEECH DIFFICULTIES, DELAYED REACTION TIMES, SPATIAL DISORIENTATION, NIGHTMARES, SLEEPWALKING, AND DROWSINESS OR INSOMNIA. AN INFLUENZA-LIKE CONDITION WITH HEADACHE, NAUSEA, WEAKNESS, ANOREXIA AND MALAISE HAS ALSO BEEN REPORTED.

FIRST AID- REMOVE FROM EXPOSURE AREA TO FRESH AIR IMMEDIATELY. IF BREATHING HAS STOPPED, GIVE ARTIFICIAL RESPIRATION. MAINTAIN AIRWAY AND BLOOD PRESSURE AND ADMINISTER OXYGEN IF AVAILABLE. KEEP AFFECTED PERSON WARM AND AT REST. TREAT SYMPTOMATICALLY AND SUPPORTIVELY. ADMINISTRATION OF OXYGEN SHOULD BE PERFORMED BY QUALIFIED PERSONNEL. GET MEDICAL ATTENTION IMMEDIATELY.

SKIN CONTACT: PHORATOXON: SEE INFORMATION ON ORGANOPHOSPHATES.
ORGANOPHOSPHATES: CHOLINESTERASE INHIBITOR. **ACUTE EXPOSURE-** LOCALIZED SWEATING AND FASCICULATIONS MAY OCCUR AT THE SITE OF CONTACT. IF SUFFICIENT AMOUNTS ARE ABSORBED, OTHER EFFECTS OF CHOLINESTERASE INHIBITION AS DESCRIBED IN ACUTE INHALATION MAY OCCUR. SYMPTOMS MAY BE DELAYED 2-3 HOURS, BUT USUALLY NO MORE THAN 12 HOURS. THE RATE OF ABSORPTION IS INCREASED BY THE PRESENCE OF DERMATITIS OR HIGH AMBIENT TEMPERATURES. DELAYED NEUROPATHY IS ALSO POSSIBLE. **CHRONIC EXPOSURE-** REPEATED OR PROLONGED EXPOSURE MAY CAUSE EFFECTS AS DESCRIBED IN ACUTE EXPOSURE. SOME ORGANOPHOSPHATES MAY CAUSE SENSITIZATION.

FIRST AID- REMOVE CONTAMINATED CLOTHING IMMEDIATELY. WASH CONTAMINATED AREAS WITH SOAP AND WATER FOLLOWED BY ALCOHOL (ARENA, POISONING, 4TH ED.). EMERGENCY PERSONNEL SHOULD WEAR GLOVES AND AVOID CONTAMINATION. TREAT RESPIRATORY DIFFICULTY WITH ARTIFICIAL RESPIRATION. GET MEDICAL ATTENTION IMMEDIATELY.

EYE CONTACT: PHORATOXON: SEE INFORMATION ON ORGANOPHOSPHATES.
ORGANOPHOSPHATES: CHOLINESTERASE INHIBITOR. **ACUTE EXPOSURE-** DIRECT CONTACT MAY CAUSE PAIN, HYPEREMIA, LACRIMATION, TWITCHING OF THE EYELIDS, MIOSIS, AND CILIARY MUSCLE SPASM WITH LOSS OF ACCOMODATION, BLURRED OR DIMMED VISION AND BROWACHE. SOMETIMES MYDRIASIS MAY OCCUR INSTEAD OF MIOSIS. WITH SUFFICIENT EXPOSURE, OTHER SYMPTOMS OF CHOLINESTERASE INHIBITION AS DESCRIBED IN ACUTE INHALATION MAY OCCUR. **CHRONIC EXPOSURE-** REPEATED OR PROLONGED EXPOSURE MAY CAUSE EFFECTS AS DESCRIBED IN ACUTE EXPOSURE. SOME COMPOUNDS HAVE CAUSED TOXIC EFFECTS ON THE CRYSTALLINE LENS, CONJUNCTIVAL THICKENING AND OBSTRUCTION OF THE NASOLACRIMAL CANALS WHEN USED AS MIOTIC EYEDROPS.

FIRST AID- IRRIGATE EYES WITH WATER OR SALINE SOLUTION. IF SYMPTOMS OF POISONING OCCUR, TREAT RESPIRATORY DIFFICULTY WITH ARTIFICIAL RESPIRATION AND OXYGEN. OBSERVE PATIENT FOR AT LEAST 24-36 HOURS (GOSSELIN, CLINICAL TOXICOLOGY OF COMMERCIAL PRODUCTS, 5TH ED.). GET MEDICAL ATTENTION IMMEDIATELY. OXYGEN SHOULD BE ADMINISTERED BY QUALIFIED MEDICAL PERSONNEL.

INGESTION: PHORATOXON: HIGHLY TOXIC. SEE INFORMATION ON ORGANOPHOSPHATES.
ORGANOPHOSPHATES: CHOLINESTERASE INHIBITOR. **ACUTE EXPOSURE-** WHEN INGESTED, THE FIRST EFFECTS MAY BE NAUSEA, VOMITING, ANOREXIA, ABDOMINAL CRAMPS AND DIARRHEA. GASTROINTESTINAL ABSORPTION MAY CAUSE SYMPTOMS OF CHOLINESTERASE INHIBITION AS DESCRIBED IN ACUTE INHALATION. SYMPTOMS MAY BEGIN WITHIN MINUTES OR BE DELAYED FOR HOURS. DELAYED EFFECTS INCLUDING NEUROPATHY MAY ALSO OCCUR. **CHRONIC EXPOSURE-** REPEATED INGESTION MAY CAUSE EFFECTS AS DESCRIBED IN ACUTE EXPOSURE.

FIRST AID- IF PERSON IS ALERT AND RESPIRATION IS NOT DEPRESSED, GIVE SYRUP OF IPECAC FOLLOWED BY WATER (IF VOMITING OCCURS, KEEP HEAD BELOW HIPS TO PREVENT ASPIRATION). IF CONSCIOUSNESS LEVEL DECLINES OR VOMITING HAS NOT OCCURRED IN 15 MINUTES EMPTY STOMACH BY GASTRIC LAVAGE WITH THE AID OF CUFFED ENDOTRACHEAL TUBE USING ISOTONIC SALINE OR 5% SODIUM BICARBONATE FOLLOW WITH ACTIVATED CHARCOAL. ESTABLISH AND MAINTAIN AIRWAY. TREAT RESPIRATORY DIFFICULTY WITH ARTIFICIAL RESPIRATION AND OXYGEN. DO NOT GIVE MORPHINE, AMINOPHYLLINE, PHENOTHIAZINES, RESERPINE, FUROSEMIDE, OR ETHACRYNIC ACID (MORGAN, RECOGNITION AND MANAGEMENT OF PESTICIDE POISONINGS, 3RD ED.). TREAT SYMPTOMATICALLY AND SUPPORTIVELY. ADMINISTRATION OF OXYGEN AND LAVAGE MUST BE PERFORMED BY QUALIFIED MEDICAL PERSONNEL. GET MEDICAL ATTENTION IMMEDIATELY.

ANTIDOTE: THE FOLLOWING ANTIDOTE(S) HAVE BEEN RECOMMENDED. HOWEVER, THE DECISION AS TO WHETHER THE SEVERITY OF POISONING REQUIRES ADMINISTRATION OF ANY ANTIDOTE AND ACTUAL DOSE REQUIRED SHOULD BE MADE BY QUALIFIED MEDICAL PERSONNEL.
FOR CHOLINESTERASE INHIBITORS: ESTABLISH CLEAR AIRWAY AND TISSUE OXYGENATION BY ASPIRATION OF SECRETIONS, AND IF NECESSARY, BY ASSISTED PULMONARY VENTILATION WITH OXYGEN. IMPROVE TISSUE OXYGENATION AS MUCH AS POSSIBLE BEFORE ADMINISTERING ATROPINE TO MINIMIZE THE RISK OF VENTRICULAR FIBRILLATION. ADMINISTER ATROPINE SULFATE INTRAVENOUSLY, OR INTRAMUSCULARLY IF IV INJECTION IS NOT POSSIBLE. IN MODERATELY SEVERE POISONING ADMINISTER ATROPINE SULFATE, 0.4-2.0 MG REPEATED EVERY 15 MINUTES UNTIL ATROPINIZATION IS ACHIEVED (TACHYCARDIA, FLUSHING, DRY MOUTH, MYDRIASIS). MAINTAIN ATROPINIZATION BY REPEATED DOSES FOR 2-12 HOURS, OR LONGER, DEPENDING ON THE SEVERITY OF POISONING. THE APPEARANCE OF RALES IN THE LUNG BASES, MIOSIS, SALIVATION, NAUSEA, BRADYCARDIA, ARE ALL INDICATIONS OF INADEQUATE ATROPINIZATION. SEVERELY POISONED INDIVIDUALS MAY EXHIBIT REMARKABLE TOLERANCE TO ATROPINE; TWO OR MORE TIMES THE DOSAGES SUGGESTED ABOVE MAY BE NEEDED. PERSONS NOT POISONED OR ONLY SLIGHTLY POISONED, HOWEVER, MAY DEVELOP SIGNS OF ATROPINE TOXICITY FROM SUCH LARGE DOSAGES: FEVER, MUSCLE FIBRILLATIONS, AND DELIRIUM ARE THE MAIN SIGNS OF ATROPINE TOXICITY. IF THESE SIGNS APPEAR WHILE THE PATIENT IS FULLY ATROPINIZED, ATROPINE ADMINISTRATION SHOULD BE DISCONTINUED, AT LEAST TEMPORARILY. OBSERVE TREATED PATIENTS CLOSELY AT LEAST 24 HOURS TO INSURE THAT SYMPTOMS (POSSIBLY PULMONARY EDEMA) DO NOT RECUR AS ATROPINIZATION WEARS OFF. IN VERY SEVERE POISONINGS, METABOLIC DISPOSITION OF TOXICANT MAY REQUIRE SEVERAL HOURS OR DAYS DURING WHICH ATROPINIZATION MUST BE MAINTAINED. MARKEDLY LOWER LEVELS OF URINARY METABOLITES INDICATE THAT ATROPINE DOSAGE CAN BE TAPERED OFF. AS DOSAGE IS REDUCED, CHECK THE LUNG BASES FREQUENTLY FOR RALES. IF RALES ARE HEARD OR OTHER SYMPTOMS RETURN, RE-ESTABLISH ATROPINIZATION PROMPTLY (MORGAN, RECOGNITION AND MANAGEMENT OF PESTICIDE POISONINGS, 3RD ED.). ADMINISTRATION OF ANTIDOTE MUST BE PERFORMED BY QUALIFIED MEDICAL PERSONNEL.
IN CASES OF SEVERE POISONING BY ORGANOPHOSPHATE PESTICIDES IN WHICH RESPIRATORY DEPRESSION, MUSCLE WEAKNESS AND TWITCHINGS ARE SEVERE, GIVE PRALIDOXIME (PROTOPAM-AYERST, 2-PAM), 1.0 GRAM INTRAVENOUSLY AT NO MORE THAN 0.5 GRAM PER MINUTE. DOSAGE OF PRALIDOXIME MAY BE REPEATED IN 1-2 HOURS, THEN AT 10-12 HOUR INTERVALS IF NEEDED. IN VERY SEVERE POISONINGS, DOSAGE RATES MAY BE DOUBLED. TREATMENT WITH PRALIDOXIME WILL BE MOST EFFECTIVE IF GIVEN WITHIN THIRTY-SIX HOURS AFTER POISONING (MORGAN, RECOGNITION AND MANAGEMENT OF PESTICIDE POISONINGS, 3RD ED.). ANTIDOTE SHOULD BE ADMINISTERED BY QUALIFIED MEDICAL PERSONNEL.

REACTIVITY

REACTIVITY: STABLE UNDER NORMAL TEMPERATURES AND PRESSURES.

INCOMPATIBILITIES: PHORATOXON: OXIDIZERS (STRONG): FIRE AND EXPLOSION HAZARD.

DECOMPOSITION: THERMAL DECOMPOSITION PRODUCTS MAY INCLUDE TOXIC OXIDES OF CARBON, SULFUR, AND PHOSPHORUS.

POLYMERIZATION: HAZARDOUS POLYMERIZATION HAS NOT BEEN REPORTED TO OCCUR UNDER NORMAL TEMPERATURES AND PRESSURES.

STORAGE AND DISPOSAL

OBSERVE ALL FEDERAL, STATE AND LOCAL REGULATIONS WHEN STORING OR DISPOSING OF THIS SUBSTANCE. FOR ASSISTANCE, CONTACT THE DISTRICT DIRECTOR OF THE ENVIRONMENTAL PROTECTION AGENCY.

STORAGE

STORE IN ACCORDANCE WITH 40 CFR 165 RECOMMENDED PROCEDURES FOR THE DISPOSAL AND STORAGE OF PESTICIDES AND PESTICIDE CONTAINERS.
STORE AWAY FROM INCOMPATIBLE SUBSTANCES.

DISPOSAL

DISPOSAL MUST BE IN ACCORDANCE WITH 40 CFR 165 RECOMMENDED PROCEDURES FOR THE DISPOSAL AND STORAGE OF PESTICIDES AND PESTICIDE CONTAINERS.

CONDITIONS TO AVOID

AVOID CONTACT WITH HEAT, SPARKS, FLAMES OR OTHER IGNITION SOURCES. VAPORS MAY BE EXPLOSIVE. MATERIAL IS POISONOUS; AVOID INHALATION OF VAPORS OR CONTACT WITH SKIN. DO NOT ALLOW MATERIAL TO CONTAMINATE WATER SOURCES.

SPILL AND LEAK PROCEDURES

OCCUPATIONAL SPILL: SHUT OFF IGNITION SOURCES. DO NOT TOUCH SPILLED MATERIAL. STOP LEAK IF YOU CAN DO IT WITHOUT RISK. USE WATER SPRAY TO REDUCE VAPORS. FOR SMALL SPILLS, TAKE UP WITH SAND OR OTHER ABSORBENT MATERIAL AND PLACE INTO CONTAINERS FOR LATER DISPOSAL. FOR LARGER SPILLS, DIKE FAR AHEAD OF SPILL FOR LATER DISPOSAL. NO SMOKING, FLAMES OR FLARES IN HAZARD AREA! KEEP UNNECESSARY PEOPLE AWAY; ISOLATE HAZARD AREA AND DENY ENTRY.

PROTECTIVE EQUIPMENT

VENTILATION: PROVIDE LOCAL EXHAUST OR PROCESS ENCLOSURE VENTILATION. VENTILATION EQUIPMENT MUST BE EXPLOSION-PROOF.

RESPIRATOR: THE FOLLOWING RESPIRATORS ARE RECOMMENDED BASED ON INFORMATION FOUND IN THE PHYSICAL DATA, TOXICITY AND HEALTH EFFECTS SECTIONS. THEY ARE RANKED IN ORDER FROM MINIMUM TO MAXIMUM RESPIRATORY PROTECTION. THE SPECIFIC RESPIRATOR SELECTED MUST BE BASED ON CONTAMINATION LEVELS FOUND IN THE WORK PLACE, MUST NOT EXCEED THE WORKING LIMITS OF THE RESPIRATOR AND BE JOINTLY APPROVED BY THE NATIONAL INSTITUTE FOR OCCUPATIONAL SAFETY AND HEALTH AND THE MINE

SAFETY AND HEALTH ADMINISTRATION (NIOSH-MSHA).
TYPE 'C' SUPPLIED-AIR RESPIRATOR WITH A FULL FACEPIECE OPERATED IN PRESSURE-DEMAND OR OTHER POSITIVE PRESSURE MODE OR WITH A FULL FACEPIECE, HELMET OR HOOD OPERATED IN CONTINOUS-FLOW MODE.
SELF-CONTAINED BREATHING APPARATUS WITH A FULL FACEPIECE OPERATED IN PRESSURE-DEMAND OR OTHER POSITIVE PRESSURE MODE.
FOR FIREFIGHTING AND OTHER IMMEDIATELY DANGEROUS TO LIFE OR HEALTH CONDITIONS:
SELF-CONTAINED BREATHING APPARATUS WITH FULL FACEPIECE OPERATED IN PRESSURE-DEMAND OR OTHER POSITIVE PRESSURE MODE.
SUPPLIED-AIR RESPIRATOR WITH FULL FACEPIECE AND OPERATED IN PRESSURE-DEMAND OR OTHER POSITIVE PRESSURE MODE IN COMBINATION WITH AN AUXILIARY SELF-CONTAINED BREATHING APPARATUS OPERATED IN PRESSURE-DEMAND OR OTHER POSITIVE PRESSURE MODE.

CLOTHING: EMPLOYEE MUST WEAR APPROPRIATE PROTECTIVE (IMPERVIOUS) CLOTHING AND EQUIPMENT TO PREVENT ANY POSSIBILITY OF SKIN CONTACT WITH THIS SUBSTANCE.

GLOVES: EMPLOYEE MUST WEAR APPROPRIATE PROTECTIVE GLOVES TO PREVENT CONTACT WITH THIS SUBSTANCE.

EYE PROTECTION: EMPLOYEE MUST WEAR SPLASH-PROOF OR DUST-RESISTANT SAFETY GOGGLES TO PREVENT EYE CONTACT WITH THIS SUBSTANCE.
EMERGENCY EYE WASH: WHERE THERE IS ANY POSSIBILITY THAT AN EMPLOYEE'S EYES MAY BE EXPOSED TO THIS SUBSTANCE, THE EMPLOYER SHOULD PROVIDE AN EYE WASH FOUNTAIN WITHIN THE IMMEDIATE WORK AREA FOR EMERGENCY USE.

AUTHORIZED BY- OCCUPATIONAL HEALTH SERVICES, INC.
CREATION DATE: 10/04/89 ***REVISION DATE:*** 05/11/90

MATERIAL SAFETY DATA SHEET

OCCUPATIONAL HEALTH SERVICES, INC.
AGRICULTURE AND PESTICIDE DIVISION
450 SEVENTH AVENUE, SUITE 2407
NEW YORK, NEW YORK 10123
1-800-445-MSDS OR (212) 967-1100

EMERGENCY CONTACT:
JOHN S. BRANSFORD, JR. (615) 292-1180

SUBSTANCE IDENTIFICATION

CAS-NUMBER 2588-06-9

SUBSTANCE: PHORATE OXYGEN ANALOG SULFONE

TRADE NAMES/SYNONYMS: PHOSPHOROTHIOIC ACID, O,O-DIETHYL S-((ETHYLSULFONYL)METHYL)ESTER; O,O-DIETHYL-S-(ETHYLSULFONYL)METHYL)PHOSPHOROTHIOATE; PHORATE OXON SULFONE; PHORATOXON SULFONE; PO-PHORATE SULFONE; THIMET OXYGEN ANALOG SULFONE; C7H17O5PS2; PST18642

CHEMICAL FAMILY: ORGANOPHOSPHATE

MOLECULAR FORMULA: (C2-H5-O)2-P-(O)-S-C-H2-S-(O2)-C2-H5

MOLECULAR WEIGHT: 276.31

CERCLA RATINGS (SCALE 0-3): HEALTH=3 FIRE=U REACTIVITY=0 PERSISTENCE=2

NFPA RATINGS (SCALE 0-4): HEALTH=3 FIRE=U REACTIVITY=0

COMPONENTS AND CONTAMINANTS

COMPONENT: PHORATE OXYGEN ANALOG SULFONE ***PERCENT:*** 100.0
CAS# 2588-06-9

OTHER CONTAMINANTS: NONE

EXPOSURE LIMITS: NO OCCUPATIONAL EXPOSURE LIMITS ESTABLISHED BY OSHA, ACGIH, OR NIOSH.

PHYSICAL DATA

DESCRIPTION: CLEAR LIQUID. ***BOILING POINT:*** NOT AVAILABLE
SPECIFIC GRAVITY: NOT AVAILABLE ***SOLUBILITY IN WATER:*** NOT AVAILABLE
VAPOR DENSITY: NOT AVAILABLE

FIRE AND EXPLOSION DATA

FIRE AND EXPLOSION HAZARD: UNKNOWN FIRE AND EXPLOSION HAZARD.

FLASH POINT: NOT AVAILABLE

FIREFIGHTING MEDIA: DRY CHEMICAL, CARBON DIOXIDE, HALON, WATER SPRAY OR STANDARD FOAM (1987 EMERGENCY RESPONSE GUIDEBOOK, DOT P 5800.4).
FOR LARGER FIRES, USE WATER SPRAY, FOG OR STANDARD FOAM (1987 EMERGENCY RESPONSE GUIDEBOOK, DOT P 5800.4).

FIREFIGHTING: MOVE CONTAINER FROM FIRE AREA IF POSSIBLE. DIKE FIRE CONTROL WATER FOR LATER DISPOSAL; DO NOT SCATTER THE MATERIAL. COOL FIRE-EXPOSED CONTAINERS WITH WATER FROM SIDE UNTIL WELL AFTER FIRE IS OUT. STAY AWAY FROM STORAGE TANK ENDS. WITHDRAW IMMEDIATELY IN CASE OF RISING SOUND FROM VENTING SAFETY DEVICE OR ANY DISCOLORATION OF STORAGE TANK DUE TO FIRE (1987 EMERGENCY RESPONSE GUIDEBOOK, DOT P 5800.4, GUIDE PAGE 28).
EXTINGUISH ONLY IF FLOW CAN BE STOPPED. USE FLOODING AMOUNTS OF WATER AS A FOG; SOLID STREAMS MAY BE INEFFECTIVE. COOL CONTAINERS WITH FLOODING AMOUNTS OF WATER FROM AS FAR A DISTANCE AS POSSIBLE. AVOID BREATHING POISONOUS VAPORS, KEEP UPWIND.

TRANSPORTATION DATA

DEPARTMENT OF TRANSPORTATION HAZARD CLASSIFICATION 49 CFR 172.101: POISON B
DEPARTMENT OF TRANSPORTATION LABELING REQUIREMENTS 49 CFR 172.101 AND SUBPART E: POISON
DEPARTMENT OF TRANSPORTATION PACKAGING REQUIREMENTS: 49 CFR 173.359 EXCEPTIONS: 49 CFR 173.359

TOXICITY

PHORATE OXYGEN ANALOG SULFONE: TOXICITY DATA: 500 UG/KG ORAL-RAT LD50. CARCINOGEN STATUS: NONE. ACUTE TOXICITY LEVEL: HIGHLY TOXIC BY INGESTION. TARGET EFFECTS: CHOLINESTERASE INHIBITOR. POISONING MAY AFFECT THE NERVOUS SYSTEM.* AT INCREASED RISK FROM EXPOSURE: PERSONS WITH RESPIRATORY AILMENTS, RECENT EXPOSURE TO CHOLINESTERASE INHIBITORS OR IMPAIRED CHOLINESTERASE PRODUCTION, OR LIVER MALFUNCTION.* ADDITIONAL DATA: MAY CROSS THE PLACENTA. HIGH ENVIRONMENTAL TEMPERATURES OR EXPOSURE OF THE CHEMICAL TO VISIBLE OR ULTRAVIOLET LIGHT MAY ENHANCE THE TOXICITY. INTERACTIONS WITH MEDICATIONS MAY OCCUR.*
* MAY BE BASED ON GENERAL INFORMATION ON ORGANOPHOSPHATES.

HEALTH EFFECTS AND FIRST AID

INHALATION: PHORATE OXYGEN ANALOG SULFONE: SEE INFORMATION ON ORGANOPHOSPHATES.
ORGANOPHOSPHATES: CHOLINESTERASE INHIBITOR. **ACUTE EXPOSURE**- WHEN INHALED, THE FIRST EFFECTS OF CHOLINESTERASE INHIBITORS ARE USUALLY RESPIRATORY AND MAY INCLUDE NASAL HYPEREMIA AND WATERY DISCHARGE, COUGH, CHEST DISCOMFORT, DYSPNEA, AND WHEEZING DUE TO INCREASED BRONCHIAL SECRETIONS AND BRONCHOCONSTRICTION. IF SUFFICIENT AMOUNTS ARE ABSORBED, OTHER SYSTEMIC EFFECTS MAY BEGIN WITHIN A FEW MINUTES OR BE DELAYED FOR UP TO 12 HOURS. SYMPTOMS MAY INCLUDE PALLOR, NAUSEA, VOMITING, DIARRHEA, ABDOMINAL CRAMPS, HEADACHE, DIZZINESS, OCULAR PAIN, BLURRED VISION, MIOSIS OR IN SOME CASES, ESPECIALLY INITIALLY, MYDRIASIS, LACRIMATION, SALIVATION, SWEATING, AND CONFUSION. OTHER REPORTED CENTRAL NERVOUS SYSTEM OR NEUROMUSCULAR EFFECTS MAY INCLUDE ATAXIA, SLURRED SPEECH, AREFLEXIA, WEAKNESS, FATIGUE, FASCICULATIONS, TWITCHING, TREMORS POSSIBLY OF THE TONGUE AND EYELIDS, AND EVENTUALLY PARALYSIS OF THE EXTREMITIES AND POSSIBLY OF THE RESPIRATORY MUSCLES. IN SEVERE CASES THERE MAY ALSO BE INVOLUNTARY DEFECATION AND URINATION, CYANOSIS, PSYCHOSIS, HYPERGLYCEMIA, ACUTE PANCREATITIS, CARDIAC IRREGULARITIES, PULMONARY EDEMA, UNCONSCIOUSNESS, CONVULSIONS, AND COMA. DEATH IS PRIMARILY DUE TO RESPIRATORY FAILURE, ALTHOUGH CARDIOVASCULAR EFFECTS INCLUDING CARDIAC ARREST MAY ALSO BE IMPLICATED. LONG TERM SEQUELAE ARE RARE BUT MAY INCLUDE NEUROPSYCHIATRIC DISORDERS AND MYOPATHY WITH MUSCLE TENDERNESS. SOME ORGANOPHOSPHATES MAY CAUSE A DELAYED NEUROPATHY BEGINNING 1-4 WEEKS AFTER AN ACUTE EXPOSURE WHICH MAY OR MAY NOT HAVE CAUSED ACUTE CHOLINERGIC EFFECTS. NUMBNESS, TINGLING, WEAKNESS AND CRAMPING BEGINNING SYMMETRICALLY IN THE LOWER LIMBS MAY PROGRESS TO ATAXIA AND PARALYSIS. IN SEVERE CASES, UPPER LIMB INVOLVEMENT IS POSSIBLE AND FLACCID PARALYSIS MAY PROGRESS TO SPASTIC PARALYSIS WITH EXAGGERATED REFLEXES. IMPROVEMENT MAY OCCUR OVER MONTHS TO YEARS, BUT SOME RESIDUAL IMPAIRMENT USUALLY REMAINS.
CHRONIC EXPOSURE- REPEATED OR PROLONGED EXPOSURE MAY RESULT IN THE EFFECTS OF ACUTE EXPOSURE INCLUDING THE DELAYED NEUROPATHY. OTHER EFFECTS REPORTED IN WORKERS REPEATEDLY EXPOSED INCLUDE IMPAIRED MEMORY AND CONCENTRATION, ACUTE PSYCHOSIS, SEVERE DEPRESSIONS, IRRITABILTY, CONFUSION, APATHY, EMOTIONAL LABILITY, SOCIAL WITHDRAWAL, CONFUSION, HEADACHE, SPEECH DIFFICULTIES, DELAYED REACTION TIMES, SPATIAL DISORIENTATION, NIGHTMARES, SLEEPWALKING, AND DROWSINESS OR INSOMNIA. AN INFLUENZA-LIKE CONDITION WITH HEADACHE, NAUSEA, WEAKNESS, ANOREXIA AND MALAISE HAS ALSO BEEN REPORTED.

FIRST AID- REMOVE FROM EXPOSURE AREA TO FRESH AIR IMMEDIATELY. IF BREATHING HAS STOPPED, GIVE ARTIFICIAL RESPIRATION. MAINTAIN AIRWAY AND

BLOOD PRESSURE AND ADMINISTER OXYGEN IF AVAILABLE. KEEP AFFECTED PERSON WARM AND AT REST. TREAT SYMPTOMATICALLY AND SUPPORTIVELY. ADMINISTRATION OF OXYGEN SHOULD BE PERFORMED BY QUALIFIED PERSONNEL. GET MEDICAL ATTENTION IMMEDIATELY.

SKIN CONTACT: PHORATE OXYGEN ANALOG SULFONE: SEE INFORMATION ON ORGANOPHOSPHATES.
ORGANOPHOSPHATES: CHOLINESTERASE INHIBITOR. **ACUTE EXPOSURE**- LOCALIZED SWEATING AND FASCICULATIONS MAY OCCUR AT THE SITE OF CONTACT. IF SUFFICIENT AMOUNTS ARE ABSORBED, OTHER EFFECTS OF CHOLINESTERASE INHIBITION AS DESCRIBED IN ACUTE INHALATION MAY OCCUR. SYMPTOMS MAY BE DELAYED 2-3 HOURS, BUT USUALLY NO MORE THAN 12 HOURS. THE RATE OF ABSORPTION IS INCREASED BY THE PRESENCE OF DERMATITIS OR HIGH AMBIENT TEMPERATURES. DELAYED NEUROPATHY IS ALSO POSSIBLE. **CHRONIC EXPOSURE**- REPEATED OR PROLONGED EXPOSURE MAY CAUSE EFFECTS AS DESCRIBED IN ACUTE EXPOSURE. SOME ORGANOPHOSPHATES MAY CAUSE SENSITIZATION.
FIRST AID- REMOVE CONTAMINATED CLOTHING IMMEDIATELY. WASH CONTAMINATED AREAS WITH SOAP AND WATER FOLLOWED BY ALCOHOL (ARENA, POISONING, 4TH ED.). EMERGENCY PERSONNEL SHOULD WEAR GLOVES AND AVOID CONTAMINATION. TREAT RESPIRATORY DIFFICULTY WITH ARTIFICIAL RESPIRATION. GET MEDICAL ATTENTION IMMEDIATELY.

EYE CONTACT: PHORATE OXYGEN ANALOG SULFONE: SEE INFORMATION ON ORGANOPHOSPHATES.
ORGANOPHOSPHATES: CHOLINESTERASE INHIBITOR. **ACUTE EXPOSURE**- DIRECT CONTACT MAY CAUSE PAIN, HYPEREMIA, LACRIMATION, TWITCHING OF THE EYELIDS, MIOSIS, AND CILIARY MUSCLE SPASM WITH LOSS OF ACCOMODATION, BLURRED OR DIMMED VISION AND BROWACHE. SOMETIMES MYDRIASIS MAY OCCUR INSTEAD OF MIOSIS. WITH SUFFICIENT EXPOSURE, OTHER SYMPTOMS OF CHOLINESTERASE INHIBITION AS DESCRIBED IN ACUTE INHALATION MAY OCCUR. **CHRONIC EXPOSURE**- REPEATED OR PROLONGED EXPOSURE MAY CAUSE EFFECTS AS DESCRIBED IN ACUTE EXPOSURE. SOME COMPOUNDS HAVE CAUSED TOXIC EFFECTS ON THE CRYSTALLINE LENS, CONJUNCTIVAL THICKENING AND OBSTRUCTION OF THE NASOLACRIMAL CANALS WHEN USED AS MIOTIC EYEDROPS.
FIRST AID- IRRIGATE EYES WITH WATER OR SALINE SOLUTION. IF SYMPTOMS OF POISONING OCCUR, TREAT RESPIRATORY DIFFICULTY WITH ARTIFICIAL RESPIRATION AND OXYGEN. OBSERVE PATIENT FOR AT LEAST 24-36 HOURS (GOSSELIN, CLINICAL TOXICOLOGY OF COMMERCIAL PRODUCTS, 5TH ED.). GET MEDICAL ATTENTION IMMEDIATELY. OXYGEN SHOULD BE ADMINISTERED BY QUALIFIED MEDICAL PERSONNEL.

INGESTION: PHORATE OXYGEN ANALOG SULFONE: HIGHLY TOXIC. SEE INFORMATION ON ORGANOPHOSPHATES.
ORGANOPHOSPHATES: CHOLINESTERASE INHIBITOR. **ACUTE EXPOSURE**- WHEN INGESTED, THE FIRST EFFECTS MAY BE NAUSEA, VOMITING, ANOREXIA, ABDOMINAL CRAMPS AND DIARRHEA. GASTROINTESTINAL ABSORPTION MAY CAUSE SYMPTOMS OF CHOLINESTERASE INHIBITION AS DESCRIBED IN ACUTE INHALATION. SYMPTOMS MAY BEGIN WITHIN MINUTES OR BE DELAYED FOR HOURS. DELAYED EFFECTS INCLUDING NEUROPATHY MAY ALSO OCCUR. **CHRONIC EXPOSURE**- REPEATED INGESTION MAY CAUSE EFFECTS AS DESCRIBED IN ACUTE EXPOSURE.
FIRST AID- IF PERSON IS ALERT AND RESPIRATION IS NOT DEPRESSED, GIVE SYRUP OF IPECAC FOLLOWED BY WATER (IF VOMITING OCCURS, KEEP HEAD BELOW HIPS TO PREVENT ASPIRATION). IF CONSCIOUSNESS LEVEL DECLINES OR VOMITING HAS NOT OCCURRED IN 15 MINUTES EMPTY STOMACH BY GASTRIC LAVAGE WITH THE AID OF CUFFED ENDOTRACHEAL TUBE USING ISOTONIC SALINE OR 5% SODIUM BICARBONATE FOLLOW WITH ACTIVATED CHARCOAL. ESTABLISH AND MAINTAIN AIRWAY. TREAT RESPIRATORY DIFFICULTY WITH ARTIFICIAL RESPIRATION AND OXYGEN. DO NOT GIVE MORPHINE, AMINOPHYLLINE, PHENOTHIAZINES, RESERPINE, FUROSEMIDE, OR ETHACRYNIC ACID (MORGAN, RECOGNITION AND MANAGEMENT OF PESTICIDE POISONINGS, 3RD ED.). TREAT SYMPTOMATICALLY AND SUPPORTIVELY. ADMINISTRATION OF OXYGEN AND LAVAGE MUST BE PERFORMED BY QUALIFIED MEDICAL PERSONNEL. GET MEDICAL ATTENTION IMMEDIATELY.
ANTIDOTE: THE FOLLOWING ANTIDOTE(S) HAVE BEEN RECOMMENDED. HOWEVER, THE DECISION AS TO WHETHER THE SEVERITY OF POISONING REQUIRES ADMINISTRATION OF ANY ANTIDOTE AND ACTUAL DOSE REQUIRED SHOULD BE MADE BY QUALIFIED MEDICAL PERSONNEL.
FOR CHOLINESTERASE INHIBITORS: ESTABLISH CLEAR AIRWAY AND TISSUE OXYGENATION BY ASPIRATION OF SECRETIONS, AND IF NECESSARY, BY ASSISTED PULMONARY VENTILATION WITH OXYGEN. IMPROVE TISSUE OXYGENATION AS MUCH AS POSSIBLE BEFORE ADMINISTERING ATROPINE TO MINIMIZE THE RISK OF VENTRICULAR FIBRILLATION. ADMINISTER ATROPINE SULFATE INTRAVENOUSLY, OR INTRAMUSCULARLY IF IV INJECTION IS NOT POSSIBLE. IN MODERATELY SEVERE POISONING ADMINISTER ATROPINE SULFATE, 0.4-2.0 MG REPEATED EVERY 15 MINUTES UNTIL ATROPINIZATION IS ACHIEVED (TACHYCARDIA, FLUSHING, DRY MOUTH, MYDRIASIS). MAINTAIN ATROPINIZATION BY REPEATED DOSES FOR 2-12 HOURS, OR LONGER, DEPENDING ON THE SEVERITY OF POISONING. THE APPEARANCE OF RALES IN THE LUNG BASES, MIOSIS, SALIVATION, NAUSEA, BRADYCARDIA, ARE ALL INDICATIONS OF INADEQUATE ATROPINIZATION. SEVERELY POISONED INDIVIDUALS MAY EXHIBIT REMARKABLE TOLERANCE TO ATROPINE; TWO OR MORE TIMES THE DOSAGES SUGGESTED ABOVE MAY BE NEEDED. PERSONS NOT POISONED OR ONLY SLIGHTLY POISONED, HOWEVER, MAY DEVELOP SIGNS OF ATROPINE TOXICITY FROM SUCH LARGE DOSAGES: FEVER, MUSCLE FIBRILLATIONS, AND DELIRIUM ARE THE MAIN SIGNS OF ATROPINE TOXICITY. IF THESE SIGNS APPEAR WHILE THE PATIENT IS FULLY ATROPINIZED, ATROPINE ADMINISTRATION SHOULD BE DISCONTINUED, AT LEAST TEMPORARILY. OBSERVE TREATED PATIENTS CLOSELY AT LEAST 24 HOURS TO INSURE THAT SYMPTOMS (POSSIBLY PULMONARY EDEMA) DO NOT RECUR AS ATROPINIZATION WEARS OFF. IN VERY SEVERE POISONINGS, METABOLIC DISPOSITION OF TOXICANT MAY REQUIRE SEVERAL HOURS OR DAYS DURING WHICH ATROPINIZATION MUST BE MAINTAINED. MARKEDLY LOWER LEVELS OF URINARY METABOLITES INDICATE THAT ATROPINE DOSAGE CAN BE TAPERED OFF. AS DOSAGE IS REDUCED, CHECK THE LUNG BASES FREQUENTLY FOR RALES. IF RALES ARE HEARD OR OTHER SYMPTOMS RETURN, RE-ESTABLISH ATROPINIZATION PROMPTLY (MORGAN, RECOGNITION AND MANAGEMENT OF PESTICIDE POISONINGS, 3RD ED.). ADMINISTRATION OF ANTIDOTE MUST BE PERFORMED BY QUALIFIED MEDICAL PERSONNEL.
IN CASES OF SEVERE POISONING BY ORGANOPHOSPHATE PESTICIDES IN WHICH RESPIRATORY DEPRESSION, MUSCLE WEAKNESS AND TWITCHINGS ARE SEVERE, GIVE PRALIDOXIME (PROTOPAM-AYERST, 2-PAM), 1.0 GRAM INTRAVENOUSLY AT NO MORE THAN 0.5 GRAM PER MINUTE. DOSAGE OF PRALIDOXIME MAY BE REPEATED IN 1-2 HOURS, THEN AT 10-12 HOUR INTERVALS IF NEEDED. IN VERY SEVERE POISONINGS, DOSAGE RATES MAY BE DOUBLED. TREATMENT WITH PRALIDOXIME WILL BE MOST EFFECTIVE IF GIVEN WITHIN THIRTY-SIX HOURS AFTER POISONING (MORGAN, RECOGNITION AND MANAGEMENT OF PESTICIDE POISONINGS, 3RD ED.). ANTIDOTE SHOULD BE ADMINISTERED BY QUALIFIED MEDICAL PERSONNEL.

REACTIVITY

REACTIVITY: STABLE UNDER NORMAL TEMPERATURES AND PRESSURES.
INCOMPATIBILITIES: PHORATE OXYGEN ANALOG SULFONE: OXIDIZERS (STRONG): FIRE AND EXPLOSION HAZARD.
DECOMPOSITION: THERMAL DECOMPOSITION PRODUCTS MAY INCLUDE TOXIC OXIDES OF CARBON, SULFUR, AND PHOSPHORUS.
POLYMERIZATION: HAZARDOUS POLYMERIZATION HAS NOT BEEN REPORTED TO OCCUR UNDER NORMAL TEMPERATURES AND PRESSURES.

STORAGE AND DISPOSAL

OBSERVE ALL FEDERAL, STATE AND LOCAL REGULATIONS WHEN STORING OR DISPOSING OF THIS SUBSTANCE. FOR ASSISTANCE, CONTACT THE DISTRICT DIRECTOR OF THE ENVIRONMENTAL PROTECTION AGENCY.

STORAGE

STORE IN ACCORDANCE WITH 40 CFR 165 RECOMMENDED PROCEDURES FOR THE DISPOSAL AND STORAGE OF PESTICIDES AND PESTICIDE CONTAINERS.
STORE AWAY FROM INCOMPATIBLE SUBSTANCES.

DISPOSAL

DISPOSAL MUST BE IN ACCORDANCE WITH 40 CFR 165 RECOMMENDED PROCEDURES FOR THE DISPOSAL AND STORAGE OF PESTICIDES AND PESTICIDE CONTAINERS.

CONDITIONS TO AVOID

AVOID CONTACT WITH HEAT, SPARKS, FLAMES OR OTHER IGNITION SOURCES. VAPORS MAY BE EXPLOSIVE. MATERIAL IS POISONOUS; AVOID INHALATION OF VAPORS OR CONTACT WITH SKIN. DO NOT ALLOW MATERIAL TO CONTAMINATE WATER SOURCES.

SPILL AND LEAK PROCEDURES

OCCUPATIONAL SPILL: SHUT OFF IGNITION SOURCES. DO NOT TOUCH SPILLED MATERIAL. STOP LEAK IF YOU CAN DO IT WITHOUT RISK. USE WATER SPRAY TO REDUCE VAPORS. FOR SMALL SPILLS, TAKE UP WITH SAND OR OTHER ABSORBENT MATERIAL AND PLACE INTO CONTAINERS FOR LATER DISPOSAL. FOR LARGER SPILLS, DIKE FAR AHEAD OF SPILL FOR LATER DISPOSAL. NO SMOKING, FLAMES OR FLARES IN HAZARD AREA! KEEP UNNECESSARY PEOPLE AWAY; ISOLATE HAZARD AREA AND DENY ENTRY.

PROTECTIVE EQUIPMENT

VENTILATION: PROVIDE LOCAL EXHAUST OR PROCESS ENCLOSURE VENTILATION. VENTILATION EQUIPMENT MUST BE EXPLOSION-PROOF.
RESPIRATOR: THE FOLLOWING RESPIRATORS ARE RECOMMENDED BASED ON INFORMATION FOUND IN THE PHYSICAL DATA, TOXICITY AND HEALTH EFFECTS

SECTIONS. THEY ARE RANKED IN ORDER FROM MINIMUM TO MAXIMUM RESPIRATORY PROTECTION. THE SPECIFIC RESPIRATOR SELECTED MUST BE BASED ON CONTAMINATION LEVELS FOUND IN THE WORK PLACE, MUST NOT EXCEED THE WORKING LIMITS OF THE RESPIRATOR AND BE JOINTLY APPROVED BY THE NATIONAL INSTITUTE FOR OCCUPATIONAL SAFETY AND HEALTH AND THE MINE SAFETY AND HEALTH ADMINISTRATION (NIOSH-MSHA).
TYPE 'C' SUPPLIED-AIR RESPIRATOR WITH A FULL FACEPIECE OPERATED IN PRESSURE-DEMAND OR OTHER POSITIVE PRESSURE MODE OR WITH A FULL FACEPIECE, HELMET OR HOOD OPERATED IN CONTINOUS-FLOW MODE.
SELF-CONTAINED BREATHING APPARATUS WITH A FULL FACEPIECE OPERATED IN PRESSURE-DEMAND OR OTHER POSITIVE PRESSURE MODE.
FOR FIREFIGHTING AND OTHER IMMEDIATELY DANGEROUS TO LIFE OR HEALTH CONDITIONS:
SELF-CONTAINED BREATHING APPARATUS WITH FULL FACEPIECE OPERATED IN PRESSURE-DEMAND OR OTHER POSITIVE PRESSURE MODE.
SUPPLIED-AIR RESPIRATOR WITH FULL FACEPIECE AND OPERATED IN PRESSURE-DEMAND OR OTHER POSITIVE PRESSURE MODE IN COMBINATION WITH AN AUXILIARY SELF-CONTAINED BREATHING APPARATUS OPERATED IN PRESSURE-DEMAND OR OTHER POSITIVE PRESSURE MODE.

CLOTHING: EMPLOYEE MUST WEAR APPROPRIATE PROTECTIVE (IMPERVIOUS) CLOTHING AND EQUIPMENT TO PREVENT ANY POSSIBILITY OF SKIN CONTACT WITH THIS SUBSTANCE.

GLOVES: EMPLOYEE MUST WEAR APPROPRIATE PROTECTIVE GLOVES TO PREVENT CONTACT WITH THIS SUBSTANCE.

EYE PROTECTION: EMPLOYEE MUST WEAR SPLASH-PROOF OR DUST-RESISTANT SAFETY GOGGLES TO PREVENT EYE CONTACT WITH THIS SUBSTANCE.
EMERGENCY EYE WASH: WHERE THERE IS ANY POSSIBILITY THAT AN EMPLOYEE'S EYES MAY BE EXPOSED TO THIS SUBSTANCE, THE EMPLOYER SHOULD PROVIDE AN EYE WASH FOUNTAIN WITHIN THE IMMEDIATE WORK AREA FOR EMERGENCY USE.

AUTHORIZED BY- OCCUPATIONAL HEALTH SERVICES, INC.
CREATION DATE: 10/04/89 ***REVISION DATE:*** 04/26/90

MATERIAL SAFETY DATA SHEET

OCCUPATIONAL HEALTH SERVICES, INC.
AGRICULTURE AND PESTICIDE DIVISION
450 SEVENTH AVENUE, SUITE 2407
NEW YORK, NEW YORK 10123
1-800-445-MSDS OR (212) 967-1100

EMERGENCY CONTACT:
JOHN S. BRANSFORD, JR. (615) 292-1180

SUBSTANCE IDENTIFICATION

CAS-NUMBER 2588-04-7

SUBSTANCE: **PHORATE SULFONE**

TRADE NAMES/SYNONYMS: PHOSPHORODITHIOIC ACID, O,O-DIETHYL S-((ETHYLSULFONYL)METHYL) ESTER; PHOSPHORODITHIOIC ACID, O,O-DIETHYL (ETHYLSULFONYL)METHYL ESTER; O,O-DIETHYL S-(ETHYLSULFONYL)METHYL PHOSPHORODITHIOATE; THIMET SULFONE; O,O-DIETHYL S-((ETHYLSULFONYLMETHYL) PHOSPHORODITHIOATE; C7H17O4PS3; PST18643

CHEMICAL FAMILY: ORGANOPHOSPHATE

MOLECULAR FORMULA: (C2-H5-O)2-P-(S)-S-C-H2-S-(O2)-C2-H5

MOLECULAR WEIGHT: 292.38

CERCLA RATINGS (SCALE 0-3): HEALTH=3 FIRE=U REACTIVITY=0 PERSISTENCE=1

NFPA RATINGS (SCALE 0-4): HEALTH=3 FIRE=U REACTIVITY=0

COMPONENTS AND CONTAMINANTS

COMPONENT: PHORATE SULFONE ***PERCENT:*** 100.0
CAS# 2588-04-7

OTHER CONTAMINANTS: NONE

EXPOSURE LIMITS: NO OCCUPATIONAL EXPOSURE LIMITS ESTABLISHED BY OSHA, ACGIH, OR NIOSH.

PHYSICAL DATA

DESCRIPTION: CLEAR LIQUID. ***BOILING POINT:*** NOT AVAILABLE

SPECIFIC GRAVITY: NOT AVAILABLE ***SOLUBILITY IN WATER:*** NOT AVAILABLE

VAPOR DENSITY: NOT AVAILABLE

FIRE AND EXPLOSION DATA

FIRE AND EXPLOSION HAZARD: UNKNOWN FIRE AND EXPLOSION HAZARD.

FLASH POINT: NOT AVAILABLE

FIREFIGHTING MEDIA: DRY CHEMICAL, CARBON DIOXIDE, HALON, WATER SPRAY OR STANDARD FOAM (1987 EMERGENCY RESPONSE GUIDEBOOK, DOT P 5800.4).
FOR LARGER FIRES, USE WATER SPRAY, FOG OR STANDARD FOAM (1987 EMERGENCY RESPONSE GUIDEBOOK, DOT P 5800.4).

FIREFIGHTING: MOVE CONTAINER FROM FIRE AREA IF POSSIBLE. DIKE FIRE CONTROL WATER FOR LATER DISPOSAL; DO NOT SCATTER THE MATERIAL. COOL FIRE-EXPOSED CONTAINERS WITH WATER FROM SIDE UNTIL WELL AFTER FIRE IS OUT. STAY AWAY FROM STORAGE TANK ENDS. WITHDRAW IMMEDIATELY IN CASE OF RISING SOUND FROM VENTING SAFETY DEVICE OR ANY DISCOLORATION OF STORAGE TANK DUE TO FIRE (1987 EMERGENCY RESPONSE GUIDEBOOK, DOT P 5800.4, GUIDE PAGE 28).
EXTINGUISH ONLY IF FLOW CAN BE STOPPED. USE FLOODING AMOUNTS OF WATER AS A FOG; SOLID STREAMS MAY BE INEFFECTIVE. COOL CONTAINERS WITH FLOODING AMOUNTS OF WATER FROM AS FAR A DISTANCE AS POSSIBLE. AVOID BREATHING POISONOUS VAPORS, KEEP UPWIND.

TRANSPORTATION DATA

DEPARTMENT OF TRANSPORTATION HAZARD CLASSIFICATION 49 CFR 172.101: POISON B
DEPARTMENT OF TRANSPORTATION LABELING REQUIREMENTS 49 CFR 172.101 AND SUBPART E: POISON
DEPARTMENT OF TRANSPORTATION PACKAGING REQUIREMENTS: 49 CFR 173.359 EXCEPTIONS: 49 CFR 173.359

TOXICITY

PHORATE SULFONE: TOXICITY DATA: 1700 UG/KG ORAL-RAT LD50. CARCINOGEN STATUS: NONE. ACUTE TOXICITY LEVEL: HIGHLY TOXIC BY INGESTION. TARGET EFFECTS: CHOLINESTERASE INHIBITOR. POISONING MAY AFFECT THE NERVOUS SYSTEM.* AT INCREASED RISK FROM EXPOSURE: PERSONS WITH RESPIRATORY AILMENTS, RECENT EXPOSURE TO CHOLINESTERASE INHIBITORS OR IMPAIRED CHOLINESTERASE PRODUCTION, OR LIVER MALFUNCTION.* ADDITIONAL DATA: MAY CROSS THE PLACENTA. HIGH ENVIRONMENTAL TEMPERATURES OR EXPOSURE OF THE CHEMICAL TO VISIBLE OR ULTRAVIOLET LIGHT MAY ENHANCE THE TOXICITY. INTERACTIONS WITH MEDICATIONS MAY OCCUR.*
* MAY BE BASED ON GENERAL INFORMATION ON ORGANOPHOSPHATES.

HEALTH EFFECTS AND FIRST AID

INHALATION: PHORATE SULFONE: SEE INFORMATION ON ORGANOPHOSPHATES.
ORGANOPHOSPHATES: CHOLINESTERASE INHIBITOR. **ACUTE EXPOSURE**- WHEN INHALED, THE FIRST EFFECTS OF CHOLINESTERASE INHIBITORS ARE USUALLY RESPIRATORY AND MAY INCLUDE NASAL HYPEREMIA AND WATERY DISCHARGE, COUGH, CHEST DISCOMFORT, DYSPNEA, AND WHEEZING DUE TO INCREASED BRONCHIAL SECRETIONS AND BRONCHOCONSTRICTION. IF SUFFICIENT AMOUNTS ARE ABSORBED, OTHER SYSTEMIC EFFECTS MAY BEGIN WITHIN A FEW MINUTES OR BE DELAYED FOR UP TO 12 HOURS. SYMPTOMS MAY INCLUDE PALLOR, NAUSEA, VOMITING, DIARRHEA, ABDOMINAL CRAMPS, HEADACHE, DIZZINESS, OCULAR PAIN, BLURRED VISION, MIOSIS OR IN SOME CASES, ESPECIALLY INITIALLY, MYDRIASIS, LACRIMATION, SALIVATION, SWEATING, AND CONFUSION. OTHER REPORTED CENTRAL NERVOUS SYSTEM OR NEUROMUSCULAR EFFECTS MAY INCLUDE ATAXIA, SLURRED SPEECH, AREFLEXIA, WEAKNESS, FATIGUE, FASCICULATIONS, TWITCHING, TREMORS POSSIBLY OF THE TONGUE AND EYELIDS, AND EVENTUALLY PARALYSIS OF THE EXTREMITIES AND POSSIBLY OF THE RESPIRATORY MUSCLES. IN SEVERE CASES THERE MAY ALSO BE INVOLUNTARY DEFECATION AND URINATION, CYANOSIS, PSYCHOSIS, HYPERGLYCEMIA, ACUTE PANCREATITIS, CARDIAC IRREGULARITIES, PULMONARY EDEMA, UNCONSCIOUSNESS, CONVULSIONS, AND COMA. DEATH IS PRIMARILY DUE TO RESPIRATORY FAILURE, ALTHOUGH CARDIOVASCULAR EFFECTS INCLUDING CARDIAC ARREST MAY ALSO BE IMPLICATED. LONG TERM SEQUELAE ARE RARE BUT MAY INCLUDE NEUROPSYCHIATRIC DISORDERS AND MYOPATHY WITH MUSCLE TENDERNESS. SOME ORGANOPHOSPHATES MAY CAUSE A DELAYED NEUROPATHY BEGINNING 1-4 WEEKS AFTER AN ACUTE EXPOSURE WHICH MAY OR MAY NOT HAVE CAUSED ACUTE CHOLINERGIC EFFECTS. NUMBNESS, TINGLING, WEAKNESS AND CRAMPING BEGINNING SYMMETRICALLY IN THE LOWER LIMBS MAY PROGRESS TO ATAXIA AND PARALYSIS. IN SEVERE CASES, UPPER LIMB INVOLVEMENT IS POSSIBLE AND FLACCID PARALYSIS MAY PROGRESS TO SPASTIC PARALYSIS WITH EXAGGERATED REFLEXES. IMPROVEMENT MAY OCCUR OVER MONTHS TO YEARS, BUT SOME RESIDUAL IMPAIRMENT USUALLY REMAINS.
CHRONIC EXPOSURE- REPEATED OR PROLONGED EXPOSURE MAY RESULT IN THE EFFECTS OF ACUTE EXPOSURE INCLUDING THE DELAYED NEUROPATHY. OTHER EFFECTS REPORTED IN WORKERS REPEATEDLY EXPOSED INCLUDE IMPAIRED MEMORY AND CONCENTRATION, ACUTE PSYCHOSIS, SEVERE DEPRESSIONS, IRRITABILTY, CONFUSION, APATHY, EMOTIONAL LABILITY, SOCIAL WITHDRAWAL, CONFUSION, HEADACHE, SPEECH DIFFICULTIES, DELAYED REACTION TIMES, SPATIAL DISORIENTATION, NIGHTMARES, SLEEPWALKING, AND DROWSINESS OR INSOMNIA. AN INFLUENZA-LIKE CONDITION WITH HEADACHE, NAUSEA,

WEAKNESS, ANOREXIA AND MALAISE HAS ALSO BEEN REPORTED.

FIRST AID- REMOVE FROM EXPOSURE AREA TO FRESH AIR IMMEDIATELY. IF BREATHING HAS STOPPED, GIVE ARTIFICIAL RESPIRATION. MAINTAIN AIRWAY AND BLOOD PRESSURE AND ADMINISTER OXYGEN IF AVAILABLE. KEEP AFFECTED PERSON WARM AND AT REST. TREAT SYMPTOMATICALLY AND SUPPORTIVELY. ADMINISTRATION OF OXYGEN SHOULD BE PERFORMED BY QUALIFIED PERSONNEL. GET MEDICAL ATTENTION IMMEDIATELY.

SKIN CONTACT: PHORATE: SEE INFORMATION ON ORGANOPHOSPHATES. ORGANOPHOSPHATES: CHOLINESTERASE INHIBITOR. **ACUTE EXPOSURE**- LOCALIZED SWEATING AND FASCICULATIONS MAY OCCUR AT THE SITE OF CONTACT. IF SUFFICIENT AMOUNTS ARE ABSORBED, OTHER EFFECTS OF CHOLINESTERASE INHIBITION AS DESCRIBED IN ACUTE INHALATION MAY OCCUR. SYMPTOMS MAY BE DELAYED 2-3 HOURS, BUT USUALLY NO MORE THAN 12 HOURS. THE RATE OF ABSORPTION IS INCREASED BY THE PRESENCE OF DERMATITIS OR HIGH AMBIENT TEMPERATURES. DELAYED NEUROPATHY IS ALSO POSSIBLE. **CHRONIC EXPOSURE**- REPEATED OR PROLONGED EXPOSURE MAY CAUSE EFFECTS AS DESCRIBED IN ACUTE EXPOSURE. SOME ORGANOPHOSPHATES MAY CAUSE SENSITIZATION.

FIRST AID- REMOVE CONTAMINATED CLOTHING IMMEDIATELY. WASH CONTAMINATED AREAS WITH SOAP AND WATER FOLLOWED BY ALCOHOL (ARENA, POISONING, 4TH ED.). EMERGENCY PERSONNEL SHOULD WEAR GLOVES AND AVOID CONTAMINATION. TREAT RESPIRATORY DIFFICULTY WITH ARTIFICIAL RESPIRATION. GET MEDICAL ATTENTION IMMEDIATELY.

EYE CONTACT: PHORATE SULFONE: SEE INFORMATION ON ORGANOPHOSPHATES. ORGANOPHOSPHATES: CHOLINESTERASE INHIBITOR. **ACUTE EXPOSURE**- DIRECT CONTACT MAY CAUSE PAIN, HYPEREMIA, LACRIMATION, TWITCHING OF THE EYELIDS, MIOSIS, AND CILIARY MUSCLE SPASM WITH LOSS OF ACCOMODATION, BLURRED OR DIMMED VISION AND BROWACHE. SOMETIMES MYDRIASIS MAY OCCUR INSTEAD OF MIOSIS. WITH SUFFICIENT EXPOSURE, OTHER SYMPTOMS OF CHOLINESTERASE INHIBITION AS DESCRIBED IN ACUTE INHALATION MAY OCCUR. **CHRONIC EXPOSURE**- REPEATED OR PROLONGED EXPOSURE MAY CAUSE EFFECTS AS DESCRIBED IN ACUTE EXPOSURE. SOME COMPOUNDS HAVE CAUSED TOXIC EFFECTS ON THE CRYSTALLINE LENS, CONJUNCTIVAL THICKENING AND OBSTRUCTION OF THE NASOLACRIMAL CANALS WHEN USED AS MIOTIC EYEDROPS.

FIRST AID- IRRIGATE EYES WITH WATER OR SALINE SOLUTION. IF SYMPTOMS OF POISONING OCCUR, TREAT RESPIRATORY DIFFICULTY WITH ARTIFICIAL RESPIRATION AND OXYGEN. OBSERVE PATIENT FOR AT LEAST 24-36 HOURS (GOSSELIN, CLINICAL TOXICOLOGY OF COMMERCIAL PRODUCTS, 5TH ED.). GET MEDICAL ATTENTION IMMEDIATELY. OXYGEN SHOULD BE ADMINISTERED BY QUALIFIED MEDICAL PERSONNEL.

INGESTION: PHORATE SULFONE: HIGHLY TOXIC. SEE INFORMATION ON ORGANOPHOSPHATES.
ORGANOPHOSPHATES: CHOLINESTERASE INHIBITOR. **ACUTE EXPOSURE**- WHEN INGESTED, THE FIRST EFFECTS MAY BE NAUSEA, VOMITING, ANOREXIA, ABDOMINAL CRAMPS AND DIARRHEA. GASTROINTESTINAL ABSORPTION MAY CAUSE SYMPTOMS OF CHOLINESTERASE INHIBITION AS DESCRIBED IN ACUTE INHALATION. SYMPTOMS MAY BEGIN WITHIN MINUTES OR BE DELAYED FOR HOURS. DELAYED EFFECTS INCLUDING NEUROPATHY MAY ALSO OCCUR. **CHRONIC EXPOSURE**- REPEATED INGESTION MAY CAUSE EFFECTS AS DESCRIBED IN ACUTE EXPOSURE.

FIRST AID- IF PERSON IS ALERT AND RESPIRATION IS NOT DEPRESSED, GIVE SYRUP OF IPECAC FOLLOWED BY WATER (IF VOMITING OCCURS, KEEP HEAD BELOW HIPS TO PREVENT ASPIRATION). IF CONSCIOUSNESS LEVEL DECLINES OR VOMITING HAS NOT OCCURRED IN 15 MINUTES EMPTY STOMACH BY GASTRIC LAVAGE WITH THE AID OF CUFFED ENDOTRACHEAL TUBE USING ISOTONIC SALINE OR 5% SODIUM BICARBONATE FOLLOW WITH ACTIVATED CHARCOAL. ESTABLISH AND MAINTAIN AIRWAY. TREAT RESPIRATORY DIFFICULTY WITH ARTIFICIAL RESPIRATION AND OXYGEN. DO NOT GIVE MORPHINE, AMINOPHYLLINE, PHENOTHIAZINES, RESERPINE, FUROSEMIDE, OR ETHACRYNIC ACID (MORGAN, RECOGNITION AND MANAGEMENT OF PESTICIDE POISONINGS, 3RD ED.). TREAT SYMPTOMATICALLY AND SUPPORTIVELY. ADMINISTRATION OF OXYGEN AND LAVAGE MUST BE PERFORMED BY QUALIFIED MEDICAL PERSONNEL. GET MEDICAL ATTENTION IMMEDIATELY.

ANTIDOTE: THE FOLLOWING ANTIDOTE(S) HAVE BEEN RECOMMENDED. HOWEVER, THE DECISION AS TO WHETHER THE SEVERITY OF POISONING REQUIRES ADMINISTRATION OF ANY ANTIDOTE AND ACTUAL DOSE REQUIRED SHOULD BE MADE BY QUALIFIED MEDICAL PERSONNEL.
FOR CHOLINESTERASE INHIBITORS: ESTABLISH CLEAR AIRWAY AND TISSUE OXYGENATION BY ASPIRATION OF SECRETIONS, AND IF NECESSARY, BY ASSISTED PULMONARY VENTILATION WITH OXYGEN. IMPROVE TISSUE OXYGENATION AS MUCH AS POSSIBLE BEFORE ADMINISTERING ATROPINE TO MINIMIZE THE RISK OF VENTRICULAR FIBRILLATION. ADMINISTER ATROPINE SULFATE INTRAVENOUSLY, OR INTRAMUSCULARLY IF IV INJECTION IS NOT POSSIBLE. IN MODERATELY SEVERE POISONING ADMINISTER ATROPINE SULFATE, 0.4-2.0 MG REPEATED EVERY 15 MINUTES UNTIL ATROPINIZATION IS ACHIEVED (TACHYCARDIA, FLUSHING, DRY MOUTH, MYDRIASIS). MAINTAIN ATROPINIZATION BY REPEATED DOSES FOR 2-12 HOURS, OR LONGER, DEPENDING ON THE SEVERITY OF POISONING. THE APPEARANCE OF RALES IN THE LUNG BASES, MIOSIS, SALIVATION, NAUSEA, BRADYCARDIA, ARE ALL INDICATIONS OF INADEQUATE ATROPINIZATION. SEVERELY POISONED INDIVIDUALS MAY EXHIBIT REMARKABLE TOLERANCE TO ATROPINE; TWO OR MORE TIMES THE DOSAGES SUGGESTED ABOVE MAY BE NEEDED. PERSONS NOT POISONED OR ONLY SLIGHTLY POISONED, HOWEVER, MAY DEVELOP SIGNS OF ATROPINE TOXICITY FROM SUCH LARGE DOSAGES: FEVER, MUSCLE FIBRILLATIONS, AND DELIRIUM ARE THE MAIN SIGNS OF ATROPINE TOXICITY. IF THESE SIGNS APPEAR WHILE THE PATIENT IS FULLY ATROPINIZED, ATROPINE ADMINISTRATION SHOULD BE DISCONTINUED, AT LEAST TEMPORARILY. OBSERVE TREATED PATIENTS CLOSELY AT LEAST 24 HOURS TO INSURE THAT SYMPTOMS (POSSIBLY PULMONARY EDEMA) DO NOT RECUR AS ATROPINIZATION WEARS OFF. IN VERY SEVERE POISONINGS, METABOLIC DISPOSITION OF TOXICANT MAY REQUIRE SEVERAL HOURS OR DAYS DURING WHICH ATROPINIZATION MUST BE MAINTAINED. MARKEDLY LOWER LEVELS OF URINARY METABOLITES INDICATE THAT ATROPINE DOSAGE CAN BE TAPERED OFF. AS DOSAGE IS REDUCED, CHECK THE LUNG BASES FREQUENTLY FOR RALES. IF RALES ARE HEARD OR OTHER SYMPTOMS RETURN, RE-ESTABLISH ATROPINIZATION PROMPTLY (MORGAN, RECOGNITION AND MANAGEMENT OF PESTICIDE POISONINGS, 3RD ED.). ADMINISTRATION OF ANTIDOTE MUST BE PERFORMED BY QUALIFIED MEDICAL PERSONNEL.
IN CASES OF SEVERE POISONING BY ORGANOPHOSPHATE PESTICIDES IN WHICH RESPIRATORY DEPRESSION, MUSCLE WEAKNESS AND TWITCHINGS ARE SEVERE, GIVE PRALIDOXIME (PROTOPAM-AYERST, 2-PAM), 1.0 GRAM INTRAVENOUSLY AT NO MORE THAN 0.5 GRAM PER MINUTE. DOSAGE OF PRALIDOXIME MAY BE REPEATED IN 1-2 HOURS, THEN AT 10-12 HOUR INTERVALS IF NEEDED. IN VERY SEVERE POISONINGS, DOSAGE RATES MAY BE DOUBLED. TREATMENT WITH PRALIDOXIME WILL BE MOST EFFECTIVE IF GIVEN WITHIN THIRTY-SIX HOURS AFTER POISONING (MORGAN, RECOGNITION AND MANAGEMENT OF PESTICIDE POISONINGS, 3RD ED.). ANTIDOTE SHOULD BE ADMINISTERED BY QUALIFIED MEDICAL PERSONNEL.

REACTIVITY

REACTIVITY: STABLE UNDER NORMAL TEMPERATURES AND PRESSURES.

INCOMPATIBILITIES: PHORATE SULFONE: OXIDIZERS (STRONG): FIRE AND EXPLOSION HAZARD.

DECOMPOSITION: THERMAL DECOMPOSITION PRODUCTS MAY INCLUDE TOXIC OXIDES OF CARBON, SULFUR, AND PHOSPHORUS.

POLYMERIZATION: HAZARDOUS POLYMERIZATION HAS NOT BEEN REPORTED TO OCCUR UNDER NORMAL TEMPERATURES AND PRESSURES.

STORAGE AND DISPOSAL

OBSERVE ALL FEDERAL, STATE AND LOCAL REGULATIONS WHEN STORING OR DISPOSING OF THIS SUBSTANCE. FOR ASSISTANCE, CONTACT THE DISTRICT DIRECTOR OF THE ENVIRONMENTAL PROTECTION AGENCY.

****STORAGE****

STORE IN ACCORDANCE WITH 40 CFR 165 RECOMMENDED PROCEDURES FOR THE DISPOSAL AND STORAGE OF PESTICIDES AND PESTICIDE CONTAINERS.
STORE AWAY FROM INCOMPATIBLE SUBSTANCES.

****DISPOSAL****

DISPOSAL MUST BE IN ACCORDANCE WITH 40 CFR 165 RECOMMENDED PROCEDURES FOR THE DISPOSAL AND STORAGE OF PESTICIDES AND PESTICIDE CONTAINERS.

CONDITIONS TO AVOID

AVOID CONTACT WITH HEAT, SPARKS, FLAMES OR OTHER IGNITION SOURCES. VAPORS MAY BE EXPLOSIVE. MATERIAL IS POISONOUS; AVOID INHALATION OF VAPORS OR CONTACT WITH SKIN. DO NOT ALLOW MATERIAL TO CONTAMINATE WATER SOURCES.

SPILL AND LEAK PROCEDURES

OCCUPATIONAL SPILL: SHUT OFF IGNITION SOURCES. DO NOT TOUCH SPILLED MATERIAL. STOP LEAK IF YOU CAN DO IT WITHOUT RISK. USE WATER SPRAY TO REDUCE VAPORS. FOR SMALL SPILLS, TAKE UP WITH SAND OR OTHER ABSORBENT MATERIAL AND PLACE INTO CONTAINERS FOR LATER DISPOSAL. FOR LARGER SPILLS, DIKE FAR AHEAD OF SPILL FOR LATER DISPOSAL. NO SMOKING, FLAMES OR FLARES IN HAZARD AREA! KEEP UNNECESSARY PEOPLE AWAY; ISOLATE HAZARD AREA AND DENY ENTRY.

PROTECTIVE EQUIPMENT

VENTILATION: PROVIDE LOCAL EXHAUST OR PROCESS ENCLOSURE VENTILATION. VENTILATION EQUIPMENT MUST BE EXPLOSION-PROOF.

RESPIRATOR: THE FOLLOWING RESPIRATORS ARE RECOMMENDED BASED ON INFORMATION FOUND IN THE PHYSICAL DATA, TOXICITY AND HEALTH EFFECTS SECTIONS. THEY ARE RANKED IN ORDER FROM MINIMUM TO MAXIMUM RESPIRATORY PROTECTION. THE SPECIFIC RESPIRATOR SELECTED MUST BE BASED ON CONTAMINATION LEVELS FOUND IN THE WORK PLACE, MUST NOT EXCEED THE WORKING LIMITS OF THE RESPIRATOR AND BE JOINTLY APPROVED BY THE NATIONAL INSTITUTE FOR OCCUPATIONAL SAFETY AND HEALTH AND THE MINE SAFETY AND HEALTH ADMINISTRATION (NIOSH-MSHA).
TYPE 'C' SUPPLIED-AIR RESPIRATOR WITH A FULL FACEPIECE OPERATED IN PRESSURE-DEMAND OR OTHER POSITIVE PRESSURE MODE OR WITH A FULL FACEPIECE, HELMET OR HOOD OPERATED IN CONTINOUS-FLOW MODE.
SELF-CONTAINED BREATHING APPARATUS WITH A FULL FACEPIECE OPERATED IN PRESSURE-DEMAND OR OTHER POSITIVE PRESSURE MODE.
FOR FIREFIGHTING AND OTHER IMMEDIATELY DANGEROUS TO LIFE OR HEALTH CONDITIONS:
SELF-CONTAINED BREATHING APPARATUS WITH FULL FACEPIECE OPERATED IN PRESSURE-DEMAND OR OTHER POSITIVE PRESSURE MODE.
SUPPLIED-AIR RESPIRATOR WITH FULL FACEPIECE AND OPERATED IN PRESSURE-DEMAND OR OTHER POSITIVE PRESSURE MODE IN COMBINATION WITH AN AUXILIARY SELF-CONTAINED BREATHING APPARATUS OPERATED IN PRESSURE-DEMAND OR OTHER POSITIVE PRESSURE MODE.

CLOTHING: EMPLOYEE MUST WEAR APPROPRIATE PROTECTIVE (IMPERVIOUS) CLOTHING AND EQUIPMENT TO PREVENT ANY POSSIBILITY OF SKIN CONTACT WITH THIS SUBSTANCE.

GLOVES: EMPLOYEE MUST WEAR APPROPRIATE PROTECTIVE GLOVES TO PREVENT CONTACT WITH THIS SUBSTANCE.

EYE PROTECTION: EMPLOYEE MUST WEAR SPLASH-PROOF OR DUST-RESISTANT SAFETY GOGGLES TO PREVENT EYE CONTACT WITH THIS SUBSTANCE.
EMERGENCY EYE WASH: WHERE THERE IS ANY POSSIBILITY THAT AN EMPLOYEE'S EYES MAY BE EXPOSED TO THIS SUBSTANCE, THE EMPLOYER SHOULD PROVIDE AN EYE WASH FOUNTAIN WITHIN THE IMMEDIATE WORK AREA FOR EMERGENCY USE.

AUTHORIZED BY- OCCUPATIONAL HEALTH SERVICES, INC.
CREATION DATE: 10/04/89 ***REVISION DATE:*** 04/26/90

MATERIAL SAFETY DATA SHEET

OCCUPATIONAL HEALTH SERVICES, INC.
AGRICULTURE AND PESTICIDE DIVISION
450 SEVENTH AVENUE, SUITE 2407
NEW YORK, NEW YORK 10123
1-800-445-MSDS OR (212) 967-1100

EMERGENCY CONTACT:
JOHN S. BRANSFORD, JR. (615) 292-1180

SUBSTANCE IDENTIFICATION

CAS-NUMBER 2588-05-8

SUBSTANCE: PHORATOXON SULFOXIDE

TRADE NAMES/SYNONYMS: PHOSPHOROTHIOIC ACID, O,O-DIETHYL S-((ETHYLSULFINYL)METHYL)ESTER; PHORATE OXON SULFOXIDE; PHORATE OXYGEN ANALOG SULFOXIDE; O,O-DIMETHYL S-(ETHYLSULFINYLMETHYL) PHOSPHOROTHIOATE; THIMET O.A. SULFOXIDE; THIMET OXYGEN ANALOG SULFOXIDE; PHORATE O.A. SULFOXIDE; C7H17O4PS2; PST18644

CHEMICAL FAMILY: ORGANOPHOSPHATE

MOLECULAR FORMULA: (C2-H5-O)2-P(O)-S-C-H2-S(O)-C2-H5

MOLECULAR WEIGHT: 260.31

CERCLA RATINGS (SCALE 0-3): HEALTH=3 FIRE=U REACTIVITY=0 PERSISTENCE=1

NFPA RATINGS (SCALE 0-4): HEALTH=3 FIRE=U REACTIVITY=0

COMPONENTS AND CONTAMINANTS

COMPONENT: PHORATOXON SULFOXIDE ***PERCENT:*** 100.0
CAS# 2588-05-8

OTHER CONTAMINANTS: NONE

EXPOSURE LIMITS: NO OCCUPATIONAL EXPOSURE LIMITS ESTABLISHED BY OSHA, ACGIH, OR NIOSH.

PHYSICAL DATA

DESCRIPTION: CLEAR LIQUID. ***BOILING POINT:*** NOT AVAILABLE
SPECIFIC GRAVITY: NOT AVAILABLE ***SOLUBILITY IN WATER:*** NOT AVAILABLE

FIRE AND EXPLOSION DATA

FIRE AND EXPLOSION HAZARD: UNKNOWN FIRE AND EXPLOSION HAZARD.

FLASH POINT: NOT AVAILABLE

FIREFIGHTING MEDIA: DRY CHEMICAL, CARBON DIOXIDE, HALON, WATER SPRAY OR STANDARD FOAM (1987 EMERGENCY RESPONSE GUIDEBOOK, DOT P 5800.4).
FOR LARGER FIRES, USE WATER SPRAY, FOG OR STANDARD FOAM (1987 EMERGENCY RESPONSE GUIDEBOOK, DOT P 5800.4).

FIREFIGHTING: MOVE CONTAINER FROM FIRE AREA IF POSSIBLE. DIKE FIRE CONTROL WATER FOR LATER DISPOSAL; DO NOT SCATTER THE MATERIAL. COOL FIRE-EXPOSED CONTAINERS WITH WATER FROM SIDE UNTIL WELL AFTER FIRE IS OUT. STAY AWAY FROM STORAGE TANK ENDS. WITHDRAW IMMEDIATELY IN CASE OF RISING SOUND FROM VENTING SAFETY DEVICE OR ANY DISCOLORATION OF STORAGE TANK DUE TO FIRE (1987 EMERGENCY RESPONSE GUIDEBOOK, DOT P 5800.4, GUIDE PAGE 28).
EXTINGUISH ONLY IF FLOW CAN BE STOPPED. USE FLOODING AMOUNTS OF WATER AS A FOG; SOLID STREAMS MAY BE INEFFECTIVE. COOL CONTAINERS WITH FLOODING AMOUNTS OF WATER FROM AS FAR A DISTANCE AS POSSIBLE. AVOID BREATHING POISONOUS VAPORS, KEEP UPWIND.

TRANSPORTATION DATA

DEPARTMENT OF TRANSPORTATION HAZARD CLASSIFICATION 49 CFR 172.101: POISON B
DEPARTMENT OF TRANSPORTATION LABELING REQUIREMENTS 49 CFR 172.101 AND SUBPART E: POISON
DEPARTMENT OF TRANSPORTATION PACKAGING REQUIREMENTS: 49 CFR 173.365 EXCEPTIONS: 49 CFR 173.364

TOXICITY

PHORATOXON SULFOXIDE: TOXICITY DATA: 1 MG/KG ORAL-RAT LD50. CARCINOGEN STATUS: NONE. ACUTE TOXICITY LEVEL: HIGHLY TOXIC BY INGESTION. TARGET EFFECTS: CHOLINESTERASE INHIBITOR. POISONING MAY AFFECT THE NERVOUS SYSTEM.* AT INCREASED RISK FROM EXPOSURE: PERSONS WITH RESPIRATORY AILMENTS, RECENT EXPOSURE TO CHOLINESTERASE INHIBITORS OR IMPAIRED CHOLINESTERASE PRODUCTION, OR LIVER MALFUNCTION.* ADDITIONAL DATA: MAY CROSS THE PLACENTA. HIGH ENVIRONMENTAL TEMPERATURES OR EXPOSURE OF THE CHEMICAL TO VISIBLE OR ULTRAVIOLET LIGHT MAY ENHANCE THE TOXICITY. INTERACTIONS WITH MEDICATIONS MAY OCCUR.*
* MAY BE BASED ON GENERAL INFORMATION ON ORGANOPHOSPHATES.

HEALTH EFFECTS AND FIRST AID

INHALATION: PHORATOXON SULFOXIDE: SEE INFORMATION ON ORGANOPHOSPHATES.
ORGANOPHOSPHATES: CHOLINESTERASE INHIBITOR. **ACUTE EXPOSURE**- WHEN INHALED, THE FIRST EFFECTS OF CHOLINESTERASE INHIBITORS ARE USUALLY RESPIRATORY AND MAY INCLUDE NASAL HYPEREMIA AND WATERY DISCHARGE, COUGH, CHEST DISCOMFORT, DYSPNEA, AND WHEEZING DUE TO INCREASED BRONCHIAL SECRETIONS AND BRONCHOCONSTRICTION. IF SUFFICIENT AMOUNTS ARE ABSORBED, OTHER SYSTEMIC EFFECTS MAY BEGIN WITHIN A FEW MINUTES OR BE DELAYED FOR UP TO 12 HOURS. SYMPTOMS MAY INCLUDE PALLOR, NAUSEA, VOMITING, DIARRHEA, ABDOMINAL CRAMPS, HEADACHE, DIZZINESS, OCULAR PAIN, BLURRED VISION, MIOSIS OR IN SOME CASES, ESPECIALLY INITIALLY, MYDRIASIS, LACRIMATION, SALIVATION, SWEATING, AND CONFUSION. OTHER REPORTED CENTRAL NERVOUS SYSTEM OR NEUROMUSCULAR EFFECTS MAY INCLUDE ATAXIA, SLURRED SPEECH, AREFLEXIA, WEAKNESS, FATIGUE, FASCICULATIONS, TWITCHING, TREMORS POSSIBLY OF THE TONGUE AND EYELIDS, AND EVENTUALLY PARALYSIS OF THE EXTREMITIES AND POSSIBLY OF THE RESPIRATORY MUSCLES. IN SEVERE CASES THERE MAY ALSO BE INVOLUNTARY DEFECATION AND URINATION, CYANOSIS, PSYCHOSIS, HYPERGLYCEMIA, ACUTE PANCREATITIS, CARDIAC IRREGULARITIES, PULMONARY EDEMA, UNCONSCIOUSNESS, CONVULSIONS, AND COMA. DEATH IS PRIMARILY DUE TO RESPIRATORY FAILURE, ALTHOUGH CARDIOVASCULAR EFFECTS INCLUDING CARDIAC ARREST MAY ALSO BE IMPLICATED. LONG TERM SEQUELAE ARE RARE BUT MAY INCLUDE NEUROPSYCHIATRIC DISORDERS AND MYOPATHY WITH MUSCLE TENDERNESS. SOME ORGANOPHOSPHATES MAY CAUSE A DELAYED NEUROPATHY BEGINNING 1-4 WEEKS AFTER AN ACUTE EXPOSURE WHICH MAY OR MAY NOT HAVE CAUSED ACUTE CHOLINERGIC EFFECTS. NUMBNESS, TINGLING, WEAKNESS AND CRAMPING BEGINNING SYMMETRICALLY IN THE LOWER LIMBS MAY PROGRESS TO ATAXIA AND PARALYSIS. IN SEVERE CASES, UPPER LIMB INVOLVEMENT IS POSSIBLE AND FLACCID PARALYSIS MAY PROGRESS TO SPASTIC PARALYSIS WITH EXAGGERATED REFLEXES. IMPROVEMENT MAY OCCUR OVER MONTHS TO YEARS, BUT SOME RESIDUAL IMPAIRMENT USUALLY REMAINS.
CHRONIC EXPOSURE- REPEATED OR PROLONGED EXPOSURE MAY RESULT IN THE EFFECTS OF ACUTE EXPOSURE INCLUDING THE DELAYED NEUROPATHY. OTHER EFFECTS REPORTED IN WORKERS REPEATEDLY EXPOSED INCLUDE IMPAIRED MEMORY AND CONCENTRATION, ACUTE PSYCHOSIS, SEVERE DEPRESSIONS, IRRITABILTY, CONFUSION, APATHY, EMOTIONAL LABILITY, SOCIAL WITHDRAWAL,

CONFUSION, HEADACHE, SPEECH DIFFICULTIES, DELAYED REACTION TIMES, SPATIAL DISORIENTATION, NIGHTMARES, SLEEPWALKING, AND DROWSINESS OR INSOMNIA. AN INFLUENZA-LIKE CONDITION WITH HEADACHE, NAUSEA, WEAKNESS, ANOREXIA AND MALAISE HAS ALSO BEEN REPORTED.

FIRST AID- REMOVE FROM EXPOSURE AREA TO FRESH AIR IMMEDIATELY. IF BREATHING HAS STOPPED, GIVE ARTIFICIAL RESPIRATION. MAINTAIN AIRWAY AND BLOOD PRESSURE AND ADMINISTER OXYGEN IF AVAILABLE. KEEP AFFECTED PERSON WARM AND AT REST. TREAT SYMPTOMATICALLY AND SUPPORTIVELY. ADMINISTRATION OF OXYGEN SHOULD BE PERFORMED BY QUALIFIED PERSONNEL. GET MEDICAL ATTENTION IMMEDIATELY.

SKIN CONTACT: PHORATOXON SULFOXIDE: SEE INFORMATION ON ORGANOPHOSPHATES.

ORGANOPHOSPHATES: CHOLINESTERASE INHIBITOR. **ACUTE EXPOSURE**- LOCALIZED SWEATING AND FASCICULATIONS MAY OCCUR AT THE SITE OF CONTACT. IF SUFFICIENT AMOUNTS ARE ABSORBED, OTHER EFFECTS OF CHOLINESTERASE INHIBITION AS DESCRIBED IN ACUTE INHALATION MAY OCCUR. SYMPTOMS MAY BE DELAYED 2-3 HOURS, BUT USUALLY NO MORE THAN 12 HOURS. THE RATE OF ABSORPTION IS INCREASED BY THE PRESENCE OF DERMATITIS OR HIGH AMBIENT TEMPERATURES. DELAYED NEUROPATHY IS ALSO POSSIBLE. **CHRONIC EXPOSURE**- REPEATED OR PROLONGED EXPOSURE MAY CAUSE EFFECTS AS DESCRIBED IN ACUTE EXPOSURE. SOME ORGANOPHOSPHATES MAY CAUSE SENSITIZATION.

FIRST AID- REMOVE CONTAMINATED CLOTHING IMMEDIATELY. WASH CONTAMINATED AREAS WITH SOAP AND WATER FOLLOWED BY ALCOHOL (ARENA, POISONING, 4TH ED.). EMERGENCY PERSONNEL SHOULD WEAR GLOVES AND AVOID CONTAMINATION. TREAT RESPIRATORY DIFFICULTY WITH ARTIFICIAL RESPIRATION. GET MEDICAL ATTENTION IMMEDIATELY.

EYE CONTACT: PHORATOXON SULFOXIDE: SEE INFORMATION ON ORGANOPHOSPHATES.

ORGANOPHOSPHATES: CHOLINESTERASE INHIBITOR. **ACUTE EXPOSURE**- DIRECT CONTACT MAY CAUSE PAIN, HYPEREMIA, LACRIMATION, TWITCHING OF THE EYELIDS, MIOSIS, AND CILIARY MUSCLE SPASM WITH LOSS OF ACCOMODATION, BLURRED OR DIMMED VISION AND BROWACHE. SOMETIMES MYDRIASIS MAY OCCUR INSTEAD OF MIOSIS. WITH SUFFICIENT EXPOSURE, OTHER SYMPTOMS OF CHOLINESTERASE INHIBITION AS DESCRIBED IN ACUTE INHALATION MAY OCCUR. **CHRONIC EXPOSURE**- REPEATED OR PROLONGED EXPOSURE MAY CAUSE EFFECTS AS DESCRIBED IN ACUTE EXPOSURE. SOME COMPOUNDS HAVE CAUSED TOXIC EFFECTS ON THE CRYSTALLINE LENS, CONJUNCTIVAL THICKENING AND OBSTRUCTION OF THE NASOLACRIMAL CANALS WHEN USED AS MIOTIC EYEDROPS.

FIRST AID- IRRIGATE EYES WITH WATER OR SALINE SOLUTION. IF SYMPTOMS OF POISONING OCCUR, TREAT RESPIRATORY DIFFICULTY WITH ARTIFICIAL RESPIRATION AND OXYGEN. OBSERVE PATIENT FOR AT LEAST 24-36 HOURS (GOSSELIN, CLINICAL TOXICOLOGY OF COMMERCIAL PRODUCTS, 5TH ED.). GET MEDICAL ATTENTION IMMEDIATELY. OXYGEN SHOULD BE ADMINISTERED BY QUALIFIED MEDICAL PERSONNEL.

INGESTION: PHORATOXON SULFOXIDE: HIGHLY TOXIC. SEE INFORMATION ON ORGANOPHOSPHATES.

ORGANOPHOSPHATES: CHOLINESTERASE INHIBITOR. **ACUTE EXPOSURE**- WHEN INGESTED, THE FIRST EFFECTS MAY BE NAUSEA, VOMITING, ANOREXIA, ABDOMINAL CRAMPS AND DIARRHEA. GASTROINTESTINAL ABSORPTION MAY CAUSE SYMPTOMS OF CHOLINESTERASE INHIBITION AS DESCRIBED IN ACUTE INHALATION. SYMPTOMS MAY BEGIN WITHIN MINUTES OR BE DELAYED FOR HOURS. DELAYED EFFECTS INCLUDING NEUROPATHY MAY ALSO OCCUR. **CHRONIC EXPOSURE**- REPEATED INGESTION MAY CAUSE EFFECTS AS DESCRIBED IN ACUTE EXPOSURE.

FIRST AID- IF PERSON IS ALERT AND RESPIRATION IS NOT DEPRESSED, GIVE SYRUP OF IPECAC FOLLOWED BY WATER (IF VOMITING OCCURS, KEEP HEAD BELOW HIPS TO PREVENT ASPIRATION). IF CONSCIOUSNESS LEVEL DECLINES OR VOMITING HAS NOT OCCURRED IN 15 MINUTES EMPTY STOMACH BY GASTRIC LAVAGE WITH THE AID OF CUFFED ENDOTRACHEAL TUBE USING ISOTONIC SALINE OR 5% SODIUM BICARBONATE FOLLOW WITH ACTIVATED CHARCOAL. ESTABLISH AND MAINTAIN AIRWAY. TREAT RESPIRATORY DIFFICULTY WITH ARTIFICIAL RESPIRATION AND OXYGEN. DO NOT GIVE MORPHINE, AMINOPHYLLINE, PHENOTHIAZINES, RESERPINE, FUROSEMIDE, OR ETHACRYNIC ACID (MORGAN, RECOGNITION AND MANAGEMENT OF PESTICIDE POISONINGS, 3RD ED.). TREAT SYMPTOMATICALLY AND SUPPORTIVELY. ADMINISTRATION OF OXYGEN AND LAVAGE MUST BE PERFORMED BY QUALIFIED MEDICAL PERSONNEL. GET MEDICAL ATTENTION IMMEDIATELY.

ANTIDOTE: THE FOLLOWING ANTIDOTE(S) HAVE BEEN RECOMMENDED. HOWEVER, THE DECISION AS TO WHETHER THE SEVERITY OF POISONING REQUIRES ADMINISTRATION OF ANY ANTIDOTE AND ACTUAL DOSE REQUIRED SHOULD BE MADE BY QUALIFIED MEDICAL PERSONNEL.

FOR CHOLINESTERASE INHIBITORS: ESTABLISH CLEAR AIRWAY AND TISSUE OXYGENATION BY ASPIRATION OF SECRETIONS, AND IF NECESSARY, BY ASSISTED PULMONARY VENTILATION WITH OXYGEN. IMPROVE TISSUE OXYGENATION AS MUCH AS POSSIBLE BEFORE ADMINISTERING ATROPINE TO MINIMIZE THE RISK OF VENTRICULAR FIBRILLATION. ADMINISTER ATROPINE SULFATE INTRAVENOUSLY, OR INTRAMUSCULARLY IF IV INJECTION IS NOT POSSIBLE. IN MODERATELY SEVERE POISONING ADMINISTER ATROPINE SULFATE, 0.4-2.0 MG REPEATED EVERY 15 MINUTES UNTIL ATROPINIZATION IS ACHIEVED (TACHYCARDIA, FLUSHING, DRY MOUTH, MYDRIASIS). MAINTAIN ATROPINIZATION BY REPEATED DOSES FOR 2-12 HOURS, OR LONGER, DEPENDING ON THE SEVERITY OF POISONING. THE APPEARANCE OF RALES IN THE LUNG BASES, MIOSIS, SALIVATION, NAUSEA, BRADYCARDIA, ARE ALL INDICATIONS OF INADEQUATE ATROPINIZATION. SEVERELY POISONED INDIVIDUALS MAY EXHIBIT REMARKABLE TOLERANCE TO ATROPINE; TWO OR MORE TIMES THE DOSAGES SUGGESTED ABOVE MAY BE NEEDED. PERSONS NOT POISONED OR ONLY SLIGHTLY POISONED, HOWEVER, MAY DEVELOP SIGNS OF ATROPINE TOXICITY FROM SUCH LARGE DOSAGES: FEVER, MUSCLE FIBRILLATIONS, AND DELIRIUM ARE THE MAIN SIGNS OF ATROPINE TOXICITY. IF THESE SIGNS APPEAR WHILE THE PATIENT IS FULLY ATROPINIZED, ATROPINE ADMINISTRATION SHOULD BE DISCONTINUED, AT LEAST TEMPORARILY. OBSERVE TREATED PATIENTS CLOSELY AT LEAST 24 HOURS TO INSURE THAT SYMPTOMS (POSSIBLY PULMONARY EDEMA) DO NOT RECUR AS ATROPINIZATION WEARS OFF. IN VERY SEVERE POISONINGS, METABOLIC DISPOSITION OF TOXICANT MAY REQUIRE SEVERAL HOURS OR DAYS DURING WHICH ATROPINIZATION MUST BE MAINTAINED. MARKEDLY LOWER LEVELS OF URINARY METABOLITES INDICATE THAT ATROPINE DOSAGE CAN BE TAPERED OFF. AS DOSAGE IS REDUCED, CHECK THE LUNG BASES FREQUENTLY FOR RALES. IF RALES ARE HEARD OR OTHER SYMPTOMS RETURN, RE-ESTABLISH ATROPINIZATION PROMPTLY (MORGAN, RECOGNITION AND MANAGEMENT OF PESTICIDE POISONINGS, 3RD ED.). ADMINISTRATION OF ANTIDOTE MUST BE PERFORMED BY QUALIFIED MEDICAL PERSONNEL.

IN CASES OF SEVERE POISONING BY ORGANOPHOSPHATE PESTICIDES IN WHICH RESPIRATORY DEPRESSION, MUSCLE WEAKNESS AND TWITCHINGS ARE SEVERE, GIVE PRALIDOXIME (PROTOPAM-AYERST, 2-PAM), 1.0 GRAM INTRAVENOUSLY AT NO MORE THAN 0.5 GRAM PER MINUTE. DOSAGE OF PRALIDOXIME MAY BE REPEATED IN 1-2 HOURS, THEN AT 10-12 HOUR INTERVALS IF NEEDED. IN VERY SEVERE POISONINGS, DOSAGE RATES MAY BE DOUBLED. TREATMENT WITH PRALIDOXIME WILL BE MOST EFFECTIVE IF GIVEN WITHIN THIRTY-SIX HOURS AFTER POISONING (MORGAN, RECOGNITION AND MANAGEMENT OF PESTICIDE POISONINGS, 3RD ED.). ANTIDOTE SHOULD BE ADMINISTERED BY QUALIFIED MEDICAL PERSONNEL.

REACTIVITY

REACTIVITY: STABLE UNDER NORMAL TEMPERATURES AND PRESSURES.

INCOMPATIBILITIES: PHORATOXON SULFOXIDE: OXIDIZERS (STRONG): FIRE AND EXPLOSION HAZARD.

DECOMPOSITION: THERMAL DECOMPOSITION PRODUCTS MAY INCLUDE TOXIC OXIDES OF CARBON, SULFUR, AND PHOSPHORUS.

POLYMERIZATION: HAZARDOUS POLYMERIZATION HAS NOT BEEN REPORTED TO OCCUR UNDER NORMAL TEMPERATURES AND PRESSURES.

STORAGE AND DISPOSAL

OBSERVE ALL FEDERAL, STATE AND LOCAL REGULATIONS WHEN STORING OR DISPOSING OF THIS SUBSTANCE. FOR ASSISTANCE, CONTACT THE DISTRICT DIRECTOR OF THE ENVIRONMENTAL PROTECTION AGENCY.

****STORAGE****

STORE IN ACCORDANCE WITH 40 CFR 165 RECOMMENDED PROCEDURES FOR THE DISPOSAL AND STORAGE OF PESTICIDES AND PESTICIDE CONTAINERS. STORE AWAY FROM INCOMPATIBLE SUBSTANCES.

****DISPOSAL****

DISPOSAL MUST BE IN ACCORDANCE WITH 40 CFR 165 RECOMMENDED PROCEDURES FOR THE DISPOSAL AND STORAGE OF PESTICIDES AND PESTICIDE CONTAINERS.

CONDITIONS TO AVOID

AVOID CONTACT WITH HEAT, SPARKS, FLAMES OR OTHER IGNITION SOURCES. VAPORS MAY BE EXPLOSIVE. MATERIAL IS POISONOUS; AVOID INHALATION OF VAPORS OR CONTACT WITH SKIN. DO NOT ALLOW MATERIAL TO CONTAMINATE WATER SOURCES.

SPILL AND LEAK PROCEDURES

OCCUPATIONAL SPILL: SHUT OFF IGNITION SOURCES. DO NOT TOUCH SPILLED MATERIAL. STOP LEAK IF YOU CAN DO IT WITHOUT RISK. USE WATER SPRAY TO REDUCE VAPORS. FOR SMALL SPILLS, TAKE UP WITH SAND OR OTHER ABSORBENT MATERIAL AND PLACE INTO CONTAINERS FOR LATER DISPOSAL. FOR LARGER SPILLS, DIKE FAR AHEAD OF SPILL FOR LATER DISPOSAL. NO SMOKING, FLAMES OR FLARES IN HAZARD AREA! KEEP UNNECESSARY PEOPLE AWAY; ISOLATE HAZARD AREA AND DENY ENTRY.

PROTECTIVE EQUIPMENT

VENTILATION: PROVIDE LOCAL EXHAUST OR PROCESS ENCLOSURE VENTILATION. VENTILATION EQUIPMENT MUST BE EXPLOSION-PROOF.

RESPIRATOR: THE FOLLOWING RESPIRATORS ARE RECOMMENDED BASED ON INFORMATION FOUND IN THE PHYSICAL DATA, TOXICITY AND HEALTH EFFECTS SECTIONS. THEY ARE RANKED IN ORDER FROM MINIMUM TO MAXIMUM RESPIRATORY PROTECTION. THE SPECIFIC RESPIRATOR SELECTED MUST BE BASED ON CONTAMINATION LEVELS FOUND IN THE WORK PLACE, MUST NOT EXCEED THE WORKING LIMITS OF THE RESPIRATOR AND BE JOINTLY APPROVED BY THE NATIONAL INSTITUTE FOR OCCUPATIONAL SAFETY AND HEALTH AND THE MINE SAFETY AND HEALTH ADMINISTRATION (NIOSH-MSHA).

TYPE 'C' SUPPLIED-AIR RESPIRATOR WITH A FULL FACEPIECE OPERATED IN PRESSURE-DEMAND OR OTHER POSITIVE PRESSURE MODE OR WITH A FULL FACEPIECE, HELMET OR HOOD OPERATED IN CONTINOUS-FLOW MODE.

SELF-CONTAINED BREATHING APPARATUS WITH A FULL FACEPIECE OPERATED IN PRESSURE-DEMAND OR OTHER POSITIVE PRESSURE MODE.

FOR FIREFIGHTING AND OTHER IMMEDIATELY DANGEROUS TO LIFE OR HEALTH CONDITIONS:

SELF-CONTAINED BREATHING APPARATUS WITH FULL FACEPIECE OPERATED IN PRESSURE-DEMAND OR OTHER POSITIVE PRESSURE MODE.

SUPPLIED-AIR RESPIRATOR WITH FULL FACEPIECE AND OPERATED IN PRESSURE-DEMAND OR OTHER POSITIVE PRESSURE MODE IN COMBINATION WITH AN AUXILIARY SELF-CONTAINED BREATHING APPARATUS OPERATED IN PRESSURE-DEMAND OR OTHER POSITIVE PRESSURE MODE.

CLOTHING: EMPLOYEE MUST WEAR APPROPRIATE PROTECTIVE (IMPERVIOUS) CLOTHING AND EQUIPMENT TO PREVENT ANY POSSIBILITY OF SKIN CONTACT WITH THIS SUBSTANCE.

GLOVES: EMPLOYEE MUST WEAR APPROPRIATE PROTECTIVE GLOVES TO PREVENT CONTACT WITH THIS SUBSTANCE.

EYE PROTECTION: EMPLOYEE MUST WEAR SPLASH-PROOF OR DUST-RESISTANT SAFETY GOGGLES TO PREVENT EYE CONTACT WITH THIS SUBSTANCE.

EMERGENCY EYE WASH: WHERE THERE IS ANY POSSIBILITY THAT AN EMPLOYEE'S EYES MAY BE EXPOSED TO THIS SUBSTANCE, THE EMPLOYER SHOULD PROVIDE AN EYE WASH FOUNTAIN WITHIN THE IMMEDIATE WORK AREA FOR EMERGENCY USE.

AUTHORIZED BY- OCCUPATIONAL HEALTH SERVICES, INC.

CREATION DATE: 10/04/89 ***REVISION DATE:*** 04/26/90

MATERIAL SAFETY DATA SHEET

OCCUPATIONAL HEALTH SERVICES, INC.
AGRICULTURE AND PESTICIDE DIVISION
450 SEVENTH AVENUE, SUITE 2407
NEW YORK, NEW YORK 10123
1-800-445-MSDS OR (212) 967-1100

EMERGENCY CONTACT:
JOHN S. BRANSFORD, JR. (615) 292-1180

SUBSTANCE IDENTIFICATION

CAS-NUMBER 2588-03-6

SUBSTANCE: **PHORATE SULFOXIDE**

TRADE NAMES/SYNONYMS: PHOSPHORODITHIOIC ACID, O,O-DIETHYL S-((ETHYLSULFINYL)METHYL) ESTER; PHOSPHORODITHIOIC ACID, O,O-DIETHYL (ETHYLSULFINYL)METHYL ESTER; PHORATE O-SULFOXIDE; THIMET SULFOXIDE; O,O-DIETHYL S-((ETHYLSULFINYL)METHYL) PHOSPHORODITHIOATE; O,O-DIETHYL (ETHYLSULFINYL)METHYL ESTER; C7H17O3PS3; PST18646

CHEMICAL FAMILY: ORGANOPHOSPHATE

MOLECULAR FORMULA: (C2-H5-O)2-P-(S)-S-C-H2-S-(O)-C2-H5

MOLECULAR WEIGHT: 276.39

CERCLA RATINGS (SCALE 0-3): HEALTH=3 FIRE=U REACTIVITY=0 PERSISTENCE=1

NFPA RATINGS (SCALE 0-4): HEALTH=3 FIRE=U REACTIVITY=0

COMPONENTS AND CONTAMINANTS

COMPONENT: PHORATE SULFOXIDE ***PERCENT:*** 100.0
CAS# 2588-03-6

OTHER CONTAMINANTS: NONE

EXPOSURE LIMITS: NO OCCUPATIONAL EXPOSURE LIMITS ESTABLISHED BY OSHA, ACGIH, OR NIOSH.

PHYSICAL DATA

DESCRIPTION: CLEAR LIQUID. ***BOILING POINT:*** NOT AVAILABLE
SPECIFIC GRAVITY: NOT AVAILABLE ***SOLUBILITY IN WATER:*** NOT AVAILABLE
VAPOR DENSITY: NOT AVAILABLE

FIRE AND EXPLOSION DATA

FIRE AND EXPLOSION HAZARD: UNKNOWN FIRE AND EXPLOSION HAZARD.

FLASH POINT: NOT AVAILABLE

FIREFIGHTING MEDIA: DRY CHEMICAL, CARBON DIOXIDE, HALON, WATER SPRAY OR STANDARD FOAM (1987 EMERGENCY RESPONSE GUIDEBOOK, DOT P 5800.4). FOR LARGER FIRES, USE WATER SPRAY, FOG OR STANDARD FOAM (1987 EMERGENCY RESPONSE GUIDEBOOK, DOT P 5800.4).

FIREFIGHTING: MOVE CONTAINER FROM FIRE AREA IF POSSIBLE. DIKE FIRE CONTROL WATER FOR LATER DISPOSAL; DO NOT SCATTER THE MATERIAL. COOL FIRE-EXPOSED CONTAINERS WITH WATER FROM SIDE UNTIL WELL AFTER FIRE IS OUT. STAY AWAY FROM STORAGE TANK ENDS. WITHDRAW IMMEDIATELY IN CASE OF RISING SOUND FROM VENTING SAFETY DEVICE OR ANY DISCOLORATION OF STORAGE TANK DUE TO FIRE (1987 EMERGENCY RESPONSE GUIDEBOOK, DOT P 5800.4, GUIDE PAGE 28).

EXTINGUISH ONLY IF FLOW CAN BE STOPPED. USE FLOODING AMOUNTS OF WATER AS A FOG; SOLID STREAMS MAY BE INEFFECTIVE. COOL CONTAINERS WITH FLOODING AMOUNTS OF WATER FROM AS FAR A DISTANCE AS POSSIBLE. AVOID BREATHING POISONOUS VAPORS, KEEP UPWIND.

TRANSPORTATION DATA

DEPARTMENT OF TRANSPORTATION HAZARD CLASSIFICATION 49 CFR 172.101: POISON B

DEPARTMENT OF TRANSPORTATION LABELING REQUIREMENTS 49 CFR 172.101 AND SUBPART E: POISON

DEPARTMENT OF TRANSPORTATION PACKAGING REQUIREMENTS: 49 CFR 173.359 EXCEPTIONS: 49 CFR 173.359

TOXICITY

PHORATE SULFOXIDE: TOXICITY DATA: 2 MG/KG ORAL-RAT LD50. CARCINOGEN STATUS: NONE. ACUTE TOXICITY LEVEL: HIGHLY TOXIC BY INGESTION. TARGET EFFECTS: CHOLINESTERASE INHIBITOR. POISONING MAY AFFECT THE NERVOUS SYSTEM.* AT INCREASED RISK FROM EXPOSURE: PERSONS WITH RESPIRATORY AILMENTS, RECENT EXPOSURE TO CHOLINESTERASE INHIBITORS OR IMPAIRED CHOLINESTERASE PRODUCTION, OR LIVER MALFUNCTION.* ADDITIONAL DATA: MAY CROSS THE PLACENTA. HIGH ENVIRONMENTAL TEMPERATURES OR EXPOSURE OF THE CHEMICAL TO VISIBLE OR ULTRAVIOLET LIGHT MAY ENHANCE THE TOXICITY.*

* MAY BE BASED ON GENERAL INFORMATION ON ORGANOPHOSPHATES.

HEALTH EFFECTS AND FIRST AID

INHALATION: PHORATE SULFOXIDE: SEE INFORMATION ON ORGANOPHOSPHATES. ORGANOPHOSPHATES: CHOLINESTERASE INHIBITOR. **ACUTE EXPOSURE-** WHEN INHALED, THE FIRST EFFECTS OF CHOLINESTERASE INHIBITORS ARE USUALLY RESPIRATORY AND MAY INCLUDE NASAL HYPEREMIA AND WATERY DISCHARGE, COUGH, CHEST DISCOMFORT, DYSPNEA, AND WHEEZING DUE TO INCREASED BRONCHIAL SECRETIONS AND BRONCHOCONSTRICTION. IF SUFFICIENT AMOUNTS ARE ABSORBED, OTHER SYSTEMIC EFFECTS MAY BEGIN WITHIN A FEW MINUTES OR BE DELAYED FOR UP TO 12 HOURS. SYMPTOMS MAY INCLUDE PALLOR, NAUSEA, VOMITING, DIARRHEA, ABDOMINAL CRAMPS, HEADACHE, DIZZINESS, OCULAR PAIN, BLURRED VISION, MIOSIS OR IN SOME CASES, ESPECIALLY INITIALLY, MYDRIASIS, LACRIMATION, SALIVATION, SWEATING, AND CONFUSION. OTHER REPORTED CENTRAL NERVOUS SYSTEM OR NEUROMUSCULAR EFFECTS MAY INCLUDE ATAXIA, SLURRED SPEECH, AREFLEXIA, WEAKNESS, FATIGUE, FASCICULATIONS, TWITCHING, TREMORS POSSIBLY OF THE TONGUE AND EYELIDS, AND EVENTUALLY PARALYSIS OF THE EXTREMITIES AND POSSIBLY OF THE RESPIRATORY MUSCLES. IN SEVERE CASES THERE MAY ALSO BE INVOLUNTARY DEFECATION AND URINATION, CYANOSIS, PSYCHOSIS, HYPERGLYCEMIA, ACUTE PANCREATITIS, CARDIAC IRREGULARITIES, PULMONARY EDEMA, UNCONSCIOUSNESS, CONVULSIONS, AND COMA. DEATH IS PRIMARILY DUE TO RESPIRATORY FAILURE, ALTHOUGH CARDIOVASCULAR EFFECTS INCLUDING CARDIAC ARREST MAY ALSO BE IMPLICATED. LONG TERM SEQUELAE ARE RARE BUT MAY INCLUDE NEUROPSYCHIATRIC DISORDERS AND MYOPATHY WITH MUSCLE TENDERNESS. SOME ORGANOPHOSPHATES MAY CAUSE A DELAYED NEUROPATHY BEGINNING 1-4 WEEKS AFTER AN ACUTE EXPOSURE WHICH MAY OR MAY NOT HAVE CAUSED ACUTE CHOLINERGIC EFFECTS. NUMBNESS, TINGLING, WEAKNESS AND CRAMPING BEGINNING SYMMETRICALLY IN THE LOWER LIMBS MAY PROGRESS TO ATAXIA AND PARALYSIS. IN SEVERE CASES, UPPER LIMB INVOLVEMENT IS POSSIBLE AND FLACCID PARALYSIS MAY PROGRESS TO SPASTIC PARALYSIS WITH EXAGGERATED REFLEXES. IMPROVEMENT MAY OCCUR OVER MONTHS TO YEARS, BUT SOME RESIDUAL IMPAIRMENT USUALLY REMAINS.

CHRONIC EXPOSURE- REPEATED OR PROLONGED EXPOSURE MAY RESULT IN THE EFFECTS OF ACUTE EXPOSURE INCLUDING THE DELAYED NEUROPATHY. OTHER

EFFECTS REPORTED IN WORKERS REPEATEDLY EXPOSED INCLUDE IMPAIRED MEMORY AND CONCENTRATION, ACUTE PSYCHOSIS, SEVERE DEPRESSIONS, IRRITABILTY, CONFUSION, APATHY, EMOTIONAL LABILITY, SOCIAL WITHDRAWAL, CONFUSION, HEADACHE, SPEECH DIFFICULTIES, DELAYED REACTION TIMES, SPATIAL DISORIENTATION, NIGHTMARES, SLEEPWALKING, AND DROWSINESS OR INSOMNIA. AN INFLUENZA-LIKE CONDITION WITH HEADACHE, NAUSEA, WEAKNESS, ANOREXIA AND MALAISE HAS ALSO BEEN REPORTED.

FIRST AID- REMOVE FROM EXPOSURE AREA TO FRESH AIR IMMEDIATELY. IF BREATHING HAS STOPPED, GIVE ARTIFICIAL RESPIRATION. MAINTAIN AIRWAY AND BLOOD PRESSURE AND ADMINISTER OXYGEN IF AVAILABLE. KEEP AFFECTED PERSON WARM AND AT REST. TREAT SYMPTOMATICALLY AND SUPPORTIVELY. ADMINISTRATION OF OXYGEN SHOULD BE PERFORMED BY QUALIFIED PERSONNEL. GET MEDICAL ATTENTION IMMEDIATELY.

SKIN CONTACT: PHORATE SULFOXIDE: SEE INFORMATION ON ORGANOPHOSPHATES. ORGANOPHOSPHATES: CHOLINESTERASE INHIBITOR. **ACUTE EXPOSURE-** LOCALIZED SWEATING AND FASCICULATIONS MAY OCCUR AT THE SITE OF CONTACT. IF SUFFICIENT AMOUNTS ARE ABSORBED, OTHER EFFECTS OF CHOLINESTERASE INHIBITION AS DESCRIBED IN ACUTE INHALATION MAY OCCUR. SYMPTOMS MAY BE DELAYED 2-3 HOURS, BUT USUALLY NO MORE THAN 12 HOURS. THE RATE OF ABSORPTION IS INCREASED BY THE PRESENCE OF DERMATITIS OR HIGH AMBIENT TEMPERATURES. DELAYED NEUROPATHY IS ALSO POSSIBLE. **CHRONIC EXPOSURE-** REPEATED OR PROLONGED EXPOSURE MAY CAUSE EFFECTS AS DESCRIBED IN ACUTE EXPOSURE. SOME ORGANOPHOSPHATES MAY CAUSE SENSITIZATION.

FIRST AID- REMOVE CONTAMINATED CLOTHING IMMEDIATELY. WASH CONTAMINATED AREAS WITH SOAP AND WATER FOLLOWED BY ALCOHOL (ARENA, POISONING, 4TH ED.). EMERGENCY PERSONNEL SHOULD WEAR GLOVES AND AVOID CONTAMINATION. TREAT RESPIRATORY DIFFICULTY WITH ARTIFICIAL RESPIRATION. GET MEDICAL ATTENTION IMMEDIATELY.

EYE CONTACT: PHORATE SULFOXIDE: SEE INFORMATION ON ORGANOPHOSPHATES. ORGANOPHOSPHATES: CHOLINESTERASE INHIBITOR. **ACUTE EXPOSURE-** DIRECT CONTACT MAY CAUSE PAIN, HYPEREMIA, LACRIMATION, TWITCHING OF THE EYELIDS, MIOSIS, AND CILIARY MUSCLE SPASM WITH LOSS OF ACCOMODATION, BLURRED OR DIMMED VISION AND BROWACHE. SOMETIMES MYDRIASIS MAY OCCUR INSTEAD OF MIOSIS. WITH SUFFICIENT EXPOSURE, OTHER SYMPTOMS OF CHOLINESTERASE INHIBITION AS DESCRIBED IN ACUTE INHALATION MAY OCCUR. **CHRONIC EXPOSURE-** REPEATED OR PROLONGED EXPOSURE MAY CAUSE EFFECTS AS DESCRIBED IN ACUTE EXPOSURE. SOME COMPOUNDS HAVE CAUSED TOXIC EFFECTS ON THE CRYSTALLINE LENS, CONJUNCTIVAL THICKENING AND OBSTRUCTION OF THE NASOLACRIMAL CANALS WHEN USED AS MIOTIC EYEDROPS.

FIRST AID- IRRIGATE EYES WITH WATER OR SALINE SOLUTION. IF SYMPTOMS OF POISONING OCCUR, TREAT RESPIRATORY DIFFICULTY WITH ARTIFICIAL RESPIRATION AND OXYGEN. OBSERVE PATIENT FOR AT LEAST 24-36 HOURS (GOSSELIN, CLINICAL TOXICOLOGY OF COMMERCIAL PRODUCTS, 5TH ED.). GET MEDICAL ATTENTION IMMEDIATELY. OXYGEN SHOULD BE ADMINISTERED BY QUALIFIED MEDICAL PERSONNEL.

INGESTION: PHORATE SULFOXIDE: HIGHLY TOXIC. SEE INFORMATION ON ORGANOPHOSPHATES.
ORGANOPHOSPHATES: CHOLINESTERASE INHIBITOR. **ACUTE EXPOSURE-** WHEN INGESTED, THE FIRST EFFECTS MAY BE NAUSEA, VOMITING, ANOREXIA, ABDOMINAL CRAMPS AND DIARRHEA. GASTROINTESTINAL ABSORPTION MAY CAUSE SYMPTOMS OF CHOLINESTERASE INHIBITION AS DESCRIBED IN ACUTE INHALATION. SYMPTOMS MAY BEGIN WITHIN MINUTES OR BE DELAYED FOR HOURS. DELAYED EFFECTS INCLUDING NEUROPATHY MAY ALSO OCCUR. **CHRONIC EXPOSURE-** REPEATED INGESTION MAY CAUSE EFFECTS AS DESCRIBED IN ACUTE EXPOSURE.

FIRST AID- IF PERSON IS ALERT AND RESPIRATION IS NOT DEPRESSED, GIVE SYRUP OF IPECAC FOLLOWED BY WATER (IF VOMITING OCCURS, KEEP HEAD BELOW HIPS TO PREVENT ASPIRATION). IF CONSCIOUSNESS LEVEL DECLINES OR VOMITING HAS NOT OCCURRED IN 15 MINUTES EMPTY STOMACH BY GASTRIC LAVAGE WITH THE AID OF CUFFED ENDOTRACHEAL TUBE USING ISOTONIC SALINE OR 5% SODIUM BICARBONATE FOLLOW WITH ACTIVATED CHARCOAL. ESTABLISH AND MAINTAIN AIRWAY. TREAT RESPIRATORY DIFFICULTY WITH ARTIFICIAL RESPIRATION AND OXYGEN. DO NOT GIVE MORPHINE, AMINOPHYLLINE, PHENOTHIAZINES, RESERPINE, FUROSEMIDE, OR ETHACRYNIC ACID (MORGAN, RECOGNITION AND MANAGEMENT OF PESTICIDE POISONINGS, 3RD ED.). TREAT SYMPTOMATICALLY AND SUPPORTIVELY. ADMINISTRATION OF OXYGEN AND LAVAGE MUST BE PERFORMED BY QUALIFIED MEDICAL PERSONNEL. GET MEDICAL ATTENTION IMMEDIATELY.

ANTIDOTE: THE FOLLOWING ANTIDOTE(S) HAVE BEEN RECOMMENDED. HOWEVER, THE DECISION AS TO WHETHER THE SEVERITY OF POISONING REQUIRES ADMINISTRATION OF ANY ANTIDOTE AND ACTUAL DOSE REQUIRED SHOULD BE MADE BY QUALIFIED MEDICAL PERSONNEL.

FOR CHOLINESTERASE INHIBITORS: ESTABLISH CLEAR AIRWAY AND TISSUE OXYGENATION BY ASPIRATION OF SECRETIONS, AND IF NECESSARY, BY ASSISTED PULMONARY VENTILATION WITH OXYGEN. IMPROVE TISSUE OXYGENATION AS MUCH AS POSSIBLE BEFORE ADMINISTERING ATROPINE TO MINIMIZE THE RISK OF VENTRICULAR FIBRILLATION. ADMINISTER ATROPINE SULFATE INTRAVENOUSLY, OR INTRAMUSCULARLY IF IV INJECTION IS NOT POSSIBLE. IN MODERATELY SEVERE POISONING ADMINISTER ATROPINE SULFATE, 0.4-2.0 MG REPEATED EVERY 15 MINUTES UNTIL ATROPINIZATION IS ACHIEVED (TACHYCARDIA, FLUSHING, DRY MOUTH, MYDRIASIS). MAINTAIN ATROPINIZATION BY REPEATED DOSES FOR 2-12 HOURS, OR LONGER, DEPENDING ON THE SEVERITY OF POISONING. THE APPEARANCE OF RALES IN THE LUNG BASES, MIOSIS, SALIVATION, NAUSEA, BRADYCARDIA, ARE ALL INDICATIONS OF INADEQUATE ATROPINIZATION. SEVERELY POISONED INDIVIDUALS MAY EXHIBIT REMARKABLE TOLERANCE TO ATROPINE; TWO OR MORE TIMES THE DOSAGES SUGGESTED ABOVE MAY BE NEEDED. PERSONS NOT POISONED OR ONLY SLIGHTLY POISONED, HOWEVER, MAY DEVELOP SIGNS OF ATROPINE TOXICITY FROM SUCH LARGE DOSAGES: FEVER, MUSCLE FIBRILLATIONS, AND DELIRIUM ARE THE MAIN SIGNS OF ATROPINE TOXICITY. IF THESE SIGNS APPEAR WHILE THE PATIENT IS FULLY ATROPINIZED, ATROPINE ADMINISTRATION SHOULD BE DISCONTINUED, AT LEAST TEMPORARILY. OBSERVE TREATED PATIENTS CLOSELY AT LEAST 24 HOURS TO INSURE THAT SYMPTOMS (POSSIBLY PULMONARY EDEMA) DO NOT RECUR AS ATROPINIZATION WEARS OFF. IN VERY SEVERE POISONINGS, METABOLIC DISPOSITION OF TOXICANT MAY REQUIRE SEVERAL HOURS OR DAYS DURING WHICH ATROPINIZATION MUST BE MAINTAINED. MARKEDLY LOWER LEVELS OF URINARY METABOLITES INDICATE THAT ATROPINE DOSAGE CAN BE TAPERED OFF. AS DOSAGE IS REDUCED, CHECK THE LUNG BASES FREQUENTLY FOR RALES. IF RALES ARE HEARD OR OTHER SYMPTOMS RETURN, RE-ESTABLISH ATROPINIZATION PROMPTLY (MORGAN, RECOGNITION AND MANAGEMENT OF PESTICIDE POISONINGS, 3RD ED.). ADMINISTRATION OF ANTIDOTE MUST BE PERFORMED BY QUALIFIED MEDICAL PERSONNEL.
IN CASES OF SEVERE POISONING BY ORGANOPHOSPHATE PESTICIDES IN WHICH RESPIRATORY DEPRESSION, MUSCLE WEAKNESS AND TWITCHINGS ARE SEVERE, GIVE PRALIDOXIME (PROTOPAM-AYERST, 2-PAM), 1.0 GRAM INTRAVENOUSLY AT NO MORE THAN 0.5 GRAM PER MINUTE. DOSAGE OF PRALIDOXIME MAY BE REPEATED IN 1-2 HOURS, THEN AT 10-12 HOUR INTERVALS IF NEEDED. IN VERY SEVERE POISONINGS, DOSAGE RATES MAY BE DOUBLED. TREATMENT WITH PRALIDOXIME WILL BE MOST EFFECTIVE IF GIVEN WITHIN THIRTY-SIX HOURS AFTER POISONING (MORGAN, RECOGNITION AND MANAGEMENT OF PESTICIDE POISONINGS, 3RD ED.). ANTIDOTE SHOULD BE ADMINISTERED BY QUALIFIED MEDICAL PERSONNEL.

REACTIVITY

REACTIVITY: STABLE UNDER NORMAL TEMPERATURES AND PRESSURES.

INCOMPATIBILITIES: PHORATE SULFOXIDE: OXIDIZERS (STRONG): FIRE AND EXPLOSION HAZARD.

DECOMPOSITION: THERMAL DECOMPOSITION PRODUCTS MAY INCLUDE TOXIC OXIDES OF CARBON, SULFUR, AND PHOSPHORUS.

POLYMERIZATION: HAZARDOUS POLYMERIZATION HAS NOT BEEN REPORTED TO OCCUR UNDER NORMAL TEMPERATURES AND PRESSURES.

STORAGE AND DISPOSAL

OBSERVE ALL FEDERAL, STATE AND LOCAL REGULATIONS WHEN STORING OR DISPOSING OF THIS SUBSTANCE. FOR ASSISTANCE, CONTACT THE DISTRICT DIRECTOR OF THE ENVIRONMENTAL PROTECTION AGENCY.

****STORAGE****

STORE IN ACCORDANCE WITH 40 CFR 165 RECOMMENDED PROCEDURES FOR THE DISPOSAL AND STORAGE OF PESTICIDES AND PESTICIDE CONTAINERS. STORE AWAY FROM INCOMPATIBLE SUBSTANCES.

****DISPOSAL****

DISPOSAL MUST BE IN ACCORDANCE WITH 40 CFR 165 RECOMMENDED PROCEDURES FOR THE DISPOSAL AND STORAGE OF PESTICIDES AND PESTICIDE CONTAINERS.

CONDITIONS TO AVOID

AVOID CONTACT WITH HEAT, SPARKS, FLAMES OR OTHER IGNITION SOURCES. VAPORS MAY BE EXPLOSIVE. MATERIAL IS POISONOUS; AVOID INHALATION OF VAPORS OR CONTACT WITH SKIN. DO NOT ALLOW MATERIAL TO CONTAMINATE WATER SOURCES.

SPILL AND LEAK PROCEDURES

OCCUPATIONAL SPILL: SHUT OFF IGNITION SOURCES. DO NOT TOUCH SPILLED MATERIAL. STOP LEAK IF YOU CAN DO IT WITHOUT RISK. USE WATER SPRAY TO REDUCE VAPORS. FOR SMALL SPILLS, TAKE UP WITH SAND OR OTHER ABSORBENT MATERIAL AND PLACE INTO CONTAINERS FOR LATER DISPOSAL. FOR LARGER SPILLS, DIKE FAR AHEAD OF SPILL FOR LATER DISPOSAL. NO SMOKING, FLAMES

OR FLARES IN HAZARD AREA! KEEP UNNECESSARY PEOPLE AWAY; ISOLATE HAZARD AREA AND DENY ENTRY.

PROTECTIVE EQUIPMENT

VENTILATION: PROVIDE LOCAL EXHAUST OR PROCESS ENCLOSURE VENTILATION. VENTILATION EQUIPMENT MUST BE EXPLOSION-PROOF.

RESPIRATOR: THE FOLLOWING RESPIRATORS ARE RECOMMENDED BASED ON INFORMATION FOUND IN THE PHYSICAL DATA, TOXICITY AND HEALTH EFFECTS SECTIONS. THEY ARE RANKED IN ORDER FROM MINIMUM TO MAXIMUM RESPIRATORY PROTECTION. THE SPECIFIC RESPIRATOR SELECTED MUST BE BASED ON CONTAMINATION LEVELS FOUND IN THE WORK PLACE, MUST NOT EXCEED THE WORKING LIMITS OF THE RESPIRATOR AND BE JOINTLY APPROVED BY THE NATIONAL INSTITUTE FOR OCCUPATIONAL SAFETY AND HEALTH AND THE MINE SAFETY AND HEALTH ADMINISTRATION (NIOSH-MSHA).

TYPE 'C' SUPPLIED-AIR RESPIRATOR WITH A FULL FACEPIECE OPERATED IN PRESSURE-DEMAND OR OTHER POSITIVE PRESSURE MODE OR WITH A FULL FACEPIECE, HELMET OR HOOD OPERATED IN CONTINOUS-FLOW MODE.

SELF-CONTAINED BREATHING APPARATUS WITH A FULL FACEPIECE OPERATED IN PRESSURE-DEMAND OR OTHER POSITIVE PRESSURE MODE.

FOR FIREFIGHTING AND OTHER IMMEDIATELY DANGEROUS TO LIFE OR HEALTH CONDITIONS:

SELF-CONTAINED BREATHING APPARATUS WITH FULL FACEPIECE OPERATED IN PRESSURE-DEMAND OR OTHER POSITIVE PRESSURE MODE.

SUPPLIED-AIR RESPIRATOR WITH FULL FACEPIECE AND OPERATED IN PRESSURE-DEMAND OR OTHER POSITIVE PRESSURE MODE IN COMBINATION WITH AN AUXILIARY SELF-CONTAINED BREATHING APPARATUS OPERATED IN PRESSURE-DEMAND OR OTHER POSITIVE PRESSURE MODE.

CLOTHING: EMPLOYEE MUST WEAR APPROPRIATE PROTECTIVE (IMPERVIOUS) CLOTHING AND EQUIPMENT TO PREVENT ANY POSSIBILITY OF SKIN CONTACT WITH THIS SUBSTANCE.

GLOVES: EMPLOYEE MUST WEAR APPROPRIATE PROTECTIVE GLOVES TO PREVENT CONTACT WITH THIS SUBSTANCE.

EYE PROTECTION: EMPLOYEE MUST WEAR SPLASH-PROOF OR DUST-RESISTANT SAFETY GOGGLES TO PREVENT EYE CONTACT WITH THIS SUBSTANCE.

EMERGENCY EYE WASH: WHERE THERE IS ANY POSSIBILITY THAT AN EMPLOYEE'S EYES MAY BE EXPOSED TO THIS SUBSTANCE, THE EMPLOYER SHOULD PROVIDE AN EYE WASH FOUNTAIN WITHIN THE IMMEDIATE WORK AREA FOR EMERGENCY USE.

AUTHORIZED BY- OCCUPATIONAL HEALTH SERVICES, INC.
CREATION DATE: 10/04/89 ***REVISION DATE:*** 04/26/90

MATERIAL SAFETY DATA SHEET

OCCUPATIONAL HEALTH SERVICES, INC.
AGRICULTURE AND PESTICIDE DIVISION
450 SEVENTH AVENUE, SUITE 2407
NEW YORK, NEW YORK 10123
1-800-445-MSDS OR (212) 967-1100

EMERGENCY CONTACT:
JOHN S. BRANSFORD, JR. (615) 292-1180

SUBSTANCE IDENTIFICATION

CAS-NUMBER 7786-34-7

SUBSTANCE: MEVINPHOS

TRADE NAMES/SYNONYMS: 2-BUTENOIC ACID, 3-((DIMETHOXYPHOSPHINYL)OXY)-, METHYL ESTER; CROTONIC ACID, 3-HYDROXY-, METHYL ESTER, DIMETHYL PHOSPHATE; METHYL 3-(DIMETHOXYPHOSPHINOYLOXY)BUT-2-ENOATE; 2-METHOXYCARBONYL-1-METHYLVINYL DIMETHYL PHOSPHATE; METHYL 3-((DIMETHOXYPHOSPHINYL)OXY)-2-BUTENOATE; METHYL 3-HYDROXYCROTONATE DIMETHYL PHOSPHATE ESTER; 2-CARBOMETHOXY-1-METHYLVINYL DIMETHYL PHOSPHATE; 3-HYDROXYCROTONIC ACID METHYL ESTER DIMETHYL PHOSPHATE; DIMETHYL 1-METHOXYCARBONYL-1-PROPEN-2-YL PHOSPHATE; 3-((DIMETHOXYPHOSPHINYL)OXYL-2-BUTENOIC ACID METHYL ESTER; O,O-DIMETHYL 1-CARBOMETHOXY-1-PROPEN-2-YL PHOSPHATE; 1-METHOXYCARBONYL-1-PROPEN-2-YL DIMETHYL PHOSPHATE; ENT 22,374; PHOSDRIN; STCC 4921531; PST18650

CHEMICAL FAMILY: ORGANOPHOSPHATE

MOLECULAR FORMULA: C7-H13-O6-P

MOLECULAR WEIGHT: 224.16

CERCLA RATINGS (SCALE 0-3): HEALTH=3 FIRE=1 REACTIVITY=0 PERSISTENCE=0

NFPA RATINGS (SCALE 0-4): HEALTH=4 FIRE=1 REACTIVITY=0

COMPONENTS AND CONTAMINANTS

COMPONENT: MEVINPHOS ***PERCENT:*** 100.00
CAS# 7786-34-7

OTHER CONTAMINANTS: METHYL ACETOACETATE, METHYL 2-CHLOROACETOACETATE, DIMETHYL METHYL PHOSPHONATE

EXPOSURE LIMITS: MEVINPHOS (PHOSDRIN): 0.01 PPM (0.1 MG/M3) OSHA TWA (SKIN); 0.03 PPM (0.3 MG/M3) OSHA STEL 0.01 PPM (0.1 MG/M3) ACGIH TWA (SKIN); 0.03 PPM (0.3 MG/M3) ACGIH STEL

500 POUNDS SARA SECTION 302 THRESHOLD PLANNING QUANTITY 10 POUNDS SARA SECTION 304 REPORTABLE QUANTITY 10 POUNDS CERCLA SECTION 103 REPORTABLE QUANTITY

PHYSICAL DATA

DESCRIPTION: PALE YELLOW LIQUID WITH MILD ODOR

BOILING POINT: 617 F (325C)

MELTING POINT: -69 F (-56 C) ***SPECIFIC GRAVITY:*** 1.25

VAPOR PRESSURE: .003 MM HG @ 20 C ***SOLUBILITY IN WATER:*** MISCIBLE

VAPOR DENSITY: 7.5

SOLVENT SOLUBILITY: SOLUBLE IN ACETONE, CARBON TETRACHLORIDE, CHLOROFORM, ALCOHOL, BENZENE, TOLUENE, AND XYLENE; SLIGHTLY SOLUBLE IN PETROLEUM ETHER, KEROSENE, AND CARBON DISULFIDE; INSOLUBLE IN HEXANE

FIRE AND EXPLOSION DATA

FIRE AND EXPLOSION HAZARD: SLIGHT FIRE HAZARD WHEN EXPOSED TO HEAT OR FLAME.

FLASH POINT: 175 F (79 C) (OC)

FIREFIGHTING MEDIA: DRY CHEMICAL, CARBON DIOXIDE, HALON, WATER SPRAY OR STANDARD FOAM (1987 EMERGENCY RESPONSE GUIDEBOOK, DOT P 5800.4).

FOR LARGER FIRES, USE WATER SPRAY, FOG OR STANDARD FOAM (1987 EMERGENCY RESPONSE GUIDEBOOK, DOT P 5800.4).

FIREFIGHTING: MOVE CONTAINERS FROM FIRE AREA IF POSSIBLE. FIGHT FIRE FROM MAXIMUM DISTANCE. STAY AWAY FROM STORAGE TANK ENDS. DIKE FIRE CONTROL WATER FOR LATER DISPOSAL. DO NOT SCATTER MATERIAL (1987 EMERGENCY RESPONSE GUIDEBOOK, DOT P 5800.4, GUIDE PAGE 55).

EXTINGUISH USING AGENT SUITABLE FOR TYPE OF SURROUNDING FIRE. AVOID BREATHING VAPORS AND DUSTS. KEEP UPWIND.

TRANSPORTATION DATA

DEPARTMENT OF TRANSPORTATION HAZARD CLASSIFICATION 49 CFR 172.101: POISON B

DEPARTMENT OF TRANSPORTATION LABELING REQUIREMENTS 49 CFR 172.101 AND SUBPART E: POISON

DEPARTMENT OF TRANSPORTATION PACKAGING REQUIREMENTS: 49 CFR 173.358 EXCEPTIONS: NONE

TOXICITY

MEVINPHOS (PHOSDRIN): TOXICITY DATA: 14 PPM/1 HOUR INHALATION-RAT; 4700 UG/KG SKIN-RABBIT LD50; 4200 UG/KG SKIN-RAT LD50; 12 MG/KG SKIN-MOUSE LD50; 700 UG/KG/28 DAY INTERMITTENT ORAL-MAN TDLO; 3 MG/KG ORAL-RAT LD50; 4 MG/KG ORAL-MOUSE LD50; 940 UG/KG SUBCUTANEOUS-RAT LD50; 1180 UG/KG SUBCUTANEOUS-MOUSE LD50; 680 UG/KG INTRAVENOUS-MOUSE LD50; 800 UG/KG INTRAPERITONEAL-RAT LD50; 2 MG/KG INTRAPERITONEAL-MOUSE LD50; 450 UG/KG INTRAPERITONEAL-GERBIL LD50; MUTAGENIC DATA (RTECS). CARCINOGEN STATUS: NONE. ACUTE TOXICITY LEVEL: HIGHLY TOXIC BY INHALATION, DERMAL ABSORPTION, AND INGESTION. TARGET EFFECTS: CHOLINESTERASE INHIBITOR. POISONING MAY AFFECT THE NERVOUS SYSTEM.* AT INCREASED RISK FROM EXPOSURE: PERSONS WITH RESPIRATORY AILMENTS. RECENT EXPOSURE TO CHOLINESTERASE INHIBITORS OR IMPAIRED CHOLINESTERASE PRODUCTION, OR LIVER MALFUNCTION.* ADDITIONAL DATA: MAY CROSS THE PLACENTA. HIGH ENVIRONMENTAL TEMPERATURES OR EXPOSURE OF THE CHEMICAL TO VISIBLE OR ULTRAVIOLET LIGHT MAY ENHANCE THE TOXICITY. INTERACTIONS WITH MEDICATIONS MAY OCCUR.*

* MAY BE BASED ON GENERAL INFORMATION ON ORGANOPHOSPHATES.

HEALTH EFFECTS AND FIRST AID

INHALATION: MEVINPHOS (PHOSDRIN): HIGHLY TOXIC. 40 MG/M3 IMMEDIATELY DANGEROUS TO LIFE OR HEALTH. SEE INFORMATION ON ORGANOPHOSPHATES. ORGANOPHOSPHATES: CHOLINESTERASE INHIBITOR. ACUTE EXPOSURE- WHEN INHALED, THE FIRST EFFECTS OF CHOLINESTERASE INHIBITORS ARE USUALLY RESPIRATORY AND MAY INCLUDE NASAL HYPEREMIA AND WATERY DISCHARGE, COUGH, CHEST DISCOMFORT, DYSPNEA, AND WHEEZING DUE TO INCREASED BRONCHIAL SECRETIONS AND BRONCHOCONSTRICTION. IF SUFFICIENT AMOUNTS ARE ABSORBED, OTHER SYSTEMIC EFFECTS MAY BEGIN WITHIN A FEW MINUTES OR BE DELAYED FOR UP TO 12 HOURS. SYMPTOMS MAY INCLUDE PALLOR, NAUSEA, VOMITING, DIARRHEA, ABDOMINAL CRAMPS, HEADACHE, DIZZINESS, OCULAR PAIN, BLURRED VISION, MIOSIS OR IN SOME CASES, ESPECIALLY

INITIALLY, MYDRIASIS, LACRIMATION, SALIVATION, SWEATING, AND CONFUSION. OTHER REPORTED CENTRAL NERVOUS SYSTEM OR NEUROMUSCULAR EFFECTS MAY INCLUDE ATAXIA, SLURRED SPEECH, AREFLEXIA, WEAKNESS, FATIGUE, FASCICULATIONS, TWITCHING, TREMORS POSSIBLY OF THE TONGUE AND EYELIDS, AND EVENTUALLY PARALYSIS OF THE EXTREMITIES AND POSSIBLY OF THE RESPIRATORY MUSCLES. IN SEVERE CASES THERE MAY ALSO BE INVOLUNTARY DEFECATION AND URINATION, CYANOSIS, PSYCHOSIS, HYPERGLYCEMIA, ACUTE PANCREATITIS, CARDIAC IRREGULARITIES, PULMONARY EDEMA, UNCONSCIOUSNESS, CONVULSIONS, AND COMA. DEATH IS PRIMARILY DUE TO RESPIRATORY FAILURE, ALTHOUGH CARDIOVASCULAR EFFECTS INCLUDING CARDIAC ARREST MAY ALSO BE IMPLICATED. LONG TERM SEQUELAE ARE RARE BUT MAY INCLUDE NEUROPSYCHIATRIC DISORDERS AND MYOPATHY WITH MUSCLE TENDERNESS. SOME ORGANOPHOSPHATES MAY CAUSE A DELAYED NEUROPATHY BEGINNING 1-4 WEEKS AFTER AN ACUTE EXPOSURE WHICH MAY OR MAY NOT HAVE CAUSED ACUTE CHOLINERGIC EFFECTS. NUMBNESS, TINGLING, WEAKNESS AND CRAMPING BEGINNING SYMMETRICALLY IN THE LOWER LIMBS MAY PROGRESS TO ATAXIA AND PARALYSIS. IN SEVERE CASES, UPPER LIMB INVOLVEMENT IS POSSIBLE AND FLACCID PARALYSIS MAY PROGRESS TO SPASTIC PARALYSIS WITH EXAGGERATED REFLEXES. IMPROVEMENT MAY OCCUR OVER MONTHS TO YEARS, BUT SOME RESIDUAL IMPAIRMENT USUALLY REMAINS.
CHRONIC EXPOSURE- REPEATED OR PROLONGED EXPOSURE MAY RESULT IN THE EFFECTS OF ACUTE EXPOSURE INCLUDING THE DELAYED NEUROPATHY. OTHER EFFECTS REPORTED IN WORKERS REPEATEDLY EXPOSED INCLUDE IMPAIRED MEMORY AND CONCENTRATION, ACUTE PSYCHOSIS, SEVERE DEPRESSIONS, IRRITABILTY, CONFUSION, APATHY, EMOTIONAL LABILITY, SOCIAL WITHDRAWAL, CONFUSION, HEADACHE, SPEECH DIFFICULTIES, DELAYED REACTION TIMES, SPATIAL DISORIENTATION, NIGHTMARES, SLEEPWALKING, AND DROWSINESS OR INSOMNIA. AN INFLUENZA-LIKE CONDITION WITH HEADACHE, NAUSEA, WEAKNESS, ANOREXIA AND MALAISE HAS ALSO BEEN REPORTED.

FIRST AID- REMOVE FROM EXPOSURE AREA TO FRESH AIR IMMEDIATELY. IF BREATHING HAS STOPPED, GIVE ARTIFICIAL RESPIRATION. MAINTAIN AIRWAY AND BLOOD PRESSURE AND ADMINISTER OXYGEN IF AVAILABLE. KEEP AFFECTED PERSON WARM AND AT REST. TREAT SYMPTOMATICALLY AND SUPPORTIVELY. ADMINISTRATION OF OXYGEN SHOULD BE PERFORMED BY QUALIFIED PERSONNEL. GET MEDICAL ATTENTION IMMEDIATELY.

SKIN CONTACT: MEVINPHOS (PHOSDRIN): HIGHLY TOXIC. SEE INFORMATION ON ORGANOPHOSPHATES.
ORGANOPHOSPHATES: CHOLINESTERASE INHIBITOR. **ACUTE EXPOSURE-** LOCALIZED SWEATING AND FASCICULATIONS MAY OCCUR AT THE SITE OF CONTACT. IF SUFFICIENT AMOUNTS ARE ABSORBED, OTHER EFFECTS OF CHOLINESTERASE INHIBITION AS DESCRIBED IN ACUTE INHALATION MAY OCCUR. SYMPTOMS MAY BE DELAYED 2-3 HOURS, BUT USUALLY NO MORE THAN 12 HOURS. THE RATE OF ABSORPTION IS INCREASED BY THE PRESENCE OF DERMATITIS OR HIGH AMBIENT TEMPERATURES. DELAYED NEUROPATHY IS ALSO POSSIBLE. **CHRONIC EXPOSURE-** REPEATED OR PROLONGED EXPOSURE MAY CAUSE EFFECTS AS DESCRIBED IN ACUTE EXPOSURE. SOME ORGANOPHOSPHATES MAY CAUSE SENSITIZATION.

FIRST AID- REMOVE CONTAMINATED CLOTHING IMMEDIATELY. WASH CONTAMINATED AREAS WITH SOAP AND WATER FOLLOWED BY ALCOHOL (ARENA, POISONING, 4TH ED.). EMERGENCY PERSONNEL SHOULD WEAR GLOVES AND AVOID CONTAMINATION. TREAT RESPIRATORY DIFFICULTY WITH ARTIFICIAL RESPIRATION. GET MEDICAL ATTENTION IMMEDIATELY.

EYE CONTACT: MEVINPHOS (PHOSDRIN): SEE INFORMATION ON ORGANOPHOSPHATES.
ORGANOPHOSPHATES: CHOLINESTERASE INHIBITOR. **ACUTE EXPOSURE-** DIRECT CONTACT MAY CAUSE PAIN, HYPEREMIA, LACRIMATION, TWITCHING OF THE EYELIDS, MIOSIS, AND CILIARY MUSCLE SPASM WITH LOSS OF ACCOMODATION, BLURRED OR DIMMED VISION AND BROWACHE. SOMETIMES MYDRIASIS MAY OCCUR INSTEAD OF MIOSIS. WITH SUFFICIENT EXPOSURE, OTHER SYMPTOMS OF CHOLINESTERASE INHIBITION AS DESCRIBED IN ACUTE INHALATION MAY OCCUR. **CHRONIC EXPOSURE-** REPEATED OR PROLONGED EXPOSURE MAY CAUSE EFFECTS AS DESCRIBED IN ACUTE EXPOSURE. SOME COMPOUNDS HAVE CAUSED TOXIC EFFECTS ON THE CRYSTALLINE LENS, CONJUNCTIVAL THICKENING AND OBSTRUCTION OF THE NASOLACRIMAL CANALS WHEN USED AS MIOTIC EYEDROPS.

FIRST AID- IRRIGATE EYES WITH WATER OR SALINE SOLUTION. IF SYMPTOMS OF POISONING OCCUR, TREAT RESPIRATORY DIFFICULTY WITH ARTIFICIAL RESPIRATION AND OXYGEN. OBSERVE PATIENT FOR AT LEAST 24-36 HOURS (GOSSELIN, CLINICAL TOXICOLOGY OF COMMERCIAL PRODUCTS, 5TH ED.). GET MEDICAL ATTENTION IMMEDIATELY. OXYGEN SHOULD BE ADMINISTERED BY QUALIFIED MEDICAL PERSONNEL.

INGESTION: MEVINPHOS (PHOSDRIN): HIGHLY TOXIC. SEE INFORMATION ON ORGANOPHOSPHATES.
ORGANOPHOSPHATES: CHOLINESTERASE INHIBITOR. **ACUTE EXPOSURE-** WHEN INGESTED, THE FIRST EFFECTS MAY BE NAUSEA, VOMITING, ANOREXIA, ABDOMINAL CRAMPS AND DIARRHEA. GASTROINTESTINAL ABSORPTION MAY CAUSE SYMPTOMS OF CHOLINESTERASE INHIBITION AS DESCRIBED IN ACUTE INHALATION. SYMPTOMS MAY BEGIN WITHIN MINUTES OR BE DELAYED FOR HOURS. DELAYED EFFECTS INCLUDING NEUROPATHY MAY ALSO OCCUR. **CHRONIC EXPOSURE-** REPEATED INGESTION MAY CAUSE EFFECTS AS DESCRIBED IN ACUTE EXPOSURE.

FIRST AID- IF PERSON IS ALERT AND RESPIRATION IS NOT DEPRESSED, GIVE SYRUP OF IPECAC FOLLOWED BY WATER (IF VOMITING OCCURS, KEEP HEAD BELOW HIPS TO PREVENT ASPIRATION). IF CONSCIOUSNESS LEVEL DECLINES OR VOMITING HAS NOT OCCURRED IN 15 MINUTES EMPTY STOMACH BY GASTRIC LAVAGE WITH THE AID OF CUFFED ENDOTRACHEAL TUBE USING ISOTONIC SALINE OR 5% SODIUM BICARBONATE FOLLOW WITH ACTIVATED CHARCOAL. ESTABLISH AND MAINTAIN AIRWAY. TREAT RESPIRATORY DIFFICULTY WITH ARTIFICIAL RESPIRATION AND OXYGEN. DO NOT GIVE MORPHINE, AMINOPHYLLINE, PHENOTHIAZINES, RESERPINE, FUROSEMIDE, OR ETHACRYNIC ACID (MORGAN, RECOGNITION AND MANAGEMENT OF PESTICIDE POISONINGS, 3RD ED.). TREAT SYMPTOMATICALLY AND SUPPORTIVELY. ADMINISTRATION OF OXYGEN AND LAVAGE MUST BE PERFORMED BY QUALIFIED MEDICAL PERSONNEL. GET MEDICAL ATTENTION IMMEDIATELY.

ANTIDOTE: THE FOLLOWING ANTIDOTE(S) HAVE BEEN RECOMMENDED. HOWEVER, THE DECISION AS TO WHETHER THE SEVERITY OF POISONING REQUIRES ADMINISTRATION OF ANY ANTIDOTE AND ACTUAL DOSE REQUIRED SHOULD BE MADE BY QUALIFIED MEDICAL PERSONNEL.
FOR CHOLINESTERASE INHIBITORS: ESTABLISH CLEAR AIRWAY AND TISSUE OXYGENATION BY ASPIRATION OF SECRETIONS, AND IF NECESSARY, BY ASSISTED PULMONARY VENTILATION WITH OXYGEN. IMPROVE TISSUE OXYGENATION AS MUCH AS POSSIBLE BEFORE ADMINISTERING ATROPINE TO MINIMIZE THE RISK OF VENTRICULAR FIBRILLATION. ADMINISTER ATROPINE SULFATE INTRAVENOUSLY, OR INTRAMUSCULARLY IF IV INJECTION IS NOT POSSIBLE. IN MODERATELY SEVERE POISONING ADMINISTER ATROPINE SULFATE, 0.4-2.0 MG REPEATED EVERY 15 MINUTES UNTIL ATROPINIZATION IS ACHIEVED (TACHYCARDIA, FLUSHING, DRY MOUTH, MYDRIASIS). MAINTAIN ATROPINIZATION BY REPEATED DOSES FOR 2-12 HOURS, OR LONGER, DEPENDING ON THE SEVERITY OF POISONING. THE APPEARANCE OF RALES IN THE LUNG BASES, MIOSIS, SALIVATION, NAUSEA, BRADYCARDIA, ARE ALL INDICATIONS OF INADEQUATE ATROPINIZATION. SEVERELY POISONED INDIVIDUALS MAY EXHIBIT REMARKABLE TOLERANCE TO ATROPINE; TWO OR MORE TIMES THE DOSAGES SUGGESTED ABOVE MAY BE NEEDED. PERSONS NOT POISONED OR ONLY SLIGHTLY POISONED, HOWEVER, MAY DEVELOP SIGNS OF ATROPINE TOXICITY FROM SUCH LARGE DOSAGES: FEVER, MUSCLE FIBRILLATIONS, AND DELIRIUM ARE THE MAIN SIGNS OF ATROPINE TOXICITY. IF THESE SIGNS APPEAR WHILE THE PATIENT IS FULLY ATROPINIZED, ATROPINE ADMINISTRATION SHOULD BE DISCONTINUED, AT LEAST TEMPORARILY. OBSERVE TREATED PATIENTS CLOSELY AT LEAST 24 HOURS TO INSURE THAT SYMPTOMS (POSSIBLY PULMONARY EDEMA) DO NOT RECUR AS ATROPINIZATION WEARS OFF. IN VERY SEVERE POISONINGS, METABOLIC DISPOSITION OF TOXICANT MAY REQUIRE SEVERAL HOURS OR DAYS DURING WHICH ATROPINIZATION MUST BE MAINTAINED. MARKEDLY LOWER LEVELS OF URINARY METABOLITES INDICATE THAT ATROPINE DOSAGE CAN BE TAPERED OFF. AS DOSAGE IS REDUCED, CHECK THE LUNG BASES FREQUENTLY FOR RALES. IF RALES ARE HEARD OR OTHER SYMPTOMS RETURN, RE-ESTABLISH ATROPINIZATION PROMPTLY (MORGAN, RECOGNITION AND MANAGEMENT OF PESTICIDE POISONINGS, 3RD ED.). ADMINISTRATION OF ANTIDOTE MUST BE PERFORMED BY QUALIFIED MEDICAL PERSONNEL.
IN CASES OF SEVERE POISONING BY ORGANOPHOSPHATE PESTICIDES IN WHICH RESPIRATORY DEPRESSION, MUSCLE WEAKNESS AND TWITCHINGS ARE SEVERE, GIVE PRALIDOXIME (PROTOPAM-AYERST, 2-PAM), 1.0 GRAM INTRAVENOUSLY AT NO MORE THAN 0.5 GRAM PER MINUTE. DOSAGE OF PRALIDOXIME MAY BE REPEATED IN 1-2 HOURS, THEN AT 10-12 HOUR INTERVALS IF NEEDED. IN VERY SEVERE POISONINGS, DOSAGE RATES MAY BE DOUBLED. TREATMENT WITH PRALIDOXIME WILL BE MOST EFFECTIVE IF GIVEN WITHIN THIRTY-SIX HOURS AFTER POISONING (MORGAN, RECOGNITION AND MANAGEMENT OF PESTICIDE POISONINGS, 3RD ED.). ANTIDOTE SHOULD BE ADMINISTERED BY QUALIFIED MEDICAL PERSONNEL.

REACTIVITY

REACTIVITY: STABLE UNDER NORMAL TEMPERATURES AND PRESSURES. DECOMPOSES VIGOROUSLY ABOVE 300 C (572 F), CAUSING CONTAINERS TO BURST.

INCOMPATIBILITIES: MEVINPHOS (PHOSDRIN): ALKALINE MATERIAL: HYDROLYZE. BRASS: CORROSIVE. BORDEAUX MIXTURE: HYDROLYZE. CAST IRON: HYDROLYZE. LIME SULPHUR: HYDROLYZE. OXIDIZERS: MAY CAUSE EXPLOSION AND FIRE HAZARD ON CONTACT. SOME FORMS OF PLASTICS, RUBBER, AND COATINGS: MAY ATTACK. MILD AND SOME STAINLESS STEELS: CORROSIVE. WATER: HYDROLYSE.

DECOMPOSITION: THERMAL DECOMPOSITION MAY RELEASE TOXIC OXIDES OF PHOSPHORUS AND CARBON.
POLYMERIZATION: HAZARDOUS POLYMERIZATION HAS NOT BEEN REPORTED TO OCCUR UNDER NORMAL TEMPERATURES AND PRESSURES.

STORAGE AND DISPOSAL

OBSERVE ALL FEDERAL, STATE AND LOCAL REGULATIONS WHEN STORING OR DISPOSING OF THIS SUBSTANCE. FOR ASSISTANCE, CONTACT THE DISTRICT DIRECTOR OF THE ENVIRONMENTAL PROTECTION AGENCY.

STORAGE

STORE IN ACCORDANCE WITH 40 CFR 165 RECOMMENDED PROCEDURES FOR THE DISPOSAL AND STORAGE OF PESTICIDES AND PESTICIDE CONTAINERS.
STORE AWAY FROM INCOMPATIBLE SUBSTANCES.
THRESHOLD PLANNING QUANTITY (TPQ): THE SUPERFUND AMENDMENTS AND REAUTHORIZATION ACT (SARA) SECTION 302 REQUIRES THAT EACH FACILITY WHERE ANY EXTREMELY HAZARDOUS SUBSTANCE IS PRESENT IN A QUANTITY EQUAL TO OR GREATER THAN THE TPQ ESTABLISHED FOR THAT SUBSTANCE NOTIFY THE STATE EMERGENCY RESPONSE COMMISSION FOR THE STATE IN WHICH IT IS LOCATED. SECTION 303 OF SARA REQUIRES THESE FACILITIES TO PARTICIPATE IN LOCAL EMERGENCY RESPONSE PLANNING (40 CFR 355.30).

DISPOSAL

DISPOSAL MUST BE IN ACCORDANCE WITH 40 CFR 165 RECOMMENDED PROCEDURES FOR THE DISPOSAL AND STORAGE OF PESTICIDES AND PESTICIDE CONTAINERS.

CONDITIONS TO AVOID

MAY BURN BUT DOES NOT IGNITE READILY. CONTAINERS MAY EXPLODE IN HEAT OF FIRE.

SPILL AND LEAK PROCEDURES

SOIL SPILL: DIG A PIT, POND, LAGOON OR HOLDING AREA TO CONTAIN LIQUID OR SOLID MATERIAL. DIKE SURFACE FLOW USING SOIL, SANDBAGS, FOAMED POLYURETHANE OR FOAMED CONCRETE. ABSORB BULK LIQUID WITH FLY ASH OR CEMENT POWDER. ADD CAUSTIC SODA.
AIR SPILL: KNOCK DOWN VAPORS WITH WATER SPRAY. KEEP UPWIND.
WATER SPILL: IF DISSOLVED, AT A CONCENTRATION OF 10 PPM OR GREATER, APPLY ACTIVATED CARBON AT TEN TIMES THE AMOUNT THAT HAS BEEN SPILLED.
USE MECHANICAL DREDGES OR LIFTS TO EXTRACT IMMOBILIZED MASSES OF POLLUTION AND PRECIPITATES.
OCCUPATIONAL SPILL: DO NOT TOUCH SPILLED MATERIAL. STOP LEAK IF YOU CAN DO IT WITHOUT RISK. USE WATER SPRAY TO REDUCE VAPORS. FOR SMALL SPILLS, TAKE UP WITH SAND OR OTHER ABSORBENT MATERIAL AND PLACE INTO CONTAINERS FOR LATER DISPOSAL. FOR SMALL DRY SPILLS, WITH A CLEAN SHOVEL PLACE MATERIAL INTO CLEAN, DRY CONTAINERS AND COVER. MOVE CONTAINERS FROM SPILL AREA. FOR LARGER SPILLS, DIKE FAR AHEAD OF SPILL FOR LATER DISPOSAL. KEEP UNNECESSARY PEOPLE AWAY. ISOLATE HAZARD AREA AND DENY ENTRY. VENTILATE CLOSED SPACES BEFORE ENTERING.
REPORTABLE QUANTITY (RQ): 10 POUNDS THE SUPERFUND AMENDMENTS AND REAUTHORIZATION ACT (SARA) SECTION 304 REQUIRES THAT A RELEASE EQUAL TO OR GREATER THAN THE REPORTABLE QUANTITY FOR THIS SUBSTANCE BE IMMEDIATELY REPORTED TO THE LOCAL EMERGENCY PLANNING COMMITTEE AND THE STATE EMERGENCY RESPONSE COMMISSION (40 CFR 355.40). IF THE RELEASE OF THIS SUBSTANCE IS REPORTABLE UNDER CERCLA SECTION 103, THE NATIONAL RESPONSE CENTER MUST BE NOTIFIED IMMEDIATELY AT (800) 424-8802 OR (202) 426-2675 IN THE METROPOLITAN WASHINGTON, D.C. AREA (40 CFR 302.6).

PROTECTIVE EQUIPMENT

VENTILATION: PROCESS ENCLOSURE RECOMMENDED TO MEET PUBLISHED EXPOSURE LIMITS.
RESPIRATOR: THE FOLLOWING RESPIRATORS AND MAXIMUM USE CONCENTRATIONS ARE RECOMMENDATIONS BY THE U.S. DEPARTMENT OF HEALTH AND HUMAN SERVICES, NIOSH POCKET GUIDE TO CHEMICAL HAZARDS; NIOSH CRITERIA DOCUMENTS OR BY THE U.S. DEPARTMENT OF LABOR, 29 CFR 1910 SUBPART Z. THE SPECIFIC RESPIRATOR SELECTED MUST BE BASED ON CONTAMINATION LEVELS FOUND IN THE WORK PLACE, MUST NOT EXCEED THE WORKING LIMITS OF THE RESPIRATOR AND BE JOINTLY APPROVED BY THE NATIONAL INSTITUTE FOR OCCUPATIONAL SAFETY AND HEALTH AND THE MINE SAFETY AND HEALTH ADMINISTRATION (NIOSH-MSHA).
1 MG/M3- ANY SUPPLIED-AIR RESPIRATOR. ANY SELF-CONTAINED BREATHING APPARATUS.
2.5 MG/M3- ANY SUPPLIED-AIR RESPIRATOR OPERATED IN A CONTINUOUS FLOW MODE.
5 MG/M3- ANY SUPPLIED-AIR RESPIRATOR WITH A FULL FACEPIECE ANY SELF-CONTAINED BREATHING APPARATUS WITH A FULL FACEPIECE. ANY SUPPLIED-AIR RESPIRATOR WITH A TIGHT-FITTING FACEPIECE OPERATED IN A CONTINOUS FLOW MODE.
40 MG/M3- ANY SUPPLIED-AIR RESPIRATOR WITH A HALF-MASK AND OPERATED IN A PRESSURE-DEMAND OR OTHER POSITIVE PRESSURE MODE.
ESCAPE- ANY AIR-PURIFYING FULL FACEPIECE RESPIRATOR (GAS MASK) WITH A CHIN-STYLE OR FRONT- OR BACK-MOUNTED ORGANIC VAPOR CANISTER HAVING A HIGH-EFFICIENCY PARTICULATE FILTER. ANY APPROPRIATE ESCAPE-TYPE SELF-CONTAINED BREATHING APPARATUS.
FOR FIREFIGHTING AND OTHER IMMEDIATELY DANGEROUS TO LIFE OR HEALTH CONDITIONS:
SELF-CONTAINED BREATHING APPARATUS WITH FULL FACEPIECE OPERATED IN PRESSURE-DEMAND OR OTHER POSITIVE PRESSURE MODE.
SUPPLIED-AIR RESPIRATOR WITH FULL FACEPIECE AND OPERATED IN PRESSURE-DEMAND OR OTHER POSITIVE PRESSURE MODE IN COMBINATION WITH AN AUXILIARY SELF-CONTAINED BREATHING APPARATUS OPERATED IN PRESSURE-DEMAND OR OTHER POSITIVE PRESSURE MODE.
CLOTHING: EMPLOYEE MUST WEAR APPROPRIATE PROTECTIVE (IMPERVIOUS) CLOTHING AND EQUIPMENT TO PREVENT ANY POSSIBILITY OF SKIN CONTACT WITH THIS SUBSTANCE.
GLOVES: EMPLOYEE MUST WEAR APPROPRIATE PROTECTIVE GLOVES TO PREVENT CONTACT WITH THIS SUBSTANCE.
EYE PROTECTION: EMPLOYEE MUST WEAR SPLASH-PROOF OR DUST-RESISTANT SAFETY GOGGLES AND A FACESHIELD TO PREVENT CONTACT WITH THIS SUBSTANCE.
EMERGENCY WASH FACILITIES: WHERE THERE IS ANY POSSIBILITY THAT AN EMPLOYEE'S EYES AND/OR SKIN MAY BE EXPOSED TO THIS SUBSTANCE, THE EMPLOYER SHOULD PROVIDE AN EYE WASH FOUNTAIN AND QUICK DRENCH SHOWER WITHIN THE IMMEDIATE WORK AREA FOR EMERGENCY USE.

AUTHORIZED BY- OCCUPATIONAL HEALTH SERVICES, INC.
CREATION DATE: 10/04/89 ***REVISION DATE:*** 05/03/90

MATERIAL SAFETY DATA SHEET

OCCUPATIONAL HEALTH SERVICES, INC.
AGRICULTURE AND PESTICIDE DIVISION
450 SEVENTH AVENUE, SUITE 2407
NEW YORK, NEW YORK 10123
1-800-445-MSDS OR (212) 967-1100

EMERGENCY CONTACT:
JOHN S. BRANSFORD, JR. (615) 292-1180

SUBSTANCE IDENTIFICATION

CAS-NUMBER 3735-33-9
SUBSTANCE: PHOSMET OXYGEN ANALOG
TRADE NAMES/SYNONYMS: PHOSPHOROTHIOIC ACID, S-((1,3-DIHYDRO-1,3-DIOXO-2H-ISOINDOL-2-YL) METHYL)O,O-DIMETHYL ESTER; PHOSPHOROTHIOIC ACID, O,O-DIMETHYL ESTER, S-ESTER WITH N- (MERCAPTOMETHYL)PHTHALIMIDE; IMIDOXON; PHOSMETOXON; STAUFFER R 1571A; IMIDAN O.A.; N(MERCAPTOMETHYL)PHTHALIMIDE S-(O,O-DIMETHYL)PHOSPHOROTHIOATE; S-((1,3-DIHYDRO-1,3-DIAXO-2H-ISOINDOL-2-YL)METHYL)O,O-DIMETHYL PHOSPHOROTHIOATE; C11H12NO5PS; PST18665
CHEMICAL FAMILY: PHTHALIMIDE
ORGANOPHOSPHATE
MOLECULAR FORMULA: C11-H12-N-O5-P-S
MOLECULAR WEIGHT: 301.27
CERCLA RATINGS (SCALE 0-3): HEALTH=3 FIRE=1 REACTIVITY=0
PERSISTENCE=3
NFPA RATINGS (SCALE 0-4): HEALTH=3 FIRE=1 REACTIVITY=0

COMPONENTS AND CONTAMINANTS

COMPONENT: PHOSMET OXYGEN ANALOG ***PERCENT:*** 100.0
CAS# 3735-33-9
OTHER CONTAMINANTS: NONE
EXPOSURE LIMITS: NO OCCUPATIONAL EXPOSURE LIMITS ESTABLISHED BY OSHA, ACGIH, OR NIOSH.

PHYSICAL DATA

DESCRIPTION: SOLID. ***MELTING POINT:*** NOT AVAILABLE
SPECIFIC GRAVITY: NOT AVAILABLE ***SOLUBILITY IN WATER:*** NOT AVAILABLE

FIRE AND EXPLOSION DATA

FIRE AND EXPLOSION HAZARD: SLIGHT FIRE HAZARD WHEN EXPOSED TO HEAT OR FLAME.

FIREFIGHTING MEDIA: DRY CHEMICAL, CARBON DIOXIDE, HALON, WATER SPRAY OR STANDARD FOAM (1987 EMERGENCY RESPONSE GUIDEBOOK, DOT P 5800.4). FOR LARGER FIRES, USE WATER SPRAY, FOG OR STANDARD FOAM (1987 EMERGENCY RESPONSE GUIDEBOOK, DOT P 5800.4).

FIREFIGHTING: MOVE CONTAINERS FROM FIRE AREA IF POSSIBLE (1987 EMERGENCY RESPONSE GUIDEBOOK, DOT P 5800.4, GUIDE PAGE 53). EXTINGUISH USING AGENT SUITABLE FOR TYPE OF SURROUNDING FIRE. AVOID BREATHING VAPORS AND DUSTS. KEEP UPWIND.

TRANSPORTATION DATA

DEPARTMENT OF TRANSPORTATION HAZARD CLASSIFICATION 49 CFR 172.101: POISON B

DEPARTMENT OF TRANSPORTATION LABELING REQUIREMENTS 49 CFR 172.101 AND SUBPART E: POISON

DEPARTMENT OF TRANSPORTATION PACKAGING REQUIREMENTS: 49 CFR 173.365 EXCEPTIONS: 49 CFR 173.364

TOXICITY

PHOSMET OXYGEN ANALOG: TOXICITY DATA: 50 MG/KG ORAL-RAT LD50. CARCINOGEN STATUS: NONE. ACUTE TOXICITY LEVEL: HIGHLY TOXIC BY INGESTION. TARGET EFFECTS: CHOLINESTERASE INHIBITOR. POISONING MAY AFFECT THE NERVOUS SYSTEM.* AT INCREASED RISK FROM EXPOSURE: PERSONS WITH RESPIRATORY AILMENTS, RECENT EXPOSURE TO CHOLINESTERASE INHIBITORS OR IMPAIRED CHOLINESTERASE PRODUCTION, OR LIVER MALFUNCTION.* ADDITIONAL DATA: MAY CROSS THE PLACENTA. HIGH ENVIRONMENTAL TEMPERATURES OR EXPOSURE OF THE CHEMICAL TO VISIBLE OR ULTRAVIOLET LIGHT MAY ENHANCE THE TOXICITY. INTERACTIONS WITH MEDICATIONS MAY OCCUR.*

* MAY BE BASED ON GENERAL INFORMATION ON ORGANOPHOSPHATES.

HEALTH EFFECTS AND FIRST AID

INHALATION: PHOSMET OXYGEN ANALOG: SEE INFORMATION ON ORGANOPHOSPHATES.

ORGANOPHOSPHATES: CHOLINESTERASE INHIBITOR. **ACUTE EXPOSURE-** WHEN INHALED, THE FIRST EFFECTS OF CHOLINESTERASE INHIBITORS ARE USUALLY RESPIRATORY AND MAY INCLUDE NASAL HYPEREMIA AND WATERY DISCHARGE, COUGH, CHEST DISCOMFORT, DYSPNEA, AND WHEEZING DUE TO INCREASED BRONCHIAL SECRETIONS AND BRONCHOCONSTRICTION. IF SUFFICIENT AMOUNTS ARE ABSORBED, OTHER SYSTEMIC EFFECTS MAY BEGIN WITHIN A FEW MINUTES OR BE DELAYED FOR UP TO 12 HOURS. SYMPTOMS MAY INCLUDE PALLOR, NAUSEA, VOMITING, DIARRHEA, ABDOMINAL CRAMPS, HEADACHE, DIZZINESS, OCULAR PAIN, BLURRED VISION, MIOSIS OR IN SOME CASES, ESPECIALLY INITIALLY, MYDRIASIS, LACRIMATION, SALIVATION, SWEATING, AND CONFUSION. OTHER REPORTED CENTRAL NERVOUS SYSTEM OR NEUROMUSCULAR EFFECTS MAY INCLUDE ATAXIA, SLURRED SPEECH, AREFLEXIA, WEAKNESS, FATIGUE, FASCICULATIONS, TWITCHING, TREMORS POSSIBLY OF THE TONGUE AND EYELIDS, AND EVENTUALLY PARALYSIS OF THE EXTREMITIES AND POSSIBLY OF THE RESPIRATORY MUSCLES. IN SEVERE CASES THERE MAY ALSO BE INVOLUNTARY DEFECATION AND URINATION, CYANOSIS, PSYCHOSIS, HYPERGLYCEMIA, ACUTE PANCREATITIS, CARDIAC IRREGULARITIES, PULMONARY EDEMA, UNCONSCIOUSNESS, CONVULSIONS, AND COMA. DEATH IS PRIMARILY DUE TO RESPIRATORY FAILURE, ALTHOUGH CARDIOVASCULAR EFFECTS INCLUDING CARDIAC ARREST MAY ALSO BE IMPLICATED. LONG TERM SEQUELAE ARE RARE BUT MAY INCLUDE NEUROPSYCHIATRIC DISORDERS AND MYOPATHY WITH MUSCLE TENDERNESS. SOME ORGANOPHOSPHATES MAY CAUSE A DELAYED NEUROPATHY BEGINNING 1-4 WEEKS AFTER AN ACUTE EXPOSURE WHICH MAY OR MAY NOT HAVE CAUSED ACUTE CHOLINERGIC EFFECTS. NUMBNESS, TINGLING, WEAKNESS AND CRAMPING BEGINNING SYMMETRICALLY IN THE LOWER LIMBS MAY PROGRESS TO ATAXIA AND PARALYSIS. IN SEVERE CASES, UPPER LIMB INVOLVEMENT IS POSSIBLE AND FLACCID PARALYSIS MAY PROGRESS TO SPASTIC PARALYSIS WITH EXAGGERATED REFLEXES. IMPROVEMENT MAY OCCUR OVER MONTHS TO YEARS, BUT SOME RESIDUAL IMPAIRMENT USUALLY REMAINS. **CHRONIC EXPOSURE-** REPEATED OR PROLONGED EXPOSURE MAY RESULT IN THE EFFECTS OF ACUTE EXPOSURE INCLUDING THE DELAYED NEUROPATHY. OTHER EFFECTS REPORTED IN WORKERS REPEATEDLY EXPOSED INCLUDE IMPAIRED MEMORY AND CONCENTRATION, ACUTE PSYCHOSIS, SEVERE DEPRESSIONS, IRRITABILTY, CONFUSION, APATHY, EMOTIONAL LABILITY, SOCIAL WITHDRAWAL, CONFUSION, HEADACHE, SPEECH DIFFICULTIES, DELAYED REACTION TIMES, SPATIAL DISORIENTATION, NIGHTMARES, SLEEPWALKING, AND DROWSINESS OR INSOMNIA. AN INFLUENZA-LIKE CONDITION WITH HEADACHE, NAUSEA, WEAKNESS, ANOREXIA AND MALAISE HAS ALSO BEEN REPORTED.

FIRST AID- REMOVE FROM EXPOSURE AREA TO FRESH AIR IMMEDIATELY. IF BREATHING HAS STOPPED, PERFORM ARTIFICIAL RESPIRATION. KEEP PERSON WARM AND AT REST. TREAT SYMPTOMATICALLY AND SUPPORTIVELY. GET MEDICAL ATTENTION IMMEDIATELY.

SKIN CONTACT: PHOSMET OXYGEN ANALOG: SEE INFORMATION ON ORGANOPHOSPHATES.

ORGANOPHOSPHATES: CHOLINESTERASE INHIBITOR. **ACUTE EXPOSURE-** LOCALIZED SWEATING AND FASCICULATIONS MAY OCCUR AT THE SITE OF CONTACT. IF SUFFICIENT AMOUNTS ARE ABSORBED, OTHER EFFECTS OF CHOLINESTERASE INHIBITION AS DESCRIBED IN ACUTE INHALATION MAY OCCUR. SYMPTOMS MAY BE DELAYED 2-3 HOURS, BUT USUALLY NO MORE THAN 12 HOURS. THE RATE OF ABSORPTION IS INCREASED BY THE PRESENCE OF DERMATITIS OR HIGH AMBIENT TEMPERATURES. DELAYED NEUROPATHY IS ALSO POSSIBLE. **CHRONIC EXPOSURE-** REPEATED OR PROLONGED EXPOSURE MAY CAUSE EFFECTS AS DESCRIBED IN ACUTE EXPOSURE. SOME ORGANOPHOSPHATES MAY CAUSE SENSITIZATION.

FIRST AID- REMOVE CONTAMINATED CLOTHING IMMEDIATELY. WASH CONTAMINATED AREAS WITH SOAP AND WATER FOLLOWED BY ALCOHOL (ARENA, POISONING, 4TH ED.). EMERGENCY PERSONNEL SHOULD WEAR GLOVES AND AVOID CONTAMINATION. TREAT RESPIRATORY DIFFICULTY WITH ARTIFICIAL RESPIRATION. GET MEDICAL ATTENTION IMMEDIATELY.

EYE CONTACT: PHOSMET OXYGEN ANALOG: SEE INFORMATION ON ORGANOPHOSPHATES.

ORGANOPHOSPHATES: CHOLINESTERASE INHIBITOR. **ACUTE EXPOSURE-** DIRECT CONTACT MAY CAUSE PAIN, HYPEREMIA, LACRIMATION, TWITCHING OF THE EYELIDS, MIOSIS, AND CILIARY MUSCLE SPASM WITH LOSS OF ACCOMODATION, BLURRED OR DIMMED VISION AND BROWACHE. SOMETIMES MYDRIASIS MAY OCCUR INSTEAD OF MIOSIS. WITH SUFFICIENT EXPOSURE, OTHER SYMPTOMS OF CHOLINESTERASE INHIBITION AS DESCRIBED IN ACUTE INHALATION MAY OCCUR. **CHRONIC EXPOSURE-** REPEATED OR PROLONGED EXPOSURE MAY CAUSE EFFECTS AS DESCRIBED IN ACUTE EXPOSURE. SOME COMPOUNDS HAVE CAUSED TOXIC EFFECTS ON THE CRYSTALLINE LENS, CONJUNCTIVAL THICKENING AND OBSTRUCTION OF THE NASOLACRIMAL CANALS WHEN USED AS MIOTIC EYEDROPS.

FIRST AID- IRRIGATE EYES WITH WATER OR SALINE SOLUTION. IF SYMPTOMS OF POISONING OCCUR, TREAT RESPIRATORY DIFFICULTY WITH ARTIFICIAL RESPIRATION AND OXYGEN. OBSERVE PATIENT FOR AT LEAST 24-36 HOURS (GOSSELIN, CLINICAL TOXICOLOGY OF COMMERCIAL PRODUCTS, 5TH ED.). GET MEDICAL ATTENTION IMMEDIATELY. OXYGEN SHOULD BE ADMINISTERED BY QUALIFIED MEDICAL PERSONNEL.

INGESTION: PHOSMET OXYGEN ANALOG: HIGHLY TOXIC. SEE INFORMATION ON ORGANOPHOSPHATES. PHOSMET FED TO FEMALE RATS ON DAY 13 OF PREGNANCY PRODUCED HYDROCEPHALY IN A LARGE NUMBER OF EMBRYOS. OTHER REPRODUCTIVE EFFECTS HAVE BEEN REPORTED IN ANIMALS.

ORGANOPHOSPHATES: CHOLINESTERASE INHIBITOR. **ACUTE EXPOSURE-** WHEN INGESTED, THE FIRST EFFECTS MAY BE NAUSEA, VOMITING, ANOREXIA, ABDOMINAL CRAMPS AND DIARRHEA. GASTROINTESTINAL ABSORPTION MAY CAUSE SYMPTOMS OF CHOLINESTERASE INHIBITION AS DESCRIBED IN ACUTE INHALATION. SYMPTOMS MAY BEGIN WITHIN MINUTES OR BE DELAYED FOR HOURS. DELAYED EFFECTS INCLUDING NEUROPATHY MAY ALSO OCCUR. **CHRONIC EXPOSURE-** REPEATED INGESTION MAY CAUSE EFFECTS AS DESCRIBED IN ACUTE EXPOSURE.

FIRST AID- IF PERSON IS ALERT AND RESPIRATION IS NOT DEPRESSED, GIVE SYRUP OF IPECAC FOLLOWED BY WATER (IF VOMITING OCCURS, KEEP HEAD BELOW HIPS TO PREVENT ASPIRATION). IF CONSCIOUSNESS LEVEL DECLINES OR VOMITING HAS NOT OCCURRED IN 15 MINUTES EMPTY STOMACH BY GASTRIC LAVAGE WITH THE AID OF CUFFED ENDOTRACHEAL TUBE USING ISOTONIC SALINE OR 5% SODIUM BICARBONATE FOLLOW WITH ACTIVATED CHARCOAL. ESTABLISH AND MAINTAIN AIRWAY. TREAT RESPIRATORY DIFFICULTY WITH ARTIFICIAL RESPIRATION AND OXYGEN. DO NOT GIVE MORPHINE, AMINOPHYLLINE, PHENOTHIAZINES, RESERPINE, FUROSEMIDE, OR ETHACRYNIC ACID (MORGAN, RECOGNITION AND MANAGEMENT OF PESTICIDE POISONINGS, 3RD ED.). TREAT SYMPTOMATICALLY AND SUPPORTIVELY. ADMINISTRATION OF OXYGEN AND LAVAGE MUST BE PERFORMED BY QUALIFIED MEDICAL PERSONNEL. GET MEDICAL ATTENTION IMMEDIATELY.

ANTIDOTE: THE FOLLOWING ANTIDOTE HAS BEEN RECOMMENDED. HOWEVER, THE DECISION AS TO WHETHER THE SEVERITY OF POISONING REQUIRES ADMINISTRATION OF ANY ANTIDOTE AND ACTUAL DOSE REQUIRED SHOULD BE MADE BY QUALIFIED MEDICAL PERSONNEL.

FOR CHOLINESTERASE INHIBITORS: ESTABLISH CLEAR AIRWAY AND TISSUE OXYGENATION BY ASPIRATION OF SECRETIONS, AND IF NECESSARY, BY ASSISTED PULMONARY VENTILATION WITH OXYGEN. IMPROVE TISSUE OXYGENATION AS MUCH AS POSSIBLE BEFORE ADMINISTERING ATROPINE TO MINIMIZE THE RISK OF VENTRICULAR FIBRILLATION. ADMINISTER ATROPINE SULFATE INTRAVENOUSLY, OR INTRAMUSCULARLY IF IV INJECTION IS NOT POSSIBLE. IN MODERATELY SEVERE POISONING ADMINISTER ATROPINE SULFATE, 0.4-2.0 MG REPEATED EVERY 15 MINUTES UNTIL ATROPINIZATION IS ACHIEVED (TACHYCARDIA, FLUSHING, DRY MOUTH, MYDRIASIS). MAINTAIN ATROPINIZATION BY REPEATED DOSES FOR 2-12 HOURS, OR LONGER, DEPENDING ON THE SEVERITY OF POISONING. THE

APPEARANCE OF RALES IN THE LUNG BASES, MIOSIS, SALIVATION, NAUSEA, BRADYCARDIA, ARE ALL INDICATIONS OF INADEQUATE ATROPINIZATION. SEVERELY POISONED INDIVIDUALS MAY EXHIBIT REMARKABLE TOLERANCE TO ATROPINE; TWO OR MORE TIMES THE DOSAGES SUGGESTED ABOVE MAY BE NEEDED. PERSONS NOT POISONED OR ONLY SLIGHTLY POISONED, HOWEVER, MAY DEVELOP SIGNS OF ATROPINE TOXICITY FROM SUCH LARGE DOSAGES: FEVER, MUSCLE FIBRILLATIONS, AND DELIRIUM ARE THE MAIN SIGNS OF ATROPINE TOXICITY. IF THESE SIGNS APPEAR WHILE THE PATIENT IS FULLY ATROPINIZED, ATROPINE ADMINISTRATION SHOULD BE DISCONTINUED, AT LEAST TEMPORARILY. OBSERVE TREATED PATIENTS CLOSELY AT LEAST 24 HOURS TO INSURE THAT SYMPTOMS (POSSIBLY PULMONARY EDEMA) DO NOT RECUR AS ATROPINIZATION WEARS OFF. IN VERY SEVERE POISONINGS, METABOLIC DISPOSITION OF TOXICANT MAY REQUIRE SEVERAL HOURS OR DAYS DURING WHICH ATROPINIZATION MUST BE MAINTAINED. MARKEDLY LOWER LEVELS OF URINARY METABOLITES INDICATE THAT ATROPINE DOSAGE CAN BE TAPERED OFF. AS DOSAGE IS REDUCED, CHECK THE LUNG BASES FREQUENTLY FOR RALES. IF RALES ARE HEARD OR OTHER SYMPTOMS RETURN, RE-ESTABLISH ATROPINIZATION PROMPTLY (MORGAN, RECOGNITION AND MANAGEMENT OF PESTICIDE POISONINGS, 3RD ED.). ADMINISTRATION OF ANTIDOTE MUST BE PERFORMED BY QUALIFIED MEDICAL PERSONNEL.

REACTIVITY

REACTIVITY: STABLE UNDER NORMAL TEMPERATURES AND PRESSURES.

INCOMPATIBILITIES: PHOSMET OXYGEN ANALOG: OXIDIZERS (STRONG): FIRE AND EXPLOSION HAZARD.

DECOMPOSITION: THERMAL DECOMPOSITION PRODUCTS MAY INCLUDE TOXIC OXIDES OF NITROGEN, CARBON, PHOSPHORUS, AND SULFUR.

POLYMERIZATION: HAZARDOUS POLYMERIZATION HAS NOT BEEN REPORTED TO OCCUR UNDER NORMAL TEMPERATURES AND PRESSURES.

STORAGE AND DISPOSAL

OBSERVE ALL FEDERAL, STATE AND LOCAL REGULATIONS WHEN STORING OR DISPOSING OF THIS SUBSTANCE. FOR ASSISTANCE, CONTACT THE DISTRICT DIRECTOR OF THE ENVIRONMENTAL PROTECTION AGENCY.

STORAGE

STORE IN ACCORDANCE WITH 40 CFR 165 RECOMMENDED PROCEDURES FOR THE DISPOSAL AND STORAGE OF PESTICIDES AND PESTICIDE CONTAINERS.
STORE AWAY FROM INCOMPATIBLE SUBSTANCES.

DISPOSAL

DISPOSAL MUST BE IN ACCORDANCE WITH 40 CFR 165 RECOMMENDED PROCEDURES FOR THE DISPOSAL AND STORAGE OF PESTICIDES AND PESTICIDE CONTAINERS.

CONDITIONS TO AVOID

MAY BURN BUT DOES NOT IGNITE READILY.

SPILL AND LEAK PROCEDURES

OCCUPATIONAL SPILL: DO NOT TOUCH SPILLED MATERIAL. STOP LEAK IF YOU CAN DO IT WITHOUT RISK. FOR SMALL SPILLS, TAKE UP WITH SAND OR OTHER ABSORBENT MATERIAL AND PLACE INTO CONTAINERS FOR LATER DISPOSAL. FOR SMALL DRY SPILLS, WITH A CLEAN SHOVEL PLACE MATERIAL INTO CLEAN, DRY CONTAINER AND COVER. MOVE CONTAINERS FROM SPILL AREA. FOR LARGER SPILLS, DIKE FAR AHEAD OF SPILL FOR LATER DISPOSAL. KEEP UNNECESSARY PEOPLE AWAY. ISOLATE HAZARD AREA AND DENY ENTRY.

PROTECTIVE EQUIPMENT

VENTILATION: PROVIDE LOCAL EXHAUST OR PROCESS ENCLOSURE VENTILATION SYSTEM.

RESPIRATOR: THE FOLLOWING RESPIRATORS ARE RECOMMENDED BASED ON INFORMATION FOUND IN THE PHYSICAL DATA, TOXICITY AND HEALTH EFFECTS SECTIONS. THEY ARE RANKED IN ORDER FROM MINIMUM TO MAXIMUM RESPIRATORY PROTECTION. THE SPECIFIC RESPIRATOR SELECTED MUST BE BASED ON CONTAMINATION LEVELS FOUND IN THE WORK PLACE, MUST NOT EXCEED THE WORKING LIMITS OF THE RESPIRATOR AND BE JOINTLY APPROVED BY THE NATIONAL INSTITUTE FOR OCCUPATIONAL SAFETY AND HEALTH AND THE MINE SAFETY AND HEALTH ADMINISTRATION (NIOSH-MSHA).
TYPE 'C' SUPPLIED-AIR RESPIRATOR WITH A FULL FACEPIECE OPERATED IN PRESSURE-DEMAND OR OTHER POSITIVE PRESSURE MODE OR WITH A FULL FACEPIECE, HELMET OR HOOD OPERATED IN CONTINOUS-FLOW MODE.
SELF-CONTAINED BREATHING APPARATUS WITH A FULL FACEPIECE OPERATED IN PRESSURE-DEMAND OR OTHER POSITIVE PRESSURE MODE.
FOR FIREFIGHTING AND OTHER IMMEDIATELY DANGEROUS TO LIFE OR HEALTH CONDITIONS:
SELF-CONTAINED BREATHING APPARATUS WITH FULL FACEPIECE OPERATED IN PRESSURE-DEMAND OR OTHER POSITIVE PRESSURE MODE. SUPPLIED-AIR RESPIRATOR WITH FULL FACEPIECE AND OPERATED IN PRESSURE-DEMAND OR OTHER POSITIVE PRESSURE MODE IN COMBINATION WITH AN AUXILIARY SELF-CONTAINED BREATHING APPARATUS OPERATED IN PRESSURE-DEMAND OR OTHER POSITIVE PRESSURE MODE.

CLOTHING: EMPLOYEE MUST WEAR APPROPRIATE PROTECTIVE (IMPERVIOUS) CLOTHING AND EQUIPMENT TO PREVENT REPEATED OR PROLONGED SKIN CONTACT WITH THIS SUBSTANCE.

GLOVES: EMPLOYEE MUST WEAR APPROPRIATE PROTECTIVE GLOVES TO PREVENT CONTACT WITH THIS SUBSTANCE.

EYE PROTECTION: EMPLOYEE MUST WEAR SPLASH-PROOF OR DUST-RESISTANT SAFETY GOGGLES TO PREVENT EYE CONTACT WITH THIS SUBSTANCE.
EMERGENCY EYE WASH: WHERE THERE IS ANY POSSIBILITY THAT AN EMPLOYEE'S EYES MAY BE EXPOSED TO THIS SUBSTANCE, THE EMPLOYER SHOULD PROVIDE AN EYE WASH FOUNTAIN WITHIN THE IMMEDIATE WORK AREA FOR EMERGENCY USE.

AUTHORIZED BY- OCCUPATIONAL HEALTH SERVICES, INC.
CREATION DATE: 10/04/89 ***REVISION DATE:*** 04/26/90

MATERIAL SAFETY DATA SHEET

OCCUPATIONAL HEALTH SERVICES, INC.
AGRICULTURE AND PESTICIDE DIVISION
450 SEVENTH AVENUE, SUITE 2407
NEW YORK, NEW YORK 10123
1-800-445-MSDS OR (212) 967-1100

EMERGENCY CONTACT:
JOHN S. BRANSFORD, JR. (615) 292-1180

SUBSTANCE IDENTIFICATION

CAS-NUMBER 13171-21-6

SUBSTANCE: PHOSPHAMIDON

TRADE NAMES/SYNONYMS: PHOSPHOROIC ACID, 2-CHLORO-3-(DIETHYLAMINO)-1-METHYL-3-OXO-1-PROPENYL DIMETHYL ESTER; PHOSPHORIC ACID, DIMETHYL ESTER, ESTER WITH 2-CHLORO-N,N-DIETHYL -3-HYDROXYCROTONAMIDE; 2-CHLORO-2-DIETHYLCARBAMOYL-1-METHYLVINYL DIMETHYL PHOSPHATE; 2-CHLORO-3-DIMETHOXYPHOSPHINOYLOXY-N,N-DIETHYLBUT-2-ENAMIDE; 2-CHLORO-3-(DIETHYLAMINO-1-METHYL-3-OXO-1-PROPENYL DIMETHYL PHOSPHATE; DIMETHYL PHOSPHATE ESTER WITH 2-CHLORO-N,N-DIETHYL -3-HYDROXYCROTONAMIDE; O,O-DIMETHYL-O-(2-CHLORO-2-DIETHYCARBAMOYL-1-METHYLVINYL) PHOSPHATE; 1-CHLORO-1-N,N-DIETHYLCARBAMOYL-1-PROPEN-2-YL DIMETHYL PHOSPHATE; DIMECRON; MERKON PHOSPHAMIDONE; C-570; ENT 25,515; PST18670

CHEMICAL FAMILY: ORGANOPHOSPHATE

MOLECULAR FORMULA: C10-H19-CL-N-O5-P

MOLECULAR WEIGHT: 299.72

CERCLA RATINGS (SCALE 0-3): HEALTH=3 FIRE=1 REACTIVITY=0 PERSISTENCE=0

NFPA RATINGS (SCALE 0-4): HEALTH=4 FIRE=1 REACTIVITY=0

COMPONENTS AND CONTAMINANTS

COMPONENT: PHOSPHAMIDON ***PERCENT:*** 100
CAS# 13171-21-6

EXPOSURE LIMITS: PHOSPHAMIDON: NO OCCUPATIONAL EXPOSURE LIMITS ESTABLISHED BY OSHA, ACGIH, OR NIOSH.
100 POUNDS SARA SECTION 302 THRESHOLD PLANNING QUANTITY 1 POUND SARA SECTION 304 REPORTABLE QUANTITY

PHYSICAL DATA

DESCRIPTION: PALE YELLOW LIQUID WITH A FAINT ODOR

BOILING POINT: 324 F (162-C) @ 1.5 MMHG ***MELTING POINT:*** -49 F (-45 C)

SPECIFIC GRAVITY: 1.2132 ***VISCOSITY:*** 70 CP @ 25 C ***VOLATILITY:*** LOW

VAPOR PRESSURE: 0.000025 MMHG @ 20 C ***SOLUBILITY IN WATER:*** MISCIBLE

SOLVENT SOLUBILITY: SOLUBLE IN ACETONE, DICHLOROMETHANE, OCTAN-1-OL, TOLUENE AND MOST ORGANIC SOLVENTS EXCEPT PARAFFINS; SLIGHTLY SOLUBLE IN HEXANE

FIRE AND EXPLOSION DATA

FIRE AND EXPLOSION HAZARD: SLIGHT FIRE HAZARD WHEN EXPOSED TO HEAT OR FLAME.

FLASH POINT: 302 F (150 C) (CC) ***AUTOIGNITION TEMP.:*** 491 F (255 C)

FIREFIGHTING MEDIA: DRY CHEMICAL, CARBON DIOXIDE, HALON, WATER SPRAY OR STANDARD FOAM (1987 EMERGENCY RESPONSE GUIDEBOOK, DOT P 5800.4).
FOR LARGER FIRES, USE WATER SPRAY, FOG OR STANDARD FOAM (1987 EMERGENCY RESPONSE GUIDEBOOK, DOT P 5800.4).

FIREFIGHTING: MOVE CONTAINERS FROM FIRE AREA IF POSSIBLE. FIGHT FIRE FROM MAXIMUM DISTANCE. STAY AWAY FROM STORAGE TANK ENDS. DIKE FIRE CONTROL WATER FOR LATER DISPOSAL. DO NOT SCATTER MATERIAL (1987 EMERGENCY RESPONSE GUIDEBOOK, DOT P 5800.4, GUIDE PAGE 55). EXTINGUISH ONLY IF FLOW CAN BE STOPPED; USE FLOODING AMOUNTS OF WATER AS FOG, SOLID STREAMS MAY BE INEFFECTIVE. COOL CONTAINERS WITH FLOODING AMOUNTS OF WATER FROM AS FAR A DISTANCE AS POSSIBLE. USE WATER SPRAY TO ABSORB TOXIC VAPORS. AVOID BREATHING TOXIC VAPORS; KEEP UPWIND. CONSIDER EVACUATION OF DOWNWIND AREA IF MATERIAL IS LEAKING.

TRANSPORTATION DATA

DEPARTMENT OF TRANSPORTATION HAZARD CLASSIFICATION 49 CFR 172.101: POISON B

DEPARTMENT OF TRANSPORTATION LABELING REQUIREMENTS 49 CFR 172.101 AND SUBPART E: POISON

TOXICITY

PHOSPAMIDON: TOXICITY DATA: 135 MG/M3/4 HOURS INHALATION-RAT LC50; 30 MG/M3/1 HOUR INHALATION-MOUSE LC50; 1300 MG/M3/4 HOURS INHALATION-GUINEA PIG LC50; 80 MG/KG SKIN-RABBIT LD50; 125 MG/KG SKIN-RAT LD50; 8 MG/KG ORAL-RAT LD50; 6 MG/KG ORAL-MOUSE LD50; 70 MG/KG ORAL-RABBIT LD50; 15 MG/KG SUBCUTANEOUS-RAT LD50; 13,200 UG/KG SUBCUTANEOUS-MOUSE LD50; 6 MG/KG INTRAVENOUS-MOUSE LD50; 8700 UG/KG INTRAPERITONEAL-RAT LD50; 5800 UG/KG INTRAPERITONEAL-MOUSE LD50; MUTAGENIC DATA (RTECS); REPRODUCTIVE EFFECTS DATA (RTECS); TUMORIGENIC DATA (RTECS). CARCINOGEN STATUS: NONE. ACUTE TOXICITY LEVEL: HIGHLY TOXIC BY INHALATION, DERMAL ABSORPTION, AND INGESTION. TARGET EFFECTS: CHOLINESTERASE INHIBITOR. POISONING MAY AFFECT THE NERVOUS SYSTEM.* AT INCREASED RISK FROM EXPOSURE: PERSONS WITH RESPIRATORY AILMENTS, RECENT EXPOSURE TO CHOLINESTERASE INHIBITORS OR IMPAIRED CHOLINESTERASE PRODUCTION, OR LIVER MALFUNCTION.* ADDITIONAL DATA: MAY CROSS THE PLACENTA. HIGH ENVIRONMENTAL TEMPERATURES OR EXPOSURE OF THE CHEMICAL TO VISIBLE OR ULTRAVIOLET LIGHT MAY ENHANCE THE TOXICITY. INTERACTIONS WITH MEDICATIONS MAY OCCUR.*

* MAY BE BASED ON GENERAL INFORMATION ON ORGANOPHOSPHATES.

HEALTH EFFECTS AND FIRST AID

INHALATION: PHOSPHAMIDOM: HIGHLY TOXIC. SEE INFORMATION ON ORGANOPHOSPHATES.

ORGANOPHOSPHATES: CHOLINESTERASE INHIBITOR. **ACUTE EXPOSURE-** WHEN INHALED, THE FIRST EFFECTS OF CHOLINESTERASE INHIBITORS ARE USUALLY RESPIRATORY AND MAY INCLUDE NASAL HYPEREMIA AND WATERY DISCHARGE, COUGH, CHEST DISCOMFORT, DYSPNEA, AND WHEEZING DUE TO INCREASED BRONCHIAL SECRETIONS AND BRONCHOCONSTRICTION. IF SUFFICIENT AMOUNTS ARE ABSORBED, OTHER SYSTEMIC EFFECTS MAY BEGIN WITHIN A FEW MINUTES OR BE DELAYED FOR UP TO 12 HOURS. SYMPTOMS MAY INCLUDE PALLOR, NAUSEA, VOMITING, DIARRHEA, ABDOMINAL CRAMPS, HEADACHE, DIZZINESS, OCULAR PAIN, BLURRED VISION, MIOSIS OR IN SOME CASES, ESPECIALLY INITIALLY, MYDRIASIS, LACRIMATION, SALIVATION, SWEATING, AND CONFUSION. OTHER REPORTED CENTRAL NERVOUS SYSTEM OR NEUROMUSCULAR EFFECTS MAY INCLUDE ATAXIA, SLURRED SPEECH, AREFLEXIA, WEAKNESS, FATIGUE, FASCICULATIONS, TWITCHING, TREMORS POSSIBLY OF THE TONGUE AND EYELIDS, AND EVENTUALLY PARALYSIS OF THE EXTREMITIES AND POSSIBLY OF THE RESPIRATORY MUSCLES. IN SEVERE CASES THERE MAY ALSO BE INVOLUNTARY DEFECATION AND URINATION, CYANOSIS, PSYCHOSIS, HYPERGLYCEMIA, ACUTE PANCREATITIS, CARDIAC IRREGULARITIES, PULMONARY EDEMA, UNCONSCIOUSNESS, CONVULSIONS, AND COMA. DEATH IS PRIMARILY DUE TO RESPIRATORY FAILURE, ALTHOUGH CARDIOVASCULAR EFFECTS INCLUDING CARDIAC ARREST MAY ALSO BE IMPLICATED. LONG TERM SEQUELAE ARE RARE BUT MAY INCLUDE NEUROPSYCHIATRIC DISORDERS AND MYOPATHY WITH MUSCLE TENDERNESS. SOME ORGANOPHOSPHATES MAY CAUSE A DELAYED NEUROPATHY BEGINNING 1-4 WEEKS AFTER AN ACUTE EXPOSURE WHICH MAY OR MAY NOT HAVE CAUSED ACUTE CHOLINERGIC EFFECTS. NUMBNESS, TINGLING, WEAKNESS AND CRAMPING BEGINNING SYMMETRICALLY IN THE LOWER LIMBS MAY PROGRESS TO ATAXIA AND PARALYSIS. IN SEVERE CASES, UPPER LIMB INVOLVEMENT IS POSSIBLE AND FLACCID PARALYSIS MAY PROGRESS TO SPASTIC PARALYSIS WITH EXAGGERATED REFLEXES. IMPROVEMENT MAY OCCUR OVER MONTHS TO YEARS, BUT SOME RESIDUAL IMPAIRMENT USUALLY REMAINS. **CHRONIC EXPOSURE-** REPEATED OR PROLONGED EXPOSURE MAY RESULT IN THE EFFECTS OF ACUTE EXPOSURE INCLUDING THE DELAYED NEUROPATHY. OTHER EFFECTS REPORTED IN WORKERS REPEATEDLY EXPOSED INCLUDE IMPAIRED MEMORY AND CONCENTRATION, ACUTE PSYCHOSIS, SEVERE DEPRESSIONS, IRRITABILTY, CONFUSION, APATHY, EMOTIONAL LABILITY, SOCIAL WITHDRAWAL, CONFUSION, HEADACHE, SPEECH DIFFICULTIES, DELAYED REACTION TIMES, SPATIAL DISORIENTATION, NIGHTMARES, SLEEPWALKING, AND DROWSINESS OR INSOMNIA. AN INFLUENZA-LIKE CONDITION WITH HEADACHE, NAUSEA, WEAKNESS, ANOREXIA AND MALAISE HAS ALSO BEEN REPORTED. **FIRST AID-** REMOVE FROM EXPOSURE AREA TO FRESH AIR IMMEDIATELY. IF BREATHING HAS STOPPED, GIVE ARTIFICIAL RESPIRATION. MAINTAIN AIRWAY AND BLOOD PRESSURE AND ADMINISTER OXYGEN IF AVAILABLE. KEEP AFFECTED PERSON WARM AND AT REST. TREAT SYMPTOMATICALLY AND SUPPORTIVELY. ADMINISTRATION OF OXYGEN SHOULD BE PERFORMED BY QUALIFIED PERSONNEL. GET MEDICAL ATTENTION IMMEDIATELY.

SKIN CONTACT: PHOSPHAMIDOM: HIGHLY TOXIC. MAY CAUSE IRRITATION. SEE INFORMATION ON ORGANOPHOSPHATES.

ORGANOPHOSPHATES: CHOLINESTERASE INHIBITOR. **ACUTE EXPOSURE-** LOCALIZED SWEATING AND FASCICULATIONS MAY OCCUR AT THE SITE OF CONTACT. IF SUFFICIENT AMOUNTS ARE ABSORBED, OTHER EFFECTS OF CHOLINESTERASE INHIBITION AS DESCRIBED IN ACUTE INHALATION MAY OCCUR. SYMPTOMS MAY BE DELAYED 2-3 HOURS, BUT USUALLY NO MORE THAN 12 HOURS. THE RATE OF ABSORPTION IS INCREASED BY THE PRESENCE OF DERMATITIS OR HIGH AMBIENT TEMPERATURES. DELAYED NEUROPATHY IS ALSO POSSIBLE. **CHRONIC EXPOSURE-** REPEATED OR PROLONGED EXPOSURE MAY CAUSE EFFECTS AS DESCRIBED IN ACUTE EXPOSURE. SOME ORGANOPHOSPHATES MAY CAUSE SENSITIZATION.

FIRST AID- REMOVE CONTAMINATED CLOTHING IMMEDIATELY. WASH CONTAMINATED AREAS WITH SOAP AND WATER FOLLOWED BY ALCOHOL (ARENA, POISONING, 4TH ED.). EMERGENCY PERSONNEL SHOULD WEAR GLOVES AND AVOID CONTAMINATION. TREAT RESPIRATORY DIFFICULTY WITH ARTIFICIAL RESPIRATION. GET MEDICAL ATTENTION IMMEDIATELY.

EYE CONTACT: PHOSPHAMIDOM: MAY CAUSE IRRITATION. SEE INFORMATION ON ORGANOPHOSPHATES.

ORGANOPHOSPHATES: CHOLINESTERASE INHIBITOR. **ACUTE EXPOSURE-** DIRECT CONTACT MAY CAUSE PAIN, HYPEREMIA, LACRIMATION, TWITCHING OF THE EYELIDS, MIOSIS, AND CILIARY MUSCLE SPASM WITH LOSS OF ACCOMODATION, BLURRED OR DIMMED VISION AND BROWACHE. SOMETIMES MYDRIASIS MAY OCCUR INSTEAD OF MIOSIS. WITH SUFFICIENT EXPOSURE, OTHER SYMPTOMS OF CHOLINESTERASE INHIBITION AS DESCRIBED IN ACUTE INHALATION MAY OCCUR. **CHRONIC EXPOSURE-** REPEATED OR PROLONGED EXPOSURE MAY CAUSE EFFECTS AS DESCRIBED IN ACUTE EXPOSURE. SOME COMPOUNDS HAVE CAUSED TOXIC EFFECTS ON THE CRYSTALLINE LENS, CONJUNCTIVAL THICKENING AND OBSTRUCTION OF THE NASOLACRIMAL CANALS WHEN USED AS MIOTIC EYEDROPS.

FIRST AID- IRRIGATE EYES WITH WATER OR SALINE SOLUTION. IF SYMPTOMS OF POISONING OCCUR, TREAT RESPIRATORY DIFFICULTY WITH ARTIFICIAL RESPIRATION AND OXYGEN. OBSERVE PATIENT FOR AT LEAST 24-36 HOURS (GOSSELIN, CLINICAL TOXICOLOGY OF COMMERCIAL PRODUCTS, 5TH ED.). GET MEDICAL ATTENTION IMMEDIATELY. OXYGEN SHOULD BE ADMINISTERED BY QUALIFIED MEDICAL PERSONNEL.

INGESTION: PHOSPHAMIDOM: HIGHLY TOXIC. ADVERSE EFFECTS ON FERTILITY AND THE FETUS WAS OBSERVED IN RATS GIVEN 5 MG/KG ON DAY 7 OF PREGNANCY. SEE INFORMATION ON ORGANOPHOSPHATES.

ORGANOPHOSPHATES: CHOLINESTERASE INHIBITOR. **ACUTE EXPOSURE-** WHEN INGESTED, THE FIRST EFFECTS MAY BE NAUSEA, VOMITING, ANOREXIA, ABDOMINAL CRAMPS AND DIARRHEA. GASTROINTESTINAL ABSORPTION MAY CAUSE SYMPTOMS OF CHOLINESTERASE INHIBITION AS DESCRIBED IN ACUTE INHALATION. SYMPTOMS MAY BEGIN WITHIN MINUTES OR BE DELAYED FOR HOURS. DELAYED EFFECTS INCLUDING NEUROPATHY MAY ALSO OCCUR. **CHRONIC EXPOSURE-** REPEATED INGESTION MAY CAUSE EFFECTS AS DESCRIBED IN ACUTE EXPOSURE.

FIRST AID- IF PERSON IS ALERT AND RESPIRATION IS NOT DEPRESSED, GIVE SYRUP OF IPECAC FOLLOWED BY WATER (IF VOMITING OCCURS, KEEP HEAD BELOW HIPS TO PREVENT ASPIRATION). IF CONSCIOUSNESS LEVEL DECLINES OR VOMITING HAS NOT OCCURRED IN 15 MINUTES EMPTY STOMACH BY GASTRIC LAVAGE WITH THE AID OF CUFFED ENDOTRACHEAL TUBE USING ISOTONIC SALINE OR 5% SODIUM BICARBONATE FOLLOW WITH ACTIVATED CHARCOAL. ESTABLISH AND MAINTAIN AIRWAY. TREAT RESPIRATORY DIFFICULTY WITH ARTIFICIAL RESPIRATION AND OXYGEN. DO NOT GIVE MORPHINE, AMINOPHYLLINE, PHENOTHIAZINES, RESERPINE, FUROSEMIDE, OR ETHACRYNIC ACID (MORGAN, RECOGNITION AND MANAGEMENT OF PESTICIDE POISONINGS, 3RD ED.). TREAT SYMPTOMATICALLY AND SUPPORTIVELY. ADMINISTRATION OF OXYGEN AND LAVAGE MUST BE PERFORMED BY QUALIFIED MEDICAL PERSONNEL. GET MEDICAL ATTENTION IMMEDIATELY.

ANTIDOTE: THE FOLLOWING ANTIDOTE(S) HAVE BEEN RECOMMENDED. HOWEVER, THE DECISION AS TO WHETHER THE SEVERITY OF POISONING REQUIRES ADMINISTRATION OF ANY ANTIDOTE AND ACTUAL DOSE REQUIRED SHOULD BE MADE BY QUALIFIED MEDICAL PERSONNEL.

FOR CHOLINESTERASE INHIBITORS: ESTABLISH CLEAR AIRWAY AND TISSUE OXYGENATION BY ASPIRATION OF SECRETIONS, AND IF NECESSARY, BY ASSISTED

PULMONARY VENTILATION WITH OXYGEN. IMPROVE TISSUE OXYGENATION AS MUCH AS POSSIBLE BEFORE ADMINISTERING ATROPINE TO MINIMIZE THE RISK OF VENTRICULAR FIBRILLATION. ADMINISTER ATROPINE SULFATE INTRAVENOUSLY, OR INTRAMUSCULARLY IF IV INJECTION IS NOT POSSIBLE. IN MODERATELY SEVERE POISONING ADMINISTER ATROPINE SULFATE, 0.4-2.0 MG REPEATED EVERY 15 MINUTES UNTIL ATROPINIZATION IS ACHIEVED (TACHYCARDIA, FLUSHING, DRY MOUTH, MYDRIASIS). MAINTAIN ATROPINIZATION BY REPEATED DOSES FOR 2-12 HOURS, OR LONGER, DEPENDING ON THE SEVERITY OF POISONING. THE APPEARANCE OF RALES IN THE LUNG BASES, MIOSIS, SALIVATION, NAUSEA, BRADYCARDIA, ARE ALL INDICATIONS OF INADEQUATE ATROPINIZATION. SEVERELY POISONED INDIVIDUALS MAY EXHIBIT REMARKABLE TOLERANCE TO ATROPINE; TWO OR MORE TIMES THE DOSAGES SUGGESTED ABOVE MAY BE NEEDED. PERSONS NOT POISONED OR ONLY SLIGHTLY POISONED, HOWEVER, MAY DEVELOP SIGNS OF ATROPINE TOXICITY FROM SUCH LARGE DOSAGES: FEVER, MUSCLE FIBRILLATIONS, AND DELIRIUM ARE THE MAIN SIGNS OF ATROPINE TOXICITY. IF THESE SIGNS APPEAR WHILE THE PATIENT IS FULLY ATROPINIZED, ATROPINE ADMINISTRATION SHOULD BE DISCONTINUED, AT LEAST TEMPORARILY. OBSERVE TREATED PATIENTS CLOSELY AT LEAST 24 HOURS TO INSURE THAT SYMPTOMS (POSSIBLY PULMONARY EDEMA) DO NOT RECUR AS ATROPINIZATION WEARS OFF. IN VERY SEVERE POISONINGS, METABOLIC DISPOSITION OF TOXICANT MAY REQUIRE SEVERAL HOURS OR DAYS DURING WHICH ATROPINIZATION MUST BE MAINTAINED. MARKEDLY LOWER LEVELS OF URINARY METABOLITES INDICATE THAT ATROPINE DOSAGE CAN BE TAPERED OFF. AS DOSAGE IS REDUCED, CHECK THE LUNG BASES FREQUENTLY FOR RALES. IF RALES ARE HEARD OR OTHER SYMPTOMS RETURN, RE-ESTABLISH ATROPINIZATION PROMPTLY (MORGAN, RECOGNITION AND MANAGEMENT OF PESTICIDE POISONINGS, 3RD ED.). ADMINISTRATION OF ANTIDOTE MUST BE PERFORMED BY QUALIFIED MEDICAL PERSONNEL.

IN CASES OF SEVERE POISONING BY ORGANOPHOSPHATE PESTICIDES IN WHICH RESPIRATORY DEPRESSION, MUSCLE WEAKNESS AND TWITCHINGS ARE SEVERE, GIVE PRALIDOXIME (PROTOPAM-AYERST, 2-PAM), 1.0 GRAM INTRAVENOUSLY AT NO MORE THAN 0.5 GRAM PER MINUTE. DOSAGE OF PRALIDOXIME MAY BE REPEATED IN 1-2 HOURS, THEN AT 10-12 HOUR INTERVALS IF NEEDED. IN VERY SEVERE POISONINGS, DOSAGE RATES MAY BE DOUBLED. TREATMENT WITH PRALIDOXIME WILL BE MOST EFFECTIVE IF GIVEN WITHIN THIRTY-SIX HOURS AFTER POISONING (MORGAN, RECOGNITION AND MANAGEMENT OF PESTICIDE POISONINGS, 3RD ED.). ANTIDOTE SHOULD BE ADMINISTERED BY QUALIFIED MEDICAL PERSONNEL.

REACTIVITY

REACTIVITY: STABLE UNDER NORMAL TEMPERATURES AND PRESSURES.

INCOMPATIBILITIES: PHOSPHAMIDOM: ALKALINE MATERIAL: MAY CAUSE HYDROLYSIS. ALUMINUM: MAY BE CORRODED. IRON: MAY BE CORRODED. STRONG OXIDIZING MATERIALS: MAY REACT. STAINLESS STELL: MAY BE CORRODED. TINPLATE: MAY BE CORRODED.

DECOMPOSITION: THERMAL DECOMPOSITION MAY RELEASE TOXIC OXIDES OF NITROGEN AND PHOSPHORUS AND CORROSIVE HYDROGEN CHLORIDE.

POLYMERIZATION: HAZARDOUS POLYMERIZATION HAS NOT BEEN REPORTED TO OCCUR UNDER NORMAL TEMPERATURES AND PRESSURES.

STORAGE AND DISPOSAL

OBSERVE ALL FEDERAL, STATE AND LOCAL REGULATIONS WHEN STORING OR DISPOSING OF THIS SUBSTANCE. FOR ASSISTANCE, CONTACT THE DISTRICT DIRECTOR OF THE ENVIRONMENTAL PROTECTION AGENCY.

STORAGE

STORE IN ACCORDANCE WITH 40 CFR 165 RECOMMENDED PROCEDURES FOR THE DISPOSAL AND STORAGE OF PESTICIDES AND PESTICIDE CONTAINERS.

STORE AWAY FROM INCOMPATIBLE SUBSTANCES.

THRESHOLD PLANNING QUANTITY (TPQ): THE SUPERFUND AMENDMENTS AND REAUTHORIZATION ACT (SARA) SECTION 302 REQUIRES THAT EACH FACILITY WHERE ANY EXTREMELY HAZARDOUS SUBSTANCE IS PRESENT IN A QUANTITY EQUAL TO OR GREATER THAN THE TPQ ESTABLISHED FOR THAT SUBSTANCE NOTIFY THE STATE EMERGENCY RESPONSE COMMISSION FOR THE STATE IN WHICH IT IS LOCATED. SECTION 303 OF SARA REQUIRES THESE FACILITIES TO PARTICIPATE IN LOCAL EMERGENCY RESPONSE PLANNING (40 CFR 355.30).

DISPOSAL

DISPOSAL MUST BE IN ACCORDANCE WITH 40 CFR 165 RECOMMENDED PROCEDURES FOR THE DISPOSAL AND STORAGE OF PESTICIDES AND PESTICIDE CONTAINERS.

CONDITIONS TO AVOID

MAY BURN BUT DOES NOT IGNITE READILY. CONTAINERS MAY EXPLODE IN HEAT OF FIRE.

SPILL AND LEAK PROCEDURES

OCCUPATIONAL SPILL: DO NOT TOUCH SPILLED MATERIAL. STOP LEAK IF YOU CAN DO IT WITHOUT RISK. USE WATER SPRAY TO REDUCE VAPORS. FOR SMALL SPILLS, TAKE UP WITH SAND OR OTHER ABSORBENT MATERIAL AND PLACE INTO CONTAINERS FOR LATER DISPOSAL. FOR SMALL DRY SPILLS, WITH A CLEAN SHOVEL PLACE MATERIAL INTO CLEAN, DRY CONTAINERS AND COVER. MOVE CONTAINERS FROM SPILL AREA. FOR LARGER SPILLS, DIKE FAR AHEAD OF SPILL FOR LATER DISPOSAL. KEEP UNNECESSARY PEOPLE AWAY. ISOLATE HAZARD AREA AND DENY ENTRY. VENTILATE CLOSED SPACES BEFORE ENTERING.

REPORTABLE QUANTITY (RQ): 1 POUND THE SUPERFUND AMENDMENTS AND REAUTHORIZATION ACT (SARA) SECTION 304 REQUIRES THAT A RELEASE EQUAL TO OR GREATER THAN THE REPORTABLE QUANTITY FOR THIS SUBSTANCE BE IMMEDIATELY REPORTED TO THE LOCAL EMERGENCY PLANNING COMMITTEE AND THE STATE EMERGENCY RESPONSE COMMISSION (40 CFR 355.40). IF THE RELEASE OF THIS SUBSTANCE IS REPORTABLE UNDER CERCLA SECTION 103, THE NATIONAL RESPONSE CENTER MUST BE NOTIFIED IMMEDIATELY AT (800) 424-8802 OR (202) 426-2675 IN THE METROPOLITAN WASHINGTON, D.C. AREA (40 CFR 302.6).

PROTECTIVE EQUIPMENT

VENTILATION: PROCESS ENCLOSURE RECOMMENDED.

RESPIRATOR: THE FOLLOWING RESPIRATORS ARE RECOMMENDED BASED ON INFORMATION FOUND IN THE PHYSICAL DATA, TOXICITY AND HEALTH EFFECTS SECTIONS. THEY ARE RANKED IN ORDER FROM MINIMUM TO MAXIMUM RESPIRATORY PROTECTION. THE SPECIFIC RESPIRATOR SELECTED MUST BE BASED ON CONTAMINATION LEVELS FOUND IN THE WORK PLACE, MUST NOT EXCEED THE WORKING LIMITS OF THE RESPIRATOR AND BE JOINTLY APPROVED BY THE NATIONAL INSTITUTE FOR OCCUPATIONAL SAFETY AND HEALTH AND THE MINE SAFETY AND HEALTH ADMINISTRATION (NIOSH-MSHA).

TYPE 'C' SUPPLIED-AIR RESPIRATOR WITH A FULL FACEPIECE OPERATED IN PRESSURE-DEMAND OR OTHER POSITIVE PRESSURE MODE OR WITH A FULL FACEPIECE, HELMET OR HOOD OPERATED IN CONTINOUS-FLOW MODE.

SELF-CONTAINED BREATHING APPARATUS WITH A FULL FACEPIECE OPERATED IN PRESSURE-DEMAND OR OTHER POSITIVE PRESSURE MODE.

FOR FIREFIGHTING AND OTHER IMMEDIATELY DANGEROUS TO LIFE OR HEALTH CONDITIONS:

SELF-CONTAINED BREATHING APPARATUS WITH FULL FACEPIECE OPERATED IN PRESSURE-DEMAND OR OTHER POSITIVE PRESSURE MODE.

SUPPLIED-AIR RESPIRATOR WITH FULL FACEPIECE AND OPERATED IN PRESSURE-DEMAND OR OTHER POSITIVE PRESSURE MODE IN COMBINATION WITH AN AUXILIARY SELF-CONTAINED BREATHING APPARATUS OPERATED IN PRESSURE-DEMAND OR OTHER POSITIVE PRESSURE MODE.

CLOTHING: EMPLOYEE MUST WEAR APPROPRIATE PROTECTIVE (IMPERVIOUS) CLOTHING AND EQUIPMENT TO PREVENT ANY POSSIBILITY OF SKIN CONTACT WITH THIS SUBSTANCE.

GLOVES: EMPLOYEE MUST WEAR APPROPRIATE PROTECTIVE GLOVES TO PREVENT CONTACT WITH THIS SUBSTANCE.

EYE PROTECTION: EMPLOYEE MUST WEAR SPLASH-PROOF OR DUST-RESISTANT SAFETY GOGGLES AND A FACESHIELD TO PREVENT CONTACT WITH THIS SUBSTANCE.

EMERGENCY WASH FACILITIES: WHERE THERE IS ANY POSSIBILITY THAT AN EMPLOYEE'S EYES AND/OR SKIN MAY BE EXPOSED TO THIS SUBSTANCE, THE EMPLOYER SHOULD PROVIDE AN EYE WASH FOUNTAIN AND QUICK DRENCH SHOWER WITHIN THE IMMEDIATE WORK AREA FOR EMERGENCY USE.

AUTHORIZED BY- OCCUPATIONAL HEALTH SERVICES, INC.

CREATION DATE: 10/04/89 ***REVISION DATE:*** 05/04/90

ALPHABETICAL INDEX

ALPHABETICAL INDEX

ALPHABETICAL INDEX

ALPHABETICAL INDEX

ALPHABETICAL INDEX

SUBSTANCE NAME	CAS #	PST #
ACETIC ACID, MERCAPTO-, ETHYL ESTER, S-ESTER WITH O,O-DIETHYL PHOSPHORODITHIOATE	919-54-0	PST00117
ACETIC ACID, MERCAPTO-, ETHYL ESTER, S-ESTER WITH O,O-DIETHYL -PHOSPHOROTHIOATE	2425-25-4	PST73057
ACETIC ACID, MERCAPTOPHENYL-, ETHYL ESTER, S-ESTER WITH O,O-DIMETHYLPHOSPHORODITHIOATE	2597-03-7	PST72337
ACETIC ACID, N-AMYL ESTER	628-63-7	PST15270
ACETIC ACID, PENTYL ESTER	628-63-7	PST15270
ACETIC ACID, PHENYL MERCURY DERIV.	62-38-4	PST18560
ACETIC ACID, SODIUM SALT	126-96-5	PST71497
ACETIC ACID, SODIUM SALT (2:1)	126-96-5	PST71497
ACETIC ACID, SODIUM SALT, COMPOUND WITH ACETIC ACID (1:1)	126-96-5	PST71497
ACETIC ACID, TRICHLORO-	76-03-9	PST23810
ACETIC ACID, TRICHLORO-, COMPOUND WITH N,N-DIMETHYL-N'- -PHENYLUREA (1:1)	4482-55-7	PST71389
ACETIC ACID, TRICHLORO-, COMPOUND WITH N'-(4-CHLOROPHENYL)-N,N-DIMETHYLUREA (1:1)	140-41-0	PST15197
ACETIC ACID, TRICHLORO-, COMPOUND WITH 3-(P-CHLOROPHENYL)-1,1-DIMETHYLUREA (1:1)	140-41-0	PST15197
ACETIC ACID, TRICHLORO-, COMPUND WITH 1,1-DIMETHYL-	4482-55-7	PST71389
ACETIC ACID, TRICHLORO-, SODIUM SALT	650-51-1	PST73307
ACETIC ACID, 2,6-DIMETHYL-M-DIOXAN-4-OL ESTER	828-00-2	PST28395
ACETIC ESTER	141-78-6	PST08750
ACETIC ETHER	141-78-6	PST08750
ACETIC PEROXIDE	79-21-0	PST18310
ACETIDIN	141-78-6	PST08750
ACETIMIDOYLPHOSPHORAMIDOTHIOIC ACID O,O-BIS(P-CHLOROPHENYL) ESTER	4104-14-7	PST71150
ACETO-CAUSTIN	76-03-9	PST23810
ACETOCHLOR	34256-82-1	PST72539
ACETOFOS	2425-25-4	PST73057
ACETOMETHOXANE	828-00-2	PST28395
ACETONE	67-64-1	PST00140
ACETOPHENETIDIN	62-44-2	PST18340
ACETOPHOS	2425-25-4	PST73057
ACETOXON	2425-25-4	PST73057
ACETOXY(2-METHOXYETHYL)MERCURY	151-38-2	PST83031
ACETOXYETHANE	141-78-6	PST08750
ACETOXYETHYLMERCURY	109-62-6	PST71476
ACETOXYPHENYLMERCURY	62-38-4	PST18560
ACETOXYTRIBUTYLSTANNANE	56-36-0	PST72220
ACETOXYTRIBUTYLTIN	56-36-0	PST72220
ACETOXYTRIPHENYLSTANNANE	900-95-8	PST24378
ACETYL HYDROPEROXIDE	79-21-0	PST18310
ACETYLPHENETIDIN	62-44-2	PST18340
ACETYLPHOSPHORAMIDOTHIOIC ACID O,S-DIMETHYL ESTER	30560-19-1	PST00065
ACID BLUE 9 (DIAMMONIUM SALT)	2650-18-2	PST08277
ACID LEAD ARSENATE	7784-40-9	PST12540
ACID LEAD ORTHOARSENATE	7784-40-9	PST12540
ACID POTASSIUM SULFATE	7646-93-7	PST19255
ACID SODIUM PHOSPHATE	7558-80-7	PST15190
ACIFLUORFEN	50594-66-6	PST72452
ACIFLUORFEN AMINO METABOLITE	UNASSIGNED	PST00316
ACIFLUORFEN SODIUM	62476-59-9	PST72453
ACIFLUORFEN SODIUM SALT	62476-59-9	PST72453

ALPHABETICAL INDEX

ALPHABETICAL INDEX

SUBSTANCE NAME	CAS #	PST #
AGRI-SUL	7704-34-9	PST22280
AGRIMYCIN	57-92-1	PST21917
AGRIMYCIN 17	57-92-1	PST21917
AGRIMYCIN 17	3810-74-0	PST84290
AGRISIL	327-98-0	PST00478
AGRITOX	327-98-0	PST00478
AGRITOX OXON	6492-18-8	PST23871
AGROCERES	76-44-8	PST10660
AGROCIT	17804-35-2	PST02580
AGROTHION	122-14-5	PST09678
AGROXON	94-74-6	PST27880
AGROXONE	94-74-6	PST27880
AGUATHOL	129-67-9	PST08590
AI 3-29054	35367-38-5	PST07388
AIP	20859-73-8	PST00970
AITC	57-06-7	PST00680
AIZEN MALACHITE GREEN	569-64-2	PST13533
AKAR	510-15-6	PST04740
AKTICON	1912-24-9	PST02150
AKTIKON	1912-24-9	PST02150
AKTISAL	144-62-7	PST17360
AKTON	1757-18-2	PST00493
AL	7429-90-5	PST01000
AL-PHOS	20859-73-8	PST00970
ALACHLOR	15972-60-8	PST00506
ALANAP	132-66-1	PST71340
ALANAP	132-67-2	PST71341
ALANAP 3	132-67-2	PST71341
ALANEX	15972-60-8	PST00506
ALAOURIN	8006-54-0	PST12425
ALAR	1596-84-5	PST06195
ALATEX	75-99-0	PST06200
ALBOCARBON	91-20-3	PST16120
ALBONE	7722-84-1	PST11190
ALBONE DS	7722-84-1	PST11190
ALBRASS	1918-16-7	PST19686
ALCIDE	10049-04-4	PST04610
ALCL3	7446-70-0	PST00900
ALCOHOL	64-17-5	PST08700
ALCOHOL ANHYDROUS	64-17-5	PST08700
ALCOHOL C-10	112-30-1	PST06285
ALCOHOL C-6	111-27-3	PST15630
ALCOHOLS, C11-15-SECONDARY, ETHOXYLATED	68131-40-8	PST85315
ALCOHOLS, LANOLIN, ETHOXYLATED	61790-81-6	PST08741
ALDACIDE	30525-89-4	PST18000
ALDEHYDE C18	104-61-0	PST10334
ALDICARB	116-06-3	PST00500
ALDICARB SULFONE	1646-88-4	PST72406
ALDICARB SULFOXIDE	1646-87-3	PST00503
ALDIFEN	51-28-5	PST28620
ALDOXYCARB	1646-88-4	PST72406
ALDRIN	309-00-2	PST00520
ALENTISAN	21564-17-0	PST71392
ALFACRON	18181-70-9	PST73035

ALPHABETICAL INDEX

ALPHABETICAL INDEX

ALPHABETICAL INDEX

ALPHABETICAL INDEX

SUBSTANCE NAME	CAS #	PST #
ETHOXY)ETHYL)-, CHLORIDE		
AMMONIUM, BENZYLDIMETHYL(2-(2-(P-1,1,3,3-TETRAMETHYLBUTYLCRESOXY)ETHOXY)ETHYL)-, CHLORIDE	25155-18-4	PST71862
AMMONIUM, DIMETHYLOCTADECYL(3-TRIMETHOXYSILYL)PROPYL)-, CHLORIDE	27668-52-6	PST72370
AMOBEN	133-90-4	PST29084
AMORPHOUS SILICA DUST	7631-86-9	PST20610
AMORPHOUS, RED PHOSPHORUS	7723-14-0	PST18790
AMS	7773-06-0	PST01400
AMYL ACETATE	628-63-7	PST15270
AMYL ACETATE ETHER	628-63-7	PST15270
AMYL ACETIC ESTER	628-63-7	PST15270
AMYL ACETIC ETHER	628-63-7	PST15270
AMYLCARBINOL	111-27-3	PST15630
AMYLIN	9004-53-9	PST06363
ANACEL	136-47-0	PST72269
ANALAP-1	132-66-1	PST71340
ANALAPE	132-66-1	PST71340
ANALGIT	119-36-8	PST14720
ANATOX	8001-35-2	PST23640
ANELDA	2008-41-5	PST71474
ANESTARON	136-47-0	PST72269
ANESTHESINE	94-09-7	PST72267
ANHYDROGLUCOCHLORAL	15879-93-3	PST00775
ANHYDROL	64-17-5	PST08700
ANHYDROUS BORIC ACID	1303-86-2	PST03290
ANHYDROUS CALCIUM SULFATE	7778-18-9	PST04110
ANHYDROUS CITRIC ACID	77-92-9	PST05200
ANHYDROUS GYPSUM	7778-18-9	PST04110
ANHYDROUS HYDROCHLORIC ACID	7647-01-0	PST11150
ANHYDROUS SODIUM ACID PHOSPHATE	7558-79-4	PST08330
ANHYDROUS SODIUM SULFITE	7757-83-7	PST21660
ANHYDROUS SULFATE OF LIME	7778-18-9	PST04110
ANICON KOMBI	94-74-6	PST27880
ANICON M	94-74-6	PST27880
ANILAZIN	101-05-3	PST01526
ANILAZINE	101-05-3	PST01526
ANILINE GREEN	569-64-2	PST13533
ANILINE, N-SEC-BUTYL-4-TERT-BUTYL-2,6-DINITRO-	33629-47-9	PST03525
ANILINE, 2,6-DICHLORO-4-NITRO-	99-30-9	PST28910
ANILINE, 4-(METHYLSULFONYL)-2,6-DINITRO-N,N-DIPROPYL-	4726-14-1	PST16525
ANILINOBENZENE	122-39-4	PST08100
ANIMAL OIL	8001-85-2	PST03250
ANISE OIL	8007-70-3	PST71028
ANISEED OIL	8007-70-3	PST71028
ANISOLE, 2-SEC-BUTYL-4,6-DINITRO-	6099-79-2	PST08022
ANIYALINE	101-05-3	PST01526
ANKILOSTIN	127-18-4	PST22900
ANON	108-94-1	PST05890
ANONE	108-94-1	PST05890
ANOZOL	84-66-2	PST07210
ANSAR 138	75-60-5	PST03710
ANTABUSE	97-77-8	PST08370
ANTAK	112-30-1	PST06285
ANTERGON	123-33-1	PST13570

ALPHABETICAL INDEX

ALPHABETICAL INDEX

ALPHABETICAL INDEX

ALPHABETICAL INDEX

ALPHABETICAL INDEX

ALPHABETICAL INDEX

SUBSTANCE NAME	CAS #	PST #
BAY-FCR 1272	68359-37-5	PST72630
BAY-SYM 1500	64529-56-2	PST09111
BAYCID (FORMULATION)	55-38-9	PST02550
BAYER NTN 9306	35400-43-2	PST22387
BAYER 16259	2642-71-9	PST02205
BAYER 18.436	919-86-8	PST83065
BAYER 19639	298-04-4	PST08380
BAYER 21/116	8022-00-2	PST14438
BAYER 22/190	500-28-7	PST71379
BAYER 22190	500-28-7	PST71379
BAYER 22555	140-56-7	PST73084
BAYER 25/154	919-86-8	PST83065
BAYER 29493	55-38-9	PST02550
BAYER 33172	3878-19-1	PST73188
BAYER 37289	327-98-0	PST00478
BAYER 39007	114-26-1	PST02540
BAYER 41 367C	3766-81-2	PST03324
BAYER 44646	2032-59-9	PST71500
BAYER 5360	443-48-1	PST72529
BAYER 60618	1929-88-0	PST72971
BAYER 74283	18691-97-9	PST14108
BAYER 77049	13593-03-8	PST73112
BAYER 77488	14816-18-3	PST73292
BAYER 78418	17109-49-8	PST08555
BAYER 8169	8065-48-3	PST06320
BAYGON	114-26-1	PST02540
BAYPIVAL	38083-17-9	PST05208
BAYRUSIL	13593-03-8	PST73112
BAYSAN	38083-17-9	PST05208
BAYTEX (FORMULATION)	55-38-9	PST02550
BAYTEX OXON	6552-12-1	PST02551
BAYTEX OXON SULFONE	14086-35-2	PST02552
BAYTEX OXON SULFOXIDE	6552-13-2	PST02553
BAYTEX SULFONE	3761-42-0	PST02554
BAYTHION	14816-18-3	PST73292
BAYTHROID	68359-37-5	PST72630
BCF-BUSHKILLER	93-76-5	PST28690
BEET-KLEEN	101-42-8	PST09679
BEET-KLEEN	101-21-3	PST71148
BELGRAN	34123-59-6	PST12254
BELMARK	51630-58-1	PST19948
BENALAN	1861-40-1	PST02570
BENAZOLIN	3813-05-6	PST72725
BENAZOLINE	3813-05-6	PST72725
BENCARBATE	22781-23-3	PST02560
BENDIOCARB	22781-23-3	PST02560
BENDIOXIDE	25057-89-0	PST02584
BENE OIL	8008-74-0	PST20575
BENEFEX	1861-40-1	PST02570
BENEFIN	1861-40-1	PST02570
BENELUX	39196-18-4	PST23330
BENFLURALIN	1861-40-1	PST02570
BENFURACARB	82560-54-1	PST72562
BENI OIL	8008-74-0	PST20575

SUBSTANCE NAME	CAS #	PST #
BENIROL	8001-54-5	PST00539
BENLATE	17804-35-2	PST02580
BENNE OIL	8008-74-0	PST20575
BENOMYL	17804-35-2	PST02580
BENSULFOID	7704-34-9	PST22280
BENSULIDE	741-58-2	PST02583
BENSULIDE OXON	UNASSIGNED	PST02582
BENSULIDE OXYGEN ANALOG	UNASSIGNED	PST02582
BENTAZON	25057-89-0	PST02584
BENTAZON A.I.B.A. METABOLITE	UNASSIGNED	PST02581
BENTAZON AMINO ISOPROPYL BENZOIC ACID METABOLITE	UNASSIGNED	PST02581
BENTAZONE	25057-89-0	PST02584
BENTHIAZOLE	21564-17-0	PST71392
BENTHIOCARB	28249-77-6	PST72381
BENTROL	1689-83-4	PST11468
BENYLATE	120-51-4	PST02805
BENZAC	50-31-7	PST71134
BENZADOX	5251-93-4	PST72964
BENZAL GREEN	569-64-2	PST13533
BENZALDEHYDE	100-52-7	PST02590
BENZALDEHYDE FFC	100-52-7	PST02590
BENZALKON	8001-54-5	PST00537
BENZALKONIUM CHLORIDE	8001-54-5	PST00537
BENZALKONIUM CHLORIDE	8001-54-5	PST00539
BENZALKONIUM CHLORIDE	53516-76-0	PST71834
BENZALKONIUM CHLORIDE	68424-85-1	PST71835
BENZAMIDE, N-(((4-CHLOROPHENYL)AMINO)CARBONYL)-2,6-DIFLUORO	35367-38-5	PST07388
BENZAMIDE, N-(3,4-DICHLOROPHENYL)-N-((DIMETHYLAMINO)CARBONYL)-	3134-12-1	PST72972
BENZAMIDE, N,N-DIETHYL-3-METHYL-	134-62-3	PST84230
BENZAMIDE, 2,6-DICHLOROTHIO-	1918-13-4	PST73046
BENZAMIDE, 3,5-DICHLORO-N-(1,1-DIMETHYL-2-PROPYNYL)-	23950-58-5	PST19670
BENZAMIDO-OXYACETIC ACID	5251-93-4	PST72964
BENZAR	3813-05-6	PST72725
BENZENAMINE, N-BUTYL-N-ETHYL-2,6-DINITRO-4-(TRIFLUOROMETHYL)-	1861-40-1	PST02570
BENZENAMINE, N-ETHYL-N-(2-METHYL-2-PROPENYL)-2,6-DINITRO-4-(TRIFLUOROMETHYL)-	55283-68-6	PST72436
BENZENAMINE, N-PHENYL-	122-39-4	PST08100
BENZENAMINE, 2,6-DICHLORO-4-NITRO-	99-30-9	PST28910
BENZENAMINE, 2,6-DINITRO-N,N-DIPROPYL-4-(TRIFLUOROMETHYL)-	1582-09-8	PST24085
BENZENAMINE, 4-(METHYLSULFONYL)-2,6-DINITRO-N,N-DIPROPYL-	4726-14-1	PST16525
BENZENAMINE, 4-(1,1-DIMETHYLETHYL)-N-(1-METHYLPROPYL)-2,6-DINITRO-	33629-47-9	PST03525
BENZENE HEXACHLORIDE	319-84-6	PST00770
BENZENE HEXACHLORIDE	608-73-1	PST03080
BENZENE HEXACHLORIDE	319-86-8	PST06310
BENZENE HEXACHLORIDE	58-89-9	PST12810
BENZENE METHYLAL	100-52-7	PST02590
BENZENE, DIMETHYL-	1330-20-7	PST25150
BENZENE, O-DICHLORO-	95-50-1	PST16970
BENZENE, P-DICHLORO-	106-46-7	PST17640
BENZENE, 1-CHLORO-2-(2-CHLORO-1-(4-CHLOROPHENYL)ETHENYL-	14835-94-0	PST04753
BENZENE, 1-CHLORO-2-(2,2-DICHLORO-1-(4-CHLOROPHENYL)ETHENYL)	3424-82-6	PST06245
BENZENE, 1-CHLORO-3-(2,2-DICHLORO-1-(4-CHLOROPHENYL)ETHYL)-	4329-12-8	PST04752
BENZENE, 1-CHLORO-4-(((4-CHLOROPHENYL)METHYL)THIO)-	103-17-3	PST71139
BENZENE, 1-CHLORO-4-(PHENYLSULFONYL)-	80-00-2	PST71663

ALPHABETICAL INDEX

SUBSTANCE NAME	CAS #	PST #
BENZENE, 1,1'-(CHLOROETHENYLIDENE)BIS(4-CHLORO-	1022-22-6	PST06322
BENZENE, 1,1'-(DICHLOROETHENYLIDENE)BIS(4-CHLORO-	72-55-9	PST06247
BENZENE, 1,1'-(2-NITROBUTYLIDENE)BIS(4-CHLORO-	117-26-0	PST71635
BENZENE, 1,1'-(2,2-DICHLOROETHYLIDENE)BIS(4-CHLORO-	72-54-8	PST06240
BENZENE, 1,1'-(2,2-DICHLOROETHYLIDENE)BIS(4-ETHYL-	72-56-0	PST71373
BENZENE, 1,1'-(2,2,2-TRICHLOROETHYLIDENE)BIS(4-CHLORO-	50-29-3	PST06250
BENZENE, 1,1'-(2,2,2-TRICHLOROETHYLIDENE)BIS(4-METHOXY-	72-43-5	PST14220
BENZENE, 1,1'METHYLENEBIS(4-CHLORO-	101-76-8	PST06321
BENZENE, 1,2-DICHLORO-	95-50-1	PST16970
BENZENE, 1,2,4,5-TETRACHLORO-3-NITRO-	117-18-0	PST71616
BENZENE, 1,3,5-TRICHLORO-2-(4-NITROPHENOXY)-	1836-77-7	PST23865
BENZENE, 1,4-DICHLORO-	106-46-7	PST17640
BENZENE, 1,4-DICHLORO-2,5-DIMETHOXY-	2675-77-6	PST71229
BENZENE, 2-CHLORO-1-(3-ETHOXY-4-NITROPHENOXY)-4-(TRIFLUOROMETHYL)-	42874-03-3	PST72413
BENZENE, 2-METHOXY-1-(1-METHYLPROPYL)-3,5-DINITRO-	6099-79-2	PST08022
BENZENE, 2-NITRO-1-(4-NITROPHENOXY)-4-(TRIFLUOROMETHYL)-	15457-05-3	PST72248
BENZENE, 2,4-DICHLORO-1-(4-NITROPHENOXY)-	1836-75-5	PST23580
BENZENEACETAMIDE, N,N-DIMETHYL-ALPHA-PHENYL-	957-51-7	PST71406
BENZENEACETIC ACID, ALPHA-((DIMETHOXYPHOSPHINOTHIOYL)THIO)-, ETHYL ESTER	2597-03-7	PST72337
BENZENEACETIC ACID, 4-CHLORO-ALPHA-(4-CHLOROPHENYL)-	83-05-6	PST06232
BENZENEACETIC ACID, 4-CHLORO-ALPHA-(4-CHLOROPHENYL)-ALPHA-HYDROXY-, ETHYL ESTER	510-15-6	PST04740
BENZENECARBINOL	100-51-6	PST02800
BENZENECARBONAL	100-52-7	PST02590
BENZENECARBOTHIOAMIDE, 2,6-DICHLORO-	1918-13-4	PST73046
BENZENECARBOXALDEHYDE	100-52-7	PST02590
BENZENECARBOXYLIC ACID	65-85-0	PST02720
BENZENEDIAZOSULFONIC ACID, P-(DIMETHYLAMINO)-, SODIUM SALT	140-56-7	PST73084
BENZENEETHANOL, 4-CHLORO-BETA-(4-CHLOROPHENYL)-	2642-82-2	PST06323
BENZENEFORMIC ACID	65-85-0	PST02720
BENZENEMETHANAMINIUM, AR-DODECYL-N,N,N-TRIMETHYL-, CHLORIDE	1330-85-4	PST71854
BENZENEMETHANAMINIUM, N,N-DIMETHYL-N-(2-(2-(METHYL-4-(1,1,3,3-TETRAMETHYLBUTYL)PHENOXY)ETHOXY)ETHYL)-, CHLORIDE	25155-18-4	PST71862
BENZENEMETHANAMINIUM, N,N-DIMETHYL-N-(2-(2-(4-(1,1,3,3-TETRAMETHYLBUTYL)PHENOXY)ETHOXY)ETHYL)-, CHLORIDE	121-54-0	PST71851
BENZENEMETHANOIC ACID	65-85-0	PST02720
BENZENEMETHANOL	100-51-6	PST02800
BENZENEMETHANOL, 4-CHLORO-ALPHA-(4-CHLOROPHENYL)-ALPHA-(TRICHLOROMETHYL)-	115-32-2	PST07010
BENZENESULFONAMIDE, 2-CHLORO-N-(((4-METHOXY-6-METHYL-1,3,5-TRIAZIN-2-YL)AMINO)CARBONYL)-	64902-72-3	PST72504
BENZENESULFONAMIDE, 4-(DIPROPYLAMINO)-3,5-DINITRO-	19044-88-3	PST17324
BENZENESULFONAMIDE, 4-AMINO-N-2-QUINOXALINYL-	59-40-5	PST72046
BENZENESULFONAMIDE, 4-AMINO-N-2-THIAZOLYL	72-14-0	PST72047
BENZENESULFONIC ACID 2,4-DICHLOROPHENYL ESTER	97-16-5	PST71350
BENZENESULFONIC ACID, DIMETHYL-, SODIUM SALT	1300-72-7	PST75603
BENZENESULFONIC ACID, DODECYL-, SODIUM SALT	25155-30-0	PST21220
BENZENESULFONIC ACID, P-CHLOROPHENYL ESTER	80-38-6	PST09677
BENZENESULFONIC ACID, 2,4-DICHLOROPHENYL ESTER	97-16-5	PST71350
BENZENESULFONIC ACID, 4-CHLOROPHENYL ESTER	80-38-6	PST09677
BENZENESULFONIC ACID, 4-METHYL-	104-15-4	PST67915
BENZENOL	108-95-2	PST18380
BENZETHONIUM CHLORIDE	121-54-0	PST71851

ALPHABETICAL INDEX

ALPHABETICAL INDEX

ALPHABETICAL INDEX

ALPHABETICAL INDEX

ALPHABETICAL INDEX

ALPHABETICAL INDEX

ALPHABETICAL INDEX

SUBSTANCE NAME	CAS #	PST #
CALCIUM CHLORIDE	10043-52-4	PST03900
CALCIUM CHLORIDE (CACL2)	10043-52-4	PST03900
CALCIUM CYANAMID	156-62-7	PST03930
CALCIUM CYANAMIDE, NOT HYDRATED	156-62-7	PST03930
CALCIUM DICHLORIDE	10043-52-4	PST03900
CALCIUM DIHYDROXIDE	1305-62-0	PST03980
CALCIUM DIOXYTETRACYCLINE	15251-48-6	PST84256
CALCIUM HYDRATE	1305-62-0	PST03980
CALCIUM HYDROXIDE	1305-62-0	PST03980
CALCIUM HYDROXIDE (CA(OH)2)	1305-62-0	PST03980
CALCIUM HYPOCHLORITE	7778-54-3	PST03990
CALCIUM MONOXIDE	1305-78-8	PST04030
CALCIUM ORTHOARSENATE	7778-44-1	PST03850
CALCIUM OXIDE	1305-78-8	PST04030
CALCIUM OXIDE (CAO)	1305-78-8	PST04030
CALCIUM OXYCHLORIDE	7778-54-3	PST03990
CALCIUM OXYTETRACYCLINE	15251-48-6	PST84256
CALCIUM SULFATE	7778-18-9	PST04110
CALCIUM SULFATE(CASO4)	7778-18-9	PST04110
CALCIUM SULFATE(1:1)	7778-18-9	PST04110
CALCIUM SULFATE, ANHYDROUS	7778-18-9	PST04110
CALCIUM SULPHATE	7778-18-9	PST04110
CALCOSAN	10043-52-4	PST03900
CALDON	88-85-7	PST08020
CALIXIN (FORMULATION)	24602-86-6	PST72537
CALSOFT LAS 99	27176-87-0	PST08480
CALSOL	64-02-8	PST23137
CALX	1305-78-8	PST04030
CALXYL	1305-78-8	PST04030
CAMPHECHLOR	8001-35-2	PST23640
CAMPHOCHLOR	8001-35-2	PST23640
CAMPHOR	76-22-2	PST04130
CAMPHOR OIL	8008-51-3	PST04140
CAMPHOR OIL WHITE	8008-51-3	PST04140
CAMPHOR OIL YELLOW	8008-51-3	PST04140
CAMPHOR OIL, RECTIFIED	8008-51-3	PST04140
CAMPHOR TAR	91-20-3	PST16120
CAMPOSAN	16672-87-0	PST72293
CANADA BALSAM	8007-47-4	PST04145
CANADA TURPENTINE	8007-47-4	PST04145
CANDASEPTIC	59-50-7	PST29890
CAO	1305-78-8	PST04030
CAPAROL	7287-19-6	PST19968
CAPMUL POE-O	9005-65-6	PST40200
CAPORIT	7778-54-3	PST03990
CAPRANE	39300-45-3	PST71402
CAPRIC ALCOHOL	112-30-1	PST06285
CAPRINIC ALCOHOL	112-30-1	PST06285
CAPROYL ALCOHOL	111-27-3	PST15630
CAPRYLIC ACID SODIUM SALT	1984-06-1	PST72105
CAPRYLIC ALCOHOL	111-87-5	PST17270
CAPTAF	133-06-2	PST04210
CAPTAF 85W	133-06-2	PST04210
CAPTAFOL	2425-06-1	PST04200

ALPHABETICAL INDEX

SUBSTANCE NAME	CAS #	PST #
CARBAMOTHIOIC ACID, CYCLOHEXYLETHYL-, S-ETHYL ESTER	1134-23-2	PST71469
CARBAMOTHIOIC ACID, DIETHYL-, S-((4-CHLOROPHENYL)METHYL) ESTER	28249-77-6	PST72381
CARBAMOTHIOIC ACID, DIETHYL-, S-ETHYL ESTER	2941-55-1	PST72327
CARBAMOTHIOIC ACID, DIPROPYL-, S-ETHYL ESTER	759-94-4	PST71470
CARBAMOTHIOIC ACID, DIPROPYL-, S-PROPYL ESTER	1929-77-7	PST71473
CARBAMOTHIOIC ACID, S,S'-(2-(SIMETHYLAMINO)-1,3-PROPANEDIYL) ESTER, MONOHYDROCHLORIDE	15263-52-2	PST04359
CARBAMULT	2631-37-0	PST72957
CARBANILIC ACID, ISOPROPYL ESTER	122-42-9	PST71564
CARBANILIC ACID, M-CHLORO-, ISOPROPYL ESTER	101-21-3	PST71148
CARBANILIC ACID, M-CHLORO-, 1-METHYL-2-PROPYNYL ESTER	1967-16-4	PST73265
CARBANILIC ACID, M-CHLORO-, 4-CHLORO-2-BUTYNYL ESTER	101-27-9	PST71143
CARBANILIC ACID, M-HYDROXY-, ETHYL ESTER, CARBANILATE (ESTER)	13684-56-5	PST72336
CARBANILIC ACID, M-HYDROXY-, METHYL ESTER, M-METHYLCARBANILATE (ESTER)	13684-63-4	PST72282
CARBANILIC ACID, 3-ISOPROPYL-5-METHYL-, METHYL ESTER	2631-37-0	PST72957
CARBANILIC ACID, 3,4-DICHLORO, METHYL ESTER	1918-18-9	PST72247
CARBANOLATE	671-04-5	PST02250
CARBARYL	63-25-2	PST04220
CARBATENE	9006-42-2	PST71123
CARBAZINC	137-30-4	PST25397
CARBETAMEX	16118-49-3	PST72941
CARBETAMIDE	16118-49-3	PST72941
CARBETHAMIDE	16118-49-3	PST72941
CARBICRON	141-66-2	PST03090
CARBIMIDE	420-04-2	PST05760
CARBINOL	67-56-1	PST14280
CARBOFENOTHION	786-19-6	PST04340
CARBOFENOTHION SULFOXIDE	17297-40-4	PST04345
CARBOFENTHION	786-19-6	PST04340
CARBOFURAN	1563-66-2	PST04240
CARBOFURAN-3-KETO-7-PHENOL	17781-16-7	PST72799
CARBOLIC ACID	108-95-2	PST18380
CARBOMER	9003-01-4	PST04349
CARBON CHLORIDE (CCL4)	56-23-5	PST04310
CARBON ELEMENT	7440-44-0	PST04246
CARBON TETRACHLORIDE	56-23-5	PST04310
CARBON-12	7440-44-0	PST04246
CARBON, ACTIVATED	7440-44-0	PST04246
CARBONIC ACID MONOSODIUM SALT	144-55-8	PST20970
CARBONIC ACID SODIUM SALT	497-19-8	PST21080
CARBONIC ACID SODIUM SALT (1:1)	144-55-8	PST20970
CARBONIC ACID SODIUM SALT (1:2)	497-19-8	PST21080
CARBONIC ACID 1-METHYLETHYL 2-(1-METHYLPROPYL)-4,6-DINITROPHENYL ESTER	973-21-7	PST07990
CARBONIC ACID 2-SEC-BUTYL-4,6-DINITROPHENYL ISOPROPYL ESTER	973-21-7	PST07990
CARBONIC ACID, DIPOTASSIUM SALT	584-08-7	PST19290
CARBONIC ACID, DISODIUM SALT	497-19-8	PST21080
CARBONIC ACID, 1-METHYLETHYL 2-(1-METHYLPROPYL)-4,6-DINITROPHENYL ESTER	973-21-7	PST07990
CARBONIC ACID, 2-SEC-BUTYL-4,6-DINITROPHENYL ISOPROPYL ESTER	973-21-7	PST07990
CARBOPHENOTHION	786-19-6	PST04340
CARBOPHENOTHION METHYL	953-17-3	PST71647
CARBOPHENOTHION OXON	7173-84-4	PST04341
CARBOPHENOTHION OXON SULFOXIDE	16662-86-5	PST04343
CARBOPHENOTHION OXYGEN ANALOG	7173-84-4	PST04341

ALPHABETICAL INDEX

SUBSTANCE NAME	CAS #	PST #
CEDRUS ATLANTICA OIL	8000-27-9	PST04365
CEKUMETA	108-62-3	PST14090
CELA S 1942	2104-96-3	PST71064
CELA W 524	26644-46-2	PST24086
CELFUME	74-83-9	PST14300
CELMONE	86-87-3	PST26130
CELON ATH	60-00-4	PST09570
CELON E	64-02-8	PST23137
CELPHOS	20859-73-8	PST00970
CEPA	16672-87-0	PST72293
CEPHALON	330-55-2	PST12826
CEQUARTYL	8001-54-5	PST00539
CERCOBIN	23564-06-9	PST72322
CERCOBIN M	23564-05-8	PST72308
CERCOBIN METHYL	23564-05-8	PST72308
CERTOX	57-24-9	PST22080
CES	140-57-8	PST01850
CET	122-34-9	PST20837
CETOL	36653-82-4	PST04525
CETYL ALCOHOL	36653-82-4	PST04525
CETYLIC ALCOHOL	36653-82-4	PST04525
CEVADINE MIXTURE WITH VERATRIDINE	8051-02-3	PST71010
CF 12	75-71-8	PST06880
CFC 11	75-69-4	PST09990
CFC 12	75-71-8	PST06880
CGA 15324	41198-08-7	PST72412
CGA 15646	15545-48-9	PST04912
CGA 17020	50563-36-5	PST07677
CGA 18731	34123-59-6	PST12254
CGA 45156	59669-26-0	PST72456
CGA 72662	66215-27-8	PST72536
CGA-12223	42509-80-8	PST15035
CGA-18762	32889-48-8	PST72398
CGA-24705	51218-45-2	PST15003
CHAMELEON MINERAL	7722-64-7	PST19520
CHEELOX	60-00-4	PST09570
CHEELOX BF-12	64-02-8	PST23137
CHELAPLEX	139-33-3	PST08305
CHEM BAM	142-59-6	PST16080
CHEM-HOE (FORMULATION)	122-42-9	PST71564
CHEMAGRO B-1776	78-48-8	PST06300
CHEMAID	124-65-2	PST21070
CHEMCOLOX 200	64-02-8	PST23137
CHEMCOLOX 340	60-00-4	PST09570
CHEMFORM	57-92-1	PST21917
CHEMICAL 109	86-88-4	PST01830
CHEMOCIDE PK	94-13-3	PST19941
CHEMOX	88-85-7	PST08020
CHILE SALTPETER	7631-99-4	PST21400
CHINA GREEN	569-64-2	PST13533
CHINALPHOS	13593-03-8	PST73112
CHINESE BEAN OIL	8001-22-7	PST21765
CHINESE WHITE	1314-13-2	PST25490
CHINORTO	311-45-5	PST07200

ALPHABETICAL INDEX

ALPHABETICAL INDEX

SUBSTANCE NAME	CAS #	PST #
CHLOROTHION	500-28-7	PST71379
CHLOROTOLURON	15545-48-9	PST04912
CHLOROTRIBUTYLSTANNANE	1461-22-9	PST72222
CHLOROTRIBUTYLTIN	1461-22-9	PST72222
CHLOROTRIPHENYL-STANNANE	639-58-7	PST24380
CHLOROTRIPHENYLSTANNANE	639-58-7	PST24380
CHLOROTRIPHENYLTIN	639-58-7	PST24380
CHLOROUS ACID, SODIUM SALT	7758-19-2	PST21110
CHLOROXIFENIDIM	1982-47-4	PST04905
CHLOROXURON	1982-47-4	PST04905
CHLOROXYLENOL	88-04-0	PST72258
CHLORPARACIDE	103-17-3	PST71139
CHLORPENTAN	2307-68-8	PST71164
CHLORPHACINONE	3691-35-8	PST04826
CHLORPHENACONE	3691-35-8	PST04826
CHLORPHENAMIDINE	6164-98-3	PST04570
CHLORPHENAMIDINE MONOHYDROCHLORIDE	19750-95-9	PST71656
CHLORPROPHAM	101-21-3	PST71148
CHLORPYRIFOS	2921-88-2	PST04910
CHLORPYRIFOS OXON	5598-15-2	PST04911
CHLORPYRIFOS OXYGEN ANALOG	5598-15-2	PST04911
CHLORPYRIFOS-METHYL	5598-13-0	PST71652
CHLORPYRIFOXON	5598-15-2	PST04911
CHLORPYRIPHOS	2921-88-2	PST04910
CHLORPYRIPHOXON	5598-15-2	PST04911
CHLORSULFURON	64902-72-3	PST72504
CHLORSULPHACIDE	103-17-3	PST71139
CHLORTEN	71-55-6	PST14370
CHLORTHAL DIMETHYL	1861-32-1	PST04913
CHLORTHAL DIMETHYL ESTER	1861-32-1	PST04913
CHLORTHAL-DIMETHYL	1861-32-1	PST04913
CHLORTHAL-METHYL	1861-32-1	PST04913
CHLORTHIAMID	1918-13-4	PST73046
CHLORTHIAMIDE	1918-13-4	PST73046
CHLORTHION	500-28-7	PST71379
CHLORTHION METHYL	500-28-7	PST71379
CHLORTHIOPHOS	60238-56-4	PST64913
CHLORTOLURON	15545-48-9	PST04912
CHLORYL RADICAL	10049-04-4	PST04610
CHNAO3	144-55-8	PST20970
CHOLECALCIFEROL	67-97-0	PST60913
CHROMIC ACID	7738-94-5	PST04930
CHROMIC ACID (H2CR207), DISODIUM SALT	10588-01-9	PST21190
CHROMIC ACID, DIPOTASSIUM SALT	7778-50-9	PST19370
CHROMIC ACID, SOLUTION	7738-94-5	PST04930
CHROMIC(VI) ACID	7738-94-5	PST04930
CHROMIUM SODIUM OXIDE (CR3NA207)	10588-01-9	PST21190
CHROMIUM TRIOXIDE, SOLUTION	7738-94-5	PST04930
CHRYSANTHEMUMMONOCARBOXYLIC ACID ESTER WITH 3-(2-CYCLOPENTEN-1-YL) -2-METHYL-4-OXO-2-CYCLOPENTEN-1-OL	97-11-0	PST19949
CHRYSON	10453-86-8	PST20095
CHWASTOX F	94-74-6	PST27880
CHWASTOX 30	94-74-6	PST27880
CH2CL2	75-09-2	PST14930

ALPHABETICAL INDEX

ALPHABETICAL INDEX

ALPHABETICAL INDEX

ALPHABETICAL INDEX

ALPHABETICAL INDEX

ALPHABETICAL INDEX

ALPHABETICAL INDEX

SUBSTANCE NAME	CAS #	PST #
C10H13CLN6	32889-48-8	PST72398
C10H13CL2FN2O2S2	731-27-1	PST73030
C10H13NO2	62-44-2	PST18340
C10H13NO2	2655-14-3	PST25171
C10H13NO2	122-42-9	PST71564
C10H14CL2NO2PS	299-85-4	PST71236
C10H14CL2N2	19750-95-9	PST71656
C10H14CL6N4O2	26644-46-2	PST24086
C10H14NO5PS	56-38-2	PST18040
C10H14N2NA2O8	139-33-3	PST08305
C10H14O	98-54-4	PST17440
C10H14ON2	UNASSIGNED	PST02581
C10H15O4PS	6552-12-1	PST02551
C10H15O4PS2	3761-41-9	PST02555
C10H15O5PS	6552-13-2	PST02553
C10H15O5PS2	3761-42-0	PST02554
C10H15O6PS	14086-35-2	PST02552
C10H15O3PS2	55-38-9	PST02550
C10H16NO5PS2	52-85-7	PST09675
C10H16N2O8	60-00-4	PST09570
C10H16N4O2	UNASSIGNED	PST06336
C10H16N4O3	644-64-4	PST83057
C10H17CL2NOS	2303-16-4	PST06480
C10H17N2O4PS	38260-54-7	PST73148
C10H17N2O5P	UNASSIGNED	PST09666
C10H17N3O2	55861-78-4	PST72586
C10H17N3O2	119-38-0	PST83027
C10H18N4O4S3	59669-26-0	PST72456
C10H19N2O4PS	3734-95-0	PST72949
C10H19N5O	1610-18-0	PST19967
C10H19N2O4PS	26259-45-0	PST73051
C10H19N5S	7287-19-6	PST19968
C10H19N5S	886-50-0	PST22538
C10H19N5O	33693-04-8	PST72770
C10H19O7PS	1634-78-2	PST13541
C10H19PS2O6	121-75-5	PST13540
C10H20NO4PS	31218-83-4	PST72440
C10H22O	112-30-1	PST06285
C10H4CL8O	27304-13-8	PST17372
C10H5CL7	76-44-8	PST10660
C10H5CL7O	1024-57-3	PST10670
C10H5CL9	39765-80-5	PST23079
C10H6CL4O4	1861-32-1	PST04913
C10H6CL6	3734-48-3	PST04565
C10H6CL6	56534-02-2	PST04566
C10H6CL6	56641-38-4	PST04567
C10H6CL8	5103-71-9	PST00776
C10H6CL8	57-74-9	PST04560
C10H6CL8	5103-74-2	PST10331
C10H6CL8	12789-03-6	PST71948
C10H7BRN3O	3042-84-0	PST72769
C10H8CLN3O	1698-60-8	PST71928
C10H9CL2NO	2164-09-2	PST71378
C10H9CL3O3	4841-20-7	PST20831

ALPHABETICAL INDEX

ALPHABETICAL INDEX

SUBSTANCE NAME	CAS #	PST #
C11H22N2O	2163-69-1	PST05996
C11H22O	112-12-9	PST14675
C11H26NO2PS	50782-69-9	PST83104
C11H9BR2NO2	3861-41-4	PST71388
C11H9CL2NO2	101-27-9	PST71143
C12H10O	90-43-7	PST18470
C12H10O2	86-87-3	PST26130
C12H11BHG2O3	6273-99-0	PST71754
C12H11CL2NO	23950-58-5	PST19670
C12H11N	122-39-4	PST08100
C12H12CLNO	21267-72-1	PST73038
C12H12CLN5O4S	64902-72-3	PST72504
C12H12N2.2BR	85-00-7	PST08250
C12H13CLN2O	3766-60-7	PST03523
C12H13NO2S	5234-68-4	PST04348
C12H13NO4S	5259-88-1	PST17373
C12H14CL2O3	94-80-4	PST71295
C12H14CL3O3PS	1757-18-2	PST00493
C12H14CL3O4P	470-90-6	PST04575
C12H14NO4PS	5131-24-8	PST72347
C12H14N2	4685-14-7	PST71671
C12H14N2.2CL	1910-42-5	PST18020
C12H14N2O6	2813-95-8	PST08021
C12H14N4O4S2	23564-05-8	PST72308
C12H15CLNO4PS2	2310-17-0	PST25720
C12H15NO3	1563-66-2	PST04240
C12H15NO4	16655-82-6	PST72800
C12H15N2O3PS	13593-03-8	PST73112
C12H15N2O3PS	14816-18-3	PST73292
C12H16CL2N2O	555-37-3	PST16143
C12H16N2O3	16118-49-3	PST72941
C12H16N3O3PS2	2642-71-9	PST02205
C12H17NAO7	52508-35-7	PST72391
C12H17NO	134-62-3	PST84230
C12H17NO2	3766-81-2	PST03324
C12H17NO2	2631-37-0	PST72957
C12H17N3O2	17702-57-7	PST73082
C12H17O4PS2	2597-03-7	PST72337
C12H18N2O	34123-59-6	PST12254
C12H18N2O2	315-18-4	PST15010
C12H18N4O6S	19044-88-3	PST17324
C12H18O4S2	50512-35-1	PST12253
C12H19CLNO3P	299-86-5	PST05550
C12H19O5PS2	42795-00-6	PST03231
C12H20N4O2	51235-04-2	PST10994
C12H20N4OS	57052-04-7	PST11844
C12H21N2O3PS	333-41-5	PST06540
C12H21N2O4P	962-58-3	PST06541
C12H23KO2	10124-65-9	PST72072
C12H23N5O2S	845-52-3	PST72212
C12H25NAO4S	151-21-3	PST08485
C12H26O	112-53-8	PST12500
C12H26O6P2S4	78-34-2	PST08050
C12H27CLSN	1461-22-9	PST72222

SUBSTANCE NAME	CAS #	PST #
C12H27FSN	1983-10-4	PST72227
C12H28O5P2S2	3244-90-4	PST72135
C12H4CL4O2	1746-01-6	PST08060
C12H6CL3NO3	1836-77-7	PST23865
C12H7CL2NO3	1836-75-5	PST23580
C12H8CL2O2S	97-24-5	PST71737
C12H8CL2O3S	97-16-5	PST71350
C12H8CL6	309-00-2	PST00520
C12H8CL6	465-73-6	PST11810
C12H8CL6O	60-57-1	PST07080
C12H8CL6O	72-20-8	PST08600
C12H9CLF3N3O	27314-13-2	PST72343
C12H9CLO	85-97-2	PST71680
C12H9CLO2S	80-00-2	PST71663
C12H9CLO3S	80-38-6	PST09677
C13H10BRCL2O3P	25006-32-0	PST12776
C13H10CL2	101-76-8	PST06321
C13H10CL2O2	97-23-4	PST71611
C13H10CL2S	103-17-3	PST71139
C13H12N4O3	53558-25-1	PST72334
C13H14F3N3O4	55283-68-6	PST72436
C13H15N3O2	87-47-8	PST73263
C13H16F3N3O4	1861-40-1	PST02570
C13H16F3N3O4	1582-09-8	PST24085
C13H16NO4PS	18854-01-8	PST12280
C13H16O2	126-15-8	PST71487
C13H18CLNO	2307-68-8	PST71164
C13H18CLNO2	50563-36-5	PST07677
C13H18N2O2	2164-08-1	PST73238
C13H18O5S	26225-79-6	PST72404
C13H19NO2	8065-36-9	PST03480
C13H19N3O6S	4726-14-1	PST16525
C13H22NO3PS	22224-92-6	PST16145
C13H22NO4PS	31972-43-7	PST16146
C13H22NO5PS	31972-44-8	PST16144
C13H22N2O	18530-56-8	PST71400
C13H22N2O	28805-78-9	PST73199
C13H7F3N2O5	15457-05-3	PST72248
C13H8CL2O	90-98-2	PST06246
C13N18CLNO	7287-36-7	PST72987
C14H10CL2O2	83-05-6	PST06232
C14H10CL4	4329-12-8	PST04752
C14H10CL4	72-54-8	PST06240
C14H12CL2O	2642-82-2	PST06323
C14H12F3NO4S2	37924-13-3	PST72375
C14H12N4O2S	59-40-5	PST72046
C14H13CL2N2O2PS	4104-14-7	PST71150
C14H13CL2O2PS	3792-59-4	PST73239
C14H14NO4PS	2104-64-5	PST08650
C14H14O2	2122-70-5	PST71628
C14H14O3	83-26-1	PST18970
C14H14O3	83-28-3	PST24738
C14H15N5O6S	74223-64-6	PST72546
C14H16CLN3O	67129-08-2	PST14106

ALPHABETICAL INDEX

ALPHABETICAL INDEX

ALPHABETICAL INDEX

SUBSTANCE NAME	CAS #	PST #
C2H4N4	61-82-5	PST01040
C2H40	75-21-8	PST09520
C2H402	64-19-7	PST00120
C2H5CLHG	107-27-7	PST09620
C2H6CL03	16672-87-0	PST72293
C2H60	64-17-5	PST08700
C2H602	107-21-1	PST09400
C2H7AS02	75-60-5	PST03710
C2H7HG04P	2235-25-8	PST71479
C2H7NO	141-43-5	PST08710
C2H704P	813-78-5	PST07882
C2H8N2	107-15-3	PST09560
C20H1404	84-62-8	PST08095
C20H22N805	59-05-2	PST14210
C20H22N805	15475-56-6	PST14211
C20H2803	25402-06-6	PST05090
C20H30N205S	82560-54-1	PST72562
C20H32N203S	55285-14-8	PST72266
C20H38NA07S	577-11-7	PST00406
C20H4808P4S8	37333-40-7	PST18807
C21H20CL203	51877-74-8	PST23708
C21H22N202	57-24-9	PST22080
C21H2803	121-21-1	PST19960
C22H18CL2FN03	68359-37-5	PST72630
C22H19BR2N03	52918-63-5	PST72784
C22H19BR4N03	66841-25-6	PST72538
C22H19CL2N03	67375-30-8	PST06118
C22H19CL2N03	52315-07-8	PST72392
C22H2603	10453-86-8	PST20095
C22H2805	121-29-9	PST19970
C22H40CLN	1330-85-4	PST71854
C23H15CL03	3691-35-8	PST04826
C23H2206	83-79-4	PST20200
C23H2603	26002-80-2	PST71954
C24H38HG02	104-60-9	PST71769
C24H3804	117-84-0	PST08040
C24H3804	117-81-7	PST06440
C24H4008	5281-13-0	PST71828
C25H24F6N4	67485-29-4	PST01009
C26H58CLN03SI	27668-52-6	PST72370
C27H42CLN02	121-54-0	PST71851
C28H44CLN02	25155-18-4	PST71862
C3H3CL2NA02	127-20-8	PST71239
C3H4CLN5	UNASSIGNED	PST06504
C3H4CL2	542-75-6	PST26820
C3H40	107-02-8	PST00330
C3H5BR2CL	96-12-8	PST26490
C3H502NA	137-40-6	PST21575
C3H6BRN04	52-51-7	PST72832
C3H6HGN4	502-39-6	PST83040
C3H60	67-64-1	PST00140
C3H602	79-09-4	PST19750
C3H7C12	78-87-5	PST19860
C3H8N05P	1071-83-6	PST10515

ALPHABETICAL INDEX

ALPHABETICAL INDEX

SUBSTANCE NAME	CAS #	PST #
C6H2CL2	95-50-1	PST16970
C6H2CL4O	25167-83-3	PST71689
C6H3CL2NO2	1702-17-6	PST05211
C6H3CL3N2O2	1918-02-1	PST18840
C6H3CL4N	1929-82-4	PST16530
C6H4CL2	106-46-7	PST17640
C6H4CL2N2O2	99-30-9	PST28910
C6H4N2O5	51-28-5	PST28620
C6H6CL6	319-84-6	PST00770
C6H6CL6	319-85-7	PST03010
C6H6CL6	608-73-1	PST03080
C6H6CL6	319-86-8	PST06310
C6H6CL6	58-89-9	PST12810
C6H6O	108-95-2	PST18380
C6H8O7	77-92-9	PST05200
C6H9N3O3	443-48-1	PST72529
C7H11N7S	4658-28-0	PST02216
C7H12CLN5	122-34-9	PST20837
C7H12N4O3S2	30043-49-3	PST72551
C7H13N2O4PS3	2669-32-1	PST73147
C7H13N3O2S	23135-22-0	PST17370
C7H14NO4PS2	29173-31-7	PST73246
C7H14N2O2S	116-06-3	PST00500
C7H14N2O2S	34681-10-2	PST73270
C7H14N2O3S	1646-87-3	PST00503
C7H14N2O4S	1646-88-4	PST72406
C7H14N2O4S	34681-23-7	PST72434
C7H15NOS	2941-55-1	PST72327
C7H16CLN	24307-26-4	PST72386
C7H16CLN3O2S2	15263-52-2	PST04359
C7H17O2PS3	36614-38-7	PST12275
C7H17O2PS3	298-02-2	PST18640
C7H17O3PS2	2600-69-3	PST18641
C7H17O3PS3	2588-03-6	PST18646
C7H17O4PS2	2588-05-8	PST18644
C7H17O4PS3	2588-04-7	PST18643
C7H17O5PS2	2588-06-9	PST18642
C7H2CL3NAO2	2078-42-4	PST71136
C7H3BR2NO	1689-84-5	PST03542
C7H3CL2N	1194-65-6	PST06800
C7H3CL3O2	50-31-7	PST71134
C7H3I2NNAO	2961-62-8	PST73074
C7H3I2NO	1689-83-4	PST11468
C7H4CL2NANO2	1954-81-0	PST71256
C7H4CL3NO3	55335-06-3	PST72472
C7H4F3NO3	88-30-2	PST71405
C7H5CL2NO2	133-90-4	PST29084
C7H5CL2NS	1918-13-4	PST73046
C7H5NS2	149-30-4	PST13738
C7H5N2NAO5	2312-76-7	PST71411
C7H6N2O5	534-52-1	PST07910
C7H6O	100-52-7	PST02590
C7H6O2	65-85-0	PST02720
C7H6O3	69-72-7	PST20315

ALPHABETICAL INDEX

SUBSTANCE NAME	CAS #	PST #
C9H10BRCLN2O2	13360-45-7	PST04552
C9H10CL2N2O	330-54-1	PST08420
C9H10CL2N2O2	330-55-2	PST12826
C9H10NO3PS	2636-26-2	PST72950
C9H11BRN2O2	3060-89-7	PST15008
C9H11CLN2O	150-68-5	PST15196
C9H11CLN2O2	1746-81-2	PST15174
C9H11CL2FN2O2S2	1085-98-9	PST73026
C9H11CL3NO3PS	2921-88-2	PST04910
C9H11CL3NO4P	5598-15-2	PST04911
C9H11NO2	94-09-7	PST72267
C9H12CLO2PS3	953-17-3	PST71647
C9H12N2O	101-42-8	PST09679
C9H13BRN2O2	314-40-9	PST03330
C9H13CLN2O2	5902-51-2	PST71099
C9H13CLN6	21725-46-2	PST05762
C9H14CLN5	22936-86-3	PST72296
C9H15O8P	122-10-1	PST03240
C9H16CLN5	139-40-2	PST19736
C9H16CLN5	5915-41-3	PST22536
C9H16CLN9	1912-26-1	PST23927
C9H16N4OS	64529-56-2	PST09111
C9H16N4OS	34014-18-1	PST72340
C9H17CLN3O3PS	42509-80-8	PST15035
C9H17NO2S	112-56-1	PST75661
C9H17N5O	1610-17-9	PST02148
C9H17N5S	834-12-8	PST01006
C9H18N2O2S	39196-18-4	PST23330
C9H19NOS	759-94-4	PST71470
C9H21O2PS3	13071-79-9	PST22545
C9H21O5PS2	56070-15-6	PST22537
C9H4CL8O	297-78-9	PST83032
C9H5CL3N4	101-05-3	PST01526
C9H6CLNO3S	3813-05-6	PST72725
C9H6CL2N2O3	20354-26-1	PST72344
C9H6CL6O3S	959-98-8	PST00800
C9H6CL6O3S	33213-65-9	PST03040
C9H6CL6O3S	115-29-7	PST08560
C9H6CL8	2550-75-6	PST73193
C9H7CL3O3	1928-37-6	PST22392
C9H8CL2O3	1928-38-7	PST71307
C9H8CL2O3	6597-78-0	PST73131
C9H8N4OS	51707-55-2	PST23299
C9H9NO4	5251-93-4	PST72964
C9H9N3OS	1929-88-0	PST72971
C9H9N3O2S2	72-14-0	PST72047
D AND C BLUE NO. 1	2650-18-2	PST08277
D 014	2312-35-8	PST19720
D 25 ANTIMYKOTIKUM	97-24-5	PST71737
D 735	5234-68-4	PST04348
D-(-)-N-ETHYL-2-(PHENYLCARBAMOYLOXY)PROPIONAMIDE	16118-49-3	PST72941
D-ALLETHRIN	584-79-2	PST00550
D-CIS-RESMETHRIN	35764-59-1	PST20094
D-GLUCONIC ACID	526-95-4	PST10408

ALPHABETICAL INDEX

SUBSTANCE NAME	CAS #	PST #
D-N-ETHYLLACTAMIDE CARBANILATE (ESTER)	16118-49-3	PST72941
D-STREPTAMINE	57-92-1	PST21917
D-STREPTAMINE, O-2-DEOXY-2-(METHYLAMINO)-ALPHA-L-GLUCOPYRANOSYL-(1->2) -O-5-DEOXY-3-C-FORMYL-ALPHA-L-LYXOFURANOSYL-(1->4)-N,N'-BIS	298-39-5	PST71042
D-STREPTAMINE, O-2-DEOXY-2-(METHYLAMINO)-ALPHA-L-GLUCOPYRANOSYL-(1->2) -O-5-DEOXY-3-C-FORMYL-ALPHA-L-LYXOFURANOSYL-(1->4)-N,N'-BIS	3810-74-0	PST84290
D-TRANS-ALLETHRIN	UNASSIGNED	PST00553
D-TRANS-ALLETHRIN	28434-00-6	PST71013
D-TRANS-RESMETHRIN	28434-01-7	PST20093
D-29	84-74-2	PST06740
D-30	84-74-2	PST06740
D-7	9004-53-9	PST06363
DABICYCLINE	79-57-2	PST17414
DAC 2787	1897-45-6	PST04890
DAC 893	1861-32-1	PST04913
DACAMOX	39196-18-4	PST23330
DACONIL	1897-45-6	PST04890
DACTHAL	1861-32-1	PST04913
DACTHALOR	1861-32-1	PST04913
DACTIN	118-52-5	PST26800
DAILON	330-54-1	PST08420
DALAPON	75-99-0	PST06200
DALAPON SODIUM	127-20-8	PST71239
DALAPON SODIUM SALT	127-20-8	PST71239
DALAPON 85	75-99-0	PST06200
DALAPON-SODIUM	127-20-8	PST71239
DALTOGEN	102-71-6	PST23932
DAMINOZIDE	1596-84-5	PST06195
DANTOIN	118-52-5	PST26800
DAPACRYL	485-31-4	PST71960
DARCO KB	7440-44-0	PST04246
DASANIT (FORMULATION)	115-90-2	PST06210
DASANIT O	6552-21-2	PST09684
DASANIT O ANALOG	6552-21-2	PST09684
DASANIT OXYGEN ANALOG	6552-21-2	PST09684
DASANIT SULPHONE	14255-72-2	PST06228
DATC	2303-16-4	PST06480
DAZOMET	533-74-4	PST06230
DBCP	96-12-8	PST26490
DBM	101-76-8	PST06321
DBN	1194-65-6	PST06800
DBP	84-74-2	PST06740
DBSC	55285-14-8	PST72266
DCA	118-52-5	PST26800
DCB	1194-65-6	PST06800
DCBP	90-98-2	PST06246
DCDMH	118-52-5	PST26800
DCMA	2164-09-2	PST71378
DCMO	5234-68-4	PST04348
DCMOD	5259-88-1	PST17373
DCMU	330-54-1	PST08420
DCNA	99-30-9	PST28910
DCPA	1861-32-1	PST04913
DCU	116-52-9	PST06817

SUBSTANCE NAME	CAS #	PST #
DDA	83-05-6	PST06232
DDA (DEGRADATION PRODUCT)	83-05-6	PST06232
DDA-P,P'	83-05-6	PST06232
DDBSA	27176-87-0	PST08480
DDD	72-54-8	PST06240
DDD-M,P'	4329-12-8	PST04752
DDE	3424-82-6	PST06245
DDE	72-55-9	PST06247
DDH	118-52-5	PST26800
DDM	101-76-8	PST06321
DDMU	1022-22-6	PST06322
DDOH	2642-82-2	PST06323
DDOM	2642-82-2	PST06323
DDT	50-29-3	PST06250
DDVP	62-73-7	PST07000
DE-GREEN	78-48-8	PST06300
DEAD OIL	8001-58-9	PST05230
DECABANE	1194-65-6	PST06800
DECACHLORO-OCTAHYDRO-1,3,4-METHENO-2H-CYCLOBUTA(CD)PENTALEN-2-ONE	143-50-0	PST12330
DECACHLOROKETONE	143-50-0	PST12330
DECACHLOROOCTAHYDRO-1,3,4-METHENO-2H-CYCLOBUTA(CD)PENTALEN-2-ONE	143-50-0	PST12330
DECAMETHRIN	52918-63-5	PST72784
DECANOL	112-30-1	PST06285
DECCO SALT NO 5	7673-09-8	PST80113
DECEMTHION	732-11-6	PST11307
DECHLORANE	2385-85-5	PST09690
DECIS	52918-63-5	PST72784
DECOFOL	115-32-2	PST07010
DECYL ALCOHOL	112-30-1	PST06285
DECYLIC ALCOHOL	112-30-1	PST06285
DED-WEED	75-99-0	PST06200
DED-WEED	93-72-1	PST20830
DEDEVAP	62-73-7	PST07000
DEET	134-62-3	PST84230
DEF	78-48-8	PST06300
DEF DEFOLIANT	78-48-8	PST06300
DEFENDION	60-51-5	PST07670
DEFTOR	19937-59-8	PST15009
DEGUMMED SOYBEAN OIL	8001-22-7	PST21765
DEHP	117-81-7	PST06440
DEIQUAT	85-00-7	PST08250
DEKETON	137-40-6	PST21575
DEKRYSIL	534-52-1	PST07910
DEKSONAL	140-56-7	PST73084
DELAN	3347-22-6	PST72290
DELAN-COL	3347-22-6	PST72290
DELIA	20859-73-8	PST00970
DELICIA	20859-73-8	PST00970
DELICIA GASTOXIN	20859-73-8	PST00970
DELNATEX	78-34-2	PST08050
DELNAV	78-34-2	PST08050
DELSTEROL	67-97-0	PST60913
DELTA	134-62-3	PST84230
DELTA-BENZENE HEXACHLORIDE	319-86-8	PST06310

ALPHABETICAL INDEX

ALPHABETICAL INDEX

ALPHABETICAL INDEX

ALPHABETICAL INDEX

SUBSTANCE NAME	CAS #	PST #
DIMETHYL PARA-(DIMETHYLSULFAMOYL)PHENYL PHOSPHOROTHIONATE	52-85-7	PST09675
DIMETHYL PARAOXON	950-35-6	PST14678
DIMETHYL PARATHION	298-00-0	PST14680
DIMETHYL PHENOL	1300-71-6	PST25160
DIMETHYL PHOSPHATE	813-78-5	PST07882
DIMETHYL PHOSPHATE ESTER WITH (E)-3-HYDROXY-N-METHYLCROTONAMIDE	6923-22-4	PST15165
DIMETHYL PHOSPHATE ESTER WITH (E)-3-HYDROXY-N,N-DIMETHYLCROTONAMIDE	141-66-2	PST03090
DIMETHYL PHOSPHATE ESTER WITH 2-CHLORO-N,N-DIETHYL -3-HYDROXYCROTONAMIDE	13171-21-6	PST18670
DIMETHYL PHOSPHATE OF ALPHA-METHYLBENZYL 3-HYDROXY-CIS-CROTONATE	7700-17-6	PST05115
DIMETHYL PHOSPHATE OF 3-HYDROXY-N-METHYL-CIS-CROTONAMIDE	6923-22-4	PST15165
DIMETHYL PHTHALATE	131-11-3	PST07740
DIMETHYL S-(MORPHOLINOCARBONYLMETHYL)PHOSPHOROTHIOLOTHIONATE	144-41-2	PST73096
DIMETHYL S-(N-ETHYLCARBAMOYLMETHYL)PHOSPHOROTHIOLOTHIONATE	116-01-8	PST08723
DIMETHYL S-(N-FORMYL-N-METHYLCARBAMOYLEMETHYL) PHOSPHOROTHIOLOTHIONATE	2540-82-1	PST10081
DIMETHYL S-(N-METHOXYETHYLCARBAMOYLMETHYL)PHOSPHOROTHIOLOTHIONATE	919-76-6	PST01007
DIMETHYL S-(N-METHYLCARBAMOYLMETHYL)PHOSPHOROTHIOLATE	1113-02-6	PST17328
DIMETHYL S-(2-ETHYLSULFINYLETHYL)PHOSPHOROTHIOLATE	301-12-2	PST17375
DIMETHYL S-(2-ETHYLSULFINYLISOPROPYL) PHOSPHOROTHIOLATE	2674-91-1	PST14105
DIMETHYL TETRACHLOROTEREPHTHALATE	1861-32-1	PST04913
DIMETHYL TRICHLOROPHENYL THIOPHOSPHATE	299-84-3	PST20180
DIMETHYL VIOLGEN	4685-14-7	PST71671
DIMETHYL VIOLGEN CHLORIDE	1910-42-5	PST18020
DIMETHYL 1-METHOXYCARBONYL-1-PROPEN-2-YL PHOSPHATE	7786-34-7	PST18650
DIMETHYL 1,2-BENZENEDICARBOXYLATE	131-11-3	PST07740
DIMETHYL 1,2-DIBROMO-2,2-DICHLOROETHYL PHOSPHATE	300-76-5	PST06660
DIMETHYL 1,3 BIS(CARBOMETHOXY)-1-PROPEN-2-YL PHOSPHATE	122-10-1	PST03240
DIMETHYL 1,3 DI(CARBOMETHOXY)-1-PROPEN-2-YL PHOSPHATE	122-10-1	PST03240
DIMETHYL 2-DIETHYLAMINO-4-METHYLPYRIMIDIN-6-YL PHOSPHOROTHIONATE	29232-93-7	PST72378
DIMETHYL 2-METHYLCARBAMOYL-1-METHYLVINYL PHOSPHATE	6923-22-4	PST15165
DIMETHYL 2,2-DICHLOROVINYL PHOSPHATE	62-73-7	PST07000
DIMETHYL 2,2,2-TRICHLORO-1-HYDROXYETHYLPHOSPHONATE	52-68-6	PST23790
DIMETHYL 2,3,5,6-TETRACHLORO-1,4-BENZENEDICARBOXYLATE	1861-32-1	PST04913
DIMETHYL 2,3,5,6-TETRACHLOROTEREPHTHALATE	1861-32-1	PST04913
DIMETHYL 2,4,5-TRICHLOROPHENYL PHOSPHOROTHIONATE	299-84-3	PST20180
DIMETHYL 2,4,5-TRICHLOROPHENYLPHOSPHATE	3983-45-7	PST25082
DIMETHYL 3-HYDROXYGLUTACONATE DIMETHYL PHOSPHATE	122-10-1	PST03240
DIMETHYL 3-METHYL-4-(METHYLSULFINYL)PHENYL PHOSPHATE	6552-13-2	PST02553
DIMETHYL 3-METHYL-4-(METHYLSULFINYL)PHENYL PHOSPHOROTHIOATE	14086-35-2	PST02552
DIMETHYL 3-METHYL-4-(METHYLTHIO)PHENYL PHOSPHATE	6552-12-1	PST02551
DIMETHYL 3-METHYL-4-NITROPHENYL PHOSPHOROTHIONATE	122-14-5	PST09678
DIMETHYL 4-(METHYLSULFINYL)-M-TOLYL PHOSPHATE	6552-13-2	PST02553
DIMETHYL 4-(METHYLSULFONYL)-M-TOLYL PHOSPHOROTHIOATE	14086-35-2	PST02552
DIMETHYL 4-(METHYLTHIO)-M-TOLYL PHOSPHATE	6552-12-1	PST02551
DIMETHYL 4-(METHYLTHIO)PHENYL ESTER PHOSPHORIC ACID	3254-63-5	PST73095
DIMETHYL 4-NITROPHENYL PHOSPHATE	950-35-6	PST14678
DIMETHYL 4,4'-O-PHENYLENE-BIS(3-THIOALLOPHANATE)	23564-05-8	PST72308
DIMETHYL-5-(1-ISOPROPYL-3-METHYLPYRAZOLYL)CARBAMATEE	119-38-0	PST83027
DIMETHYLARSINIC ACID	75-60-5	PST03710
DIMETHYLARSINIC ACID, SODIUM SALT	124-65-2	PST21070
DIMETHYLBENZENE	1330-20-7	PST25150
DIMETHYLBENZYLAMMONIUM, (2-(2-(P-OCTYLCRESOXY)ETHOXY)ETHYL)-, CHLORIDE	25155-18-4	PST71862
DIMETHYLCARBAMATE ESTER OF 3-HYDROXY-N,N,5-TRIMETHYLPYRAZOLE -1-CARBOXAMIDE	644-64-4	PST83057

ALPHABETICAL INDEX

SUBSTANCE NAME	CAS #	PST #
DIOCTYL-MEDO FORTE	577-11-7	PST00406
DIOCTYLAL	577-11-7	PST00406
DIORTHO LEAD ARSENATE	7784-40-9	PST12540
DIOTHYL	5221-49-8	PST08049
DIOTILAN	577-11-7	PST00406
DIOVAC	577-11-7	PST00406
DIOXABENZOFOS	3811-49-2	PST20325
DIOXACARB	6988-21-2	PST73123
DIOXATHION	78-34-2	PST08050
DIOXIN	1746-01-6	PST08060
DIPAXIN	82-66-6	PST08068
DIPEL 2X	UNASSIGNED	PST08603
DIPHACIN	82-66-6	PST08068
DIPHACINON	82-66-6	PST08068
DIPHACINONE	82-66-6	PST08068
DIPHENACIN	82-66-6	PST08068
DIPHENACOUM	56073-07-5	PST07385
DIPHENADION	82-66-6	PST08068
DIPHENADIONE	82-66-6	PST08068
DIPHENAMID	957-51-7	PST71406
DIPHENAMIDE	957-51-7	PST71406
DIPHENOXURON	14214-32-5	PST07386
DIPHENYL PHTHALATE	84-62-8	PST08095
DIPHENYLAMINE	122-39-4	PST08100
DIPHENYLMETHANE, 5,5'-DICHLORO-2,2'-HYDROXY-	97-23-4	PST71611
DIPHOSPHORAMIDE, OCTAMETHYL-	152-16-9	PST20350
DIPHOSPHORIC ACID TETRAETHYL ESTER	107-49-3	PST22520
DIPHOSPHORIC ACID, TETRAPOTASSIUM SALT	7320-34-5	PST19546
DIPHOSPHORIC ACID, TETRASODIUM SALT	7722-88-5	PST23140
DIPOTASSIUM CARBONATE	584-08-7	PST19290
DIPOTASSIUM DICHROMATE	7778-50-9	PST19370
DIPOTASSIUM SALT	7778-50-9	PST19370
DIPOTASSIUM SULFATE	7778-80-5	PST19590
DIPPEL'S OIL	8001-85-2	PST03250
DIPPING ACID	7664-93-9	PST22350
DIPROPETRYN	4147-51-7	PST72333
DIPROPYLCARBAMOTHIOIC ACID S-ETHYL ESTER	759-94-4	PST71470
DIPROPYLCARBAMOTHIOIC ACID S-PROPYL ESTER	1929-77-7	PST71473
DIPROPYLTHIOCARBAMIC ACID S-ETHYL ESTER	759-94-4	PST71470
DIPROPYLTHIOCARBAMIC ACID S-PROPYL ESTER	1929-77-7	PST71473
DIPTEREX	52-68-6	PST23790
DIPTHAL	2303-17-5	PST72050
DIPYRIDO(1,2-A:2',1'-C)PYRAZINEDIIUM, 6,7-DIHYDRO-, DIBROMIDE	85-00-7	PST08250
DIQUAT	85-00-7	PST08250
DIQUAT DIBROMIDE	85-00-7	PST08250
DIRAX	86-88-4	PST01830
DIRIMAL	19044-88-3	PST17324
DIS(DIETHYLAMINO)THIOXOMETHYL DISULFIDE	97-77-8	PST08370
DISAN	741-58-2	PST02583
DISK DRIVE HEAD CLEANING KIT (DIGITAL EQUIPMENT CORPORATION)	67-63-0	PST12090
DISODIUM ACID ORTHOPHOSPHATE	7558-79-4	PST08330
DISODIUM ACID PHOSPHATE	7558-79-4	PST08330
DISODIUM CARBONATE	497-19-8	PST21080
DISODIUM DICHROMATE	10588-01-9	PST21190

SUBSTANCE NAME	CAS #	PST #
DITHIOSYSTOX	298-04-4	PST08380
DITION	572-48-5	PST73073
DIUREX	330-54-1	PST08420
DIURON	330-54-1	PST08420
DIVIPAN	62-73-7	PST07000
DKHM	116-52-9	PST06817
DL-HOMOALANIN-4-YL(METHYL)PHOSPHINIC ACID, AMMONIUM	77182-82-2	PST72647
DL-HOMOALANIN-4-YL(METHYL)PHOSPHINIC ACID, MONOAMMONIUM SALT	77182-82-2	PST72647
DL-2-ALLYL-4-HYDROXY-3-METHYL-2-CYCLOPENTEN-1-ONE ESTER OF D-TRANS CHRYSANTHEMUM MONOCARBOXYLIC ACID	UNASSIGNED	PST00553
DL-2-ALLYL-4-HYDROXY-3-METHYL-2-CYCLOPENTEN-1-ONE ESTER OF D-TRANS-2,2-DIMETHYL-3-(2-METHYLPROPENYL)CYCLOPROPANECARBOXYLIC ACID	UNASSIGNED	PST00553
DL-3-(2-FURFURYL)-4-HYDROXY-2-METHYL-2-CYCLOPENTEN-1-ONE ESTER OF DL-CIS-TRANS-CHRYSANTHEMUM MONOCARBOXYLIC ACID	17080-02-3	PST10175
DMAP	30560-19-1	PST00065
DMASA	1596-84-5	PST06195
DMCP	3309-87-3	PST72763
DMDT	72-43-5	PST14220
DMOC	5234-68-4	PST04348
DMP	131-11-3	PST07740
DMP	813-78-5	PST07882
DMPA	299-85-4	PST71236
DMTT	533-74-4	PST06230
DMU	330-54-1	PST08420
DN 289	88-85-7	PST08020
DNBP	88-85-7	PST08020
DNBP	6099-79-2	PST08022
DNC	534-52-1	PST07910
DNOC	534-52-1	PST07910
DNOC SODIUM SALT	2312-76-7	PST71411
DNOCP	39300-45-3	PST71402
DNOP	117-84-0	PST08040
DNTBP	1420-07-1	PST72921
DOCUSATE SODIUM	577-11-7	PST00406
DODANIC ACID 83	27176-87-0	PST08480
DODECACHLOROOCTAHYDRO-1,3,4-METHENO-1H-CYCLOBUTA(CD)PENTALENE	2385-85-5	PST09690
DODECACHLOROPENTACYCLODECANE	2385-85-5	PST09690
DODECANOIC ACID, POTASSIUM SALT	10124-65-9	PST72072
DODECANOL	112-53-8	PST12500
DODECYL ALCOHOL	112-53-8	PST12500
DODECYL BENZENE SODIUM SULPHONATE	25155-30-0	PST21220
DODECYL SODIUM SULFATE	151-21-3	PST08485
DODECYL SULFATE, SODIUM SALT	151-21-3	PST08485
DODECYLBENZENE SODIUM SULFONATE	25155-30-0	PST21220
DODECYLBENZENESULFONIC ACID	27176-87-0	PST08480
DODECYLBENZENESULFONIC ACID, SODIUM SALT	25155-30-0	PST21220
DODECYLBENZENESULPHONATE, SODIUM SALT	25155-30-0	PST21220
DODECYLBENZENESULPHONIC ACID	27176-87-0	PST08480
DODECYLBENZYLTRIMETHYLAMMONIUM CHLORIDE	1330-85-4	PST71854
DOLOCHLOR	76-06-2	PST04830
DOP	117-81-7	PST06440
DOSAFLO	19937-59-8	PST15009
DOSANEX	19937-59-8	PST15009
DOTAN	24934-91-6	PST04655

ALPHABETICAL INDEX

SUBSTANCE NAME	CAS #	PST #
DRIERITE	7778-18-9	PST04110
DRILLZID	2104-96-3	PST71064
DRINOX	76-44-8	PST10660
DROPP	51707-55-2	PST23299
DRW-1139	41394-05-2	PST14095
DS 15647	39196-18-4	PST23330
DSDP	78-53-5	PST83006
DSE	142-59-6	PST16080
DSP	7558-79-4	PST08330
DTMC761	115-32-2	PST07010
DU PONT 1991	17804-35-2	PST02580
DU PONT 326	330-55-2	PST12826
DU PONT 634	2164-08-1	PST73238
DU PONT 732	5902-51-2	PST71099
DUAL	51218-45-2	PST15003
DUATEX	72-14-0	PST72047
DULCIDOR	15879-93-3	PST00775
DUPHAR PH 60-40	35367-38-5	PST07388
DUPONOL	151-21-3	PST08485
DUPONT HERBICIDE 326	330-55-2	PST12826
DURAFUR DEVELOPER C	120-80-9	PST04360
DURATOX (FORMULATION)	919-86-8	PST83065
DURSBAN	2921-88-2	PST04910
DURSBAN (R) L.O. INSECTICIDE	UNASSIGNED	PST08522
DURSBAN (R) 4E INSECTICIDE	UNASSIGNED	PST08521
DURSBAN L.O. INSECTICIDE	UNASSIGNED	PST08522
DURSBAN METHYL	5598-13-0	PST71652
DURSBAN OXON	5598-15-2	PST04911
DURSBAN OXYGEN ANALOG	5598-15-2	PST04911
DURSBAN 4E EMULSIFIABLE INSECTICIDE	UNASSIGNED	PST08521
DURSBAN 4E INSECTICIDE	UNASSIGNED	PST08521
DURSBANOXON	5598-15-2	PST04911
DUTCH LIQUID	107-06-2	PST09390
DUTOM	2307-68-8	PST71164
DW3418	21725-46-2	PST05762
DXP 5648	74222-97-2	PST72544
DYBAR	101-42-8	PST09679
DYCARB	22781-23-3	PST02560
DYCLOMEC	1194-65-6	PST06800
DYFLOS	55-91-4	PST07590
DYFONAT	944-22-9	PST10020
DYFONATE	944-22-9	PST10020
DYKON	126-96-5	PST71497
DYLOX	52-68-6	PST23790
DYMID	957-51-7	PST71406
DYNACHEM (R) DEVELOPER DCR (THIOKOL/DYNACHEM CORPORATION)	1330-20-7	PST25150
DYNEX	330-54-1	PST08420
DYRENE	101-05-3	PST01526
DYREX	52-68-6	PST23790
DYTOL S-91	112-30-1	PST06285
D3-VIGANTOL	67-97-0	PST60913
E 1059	8065-48-3	PST06320
E 20	7440-22-4	PST20770
E 600	311-45-5	PST07200

ALPHABETICAL INDEX

ALPHABETICAL INDEX

SUBSTANCE NAME	CAS #	PST #
ENT 24969	470-90-6	PST04575
ENT 24988	300-76-5	PST06660
ENT 25 726	2032-65-7	PST14190
ENT 25,506	116-01-8	PST08723
ENT 25,515	13171-21-6	PST18670
ENT 25,545-X	297-78-9	PST83032
ENT 25,552-X	12789-03-6	PST71948
ENT 25,554-X	3735-23-7	PST73085
ENT 25,580	297-97-2	PST25590
ENT 25,586	953-17-3	PST71647
ENT 25,602-X	299-86-5	PST05550
ENT 25,613	2665-30-7	PST73278
ENT 25,640	115-93-5	PST06135
ENT 25,644	52-85-7	PST09675
ENT 25,671	114-26-1	PST02540
ENT 25,674	2674-91-1	PST14105
ENT 25,705	732-11-6	PST11307
ENT 25,715	122-14-5	PST09678
ENT 25,766	315-18-4	PST15010
ENT 25,776	1113-02-6	PST17328
ENT 25,784	2032-59-9	PST71500
ENT 25,793	485-31-4	PST71960
ENT 25,830	947-02-4	PST06115
ENT 25,832	13067-93-1	PST05805
ENT 25,962	15271-41-7	PST73177
ENT 25445	61-82-5	PST01040
ENT 25500	64-00-6	PST29423
ENT 25540	55-38-9	PST02550
ENT 25567	1491-41-4	PST72737
ENT 25584	1024-57-3	PST10670
ENT 25585	2275-14-1	PST18373
ENT 25647	299-85-4	PST71236
ENT 25650	919-54-0	PST00117
ENT 25670	2631-40-5	PST73231
ENT 25685	3309-87-3	PST72763
ENT 25712	327-98-0	PST00478
ENT 25719	2385-85-5	PST09690
ENT 25734	3254-63-5	PST73095
ENT 25760	78-57-9	PST72980
ENT 25922	644-64-4	PST83057
ENT 25991	950-10-7	PST13735
ENT 26,058	101-05-3	PST01526
ENT 26613	2275-23-2	PST73108
ENT 27 258	4824-78-6	PST03458
ENT 27 566	23422-53-9	PST10050
ENT 27 822	30560-19-1	PST00065
ENT 27,093	116-06-3	PST00500
ENT 27,102	1757-18-2	PST00493
ENT 27,160	919-76-6	PST01007
ENT 27,165	3383-96-8	PST00020
ENT 27,305	17702-57-7	PST73082
ENT 27,341	16752-77-5	PST14200
ENT 27,395-X	13121-70-5	PST06110
ENT 27,396	10265-92-6	PST15160

ALPHABETICAL INDEX

SUBSTANCE NAME	CAS #	PST #
ENT 27041	1079-33-0	PST29855
ENT 27127	8065-36-9	PST03480
ENT 27129	6923-22-4	PST15165
ENT 27162	2104-96-3	PST71064
ENT 27163	2310-17-0	PST25720
ENT 27164	1563-66-2	PST04240
ENT 27193	950-37-8	PST14175
ENT 27226	2312-35-8	PST19720
ENT 27244	973-21-7	PST07990
ENT 27257	2540-82-1	PST10081
ENT 27300	2631-37-0	PST72957
ENT 27311	2921-88-2	PST04910
ENT 27318	13194-48-4	PST15080
ENT 27320	10311-84-9	PST23630
ENT 27335	6164-98-3	PST04570
ENT 27339	7696-12-0	PST23061
ENT 27386	2597-03-7	PST72337
ENT 27389	6988-21-2	PST73123
ENT 27395	13121-70-5	PST06110
ENT 27520	5598-13-0	PST71652
ENT 27567	19750-95-9	PST71656
ENT 27635	60238-56-4	PST64913
ENT 27696	26419-73-8	PST73088
ENT 27699GC	29232-93-7	PST72378
ENT 27766	23103-98-2	PST72345
ENT 27851	39196-18-4	PST23330
ENT 27972	26002-80-2	PST71954
ENT 28344	5281-13-0	PST71828
ENT 29 261	1646-88-4	PST72406
ENT 29054	35367-38-5	PST07388
ENT 38	92-84-2	PST18400
ENT 4225	72-54-8	PST06240
ENT 6	112-56-1	PST75661
ENT 7,796	58-89-9	PST12810
ENT 785	2550-75-6	PST73193
ENT 8,538	94-75-7	PST28510
ENT 8,601	608-73-1	PST03080
ENT 9,232	319-84-6	PST00770
ENT 9,233	319-85-7	PST03010
ENT 9,234	319-86-8	PST06310
ENT 9,932	57-74-9	PST04560
ENT 9,932	12789-03-6	PST71948
ENT 987	137-26-8	PST23430
ENTEX (FORMULATION)	55-38-9	PST02550
ENTEX OXON	6552-12-1	PST02551
ENTEX OXON SULFONE	14086-35-2	PST02552
ENTEX OXON SULFOXIDE	6552-13-2	PST02553
EO	75-21-8	PST09520
EP 332	23422-53-9	PST10050
EP 475	13684-56-5	PST72336
EPA REG. NO. 2724-312-50809	UNASSIGNED	PST10348
EPA REG. NO. 4581-335	UNASSIGNED	PST12357
EPA REG. NO. 464-360	UNASSIGNED	PST08521
EPA REG. NO. 464-571	UNASSIGNED	PST08522

ALPHABETICAL INDEX

SUBSTANCE NAME	CAS #	PST #
EPA REG. NO. 499-157	UNASSIGNED	PST25105
EPA REG. NO. 524-329	UNASSIGNED	PST12481
EPA REG. NO. 524-329-AA	UNASSIGNED	PST12471
EPA REG. NO. 524-341	UNASSIGNED	PST03451
EPA SHAUGHNESSY CODE: 098301	116-06-3	PST00500
EPAL	39148-24-8	PST72563
EPAL 10	112-30-1	PST06285
EPBP	3792-59-4	PST73239
EPN	2104-64-5	PST08650
EPOXYETHANE	75-21-8	PST09520
EPOXYHEPTACHLOR	1024-57-3	PST10670
EPOXYPROPANE	75-56-9	PST19910
EPTAM	759-94-4	PST71470
EPTAPUR	3766-60-7	PST03523
EPTC	759-94-4	PST71470
EQUIGARD	62-73-7	PST07000
EQUIPMENT FLUSHING SOLVENT (LOCTITE CORPORATION)	75-09-2	PST14930
ERIOGLAUCINE	2650-18-2	PST08277
ERYTHROSIN B	16423-68-0	PST08685
ERYTHROSINE B (BIOLOGICAL STAIN)	16423-68-0	PST08685
ERYTHROSINE BLUISH	16423-68-0	PST08685
ESBIOL	28434-00-6	PST71013
ESCORT	74223-64-6	PST72546
ESP	2674-91-1	PST14105
ESPADOL	88-04-0	PST72258
ESTAFILOL	72-14-0	PST72047
ESTER	2104-96-3	PST71064
ESTER 25	311-45-5	PST07200
ESTER, (1R-(1ALPHA(S*(Z),3BETA))-	121-29-9	PST19970
ESTONOX	8001-35-2	PST23640
ESTOX	2674-91-1	PST14105
ETAZIN	26259-45-0	PST73051
ETAZINE	26259-45-0	PST73051
ETHAL	36653-82-4	PST04525
ETHALFLURALIN	55283-68-6	PST72436
ETHANAMINIUM, 2-CHLORO-N,N,N-TRIMETHYL-, CHLORIDE	999-81-5	PST71147
ETHANE-1,2-DIOL	107-21-1	PST09400
ETHANE, 1,1-DICHLORO-2-(M-CHLOROPHENYL)-2-(P-CHLOROPHENYL)-	4329-12-8	PST04752
ETHANE, 1,1-DICHLORO-2,2-BIS(P-CHLOROPHENYL)-	72-54-8	PST06240
ETHANE, 1,1-DICHLORO-2,2-BIS(P-ETHYLPHENYL)-	72-56-0	PST71373
ETHANE, 1,1,1-TRICHLORO-2,2-BIS(P-CHLOROPHENY)-	50-29-3	PST06250
ETHANE, 1,1,1-TRICHLORO-2,2-BIS(P-METHOXYPHENYL)-	72-43-5	PST14220
ETHANE, 1,1,1-TRICHLOROETHANE	71-55-6	PST14370
ETHANE, 1,2-DIBROMO-	106-93-4	PST09380
ETHANE, 1,2-DICHLORO-	107-06-2	PST09390
ETHANECARBOXYLIC ACID	79-09-4	PST19750
ETHANEDIAL, DIOXIME	557-30-2	PST73143
ETHANEDIOIC ACID	144-62-7	PST17360
ETHANEDIOIC ACID, COPPER (2+) SALT (1:1)	814-91-5	PST05650
ETHANEDIONE DIOXIME	557-30-2	PST73143
ETHANEPEROXOIC ACID	79-21-0	PST18310
ETHANETHIOL, 2-(ETHYLTHIO)-, S-ESTER WITH O,O-DIETHYL PHOSPHOROTHIOATE	126-75-0	PST71646
ETHANIMIDOTHIOIC ACID, N-(((METHYLAMINO)CARBONYL)OXY)-, METHYL ESTER	16752-77-5	PST14200
ETHANIMIDOTHIOIC ACID, N,N'-(THIOBIS((METHYLIMINO)CARBONYLOXY))BIS-,	59669-26-0	PST72456

SUBSTANCE NAME	CAS #	PST #
DIMETHYL ESTER		
ETHANOIC ACID	64-19-7	PST00120
ETHANOL	64-17-5	PST08700
ETHANOL, 2-(ETHYLTHIO)-, DIETHYL PHOSPHATE	23052-51-9	PST06317
ETHANOL, 2-(HYDROXYMETHYLAMINE)-	34375-28-5	PST72288
ETHANOL, 2-(2,4-DICHLOROPHENOXY)-	120-67-2	PST06915
ETHANOL, 2-AMINO-	141-43-5	PST08710
ETHANOL, 2-BUTOXY-	111-76-2	PST03540
ETHANOL, 2-METHOXY	109-86-4	PST14340
ETHANOL, 2,2-BIS(P-CHLOROPHENYL)-	2642-82-2	PST06323
ETHANOL, 2,2',2''-NITRILOTRI-	102-71-6	PST23932
ETHANOL, 2,2',2''-NITRILOTRIS-	102-71-6	PST23932
ETHANOL,2,2'-(1,2-ETHANEDIYLBIS(OXY))BIS-,	112-27-6	PST24000
ETHANOLAMINE	141-43-5	PST08710
ETHEFON	16672-87-0	PST72293
ETHENE	74-85-1	PST09330
ETHENE OXIDE	75-21-8	PST09520
ETHENE, HOMOPOLYMER	9002-88-4	PST19119
ETHENE, TETRACHLORO-	127-18-4	PST22900
ETHEPHON	16672-87-0	PST72293
ETHER, P-NITROPHENYL ALPHA,ALPHA,ALPHA-TRIFLUORO-2-NITRO-P-TOLYL	15457-05-3	PST72248
ETHER, P-NITROPHENYL 2,4,6-TRICHLOROPHENYL	1836-77-7	PST23865
ETHER, 2,4-DICHLOROPHENYL P-NITROPHENYL	1836-75-5	PST23580
ETHIDIMURON	30043-49-3	PST72551
ETHIOFENCARB	29973-13-5	PST72421
ETHIOLAT	2941-55-1	PST72327
ETHIOLATE	2941-55-1	PST72327
ETHION	563-12-2	PST08720
ETHIOZIN	64529-56-2	PST09111
ETHIRIMOL	23947-60-6	PST08721
ETHOATE-METHYL	116-01-8	PST08723
ETHOFUMESATE	26225-79-6	PST72404
ETHOHEXADIOL	94-96-2	PST71458
ETHOL	36653-82-4	PST04525
ETHOPROP	13194-48-4	PST15080
ETHOPROPHOS	13194-48-4	PST15080
ETHOXYLAN 1685	61790-81-6	PST08741
ETHOXYLAN 1685 PEG (75) LANOLIN	61790-81-6	PST08741
ETHOXYLATED ALCOHOLS (C11-C15):	68131-40-8	PST85315
ETHOXYLATED ALCOHOLS, C11-15-SECONDARY	68131-40-8	PST85315
ETHOXYLATED LANOLIN	61790-81-6	PST08741
ETHOXYLATED LANOLIN ALCOHOLS	61790-81-6	PST08741
ETHOXYLATED NONYLPHENOL	9016-45-9	PST16835
ETHOXYLATED SORBITAN MONOOLAURATE	9005-64-5	PST80107
ETHOXYLATED WOOL WAX ALCOHOLS	61790-81-6	PST08741
ETHOXYPHAS	919-54-0	PST00117
ETHOXYPHOS	919-54-0	PST00117
ETHOXYQUIN	91-53-2	PST08740
ETHOXYQUINE	91-53-2	PST08740
ETHREL	16672-87-0	PST72293
ETHYL (((DIETHOXYPHOSPHINOTHIOYL)THIO)ACETYL)METHYLCARBAMATE	2595-54-2	PST13675
ETHYL (DIETHOXYPHOSPHINOTHIOYLTHIO)ACETYL(METHYL)CARBAMATE	2595-54-2	PST13675
ETHYL (MERCAPTOACETYL)METHYLCARBAMATE S-ESTER WITH O,O-DIETHYL PHOSPHORODITHIOATE	2595-54-2	PST13675

ALPHABETICAL INDEX

SUBSTANCE NAME	CAS #	PST #
ETHYLENEDINITRILOTETRAACETIC ACID	60-00-4	PST09570
ETHYLFORMIC ACID	79-09-4	PST19750
ETHYLHEXYL PHTHALATE	117-81-7	PST06440
ETHYLIC ACID	64-19-7	PST00120
ETHYLMERCURIC ACETATE	109-62-6	PST71476
ETHYLMERCURIC CHLORIDE	107-27-7	PST09620
ETHYLMERCURIC PHOSPHATE	2235-25-8	PST71479
ETHYLMERCURY ACETATE	109-62-6	PST71476
ETHYLMERCURY CHLORIDE	107-27-7	PST09620
ETHYLOLAMINE	141-43-5	PST08710
ETHYLPHOSPHONODITHIOIC ACID O-ETHYL S-PHENYL ESTER	944-22-9	PST10020
ETHYLPHOSPHONOTHIOIC ACID O-ETHYL O-(2,4,5-TRICHLOROPHENYL)ESTER	327-98-0	PST00478
ETHYLTHIODEMETON	298-04-4	PST08380
ETHYLTHIOMETON SULFOXIDE	2497-07-6	PST17385
ETHYLTHIONODEMETON	126-75-0	PST71646
ETICOL	311-45-5	PST07200
ETIROX	2941-55-1	PST72327
ETO	75-21-8	PST09520
ETRIMFOS	38260-54-7	PST73148
ETRIMFOS OXYGEN ANALOG	UNASSIGNED	PST09666
ETRIMPHOS	38260-54-7	PST73148
ETRIMPHOS OXON	UNASSIGNED	PST09666
ETROFOLAN	2631-40-5	PST73231
ETROLENE	299-84-3	PST20180
ETSAN	1134-23-2	PST71469
EUCALYPTUS OIL	8000-48-4	PST71453
EUDERMOL	29790-52-1	PST16450
EUNATROL	143-19-1	PST21418
EUPAREN	1085-98-9	PST73026
EUPAREN M	731-27-1	PST73030
EUREX	1134-23-2	PST71469
EVIK	834-12-8	PST01006
EVITAL	27314-13-2	PST72343
EVOLA	106-46-7	PST17640
EXAGIEN	119-36-8	PST14720
EXO-1,4,5,6,7,7-HEXACHLORO-5-NORBORNENE-2,3-DIMETHANOL CYCLIC SULFITE	33213-65-9	PST03040
EXO-3-CHLORO-ENDO-6-CYANO-2-NORBORANONE O-(METHYLCARBAMOYL)OXIME	15271-41-7	PST73177
EXO,ENDO-1,2,4,5,6,7,8,8-OCTACHLORO-2,3-EPOXY-3A,4,7,7,7A-TETRAHYDRO-4,7-METHANOINDAN	27304-13-8	PST17372
EXOFENE	70-30-4	PST10780
EXP 1659	39148-24-8	PST72563
EXPAND	74051-80-2	PST20577
EXPERIMENTAL HERBICIDE	116-52-9	PST06817
EXPERIMENTAL HERBICIDE 1	136-78-7	PST05500
EXPERIMENTAL HERBICIDE 732	5902-51-2	PST71099
EXPERIMENTAL INSECTICIDE 269	72-20-8	PST08600
EXPERIMENTAL INSECTICIDE 3911	298-02-2	PST18640
EXSICCATED SODIUM PHOSPHATE	7558-79-4	PST08330
EXSICCATED SODIUM SULFITE	7757-83-7	PST21660
EXTRACT OF CHRYSANTHEMUM CINERARIAEFOLIUM CONTAINING: CINERIN I AND II JASMOLIN I AND II AND PYRETHRIN I AND II	8003-34-7	PST19980
EZ FLOW	10049-04-4	PST04610
EZITAN	26259-45-0	PST73051
F 11	75-69-4	PST09990

SUBSTANCE NAME	CAS #	PST #
F 139	126-22-7	PST71399
F 461	5259-88-1	PST17373
F-319	10004-44-1	PST22404
FAA	640-19-7	PST09930
FAC	2275-18-5	PST19943
FAC 20	2275-18-5	PST19943
FAK-40	2275-18-5	PST19943
FALCON DUST OFF II (FALCON SAFETY PRODUCT INC.)	75-71-8	PST06880
FALISILVAN	101-42-8	PST09679
FALTAN	133-07-3	PST10012
FAMID	6988-21-2	PST73123
FAMOPHOS	52-85-7	PST09675
FAMPHOS	52-85-7	PST09675
FAMPHUR	52-85-7	PST09675
FANAL	7681-38-1	PST20990
FANTERRIN	79-57-2	PST17414
FAP	525-79-1	PST72483
FAR-GO	2303-17-5	PST72050
FARTOX	82-68-8	PST18140
FAST GREEN	569-64-2	PST13533
FASTAC	67375-30-8	PST06118
FATSCO ANT POISON	7631-89-2	PST20940
FB/2	85-00-7	PST08250
FC 11	75-69-4	PST09990
FCR 1272	68359-37-5	PST72630
FD AND C RED NO. 3	16423-68-0	PST08685
FD[C YELLOW NO.5	1934-21-0	PST22465
FDA 0101	7681-49-4	PST21230
FDA 1541	759-94-4	PST71470
FEDONA	67375-30-8	PST06118
FEENO	92-84-2	PST18400
FEH7011S	7782-63-0	PST09870
FELAN	2212-67-1	PST71471
FELIDERM K	7773-06-0	PST01400
FENAM	957-51-7	PST71406
FENAMINOSULF	140-56-7	PST73084
FENAMIPHOS	22224-92-6	PST16145
FENAMIPHOS SULFONE	31972-44-8	PST16144
FENAMIPHOS SULFOXIDE	31972-43-7	PST16146
FENBUTATIN OXIDE	13356-08-6	PST24866
FENCAL	7778-44-1	PST03850
FENCHLOFOS	299-84-3	PST20180
FENCHLORFOS	299-84-3	PST20180
FENCHLORPHOS	299-84-3	PST20180
FENCHLORPHOS-OXON	3983-45-7	PST25082
FENDONA	52315-07-8	PST72392
FENFOSPHORIN	3811-49-2	PST20325
FENIDIM	101-42-8	PST09679
FENITROTHION	122-14-5	PST09678
FENMEDIFAM	13684-63-4	PST72282
FENOBUCARB	3766-81-2	PST03324
FENORMONE	93-72-1	PST20830
FENOVERM	92-84-2	PST18400
FENOXAPROP-ETHYL	66441-23-4	PST72723

SUBSTANCE NAME	CAS #	PST #
FENOXON	6552-12-1	PST02551
FENOXON SULFONE	14086-35-2	PST02552
FENOXON SULFOXIDE	6552-13-2	PST02553
FENOXYCARB	72490-01-8	PST72618
FENSON	80-38-6	PST09677
FENSONE	80-38-6	PST09677
FENSULFOTHION	115-90-2	PST06210
FENSULFOTHION OXON	6552-21-2	PST09684
FENSULFOTHION OXON SULFONE	6132-17-8	PST06211
FENSULFOTHION OXYGEN ANALOG	6552-21-2	PST09684
FENSULFOTHION OXYGEN ANALOG SULFONE	6132-17-8	PST06211
FENSULFOTHION SULFONE	14255-72-2	PST06228
FENSULFOXIDE	3761-41-9	PST02555
FENTHION	55-38-9	PST02550
FENTHION O-ANALOG SULFONE	14086-35-2	PST02552
FENTHION OXON	6552-12-1	PST02551
FENTHION OXON SULFONE	14086-35-2	PST02552
FENTHION OXON SULFOXIDE	6552-13-2	PST02553
FENTHION OXYGEN ANALOG	6552-12-1	PST02551
FENTHION SULFONE	3761-42-0	PST02554
FENTHION SULFOXIDE	3761-41-9	PST02555
FENTIAZIN	92-84-2	PST18400
FENTICHLOR	97-24-5	PST71737
FENTICLOR	97-24-5	PST71737
FENTIN ACETATE	900-95-8	PST24378
FENTIN CHLORIDE	639-58-7	PST24380
FENULON	101-42-8	PST09679
FENURON	101-42-8	PST09679
FENURON TCA	4482-55-7	PST71389
FENURON TRICHLOROACETATE	4482-55-7	PST71389
FENURON-TCA	4482-55-7	PST71389
FENVALERATE	51630-58-1	PST19948
FERBAM	14484-64-1	PST09680
FERBERK	14484-64-1	PST09680
FERMATE	14484-64-1	PST09680
FERMENTICIDE LIQUID	7446-09-5	PST22290
FERMINE	131-11-3	PST07740
FERNASAN	137-26-8	PST23430
FERNEX	23505-41-1	PST72377
FERNIMINE	94-75-7	PST28510
FERNOS	23103-98-2	PST72345
FEROPROP	93-72-1	PST20830
FERRADOW	14484-64-1	PST09680
FERRIC DIMETHYLDITHIOCARBAMATE	14484-64-1	PST09680
FERRIC N,N-DIMETHYLDITHIOCARBAMATE	14484-64-1	PST09680
FERRIC SULFATE	10028-22-5	PST09790
FERROUS AMMONIUM SULFATE	10045-89-3	PST09820
FERROUS DIAMMONIUM SULFATE	10045-89-3	PST09820
FERROUS SULFATE	7782-63-0	PST09870
FERROUS SULFATE HEPTAHYDRATE	7782-63-0	PST09870
FERROUS SULFATE, HEPTAHYDRATE	7782-63-0	PST09870
FICAM	22781-23-3	PST02560
FICHLOR 91	87-90-1	PST23860
FILARIOL	4824-78-6	PST03458

ALPHABETICAL INDEX

ALPHABETICAL INDEX

ALPHABETICAL INDEX

ALPHABETICAL INDEX

ALPHABETICAL INDEX

ALPHABETICAL INDEX

SUBSTANCE NAME	CAS #	PST #
H 9789	27314-13-2	PST72343
H-119	1698-60-8	PST71928
HACHE UNO SUPER	69806-50-4	PST72554
HAIPEN 50	2425-06-1	PST04200
HALANE	118-52-5	PST26800
HALENOL	97-23-4	PST71611
HALIMIDE	1330-85-4	PST71854
HALITE	7647-14-5	PST21105
HALIZAN	108-62-3	PST14090
HALOFLEX 208	9003-01-4	PST04349
HALON 1001	74-83-9	PST14300
HALOXYFOP	69806-34-4	PST72580
HALOXYFOP-METHYL	69806-40-2	PST72579
HAMPSHIRE DEG	139-41-3	PST71447
HANANE	115-26-4	PST07655
HARNESS	34256-82-1	PST72539
HAVIDOTE	60-00-4	PST09570
HAVOC	56073-10-0	PST03327
HC 2072	311-45-5	PST07200
HCE	1024-57-3	PST10670
HCH	319-84-6	PST00770
HCH	319-85-7	PST03010
HCH	608-73-1	PST03080
HCH	319-86-8	PST06310
HCH	58-89-9	PST12810
HCS 3260	12789-03-6	PST71948
HEAVY OIL	8001-58-9	PST05230
HEBACID OXON SULFONE	14086-35-2	PST02552
HEBURID OXON	6552-12-1	PST02551
HEDAPUR M 52	94-74-6	PST27880
HEDONAL	94-75-7	PST28510
HELMETINA	92-84-2	PST18400
HELOTHION	35400-43-2	PST22387
HEOLITE	84-65-1	PST01600
HEPTA	76-44-8	PST10660
HEPTACHLOR	76-44-8	PST10660
HEPTACHLOR CIS-OXIDE	1024-57-3	PST10670
HEPTACHLOR EPOXIDE	1024-57-3	PST10670
HEPTENOPHOS	23560-59-0	PST10685
HEPTYL CARBINOL	111-87-5	PST17270
HERBAN	18530-56-8	PST71400
HERBATOX	330-54-1	PST08420
HERBATOXOL	1912-24-9	PST02150
HERBAZIN	122-34-9	PST20837
HERBICIDE 326	330-55-2	PST12826
HERBICIDE 976	314-40-9	PST03330
HERBICIDES, SILVEX	93-72-1	PST20830
HERBOGIL	1420-07-1	PST72921
HERCO AND YARMOR 80 PINE OIL (HERCULES, INC.)	8002-09-3	PST18900
HERCULES AC 5727	64-00-6	PST29423
HERCULES AC528	78-34-2	PST08050
HERCULES 14 503	10311-84-9	PST23630
HERCULES 22234	38727-55-8	PST72968
HERCULES 426	2550-75-6	PST73193

ALPHABETICAL INDEX

SUBSTANCE NAME	CAS #	PST #
HERCULES 5727	64-00-6	PST29423
HERCULES 7531	18530-56-8	PST71400
HEXABALM	70-30-4	PST10780
HEXACHLORO-HEXAHYDRO-ENDO,ENDO-DIMETHANONAPHTHALENE	465-73-6	PST11810
HEXACHLOROBENZENE	319-85-7	PST03010
HEXACHLOROBENZENE	608-73-1	PST03080
HEXACHLOROBENZENE	118-74-1	PST10730
HEXACHLOROCYCLOHEXANE	319-84-6	PST00770
HEXACHLOROCYCLOHEXANE	319-85-7	PST03010
HEXACHLOROCYCLOHEXANE	608-73-1	PST03080
HEXACHLOROCYCLOHEXANE	319-86-8	PST06310
HEXACHLOROCYCLOHEXANE	58-89-9	PST12810
HEXACHLOROCYCLOPENTADIENE DIMER	2385-85-5	PST09690
HEXACHLOROPHENE	70-30-4	PST10780
HEXACOL TARTRAZINE	1934-21-0	PST22465
HEXADECANOL	36653-82-4	PST04525
HEXADECYL ALCOHOL	36653-82-4	PST04525
HEXAFERB	14484-64-1	PST09680
HEXAHYDRO-1H-AZEPINE-1-CARBOTHIOIC ACID S-ETHYL ESTER	2212-67-1	PST71471
HEXAHYDROXY-6-METHYL-1,11-DIOXO-2-NAPHTHACENECARBOXAMIDE, MONOHYDROCHLORIDE	2058-46-0	PST84045
HEXAKIS(B,B-DIMETHYLPHENETHYL)-DISTANNOXANE	13356-08-6	PST24866
HEXAKIS(2-METHYL-2-PHENYLPROPYL)-DISTANNOXANE	13356-08-6	PST24866
HEXAN-1-OL	111-27-3	PST15630
HEXANEMA	97-17-6	PST06805
HEXANOL	111-27-3	PST15630
HEXANON	108-94-1	PST05890
HEXASUL	7704-34-9	PST22280
HEXATHION	786-19-6	PST04340
HEXAZINONE	51235-04-2	PST10994
HEXAZIR	137-30-4	PST25397
HEXONE	108-10-1	PST14550
HEXYL ALCOHOL	111-27-3	PST15630
HEXYLTHIOCARBAM	1134-23-2	PST71469
HHDN	309-00-2	PST00520
HI-SIL	63231-67-4	PST20670
HI-YIELD DESICCANT H-10	7778-39-4	PST01990
HILTACHLOR	23184-66-9	PST03497
HINOSAN	17109-49-8	PST08555
HIZAROCIN	66-81-9	PST05930
HKO	1310-58-3	PST19430
HKO4S	7646-93-7	PST19255
HNAO4S	7681-38-1	PST20990
HNA2O4P	7558-79-4	PST08330
HOE 16410	34123-59-6	PST12254
HOE 2747	1746-81-2	PST15174
HOE 2784	485-31-4	PST71960
HOE 2872	639-58-7	PST24380
HOE 2873	13457-18-6	PST73169
HOE 2960	24017-47-8	PST73068
HOE 2982	23560-59-0	PST10685
HOE 2991	27954-37-6	PST23002
HOE 33171	66441-23-4	PST72723
HOE 39 866	77182-82-2	PST72647

ALPHABETICAL INDEX

SUBSTANCE NAME	CAS #	PST #
HOE-0066	77182-82-2	PST72647
HOKKO-MYCIN	57-92-1	PST21917
HORMEX	133-32-4	PST29325
HORMODIN	133-32-4	PST29325
HORTOX	2307-68-8	PST71164
HOSALON	36614-38-7	PST12275
HOSDON	36614-38-7	PST12275
HOSTAQUICK	23560-59-0	PST10685
HOSTATHION	24017-47-8	PST73068
HOSTATION	24017-47-8	PST73068
HOX 1901	29973-13-5	PST72421
HS 61	2163-69-1	PST05996
HUBBUCK'S WHITE	1314-13-2	PST25490
HUMISEAL THINNER NO. 521 (M.W. RIEDEL AND COMPANY)	1330-20-7	PST25150
HUMISEAL THINNER NO.SP 420 (HUMISEAL DIV.)	1330-20-7	PST25150
HUMISEAL THINNER NO.33 (HUMISEAL DIV.)	1330-20-7	PST25150
HUNGAZIN	1912-24-9	PST02150
HUSEPT EXTRA	88-04-0	PST72258
HYAMINE 10X	25155-18-4	PST71862
HYAMINE 1622	121-54-0	PST71851
HYDOUT	145-73-3	PST08580
HYDRAM	2212-67-1	PST71471
HYDRAMETHYLNON	67485-29-4	PST01009
HYDRATED AMORPHOUS SILICA	63231-67-4	PST20670
HYDRATED LIME	1305-62-0	PST03980
HYDRAZINE YELLOW	1934-21-0	PST22465
HYDRAZOIC ACID, SODIUM SALT	26628-22-8	PST20960
HYDRAZONE	67485-29-4	PST01009
HYDRAZONE	67485-29-4	PST01009
HYDROCEROL A	77-92-9	PST05200
HYDROCHLORIC ACID	7647-01-0	PST11150
HYDROCHLORIC ACID GAS	7647-01-0	PST11150
HYDROCHLORIC ACID, ANHYDROUS	7647-01-0	PST11150
HYDROCYANIC ACID, POTASSIUM SALT	151-50-8	PST19350
HYDROGEN ARSENIDE	7784-42-1	PST02100
HYDROGEN CHLORIDE	7647-01-0	PST11150
HYDROGEN CHLORIDE (HCL)	7647-01-0	PST11150
HYDROGEN CHLORIDE, ANHYDROUS	7647-01-0	PST11150
HYDROGEN CYANAMIDE	420-04-2	PST05760
HYDROGEN DIOXIDE	7722-84-1	PST11190
HYDROGEN DISODIUM PHOSPHATE	7558-79-4	PST08330
HYDROGEN OXIDE	7722-84-1	PST11190
HYDROGEN PEROXIDE	7722-84-1	PST11190
HYDROGEN PEROXIDE (H2O2)	7722-84-1	PST11190
HYDROGEN POTASSIUM SULFATE	7646-93-7	PST19255
HYDROGEN SODIUM SULFATE	7631-90-5	PST21000
HYDROGEN SULFATE	7664-93-9	PST22350
HYDROGEN SULFITE SODIUM	7631-90-5	PST21000
HYDROGENATED CASTOR OIL	8001-78-3	PST11225
HYDROL	6392-46-7	PST72977
HYDROLYSED DEXTRIN	9004-53-9	PST06363
HYDROXY-2,4-DIMETHYLBENZENE	105-67-9	PST28670
HYDROXYACETIC ACID	79-14-1	PST10500
HYDROXYACETIC ACID, MONOSODIUM SALT	2836-32-0	PST11235

SUBSTANCE NAME	CAS #	PST #
INDOLEBUTYRIC ACID	133-32-4	PST29325
INDOPOL L-50	9003-29-6	PST75671
INFERNO	78-53-5	PST83006
INHIBINE	7722-84-1	PST11190
INPC	122-42-9	PST71564
INPERON FIXER T	545-55-1	PST22510
INSECT REPELLENT-11	126-15-8	PST71487
INSECTOL	7696-12-0	PST23061
INSEGAR	72490-01-8	PST72618
INTERCIDE TMP	133-07-3	PST10012
INTEXAN LB-50	8001-54-5	PST00537
INTRATHION	640-15-3	PST83056
INTRATION	640-15-3	PST83056
INVALON OP	90-43-7	PST18470
IODINE	7553-56-2	PST11400
IODINE A.R. CRYSTALS (MALLINCKRODT)	7553-56-2	PST11400
IODINE CRYSTALS	7553-56-2	PST11400
IODINE MOLECULE (I2)	7553-56-2	PST11400
IODINE, SUBLIMED	7553-56-2	PST11400
IODOFENFOS	18181-70-9	PST73035
IODOFENPHOS	18181-70-9	PST73035
IODOPHOS	18181-70-9	PST73035
IOPEZITE	7778-50-9	PST19370
IOXYNIL	1689-83-4	PST11468
IOXYNIL OCTANOATE	3861-47-0	PST73075
IOXYNIL SODIUM	2961-62-8	PST73074
IP 50	34123-59-6	PST12254
IPC	122-42-9	PST71564
IPPC	122-42-9	PST71564
IPT	50512-35-1	PST12253
IPURON	34123-59-6	PST12254
IRON (III) DIMETHYLDITHIOCARBAMATE	14484-64-1	PST09680
IRON AMMONIUM SULFATE	10045-89-3	PST09820
IRON PERSULFATE	10028-22-5	PST09790
IRON SESQUISULFATE	10028-22-5	PST09790
IRON SULFATE	7782-63-0	PST09870
IRON SULFATE (2:3)	10028-22-5	PST09790
IRON TERSULFATE	10028-22-5	PST09790
IRON TRIS(DIMETHYLDITHIOCARBAMATE)	14484-64-1	PST09680
IRON(II) SULFATE	7782-63-0	PST09870
IRON(II) SULFATE (1:1), HEPTAHYDRATE	7782-63-0	PST09870
IRON(2+) SULFATE HEPTAHYDRATE	7782-63-0	PST09870
IRON(3+) SULFATE	10028-22-5	PST09790
IS	126-75-0	PST71646
ISAZOFOS	42509-80-8	PST15035
ISAZOPHOS	42509-80-8	PST15035
ISCOBROME	74-83-9	PST14300
ISOBENZAN	297-78-9	PST83032
ISOBUMETONE	26259-45-0	PST73051
ISOBUTYL KETONE	108-83-8	PST07500
ISOBUTYL METHYL KETONE	108-10-1	PST14550
ISOCHLOROTHION	2463-84-5	PST71380
ISOCHLORTHION	2463-84-5	PST71380
ISOCIL	314-42-1	PST71090

SUBSTANCE NAME	CAS #	PST #
ISOCOTHANE	39300-45-3	PST71402
ISOCTHANE	39300-45-3	PST71402
ISOCYANURIC CHLORIDE	87-90-1	PST23860
ISODRIN	465-73-6	PST11810
ISOFENPHOS	25311-71-1	PST11985
ISOFLUROPHATE	55-91-4	PST07590
ISOHOL	67-63-0	PST12090
ISOLAN	119-38-0	PST83027
ISOMERIC CHLORHTION	2463-84-5	PST71380
ISOMETASYSTOX (FORMULATION)	919-86-8	PST83065
ISOMETHIOZIN	57052-04-7	PST11844
ISOMETHIOZINE	57052-04-7	PST11844
ISONAPHTHOL	135-19-3	PST03050
ISONORURON	28805-78-9	PST73199
ISOPESTOX	371-86-8	PST15030
ISOPHENPHOS	25311-71-1	PST11985
ISOPHTHALONITRILE, TETRACHLORO-	1897-45-6	PST04890
ISOPROCARB	2631-40-5	PST73231
ISOPROCIL	314-42-1	PST71090
ISOPROPANOL	67-63-0	PST12090
ISOPROPYL ACETONE	108-10-1	PST14550
ISOPROPYL ALCOHOL	67-63-0	PST12090
ISOPROPYL ALCOHOL, ANHYDROUS (EXXON)	67-63-0	PST12090
ISOPROPYL CARBANILATE	122-42-9	PST71564
ISOPROPYL FLUOPHOSPHATE	55-91-4	PST07590
ISOPROPYL M-CHLOROCARBANILATE	101-21-3	PST71148
ISOPROPYL N-(3-CHLOROPHENYL)CARBAMATE	101-21-3	PST71148
ISOPROPYL O-(ETHOXY(ISOPROPYLAMINO)PHOSPHINOTHIOYL)SALICYLATE	25311-71-1	PST11985
ISOPROPYL O-(ETHOXY-N-ISOPROPYLAMINO(THIOPHOSPHORYL))SALICYLATE	25311-71-1	PST11985
ISOPROPYL PHENYL URETHANE	122-42-9	PST71564
ISOPROPYL PHENYLCARBAMATE	122-42-9	PST71564
ISOPROPYL PHOSPHOROFLUORIDATE	55-91-4	PST07590
ISOPROPYL SALICYLATE O-ESTER WITH O-ETHYL ISOPROPYLPHOSPHORAMIDO-THIOATE	25311-71-1	PST11985
ISOPROPYL 2,4-DINITRO-6-SEC-BUTYLPHENYL CARBONATE	973-21-7	PST07990
ISOPROPYL 3-(ETHYLAMINO(METHOXY)PHOSPHINOTHIOYLOXY)ISOCROTONATE	31218-83-4	PST72440
ISOPROPYL 3-CHLOROCARBANILATE	101-21-3	PST71148
ISOPROPYL-CRESOL	89-83-8	PST23475
ISOPROPYL-META-CRESOL	89-83-8	PST23475
ISOPROPYLENE GLYCOL	57-55-6	PST19870
ISOPROPYLMETHYLPYRAZOLYL DIMETHYLCARBAMATE	119-38-0	PST83027
ISOPROPYLPHOSPHORAMIDIC ACID ETHYL 4-(ETHYLSULFINYL)-M-TOLYL ESTER	31972-43-7	PST16146
ISOPROPYLPHOSPHORAMIDIC ACID ETHYL 4-(METHYLTHIO)-M-TOLYL ESTER	22224-92-6	PST16145
ISOPROPYLPHOSPHORAMIDIC ACID ETHYL-4-(METHYLSULFONYL)-M-TOLYL ESTER	31972-44-8	PST16144
ISOPROPYLPHOSPHORAMIDOTHIOIC ACID, O-(2,4-DICHLOROPHENYL) O-METHYL ESTER	299-85-4	PST71236
ISOPROTHIOLANE	50512-35-1	PST12253
ISOPROTURON	34123-59-6	PST12254
ISORPOPYL 3-CHLOROPHENYLCARBAMATE	101-21-3	PST71148
ISOSYSTOX	126-75-0	PST71646
ISOSYSTOX SULFONE	2496-91-5	PST06306
ISOSYSTOX SULFOXIDE	2496-92-6	PST06316
ISOTHIOATE	36614-38-7	PST12275
ISOTHIOCYANATOMETHANE	556-61-6	PST14950

ALPHABETICAL INDEX

ALPHABETICAL INDEX

SUBSTANCE NAME	CAS #	PST #
L-GLUTAMIC ACID, N-(4-(((2,4-DIAMINO-6-PTERIDINYL)METHYL)METHYLAMINO) BENZOYL)-, SODIUM SALT	15475-56-6	PST14211
L-METHOTREXATE	59-05-2	PST14210
L-METHOTREXATE SODIUM	15475-56-6	PST14211
L-3-(1-METHYL 1-2-PYRROLIDYL) PYRIDINE	54-11-5	PST16430
L-7	8006-54-0	PST12425
LACCO METHYLENE CHLORIDE (PPG INDUSTRIES INC.)	75-09-2	PST14930
LACTAMIDE, N-ETHYL-, CARBANILATE (ESTER), D-	16118-49-3	PST72941
LAKE YELLOW	1934-21-0	PST22465
LAMBAST	23184-66-9	PST03497
LAMBAST	845-52-3	PST72212
LAMPRECID	88-30-2	PST71405
LANAIN	8006-54-0	PST12425
LANALIN	8006-54-0	PST12425
LANCE	51487-69-5	PST72572
LANDRIN	12407-86-2	PST12420
LANESIN	8006-54-0	PST12425
LANEX	2164-17-2	PST09907
LANICHOL	8006-54-0	PST12425
LANIOL	8006-54-0	PST12425
LANNATE	16752-77-5	PST14200
LANOLIN	8006-54-0	PST12425
LANUM	8006-54-0	PST12425
LAPIS INFERNALIS	7761-88-8	PST20810
LAPROL	25322-69-4	PST19140
LARIAT FLOWABLE HERBICIDE	UNASSIGNED	PST12471
LARVACIDE	76-06-2	PST04830
LARVADEX	66215-27-8	PST72536
LARVAKIL	35367-38-5	PST07388
LARVIN	59669-26-0	PST72456
LASER GUARD (DYNATEX CORPORATION)	127-18-4	PST22900
LASSO	15972-60-8	PST00506
LASSO AND ATRAZINE FLOWABLE HERBICIDE	UNASSIGNED	PST12481
LAURIC ACID, POTASSIUM SALT	10124-65-9	PST72072
LAURIC ALCOHOL	112-53-8	PST12500
LAURINIC ALCOHOL	112-53-8	PST12500
LAURYL ALCOHOL	112-53-8	PST12500
LAURYL SODIUM SULFATE	151-21-3	PST08485
LAURYL SULFATE SODIUM	151-21-3	PST08485
LAURYL SULFATE SODIUM SALT	151-21-3	PST08485
LAURYLBENZENESULFONATE	27176-87-0	PST08480
LAURYLBENZENESULFONIC ACID	27176-87-0	PST08480
LAUXTOL	87-86-5	PST18150
LAZO	15972-60-8	PST00506
LB-BUTYLENE GLYCOL	107-88-0	PST26730
LEAD ARSENATE	7784-40-9	PST12540
LEAD ARSENATE, SOLID	7784-40-9	PST12540
LEBAYCID (FORMULATION)	55-38-9	PST02550
LEGURAME	16118-49-3	PST72941
LEIOCOM	9004-53-9	PST06363
LEMON YELOW A	1934-21-0	PST22465
LENACIL	2164-08-1	PST73238
LENOCYCLINE	79-57-2	PST17414
LENS CLENS #3 (GENERAL PRODUCTION SERVICES INC.)	67-63-0	PST12090

SUBSTANCE NAME	CAS #	PST #
LEPICRON	59669-26-0	PST72456
LEPTOPHOS	21609-90-5	PST12780
LEPTOPHOS OA	25006-32-0	PST12776
LEPTOPHOS OXON	25006-32-0	PST12776
LEPTOPHOS OXYGEN ANALOG	25006-32-0	PST12776
LETHANE	112-56-1	PST75661
LETHANE 384	112-56-1	PST75661
LETHANE 384 REGULAR	112-56-1	PST75661
LETHELMIN	92-84-2	PST18400
LEXONEEX	21087-64-9	PST15006
LEY-CORNOX	3813-05-6	PST72725
LIDAMYCIN CREME	1405-10-3	PST84263
LIGHT CAMPHOR OIL	8008-51-3	PST04140
LIGNASAN	2235-25-8	PST71479
LIME	1305-78-8	PST04030
LIME CHLORIDE	7778-54-3	PST03990
LIME WATER	1305-62-0	PST03980
LIME, UNSLAKED	1305-78-8	PST04030
LINDANE	58-89-9	PST12810
LINSEED OIL	8001-26-1	PST71365
LINSEED OIL, BLEACHED	8001-26-1	PST71365
LINSEED OIL, RAW	8001-26-1	PST71365
LINUREX	330-55-2	PST12826
LINURON	330-55-2	PST12826
LIPHADIONE	3691-35-8	PST04826
LIPOSORB L-20	9005-65-6	PST40200
LIPOSORB O-20	9005-65-6	PST40200
LIQUAMYCIN	79-57-2	PST17414
LIQUAMYCIN INJECTABLE	2058-46-0	PST84045
LIQUID PITCH OIL	8001-58-9	PST05230
LIROMATIN	900-95-8	PST24378
LIRONION	14214-32-5	PST07386
LIRONOX	94-80-4	PST71295
LIROPON	75-99-0	PST06200
LIROPREM	87-86-5	PST18150
LIROSTANOL	900-95-8	PST24378
LITHIUM HYPOCHLORITE	13840-33-0	PST12920
LITHIUM HYPOCHLORITE COMPOUND, DRY	13840-33-0	PST12920
LM 91	3691-35-8	PST04826
LOGIC	72490-01-8	PST72618
LONTREL	1702-17-6	PST05211
LOREX	330-55-2	PST12826
LOROX	330-55-2	PST12826
LORSBAN	2921-88-2	PST04910
LOSANTIN	7778-54-3	PST03990
LS 4442	639-58-7	PST24380
LS 74-783	39148-24-8	PST72563
LS-303 (POLYTECH)	75-09-2	PST14930
LUBRICATING BASE OIL	64742-52-5	PST17323
LUNAR CAUSTIC	7761-88-8	PST20810
LUPRISOL	79-09-4	PST19750
LUTROL-9	107-21-1	PST09400
LYE	1310-58-3	PST19430
LYE	1310-73-2	PST21300

ALPHABETICAL INDEX

SUBSTANCE NAME	CAS #	PST #
MBX	74-83-9	PST14300
MC 1053	973-21-7	PST07990
MC 2188	24934-91-6	PST04655
MC 4379	42576-02-3	PST72332
MCA 600	1079-33-0	PST29855
MCN 1025	991-42-4	PST72254
MCP	94-74-6	PST27880
MCP METHYL ESTER	2436-73-9	PST27881
MCPA	94-74-6	PST27880
MCPA METHYL ESTER	2436-73-9	PST27881
MDBA	1918-00-9	PST02260
MEA	141-43-5	PST08710
MEBETIZOLE	149-30-4	PST13738
MEBT	33693-04-8	PST72770
MECARBAM	2595-54-2	PST13675
MECARPHON	29173-31-7	PST73246
MEDIBEN	1918-00-9	PST02260
MEEHG	151-38-2	PST83031
MEFLORIN	97-24-5	PST71737
MEFLUIDIDE	53780-34-0	PST72444
MEGATOX	640-19-7	PST09930
MEK	78-93-3	PST14460
MELIPAX	8001-35-2	PST23640
MEMA	151-38-2	PST83031
MENADIONE	58-27-5	PST71050
MENAQUINONE 0	58-27-5	PST71050
MENAZON	78-57-9	PST72980
MEP	122-14-5	PST09678
MEPATAR	2058-46-0	PST84045
MEPHANAC	94-74-6	PST27880
MEPHOSFOLAN	950-10-7	PST13735
MEPIQUAT CHLORIDE	24307-26-4	PST72386
MERCAPROFOS	35400-43-2	PST22387
MERCAPROPHOS	35400-43-2	PST22387
MERCAPTOACETIC ACID ETHYL ESTER, S-ESTER WITH O,O-DIETHYL PHOSPHORODITHIOATE	919-54-0	PST00117
MERCAPTOACETIC ACID ETHYL ESTER, S-ESTER WITH O,O-DIETHYL -PHOSPHOROTHIOATE	2425-25-4	PST73057
MERCAPTOBENZOTHIAZOLE	149-30-4	PST13738
MERCAPTODIMETHUR	2032-65-7	PST14190
MERCAPTOFOS	8065-48-3	PST06320
MERCAPTOPHENYLACETIC ACID, ETHYL ESTER , S-ESTER WITH O,O-DIMETHYL PHOSPHORODITHIOATE	2597-03-7	PST72337
MERCAPTOPHOS	8065-48-3	PST06320
MERCAPTOPHOS (FORMULATION)	55-38-9	PST02550
MERCAPTOPHOS OXON	6552-12-1	PST02551
MERCAPTOPHOS OXON SULFONE	14086-35-2	PST02552
MERCAPTOPHOS OXON SULFOXIDE	6552-13-2	PST02553
MERCAPTOSUCCINIC ACID DIETHYL ESTER, S-ESTER WITH O,O-DIMETHYL PHOSPHORODITHIOATE	121-75-5	PST13540
MERCAPTOSUCCINIC ACID DIETHYL ESTER, S-ESTER WITH O,O-DIMETHYL PHOSPHOROTHIOATE	1634-78-2	PST13541
MERCAZIN	7287-19-6	PST19968
MERCKOSORB M.SI.	63231-67-4	PST20670

SUBSTANCE NAME	CAS #	PST #
MERCURAN	151-38-2	PST83031
MERCURATE(2), ETHYL(PHOSPHATO(3-)-O-)-, DIHYDROGEN	2235-25-8	PST71479
MERCURIC BICHLORIDE	7487-94-7	PST13800
MERCURIC CHLORIDE	7487-94-7	PST13800
MERCURIC CHLORIDE, SOLID	7487-94-7	PST13800
MERCURIPHENYL ACETATE	62-38-4	PST18560
MERCURIPHENYL CHLORIDE	100-56-1	PST18570
MERCURY BICHLORIDE	7487-94-7	PST13800
MERCURY PERCHLORIDE	7487-94-7	PST13800
MERCURY(II) CHLORIDE	7487-94-7	PST13800
MERCURY(1+), (2,2',2''-NITRILOTRIS(ETHANOL)-N,O,O',O'') PHENYL-, SALT WITH 2-HYDROXYPROPANOIC ACID(1:1)	23319-66-6	PST71768
MERCURY, (ACETATO)ETHYL-	109-62-6	PST71476
MERCURY, (ACETATO-O)ETHYL-	109-62-6	PST71476
MERCURY, (CYANOGUANIDINATO)METHYL-	502-39-6	PST83040
MERCURY, (CYANOGUANIDINATO-N')METHYL-	502-39-6	PST83040
MERCURY, (CYANOGUANIDINE)METHYL-	502-39-6	PST83040
MERCURY, (DIHYDROGEN PHOSPHATO)ETHYL-	2235-25-8	PST71479
MERCURY, (MU-(HYDROGEN ORTHOBORATO))DIPHENYLDI-	6273-99-0	PST71754
MERCURY, (MU-(ORTHOBORATO(2-)-O:O'))DIPHENYLDI-	6273-99-0	PST71754
MERCURY, (OLEATO)PHENYL	104-60-9	PST71769
MERCURY, (OLEOYLOXY)PHENYL-	104-60-9	PST71769
MERCURY, (9-OCTADECENOATO-O)PHENYL-, (Z)-	104-60-9	PST71769
MERCURY, ACETOXYETHYL-	109-62-6	PST71476
MERCURY, CHLOROETHYL-	107-27-7	PST09620
MERFAZIN	100-56-1	PST18570
MERKAZIN	7287-19-6	PST19968
MERKON	13171-21-6	PST18670
MERKURAN	151-38-2	PST83031
MERPAFOS	35400-43-2	PST22387
MERPAN	133-06-2	PST04210
MERPHOS	150-50-5	PST10010
MERSOLITE	62-38-4	PST18560
MERSOLITE 1	100-57-2	PST18580
MERSOLITE 2	100-56-1	PST18570
MERTAX	149-30-4	PST13738
MESORANIL	4658-28-0	PST02216
MESULFENFOS	3761-41-9	PST02555
MESUROL	2032-65-7	PST14190
MESUROL SULFOXIDE	2635-10-1	PST14191
MET 1486	30043-49-3	PST72551
META	108-62-3	PST14090
META-CRESOL,6 ISO-PROPYL	89-83-8	PST23475
METABENZTHIAZURON	18691-97-9	PST14108
METABROM	2104-96-3	PST71064
METACETALDEHYDE	108-62-3	PST14090
METACETONIC ACID	79-09-4	PST19750
METACHLOR	15972-60-8	PST00506
METACIDE	298-00-0	PST14680
METACRATE	1129-41-5	PST83074
METADELPHENE	134-62-3	PST84230
METAFUME	74-83-9	PST14300
METAISOSYSTOX SULFOXIDE	301-12-2	PST17375

ALPHABETICAL INDEX

SUBSTANCE NAME	CAS #	PST #
METHANIMIDAMIDE, N'-(4-CHLORO-2-METHYLPHENYL) N,N-DIMETHYL-	6164-98-3	PST04570
METHANIMIDAMIDE, N'-(4-CHLORO-2-METHYLPHENYL)-N,N-DIMETHYL-, MONOHYDROCHLORIDE	19750-95-9	PST71656
METHANOL	67-56-1	PST14280
METHANOL (ELECTROKLEIN) (ROK)	67-56-1	PST14280
METHANOL, SPECTRO QUALITY (MCB MANF. CHEMIST)	67-56-1	PST14280
METHANONE, BIS(4-CHLOROPHENYL)-	90-98-2	PST06246
METHASAN	137-30-4	PST25397
METHAZOLE	20354-26-1	PST72344
METHBENZTHIAZURON	18691-97-9	PST14108
METHIDATHION	950-37-8	PST14175
METHIOCARB	2032-65-7	PST14190
METHIOCARB SULFOXIDE	2635-10-1	PST14191
METHOGAS	74-83-9	PST14300
METHOMYL	16752-77-5	PST14200
METHOPROPTRYNE	841-06-5	PST14204
METHOPROTRYN	841-06-5	PST14204
METHOPROTRYNE	841-06-5	PST14204
METHOTREXATE	59-05-2	PST14210
METHOTREXATE	15475-56-6	PST14211
METHOTREXATE SODIUM	15475-56-6	PST14211
METHOTRYNE	841-06-5	PST14204
METHOXONE	94-74-6	PST27880
METHOXY-DDT	72-43-5	PST14220
METHOXYCHLOR	72-43-5	PST14220
METHOXYDIURON	330-55-2	PST12826
METHOXYETHANOL	109-86-4	PST14340
METHOXYETHYLENE GLYCOL	109-86-4	PST14340
METHOXYETHYLMERCURIC ACETATE	151-38-2	PST83031
METHOXYHYDROXYETHANE	109-86-4	PST14340
METHOXYPROPAZINE	1610-18-0	PST19967
METHYL ((METHOXY(METHYLPHOSPHINOTHIOYL)THIO)ACETYL)METHYLCARBAMATE	29173-31-7	PST73246
METHYL ((4-AMINOPHENYL)SULFONYL)CARBAMATE	3337-71-1	PST72352
METHYL (MERCAPTOACETYL)METHYLCARBAMATE S-ESTER WITH O-METHYL METHYLPHOSPHONODITHIOATE	29173-31-7	PST73246
METHYL (1-((BUTYLAMINO)CARBONYL)-1H-BENZIMIDAZOL-2-YL)CARBAMATE	17804-35-2	PST02580
METHYL ACETIC ACID	79-09-4	PST19750
METHYL ACETONE	78-93-3	PST14460
METHYL ALCOHOL	67-56-1	PST14280
METHYL ALDEHYDE	50-00-0	PST50003
METHYL ARSONIC ACID, MONOSODIUM SALT	2163-80-6	PST15180
METHYL BROMIDE	74-83-9	PST14300
METHYL BROMIDE, LIQUID	74-83-9	PST14300
METHYL CARBAMIC ACID 1-NAPHTHYL ESTER	63-25-2	PST04220
METHYL CARBAMIC ACID 4-(DIALLYLAMINO)-3,5-XYLYL ESTER	6392-46-7	PST72977
METHYL CARBAMIC ACID, M-TOLY ESTER	1129-41-5	PST83074
METHYL CARBAMIC ACID, 3-METHYLPHENYL ESTER	1129-41-5	PST83074
METHYL CARBOPHENOTHION	953-17-3	PST71647
METHYL CELLOSOLVE	109-86-4	PST14340
METHYL CHEMOSEPT	99-76-3	PST14677
METHYL CHLORAMBEN	7286-84-2	PST71255
METHYL CHLOROFORM	71-55-6	PST14370
METHYL CHLORPYRIFOS	5598-13-0	PST71652
METHYL DEMETON	8022-00-2	PST14438

SUBSTANCE NAME	CAS #	PST #
METHYL DEMETON THIOESTER	919-86-8	PST83065
METHYL DURSBAN	5598-13-0	PST71652
METHYL ETHYL KETONE	78-93-3	PST14460
METHYL ETHYLENE OXIDE	75-56-9	PST19910
METHYL GLYCOL	109-86-4	PST14340
METHYL HYDROXIDE	67-56-1	PST14280
METHYL ISOBUTYL KETONE	108-10-1	PST14550
METHYL ISOTHIOCYANATE	556-61-6	PST14950
METHYL KETONE	67-64-1	PST00140
METHYL M-HYDROXYCARBANILATE M-METHYLCARBANILATE (ESTER)	13684-63-4	PST72282
METHYL MERCURIC DICYANAMIDE	502-39-6	PST83040
METHYL MUSTARD	556-61-6	PST14950
METHYL MUSTARD OIL	556-61-6	PST14950
METHYL N-(((METHYLAMINO)CARBONYL)OXY)ETHANIMIDOTHIOATE	16752-77-5	PST14200
METHYL N-((METHYLCARBOMOYL)OXY)THIOACETIMIDATE	16752-77-5	PST14200
METHYL N-(METHOXY(METHYL)THIOPHOSPHORYLTHIOACETYL)-N-METHYLCARBAMATE	29173-31-7	PST73246
METHYL N-(3,4-DICHLOROPHENYL)CARBAMATE	1918-18-9	PST72247
METHYL N-NONYL KETONE	112-12-9	PST14675
METHYL N',N'-DIMETHYL-N-((METHYLCARBAMOYL)OXY)-1-THIOOXAMIMIDATE	23135-22-0	PST17370
METHYL NONYL KETONE	112-12-9	PST14675
METHYL O-(METHYLCARBAMOYL)THIOLACETOHYDROXAMATE	16752-77-5	PST14200
METHYL O-HYDROXYBENZOATE	119-36-8	PST14720
METHYL OXIRANE	75-56-9	PST19910
METHYL OXITOL	109-86-4	PST14340
METHYL OXYDEMETON S	301-12-2	PST17375
METHYL P-HYDROXYBENZOATE	99-76-3	PST14677
METHYL P-OXYBENZOATE	99-76-3	PST14677
METHYL PARABEN	99-76-3	PST14677
METHYL PARAHYDROXYBENZOATE	99-76-3	PST14677
METHYL PARAOXON	950-35-6	PST14678
METHYL PARASEPT	99-76-3	PST14677
METHYL PARATHION	298-00-0	PST14680
METHYL PARATHION OXYGEN ANALOG	950-35-6	PST14678
METHYL PARATHION 80%	UNASSIGNED	PST14681
METHYL PHENCAPTON	3735-23-7	PST73085
METHYL PHENKAPTON	3735-23-7	PST73085
METHYL PHOSPHORAMIDOTHIOATE	10265-92-6	PST15160
METHYL PYRIMIPHOS	29232-93-7	PST72378
METHYL SALICYLATE	119-36-8	PST14720
METHYL SULFANILYLCARBAMATE	3337-71-1	PST72352
METHYL SULPHANILYLCARBAMATE	3337-71-1	PST72352
METHYL SYSTOX	8022-00-2	PST14438
METHYL THIOISOCYANATE	556-61-6	PST14950
METHYL TRITHION	953-17-3	PST71647
METHYL VIOLOGEN	1910-42-5	PST18020
METHYL VIOLOGEN (2+)	4685-14-7	PST71671
METHYL VIOLOGEN DICHLORIDE	1910-42-5	PST18020
METHYL 1-(BUTYLCARBAMOYL)-2-BENZIMIDAZOLECARBAMATE	17804-35-2	PST02580
METHYL 1-(BUTYLCARBAMOYL)BENZIMIDAZOL-2-YLCARBAMATE	17804-35-2	PST02580
METHYL 2-((((4,6-DIMETHYL-2-PYRIMIDINYL)AMINO)CARBONYL)AMINO)-SULFONYL)BENZOATE	74222-97-2	PST72544
METHYL 2-(DIMETHYLAMINO)N-(((METHYLAMINO)CARBONYL)OXYL)-2-OXOETHANIMIDOTHIOATE	23135-22-0	PST17370
METHYL 2-(3-(4,6-DIMETHYLPYRIMIDIN-2-YL)UREIDOSULPHONYL)BENZOATE	74222-97-2	PST72544

ALPHABETICAL INDEX

SUBSTANCE NAME	CAS #	PST #
MOLINATE	2212-67-1	PST71471
MON 0139	38641-94-0	PST20205
MON 0573	1071-83-6	PST10515
MON 097	34256-82-1	PST72539
MONALIDE	7287-36-7	PST72987
MONAQUEST IA	139-41-3	PST71447
MONCEREN	66063-05-6	PST72622
MONITAN	9005-65-6	PST40200
MONITOR	10265-92-6	PST15160
MONO(2,2-DIMETHLYHYDRAZIDE)SUCCINIC ACID	1596-84-5	PST06195
MONOAMMONIUM SULFAMATE	7773-06-0	PST01400
MONOBASIC SODIUM PHOSPHATE	7558-80-7	PST15190
MONOBROMOMETHANE	74-83-9	PST14300
MONOBUTYL GLYCOL ETHER	111-76-2	PST03540
MONOCHLOROTRIBUTYLTIN	1461-22-9	PST72222
MONOCROTOPHOS	6923-22-4	PST15165
MONODODECYL SODIUM SULFATE	151-21-3	PST08485
MONOETHANOLAMINE	141-43-5	PST08710
MONOETHYLENE GLYCOL	107-21-1	PST09400
MONOFLUOROTRICHLOROMETHANE	75-69-4	PST09990
MONOHYDROCHLORIDE, (4S-(4 ALPHA,4A ALPHA,5 ALPHA,5A ALPHA,6 BETA, 12A ALPHA))-	2058-46-0	PST84045
MONOHYDROGEN DISODIUM PHOSPHATE	7558-79-4	PST08330
MONOHYDROXYBENZENE	108-95-2	PST18380
MONOHYDROXYMETHANE	67-56-1	PST14280
MONOLINURON	1746-81-2	PST15174
MONOMETHYLGLYCOL	109-86-4	PST14340
MONOPHENOL	108-95-2	PST18380
MONOPOLE OIL MDD	8002-33-3	PST24575
MONOPOTASSIUM SALT	125-67-7	PST71492
MONOPOTASSIUM SULFATE	7646-93-7	PST19255
MONOPROPYLENE GLYCOL	57-55-6	PST19870
MONOROTOX	1746-81-2	PST15174
MONOSODIUM ACID METHANE ARSONATE	2163-80-6	PST15180
MONOSODIUM ARSENITE LIQUID	7784-46-5	PST52136
MONOSODIUM CARBONATE	144-55-8	PST20970
MONOSODIUM DIHYDROGEN PHOSPHATE	7558-80-7	PST15190
MONOSODIUM HYDROGEN CARBONATE	144-55-8	PST20970
MONOSODIUM HYDROGEN PHOSPHATE	7558-80-7	PST15190
MONOSODIUM HYDROGEN SULFATE	7681-38-1	PST20990
MONOSODIUM METHANE ARSONATE	2163-80-6	PST15180
MONOSODIUM METHANEARSONATE	2163-80-6	PST15180
MONOSODIUM ORTHOPHOSPHATE	7558-80-7	PST15190
MONOSODIUM PHOSPHATE	7558-80-7	PST15190
MONOSODIUM SULFATE	7681-38-1	PST20990
MONOSODIUM SULFITE	7631-90-5	PST21000
MONSANTO CP-19699	13067-93-1	PST05805
MONTREL	299-86-5	PST05550
MONUREX	150-68-5	PST15196
MONURON	150-68-5	PST15196
MONURON TCA	140-41-0	PST15197
MONURON TRICHLOROACETATE	140-41-0	PST15197
MOROCIDE	485-31-4	PST71960
MORPHACTIN	2536-31-4	PST72283

SUBSTANCE NAME	CAS #	PST #
N-DECANOL	112-30-1	PST06285
N-DECATYL ALCOHOL	112-30-1	PST06285
N-DECYL ALCOHOL	112-30-1	PST06285
N-DICHLOROFLUOROMETHANESULPHENYL-N',N'-DIMETHYL-N-PHENYLSULPHAMIDE	1085-98-9	PST73026
N-DICHLOROFLUOROMETHYLTHIO-N',N'-DIMETHYL-N-PHENYLSULPHAMIDE	1085-98-9	PST73026
N-DIETHOXYPHOSPHINOTHIOYLPHTHALIMIDE	5131-24-8	PST72347
N-DIMETHYLAMINOSUCCINAMIC ACID	1596-84-5	PST06195
N-DIPHENYLANILINE	122-39-4	PST08100
N-DODECYL SULFATE SODIUM	151-21-3	PST08485
N-DODECYLBENZENESULFONIC ACID	27176-87-0	PST08480
N-ETHYL-ALPHA,ALPHA,ALPHA-TRIFLUORO-N-(2-METHYLALLYL)-2,6-DINITRO-P-TOLUIDINE	55283-68-6	PST72436
N-ETHYL-N-(2-METHYL-2-PROPENYL)-2,6-DINITRO-4-(TRIFLUOROMETHYL)-BENZENAMINE	55283-68-6	PST72436
N-ETHYL-N-(2-METHYLALLYL)-2,6-DINITRO-4-TRIFLUOROMETHYLANILINE	55283-68-6	PST72436
N-ETHYL-N-(4((4-ETHYL((3-SULFOPHENYL)METHYL)AMINO)PHENYL)(2-SULFOPHENYL)METHYLENE)-2,5-CYCLOHEXADIEN-1-YLIDENE)-3-SULFOBENZENE	2650-18-2	PST08277
N-ETHYL-N'-(1-METHYLETHYL)-6-(METHYLTHIO)-1,3,5-TRIAZINE-2,4-DIAMINE	834-12-8	PST01006
N-ETHYL-6-METHOXY-N'-(1-METHYLETHYL)-1,3,5-TRIAZINE-2,4-DIAMINE	1610-17-9	PST02148
N-ETHYL-6-METHOXY-N'-(1-METHYLPROPYL)-1,3,5-TRIAZINE-2,4-DIAMINE	26259-45-0	PST73051
N-ETHYLAMIDE OF O,O-DIMETHYL DITHIOPHOSPHORYLACETIC ACID	116-01-8	PST08723
N-ETHYLTHIOCYLCLOHEXANECARBAMIC ACID S-ETHYL ESTER	1134-23-2	PST71469
N-FURFURYLADENINE	525-79-1	PST72483
N-HEXADECANOL	36653-82-4	PST04525
N-HEXAN-1-OL	111-27-3	PST15630
N-HEXANOL	111-27-3	PST15630
N-HEXYL ALCOHOL	111-27-3	PST15630
N-HYDROXYNAPTHALIMIDE DIETHYL PHOSPHATE	1491-41-4	PST72737
N-ISOPROPYL-ALPHA-CHLOROACETANILIDE	1918-16-7	PST19686
N-METHYL-N'-(1-METHYLETHYL)-6-(METHYLTHIO)-1,3,5-TRIAZINE-2,4-DIAMINE	1014-69-3	PST06353
N-METHYL-1-NAPHTHYLCARBAMATE	63-25-2	PST04220
N-METHYL-2-ISOPROPOXYPHENYLCARBAMATE	114-26-1	PST02540
N-METHYLCARBAMIC ACID 3-METHYL-5-ISOPROPYLPHENYL ESTER	2631-37-0	PST72957
N-METHYLDITHIOCARBAMIC ACID, SODIUM SALT	137-42-8	PST71430
N-OCTANOL	111-87-5	PST17270
N-OCTYL ALCOHOL	111-87-5	PST17270
N-OCTYL BICYCLOHEPTENE DICARBOXIMIDE	113-48-4	PST15955
N-OCTYL PHTHALATE	117-84-0	PST08040
N-PARA-ETHOXYACETANILIDE	62-44-2	PST18340
N-PENTYL ACETATE	628-63-7	PST15270
N-PHENYL ISOPROPYL CARBAMATE	122-42-9	PST71564
N-PHENYL-N'-1,2,3-THIADIAZOL-5-YL UREA	51707-55-2	PST23299
N-PHENYL-N'-1,2,3-THIADIAZOL-5-YL-UREA	51707-55-2	PST23299
N-PHENYL-N',N'-DIMETHYLUREA	101-42-8	PST09679
N-PHENYLANILINE	122-39-4	PST08100
N-PHENYLBENZENAMINE	122-39-4	PST08100
N-PHOSPHOMETHYLGLYCINE	1071-83-6	PST10515
N-PHOSPHONOMETHYLGLYCINE	1071-83-6	PST10515
N-PROPYL ETHYL-N-BUTYLTHIOLCARBAMATE	1114-71-2	PST71472
N-PROPYL-N-(2-(2,4,6-TRICHLOROPHENOXY)ETHYL)-1-IMIDAZOLE-1-CARBOXAMIDE	67747-09-5	PST72648
N-SEC-BUTYL-N-ETHYL-6-METHOXY-1,3,5-TRIAZINE-2,6-DIAMINE	26259-45-0	PST73051
N-SEC-BUTYL-4-TERT-BUTYL-2,6-DINITROANILINE	33629-47-9	PST03525
N-SERVE	1929-82-4	PST16530
N-TRICHLOROMETHYLMERCAPTO-4-CYCLOHEXENE-1,2-DICARBOXIMIDE	133-06-2	PST04210

SUBSTANCE NAME	CAS #	PST #
NA 1989	100-52-7	PST02590
NA 1999	8052-42-4	PST02140
NA 1999	8052-42-4	PST71177
NA 2020	87-86-5	PST18150
NA 2020	95-95-4	PST28700
NA 2131	79-21-0	PST18310
NA 2465	2244-21-5	PST19360
NA 2762	12789-03-6	PST71948
NA 9078	10043-01-3	PST00980
NA 9089	7773-06-0	PST01400
NA 9093	7783-18-8	PST01460
NA 9099	133-06-2	PST04210
NA 9109	7758-98-7	PST05670
NA 9109	7758-99-8	PST05690
NA 9121	10028-22-5	PST09790
NA 9122	10045-89-3	PST09820
NA 9147	7558-79-4	PST08330
NA 9148	7601-54-9	PST24480
NA 9188	2163-80-6	PST15180
NA-X	497-19-8	PST21080
NAA	86-87-3	PST26130
NAA ETHYL ESTER	2122-70-5	PST71628
NABAC	70-30-4	PST10780
NABAM	142-59-6	PST16080
NABR	7647-15-6	PST21060
NABU	74051-80-2	PST20577
NACAR	7440-44-0	PST04246
NACCONAL 90F	25155-30-0	PST21220
NACCONOL 98 SA	27176-87-0	PST08480
NADEX	9004-53-9	PST06363
NADONE	108-94-1	PST05890
NAFTALOFOS	1491-41-4	PST72737
NAFUSAKU	86-87-3	PST26130
NAH2PO4	7558-80-7	PST15190
NALCO 7046	2425-06-1	PST04200
NALED	300-76-5	PST06660
NAMEKIL	108-62-3	PST14090
NANKOR	299-84-3	PST20180
NANSA SSA	27176-87-0	PST08480
NAOH	1310-73-2	PST21300
NAPHTHALEN	91-20-3	PST16120
NAPHTHALENE	91-20-3	PST16120
NAPHTHALENE OIL	8001-58-9	PST05230
NAPHTHALENEACETIC ACID	86-87-3	PST26130
NAPHTHALENEACETIC ACID, ETHYL ESTER	2122-70-5	PST71628
NAPHTHALIN	91-20-3	PST16120
NAPHTHALINE	91-20-3	PST16120
NAPHTHALOPHOS	1491-41-4	PST72737
NAPHTHENE	91-20-3	PST16120
NAPHTHENIC ACID, COPPER SALT	1338-02-9	PST05460
NAPHTHO(2,3-B)-P-DITHIIN-2,3-DICARBONITRILE, 5,10-DIHYDRO-5,10-DIOXO-	3347-22-6	PST72290
NAPHTHO(2,3-B)-1,4-DITHIIN-2,3-DICARBONITRILE, 5,10-DIHYDRO-5, 10-DIOXO-	3347-22-6	PST72290
NAPROPAMIDE	15299-99-7	PST72319

SUBSTANCE NAME	CAS #	PST #
NAPROPION	137-40-6	PST21575
NAPTALAM	132-66-1	PST71340
NAPTALAM	132-67-2	PST71341
NAPTALAM SODIUM	132-67-2	PST71341
NAPTHALIMIDE, N-HYDROXY-, DIETHYL PHOSPHATE	1491-41-4	PST72737
NARAMYCIN	66-81-9	PST05930
NARAMYCIN A	66-81-9	PST05930
NARKOTIL	75-09-2	PST14930
NATA	650-51-1	PST73307
NATURAL ANHYDRITE	7778-18-9	PST04110
NATURAL ARCANITE	7778-80-5	PST19590
NATURAL TENORITE	1317-38-0	PST05655
NATURAL VILLIAUMITE	7681-49-4	PST21230
NAVADEL	78-34-2	PST08050
NAVRON	640-19-7	PST09930
NAXONATE	1300-72-7	PST75603
NAXONATE G	1300-72-7	PST75603
NA2SIO3	6834-92-0	PST21373
NA3O4P	7601-54-9	PST24480
NA4O7P2	7722-88-5	PST23140
NA5O10P3	7758-29-4	PST21730
NC 1667	1912-26-1	PST23927
NC 3363	3615-21-2	PST73047
NC 6897	22781-23-3	PST02560
NC 8438	26225-79-6	PST72404
NCB	118-74-1	PST10730
NCI-C00099	57-74-9	PST04560
NCI-C00099	12789-03-6	PST71948
NCI-C00180	76-44-8	PST10660
NCI-C00453	95-06-7	PST22190
NCI-C00486	115-32-2	PST07010
NCI-C02971	298-00-0	PST14680
NCI-C08640	116-06-3	PST00500
NCI-C08673	333-41-5	PST06540
NCI-C00113	62-73-7	PST07000
NCI-C00191	143-50-0	PST12330
NCI-C00204	58-89-9	PST12810
NCI-C00237	1918-02-1	PST18840
NCI-C00408	510-15-6	PST04740
NCI-C00475	72-54-8	PST06240
NCI-C00500	96-12-8	PST26490
NCI-C0054	315-18-4	PST15010
NCI-C00555	72-55-9	PST06247
NCI-C04580	127-18-4	PST22900
NCI-C08684	101-05-3	PST01526
NCI-C54831	52-68-6	PST23790
NCI-C55298	148-24-3	PST30450
NCI-C60048	84-66-2	PST07210
NCI-C60413	510-15-6	PST04740
NCI-000077	133-06-2	PST04210
NEANTINE	84-66-2	PST07210
NEBUREA	555-37-3	PST16143
NEBUREX	555-37-3	PST16143
NEBURON	555-37-3	PST16143

ALPHABETICAL INDEX

SUBSTANCE NAME	CAS #	PST #
NORSULFAZOL	72-14-0	PST72047
NORTON	26225-79-6	PST72404
NORURON	18530-56-8	PST71400
NOVEX	97-24-5	PST71737
NOVOSCABIN	120-51-4	PST02805
NOXAL	97-77-8	PST08370
NOXFISH	83-79-4	PST20200
NPA	132-66-1	PST71340
NPA-3	132-67-2	PST71341
NPD	3244-90-4	PST72135
NPH 1320	1689-99-2	PST03543
NP55	74051-80-2	PST20577
NRDC 107	28434-01-7	PST20093
NRDC 119	35764-59-1	PST20094
NRDC 149	52315-07-8	PST72392
NRDC 161	52918-63-5	PST72784
NSC 14083	57-92-1	PST21917
NSC-423	94-75-7	PST28510
NSN 6840-00-402-5411	UNASSIGNED	PST08521
NTA TRISODIUM SALT	5064-31-3	PST24475
NTN 19701	66063-05-6	PST72622
NUDRIN	16752-77-5	PST14200
NULLAPON	60-00-4	PST09570
NUVACRON	6923-22-4	PST15165
NUVAN	62-73-7	PST07000
NUVANOL	122-14-5	PST09678
NUVANOL N	18181-70-9	PST73035
NUX VOMICA	57-24-9	PST22080
N1-(2-QUINOXALINYL)SULFANILAMIDE	59-40-5	PST72046
N1-(2-THIAZOLYL)SULFANILAMIDE	72-14-0	PST72047
N1-METHOXYCARBONYLSULFANILAMIDE	3337-71-1	PST72352
N1-2-THIAZOLYLSULFANILAMIDE	72-14-0	PST72047
N1-4-THIAZOLIN-2-YLIDENESULFANILAMIDE	72-14-0	PST72047
N2,N4-DI-ISOPROPYL-6-METHYLTHIO-1,3,5-TRIAZINE-2,4-DIAMINE	7287-19-6	PST19968
N3NA	26628-22-8	PST20960
O-(1,6-DIHYDRO-6-OXO-1-PHENYL-3-PYRIDAZINYL) O,O-DIETHYL PHOSPHOROTHIOATE	119-12-0	PST71604
O-(2-CHLORO-4-NITROPHENYL) O,O-DIMETHYLPHOSPHOROTHIOATE	2463-84-5	PST71380
O-(2,4-DICHLOROPHENYL) O-ETHYL PHENYLPHOSPHONOTHIOATE	3792-59-4	PST73239
O-(2,4-DICHLOROPHENYL) O-ETHYL S-PROPYL PHOSPHORODITHIOATE	34643-46-4	PST72655
O-(2,4-DICHLOROPHENYL) O-METHYL (1-METHYLETHYL)PHOSPHORAMIDOTHIOATE	299-85-4	PST71236
O-(2,4-DICHLOROPHENYL) O-METHYL ISOPROPYLPHOSPHORAMIDOTHIOATE	299-85-4	PST71236
O-(2,5-DICHLORO-4-IODOPHENYL) O,O-DIMETHYL ESTER PHOSPHOROTHIOATE	18181-70-9	PST73035
O-(3-CHLORO-4-METHYL-2-OXO-2H-1-BENZOPYRAN-7-YL) O,O DIETHYL PHOSPHOROTHIOATE	56-72-4	PST05490
O-(3-CHLORO-4-NITROPHENYL) O,O-DIMETHYL PHOSPHOROTHIOATE	500-28-7	PST71379
O-(4-((DIMETHYLAMINO)SULFONYL)PHENYL) O,O-DIMETHYL PHOSPHOROTHIOATE	52-85-7	PST09675
O-(4-BROMO-2-CHLOROPHENYL)O-ETHYL S-PROPYL PHOSPHOROTHIOATE	41198-08-7	PST72412
O-(4-BROMO-2,5-DICHLOROPHENYL) O,O-DIETHYL PHOSPHOROTHIOATE	4824-78-6	PST03458
O-(4-BROMO-2,5-DICHLOROPHENYL) O,O-DIMETHYL PHOSPHOROTHIOATE	2104-96-3	PST71064
O-(4-CYANOPHENYL) O,O-DIMETHYL PHOSPHOROTHIOATE	2636-26-2	PST72950
O-(5-CHLORO-1-(1-METHYLETHYL)-1H-1,2,4-TRIAZOL-3-YL) O,O-DIETHYL PHOSPHOROTHIOATE	42509-80-8	PST15035
O-(6-ETHOXY-2-ETHYL-4-PYRIMIDINYL) O,O-DIMETHYL PHOSPHOROTHIOATE	38260-54-7	PST73148

ALPHABETICAL INDEX

SUBSTANCE NAME	CAS #	PST #
OCTYL ALCOHOL	111-87-5	PST17270
OCTYL PHTHALATE	117-81-7	PST06440
OCTYL PHTHALATE	117-84-0	PST08040
OCTYL/OCTADECYL DIMETHYL ETHYLBENZYL AMMONIUM CHLORIDES	8001-54-5	PST00539
OCTYLENE GLYCOL	94-96-2	PST71458
OCUSEPTINE	137-40-6	PST21575
ODM	301-12-2	PST17375
OESIPOS	8006-54-0	PST12425
OFF (FORMULATION)	134-62-3	PST84230
OFNACK	119-12-0	PST71604
OFTANOL	25311-71-1	PST11985
OFUNACK	119-12-0	PST71604
OIL CAMPHOR SASSAFRASSY	8008-51-3	PST04140
OIL CEDAR	8000-27-9	PST04365
OIL OF ANISE	8007-70-3	PST71028
OIL OF BITTER ALMOND	100-52-7	PST02590
OIL OF CITRONELLA	8000-29-1	PST71180
OIL OF EUCALYPTUS	8000-48-4	PST71453
OIL OF GARLIC	8000-78-0	PST72626
OIL OF GERANIUM	8000-46-2	PST73283
OIL OF HARTSHORN	8001-85-2	PST03250
OIL OF HEDEOMA	8007-44-1	PST71456
OIL OF MUSTARD, ARTIFICIAL	57-06-7	PST00680
OIL OF PELARGONIUM	8000-46-2	PST73283
OIL OF PENNYROYAL	8007-44-1	PST71456
OIL OF PENNYROYAL-AMERICAN	8007-44-1	PST71456
OIL OF PINE	8002-09-3	PST18900
OIL OF ROSE GERANIUM	8000-46-2	PST73283
OIL OF TURPENTINE	8006-64-2	PST24580
OIL OF TURPENTINE, RECTIFIED	8006-64-2	PST24580
OIL OF VITRIOL	7664-93-9	PST22350
OIL OF VITRIOL BATTERY ACID (SPECTRUM CHEMICAL MFG.CORP.)	7664-93-9	PST22350
OIL SESAME 4742	8008-74-0	PST20575
OILS, ANISE	8007-70-3	PST71028
OILS, CITRONELLA	8000-29-1	PST71180
OILS, EUCALYPTUS	8000-48-4	PST71453
OILS, GARLIC	8000-78-0	PST72626
OILS, GERANIUM	8000-46-2	PST73283
OILS, PENNYROYAL, HEDEOMA PULEGIOIDES	8007-44-1	PST71456
OILS, PINE	8002-09-3	PST18900
OILS, SESAME	8008-74-0	PST20575
OK 174	82560-54-1	PST72562
OKSID	97-24-5	PST71737
OKULTIN M	94-74-6	PST27880
OLEFIANT GAS	74-85-1	PST09330
OLEIC ACID	112-80-1	PST17305
OLEIC ACID, POTASSIUM SALT	143-18-0	PST72131
OLEIC ACID, SODIUM SALT	143-19-1	PST21418
OLEO NORDOX	1317-39-1	PST05470
OLEOPHOSVEL	21609-90-5	PST12780
OLEOVITAMIN D3	67-97-0	PST60913
OLEUM LINI	8001-26-1	PST71365
OLEUM SINAPIS VOLATILE	57-06-7	PST00680
OLITREF	1582-09-8	PST24085

SUBSTANCE NAME	CAS #	PST #
OLOTHORB	9005-65-6	PST40200
OLPISAN	82-68-8	PST18140
OMACIDE 24	15922-78-8	PST21420
OMADINE SODIUM	15922-78-8	PST21420
OMADINE SODIUM SALT	15922-78-8	PST21420
OMCHLOR	118-52-5	PST26800
OMETHOATE	1113-02-6	PST17328
OMEXAN	2104-96-3	PST71064
OMITE	2312-35-8	PST19720
OMPA	152-16-9	PST20350
OMS 1056	973-21-7	PST07990
OMS 1075	2597-03-7	PST72337
OMS 1078	72-54-8	PST06240
OMS 1102	6988-21-2	PST73123
OMS 115	299-85-4	PST71236
OMS 1155	5598-13-0	PST71652
OMS 1170	14816-18-3	PST73292
OMS 1206	10453-86-8	PST20095
OMS 1209	6164-98-3	PST04570
OMS 1211	18181-70-9	PST73035
OMS 123	299-84-3	PST20180
OMS 1328	470-90-6	PST04575
OMS 1344	1757-18-2	PST00493
OMS 1437	57-74-9	PST04560
OMS 1478	29173-31-7	PST73246
OMS 15	64-00-6	PST29423
OMS 1502	31218-83-4	PST72440
OMS 16	50-29-3	PST06250
OMS 162	64-00-6	PST29423
OMS 17	58-89-9	PST12810
OMS 17KO	2032-59-9	PST71500
OMS 1804	35367-38-5	PST07388
OMS 1809	26002-80-2	PST71954
OMS 186	86-50-0	PST02210
OMS 193	76-44-8	PST10660
OMS 197	72-20-8	PST08600
OMS 20	87-47-8	PST73263
OMS 206N	297-78-9	PST83032
OMS 214	2463-84-5	PST71380
OMS 217	500-28-7	PST71379
OMS 227	8065-36-9	PST03480
OMS 244	786-19-6	PST04340
OMS 32	2631-40-5	PST73231
OMS 33	114-26-1	PST02540
OMS 43	122-14-5	PST09678
OMS 466	72-43-5	PST14220
OMS 47	315-18-4	PST15010
OMS 503	78-57-9	PST72980
OMS 658	2104-96-3	PST71064
OMS 659	4824-78-6	PST03458
OMS 708	1079-33-0	PST29855
OMS 771	116-06-3	PST00500
OMS 773	6392-46-7	PST72977
OMS 870	13067-93-1	PST05805

ALPHABETICAL INDEX

SUBSTANCE NAME	CAS #	PST #
PARASEPT	99-76-3	PST14677
PARASEPT	94-13-3	PST19941
PARATHESINE	94-09-7	PST72267
PARATHION	56-38-2	PST18040
PARATHION-ETHYL	56-38-2	PST18040
PARATHION-METHYL	298-00-0	PST14680
PARATHION-METHYL HOMOLOG	298-00-0	PST14680
PARAZATE	142-59-6	PST16080
PARDNER	1689-84-5	PST03542
PARIDOL	99-76-3	PST14677
PARTISIL	63231-67-4	PST20670
PASEPTOL	94-13-3	PST19941
PATENT ALUM	10043-01-3	PST00980
PATORAN	3060-89-7	PST15008
PAXILON	20354-26-1	PST72344
PCA	1698-60-8	PST71928
PCI	80-38-6	PST09677
PCMC	59-50-7	PST29890
PCMX	88-04-0	PST72258
PCNB	82-68-8	PST18140
PCP	87-86-5	PST18150
PCP SODIUM SALT	131-52-2	PST08506
PCP-SODIUM	131-52-2	PST08506
PCPBS	80-38-6	PST09677
PDU	101-42-8	PST09679
PEACOCK BLUE X 1756	2650-18-2	PST08277
PEARL ASH	584-08-7	PST19290
PEBBLE LIME	1305-78-8	PST04030
PEBC	1114-71-2	PST71472
PEBULATE	1114-71-2	PST71472
PELARGONIUM OIL	8000-46-2	PST73283
PELT	23564-06-9	PST72322
PENCAL	7778-44-1	PST03850
PENCHLOROL	87-86-5	PST18150
PENCYCURON	66063-05-6	PST72622
PENNAC ZT	155-04-4	PST27776
PENNYROYAL OIL	8007-44-1	PST71456
PENTACHLORIN	50-29-3	PST06250
PENTACHLORONITROBENZENE	82-68-8	PST18140
PENTACHLOROPHENATE SODIUM	131-52-2	PST08506
PENTACHLOROPHENOL	87-86-5	PST18150
PENTACHLOROPHENOL SODIUM SALT	131-52-2	PST08506
PENTACHLOROPHENOXY SODIUM	131-52-2	PST08506
PENTACHLOROPHENYL CHLORIDE	118-74-1	PST10730
PENTAGEN	82-68-8	PST18140
PENTAHYDROXYCAPROIC ACID	526-95-4	PST10408
PENTANAMIDE, N-(3-CHLORO-4-METHYLPHENYL)-2-METHYL-	2307-68-8	PST71164
PENTANAMIDE, N-(4-CHLOROPHENYL)-2,2-DIMETHYL-	7287-36-7	PST72987
PENTANOCHLOR	2307-68-8	PST71164
PENTAPHEN	80-46-6	PST71715
PENTASODIUM TRIPHOSPHATE	7758-29-4	PST21730
PENTASODIUM TRIPOLYPHOSPHATE	7758-29-4	PST21730
PENTHAZINE	92-84-2	PST18400
PENTYL ACETATE	628-63-7	PST15270

SUBSTANCE NAME	CAS #	PST #
PHENIC ACID	108-95-2	PST18380
PHENKAPTON	2275-14-1	PST18373
PHENKAPTONE	2275-14-1	PST18373
PHENMAD	62-38-4	PST18560
PHENMEDIPHAM	13684-63-4	PST72282
PHENO, 2-SEC-BUTYL-4,6-DINITRO, ACETATE	2813-95-8	PST08021
PHENOBENZURON	3134-12-1	PST72972
PHENOL	108-95-2	PST18380
PHENOL SODIUM	139-02-6	PST21530
PHENOL-2-CARBOXYLIC ACID	69-72-7	PST20315
PHENOL, DIMETHYL	1300-71-6	PST25160
PHENOL, METHYL-	1319-77-3	PST05510
PHENOL, P-TERT-BUTYL-	98-54-4	PST17440
PHENOL, PENTACHLORO-	87-86-5	PST18150
PHENOL, PENTACHLORO-, SODIUM SALT	131-52-2	PST08506
PHENOL, SODIUM SALT, (SOLID)	139-02-6	PST21530
PHENOL, TETRACHLORO-	25167-83-3	PST71689
PHENOL, 2-((ETHYLTHIO)METHYL)-, METHYLCARBAMATE	29973-13-5	PST72421
PHENOL, 2-(1-METHYLETHOXY)-, METHYLCARBAMATE	114-26-1	PST02540
PHENOL, 2-(1-METHYLETHYL)-, METHYLCARBAMATE	2631-40-5	PST73231
PHENOL, 2-(1-METHYLPROPYL)-, METHYLCARBAMATE	3766-81-2	PST03324
PHENOL, 2-(1-METHYLPROPYL)-4,6-DINITRO-	88-85-7	PST08020
PHENOL, 2-(1-METHYLPROPYL)-4,6-DINITRO-, ACETATE (ESTER)	2813-95-8	PST08021
PHENOL, 2-(1,1-DIMETHYLETHYL)-4,6-DINITRO-	1420-07-1	PST72921
PHENOL, 2-(1,3-DIOXOLAN-2YL)-, METHYLCARBAMATE	6988-21-2	PST73123
PHENOL, 2-(2-CHLORO-1-METHOXYETHOXY)-, METHYLCARBAMATE	51487-69-5	PST72572
PHENOL, 2-CHLORO-4,5-DIMETHYL-, METHYLCARBAMATE	671-04-5	PST02250
PHENOL, 2-METHYL-4,6-DINITRO-	534-52-1	PST07910
PHENOL, 2-METHYL-4,6-DINITRO-, SODIUM SALT	2312-76-7	PST71411
PHENOL, 2-SEC-BUTYL-4,6-DINITRO-	88-85-7	PST08020
PHENOL, 2-SEC-BUTYL-4,6-DINITRO-, ACETATE (ESTER)	2813-95-8	PST08021
PHENOL, 2-TERT-BUTYL-4,6-DINITRO-	1420-07-1	PST72921
PHENOL, 2,2'-METHYLENEBIS(4-CHLORO-	97-23-4	PST71611
PHENOL, 2,2'-THIOBIS(4-CHLORO-	97-24-5	PST71737
PHENOL, 2,3,5(OR 3,4,5)-TRIMETHYL-, METHYLCARBAMATE	12407-86-2	PST12420
PHENOL, 2,4-DICHLORO-, BENZENESULFONATE	97-16-5	PST71350
PHENOL, 2,4-DIMETHYL	105-67-9	PST28670
PHENOL, 2,4-DINITRO-	51-28-5	PST28620
PHENOL, 3-(1-ETHYLPROPYL)-, METHYLCARBAMATE, MIXTURE WITH 3-(1-METHYLBUTYL)PHENYL METHYLCARBAMATE	8065-36-9	PST03480
PHENOL, 3-(1-METHYLETHYL)-, METHYLCARBAMATE	64-00-6	PST29423
PHENOL, 3-METHYL-5-(1-METHYLETHYL)-, METHYLCARBAMATE	2631-37-0	PST72957
PHENOL, 3,5-BIS(1,1-DIMETHYLETHYL)-, METHYLCARBAMATE	2655-19-8	PST72994
PHENOL, 3,5-DIMETHYL-, METHYLCARBAMATE	2655-14-3	PST25171
PHENOL, 3,5-DIMETHYL-4-(METHYLSULFINYL)-, METHYLCARBAMATE	2635-10-1	PST14191
PHENOL, 3,5-DIMETHYL-4-(METHYLTHIO)-, METHYLCARBAMATE	2032-65-7	PST14190
PHENOL, 4-(DI-2-PROPENYLAMINO)-3,5-DIMETHYL-, METHYLCARBAMATE (ESTER)	6392-46-7	PST72977
PHENOL, 4-(DIMETHYLAMINO)-3-METHYL-, METHYLCARBAMATE (ESTER)	2032-59-9	PST71500
PHENOL, 4-(DIMETHYLAMINO)-3,5-DIMETHYL-, METHYLCARBAMATE (ESTER)	315-18-4	PST15010
PHENOL, 4-(1,1-DIMETHYLETHYL)-	98-54-4	PST17440
PHENOL, 4-CHLORO-2-CYCLOPENTYL-	13347-42-7	PST71731
PHENOL, 4-CHLORO-3-METHYL-	59-50-7	PST29890
PHENOL, 4-CHLORO-3,5-DIMETHYL-	88-04-0	PST72258
PHENOL, 4-NITRO-3-(TRIFLUOROMETHYL)-	88-30-2	PST71405

ALPHABETICAL INDEX

SUBSTANCE NAME	CAS #	PST #
PHENOMERCURIC ACETATE	62-38-4	PST18560
PHENOPYRIDINE	148-24-3	PST30450
PHENOTHIAZINE	92-84-2	PST18400
PHENOTHRIN	26002-80-2	PST71954
PHENOXAPROP-ETHYL	66441-23-4	PST72723
PHENTHOATE	2597-03-7	PST72337
PHENTIN ACETATE	900-95-8	PST24378
PHENUDIN	2275-14-1	PST18373
PHENUDINE	2275-14-1	PST18373
PHENVALERATE	51630-58-1	PST19948
PHENYL ALCOHOL	108-95-2	PST18380
PHENYL CARBOXYLIC ACID	65-85-0	PST02720
PHENYL CHLOROMERCURY	100-56-1	PST18570
PHENYL HYDRATE	108-95-2	PST18380
PHENYL HYDROXIDE	108-95-2	PST18380
PHENYL HYDROXYMERCURY	100-57-2	PST18580
PHENYL MERCURIC ACETATE	62-38-4	PST18560
PHENYL MERCURIC CHLORIDE	100-56-1	PST18570
PHENYL MERCURIC TRIETHANOL AMMONIUM LACTATE	23319-66-6	PST71768
PHENYL N,N'-DIMETHYL PHOSPHOROMIADATE	1754-58-1	PST72310
PHENYL PERCHLORYL	118-74-1	PST10730
PHENYL PHOSPHONOTHIOIC ACID, O-ETHYL O-(4-NITROPHENYL)ESTER	2104-64-5	PST08650
PHENYL PHTHALATE	84-62-8	PST08095
PHENYLANILINE	122-39-4	PST08100
PHENYLCARBAMIC ACID 1-METHYLETHYL ESTER	122-42-9	PST71564
PHENYLCARBINOL	100-51-6	PST02800
PHENYLCARBOXYLIC ACID	65-85-0	PST02720
PHENYLETHYL PROPIONATE	122-70-3	PST72314
PHENYLFORMIC ACID	65-85-0	PST02720
PHENYLGLYOXYLONITRILE OXIME O,O-DIETHYL PHOSPHOROTHIOATE	14816-18-3	PST73292
PHENYLIC ACID	108-95-2	PST18380
PHENYLIC ALCOHOL	108-95-2	PST18380
PHENYLMERCURIC ACETATE	62-38-4	PST18560
PHENYLMERCURIC BORATE	6273-99-0	PST71754
PHENYLMERCURIC CHLORIDE	100-56-1	PST18570
PHENYLMERCURIC HYDROXIDE	100-57-2	PST18580
PHENYLMERCURIC OLEATE	104-60-9	PST71769
PHENYLMERCURY ACETATE	62-38-4	PST18560
PHENYLMERCURY BORATE	6273-99-0	PST71754
PHENYLMERCURY CHLORIDE	100-56-1	PST18570
PHENYLMERCURY HYDROXIDE	100-57-2	PST18580
PHENYLMERCURY OLEATE	104-60-9	PST71769
PHENYLMETHANAL	100-52-7	PST02590
PHENYLMETHANOL	100-51-6	PST02800
PHENYLMETHYL ALCOHOL	100-51-6	PST02800
PHENYLPHOSPHONOTHIOIC ACID O-(4-CYANOPHENYL) O-ETHYL ESTER	13067-93-1	PST05805
PHENYLPHOSPHONOTHIOIC ACID O-ETHYL ESTER O-ESTER WITH P-HYDROXYBENZONITRILE	13067-93-1	PST05805
PHENYLPHOSPHONOTHIOIC ACID, ETHYL P-NITROPHENYL ESTER	2104-64-5	PST08650
PHENYLPHOSPHONOTHIOIC ACID, O-(2,4-DICHLOROPHENYL)-O-ETHYL ESTER	3792-59-4	PST73239
PHENYLPHOSPHONOTHIOIC ACID, O-(4-BROMO-2,5-DICHLOROPHENYL)O-METHYL ESTER	21609-90-5	PST12780
PHENYLPHOSPHONOTHIOIC ACID, O-ETHYL O-(P-NITROPHENYL)ESTER	2104-64-5	PST08650
PHILLIPS REPELLENT 11	126-15-8	PST71487

SUBSTANCE NAME	CAS #	PST #
PHILOSOPHER'S WOOL	1314-13-2	PST25490
PHODA-NIDE	333-20-0	PST19640
PHORATE	298-02-2	PST18640
PHORATE O.A. SULFOXIDE	2588-05-8	PST18644
PHORATE O-SULFOXIDE	2588-03-6	PST18646
PHORATE OXON	2600-69-3	PST18641
PHORATE OXON SULFONE	2588-06-9	PST18642
PHORATE OXON SULFOXIDE	2588-05-8	PST18644
PHORATE OXYGEN ANALOG	2600-69-3	PST18641
PHORATE OXYGEN ANALOG SULFONE	2588-06-9	PST18642
PHORATE OXYGEN ANALOG SULFOXIDE	2588-05-8	PST18644
PHORATE SULFONE	2588-04-7	PST18643
PHORATE SULFOXIDE	2588-03-6	PST18646
PHORATE THIOLATE ANALOG	2600-69-3	PST18641
PHORATOXON	2600-69-3	PST18641
PHORATOXON SULFONE	2588-06-9	PST18642
PHORATOXON SULFOXIDE	2588-05-8	PST18644
PHOSACETIM	4104-14-7	PST71150
PHOSALON	2310-17-0	PST25720
PHOSALONE	2310-17-0	PST25720
PHOSDRIN	7786-34-7	PST18650
PHOSETHYL AL	39148-24-8	PST72563
PHOSFOLAN	947-02-4	PST06115
PHOSMET	732-11-6	PST11307
PHOSMET OXYGEN ANALOG	3735-33-9	PST18665
PHOSMETOXON	3735-33-9	PST18665
PHOSPHACHOLE	311-45-5	PST07200
PHOSPHACOL; PHOSPHAKOL	311-45-5	PST07200
PHOSPHAMIDE	60-51-5	PST07670
PHOSPHAMIDON	13171-21-6	PST18670
PHOSPHOLAN	947-02-4	PST06115
PHOSPHONIC ACID, (2-CHLOROETHYL)-	16672-87-0	PST72293
PHOSPHONIC ACID, (2,2,2-TRICHLORO-1-HYDROXYETHYL)-, DIMETHYL ESTER	52-68-6	PST23790
PHOSPHONIC ACID, ETHYL-, ETHYL 2,4,5-TRICHLOROPHENYL ESTER	6492-18-8	PST23871
PHOSPHONIC ACID, MONOETHYL ESTER, ALUMINUM SALT	39148-24-8	PST72563
PHOSPHONIC ACID, PHENYL-, 4-BROMO-2,5-DICHLOROPHENYL METHYL ESTER	25006-32-0	PST12776
PHOSPHONIC DIAMIDE, P-(5-AMINO-3-PHENYL-1H-1,2,4-TRIAZOL-1-YL)-N,N,N', N'-TETRAMETHYL	1031-47-6	PST72937
PHOSPHONODITHIOIC ACID, ETHYL-, O-ETHYL S-PHENYL ESTER	944-22-9	PST10020
PHOSPHONODITHIOIMIDOCARBONIC ACID CYCLIC METHYLENE P,P-DIETHYL ESTER	21548-32-3	PST16141
PHOSPHONODITHIOIMIDOCARBONIC ACID CYCLIC PROPYLENE P,P-DIETHYL ESTER	950-10-7	PST13735
PHOSPHONOMETHYLGLYCINE	1071-83-6	PST10515
PHOSPHONOMETHYLIMINOACETIC ACID	1071-83-6	PST10515
PHOSPHONOTHIOIC ACID, (1,3-DIHYDRO-1,3-DIOXO-2H-ISOINDOL-2-YL)-, O,O-DIETHYL ESTER	5131-24-8	PST72347
PHOSPHONOTHIOIC ACID, ETHYL-, O-ETHYL O-(2,4,5-TRICHLOROPHENYL)ESTER	327-98-0	PST00478
PHOSPHONOTHIOIC ACID, PHENYL ETHYL P-NITROPHENYL ESTER	2104-64-5	PST08650
PHOSPHONOTHIOIC ACID, PHENYL-, O-(2,4-DICHLOROPHENYL)-O-ETHYL ESTER	3792-59-4	PST73239
PHOSPHONOTHIOIC ACID, PHENYL-, O-(4-CYANOPHENYL) O-ETHYL ESTER	13067-93-1	PST05805
PHOSPHONOTHIOIC ACID, PHENYL-, O-ETHYL ESTER, O-ESTER WITH P-HYDROXYBENZONITRILE	13067-93-1	PST05805
PHOSPHONOTHIOIC ACID, PHENYL-, O-ETHYL O-(P-NITROPHENYL)ESTER	2104-64-5	PST08650
PHOSPHONOTHIOIC ACID, PHENYL-, O-ETHYL O-(4-NITROPHENYL)ESTER	2104-64-5	PST08650
PHOSPHONOTHIOIC ACID, PHTHALIMIDO-, O,O-DIETHYL ESTER	5131-24-8	PST72347

SUBSTANCE NAME	CAS #	PST #
PHOSPHONOTHIONIC ACID, METHYL-, S-(2-(BIS(1-METHYLETHYL)AMINO)ETHYL) O-ETHYL ESTER	50782-69-9	PST83104
PHOSPHORAMIDIC ACID, (1-METHYLETHYL)-, ETHYL 3-METHYL-4-(METHYLSULFONYL)PHENYL ESTER	31972-44-8	PST16144
PHOSPHORAMIDIC ACID, (1-METHYLETHYL)-, ETHYL 3-METHYL-4-(METHYLSULFINYL)PHENYL ESTER	31972-43-7	PST16146
PHOSPHORAMIDIC ACID, (1-METHYLETHYL)-, ETHYL 3-METHYL-4-(METHYLTHIO) PHENYL ESTER	22224-92-6	PST16145
PHOSPHORAMIDIC ACID, (4-METHYL-1,3-DITHIOLAN-2-YLIDENE)-, DIETHYL ESTER	950-10-7	PST13735
PHOSPHORAMIDIC ACID, ISOPROPYL-, ETHYL 4-(ETHYLSULFINYL)-M-TOLYL ESTER	31972-43-7	PST16146
PHOSPHORAMIDIC ACID, ISOPROPYL-, ETHYL 4-(METHYLTHIO)-M-TOLYL ESTER	22224-92-6	PST16145
PHOSPHORAMIDIC ACID, ISOPROPYL-, ETHYL-4-(METHYLSULFONYL)-M-TOLYL ESTER	31972-44-8	PST16144
PHOSPHORAMIDIC ACID, METHYL-, 4-TERT-BUTYL-2-CHLOROPHENYL METHYL ESTER	299-86-5	PST05550
PHOSPHORAMIDIC ACID, METHYL-,2-CHLORO-4-(1,1-DIMETHYLETHYL)PHENYL METHYL ESTER	299-86-5	PST05550
PHOSPHORAMIDIC ACID, 1-3-DITHIOLAN-2-YLIDENE-, DIETHYL ESTER	947-02-4	PST06115
PHOSPHORAMIDIC ACID, 1,3-DITHIETAN-2-YLIDENE-, DIETHYL ESTER	21548-32-3	PST16141
PHOSPHORAMIDOTHIOIC ACID, (1-IMINOETHYL)-, O,O-BIS(P-CHLOROPHENYL) ESTER	4104-14-7	PST71150
PHOSPHORAMIDOTHIOIC ACID, (1-METHYLETHYL)-, O-(2,4-DICHLOROPHENYL) O-METHYL ESTER	299-85-4	PST71236
PHOSPHORAMIDOTHIOIC ACID, ACETIMIDOYL-, O,O-BIS(P-CHLOROPHENYL) ESTER	4104-14-7	PST71150
PHOSPHORAMIDOTHIOIC ACID, ISOPROPYL-, O-(2,4-DICHLOROPHENYL) O-METHYL ESTER	299-85-4	PST71236
PHOSPHORAMIDOTHIOIC ACID, O,S-DIMETHYL ESTER	10265-92-6	PST15160
PHOSPHORIC ACID	7664-38-2	PST18690
PHOSPHORIC ACID SODIUM SALT (1:3)	7601-54-9	PST24480
PHOSPHORIC ACID TRIETHYLENEIMINE	545-55-1	PST22510
PHOSPHORIC ACID, DIETHYL P-(METHYLSULFINYL)PHENYL ESTER	6552-21-2	PST09684
PHOSPHORIC ACID, DIETHYL P-(METHYLSULFONYL)PHENYL ESTER	6132-17-8	PST06211
PHOSPHORIC ACID, DIETHYL P-NITROPHENYL ESTER	311-45-5	PST07200
PHOSPHORIC ACID, DIETHYL PYRAZINYL ESTER	7359-55-9	PST71377
PHOSPHORIC ACID, DIETHYL 2-(ETHYLTHIO)ETHYL ESTER	23052-51-9	PST06317
PHOSPHORIC ACID, DIETHYL 2-ISOPROPYL-6-METHYL-4-PYRIMIDINYL ESTER	962-58-3	PST06541
PHOSPHORIC ACID, DIETHYL 3,5,6-TRICHLORO-2-PYRIDINYL ESTER	5598-15-2	PST04911
PHOSPHORIC ACID, DIETHYL 3,5,6-TRICHLORO-2-PYRIDYL ESTER	5598-15-2	PST04911
PHOSPHORIC ACID, DIETHYL 4-(METHYLSULFINYL)PHENYL ESTER	6552-21-2	PST09684
PHOSPHORIC ACID, DIETHYL 4-(METHYLSULFONYL)PHENYL ESTER	6132-17-8	PST06211
PHOSPHORIC ACID, DIETHYL 4-NITROPHENYL ESTER	311-45-5	PST07200
PHOSPHORIC ACID, DIETHYL 6-METHYL-2-(1-METHYLETHYL)-4-PYRIMIDINYL ESTER	962-58-3	PST06541
PHOSPHORIC ACID, DIMETHYL ESTER	813-78-5	PST07882
PHOSPHORIC ACID, DIMETHYL ESTER, ESTER WITH 2-CHLORO-N,N-DIETHYL -3-HYDROXYCROTONAMIDE	13171-21-6	PST18670
PHOSPHORIC ACID, DIMETHYL ESTER, ESTER WITH 3-HYDROXY-N-METHYL CROTONAMIDE, (E)-	6923-22-4	PST15165
PHOSPHORIC ACID, DIMETHYL ESTER, ESTER WITH 3-HYDROXY-N,N -DIMETHYLCROTONAMIDE, (E)-	141-66-2	PST03090
PHOSPHORIC ACID, DIMETHYL P-NITROPHENYL ESTER	950-35-6	PST14678
PHOSPHORIC ACID, DIMETHYL 1-METHYL-3-(METHYLAMINO)-3-OXO-1-PROPENYL ESTER, (E)	6923-22-4	PST15165
PHOSPHORIC ACID, DIMETHYL 2,4,5-TRICHLOROPHENYL ESTER	3983-45-7	PST25082

SUBSTANCE NAME	CAS #	PST #
PHOSPHOROTHIOIC ACID, O-(2-CHLORO-4-NITROPHENYL) O,O-DIMETHYL ESTER	2463-84-5	PST71380
PHOSPHOROTHIOIC ACID, O-(2,4-DICHLOROPHENYL) O,O-DIETHYL ESTER	97-17-6	PST06805
PHOSPHOROTHIOIC ACID, O-(2,5-DICHLORO-4-IODOPHENYL) O,O-DIMETHYL ESTER	18181-70-9	PST73035
PHOSPHOROTHIOIC ACID, O-(3-CHLORO-4-METHYL-2-OXO-2H-1-BENZOPYRAN-7-YL) O,O-DIETHYL ESTER	56-72-4	PST05490
PHOSPHOROTHIOIC ACID, O-(3-CHLORO-4-NITROPHENYL) O,O-DIMETHYL ESTER	500-28-7	PST71379
PHOSPHOROTHIOIC ACID, O-(4-((DIMETHYLAMINO)SULFONYL)PHENYL) O,O-DIMETHYL ESTER	52-85-7	PST09675
PHOSPHOROTHIOIC ACID, O-(4-(AMINOSULFONYL)PHENYL) O,O-DIMETHYL ESTER	115-93-5	PST06135
PHOSPHOROTHIOIC ACID, O-(4-BROMO-2-CHLOROPHENYL)O-ETHYL S-PROPYL ESTER	41198-08-7	PST72412
PHOSPHOROTHIOIC ACID, O-(4-BROMO-2,5-DICHLOROPHENYL) O,O-DIETHYL ESTER	4824-78-6	PST03458
PHOSPHOROTHIOIC ACID, O-(4-BROMO-2,5-DICHLOROPHENYL) O,O-DIMETHYL	2104-96-3	PST71064
PHOSPHOROTHIOIC ACID, O-(4-CYANOPHENYL) O,O-DIMETHYL ESTER	2636-26-2	PST72950
PHOSPHOROTHIOIC ACID, O-(5-CHLORO-1-(1-METHYLETHYL)-1H-1,2,4-TRIAZOL -3-YL) O,O-DIETHYL ESTER	42509-80-8	PST15035
PHOSPHOROTHIOIC ACID, O-(6-ETHOXY-2-ETHYL-4-PYRIMIDINYL)-O,O-DIMETHYL ESTER	38260-54-7	PST73148
PHOSPHOROTHIOIC ACID, O-ETHYL O-(4-(METHYLSULFONYL)PHENYL) S-PROPYL ESTER	42795-00-6	PST03231
PHOSPHOROTHIOIC ACID, O-METHYL ESTER, CYCLIC O,O-ESTER WITH O-HYDROXYBENZYL ALCOHOL	3811-49-2	PST20325
PHOSPHOROTHIOIC ACID, O,O-BIS(1-METHYLETHYL)S-(PHENYLMETHYL) ESTER	26087-47-8	PST12355
PHOSPHOROTHIOIC ACID, O,O-DIETHYL ESTER, O-ESTER WITH 6-HYDROXY -2-PHENYL-3(2H)-PYRIDAZINONE	119-12-0	PST71604
PHOSPHOROTHIOIC ACID, O,O-DIETHYL ESTER, O-ESTER WITH 7,8,9,10 -TETRAHYDRO-3-HYDROXY-6H-DIBENZO(B,D)PYRAN-6-ONE	572-48-5	PST73073
PHOSPHOROTHIOIC ACID, O,O-DIETHYL ESTER, S-ESTER WITH N-(1-CYANO-1-METHYLETHYL)-2-MERCAPTOACETAMIDE	3734-95-0	PST72949
PHOSPHOROTHIOIC ACID, O,O-DIETHYL O-(P-(METHYLSULFINYL)PHENYL) ESTER	115-90-2	PST06210
PHOSPHOROTHIOIC ACID, O,O-DIETHYL O-(P-(METHYLSULFONYL)PHENYL) ESTER	14255-72-2	PST06228
PHOSPHOROTHIOIC ACID, O,O-DIETHYL O-(P-NITROPHENYL)ESTER	56-38-2	PST18040
PHOSPHOROTHIOIC ACID, O,O-DIETHYL O-(1-PHENYL-1H-1,2,4-TRIAZOL-3-YL) ESTER	24017-47-8	PST73068
PHOSPHOROTHIOIC ACID, O,O-DIETHYL O-(2-(ETHYLSULFONYL)ETHYL) ESTER	4891-54-7	PST06309
PHOSPHOROTHIOIC ACID, O,O-DIETHYL O-(2-(ETHYLTHIO)ETHYL)ESTER	298-03-3	PST71645
PHOSPHOROTHIOIC ACID, O,O-DIETHYL O-(2-(ETHYLTHIO)ETHYL)ESTER, MIXED WITH O,O-DIETHYL S-(2-(ETHYLTHIO)ETHYL)PHOSPHOROTHIOATE	8065-48-3	PST06320
PHOSPHOROTHIOIC ACID, O,O-DIETHYL O-(2-ISOPROPYL-6-METHYL -4-PYRIMIDINYL) ESTER	333-41-5	PST06540
PHOSPHOROTHIOIC ACID, O,O-DIETHYL O-(3,5,6-TRICHLORO-2-PYRIDINYL) ESTER	2921-88-2	PST04910
PHOSPHOROTHIOIC ACID, O,O-DIETHYL O-(3,5,6-TRICHLORO-2-PYRIDYL) ESTER	2921-88-2	PST04910
PHOSPHOROTHIOIC ACID, O,O-DIETHYL O-(4-(METHYLSULFINYL)PHENYL) ESTER	115-90-2	PST06210
PHOSPHOROTHIOIC ACID, O,O-DIETHYL O-(4-(METHYLSULFONYL)PHENYL) ESTER	14255-72-2	PST06228
PHOSPHOROTHIOIC ACID, O,O-DIETHYL O-(4-NITROPHENYL)ESTER	56-38-2	PST18040
PHOSPHOROTHIOIC ACID, O,O-DIETHYL O-(5-PHENYL-3-ISOXAZOLYL)ESTER	18854-01-8	PST12280
PHOSPHOROTHIOIC ACID, O,O-DIETHYL O-(6-METHYL-2-(1-METHYLETHYL)-4-PYRIMIDINYL) ESTER	333-41-5	PST06540
PHOSPHOROTHIOIC ACID, O,O-DIETHYL O-(7,8,9,10-TETRAHYDRO-6-OXO-6H -DIBENZO(B,D)PYRAN-3-YL) ESTER	572-48-5	PST73073
PHOSPHOROTHIOIC ACID, O,O-DIETHYL S-((ETHYLSULFINYL)METHYL)ESTER	2588-05-8	PST18644
PHOSPHOROTHIOIC ACID, O,O-DIETHYL S-((ETHYLSULFONYL)METHYL)ESTER	2588-06-9	PST18642
PHOSPHOROTHIOIC ACID, O,O-DIETHYL S-((ETHYLTHIO)METHYL)ESTER	2600-69-3	PST18641
PHOSPHOROTHIOIC ACID, O,O-DIETHYL S-(2-(ETHYLSULFINYL)ETHYL) ESTER	2496-92-6	PST06316

SUBSTANCE NAME	CAS #	PST #
POLYRAM	9006-42-2	PST71123
POLYRAM M	12427-38-2	PST13589
POLYSORBATE 20	9005-64-5	PST80107
POLYSORBATE 80	9005-65-6	PST40200
POLYSORBATE 80 B.P.C.	9005-65-6	PST40200
POMARSOL	137-26-8	PST23430
PONTOCAINE HYDROCHLORIDE	136-47-0	PST72269
POSSE	55285-14-8	PST72266
POTABLAN	7287-36-7	PST72987
POTASH	584-08-7	PST19290
POTASSA	1310-58-3	PST19430
POTASSIUM ACID SULFATE	7646-93-7	PST19255
POTASSIUM ANTIMONY TARTRATE	28300-74-5	PST01690
POTASSIUM ANTIMONYL D-TARTRATE	28300-74-5	PST01690
POTASSIUM ANTIMONYL TARTRATE	28300-74-5	PST01690
POTASSIUM BICHROMATE	7778-50-9	PST19370
POTASSIUM BISULFATE	7646-93-7	PST19255
POTASSIUM BISULPHATE	7646-93-7	PST19255
POTASSIUM BROMIDE	7758-02-3	PST19280
POTASSIUM CARBONATE	584-08-7	PST19290
POTASSIUM CIS-9-OCTADECENOIC ACID	143-18-0	PST72131
POTASSIUM CYANIDE	151-50-8	PST19350
POTASSIUM CYANIDE (K(CN))	151-50-8	PST19350
POTASSIUM CYANIDE, SOLID	151-50-8	PST19350
POTASSIUM DICHLORO-S-TRIAZINETRIONE	2244-21-5	PST19360
POTASSIUM DICHLOROCYANURATE	2244-21-5	PST19360
POTASSIUM DICHLOROISOCYANURATE	2244-21-5	PST19360
POTASSIUM DICHROMATE	7778-50-9	PST19370
POTASSIUM DICHROMATE (VI)	7778-50-9	PST19370
POTASSIUM DIPHOSPHATE(K4P207)	7320-34-5	PST19546
POTASSIUM DODECANOATE	10124-65-9	PST72072
POTASSIUM GIBBERELLATE	125-67-7	PST71492
POTASSIUM HYDRATE	1310-58-3	PST19430
POTASSIUM HYDROGEN SULFATE	7646-93-7	PST19255
POTASSIUM HYDROGEN SULFATE, SOLID	7646-93-7	PST19255
POTASSIUM HYDROXIDE	1310-58-3	PST19430
POTASSIUM HYDROXIDE, SOLUTION	1310-58-3	PST19430
POTASSIUM IODIDE	7681-11-0	PST19435
POTASSIUM ISOTHIOCYANATE	333-20-0	PST19640
POTASSIUM LAURATE	10124-65-9	PST72072
POTASSIUM MYRISTATE	13429-27-1	PST72073
POTASSIUM N-DODECANOATE	10124-65-9	PST72072
POTASSIUM NITRATE	7757-79-1	PST19470
POTASSIUM NITRATE (JT BAKER)	7757-79-1	PST19470
POTASSIUM OLEATE	143-18-0	PST72131
POTASSIUM PERMANGANATE	7722-64-7	PST19520
POTASSIUM PHOSPHATE TRIBASIC	7778-53-2	PST19544
POTASSIUM PHOSPHATE(K4P207)	7320-34-5	PST19546
POTASSIUM PHOSPHATE, NEUTRAL	7778-53-2	PST19544
POTASSIUM PHOSPHATE, NORMAL	7778-53-2	PST19544
POTASSIUM PHOSPHATE, TERTIARY	7778-53-2	PST19544
POTASSIUM POLYSULFIDE	37199-66-9	PST19548
POTASSIUM PYROPHOSPHATE, ANHYDROUS	7320-34-5	PST19546
POTASSIUM PYROPHOSPHATE, NORMAL	7320-34-5	PST19546

ALPHABETICAL INDEX

ALPHABETICAL INDEX

ALPHABETICAL INDEX

SUBSTANCE NAME	CAS #	PST #
RAD-E-CATE	75-60-5	PST03710
RADAPON	75-99-0	PST06200
RADAZIN	1912-24-9	PST02150
RADOSAN	151-38-2	PST83031
RAGADAN	23560-59-0	PST10685
RAID (R) ANT AND ROACH KILLER-LIQUID	UNASSIGNED	PST86204
RAMETIN	1491-41-4	PST72737
RAMROD	1918-16-7	PST19686
RANDOX	93-71-0	PST71155
RANGE OIL	8008-20-6	PST10090
RAT-NIP	7723-14-0	PST18800
RATAFIN	117-52-2	PST05476
RATAK	56073-07-5	PST07385
RATAK +	56073-10-0	PST03327
RATBANE 1080	62-74-8	PST21240
RATICATE	991-42-4	PST72254
RATINDAN	82-66-6	PST08068
RATOL	1314-84-7	PST25540
RATSUL SOLUBLE	129-06-6	PST83008
RATTRACK	86-88-4	PST01830
RAX	81-81-2	PST25090
RC 9485	116-52-9	PST06817
RCRA P001	81-81-2	PST25090
RCRA P001	129-06-6	PST83008
RCRA P003	107-02-8	PST00330
RCRA P004	309-00-2	PST00520
RCRA P006	20859-73-8	PST00970
RCRA P008	504-24-5	PST02180
RCRA P010	7778-39-4	PST01990
RCRA P011	1303-28-2	PST02020
RCRA P012	1327-53-3	PST02070
RCRA P020	88-85-7	PST08020
RCRA P037	60-57-1	PST07080
RCRA P039	298-04-4	PST08380
RCRA P040	297-97-2	PST25590
RCRA P041	311-45-5	PST07200
RCRA P043	55-91-4	PST07590
RCRA P044	60-51-5	PST07670
RCRA P045	39196-18-4	PST23330
RCRA P047	534-52-1	PST07910
RCRA P047	2312-76-7	PST71411
RCRA P048	51-28-5	PST28620
RCRA P050	115-29-7	PST08560
RCRA P051	72-20-8	PST08600
RCRA P057	640-19-7	PST09930
RCRA P058	62-74-8	PST21240
RCRA P059	76-44-8	PST10660
RCRA P060	465-73-6	PST11810
RCRA P066	16752-77-5	PST14200
RCRA P070	116-06-3	PST00500
RCRA P071	298-00-0	PST14680
RCRA P072	86-88-4	PST01830
RCRA P075	54-11-5	PST16430
RCRA P085	152-16-9	PST20350

ALPHABETICAL INDEX

ALPHABETICAL INDEX

ALPHABETICAL INDEX

SUBSTANCE NAME	CAS #	PST #
S-2-ETHYLSULFINYLETHYL O,O-DIMETHYL PHOSPHOROTHIOATE	301-12-2	PST17375
S-2-ETHYLSULPHINYL-1-METHYLETHYL O,O-DIMETHYL PHOSPHOROTHIOATE	2674-91-1	PST14105
S-2-ETHYLSULPHINYLETHYL O,O-DIMETHYL PHOSPHOROTHIOATE	301-12-2	PST17375
S-2-ETHYLTHIOETHYL O,O-DIMETHYL PHOSPHORODITHIOATE	640-15-3	PST83056
S-2-ETHYLTHIOETHYL O,O-DIMETHYL PHOSPHOROTHIOATE	919-86-8	PST83065
S-2-ISOPROPYLTHIOETHYL O,O-DIMETHYL PHOSPHORODITHIOATE	36614-38-7	PST12275
S-2-METHOXYETHYLCARBAMOYLMETHYL O,O-DIMETHYL PHOSPHORODITHIOATE	919-76-6	PST01007
S-2,3-DICHLOROALLYL DI-ISOPROPYL(THIOCARBAMATE)	2303-16-4	PST06480
S-2,3-DICHLOROALLYL DIISOPROPYLTHIOCARBAMATE	2303-16-4	PST06480
S-2,3-DIHYDRO-5-METHOXY-2-OXO-1,3,4-THIADIAZOL-3-YLMETHYL O,O DIMETHYL PHOSPHORODITHIOATE	950-37-8	PST14175
S-2,3,3-TRICHLOROALLYL DI-ISOPROPYL THIOCARBAMATE	2303-17-5	PST72050
S-2,3,3-TRICHLOROALLYL DI-ISOPROPYL(THIOCARBAMATE)	2303-17-5	PST72050
S-2,5,-DICHLOROPHENYLTHIOMETHYL O,O-DIETHYL PHOSPHORODITHIOATE	2275-14-1	PST18373
S-224	532-32-1	PST20965
S-255	7647-15-6	PST21060
S-268	7775-09-9	PST21100
S-283; S-284	143-33-9	PST21160
S-299	7681-49-4	PST21230
S-3,4-DIHYDRO-4-OXO-1,2,3-BENZOTRIAZIN-3-YLMETHYL O,O-DIETHYL PHOSPHORODITHIOATE	2642-71-9	PST02205
S-3,4-DIHYDRO-4-OXO-1,2,3-BENZOTRIAZIN-3-YLMETHYL O,O-DIMETHYL PHOSPHORODITHIOATE	86-50-0	PST02210
S-3,4-DIHYDRO-4-OXOBENZO(D)(1,2,3)TRIAZIN-3-YLMETHYL O,O,-DIMETHYL PHOSPHORODITHIOATE	86-50-0	PST02210
S-311; O-2793	139-33-3	PST08305
S-343,S-342	7631-99-4	PST21400
S-4-CHLOROBENZYL DIETHYL(THIOCARBAMATE)	28249-77-6	PST72381
S-4-CHLOROBENZYL DIETHYLTHIOCARBAMATE	28249-77-6	PST72381
S-4-CHLOROPHENYLTHIOMETHYL O,O-DIETHYL PHOSPHORODITHIOATE	786-19-6	PST04340
S-4-CHLOROPHENYLTHIOMETHYL O,O-DIMETHYL PHOSPHORODITHIOATE	953-17-3	PST71647
S-4,6-DIAMINO-1,3,5-TRIAZIN-2-YLMETHYL O,O-DIMETHYL PHOSPORODITHIOATE	78-57-9	PST72980
S-5-ETHOXY-2,3-DIHYDRO-2-OXO-1,3,4-THIADIAZOL-3-YLMETHYL O,O-DIMETHYL PHOSPHORODITHIOATE	2669-32-1	PST73147
S-5-METHOXY-4-OXOPYRAN-2-YLMETHYL DIMETHYL PHOSPHOROTHIOATE	2778-04-3	PST73139
S-6-CHLORO-2,3-DIHYDRO-2-OXO-1,3-BENZOXAZOL-3-YLMETHYL O,O-DIETHYL PHOSPHORODITHIOATE	2310-17-0	PST25720
S-6-CHLORO-2,3-DIHYDRO-2-OXOBENZOXAZOL-3-YLMETHYL O,O-DIETHYL PHOSPHORODITHIOATE	2310-17-0	PST25720
S-657; S-660	64-02-8	PST23137
S,S-BIS(O,O-DIETHYL PHOSPHORODITHIOATE)	78-34-2	PST08050
S,S-DIPROPYL ETHYL PHOSPHORODITHIOLATE	13194-48-4	PST15080
S,S,S-TRIBUTYL PHOSPHOROTRITHIOATE	78-48-8	PST06300
S,S,S-TRIBUTYL PHOSPHOROTRITHIOITE	150-50-5	PST10010
S,S,S-TRIBUTYL TRITHIOPHOSPHATE	78-48-8	PST06300
S,S'-(1,4-DIOXANE-2,3-DIYL) O,O,O',O'-TETRAETHYL BIS(PHOSPHORODITHIOATE)	78-34-2	PST08050
S,S'-(2-(DIMETHYLAMINO)-1,3-PROPANEDIYL) DICARBANOTHIOATE HYDROCHLORIDE	15263-52-2	PST04359
S,S'-(2-DIMETHYLAMINOTRIMETHYLENE) BIS(THIOCARBAMATE) HYDROCHLORIDE	15263-52-2	PST04359
S,S'-METHYLENE BIS (O,O-DIETHYL PHOSPHORODITHIOATE)	563-12-2	PST08720
S,S'-METHYLENE O,O,O',O'-TETRAETHYL DI(PHOSPHORODITHIOATE)	563-12-2	PST08720
S,S'-PARA-DIOXANE-2,3-DIYL BIS(O,O-DIETHYL PHOSPHORODITHIOATE)	78-34-2	PST08050
S,S'-1,4-DIOXANE,2,3-DIYL BIS(O,O-DIETHYL PHOSPHORODITHIOATE)	78-34-2	PST08050

ALPHABETICAL INDEX

ALPHABETICAL INDEX

ALPHABETICAL INDEX

SUBSTANCE NAME	CAS #	PST #
SODIUM FLUOACETIC ACID	62-74-8	PST21240
SODIUM FLUOALUMINATE	15096-52-3	PST05560
SODIUM FLUORACETATE	62-74-8	PST21240
SODIUM FLUORIDE	7681-49-4	PST21230
SODIUM FLUORIDE(NAF)	7681-49-4	PST21230
SODIUM FLUORIDE, SOLID	7681-49-4	PST21230
SODIUM FLUOROACETATE	62-74-8	PST21240
SODIUM FLUOROSILICATE	16893-85-9	PST21620
SODIUM FLUOSILICATE	16893-85-9	PST21620
SODIUM GLYCOLATE	2836-32-0	PST11235
SODIUM HEXAFLUOROALUMINATE	15096-52-3	PST05560
SODIUM HEXAFLUOROSILICATE	16893-85-9	PST21620
SODIUM HEXAFLUOSILICATE	16893-85-9	PST21620
SODIUM HYDRATE	1310-73-2	PST21300
SODIUM HYDROGEN CARBONATE	144-55-8	PST20970
SODIUM HYDROGEN DIACETATE	126-96-5	PST71497
SODIUM HYDROGEN SULFATE	7681-38-1	PST20990
SODIUM HYDROGEN SULFITE	7631-90-5	PST21000
SODIUM HYDROSULFATE	7681-38-1	PST20990
SODIUM HYDROXIDE	1310-73-2	PST21300
SODIUM HYDROXIDE (NA(OH))	1310-73-2	PST21300
SODIUM HYDROXIDE, DRY	1310-73-2	PST21300
SODIUM HYDROXIDE, DRY SOLID, FLAKE, BEAD, OR GRANULAR	1310-73-2	PST21300
SODIUM HYDROXIDE, FLAKE	1310-73-2	PST21300
SODIUM HYDROXIDE, SOLID	1310-73-2	PST21300
SODIUM HYDROXYACETATE	2836-32-0	PST11235
SODIUM HYPOCHLORITE	7681-52-9	PST21310
SODIUM HYPOCHLORITE (NACLO)	7681-52-9	PST21310
SODIUM HYPOCHLORITE (NAOCL)	7681-52-9	PST21310
SODIUM HYPOCHLORITE SOLUTION	7681-52-9	PST21310
SODIUM HYPOCHLORITE, PHOSPHATE	56802-99-4	PST80117
SODIUM LAURYL SULFATE	151-21-3	PST08485
SODIUM LAURYL SULPHATE	151-21-3	PST08485
SODIUM LAURYLBENZENESULFONATE	25155-30-0	PST21220
SODIUM META-ARSENITE LIQUID (SOLUTION)	7784-46-5	PST52136
SODIUM METAARSENATE	7631-89-2	PST20940
SODIUM METAM	137-42-8	PST71430
SODIUM METASILICATE	6834-92-0	PST21373
SODIUM METASILICATE (NA2SIO3)	6834-92-0	PST21373
SODIUM METASILICATE, ANHYDROUS	6834-92-0	PST21373
SODIUM METHAM	137-42-8	PST71430
SODIUM METHYLCARBAMODITHIOATE	137-42-8	PST71430
SODIUM METHYLDITHIOCARBAMATE	137-42-8	PST71430
SODIUM MONOCHLORIDE	7647-14-5	PST21105
SODIUM MONODODECYL SULFATE	151-21-3	PST08485
SODIUM MONOFLUORIDE	7681-49-4	PST21230
SODIUM MONOFLUOROACETATE	62-74-8	PST21240
SODIUM MONOHYDROGEN PHOSPHATE	7558-79-4	PST08330
SODIUM MONOLAURYL SULFATE	151-21-3	PST08485
SODIUM MONOMETHYLDITHIOCARBAMATE	137-42-8	PST71430
SODIUM N-DODECYL SULFATE	151-21-3	PST08485
SODIUM N-METHYLDITHIOCARBAMATE	137-42-8	PST71430
SODIUM N-OCTANOATE	1984-06-1	PST72105
SODIUM N-1-NAPHTHYLPHTHALAMATE	132-67-2	PST71341

SUBSTANCE NAME	CAS #	PST #
SODIUM N-1-NAPHTHYLPHTHALAMIC ACID	132-67-2	PST71341
SODIUM N,N-DIMETHYLDITHIOCARBAMATE	128-04-1	PST71383
SODIUM NAPTALAM	132-67-2	PST71341
SODIUM NITER	7631-99-4	PST21400
SODIUM NITRATE	7631-99-4	PST21400
SODIUM NITRITE	7632-00-0	PST21410
SODIUM NPA	132-67-2	PST71341
SODIUM OCTANOATE	1984-06-1	PST72105
SODIUM OCTOATE	1984-06-1	PST72105
SODIUM OLEATE	143-19-1	PST21418
SODIUM OMADINE	15922-78-8	PST21420
SODIUM ORTHOARSENITE LIQUID	7784-46-5	PST52136
SODIUM PCP	131-52-2	PST08506
SODIUM PENTACHLOROPHENATE	131-52-2	PST08506
SODIUM PENTACHLOROPHENOL	131-52-2	PST08506
SODIUM PENTACHLOROPHENOLATE	131-52-2	PST08506
SODIUM PENTACHLOROPHENOXIDE	131-52-2	PST08506
SODIUM PETROLEUM SULFONIC ACIDS	68608-26-4	PST18339
SODIUM PHENATE	139-02-6	PST21530
SODIUM PHENOLATE	139-02-6	PST21530
SODIUM PHENOXIDE	139-02-6	PST21530
SODIUM PHENYLATE	139-02-6	PST21530
SODIUM PHOSPHATE	7558-79-4	PST08330
SODIUM PHOSPHATE	7558-80-7	PST15190
SODIUM PHOSPHATE	7758-29-4	PST21730
SODIUM PHOSPHATE	7601-54-9	PST24480
SODIUM PHOSPHATE (NA(H2PO4))	7558-80-7	PST15190
SODIUM PHOSPHATE (NA2HPO4)	7558-79-4	PST08330
SODIUM PHOSPHATE (NA3PO4)	7601-54-9	PST24480
SODIUM PHOSPHATE (NA4P207)	7722-88-5	PST23140
SODIUM PHOSPHATE (NA5P3010)	7758-29-4	PST21730
SODIUM PHOSPHATE, DIBASIC	7558-79-4	PST08330
SODIUM PHOSPHATE, MONOBASIC	7558-80-7	PST15190
SODIUM PHOSPHATE, TRIBASIC	7601-54-9	PST24480
SODIUM PHOSPHATTE	7722-88-5	PST23140
SODIUM POLYPHOSPHATE	7758-29-4	PST21730
SODIUM POLYPHOSPHATE (NA5P3010)	7758-29-4	PST21730
SODIUM PRIMARY PHOSPHATE	7558-80-7	PST15190
SODIUM PROPANOATE	137-40-6	PST21575
SODIUM PROPIONATE	137-40-6	PST21575
SODIUM PROPIONATE, ANHYDROUS	137-40-6	PST21575
SODIUM PYRIDINETHIONE	15922-78-8	PST21420
SODIUM PYRITHIONE	15922-78-8	PST21420
SODIUM PYROBORATE DECAHYDRATE	1303-96-4	PST21010
SODIUM PYROPHOSPHATE	7722-88-5	PST23140
SODIUM PYROPHOSPHATE (NA4P207)	7722-88-5	PST23140
SODIUM PYROSULFATE	7681-38-1	PST20990
SODIUM SALT OF CACODYLAC ACID	124-65-2	PST21070
SODIUM SALT OF CHLORAMBEN	1954-81-0	PST71256
SODIUM SILICATE	6834-92-0	PST21373
SODIUM SILICATE (NA2SIO3)	6834-92-0	PST21373
SODIUM SILICOFLUORIDE	16893-85-9	PST21620
SODIUM SILICON FLUORIDE	16893-85-9	PST21620
SODIUM SULFITE	7631-90-5	PST21000

ALPHABETICAL INDEX

SUBSTANCE NAME	CAS #	PST #
SODIUM SULFITE	7757-83-7	PST21660
SODIUM SULFITE, ANHYDROUS	7757-83-7	PST21660
SODIUM SULPHITE	7757-83-7	PST21660
SODIUM TCA	650-51-1	PST73307
SODIUM TETRABORATE DECAHYDRATE	1303-96-4	PST21010
SODIUM TRICHLOROACETATE	650-51-1	PST73307
SODIUM TRIPHOSPHATE	7758-29-4	PST21730
SODIUM TRIPHOSPHATE (NA5P3O10)	7758-29-4	PST21730
SODIUM TRIPOLYPHOSPHATE	7758-29-4	PST21730
SODIUM TRIPOLYPHOSPHATE (NA5P3O10)	7758-29-4	PST21730
SODIUM WARFARIN	129-06-6	PST83008
SODIUM XYLENE SULFONATE	1300-72-7	PST75603
SODIUM XYLENESULFONATE	1300-72-7	PST75603
SODIUM 2-((1-NAPHTHALENYLAMINO)CARBONYL)BENZOATE	132-67-2	PST71341
SODIUM 2-(2,4-DICHLOROPHENOXY)ETHYL SULFATE	136-78-7	PST05500
SODIUM 2,2-DICHLOROPROPIONATE	127-20-8	PST71239
SODIUM 2,2-DICHLOROPROPIONIC ACID	127-20-8	PST71239
SODIUM 2,3,6-TRICHLOROBENZOATE	2078-42-4	PST71136
SODIUM 2,3,6-TRICHLOROBENZOIC ACID	2078-42-4	PST71136
SODIUM 2,3:4,6-BIS-O-(1-METHYLETHYLIDENE)-A-L-XYOL -2-HEXULOFURANOSONATE	52508-35-7	PST72391
SODIUM 2,4-DICHLOROPHENOXYETHYL SULFATE	136-78-7	PST05500
SODIUM 2,4,5- TRICHLOROPHENOLATE	136-32-3	PST21713
SODIUM 2,4,5-TRICHLOROPHENATE	136-32-3	PST21713
SODIUM 2,4,5-TRICHLOROPHENOXIDE	136-32-3	PST21713
SODIUM 4,6-DINITRO-O-CRESYLATE	2312-76-7	PST71411
SODIUM 5-(2-CHLORO-4-(TRIFLUOROMETHYL)-PHENOXY)-2-NITROBENZOATE	62476-59-9	PST72453
SODIUM(+1) NITRATE	7631-99-4	PST21400
SODIUM(I) NITRATE	7631-99-4	PST21400
SODIUM(1-) ION	55635-13-7	PST72430
SODIUM-2-BIPHENOLATE	132-27-4	PST08500
SODIUM, ((4,6-DINITRO-O-TOLYL)OXY)-	2312-76-7	PST71411
SODIUM, (4-CYANO-2,6-DIIODOPHENOXY)-	2961-62-8	PST73074
SOK	671-04-5	PST02250
SOL 9050 XYLENE (CHEMTECH INDUSTRIES, INC.)	1330-20-7	PST25150
SOLAESTHIN	75-09-2	PST14930
SOLAN	2307-68-8	PST71164
SOLANE	2307-68-8	PST71164
SOLBROL M	99-76-3	PST14677
SOLBROL P	94-13-3	PST19941
SOLFRIL	7704-34-9	PST22280
SOLGARD	23505-41-1	PST72377
SOLICAM	27314-13-2	PST72343
SOLMETHINE	75-09-2	PST14930
SOLUDAL	144-55-8	PST20970
SOLVAN	82-66-6	PST08068
SOLVANOL	84-66-2	PST07210
SOLVENT, THINNER AND SCREEN WASH (NAZ-DAR CO.)	111-76-2	PST03540
SOLVESSO XYLENE (HUMBLE OIL AND REFINING COMPANY)	1330-20-7	PST25150
SOLVIREX	298-04-4	PST08380
SOLVO POWDER	65-85-0	PST02720
SOMIO	15879-93-3	PST00775
SONAC	7664-38-2	PST18690
SONACIDE	111-30-8	PST10423

ALPHABETICAL INDEX

SUBSTANCE NAME	CAS #	PST #
SONALAN	55283-68-6	PST72436
SONALEN	55283-68-6	PST72436
SOPRABEL	7784-40-9	PST12540
SORBIMACROGOL OLEATE 300	9005-65-6	PST40200
SORBITAN POLYETHOXY MONOLAURATE	9005-64-5	PST80107
SORBITAN, MONODODECANOTE, POLY(OXY-1,2-ETHANEDIYL) DERIVATIVES	9005-64-5	PST80107
SORBSIL	63231-67-4	PST20670
SORLATE	9005-65-6	PST40200
SOVINEXION	2104-96-3	PST71064
SOY BEAN OIL	8001-22-7	PST21765
SOY OIL	8001-22-7	PST21765
SOYA BEAN OIL	8001-22-7	PST21765
SOYBEAN OIL	8001-22-7	PST21765
SPANON MONOHYDROCHLORIDE	19750-95-9	PST71656
SPECTRACIDE	333-41-5	PST06540
SPERGON	118-75-2	PST72136
SPIKE	34014-18-1	PST72340
SPILL TAMER ABSORBENT (MALLINCKRODT)	7631-86-9	PST20610
SPIN-AID	13684-63-4	PST72282
SPIRIT OF CAMPHOR	76-22-2	PST04130
SPIRITS OF SALT	7647-01-0	PST11150
SPIRITS OF TURPENTINE	8006-64-2	PST24580
SPOLACID	133-07-3	PST10012
SPOR-KIL	62-38-4	PST18560
SPORTAK	67747-09-5	PST72648
SPOTTON (FORMULATION)	55-38-9	PST02550
SPRACAL	7778-44-1	PST03850
SPROUT-NIP	101-21-3	PST71148
SR 999	7440-22-4	PST20770
SRA 12869	25311-71-1	PST11985
ST-1000A CLEANER (STRESSCOAT)	71-55-6	PST14370
STA-FAST	93-72-1	PST20830
STABOND C-THINNER (STABOND CORP.)	78-93-3	PST14460
STANDAK	1646-88-4	PST72406
STANDARD WATER IN METHANOL	67-56-1	PST14280
STANNANE, (ACETYLOXY)TRIBUTYL-	56-36-0	PST72220
STANNANE, ACETOXYTRIBUTYL-	56-36-0	PST72220
STANNANE, TRIBUTYLCHLORO-	1461-22-9	PST72222
STANNANE, TRIBUTYLFLUORO-	1983-10-4	PST72227
STAR ANISE OIL	8007-70-3	PST71028
STARCH GUM	9004-53-9	PST06363
STAUFFER FERBAM	14484-64-1	PST09680
STAUFFER N 2790	944-22-9	PST10020
STAUFFER R 1303	786-19-6	PST04340
STAUFFER R 1492	953-17-3	PST71647
STAUFFER R 1504	732-11-6	PST11307
STAUFFER R 1571A	3735-33-9	PST18665
STAUFFER R 1608	759-94-4	PST71470
STAUFFER R 1910	2008-41-5	PST71474
STAUFFER R 2061	1114-71-2	PST71472
STCC 4904120	7782-50-5	PST04600
STCC 4904205	67-63-0	PST12090
STCC 4904230	67-56-1	PST14280
STCC 4904243	78-93-3	PST14460

SUBSTANCE NAME	CAS #	PST #
STCC 4921414	76-06-2	PST04830
STCC 4921442	UNASSIGNED	PST14681
STCC 4921443	298-00-0	PST14680
STCC 4921452	65-30-5	PST16460
STCC 4921469	56-38-2	PST18040
STCC 4921477	57-24-9	PST22080
STCC 4921480	3689-24-5	PST22470
STCC 4921486	107-49-3	PST22520
STCC 4921497	106-93-4	PST09380
STCC 4921505	56-72-4	PST05490
STCC 4921513	298-04-4	PST08380
STCC 4921522	115-29-7	PST08560
STCC 4921523	72-20-8	PST08600
STCC 4921525	1563-66-2	PST04240
STCC 4921528	86-50-0	PST02210
STCC 4921531	7786-34-7	PST18650
STCC 4921534	62-73-7	PST07000
STCC 4921542	315-18-4	PST15010
STCC 4921567	563-12-2	PST08720
STCC 4921670	117-26-0	PST71635
STCC 4923106	7778-39-4	PST01990
STCC 4923112	1303-28-2	PST02020
STCC 4923217	7778-44-1	PST03850
STCC 4923226	151-50-8	PST19350
STCC 4923228	143-33-9	PST21160
STCC 4923235	7784-40-9	PST12540
STCC 4923245	7487-94-7	PST13800
STCC 4923290	7631-89-2	PST20940
STCC 4923291	7784-46-5	PST52136
STCC 4923465	26628-22-8	PST20960
STCC 4923496	1314-84-7	PST25540
STCC 4930040	7664-93-9	PST22350
STCC 4930206	7738-94-5	PST04930
STCC 4930248	7664-38-2	PST18690
STCC 493115	1327-53-3	PST02070
STCC 4931303	64-19-7	PST00120
STCC 4931417	1319-77-3	PST05510
STCC 4931448	79-09-4	PST19750
STCC 4931470	76-03-9	PST23810
STCC 4935230	1310-58-3	PST19430
STCC 4935235	1310-73-2	PST21300
STCC 4935270	139-02-6	PST21530
STCC 4935520	545-55-1	PST22510
STCC 4935628	107-15-3	PST09560
STCC 4935630	13426-91-0	PST05710
STCC 4935665	141-43-5	PST08710
STCC 4940320	56-23-5	PST04310
STCC 4940355	127-18-4	PST22900
STCC 4940361	91-20-3	PST16120
STCC 4940370	72-54-8	PST06240
STCC 4940377	52-68-6	PST23790
STCC 4941122	63-25-2	PST04220
STCC 4941124	2921-88-2	PST04910
STCC 4941126	94-75-7	PST28510

ALPHABETICAL INDEX

ALPHABETICAL INDEX

ALPHABETICAL INDEX

ALPHABETICAL INDEX

SUBSTANCE NAME	CAS #	PST #
TAT	12789-03-6	PST71948
TATD	97-77-8	PST08370
TATTOO	22781-23-3	PST02560
TBPT	78-48-8	PST06300
TBTP	78-48-8	PST06300
TC 523 EPOXY DISSOLVER (TECHFORM)	75-09-2	PST14930
TCA	76-03-9	PST23810
TCA SODIUM	650-51-1	PST73307
TCB	50-31-7	PST71134
TCBA	50-31-7	PST71134
TCDBD	1746-01-6	PST08060
TCDD	1746-01-6	PST08060
TCG 7R	7440-22-4	PST20770
TCM	7673-09-8	PST80113
TCMTB	21564-17-0	PST71392
TCNB	117-18-0	PST71616
TCP	95-95-4	PST28700
TDE	72-54-8	PST06240
TDE-M,P'	4329-12-8	PST04752
TDEE	1022-22-6	PST06322
TEA	102-71-6	PST23932
TEAL OIL	8008-74-0	PST20575
TEBUTAM	35256-85-0	PST72852
TEBUTHIURON	34014-18-1	PST72340
TECNAZEN	117-18-0	PST71616
TECNAZENE	117-18-0	PST71616
TECSOL	64-17-5	PST08700
TEDP	3689-24-5	PST22470
TEEL OIL	8008-74-0	PST20575
TEG	112-27-6	PST24000
TEGOSEPT M	99-76-3	PST14677
TEGOSEPT P	94-13-3	PST19941
TEKRESOL	1319-77-3	PST05510
TEKTAMER 38	35691-65-7	PST26487
TELAR	64902-72-3	PST72504
TELODRIN	297-78-9	PST83032
TELOK	27314-13-2	PST72343
TELVAR	150-68-5	PST15196
TELVAR DIURON WEED KILLER	330-54-1	PST08420
TEMEFOS	3383-96-8	PST00020
TEMEPHOS	3383-96-8	PST00020
TEMEPHOS SULFOXIDE	17210-55-8	PST71651
TEMIK	116-06-3	PST00500
TEMIK SULFOXIDE	1646-87-3	PST00503
TENIATOL	97-23-4	PST71611
TENN-PLAS	65-85-0	PST02720
TENORAN	1982-47-4	PST04905
TENOX P GRAIN PRESERVATIVE	79-09-4	PST19750
TEPA	545-55-1	PST22510
TEPP	107-49-3	PST22520
TEPPEL'S OIL	8001-85-2	PST03250
TERAVIT	79-57-2	PST17414
TERBACIL	5902-51-2	PST71099
TERBUFOS	13071-79-9	PST22545

ALPHABETICAL INDEX

ALPHABETICAL INDEX

ALPHABETICAL INDEX

SUBSTANCE NAME	CAS #	PST #
THIOPHANATE-METHYL	23564-05-8	PST72308
THIOPHOS	56-38-2	PST18040
THIOPHOSPHORIC ACID 2-ISOPROPYL-4-METHYL-6-PYRIMIDYL DIETHYL ESTER	333-41-5	PST06540
THIOPYROPHOSPHORIC ACID (((HO)2PS)2O), TETRAETHYL ESTER	3689-24-5	PST22470
THIOPYROPHOSPHORIC ACID (((HO)2PS)2O), TETRAPROPYL ESTER	3244-90-4	PST72135
THIOPYROPHOSPHORIC ACID, TETRAETHYL ESTER	3689-24-5	PST22470
THIOSAN	137-26-8	PST23430
THIOSULFURIC ACID, DIAMMONIUM SALT	7783-18-8	PST01460
THIOTAX A	149-30-4	PST13738
THIOTAX ACCELERATOR	149-30-4	PST13738
THIOTEPP	3689-24-5	PST22470
THIOTOX	137-26-8	PST23430
THIOUREA, 1-NAPHTHALENYL-	86-88-4	PST01830
THIOVIT	7704-34-9	PST22280
THIOXAMYL	23135-22-0	PST17370
THIRAM	137-26-8	PST23430
THOMPSON-HAYWARD 6040	35367-38-5	PST07388
THYLOQUINONE	58-27-5	PST71050
THYME CAMPHOR	89-83-8	PST23475
THYMIC ACID	89-83-8	PST23475
THYMOL	89-83-8	PST23475
TIGUVON OXON	6552-12-1	PST02551
TIGUVON OXON SULFONE	14086-35-2	PST02552
TIGUVON OXON SULFOXIDE	6552-13-2	PST02553
TIL OIL	8008-74-0	PST20575
TILLAM	1114-71-2	PST71472
TIMET (FORMULATION)	298-02-2	PST18640
TIN TRIPHENYL ACETATE	900-95-8	PST24378
TIN, TRIBUTYLFLUORO-	1983-10-4	PST72227
TINESTAN	900-95-8	PST24378
TINTORANE	129-06-6	PST83008
TIOCABAZIL	36756-79-3	PST72405
TIRPATE	26419-73-8	PST73088
TKPP	7320-34-5	PST19546
TM 5	2058-46-0	PST84045
TMTD	137-26-8	PST23430
TOK	1836-75-5	PST23580
TOKUTHION	34643-46-4	PST72655
TOLILFLUANIDE	731-27-1	PST73030
TOLKAN	34123-59-6	PST12254
TOLUENE, ALPHA-(2-(2-BUTOXYETHOXY)ETHOXY)-4,5-(METHYLENEDIOXY)-2-PROPYL-	51-03-6	PST75640
TOLUENESULFONIC ACID	104-15-4	PST67915
TOLUREX	15545-48-9	PST04912
TOLYLFLUANID	731-27-1	PST73030
TOMARIN	117-52-2	PST05476
TOMILON	27954-37-6	PST23002
TONEXOL	136-47-0	PST72269
TOPANE	132-27-4	PST08500
TOPROSE	2540-82-1	PST10081
TOPSIN	23564-06-9	PST72322
TOPSIN M	23564-05-8	PST72308
TOPSIN METHYL	23564-05-8	PST72308
TOPUSYN	1014-69-3	PST06353

SUBSTANCE NAME	CAS #	PST #
TORAK	10311-84-9	PST23630
TORBIN	759-94-4	PST71470
TORDON	1918-02-1	PST18840
TORQUE	13356-08-6	PST24866
TORREFACTION DEXTRIN	9004-53-9	PST06363
TORSITE	90-43-7	PST18470
TOSIC ACID	104-15-4	PST67915
TOTAL	77182-82-2	PST72647
TOTRIL	3861-47-0	PST73075
TOXAKIL	8001-35-2	PST23640
TOXAPHEN	8001-35-2	PST23640
TOXAPHENE	8001-35-2	PST23640
TOXICHLOR	57-74-9	PST04560
TOXICHLOR	12789-03-6	PST71948
TOXYNIL	1689-83-4	PST11468
TOYODAN	34643-46-4	PST72655
TOYOTHION	34643-46-4	PST72655
TPTA	900-95-8	PST24378
TPTC	639-58-7	PST24380
TRALOMETHRIN	66841-25-6	PST72538
TRAMAT	26225-79-6	PST72404
TRANID	15271-41-7	PST73177
TRANS-(+)-ALLETHRIN	28434-00-6	PST71013
TRANS-(+)-2,2-DIMETHYL-3-(2-METHYLPROPENYL)-CYCLOPROPANECARBOXYLIC ACID ESTER WITH (+)-2-ALLYL-4-HYDROXY-3-METHYL-2-CYCLOPENTEN-1-ONE	28434-00-6	PST71013
TRANS-ALLETHRIN	584-79-2	PST00550
TRANS-CHLORDAN	5103-74-2	PST10331
TRANS-CHLORDANE	5103-74-2	PST10331
TRANS-GARDONA	22350-76-1	PST72245
TRANS-NONACHLOR	39765-80-5	PST23079
TRANS-PERMETHRIN	51877-74-8	PST23708
TRANS-2,2-DIMETHYL-3-(2-METHYL PROPENYL)CYCLOPROPANECARBOXYLIC ACID ESTER WITH 2-ALLYL-4-HYDROXY-3-METHYL-2-CYCLOPENTEN-1-ONE	UNASSIGNED	PST00554
TRAPEX	556-61-6	PST14950
TRAVEX	7775-09-9	PST21100
TREFANOCIDE	1582-09-8	PST24085
TREFLAN	1582-09-8	PST24085
TRENAMINE D 200	143-18-0	PST72131
TRENAMINE D 201	143-18-0	PST72131
TREVESPAN	1689-83-4	PST11468
TRI(HYDROXYETHYL)AMINE	102-71-6	PST23932
TRI-ALLATE	2303-17-5	PST72050
TRI-CLOR	76-06-2	PST04830
TRI-N-BUTYLSTANNYLFLUORIDE	1983-10-4	PST72227
TRI-N-BUTYLTIN ACETATE	56-36-0	PST72220
TRI-N-BUTYLTIN FLUORIDE	1983-10-4	PST72227
TRIAETHYLENPHOSPHORSAEUREAMID	545-55-1	PST22510
TRIALLATE	2303-17-5	PST72050
TRIAMIPHOS	1031-47-6	PST72937
TRIANGLE	7758-99-8	PST05690
TRIANTINE LIGHT BROWN	2650-18-2	PST08277
TRIAZIN	101-05-3	PST01526
TRIAZIRIDINOPHOSPHINE OXIDE	545-55-1	PST22510
TRIAZOFOS	24017-47-8	PST73068

SUBSTANCE NAME	CAS #	PST #
TRIAZOPHOS	24017-47-8	PST73068
TRIBAN	83-26-1	PST18970
TRIBASIC SODIUM ORTHOPHOSPHATE	7601-54-9	PST24480
TRIBASIC SODIUM PHOSPHATE	7601-54-9	PST24480
TRIBUFON	126-22-7	PST71399
TRIBUNIL	18691-97-9	PST14108
TRIBUTYL ESTER PHOSPHOROTRITHIOUS ACID	150-50-5	PST10010
TRIBUTYL PHOSPHOROTRITHIOITE	150-50-5	PST10010
TRIBUTYL TRITHIOPHOSPHITE	150-50-5	PST10010
TRIBUTYLACETOXYSTANNANE	56-36-0	PST72220
TRIBUTYLCHLOROSTANNANE	1461-22-9	PST72222
TRIBUTYLCHLOROTIN	1461-22-9	PST72222
TRIBUTYLFLUOROSTANNANE	1983-10-4	PST72227
TRIBUTYLFLUOROTIN	1983-10-4	PST72227
TRIBUTYLSTANNYL ACETATE	56-36-0	PST72220
TRIBUTYLTIN ACETATE	56-36-0	PST72220
TRIBUTYLTIN CHLORIDE	1461-22-9	PST72222
TRIBUTYLTIN FLUORIDE	1983-10-4	PST72227
TRICALCIUM ORTHO-ARSENATE	7778-44-1	PST03850
TRICHLORACETIC ACID	76-03-9	PST23810
TRICHLORFON	52-68-6	PST23790
TRICHLORMETAPHOS	299-84-3	PST20180
TRICHLORO-S-TRIAZINE-2,4,6(1H,3H,5H)-TRIONE	87-90-1	PST23860
TRICHLORO-S-TRIAZINETRIONE	87-90-1	PST23860
TRICHLOROACETIC ACID COMPOUND WITH N,N-DIMETHYL-N'-PHENYLUREA	4482-55-7	PST71389
TRICHLOROACETIC ACID COMPOUND WITH N'-(4-CHLOROPHENYL)-N,N-DIMETHYLUREA	140-41-0	PST15197
TRICHLOROACETIC ACID COMPOUND WITH N'-(4-CHLOROPHENYL)-N,N-DIMETHYL UREA(1:1)	140-41-0	PST15197
TRICHLOROACETIC ACID COMPOUND WITH 1,1-DIMETHYL-3-PHENYLUREA	4482-55-7	PST71389
TRICHLOROACETIC ACID COMPOUND WITH 3-(P-CHLOROPHENYL)-1,1-DIMETHYL UREA(1:1)	140-41-0	PST15197
TRICHLOROACETIC ACID COMPOUND WITH 3-(P-CHLOROPHENYL)-1,1-DIMETHYLUREA	140-41-0	PST15197
TRICHLOROACETIC ACID SODIUM SALT	650-51-1	PST73307
TRICHLOROACETIC ACID, SOLID	76-03-9	PST23810
TRICHLOROALUMINUM	7446-70-0	PST00900
TRICHLOROBENZOIC ACID	50-31-7	PST71134
TRICHLOROCYANURIC ACID	87-90-1	PST23860
TRICHLOROETHANE	71-55-6	PST14370
TRICHLOROETHANE 111 DEGREASE COLD/VAPOR (ASHLAND)	71-55-6	PST14370
TRICHLOROETHANOIC ACID	76-03-9	PST23810
TRICHLOROFLUOROCARBON	75-69-4	PST09990
TRICHLOROFLUOROMETHANE	75-69-4	PST09990
TRICHLOROISOCYANURIC ACID	87-90-1	PST23860
TRICHLOROMELAMINE	7673-09-8	PST80113
TRICHLOROMETAPHOS	299-84-3	PST20180
TRICHLOROMETHYL-CYCLOHEXENE DICARBOMIDE	133-06-2	PST04210
TRICHLOROMETHYLMETHANE	71-55-6	PST14370
TRICHLOROMONOFLUOROMETHANE	75-69-4	PST09990
TRICHLORONAT	327-98-0	PST00478
TRICHLORONATE	327-98-0	PST00478
TRICHLORONATE OXON	6492-18-8	PST23871
TRICHLORONATE OXYGEN ANALOG	6492-18-8	PST23871
TRICHLORONATOXON	6492-18-8	PST23871

ALPHABETICAL INDEX

ALPHABETICAL INDEX

SUBSTANCE NAME	CAS #	PST #
UN 1403	156-62-7	PST03930
UN 1452	10137-74-3	PST03890
UN 1471	13840-33-0	PST12920
UN 1486	7757-79-1	PST19470
UN 1490	7722-64-7	PST19520
UN 1493	7761-88-8	PST20810
UN 1495	7775-09-9	PST21100
UN 1496	7758-19-2	PST21110
UN 1498	7631-99-4	PST21400
UN 1500	7632-00-0	PST21410
UN 1545	57-06-7	PST00680
UN 1551	86-88-4	PST01830
UN 1553	7778-39-4	PST01990
UN 1557	2163-80-6	PST15180
UN 1559	1303-28-2	PST02020
UN 1561	1327-53-3	PST02070
UN 1572	75-60-5	PST03710
UN 1573	7778-44-1	PST03850
UN 1580	76-06-2	PST04830
UN 1591	95-50-1	PST16970
UN 1592	106-46-7	PST17640
UN 1593	75-09-2	PST14930
UN 1598	534-52-1	PST07910
UN 1604	107-15-3	PST09560
UN 1605	106-93-4	PST09380
UN 1617	7784-40-9	PST12540
UN 1624	7487-94-7	PST13800
UN 1654	54-11-5	PST16430
UN 1658	65-30-5	PST16460
UN 1663	100-02-7	PST17800
UN 1671	108-95-2	PST18380
UN 1674	62-38-4	PST18560
UN 1680	151-50-8	PST19350
UN 1685	7631-89-2	PST20940
UN 1686	7784-46-5	PST52136
UN 1687	26628-22-8	PST20960
UN 1688	124-65-2	PST21070
UN 1689	143-33-9	PST21160
UN 1690	7681-49-4	PST21230
UN 1692	57-24-9	PST22080
UN 1704	3689-24-5	PST22470
UN 1714	1314-84-7	PST25540
UN 1726	7446-70-0	PST00900
UN 1744	7726-95-6	PST03340
UN 1748	7778-54-3	PST03990
UN 1755	7738-94-5	PST04930
UN 1761	13426-91-0	PST05710
UN 1791	7681-52-9	PST21310
UN 1805	7664-38-2	PST18690
UN 1814	1310-58-3	PST19430
UN 1821	7681-38-1	PST20990
UN 1823	1310-73-2	PST21300
UN 1830	7664-93-9	PST22350
UN 1839	76-03-9	PST23810

ALPHABETICAL INDEX

SUBSTANCE NAME	CAS #	PST #
UREA, 3-(P-CHLOROPHENYL)-1,1-DIMETHYL-	150-68-5	PST15196
UREA, 3-(3-CHLORO-P-TOLYL)-1,1-DIMETHYL-	15545-48-9	PST04912
UREA, 3-(3-CHLORO-4-METHOXYPHENYL)-1,1-DIMETHYL-	19937-59-8	PST15009
UREA, 3-(3,4-DICHLOROPHENYL)-1-METHOXY-1-METHYL-	330-55-2	PST12826
UREA, 3-(3,4-DICHLOROPHENYL)-1,1-DIMETHYL-	330-54-1	PST08420
UREA, 3-(4-BROMO-3-CHLOROPHENYL)-1-METHOXY-1-METHYL-	13360-45-7	PST04552
UREA, 3-CYCLOOCTYL-1,1-DIMETHYL-	2163-69-1	PST05996
UREA, 3-P-CUMENYL-1,1-DIMETHYL-	34123-59-6	PST12254
UROX	140-41-0	PST15197
UROX B	314-40-9	PST03330
USR 604	117-80-6	PST06810
USTILAN	30043-49-3	PST72551
UZGEN	17804-35-2	PST02580
U052	1319-77-3	PST05510
U052	108-39-4	PST13080
U088	84-66-2	PST07210
U165	91-20-3	PST16120
U230	95-95-4	PST28700
U232	93-76-5	PST28690
V 9	7440-22-4	PST20770
VACOR	53558-25-1	PST72334
VAGIMID	443-48-1	PST72529
VALERANILIDE, 4'-CHLORO-2,2-DIMETHYL-	7287-36-7	PST72987
VALERONE	108-83-8	PST07500
VALEXON	14816-18-3	PST73292
VALONE	83-28-3	PST24738
VAMIDOATE	2275-23-2	PST73108
VAMIDOTHION	2275-23-2	PST73108
VAMPIROL	60-41-3	PST22090
VAN DYKE 264	113-48-4	PST15955
VANALATE	1929-77-7	PST71473
VANZOATE	120-51-4	PST02805
VAPAM	137-42-8	PST71430
VAPONA	62-73-7	PST07000
VAPOTONE	107-49-3	PST22520
VARFINE	129-06-6	PST83008
VARITOX	650-51-1	PST73307
VC 13	97-17-6	PST06805
VC 9-104	13194-48-4	PST15080
VCS 438	20354-26-1	PST72344
VCS 506	21609-90-5	PST12780
VEGADEX	95-06-7	PST22190
VEGADEX SUPER	95-06-7	PST22190
VEGETOX	15263-52-2	PST04359
VEGIBEN	133-90-4	PST29084
VEL 3973	53780-34-0	PST72444
VELPAR	51235-04-2	PST10994
VELSICOL COMPOUND R	1918-00-9	PST02260
VELSICOL 104	76-44-8	PST10660
VELSICOL 506	21609-90-5	PST12780
VELSICOL 53-CS-17	1024-57-3	PST10670
VELSICOL 58-CS-11	1918-00-9	PST02260
VELTIN	640-15-3	PST83056
VENDEX	13356-08-6	PST24866

ALPHABETICAL INDEX

SUBSTANCE NAME	CAS #	PST #
VORANOL P	25322-69-4	PST19140
VP 19-40	900-95-8	PST24378
VPM	137-42-8	PST71430
VULKACIT	155-04-4	PST27776
VULKLOR	118-75-2	PST72136
VX	50782-69-9	PST83104
VYDATE	23135-22-0	PST17370
W.A.R.F. 42	81-81-2	PST25090
WARAN	129-06-6	PST83008
WARBEX	52-85-7	PST09675
WARF COMPOUND 42	81-81-2	PST25090
WARFARIN	81-81-2	PST25090
WARFARIN SODIUM	129-06-6	PST83008
WARFARIN SODIUM SALT	129-06-6	PST83008
WARFILONE SODIUM SALT	129-06-6	PST83008
WARKEELATE PS-42	64-02-8	PST23137
WASH OIL	8001-58-9	PST05230
WATER BLUE 9	2650-18-2	PST08277
WATER GLASS	6834-92-0	PST21373
WBA 8119	56073-10-0	PST03327
WC-PERFECT	7681-38-1	PST20990
WC-REINIGER	7664-38-2	PST18690
WC-SUPER	7681-38-1	PST20990
WEED-B-GON	93-72-1	PST20830
WEEDAZOL	61-82-5	PST01040
WEPSYN	1031-47-6	PST72937
WHI-PRO	137-40-6	PST21575
WHIP	66441-23-4	PST72723
WHITE ARSENIC	1327-53-3	PST02070
WHITE CAMPHOR OIL	8008-51-3	PST04140
WHITE CAUSTIC	1310-73-2	PST21300
WHITE CYANIDE	143-33-9	PST21160
WHITE OLEIC ACID	112-80-1	PST17305
WHITE PHOSPHORIC ACID	7664-38-2	PST18690
WHITE PHOSPHOROUS	7723-14-0	PST18800
WHITE PHOSPHORUS	7723-14-0	PST18800
WHITE TAR	91-20-3	PST16120
WHITE VITRIOL	7733-02-0	PST25570
WHITE ZINC	1314-13-2	PST25490
WHITMIRE PT 250	UNASSIGNED	PST25105
WITTOX C	1338-02-9	PST05460
WL 19805	21725-46-2	PST05762
WL 5792	1918-13-4	PST73046
WL 85871	67375-30-8	PST06118
WOOD ALCOHOL	67-56-1	PST14280
WOOD CREOSOTE	8021-39-4	PST71221
WOOD NAPHTHA	67-56-1	PST14280
WOOD SPIRIT	67-56-1	PST14280
WOOL FAT	8006-54-0	PST12425
WOOL WAX ALCOHOLS, ETHOXYLATED	61790-81-6	PST08741
WOOL YELLOW	1934-21-0	PST22465
WP	7723-14-0	PST18800
WP 155	1031-47-6	PST72937
WS 24	9003-01-4	PST04349

SUBSTANCE NAME	CAS #	PST #
XA 208	7440-22-4	PST20770
XEROX FILM REMOVER (UNION CARBIDE)	67-63-0	PST12090
XMC	2655-14-3	PST25171
XMC (PESTICIDE)	2655-14-3	PST25171
XPA	9003-01-4	PST04349
XYLENE	1330-20-7	PST25150
XYLENE BLUE VSG	2650-18-2	PST08277
XYLENESULFONIC ACID, SODIUM SALT	1300-72-7	PST75603
XYLENOL	1300-71-6	PST25160
XYLENOL	105-67-9	PST28670
XYLENOL (MIXED ISOMERS)	1300-71-6	PST25160
XYLOL	1330-20-7	PST25150
YALAN	2212-67-1	PST71471
YANOCK	640-19-7	PST09930
YARMOR	8002-09-3	PST18900
YELLOW CUPROCIDE	1317-39-1	PST05470
YELLOW LAKE 69	1934-21-0	PST22465
YELLOW PHOSPHOROUS	7723-14-0	PST18800
YELLOW PHOSPHORUS	7723-14-0	PST18800
YULAN	2212-67-1	PST71471
Z-31	7646-85-7	PST25350
Z-33	7646-85-7	PST25350
Z-68	297-97-2	PST25590
Z-70	297-97-2	PST25590
Z-76	297-97-2	PST25590
Z-83	1314-23-4	PST25635
ZEAZIN	1912-24-9	PST02150
ZECTANE	315-18-4	PST15010
ZECTRAN	315-18-4	PST15010
ZEPHIRAN CHLORIDE	8001-54-5	PST00537
ZEPHIRAN CHLORIDE	8001-54-5	PST00539
ZEPHIROL	8001-54-5	PST00539
ZERLATE	137-30-4	PST25397
ZETAX	155-04-4	PST27776
ZEXTRAN	315-18-4	PST15010
ZIMATE	137-30-4	PST25397
ZIMTALDEHYDE	104-55-2	PST05100
ZINC AMMONIATE ETHYLENEBIS(DITHIOCARBAMATE)-POLY(ETHYLENETHIURAM DISULPHIDE)	9006-42-2	PST71123
ZINC AMMONIATE ETHYLENEBIS(DITHIOCARBAMATE)-POLY(ETHYLENETHIURAM DISULFIDE)	9006-42-2	PST71123
ZINC BENZOTHIAZOL-2-YLTHIOLATE	155-04-4	PST27776
ZINC BIS(DIMETHYLDITHIOCARBAMATE)	137-30-4	PST25397
ZINC BUTTER	7646-85-7	PST25350
ZINC CHLORIDE	7646-85-7	PST25350
ZINC CHLORIDE, SOLID	7646-85-7	PST25350
ZINC DICHLORIDE	7646-85-7	PST25350
ZINC DIMETHYLDITHIOCARBAMATE	137-30-4	PST25397
ZINC FLUOROSILICATE	16871-71-9	PST25410
ZINC FLUOSILICATE	16871-71-9	PST25410
ZINC GELATIN	1314-13-2	PST25490
ZINC HEXAFLUOROSILICATE	16871-71-9	PST25410
ZINC HEXAFLUOROSILICATE(2-)	16871-71-9	PST25410
ZINC MONOXIDE	1314-13-2	PST25490

SUBSTANCE NAME	CAS #	PST #
ZINC OXIDE	1314-13-2	PST25490
ZINC PHOSPHIDE	1314-84-7	PST25540
ZINC SILICOFLUORIDE	16871-71-9	PST25410
ZINC SULFATE	7733-02-0	PST25570
ZINC SULFATE (ZNSO4)	7733-02-0	PST25570
ZINC SULFATE (1:1)	7733-02-0	PST25570
ZINC SULPHATE	7733-02-0	PST25570
ZINC VITRIOL	7733-02-0	PST25570
ZINC WHITE	1314-13-2	PST25490
ZINC-TOX	1314-84-7	PST25540
ZINC, BIS(DIMETHYLCARBAMODITHIOATO-S,S')-,(T-4)	137-30-4	PST25397
ZINC, BIS(DIMETHYLDITHIOCARBAMATO)-	137-30-4	PST25397
ZINCOID	1314-13-2	PST25490
ZINCOMED	7733-02-0	PST25570
ZINKOSITE	7733-02-0	PST25570
ZINOCHLOR	101-05-3	PST01526
ZINOPHOS	297-97-2	PST25590
ZINPOL	9003-01-4	PST04349
ZIRAM	137-30-4	PST25397
ZIRBEADS	1314-23-4	PST25635
ZIRBERK	137-30-4	PST25397
ZIRCONIA	1314-23-4	PST25635
ZIRCONIC ANHYDRIDE	1314-23-4	PST25635
ZIRCONIUM DIOXIDE	1314-23-4	PST25635
ZIRCONIUM OXIDE	1314-23-4	PST25635
ZIRCONIUM WHITE	1314-23-4	PST25635
ZIRCONIUM(IV) OXIDE	1314-23-4	PST25635
ZIRCONOTRAST	1314-23-4	PST25635
ZMBT	155-04-4	PST27776
ZNBT	155-04-4	PST27776
ZNO	1314-13-2	PST25490
ZOECON RF 226 AEROSOL	UNASSIGNED	PST10348
ZOLONE	2310-17-0	PST25720
ZOOCOUMARIN	81-81-2	PST25090
ZORIAL	27314-13-2	PST72343
ZOTOX	7778-39-4	PST01990
ZYMAFLUOR	7681-49-4	PST21230
ZYNOPHOS	297-97-2	PST25590
ZYTOX	74-83-9	PST14300
ZYTRON	299-85-4	PST71236
0-63	8001-29-4	PST05475
1- ACETAMIDO-4-ETHOXYBENZENE	62-44-2	PST18340
1-((DIMETHYLAMINO)CARBONYL)-5-METHYL-1H-PYRAZOL-3-YL DIMETHYLCARBAMATE	644-64-4	PST83057
1-(BETA-ETHYLOL)-2-METHYL-5-NITRO-3-AZAPYRROLE	443-48-1	PST72529
1-(BETA-HYDROXYETHYL)-2-METHYL-5-NITROIMIDAZOLE	443-48-1	PST72529
1-(BUTYLCARBAMOYL)-2-BENZIMIDAZOLECARBAMIC ACID METHYL ESTER	17804-35-2	PST02580
1-(N-PROPYL.N-(2-(2,4,6-(TRICHLOROPHENOXY)ETHYL)CARBAMOYL)IMIDAZOLE	67747-09-5	PST72648
1-(1-NAPHTHYL)-2-THIOUREA	86-88-4	PST01830
1-(1-NAPHTHYL)THIOUREA	86-88-4	PST01830
1-(1,3-BENZOTHIAZOL-2-YL)-3-METHYLUREA	1929-88-0	PST72971
1-(2-BENZOTHIAZOLYL)-1,3-DIMETHYLUREA	18691-97-9	PST14108
1-(2-BENZOTHIAZOLYL)-3-METHYLUREA	1929-88-0	PST72971
1-(2-CHLOROPHENYLSULFONYL)-3-(4-METHOXY-6-METHYL-1,3,5-TRIAZIN-2-YL)-UREA	64902-72-3	PST72504

ALPHABETICAL INDEX

ALPHABETICAL INDEX

SUBSTANCE NAME	CAS #	PST #
1,2-BENZENEDICARBOXYLIC ACID, DIOCTYL ESTER	117-84-0	PST08040
1,2-BENZENEDICARBOXYLIC ACID, DIPHENYL ESTER	84-62-8	PST08095
1,2-BENZENEDIOL	120-80-9	PST04360
1,2-BICHLOROETHANE	107-06-2	PST09390
1,2-BIS(3-ETHOXYCARBONYL-2-THIOUREIDO)BENZENE	23564-06-9	PST72322
1,2-BIS(3-METHOXYCARBONYL-2-THIOUREIDO)BENZENE	23564-05-8	PST72308
1,2-DI(3-ETHOXYCARBONYL-2-THIOUREIDO)BENZENE	23564-06-9	PST72322
1,2-DI(3-METHOXYCARBONYL-2-THIOUREIDO)BENZENE	23564-05-8	PST72308
1,2-DI-(3-METHOXYCARBONYL-2-THIOUREIDO)BENZENE	23564-05-8	PST72308
1,2-DIAMINOETHANE	107-15-3	PST09560
1,2-DIBROMO-2,2-DICHLOROETHYL DIMETHYL PHOSPHATE	300-76-5	PST06660
1,2-DIBROMO-2,4-DICYANOBUTANE	35691-65-7	PST26487
1,2-DIBROMO-3-CHLOROPROPANE	96-12-8	PST26490
1,2-DIBROMOETHANE	106-93-4	PST09380
1,2-DICARBOXY 3,6-ENDOXOCYCLOHEXANE	145-73-3	PST08580
1,2-DICHLORETHANE	107-06-2	PST09390
1,2-DICHLOROBENZENE	95-50-1	PST16970
1,2-DICHLOROETHANE	107-06-2	PST09390
1,2-DICHLOROPROPANE	78-87-5	PST19860
1,2-DIHYDRO-3,6-PYRIDAZINEDIONE	123-33-1	PST13570
1,2-DIHYDRO-6-ETHOXY-2,2,4-TRIMETHYLQUINOLINE	91-53-2	PST08740
1,2-DIHYDROXYBENZENE	120-80-9	PST04360
1,2-DIHYDROXYETHANE	107-21-1	PST09400
1,2-DIHYDROXYPROPANE	57-55-6	PST19870
1,2-DIMETHYL-3,5-DIPHENYL-1H-PYRAZOLIUM	49866-87-7	PST72349
1,2-DIMETHYL-3,5-DIPHENYL-1H-PYRAZOLIUM METHYL SULFATE	43222-48-6	PST72348
1,2-DIMETHYL-3,5-DIPHENYLPYRAZOLIUM ION	49866-87-7	PST72349
1,2-DIMETHYL-3,5-DIPHENYLPYRAZOLIUM METHYL SULFATE	43222-48-6	PST72348
1,2-EPOXYETHANE	75-21-8	PST09520
1,2-EPOXYPROPANE	75-56-9	PST19910
1,2-EPOXYPROPANE POLYMER	25322-69-4	PST19140
1,2-ETHANEDIAMINE	107-15-3	PST09560
1,2-ETHANEDIOL	107-21-1	PST09400
1,2-ETHANEDIYLBISCARBAMODITHIOIC ACID DISODIUM SALT	142-59-6	PST16080
1,2-ETHYLENE DIBROMIDE	106-93-4	PST09380
1,2-ETHYLENEDIAMINE	107-15-3	PST09560
1,2-PROPANEDIOL	57-55-6	PST19870
1,2-PROPYLENE GLYCOL	57-55-6	PST19870
1,2-PROPYLENE OXIDE	75-56-9	PST19910
1,2,12,12A ALPHA-TETRAHYDRO-2A ALPHA-ISOPROPENYL-8,9-DIMETHOXY(1) BENZOPYRANOL(3,4-B)FURO(2,3-H(1)BENZOPYRAN-6(6A ALPHA H)-ONE	83-79-4	PST20200
1,2,12,12A-TETRAHYDRO-8,9-DIMETHOXY-2-(1-METHYLETHENYL)-(1) BENZOPYRANO(3,4-B)FURO(2,3-H(1)-BENZOPYRAN-6(6AH)-ONE	83-79-4	PST20200
1,2,3-PROPANETRICARBOXYLIC ACID, 2-HYDROXY-	77-92-9	PST05200
1,2,3-PROPANETRICARBOXYLIC ACID, 2-HYDROXY-, COPPER SALT	10402-15-0	PST71496
1,2,3-PROPANETRIOL	56-81-5	PST10440
1,2,3-TRIHYDROXYPROPANE	56-81-5	PST10440
1,2,3,4,10,10-HEXACHLORO-1,4,4A,5,8,8A-HEXAHYDRO-EXO-1,4-ENDO-5,8 DIMETHANONAPHTHALENE	309-00-2	PST00520
1,2,3,4,10,10-HEXACHLORO-1,4,4A,5,8,8A-HEXAHYDRO-1,4-ENDO,ENDO-5,8 -DIMETHANONAPHTHALENE	465-73-6	PST11810
1,2,3,4,10,10-HEXACHLORO-1,4,4A,5,8,8A-HEXAHYDRO-1,4,:5,8 -DIMETHANONAPHTHALENE	309-00-2	PST00520
1,2,3,4,10,10-HEXACHLORO-1,4,4A,5,8,8A-HEXAHYDRO-1,4:5,8	465-73-6	PST11810

SUBSTANCE NAME	CAS #	PST #
-DIMETHANONAPHTHALENE		
1,2,3,4,10,10-HEXACHLORO-6,7-EPOXY-1,4,4A,5,6,7,8,8A-OCTAHYDRO-ENDO -1,4-EXO-5,8-DIMETHANONAPHTHALENE	60-57-1	PST07080
1,2,3,4,10,10-HEXACHLORO-6,7-EPOXY-1,4,4A,5,6,7,8,8A-OCTAHYDRO-ENDO ENDO-1,4:5,8-DIMETHANONAPHTHALENE	72-20-8	PST08600
1,2,3,4,10,10-HEXACHLORO-6,7-EPOXY-1,4,4A,5,6,7,8,8A-OCTAHYDRO-1, 4-ENDO-EXO-5,8-DIMETHANONAPHTHALENE	60-57-1	PST07080
1,2,3,4,5,6-HEXACHLOROCYCLOHEXANE	319-84-6	PST00770
1,2,3,4,5,6-HEXACHLOROCYCLOHEXANE	608-73-1	PST03080
1,2,3,4,5,6-HEXACHLOROCYCLOHEXANE	319-86-8	PST06310
1,2,3,4,5,6-HEXACHLOROCYCLOHEXANE	58-89-9	PST12810
1,2,3,4,5,6,-HEXACHLOROCYCLOHEXANE	319-85-7	PST03010
1,2,3,4,7,7-HEXACHLORO-5,6-BIS(CHLOROMETHYL)-BICYCLO(2.2.1)HEPT-2-ENE	2550-75-6	PST73193
1,2,3,4,7,7-HEXACHLORO-5,6-BIS(CHLOROMETHYL)-2-NORBORNENE	2550-75-6	PST73193
1,2,3,4,7,7-HEXACHLORO-5,6-BIS(CHLOROMETHYL)-8,9,10-TRINORBORN-2-ENE	2550-75-6	PST73193
1,2,3,4,7,7-HEXACHLORO-5,6-BIS-(CHLOROMETHYL)-2-NORBON-ENE	2550-75-6	PST73193
1,2,3,4,7,7-HEXACHLOROBICYCLO(2.2.1)-2-HEPTENE-5,6-BISOXYMETHYLENE SULFITE	115-29-7	PST08560
1,2,4-OXADIAZOLIDINE-3,5-DIONE, 2-(3,4-DICHLOROPHENYL)-4-METHYL-	20354-26-1	PST72344
1,2,4-TRIAZIN-5(4H)-ONE, 4-AMINO-6-(1,1-DIMETHYLETHYL)-3-(ETHYLTHIO)-	64529-56-2	PST09111
1,2,4-TRIAZIN-5(4H)-ONE, 4-AMINO-6-(1,1-DIMETHYLETHYL)-3-(METHYLTHIO)-	21087-64-9	PST15006
1,2,4-TRIAZIN-5(4H)-ONE, 6-(1,1-DIMETHYLETHYL)-4-((2-METHYLPROPYLIDENE)AMINO)-3-(METHYLTHIO)-	57052-04-7	PST11844
1,2,4-TRIAZINE-5-(4H)-ONE, 4-AMINO-3-METHYL-6-PHENYL-	41394-05-2	PST14095
1,2,4,5-TETRACHLORO-3-NITRO-BENZENE	117-18-0	PST71616
1,2,4,5,6,7,8,8-OCTACHLORO-2,3,3A,4,7,7A-HEXAHYDRO-4,7-METHANO-1H -INDENE	57-74-9	PST04560
1,2,4,5,6,7,8,8-OCTACHLORO-2,3,3A,4,7,7A-HEXAHYDRO-4,7-METHANO-1H -INDENE	12789-03-6	PST71948
1,2,4,5,6,7,8,8-OCTACHLORO-2,3,3A,4,7,7A-HEXAHYDRO-4,7-METHANOINDENE	57-74-9	PST04560
1,2,4,5,6,7,8,8-OCTACHLORO-3A,4,7,7A-TETRAHYDRO-4,7-METHANOINDAN	57-74-9	PST04560
1,2,4,5,6,7,8,8-OCTACHLORO-3A,4,7,7A-TETRAHYDRO-4,7-METHANOINDAN	12789-03-6	PST71948
1,2,4,5,6,7,8,8-OCTACHLORO-3A,4,7,7A-TETRAHYDRO-4,7-METHANOINDANE	57-74-9	PST04560
1,2,4,5,6,7,8,8-OCTACHLORO-4,7-METHANE-3A,4,7,7A-TETRAHYDROINDANE	57-74-9	PST04560
1,3-BENZENEDICARBONITRILE, 2,4,5,6-TETRACHLORO-	1897-45-6	PST04890
1,3-BENZODIOXOL-4-OL, 2,2-DIMETHYL-, METHYLCARBAMATE	22781-23-3	PST02560
1,3-BENZODIOXOLE, 5-((2-(2-BUTOXYETHOXY)ETHOXY)METHYL)-6-PROPYL-	51-03-6	PST75640
1,3-BENZODIOXOLE, 5-(BIS(2-(2-BUTOXYETHOXY)ETHOXY)METHYL)-	5281-13-0	PST71828
1,3-BIS(CARBAMOYLTHIO)-2-(N,N-DIMETHYLAMINO)PROPANE HYDROCHLORIDE	15263-52-2	PST04359
1,3-BIS(2,2,2-TRICHLORO-1-HYDROXYETHYL)UREA	116-52-9	PST06817
1,3-BUTANEDIOL	107-88-0	PST26730
1,3-BUTYLENE GLYCOL	107-88-0	PST26730
1,3-D	542-75-6	PST26820
1,3-DI(CARBAMOYLTHIO)-2-DIMETHYLAMINOPROPANE-HYDROCHLORIDE	15263-52-2	PST04359
1,3-DICHLORO-S-TRIAZINE-2,4,6(1H,3H,5H)-TRIONE POTASSIUM SALT	2244-21-5	PST19360
1,3-DICHLORO-S-TRIAZINE-2,4,6,(1H,3H,5H) -TRIONE	2782-57-2	PST06975
1,3-DICHLORO-1-PROPENE	542-75-6	PST26820
1,3-DICHLORO-1,3,5-TRIAZINE-2,4,6(1H,3H,5H)-TRIONE POTASSIUM SALT	2244-21-5	PST19360
1,3-DICHLORO-5,5-DIMETHYL-2-IMIDAZOLIDINEDIONE	118-52-5	PST26800
1,3-DICHLORO-5,5-DIMETHYLHYDANTOIN	118-52-5	PST26800
1,3-DICHLORO-5,5-METHYLHYDANTOIN	118-52-5	PST26800
1,3-DICHLOROPROPENE	542-75-6	PST26820
1,3-DICHLOROPROPYLENE	542-75-6	PST26820
1,3-DICYANOTETRACHLOROBENZENE	1897-45-6	PST04890

ALPHABETICAL INDEX

ALPHABETICAL INDEX

SUBSTANCE NAME	CAS #	PST #
2-((1-NAPHTHALENYLAMINO)CARBONYL)BENZOIC ACID	132-66-1	PST71340
2-((1-NAPHTHALENYLAMINO)CARBONYL)BENZOIC ACID MONOSODIUM SALT	132-67-2	PST71341
2-((1,2-DIMETHYLPROPYL)AMINO)-4-(ETHYLAMINO)-6-(METHYLTHIO)-S-TRIAZINE	22936-75-0	PST72145
2-((4-CHLORO-6-(CYCLOPROPYLAMINO)-S-TRIAZIN-2-YL)AMINO)-2-METHYL PROPIONITRILE	32889-48-8	PST72398
2-((4-CHLORO-6-(CYCLOPROPYLAMINO)-1,3,5-TRIAZIN-2-YL)AMINO)-2-METHYL PROPANENITRILE	32889-48-8	PST72398
2-((4-CHLORO-6-(ETHYLAMINO)-S-TRIAZIN-2-YL))AMINO)-2-METHYLPROPIONITRILE	21725-46-2	PST05762
2-((4-CHLORO-6-(ETHYLAMINO)-S-TRIAZIN-2-YL)AMINO-2-METHYLPROPIONITRILE	21725-46-2	PST05762
2-((4-CHLORO-6-(ETHYLAMINO)-1,3,5-TRIAZIN-2-YL)AMINO)-2-METHYLPROPANENITRILE	21725-46-2	PST05762
2-((4-CHLOROPHENYL)PHENYLACETYL)-1H-INDENE-1,3(2H)-DIONE	3691-35-8	PST04826
2-(ALPHA-NAPHTHOXY)-N,N-DIETHYLPROPIONAMIDE	15299-99-7	PST72319
2-(DIETHOXYPHOSPHINOTHIOYLOXYIMINO)-2-PHENYLACETONITRILE	14816-18-3	PST73292
2-(DIETHOXYPHOSPHINYLIMINO)-1,3-DIETHIETANE	21548-32-3	PST16141
2-(DIETHOXYPHOSPHINYLIMINO)-1,3-DITHIOLAN	947-02-4	PST06115
2-(DIETHOXYPHOSPHINYLIMINO)-1,3-DITHIOLANE	947-02-4	PST06115
2-(DIETHOXYPHOSPHINYLIMINO)-4-METHYL-1,3-DITHIOLANE	950-10-7	PST13735
2-(DIMETHYLAMINO)-N-(((METHYLAMINO)CARBONYL)OXYL)-2 -OXOETHANIMIDOTHIOIC ACID METHYL ESTER	23135-22-0	PST17370
2-(DIMETHYLAMINO)-5,6-DIMETHYL-4-PYRIMIDINYL DIMETHYLCARBAMATE	23103-98-2	PST72345
2-(DIMETHYLAMINO)ETHYL-P-(BUTYLAMINO) BENZOATE MONOHYDROCHLORIDE	136-47-0	PST72269
2-(DIPHENYLACETYL)-1,3-INDANDIONE	82-66-6	PST08068
2-(DIPHENYLACETYL)-1H-INDEND-1,3(2H)-DIONE	82-66-6	PST08068
2-(ETHYLAMINO)-4-(ISOPROPYLAMINO)-6-(METHYLTHIO)-S-TRIAZINE	834-12-8	PST01006
2-(ETHYLAMINO)-4-(ISOPROPYLAMINO)-6-METHOXY-S-TRIAZINE	1610-17-9	PST02148
2-(ETHYLTHIO)-4,6-BIS(ISOPROPYLAMINO)-S-TRIAZINE	4147-51-7	PST72333
2-(ETHYLTHIO)-4,6-BIS(ISOPROPYLAMINO)-1,3,5-TRIAZINE	4147-51-7	PST72333
2-(HYDROXYMETHYL)-2-NITRO-1,3-PROPANEDIOL	126-11-4	PST24430
2-(ISOPROPYLAMINO)-4-((3-METHOXYPROPYL)AMINO)-6-(METHYLTHIO) -S-TRIAZINE	841-06-5	PST14204
2-(ISOPROPYLAMINO)-4-(METHYLAMINO)-6-(METHYLTHIO)-S-TRIAZINE	1014-69-3	PST06353
2-(M-CHLOROPHENYL) 2-(P-CHLOROPHENYL-1,1-DICHLOROETHANE	4329-12-8	PST04752
2-(METHOXYCARBONYL)PHENOL	119-36-8	PST14720
2-(P-SULFANILAMIDO)QUINOZALINE	59-40-5	PST72046
2-(P-TERT-BUTYLPHENOXY)CYCLOHEXYL 2-PROPYNYL SULFITE	2312-35-8	PST19720
2-(P-TERT-BUTYLPHENOXY)ISOPROPYL 2-CHLOROETHYL SULPHITE	140-57-8	PST01850
2-(SEC-BUTYLAMINO)-4-(ETHYLAMINO)-6-METHOXY-S-TRIAZINE	26259-45-0	PST73051
2-(SULFANILYLAMINO)THIAZOLE	72-14-0	PST72047
2-(TERT-BUTYLAMINO)-4-(ETHYLAMINO)-6-(METHYLTHIO)-S-TRIAZINE	886-50-0	PST22538
2-(TERT-BUTYLAMINO)-4-(ETHYLAMINO)-6-METHOXY-S-TRIAZINE	33693-04-8	PST72770
2-(TERT-BUTYLAMINO)-4-CHLORO-6-(ETHYLAMINO)-S-TRIAZINE	5915-41-3	PST22536
2-(THIOCYANOMETHYLTHIO)BENZOTHIAZOLE	21564-17-0	PST71392
2-(1-(ETHOXYAMINO)BUTYLIDENE)-5-(2-(ETHYLTHIO)PROPYL)-1,3-CYCLOHEXANEDIONE	74051-80-2	PST20577
2-(1-(ETHXOYIMINOBUTYL)-5-(2-(ETHYLTHIO)PROPYL)-3-HYDROXY-2-CYCLOHEXENE-1-ONE	74051-80-2	PST20577
2-(1-METHYLETHOXY)PHENOL METHYLCARBAMATE	114-26-1	PST02540
2-(1-METHYLETHOXY)PHENYL METHYLCARBAMATE	114-26-1	PST02540
2-(1-METHYLETHYL)PHENOL METHYLCARBAMATE	2631-40-5	PST73231
2-(1-METHYLETHYL)PHENYL METHYLCARBAMATE	2631-40-5	PST73231
2-(1-METHYLPROPYL)-4,6-DINITROPHENOL	88-85-7	PST08020
2-(1-METHYLPROPYL)-4,6-DINITROPHENOL ACETATE (ESTER)	2813-95-8	PST08021

ALPHABETICAL INDEX

ALPHABETICAL INDEX

SUBSTANCE NAME	CAS #	PST #
2-CHLORO-N-(2,6-DIETHYLPHENYL)-N-(METHOXYMETHYL)ACETAMIDE	15972-60-8	PST00506
2-CHLORO-N-(2,6-DIMETHYLPHENYL)-N-(1H-PYRAZOL-1-YLMETHYL)ACETAMIDE	67129-08-2	PST14106
2-CHLORO-N-(2,6-DIMETHYLPHENYL)-N-(2-METHOXYETHYL))ACETAMIDE	50563-36-5	PST07677
2-CHLORO-N-(2,6-DIMETHYLPHENYL)-N-(2-METHOXYETHYL)ACETAMIDE	50563-36-5	PST07677
2-CHLORO-N-(4,6-DICHLORO-1,3,5-TRIAZIN-2-YL)ANILINE	101-05-3	PST01526
2-CHLORO-N-ETHOXYMETHYL-6'-ETHYLACET-O-TOLUIDIDE	34256-82-1	PST72539
2-CHLORO-N-ISOPROPYLACETANILIDE	1918-16-7	PST19686
2-CHLORO-N,N-DI-2-PROPENYLACETAMIDE	93-71-0	PST71155
2-CHLORO-N,N-DIALLYLACETAMIDE	93-71-0	PST71155
2-CHLORO-1-(O-CHLOROPHENYLO-1-(P-CHLOROPHENYL)ETHYLENE	14835-94-0	PST04753
2-CHLORO-1-(2,4-DICHLOROPHENYL)ETHENYL DIETHYL PHOSPHATE	470-90-6	PST04575
2-CHLORO-1-(2,4-DICHLOROPHENYL)VINYL DIETHYL PHOSPHATE	470-90-6	PST04575
2-CHLORO-1-(2,4,5-TRICHLOROPHENYL)ETHENYL DIMETHYL PHOSPHATE	961-11-5	PST72243
2-CHLORO-1-(2,4,5-TRICHLOROPHENYL)VINYL DIMETHYL PHOSPHATE	961-11-5	PST72243
2-CHLORO-1-(2',5'-DICHLOROPHENYL)VINYL DIETHYL PHOSPHOROTHIONATE	1757-18-2	PST00493
2-CHLORO-1-(3-ETHOXY-4-NITROPHENOXY)-4-(TRIFLUOROMETHYL)BENZENE	42874-03-3	PST72413
2-CHLORO-1,1-BIS(P-CHLOROPHENYL)ETHYLENE	1022-22-6	PST06322
2-CHLORO-2-DIETHYLCARBAMOYL-1-METHYLVINYL DIMETHYL PHOSPHATE	13171-21-6	PST18670
2-CHLORO-2-PROPENE-1-THIOL DIETHYLDITHIOCARBAMATE	95-06-7	PST22190
2-CHLORO-2-PROPENYL DIETHYLCARBAMODITHIOATE	95-06-7	PST22190
2-CHLORO-2',6'-DIETHYL-N-(BUTOXYMETHYL)ACETANILIDE	23184-66-9	PST03497
2-CHLORO-2',6'-DIETHYL-N-(METHOXYMETHYL)ACETANILIDE	15972-60-8	PST00506
2-CHLORO-2',6'-DIETHYL-N-METHOXYMETHYLACETANILIDE	15972-60-8	PST00506
2-CHLORO-3-(DIETHYLAMINO-1-METHYL-3-OXO-1-PROPENYL DIMETHYL PHOSPHATE	13171-21-6	PST18670
2-CHLORO-3-DIMETHOXYPHOSPHINOYLOXY-N,N-DIETHYLBUT-2-ENAMIDE	13171-21-6	PST18670
2-CHLORO-4-(CYCLOPROPYLAMINO)-6-(ISOPROPYLAMINO)-S-TRIAZINE	22936-86-3	PST72296
2-CHLORO-4-(DIETHYLAMINO)-6-(ETHYLAMINO)-S-TRIAZINE	1912-26-1	PST23927
2-CHLORO-4-(ETHYLAMINO)-6-(ISOPROPYLAMINO)-S-TRIAZINE	1912-24-9	PST02150
2-CHLORO-4-(1-CYANO-1-METHYLETHYLAMINO)-6-ETHYLAMINO-1,3,5-TRIAZINE	21725-46-2	PST05762
2-CHLORO-4-(1,1-DIMETHYLETHYL)PHENYL METHYL METHYLPHOSPHORAMIDATE	299-86-5	PST05550
2-CHLORO-4-CYCLOPROPYLAMINO-6-ISOPROPYLAMINO-1,3,5-TRIAZINE	22936-86-3	PST72296
2-CHLORO-4-DIETHYLAMINO-6-ETHYLAMINO-1,3,5-TRIAZINE	1912-26-1	PST23927
2-CHLORO-4-ETHYLAMINO-6-ISOPROPYLAMINE-S-TRIAZINE	1912-24-9	PST02150
2-CHLORO-4-TERT-BUTYLPHENYL METHYL N-METHYLPHOSPHORAMIDATE	299-86-5	PST05550
2-CHLORO-4-TRIFLUOROMETHYLPHENYL 3-ETHOXY-4-NITROPHENYL ETHER	42874-03-3	PST72413
2-CHLORO-4,5-DIMETHYLPHENYL METHYLCARBAMATE	671-04-5	PST02250
2-CHLORO-4,6-BIS(DIETHYLAMINO)-S-TRIAZINE	580-48-3	PST72143
2-CHLORO-4,6-BIS(DIETHYLAMINO)-1,3,5-TRIAZINE	580-48-3	PST72143
2-CHLORO-4,6-BIS(ETHYLAMINO)-S-TRIAZINE	122-34-9	PST20837
2-CHLORO-4,6-BIS(ETHYLAMINO)-1,3,5-TRIAZINE	122-34-9	PST20837
2-CHLORO-4,6-BIS(ISOPROPYLAMINO)-S-TRIAZINE	139-40-2	PST19736
2-CHLORO-4,6-BIS(ISOPROPYLAMINO)-1,3,5-TRIAZINE	139-40-2	PST19736
2-CHLORO-5-HYDROXYTOLUENE	59-50-7	PST29890
2-CHLORO-6-(TRICHLOROMETHYL)PYRIDINE	1929-82-4	PST16530
2-CHLORO-6-TRICLOROMETHYLPYRIDINE	1929-82-4	PST16530
2-CHLORO-6'-ETHYL-N-(2-METHOXY-1-METHYLETHYL)ACETO-O-TOLUIDIDE	51218-45-2	PST15003
2-CHLORO-9-HYDROXY-FLUORENE-9-CARBOXYLIC ACID METHYL ESTER	2536-31-4	PST72283
2-CHLORO-9-HYDROXY-9H-FLUORENE-9-CARBOXYLIC ACID METHYL ESTER	2536-31-4	PST72283
2-CHLOROALLYL DIETHYLDITHIOCARBAMATE	95-06-7	PST22190
2-CHLOROALLYL N,N-DIETHYLDITHIOCARBAMATE	95-06-7	PST22190
2-CHLOROETHYLPHOSPHONIC ACID	16672-87-0	PST72293
2-CHLOROETHYLTRIMETHYLAMMONIUM CHLORIDE	999-81-5	PST71147
2-CYCLOHEXEN-1-ONE, 2-(1-(ETHOXYIMINO)BUTYL)-5-(2-(ETHYLTHIO)PROPYL) -3-HYDROXY-	74051-80-2	PST20577

SUBSTANCE NAME	CAS #	PST #
2-CYCLOPENTEN-1-YL ESTER	121-21-1	PST19960
2-CYCLOPROPYLAMINO-4,6-DIAMINO-S-TRIAZINE	66215-27-8	PST72536
2-DIBROMO-3-CHLOROPROPANE	96-12-8	PST26490
2-DIETHOXYPHOSPHINOTHIOYLTHIO-N-ISOPROPYLACETAMIDE	2275-18-5	PST19943
2-DIMETHOXYPHOSPHINOTHIOYLTHIO-N-(2-METHOXYETHYL)ACETAMIDE	919-76-6	PST01007
2-DIMETHOXYPHOSPHINOTHIOYLTHIO-N-ETHYLACETAMIDE	116-01-8	PST08723
2-DIMETHOXYPHOSPHINOTHIOYLTHIO-N-FORMYL-N-METHYLACETAMIDE	2540-82-1	PST10081
2-DIMETHOXYPHOSPHINOTHIOYLTHIO-N-METHYLACETAMIDE	60-51-5	PST07670
2-DIMETHOXYPHOSPHINOTHIOYLTHIOMETHYL-4,6-DIAMINO-S-TRIAZINE	78-57-9	PST72980
2-DIMETHOXYPHOSPHINOYLTHIO-N-METHYLACETAMIDE	1113-02-6	PST17328
2-DIMETHYL CIS-2-DIMETHYL-CARBAMOYL-1-METHYLVINYL PHOSPHATE	141-66-2	PST03090
2-DIMETHYLAMINO-5,6-DIMETHYLPYRIMIDIN-4-YL DIMETHYLCARBAMATE	23103-98-2	PST72345
2-DIMETHYLCARBAMOYL-3-METHYL-4-PYRAZOLYL DIMETHYLCARBAMATE	644-64-4	PST83057
2-ETHANOLAMINE	141-43-5	PST08710
2-ETHOXY-2,3-DIHYDRO-3,3-DIMETHYL-5-BENZOFURANOL METHANESULFONATE	26225-79-6	PST72404
2-ETHOXY-2,3-DIHYDRO-3,3-DIMETHYL-5-BENZOFURANYL METHANESULPHONATE	26225-79-6	PST72404
2-ETHYL-1,3-HEXANEDIOL	94-96-2	PST71458
2-ETHYL-3-PROPYL-1,3-PROPANEDIOL	94-96-2	PST71458
2-ETHYLAMINO-4-DIETHYLAMINO-6-CHLORO-S-TRIAZINE	1912-26-1	PST23927
2-ETHYLAMINO-4-ISOPROPYLAMINO-6-METHOXY-1,3,5-TRIZAINE	1610-17-9	PST02148
2-ETHYLAMINO-4-ISOPROPYLAMINO-6-METHYLMERCAPTO-S-TRIAZINE	834-12-8	PST01006
2-ETHYLAMINO-4-ISOPROPYLAMINO-6-METHYLTHIO-1,3,5-TRIAZINE 2-METHYLTHIO-4-ETHYLAMINO-6-ISOPROPYLAMINO-S-TRIAZINE	834-12-8	PST01006
2-ETHYLHEXANEDIOL	94-96-2	PST71458
2-ETHYLHEXYL PHTHALATE	117-81-7	PST06440
2-ETHYLTHIOMETHYLPHENYL METHYLCARBAMATE	29973-13-5	PST72421
2-FLUOROACETAMIDE	640-19-7	PST09930
2-FURALDEHYDE	98-01-1	PST10180
2-FURANALDEHYDE	98-01-1	PST10180
2-FURANCARBONAL	98-01-1	PST10180
2-FURANCARBOXALDEHYDE	98-01-1	PST10180
2-FURFURAL	98-01-1	PST10180
2-FURYL-METHANOAL	98-01-1	PST10180
2-HENDECANONE	112-12-9	PST14675
2-HYDROXY-1,2,3-PROPANETRICARBOXYLIC ACID	77-92-9	PST05200
2-HYDROXY-1,2,3-PROPANETRICARBOXYLIC ACID, COPPER SALT	10402-15-0	PST71496
2-HYDROXY-3-CHLOROBIPHENYL	85-97-2	PST71680
2-HYDROXY-5-METHYLPYRAZOLO(1,5-A)PYRIMIDINE-6-CARBOXYLIC ACID, ETHYL ESTER, O-ESTER WITH O,O-DIETHYLPHOSPHOROTHIOATE	13457-18-6	PST73169
2-HYDROXYBENZENECARBOXYLIC ACID	69-72-7	PST20315
2-HYDROXYBENZOIC ACID	69-72-7	PST20315
2-HYDROXYBENZOIC ACID METHYL ESTER	119-36-8	PST14720
2-HYDROXYBIPHENYL	90-43-7	PST18470
2-HYDROXYBIPHENYL SODIUM SALT	132-27-4	PST08500
2-HYDROXYDIPHENYL	90-43-7	PST18470
2-HYDROXYDIPHENYL SODIUM SALT	132-27-4	PST08500
2-HYDROXYETHANAMINE	141-43-5	PST08710
2-HYDROXYETHANOL	107-21-1	PST09400
2-HYDROXYETHYLAMINE	141-43-5	PST08710
2-HYDROXYNAPHTHLALENE	135-19-3	PST03050
2-HYDROXYPHENOL	120-80-9	PST04360
2-HYDROXYPROPANOL	57-55-6	PST19870
2-ISOPROPOXYPHENYL METHYLCARBAMATE	114-26-1	PST02540
2-ISOPROPOXYPHENYL N-METHYLCARBAMATE	114-26-1	PST02540

SUBSTANCE NAME	CAS #	PST #
2-ISOPROPYL-5-METHYL-PHENOL	89-83-8	PST23475
2-ISOPROPYLAMINO-4-(3-METHOXYPROPYLAMINO)-6-METHYLTHIO-1,3,5-TRIAZINE	841-06-5	PST14204
2-ISOPROPYLAMINO-4-METHYLAMINO-6-METHYLTHIO-1,3,5-TRIAZINE	1014-69-3	PST06353
2-ISOPROPYLPHENYL METHYLCARBAMATE	2631-40-5	PST73231
2-ISOVALERYL-1,3-INDANDIONE	83-28-3	PST24738
2-MERCAPTOBENZOTHIAZOLE	149-30-4	PST13738
2-MERCAPTOBENZOTHIAZOLE, ZINC SALT	155-04-4	PST27776
2-MESYL-2-METHYLPROPIONALDEHYDE O-METHYLCARBAMOYLOXIME	1646-88-4	PST72406
2-METHOXY-1-(1-METHYLPROPYL)-3,5-DINITROBENZENE	6099-79-2	PST08022
2-METHOXY-3,6-DICHLOROBENZOIC ACID	1918-00-9	PST02260
2-METHOXY-4H-BENZO-1,3,2-DIOXAPHOSPHORIN 2-SULPHIDE	3811-49-2	PST20325
2-METHOXY-4H-BENZO-1,3,2-DIOXAPHOSPHORINE-2-SULFIDE	3811-49-2	PST20325
2-METHOXY-4H-1,3,2-BENZODIOXAPHOSPHININE 2-SULPHIDE	3811-49-2	PST20325
2-METHOXY-4H-1,3,2-BENZODIOXAPHOSPHORIN 2-SULFIDE	3811-49-2	PST20325
2-METHOXY-4H-1,3,2LAMBDA-BENZODIOXAPHOSPHINE 2-SULPHIDE	3811-49-2	PST20325
2-METHOXY-4H-1,3,2LAMBDA-BENZODIOXAPHOSPHORINE 2-SULFIDE	3811-49-2	PST20325
2-METHOXYCARBONYL-1-METHYLVINYL DIMETHYL PHOSPHATE	7786-34-7	PST18650
2-METHOXYETHANOL	109-86-4	PST14340
2-METHOXYETHYL ALCOHOL	109-86-4	PST14340
2-METHYL-1,4-NAPHTHALENEDION	58-27-5	PST71050
2-METHYL-1,4-NAPHTHOQUINONE	58-27-5	PST71050
2-METHYL-2(METHYLTHIO)PROPANAL O-((METHYLAMINO)CARBONYL)OXIME	116-06-3	PST00500
2-METHYL-2-(METHYLSULFINYL)PROPANOL, O-((METHYLAMINO)CARBONYL)OXIME	1646-87-3	PST00503
2-METHYL-2-(METHYLSULFINYL)PROPIONALDEHYDE-O-(METHYLCARBAMOYL)OXIME	1646-87-3	PST00503
2-METHYL-2-(METHYLSULFONYL)PROPANAL O-((METHYLAMINO)CARBONYL)OXIME	1646-88-4	PST72406
2-METHYL-2-(METHYLSULFONYL)PROPIONALDEHYDE O-(METHYLCARBAMOYL)OXIME	1646-88-4	PST72406
2-METHYL-2-(METHYLTHIO)PROPIONALDEHYDE O-(METHYLCARBAMOYL)OXIME	116-06-3	PST00500
2-METHYL-2-METHYLSULPHONYLPROPIONALDEHYDE O-METHYLCARBAMOYLOXIME	1646-88-4	PST72406
2-METHYL-2-P-HYDROXYPHENYLBUTANE	80-46-6	PST71715
2-METHYL-2-PROPANOL	75-65-0	PST22630
2-METHYL-3(2)-ISOTHIAZOLONE	2682-20-4	PST72362
2-METHYL-4-CHLOROPHENOXYACETIC ACID	94-74-6	PST27880
2-METHYL-4-ISOTHIAZOLIN-3-ONE	2682-20-4	PST72362
2-METHYL-4-OXO-3-(2-CYCLOPENTEN-1-YL 2,2-DIMETHYL-3-(2-METHYL-1 -PROPENYL) CYCLOPROPANE CARBOXYILATE	584-79-2	PST00550
2-METHYL-4,6-DINITROPHENOL	534-52-1	PST07910
2-METHYL-4,6-DINITROPHENOL SODIUM SALT	2312-76-7	PST71411
2-METHYL-5-NITRO-1-IMIDAZOLE-ETHANOL	443-48-1	PST72529
2-METHYL-5-NITRO-1H-IMIDAZOLE-1-ETHANOL	443-48-1	PST72529
2-METHYL-5-NITROIMIDAZOLE-1-ETHANOL	443-48-1	PST72529
2-METHYLPROPYL METHYL KETONE	108-10-1	PST14550
2-METHYLTHIO-4-ETHYLAMINO-6-ISOPROPYLAMINO-S-TRIAZINE	834-12-8	PST01006
2-METHYLTHIO-4,6-BIS(ISOPROPYLAMINO)-S-TRIAZINE	7287-19-6	PST19968
2-METHYLTHIO-4,6-BIS(MONOETHYLAMINO)-S-TRIAZINE	1014-70-6	PST02838
2-MONOFLUOROACETAMIDE	640-19-7	PST09930
2-N-OCTYL-4-ISOTHIAZOLIN-3-ONE	26530-20-1	PST72294
2-N-PROPYL-4-METHYLPYRIMIDYL-(6)-DIMETHYLCARBAMATE	2532-49-2	PST73266
2-NAPHTHACENECARBOXAMIDE, 4-(DIMETHYLAMINO)-1,4,4A,5,5A,6,11,12A-OCTAHYDRO-3,5,6,10,12,12A-HEXAHYDROXY-6-METHYL-1,11-DIOXO-, (4S-(4	79-57-2	PST17414
2-NAPHTHACENECARBOXAMIDE, 4-(DIMETHYLAMINO)-1,4,4A,5,5A,6,11,12A-OCTAHYDRO-3,5,6,10,12,12A-HEXAHYDROXY-6-METHYL-1,11-DIOXO,	2058-46-0	PST84045
2-NAPHTHACENECARBOXAMIDE, 4-(DIMETHYLAMINO)-1,4,4A,5,5A,6,11,12A-	2058-46-0	PST84045
2-NAPHTHACENECARBOXAMIDE, 4-(DIMETHYLAMINO)-1,4,4A,5,5A,6,11,12A-OCTA-HYDRO-3,5,6,10,12,12A-HEXAHYDROXY-6-METHYL-1,11-DIOXO-, CALCIUM SALT,	15251-48-6	PST84256

ALPHABETICAL INDEX

SUBSTANCE NAME	CAS #	PST #
2-NAPHTHACENECARBOXAMIDE, 4-(DIMETHYLAMINO)-1,4,4A,5,5A,6,11,12A-OCTA-HYDRO-3,5,6,10,12,12A-HEXAHYDROXY-6-METHYL-1,11-DIOXO-, CALCIUM SALT	15251-48-6	PST84256
2-NAPHTHACENECARBOXAMIDE, 4-(DIMETHYLAMINO)-1,4,4S,5,5A,6,11,12A-OCTAHYDRO-3,5,6,10,12,12A-HEXAHYDROXY-6-METHYL-1,11-DIOXO-	79-57-2	PST17414
2-NAPHTHOL	135-19-3	PST03050
2-NITRO-1-(4-NITROPHENOXY)-4-(TRIFLUOROMETHYL)BENZENE	15457-05-3	PST72248
2-NITRO-2-ETHYL-1,3-PROPANEDIOL	597-09-1	PST71953
2-NORBORNENE, 1,2,3,4,7,7-HEXACHLORO-5,6-BIS(CHLOROMETHYL)-	2550-75-6	PST73193
2-OCTYL-3(2H)-ISOTHIAZOLONE	26530-20-1	PST72294
2-OCTYL-4-ISOTHIAZOLIN-3-ONE	26530-20-1	PST72294
2-OXA-4-THIA-7-AZA-3-PHOSPHAOCTAN-8-OIC ACID, 3,7-DIMETHYL-6-OXO-, METHYL ESTER, 3-SULFIDE	29173-31-7	PST73246
2-PENTANONE, 4-METHYL-	108-10-1	PST14550
2-PENTENEDIOIC ACID, 3-((DIMETHOXYPHOSPHINYL)OXY)-, DIMETHYL ESTER	122-10-1	PST03240
2-PHENETHYL PROPIONATE	122-70-3	PST72314
2-PHENYLETHYL PROPANOATE	122-70-3	PST72314
2-PHENYLETHYL PROPANOIC ACID ESTER	122-70-3	PST72314
2-PHENYLETHYL PROPIONATE	122-70-3	PST72314
2-PHENYLPHENOL	90-43-7	PST18470
2-PHENYLPHENOL SODIUM SALT	132-27-4	PST08500
2-PIVALOYL-1,3-INDANDIONE	83-26-1	PST18970
2-PIVALOYLINDAN-1,3-DIONE	83-26-1	PST18970
2-PIVALYL-1,3-INDANDIONE	83-26-1	PST18970
2-PROPANOL	67-63-0	PST12090
2-PROPANOL, 2-METHYL-	75-65-0	PST22630
2-PROPANONE	67-64-1	PST00140
2-PROPEN-1-AL	107-02-8	PST00330
2-PROPENAL	107-02-8	PST00330
2-PROPENAMIDE, N-(3,4-DICHLOROPHENYL)-2-METHYL-	2164-09-2	PST71378
2-PROPENE-1-THIOL,2-CHLORO-, DIETHYLDITHIOCARBAMATE	95-06-7	PST22190
2-PROPENOIC ACID HOMOPOLYMER	9003-01-4	PST04349
2-PROPENYL ISOTHIOCYANATE	57-06-7	PST00680
2-PYRIDINECARBOXYLIC ACID, 3,6-DICHLORO-	1702-17-6	PST05211
2-PYRIDINECARBOXYLIC ACID, 4-AMINO-2,5,6-TRICHLORO-	1918-02-1	PST18840
2-SEC-BUTYL-4,6-DINITROANISOLE	6099-79-2	PST08022
2-SEC-BUTYL-4,6-DINITROPHENOL	88-85-7	PST08020
2-SEC-BUTYL-4,6-DINITROPHENOL ACETATE	2813-95-8	PST08021
2-SEC-BUTYL-4,6-DINITROPHENOL ACETATE (ESTER)	2813-95-8	PST08021
2-SEC-BUTYL-4,6-DINITROPHENYL ISOPROPYL CARBONATE	973-21-7	PST07990
2-SEC-BUTYL-4,6-DINITROPHENYL-3-METHYL-2-BUTENOATE	485-31-4	PST71960
2-SEC-BUTYLAMINO-4-ETHYLAMINO-6-METHOXY-S-TRIAZINE	26259-45-0	PST73051
2-SEC-BUTYLAMINO-4-ETHYLAMINO-6-METHOXY-1,3,5-TRIAZINE	26259-45-0	PST73051
2-SEC-BUTYLPHENYL METHYLCARBAMATE	3766-81-2	PST03324
2-SULFANILAMIDOBENZOPYRAZINE	59-40-5	PST72046
2-SULFANILAMIDOTHIAZOLE	72-14-0	PST72047
2-SULFATHIAZOLE	72-14-0	PST72047
2-TERT-BUTYL-4-(2,4-DICHLORO-5-ISOPROPOXYPHENYL)-(DELTA)2-1,3,4-OXADIAZOLIN-5-ONE	19666-30-9	PST72385
2-TERT-BUTYL-4,6-DINITROPHENOL	1420-07-1	PST72921
2-TERT-BUTYLAMINO-4-CHLORO-6-ETHYLAMINO-1,3,5-TRIAZINE	5915-41-3	PST22536
2-TERT-BUTYLAMINO-4-ETHYLAMINO-6-METHOXY-1,3,5-TRIAZINE	33693-04-8	PST72770
2-TERT-BUTYLAMINO-4-ETHYLAMINO-6-METHYLTHIO-1,3,5-TRIAZINE	886-50-0	PST22538
2-THIO-3,5-DIMETHYLTETRAHYDRO-1,3,5,-THIADIAZINE	533-74-4	PST06230
2-TRIMETHYLACETYL-1,3-INDANDIONE	83-26-1	PST18970

ALPHABETICAL INDEX

ALPHABETICAL INDEX

SUBSTANCE NAME	CAS #	PST #
2,6-DICHLOROCYANOBENZENE	1194-65-6	PST06800
2,6-DICHLOROTHIOBENZAMIDE	1918-13-4	PST73046
2,6-DIMETHYL-HEPT-4-ONE	108-83-8	PST07500
2,6-DIMETHYL-M-DIOXAN-4-OL ACETATE	828-00-2	PST28395
2,6-DIMETHYL-N-(2-METHOXYETHYL)CHLOROACETANILIDE	50563-36-5	PST07677
2,6-DIMETHYL-1,3-DIOXAN-4-OL ACETATE	828-00-2	PST28395
2,6-DIMETHYL-4-HEPTANONE	108-83-8	PST07500
2,6-DIMETHYL-4-TRIDECYLMORPHOLINE	24602-86-6	PST72537
2,6-DIMETHYL-4-TRIDECYLTETRAHYDRO-1,4-OXAZINE	24602-86-6	PST72537
2,6-DINITRO-N,N-DIPROPYL-ALPHA,ALPHA,ALPHA-TRIFLUORO-P-TOLUIDINE	1582-09-8	PST24085
2,6-DINITRO-N,N-DIPROPYL-4-(TRIFLUOROMETHYL)BENZENAMINE	1582-09-8	PST24085
2,6-DINITRO-N,N-DIPROPYL-4-TRIFLUOROMETHYLANILINE	1582-09-8	PST24085
2,7:3,6-DIMETHANONAPHTH(2,3-B)OXIRENE, 3,4,5,6,9,9-HEXACHLORO-1A, 2, 2A,3,6,6A,7,7A-OCTAHYDRO-, (1A ALPHA, 2 BETA, 2A BETA, 3 ALPHA,	72-20-8	PST08600
2,7:3,6-DIMETHANONAPHTH(2,3-B)OXIRENE, 3,4,5,6,9,9-HEXACHLORO-1A,2,2A, 3,6,6A,7,7A-OCTAHYDRO-, (1A ALPHA, 2 BETA, 2A ALPHA, 3 BETA, 6 BETA,	60-57-1	PST07080
2',4'-DIMETHYL-5-((TRIFLUOROMETHYL)SULFONAMIDO)ACETANILIDE	53780-34-0	PST72444
2',4',5',7'-TETRA IODO FLUORESCEIN-DISODIUM SALT	16423-68-0	PST08685
2H-1-BENZOPYRAN-2-ONE, 3-(1-(2-FURANYL)-3-OXOBUTYL)-4-HYDROXY-	117-52-2	PST05476
2H-1-BENZOPYRAN-2-ONE, 3-(3-(1,1'-BIPHENYL)-4-YL-1,2,3,4-TETRAHYDRO-1-NAPHTHALENYL)-4-HYDROXY-	56073-07-5	PST07385
2H-1-BENZOPYRAN-2-ONE, 3-(3-(4'-BROMO(1,1'-BIPHENYL)-4-YL)-1,2,3,4-TETRAHYDRO-1-NAPHTHALENYL)-4-HYDROXY-	56073-10-0	PST03327
2H-1-BENZOPYRAN-2-ONE, 3-(3-(4'-BROMO(1,1'-BIPHENYL)-4-YL)-3-HYDROXY-1-PHENYLPROPYL)-4-HYDROXY-	28772-56-7	PST03334
2H-1-BENZOPYRAN-2-ONE, 4-HYDROXY-3-(1,2,3,4-TETRAHYDRO-1-NAPHTHALENYL)-	5836-29-3	PST05493
2H-1-BENZOPYRAN-2-ONE, 4-HYDROXY-3-(3-OXO-1-PHENYLBUTYL)-	81-81-2	PST25090
2H-1-BENZOPYRAN-2-ONE, 4-HYDROXY-3-(3-OXO-1-PHENYLBUTYL)-, SODIUM SALT	129-06-6	PST83008
2H-1,3,5-THIADIAZINE-2-THIONEETRAHYDRO-3,5-DIMETHYL	533-74-4	PST06230
2M-4CH	94-74-6	PST27880
21 DIAZINON 4E NAMCO 05628671	UNASSIGNED	PST75469
21 DIAZINON 4S 05622664	UNASSIGNED	PST75469
21 MALATHION 57E 05623441	UNASSIGNED	PST75465
21 NAMFUME 05001667	UNASSIGNED	PST75470
21 NAMTOX 05623598	UNASSIGNED	PST75467
21 PATHOFUME B 67-33 05360954	UNASSIGNED	PST75471
21 PATHOFUME 57-43 05224650	UNASSIGNED	PST75471
21 PATHOFUME 75-25 50 LB CYL 05131200	UNASSIGNED	PST75471
21 PINTOFUME 05623736	UNASSIGNED	PST75470
21 PYRENONE CONCENTRATE 05623838	UNASSIGNED	PST75472
21 PYRENONE FOOD STORAGE SPRAY 05623871	UNASSIGNED	PST75472
21 PYROCIDE FOGGING CONC 1-2-3 05141258	UNASSIGNED	PST75473
21 PYROCIDE FOGGING CONC 3-6-10 05141622	UNASSIGNED	PST75473
21 PYROCIDE FOGGING CONC(0.5-1-1.67) NAMCO 05194935	UNASSIGNED	PST75473
21 TRIFUME 2+2 05066709	UNASSIGNED	PST75474
21 TRIFUME 43-57 05066695	UNASSIGNED	PST75474
3(2H)-BENZOFURANONE, 7-HYDROXY-2,2-DIMETHYL-	17781-16-7	PST72799
3(2H)-BENZOTHIAZOLEACETIC ACID, 4-CHLORO-2-OXO'	3813-05-6	PST72725
3(2H)-ISOTHIAZOLONE, 2-METHYL-	2682-20-4	PST72362
3(2H)-ISOTHIAZOLONE, 2-OCTYL-	26530-20-1	PST72294
3(2H)-ISOXAZOLONE, 5-METHYL-	10004-44-1	PST22404
3(2H)-PYRIDAZINONE, 4-CHLORO-5-(METHYLAMINO)-2-(ALPHA,ALPHA,ALPHA,-TRIFLUORO-M-TOLYL)-	27314-13-2	PST72343

SUBSTANCE NAME	CAS #	PST #
3(2H)-PYRIDAZINONE, 4-CHLORO-5-(METHYLAMINO)-2-(3-(TRIFLUOROMETHYL) PHENYL)-	27314-13-2	PST72343
3(2H)-PYRIDAZINONE, 5-AMINO-4-BROMO-2-PHENYL-	3042-84-0	PST72769
3(2H)-PYRIDAZINONE, 5-AMINO-4-CHLORO-2-PHENYL-	1698-60-8	PST71928
3-(((DIMETHYLAMINO)CARBONYL)AMINO)PHENYL (1,1-DIMETHYLETHYL)CARBAMATE	4849-32-5	PST72271
3-((DIMETHOXYPHOSPHINYL)OXY-2-PENTENEDIOIC ACID DIMETHYL ESTER	122-10-1	PST03240
3-((DIMETHOXYPHOSPHINYL)OXYL-2-BUTENOIC ACID METHYL ESTER	7786-34-7	PST18650
3-((METHOXYCARBONYL)AMINO)PHENYL (3-METHYLPHENYL)CARBAMATE	13684-63-4	PST72282
3-(ALPHA-(P-(P-BROMOPHENYL)-BETA-HYDROXYPHENETHYL)BENZYL)-4-HYDROXY-COUMARIN	28772-56-7	PST03334
3-(ALPHA-(2-FURYL)-BETA-ACETYLETHYL)4-HYDROXYCOUMARIN	117-52-2	PST05476
3-(ALPHA-ACETONYLBENZYL)-4-HYDROXYCOUMARIN	81-81-2	PST25090
3-(ALPHA-ACETONYLBENZYL)-4-HYDROXYCOUMARIN, SODIUM SALT	129-06-6	PST83008
3-(ALPHA-ACETONYLFURFURYL)-4-HYDROXYCOUMARIN	117-52-2	PST05476
3-(DIMETHOXYPHOSPHINYLOXY)-N-METHYL-CIS-CROTONAMIDE	6923-22-4	PST15165
3-(DIMETHOXYPHOSPHINYLOXY)-N-METHYLISOCROTONAMIDE	6923-22-4	PST15165
3-(DIMETHOXYPHOSPHINYLOXY)-N,N-DIMETHYL-CIS-CROTONAMIDE	141-66-2	PST03090
3-(HEXAHYDRO-4,7-METHANOINDAN-1(OR 2)-YL)-1,1-DIMETHYLUREA	28805-78-9	PST73199
3-(HEXAHYDRO-4,7-METHANOINDAN-1-YL)-1,1-DIMETHYLUREA + 3-HEXAHYDRO-4,7-METHANOINDAN-2-YL)-1,1-DIMETHYLUREA	28805-78-9	PST73199
3-(HEXAHYDRO-4,7-METHANOINDAN-5-YL)-1,1-DIMETHYLUREA	18530-56-8	PST71400
3-(METHYLSULFONYL)-2-BUTANONE O-((METHYLAMINO)CARBONYL)OXIME	34681-23-7	PST72434
3-(METHYLSULFONYL)-2-BUTANONE O-(METHYLCARBAMOYL)OXIME	34681-23-7	PST72434
3-(METHYLTHIO)-2-BUTANONE O-((METHYLAMINO)CARBONYL)OXIME	34681-10-2	PST73270
3-(METHYLTHIO)-2-BUTANONE O-(METHYLCARBAMOYL)OXIME	34681-10-2	PST73270
3-(METHYLTHIO)BUTANONE O-METHYLCARBAMOYLOXIME	34681-10-2	PST73270
3-(P-(P-CHLOROPHENOXY)PHENYL)-1,1-DIMETHYLUREA	1982-47-4	PST04905
3-(P-(P-METHOXYPHENOXY)PHENYL)-1,1-DIMETHYLUREA	14214-32-5	PST07386
3-(P-BROMOPHENYL)-1-METHOXY-1-METHYLUREA	3060-89-7	PST15008
3-(P-CHLOROPHENYL)-1-METHOXY-1-METHYLUREA	1746-81-2	PST15174
3-(P-CHLOROPHENYL)-1-METHYL-1-(1-METHYL-2-PROPYNYL)UREA	3766-60-7	PST03523
3-(P-CHLOROPHENYL)-1,1-DIMETHYLUREA	150-68-5	PST15196
3-(P-CHLOROPHENYL)-1,1-DIMETHYLUREA TRICHLOROACETATE	140-41-0	PST15197
3-(PHENOXYPHENYL)METHYL-TRANS-3-(2,2-DICHLOROETHENYL)-2,2-DIMETHYLCYCLOPROPANECARBOXYLATE	51877-74-8	PST23708
3-(PHENOXYPHENYL)METHYL-TRANS-3-(2,2-DICHLOROVINYL)-2,2-DIMETHYLCYCLOPROPANECARBOXYLATE	51877-74-8	PST23708
3-(TRIMETHOXYSILYL)PROPYLDIMETHYLOCTADECYLAMMONIUM CHLORIDE	27668-52-6	PST72370
3-(1 OR 2-HEXAHYDRO-4,7-METHANOINDANLYL)-1,1-DIMETHYLUREA	28805-78-9	PST73199
3-(1-(2-FURANYL)-3-OXOBUTYL)-4-HYDROXY-2H-1-BENZOPYRAN-2-ONE	117-52-2	PST05476
3-(1-ETHYLPROPYL)PHENOL METHYLCARBAMATE MIXTURE WITH 3-(1-METHYLBUTYL) PHENYL METHYLCARBAMATE	8065-36-9	PST03480
3-(1-METHYLETHYL)-1H-2,1,3-BENZOTHIADIAZIN-4(3H)-ONE 2,2-DIOXIDE	25057-89-0	PST02584
3-(1-METHYLETHYL)PHENOL METHYLCARBAMATE	64-00-6	PST29423
3-(2-CYCLOPENTENYL)-2-METHYL-4-OXO-2-CYCLOPENTENYL ESTER OF CHRYSANTHEMUMMONOCARBOXYLIC ACID	97-11-0	PST19949
3-(2-FURANYLMETHYL)-2-METHYL-4-OXO-2-CYCLOPENTEN-1-YL 2,2-DIMETHYL -3-(2-METHYL-1-PROPENYL)CYCLOPROPANECARBOXYLATE	17080-02-3	PST10175
3-(2,2-DIBROMOETHENYL)-2,2-DIMETHYLCYCLOPROPANECARBOXYLIC ACID CYANO(3-PHENOXYPHENYL)METHYL ESTER	52918-63-5	PST72784
3-(2,2-DICHLOROETHENYL)-2,2-DIMETHYLCYCLOPROPANECARBOXYLIC ACID CYANO(3-PHENOXYPHENYL) METHYL ESTER	52315-07-8	PST72392
3-(2,4-DICHLORO-5-(1-METHYLETHOXY)PHENYL)-5-(1,1-DIMETHYLETHYL)-1,3,4-OXADIAZOL-2(3H)-ONE	19666-30-9	PST72385

SUBSTANCE NAME	CAS #	PST #
3-(3-(1,1'-BIPHENYL)-4-YL-1,2,3,4-TETRAHYDRO-1-NAPHTHALENYL)-4-HYDROXY-2H-1-BENZOPYRAN-2-ONE	56073-07-5	PST07385
3-(3-(4'-BROMO(1,1'-BIPHENYL)-4-YL)-1,2,3,4-TETRAHYDRO-1-NAPHTHALENYL)-4-HYDROXY-2H-1-BENZOPYRAN-2-ONE	56073-10-0	PST03327
3-(3-(4'-BROMO(1,1'-BIPHENYL)-4-YL)-3-HYDROXY-1-PHENYLPROPYL)-4-HYDROXY-2H-1-BENZOPYRAN-2-ONE	28772-56-7	PST03334
3-(3-(4'-BROMOBIPHENYL-4-YL)-1,2,3,4-TETRAHYDRO-1-NAPHTHYL-4-HYDROXYCOUMARIN	56073-10-0	PST03327
3-(3-(4'-BROMOBIPHENYL-4-YL)-3-HYDROXY-1-PHENYLPROPYL)-4-HYDROXY-COUMARIN	28772-56-7	PST03334
3-(3-BIPHENYL-4-YL-1,2,3,4-TETRAHYDRO-1-NAPHTHYL)-4-HYDROXYCOUMARIN	56073-07-5	PST07385
3-(3-CHLORO-P-TOLYL)-1,1-DIMETHYLUREA	15545-48-9	PST04912
3-(3-CHLORO-4-METHOXYPHENYL)-1,1-DIMETHYLUREA	19937-59-8	PST15009
3-(3,3-DIMETHYLUREIDO)PHENYL TERT-BUTYLCARBAMATE	4849-32-5	PST72271
3-(3,4-DICHLOROPHENYL)-1-METHOXY-1-METHYLUREA	330-55-2	PST12826
3-(3,4-DICHLOROPHENYL)-1-METHYL-1-N-BUTYLUREA	555-37-3	PST16143
3-(3,4-DICHLOROPHENYL)-1,1-DIMETHYLUREA	330-54-1	PST08420
3-(4-(4-CHLOROPHENOXY)PHENYL)-1,1-DIMETHYLUREA	1982-47-4	PST04905
3-(4-(4-METHOXYPHENOXY)PHENYL)-1,1-DIMETHYLUREA	14214-32-5	PST07386
3-(4-BROMO-3-CHLOROPHENYL)-1-METHOXY-1-METHYLUREA	13360-45-7	PST04552
3-(4-BROMOPHENYL)-1-METHOXY-1-METHYLUREA	3060-89-7	PST15008
3-(4-CHLOROPHENYL)-1-METHOXY-1-METHYLUREA	1746-81-2	PST15174
3-(4-CHLOROPHENYL)-1-METHYL-1-(1-METHYLPROP-2-YNYL)UREA	3766-60-7	PST03523
3-(4-CHLOROPHENYL)-1,1-DIMETHYLUREA	150-68-5	PST15196
3-(4-CHLOROPHENYL)-1,1-DIMETHYLURONIUM TRICHLOROACETATE	140-41-0	PST15197
3-(4-ISOPROPYLPHENYL)-1,1-DIMETHYLUREA	34123-59-6	PST12254
3-(5-TERT-BUTYLISOXAZOL-3-YL)-1,1-DIMETHYLUREA	55861-78-4	PST72586
3-ALPHA-PHENYL-BETA-ACETYLETHYL-4-HYDROXYCOUMARIN	81-81-2	PST25090
3-AMINO-S-TRIAZOLE	61-82-5	PST01040
3-AMINO-1,2,4-TRIAZOLE	61-82-5	PST01040
3-AMINO-1H-1,2,4-TRIAZOLE	61-82-5	PST01040
3-AMINO-2,5-DICHLOROBENZOIC ACID	133-90-4	PST29084
3-AMINO-2,5-DICHLOROBENZOIC ACID, METHYL ESTER	7286-84-2	PST71255
3-AMINO-2,5-DICHLOROBENZOIC ACID, MONOAMMONIUM SALT	1076-46-6	PST71252
3-AMINO-2,5-DICHLOROBENZOIC ACID, MONOSODIUM SALT	1954-81-0	PST71256
3-AMINOTRIAZOLE	61-82-5	PST01040
3-BENZOTHIAZOLINEACETIC ACID, 4-CHLORO-2-OXO'	3813-05-6	PST72725
3-BUTANONE	78-93-3	PST14460
3-CARBOXY-ALPHA,2-2-TRIMETHYLCYCLOPROPANEACRYLIC ACID, 1-METHYL ESTER, ESTER WITH 4-HYDROXY-3-METHYL-2-(2,4-PENTADIENYL)-2-CYCLOPENTEN-1-ONE	121-29-9	PST19970
3-CHLORO-ALPHA-ETHOXYIMINO-2,6-DIMETHOXYBENZYL BENZOATE	29104-30-1	PST72988
3-CHLORO-1,2-DIBROMOPROPANE	96-12-8	PST26490
3-CHLORO-4-METHYL-2-OXO-2H-1-BENZOPYRAN-7-YL DIETHYL ESTER PHOSPHORIC ACID	321-54-0	PST65468
3-CHLORO-4-METHYLCOUMARIN-7-YL DIETHYL PHOSPHATE	321-54-0	PST65468
3-CHLORO-4-METHYLCOUMARIN-7-YL DIETHYL PHOSPHOROTHIONATE	56-72-4	PST05490
3-CHLORO-4-NITROPHENYL DIMETHYL PHOSPHOROTHIONATE	500-28-7	PST71379
3-CHLORO-7-DIETHOXYPHOSPHINOTHIOYLOXY-4-METHYLCOUMARIN	56-72-4	PST05490
3-CHLORO-7-HYDROXY-4-METHYL-COUMARIN-O,O-DIETHYL PHOSPHOROTHIOATE	56-72-4	PST05490
3-CHLORO-7-HYDROXY-4-METHYLCOUMARIN DIETHYL PHOSPHATE	321-54-0	PST65468
3-CHLORO-7-HYDROXY-4-METHYLCOUMARIN O-ESTER WITH O,O DIETHYL PHOSPHOROTHIOATE	56-72-4	PST05490
3-CHLOROALLYL CHLORIDE	542-75-6	PST26820
3-CHLOROPROPENYL CHLORIDE	542-75-6	PST26820

SUBSTANCE NAME	CAS #	PST #
3-CRESOL	108-39-4	PST13080
3-CRESOLE	108-39-4	PST13080
3-CYCLO-OCTYL-1,1-DIMETHYLUREA	2163-69-1	PST05996
3-CYCLOHEXYL-1,5,6,7-TETRAHYDRO-2H-CYCLOPENTAPYRIMIDINE-2,4(3H)-DIONE	2164-08-1	PST73238
3-CYCLOHEXYL-1,5,6,7-TETRAHYDROCYCLOPENTAPYRIMIDINE-2,4(3H)-DIONE	2164-08-1	PST73238
3-CYCLOHEXYL-5,6-TRIMETHYLENEURACIL	2164-08-1	PST73238
3-CYCLOHEXYL-6-(DIMETHYLAMINO)-1-METHYL-S-TRIAZINE-3,4(1H,3H)-DIONE	51235-04-2	PST10994
3-CYCLOHEXYL-6-(DIMETHYLAMINO)-1-METHYL-1,3,5-TRIAZINE-2,4(1H,3H)-DIONE	51235-04-2	PST10994
3-CYCLOHEXYL-6-DIMETHYLAMINO-1-METHYL-1,3,5-TRIAZINE-2,4(1H,3H)-DIONE	51235-04-2	PST10994
3-CYCLOHEXYL-6-DIMETHYLAMINO-1-METHYL-1,3,5-TRIAZINE-2,4-DIONE	51235-04-2	PST10994
3-CYCLOHEXYL-6,7-DIHYDRO-1H-CYCLOPENTAPYRIMIDINE-2,4(3H,5H)-DIONE	2164-08-1	PST73238
3-CYCLOOCTYL-1,1-DIMETHYLUREA	2163-69-1	PST05996
3-DIETHOXYPHOSPHINOTHIOYLTHIOMETHYL-1,2,3-BENZOTRIAZIN-4(3H)-ONE	2642-71-9	PST02205
3-DIMETHOXYPHOSPHINITHIOYLTHIOMETHYL-1,2,3-BENZOTRIAZIN-4(3H)-ONE	86-50-0	PST02210
3-DIMETHOXYPHOSPHINOTHIOYLTHIOMETHYL-5-ETHOXY-1,3,4-THIADIAZOL-2(3H)-ONE	2669-32-1	PST73147
3-DIMETHOXYPHOSPHINOTHIOYLTHIOMETHYL-5-METHOXY-1,3,4-THIADIAZOL-2(3H)ONE	950-37-8	PST14175
3-DIMETHOXYPHOSPHINOYLOXY-N-METHYLISOCROTONAMIDE	6923-22-4	PST15165
3-DIMETHOXYPHOSPHINOYLOXY-N,N-DIMETHYLISOCROTONAMIDE	141-66-2	PST03090
3-DIMETHOXYPHOSPHINYLOXY-N,N-DIMETHYLISOCROTONAMIDE	141-66-2	PST03090
3-DIMETHYLAMINOMETHYLENEAMINOPHENYL METHYLCARBAMATE	22259-30-9	PST73187
3-ETHOXYCARBONYLAMINOPHENYL PHENYLCARBAMATE	13684-56-5	PST72336
3-ETHYLTHIO-4-AMINO-6-TERT-BUTYL-1,2,4-TRIAZINE-5-ONE	64529-56-2	PST09111
3-FURFURYL-2-METHYL-4-OXO-2-CYCLOPENTEN-1-YL CHRYSANTHEMUMATE	17080-02-3	PST10175
3-HYDROXY-P-CYMENE	89-83-8	PST23475
3-HYDROXY-2-PENTENEDIOIC ACID DIMETHYL ESTER DIMETHYL PHOSPHATE	122-10-1	PST03240
3-HYDROXY-5-METHYLISOXAZOLE	10004-44-1	PST22404
3-HYDROXYCARBOFURAN	16655-82-6	PST72800
3-HYDROXYCROTONIC ACID METHYL ESTER DIMETHYL PHOSPHATE	7786-34-7	PST18650
3-HYDROXYGLUTACONIC ACID DIMETHYL ESTER DIMETHYL PHOSPHATE	122-10-1	PST03240
3-HYDROXYTOLUENE	108-39-4	PST13080
3-INDOLEBUTYRIC ACID	133-32-4	PST29325
3-INDOLYLBUTRIC ACID	133-32-4	PST29325
3-ISOPROPYL-1H-BENZO-2,1,3-THIADIAZIN-4-ONE 2,2-DIOXIDE	25057-89-0	PST02584
3-ISOPROPYL-1H-2,1,3-BENZOTHIADIAZIN-4(3H)-ONE 2,2-DIOXIDE	25057-89-0	PST02584
3-ISOPROPYL-5-METHYLCARBAMIC ACID METHYL ESTER	2631-37-0	PST72957
3-ISOPROPYLL-5-METHYLPHENYL-N-METHYLCARBAMATE	2631-37-0	PST72957
3-ISOPROPYLPHENYL METHYLCARBAMATE	64-00-6	PST29423
3-ISOPROPYLPHENYL N-METHYLCARBAMATE	64-00-6	PST29423
3-ISOXAZOLOL, 5-METHYL-	10004-44-1	PST22404
3-KETO-7-CARBOFURAN PHENOL	17781-16-7	PST72799
3-KETOCARBOFURAN PHENOL	17781-16-7	PST72799
3-MESYLBUTANONE O-METHYLCARBAMOYLOXIME	34681-23-7	PST72434
3-METHOXYCARBONYLAMINOPHENYL 3'-METHYLCARBANILATE	13684-63-4	PST72282
3-METHYL-1-(1-METHYLETHYL)-1H-PYRAZOL-5-YL DIMETHYLCARBAMATE	119-38-0	PST83027
3-METHYL-1-PHENYL-1H-PYRAZOL-5-YL DIMETHYLCARBAMATE	87-47-8	PST73263
3-METHYL-1-PHENYL-5-PYRAZOLYL DIMETHYLCARBAMATE	87-47-8	PST73263
3-METHYL-1-PHENYLPYRAZOL-5-YL DIMETHYLCARBAMATE	87-47-8	PST73263
3-METHYL-2-BUTENOIC ACID-2-(1-METHYLPROPYL)-4,6-DINITROPHENYL ESTER	485-31-4	PST71960
3-METHYL-4-CHLOROPHENOL	59-50-7	PST29890
3-METHYL-5-(1-METHYLETHYL)PHENOL METHYLCARBAMATE	2631-37-0	PST72957
3-METHYL-5-(1-METHYLETHYL)PHENYL-CARBAMIC ACID METHYL ESTER	2631-37-0	PST72957

ALPHABETICAL INDEX

SUBSTANCE NAME	CAS #	PST #
4-(METHYLSULFONYL)-2,6-DINITRO-N,N-DIPROPYLANILINE	4726-14-1	PST16525
4-(METHYLSULFONYL)-2,6-DINITRO-N,N-DIPROPYLBENZENAMINE	4726-14-1	PST16525
4-(METHYLTHIO)-3,5-XYLYL METHYLCARBAMATE	2032-65-7	PST14190
4-(1,1-DIMETHYLETHYL)-N-(1-METHYLPROPYL)-2,6-DINITROBENZENAMINE	33629-47-9	PST03525
4-(1,1-DIMETHYLETHYL)PHENOL	98-54-4	PST17440
4-(1,1-DIMETHYLPROPYL)PHENOL	80-46-6	PST71715
4-(2,4-DB) METHYL ESTER	18625-12-2	PST06227
4-(2,4-DICHLOROPHENOXY) METHYL BUTYRATE	18625-12-2	PST06227
4-(2,4-DICHLOROPHENOXY)BUTANOIC ACID METHYL ESTER	18625-12-2	PST06227
4-(2,4-DICHLOROPHENOXY)BUTYRIC ACID METHYL ESTER	18625-12-2	PST06227
4-(2,4-DICHLOROPHENOXY)METHYL BUTANOATE	18625-12-2	PST06227
4-(2,4,5-TB)	93-80-1	PST73203
4-(2,4,5-TRICHLOROPHENOXY) BUTANOIC ACID	93-80-1	PST73203
4-(2,4,5-TRICHLOROPHENOXY) BUTYRIC ACID	93-80-1	PST73203
4-AMINO-N-2-QUINOXALINYL-BENZENESULFONAMIDE	59-40-5	PST72046
4-AMINO-N-2-THIAZOLYLBENZENESULFONAMIDE	72-14-0	PST72047
4-AMINO-3-METHYL-6-PHENYL-1,2,4-TRIAZIN-5(4H)-ONE	41394-05-2	PST14095
4-AMINO-3-METHYL-6-PHENYL-1,2,4-TRIAZINE-5(4H)-ONE	41394-05-2	PST14095
4-AMINO-3,5,6-TRICHLORO-2-PICOLINIC ACID	1918-02-1	PST18840
4-AMINO-3,5,6-TRICHLORO-2-PYRIDINECARBOXYLIC ACID	1918-02-1	PST18840
4-AMINO-3,5,6-TRICHLOROPICOLINIC ACID	1918-02-1	PST18840
4-AMINO-3,5,6-TRICHLOROPYRIDINE-2-CARBOXYLIC ACID	1918-02-1	PST18840
4-AMINO-4,5-DIHYDRO-3-METHYL-6-PHENYL-1,2,4-TRIAZIN-5-ONE	41394-05-2	PST14095
4-AMINO-6-(1,1-DIMETHYLETHYL)-3-(ETHYLTHIO)-1,2,4-TRIAZIN-5(4H)-ONE	64529-56-2	PST09111
4-AMINO-6-(1,1-DIMETHYLETHYL)-3-(METHYLTHIO)-1,2,4-TRIAZIN-5(4H)-ONE	21087-64-9	PST15006
4-AMINO-6-TERT-BUTYL-3-(METHYLTHIO)-AS-TRIAZIN-5(4H)-ONE	21087-64-9	PST15006
4-AMINO-6-TERT-BUTYL-3-METHYLTHIO-1,2,4-TRIAZIN-5(4H)-ONE	21087-64-9	PST15006
4-AMINO-6-TERT-BUTYL-4,5-DIHYDRO-3-METHYLTHIO-1,2,4-TRIAZIN-5-ONE	21087-64-9	PST15006
4-AMINOBENZOIC ACID, ETHYL ESTER	94-09-7	PST72267
4-AMINOPYRIDINE	504-24-5	PST02180
4-AMINOTRICHLOROPICOLINIC ACID	1918-02-1	PST18840
4-AP	504-24-5	PST02180
4-AZIDO-N-(1-METHYLETHYL)-6-(METHYLTHIO)-1,3,5-TRIAZIN-2-AMINE	4658-28-0	PST02216
4-AZIDO-N-ISOPROPYL-6-METHYLTHIO-1,3,5-TRIAZIN-2-YLAMINE	4658-28-0	PST02216
4-BENZOTHIENYL METHYLCARBAMATE	1079-33-0	PST29855
4-BENZOTHIENYL-N-METHYLCARBAMATE	1079-33-0	PST29855
4-BROMO-2,5-DICHLOROPHENYL DIMETHYL PHOSPHOROTHIONATE	4824-78-6	PST03458
4-BROMO-2,5-DICHLOROPHENYL DIMETHYL PHOSPHOROTHIONATE	2104-96-3	PST71064
4-BROMO-2,5-DICHLOROPHENYL METHYL PHENYLPHOSPHONATE	25006-32-0	PST12776
4-BUTYLAMINOBENZOIC ACID, 2-(DIMETHYLAMINO)ETHYL ESTER, MONOHYDROCHLORIDE	136-47-0	PST72269
4-CARBETHOXYANILINE	94-09-7	PST72267
4-CHLORO-(ALPHA-(1-METHYLETHYL)BENZENEACETIC ACID CYANO (3-PHENOXYPHENYL)METHYL ESTER	51630-58-1	PST19948
4-CHLORO-ALPHA-(4-CHLOROPHENYL)-ALPHA(TRICHLOROMETHYL)BENZENEMETHANOL	115-32-2	PST07010
4-CHLORO-ALPHA-(4-CHLOROPHENYL)-ALPHA-HYDROXYBENZENEACETIC ACID ETHYL ESTER	510-15-6	PST04740
4-CHLORO-ALPHA-(4-CHLOROPHENYL)BENZENEACETIC ACID	83-05-6	PST06232
4-CHLORO-BETA-(4-CHLOROPHENYL)BENZENEETHANOL	2642-82-2	PST06323
4-CHLORO-M-CRESOL	59-50-7	PST29890
4-CHLORO-1-HYDROXY-3-METHYLBENZENE	59-50-7	PST29890
4-CHLORO-2-BUTYNYL M-CHLOROPHENYLCARBAMATE	101-27-9	PST71143
4-CHLORO-2-BUTYNYL N-(3-CHLOROPHENYL)CARBAMATE	101-27-9	PST71143
4-CHLORO-2-BUTYNYL 3-CHLOROPHENYLCARBAMATE	101-27-9	PST71143

SUBSTANCE NAME	CAS #	PST #
4-CHLORO-2-CYCLOPENTYLPHENOL	13347-42-7	PST71731
4-CHLORO-2-OXO-3(2H)-BENZOTHIAZOLEACETIC ACID	3813-05-6	PST72725
4-CHLORO-2-OXO-3-BENZOTHIAZOLINEACETIC ACID	3813-05-6	PST72725
4-CHLORO-2-OXOBENZOTHIAZOLIN-3-YLACETIC ACID	3813-05-6	PST72725
4-CHLORO-2,3-DIHYDRO-2-OXO-1,3-BENZOTHIAZOL-3-YLACETIC ACID	3813-05-6	PST72725
4-CHLORO-3-METHYLPHENOL	59-50-7	PST29890
4-CHLORO-3,5-DIMETHYLPHENOL	88-04-0	PST72258
4-CHLORO-3,5-XYLENOL	88-04-0	PST72258
4-CHLORO-5-(METHYLAMINO)-2-(ALPHA,ALPHA,ALPHA-TRIFLUORO-M-TOLYL)-3(2H)-PYRIDAZINONE	27314-13-2	PST72343
4-CHLORO-5-(METHYLAMINO)-2-(3-(TRIFLUOROMETHYL)PHENYL-3(2H)-PYRIDAZINONE	27314-13-2	PST72343
4-CHLORO-5-METHYLAMINO-2-(ALPHA,ALPHA,ALPHA-TRIFLUORO-M-TOLYL)-PYRIDAZIN-3(2H)-ONE	27314-13-2	PST72343
4-CHLORO-5-METHYLAMINO-2-(3-TRIFLUOROMETHYLPHENYL)PYRIDAZIN-3-ONE	27314-13-2	PST72343
4-CHLOROBENZYL 4-CHLOROPHENYL SULFIDE	103-17-3	PST71139
4-CHLOROBUT-2-YNYL 3-CHLOROCARBANILATE	101-27-9	PST71143
4-CHLOROBUT-2-YNYL 3-CHLOROPHENYLCARBAMATE	101-27-9	PST71143
4-CHLORODIPHENYL SULFONE	80-00-2	PST71663
4-CHLOROPHENYL BENZENESULFONATE	80-38-6	PST09677
4-CHLOROPHENYL BENZENESULFONIC ACID ESTER	80-38-6	PST09677
4-CHLOROPHENYL BENZENESULPHONATE	80-38-6	PST09677
4-CHLOROPHENYL PHENYL SULFONE	80-00-2	PST71663
4-CYANO-2,6-DI-IODOPHENYL OCTANOATE	3861-47-0	PST73075
4-CYANO-2,6-DIIODOPHENOL	1689-83-4	PST11468
4-CYANO-2,6-DIIODOPHENYL OCTANOATE	3861-47-0	PST73075
4-CYANOPHENYLETHYLPHENYL PHOSPHONOTHIONATE	13067-93-1	PST05805
4-DIALLYLAMINO-3,5-XYLYL METHYLCARBAMATE	6392-46-7	PST72977
4-DIMETHYLAMINO-M-CRESYL METHYLCARBAMATE	2032-59-9	PST71500
4-DIMETHYLAMINO-M-TOLYL METHYLCARBAMATE	2032-59-9	PST71500
4-DIMETHYLAMINO-3-CRESYL METHYLCARBAMATE	2032-59-9	PST71500
4-DIMETHYLAMINO-3-METHYL-PHENYL-N-METHYLCARBAMATE	2032-59-9	PST71500
4-ETHOXY-7-PHENYL-3,5-DIOXA-6-AZA-4-PHOSPHAOCT-6-ENE-8-NITRILE -4-SULFIDE	14816-18-3	PST73292
4-ETHOXYACETANILIDE	62-44-2	PST18340
4-HYDROXY-3-(1,2,3,4-TETRAHYDRO-1-NAPHTHALENYL)-2H-1-BENZOPYRAN-2-ONE	5836-29-3	PST05493
4-HYDROXY-3-(1,2,3,4-TETRAHYDRO-1-NAPHTHYL)COUMARIN	5836-29-3	PST05493
4-HYDROXY-3-(3-OXO-1-PHENYLBUTYL)-2H-1-BENZOPYRAN-2-ONE	81-81-2	PST25090
4-HYDROXY-3-(3-OXO-1-PHENYLBUTYL)-2H-1-BENZOPYRAN-2-ONE, SODIUM SALT	129-06-6	PST83008
4-HYDROXY-3-(3-OXO-1-PHENYLBUTYL)COUMARIN	81-81-2	PST25090
4-HYDROXY-3,5-DIIODOBENZONITRILE	1689-83-4	PST11468
4-HYDROXY-3,5-DIIODOBENZONITRILE, SODIUM SALT	2961-62-8	PST73074
4-HYDROXY-3,5-DIIODOPHENYL CYANIDE	1689-83-4	PST11468
4-HYDROXYBENZOIC ACID, METHYL ESTER	99-76-3	PST14677
4-HYDROXYBENZOIC ACID, PROPYL ESTER	94-13-3	PST19941
4-HYDROXYNITROBENZENE	100-02-7	PST17800
4-HYDROXYNONANOIC ACID LACTONE	104-61-0	PST10334
4-ISOTHIAZOLIN-3-ONE, 2-METHYL-	2682-20-4	PST72362
4-ISOTHIAZOLIN-3-ONE, 2-N-OCTYL-	26530-20-1	PST72294
4-ISOTHIAZOLIN-3-ONE, 2-OCTYL-	26530-20-1	PST72294
4-METHYL-2-PENTANONE	108-10-1	PST14550
4-METHYLBENZENESULFONIC ACID	104-15-4	PST67915
4-METHYLSULFONYL-2,6-DINITRO-N,N-DIPROPYLANILINE	4726-14-1	PST16525
4-METHYLSULPHONYL-2,6-DINITRO-N,N-DIPROPYLANILINE	4726-14-1	PST16525

SUBSTANCE NAME	CAS #	PST #
TETRAHYDRO-, EXO,ENDO-		
4,7-METHANOINDAN, 1,2,4,5,6,7,8,8-OCTACHLORO-3A,4,7,7A-TETRAHYDRO-	57-74-9	PST04560
4,7-METHANOINDAN, 1,4,5,6,7,8,8-HEPTACHLORO-2,3-EPOXY-3A,4,7,7A-TETRAHYDRO-	1024-57-3	PST10670
4,7-METHANOINDAN, 1ALPHA,2ALPHA,4BETA,5,6,7BETA,8,8-OCTACHLORO-3A ALPHA,4,7,7A ALPHA-TETRAHYDRO-	5103-71-9	PST00776
4,7-METHANOINDAN, 1BETA,2ALPHA,4ALPHA,5,6,7ALPHA,8,8-OCTACHLORO-3A BETA,4,7,7A BETA-TETRAHYDRO-	5103-74-2	PST10331
4,7-METHANOINDENE, 1,4,5,6,7,8,8-HEPTACHLORO-3A,4,7,7A-TETRAHYDRO-	76-44-8	PST10660
4,7-METHANOINDENE, 4,5,6,7,8,8-HEXACHLORO-3A,4,7,7A-TETRAHYDRO-	3734-48-3	PST04565
4,7-METHANOISOBENZOFURAN, 1,3,4,5,6,7,8,8-OCTACHLORO-1,3,3A,4,7,7A-HEXAHYDRO-	297-78-9	PST83032
4,7-METHANOISOBENZOFURAN, 1,3,4,5,6,7,8,8-OCTACHLORO-3A,4,7,7A -TETRAHYDRO-	297-78-9	PST83032
4'-CHLORO-ALPHA,ALPHA-DIMETHYLVALERANILIDE	7287-36-7	PST72987
4'-CHLORO-2,2-DIMETHYLVALERANILIDE	7287-36-7	PST72987
4A(ALPHA), 4B(BETA), 10 BETA)-	125-67-7	PST71492
4A(4H)-DIBENZOFURANCARBOXALDEHYDE, 1,5A,6,9,9A,9B-HEXAHYDRO-	126-15-8	PST71487
4H-1,3,2-BENZODIOXAPHOSPHORIN, 2-METHOXY-, 2-SULFIDE	3811-49-2	PST20325
5-((2-(2-BUTOXYETHOXY)ETHOXY)METHYL)-6-PROPYL-1,3-BENZODIOXOLE	51-03-6	PST75640
5-(ALPHA-HYDROXY-ALPHA-2-PYRIDYLBENZYL)-7-(ALPHA-2 -PYRIDYLBENZYLIDENE)-5-NORBORNENE-2,3-DICARBOXIMIDE	991-42-4	PST72254
5-(BIS(2-(2-BUTOXYETHOXY)ETHOXY)METHYL)-1,3-BENZODIOXOLE	5281-13-0	PST71828
5-(2-CHLORO-4-(TRIFLUOROMETHYL)PHENOXY)-2-NITROBENZOIC ACID	50594-66-6	PST72452
5-(2-CHLORO-4-(TRIFLUOROMETHYL)PHENOXY)-2-NITROBENZOIC ACID SODIUM SALT	62476-59-9	PST72453
5-(2,4-DICHLOROPHENOXY)-2-NITROBENZOIC ACID METHYL ESTER	42576-02-3	PST72332
5-ACETAMIDO-2,4-DIMETHYLTRIFLUOROMETHANESULFONANILIDE	53780-34-0	PST72444
5-AMINO-1-(BIS(DIMETHYLAMINO)PHOSPHINYL)-3-PHENYL-1,2,4-TRIAZOLE	1031-47-6	PST72937
5-AMINO-1-BIS(DIMETHYLAMIDO)PHOSPHORYL-3-PHENYL-1,2,4-TRIAZOLE	1031-47-6	PST72937
5-AMINO-3-PHENYL-1,2,4-TRIAZOLE-1-YL-N,N,N',N' -TETRAMETHYLPHOSPHODIAMIDE	1031-47-6	PST72937
5-AMINO-4-BROMO-2-PHENYL-3(2H)-PYRIDAZINONE	3042-84-0	PST72769
5-AMINO-4-BROMO-2-PHENYLPYRIDAZIN-3(2H)-ONE	3042-84-0	PST72769
5-AMINO-4-BROMO-2-PHENYLPYRIDAZINE-3-ONE	3042-84-0	PST72769
5-AMINO-4-CHLORO-2-PHENYL-3(2H)-PYRIDAZINONE	1698-60-8	PST71928
5-AMINO-4-CHLORO-2-PHENYLPYRIDAZIN-3(2H)-ONE	1698-60-8	PST71928
5-BENZOFURANOL, 2-ETHOXY-2,3-DIHYDRO-3,3-DIMETHYL-, METHANESULFONATE, (+,-)-	26225-79-6	PST72404
5-BENZYL-3-FURYLMETHYL (+)-CIS-CHRYSANTHEMATE	35764-59-1	PST20094
5-BENZYL-3-FURYLMETHYL (+)-TRANS-CHRYSANTHEMATE	28434-01-7	PST20093
5-BENZYL-3-FURYLMETHYL (+-)-CIS-TRANS-CHRYSANTHEMATE	10453-86-8	PST20095
5-BENZYLFURFURYL CHRYSANTHEMATE	10453-86-8	PST20095
5-BROMO-3-ISOPROPYL-6-METHYLURACIL	314-42-1	PST71090
5-BROMO-3-SEC-BUTYL-6-METHYLURACIL	314-40-9	PST03330
5-BROMO-6-METHYL-3-(1-METHYLETHYL)-2,4(1H,3H)-PYRIMIDINEDIONE	314-42-1	PST71090
5-BROMO-6-METHYL-3-(1-METHYLPROPYL)-2,4(1H,3H)-PYRIMIDINEDIONE	314-40-9	PST03330
5-BUTYL-2-(DIMETHYLAMINO)-6-METHYL-4(1H)-PYRIMIDINONE	5221-53-4	PST72919
5-BUTYL-2-(DIMETHYLAMINO)-6-METHYL-4-PYRIMIDINOL	5221-53-4	PST72919
5-BUTYL-2-(ETHYLAMINO)-6-METHYL-4(1H)-PYRIMIDINONE	23947-60-6	PST08721
5-BUTYL-2-(ETHYLAMINO)-6-METHYL-4(3H)-PYRIMIDINONE	23947-60-6	PST08721
5-CHLORO-3-(1,1-DIMETHYLETHYL)-6-METHYL-2,4(1H,3H)-PYRIMIDINEDIONE	5902-51-2	PST71099
5-CHLORO-6-((((METHYLAMINO)CARBONYL)OXY)IMINO)-BICYCLO(2.2.1)HEPTANE 2-CARBONITRILE, (1S-(1 ALPHA, 2 BETA, 4 ALPHA, 5 ALPHA, 6 EPSILON))	15271-41-7	PST73177

ALPHABETICAL INDEX

SUBSTANCE NAME	CAS #	PST #
6-CHLORO-N,N'-DIETHYL-1,3,5-TRIAZINE-2,4-DIAMINE	122-34-9	PST20837
6-CHLORO-2-PHENYLPHENOL	85-97-2	PST71680
6-CHLORO-3-DIETHOXYPHOSPHINOTHIOYLTHIOMETHYL-1,3-BENZOXAZOL-2(3H)-ONE	2310-17-0	PST25720
6-CHLORO-3-HYDROXYTOLUENE	59-50-7	PST29890
6-CHLORO-3,4-XYLYL ESTER METHYLCARBAMIC ACID	671-04-5	PST02250
6-CHLORO-3,4-XYLYL METHYLCARBAMATE	671-04-5	PST02250
6-CHLOROXENOL	85-97-2	PST71680
6-ETHOXY-1,2-DIHYDRO-2,2,4-TRIMETHYLQUINOLINE	91-53-2	PST08740
6-ETHYLTHIO-N,N-DI-ISOPROPYL-1,3,5-TRIAZINE-2,4-DIAMINE	4147-51-7	PST72333
6-FURFURYLADENINE	525-79-1	PST72483
6-FURFURYLAMINO PURINE	525-79-1	PST72483
6-HYDROXY-3(2H)-PYRIDAZINONE	123-33-1	PST13570
6-METHOXY-N,N'-BIS(1-METHYLETHYL)-1,3,5-TRIAZINE-2,4-DIAMINE	1610-18-0	PST19967
6-METHYL-2-PROPYL-4-PYRIMIDINYL DIMETHYLCARBAMATE	2532-49-2	PST73266
6-TERT-BUTYL-4-ISOBUTYLIDENEAMINO-3-METHYLTHIO-1,2,4-TRIAZIN-5(4H) -ONE	57052-04-7	PST11844
6,7-DIHYDRODIPYRIDO(1,2-A:2',1'-C)PYRAZINEDIIUM DIBROMIDE	85-00-7	PST08250
6,7-DIHYDRODIPYRIDOL(1,2-A:2',1'-C)PYRAZIDIINIUM DIBROMIDE	85-00-7	PST08250
6,7,8,9,10,10-HEXACHLORO-1,5,5A,6,9,9A-HEXAHYDRO-6,9-METHANO-2,4, 3-BENZODIOXATHIEPIN 3-OXIDE	115-29-7	PST08560
6,9-METHANO-2,4,3-BENZODIOXATHIEPIN, 6, 7,8,9,10,10-HEXACHLORO-1,5, 5A,6,9,9A-HEXAHYDRO-,3-OXIDE	115-29-7	PST08560
6,9-METHANO-2,4,3-BENZODIOXATHIEPIN, 6,7,8,9,10,10-HEXACHLORO-1, 5,5A,6,9,9A-HEXAHYDRO-, 3-OXIDE, (3 ALPHA, 5A BETA, 6 ALPHA, 9 ALPHA,	959-98-8	PST00800
6,9-METHANO-2,4,3-BENZODIOXATHIEPIN, 6,7,8,9,10,10-HEXACHLORO-1, 5,5A,6,9,9A-HEXAHYDRO-, 3-OXIDE, (3 ALPHA, 5A ALPHA, 6 BETA, 9 BETA,	33213-65-9	PST03040
6A ALPHA, 7 BETA, 7A ALPHA)-	60-57-1	PST07080
6BETA,6A ALPHA)-	27304-13-8	PST17372
7-BENZOFURANOL, 2,3-DIHYDRO-2,2-DIMETHYL-, METHYLCARBAMATE	1563-66-2	PST04240
7-CHLOROBICYCLO(3.2.0)HEPTA-2.6-DIEN-6-YL DIMETHYL PHOSPHATE	23560-59-0	PST10685
7-HYDROXY-2,2-DIMETHYL-3(2H)-BENZOFURANONE	17781-16-7	PST72799
7-OXA-5-THIA-2-AZA-6-PHOSPHANONANOIC ACID, 6-ETHOXY-2-METHYL-3-, OXO-, ETHYL ESTER, 6-SULFIDE	2595-54-2	PST13675
7-OXABICYCLO(2.2.1)HEPTANE-2,3-DICARBOSYLIC ACID, DISODIUM SALT	129-67-9	PST08590
7-OXABICYCLO(2.2.1)HEPTANE-2,3-DICARBOXYLIC ACID	145-73-3	PST08580
7,11-HEXADECADIEN-1-OL, ACETATE, (Z,Z)-	52207-99-5	PST72448
8-HYDROXYQUINOLINE	148-24-3	PST30450
8-HYDROXYQUINOLINE BENZOATE (SALT)	7091-57-8	PST71657
8-OQ	148-24-3	PST30450
8-OXYQUINOLINE	148-24-3	PST30450
8-QUINOLINOL	148-24-3	PST30450
8-QUINOLINOL BENZOATE	7091-57-8	PST71657
88R	140-57-8	PST01850
9-OCTADECANOIC ACID (Z)-	112-80-1	PST17305
9-OCTADECENOIC ACID (Z)-,POTASSIUM SALT	143-18-0	PST72131
9-OCTADECENOIC ACID, 12-HYDROXY-, MONOPOTASSIUM SALT	7492-30-0	PST72074
9-OCTADECENOIC ACID, 12-HYDROXY-, MONOPOTASSIUM SALT, (R-(Z))-	7492-30-0	PST72074
9-TRICOSENE, (Z)-	27519-02-4	PST05185
9,10-ANTHRACENEDIONE	84-65-1	PST01600
9,10-ANTHRAQUINONE	84-65-1	PST01600
9,10-DIHYDRO-9,10-DIKETOANTHRACENE	84-65-1	PST01600
9,10-DIOXOANTHRACENE	84-65-1	PST01600
9A ALPHA)-	33213-65-9	PST03040
9A BETA)-	959-98-8	PST00800

ALPHABETICAL INDEX

SUBSTANCE NAME	CAS #	PST #
9H-FLUORENE-9-CARBOXYLIC ACID, 2-CHLORO-9-HYDROXY-, METHYL ESTER	2536-31-4	PST72283
998	79-14-1	PST10500

CAS NUMBER INDEX

CAS #	PST #	SUBSTANCE NAME
100-02-7	PST17800	P-NITROPHENOL
100-51-6	PST02800	BENZYL ALCOHOL
100-52-7	PST02590	BENZALDEHYDE
100-56-1	PST18570	PHENYLMERCURIC CHLORIDE
100-57-2	PST18580	PHENYLMERCURIC HYDROXIDE
10004-44-1	PST22404	HYMEXAZOL
10028-22-5	PST09790	FERRIC SULFATE
10043-01-3	PST00980	ALUMINUM SULFATE
10043-35-3	PST03260	BORIC ACID
10043-52-4	PST03900	CALCIUM CHLORIDE
10045-89-3	PST09820	FERROUS AMMONIUM SULFATE
10049-04-4	PST04610	CHLORINE DIOXIDE
101-05-3	PST01526	ANILAZINE
101-21-3	PST71148	CHLORPROPHAM
101-27-9	PST71143	BARBAN
101-42-8	PST09679	FENURON
101-76-8	PST06321	4,4'-DICHLORODIPHENYLMETHANE
10101-97-0	PST16410	NICKEL SULFATE, HEXAHYDRATE
10108-64-2	PST03740	CADMIUM CHLORIDE
10124-65-9	PST72072	POTASSIUM LAURATE
10125-13-0	PST05625	CUPRIC CHLORIDE, DIHYDRATE
10137-74-3	PST03890	CALCIUM CHLORATE
1014-69-3	PST06353	DESMETRYNE
1014-70-6	PST02838	SIMETRYN
102-71-6	PST23932	TRIETHANOLAMINE
1022-22-6	PST06322	2,2-BIS(4-CHLOROPHENYL)-1-CHLOROETHENE
1024-57-3	PST10670	HEPTACHLOR EPOXIDE
10257-54-2	PST05675	CUPRIC SULFATE, MONOHYDRATE
10265-92-6	PST15160	METHAMIDOPHOS
103-17-3	PST71139	CHLORBENSIDE
1031-47-6	PST72937	TRIAMIPHOS
10311-84-9	PST23630	DIALIFOR
104-15-4	PST67915	P-TOLUENESULFONIC ACID
104-55-2	PST05100	CINNAMALDEHYDE
104-60-9	PST71769	PHENYLMERCURIC OLEATE
104-61-0	PST10334	GAMMA-NONANOLACTONE
10402-15-0	PST71496	COPPER CITRATE
10453-86-8	PST20095	RESMETHRIN
105-67-9	PST28670	2,4-XYLENOL
10588-01-9	PST21190	SODIUM DICHROMATE
106-46-7	PST17640	P-DICHLOROBENZENE
106-93-4	PST09380	ETHYLENE DIBROMIDE
107-02-8	PST00330	ACROLEIN, INHIBITED
107-06-2	PST09390	ETHYLENE DICHLORIDE
107-15-3	PST09560	ETHYLENEDIAMINE
107-21-1	PST09400	ETHYLENE GLYCOL
107-27-7	PST09620	ETHYLMERCURIC CHLORIDE
107-49-3	PST22520	TETRAETHYL PYROPHOSPHATE
107-88-0	PST26730	1,3-BUTANEDIOL
1071-83-6	PST10515	GLYPHOSATE
1076-46-6	PST71252	CHLORAMBEN AMMONIUM SALT
1079-33-0	PST29855	4-BENZOTHIENYL METHYLCARBAMATE
108-10-1	PST14550	METHYL ISOBUTYL KETONE
108-39-4	PST13080	M-CRESOL

CAS NUMBER INDEX

CAS NUMBER INDEX

CAS NUMBER INDEX

CAS #	PST #	SUBSTANCE NAME
13347-42-7	PST71731	4-CHLORO-2-CYCLOPENTYLPHENOL
13356-08-6	PST24866	VENDEX
13360-45-7	PST04552	CHLORBROMURON
1338-02-9	PST05460	COPPER NAPHTHENATE
134-62-3	PST84230	DEET
13426-91-0	PST05710	CUPRIETHYLENEDIAMINE
13429-27-1	PST72073	POTASSIUM MYRISTATE
13457-18-6	PST73169	PYRAZOPHOS
135-19-3	PST03050	2-NAPHTHOL
13593-03-8	PST73112	QUINALPHOS
136-32-3	PST21713	2,4,5-SODIUM TRICHLOROPHENATE
136-47-0	PST72269	TETRACAINE HYDROCHLORIDE
136-78-7	PST05500	SODIUM 2,4-DICHLOROPHENOXYETHYL SULFATE
13684-56-5	PST72336	DESMEDIPHAM
13684-63-4	PST72282	PHENMEDIPHAM
137-26-8	PST23430	THIRAM
137-30-4	PST25397	ZINC DIMETHYLDITHIOCARBAMATE
137-40-6	PST21575	SODIUM PROPIONATE
137-42-8	PST71430	SODIUM METHYLDITHIOCARBAMATE
138-87-4	PST03075	BETA-TERPINEOL
13840-33-0	PST12920	LITHIUM HYPOCHLORITE
139-02-6	PST21530	SODIUM PHENOLATE
139-33-3	PST08305	ETHYLENEDIAMINETETRAACETIC ACID, DISODIUM SALT
139-40-2	PST19736	PROPAZINE
139-41-3	PST71447	SODIUM DIHYDROXYETHYLGLYCINE
13932-13-3	PST72015	POTASSIUM TETRATHIONATE
1397-94-0	PST83076	ANTIMYCIN A
140-41-0	PST15197	MONURON TCA
140-56-7	PST73084	FENAMINOSULF
140-57-8	PST01850	ARAMITE
1405-10-3	PST84263	NEOMYCIN SULFATE
14086-35-2	PST02552	FENTHION OXON SULFONE
141-43-5	PST08710	ETHANOLAMINE
141-66-2	PST03090	DICROTOPHOS
141-78-6	PST08750	ETHYL ACETATE
142-59-6	PST16080	NABAM
1420-07-1	PST72921	DINOTERB
14214-32-5	PST07386	DIFENOXURON
14255-72-2	PST06228	FENSULFOTHION SULFONE
143-18-0	PST72131	POTASSIUM OLEATE
143-19-1	PST21418	SODIUM OLEATE
143-33-9	PST21160	SODIUM CYANIDE, SOLID
143-50-0	PST12330	CHLORDECONE
144-41-2	PST73096	MORPHOTHION
144-55-8	PST20970	SODIUM BICARBONATE
144-62-7	PST17360	OXALIC ACID
14484-64-1	PST09680	FERBAM
145-73-3	PST08580	ENDOTHALL
1461-22-9	PST72222	TRIBUTYLTIN CHLORIDE
148-24-3	PST30450	8-HYDROXYQUINOLINE
14816-18-3	PST73292	PHOXIM
14835-94-0	PST04753	1-CHLORO-2-(O-CHLOROPHENYL)-2-(P-CHLOROPHENYL)ETHYLENE
149-30-4	PST13738	MERCAPTOBENZOTHIAZOLE
1491-41-4	PST72737	NAPHTHALOPHOS

CAS NUMBER INDEX

CAS #	PST #	SUBSTANCE NAME
150-50-5	PST10010	MERPHOS
150-68-5	PST15196	MONURON
15096-52-3	PST05560	SODIUM FLUOALUMINATE
151-21-3	PST08485	DODECYL SODIUM SULFATE
151-38-2	PST83031	METHOXYETHYLMERCURIC ACETATE
151-50-8	PST19350	POTASSIUM CYANIDE, SOLID
152-16-9	PST20350	SCHRADAN
15251-48-6	PST84256	CALCIUM OXYTETRACYCLINE
15263-52-2	PST04359	CARTAP HYDROCHLORIDE
15271-41-7	PST73177	EXO-3-CHLORO-ENDO-6-CYANO-2-NORBORANONE O-(METHYLCARBAMOYL)OXIME
15299-99-7	PST72319	NAPROPAMIDE
15457-05-3	PST72248	FLUORODIFEN
15475-56-6	PST14211	METHOTREXATE SODIUM
155-04-4	PST27776	2-MERCAPTOBENZOTHIAZOLE, ZINC SALT
15545-48-9	PST04912	CHLOROTOLURON
156-62-7	PST03930	CALCIUM CYANAMIDE, NOT HYDRATED
1563-66-2	PST04240	CARBOFURAN
1582-09-8	PST24085	TRIFLURALIN
15879-93-3	PST00775	ALPHA-CHLORALOSE
15922-78-8	PST21420	SODIUM PYRIDINETHIONE
1596-84-5	PST06195	DAMINOZIDE
15972-60-8	PST00506	ALACHLOR
1610-17-9	PST02148	ATRATON
1610-18-0	PST19967	PROMETON
16118-49-3	PST72941	CARBETAMIDE
1634-78-2	PST13541	MALATHION OXYGEN ANALOG
16423-68-0	PST08685	ERYTHROSIN B
1646-87-3	PST00503	ALDICARB SULFOXIDE
1646-88-4	PST72406	ALDOXYCARB
16655-82-6	PST72800	3-HYDROXYCARBOFURAN
16662-85-4	PST04344	CARBOPHENOTHION SULFONE
16662-86-5	PST04343	CARBOPHENOTHION OXYGEN ANALOG SULFOXIDE
16662-87-6	PST04342	CARBOPHENOTHION OXYGEN ANALOG SULFONE
16672-87-0	PST72293	ETHEPHON
16752-77-5	PST14200	METHOMYL
16871-71-9	PST25410	ZINC SILICOFLUORIDE
1689-83-4	PST11468	IOXYNIL
1689-84-5	PST03542	BROMOXYNIL
1689-99-2	PST03543	BROMOXYNIL OCTANOATE
16893-85-9	PST21620	SODIUM SILICOFLUORIDE
1698-60-8	PST71928	PYRAZON
1702-17-6	PST05211	CLOPYRALID
17040-19-6	PST06319	DEMETON-S-METHYL SULFONE
17080-02-3	PST10175	FURETHRIN
17109-49-8	PST08555	EDIFENPHOS
17210-55-8	PST71651	TEMEPHOS SULFOXIDE
17297-40-4	PST04345	CARBOPHENOTHION SULFOXIDE
1746-01-6	PST08060	2,3,7,8-TETRACHLORODIBENZO-P-DIOXIN
1746-81-2	PST15174	MONOLINURON
1754-58-1	PST72310	DIAMIDOFOS
1757-18-2	PST00493	AKTON
17702-57-7	PST73082	FORMPARANATE
17781-16-7	PST72799	7-HYDROXY-2,2-DIMETHYL-3(2H)-BENZOFURANONE
17804-35-2	PST02580	BENOMYL

CAS NUMBER INDEX

CAS #	PST #	SUBSTANCE NAME
18181-70-9	PST73035	IODOFENPHOS
1836-75-5	PST23580	NITROFEN
1836-77-7	PST23865	CHLORNITROFEN
18530-56-8	PST71400	NOREA
1861-32-1	PST04913	CHLORTHAL-DIMETHYL
1861-40-1	PST02570	BENFLURALIN
18625-12-2	PST06227	2,4-DB METHYL ESTER
18691-97-9	PST14108	METHABENZTHIAZURON
18854-01-8	PST12280	ISOXATHION
1897-45-6	PST04890	CHLOROTHALONIL
19044-88-3	PST17324	ORYZALIN
1910-42-5	PST18020	PARAQUAT DICHLORIDE
1912-24-9	PST02150	ATRAZINE
1912-26-1	PST23927	TRIETAZINE
1918-00-9	PST02260	DICAMBA
1918-02-1	PST18840	PICLORAM
1918-13-4	PST73046	CHLORTHIAMID
1918-16-7	PST19686	PROPACHLOR
1918-18-9	PST72247	SWEP
1928-37-6	PST22392	2,4,5-T METHYL ESTER
1928-38-7	PST71307	METHYL 2,4-DICHLOROPHENOXY ACETATE
1928-45-6	PST71294	2,4-D PROPYLENE GLYCOL BUTYL ETHER ESTER
1929-77-7	PST71473	VERNOLATE
1929-82-4	PST16530	NITRAPYRIN
1929-88-0	PST72971	BENZTHIAZURON
1934-21-0	PST22465	TARTRAZINE YELLOW DYE
1954-81-0	PST71256	CHLORAMBEN, SODIUM SALT
19666-30-9	PST72385	OXADIAZON
1967-16-4	PST73265	CHLORBUFAM
19750-95-9	PST71656	CHLORDIMEFORM HYDROCHLORIDE
1982-47-4	PST04905	CHLOROXURON
1982-49-6	PST20586	SIDURON
1982-69-0	PST71250	SODIUM DICAMBA
1983-10-4	PST72227	TRIBUTYLTIN FLUORIDE
1984-06-1	PST72105	SODIUM CAPRYLATE
19937-59-8	PST15009	METOXURON
2008-41-5	PST71474	BUTYLATE
2032-59-9	PST71500	AMINOCARB
2032-65-7	PST14190	METHIOCARB
20354-26-1	PST72344	METHAZOLE
20427-59-2	PST05640	CUPRIC HYDROXIDE
2058-46-0	PST84045	OXYTETRACYCLINE HYDROCHLORIDE
2074-50-2	PST71670	PARAQUAT DIMETHYL SULFATE
2078-42-4	PST71136	SODIUM 2,3,6-TRICHLOROBENZOIC ACID
20859-73-8	PST00970	ALUMINUM PHOSPHIDE
2104-64-5	PST08650	EPN
2104-96-3	PST71064	BROMOPHOS
21087-64-9	PST15006	METRIBUZIN
2122-70-5	PST71628	ETHYL 1-NAPHTHALENEACETATE
21267-72-1	PST73038	PRYNACHLOR
21548-32-3	PST16141	FOSTHIETAN
21564-17-0	PST71392	2-(THIOCYANOMETHYLTHIO)BENZOTHIAZOLE
21609-90-5	PST12780	LEPTOPHOS
2163-69-1	PST05996	CYCLURON

CAS NUMBER INDEX

CAS #	PST #	SUBSTANCE NAME
2163-80-6	PST15180	MONOSODIUM METHANE ARSONATE
2164-08-1	PST73238	LENACIL
2164-09-2	PST71378	DICRYL
2164-17-2	PST09907	FLUOMETURON
21725-46-2	PST05762	CYANAZINE
2212-67-1	PST71471	MOLINATE
22224-92-6	PST16145	FENAMIPHOS
22248-79-9	PST72244	(Z)-2-CHLORO-1-(2,4,5-TRICHLOROPHENYL)VINYL DIMETHYL PHOSPHATE
22259-30-9	PST73187	FORMETANATE
2235-25-8	PST71479	ETHYLMERCURIC PHOSPHATE
22350-76-1	PST72245	(E)-2-CHLORO-1-(2,4,5-TRICHLOROPHENYL)VINYL DIMETHYL PHOSPHATE
2244-21-5	PST19360	POTASSIUM DICHLOROISOCYANURATE
2275-14-1	PST18373	PHENCAPTON
2275-18-5	PST19943	PROTHOATE
2275-23-2	PST73108	VAMIDOTHION
22781-23-3	PST02560	BENDIOCARB
22936-75-0	PST72145	DIMETHAMETRYN
22936-86-3	PST72296	CYPRAZINE
2303-16-4	PST06480	DIALLATE
2303-17-5	PST72050	TRIALLATE
23052-51-9	PST06317	DEMETON-O OXYGEN ANALOG
2307-68-8	PST71164	PENTANOCHLOR
2310-17-0	PST25720	PHOSALONE
23103-98-2	PST72345	PIRIMICARB
2312-35-8	PST19720	PROPARGITE
2312-76-7	PST71411	DINITRO-O-CRESOL SODIUM SALT
23135-22-0	PST17370	OXAMYL
23184-66-9	PST03497	BUTACHLOR
23319-66-6	PST71768	PHENYL MERCURIC TRIETHANOL AMMONIUM LACTATE
23422-53-9	PST10050	FORMETANATE HYDROCHLORIDE
23505-41-1	PST72377	PIRIMIFOS-ETHYL
23560-59-0	PST10685	HEPTENOPHOS
23564-05-8	PST72308	THIOPHANATE-METHYL
23564-06-9	PST72322	THIOPHANATE
2385-85-5	PST09690	MIREX
23947-60-6	PST08721	ETHIRIMOL
23950-58-5	PST19670	PRONAMIDE
24017-47-8	PST73068	TRIAZOPHOS
2425-06-1	PST04200	CAPTAFOL
2425-25-4	PST73057	ACETOXON
24307-26-4	PST72386	MEPIQUAT CHLORIDE
2436-73-9	PST27881	MCPA METHYL ESTER
24602-86-6	PST72537	2,6-DIMETHYL-4-TRIDECYLMORPHOLINE
2463-84-5	PST71380	DICAPTHON
24934-91-6	PST04655	CHLORMEPHOS
2496-91-5	PST06306	DEMETON-S-SULFONE
2496-92-6	PST06316	DEMETON-S SULFOXIDE
2497-06-5	PST08381	DISULFOTON SULFONE
2497-07-6	PST17385	OXYDISULFOTON
25006-32-0	PST12776	LEPTOPHOS OXYGEN ANALOG
25057-89-0	PST02584	BENTAZON
25155-18-4	PST71862	METHYLBENZETHONIUM CHLORIDE
25155-30-0	PST21220	SODIUM DODECYLBENZENESULFONATE
25167-83-3	PST71689	TETRACHLOROPHENOL

CAS #	PST #	SUBSTANCE NAME
25311-71-1	PST11985	ISOFENPHOS
2532-49-2	PST73266	PYRAMAT
25322-69-4	PST19140	POLYPROPYLENE GLYCOLS
2536-31-4	PST72283	CHLORFLURENOL METHYL ESTER
2540-82-1	PST10081	FORMOTHION
25402-06-6	PST05090	CINERIN I
2550-75-6	PST73193	CHLORBICYCLEN
25537-26-2	PST72194	BUTOXYPROPYL SILVEX
2587-90-8	PST73094	DEMEPHION-S
2588-03-6	PST18646	PHORATE SULFOXIDE
2588-04-7	PST18643	PHORATE SULFONE
2588-05-8	PST18644	PHORATOXON SULFOXIDE
2588-06-9	PST18642	PHORATE OXYGEN ANALOG SULFONE
2595-54-2	PST13675	MECARBAM
2597-03-7	PST72337	PHENTHOATE
2600-69-3	PST18641	PHORATOXON
26002-80-2	PST71954	PHENOTHRIN
26087-47-8	PST12355	IBP
26225-79-6	PST72404	ETHOFUMESATE
26259-45-0	PST73051	SECBUMETON
2631-37-0	PST72957	PROMECARB
2631-40-5	PST73231	ISOPROCARB
2635-10-1	PST14191	METHIOCARB SULFOXIDE
2636-26-2	PST72950	CYANOPHOS
26419-73-8	PST73088	TIRPATE
2642-71-9	PST02205	AZINPHOS-ETHYL
2642-82-2	PST06323	2,2-BIS(4-CHLOROPHENYL)ETHANOL
2650-18-2	PST08277	ACID BLUE 9 (DIAMMONIUM SALT)
26530-20-1	PST72294	2-N-OCTYL-4-ISOTHIAZOLIN-3-ONE
2655-14-3	PST25171	3,5-XYLYL METHYLCARBAMATE
2655-19-8	PST72994	BUTACARB
26628-22-8	PST20960	SODIUM AZIDE
26644-46-2	PST24086	TRIFORINE
2665-30-7	PST73278	METHYLPHOSPHONOTHIOIC ACID, O-(4-NITROPHENYL) O-PHENYL ESTER
2669-32-1	PST73147	LYTHIDATION
2674-91-1	PST14105	METASYSTOX-S
2675-77-6	PST71229	CHLORONEB
2682-20-4	PST72362	2-METHYL-4-ISOTHIAZOLIN-3-ONE
2699-79-8	PST22380	SULFURYL FLUORIDE
27176-87-0	PST08480	DODECYLBENZENESULFONIC ACID
27304-13-8	PST17372	OXYCHLORDANE
27314-13-2	PST72343	NORFLURAZON
27519-02-4	PST05185	CIS-9-TRICOSENE
27668-52-6	PST72370	3-(TRIMETHOXYSILYL)PROPYLDIMETHYLOCTADECYLAMMONIUM CHLORIDE
2778-04-3	PST73139	ENDOTHION
2782-57-2	PST06975	DICHLORO-S-TRIAZINE TRIONE
27954-37-6	PST23002	TETRAFLUORON
2813-95-8	PST08021	DINOSEB ACETATE
28249-77-6	PST72381	THIOBENCARB
28300-74-5	PST01690	ANTIMONY POTASSIUM TARTRATE
2836-32-0	PST11235	HYDROXYACETIC ACID, SODIUM SALT
28434-00-6	PST71013	BIOALLETHRIN
28434-01-7	PST20093	BIORESMETHRIN
28772-56-7	PST03334	BROMADIOLONE

CAS #	PST #	SUBSTANCE NAME
33629-47-9	PST03525	BUTRALIN
33693-04-8	PST72770	TERBUMETON
3383-96-8	PST00020	TEMEPHOS
33911-28-3	PST20098	(-)-TRANS-RESMETHRIN
34014-18-1	PST72340	TEBUTHIURON
34123-59-6	PST12254	ISOPROTURON
3424-82-6	PST06245	2-(2-CHLOROPHENYL)-2-(4-CHLOROPHENYL)-1,1-DICHLOROETHENE
34256-82-1	PST72539	ACETOCHLOR
34375-28-5	PST72288	2-((HYDROXYMETHYL)AMINO)ETHANOL
34624-48-1	PST00551	CIS-ALLETHRIN
34643-46-4	PST72655	PROTHIOPHOS
34681-10-2	PST73270	BUTOCARBOXIM
34681-23-7	PST72434	BUTOXYCARBOXIM
35256-85-0	PST72852	TEBUTAM
35367-38-5	PST07388	DIFLUBENZURON
35400-43-2	PST22387	SULPROFOS
35691-65-7	PST26487	1,2-DIBROMO-2,4-DICYANOBUTANE
35764-59-1	PST20094	CISMETHRIN
3615-21-2	PST73047	CHLORFLURAZOLE
36614-38-7	PST12275	ISOTHIOATE
36653-82-4	PST04525	CETYL ALCOHOL
36756-79-3	PST72405	TIOCABAZIL
3689-24-5	PST22470	SULFOTEP
3691-35-8	PST04826	CHLOROPHACINONE
371-86-8	PST15030	MIPAFOX
37199-66-9	PST19548	POTASSIUM POLYSULFIDE
37333-40-7	PST18807	PHOSTEX
3734-48-3	PST04565	CHLORDENE
3734-95-0	PST72949	CYANTHOATE
3734-97-2	PST71642	AMITON OXALATE
3735-23-7	PST73085	METHYL PHENCAPTON
3735-33-9	PST18665	PHOSMET OXYGEN ANALOG
3761-41-9	PST02555	FENTHION SULFOXIDE
3761-42-0	PST02554	FENTHION SULFONE
3766-60-7	PST03523	BUTURON
3766-81-2	PST03324	FENOBUCARB
3792-59-4	PST73239	O-(2,4-DICHLOROPHENYL) O-ETHYL PHENYLPHOSPHONOTHIOATE
37924-13-3	PST72375	PERFLUIDONE
38083-17-9	PST05208	CLIMBAZOLE
3810-74-0	PST84290	STREPTOMYCIN SULFATE (2:3) SALT
3811-49-2	PST20325	SALITHION
3813-05-6	PST72725	BENAZOLIN
38260-54-7	PST73148	ETRIMFOS
3861-41-4	PST71388	BROMOXYNIL BUTYRATE
3861-47-0	PST73075	IOXYNIL OCTANOATE
38641-94-0	PST20205	GLYPHOSATE ISOPROPYLAMINE SALT
38727-55-8	PST72968	DIETHATYL-ETHYL
3878-19-1	PST73188	FUBERIDAZOLE
39148-24-8	PST72563	FOSETYL AL
39196-18-4	PST23330	THIOFANOX
39300-45-3	PST71402	DINOCAP
39765-80-5	PST23079	TRANS-NONACHLOR
3983-45-7	PST25082	VIOZENE OXON
4104-14-7	PST71150	PHOSACETIM

CAS NUMBER INDEX

CAS #	PST #	SUBSTANCE NAME
41198-08-7	PST72412	PROFENOFOS
41394-05-2	PST14095	METAMITRON
4147-51-7	PST72333	DIPROPETRYN
420-04-2	PST05760	CYANAMIDE
42509-80-8	PST15035	ISAZOPHOS
42576-02-3	PST72332	BIFENOX
42795-00-6	PST03231	SULPROFOS OXYGEN ANALOG SULFONE
42874-03-3	PST72413	OXYFLUORFEN
43222-48-6	PST72348	DIFENZOQUAT METHYL SULFATE
4329-12-8	PST04752	1-CHLORO-3-(2,2-DICHLORO-1-(4-CHLOROPHENYL)ETHYL)BENZENE
443-48-1	PST72529	METRONIDAZOLE
4482-55-7	PST71389	FENURON-TCA
465-73-6	PST11810	ISODRIN
4658-28-0	PST02216	AZIPROTRYN
4685-14-7	PST71671	PARAQUAT ION
470-90-6	PST04575	CHLORFENVINPHOS
47000-92-0	PST73184	FLUORIDAMID
4726-14-1	PST16525	NITRALIN
4824-78-6	PST03458	BROMOPHOS-ETHYL
4841-20-7	PST20831	SILVEX, METHYL ESTER
4849-32-5	PST72271	KARBUTILATE
485-31-4	PST71960	BINAPACRYL
4891-54-7	PST06309	DEMETON-O-SULFONE
497-19-8	PST21080	SODIUM CARBONATE
49866-87-7	PST72349	DIFENZOQUAT ION
50-00-0	PST50003	FORMALDEHYDE SOLUTION, 37%
50-29-3	PST06250	DICHLORODIPHENYLTRICHLOROETHANE
50-31-7	PST71134	2,3,6-TRICHLOROBENZOIC ACID
500-28-7	PST71379	CHLORTHION
502-39-6	PST83040	METHYLMERCURIC DICYANAMIDE
504-24-5	PST02180	AVITROL
50512-35-1	PST12253	ISOPROTHIOLANE
50563-36-5	PST07677	DIMETHACHLOR
50594-66-6	PST72452	ACIFLUORFEN
5064-31-3	PST24475	TRISODIUM NITRILOTRIACETATE
50782-69-9	PST83104	VX
51-03-6	PST75640	PIPERONYL BUTOXIDE
51-28-5	PST28620	2,4-DINITROPHENOL
510-15-6	PST04740	CHLOROBENZILATE
5103-71-9	PST00776	ALPHA-CHLORDANE
5103-74-2	PST10331	BETA-CHLORDANE
51218-45-2	PST15003	METOLACHLOR
51235-04-2	PST10994	HEXAZINONE
5131-24-8	PST72347	DITALIMFOS
51348-90-4	PST23062	(+)-CIS-TETRAMETHRIN
51487-69-5	PST72572	CLOETHOCARB
51630-58-1	PST19948	FENVALERATE
51707-55-2	PST23299	THIDIAZURON
51877-74-8	PST23708	TRANS-PERMETHRIN
52-51-7	PST72832	2-BROMO-2-NITROPROPANE-1,3-DIOL
52-68-6	PST23790	TRICHLORFON
52-85-7	PST09675	FAMPHUR
52207-99-5	PST72448	(Z,Z)-7,11-HEXADECADIEN-1-OL ACETATE
5221-49-8	PST08049	DIOTHYL

CAS #	PST #	SUBSTANCE NAME
5221-53-4	PST72919	DIMETHIRIMOL
52315-07-8	PST72392	CYPERMETHRIN
5234-68-4	PST04348	CARBOXIN
525-79-1	PST72483	KINETIN
52508-35-7	PST72391	SODIUM DIKEGULAC
5251-93-4	PST72964	BENZADOX
5259-88-1	PST17373	OXYCARBOXIN
526-95-4	PST10408	GLUCONIC ACID
5281-13-0	PST71828	PIPROTAL
52918-63-5	PST72784	DELTAMETHRIN
532-32-1	PST20965	SODIUM BENZOATE
5329-14-6	PST22200	SULFAMIC ACID
533-74-4	PST06230	DAZOMET
534-52-1	PST07910	DINITRO-ORTHO-CRESOL
53516-76-0	PST71834	ALKYLDIMETHYLBENZYLAMMONIUM CHLORIDE (60% C14, 30% C16, 5% C18,
53558-25-1	PST72334	PYRIMINIL
53780-34-0	PST72444	MEFLUIDIDE
53939-28-9	PST72519	(Z)-11-HEXADECENAL
54-11-5	PST16430	NICOTINE
542-75-6	PST26820	1,3-DICHLOROPROPENE
545-55-1	PST22510	TEPA
55-38-9	PST02550	FENTHION
55-91-4	PST07590	ISOFLUROPHATE
55-98-1	PST03482	BUSULFAN
55283-68-6	PST72436	ETHALFLURALIN
55285-14-8	PST72266	CARBOSULFAN
55335-06-3	PST72472	TRICLOPYR
555-37-3	PST16143	NEBURON
556-61-6	PST14950	METHYLISOTHIOCYANATE
55635-13-7	PST72430	SODIUM ALLOXYDIM
557-30-2	PST73143	GLYOXIME
55861-78-4	PST72586	ISOURON
5598-13-0	PST71652	CHLORPYRIFOS-METHYL
5598-15-2	PST04911	CHLORPYRIFOS OXYGEN ANALOG
56-23-5	PST04310	CARBON TETRACHLORIDE
56-36-0	PST72220	TRIBUTYLTIN ACETATE
56-38-2	PST18040	PARATHION
56-72-4	PST05490	COUMAPHOS
56-81-5	PST10440	GLYCERIN
56070-15-6	PST22537	TERBUFOS OXYGEN ANALOG SULFONE
56073-07-5	PST07385	DIFENACOUM
56073-10-0	PST03327	BRODIFACOUM
563-12-2	PST08720	ETHION
56534-02-2	PST04566	ALPHA-CHLORDENE
56641-38-4	PST04567	GAMMA-CHLORDENE
56802-99-4	PST80117	CHLORINATED TRISODIUM PHOSPHATE
569-64-2	PST13533	MALACHITE GREEN CHLORIDE
57-06-7	PST00680	ALLYL ISOTHIOCYANATE
57-24-9	PST22080	STRYCHNINE
57-55-6	PST19870	PROPYLENE GLYCOL
57-74-9	PST04560	CHLORDANE
57-92-1	PST21917	STREPTOMYCIN
57052-04-7	PST11844	ISOMETHIOZIN
572-48-5	PST73073	COUMITHOATE

CAS NUMBER INDEX

CAS #	PST #	SUBSTANCE NAME
577-11-7	PST00406	DIOCTYL SODIUM SULFOSUCCINATE
58-27-5	PST71050	MENADIONE
58-36-6	PST30500	10, 10'-OXYDIPHENOXARSINE
58-89-9	PST12810	LINDANE
580-48-3	PST72143	CHLORAZINE
5836-29-3	PST05493	COUMATETRALYL
584-08-7	PST19290	POTASSIUM CARBONATE
584-79-2	PST00550	ALLETHRIN
59-05-2	PST14210	METHOTREXATE
59-40-5	PST72046	SULFAQUINOXALINE
59-50-7	PST29890	4-CHLORO-M-CRESOL
5902-51-2	PST71099	TERBACIL
5915-41-3	PST22536	TERBUTHYLAZINE
59669-26-0	PST72456	THIODICARB
597-09-1	PST71953	2-NITRO-2-ETHYL-1,3-PROPANEDIOL
60-00-4	PST09570	ETHYLENEDIAMINETETRAACETIC ACID
60-41-3	PST22090	STRYCHNINE SULFATE
60-51-5	PST07670	DIMETHOATE
60-57-1	PST07080	DIELDRIN
60238-56-4	PST64913	CHLORTHIOPHOS
608-73-1	PST03080	1,2,3,4,5,6-HEXACHLOROCYCLOHEXANE
6099-79-2	PST08022	DINOSEB METHYL ETHER
61-82-5	PST01040	AMITROLE
6132-17-8	PST06211	FENSULFOTHION OXYGEN ANALOG SULFONE
6164-98-3	PST04570	CHLORDIMEFORM
61790-81-6	PST08741	ETHOXYLAN 1685
62-38-4	PST18560	PHENYLMERCURIC ACETATE
62-44-2	PST18340	PHENACETIN
62-73-7	PST07000	DICHLORVOS
62-74-8	PST21240	SODIUM FLUOROACETATE
62476-59-9	PST72453	SODIUM ACIFLUORFEN
6273-99-0	PST71754	PHENYLMERCURIC BORATE
628-63-7	PST15270	N-AMYL ACETATE
63-25-2	PST04220	CARBARYL
63231-67-4	PST20670	SILICA GEL
639-58-7	PST24380	TRIPHENYLTIN CHLORIDE
6392-46-7	PST72977	ALLYXYCARB
64-00-6	PST29423	3-ISOPROPYLPHENYL N-METHYLCARBAMATE
64-02-8	PST23137	ETHYLENEDIAMINETETRAACETIC ACID, TETRASODIUM SALT
64-17-5	PST08700	ETHYL ALCOHOL
64-19-7	PST00120	ACETIC ACID, GLACIAL
640-15-3	PST83056	THIOMETON
640-19-7	PST09930	FLUOROACETAMIDE
644-64-4	PST83057	DIMETILAN
64529-56-2	PST09111	ETHYL METRIBUZIN
64742-52-5	PST17323	ORTHO SPRAY STOCK "L"
64902-72-3	PST72504	CHLORSULFURON
6492-18-8	PST23871	TRICHLORONATE OXYGEN ANALOG
65-30-5	PST16459	NICOTINE SULFATE, LIQUID
65-30-5	PST16460	NICOTINE SULFATE, SOLID
65-31-6	PST16470	NICOTINE TARTRATE
65-85-0	PST02720	BENZOIC ACID
650-51-1	PST73307	SODIUM TRICHLOROACETATE
65195-55-3	PST72553	AVERMECTIN B1A

CAS #	PST #	SUBSTANCE NAME
65195-56-4	PST02156	AVERMECTIN B1B
6552-12-1	PST02551	FENTHION OXYGEN ANALOG
6552-13-2	PST02553	FENTHION OXON SULFOXIDE
6552-21-2	PST09684	FENSULFOTHION OXYGEN ANALOG
6597-78-0	PST73131	DICAMBA METHYL ESTER
66-81-9	PST05930	CYCLOHEXIMIDE
66063-05-6	PST72622	PENCYCURON
66215-27-8	PST72536	CYROMAZINE
66441-23-4	PST72723	FENOXAPROP-ETHYL
66841-25-6	PST72538	TRALOMETHRIN
67-56-1	PST14280	METHYL ALCOHOL
67-63-0	PST12090	ISOPROPYL ALCOHOL
67-64-1	PST00140	ACETONE
67-97-0	PST60913	CHOLECALCIFEROL
671-04-5	PST02250	CARBANOLATE
67129-08-2	PST14106	METAZACHLOR
67375-30-8	PST06118	ALPHACYPERMETHRIN
67485-29-4	PST01009	HYDRAMETHYLNON
67747-09-5	PST72648	PROCHLORAZ
68131-40-8	PST85315	ETHOXYLATED ALCOHOLS (C11-C15):
682-80-4	PST73093	DEMEPHION-O
6834-92-0	PST21373	SODIUM METASILICATE, ANHYDROUS
68359-37-5	PST72630	CYFLUTHRIN
68424-85-1	PST71835	ALKYLDIMETHYLBENZYLAMMONIUM CHLORIDE (50% C14, 40% C12, 10% C16)
68608-26-4	PST18339	PETRONATE L
69-72-7	PST20315	SALICYLIC ACID
6923-22-4	PST15165	MONOCROTOPHOS
69806-34-4	PST72580	HALOXYFOP
69806-40-2	PST72579	HALOXYFOP-METHYL
69806-50-4	PST72554	FLUAZIFOP-BUTYL
6988-21-2	PST73123	DIOXACARB
70-30-4	PST10780	HEXACHLOROPHENE
70-38-2	PST07676	DIMETHRIN
7091-57-8	PST71657	8-QUINOLINOL BENZOATE
71-55-6	PST14370	METHYL CHLOROFORM
7173-84-4	PST04341	CARBOPHENOTHION OXYGEN ANALOG
72-14-0	PST72047	SULFATHIAZOLE
72-20-8	PST08600	ENDRIN
72-43-5	PST14220	METHOXYCHLOR
72-54-8	PST06240	1,1-DICHLORO-2,2-BIS(P-CHLOROPHENYL)ETHANE
72-55-9	PST06247	2,2-BIS-(4-CHLOROPHENYL)-1,1-DICHLOROETHENE
72-56-0	PST71373	ETHYLAN
72490-01-8	PST72618	FENOXYCARB
7286-84-2	PST71255	CHLORAMBEN METHYL ESTER
7287-19-6	PST19968	PROMETRYN
7287-36-7	PST72987	MONALIDE
731-27-1	PST73030	TOLYLFLUANID
732-11-6	PST11307	PHOSMET
7320-34-5	PST19546	POTASSIUM PYROPHOSPHATE, ANHYDROUS
7359-55-9	PST71377	THIONAZIN OXYGEN ANALOG
74-83-9	PST14300	METHYL BROMIDE
74-85-1	PST09330	ETHYLENE
74051-80-2	PST20577	SETHOXYDIM
741-58-2	PST02583	BENSULIDE

CAS #	PST #	SUBSTANCE NAME
7722-84-1	PST11190	HYDROGEN PEROXIDE
7722-88-5	PST23140	TETRASODIUM PYROPHOSPHATE, ANHYDROUS
7723-14-0	PST18790	PHOSPHORUS, RED
	PST18800	PHOSPHORUS, WHITE
7726-95-6	PST03340	BROMINE
7733-02-0	PST25570	ZINC SULFATE
7738-94-5	PST04930	CHROMIC ACID
7757-79-1	PST19470	POTASSIUM NITRATE
7757-83-7	PST21660	SODIUM SULFITE
7758-02-3	PST19280	POTASSIUM BROMIDE
7758-19-2	PST21110	SODIUM CHLORITE
7758-29-4	PST21730	SODIUM TRIPOLYPHOSPHATE
7758-98-7	PST05670	CUPRIC SULFATE
7758-99-8	PST05690	CUPRIC SULFATE, PENTAHYDRATE
7761-88-8	PST20810	SILVER NITRATE
7773-06-0	PST01400	AMMONIUM SULFAMATE
7775-09-9	PST21100	SODIUM CHLORATE
7778-18-9	PST04110	CALCIUM SULFATE, ANHYDROUS
7778-39-4	PST01990	ARSENIC ACID
7778-44-1	PST03850	CALCIUM ARSENATE
7778-50-9	PST19370	POTASSIUM DICHROMATE
7778-53-2	PST19544	POTASSIUM PHOSPHATE TRIBASIC
7778-54-3	PST03990	CALCIUM HYPOCHLORITE
7778-80-5	PST19590	POTASSIUM SULFATE
7782-50-5	PST04600	CHLORINE
7782-63-0	PST09870	FERROUS SULFATE, HEPTAHYDRATE
7783-18-8	PST01460	AMMONIUM THIOSULFATE
7783-90-6	PST20787	SILVER CHLORIDE
7784-40-9	PST12540	LEAD ARSENATE
7784-42-1	PST02100	ARSINE
7784-46-5	PST52136	SODIUM ARSENITE, LIQUID
7786-30-3	PST13360	MAGNESIUM CHLORIDE
7786-34-7	PST18650	MEVINPHOS
78-34-2	PST08050	DIOXATHION
78-48-8	PST06300	DEF
78-53-5	PST83006	AMITON
78-57-9	PST72980	MENAZON
78-87-5	PST19860	PROPYLENE DICHLORIDE
78-93-3	PST14460	METHYL ETHYL KETONE
786-19-6	PST04340	CARBOPHENOTHION
79-09-4	PST19750	PROPIONIC ACID
79-14-1	PST10500	GLYCOLIC ACID
79-21-0	PST18310	PEROXYACETIC ACID
79-57-2	PST17414	OXYTETRACYCLINE
79241-46-6	PST72557	FLUAZIFOP-P-BUTYL
80-00-2	PST71663	P-CHLOROPHENYL PHENYL SULFONE
80-38-6	PST09677	FENSON
80-46-6	PST71715	4-TERT-AMYLPHENOL
8000-27-9	PST04365	CEDARWOOD OIL
8000-29-1	PST71180	OIL OF CITRONELLA
8000-46-2	PST73283	OIL OF GERANIUM
8000-48-4	PST71453	OIL OF EUCALYPTUS
8000-78-0	PST72626	GARLIC OIL
8001-22-7	PST21765	SOYBEAN OIL

CAS NUMBER INDEX

CAS NUMBER INDEX

CAS #	PST #	SUBSTANCE NAME
87-47-8	PST73263	PYROLAN
87-86-5	PST18150	PENTACHLOROPHENOL
87-90-1	PST23860	TRICHLOROISOCYANURIC ACID
88-04-0	PST72258	4-CHLORO-3,5-DIMETHYLPHENOL
88-30-2	PST71405	ALPHA, ALPHA, ALPHA-TRIFLUORO-4-NITRO-M-CRESOL
88-85-7	PST08020	DINOSEB
886-50-0	PST22538	TERBUTRYN
89-83-8	PST23475	THYMOL
90-43-7	PST18470	ORTHO-PHENYLPHENOL
90-98-2	PST06246	4,4'-DICHLOROBENZOPHENONE
900-95-8	PST24378	TRIPHENYLTIN ACETATE
9002-88-4	PST19119	POLYETHYLENE
9003-01-4	PST04349	POLYACRYLIC ACID
9003-29-6	PST75671	POLYBUTENE
9004-53-9	PST06363	DEXTRIN, CORN
9005-64-5	PST80107	POLYOXYETHYLENE (20) SORBITAN MONOLAURATE
9005-65-6	PST40200	POLYOXYETHYLENE (20) SORBITAN MONOOLEATE
9006-42-2	PST71123	METIRAM
9016-45-9	PST16835	ETHOXYLATED NONYLPHENOL
9080-17-5	PST01380	AMMONIUM POLYSULFIDE SOLUTION
91-20-3	PST16120	NAPHTHALENE
91-53-2	PST08740	ETHOXYQUIN
919-54-0	PST00117	ACETHION
919-76-6	PST01007	AMIDITHION
919-86-8	PST83065	DEMETON-S-METHYL
92-84-2	PST18400	PHENOTHIAZINE
93-71-0	PST71155	ALLIDOCHLOR
93-72-1	PST20830	SILVEX
93-76-5	PST28690	2,4,5-TRICHLOROPHENOXYACETIC ACID
93-80-1	PST73203	4-(2,4,5-TRICHLOROPHENOXY) BUTYRIC ACID
94-09-7	PST72267	BENZOCAINE
94-13-3	PST19941	PROPYL PARABEN
94-74-6	PST27880	MCPA
94-75-7	PST28510	2,4-DICHLOROPHENOXYACETIC ACID
94-80-4	PST71295	BUTYL 2,4-DICHLOROPHENOXYACETATE
94-96-2	PST71458	2-ETHYL-1,3-HEXANEDIOL
944-22-9	PST10020	FONOFOS
947-02-4	PST06115	PHOSFOLAN
95-06-7	PST22190	SULFALLATE
95-50-1	PST16970	O-DICHLOROBENZENE, LIQUID
95-95-4	PST28700	2,4,5-TRICHLOROPHENOL
950-10-7	PST13735	MEPHOSFOLAN
950-35-6	PST14678	METHYL PARAOXON
950-37-8	PST14175	METHIDATHION
953-17-3	PST71647	METHYL CARBOPHENOTHION
957-51-7	PST71406	DIPHENAMID
959-98-8	PST00800	ALPHA-ENDOSULFAN
96-12-8	PST26490	1,2-DIBROMO-3-CHLOROPROPANE
961-11-5	PST72243	TETRACHLORVINPHOS
961-22-8	PST10585	GUTHION OXYGEN ANALOG
962-58-3	PST06541	DIAZINON OXYGEN ANALOG
97-11-0	PST19949	PYPYRETHRIN
97-16-5	PST71350	GENITE
97-17-6	PST06805	DICHLOFENTHION

CAS #	PST #	SUBSTANCE NAME
97-23-4	PST71611	2,2'-METHYLENEBIS(4-CHLOROPHENOL)
97-24-5	PST71737	2,2'-THIOBIS(4-CHLOROPHENOL)
97-77-8	PST08370	DISULFIRAM
973-21-7	PST07990	DINOBUTON
98-01-1	PST10180	FURFURAL
98-54-4	PST17440	P-TERT-BUTYLPHENOL
99-30-9	PST28910	2,6-DICHLORO-4-NITROANILINE
99-76-3	PST14677	METHYL PARABEN
991-42-4	PST72254	NORBORMIDE
999-81-5	PST71147	CHLORMEQUAT CHLORIDE